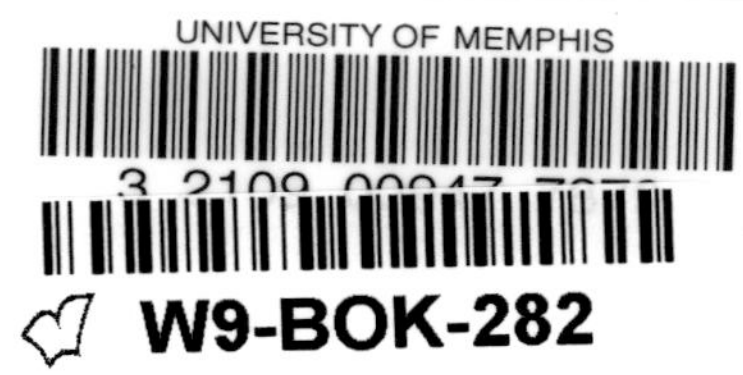

WITHDRAWAL
University of Memphis Libraries

2004 SAE Handbook

Volume 1 Metals, Materials, Fuels, Emissions, Threads, Fasteners, and Common Parts

Standards Development Program

Published by:
Society of Automotive Engineers, Inc.
400 Commonwealth Drive
Warrendale, PA 15096-0001
U.S.A.
Phone: (724) 776-4841
Fax: (724) 776-5760
http://www.sae.org

All SAE Standards are submitted to the American National Standards Institute for recognition as American National Standards. The second printing of the standard will indicate the recognition.

The 2004 SAE Handbook is comprised of three volumes, the titles of which are:

Volume 1—Metals, Materials, Emissions, Threads, Fasteners, and Common Parts

Volume 2—Parts & Components and On-Highway Vehicles (Part I)

Volume 3—On-Highway Vehicles (Part II) and Off-Highway Machinery

Volume 1 contains a complete Subject Index in addition to a Numerical Index of Standards.

Page numbers shown in the indexes include the volume number followed by the section number and the page number within that section.

ISBN 0-7680-1315-1
ISSN 0362-8205

Copyright © 2004 Society of Automotive Engineers, Inc.

All rights reserved. Printed in Canada.

Permission to photocopy for internal or personal use, or the internal or personal use of specific clients, is granted by SAE for libraries and other users registered with the Copyright Clearance Center (CCC), provided that the base fee of $10.00 per report is paid directly to CCC, 222 Rosewood Dr., Danvers, MA 01923. Special requests should be addressed to the SAE Publications Group. 0-7680-1315-1/04 $10.00.

HOW TO USE THE 2004 SAE HANDBOOK

Each surface vehicle Standard, Recommended Practice, or Information Report has a designation consisting of the letter "J" combined with a number. The letter "J" is combined with a nonsignificant number to eliminate any possible confusion between the report number and the SAE numbers within the report.

In SAE usage, the term "technical report" includes standards, recommended practices, information reports, and draft technical reports.

Effective with the 1981 Handbook, revisions of reports are indicated by the month and year of revision; for example, J300 MAR93. A lower case "a," "b," etc., appended to the report designation number indicates successive revisions of reports before 1981.

Because the SAE Handbook is published on an annual basis, certain reports in this book may not be the latest issue of the document. Therefore, users are cautioned to contact SAE Headquarters to determine the status of specific documents.

All new and revised reports contain SI (metric) equivalents of all dimensions. The SAE Editorial Advisory Committee appreciates receiving any comments and/or suggestions regarding the conversions.

The ϕ or (R) symbol, or a change bar (l) next to a section or line of a report indicates areas where technical revisions have been made since the previous issue of the report. If the symbol is next to the report title, it indicates a complete revision of the report. The notation "ed." was used on older reports to indicate editorial changes.

Reports not included in the Handbook are listed under "Related Technical Reports" in Volume 1.

A "†" or "*" next to a report title in the index indicates the report is new or has been revised, respectively, in the past year.

Page numbers shown in the indexes include the volume number followed by the section number and the page number within that section.

NOTE

All technical reports, including standards approved and practices recommended, are advisory only. Their use by anyone engaged in industry or trade or their use by governmental agencies is entirely voluntary. There is no agreement to adhere to any SAE Standard or Recommended Practice, and no commitment to conform to or be guided by any technical report. In formulating and approving technical reports, the Technical Board, its councils, and committees will not investigate or consider patents which may apply to the subject matter. Prospective users of the report are responsible for protecting themselves against liability for infringement of patents, trademarks, and copyrights.

2004 SAE HANDBOOK CONTENTS—VOLUME 1

Ref.
TL
151
.S62
2004
V. 1

Numerical Index

* Technical Revision † New Document (D)—DODISS Adopted (A)—ANSI Recognized

Numerical Index

Numerical Index

Numerical Index

SAE **J552** **External Electromagnetic Radiation Suppressor** .... Cancelled 1982.01
SAE **J553** APR96 **Circuit Breakers** **2:23.270**
SAE **J554** AUG87 **Electric Fuses (Cartridge Type)** (A) **2:23.241**
SAE **J555** **Truck, Truck-Tractor, Trailer, and Motor-Coach Wiring** .... Cancelled 1981.01 *(Superseded by J1292)*
SAE **J556** **Automobile Wiring** .... Cancelled 1981.01 *(Superseded by J1292)*
SAE **J557** **High Tension Ignition Cable** .... Cancelled 1990.01 *(Superseded by J2031)*
SAE **J558** **Low Tension Cable** .... Cancelled 1978.01 *(Superseded by J1127, J1128)*
SAE **J559** **Seven Conductor Jacketed Cable for Truck and Trailer connections** .... Cancelled 1974.12
SAE **J560** JUL98 **Seven Conductor Electrical Connector for Truck-Trailer Jumper cable** (A) **2:23.363**
SAE **J561** DEC01 **Electrical Terminals—Eyelet and Spade Type** **2:23.395**
SAE **J562** APR86 **Nonmetallic Loom** (A) **2:23.401**
SAE **J563** MAR90 **Six- and Twelve-Volt Cigar Lighter Receptacles** (A) **2:23.405**
SAE **J564** MAR90 **Headlamp Beam Switching** (A) **2:24.13**
SAE **J565** JUN89 **Semiautomatic Headlamp Beam Switching Devices** (D) **2:24.14**
SAE **J566** **Headlamp Mountings** .... Cancelled 1971.01
SAE **J567** MAR98 **Lamp Bulb Retention System** (A) **2:24.16**
SAE **J568** **Sockets Receiving Prefocus Base Lamps** .... Cancelled 1978.01
SAE **J569** **Lamp Bulbs and Bases** .... Cancelled 1970.01
SAE **J570** **Wedge Base Bulbs** .... Cancelled 1964.12
SAE **J571** **Dimensional Specifications for Sealed Beam Headlamp Units** .... Cancelled 1988.01
SAE **J572** DEC98 **Requirements for Sealed Lighting Unit for Construction and Industrial Machines** **3:40.313**
SAE **J573** JUN98 **Miniature Lamp Bulbs** (A) (D) **2:24.21**
SAE **J574** **12-Volt Lamp Bulbs and Sealed Units for Heavy Duty Commercial vehicles** .... Cancelled 1964.01 *(Superseded by J573)*
SAE **J575** JUN92 **Test Methods and Equipment for Lighting Devices and components for Use on Vehicles Less Than 2032 mm in Overall Width** **2:24.29**
SAE **J576** JUL91 **Plastic Materials for Use in Optical Parts Such as Lenses and reflectors of Motor Vehicle Lighting Devices** **2:24.38**
SAE **J577** **Vibration Test Machine** .... Cancelled 1980.01
SAE **J578** JUL02 **Color Specification** **2:24.42**
SAE **J579** **Sealed Beam Headlamp Units for Motor Vehicles** .... Cancelled 1992.01
SAE **J580** **Sealed Beam Headlamp Assembly** .... Cancelled 1992.01
SAE **J581** JUN98 **Auxiliary High Beam Lamps** (A) **2:24.137**
SAE **J582** MAR95 **Auxiliary Low Beam Lamps** **2:24.138**
SAE **J583** APR01 **Front Fog Lamps** **2:24.139**
SAE **J584** JAN03 * **Motorcycle Headlamps** (A) (J584) **2:24.142**
SAE **J585** MAR00 **Tail Lamps (Rear Position Lamps) for Use on Motor Vehicles Less Than 2032 mm in Overall Width** **2:24.162**
SAE **J586** MAR00 **Stop Lamps for Use on Motor Vehicles Less Than 2032 mm in Overall Width** .. **2:24.169**
SAE **J587** SEP03 * **License Plate Illumination Devices (Rear Registration Plate Illumination Devices)** (J587) **2:24.176**
SAE **J588** MAR00 **Turn Signal Lamps for Use on Motor Vehicles Less Than 2032 mm in Overall Width** **2:24.178**
SAE **J589B** **Turn Signal Switch** (D) **2:24.196**
SAE **J590** **Turn Signal Flashers** (A) .... Cancelled 1999.07
SAE **J591** SEP03 * **Spot Lamps** (J591) **2:24.202**
SAE **J592** AUG00 **Sidemarker Lamps for Use on Road Vehicles Less Than 2032 mm in Overall Width** **2:24.208**
SAE **J593** MAR00 **Backup Lamps (Reversing Lamps)** **2:24.212**
SAE **J594** DEC03 * **Reflex Reflectors** (J594) **2:24.216**
SAE **J595** JAN90 **Flashing Warning Lamps for Authorized Emergency, Maintenance and service Vehicles** (A) **2:24.227**
SAE **J596** **Electric Emergency Lanterns** .... Cancelled 1979.01
SAE **J597** **Liquid Burning Emergency Flares** ..... Cancelled 1979.01
SAE **J598** **Sealed Lighting Units for Construction, Industrial and Forest machinery** .... Cancelled 1998.12
SAE **J599** AUG97 **Lighting Inspection Code** (A) **2:24.250**
SAE **J600** FEB93 **Headlamp Aim Testing Machines** **2:24.253**
SAE **J601** **Light Output Meter** .... Cancelled 1965.01
SAE **J602** DEC89 **Headlamp Aiming Device for Mechanically Aimable Headlamp Units** (A) **2:24.254**
SAE **J603** **Incandescent Lamp Impact Test** .... Cancelled 1981.01
SAE **J604** JUN95 **Engine Terminology and Nomenclature—General** **2:26.1**
SAE **J605** **Free Piston Engine Nomenclature** ..... Cancelled 1973.01
SAE **J607** **Small Spark Ignition Engine Test Code** (A) .... Cancelled 1988.08 *(Superseded by J1349)*
SAE **J608** **Minimum Identification Markings for Small Air-Cooled Engines** .... Cancelled 1974.12
SAE **J609** JUL03 * **Mounting Flanges and Power Take-Off Shafts for Small Engines** (J609) **2:26.25**
SAE **J610** **Valve Seat Inserts—Engine** .... Cancelled 1987.01
SAE **J611** **Piston Rings and Pistons** .... Cancelled 1965.01 *(Superseded by J929)*
SAE **J612** **Piston and Piston Ring Nomenclature** . Cancelled 1965.01 *(Superseded by J929)*
SAE **J613** **Turbocharger Connections** .... Cancelled 1976.01 *(Superseded by J1135)*
SAE **J614** JUN95 **Engine and Transmission Dipstick Marking** **2:26.221**
SAE **J615** JUL95 **Engine Mountings** **2:26.222**
SAE **J616** JUL95 **Engine Foot Mounting (Front and Rear)** **2:26.227**
SAE **J617** MAY92 **Engine Flywheel Housing and Mating Transmission Housing flanges** **3:40.299**
SAE **J618** JAN91 **Flywheels for Single-Plate Spring-Loaded Clutches** (A) **2:26.228**
SAE **J619** DEC93 **Flywheels for Two-Plate Spring-Loaded Clutches** **2:26.230**
SAE **J620** MAY93 **Flywheels for Industrial Engines Used with Industrial Power take-Offs Equipped with Driving-Ring Type Overcenter Clutches and engine-Mounted Marine Gears and Single Bearing Engine-Mounted power Generators** **3:40.309**
SAE **J621** MAR95 **Industrial Power Take-offs with Driving Ring-Type Overcenter clutches** **3:40.295**
SAE **J622** **Airflow or Vacuum Governor Flanges** Cancelled 1987.01
SAE **J623** **Automotive Carburetor Flanges** .... Cancelled 1983.01
SAE **J624** **Tapped and Flanged Exhaust Connections for Small Engines** .... Cancelled 2001.07
SAE **J625** **Fuel Pump Mountings for Diaphragm Type Pumps** .... Cancelled 1987.01
SAE **J626** AUG98 **Diesel Fuel Injection—End-Mounting Flanges for Fuel Injection Pumps** (A) **2:26.289**
SAE **J627** **Diesel Fuel Injection Pump Mounting, Flange No. 5** .... Cancelled 1965.01 *(Superseded by J626)*
SAE **J628** **Diesel Fuel Injection Pump Mounting, Flange No. 6** .... Cancelled 1965.01 *(Superseded by J626)*

Numerical Index

Numerical Index

* Technical Revision † New Document (D)—DODISS Adopted (A)—ANSI Recognized

Numerical Index

* Technical Revision † New Document (D)—DODISS Adopted (A)—ANSI Recognized

Numerical Index

Numerical Index

SAE J1547 Electromagnetic Susceptibility Procedures for Common Mode injection (1—400 MHz), Module Testing Cancelled 1995.07
SAE J1548 Drawbars—Agricultural Wheel Tractors Cancelled 1996.07 *(Superseded by ASAE S482)*
SAE J1549 APR88 Diesel Fuel Injection Pump—Validation of Calibrating Nozzle holder assemblies (A) 2:26.315
SAE J1553 APR95 Cross Peel Test for Automotive-Type Adhesives for Fiber reinforced plastic (FRP) Bonding 1:11.133
SAE J1554 Identifying and Repairing High Strength Steel Vehicle components .... Cancelled 1993.12
SAE J1555 JUN00 Recommended Practice for Optimizing Automobile Damageability 3:42.22
SAE J1556 JUL97 Stationary Safety Glazing Replacement 3:42.32
SAE J1559 JUL95 Measurement of Solar Heating Effect .. 3:40.602
SAE J1560 Low Tension Thin Wall Primary Cable (J1560) .... Cancelled 1995.06 *(Superseded by J1128)*
SAE J1561 FEB01 Laboratory Speed Test Procedure for Passenger Car Tires 2:30.67
SAE J1562 DEC99 Selection of Zinc and Zinc-Alloy (Hot-Dipped and Electrodeposited Coated Steel Sheet 1:10.161
SAE J1563 OCT93 Guidelines for Laboratory Cyclic Corrosion Test Procedures for painted Automotive Parts 1:03.99
SAE HS1566 FEB86 Aerodynamic Flow Visualization Techniques and Procedures .... Available as a separate publication *(See Related Technical Reports Section)*
SAE J1567 Collision Detection Serial Data Communications Multiplex Bus .... Cancelled 1994.12
SAE J1568 MAY01 Materials for Plastic Pistons for Hydraulic Disc Brake Cylinders 2:25.18
SAE J1570 SEP91 Rubber Dust Boots for the Hydraulic Disc Brake Piston 2:25.230
SAE J1571 Inspection of Energy Absorbing Bumper Mounts (A) .... Cancelled 1993.12
SAE J1573 FEB03 * OEM Plastic Parts Repair (J1573) .. 3:42.33
SAE J1574-1 MAR00 Measurement of Vehicle and Suspension Parameters for Directional Control Studies 3:34.463
SAE J1574-2 MAR00 Measurement of Vehicle and Suspension Parameters for Directional Control Studies—Rationale 3:34.516
SAE HS1576 SEP94 Manual for Incorporating Pneumatic Springs in Vehicle suspension designs Available as a separate publication *(See Related Technical Reports Section)*
SAE J1577 JUN91 Replaceable Motorcycle Headlamp Bulbs (A) 2:24.147
SAE J1578 AUG03 * Motorcycle Side Stand Retraction Test Procedure (A) (J1578) 3:37.16
SAE J1579 MAY03 * Motorcycle Side Stand Retraction Performance Requirements (A) (J1579) 3:37.19
SAE J1580 DEC89 Metric Countersunk Holes for Cutting Edges and End Bits (A) 3:40.286
SAE J1581 SEP89 Cutting Edge—Optional Cross-Sections and Dimensions Loader straight (A) 3:40.292
SAE HS1582 JUN88 Manual on Design and Manufacture of Coned Disk Springs (Belleville springs) and Spring Washers .... Available as a separate publication *(See Related Technical Reports Section)*
SAE J1583 Controller Area Network (CAN), An In-Vehicle Serial Communication Protocol Cancelled 1999.07
SAE J1587 FEB02 Joint SAE/TMC Electronic Data Interchange Between Microcomputer Systems in Heavy-Duty Vehicle Applications 2:23.937
SAE J1588 APR98 Internal Combustion Engines—Piston Rings—Vocabulary (A) 2:26.47
SAE J1589 APR98 Internal Combustion Engines—Piston Rings—Inspection Measuring Principles (A) 2:26.55
SAE J1590 APR98 Internal Combustion Engines—Piston Rings—Material specifications (A) .. 2:26.68
SAE J1591 APR98 Internal Combustion Engines—Piston Rings—General Specifications (A) 2:26.70
SAE J1594 DEC94 Vehicle Aerodynamics Terminology ... 2:28.24
SAE J1595 Electrostatic Discharge Test for Vehicles .... Cancelled 1995.07
SAE J1596 JUN89 Automotive V-Ribbed Belt Drives and Test Methods 1:19.26
SAE J1597 FEB99 Laboratory Testing of Vehicle and Industrial Heat Exchangers for Pressure-Cycle Durability 2:26.395
SAE J1598 DEC99 Laboratory Testing of Vehicle and Industrial Heat Exchangers for Durability Under Vibration-Induced Loading 2:26.397
SAE J1600 Method for Evaluating the Adhesion Characteristics of automotive Sealers . Cancelled 2001.01
SAE J1601 JUL97 Rubber Cups for Hydraulic Actuating Cylinders (A) 2:25.224
SAE J1603 JAN95 Rubber Seals for Hydraulic Disc Brake Cylinders 2:25.19
SAE J1604 JAN95 Rubber Boots for Drum-Type Hydraulic Brake Wheel Cylinders 2:25.24
SAE J1605 MAR92 Brake Master Cylinder Reservoir Diaphragm Gasket 2:25.22
SAE J1606 OCT97 Headlamp Design Guidelines for Mature Drivers 3:34.306
SAE J1608 SEP01 Manual Transmission Shift Patterns ... 2:29.75
SAE J1609 AUG02 Air Reservoir Capacity Performance Guide—Commercial Vehicles 3:36.167
SAE J1610 JUN01 Test Method for Evaluating the Sealing Capability of Hose Connections with a PVT Test Facility 1:16.6
SAE J1611 AUG98 Operator Controls—Horizontal Earthboring Machines (A) 3:40.19
SAE J1614 MAR98 Wiring distribution systems for construction, agricultural, and off-road work machines 3:40.320
SAE J1615 AUG01 Thread Sealants 1:22.325
SAE J1616 FEB94 Recommended Practice for Compressed Natural Gas Vehicle Fuel . 1:12.127
SAE J1617 NOV93 Body Corrosion—A Comprehensive Introduction 1:03.47
SAE J1618 APR00 Continuously Variable Transmission Test Code for Passenger cars 2:29.76
SAE J1619 JAN97 Single Tooth Gear Bending Fatigue Test 3:42.49
SAE J1621 AUG94 Engine Retarder Dynamometer Test and Capability Rating procedure 3:40.361
SAE J1623 FEB94 All-Terrain Vehicle Headlamps 2:24.144
SAE J1624 SEP00 Fuel Crossover Line 3:36.250
SAE J1625 APR96 Heavy-Duty Circuit Breakers 2:23.280
SAE J1626 JUN99 Braking, Stability, and Control Performance Test Procedures for Air- and Hydraulic-Brake-Equipped Trucks, Truck-Tractors and Buses 3:36.143
SAE J1627 AUG95 Performance Criteria for Electronic Refrigerant Leak detectors 3:34.89

Numerical Index

* Technical Revision † New Document (D)—DODISS Adopted (A)—ANSI Recognized

Numerical Index

* Technical Revision † New Document (D)—DODISS Adopted (A)—ANSI Recognized

Numerical Index

Numerical Index

Subject Index

Subject Index

Subject Index

* Technical Revision   † New Document   (D)—DODISS Adopted   (A)—ANSI Recognized

Subject Index

DIMENSIONS (continued)

Connections (continued)

Couplers

Crane shovels

Electric cables

Electric terminals

Fabrics

Fasteners

Filters

Fittings

Flanges

Flywheels

Forestry equipment

Frames

Fuel filler caps

Fuel injection nozzles

Subject Index

Subject Index

* Technical Revision † New Document (D)—DODISS Adopted (A)—ANSI Recognized

Subject Index

RELIABILITY (continued)

Reliability Program Standard **(A)**—SAE **JA 1000** JUN98 . **3:45.1**

Reliability Program Standard Implementation Guide—SAE **JA 1000-1** MAR99 .... **3:45.3**

Software Reliability Program Standard **(A)**—SAE **JA 1002** JUL98 .... **3:45.32**

Software Supportability Program Implementation Guide—SAE **JA 1005** MAY01 .... **3:43.41**

Software Supportability Program Standard **(A)**—SAE **JA 1004** JUL98 .... **3:45.36**

REMANUFACTURING

Alternator Remanufacturing/Rebuilding Procedures Includes Passenger Car, Heavy Duty, Industrial, Agricultural, and Marine—SAE **J2075** MAR01 .... **3:42.77**

Automotive Starter Drive Assembly Remanufacturing Procedures—SAE **J2241** DEC98 .... **3:42.75**

Automotive Starter Remanufactured Procedures—SAE **J2073** DEC98 .... **3:42.67**

Automotive Starter Solenoid Remanufacturing Procedures—SAE **J2242** DEC98 .... **3:42.76**

Heavy-Duty Starter Remanufacturing Procedures—SAE **J2237** FEB95 .... **3:42.71**

Recommended Remanufacturing Procedures for Manual Transmission Clutch Assemblies—SAE **J1915** AUG00 .... **3:42.64**

SAE Maintainability, Repairability, and Serviceability Standards Manual—1999 Edition—SAE **HS 2600** NOV98 Available as a separate publication *(See Related Technical Reports Section)*

Starter Armature Remanufacturing Procedures—SAE **J2240** NOV99 .... **3:46.3**

REMOTE CONTROL SYSTEMS

Bluetooth Wireless Protocol for Automotive Applications—SAE **J2561** DEC01 .... **2:23.885**

REPAIR

***See also:* MAINTENANCE**

Engine Water Pump Remanufacture Procedures and Acceptance criteria—SAE **J1916** MAY89 .... **3:42.66**

New-vehicle collision repair information—SAE **J2376** DEC97 .... **3:42.93**

Recommended Practice for Optimizing Automobile Damageability—SAE **J1555** JUN00 .... **3:42.22**

Recommended Remanufacturing Procedures for Manual Transmission Clutch Assemblies—SAE **J1915** AUG00 .... **3:42.64**

SAE Maintainability, Repairability, and Serviceability Standards Manual—1999 Edition—SAE **HS 2600** NOV98 Available as a separate publication *(See Related Technical Reports Section)*

Stationary Safety Glazing Replacement—SAE **J1556** JUL97 .... **3:42.32**

Uniform Reference and Dimensional Guidelines for Collision Repair—SAE **J1828** OCT96 .... **3:42.37**

Plastics

*OEM Plastic Parts Repair—SAE **J1573** FEB03 .... **3:42.33**

Service technicians

Assessing Technician Training **(A)**—SAE **J2018** JUL89 .... **3:42.83**

Guidelines for the Development of Performance-Based technician Training Programs—SAE **J2017** JUL95 .... **3:42.80**

RESISTANCE TESTING

60 V and 600 V Single Core Cables—SAE **J2183** MAR01 **2:23.342**

American National Standard for Safety Glazing Materials for Glazing Motor Vehicles and Motor Vehicle Equipment Operating on Land Highways—Safety Code—ANSI **Z26.1** FEB96 .... Available as a separate publication *(See Related Technical Reports Section)*

*Classification System for Rubber Materials—SAE **J200** NOV03 .... **1:11.1**

High Tension Ignition Cable—SAE **J2031** DEC01 .... **2:23.306**

Hose and Hose Assemblies for Marine Applications—SAE **J1942** NOV02 .... **1:22.209**

Hot Plate Method for Evaluating Heat Resistance and Thermal insulation Properties of Materials—SAE **J1361** OCT01 .... **1:11.218**

*Hydraulic Hose—SAE **J517** JUL03 .... **1:22.234**

Test Method for Evaluating the Electrochemical Resistance of Coolant System Hoses and Materials—SAE **J1684** JUN00 .... **1:11.320**

Thermal Effectiveness of Sleeve Insulation—SAE **J2302** NOV96 .... **1:11.141**

RESTRAINT SYSTEMS

***See also:* INFLATABLE RESTRAINTS, PASSIVE RESTRAINT SYSTEMS, SAFETY BELTS**

*Cab Sleeper Occupant Restraint System Test—SAE **J1948** MAR03 .... **3:34.374**

Combination Pelvic/Upper Torso (Type 2) Operator Restraint Systems for Off-Road Work Machines—SAE **J2292** OCT00 .... **3:40.1**

Guidelines for Evaluating Out-of-Position Vehicle Occupant interactions with Deploying Airbags **(A)**—SAE **J1980** DEC01 .... **2:33.66**

*Occupant Restraint System Evaluation—Frontal Impact Component-Level Heavy Trucks **(A)**—SAE **J2418** MAR03 .... **3:36.253**

*Occupant Restraint System Evaluation—Frontal Impact System-Level Heavy Trucks **(A)**—SAE **J2419** MAR03 .... **3:36.254**

*Occupant Restraint System Evaluation—Lateral Rollover System-Level Heavy Trucks **(A)**—SAE **J2426** APR03 ... **3:36.267**

Occupant Restraint System Evaluation—Passenger Cars and light-Duty trucks—SAE **J128** NOV94 .... **2:33.24**

Operator Restraint System for Off-Road Work Machines **(A)**—SAE **J386** NOV97 .... **3:40.577**

Recommended Design and Performance Standard for Seats with Integrated Lap and Shoulder Restraints—SAE **J2287** APR99 .... **3:34.377**

SAE Vehicle Occupant Restraint Systems and Components Standards Manual—1999 Edition—SAE **HS 13** JAN99 Available as a separate publication *(See Related Technical Reports Section)*

Seat Belt Comfort, Fit, and Convenience **(A)**—SAE **J1834** JAN00 .... **3:34.375**

Wheelchair Tiedown and Occupant Restraint Systems for Use in Motor Vehicles—SAE **J2249** JAN99 .... **3:34.230**

Child

Anchorage Provisions for Installation of Child Restraint Tether Straps in Rear Seating Positions **(A)**—SAE **J1369** OCT97 .... **2:33.29**

Child Restraint Anchorages and Attachment Hardware **(A)**—SAE **J1368** OCT97 .... **2:33.28**

Guidelines for Evaluating Child Restraint System Interactions with deploying Airbags—SAE **J2189** DEC01 **2:33.41**

Securing Child Restraint Systems in Motor Vehicles—SAE **J1819** JUL99 .... **2:33.31**

Hardware

Child Restraint Anchorages and Attachment Hardware **(A)**—SAE **J1368** OCT97 .... **2:33.28**

Seat Belt Restraint Systems Hardware-Glossary of Terms—SAE **J1803** APR97 .... **2:33.16**

Head

Motor Vehicle Seating Manual—SAE **J782** FEB80 .... **3:34.92**

Passive

Instrumentation for Measuring Acoustic Impulses Within vehicles **(A)**—SAE **J247** FEB87 .... **1:14.8**

The Air Bag Systems in Your Car 'What the Public Needs to Know'—SAE **J2074** MAR00 .... **2:33.73**

Subject Index

* Technical Revision † New Document (D)—DODISS Adopted (A)—ANSI Recognized

SCRAPERS (continued)

Loading Ability Test Procedure—Scrapers—SAE **J764** AUG95 . . . . **3:40.180**

Noise

Sound Measurement—Off-Road Self-Propelled Work Machines—Operator—Work Cycle **(A)**—SAE **J1166** OCT98 . . . . **1:14.71**

Tire guards

Tire Guards for Operator Protection—Earthmoving Haulage Machines—SAE **J321** MAY99 . . . . **3:40.418**

SCREWS

See also: **FASTENERS**

Bolt and Capscrew Sizes for Use in Construction and Industrial Machinery **(A)**—SAE **J370** MAY98 . . . **1:04.39**

† Fastener Part Standard - Machine Screw Nuts (Metric and Inch)—SAE **J2485** JAN03 . . . . **3:41.198**

Fastener Part Standard—Machine Screws—SAE **J2484** JUL02 . . . . **3:41.144**

Flanged 12-Point Screws **(A)**—SAE **J58** MAY98 . . . . . . **1:04.24**

Holes in Bolt and Screw Shanks and Slots in Nuts for Cotter Pins **(A)**—SAE **J485** MAY98 . . . . **1:04.75**

Mechanical and Material Requirements for Externally Threaded Fasteners **(A)**—SAE **J429** JAN99 . . . . **1:04.1**

Mechanical and Material Requirements for Metric Externally Threaded Steel Fasteners **(A)**—SAE **J1199** MAR01 . . . . **1:04.8**

Mechanical and Quality Requirements for Machine Screws **(A)**—SAE **J82** MAY98 . . . . **1:04.22**

Mechanical and Quality Requirements for Tapping Screws **(A)**—SAE **J933** MAY98 . . . . **1:04.37**

Metric Thread Rolling Screws—SAE **J1237** MAR01 . . . . **1:04.50**

Steel Self-Drilling Tapping Screws **(A)**—SAE **J78** MAY98 **1:04.40**

Surface Discontinuities on Bolts, Screws, and Studs in Fatigue Applications—SAE **J123** MAR94 . . . . **1:04.58**

Surface Discontinuities on General Application Bolts, Screws, and Studs—SAE **J1061** MAY98 . . . . **1:04.55**

Thread Rolling Screws **(A)**—SAE **J81** SEP97 . . . . **1:04.46**

SEALANTS

See also: **ADHESIVES**

Design Guide for Formed-In-Place Gaskets—SAE **J1497** APR94 . . . . **1:11.246**

Electrocoat Compatibilities of Automotive Sealers—SAE **J1969** OCT88 . . . . **1:11.123**

Method for Evaluating Material Separation in Automotive sealers Under Pressure in Static Conditions—SAE **J1864** MAR96 . . . . **1:11.125**

Method for Evaluating the Flow Properties of Pumpable Sealers—SAE **J2025** JUN89 . . . . **1:11.93**

Method for Evaluating the Paintable Characteristics of automotive sealers—SAE **J1800** APR87 . . . . **1:11.116**

Method for the Determination of Expansion and Water absorption of automotive Sealers **(A)**—SAE **J1918** JAN02 **1:11.119**

Method of Viscosity Test for Automotive Type Adhesives, sealers, and deadeners—SAE **J1524** AUG95 . . . . **1:11.109**

Methods of Tests for Automotive-Type Sealers, Adhesives, and deadeners—SAE **J243** OCT71 . . . . **1:11.95**

Overlap Shear Test for Automotive Type Sealant for Stationary glass bonding **(A)**—SAE **J1529** MAY86 . . . . **1:11.129**

Overlap Shear Test for Sealant Adhesive Bonding of Automotive glass encapsulating Material to Body Opening—SAE **J1836** OCT88 . . . . **1:11.130**

Synthetic Resin Plastic Sealers, Nondrying Type—SAE **J250** MAY59 . . . . **1:11.92**

Thread Sealants—SAE **J1615** AUG01 . . . . **1:22.325**

Urethane

Stationary Safety Glazing Replacement—SAE **J1556** JUL97 . . . . **3:42.32**

SEALS

See also: **GASKETS, O-RINGS, PISTON RINGS**

Cast Iron Sealing Rings (Metric)—SAE **J1236** MAY95 . . **2:29.201**

Connections for Fluid Power and High Pressure Use - Ports, Stud Ends, and Plugs with ISO 261 Threads and O-Rings Sealing—Part 2: Stud End Requirements, Dimensions, Design and Test Methods—SAE **J2337-2** OCT02 . . . . **1:22.376**

Connections for Fluid Power and High Pressure Use—Ports, Stud Ends, and Plugs with ISO 261 Threads and O-Ring Sealing—Part 1: Ports with Recessed Conical Seat Requirements, Dimensions, Design, and Test Methods—SAE **J2337-1** OCT02 . . . . **1:22.374**

Connections for Fluid Power and High Pressure Use—Ports, Stud Ends, and Plugs with ISO 261 Threads and O-Rings Sealing—Part 3: Port Plug Requirements, Dimensions, Design, and Test Methods—SAE **J2337-3** OCT02 . . . . **1.22.381**

Fitting—O-Ring Face Seal **(A)**—SAE **J1453** JUN02 . . . . **1:22.342**

Front-Wheel-Drive Constant Velocity Joint Boot Seals—SAE **J2028** MAY00 . . . . **2:29.9**

Rectangular Cross Section Polymeric Sealing Rings (Metric)—SAE **J2310** JAN99 . . . . **2:29.51**

Test Method for Evaluating the Sealing Capability of Hose Connections with a PVT Test Facility—SAE **J1610** JUN01 **1:16.6**

Hoses

* Recommended Practices for Design and Evaluation of Passenger and Light Truck Coolant Hose Clamped Joints—SAE **J1697** NOV03 . . . . **1:16.1**

Hydraulic cylinders

Hydraulic Cylinder Leakage Test—SAE **J1336** JUN87 . . **3:40.411**

Hydraulic Cylinder Rod Seal Endurance Test Procedure **(A)**—SAE **J1374** MAY85 . . . . **3:40.163**

Rubber Boots for Drum-Type Hydraulic Brake Wheel Cylinders—SAE **J1604** JAN95 . . . . **2:25.24**

Rubber Seals for Hydraulic Disc Brake Cylinders—SAE **J1603** JAN95 . . . . **2:25.19**

Radial lip

SAE Fluid Sealing Handbook Radial Lip Seals—SAE **HS 1417** FEB96 . . . . Available as a separate publication *(See Related Technical Reports Section)*

Rubber

* Borate Ester Based Brake Fluids—SAE **J1704** JUN03 . . **2:25.61**

Brake Master Cylinder Reservoir Diaphragm Gasket—SAE **J1605** MAR92 . . . . **2:25.22**

Low Water Tolerant Brake Fluids—SAE **J1705** MAY95 . . **2:25.71**

* Motor Vehicle Brake Fluid—SAE **J1703** JUN03 . . . . . . **2:25.54**

Rubber Seals for Hydraulic Disc Brake Cylinders—SAE **J1603** JAN95 . . . . **2:25.19**

Symbols

Identification of Truck, Trailer, and Bus Wheel Seals and associated packaging—SAE **J2224** MAY02 . . . . **2:31.47**

SEAT BELTS

See: **SAFETY BELTS**

SEATS

SAE Automotive Textiles and Trim Standards Manual—1999 Edition—SAE **HS 2700** FEB99 . . . . Available as a separate publication *(See Related Technical Reports Section)*

Automobiles and trucks

Accommodation Tool Reference Point—SAE **J1516** DEC98 . . . . **3:34.349**

Driver Hand Control Reach **(A)**—SAE **J287** JUN88 . . . . **3:34.180**

Driver Selected Seat Position **(A)**—SAE **J1517** DEC98 . . **3:34.353**

H-Point Machine and Design Tool Procedures and Specifications—SAE **J826** JUN02 . . . . **3:34.108**

Subject Index

Subject Index

* Technical Revision † New Document (D)—DODISS Adopted (A)—ANSI Recognized

Subject Index

* Technical Revision † New Document (D)—DODISS Adopted (A)—ANSI Recognized

TRUCKS AND BUSES (continued)

Air reservoir

Axles

Brakes

Clutches

Compressors

Cornering

Crashworthiness

Data communications

Defrosters

Dimensions

Electric equipment

Electronic equipment

Subject Index

TUBING (continued)

Connections

Connections for Fluid Power and General Use—Ports and Stud ends with iSO 261 Threads and O-Ring Sealing Part 1: Port with O-Ring Seal in truncated Housing—SAE **J2244/1** DEC91 .... **1:22.384**

Connections for Fluid Power and General Use—Ports and Stud ends with iSO 261 Threads and O-Ring Sealing Part 2: Heavy-Duty (S Series) stud ends— Dimensions, Design, Test Methods, and Requirements—SAE **J2244/2** DEC91 .... **1:22.387**

Hydraulic Flanged Tube, Pipe, and Hose Connections, Four-Bolt split flange Type—SAE **J518** JUN93 .... **1:22.265**

Metallic Tube Connections for Fluid Power and General Use-Test Methods for Threaded Hydraulic Fluid Power Connectors—SAE **J1644** OCT98 .... **1:22.370**

Quick Connector Specification for Liquid Fuel and Vapor/ Emissions Systems—SAE **J2044** SEP02 **2:26.483**

Copper

Seamless Copper Tube **(A)**—SAE **J528** JUN91 .... **1:22.303**

Copper alloys

Tests and Procedures for SAE Low-Carbon Steel and Copper nickel Tubing—SAE **J1677** JAN96 .... **1:22.304**

Wrought Copper and Copper Alloys—SAE **J463** DEC02 **1:10.87**

Ferrous materials

Detection of Surface Imperfections in Ferrous Rods, Bars, tubes, and wires—SAE **J349** FEB91 .... **1:03.110**

Fittings

Automotive Tube Fittings—SAE **J512** APR97 .... **1:22.49**

* Coding Systems for Identification of Fluid Conductors and Connectors—SAE **J846** FEB03 .... **1:22.41**

Fitting—O-Ring Face Seal **(A)**—SAE **J1453** JUN02 .... **1:22.342**

Formed Tube Ends for Hose Connections and Hose Fittings—SAE **J1231** JAN01 .... **1:22.226**

Hydraulic Tube Fittings **(A)**—SAE **J514** JUL01 .... **1:22.110**

* Nominal Reference Working Pressures for Steel Hydraulic Tubing—SAE **J1065** FEB03 .... **1:22.299**

Refrigeration Tube Fittings—General Specifications—SAE **J513** JAN99 .... **1:22.83**

Spherical and Flanged Sleeve (Compression) Tube Fittings—SAE **J246** FEB00 .... **1:22.71**

Fuel injection

Diesel Engines—Steel Tubes for High-Pressure Fuel Injection Pipes (Tubing)—SAE **J1958** OCT02 .... **2:26.246**

Fuel Injection Pumps—High Pressure Pipes (Tubing) for Testing—SAE **J1418** OCT02 .... **2:26.248**

Fuel systems

Low-Permeation Fuel Fill and Vent Tube **(A)**—SAE **J2405** AUG97 .... **1:12.146**

Nonmetallic Fuel System Tubing with One or More Layers—SAE **J2260** NOV96 .... **1:12.139**

Performance Requirements for Fuel System Tubing Assemblies **(A)**—SAE **J2045** FEB98 .... **1:12.149**

Standard for Protective Covers for Gasoline Fuel Line Tubing **(A)**—SAE **J2027** JUN98 .... **2:26.446**

Nylon

Metric Nonmetallic Air Brake System Tubing **(A)**—SAE **J1394** APR00 .... **1:22.313**

Steel

Brazed Double Wall Low-Carbon Steel Tubing—SAE **J527** NOV00 .... **1:22.291**

Diesel Engines—Steel Tubes for High-Pressure Fuel Injection Pipes (Tubing)—SAE **J1958** OCT02 .... **2:26.246**

* Nominal Reference Working Pressures for Steel Hydraulic Tubing—SAE **J1065** FEB03 .... **1:22.299**

Seamless Low-Carbon Steel Tubing Annealed for Bending and flaring—SAE **J524** FEB96 .... **1:22.287**

Tests and Procedures for SAE Low-Carbon Steel and Copper nickel Tubing—SAE **J1677** JAN96 .... **1:22.304**

Welded and Cold Drawn Low-Carbon Steel Tubing Annealed for bending and Flaring—SAE **J525** MAY99 .... **1:22.288**

Welded and Cold-Drawn, SAE 1021 Carbon Steel Tubing Normalized for Bending and Flaring—SAE **J2467** APR99 **1:22.295**

Welded Flash Controlled, High Strength Low Alloy Steel Hydraulic Tubing, Sub-Critically Annealed for Bending, Double Flaring, and Bending—SAE **J2613** OCT02 .... **1:22.285**

Welded Flash Controlled, SAE 1021 Carbon Steel Tubing, Normalized for Bending, Double Flaring, and Beading—SAE **J2435** APR99 .... **1:22.297**

Welded Flash-Controlled Low-Carbon Steel Tubing Normalized for Bending, Double Flaring, and Beading—SAE **J356** MAY99 .... **1:22.293**

Welded Low-Carbon Steel Tubing—SAE **J526** JAN00 .... **1:22.290**

Windshield washers

Truck and Bus Multipurpose Vehicle Windshield Washer System **(A)**—SAE **J1944** SEP00 .... **3:34.10**

Windshield Washer Tubing **(A)**—SAE **J1037** AUG01 .... **1:11.340**

TUBULAR ASSEMBLIES

† Metallic Tube Conductor Assemblies for Fluid Power and General Use—Test Methods for Hydraulic Fluid Power Metallic Tube Assemblies—SAE **J2658** JUL03 .... **1.22.401**

TURBOCHARGERS

Spark Arrester Test Procedure for Large Size Engines **(A)**—SAE **J342** JAN91 .... **2:26.365**

Turbocharger Gas Stand Test Code—SAE **J1826** MAR95 **2:26.358**

Terminology

Turbocharger Nomenclature and Terminology—SAE **J922** JUN95 .... **2:26.4**

TURN INDICATORS

Flasher Test—SAE **J823** JAN94 .... **2:24.258**

Flashers—SAE **J1690** AUG96 .... **2:24.200**

Minimum Performance of the Warning Light System Used on Emergency Vehicles—SAE **J2498** AUG99 .... **2:24.224**

* Motorcycle Turn Signal Lamps **(A)**—SAE **J131** JUN03 .... **2:24.161**

SAE Ground Vehicle Lighting Standards Manual—2002 Edition—SAE **HS 34** FEB02 Available as a separate publication *(See Related Technical Reports Section)*

Side Turn Signal Lamps for Large Vehicles—SAE **J2039** MAY01 .... **2:24.191**

* Side Turn Signal Lamps for Vehicles Less Than 12 m in Length—SAE **J914** JUL03 .... **2:24.197**

Stop Lamps and Front- and Rear-Turn Signal Lamps for Use on Motor Vehicles 2032 mm or More in Overall Width—SAE **J2261** JAN02 .... **2:24.193**

Tail Lamps (Rear Position Lamps) for Use on Motor Vehicles Less Than 2032 mm in Overall Width—SAE **J585** MAR00 .... **2:24.162**

Turn Signal Lamps for Use on Motor Vehicles Less Than 2032 mm in Overall Width—SAE **J588** MAR00 .... **2:24.178**

Turn Signal Switch **(D)**—SAE **J589B** OCT77 .... **2:24.196**

TURNING BEHAVIOR

Trucks and buses

Turning Ability and Off Tracking—Motor Vehicles **(A)**—SAE **J695** DEC98 .... **3:36.74**

TWO STROKE CYCLE ENGINES

***See also:* SPARK IGNITION ENGINES**

Engine Oil Performance and Engine Service Classification (Other Than 'Energy-Conserving')—SAE **J183** JAN02 .... **1:12.2**

Lubricants for Two-Stroke-Cycle Gasoline Engines—SAE **J1510** NOV01 .... **1:12.48**

* Two-Stroke-Cycle Gasoline Engine Lubricants Performance and Service Classification **(A)**—SAE **J2116** JUL03 .... **1:12.50**

Fuels

Impact of Alternative Fuels on Engine Test and Reporting procedures—SAE **J1515** JUN95 .... **1:12.153**

REFEREE MATERIALS FOR TESTING MOTOR VEHICLE BRAKE FLUIDS

The materials listed below fall within the auspices of the Referee Materials Subcommittee of the SAE Hydraulic Brake Systems Actuating Committee and are available from SAE for use in testing a variety of products for compliance with SAE documents. Where those materials are referenced in a specific document, the number of the document is provided. For information on how to order Referee Materials, contact SAE Customer Sales and Satisfaction, SAE, 400 Commonwealth Dr., Warrendale, PA 15096-0001, (724) 772-7103.

SAE Part No.	Description	Reference Document
RM-3a	SBR Brake Cups—Wheel Cylinder	J1703 OCT2000/ISO 4925
RM-4a	SBR Brake Cups—Primary Master Cylinder	J1703 OCT2000
RM-5a	SBR Brake Cups—Secondary Master Cylinder	J1703 OCT2000
RM-6a	Corrosion Test Strip—Tinned Iron	J1703 OCT2000
RM-7	Corrosion Test Strip—Steel	J1703 OCT2000
RM-8	Corrosion Test Strip—Aluminum	J1703 OCT2000
RM-9	Corrosion Test Strip—Cast Iron	J1703 OCT2000
RM-10	Corrosion Test Strip—Brass	J1703 OCT2000
RM-11	Corrosion Test Strip—Copper	J1703 OCT2000
RM-12	Wheel Cylinder Piston	J1703 OCT2000
RM-13	Aluminum Master Cylinder Piston	J1703 OCT2000
RM-14b	Wheel Cylinder Assembly	J1703 OCT2000
RM-15b	Master Cylinder Assembly	J1703 OCT2000
RM-25	Copper Gasket	—
RM-26	Inverted Tube Nut	—
RM-27	Tinfoil (Approximately 6×6 Inch Sheet)	J1703 OCT2000
RM-28	Hiding Power Test Chart	J1703 OCT2000
RM-29	320A Abrasive Grit Paper (9"×11")	J1703 OCT2000
RM-49	Corrosion Test Jar with RM-63 Lid	J1703 OCT2000
RM-51	Effect on Rubber Test Jar	J1703 OCT2000
RM-52a	Tinned Lid—Effect on Rubber Test Jar	J1703 OCT2000
RM-57	Tubing—¼" O.D.	J1703 OCT2000
RM-58	Tubing—3/16" O.D.	J1703 OCT2000
RM-59a	Glass Oil Sample Bottle (4 oz.) with Cork	J1703 OCT2000
RM-60	Storage Corrosion Test Fluid	J1703 OCT2000
RM-62	Screws and Nuts for Resistance to Oxidation Test	—
RM-63	Jar Lids for Humidification Procedures, MVSS116, S6.2	J1703 OCT2000
RM-64	Jar Lids for Corrosion Test (w/ hole)	J1703 OCT2000
RM-66-05	High Boiling Compatibility Fluid	J1703 OCT2000
RM-69	EPDM Stock (ASTM D15 Test Slab)	J1703 OCT2000
RM-70	Silicone Base Compatibility Fluid	—
RM-71	Triethylene Glycol Monomethyl Ether	J1703 OCT2000
RM-75	Silicon Carbide Grain, #8 grit	J1703 OCT2000
ISO-1	Natural Rubber Cups	—

TESTING MATERIALS

The following Referee Materials are sold by SAE and fall within the realm of SAE Technical Committees as indicated:

Lubricants Review Institute

Engine Oil Review Committee

RM-93	Storage, Stability and Compatibility Fluid

Aerospace Materials Specifications Products

ARM-200	Fluid, Reference for Testing Polyol Ester (and Diester) Resistant Material. A trimethylol propane triheptanoate fluid representative of gas turbine engine oils as defined in AMS Draft Specification CE93AT.
ARM-201	AMS 3020, "Oil, Reference, for 'L' Stock Rubber Testing." Used primarily as a reference oil to estimate the ability of elastomeric compounds to conform to specified requirements after immersion at a specified temperature for a specified time.
ARM-202	AMS 3021, Fluid, Reference for Testing DI-Ester (POLYOL) Resistant Material. Properties listed in Table 1 of AMS 3021C.

ENGINEERING AIDS

SAE is the supplier of drafting templates and machines in its Engineering Aids Program. These drafting templates and machines are referred to in reports prepared by the SAE Human Factors Engineering Committee.

The two-dimensional drafting templates and three-dimensional H-point machine have been certified by SAE for adherence to the SAE Standards and for exact repeatability between individual templates and machines.

The reports, templates and machines are as follows:

SAE J400 DEC2001—TEST FOR CHIP RESISTANCE OF SURFACE COATINGS

SAE PART #EA-400—CHIP RATING STANDARDS—A set of photographic transparencies, each depicting one size of chip and the fewest number of chips in each rating category.

SAE J406 MAY1998—METHODS OF DETERMINING HARDENABILITY OF STEELS

SAE PART #EA-406CD—HARDENABILITY CALCULATOR—This product consists of a CD with a program that calculates the predicted hardenability for wrought steel compositions within the limits listed in SAE J406. Carbon and alloy multiplying factors and the correlation of boron factor with carbon and alloy content are based on the analysis of thousands of heats of boron and non-boron steels consisting of 1500; 4100; 5000; and 8600 series grades.

The IE38 method of Jominy hardenability calculation from the chemical Ideal Diameter* (DI) of a steel is based on the original work of M.A. Grossman. Caterpillar, Inc. subsequently refined the carbon multiplying factors and improved the correlation of the boron factor with both carbon and alloy content to provide increased accuracy of both the calculated DI and Jominy hardenability curves.

SAE J826 JUL1995—DEVICES FOR USE IN DEFINING AND MEASURING SEATING ACCOMMODATIONS

SAE PART #EA-3—THREE-DIMENSIONAL H-POINT MACHINE—

The three-dimensional H-point machine is used in the following applications: 1) aid in the design an development of seats and seat materials; and 2) check vehicle seating compartment for conformance to design specifications, that is, relationship of H-point to body structures, seats, controls, etc. The H-point machine measures 33" x 24" x 37" and weighs 167 lbs. uncrated

EA-3 SPARE PARTS—A full range of Spare Parts and Repair Services are available through the original Equipment Supplier of the SAE J826 EA-3, Three-Dimensional H-Point Machine. Quotations for replacement parts and repairs can be received by contacting the SAE Customer Sales and Satisfaction area for instructions.

SAE PART #EA-30—STORAGE CART FOR THREE-DIMENSIONAL H-POINT MACHINE—The 3-D H-Point Cart offers many features, from keeping your 3-D mannequin clean and free of damage, to the security of locking up the machine and attachments when not in use. It has a top work surface so it can be moved easily and used anywhere in the plant or lab. The cart is constructed of 16 gauge steel with a 14 gauge heavy-duty locking door and hinge. The physical dimensions are 30" long × 24" wide × 35" tall with casters.

SAE J4002 FEB2004—H-Point Machine and Design Tool Procedures and Specifications

SAE PART #EA-3.01—THREE-DIMENSIONAL H-POINT MACHINE—

The HPM-II defines and locates the standard seating reference point – the H-Point – plus additional leg, shoe, and pedal reference points. The HPM-II's key uses are:

- Design – Establishes interior reference points and dimensions
- Audit – Verifies location of key reference points throughout development and production cycle
- Benchmark – Compare reference points of competive vehicles

SAE PART #EA-30.01—HPM-II STORAGE/SHIPPING CART
For the safety of your newly purchased H-Point machine (HPM II), SAE offers this highly protective steel shipping and storage case, ensuring the longevity and reliability of your investment.
The case has a front open lid with anvil front clamps that converts into a table, providing a convenient place for machine assembly. The case is equipped with casters, cardholder, shipping label plate and hasp latch tie down rings. The case will hold the machine in (4) foam lined compartments with the weights stored in foam lined drawers. The head probe is stored separately in the lid.

SAE J941 JUN1997—MOTOR VEHICLE DRIVER'S EYE RANGE

SAE PART #EA-5—EYELLIPSE AND HEAD CONTOUR LOCATOR LINE—ADJUSTABLE SEAT—The EA-5 is a drafting tool that describes the position of the eyellipse and the occupant head contour for horizontally adjustable seats with back angles between 5 and 40 degrees.

SAE PART #EA-23—OWNER'S MANUAL FOR HYBRID III DUMMY

SAE PART #EA-24—OWNER'S MANUAL FOR BIOSID/SIDE IMPACT TEST DUMMY

SAE PART #EA-25—CALIBRATION PROCEDURES—HYBRID III SMALL FEMALE DUMMY

SAE PART #EA-26—CALIBRATION PROCEDURES—HYBRID III LARGE MALE TEST DUMMY

SAE PART #EA-28—USER'S GUIDE FOR THE SIX MONTH OLD INFANT DUMMY (CRABI)

SAE Part #EA-29—HYBRID III SIX-YEAR OLD CHILD DUMMY USER'S MANUAL

SAE PART #EA-31—HYBRID III 3-YEAR OLD CHILD DUMMY USERS MANUAL

SAE J1128 JAN1995—LOW TENSION PRIMARY CABLE

SAE PART #EA-1128—WIRE COLOR CHARTS—Color charts are for use in connection with SAE J1128 Standard on Low Tension Primary Cable and provide a reference for color comparison. Complete set including black and white charts. Individual black and white charts are available upon request for an individual sheet cost.

SAE J1362 JUL1997—SYMBOLS FOR CONTROLS, INDICATORS AND TELL-TALES FOR OFF-ROAD, SELF-PROPELLED WORK MACHINES

SAE PART #EA-35—STATS OF SYMBOLS—SAE J1362 presents the symbols with which certain controls, indicators, and tell-tales for off-road, self-propelled work machines are to be provided in order to ensure their identification and facilitate their utilization. It also indicates the colors of possible optical tell-tales which warn the operator of the operation or malfunctioning of the devices and equipment represented by the corresponding symbols. It is applicable to those controls, indicators, and tell-tales which are fitted on the instrument panel or in the immediate vicinity of the operator on Construction, General Purpose Industrial, Agricultural, Forestry, and Specialized Mining categories of off-road, self-propelled work machines, as defined in SAE J1116 JUN86.

AEROSPACE ENGINEERING AIDS

AEA-0001—SAE Aerospace Hand Tool Committee "Worn Out Tool Reference Chart"

All tools wear out eventually through use. Discard any tool that shows evidence of dents, cracks, and mushrooming or excessive wear. This includes tools with spread, nicked or battered jaws; battered gripping surfaces; or broken or bent handles. Wooden handles on some tools can be replaced with handles of equal size and type. Indicators of wear include tools where chrome is worn, flaking or there is evidence of rust. Flaking chrome can cause serious cuts and injury to the operator.

* * * * *

The templates and machine may be ordered through SAE Customer Sales and Satisfaction, SAE, 400 Commonwealth Dr., Warrendale, PA 15096-0001, (724) 776-4970.

SAE Standards Manuals

Comprehensive Collections of SAE Ground Vehicle Standards

(Related Technical Reports Section)

SAE HS 1086	Metals and Alloys in the Unified Numbering System Handbook~9th Edition
SAE HS 124	SAE Manual on Blast Cleaning~SAE J792a
SAE HS 13	SAE Vehicle Occupant Restraint Systems and Components Standards Manual
SAE HS 1417	SAE Fluid Sealing Handbook Radial Lip Seals
SAE HS 150	SAE Fluid Conductors and Connectors Standards Manual
SAE HS 1566	Aerodynamic Flow Visualization Techniques and Procedures
SAE HS 1576	Manual for Incorporating Pneumatic Springs in Vehicle suspension designs
SAE HS 1582	Manual on Design and Manufacture of Coned Disk Springs (Belleville springs) and Spring Washers
SAE HS 1738	SAE Standard for Electrical Equipment for Automotive Industrial Machinery
SAE HS 184	Surface Vehicle Sound Measurement Standards Manual
SAE HS 19	SAE Documents Referenced in Federal Motor Vehicle Safety standards
SAE HS 1939	SAE Truck and Bus Control Communications Network Standards Manual
SAE HS 210	Laboratory Testing Machines and Procedures for Measuring the Steady State Force and Movement Properties of Passenger Car Tires~SAE J1106 and SAE J1107
SAE HS 2100	Numbering System for Standard Drills, Standard Taps, and reamers
SAE HS 215	SAE Motor Vehicle Safety and Environmental Terminology
SAE HS 2200	SAE Piston Ring Standards Manual
SAE HS 2293	SAE Energy Transfer System for Electric Vehicles Parts 1 and 2
SAE HS 23	SAE Fuels and Lubricants Standards Manual
SAE HS 2300	Introduction to All-Wheel Drive
SAE HS 24	SAE Surface Vehicle Brake Systems Standards Manual
SAE HS 2400	SAE Surface Vehicle Emissions Standards Manual
SAE HS 2500	SAE Motorcycle Standards Manual
SAE HS 2600	SAE Maintainability, Repairability, and Serviceability Standards Manual
SAE HS 2700	SAE Automotive Textiles and Trim Standards Manual
SAE HS 2800	SAE Construction, Agricultural, and Off-Road Machinery Standards Manual
SAE HS 2900	SAE Interior Climate Control Standards Manual
SAE HS 3	Surface Rolling and Other Methods for Mechanical Prestressing of metals
SAE HS 30	SAE Ferrous Materials Standards Manual
SAE HS 3000	SAE On-Board Diagnostics for Light and Medium Duty Vehicles Standards Manual
SAE HS 3200	SAE Passenger Car Safety Standards Manual
SAE HS 3300	SAE Wheel Standards Manual
SAE HS 34	SAE Ground Vehicle Lighting Standards Manual
SAE HS 3458	SAE Fuel Injection Systems and Testing Methods Standards manual

SAE HS 3500	SAE Fuel, Oil, Emissions, and Coolant System Hose and Hose Clamp Standards Manual
SAE HS 3600	SAE Surface Vehicle Electromagnetic Compatibility (EMC) Standards Manual
SAE HS 40	Principles of Engine Cooling Systems, Components and maintenance
SAE HS 4000	SAE Fastener Standards Manual
SAE HS 4040	SAE Vehicle Cooling Systems Standards Manual
SAE HS 4200	SAE Crane Standards Manual
SAE HS 5600	SAE Agricultural Tractor and Related Standards Handbook
SAE HS 58	Diesel Fuel Injection Equipment and Test Methods
SAE HS 63	Manual on Design and Manufacture of Coned Disk Springs or belleville springs
SAE HS 788	Manual on Design and Application of Leaf Springs
SAE HS 795	SAE Manual on Design and Application of Helical and Spiral springs
SAE HS 796	Manual on Design and Manufacture of Torsion Bar Springs and Stabilizer Bars
SAE HS 806	Oil Filter Test Procedure
SAE HS 82	Truck Ability Prediction Procedure~SAE J688
SAE HS 83	Truck Ability Work Sheet Pad
SAE HS 83a	SAE Commercial Vehicle Ability Report Form
SAE HS 84	Manual on Shot Peening
SAE HS 87	Fiberboards
SAE HSJ 1066	Recommended Guidelines for Company Metrication Programs in the metalworking Industry
SAE HSJ 1093	Latticed Crane Boom Systems~Analytical Procedure
SAE HSJ 1156	Automotive Resistance Spot Welding Electrodes
SAE HSJ 1188	Specification for Automotive Weld Quality~Resistance Spot welding
SAE HSJ 1196	Specification for Automotive Frame Weld Quality~Arc Welding
SAE HSJ 1213	Glossary of Automotive Electronic Terms
SAE HSJ 1451	A Dictionary of Terms for the Dynamics and Handling of Single track vehicles (Motorcycles, Mopeds, and Bicycles)
SAE HSJ 390	Dual Dimensioning
SAE HSJ 670	Vehicle Dynamics Terminology
SAE HSJ 73	Multipurpose Petroleum Base Fluids
SAE HSJ 762	Reinforced Thermosetting for Ground Vehicle Applications
SAE HSJ 782	Motor Vehicle Seating Manual
SAE HSJ 784a	Residual Stress Measurements by X-Ray Diffraction
SAE HSJ 836	Automotive Metallurgical Joining
SAE HSJ 885	Human Tolerance to Impact Conditions as Related to Motor vehicle design
SAE HSJ 905	Fuel Filter Test Method
SAE HSJ 906	Automotive Safety Glazing Manual
SAE HSJ 965	Abrasive Wear

FERROUS METALS

1 Numbering System, Chemical Compositions

NUMBERING METALS AND ALLOYS —SAE J1086 JUL1995 and ASTM E 527

SAE Recommended Practice

Report of the SAE Unified Numbering System Advisory Board approved August 1974, revised June 1989. Revised by the SAE Unified Numbering System Advisory Board December 1992 and July 1995.

Foreword—This Document has not changed other than to put it into the new SAE Technical Standards Board Format.

UNS designations shall not be used for metals and alloys which are not registered under the system described herein, or for any metal or alloy whose composition differs from those registered.

1. Scope

1.1 This SAE Recommended Practice describes a unified numbering system (UNS) for metals and alloys which have a "commercial standing" (see 6.1), and covers the procedure by which such numbers are assigned.

Section 2 describes the system of alphanumeric designations or "numbers" established for each family of metals and alloys.

Section 3 outlines the organization established for administering the system.

Section 4 describes the procedure for requesting number assignment to metals and alloys for which UNS numbers have not previously been assigned.

1.2 The UNS provides a means of correlating many nationally used numbering systems currently administered by societies, trade associations, and individual users and producers of metals and alloys, thereby avoiding confusion caused by use of more than one identification number for the same material; and by the opposite situation of having the same number assigned to two or more entirely different materials. It provides, also, the uniformity necessary for efficient indexing, record keeping, data storage and retrieval, and cross referencing.

1.3 A UNS number is not in itself a specification, since it establishes no requirements for form, condition, quality, etc. It is a unified identification of metals and alloys for which controlling limits have been established in specifications published elsewhere. (See 6.2.)

2. References

2.1 Related Publications—The following publications are provided for information purposes only and are not a required part of this document.

2.1.1 SAE PUBLICATIONS—Available from SAE, 400 Commonwealth Drive, Warrendale, PA 15096-0001.

SAE HS-1086—Metals and Alloys in the Unified Numbering System

2.1.2 ASTM PUBLICATIONS—Available from ASTM, 100 Barr Harbor Drive, West Conshohocken, PA 19428-2959.

ASTM E 527—Practice for Numbering Metals and Alloys (UNS)

ASTM Publication No. DS-56—Metals and Alloys and the Unified Numbering System

3. Description of Numbers (or Codes) Established for Metals and Alloys

3.1 The unified numbering system (UNS) establishes 18 series of numbers for metals and alloys, as shown in Table 1. Each UNS number consists of a single letter-prefix followed by five digits. In most cases the letter is suggestive of the family of metals identified, for example, A for aluminum, P for precious metals, S for stainless steels. Table 2 shows the secondary division of some primary series of numbers.

3.2 Whereas some of the digits in certain of the UNS number groups have special assigned meaning, each series is independent of the others in such significance; this practice permits greater flexibility and avoids complicated and lengthy UNS numbers. (See 6.3.)

TABLE 1—PRIMARY SERIES OF NUMBERS

UNS Series	Metal
Nonferrous metals and alloys	
A00001-A99999	Aluminum and aluminum alloys
C00001-C99999	Copper and copper alloys
E00001-E99999	Rare earth and rare earth-like metals and alloys (18 Items, see Table 2)
L00001-L99999	Low melting metals and alloys (14 Items, see Table 2)
M00001-M99999	Miscellaneous nonferrous metals and alloys (12 Items, see Table 2)
N00001-N99999	Nickel and nickel alloys
P00001-P99999	Precious metals and alloys (8 Items, see Table 2)
R00001-R99999	Reactive and refractory metals and alloys (14 Items, see Table 2)
Z00001-Z99999	Zinc and zinc alloys
Ferrous metals and alloys	
D00001-D99999	Specified mechanical properties steels
F00001-F99999	Cast irons
G00001-G99999	AISI and SAE carbon and alloy steels (except tool steels)
H00001-H99999	AISI H-steels
J00001-J99999	Cast steels (except tool steels)
K00001-K99999	Miscellaneous steels and ferrous alloys
S00001-S99999	Heat and corrosion resistant (stainless) steels
T00001-T99999	Tool steels
Welding filler metals	
W00001-W99999	Welding filler metals, covered and tubular electrodes, classified by weld deposit composition (see Table 2)

3.3 Wherever feasible, identification "numbers" from existing systems are incorporated into the UNS numbers. For example: The carbon steel which is presently identified by "AISI 1020" (American Iron & Steel Institute) is covered by "UNS G10200" and the nickel alloy presently identified by "M252" is covered by "UNS N07252."

3.4 Welding filler metals fall into two general categories: those whose compositions are determined by the filler metal analysis (e.g., solid bare wire or rods and cast rods), and those whose composition is determined by the weld deposit analysis (e.g., covered electrodes, flux-cored and other composite wire electrodes). The latter are assigned to a new primary series with the letter W as shown in Table 1. The solid bare wire and rods continue to be assigned in the established number series according to their composition.

(Readers are cautioned not to make their own "assignments" of numbers from such listings, as this can result in unintended and unexpected duplication and conflict.)

3.5 The ASTM and the SAE periodically publish up-to-date listings of all UNS numbers assigned to specific metals and alloys, with appropriate reference information on each. (See 6.6.) Many trade associations also publish similar listings related to materials of primary interest to their organizations.

TABLE 2—SECONDARY DIVISION OF SOME SERIES OF NUMBERS

UNS Series	Metal
E00001-E99999 Rare earth and rare earthlike metals and alloys	
E00000-E00999	Actinium
E01000-E20999	Cerium
E21000-E45999	Mixed rare earths(1)
E46000-E47999	Dysprosium
E48000-E49999	Erbium
E50000-E51999	Europium
E52000-E55999	Gadolinium
E56000-E57999	Holmium
E58000-E67999	Lanthanum
E68000-E68999	Lutetium
E69000-E73999	Neodymium
E74000-E77999	Praseodymium
E78000-E78999	Promethium
E79000-E82999	Samarium
E83000-E84999	Scandium
E85000-E86999	Terbium
E87000-E87999	Thulium
E88000-E89999	Ytterbium
E90000-E99999	Yttrium
F00001-F99999 Cast irons	Gray, malleable, pearlitic malleable, and ductile (nodular) cast irons
K00001-K99999 Miscellaneous steels and ferrous alloys	
L00001-L99999 Low-melting metals and alloys	
L00001-L00999	Bismuth
L01001-L01999	Cadmium
L02001-L02999	Cesium
L03001-L03999	Gallium
L04001-L04999	Indium
L06001-L06999	Lithium
L07001-L07999	Mercury
L08001-L08999	Potassium
L09001-L09999	Rubidium
L10001-L10999	Selenium
L11001-L11999	Sodium
L13001-L13999	Tin
L50001-L59999	Lead
M00001-M99999 Miscellaneous nonferrous metals and alloys	
M00001-M00999	Antimony
M01001-M01999	Arsenic
M02001-M02999	Barium
M03001-M03999	Calcium
M04001-M04999	Germanium
M05001-M05999	Plutonium
M06001-M06999	Strontium
M07001-M07999	Tellurium
M08001-M08999	Uranium
M10001-M19999	Magnesium
M20001-M29999	Manganese
M30001-M39999	Silicon

UNS Series	Metal
P00001-P99999 Precious metals and alloys	
P00001-P00999	Gold
P01001-P01999	Iridium
P02001-P02999	Osmium
P03001-P03999	Palladium
P04001-P04999	Platinum
P05001-P05999	Rhodium
P06001-P06999	Ruthenium
P07001-P07999	Silver
R00001-R99999 Reactive and refractory metals and alloys	
R01001-R01999	Boron
R02001-R02999	Hafnium
R03001-R03999	Molybdenum
R04001-R04999	Niobium (Columbium)
R05001-R05999	Tantalum
R06001-R06999	Thorium
R07001-R07999	Tungsten
R08001-R08999	Vanadium
R10001-R19999	Beryllium
R20001-R29999	Chromium
R30001-R39999	Cobalt
R40001-R49999	Rhenium
R50001-R59999	Titanium
R60001-R69999	Zirconium
W00001-W99999 Welding filler metals, classified by weld deposit composition	
W00001-W09999	Carbon steel with no significant alloying elements
W10000-W19999	Manganese-molybdenum low alloy steels
W20000-W29999	Nickel low alloy steels
W30000-W39999	Austenitic stainless steels
W40000-W49999	Ferritic stainless steels
W50000-W59999	Chromium low alloy steels
W60000-W69999	Copper base alloys
W70000-W79999	Surfacing alloys
W80000-W89999	Nickel base alloys
Z00001-Z99999 Zinc and zinc alloys	Zinc

1. Alloys in which the rare earths are used in the ratio of their natural occurrence (that is, unseparated rare earths). In this mixture, cerium is the most abundant of the rare earth elements.

4. Organization for Administering Unified Numbering System for Metals and Alloys

4.1 The organization for administering the UNS consists of: (1) an advisory board, (2) several number-assigning offices, (3) a corps of volunteer consultants, and (4) staffs at ASTM and SAE. In addition, SAE and ASTM committees dealing with various groups of materials may be consulted.

4.1.1 The Advisory Board has approximately 20 volunteer members who are affiliated with major producing and using industries, trade associations, government agencies, and standards societies, and who have extensive experience with identification, classification, and specification of materials. The Board is the administrative arm of SAE and ASTM on all matters pertaining to the UNS. It coordinates thinking on the format of each series of numbers and the administration of each by selected experts. It sets up ground rules for determining eligibility of any material for a UNS number, for requesting such numbers, and for appealing unfavorable rulings. It is the final referee on matters of disagreement between requesters and assigners.

4.1.2 UNS number assigners for certain materials are set up at trade associations which have successfully administered their own numbering systems; for other materials, assigners are located at the offices of SAE and ASTM. Each of these assigners has the responsibility for administering a specific series of numbers, as shown in Table 3. Each considers requests for assignment of new UNS numbers, and informs applicants of the action taken. Trade association UNS number assigners also report immediately to both SAE and ASTM details of each number assignment. ASTM and SAE assigners collaborate with designated consultants when considering requests for assignment of new numbers.

TABLE 3—NUMBER ASSIGNERS AND AREAS OF RESPONSIBILITY

Assigner	Area of responsibility
The Aluminum Association 900 19th Street, NW, Suite 30 Washington, DC 20006 Telephone: (202) 862-5100	Aluminum and aluminum alloys UNS Number Series: A00001-A99999
American Society for Testing and Materials 100 Barr Harbor Drive West Conshohocken, PA 19428-2959 Attention: Office for Unified Numbering System for Metals Telephone: (215) 299-5400	Rare earth and rare earth-like metals and alloys UNS Number Series: E00001-E99999 Cast irons UNS Number Series: F00001-F99999 Cast steels UNS Number Series: J00001-J99999 Miscellaneous steels and ferrous alloys UNS Number Series: K00001-K99999 Low melting metals and alloys UNS Number Series: L00001-L99999 Miscellaneous nonferrous metals and alloys UNS Number Series: M00001-M99999 Precious metals and alloys UNS Number Series: P00001-P99999
American Welding Society 550 N.W. LeJeune Road P.O. Box 351040 Miami, FL 33135 Attention: Office for Unified Numbering System Telephone: (800) 443-9353 Fax: 303-443-7559	Welding filler metals UNS Number Series: W00001-W99999
Copper Development Association 260 Madison Avenue New York, NY 10016-2401 Attention: Office for Unified Numbering System for Metals Telephone: (212) 251-7200	Copper and copper alloys UNS Number Series: C00001-C99999
SAE (Society of Automotive Engineers) 400 Commonwealth Drive Warrendale, PA 15096-0001 Attention: Office for Unified Numbering System for Metals Telephone: (412) 776-4841	Carbon and alloy steels UNS Number Series: G00001 - G99999 H-steels UNS Number Series: H00001-H99999 Nickel and nickel alloys UNS Number Series: N00001-N99999 Heat and corrosion resistant (stainless) steels UNS Number Series: S00001 - S99999 Tool steels UNS Number Series: T00001 - T99999
Zinc Institute, Inc. 292 Madison Avenue New York, NY 10017 Attention: Office for Unified Numbering System for Metals Telephone: (212) 578-4750	Zinc and zinc alloys UNS Number Series: Z00001 - Z99999

4.1.3 Consultants are selected by the Advisory Board to provide expert knowledge of a specific field of materials. Since they are utilized primarily by the Board and the SAE and ASTM number assigners, they are not listed in this document. At the request of the ASTM or SAE number assigner, a consultant considers a request for a new number in light of the ground rules established for the material involved, decides whether a new number is justified, and informs the ASTM or SAE number assigner accordingly.

This utilization of experts (consultants and number assigners) is intended to insure prompt and fair consideration of all requests. It permits each decision to be based on current knowledge of the needs of a specific industry of producers and users.

4.1.4 Staff members at SAE and ASTM maintain duplicate master listings of all UNS numbers assigned.

4.1.5 Established SAE and ASTM committees which normally deal with standards and specifications for the materials covered by the UNS, and other knowledgeable persons, are called upon by the Advisory Board for advice when considering appeals from unfavorable rulings in the matter of UNS number assignments.

*5. **Procedure for Requesting Number Assignment to Metals and Alloys Not Already Covered by UNS Numbers (or Codes)***

5.1 UNS numbers are assigned only to metals and alloys which have a commercial standing (as defined in 6.1).

5.2 The need for a new number should always be verified by determining from the latest complete listing of already assigned UNS numbers that a usable number is not available. (See 6.4.)

5.3 For a new UNS number to be assigned, the composition (or other properties, as applicable) must be significantly different from those of any metal or alloy which has already been assigned a UNS number.

5.3.1 In the case of metals or alloys that are normally identified or specified by chemical composition, the chemical composition limits must be reported.

5.3.2 In the case of metals or alloys which are normally identified or specified by mechanical (or other) properties, such properties and limits thereof must be reported. Only those chemical elements and limits, if any, which are significant in defining such materials need be reported.

5.4 Requests for new numbers shall be submitted on "Application for UNS Number Assignment" forms (Figure 1). Copies of these are available from any UNS number assigning office (Table 3) or facsimiles may be made of the one herein.

5.5 All instructions on the printed application form should be read carefully and all information provided as indicated. (See 6.5.)

5.6 To further assist in assigning UNS numbers, the requester is encouraged to suggest a possible UNS number in each request, giving appropriate consideration to any existing number presently used by a trade association, standards society, producer, or user.

5.7 Each completed application form shall be sent to the UNS number assigning office having responsibility for the series of numbers which appears to most closely relate to the material described on the form (Table 3).

*6. **Notes***

6.1 The terms "commercial standing," "production usage," and others, are intended to portray a material in active industrial use, although the actual amount of such use will depend, among other things, upon the type of materials. (Obviously gold will not be used in the same "tonnages" as hot rolled steel.)

Different standardizing groups use different criteria to define the status that a material has to attain before a standard number will be assigned to it. For instance, the American Iron and Steel Institute requires for stainless steels "two or more producers with combined production of 200 tons per year for at least two years"; the Copper Development Association requires that the material be "in commercial use (without tonnage limits)"; the Aluminum Association requires that the alloy must be "offered for sale (not necessarily in commercial use)"; the SAE Aerospace Materials Division calls for "repetitive procurement by at least two users."

While it is apparent that no hard and fast usage definition can be set up for an all-encompassing system, the UNS numbers are intended to identify metals and alloys that are in more or less regular production and use.

A UNS number will not ordinarily be issued for a material which has just been conceived or which is still in only experimental trial.

6.2 Organizations that issue specifications should report to appropriate UNS number assigning offices (see 4.1.2) any specification changes which affect descriptions shown in published UNS listings.

APPLICATION FOR UNS NUMBER ASSIGNMENT
and
Data Input Sheet for Entering a Specific Material in the SAE-ASTM Unified Numbering System for Metals and Alloys
(See Reverse Side for Instructions for Completing This Form)

Material Description ____________________

____________________ **Suggested UNS No.** ____________________

***UNS Assigned Description** ____________________

____________________ ***UNS Assigned No.** ____________________

***Chemical Composition (percent by wt.)**

Silver	Ag	____	Hafnium	Hf	____	Sulfur	S	____
Aluminum	Al	____	Mercury	Hg	____	Antimony	Sb	____
Arsenic	As	____	Indium	In	____	Selenium	Se	____
Gold	Au	____	Iridium	Ir	____	Silicon	Si	____
Boron	B	____	Lithium	Li	____	Tin	Sn	____
Beryllium	Be	____	Magnesium	Mg	____	Tantalum	Ta	____
Bismuth	Bi	____	Manganese	Mn	____	Tellurium	Te	____
Carbon	C	____	Molybdenum	Mo	____	Thorium	Th	____
Columbium	Cb	____	Nitrogen	N	____	Titanium	Ti	____
Cadmium	Cd	____	Nickel	Ni	____	Uranium	U	____
Cobalt	Co	____	Oxygen	O	____	Vanadium	V	____
Chromium	Cr	____	Phosphorus	P	____	Tungsten	W	____
Copper	Cu	____	Lead	Pb	____	Zinc	Zn	____
Iron	Fe	____	Platinum	Pt	____	Zirconium	Zr	____
Germanium	Ge	____	Rhenium	Re	____			
Hydrogen	H	____	Rhodium	Rh	____			

Other ____________________

***Cross References**

AA ____________________
ACI ____________________
AISI ____________________
AMS ____________________
ANSI ____________________
ASME ____________________
ASTM ____________________
AWS ____________________
CDA ____________________
FED ____________________
MIL SPEC ____________________
SAE ____________________
OTHER ____________________

Requesting Person and Organization (full address) ____________________

____________________ **Date of Request** ____________________

***Assigning Org.** ____________________ ***Date of UNS Assignment** ____________________

Assigner's Name and Office ____________________

Applicant: DO NOT write in shaded areas. *** These items for Computer Operator**

FIGURE 1A—APPLICATION FORM FOR UNS NUMBER ASIGNMENT (FRONT)

GENERAL

Before attempting to complete this form, the applicant should be thoroughly familiar with the objectives of the UNS and the "ground rules" for assigning numbers, as stated in Section 4 of SAE J1086 and ASTM E 527.

MATERIAL DESCRIPTION

Identify: the base element; the single alloying element that constitutes 50% or more of the total alloy content; other distinguishing predominant characteristics (such as "casting"); and common or generic names if any (such as "ounce metal" or "Waspalloy"). When no single element makes up 50% or more of the total alloy content, list in decreasing order of abundance the two alloying elements which together constitute the largest portion of the total alloy content; except that if no two elements make up at least 50% of the total alloy content, list the three most abundant, and so on. Instead of "iron," use "steel" to identify the base element of those iron-low-carbon alloys commonly known as steels.

When mechanical properties or physical characteristics are the primary defining criteria and chemical composition is secondary or nonsignificant, enter such properties and characteristics with the appropriate values or limits for each.

SUGGESTED UNS NO.

While applicant's suggestion may or may not be the one finally assigned, it will assist proper identification of the material by the UNS Number Assigner.

CHEMICAL COMPOSITION

Enter limits such as 0.13-0.18 (not .13-.18 or 0.13 to 0.18), 1.5 max, 0.040 min, and balance. In space designated "other," enter information such as "0.05 max each, 0.15 max total" and "Sn+Pb 2.0 min." Additional specific elements not included in the list on this form may be entered in the spaces provided at the end of the list.

CROSS REFERENCES

Letter symbols listed indicate widely known trade associations and standards issuing organizations. Enter after appropriate symbols any known specification numbers or identification numbers issued by such groups to cover material equivalent to, similar to, or closely resembling the subject material.

Examples: SAE J404 (50B44), AISI 415, ASTM A 638 (660)

In space designated "other" enter any pertinent numbers issued by groups not listed above. In these instances, the full name and address of the issuing group shall be included.

SUBMIT COMPLETED FORM TO APPROPRIATE UNS NUMBER ASSIGNER, AS LISTED IN SAE J1086 AND ASTM E 527

FIGURE 1B—APPLICATION FORM FOR UNS NUMBER ASSIGNMENT (BACK)

6.3 This arrangement of alphanumeric six character numbers is a compromise of the thinking that identification numbers should indicate many characteristics of the material, and the thinking that numbers should be short and uncomplicated to be widely accepted and used.

6.4 In assigning UNS numbers, and consequently in searching complete listings of numbers, the predominant element of the metal or alloy usually determines the prefix letter of the series to which it is assigned. In certain instances where no one element predominates, arbitrary decisions are made as to what prefix letter to use, depending upon the producing industry and other factors.

6.5 The application form is designed to serve also as a data input sheet to facilitate processing each request through to final printout of the data on electronic data processing equipment and to minimize transcription errors at number-assigning offices and data processing centers.

6.6 One such listing is ASTM Publication No. DS-56 and SAE Handbook Supplement HS-1086 (a joint ASTM-SAE publication).

SELECTION AND USE OF STEELS—SAE J401 APR2000 SAE Information Report

Report of the SAE Iron and Steel Technical Committee approved June 1911, revised April 1981, and reaffirmed December 1988. Reaffirmed by the SAE Iron and Steel Technical Committee Division 1—Carbon and Alloy Steels of the SAE Iron and Steel Technical Committee November 1992 and revised April 2000. Rationale statement available.

1. Scope—The SAE system of designating steels, described in SAE J402, classifies and numbers them according to chemical composition. In the case of the high-strength, low-alloy steels in SAE J1392 and J1442 and the high-strength carbon and alloy die drawn steels in SAE J935, minimum mechanical property requirements have been included in the designations. In addition, hardenability data on most of the alloy steels and some of the carbon steels will be found in SAE J1268.

2. References

2.1 Applicable Publications—The following publications form a part of this specification to the extent specified herein. The latest issue of SAE publications shall apply.

2.1.1 SAE PUBLICATIONS—Available from SAE, 400 Commonwealth Drive, Warrendale, PA 15096-0001.

SAE J402—SAE Numbering System for Wrought or Rolled Steels
SAE J935—High Strength Carbon and Alloy Die Drawn Steels
SAE J412—General Characteristics and Heat Treatments of Steels
SAE J1099—Technical Report on Fatigue Properties
SAE J1268—Hardenability Bands for Carbon and Alloy H Steels
SAE J1392—Steel, High-Strength, Hot-Rolled Sheet and Strip, Cold-Rolled Sheet and Coated Sheet
SAE J1442—High-Strength, Hot-Rolled Steel Plates, Bars and Shapes
SAE AE-4—Fatigue Design Handbook

2.1.2 ASM PUBLICATIONS—Available from American Society for Metals, Metals Park, OH.

The Selection of Steel for Metal Toughness, ASM Handbook, 9th Edition, Vol. 1, p. 403
Toughness and Fracture Mechanics, ASM Handbook, 8th Edition, Vol. 10, p. 30

2.2 Related Publications—The following publications are provided for information purposes only and are not a required part of this document.

More detailed information on the characteristics, application and heat treatment of SAE steels is given in the SAE Information Report J412 in the SAE Handbook. References 1–4, 7, 8, and 10 are representative of meaningful articles that have appeared in other publications. References 5 and 9 deal with the various tests for toughness and their significance. Reference 6 details the application of linear elastic fracture mechanics. Reference 11 fatigue strength and design.

a. Kern, R. F., "Selection of Steels for Heat Treated Parts." *Metal Progress*, Vol. 94, No. 5, November, 1968, p. 60 and No. 6, December, 1968, p. 71.
b. Weymueller, C. F., "Selecting Steels for Heat Treated Auto and Truck Parts." *Metal Progress*, Vol. 94, No. 4, October, 1968, p. 125.
c. Fox, M. M., "Saving by Substituting for Alloy Steels." *Metal Progress*, Vol. 96, No. 6, December, 1969, p. 95.
d. Kern, R. F., "Selecting Steels for Carburized Gears." *Metal Progress*, Vol. 102, No. 1, July, 1972, p. 53.
e. "The Variations in Charpy V-notch Impact Properties in Plates." American Iron and Steel Institute, Washington, DC, 1989.
f. Barsom, J. M. and Rolfe, S. T., "Fracture and Fatigue Control in Structures—Applications of Fracture Mechanics." 2nd Edition, Prentice-Hall, Inc., Englewood Cliffs, NJ, 1987.
g. Nagaraja Rao, N. R., Lohmann, M., and Tall, L., "Effect of Strain Rate on the Yield Stress of Structural Steels." *Journal of Materials*, March, 1966.
h. Barsom, J. M., "Material Considerations in Structural Steel Design." *Engineering Journal*, American Institute of Steel Construction, Chicago, IL, Vol. 24, No. 3, 1987.
i. Barsom, J. M., "Properties of Bridge Steels." Vol. I, Chap. 3, *Highway Structures Design Handbooks*, American Institute of Steel Construction, Chicago, IL, May, 1991.
j. "Commentary on Highly Restrained Welded Connections." *Engineering Journal*, American Institute of Steel Construction, Third quarter, 1973.
k. Signes, E. G., et al, "Factors Affecting Fatigue Strength of Welded High Strength Steels." *British Welding Journal*, Vol. 14, No. 3, 1967.

3. Steel Designation—The steels so designated have been developed cooperatively by producers and users and have been found through long experience to cover most of the wrought ferrous materials used in automotive vehicles and related equipment. Because the SAE designations provide a convenient way for engineers to state briefly but clearly the chemical composition, and in some instances, some of the properties desired, they are widely recognized and used throughout the United States and in many other countries.

It should be recognized that the many technological variations of the steel-making process, coupled with the diverse requirements of the numerous processes used in the manufacture of components, make it impossible for these brief SAE designations to completely describe any steel. A specification consists of a designation and whatever supplementary information may be necessary to describe the product desired. For this reason these designations should never be referred to as specifications, nor should they be used for purchasing unless accompanied by the necessary supplementary information to describe commercially the product desired.

4. Selection—A material for any particular use is properly selected when a part made from it satisfies the engineering and service requirements at the lowest final cost. Many factors enter into such a selection, the principal ones being: the mechanical and physical properties required to satisfy the engineering and service requirements; the cost and availability of the material; the cost of processing, such as machining, welding, or heat-treating; and the suitability of available processing equipment or the cost of new equipment that must be purchased. These considerations require input from the designer, the test engineer, the metallurgist, the manufacturing or process engineer, and the buyer. Since the pertinent factors vary widely, the correct choice of material for any set of conditions is the one that provides the best balance among all the factors. Thus, a categorical selection for a given part is impractical. The successful use of different steels for similar parts is ample evidence of the complexity of the problem.

5. Static Loading—Selection of materials is least complicated when the loading is static or the frequency of application of load during the expected life is so low that the possibility of fatigue may be neglected. In such cases, yield strength or the more precisely determined proportional limit is the strength criterion, together with a determination of the section modulus (stiffness) required to keep the stress within the elastic range. The finished structure is designed to operate only within the elastic range of its members; no part is intended to deform plastically under any reasonably expected overload.

The opposite is true in those cases where the structure is intended to provide maximum protection with minimum weight for only one major load application as in roll-over or falling object protection structures (ROPS and FOPS). Here the maximum yield strength and the section modulus are so controlled that the structure will plastically deform under load; that is, it is the major energy absorber in the system and is an expendable item.

6. Dynamic Loading—When the loading is primarily dynamic (cyclic) as is the case in many automotive applications, resistance to fatigue becomes the foremost consideration. When tested as a rotating beam (R. R. Moore) specimen with a surface finish of 0.2 μm (10 μin) or less, the fatigue resistance of any steel, regardless of composition or condition, is more closely related to tensile strength than to any other property. For material up to about 1210 MPa (175 000 psi) the fatigue strength is about 50% of the tensile strength. For higher strength materials, this percentage decreases somewhat and the test results show increased scatter. See also SAE AE-4.

The fatigue limits thus determined are seldom realized in practice because few actual components are so highly finished, that is, free from surface imperfections in critical areas. If the surface of a critically stressed area is as-cast, as-forged, turned only, or decarburized, the fatigue strength may be reduced. Because they concentrate stress, undersize fillets, undercuts, notches, grooves, tool marks, weld cracks, and the like are highly detrimental. Since the effect increases as tensile strength rises, an attempt to increase fatigue strength by increasing tensile strength may actually decrease component life. The remedy lies in improving the design to remove the cause of the damaging stress concentration.

If the stress concentration is caused by excessive elastic deflection under load then the best and, usually, the least expensive way to remedy the difficulty is to either increase the section modulus of the affected area or decrease that of the adjacent areas, or both, the effect in either case being to reduce the deflection and the unit stress in the troubled area. This is because the elastic modulus (Young's modulus) is, for all practical purposes, the same for all steels regardless of composition or condition.

It is well established that the fatigue strength of a component can often be substantially increased by inducing compressive stresses into the outer layer in critical areas in such a way that a significant portion of the induced stress is retained after processing. In service the algebraic sum of this residual compressive stress and the applied stress (usually a tensile stress from a bending or a torsional load) results in a net decrease in the stress on the component, thus increasing fatigue life. Processes commonly used to induce residual compressive stresses are shot peening, cold rolling of radii, induction hardening, shell hardening, nitriding, carbonitriding, and, sometimes, carburizing and hardening.

The corollary of the previous is that any process or condition that leaves a residual tensile stress in the outer layer of a component is usually detrimental to fatigue life.

SAE J1099 gives some basic information on the approach to fatigue problems. The fact remains, however, that the surest guide to satisfactory fatigue resistance of a part or a structure is life testing either in actual service or under conditions that closely simulate it. The method is expensive, but the alternative can be a disappointing lack of product reliability.

*7. **Brittle Fracture***—When improved resistance to failure by brittle fracture is of concern, toughness becomes an important additional consideration. The principal factors in determining if a material behaves in a tough or brittle manner are: (a) the type of load, static or dynamic, and its magnitude; (b) the rate of loading; (c) the stress pattern, uniaxial, biaxial, or triaxial; (d) the minimum service temperature; (e) the metallurgical history of the material, rimmed, semi-killed or killed, and its microstructure, including grain size; (f) the tensile strength; and (g) the section size, rolling direction, and surface condition. In the structure in which the material is used, the presence of stress raisers of any kind from any cause will affect the behavior of the material. A detailed discussion of these factors and their interrelationship is beyond the scope of this document. See 2.1.2.

*8. **Notch Toughness***—The most commonly used measure of toughness is the charpy V-notch (CVN) test, a single-blow impact test employing a sharply notched test bar and a high strain rate. The results are reported in footpounds (joules) absorbed in breaking the specimen or by measuring the lateral expansion at the fracture site. The test has two serious limitations: first, it is not applicable to material less than 2.5 mm (0.10 in) thick and, second, because the strain rate employed is considerably higher than that normally encountered in commercial applications of steel, the results cannot be used directly in design calculations, and it is often impossible to correlate them with service.

The test is of value in two areas: first, many times, it is successfully used to compare the relative toughness of different conditions of the same steel or of different steels in any desired condition; second, it is used to determine the temperature at which the ductile-brittle transition occurs. This measure of behavior is used to provide some degree of insurance against unexpected catastrophic failure when selecting steels for low-temperature applications, provided the charpy values are related to a particular design which has been tested at the service temperature. This correlation is, perhaps, the most important use of the test, and it should, wherever and whenever possible, precede the addition of CVN requirements to a specification.

The fact remains that many machines and structures operate successfully at low temperatures without any consideration of the notch-toughness level of the material used simply because the test is so much more severe than the application that the added protection is not needed. Since the addition of a notch-toughness requirement to the material specification increases cost, failure to carefully consider the need for it can mean unnecessary material cost.

*9. **Fracture Toughness***—This test is growing in favor for evaluating the toughness of materials and structures subjected to various loading rates. It is based on the concepts of linear elastic fracture mechanics and its results are considered to be a constant of the material for a given temperature and loading rate under conditions of plane strain. The results are used to determine the stress required to cause a flaw of any given size, such as a scratch, a crack, or any unfused portion of the weld, to propagate unstably.

The concepts of fracture mechanics have also been applied extensively to analyze subcritical crack growth rates under static loading in an aggressive environment (stress-corrosion cracking), cyclic loading in a noncorrosive environment (fatigue), and under the combined effects of cyclic loading and aggressive environment (corrosive fatigue).

SAE NUMBERING SYSTEM FOR WROUGHT OR ROLLED STEEL—SAE J402 MAY1997

SAE Standard

Report of the SAE Iron and Steel Division approved January 1912, corrected June 1984. Reaffirmed by the SAE Iron and Steel Technical Committee December 1988. Revised by the SAE Iron and Steel Technical Committee Division 1—Carbon and Alloy Steels November 1993 and May 1997. Rationale statement available.

1. Scope—This SAE Standard is intended to supply a uniform means of designating wrought ferrous materials reported in SAE Standards and Recommended Practices.

A numerical index system is used to identify the compositions of the SAE steels. This system makes it possible to use numbers on shop drawings and blueprints to describe partially the composition of the material. A four-numeral series is usually used to designate standard alloy and carbon steels specified to chemical composition ranges. There are certain types of alloy steels which are designated by five numerals. The prefix E is used to designate steels which are made by the basic electric furnace process with special practices. The suffix H is used to designate standard hardenability steels. The last two digits of the four-numeral series and the last three digits of the five-numeral series are intended to indicate the approximate mean of the carbon range. For example, in the Grade 1035, 35 represents a carbon range of 0.32 to 0.38% and in Grade E52100, 100 represents a carbon range of 0.98 to 1.10%. It is necessary, however, to deviate from this system and to interpolate numbers in the case of some carbon ranges, and for variations in manganese, sulfur, or other elements with the same carbon range. The first two digits of the SAE numeral series for the various grades of alloy and carbon steel are given in Table 1.

The Unified Numbering System (UNS) is described in greater detail in SAE J1086 and ASTM E 527.

The basic numerals of the various types of standard and formerly standard SAE steels are given in Table 1.

2. References

2.1 Applicable Publications—The following publications form a part of this specification to the extent specified herein. Unless otherwise specified, the latest issue of SAE publications shall apply.

2.1.1 SAE PUBLICATIONS—Available from SAE, 400 Commonwealth Drive, Warrendale, PA 15096-0001.

SAE J403—Chemical Compositions of SAE Carbon Steels
SAE J404—Chemical Compositions of SAE Alloy Steels
SAE J405—Chemical Compositions of SAE Wrought Stainless Steels
SAE J1081—Potential Standard Steels
SAE J1086—Numbering Metals and Alloys
SAE J1249—Former SAE Standard and Former SAE Ex-Steels

2.1.2 ASTM PUBLICATION—Available from ASTM, 100 Barr Harbor Drive, West Conshohocken, PA 19428-2959.

ASTM E 527—Practice for Numbering Metals and Alloys (UNS)

TABLE 1—VARIOUS GRADES OF ALLOY AND CARBON STEEL

Numerals and Digits UNS	Numerals and Digits SAE	Type of Identifying Elements	Refer to SAE Standard or Information Report - JXXX for Composition Limits
		CARBON STEELS	
G10XX0	10XX	Nonresulfurized, Manganese 1.00% maximum	403 and 1249
G11XX0	11XX	Resulfurized	403 and 1249
G12XX0	12XX	Rephosphorized and Resulfurized	403
G15XX0	15XX	Nonresulfurized, Manganese Maximum over 1.00%	403 and 1249
		ALLOY STEELS	
G13XX0	13XX	Manganese Steels	404 and 1249
G23XX0	23XX	Nickel Steels	1249
G25XX0	25XX	Nickel Steels	1249
G31XX0	31XX	Nickel-Chromium Steels	1249
G32XX0	32XX	Nickel-Chromium Steels	1249
G33XX0	33XX	Nickel-Chromium Steels	1249
G34XX0	34XX	Nickel-Chromium Steels	1249
G40XX0	40XX	Molybdenum Steels	404 and 1249
G41XX0	41XX	Chromium-Molybdenum Steels	404 and 1249
G43XX0	43XX	Nickel-Chromium-Molybdenum Steels	404 and 1249
G44XX0	44XX	Molybdenum Steels	404 and 1249
G46XX0	46XX	Nickel-Molybdenum Steels	404 and 1249
G47XX0	47XX	Nickel-Chromium-Molybdenum Steels	404
G48XX0	48XX	Nickel-Molybdenum Steels	404 and 1249
G50XX0	50XX	Chromium Steels	404 and 1249
G51XX0	51XX	Chromium Steels	404 and 1249
G50XX6	50XXX	Chromium Steels	404
G51XX6	51XXX	Chromium Steels	404
G52XX6	52XXX	Chromium Steels	404
G61XX0	61XX	Chromium-Vanadium Steels	404 and 1249
G71XX0	71XXX	Tungsten-Chromium Steels	1249
G72XX0	72XX	Tungsten-Chromium Steels	1249
G81XX0	81XX	Nickel-Chromium-Molybdenum Steels	404
G86XX0	86XX	Nickel-Chromium-Molybdenum Steels	404 and 1249
G87XX0	87XX	Nickel-Chromium-Molybdenum Steels	404 and 1249
G88XX0	88XX	Nickel-Chromium-Molybdenum Steels	404
G92XX0	92XX	Silicon-Manganese Steels	404 and 1249
G93XX0	93XX	Nickel-Chromium-Molybdenum Steels	404 and 1249
G94XX0	94XX	Nickel-Chromium-Molybdenum Steels	404 and 1249
G97XX0	97XX	Nickel-Chromium-Molybdenum Steels	1249

TABLE 1—VARIOUS GRADES OF ALLOY AND CARBON STEEL (continued)

Numerals and Digits UNS	Numerals and Digits SAE	Type of Identifying Elements	Refer to SAE Standard or Information Report - JXXX for Composition Limits
G98XX0	98XX	Nickel-Chromium-Molybdenum Steels	1249
		CARBON AND ALLOY STEELS	
GXXXX1	XXBXX	B denotes Boron Steels	403 and 404
GXXXX4	XXLXX	L denotes Leaded Steels	403 and 404
------	XXVXX	V denotes Vanadium Steels	J403(1)
		STAINLESS STEELS	
S2XXXX	302XX	Chromium-Nickel Steels	405
S3XXXX	303XX	Chromium-Nickel Steels	405
S4XXXX	514XX	Chromium Steels	405
S5XXXX	515XX	Chromium Steels	405
		POTENTIAL STANDARD STEELS	
None	PS--	SAE Experimental Steels	1081

1. Applies to carbon steels only.

SELECTING AND SPECIFYING HOT-ROLLED STEEL BAR PRODUCTS—SAE J2281 MAY1997

SAE Information Report

Report of the SAE Iron and Steel Technical Committee Division 1—Carbon and Alloy Steels approved May 1997.

1. Scope—This SAE Information Report relates to hot-rolled steel bar products. It is intended as a guideline to assist in the selection and specification of hot-rolled steel bar; however, it is not to be interpreted as a material specification in itself.

1.1 Purpose—To provide general information about steel bar products and to provide a guideline for their selection and specification.

1.2 Field of Application—This document may be used as a guideline for the selection, specification, and ordering of steel bar products and as a reference and an educational document. It is intended for use by material, design, and product engineers, purchasing and material-control personnel, and educators.

2. References

2.1 Applicable Publications—The following publications form a part of this specification to the extent specified herein. Unless otherwise indicated, the latest issue of SAE publications shall apply.

2.1.1 SAE PUBLICATIONS—Available from SAE, 400 Commonwealth Drive, Warrendale, PA 15096-0001.

SAE J401—Selection and Use of Steels
SAE J403—Chemical Compositions of SAE Carbon Steels
SAE J404—Chemical Compositions of SAE Alloy Steels
SAE J406—Methods of Determining Hardenability of Steels
SAE J411—Carbon and Alloy Steels
SAE J412—General Characteristics and Heat Treatments of Steels
SAE J413—Mechanical Properties of Heat Treated Wrought Steels
SAE J416—Tensile Test Specimens
SAE J417—Hardness Tests and Hardness Number Conversions
SAE J418—Grain Size Determination of Steels
SAE J419—Methods of Measuring Decarburization
SAE J420—Magnetic Particle Inspection
SAE J422—Microscopic Determination of Inclusions in Steels
SAE J423—Methods of Measuring Case Depth
SAE J425—Electromagnetic Testings by Eddy Current Methods
SAE J428—Ultrasonic Inspection
SAE J1081—Potential Standard Steels
SAE J1099—Technical Report on Fatigue Properties
SAE J1123—Leaf Springs for Motor Vehicle Suspension
SAE J1268—Hardenability Bands for Carbon and Alloy H Steels
SAE J1397—Estimated Mechanical Properties and Machinability of Steel Bars
SAE J1868—Restricted Hardenability Bands for Selected Alloy Steels
SAE J1975—Case Hardenability of Carburized Steels

2.1.2 ANSI PUBLICATION—Available from ANSI, 11 West 42nd Street, New York, NY 10036-8002.

ANSI B 32.4-1980—Preferred Metric Sizes for Round, Square, Rectangle, and Hexagon Metal Products

2.1.3 ASTM PUBLICATIONS—Available from ASTM, 100 Barr Harbor Drive, West Conshohocken, PA 19428-2959.

ASTM A 29/A 29M—Steel Bar, Carbon and Alloy, Hot-Wrought and Cold-Finished, General Requirements for
ASTM A 255—Method for End-Quench Test for Hardenability of Steel
ASTM A 295—High-Carbon Anti-Friction Bearing Steel
ASTM A 321—Steel Bars, Carbon, Quenched and Tempered
ASTM A 370—Test Methods and Definitions for Mechanical Testing of Steel Products
ASTM A 434—Specification for Steel Bars, Alloy, Hot-Wrought or Cold-Finished, Quenched and Tempered
ASTM A 485—High Hardenability Antifriction Bearing Steel
ASTM A 534—Carburizing Steels for Anti-Friction Bearings
ASTM A 675/A 675M—Steel Bars, Carbon, Special Quality, Mechanical Properties
ASTM E 8—Test Methods of Tension Testing of Metallic Materials
ASTM E 12—Definitions of Terms Relating to Density and Specific Gravity of Solids, Liquids, and Gases
ASTM E 45—Practice for Determining the Inclusion Content of Steel
ASTM E 381—Method of Macroetch Testing, Inspection, and Rating Steel Products, Comprising Bars, Billets, Blooms, and Forgings
ASTM E 399—Test Method for Plane-Strain Fracture Toughness of Metallic Materials

2.1.4 ASM PUBLICATION—ATTN: MSC/Book Order, ASM International, PO Box 473, Novelty, OH 44072-9901.

Metals Handbook, Volume 1, Properties and Selection: Irons, Steels and High-Performance Alloys

2.1.5 FORGING INDUSTRY ASSOCIATION PUBLICATION—FIA, 25 Prospect Avenue West #300, Cleveland, OH 44115.

FIA/ASM International Forging Handbook

2.2 Related Publications—The following publications are provided for information purposes only and are not a required part of this document.

2.2.1 SAE PUBLICATIONS—Available from SAE, 400 Commonwealth Drive, Warrendale, PA 15096-0001.

SAE J402—SAE Numbering System for Wrought or Rolled Steel
SAE J409—Product Analysis—Permissible Variations from Specified Chemical Analysis of a Heat or Cast of Steel
SAE J491—Steering Ball Studs and Socket Assemblies
SAE J1121—Helical Compression and Extension Spring Terminology
SAE J1442—High-Strength, Hot Rolled Steel Plates, Bars and Shapes

2.2.2 ASTM PUBLICATIONS—Available from ASTM, 100 Barr Harbor Drive, West Conshohocken, PA 19428-2959.

ASTM A 108—Steel Bars, Carbon, Cold Finished, Standard Quality
ASTM A 291—Steel Forgings, Carbon and Alloy, for Pinions, Gears and Shafts for Reduction Gears
ASTM A 322—Steel Bars, Alloy, Standard Grades
ASTM A 331—Steel Bars, Alloy, Cold Finished
ASTM A 355—Steel Bars, Alloys for Nitriding
ASTM A 400—Steel Bars, Selection Guide, Composition, and Mechanical Properties, Standard Practice for
ASTM A 535—Special Quality Ball and Roller Bearing Steel
ASTM A 521—Steel, Closed-Impression Die Forgings for General Industrial Use
ASTM A 576—Steel Bars, Carbon, Hot-Wrought, Special Quality
ASTM A 688/A 688M—Steel Forgings, Carbon and Alloy, for General Industrial Use
ASTM A 689—Carbon and Alloy Steel Bars for Springs
ASTM A 920—Steel Bars, Microalloy, Hot-Wrought, Special Quality, Mechanical Properties
ASTM A 921—Steel Bars, Microalloy, Hot-Wrought, Special Quality, for Subsequent Hot Forging

2.2.3 AMERICAN IRON AND STEEL INSTITUTE PUBLICATION—Available from AISI, 2000 Town Center, 1900 Southfield, MI 48075-1137.

Steel Bar Product Guidelines, Bar Steel Alloy, Carbon and Microalloy Steels: Semifinished, Hot Rolled Bars, Cold Finished Bars, Hot Rolled Deformed and Plain Concrete Reinforcing Bars

3. Manufacture—As a means of introducing the product, the following briefly describes the methods of hot-rolled steel bar manufacture. Refer also to SAE J412 for a definition of some of the steel making terms. A steel bar may be derived from an ingot which is the product of a steel heat "teemed" into individual molds or from a strand casting process which involves pouring and solidifying steel heats continuously in a strand. Strand casting is the predominant method of steel bar manufacture in North America. There are two strand casting techniques associated with bar products, namely bloom casting and billet casting. A cast bloom or ingot is relatively large and requires reduction by hot rolling into a billet. Billets, whether from cast blooms or ingots, are frequently inspected and conditioned to enhance surface quality. Billets are the feedstock used in a bar mill to roll a bar product or by an open die forger to produce a forged product. Dimensional accuracy and other requirements for billets are normally subject to agreement between steel producer and purchaser. Hot-rolled steel bar is the finished product rolled from a billet, produced in lengths and coils, in numerous sections and sizes and to specific tolerances related to chemistry, dimension, surface, internal condition, mechanical properties and hardenability. Bar products may be further processed by thermal treating, descaling, and cold drawing prior to use.

4. Selection Guidelines—Hot-rolled steel bar is widely used in, but not limited to, original equipment manufacturing such as automotive, off highway, agriculture, military, railway, industrial equipment, and appliance industries. Manufacturing processing may involve forming (hot, warm, or cold forming, and cold drawing), heat treating (quench and tempering and surface hardening), machining (turning, drilling, broaching, and grinding) and surface finishing (plating and painting).

Hot-rolled bars may be selected on the basis of one or several application requirements including static, cyclic (fatigue) and dynamic (impact) load resistance, rolling contact fatigue resistance and response to various manufacturing processes. SAE J401 will assist the reader in designing parts from steel including hot-rolled bar. Further, SAE J412 is a useful selection guide showing the chemistry (grade), grain size, microstructure, cleanliness, and surface quality are important factors when selecting a hot-rolled bar product and how these factors influence processing and ultimate end use.

4.1 Mechanical Properties—Hot-rolled steel bar products can be furnished to specified minimum strengths (tensile and yield strength) or, as is more often the case, they are processed into varying hardness levels through heat treatment by the end user. SAE J413 provides mechanical properties for a range of material hardness resulting from heat treatment. It further illustrates the principle that regardless of chemical composition (grade), steels of the same cross-section hardness produced by tempering after through hardening, will have approximately the same tensile strength. Yield strength, as a percentage of tensile strength, is highest if the section is through hardened to a martensitic structure before tempering. Hot-rolled steel bar products can be furnished with certain hardenability requirements which assure the end user that minimum hardness can be achieved via proper quench and temper heat treatment (see 5.8).

4.1.1 FATIGUE PROPERTIES—Parts and components made from hot-rolled steel bar are frequently subject to fatigue loading. Designing to avoid fatigue failures requires, among other factors, a knowledge of material properties existing in the finished part at the most critically stressed location. SAE J1099 contains fatigue properties of several steel bar grades (carbon and alloy steels).

4.1.2 FRACTURE TOUGHNESS—Parts are frequently subjected to impact loads and their constituent material should possess sufficient fracture toughness to withstand the load at service temperature without failing. Parts made from steel and steel bar generally have good fracture toughness and resistance. Steels are frequently tested using impact loading on specimens with prepared notches to examine the nature of the fracture (ductile or brittle) and the energy absorption. Charpy V Notch testing, as specified in ASTM A 370 is a popular method, however, it and similar tests are comparative and can only show relative performance. Fracture mechanics provides a more engineered prediction of fracture resistance. Fracture mechanics treats fracture toughness as the resistance to crack growth. Cracks are frequently present, either introduced during manufacture or initiated early in the life of the component. Resistance offered by the material to crack growth is as significant as the type of loading and environment in predicting crack growth resistance. Fracture mechanics uses a parameter called the plane strain fracture toughness, K_{Ic}, a type of stress intensity factor. The property K_{Ic} determined by the test method outlined in ASTM E 399 characterizes material fracture resistance in a non-corrosive environment in the presence of a sharp crack under severe tensile constraint. A K_{Ic} value is believed to represent the lower limiting value of fracture toughness and can be used to estimate the relationship between failure stress and defect size in a material in service.

4.1.3 ROLLING CONTACT FATIGUE—Contact stress resistance is often defined as rolling contact fatigue resistance in bearing applications. Rolling contact fatigue strength measures the Hertzian contact stress between two rotating surfaces. This fatigue strength is measured by the resistance to failure from pitting or spalling when constant load is applied under controlled lubricant conditions. Bearing steel cleanliness strongly influences the rolling contract fatigue strength of a component since pitting or spalling sites are often initiated from subsurface nonmetallic inclusions. The oxide type inclusion has the most deleterious effect on rolling contact fatigue. Oxide type nonmetallic inclusions form a poor interface with the steel matrix due to their very hard and brittle properties. They tend to be grouped in small clusters that increase the stress concentration critical for initiating fatigue failures. Bar steels intended for rolling contact applications are frequently specified to have certain cleanliness levels or ratings.

Maximum bearing steel inclusion cleanliness ratings are specified in ASTM A 295 for high carbon grades, ASTM A 485 for high carbon/high hardenability steel grades, and ASTM A 534 for carburized grades. The nonmetallic inclusion rating scales used in any of the previous specifications are shown in the Jernkontoret ("J") charts described in ASTM E 45. The nonmetallic inclusion field rating charts include sulfides (A type), aluminates (B types), silicates (C types), and oxides (D types).

4.2 Processing

4.2.1 FORMING—Bulk forming of hot-rolled bars is employed in the manufacture of numerous parts and components. Hot forging is a widely used method as is cold forming. Warm forming is an increasing popular technique which takes advantage of reduced metal flow resistance through an intermediate temperature warming of the material. Warm and cold forming are near net shape techniques which reduce the amount of machining for the final part. The primary feature of forming is the enhancement of mechanical properties in the direction of major metal flow during forming. Microalloyed forging steels take advantage of the heat of hot forging and, by control of cooling, achieve desirable mechanical properties without subsequent heat treatment. Many steel bar products are suitable for forming. Steel bars in the 10XX, 11XX, and 15XX Carbon series and the 13XX, 40XX, 41XX, and 43XX Alloy series are popular. Products with relatively low carbon content, for example SAE 1020, 1038, 4137, 5140, and 8620 are commonly cold formed. Detailed information about bulk forming may be found in the FIA/ASM International Forging Handbook.

4.2.2 MACHINING—Machining can be a major and therefore important factor in overall processing cost when considering steel bar selection. Machinability is the relative measure of the ease of machining in a given set of circumstances. This may mean the amount of tool force and wear, required cycle time, ease of chip formation, and surface finish. The material selection has a major impact on machinability and certain steel bar grades produced with machining in mind. Cold drawing markedly improves consistency of machining. An interpretation widely used in the industry is SAE J1397 which provides a machinability rating for various SAE grades of steel bar in hot-rolled and cold-drawn condition.

4.2.3 HEAT TREATING—Hot-rolled steel bars and parts made from hot-rolled bars are heat treated in order attain the hardness and microstructure required in the final product or to make them suitable for further processing. Heat treating can consist of annealing, stress relieving, quench and tempering, and surface hardening. The various types of annealing are performed to soften the material and to alter the microstructure. A frequently employed method of increasing hardness and strength of the higher carbon and alloy steel grades, particularly after forming of the part, is quench and tempering. This involves heating and holding above the critical temperature, rapid cooling by quenching followed by a subcritical heating called tempering to restore ductility. Surface hardening describes techniques that selectively harden the surface of the bar or part to increase surface strength and wear resistance. Reference may be made to the ASM Handbook for further information about these heat treatment methods.

5. Specification Guidelines—Hot-rolled steel bars are normally specified on the basis of the following:

5.1 Carbon, Alloy, and Microalloy Steel—The designations carbon steel and alloy steel, which are defined in SAE J411, are frequently used when specifying hot-rolled steel bars. The common practice is to designate "C" for carbon steel and "Alloy" for alloy steel. Microalloy steels (sometimes referred to as high strength low alloy) are intended for use in the as-rolled condition or in hot forging where the desired mechanical properties are developed during the forge process.

5.2 Grade—Steel grade or chemical composition determines strength, hardness, and response to thermal treatment in steel products. Hot-rolled steel bars are produced in the standard grades shown in SAE J403, J404, and J1081 and in many modified versions of these SAE chemical compositions. The SAE grade designation should be used when specifying hot-rolled bars.

5.3 Quality—A quality designation is often used in specifying steel bar. The designation implies material characteristics that are important for the intended end use. Characteristics such as surface and internal condition, and the steps taken during manufacture to assure their adequate level, are associated with a quality designation. Special Bar Quality, Special Quality, or "SQ" are carbon steel bar designations. Similarly, Regular Quality Alloy or simply "Alloy," as shown in 5.1, implies an alloy steel bar product. Sometimes more specific designations are used: for example Axle Shaft, Bearing, Cold Heading, Aircraft, and Magnaflux Qualities identifying a very specific end use. Merchant Quality is the base quality for hot-rolled carbon steel bars intended for non-critical end uses.

5.4 Dimensional Characteristics—Bar products are produced to specified shape (or section), dimension, and tolerances commonly available as follows:

5.4.1 SECTIONS AND SIZE RANGES

Rounds[1] (RDS): 12 mm to 320 mm
Squares[1] (SQS): from 12 mm to 150 mm across flat
Hexagons[1] (HEX): 12 mm to 100 mm across flat
Flats and Rectangles[1]: Over 5.0 mm thick and up to 150 mm width
Round Edge Flats[2]: 5.0 mm thick and over and up to 150 mm width

Producers should be consulted to determine availability of sizes of Round Corner Squares (RCS) or of a particular section and size within or outside the ranges shown previously.

5.4.2 LENGTHS AND COILS—Bars are rolled and cut to specified length (order length) by shearing and sawing or are rolled and coiled. Bar lengths, coil weights, and their dimensions vary by producer.

5.4.3 DIMENSIONAL TOLERANCES—Applicable section and size tolerances are shown in ASTM A 29/A 29M. Straightness and length tolerances for length products are also defined in ASTM A 29/A29M. More restrictive tolerances than are shown in ASTM A 29/A 29M may be agreed upon between supplier and purchaser.

5.5 Mechanical Properties—Hot-rolled carbon steel bars can be produced to meet mechanical properties with associated limited chemical requirements. Mechanical property requirements for Carbon and Microalloy steel bars are found in ASTM A 675/A 675M and A 920 respectively. Somewhat higher properties for Carbon and Alloy bars are obtained by quench and tempering as shown in ASTM A 321 and A 434, respectively. Mechanical properties can also be subject to agreement between producer and user.

5.5.1 TENSILE TESTING—Tensile testing is a requirement for products produced to minimum tensile requirements. Tensile tests measure strength, elongation, and reduction of area in a prepared sample obtained from a product. Tensile test methods are described in ASTM A 370 and ASTM E 8. Specimens for tensile testing may be prepared in accordance with SAE J416.

5.6 Surface Characteristics—Users should recognize that hot-rolled steel bars are the product of hot rolling with inherent surface characteristics. Although great care is taken during steelmaking and bar rolling, the surface may contain certain discontinuities. Seams, lamps, and slivers are types of physical discontinuities that can have an impact in forming operations and where cyclic stress is present. Decarburization which is the absence of base carbon on and below the bar surface, is a concern for applications involving surface hardening, quench and tempering and peening. In the interest of simplicity and cost, the supplier and purchaser should determine limits on acceptable surface discontinuities. Nondestructive, sophisticated methods of inspection, particularly for physical discontinuities can be employed during or after the hot bar rolling to detect and limit them. Also, several surface metal removal processes can be employed to improve surface quality in terms of level, frequency, and smoothness. Decarburization can result from both rolling and post rolling processes. The user should consider the level of decarburization generally allowed for the bar (up to 1.6% of diameter) prior to ordering. Some grades are more prone to decarburization and, prior to further processing, may require some degree of surface metal removal.

5.6.1 SURFACE DECARBURIZATION TESTING—SAE J419 describes a method for rating the types and level of decarburization on and below the bar surface.

5.6.2 MAGNETIC PARTICLE INSPECTION—Refer to Section 6 and 6.3.

5.7 Internal Characteristics

5.7.1 GRAIN SIZE—Grain size, normally refers to the size of prior austenite grains, is largely dependent on the steel making practice and is an important factor governing mechanical properties. A fine austentite grain size generally improves toughness, ductility, and fatigue strength, but may reduce hardenability. The benefits associated with fine austenite grain size are such that fine grain size is almost always desired. Grain size can also refer to as-rolled pearlite-ferrite grain size. SAE J418 and ASTM E 12 describe methods for determining grain size of steel and steel bars.

5.7.1.1 Grain Size Determination—A rating system to indicate size and density (measured as number of grains per unit area) is provided by SAE J418. Fine austenite grain size is normally desirable and, in the interest of time and cost, ASTM A 29/A 29M allows a certain minimum content of aluminum (0.020) or acid soluble aluminum (0.015) to indicate the fine grain structure.

5.7.2 MICROCLEANLINESS—Cleanliness refers to the level of non-metallic inclusions within the metal matrix. Inclusion type (mainly oxides, sulfides, and silicates) and aspect ratio (length and width) can affect the response of the material to processing (particularly machining) and service (particularly fatigue and rolling fatigue loading). Ultra-clean steels are not always desirable for machining operations.

5.7.2.1 Cleanliness Evaluation—Cleanliness is determined by two popular methods which outline rating systems to quantitatively measure steel cleanliness. Microscopic methods are described in SAE J422 and ASTM E 45. Resulfurized steels are not normally produced to sulfide inclusion ratings.

5.7.3 MACRO EVALUATION—Macroetch tests evaluate homogeneity in steel products such as bars, billets, blooms and forgings of carbon and alloy steels. ASTM E 381 describes a macroetch test method for the purpose of assessing specimens by a series of photographs showing certain conditions and forming a basis of agreement between supplier and purchaser.

5.8 Hardenability—Hardenability is an important consideration as it defines the response of steel to heat treatment by determining the depth and distribution of hardness induced by quenching from above the transformation temperature. Chemical composition and grain size influence hardenability with many elements making varying degrees of contribution. Hardenability bands in SAE J1268 and SAE J1868 indicate achievable hardness by appropriate thermal treating for several grades. Hot-rolled steel bar may be ordered to meet specified hardenability and restricted hardenability band limits of SAE J1268 and SAE J1868 by adding suffix "H" or "RH", respectively, to the conventional grade number (e.g., SAE 1541H or SAE 4140RH). SAE J406 defines the methods of determining hardenability of steel and steel bars.

5.8.1 HARDENABILITY TESTS—Physical tests which determine hardenability of bar steels are given in SAE J406 and ASTM A 255. Specifiers should also consider the Ideal Critical Diameter or D_I calculation methods of hardenability prediction as described in SAE J406 in the interests of time and cost. Methods for determining case hardenability are given in SAE J1975.

5.9 Hardness—Hardness, which is more or less proportional to Tensile Strength as shown in SAE J413 and which should not be confused with hardenability, depends mainly on carbon for a given cooling rate during heat treatment (i.e., cooling after hot rolling or quenching after austenitizing). A maximum hardness limit may be important in certain cold-forming operations (e.g., cold heading), cold shearing, or machining.

5.9.1 HARDNESS TESTS—Hardness testing as outlined by SAE J417 and ASTM A 370 measure the material resistance to local deformation by application of a small, relatively hard object onto the surface of a prepared sample. Several methods are used including the Brinell and Rockwell tests.

5.9.2 CASE DEPTH MEASUREMENT—Case hardening describes several processing methods for hardening in such a manner that the surface layer or case is substantially harder than the remaining material or core. Methods for measuring case depth are contained in SAE J423.

6. Nondestructive Testing—Nondestructive methods of testing and inspection are increasingly utilized in the manufacture of hot-rolled bar and by end users as cost-effective means of evaluating the product and parts produced. Nondestructive tests can be employed to measure more than one characteristic of the product and are described separately here.

6.1 Electromagnetic/Eddy Current Testing—Eddy current testing is an electromagnetic method that uses induced electrical current (Eddy current) to indicate or measure certain characteristics. Eddy current testing is used to detect surface and subsurface discontinuities, sort for chemical composition, and sort for such properties as hardness and case depth. SAE J425 provides general information and further references on Eddy current testing.

6.2 Ultrasonic Inspection—Ultrasonic inspection is based on the ability of most solids to transmit high-frequency sound waves. Controlled ultrasonic energy is introduced into the object and effects on the passage of sound are observed. Discontinuities in the material reflect, disperse, or attenuate the energy. Ultrasonic inspection is used for detection of both surface and subsurface discontinuities. SAE J428 provides further information and references.

6.3 Magnetic Particle Inspection—Magnetic particle inspection is used as an aid in visual inspection. It uses the principle of magnetic flux leakage at a discontinuity, for example a surface seam, to show a defect. Fine magnetic particles, introduced onto the surface of a magnetized test object, accumulate at the leakage flux for ready visual detection. SAE J420 provides details of the magnetic particle inspection method.

1. Based on American National Standard B32.4M-1980, Reaffirmed 1994, Preferred Metric Sizes for Round, Square, Rectangle and Hexagon Metal Products, published by the American Society of Mechanical Engineers.
2. SAE J1123, Leaf Springs for Motor Vehicle Suspension - Made to Metric Units

CHEMICAL COMPOSITIONS OF SAE CARBON STEELS—SAE J403 NOV2001

SAE Standard

Report of the SAE Iron and Steel Division approved June 1911. Revised by the SAE Iron and Steel Technical Committee December 1988, and completely revised February 1991. Revised by the SAE Iron and Steel Division 1—Carbon and Alloy Steels, May 1992, May 1994, August 1995, June 2000, and November 2001. Rationale statement available.

1. Scope—In 1941, the SAE Iron and Steel Division, in collaboration with the American Iron and Steel Institute (AISI), made a major change in the method of expressing composition ranges for the SAE steels. The plan, as now applied, is based in general on narrower cast or heat analysis ranges plus certain product analysis allowances on individual samples, in place of the fixed ranges and limits without tolerances formerly provided for carbon and other elements in SAE steels.

For years the variety of chemical compositions of steel has been a matter of concern in the steel industry. It was recognized that production of fewer grades of steel could result in improved deliveries and provide a better opportunity to achieve advances in technology, manufacturing practices, and quality, and thus develop more fully the possibilities of application inherent in those grades.

Comprehensive and impartial studies were directed toward determining which of the many grades being specified were the ones in most common demand, and the feasibility of combining compositions having like requirements. From these studies, the most common grades of steel have been selected and kept in the current revision. The cast or heat chemical composition limits or ranges of these grades are given in Tables 1, 2, 3A, and 3B. These cast or heat limits or ranges are subject to standard variations for product analysis as given in SAE J409. Since AISI is no longer issuing steel grade designations, grades listed in this document are SAE grades.

It is recognized that chemical compositions other than those listed in the previously mentioned tables will at times be needed for specialized applications or processing. When such a steel is required, the elements comprising the desired chemical composition are specified in one of three ways: (a) by a minimum limit, (b) by a maximum limit, or (c) by minimum and maximum limits, termed a range.

Standard cast or heat analysis limits and ranges for the various elements of carbon steels are given in Table 4. In this table, range is the arithmetical difference between the minimum and maximum limits (that is, 0.19 to 0.25 is a 0.06 range). These cast or heat limits and ranges are also subject to standard variations for product analysis as given in SAE J409.

ISTC Division 1 has developed a procedure which allows for the maintenance of the grade lists in this document. This will involve conducting an industry-wide survey to solicit input. This survey will be conducted at a frequency deemed necessary by the technical committee.

Criteria have been established for the addition to or the deletion of grades from the grade lists. New grades will be considered based on the grade meeting a SAE grade designation and chemistry, having a minimum production or consumption of 225 tonnes/year (250 tons/year) and has the sponsorship of at least two individual users or producers. New steel compositions will be considered as Potential Standard (PS) steels, based on the guidelines in SAE J1081, until such time as production of the new steel achieves a level of production or usage qualifying it for consideration as a standard steel.

Deletion of grades will be by consensus based on the grade survey. Deleted grades will be archived in SAE J1249.

When the cast or heat analysis is requested to be reported to demonstrate conformance to the chemical limits shown in Tables 1, 2, 3A, or 3B, in addition to the quantities of carbon, manganese, phosphorus, and sulfur, the following elements and their quantities shall also be reported: copper, chromium, nickel, molybdenum, and silicon. When the amount of any one of these last five elements is less than 0.02% that analysis may be reported as "<0.02%."

Based on a survey question in the 1998 Grade Survey, the grade lists have been revised such that chemistries of all product forms are now consolidated into single tables. The chemistry ranges listed will be the narrowest range for the various product forms with the exception of S content. It is acknowledged however that due to differences in the section size of the various product forms, chemical composition demands for the product forms should be different to allow for adequate flexibility of steel application. These differences are reflected in Tables 4 and 5.

2. References

2.1 Applicable Publications—The following publications form a part of this specification to the extent specified herein. Unless otherwise indicated, the latest issue of SAE publications shall apply.

2.1.1 SAE PUBLICATIONS—Available from SAE, 400 Commonwealth Drive, Warrendale, PA 15096-0001.

SAE J409—Product Analysis—Permissible Variations from Specified Chemical Analysis of a Heat or Cast of Steel
SAE J411—Carbon and Alloy Steel
SAE J1081—Potential Standard Steels
SAE J1249—Former SAE Standard and Former SAE Ex-Steels
SAE J1268—Hardenability Bands for Carbon and Alloy H Steels
SAE J1868—Restricted Hardenabilty Bands for Selected Alloy Steels

2.1.2 ISS PUBLICATION—Available from ISS, 410 Commonwealth Drive, Warrendale, PA 15086.

ISS Carbon and Alloy Steel Bar and Semi-Finished Products Manual

3. Chemical Reporting Requirements

3.1 When the cast or heat analysis is requested to be reported to demonstrate conformance to the chemical limits shown in Tables 1, 2, 3A, and 3B, in addition to the quantities of carbon, manganese, phosphorus, and sulfur, the elements and their quantities, as shown in Table 6, shall also be reported.

TABLE 1—NONRESULFURIZED CARBON STEEL COMPOSITIONS APPLICABLE TO SEMIFINISHED PRODUCTS FOR FORGING, TO HOT-ROLLED AND COLD-FINISHED BARS, TO WIRE RODS, PLATES, STRIP, SHEETS, WELDED TUBING, AND TO SEAMLESS TUBING CAST OR HEAT CHEMICAL RANGES AND LIMITS

UNS No.	SAE No.	Chemical Composition Limits, %(1)(2) C	Chemical Composition Limits, %(1) Mn	Chemical Composition Limits, %(1) P, Max	Chemical Composition Limits, %(1) S, Max
G10050	1005	0.06 Max	0.35 Max	0.030	0.050
G10060*	1006	0.08 Max	0.25–0.40	0.030	0.050
G10080*	1008	0.10 Max	0.30–0.50	0.030	0.050
G10090	1009	0.15 Max	0.60 Max	0.030	0.050
G10100	1010	0.08–0.13	0.30–0.60	0.030	0.050
G10120	1012	0.10–0.15	0.30–0.60	0.030	0.050
G10130	1013	0.11–0.16	0.30–0.60	0.030	0.050
G10150	1015	0.13–0.18	0.30–0.60	0.030	0.050
G10160	1016	0.13–0.18	0.60–0.90	0.030	0.050
G10170	1017	0.15–0.20	0.30–0.60	0.030	0.050
G10180	1018	0.15–0.20	0.60–0.90	0.030	0.050
G10190	1019	0.15–0.20	0.70–1.00	0.030	0.050
G10200	1020	0.18–0.23	0.30–0.60	0.030	0.050
G10210	1021	0.18–0.23	0.60–0.90	0.030	0.050
G10220	1022	0.18–0.23	0.70–1.00	0.030	0.050
G10230	1023	0.20–0.25	0.30–0.60	0.030	0.050
G10250	1025	0.22–0.28	0.30–0.60	0.030	0.050
G10260	1026	0.22–0.28	0.60–0.90	0.030	0.050

TABLE 1—NONRESULFURIZED CARBON STEEL COMPOSITIONS APPLICABLE TO SEMIFINISHED PRODUCTS FOR FORGING, TO HOT-ROLLED AND COLD-FINISHED BARS, TO WIRE RODS, PLATES, STRIP, SHEETS, WELDED TUBING, AND TO SEAMLESS TUBING CAST OR HEAT CHEMICAL RANGES AND LIMITS (continued)

UNS No.	SAE No.	Chemical Composition Limits, %(1)(2) C	Chemical Composition Limits, %(1) Mn	Chemical Composition Limits, %(1) P, Max	Chemical Composition Limits, %(1) S, Max
G10290	1029	0.25–0.31	0.60–0.90	0.030	0.050
G10300	1030	0.28–0.34	0.60–0.90	0.030	0.050
G10330	1033	0.30–0.36	0.70–1.00	0.030	0.050
G10350	1035	0.32–0.38	0.60–0.90	0.030	0.050
G10370	1037	0.32–0.38	0.70–1.00	0.030	0.050
G10380	1038	0.35–0.42	0.60–0.90	0.030	0.050
G10390	1039	0.37–0.44	0.70–1.00	0.030	0.050
G10400	1040	0.37–0.44	0.60–0.90	0.030	0.050
G10420	1042	0.40–0.47	0.60–0.90	0.030	0.050
G10430	1043	0.40–0.47	0.70–1.00	0.030	0.050
G10440	1044	0.43–0.50	0.30–0.60	0.030	0.050
G10450	1045	0.43–0.50	0.60–0.90	0.030	0.050
G10460	1046	0.43–0.50	0.70–1.00	0.030	0.050
G10490	1049	0.46–0.53	0.60–0.90	0.030	0.050
G10500	1050	0.48–0.55	0.60–0.90	0.030	0.050
G10530	1053	0.48–0.55	0.70–1.00	0.030	0.050
G10550	1055	0.50–0.60	0.60–0.90	0.030	0.050
G10600	1060	0.55–0.65	0.60–0.90	0.030	0.050
G10650	1065	0.60–0.70	0.60–0.90	0.030	0.050
G10700	1070	0.65–0.75	0.60–0.90	0.030	0.050
G10740	1074	0.70–0.80	0.50–0.80	0.030	0.050
G10750	1075	0.70–0.80	0.40–0.70	0.030	0.050
G10780	1078	0.72–0.85	0.30–0.60	0.030	0.050
G10800	1080	0.75–0.88	0.60–0.90	0.030	0.050
G10840	1084	0.80–0.93	0.60–0.90	0.030	0.050
G10850	1085	0.80–0.93	0.70–1.00	0.030	0.050
G10860	1086	0.80–0.93	0.30–0.50	0.030	0.050
G10900	1090	0.85–0.98	0.60–0.90	0.030	0.050
G10950	1095	0.90–1.03	0.30–0.50	0.030	0.050

1. Certain qualities and commodities are customarily produced to lower limits of phosphorus and sulfur. (See SAE J411, Table 1.)
2. NOTES

Lead—Standard carbon steels can be produced with a lead range of 0.15 to 0.35% to improve machinability. Such steels are identified by inserting the letter "L" between the second and third numerals of the grade number, for example, 10L45. The UNS designation is also modified by changing the last digit to "4" to indicate lead, for example, G10454.

BORON—Standard killed carbon steels, which are fine grain, may be produced with a boron addition to improve hardenability. Such steels are produced to a range of 0.0005 to 0.003% boron. These steels are identified by inserting the letter "B" between the second and third numerals of the grade number, for example, 10B46. The UNS designation is also modified by changing the last digit to "1" to indicate boron, for example, G10461.

COPPER—When copper is required, 0.20% minimum is generally specified.

*MANGANESE—For grades G10060 and G10080 applicable to Structural Shapes, Plates, Strip, Sheets and Welded Tubing, the manganese limit is 0.45% maximum and 0.50% maximum, respectively, with no minimum.

SILICON—BARS AND SEMIFINISHED—When silicon ranges or limits are required, the following ranges are commonly used: 0.10% max; 0.10 to 0.20%; 0.15 to 0.35%; 0.20 to 0.40%; or 0.30 to 0.60%.

RODS—When silicon is required, the following ranges and limits are commonly used for nonresulfurized steels: 0.10% max; 0.07 to 0.15%; 0.10 to 0.20%; 0.15 to 0.35%; 0.20 to 0.40%; 0.30 to 0.60%.

ADDITIONAL ELEMENTS—See 3.1 for additional elements to be reports

TABLE 2—HIGH MANGANESE CARBON STEEL COMPOSITIONS APPLICABLE ONLY TO SEMIFINISHED PRODUCTS FOR FORGING, TO HOT-ROLLED AND COLD-FINISHED BARS, PLATES, STRIP, SHEETS, AND TO SEAMLESS TUBING CAST OR HEAT CHEMICAL RANGES AND LIMITS

UNS No.	SAE No.	Chemical Composition Limits, % C	Chemical Composition Limits, % Mn	Chemical Composition Limits, % P, Max	Chemical Composition Limits, % S, Max
G15220	1522	0.18–0.24	1.10–1.40	0.030	0.050
G15240	1524	0.19–0.25	1.35–1.65	0.030	0.050
G15260	1526	0.22–0.29	1.10–1.40	0.030	0.050
G15270	1527	0.22–0.29	1.20–1.50	0.030	0.050
G15360	1536	0.30–0.37	1.20–1.50	0.030	0.050
G15410	1541	0.36–0.44	1.35–1.65	0.030	0.050
G15470	1547	0.43–0.51	1.35–1.65	0.030	0.050
G15480	1548	0.44–0.52	1.10–1.40	0.030	0.050
G15520	1552	0.47–0.55	1.20–1.50	0.030	0.050
G15660	1566	0.60–0.71	0.85–1.15	0.030	0.050

LEAD—See footnote under Table 1.

BORON—See footnote under Table 1.

PHOSPHORUS AND SULFUR—See footnote under Table 1.

SILICON—See footnote under Table 1.

ADDITIONAL ELEMENTS—(see 3)For additional elements to be reported, see 3.1.

Chemical analyses of additional high-manganese steels produced to hardenability requirements are shown in SAE J1268 and SAE J1868

TABLE 3A—FREE CUTTING CARBON STEEL COMPOSITIONS APPLICABLE TO SEMIFINISHED PRODUCTS FOR FORGING, HOT-ROLLED AND COLD-FINISHED BARS, WIRE RODS, AND SEAMLESS TUBING—RESULFURIZED CARBON STEELS CAST OR HEAT CHEMICAL RANGES AND LIMITS

UNS No.	SAE No.	Chemical Composition Limits, % C	Chemical Composition Limits, % Mn	Chemical Composition Limits, % P, Max	Chemical Composition Limits, % S, Max
G11170	1117	0.14–0.20	1.00–1.30	0.030	0.08–0.13
G11180	1118	0.14–0.20	1.30–1.60	0.030	0.08–0.13
G11260	1126	0.23–0.29	0.70–1.00	0.030	0.08–0.13
G11320	1132	0.27–0.34	1.35–1.65	0.030	0.08–0.13
G11370	1137	0.32–0.39	1.35–1.65	0.030	0.08–0.13
G11380	1138	0.34–0.40	0.70–1.00	0.030	0.08–0.13
G11400	1140	0.37–0.44	0.70–1.00	0.030	0.08–0.13
G11410	1141	0.37–0.45	1.35–1.65	0.030	0.08–0.13
G11440	1144	0.40–0.48	1.35–1.65	0.030	0.24–0.33
G11460	1146	0.42–0.49	0.70–1.00	0.030	0.08–0.13
G11510	1151	0.48–0.55	0.70–0.90	0.030	0.08–0.13

LEAD—See footnote under Table 1.

SILICON—Bars and Semifinished—See footnote under Table 1.

RODS—When silicon is required, the following ranges and limits are commonly used: 0.10 Max, 0.10–0.20 or 0.15–0.35.

ADDITIONAL ELEMENTS—(see 3) For additional elements to be reported, see 3.1.

TABLE 3B—FREE CUTTING CARBON STEEL COMPOSITIONS APPLICABLE TO SEMIFINISHED PRODUCTS FOR FORGING, HOT-ROLLED AND COLD-FINISHED BARS, WIRE RODS, AND SEAMLESS TUBING—REPHOSPHORIZED AND RESULFURIZED CARBON STEELS CAST OR HEAT CHEMICAL RANGES AND LIMITS

UNS No.	SAE No.	Chemical Composition Limits, % C, Max	Chemical Composition Limits, % Mn	Chemical Composition Limits, % P	Chemical Composition Limits, % S	Chemical Composition Limits, % Pb
G12120	1212	0.13	0.70–1.00	0.07–0.12	0.16–0.23	—
G12130	1213	0.13	0.70–1.00	0.07–0.12	0.24–0.33	—
G12150	1215	0.09	0.75–1.05	0.04–0.09	0.26–0.35	—
G12144	12L14	0.15	0.85–1.15	0.04–0.09	0.26–0.35	0.15–0.35

LEAD—See footnote under Table 1.

SILICON—It is not common practice to produce the 12xx series of steels to specified silicon because of its adverse effect on machinability.

ADDITIONAL ELEMENTS—For additional elements to be reported, (see 3)see 3.1.

TABLE 4—CARBON STEEL CAST OR HEAT CHEMICAL LIMITS AND RANGES APPLICABLE ONLY TO SEMIFINISHED PRODUCTS FOR FORGING, HOT-ROLLED AND COLD-FINISHED BARS, WIRE RODS, AND SEAMLESS TUBING

Element	Chemical Ranges and Limits, % When Maximum of Specified Element	Chemical Ranges and Limits, % Range	Chemical Ranges and Limits, % Lowest Max
Carbon[(1)]			0.06
	To 0.12 incl.	0.05	
	Over 0.12 to 0.25 incl.	0.05	
	Over 0.25 to 0.40 incl.	0.06	
	Over 0.40 to 0.55 incl.	0.07	
	Over 0.55 to 0.80 incl.	0.10	
	Over 0.80	0.13	
Manganese			0.35
	To 0.40 incl.	0.15	
	Over 0.40 to 0.50 incl.	0.20	
	Over 0.50 to 1.65 incl.	0.30	
Phosphorus			0.040
	Over 0.040 to 0.08 incl.	0.03	
	Over 0.08 to 0.13 incl.	0.05	
Sulfur			0.050
	Over 0.05 to 0.09 incl.	0.03	
	Over 0.09 to 0.15 incl.	0.05	
	Over 0.15 to 0.23 incl.	0.07	
	Over 0.23 to 0.35 incl.	0.09	
Silicon[(2)] Bars			
	To 0.15 incl.	0.08	
	Over 0.15 to 0.20 incl.	0.10	
	Over 0.20 to 0.30 incl.	0.15	
	Over 0.30 to 0.60 incl.	0.20	
Rods	When silicon is required, the following ranges and limits are commonly used: 0.10 max; 0.07–0.15, 0.10–0.20, 0.15–0.35, 0.20–0.40, or 0.30–0.60		
Copper	When copper is required, 0.20 minimum is commonly used.		
Lead[(3)]	When lead is required, a range of 0.15–0.35 is generally used.		
Boron	Boron treated fine grain steels are produced to a range of 0.0005 to 0.003% boron.		

1. The carbon ranges shown customarily apply when the specified maximum limit for manganese does not exceed 1.10%. When the maximum manganese limit exceeds 1.10%, it is customary to add 0.01 to the carbon range shown.
2. It is not common practice to produce a rephosphorized and resulfurized carbon steel to specified limits for silicon because of its adverse effect on machinability.
3. Lead is reported only as a range of 0.15 to 0.35% since it is usually added to the mold or ladle stream as the steel is poured.

TABLE 5—CARBON STEEL CAST OR HEAT CHEMICAL LIMITS AND RANGES APPLICABLE ONLY TO STRUCTURAL SHAPES, PLATES, STRIP, SHEETS, AND WELDED TUBING

Element	Standard Chemical Ranges and Limits, % Limit or Max of Specified Range	Standard Chemical Ranges and Limits, Range	Standard Chemical Ranges and Limits, % Lowest Max
Carbon[(1)]			0.08[(2)]
	To 0.15 incl.	0.05	
	Over 0.15 to 0.30 incl.	0.06	
	Over 0.30 to 0.40 incl.	0.07	
	Over 0.40 to 0.60 incl.	0.08	
	Over 0.60 to 0.80 incl.	0.11	
	Over 0.80 to 1.35 incl.	0.14	
Manganese			0.40
	To 0.50 incl.	0.20	
	Over 0.50 to 1.15 incl.	0.30	
	Over 1.15 to 1.65 incl.	0.35	
Phosphorus			0.04
	To 0.08 incl.	0.03	
	Over 0.08 to 0.15 incl.	0.05	
Sulfur			0.05
	To 0.08 incl.	0.03	
	Over 0.08 to 0.15 incl.	0.05	
	Over 0.15 to 0.23 incl.	0.07	
	Over 0.23 to 0.33 incl.	0.10	
Silicon			0.10
	To 0.15 incl.	0.08	
	Over 0.15 to 0.30 incl.	0.15	
	Over 0.30 to 0.60 incl.	0.30	
Copper	When copper is required, 0.20 minimum is commonly specified.		

1. The carbon ranges shown in the column headed "Range" apply when the specified maximum limit for manganese does not exceed 1.00%. When the maximum manganese limit exceeds 1.00%, add 0.01 to the carbon ranges shown in the table.
2. 0.12 carbon maximum for structural shapes and plates.

TABLE 6—ADDITIONAL ELEMENTS TO BE REPORTED

Table Number	Additional Elements	
1, 2, and 3A	Cu, Cr, Ni, Mo an Si[1]	Al, Nb (Cb), Ti and V[2]
3B	Cu, Cr, Ni, Mo and Si[1]	
4 and 5	Cu, Cr, Ni, Mo and Si[1]	Al[3], Nb (Cb) and V[4]

1. When the amount of any one of these five elements is less than 0.02%, that analysis may be reported as "<0.02%."
2. When the amount of these elements is less than 0.008%, that analysis may be reported as "<0.008%."
3. Applicable to Structural Shapes, Plates, and Welded Tubing.
4. Applicable to Sheet and Strip.

CHEMICAL COMPOSITIONS OF SAE ALLOY STEELS —SAE J404 JUN2000

SAE Standard

Report of the SAE Iron and Steel Division approved June 1911. Completely revised by the SAE Iron and Steel Technical Committee January 1989. Completely revised by the SAE Iron and Steel Technical Committee—Division 1—Carbon and Alloy Steels, February 1991, and revised April 1994 and June 2000. Rationale statement available.

1. Scope—In 1941, the SAE Iron and Steel Division in collaboration with the American Iron and Steel Institute (AISI) made a major change in the method of expressing composition ranges for the SAE steels. The plan, as now applied, is based in general on narrower ladle analysis ranges plus certain product (check) analysis allowances on individual samples, in place of the fixed ranges and limits without tolerances formerly provided for carbon and other elements in SAE steels (reference SAE J408).

ISTC Division 1 has developed a procedure which allows for the maintenance of the grade list in this SAE Standard. This will involve conducting an industry-wide survey to solicit input. This survey will be conducted at a frequency deemed necessary by the technical committee. Criteria have been established for the addition to or deletion of grades from the grade table. A new grade will be considered if it meets standard SAE grade ranges, has a minimum usage or production of 225 tonnes/year (250 tons/year), and has the endorsement of at least two users or producers. New steel compositions will still be considered as Potential Standard (PS) steels, based on the guidelines provided in SAE J1081, until such time as production of the new steel achieves a level of production or usage qualifying it for consideration as a standard steel.

The deletion of a grade from the grade table will be by consensus based on the grade survey results. Deleted grades will be archived in SAE J1249 for future reference.

The compositions in this document may apply to open hearth and basic oxygen, or electric furnace steels. Grades shown in Table 1 with prefix letter E are normally made by the electric furnace process with maximum limits of 0.025% phosphorus and 0.025% sulfur. The nominal chemical limits or ranges in the compositions given in Table 1 are subject to standard variations in check analysis given in SAE J409. Since AISI is no longer issuing steel grade designations, all grades listed in this document are SAE grades.

Table 1 is applicable to billets, blooms, slabs, plates, wire rods, and hot-rolled and cold-finished bars.

SAE J404 is not applicable to the following product forms:

a. Structural shapes—Not normally furnished to alloy chemistries
b. Sheet and strip, hot-rolled and cold-rolled—Refer to ASTM A 506 and A 507
c. Seamless and welded mechanical tubing—Refer to ASTM A 513 and A 519

2. References

2.1 Applicable Publications—The following publications form a part of this specification to the extent specified herein. Unless otherwise indicated, the latest issue of SAE publications shall apply.

2.1.1 AE PUBLICATIONS—Available from SAE, 400 Commonwealth Drive, Warrendale, PA 15096-0001.

SAE J408—Methods of Sampling Steel for Chemical Analysis
SAE J409—Product Analysis—Permissible Variations from Specified Chemical Analysis of a Heat or Cast of Steel
SAE J1081—Potential Standard Steels
SAE J1249—Former SAE Standard and Former SAE EX-Steels
SAE Aerospace Material Specifications (AMS) Index

2.1.2 ASTM PUBLICATIONS—Available from ASTM, 100 Barr Harbor Drive, West Conshohocken, PA 19428-2959.

ASTM A 506—Specification for Steel Sheet and Strip, Alloy, Hot-Rolled and Cold-Rolled, Regular Quality
ASTM A 507—Specification for Steel Sheet and Strip, Alloy, Hot-Rolled and Cold-Rolled, Drawing Quality
ASTM A 513—Specification for Electric-Resistance-Welded Carbon and Alloy Steel Mechanical Tubing
ASTM A 519—Specification for Seamless Carbon and Alloy Steel Mechanical Tubing

3. Cross Index to Equivalent Grades and Government Specifications—
Attention is called to the SAE Aerospace Material Specifications (AMS) Index which is published twice a year. This index gives a cross reference to AMS grades, SAE grades, AISI grades, and Government Specifications (MIL, QQS, and so on) for metals, alloys, and nonmetallic materials.

TABLE 1—ALLOY STEEL COMPOSITIONS(1)

UNS No.	SAE No.	Ladle Chemical Composition Limits, % C	Ladle Chemical Composition Limits, % Mn	Ladle Chemical Composition Limits, % P	Ladle Chemical Composition Limits, % S	Ladle Chemical Composition Limits, % Si	Ladle Chemical Composition Limits, % Ni	Ladle Chemical Composition Limits, % Cr	Ladle Chemical Composition Limits, % Mo	Ladle Chemical Composition Limits, % V
G13300	1330	0.28–0.33	1.60–1.80	0.030	0.040	0.15–0.35	—	—	—	—
G13350	1335	0.33–0.38	1.60–1.90	0.030	0.040	0.15–0.35	—	—	—	—
G13400	1340	0.38–0.43	1.60–1.90	0.030	0.040	0.15–0.35	—	—	—	—
G13450	1345	0.43–0.48	1.60-1.90	0.030	0.040	0.15-0.35	—	—	—	—
G40230	4023	0.20–0.25	0.70–0.90	0.030	0.040	0.15–0.35	—	—	0.20–0.30	—
G40270	4027	0.25–0.30	0.70–0.90	0.030	0.040	0.15–0.35	—	—	0.20–0.30	—
G40370	4037	0.35–0.40	0.70–0.90	0.030	0.040	0.15–0.35	—	—	0.20–0.30	—
G40470	4047	0.45–0.50	0.70–0.90	0.030	0.040	0.15–0.35	—	—	0.20–0.30	—
G41180	4118	0.18–0.23	0.70–0.90	0.030	0.040	0.15–0.35	—	0.40–0.60	0.08–0.15	—
G41200	4120	0.18–0.23	0.90–1.20	0.030	0.040	0.15–0.35	—	0.40–0.60	0.13–0.20	—
G41300	4130	0.28–0.33	0.40–0.60	0.030	0.040	0.15–0.35	—	0.80–1.10	0.15–0.25	—
G41350	4135	0.33–0.38	0.70–0.90	0.030	0.040	0.15–0.35	—	0.80–1.10	0.15–0.25	—
G41370	4137	0.35–0.40	0.70–0.90	0.030	0.040	0.15–0.35	—	0.80–1.10	0.15–0.25	—
G41400	4140	0.38–0.43	0.75–1.00	0.030	0.040	0.15–0.35	—	0.80–1.10	0.15–0.25	—
G41420	4142	0.40–0.45	0.75–1.00	0.030	0.040	0.15–0.35	—	0.80–1.10	0.15–0.25	—
G41450	4145	0.43–0.48	0.75–1.00	0.030	0.040	0.15–0.35	—	0.80–1.10	0.15–0.25	—
G41500	4150	0.48–0.53	0.75–1.00	0.030	0.040	0.15–0.35	—	0.80–1.10	0.15–0.25	—
G43200	4320	0.17–0.22	0.45–0.65	0.030	0.040	0.15–0.35	1.65–2.00	0.40–0.60	0.20–0.30	—
G43400	4340	0.38–0.43	0.60–0.80	0.030	0.040	0.15–0.35	1.65–2.00	0.70–0.90	0.20–0.30	—
G43406	E4340(2)	0.38–0.43	0.65–0.85	0.025	0.025	0.15–0.35	1.65–2.00	0.70–0.90	0.20–0.30	—

TABLE 1—ALLOY STEEL COMPOSITIONS[(1)] (continued)

UNS No.	SAE No.	Ladle Chemical Composition Limits, % C	Ladle Chemical Composition Limits, % Mn	Ladle Chemical Composition Limits, % P	Ladle Chemical Composition Limits, % S	Ladle Chemical Composition Limits, % Si	Ladle Chemical Composition Limits, % Ni	Ladle Chemical Composition Limits, % Cr	Ladle Chemical Composition Limits, % Mo	Ladle Chemical Composition Limits, % V
G46150	4615	0.13–0.18	0.45–0.65	0.030	0.040	0.15–0.35	1.65–2.00	—	0.20–0.30	—
G46170	4617	0.16–0.21	0.40–0.65	0.030	0.040	0.15–0.35	1.65–2.00	—	0.20–0.30	—
G46200	4620	0.17–0.22	0.45–0.65	0.030	0.040	0.15–0.35	1.65–2.00	—	0.20–0.30	—
G48200	4820	0.18–0.23	0.50–0.70	0.030	0.040	0.15–0.35	3.25–3.75	—	0.20–0.30	—
G50461	50B46[(3)]	0.44–0.49	0.75–1.00	0.030	0.040	0.15–0.35	0.20–0.35	—	—	—
G51150	5115	0.13–0.18	0.70–0.90	0.030	0.040	0.15–0.35	—	0.70–0.90	—	—
G51200	5120	0.17–0.22	0.70–0.90	0.030	0.040	0.15–0.35	—	0.70–0.90	—	—
G51300	5130	0.28–0.33	0.70–0.90	0.030	0.040	0.15–0.35	—	0.80–1.10	—	—
G51320	5132	0.30–0.35	0.60–0.80	0.030	0.040	0.15–0.35	—	0.75–1.00	—	—
G51400	5140	0.38–0.43	0.70–0.90	0.030	0.040	0.15–0.35	—	0.70–0.90	—	—
G51500	5150	0.48–0.53	0.70–0.90	0.030	0.040	0.15–0.35	—	0.70–0.90	—	—
G51600	5160	0.56–0.64	0.75–1.00	0.030	0.040	0.15–0.35	—	0.70–0.90	—	—
G51601	51B60[(3)]	0.56–0.64	0.75–1.00	0.030	0.040	0.15–0.35	—	0.70–0.90	—	—
G52986	E52100[(2)]	0.98–1.10	0.25–0.45	0.025	0.025	0.15–0.35	—	1.30–1.60	—	—
G61500	6150	0.48–0.53	0.70–0.90	0.030	0.040	0.15–0.35	—	0.80–1.10	—	0.15 min
G86150	8615	0.16–0.18	0.70–0.90	0.030	0.040	0.15–0.35	0.40–0.70	0.40–0.60	0.15–0.25	—
G86170	8617	0.15–0.20	0.70–0.90	0.030	0.040	0.15–0.35	0.40–0.70	0.40–0.60	0.15–0.25	—
G86200	8620	0.18–0.23	0.70–0.90	0.030	0.040	0.15–0.35	0.40–0.70	0.40–0.60	0.15–0.25	—
G86220	8622	0.20–0.25	0.70–0.90	0.030	0.040	0.15–0.35	0.40–0.70	0.40–0.60	0.15–0.25	—
G86250	8625	0.23–0.28	0.70–0.90	0.030	0.040	0.15–0.35	0.40–0.70	0.40–0.60	0.15–0.25	—
G86270	8627	0.25–0.30	0.70–0.90	0.030	0.040	0.15–0.35	0.40–0.70	0.40–0.60	0.15–0.25	—
G86300	8630	0.28–0.33	0.70–0.90	0.030	0.040	0.15–0.35	0.40–0.70	0.40–0.60	0.15–0.25	—
G86370	8637	0.38–0.43	0.75–1.00	0.030	0.040	0.15–0.35	0.40–0.70	0.40–0.60	0.15–0.25	—
G86400	8640	0.38–0.43	0.75–1.00	0.030	0.040	0.15–0.35	0.40–0.70	0.40–0.60	0.15–0.25	—
G86450	8645	0.43–0.48	0.75–1.00	0.030	0.040	0.15–0.35	0.40–0.70	0.40–0.60	0.15–0.25	—
G86550	8655	0.51–0.59	0.75–1.00	0.030	0.040	0.15–0.35	0.40–0.70	0.40–0.60	0.15–0.25	—
G87200	8720	0.18–0.23	0.70–0.90	0.030	0.040	0.15–0.35	0.40–0.70	0.40–0.60	0.20–0.30	—
G87420	8740	0.40–0.45	0.75–1.00	0.030	0.040	0.15–0.35	0.40–0.70	0.40–0.60	0.15–0.25	—
G88220	8822	0.20–0.25	0.75–1.00	0.030	0.040	0.15–0.35	0.40–0.70	0.40–0.60	0.30–0.40	—
G92540	9254	0.51–0.59	0.60–0.80	0.030	0.040	1.20–1.60	—	0.60–0.80	—	—
G92590	9259	0.56–0.64	0.75–1.00	0.030	0.040	0.70–1.10	—	0.45–0.65	—	—
G92600	9260	0.56–0.64	0.75–1.00	0.030	0.040	1.80–2.20	—	—	—	—

1. For standard variations in composition limits, see Table 4 of SAE J409. Small quantities of certain elements which are not specified or required may be found in alloy steels. These elements are to be considered as incidental and are acceptable to the following maximum amounts: copper to 0.35%, nickel to 0.25%, chromium to 0.20%, and molybdenum to 0.06%. Lead - Alloy steels can be produced with a lead addition of 0.15 to 0.35% to improve machinability. Such steels are identified by inserting the letter "L" between the second and third numerals of the grade number, for example, 51L40.
   The analysis of the following elements shall be reported regardless of whether they are specified:
   Aluminum, Titanium, Niobium (Columbium), Vanadium. If the analysis of any of these elements is less than 0.008%, it may be reported as <0.008%.
2. Electric furnace steel.
3. Boron content is 0.0005 to 0.003%.

(R) CHEMICAL COMPOSITIONS OF SAE WROUGHT STAINLESS STEELS—SAE J405 JUN1998

SAE Standard

Report from the Iron and Steel Division, approved June 1911, and revised by the Iron and Steel Technical Committee January 1989. Completely revised by the SAE Iron and Steel Committee Division 15—Wrought Corrosion Resistant Steels. Rationale statement available.

Foreword—This Document has also changed to comply with the new SAE Technical Standards Board Format.

1. Scope—The chemical composition of standard types of wrought stainless steels are listed in ASTM Specification A240. The UNS 20000 series designates nickel-chromium manganese, corrosion resistant types that are nonhardenable by thermal treatment. The UNS 30000 series are nickel-chromium, corrosion resistant steels, nonhardenable by thermal treatment. The UNS 40000 however, includes both a hardenable, martensitic chromium steel and nonhardenable, ferritic, chromium steel. Reference to SAE J412 is suggested for general information and usage of these types of materials. See Table 1.

2. References

2.1 Applicable Publications—The following publications form a part of the specification to the extent specified herein. Unless otherwise indicated the latest revision of SAE publications shall apply.

2.1.1 SAE PUBLICATION—Available from SAE, 400 Commonwealth Drive, Warrendale, PA 15096-0001.

SAE J412—General Characteristics and Heat Treatments of Steels

2.1.2 ASTM PUBLICATION—Available from ASTM, 100 Barr Harbor Drive, West Conshohocken, PA 19428-2959.

ASTM A 240—Specification for Heat-Resisting Chromium and Chromium-Nickel Stainless Steel Plate, Sheet, and Strip for Pressure Vessels

TABLE 1—CHEMICAL COMPOSITION REQUIREMENTS, %[(1)]

UNS Designation[(2)]	Type[(3)]	Carbon[(4)]	Manganese	Phosphorus	Sulfur	Silicon	Chromium	Nickel	Molybdenum	Nitrogen	Copper	Other Elements[(5)]
Austenitic (Chromium-Nickel) (Chromium-Manganese-Nickel)												
N08367	—	0.030	2.00	0.040	0.030	1.00	20.00–22.00	23.50–25.50	6.00–7.00	0.18–0.25	0.75	—
N08800	—	0.10	1.50	0.045	0.015	1.00	19.0–23.0	30.0–35.0	—	—	0.75	Al 0.15–0.60 Ti 0.15–0.60
N08810	—	0.05–0.10	1.50	0.045	0.015	1.00	19.0–23.0	30.0–35.0	—	—	0.75	Al 0.15–0.60 Ti 0.15–0.60
N08904	904L[(6)]	0.020	2.00	0.045	0.035	1.00	19.00–23.00	23.00–28.00	4.0–5.0	0.10	1.0–2.0	—
N08926	—	0.020	2.00	0.030	0.010	0.50	19.00–21.00	24.00–26.00	6.0–7.0	0.15–0.25	0.5–1.5	—
S20100	201	0.15	5.50–7.50	0.060	0.030	1.00	16.00–18.00	3.50–5.50	—	0.25	—	—
S20103	—	0.03	5.50–7.50	0.045	0.030	0.75	16.00–18.00	3.50–5.50	—	0.25	—	—
S20153	—	0.03	6.40–7.50	0.045	0.015	0.75	16.00–17.50	4.00–5.00	—	0.10–0.25	1.00	—
S20161	—	0.15	4.00–6.00	0.040	0.040	3.00–4.00	15.00–18.00	4.00–6.00	—	0.08–0.20	—	—
S20200	202	0.15	7.50–10.0	0.060	0.030	1.00	17.00–19.00	4.00–6.00	—	0.25	—	—
S20400	—	0.030	7.00–9.00	0.040	0.030	1.00	15.00–17.00	1.50–3.00	—	0.15–0.30	—	—
S20910	XM-19[(7)]	0.06	4.00–6.00	0.040	0.030	0.75	20.50–23.50	11.50–13.50	1.50–3.00	0.20–0.40	—	Cb 0.10–0.30 V 0.10–0.30
S21400	XM-31[(7)]	0.12	14.00–16.00	0.045	0.030	0.30–1.00	17.00–18.50	1.00	—	0.35 min	—	—
S21600	XM-17[(7)]	0.08	7.50–9.00	0.045	0.030	0.75	17.50–22.00	5.00–7.00	2.00–3.00	0.25–0.50	—	—
S21603	XM-18[(7)]	0.03	7.50–9.00	0.045	0.030	0.75	17.50–22.00	5.00–7.00	2.00–3.00	0.25–0.50	—	—
S21800	—	0.10	7.00–9.00	0.060	0.030	3.50–4.50	16.00–18.00	8.00–9.00	—	0.08–0.18	—	—
S24000	XM-29[(7)]	0.08	11.50–14.50	0.060	0.030	0.75	17.00–19.00	2.25–3.75	—	0.20–0.40	—	—
S30100	301	0.15	2.00	0.045	0.030	1.00	16.00–18.00	6.00–8.00	—	0.10	—	—
S30200	302	0.15	2.00	0.045	0.030	0.75	17.00–19.00	8.00–10.00	—	0.10	—	—
S30400	304	0.08	2.00	0.045	0.030	0.75	18.00–20.00	8.00–10.50	—	0.10	—	—
S30403	304L	0.030	2.00	0.045	0.030	0.75	18.00–20.00	8.00–12.00	—	0.10	—	—
S30409	304H	0.04–0.10	2.00	0.045	0.030	0.75	18.00–20.00	8.00—10.50	—		—	—
S30415	—	0.04–0.06	0.80	0.045	0.030	1.00–2.00	18.00–19.00	9.00–10.00	—	0.12–0.18	—	Ce 0.03–0.08
S30451	304N	0.08	2.00	0.045	0.030	0.75	18.00–20.00	8.00–10.50	—	0.10–0.16	—	—
S30452	XM-21	0.08	2.00	0.045	0.030	0.75	18.00–20.00	8.00–10.50	—	0.16–0.30	—	—
S30453	304LN	0.030	2.00	0.045	0.030	0.75	18.00–20.00	8.00–12.00	—	0.10–0.16	—	—
S30500	305	0.12	2.00	0.045	0.030	0.75	17.00–19.00	10.50–13.00	—	—	—	—
S30600	—	0.018	2.00	0.20	0.020	3.7–4.3	17.0–18.5	14.0–15.5	0.20	—	0.50	—
S30601	—	0.015	0.50–0.80	0.030	0.013	5.00–5.60	17.00–18.00	17.00–18.00	0.20	0.050	0.35	—
S30615	—	0.16–0.24	2.00	0.030	0.030	3.2–4.0	17.0–19.5	13.5–16.0	—	—	—	Al 0.8–1.5
S30815	—	0.05–0.10	0.80	0.040	0.030	1.40–2.00	20.00—22.00	10.00–12.00	—	0.14–0.20	—	Ce 0.03–0.08
S30908	309S	0.08	2.00	0.045	0.030	0.75	22.00–24.00	12.00–15.00	—	—	—	—
S30909	309H[(6)]	0.04–0.10	2.00	0.045	0.030	0.75	22.00–24.00	12.00–15.00	—	—	—	—
S30940	309Cb[(6)]	0.08	2.00	0.045	0.030	0.75	22.00–24.00	12.00–16.00	—	—	—	Cb 10 x C min, 1.10 max
S30941	309HCb[(6)]	0.04–0.10	2.00	0.045	0.030	0.75	22.00–24.00	12.00–16.00	—	—	—	Cb 10 x C min, 1.10 max
S31008	310S	0.08	2.00	0.045	0.030	1.50	24.00–26.00	19.00–22.00	—	—	—	—
S31009	310H[(6)]	0.04–0.10	2.00	0.045	0.030	0.75	24.00–26.00	19.00–22.00	—	—	—	—
S31040	310Cb[(6)]	0.08	2.00	0.045	0.030	1.50	24.00–26.00	19.00–22.00	—	—	—	Cb 10 x C min, 1.10 max
S31041	310HCb[(6)]	0.04–0.10	2.00	0.045	0.030	0.75	24.00–26.00	19.00–22.00	—	—	—	Cb 10 x C min, 1.10 max
S31050	310 MoLN[(6)]	0.030	2.00	0.030	0.010	0.50	24.00–26.00	21.00–23.00	2.00–3.00	0.10–0.16	—	—
S31254	—	0.020	1.00	0.030	0.010	0.80	19.50–20.50	17.50–18.50	6.00–6.50	0.18–0.22	0.50–1.00	—
S31266	—	0.030	2.00–4.00	0.035	0.020	1.00	23.00–25.00	21.00–24.00	5.00–7.00	0.35–0.60	0.50–3.00	W 1.00–3.00
S31600	316	0.08	2.00	0.045	0.030	0.75	16.00–18.00	10.00–14.00	2.00–3.00	0.10	—	—
S31603	316L	0.030	2.00	0.045	0.030	0.75	16.00–18.00	10.00–14.00	2.00–3.00	0.10	—	—
S31609	316H	0.04–0.10	2.00	0.045	0.030	0.75	16.00–18.00	10.00–14.00	2.00–3.00	—	—	—
S31635	316Ti[(6)]	0.08	2.00	0.045	0.030	0.75	16.00–18.00	10.00–14.00	2.0–3.0	0.10	—	Ti 5 x (C + N) min, 0.70 max
S31640	316Cb[(6)]	0.08	2.00	0.045	0.030	0.75	16.00–18.00	10.00–14.00	2.0–3.0	0.10	—	Cb 10 x C min, 1.10 max
S31651	316N	0.08	2.00	0.045	0.030	0.75	16.00–18.00	10.00–14.00	2.00–3.00	0.10–0.16	—	—
S31653	316LN	0.030	2.00	0.045	0.030	0.75	16.00–18.00	10.00–14.00	2.00–3.00	0.10–0.16	—	—
S31700	317	0.08	2.00	0.045	0.030	0.75	18.00–20.00	11.00–15.00	3.00–4.00	0.10	—	—
S31703	317L	0.030	2.00	0.045	0.030	0.75	18.00–20.00	11.00–15.00	3.00–4.00	0.10	—	—
S31725	—	0.030	2.00	0.045	0.030	0.75	18.00–20.00	13.50–17.50	4.0–5.0	0.20	—	—
S31726	—	0.030	2.00	0.045	0.030	0.75	17.00–20.00	13.50–17.50	4.0–5.0	0.10–0.20	—	—
S31753	317LN[(6)]	0.030	2.00	0.045	0.030	0.75	18.00–20.00	11.00–15.00	3.00–4.00	0.10–0.22	—	—
S32100	321	0.08	2.00	0.045	0.030	0.75	17.00–19.00	9.00–12.00	—	0.10	—	Ti 5 x (C + N) min, 0.70 max
S32109	321H	0.04–0.10	2.00	0.045	0.030	0.75	17.00–19.00	9.00–12.00	—	—	—	Ti 4 x (C + N) min, 0.70 max
S32615	—	0.07	2.00	0.045	0.030	4.8–6.0	16.5–19.5	19.0–22.0	0.30–1.5	—	1.5–2.5	—
S32654	—	0.020	2.00–4.00	0.030	0.005	0.50	24.00–25.00	21.00–23.00	7.00–8.00	0.45–0.55	0.30–0.60	—
S33228	—	0.04–0.08	1.00	0.020	0.015	0.030	26.0–28.0	31.0–33.0	—	—	—	Ce 0.05–0.10 Cb 0.6–1.0 Al 0.025
S34565	—	0.030	5.00–7.00	0.030	0.010	1.00	23.00–25.00	16.00–18.00	4.00–5.00	0.40–0.60	—	Cb 0.10

TABLE 1—CHEMICAL COMPOSITION REQUIREMENTS, %[(1)] (continued)

UNS Designation[(2)]	Type[(3)]	Carbon[(4)]	Manganese	Phos-phorus	Sulfur	Silicon	Chromium	Nickel	Molybdenum	Nitrogen	Copper	Other Elements[(5)]
S34700	347	0.08	2.00	0.045	0.030	0.75	17.00–19.00	9.00–13.00	—	—	—	Cb 10 x C min, 1.00 max
S34709	347H	0.04–0.10	2.00	0.045	0.030	0.75	17.00–19.00	9.00–13.00	—	—	—	Cb 8 x C min, 1.00 max
S34800	348	0.08	2.00	0.045	0.030	0.75	17.00–19.00	9.00–13.00	—	—	—	Cb + Ta 10 x C min, 1.00 max Ta 0.10 max Co 0.20
S34809	348H	0.04–0.10	2.00	0.045	0.030	0.75	17.00–19.00	9.00–13.00	—	—	—	Cb + Ta 8 x C min, 1.00 max Ta 0.10 max Co 0.20
S35315	—	0.04–0.08	2.00	0.040	0.030	1.20–2.00	24.00–26.00	34.00–36.00	—	0.12–0.18	—	Ce 0.03–0.08
S38100	XM-15[(7)]	0.08	2.00	0.030	0.030	1.50–2.50	17.00–19.00	17.50–18.50	—		—	—
Duplex (Austenitic-Ferritic)												
S31200	—	0.030	2.00	0.045	0.030	1.00	24.0–26.0	5.5–6.5	1.2–2.0	0.14–0.20		—
S31260	—	0.03	1.00	0.030	0.030	0.75	24.0–26.0	5.50–7.50	2.50–3.50	0.10–0.30	0.20–0.80	W 0.10–0.50
S31803	—	0.030	2.00	0.030	0.020	1.00	21.0–23.0	4.50–6.50	2.50–3.50	0.08–0.20		—
S32205	—	0.030	2.00	0.030	0.020	1.00	22.0–23.0	4.50–6.50	3.00–3.50	0.14–0.20		—
S32304	—	0.030	2.50	0.040	0.030	1.00	21.5–24.5	3.00–5.00	0.05–0.60	0.05–0.20	0.05–3.00	—
S32520	—	0.030	1.50	0.035	0.020	0.80	24.00–26.00	5.50–8.00	3.00–5.00	0.20–0.35	0.50–3.00	—
S32550	—	0.04	1.5	0.040	0.030	1.0	24.0–27.0	4.5–6.5	2.9–3.9	0.10–0.25	1.5–2.5	—
S32750	—	0.030	1.20	0.035	0.020	0.80	24.0–26.0	6.00–8.00	3.00–5.00	0.24–0.32	0.50	—
S32760	—	0.030	1.00	0.030	0.010	1.00	24.00–26.00	6.00–8.00	3.00–4.00	0.20–0.30	0.50–1.00	W 0.50–1.00 Cr + 3.3 Mo + 16 N = 40 min
S32900	329	0.08	1.00	0.040	0.030	0.75	23.00–28.00	2.50–5.00	1.0–2.0	—	—	—
S32950	—	0.03	2.00	0.035	0.010	0.60	26.00–29.00	3.50–5.20	1.00–2.50	015–0.35	—	—
Ferritic or Martensitic (Chromium)												
S32803	—	0.015	0.50	0.020	0.0035	0.55	28.00–29.00	3.0–4.0	1.8–2.5	0.020 (C + N) 0.030 max	—	Cb 0.15–0.50 12 (C + N) min
S40500	405	0.08	1.00	0.040	0.030	1.00	11.50–14.50	0.60	—	—	—	Al 0.10–0.30
S40900	409	0.08	1.00	0.045	0.030	1.00	10.50–11.75	0.50	—	—	—	Ti 6 x C min; 0.75 max
S40945	—	0.030	1.00	0.040	0.030	1.00	10.50–11.75	0.50	—	0.030	—	Cb 0.18–0.40 Ti 0.05–0.20
S40975	—	0.030	1.00	0.040	0.030	1.00	10.50–11.75	0.50–1.00	—	0.030	—	Ti 6 (C + N) min and 0.75 max
S41000	410	0.15	1.00	0.040	0.030	1.00	11.50–13.50	0.75	—	—	—	—
S41003	—	0.03	1.50	0.040	0.030	1.00	10.50–12.50	1.50	—	—	—	N 0.030 max
S41008	410S	0.08	1.00	0.040	0.030	1.00	11.50–13.50	0.60	—	—	—	—
S41045	—	0.030	1.00	0.040	0.030	1.00	12.00–13.00	0.50	—	0.030	—	Cb 9 (C + N) min,0.60 max
S41050	—	0.040	1.00	0.045	0.030	1.00	10.50–12.50	0.60–1.10	—	0.10	—	—
S41500[(5)]	—	0.05	0.5–1.0	0.030	0.030	0.60	11.5–14.0	3.5–5.5	0.5–1.0	—	—	—
S42900	429[(6)]	0.12	1.00	0.040	0.030	1.00	14.00–16.00	—	—	—	—	—
S43000	430	0.12	1.00	0.040	0.030	1.00	16.00–18.00	0.75	—	—	—	
S43035	439	0.07	1.00	0.040	0.030	1.00	17.00–19.00	0.50	—	0.04	—	Ti 0.20 + 4 (C + N) min; 1.10 max Al 0.15 max
S43400	—	0.12	1.00	0.040	0.030	1.00	16.00–18.00	—	0.75–1.25	—	—	—
S43600	—	0.12	1.00	0.040	0.030	1.00	16.00–18.00	—	0.75–1.25	—	—	Cb 5 x C min; 0.80 max
S43932	—	0.030	1.00	0.040	0.030	1.00	17.0–19.0	0.50	—	0.030	—	Ti + Cb 0.20 + 4 (C + N) min; 0.75 max Al 0.15 max
S44400	444	0.025	1.00	0.040	0.030	1.00	17.5–19.5	1.00	1.75–2.50	0.035	—	Ti + Cb 0.20 + 4 (C + N) min; 0.80 max
S44500	—	0.020	1.00	0.040	0.012	1.00	19.00–21.00	0.60	—	0.03	0.30–0.60	Cb 10 (C + N) –0.80
S44626	XM-33[(7)]	0.06	0.75	0.040	0.020	0.75	25.00–27.00	0.50	0.75–1.50	0.04	0.20	Ti 0.20–1.00 7 (C + N) min
S44627	SM-27[(7)]	0.010[(6)]	0.40	0.020	0.020	0.40	25.00–27.50	0.50	0.75–1.50	0.015[(5)]	0.20	Cb 0.05–0.20 Ni + Cu 0.50 max
S44635	—	0.025	1.00	0.040	0.030	0.75	24.5–26.0	3.5–4.5	3.5–4.5	0.035	—	Ti + Cb 0.20 + 4 (C + N) min; 0.80 max
S44660	—	0.030	1.00	0.040	0.030	1.00	25.0–28.0	1.0–3.50	3.00–4.00	0.040	—	Ti + Cb = 0.20 –1.00 and 6 (C + N) min
S44700	—	0.010	0.30	0.025	0.020	0.20	28.0–30.0	0.15	3.5–4.2	0.020	0.15	(C + N) 0.025 max
S44735	—	0.030	1.00	0.040	0.030	1.00	28.00–30.00	1.00	3.60–4.20	0.045	—	Ti + Cb = 0.20–1.00 and 6 (C + N) min
S44800	—	0.010	0.30	0.025	0.020	0.20	28.0–30.0	2.0–2.5	3.5–4.2	0.020	0.15	(C + N) 0.025 max
S46800	—	0.030	1.00	0.040	0.030	1.00	18.00–20.00	0.50	—		—	Ti 0.07–0.30 Cb 0.10–0.60 N 0.030 max Ti + Cb = 0.20 + 4 (C + N) min; 0.80 max

1. Maximum, unless range or minimum is indicated.
2. Designation established in accordance with Practice E 527 and SAE J1086.
3. Unless otherwise indicated, a grade designation originally assigned by the American Iron and Steel Institute (AISI).
4. Carbon analysis shall be reported to nearest 0.01% except for the low-carbon types, which shall be reported to nearest 0.001%.
5. The terms Columbium (Cb) and Niobium (Nb) both relate to the same element.
6. Common name, not a trademark, widely used, not associated with any one producer.
7. Naming system developed and applied by ASTM.

NOTE—**"Reprinted with permission from the Annual Book of ASTM Standards, copyright American Society for Testing and Materials, 100 Barr Harbor Drive, West Conshohocken, PA 19428-2959."**

POTENTIAL STANDARD STEELS—SAE J1081 NOV2000

SAE Information Report

Report of the SAE Iron and Steel Technical Committee approved April 1974 and revised December 1988. Revised by the SAE Iron and Steel Technical Committee Division 1—Carbon and Alloy Steels November 2000. Rationale statement available.

Foreword—This Document has also changed to comply with the new SAE Technical Standards Board Format. Scope is Section 1, References were added as Section 2.

1. Scope—This SAE Information Report provides a uniform means of designating wrought steels during a period of usage prior to the time they meet the requirements for SAE standard steel designation. The numbers consist of the prefix PS[1] followed by a sequential number starting with 1. A number once assigned is never assigned to any other composition.

A PS number may be obtained for steel composition by submitting a written request to SAE Staff, indicating the chemical composition and other pertinent characteristics of the material. If the request is approved according to established procedures, SAE Staff will assign a PS number to the grade. This number will remain in effect until the grade meets the requirements for an SAE standard steel or the grade is discontinued according to established procedures.

Table 1 is a listing of the chemical composition limits of potential standard steels which were considered active on the date of the last survey prior to the date of this report. These ladle limits are subject to standard variations for check analysis as given in SAE J409.

2. References

2.1 Applicable Publication—The following publication forms a part of the specification to the extent specified herein. Unless otherwise indicated, the latest revision of SAE publications shall apply.

2.1.1 SAE PUBLICATION—Available from SAE, 400 Commonwealth Drive, Warrendale, PA 15096-0001.

SAE J409 FEB95—Product Analysis—Permissible Variations from Specified Chemical analysis of a Heat or Cast of Steel

1. Previously noted as EX.

TABLE 1—SAE POTENTIAL STANDARD STEEL COMPOSITIONS
LADLE CHEMICAL COMPOSITION LIMITS, % BY WEIGHT

PS No.[1]	C	Mn	P, max	S, max	Si	Ni	Cr	Mo	B
PS 10	0.19–0.24	0.95–1.25	0.035	0.040	0.15–0.35	0.20–0.40	0.25–0.40	0.05–0.10	—
PS 16	0.20–0.25	0.90–1.20	0.035	0.040	0.15–0.35	—	0.40–0.60	0.13–0.20	—
PS 17	0.23–0.28	0.90–1.20	0.035	0.040	0.15–0.35	—	0.40–0.60	0.13–0.20	—
PS 18	0.25–0.30	0.90–1.20	0.035	0.040	0.15–0.35	—	0.40–0.60	0.13–0.20	—
PS 19	0.18–0.23	0.90–1.20	0.035	0.040	0.15–0.35	—	0.40–0.60	0.08–0.15	0.0005–0.003
PS 20	0.13–0.18	0.90–1.20	0.035	0.040	0.15–0.35	—	0.40–0.60	0.13–0.20	—
PS 21	0.15–0.20	0.90–1.20	0.035	0.040	0.15–0.35	—	0.40–0.60	0.13–0.20	—
PS 31	0.15–0.20	0.70–0.90	0.035	0.040	0.15–0.35	0.70–1.00	0.45–0.65	0.45–0.60	—
PS 32	0.18–0.23	0.70–0.90	0.035	0.040	0.15–0.35	0.70–1.00	0.45–0.65	0.45–0.60	—
PS 33[2]	0.17–0.24	0.85–1.25	0.035	0.040	0.15–0.35	0.20 min	0.20 min	0.05 min	—
PS 34	0.28–0.33	0.90–1.20	0.035	0.040	0.15–0.35	—	0.40–0.60	0.13–0.20	—
PS 36	0.38–0.43	0.90–1.20	0.035	0.040	0.15–0.35	—	0.45–0.65	0.13–0.20	—
PS 38	0.43–0.48	0.90–1.20	0.035	0.040	0.15–0.35	—	0.45–0.65	0.13–0.20	—
PS 39	0.48–0.53	0.90–1.20	0.035	0.040	0.15–0.35	—	0.45–0.65	0.13–0.20	—
PS 40	0.51–0.59	0.90–1.20	0.035	0.040	0.15–0.35	—	0.45–0.65	0.13–0.20	—
PS 54	0.19–0.25	0.70–1.05	0.035	0.040	0.15–0.35	—	0.40–0.70	0.05 min	—
PS 55	0.15–0.20	0.70–1.00	0.035	0.040	0.15–0.35	1.65–2.00	0.45–0.65	0.65–0.80	—
PS 56	0.080–0.13	0.70–1.00	0.035	0.040	0.15–0.35	1.65–2.00	0.45–0.65	0.65–0.80	—
PS 57	0.08 max	1.25 max	0.040	0.15–0.35	1.00 max	—	17.00–19.00	1.75–2.25	—
PS 58	0.16–0.21	1.00–1.30	0.035	0.040	0.15–0.35	—	0.45–0.65	—	—
PS 59	0.18–0.23	1.00–1.30	0.035	0.040	0.15–0.35	—	0.70–0.90	—	—
PS 61	0.23–0.28	1.00–1.30	0.035	0.040	0.15–0.35	—	0.70–0.90	—	—
PS 63	0.31–0.38	0.75–1.10	0.035	0.040	0.15–0.35	—	0.45–0.65	—	0.0005–0.003
PS 64	0.16–0.21	1.00–1.30	0.035	0.040	0.15–0.35	—	0.70–0.90	—	—
PS 65	0.21–0.26	1.00–1.30	0.035	0.040	0.15–0.35	—	0.70–0.90	—	—
PS 66[3]	0.16–0.21	0.40–0.70	0.035	0.040	0.15–0.35	1.65–2.00	0.45–0.75	0.08–0.15	—
PS 67	0.42–0.49	0.80–1.20	0.035	0.040	0.15–0.35	—	0.85–1.20	0.25–0.35	—
PS 68[4]	0.15 max	0.85-1.15	0.04-0.09	0.26-0.35					

1. Some PS steels may be supplied to a hardenability requirement.
2. Supplied to a hardenability requirement of 15 HRC points within the range of HRC 23/43 at J4, subject to agreement between producer and user.
3. PS 66 has vanadium content 0.10–0.15.
4. PS 68 has Sn content 0.04-0.08

APPENDIX A
DESIGNATION AND NUMBERING OF POTENTIAL STANDARD STEELS

A.1 Scope—This Appendix establishes a system for designating and numbering compositions for steel products during a period of limited use in which technical and commercial desirability is evaluated.

A.1.1 Designation and Numbering—Such materials shall be designated by the prefix PS and numbered by assigning a sequential, non-significant number beginning with 1 in the order of approval for listing.

A.1.1.1 Application for listing may be made by any person, acting in his own behalf or for his company or association by written application to the SAE technical staff listing the range of chemical composition and other pertinent characteristics of the proposed material. This request shall be forwarded to the Chairman of the appropriate Division of ISTC for action.

A.1.1.2 ASSIGNMENT OF NUMBER—If the Division Chairman approves, he shall inform the appropriate member of the SAE Technical Staff who will assign the number, add the material to the list, and inform the applicant of the number assigned.

A.1.2 Publication—The current numbers, their range of chemical composition, and other pertinent characteristics, shall be published yearly in the SAE Handbook in SAE J1081. Publication of interim bulletins on newly listed numbers may be authorized by the ISTC Executive Committee.

A.1.3 Discontinuance—A material may be removed from the list by any of the following:

A.1.3.1 Adoption of the material as an SAE standard steel and assignment of a permanent number.

A.1.3.2 Formal action to delist by the cognizant Division.

A.1.3.2.1 Every two years each Division shall determine the status of the steels within its jurisdiction and delete those which an ISTC ballot shows to be of insufficient interest to warrant further consideration.

A.1.3.3 A request to delist by the applicant who originally requested listing, followed by action prescribed in A.3.2.

A.1.4 Reassignment of a number once assigned is not permitted. If the material to which it was originally assigned is relisted, it shall be relisted with its original number.

FORMER SAE STANDARD AND FORMER SAE EX-STEELS—SAE J1249 JUN2000

SAE Information Report

Report of the SAE Iron and Steel Technical Committee, ISTC Division 1, approved June 1983, and completely revised January 1989. Completely revised by the SAE Iron and Steel Technical Committee—Division 1—Carbon and Alloy Steels, April 1994, revised June 1995 and June 2000. Rationale statement available.

1. Scope—This SAE Information Report provides a list of those SAE steels which, because of decreased usage, have been deleted from the standard SAE Handbook listings. Included are alloy steels from SAE J778 deleted since 1936, carbon steels from SAE J118 deleted since 1952, and all EX-steels deleted from SAE J1081. Information concerning SAE steels prior to these dates may be obtained from the SAE office on request. With the issuance of this report, SAE J778, Formerly Standard SAE Alloy Steels, and SAE J118, Formerly Standard SAE Carbon Steels, will be retired since they are now combined in SAE J1249. In the future, new assignments to SAE J1081, Chemical Compositions of SAE Experimental Steels, will be given "PS" (Potential Standard) numbers rather than "EX" numbers.

The steels listed in Tables 1 and 2 are no longer considered as standard steels. Producers should be contacted concerning availability. Steel grades can be reinstated based on usage according to the criteria indicated in SAE J403 and J404.

The last column lists the date a steel was last listed as standard in the SAE Handbook. Where applicable, the corresponding AISI and UNS numbers are given.

2. References

2.1 Applicable Publications—The following publications form a part of this specification to the extent specified herein. Unless otherwise indicated, the latest issue of SAE publications shall apply.

2.1.1 SAE PUBLICATIONS—Available from SAE, 400 Commonwealth Drive, Warrendale, PA 15096-0001.

SAE J1081—Potential Standard Steels
SAE J118 Cancelled—Formerly Standard SAE Carbon Steels
SAE J778 Cancelled—Formerly Standard SAE Alloy Steels

TABLE 1—FORMER STANDARD SAE STEELS

SAE No.	UNS No.	C	Mn	P, Max[1]	S, Max[1]	Si	Cr	Ni	Mo	V, Min	AISI No.	Date
1009	—	0.15 max	0.60 max	0.040	0.050	—	—	—	—	—	1009	1965
1011	G10110	0.09–0.14	0.60–0.90	0.040	0.050	—	—	—	—	—	1011	1993
1019[2]	G10190	0.15–0.20	0.70–1.00	0.040	0.050	—	—	—	—	—		
1033	—	0.30–0.36	0.70–1.00	0.040	0.050	—	—	—	—	—	1033	1965
1034	—	0.32–0.38	0.50–0.80	0.040	0.050	—	—	—	—	—	C1034	1968
1037[2]	G10370	0.32–0.38	0.70–1.00	0.040	0.050	—	—	—	—	—		
1059[2]	—	0.55–0.65	0.50–0.80	0.040	0.050	—	—	—	—	—		1968
1059	G10590	0.55–0.65	0.50–0.80	0.040	0.050	—	—	—	—	—	1059	1993
1062	—	0.54–0.65	0.85–1.15	0.040	0.050	—	—	—	—	—	C1062	1953
1064[2]	G10640	0.60–0.70	0.50–0.80	0.040	0.050	—	—	—	—	—		
1069[2]	G10690	0.65–0.75	0.40–0.70	0.040	0.050	—	—	—	—	—		
1074	G10740	0.70–0.80	0.50–0.80	0.040	0.050	—	—	—	—	—	1074	1993
1075[2]	G10750	0.70–0.80	0.40–0.70	0.040	0.050	—	—	—	—	—		
1084[2]	G10840	0.80–0.93	0.60–0.90	0.040	0.050	—	—	—	—	—		
1085	G10850	0.80–0.93	0.70–1.00	0.040	0.050	—	—	—	—	—		
1086[2]	G10860	0.80–0.94	0.30–0.50	0.040	0.050	—	—	—	—	—		1977
1108[2]	G11080	0.08–0.13	0.50–0.80	0.040	0.08–0.13	—	—	—	—	—		
1109	G11090	0.08–0.13	0.60–0.90	0.040	0.08–0.13	—	—	—	—	—	1109	1977
1110	G11100	0.08–0.13	0.30–0.60	0.040	0.08–0.13	—	—	—	—	—	1110	1993
1111	—	0.13 max	0.60–0.90	0.07–0.12	0.10–0.15	—	—	—	—	—	B1111	1969
1112	—	0.13 max	0.70–1.00	0.07–0.12	0.16–0.23	—	—	—	—	—	B1112	1969
1113	—	0.13 max	0.70–1.00	0.07–0.12	0.24–0.33	—	—	—	—	—	B1113	1969
1114	—	0.10–0.16	1.00–1.30	0.040	0.08–0.13	—	—	—	—	—	C1114	1952
1115	—	0.13–0.18	0.60–0.90	0.040	0.08–0.13	—	—	—	—	—	1115	1965
1116	—	0.14–0.20	1.10–1.40	0.040	0.16–0.23	—	—	—	—	—	C1116	1952
1119	G11190	0.14–0.20	1.00–1.30	0.040	0.24–0.33	—	—	—	—	—	1119	1977
1120	—	0.18–0.23	0.70–1.00	0.040	0.08–0.13	—	—	—	—	—	1120	1965
1123	G11230	0.20–0.27	1.20–1.50	0.040	0.06–0.09	—	—	—	—	—	1123	1993
1139[2]	G11390	0.35–0.43	1.35–1.65	0.040	0.13–0.20	—	—	—	—	—		
1145	G11450	0.42–0.49	0.70–1.00	0.040	0.04–0.07	—	—	—	—	—	1145	1977
1152	G11520	0.48–0.55	0.70–1.00	0.040	0.06–0.09	—	—	—	—	—	1152	1993
1211[2]	G12110	0.13 max	0.60–0.90	0.07–0.12	0.10–0.15	—	—	—	—	—		
1320	—	0.18–0.23	1.60–1.90	0.040	0.040	0.20–0.35	—	—	—	—	A1320	1956
1330	G13300	0.28–0.33	1.60–1.90	0.035	0.040	0.15–0.35	—	—	—	—	1330	1993
1345	G13450	0.43–0.48	1.60–1.90	0.035	0.040	0.15–0.35	—	—	—	—		
1513	G15130	0.10–0.16	1.10–1.40	0.040	0.050	—	—	—	—	—	1513	1993
1518	G15180	0.15–0.21	1.10–1.40	0.040	0.050	—	—	—	—	—	—	1977
1525	G15250	0.23–0.29	0.80–1.10	0.040	0.050	—	—	—	—	—	—	1977
1533	G15330	0.30–0.37	1.10–1.40	0.040	0.050	—	—	—	—	—	1533	1993
1534	G15340	0.30–0.37	1.20–1.50	0.040	0.050	—	—	—	—	—	1534	1993
1536	G15360	0.30–0.37	1.20–1.50	0.040	0.050	—	—	—	—	—		
1544	G15440	0.40–0.47	0.80–1.10	0.040	0.050	—	—	—	—	—	1544	1993
1545	G15450	0.43–0.50	0.80–1.10	0.040	0.050	—	—	—	—	—	1545	1993
1546	G15460	0.44–0.52	1.00–1.30	0.040	0.050	—	—	—	—	—	1546	1993
1551	G15510	0.45–0.56	0.85–1.15	0.040	0.050	—	—	—	—	—		
1553	G15530	0.48–0.55	0.80–1.10	0.040	0.050	—	—	—	—	—	1553	1993
1561	G15610	0.55–0.65	0.75–1.05	0.040	0.050	—	—	—	—	—		
1570	G15700	0.65–0.75	0.80–1.10	0.040	0.050	—	—	—	—	—	1570	1993
1572	G15720	0.65–0.76	1.00–1.30	0.040	0.050	—	—	—	—	—	—	1977
1580	G15800	0.75–0.88	0.80–1.10	0.040	0.050	—	—	—	—	—	1580	1993
1590	G15900	0.85–0.98	0.80–1.10	0.040	0.050	—	—	—	—	—	1590	1993

TABLE 1—FORMER STANDARD SAE STEELS (continued)

SAE No.	UNS No.	C	Mn	P, Max[1]	S, Max[1]	Si	Cr	Ni	Mo	V, Min	AISI No.	Date
2317	—	0.15–0.20	0.40–0.60	0.040	0.040	0.20–0.35	—	3.25–3.75	—	—	A2317	1956
2330	—	0.28–0.33	0.60–0.80	0.040	0.040	0.20–0.35	—	3.25–3.75	—	—	A2330	1953
2340	—	0.38–0.43	0.70–0.90	0.040	0.040	0.20–0.35	—	3.25–3.75	—	—	A2340	1953
2345	—	0.43–0.48	0.70–0.90	0.040	0.040	0.20–0.35	—	3.25–3.75	—	—	A2345	1952
2512	—	0.09–0.14	0.45–0.60	0.025	0.025	0.20–0.35	—	4.75–5.25	—	—	E2512	1953
2515	—	0.12–0.17	0.40–0.60	0.040	0.040	0.20–0.35	—	4.75–5.25	—	—	A2515	1956
2517	—	0.15–0.20	0.45–0.60	0.025	0.025	0.20–0.35	—	4.75–5.25	—	—	E2517	1959
3115	—	0.13–0.18	0.40–0.60	0.040	0.040	0.20–0.35	0.55–0.75	1.10–1.40	—	—	A3115	1953
3120	—	0.17–0.22	0.60–0.80	0.040	0.040	0.20–0.35	0.55–0.75	1.10–1.40	—	—	A3120	1956
3130	—	0.28–0.33	0.60–0.80	0.040	0.040	0.20–0.35	0.55–0.75	1.10–1.40	—	—	A3130	1956
3135	—	0.33–0.38	0.60–0.80	0.040	0.040	0.20–0.35	0.55–0.75	1.10–1.40	—	—	3135	1960
X3140	—	0.38–0.43	0.70–0.90	0.040	0.040	0.20–0.35	0.70–0.90	1.10–1.40	—	—	A3141	1947
3140	—	0.38–0.43	0.70–0.90	0.040	0.040	0.20–0.35	0.55–0.75	1.10–1.40	—	—	3140	1964
3145	—	0.43–0.48	0.70–0.90	0.040	0.040	0.20–0.35	0.70–0.90	1.10–1.40	—	—	A3145	1952
3150	—	0.48–0.53	0.70–0.90	0.040	0.040	0.20–0.35	0.70–0.90	1.10–1.40	—	—	A3150	1952
3215	—	0.10–0.20	0.30–0.60	0.040	0.050	0.15–0.30	0.90–1.25	1.50–2.00	—	—	—	1941
3220	—	0.15–0.25	0.30–0.60	0.040	0.050	0.15–0.30	0.90–1.25	1.50–2.00	—	—	—	1941
3230	—	0.25–0.35	0.30–0.60	0.040	0.050	0.15–0.30	0.90–1.25	1.50–2.00	—	—	—	1941
3240	—	0.35–0.45	0.30–0.60	0.040	0.040	0.15–0.30	0.90–1.25	1.50–2.00	—	—	A3240	1941
3245	—	0.40–0.50	0.30–0.60	0.040	0.040	0.15–0.30	0.90–1.25	1.50–2.00	—	—	—	1941
3250	—	0.45–0.55	0.30–0.60	0.040	0.040	0.15–0.30	0.90–1.25	1.50–2.00	—	—	—	1941
3310	—	0.08–0.13	0.45–0.60	0.025	0.025	0.20–0.35	1.40–1.75	3.25–3.75	—	—	E3310	1964
3312	—	0.08–0.13	0.45–0.60	0.025	0.025	0.20–0.35	1.40–1.75	3.25–3.75	—	—	—	1948
3316	—	0.14–0.19	0.45–0.60	0.025	0.025	0.20–0.35	1.40–1.75	3.25–3.75	—	—	E3316	1956
3325	—	0.20–0.30	0.30–0.60	0.040	0.050	0.15–0.30	1.25–1.75	3.25–3.75	—	—	—	1936
3335	—	0.30–0.40	0.30–0.60	0.040	0.050	0.15–0.30	1.25–1.75	3.25–3.75	—	—	—	1936
3340	—	0.35–0.45	0.30–0.60	0.040	0.050	0.15–0.30	1.25–1.75	3.25–3.75	—	—	—	1936
3415	—	0.10–0.20	0.30–0.60	0.040	0.050	0.15–0.30	0.60–0.95	2.75–3.25	—	—	—	1941
3435	—	0.30–0.40	0.30–0.60	0.040	0.050	0.15–0.30	0.60–0.95	2.75–3.25	—	—	—	1936
3450	—	0.45–0.55	0.30–0.60	0.040	0.050	0.15–0.30	0.60–0.95	2.75–3.25	—	—	—	1936
4012	G40120	0.09–0.14	0.75–1.00	0.035	0.040	0.15–0.30	—	—	0.15–0.25	—	4012	1977
4024	G40240	0.20–0.25	0.70–0.90	0.035	0.035–0.050	0.15–0.35	—	—	0.20–0.30	—		
4028	G40280	0.25–0.30	0.70–0.90	0.035	0.035–0.050	0.15–0.35	—	—	—	—	4028	1993
4032	G40320	0.30–0.35	0.70–0.90	0.035	0.040	0.15–0.35	—	—	0.20–0.30	—		
4042	G40420	0.40–0.45	0.70–0.90	0.035	0.040	0.15–0.35	—	—	0.20–0.30	—		
4053	—	0.50–0.56	0.75–1.00	0.040	0.040	0.20–0.35	—	—	0.20–0.30	—	4053	1956
4063	G40630	0.60–0.67	0.75–1.00	0.040	0.040	0.20–0.35	—	—	0.20–0.30	—	4063	1964
4068	—	0.63–0.70	0.75–1.00	0.040	0.040	0.20–0.35	—	—	0.20–0.30	—	A4068	1957
4119	—	0.17–0.22	0.70–0.90	0.040	0.040	0.20–0.35	0.40–0.60	—	0.20–0.30	—	A4119	1956
4121	G41210	0.18–0.23	0.75–1.00	0.035	0.040	0.15–0.35	0.45–0.65	—	0.20–0.30	—	4121	1993
4125	—	0.23–0.28	0.70–0.90	0.040	0.040	0.20–0.35	0.40–0.60	—	0.20–0.30	—	A4125	1950
4131	G41310	0.28–0.33	0.50–0.70	0.035	0.040	0.15–0.35	0.90–1.20	—	0.15–0.25	—	4131	1993
4135	G41350	0.33–0.38	0.70–0.90	0.035	0.040	0.15–0.35	0.80–1.10	—	0.15–0.25	—		
4147	G41470	0.45–0.50	0.75–1.00	0.035	0.040	0.15–0.35	0.80–1.10	—	0.15–0.25	—	4147	1993
4161	G41610	0.56–0.64	0.75–1.00	0.035	0.040	0.15–0.35	0.70–0.90	—	0.25–0.35	—		
4317	—	0.15–0.20	0.45–0.65	0.040	0.040	0.20–0.35	0.40–0.60	1.65–2.00	0.20–0.30	—	4317	1953
4337	G43370	0.35–0.40	0.60–0.80	0.040	0.040	0.20–0.35	0.70–0.90	1.65–2.00	0.20–0.30	—	4337	1964
4419	—	0.18–0.23	0.45–0.65	0.035	0.040	0.15–0.30	—	—	0.45–0.60	—	4520	1977
4419H	—	0.17–0.23	0.35–0.75	0.035	0.040	0.15–0.30	—	—	0.45–0.60	—	4419H	1977
4422	G44220	0.20–0.25	0.70–0.90	0.035	0.040	0.15–0.35	—	—	0.35–0.45	—		
4427	G44270	0.24–0.29	0.70–0.90	0.035	0.040	0.15–0.35	—	—	0.35–0.45	—		
4608	—	0.06–0.11	0.25–0.45	0.040	0.040	0.25 max	—	1.40–1.75	0.15–0.25	—	4608	1956
46B12[3]	—	0.10–0.15	0.45–0.65	0.040	0.040	0.20–0.35	—	1.65–2.00	0.20–0.30	—	46B12	1957
4615	G46150	0.13–0.18	0.45–0.65	0.035	0.040	0.15–0.35	—	1.65–2.00	0.20–0.30	—		
4617	G46170	0.15–0.20	0.45–0.65	0.035	0.040	0.15–0.35	—	1.65–2.00	0.20–0.30	—		
X4620	—	0.18–0.23	0.50–0.70	0.040	0.040	0.20–0.35	—	1.65–2.00	0.20–0.30	—	X4620	1956
4621	G46210	0.18–0.23	0.70–0.90	0.035	0.040	0.15–0.30	—	1.65–2.00	0.20–0.30	—	4621	1977
4621H	—	0.17–0.23	0.60–1.00	0.035	0.040	0.15–0.30	—	1.55–2.00	0.20–0.30	—	4621H	1977
4626	G46260	0.24–0.29	0.45–0.65	0.035	0.040	0.15–0.35	—	0.70–1.00	0.15–0.25	—		
4640	—	0.38–0.43	0.60–0.80	0.040	0.040	0.20–0.35	—	1.65–2.00	0.20–0.30	—	A4640	1952
4715	G47150	0.13–0.18	0.70–0.90	0.035	0.040	0.15–0.35	0.45–0.65	0.70–1.00	0.45–0.60	—	4715	1993
4718	G47180	0.16–0.21	0.70–0.90	—	—	—	0.35–0.55	0.90–1.20	0.30–0.40	—		
4720	G4720	0.17–0.22	0.50–0.70	0.035	0.040	0.15–0.35	0.35–0.55	0.90–1.20	0.15–0.25	—	4720	1993
4812	—	0.10–0.15	0.40–0.60	0.040	0.040	0.20–0.35	—	3.25–3.75	0.20–0.30	—	4817	1956
4815	G48150	0.13–0.18	0.40–0.60	0.035	0.040	0.15–0.35	—	3.25–3.75	0.20–0.30	—	4815	1993
4817	G48170	0.15–0.20	0.40–0.60	0.035	0.040	0.15–0.35	—	3.25–3.75	0.20–0.30	—		
5015	G50150	0.12–0.17	0.30–0.50	0.035	0.040	0.15–0.30	0.30–0.50	—	—	—	5015	1977
50B40[3]	B50401	0.38–0.43	0.75–1.00	0.035	0.040	0.15–0.35	0.40–0.60	—	—	—		
50B44[3]	G50441	0.43–0.48	0.75–1.00	0.035	0.040	0.15–0.35	0.40–0.60	—	—	—		
5045	—	0.43–0.48	0.70–0.90	0.040	0.040	0.20–0.35	0.55–0.75	—	—	—	5045	1953
5046	G50460	0.43–0.48	0.75–1.00	0.035	0.040	0.15–0.35	0.20–0.35	—	—	—		
50B50[3]	G50501	0.48–0.53	0.75–1.00	0.035	0.040	0.15–0.35	0.40–0.60	—	—	—		
5060	G50600	0.56–0.64	0.75–1.00	0.035	0.040	0.15–0.35	0.40–0.60	—	—	—		
50B60[3]	G50601	0.56–0.64	0.75–1.00	0.035	0.040	0.15–0.35	0.40–0.60	—	—	—		

TABLE 1—FORMER STANDARD SAE STEELS (continued)

SAE No.	UNS No.	C	Mn	P, Max(1)	S, Max(1)	Si	Cr	Ni	Mo	V, Min	AISI No.	Date
5115	G51150	0.13–0.18	0.70–0.90	0.035	0.040	0.15–0.35	0.70–0.90	—	—	—		
5117	G51170	0.15–0.20	0.70–0.90	0.040	0.040	0.15–0.35	0.70–0.90	—	—	—		
5135	G51350	0.33–0.38	0.60–0.80	0.035	0.040	0.15–0.35	0.80–1.05	—	—	—		
5145	G51450	0.43–0.48	0.70–0.90	0.035	0.040	0.15–0.30	0.70–0.90	—	—	—	5145	1977
5145H	H51450	0.42–0.49	0.60–1.00	0.035	0.040	0.15–0.30	0.60–1.00	—	—	—	5145H	1977
5147	G51470	0.46–0.51	0.70–0.95	0.035	0.040	0.15–0.35	0.85–1.15	—	—	—		
5152	—	0.48–0.55	0.70–0.90	0.040	0.040	0.20–0.35	0.90–1.20	—	—	—	5152	1956
5155	G51550	0.51–0.59	0.70–0.90	0.035	0.040	0.15–0.35	0.70–0.90	—	—	—		
50100	G50986	0.98–1.10	0.25–0.45	0.025	0.025	0.15–0.35	0.40–0.60	—	—	—		
E51100	G51986	0.98–1.10	0.25–0.45	0.025	0.025	0.15–0.35	0.90–1.15	—	—	—	E51100	1993
6115	—	0.10–0.20	0.30–0.60	0.040	0.050	0.15–0.30	0.80–1.10	—	—	0.15	—	1936
6117	—	0.15–0.20	0.70–0.90	0.040	0.040	0.20–0.35	0.70–0.90	—	—	0.10	6117	1956
6118	G61180	0.16–0.21	0.50–0.70	0.035	0.040	0.15–0.35	0.50–0.70	—	V–0.10–0.15	—		
6120	—	0.17–0.22	0.70–0.90	0.040	0.040	0.20–0.35	0.70–0.90	—	—	0.10	6120	1961
6125	—	0.20–0.30	0.60–0.90	0.040	0.050	0.15–0.30	0.80–1.10	—	—	0.15	—	1936
6130	—	0.25–0.35	0.60–0.90	0.040	0.050	0.15–0.30	0.80–1.10	—	—	0.15	—	1936
6135	—	0.30–0.40	0.60–0.90	0.040	0.050	0.15–0.30	0.80–1.10	—	—	0.15	—	1941
6140	—	0.35–0.45	0.60–0.90	0.040	0.050	0.15–0.30	0.80–1.10	—	—	0.15	—	1936
6145	—	0.43–0.48	0.70–0.90	0.040	0.050	0.20–0.35	0.80–1.10	—	—	0.15	6145	1956
6195	—	0.90–1.05	0.20–0.45	0.030	0.035	0.15–0.30	0.80–1.10	—	—	0.15	—	1936
71360	—	0.50–0.70	0.30 max	0.035	0.040	0.15–0.30	3.00–4.00	12.00–15.00W	—	—	—	1936
71660	—	0.50–0.70	0.30 max	0.035	0.040	0.15–0.30	3.00–4.00	15.00–18.00W	—	—	—	1936
7260	—	0.50–0.70	0.30 max	0.035	0.040	0.15–0.30	0.50–1.00	1.50–2.00W	—	—	—	1936
8115	G81150	0.13–0.18	0.70–0.90	0.035	0.040	0.15–0.35	0.30–0.50	0.20–0.40	0.08–0.15	—		
81B45(3)	G81451	0.43–0.48	0.75–1.00	0.035	0.040	0.15–0.35	0.35–0.55	0.20–0.40	0.08–0.15	—		
8627	G86270	0.25–0.30	0.70–0.90	0.035	0.040	0.15–0.35	0.40–0.60	0.40–0.70	0.15–0.25	—		
8632	—	0.30–0.35	0.70–0.90	0.040	0.040	0.20–0.35	0.40–0.60	0.40–0.70	0.15–0.25	—	8632	1951
8635	—	0.33–0.38	0.75–1.00	0.040	0.040	0.20–0.35	0.40–0.60	0.40–0.70	0.15–0.25	—	8635	1956
8637	G86370	0.35–0.40	0.75–1.00	0.035	0.040	0.15–0.35	0.40–0.60	0.40–0.70	0.15–0.25	—	8637	1993
8641	—	0.38–0.43	0.75–1.00	0.040	0.040-0.060	0.20–0.35	0.40–0.60	0.40–0.70	0.15–0.25	—	8641	1956
8642	G86420	0.40–0.45	0.75–1.00	0.035	0.040	0.15–0.35	0.40–0.60	0.40–0.70	0.15–0.25	—		
86B45(3)	G86451	0.43–0.48	0.75–1.00	0.035	0.040	0.15–0.35	0.40–0.60	0.40–0.70	0.15–0.25	—		
8650	G86500	0.48–0.53	0.75–1.00	0.035	0.040	0.15–0.35	0.40–0.60	0.40–0.70	0.15–0.25	—		
8653	—	0.50–0.56	0.75–1.00	0.040	0.040	0.20–0.35	0.50–0.80	0.40–0.70	0.15–0.25	—	8653	1956
8647	—	0.45–0.50	0.75–1.00	0.040	0.040	0.20–0.35	0.40–0.60	0.40–0.70	0.15–0.25	—	8647	1948
8655	G86550	0.51–0.59	0.75–1.00	0.035	0.040	0.15–0.35	0.40–0.60	0.40–0.70	0.15–0.25	—		
8660	G86600	0.56–0.64	0.75–1.00	0.035	0.040	0.15–0.35	0.40–0.60	0.40–0.70	0.15–0.25	—		
8715	—	0.13–0.18	0.70–0.90	0.040	0.040	0.20–0.35	0.40–0.60	0.40–0.70	0.20–0.30	—	8715	1956
8717	—	0.15–0.20	0.70–0.90	0.040	0.040	0.20–0.35	0.40–0.60	0.40–0.70	0.20–0.30	—	8717	1956
8719	—	0.18–0.23	0.60–0.80	0.040	0.040	0.20–0.35	0.40–0.60	0.40–0.70	0.20–0.30	—	8719	1952
8735	G87350	0.33–0.38	0.75–1.00	0.040	0.040	0.20–0.35	0.40–0.60	0.40–0.70	0.20–0.30	—	8735	1952
8740	G87400	0.38–0.43	0.75–1.00	0.035	0.040	0.15–0.35	0.40–0.60	0.40–0.70	0.20–0.30	—		
8742	G87420	0.40–0.45	0.75–1.00	0.040	0.040	0.20–0.35	0.40–0.60	0.40–0.70	0.20–0.30	—	8742	1964
8745	—	0.43–0.48	0.75–1.00	0.040	0.040	0.20–0.35	0.40–0.60	0.40–0.70	0.20–0.30	—	8745	1953
8750	—	0.48–0.53	0.75–1.00	0.040	0.040	0.20–0.35	0.40–0.60	0.40–0.70	0.20–0.30	—	8750	1956
9250	—	0.45–0.55	0.60–0.90	0.040	0.040	1.80–2.20	—	—	—	—	9250	1941
9255	G92550	0.51–0.59	0.70–0.95	0.035	0.040	1.80–2.20	—	—	—	—	9255	1977
9261	—	0.55–0.65	0.75–1.00	0.040	0.040	1.80–2.20	0.10–0.25	—	—	—	9261	1956
9262	G92620	0.55–0.65	0.75–1.00	0.040	0.040	1.80–2.20	0.25–0.40	—	—	—	9262	1961
9310	G93106	0.08–0.13	0.45–0.65	0.025	0.025	0.15–0.35	1.00–1.40	3.00–3.50	0.08–0.15	—		
9315	—	0.13–0.18	0.45–0.65	0.025	0.025	0.20–0.35	1.00–1.40	3.00–3.50	0.08–0.15	—	E9315	1959
9317	—	0.15–0.20	0.45–0.65	0.025	0.025	0.20–0.35	1.00–1.40	3.00–3.50	0.08–0.15	—	E9317	1959
94B15(3)	G94151	0.13–0.18	0.75–1.00	0.035	0.040	0.15–0.35	0.30–0.50	0.30–0.60	0.08–0.15	—		
94B17(3)	G94171	0.15–0.20	0.75–1.00	0.035	0.040	0.15–0.35	0.30–0.50	0.30–0.60	0.08–0.15	—		
94B30(3)	G94301	0.28–0.33	0.75–1.00	0.035	0.040	0.15–0.35	0.30–0.50	0.30–0.60	0.08–0.15	—		
9437	—	0.35–0.40	0.90–1.20	0.040	0.040	0.20–0.35	0.30–0.50	0.30–0.60	0.08–0.15	—	9437	1950
9440	—	0.38–0.43	0.90–1.20	0.040	0.040	0.20–0.35	0.30–0.50	0.30–0.60	0.08–0.15	—	9440	1950
94B40(3)	G94401	0.38–0.43	0.75–1.00	0.040	0.040	0.20–0.35	0.30–0.60	0.30–0.60	0.08–0.15	—	94B40	1964
9442	—	0.40–0.45	0.90–1.20	0.040	0.040	0.20–0.35	0.30–0.50	0.30–0.60	0.08–0.15	—	9442	1950
9445	—	0.43–0.48	0.90–1.20	0.040	0.040	0.20–0.35	0.30–0.50	0.30–0.60	0.08–0.15	—	9445	1950
9447	—	0.45–0.50	0.90–1.20	0.040	0.040	0.20–0.35	0.30–0.50	0.30–0.60	0.08–0.15	—	9447	1950
9747	—	0.45–0.50	0.50–0.80	0.040	0.040	0.20–0.35	0.10–0.25	0.40–0.70	0.15–0.25	—	9747	1950
9763	—	0.60–0.67	0.50–0.80	0.040	0.040	0.20–0.35	0.10–0.25	0.40–0.70	0.15–0.25	—	9763	1950
9840	G98400	0.38–0.43	0.70–0.90	0.040	0.040	0.20–0.35	0.70–0.90	0.85–1.15	0.20–0.30	—	9840	1964
9845	—	0.43–0.48	0.70–0.90	0.040	0.040	0.20–0.35	0.70–0.90	0.85–1.15	0.20–0.30	—	9845	1950
9850	G98500	0.48–0.53	0.70–0.90	0.040	0.040	0.20–0.35	0.70–0.90	0.85–1.15	0.20–0.30	—	9850	1961
43BV12(3)	—	0.08–0.13	0.75–1.00	—	—	0.20–0.35	0.40–0.60	1.65–2.00	0.20–0.30	0.03	—	
43BV14(3)	—	0.10–0.15	0.45–0.65	—	—	0.20–0.35	0.40–0.60	1.65–2.00	0.08–0.15	0.03	—	

1. Limits apply to semi-finished products for forgings, bars, wire rods, and seamless tubing.
2. These grades remain standard for wire rods.
3. Boron content 0.0005 to 0.003%.

TABLE 2—FORMER EX/PS STEELS

EX/PS No.	Composition, % C	Composition, % Mn	Composition, % Cr	Composition, % Mo	Composition, % Other	Approximate SAE Grade	Deletion Date
EX No.							
1[(1)]	0.15–0.21	0.35–0.60	—	0.20–0.30	4.80–5.30 Ni	9310	1976
2[(1)]	0.64–0.75	0.25–0.45	0.15–0.30	0.08–0.15	0.70–1.00 Ni	—	1971
3	0.56–0.64	0.75–1.00	0.40–0.60	—	—	5060	Made standard
4	0.18–0.23	0.75–1.00	0.45–0.65	0.05–0.10	—	4118	1973
5	0.18–0.23	0.75–1.00	0.45–0.65	0.08–0.15	0.40–0.70 Ni	8620	1971
6	0.20–0.25	0.75–1.00	0.45–0.65	0.08–0.15	0.40–0.70 Ni	8622	1971
7	0.23–0.28	0.75–1.00	0.45–0.65	0.08–0.15	0.40–0.70 Ni	8625	1971
8	0.25–0.30	0.75–1.00	0.45–0.65	0.08–0.15	0.40–0.70 Ni	8627	1971
9[(1)]	0.19–0.24	0.95–1.25	0.25–0.40	0.05–0.10	0.20–0.40 Ni	8620	1976
11[(1)]	0.38–0.43	0.75–1.00	0.25–0.40	0.05–0.10	0.20–0.40 Ni, 0.0005 B min	8640	1976
12	0.38–0.43	0.75–1.00	0.25–0.40	0.05–0.10	0.20–0.40 Ni, 0.0005 B min	8640	1976
13[(1)]	0.66–0.75	0.80–1.05	0.25–0.40	0.05–0.10	0.20–0.40 Ni	—	1976
14[(1)]	0.66–0.75	0.80–1.05	0.25–0.40	0.05–0.10	0.20–0.40 Ni	—	1976
15	0.18–0.23	0.90–1.20	0.40–0.60	0.13–0.20	—	—	
22	0.13–0.18	0.75–1.00	0.45–0.65	0.20–0.30	—	8615	1973
23	0.15–0.20	0.75–1.00	0.45–0.65	0.20–0.30	—	8617	1973
24	0.18–0.23	0.75–1.00	0.45–0.65	0.20–0.30	—	—	
25	0.20–0.25	0.75–1.00	0.45–0.65	0.20–0.30	—	8622	1973
26	0.23–0.28	0.75–1.00	0.45–0.65	0.20–0.30	—	8625	1973
27	0.25–0.30	0.75–1.00	0.45–0.65	0.20–0.30	—	8627	1976
28	0.16–0.21	0.75–1.00	0.45–0.65	0.30–0.40	0.40–0.70 Ni	4718	1973
29	0.18–0.23	0.75–1.00	0.45–0.65	0.30–0.40	0.40–0.70 Ni	4320	1976
30	0.13–0.18	0.70–0.90	0.45–0.65	0.45–0.60	0.70–1.00 Ni	—	
35	0.35–0.40	0.90–1.20	0.45–0.65	0.13–0.20	—	8637	1976
37	0.40–0.45	0.90–1.20	0.45–0.65	0.13–0.20	—	8642	1976
41	0.56–0.64	0.90–1.20	0.45–0.65	0.13–0.20	—	8660	1976
42	0.13–0.18	0.95–1.25	0.25–0.40	0.05–0.10	0.20–0.40 Ni	8615	1976
43	0.13–0.18	0.95–1.25	0.25–0.40	0.05–0.10	0.20–0.40 Ni, 0.0005 B min	—	1976
44	0.15–0.20	0.95–1.25	0.25–0.40	0.05–0.10	0.20–0.40 Ni	8617	1976
45	0.15–0.20	0.95–1.25	0.25–0.40	0.05–0.10	0.20–0.40 Ni, 0.0005 B min	—	1976
46	0.20–0.25	0.95–1.25	0.25–0.40	0.05–0.10	0.20–0.40 Ni	8622	1976
47	0.23–0.28	0.95–1.25	0.25–0.40	0.05–0.10	0.20–0.40 Ni	8625	1976
48	0.25–0.30	0.95–1.25	0.25–0.40	0.05–0.10	0.20–0.40 Ni	8627	1976
49	0.28–0.33	0.95–1.25	0.25–0.40	0.05–0.10	0.20–0.40 Ni	8630	1976
50	0.33–0.38	0.95–1.25	0.25–0.40	0.05–0.10	0.20–0.40 Ni	8635	1976
51	0.35–0.40	0.95–1.25	0.25–0.40	0.05–0.10	0.20–0.40 Ni	8637	1976
52	0.38–0.43	0.95–1.25	0.25–0.40	0.05–0.10	0.20–0.40 Ni	8640	1976
53	0.40–0.45	0.95–1.25	0.25–0.40	0.05–0.10	0.20–0.40 Ni	8642	1976
60	0.20–0.25	1.00–1.30	0.70–0.90	—	—	—	1983
62	0.25–0.30	1.00–1.30	0.70–0.90	—	—	—	1983
PS No.							
10	0.19–0.24	0.95–1.25	0.25–0.40	0.05–0.10	0.20–0.40 Ni	—	1993
19	0.18–0.23	0.90–1.20	0.40–0.60	0.08–0.15	0.0005–0.003 B	—	1993
21	0.15–0.20	0.90–1.20	0.40–0.60	0.13–0.20	—	—	1993
31	0.15–0.20	0.70–0.90	0.45–0.65	0.45–0.60	0.70–1.00 Ni	—	1993
32	0.18–0.23	0.70–0.90	0.45–0.65	0.45–0.60	0.70–1.00 Ni	—	1993
34	0.28–0.33	0.90–1.20	0.40–0.60	0.13–0.20	—	—	1993
36	0.38–0.43	0.90–1.20	0.45–0.65	0.13–0.20	—	—	1993
38	0.43–0.48	0.90–1.20	0.45–0.65	0.13–0.20	—	—	1993
39	0.48–0.53	0.90–1.20	0.45–0.65	0.13–0.20	—	—	1993
40	0.51–0.59	0.90–1.20	0.45–0.60	0.13–0.20	—	—	1993
56	0.08–0.13	0.70–1.00	0.45–0.65	0.65–0.80	1.65–2.00 Ni	—	1993
57	0.08 Max	1.25 Max	17.00–19.00	1.75–2.25	0.15–0.35 S, 1.00 Max Si	—	1993
58	0.16–0.21	1.00–1.30	0.45–0.65	—	—	—	1993
59	0.18–0.23	1.00–1.30	0.70–0.90	—	—	—	1993
61	0.23–0.28	1.00–1.30	0.70–0.90	—	—	—	1993
63	0.31–0.38	0.75–1.10	0.70–0.90	—	0.0005–0.003 B	—	1993
64	0.16–0.21	1.00–1.30	0.70–0.90	—	—	—	1993
65	0.21–0.26	1.00–1.30	0.70–0.90	—	—	—	1993
66	0.16–0.21	0.40–0.70	0.45–0.75	0.08–0.15	1.65–2.00 Ni	—	1993
67	0.42–0.49	0.80–1.20	0.85–1.20	0.25–0.35	—	—	1993

1. All steels contain (1) 0.035 P max except EX 1 (0.040 P max), and EX 2, EX 13, and EX 14 (0.025 P max); (2) all contain 0.040 S max except EX 2, EX 13, and EX 14 (0.025 S max); and (3) all contain 0.15–0.35 Si except EX 9, EX 11, and EX 13 (0.050 Si max).

METHODS OF DETERMINING HARDENABILITY OF STEELS—SAE J406 MAY98

SAE Standard

Report of the Iron and Steel Division approved January 1942. Completely revised by the Iron and Steel Technical Committee—Division 8—Hardenability of Carbon and Alloy Steels, May 1985, November 1990, June 1993, and February 1995. Revised by the SAE Iron and Steel Technical Committee—Division 8—Hardenability of Carbon and Alloy Steels May 1998. Rationale statement available.

1. Scope—This SAE Standard prescribes the procedure for making hardenability tests and recording results on shallow and medium hardening steels, but not deep hardening steels that will normally air harden.

Included are procedures using the 25 mm (1 in) standard hardenability end-quench specimen for both medium and shallow hardening steels and subsize method for bars less than 32 mm (1-1/4 in) in diameter. Methods for determining case hardenability of carburized steels are given in SAE J1975.

Any hardenability test made under other conditions than those given in this document will not be deemed standard and will be subject to agreement between supplier and user. Whenever check tests are made, all laboratories concerned must arrange to use the same alternate procedure with reference to test specimen and method of grinding for hardness testing.

For routine testing of the hardenability of successive heats of steel required to have hardenability within certain limits, it is sufficient to designate hardenability simply in terms of distance from the quenched end to the point at which a certain hardness is obtained. This designation may also be adequate for comparing steels of different compositions to see whether they have similar hardenability.

Hardenability limits for specifying steel in this manner are obtained by measuring the hardenability of a steel which has proved satisfactory for the use intended. The hardenability test may be used in this way as an empirical test.

For new components where manufacturing experience is lacking, hardenability data may be effectively used to estimate the hardness profile provided by any given steel. Attendantly, the ability to predict hardenability from chemical composition has become increasingly important when comparing various steel grades or developing new steels for specific applications. One such procedure is described in Appendix A. Other hardenability prediction methods are available from the selected references in Section 2. However, it should be emphasized that the use of any hardenability prediction procedure does not preclude the importance of conducting Jominy end-quench tests to determine the actual hardenability of any specific grade of steel.

Hardenability data may be used to estimate hardnesses obtainable with any steel in new machine parts not yet in production and not similar to any parts on which production experience is available. Various hardenability application methods are described in the selected references, Section 2.1, 23 to 25. It appears none of these methods are precise, but these are often useful for estimation purposes. Final correlation on actual parts is necessary.

2. References

2.1 Applicable Publications—The following publications form a part of the specification to the extent specified herein. Unless otherwise indicated the lastest revision of SAE publications shall apply.

1. SAE J417—Hardness Test and Hardness Number Conversion
2. SAE EA 406—Hardenability Prediction Calculator
3. W. E. Jominy and A. L. Boegehold, "A Hardenability Test for Carburizing Steel," ASM Transactions, Vol. 26 (1938, No. 2, pp 574–599)
4. J. L. Burns, T. L. Moore, and R. S. Archer, "Quantitative Hardenability," ASM Transactions, Vol 26 (1938), No. 1, pp 1–33
5. W. E. Jominy, "A Hardenability Test for Shallow Hardening Steels," ASM Transactions, Vol. 27 (1939) pp 1072–1085
6. Symposium on Hardenability of Alloy Steels, ASM 1939
7. M. Asimow and M. A. Grossmann, "Hardening Characteristics of Various Shapes," AMS Transactions, Vol. 28 (1940) pp 949–977
8. "Standardization Sought in Determining the Hardenability of Steels" (A symposium), SAE Journal, Vol. 49, No. 1 (July 1941) pp 266–293
9. A. E. Focke, "Hardenability of Steel," Iron Age, Aug. 20, 1942 pp 37–40: Aug. 27, 1942, pp. 43–51; Sept. 3, 1942, pp 56–59
10. Morse Hill "The End-Quench Test: Reproducibility," ASM Transactions, Vol. 31 (1943), P 923 ff.
11. Symposium on the Hardenability of Steel, Special Report No. 36, British Iron and Steel Institute, 1946
12. G. K. Manning, "End Quench Hardenability Versus Hardness of Quenched Rounds," Metal Progress, Vol. 50, No. 4 (October 1946) pp 674-650
13. E. W. Wienman, R. F. Thomson, and A. L. Boegehold, "Correlation of End Quenched Test Bars and Rounds in Terms of Hardness and Cooling Characteristics," ASM Transactions, Vol. 44 (1952) pp 802–834
14. G. K. Manning, "Comparison of Tests of Hardenability of Shallow Hardening Steels," SAE Journal, Vol. 61, July 1953, pp 30–36
15. D. J. Carney, "Another Look at Quenchants, Cooling Rates and Hardenability," ASM Transactions, Vol. 46 (1954), pp 882–925
16. John Birtalan, R. G. Henley, Jr., and A. L. Christenson, "Thermal Reproducibility of the End-Quench Test," ASM Transactions, Vol. 46 (1954), P 928 ff
17. M. A. Grossman and R. L. Stephenson, "The Effect of Grain Size on Hardenability," ASM Transactions, Vol. 29 (1941), pp 1–19
18. M. A. Grossmann, "Hardenability Calculated from Chemical Compositions," AIME Transactions, Vol. 150 (1942) pp 227–259
19. I. R. Kramer, S. Siegel, and J. Brooks, "Factors for the Calculation of Hardenability," ASM Transactions, Vol. 163 (1946), p 670 ff
20. C. F. Jatczak and D. J. Girardi, "Multiplying Factors for the Calculation of Hardenability of Hypereutectoid Steels Hardened from 1700 F," ASM Transactions Vol. 51 (1960) p 335 ff
21. E. Just, "New Formulas for Calculating Hardenability Curves," Metal Progress, November 1969, pp 87–88
22. C. F. Jatczak, "Determining Hardenability from Composition," Metal Progress, Vol. 100, No. 3 (September 1971), p 60
23. D. H. Breen, G. H. Walter, C. J. Keith, and J. T. Sponzilli, "Computer-Based System Selects Optimum Cost Steels," Metal Progress, I: Dec. 1972, p. 42; II: Feb. 1973, p. 76; III: April 1973, p. 105; IV: June 1973, p. 83; V: Nov. 1973, p. 43
24. C. S. Siebert, D. V. Doane, and D. H. Breen, "The Hardenability of Steels," American Society for Metals, Metals Park, OH 1977, p 64 ff
25. D. V. Doane, J. S. Kirkaldy, "Hardenability Concepts with Applications to Steel," The Metallurgical Society of AIME, Warrendale, PA 1978
26. C. T. Kunze and G. Keil," A New Look at Boron Effectiveness in Heat Treated Steels," Symposium on Boron Steels, TMS-AIME, Milwaukee, WI Sept. 18, 1979
27. W. Hewitt, "Hardenability - Its Prediction form Chemical Compositions," Heat Treatment of Metals, Vol. 8, 1981, pp 33–38
28. Deb. M. C. Chaturvedi and A. K. Jena, "Analytical Representation of Hardenability Data for Steels," Metals Technology, 1982, Vol 9, p 76
29. J. M. Tartaglia and G. T. Eldis, "Core Hardenability Calculations for Carburizing Steels," Met. Trans., Vol. 15A, No. 6, June 1984, pp. 1173–1183

2.2 Related Publications—The following publications are provided for information purposes only and are not a required part of this document.

2.2.1 ASTM—Available from ASTM, 100 Barr Harbor Drive, West Conshohocken, PA 19428-2959.

ASTM A 255—End-quench Test for Hardenability of Steel

2.2.2 OTHER PUBLICATIONS

DIN 50191—Hardenability Testing of Steel by End Quenching

JIS G 0561—Method of Hardenability Testing (End-Quenching Method)

3. Hardenability Test for Medium Hardening Steels

3.1 Introduction—This method covers the procedure for determining the hardenability of steel by the end-quench test for both the 25 mm (1 in) standard specimen and the subsize test specimen. Also included are charts for plotting hardenability test results and for predicting hardness U curves in various sizes of rounds.

Please note that in this revision the metric dimensions are shown to the nearest whole millimeter. Tolerances, where not indicated, are assumed to be ±0.5 mm or ±1/32 in (0.03 in).

3.2 Test Specimen—The test specimen is a 25 mm (1 in) diameter cylinder 102 mm (4 in) long with means for hanging it in a vertical position for end-quenching. Figure 1 shows a test specimen in the fixture ready for quenching illustrating the preferred form of specimen. Figure 2 gives the details of the preferred test specimen. Figure 3 is an example of an optional specimen which provides the same diameter and approximately the same length and which will provide satisfactory heat transfer characteristics.

The bar from which the specimen is machined shall be a forged or rolled 29 to 32 mm (1-1/8 to 1-1/4 in) round representing the full cross section of the product (or rolled 26 mm, 1-1/16 in, round if optional test specimen, Figure 3, is used). A cast specimen may be used in lieu of a rolled or forged specimen, except in the case of boron-treated steel; experience has shown that cast specimens of boron-treated steels give erratic results. The option of using as-cast specimens for non-boron steels, deletion of normalizing prior to heating for end-quenching or modification of other testing details shall be negotiated between supplier and user. It is of primary importance that the specimen represent the full cross section of the ingot, cast bloom or cast billet since test specimens from a portion of the bloom, billet, or bar may introduce factors tending to affect the reproducibility of test results. The condition of this hot formed bar shall be such that there is no decarburization on the 25 mm (1 in) specimen machined from it. If any test specimen shows obvious defects or flaws, the specimen should be discarded and a new specimen obtained.

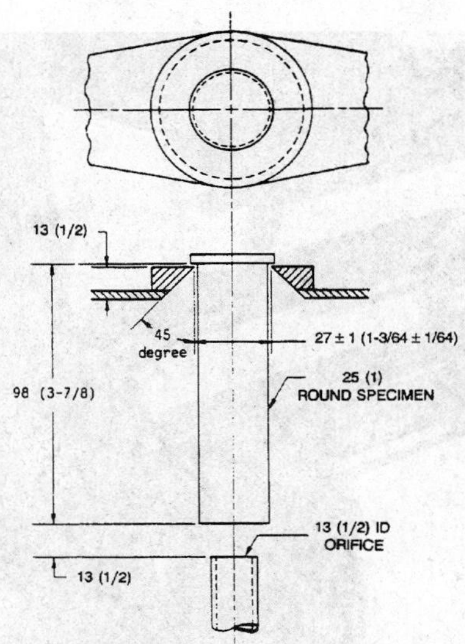

FIGURE 1—HARDENABILITY TEST SPECIMEN IN FIXTURE FOR WATER QUENCHING

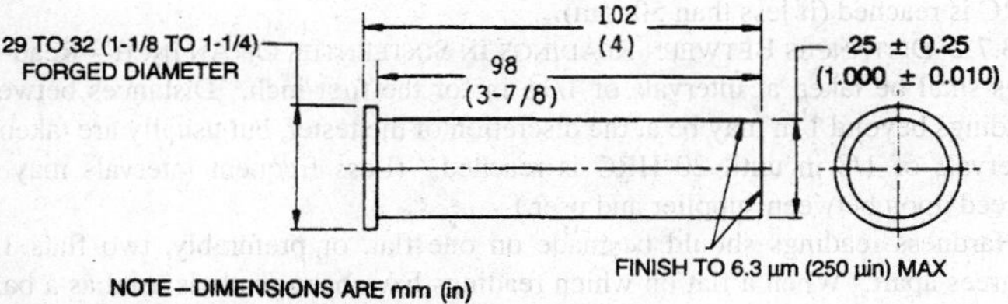

FIGURE 2—PREFERRED TEST SPECIMEN

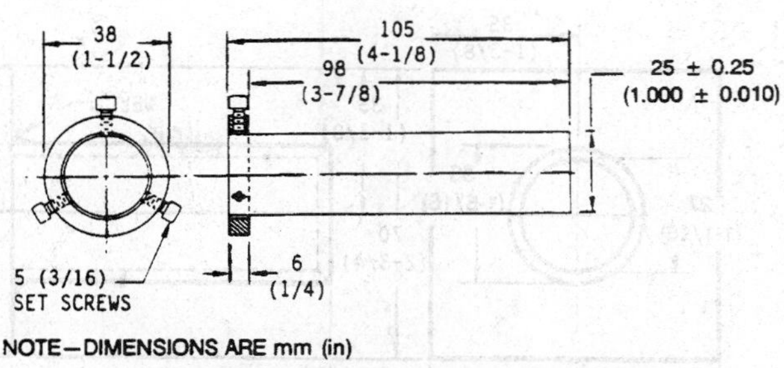

FIGURE 3—OPTIONAL TEST SPECIMEN

3.3 Optional Specimen Preparation—The following method is satisfactory for most purposes, but for check testing against specifications, the method in the preceding paragraph is mandatory.

The test specimen shall be machined from the center of the bar in the case of sections from 32 to 51 mm (1-1/4 to 2 in) round or square. In sections over 51 mm (2 in), the test specimen shall be machined from one-half of the section with the axis of the specimen located at a point halfway between the center and surface of the bar and marked to identify the position of the test bar with reference to the original bar. The hardness readings shall be made on the two sides of the test specimen corresponding to a position in the bar approximately halfway between the center and the surface.

3.4 Normalizing Prior to Heating for End-Quenching—The forged or rolled round shall be normalized prior to machining the test specimen. This is of importance since the structure of material before the final austenitizing treatment may materially affect the hardening characteristics. In order that variations in prior structure may be controlled as much as possible, the normalizing temperature listed in Table 1 should be used. The steel shall be held at such temperature for 1 h and cooled to ambient in still air. If the normalized specimen is too hard, it may be given a short time temper at about 55 °C (100 °F) below the Ac_1 to improve machinability. *Cast specimens usually are not normalized before machining.* The record of hardenability test results must always state the prior thermal history of the specimen tested.

3.5 Heating for End-Quenching—The specimen shall be heated to the austenitizing temperature shown in Table 1. The specimen shall be placed in a furnace which is at the specified temperature and shall be held at this temperature for 30 to 35 min. It is necessary to determine by means of a thermocouple the time required for a test specimen to come to the required temperature.

While heating the test specimen it is important to insure that practically no scaling or decarburization takes place on the end to be quenched. This may be achieved through the use of protective furnace atmospheres or by placing the specimen in a container which maintains a non-oxidizing atmosphere, e.g., by placing fine graphite powder or cast iron chips in the base of the container.

Figure 4 illustrates a type of container which has been used with success. However, any similar type will be satisfactory.

TABLE 1—NORMALIZING AND QUENCHING TEMPERATURES(1)(2) APPLICABLE TO STEEL ORDERED TO END-QUENCH HARDENABILITY REQUIREMENTS

Maximum Ordered Carbon Content, %	Normalizing Temperature °C	Normalizing Temperature °F	Austenitizing Temperature °C	Austenitizing Temperature °F
Steel Series 1000, 1300, 1500, 4000, 4100, 4300, 4600, 4700, 5000, 5100, 6100 (3), 8100, 8600, 8700, 8800, 9400				
Up to 0.25 incl	925	1700	925	1700
0.26 to 0.36 incl	900	1650	870	1600
0.37 and over[3]	870	1600	845	1550
Steel Series 4800, 9300				
Up to 0.25 incl	925	1700	845	1550
Steel Series 9200				
0.50 and over	900	1650	870	1600

1. A variation of ±5 °C (±10 °F) from the above temperature is permissible.
2. When testing H steels, the normalizing and austenitizing should be the same as for the equivalent standard steels. EXAMPLES: For 8622 H, the normalizing and austenitizing temperature should be the same as for SAE 8622; for 4032 H (carbon 0.30/0.37), the temperature should be the same as for SAE 4032 (carbon 0.30/0.35).
3. Normalizing and austenitizing temperatures shall be 30 °C (50 °F) higher for the 6100 series.

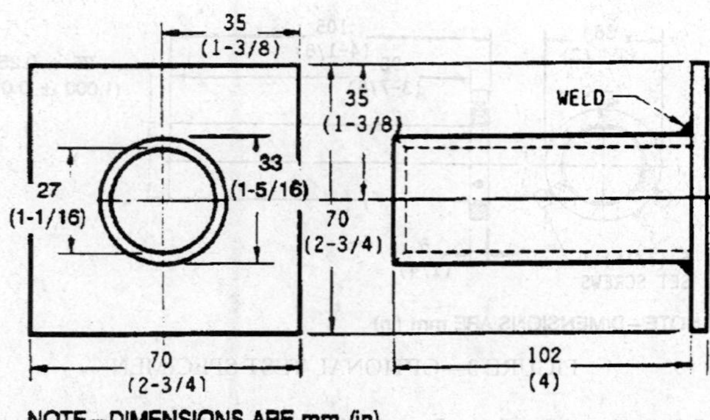

FIGURE 4—SPECIMEN PROTECTING FIXTURE TO BE CONSTRUCTED OF HEAT-RESISTING ALLOY

3.6 Quenching—The test specimen shall be placed on a fixture so that a column of water at a temperature of 5 to 30 °C (40 to 85 °F) may be directed against the bottom face of the specimen. The column of water passing through an orifice 13 mm (1/2 in) in diameter shall rise to a free height of 63 mm (2-1/2 in) above the orifice. The fixture shall be dry at the beginning of each test.

In performing the test, the water supply shall be shut off with a quick-opening valve and the hot specimen placed over the water pipe so that the bottom of the specimen is 13 mm (1/2 in) from the opening of the water pipe and the water shall then be turned on. A preferred alternate procedure is to keep the water flowing, but impose a deflecting plate above the water pipe while transferring the test specimen from the furnace to the fixture, and quickly removing the plate to start the end-quench. The time between removal of the specimen from the furnace and the beginning of the quench shall be not more than 5 s. The sample shall remain on the fixture for at least 10 min. A condition of still air shall be maintained around the specimen during cooling. (If the quenched end of the specimen is not cool when removed from the fixture, investigate whether water temperature or water flow is within specification.)

3.7 Hardness Measurement—Two flats 180 degrees apart shall be ground to a minimum depth of 0.38 mm (0.015 in) along the entire length of the bar and Rockwell C hardness measurements made along the length of the bar. Deviation from the standard depth can affect reproducibility of test results, and correlation with cooling rates in quenched bars.

The preparation of the two flats must be carried out with considerable care. They should be mutually parallel and the grinding done in such a manner that no change of the quenched structure takes place. Very light passes (less than 0.013 mm (0.0005 in)) with water cooling and a coarse, soft grinding wheel are recommended to avoid overheating the specimen. To detect tempering due to grinding, the flats may be etched as follows:

Two etchant solutions are used:

No. 1—5% nitric acid (concentrated) and 95% water by volume.

No. 2—50% hydrochloric acid (concentrated) and 50% water by volume.

Wash the sample in hot water. Etch in solution No. 1 until black. Wash in hot water. Immerse in solution No. 2 for 3 s and wash in hot water. Dry in air blast.

The presence of lighter or darker areas indicates that hardness and structure have been altered in grinding. All structural changes caused by grinding shall be removed before hardness tests are made. This may be accomplished by resurfacing and again etching, or new flats may be prepared.

When hardness indentations are made, the test specimen must rest on one of its flats on an anvil firmly attached to the hardness machine. It is important that no vertical movement be allowed when the major load is applied. The fixture must be constructed to move the test specimen past the penetrator in accurate steps of 0.5 mm (for metric fixture) or 1/16 in (for U.S. customary fixture). (Resting specimen on a V-block is not permitted.)

Figure 5 is an example of a commercially available fixture which provides for the controlled movement of the specimen.

The Rockwell tester should be checked against standard test blocks before testing the hardenability specimen. It is recommended that the test block be interposed between the specimen and the indenter to check the seating of the indenter and the specimen simultaneously.

Care must be exercised in registering the point of the indenter with the hardened end of the specimen, as well as providing for accurate spacing between indentations. A low power measuring microscope is suitable for use in determining the distance from the quenched end to the center of the first indentation and in checking the distance from center to center of the succeeding indentation. It has been found that with reasonable operating care and a well-built fixture, it is practical to locate the center of the first indentation 1.5 mm ± 0.075 mm (0.0625 in ± 0.003 in) from the quenched end. The variations between spacings should be even smaller. Obviously, it is more important to position the indenter accurately when testing shallow hardenability steels than when testing medium hardenability steels. The positioning of the indenter should be checked with sufficient frequency to provide assurance that accuracy requirements are being met. In cases of lack of reproducibility or of differences between laboratories, indenter spacing should be measured immediately.

FIGURE 5—COMMERCIALLY AVAILABLE FIXTURE FOR POSITIONING SPECIMEN FOR HARDNESS INDENTATIONS

3.7.1 METRIC DISTANCES BETWEEN READINGS—Readings shall be taken at 1.5, 3, 5, 7, 9, 11, 13, and 15 mm, then at 5 mm intervals to 50 mm, or until 20 HRC is reached (if less than 50 mm).

3.7.2 DISTANCES BETWEEN READINGS IN SIXTEENTHS OF AN INCH—Readings shall be taken at intervals of 1/16 in for the first inch. Distances between readings beyond 1 in may be at the discretion of the tester, but usually are taken at intervals of 1/8 in until 20 HRC is reached. (Less frequent intervals may be agreed upon between supplier and user.)

Hardness readings should be made on one flat, or preferably, two flats 180 degrees apart. When a flat on which readings have been made is used as a base, the ridges around the hardness indentations shall be removed by grinding unless a fixture is used which has been relieved to accommodate the irregularities due to the indentations. Testing on two flats will assist in the detection of errors in specimen preparation and hardness measurement. If the two probes on opposite sides differ by more than 4 HRC points at any one position, the test should be repeated on new flats, 90 degrees from the first two flats. If the retest also has greater than 4 HRC points spread, a new specimen should be tested.

For reporting purposes, hardness readings should be recorded to the nearest integer, with 0.5 HRC values rounded to the next higher integer.

3.8 Plotting of Tests—Tests should be plotted on a standard chart prepared for this purpose (Figure 6A or FIGURE 6B) in which the ordinates represent hardness and the abscissas represent distance from the quenched end. Readings at identical distances should be averaged and the resultant values used for plotting.

Figures 6A and 6B are Standard Forms for Plotting Hardenability Curves.

3.9 Construction of Hardness U Curves—Charts are provided for using the hardenability curve to predict hardness U curves in various sized rounds when oil or water quenched. Figure 7 shows these charts. The curves show the locations in various sizes of rounds where the cooling rates are the same as at various positions along the end-quenched hardenability test bar. It should be noted that these curves assume good heat treatment practice—separation of parts in the quench, good agitation, and good control of temperature and cleanliness of the quenchant. The ranges given reflect variations found under laboratory conditions. Under production conditions, even wider variations may be found.

DATE ____________

LABORATORY ____________

TYPE SPECIMEN ____________

TEST NO. ____________

TYPE	HEAT NO.	GRAIN SIZE	C	Mn	P	S	Si	Ni	Cr	Mo		NORMAL. TEMP. °C	QUENCH TEMP. °C

REMARKS ____________

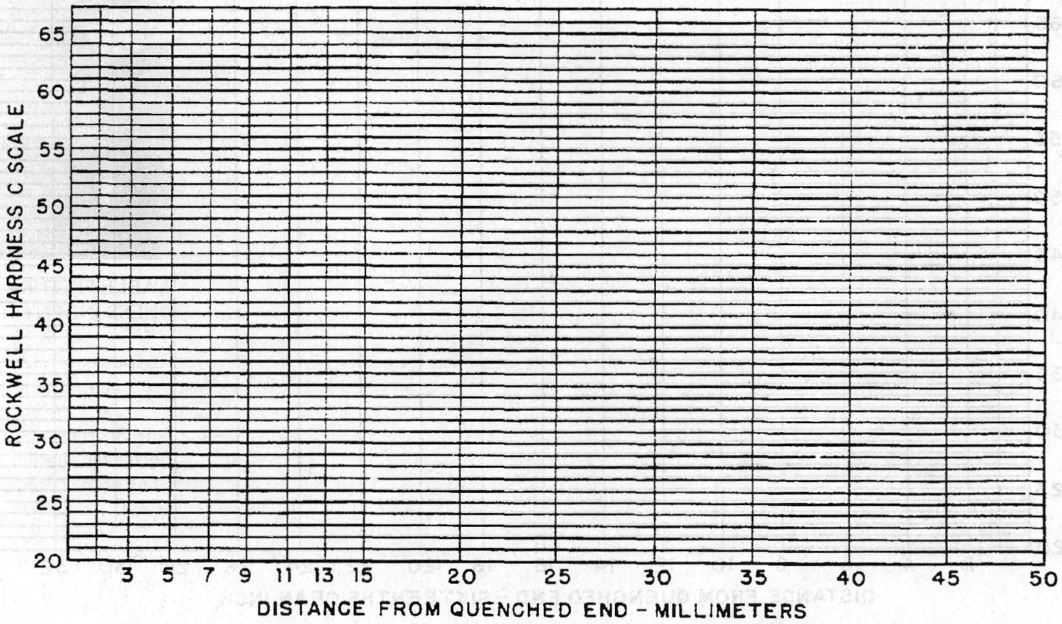

ROCKWELL HARDNESS C SCALE: 65, 60, 55, 50, 45, 40, 35, 30, 25, 20

3 5 7 9 11 13 15 20 25 30 35 40 45 50

DISTANCE FROM QUENCHED END - MILLIMETERS

FIGURE 6A—STANDARD FORM FOR PLOTTING HARDENABILITY CURVES (MILLIMETER DISTANCES)

3.10 Subsize Test Specimen—For determining hardenability of steel received in bars less than 26 mm (1-1/6 in) in diameter, the test bar may be made 19, 13, or 6 mm (3/4, 1/2, or 1/4 in) in diameter, as desired, and end-quenched as prescribed for the 25 mm (1 in) round. Modifications in the water orifice are required for quenching cylinders of less than 25 mm (1 in) diameter. The details of orifices for quenching specimens less than 25 mm (1 in) diameter are given in Table 2.

Because of the greater air-cooling effect on test specimens less than 25 mm (1 in) diameter and especially in specimens smaller than 19 mm (3/4 in) diameter, the cooling rates at various distances from the quenched end will not be the same as in the standard test specimen.

Hardenability curves obtained from smaller specimens are not comparable with curves obtained from the 25 mm (1 in) round specimen. If the standard hardenability curve is needed from subsize specimens, it becomes necessary to determine the actual cooling rates on the subsize specimens.

4. Hardenability Tests for Shallow Hardening Steels—The 25 mm (1 in) standard hardenability specimen may be used to determine the hardenability of shallow hardening steels other than the carbon tool steels by a modification in the hardness survey. The procedure for preparing the specimen prior to hardness measurement is specified in 3.1 to 3.9 for standard 25 mm (1 in) hardenability specimens. An anvil providing a means of very accurately measuring the distance from the quenched end is essential.

Only two flats 180 degrees apart need be ground if the mechanical fixture has a grooved bed which will accommodate the indentations on the flat surveyed first. The second hardness traverse is made after turning the bar over. If the fixture does not have such a grooved bed, two pairs of flats should be ground, the flats of each pair being 180 degrees apart. The two hardness surveys are made on adjacent flats.

DATE ____________________

LABORATORY ____________________

TYPE SPECIMEN ____________________

TEST NO. ____________________

TYPE	HEAT NO.	GRAIN SIZE	C	Mn	P	S	Si	Ni	Cr	Mo		NORMAL. TEMP. °F	QUENCH TEMP. °F

REMARKS ____________________

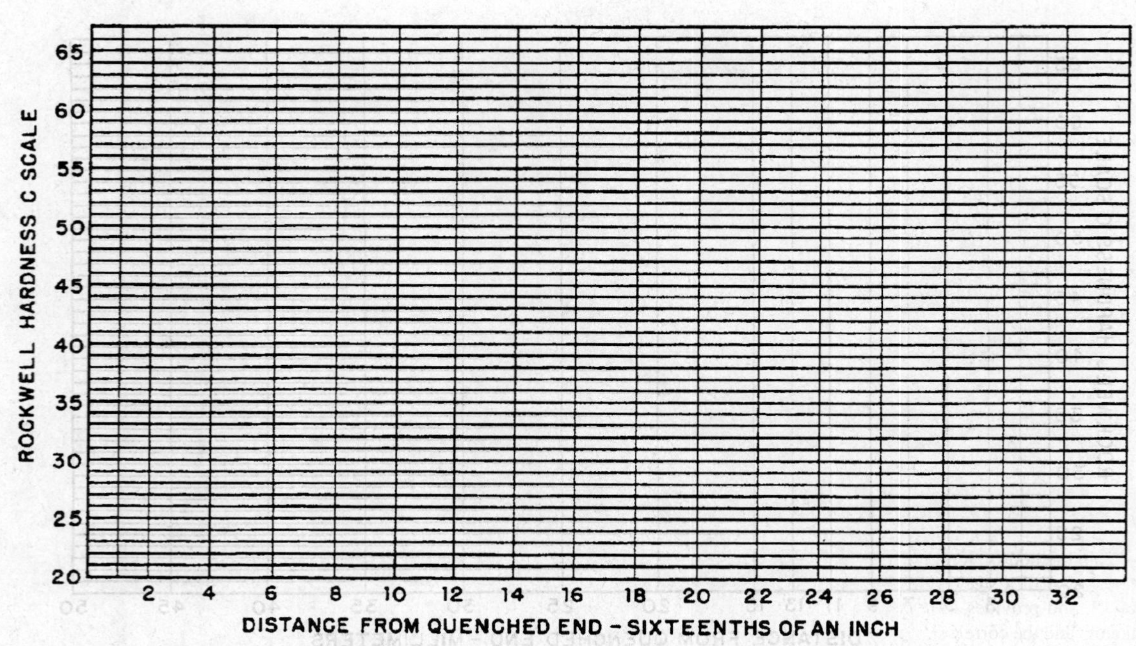

FIGURE 6B—STANDARD FORM FOR PLOTTING HARDENABILITY CURVES (SIXTEENTHS OF AN INCH DISTANCES)

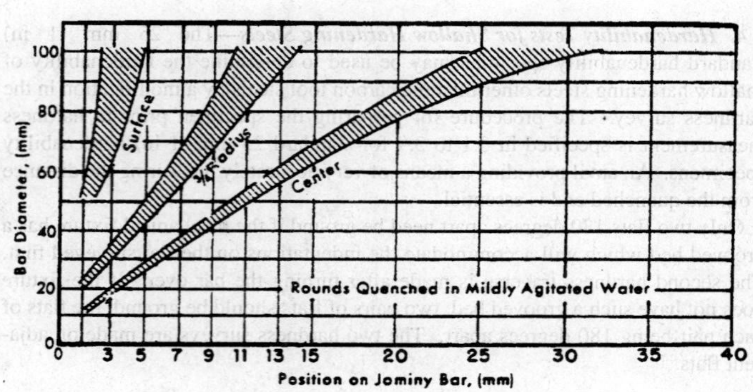

FIGURE 7A—CORRELATION OF COOLING RATES IN JOMINY BAR AND QUENCHED ROUND BARS

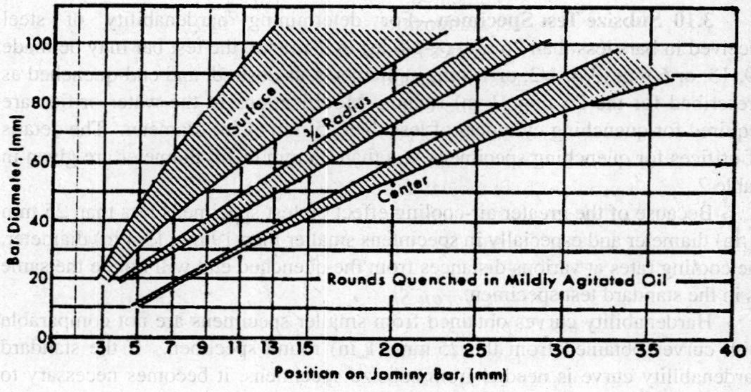

FIGURE 7B—CORRELATION OF COOLING RATES IN JOMINY BAR AND QUENCHED ROUND BARS

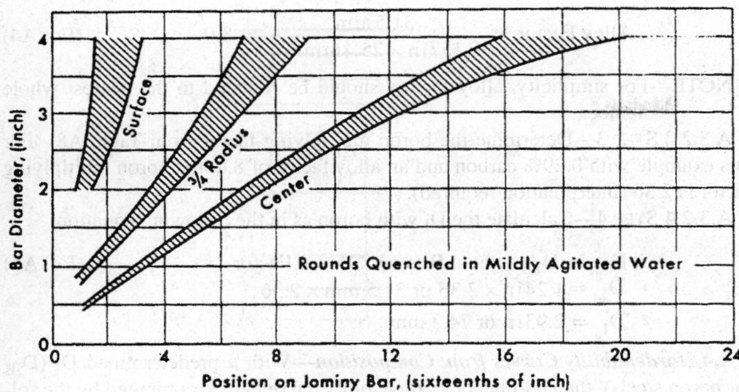

FIGURE 7C—CORRELATION OF COOLING RATES IN JOMINY BAR AND QUENCHED ROUND BARS

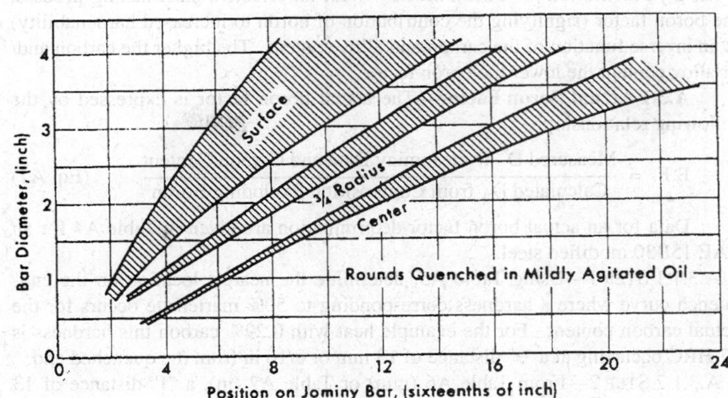

FIGURE 7D—CORRELATION OF COOLING RATES IN JOMINY BAR AND QUENCHED ROUND BARS

TABLE 2—ORIFICES FOR QUENCHING SUBSIZE SPECIMENS

Test Specimen Diameter mm (in)	Orifice Size mm (in)	Distance from Orifice to Quenched End of Specimen mm (in)	Free Height of Water Column mm (in)
19 (3/4)	13 (1/2)	13 (1/2)	63 (2–1/2)
13 (1/2)	6 (1/4)	10 (3/8)	102 (4)
6 (1/4)	3 (1/8)	6 (1/4)	203 (8)

4.1 Procedure for Distance from the Quenched End in Millimeters—Hardness values are obtained from 1 to 15 mm in intervals of 1 mm. For this distance, two hardness traverses are made, each with hardness indentations 2 mm apart, one traverse starting at 1 mm from the quenched end, the other starting at 2 mm from the quenched end. Beyond 15 mm from the quenched end, intervals can be increased to 5 mm until 20 HRC is reached.

4.2 Procedure for Distance from the Quenched End in Sixteenths of an Inch—Hardness values are obtained from 1/16 to 8/16 in from the quenched end in intervals of 1/32 in. For this distance, two hardness traverses are made, each with hardness indentations 1/16 in apart, one traverse starting at 1/16 in from the quenched end, the other starting at 3/32 in from the quenched end. Beyond 8/16 in from the quenched end, intervals can be increased to a minimum of 2/16 in until 20 HRC is reached.

For plotting test results, the Standard Form for Plotting Hardenability Curves (Figure 6A or FIGURE 6B) should be used.

APPENDIX A
METHOD FOR CALCULATING HARDENABILITY FROM COMPOSITION

A.1 Introduction—This method of Jominy hardenability calculation from the chemical ideal diameter[1] (D_I) of a steel is based on the original work of M. A. Grossman, Reference 18, and provides increased accuracy by refinement of the carbon multiplying factors and the correlation of a boron factor (B.F.) with carbon and alloy content. These refinements were based on analysis of thousands of heats of boron and non-boron 1500, 4100, 5000, and 8600 series steels encompassing a range of compositions as shown in Table A1 and a range of D_I as contained in Tables A9 to A12. The accuracy of this method and the techniques used to develop it have been documented, Reference 26. For comparison of this method to others, or for steel compositions outside the above-mentioned grades, the user should refer to other articles listed in Section 2.1, 17 to 29.

The succeeding paragraphs outline this method for calculating hardenability from chemical composition. The calculation method and data tables are also embodied in a computer program, EA406 "Hardenability Prediction Calculator" available through SAE. The program runs on an IBM compatible PC with a 3-1/2 in disc drive. It provides both tabular and graphical output of end-quench hardenability data calculated from chemical composition. To obtain a copy of the program, contact the SAE Customer Service Department, 400 Commonwealth Drive, Warrendale, PA 15096-0001.

A.2 D_I Calculation for Non-Boron Steels—This calculation relies on a series of hardenability factors (Table A2) for each alloying element in the composition which multiplied together give a D_I value. (For simplicity, only multiplying factors for D_I in inch units are given. For D_I in mm, the D_I in inches should be converted.) The effects of phosphorus and sulfur are not considered since they tend to cancel one another. A No. 7 austenitic grain size is assumed since most steels with hardenability control are melted to a fine grain practice where experience has demonstrated that an extremely high percentage of heats conform to this grain size. For austenitic grain sizes other than No. 7, Grossman's data suggest that the calculated D_I be increased about 8% for each grain size number less than 7 and decreased by about 8% for each grain size number greater than 7. Specific suggestions are:

a. For grain size 6 multiply D_I by 1.083
b. For grain size 5 multiply D_I by 1.172
c. For grain size 4 multiply D_I by 1.270

An example of D_I calculation is given in Table A3 for an SAE 4118 modified steel.

TABLE A1—COMPOSITION RANGE USED TO DEVELOP THE HARDENABILITY CALCULATION METHOD DESCRIBED IN THIS APPENDIX

Element[(1)]	Range (%)[(1)]
Carbon	0.10–0.70
Manganese	0.50–1.65
Silicon	0.15–0.60
Chromium	1.35 max
Nickel	1.50 max
Molybdenum	0.55 max

1. For element percentages outside the ranges shown, and for elements not shown (copper and vanadium), the original Grossman factors are shown in Table A2.

1. D_I (or DI in some computer programs) represents the diameter of a round steel bar that will harden at the center to 50% martensite when subjected to an ideal quench (i.e., a Grossman quench severity H = infinity).

A.3 D_I Calculation for Boron Steels—With an effective steelmaking process, the boron factor (signifying the contribution of boron to increased hardenability) is an inverse function of the carbon and alloy content. The higher the carbon and/or alloy content the lower the boron factor.

A.3.1 Actual Boron Factor—The actual boron factor is expressed by the following relationship:

$$\text{B.F.} = \frac{\text{Measured } D_I \text{ from Jominy Data and Carbon Content}}{\text{Calculated } D_I \text{ from Composition Excluding Boron}} \quad \text{(Eq. A1)}$$

Data for an actual boron factor determination are given in Table A4 for an SAE 15B30 modified steel.

A.3.1.1 STEP 1—Using Table A5, determine the nearest location on the end-quench curve where a hardness corresponding to 50% martensite occurs for the actual carbon content. For the example heat with 0.29% carbon this hardness is 37 HRC occurring at a "J" distance of 13 mm or 8/16 in from the quenched end.

A.3.1.2 STEP 2—From Table A6 (mm) or Table A7 (in), a "J" distance of 13 mm or 8/16 in equates to a measured D_I of 76.4 mm or 2.97 in (interpolation may be required).

A.3.1.3 STEP 3

$$\text{Boron Factor} = \frac{76.4\text{mm}}{31.5\text{mm}} = 2.43 \quad \text{(Eq. A2)}$$

or

$$\text{Boron Factor} = \frac{2.97\text{in}}{1.24\text{in}} = 2.4$$

NOTE—Difference in B.F. using inch versus mm is due to the use of nearest standard "J" distance. Use of exact "J" distances would resolve this difference.

A.3.2 Calculation of D_I with Boron (D_{IB})

A.3.2.1 STEP 1—Calculate the D_I without boron. For the previous example, this D_I is 31.5 mm (1.24 in).

A.3.2.2 STEP 2—Calculate the alloy factor (the product of all the multiplying factors from Table A2 excluding carbon). For the previous example:

$$\text{Alloy Factor} = \frac{\text{Calculated } D_I \text{ (without Boron)}}{\text{Carbon Multiplying Factor}} = \frac{1.24\text{in}}{0.157\text{in}} = 8.0 \quad \text{(Eq. A3)}$$

or

$$\text{Alloy Factor} = \frac{31.5\text{mm}}{0.157\text{in} \times 25.4\text{mm/in}} = 8.0 \quad \text{(Eq. A4)}$$

NOTE—For simplicity, alloy factors should be rounded to the nearest whole number.

A.3.2.3 STEP 3—Determine the boron multiplying factor from Table A8. For this example with 0.29% carbon and an alloy factor of 8.0, the boron multiplying factor is 2.36 (interpolation required).

A.3.2.4 STEP 4—Calculate the D_I with boron as in the following equation:

$$D_{I_B} = D_I \text{ (without Boron)} \times \text{Boron Factor} \quad \text{(Eq. A5)}$$
$$D_{I_B} = 1.24\text{in} \times 2.36 \text{ or } 31.5 \text{ mm} \times 2.36$$
$$D_{I_B} = 2.93\text{in or } 74.3 \text{ mm}$$

A.4 Hardenability Curves from Composition—With a predetermined D_I (D_{IB} for boron steels), the end-quench hardenability curve can be computed by the following procedure:

A.4.1 Step 1—The initial hardness (IH) at the J = 1.5 mm or 1/16 in position is a function of carbon content and independent of hardenability, and is selected from Table A5. For the example, non-boron SAE 4118 modified heat containing 0.22% C the initial hardness is 45 HRC.

A.4.2 Step 2—The hardness at other positions along the end-quench specimen (termed distance hardness) is determined by dividing the initial hardness by the appropriate factor from Table A9 (mm) or A10 (inch) for non-boron steels or from Table A11 (mm) or A12 (inch) for boron steels.

For the example shown in Tables A13 and A14, a non-boron heat of steel with an IH = 45 HRC and a calculated D_I of 45.5 mm (1.79 in), the hardness at the respective end-quench positions can be calculated by dividing 45 by the appropriate dividing factor listed in Table A9 (mm) or A10 (inch) for non-boron steels. (For simplicity, the D_I should be rounded to the nearest 0.5 mm or 0.1 in.)

A.5 Equations for Tables A2-A12—Tables A15 to A22 represent a least squares polynomial fit of data contained in Tables A2 to A12. The use of these equations to plot curves may result in random inflection points due to the characteristics of the polynomial equations. These inflections will be minor, however, and should be disregarded.

TABLE A2—HARDENABILITY MULTIPLYING FACTORS VS. % ELEMENT (NON-BORON STEELS), INCH

% Element	Carbon-Grain Size 7	Mn	Si	Ni	Cr	Mo	Cu	V
0.01	0.005	1.033	1.007	1.004	1.022	1.03	1.00	1.02
0.02	0.011	1.067	1.014	1.007	1.043	1.06	1.01	1.03
0.03	0.016	1.100	1.021	1.011	1.065	1.09	1.01	1.05
0.04	0.021	1.133	1.028	1.015	1.086	1.12	1.02	1.07
0.05	0.026	1.167	1.035	1.018	1.108	1.15	1.02	1.09
0.06	0.032	1.200	1.042	1.022	1.130	1.18	1.02	1.11
0.07	0.038	1.233	1.049	1.026	1.151	1.21	1.03	1.12
0.08	0.043	1.267	1.056	1.029	1.173	1.24	1.03	1.14
0.09	0.049	1.300	1.063	1.033	1.194	1.27	1.03	1.16
0.10	0.054	1.333	1.070	1.036	1.216	1.30	1.04	1.17
0.11	0.059	1.367	1.077	1.040	1.238	1.33	1.04	1.19
0.12	0.065	1.400	1.084	1.044	1.259	1.36	1.05	1.21
0.13	0.070	1.433	1.091	1.047	1.281	1.39	1.05	1.22
0.14	0.076	1.467	1.098	1.051	1.302	1.42	1.05	1.24
0.15	0.081	1.500	1.105	1.055	1.324	1.45	1.06	1.26
0.16	0.086	1.533	1.112	1.058	1.346	1.48	1.06	1.28
0.17	0.092	1.567	1.119	1.062	1.367	1.51	1.06	1.29
0.18	0.097	1.600	1.126	1.066	1.389	1.54	1.07	1.31
0.19	0.103	1.633	1.133	1.069	1.410	1.57	1.07	1.33
0.20	0.108	1.667	1.140	1.073	1.432	1.60	1.07	1.35
0.21	0.113	1.700	1.147	1.077	1.454	1.63	1.08	--
0.22	0.119	1.733	1.154	1.080	1.475	1.66	1.08	--
0.23	0.124	1.767	1.161	1.084	1.497	1.69	1.09	--
0.24	0.130	1.800	1.168	1.088	1.518	1.72	1.09	—
0.25	0.135	1.833	1.175	1.091	1.540	1.75	1.09	—

TABLE A2—HARDENABILITY MULTIPLYING FACTORS VS. % ELEMENT (NON-BORON STEELS), INCH (continued)

% Element	Carbon-Grain Size 7	Mn	Si	Ni	Cr	Mo	Cu	V
0.26	0.140	1.867	1.182	1.095	1.562	1.78	1.10	—
0.27	0.146	1.900	1.189	1.098	1.583	1.81	1.10	—
0.28	0.151	1.933	1.196	1.102	1.605	1.84	1.10	—
0.29	0.157	1.967	1.203	1.106	1.626	1.87	1.11	—
0.30	0.162	2.000	1.210	1.109	1.648	1.90	1.11	—
0.31	0.167	2.033	1.217	1.113	1.670	1.93	1.11	—
0.32	0.173	2.067	1.224	1.117	1.691	1.96	1.12	—
0.33	0.178	2.100	1.231	1.120	1.713	1.99	1.12	—
0.34	0.184	2.133	1.238	1.124	1.734	2.02	1.12	—
0.35	0.189	2.167	1.245	1.128	1.756	2.05	1.13	—
0.36	0.194	2.200	1.252	1.131	1.776	2.08	1.13	—
0.37	0.200	2.233	1.259	1.135	1.799	2.11	1.14	—
0.38	0.205	2.267	1.266	1.139	1.821	2.14	1.14	—
0.39	0.211	2.300	1.273	1.142	1.842	2.17	1.14	—
0.40	0.213	2.333	1.280	1.146	1.864	2.20	1.15	—
0.41	0.216	2.367	1.287	1.150	1.886	2.23	1.15	—
0.42	0.218	2.400	1.294	1.153	1.907	2.26	1.15	—
0.43	0.221	2.433	1.301	1.157	1.929	2.29	1.16	—
0.44	0.223	2.467	1.308	1.160	1.950	2.32	1.16	—
0.45	0.226	2.500	1.315	1.164	1.972	2.35	1.16	—
0.46	0.228	2.533	1.322	1.168	1.994	2.38	1.17	—
0.47	0.230	2.567	1.329	1.171	2.015	2.41	1.17	—
0.48	0.233	2.600	1.336	1.175	2.037	2.44	1.18	—
0.49	0.235	2.633	1.343	1.179	2.058	2.47	1.18	—
0.50	0.238	2.667	1.350	1.182	2.080	2.50	1.18	—
0.51	0.242	2.700	1.357	1.186	2.102	2.53	1.19	—
0.52	0.244	2.733	1.364	1.190	2.123	2.56	1.19	—
0.53	0.246	2.767	1.371	1.193	2.145	2.59	1.19	—
0.54	0.249	2.800	1.378	1.197	2.166	2.62	1.20	—
0.55	0.251	2.833	1.385	1.201	2.188	2.65	1.20	—
0.56	0.253	2.867	1.392	1.204	2.210	—	—	—
0.57	0.256	2.900	1.399	1.208	2.231	—	—	—
0.58	0.258	2.933	1.406	1.212	2.253	—	—	—
0.59	0.260	2.967	1.413	1.215	2.274	—	—	—
0.60	0.262	3.000	1.420	1.219	2.296	—	—	—
0.61	0.264	3.033	1.427	1.222	2.318	—	—	—
0.62	0.267	3.067	1.434	1.226	2.339	—	—	—
0.63	0.269	3.100	1.441	1.230	2.361	—	—	—
0.64	0.271	3.133	1.448	1.233	2.382	—	—	—
0.65	0.273	3.167	1.465	1.237	2.404	—	—	—
0.66	0.275	3.200	1.462	1.241	2.426	—	—	—
0.67	0.277	3.233	1.469	1.244	2.447	—	—	—
0.68	0.279	3.267	1.476	1.248	2.469	—	—	—
0.69	0.281	3.300	1.483	1.252	2.490	—	—	—
0.70	0.283	3.333	1.490	1.255	2.512	—	—	—
0.71	0.285	3.367	1.497	1.259	2.534	—	—	—
0.72	0.287	3.400	1.504	1.262	2.555	—	—	—
0.73	0.289	3.433	1.511	1.266	2.577	—	—	—
0.74	0.291	3.467	1.518	1.270	2.596	—	—	—
0.75	0.293	3.500	1.525	1.273	2.620	—	—	—
0.76	0.295	3.533	1.532	1.276	2.642	—	—	—
0.77	0.297	3.567	1.539	1.280	2.663	—	—	—
0.78	0.299	3.600	1.546	1.284	2.685	—	—	—
0.79	0.301	3.633	1.553	1.287	2.706	—	—	—
0.80	0.303	3.667	1.560	1.291	2.728	—	—	—

TABLE A2—HARDENABILITY MULTIPLYING FACTORS VS. % ELEMENT (NON-BORON STEELS), INCH (continued)

% Element	Carbon-Grain Size 7	Mn	Si	Ni	Cr	Mo	Cu	V
0.81	0.305	3.700	1.567	1.294	2.750	—	—	—
0.82	0.307	3.733	1.574	1.298	2.771	—	—	—
0.83	0.309	3.767	1.581	1.301	2.793	—	—	—
0.84	0.310	3.800	1.588	1.306	2.814	—	—	—
0.85	0.312	3.833	1.595	1.309	2.836	—	—	—
0.86	0.314	3.867	1.602	1.313	2.858	—	—	—
0.87	0.316	3.900	1.609	1.317	2.879	—	—	—
0.88	0.318	3.933	1.616	1.320	2.900	—	—	—
0.89	0.319	3.967	1.623	1.324	2.922	—	—	—
0.90	0.321	4.000	1.630	1.327	2.944	—	—	—
0.91	—	4.033	1.637	1.331	2.966	—	—	—
0.92	—	4.067	1.644	1.334	2.987	—	—	—
0.93	—	4.100	1.651	1.338	3.009	—	—	—
0.94	—	4.133	1.658	1.343	3.030	—	—	—
0.95	—	4.167	1.665	1.345	3.052	—	—	—
0.96	—	4.200	1.672	1.349	3.074	—	—	—
0.97	—	4.233	1.679	1.352	3.095	—	—	—
0.98	—	4.267	1.686	1.356	3.117	—	—	—
0.99	—	4.300	1.693	1.360	3.138	—	—	—
1.00	—	4.333	1.700	1.364	3.160	—	—	—
1.01	—	4.367	1.707	1.367	3.182	—	—	—
1.02	—	4.400	1.714	1.370	3.203	—	—	—
1.03	—	4.433	1.721	1.375	3.225	—	—	—
1.04	—	4.467	1.728	1.378	3.246	—	—	—
1.05	—	4.500	1.735	1.382	3.268	—	—	—
1.06	—	4.533	1.742	1.386	3.290	—	—	—
1.07	—	4.567	1.749	1.389	3.311	—	—	—
1.08	—	4.600	1.756	1.393	3.333	—	—	—
1.09	—	4.633	1.763	1.396	3.354	—	—	—
1.10	—	4.667	1.770	1.400	3.376	—	—	—
1.11	—	4.700	1.777	1.403	3.398	—	—	—
1.12	—	4.733	1.784	1.406	3.419	—	—	—
1.13	—	4.767	1.791	1.411	3.441	—	—	—
1.14	—	4.800	1.798	1.414	3.462	—	—	—
1.15	—	4.833	1.805	1.418	3.484	—	—	—
1.16	—	4.867	1.812	1.422	3.506	—	—	—
1.17	—	4.900	1.819	1.426	3.527	—	—	—
1.18	—	4.933	1.826	1.429	3.549	—	—	—
1.19	—	4.967	1.833	1.433	3.570	—	—	—
1.20	—	5.000	1.840	1.437	3.592	—	—	—
1.21	—	5.051	1.847	1.440	3.614	—	—	—
1.22	—	5.102	1.854	1.444	3.635	—	—	—
1.23	—	5.153	1.861	1.447	3.657	—	—	—
1.24	—	5.204	1.868	1.450	3.678	—	—	—
1.25	—	5.255	1.875	1.454	3.700	—	—	—
1.26	—	5.306	1.882	1.458	3.722	—	—	—
1.27	—	5.357	1.889	1.461	3.743	—	—	—
1.28	—	5.408	1.896	1.465	3.765	—	—	—
1.29	—	5.459	1.903	1.470	3.786	—	—	—
1.30	—	5.510	1.910	1.473	3.808	—	—	—
1.31	—	5.561	1.917	1.476	3.830	—	—	—
1.32	—	5.612	1.924	1.481	3.851	—	—	—
1.33	—	5.663	1.931	1.484	3.873	—	—	—
1.34	—	5.714	1.938	1.487	3.984	—	—	—
1.35	—	5.765	1.945	1.491	3.916	—	—	—
1.36	—	5.816	1.952	1.495	3.938	—	—	—
1.37	—	5.867	1.959	1.498	3.959	—	—	—

TABLE A2—HARDENABILITY MULTIPLYING FACTORS VS. % ELEMENT (NON-BORON STEELS), INCH (continued)

% Element	Carbon-Grain Size 7	Mn	Si	Ni	Cr	Mo	Cu	V
1.38	—	5.918	1.966	1.501	3.981	—	—	—
1.39	—	5.969	1.973	1.506	4.002	—	—	—
1.40	—	6.020	1.980	1.509	4.024	—	—	—
1.41	—	6.071	1.987	1.512	4.046	—	—	—
1.42	—	6.122	1.994	1.517	4.067	—	—	—
1.43	—	6.173	2.001	1.520	4.089	—	—	—
1.44	—	6.224	2.008	1.523	4.110	—	—	—
1.45	—	6.275	2.015	1.527	4.132	—	—	—
1.46	—	6.326	2.022	1.531	4.154	—	—	—
1.47	—	6.377	2.029	1.535	4.175	—	—	—
1.48	—	6.428	2.036	1.538	4.197	—	—	—
1.49	—	6.479	2.043	1.541	4.217	—	—	—
1.50	—	6.530	2.050	1.545	4.239	—	—	—
1.51	—	6.581	2.057	1.556	4.262	—	—	—
1.52	—	6.632	2.064	1.561	4.283	—	—	—
1.53	—	6.683	2.071	1.565	4.305	—	—	—
1.54	—	6.734	2.078	1.569	4.326	—	—	—
1.55	—	6.785	2.085	1.574	4.348	—	—	—
1.56	—	6.836	2.092	1.578	4.369	—	—	—
1.57	—	6.887	2.099	1.582	4.391	—	—	—
1.58	—	6.938	2.106	1.586	4.413	—	—	—
1.59	—	6.989	2.113	1.591	4.434	—	—	—
1.60	—	7.040	2.120	1.595	4.456	—	—	—
1.61	—	7.091	2.127	1.600	4.478	—	—	—
1.62	—	7.142	2.134	1.604	4.499	—	—	—
1.63	—	7.193	2.141	1.609	4.521	—	—	—
1.64	—	7.224	2.148	1.613	4.542	—	—	—
1.65	—	7.295	2.155	1.618	4.564	—	—	—
1.66	—	7.346	2.162	1.622	4.586	—	—	—
1.67	—	7.397	2.169	1.627	4.607	—	—	—
1.68	—	7.448	2.176	1.631	4.629	—	—	—
1.69	—	7.499	2.183	1.636	4.650	—	—	—
1.70	—	7.550	2.190	1.640	4.672	—	—	—
1.71	—	7.601	2.197	1.644	4.694	—	—	—
1.72	—	7.652	2.204	1.648	4.715	—	—	—
1.73	—	7.703	2.211	1.652	4.737	—	—	—
1.74	—	7.754	2.218	1.656	4.759	—	—	—
1.75	—	7.805	2.225	1.660	4.780	—	—	—
1.76	—	7.856	2.232	1.664	—	—	—	—
1.77	—	7.907	2.239	1.668	—	—	—	—
1.78	—	7.958	2.246	1.672	—	—	—	—
1.79	—	8.009	2.253	1.676	—	—	—	—
1.80	—	8.060	2.260	1.680	—	—	—	—
1.81	—	8.111	2.267	1.687	—	—	—	—
1.82	—	8.162	2.274	1.694	—	—	—	—
1.83	—	8.213	2.281	1.701	—	—	—	—
1.84	—	8.264	2.288	1.708	—	—	—	—
1.85	—	8.315	2.295	1.715	—	—	—	—
1.86	—	8.366	2.302	1.722	—	—	—	—
1.87	—	8.417	2.309	1.729	—	—	—	—
1.88	—	8.468	2.316	1.736	—	—	—	—
1.89	—	8.519	2.323	1.743	—	—	—	—
1.90	—	8.570	2.330	1.750	—	—	—	—
1.91	—	8.671	2.337	1.753	—	—	—	—
1.92	—	8.672	2.344	1.756	—	—	—	—

TABLE A2—HARDENABILITY MULTIPLYING FACTORS VS. % ELEMENT (NON-BORON STEELS), INCH (continued)

% Element	Carbon-Grain Size 7	Mn	Si	Ni	Cr	Mo	Cu	V
1.93	—	8.723	2.351	1.759	—	—	—	—
1.94	—	8.774	2.358	1.761	—	—	—	—
1.95	—	8.825	2.364	1.765	—	—	—	—
1.96	—	—	2.372	1.767	—	—	—	—
1.97	—	—	2.379	1.770	—	—	—	—
1.98	—	—	2.386	1.773	—	—	—	—
1.99	—	—	2.393	1.776	—	—	—	—
2.00	—	—	2.400	1.779	—	—	—	—

TABLE A3—EXAMPLE OF D_I CALCULATION (FOR A MODIFIED SAE 4118 STEEL, GRAIN SIZE 7)

Element	%	Multiplying Factor (Table A2)
Carbon	0.22	0.119
Manganese	0.80	3.667
Silicon	0.18	1.126
Nickel	0.10	1.036
Chromium	0.43	1.929
Molybdenum	0.25	1.75
Copper	0.10	1.04
D_I = 0.119 x 3.667 x 1.126 x 1.036 x 1.929 x 1.75 x 1.79 in (45.5 mm)		

TABLE A4—DATA FOR AN ACTUAL BORON FACTOR DETERMINATION (FOR AN SAE 15B30 STEEL)

Composition, %	C	Mn	Si	Ni	Cr	Mo	B			Calc DI (Boron Excluded)			
	0.29	1.25	0.20	0.13	0.07	0.03	0.0015			31.5 mm (1.24 in)			
End-Quench Test Results, mm													
"J" Position (mm)	1.5	3	5	7	9	11	13	15	20	25			
Hardness, HRC	50	50	49	48	46	41	37	30	24	20			
End-Quench Test Results, inches													
"J" Position													
(1/16 in)	1	2	3	4	5	6	7	8	9	10	12	14	16
Hardness, HRC	50	50	49	48	47	45	41	38	33	28	25	22	20

TABLE A5—INITIAL HARDNESS AND 50% MARTENSITE HARDNESS VS. % CARBON

% Carbon Content	Initial Hardness—HRC 100% Martensite	Hardness—HRC 50% Martensite	% Carbon Content	Initial Hardness—HRC 100% Martensite	Hardness—HRC 50% Martensite	% Carbon Content	Initial Hardness—HRC 100% Martensite	Hardness—HRC 50% Martensite
0.10	38	26	0.30	50	37	0.50	61	47
0.11	39	27	0.31	51	38	0.51	61	47
0.12	40	27	0.32	51	38	0.52	62	48
0.13	40	28	0.33	52	39	0.53	62	48
0.14	41	28	0.34	53	40	0.54	63	48
0.15	41	29	0.35	53	40	0.55	63	49
0.16	42	30	0.36	54	41	0.56	63	49
0.17	42	30	0.37	55	41	0.57	64	50
0.18	43	31	0.38	55	42	0.58	64	50
0.19	44	31	0.39	56	42	0.59	64	51
0.20	44	32	0.40	56	43	0.60	64	51
0.21	45	32	0.41	57	43	0.61	64	51
0.22	45	33	0.42	57	43	0.62	65	51
0.23	46	34	0.43	58	44	0.63	65	52
0.24	46	34	0.44	58	44	0.64	65	52
0.25	47	35	0.45	59	45	0.65	65	52
0.26	48	35	0.46	59	45	0.66	65	52
0.27	49	36	0.47	59	45	0.67	65	53
0.28	49	36	0.48	59	46	0.68	65	53
0.29	50	37	0.49	60	46	0.69	65	53

TABLE A6—D_I VS. JOMINY DISTANCE FOR 50% MARTENSITE (mm)

"J" mm	D_I mm	"J" mm	DI mm	"J" mm	D_I mm
1.0	7.9	18.0	94.5	35.0	137.3
2.0	15.8	19.0	97.7	36.0	139.3
3.0	23.2	20.0	100.8	37.0	141.2
4.0	30.2	21.0	103.7	38.0	143.0
5.0	36.6	22.0	106.6	39.0	144.8
6.0	42.7	23.0	109.3	40.0	146.6
7.0	48.4	24.0	112.0	41.0	148.3
8.0	53.8	25.0	114.7	42.0	149.9
9.0	58.9	26.0	117.2	43.0	151.5
10.0	63.7	27.0	119.7	44.0	153.1
11.0	68.2	28.0	122.1	45.0	154.6
12.0	72.5	29.0	124.5	46.0	156.1
13.0	76.6	30.0	126.7	47.0	157.6
14.0	80.5	31.0	129.0	48.0	159.0
15.0	84.3	32.0	131.2	49.0	160.5
16.0	87.8	33.0	133.3	50.0	161.9
17.0	91.2	34.0	135.3	—	—

TABLE A7—D_I VS. JOMINY DISTANCE FOR 50% MARTENSITE (inch)

"J" 1/16 in	D_I in	"J" 1/16 in	D_I in	"J" 1/16 in	D_I in
0.5	0.27	11.5	3.74	22.5	5.46
1.0	0.50	12.0	3.83	23.0	5.51
1.5	0.73	12.5	3.94	23.5	5.57
2.0	0.95	13.0	4.04	24.0	5.63
2.5	1.16	13.5	4.13	24.5	5.69
3.0	1.37	14.0	4.22	25.0	5.74
3.5	1.57	14.5	4.32	25.5	5.80
4.0	1.75	15.0	4.40	26.0	5.86
4.5	1.93	15.5	4.48	26.5	5.91
5.0	2.12	16.0	4.57	27.0	5.96
5.5	2.29	16.5	4.64	27.5	6.02
6.0	2.45	17.0	4.72	28.0	6.06
6.5	2.58	17.5	4.80	28.5	6.12
7.0	2.72	18.0	4.87	29.0	6.16
7.5	2.86	18.5	4.94	29.5	6.20
8.0	2.97	19.0	5.02	30.0	6.25
8.5	3.07	19.5	5.08	30.5	6.29
9.0	3.20	20.0	5.15	31.0	6.33
9.5	3.32	20.5	5.22	31.5	6.37
10.0	3.43	21.0	5.28	32.0	6.42
10.5	3.54	21.5	5.33	—	—
11.0	3.64	22.0	5.39	—	—

TABLE A8—BORON FACTORS VS. % CARBON AT SPECIFIC ALLOY FACTOR LEVELS

% Carbon	Alloy Factor(1) 5	Alloy Factor(1) 7	Alloy Factor(1) 9	Alloy Factor(1) 11	Alloy Factor(1) 13	Alloy Factor(1) 15	Alloy Factor(1) 18	Alloy Factor(1) 22	Alloy Factor(1) 26
0.10	6.18	5.38	5.09	4.61	4.28	4.14	3.72	3.68	3.55
0.11	5.76	5.07	4.77	4.35	4.05	3.88	3.54	3.48	3.35
0.12	5.38	4.78	4.48	4.10	3.84	3.65	3.37	3.30	3.18
0.13	5.04	4.52	4.22	3.88	3.64	3.44	3.21	3.14	3.03
0.14	4.72	4.28	3.98	3.68	3.47	3.26	3.07	2.99	2.88
0.15	4.44	4.06	3.77	3.50	3.31	3.09	2.94	2.86	2.76
0.16	4.19	3.86	3.57	3.34	3.16	2.94	2.82	2.74	2.64
0.17	3.96	3.68	3.40	3.19	3.03	2.81	2.71	2.63	2.54
0.18	3.75	3.51	3.24	3.05	2.91	2.70	2.61	2.53	2.44
0.19	3.57	3.36	3.10	2.93	2.80	2.59	2.52	2.44	2.36
0.20	3.40	3.22	2.98	2.82	2.70	2.50	2.43	2.35	2.28
0.21	3.25	3.09	2.86	2.72	2.60	2.42	2.35	2.28	2.20
0.22	3.12	2.98	2.76	2.63	2.52	2.34	2.28	2.20	2.13
0.23	3.00	2.88	2.61	2.55	2.44	2.27	2.21	2.14	2.07
0.24	2.90	2.78	2.59	2.47	2.37	2.21	2.15	2.07	2.01
0.25	2.81	2.70	2.52	2.40	2.30	2.15	2.09	2.01	1.95
0.26	2.73	2.62	2.45	2.34	2.24	2.10	2.03	1.96	1.89
0.27	2.66	2.55	2.39	2.28	2.18	2.05	1.98	1.91	1.84
0.28	2.60	2.49	2.34	2.23	2.13	2.00	1.93	1.86	1.79
0.29	2.54	2.43	2.29	2.18	2.08	1.96	1.88	1.81	1.74
0.30	2.49	2.38	2.24	2.14	2.04	1.92	1.83	1.76	1.70
0.31	2.44	2.33	2.20	2.10	1.99	1.88	1.79	1.72	1.65
0.32	2.40	2.28	2.16	2.06	1.95	1.84	1.74	1.68	1.61
0.33	2.36	2.24	2.12	2.02	1.91	1.80	1.70	1.64	1.57
0.34	2.32	2.20	2.09	1.98	1.87	1.76	1.66	1.60	1.53
0.35	2.29	2.17	2.05	1.95	1.84	1.72	1.63	1.56	1.49
0.36	2.26	2.13	2.02	1.92	1.80	1.69	1.59	1.52	1.45
0.37	2.23	2.10	1.99	1.89	1.77	1.65	1.55	1.49	1.42
0.38	2.20	2.07	1.96	1.85	1.74	1.62	1.52	1.46	1.38
0.39	2.18	2.04	1.93	1.82	1.70	1.58	1.49	1.42	1.35

TABLE A8—BORON FACTORS VS. % CARBON AT SPECIFIC ALLOY FACTOR LEVELS (continued)

% Carbon	Alloy Factor[1] 5	Alloy Factor[1] 7	Alloy Factor[1] 9	Alloy Factor[1] 11	Alloy Factor[1] 13	Alloy Factor[1] 15	Alloy Factor[1] 18	Alloy Factor[1] 22	Alloy Factor[1] 26
0.40	2.15	2.01	1.90	1.79	1.67	1.55	1.46	1.39	1.32
0.41	2.12	1.98	1.87	1.76	1.64	1.52	1.43	1.36	1.29
0.42	2.09	1.96	1.84	1.73	1.62	1.49	1.40	1.34	1.26
0.43	2.06	1.93	1.82	1.70	1.58	1.46	1.37	1.31	1.23
0.44	2.04	1.90	1.78	1.68	1.56	1.43	1.35	1.28	1.21
0.45	2.01	1.87	1.75	1.65	1.53	1.40	1.32	1.25	1.19
0.46	1.98	1.85	1.72	1.62	1.51	1.38	1.30	1.23	1.17
0.47	1.94	1.82	1.69	1.59	1.48	1.36	1.28	1.21	1.15
0.48	1.91	1.80	1.67	1.57	1.46	1.34	1.26	1.19	1.13
0.49	1.89	1.77	1.64	1.54	1.43	1.32	1.24	1.17	1.10
0.50	1.87	1.75	1.61	1.51	1.41	1.30	1.22	1.15	1.08
0.51	1.83	1.72	1.58	1.48	1.39	1.27	1.20	1.12	1.06
0.52	1.80	1.70	1.56	1.46	1.37	1.26	1.18	1.10	1.04
0.53	1.77	1.67	1.53	1.44	1.34	1.24	1.16	1.07	1.02
0.54	1.74	1.65	1.51	1.42	1.32	1.23	1.14	1.05	1.00
0.55	1.71	1.62	1.48	1.39	1.30	1.21	1.12	1.02	1.00
0.56	1.68	1.60	1.46	1.37	1.28	1.20	1.10	1.00	1.00
0.57	1.65	1.57	1.44	1.35	1.26	1.18	1.07	1.00	1.00
0.58	1.62	1.55	1.42	1.33	1.24	1.17	1.05	1.00	1.00
0.59	1.60	1.52	1.40	1.31	1.22	1.14	1.02	1.00	1.00
0.60	1.57	1.50	1.38	1.29	1.20	1.12	1.00	1.00	1.00
0.61	1.54	1.48	1.36	1.27	1.18	1.09	1.00	1.00	1.00
0.62	1.51	1.46	1.34	1.25	1.16	1.06	1.00	1.00	1.00
0.63	1.49	1.43	1.32	1.23	1.13	1.03	1.00	1.00	1.00
0.64	1.47	1.41	1.30	1.21	1.11	1.00	1.00	1.00	1.00
0.65	1.45	1.39	1.29	1.19	1.08	1.00	1.00	1.00	1.00
0.66	1.42	1.37	1.28	1.17	1.05	1.00	1.00	1.00	1.00
0.67	1.40	1.35	1.26	1.15	1.02	1.00	1.00	1.00	1.00
0.68	1.38	1.33	1.24	1.14	1.00	1.00	1.00	1.00	1.00
0.69	1.36	1.31	1.22	1.12	1.00	1.00	1.00	1.00	1.00
0.70	1.35	1.28	1.20	1.10	1.00	1.00	1.00	1.00	1.00
0.71	1.33	1.26	1.18	1.07	1.00	1.00	1.00	1.00	1.00
0.72	1.32	1.25	1.16	1.05	1.00	1.00	1.00	1.00	1.00
0.73	1.30	1.22	1.14	1.02	1.00	1.00	1.00	1.00	1.00
0.74	1.29	1.20	1.12	1.00	1.00	1.00	1.00	1.00	1.00
0.75	1.27	1.17	1.08	1.00	1.00	1.00	1.00	1.00	1.00
0.76	1.26	1.15	1.05	1.00	1.00	1.00	1.00	1.00	1.00
0.77	1.24	1.12	1.02	1.00	1.00	1.00	1.00	1.00	1.00
0.78	1.22	1.10	1.00	1.00	1.00	1.00	1.00	1.00	1.00
0.79	1.20	1.07	1.00	1.00	1.00	1.00	1.00	1.00	1.00
0.80	1.18	1.05	1.00	1.00	1.00	1.00	1.00	1.00	1.00
0.81	1.15	1.02	1.00	1.00	1.00	1.00	1.00	1.00	1.00
0.82	1.12	1.00	1.00	1.00	1.00	1.00	1.00	1.00	1.00
0.83	1.08	1.00	1.00	1.00	1.00	1.00	1.00	1.00	1.00
0.84	1.04	1.00	1.00	1.00	1.00	1.00	1.00	1.00	1.00
0.85	1.02	1.00	1.00	1.00	1.00	1.00	1.00	1.00	1.00
0.86	1.00	1.00	1.00	1.00	1.00	1.00	1.00	1.00	1.00

1. Alloy factor is the product of all the multiplying factors (Table A2) excluding that for carbon.

TABLE A9—DISTANCE HARDNESS DIVIDING FACTORS VS. JOMINY DISTANCE FOR A SPECIFIC CALCULATED Di (NON-BORON STEELS), mm

Ideal Critical Diameter (DI), mm	Jominy End-Quench Distance (mm) 3.0	Jominy End-Quench Distance (mm) 5.0	Jominy End-Quench Distance (mm) 7.0	Jominy End-Quench Distance (mm) 9.0	Jominy End-Quench Distance (mm) 11.0	Jominy End-Quench Distance (mm) 13.0	Jominy End-Quench Distance (mm) 15.0	Jominy End-Quench Distance (mm) 20.0	Jominy End-Quench Distance (mm) 25.0	Jominy End-Quench Distance (mm) 30.0	Jominy End-Quench Distance (mm) 35.0	Jominy End-Quench Distance (mm) 40.0	Jominy End-Quench Distance (mm) 45.0	Jominy End-Quench Distance (mm) 50.0
25.0	1.13	1.62	2.11	2.62	2.82	2.96	3.15	3.52						
27.5	1.11	1.54	1.99	2.50	2.70	2.84	3.01	3.37						
30.0	1.09	1.47	1.88	2.38	2.58	2.72	2.89	3.24	3.48					
32.5	1.07	1.40	1.78	2.27	2.48	2.61	2.77	3.11	3.34	3.58				
35.0	1.06	1.35	1.69	2.17	2.37	2.51	2.65	2.99	3.20	3.43				
37.5	1.05	1.30	1.61	2.07	2.28	2.41	2.54	2.87	3.08	3.28	3.52			
40.0	1.04	1.26	1.54	1.99	2.19	2.31	2.44	2.77	2.96	3.15	3.37	3.56		
42.5	1.03	1.22	1.48	1.90	2.10	2.22	2.35	2.67	2.86	3.03	3.23	3.41	3.55	
45.0	1.02	1.19	1.42	1.83	2.02	2.14	2.26	2.57	2.75	2.92	3.10	3.27	3.41	3.54
47.5	1.02	1.16	1.37	1.76	1.95	2.06	2.17	2.48	2.66	2.81	2.98	3.14	3.28	3.46
50.0	1.01	1.13	1.33	1.70	1.87	1.99	2.10	2.40	2.57	2.72	2.87	3.02	3.16	3.29
52.5	1.01	1.11	1.29	1.64	1.81	1.92	2.02	2.32	2.48	2.63	2.77	2.92	3.05	3.18
55.0	1.00	1.10	1.26	1.58	1.75	1.85	1.95	2.24	2.40	2.54	2.68	2.82	2.95	3.07
57.5	1.00	1.08	1.23	1.53	1.69	1.79	1.89	2.17	2.33	2.46	2.60	2.73	2.85	2.97
60.0	1.00	1.07	1.21	1.48	1.63	1.74	1.83	2.10	2.26	2.39	2.52	2.65	2.76	2.88
62.5	1.00	1.06	1.18	1.44	1.58	1.68	1.77	2.04	2.20	2.32	2.45	2.57	2.68	2.79
65.0	1.00	1.05	1.17	1.40	1.54	1.63	1.72	1.98	2.13	2.26	2.38	2.50	2.60	2.70
67.5	1.00	1.04	1.15	1.36	1.49	1.59	1.67	1.92	2.07	2.20	2.32	2.43	2.53	2.62
70.0	1.00	1.04	1.13	1.33	1.45	1.54	1.63	1.87	2.02	2.14	2.26	2.37	2.46	2.55
72.5	1.00	1.03	1.12	1.30	1.41	1.50	1.58	1.82	1.97	2.09	2.21	2.31	2.40	2.48
75.0	1.00	1.03	1.11	1.27	1.38	1.46	1.54	1.77	1.92	2.04	2.15	2.25	2.34	2.41
77.5	1.00	1.03	1.10	1.25	1.34	1.43	1.51	1.73	1.87	1.99	2.10	2.20	2.28	2.35
80.0	1.00	1.02	1.09	1.22	1.31	1.40	1.47	1.68	1.83	1.95	2.06	2.15	2.22	2.29
82.5	1.00	1.02	1.08	1.20	1.29	1.37	1.44	1.64	1.79	1.90	2.01	2.10	2.17	2.23
85.0	1.00	1.02	1.07	1.18	1.26	1.34	1.41	1.60	1.75	1.86	1.97	2.05	2.12	2.17
87.5	1.00	1.02	1.07	1.16	1.24	1.31	1.38	1.57	1.71	1.82	1.92	2.01	2.07	2.12
90.0	1.00	1.02	1.06	1.14	1.22	1.29	1.35	1.53	1.67	1.78	1.88	1.97	2.03	2.07
92.5	1.00	1.01	1.05	1.13	1.20	1.27	1.33	1.50	1.64	1.75	1.84	1.92	1.98	2.02
95.0	1.00	1.01	1.05	1.11	1.18	1.24	1.31	1.47	1.60	1.71	1.81	1.88	1.94	1.98
97.5	1.00	1.01	1.04	1.10	1.16	1.22	1.28	1.44	1.57	1.67	1.77	1.84	1.90	1.93
100.0	1.00	1.01	1.04	1.09	1.15	1.21	1.26	1.41	1.54	1.64	1.73	1.80	1.86	1.89
102.5	1.00	1.01	1.03	1.08	1.13	1.19	1.24	1.39	1.51	1.61	1.69	1.76	1.82	1.85
105.0	1.00	1.01	1.03	1.07	1.12	1.17	1.23	1.36	1.48	1.58	1.66	1.73	1.78	1.81
107.5	1.00	1.00	1.02	1.06	1.11	1.16	1.21	1.34	1.46	1.55	1.63	1.69	1.74	1.77
110.0	1.00	1.00	1.02	1.05	1.09	1.15	1.19	1.32	1.43	1.51	1.59	1.65	1.71	1.73
125.0	1.00	1.00	1.00	1.02	1.04	1.08	1.11	1.20	1.29	1.35	1.41	1.46	1.52	1.54
127.5	1.00	1.00	1.00	1.01	1.04	1.07	1.10	1.19	1.27	1.33	1.39	1.44	1.49	1.52
130.0	1.00	1.00	1.00	1.01	1.03	1.06	1.09	1.18	1.25	1.31	1.36	1.41	1.46	1.49
132.5	1.00	1.00	1.00	1.01	1.02	1.05	1.08	1.16	1.24	1.28	1.34	1.38	1.44	1.47
135.0	1.00	1.00	1.00	1.01	1.02	1.04	1.07	1.15	1.22	1.26	1.32	1.36	1.42	1.44
137.5	1.00	1.00	1.00	1.00	1.01	1.04	1.06	1.14	1.20	1.24	1.30	1.34	1.39	1.42
140.0	1.00	1.00	1.00	1.00	1.01	1.03	1.05	1.13	1.19	1.22	1.28	1.32	1.37	1.40
142.5	1.00	1.00	1.00	1.00	1.00	1.02	1.04	1.12	1.17	1.21	1.26	1.30	1.35	1.38
145.0	1.00	1.00	1.00	1.00	1.00	1.02	1.03	1.11	1.16	1.19	1.24	1.28	1.33	1.36
147.5	1.00	1.00	1.00	1.00	1.00	1.01	1.03	1.10	1.14	1.17	1.23	1.26	1.32	1.34
150.0	1.00	1.00	1.00	1.00	1.00	1.00	1.02	1.09	1.13	1.16	1.21	1.25	1.30	1.32
152.5	1.00	1.00	1.00	1.00	1.00	1.00	1.01	1.08	1.12	1.15	1.20	1.23	1.29	1.31
155.0	1.00	1.00	1.00	1.00	1.00	1.00	1.01	1.07	1.10	1.13	1.19	1.22	1.27	1.29
157.5	1.00	1.00	1.00	1.00	1.00	0.99	1.00	1.06	1.09	1.12	1.18	1.21	1.26	1.28
160.0	1.00	1.00	1.00	1.00	1.00	0.99	1.00	1.05	1.08	1.11	1.17	1.20	1.24	1.27
162.5	1.00	1.00	1.00	1.00	1.00	0.99	1.00	1.05	1.07	1.10	1.16	1.19	1.23	1.26
165.0	1.00	1.00	1.00	1.00	1.00	0.99	1.00	1.04	1.06	1.09	1.15	1.17	1.22	1.25
167.5	1.00	1.00	1.00	1.00	1.00	0.99	1.00	1.03	1.05	1.08	1.14	1.16	1.21	1.24
170.0	1.00	1.00	1.00	1.00	1.00	0.99	1.00	1.02	1.04	1.07	1.13	1.15	1.20	1.23
172.5	1.00	1.00	1.00	1.00	1.00	1.00	1.00	1.01	1.03	1.06	1.12	1.14	1.18	1.22
175.0	1.00	1.00	1.00	1.00	1.00	1.00	1.00	1.00	1.02	1.05	1.11	1.12	1.17	1.21
177.5	1.00	1.00	1.00	1.00	1.00	1.01	1.00	1.00	1.01	1.04	1.10	1.10	1.15	1.20

TABLE A10A—DISTANCE HARDNESS DIVIDING FACTORS VS. JOMINY DISTANCE FOR A SPECIFIC CALCULATED D_I (NON-BORON STEELS), inch

Ideal Critical Diameter (D_I), inch	Jominy End-Quench Distance (1/16 in) 2	Jominy End-Quench Distance (1/16 in) 3	Jominy End-Quench Distance (1/16 in) 4	Jominy End-Quench Distance (1/16 in) 5	Jominy End-Quench Distance (1/16 in) 6	Jominy End-Quench Distance (1/16 in) 7	Jominy End-Quench Distance (1/16 in) 8	Jominy End-Quench Distance (1/16 in) 9
1.0	1.15	1.50	2.15	2.46	2.72	2.81	2.92	3.07
1.1	1.12	1.42	1.98	2.32	2.60	2.70	2.80	2.94
1.2	1.10	1.35	1.85	2.20	2.48	2.59	2.69	2.81
1.3	1.08	1.29	1.74	2.09	2.38	2.48	2.58	2.69
1.4	1.07	1.24	1.64	1.99	2.27	2.38	2.47	2.58
1.5	1.05	1.19	1.56	1.90	2.18	2.28	2.37	2.47
1.6	1.04	1.16	1.49	1.81	2.09	2.19	2.28	2.38
1.7	1.03	1.13	1.43	1.73	2.00	2.10	2.19	2.28
1.8	1.02	1.10	1.37	1.66	1.92	2.02	2.11	2.19
1.9	1.02	1.09	1.33	1.60	1.85	1.94	2.03	2.11
2.0	1.01	1.08	1.29	1.54	1.78	1.87	1.95	2.03
2.1	1.01	1.07	1.26	1.48	1.71	1.80	1.89	1.96
2.2	1.00	1.07	1.23	1.43	1.66	1.73	1.82	1.90
2.3	1.00	1.06	1.21	1.39	1.60	1.68	1.76	1.83
2.4	1.00	1.06	1.18	1.35	1.55	1.62	1.70	1.77
2.5	1.00	1.05	1.16	1.32	1.50	1.57	1.65	1.72
2.6	1.00	1.05	1.15	1.29	1.45	1.52	1.60	1.67
2.7	1.00	1.04	1.13	1.26	1.41	1.48	1.56	1.62
2.8	1.00	1.04	1.12	1.23	1.37	1.44	1.51	1.58
2.9	1.00	1.03	1.11	1.21	1.34	1.40	1.48	1.54
3.0	1.00	1.02	1.10	1.19	1.31	1.37	1.44	1.50
3.1	1.00	1.01	1.09	1.17	1.28	1.34	1.41	1.47
3.2	1.00	1.00	1.08	1.15	1.25	1.31	1.38	1.43
3.3	1.00	1.00	1.07	1.13	1.23	1.29	1.35	1.40
3.4	1.00	1.00	1.06	1.12	1.20	1.26	1.33	1.37
3.5	1.00	1.00	1.05	1.10	1.18	1.24	1.30	1.35
3.6	1.00	1.00	1.04	1.09	1.17	1.22	1.28	1.32
3.7	1.00	1.00	1.04	1.08	1.15	1.20	1.25	1.30
3.8	1.00	1.00	1.03	1.07	1.14	1.18	1.24	1.28
3.9	1.00	1.00	1.03	1.06	1.12	1.17	1.22	1.26
4.0	1.00	1.00	1.02	1.05	1.11	1.15	1.20	1.24
4.1	1.00	1.00	1.01	1.04	1.10	1.14	1.18	1.22
4.2	1.00	1.00	1.00	1.03	1.09	1.13	1.17	1.20
4.3	1.00	1.00	1.00	1.02	1.08	1.12	1.15	1.18
4.4	1.00	1.00	1.00	1.01	1.07	1.10	1.14	1.16
4.5	1.00	1.00	1.00	1.00	1.06	1.09	1.13	1.15
4.6	1.00	1.00	1.00	1.00	1.05	1.08	1.11	1.13
4.7	1.00	1.00	1.00	1.00	1.04	1.07	1.10	1.12
4.8	1.00	1.00	1.00	1.00	1.03	1.06	1.09	1.11
4.9	1.00	1.00	1.00	1.00	1.02	1.05	1.08	1.10
5.0	1.00	1.00	1.00	1.00	1.01	1.04	1.07	1.09
5.1	1.00	1.00	1.00	1.00	1.00	1.03	1.06	1.08
5.2	1.00	1.00	1.00	1.00	1.00	1.02	1.05	1.07
5.3	1.00	1.00	1.00	1.00	1.00	1.01	1.04	1.06
5.4	1.00	1.00	1.00	1.00	1.00	1.00	1.03	1.05
5.5	1.00	1.00	1.00	1.00	1.00	1.00	1.02	1.04
5.6	1.00	1.00	1.00	1.00	1.00	1.00	1.01	1.03
5.7	1.00	1.00	1.00	1.00	1.00	1.00	1.00	1.02
5.8	1.00	1.00	1.00	1.00	1.00	1.00	1.00	1.01
5.9	1.00	1.00	1.00	1.00	1.00	1.00	1.00	1.00
6.0	1.00	1.00	1.00	1.00	1.00	1.00	1.00	1.00
6.1	1.00	1.00	1.00	1.00	1.00	1.00	1.00	1.00
6.2	1.00	1.00	1.00	1.00	1.00	1.00	1.00	1.00
6.3	1.00	1.00	1.00	1.00	1.00	1.00	1.00	1.00

TABLE A10A—DISTANCE HARDNESS DIVIDING FACTORS VS. JOMINY DISTANCE FOR A SPECIFIC CALCULATED D_I (NON-BORON STEELS), inch (continued)

Ideal Critical Diameter (D_I), inch	Jominy End-Quench Distance (1/16 in) 2	Jominy End-Quench Distance (1/16 in) 3	Jominy End-Quench Distance (1/16 in) 4	Jominy End-Quench Distance (1/16 in) 5	Jominy End-Quench Distance (1/16 in) 6	Jominy End-Quench Distance (1/16 in) 7	Jominy End-Quench Distance (1/16 in) 8	Jominy End-Quench Distance (1/16 in) 9
6.4	1.00	1.00	1.00	1.00	1.00	1.00	1.00	1.00
6.5	1.00	1.00	1.00	1.00	1.00	1.00	1.00	1.00
6.6	1.00	1.00	1.00	1.00	1.00	1.00	1.00	1.00
6.7	1.00	1.00	1.00	1.00	1.00	1.00	1.00	1.00
6.8	1.00	1.00	1.00	1.00	1.00	1.00	1.00	1.00
6.9	1.00	1.00	1.00	1.00	1.00	1.00	1.00	1.00
7.0	1.00	1.00	1.00	1.00	1.00	1.00	1.00	1.00

TABLE A10B—DISTANCE HARDNESS DIVIDING FACTORS VS. JOMINY DISTANCE FOR A SPECIFIC CALCULATED D_1 (NON-BORON STEELS), inch

Ideal Critical Diameter (D1), inch	Jominy End-Quench Distance (1/16 in) 10	Jominy End-Quench Distance (1/16 in) 12	Jominy End-Quench Distance (1/16 in) 14	Jominy End-Quench Distance (1/16 in) 16	Jominy End-Quench Distance (1/16 in) 18	Jominy End-Quench Distance (1/16 in) 20	Jominy End-Quench Distance (1/16 in) 24	Jominy End-Quench Distance (1/16 in) 28	Jominy End-Quench Distance (1/16 in) 32
1.0	3.22	3.50	—	—	—	—	—	—	—
1.1	3.07	3.34	—	—	—	—	—	—	—
1.2	2.94	3.20	3.32	3.44	—	—	—	—	—
1.3	2.81	3.07	3.19	3.30	3.53	—	—	—	—
1.4	2.69	2.95	3.06	3.17	3.37	3.50	3.78	—	—
1.5	2.58	2.83	2.94	3.05	3.22	3.35	3.61	—	—
1.6	2.47	2.73	2.83	2.94	3.09	3.20	3.45	3.67	3.77
1.7	2.38	2.62	2.73	2.83	2.96	3.08	3.30	3.51	3.63
1.8	2.29	2.53	2.63	2.73	2.85	2.96	3.17	3.37	3.49
1.9	2.20	2.44	2.54	2.64	2.74	2.85	3.05	3.24	2.36
2.0	2.12	2.35	2.45	2.55	2.65	2.74	2.94	3.12	3.24
2.1	2.05	2.27	2.37	2.47	2.56	2.65	2.83	3.00	3.13
2.2	1.98	2.20	2.30	2.39	2.47	2.56	2.74	2.90	3.03
2.3	1.91	2.13	2.22	2.32	2.40	2.48	2.65	2.81	2.93
2.4	1.85	2.06	2.16	2.25	2.32	2.41	2.57	2.72	2.84
2.5	1.80	2.00	2.09	2.19	2.26	2.34	2.50	2.64	2.76
2.6	1.74	1.94	2.03	2.13	2.19	2.27	2.43	2.56	2.68
2.7	1.69	1.88	1.97	2.07	2.14	2.21	2.37	2.50	2.61
2.8	1.65	1.83	1.92	2.02	2.08	2.16	2.31	2.43	2.54
2.9	1.60	1.78	1.87	1.97	2.03	2.10	2.25	2.37	2.48
3.0	1.57	1.73	1.82	1.92	1.98	2.05	2.20	2.31	2.41
3.1	1.53	1.68	1.77	1.87	1.94	2.00	2.14	2.26	2.36
3.2	1.49	1.64	1.73	1.83	1.89	1.96	2.10	2.21	2.30
3.3	1.46	1.60	1.69	1.79	1.85	1.92	2.05	2.16	2.25
3.4	1.43	1.56	1.65	1.75	1.81	1.87	2.00	2.11	2.20
3.5	1.40	1.53	1.61	1.71	1.77	1.83	1.96	2.07	2.15
3.6	1.37	1.49	1.58	1.68	1.73	1.80	1.92	2.02	2.10
3.7	1.35	1.46	1.54	1.64	1.70	1.76	1.87	1.98	2.06
3.8	1.32	1.43	1.51	1.61	1.66	1.72	1.83	1.94	2.01
3.9	1.30	1.40	1.48	1.58	1.63	1.69	1.79	1.90	1.97
4.0	1.28	1.38	1.45	1.55	1.60	1.65	1.76	1.86	1.93
4.1	1.26	1.35	1.42	1.52	1.57	1.62	1.72	1.82	1.89
4.2	1.24	1.32	1.39	1.49	1.54	1.58	1.68	1.78	1.86
4.3	1.22	1.30	1.37	1.46	1.51	1.55	1.65	1.75	1.82
4.4	1.21	1.28	1.35	1.43	1.48	1.52	1.61	1.71	1.78
4.5	1.19	1.26	1.32	1.41	1.45	1.49	1.58	1.67	1.75
4.6	1.18	1.24	1.30	1.39	1.42	1.46	1.54	1.64	1.71
4.7	1.16	1.22	1.28	1.36	1.40	1.43	1.50	1.60	1.68
4.8	1.15	1.20	1.26	1.34	1.37	1.40	1.47	1.57	1.65
4.9	1.13	1.19	1.24	1.32	1.35	1.37	1.44	1.54	1.62

TABLE A10B—DISTANCE HARDNESS DIVIDING FACTORS VS. JOMINY DISTANCE FOR A SPECIFIC CALCULATED D_1 (NON-BORON STEELS), inch (continued)

Ideal Critical Diameter (D1), inch	Jominy End-Quench Distance (1/16 in) 10	Jominy End-Quench Distance (1/16 in) 12	Jominy End-Quench Distance (1/16 in) 14	Jominy End-Quench Distance (1/16 in) 16	Jominy End-Quench Distance (1/16 in) 18	Jominy End-Quench Distance (1/16 in) 20	Jominy End-Quench Distance (1/16 in) 24	Jominy End-Quench Distance (1/16 in) 28	Jominy End-Quench Distance (1/16 in) 32
5.0	1.12	1.18	1.23	1.30	1.32	1.35	1.41	1.51	1.59
5.1	1.11	1.17	1.21	1.28	1.30	1.32	1.38	1.48	1.56
5.2	1.10	1.16	1.20	1.26	1.28	1.30	1.36	1.45	1.53
5.3	1.09	1.15	1.18	1.24	1.26	1.28	1.33	1.42	1.50
5.4	1.08	1.14	1.17	1.22	1.24	1.25	1.31	1.39	1.48
5.5	1.07	1.13	1.16	1.21	1.22	1.23	1.30	1.37	1.45
5.6	1.06	1.12	1.15	1.19	1.20	1.21	1.28	1.34	1.43
5.7	1.05	1.10	1.14	1.18	1.18	1.20	1.26	1.32	1.41
5.8	1.04	1.09	1.13	1.16	1.17	1.18	1.25	1.30	1.38
5.9	1.03	1.08	1.12	1.15	1.16	1.16	1.24	1.28	1.36
6.0	1.02	1.07	1.11	1.13	1.14	1.15	1.22	1.26	1.34
6.1	1.01	1.06	1.10	1.12	1.13	1.14	1.21	1.24	1.32
6.2	1.00	1.05	1.09	1.11	1.12	1.13	1.20	1.23	1.30
6.3	1.00	1.04	1.08	1.10	1.11	1.12	1.19	1.21	1.28
6.4	1.00	1.03	1.07	1.09	1.10	1.11	1.18	1.20	1.27
6.5	1.00	1.02	1.06	1.08	1.09	1.10	1.17	1.18	1.25
6.6	1.00	1.01	1.05	1.07	1.08	1.09	1.16	1.17	1.23
6.7	1.00	1.00	1.04	1.06	1.07	1.08	1.14	1.16	1.21
6.8	1.00	1.00	1.03	1.05	1.06	1.07	1.12	1.15	1.19
6.9	1.00	1.00	1.02	1.04	1.05	1.06	1.10	1.14	1.17
7.0	1.00	1.00	1.01	1.03	1.04	1.05	1.08	1.13	1.15

TABLE A11—DISTANCE HARDNESS DIVIDING FACTORS VS. JOMINY DISTANCE FORA SPECIFIC CALCULATED D_I (BORON STEELS), mm

Ideal Critical Diameter (D_{IB}), mm	Jominy End-Quench Distance (mm) 3.0	Jominy End-Quench Distance (mm) 5.0	Jominy End-Quench Distance (mm) 7.0	Jominy End-Quench Distance (mm) 9.0	Jominy End-Quench Distance (mm) 11.0	Jominy End-Quench Distance (mm) 13.0	Jominy End-Quench Distance (mm) 15.0	Jominy End-Quench Distance (mm) 20.0	Jominy End-Quench Distance (mm) 25.0	Jominy End-Quench Distance (mm) 30.0	Jominy End-Quench Distance (mm) 35.0	Jominy End-Quench Distance (mm) 40.0	Jominy End-Quench Distance (mm) 45.0	Jominy End-Quench Distance (mm) 50.0
40.00	1.07	1.25	1.92	2.56										
42.5	1.06	1.21	1.73	2.34										
45.0	1.05	1.18	1.57	2.14	2.64									
47.5	1.04	1.14	1.45	1.97	2.44									
50.0	1.03	1.12	1.35	1.83	2.26	2.57								
52.5	1.03	1.09	1.28	1.70	2.10	2.40								
55.0	1.02	1.08	1.22	1.59	1.96	2.24	2.52							
57.5	1.02	1.06	1.17	1.49	1.83	2.10	2.37							
60.0	1.01	1.05	1.14	1.41	1.71	1.97	2.23							
62.5	1.01	1.04	1.11	1.35	1.61	1.86	2.10							
65.0	1.01	1.03	1.09	1.29	1.53	1.75	1.99	2.56						
67.5	1.00	1.02	1.08	1.24	1.45	1.66	1.88	2.43						
70.0	1.00	1.02	1.07	1.20	1.38	1.57	1.78	2.32						
72.5	1.00	1.01	1.06	1.17	1.32	1.50	1.70	2.21						
75.0	1.00	1.01	1.06	1.15	1.27	1.43	1.62	2.11	2.53					
77.5	1.00	1.01	1.05	1.12	1.23	1.37	1.55	2.01	2.42	2.71				
80.0	1.00	1.00	1.05	1.11	1.19	1.32	1.48	1.93	2.31	2.59	2.82			
82.5	1.00	1.00	1.04	1.09	1.16	1.27	1.43	1.85	2.21	2.47	2.70	2.89	3.06	3.26
85.0	1.00	1.00	1.04	1.08	1.13	1.23	1.38	1.77	2.11	2.37	2.59	2.77	2.92	3.11
87.5	1.00	1.00	1.03	1.08	1.11	1.20	1.33	1.71	2.03	2.27	2.48	2.66	2.80	2.98
90.0	1.00	1.00	1.03	1.07	1.09	1.17	1.29	1.65	1.95	2.18	2.38	2.55	2.69	2.86
92.5	1.00	1.00	1.02	1.06	1.08	1.15	1.26	1.59	1.87	2.09	2.29	2.45	2.59	2.75
95.0	1.00	1.00	1.02	1.06	1.07	1.13	1.23	1.54	1.81	2.01	2.20	2.37	2.50	2.65
97.5	1.00	1.00	1.01	1.06	1.06	1.11	1.20	1.49	1.74	1.94	2.12	2.28	2.42	2.56
100.0	1.00	1.00	1.00	1.05	1.05	1.09	1.18	1.45	1.69	1.87	2.05	2.21	2.34	2.48

TABLE A11—DISTANCE HARDNESS DIVIDING FACTORS VS. JOMINY DISTANCE FORA SPECIFIC CALCULATED D_I (BORON STEELS), mm (continued)

Ideal Critical Diameter (D_{IB}), mm	Jominy End-Quench Distance (mm) 3.0	Jominy End-Quench Distance (mm) 5.0	Jominy End-Quench Distance (mm) 7.0	Jominy End-Quench Distance (mm) 9.0	Jominy End-Quench Distance (mm) 11.0	Jominy End-Quench Distance (mm) 13.0	Jominy End-Quench Distance (mm) 15.0	Jominy End-Quench Distance (mm) 20.0	Jominy End-Quench Distance (mm) 25.0	Jominy End-Quench Distance (mm) 30.0	Jominy End-Quench Distance (mm) 35.0	Jominy End-Quench Distance (mm) 40.0	Jominy End-Quench Distance (mm) 45.0	Jominy End-Quench Distance (mm) 50.0
102.5	1.00	1.00	1.00	1.05	1.04	1.08	1.16	1.41	1.63	1.81	1.98	2.13	2.27	2.41
105.0	1.00	1.00	1.00	1.05	1.04	1.07	1.14	1.37	1.58	1.75	1.92	2.07	2.21	2.34
107.5	1.00	1.00	1.00	1.04	1.03	1.06	1.13	1.34	1.54	1.70	1.86	2.01	2.15	2.27
110.0	1.00	1.00	1.00	1.04	1.03	1.06	1.12	1.31	1.50	1.65	1.80	1.95	2.09	2.21
112.5	1.00	1.00	1.00	1.03	1.03	1.05	1.11	1.28	1.46	1.61	1.75	1.89	2.03	2.16
115.0	1.00	1.00	1.00	1.03	1.03	1.05	1.10	1.25	1.43	1.56	1.70	1.84	1.98	2.10
117.5	1.00	1.00	1.00	1.03	1.02	1.05	1.09	1.23	1.39	1.53	1.66	1.80	1.93	2.05
120.0	1.00	1.00	1.00	1.02	1.02	1.04	1.08	1.21	1.36	1.49	1.62	1.75	1.88	2.01
122.5	1.00	1.00	1.00	1.02	1.02	1.04	1.07	1.19	1.34	1.46	1.58	1.71	1.84	1.96
125.0	1.00	1.00	1.00	1.02	1.02	1.04	1.07	1.17	1.31	1.43	1.55	1.67	1.79	1.92
127.5	1.00	1.00	1.00	1.01	1.02	1.04	1.06	1.15	1.29	1.40	1.52	1.64	1.75	1.87
130.0	1.00	1.00	1.00	1.01	1.02	1.03	1.06	1.14	1.27	1.38	1.49	1.60	1.71	1.83
132.5	1.00	1.00	1.00	1.00	1.01	1.03	1.05	1.13	1.25	1.36	1.46	1.57	1.68	1.79
135.0	1.00	1.00	1.00	1.00	1.01	1.03	1.05	1.11	1.23	1.33	1.44	1.54	1.64	1.76
137.5	1.00	1.00	1.00	1.00	1.01	1.03	1.04	1.10	1.21	1.31	1.41	1.51	1.61	1.72
140.0	1.00	1.00	1.00	1.00	1.01	1.02	1.04	1.09	1.19	1.29	1.39	1.48	1.57	1.69
142.5	1.00	1.00	1.00	1.00	1.01	1.02	1.03	1.08	1.18	1.27	1.37	1.45	1.54	1.65
145.0	1.00	1.00	1.00	1.00	1.01	1.01	1.03	1.07	1.16	1.25	1.35	1.43	1.52	1.62
147.5	1.00	1.00	1.00	1.00	1.00	1.01	1.02	1.06	1.15	1.24	1.32	1.41	1.49	1.59
150.0	1.00	1.00	1.00	1.00	1.00	1.01	1.02	1.05	1.14	1.22	1.30	1.38	1.46	1.56
152.5	1.00	1.00	1.00	1.00	1.00	1.00	1.01	1.05	1.12	1.20	1.28	1.36	1.44	1.53
155.0	1.00	1.00	1.00	1.00	1.00	1.00	1.01	1.04	1.11	1.18	1.26	1.34	1.42	1.51
157.5	1.00	1.00	1.00	1.00	1.00	1.00	1.01	1.03	1.10	1.17	1.24	1.31	1.39	1.48
160.0	1.00	1.00	1.00	1.00	1.00	1.00	1.00	1.03	1.09	1.15	1.22	1.29	1.37	1.45
162.5	1.00	1.00	1.00	1.00	1.00	1.00	1.00	1.02	1.08	1.13	1.20	1.27	1.35	1.43
165.0	1.00	1.00	1.00	1.00	1.00	1.00	1.00	1.01	1.06	1.12	1.18	1.25	1.32	1.40
167.5	1.00	1.00	1.00	1.00	1.00	1.00	1.00	1.01	1.05	1.10	1.16	1.22	1.30	1.37
170.0	1.00	1.00	1.00	1.00	1.00	1.00	1.00	1.00	1.04	1.08	1.14	1.20	1.26	1.33
172.5	1.00	1.00	1.00	1.00	1.00	1.00	1.00	1.00	1.03	1.07	1.12	1.17	1.23	1.30
175.0	1.00	1.00	1.00	1.00	1.00	1.00	1.00	1.00	1.02	1.05	1.10	1.14	1.19	1.25
177.5	1.00	1.00	1.00	1.00	1.00	1.00	1.01	1.00	1.01	1.04	1.08	1.11	1.14	1.20

TABLE A12A—DISTANCE HARDNESS DIVIDING FACTORS VS. JOMINY DISTANCE FOR A SPECIFIC CALCULATED D_I (BORON STEELS), inch

Ideal Critical Diameter (D_{IB}), inch	Jominy End-Quench Distance (1/16 in) 2	Jominy End-Quench Distance (1/16 in) 3	Jominy End-Quench Distance (1/16 in) 4	Jominy End-Quench Distance (1/16 in) 5	Jominy End-Quench Distance (1/16 in) 6	Jominy End-Quench Distance (1/16 in) 7	Jominy End-Quench Distance (1/16 in) 8	Jominy End-Quench Distance (1/16 in) 9
1.5	1.10	1.14	1.88	2.52	2.90	3.22	—	—
1.6	1.08	1.12	1.65	2.20	2.70	3.02	—	—
1.7	1.07	1.10	1.47	1.95	2.50	2.82	3.00	—
1.8	1.06	1.09	1.34	1.75	2.31	2.63	2.82	3.00
1.9	1.05	1.08	1.25	1.59	2.14	2.45	2.66	2.83
2.0	1.04	1.07	1.19	1.46	1.98	2.28	2.51	2.70
2.1	1.03	1.06	1.14	1.36	1.83	2.12	2.36	2.52
2.2	1.02	1.05	1.11	1.29	1.70	1.98	2.21	2.38
2.3	1.02	1.04	1.09	1.24	1.58	1.84	2.08	2.24
2.4	1.01	1.03	1.08	1.20	1.48	1.72	1.95	2.11
2.5	1.01	1.03	1.07	1.17	1.39	1.61	1.83	1.99
2.6	1.00	1.03	1.06	1.15	1.31	1.52	1.72	1.87
2.7	1.00	1.02	1.05	1.14	1.25	1.43	1.62	1.77
2.8	1.00	1.02	1.05	1.13	1.20	1.36	1.53	1.69
2.9	1.00	1.01	1.04	1.12	1.16	1.30	1.45	1.59

TABLE A12A—DISTANCE HARDNESS DIVIDING FACTORS VS. JOMINY DISTANCE FOR A SPECIFIC CALCULATED D_I (BORON STEELS), inch (continued)

Ideal Critical Diameter (D_{IB}), inch	Jominy End-Quench Distance (1/16 in) 2	Jominy End-Quench Distance (1/16 in) 3	Jominy End-Quench Distance (1/16 in) 4	Jominy End-Quench Distance (1/16 in) 5	Jominy End-Quench Distance (1/16 in) 6	Jominy End-Quench Distance (1/16 in) 7	Jominy End-Quench Distance (1/16 in) 8	Jominy End-Quench Distance (1/16 in) 9
3.0	1.00	1.00	1.04	1.11	1.14	1.24	1.38	1.50
3.1	1.00	1.00	1.03	1.10	1.12	1.20	1.31	1.42
3.2	1.00	1.00	1.03	1.09	1.10	1.17	1.25	1.37
3.3	1.00	1.00	1.02	1.08	1.09	1.14	1.20	1.32
3.4	1.00	1.00	1.02	1.07	1.08	1.12	1.17	1.28
3.5	1.00	1.00	1.01	1.06	1.07	1.10	1.14	1.24
3.6	1.00	1.00	1.00	1.05	1.06	1.09	1.12	1.22
3.7	1.00	1.00	1.00	1.04	1.05	1.08	1.10	1.19
3.8	1.00	1.00	1.00	1.04	1.05	1.07	1.09	1.17
3.9	1.00	1.00	1.00	1.03	1.04	1.06	1.08	1.15
4.0	1.00	1.00	1.00	1.02	1.04	1.06	1.08	1.13
4.1	1.00	1.00	1.00	1.02	1.04	1.06	1.07	1.12
4.2	1.00	1.00	1.00	1.02	1.03	1.05	1.07	1.11
4.3	1.00	1.00	1.00	1.01	1.03	1.04	1.06	1.10
4.4	1.00	1.00	1.00	1.01	1.03	1.04	1.06	1.09
4.5	1.00	1.00	1.00	1.00	1.03	1.04	1.06	1.08
4.6	1.00	1.00	1.00	1.00	1.02	1.04	1.06	1.07
4.7	1.00	1.00	1.00	1.00	1.02	1.03	1.05	1.07
4.8	1.00	1.00	1.00	1.00	1.01	1.03	1.05	1.06
4.9	1.00	1.00	1.00	1.00	1.01	1.03	1.04	1.06
5.0	1.00	1.00	1.00	1.00	1.00	1.02	1.04	1.05
5.1	1.00	1.00	1.00	1.00	1.00	1.01	1.03	1.04
5.2	1.00	1.00	1.00	1.00	1.00	1.01	1.03	1.04
5.3	1.00	1.00	1.00	1.00	1.00	1.00	1.02	1.03
5.4	1.00	1.00	1.00	1.00	1.00	1.00	1.02	1.03
5.5	1.00	1.00	1.00	1.00	1.00	1.00	1.01	1.02
5.6	1.00	1.00	1.00	1.00	1.00	1.00	1.01	1.02
5.7	1.00	1.00	1.00	1.00	1.00	1.00	1.00	1.01
5.8	1.00	1.00	1.00	1.00	1.00	1.00	1.00	1.01
5.9	1.00	1.00	1.00	1.00	1.00	1.00	1.00	1.00
6.0	1.00	1.00	1.00	1.00	1.00	1.00	1.00	1.00
6.1	1.00	1.00	1.00	1.00	1.00	1.00	1.00	1.00
6.2	1.00	1.00	1.00	1.00	1.00	1.00	1.00	1.00
6.3	1.00	1.00	1.00	1.00	1.00	1.00	1.00	1.00
6.4	1.00	1.00	1.00	1.00	1.00	1.00	1.00	1.00
6.5	1.00	1.00	1.00	1.00	1.00	1.00	1.00	1.00
6.6	1.00	1.00	1.00	1.00	1.00	1.00	1.00	1.00
6.7	1.00	1.00	1.00	1.00	1.00	1.00	1.00	1.00
6.8	1.00	1.00	1.00	1.00	1.00	1.00	1.00	1.00
6.9	1.00	1.00	1.00	1.00	1.00	1.00	1.00	1.00
7.0	1.00	1.00	1.00	1.00	1.00	1.00	1.00	1.00

TABLE A12B—DISTANCE HARDNESS DIVIDING FACTORS VS. JOMINY DISTANCE FOR A SPECIFIC CALCULATED D_1 (BORON STEELS), inch

Ideal Critical Diameter (DIB), inch	Jominy End-Quench Distance (1/16 in) 10	Jominy End-Quench Distance (1/16 in) 12	Jominy End-Quench Distance (1/16 in) 14	Jominy End-Quench Distance (1/16 in) 16	Jominy End-Quench Distance (1/16 in) 18	Jominy End-Quench Distance (1/16 in) 20	Jominy End-Quench Distance (1/16 in) 24	Jominy End-Quench Distance (1/16 in) 28	Jominy End-Quench Distance (1/16 in) 32
1.5	—	—	—	—	—	—	—	—	—
1.6	—	—	—	—	—	—	—	—	—
1.7	—	—	—	—	—	—	—	—	—
1.8	—	—	—	—	—	—	—	—	—
1.9	3.08	—	—	—	—	—	—	—	—
2.0	2.88	3.34	—	—	—	—	—	—	—
2.1	2.70	3.15	3.70	—	—	—	—	—	—
2.2	2.53	2.98	3.48	3.87	—	—	—	—	—
2.3	2.38	2.82	3.29	3.65	—	—	—	—	—
2.4	2.24	2.67	3.11	3.45	3.64	—	—	—	—
2.5	2.12	2.54	2.95	3.26	3.45	3.62	4.00	—	—
2.6	2.00	2.41	2.79	3.09	3.28	3.46	3.86	4.23	—
2.7	1.90	2.29	2.65	2.93	3.12	3.30	3.67	4.00	—
2.8	1.80	2.18	2.52	2.78	2.97	3.15	3.50	3.78	4.27
2.9	1.72	2.08	2.40	2.64	2.83	3.01	3.33	3.59	4.01
3.0	1.64	1.99	2.29	2.52	2.70	2.88	3.18	3.41	3.78
3.1	1.57	1.91	2.19	2.40	2.57	2.75	3.03	3.25	3.57
3.2	1.51	1.83	2.10	2.30	2.46	2.63	2.90	3.10	3.39
3.3	1.45	1.75	2.01	2.20	2.35	2.51	2.77	2.97	3.22
3.4	1.40	1.69	1.93	2.10	2.25	2.40	2.66	2.84	3.07
3.5	1.35	1.62	1.85	2.01	2.16	2.30	2.55	2.73	2.94
3.6	1.31	1.57	1.78	1.93	2.07	2.21	2.45	2.63	2.82
3.7	1.27	1.51	1.72	1.86	2.00	2.12	2.35	2.54	2.71
3.8	1.24	1.47	1.66	1.80	1.92	2.04	2.26	2.44	2.61
3.9	1.21	1.42	1.60	1.74	1.85	1.96	2.18	2.36	2.52
4.0	1.19	1.38	1.55	1.68	1.78	1.89	2.11	2.29	2.44
4.1	1.16	1.34	1.50	1.63	1.73	1.82	2.04	2.21	2.37
4.2	1.14	1.31	1.46	1.58	1.68	1.76	1.98	2.15	2.30
4.3	1.13	1.28	1.42	1.54	1.62	1.71	1.92	2.09	2.23
4.4	1.11	1.25	1.38	1.50	1.58	1.66	1.86	2.03	2.17
4.5	1.10	1.23	1.35	1.46	1.54	1.61	1.81	1.97	2.11
4.6	1.09	1.21	1.32	1.43	1.50	1.57	1.76	1.92	2.06
4.7	1.09	1.19	1.29	1.40	1.47	1.53	1.72	1.87	2.00
4.8	1.08	1.17	1.26	1.37	1.44	1.50	1.67	1.83	1.96
4.9	1.07	1.15	1.24	1.35	1.41	1.47	1.63	1.79	1.91
5.0	1.06	1.14	1.21	1.32	1.38	1.44	1.60	1.75	1.87
5.1	1.05	1.13	1.19	1.30	1.36	1.41	1.56	1.71	1.82
5.2	1.05	1.11	1.17	1.28	1.34	1.39	1.53	1.67	1.78
5.3	1.04	1.10	1.16	1.26	1.31	1.36	1.50	1.63	1.74
5.4	1.04	1.09	1.14	1.24	1.29	1.34	1.47	1.60	1.70
5.5	1.03	1.08	1.13	1.22	1.27	1.32	1.44	1.57	1.67
5.6	1.03	1.07	1.12	1.20	1.25	1.30	1.41	1.54	1.63
5.7	1.03	1.07	1.11	1.19	1.24	1.28	1.39	1.51	1.60
5.8	1.02	1.06	1.10	1.17	1.22	1.26	1.37	1.48	1.57
5.9	1.02	1.05	1.09	1.16	1.20	1.25	1.35	1.45	1.53
6.0	1.01	1.04	1.08	1.14	1.18	1.23	1.33	1.43	1.50
6.1	1.01	1.03	1.08	1.13	1.16	1.21	1.30	1.40	1.47
6.2	1.00	1.02	1.07	1.11	1.15	1.19	1.28	1.38	1.44
6.3	1.00	1.02	1.06	1.10	1.14	1.17	1.26	1.35	1.41
6.4	1.00	1.01	1.05	1.09	1.12	1.15	1.24	1.32	1.39
6.5	1.00	1.01	1.04	1.08	1.10	1.13	1.21	1.30	1.35
6.6	1.00	1.01	1.03	1.07	1.09	1.12	1.18	1.27	1.32
6.7	1.00	1.00	1.02	1.06	1.08	1.10	1.16	1.24	1.29
6.8	1.00	1.00	1.01	1.05	1.07	1.08	1.14	1.20	1.25
6.9	1.00	1.00	1.01	1.05	1.06	1.07	1.12	1.17	1.21
7.0	1.00	1.00	1.00	1.04	1.05	1.05	1.10	1.14	1.17

TABLE A13—EXAMPLE OF CALCULATION OF HARDENABILITY CURVE (mm) (FOR A MODIFIED SAE 4118 STEEL)

"J" Distance (mm)	Dividing Factor For 45.5 mm D_I (Table A9)	Distance Hardness (DH), HRC
1.5	—	45
3.0	1.02	44
5.0	1.19	38
7.0	1.41	32
9.0	1.82	25
11.0	2.01	22
13.0	2.13	21
15.0	2.25	20
20.0	2.56	18

TABLE A14—EXAMPLE OF CALCULATION OF HARDENABILITY CURVE (in) (FOR A MODIFIED SAE 4118 STEEL)

"J" Distance (1/16)	Dividing Factor for 1.8 in D1 (Table A10)	Distance Hardness (DH), HRC
1	—	45
2	1.02	44
3	1.10	41
4	1.37	33
5	1.66	27
6	1.92	23
8	2.11	21
10	2.29	20
12	2.53	18

TABLE A15—EQUATIONS FOR TABLE A2—HARDENABILITY MULTIPLYING FACTORS VS. % ELEMENT

Carbon/grain size 7	**up to 0.39% incl**	**MF = 0.54 (%C)**
	over 0.39% to 0.55% incl	**= 0.171 + 0.001 (%C) + 0.265 (%C)2**
	over 0.55% to 0.65% incl	**= 0.115 + 0.268 (%C) - 0.038 (%C)2**
	over 0.65% to 0.75% incl	**= 0.143 + 0.2 (%C)**
	over 0.75% to 0.90% incl	**= 0.062 + 0.409 (%C) - 0.135 (%C)2**
Manganese	up to 1.20% incl	= 3.3333 (%Mn) + 1.00
	over 1.20% to 1.95% incl	= 5.10 (%Mn) - 1.12
Silicon	to 2.00% incl	= 1.00 + 0.7 (%Si)
Nickel	to 2.00% incl	= 1.00 + 0.363 (%Ni)
Chromium	to 1.75% incl	= 1.00 + 2.16 (%Cr)
Molybdenum	to 0.55% incl	= 1.00 + 3.00 (%Mo)
Copper	to 0.55% incl	= 1.00 + 0.365 (%Cu)
Vanadium	to 0.20% incl	= 1.00 + 1.73 (%V)

TABLE A16—EQUATIONS FOR TABLE A5—INITIAL 100% MARTENSITE HARDNESS AND 50% MARTENSITE HARDNESS VS. PERCENT CARBON

Initial 100% Martensite Hardness, $H = 35.395 + 6.990x + 312.330x^2 - 821.744x^3 + 1015.479x^4 - 538.34\ 6x^5$ 50% Martensite Hardness, $H = 22.974 + 6.214x + 356.364x^2 - 1091.488x^3 + 1464.880x^4 - 750.441x^5$

where:

H = Hardness in HRC

x = % Carbon

TABLE A17—EQUATIONS FOR TABLE A6 AND A7—D_I VS. JOMINY DISTANCE FOR 50% MARTENSITE VS. D_I

D_I (mm) = $- 0.5203 + 8.7522X - 0.3003X^2 + 0.00778X^3 - 0.0011125X^4 + 6.5978E - 07X^5$

D_I (inch) = $- 0.0156 + 0.54358X - 0.0292133X^2 + 0.001186X^3 - 2.696E - 05X^4 + 2.49E - 07X^5$

where:

x = J Position in 1/16 in or mm

TABLE A18—EQUATIONS FOR TABLE A8—BORON FACTOR VS. % CARBON AT SPECIFIC ALLOY FACTOR LEVELS

Alloy Factor		Boron Factor
5	to 0.85% C incl	$B.F. = 13.03059 - 99.60059\ X + 374.8548\ X^2 - 707.3472\ X^3 + 649.0012\ X^4 - 231.1499\ X^5$
	over 0.85% C	B.F. = 1.00
7	to 0.81% C incl	$B.F. = 10.29157 - 69.64546\ X + 245.7061\ X^2 - 445.3980\ X^3 + 398.8044\ X^4 - 140.6225\ X^5$
	over 0.81% C	B.F. = 1.00
9	to 0.77% C incl	$B.F. = 10.45573 - 79.18534\ X + 311.9332\ X^2 - 630.5490\ X^3 + 627.6022\ X^4 - 244.4064\ X^5$
	over 0.77% C	B.F. = 1.00
11	to 0.73% C incl	$B.F. = 9.005326 - 64.37669\ X + 249.6933\ X^2 - 506.0601\ X^3 + 509.4772\ X^4 - 201.6323\ X^5$
	over 0.73% C	B.F. = 1.00
13	to 0.67% C incl	$B.F. = 8.054231 - 55.10171\ X + 213.6752\ X^2 - 447.8863\ X^3 + 477.8413\ X^4 - 204.4974\ X^5$
	over 0.67% C	B.F. = 1.00
15	to 0.63% C incl	$B.F. = 9.001263 - 76.47680\ X + 355.8714\ X^2 - 872.9646\ X^3 + 1067.359\ X^4 - 512.7757\ X^5$
	over 0.63% C	B.F. = 1.00
18	to 0.59% C incl	$B.F. = 6.849017 - 46.78647\ X + 196.6635\ X^2 - 471.3978\ X^3 + 587.8504\ X^4 - 295.0410\ X^5$
	over 0.50% C	B.F. = 1.00
22	to 0.55% C incl	$B.F. = 7.217034 - 54.73529\ X + 248.9901\ X^2 - 632.7765\ X^3 + 826.1873\ X^4 - 431.7227\ X^5$
	over 0.55% C	B.F. = 1.00
26	to 0.53% C incl	$B.F. = 7.162633 - 57.52117\ X + 279.6173\ X^2 - 756.9353\ X^3 + 1042.628\ X^4 - 568.5680\ X^5$
	over 0.53% C	B.F. = 1.00

where:

$X = D_1$ (mm)

[a] Max D_1 = 177.5 mm

TABLE A19—EQUATIONS FOR TABLE A9—DISTANCE HARDNESS DIVIDING FACTORS VS. JOMINY DISTANCE (NON-BORON STEELS), mm

"J" Distance (mm)	D_I[a]	Dividing Factor
3.0	to 52.5 mm incl	$DF = 1.5523 - 0.2706\ X + 0.00050906\ X^2 - 4.608E - 0.6\ X^3 + 2.014E - 08\ X^4 - 3.413E - 11\ X^5$
	over 52.5 mm	DF = 1.00
5.0	to 105 mm incl	$DF = 3.1355 - 0.094625\ X + 0.001698\ X^2 - 1.516E - 05\ X^3 + 6.6597E - 08\ X^4 - 1.144E - 10\ X^5$
	over 105 mm	DF = 1.00
7.0	to 125 mm incl	$DF = 4.3189 - 0.134356\ X + 0.002289\ X^2 - 1.987E - 05\ X^3 + 0.6E - 08\ X^4 - 1.466E - 10\ X^5$
	over 125 mm	DF = 1.00
9.0	to 135 mm incl	$DF = 4.4985 - 0.10237\ X + 0.001293\ X^2 - 8.811E - 06\ X^3 + 3.1843E - 08\ X^4 - 4.765E - 11\ X^5$
	over 135 mm	DF = 1.00
11.0	to 140 mm incl	$DF = 4.41404 - 0.0794\ X + 0.000685\ X^2 - 2.17E - 06\ X^3 - 1.658E - 09\ X^4 + 1.641E - 11\ X^5$
	over 140 mm	DF = 1.00
13.0	to 150 mm incl	$DF = 4.5983 - 0.08138\ X + 0.0006948\ X^2 - 2.16E - 06\ X^3 - 2.31E - 09\ X^4 + 1.8953E - 11\ X^5$
	over 150 mm	DF = 1.00
15.0	to 155 mm incl	$DF = 5.0089 - 0.09515\ X + 0.0009385\ X^2 - 4.395E - 06\ X^3 + 7.5823E - 09\ X^4 + 2.1161E - 12\ X^5$
	over 155 mm	DF = 1.00

where:

$X = D_I$ (mm)

[a] Max D_I = 177.5 mm

TABLE A19—EQUATIONS FOR TABLE A9—DISTANCE HARDNESS DIVIDING FACTORS VS. JOMINY DISTANCE (NON-BORON STEELS), mm (continued)

"J" Distance (mm)	D_I[a]	Dividing Factor
20.0		$DF = 5.5467 - 0.10681 X + 0.001215 X^2 - 8.214E-06 X^3 + 3.1118E-08 X^4 - 5.012E-11 X^5$
25.0		$DF = 6.1097 - 0.12467 X + 0.001514 X^2 - 1.054E-05 X^3 + 3.8787E-08 X^4 - 5.807E-11 X^5$
30.0		$DF = 7.17628 - 0.1724 X + 0.002455 X^2 - 1.943E-05 X^3 + 7.8367E-08 X^4 - 1.248E-10 X^5$
35.0		$DF = 8.4427 - 0.22818 X + 0.003527 X^2 - 2.952E-05 X^3 + 1.2394E-07 X^4 - 2.038E-10 X^5$
40.0		$DF = 9.0996 - 0.2505 X + 0.003909 X^2 - 3.299E-05 X^3 + 1.3976E-07 X^4 - 2.323E-10 X^5$
45.0		$DF = 8.7557 - 0.21859 X + 0.003166 X^2 - 2.544E-05 X^3 + 1.0437E-07 X^4 - 1.696E-10 X^5$
50.0		$DF = 8.09516 - 0.17014 X + 0.0021 X^2 - 1.496E-05 X^3 + 5.6151E-08 X^4 - 8.476E-11 X^5$

where:

$X = D_I$ (mm)

[a] Max D_I = 177.5 mm

TABLE A20—EQUATIONS FOR TABLE A10—DISTANCE HARDNESS DIVIDING FACTORS VS. JOMINY DISTANCE (NON-BORON STEELS), inch

"J" Distance (1/16 in)	D_I[a]	Dividing Factor
2	to 2.1 incl	$DF = 4.68961 - 11.00832 X + 13.83314 X^2 - 8.80283 X^3 + 2.78698 X^4 - 0.34880 X^5$
	over 2.1	DF = 1.00
3	to 3.1 incl	$DF = 2.34904 - 0.28254 X - 1.42995 X^2 + 1.16697 X^3 - 0.33813 X^4 + 0.03403 X^5$
	over 3.1	DF = 1.00
4	to 4.1 incl	$DF = 5.66795 - 6.14648 X + 3.52874 X^2 - 1.06026 X^3 + 0.16301 X^4 - 0.01015 X^5$
	over 4.1	DF = 1.00
5	to 4.4 incl	$DF = 4.53651 - 2.92609 X + 1.00411 X^2 - 0.17129 X^3 + 0.01369 X^4 - 0.00038 X^5$
	over 4.4	DF = 1.00
6	to 5.0 incl	$DF = 4.39436 - 2.16072 X + 0.56027 X^2 - 0.08145 X^3 + 0.00840 X^4 - 0.00053 X^5$
	over 5.0	DF = 1.00
7	to 5.3 incl	$DF = 4.20866 - 1.54405 X + 0.08294 X^2 + 0.08613 X^3 - 0.01963 X^4 - 0.00127 X^5$
	over 5.3	DF = 1.00
8	to 5.6 incl	$DF = 4.44473 - 1.79085 X + 0.24617 X^2 + 0.03374 X^3 - 0.01189 X^4 + 0.00084 X^5$
	over 5.6	DF = 1.00
9	to 5.8 incl	$DF = 4.95421 - 2.43521 X + 0.62983 X^2 - 0.07914 X^3 + 0.00399 X^4 - 0.00001 X^5$
	over 5.8	DF = 1.00
10	to 6.1 incl	$DF = 5.31610 - 2.80977 X + 0.84183 X^2 - 0.141781 X^3 + 0.01301 X^4 - 0.00051 X^5$
	over 6.1	DF = 1.00
12	to 6.6 incl	$DF = 5.63649 - 2.89264 X + 0.90309 X^2 - 0.17297 X^3 + 0.01881 X^4 - 0.00086 X^5$
	over 6.6	DF = 1.00
14		$DF = 5.83176 - 2.99646 X + 0.94088 X^2 - 0.17734 X^3 + 0.01839 X^4 - 0.00079 X^5$
16		$DF = 6.06952 - 3.15198 X + 0.99297 X^2 - 0.18010 X^3 + 0.01720 X^4 - 0.00066 X^5$
18		$DF = 7.26492 - 4.50566 X + 1.61688 X^2 - 0.31738 X^3 + 0.03146 X^4 - 0.00122 X^5$

where:

$X = D_1$ in inches

[a] Max D_1 = 7.0 in

TABLE A20—EQUATIONS FOR TABLE A10—DISTANCE HARDNESS DIVIDING FACTORS VS. JOMINY DISTANCE (NON-BORON STEELS), inch (continued)

"J" Distance (1/16 in)	D_I[a]	Dividing Factor
20		$DF = 7.68728 - 4.90380 X + 1.81034 X^2 - 0.36593 X^3 + 0.03739 X^4 - 0.00150 X^5$
24		$DF = 9.19586 - 6.71331 X + 2.77208 X^2 - 0.61510 X^3 + 0.06814 X^4 - 0.00295 X^5$
28		$DF = 9.27904 - 6.21461 X + 2.33158 X^2 - 0.46972 X^3 + 0.04727 X^4 - 0.00186 X^5$
32		$DF = 8.62857 - 5.16125 X + 1.81214 X^2 - 0.35489 X^3 + 0.03569 X^4 - 0.00143 X^5$

where:

$X = D_1$ in inches

[a]Max D_1 = 7.0 in

TABLE A21—EQUATIONS FOR TABLE A11—DISTANCE HARDNESS DIVIDING FACTORS VS. JOMINY DISTANCE (BORON STEELS), mm

"J" Distance (mm)	D_{IB}[a]	Dividing Factor
3.0	to 70.0 mm incl	$DF = 1.6078 - 0.02555 X + 0.0004179 X^2 - 3.333E-06 X^3 + 1.2994E-08 X^4 - 1.986E-11 X^5$
	over 70 mm	DF = 1.00
5.0	to 80 mm incl	$DF = 3.3021 - 0.10097 X + 0.001741 X^2 - 1.471E-05 X^3 + 6.093E-08 X^4 - 9.89E-11 X^5$
	over 80 mm	DF = 1.00
7.0	to 100 mm incl	$DF = 17.0308 - 0.90372 X + 0.02093 X^2 - 0.00025294 X^3 + 1.6771E-06 X^4 - 5.784E-09 X^5 + 8.1136E-12 X^6$
	over 100 mm	DF = 1.00
9.0	to 135 mm incl	$DF = 12.5452 - 0.4788 X + 0.007944 X^2 - 6.529E-05 X^3 + 2.6455E-07 X^4 - 4.218E-10 X^5$
	over 135 mm	DF = 1.00
11.0	to 150 mm incl	$DF = 12.079366 - 0.39065228 X + 0.0054925 X^2 - 3.828E-05 X^3 + 1.317E-07 X^4 - 1.788E-10 X^5$
	over 150 mm	DF = 1.00
13.0	to 160 mm incl	$DF = 10.4322 - 0.2718 X + 0.002896 X^2 - 1.301E-05 X^3 + 1.686E-08 X^4 + 2.0477E-11 X^5$
	over 165 mm	DF = 1.00
15.0	to 165 mm incl	$DF = 10.639 - 0.2617 X + 0.00266 X^2 - 1.15E-05 X^3 + 1.4384E-08 X^4 + 1.7322E-11 X^5$
	over 165 mm	DF = 1.00
20.0	to 170 mm incl	$DF = 11.7343 - 0.27476 X + 0.002912 X^2 - 1.577E-05 X^3 + 4.3095E-08 X^4 - 4.711E-11 X^5$
	over 170 mm	DF = 1.00
25.0		$DF = 13.0464 - 0.28015 X + 0.002638 X^2 - 1.214E-05 X^3 + 2.6094E-08 X^4 - 1.949E-11 X^5$
30.0		$DF = 10.4623 - 0.1353 X - 2.189E-05 X^2 + 1.0523E-05 X^3 - 6.624E-08 X^4 + 1.2592E-10 X^5$
35.0		$DF = 12.5309 - 0.2066 X + 0.001154 X^2 + 3.3717E-07 X^3 - 2.2E-08 X^4 + 5.001E-11 X^5$
40.0		$DF = 22.8737 - 0.624 X + 0.007925 X^2 - 5.38E-05 X^3 + 1.907E-07 X^4 - 2.788E-10 X^5$
45.0		$DF = 43.316 - 1.4589 X + 0.021437 X^2 - 0.00016129 X^3 + 6.109E-07 X^4 - 9.2353E-10 X^5$
50.0		$DF = 46.897 - 1.5553 X + 0.02238 X^2 - 0.00016453 X^3 + 6.1E-07 X^4 - 9.057E-10 X^5$

where:

$X = D_{1B}$ in m

[a] Max D_{1B} = 177.5 m

TABLE A22—EQUATIONS FOR TABLE A12—DISTANCE HARDNESS DIVIDING FACTORS VS. JOMINY DISTANCE (BORON STEELS), inch

"J" Distance (1/16 in)	D_{IB}[a]	Dividing Factor
2	to 2.5 incl	$DF = 22.9750 - 54.60177 X + 54.29984 X^2 - 26.85746 X^3 + 6.59130 X^4 - 0.64165 X^5$
	over 2.5	DF = 1.00
3	to 2.9 incl	$DF = 13.25591 - 28.28828 X + 26.35541 X^2 - 12.23150 X^3 + 2.81374 X^4 - 0.25623 X^5$
	over 2.9	DF = 1.00
4	to 3.5 incl	$DF = 28.50611 - 46.70430 X + 31.90431 X^2 - 10.91263 X^3 + 1.86570 X^4 - 0.12747 X^5$
	over 3.5	DF = 1.00
5	to 4.4 incl	$DF = 24.56368 - 33.70604 X + 19.34623 X^2 - 5.52132 X^3 + 0.78088 X^4 - 0.04375 X^5$
	over 4.4	DF = 1.00
6	to 4.9 incl	$DF = 5.32872 + 1.00334 X - 3.67571 X^2 + 1.70752 X^3 - 0.30124 X^4 + 0.02018 X^5$
	over 4.9	DF = 1.00
7	to 5.2 incl	$DF = 5.34598 + 0.98810 X 3.15067 X^2 + 1.33727 X^3 - 0.22285 X^4 + 0.01332 X^5$
	over 5.2	DF = 1.00
8	to 5.6 incl	$DF = 2.61397 + 4.69073 X - 4.71553 X^2 + 1.58031 X^3 - 0.22844 X_4 + 0.01219 X^5$
	over 5.6	DF = 1.00
9	to 5.8 incl	$DF = 3.80939 + 2.96448 X - 3.58847 X^2 + 1.22906 X^3 - 0.17730 X^4 + 0.00938 X^5$
	over 5.8	DF = 1.00
10	to 6.1 incl	$DF = 11.75138 - 8.15904 X + 2.57305 X^2 - 0.42384 X^3 + 0.03679 X^4 - 0.00136 X^5$
	over 6.1	DF = 1.00
12	to 6.6 incl	$DF = 10.94580 - 6.42904 X + 1.72900 X^2 - 0.24187 X^3 + 0.01769 X^4 - 0.00055 X^5$
	over 6.6	DF = 1.00
14	to 6.9 incl	$DF = 14.86832 - 10.16374 X + 3.32700 X^2 - 0.59480 X^3 + 0.05639 X^4 - 0.00221 X^5$
	over 6.9	DF = 1.00
16		$DF = 14.10267 - 7.94906 X + 1.93841 X^2 - 0.22357 X^3 + 0.01084 X^4 - 0.00010 X^5$
18		$DF = 11.29531 - 4.46248 X + 0.41286 X^2 + 0.09097 X^3 + 0.02034 X^4 + 0.00110 X^5$
20		$DF = 7.14752 + 0.35500 X - 1.61359 X^2 - 0.49403 X^3 - 0.05879 X^4 + 0.00251 X^5$
24		$DF = 12.3738 - 4.50690 X + 0.29009 X^2 + 0.12299 X^3 - 0.02325 X^4 + 0.00117 X^5$
28		$DF = 27.50991 - 20.45946 X + 6.97580 X^2 - 1.25184 X^3 + 0.11543 X^4 - 0.00433 X^5$
32		$DF = 43.35623 - 35.34260 + 12.58238 X^2 - 2.29821 X^3 + 0.21196 X^4 - 0.00785 X^5$

where:

$X = D_{1B}$ in inches

[a]Max D_{1B} = 7.0 in

HARDENABILITY BANDS FOR CARBON AND ALLOY H STEELS—SAE J1268 MAY95

SAE Standard

Report of the SAE Iron and Steel Technical Committee approved June 1980 and completely revised February 1988. Completely revised by the SAE Iron and Steel Technical Division 8—Carbon and Alloy Steel Hardenability, June 1993, and revised May 1995. Rationale statement available.

Foreword—This Document has not changed other than to put it into the new SAE Technical Standards Board Format

1. Scope—All carbon and alloy H-band steels are shown, along with their corresponding minimum and maximum hardenability limits, for which sufficient hardenability data have been established and for grades which use the standard end-quench test. As hardenability data are accumulated for other grades, this SAE Standard will be revised to include such grades.

2. References

2.1 Applicable Publications—The following publications form a part of the specification to the extent specified herein. Unless otherwise indicated the latest revision of SAE publications shall apply.

2.1.1 SAE PUBLICATIONS—Available from SAE, 400 Commonwealth Drive, Warrendale, PA 15096-0001.

SAE J403—Chemical Compositions of SAE Carbon Steels
SAE J404—Chemical Compositions of SAE Alloy Steels
SAE J406—Methods of Determining Hardenability of Steels
SAE J409—Product Analysis—Permissible Variations from Specified Chemical Analysis of a Heat or Cast of Steel
SAE J418—Grain Size Determination of Steels
SAE J1868—Restricted Hardenability Bands for Selected Alloy Steels

2.2 Related Publication—The following publication is provided for information purposes only and is not a required part of this document.

2.2.1 ASTM PUBLICATION—Available from ASTM, 100 Barr Harbor Drive, West Conshohocken, PA 19428-2959.

ASTM A 304—Steel Bars, Alloy, Subject to End-Quench Hardenability Requirements

3. Chemical Composition Limits—To permit steel producers the necessary latitude to meet the standard hardenability limits, the chemical composition limits of these steels have been broadened somewhat from those limits applicable to the same grades when specified by chemical composition only (SAE J403 and J404). These broader limits permit adjustments in manufacturing ranges of composition to compensate for individual plant melting procedures which might otherwise influence the levels and widths of the bands. The modifications have not been great enough to influence the general characteristics of the original compositions of the series under consideration.

The chemical composition limits for electric furnace, open hearth, and BOF steels are outlined in Tables 1 and 2 of this document and are subject to the permissible variations for product analysis outlined in Tables 1 and 3 of SAE J409.

TABLE 1—CARBON AND CARBON BORON H STEEL (ladle chemical composition, weight %, for elements shown; see Figures 3 to 16 for respective H-bands)

UNS No.	SAE Steel No.	C	Mn	Si	P,max(1)	S,max(1)
H10380	1038H	0.34/0.43	0.50/1.00	0.15/0.35	0.030	0.050
H10450	1045H	0.42/0.51	0.50/1.00	0.15/0.35	0.030	0.050
H15220	1522H	0.17/0.25	1.00/1.50	0.15/0.35	0.030	0.050
H15240	1524H	0.18/0.26	1.21/1.75	0.15/0.35	0.030	0.050
H15260	1526H	0.21/0.30	1.00/1.50	0.15/0.35	0.030	0.050
H15410	1541H	0.35/0.45	1.25/1.75	0.15/0.35	0.030	0.050
H15211	15B21H(2)	0.17/0.24	0.70/1.20	0.15/0.35	0.030	0.050
H15281	15B28H(2)	0.25/0.34	1.00/1.50	0.15/0.35	0.030	0.050
H15301	15B30H(2)	0.27/0.35	0.70/1.20	0.15/0.35	0.030	0.050
H15351	15B35H(2)	0.31/0.39	0.70/1.20	0.15/0.35	0.030	0.050
H15371	15B37H(2)	0.30/0.39	1.00/1.50	0.15/0.35	0.030	0.050
H15411	15B41H(2)	0.35/0.45	1.25/1.75	0.15/0.35	0.030	0.050
H15481	15B48H(2)	0.43/0.53	1.00/1.50	0.15/0.35	0.030	0.050
H15261	15B62H(2)	0.54/0.67	1.00/1.50	0.40/0.60	0.030	0.050

1. If electric furnace practice is specified or required, the limits for phosphorus and sulfur are 0.025%, respectively, and the prefix E is added to the SAE number, for example, E1038H.
2. These steels contain 0.0005 to 0.003% boron.

4. Identification—As a means of identifying steels specified to hardenability band limits, the suffix letter "H" has been added to the conventional series number. In the Unified Numbering System (UNS), the "H" appears as a prefix. It is important the steel consumers use this letter in specification requirements, as there is no other means of determining when hardenability band limits apply. When the letter is used, all conditions pertaining to chemical composition limits, restrictions, testing techniques, and so forth, as outlined herein apply

5. Grain Size—The H-band limits set forth are intended to apply to steels exhibiting austenitic grain size ASTM No. 5 or finer (see SAE J418). In cases where coarse grain steel is desired, the hardenability limits shall be a matter of agreement between the producer and the consumer.

6. Use of Hardenability Limits—H-band limits are shown graphically and are so depicted for convenience in estimating the hardness value obtainable at the various locations on the end quench test specimen and for quick comparisons of the various H grades.

The values of Diameter of Rounds, with Same As-Quenched Hardness shown above each H-band, are approximate and were selected from the ranges appearing in Figure 7 of SAE J406.

It should be noted that hardenability limits are presented graphically in both U.S. customary units and metric (SI) units. The metric hardenability bands were prepared by careful conversion from existing bands in U.S. customary units.

In either case, for specification purposes, the tabulated values of Rockwell C hardness (HRC) are used. Values below 20 HRC are not specified because such values are not as accurate.

Two points from the tabulated values are commonly designated according to method A, B, C, D, or E, which are defined in the following paragraphs. Those various methods are illustrated graphically in Figures 1 and 2. Note that nearest whole integers of distance and hardness are to be used, not fractions.

6.1 Method A—The minimum and maximum hardness values at any desired distance. This method is illustrated in Figures 1 and 2 as points A-A.

6.2 Method B—The minimum and maximum distance at which any desired hardness value occurs. This method is illustrated in Figures 1 and 2 as points B-B. If the desired hardness does not fall on an exact mm (or sixteenth of an inch) position, the minimum distance selected should be the nearest mm (or sixteenth of an inch) position toward the quenched end and the maximum should be the nearest mm (or sixteenth of an inch) position away from the quenched end.

6.3 Method C—Two maximum hardness values at two desired distances, illustrated in Figures 1 and 2 as points C-C.

6.4 Method D—Two minimum hardness values at two desired distances, illustrated in Figures 1 and 2 as points D-D.

6.5 Method E—Any minimum hardness plus any maximum hardness, illustrated in Figures 1 and 2 as points E-E.

When hardenability is specified according to one of the aforementioned methods, the balance of the hardenability band is not applicable.

In cases when it is considered desirable, the maximum and minimum limits at a distance of 1.5 mm (1/16 in) from the quenched end can be specified in addition to the other two points as previously described in methods A to E, inclusive.

When the full h-band is specified, the hardenability can be reported by listing hardness values for 1.5, 3, 5, 7, 9, 11, 13, 15, 20, 25, 30, 35, 40, 45, and 50 mm from the quenched end of the test specimen. In the case of the test specimen made to U.S. customary units, hardness values would be reported for each 1/6 to 16/16 in and 1/8 in increments from there to 32/16 in.

It is customary to accept a tolerance of two points HRC for a 5mm or 3/16 in portion of the curve, except at the 1.5 mm or 1/6 in position. This tolerance is necessary because curves for individual heats may vary somewhat in shape from the standard band limits and thus deviate slightly at one or more positions in the full length of the curves.

For shall hardening carbon H steels, distances form the quenched end may be reported by listing hardness values for 1 mm or 1/32 in intervals near the quenched end, as described more fully in SAE J406.

Acceptance testing shall be performed in accordance with SAE J406.

7. General—The hardenability limits in this document are those for regular quality steels produced in accordance with the Steel Products manuals published by the American Iron and Steel Institute (AISI). Some of the steels in this document can be specified to more restricted hardenability ranges, as presented in SAE J1868.

TABLE 2—[1]STANDARD ALLOY H STEEL COMPOSITIONS
(ladle chemical composition, weight %, for elements shown[2][3]
see Figures 17 to 88 for respective H-bands)

UNS No.	SAE Steel No.	C	Mn	Si	Ni	Cr	Mo	V
H13300	1330H	0.27/0.33	1.45/2.05	0.15/0.35	—	—	—	—
H13350	1335H	0.32/0.38	1.45/2.05	0.15/0.35	—	—	—	—
H13400	1340H	0.37/0.44	1.45/2.05	0.15/0.35	—	—	—	—
H13450	1345H	0.42/0.49	1.45/2.05	0.15/0.35	—	—	—	—
H40270	4027H	0.24/0.30	0.60/1.00	0.15/0.35	—	—	0.20/0.30	—
H40280[4]	4028H[4]	0.24/0.30	0.60/1.00	0.15/0.35	—	—	0.20/0.30	—
H40320	4032H	0.29/0.35	0.60/1.00	0.15/0.35	—	—	0.20/0.30	—
H40370	4037H	0.34/0.41	0.60/1.00	0.15/0.35	—	—	0.20/0.30	—
H40420	4042H	0.39/0.46	0.60/1.00	0.15/0.35	—	—	0.20/0.30	—
H40470	4047H	0.44/0.51	0.60/1.00	0.15/0.35	—	—	0.20/0.30	—
H41180	4118H	0.17/0.23	0.60/1.00	0.15/0.35	—	0.30/0.70	0.80/0.15	—
H41200	4120H	0.18/0.23	0.90/1.20	0.15/0.35	—	0.40/0.60	0.13/0.20	—
H41300	4130H	0.27/0.33	0.30/0.70	0.15/0.35	—	0.75/1.20	0.15/0.25	—
H41350	4135H	0.32/0.38	0.60/1.00	0.15/0.35	—	0.75/1.20	0.15/0.25	—
H41370	4137H	0.34/0.41	0.60/1.00	0.15/0.35	—	0.75/1.20	0.15/0.25	—
H41400	4140H	0.37/0.44	0.60/1.00	0.15/0.35	—	0.75/1.20	0.15/0.25	—
H41420	4142H	0.39/0.46	0.65/1.10	0.15/0.35	—	0.75/1.20	0.15/0.25	—
H41450	4145H	0.42/0.49	0.65/1.10	0.15/0.35	—	0.75/1.20	0.15/0.25	—
H41470	4147H	0.44/0.51	0.65/1.10	0.15/0.35	—	0.75/1.20	0.15/0.25	—
H41500	4150H	0.47/0.54	0.65/1.10	0.15/0.35	—	0.75/1.20	0.15/0.25	—
H41610	4161H	0.55/0.65	0.65/1.10	0.15/0.35	—	0.65/0.95	0.25/0.35	—
H43200	4320H	0.17/0.23	0.40/0.70	0.15/0.35	1.55/2.00	0.35/0.65	0.20/0.30	—
H43400	4340H	0.37/0.44	0.55/0.90	0.15/0.35	1.55/2.00	0.65/0.95	0.20/0.30	—
H43406[5]	E4340H[5]	0.37/0.44	0.60/0.95	0.15/0.35	1.55/2.00	0.65/0.95	0.20/0.30	—
H46200	4620H	0.17/0.23	0.35/0.75	0.15/0.35	1.55/2.00	—	0.20/0.30	—
H47180	4718H	0.15/0.21	0.60/0.95	0.15/0.35	0.85/1.25	0.30/0.60	0.30/0.40	—
H47200	4720H	0.17/0.23	0.45/0.75	0.15/0.35	0.85/1.25	0.30/0.60	0.15/0.25	—
H48150	4815H	0.12/0.18	0.30/0.70	0.15/0.35	3.20/3.80	—	0.20/0.30	—
H48170	4817H	0.14/0.20	0.30/0.70	0.15/0.35	3.20/3.80	—	0.20/0.30	—
H48200	4820H	0.17/0.23	0.40/0.80	0.15/0.35	3.20/3.80	—	0.20/0.30	—
H50401[6]	50B40H[6]	0.37/0.44	0.65/1.10	0.15/0.35	—	0.30/0.70	—	—
H50441[6]	50B44H(6)	0.42/0.49	0.65/1.10	0.15/0.35	—	0.30/0.70	—	—
H50460	5046H	0.43/0.50	0.65/1.10	0.15/0.35	—	0.13/0.43	—	—
H50461[6]	50B46H(6)	0.43/0.50	0.65/1.10	0.15/0.35	—	0.13/0.43	—	—
H50501[6]	50B50H(6)	0.47/0.54	0.65/1.10	0.15/0.35	—	0.30/0.70	—	—
H50601[6]	50B60H(6)	0.55/0.65	0.65/1.10	0.15/0.35	—	0.30/0.70	—	—
H51200	5120H	0.17/0.23	0.60/1.00	0.15/0.35	—	0.60/1.00	—	—
H51300	5130H	0.27/0.33	0.60/1.00	0.15/0.35	—	0.75/1.20	—	—
H51320	5132H	0.29/0.35	0.50/0.90	0.15/0.35	—	0.65/1.10	—	—
H51350	5135H	0.32/0.38	0.50/0.90	0.15/0.35	—	0.70/1.15	—	—
H51400	5140H	0.37/0.44	0.60/1.00	0.15/0.35	—	0.60/1.00	—	—
H51470	5147H	0.45/0.52	0.60/1.05	0.15/0.35	—	0.80/1.25	—	—
H51500	5150H	0.47/0.54	0.60/1.00	0.15/0.35	—	0.60/1.00	—	—
H51550	5155H	0.50/0.60	0.60/1.00	0.15/0.35	—	0.60/1.00	—	—
H51600	5160H	0.55/0.65	0.65/1.10	0.15/0.35	—	0.60/1.00	—	—
H51601[6]	51B60H[6]	0.55/0.65	0.65/1.10	0.15/0.35	—	0.60/1.00	—	—
H61180	6118H	0.15/0.21	0.40/0.80	0.15/0.35	—	0.40/0.80	—	0.10/0.15
H61500	6150H	0.47/0.54	0.60/1.00	0.15/0.35	—	0.75-1.20	—	0.15 min
H81451[6]	81B45H(6)	0.42/0.49	0.70/1.05	0.15/0.35	0.15/0.45	0.30/0.60	0.08/0.15	—
H86170	8617H	0.14/0.20	0.60/0.95	0.15/0.35	0.35/0.75	0.35/0.65	0.15/0.25	—

TABLE 2—[1]STANDARD ALLOY H STEEL COMPOSITIONS (continued)
(ladle chemical composition, weight %, for elements shown[2][3]
see Figures 17 to 88 for respective H-bands) (continued)

UNS No.	SAE Steel No.	C	Mn	Si	Ni	Cr	Mo	V
H86200	8620H	0.17/0.23	0.60/0.95	0.15/0.35	0.35/0.75	0.35/0.65	0.15/0.25	—
H86220	8622H	0.19/0.25	0.60/0.95	0.15/0.35	0.35/0.75	0.35/0.65	0.15/0.25	—
H86250	8625H	0.22/0.28	0.60/0.95	0.15/0.35	0.35/0.75	0.35/0.65	0.15/0.25	—
H86270	8627H	0.24/0.30	0.60/0.95	0.15/0.35	0.35/0.75	0.35/0.65	0.15/0.25	—
H86300	8630H	0.27/0.33	0.60/0.95	0.15/0.35	0.35/0.75	0.35/0.65	0.15/0.25	—
H86301[6]	86B30H[6]	0.27/0.33	0.60/0.95	0.15/0.35	0.35/0.75	0.35/0.65	0.15/0.25	—
H86370	8637H	0.34/0.41	0.70/1.05	0.15/0.35	0.35/0.75	0.35/0.65	0.15/0.25	—
H86400	8640H	0.37/0.44	0.70/1.05	0.15/0.35	0.35/0.75	0.35/0.65	0.15/0.25	—
H86420	8642H	0.39/0.46	0.70/1.05	0.15/0.35	0.35/0.75	0.35/0.65	0.15/0.25	—
H86450	8645H	0.42/0.49	0.70/1.05	0.15/0.35	0.35/0.75	0.35/0.65	0.15/0.25	—
H86451[6]	86B45H[6]	0.42/0.49	0.70/1.05	0.15/0.35	0.35/0.75	0.35/0.65	0.15/0.25	—
H86500	8650H	0.47/0.54	0.70/1.05	0.15/0.35	0.35/0.75	0.35/0.65	0.15/0.25	—
H86550	8655H	0.50/0.60	0.70/1.05	0.15/0.35	0.35/0.75	0.35/0.65	0.15/0.25	—
H86600	8660H	0.55/0.65	0.70/1.05	0.15/0.35	0.35/0.75	0.35/0.65	0.15/0.25	
H87200	8720H	0.17/0.23	0.60/0.95	0.15/0.35	0.35/0.75	0.35/0.65	0.20/0.30	—
H87400	8740H	0.37/0.44	0.70/1.05	0.15/0.35	0.35/0.75	0.35/0.65	0.20/0.30	—
H88220	8822H	0.19/0.25	0.70/1.05	0.15/0.35	0.35/0.75	0.35/0.65	0.30/0.40	—
H92590	9259H	0.56/0.64	0.65/1.10	0.70/1.20	—	0.45/0.65	—	—
H92600	9260H	0.55/0.65	0.65/1.10	1.70/2.20	—	—	—	—
H93106(5)	E9310H(5)	0.07/0.13	0.40/0.70	0.15/0.35	2.95/3.55	1.00/1.45	0.80/0.15	—
H94151(6)	94B15H(6)	0.12/0.18	0.70/1.05	0.15/0.35	0.25/0.65	0.25/0.55	0.80/0.15	—
H94171(6)	94B17H(6)	0.14/0.20	0.70/1.05	0.15/0.35	0.25/0.65	0.25/0.55	0.80/0.15	—
H94301(6)	94B30H(6)	0.27/0.33	0.70/1.05	0.15/0.35	0.25/0.65	0.25/0.55	0.80/0.15	—

1. The ranges and limits on this table apply only to material not exceeding 0.13 m^2 (200 in^2) in cross-sectional area, 460 mm (18 in) in width, or 4.5 tonne (10 000 lb) per piece in weight. Ranges and limits are subject to the permissible variations for product analysis shown in Table 4 of SAE J409.
2. Small quantities of certain elements may be found in alloy steel which are not specified or required. These elements are considered incidental and acceptable to the following maximum amounts: copper to 0.35%, nickel to 0.25%, chromium to 0.20%, and molybdenum to 0.06%.
3. For open hearth and basic oxygen steels maximum sulfur content is 0.040% and maximum phosphorus content is 0.030%. Maximum phosphorus and sulfur in basic electric furnace steels are 0.025% each.
4. Sulfur content range is 0.035/0.050%.
5. Electric furnace steel.
6. These steels contain 0.0005 to 0.003% boron.

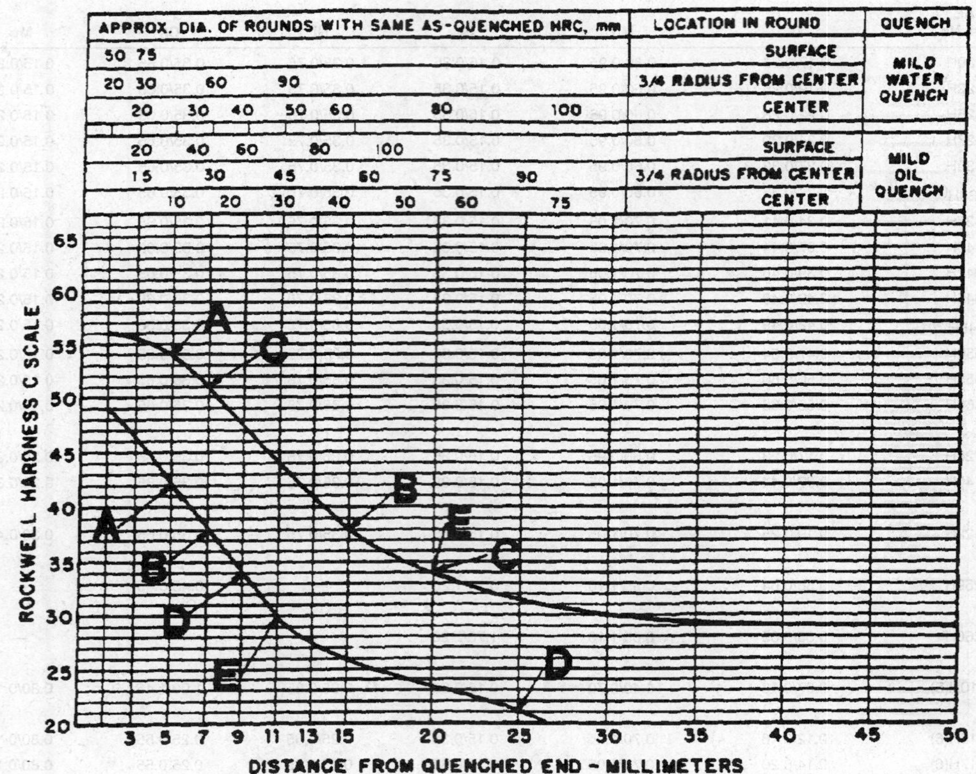

	Method	Example
A	Minimum and maximum hardness values at a designated distance	A-A 42 to 54 HRC at J 5 mm
B	A hardness value at minimum and maximum distance	B-B 38 HRC at J 7 mm min 38 HRC at J 15 mm max
C	Two maximum hardness values at two designated distances	C-C 51 HRC at J 7 mm max 34 HRC at J 20 mm max
D	Two minimum hardness values at two distances	D-D 34 HRC at J 9 mm min 21 HRC at J 25 mm min
E	Any minimum hardness plus any maximum hardness	E-E 30 HRC at J 11 mm min 34 HRC at J 20 mm max

FIGURE 1—EXAMPLES ILLUSTRATING ALTERNATE METHODS OF SPECIFYING HARDENABILITY REQUIREMENTS IN METRIC (SI) UNITS

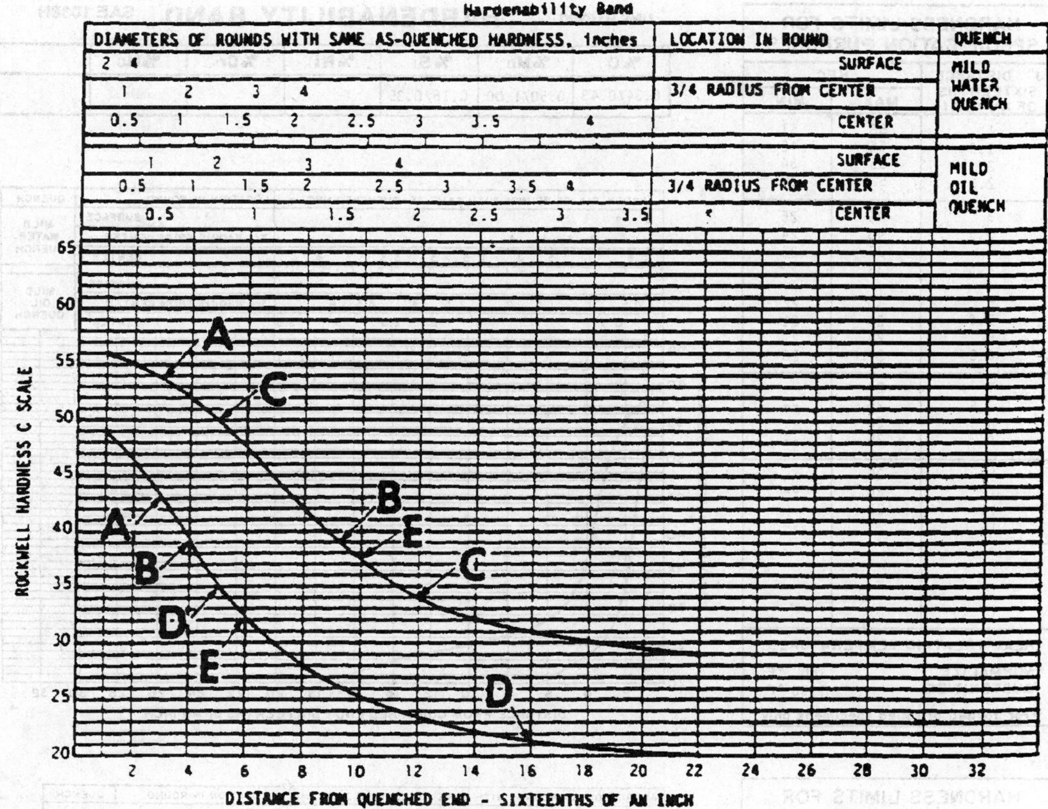

	Method		Example
A	Minimum and maximum hardness values at a designated distance	A-A	43 to 54 HRC at J 3/16
B	A hardness value at minimum and maximum distances	B-B	39 HRC at J 4/16 min 39 HRC at J 9/16 max
C	Two maximum hardness values at two designated distances	C-C	50 HRC at J 5/16 max 34 HRC at J 12/16 max
D	Two minimum hardness values at two distances	D-D	35 HRC at J 5/16 min 21 HRC at J 16/16 min
E	Any minimum hardness plus any maximum hardness	E-E	32 HRC at J 6/16 min 37 HRC at J 10/16 max

FIGURE 2—EXAMPLES ILLUSTRATING ALTERNATE METHODS OF SPECIFYING HARDENABILTY REQUIREMENTS IN U.S. CUSTOMARY UNITS

HARDENABILITY BAND

UNS H10380 SAE 1038H

%C	%Mn	%Si	%Ni	%Cr	%Mo
0.34/0.43	0.50/1.00	0.15/0.35			

HARDNESS LIMITS FOR SPECIFICATION PURPOSES

"J" DISTANCE SIXTEENTHS OF AN INCH	HRC MAX.	HRC MIN.
1	58	51
1.5	56	42
2	55	34
2.5	53	29
3	49	26
3.5	43	24
4	37	23
4.5	33	22
5	30	22
5.5	29	21
6	28	21
6.5	27	20
7	27	--
7.5	26	--
8	26	--
9	25	--
10	25	--
12	24	--
14	23	--
16	21	--

HEAT TREATING TEMPERATURES

*NORMALIZE	1600 °F
AUSTENITIZE	1550 °F

*For forged or rolled specimens only

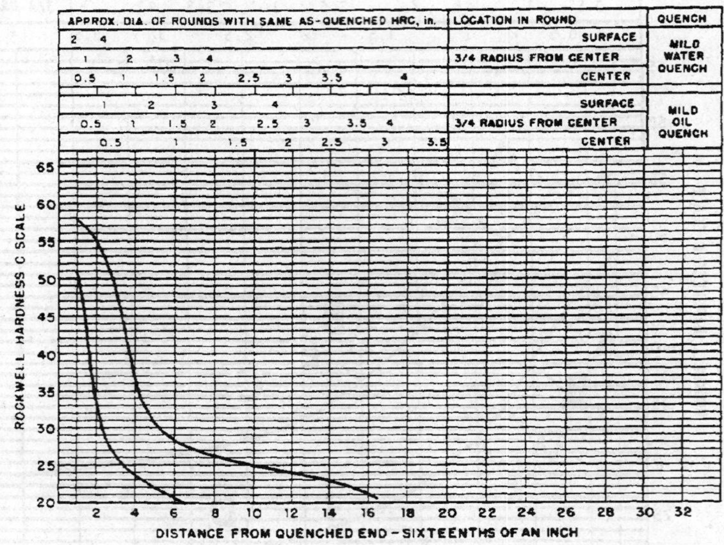

HARDNESS LIMITS FOR SPECIFICATION PURPOSES

"J" DISTANCE MILLIMETERS	HRC MAX.	HRC MIN.
1.5	58	51
3	56	37
5	49	25
7	33	22
9	29	20
11	27	--
13	26	--
15	25	--
20	24	--
25	22	--
30	--	--
35		
40		
45		
50		

HEAT TREATING TEMPERATURES

*NORMALIZE	870 °C
AUSTENITIZE	845 °C

*For forged or rolled specimens only

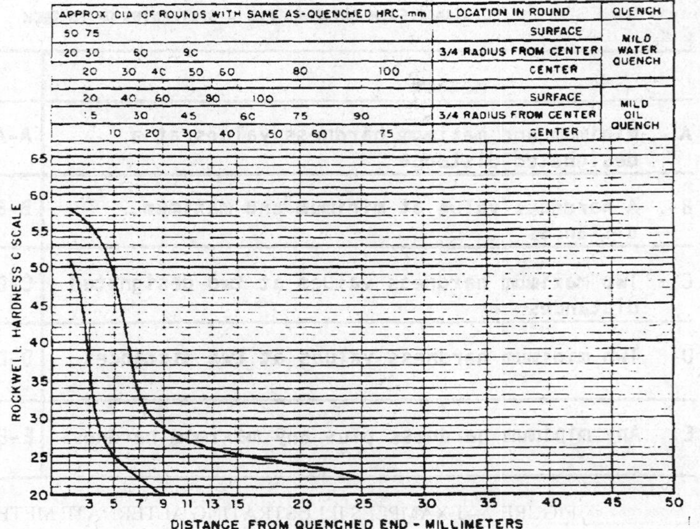

FIGURE 3—UNS H10380—HARDENABILITY BAND—SAE 1038H

UNS H10450 **HARDENABILITY BAND** SAE 1045H

%C	%Mn	%Si	%Ni	%Cr	%Mo
0.42/0.51	0.50/1.00	0.15/0.35			

HARDNESS LIMITS FOR SPECIFICATION PURPOSES

"J" DISTANCE SIXTEENTHS OF AN INCH	HRC MAX.	HRC MIN.
1	62	55
1.5	61	52
2	59	42
2.5	56	34
3	52	31
3.5	46	29
4	38	28
4.5	34	27
5	33	26
5.5	32	26
6	32	25
6.5	31	25
7	31	25
7.5	30	24
8	30	24
9	29	23
10	29	22
12	28	21
14	27	20
16	26	--

HEAT TREATING TEMPERATURES

*NORMALIZE	1600 °F
AUSTENITIZE	1550 °F

*For forged or rolled specimens only

APPROX. DIA. OF ROUNDS WITH SAME AS-QUENCHED HRC, in.

Diameters	LOCATION IN ROUND	QUENCH
2 4	SURFACE	MILD WATER QUENCH
1 2 3 4	3/4 RADIUS FROM CENTER	
0.5 1 1.5 2 2.5 3 3.5 4	CENTER	
1 2 3 4	SURFACE	MILD OIL QUENCH
0.5 1 1.5 2 2.5 3 3.5 4	3/4 RADIUS FROM CENTER	
0.5 1 1.5 2 2.5 3 3.5	CENTER	

ROCKWELL HARDNESS C SCALE (20–65)

DISTANCE FROM QUENCHED END - SIXTEENTHS OF AN INCH (2–32)

HARDNESS LIMITS FOR SPECIFICATION PURPOSES

"J" DISTANCE MILLIMETERS	HRC MAX.	HRC MIN.
1.5	62	55
3	59	44
5	50	30
7	35	27
9	32	26
11	31	25
13	30	24
15	29	22
20	28	20
25	26	--
30	--	--
35		
40		
45		
50		

HEAT TREATING TEMPERATURES

*NORMALIZE	870 °C
AUSTENITIZE	845 °C

*For forged or rolled specimens only

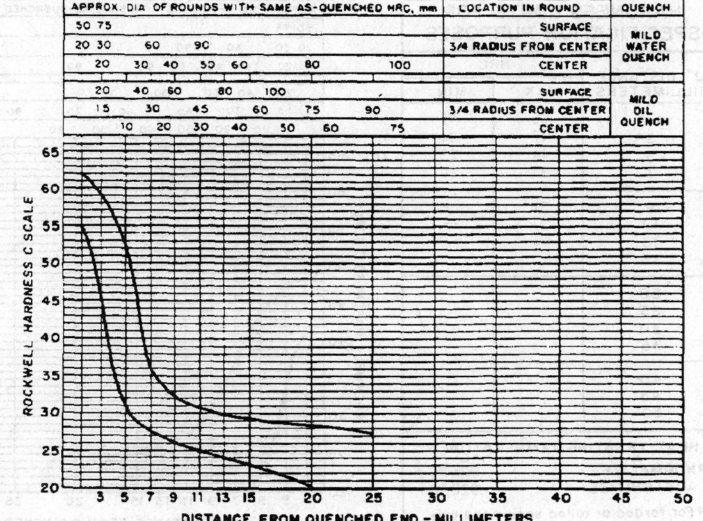

FIGURE 4—UNS H10450—HARDENABILITY BAND—SAE 1045H

UNS H15220 **HARDENABILITY BAND** SAE 1522H

%C	%Mn	%Si	%Ni	%Cr	%Mo
0.17/0.25	1.00/1.50	0.15/0.35			

HARDNESS LIMITS FOR SPECIFICATION PURPOSES

"J" DISTANCE SIXTEENTHS OF AN INCH	HRC MAX.	HRC MIN.
1	50	41
1.5	48	41
2	47	32
2.5	46	27
3	45	22
3.5	42	21
4	39	20
4.5	37	--
5	34	--
5.5	32	--
6	30	--
6.5	28	--
7	27	--
7.5	--	--
8	--	--
9	--	--
10	--	--
12	--	--
14	--	--
16	--	--

HEAT TREATING TEMPERATURES

*NORMALIZE	1700 °F
AUSTENITIZE	1700 °F

*For forged or rolled specimens only

APPROX. DIA. OF ROUNDS WITH SAME AS-QUENCHED HRC, in.	LOCATION IN ROUND	QUENCH
2 4	SURFACE	MILD WATER QUENCH
1 2 3 4	3/4 RADIUS FROM CENTER	
0.5 1 1.5 2 2.5 3 3.5 4	CENTER	
1 2 3 4	SURFACE	MILD OIL QUENCH
0.5 1 1.5 2 2.5 3 3.5 4	3/4 RADIUS FROM CENTER	
0.5 1 1.5 2 2.5 3 3.5	CENTER	

ROCKWELL HARDNESS C SCALE: 20 25 30 35 40 45 50 55 60 65

2 4 6 8 10 12 14 16 18 20 22 24 26 28 30 32

DISTANCE FROM QUENCHED END - SIXTEENTHS OF AN INCH

HARDNESS LIMITS FOR SPECIFICATION PURPOSES

"J" DISTANCE MILLIMETERS	HRC MAX.	HRC MIN.
1.5	50	41
3	47	34
5	44	22
7	37	20
9	31	--
11	27	--
13	--	--
15		
20		
25		
30		
35		
40		
45		
50		

HEAT TREATING TEMPERATURES

*NORMALIZE	925 °C
AUSTENITIZE	925 °C

*For forged or rolled specimens only

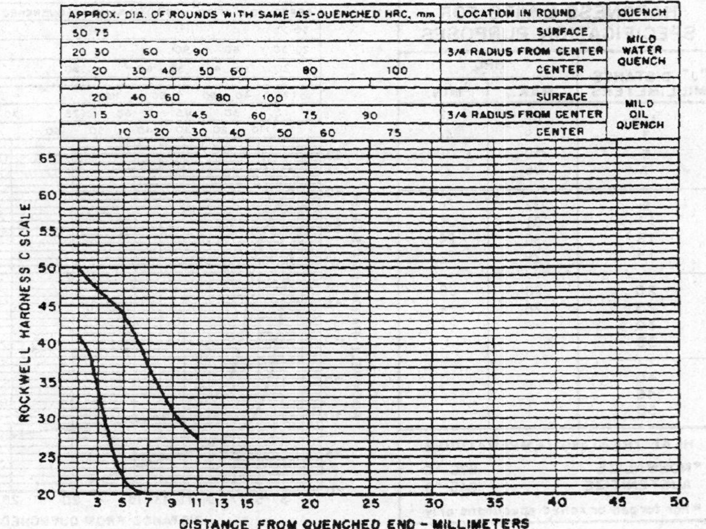

FIGURE 5—UNS H15220—HARDENABILITY BAND—SAE 1522H

HARDENABILITY BAND

UNS H15240 — SAE 1524H

%C	%Mn	%Si	%Ni	%Cr	%Mo
0.18/0.26	1.25/1.75	0.15/0.35			

HARDNESS LIMITS FOR SPECIFICATION PURPOSES

"J" DISTANCE SIXTEENTHS OF AN INCH	HRC MAX.	HRC MIN.
1	51	42
1.5	49	42
2	48	38
2.5	47	34
3	45	29
3.5	43	25
4	39	22
4.5	38	20
5	35	--
5.5	34	--
6	32	--
6.5	30	--
7	29	--
7.5	28	--
8	27	--
9	26	--
10	25	--
12	23	--
14	22	--
16	--	--
26		
28		
30		
32		

HEAT TREATING TEMPERATURES

*NORMALIZE 1650 °F
AUSTENITIZE 1600 °F

*For forged or rolled specimens only

APPROX. DIA. OF ROUNDS WITH SAME AS-QUENCHED HRC, in. — LOCATION IN ROUND — QUENCH

MILD WATER QUENCH: SURFACE 2 4; 3/4 RADIUS FROM CENTER 1 2 3 4; CENTER 0.5 1 1.5 2 2.5 3 3.5 4

MILD OIL QUENCH: SURFACE 1 2 3 4; 3/4 RADIUS FROM CENTER 0.5 1 1.5 2 2.5 3 3.5 4; CENTER 0.5 1 1.5 2 2.5 3 3.5

ROCKWELL HARDNESS C SCALE (20–65)

DISTANCE FROM QUENCHED END - SIXTEENTHS OF AN INCH (2–32)

HARDNESS LIMITS FOR SPECIFICATION PURPOSES

"J" DISTANCE MILLIMETERS	HRC MAX.	HRC MIN.
1.5	51	42
3	49	39
5	44	26
7	38	21
9	34	--
11	30	--
13	27	--
15	25	--
20	23	--
25	--	--
30		
35		
40		
45		
50		

HEAT TREATING TEMPERATURES

*NORMALIZE 900 °C
AUSTENITIZE 870 °C

*For forged or rolled specimens only

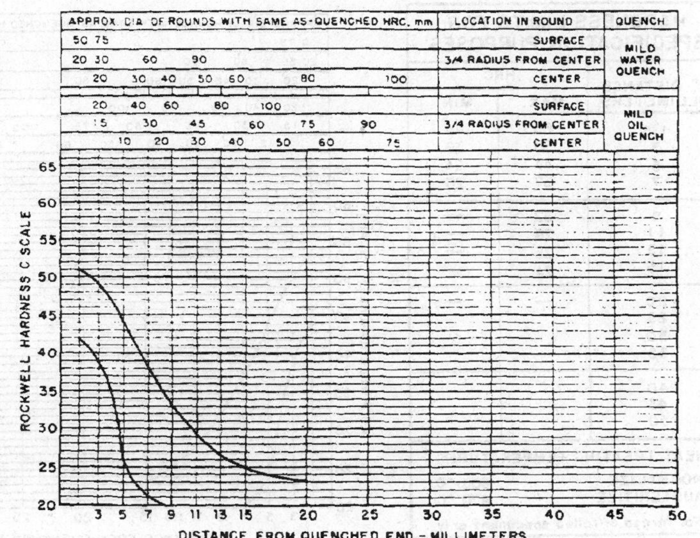

FIGURE 6—UNS H15240—HARDENABILITY BAND—SAE 1524H

UNS H15260 **HARDENABILITY BAND** SAE 1526H

%C	%Mn	%Si	%Ni	%Cr	%Mo
0.21/0.30	1.00/1.50	0.15/0.35			

HARDNESS LIMITS FOR SPECIFICATION PURPOSES

"J" DISTANCE SIXTEENTHS OF AN INCH	HRC MAX.	HRC MIN.
1	53	44
1.5	50	42
2	49	38
2.5	47	33
3	46	26
3.5	42	25
4	39	21
4.5	37	20
5	33	--
5.5	31	--
6	30	--
6.5	28	--
7	27	--
7.5	26	--
8	26	--
9	24	--
10	24	--
12	23	--
14	--	--
16	--	--

HEAT TREATING TEMPERATURES

*NORMALIZE	1650 °F
AUSTENITIZE	1600 °F

*For forged or rolled specimens only

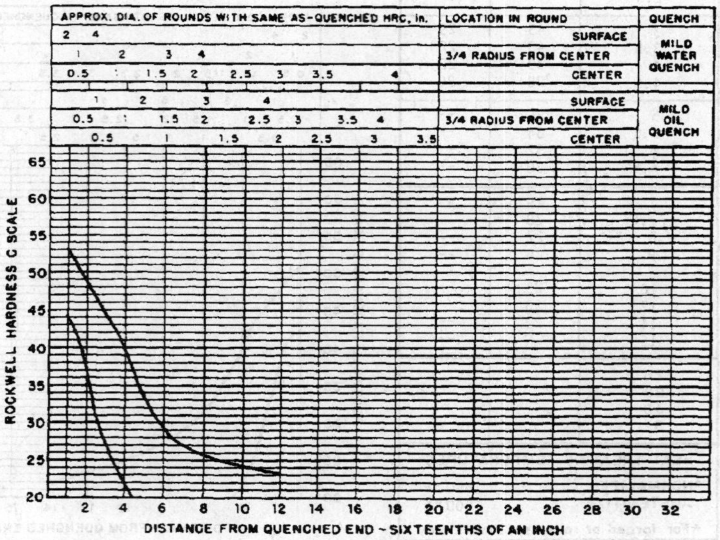

APPROX. DIA. OF ROUNDS WITH SAME AS-QUENCHED HRC, in.	LOCATION IN ROUND	QUENCH
2 4	SURFACE	MILD WATER QUENCH
1 2 3 4	3/4 RADIUS FROM CENTER	
0.5 1 1.5 2 2.5 3 3.5 4	CENTER	
1 2 3 4	SURFACE	MILD OIL QUENCH
0.5 1 1.5 2 2.5 3 3.5 4	3/4 RADIUS FROM CENTER	
0.5 1 1.5 2 2.5 3 3.5	CENTER	

ROCKWELL HARDNESS C SCALE (20–65)

DISTANCE FROM QUENCHED END ~ SIXTEENTHS OF AN INCH (2–32)

HARDNESS LIMITS FOR SPECIFICATION PURPOSES

"J" DISTANCE MILLIMETERS	HRC MAX.	HRC MIN.
1.5	53	44
3	50	39
5	44	24
7	37	20
9	32	—
11	28	—
13	25	—
15	24	—
20	—	—
25		
30		
35		
40		
45		
50		

HEAT TREATING TEMPERATURES

*NORMALIZE	900 °C
AUSTENITIZE	870 °C

*For forged or rolled specimens only

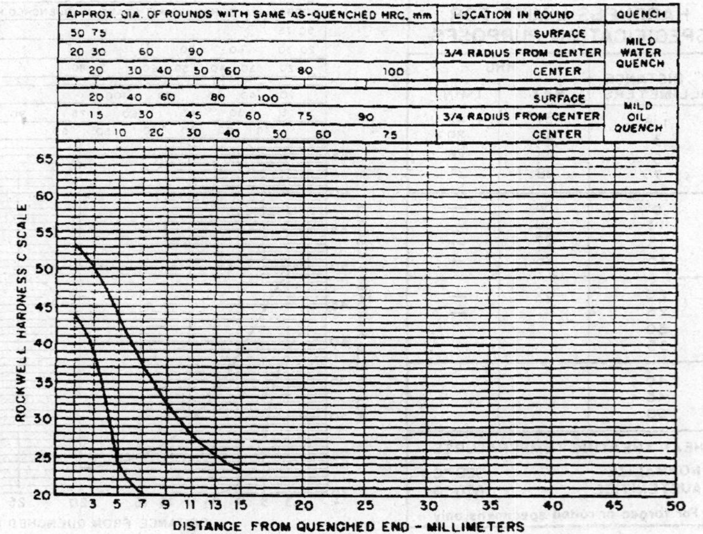

FIGURE 7—UNS H15260—HARDENABILITY BAND—SAE 1526H

UNS H15410 **HARDENABILITY BAND** SAE 1541H

%C	%Mn	%Si	%Ni	%Cr	%Mo
0.35/0.45	1.25/1.75	0.15/0.35			

HARDNESS LIMITS FOR SPECIFICATION PURPOSES

"J" DISTANCE SIXTEENTHS OF AN INCH	HRC MAX.	HRC MIN.
1	60	53
1.5	59	52
2	59	50
2.5	58	47
3	57	44
3.5	56	41
4	55	38
4.5	53	35
5	52	32
5.5	50	29
6	48	27
6.5	46	26
7	44	25
7.5	41	24
8	39	23
9	35	23
10	33	22
12	32	21
14	31	20
16	30	--

HEAT TREATING TEMPERATURES

*NORMALIZE	1600 °F
AUSTENITIZE	1550 °F

*For forged or rolled specimens only

APPROX DIA OF ROUNDS WITH SAME AS-QUENCHED HRC, in. — LOCATION IN ROUND — QUENCH

MILD WATER QUENCH: SURFACE; 3/4 RADIUS FROM CENTER; CENTER

MILD OIL QUENCH: SURFACE; 3/4 RADIUS FROM CENTER; CENTER

ROCKWELL HARDNESS C SCALE

DISTANCE FROM QUENCHED END - SIXTEENTHS OF AN INCH

HARDNESS LIMITS FOR SPECIFICATION PURPOSES

"J" DISTANCE MILLIMETERS	HRC MAX.	HRC MIN.
1.5	60	53
3	59	50
5	57	43
7	53	36
9	49	29
11	44	25
13	38	23
15	35	22
20	32	20
25	30	--
30	--	--
35		
40		
45		
50		

HEAT TREATING TEMPERATURES

*NORMALIZE	870 °C
AUSTENITIZE	845 °C

*For forged or rolled specimens only

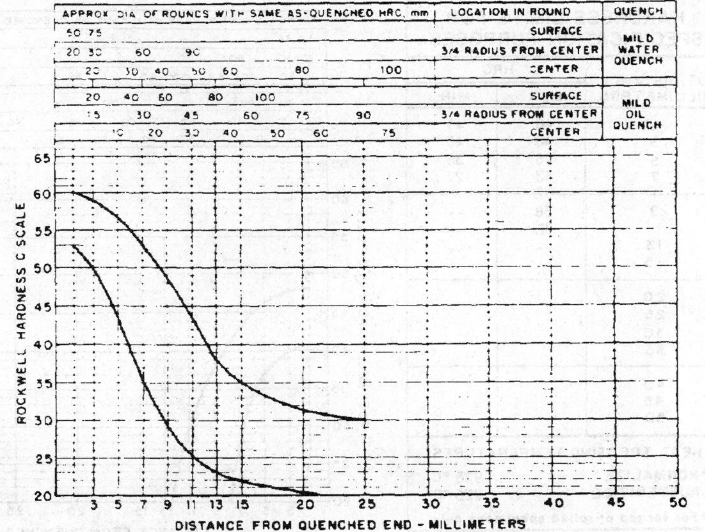

FIGURE 8—UNS H15410—HARDENABILITY BAND—SAE 1541H

UNS H15211 **HARDENABILITY BAND** SAE 15B21H

%C	%Mn	%Si	%Ni	%Cr	%Mo	%B
0.17/0.24	0.70/1.20	0.15/0.35	--	--	--	0.0005/0.003

HARDNESS LIMITS FOR SPECIFICATION PURPOSES

"J" DISTANCE SIXTEENTHS OF AN INCH	HRC MAX.	HRC MIN.
1	48	41
1.5	48	41
2	47	40
2.5	47	39
3	46	38
3.5	45	36
4	44	30
4.5	42	23
5	40	20
5.5	38	--
6	35	--
6.5	32	--
7	27	--
7.5	22	--
8	20	--
9	--	--
10		
12		
14		
16		

HEAT TREATING TEMPERATURES

*NORMALIZE 1700 °F

AUSTENITIZE 1700 °F

*For forged or rolled specimens only

APPROX. DIA. OF ROUNDS WITH SAME AS-QUENCHED HRC, in.

LOCATION IN ROUND	QUENCH
SURFACE	MILD WATER QUENCH
3/4 RADIUS FROM CENTER	MILD WATER QUENCH
CENTER	MILD WATER QUENCH
SURFACE	MILD OIL QUENCH
3/4 RADIUS FROM CENTER	MILD OIL QUENCH
CENTER	MILD OIL QUENCH

ROCKWELL HARDNESS C SCALE

DISTANCE FROM QUENCHED END - SIXTEENTHS OF AN INCH

HARDNESS LIMITS FOR SPECIFICATION PURPOSES

"J" DISTANCE MILLIMETERS	HRC MAX.	HRC MIN.
1.5	48	41
3	48	40
5	46	36
7	43	27
9	38	--
11	30	--
13	--	--
15		
20		
25		
30		
35		
40		
45		
50		

HEAT TREATING TEMPERATURES

*NORMALIZE 925 °C

AUSTENITIZE 925 °C

*For forged or rolled specimens only

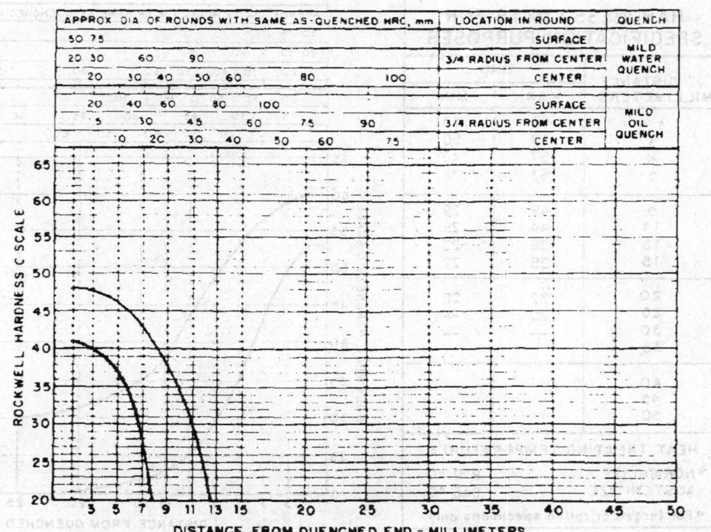

FIGURE 9—UNS H15211—HARDENABILITY BAND—SAE 15B21H

UNS H15281 **HARDENABILITY BAND** SAE 15B28H

%C	%Mn	%Si	%Ni	%Cr	%Mo	%B
0.25/0.34	1.00/1.50	0.15/0.35	--	--	--	0.0005/0.003

HARDNESS LIMITS FOR SPECIFICATION PURPOSES

"J" DISTANCE SIXTEENTHS OF AN INCH	HRC MAX.	HRC MIN.
1	53	47
2	53	47
3	52	46
4	51	45
5	51	42
6	50	32
7	49	25
8	48	21
9	46	20
10	43	--
11	40	--
12	37	--
13	34	--
14	31	--
15	30	--
16	29	--
18	27	--
20	25	--
22	25	--
24	24	--
26	23	--
28	22	--
30	21	--
32	20	--

HEAT TREATING TEMPERATURES

*NORMALIZE	1650 °F
AUSTENITIZE	1600 °F

*For forged or rolled specimens only

APPROX DIA OF ROUNDS WITH SAME AS-QUENCHED HRC, in — LOCATION IN ROUND: SURFACE, 3/4 RADIUS FROM CENTER, CENTER — QUENCH: MILD WATER QUENCH; MILD OIL QUENCH

ROCKWELL HARDNESS C SCALE

DISTANCE FROM QUENCHED END - SIXTEENTHS OF AN INCH

HARDNESS LIMITS FOR SPECIFICATION PURPOSES

"J" DISTANCE MILLIMETERS	HRC MAX.	HRC MIN.
1.5	53	47
3	53	47
5	53	46
7	52	43
9	51	35
11	50	24
13	48	21
15	45	20
20	35	--
25	29	--
30	26	--
35	25	--
40	24	--
45	23	--
50	20	--

HEAT TREATING TEMPERATURES

*NORMALIZE	900 °C
AUSTENITIZE	870 °C

*For forged or rolled specimens only

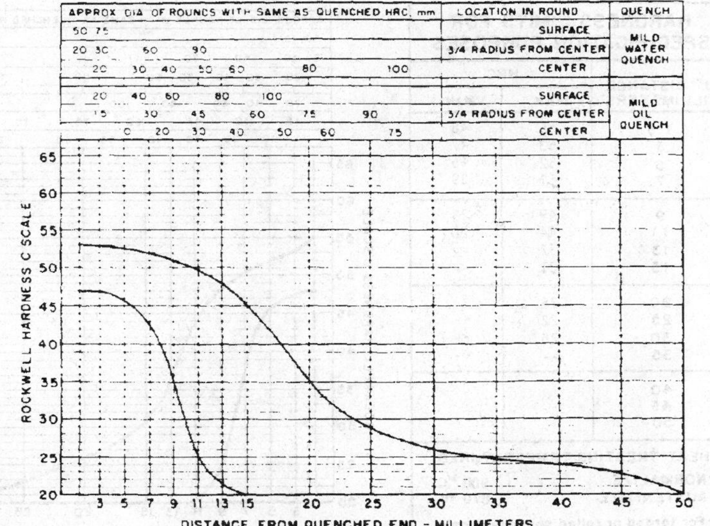

FIGURE 10—UNS H15281—HARDENABILITY BAND—SAE 15B28H

UNS H15301 **HARDENABILITY BAND** SAE 15B30H

%C	%Mn	%Si	%Ni	%Cr	%Mo	%B
0.27/0.35	0.70/1.20	0.15/0.35	--	--	--	0.0005/0.003

HARDNESS LIMITS FOR SPECIFICATION PURPOSES

"J" DISTANCE SIXTEENTHS OF AN INCH	HRC MAX.	HRC MIN.
1	55	48
2	53	47
3	52	46
4	51	44
5	50	32
6	48	22
7	43	20
8	38	--
9	33	--
10	29	--
11	27	--
12	26	--
13	25	--
14	24	--
15	23	--
16	22	--
18	20	--
20	--	--
22		
24		
26		
28		
30		
32		

HEAT TREATING TEMPERATURES

*NORMALIZE 1650 °F
AUSTENITIZE 1600 °F

*For forged or rolled specimens only

APPROX. DIA. OF ROUNDS WITH SAME AS-QUENCHED HRC, in.	LOCATION IN ROUND	QUENCH
2 4	SURFACE	MILD WATER QUENCH
1 2 3 4	3/4 RADIUS FROM CENTER	
0.5 1 1.5 2 2.5 3 3.5 4	CENTER	
1 2 3 4	SURFACE	MILD OIL QUENCH
0.5 1 1.5 2 2.5 3 3.5 4	3/4 RADIUS FROM CENTER	
0.5 1 1.5 2 2.5 3 3.5	CENTER	

ROCKWELL HARDNESS C SCALE: 20 25 30 35 40 45 50 55 60 65

DISTANCE FROM QUENCHED END - SIXTEENTHS OF AN INCH: 2 4 6 8 10 12 14 16 18 20 22 24 26 28 30 32

HARDNESS LIMITS FOR SPECIFICATION PURPOSES

"J" DISTANCE MILLIMETERS	HRC MAX.	HRC MIN.
1.5	55	48
3	53	47
5	52	46
7	51	39
9	49	25
11	44	20
13	37	--
15	31	--
20	26	--
25	22	--
30	20	--
35	--	--
40		
45		
50		

HEAT TREATING TEMPERATURES

*NORMALIZE 900 °C
AUSTENITIZE 870 °C

*For forged or rolled specimens only

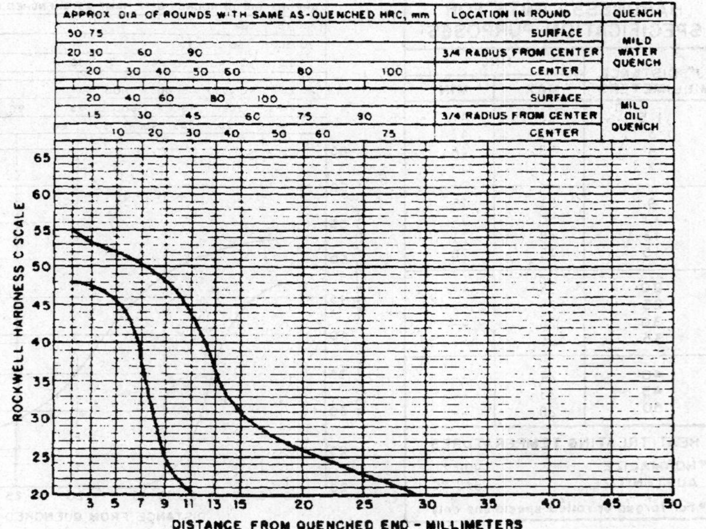

FIGURE 11—UNS H15301—HARDENABILITY BAND—SAE 15B30H

HARDNESS LIMITS FOR SPECIFICATION PURPOSES

"J" DISTANCE SIXTEENTHS OF AN INCH	HRC MAX.	HRC MIN.
1	58	51
2	56	50
3	55	49
4	54	48
5	53	39
6	51	28
7	47	24
8	41	22
9	--	--
10	30	20
11	--	--
12	27	--
13	--	--
14	26	--
15	--	--
16	25	--
18	--	--
20	24	--
22	--	--
24	22	--
26	--	--
28	20	--
30	--	--
32	--	--

HEAT TREATING TEMPERATURES

*NORMALIZE 1600 °F
AUSTENITIZE 1550 °F

*For forged or rolled specimens only

UNS H15351 **HARDENABILITY BAND** SAE 15B35H

%C	%Mn	%Si	%Ni	%Cr	%Mo	%B
0.31/0.39	0.70/1.20	0.15/0.35	--	--	--	0.0005/0.003

APPROX. DIA. OF ROUNDS WITH SAME AS-QUENCHED HRC, in. — LOCATION IN ROUND — QUENCH

SURFACE / 3/4 RADIUS FROM CENTER / CENTER — MILD WATER QUENCH

SURFACE / 3/4 RADIUS FROM CENTER / CENTER — MILD OIL QUENCH

ROCKWELL HARDNESS C SCALE

DISTANCE FROM QUENCHED END - SIXTEENTHS OF AN INCH

HARDNESS LIMITS FOR SPECIFICATION PURPOSES

"J" DISTANCE MILLIMETERS	HRC MAX.	HRC MIN.
1.5	58	51
3	56	50
5	55	49
7	54	45
9	52	32
11	47	24
13	39	21
15	32	20
20	27	--
25	25	--
30	24	--
35	23	--
40	22	--
45	20	--
50	--	--

HEAT TREATING TEMPERATURES

*NORMALIZE 870 °C
AUSTENITIZE 845 °C

*For forged or rolled specimens only

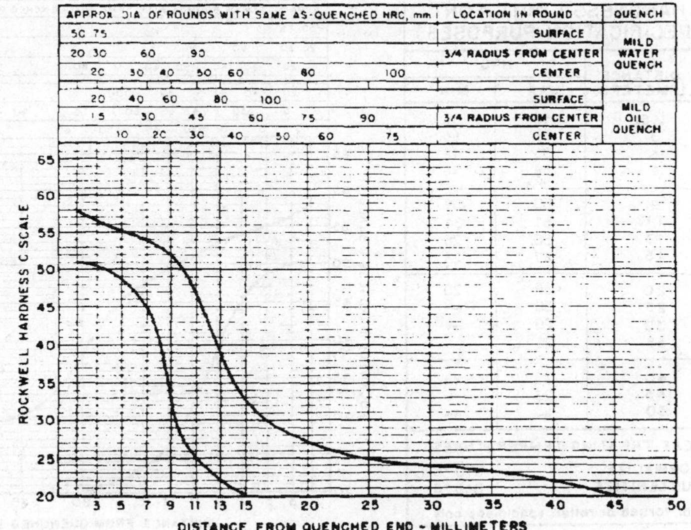

FIGURE 12—UNS H15351—HARDENABILITY BAND—SAE 15B35H

HARDNESS LIMITS FOR SPECIFICATION PURPOSES

"J" DISTANCE SIXTEENTHS OF AN INCH	HRC MAX.	HRC MIN.
1	58	50
2	56	50
3	55	49
4	54	48
5	53	43
6	52	37
7	51	33
8	50	26
9	--	--
10	45	22
11	--	--
12	40	21
13	--	--
14	33	20
15	--	--
16	29	--
18	--	--
20	27	--
22	--	--
24	25	--
26	--	--
28	23	--
30	--	--
32	--	--

HEAT TREATING TEMPERATURES

*NORMALIZE	1600 °F
AUSTENITIZE	1550 °F

* For forged or rolled specimens only

UNS H15371 **HARDENABILITY BAND** SAE 15B37H

% C	% Mn	% Si	% Ni	% Cr	% Mo	% B
0.30/0.39	1.00/1.50	0.15/0.35	--	--	--	0.0005/0.003

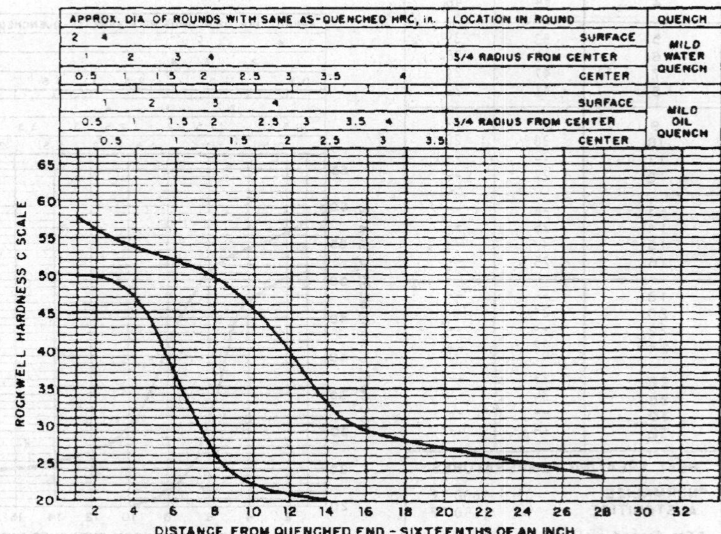

HARDNESS LIMITS FOR SPECIFICATION PURPOSES

"J" DISTANCE MILLIMETERS	HRC MAX.	HRC MIN.
1.5	58	50
3	56	50
5	55	49
7	54	46
9	53	39
11	51	31
13	50	26
15	47	23
20	38	20
25	30	--
30	28	--
35	26	--
40	25	--
45	23	--
50	--	--

HEAT TREATING TEMPERATURES

*NORMALIZE	870 °C
AUSTENITIZE	845 °C

* For forged or rolled specimens only

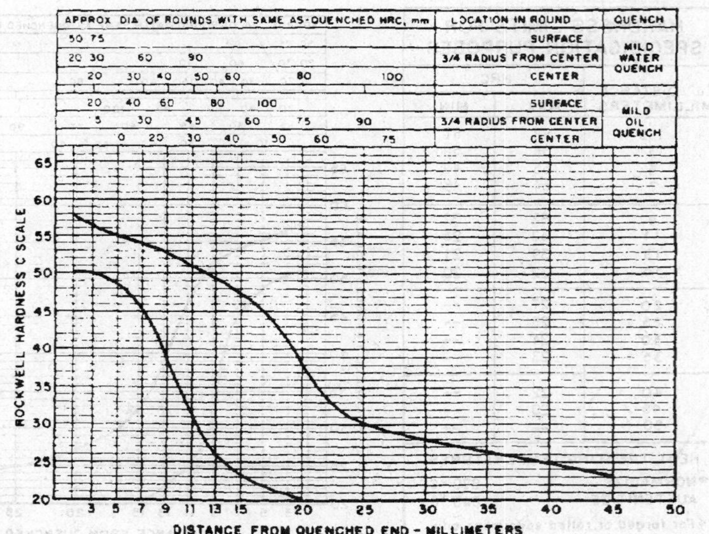

FIGURE 13—UNS H15371—HARDENABILITY BAND—SAE 15B37H

HARDNESS LIMITS FOR SPECIFICATION PURPOSES		
"J" DISTANCE SIXTEENTHS OF AN INCH	HRC	
	MAX.	MIN.
1	60	53
2	59	52
3	59	52
4	58	51
5	58	51
6	57	50
7	57	49
8	56	48
9	55	44
10	55	37
11	54	32
12	53	28
13	52	26
14	51	25
15	50	25
16	49	24
18	46	23
20	42	22
22	39	21
24	36	21
26	34	20
28	33	--
30	31	--
32	31	--

HEAT TREATING TEMPERATURES

*NORMALIZE	1600 °F
AUSTENITIZE	1550 °F

* For forged or rolled specimens only

UNS H15411 **HARDENABILITY BAND** **SAE 15B41H**

%C	%Mn	%Si	%Ni	%Cr	%Mo	%B
0.35/0.45	1.25/1.75	0.15/0.35	--	--	--	0.0005/0.003

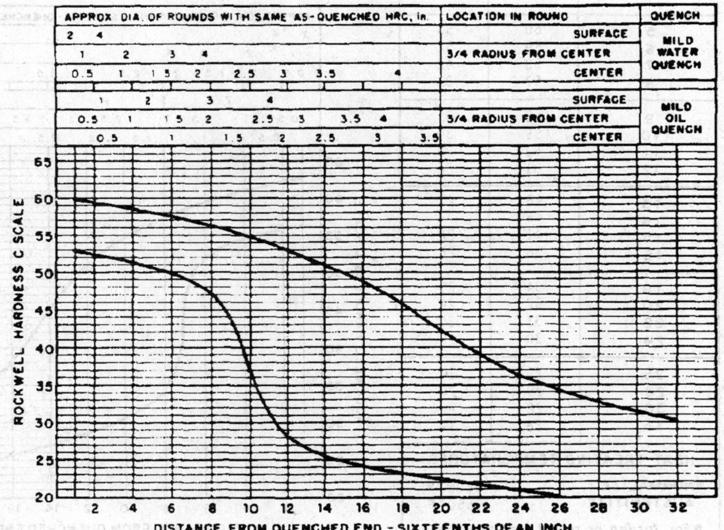

HARDNESS LIMITS FOR SPECIFICATION PURPOSES		
"J" DISTANCE MILLIMETERS	HRC	
	MAX.	MIN.
1.5	60	53
3	60	52
5	59	52
7	58	51
9	58	50
11	57	49
13	56	47
15	55	41
20	53	26
25	50	24
30	45	23
35	39	21
40	35	20
45	32	--
50	31	--

HEAT TREATING TEMPERATURES

*NORMALIZE	870 °C
AUSTENITIZE	845 °C

* For forged or rolled specimens only

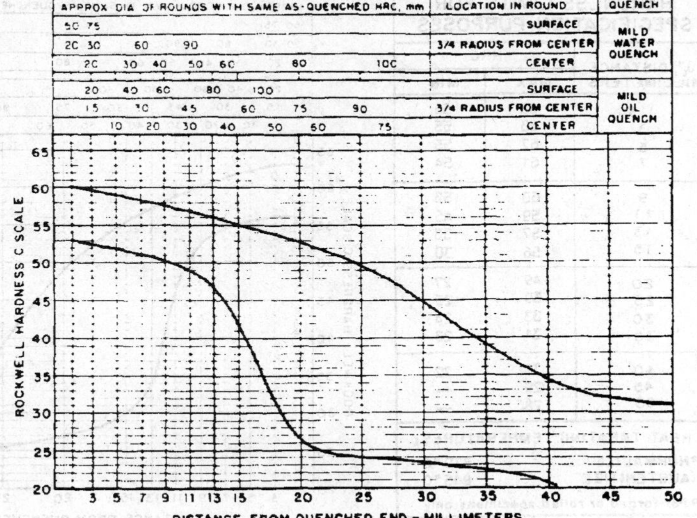

FIGURE 14—UNS H15411—HARDENABILITY BAND—SAE 15B41H

UNS H15481 **HARDENABILITY BAND** SAE 15B48H

%C	%Mn	%Si	%Ni	%Cr	%Mo	%B
0.43/0.53	1.00/1.50	0.15/0.35	--	--	--	0.0005/0.003

HARDNESS LIMITS FOR SPECIFICATION PURPOSES

"J" DISTANCE SIXTEENTHS OF AN INCH	HRC MAX.	HRC MIN.
1	63	56
2	62	56
3	62	55
4	61	54
5	60	53
6	59	52
7	58	42
8	57	34
9	56	31
10	55	30
11	53	29
12	51	28
13	48	27
14	45	27
15	41	26
16	38	26
18	34	25
20	32	24
22	31	23
24	30	22
26	29	21
28	29	20
30	28	--
32	28	--

HEAT TREATING TEMPERATURES

*NORMALIZE	1600°F
AUSTENITIZE	1550°F

*For forged or rolled specimens only

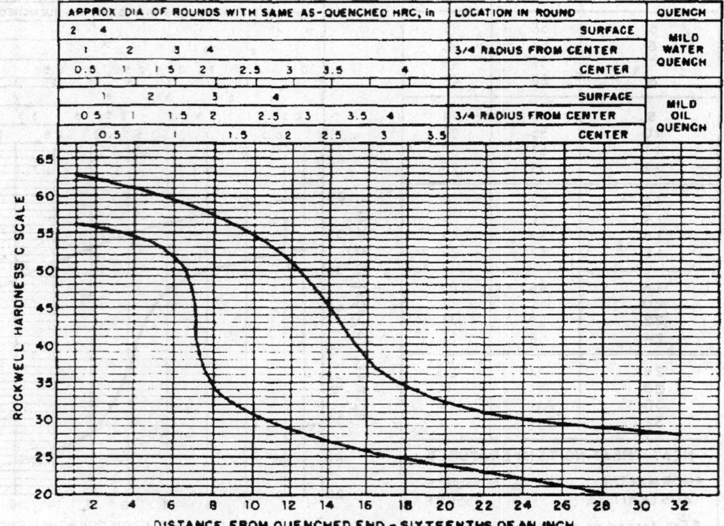

HARDNESS LIMITS FOR SPECIFICATION PURPOSES

"J" DISTANCE MILLIMETERS	HRC MAX.	HRC MIN.
1.5	63	56
3	63	55
5	62	55
7	61	54
9	60	53
11	59	45
13	57	33
15	56	30
20	49	27
25	39	25
30	33	24
35	31	23
40	30	22
45	29	—
50	28	—

HEAT TREATING TEMPERATURES

*NORMALIZE	870°C
AUSTENITIZE	845°C

*For forged or rolled specimens only

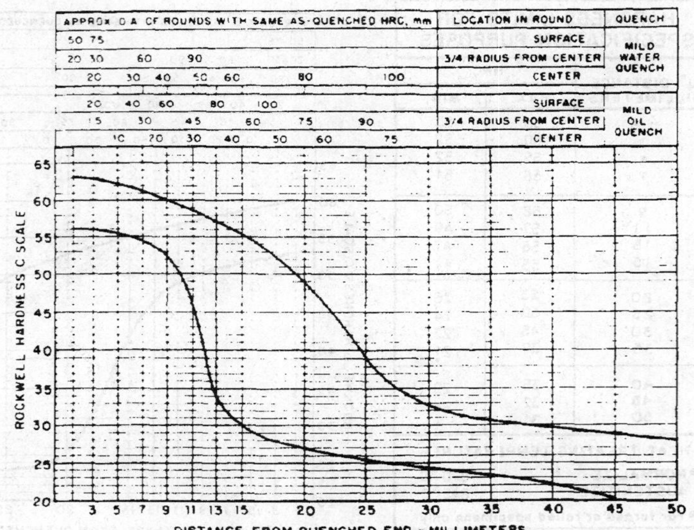

FIGURE 15—UNS H15481—HARDENABILITY BAND—SAE 15B48H

UNS H15621 **HARDENABILITY BAND** **SAE 15B62H**

%C	%Mn	%Si	%Ni	%Cr	%Mo	%B
0.54/0.67	1.00/1.50	0.40/0.60	--	--	--	0.0005/0.003

HARDNESS LIMITS FOR SPECIFICATION PURPOSES

"J" DISTANCE SIXTEENTHS OF AN INCH	HRC MAX.	HRC MIN.
1	--	60
2	--	60
3	--	60
4	--	60
5	65	59
6	65	58
7	64	57
8	64	52
9	64	43
10	63	39
11	63	37
12	63	35
13	62	35
14	62	34
15	61	33
16	60	33
18	58	32
20	54	31
22	48	30
24	43	30
26	40	29
28	37	28
30	35	27
32	34	26

HEAT TREATING TEMPERATURES	
*NORMALIZE	1600 °F
AUSTENITIZE	1550 °F

*For forged or rolled specimens only

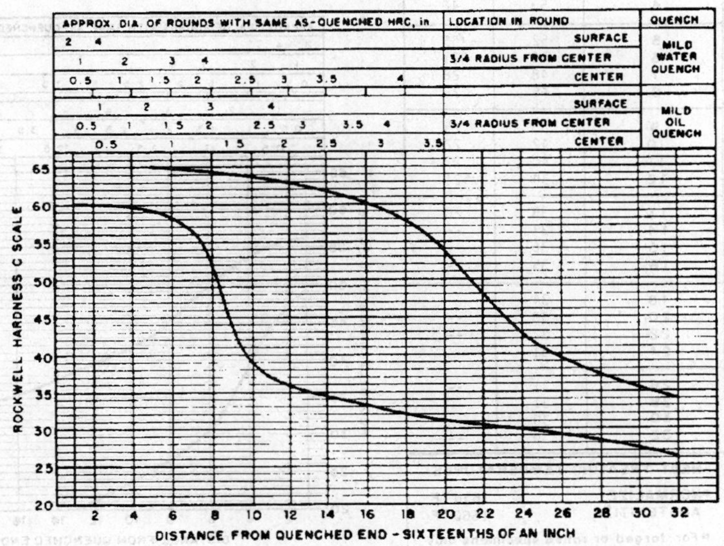

HARDNESS LIMITS FOR SPECIFICATION PURPOSES

"J" DISTANCE MILLIMETERS	HRC MAX.	HRC MIN.
1.5	--	60
3	--	60
5	65	60
7	65	59
9	65	58
11	65	56
13	64	50
15	64	42
20	63	34
25	60	32
30	56	31
35	48	30
40	42	29
45	37	27
50	34	26

HEAT TREATING TEMPERATURES	
*NORMALIZE	870 °C
AUSTENITIZE	845 °C

*For forged or rolled specimens only

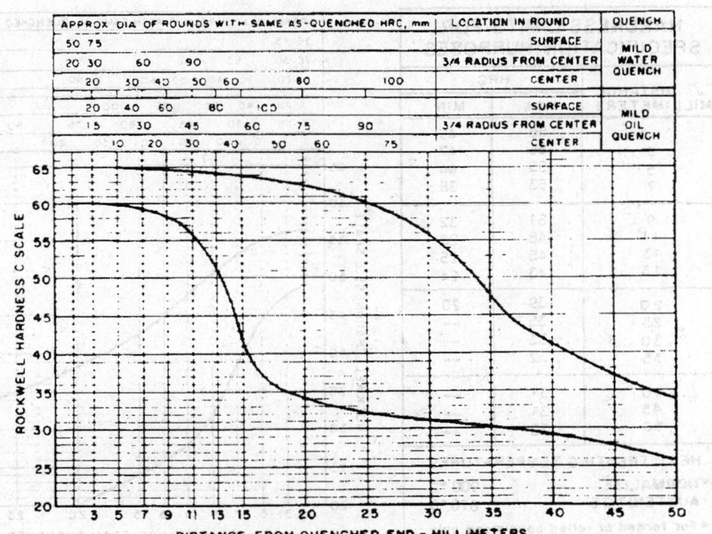

FIGURE 16—UNS H15621—HARDENABILITY BNAD—SAE 15B62H

UNS H13300 **HARDENABILITY BAND** SAE 1330H

%C	%Mn	%Si	%Ni	%Cr	%Mo
0.27/0.33	1.45/2.05	0.15/0.35			

HARDNESS LIMITS FOR SPECIFICATION PURPOSES

"J" DISTANCE SIXTEENTHS OF AN INCH	HRC MAX.	HRC MIN.
1	56	49
2	56	47
3	55	44
4	53	40
5	52	35
6	50	31
7	48	28
8	45	26
9	43	25
10	42	23
11	40	22
12	39	21
13	38	20
14	37	--
15	36	--
16	35	--
18	34	--
20	33	--
22	32	--
24	31	--
26	31	--
28	31	--
30	30	--
32	30	--

HEAT TREATING TEMPERATURES

*NORMALIZE	1650 °F
AUSTENITIZE	1600 °F

*For forged or rolled specimens only

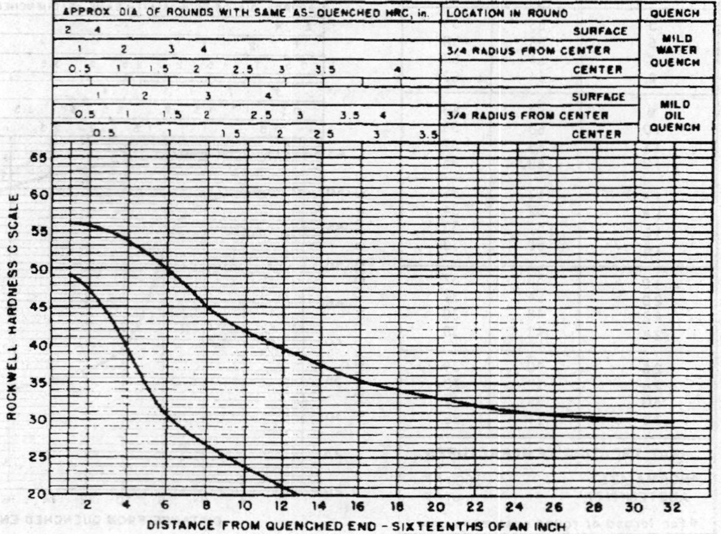

HARDNESS LIMITS FOR SPECIFICATION PURPOSES

"J" DISTANCE MILLIMETERS	HRC MAX.	HRC MIN.
1.5	56	49
3	56	47
5	55	44
7	53	38
9	51	32
11	48	28
13	45	25
15	43	24
20	39	20
25	35	--
30	33	--
35	32	--
40	31	--
45	31	--
50	30	--

HEAT TREATING TEMPERATURES

*NORMALIZE	900 °C
AUSTENITIZE	870 °C

*For forged or rolled specimens only

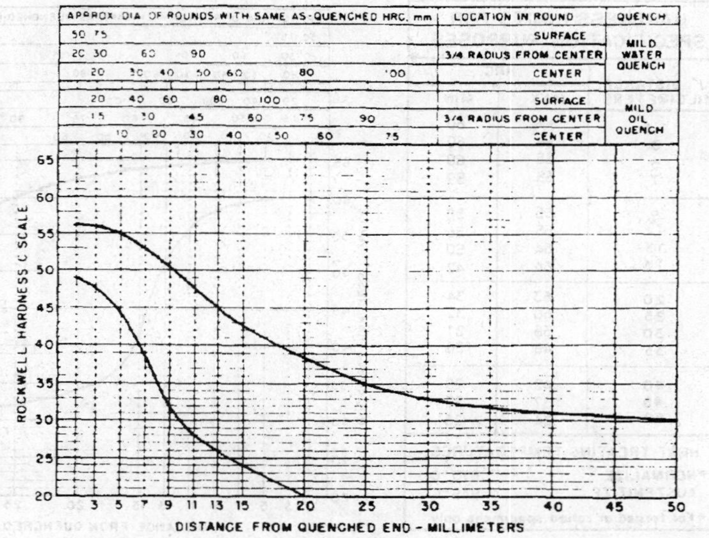

FIGURE 17—UNS H13300—HARDENABILITY BAND—SAE 1330H

UNS H13350 **HARDENABILITY BAND** SAE 1335H

%C	%Mn	%Si	%Ni	%Cr	%Mo
0.32/0.38	1.45/2.05	0.15/0.35			

HARDNESS LIMITS FOR SPECIFICATION PURPOSES

"J" DISTANCE SIXTEENTHS OF AN INCH	HRC MAX.	HRC MIN.
1	58	51
2	57	49
3	56	47
4	55	44
5	54	38
6	52	34
7	50	31
8	48	29
9	46	27
10	44	26
11	42	25
12	41	24
13	40	23
14	39	22
15	38	22
16	37	21
18	35	20
20	34	--
22	33	--
24	32	--
26	31	--
28	31	--
30	30	--
32	30	--

HEAT TREATING TEMPERATURES

*NORMALIZE	1600°F
AUSTENITIZE	1550°F

*For forged or rolled specimens only

APPROX DIA OF ROUNDS WITH SAME AS-QUENCHED HRC, in | LOCATION IN ROUND | QUENCH

2 4 — SURFACE — MILD WATER QUENCH

1 2 3 4 — 3/4 RADIUS FROM CENTER

0.5 1 1.5 2 2.5 3 3.5 4 — CENTER

1 2 3 4 — SURFACE — MILD OIL QUENCH

0.5 1 1.5 2 2.5 3 3.5 4 — 3/4 RADIUS FROM CENTER

0.5 1 1.5 2 2.5 3 3.5 — CENTER

ROCKWELL HARDNESS C SCALE (20–65)

DISTANCE FROM QUENCHED END – SIXTEENTHS OF AN INCH (2–32)

HARDNESS LIMITS FOR SPECIFICATION PURPOSES

"J" DISTANCE MILLIMETERS	HRC MAX.	HRC MIN.
1.5	58	51
3	58	49
5	57	46
7	55	42
9	53	36
11	50	31
13	47	28
15	45	27
20	41	23
25	37	21
30	35	--
35	33	--
40	32	--
45	31	--
50	30	--

HEAT TREATING TEMPERATURES

*NORMALIZE	870°C
AUSTENITIZE	845°C

*For forged or rolled specimens only

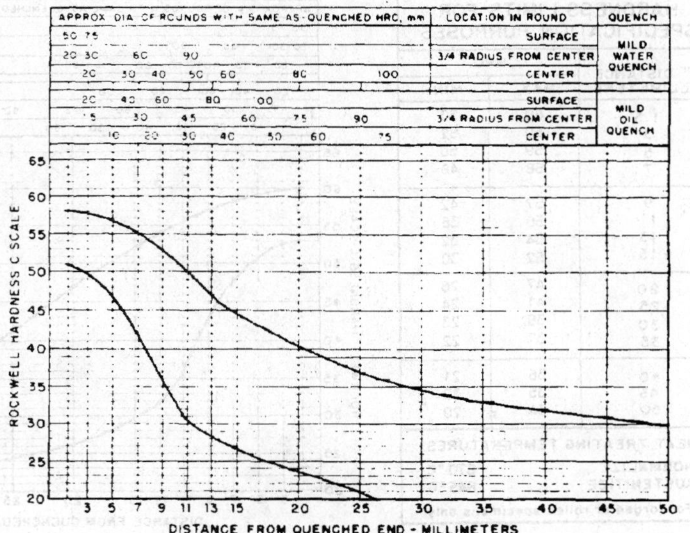

FIGURE 18—UNS H13350—HARDENABILITY BAND—SAE 1335H

UNS H13400 **HARDENABILITY BAND** SAE 1340H

%C	%Mn	%Si	%Ni	%Cr	%Mo
0.37/0.44	1.45/2.05	0.15/0.35			

HARDNESS LIMITS FOR SPECIFICATION PURPOSES

"J" DISTANCE SIXTEENTHS OF AN INCH	HRC MAX.	HRC MIN.
1	60	53
2	60	52
3	59	51
4	58	49
5	57	46
6	56	40
7	55	35
8	54	33
9	52	31
10	51	29
11	50	28
12	48	27
13	46	26
14	44	25
15	42	25
16	41	24
18	39	23
20	38	23
22	37	22
24	36	22
26	35	21
28	35	21
30	34	20
32	34	20

HEAT TREATING TEMPERATURES

*NORMALIZE	1600 °F
AUSTENITIZE	1550 °F

*For forged or rolled specimens only

APPROX. DIA. OF ROUNDS WITH SAME AS-QUENCHED HRC, in.	LOCATION IN ROUND	QUENCH
2 4	SURFACE	MILD WATER QUENCH
1 2 3 4	3/4 RADIUS FROM CENTER	
0.5 1 1.5 2 2.5 3 3.5 4	CENTER	
1 2 3 4	SURFACE	MILD OIL QUENCH
0.5 1 1.5 2 2.5 3 3.5 4	3/4 RADIUS FROM CENTER	
0.5 1 1.5 2 2.5 3 3.5	CENTER	

ROCKWELL HARDNESS C SCALE

DISTANCE FROM QUENCHED END – SIXTEENTHS OF AN INCH

HARDNESS LIMITS FOR SPECIFICATION PURPOSES

"J" DISTANCE MILLIMETERS	HRC MAX.	HRC MIN.
1.5	60	53
3	60	52
5	59	50
7	58	48
9	57	42
11	56	36
13	54	32
15	52	30
20	47	26
25	41	24
30	39	23
35	37	22
40	36	21
45	35	20
50	34	20

HEAT TREATING TEMPERATURES

*NORMALIZE	870 °C
AUSTENITIZE	845 °C

*For forged or rolled specimens only

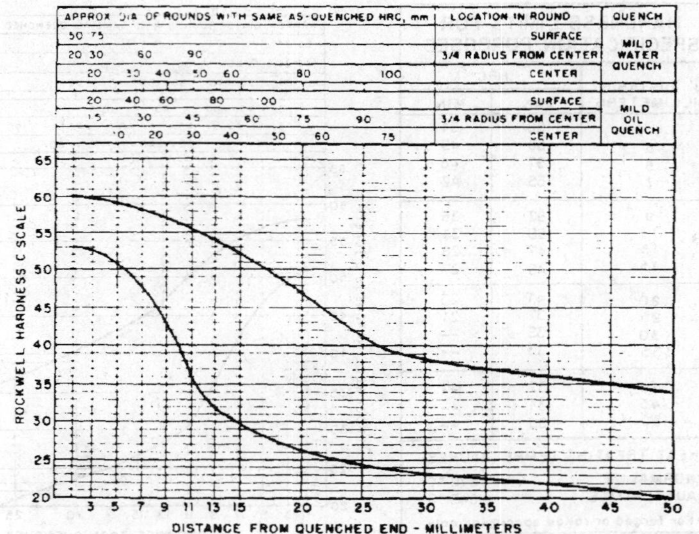

FIGURE 19—UNS H13400—HARDENABILITY BAND—SAE 1340H

HARDENABILITY BAND

UNS H13450 — SAE 1345H

%C	%Mn	%Si	%Ni	%Cr	%Mo
0.42/0.49	1.45/2.05	0.15/0.35			

HARDNESS LIMITS FOR SPECIFICATION PURPOSES

"J" DISTANCE SIXTEENTHS OF AN INCH	HRC MAX.	HRC MIN.
1	63	56
2	63	56
3	62	55
4	61	54
5	61	51
6	60	44
7	60	38
8	59	35
9	58	33
10	57	32
11	56	31
12	55	30
13	54	29
14	53	29
15	52	28
16	51	28
18	49	27
20	48	27
22	47	26
24	46	26
26	45	25
28	45	25
30	45	24
32	45	24

HEAT TREATING TEMPERATURES

*NORMALIZE	1600°F
AUSTENITIZE	1550°F

*For forged or rolled specimens only

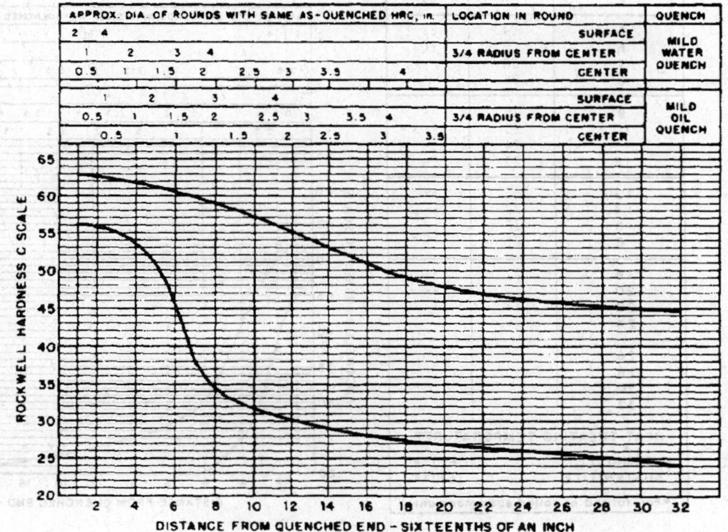

HARDNESS LIMITS FOR SPECIFICATION PURPOSES

"J" DISTANCE MILLIMETERS	HRC MAX.	HRC MIN.
1.5	63	56
3	63	56
5	63	54
7	62	52
9	61	46
11	60	38
13	59	35
15	58	31
20	55	29
25	51	27
30	48	26
35	47	25
40	46	24
45	45	24
50	45	24

HEAT TREATING TEMPERATURES

*NORMALIZE	870°C
AUSTENITIZE	845°C

*For forged or rolled specimens only

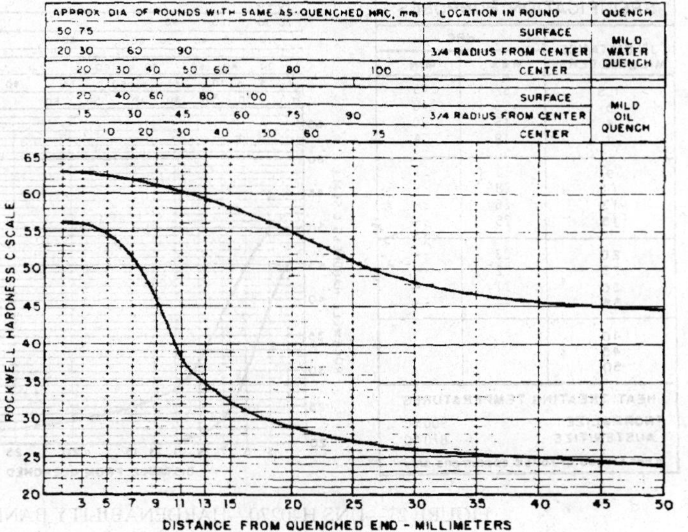

FIGURE 20—UNS H13450—HARDENABILITY BAND—SAE 1345H

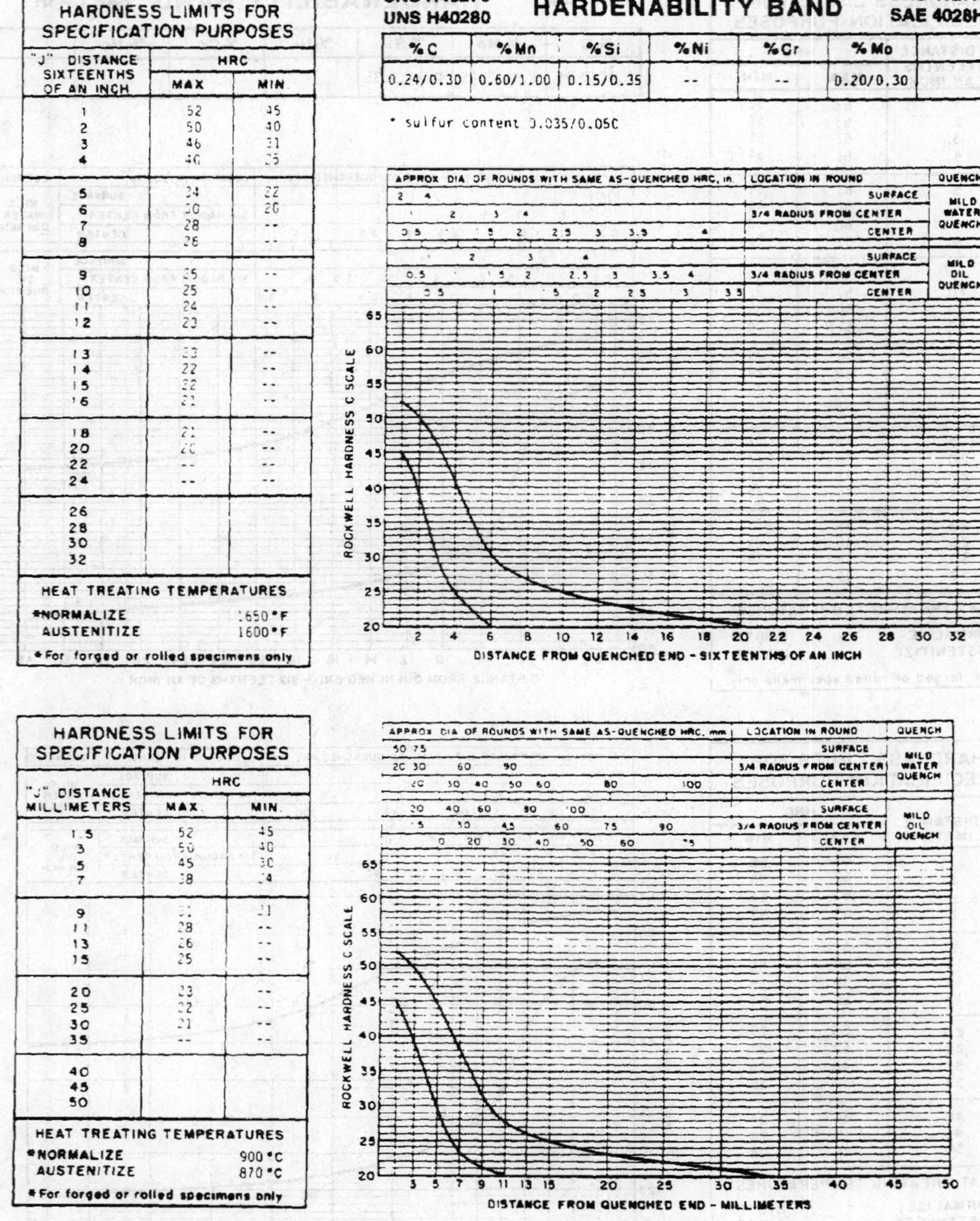

UNS H40270
UNS H40280

HARDENABILITY BAND

SAE 4027H
SAE 4028H

%C	%Mn	%Si	%Ni	%Cr	%Mo
0.24/0.30	0.60/1.00	0.15/0.35	--	--	0.20/0.30

* sulfur content 0.035/0.050

HARDNESS LIMITS FOR SPECIFICATION PURPOSES

"J" DISTANCE SIXTEENTHS OF AN INCH	HRC MAX	HRC MIN
1	52	45
2	50	40
3	46	31
4	40	25
5	34	22
6	30	20
7	28	--
8	26	--
9	25	--
10	25	--
11	24	--
12	23	--
13	23	--
14	22	--
15	22	--
16	21	--
18	21	--
20	20	--
22	--	--
24	--	--
26		
28		
30		
32		

HEAT TREATING TEMPERATURES
*NORMALIZE 1650°F
AUSTENITIZE 1600°F
* For forged or rolled specimens only

HARDNESS LIMITS FOR SPECIFICATION PURPOSES

"J" DISTANCE MILLIMETERS	HRC MAX.	HRC MIN.
1.5	52	45
3	50	40
5	45	30
7	38	24
9	31	21
11	28	--
13	26	--
15	25	--
20	23	--
25	22	--
30	21	--
35	--	--
40		
45		
50		

HEAT TREATING TEMPERATURES
*NORMALIZE 900°C
AUSTENITIZE 870°C
* For forged or rolled specimens only

FIGURE 21—UNS H40270—HARDENABILITY BAND—SAE 4027H
UNS H40280—HARDENABILITY BAND—SAE 4028H*

UNS H40320 — **HARDENABILITY BAND** — **SAE 4032H**

%C	%Mn	%Si	%Ni	%Cr	%Mo
0.29/0.35	0.60/1.00	0.15/0.35	--	--	0.20/0.30

HARDNESS LIMITS FOR SPECIFICATION PURPOSES

"J" DISTANCE SIXTEENTHS OF AN INCH	HRC MAX.	HRC MIN.
1	57	50
2	54	45
3	51	36
4	46	29
5	39	25
6	34	23
7	31	22
8	29	21
9	28	20
10	26	--
11	26	--
12	25	--
13	24	--
14	24	--
15	23	--
16	23	--
18	23	--
20	22	--
22	22	--
24	21	--
26	21	--
28	20	--
30	--	--
32	--	--

HEAT TREATING TEMPERATURES

*NORMALIZE	1650°F
AUSTENITIZE	1600°F

*For forged or rolled specimens only

APPROX DIA OF ROUNDS WITH SAME AS-QUENCHED HRC, in. / LOCATION IN ROUND / QUENCH

Approx dia, in.	Location in round	Quench
2 4	SURFACE	MILD WATER QUENCH
1 2 3 4	3/4 RADIUS FROM CENTER	MILD WATER QUENCH
0.5 1 1.5 2 2.5 3 3.5 4	CENTER	MILD WATER QUENCH
1 2 3 4	SURFACE	MILD OIL QUENCH
0.5 1 1.5 2 2.5 3 3.5 4	3/4 RADIUS FROM CENTER	MILD OIL QUENCH
0.5 1 1.5 2 2.5 3 3.5	CENTER	MILD OIL QUENCH

ROCKWELL HARDNESS C SCALE: 20, 25, 30, 35, 40, 45, 50, 55, 60, 65

DISTANCE FROM QUENCHED END – SIXTEENTHS OF AN INCH: 2, 4, 6, 8, 10, 12, 14, 16, 18, 20, 22, 24, 26, 28, 30, 32

HARDNESS LIMITS FOR SPECIFICATION PURPOSES

"J" DISTANCE MILLIMETERS	HRC MAX.	HRC MIN.
1.5	57	50
3	55	46
5	51	34
7	44	27
9	36	24
11	32	22
13	29	20
15	27	--
20	24	--
25	23	--
30	23	--
35	22	--
40	21	--
45	20	--
50	--	--

HEAT TREATING TEMPERATURES

*NORMALIZE	900°C
AUSTENITIZE	870°C

*For forged or rolled specimens only

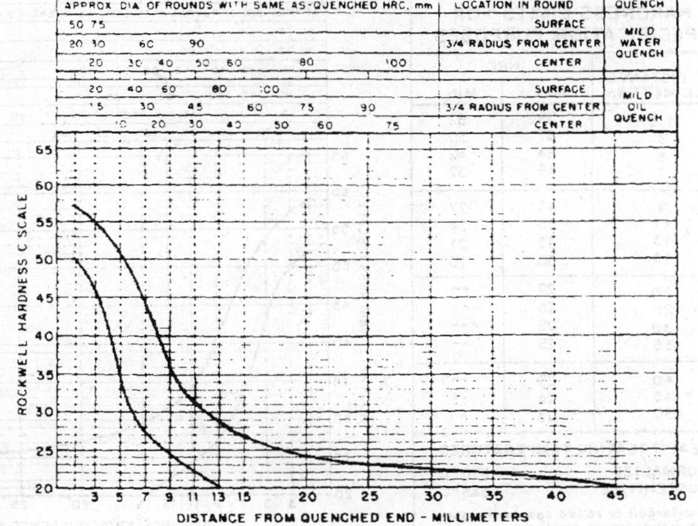

FIGURE 22—UNS H40320—HARDENABILITY BAND—SAE 4032H

UNS H40370 **HARDENABILITY BAND** SAE 4037H

%C	%Mn	%Si	%Ni	%Cr	%Mo
0.34/0.41	0.60/1.00	0.15/0.35	--	--	0.20/0.30

HARDNESS LIMITS FOR SPECIFICATION PURPOSES

"J" DISTANCE SIXTEENTHS OF AN INCH	HRC MAX.	HRC MIN.
1	59	52
2	57	49
3	54	42
4	51	35
5	45	30
6	38	26
7	34	23
8	32	22
9	30	21
10	29	20
11	28	--
12	27	--
13	26	--
14	26	--
15	26	--
16	25	--
18	25	--
20	25	--
22	25	--
24	24	--
26	24	--
28	24	--
30	23	--
32	23	--

HEAT TREATING TEMPERATURES

*NORMALIZE 1600°F
AUSTENITIZE 1550°F

*For forged or rolled specimens only

APPROX. DIA. OF ROUNDS WITH SAME AS-QUENCHED HRC, in. — LOCATION IN ROUND — QUENCH

ROCKWELL HARDNESS C SCALE

DISTANCE FROM QUENCHED END - SIXTEENTHS OF AN INCH

HARDNESS LIMITS FOR SPECIFICATION PURPOSES

"J" DISTANCE MILLIMETERS	HRC MAX.	HRC MIN.
1.5	59	52
3	57	50
5	54	42
7	49	32
9	41	27
11	35	24
13	32	21
15	30	20
20	27	--
25	26	--
30	25	--
35	25	--
40	25	--
45	24	--
50	23	--

HEAT TREATING TEMPERATURES

*NORMALIZE 870°C
AUSTENITIZE 845°C

*For forged or rolled specimens only

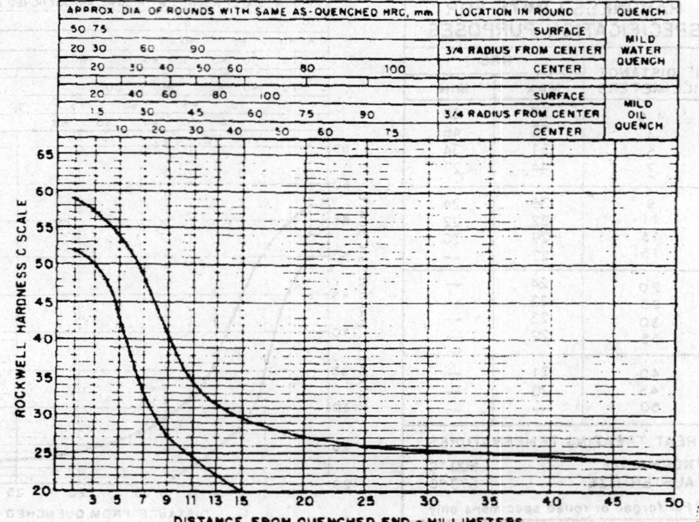

FIGURE 23—UNS H40370—HARDENABILITY BAND—SAE 4037H

UNS H40420 **HARDENABILITY BAND** **SAE 4042H**

%C	%Mn	%Si	%Ni	%Cr	%Mo
0.39/0.46	0.60/1.00	0.15/0.35	--	--	0.20/0.30

HARDNESS LIMITS FOR SPECIFICATION PURPOSES

"J" DISTANCE SIXTEENTHS OF AN INCH	HRC MAX.	HRC MIN.
1	62	55
2	60	52
3	58	48
4	55	40
5	50	33
6	45	29
7	39	27
8	36	26
9	34	25
10	33	24
11	32	24
12	31	23
13	30	23
14	30	23
15	29	22
16	29	22
18	28	22
20	28	21
22	28	20
24	27	20
26	27	--
28	27	--
30	26	--
32	26	--

HEAT TREATING TEMPERATURES	
*NORMALIZE	1600 °F
AUSTENITIZE	1550 °F

*For forged or rolled specimens only

APPROX. DIA. OF ROUNDS WITH SAME AS-QUENCHED HRC, in.	LOCATION IN ROUND	QUENCH
2 4	SURFACE	MILD WATER QUENCH
1 2 3 4	3/4 RADIUS FROM CENTER	
0.5 1 1.5 2 2.5 3 3.5 4	CENTER	
1 2 3 4	SURFACE	MILD OIL QUENCH
0.5 1 1.5 2 2.5 3 3.5 4	3/4 RADIUS FROM CENTER	
0.5 1 1.5 2 2.5 3 3.5	CENTER	

ROCKWELL HARDNESS C SCALE: 20 25 30 35 40 45 50 55 60 65

DISTANCE FROM QUENCHED END - SIXTEENTHS OF AN INCH: 2 4 6 8 10 12 14 16 18 20 22 24 26 28 30 32

HARDNESS LIMITS FOR SPECIFICATION PURPOSES

"J" DISTANCE MILLIMETERS	HRC MAX.	HRC MIN.
1.5	62	55
3	61	53
5	58	47
7	54	36
9	48	30
11	40	27
13	36	25
15	33	24
20	31	23
25	29	22
30	28	21
35	28	20
40	27	--
45	27	--
50	26	--

HEAT TREATING TEMPERATURES	
*NORMALIZE	870 °C
AUSTENITIZE	845 °C

*For forged or rolled specimens only

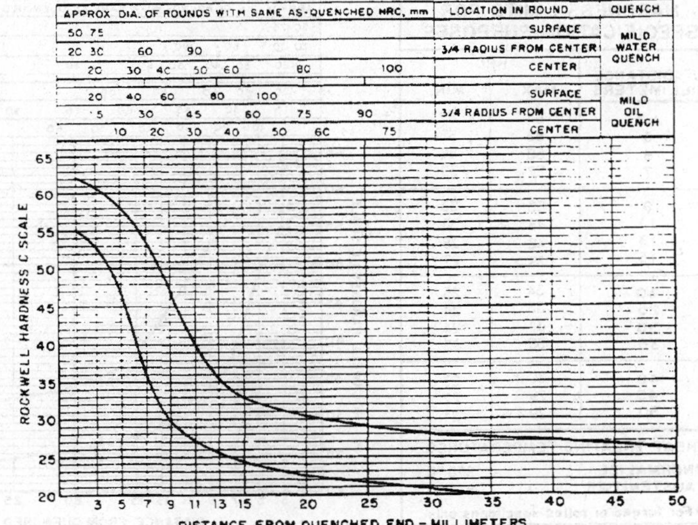

FIGURE 24—UNS H40420—HARDENABILITY BAND—SAE 4042H

UNS H40470 **HARDENABILITY BAND** SAE 4047H

%C	%Mn	%Si	%Ni	%Cr	%Mo
0.44/0.51	0.60/1.00	0.15/0.35	--	--	0.20/0.30

HARDNESS LIMITS FOR SPECIFICATION PURPOSES

"J" DISTANCE SIXTEENTHS OF AN INCH	HRC MAX.	HRC MIN.
1	64	57
2	62	55
3	60	50
4	58	42
5	55	35
6	52	32
7	47	30
8	43	28
9	40	28
10	38	27
11	37	26
12	35	26
13	34	25
14	33	25
15	33	25
16	32	25
18	31	24
20	30	24
22	30	23
24	30	23
26	30	22
28	29	22
30	29	21
32	29	21

HEAT TREATING TEMPERATURES

*NORMALIZE	1600 °F
AUSTENITIZE	1550 °F

*For forged or rolled specimens only

APPROX. DIA. OF ROUNDS WITH SAME AS-QUENCHED HRC, in. | LOCATION IN ROUND | QUENCH

MILD WATER QUENCH: SURFACE 2 4; 3/4 RADIUS FROM CENTER 1 2 3 4; CENTER 0.5 1 1.5 2 2.5 3 3.5 4

MILD OIL QUENCH: SURFACE 1 2 3 4; 3/4 RADIUS FROM CENTER 0.5 1 1.5 2 2.5 3 3.5 4; CENTER 0.5 1 1.5 2 2.5 3 3.5

ROCKWELL HARDNESS C SCALE (20–65)

DISTANCE FROM QUENCHED END - SIXTEENTHS OF AN INCH (2–32)

HARDNESS LIMITS FOR SPECIFICATION PURPOSES

"J" DISTANCE MILLIMETERS	HRC MAX.	HRC MIN.
1.5	64	57
3	63	55
5	60	49
7	57	39
9	53	33
11	48	30
13	43	28
15	39	27
20	34	25
25	33	24
30	31	24
35	30	23
40	30	23
45	29	22
50	29	21

HEAT TREATING TEMPERATURES

*NORMALIZE	870 °C
AUSTENITIZE	845 °C

*For forged or rolled specimens only

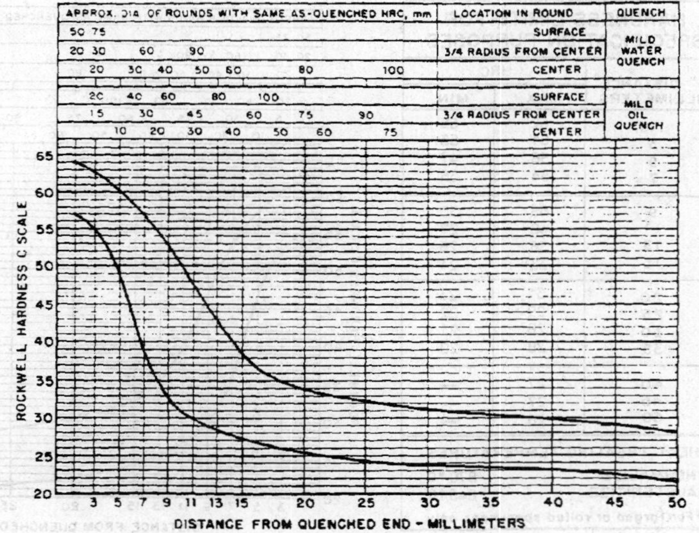

FIGURE 25—UNS H40470—HARDENABILITY BAND—SAE 4047H

UNS H41180 **HARDENABILITY BAND** **SAE 4118H**

%C	%Mn	%Si	%Ni	%Cr	%Mo
0.17/0.23	0.60/1.00	0.15/0.35	--	0.30/0.70	0.08/0.15

HARDNESS LIMITS FOR SPECIFICATION PURPOSES

"J" DISTANCE SIXTEENTHS OF AN INCH	HRC MAX.	HRC MIN.
1	48	41
2	46	36
3	41	27
4	35	23
5	31	20
6	28	--
7	27	--
8	26	--
9	24	--
10	23	--
11	22	--
12	21	--
13	21	--
14	20	--
15	--	--
16	--	--
18		
20		
22		
24		
26		
28		
30		
32		

HEAT TREATING TEMPERATURES

*NORMALIZE	1700°F
AUSTENITIZE	1700°F

*For forged or rolled specimens only

APPROX. DIA. OF ROUNDS WITH SAME AS-QUENCHED HRC, in. | LOCATION IN ROUND | QUENCH

2 4 — SURFACE — MILD WATER QUENCH
1 2 3 4 — 3/4 RADIUS FROM CENTER
0.5 1 1.5 2 2.5 3 3.5 4 — CENTER
1 2 3 4 — SURFACE — MILD OIL QUENCH
0.5 1 1.5 2 2.5 3 3.5 4 — 3/4 RADIUS FROM CENTER
0.5 1 1.5 2 2.5 3 3.5 — CENTER

ROCKWELL HARDNESS C SCALE: 20 25 30 35 40 45 50 55 60 65

DISTANCE FROM QUENCHED END - SIXTEENTHS OF AN INCH: 2 4 6 8 10 12 14 16 18 20 22 24 26 28 30 32

HARDNESS LIMITS FOR SPECIFICATION PURPOSES

"J" DISTANCE MILLIMETERS	HRC MAX.	HRC MIN.
1.5	48	41
3	46	37
5	40	27
7	34	22
9	29	--
11	27	--
13	25	--
15	24	--
20	21	--
25	--	--
30		
35		
40		
45		
50		

HEAT TREATING TEMPERATURES

*NORMALIZE	925°C
AUSTENITIZE	925°C

*For forged or rolled specimens only

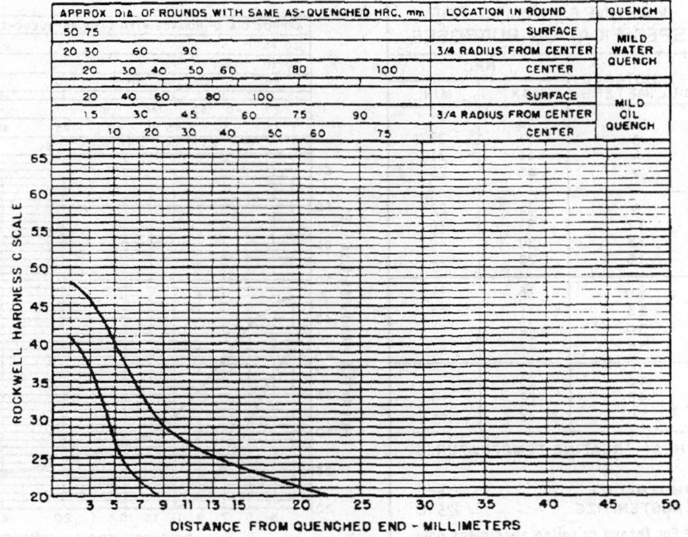

FIGURE 26—UNS H41180—HARDENABILITY BAND—SAE 4118H

UNS H41200 **HARDENABILITY BAND** **SAE 4120H**

%C	%Mn	%Si	%Ni	%Cr	%Mo
0.18/0.23	0.90/1.20	0.15/0.35	--	0.40/0.60	0.13/0.20

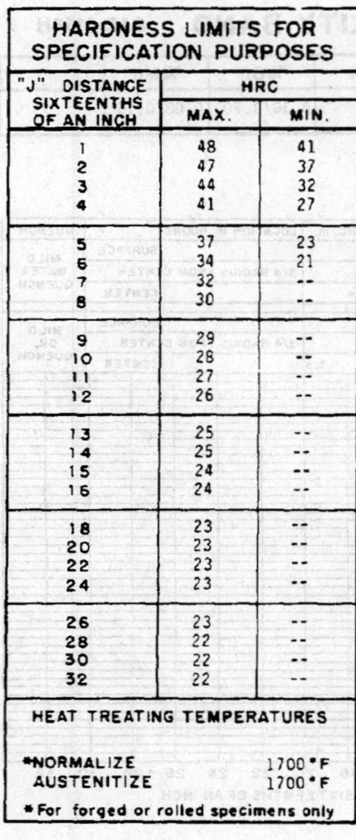

HARDNESS LIMITS FOR SPECIFICATION PURPOSES

"J" DISTANCE SIXTEENTHS OF AN INCH	HRC MAX.	HRC MIN.
1	48	41
2	47	37
3	44	32
4	41	27
5	37	23
6	34	21
7	32	--
8	30	--
9	29	--
10	28	--
11	27	--
12	26	--
13	25	--
14	25	--
15	24	--
16	24	--
18	23	--
20	23	--
22	23	--
24	23	--
26	23	--
28	22	--
30	22	--
32	22	--

HEAT TREATING TEMPERATURES

*NORMALIZE	1700 °F
AUSTENITIZE	1700 °F

* For forged or rolled specimens only

APPROX. DIA. OF ROUNDS WITH SAME AS-QUENCHED HRC, in. — LOCATION IN ROUND — QUENCH

MILD WATER QUENCH: SURFACE; 3/4 RADIUS FROM CENTER; CENTER

MILD OIL QUENCH: SURFACE; 3/4 RADIUS FROM CENTER; CENTER

ROCKWELL HARDNESS C SCALE

DISTANCE FROM QUENCHED END - SIXTEENTHS OF AN INCH

HARDNESS LIMITS FOR SPECIFICATION PURPOSES

"J" DISTANCE MILLIMETERS	HRC MAX.	HRC MIN.
1.5	48	41
3	47	37
5	44	31
7	40	25
9	35	22
11	33	20
13	30	--
15	29	--
20	26	--
25	24	--
30	23	--
35	23	--
40	23	--
45	22	--
50	22	--

HEAT TREATING TEMPERATURES

*NORMALIZE	925 °C
AUSTENITIZE	925 °C

* For forged or rolled specimens only

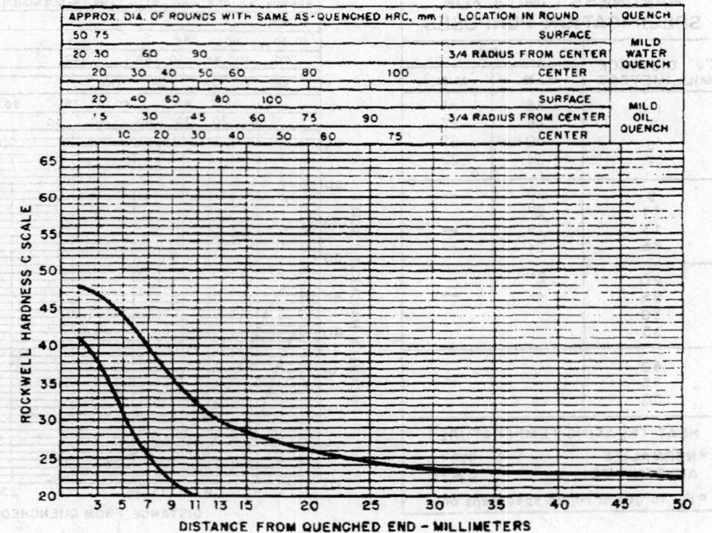

FIGURE 27—UNS H41200—HARDENABILITY BAND—SAE 4120H

UNS H41300 **HARDENABILITY BAND** SAE 4130H

%C	%Mn	%Si	%Ni	%Cr	%Mo
0.27/0.33	0.30/0.70	0.15/0.35	--	0.75/1.20	0.15/0.25

HARDNESS LIMITS FOR SPECIFICATION PURPOSES

"J" DISTANCE SIXTEENTHS OF AN INCH	HRC MAX.	HRC MIN.
1	56	49
2	55	46
3	53	42
4	51	38
5	49	34
6	47	31
7	44	29
8	42	27
9	40	26
10	38	26
11	36	25
12	35	25
13	34	24
14	34	24
15	33	23
16	33	23
18	32	22
20	32	21
22	32	20
24	31	--
26	31	--
28	30	--
30	30	--
32	29	--

HEAT TREATING TEMPERATURES

*NORMALIZE	1650°F
AUSTENITIZE	1600°F

*For forged or rolled specimens only

APPROX. DIA. OF ROUNDS WITH SAME AS-QUENCHED HRC, in. — LOCATION IN ROUND — QUENCH

ROCKWELL HARDNESS C SCALE

DISTANCE FROM QUENCHED END - SIXTEENTHS OF AN INCH

HARDNESS LIMITS FOR SPECIFICATION PURPOSES

"J" DISTANCE MILLIMETERS	HRC MAX.	HRC MIN.
1.5	56	49
3	55	46
5	53	40
7	51	36
9	48	32
11	44	28
13	41	26
15	39	25
20	34	24
25	33	23
30	33	22
35	32	20
40	31	--
45	31	--
50	30	--

HEAT TREATING TEMPERATURES

*NORMALIZE	900 °C
AUSTENITIZE	870 °C

*For forged or rolled specimens only

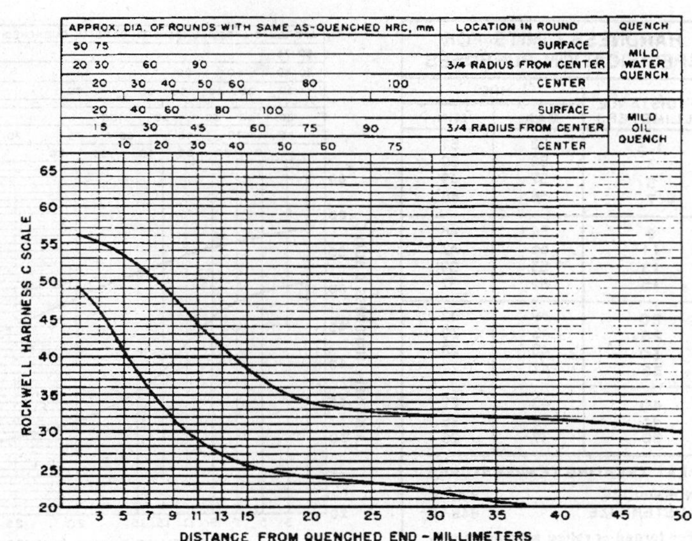

FIGURE 28—UNS H41300—HARDENABILITY BAND—SAE 4130H

UNS H41350 **HARDENABILITY BAND** SAE 4135H

%C	%Mn	%Si	%Ni	%Cr	%Mo
0.32/0.38	0.60/1.00	0.15/0.35	--	0.75/1.20	0.15/0.25

HARDNESS LIMITS FOR SPECIFICATION PURPOSES

"J" DISTANCE SIXTEENTHS OF AN INCH	HRC MAX.	HRC MIN.
1	58	51
2	58	50
3	57	49
4	56	48
5	56	47
6	55	45
7	54	42
8	53	40
9	52	38
10	51	36
11	50	34
12	49	33
13	48	32
14	47	31
15	46	30
16	45	30
18	44	29
20	42	28
22	41	27
24	40	27
26	39	27
28	38	26
30	38	26
32	37	26

HEAT TREATING TEMPERATURES	
*NORMALIZE	1600 °F
AUSTENITIZE	1550 °F

*For forged or rolled specimens only

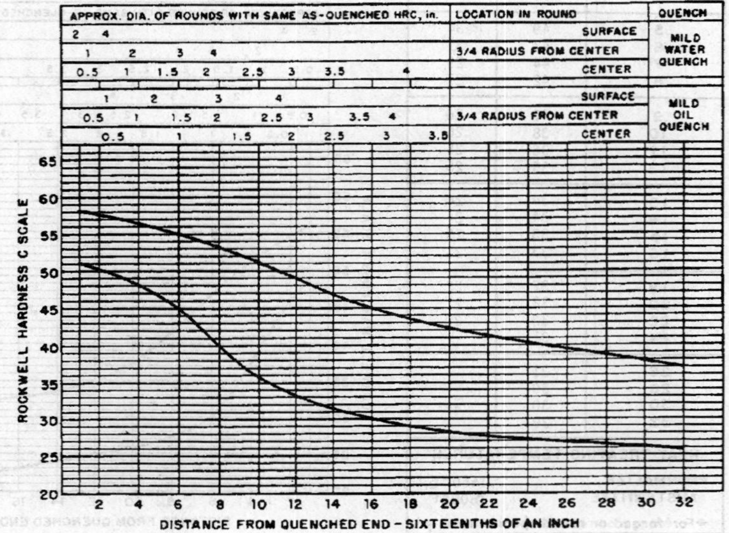

HARDNESS LIMITS FOR SPECIFICATION PURPOSES

"J" DISTANCE MILLIMETERS	HRC MAX.	HRC MIN.
1.5	58	51
3	58	50
5	57	49
7	56	48
9	56	46
11	55	42
13	53	39
15	52	37
20	49	32
25	45	30
30	43	28
35	41	27
40	40	27
45	39	26
50	37	26

HEAT TREATING TEMPERATURES	
*NORMALIZE	870 °C
AUSTENITIZE	845 °C

*For forged or rolled specimens only

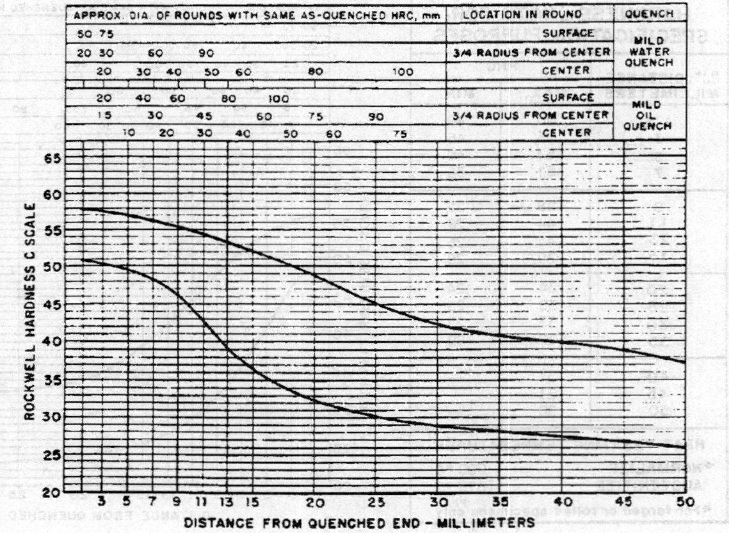

FIGURE 29—UNS H41350—HARDENABILITY BAND—SAE 4135H

UNS H41370 **HARDENABILITY BAND** SAE 4137H

%C	%Mn	%Si	%Ni	%Cr	%Mo
0.34/0.41	0.60/1.00	0.15/0.35	--	0.75/1.20	0.15/0.25

HARDNESS LIMITS FOR SPECIFICATION PURPOSES

"J" DISTANCE SIXTEENTHS OF AN INCH	HRC MAX.	HRC MIN.
1	59	52
2	59	51
3	58	50
4	58	49
5	57	49
6	57	48
7	56	45
8	55	43
9	55	40
10	54	39
11	53	37
12	52	36
13	51	35
14	50	34
15	49	33
16	48	33
18	46	32
20	45	31
22	44	30
24	43	30
26	42	30
28	42	29
30	41	29
32	41	29

HEAT TREATING TEMPERATURES

*NORMALIZE	1600 °F
AUSTENITIZE	1550 °F

*For forged or rolled specimens only

APPROX. DIA. OF ROUNDS WITH SAME AS-QUENCHED HRC, in.	LOCATION IN ROUND	QUENCH
2 4	SURFACE	MILD WATER QUENCH
1 2 3 4	3/4 RADIUS FROM CENTER	
0.5 1 1.5 2 2.5 3 3.5 4	CENTER	
1 2 3 4	SURFACE	MILD OIL QUENCH
0.5 1 1.5 2 2.5 3 3.5 4	3/4 RADIUS FROM CENTER	
0.5 1 1.5 2 2.5 3 3.5	CENTER	

ROCKWELL HARDNESS C SCALE: 20 25 30 35 40 45 50 55 60 65

DISTANCE FROM QUENCHED END - SIXTEENTHS OF AN INCH: 2 4 6 8 10 12 14 16 18 20 22 24 26 28 30 32

HARDNESS LIMITS FOR SPECIFICATION PURPOSES

"J" DISTANCE MILLIMETERS	HRC MAX.	HRC MIN.
1.5	59	52
3	59	51
5	58	50
7	58	49
9	57	48
11	56	45
13	55	42
15	55	39
20	52	35
25	48	33
30	46	31
35	44	30
40	43	29
45	42	29
50	41	29

HEAT TREATING TEMPERATURES

*NORMALIZE	870 °C
AUSTENITIZE	845 °C

*For forged or rolled specimens only

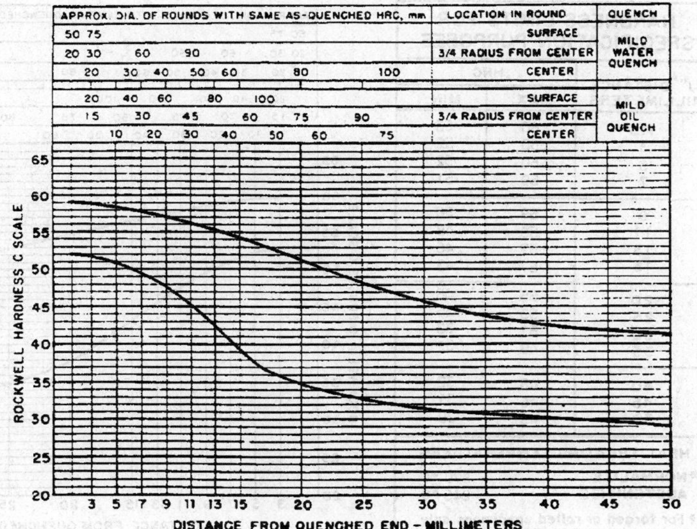

FIGURE 30—UNS 41370—HARDENABILITY BAND—SAE 4137H

UNS H41400 **HARDENABILITY BAND** SAE 4140H

%C	%Mn	%Si	%Ni	%Cr	%Mo
0.37/0.44	0.65/1.10	0.15/0.35	--	0.75/1.20	0.15/0.25

HARDNESS LIMITS FOR SPECIFICATION PURPOSES

"J" DISTANCE SIXTEENTHS OF AN INCH	HRC MAX.	HRC MIN.
1	60	53
2	60	53
3	60	52
4	59	51
5	59	51
6	58	50
7	58	48
8	57	47
9	57	44
10	56	42
11	56	40
12	55	39
13	55	38
14	54	37
15	54	36
16	53	35
18	52	34
20	51	33
22	49	33
24	48	32
26	47	32
28	46	31
30	45	31
32	44	30

HEAT TREATING TEMPERATURES

*NORMALIZE 1600 °F
AUSTENITIZE 1550 °F

*For forged or rolled specimens only

APPROX. DIA. OF ROUNDS WITH SAME AS-QUENCHED HRC, in.	LOCATION IN ROUND	QUENCH
2 4	SURFACE	MILD WATER QUENCH
1 2 3 4	3/4 RADIUS FROM CENTER	
0.5 1 1.5 2 2.5 3 3.5 4	CENTER	
1 2 3 4	SURFACE	MILD OIL QUENCH
0.5 1 1.5 2 2.5 3 3.5 4	3/4 RADIUS FROM CENTER	
0.5 1 1.5 2 2.5 3 3.5	CENTER	

ROCKWELL HARDNESS C SCALE
65 60 55 50 45 40 35 30 25 20
2 4 6 8 10 12 14 16 18 20 22 24 26 28 30 32
DISTANCE FROM QUENCHED END - SIXTEENTHS OF AN INCH

HARDNESS LIMITS FOR SPECIFICATION PURPOSES

"J" DISTANCE MILLIMETERS	HRC MAX.	HRC MIN.
1.5	60	53
3	60	52
5	60	52
7	59	51
9	59	50
11	58	48
13	57	46
15	57	43
20	55	38
25	53	35
30	51	33
35	49	32
40	48	32
45	46	31
50	45	30

HEAT TREATING TEMPERATURES

*NORMALIZE 870 °C
AUSTENITIZE 845 °C

*For forged or rolled specimens only

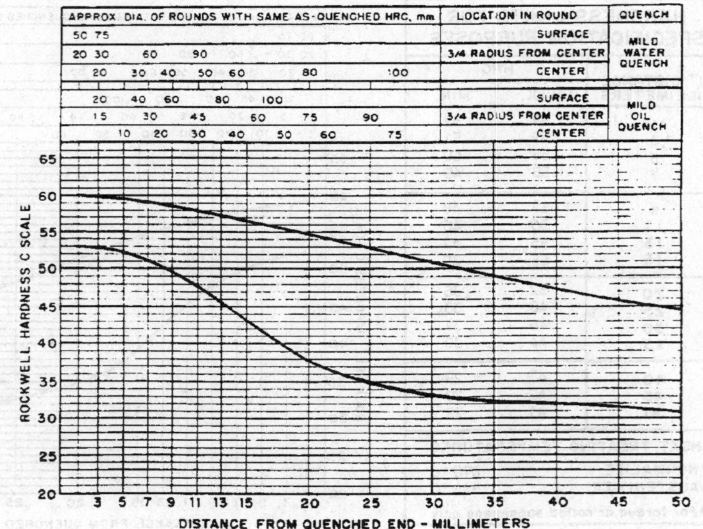

FIGURE 31—UNS H41400—HARDENABILITY BAND—4140H

HARDENABILITY BAND

UNS H41420 — SAE 4142H

%C	%Mn	%Si	%Ni	%Cr	%Mo
0.39/0.46	0.65/1.10	0.15/0.35	--	0.75/1.20	0.15/0.35

HARDNESS LIMITS FOR SPECIFICATION PURPOSES

"J" DISTANCE SIXTEENTHS OF AN INCH	HRC MAX.	HRC MIN.
1	62	55
2	62	55
3	62	54
4	61	53
5	61	53
6	61	52
7	60	51
8	60	50
9	60	49
10	59	47
11	59	46
12	58	44
13	58	42
14	57	41
15	57	40
16	56	39
18	55	37
20	54	36
22	53	35
24	53	34
26	52	34
28	51	34
30	51	33
32	50	33

HEAT TREATING TEMPERATURES	
*NORMALIZE	1600 °F
AUSTENITIZE	1550 °F

*For forged or rolled specimens only

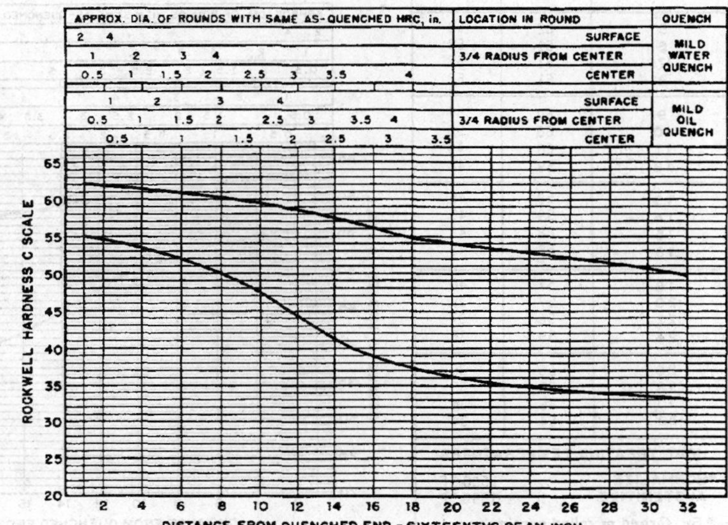

HARDNESS LIMITS FOR SPECIFICATION PURPOSES

"J" DISTANCE MILLIMETERS	HRC MAX.	HRC MIN.
1.5	62	55
3	62	54
5	62	54
7	62	53
9	61	52
11	61	51
13	60	49
15	60	48
20	58	43
25	56	39
30	55	36
35	53	35
40	52	34
45	51	33
50	50	33

HEAT TREATING TEMPERATURES	
*NORMALIZE	870 °C
AUSTENITIZE	845 °C

*For forged or rolled specimens only

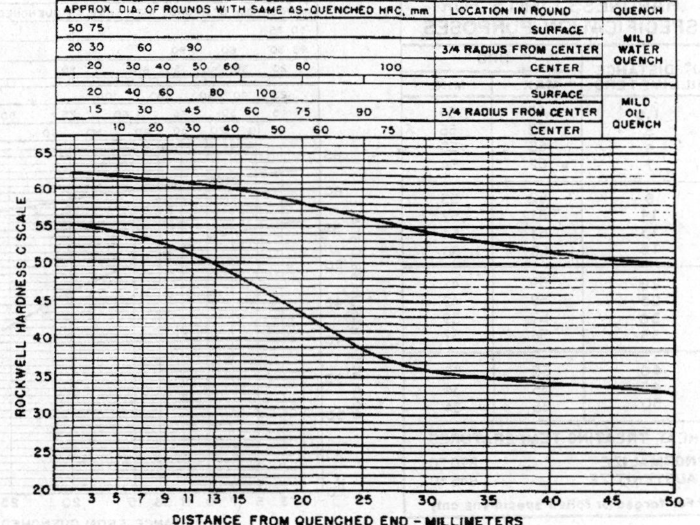

FIGURE 32—UNS H41420—HARDENABILITY BAND—SAE 4142H

UNS H41450 **HARDENABILITY BAND** SAE 4145H

%C	%Mn	%Si	%Ni	%Cr	%Mo
0.42/0.49	0.65/1.10	0.15/0.35	--	0.75/1.20	0.15/0.25

HARDNESS LIMITS FOR SPECIFICATION PURPOSES

"J" DISTANCE SIXTEENTHS OF AN INCH	HRC MAX.	HRC MIN.
1	63	56
2	63	55
3	62	55
4	62	54
5	62	53
6	61	53
7	61	52
8	61	52
9	60	51
10	60	50
11	60	49
12	59	48
13	59	46
14	59	45
15	58	43
16	58	42
18	57	40
20	57	38
22	56	37
24	55	36
26	55	35
28	55	35
30	55	34
32	54	34

HEAT TREATING TEMPERATURES

*NORMALIZE	1600 °F
AUSTENITIZE	1550 °F

*For forged or rolled specimens only

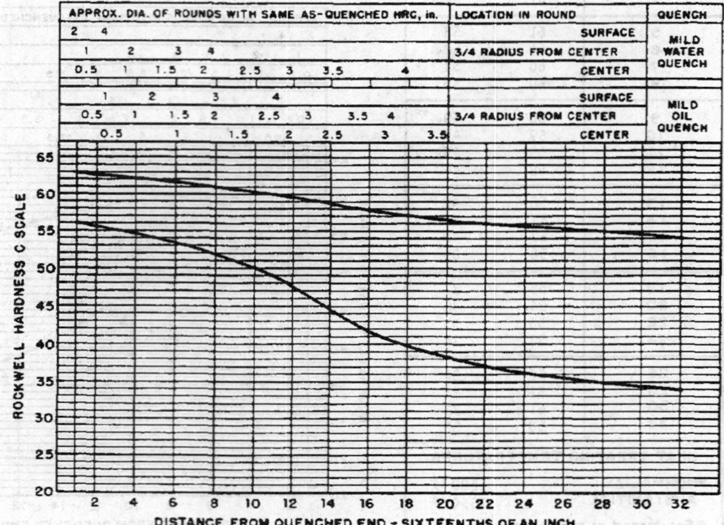

HARDNESS LIMITS FOR SPECIFICATION PURPOSES

"J" DISTANCE MILLIMETERS	HRC MAX.	HRC MIN.
1.5	63	56
3	63	55
5	63	55
7	62	54
9	62	53
11	61	52
13	61	51
15	60	50
20	59	47
25	58	42
30	57	39
35	56	37
40	55	35
45	55	34
50	55	34

HEAT TREATING TEMPERATURES

*NORMALIZE	870 °C
AUSTENITIZE	845 °C

*For forged or rolled specimens only

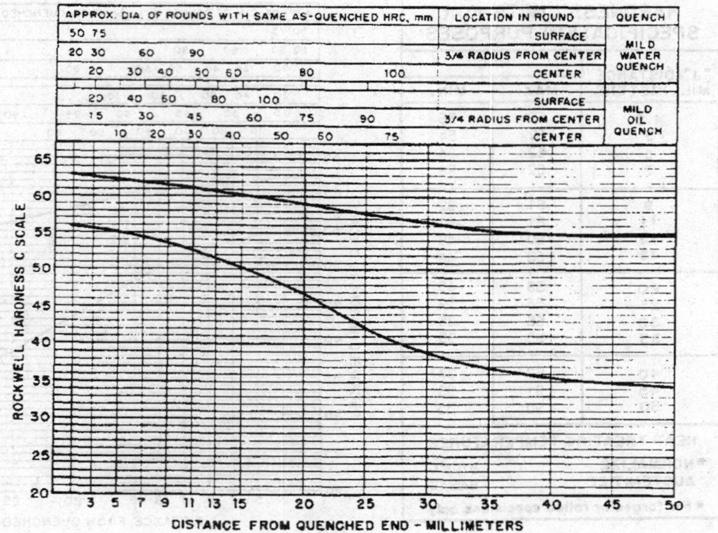

FIGURE 33—UNS H41450—HARDENABILITY BAND—SAE 4145H

HARDNESS LIMITS FOR SPECIFICATION PURPOSES		
"J" DISTANCE SIXTEENTHS OF AN INCH	HRC MAX.	HRC MIN.
1	64	57
2	64	57
3	64	56
4	64	56
5	63	55
6	63	55
7	63	55
8	63	54
9	63	54
10	62	53
11	62	52
12	62	51
13	61	49
14	61	48
15	60	46
16	60	45
18	59	42
20	59	40
22	58	39
24	57	38
26	57	37
28	57	37
30	56	37
32	56	36

HEAT TREATING TEMPERATURES	
*NORMALIZE	1600 °F
AUSTENITIZE	1550 °F

*For forged or rolled specimens only

UNS H41470 **HARDENABILITY BAND** SAE 4147H

%C	%Mn	%Si	%Ni	%Cr	%Mo
0.44/0.51	0.65/1.10	0.15/0.35	--	0.75/1.20	0.15/0.25

APPROX. DIA. OF ROUNDS WITH SAME AS-QUENCHED HRC, in. — LOCATION IN ROUND — QUENCH

SURFACE: 2 4 — MILD WATER QUENCH
3/4 RADIUS FROM CENTER: 1 2 3 4
CENTER: 0.5 1 1.5 2 2.5 3 3.5 4
SURFACE: 1 2 3 4 — MILD OIL QUENCH
3/4 RADIUS FROM CENTER: 0.5 1 1.5 2 2.5 3 3.5 4
CENTER: 0.5 1 1.5 2 2.5 3 3.5

ROCKWELL HARDNESS C SCALE: 20 25 30 35 40 45 50 55 60 65

DISTANCE FROM QUENCHED END – SIXTEENTHS OF AN INCH: 2 4 6 8 10 12 14 16 18 20 22 24 26 28 30 32

HARDNESS LIMITS FOR SPECIFICATION PURPOSES		
"J" DISTANCE MILLIMETERS	HRC MAX.	HRC MIN.
1.5	64	57
3	64	57
5	64	56
7	64	55
9	63	55
11	63	55
13	63	54
15	63	53
20	62	50
25	60	45
30	59	42
35	58	39
40	57	37
45	57	36
50	56	36

HEAT TREATING TEMPERATURES	
*NORMALIZE	870 °C
AUSTENITIZE	845 °C

*For forged or rolled specimens only

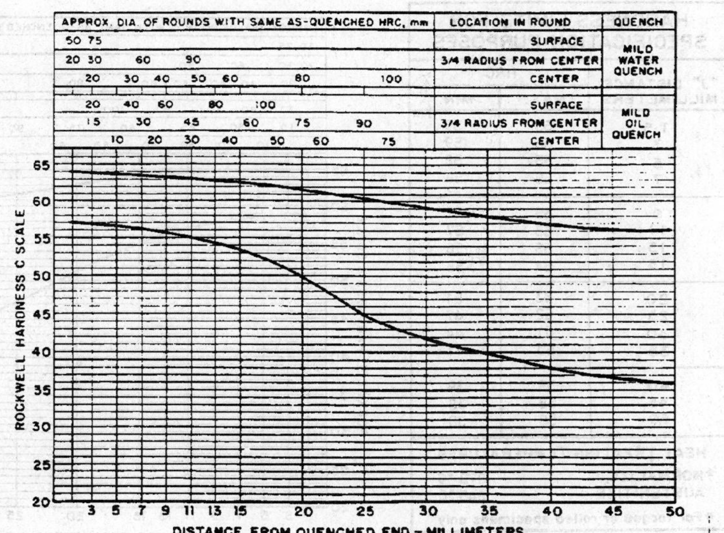

FIGURE 34—UNS H41470—HARDENABILITY BAND—SAE 4147H

UNS H41500 **HARDENABILITY BAND** SAE 4150H

%C	%Mn	%Si	%Ni	%Cr	%Mo
0.47/0.54	0.65/1.10	0.15/0.35	--	0.75/1.20	0.15/0.25

HARDNESS LIMITS FOR SPECIFICATION PURPOSES

"J" DISTANCE SIXTEENTHS OF AN INCH	HRC MAX.	HRC MIN.
1	65	59
2	65	59
3	65	59
4	65	58
5	65	58
6	65	57
7	65	57
8	64	56
9	64	56
10	64	55
11	64	54
12	63	53
13	63	51
14	62	50
15	62	48
16	62	47
18	61	45
20	60	43
22	59	41
24	59	40
26	58	39
28	58	38
30	58	38
32	58	38

HEAT TREATING TEMPERATURES

*NORMALIZE	1600 °F
AUSTENITIZE	1550 °F

*For forged or rolled specimens only

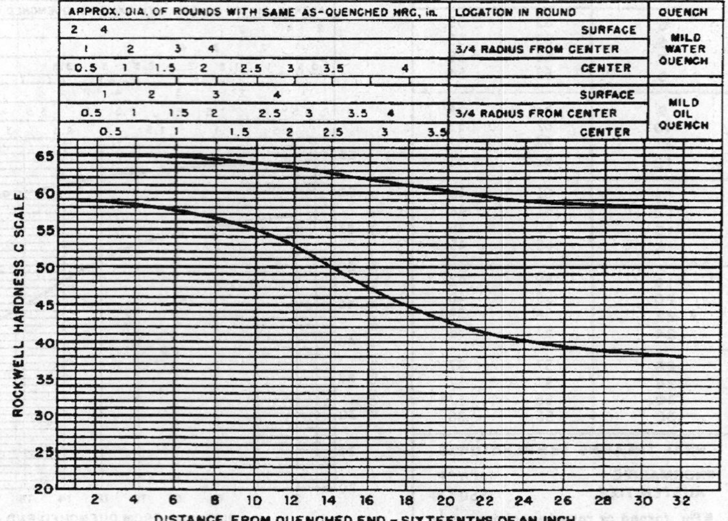

HARDNESS LIMITS FOR SPECIFICATION PURPOSES

"J" DISTANCE MILLIMETERS	HRC MAX.	HRC MIN.
1.5	65	59
3	65	59
5	65	58
7	65	58
9	65	57
11	65	57
13	65	56
15	64	55
20	63	51
25	62	47
30	61	44
35	60	41
40	59	39
45	58	38
50	58	38

HEAT TREATING TEMPERATURES

*NORMALIZE	870 °C
AUSTENITIZE	845 °C

*For forged or rolled specimens only

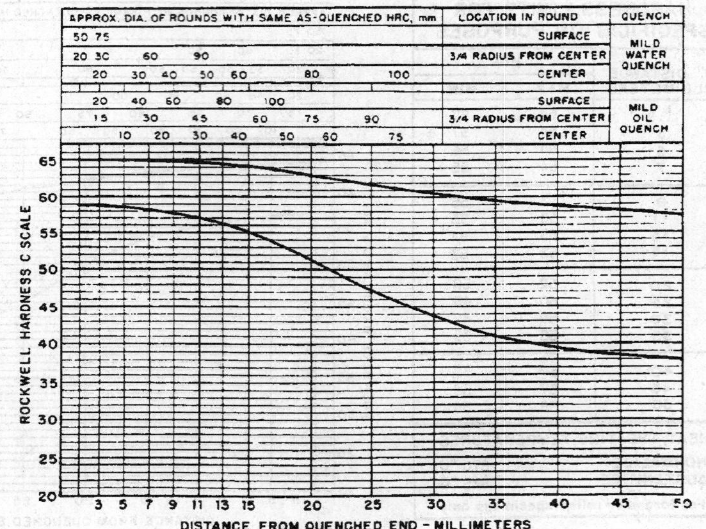

FIGURE 35—UNS H41500—HARDENABILITY BAND—SAE 4150H

UNS H41610 **HARDENABILITY BAND** SAE 4161H

%C	%Mn	%Si	%Ni	%Cr	%Mo
0.55/0.65	0.65/1.10	0.15/0.35	--	0.65/0.95	0.25/0.35

HARDNESS LIMITS FOR SPECIFICATION PURPOSES

"J" DISTANCE SIXTEENTHS OF AN INCH	HRC MAX.	HRC MIN.
1	65	60
2	65	60
3	65	60
4	65	60
5	65	60
6	65	60
7	65	60
8	65	60
9	65	59
10	65	59
11	65	59
12	64	59
13	64	58
14	64	58
15	64	57
16	64	56
18	64	55
20	63	53
22	63	50
24	63	48
26	63	45
28	63	43
30	63	42
32	63	41

HEAT TREATING TEMPERATURES

*NORMALIZE	1600 °F
AUSTENITIZE	1550 °F

*For forged or rolled specimens only

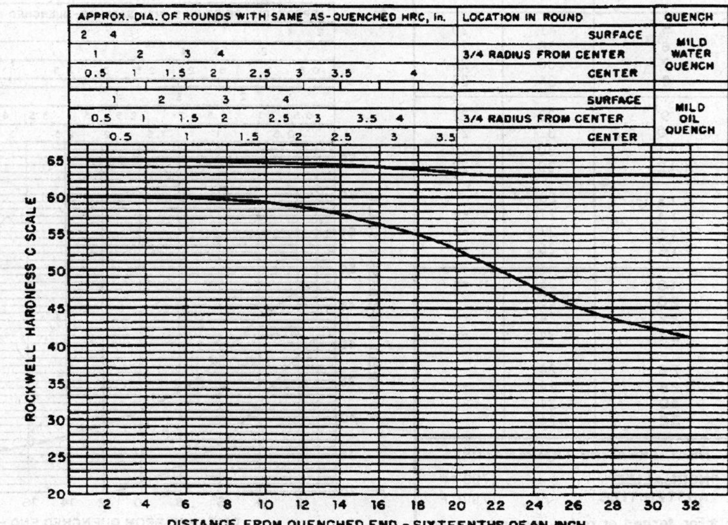

HARDNESS LIMITS FOR SPECIFICATION PURPOSES

"J" DISTANCE MILLIMETERS	HRC MAX.	HRC MIN.
1.5	65	60
3	65	60
5	65	60
7	65	60
9	65	60
11	65	60
13	65	60
15	65	60
20	65	58
25	64	56
30	63	53
35	63	50
40	63	46
45	63	43
50	63	41

HEAT TREATING TEMPERATURES

*NORMALIZE	870 °C
AUSTENITIZE	845 °C

*For forged or rolled specimens only

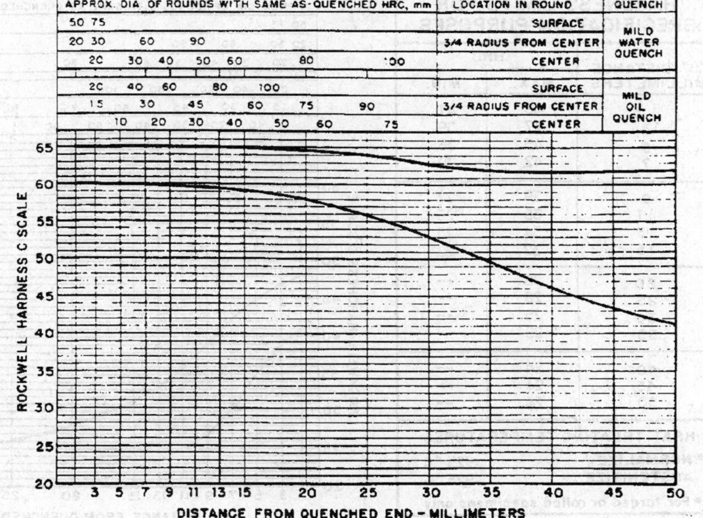

FIGURE 36—UNS H41610—HARDENABILITY BAND—SAE 4161H

UNS H43200 — **HARDENABILITY BAND** — **SAE 4320H**

%C	%Mn	%Si	%Ni	%Cr	%Mo
0.17/0.23	0.40/0.70	0.15/0.35	1.55/2.00	0.35/0.65	0.20/0.30

HARDNESS LIMITS FOR SPECIFICATION PURPOSES

"J" DISTANCE SIXTEENTHS OF AN INCH	HRC MAX.	HRC MIN.
1	48	41
2	47	38
3	45	35
4	43	32
5	41	29
6	38	27
7	36	25
8	34	23
9	33	22
10	31	21
11	30	20
12	29	20
13	28	--
14	27	--
15	27	--
16	26	--
18	25	--
20	25	--
22	24	--
24	24	--
26	24	--
28	24	--
30	24	--
32	24	--

HEAT TREATING TEMPERATURES

*NORMALIZE	1700 °F
AUSTENITIZE	1700 °F

*For forged or rolled specimens only

APPROX. DIA. OF ROUNDS WITH SAME AS-QUENCHED HRC, in.	LOCATION IN ROUND	QUENCH
2 4	SURFACE	MILD WATER QUENCH
1 2 3 4	3/4 RADIUS FROM CENTER	
0.5 1 1.5 2 2.5 3 3.5 4	CENTER	
1 2 3 4	SURFACE	MILD OIL QUENCH
0.5 1 1.5 2 2.5 3 3.5 4	3/4 RADIUS FROM CENTER	
0.5 1 1.5 2 2.5 3 3.5	CENTER	

ROCKWELL HARDNESS C SCALE: 20 25 30 35 40 45 50 55 60 65

DISTANCE FROM QUENCHED END – SIXTEENTHS OF AN INCH: 2 4 6 8 10 12 14 16 18 20 22 24 26 28 30 32

HARDNESS LIMITS FOR SPECIFICATION PURPOSES

"J" DISTANCE MILLIMETERS	HRC MAX.	HRC MIN.
1.5	48	41
3	47	39
5	45	35
7	42	30
9	39	27
11	36	25
13	34	23
15	32	22
20	28	--
25	26	--
30	25	--
35	25	--
40	24	--
45	24	--
50	24	--

HEAT TREATING TEMPERATURES

*NORMALIZE	925 °C
AUSTENITIZE	925 °C

*For forged or rolled specimens only

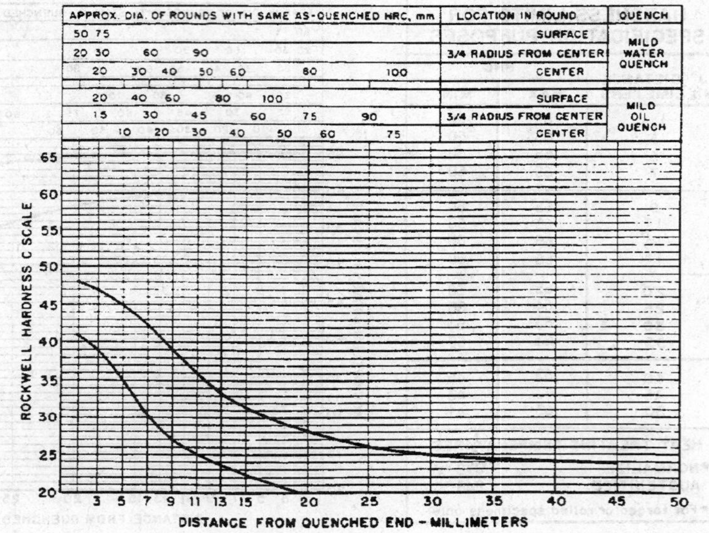

FIGURE 37—UNS H43200—HARDENABILITY BAND—SAE 4320H

HARDENABILITY BAND

UNS H43400 — SAE 4340H

%C	%Mn	%Si	%Ni	%Cr	%Mo
0.37/0.44	0.55/0.90	0.15/0.35	1.55/2.00	0.65/0.95	0.20/0.30

HARDNESS LIMITS FOR SPECIFICATION PURPOSES

"J" DISTANCE SIXTEENTHS OF AN INCH	HRC MAX.	HRC MIN.
1	60	53
2	60	53
3	60	53
4	60	53
5	60	53
6	60	53
7	60	53
8	60	52
9	60	52
10	60	52
11	59	51
12	59	51
13	59	50
14	58	49
15	58	49
16	58	48
18	58	47
20	57	46
22	57	45
24	57	44
26	57	43
28	56	42
30	56	41
32	56	40

HEAT TREATING TEMPERATURES

*NORMALIZE	1600 °F
AUSTENITIZE	1550 °F

*For forged or rolled specimens only

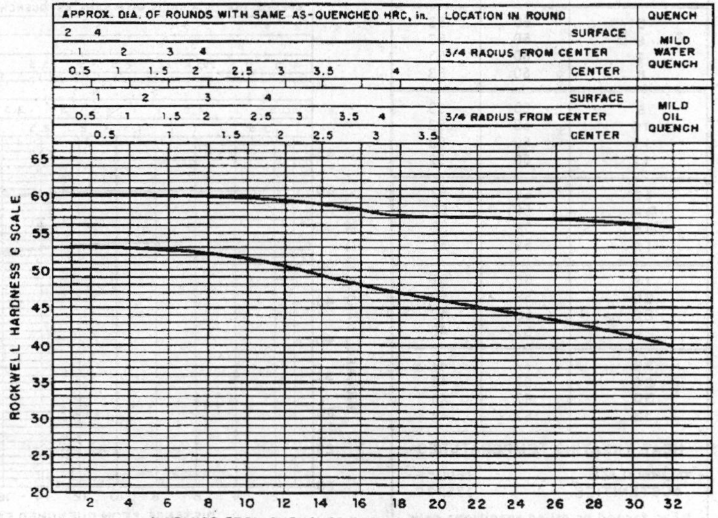

HARDNESS LIMITS FOR SPECIFICATION PURPOSES

"J" DISTANCE MILLIMETERS	HRC MAX.	HRC MIN.
1.5	60	53
3	60	53
5	60	53
7	60	53
9	60	53
11	60	53
13	60	52
15	60	52
20	59	50
25	58	48
30	58	46
35	57	44
40	57	43
45	56	42
50	56	40

HEAT TREATING TEMPERATURES

*NORMALIZE	870 °C
AUSTENITIZE	845 °C

*For forged or rolled specimens only

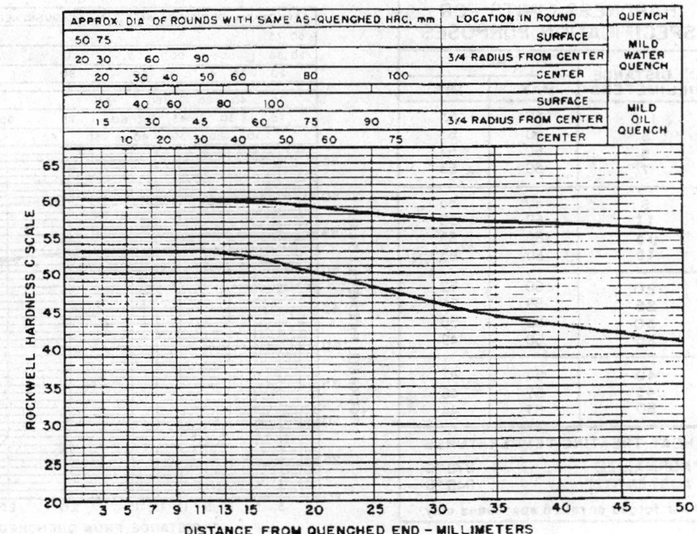

FIGURE 38—UNS H43400—HARDENABILITY BAND—SAE 4340H

UNS H43406 **HARDENABILITY BAND** SAE E4340H

%C	%Mn	%Si	%Ni	%Cr	%Mo
0.37/0.44	0.60/0.95	0.15/0.35	1.55/2.00	0.65/0.95	0.20/0.30

HARDNESS LIMITS FOR SPECIFICATION PURPOSES

"J" DISTANCE SIXTEENTHS OF AN INCH	HRC MAX.	HRC MIN.
1	60	53
2	60	53
3	60	53
4	60	53
5	60	53
6	60	53
7	60	53
8	60	53
9	60	53
10	60	53
11	60	53
12	60	52
13	60	52
14	59	52
15	59	52
16	59	51
18	58	51
20	58	50
22	58	49
24	57	48
26	57	47
28	57	46
30	57	45
32	57	44

HEAT TREATING TEMPERATURES

*NORMALIZE	1600 °F
AUSTENITIZE	1550 °F

* For forged or rolled specimens only

APPROX. DIA. OF ROUNDS WITH SAME AS-QUENCHED HRC, in. | LOCATION IN ROUND | QUENCH

2 4 — SURFACE — MILD WATER QUENCH
1 2 3 4 — 3/4 RADIUS FROM CENTER
0.5 1 1.5 2 2.5 3 3.5 4 — CENTER
1 2 3 4 — SURFACE — MILD OIL QUENCH
0.5 1 1.5 2 2.5 3 3.5 4 — 3/4 RADIUS FROM CENTER
0.5 1 1.5 2 2.5 3 3.5 — CENTER

ROCKWELL HARDNESS C SCALE: 20 25 30 35 40 45 50 55 60 65

2 4 6 8 10 12 14 16 18 20 22 24 26 28 30 32

DISTANCE FROM QUENCHED END - SIXTEENTHS OF AN INCH

HARDNESS LIMITS FOR SPECIFICATION PURPOSES

"J" DISTANCE MILLIMETERS	HRC MAX.	HRC MIN.
1.5	60	53
3	60	53
5	60	53
7	60	53
9	60	53
11	60	53
13	60	53
15	60	53
20	60	52
25	59	51
30	58	50
35	58	49
40	57	47
45	57	46
50	57	44

HEAT TREATING TEMPERATURES

*NORMALIZE	870 °C
AUSTENITIZE	845 °C

* For forged or rolled specimens only

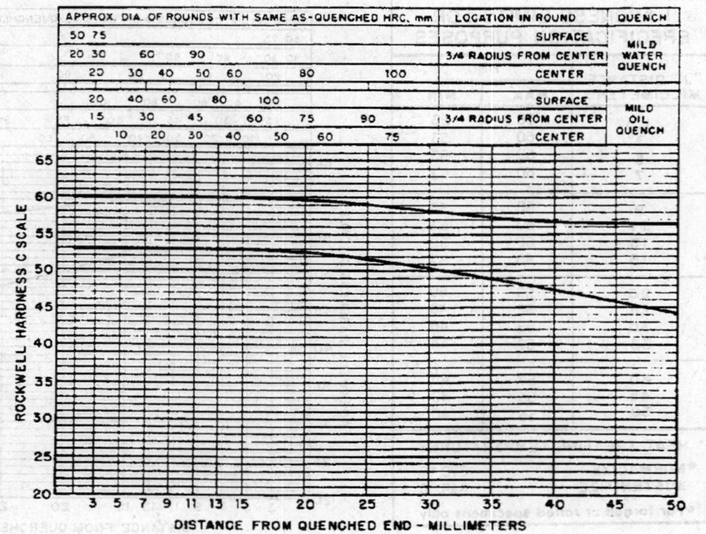

FIGURE 39—UNS H43406—HARDENABILITY BAND—SAE E4340H

UNS H46200 **HARDENABILITY BAND** SAE 4620H

%C	%Mn	%Si	%Ni	%Cr	%Mo
0.17/0.23	0.35/0.75	0.15/0.35	1.55/2.00	--	0.20/0.30

HARDNESS LIMITS FOR SPECIFICATION PURPOSES

"J" DISTANCE SIXTEENTHS OF AN INCH	HRC MAX.	HRC MIN.
1	48	41
2	45	35
3	42	27
4	39	24
5	34	21
6	31	--
7	29	--
8	27	--
9	26	--
10	25	--
11	24	--
12	23	--
13	22	--
14	22	--
15	22	--
16	21	--
18	21	--
20	20	--
22	--	--
24	--	--
26		
28		
30		
32		

HEAT TREATING TEMPERATURES	
*NORMALIZE	1700 °F
AUSTENITIZE	1700 °F

*For forged or rolled specimens only

APPROX. DIA. OF ROUNDS WITH SAME AS-QUENCHED HRC, in. — LOCATION IN ROUND — QUENCH

SURFACE: 2 4 — MILD WATER QUENCH
3/4 RADIUS FROM CENTER: 1 2 3 4
CENTER: 0.5 1 1.5 2 2.5 3 3.5 4
SURFACE: 1 2 3 4 — MILD OIL QUENCH
3/4 RADIUS FROM CENTER: 0.5 1 1.5 2 2.5 3 3.5 4
CENTER: 0.5 1 1.5 2 2.5 3 3.5

ROCKWELL HARDNESS C SCALE: 20 25 30 35 40 45 50 55 60 65

DISTANCE FROM QUENCHED END – SIXTEENTHS OF AN INCH: 2 4 6 8 10 12 14 16 18 20 22 24 26 28 30 32

HARDNESS LIMITS FOR SPECIFICATION PURPOSES

"J" DISTANCE MILLIMETERS	HRC MAX.	HRC MIN.
1.5	48	41
3	46	37
5	42	28
7	37	23
9	33	—
11	30	—
13	27	—
15	26	—
20	23	—
25	22	—
30	21	—
35	—	—
40		
45		
50		

HEAT TREATING TEMPERATURES	
*NORMALIZE	925 °C
AUSTENITIZE	925 °C

*For forged or rolled specimens only

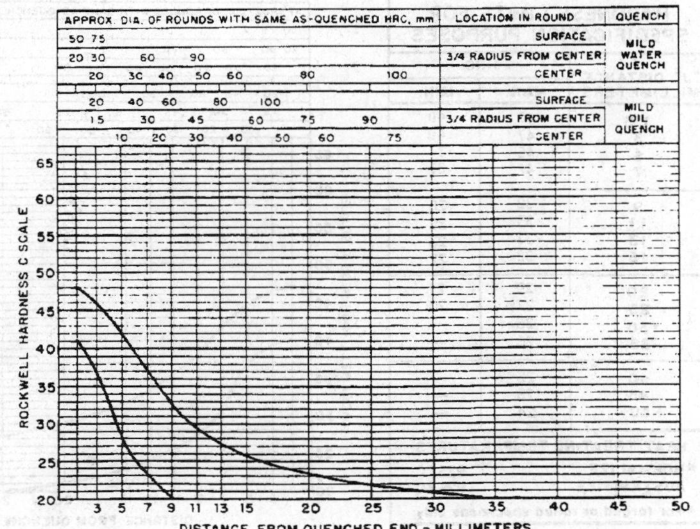

FIGURE 40—UNS H46200—HARDENABILITY BAND—SAE 4620H

UNS H47180 — **HARDENABILITY BAND** — **SAE 4718H**

%C	%Mn	%Si	%Ni	%Cr	%Mo
0.15/0.21	0.60/0.95	0.15/0.35	0.85/1.25	0.30/0.60	0.30/0.40

HARDNESS LIMITS FOR SPECIFICATION PURPOSES

"J" DISTANCE SIXTEENTHS OF AN INCH	HRC MAX.	HRC MIN.
1	47	40
2	47	40
3	45	38
4	43	33
5	40	29
6	37	27
7	35	25
8	33	24
9	32	23
10	31	22
11	30	22
12	29	21
13	29	21
14	28	21
15	27	20
16	27	20
18	27	--
20	26	--
22	26	--
24	25	--
26	25	--
28	24	--
30	24	--
32	24	--

HEAT TREATING TEMPERATURES

*NORMALIZE 1700 °F
AUSTENITIZE 1700 °F

*For forged or rolled specimens only

APPROX. DIA. OF ROUNDS WITH SAME AS-QUENCHED HRC, in. — LOCATION IN ROUND — QUENCH

MILD WATER QUENCH: SURFACE 2 4; 3/4 RADIUS FROM CENTER 1 2 3 4; CENTER 0.5 1 1.5 2 2.5 3 3.5 4

MILD OIL QUENCH: SURFACE 1 2 3 4; 3/4 RADIUS FROM CENTER 0.5 1 1.5 2 2.5 3 3.5 4; CENTER 0.5 1 1.5 2 2.5 3 3.5

ROCKWELL HARDNESS C SCALE: 20 25 30 35 40 45 50 55 60 65

DISTANCE FROM QUENCHED END - SIXTEENTHS OF AN INCH: 2 4 6 8 10 12 14 16 18 20 22 24 26 28 30 32

HARDNESS LIMITS FOR SPECIFICATION PURPOSES

"J" DISTANCE MILLIMETERS	HRC MAX.	HRC MIN.
1.5	47	40
3	47	40
5	45	37
7	42	31
9	38	28
11	35	25
13	33	23
15	32	22
20	29	21
25	27	20
30	26	—
35	26	—
40	25	—
45	25	—
50	24	—

HEAT TREATING TEMPERATURES

*NORMALIZE 925 °C
AUSTENITIZE 925 °C

*For forged or rolled specimens only

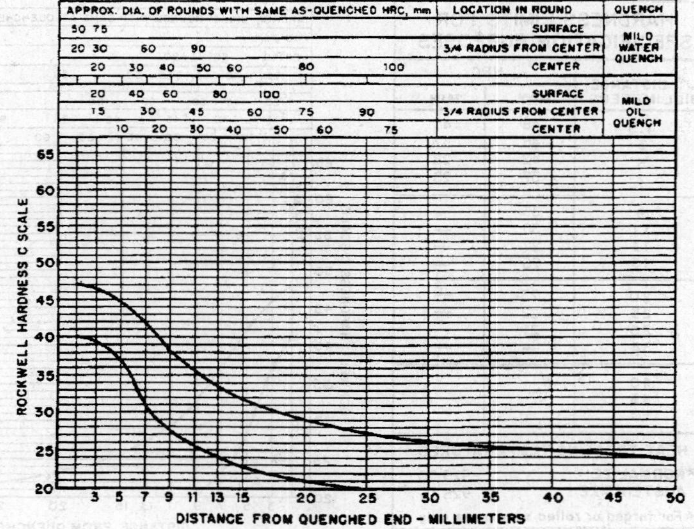

FIGURE 41—UNS H47180—HARDENABILITY BAND—SAE 4718H

UNS H47200 **HARDENABILITY BAND** SAE 4720H

%C	%Mn	%Si	%Ni	%Cr	%Mo
0.17/0.23	0.45/0.75	0.15/0.35	0.85/1.25	0.30/0.60	0.15/0.25

HARDNESS LIMITS FOR SPECIFICATION PURPOSES

"J" DISTANCE SIXTEENTHS OF AN INCH	HRC MAX.	HRC MIN.
1	48	41
2	47	39
3	43	31
4	39	27
5	35	23
6	32	21
7	29	--
8	28	--
9	27	--
10	26	--
11	25	--
12	24	--
13	24	--
14	23	--
15	23	--
16	22	--
18	21	--
20	21	--
22	21	--
24	20	--
26	--	--
28	--	--
30	--	--
32	--	--

HEAT TREATING TEMPERATURES

*NORMALIZE	1700 °F
AUSTENITIZE	1700 °F

*For forged or rolled specimens only

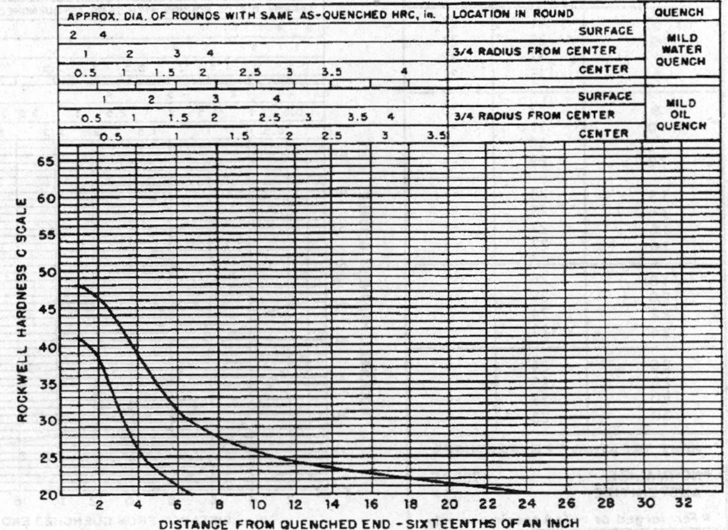

HARDNESS LIMITS FOR SPECIFICATION PURPOSES

"J" DISTANCE MILLIMETERS	HRC MAX.	HRC MIN.
1.5	48	41
3	47	39
5	43	30
7	38	25
9	33	22
11	30	20
13	28	--
15	27	--
20	24	--
25	23	--
30	22	--
35	21	--
40	20	--
45	—	--
50		

HEAT TREATING TEMPERATURES

*NORMALIZE	925 °C
AUSTENITIZE	925 °C

*For forged or rolled specimens only

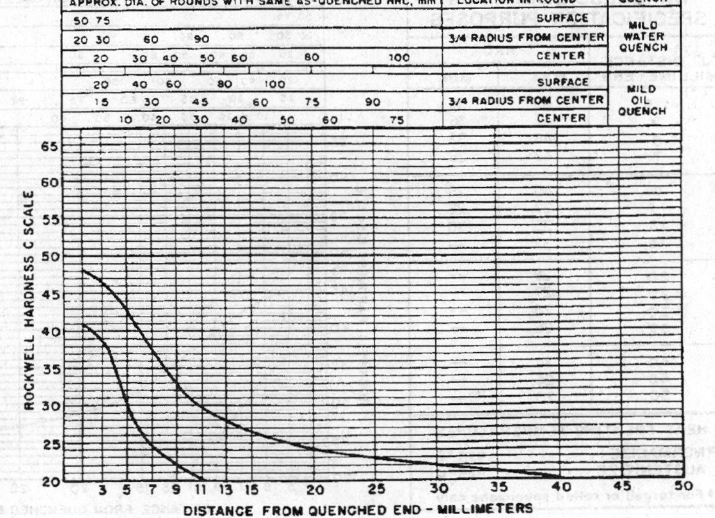

FIGURE 42—UNS H47200—HARDENABILITY BAND—SAE 4720H

UNS H48150 **HARDENABILITY BAND** SAE 4815H

%C	%Mn	%Si	%Ni	%Cr	%Mo
0.12/0.18	0.30/0.70	0.15/0.35	3.20/3.80	--	0.20/0.30

HARDNESS LIMITS FOR SPECIFICATION PURPOSES

"J" DISTANCE SIXTEENTHS OF AN INCH	HRC MAX.	HRC MIN.
1	45	38
2	44	37
3	44	34
4	42	30
5	41	27
6	39	24
7	37	22
8	35	21
9	33	20
10	31	--
11	30	--
12	29	--
13	28	--
14	28	--
15	27	--
16	27	--
18	26	--
20	25	--
22	24	--
24	24	--
26	24	--
28	23	--
30	23	--
32	23	--

HEAT TREATING TEMPERATURES

*NORMALIZE 1700°F
AUSTENITIZE 1550°F

*For forged or rolled specimens only

HARDNESS LIMITS FOR SPECIFICATION PURPOSES

"J" DISTANCE MILLIMETERS	HRC MAX.	HRC MIN.
1.5	45	38
3	45	36
5	44	33
7	42	28
9	40	25
11	37	22
13	35	20
15	32	--
20	29	--
25	27	--
30	26	--
35	25	--
40	24	--
45	24	--
50	23	--

HEAT TREATING TEMPERATURES

*NORMALIZE 925°C
AUSTENITIZE 845°C

*For forged or rolled specimens only

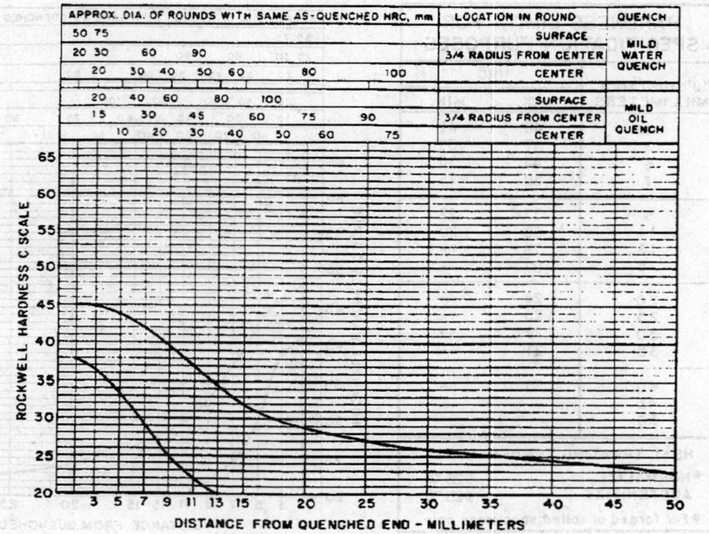

FIGURE 43—UNS H48150—HARDENABILITY BAND—SAE 4815H

HARDENABILITY BAND

UNS H48170 SAE 4817H

%C	%Mn	%Si	%Ni	%Cr	%Mo
0.14/0.20	0.30/0.70	0.15/0.35	3.20/3.80	--	0.20/0.30

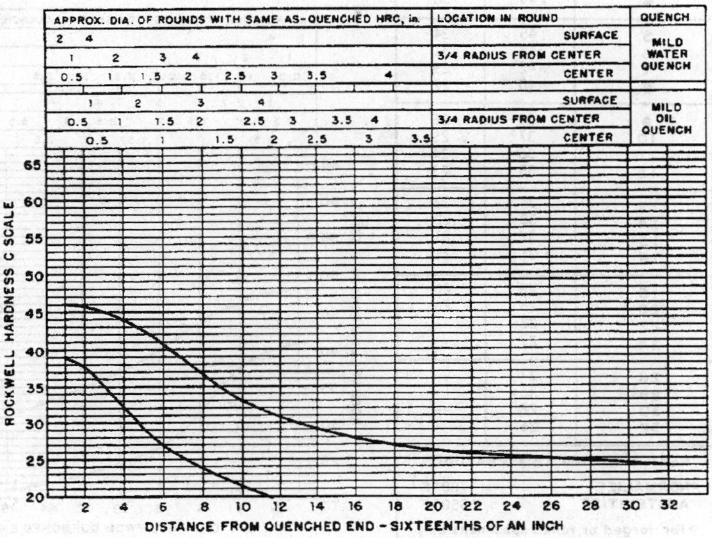

HARDNESS LIMITS FOR SPECIFICATION PURPOSES

"J" DISTANCE SIXTEENTHS OF AN INCH	HRC MAX.	HRC MIN.
1	46	39
2	46	38
3	45	35
4	44	32
5	42	29
6	41	27
7	39	25
8	37	23
9	35	22
10	33	21
11	32	20
12	31	20
13	30	--
14	29	--
15	28	--
16	28	--
18	27	--
20	26	--
22	25	--
24	25	--
26	25	--
28	25	--
30	24	--
32	24	--

HEAT TREATING TEMPERATURES

*NORMALIZE	1700 °F
AUSTENITIZE	1550 °F

* For forged or rolled specimens only

APPROX. DIA. OF ROUNDS WITH SAME AS-QUENCHED HRC, in.	LOCATION IN ROUND	QUENCH
2 4	SURFACE	MILD WATER QUENCH
1 2 3 4	3/4 RADIUS FROM CENTER	
0.5 1 1.5 2 2.5 3 3.5 4	CENTER	
1 2 3 4	SURFACE	MILD OIL QUENCH
0.5 1 1.5 2 2.5 3 3.5 4	3/4 RADIUS FROM CENTER	
0.5 1 1.5 2 2.5 3 3.5	CENTER	

ROCKWELL HARDNESS C SCALE (20–65)

DISTANCE FROM QUENCHED END – SIXTEENTHS OF AN INCH (2–32)

HARDNESS LIMITS FOR SPECIFICATION PURPOSES

"J" DISTANCE MILLIMETERS	HRC MAX.	HRC MIN.
1.5	46	39
3	46	38
5	45	35
7	44	31
9	42	28
11	39	25
13	37	23
15	34	21
20	31	--
25	28	--
30	27	--
35	26	--
40	25	--
45	25	--
50	25	--

HEAT TREATING TEMPERATURES

*NORMALIZE	925 °C
AUSTENITIZE	845 °C

* For forged or rolled specimens only

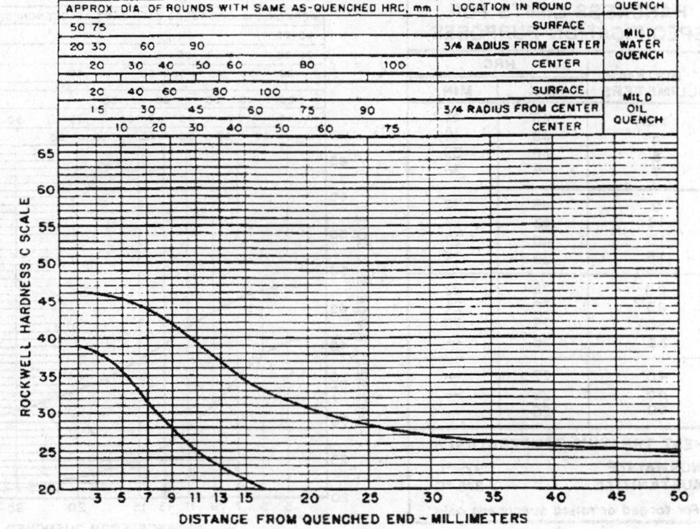

FIGURE 44—UNS H48170—HARDENABILITY BAND—SAE 4817H

UNS H48200 **HARDENABILITY BAND** **SAE 4820H**

%C	%Mn	%Si	%Ni	%Cr	%Mo
0.17/0.23	0.40/0.80	0.15/0.35	3.20/3.80	--	0.20/0.30

HARDNESS LIMITS FOR SPECIFICATION PURPOSES

"J" DISTANCE SIXTEENTHS OF AN INCH	HRC MAX.	HRC MIN.
1	48	41
2	48	40
3	47	39
4	46	38
5	45	34
6	43	31
7	42	29
8	40	27
9	39	26
10	37	25
11	36	24
12	35	23
13	34	22
14	33	22
15	32	21
16	31	21
18	29	20
20	28	20
22	28	--
24	27	--
26	27	--
28	26	--
30	26	--
32	25	--

HEAT TREATING TEMPERATURES

*NORMALIZE 1700°F
AUSTENITIZE 1550°F

*For forged or rolled specimens only

APPROX. DIA. OF ROUNDS WITH SAME AS-QUENCHED HRC, in. | LOCATION IN ROUND | QUENCH
2 4 | SURFACE | MILD WATER QUENCH
1 2 3 4 | 3/4 RADIUS FROM CENTER
0.5 1 1.5 2 2.5 3 3.5 4 | CENTER
1 2 3 4 | SURFACE | MILD OIL QUENCH
0.5 1 1.5 2 2.5 3 3.5 4 | 3/4 RADIUS FROM CENTER
0.5 1 1.5 2 2.5 3 3.5 | CENTER

ROCKWELL HARDNESS C SCALE (20–65)

DISTANCE FROM QUENCHED END – SIXTEENTHS OF AN INCH (2–32)

HARDNESS LIMITS FOR SPECIFICATION PURPOSES

"J" DISTANCE MILLIMETERS	HRC MAX.	HRC MIN.
1.5	48	41
3	48	40
5	48	39
7	46	36
9	45	32
11	43	29
13	40	27
15	39	25
20	35	22
25	32	21
30	29	20
35	28	--
40	27	--
45	26	--
50	26	--

HEAT TREATING TEMPERATURES

*NORMALIZE 925°C
AUSTENITIZE 845°C

*For forged or rolled specimens only

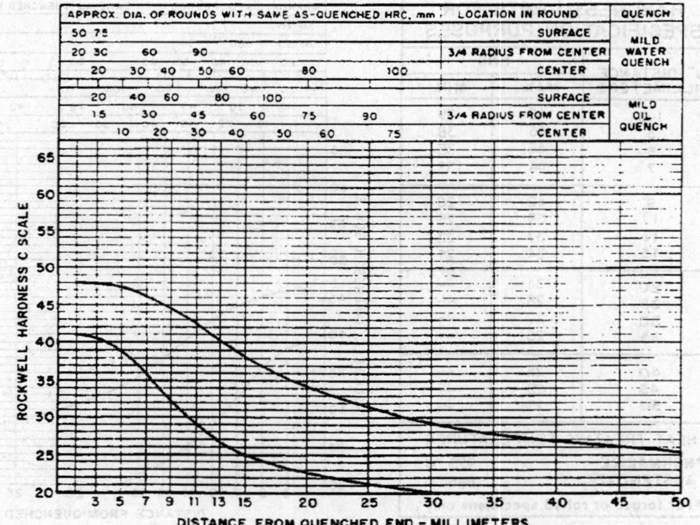

FIGURE 45—UNS H48200—HARDENABILITY BAND—SAE 4820H

UNS H50401 **HARDENABILITY BAND** SAE 50B40H

%C	%Mn	%Si	%Ni	%Cr	%Mo	%B
0.37/0.44	0.65/1.10	0.15/0.35	--	0.30/0.70	--	0.0005/0.003

HARDNESS LIMITS FOR SPECIFICATION PURPOSES

"J" DISTANCE SIXTEENTHS OF AN INCH	HRC MAX.	HRC MIN.
1	60	53
2	60	53
3	59	52
4	59	51
5	58	50
6	58	48
7	57	44
8	57	39
9	56	34
10	55	31
11	53	29
12	51	28
13	49	27
14	47	26
15	44	25
16	41	25
18	38	23
20	36	21
22	35	--
24	34	--
26	33	--
28	32	--
30	30	--
32	29	--

HEAT TREATING TEMPERATURES

*NORMALIZE	1600 °F
AUSTENITIZE	1550 °F

*For forged or rolled specimens only

APPROX. DIA. OF ROUNDS WITH SAME AS-QUENCHED HRC, in.	LOCATION IN ROUND	QUENCH
2 4	SURFACE	MILD WATER QUENCH
1 2 3 4	3/4 RADIUS FROM CENTER	
0.5 1 1.5 2 2.5 3 3.5 4	CENTER	
1 2 3 4	SURFACE	MILD OIL QUENCH
0.5 1 1.5 2 2.5 3 3.5 4	3/4 RADIUS FROM CENTER	
0.5 1 1.5 2 2.5 3 3.5	CENTER	

ROCKWELL HARDNESS C SCALE

DISTANCE FROM QUENCHED END – SIXTEENTHS OF AN INCH

HARDNESS LIMITS FOR SPECIFICATION PURPOSES

"J" DISTANCE MILLIMETERS	HRC MAX.	HRC MIN.
1.5	60	53
3	60	53
5	60	52
7	59	51
9	59	49
11	58	44
13	57	38
15	56	33
20	50	27
25	43	24
30	37	22
35	35	—
40	34	—
45	32	—
50	30	—

HEAT TREATING TEMPERATURES

*NORMALIZE	870 °C
AUSTENITIZE	845 °C

*For forged or rolled specimens only

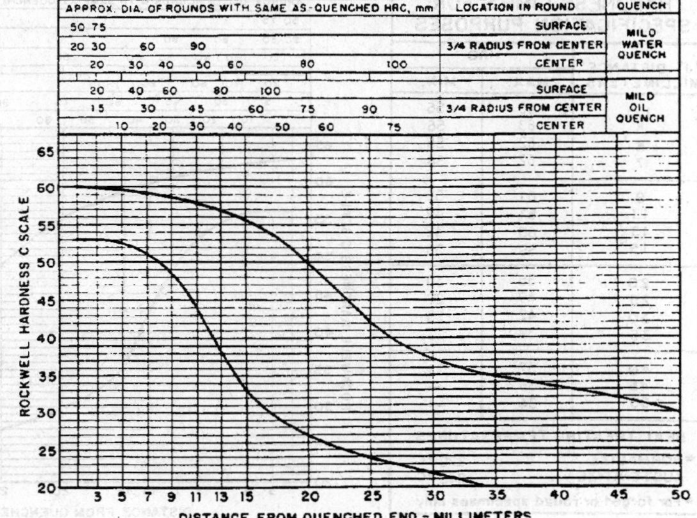

FIGURE 46—UNS H50401—HARDENABILITY BAND—SAE 50B40H

UNS H50441 HARDENABILITY BAND SAE 50B44H

%C	%Mn	%Si	%Ni	%Cr	%Mo	%B
0.42/0.49	0.65/1.10	0.15/0.35	--	0.30/0.70	--	0.0005/0.003

HARDNESS LIMITS FOR SPECIFICATION PURPOSES

"J" DISTANCE SIXTEENTHS OF AN INCH	HRC MAX.	HRC MIN.
1	63	56
2	63	56
3	62	55
4	62	55
5	61	54
6	61	52
7	60	48
8	60	43
9	59	38
10	58	34
11	57	31
12	56	30
13	54	29
14	52	29
15	50	28
16	48	27
18	44	26
20	40	24
22	38	23
24	37	21
26	36	20
28	35	--
30	34	--
32	33	--

HEAT TREATING TEMPERATURES

*NORMALIZE	1600 °F
AUSTENITIZE	1550 °F

* For forged or rolled specimens only

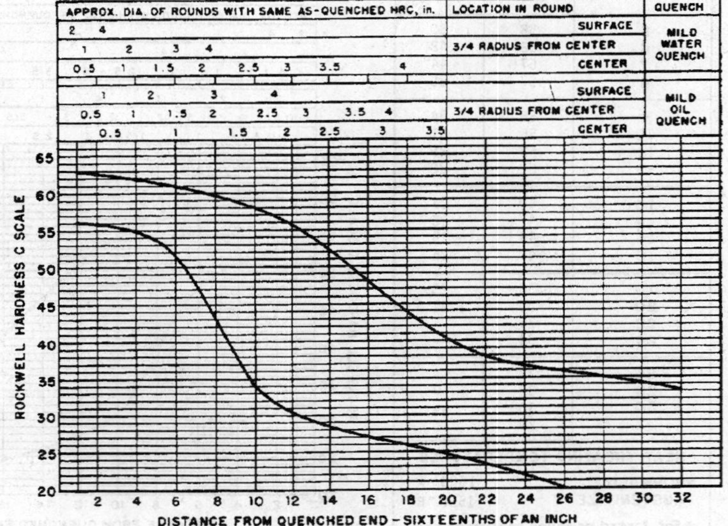

HARDNESS LIMITS FOR SPECIFICATION PURPOSES

"J" DISTANCE MILLIMETERS	HRC MAX.	HRC MIN.
1.5	63	56
3	63	56
5	62	55
7	62	54
9	61	52
11	61	49
13	60	42
15	59	36
20	55	30
25	49	27
30	42	25
35	38	23
40	37	21
45	35	—
50	34	—

HEAT TREATING TEMPERATURES

*NORMALIZE	870 °C
AUSTENITIZE	845 °C

* For forged or rolled specimens only

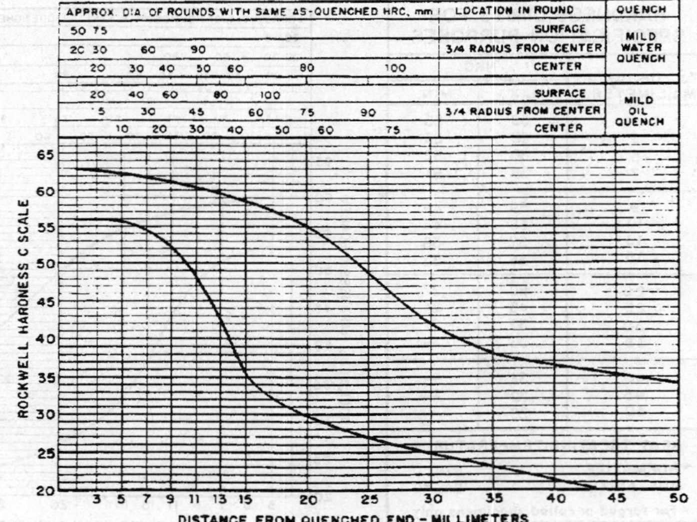

FIGURE 47—UNS H50441—HARDENABILITY BAND—SAE 50B44H

UNS H50460 **HARDENABILITY BAND** SAE 5046H

%C	%Mn	%Si	%Ni	%Cr	%Mo
0.43/0.50	0.65/1.10	0.15/0.35	--	0.13/0.43	--

HARDNESS LIMITS FOR SPECIFICATION PURPOSES

"J" DISTANCE SIXTEENTHS OF AN INCH	HRC MAX.	HRC MIN.
1	63	56
2	62	55
3	60	45
4	56	32
5	52	28
6	46	27
7	39	26
8	35	25
9	34	24
10	33	24
11	33	23
12	32	23
13	32	22
14	31	22
15	31	21
16	30	21
18	29	20
20	28	--
22	27	--
24	26	--
26	25	--
28	24	--
30	23	--
32	23	--

HEAT TREATING TEMPERATURES

*NORMALIZE 1600°F
AUSTENITIZE 1550°F

*For forged or rolled specimens only

APPROX. DIA. OF ROUNDS WITH SAME AS-QUENCHED HRC, in. — LOCATION IN ROUND — QUENCH

MILD WATER QUENCH: SURFACE 2 4; 3/4 RADIUS FROM CENTER 1 2 3 4; CENTER 0.5 1 1.5 2 2.5 3 3.5 4

MILD OIL QUENCH: SURFACE 1 2 3 4; 3/4 RADIUS FROM CENTER 0.5 1 1.5 2 2.5 3 3.5 4; CENTER 0.5 1 1.5 2 2.5 3 3.5

ROCKWELL HARDNESS C SCALE (20–65)

DISTANCE FROM QUENCHED END - SIXTEENTHS OF AN INCH (2–32)

HARDNESS LIMITS FOR SPECIFICATION PURPOSES

"J" DISTANCE MILLIMETERS	HRC MAX.	HRC MIN.
1.5	63	56
3	62	54
5	59	40
7	54	30
9	48	27
11	39	26
13	35	25
15	34	25
20	32	22
25	30	20
30	29	--
35	27	--
40	26	--
45	24	--
50	23	--

HEAT TREATING TEMPERATURES

*NORMALIZE 870°C
AUSTENITIZE 845°C

*For forged or rolled specimens only

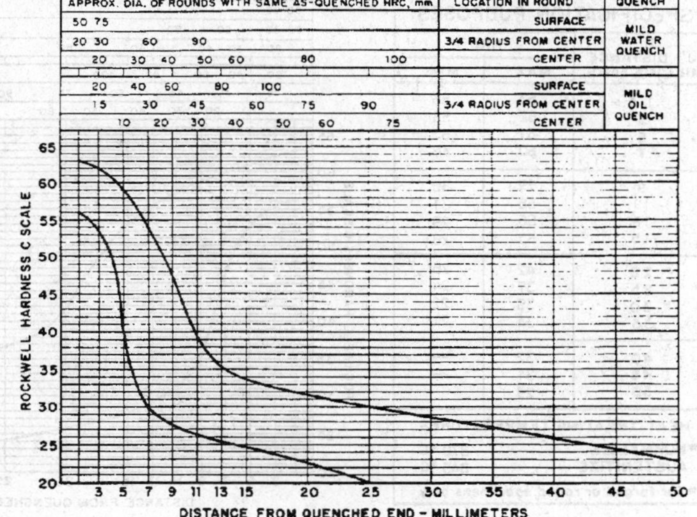

FIGURE 48—UNS H50460—HARDENABILITY BAND—SAE 5046H

HARDNESS LIMITS FOR SPECIFICATION PURPOSES		
"J" DISTANCE SIXTEENTHS OF AN INCH	HRC MAX.	HRC MIN.
1	63	56
2	62	54
3	61	52
4	60	50
5	59	41
6	58	32
7	57	31
8	56	30
9	54	29
10	51	28
11	47	27
12	43	26
13	40	26
14	38	25
15	37	25
16	36	24
18	35	23
20	34	22
22	33	21
24	32	20
26	31	--
28	30	--
30	29	--
32	28	--

HEAT TREATING TEMPERATURES

*NORMALIZE 1600 °F
AUSTENITIZE 1550 °F

*For forged or rolled specimens only

UNS H50461 **HARDENABILITY BAND** SAE 50B46H

%C	%Mn	%Si	%Ni	%Cr	%Mo	%B
0.43/0.50	0.65/1.10	0.15/0.35	--	0.13/0.43	--	0.0005/0.003

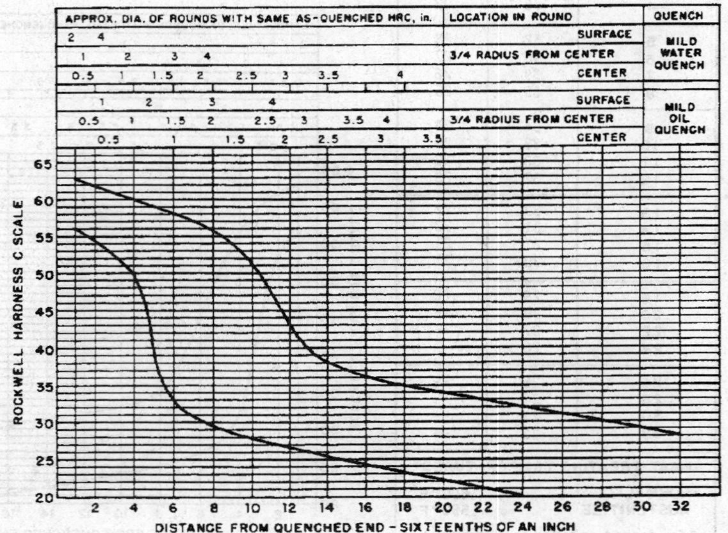

HARDNESS LIMITS FOR SPECIFICATION PURPOSES		
"J" DISTANCE MILLIMETERS	HRC MAX.	HRC MIN.
1.5	63	56
3	62	55
5	61	53
7	60	47
9	59	35
11	58	31
13	56	29
15	53	28
20	42	26
25	37	24
30	35	22
35	34	21
40	32	—
45	31	—
50	29	—

HEAT TREATING TEMPERATURES

*NORMALIZE 870 °C
AUSTENITIZE 845 °C

*For forged or rolled specimens only

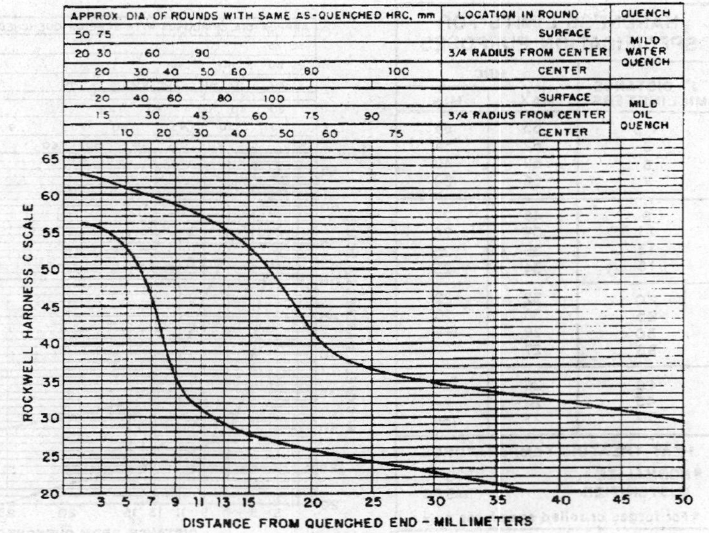

FIGURE 49—UNS H50461—HARDENABILITY BAND—SAE 50B46H

UNS H50501 **HARDENABILITY BAND** SAE 50B50H

%C	%Mn	%Si	%Ni	%Cr	%Mo	%B
0.47/0.54	0.65/1.10	0.15/0.35	--	0.30/0.70	--	0.0005/0.003

HARDNESS LIMITS FOR SPECIFICATION PURPOSES

"J" DISTANCE SIXTEENTHS OF AN INCH	HRC MAX.	HRC MIN.
1	65	59
2	65	59
3	64	58
4	64	57
5	63	56
6	63	55
7	62	52
8	62	47
9	61	42
10	60	37
11	60	35
12	59	33
13	58	32
14	57	31
15	56	30
16	54	29
18	50	28
20	47	27
22	44	26
24	41	25
26	39	24
28	38	22
30	37	21
32	36	20

HEAT TREATING TEMPERATURES

*NORMALIZE	1600 °F
AUSTENITIZE	1550 °F

*For forged or rolled specimens only

APPROX. DIA. OF ROUNDS WITH SAME AS-QUENCHED HRC, in.	LOCATION IN ROUND	QUENCH
2 4	SURFACE	MILD WATER QUENCH
1 2 3 4	3/4 RADIUS FROM CENTER	MILD WATER QUENCH
0.5 1 1.5 2 2.5 3 3.5 4	CENTER	MILD WATER QUENCH
1 2 3 4	SURFACE	MILD OIL QUENCH
0.5 1 1.5 2 2.5 3 3.5 4	3/4 RADIUS FROM CENTER	MILD OIL QUENCH
0.5 1 1.5 2 2.5 3 3.5	CENTER	MILD OIL QUENCH

ROCKWELL HARDNESS C SCALE (20–65) vs. DISTANCE FROM QUENCHED END - SIXTEENTHS OF AN INCH (2–32)

HARDNESS LIMITS FOR SPECIFICATION PURPOSES

"J" DISTANCE MILLIMETERS	HRC MAX.	HRC MIN.
1.5	65	59
3	65	59
5	65	58
7	64	57
9	63	55
11	63	52
13	62	46
15	61	39
20	59	32
25	54	29
30	49	27
35	44	26
40	40	24
45	38	22
50	37	20

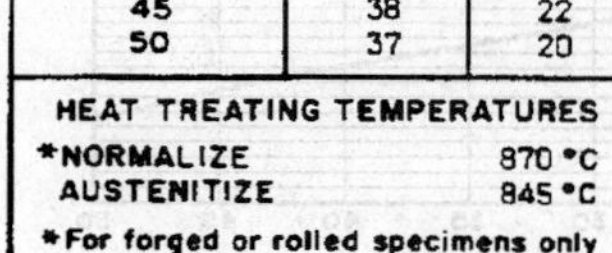

HEAT TREATING TEMPERATURES

*NORMALIZE	870 °C
AUSTENITIZE	845 °C

*For forged or rolled specimens only

APPROX. DIA. OF ROUNDS WITH SAME AS-QUENCHED HRC, mm	LOCATION IN ROUND	QUENCH
50 75	SURFACE	MILD WATER QUENCH
20 30 60 90	3/4 RADIUS FROM CENTER	MILD WATER QUENCH
20 30 40 50 60 80 100	CENTER	MILD WATER QUENCH
20 40 60 80 100	SURFACE	MILD OIL QUENCH
15 30 45 60 75 90	3/4 RADIUS FROM CENTER	MILD OIL QUENCH
10 20 30 40 50 60 75	CENTER	MILD OIL QUENCH

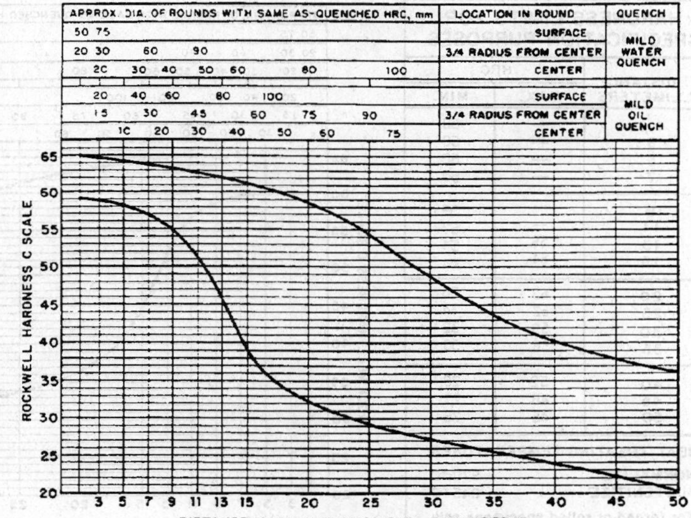

FIGURE 50—UNS H50501—HARDENABILITY BAND—SAE 50B50H

UNS H50601 **HARDENABILITY BAND** SAE 50B60H

%C	%Mn	%Si	%Ni	%Cr	%Mo	%B
0.55/0.65	0.65/1.10	0.15/0.35	--	0.30/0.70	--	0.0005/0.003

HARDNESS LIMITS FOR SPECIFICATION PURPOSES

"J" DISTANCE SIXTEENTHS OF AN INCH	HRC MAX.	HRC MIN.
1	--	60
2	--	60
3	--	60
4	--	60
5	--	60
6	--	59
7	--	57
8	65	53
9	65	47
10	64	42
11	64	39
12	64	37
13	63	36
14	63	35
15	63	34
16	62	34
18	60	33
20	58	31
22	55	30
24	53	29
26	51	28
28	49	27
30	47	26
32	44	25

HEAT TREATING TEMPERATURES

*NORMALIZE	1600°F
AUSTENITIZE	1550°F

*For forged or rolled specimens only

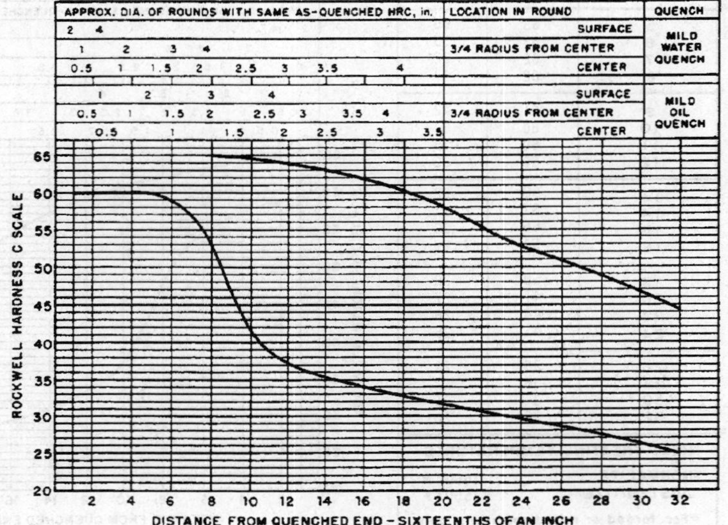

HARDNESS LIMITS FOR SPECIFICATION PURPOSES

"J" DISTANCE MILLIMETERS	HRC MAX.	HRC MIN.
1.5	—	60
3	—	60
5	—	60
7	—	60
9	--	59
11	--	57
13	65	51
15	64	44
20	63	36
25	62	34
30	59	32
35	56	30
40	52	28
45	48	27
50	45	25

HEAT TREATING TEMPERATURES

*NORMALIZE	870°C
AUSTENITIZE	845°C

*For forged or rolled specimens only

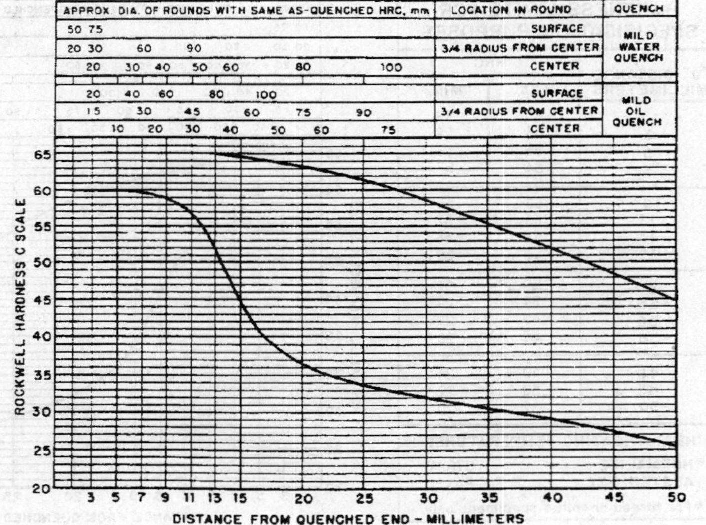

FIGURE 51—UNS H50601—HARDENABILITY BAND—SAE 50B60H

UNS H51200 HARDENABILITY BAND **SAE 5120H**

%C	%Mn	%Si	%Ni	%Cr	%Mo
0.17/0.23	0.60/1.00	0.15/0.35	--	0.60/1.00	--

HARDNESS LIMITS FOR SPECIFICATION PURPOSES

"J" DISTANCE SIXTEENTHS OF AN INCH	HRC MAX.	HRC MIN.
1	48	40
2	46	34
3	41	26
4	36	23
5	33	20
6	30	--
7	28	--
8	27	--
9	25	--
10	24	--
11	23	--
12	22	--
13	21	--
14	21	--
15	20	--
16	--	--
18		
20		
22		
24		
26		
28		
30		
32		

HEAT TREATING TEMPERATURES	
*NORMALIZE	1700 °F
AUSTENITIZE	1700 °F

*For forged or rolled specimens only

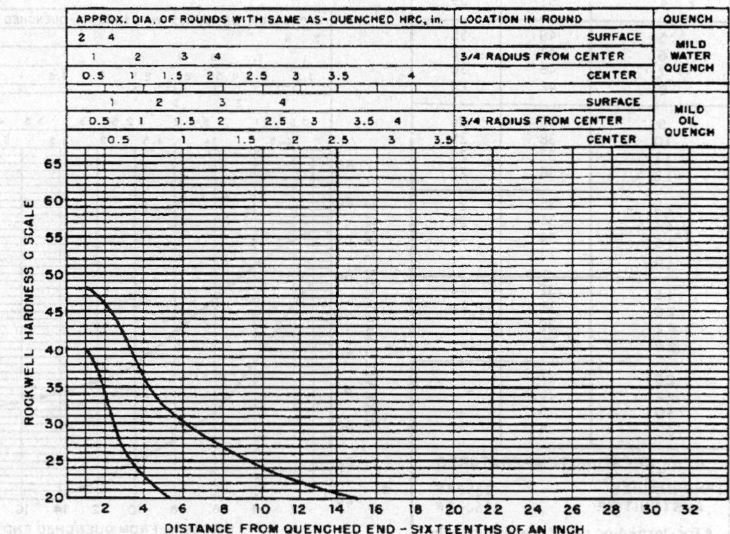

HARDNESS LIMITS FOR SPECIFICATION PURPOSES

"J" DISTANCE MILLIMETERS	HRC MAX.	HRC MIN.
1.5	48	40
3	46	35
5	41	25
7	34	22
9	31	20
11	29	--
13	27	--
15	25	--
20	22	--
25	--	--
30		
35		
40		
45		
50		

HEAT TREATING TEMPERATURES	
*NORMALIZE	925 °C
AUSTENITIZE	925 °C

*For forged or rolled specimens only

APPROX. DIA. OF ROUNDS WITH SAME AS-QUENCHED HRC, mm — LOCATION IN ROUND — QUENCH
SURFACE / 3/4 RADIUS FROM CENTER / CENTER — MILD WATER QUENCH
SURFACE / 3/4 RADIUS FROM CENTER / CENTER — MILD OIL QUENCH
ROCKWELL HARDNESS C SCALE
DISTANCE FROM QUENCHED END - MILLIMETERS

FIGURE 52—UNS H51200—HARDENABILITY BAND—SAE 5120H

UNS H51300 **HARDENABILITY BAND** SAE 5130H

%C	%Mn	%Si	%Ni	%Cr	%Mo
0.27/0.33	0.60/1.00	0.15/0.35	--	0.75/1.20	--

HARDNESS LIMITS FOR SPECIFICATION PURPOSES

"J" DISTANCE SIXTEENTHS OF AN INCH	HRC MAX.	HRC MIN.
1	56	49
2	55	46
3	53	42
4	51	39
5	49	35
6	47	32
7	45	30
8	42	28
9	40	26
10	38	25
11	37	23
12	36	22
13	35	21
14	34	20
15	34	--
16	33	--
18	32	--
20	31	--
22	30	--
24	29	--
26	27	--
28	26	--
30	25	--
32	24	--

HEAT TREATING TEMPERATURES

*NORMALIZE 1650°F
AUSTENITIZE 1600°F

*For forged or rolled specimens only

APPROX. DIA. OF ROUNDS WITH SAME AS-QUENCHED HRC, in. — LOCATION IN ROUND — QUENCH
SURFACE / 3/4 RADIUS FROM CENTER / CENTER — MILD WATER QUENCH
SURFACE / 3/4 RADIUS FROM CENTER / CENTER — MILD OIL QUENCH
ROCKWELL HARDNESS C SCALE
DISTANCE FROM QUENCHED END – SIXTEENTHS OF AN INCH

HARDNESS LIMITS FOR SPECIFICATION PURPOSES

"J" DISTANCE MILLIMETERS	HRC MAX.	HRC MIN.
1.5	56	49
3	55	46
5	53	42
7	50	37
9	48	33
11	45	30
13	42	27
15	39	25
20	35	21
25	33	--
30	31	--
35	30	--
40	28	--
45	26	--
50	24	--

HEAT TREATING TEMPERATURES

*NORMALIZE 900°C
AUSTENITIZE 870°C

*For forged or rolled specimens only

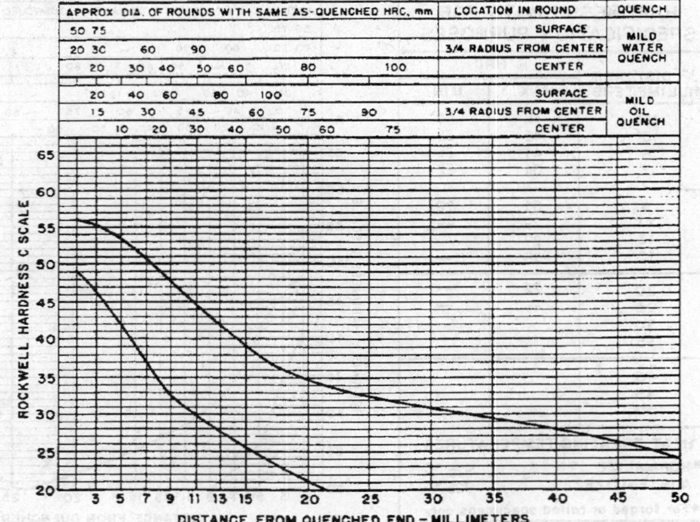

FIGURE 53—UNS H51300—HARDENABILITY BAND—SAE 5130H

HARDNESS LIMITS FOR SPECIFICATION PURPOSES

"J" DISTANCE SIXTEENTHS OF AN INCH	HRC MAX.	HRC MIN.
1	57	50
2	56	47
3	54	43
4	52	40
5	50	35
6	48	32
7	45	29
8	42	27
9	40	25
10	38	24
11	37	23
12	36	22
13	35	21
14	34	20
15	34	--
16	33	--
18	32	--
20	31	--
22	30	--
24	29	--
26	28	--
28	27	--
30	26	--
32	25	--

HEAT TREATING TEMPERATURES

*NORMALIZE	*1650°F
AUSTENITIZE	1600°F

*For forged or rolled specimens only

UNS H51320 **HARDENABILITY BAND** SAE 5132H

%C	%Mn	%Si	%Ni	%Cr	%Mo
0.29/0.35	0.50/0.90	0.15/0.35	--	0.65/1.10	--

APPROX. DIA. OF ROUNDS WITH SAME AS-QUENCHED HRC, in.	LOCATION IN ROUND	QUENCH
2 4	SURFACE	MILD WATER QUENCH
1 2 3 4	3/4 RADIUS FROM CENTER	
0.5 1 1.5 2 2.5 3 3.5 4	CENTER	
1 2 3 4	SURFACE	MILD OIL QUENCH
0.5 1 1.5 2 2.5 3 3.5 4	3/4 RADIUS FROM CENTER	
0.5 1 1.5 2 2.5 3 3.5	CENTER	

ROCKWELL HARDNESS C SCALE

65 60 55 50 45 40 35 30 25 20

2 4 6 8 10 12 14 16 18 20 22 24 26 28 30 32

DISTANCE FROM QUENCHED END - SIXTEENTHS OF AN INCH

HARDNESS LIMITS FOR SPECIFICATION PURPOSES

"J" DISTANCE MILLIMETERS	HRC MAX.	HRC MIN.
1.5	57	50
3	56	47
5	54	42
7	52	38
9	49	33
11	45	29
13	42	26
15	39	25
20	35	21
25	33	--
30	32	--
35	31	--
40	29	--
45	27	--
50	25	--

HEAT TREATING TEMPERATURES

*NORMALIZE	900°C
AUSTENITIZE	870°C

*For forged or rolled specimens only

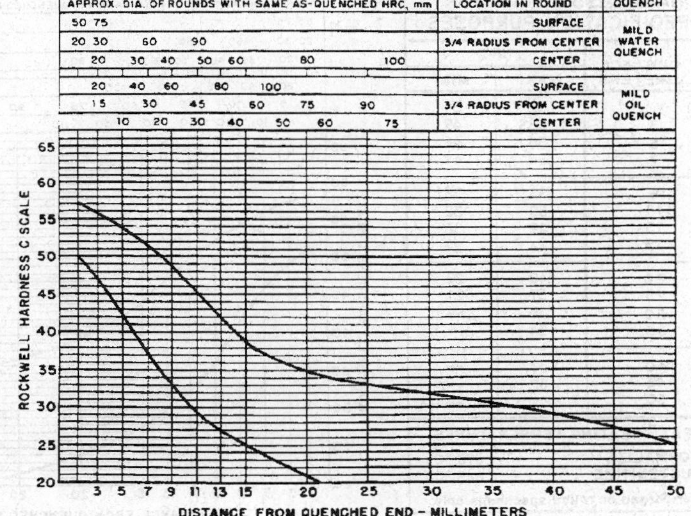

FIGURE 54—UNS H51320—HARDENABILITY BAND—SAE 5132H

UNS H51350 HARDENABILITY BAND SAE 5135H

%C	%Mn	%Si	%Ni	%Cr	%Mo
0.32/0.38	0.50/0.90	0.15/0.35	--	0.70/1.15	--

HARDNESS LIMITS FOR SPECIFICATION PURPOSES

"J" DISTANCE SIXTEENTHS OF AN INCH	HRC MAX.	HRC MIN.
1	58	51
2	57	49
3	56	47
4	55	43
5	54	38
6	52	35
7	50	32
8	47	30
9	45	28
10	43	27
11	41	25
12	40	24
13	39	23
14	38	22
15	37	21
16	37	21
18	36	20
20	35	--
22	34	--
24	33	--
26	32	--
28	32	--
30	31	--
32	30	--

HEAT TREATING TEMPERATURES

*NORMALIZE 1650 °F
AUSTENITIZE 1600 °F

*For forged or rolled specimens only

APPROX. DIA. OF ROUNDS WITH SAME AS-QUENCHED HRC, in. — LOCATION IN ROUND — QUENCH

ROCKWELL HARDNESS C SCALE

DISTANCE FROM QUENCHED END - SIXTEENTHS OF AN INCH

HARDNESS LIMITS FOR SPECIFICATION PURPOSES

"J" DISTANCE MILLIMETERS	HRC MAX.	HRC MIN.
1.5	58	51
3	58	49
5	56	46
7	54	41
9	53	36
11	50	32
13	47	30
15	44	27
20	40	23
25	37	21
30	35	--
35	34	--
40	33	--
45	32	--
50	31	--

HEAT TREATING TEMPERATURES

*NORMALIZE 870 °C
AUSTENITIZE 845 °C

*For forged or rolled specimens only

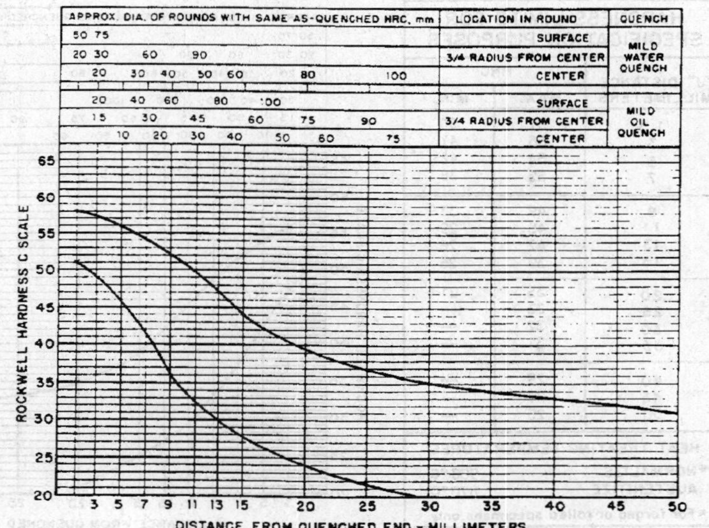

FIGURE 55—UNS H51350—HARDENABILITY BAND—SAE 5135H

HARDENABILITY BAND

UNS H51400 — SAE 5140H

%C	%Mn	%Si	%Ni	%Cr	%Mo
0.37/0.44	0.60/1.00	0.15/0.35	--	0.60/1.00	--

HARDNESS LIMITS FOR SPECIFICATION PURPOSES

"J" DISTANCE SIXTEENTHS OF AN INCH	HRC MAX.	HRC MIN.
1	60	53
2	59	52
3	58	50
4	57	48
5	56	43
6	54	38
7	52	35
8	50	33
9	48	31
10	46	30
11	45	29
12	43	28
13	42	27
14	40	27
15	39	26
16	38	25
18	37	24
20	36	23
22	35	21
24	34	20
26	34	--
28	33	--
30	33	--
32	32	--

HEAT TREATING TEMPERATURES

*NORMALIZE	1600 °F
AUSTENITIZE	1550 °F

*For forged or rolled specimens only

APPROX. DIA. OF ROUNDS WITH SAME AS-QUENCHED HRC, in.	LOCATION IN ROUND	QUENCH
2 4	SURFACE	MILD WATER QUENCH
1 2 3 4	3/4 RADIUS FROM CENTER	
0.5 1 1.5 2 2.5 3 3.5 4	CENTER	
1 2 3 4	SURFACE	MILD OIL QUENCH
0.5 1 1.5 2 2.5 3 3.5 4	3/4 RADIUS FROM CENTER	
0.5 1 1.5 2 2.5 3 3.5	CENTER	

ROCKWELL HARDNESS C SCALE: 20 25 30 35 40 45 50 55 60 65

DISTANCE FROM QUENCHED END – SIXTEENTHS OF AN INCH: 2 4 6 8 10 12 14 16 18 20 22 24 26 28 30 32

HARDNESS LIMITS FOR SPECIFICATION PURPOSES

"J" DISTANCE MILLIMETERS	HRC MAX.	HRC MIN.
1.5	60	53
3	59	52
5	58	50
7	57	45
9	55	40
11	53	35
13	50	32
15	47	30
20	42	28
25	39	25
30	36	23
35	35	21
40	34	--
45	33	--
50	32	--

HEAT TREATING TEMPERATURES

*NORMALIZE	870 °C
AUSTENITIZE	845 °C

*For forged or rolled specimens only

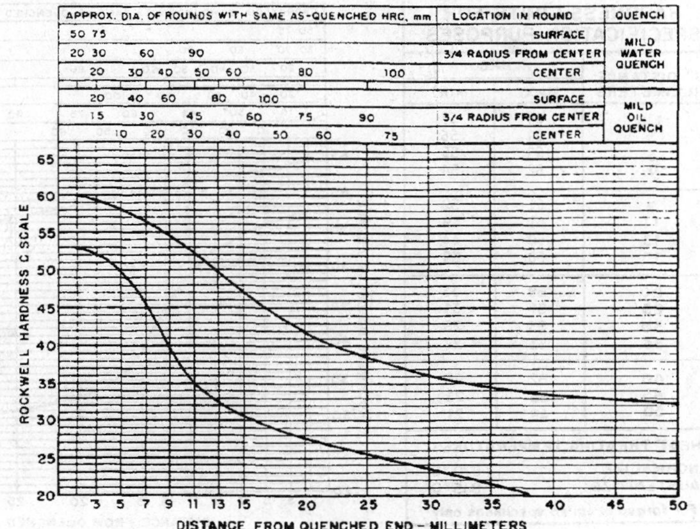

FIGURE 56—UNS H51400—HARDENABILITY BAND—SAE 5140H

UNS 51470 **HARDENABILITY BAND** SAE 5147H

%C	%Mn	%Si	%Ni	%Cr	%Mo
0.45/0.52	0.60/1.05	0.15/0.35	--	0.80/1.25	--

HARDNESS LIMITS FOR SPECIFICATION PURPOSES

"J" DISTANCE SIXTEENTHS OF AN INCH	HRC MAX.	HRC MIN.
1	64	57
2	64	56
3	63	55
4	62	54
5	62	53
6	61	52
7	61	49
8	60	45
9	60	40
10	59	37
11	59	35
12	58	34
13	58	33
14	57	32
15	57	32
16	56	31
18	55	30
20	54	29
22	53	27
24	52	26
26	51	25
28	50	24
30	49	22
32	48	21

HEAT TREATING TEMPERATURES

*NORMALIZE 1600 °F
AUSTENITIZE 1550 °F

*For forged or rolled specimens only

APPROX. DIA. OF ROUNDS WITH SAME AS-QUENCHED HRC, in. | LOCATION IN ROUND | QUENCH

MILD WATER QUENCH: SURFACE 2 4; 3/4 RADIUS FROM CENTER 1 2 3 4; CENTER 0.5 1 1.5 2 2.5 3 3.5 4

MILD OIL QUENCH: SURFACE 1 2 3 4; 3/4 RADIUS FROM CENTER 0.5 1 1.5 2 2.5 3 3.5 4; CENTER 0.5 1 1.5 2 2.5 3 3.5

ROCKWELL HARDNESS C SCALE

DISTANCE FROM QUENCHED END - SIXTEENTHS OF AN INCH

HARDNESS LIMITS FOR SPECIFICATION PURPOSES

"J" DISTANCE MILLIMETERS	HRC MAX.	HRC MIN.
1.5	64	57
3	64	56
5	63	55
7	62	54
9	61	52
11	61	49
13	60	44
15	60	39
20	58	33
25	57	31
30	55	29
35	53	27
40	52	25
45	50	23
50	49	21

HEAT TREATING TEMPERATURES

*NORMALIZE 870 °C
AUSTENITIZE 845 °C

*For forged or rolled specimens only

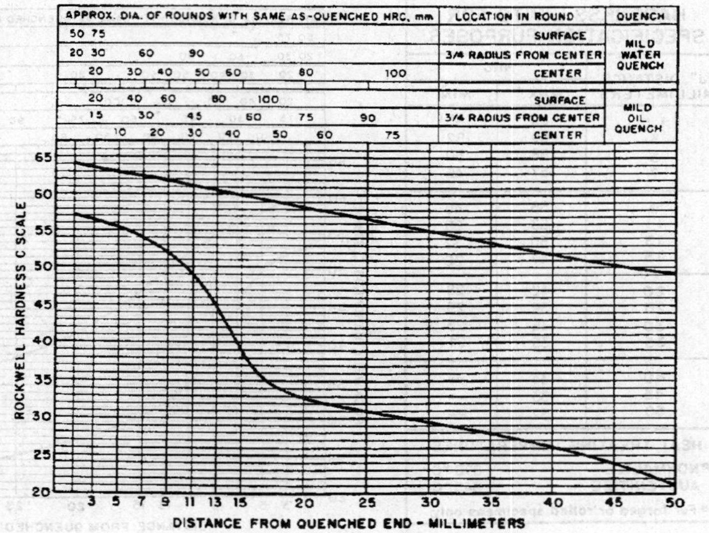

FIGURE 57—UNS 51470—HARDENABILITY BAND—SAE 5147H

UNS H51500 **HARDENABILITY BAND** SAE 5150H

%C	%Mn	%Si	%Ni	%Cr	%Mo
0.47/0.54	0.60/1.00	0.15/0.35	--	0.60/1.00	--

HARDNESS LIMITS FOR SPECIFICATION PURPOSES

"J" DISTANCE SIXTEENTHS OF AN INCH	HRC MAX.	HRC MIN.
1	65	59
2	65	58
3	64	57
4	63	56
5	62	53
6	61	49
7	60	42
8	59	38
9	58	36
10	56	34
11	55	33
12	53	32
13	51	31
14	50	31
15	48	30
16	47	30
18	45	29
20	43	28
22	42	27
24	41	26
26	40	25
28	39	24
30	39	23
32	38	22

HEAT TREATING TEMPERATURES	
*NORMALIZE	1600 °F
AUSTENITIZE	1550 °F

*For forged or rolled specimens only

APPROX. DIA. OF ROUNDS WITH SAME AS-QUENCHED HRC, in.	LOCATION IN ROUND	QUENCH
2 4	SURFACE	MILD WATER QUENCH
1 2 3 4	3/4 RADIUS FROM CENTER	
0.5 1 1.5 2 2.5 3 3.5 4	CENTER	
1 2 3 4	SURFACE	MILD OIL QUENCH
0.5 1 1.5 2 2.5 3 3.5 4	3/4 RADIUS FROM CENTER	
0.5 1 1.5 2 2.5 3 3.5	CENTER	

ROCKWELL HARDNESS C SCALE (20–65)

DISTANCE FROM QUENCHED END – SIXTEENTHS OF AN INCH (2–32)

HARDNESS LIMITS FOR SPECIFICATION PURPOSES

"J" DISTANCE MILLIMETERS	HRC MAX.	HRC MIN.
1.5	65	59
3	65	58
5	64	57
7	63	54
9	62	50
11	60	43
13	58	37
15	57	35
20	52	31
25	47	29
30	44	28
35	42	27
40	40	26
45	39	24
50	38	22

HEAT TREATING TEMPERATURES	
*NORMALIZE	870 °C
AUSTENITIZE	845 °C

*For forged or rolled specimens only

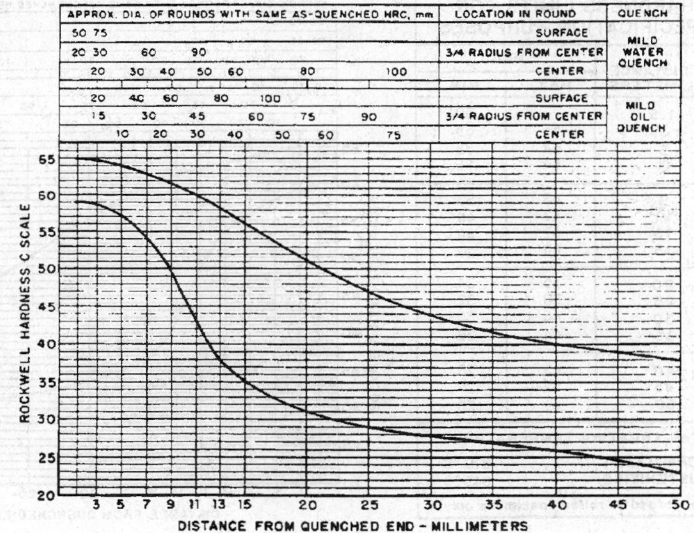

FIGURE 58—UNS H51500—HARDENABILITY BAND—SAE 5150H

UNS H51550 **HARDENABILITY BAND** SAE 5155H

%C	%Mn	%Si	%Ni	%Cr	%Mo
0.50/0.60	0.60/1.00	0.15/0.35	--	0.60/1.00	--

HARDNESS LIMITS FOR SPECIFICATION PURPOSES

"J" DISTANCE SIXTEENTHS OF AN INCH	HRC MAX.	HRC MIN.
1	--	60
2	65	59
3	64	58
4	64	57
5	63	55
6	63	52
7	62	47
8	62	41
9	61	37
10	60	36
11	59	35
12	57	34
13	55	34
14	52	33
15	51	33
16	49	32
18	47	31
20	45	31
22	44	30
24	43	29
26	42	28
28	41	27
30	41	26
32	40	25

HEAT TREATING TEMPERATURES

*NORMALIZE	1600°F
AUSTENITIZE	1550°F

* For forged or rolled specimens only

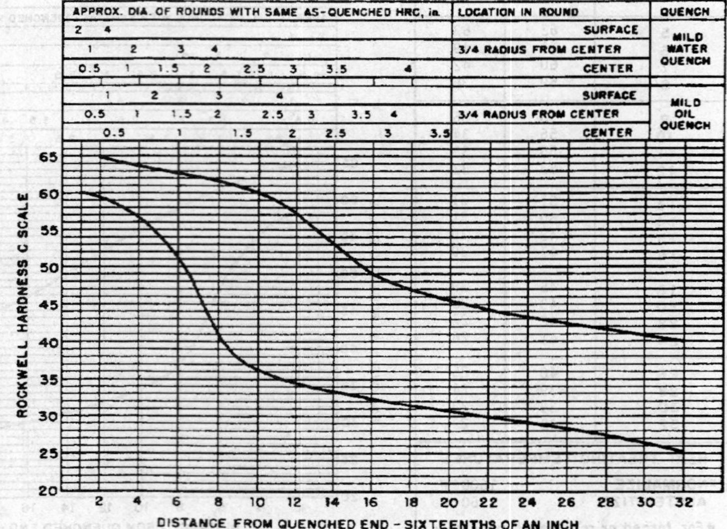

HARDNESS LIMITS FOR SPECIFICATION PURPOSES

"J" DISTANCE MILLIMETERS	HRC MAX.	HRC MIN.
1.5	--	60
3	65	59
5	64	58
7	64	56
9	63	53
11	62	48
13	61	40
15	60	37
20	56	34
25	50	32
30	46	30
35	44	29
40	43	28
45	42	27
50	41	25

HEAT TREATING TEMPERATURES

*NORMALIZE	870°C
AUSTENITIZE	845°C

* For forged or rolled specimens only

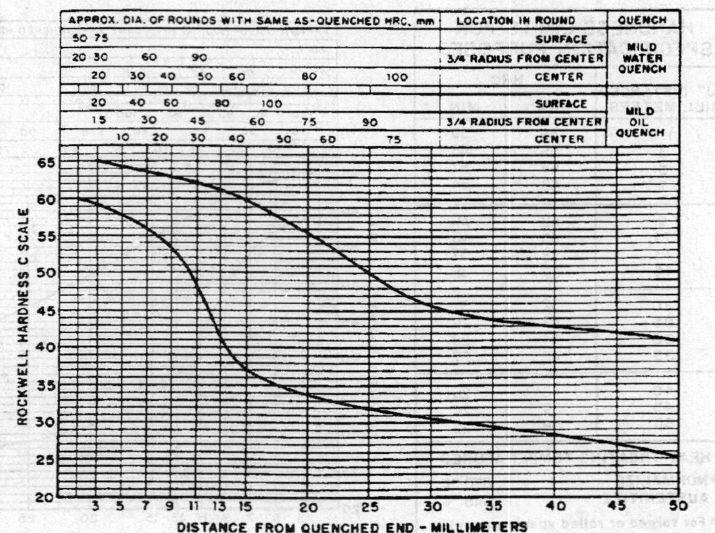

FIGURE 59—UNS H51550—HARDENABILITY BAND—SAE 5155H

UNS H51600 **HARDENABILITY BAND** SAE 5160H

%C	%Mn	%Si	%Ni	%Cr	%Mo
0.55/0.65	0.65/1.00	0.15/0.35	--	0.60/1.00	--

HARDNESS LIMITS FOR SPECIFICATION PURPOSES

"J" DISTANCE SIXTEENTHS OF AN INCH	HRC MAX.	HRC MIN.
1	--	60
2	--	60
3	--	60
4	65	59
5	65	58
6	64	56
7	64	52
8	63	47
9	62	42
10	61	39
11	60	37
12	59	36
13	58	35
14	56	35
15	54	34
16	52	34
18	48	33
20	47	32
22	46	31
24	45	30
26	44	29
28	43	28
30	43	28
32	42	27

HEAT TREATING TEMPERATURES	
*NORMALIZE	1600°F
AUSTENITIZE	1550°F

*For forged or rolled specimens only

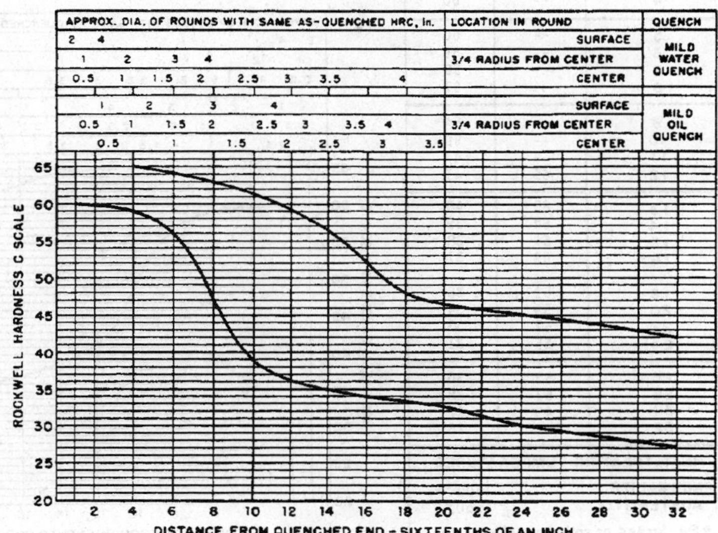

HARDNESS LIMITS FOR SPECIFICATION PURPOSES

"J" DISTANCE MILLIMETERS	HRC MAX.	HRC MIN.
1.5	--	60
3	—	60
5	—	60
7	—	59
9	65	57
11	64	52
13	64	46
15	62	40
20	58	36
25	52	34
30	48	32
35	46	30
40	44	28
45	42	27
50	41	27

HEAT TREATING TEMPERATURES	
*NORMALIZE	870°C
AUSTENITIZE	845°C

*For forged or rolled specimens only

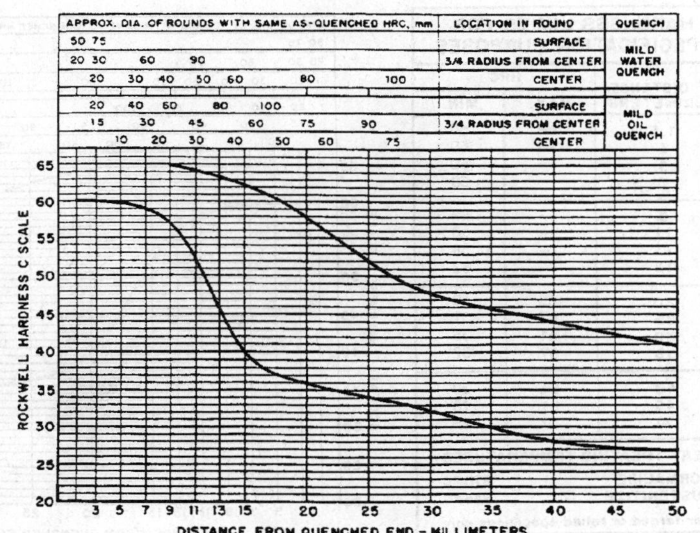

FIGURE 60—UNS H51600—HARDENABILITY BAND—SAE 5160H

UNS H51601 **HARDENABILITY BAND** SAE 51B60H

%C	%Mn	%Si	%Ni	%Cr	%Mo	%B
0.55/0.65	0.65/1.10	0.15/0.35	--	0.60/1.00	--	0.0005/0.003

HARDNESS LIMITS FOR SPECIFICATION PURPOSES

"J" DISTANCE SIXTEENTHS OF AN INCH	HRC MAX.	HRC MIN.
1	--	60
2	--	60
3	--	60
4	--	60
5	--	60
6	--	59
7	--	58
8	--	57
9	--	54
10	--	50
11	--	44
12	65	41
13	65	40
14	64	39
15	64	38
16	63	37
18	61	36
20	59	34
22	57	33
24	55	31
26	53	30
28	51	28
30	49	27
32	47	25

HEAT TREATING TEMPERATURES

*NORMALIZE 1600 °F
AUSTENITIZE 1550 °F

* For forged or rolled specimens only

APPROX. DIA. OF ROUNDS WITH SAME AS-QUENCHED HRC, in. — LOCATION IN ROUND — QUENCH
2 4 — SURFACE — MILD WATER QUENCH
1 2 3 4 — 3/4 RADIUS FROM CENTER
0.5 1 1.5 2 2.5 3 3.5 4 — CENTER
1 2 3 4 — SURFACE — MILD OIL QUENCH
0.5 1 1.5 2 2.5 3 3.5 4 — 3/4 RADIUS FROM CENTER
0.5 1 1.5 2 2.5 3 3.5 — CENTER

ROCKWELL HARDNESS C SCALE: 20 25 30 35 40 45 50 55 60 65
DISTANCE FROM QUENCHED END - SIXTEENTHS OF AN INCH: 2 4 6 8 10 12 14 16 18 20 22 24 26 28 30 32

HARDNESS LIMITS FOR SPECIFICATION PURPOSES

"J" DISTANCE MILLIMETERS	HRC MAX.	HRC MIN.
1.5	—	60
3	—	60
5	—	60
7	—	60
9	--	59
11	—	58
13	—	56
15	—	52
20	65	40
25	63	37
30	61	35
35	57	32
40	54	30
45	51	28
50	47	25

HEAT TREATING TEMPERATURES

*NORMALIZE 870 °C
AUSTENITIZE 845 °C

* For forged or rolled specimens only

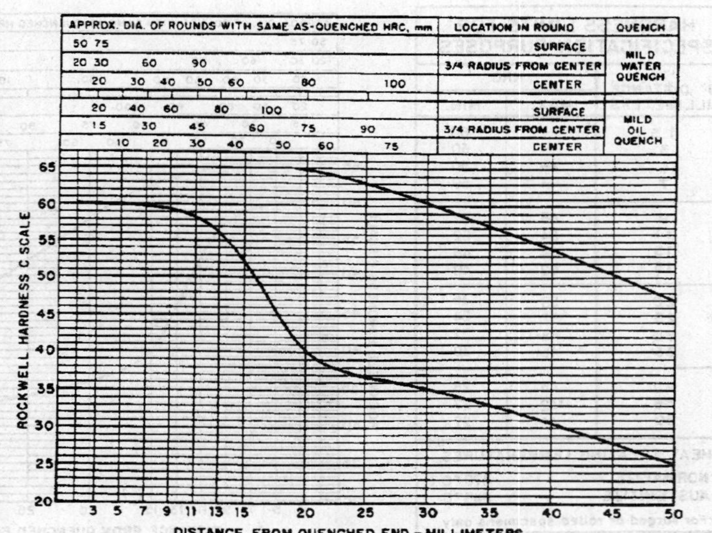

FIGURE 61—UNS H51601—HARDENABILITY BAND—SAE 51B60H

UNS H61180 **HARDENABILITY BAND** SAE 6118H

%C	%Mn	%Si	%Ni	%Cr	%Mo	% V
0.15/0.21	0.40/0.80	0.15/0.35	--	0.40/0.80	--	0.10/0.15

HARDNESS LIMITS FOR SPECIFICATION PURPOSES

"J" DISTANCE SIXTEENTHS OF AN INCH	HRC MAX.	HRC MIN.
1	46	39
2	44	36
3	38	28
4	33	24
5	30	22
6	28	20
7	27	--
8	26	--
9	26	--
10	25	--
11	25	--
12	24	--
13	24	--
14	23	--
15	23	--
16	22	--
18	22	--
20	21	--
22	21	--
24	20	--
26	--	--
28	--	--
30	--	--
32	--	--

HEAT TREATING TEMPERATURES

*NORMALIZE 1700 °F
AUSTENITIZE 1700 °F

*For forged or rolled specimens only

APPROX. DIA. OF ROUNDS WITH SAME AS-QUENCHED HRC, in. | LOCATION IN ROUND | QUENCH

2 4 — SURFACE — MILD WATER QUENCH
1 2 3 4 — 3/4 RADIUS FROM CENTER
0.5 1 1.5 2 2.5 3 3.5 4 — CENTER
1 2 3 4 — SURFACE — MILD OIL QUENCH
0.5 1 1.5 2 2.5 3 3.5 4 — 3/4 RADIUS FROM CENTER
0.5 1 1.5 2 2.5 3 3.5 — CENTER

ROCKWELL HARDNESS C SCALE
DISTANCE FROM QUENCHED END – SIXTEENTHS OF AN INCH

HARDNESS LIMITS FOR SPECIFICATION PURPOSES

"J" DISTANCE MILLIMETERS	HRC MAX.	HRC MIN.
1.5	46	39
3	44	36
5	37	28
7	32	23
9	30	20
11	28	--
13	27	--
15	25	--
20	24	--
25	23	--
30	22	--
35	21	--
40	20	--
45	--	--
50		--

HEAT TREATING TEMPERATURES

*NORMALIZE 925 °C
AUSTENITIZE 925 °C

*For forged or rolled specimens only

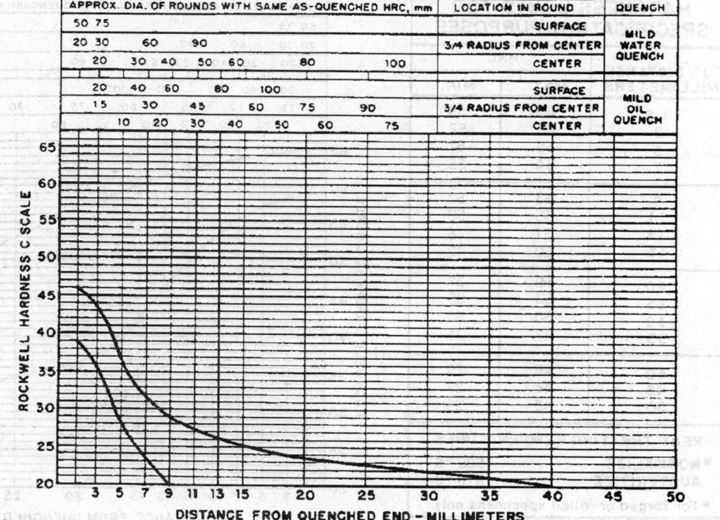

FIGURE 62—UNS H61180—HARDENABILITY BAND—SAE 6118H

HARDNESS LIMITS FOR SPECIFICATION PURPOSES		
"J" DISTANCE SIXTEENTHS OF AN INCH	HRC MAX.	HRC MIN.
1	65	59
2	65	58
3	64	57
4	64	56
5	63	55
6	63	53
7	62	50
8	61	47
9	61	43
10	60	41
11	59	39
12	58	38
13	57	37
14	55	36
15	54	35
16	52	35
18	50	34
20	48	32
22	47	31
24	46	30
26	45	29
28	44	27
30	43	26
32	42	25

HEAT TREATING TEMPERATURES

*NORMALIZE 1650 °F
AUSTENITIZE 1600 °F

*For forged or rolled specimens only

UNS H61500 **HARDENABILITY BAND** SAE 6150H

%C	%Mn	%Si	%Ni	%Cr	%Mo	% V
0.47/0.54	0.60/1.00	0.15/0.35	--	0.75/1.20	--	0.15 min.

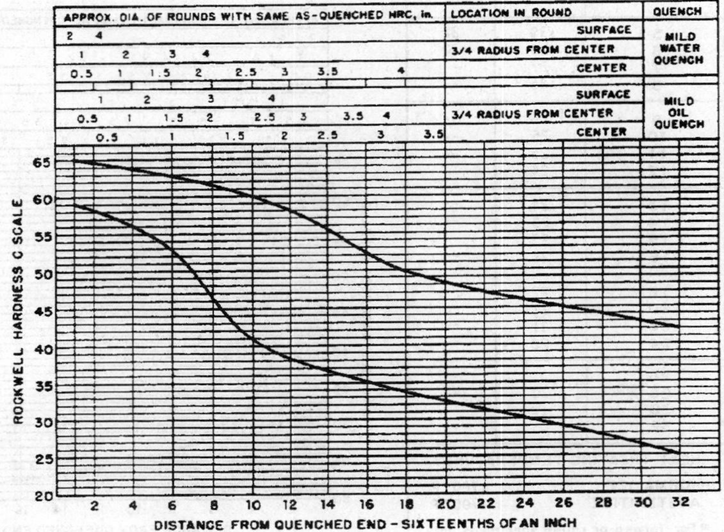

HARDNESS LIMITS FOR SPECIFICATION PURPOSES		
"J" DISTANCE MILLIMETERS	HRC MAX.	HRC MIN.
1.5	65	59
3	65	58
5	65	57
7	64	55
9	63	53
11	63	50
13	61	46
15	60	42
20	58	37
25	53	35
30	50	33
35	47	31
40	45	29
45	44	27
50	43	25

HEAT TREATING TEMPERATURES

*NORMALIZE 900 °C
AUSTENITIZE 870 °C

*For forged or rolled specimens only

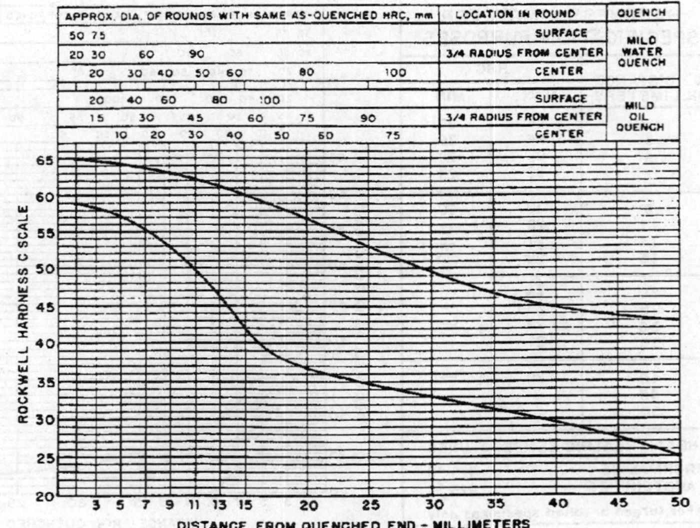

FIGURE 63—UNS H61500—HARDENABILITY BAND—SAE 6150H

UNS H81451 — **HARDENABILITY BAND** — SAE 81B45H

%C	%Mn	%Si	%Ni	%Cr	%Mo	%B
0.42/0.49	0.70/1.05	0.15/0.35	0.15/0.45	0.30/0.60	0.08/0.15	0.0005/0.003

HARDNESS LIMITS FOR SPECIFICATION PURPOSES

"J" DISTANCE SIXTEENTHS OF AN INCH	HRC MAX.	HRC MIN.
1	63	56
2	63	56
3	63	56
4	63	56
5	63	55
6	63	54
7	62	53
8	62	51
9	61	48
10	60	44
11	60	41
12	59	39
13	58	38
14	57	37
15	57	36
16	56	35
18	55	34
20	53	32
22	52	31
24	50	30
26	49	29
28	47	28
30	45	28
32	43	27

HEAT TREATING TEMPERATURES	
*NORMALIZE	1600 °F
AUSTENITIZE	1550 °F

* For forged or rolled specimens only

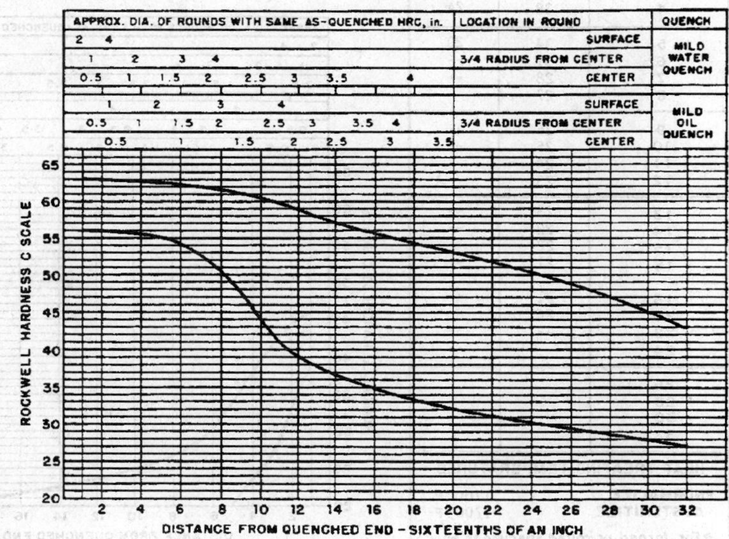

HARDNESS LIMITS FOR SPECIFICATION PURPOSES

"J" DISTANCE MILLIMETERS	HRC MAX.	HRC MIN.
1.5	63	56
3	63	56
5	63	56
7	63	56
9	63	55
11	63	53
13	62	49
15	60	47
20	58	38
25	56	35
30	54	33
35	52	31
40	50	29
45	47	28
50	44	27

HEAT TREATING TEMPERATURES	
*NORMALIZE	870 °C
AUSTENITIZE	845 °C

* For forged or rolled specimens only

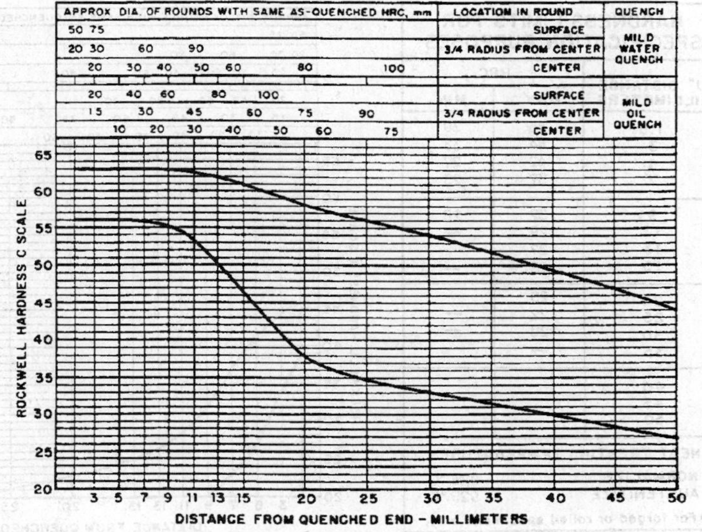

FIGURE 64—UNS H81451—HARDENABILITY BAND—SAE 81B45H

HARDENABILITY BAND

UNS H86170 — SAE 8617H

%C	%Mn	%Si	%Ni	%Cr	%Mo
0.14/0.20	0.60/0.95	0.15/0.35	0.35/0.75	0.35/0.65	0.15/0.25

HARDNESS LIMITS FOR SPECIFICATION PURPOSES

"J" DISTANCE SIXTEENTHS OF AN INCH	HRC MAX.	HRC MIN.
1	46	39
2	44	33
3	41	27
4	38	24
5	34	20
6	31	--
7	28	--
8	27	--
9	26	--
10	25	--
11	24	--
12	23	--
13	23	--
14	22	--
15	22	--
16	21	--
18	21	--
20	20	--
22	--	--
24	--	--
26		
28		
30		
32		

HEAT TREATING TEMPERATURES	
*NORMALIZE	1700°F
AUSTENITIZE	1700°F

*For forged or rolled specimens only

APPROX. DIA. OF ROUNDS WITH SAME AS-QUENCHED HRC, in. — LOCATION IN ROUND — QUENCH: SURFACE, 3/4 RADIUS FROM CENTER, CENTER — MILD WATER QUENCH; SURFACE, 3/4 RADIUS FROM CENTER, CENTER — MILD OIL QUENCH

ROCKWELL HARDNESS C SCALE

DISTANCE FROM QUENCHED END - SIXTEENTHS OF AN INCH

HARDNESS LIMITS FOR SPECIFICATION PURPOSES

"J" DISTANCE MILLIMETERS	HRC MAX.	HRC MIN.
1.5	46	39
3	44	33
5	42	27
7	37	23
9	32	20
11	29	--
13	27	--
15	25	--
20	23	--
25	22	--
30	20	--
35	—	--
40		
45		
50		

HEAT TREATING TEMPERATURES	
*NORMALIZE	925°C
AUSTENITIZE	925°C

*For forged or rolled specimens only

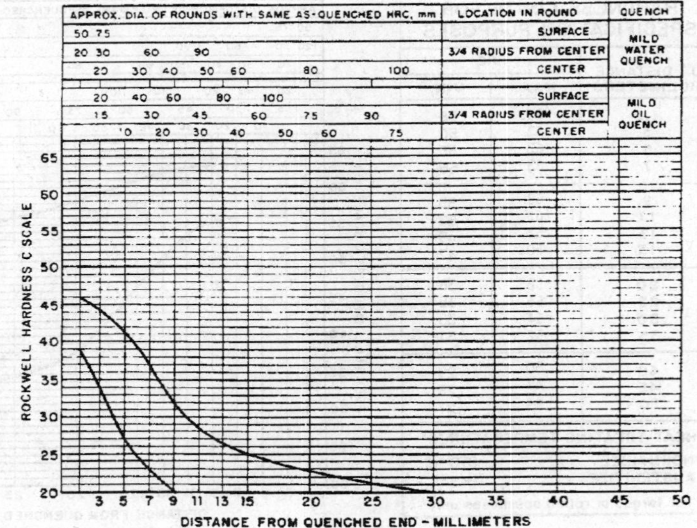

FIGURE 65—UNS H86170—HARDENABILITY BAND—SAE 8617H

UNS H86200 **HARDENABILITY BAND** **SAE 8620H**

%C	%Mn	%Si	%Ni	%Cr	%Mo
0.17/0.23	0.60/0.95	0.15/0.35	0.35/0.75	0.35/0.65	0.15/0.25

HARDNESS LIMITS FOR SPECIFICATION PURPOSES

"J" DISTANCE SIXTEENTHS OF AN INCH	HRC MAX.	HRC MIN.
1	48	41
2	47	37
3	44	32
4	41	27
5	37	23
6	34	21
7	32	--
8	30	--
9	29	--
10	28	--
11	27	--
12	26	--
13	25	--
14	25	--
15	24	--
16	24	--
18	23	--
20	23	--
22	23	--
24	23	--
26	23	--
28	22	--
30	22	--
32	22	--

HEAT TREATING TEMPERATURES

*NORMALIZE 1700 °F

AUSTENITIZE 1700 °F

*For forged or rolled specimens only

APPROX. DIA. OF ROUNDS WITH SAME AS-QUENCHED HRC, in. | LOCATION IN ROUND | QUENCH

MILD WATER QUENCH: SURFACE 2 4; 3/4 RADIUS FROM CENTER 1 2 3 4; CENTER 0.5 1 1.5 2 2.5 3 3.5 4

MILD OIL QUENCH: SURFACE 1 2 3 4; 3/4 RADIUS FROM CENTER 0.5 1 1.5 2 2.5 3 3.5 4; CENTER 0.5 1 1.5 2 2.5 3 3.5

ROCKWELL HARDNESS C SCALE (20–65)

DISTANCE FROM QUENCHED END – SIXTEENTHS OF AN INCH (2–32)

HARDNESS LIMITS FOR SPECIFICATION PURPOSES

"J" DISTANCE MILLIMETERS	HRC MAX.	HRC MIN.
1.5	48	41
3	47	37
5	44	31
7	40	25
9	35	22
11	33	20
13	30	--
15	29	--
20	26	--
25	24	--
30	23	--
35	23	--
40	23	--
45	22	--
50	22	--

HEAT TREATING TEMPERATURES

*NORMALIZE 925 °C

AUSTENITIZE 925 °C

*For forged or rolled specimens only

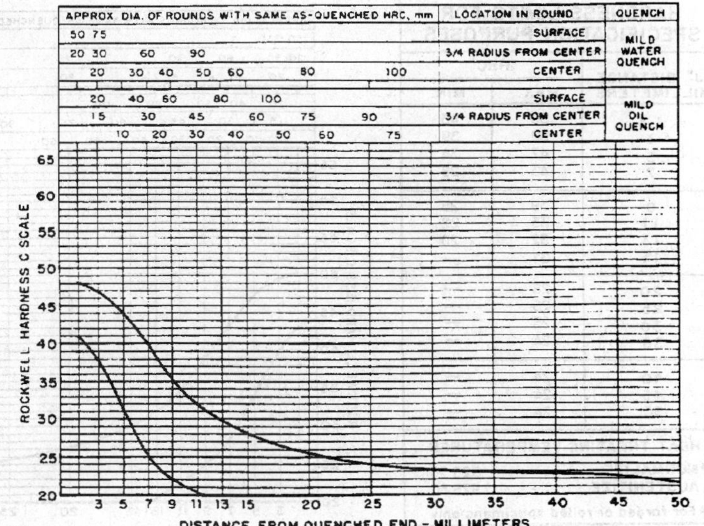

FIGURE 66—UNS H86200—HARDENABILITY BAND—SAE 8620H

HARDNESS LIMITS FOR SPECIFICATION PURPOSES

"J" DISTANCE SIXTEENTHS OF AN INCH	HRC MAX.	HRC MIN.
1	50	43
2	49	39
3	47	34
4	44	30
5	40	26
6	37	24
7	34	22
8	32	20
9	31	--
10	30	--
11	29	--
12	28	--
13	27	--
14	26	--
15	26	--
16	25	--
18	25	--
20	24	--
22	24	--
24	24	--
26	24	--
28	24	--
30	24	--
32	24	--

HEAT TREATING TEMPERATURES

*NORMALIZE 1700°F

AUSTENITIZE 1700°F

*For forged or rolled specimens only

UNS H86220 — **HARDENABILITY BAND** — **SAE 8622H**

%C	%Mn	%Si	%Ni	%Cr	%Mo
0.19/0.25	0.60/0.95	0.15/0.35	0.35/0.75	0.35/0.65	0.15/0.25

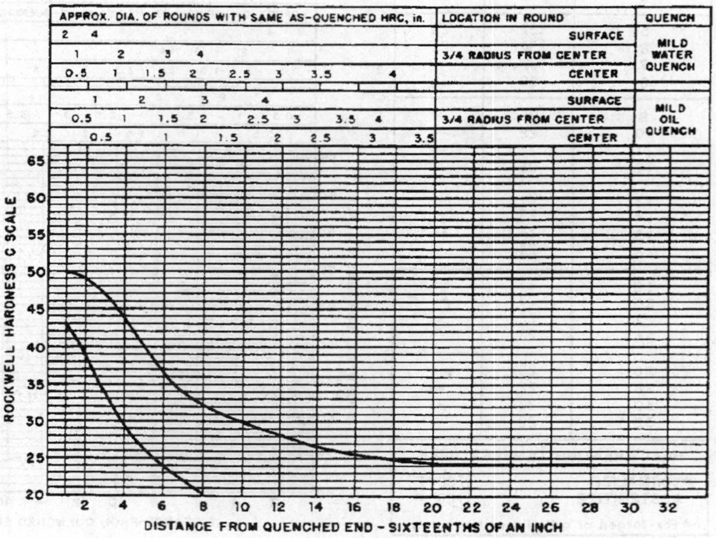
APPROX. DIA. OF ROUNDS WITH SAME AS-QUENCHED HRC, in.
LOCATION IN ROUND
QUENCH
SURFACE
3/4 RADIUS FROM CENTER
CENTER
MILD WATER QUENCH
MILD OIL QUENCH
ROCKWELL HARDNESS C SCALE
DISTANCE FROM QUENCHED END - SIXTEENTHS OF AN INCH

HARDNESS LIMITS FOR SPECIFICATION PURPOSES

"J" DISTANCE MILLIMETERS	HRC MAX.	HRC MIN.
1.5	50	43
3	50	39
5	47	34
7	43	28
9	39	25
11	35	22
13	32	20
15	31	--
20	28	--
25	26	--
30	25	--
35	24	--
40	24	--
45	24	--
50	24	--

HEAT TREATING TEMPERATURES

*NORMALIZE 925°C

AUSTENITIZE 925°C

*For forged or rolled specimens only

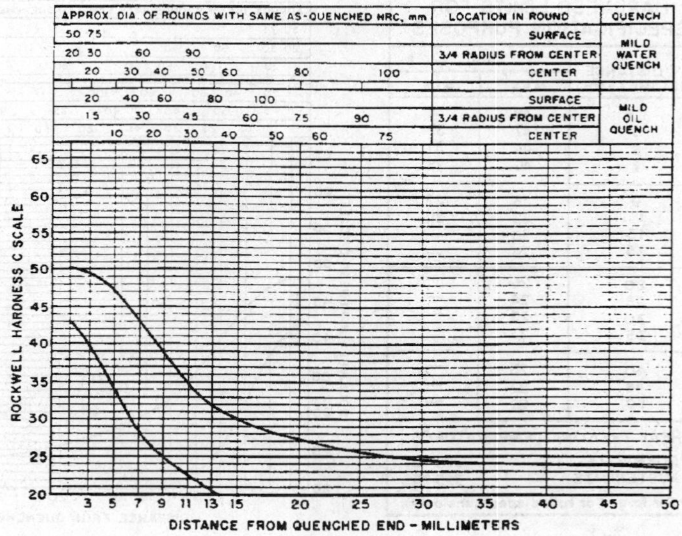
APPROX. DIA. OF ROUNDS WITH SAME AS-QUENCHED HRC, mm
LOCATION IN ROUND
QUENCH
SURFACE
3/4 RADIUS FROM CENTER
CENTER
MILD WATER QUENCH
MILD OIL QUENCH
ROCKWELL HARDNESS C SCALE
DISTANCE FROM QUENCHED END - MILLIMETERS

FIGURE 67—UNS H86220—HARDENABILITY BAND—SAE 8622H

UNS H86250 **HARDENABILITY BAND** SAE 8625H

%C	%Mn	%Si	%Ni	%Cr	%Mo
0.22/0.28	0.60/0.95	0.15/0.35	0.35/0.75	0.35/0.65	0.15/0.25

HARDNESS LIMITS FOR SPECIFICATION PURPOSES

"J" DISTANCE SIXTEENTHS OF AN INCH	HRC MAX.	HRC MIN.
1	52	45
2	51	41
3	48	36
4	46	32
5	43	29
6	40	27
7	37	25
8	35	23
9	33	22
10	32	21
11	31	20
12	30	--
13	29	--
14	28	--
15	28	--
16	27	--
18	27	--
20	26	--
22	26	--
24	26	--
26	26	--
28	25	--
30	25	--
32	25	--

HEAT TREATING TEMPERATURES

*NORMALIZE	1650 °F
AUSTENITIZE	1600 °F

*For forged or rolled specimens only

APPROX. DIA. OF ROUNDS WITH SAME AS-QUENCHED HRC, in. — LOCATION IN ROUND — QUENCH: SURFACE, 3/4 RADIUS FROM CENTER, CENTER — MILD WATER QUENCH; SURFACE, 3/4 RADIUS FROM CENTER, CENTER — MILD OIL QUENCH

ROCKWELL HARDNESS C SCALE

DISTANCE FROM QUENCHED END - SIXTEENTHS OF AN INCH

HARDNESS LIMITS FOR SPECIFICATION PURPOSES

"J" DISTANCE MILLIMETERS	HRC MAX.	HRC MIN.
1.5	52	45
3	51	40
5	48	35
7	45	31
9	41	28
11	38	25
13	35	23
15	33	21
20	29	--
25	28	--
30	27	--
35	26	--
40	26	--
45	26	--
50	25	--

HEAT TREATING TEMPERATURES

*NORMALIZE	900 °C
AUSTENITIZE	870 °C

*For forged or rolled specimens only

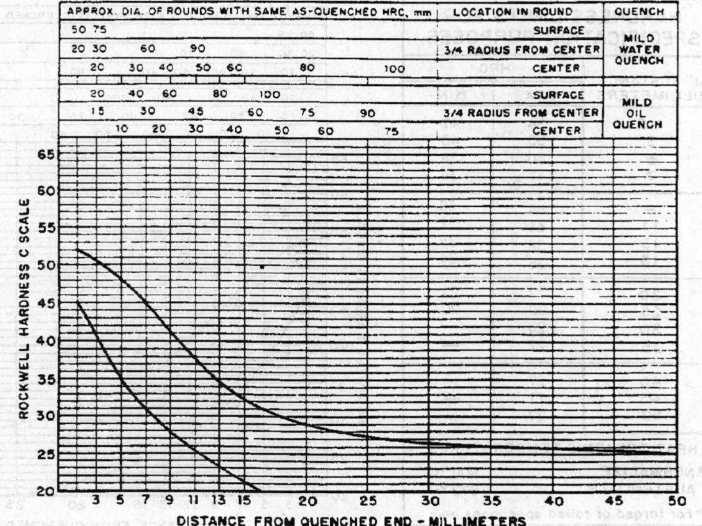

FIGURE 68—UNS H86250—HARDENABILITY BAND—SAE 8625H

UNS H86270 **HARDENABILITY BAND** SAE 8627H

%C	%Mn	%Si	%Ni	%Cr	%Mo
0.24/0.30	0.60/0.95	0.15/0.35	0.35/0.75	0.35/0.65	0.15/0.25

HARDNESS LIMITS FOR SPECIFICATION PURPOSES

"J" DISTANCE SIXTEENTHS OF AN INCH	HRC MAX.	HRC MIN.
1	54	47
2	52	43
3	50	38
4	48	35
5	45	32
6	43	29
7	40	27
8	38	26
9	36	24
10	34	24
11	33	23
12	32	22
13	31	21
14	30	21
15	30	20
16	29	20
18	28	--
20	28	--
22	28	--
24	27	--
26	27	--
28	27	--
30	27	--
32	27	--

HEAT TREATING TEMPERATURES

*NORMALIZE	1650 °F
AUSTENITIZE	1600 °F

*For forged or rolled specimens only

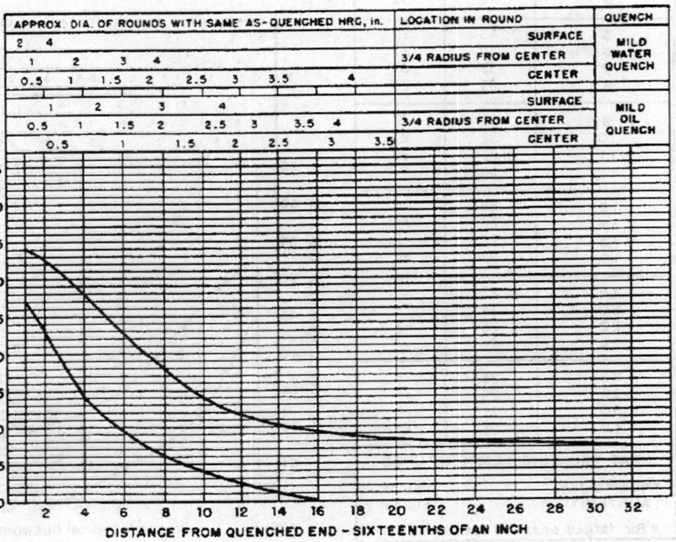

APPROX. DIA. OF ROUNDS WITH SAME AS-QUENCHED HRC, in.	LOCATION IN ROUND	QUENCH
2 4	SURFACE	MILD WATER QUENCH
1 2 3 4	3/4 RADIUS FROM CENTER	
0.5 1 1.5 2 2.5 3 3.5 4	CENTER	
1 2 3 4	SURFACE	MILD OIL QUENCH
0.5 1 1.5 2 2.5 3 3.5 4	3/4 RADIUS FROM CENTER	
0.5 1 1.5 2 2.5 3 3.5	CENTER	

ROCKWELL HARDNESS C SCALE (20–65)

DISTANCE FROM QUENCHED END - SIXTEENTHS OF AN INCH (2–32)

HARDNESS LIMITS FOR SPECIFICATION PURPOSES

"J" DISTANCE MILLIMETERS	HRC MAX.	HRC MIN.
1.5	54	47
3	53	43
5	50	38
7	47	34
9	44	30
11	41	27
13	38	25
15	35	24
20	32	21
25	30	20
30	28	—
35	27	—
40	27	—
45	27	—
50	27	—

HEAT TREATING TEMPERATURES

*NORMALIZE	900 °C
AUSTENITIZE	870 °C

*For forged or rolled specimens only

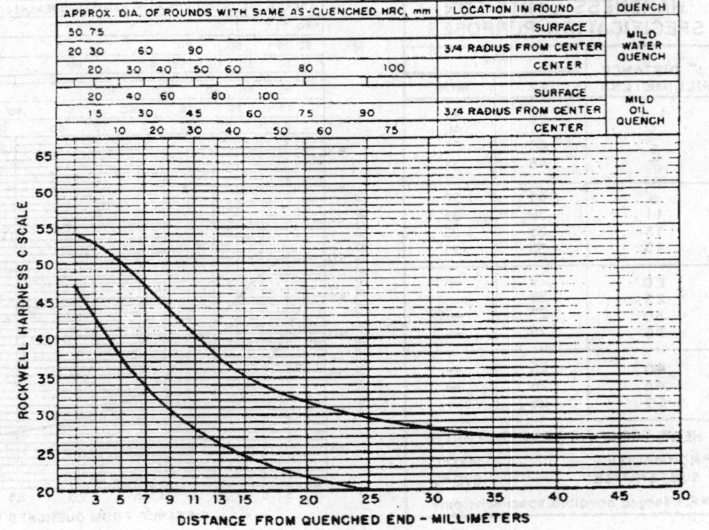

FIGURE 69—UNS H86270—HARDENABILITY BAND—SAE H8627H

UNS H86300 **HARDENABILITY BAND** SAE 8630H

%C	%Mn	%Si	%Ni	%Cr	%Mo
0.27/0.33	0.60/0.95	0.15/0.35	0.35/0.75	0.35/0.65	0.15/0.25

HARDNESS LIMITS FOR SPECIFICATION PURPOSES

"J" DISTANCE SIXTEENTHS OF AN INCH	HRC MAX.	HRC MIN.
1	56	49
2	55	46
3	54	43
4	52	39
5	50	35
6	47	32
7	44	29
8	41	28
9	39	27
10	37	26
11	35	25
12	34	24
13	33	23
14	33	22
15	32	22
16	31	21
18	30	21
20	30	20
22	29	20
24	29	--
26	29	--
28	29	--
30	29	--
32	29	--

HEAT TREATING TEMPERATURES

*NORMALIZE	1650 °F
AUSTENITIZE	1600 °F

*For forged or rolled specimens only

APPROX. DIA. OF ROUNDS WITH SAME AS-QUENCHED HRC, in.	LOCATION IN ROUND	QUENCH
2 4	SURFACE	MILD WATER QUENCH
1 2 3 4	3/4 RADIUS FROM CENTER	
0.5 1 1.5 2 2.5 3 3.5 4	CENTER	
1 2 3 4	SURFACE	MILD OIL QUENCH
0.5 1 1.5 2 2.5 3 3.5 4	3/4 RADIUS FROM CENTER	
0.5 1 1.5 2 2.5 3 3.5	CENTER	

ROCKWELL HARDNESS C SCALE

DISTANCE FROM QUENCHED END – SIXTEENTHS OF AN INCH

HARDNESS LIMITS FOR SPECIFICATION PURPOSES

"J" DISTANCE MILLIMETERS	HRC MAX.	HRC MIN.
1.5	56	49
3	55	46
5	54	42
7	51	37
9	48	33
11	44	29
13	41	27
15	38	26
20	34	23
25	31	21
30	30	20
35	29	--
40	29	--
45	29	--
50	29	--

HEAT TREATING TEMPERATURES

*NORMALIZE	900 °C
AUSTENITIZE	870 °C

*For forged or rolled specimens only

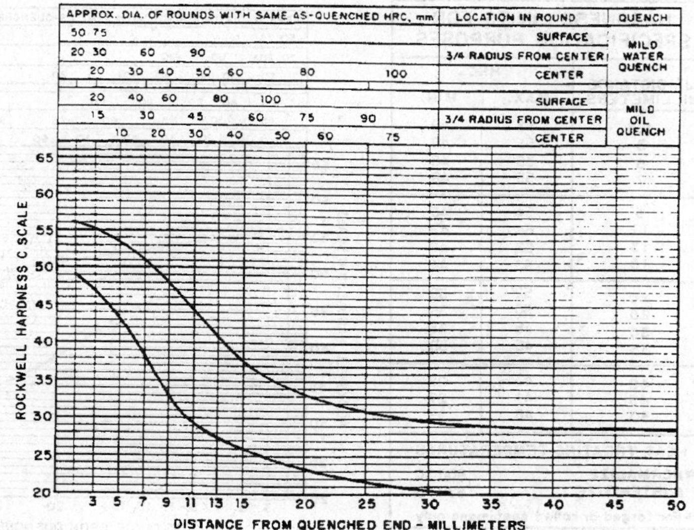

FIGURE 70—UNS H86300—HARDENABILITY BAND—SAE 8630H

UNS H86301 **HARDENABILITY BAND** **SAE 86B30H**

%C	%Mn	%Si	%Ni	%Cr	%Mo	%B
0.27/0.33	0.60/0.95	0.15/0.35	0.35/0.75	0.35/0.65	0.15/0.25	0.0005/0.003

HARDNESS LIMITS FOR SPECIFICATION PURPOSES

"J" DISTANCE SIXTEENTHS OF AN INCH	HRC MAX.	HRC MIN.
1	56	49
2	55	49
3	55	48
4	55	48
5	54	48
6	54	48
7	53	48
8	53	47
9	52	46
10	52	44
11	52	42
12	51	40
13	51	39
14	50	38
15	50	36
16	49	35
18	48	34
20	47	32
22	45	31
24	44	29
26	43	28
28	41	27
30	40	26
32	39	25

HEAT TREATING TEMPERATURES

*NORMALIZE	1650°F
AUSTENITIZE	1600°F

*For forged or rolled specimens only

APPROX. DIA. OF ROUNDS WITH SAME AS-QUENCHED HRC, in. — LOCATION IN ROUND — QUENCH

MILD WATER QUENCH: SURFACE 2, 4; 3/4 RADIUS FROM CENTER 1, 2, 3, 4; CENTER 0.5, 1, 1.5, 2, 2.5, 3, 3.5, 4

MILD OIL QUENCH: SURFACE 1, 2, 3, 4; 3/4 RADIUS FROM CENTER 0.5, 1, 1.5, 2, 2.5, 3, 3.5, 4; CENTER 0.5, 1, 1.5, 2, 2.5, 3, 3.5

ROCKWELL HARDNESS C SCALE (20–65)

DISTANCE FROM QUENCHED END – SIXTEENTHS OF AN INCH (2–32)

HARDNESS LIMITS FOR SPECIFICATION PURPOSES

"J" DISTANCE MILLIMETERS	HRC MAX.	HRC MIN.
1.5	56	49
3	56	49
5	55	48
7	55	48
9	54	48
11	54	47
13	53	46
15	53	44
20	52	39
25	50	35
30	48	33
35	46	30
40	43	28
45	41	27
50	40	25

HEAT TREATING TEMPERATURES

*NORMALIZE	900°C
AUSTENITIZE	870°C

*For forged or rolled specimens only

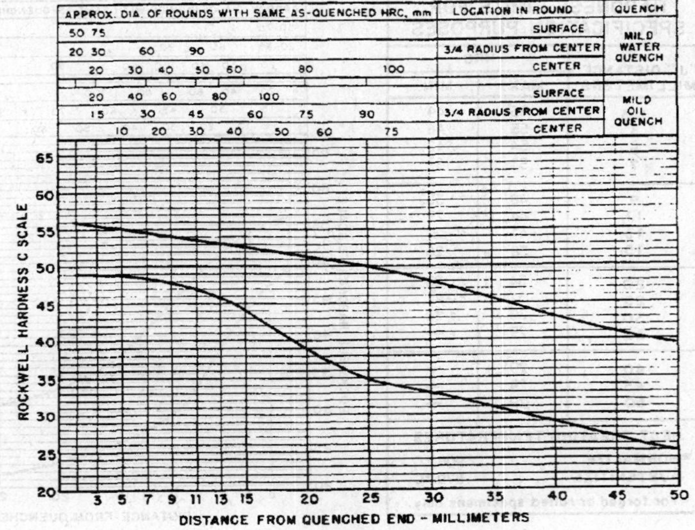

FIGURE 71—UNS H86301—HARDENABILITY BAND—SAE 86B30H

UNS H86370 **HARDENABILITY BAND** SAE 8637H

%C	%Mn	%Si	%Ni	%Cr	%Mo
0.34/0.41	0.70/1.05	0.15/0.35	0.35/0.75	0.35/0.65	0.15/0.25

HARDNESS LIMITS FOR SPECIFICATION PURPOSES

"J" DISTANCE SIXTEENTHS OF AN INCH	HRC MAX.	HRC MIN.
1	59	52
2	58	51
3	58	50
4	57	48
5	56	45
6	55	42
7	54	39
8	53	36
9	51	34
10	49	32
11	47	31
12	46	30
13	44	29
14	43	28
15	41	27
16	40	26
18	39	25
20	37	25
22	36	24
24	36	24
26	35	24
28	35	24
30	35	23
32	35	23

HEAT TREATING TEMPERATURES

*NORMALIZE	1600 °F
AUSTENITIZE	1550 °F

*For forged or rolled specimens only

APPROX. DIA. OF ROUNDS WITH SAME AS-QUENCHED HRC, in. — LOCATION IN ROUND — QUENCH

SURFACE / 3/4 RADIUS FROM CENTER / CENTER — MILD WATER QUENCH

SURFACE / 3/4 RADIUS FROM CENTER / CENTER — MILD OIL QUENCH

ROCKWELL HARDNESS C SCALE

DISTANCE FROM QUENCHED END - SIXTEENTHS OF AN INCH

HARDNESS LIMITS FOR SPECIFICATION PURPOSES

"J" DISTANCE MILLIMETERS	HRC MAX.	HRC MIN.
1.5	59	52
3	59	51
5	58	49
7	57	47
9	55	43
11	54	39
13	52	36
15	50	33
20	45	29
25	40	27
30	38	25
35	36	24
40	35	24
45	35	23
50	35	23

HEAT TREATING TEMPERATURES

*NORMALIZE	870 °C
AUSTENITIZE	845 °C

*For forged or rolled specimens only

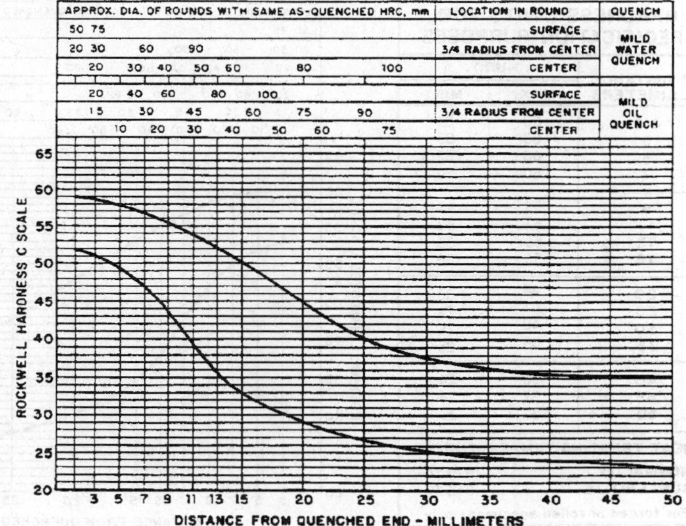

FIGURE 72—UNS H86370—HARDENABILITY BAND—SAE 8637H

UNS H86400 **HARDENABILITY BAND** SAE 8640H

%C	%Mn	%Si	%Ni	%Cr	%Mo
0.37/0.44	0.70/1.05	0.15/0.35	0.35/0.75	0.35/0.65	0.15/0.25

HARDNESS LIMITS FOR SPECIFICATION PURPOSES

"J" DISTANCE SIXTEENTHS OF AN INCH	HRC MAX.	HRC MIN.
1	60	53
2	60	53
3	60	52
4	59	51
5	59	49
6	58	46
7	57	42
8	55	39
9	54	36
10	52	34
11	50	32
12	49	31
13	47	30
14	45	29
15	44	28
16	42	28
18	41	26
20	39	26
22	38	25
24	38	25
26	37	24
28	37	24
30	37	24
32	37	24

HEAT TREATING TEMPERATURES

*NORMALIZE	1600 °F
AUSTENITIZE	1550 °F

*For forged or rolled specimens only

ROCKWELL HARDNESS C SCALE

DISTANCE FROM QUENCHED END – SIXTEENTHS OF AN INCH

HARDNESS LIMITS FOR SPECIFICATION PURPOSES

"J" DISTANCE MILLIMETERS	HRC MAX.	HRC MIN.
1.5	60	53
3	60	53
5	60	52
7	60	50
9	58	47
11	57	42
13	55	38
15	53	35
20	48	30
25	43	28
30	40	26
35	39	25
40	38	24
45	37	24
50	37	24

HEAT TREATING TEMPERATURES

*NORMALIZE	870 °C
AUSTENITIZE	845 °C

*For forged or rolled specimens only

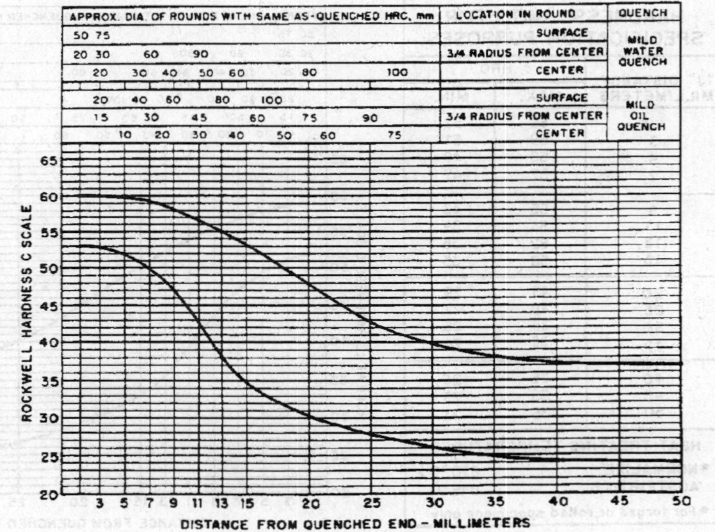

FIGURE 73—UNS H86400—HARDENABILITY BAND—SAE 8640H

UNS H86420 **HARDENABILITY BAND** SAE 8642H

%C	%Mn	%Si	%Ni	%Cr	% Mo
0.39/0.46	0.70/1.05	0.15/0.35	0.35/0.75	0.35/0.65	0.15/0.25

HARDNESS LIMITS FOR SPECIFICATION PURPOSES

"J" DISTANCE SIXTEENTHS OF AN INCH	HRC MAX.	HRC MIN.
1	62	55
2	62	54
3	62	53
4	61	52
5	61	50
6	60	48
7	59	45
8	58	42
9	57	39
10	55	37
11	54	34
12	52	33
13	50	32
14	49	31
15	48	30
16	46	29
18	44	28
20	42	28
22	41	27
24	40	27
26	40	26
28	39	26
30	39	26
32	39	26

HEAT TREATING TEMPERATURES	
*NORMALIZE	1600 °F
AUSTENITIZE	1550 °F

*For forged or rolled specimens only

APPROX. DIA. OF ROUNDS WITH SAME AS-QUENCHED HRC, in. — LOCATION IN ROUND — QUENCH

MILD WATER QUENCH: SURFACE 2 4; 3/4 RADIUS FROM CENTER 1 2 3 4; CENTER 0.5 1 1.5 2 2.5 3 3.5 4

MILD OIL QUENCH: SURFACE 1 2 3 4; 3/4 RADIUS FROM CENTER 0.5 1 1.5 2 2.5 3 3.5 4; CENTER 0.5 1 1.5 2 2.5 3 3.5

ROCKWELL HARDNESS C SCALE: 20 25 30 35 40 45 50 55 60 65

DISTANCE FROM QUENCHED END – SIXTEENTHS OF AN INCH: 2 4 6 8 10 12 14 16 18 20 22 24 26 28 30 32

HARDNESS LIMITS FOR SPECIFICATION PURPOSES

"J" DISTANCE MILLIMETERS	HRC MAX.	HRC MIN.
1.5	62	55
3	62	54
5	62	53
7	61	51
9	60	49
11	59	46
13	58	42
15	56	38
20	52	32
25	47	29
30	44	28
35	41	27
40	40	27
45	39	26
50	39	26

HEAT TREATING TEMPERATURES	
*NORMALIZE	870 °C
AUSTENITIZE	845 °C

*For forged or rolled specimens only

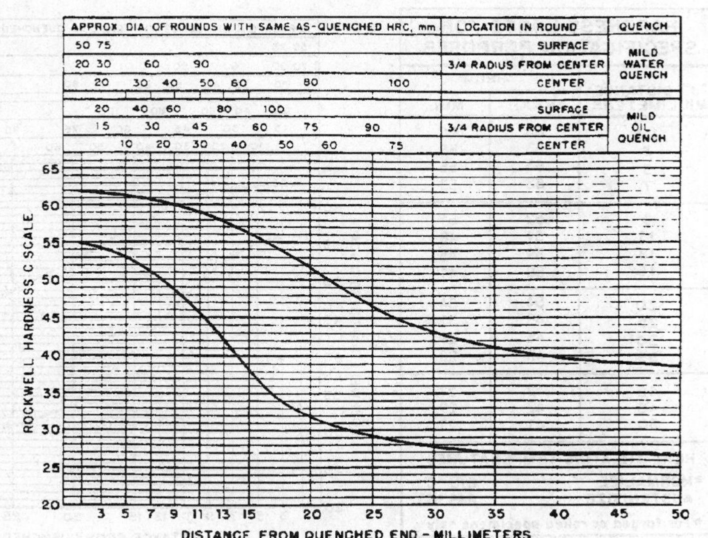

FIGURE 74—UNS H86420—HARDENABILITY BAND—SAE 8642H

UNS H86450 **HARDENABILITY BAND** SAE 8645H

%C	%Mn	%Si	%Ni	%Cr	%Mo
0.42/0.49	0.70/1.05	0.15/0.35	0.35/0.75	0.35/0.65	0.15/0.25

HARDNESS LIMITS FOR SPECIFICATION PURPOSES

"J" DISTANCE SIXTEENTHS OF AN INCH	HRC MAX.	HRC MIN.
1	63	56
2	63	56
3	63	55
4	63	54
5	62	52
6	61	50
7	61	48
8	60	45
9	59	41
10	58	39
11	56	37
12	55	35
13	54	34
14	52	33
15	51	32
16	49	31
18	47	30
20	45	29
22	43	28
24	42	28
26	42	27
28	41	27
30	41	27
32	41	27

HEAT TREATING TEMPERATURES

*NORMALIZE 1600°F
AUSTENITIZE 1550°F

*For forged or rolled specimens only

APPROX. DIA. OF ROUNDS WITH SAME AS-QUENCHED HRC, in.	LOCATION IN ROUND	QUENCH
2 4	SURFACE	MILD WATER QUENCH
1 2 3 4	3/4 RADIUS FROM CENTER	
0.5 1 1.5 2 2.5 3 3.5 4	CENTER	
1 2 3 4	SURFACE	MILD OIL QUENCH
0.5 1 1.5 2 2.5 3 3.5 4	3/4 RADIUS FROM CENTER	
0.5 1 1.5 2 2.5 3 3.5	CENTER	

ROCKWELL HARDNESS C SCALE

DISTANCE FROM QUENCHED END - SIXTEENTHS OF AN INCH

HARDNESS LIMITS FOR SPECIFICATION PURPOSES

"J" DISTANCE MILLIMETERS	HRC MAX.	HRC MIN.
1.5	63	56
3	63	56
5	63	55
7	63	53
9	62	51
11	61	48
13	59	45
15	58	41
20	54	34
25	49	31
30	46	29
35	43	28
40	42	27
45	42	27
50	41	27

HEAT TREATING TEMPERATURES

*NORMALIZE 870°C
AUSTENITIZE 845°C

*For forged or rolled specimens only

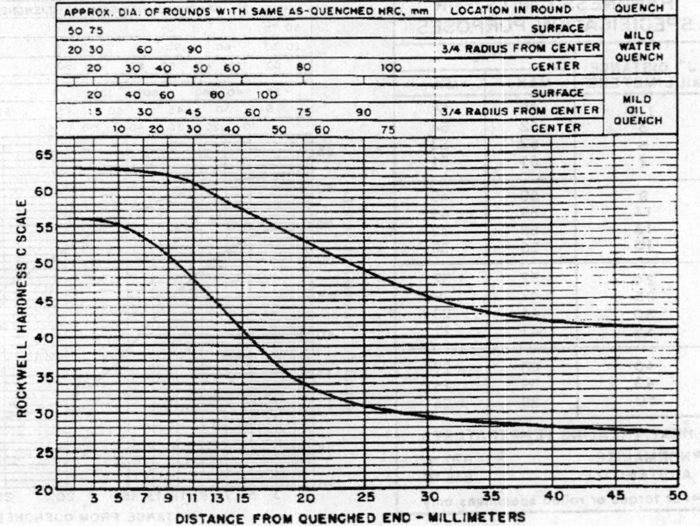

FIGURE 75—UNS H86450—HARDENABILITY BAND—SAE 8645H

UNS H86451 **HARDENABILITY BAND** SAE 86B45H

%C	%Mn	%Si	%Ni	%Cr	%Mo	%B
0.42/0.49	0.70/1.05	0.15/0.35	0.35/0.75	0.35/0.65	0.15/0.25	0.0005/0.003

HARDNESS LIMITS FOR SPECIFICATION PURPOSES

"J" DISTANCE SIXTEENTHS OF AN INCH	HRC MAX.	HRC MIN.
1	63	56
2	63	56
3	62	55
4	62	54
5	62	54
6	61	53
7	61	52
8	60	52
9	60	51
10	60	51
11	59	50
12	59	50
13	59	49
14	59	48
15	58	46
16	58	45
18	58	42
20	58	39
22	57	37
24	57	35
26	57	34
28	57	32
30	56	32
32	56	31

HEAT TREATING TEMPERATURES

*NORMALIZE	1600 °F
AUSTENITIZE	1550 °F

*For forged or rolled specimens only

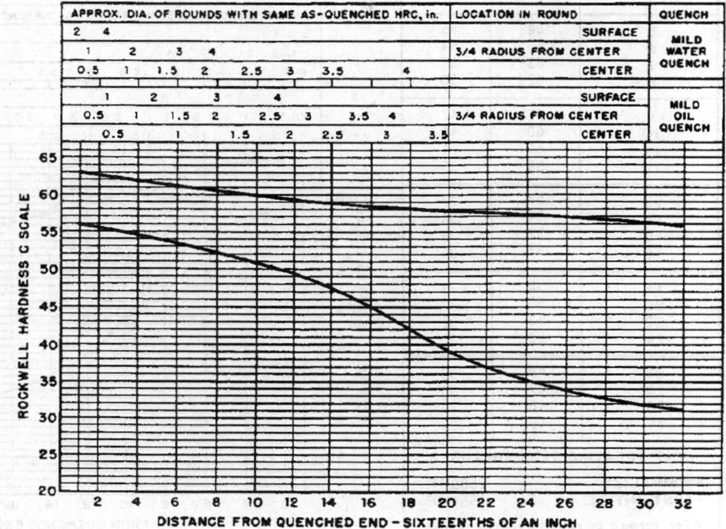

HARDNESS LIMITS FOR SPECIFICATION PURPOSES

"J" DISTANCE MILLIMETERS	HRC MAX.	HRC MIN.
1.5	63	56
3	63	56
5	63	55
7	62	54
9	62	53
11	61	52
13	61	51
15	60	51
20	59	49
25	58	45
30	58	40
35	57	36
40	57	33
45	56	32
50	56	31

HEAT TREATING TEMPERATURES

*NORMALIZE	870 °C
AUSTENITIZE	845 °C

*For forged or rolled specimens only

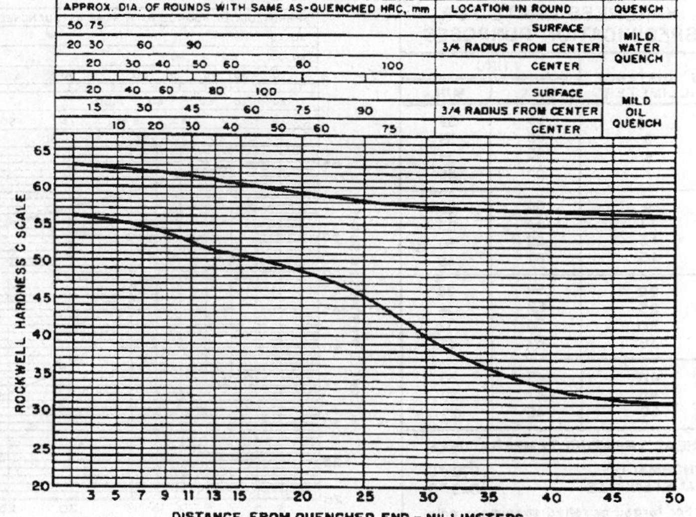

FIGURE 76—UNS H86451—HARDENABILITY BAND—SAE 86B45H

HARDENABILITY BAND

UNS H86500 — SAE 8650H

%C	%Mn	%Si	%Ni	%Cr	%Mo
0.47/0.54	0.70/1.05	0.15/0.35	0.35/0.75	0.35/0.65	0.15/0.25

HARDNESS LIMITS FOR SPECIFICATION PURPOSES

"J" DISTANCE SIXTEENTHS OF AN INCH	HRC MAX.	HRC MIN.
1	65	59
2	65	58
3	65	57
4	64	57
5	64	56
6	63	54
7	63	53
8	62	50
9	61	47
10	60	44
11	60	41
12	59	39
13	58	37
14	58	36
15	57	35
16	56	34
18	55	33
20	53	32
22	52	31
24	50	31
26	49	30
28	47	30
30	46	29
32	45	29

HEAT TREATING TEMPERATURES

*NORMALIZE 1600 °F

AUSTENITIZE 1550 °F

*For forged or rolled specimens only

APPROX. DIA. OF ROUNDS WITH SAME AS-QUENCHED HRC, in. — LOCATION IN ROUND — QUENCH

Approx. dia., in.	Location in round	Quench
2 4	SURFACE	MILD WATER QUENCH
1 2 3 4	3/4 RADIUS FROM CENTER	MILD WATER QUENCH
0.5 1 1.5 2 2.5 3 3.5 4	CENTER	MILD WATER QUENCH
1 2 3 4	SURFACE	MILD OIL QUENCH
0.5 1 1.5 2 2.5 3 3.5 4	3/4 RADIUS FROM CENTER	MILD OIL QUENCH
0.5 1 1.5 2 2.5 3 3.5	CENTER	MILD OIL QUENCH

ROCKWELL HARDNESS C SCALE: 20 25 30 35 40 45 50 55 60 65

DISTANCE FROM QUENCHED END - SIXTEENTHS OF AN INCH: 2 4 6 8 10 12 14 16 18 20 22 24 26 28 30 32

HARDNESS LIMITS FOR SPECIFICATION PURPOSES

"J" DISTANCE MILLIMETERS	HRC MAX.	HRC MIN.
1.5	65	59
3	65	59
5	65	58
7	65	56
9	64	55
11	63	53
13	62	50
15	61	46
20	59	38
25	57	34
30	54	32
35	52	31
40	49	30
45	47	29
50	46	29

HEAT TREATING TEMPERATURES

*NORMALIZE 870 °C

AUSTENITIZE 845 °C

*For forged or rolled specimens only

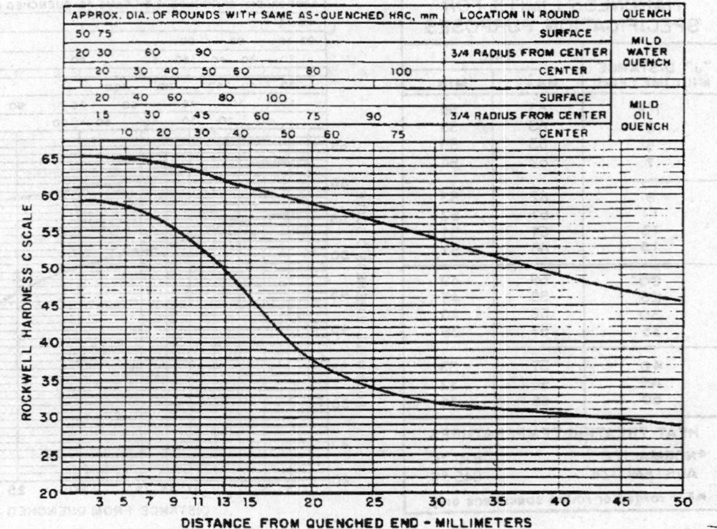

FIGURE 77—UNS H86500—HARDENABILITY BAND—SAE 8650H

UNS H86550 **HARDENABILITY BAND** SAE 8655H

%C	%Mn	%Si	%Ni	%Cr	%Mo
0.50/0.60	0.70/1.05	0.15/0.35	0.35/0.75	0.35/0.65	0.15/0.25

HARDNESS LIMITS FOR SPECIFICATION PURPOSES

"J" DISTANCE SIXTEENTHS OF AN INCH	HRC MAX.	HRC MIN.
1	--	60
2	--	59
3	--	59
4	--	58
5	--	57
6	--	56
7	--	55
8	--	54
9	--	52
10	65	49
11	65	46
12	64	43
13	64	41
14	63	40
15	63	39
16	62	38
18	61	37
20	60	35
22	59	34
24	58	34
26	57	33
28	56	33
30	55	32
32	53	32

HEAT TREATING TEMPERATURES

*NORMALIZE	1600 °F
AUSTENITIZE	1550 °F

*For forged or rolled specimens only

HARDNESS LIMITS FOR SPECIFICATION PURPOSES

"J" DISTANCE MILLIMETERS	HRC MAX.	HRC MIN.
1.5	--	60
3	--	60
5	--	59
7	--	57
9	--	56
11	--	55
13	--	53
15	65	51
20	64	42
25	62	39
30	61	36
35	59	34
40	57	34
45	56	33
50	54	32

HEAT TREATING TEMPERATURES

*NORMALIZE	870 °C
AUSTENITIZE	845 °C

*For forged or rolled specimens only

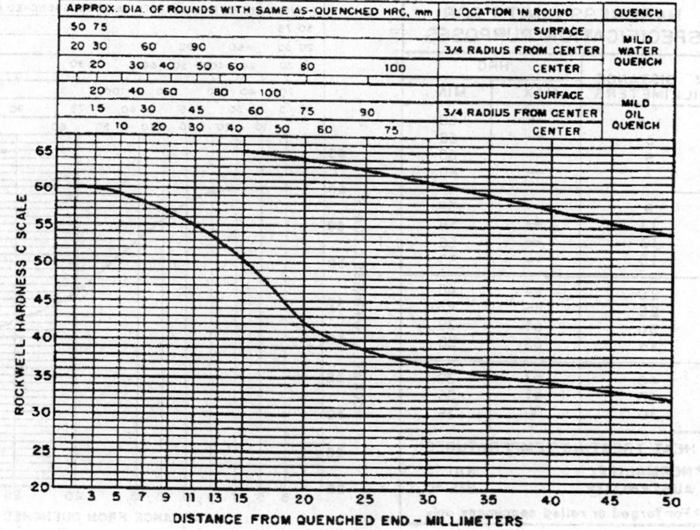

FIGURE 78—UNS H86550—HARDENABILITY BAND—SAE 8655H

UNS H86600 **HARDENABILITY BAND** SAE 8660H

%C	%Mn	%Si	%Ni	%Cr	%Mo
0.55/0.65	0.70/1.05	0.15/0.35	0.35/0.75	0.35/0.65	0.15/0.25

HARDNESS LIMITS FOR SPECIFICATION PURPOSES

"J" DISTANCE SIXTEENTHS OF AN INCH	HRC MAX.	HRC MIN.
1	--	60
2	--	60
3	--	60
4	--	60
5	--	60
6	--	59
7	--	58
8	--	57
9	--	55
10	--	53
11	--	50
12	--	47
13	--	45
14	--	44
15	--	43
16	65	42
18	64	40
20	64	39
22	63	38
24	62	37
26	62	36
28	61	36
30	60	35
32	60	35

HEAT TREATING TEMPERATURES

*NORMALIZE 1600 °F
AUSTENITIZE 1550 °F

*For forged or rolled specimens only

HARDNESS LIMITS FOR SPECIFICATION PURPOSES

"J" DISTANCE MILLIMETERS	HRC MAX.	HRC MIN.
1.5	—	60
3	—	60
5	—	60
7	—	60
9	—	59
11	—	58
13	—	56
15	—	53
20	--	46
25	65	42
30	64	39
35	63	38
40	62	37
45	61	36
50	60	35

HEAT TREATING TEMPERATURES

*NORMALIZE 870 °C
AUSTENITIZE 845 °C

*For forged or rolled specimens only

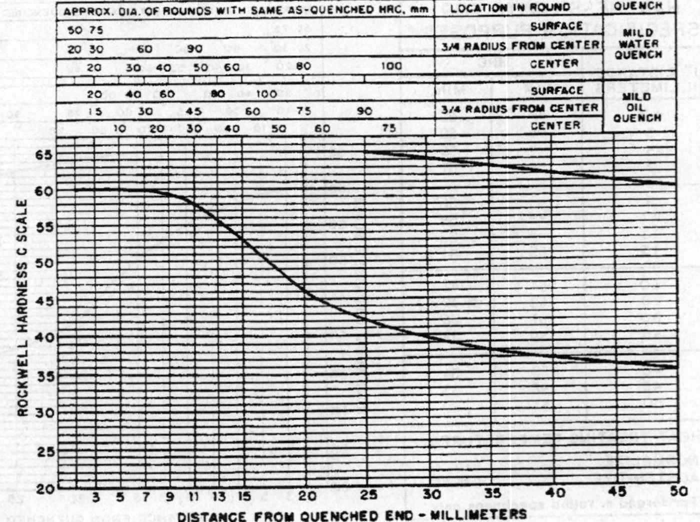

FIGURE 79—UNS H86600—HARDENABILITY BAND—SAE 8660H

HARDNESS LIMITS FOR SPECIFICATION PURPOSES		
"J" DISTANCE SIXTEENTHS OF AN INCH	HRC MAX.	HRC MIN.
1	48	41
2	47	38
3	45	35
4	42	30
5	38	26
6	35	24
7	33	22
8	31	21
9	30	20
10	29	--
11	28	--
12	27	--
13	26	--
14	26	--
15	25	--
16	25	--
18	24	--
20	24	--
22	23	--
24	23	--
26	23	--
28	23	--
30	22	--
32	22	--

HEAT TREATING TEMPERATURES

*NORMALIZE 1700 °F

AUSTENITIZE 1700 °F

*For forged or rolled specimens only

UNS H87200 **HARDENABILITY BAND** SAE 8720H

%C	%Mn	%Si	%Ni	%Cr	%Mo
0.17/0.23	0.60/0.95	0.15/0.35	0.35/0.75	0.35/0.65	0.20/0.30

APPROX. DIA. OF ROUNDS WITH SAME AS-QUENCHED HRC, in. — LOCATION IN ROUND — QUENCH

MILD WATER QUENCH:
- SURFACE: 2 4
- 3/4 RADIUS FROM CENTER: 1 2 3 4
- CENTER: 0.5 1 1.5 2 2.5 3 3.5 4

MILD OIL QUENCH:
- SURFACE: 1 2 3 4
- 3/4 RADIUS FROM CENTER: 0.5 1 1.5 2 2.5 3 3.5 4
- CENTER: 0.5 1 1.5 2 2.5 3 3.5

ROCKWELL HARDNESS C SCALE: 20 25 30 35 40 45 50 55 60 65

DISTANCE FROM QUENCHED END – SIXTEENTHS OF AN INCH: 2 4 6 8 10 12 14 16 18 20 22 24 26 28 30 32

HARDNESS LIMITS FOR SPECIFICATION PURPOSES		
"J" DISTANCE MILLIMETERS	HRC MAX.	HRC MIN.
1.5	48	41
3	47	38
5	44	34
7	40	28
9	36	25
11	33	22
13	31	21
15	29	--
20	27	--
25	25	--
30	24	--
35	23	--
40	23	--
45	23	--
50	22	--

HEAT TREATING TEMPERATURES

*NORMALIZE 925 °C

AUSTENITIZE 925 °C

*For forged or rolled specimens only

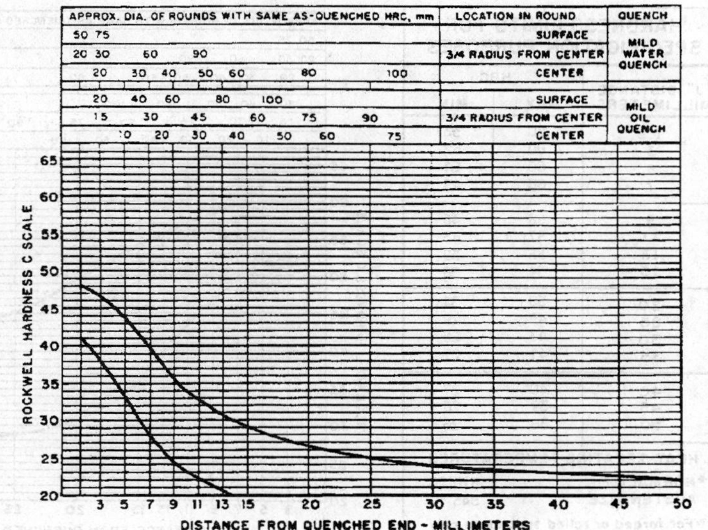

FIGURE 80—UNS H87200—HARDENABILITY BAND—SAE 8720H

UNS H87400 **HARDENABILITY BAND** SAE 8740H

%C	%Mn	%Si	%Ni	%Cr	%Mo
0.37/0.44	0.70/1.05	0.15/0.35	0.35/0.75	0.35/0.65	0.20/0.30

HARDNESS LIMITS FOR SPECIFICATION PURPOSES

"J" DISTANCE SIXTEENTHS OF AN INCH	HRC MAX.	HRC MIN.
1	60	53
2	60	53
3	60	52
4	60	51
5	59	49
6	58	46
7	57	43
8	56	40
9	55	37
10	53	35
11	52	34
12	50	32
13	49	31
14	48	31
15	46	30
16	45	29
18	43	28
20	42	28
22	41	27
24	40	27
26	39	27
28	39	27
30	38	26
32	38	26

HEAT TREATING TEMPERATURES

*NORMALIZE	1600 °F
AUSTENITIZE	1550 °F

*For forged or rolled specimens only

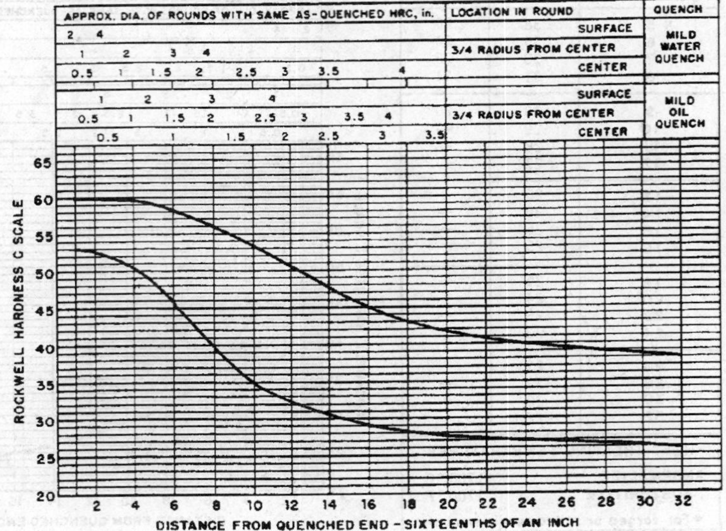

HARDNESS LIMITS FOR SPECIFICATION PURPOSES

"J" DISTANCE MILLIMETERS	HRC MAX.	HRC MIN.
1.5	60	53
3	60	52
5	60	51
7	60	49
9	58	46
11	57	43
13	56	39
15	54	36
20	50	31
25	45	29
30	43	28
35	41	27
40	40	27
45	39	26
50	38	26

HEAT TREATING TEMPERATURES

*NORMALIZE	870 °C
AUSTENITIZE	845 °C

*For forged or rolled specimens only

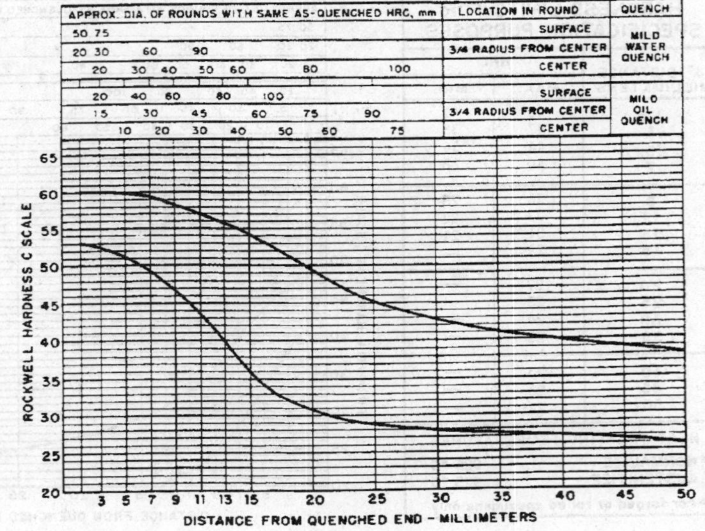

FIGURE 81—UNS H87400—HARDENABILITY BAND—SAE 8740H

HARDNESS LIMITS FOR SPECIFICATION PURPOSES

"J" DISTANCE SIXTEENTHS OF AN INCH	HRC MAX.	HRC MIN.
1	50	43
2	49	42
3	48	39
4	46	33
5	43	29
6	40	27
7	37	25
8	35	24
9	34	24
10	33	23
11	32	23
12	31	22
13	31	22
14	30	22
15	30	21
16	29	21
18	29	20
20	28	--
22	27	--
24	27	--
26	27	--
28	27	--
30	27	--
32	27	--

HEAT TREATING TEMPERATURES

*NORMALIZE	1700°F
AUSTENITIZE	1700°F

*For forged or rolled specimens only

UNS H88220 **HARDENABILITY BAND** SAE 8822H

%C	%Mn	%Si	%Ni	%Cr	%Mo
0.19/0.25	0.70/1.05	0.15/0.35	0.35/0.75	0.35/0.65	0.30/0.40

APPROX. DIA. OF ROUNDS WITH SAME AS-QUENCHED HRC, in. — LOCATION IN ROUND — QUENCH

MILD WATER QUENCH: SURFACE: 2, 4; 3/4 RADIUS FROM CENTER: 1, 2, 3, 4; CENTER: 0.5, 1, 1.5, 2, 2.5, 3, 3.5, 4

MILD OIL QUENCH: SURFACE: 1, 2, 3, 4; 3/4 RADIUS FROM CENTER: 0.5, 1, 1.5, 2, 2.5, 3, 3.5, 4; CENTER: 0.5, 1, 1.5, 2, 2.5, 3, 3.5

ROCKWELL HARDNESS C SCALE: 20, 25, 30, 35, 40, 45, 50, 55, 60, 65

DISTANCE FROM QUENCHED END - SIXTEENTHS OF AN INCH: 2, 4, 6, 8, 10, 12, 14, 16, 18, 20, 22, 24, 26, 28, 30, 32

HARDNESS LIMITS FOR SPECIFICATION PURPOSES

"J" DISTANCE MILLIMETERS	HRC MAX.	HRC MIN.
1.5	50	43
3	49	42
5	47	38
7	45	31
9	41	28
11	38	26
13	35	24
15	33	23
20	31	22
25	29	21
30	29	20
35	28	--
40	27	--
45	27	--
50	27	--

HEAT TREATING TEMPERATURES

*NORMALIZE	925°C
AUSTENITIZE	925°C

*For forged or rolled specimens only

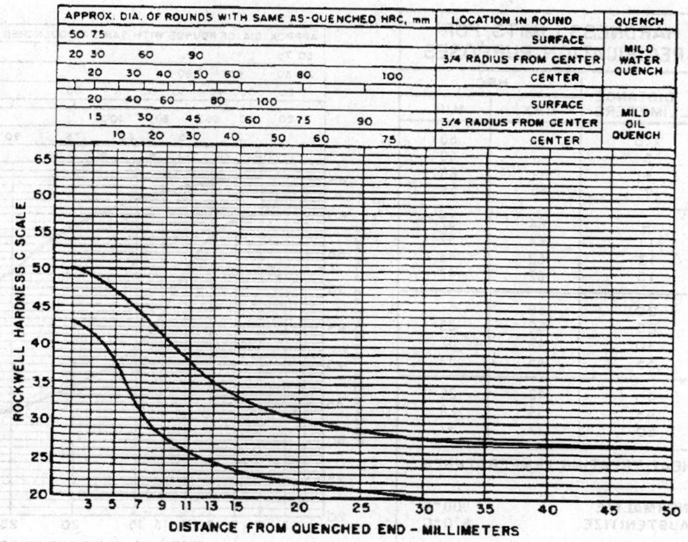

FIGURE 82—UNS H88220—HARDENABILITY BAND—SAE 8822H

UNS H92590 **HARDENABILITY BAND** SAE 9259H

%C	%Mn	%Si	%Ni	%Cr	%Mo
0.56/0.64	0.65/1.10	0.70/1.20		0.45/0.65	

HARDNESS LIMITS FOR SPECIFICATION PURPOSES

"J" DISTANCE SIXTEENTHS OF AN INCH	HRC MAX.	HRC MIN.
1	--	60
2	--	60
3	--	60
4	65	59
5	65	58
6	64	56
7	64	52
8	63	47
9	62	43
10	62	40
11	61	39
12	60	38
13	58	37
14	56	35
15	54	34
16	52	33
18	49	32
20	46	31
22	45	31
24	43	30
26	41	29
28	39	28
30	38	28
32	36	27

HEAT TREATING TEMPERATURES

*NORMALIZE	1650 °F
AUSTENITIZE	1600 °F

*For forged or rolled specimens only

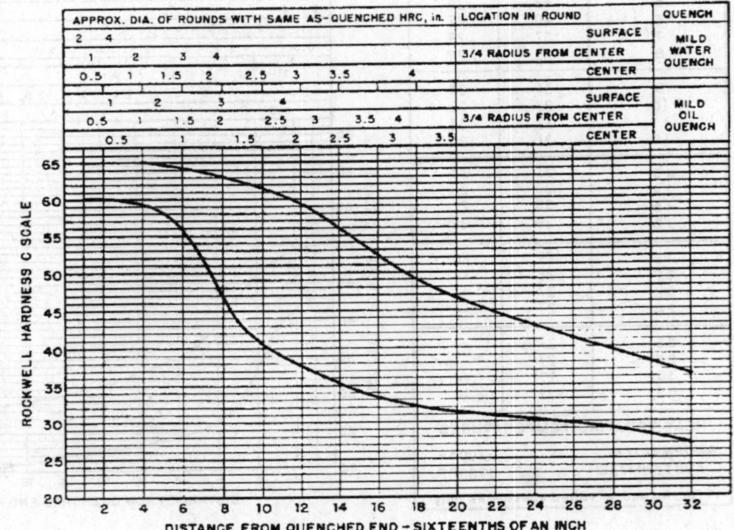

HARDNESS LIMITS FOR SPECIFICATION PURPOSES

"J" DISTANCE MILLIMETERS	HRC MAX.	HRC MIN.
1.5	--	60
3	--	60
5	--	60
7	65	59
9	64	57
11	64	52
13	63	46
15	62	42
20	59	37
25	52	33
30	48	32
35	45	33
40	42	29
45	39	28
50	37	27

HEAT TREATING TEMPERATURES

*NORMALIZE	900 °C
AUSTENITIZE	870 °C

*For forged or rolled specimens only

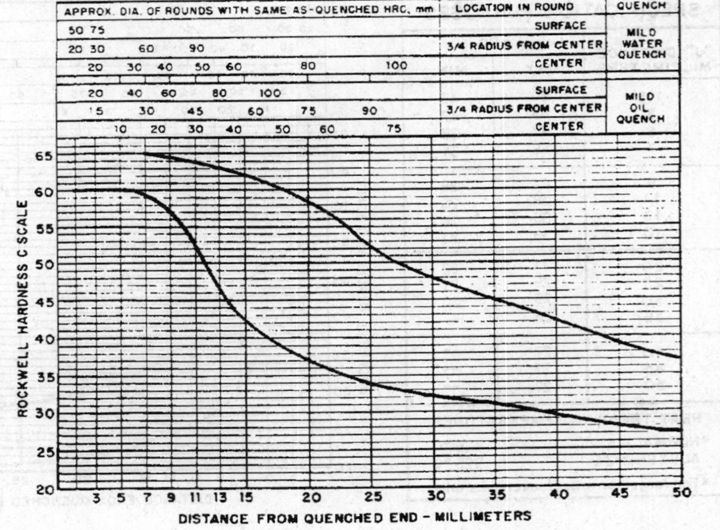

FIGURE 83—UNS H92590—HARDENABILITY BAND—SAE 9259H

UNS H92600 **HARDENABILITY BAND** SAE 9260H

%C	%Mn	%Si	%Ni	%Cr	%Mo
0.55/0.65	0.65/1.10	1.70/2.20			

HARDNESS LIMITS FOR SPECIFICATION PURPOSES

"J" DISTANCE SIXTEENTHS OF AN INCH	HRC MAX.	HRC MIN.
1	--	60
2	--	60
3	65	57
4	64	53
5	63	46
6	62	41
7	60	38
8	58	36
9	55	36
10	52	35
11	49	34
12	47	34
13	45	33
14	43	33
15	42	32
16	40	32
18	38	31
20	37	31
22	36	30
24	36	30
26	35	29
28	35	29
30	35	28
32	34	28

HEAT TREATING TEMPERATURES

*NORMALIZE	1650 °F
AUSTENITIZE	1600 °F

*For forged or rolled specimens only

APPROX. DIA. OF ROUNDS WITH SAME AS-QUENCHED HRC, in. — LOCATION IN ROUND — QUENCH
SURFACE / 3/4 RADIUS FROM CENTER / CENTER — MILD WATER QUENCH
SURFACE / 3/4 RADIUS FROM CENTER / CENTER — MILD OIL QUENCH
ROCKWELL HARDNESS C SCALE
DISTANCE FROM QUENCHED END – SIXTEENTHS OF AN INCH

HARDNESS LIMITS FOR SPECIFICATION PURPOSES

"J" DISTANCE MILLIMETERS	HRC MAX.	HRC MIN.
1.5	—	60
3	—	60
5	65	58
7	63	50
9	62	42
11	60	38
13	58	36
15	54	35
20	47	33
25	40	32
30	38	31
35	37	30
40	36	29
45	35	28
50	35	28

HEAT TREATING TEMPERATURES

*NORMALIZE	900 °C
AUSTENITIZE	870 °C

*For forged or rolled specimens only

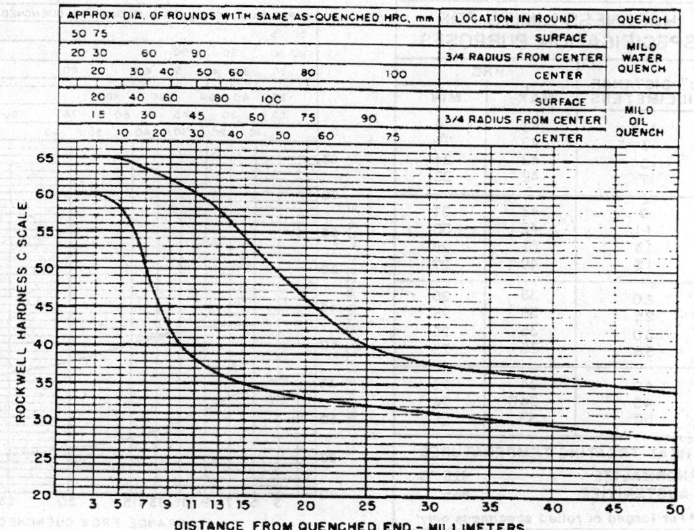

FIGURE 84—UNS H92600—HARDENABILITY BAND—SAE 9260H

UNS H93106 — HARDENABILITY BAND — SAE E9310H

%C	%Mn	%Si	%Ni	%Cr	%Mo
0.07/0.13	0.40/0.70	0.15/0.35	2.95/3.55	1.00/1.45	0.08/0.15

HARDNESS LIMITS FOR SPECIFICATION PURPOSES

"J" DISTANCE SIXTEENTHS OF AN INCH	HRC MAX.	HRC MIN.
1	43	36
2	43	35
3	43	35
4	42	34
5	42	32
6	42	31
7	42	30
8	41	29
9	40	28
10	40	27
11	39	27
12	38	26
13	37	26
14	36	26
15	36	26
16	35	26
18	35	26
20	35	25
22	34	25
24	34	25
26	34	25
28	34	25
30	33	24
32	33	24

HEAT TREATING TEMPERATURES

*NORMALIZE	1700 °F
AUSTENITIZE	1550 °F

*For forged or rolled specimens only

APPROX. DIA. OF ROUNDS WITH SAME AS-QUENCHED HRC, in.	LOCATION IN ROUND	QUENCH
2 4	SURFACE	MILD WATER QUENCH
1 2 3 4	3/4 RADIUS FROM CENTER	
0.5 1 1.5 2 2.5 3 3.5 4	CENTER	
1 2 3 4	SURFACE	MILD OIL QUENCH
0.5 1 1.5 2 2.5 3 3.5 4	3/4 RADIUS FROM CENTER	
0.5 1 1.5 2 2.5 3 3.5	CENTER	

ROCKWELL HARDNESS C SCALE (20–65)

DISTANCE FROM QUENCHED END – SIXTEENTHS OF AN INCH (2–32)

HARDNESS LIMITS FOR SPECIFICATION PURPOSES

"J" DISTANCE MILLIMETERS	HRC MAX.	HRC MIN.
1.5	43	36
3	43	35
5	43	34
7	42	33
9	42	31
11	42	30
13	41	28
15	40	27
20	38	26
25	36	25
30	35	25
35	35	25
40	34	25
45	34	24
50	33	24

HEAT TREATING TEMPERATURES

*NORMALIZE	925 °C
AUSTENITIZE	845 °C

*For forged or rolled specimens only

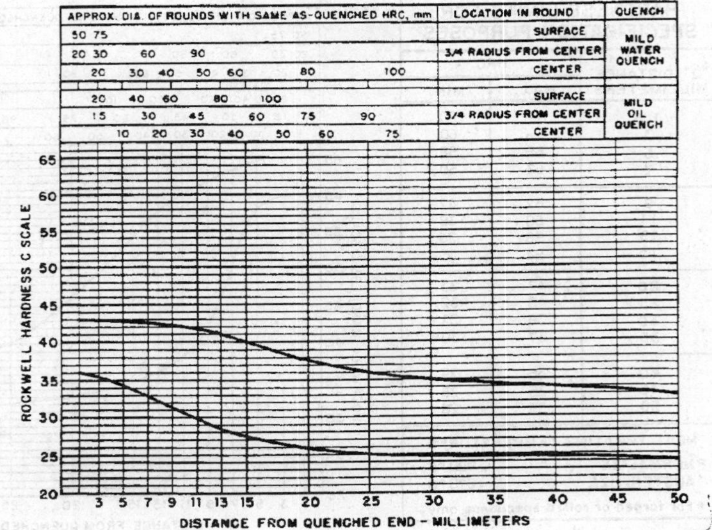

FIGURE 85—UNS H93106—HARDENABILITY BAND—SAE E9310H

HARDNESS LIMITS FOR SPECIFICATION PURPOSES		
"J" DISTANCE SIXTEENTHS OF AN INCH	HRC MAX.	HRC MIN.
1	45	38
2	45	38
3	44	37
4	44	36
5	43	32
6	42	28
7	40	25
8	38	23
9	36	21
10	34	20
11	33	--
12	31	--
13	30	--
14	29	--
15	28	--
16	27	--
18	26	--
20	25	--
22	24	--
24	23	--
26	23	--
28	22	--
30	22	--
32	22	--

HEAT TREATING TEMPERATURES

*NORMALIZE 1700 °F
AUSTENITIZE 1700 °F

*For forged or rolled specimens only

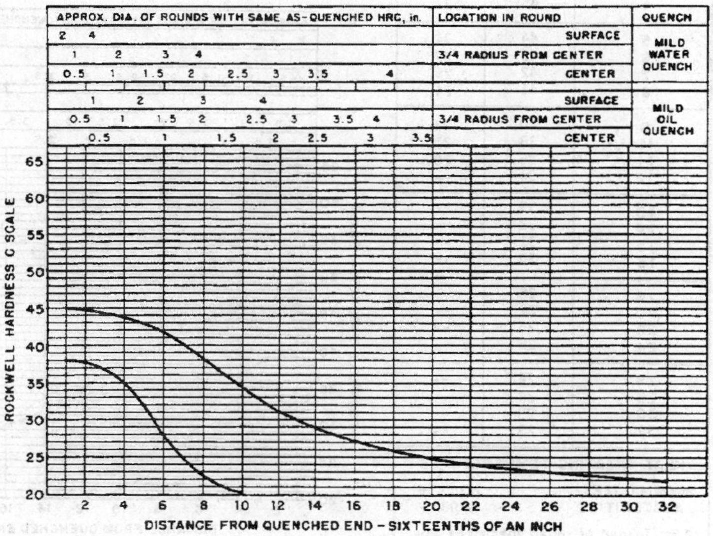

UNS H94151 **HARDENABILITY BAND** SAE 94B15H

%C	%Mn	%Si	%Ni	%Cr	%Mo	%B
0.12/0.18	0.70/1.05	0.15/0.35	0.25/0.65	0.25/0.55	0.08/0.15	0.0005/0.003

HARDNESS LIMITS FOR SPECIFICATION PURPOSES		
"J" DISTANCE MILLIMETERS	HRC MAX.	HRC MIN.
1.5	45	38
3	45	38
5	45	37
7	44	34
9	42	29
11	40	25
13	38	23
15	36	20
20	31	--
25	28	--
30	26	--
35	24	--
40	23	--
45	22	--
50	22	--

HEAT TREATING TEMPERATURES

*NORMALIZE 925 °C
AUSTENITIZE 925 °C

*For forged or rolled specimens only

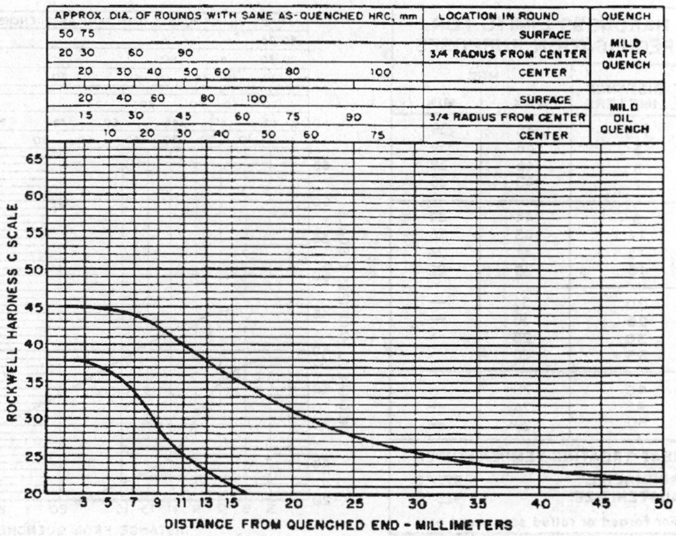

FIGURE 86—UNS H94151—HARDENABILITY BAND—SAE 94B15H

UNS H94171 **HARDENABILITY BAND** SAE 94B17H

%C	%Mn	%Si	%Ni	%Cr	%Mo	%B
0.14/0.20	0.70/1.05	0.15/0.35	0.25/0.65	0.25/0.55	0.08/0.15	0.0005/0.003

HARDNESS LIMITS FOR SPECIFICATION PURPOSES

"J" DISTANCE SIXTEENTHS OF AN INCH	HRC MAX.	HRC MIN.
1	46	39
2	46	39
3	45	38
4	45	37
5	44	34
6	43	29
7	42	26
8	41	24
9	40	23
10	38	21
11	36	20
12	34	--
13	33	--
14	32	--
15	31	--
16	30	--
18	28	--
20	27	--
22	26	--
24	25	--
26	24	--
28	24	--
30	23	--
32	23	--

HEAT TREATING TEMPERATURES	
*NORMALIZE	1700 °F
AUSTENITIZE	1700 °F

*For forged or rolled specimens only

APPROX. DIA. OF ROUNDS WITH SAME AS-QUENCHED HRC, in. — LOCATION IN ROUND — QUENCH

MILD WATER QUENCH: SURFACE 2 4; 3/4 RADIUS FROM CENTER 1 2 3 4; CENTER 0.5 1 1.5 2 2.5 3 3.5 4

MILD OIL QUENCH: SURFACE 1 2 3 4; 3/4 RADIUS FROM CENTER 0.5 1 1.5 2 2.5 3 3.5 4; CENTER 0.5 1 1.5 2 2.5 3 3.5

ROCKWELL HARDNESS C SCALE (20–65)

DISTANCE FROM QUENCHED END – SIXTEENTHS OF AN INCH (2–32)

HARDNESS LIMITS FOR SPECIFICATION PURPOSES

"J" DISTANCE MILLIMETERS	HRC MAX.	HRC MIN.
1.5	46	39
3	46	39
5	46	38
7	45	36
9	44	31
11	43	26
13	41	24
15	39	22
20	34	—
25	30	—
30	28	—
35	26	—
40	25	—
45	24	—
50	23	—

HEAT TREATING TEMPERATURES	
*NORMALIZE	925 °C
AUSTENITIZE	925 °C

*For forged or rolled specimens only

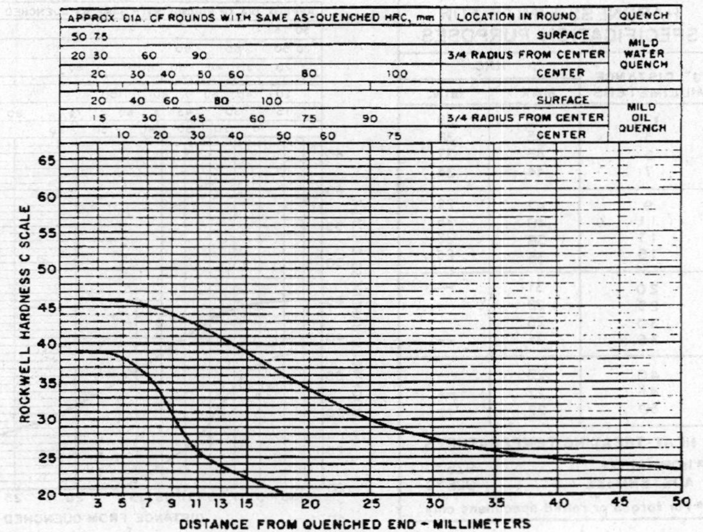

FIGURE 87—UNS H94171—HARDENABILITY BAND—SAE 94B17H

UNS H94301 HARDENABILITY BAND SAE 94B30H

%C	%Mn	%Si	%Ni	%Cr	%Mo	%B
0.27/0.33	0.70/1.05	0.15/0.35	0.25/0.65	0.25/0.55	0.08/0.15	0.0005/0.003

HARDNESS LIMITS FOR SPECIFICATION PURPOSES

"J" DISTANCE SIXTEENTHS OF AN INCH	HRC MAX.	HRC MIN.
1	56	49
2	56	49
3	55	48
4	55	48
5	54	47
6	54	46
7	53	44
8	53	42
9	52	39
10	52	37
11	51	34
12	51	32
13	50	30
14	49	29
15	48	28
16	46	27
18	44	25
20	42	24
22	40	23
24	38	23
26	37	22
28	35	21
30	34	21
32	34	20

HEAT TREATING TEMPERATURES

*NORMALIZE	1650 °F
AUSTENITIZE	1600 °F

*For forged or rolled specimens only

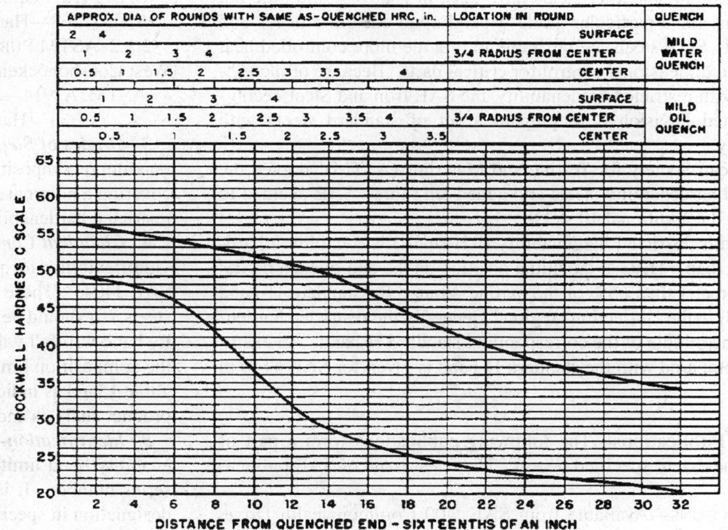

HARDNESS LIMITS FOR SPECIFICATION PURPOSES

"J" DISTANCE MILLIMETERS	HRC MAX.	HRC MIN.
1.5	56	49
3	56	49
5	55	48
7	55	47
9	54	46
11	53	44
13	53	41
15	52	38
20	50	31
25	46	26
30	43	24
35	40	23
40	37	22
45	36	21
50	34	20

HEAT TREATING TEMPERATURES

*NORMALIZE	900 °C
AUSTENITIZE	870 °C

*For forged or rolled specimens only

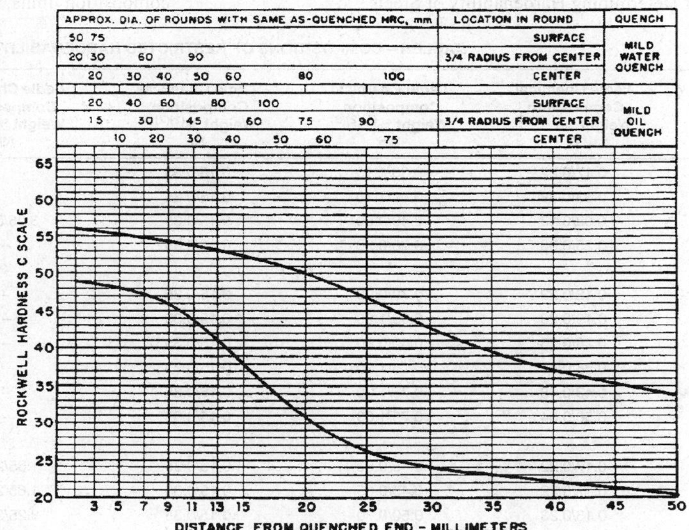

FIGURE 88—UNS 94301—HARDENABILITY BAND—SAE 94B30H

RESTRICTED HARDENABILITY BANDS FOR SELECTED ALLOY STEELS—SAE J1868 SEP1993

SAE Standard

Report of the SAE Iron and Steel Technical Committee approved February 1988, and completely revised June 1980. Completely revised by the SAE Iron and Steel Technical Committee Division 8—Carbon and Alloy Steel Hardenability, September 1993. Rationale statement available.

Foreword—This Document has not changed other than to put it into the new SAE Technical Standards Board Format.

1. Scope—Restricted hardenability steels have been in use for some time but the specific restrictions for a particular grade depend upon customer needs and vary from mill to mill. Such steels are desirable to provide more controlled heat treatment response and dimensional control for critical parts. Because of increasing interest in steels with restricted hardenability, the SAE Iron and Steel Technical Committee directed Division 8 to prepare a set of standard steels with restricted hardenability.

In 1993, the American Society for Testing and Materials (ASTM) adopted the twelve SAE restricted hardenability steels and added ten more. SAE decided to include in SAE J1868 the additional 10 steels.

In general, steels with restricted hardenability (RH steels) will exhibit a hardness range not greater than 5 HRC at the initial position on the end-quench hardenability bar and not greater than 65% of the hardness range for standard H-band steels (see SAE J1268) in the "inflection" region. Generally the restricted hardenability band follows the middle of the corresponding standard H-band. An example of the RH band compared with the standard H-band is given for SAE 4140 in Figure 1.

2. References

2.1 Applicable Publications—The following publications form a part of this specification to the extent specified herein. The latest issue of SAE publications shall apply.

2.1.1 SAE PUBLICATIONS—Available from SAE, 400 Commonwealth Drive, Warrendale, PA 15096-0001.

SAE J404—Chemical Compositions of SAE Alloy Steels

SAE J406—Methods of Determining Hardenability of Steels

SAE J409—Product Analysis—Permissible Variations from Specified Chemical Analysis of a Heat or Cast of Steel

SAE J418—Grain Size Determination of Steels

SAE J1268—Hardenability Bands for Carbon and Alloy H Steels

2.1.2 ASTM PUBLICATION—Available from ASTM, 100 Barr Harbor Drive, West Conshohocken, PA 19428-2959.

ASTM A 914—Standard Specification for Steel Bars Subject to Restricted Hardenability Requirements

3. Grades of Steel—The RH steels and their corresponding minimum and maximum composition limits are shown in Table 1 for a group of 22 alloy steels covering a nominal carbon content range of 0.10 to 0.60%. As the need arises for restricted hardenability in other grades, they will be added to the standard.

4. Chemical Composition Limits—To meet restricted hardenability, yet provide flexibility for producers, composition limits are the same as those given in SAE J404. (These limits are somewhat narrower than allowed for standard H-steels.) It should be understood that alloys which satisfy the restricted hardenability band will fall within SAE J404 composition limits, but not all steels melted to the composition limits would meet the required RH-band. The limits are given in Table 1, and as indicated in the footnotes, are subject to permissible variations for product analysis and may contain certain levels of elements not specified.

5. Identification—As a means of identifying steels specified to restricted hardenability band limits, the suffix letters RH have been added to the conventional series number. It is important that steel consumers use this special identifying designation in specification requirements, as there is no other means of determining when restricted hardenability band limits apply. When the special identification is used, the steel shall conform to all conditions pertaining to chemical composition limits, restrictions, testing technique, and so forth, as outlined herein.

TABLE 1—COMPOSITIONS OF RESTRICTED HARDENABILITY STEELS

SAE Steel No.	Ladle Chemical Composition, Weight %[1][2][3] C	Ladle Chemical Composition, Weight %[1][2][3] Mn	Ladle Chemical Composition, Weight %[1][2][3] Si	Ladle Chemical Composition, Weight %[1][2][3] Ni	Ladle Chemical Composition, Weight %[1][2][3] Cr	Ladle Chemical Composition, Weight %[1][2][3] Mo
SAE 15B21RH[4]	0.17/0.22	0.80/1.10	0.15/0.35			
SAE 15B35RH[4]	0.33/0.38	0.80/1.10	0.15/0.35			
SAE 3310RH	0.08/0.13	0.40/0.60	0.15/0.35	3.25/3.75	1.40/1.75	
SAE 4027RH	0.25/0.30	0.70/0.90	0.15/0.35	--	--	0.20/0.30
SAE 4118RH	0.18/0.23	0.70/0.90	0.15/0.35	--	0.40/0.60	0.08/0.15
SAE 4120RH	0.18/0.23	0.90/1.20	0.15/0.35	--	0.40/0.60	0.13/0.20
SAE 4130RH	0.28/0.33	0.40/0.60	0.15/0.35	--	0.80/1.10	0.15/0.25
SAE 4140RH	0.38/0.43	0.75/1.00	0.15/0.35	--	0.80/1.10	0.15/0.25
SAE 4145RH	0.43/0.48	0.75/1.00	0.15/0.35	--	0.80/1.10	0.15/0.25
SAE 4161RH	0.56/0.64	0.75/1.00	0.15/0.35	--	0.70/0.90	0.25/0.35
SAE 4320RH	0.17/0.22	0.45/0.65	0.15/0.35	1.65/2.00	0.40/0.60	0.20/0.30
SAE 4620RH	0.17/0.22	0.45/0.65	0.15/0.35	1.65/2.00	--	0.20/0.30
SAE 4820RH	0.18/0.23	0.50/0.70	0.15/0.35	3.25/3.75	--	0.20/0.30
SAE 50B40RH[4]	0.38/0.43	0.75/1.00	0.15/0.35	--	0.40/0.60	
SAE 5130RH	0.28/0.33	0.70/0.90	0.15/0.35	--	0.80/1.10	--
SAE 5140RH	0.38/0.43	0.70/0.90	0.15/0.35	--	0.70/0.90	--
SAE 5160RH	0.56/0.64	0.75/1.00	0.15/0.35	--	0.70/0.90	--
SAE 8620RH	0.18/0.23	0.70/0.90	0.15/0.35	0.40/0.70	0.40/0.60	0.15/0.25
SAE 8622RH	0.20/0.25	0.70/0.90	0.15/0.35	0.40/0.70	0.40/0.60	0.15/0.25
SAE 8720RH	0.18/0.23	0.70/0.90	0.15/0.35	0.40/0.70	0.40/0.60	0.20/0.30
SAE 8822RH	0.20/0.25	0.75/1.00	0.15/0.35	0.40/0.70	0.40/0.60	0.30/0.40
SAE 9310RH	0.08/0.13	0.45/0.65	0.15/0.35	3.00/3.50	1.00/1.40	0.08/0.15

Restricted Hardenability Limits for Steels in Table 1 appear in Figures 2 through 23.

1. Small quantities of certain elements may be found in alloy steel which are not specified or required. These elements are considered as incidental and acceptable to the following maximum amounts: copper to 0.35%, nickel to 0.25%, chromium to 0.20%, and molybdenum to 0.06%.
2. Maximum sulfur content is 0.040% and maximum phosphorus content is 0.025%.
3. Ranges and limits are subject to the permissible variations for product analysis shown in Table 4 of SAE J409.
4. These steels can be expected to contain 0.0005 to 0.003% boron.

HARDENABILITY BAND SAE 4140 H/RH

	%C	%Mn	%Si	%Ni	%Cr	%Mo
H	0.37/0.44	0.65/1.10	0.15/0.35	--	0.75/1.20	0.15/0.25
RH	0.38/0.43	0.75/1.00	0.15/0.35	--	0.80/1.10	0.15/0.25

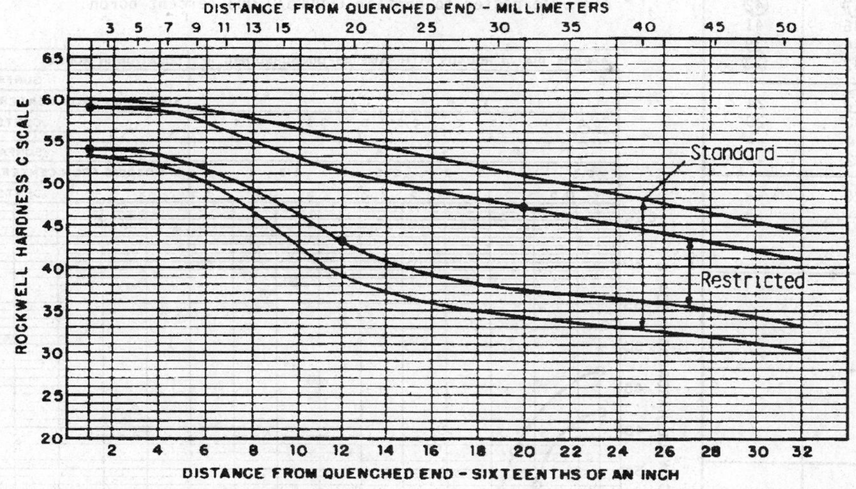

HARDNESS LIMITS FOR SPECIFICATION PURPOSES

"J" DISTANCE MILLIMETERS	MAX HRC		MIN HRC	
	4140 H	4140 RH	4140 RH	4140 H
1.5	60	59	54	53
3	60	59	54	52
5	60	59	59	52
7	59	59	53	51
9	59	58	52	50
11	58	56	50	48
13	57	55	49	46
15	57	54	47	43
20	55	51	42	38
25	53	49	39	35
30	51	48	38	33
35	49	46	37	32
40	48	44	36	32
45	46	43	35	31
50	45	41	33	30

HEAT TREATING TEMPERATURES

*NORMALIZE	870 °C
AUSTENITIZE	845 °C

*For forged or rolled specimens only

HARDNESS LIMITS FOR SPECIFICATION PURPOSES

"J" DISTANCE SIXTEENTHS OF AN INCH	MAX HRC		MIN HRC	
	4140 H	4140 RH	4140 RH	4140 H
1	60	59	54	53
2	60	59	54	53
3	60	59	54	52
4	59	59	53	51
5	59	58	52	51
6	58	57	51	50
7	58	56	50	48
8	57	55	49	47
9	57	54	48	44
10	56	53	46	42
11	56	52	44	40
12	55	52	43	39
13	55	51	42	38
14	54	50	41	37
15	54	50	40	36
16	53	49	39	35
18	52	48	38	34
20	51	47	37	33
22	49	46	37	33
24	48	45	36	32
26	47	44	35	32
28	46	43	35	31
30	46	42	34	31
32	44	41	33	30

HEAT TREATING TEMPERATURES

*NORMALIZE	1600 °F
AUSTENITIZE	1550 °F

*For forged or rolled specimens only

FIGURE 1—COMPARISON OF H-BAND AND RH-BAND FOR SAE 4140 STEEL

HARDENABILITY BAND SAE 15B21 RH

%C	%Mn	%Si	%Ni	%Cr	%Mo	%B
0.17/0.22	0.80/1.10	0.15/0.35	--	--	--	*

* can be expected to contain 0.0005/0.003 percent boron.

HARDNESS LIMITS FOR SPECIFICATION PURPOSES

"J" DISTANCE SIXTEENTHS OF AN INCH	HRC MAX.	HRC MIN.
1	(47)	(42)
2	46	41
3	44	39
4	42	(33)
5	(37)	24
6	30	20
7	24	--
8	22	--
9	20	--
10	--	--
11		
12		
13		
14		
15		
16		
18		
20		
22		
24		
26		
28		
30		
32		

HEAT TREATING TEMPERATURES	
*NORMALIZE	1700 °F
AUSTENITIZE	1700 °F

*For forged or rolled specimens only

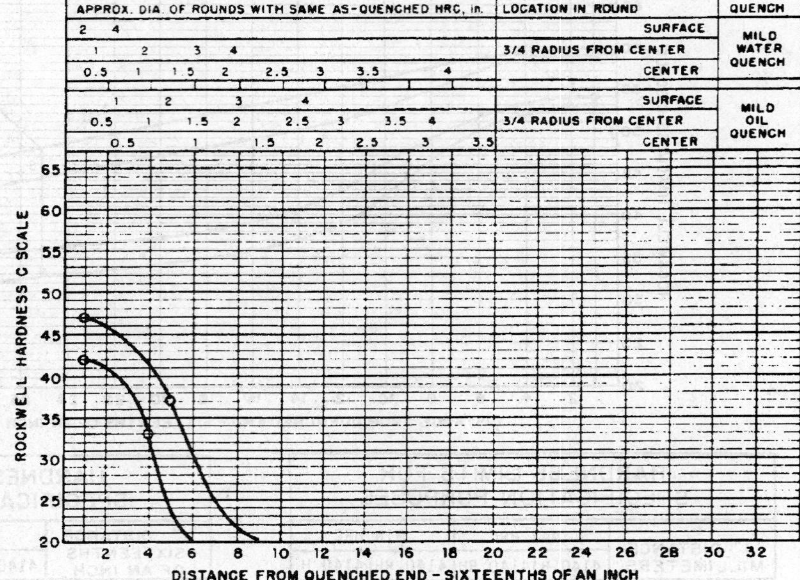

HARDNESS LIMITS FOR SPECIFICATION PURPOSES

"J" DISTANCE MILLIMETERS	HRC MAX.	HRC MIN.
1.5	(47)	(42)
3	46	41
5	44	38
7	40	(29)
9	(32)	21
11	24	--
13	22	--
15	20	--
20	--	--
25		
30		
35		
40		
45		
50		

HEAT TREATING TEMPERATURES	
*NORMALIZE	925 °C
AUSTENITIZE	925 °C

*For forged or rolled specimens only

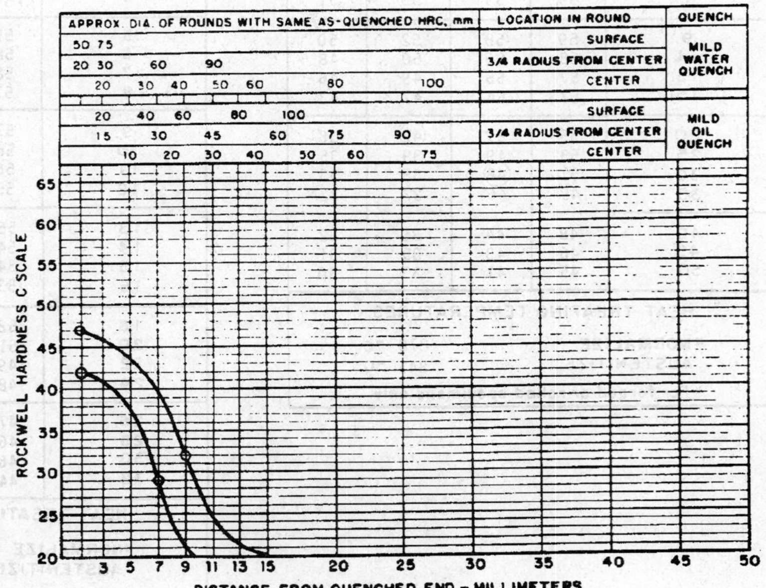

FIGURE 2—LIMITS FOR HARDENABILITY BAND 15B21RH

HARDENABILITY BAND SAE 15B35 RH

%C	%Mn	%Si	%Ni	%Cr	%Mo	%B
0.33/0.38	0.80/1.10	0.15/0.35	--	--	--	*

* can be expected to contain 0.0005/0.003 percent boron.

HARDNESS LIMITS FOR SPECIFICATION PURPOSES

"J" DISTANCE SIXTEENTHS OF AN INCH	HRC MAX.	HRC MIN.
1	57	52
2	55	51
3	54	50
4	53	49
5	50	41
6	46	33
7	42	28
8	36	24
9	32	23
10	28	21
11		
12	25	--
13		
14	24	--
15		
16	23	--
18		
20	22	--
22		
24	20	--
26		
28	--	--
30		
32		

HEAT TREATING TEMPERATURES

*NORMALIZE	1600 °F
AUSTENITIZE	1550 °F

*For forged or rolled specimens only

APPROX. DIA. OF ROUNDS WITH SAME AS-QUENCHED HRC, in. — LOCATION IN ROUND — QUENCH

Mild water quench: Surface 2 4; 3/4 Radius from center 1 2 3 4; Center 0.5 1 1.5 2 2.5 3 3.5 4

Mild oil quench: Surface 1 2 3 4; 3/4 Radius from center 0.5 1 1.5 2 2.5 3 3.5 4; Center 0.5 1 1.5 2 2.5 3 3.5

ROCKWELL HARDNESS C SCALE (20–65)

DISTANCE FROM QUENCHED END - SIXTEENTHS OF AN INCH (2–32)

HARDNESS LIMITS FOR SPECIFICATION PURPOSES

"J" DISTANCE MILLIMETERS	HRC MAX.	HRC MIN.
1.5	57	52
3	55	51
5	54	50
7	52	46
9	47	35
11	42	28
13	35	24
15	30	21
20	25	--
25	23	--
30	22	--
35	21	--
40	20	--
45		
50		

HEAT TREATING TEMPERATURES

*NORMALIZE	870 °C
AUSTENITIZE	845 °C

*For forged or rolled specimens only

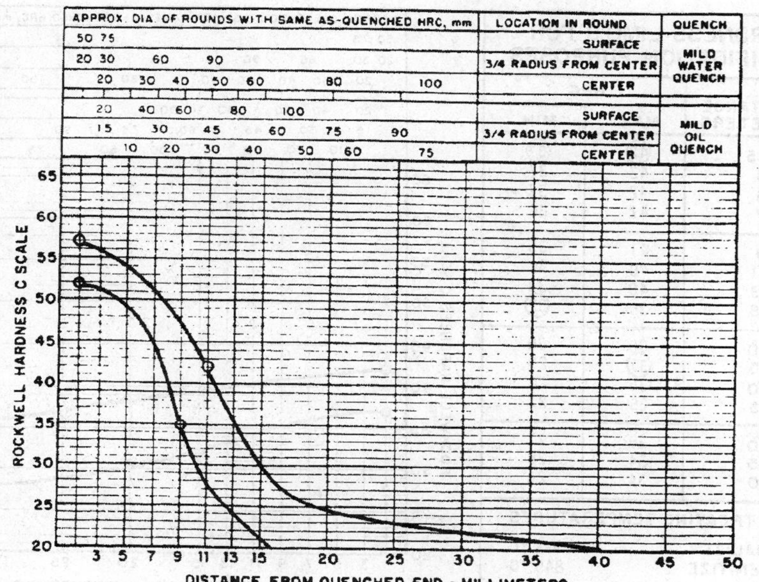

FIGURE 3—LIMITS FOR HARDENABILITY BAND 15B35RH

HARDENABILITY BAND

SAE 3310 RH

%C	%Mn	%Si	%Ni	%Cr	%Mo
0.08/0.13	0.40/0.60	0.15/0.35	3.25/3.75	1.40/1.75	--

HARDNESS LIMITS FOR SPECIFICATION PURPOSES

"J" DISTANCE SIXTEENTHS OF AN INCH	HRC MAX.	HRC MIN.
1	(42)	(37)
2	42	37
3	42	37
4	41	36
5	41	36
6	41	35
7	40	34
8	40	33
9	39	32
10	39	(32)
11	39	31
12	39	31
13	38	30
14	38	30
15	(37)	29
16	37	29
18	36	28
20	36	28
22	35	27
24	35	27
26	35	27
28	34	26
30	34	26
32	34	26

HEAT TREATING TEMPERATURES

*NORMALIZE 1700 °F

AUSTENITIZE 1550 °F

*For forged or rolled specimens only

APPROX. DIA. OF ROUNDS WITH SAME AS-QUENCHED HRC, in.

LOCATION IN ROUND — QUENCH

MILD WATER QUENCH: SURFACE 2 4; 3/4 RADIUS FROM CENTER 1 2 3 4; CENTER 0.5 1 1.5 2 2.5 3 3.5 4

MILD OIL QUENCH: SURFACE 1 2 3 4; 3/4 RADIUS FROM CENTER 0.5 1 1.5 2 2.5 3 3.5 4; CENTER 0.5 1 1.5 2 2.5 3 3.5

ROCKWELL HARDNESS C SCALE

65 60 55 50 45 40 35 30 25 20

2 4 6 8 10 12 14 16 18 20 22 24 26 28 30 32

DISTANCE FROM QUENCHED END - SIXTEENTHS OF AN INCH

HARDNESS LIMITS FOR SPECIFICATION PURPOSES

"J" DISTANCE MILLIMETERS	HRC MAX.	HRC MIN.
1.5	(42)	(37)
3	42	37
5	42	37
7	41	36
9	41	35
11	40	34
13	40	33
15	39	(32)
20	38	30
25	(37)	29
30	36	28
35	35	27
40	35	27
45	34	26
50	34	26

HEAT TREATING TEMPERATURES

*NORMALIZE 925 °C

AUSTENITIZE 845 °C

*For forged or rolled specimens only

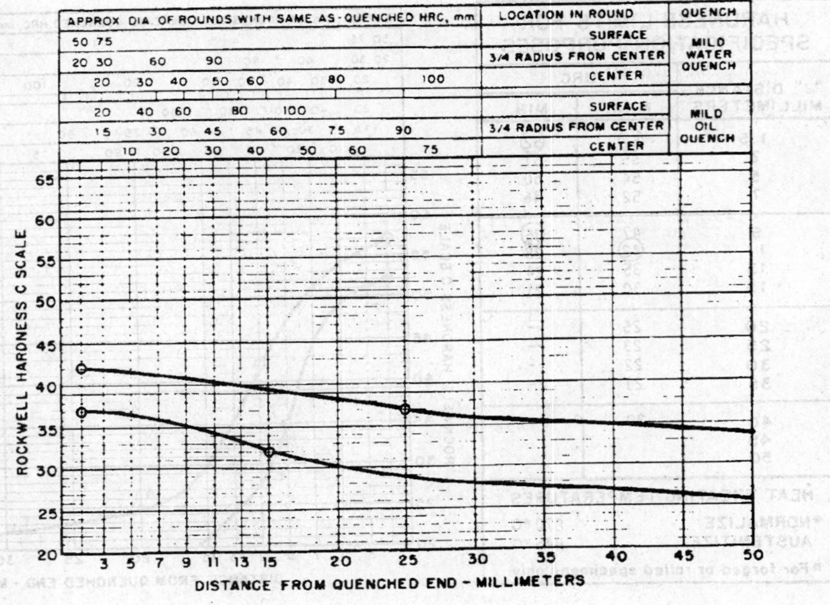

FIGURE 4—LIMITS FOR HARDENABILITY BAND 3310 RH

HARDENABILITY BAND SAE 4027 RH

%C	%Mn	%Si	%Ni	%Cr	%Mo
0.25/0.30	0.70/0.90	0.15/0.35	--	--	0.20/0.30

HARDNESS LIMITS FOR SPECIFICATION PURPOSES

"J" DISTANCE SIXTEENTHS OF AN INCH	HRC MAX.	HRC MIN.
1	51	46
2	48	42
3	43	34
4	37	28
5	32	24
6	28	22
7	26	20
8	24	--
9	23	--
10	22	--
11	22	--
12	21	--
13	21	--
14	20	--
15	--	--
16		
18		
20		
22		
24		
26		
28		
30		
32		

HEAT TREATING TEMPERATURES

*NORMALIZE	1650 °F
AUSTENITIZE	1600 °F

*For forged or rolled specimens only

APPROX. DIA. OF ROUNDS WITH SAME AS-QUENCHED HRC, in.

LOCATION IN ROUND: SURFACE / 3/4 RADIUS FROM CENTER / CENTER — QUENCH: MILD WATER QUENCH; MILD OIL QUENCH

ROCKWELL HARDNESS C SCALE

DISTANCE FROM QUENCHED END - SIXTEENTHS OF AN INCH

HARDNESS LIMITS FOR SPECIFICATION PURPOSES

"J" DISTANCE MILLIMETERS	HRC MAX.	HRC MIN.
1.5	51	46
3	48	42
5	42	33
7	35	26
9	29	23
11	26	20
13	24	--
15	23	--
20	21	--
25	--	--
30		
35		
40		
45		
50		

HEAT TREATING TEMPERATURES

*NORMALIZE	900 °C
AUSTENITIZE	870 °C

*For forged or rolled specimens only

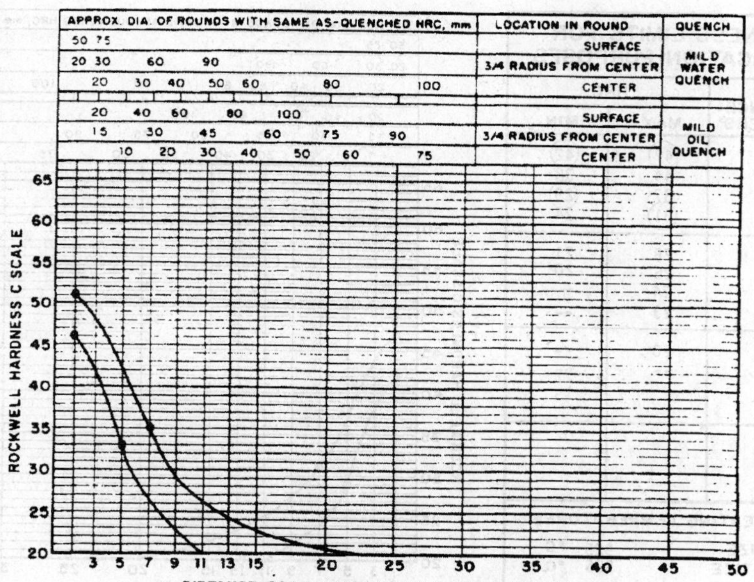

FIGURE 5—LIMITS FOR HARDENABILITY BAND 4027 RH

HARDENABILITY BAND

SAE 4118 RH

%C	%Mn	%Si	%Ni	%Cr	%Mo
0.18/0.23	0.70/0.90	0.15/0.35	--	0.40/0.60	0.08/0.15

HARDNESS LIMITS FOR SPECIFICATION PURPOSES

"J" DISTANCE SIXTEENTHS OF AN INCH	HRC MAX.	HRC MIN.
1	(47)	(42)
2	44	38
3	38	(30)
4	(33)	25
5	29	22
6	27	20
7	25	--
8	24	--
9	23	--
10	22	--
11	21	--
12	20	--
13	--	--
14		
15		
16		
18		
20		
22		
24		
26		
28		
30		
32		

HEAT TREATING TEMPERATURES

*NORMALIZE	1700 °F
AUSTENITIZE	1700 °F

*For forged or rolled specimens only

APPROX. DIA. OF ROUNDS WITH SAME AS-QUENCHED HRC, in.

LOCATION IN ROUND	QUENCH
SURFACE	MILD WATER QUENCH
3/4 RADIUS FROM CENTER	MILD WATER QUENCH
CENTER	MILD WATER QUENCH
SURFACE	MILD OIL QUENCH
3/4 RADIUS FROM CENTER	MILD OIL QUENCH
CENTER	MILD OIL QUENCH

ROCKWELL HARDNESS C SCALE

DISTANCE FROM QUENCHED END - SIXTEENTHS OF AN INCH

HARDNESS LIMITS FOR SPECIFICATION PURPOSES

"J" DISTANCE MILLIMETERS	HRC MAX.	HRC MIN.
1.5	(47)	(42)
3	44	38
5	37	(29)
7	(31)	24
9	28	21
11	25	20
13	24	--
15	23	--
20	20	--
25	--	--
30		
35		
40		
45		
50		

HEAT TREATING TEMPERATURES

*NORMALIZE	925 °C
AUSTENITIZE	925 °C

*For forged or rolled specimens only

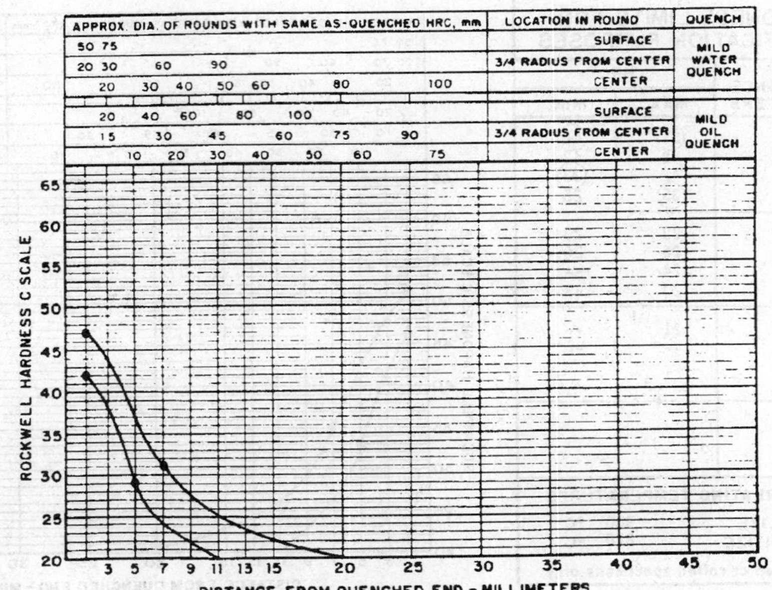

FIGURE 6—LIMITS FOR HARDENABILITY BAND 4118 RH

HARDENABILITY BAND SAE 4120 RH

%C	%Mn	%Si	%Ni	%Cr	%Mo
0.18/0.23	0.90/1.20	0.15/0.35	--	0.40/0.60	0.13/0.20

HARDNESS LIMITS FOR SPECIFICATION PURPOSES

"J" DISTANCE SIXTEENTHS OF AN INCH	HRC MAX.	HRC MIN.
1	(47)	(42)
2	45	39
3	41	35
4	38	(30)
5	(34)	26
6	31	24
7	29	22
8	28	21
9	26	20
10	25	--
11	24	--
12	23	--
13	23	--
14	22	--
15	22	--
16	21	--
18	20	--
20	--	--
22		
24		
26		
28		
30		
32		

HEAT TREATING TEMPERATURES

*NORMALIZE	1700 °F
AUSTENITIZE	1700 °F

*For forged or rolled specimens only

APPROX. DIA. OF ROUNDS WITH SAME AS-QUENCHED HRC, in. — LOCATION IN ROUND — QUENCH

Mild water quench: Surface 2, 4; 3/4 radius from center 1, 2, 3, 4; Center 0.5, 1, 1.5, 2, 2.5, 3, 3.5, 4

Mild oil quench: Surface 1, 2, 3, 4; 3/4 radius from center 0.5, 1, 1.5, 2, 2.5, 3, 3.5, 4; Center 0.5, 1, 1.5, 2, 2.5, 3, 3.5

ROCKWELL HARDNESS C SCALE (20–65)

DISTANCE FROM QUENCHED END - SIXTEENTHS OF AN INCH (2–32)

HARDNESS LIMITS FOR SPECIFICATION PURPOSES

"J" DISTANCE MILLIMETERS	HRC MAX.	HRC MIN.
1.5	(47)	(42)
3	45	39
5	41	(34)
7	(36)	28
9	32	25
11	29	22
13	28	21
15	26	20
20	23	--
25	21	--
30	--	--
35		
40		
45		
50		

HEAT TREATING TEMPERATURES

*NORMALIZE	925 °C
AUSTENITIZE	925 °C

*For forged or rolled specimens only

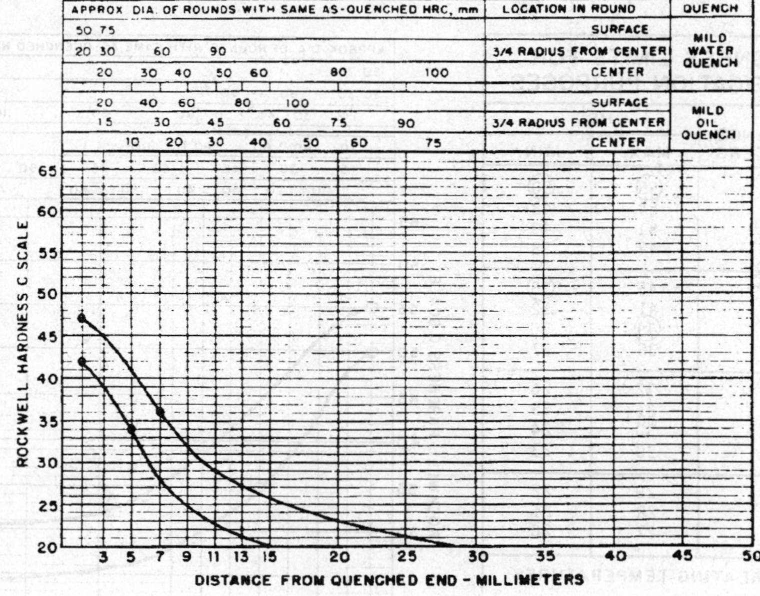

FIGURE 7—LIMITS FOR HARDENABILITY BAND 4120 RH

HARDENABILITY BAND SAE 4130 RH

%C	%Mn	%Si	%Ni	%Cr	%Mo
0.28/0.33	0.40/0.60	0.15/0.35	--	0.80/1.10	0.15/0.25

HARDNESS LIMITS FOR SPECIFICATION PURPOSES

"J" DISTANCE SIXTEENTHS OF AN INCH	HRC MAX	HRC MIN.
1	(55)	(50)
2	54	48
3	52	44
4	49	40
5	46	(36)
6	44	34
7	41	32
8	(39)	30
9	37	28
10	35	27
11	33	26
12	32	26
13	32	26
14	31	25
15	31	25
16	31	25
18	30	24
20	30	23
22	30	23
24	29	22
26	29	22
28	28	21
30	28	21
32	27	20

HEAT TREATING TEMPERATURES

*NORMALIZE	1650 °F
AUSTENITIZE	1600 °F

* For forged or rolled specimens only

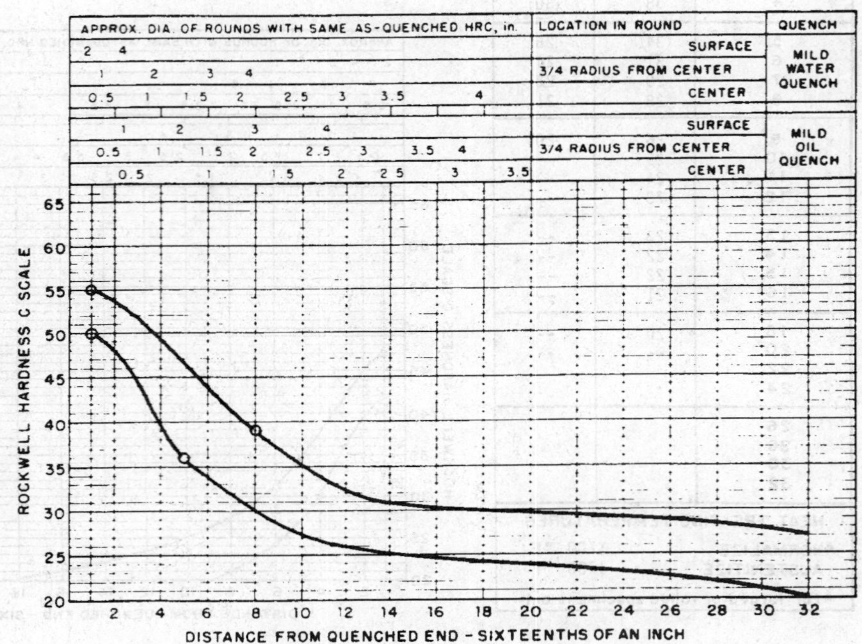

HARDNESS LIMITS FOR SPECIFICATION PURPOSES

"J" DISTANCE MILLIMETERS	HRC MAX.	HRC MIN.
1.5	(55)	(50)
3	54	48
5	51	43
7	48	38
9	45	(35)
11	41	32
13	(39)	30
15	36	27
20	32	26
25	31	25
30	30	24
35	30	23
40	29	22
45	28	21
50	27	20

HEAT TREATING TEMPERATURES

*NORMALIZE	900 °C
AUSTENITIZE	870 °C

* For forged or rolled specimens only

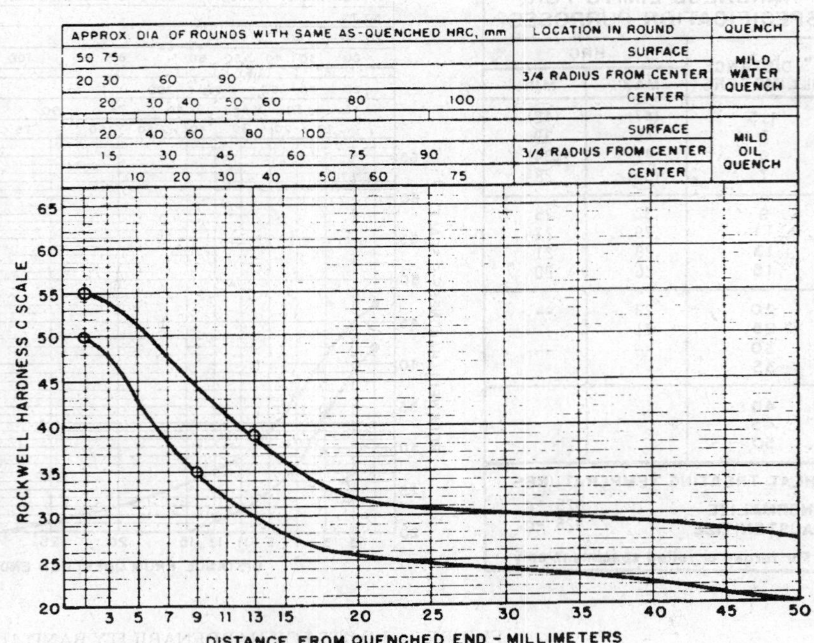

FIGURE 8—LIMITS FOR HARDENABILITY BAND 4130 RH

HARDENABILITY BAND SAE 4140 RH

%C	%Mn	%Si	%Ni	%Cr	%Mo
0.38/0.43	0.75/1.00	0.15/0.35	--	0.80/1.10	0.15/0.25

HARDNESS LIMITS FOR SPECIFICATION PURPOSES

"J" DISTANCE SIXTEENTHS OF AN INCH	HRC MAX.	HRC MIN.
1	59	54
2	59	54
3	59	54
4	59	53
5	58	52
6	57	51
7	56	50
8	55	49
9	54	48
10	53	46
11	52	44
12	52	43
13	51	42
14	50	41
15	50	40
16	49	39
18	48	38
20	47	37
22	46	37
24	45	36
26	44	35
28	43	35
30	42	34
32	41	33

HEAT TREATING TEMPERATURES

*NORMALIZE	1600 °F
AUSTENITIZE	1550 °F

*For forged or rolled specimens only

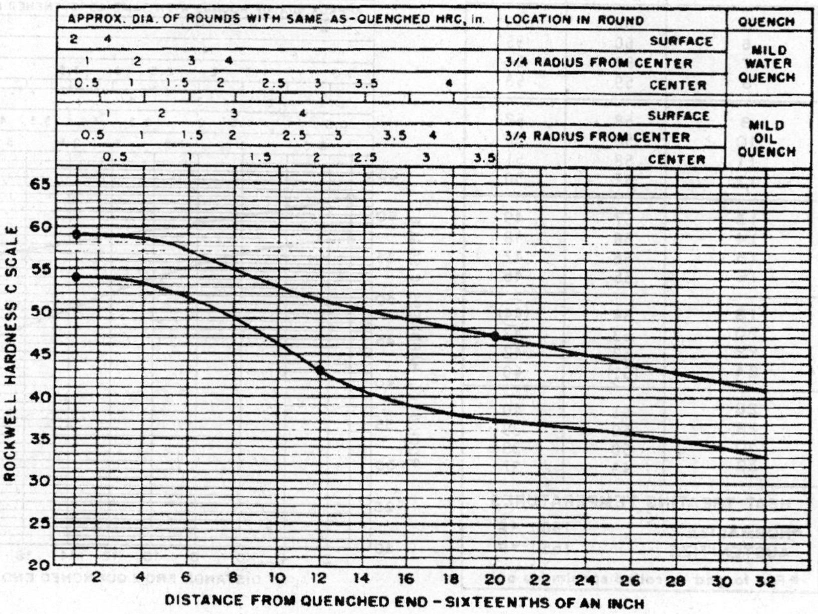

APPROX. DIA. OF ROUNDS WITH SAME AS-QUENCHED HRC, in.	LOCATION IN ROUND	QUENCH
2 4	SURFACE	MILD WATER QUENCH
1 2 3 4	3/4 RADIUS FROM CENTER	
0.5 1 1.5 2 2.5 3 3.5 4	CENTER	
1 2 3 4	SURFACE	MILD OIL QUENCH
0.5 1 1.5 2 2.5 3 3.5 4	3/4 RADIUS FROM CENTER	
0.5 1 1.5 2 2.5 3 3.5	CENTER	

ROCKWELL HARDNESS C SCALE (20–65)

DISTANCE FROM QUENCHED END – SIXTEENTHS OF AN INCH (2–32)

HARDNESS LIMITS FOR SPECIFICATION PURPOSES

"J" DISTANCE MILLIMETERS	HRC MAX.	HRC MIN.
1.5	59	54
3	59	54
5	59	54
7	59	53
9	58	52
11	56	50
13	55	49
15	54	47
20	51	42
25	49	39
30	48	38
35	46	37
40	44	36
45	43	35
50	41	33

HEAT TREATING TEMPERATURES

*NORMALIZE	870 °C
AUSTENITIZE	845 °C

*For forged or rolled specimens only

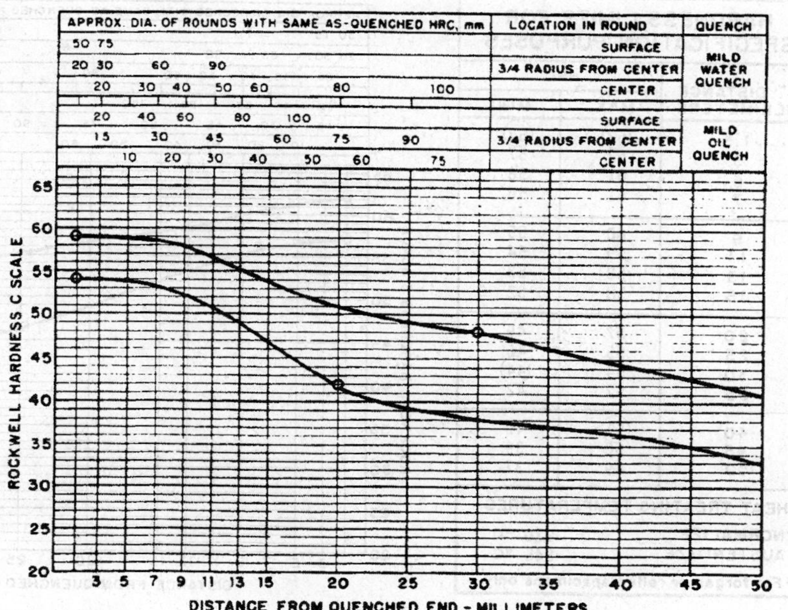

FIGURE 9—LIMITS FOR HARDENABILITY BAND 4140 RH

HARDENABILITY BAND

SAE 4145 RH

%C	%Mn	%Si	%Ni	%Cr	%Mo
0.43/0.48	0.75/1.00	0.15/0.35	--	0.80/1.10	0.15/0.25

HARDNESS LIMITS FOR SPECIFICATION PURPOSES

"J" DISTANCE SIXTEENTHS OF AN INCH	HRC MAX.	HRC MIN.
1	(62)	(57)
2	62	57
3	61	56
4	61	56
5	60	55
6	60	55
7	59	54
8	59	53
9	58	52
10	58	52
11	58	51
12	57	50
13	57	49
14	56	48
15	56	47
16	55	46
18	54	(44)
20	53	43
22	52	42
24	(51)	40
26	51	40
28	50	39
30	50	38
32	49	37

HEAT TREATING TEMPERATURES

*NORMALIZE 1600 °F

AUSTENITIZE 1550 °F

*For forged or rolled specimens only

APPROX. DIA. OF ROUNDS WITH SAME AS-QUENCHED HRC, in. — LOCATION IN ROUND — QUENCH

MILD WATER QUENCH: SURFACE; 3/4 RADIUS FROM CENTER; CENTER

MILD OIL QUENCH: SURFACE; 3/4 RADIUS FROM CENTER; CENTER

ROCKWELL HARDNESS C SCALE

DISTANCE FROM QUENCHED END - SIXTEENTHS OF AN INCH

HARDNESS LIMITS FOR SPECIFICATION PURPOSES

"J" DISTANCE MILLIMETERS	HRC MAX.	HRC MIN.
1.5	(62)	(57)
3	62	57
5	61	56
7	61	56
9	60	55
11	59	54
13	59	53
15	58	52
20	57	49
25	55	46
30	54	(44)
35	52	42
40	(51)	40
45	50	39
50	49	37

HEAT TREATING TEMPERATURES

*NORMALIZE 870 °C

AUSTENITIZE 845 °C

*For forged or rolled specimens only

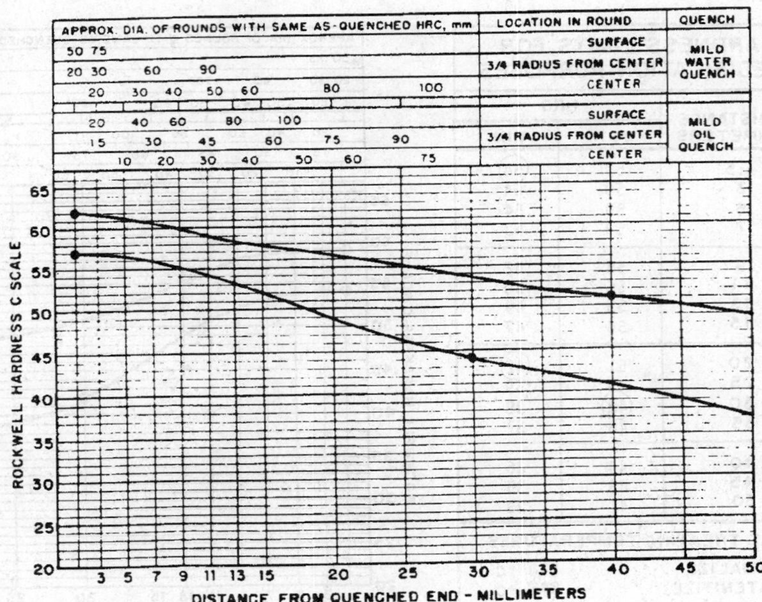

FIGURE 10—LIMITS FOR HARDENABILITY BAND 4145 RH

HARDENABILITY BAND SAE 4161 RH

%C	%Mn	%Si	%Ni	%Cr	%Mo
0.56/0.64	0.75/1.00	0.15/0.35	--	0.70/0.90	0.25/0.35

HARDNESS LIMITS FOR SPECIFICATION PURPOSES

"J" DISTANCE SIXTEENTHS OF AN INCH	HRC MAX.	HRC MIN.
1	(65)	(60)
2	65	60
3	65	60
4	65	60
5	65	60
6	65	60
7	65	60
8	65	60
9	65	60
10	65	60
11	65	60
12	64	59
13	64	59
14	64	59
15	63	58
16	63	57
18	62	56
20	62	(54)
22	61	53
24	(60)	51
26	59	49
28	58	47
30	57	46
32	57	45

HEAT TREATING TEMPERATURES

*NORMALIZE 1600 °F
AUSTENITIZE 1550 °F

* For forged or rolled specimens only

APPROX. DIA. OF ROUNDS WITH SAME AS-QUENCHED HRC, in. — LOCATION IN ROUND — QUENCH
MILD WATER QUENCH: SURFACE 2 4; 3/4 RADIUS FROM CENTER 1 2 3 4; CENTER 0.5 1 1.5 2 2.5 3 3.5 4
MILD OIL QUENCH: SURFACE 1 2 3 4; 3/4 RADIUS FROM CENTER 0.5 1 1.5 2 2.5 3 3.5 4; CENTER 0.5 1 1.5 2 2.5 3 3.5

ROCKWELL HARDNESS C SCALE: 65 60 55 50 45 40 35 30 25 20

DISTANCE FROM QUENCHED END - SIXTEENTHS OF AN INCH: 2 4 6 8 10 12 14 16 18 20 22 24 26 28 30 32

HARDNESS LIMITS FOR SPECIFICATION PURPOSES

"J" DISTANCE MILLIMETERS	HRC MAX.	HRC MIN.
1.5	(65)	(60)
3	65	60
5	65	60
7	65	60
9	65	60
11	65	60
13	65	60
15	65	60
20	64	59
25	63	57
30	62	(55)
35	(61)	53
40	59	50
45	58	47
50	57	45

HEAT TREATING TEMPERATURES

*NORMALIZE 870 °C
AUSTENITIZE 845 °C

* For forged or rolled specimens only

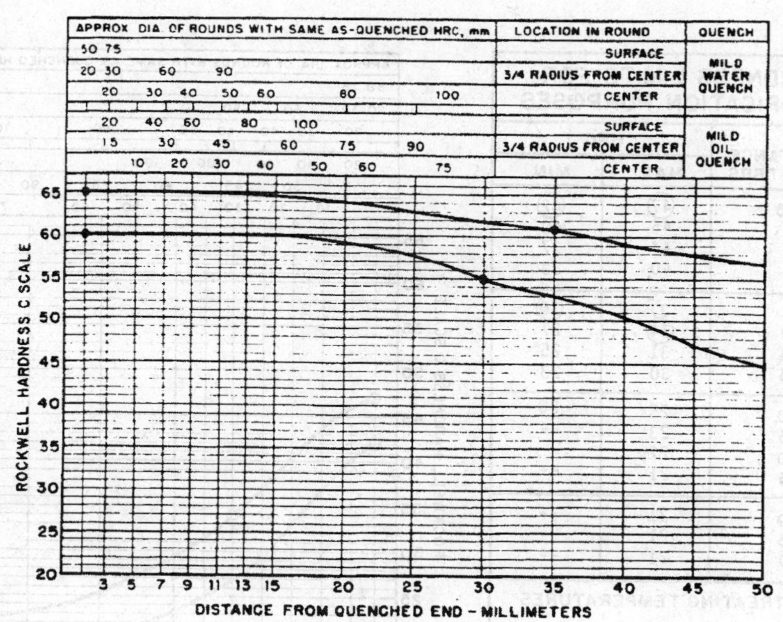

FIGURE 11—LIMITS FOR HARDENABILITY BAND 4161 RH

HARDENABILITY BAND SAE 4320 RH

%C	%Mn	%Si	%Ni	%Cr	%Mo
0.17/0.22	0.45/0.65	0.15/0.35	1.65/2.00	0.40/0.60	0.20/0.30

HARDNESS LIMITS FOR SPECIFICATION PURPOSES

"J" DISTANCE SIXTEENTHS OF AN INCH	HRC MAX.	HRC MIN.
1	(47)	(42)
2	46	40
3	44	37
4	41	34
5	39	(31)
6	36	29
7	(34)	27
8	32	25
9	31	24
10	29	23
11	28	22
12	26	21
13	25	20
14	24	--
15	24	--
16	23	--
18	22	--
20	22	--
22	21	--
24	21	--
26	21	--
28	21	--
30	21	--
32	21	--

HEAT TREATING TEMPERATURES	
*NORMALIZE	1700 °F
AUSTENITIZE	1700 °F

*For forged or rolled specimens only

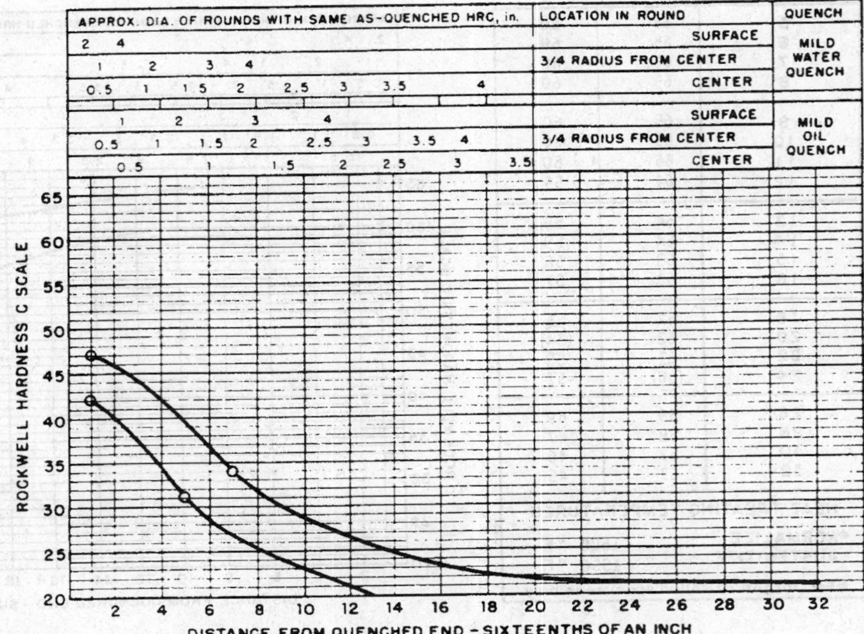

HARDNESS LIMITS FOR SPECIFICATION PURPOSES

"J" DISTANCE MILLIMETERS	HRC MAX.	HRC MIN.
1.5	(47)	(42)
3	46	40
5	44	37
7	40	33
9	37	(30)
11	(34)	27
13	31	25
15	30	23
20	25	20
25	23	--
30	22	--
35	21	--
40	21	--
45	21	--
50	21	--

HEAT TREATING TEMPERATURES	
*NORMALIZE	925 °C
AUSTENITIZE	925 °C

*For forged or rolled specimens only

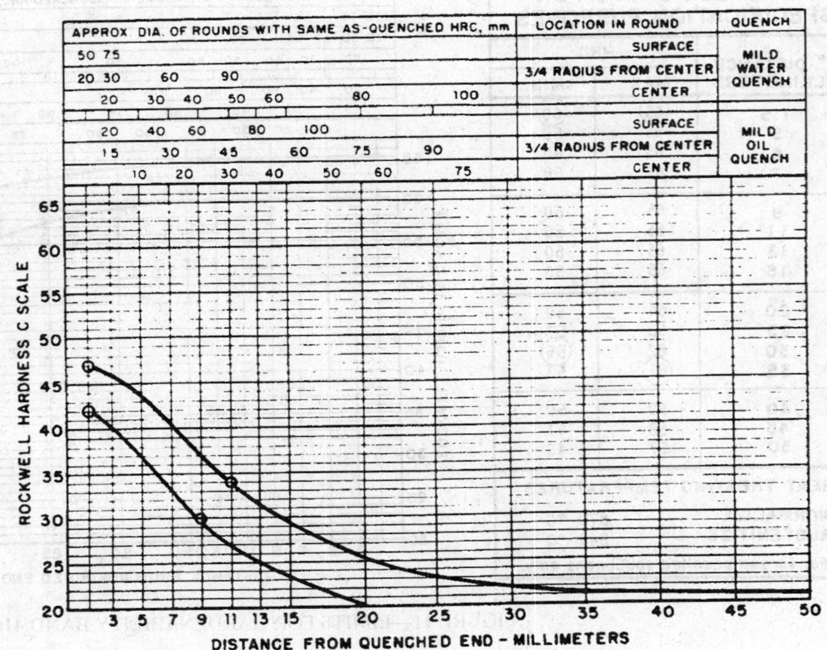

FIGURE 12—LIMITS FOR HARDENABILITY BAND 4320 RH

HARDENABILITY BAND SAE 4620 RH

%C	%Mn	%Si	%Ni	%Cr	%Mo
0.17/0.22	0.45/0.65	0.15/0.35	1.65/2.00	--	0.20/0.30

HARDNESS LIMITS FOR SPECIFICATION PURPOSES

"J" DISTANCE SIXTEENTHS OF AN INCH	HRC MAX.	HRC MIN.
1	(47)	(42)
2	44	37
3	40	30
4	37	(27)
5	(32)	24
6	29	21
7	27	20
8	25	--
9	24	--
10	23	--
11	22	--
12	21	--
13	20	--
14	--	--
15		
16		
18		
20		
22		
24		
26		
28		
30		
32		

HEAT TREATING TEMPERATURES

*NORMALIZE	1700 °F
AUSTENITIZE	1700 °F

*For forged or rolled specimens only

APPROX. DIA. OF ROUNDS WITH SAME AS-QUENCHED HRC, in. — LOCATION IN ROUND — QUENCH

MILD WATER QUENCH: SURFACE 2 4; 3/4 RADIUS FROM CENTER 1 2 3 4; CENTER 0.5 1 1.5 2 2.5 3 3.5 4

MILD OIL QUENCH: SURFACE 1 2 3 4; 3/4 RADIUS FROM CENTER 0.5 1 1.5 2 2.5 3 3.5 4; CENTER 0.5 1 1.5 2 2.5 3 3.5

ROCKWELL HARDNESS C SCALE (20–65)

DISTANCE FROM QUENCHED END - SIXTEENTHS OF AN INCH (2–32)

HARDNESS LIMITS FOR SPECIFICATION PURPOSES

"J" DISTANCE MILLIMETERS	HRC MAX.	HRC MIN.
1.5	(47)	(42)
3	44	37
5	39	(29)
7	35	26
9	(30)	22
11	27	20
13	25	--
15	23	--
20	21	--
25	--	--
30		
35		
40		
45		
50		

HEAT TREATING TEMPERATURES

*NORMALIZE	925 °C
AUSTENITIZE	925 °C

*For forged or rolled specimens only

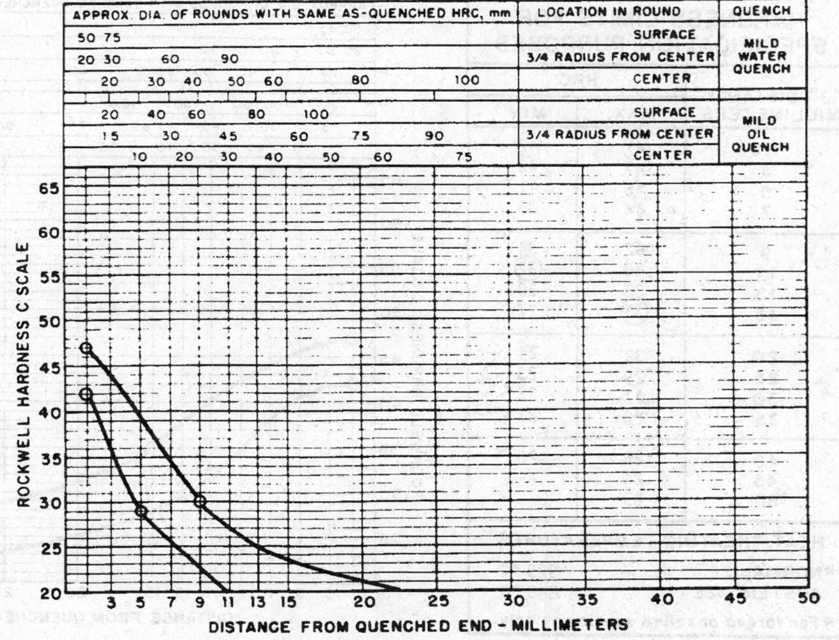

FIGURE 13—LIMITS FOR HARDENABILITY BAND 4620 RH

HARDENABILITY BAND SAE 4820 RH

%C	%Mn	%Si	%Ni	%Cr	%Mo
0.18/0.23	0.50/0.70	0.15/0.35	3.25/3.75	--	0.20/0.30

HARDNESS LIMITS FOR SPECIFICATION PURPOSES

"J" DISTANCE SIXTEENTHS OF AN INCH	HRC MAX.	HRC MIN.
1	(47)	(42)
2	47	42
3	46	41
4	45	40
5	43	36
6	41	33
7	40	32
8	38	(30)
9	36	28
10	35	27
11	(34)	26
12	33	25
13	32	24
14	31	24
15	30	23
16	29	23
18	28	22
20	27	22
22	26	21
24	25	20
26	25	20
28	25	--
30	24	--
32	23	--

HEAT TREATING TEMPERATURES

*NORMALIZE	1700 °F
AUSTENITIZE	1550 °F

*For forged or rolled specimens only

APPROX. DIA. OF ROUNDS WITH SAME AS-QUENCHED HRC, in. / LOCATION IN ROUND / QUENCH

Approx. dia.	Location in round	Quench
2 4	SURFACE	MILD WATER QUENCH
1 2 3 4	3/4 RADIUS FROM CENTER	MILD WATER QUENCH
0.5 1 1.5 2 2.5 3 3.5 4	CENTER	MILD WATER QUENCH
1 2 3 4	SURFACE	MILD OIL QUENCH
0.5 1 1.5 2 2.5 3 3.5 4	3/4 RADIUS FROM CENTER	MILD OIL QUENCH
0.5 1 1.5 2 2.5 3 3.5	CENTER	MILD OIL QUENCH

ROCKWELL HARDNESS C SCALE (20–65)

DISTANCE FROM QUENCHED END - SIXTEENTHS OF AN INCH (2–32)

HARDNESS LIMITS FOR SPECIFICATION PURPOSES

"J" DISTANCE MILLIMETERS	HRC MAX.	HRC MIN.
1.5	(47)	(42)
3	47	42
5	46	41
7	44	38
9	42	34
11	40	(32)
13	38	30
15	(35)	27
20	32	24
25	29	23
30	27	22
35	26	21
40	25	20
45	24	--
50	23	--

HEAT TREATING TEMPERATURES

*NORMALIZE	925 °C
AUSTENITIZE	845 °C

*For forged or rolled specimens only

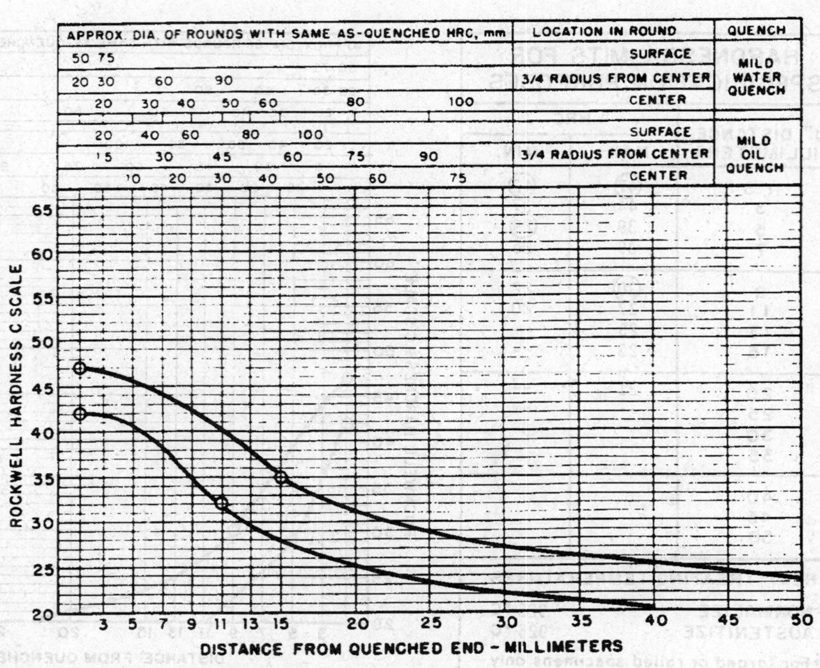

FIGURE 14—LIMITS FOR HARDENABILITY BAND 4820 RH

HARDENABILITY BAND SAE 50B40 RH

%C	%Mn	%Si	%Ni	%Cr	%Mo	%B
0.38/0.43	0.75/1.00	0.15/0.35	--	0.40/0.60	--	*

* can be expected to contain 0.0005/0.003 percent boron.

HARDNESS LIMITS FOR SPECIFICATION PURPOSES

"J" DISTANCE SIXTEENTHS OF AN INCH	HRC MAX.	HRC MIN.
1	(59)	(54)
2	59	54
3	58	53
4	58	53
5	57	52
6	56	50
7	55	47
8	54	(43)
9	52	38
10	50	35
11	49	33
12	47	32
13	(45)	31
14	44	30
15	41	29
16	38	28
18	36	26
20	34	24
22	33	23
24	32	22
26	31	21
28	30	20
30	29	--
32	28	--

HEAT TREATING TEMPERATURES

*NORMALIZE	1600°F
AUSTENITIZE	1550°F

*For forged or rolled specimens only

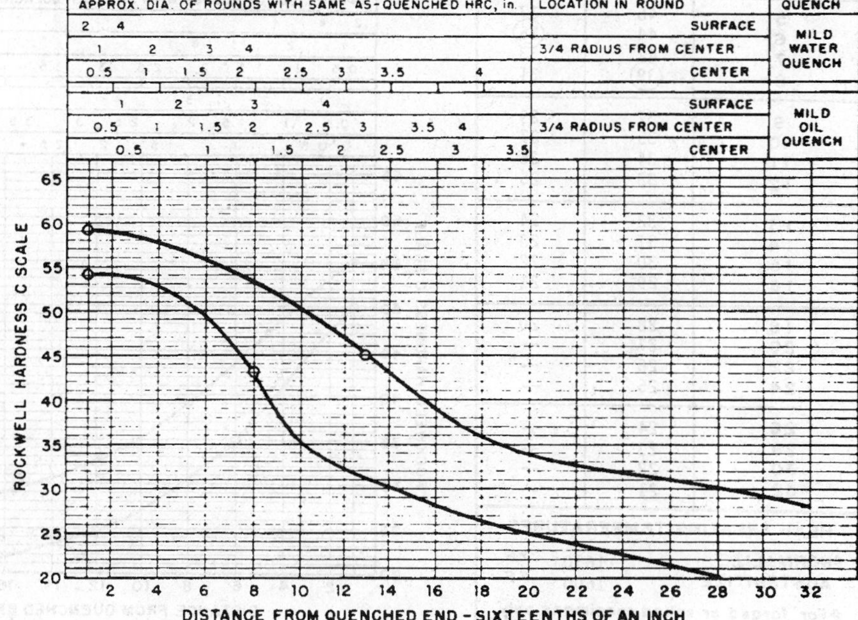

HARDNESS LIMITS FOR SPECIFICATION PURPOSES

"J" DISTANCE MILLIMETERS	HRC MAX.	HRC MIN.
1.5	(59)	(54)
3	59	54
5	58	53
7	58	53
9	56	51
11	55	47
13	54	(42)
15	51	36
20	(46)	31
25	39	28
30	35	25
35	33	23
40	31	21
45	29	20
50	28	--

HEAT TREATING TEMPERATURES

*NORMALIZE	870°C
AUSTENITIZE	845°C

*For forged or rolled specimens only

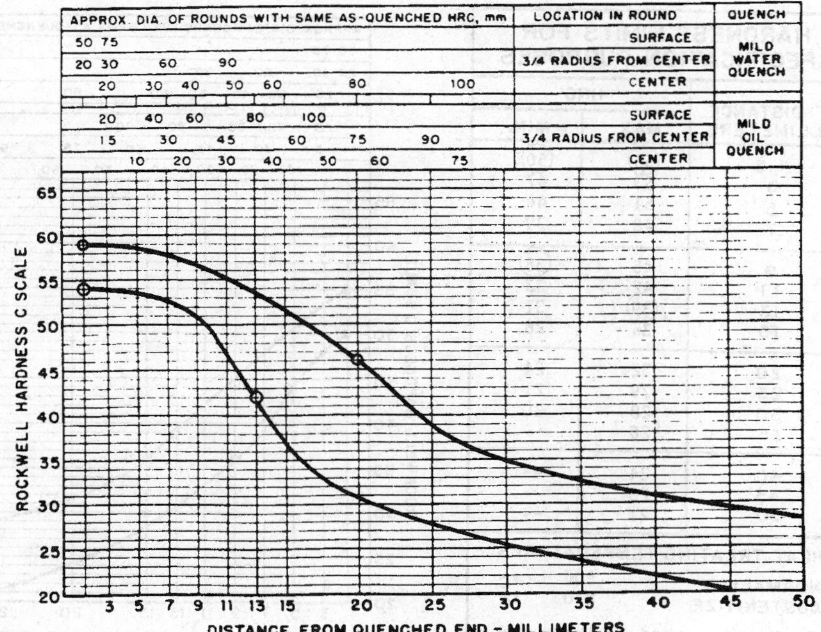

FIGURE 15—LIMITS FOR HARDENABILITY BAND 50B40 RH

HARDENABILITY BAND SAE 5130 RH

%C	%Mn	%Si	%Ni	%Cr	%Mo
0.28/0.33	0.70/0.90	0.15/0.35	--	0.80/1.10	--

HARDNESS LIMITS FOR SPECIFICATION PURPOSES

"J" DISTANCE SIXTEENTHS OF AN INCH	HRC MAX.	HRC MIN.
1	(55)	(50)
2	53	47
3	51	44
4	49	41
5	46	37
6	44	(35)
7	42	33
8	(39)	31
9	37	29
10	35	27
11	34	26
12	33	25
13	32	24
14	31	23
15	30	22
16	29	21
18	28	20
20	27	--
22	26	--
24	25	--
26	24	--
28	23	--
30	22	--
32	21	--

HEAT TREATING TEMPERATURES

*NORMALIZE	1650	°F
AUSTENITIZE	1600	°F

*For forged or rolled specimens only

APPROX. DIA. OF ROUNDS WITH SAME AS-QUENCHED HRC, in. — LOCATION IN ROUND — QUENCH

MILD WATER QUENCH: SURFACE: 2, 4; 3/4 RADIUS FROM CENTER: 1, 2, 3, 4; CENTER: 0.5, 1, 1.5, 2, 2.5, 3, 3.5, 4

MILD OIL QUENCH: SURFACE: 1, 2, 3, 4; 3/4 RADIUS FROM CENTER: 0.5, 1, 1.5, 2, 2.5, 3, 3.5, 4; CENTER: 0.5, 1, 1.5, 2, 2.5, 3, 3.5

ROCKWELL HARDNESS C SCALE: 20, 25, 30, 35, 40, 45, 50, 55, 60, 65

DISTANCE FROM QUENCHED END – SIXTEENTHS OF AN INCH: 2, 4, 6, 8, 10, 12, 14, 16, 18, 20, 22, 24, 26, 28, 30, 32

HARDNESS LIMITS FOR SPECIFICATION PURPOSES

"J" DISTANCE MILLIMETERS	HRC MAX.	HRC MIN.
1.5	(55)	(50)
3	53	47
5	51	44
7	48	39
9	45	(36)
11	42	33
13	(39)	31
15	36	28
20	32	24
25	29	21
30	28	20
35	26	--
40	24	--
45	23	--
50	21	--

HEAT TREATING TEMPERATURES

*NORMALIZE	900	°C
AUSTENITIZE	870	°C

*For forged or rolled specimens only

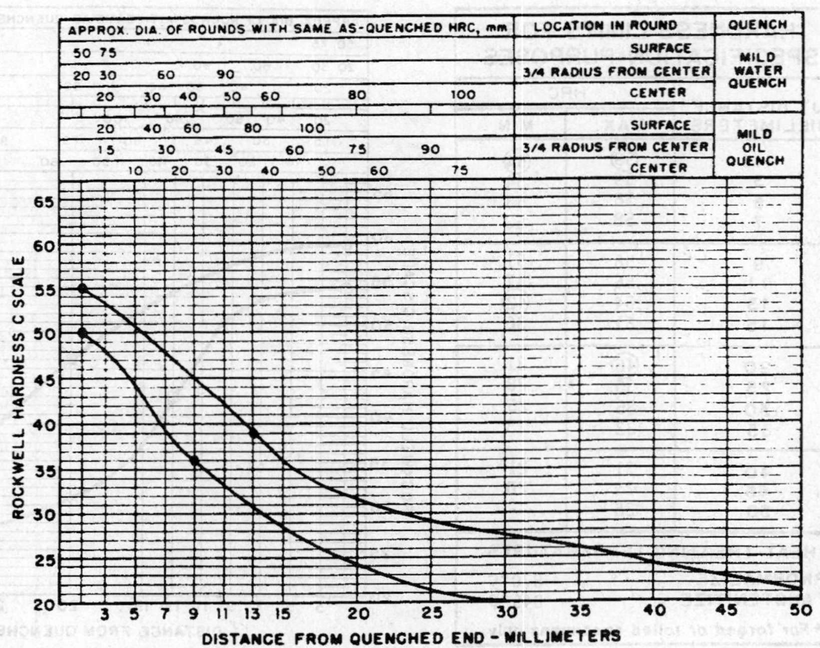

FIGURE 16—LIMITS FOR HARDENABILITY BAND 5130 RH

HARDENABILITY BAND SAE 5140 RH

%C	%Mn	%Si	%Ni	%Cr	%Mo
0.38/0.43	0.70/0.90	0.15/0.35	--	0.70/0.90	--

HARDNESS LIMITS FOR SPECIFICATION PURPOSES

"J" DISTANCE SIXTEENTHS OF AN INCH	HRC MAX.	HRC MIN.
1	(59)	(54)
2	58	53
3	57	51
4	55	49
5	53	45
6	51	(41)
7	48	38
8	46	36
9	(44)	34
10	43	33
11	41	32
12	40	31
13	39	30
14	37	29
15	36	28
16	35	27
18	34	26
20	33	25
22	32	24
24	31	23
26	30	22
28	30	21
30	29	20
32	29	--

HEAT TREATING TEMPERATURES

*NORMALIZE	1600	°F
AUSTENITIZE	1550	°F

* For forged or rolled specimens only

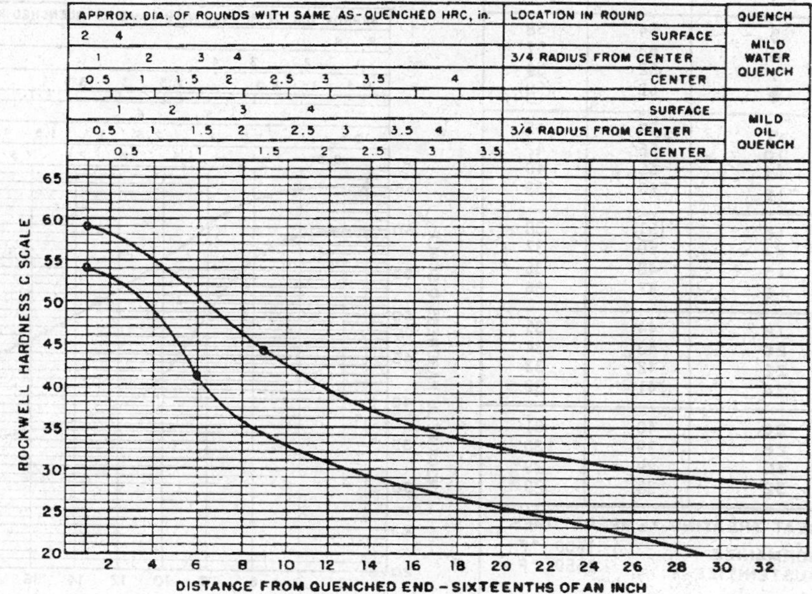

HARDNESS LIMITS FOR SPECIFICATION PURPOSES

"J" DISTANCE MILLIMETERS	HRC MAX.	HRC MIN.
1.5	(59)	(54)
3	58	53
5	57	51
7	55	47
9	52	(42)
11	48	38
13	46	36
15	(44)	34
20	39	30
25	35	27
30	33	25
35	32	24
40	31	22
45	30	21
50	29	20

HEAT TREATING TEMPERATURES

*NORMALIZE	870	°C
AUSTENITIZE	845	°C

* For forged or rolled specimens only

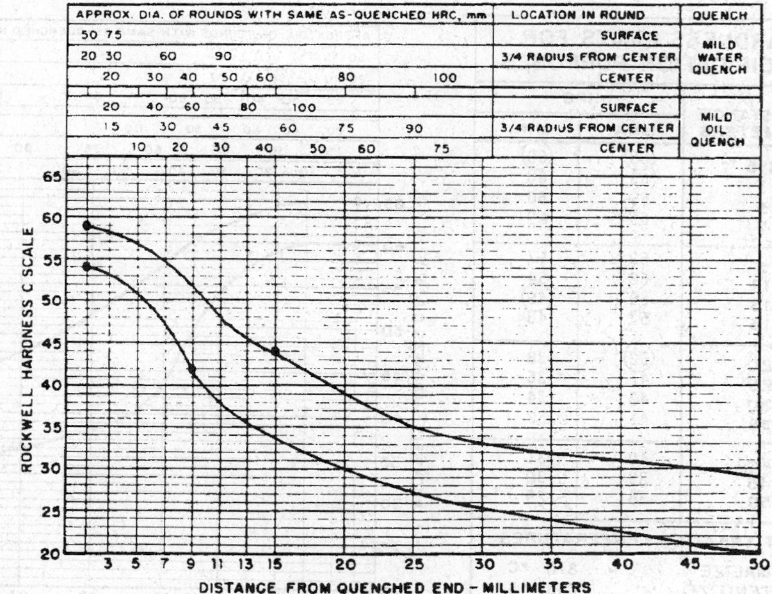

FIGURE 17—LIMITS FOR HARDENABILITY BAND 5140 RH

HARDENABILITY BAND SAE 5160 RH

%C	%Mn	%Si	%Ni	%Cr	%Mo
0.56/0.64	0.75/1.00	0.15/0.35	--	0.70/0.90	--

HARDNESS LIMITS FOR SPECIFICATION PURPOSES

"J" DISTANCE SIXTEENTHS OF AN INCH	HRC MAX.	HRC MIN.
1	(65)	(60)
2	65	60
3	65	60
4	65	59
5	64	58
6	63	57
7	62	54
8	60	(50)
9	58	45
10	56	42
11	55	40
12	63	39
13	(51)	38
14	50	37
15	48	36
16	47	36
18	44	35
20	43	34
22	42	33
24	41	32
26	40	31
28	39	30
30	39	29
32	38	29

HEAT TREATING TEMPERATURES

*NORMALIZE	1600 °F
AUSTENITIZE	1550 °F

*For forged or rolled specimens only

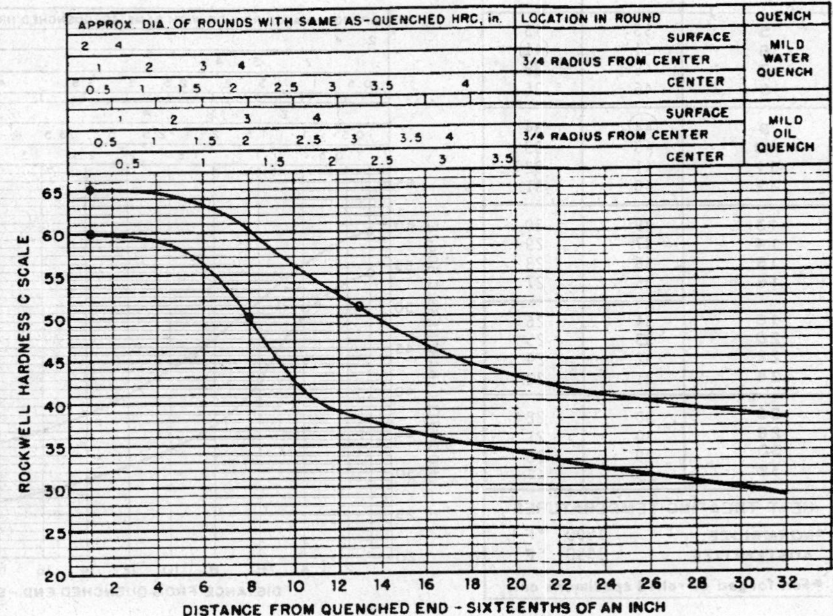

HARDNESS LIMITS FOR SPECIFICATION PURPOSES

"J" DISTANCE MILLIMETERS	HRC MAX.	HRC MIN.
1.5	(65)	(60)
3	65	60
5	65	60
7	65	59
9	63	57
11	62	54
13	60	(49)
15	57	43
20	(52)	38
25	47	36
30	43	34
35	41	32
40	40	31
45	39	30
50	38	29

HEAT TREATING TEMPERATURES

*NORMALIZE	870 °C
AUSTENITIZE	845 °C

*For forged or rolled specimens only

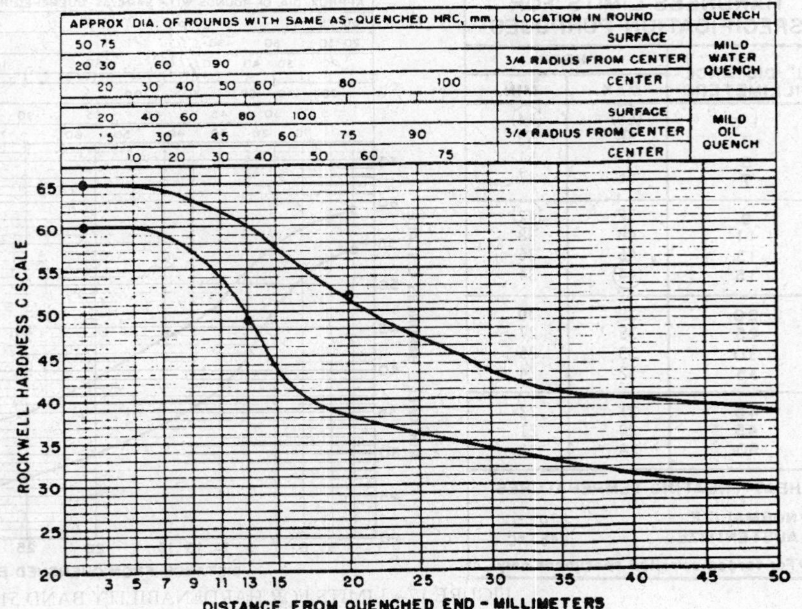

FIGURE 18—LIMITS FOR HARDENABILITY BAND 5160 RH

HARDENABILITY BAND SAE 8620 RH

%C	%Mn	%Si	%Ni	%Cr	%Mo
0.18/0.23	0.70/0.90	0.15/0.35	0.40/0.70	0.40/0.60	0.15/0.25

HARDNESS LIMITS FOR SPECIFICATION PURPOSES

"J" DISTANCE SIXTEENTHS OF AN INCH	HRC MAX.	HRC MIN.
1	(47)	(42)
2	45	39
3	41	35
4	38	(30)
5	(34)	26
6	31	24
7	29	22
8	28	21
9	26	20
10	25	--
11	24	--
12	23	--
13	23	--
14	22	--
15	22	--
16	21	--
18	20	--
20	--	--
22		
24		
26		
28		
30		
32		

HEAT TREATING TEMPERATURES

*NORMALIZE	1700 °F
AUSTENITIZE	1700 °F

*For forged or rolled specimens only

APPROX. DIA. OF ROUNDS WITH SAME AS-QUENCHED HRC, in. | LOCATION IN ROUND | QUENCH

2 4 — SURFACE — MILD WATER QUENCH

1 2 3 4 — 3/4 RADIUS FROM CENTER

0.5 1 1.5 2 2.5 3 3.5 4 — CENTER

1 2 3 4 — SURFACE — MILD OIL QUENCH

0.5 1 1.5 2 2.5 3 3.5 4 — 3/4 RADIUS FROM CENTER

0.5 1 1.5 2 2.5 3 3.5 — CENTER

ROCKWELL HARDNESS C SCALE: 20 25 30 35 40 45 50 55 60 65

2 4 6 8 10 12 14 16 18 20 22 24 26 28 30 32

DISTANCE FROM QUENCHED END - SIXTEENTHS OF AN INCH

HARDNESS LIMITS FOR SPECIFICATION PURPOSES

"J" DISTANCE MILLIMETERS	HRC MAX.	HRC MIN.
1.5	(47)	(42)
3	45	39
5	41	(34)
7	(36)	28
9	32	25
11	29	22
13	28	21
15	26	20
20	23	--
25	21	--
30	--	--
35		
40		
45		
50		

HEAT TREATING TEMPERATURES

*NORMALIZE	925 °C
AUSTENITIZE	925 °C

*For forged or rolled specimens only

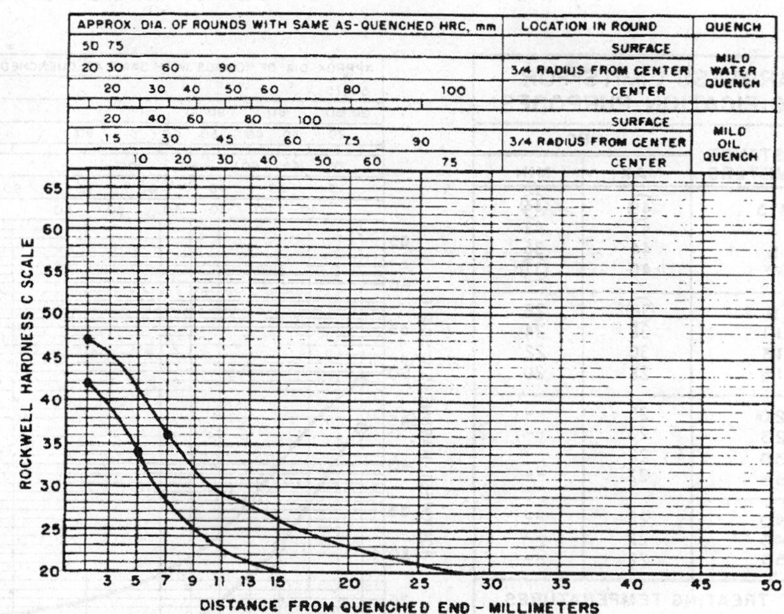

FIGURE 19—LIMITS FOR HARDENABILITY BAND 8620 RH

HARDENABILITY BAND SAE 8622 RH

%C	%Mn	%Si	%Ni	%Cr	%Mo
0.20/0.25	0.70/0.90	0.15/0.35	0.40/0.70	0.40/0.60	0.15/0.25

HARDNESS LIMITS FOR SPECIFICATION PURPOSES

"J" DISTANCE SIXTEENTHS OF AN INCH	HRC MAX.	HRC MIN.
1	(49)	(44)
2	47	41
3	45	37
4	41	(32)
5	38	29
6	(35)	27
7	32	24
8	30	22
9	29	21
10	28	20
11	27	--
12	26	--
13	25	--
14	24	--
15	24	--
16	23	--
18	23	--
20	22	--
22	22	--
24	22	--
26	22	--
28	22	--
30	22	--
32	22	--

HEAT TREATING TEMPERATURES	
*NORMALIZE	1700 °F
AUSTENITIZE	1700 °F

*For forged or rolled specimens only

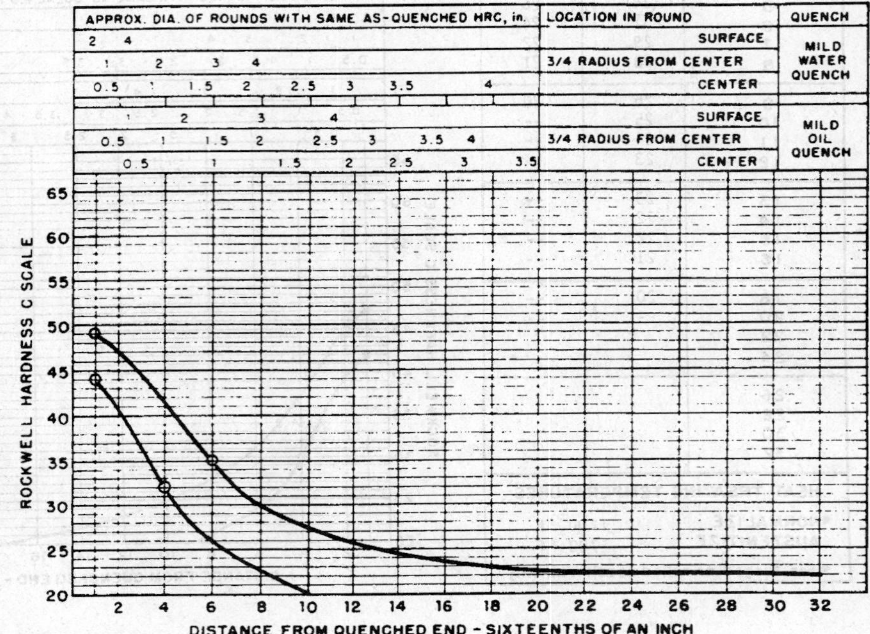

HARDNESS LIMITS FOR SPECIFICATION PURPOSES

"J" DISTANCE MILLIMETERS	HRC MAX.	HRC MIN.
1.5	(49)	(44)
3	47	41
5	44	36
7	40	(31)
9	(36)	28
11	32	24
13	30	22
15	28	20
20	25	--
25	23	--
30	22	--
35	22	--
40	22	--
45	22	--
50	22	--

HEAT TREATING TEMPERATURES	
*NORMALIZE	925 °C
AUSTENITIZE	925 °C

*For forged or rolled specimens only

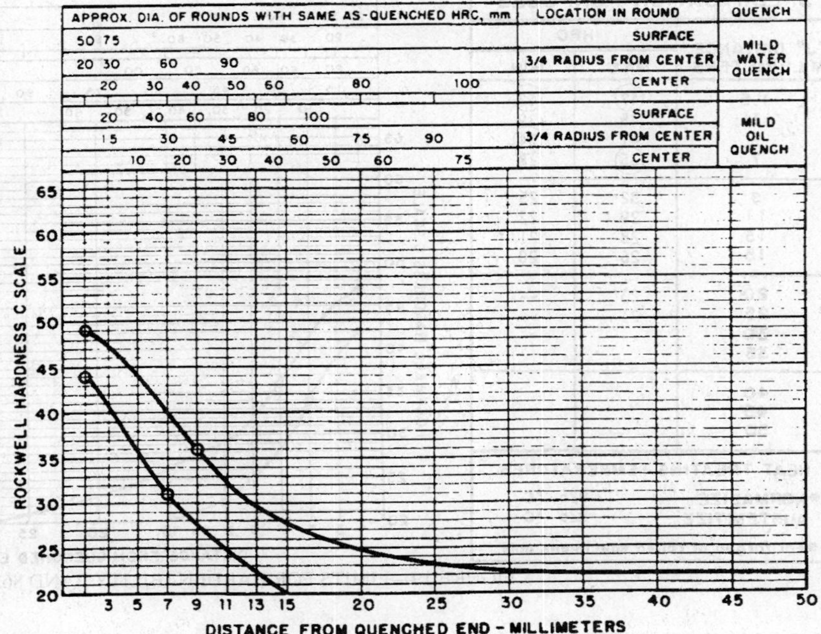

FIGURE 20—LIMITS FOR HARDENABILITY BAND 8622 RH

HARDENABILITY BAND SAE 8720 RH

%C	%Mn	%Si	%Ni	%Cr	%Mo
0.18/0.23	0.70/0.90	0.15/0.35	0.40/0.70	0.40/0.60	0.20/0.30

HARDNESS LIMITS FOR SPECIFICATION PURPOSES

"J" DISTANCE SIXTEENTHS OF AN INCH	HRC MAX.	HRC MIN.
1	(47)	(42)
2	45	39
3	43	37
4	40	(32)
5	36	28
6	(33)	26
7	31	24
8	29	23
9	28	22
10	27	21
11	26	20
12	25	--
13	25	--
14	24	--
15	24	--
16	23	--
18	23	--
20	22	--
22	22	--
24	21	--
26	20	--
28	--	--
30		
32		

HEAT TREATING TEMPERATURES

*NORMALIZE 1700 °F
AUSTENITIZE 1700 °F

*For forged or rolled specimens only

APPROX. DIA. OF ROUNDS WITH SAME AS-QUENCHED HRC, in. | LOCATION IN ROUND | QUENCH

MILD WATER QUENCH: SURFACE 2 4; 3/4 RADIUS FROM CENTER 1 2 3 4; CENTER 0.5 1 1.5 2 2.5 3 3.5 4

MILD OIL QUENCH: SURFACE 1 2 3 4; 3/4 RADIUS FROM CENTER 0.5 1 1.5 2 2.5 3 3.5 4; CENTER 0.5 1 1.5 2 2.5 3 3.5

ROCKWELL HARDNESS C SCALE (20–65)

DISTANCE FROM QUENCHED END - SIXTEENTHS OF AN INCH (2–32)

HARDNESS LIMITS FOR SPECIFICATION PURPOSES

"J" DISTANCE MILLIMETERS	HRC MAX.	HRC MIN.
1.5	(47)	(42)
3	45	39
5	42	35
7	38	(30)
9	(34)	27
11	31	24
13	29	23
15	28	22
20	25	--
25	23	--
30	23	--
35	22	--
40	20	--
45	--	--
50		

HEAT TREATING TEMPERATURES

*NORMALIZE 925 °C
AUSTENITIZE 925 °C

*For forged or rolled specimens only

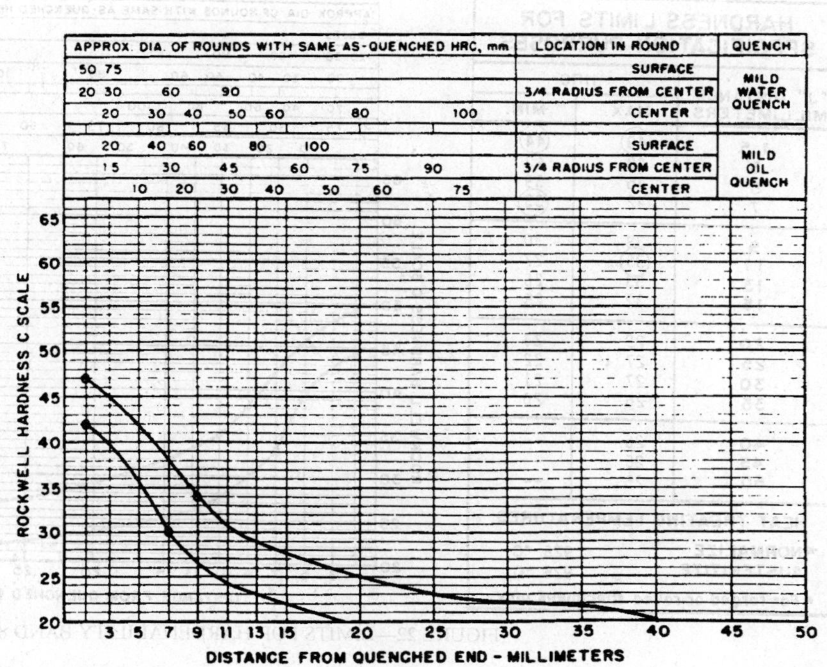

FIGURE 21—LIMITS FOR HARDENABILITY BAND 8720 RH

HARDENABILITY BAND

SAE 8822 RH

%C	%Mn	%Si	%Ni	%Cr	%Mo
0.20/0.25	0.75/1.00	0.15/0.35	0.40/0.70	0.40/0.60	0.30/0.40

HARDNESS LIMITS FOR SPECIFICATION PURPOSES

"J" DISTANCE SIXTEENTHS OF AN INCH	HRC MAX.	HRC MIN.
1	(49)	(44)
2	48	43
3	47	40
4	43	35
5	40	(31)
6	37	29
7	(35)	27
8	33	26
9	32	25
10	31	25
11	30	24
12	30	23
13	29	23
14	28	23
15	28	22
16	27	22
18	27	21
20	26	20
22	26	--
24	26	--
26	26	--
28	25	--
30	25	--
32	25	--

HEAT TREATING TEMPERATURES

*NORMALIZE	1700 °F
AUSTENITIZE	1700 °F

*For forged or rolled specimens only

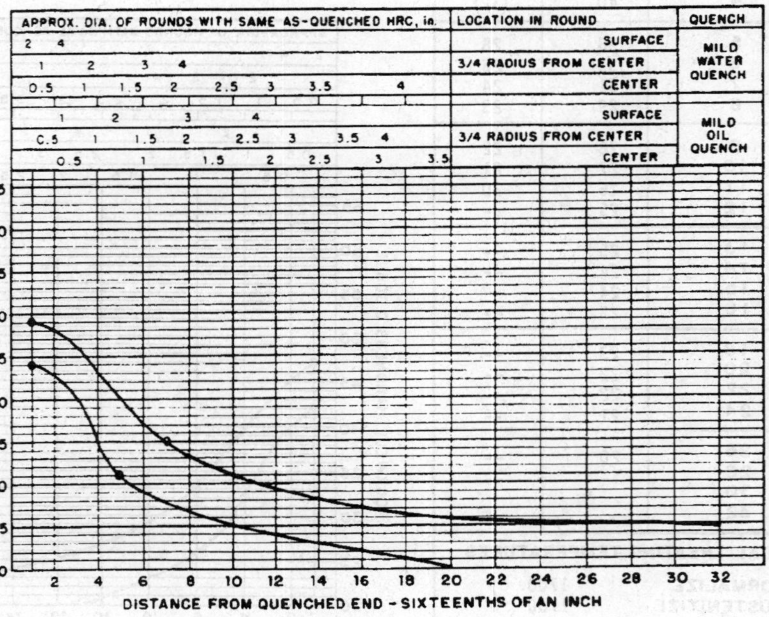

APPROX. DIA. OF ROUNDS WITH SAME AS-QUENCHED HRC, in.	LOCATION IN ROUND	QUENCH
2 4	SURFACE	MILD WATER QUENCH
1 2 3 4	3/4 RADIUS FROM CENTER	MILD WATER QUENCH
0.5 1 1.5 2 2.5 3 3.5 4	CENTER	MILD WATER QUENCH
1 2 3 4	SURFACE	MILD OIL QUENCH
0.5 1 1.5 2 2.5 3 3.5 4	3/4 RADIUS FROM CENTER	MILD OIL QUENCH
0.5 1 1.5 2 2.5 3 3.5	CENTER	MILD OIL QUENCH

ROCKWELL HARDNESS C SCALE

DISTANCE FROM QUENCHED END - SIXTEENTHS OF AN INCH

HARDNESS LIMITS FOR SPECIFICATION PURPOSES

"J" DISTANCE MILLIMETERS	HRC MAX.	HRC MIN.
1.5	(49)	(44)
3	48	43
5	46	39
7	42	(33)
9	38	30
11	(35)	27
13	33	26
15	32	25
20	29	23
25	27	22
30	27	21
35	26	20
40	26	--
45	25	--
50	25	--

HEAT TREATING TEMPERATURES

*NORMALIZE	925 °C
AUSTENITIZE	925 °C

*For forged or rolled specimens only

APPROX. DIA. OF ROUNDS WITH SAME AS-QUENCHED HRC, mm	LOCATION IN ROUND	QUENCH
50 75	SURFACE	MILD WATER QUENCH
20 30 60 90	3/4 RADIUS FROM CENTER	MILD WATER QUENCH
20 30 40 50 60 80 100	CENTER	MILD WATER QUENCH
20 40 60 80 100	SURFACE	MILD OIL QUENCH
15 30 45 60 75 90	3/4 RADIUS FROM CENTER	MILD OIL QUENCH
10 20 30 40 50 60 75	CENTER	MILD OIL QUENCH

ROCKWELL HARDNESS C SCALE

DISTANCE FROM QUENCHED END - MILLIMETERS

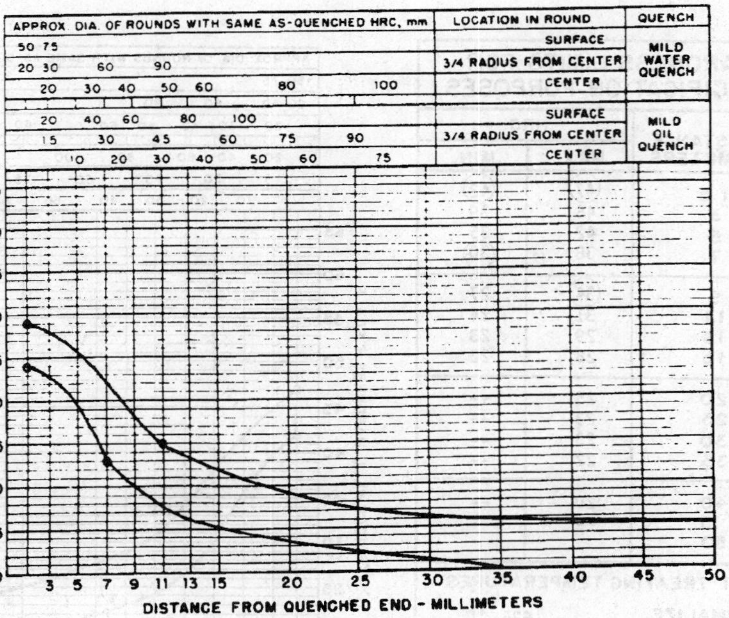

FIGURE 22—LIMITS FOR HARDENABILITY BAND 8822 RH

HARDNESS LIMITS FOR SPECIFICATION PURPOSES		
"J" DISTANCE SIXTEENTHS OF AN INCH	HRC	
	MAX.	MIN.
1	(42)	(37)
2	42	36
3	42	36
4	41	35
5	41	34
6	40	33
7	40	(32)
8	39	31
9	38	30
10	(37)	29
11	37	29
12	36	28
13	35	28
14	34	28
15	34	28
16	33	27
18	33	27
20	32	26
22	32	26
24	32	26
26	32	26
28	32	26
30	31	25
32	31	25

HEAT TREATING TEMPERATURES

*NORMALIZE	1700 °F
AUSTENITIZE	1550 °F

*For forged or rolled specimens only

HARDENABILITY BAND SAE 9310 RH

% C	% Mn	% Si	% Ni	% Cr	% Mo
0.08/0.13	0.45/0.65	0.15/0.35	3.00/3.50	1.00/1.40	0.08/0.15

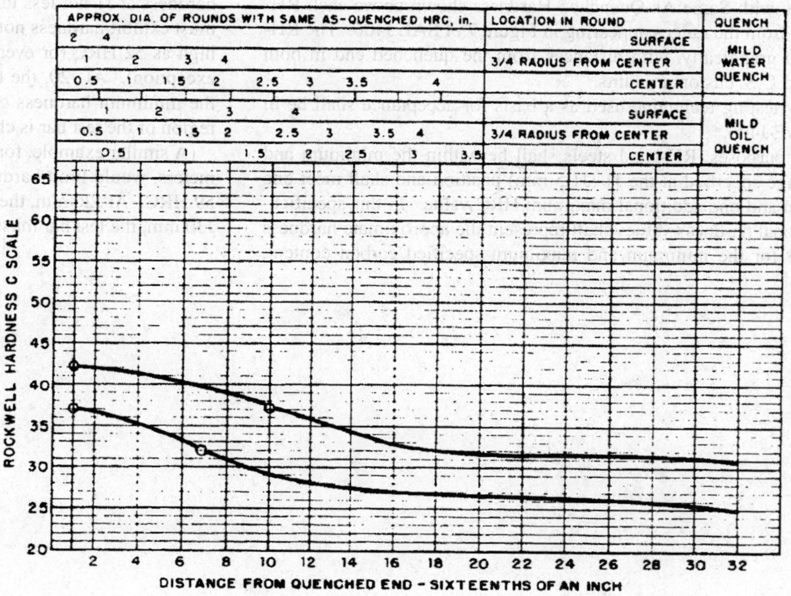 APPROX. DIA. OF ROUNDS WITH SAME AS-QUENCHED HRC, in.	LOCATION IN ROUND	QUENCH
2 4	SURFACE	MILD WATER QUENCH
1 2 3 4	3/4 RADIUS FROM CENTER	
0.5 1 1.5 2 2.5 3 3.5 4	CENTER	
1 2 3	SURFACE	MILD OIL QUENCH
0.5 1 1.5 2 2.5 3 3.5 4	3/4 RADIUS FROM CENTER	
0.5 1 1.5 2 2.5 3	CENTER	

ROCKWELL HARDNESS C SCALE

DISTANCE FROM QUENCHED END – SIXTEENTHS OF AN INCH

HARDNESS LIMITS FOR SPECIFICATION PURPOSES		
"J" DISTANCE MILLIMETERS	HRC	
	MAX.	MIN.
1.5	(42)	(37)
3	42	36
5	42	36
7	41	35
9	40	33
11	40	(32)
13	39	31
15	(37)	29
20	35	28
25	33	27
30	32	26
35	32	26
40	32	26
45	32	25
50	31	25

HEAT TREATING TEMPERATURES

*NORMALIZE	925 °C
AUSTENITIZE	845 °C

*For forged or rolled specimens only

APPROX. DIA. OF ROUNDS WITH SAME AS-QUENCHED HRC, mm	LOCATION IN ROUND	QUENCH
50 75	SURFACE	MILD WATER QUENCH
20 30 60 90	3/4 RADIUS FROM CENTER	
20 30 40 50 60 80 100	CENTER	
20 40 60 80 100	SURFACE	MILD OIL QUENCH
15 30 45 60 75 90	3/4 RADIUS FROM CENTER	
10 20 30 40 50 60 75	CENTER	

ROCKWELL HARDNESS C SCALE

DISTANCE FROM QUENCHED END – MILLIMETERS

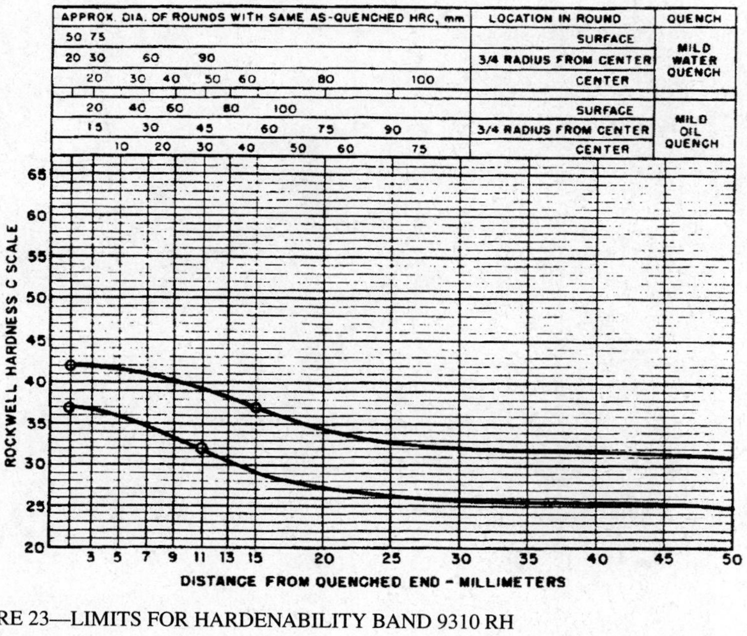

FIGURE 23—LIMITS FOR HARDENABILITY BAND 9310 RH

6. Grain Size—The limits set forth for RH-bands are intended to apply to steels exhibiting a fine austenitic grain size (ASTM No. 5 or finer; see SAE J418).

7. Use of Restricted Hardenability Limits—For specification purposes, one must use the tabulated values of Rockwell hardness (HRC) as a function of distance from the quenched end of the hardenability bar, either in metric (SI) units (millimeters) or U.S. customary units (sixteenths of an inch). Values below 20 HRC are not specified because such values are not as accurate. Band limits are also shown graphically and are so depicted for convenience in estimating the hardness values at various intermediate locations on the end quench test bar and for quick comparisons of the various RH grades. The values of Approximate Diameter of Rounds with Same As-Quenched Hardness shown above each RH-band, were selected from the ranges appearing in Figure 7 of SAE J406. The RH-bands are presented graphically, with distances from the quenched end in both metric (SI) units and U.S. customary units.

The hardenability testing technique used as a basis for acceptance shall be in accordance with SAE J406.

For specification purposes, RH-band steels shall be within the minimum and maximum HRC range specified at the J1 (J1.5 mm) position and shall meet one additional minimum and one additional maximum HRC value. In this specification, the two additional hardness values shall represent the approximate hardness for 50% martensite for the minimum and maximum specified carbon content, respectively (except where hardenability is too high to exhibit 50% martensite hardness; then the additional two control hardness points shall be 5 HRC below the minimum and maximum hardness specified at the J1 (J1.5 mm) position). In general, these points define the critical locations of the Jominy hardenability band for purposes of characterizing heat treatment response. The four specification points are circled in the tables of hardness versus Jominy distance and on the RH-bands. For a portion of the curve not exceeding 5 mm or 3/16 in (not including the control points), a tolerance of two points HRC is permitted.

For example, referring to the right-hand hardness limit table in Figure 1, a hardenability test bar of a steel meeting the requirements for 4140RH must exhibit a hardness at J1 not less than 54 HRC nor more than 59 HRC. At J12, the test bar must exhibit hardness not less than 43 HRC, but the maximum hardness can be as high as 52 HRC (or even 54 HRC if this region of the test bar is chosen as the exception). At J20, the bar must exhibit hardness not greater than 47 HRC, but the minimum hardness can be as low as 37 HRC (or as low as 35 HRC if this region of the test bar is chosen as the exception).

(A similar example, for 4140RH with distances from the quenched end in millimeters, would limit hardness at J1.5 mm to not less than 54 HRC nor more than 59 HRC. At J20 mm, the test bar must exhibit hardness not less than 42 HRC. At J30 mm, the test bar must exhibit hardness not greater than 48 HRC.)

PRODUCT ANALYSIS—PERMISSIBLE VARIATIONS FROM SPECIFIED CHEMICAL ANALYSIS OF A HEAT OR CAST OF STEEL—SAE J409 FEB1995

SAE Standard

Report of the SAE Iron and Steel Division approved January 1942. Revised by the SAE Iron and Steel Technical Committee, Division 1, June 1984. Reaffirmed by the SAE Iron and Steel Technical Committee December 1988, and completely revised December 1990. Reaffirmed by the SAE Iron and Steel Technical Committee Division 1—Carbon and Alloy Steels, February 1995.

Foreword—This reaffirmed document has been changed only to reflect the new SAE Technical Standards Board format.

1. Scope—Supplementary to the heat or cast analysis, a product analysis may be made on steel in the semifinished or finished form. For definitions and methods of sampling steel for product chemical analysis, refer to SAE J408.

A product analysis is a chemical analysis of the semifinished or finished steel to determine conformance to the specification requirements. The range of the specified chemical composition is normally expanded to take into account deviations associated with analytical reproducibility and the heterogeneity of the steel. Individual determinations may vary from the specified heat or cast analysis ranges or limits to the extent shown in Tables 1 through 5. The several determinations of any element in a heat or cast may not vary both above and below the specified range except for lead. Tables 1 through 5 provide permissible limits for various steel forms and composition types.

Rimmed or capped steels are not subject to product analysis limits because they are characterized by an inherently large variation in chemical composition. Also, for rephosphorized and resulfurized steels, the product analysis tolerance limits are not applicable for phosphorus and sulfur because of the degree to which these elements segregate.

Boron is not subject to product analysis tolerances.

TABLE 1—PERMISSIBLE VARIATIONS FROM SPECIFIED CHEMICAL RANGES AND LIMITS FOR CARBON STEEL IN HOT ROLLED AND COLD FINISHED BARS AND SEMIFINISHED FOR FORGING, WIRE ROD, AND SEAMLESS TUBING

Element	Limit or Max of Specified Range, %	Variation, %, Over Max Limit or Under Min Limit Bars, Wire Rod, Seamless Tubing and Semifinished for Forging to 0.065 m^2 (100 in^2) incl	Variation, %, Over Max Limit or Under Min Limit Semifinished Products for Forging Over 0.065 to 0.129 m^2 (100 to 200 in^2) incl	Variation, %, Over Max Limit or Under Min Limit Semifinished Products for Forging Over 0.129 to 0.258 m^2 (200 to 400 in^2) incl	Variation, %, Over Max Limit or Under Min Limit Semifinished Products for Forging Over 0.258 to 0.516 m^2 (400 to 800 in^2) incl
Carbon	To 0.25 incl	0.02	0.03	0.04	0.05
	Over 0.25 to 0.55 incl	0.03	0.04	0.05	0.06
	Over 0.55	0.04	0.05	0.06	0.07
Manganese	To 0.90 incl	0.03	0.04	0.06	0.07
	Over 0.90 to 1.65 incl	0.06	0.06	0.07	0.08
Phosphorus	Over max only to 0.040 incl	0.008	0.008	0.010	0.015
Sulfur	Over max only to 0.050 incl	0.008	0.010	0.010	0.015
Silicon	To 0.35 incl	0.02	0.02	0.03	0.04
	Over 0.35 to 0.60	0.05	—	—	—
Copper	Under min only for copper bearing steels	0.02	0.03	—	—
Lead[1]	0.15 to 0.35 incl	0.03	0.03	—	—

1. Product analysis tolerance for lead applies, both over and under, to a range of 0.15 to 0.35% lead.

TABLE 2—PERMISSIBLE VARIATIONS FROM SPECIFIED CHEMICAL RANGES AND LIMITS FOR CARBON STEEL SHEETS, STRIP, AND WELDED TUBING

Element	Limit or Max of Specified Range, %	Limit Variation, % Under Min Limit	Limit Variation, % Over Max Limit
Carbon	To 0.15 incl	0.02	0.03
	Over 0.15 to 0.40 incl	0.03	0.04
	Over 0.40 to 0.80 incl	0.03	0.05
	Over 0.80	0.03	0.06
Manganese	To 0.60 incl	0.03	0.03
	Over 0.60 to 1.15 incl	0.04	0.04
	Over 1.15 to 1.65 incl	0.05	0.05
Phosphorus	—	—	0.01
Sulfur	—	—	0.01
Silicon	To 0.30 incl	0.02	0.03
	Over 0.30 to 0.60	0.05	0.05
Copper	Under min only for copper bearing steels	0.02	—
Lead[1]	0.15 to 0.35 incl	0.03	0.03

1. Product analysis tolerance for lead applies both over and under a range of 0.15 to 0.35% lead.

TABLE 3—PERMISSIBLE VARIATIONS FROM SPECIFIED CHEMICAL RANGES AND LIMITS FOR ALLOY STEELS

Element	Limit or Max of Specified Range, %	Variation, %, Over Max Limit or Under Min Limit Bars, Sheet, Strip, Tubing(1), and Semifinished Products to 0.065 m^2 (100 in^2) incl	Variation, %, Over Max Limit or Under Min Limit Semifinished Products Over 0.065 to 0.129 m^2 (100 to 200 in^2) incl	Variation, %, Over Max Limit or Under Min Limit Semifinished Products Over 0.129 to 0.0258 m^2 (200 to 400 in^2) incl	Variation, %, Over Max Limit or Under Min Limit Semifinished Products Over 0.258 to 0.516 m^2 (400 to 800 in^2) incl
Carbon	To 0.30 incl	0.01	0.02	0.03	0.04
	Over 0.30 to 0.75 incl	0.02	0.03	0.04	0.05
	Over 0.75	0.03	0.04	0.05	0.06
Manganese	To 0.90 incl	0.03	0.04	0.05	0.06
	Over 0.90 to 2.10 incl	0.04	0.05	0.06	0.07
Phosphorus	Over max only	0.005	0.010	0.010	0.010
Sulfur	To 0.060 incl(2)	0.005	0.010	0.010	0.010
Silicon	To 0.40 incl	0.02	0.02	0.03	0.04
	Over 0.40 to 2.20 incl	0.05	0.06	0.06	0.07
Nickel	To 1.00 incl	0.03	0.03	0.03	0.03
	Over 1.00 to 2.00 incl	0.05	0.05	0.05	0.05
	Over 2.00 to 5.30 incl	0.07	0.07	0.07	0.07
	Over 5.30 to 10.00 incl	0.10	0.10	0.10	0.10
Chromium	To 0.90 incl	0.03	0.04	0.04	0.05
	Over 0.90 to 2.10 incl	0.05	0.06	0.06	0.07
	Over 2.10 to 3.99	0.10	0.10	0.12	0.14
Molybdenum	To 0.20 incl	0.01	0.01	0.02	0.03
	Over 0.20 to 0.40 incl	0.02	0.03	0.03	0.04
	Over 0.40 to 1.15 incl	0.03	0.04	0.05	0.06
Tungsten	To 1.00 incl	0.04	0.05	0.05	0.06
	Over 1.00 to 4.00 incl	0.08	0.09	0.10	0.12
Vanadium	To 0.10 incl	0.01	0.01	0.01	0.01
	Over 0.10 to 0.25 incl	0.02	0.02	0.02	0.02
	Over 0.25 to 0.50 incl	0.03	0.03	0.03	0.03
	Min value specified check under min limit	0.01	0.01	0.01	0.01
Aluminum(3)	Up to 0.10 incl	0.03	—	—	—
	Over 0.10 to 0.20 incl	0.04	—	—	—
	Over 0.20 to 0.30 incl	0.05	—	—	—
	Over 0.30 to 0.80 incl	0.07	—	—	—
	Over 0.80 to 1.80 incl	0.10	—	—	—
Lead(3)	0.15 to 0.35 incl	0.03(4)	—	—	—
Copper(3)	To 1.00 incl	0.03	—	—	—
	Over 1.00 to 2.00 incl	0.05	—	—	—

1. From ASTM A 513 and A 519.
2. Sulfur over 0.060% is not subject to check analysis.
3. Tolerances shown apply only to 100 in^2 or less.
4. Tolerance is over and under.

2. *References*

2.1 Applicable Publications—The following publications form a part of this specification to the extent specified herein. The latest issue of SAE publications shall apply.

2.1.1 SAE PUBLICATION—Available from SAE, 400 Commonwealth Drive, Warrendale, PA 15096-0001.

SAE J408—Methods of Sampling Steel for Chemical Analysis

2.1.2 ASTM PUBLICATION—Available from ASTM, 100 Barr Harbor Drive, West Conshohocken, PA 19428-2959.

ASTM A 6—Specification for General Requirements for Rolled Steel Plates, Shapes, Sheet Piling, and Bars for Structural Use

ASTM A 480/A 480M—Specification for General Requirements for Flat-Rolled Stainless and Heat-Resisting Steel Plate, Sheet, and Strip

ASTM A 513—Specification for Electric-Resistance-Welded Carbon and Alloy Steel Mechanical Tubing

ASTM A 519—Specification for Seamless Carbon and Alloy Steel Mechanical Tubing

TABLE 4—PERMISSIBLE VARIATIONS FROM SPECIFIED CHEMICAL RANGES AND LIMITS FOR STAINLESS STEELS (FROM ASTM A 480/A 480M)

Element	Limit or Max of Specified Range, %	Variation, %, Over Max Limit or Under Min Limit
Carbon	To 0.010 incl	0.002
	Over 0.010 to 0.030 incl	0.005
	Over 0.030 to 0.20 incl	0.01
	Over 0.20 to 0.60 incl	0.02
	Over 0.60 to 1.20 incl	0.03
Manganese	To 1.00 incl	0.03
	Over 1.00 to 3.00 incl	0.04
	Over 3.00 to 6.00 incl	0.05
	Over 6.00 to 10.00 incl	0.06
	Over 10.00 to 15.00 incl	0.10
	Over 15.00 to 20.00 incl	0.15
Phosphorus	To 0.040 incl	0.005
	Over 0.040 to 0.20 incl	0.010
Sulfur	To 0.040 incl	0.005
	Over 0.040 to 0.20 incl	0.010
	Over 0.20 to 0.50 incl	0.020
Silicon	To 1.00 incl	0.05
	Over 1.00 to 3.00 incl	0.10
Chromium	Over 4.00 to 10.00 incl	0.10
	Over 10.00 to 15.00 incl	0.15
	Over 15.00 to 20.00 incl	0.20
	Over 20.00 to 30.00 incl	0.25
Nickel	To 1.00 incl	0.03
	Over 1.00 to 5.00 incl	0.07
	Over 5.00 to 10.00 incl	0.10
	Over 10.00 to 20.00 incl	0.15
	Over 20.00 to 22.00 incl	0.20
Molybdenum	Over 0.20 to 0.60 incl	0.03
	Over 0.60 to 2.00 incl	0.05
	Over 2.00 to 7.00 incl	0.10
Titanium	To 1.00 incl	0.05
	Over 1.00 to 3.00 incl	0.07
Columbian-Tantalum		
	All ranges	0.05
Tantalum	To 0.10 incl	0.02
Cobalt[1]	Over 0.05 to 0.50 incl	0.01
	Over 0.50 to 2.00 incl	0.02
	Over 2.00 to 5.00 incl	0.05
Aluminum	To 0.15 incl	−0.005, +0.01
	Over 0.15 to 0.50 incl	0.05
	Over 0.50 to 2.00 incl	0.10
Selenium	All ranges	0.03
Nitrogen	To 0.02 incl	0.005
	Over 0.02 to 0.19 incl	0.01
	Over 0.19 to 0.25 incl	0.02
	Over 0.25 to 0.35 incl	0.03
	Over 0.35 to 0.45 incl	0.04
Tungsten	To 1.00 incl	0.03
	Over 1.00 to 2.00 incl	0.05
Vanadium	To 0.50 incl	0.03
	Over 0.50 to 1.50 incl	0.05

1. Product analysis limits for cobalt under 0.05% have not been established, and the manufacturer should be consulted for those limits.

TABLE 5—PRODUCT ANALYSIS TOLERANCES—STRUCTURAL SHAPES AND PLATES (FROM ASTM A 6)

Element	Upper Limit, or Max Specified Value, %	Tolerances, % Under Min Limit	Tolerances, % Over Max Limit
Carbon	To 0.15 incl	0.02	0.03
	Over 0.15 to 0.40 incl	0.03	0.04
	Over 0.40 to 0.75 incl	0.04	0.05
	Over 0.75	0.04	0.06
Manganese	To 0.60 incl	0.05	0.06
	Over 0.60 to 0.90 incl	0.06	0.08
	Over 0.90 to 1.20 incl	0.08	0.10
	Over 1.20 to 1.35 incl	0.09	0.11
	Over 1.35 to 1.65 incl	0.09	0.12
	Over 1.65 to 1.95 incl	0.11	0.14
	Over 1.95	0.12	0.16
Phosphorus	To 0.04 incl	—	0.010
	Over 0.04 to 0.15 incl	—	N.A.[1]
Sulfur	To 0.060 incl	—	0.010
	Over 0.060		N.A.[1]
Silicon	To 0.30 incl	0.02	0.03
	Over 0.30 to 0.40 incl	0.05	0.05
	Over 0.40 to 2.20 incl	0.06	0.06
Nickel	To 1.00 incl	0.03	0.03
	Over 1.00 to 2.00 incl	0.05	0.05
	Over 2.00 to 3.75 incl	0.07	0.07
	Over 3.75 to 5.30 incl	0.08	0.08
	Over 5.30	0.10	0.10
Chromium	To 0.90 incl	0.04	0.04
	Over 0.90 to 2.00 incl	0.06	0.06
	Over 2.00 to 4.00 incl	0.10	0.10
Molybdenum	To 0.20 incl	0.01	0.01
	Over 0.20 to 0.40 incl	0.03	0.03
	Over 0.40 to 1.15 incl	0.04	0.04
Aluminum	Up to 0.10 incl	0.03	0.03
Copper	0.20 min only	0.02	—
	To 1.00 incl	0.03	0.03
	Over 1.00 to 2.00 incl	0.05	0.05
Titanium	To 0.10 incl	0.01[2]	0.01[2]
Vanadium	To 0.10 incl	0.01[2]	0.01[2]
	Over 0.10 to 0.25 incl	0.02	0.02
	Over 0.25 to 0.50	0.02	0.03
	Min only specified	0.01	—
Boron	Any	N.A.[1]	N.A.[1]
Columbium	To 0.10 incl	0.01[2]	0.01[2]
Zirconium	To 0.15 incl	0.03	0.03
Nitrogen	To 0.030 incl	0.005	0.005

1. N.A.—Product analysis not applicable.
2. If the minimum of the range is 0.01%, the under tolerance is 0.005%.

(R) STEEL, HIGH STRENGTH, HOT ROLLED SHEET AND STRIP, COLD ROLLED SHEET, AND COATED SHEET[1]—SAE J1392 FEB2001

SAE Recommended Practice

Report of the SAE Iron and Steel Technical Committee, prepared by the SAE Division 32 approved May 1982, corrected June 1984. Completely revised by the SAE Iron and Steel Technical Committee 32—Sheet and Strip Steel February 2001. Rationale statement available.

NOTE 1—This document shall not be used on new designs—Superseded by SAE J2340.

NOTE 2—NOTE—High-strength, low-alloy Sheet and Strip products formerly were included in SAE J410c (Cancelled), but are now detailed in this separate SAE Recommended Practice.

1. Scope—This SAE Recommended Practice covers seven levels of high strength carbon and low-alloy hot rolled sheet and strip, cold rolled sheet, and coated sheet steels. The strength is achieved through chemical composition and special processing.

2. References

2.1 Applicable Publications—The following publications form a part of the specification to the extent specified herein. Unless otherwise indicated, the latest revision of SAE publications shall apply.

2.1.1 SAE PUBLICATIONS—Available from SAE, 400 Commonwealth Drive, Warrendale, PA 15096-0001.

SAE J410c (Cancelled)—High Strength, Low Alloy Steel

SAE J2340—Categorization and Properties of Dent Resistant, High Strength, and Ultra High Strength Automotive Sheet Steel

2.1.2 ASTM PUBLICATIONS—Available from ASTM, 100 Barr Harbor Drive, West Conshohocken, PA 19428-2959.

ASTM A 308—Specification for Steel, Sheet, Cold-Rolled, Long Terne Coated

ASTM A 370—Test Methods and Definitions for Mechanical Testing of Steel Products

ASTM A 463—Specification for Steel Sheet, Cold-Rolled, Aluminum-Coated Type I and Type II

ASTM A 568—Specification for General Requirements for Steel, Carbon and High-Strength Low-Alloy Hot-Rolled Sheet and Cold-Rolled Sheet

ASTM A 568M—Specification for General Requirements for Steel, Carbon, and High-Strength Low-Alloy Hot-Rolled Sheet and Cold-Rolled Sheet (Metric)

ASTM A 591—Specification for Steel Sheet, Electrolytic Zinc-Coated, for Light Coating Mass Applications

ASTM A 924—Standard Specification for General Requirements for Steel Sheet, Metallic-Coated by the Hot-Dip-Process

3. Introduction—High strength steel discussed in this document involves hot rolled sheet and strip and cold rolled sheet as dimensionally described in ASTM A 568 (A 568M) latest revision (Steel, Carbon and High-Strength Low-Alloy Hot-Rolled Sheet, Hot-Rolled Strip and Cold-Rolled Sheet, General Requirements). It also includes coated sheet, that is, sheet coated by hot dipping, electroplating, or vapor deposition of zinc, terne, aluminum, and organic compounds normally applied by coil coating. Public specifications related to these coated products are the latest revisions of ASTM A 924 (Steel Sheet, Zinc-Coated (Galvanized) by the Hot-Dip Process, General Requirements), A 591 (Steel Sheet, Cold Rolled, Electrolytic Zinc-Coated), A 463 (Steel Sheet, Cold-Rolled, Aluminum-Coated Type 1), and A 308 (Steel, Sheet, Cold-Rolled, Long Terne Coated).

The strength is achieved through chemical composition and special processing. Special processing includes mechanical rolling techniques, and temperature control in hot rolling and subsequent heat treatments. The primary use of high strength steel is based on the increased yield and tensile properties which are higher than those of conventional sheet and strip for which minimum mechanical properties are not normally specified.

The seven strength levels are 240 (35), 280 (40), 310 (45), 340 (50), 410 (60), 480 (70), and 550 (80) MPa (ksi) minimum yield strength. Different chemical compositions are normally used to achieve the specified mechanical properties. These compositions are significantly different at the same strength level depending on additional material requirements, that is, weldability, formability, toughness, fatigue life, atmospheric corrosion resistance, and economics. The correct type of high strength sheet or strip should be specified to establish compatibility of the producers' chemical composition with the fabrication and application requirements.

Because high strength steel is characterized by special mechanical properties, consultation of producer and user in grade selection is recommended to insure compatibility of the strength and forming requirements. Care must be taken in designing parts, tooling, and fabrication processes to obtain the greatest benefit from the high strength sheet and strip steels. It is advisable that the purchaser furnish information to the producer relating the individual requirements of an identified part; this may be accomplished by visual examination of the part, by prints, through a description, or a combination of these. Also, it is highly desirable for the producer to observe the fabricating practices, or at least be provided with a detailed description of the operations.

The steels discussed in this document are characterized by their special mechanical properties achieved through chemical composition and special processing. They normally are not intended for any heat treatment by the purchaser. Subjecting these steels to such heat treatments will modify the original mechanical properties. For certain applications these steels may be annealed, normalized, or stress relieved with some effect on the mechanical properties. It is recommended that prior to such heat treatments the producer and purchaser consult to determine the need for a heat treatment and its effect on mechanical properties.

All grades and chemical compositions in this practice are weldable despite the differences in carbon, manganese, and alloying additions. However, as variations in composition from one producer to another do exist, it is advisable to discuss with the producers the features of their chemical composition relative to specific types of welding and any special considerations for each application.

These steels, because of their strength-to-weight ratio, may be adapted for use in mobile equipment and other structures where substantial weight savings are generally desirable.

4. General Information—The specific grades are identified by a six character code that describes the strength level, general chemical composition, general carbon level, and deoxidation/sulfide inclusion control system, as follows:

4.1 First, Second and Third Characters—Minimum yield strength expressed in megapascals (MPa 240, 280, 310, 340, 410, 480, and 550 or as kips per square inch (ksi): 35, 40, 45, 50, 60, 70, and 80, expressed as 035, 040, 045, 050, 060, 070, and 080 respectively.

4.2 Fourth Character—General chemical composition:

A—C and Mn only

B—C, Mn, N

C—C, Mn, P

S—C, Mn, (N and/or P added at producer option)

W—Weathering composition (Si, P, Cu, Ni, and Cr in various combinations)

X—High Strength Low Alloy (HSLA), that is, Cb, Cr, Cu, Mo, Ni, Si, Ti, V, Zr either singly or in combination, with a 70 MPa (10 ksi) spread between the specified minima of the yield and tensile strengths. N and P may be used in combination with any of the aforementioned elements.

Y—Same as X with a 100 MPa (15 ksi) spread between the specified minima of the yield and tensile strengths.

Z—Same as X with a 140 MPa (20 ksi) spread between the specified minima of the yield and tensile strengths.

4.3 Fifth Character—General carbon level:

H—Maximum carbon as shown in Table 3 and Table 4

L—0.13% carbon max except as indicated in Table 4

4.4 Sixth Character—Deoxidation/sulfide inclusion control practices:

K—Killed, made to a fine grain practice

F—Sulfide inclusion controlled, killed, made to a fine grain practice

O—Other than K and F

4.5 A material grade corresponding to every combination of numbers and letters is not available. Therefore, it is recommended that the purchaser consult with the producers to determine that the desired grade is available before releasing engineering approved prints and specifications, and before purchase orders are placed.

1. The values stated in U.S. customary units are to be regarded as the standard recommended practice.

These steels are generally produced as semi-killed or killed steel, although rimmed and capped practices may be used in certain situations. When selecting a deoxidation practice, the following items should be considered. Rimmed and capped steels are less homogeneous than killed steels. Therefore, the producer must plan his processing to compensate for variations in chemical composition and maintain mechanical strength properties specified. With the greater range in chemical composition of rimmed and capped steels, variations in fabrication, such as maintaining part dimensions, springback, and breakage, on complex parts can result. If these material variations are not compatible with specific part designs and tooling, a deoxidation practice resulting in a more homogeneous steel should be considered.

5. Mechanical Properties—The mechanical properties of these high strength sheet and strip steels are shown in Table 1 (hot rolled) and Table 2 (cold rolled and coated). Current steel industry practice is to determine the yield point of these materials by the drop of the beam, halt of pointer, dividers, 0.2% offset, or 0.5% extension under load method. In cases involving dispute between two or more parties, the yield strength shall be determined by the 0.2% offset method as described in ASTM A 370, Paragraph 13.2.1, which describes yield strength.

Because of the different rates of heat transfer in the various parts of a coil of hot rolled sheet steel, and to a lesser degree, the variation in chemical composition, especially when deoxidation practices other than killed are employed, mechanical properties will vary in a coil or cut lengths which are sheared from a coil. Because of the faster cooling rates that may occur on the outside and inside (eye) wraps of a coil, the leading and trailing ends of a coil tend to be harder and higher in yield and tensile strength than the material from the interior of the coil. Cooling is generally faster as the thickness decreases, thus the strength tends to increase as the thickness decreases. For a specified grade and thickness, both coils and cut lengths will be produced to the same mill practices. Testing within the body of the coil cannot be performed by the producer, thus producer testing is limited practically to coil ends and random pieces sheared from coils for cut length orders. Considering this practical limitation on testing, the producer has specific knowledge of material properties only at the test location. Therefore, the mechanical properties in the body of a coil may vary from those at the ends.

Based on the data developed from above, each producer establishes testing procedures and frequency to ensure that the processes designed to produce the specified mechanical properties are under control. These procedures also provide knowledge of the product properties and guidance in evaluating the product for the intended application. Since the local manufacturing conditions vary from one producer location to another, and the characteristics of the grades within the scope of this report vary, there is no one testing frequency plan. If the purchaser requires any special testing program it should be discussed with the producer at the time of evaluating the steel grades for the intended application.

TABLE 1—MECHANICAL PROPERTIES—HOT ROLLED

Grade	Yield Strength, MPa (ksi) min.	Tensile Strength, MPa (ksi) min.	% Elongation(1) (50 mm or 2 in) min
035 A, B, C, S	240 (35)	(2)	21
035 X, Y, Z	240 (35)	(2)	28
040 A, B, C, S	280 (40)	(2)	20
040 X, Y, Z	280 (40)	(2)	27
045 A, B, C, S	310 (45)	(2)	18
045 W	310 (45)	450 (65)	25
045 X	310 (45)	380 (55)	25
045 Y	310 (45)	410 (60)	25
045 Z	310 (45)	450 (65)	25
050 A, B, C, S	340 (50)	(2)	16
050 W	340 (50)	480 (70)	22
050 X	340 (50)	410 (60)	22
050 Y	340 (50)	450 (65)	22
050 Z	340 (50)	480 (70)	22
060 X	410 (60)	480 (70)	20
060 Y	410 (60)	520 (75)	20
070 X	480 (70)	550 (80)	17
070 Y	480 (70)	590 (85)	17
080 X	550 (80)	620 (90)	14
080 Y	550 (80)	650 (95)	14

1. Elongation values are dependent upon specimen geometry (cross-sectional area). Thicker and wider specimens normally result in higher percentages.
2. Minimum tensile strength normally does not apply.

TABLE 2—MECHANICAL PROPERTIES—COLD ROLLED AND COATED

Grade	Yield Strength, MPa (ksi) min.	Tensile Strength, MPa (ksi) min.	% Elongation(1) (50 mm or 2 in) min
035 A, B, C, S	240 (35)	(2)	22
035 X, Y, Z	240 (35)	(2)	27
040 A, B, C, S	280 (40)	(2)	20
040 X, Y, Z	280 (40)	(2)	25
045 A, B, C, S	310 (45)	(2)	18
045 W	310 (45)	450 (65)	22
045 X	310 (45)	380 (55)	22
045 Y	310 (45)	410 (60)	22
045 Z	310 (45)	450 (65)	22
050 A, B, C, S	340 (50)	(2)	16
050 X	340 (50)	410 (60)	20
050 Y	340 (50)	450 (65)	20
050 Z	340 (50)	480 (70)	20

1. Elongation values are dependent upon specimen geometry (cross-sectional area). Thicker and wider specimens normally result in higher percentages.
2. Minimum tensile strength normally does not apply.

6. Chemical Composition—The chemical composition of the steels in this document may vary from one producing facility to another for the same strength level. Therefore, it is not practical to list all the combinations for each strength level and general chemical compositions. While all producers comply with the carbon and manganese content shown in Tables 3 and 4, a more precise value or range is dependent on the alloys, if used, and their specific amounts, the thickness of the steel being produced on a given unit, and the special characteristics of the producing unit. Chemical composition is important for achieving the specified minimum mechanical properties. Chemical composition also affects other properties such as weldability, formability, toughness, and fatigue. When these are critical, the fabricator should discuss the details with the producer so that the material selected will be compatible with the fabrication and application requirements.

The following provides a brief description and comparison of the eight compositional systems.

6.1 A—Carbon/Manganese—Only carbon and manganese are used to meet the minimum strength requirements. No other elements that significantly add to strength and hardness are intentionally added. As the carbon and/or manganese are increased, the strength and hardness are increased, but ductility and weldability are decreased. Carbon has a greater effect on these properties than manganese.

6.2 B—Nitrogenized—Nitrogen is used to increase strength and hardness. Producers of this system generally lower the carbon and/or manganese of the A system. Nitrogen is inherently present in all steels. When added intentionally, so that the content is higher than that normally exhibited in SAE 1006/1008/1010 type steels, the resulting product not only increases in strength and hardness, but, by additional processing, provides the potential to increase in strength beyond as-rolled strength. The additional processing usually involves straining in part fabrication followed by a thermal treatment, such as a paint bake cycle. The nitrogen encountered in this chemical composition is responsible for the accelerated aging phenomenon. This also reduces ductility, and with this consideration, nitrogenized steel may be specified when higher strength is desired beyond that achieved by simply forming the intended part. Toughness may be reduced with the addition of nitrogen in heavier thicknesses.

6.3 C—Phosphorized—As in previous case B, this system utilizes another strengthener, phosphorus, in combination with carbon and manganese. The carbon and/or manganese of this system is usually lower than that found in carbon/manganese steel (A). Phosphorus increases strength and hardness, but generally reduces ductility and toughness. Phosphorized steel may be specified when nitrogenized steel (B) is not suitable. Phosphorus is intentionally added so that the content is higher than that normally exhibited in SAE 1006/1008/1010 steel.

6.4 S—Optional (A or B or C)—This system may be specified when the carbon/manganese steel (A), nitrogenized steel (B), and phosphorized steel (C) chemical compositions are satisfactory for the intended application. The advantage of using this system is that it provides more options.

6.5 W—Weathering—This system utilizes two or more elements to produce a weathering steel. The elements most commonly used are silicon, phosphorus, nickel, copper, and chromium. The "atmospheric" corrosion resistance is improved at least fourfold compared to plain carbon steel with less than 0.02% copper. As "vehicle" corrosion is not limited to "atmospheric" corrosive environments, weathering steel will not provide adequate protection.

6.6 X, Y, and Z—High Strength Low Alloy (HSLA)—From a chemical composition standpoint, these systems can be grouped together. They are alloyed systems in which the alloying is a major source of strength. The elements most commonly used are columbium (niobium), titanium, vanadium, and zirconium. Other elements such as chromium, copper, molybdenum, nickel and silicon may be used. The elements may be used singularly or in combination to achieve the specified minimum mechanical properties. Nitrogen and/or phosphorus may be used in combination with any of the aforementioned elements. The use of these elements enables the producer to reduce the carbon and/or manganese content. The major difference in these systems is the spread between the specified minima of the yield and tensile strengths. This spread is mainly dependent on the carbon content, although other factors such as hot and cold rolling practices, and associated thermal practices have some influence. Thus, steels in the X system usually contain less carbon than the Y and Z systems, and steels in the Y system usually contain less carbon than the Z system. These HSLA steels provide better formability, weldability, and toughness at a given strength level than the steels produced by the A, B, and C systems.

7. ***Cold Bending***—High strength steels are frequently fabricated by cold bending. There are a multiplicity of inter-related factors which affect the ability of a given piece of steel to form over any given radius in shop practice. These factors include thickness, strength level, degree of restraint in bending, relationship to rolling direction, chemical composition, and microstructure. The table of Suggested Minimum Inside Radii for Cold Bending, for Hot Rolled Sheet and Strip, Table 5, lists those ratios which should be used as minimums for 90 degree bends in actual shop practice. It recognizes that "hard way" bending (bend axis parallel to rolling direction) is common in production and presupposes that reasonably good forming practices will be employed. Where design permits, users are encouraged to employ larger radii than shown in Table 5 for improved performance. Where the bend axis can be designed across the width ("easy way") of the sheet or strip, or bends less than 90 degrees, slightly tighter radii can be employed. As the cold forming becomes progressively more difficult, that is from a straight bend to a curved or offset bend to stretching or drawing, it is advisable that the producer and user consult to determine the special material, design, and tooling requirements of the application. The fabricator should be aware that steel may crack to some degree when bent on a sheared or burned edge. This is not considered to be the fault of the steel, but rather a function of the induced cold work or heat affected zone (HAZ).

TABLE 3—CHEMICAL COMPOSITION (HEAT OR CAST ANALYSIS) HOT ROLLED (ALL MAXIMUMS UNLESS OTHERWISE NOTED)

Grade	Carbon[1] H	Carbon[1] L	Manganese	Additional
035 A	0.25	0.13	0.60	None
035 B	0.25	0.13	0.60	Nitrogen
035 C	0.25	0.13	0.60	Phosphorus
035 S	0.25	0.13	0.60	Producer option, i.e., A or B or C
035 X, Y, Z		0.13	0.60	Microalloy[2]
040 A, B, C, S	0.25	0.13	0.90	Same as 035 A, B, C, S above
040 X, Y, Z	—	0.13	0.60	Microalloy[2]
045 A, B, C, S	0.25	0.13	0.90	Same as 035 A, B, C, S above
045 W	0.22	—	1.25	Various combinations of Si, P, Cu, Ni, Cr
045 X		0.13	1.35	Microalloy[2]
045 Y, Z	0.22	—	1.35	Microalloy[2]
050 A, B, C, S	0.25	—	1.35	Same as 035 A, B, C, S above
050 W	0.22	—	1.25	Various combinations of Si, P, Cu, Ni, Cr
050 X		0.13	0.90	Microalloy[2]
050 Y, Z	0.23	—	1.35	Microalloy[2]
060 X		0.13	0.90	Microalloy[2]
060 Y, Z	0.26	—	1.50	Microalloy[2]
070 X		0.13	1.65	Microalloy[2]
070 Y, Z	0.26	—	1.65	Microalloy[2]
080 X		0.13	1.65	Microalloy[2]
080 Y	0.18	—	1.65	Microalloy[2]

1. Lower levels are available upon inquiry.
2. Cb, V, and Ti are commonly used singly or in combination. Combinations of the following elements are sometimes used with or without Cb, V, and Ti: Cr, Cu, Mo, Ni, Si, and Zr. P and/or N may be added to any of the foregoing.

TABLE 4—CHEMICAL COMPOSITION (HEAT OR CAST ANALYSIS) COLD ROLLED AND COATED (ALL MAXIMUMS UNLESS OTHERWISE NOTED)

Grade	Carbon[1] H	Carbon[1] L	Manganese	Additional
035 A	0.20	0.13	0.60	None
035 B	0.20	0.13	0.60	Nitrogen
035 C	0.20	0.13	0.60	Phosphorus
035 S	0.20	0.13	0.60	Producer option, i.e., A or B or C
035 X, Y, Z	0.18	0.13	0.60	Microalloy[2]
040 A, B, C, S	0.24	0.15	0.90	Same as 035 A, B, C, S
040 X, Y, Z	0.20	0.13	0.90	Microalloy[2]
045 A, B, C, S	0.25	0.17	1.20	Same as 035 A, B, C, S
045 W	0.22	—	1.35	Various combinations of Si, P, Cu, Cr, Ni
045 X, Y, Z	0.22	0.15	1.20	Microalloy[2]
050 A, B, C, S	0.25	0.20	1.35	Same as 035 A, B, C, S
050 X, Y, Z	0.23	0.17	1.35	Microalloy[2]

1. Lower levels are available upon inquiry.
2. Cb, V, and Ti are commonly used singly or in combination. Combinations of the following elements are sometimes used with or without Cb, V, and Ti: Cr, Cu, Mo, Ni, Si, and Zr. P and/or N may be added to any of the foregoing.

8. ***Suggested Ordering Practice***—Orders for material under this document should include the following information to adequately describe the desired material:

(1) SAE Recommended Practice number (J1392).
(2) Name of material (hot rolled or cold rolled or coated sheet, or hot rolled strip; in the case of coated sheet, the specific coating should be described, such as electrozinc coated, hot dip zinc coated (galvanized), aluminum coated, etc.)
(3) Grade (six character identification including minimum yield strength, chemical composition system, general carbon level, deoxidation/sulfide inclusion control practice).
(4) Condition (specify pickled if required, specify oiled or not oiled as required, specify chemical treatment for coated product if required).
(5) Copper bearing steel (when required).
(6a) Surface condition—Cold Rolled (indicate exposed, E, or unexposed, U; matte, or dull finish will be supplied unless otherwise specified).
(6b) Surface condition—Coated (indicate regular spangle or minimized spangle or minimized spangle extra smooth, and coating weight for hot dip zinc coated (galvanized) sheet).
(7) Edges (must be specified for hot rolled sheet and strip, that is, mill edge or cut edge).
(8) Dimensions (thickness, width, and length for cut lengths).
(9) Coil size and weight requirements (must include inside diameter, outside diameter, and maximum weight).
(10) Cut length weight restrictions, that is, maximum weight of individual bundle.
(11) Application (show part identification and description).
(12) Heat or cast analysis and mechanical property report (if required).

8.1 Typical ordering descriptions are as follows:

A—SAE J1392, Grade 050YLO, Hot Rolled Sheet, High Strength Low Alloy, pickled and oiled, cut edge, 0.095 in min. x 46.50 in x coil for front lower control arm (the metric grade equivalent is 340YLO)

B—SAE J1392, Grade 040CHO, Hot Dipped Zinc Coated (Galvanized) Sheet, High Strength Carbon, Regular Spangle, G90 coating weight, oiled, 0.035 in min. x 41.25 in x 94 in for member front side front upper (the metric grade equivalent is 280CHO)

C—SAE J1392, Grade 050XLF, Cold Rolled Sheet, High Strength Low Alloy, oiled, U finish, 0.031 in min. x 39.37 in x coil for frame back window upper (the metric grade equivalent is 340XLF)

D—SAE J1392, Grade 410XLK, Hot Dipped Zinc Coated (Galvanized) Sheet, High Strength Low Alloy, Regular Spangle, G60 coating weight, chemically treated not oiled, 1.30 mm min. x 1220 mm x coil for railmotor side inner.

9. ***Tolerances***—Tolerances for dimensions and chemical compositions shown in ASTM A 568 (A 568M), A 525, and A 463 apply to the material described in this document.

TABLE 5—SUGGESTED MINIMUM INSIDE RADII FOR COLD BENDING(1)(2)(3)(4) FOR HOT ROLLED SHEET AND STRIP

	H(5) Up to 4.55 mm (0.179 in) O	H(5) Up to 4.55 mm (0.179 in) K	H(5) Up to 4.55 mm (0.179 in) F	L(5) Up to 4.55 mm (0.179 in) Q	L(5) Up to 4.55 mm (0.179 in) K	L(5) Up to 4.55 mm (0.179 in) F
035 A, B, C, S	1-1/2	—	—	1	—	—
035 X, Y, Z	—	—	—	—	1/2	—
040 A, B, C, S	1-1/2	—	—	1	—	—
045 A, B, C, S	2	—	—	1-1/2	1	—
045 W	—	2	1	—	—	—
045 X	—	—	—	1-1/2	1	1/2
045 Y, Z	1-1/2	1	—	—	—	—
050 A, B, C, S	2-1/2	—	—	—	—	—
050 W	—	2-1/2	1-1/2	—	2	1
050 X	—	—	—	1-1/2	1	1/2
050 Y, Z	2	1-1/2	1	—	—	—
060 X	—	—	—	—	2	1
060 Y, Z	2-1/2	2	1-1/2	—	—	—
070 X	—	—	—	—	3	1
070 Y, Z	—	3-1/2	1-1/2	—	—	—
080 X	—	—	—	—	—	1
080 Y, Z	—	—	1-1/2	—	—	—

1. Ratio of bend radius to thickness.
2. Refer to the paragraph headed "Cold Bending" for a more detailed explanation of the use of this table.
3. The suggested minimum bending radius is based on the nominal rolled thickness, not the minimum ordered thickness.
4. For thicknesses over 4.55 mm (0.180 in) to 5.85 mm (0.230 in) inclusive, add 1/2t to the radii shown in the table above.
5. H–maximum carbon as shown in Tables 3 and 4; L–0.13% maximum carbon except as noted in Table 4.

(R) HIGH-STRENGTH, HOT-ROLLED STEEL BARS—SAE J1442 SEP2003

SAE Recommended Practice

Report of the SAE Iron and Steel Technical Committee, Division 13, approved June 1984, and reaffirmed December 1988. Completely revised by the SAE Iron and Steel Technical Committee Division 1—Carbon and Alloy Steels, November 1993 and September 2003. Rationale statement available.

Foreword—High-strength steel discussed in this SAE Recommended Practice involves hot-rolled bars only. The strength is achieved through chemical composition and rolling practice; it is not achieved through quenching and tempering or additional rolling operations.

1. Scope—This SAE Recommended Practice covers two levels of high strength structural low-alloy steel bars having minimum Yield Points of 345 MPa (50 ksi) and 450 MPa (65 ksi).

The two strength levels are 345 and 450 MPa or 50 and 65 ksi minimum yield point. Different chemical compositions are used to achieve the specified mechanical properties. In some cases there are significant differences in chemical composition for the same strength level, depending on the fabricating requirements.

It should be noted that although the mechanical properties for a steel grade sourced from different suppliers may be the same, the chemical composition may vary significantly. The fabricator should be aware that certain compositional differences may effect the forming, welding, and/or service requirements of the material. It is therefore recommended that the fabricator consult with the producer to understand the effect of chemical composition.

The products within the scope of this document include bars of the following types and sizes:

Rounds, squares, and hexagons of all sizes (cut length only), flats 5.2 mm (0.203 in) and greater in thickness but not greater than 150 mm (6 in) wide, and flats greater than 5.8 mm (0.229 in) thick and over 150 mm (6 in) to 204 mm (8 in) wide.

This document previously covered plates, structural shapes, and bar size shapes of Grades 290A, 345A, 415A, 450A, 345W, 345F, 415F, 485F, and 550F as well as bars of Grades 290A, 415A, and 345W. These products are no longer covered; requirements for these products and grades can be found in ASTM Specifications as follows in Table 1:

TABLE 1—EQUIVALENT ASTM SPECIFICATIONS

Product	Previous SAE Grade	ASTM Specification/Grade
Plates, Structural Shapes, Bar Size Shapes, Bars	290A	A 572/A 572M, Grade 42
Plates, Structural Shapes, Bar Size Shapes	345A	A 572/A 572M, Grade 50
Plates, Structural Shapes, Bar Size Shapes, Bars	415A	A 572/A 572M, Grade 60
Plates, Structural Shapes, Bar Size Shapes	450A	A 57/A 572M, Grade 65
Plates, Structural Shapes, Bar Size Shapes, Bars	345W	A 588/A 588M
Plates	345F	A 656/A 656M, Grade 50
Plates	415F	A 656/A 656M, Grade 60
Plates	485F	A 656/A 656M, Grade 70
Plates	550F	A 656/A 656M, Grade 80

2. References

2.1 Applicable Publications—The following publications form a part of the specification to the extent specified herein.

2.1.1 ASTM PUBLICATIONS—Available from ASTM, 100 Barr Harbor Drive, West Conshohocken, PA 19428-2959.

ASTM A 6/A 6M—General Requirements for Rolled Steel Plates, Shapes, Sheet Piling, and Bars of Structural Use

ASTM A 370—Standard Methods and Definitions for Mechanical Testing of Steel Products

ASTM A 572/A 572M—Specification for High-Strength Low-Alloy Columbium-Vanadium Steels of Structural Quality

ASTM A 588/A 588M—Specification for High-Strength Low-Alloy Structural Steel with 50 ksi (345 MPa) Minimum Yield Point to 4 in thick

ASTM A 656/A 656M—Specification for Hot-Rolled Structural Steel, High-Strength Low-Alloy Plate with Improved Formability

2.2 Related Publications—The following publication is provided for information purposes only and is not a required part of this specification. Unless otherwise indicated, the latest version of SAE publications shall apply.

SAE J450—Use of Terms Yield Strength and Yield Point

3. General Information—The specific grades are identified by the minimum yield point expressed in MPa, that is 345 and 450 or in ksi, that is 50 and 65 ksi. Grades 345 and 450 are similar to grades contained in ASTM A 572/A 572M. These Grades were previously covered under this specification as Grades 345A and 450A; the "A" suffix has been dropped in this revision.

Because these steels are characterized by their special mechanical properties obtained in the as-rolled conditions, they are not intended for any heat treatment by the purchaser either before, during, or after fabrication. The fabricator should not subject these steels to such heat treatments without assuming responsibility for the resulting mechanical properties. For certain applications, these steels may be annealed, normalized, or stress relieved with some effect on the mechanical properties; it is recommended that prior to such heat treatments, the purchaser should consult the producer to determine the need for and the effect on mechanical properties.

Both grades and chemical compositions discussed in the practice are weldable despite the differences in carbon, manganese, and alloying addition. Because of the aforementioned variations in composition from one producer to another, it is advisable to discuss with the producers the features of their chemical composition relative to the various types of welding and any special consideration for each application.

These steels, because of their high strength-to-weight ratio, are adapted particularly for use in mobile equipment and other structures where substantial weight savings are generally desirable.

4. Mechanical Properties—The mechanical properties of these steels are shown in Table 2. If thicknesses greater than those shown in the table are required, consultation with the producers regarding availability and characteristics is suggested.

5. Chemical Composition—The chemical composition (heat analysis) of steel furnished to this practice shall conform to Table 3.

Because the chemical compositions vary significantly among the producers despite the required mechanical properties being the same, it is advisable for the purchaser to discuss specific compositions with each producer, especially if welding, and/or forming are critical factors. The commonly used alloying elements are: chromium, columbium (niobium), copper, molybdenum, nickel, titanium, vanadium, and zirconium. The selection and chemical ranges for any alloying elements not in Table 3, which are considered necessary to attain the required properties, may be specified by mutual agreement between purchaser and producer at the time of ordering. Once specified, they may not be changed without both parties' consent.

6. Suggested Bending Practice—The suggested minimum inside bend radii for cold forming are shown in Table 4. The suggested radii listed in Table 4 should be used as minimums in typical shop fabrication. Material that does not form satisfactorily when fabricated in accordance with Table 4 may be subject to rejection pending negotiation with the steel supplier. When tighter bends are required, the manufacturer should be consulted. the bend radius and the radius of the male die should be as liberal as the finished part will permit. The width across the shoulders of the female die should be at least eight times the plate thickness. Higher strength steels require larger die openings. The surface of the dies in the area of radius should be smooth.

Since cracks in cold bending commonly originate from the outside edges, shear burrs and gas cut edges should be removed by grinding. Sharp corners on edges and on punched or gas cut holes should be removed by chamfering or grinding to a radius. It should be noted that all steel has a tendency to crack when bent on a sheared or gas cut edge. This is not to be considered a fault of the steel, but rather a function of the induced cold work or heat affected zone. Where bends are to be made on a sheared edge, best performance is attained when the shear burr is located on the inside of the bend.

If possible, parts should be formed such that the bend line is perpendicular to the direction of final rolling. If it is necessary to bend with the bend line parallel to the direction of final rolling, a more generous radius is suggested (1-1/2 times applicable value given in Table 4 for bend lines perpendicular to the direction of rolling.)

7. Dimensional Tolerances—Standard manufacturing tolerances for dimensions, as shown in the latest edition of ASTM A 6/A 6M shall apply.

TABLE 2—MECHANICAL PROPERTIES[1]

Grade	Nominal Maximum Thickness mm	Nominal Maximum Thickness in	Yield Point[2][3] Minimum MPa	Yield Point[2][3] Minimum ksi	Tensile Strength[3][4] Minimum MPa	Tensile Strength[3][4] Minimum ksi	Elongation[3] Minimum % Minimum 200 mm (8 in)	Elongation[3][5] Minimum % Minimum 50 mm (2 in)	Tensile Strength,[4] Max MPa	Tensile Strength,[4] Max ksi
345	100	4	345	50	450	65	18	21	655	95
450	32	1-1/4	450	65	550	80	15	17	725	105

1. Mechanical testing (location, number of tests, preparation, and method) is to be in accordance with the latest revision of ASTM A 6/A 6M.
2. Yield point may be reported as yield strength as measured by the 0.2% offset or 0.5% extension under load method as agreed upon between the producer and the purchaser.
3. Only one set of units apply to yield and tensile and the reported value should be based on the units of the purchase order. In addition only one set of elongation values 50 mm (2 in) or 200 mm (8 in) need to be met and reported.
4. Some applications may require a maximum tensile strength. In such cases, the following values must be determined from the producer for acceptance prior to issuing a purchase order.
5. Refer to ASTM A 6/A 6M elongation requirement adjustments.

TABLE 3—CHEMICAL COMPOSITION, HEAT ANALYSIS, MAX, % BY WEIGHT

Grade	C	Mn	Si	P	S	Other
345	0.21	1.50	0.40	0.040	0.050	(1)
450	0.26	1.65	0.40	0.040	0.050	(1)

1. Choice and use of alloying elements, combined with carbon, manganese, silicon, phosphorus and sulfur within the limits of Table 3 to give the mechanical properties prescribed in Table 2, shall be made by the manufacturer and included and reported in the heat analysis to identify the type of steel applied. Element commonly added include: chromium, copper, molybdenum, nickel, niobium (columbium), vanadium, titanium, and zirconium.

TABLE 4—SUGGESTED MINIMUM INSIDE RADII FOR 90-DEGREE COLD BENDING—RATIO OF BEND RADIUS TO THICKNESS THICKNESS OF MATERIAL, mm (in)

Grade	to 20 (3/4) incl.	Over 20 (3/4) to 25 (1) incl.	Over 25 (1) to 50 (2) incl.	Over 50 (2)
345	1.5	1.5	2.0	2.5
450	1.5	1.5	3.0	3.5

ENGINE POPPET VALVE INFORMATION REPORT—SAE J775 AUG93

SAE Information Report

Report of the SAE Iron and Steel Technical Committee approved June 1961 and completely revised January 1988. This specification adopts the International Organization for Standardization (ISO) chemical compositions from their Regulation 683/15. Completely revised by the SAE Iron and Steel Technical Committee Division 35—Elevated Temperature Properties of Ferrous Metals, August 1993.

Foreword—This Document has not changed other than to put it into the new SAE Technical Standards Board Format.

Poppet valves control combustion chamber induction and exhaust gas flow in reciprocating combustion engines. Poppet valves are manufactured from iron, nickel, titanium, and cobalt-base metallic alloys which are often welded together in various combinations.

Martensitic and austenitic steels are used for intake valves. Specially designed high temperature martensitic alloys, austenitic alloys, and superalloys are used for exhaust valves. Titanium alloys have been used for both intake and exhaust valves in some limited production, high performance applications. Special iron, nickel, and cobalt-base alloys are welded to many of the valve head alloys to improve seat face wear and corrosion resistance.

1. Scope—This specification supplies engineers and designers with:

a. Poppet valve nomenclature
b. Poppet valve alloy designations
c. Chemical compositions of poppet valve alloys
d. A guide to valve alloy metallurgy and heat treatments
e. General information on properties of valve alloys
f. A guide to the application of valve alloys
g. A description of valve design and construction, and their relation to valve alloy selection
h. Valve gear design considerations that affect valves

2. References—There are no referenced publications specified herein.

3. Valve Nomenclature—Valve nomenclature and constructions are illustrated in Figures 1 to 5.

4. Valve Alloy Designation

4.1 UNS Designations—SAE, in conjunction with American Society for Testing and Materials (ASTM), has adopted the Unified Numbering System (UNS) for the identification of all metallic alloys. Tables 1A to 1E use the UNS identification codes for valve alloys. These UNS numbers supersede the previous SAE functional numbering system, which is still included for reference purposes.

Each UNS designation is a five-digit identification number preceded by a type identification prefix letter. Valve alloys have six identification prefixes:

G - General purpose carbon and low alloy structural steels
H - Controlled hardenability carbon and low alloy steels
K - Special purpose iron-base alloys
N - Nickel-base alloys
R - Cobalt, titanium, and other refractory alloys
S - Stainless steels, heat-resistant steels, corrosion-resistant steels, and iron-base superalloys

The five-digit identification number often incorporates the most popular previous designation for the alloy. The UNS designations are controlled by individual SAE and ASTM committees which work in concert.

4.2 Obsolete SAE Functional Designations—The former SAE numbering system was based on the type of valve for which the material was commonly used. Numbers were assigned on the following bases:

a. Letter Prefix—Intake valves may be made of carbon, low alloy, or heat and corrosion resistant high-alloy steels. The prefix NV designated carbon and low alloy intake valve steels. HNV designated high alloy intake valve steels.

Exhaust valves may be made of hardenable martensitic steels, austenitic steels, or superalloys. Alloys used for exhaust valves may be iron, nickel, or cobalt-base alloys. The prefix letters EV designated austenitic exhaust valve steels. The letters HEV were used for high strength exhaust valve alloys in severe spark and compression ignition engine service.

The prefix VF designated high alloy valve seat facing overlays used at critical points of wear or corrosion.

The prefix X designated experimental and limited usage alloys preceding a conventional prefix, such as XEV.

b. Number Suffix—A number was arbitrarily assigned, based on the order in which the alloy was codified.

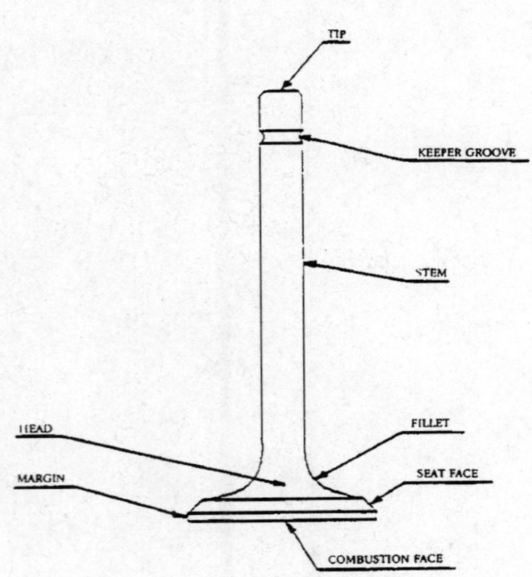

The majority of intake valves for all applications are one-piece construction which also has significant usage in spark ignition engine exhaust valves.

FIGURE 1—ONE-PIECE CONSTRUCTION

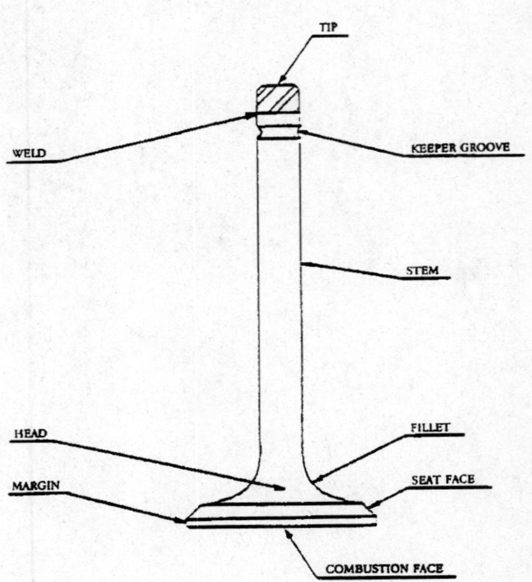

Welded tip construction has significant usage in spark and compression ignition engine exhaust valves.

FIGURE 2—WELDED TIP CONSTRUCTION

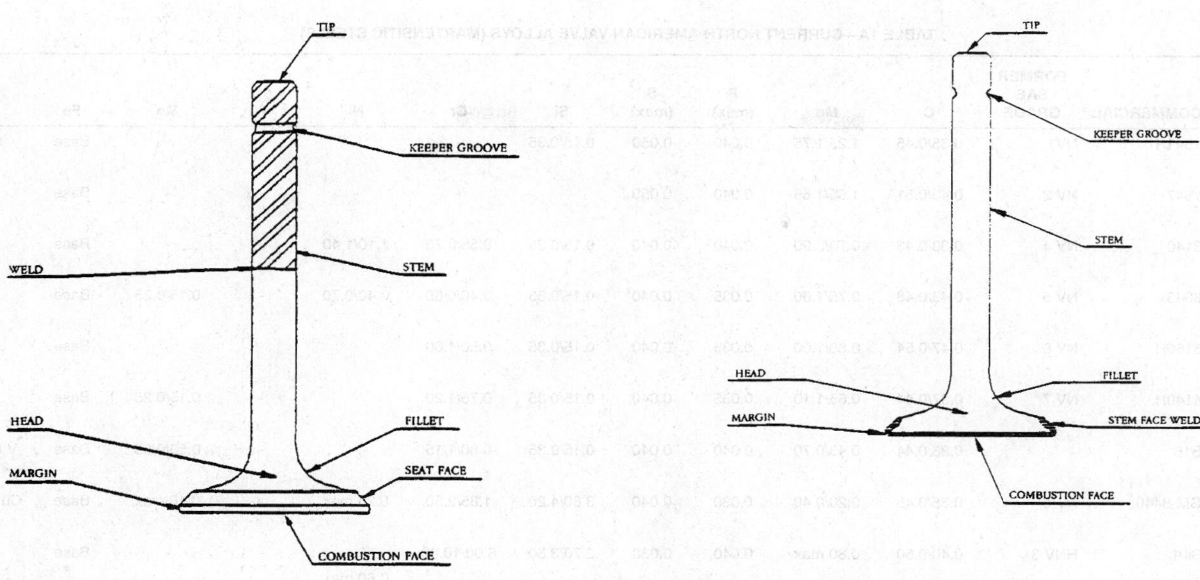

Two-piece construction has significant usage in spark and compression ignition engine exhaust valves.

FIGURE 3—TWO-PIECE CONSTRUCTION

Welded seat face construction predominates in compression ignition engine exhaust valves and has some usage in other valves. It supplements other types of valve construction.

FIGURE 5—WELDED SEAT FACE CONSTRUCTION

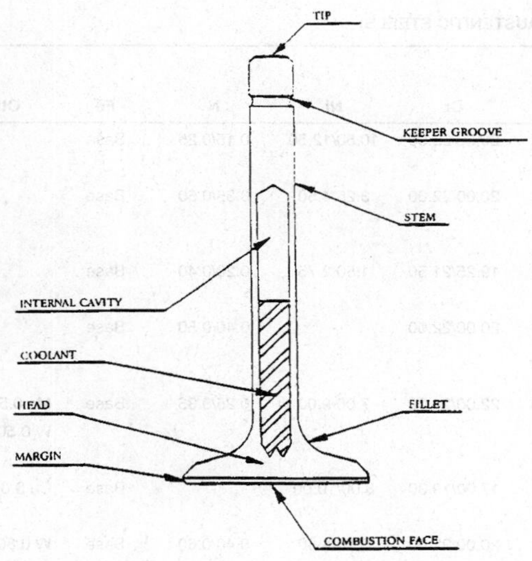

Internally-cooled construction is used in extreme duty truck, high performance, and aircraft spark ignition engine exhaust valves.

FIGURE 4—INTERNALLY-COOLED CONSTRUCTION

4.3 Other Designations—Tables 2A to 2C list other important national and international valve alloys, together with their specific chemistries.

5. Valve Alloy Chemical Compositions

5.1 General—There are many overlapping and conflicting specifications for the chemical compositions of valve alloys. This specification adopts the ISO chemical compositions from their Regulation 683/15. Unfortunately, a number of alloys in common use are not listed in this regulation, so lowest common denominator compositions, conforming with most specifications in common usage, were developed.

5.2 UNS (SAE) Compositions—The UNS (SAE) standard compositions for valve alloys are listed in Tables 1A to 1E.

5.3 Other Compositions—The compositions of other international valve alloys are listed in Tables 2A to 2C.

6. Valve Alloy Metallurgy and Heat Treatment

6.1 General—The performance characteristics of a valve alloy are a cross product of composition and heat treatment. Alloy selection depends upon stresses, corrosive agents, and temperatures encountered in service, as well as the economic and durability objectives. Heat treatments used to improve the mechani cal properties of valves depend upon the specific alloy, economics, and the level of properties desired. They can be general or selective, and it is not uncommon for a single valve to be subjected to two or more heat treatments in different locations.

6.2 Martensitic Alloys—Plain carbon, low alloy, and high alloy martensitic steels are primarily used for intake valves. Extreme duty martensitic steels generally have the highest carbon and alloy content to resist wear, to resist seat face indention by deposits, and to provide increased strength. Elements such as chromium and silicon are added when increased oxidation or corrosion resistance is needed. Manganese and nickel are added as strengthening agents. Occasionally, refractory elements, such as molybdenum, tungsten, and vanadium are used to enhance certain elevated temperature properties.

Martensitic valves are most often quench hardened and tempered to hardness readings in the 25 to 45 Rockwell "C" scale range. This is a compromise among good strength, adequate ductility, impact performance, and wear resistance along the stem. In some less demanding applications, martensitic valves can be used in the annealed condition.

Tips and seats are often selectively hardened to create high hardness and wear resistant surfaces. These surfaces are selectively hardened, generally to the greatest hardness practical for the alloy. Tip hardening may extend beyond the keeper groove to improve the fatigue strength and the wear resistance of this region.

TABLE 1A—CURRENT NORTH AMERICAN VALVE ALLOYS (MARTENSITIC STEELS)

UNS NR/ ISO 683/15	COMMERCIAL	FORMER SAE GRADE	C	Mn	P (max)	S (max)	Si	Cr	Ni	W	Mo	Fe	Other
H15410	1541H	NV1	0.35/0.45	1.25/1.75	0.040	0.050	0.15/0.35	-	-	-	-	Base	
G15470	1547	NV 2	0.43/0.51	1.35/1.65	0.040	0.050	-	-	-	-	-	Base	
G31400	3140	NV 4	0.38/0.43	0.70/0.90	0.040	0.040	0.15/0.35	0.55/0.75	1.10/1.40	-	-	Base	
G86450	8645	NV 5	0.43/0.48	0.75/1.00	0.035	0.040	0.15/0.35	0.40/0.60	0.40/0.70	-	0.15/0.25	Base	
H51500	5150H	NV 6	0.47/0.54	0.60/1.00	0.035	0.040	0.15/0.35	0.60/1.00	-	-	-	Base	
H41400	4140H	NV 7	0.37/0.44	0.65/1.10	0.035	0.040	0.15/0.35	0.75/1.20	-	-	0.15/0.25	Base	
K14072	B16		0.36/0.44	0.45/0.70	0.040	0.040	0.15/0.35	0.80/1.15	-	-	0.50/0.65	Base	V 0.25/0.35
	GM-8440	NV 8	0.35/0.45	0.20/0.40	0.030	0.040	3.60/4.20	1.85/2.50	0.25 max	-	0.10 max	Base	Cu 0.25 max
S65007/X 45 CrSi 9 3	Sil 1	HNV 3	0.40/0.50	0.80 max	0.040	0.030	2.70/3.30	8.00/10.00	0.60 max	-	-	Base	
S65006	Sil XB	HNV 6	0.75/0.90	0.80 max	0.040	0.040	1.75/2.60	19.00/21.00	1.00/1.70	-	-	Base	
S42200	422 SS	HNV 8	0.20/0.25	1.00 max	0.040	0.030	0.75 max	11.00/12.50	0.50/1.00	0.75/1.25	0.75/1.25	Base	V 0.15/0.30 Cu 0.50 max
S64004	SUH 11M		0.47/0.55	0.60 max	0.030	0.030	1.00/2.00	7.50/9.50	0.60 max	-	-	Base	

All chemical contents are expressed in weight percent.

TABLE 1B—CURRENT NORTH AMERICAN VALVE ALLOYS (AUSTENITIC STEELS)

UNS NR/ISO 683/15	COMMERCIAL	FORMER SAE GRADE	C	Mn	P (max)	S (max)	Si	Cr	Ni	N	Fe	Other
S63017	21-12N	EV 4	0.15/0.25	1.00/1.50	0.045	0.030	0.70/1.25	20.00/22.00	10.50/12.50	0.15/0.25	Base	
S63008/ X 53 CrMnNiN21 9	21-4N	EV 8	0.48/0.58	8.00/10.00	0.050	0.030	0.25 max	20.00/22.00	3.25/4.50	0.35/0.50	Base	
S63012	21-2N	EV 12	0.50/0.60	7.00/10.00	0.050	0.030	0.25 max	19.25/21.50	1.50/2.75	0.20/0.40	Base	
S63013	Gaman H	EV 13	0.47/0.57	11.00/ 13.00	0.030	0.050	2.00/3.00	20.00/22.00	-	0.40/0.50	Base	
S63018/ X 33 CrNiMnN 23 8	23-8N	EV 16	0.28/0.38	1.50/3.50	0.050	0.030	0.50/1.00	22.00/24.00	7.00/9.00	0.25/0.35	Base	Mo 0.50 max W 0.50 max
S30430	302 HQ	EV 17	0.10 max	2.00 max	0.045	0.030	1.00 max	17.00/19.00	8.00/10.00	-	Base	Cu 3.00/4.00
S63019/ X 50 CrMnNiNbN 21 9	21-4N + Nb + W	XEV-F	0.45/0.55	8.00/10.00	0.050	0.030	0.45 max	20.00/22.00	3.50/5.50	0.40/0.60	Base	W 0.80/1.50 Nb + Ta 1.80/2.50

All chemical contents are expressed in weight percent.

TABLE 1C—CURRENT VALVE ALLOYS (SUPERALLOYS)

UNS NR/ISO 683/15	COMMERCIAL	FORMER SAE GRADE	C	Mn (max)	P (max)	S (max)	Si (max)	Cr	Ni	Co	Mo	Fe	Other
N07751/ NiCr 15 Fe 7 TiAl	Inconel 751	HEV 3	0.03/0.10	0.50	0.015	0.015	0.50	14.00/17.00	Base	1.00 max	0.50 max	5.00/9.00	Ti 2.00/2.60 Al 1.10/1.35 Nb + Ta 0.70/1.20 Zr 0.04/0.10 B 0.0015/0.009 Cu 0.50 max
N07080/ NiCr 20 TiAl	Nimonic 80-A	HEV 5	0.04/0.10	1.00	0.020	0.015	1.00	18.00/21.00	Base	2.00 max	-	3.00 max	B 0.008 max Zr 0.04/0.10 Ti 1.80/2.70 Al 1.00/1.80 Cu 0.20 max
N07032	Pyromet 31V	HEV 8	0.03/0.06	0.20	0.015	0.015	0.20	22.30/22.90	55.00/58.00	1.00 max	1.70/2.30	Balance	Ti 2.10/2.40 Al 1.10/1.40 Nb 0.70/1.00 B 0.003/0.007 Cu 0.50 max
N07001	Waspaloy	XEV-H	0.03/0.10	1.00	0.030	0.030	0.75	18.00/21.00	Base	12.00/15.00	3.50/5.00	2.00 max	Ti 2.75/3.25 Al 1.20/1.60 Zr 0.02/0.12 B 0.003/0.010 Cu 0.50 max

All chemical contents are expressed in weight percent.

TABLE 1D—CURRENT VALVE ALLOYS (FACING ALLOYS)

UNS NR	COMMERCIAL	FORMER SAE GRADE	C	Mn (max)	P (max)	S (max)	Si	Cr	Ni	Co	W	Mo	Fe	Other
R30006	Stellite 6	VF 2	0.90/1.40	1.00	0.030	0.030	1.50 max	26.00/32.00	5.00 max	Base	3.50/5.50	1.50 max	6.00 max	
N06005	Eatonite	VF 3	2.00/2.75	0.50	0.030	0.030	0.50/1.00	27.00/31.00	Base	9.00/11.00	14.00/16.00		8.00 max	
N06782	X-782	VF 4	1.75/2.25	1.00	0.030	0.030	0.50 max	25.00/27.00	Base	0.50 max	8.00/9.50	–	4.00 max	
R30002	Stellite F	VF 5	1.50/2.00	1.00	0.030	0.030	0.80/1.50	23.00/27.00	20.50/23.50	Base	10.50/13.50	1.00 max	6.00 max	
R30001	Stellite 1	VF 6	2.00/3.00	1.00	0.030	0.030	0.40/2.00	26.00/33.00	3.00 max	Base	11.00/14.00	1.00 max	6.00 max	
R30012	Stellite 12	VF 7	1.10/1.70	1.00	0.030	0.030	0.40/2.00	26.00/33.00	3.00 max	Base	7.00/9.50	1.00 max	3.00 max	
R30400	Tribaloy T-400	VF 8	0.08 max	–	0.030	0.030	2.20/3.00	7.50/10.00	–	61.00/63.00		26.50/30.00		Fe + Ni 3.00 max
N06013	Eatonite 3	VF 9	1.80/2.20	1.00	0.030	0.030	0.80/1.20	28.00/30.00	Base	–	–	4.00/6.00	1.00/8.00	
N06015	Eatonite 5	VF 10	1.80/2.20	1.00	0.030	0.030	0.80/1.20	28.00/30.00	Base	–	–	7.00/9.00	1.00/8.00	
	VMS 585	VF 11	2.00/2.50	–	–	–	0.80/1.30	22.00/26.00	10.00/12.00	–	–	5.00/6.00	Base	
S68000														
	Eatonite 6		1.50/2.00	1.00	0.025	0.020	1.10/1.50	26.00/30.00	15.00/18.00	–		4.00/5.00	Base	
	Tribaloy T-800		0.08 max	–	0.030	0.030	3.00/3.80	16.50/18.50	1.50 max	Base	–	27.00/30.00	1.50 max	

All chemical contents are expressed in weight percent.

TABLE 1E—CURRENT VALVE ALLOYS (TITANIUM ALLOYS)

UNS NR	COMMERCIAL	FORMER SAE GRADE	C (max)	Al	V	Zr	Mo	Sn	O (max)	Fe (max)	H (max)	Y (max)	Ti	Other (max)
R56401	Ti 6-4	XEV-J	0.10	5.25/6.75	3.35/4.65	–	–	–	0.40	0.80	0.020	0.005	Base	N 0.10
R54620	Ti 6-2-4-2		0.05	5.50/6.50	–	3.60/4.40	1.80/2.20	1.80/2.20	0.20	0.25	0.015	0.005	Base	Si 0.20 N 0.07

All chemical contents are expressed in weight percent.

TABLE 2A—ISO VALVE ALLOYS

UNS NR	ISO 683/15	C	Mn	P (max)	S (max)	Si	Cr	Ni	N	W	Mo	Fe	Other
S65007	x 45 CrSi 9 3	0.40/0.50	0.80 max	0.040	0.030	2.7/3.3	8.0/10.0	0.60 max	–	–	–	Base	
	X 50 CrSi 8 2	0.45/0.55	0.60 max	0.030	0.030	1.0/2.0	7.5/9.5	0.60 max	–	–	–	Base	
	X 85 CrMoV 18 2	0.80/0.90	1.5 max	0.040	0.030	1.0 max	16.5/18.5	–	–	–	2.0/2.5	Base	V 0.30/0.60
S63008	X 53 CrMnNiN 21 9	0.48/0.58	8.0/10.0	0.050	0.030	0.25 max	20.0/22.0	3.25/4.5	0.35/0.50	–	–	Base	
	X 55 CrMnNiN 20 8	0.50/0.60	7.0/10.0	0.050	0.030	0.25 max	19.5/21.5	1.5/2.75	0.20/0.40	–	–	Base	
S63018	X 33 CrNiMnN 23 8	0.28/0.38	1.5/3.5	0.050	0.030	0.50/1.00	22.0/24.0	7.0/9.0	0.25/0.35	0.50 max	0.50 max	Base	
S63019	X 50 CrMnNiNbN 21 9	0.45/0.55	8.0/10.0	0.050	0.030	0.45 max	20.0/22.0	3.5/5.5	0.40/0.60	0.80/1.50	–	Base	Nb + Ta 1.80/2.50
	X 53 CrMnNiNbN 21 9	0.48/0.58	8.0/10.0	0.050	0.030	0.45 max	20.0/22.0	3.25/4.5	0.38/0.50	–	–	Base	C + N ρ 0.90 Nb + Ta 2.00/3.00
N07080	NiCr 20 TiAl	0.04/0.10	1.0 max	0.020	0.015	1.0 max	18.0/21.0	Base	–	–	–	3.0 max	Al 1.0/1.8 Ti 1.8/2.7 Co 2.0 max Cu 0.2 max B 0.008 max
N07751	NiCr 15 Fe 7 TiAl	0.03/0.10	0.50 max	0.015	0.015	0.50 max	14.0/17.0	Base	–	–	0.50 max	5.0/9.0	Al 1.10/1.35 Nb + Ta 0.70/1.20 Ti 2.0/2.6
	NiFe 25 Cr 20 NbTi	0.10 max	1.0 max	0.030	0.015	1.0 max	18.0/21.0	Base	–	–	–	23.0/28.0	Al 0.30/1.00 Nb + Ta 1.0/2.0 B 0.008 max

All chemical contents are expressed in weight percent.

TABLE 2B—JIS HEAT RESISTING STEELS (VALVE ALLOYS)

UNS NR	JASO GRADE	C	Mn	P (max)	S (max)	Si	Cr	Ni	Co	W	Mo	Fe	Other
R30001	Co Cr 1	2.00/3.00	1.00 max	-	-	0.40/2.00	26.0/33.0	3.00 max	Base	11.00/14.00	1.00 max	3.00 max	0.50 max
R30006	Co Cr 6	0.90/1.40	1.00 max	-	-	0.40/2.00	26.0/32.0	3.00 max	Base	3.00/6.00	1.00 max	3.00 max	0.50 max
R30012	Co Cr 12	1.20/1.70	1.00 max	-	-	0.40/2.00	26.0/33.0	3.00 max	Base	7.00/9.50	1.00 max	3.00 max	0.50 max

All chemical contents are expressed in weight percent.

UNS NR	JIS G 4106 GRADE	C	Mn	P (max)	S (max)	Si	Cr	Ni	Co	W	Mo	Fe	Other
G15470	SMnC443	0.40/0.46	1.35/1.65	0.030	0.030	0.15/0.35	0.35/0.70	-	-				

All chemical contents are expressed in weight percent.

UNS NR	JIS G 4103 GRADE	C	Mn	P (max)	S (max)	Si	Cr	Ni	Co	W	Mo	Fe	Other
G86450	SNCM 240	0.38/0.43	0.70/1.00	0.030	0.030	0.15/0.35	0.40/0.65	0.40/0.70	-	-	0.15/0.30	-	

All chemical contents are expressed in weight percent.

UNS NR	JIS G 4311 GRADE	C	Mn	P (max)	S (max)	Si	Cr	Ni	Co	W	Mo	Fe	Other
S65007	SUH 1	0.40/0.50	0.60 max	0.030	0.030	3.00/3.50	7.50/9.50	0.60 max	-	-	-	-	
S65006	SUH 4	0.75/0.85	0.20/0.60	0.030	0.030	1.75/2.25	19.00/20.50	1.15/1.65	-	-	-	-	
S63008	SUH 35	0.48/0.58	8.00/10.00	0.040	0.030	0.35 max	20.00/22.00	3.25/4.50	-	-	-	-	N 0.35/0.50
S63017	SUH 37	0.15/0.25	1.00/1.60	0.040	0.030	1.00 max	20.50/22.50	10.00/12.00	-	-	-	-	N 0.15/0.30
S42200	SUH 616	0.20/0.25	0.50/1.00	0.040	0.030	0.50 max	11.00/13.00	0.50/1.00	-	0.75/1.25	0.75/1.25	-	V 0.20/0.30

All chemical contents are expressed in weight percent.

TABLE 2C—JIS HEAT RESISTING STEELS (VALVE ALLOYS)

UNS NR	JIS G 4902 GRADE	C	Mn (max)	P (max)	S (max)	Si (max)	Cr	Ni	Fe	Other
N07080	NCF 80A	0.04/0.10	1.00	0.030	0.015	1.00	18.00/21.00	Base	1.50 max	Ti 1.80/2.70 Al 1.00/1.80 Cu 0.20 max
	NCF 751	0.10 max	1.00	0.030	0.015	0.50	14.00/17.00	70.00 min	5.00/9.00	Ti 2.00/2.60 Al 0.90/1.50 Nb + Ta 0.70/1.20 Cu 0.50 max

All chemical contents are expressed in weight percent.

6.3 Austenitic Alloys—Austenitic alloys have a face-centered cubic crystal structure which is termed austenite. The elements that stabilize the austenitic structure are carbon, manganese, nickel, copper, and nitrogen. Chromium, silicon, and sometimes, aluminum are added for oxidation or corrosion resistance. Refractory elements such as molybdenum, niobium, tantalum, tungsten, and vanadium may be added for high temperature strength. These alloys are termed steels when the base element is iron. The cobalt and nickel-base austenitic materials are termed superalloys. Iron-base austenitic steels are hardened by carbonitride precipitation. Nickel-base superalloys are hardened by precipitation of aluminum, nickel, niobium, tantalum, and titanium in the form of intermetallic compounds. They may be used in either wrought or cast form, although cast valves are diminishing in commercial importance.

Austenitic valve alloys may be as simple in composition as 18-8 stainless steels, or as complicated as gas turbine alloys. The selection is strongly influenced by economic considerations, as well as the mechanical, physical, and chemical attributes required to satisfy specific engine requirements.

Mechanical properties are improved in austenitic valve alloys by precipitation hardening or strain hardening, rather than the martensitic transformation hardening of low alloy steels. The most common austenitic alloy hardening processes are:

a. High temperature forging followed by aging heat treatment(s)
b. High temperature forging followed by a solution treatment and then aging heat treatment(s)
c. Cold forming

In lower temperature applications, austenitic engine valves are frequently used in the forged and aged condition. More severe and higher temperature service generally requires solution treatment followed by one or more aging treatments. These operations produce hardness readings in the 20 to 40 Rockwell "C" scale range. The hardness developed depends upon the capability of the individual alloy. These alloys develop fatigue, creep, wear, and seat face indentation resistance from the heat treatments.

The cold formed austentic alloys (302HQ) are often used in small light-duty engines.

6.4 Titanium Alloys—Titanium alloys can be divided into three categories: alpha, alpha-beta, and beta alloys. Alpha alloys have a close-packed hexagonal structure, beta alloys have a body-centered cubic structure, and alpha-beta alloys have mixtures of the two different structures. The alloying elements that stabilize the alpha structure include oxygen, nitrogen, aluminum, and carbon. Alloying elements that stabilize the beta structure include vanadium and molybdenum. Zirconium and tin have minor effects upon phase stability, but are widely used as solid-solution strengtheners in both alpha and beta alloys.

Most titanium intake valves are made from alpha-beta alloys which have superior low temperature strength. Exhaust valves are generally manufactured from alpha or near alpha alloys because they have better high temperature creep properties. Beta alloys have not been used in any engine valve applications of consequence.

Titanium alloy heat treatments for engine valve applications are less established than the heat treatments for high volume production alloys. Most titanium alloys used in engine valves are precipitation hardenable and receive some type of solution treatment and aging after forming.

It is important to note that the development of titanium alloy engine valves has been primarily for high performance applications where extended durability is not a primary concern. Heat treatment procedures and precision are believed to be critical parameters in long-term titanium valve durability.

Titanium aluminides are being investigated on an experimental basis for passenger car exhaust valve applications.

6.5 Ceramic Materials—Although not yet used in any commercial applications, ceramic materials are being investigated for high temperature valve service. The primary material being investigated for this application is Si_3N_4. Much experimentation has been done to develop plasma sprayed cermets, but these are being used only on a limited basis.

6.6 Seat Facing Alloys—Seat facing alloys are composed of hard precipitates in cobalt, nickel, or iron-base austenitic matrices. The hard precipitates are generally chromium, molybdenum, tungsten, or vanadium carbides. Some compositions use intermetallic compounds, such as Laves phase, as the hard precipitates. Chromium is added to the matrix to increase corrosion resistance. Silicon additions provide the fluidity necessary for welding the facing to the valve seat and can improve wear resistance.

Seat facing alloys derive their wear resistance from the volume fraction of precipitates which possess great hot hardness and compressive strength. A significant portion of the adhesive wear resistance in these seat facing alloys, as well as other high chromium alloys, is derived from the tenacious chromium oxide layer formed on the wear surface by oxidation during service. When extremely severe conditions of corrosion are encountered, such as those which occur when sulfur-containing fuels are used, cobalt or iron-base hard-facing alloys may be required to assure valve seat durability.

Selection of a particular seat facing alloy usually depends upon temperatures, stresses, and corrodents encountered in service. Manufacturing considerations may preclude some seat facing alloy/valve head alloy combinations.

7. *Valve Alloy Physical and Mechanical Properties*

7.1 General—No single property can define the varying conditions encountered in different internal combustion engines. Spark and compression ignition engines place different demands on engine valves, so the properties of interest vary.

Common causes of valve failures include:

a. Adhesive or Abrasive Wear
   1. Of the stem surface
   2. Of the seat surface
   3. Of the tip surface
b. General or Localized Corrosion
   1. Primarily at elevated temperatures
   2. Often combined with fatigue
c. Fatigue
   1. Head radial cracking by thermal fatigue
   2. Head chordal cracking by mechanical fatigue
   3. Fillet transverse cracking by mechanical fatigue
   4. Keeper groove transverse cracking by mechanical fatigue
   5. Often assisted by corrosion

7.2 Wear Properties—The wear resistance of valve materials cannot be adequately assessed by a single type of wear or mechanical property test because of the different modes of wear encountered at different locations on the valve. Often a secondary mode of wear can be initiated by the wear particles generated by the primary wear mode. Valve wear service must be considered individually at each of these locations: valve tip, stem, and seat.

a. Valve Tip—Against rocker arm type valve gear, valve tips are subjected to combined sliding and rolling contact with the rocker arm surface, potentially causing adhesive wear.
b. Valve Stem—Valve stems are subjected to a normal amount of sliding wear, which is not severe unless aggravated by inadequate lubrication or applied transverse loads. Excessive transverse loads are often due to improper rocker arm geometry or thermal distortion of the cylinder seat.

c. Valve Seat—The valve seat/cylinder head seat contact is characterized by high normal stresses and severe sliding conditions, generally at high temperatures and in a corrosive environment. The high combustion pressures in heavy-duty compression-ignition engines impose high shear stresses across the contact interface which damage the seat face surfaces by sliding. Valve seat wear is often accelerated because of dimensional misalignment as a result of manufacturing variability or thermal distortion.

Valve wear performance is most often determined by evaluating valves that are run in durability test engines, but some laboratory tests are also used to rate the relative performance of alloys. These laboratory tests include:

a. Pin on disc tests
b. Crossed cylinder wear tests
c. Thrust washer tests
d. Cylinder - vee block tests
e. Functional tests of components in fixtures or actual engines

At the present time, there is little experience to suggest that the data generated by these tests can be used to design an engine valve from the first principles, but test data are invaluable in improving the wear performance of existing valve designs.

7.3 Corrosion Properties—Because of the variety of corrosive environments, there is no industry standard laboratory corrosion test. Some of the tests used to rate the corrosion resistance of valve alloys are:

a. Crucible immersion tests with various corrodents
b. Engine tests with a hole drilled through the head of the valve
c. Air oxidation tests run at high temperatures for a given time
d. Sulfidation tests using gas atmospheres

The corrosion of valves is accelerated by their temperature and environment. Corrosion occurs through four mechanisms:

a. Oxidation
b. Attack by various liquid metal oxides and salts
c. Attack by combustion products
d. Attack by fuel and lubricant additives or contaminants

Valve manufacturers and valve steel suppliers can generally supply representative corrosion resistance data.

7.4 Fatigue Properties—Fatigue data and corrosion-accelerated fatigue data are limited because of the lengthy testing programs required to generate meaningful data. The situation is improving, and more data are being gathered by valve and steel manufacturers. In lieu of these data, estimates of fatigue resistance are usually established on the basis of elevated temperature tensile, creep, and stress rupture performances.

The tensile properties of finished valves are dependent upon processing and heat treatment during manufacture. Typical tensile data for individual alloys are provided in Table 3. This table contains data of unknown origin, therefore, its accuracy cannot be presumed. The data should be used only as a guideline. Valve manufacturers can generally supply expected mechanical properties in different regions of a valve, once a design envelope is established.

7.5 Physical Properties—The physical properties of various valve steels and alloys are listed in Table 4. These data are of unknown origin and their accuracy cannot be presumed. The data should be used only as a guideline.

8. Valve Alloy Application

8.1 General—Alloys are selected for the body of the valve after considering the required mechanical and physical properties. Final selection and validation are usually decided, based on the outcome of engine tests. It is well worth noting that there are many thermodynamic adjustments that can be made to an engine system which dramatically change the operating environment of the valves. The cost penalties of the more sophisticated valve alloys which may be required must be considered when analyzing the benefits of thermodynamic cycle improvements.

The severity of valve duty is determined by the operating environment in which the valve functions. The preeminent environmental factors are temperature, imposed stress, and chemical activity. Poppet valve operating temperature is generally a function of combustion process efficiency and engine cooling system effectiveness. Peak engine firing pressures and the valve seating velocities determine the stresses of most concern in a valve. The combustion gases which flow past the exhaust valve can be quite active chemically and generally dictate the use of corrosion resistant alloys.

8.2 Intake Valves—Intake valves require wear resistance and fatigue strength. Intake valves for light-duty service are generally manufactured from carbon or low alloy steels. Heavy-duty service intake valves are typically made from high alloy martensitic or austenitic steels. Titanium alloys are used in selected high speed spark ignition engine valves where valve train mass reduction is a prime design criterion.

Maximum intake valve temperatures are typically less than 425 °C (800 °F) in light-duty spark ignition engines and 500 °C (930 °F) in heavy-duty compression ignition engines. Plain carbon steels are used for the lowest temperature intake valve applications. Low alloy martensitic steels, high alloy martensitic steels, and austenitic steels are used progressively as intake valve temperatures and peak firing pressures increase.

Spark ignition engine intake valve seats that operate at moderate temperatures achieve adequate adhesive wear durability by using low alloy martensitic steels hardened to 35 Rockwell "C" scale or harder. Higher temperature spark ignition engine valves generally use hardened high carbon, high chromium alloys. In the most demanding application, intake valve seats are hard-faced with a seat facing alloy.

8.3 Exhaust Valves—Principal exhaust valve requirements are resistance to seat face burning (commonly referred to as guttering), resistance to wear, fatigue strength resistance to bending loads, and creep strength sufficient to prevent head doming (commonly referred to as tuliping). Exhaust valves are typically made from austenitic steels or superalloys. Titanium alloys are also used in spark ignition engine exhaust valves when mass reduction is a paramount consideration.

Austenitic exhaust valve operating temperatures are typically 700 to 760 °C (1300 to 1400 °F), but transient temperatures as hot as 815 to 850 °C (1500 to 1560 °F) are encountered in service. UNS S3XXXX series for austenitic stainless steels are used for the lowest temperature exhaust valve applications. Low nickel content nitrogen-strengthened austenitic steels, high nickel content nitrogen-strengthened austenitic steels, and superalloys are used progressively as exhaust valve temperatures increase. The maximum service temperature for superalloys can be as high as 870 to 900 °C (1600 to 1650 °F) depending upon imposed stresses.

Seat face burning resistance is achieved by alloy composition rather than valve design such as valve face angle. The precipitation strengthened austenitic stainless steels used in light-duty spark ignition exhaust valves possess adequate hot hardness and oxidation/corrosion resistance to prevent undue seat wear. In demanding applications, the seats are hard-faced with a high hot hardness and corrosion resistant alloy.

Many exhaust valves have martensitic steel wafers welded to their stem tips or martensitic steel stems welded to their austenitic heads. These martensitic steel tips, when hardened, generally provide sufficient wear resistance. When a martensitic stem extends into the valve guide, the valve is referred to as a two-piece construction. This construction minimizes stem wear, provides superior fatigue strength in the keeper groove, and conserves alloying elements.

9. Valve Design Relationship to Materials

9.1 General—The design of a valve and its application to the engine are as important as the selection of the valve's alloy(s). As many as six different materials are used in the valve construction for some applications. Valve durability is limited by the operating temperature and stress imposed on it. It is sometimes possible to select a stronger or a more temperature resistant material to overcome limitations in valve design and application.

Optimizing stresses, temperature, and cooling for valve durability may impede overall engine efficiency, particularly when advanced thermodynamic concepts are employed. Fortunately, many of the valve design enhancements can compensate for excessive temperatures; delivering satisfactory valve durability under otherwise difficult circumstances.

TABLE 3—TYPICAL MECHANICAL PROPERTIES OF VALVE ALLOYS[1][2]

UNS NR	ISO 683/15	SAE GRADE	Temperature °C	Temperature (°F)	Tensile Properties Tensile Strength MPa	Tensile Properties Tensile Strength (ksi)	Tensile Properties Yield Strength MPa	Tensile Properties Yield Strength (ksi)	Tensile Properties Elongation %	Tensile Properties Reduction of Area %	Brinell Mutual Indentation BHN	Hot Hardness Cold Ball BHN 760 °C (1400 °F)
H15410		1541H	Room	Room	970	(141)	910	(132)	-	63		-
			540	(1000)	420	(61)	330	(48)	-	75		-
G15470		1547	Room	Room	1240	(180)	1140	(165)	-	40		-
G31400		3140	Room	Room	790	(114)	520	(76)	-	-		-
			540	(1000)	140	(21)	110	(16.1)	-	-		-
			650	(1200)	86	(12.5)	57	(8.3)	-	-		-
G86450		8645	Room	Room	1240	(180)	1140	(165)	-	40		-
H51500		5150H	Room	Room	990	(143)	910	(132)	-	57		-
H41400		4140H	Room	Room	900	(131)	800	(116)	-	-		-
			540	(1000)	500	(72)	390	(56)	-	-		-
		NV 8	Room	Room	920	(134)	690	(100)		53		-
			540	(1000)	270	(39)	220	(32)		44		
			650	(1200)	130	(18.2)	110	(16.1)	-	97		-
S65007	X 45 CrSi 9 3	HNV 3	Room	Room	920	(133)	690	(100)	22	50	-	-
			650	(1200)	210	(31)	150	(22)		89	63	-
			760	(1400)	69	(10)	62	(9)	-	99	31	-
S65006		HNV 6	Room	Room	940	(136)	840	(122)	15.5	10		-
			650	(1200)	200	(29)	160	(23)	-	62	85	-
			760	(1400)	100	(14.5)	75	(10.9	72	80	40	70
S42200		HNV 8	Room	Room	1030	(149)	860	(125)	-	52	-	-
			650	(1200)	360	(52)	310	(45)	-	83	-	-
S63017		EV 4	Room	Room	820	(119)	430	(63)	26.2	20		-
			650	(1200)	420	(61)	230	(34)		18	100	
			760	(1400)	300	(43)	220	(31)	13.3	18	80	115
S63008	X 53 CrMnNiN 21 9	EV 8	Room	Room	1140	(166)	740	(107)	-	9	-	-
			650	(1200)	590	(86)	330	(48)	-	18	185	-
			760	(1400)	430	(62)	260	(37)	18	25	100	193
S63012		EV 12	Room	Room	1080	(157)	700	(102)	-	5	-	-
			650	(1200)	590	(85)	340	(49)		27	185	-
			760	(1400)	390	(57)	280	(41)		22	100	193
S63013		EV 13	Room	Room	1080	(157)	520	(75)		5		-
			650	(1200)	940	(78)	350	(51)		49	220	-
			760	(1400)	430	(62)	330	(48)		22	130	-
S63018	X 33 CrNiMnN 23 8	EV 16	Room	Room	1010	(147)	580	(84)		33		-
			650	(1200)	580	(84)	270	(39)		32		-
			760	(1400)	470	(68)	260	(37)	-	30		190
S63019	X 50 CrMnNiNbN 21 9	XEV-F	Room	Room	1190	(172)	880	(127)		6		-
			650	(1200)	720	(105)	570	(82)		8		-
			760	(1400)	340	(50)	280	(40)	-	13		-
N07751	NiCr 15 Fe 7 TiAl	HEV 3	Room	Room	1120	(162)	630	(92)	-	30		-
			650	(1200)	830	(120)	570	(82)	-	21	225	-
			760	(1400)	550	(80)	450	(65)	10	22	195	-
N07080	NiCr 20 TiAl	HEV 5	Room	Room	1070	(155)	620	(90)	39	38	-	-
			650	(1200)	790	(114)	550	(80)	-	17	200	-
			760	(1400)	590	(86)	500	(73)	-	20	150	-
N07032		HEV 8	Room	Room	1300	(189)	770	(112)	-	45	-	-
			650	(1200)	1150	(167)	750	(109)	-	15	-	-
			760	(1400)	850	(123)	730	(106)	-	23	-	227
N07001		XEV-H	Room	Room	1280	(185)	1030	(150)	-	15	-	-
			650	(1200)	1000	(145)	860	(125)	-	12	-	240

1. These data are of unknown origin and their accuracy cannot be presumed.
2. The data should be used onl y as a guideline.

TABLE 4—TYPICAL PHYSICAL PROPERTIES OF VALVE ALLOYS

UNS NR	ISO 683/15	FORMER SAE GRADE	Specific Gravity g/cc	Density kg/m3	Density (lb/in3)	Coefficient of Thermal Expansion 21 to 760 °C 1/ °C × 10–6	Coefficient of Thermal Expansion (70 to 1400 °F) (1/ °F × 10–6)
S65007	X 45 CrSi 9 3	HNV 3	7.44	7442	0.276	13.0	7.2
S65006		HNV 6	7.42	7415	0.275	13.3	7.4
S42200		HNV 8	7.55	7550	0.280	-	-
S63017		EV 4	7.71	7712	0.286	18.5	10.30
S63008	X 53 CrMnNiN 21 9	EV 8	7.60	7604	0.282	18.4	10.25
S63012		EV 12	7.63	7631	0.283	18.4	10.22
S63019	X 50 CrMnNiNbN 21 9	XEV-F	7.87	7874	0.292	17.3	9.61
N07751	NiCr 15 Fe 7 TiAl	HEV 3	8.06	8062	0.299	14.9	8.30
N07080	NiCr 20 TiAl	HEV 5	8.06	8062	0.299	14.9	8.30
N07032		HEV 8	7.87	7874	0.292	15.7	8.73
R56401		XEV-J	4.34	4341	0.161	10.4	5.80
R54620			4.42	4422	0.164	9.7	5.40

These data are of unknown origin and their accuracy cannot be presumed.
These data should be used only as guideline.

9.2 Design Enhancements—When valve alloys with the properties necessary to obtain the desired durability are not available (or cannot be used economically), various valve design enhancements are employed. The most important of these are:

a. Seat Face Welding—When wear, corrosion, or duty service conditions are extreme, the valve face of an otherwise satisfactory head alloy may be inadequate. In these cases, the valve seat may be welded with a hard overlay alloy to better withstand wear and corrosion at the valve seating surface. Special cobalt, nickel, or iron-base alloys have been developed for this purpose.
b. Seat Face Strain Hardening—When seat wear conditions are moderately beyond the endurance of an otherwise satisfactory head alloy, the valve seat may be strain hardened to better withstand wear. This is accomplished by mechanically cold working the seat face region after high temperature heat treating operations.
c. Stem Surface Treatments—Chromium plating, nitriding, moly spray coating, and other surface treatments are applied to valve stems to reduce friction, wear, or both, in service. A light film of engine oil (commonly referred to as a pre-lube), generally prevents stem/guide wear, but adhesive wear can still occur under some circumstances. Valve stem surface treatments have effectively prevented adhesive wear in these instances.
d. Aluminizing—This is a special type of protective coating. A thin layer of aluminum is deposited on the valve seat face and, sometimes, the combustion face. The aluminum diffuses and alloys with the base material, resulting in a hard oxidation resistant coating that improves corrosion resistance, particularly in a lead oxide environment. This approach is becoming less popular as leaded fuel is being phased out.
e. Internal Cooling—Hollow valves, partially filled with metallic sodium or sodium-potassium mixtures, transfer heat by convection from the hot head end of the valve to the stem. Internal cooling reduces peak valve temperatures, which may reduce engine octane sensitivity or permit a reduction in valve alloy content. Hollow intake valves and internally cooled exhaust valves are being increasingly considered to decrease valve mass.
f. Tip Caps—Occasionally a hardened martensitic steel cap is mechanically fitted on the end of the valve stem to improve tip wear resistance. These tip caps are sometimes used on valves where dissimilar metal welding is a problem.
g. Seat Face Angle—Changing to a seat face that is more perpendicular to the longitudinal axis of the valve stem can greatly reduce seat wear although valve seat burning and deposit build-up may be accentuated if a flex head valve design is not utilized.

10. Valve Gear Design Considerations

10.1 General—The design of a poppet valve is generally dictated by a pre-established operating environment. Since overall engine cost effectiveness is paramount, valve gear design parameters that intensify valve stresses must be carefully considered. Actuating geometry and valve gear dynamic performance are the most significant parameters.

10.2 Actuating Geometry—Valve actuating mechanisms often have a resolved force vector at the valve tip that is not coaxial with the valve stem. The greater the divergence, the greater the concentration of stem to guide contact forces at the ends of the guide. This concentrates the contact forces at the guide ends that may cause severe adhesion of the guide material to the valve stem, often referred to as valve stem scuffing.

Valve rotators are mechanical devices which rotate the valve during the opening portion of the operating cycle. Valve rotation dissipates hot spots and reduces deposits on the seat face so that heat transfer to the seat is improved. Valve rotators can be used to reduce stem and guide wear as well as stem scuffing.

10.3 Dynamic Performance—Valve stresses arise primarily from the dynamics of the valve gear and from the manner in which the valve closes against its seat. Compression ignition engines generate peak combustion pressures several times higher than spark ignition engines. Careful analysis of the valve gear kinematics and pressure induced stress is essential in assuring adequate valve durability.

Hydraulic valve lifters compensate for wear and thermal expansion/contraction in the valve gear. Automatic lash adjustment eliminates the undue stresses caused by excessive lash, extreme valve temperatures, and valve burning/guttering that develop from inadequate lash.

Optimizing actuating geometry and dynamic performance for valve durability may impede overall engine efficiency, particularly when advanced concepts are employed. Fortunately, many of the valve design enhancements compensate for sub-optimal geometry and dynamics, permitting adequate valve durability under difficult circumstances.

VALVE GUIDE INFORMATION REPORT —SAE J1682 SEP1993

SAE Information Report

Report of the SAE Iron and Steel Technical Committee Division 35—Elevated Temperature Proporties of Ferrous Metals, approved September 1993.

Foreword—This Document has not changed other than to put it into the new SAE Technical Standards Board Format.

Valve guides are installed in internal combustion engine heads as axial bearings for the valve stem, and they hold the valve face coaxial to the head or block seat. They also serve as heat sinks to cool the valves.

Valve guides are typically hollow metallic cylinders. Other materials such as ceramic and ceramic-coated metals have been used on an experimental basis.

The most common installation practice is to retain the valve guide through an interference fit between it and the mating counterbore. In addition to retaining the guide, the fit promotes efficient heat transfer from the guide to the mating counterbore material.

1. Scope—This SAE Information Report provides:

a. Types of valve guides and their nomenclature
b. Valve guide alloy designations and their chemistries
c. Valve guide alloy metallurgy
d. Typical mechanical and physical properties of guide alloys
e. Typical dimensional tolerances of valve guides and their counterbores
f. Recommended interference fits
g. Installation procedures
h. Application considerations

2. References—There are no referenced publications specified herein.

3. Types of Valve Guides

3.1 Standard Valve Guides—Figure 1 shows the most common types of valve guides. Smooth bore guides are most common in passenger car operations. For heavy-duty engines, helical grooves are often machined, as shown in Figure 1B, into the valve guide bore for oil retention. However, heavy-duty engine manufacturers are abandoning this practice because of emission concerns. Figure 1C shows a guide with a retaining flange which can be used for location as well as retention. A typical valve guide installation showing the relationship of the valve guide to other components is illustrated in Figure 2.

4. Valve Guide Alloy Designations—Table 1 enumerates typical valve guide materials and chemical compositions. Table 2 lists the manufacturers and their usage. All tabular data is submitted by the manufacturers as typical.

5. Valve Guide Alloy Metallurgy

5.1 General—Valve guides are manufactured using cast, wrought, or sintered powder metal (P/M) processes. Wear resistance is generally related to bulk hardness and volume fractions of soft and hard phases present, as well as to lubrication. Valve guides may be heat treated or surface coated for wear resistance. Table 3 describes the typical microstructural constituents of the valve guide materials enumerated in this document. Table 4 lists typical valve guide processing information.

5.2 Cast Alloys—Valve guides are most frequently made from pearlitic cast iron. The microstructure of these guides should consist primarily of type A and B graphite, size 4 to 7. Type D and E graphite should be held to a minimum. The graphite morphology should be evaluated at 100X magnification. The matrix structure after etching shall consist of a pearlitic matrix with a maximum of 5% free ferrite. The phosphide constituent should be uniformly distributed as a noncontinuous network.

Applications requiring greater wear resistance can be obtained by higher alloy contents providing uniformly dispersed phosphide and/or carbide constituents and by providing a harder matrix consisting of tempered martensite and/or bainite.

5.3 Nonferrous Wrought Alloys—Copper-base wrought alloys are occasionally used for high-performance applications to promote more efficient heat transfer from the guide to the mating counterbore. However, these materials generally have inadequate long-term wear durability.

5.4 Sintered Powder Metallurgy Alloys—Sintered powder metallurgy alloys have been developed for automotive and heavy-duty engine valve guides. P/M valve guide compositions are Fe-C-Graphite alloys. Alloying additions may include copper, lead, tin, phosphorus, molybdenum, or nickel. A solid lubricant is often added to improve wear resistance. The microstructure consists of free graphite, pores, and a hard phase (such as Fe-P-C) in a lamellar pearlitic matrix. Sintered valve guides can be oil impregnated prior to installation to lubricate the valve guide/valve stem interface, providing additional wear resistance particularly during the break-in period.

6. Mechanical and Physical Properties of Valve Guide Alloys—Tables 5 and 6 list mechanical and physical properties of typical valve guide materials.

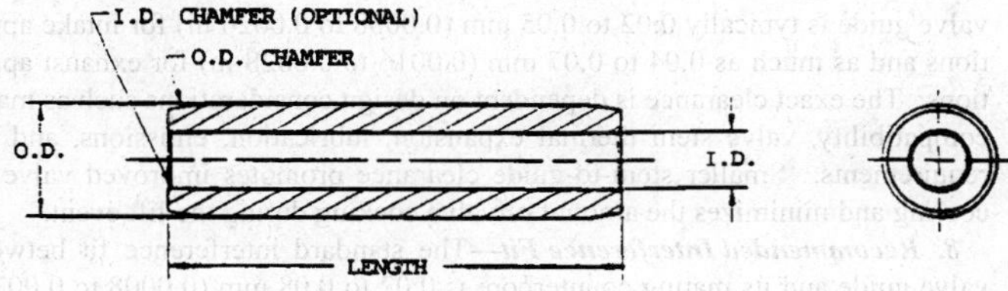

FIGURE 1A—SMOOTH BORE

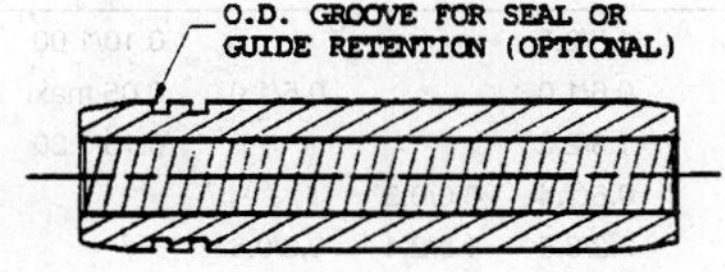

FIGURE 1B—HELICAL GROOVED BORE

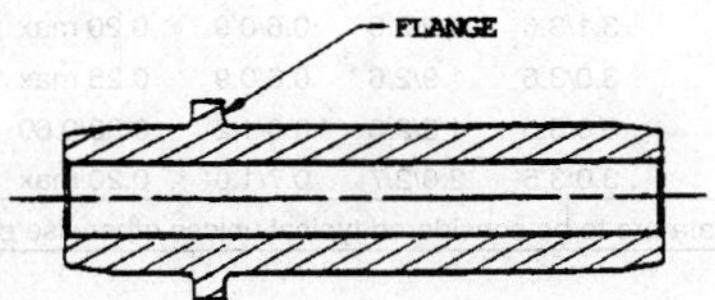

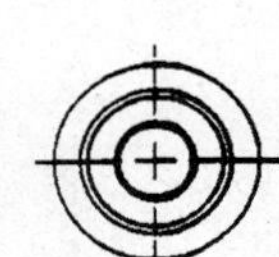

FIGURE 1C—FLANGED ON OUTSIDE DIAMETER SURFACE

FIGURE 1—CROSS SECTION OF VALVE GUIDES

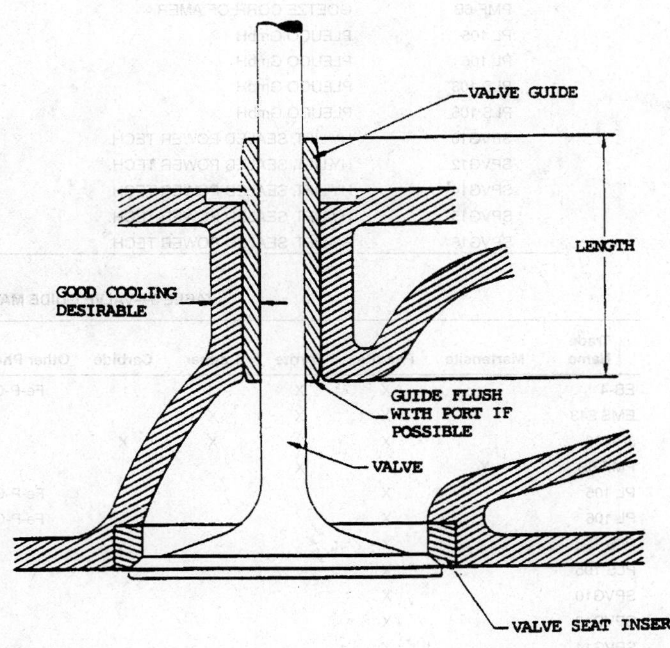

FIGURE 2—CROSS-SECTIONAL VIEW OF CYLINDER HEAD SHOWING INSTALLED VALVE GUIDE

*7. **Dimensional Tolerances***—The length of the valve guide should be as long as space permits. This is to reduce the contact stresses arising from the cocking action imparted to the valve from side loading. The hot end of the guide should be located as close as possible to the valve head without effecting port restriction. It is good practice to avoid exhaust valve guide protrusion into the hot exhaust gas stream, as this will greatly reduce its ability to serve as a heat sink and enhance scuffing tendencies. The diametric clearance between the valve stem and the valve guide is typically 0.02 to 0.05 mm (0.0008 to 0.0020 in) for intake applications and as much as 0.04 to 0.07 mm (0.0016 to 0.0028 in) for exhaust applications. The exact clearance is dependent on design considerations such as material compatibility, valve stem thermal expansion, lubrication, emissions, and noise requirements. Smaller stem-to-guide clearance promotes improved valve stem cooling and minimizes the amount of valve cocking during the lift event.

*8. **Recommended Interference Fit***—The standard interference fit between a valve guide and its mating counterbore is 0.02 to 0.08 mm (0.0008 to 0.0031 in) although this should be confirmed with the manufacturer.

*9. **Installation Procedure***—Valve guides are installed by pressing the guide into the counterbore such that the guide can fit directly against the full length of the metal counterbore (dry) or so that the guide ends fit snugly against the counterbore and the center of the guide is exposed to coolant (wet). Guides are usually inserted at ambient temperatures, although liquid nitrogen is used for cryogenic insertion. One must be careful not to crack or deform the guide during installation. Particular care must be taken if the bore is not machined after installation. One must also start the guide squarely and press without interruption until it is flush with the counterbore in the cylinder head port surface or reaches its final location. If the guide has a retaining flange (see Figure 1C), it can be held in place by the valve gear.

*10. **Application Considerations***—Valve guide lubrication must be adequate to prevent valve stem scuffing. However, excessive lubrication may increase emissions or lead to valve burning because of heavy deposits at the hot end of the valve stem. It is common to use an oil seal on the intake and exhaust valve stem to control lubrication conditions.

TABLE 1—VALVE GUIDE MATERIAL CHEMICAL COMPOSITIONS (MINIMUM/MAXIMUM - WEIGHT %)

Trade Name	C	Si	Mn	P	S	Cu	Mo	Ni	Sn	Fe	Others
EB-4	1.5/2.5			0.10/1.00		2.0/6.0			0.1/1.0	BAL	
EMS 543	0.6/1.0		0.5/1.0	0.05 max	0.15/0.35	3.5/5.5				BAL	0.0/5.0 (Ca,Mg) Silicate
JP-406	1.8/2.2			0.15/0.30		4.0/5.0				BAL	2.0 max
PMF-6B	0.5/1.4	0.0/0.5					1.0/4.5	0.00/0.75		BAL	SOLID LUBE
PL 105	3.2/3.5	1.8/2.4	0.3/0.8		0.00/0.12					BAL	
PL 106	3.2/3.5	1.8/2.4	0.3/0.8	0.35/0.55	0.00/0.12					BAL	Cr 0.0/0.2
PLS 103	1.8/2.2	0.0/0.3	0.0/0.3	0.40/0.60						BAL	
PLS 105	0.8/1.2	0.0/0.3	0.4/0.6		0.10/0.20	1.8/2.2		0.00/0.20		BAL	
SPVG10	3.1/3.8	2.2/2.9	0.5/0.9	0.20 max	0.15 max					BAL	
SPVG12	3.1/3.6	2.2/2.8	0.6/0.9	0.20 max	0.15 max					BAL	
SPVG14	3.0/3.6	1.9/2.6	0.6/0.9	0.25 max	0.15 max	0.6 max	0.2/0.4	0.20/0.80		BAL	Cr 0.2/08
SPVG15	3.0/3.5	1.8/2.6	0.6/1.2	0.30/0.60	0.12 max					BAL	Cr 0.25 max
SPVG16	3.0/3.5	2.0/2.7	0.7/1.0	0.20 max	0.10 max		0.3/0.7	0.40/0.70		BAL	Cr 0.8/1.3

All property data are to be considered typical unless otherwise designated.

TABLE 2—VALVE GUIDE MATERIAL MANUFACTURING AND USAGE

Trade Name	Manufacturer	Engine Type Gas	Engine Type Diesel	Engine Type Others	Maximum Temperature (°C)
EB-4	HITACHI P/M CO., LTD	X	X	LPG, LNG	500
EMS 543	EATON CORP., ECD	X	X	LPG, LNG	525
JP-406	HY-LIFT, SEALED POWER TECH.	X	X	LPG, LNG	
PMF-6B	GOETZE CORP. OF AMER.	X	X	LPG, LNG	590
PL 105	PLEUCO GmbH	X	X	LPG, LNG	600
PL 106	PLEUCO GmbH	X	X	LPG, LNG	600
PLS 103	PLEUCO GmbH	X	X	LPG, LNG	600
PLS 105	PLEUCO GmbH	X	X	LPG, LNG	600
SPVG10	HY-LIFT, SEALED POWER TECH.	X	X	LPG, LNG	600
SPVG12	HY-LIFT, SEALED POWER TECH.	X	X	LPG, LNG	600
SPVG14	HY-LIFT, SEALED POWER TECH.	X	X	LPG, LNG	600
SPVG15	HY-LIFT, SEALED POWER TECH.	X	X	LPG, LNG	600
SPVG16	HY-LIFT, SEALED POWER TECH.	X	X	LPG, LNG	600

TABLE 3—VALVE GUIDE MATERIAL MICROSTRUCTURAL CONSTITUENTS

Trade Name	Martensite	Pearlite	Ferrite	Copper	Carbide	Other Phases	Vickers Hard Phase/Hardness		Solid Lubricant	Impregnating Lubricant	Method
EB-4		X	X	X		Fe-P-C	Fe-P-C	400/700	GRAPHITE	OIL	VACUUM
EMS 543		X	X	X			MATRIX	200/400	(Ca,Mg) SILICATE	OIL OR HIGH TEMP. LUBE	VACUUM
JP-406		X		X	X		CARBIDE	900	GRAPHITE	PROPRIETARY LUBE	VACUUM
PMF-6B	X	X	X				MATRIX	300/600	YES		
PL 105		X				Fe-P-C	Fe-P-C	750	GRAPHITE	NONE	
PL 106		X				Fe-P-C	Fe-P-C	750	GRAPHITE	NONE	
PLS 103		X			X		CARBIDE	1000			
PLS 105		X					NONE		YES		
SPVG10		X							GRAPHITE		
SPVG12		X							GRAPHITE		
SPVG14		X							GRAPHITE		
SPVG15		X				Fe-P-C	Fe-P-C	750	GRAPHITE		
SPVG16					X				GRAPHITE		

TABLE 4—VALVE GUIDE MATERIAL PROCESSING

Trade Name	% Open Porosity[1] (Inside Diameter)	Process	Heat Treatment
EB-4	3 – 10	CONVENTIONAL P/M	NONE
EMS 543		CONVENTIONAL P/M	NONE
JP-406	5 – 15	CONVENTIONAL P/M	NONE
PMF-6B		CONVENTIONAL P/M	YES
PL 105		CAST (SAND)	NONE
PL 106		CAST (SAND)	NONE
PLS 103		CONVENTIONAL P/M	NONE
PLS 105		CONVENTIONAL P/M	NONE
SPVG10		CAST (SAND)	NONE
SPVG12		CAST (SAND)	NONE
SPVG14		CAST (SAND)	NONE
SPVG15		CAST (SAND)	NONE
SPVG16		CAST (SAND)	NONE

1. Prior to machining.

TABLE 5—VALVE GUIDE MECHANICAL PROPERTY DATA

Trade Name	Macrohardness	0.2% YS (MPa) @ Room Temperature (Unless Otherwise Noted)	UTS (MPa) @ Room Temperature (Unless Otherwise Noted)	% Elongation @ Room Temperature (Unless Otherwise Noted)	Elastic Modulus (MPa)	Poisson's Ratio	Impact Strength (kg_f-m/cm²)
EB-4	70/85 HRB	280	340	0.2	101 000	0.22	0.26
		270 (@ 100 °C)	340 (@ 100 °C)	0.2 (@ 100 °C)			
		270 (@ 200 °C)	340 (@ 200 °C)	0.2 (@ 200 °C)			
		230 (@ 400 °C)	260 (@ 400 °C)	0.2 (@ 300 °C)			
				0.2 (@ 400 °C)			
EMS 543	70/85 HRB						
JP-406	50/70 HRB						
PMF-6B	75/100 HRB		350		67 000		
PL 105	200/260 HBN		250		110 000	0.3	
PL 106	210/270 HBN		250		120 000	0.3	
PLS 103	210/270 HBN	250	300	2	100 000	0.3	
PLS 105	130/190 HBN	250	300	2	80 000	0.3	
SPVG10	90/100 HRB		250				
SPVG12	93/100 HRB		250				
SPVG14	96/105 HRB		250				
SPVG15	93/105 HRB		250				
SPVG16	94/104 HRB		250				

TABLE 6—VALVE GUIDE PHYSICAL PROPERTY DATA

Trade Name	Density (g/cm³)	Coefficient of Thermal Expansion (m/m°/C x 10^{-6}) at Room Temperature (Unless Otherwise Noted)	Thermal Conductivity (Cal/s-cm²-°C/cm) at Room Temperature (Unless Otherwise Noted)
EB-4	6.5	7.4	0.07
		10.4 (@ 100 °C)	0.067 (@ 100 °C)
		10.7 (@ 200 °C)	0.064 (@ 200 °C)
		12.5 (@ 400 °C)	0.055 (@ 400 °C)
EMS 543	6.5 min		
JP-406	6.2 min		
PMF-6B	6.3 min		
PL 105	7.1	10.0	0.12
PL 106	7.1	10.0	0.12
PLS 103	6.8 min	13.0	0.10
PLS 105		13.0	0.10
SPVG10	7.1		
SPVG12	7.1		
SPVG14	7.1		
SPVG15	7.1		
SPVG16	7.1		

VALVE SEAT INSERT INFORMATION REPORT—SAE J1692 AUG93

SAE Information Report

Report of the SAE Iron and Steel Technical Commitee Division 35—Elevated Temperature Properties of Ferrous Metals, approved August 1993.

Foreword—This Document has not changed other than to put it into the new SAE Technical standards Board format.

Valve seat inserts are installed in internal combustion engine heads or blocks to provide a seating surface for poppet valves. Inserts are usually metallic rings; however, other geometries are also employed. Other materials such as ceramics and ceramic-coated metals have been used on an experimental basis and copper beryllium inserts are used in some racing applications.

Inserts are used for two fundamental reasons. First, and most important, insert alloys are more wear and heat resistant than the block or head material, making them better suited for the harsh environment encountered during valve seating. Engine durability can thus be improved. Second, the use of inserts permits easier field repair or rebuild of engines.

The most common installation practice is to retain the insert through an interference fit between it and the mating counterbore. In addition to retaining the insert, the fit promotes efficient heat transfer from the insert to the mating material. In special applications, the valve seat insert is held in place by mechanical means such as threads or retaining rings. Inserts may also be cast in place.

1. Scope—This SAE Information Report provides engineers and designers with:

a. Types of valve seat inserts and their nomenclature
b. Valve seat insert alloy designations and their chemistries
c. Valve seat insert alloy metallurgy
d. Typical mechanical and physical properties of insert alloys
e. Recommended interference fits
f. Installation procedures
g. Application considerations

2. References—There are no referenced publications specified herein.

3. Types of Valve Seat Inserts

3.1 Standard Valve Seat Insert—Figures 1 and 2 show the most common type of insert and counterbore in use today along with their nomenclature. This valve seat insert is a cylindrical, ring-shaped component which is usually pressed into a head or block counterbore.

3.2 Skirted Insert—The flexible or skirted insert shown in Figure 3 is used in some air-cooled engine applications. The clearance between the flange diameter and the cylinder head allows slight movement of the cylinder head to occur without distorting the seating surface. Insert retention is accomplished by an interference fit between the skirt diameter and the head. This puts the insert head interface farther away from the port in a relatively cooler area, thus aiding retention. Insert retention is also aided by a nominal 1/4 degree reverse taper on the skirt outside diameter.

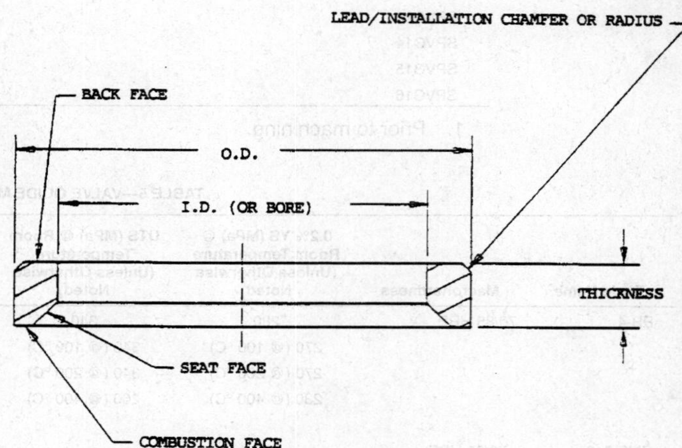

FIGURE 1—STANDARD VALVE SEAT INSERT

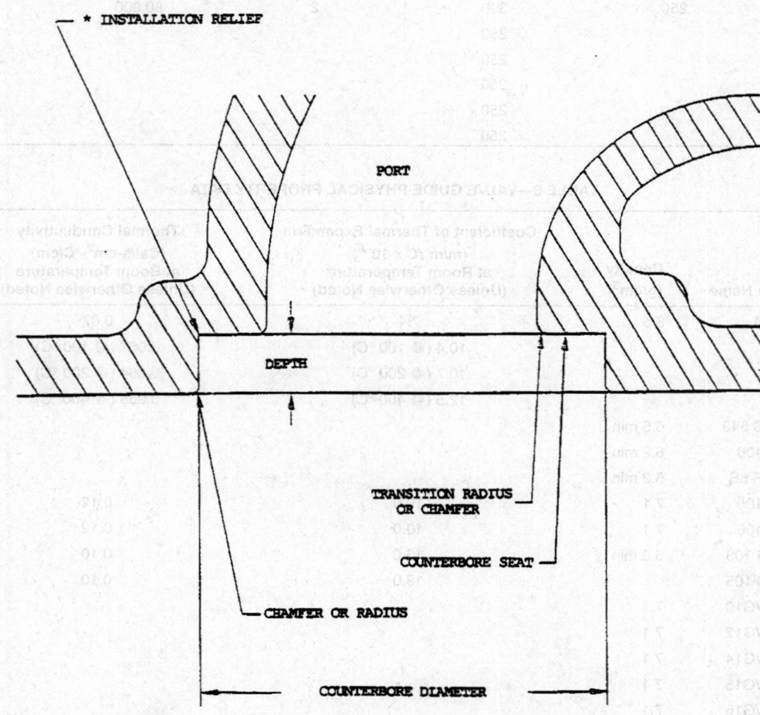

FIGURE 2—STANDARD INSERT COUNTERBORE

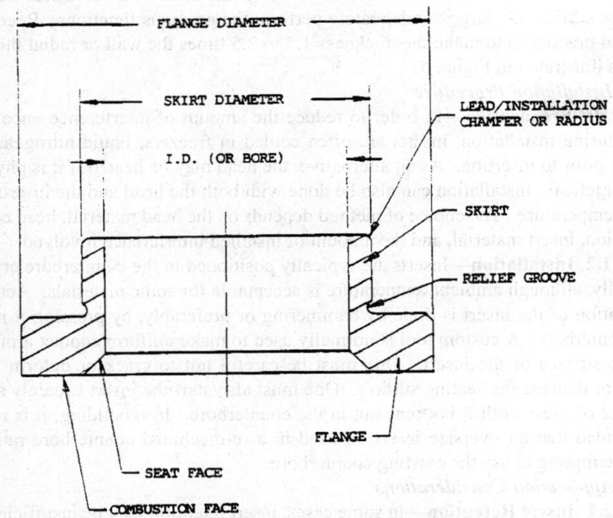

FIGURE 3—FLEXIBLE OR SKIRTED VALVE SEAT INSERT

4. Valve Seat Insert Alloy Designations—Table 1 describes the valve seat insert chemical compositions. Table 2 enumerates the valve seat insert materials, manufacturers, and usage. All tabularized data is submitted by the manufacturers as typical.

5. Valve Seat Insert Alloy Metallurgy

5.1 General—Valve seat inserts are manufactured using cast, wrought, or sintered powder metallurgy processes. Wear resistance is generally related to the volume fraction of hard phases such as martensite, carbides, nitrides, and oxides. The major alloy categories in each of these three groups follows along with a brief metallurgical description of each category.

Table 3 lists the typical microstructural constituents of the valve seat materials identified in the document.

6. Cast Alloys

6.1 Grey Cast Iron—Low alloy grey iron is used for light- to moderate-duty intake applications and light-duty exhaust applications. It is sometimes used in the as-cast condition, but may also be heat treated for improved strength and hardness. Grey iron offers low alloy cost and good machinability. For certain applications, it is also less abrasive to the mating valve.

6.2 Ductile Cast Iron—Ductile iron finds limited use in high performance applications seating against titanium valves. It is usually supplied in the hardened and tempered condition.

6.3 White Cast Iron—White iron is employed primarily in heavy-duty intake applications for wear resistance. White irons used for inserts normally have significant additions of carbide formers such as chromium, tungsten, vanadium, or molybdenum. They are also normally heat treated so that the final microstructure consists of alloy carbides in a martensitic matrix.

6.4 Austenitic Cast Iron Alloys—UNS[1] (Ni-resist™) is a typical example of these alloys and is used in some aluminum head applications. It is a highly alloyed austenitic iron which possesses a high coefficient of thermal expansion.

6.5 Cast Martensitic Alloys—Martensitic alloys find application in moderate- to heavy-duty intake inserts and moderate-duty exhaust inserts. They have a temperature capability of approximately 430 to 600 °C (800 to 1100 °F). These alloys are based on tool steel or martensitic stainless steel compositions and are supplied in the hardened and tempered condition. Their microstructures typically consist of alloy carbides in a martensitic matrix. Alloys possessing in excess of 12% chromium generally exhibit excellent hot corrosion resistance.

6.6 Cast Nonferrous Alloys—These cobalt or nickel-base alloys are used for heavy-duty exhaust valve applications. These materials are heavily alloyed with chromium and other elements such as tungsten and molybdenum with nickel or cobalt as the matrix. As such, the cast nonferrous group is more costly than the iron-base materials discussed previously. The microstructure generally consists of large primary alloy carbides in a cobalt or nickel matrix. These alloys possess very good high temperature properties and will retain their hardness up to 875 °C (1600 °F). They also possess good hot corrosion resistance. However, in addition to cost, they have the disadvantages of both poor thermal conductivity and a relatively low compressive yield strength.

1. No UNS number assigned.

7. Wrought Alloys

7.1 Tool Steel Alloys—Tool steel inserts are generally used for small production runs of engines or experimental engines. Often, it is most economical to machine these inserts from materials such as UNS T30402 (D-2), UNS T30102 (A-2), etc.

7.2 Martensitic Stainless Steel Alloys—Such alloys are often used for applications similar to those described in the previous paragraph as well as for piston driven aircraft engines. Wrought UNS S41000 (410SS) is often used when only a small number of inserts are required. UNS S65006 (AMS 5710) in the hardened and tempered condition is used in a limited number of aircraft engines.

7.3 Austenitic Stainless Steel Alloys—These wrought alloys are used extensively in piston aircraft engines. UNS S66009 (AMS 5700) is the most common and has a tungsten-rich carbide phase.

8. Sintered Powder Alloys

8.1 Low Alloy Steels—These powder metallurgy (P/M) materials are generally used for light- to moderate-duty intake applications and light-duty exhaust applications. These steels are of the type Fe + Cu + C, but may also contain small amounts of other alloying elements such as nickel, molybdenum, chromium, tungsten, and cobalt, depending on the severity of the application. The total alloy content is normally less than 5%. The parts typically have a density range that is 80 to 97% of the theoretical density and are used in the tempered or steam treated condition.

The matrix, carbide morphology, and the degree of heterogeneity of the microstructure will vary depending on the specific alloy/carbon contents and the types of powders being used in the manufacture of these inserts (e.g., pre-alloyed or elementally added).

8.2 Tool Steels—There are several P/M tool steel compositions currently being used in light-, moderate-, and heavy-duty exhaust applications as well as heavy-duty intake applications. These do not correspond to any standard tool steels with the possible exception of some high-speed steels such as UNS T11302 (M2), UNS[2] (M35), and UNS T12015 (T15). Typically, the microstructure consists of evenly distributed, discontinuous alloy carbides in an alloy-rich martensitic matrix. The densities of these inserts vary from 80 to 100% of the theoretical density.

These inserts are supplied in the as-sintered, tempered, steam treated, hot formed, or copper infiltrated condition. Copper infiltration serves a dual purpose. In addition to acting as a solid lubricant, it also enhances the heat transfer from the insert to the head material by increasing the thermal conductivity of the insert.

In many high-temperature applications which require resistance to adhesive wear, solid lubricants are added either through the powder blend or through infiltration. Some of the commonly used solid lubricants besides Fe_3O_4 (from steam treating) and Cu_2O (from copper infiltration) are MnS, MoS_2 Cu_2S, Pb, CaF_2, graphite, and talc. Solid lubricants also offer the benefits of improved machinability. The solid lubricant containing inserts are particularly effective under dry operating conditions such as natural gas, LPG, and propane applications. Unlike gasoline fuels, the dry fuels do not provide sufficient lubrication through combustion deposits in order to prevent adhesion between the valve seat and the insert.

Heavy-duty inserts are more heavily alloyed with elements that provide resistance to the effects of temperature and corrosion (e.g., Cr, Mo, V, W, Co). Heavy-duty inserts also demand superior surface flow strength and indentation resistance which can be achieved through densification and more allowing. Densities better than 95% of the theoretical density may be required in some applications and can be obtained by hot forming or liquid phase sintering at high temperatures, normally in a vacuum.

8.3 Martensitic Stainless Steels—These alloys are used in applications requiring high temperature oxidation and corrosion resistance such as moderate- to heavy-duty intake inserts and light- to moderate-duty exhaust inserts. The microstructure typically consists of martensite and in the case of alloys with higher carbon (≥0.70%), may also contain alloy carbides. Typically, the parts have a minimum density that is 80% of the theoretical density and are supplied in the as-sintered or steam-treated condition. These may also contain solid lubricants.

8.4 Austenitic Stainless Steels—Typical applications for these alloys are moderate- to heavy-duty exhaust inserts. These materials have high chromium and nickel contents to provide high-temperature oxidation resistance and thermal stability, especially above 590 °C (1100 °F). Hard particles such as cermets, borides, silicides, nitrides, and carbides are often present to provide superior wear resistance. Densities range from 80 to 100% of the theoretical density.

2. No UNS number assigned.

8.5 Valve Steels—Typical applications for these alloys are light- to moderate-duty exhaust inserts and heavy-duty intake inserts. Two of the most commonly used exhaust valve materials are UNS S63012 (21-2N) and UNS S63018 (23-8N) austenitic steels. Powders of equivalent valve steel compositions are blended with other alloy steel powders in varying amounts. The resultant heterogeneous microstructure consists of a uniform distribution of austenitic alloy phase containing carbonitrides in an alloy steel matrix. Such an alloy provides wear resistance by virtue of material compatibility between the valve and the insert. The parts typically have a minimum density that is 80% of the theoretical density. These inserts are supplied in the as-sintered or heat treated condition.

8.6 Nonferrous Alloys—These are nickel-base or cobalt-base materials for heavy-duty engine applications where the valve seat inserts operate above 650 °C (1200 °F). These alloys are particularly resistant to high temperature wear and corrosion. The microstructure generally consists of alloy carbides in a refractory metal strengthened matrix of cobalt and/or nickel. Due to their relatively high cost, they are limited to applications where other alloys with less strategic alloy content cannot be used.

8.7 Dual Materials or Bimetallics—These are often used for heavy-duty applications where excessive wear is a problem, but strategic alloy content is to be minimized. A double layered valve seat insert is made using two different powders. The top half of the insert, which contains the seat, is made of a heavy-duty alloy with superior strength and wear characteristics. The bottom half of the insert is generally made of an inexpensive material with higher thermal conductivity and good heat resistance. The resultant product provides superior wear resistance and improved creep properties at reduced material costs.

9. Mechanical and Physical Properties of Insert Alloys—Tables 4 and 5 provide the nominal mechanical and physical properties of the valve seat insert alloys.

10. Design Considerations

10.1 Recommended Interference Fit—The standard tolerance for interference fit between a valve seat insert and its mating counterbore is 0.05 to 0.13 mm (0.002 to 0.005 in) although this should be confirmed with the manufacturer.

10.2 Lead Chamfer/Radius—The purpose of the lead chamfer or radius is to guide the insert into the counterbore during insertion. For cast iron cylinder heads, a 45 degree chamfer with a slight break at the chamfer/OD intersection is generally adequate. With aluminum heads, however, care must be taken to prevent the harder insert from scraping or shaving the counterbore. If a radius is employed, it should be well blended with the outside diameter of the insert. Lead chamfers for aluminum head applications should be a shallow angle as shown in Figure 4.

10.3 Valve Seat Insert Thickness—After installation, the outside diameter of the insert is in intimate contact with the counterbore. This contact serves two purposes. First, it provides an interface over which heat is conducted from the insert to the cylinder head. Secondly, the frictional forces set up by the interference fit retain the insert in the counterbore. The thickness of a valve seat insert must be sufficiently large to adequately perform the previous functions. Recommended practice is to make the thickness 1.7 to 2.5 times the wall or radial thickness as illustrated in Figure 5.

11. Installation Procedure

11.1 Preparation—In order to reduce the amount of interference encountered during installation, inserts are often cooled in freezers, liquid nitrogen, or dry ice prior to insertion. As an alternative, the head may be heated if it is physically practical. Installation can also be done with both the head and the inserts at room temperature. The choice of method depends on the head material, head configuration, insert material, and the amount of installed interference involved.

11.2 Installation—Inserts are typically positioned in the counterbore cryogenically, although ambient temperature is acceptable for some materials. Actual installation of the insert is done by hammering or preferably, by pressing it into the counterbore. A custom tool is normally used to make uniform contact around the top surface of the insert. One must be careful not to crack or deform the insert, or damage the seating surface. One must also start the insert squarely and hammer or press until it bottoms out in the counterbore. In rebuilding, it is recommended that an oversize insert be used in a re-machined counterbore rather than attempting to use the existing counterbore.

12. Application Considerations

12.1 Insert Retention—In some cases, insert retention may be insufficient. This is a serious problem as a dropped insert can result in engine damage or failure. In addition to the foregoing recommendations, retention may be improved by:

a. Increasing the compressive yield strength of the existing insert material or choosing an alternative material with a higher compressive yield strength—Inserts can plastically deform in compression. This may occur during the initial insertion, resulting in an interference after insertion which is less than the originally designed fit. In operation, the thermal stresses placed on the insert can cause additional deformation, commonly referred to as creep, to the point where it becomes loose in the counterbore upon cooling. A higher compressive yield strength will minimize this plastic deformation.
b. Increasing the depth of the insert—This increases the amount of wall contact between the insert and the counterbore which increases the frictional holding force. In addition, increasing the depth will deepen the insert counterbore contact into a cooler region of the head away from the combustion chamber.
c. Deforming the head material over the insert and mechanically holding it in place—This can be done by staking or rolling, but caution should be employed to prevent initiating cracks in the head. It must also be done uniformly to avoid the occurrence of nonuniform stress relaxation during engine operation with consequent seat distortion and leakage.

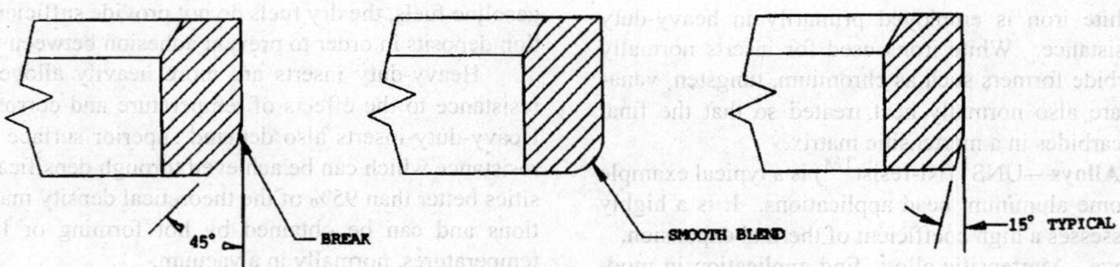

FIGURE 4—LEAD CHAMFERS FOR ALUMINUM HEAD APPLICATIONS

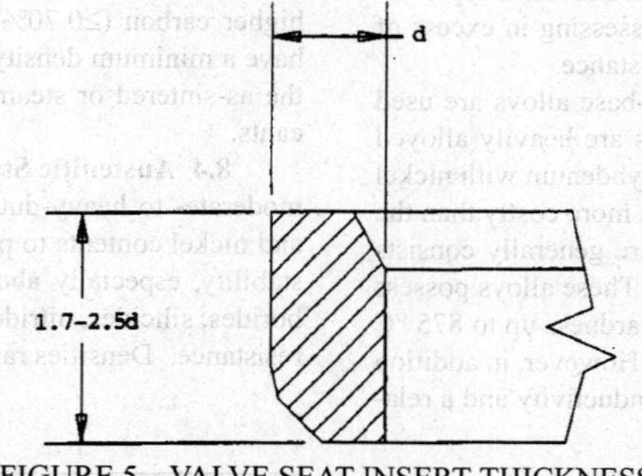

FIGURE 5—VALVE SEAT INSERT THICKNESS

TABLE 1—(1) VALVE SEAT INSERT MATERIAL CHEMICAL COMPOSITIONS (MINIMUM/MAXIMUM - WEIGHT %)

Trade Name	C	Si	Mn	P	S	Co	Cr	Mo	Ni	V	W	Fe	Others
ALLOY 1H	3.50/3.90	2.20/3.10	0.40/0.80	0.30/0.80	0.00/0.10		0.10/0.20	1.00/1.20	0.20/0.50			BAL	Cu 0.10/0.25 Combined C 0.45/0.75
ALLOY 7	2.50/3.00	1.50/2.50	0.50/0.80	0.00/0.20	0.00/0.10		2.75/3.25	4.00/5.00				BAL	
ALLOY 11	1.25/1.75	1.90/2.60	0.20/0.60	0.00/0.15	0.00/0.10		19.00/21.00		1.00/1.60			BAL	
ALLOY 13	1.35/1.75	1.90/2.60	0.20/0.60	0.00/0.03	0.00/0.03		19.00/21.00		1.00/1.60			BAL	
ALLOY 79	1.30/1.50	0.00/1.00	0.00/0.75			9.00/11.00	25.00/28.00	9.00/11.00	BAL		9.00/11.00	10.50/14.00	
ALLOY 81	2.00/2.75	0.00/1.00					27.00/31.00		46.00/52.00		14.00/16.00	0.00/3.00	
ALLOY 589	2.90/3.40	0.50/1.50	0.00/0.50				15.50/18.50	14.50/17.50		1.65/2.10		BAL	
EH-2	0.70/1.10						2.00/4.00	0.20/0.40		0.20/0.40		BAL	
EH-8	0.60/1.10	0.10/0.30				5.00/10.00	1.00/2.00	1.50/4.00	0.50/1.00	0.10/0.20		BAL	
EH-9	0.60/1.10						1.00/4.00	2.50/8.00	0.50/3.00			BAL	Cu 0.50/2.00
EH-10	0.60/1.10	0.10/0.50				10.00/15.00	2.00/4.00	4.00/7.00	0.50/2.00	0.10/0.20		BAL	
EH-11	0.40/0.80	0.10/0.50				10.00/15.00	0.50/2.00	3.00/7.00	0.50/1.00			BAL	Pb 13.00/ 23.00
EMS 541	0.70/1.10		3.00/4.70	0.00/0.05	0.10/0.25		8.00/10.75		0.75/1.50			BAL	Cu 1.50/2.50 Mg 0.13/0.30
EMS 542	0.55/0.90		0.20/0.45	0.00/0.05	0.00/0.05			0.65/0.85	0.35/0.55			BAL	Cu 1.50/2.50 Mg 0.13/0.30
EMS 544	0.70/1.10		3.00/5.00		0.04/0.15		8.00/10.75	0.30/0.45	0.75/1.80			BAL	Cu 1.50/2.50 Mg 0.13/0.30
EMS 554	1.60/2.00		1.00/2.70	0.00/0.05	0.03/0.06		4.00/6.50	0.30/0.45	1.60/2.40			BAL	Cu 2.50/4.00 Mg 0.13/0.30
GM 76135	1.20/1.50	0.30/0.60	0.30/0.60	0.00/0.20	0.00/0.10		3.50/4.25	6.00/7.00	0.00/1.00		5.00/6.00	BAL	Cu 0.00/0.25
J3	2.20/2.70	0.00/1.50	0.00/1.00			BAL	29.00/33.00		0.00/3.00		11.00/14.00	0.00/3.00	
J6	0.90/1.40	0.00/1.50	0.00/1.00			BAL	27.00/31.00		0.00/3.00		3.50/5.50	0.00/3.00	
J10	0.00/0.08	2.20/2.60				BAL	7.50/8.50	26.50/29.00				0.00/3.00	(with Ni)
J70	2.20/2.80	0.00/1.25				15.00/18.50	26.50/31.50	1.75/2.75	BAL	1.75/2.75	0.00/1.50	0.00/9.00	
J96	2.00/2.75	0.00/1.50					27.00/31.00		BAL		14.00/16.00	0.00/8.00	
J100	2.00/2.75	0.00/1.00				9.00/11.00	27.00/31.00		BAL		14.00/16.00	0.00/8.00	
J101 H	0.00/3.00	1.00/3.00	1.00/2.00				1.75/3.00		13.50/17.50			BAL	Cu 4.50/7.50
J120	1.20/1.50	0.30/0.60	0.30/0.60	0.00/0.20	0.00/0.10		3.50/4.25	6.00/7.00	0.00/1.00		5.00/6.00	BAL	
J122	2.50/3.00	1.50/2.50	0.50/0.80				2.75/3.25	4.00/5.00				BAL	
J125	1.25/1.75	1.90/2.60	0.20/0.60	0.00/0.15	0.00/0.10		19.00/21.00		1.00/1.75			BAL	
PL 7N	3.10/3.50	1.80/2.40	0.40/0.80	0.40/0.60	0.00/0.08		0.50/0.80	1.00/1.30	0.80/1.20			BAL	
PL 12M	1.80/2.30	0.80/1.20	0.00/0.60	0.00/0.06	0.00/0.04		12.00/14.00	2.00/2.50	0.00/0.50			BAL	
PL 33M	1.80/2.30	1.80/2.30	0.00/0.60	0.00/0.06	0.00/0.04		33.00/35.00	2.00/2.50	0.00/0.50			BAL	
PL 476	1.20/1.60	0.00/1.00	0.00/0.70	0.00/0.06	0.00/0.15		3.50/4.50	6.00/8.00		1.50/1.90	5.00/7.00	BAL	
PLS 100	1.00/1.40											BAL	Cu 8.00/10.00
PLS 250	0.70/1.10		1.50/2.00		0.60/0.90		3.00/4.00	4.00/5.00		1.50/2.00	5.00/6.00	BAL	Cu 15.00/ 20.00
PLS 300	0.30/0.60						1.40/1.70	4.50/3.00	2.00/3.00			BAL	Cu 18.00/ 20.00
PLS 301	0.30/0.60						0.50/0.80	2.40/3.00	3.00/3.50			BAL	Cu 18.00/ 20.00
PMF-2	0.50/1.40	0.00/0.50						0.00/1.00	0.00/0.75			BAL	Cu 1.75/3.75
PMF-3	0.50/1.40	0.00/0.50						0.00/1.00	0.00/0.75			BAL	Cu 1.75/3.75
PMF-4	0.25/0.90						11.50/14.50					BAL	
PMF-15	0.60/1.40		0.00/0.75				3.50/7.50	3.50/7.50		1.50/3.50	4.50/7.50	BAL	
PMF-16	0.60/1.40		0.00/0.75				3.50/7.50	3.50/7.50		1.50/3.50	4.50/7.50	BAL	
VMS 450	0.65/0.90	0.00/0.50						0.67/0.87	0.30/0.60			BAL	Cu 1.75/2.25
VMS 586	0.00/0.10	0.00/1.00	0.00/1.00				11.50/13.50					BAL	
VMS 587	1.60/2.00		0.20/0.50			0.30/0.50	0.10/0.30	0.40/0.65	0.70/0.90			BAL	Cu 0.00/0.50
VMS 622	1.60/2.00		0.20/0.50			0.30/0.50	0.10/0.30	0.45/0.65	0.70/0.90			BAL	Cu 0.00/0.50
VMS 643	0.80/1.20	0.00/0.50	0.00/0.50				1.50/2.50	7.00/9.00	0.10/0.40	0.50/1.50	2.25/3.50	BAL	Cu 8.00/11.00
VMS 644	0.65/0.90	0.00/0.50	0.50/0.90					0.67/0.87	0.30/0.60			BAL	Cu 1.75/2.25
W50	2.50/3.00	1.50/2.50	0.50/0.80				2.75/3.25	4.00/5.00				BAL	
W60	0.00/3.00	1.00/2.80	1.00/1.50		0.00/0.12		1.75/3.00		13.50/17.50			BAL	Cu 5.50/7.50
W70	1.20/1.50	0.30/0.60	0.30/0.60	0.00/0.02	0.00/0.10		3.50/4.25	6.00/7.00	0.00/1.00		5.00/6.00	BAL	Cu 0.00/0.25
W70V	1.20/1.50	0.30/0.60	0.30/0.60	0.00/0.04	0.00/0.04		3.50/4.25	6.00/7.00		1.35/1.65	5.00/6.00	BAL	
W76	1.20/1.50	0.40/0.80	0.30/0.60	0.00/0.04	0.00/0.04	3.00/5.00	4.00/5.00	6.00/7.00		1.35/1.65	5.00/6.00	BAL	
W90	1.25/1.75	1.90/2.60	0.20/0.60	0.00/0.15	0.00/0.10		19.00/21.00		1.00/1.60			BAL	
W93	2.00/2.50	0.00/1.50	0.00/1.00	0.00/0.04	0.00/0.04	5.50/7.50	14.00/18.00	10.00/14.00	1.00/2.00	1.30/1.70		BAL	
W100	2.25/2.65	0.00/1.00	0.00/1.00			BAL	29.00/32.00		0.00/3.00		11.00/14.00	0.00/3.00	
W150	0.00/0.08	2.20/2.60				BAL	7.50/8.50	26.50/29.50	0.00/1.50			0.00/1.50	
W230	1.80/2.50	0.00/1.50					27.00/31.00	7.00/9.00	BAL		0.00/1.00	0.00/25.00	
W240	2.00/2.75	0.00/1.00					27.00/31.00		46.00/52.00		14.00/16.00	0.00/8.00	
W260	2.00/2.75	0.00/1.00				9.00/11.00	27.00/31.00		37.00/41.00		14.00/16.00	0.00/8.00	
XL8	2.00/2.75	0.00/1.15	0.00/0.50			9.00/11.00	27.00/31.00		37.00/41.00		14.00/16.00	0.00/8.00	

1. All chemistry and property data are to be considered typical unless otherwise designated.

TABLE 2—VALVE SEAT INSERT MATERIAL MANUFACTURERS AND USAGE

Trade Name	Product Manufacturer	Gas Intake	Gas Exhaust	Diesel Intake	Diesel Exhaust	Others	Maximum Operating Temperature of Metallic Surface (° C)	Process	Heat Treatment
ALLOY 1H	GOETZE CORP. OF AMERICA	X		X				CAST	YES
ALLOY 7	GOETZE CORP. OF AMERICA	X		X				CAST	YES
ALLOY 11	GOETZE CORP. OF AMERICA		X	X	X			CAST	YES
ALLOY 13	GOETZE CORP. OF AMERICA		X	X	X			CAST	YES
ALLOY 79	GOETZE CORP. OF AMERICA				X			CAST	YES
ALLOY 81	GOETZE CORP. OF AMERICA		X		X			CAST	YES
ALLOY 589	GOETZE CORP. OF AMERICA		X		X			CAST	YES
EH-2	HITACHI P/M CO., LTD	X					250	CONVENTIONAL P/M	NONE
EH-8	HITACHI P/M CO., LTD	X	X				400	CONVENTIONAL P/M	NONE
EH-9	HITACHI P/M CO., LTD	X	X				400	CONVENTIONAL P/M	NONE
EH-10	HITACHI P/M CO., LTD	X	X	X	X	LPG, LNG	500	CONVENTIONAL P/M	NONE
EH-11	HITACHI P/M CO., LTD	X	X	X	X	LPG, LNG	500	CONVENTIONAL P/M	NONE
EMS 541	EATON CORP., ECD		X			DRY FUEL, EXHAUST	600	CONVENTIONAL P/M	AGE HARDEN
EMS 542	EATON CORP., ECD	X				DRY FUEL, INTAKE	425	CONVENTIONAL P/M	TEMPER
EMS 544	EATON CORP., ECD		X			DRY FUEL, EXHAUST	600	CONVENTIONAL P/M	AGE HARDEN
EMS 554	EATON CORP., ECD		X			DRY FUEL, EXHAUST	600	CONVENTIONAL P/M	CARBURIZE Cr/YES
GM 76135	GOETZE CORP. OF AMERICA		X		X			CAST	YES
J3	L.E. JONES CO.		X	X	X	DRY FUEL, EXHAUST	750	STATIC SHELL MOLD CAST	STRESS RELIEF
J6	L.E. JONES CO.		X		X		700	STATIC SHELL MOLD CAST	STRESS RELIEF
J10	L.E. JONES CO.			X		DRY FUEL, INTAKE	500	STATIC SHELL MOLD CAST	NONE
J70	L.E. JONES CO.		X		X		750	STATIC SHELL MOLD CAST	STRESS RELIEF
J96	L.E. JONES CO.		X		X	DRY FUEL, EXHAUST	750	STATIC SHELL MOLD CAST	NONE
J100	L.E. JONES CO.		X		X	DRY FUEL, EXHAUST	750	STATIC SHELL MOLD CAST	NONE
J101 H	L.E. JONES CO.	X		X			300	STATIC SHELL MOLD CAST	NONE
J120	L.E. JONES CO.	X		X		DRY FUEL, INTAKE	500	STATIC SHELL MOLD CAST	HARDEN & TEMPER
J122	L.E. JONES CO.	X		X		DRY FUEL, INTAKE	500	STATIC SHELL MOLD CAST	HARDEN & TEMPER
J125	L.E. JONES CO.	X	X	X	X	DRY FUEL, INTAKE	500	STATIC SHELL MOLD CAST	HARDEN & TEMPER
PL 7N	PLEUCO GmbH	X		X	X		800	CENTRIFUGAL CAST	YES
PL 12M	PLEUCO GmbH	X	X	X	X	LPG, LNG	850	CENTRIFUGAL CAST	YES
PL 33M	PLEUCO GmbH		X	X	X	LPG, LNG	900	CENTRIFUGAL CAST	YES
PL 476	PLEUCO GmbH		X	X	X	LPG, LNG	900	CENTRIFUGAL CAST	YES
PLS 100	PLEUCO GmbH	X		X			350	CONVENTIONAL P/M	YES
PLS 250	PLEUCO GmbH		X	X	X	LPG, LNG	900	CONVENTIONAL P/M	YES
PLS 300	PLEUCO GmbH		X	X	X	LPG, LNG		CONVENTIONAL P/M	YES
PLS 301	PLEUCO GmbH	X	X	X	X	LPG, LNG	800	CONVENTIONAL P/M	YES
PMF-2	GOETZE CORP. OF AMERICA	X	X				600	CONVENTIONAL P/M	YES
PMF-3	GOETZE CORP. OF AMERICA	X	X				600	CONVENTIONAL P/M	YES
PMF-4	GOETZE CORP. OF AMERICA	X	X				650	CONVENTIONAL P/M	YES
PMF-15	GOETZE CORP. OF AMERICA	X	X			DRY FUEL, INT. & EXH.	650	CONVENTIONAL P/M	YES
PMF-16	GOETZE CORP. OF AMERICA	X	X		X	DRY FUEL, INT. & EXH.	650	CONVENTIONAL P/M	YES
VMS 450	TRW VALVE DIVISION	X	X	X				CONVENTIONAL P/M	YES (STEAM TEMPER)
VMS 586	TRW VALVE DIVISION		X					CONVENTIONAL P/M	YES (STEAM TEMPER)
VMS 587	TRW VALVE DIVISION		X					CONVENTIONAL P/M	NONE
VMS 622	TRW VALVE DIVISION		X					HOT FORMED P/M	NONE
VMS 643	TRW VALVE DIVISION		X		X			HOT FORMED P/M	TEMPER
VMS 644	TRW VALVE DIVISION	X	X	X				CONVENTIONAL P/M	YES (STEAM TEMPER)
W50	WINSERT, INC.	X		X		DRY FUEL, INTAKE	500	STATIC SHELL MOLD CAST	HARDEN & TEMPER
W60	WINSERT, INC.	X					400	STATIC SHELL MOLD CAST	STRESS RELIEF
W70	WINSERT, INC.	X	X	X	X	DRY FUEL, INTAKE	500	STATIC SHELL MOLD CAST	HARDEN & TEMPER
W70V	WINSERT, INC.		X				500	STATIC SHELL MOLD CAST	HARDEN & TEMPER
W76	WINSERT, INC.		X		X		550	STATIC SHELL MOLD CAST	HARDEN & TEMPER
W90	WINSERT, INC.	X	X	X		DRY FUEL, INTAKE	500	STATIC SHELL MOLD CAST	HARDEN & TEMPER
W93	WINSERT, INC.		X			DRY FUEL, EXHAUST	500	STATIC SHELL MOLD CAST	HARDEN & TEMPER
W100	WINSERT, INC.		X	X	X	DRY FUEL, EXHAUST	750	STATIC SHELL MOLD CAST	STRESS RELIEF
W150	WINSERT, INC.			X		DRY FUEL, INTAKE	600	STATIC SHELL MOLD CAST	STRESS RELIEF
W230	WINSERT, INC.		X		X		700	STATIC SHELL MOLD CAST	STRESS RELIEF
W240	WINSERT, INC.		X		X		700	STATIC SHELL MOLD CAST	STRESS RELIEF
W260	WINSERT, INC.		X		X		700	STATIC SHELL MOLD CAST	STRESS RELIEF
XL8	GOETZE CORP. OF AMERICA		X		X			CAST	YES

NOTES

X = Potential application

Blank = Not a recommended application

TABLE 3—VALVE SEAT INSERT MATERIAL MICROSTRUCTURAL CONSTITUENTS (IN HEAT TREATED CONDITION)

Trade Name	Martensite	Pearlite	Ferrite	Copper	Carbide	Other	Hard Phase	Vickers Hardness	Solid Lubricant
ALLOY 1H		X				GRAPHITE			
ALLOY 7	X	X				GRAPHITE			
ALLOY 11	X				X				
ALLOY 13	X				X				
ALLOY 79					X	AUSTENITE			
ALLOY 81					X	AUSTENITE			
ALLOY 589									
EH-2		X							NONE
EH-8		X					CoMoCrSi	800	NONE
EH-9		X					FeMo	1200/1400	NONE
EH-10		X					CoMoCrSi	800	NONE
EH-11		X					CoMoCrSi	800	Pb
EMS 541	X	X	X	X	X	AUSTENITE; CARBONITRIDE	21-2N	400/650	(Ca,Mg)SILICATE
EMS 542	X	X	X	X		BAINITE		400/650	(Ca,Mg)SILICATE
EMS 544	X	X	X	X	X	AUSTENITE; CARBONITRIDE	21-2N	400/650	(Ca,Mg)SILICATE
EMS 554	X			X	X	AUSTENITE; CARBONITRIDE	21-2N	450/850	(Ca,Mg)SILICATE
GM 76135	X				X				
J3					X	FCC SOLID SOLUTION			
J6					X	FCC SOLID SOLUTION			
J10						LAVES PHASE; FCC SOLID SOLUTION			
J70					X	Ni SOLID SOLUTION			
J96					X	Ni SOLID SOLUTION			
J100					X	Ni SOLID SOLUTION			
J101 H					X	AUSTENITE			
J120	X				X				
J122	X				X				
J125	X				X				
PL 7N	X				X	Fe-P-C	CARBIDE	1000	
PL 12M	X				X		CARBIDE	1000	
PL 33M			X		X		CrMoCARBIDE	1200	
PL 476	X				X		CrMoWVCARBIDE	1300	
PLS 100	X			X	X		CARBIDE	800	
PLS 250	X			X	X		CARBIDE	1200	
PLS 300	X			X			INTERMETALLIC	1100	
PLS 301	X			X			INTERMETALLIC	1200	
PMF-2	X	X							NONE
PMF-3	X	X							YES
PMF-4	X				X				YES
PMF-15	X				X				YES
PMF-16	X				X				YES
VMS 450	X	X	X						
VMS 586	X								
VMS 587	X				X				
VMS 622	X				X				
VMS 643	X			X	X				
VMS 644	X	X	X						
W50	X				X				
W60					X	AUSTENITE			
W70	X				X				
W70V	X				X				
W76	X				X				
W90	X				X				
W93	X				X				
W100					X	Co SOLID SOLUTION			
W150						LAVES PHASE			
W230					X	Ni SOLID SOLUTION			
W240					X	Ni SOLID SOLUTION			
W260					X	Ni SOLID SOLUTION			
XL8					X	AUSTENITE			

NOTES

X = Phase or element apparent in microstructure at 100X
Blank = Phase or element not apparent in microstructure at 100X

TABLE 4—VALVE SEAT INSERT MECHANICAL PROPERTY DATA

Trade Name	Compressive Yield Strength (MPa) @ RT	Compressive Yield Strength (MPa) @ 300 °C	Compressive Yield Strength (MPa) @ 400 °C	Compressive Yield Strength (MPa) @ 500 °C	0.2% YS (MPa) @ Room Temperature	UTS (MPa) @ RT	UTS (MPa) @ 200 °C	UTS (MPa) @ 300 °C	UTS (MPa) @ 400 °C	% Elongation	RT Macroharness	Hot Hardness Scale	Hot Hardness RT	Hot Hardness 200 °C	Hot Hardness 300 °C	Hot Hardness 400 °C	Hot Hardness 500 °C	Hot Hardness 600 °C	Charpy Impact Strength (kg-m/cm^2)
ALLOY 1H											40/50 HRC								
ALLOY 7						232					50/60 HRC								
ALLOY 11											35/45 HRC								
ALLOY 13											42/48 HRC								
ALLOY 79											45/55 HRC								
ALLOY 81											37/47 HRC								
ALLOY 589						793				0.1	60 MIN HRC								
EH-2					600	750	720	700	680	0.8	50/70 HRA	DPH	370	320	300	280	230		0.6
EH-8						600	500	500	400	0.7	45/65 HRA	DPH	300	300	250	250			0.5
EH-9					310	380	380	380	390	0.5	40/65 HRA	DPH	350	350	300	250			0.6
EH-10					350	400	380		370	0.3	45/65 HRA	DPH	300	300	250	250			0.3
EH-11						400	480		450	0.3	50/70 HRA	DPH	400	350	300	290			0.2
EMS 541											85/100 HRB	HRA	52.0	49.0	46.0	43.0	32.0		
EMS 542											90/105 HRB	HRA		61.0	57.0	55.0			
EMS 544											85/100 HRB	HRA	58.0			52.5	46.0	42.0	
EMS 554											95/110 HRB	HRA	65.5		62.0	56.5	54.0	41.5	
GM 76135											42/52 HRC								
J3											54 HRC	HRA	80.5	78.5		77.0		75.0	
J6											48 HRC	HRA	75.0	73.5		71.0		68.0	
J10											53 HRC								
J70											38 HRC	HRA	70.0	69.5		69.0		665	
J96	386										42 HRC	HRA	71.5	70.0		69.0		64.0	
J100	448										43 HRC	HRA	73.5	73.5		71.5		67.0	
J101 H											37 HRC								
J120	876										45 HRC	HRA	76.0	75.0	74.0	72.5	68.0		
J122											55 HRC	HRA	79.4	79.0	76.5	76.5	66.5		
J125	1190										40 HRC	HRA	74.5	73.5	72.0	71.0	63.0		
PL 7N						250	400				27/43 HRC	HBN	400	390	370	330	300		
PL 12M					650	800				2	27/46 HRC	HBN	425	420	410	390	350		
PL 33M					700	800				1	37/44 HRC	HBN	400	400	380	360	300		
PL 476					800	900				1	38/46 HRC	HBN	450	430	400	400	420		
PLS 100					250	350				5	27/34 HRC	HRC	30.0	28.0	27.0				
PLS 250					380	400				1	38/40 HRC	HRC	42.0	40.0	38.0	36.0	34.0		
PLS 300					380	450				2	38/46 HRC	HRC	40.0	39.0	37.0	36.0	32.0		
PLS 301					380	450				2	38/46 HRC	HRC	40.0	38.0	36.0	34.0	30.0		
PMF-2						505					95/110 HRB								
PMF-3						485					95/110 HRB								
PMF-4	405					405					110/115 HRB								
PMF-15						320					100/115 HRB								
PMF-16						270					100/115 HRB								
VMS 450		552	545	434							95 MIN HRB	BHN		240	220	180	140		
VMS 586			717								95 MIN HRB	BHN		280	255	205	155		
VMS 587			705								95 MIN HRB	BHN		280	255	205	155	130	
VMS 622			815								95 MIN HRB	BHN		320	285	255	185		
VMS 643			810								104/112 HRB	BHN		390	350	285	230		
VMS 644			545								95 MIN HRB	BHN		240	220	180	140		
W50											50/60 HRC	DPH	613	577		532	346	176	
W60						200					30/40 HRC								
W70											42/52 HRC	DPH	505	486	462	434	372	243	
W70V						690					38/45 HRC	DPH	423	401	389	374	325	251	
W76						690					38/45 HRC								
W90						1090					35/45 HRC	DPH	464	446	421	377	299	170	
W93											50/60 HRC								
W100											50/60 HRC	DPH	520	498	475	450	421	399	
W150						690					50/60 HRC	DPH	680	660	640	615	550	465	
W230											38/49 HRC	DPH	450			420	380	330	
W240						345					35/48 HRC	DPH	430			390	340	300	
W260						365					35/48 HRC	DPH	490			445	410	380	
XL8											37/48 HRC								

Inconsistencies between the Hot Hardness columns are due to nonstandardized equipment and procedures.

TABLE 5—VALVE SEAT INSERT PHYSICAL PROPERTY DATA

Trade Name	Density (g/cm^3)	Coefficient Thermal Expansion (m/m °C x 106) RT	Coefficient of Thermal Expansion (m/m °C x 10^6) 300 °C	Coefficient of Thermal Expansion (m/m °C x 10^6) 400 °C	Coefficient of Thermal Expansion (m/m °C x 10^6) 600 °C	Coefficient of Thermal Expansion (m/m °C x 10^6) 800 °C	Thermal Conductivity (Cal/s-cm^2-°C/cm) RT	Thermal Conductivity (cal/s-cm^2-°C/cm) 200 °C	Thermal Conductivity (Cal/s-cm^2-°C/cm) 300 °C	Elastic Modulus (MPa)
ALLOY 1H										
ALLOY 7	7.5									
ALLOY 11										
ALLOY 13										
ALLOY 79										
ALLOY 81										
ALLOY 589	7.7									
EH-2	5.8		10.2	12.1			0.07	0.08		120 000
EH-8	6.8	11.3	12.0	13.7			0.05	0.06		126 000
EH-9	6.8		13.8	15.4			0.04	0.04	0.05	138 000
EH-10	6.8	11.6	12.0	12.8	13.8		0.06	0.07		127 000
EH-11	8.2	10.8	11.5	12.5	13.2		0.06	0.07		148 000
EMS 541	6.2 min									
EMS 542	6.7 min									
EMS 544	6.4 min									
EMS 554	6.7 min									
GM 76135										
J3										
J6										
J10						13.4				265 000
J70		12.5	12.5		13.5	13.8				
J96		13.6	13.6		14.8	15.9				120 000
J100		11.4	11.4		12.6	13.5				125 000
J101 H		11.7		14.3	15.7					
J120			9.4		10.0	10.9				
J122										
J125				8.5	9.1	10.3				220 000
PL 7N		12.0					0.10			120 000
PL 12M		12.0					0.07			180 000
PL 33M		11.0					0.10			180 000
PL 476		12.0					0.05			200 000
PLS 100	7.2	13.0					0.10			100 000
PLS 250	8.0	13.0					0.10			130 000
PLS 300	8.0	13.0					0.10			130 000
PLS 301		13.0					0.10			130 000
PMF-2	6.7 min									79 000
PMF-3	6.7 min									58 000
PMF-4	6.7 min									117 000
PMF-15	6.7 min									65 000
PMF-16	6.8 min									115 000
VMS 450	6.5 min	8.4	10.8	12.0	12.7					
VMS 586	6.4 min		11.0	11.5	11.7					
VMS 587	6.8									
VMS 622	7.3 min									
VMS 643	7.6 min		13.9							
VMS 644	6.5 min	8.4	10.8	12.0	12.7					
W50										
W60	7.3						0.095			
W70	7.6									
W70V	7.6	12.6	12.7	13.3	13.8		0.056			
W76	7.6									
W90	7.6	9.6		11.8		12.4				
W93										
W100	8.7	10.0		11.8		12.7	0.031			
W150	8.8					13.5	0.035			
W230	8.1									
W240	8.6	11.5	11.9	12.2	12.9	13.3				
W260	8.6	12.6	12.8	13.3	13.8	14.2	0.039			
XL8										

2 General Data on Steels

CARBON AND ALLOY STEELS—SAE J411 SEP1997 SAE Information Report

Report of the Iron and Steel Technical Committee, approved February 1948, sixth revision June 1981. Completely revised by the SAE Iron and Steel Technical Committee November 1989 and September 1997.

1. Scope—This SAE Information Report describes the processing and fabrication of carbon and alloy steels. The basic steelmaking process including iron ore reduction, the uses of fluxes, and the various melting furnaces are briefly described. The various types of steels: killed, rimmed, semikilled, and capped are described in terms of their melting and microstructural differences and their end product use. This document also provides a list of the commonly specified elements used to alloy elemental iron into steel. Each element's structural benefits and effects are also included. A list of the AISI Steel Products Manuals is included and describes the various finished shapes in which steel is produced.

2. References

2.1 Applicable Publications—The following publications form a part of this specification to the extent specified herein.

2.1.1 AISI MANUALS—Available from the Iron and Steel Society, 410 Commonwealth Drive, Warrendale, PA 15086, Telephone (412) 776-1535.

- Bar Steel: Alloy, Carbon, and Microalloy Steels: Semifinished, Hot-Rolled Bars, Cold Finished Bars, Hot-Rolled Deformed and Plain Concrete Reinforcing Bars
- Plates and Rolled Floor Plates: Carbon, High-Strength Low-Alloy and Alloy
- Carbon Steel Pipe, Structural Tubing, Line Pipe, Oil Country Tubular Goods
- Sheet Steel: Carbon, High-Strength Low Alloy, and Alloy: Coils and Cut Lengths (Including Coated Products)
- Strip Steel: Carbon, High-Strength Low Alloy, and Alloy
- Tin Mill Products
- Carbon Steel, Wire and Rods
- Cold Rolled Flat Steel Wire
- Railway Track Material
- Stainless and Heat Resisting Steels
- Tool Steels
- Steel Specialty Tubular Products
- Hot-Rolled Structural Shapes, H-Piles and Sheet Piling

2.1.2 ASTM PUBLICATION—Available from ASTM, 100 Barr Harbor Drive, West Conshohocken, PA 19428-2959.

ASTMA29—Specification for Steel Bars, Carbon and Alloy, Hot-Wrought and Cold-FInished, General Requirements for

3. Steel—Steel is a malleable alloy of iron and carbon that has been made molten in the process of manufacture and contains approximately 0.05 to 2.0% carbon, as well as some manganese and sometimes other alloying elements.

3.1 Carbon Steel—Steel is considered to be carbon steel when no minimum content is specified or required for aluminum, chromium, cobalt, columbium, molybdenum, nickel, titanium, tungsten, vanadium, or zirconium, or any other element added to obtain a desired alloying effect: when the specified minimum for copper does not exceed 0.40%; or when the maximum content specified for any of the following elements does not exceed the following percentage: manganese, 1.65%; silicon, 0.60%; copper, 0.60%. For fine grain carbon steels, minimum or maximum levels of grain refiners (Al, Cb, V) can be specified. Boron may be added to killed fine grain carbon steel to improve hardenability.

In all carbon steels, small quantities of certain residual elements, such as copper, nickel, molybdenum, chromium, etc., are unavoidably retained from raw materials. Those elements are considered detrimental for special applications, the maximum acceptable content of these incidental elements should be specified by the purchaser.

3.2 Alloy Steel—Steel is considered to be alloy steel when the maximum of the range given for the content of alloying elements exceeds one or more of the following limits: manganese, 1.65%; silicon, 0.60%; copper, 0.60%; or in which a definite range or definite minimum quantity for any of the following elements is specified or required within the limits of the recognized field of constructional alloy steels: aluminum and chromium up to 3.99%: cobalt, columbium, molybdenum, nickel, titanium, tungsten, vanadium, zirconium, or any other alloying element added to obtain a desired alloying effect.

4. Steelmaking Processes—These fall into two general groups: acid or basic, according to the character of the furnace lining. Thus electric processes may be either acid or basic. Basic oxygen, as the name implies, is an exclusively basic process. The choice of an acid or basic furnace is usually determined mainly by the phosphorus in the available raw materials and the content of phosphorus permissible in the finished steel.

Phosphorus is an acid-forming element and, in its oxide form, will react with any suitable base to form a slag in the steelmaking furnace. In basic processes, the metallurgist and steelmaker take advantage of this chemical behavior by oxidizing the phosphorus with iron oxide, which yields up its oxygen to the phosphorus. This permits the iron to remain as part of the steelmaking bath, while the acid phosphoric oxide is separated by floating up into the molten basic lime slag. In acid processes, furnaces are generally lined with silica, which is acid in nature and will not tolerate the use of basic materials for fluxes. Since an acid slag has no affinity for impurities such as phosphorus, the steel cannot be dephosphorized by fluxing and the content of this element remains at the level contained in the raw material, or may be concentrated somewhat in the finished steel due to loss of other materials from the original metallic charge.

Most iron ores in the United States are of a phosphorus content suitable only for basic steelmaking processes: hence, all of the nation's wrought steel is so made. The following are the principal steelmaking processes used in the United States:

4.1 Basic Electric—The principal advantage of this process is optional control in the furnace permitting steel to be treated under oxidizing, reducing, or neutral slags, and pouring off and replacement of slags during the process. In this manner, and depending on specified requirements, objectionable elements may be substantially reduced and a high degree of refinement obtained in the steel bath. Practically all grades of steel can be made by the basic electric furnace, and the process with or without supplementary processes is used for producing SAE Wrought stainless steels.

4.2 Basic Oxygen—The prime advantage of this process is the rate at which steel can be produced. The nature of the process is such that large quantities of molten iron must be readily available, since refining is accomplished by the exothermic reactions of high purity oxygen with the various elements contained in the molten iron.

4.3 Ladle Refining—Today the majority of steels are actually refined to final chemistry and cleanliness requirements in a ladle refining facility. This facility takes the ladle of steel which was tapped from the electric arc furnace (EAF) or basic oxygen furnace (BOF), and through the use of the ladle as a vessel further refines the steel. Through the use of optional electric arc reheating capability, inert gas stirring, and optional degassing capabilities; the ladle of steel is trimmed to the final chemistry requirements and inclusions are removed for cleaner steel. The ladle refining station is the facility which actually makes the specific grade of steel to the customer's specification.

4.4 Other—Another method increasing in use in the production of stainless, tool, and specialty steels is ESR (electroslag refining). In this process, as-cast electric furnace melted electrodes are progressively melted and solidified in a water cooled copper mold under a blanket of molten flus. Melting results from the heat generated by the resistance of the molten flux to electric current passing between the electrode and the solidifying ingot. Refining occurs as the electrode melts and droplets of molten metal pass through the flux and their impurities are removed by reaction with the flux. The progressively solidified ingot thus produced is very homogeneous and sound, and may be directly processed into mill products.

The AOD (argon oxygen decarburization) process has become an important steel refining system for specialty steel grades. Originally employed to replace electric furnace basic slag practice for stainless steels, it is now refining alloy, tool, silicon-iron, electrical, and other specialties. The AOD system refining vessel simply accepts molten iron from whatever source is available, that is, electric furnace, BOF, blast furnace or cupola and completes all chemical and refining stages.

The process is based on the principle that when argon gas is mixed with oxygen and injected into the melt, the inert gas dilutes the carbon monoxide resulting from the oxidation of carbon and reduces its partial pressure. This shifts the reaction equilibrium to favor the oxidation of carbon over other oxidizable metals such as chromium. As a result, a higher chromium content can be charged in the melt allowing the conservation of ferrochromium and making this attractive in the economic production of stainless steel.

AOD melting also allows control of hydrogen in flake sensitive grades to the point that the need for long anneals is eliminated.

4.5 Vacuum Treatment—The use of vacuum treatment can be employed with electric furnace, BOF, and ladle metallurgy furnace steelmaking, and is adaptable to all grades of carbon and alloy steel.

There are two types of treatments commonly used. The first is simply "vacuum degassing" the steel to remove hydrogen gas and avoid the necessity for long slow cooling cycles for heavy sections such as blooms, billets, and slabs. The reduced hydrogen content provides steel with improved internal soundness and resistance to internal rupturing or "flaking." The second treatment is infrequently utilized since the advent of ladle metallurgy facilities. It is referred to as "vacuum carbon deoxidation" (VCD). While this process will also remove hydrogen from the liquid steel, it serves the added purpose of deoxiding the steel. These steels exhibit improved cleanliness compared with conventional product.

In today's modern steelmaking practices, the steel cleanliness is usually achieved in the ladle metallurgy treatment, and VCD treatments are not frequently used. During the ladle metallurgy treatment, the liquid steel is constantly being stirred via argon gas or induction stirring. This induces the liquid steel to have contact with the artificial slag cover on the ladle, the artificial slag captures the inclusions in the steel and prevents them from reentering the molten steel.

4.6 Strand Casting—This process involves the direct casting of steel from the ladle into slabs, blooms, or billets. In strand casting, a heat of steel is tapped into ladle in the conventional manner. The liquid steel is then teemed into a tundish, which acts as a reservoir to provide for a controlled casting rate. The steel flows from the tundish into the casting machine and rapid solidification begins in the open-ended water cooled copper molds. The partially solidified slab, bloom, or billet is continuously extracted from the mold by an up and down oscillating movement of the mold. Solidification is completed by cooling the moving cast shape through a water cooling spray system. Several strands may be cast simultaneously, depending on the heat size and section size. A reduction in size may be carried out by hot working the product prior to cutting the standard into lengths. Chemical segregation is minimized, due to the rapid solidification rate of the strand cast product.

Good casting practice should include measures to protect the molten steel from reoxidation (exposure to air). These measures include, but are not limited to, ladle to tundish shrouding, artificial tundish slag, tundish to mold shrouding, and mold powder. The shrouding technique can employ ceramic shrouds, gaseous shrouds or some combination of both.

When two or more heats of steel are cast without interruption, the process is called continuous casting or sequence casting.

Some strand casting machines can incorporate electromagnetic stirring (EMS) in the molds and/or below the molds. The EMS stirs the molten steel within the solidified shell. Also below the mold or prior to complete solidification soft or hard reduction of the strand can be employed. These steps help to improve as-cast center quality, reduce segregation, and promote the formation of an equiaxed grain zone.

The process of strand casting steel has become the predominant process for the manufacture of steel products. This is due to the advances in the technology of strand casting both from a production aspect and material quality aspect. The quality of strand cast material has become at least equivalent, and in many cases better than the traditional ingot casting process.

4.7 Ingot Casting—This process has been designed to meet a variety of conditions of manufacture. Ingots are usually cast as square or rectangular in cross section with rounded corners. Occasionally they are cast in round cross sections. They are usually tapered and cast big end up and hot topped. Ingot steel is subject to internal variations in chemical composition and structure due to the natural phenomena which occur as the steel solidifies.

Shrinkage in the ingot during solidification results in the formation of a central cavity known as pipe. Primary pipe is located in the upper portion of the ingot. Under some conditions, another shrinkage cavity, known as secondary pipe, may form in the ingot below but not connected with the primary pipe. Secondary pipe is normally not exposed to the air and therefore not oxidized. This allows it to be welded during hot working of the ingot, and results in no detriment to the integrity of the product. Primary pipe is controlled by the hot topping system and any remnants are cropped during the ingot breakdown.

There are two methods of ingot production, bottom pouring and top pouring. In bottom pouring, the molten steel flows through a center sprue or trumpet into a runner system filling the ingots from the bottom. Generally there are multiple ingots filled simultaneously from one runner system. The molten steel in the ingot molds is covered by a bottom pouring flux compound.

Additionally, the teeming stream can be shrouded to reduce the potential for steel reoxidation and the generation of exogenous inclusions. Once the ingots are filled, a hot topping compound is applied to each ingot.

Top pouring is accomplished by filling each ingot individually by teeming the molten steel directly into the top of each ingot much like filling a glass of water. Once the mold is filled, a hot topping compound may be applied to each ingot. Shrouding of the teeming stream is generally more difficult and not as effective in top pouring.

5. Steel Processing—After the molten steel has solidified into a solid in either the strand casting process or the ingot process the as-cast product is processed into a finished product through several stages. These include primary rolling, inspection, conditioning, hot-rolling, and sometimes cold finishing.

5.1 Primary Rolling, Inspection, and Conditioning—Cast blooms and ingots are reduced into billets by hot-rolling. This is called primary rolling, and it is also a phase where manufacturers have an opportunity to inspect and enhance the surface of the billet by conditioning.

Primary rolling involves the reheating or "soaking" of the ingot or cast bloom followed by the reduction of the heated section by rolling in continuous or reversing type primary mills. In a continuous mill, the section is continuously passed through one or more strands to produce the billet or bloom. In a reversing mill, the section is alternately passed forward and backward, reducing the section into a billet or bloom.

Generally, at some point in the primary rolling process, the surface of the section is inspected and conditioned. Inspection is the process of detecting surface imperfections and conditioning is the means of removing them. Inspection of the surface may be visual or automatic by magnetic particle or other means. Conditioning generally involves the removal of surface imperfections by grinding, torching, or other means.

Ultrasonic testing of billets can also be performed to test internal quality of the billets.

5.2 Hot-Rolling—Hot-rolling initially involves the reheating of billets in continuous furnaces that tightly control temperature and atmosphere to limit surface decarburization. Heated billets exit the furnace and pass through a series of rolling stands for reduction into the bar section, which goes on to a cooling bed or into a coiling tub. Interstand cooling, tension-free rolling and continuous, electronic dimensional measuring with feedback are some of the measures employed to achieve high quality, hot-rolled product.

5.3 Cold Finishing—Some products receive additional processing through cold finishing operations. These operations are designed to enhance the steel's surface quality and/or mechanical properties.

6. Quality Classifications—Technically, quality, as the term relates to steel products, may be indicative of many conditions, such as the degree of internal soundness, relative uniformity of composition, relative freedom from detrimental surface imperfections, and finish. Steel quality also relates to general suitability for particular applications. Sheet steel surface requirements may be broadly identified as to the end use by the suffix E for exposed parts requiring a good painted surface, and the suffix U for unexposed parts for which surface finish is less important.

Carbon steel may be obtained in a number of fundamental qualities, which reflect various degrees of the quality conditions mentioned. Some of those qualities may be modified by such requirements as austenitic grain size, special discard, macroetch test, special hardenability, maximum incidental alloy elements, restricted chemical composition, and nonmetallic inclusions. In addition, several of the products have special qualities, which are intended for specific end uses or fabricating practices, that is, scrapless nut quality, axle shaft quality, gun barrel quality, or shell quality.

Alloy steels also may be obtained in special qualities. Superimposed on some of these qualities may be such requirements as extensometer test, fracture test, impact test, macroetch test, nonmetallic inclusion tests, special hardenability test, and grain size test.

For complete descriptions of the qualities and supplementary requirements for carbon and alloy steels, reference should be made to the latest applicable Steel Products Manual Section. Titles of these manuals are listed in Section 2.

7. Types of Steel—In steelmaking, the principal reaction is the combination of carbon and oxygen to form a gas. If the oxygen available for this reaction is not removed prior to or during casting, the gaseous products continue to evolve during solidification. Proper control of the evolution of gas determines the type of steel produced. All alloy steels and strand cast steels are killed steels. Killed steels refers to those steels which have a deoxidizing element (such as aluminum or silicon) added to eliminate the gaseous oxygen. Carbon steel may be produced as killed, semi-killed, or rimmed. The vast majority of steels are of the killed type.

7.1 Killed steel is a type of steel from which there may be only a slight evolution of gases during solidification of the metal. Killed steels have more uniform chemical composition and properties than the other types. However, there may be variations in composition, depending on the steelmaking practices used. Alloy steels are of the killed type, while carbon steels may be killed or may be of the following types:

7.2 Rimmed steels have marked differences in chemical composition across the section. The typical structure of rimmed steel results from a marked gas evolution during solidification of the outer rim, caused by a reaction between the carbon in the solidifying metal and dissolved oxygen. The outer rim is lower in carbon, phosphorus, and sulfur than the average composition, whereas the inner portion, or core, is higher than the average in those elements. The technology of manufacturing rimmed steels limits the maximum contents of carbon and manganese and those maximum contents vary among producers. Rimmed steels do not retain any significant percentages of highly oxidizible elements, such as aluminum, silicon, or titanium.

Rimmed steel products, because of their chemical composition and their surface and other characteristics, may be used advantageously for the manufacture of finished articles involving cold bending, cold forming, deep drawing, and in some cases, cold heading applications.

7.3 Semi-killed steels have characteristics intermediate between those of killed and rimmed steels. During the solidification of semikilled steel, some gas is evolved and entrapped within the body of the ingot. This tends to compensate for the shrinkage that accompanies solidification.

7.4 Capped steels have characteristics, which combine some features of rimmed and semi-killed steels. After pouring, the rimming action is stopped after a brief interval by means of mechanical or chemical capping. The thin lower carbon rim has surface and forming properties comparable to those of rimmed steel, whereas the uniformity of composition and properties more nearly approaches that of semi-killed steels. Capped steel products, because of their chemical composition, surface, and other characteristics, may be used to advantage when the material is to withstand cold bending, cold forming, or cold heading.

8. Commonly Specified Elements—It is the purpose here to outline briefly the effects of various elements on the steelmaking practices and steel characteristics. The effects of a single element on either practice or characteristics are modified by the influence of other elements. These interrelations, frequently of a synergistic nature, must be considered when evaluating a change in specified composition. However, to simplify this presentation, the various elements will be discussed individually. The scope of this discussion will permit only suggestions of the modifying effects of other elements or of steelmaking practices on the effects of the element under consideration. Aluminum, titanium, and columbium, though not specified in SAE standard steels, are at times present to achieve deoxidation or fine grain size.

8.1 Carbon is present in all steel and is the principal hardening element. The hot-rolled strength and hardness increase significantly with increased carbon content, particularly at the low and medium carbon levels. Ductility and weldability decrease with increasing carbon content. Carbon also determines the level of hardness or strength attainable by quenching. Carbon segregates, and because of its major effect on properties, carbon segregation is frequently of more significance and importance than the segregation of other elements.

8.2 Manganese contributes to strength and hardness, but to a lesser degree than carbon. The amount of increase in these properties is dependent upon the carbon content, that is, higher carbon steels are affected more by manganese than lower carbon steels. Increasing the manganese content decreases weldability, but to a lesser extent than carbon. Manganese tends to increase the rate of carbon penetration during carburizing and enhances hardenability in quenching. Manganese is generally beneficial to surface quality, particularly in resulfurized steels. Manganese has a moderate tendency to segregate during solidification.

8.3 Phosphorus in appreciable amounts increases the hot-rolled strength and hardness, but at the sacrifice of ductility and toughness. Increased phosphorus content in quenched and tempered steels is also detrimental to ductility, toughness, and fatigue. Consequently, for most applications, phosphorus is maintained below a specific maximum. This varies with the grade and quality level. In certain low carbon, free machining steels, higher phosphorus content is specified for its effect on machinability. Phosphorus has a pronounced tendency to segregate.

8.4 Sulfur lowers ductility and toughness in the transverse direction as the content increases. Weldability decreases with increasing sulfur. Sulfur is very detrimental to surface quality, particularly in the lower manganese steels. For these reasons, a maximum sulfur content is specified for most steels. However, for some steels, sulfur is added to improve the machinability. Sulfur also has a pronounced tendency to segregate. Sulfur occurs in steel primarily in the form of manganese sulfide inclusions. Obviously, greater frequency of such inclusions is to be expected in the resulfurized grades.

8.5 Silicon is one of the principal deoxidizers used in steelmaking and, therefore, the amount of silicon present is related to the type of steel. Rimmed and capped steels contain no significant amounts of silicon. Semi-killed steels may contain moderate amounts of silicon, although there is a definite maximum amount that can be tolerated in such steels. Killed carbon steels may contain any amount of silicon up to 0.60% maximum.

Silicon is somewhat less effective than manganese in increasing as-rolled strength and hardness. Silicon has only a slight tendency to segregate. In low-carbon steels, silicon is usually detrimental to surface quality, and this condition is more pronounced in low-carbon resulfurized grades.

Silicon can help improve toughness and reduce relaxator in heat-treated spring steels.

8.6 Copper has a moderate tendency to segregate. Copper in appreciable amounts is detrimental to hot working operations. Copper adversely affects forge welding, but it does not seriously affect arc or acetylene welding. Copper is detrimental to surface quality and exaggerates the surface defects inherent in resulfurized steels. Copper is, however, beneficial to atmospheric corrosion resistance when present in amounts exceeding 0.20%.

8.7 Lead is an element sometimes added to carbon and alloy steels through mechanical dispersion during teeming or casting for the purpose of improving the machining characteristics of such steels. When so added, the range is generally 0.15 to 0.35%.

8.8 Boron is added to steel in small amounts (0.0005 to 0.0030%) to increase hardenability. Special melting and heating techniques are essential to obtain the desired hardenability results. Boron does not measurably affect the hot-rolled, normalized, or annealed properties of steel. Boron is most effective as a hardenability agent in lower carbon steels.

8.9 Chromium is generally added to steel to increase resistance to corrosion and oxidation, increase hardenability, improve high temperature strength, or improve abrasion resistance in high-carbon compositions. Chromium is a strong carbide former. Complex chromium-iron carbides go into solution in austenite slowly; therefore, a sufficient heating time before quenching is necessary.

Chromium is essentially a hardening element and is frequently used with a toughening element such as nickel to produce superior mechanical properties. At higher temperatures, chromium contributes increased strength, but is ordinarily used for applications of this nature in conjunction with molybdenum.

8.10 Nickel, when used as an alloying element, is a ferrite strengthener. Since nickel does not form any carbide compounds in steel, it remains in solution in the ferrite, thus strengthening and toughening the ferrite phase. Nickel steels are easily heat treated because nickel lowers the critical cooling rate. In combination with chromium, nickel produces alloy steels with greater hardenability, higher impact strength, and greater fatigue resistance than are possible with carbon steels.

8.11 Molybdenum promotes hardenability of steel and is useful where hardenability control is essential. When molybdenum is in solid solution in austenite prior to quenching, the reaction rates for transformation become considerably slower as compared with carbon steel. It widens the temperature range of effective heat treated response since it has a tendency to form stable carbides. Molybdenum provides hardenability with a minimum detrimental effect on cold-forming characteristics. Molybdenum steels in the quenched condition require higher tempering temperatures to obtain the same degree of softness as comparable carbon and alloy steels. It also increases the tensile and creep strengths of steel at high temperatures. Alloy steels that contain 0.15% to 0.30% molybdenum show a minimized susceptibility to temper embrittlement.

8.12 Vanadium increases the hot-rolled mechanical properties of steel and may be used to enhance hardenability. It can be used to inhibit austenitic grain growth through the formation of precipitates. The grain growth inhibiting effects promote a fine grain structure that imparts strength and toughness to steels. However, the precipitates of Al, Cb, and/or Ti offer a more effective means of austenitic grain coarsening resistance. Vanadium is also used in some microalloy steel since its ability to produce vanadium carbonitride precipitates from hot forging or hot-rolling temperatures imparts strength and hardness levels comparable to quench and tempered steels. It can be used in combination with columbium, aluminum, and/or titanium.

8.13 Aluminum is primarily used as a deoxidizer and austenitic grain refiner. In increased amounts, it combines readily with nitrogen to form aluminum nitrides which combines readily with nitrogen to form aluminum nitrides which contribute to high surface hardness and superior wear resistance.

8.14 Selenium is added to enhance machinability. It combines with manganese sulfide inclusions to modify their shape to be more globular; it also combines with manganese to form manganese selenides, which are inclusions which behave like manganese sulfides and are beneficial to machining.

8.15 Tellurium is added to enhance machinability. Its main purpose is to modify the shape of the manganese sulfides. However, tellurium will form iron tellurides, which result in hot shortness problems and require special hot-rolling considerations.

8.16 Bismuth is added to enhance machinability. It behaves much like lead in that it is present in a finely dispersed form in the solid steel.

8.17 Calcium is added to steel to promote the strand castability of aluminum grain refined steel. It forms calcium aluminate inclusions which remain liquid at steel casting temperatures, as opposed to alumina inclusions which are solid at casting temperatures. The alumina inclusions build up on nozzles and shrouds and cause clogging problems. Calcium is also added to strand cast or ingot steels to modify the alumina inclusions from a hard, brittle stringer to a softer, globular inclusion which is less detrimental to carbide tooling during machining operations.

8.18 Columbium (Niobium) can be added to steel for two purposes. It can be a grain refiner in lieu of aluminum in quantities up to 0.05% maximum (ASTM A 29). It can also be added as a microalloying agent (alone or in combination with V or Ti) when aluminum is a grain refiner, or when columbium exceeds the 0.05% level in a columbium grain refined steel. The columbium forms columbium carbonitride precipitates from hot forging or hot-rolling temperatures. The particles impart strength and hardness levels comparable to quench and tempered steels.

8.19 Titanium can be added to steel as a grain refiner in conjunction with aluminum. It can also be added to microalloy steels in combination with V and/or Cb to help control austenitic grain size during reheating. In boron treated steels, titanium is added to protect boron from nitrogen.

8.20 Nitrogen is intentionally added to some steels as a solid solution strengthener which improves machinability with respect to chip breaking and surface finish. Nitrogen is also added with microalloy additions such as vanadium, columbium (niobium) or titanium to promote precipitation strengthening and/or grina refinement. Nitrogen, however, reduces cold workability and notch toughness. Thus, users who cold draw or cold forge may require control of free nitrogen in the steel.

8.21 Other Elements such as Co, W, Zr, and so forth may be specified when their particular alloying effect is desired.

8.22 Residual Elements—Certain elements are present in small quantities in most steels. They are not intentionally added, but have been retained from the raw materials used during the production of the steel. These elements are considered incidental or residual as long as they do not exceed certain maximum limits. The most common residual elements of concern are copper, nickel, chromium, and molybdenum, and their maximum limits are: copper – 0.35%, nickel – 0.25%, chromium – 0.20%, and molybdenum – 0.06%. Other maximum limits for these particular elements, or limiting maximums for other elements, can be established between producer and purchaser.

HIGH-STRENGTH CARBON AND ALLOY DIE DRAWN STEELS—SAE J935 FEB2002

SAE Recommended Practice

Report of the SAE Iron and Steel Committee approved September 1965, completely revised July 1981, and reaffirmed June 1990. Rationale statement available. Reaffirmed by the SAE Iron and Steel Technical Committee—Division 1—Carbon and Alloy Steels, March 1996 and February 2002. Rationale statement available.

Foreword—Die drawing of hot-rolled bars increases the strength and hardness. At the same time, the ratio of yield strength to tensile strength is increased and the notched bar impact values are reduced. Various factors control the degree of change in the mechanical properties. The final properties are dependent upon chemical composition, hot-rolled microstructure (except in the case of alloy steel where a normalize treatment is used prior to drawing), size, shape, and the amount of reduction in cross-sectional area, die geometry, straightening procedures, and manner or temperature level of the stress-relieving operation.

As noted in Table 1, carbon and alloy steels of medium carbon content respond readily to this special processing. Compositional additives may be employed to improve machinability.

In the production of these products, drafts of approximately 10 to 35% reduction in cross-sectional areas are employed at either room or elevated temperatures depending on the practices and facilities of the individual producer. Stress-relieving temperatures vary over a similarly wide range, depending on producer facilities and the end product requirements.

Die drawn and stress-relieved bars are employed instead of quenched and tempered bars because of their unique combinations of properties. The die drawn and stress-relieved bars can be machined more readily than quenched and tempered bars, and except when the latter have high hardenability, the die drawn and stress-relieved bars have more uniform hardness throughout the cross section. When dimensional stability is critical during or after machining, or after cold-forming operations, the individual producer should be consulted for special processing to meet such conditions.

The torsional strength and endurance limit are similar to those of quenched and tempered grades at the same strength level. The wear resistance of these special processed steels is approximately equal to that of quenched and tempered bars of the same surface hardness.

1. Scope—This SAE Recommended Practice is intended to provide basic information on properties and characteristics of high-strength carbon and alloy steels which have been subjected to special die drawing. This includes both cold drawing with heavier-than-normal drafts and die drawing at elevated temperatures.

2. References

2.1 Applicable Publication—The following publication forms a part of this specification to the extent specified herein. Unless otherwise specified, the latest issue of SAE publications shall apply.

2.1.1 SAE PUBLICATION—Available from SAE, 400 Commonwealth Drive, Warrendale, PA 15096-0001.

SAE J429—Mechanical and Material Requirements for Externally Threaded Fasteners

3. Hardness—The hardness values for all grades are shown in Table 1. The typical hardness ranges indicated for the 825 MPa tensile strength steels are subject to negotiation between producer and consumer. Hardness determinations are commonly made on a flat ground on the outside diameter or on a cross section from the mid-radius to within 6 mm of the surface. If, when testing the finished product, there is disagreement between the typical hardness and tensile or yield strength values, the latter properties shall govern.

4. Impact Characteristics—The impact test values of special die drawn bars, as measured by the Izod or Charpy notched bar test, are lower than those of quenched and tempered carbon bars and they are significantly lower than those of quenched and tempered alloy steels. Failures of machine components usually result from fatigue, corrosion, wear, or shock loading. With the possible exception of the latter, there is no known correlation between the cases of failure and the notched bar impact test. In the case of shock loading, whatever relation exists must be derived empirically, that is, from experience. When low temperatures or high pressures are involved and where doubt exists as to the suitability of these steels, the design of the part should be reviewed.

5. Surface Finish—A number of surface finishes are available depending on producers' facilities and end use requirements. Bars can be supplied in the die drawn condition turned and polished, or ground and polished from die drawn or turned bars. The bars frequently have a dark appearance when the last operation is stress relieving. Surface finishes are subject to negotiation with each producer. The ranges of Arithmetical Average (AA) values in Table 5 are considered normal for each condition.

TABLE 1—MINIMUM MECHANICAL PROPERTIES

Tensile Strength MPa	Tensile Strength ksi	Yield Strength MPa	Yield Strength ksi	Elongation in 50 mm (2 In), %	Reduction in Area, %(1)	Brinell Hardness	Grades	Size Range mm	Size Range in	Tolerance
CARBON STEELS										
825	120	690	100	10.0	25.0	241/321(2)	1541	up to 80 (round)	3	See Table 2
							1045			
							1052	6-90 (round)	1/4 - 3-1/2	
							1141			
						248/321(2)	1144	6-120 (round)	1/4 - 4-1/2	See Table 2
							1151	6-55 (hexagon)	1/4 -2	
965	140	860	125	5.0	15.0	280	1144	6-60 (round)	1/4 - 2-1/2	See Table 3
								6-40 (hexagon)	1/4 - 1-1/2	
ALLOY STEELS										
860	125	725	105	14.0	45.0	269	41XX	12–90 (hexagon)	7/16–3-1/2	See Table 4
							51XX(3)			
1035(4)	150	895	130	10.0	35.0	302	41XX(3)			
							51XX(3)			
1170	170	1070	155	5.0	20.0	355	41XX(3)			

1. Typical minimum.
2. Typical hardness ranges, subject to negotiation. Hardness to be taken on a flat below decarb or on the mid-radius. In case of disagreement between hardness and tensile or yield strength, the latter properties govern.
3. May contain Pb or Te or other additives for improved machinability.
4. See SAE J429.

6. Machinability—Machinability values for any given grade or condition will vary considerably from shop to shop as a function of equipment, tooling grade and design, set up conditions, lubrication, and personnel. The ratings in Table 6 which are considered typical and which are offered only for purposes of comparison are based on a value of 100% for SAE 1212.

TABLE 2—SIZE TOLERANCES FOR CARBON STEELS

	Size Range, mm (in)	Tolerance, mm(1)	Tolerance, in(1)
Rounds	6 – 40, incl (1/4 - 1 - 1/2)	0.10	0.004
	Over 40 – 60, incl (Over 1-1/2 - 2-1/2, incl)	0.12	0.005
	Over 60 – 100, incl (Over 2-1/2 - 4, incl)	0.15	0.006
	Over 100 – 120, incl (Over 4 - 4-1/2, incl)	0.18	0.007
Hexagons	7 – 18, incl (1/4 - 3/4, incl)	0.10	0.004
	Over 18 – 36, incl (Over 3/4 - 1-1/2, incl)	0.12	0.005
	Over 36 – 55, incl (Over 1-1/2 - 2, incl)	0.15	0.006

1. All tolerances are minus.

TABLE 3—SIZE TOLERANCES FOR CARBON STEELS

	Size Range, mm (in)	Tolerance, mm(1)	Tolerance, in(1)
Rounds	8 to less than 12 (5/16 to less than 7/16)	0.10	0.004
	12 – 40, incl (7/16 - 1-1/2, incl)	0.12	0.005
	Over 40 – 60, incl (Over 1-1/2 - 2-1/2, incl)	0.15	0.006
Hexagons	7 to less than 10 (1/4 to less than 3/8)	0.10	0.004
	10 to less than 13 (3/8 to less than 7/16)	0.12	0.005
	13 – 36, incl (7/16 - 1-1/2, incl)	0.15	0.006

1. All tolerances are minus.

TABLE 4—SIZE TOLERANCES FOR ALLOY STEELS (ROUNDS)

Size Range, mm (in)	Tolerance, mm(1)	Tolerance, in(1)
12 – 40, incl (7/16 - 1-1/2, incl)	0.12	0.005
Over 40 – 60, incl (Over 1-1/2 - 2-1/2, incl)	0.15	0.006
Over 60–90, incl (Over 2-1/2 - 3-1/2, incl)	0.18	0.007

1. All tolerances are minus.

TABLE 5—RANGES OF ARITHMETICAL AVERAGE (AA) VALUES

	µm		µin
Cold Drawn	1.25/3.20	AA	(50/125)
Turned and Polished	0.40/1.00	AA	(15/40)
Cold Drawn-Ground and Polished	0.20/0.50	AA	(8/20)
Turned-Ground and Polished	0.20/0.50	AA	(8/20)

TABLE 6—TYPICAL MACHINABILITY RATINGS

SAE Grade		Heavy Drafted, Stress Relieved, %
1045		56
1050		54
1141		67
1144		85
High Tensile 1144		80
41XX	1035 MPa (150 ksi), TS	75 with free machining additives
51XX	1035 MPa (150 ksi), TS	75 with free machining additives
41XX	1170 MPa (170 ksi), TS	60 with free machining additives

GENERAL CHARACTERISTICS AND HEAT TREATMENTS OF STEELS—SAE J412 OCT1995

SAE Information Report

Report of the SAE Iron and Steel Division approved January 1912, editorial change April 1970. Completely revised by the SAE Iron and Steel Technical Committee June 1989, and revised October 1995.

Foreword—This Document has not changed other than to put it into the new SAE Technical Standards Board Format.

1. Scope—The information and data contained in this SAE Information Report are intended as a guide in the selection of steel types and grades for various purposes. Consideration of the individual types of steel is preceded by a discussion of the factors affecting steel properties and characteristics.

SAE steels are generally purchased on the basis of chemical composition requirements (SAE J403, J404, and J405). High-strength, low alloy (HSLA) steels (SAE J1392 and J1442) are generally purchased on the basis of mechanical properties; different chemical compositions are used to achieve the specified mechanical properties. Because these steels are characterized by their special mechanical properties obtained in the as-rolled condition, they are not intended for any heat treatment by the purchaser either before, during, or after fabrication.

In many instances, as in the case of steels listed in SAE J1268 and J1868, hardenability is also a specification requirement. This information report can be used as a reference for determining the general characteristics and applications of commonly used SAE steels. The use of the typical heat treatments listed in Tables 1 through 7 is recommended. These and other heat treatments commonly used on steel are briefly described at the end of this section.

2. References

2.1 Applicable Publications—The following publications form a part of this specification to the extent specified herein. The latest issue of SAE publications shall apply.

All of the heat treatments briefly described in this article are discussed in detail in *Metals Handbook—Ninth Edition—Volume 4—Heat Treating*, published by ASM International.

2.1.1 SAE PUBLICATIONS—Available from SAE, 400 Commonwealth Drive, Warrendale, PA 15096-0001.

SAE J403—Chemical Compositions of SAE Carbon Steels
SAE J404—Chemical Compositions of SAE Alloy Steels
SAE J405—Chemical Compositions of SAE Wrought Stainless Steels
SAE J406—Methods of Determining Hardenability of Steels
SAE J411—Carbon and Alloy Steels
SAE J1868—Restricted Hardenability Bands for Selected Alloy Steels

3. Factors Affecting Properties and Characteristics of Steel

3.1 Hardenability—Hardenability, or response to heat treatment, is one of the most important characteristics of heat-treated steels. Hardenability is the property of steels that determines the depth and distribution of hardness induced by quenching the steel from above the transformation temperature. Hardenability is usually measured by the end quench test described in SAE J406. Specified hardenability bands for standard carbon and alloy steels are shown in SAE J1268 and J1868.

The chemical composition and grain size of the steel completely determine its hardenability with almost all of the elements making varying degrees of contribution. Many elements are discussed in SAE J411; however, carbon, boron, manganese, chromium, and molybdenum have the strongest effect. Boron is a particularly potent hardenability agent. Typical additions in the range of 0.0005 to 0.003% will have a major effect on hardenability. Boron is most effective in lower carbon steels; it becomes less effective as carbon content increases. Carbon-manganese-boron steels generally fill a gap between plain carbon and alloy steels in terms of hardenability. Empirical relationships can be used to calculate or predict the hardenability for a given chemistry of steel. Actual depth and distribution of hardness will depend on quench severity.

Hardenability should not be confused with hardness per se or with maximum hardness. The maximum hardness obtainable with any steel quenched at the critical cooling rate depends only on the carbon content. That is to say, the maximum martensitic hardness obtainable on hardened steels is governed by the carbon content at the surface. It has been established that, under the conditions of scale-free heating, complete solution and achievement of critical cooling rate, maximum hardness is attained at about 0.60% carbon. If the material is decarburized, scaled, or overheated, or if it is quenched at less than the critical cooling rate, full hardness will not be achieved.

The term hardening implies that the hardness of the material is increased by suitable treatment, usually involving heating to a suitable austenitizing temperature followed by cooling at a certain minimum rate which depends upon the alloy content. If quenching is complete, the resulting structure is untempered martensite. If the quenching conditions produce a minimum of 90% martensite, followed by proper tempering, it may be reasonably expected that the surface hardness and the cross-sectional hardness will have achieved the commercial possibilities for that material and section size. Smaller percentages of martensite will result in a corresponding reduction in mechanical properties.

3.2 Grain Size—When used in reference to heat-treated steels, the term grain size implies austenitic grain size. It is an important parameter governing mechanical properties. A fine austenitic grain size will improve toughness, ductility, and fatigue strength, but will reduce hardenability. The inherent austenitic grain size is determined by the choice of deoxidizer or grain refiner used in the steel-making process. With few exceptions, steels to be heat-treated should have a fine austenitic grain size.

Ferritic grain size is a parameter that is important to nonheat-treated steels as it will affect formability, toughness, and ductility. Fine grain steels are stronger but will have less formability and ductility.

3.3 Microstructure—Microstructure means the quantity, size, shape, and distribution of various phases in steel. It depends totally on the chemistry, hardenability, heat treatment, and cooling rates employed. Ferrite, the purest form of iron in steel, is the softest and lowest strength constituent with highest ductility. Martensite, supersaturated solution of carbon in iron, is the hardest. Controlled diffusion of carbon from martensite achieved by controlling the heat treatment (tempering time and temperature) softens the steel and improves ductility. Slow cooling from high temperatures causes the carbon to precipitate out as iron carbide or cementite which is a hard phase. A mixture of ferrite and lamellar or plate-like cementite is called pearlite.

Austenite is a term applied to the solid solution of carbon in gamma iron (or face centered cubic) and is present in carbon steels when they are heated above the A3 transformation temperature. Retained austenite is austenite that remains in the microstructure after a part is quenched from its austenitizing temperature. It is a softer microstructure constituent.

3.4 Cleanliness—Cleanliness is a measure of nonmetallic oxides, sulfides, coarse-nitrides, silicates, and other such inclusions developed during the steel-making process. Depending on their size, shape, population, and distribution, nonmetallic inclusions may adversely affect toughness, ductility, and fatigue properties. Cleanliness is of utmost importance in critical components under high stresses, impact, cyclic loading, or low temperatures.

3.5 Surface Quality—Surface quality, a measure of the surface condition of steel, is important in cyclic loading, contact fatigue, and wear resistance applications. It is also very important in applications requiring surface coating, plating, painting, or aesthetics in exposed parts. Surface conditioning or scarfing of ingots, slabs, blooms, and billets may be utilized to improve surface quality.

3.6 Homogeneity—Chemical and microstructural homogeneity and soundness (absence of voids, pinholes, and porosity) are important in predicting the consistency of product performance and integrity. Proper deoxidation and stirring of molten steel alleviate some of these problems.

4. Characteristics of Plain Carbon Steels

4.1 Group I (SAE 1005, 1006, 1008, 1010, 1012, 1013)—These steels are the lowest carbon steels of the plain carbon type and are selected when cold formability or drawability is the primary requisite. These steels have relatively low tensile values. Within the carbon range of the group, strength and hardness will increase with increase in carbon and with cold work. Such increases in strength are at the sacrifice of ductility or the ability to withstand cold deformation.

When under 0.15% carbon, the steels are susceptible to grain growth and consequent brittleness if they are cold worked and subsequently heated to temperatures between 595 °C (1100 °F) and the lower transformation temperature. If coarse grains develop, they can be refined by heating above the A3 transformation temperature and then cooling.

Cold-rolled sheets are made from the lower carbon steels in the group. They have excellent surface appearance and are used in automobile panels, appliances, and so forth. The machinability of bar, rod, and wire products in this group is improved by cold drawing. In general, these steels are considered suitable for welding or brazing but may suffer strength reductions either locally in the heat affected zone or overall, depending upon process details.

TABLE 1—TYPICAL TREATMENTS FOR CASE HARDENING GRADES OF CARBON STEELS

UNS No.	SAE Steels[1]	Carburizing Temperature °C	Carburizing Temperature °F	Cooling Medium	Reheat Temperature °C	Reheat Temperature °F	Cooling Medium	Carbonitriding Temperature °C[2]	Carbonitriding Temperature °F[2]	Cooling Medium	Temper °C[3]	Temper °F[3]
G10100	1010	—	—	—	—	—	—	790–900	1450–1650	Oil	120–205	250–400
G10150	1015	—	—	—	—	—	—	790–900	1450–1650	Oil	120–205	250–400
G10160	1016	900–925	1650–1700	Water or Caustic	—	—	—	790–900	1450–1650	Oil	120–205	250–400
G10180	1018	900–925	1650–1700	Water or Caustic	790	1450	Water or Caustic[4]	790–900	1450–1650	Oil	120–205	250–400
G10200	1020	900–925	1650–1700	Water or Caustic	790	1450	Water or Caustic[4]	790–900	1450–1650	Oil	120–205	250–400
G10220	1022	900–925	1650–1700	Water or Caustic	790	1450	Water or Caustic[4]	790–900	1450–1650	Oil	120–205	250–400
G10260	1026	900–925	1650–1700	Water or Caustic	790	1450	Water or Caustic[4]	790–900	1450–1650	Oil	120–205	250–400
G10300	1030	900–925	1650–1700	Water or Caustic	790	1450	Water or Caustic[4]	790–900	1450–1650	Oil	120–205	250–400
G11170	1117	900–925	1650–1700	Water or Oil	790–870	1450–1600	Water or Caustic[4]	790–900	1450–1650	Oil	120–205	250–400
G11180	1118	900–925	1650–1700	Oil	790–870	1450–1600	Oil	—	—	—	120–205	250–400
G15130	1513	900–925	1650–1700	Oil	790	1450	Oil	—	—	—	120–205	250–400
G15220	1522	900–925	1650–1700	Oil	790	1450	Oil	—	—	—	120–205	250–400
G15240	1524	900–925	1650–1700	Oil	790	1450	Oil	—	—	—	120–205	250–400
G15260	1526	900–925	1650–1700	Oil	790	1450	Oil	—	—	—	120–205	250–400
G15270	1527	900–925	1650–1700	Oil	790	1450	Oil	—	—	—	120–205	250–400

1. Generally, it is not necessary to normalize the carbon grades for fulfilling either dimensional or machinability requirements of parts made from the steel grades listed in the table although, where dimension is of vital importance, normalizing temperatures of at least 50 °F above the carburizing temperatures are sometimes required.
2. The higher manganese steels such as 1118 and the 1500 series are not usually carbonitrided. If carbonitriding is performed, care must be taken to limit the nitrogen content because high nitrogen will increase their tendency to retain austenite.
3. Even where recommended tempering temperatures are shown, the temper is not mandatory on many applications. Tempering is generally employed for a partial stress relief and improves resistance to cracking from grinding operations. Higher temperatures than those shown may be employed where the hardness specification on the finished parts permits.
4. 3% sodium hydroxide.

TABLE 2—TYPICAL TREATMENTS FOR HEAT-TREATING GRADES OF CARBON STEELS

UNS No.	SAE Steels	Normalizing Temperature, °C	Normalizing Temperature, °F	Annealing Temperature, °C	Annealing Temperature, °F	Hardening Temperature, °C	Hardening Temperature, °F	Quenching[1] Medium
G10300	1030	—	—	—	—	855–870	1575–1600	Water or Caustic
G10350	1035	—	—	—	—	840–870	1550–1600	Water or Caustic
G10380[2]	1038[2]	—	—	—	—	830–855	1525–1575	Water or Caustic
G10390[2]	1039[2]	—	—	—	—	830–855	1525–1575	Water or Caustic
G10400[2]	1040[2]	—	—	—	—	830–855	1525–1575	Water or Caustic
G10420	1042	—	—	—	—	815–845	1500–1550	Water or Caustic
G10430[2]	1043[2]	—	—	—	—	815–845	1500–1550	Water or Caustic
G10450[2]	1045[2]	—	—	—	—	815–845	1500–1550	Water or Caustic
G10460[2]	1046[2]	—	—	—	—	815–845	1500–1550	Water or Caustic
G10500[2]	1050[2]	870–925	1600–1700	—	—	815–845	1500–1550	Water or Caustic
G10530	1053	870–925	1600–1700	—	—	815–845	1500–1550	Water or Caustic
G10600	1060	870–925	1600–1700	760–815	1400–1500	855–885	1575–1625	Oil
G10740	1074	870–900	1550–1650	760–815	1400–1500	855–885	1575–1625	Oil
G10800	1080	845–900	1550–1650	760–815[3]	1400–1500[3]	855–885	1575–1625	Oil[4]
G10900	1090	845–900	1550–1650	760–815[3]	1400–1500[3]	855–885	1575–1625	Oil[4]
G10950	1095	845–900	1550–1650	760–815[3]	1400–1500[3]	855–885	1575–1625	Water and Oil
G11370	1137	—	—	—	—	845–870	1550–1600	Oil
G11410	1141	—	—	760–815	1400–1500	815–845	1500–1550	Oil
G11450	1145	870–925	1600–1700	760–815	1400–1500	815–845	1500–1550	Oil
G11450	1145	—	—	—	—	800–815	1475–1500	Water or Oil
G11460	1146	—	—	—	—	800–815	1475–1500	Water or Oil
G15410	1541	870–925	1600–1700	760–815	1400–1500	815–845	1500–1550	Water or Oil
G15480	1548	870–925	1600–1700	—	—	815–845	1500–1550	Oil
G15520	1552	870–925	1600–1700	—	—	815–845	1500–1550	Oil
G15660	1566	870–925	1600–1700	—	—	855–885	1575–1625	Oil

1. All steels are tempered to desired hardness: however, tempering is not mandatory on many applications. Tempering is generally employed for a partial stress relief and improves resistance to cracking from grinding operations. Higher temperatures than those shown may be employed where the hardness specification on the finished parts permits.
2. Commonly used on parts where induction hardening is employed. However, all steels from SAE 1030 up may have induction hardening applications.
3. Spheroidal structures are often required for machining purposes and should be cooled very slowly or be isothermally transformed to produce the desired structure.
4. May be water or brine quenched by special techniques such as partial immersion or time quenched; otherwise they are subject to quench cracking.

4.2 Group II (SAE 1015, 1016, 1017, 1018, 1019, 1020, 1021, 1022, 1023, 1025, 1026, 1029, 1513, 1522, 1524, 1526, 1527)—Steels in this group have increased strength and hardness and reduced cold formability compared to the lowest carbon group. For heat treating purposes, they are commonly known as carburizing or case hardening grades.

Selection of one of these steels for carburizing applications depends on the nature of the part, the properties desired, and the processing practices preferred. Increase in carbon content of the base steel results in greater core hardness with a given quench. Increase in manganese improves the hardenability of both the core and the case.

In this group, the intermediate manganese grades (0.60 to 1.00) machine better than the lower manganese grades. For carburizing applications, SAE 1016, 1018, and 1019 are widely used for water quenched parts. SAE 1022 and the 1500 series in this group are used for heavier sections or with thin sections where oil quenching is desired.

In cold-formed or cold-heated parts, the lowest manganese grades offer the best formability at a given carbon level. The next higher manganese types (SAE 1018, 1021, and 1026) provide increased strength.

These steels are used for numerous forged parts. In general, these steels are suitable for welding or brazing prior to carburizing. If welding is to be performed after carburizing, the area to be welded must be protected from the carburizing media during the process. An alternative to protection is to machine away the area to be welded after carburizing, but before hardening.

A typical application for carburized plain carbon steel is for parts requiring a hard wear-resistant surface, but with little need for increased mechanical properties in the core; e.g., small shafts, plungers, and lightly loaded gearing.

4.3 Group III (SAE 1030, 1035, 1037, 1038, 1039, 1040, 1042, 1043, 1044, 1045, 1046, 1049, 1050, 1053, 1536, 1541, 1548, 1551, 1552)—Steels of the medium carbon type are selected for uses where higher mechanical properties are needed. They are frequently further hardened and strengthened by heat treatment or by cold work. Steels in this group are suitable for a wide variety of automotive applications. Selection of the particular carbon and manganese level is governed by a number of factors. Increase in mechanical properties required, section thickness, or depth of hardening ordinarily necessitate either higher carbon, higher manganese, or both. The heat treating practice used, especially the quenching medium, also has a great effect on the steels selected. In general, any of the grades over 0.30% carbon may be induction or flame hardened.

The lower carbon and manganese steels in this group find wide usage for certain types of cold-formed parts. In nearly all cases, the parts cold formed from these steels are annealed, normalized, or quenched and tempered prior to use. Stampings are usually limited to flat parts or simple bends. The higher carbon grades are frequently cold drawn to specified mechanical properties for use without heat treatment for some applications.

All of these steels can be used for forgings, the selection being governed by the section size and the mechanical properties desired after heat treatment. Thus, SAE 1030 and 1035 are used for many small forgings where moderate properties are desired. SAE 1536 is used for more critical parts where a higher strength level and better uniformity is essential. The SAE 1038, 1052, 1053, and 1500 groups are used for larger forgings. They are also used for small forgings where high hardness after oil quenching is desired. Suitable heat treatment is necessary on forgings from this group to provide machinability.

These steels are also widely used for parts machined from bar stock. They are used both with and without heat treatment, depending upon the application and the level of properties needed. As a class, they are considered good for normal machining operations. It is possible to weld these steels by most commercial methods, but precautions should be taken to avoid cracking from rapid heating or cooling.

4.4 Group IV (SAE 1055, 1059, 1060, 1065, 1069, 1070, 1074, 1075, 1078, 1080, 1085, 1086, 1090, 1095, 1561, 1566)—Steels in this group are of the high carbon type which are used for applications where the higher carbon is needed to improve wear characteristics and where strength levels required are higher than those attainable with the lower carbon groups.

In general, cold-forming methods are not practical with this group of steels as they are limited to flat stampings and springs coiled from small-diameter wire. Practically all parts from these steels are heat-treated before use. Variations in heat-treating methods are required to obtain optimum properties for particular composition and application.

Typical uses in the spring industry include SAE 1065 for pretempered wire, SAE 1064 for small washers and thin stamped parts, SAE 1074 for light, flat springs formed from annealed stock, and SAE 1080 and 1085 for thicker flat springs. SAE 1085 is also used for heavier coiled springs.

Because of good wearing properties when properly heat-treated, the high carbon steels find wide usage in the farm implement industry. Typical applications are plow beams, plow shares, scraper blades, discs, mower knives, and harrow teeth.

5. Characteristics of Free-Cutting Carbon Steels—This class of steel is intended for uses where improved machinability is desired as compared with carbon steels of similar carbon and manganese content. Machinability refers to the effects of hardness, strength, ductility, grain size, microstructure, and chemical composition on cutting tool wear, chip formation, ease of metal removal, and surface finish quality of the steel being cut. Lower costs are achieved either by increased production through greater machining speeds and improved tool life, or by eliminating secondary operations through an improvement in finish.

These steels contain sulfur for chip formation and, in the 1200 series, phosphorus to increase the strength and reduce the ductility of ferrite so chips will break up more easily. Calcium is also used to improve shape of the sulfides. The use of other additions such as lead, bismuth, or selenium has declined due to environmental restrictions. Sulfur and phosphorus negatively affect weldability, cold-forming, forging, and so forth. Lead in steel wire causes a poor quality, low-strength welded, or brazed joint. The lower carbon grades can be used for case hardening operations while the grades over 0.30 carbon can be quenched and tempered or induction hardened.

Machinability improves within the 1100 series as sulfur levels increase. Sulfur combines mostly with the manganese and precipitates as sulfide inclusions. These inclusions favor machining by causing the formation of a broken chip and by providing a built-in lubricant that prevents the chips from sticking to the tool and undermining the cutting edge. By minimizing this adherence, less power is required, finish is improved, and the speed of machining may often be doubled as compared with a similar nonresulfurized grade. The 1200 series steels are both rephosphorized and resulfurized. Phosphorus is soluble in iron and promotes chip breakage in cutting operations through increased hardness and brittleness. Steels high in phosphorus are notoriously notch sensitive. As with carbon, an excessive amount of phosphorus can raise strength and hardness levels so high as to impair machinability. Hence, the 1200 series phosphorus content is limited to either a 0.04 to 0.09% or 0.07 to 0.12% range and carbon is limited to 0.13% maximum for the same reason. 1200 series steels are normally used in applications where ease of machining is the primary requisite. They are not normally heat-treated, but they may be case hardened by carburizing or carbonitriding.

5.1 Group I (SAE 1117, 1118)—Steels in this group are used where a combination of good machinability and response to heat treatment is needed. These varieties can be used for small parts that are to be carbonitrided. SAE 1117 and 1118 carry more manganese for better hardenability, permitting oil quenching after case hardening heat treatments.

5.2 Group II (SAE 1137, 1140, 1141, 1144, 1146)—This group of steels has characteristics comparable to carbon steels of the same carbon content. They are widely used for parts where a large amount of machining is necessary, or where threads, splines, grooves, or other operations offer special tooling problems. SAE 1137, for example, is widely used for nuts, bolts, and studs with machined threads. The higher manganese SAE 1137, 1141, and 1144 offer greater hardenability, the higher carbon types being suitable for oil quenching for many parts. All of these steels may be selectively hardened by induction or flame heating, if desired.

6. Structural steels are purchased on the basis of mechanical properties and are available as carbon (J368 and J1392), HSLA (J1392 and J1442), and alloy (J368) steels. These steels are available in the as-rolled condition (J1392 and J1442) with yield strengths of 240 to 550 MPa or quenched and tempered (J368) with yield strengths of 550 to 690 MPa. These steels are normally not intended for any heat treatment by the purchaser. Subjecting these steels to such heat treatments will modify their mechanical properties. For certain applications, these steels may be annealed, normalized, or stress relieved with some effect on the mechanical properties; it is recommended that prior to such heat treatments, the purchaser should consult the producer to determine the need for and the effect on mechanical properties.

The term "Microalloyed Steels" has come into common use to denote a family of hot-rolled bar steels which develop higher strength in the as-rolled or as-forged condition. These steels, as in the case of HSLA steels, are not generally intended for heat-treatment after rolling or hot forging. Medium carbon microalloy steels, however, may be induction case hardened using practices similar to carbon steels of equivalent carbon content. This is common practice for applications such as hydraulic shafts.

6.1 Carburizing Grades of Alloy Steels

6.1.1 PROPERTIES OF THE CASE—The properties of carburized and hardened cases depend on the carbon and alloy content, the depth of case, the structure of the case, and the degree and distribution of residual stresses. The carbon content of the case depends on the details of the carburizing process along with the response of iron and the alloying elements. The original carbon content of the steel has little or no effect on the carbon content produced in the case. The hardenability in the case, therefore, depends on the alloy content of the steel and the final carbon content produced by carburizing.

When heating for hardening results in complete carbide solution in the case, the effect of alloying elements on the hardenability of the case will in general be the same as the effect of these elements on the hardenability of the core. An exception is that boron significantly increases the hardenability of the low carbon core, but has little effect on the hardenability of the higher carbon case. Other less dramatic exceptions involve alloy interactions, which may enhance core hardenability but not case hardenability. It is also true that some elements, which raise the hardenability of the core, may tend to produce more retained austenite and consequently somewhat lower indentation hardness in the case.

Alloy steels are frequently used for case hardening because the required surface hardness can be obtained by moderate rates of cooling, which can result from an oil quench. This may mean less distortion than would be encountered with water quenching. It is usually desirable to select a steel that will attain a minimum surface hardness of Rockwell C 58, after carburizing and oil quenching. Where section sizes are large, a high hardenability alloy steel may be necessary; for medium and light sections, a low hardenability steel will suffice.

In general, case hardening alloy steels may be divided into three classes as far as the hardenability of the case is concerned. The three classes are: 1) low hardenability, such as the 4000, 5000, 5100, 6100, and 8100 series; 2) intermediate hardenability, such as the 4300, 4400, 4500, 4600, 4700, 8600, 8800, and 94B00 series; and 3) high hardenability, such as the 4800 and 9300 series. (The 8800 series is borderline with the high hardenability class.) Since the original carbon content has little effect on the case carbon level (and case hardenability) after carburizing, there is no significant difference between the case hardenabilities of two steels having similar alloy content, but varied original carbon percentage, e.g., 4815 and 4820 steels.

The steels having high case hardenability generally have reasonably high core hardenabilities, although the core hardenability is dependent upon the carbon content of the basic steel as well as the alloy content. These steels are used particularly for carburized parts having thick sections, such as heavy-duty truck drive pinions and gears and large roller bearings. Good case properties can be obtained by oil quenching. These steels are likely to have substantial amounts of retained austenite in the case after carburizing and quenching. The amount of retained austenite may be held to reasonable limits by controlling the carbon content of the case to produce a near eutectoid case, by refrigerating the parts, or by reheating and quenching after carburizing. Lower case hardenability steels are used in smaller parts that are less heavily loaded. Steels with intermediate case hardenability are used for tractor and automotive gears, piston pins, ball studs, universal crosses, and roller bearings. Satisfactory case hardness should be produced in most cases by oil quenching.

6.1.2 CORE PROPERTIES—The core properties of case hardened steels depend on the carbon and alloy content of the original steel and the severity of the quench. Many of the generally used types of alloy case hardening steels are made with two or more carbon contents so a choice of core hardness is provided. The most desirable hardness for the core depends on the design and function of the individual part. In general, where high compressive loads are encountered, relatively high core hardness is beneficial in supporting the case. Lower core hardnesses may be desirable where more than normal toughness is essential.

The case hardening steels may be divided into three general classes with respect to hardenability of the core. For hardenability of individual steels, see SAE J1268. Because H-bands have not been established for all steels, it is impossible to give an accurate comparative rating of hardenability of all the steels in any one group. Low hardenability core steels include SAE 4023, 4024, 4027*, 4028*, 4118*, 4422*, 4615, 4617, 4626*, 5115, 5120*, 6118*, and 8615. The steels followed by a "*" are borderline and might be considered medium hardenability.

Medium hardenability core steels include SAE 4032, 4427, 4620, 4720, 4815 (borderline with high), 8617, 8620, 8622, and 8720. High hardenability core steels include SAE 4320, 4718, 4817, 4820, 8625, 8627, 8822, 9310, 94B15, and 94B17. SAE 94B15 and 94B17 have been classed as high hardenability steels in the core because of the marked effect of boron on the hardenability of low carbon steels.

6.1.3 HEAT TREATMENT—With few exceptions, the alloy carburizing steels are made to fine grain practices, and most are, therefore, suitable for direct quenching from the carburizing temperature of 925 °C (1700 °F) or from a reduced temperature of 815 to 870 °C (1500 to 1600 °F). If the carburizing is to be done at temperatures above 925 °C (1700 °F) and the parts are direct quenched, careful studies should be made of the suitability of the products so treated. Several other types of heat treatment involving single and double quenching are also used for some of these steels. Table 3.

6.2 Nitriding Grades of Alloy Steels—A nitrided case is desirable for parts requiring resistance to sliding wear. Furthermore, since nitriding is carried out at relatively low temperatures (495 to 565 °C or 925 to 1050 °F), and no quenching after nitriding is required, this process produces very little distortion. However, nitriding produces a relatively shallow case (0.2 to 0.3 mm or 0.008 to 0.012 in).

The following steels can be nitrided for specific applications:

a. Aluminum containing low-alloy steels
b. Medium carbon, chromium containing low-alloy steels; e.g., SAE 4100, 4300, 5100, 6100, 8600, 9300, and 9800 series
c. Hot work die steels containing 5% chromium; e.g., H11, H12, H13
d. 400 series stainless steels
e. Austenitic 300 series stainless steels
f. Precipitation hardening stainless steels; e.g., 17-4 PH or A-286

A very hard, low-ductility nitrided case is produced from aluminum containing steels where a chromium containing steel produces a lower hardness case with improved ductility. Except for martensitic stainless, all steels that are to be nitrided must first be hardened and tempered. The tempering temperature is usually 10 °C (50 °F) higher than the maximum nitriding temperature to ensure that the core hardness is not reduced during the nitriding operation. Typical nitriding applications include gears designed for low contact stresses, spindles, seal rings, and pins.

6.3 Directly Hardenable Grades of Alloy Steel—These steels may be considered in five groups on the basis of approximate mean carbon content of the SAE specification. In general, the last two figures of the specification agree with the mean carbon content. Consequently, the heading "0.30 to 0.37 Mean Carbon Content of SAE Specification" includes steels such as SAE 1330 and 4137.

It is necessary to deviate from the preceding plan in the classification of the carbon-molybdenum steels. When these steels are used, it is customary to specify higher carbon content, for specific applications, than would be specified for other alloy steels because of the low alloy content of these steels. For example, SAE 4047 is used for the same applications as SAE 4140 and 5140. Consequently, in the following tables and discussion, the carbon-molybdenum steels are shown in the groups where they belong on the basis of applications rather than carbon content.

For the present discussion, steels of each carbon content are divided into two or three groups on the basis of hardenability. Transformation ranges and consequently heat-treating practices vary somewhat with different alloying elements even though the hardenability is not changed.

6.3.1 0.30 TO 0.37 MEAN CARBON CONTENT—These steels are frequently used for water-quenched parts of moderate section size and for oil-quenched parts of small section size. Typical applications are connecting rods, steering arms and steering knuckles, axle shafts, bolts, studs, screws, and other parts requiring strength and toughness where the section size is small enough to permit obtaining the desired mechanical properties with the customary heat treatment. Steels falling into this classification may be subdivided into two groups on the basis of hardenability.

Low hardenability steels in the 0.30 to 0.37 mean carbon content classification include SAE 1330, 1335, 4037, 4130, 5130, 5132, 5135, and 8630. Medium hardenability steels in this same carbon range include SAE 4135, 4137, 8637, and 94B30.

TABLE 3—TYPICAL HEAT TREATMENTS FOR CARBURIZING GRADES OF ALLOY STEELS

UNS No.	SAE Steels[1]	Pretreatments Normalize[2]	Pretreatments Normalize and Temper[3]	Pretreatments Cycle Anneal[4]	Carburizing[5] Temperature, °C	Carburizing[5] Temperature, °F	Cooling Method	Reheat[6] Temperature, °C	Reheat[6] Temperature, °F	Quenching Medium	Tempering[7] Temperature, °C	Tempering[7] Temperature, °F
G40120	4012											
G40230	4023											
G40270	4027	Yes	—	—	900–925	1650–1700	Quench in oil[8]	—	—	—	120–175	250–350
G40280	4028											
G40320	4032											
G41180	4118	Yes	—	—	900–925	1650–1700	Quench in oil[8]	—	—	—	120–175	250–350
G43200	4320	Yes	—	Yes	900–925	1650–1700	Quench in oil[8]	—	—	—	120–175	250–350
					900–925	1650–1700	Cool slowly	830–845	1525–1550[9]	Oil	120–175	250–350
G44220	4422	Yes	—	Yes	900–925	1650–1700	Quench in oil[8]	—	—	—	120–175	250–350
G44270	4427											
G46200	4620	Yes	—	Yes	900–925	1650–1700	Cool slowly	815–845	1500–1550[9]	Oil	120–175	250–350
G47200	4720	Yes	—	Yes	900–925	1650–1700	Quench in oil	815–845	1500–1550[9]	Oil	120–175	250–350
G48150	4815	—	Yes	Yes	900–925	1650–1700	Quench in oil[8]	—	—	—	120–175	250–325
G48200	4820				900–925	1650–1700	Quench in oil	800–830	1475–1525[9]	Oil	120–175	250–325
G51200	5120	Yes	—	—	900–925	1650–1700	Quench in oil[8]	—	—	—	120–175	250–350
G86150	8615	Yes	—	—								
G86170	8617											
G86200	8620				900–925	1650–1700	Quench in oil[8]	845–870	—	—	120–175	250–350
G86220	8622				900–925	1650–1700	Cool slowly	845–870	1550–1600[9]	Oil	120–175	250–350
G86250	8625				900–925	1650–1700	Quench in oil	845–870	1550–1600[9]	Oil	120–175	250–350
G86270	8627	Yes	—	Yes								
G87200	8720											
G88220	8822											
G93100	9310	—	Yes	—	900–925	1600–1700	Quench in oil	790–830	1450–1525[9]	Oil	120–175	250–325
					900–925	1600–1700	Cool slowly	790–830	1450–1525[9]	Oil	120–175	250–325
G94151	94B15	Yes	—	—	900–925	1650–1700	Quench in oils	—	—	—	120–175	250–350
G94171	94B17											

1. These steels are fine grain. Heat treatments are not necessarily correct for coarse grain.
2. Normalizing temperature should be at least as high as the carburizing temperature followed by air cooling.
3. After normalizing, reheat to temperature of 1100 to 1200 °F and hold at temperature approximately 1 h per in of maximum section or 4 h minimum time.
4. Where cycle annealing is desired, heat to at least as high as the carburizing temperature, hold for uniformity, cool rapidly to 1000 to 1250 °F, hold 1 to 3 h, then air cool or furnace cool to obtain a structure suitable for machining and finish.
5. It is general practice to reduce carburizing temperatures to approximately 1550 °F before quenching to minimize distortion and retained austenite. For 4800 series steels, the carburizing temperature is reduced to approximately 1500 °F before quenching.
6. In this treatment the parts are slowly cooled, preferably under a protective atmosphere. They are then reheated and oil quenched. A tempering operation follows as required. This treatment is used when machining must be done between carburizing and hardening or when facilities for quenching from the carburizing cycle are not available. Distortion is at least equal to that obtained by a single quench from the carburizing cycle, as described in note 5.
7. Tempering treatment is optional. Tempering is generally employed for partial stress relief and improved resistance to cracking from grinding operations. Temperatures higher than those shown are used in some instances where application requires.
8. This treatment is most commonly used and generally produces a minimum of distortion.
9. This treatment is used where the maximum grain refinement is required and/or where parts are subsequently ground on critical dimensions. A combination of good case and core properties is secured with somewhat greater distortion than is obtained by a single quench from the carburizing treatment.

6.3.2 0.40 TO 0.42 MEAN CARBON CONTENT—In general, these steels are used for medium and large size parts requiring a high degree of strength and toughness. The choice of the proper steel depends on the section size and the mechanical properties that must be produced. The low and medium hardenability steels are used for average size automotive parts such as steering knuckles or axle shafts. The high-hardenability steels are used particularly for large axles and shafts and for large aircraft parts. These steels are usually considered for oil quenching, although some large parts made of the low and medium hardenability classifications may be quenched in water under properly controlled conditions. These steels may be roughly divided into three groups as follows, on the basis of hardenability:

a. Low hardenability steels in the 0.40 to 0.42 mean carbon content classification include SAE 1340, 4047, and 5140.

b. Medium hardenability steels in the 0.40 to 0.42 classification include 4140, 4142, 50B40, 8640, 8642, and 8740.

c. High hardenability steels in this classification include SAE 4340.

6.3.3 0.45 TO 0.50 MEAN CARBON CONTENT—These steels are used primarily for gears and other parts requiring fairly high hardness as well as strength and toughness. Such parts are usually oil quenched. A minimum of 90% martensite in the as-quenched condition is desirable. These steels are as follows:

a. Low hardenability steels in the 0.45 to 0.50 mean carbon content classification include SAE 5046, 50B44, 50B46, and 5147.

b. Medium hardenability steels in the 0.45 to 0.50 classification include SAE 4145, 5147, 5150, 81B45, 8645, and 8650.

c. High hardenability steels in this classification include SAE 4150 and 86B45.

6.3.4 0.50 TO 0.60 MEAN CARBON CONTENT—These steels are used primarily for springs and hand tools. The hardenability necessary depends on the thickness of the material and the quenching practice. These steels are as follows:

a. Medium hardenability steels in the 0.50 to 0.60 mean carbon content classification include SAE 50B50, 5060, 50B60, 5150, 5155, 51B60, 6150, 8650, 9254, and 9260.
b. High hardenability steels in this classification include SAE 4161, 8655, and 8660.

6.3.5 1.02 MEAN CARBON CONTENT—These are straight chromium electric furnace steels used primarily for the races and balls or rollers of antifriction bearings. They are also used for other parts requiring high hardness and wear resistance. The compositions of the three steels are identical except for a variation in chromium with a corresponding variation in hardenability. These steels are as follows:

a. The low hardenability steel in the 1.02 mean carbon content classification is SAE 50100.
b. The medium hardenability steels in this classification are SAE 51100 and 52100.

6.3.6 HEAT TREATMENTS—Typical treatments are given in Table 4.

6.3.7 RESULFURIZED STEEL—Some of the alloy steels (SAE 4024 and 4028) are resulfurized to give better machinability at a relatively high hardness.

7. ***Characteristics of Wrought Stainless Steels***—The composition and corresponding physical characteristics of these steels can be divided into several broad groups or types as follows:

7.1 Stainless Chromium-Nickel-Manganese Austenitic Steels (Not Hardenable)—These steels are austenitic at room temperature and higher and cannot be hardened by thermal treatment. Table 5 gives typical heat treatments for the following steels:

a. SAE 30201 is an austenitic chromium-nickel-manganese stainless steel usually required for flat products. It is nonmagnetic in the annealed condition but may be magnetic when cold worked. SAE 30201, as with 30301, can be used to obtain a high-strength product by cold rolling. It is well suited for corrosion-resistant structural members requiring high strength with low weight and has excellent resistance to a wide variety of corrosive media, showing behavior comparable to stainless grade SAE 30301. With high ductility and excellent forming properties, it has been used for automotive trim, automotive wheel covers, railroad passenger car bodies and structural members, truck trailer bodies, and cookware.
b. SAE 30202, like its corresponding chromium-nickel stainless steel SAE 30304, is a general-purpose stainless steel. It has good corrosion resistance, deep drawing, and stretch forming qualities. It is nonhardenable by thermal treatments but may be cold worked to high strengths. In the annealed condition, it is nonmagnetic but turns magnetic when cold worked. Applications for this stainless steel are hub caps, railcar and truck trailer bodies, and spring wire.

TABLE 4—TYPICAL HEAT TREAMENTS FOR DIRECTLY HARDENABLE GRADES OF ALLOY STEELS

UNS No.	SAE Steels [1]	Normalizing Temperature, 6C	Normalizing Temperature, °F	Annealing [2] Temperature, °C	Annealing [2] Temperature, °F	Hardening [3] Temperature, °C	Hardening [3] Temperature °F	Quenching Medium [4]
G13300	1330	870-925 [5]	1600-1700 [5]	845-900	1550-1650	830-855	1525-1575	Water or oil
G13350	1335	870-925 [5]	1600-1700 [5]	845-900	1550-1650	815-845	1500-1550	Oil
G13400	1340							
G40370	4037		—	815-855	1500-1575	830-855	1525-1575	Oil
G40470	4047		—	790-845	1450-1550	815-855	1500-1575	Oil
G41300	4130	870-925 [5]	1600-1700 [5]	790-845	1450-1550	815-870	1500-1600	Water or oil
G41370	4137							
G41400	4140		—	790-845	1450-1550	845-900	1550-160	Oil
G41420	4142							
G41450	4145							
G41470	4147		—	790-845	1450-1550	815-845	1500-1550	Oil
G41450	4140							
G43400	4340	870-925 [5][6]	1600-1700 [5][6]	790-845	1450-1550	815-845	1500-1550	Oil
G50461	5046	870-925 [5]	1600-1700 [5]	815-870	1500-1600	815-845	1500-1550	Oil
G51300	5130	870-925 [5]	1600-1700 [5]	790-845	1450-1550	830-855	1525-1575	Water, caustic solution, or oil
G51320	5132							
G51400	5140	870-925 [5]	1600-1700 [5]	815-870	1500-1600	815-845	1500-1550	Oil
G51500	5150							
G51600	5160	870-925 [5]	1600-1700 [5]	815-870	1500-1600	800-845	1475-1550	Oil
G51601	5160							
G61500	6150		—	845-900	1550-1650	845-885	1550-1625	Oil
G86300	8630	870-925 [5]	1600-1700 [5]	790-845	1450-1550	830-870	1525-1600	Water or oil
G86370	8637		—	815-870	1500-1600	830-855	1525-1575	Oil
G86400	8640							
G86450	8645		—	815-870	1500-1600	815-855	1500-1575	Oil
G92600	9260			—	—	815-900	1500-1650	Oil

1. These steels are fine grain unless otherwise specified.
2. The specific annealing cycle is dependent on the alloy content of the steel, the type of subsequent machining operations, and de sired surface finish.
3. Frequenty, these steels, with the exception of 4340, 50100, 51100, and 52100, are hardened and tempered to a final machinable hardness without preliminary heat treatment.
4. All steels are tempered to desired hardness.
5. These steels should be either normalized or annealed for optimum machinability.
6. Temper at 595 to 665 °C (1100 to 1225 °F).

TABLE 5A—TYPICAL HEAT TREATMENTS FOR GRADES OF CHROMIUM-NICKEL AUSTENITIC STEELS NOT HARDENABLE BY THERMAL TREATMENT

SAE Steels	AISI No.	Annealing[1] Temperature, °C	Annealing[1] Temperature, °F
20201	201	1010-1120	1850-2050
20202	202	1010-1120	1850-2050
30301	301	1010-1120	1850-2050
30302	302	1010-1120	1850-2050
30303	303	1010-1120	1850-2050
30304	304	1010-1120	1850-2050
30305	305	1010-1120	1850-2050
30309	309	1040-1120	1900-2050
30310	310	1040-1120	1900-2100
30316	316	1010-1120	1850-2050
30317	317	1010-1120	1850-2050
30321	321	955-1120	1750-2050
30325	325	980-1150	1800-2100
30330	—	1065-1175	1950-2150
30347	347	1010-1120	1850-2050

1. Quench to produce full austenitic structure using water or air in accordance with thickness of section. Annealing temperatures given cover process and full annealing as already established and used by industry, the lower end of the range being used for process annealing. All steels are quenched in air.

TABLE 5B—TYPICAL HEAT TREATMENTS FOR GRADES OF CHROMIUM-NICKEL AUSTENITIC STEELS NOT HARDENABLE BY THERMAL TREATMENT

Mean Carbon Content of SAE Specification, %	Common Applications (See also more detailed discussion below)
0.30-0.37	Heat-treated parts requiring moderate strength and great toughness
0.40-0.42	Heat-treated parts requiring higher strength and good toughness.
0.45-0.50	Heat-treated parts requiring fairly high hardness and strength with moderate toughness.
0.50-0.60	Springs and hand tools.
1.02	Ball and roller bearings

7.2 Stainless Chromium-Nickel Austenitic Steels (Not Hardenable)—These steels are austenitic at room temperature and higher and cannot be hardened by thermal treatment. Table 5 gives typical heat treatments for the following steels:

a. SAE 30301 is capable of developing high-tensile strength, while retaining high ductility by moderate to severe cold working. It is often used in the cold-rolled or cold-drawn condition in the form of sheet, strip, and wire. It is nonmagnetic when annealed but is magnetic when cold worked. Its corrosion resistance is not quite equal to SAE 30302. This steel is used for applications requiring a combination of high strength and excellent forming properties such as in structural members, automotive trim, and wheel discs and rings. It is used for flat and wire springs, windshield wiper arms, grills, steering wheel spokes, and similar applications. It is also used for cream separators and milking machine parts.
b. SAE 30302 is the general-purpose stainless steel of this type. Its corrosion resistance is better than that of SAE 30301, and it is the most widely used of all the chromium-nickel stainless and heat-resisting steels. It is used for deep drawing largely in the softer tempers. It can be worked to high-tensile strength but with lower ductility than SAE 30301. It is nonmagnetic when annealed but is magnetic when cold worked. This steel is used on automotive parts where excellent corrosion resistance or good forming and drawing properties are required. It is used for hub caps, radiator grills, windshield wiper parts such as tension bars and binder strips, hose clamps, antennas, control cables, fender guards, fire walls, and hydraulic tubing. It is used for other similar parts that have severe forming requirements combined with a need for corrosion resistance.
c. SAE 30303 has elements added to improve machining and nonseizing characteristics. This steel, the free machining modification of SAE 30302, is recommended for the manufacture of parts produced on automatic machines. It can be forged but requires much more care than is necessary with SAE 30302. Its corrosion resistance is slightly inferior to that of SAE 30302. It is nonmagnetic when annealed but is slightly magnetic when cold worked. It is used for screws, nuts, carburetor parts, aircraft fittings, water pump shafts, and other machined parts requiring some corrosion resistance. It is not recommended for applications involving severe cold working, cold upsetting, or welding.
d. SAE 30304 is a lower carbon steel similar to SAE 30302 but has superior welding properties for certain types of equipment. It is nonmagnetic when annealed but slightly magnetic when cold worked. It is used for diesel injection pump valve springs, roller chains, parachute hardware, and welded parts that can be heat treated after welding or parts that are not liable to damage by intergranular corrosion if heat treating after welding is not performed. This steel is also available with 0.03 to 0.05% carbon for even better corrosion resistance in the as-welded state.
e. SAE 30305 is similar to SAE 30302 and 30304, but because of a higher nickel content does not harden as rapidly with cold working as either of the similar grades. It also has much less change in magnetic permeability when cold worked. Because of its lower work hardening tendency, it is better suited for spun parts, multiple drawing operations, severe cold heading, and parts requiring large amounts of cold deformation.
f. SAE 30309 has higher corrosion and oxidation resistance than SAE 30304. It is resistant to oxidation at temperatures up to about 1095 °C (2000 °F). It is nonmagnetic when annealed but may be slightly magnetic when cold worked. It is used primarily in high temperature applications such as thermocouple wells, heat exchangers, glass lehr belts, and aircraft cabin heaters.
g. SAE 30310 has very high corrosion and heat resisting properties. As with SAE 30309, it resists oxidation at temperatures up to about 1095 °C (2000 °F). It is more stable and somewhat stronger at high temperatures and is more safely hot worked than SAE 30309. It is nonmagnetic when annealed or cold worked. It is used in such applications as diesel injector cup wipers, jet engine burner liners, and nozzle vanes.
h. SAE 30316 is similar to SAE 30304 in fabricating qualities. However, it has superior corrosion resistance to other chromium-nickel steels when exposed to sea water and many types of chemical corrodents, especially those of a reducing nature. It also has superior strength at elevated temperatures. It is nonmagnetic when annealed but is slightly magnetic when cold worked. It is used in applications such as wire screens, dye making and chemical processing equipment, and in elevated temperature service, especially where strength is important, up to about 815 °C (1500 °F). This steel has a specified molybdenum content which reduces susceptibility to pitting attack. The low carbon content stabilizes against intergranular carbide precipitation during welding. It is available with less than 0.05% carbon for further resistance to sensitization.
i. SAE 30317 is similar to SAE 30316 but with greater corrosion resistance in many environments and with somewhat greater high-temperature strength. It is primarily used for paper-making equipment and scrubber components.
j. SAE 30321 has a specified titanium content which acts to stabilize the alloy against sensitization. Its properties are similar to those of SAE 30304 except that it can be recommended for use in the manufacture of welded parts requiring immunity to intergranular attack and where heat treating after welding is not feasible. It may also be used where temperatures in the range of about 425 to 900 °C (800 to 1650 °F) are encountered in fabrication or service and where the possibility of intergranular corrosion exists. It is nonmagnetic when annealed but is slightly magnetic when cold worked. It has been used for exhaust manifolds, manifold flanges, and high temperature bolts and locknuts.
k. SAE 30330 alloy in the wrought and cast form is used for high temperature oxidation resistance essentially over 900 °C (1650 °F) and utilized in the construction of heat-treating baskets, similar items, and heat-treating furnace parts.
l. SAE 30347 is similar to SAE 30321 except it contains columbium instead of titanium. The columbium-bearing alloy is used in the same applications as SAE 30321.

7.3 Stainless Martensitic Chromium Steels (Hardenable)—These alloys combine carbon and chromium to produce a hardenable, high-strength stainless steel after proper heat treatment. They are ferritic at room temperature but become austenitic at elevated temperature. They can be rapidly cooled to produce a hard, martensitic structure in the same manner as other hardenable steels. Since they can be heat treated to produce martensite, they are commonly known as martensitic stainless steels.

a. SAE 51410 is the general-purpose steel of this type. It can be hardened by heat-treating to develop a wide range of mechanical properties. 39/45 RC is about the maximum useful hardness obtainable. It has fair machining properties and corrosion resistance, although in this respect, it is inferior to SAE51430. Best corrosion resistance is obtained in the heat-treated condition. It is magnetic in all conditions. It is used in applications requiring high strength combined with moderate resistance to corrosion. Possessing fair strength and good oxidation resistance to about 650 °C (1200 °F), it is used in manifold stud bolts, heat control shafts, steam valves, bourdon tubes, and gun mounts.

b. SAE 51414 has somewhat better corrosion resistance than SAE 51410. It will attain slightly higher mechanical properties when heat-treated than SAE 51410 and develop a maximum useful hardness of about 41/43 RC. It is magnetic in all conditions. It is used in the form of tempered strip and in bars and forgings for heat-treated parts for valve trim and stems.

c. SAE 51416 is similar to SAE 51410. It can be heat-treated to a maximum hardness of about 39/41 RC. Elements have been added to improve its machining and nonseizing characteristics at some sacrifice in corrosion resistance and weldability. It is the most readily machinable of all the stainless steels and is suited for use on automatic screw machines. It is magnetic in all conditions. This steel is available in bars, wire, and forgings and is used for water pump shafts, carburetor needle valves, heat control valve shafts, manifold parts, and other parts requiring a hardenable, free-machining corrosion and heat-resisting steel. Free-machining types are not recommended for welding.

d. SAE 51420 is capable of being hardened to a wide range of mechanical properties depending on the actual carbon and chromium contents. With low side of carbon range and chromium, the grade behaves similarly to SAE 51410. With 12.5%, or higher, chromium and 0.35% carbon, the maximum heat-treating response expected is about 53/56 RC. It offers its maximum corrosion-resistant properties only in fully hardened conditions. It is magnetic in all conditions. This steel is used in wire cutter blades, garden shears, cutlery, hardened pump shafts, water pump parts, glass and plastic molds, bomb shackle parts, and drive screws.

e. SAE 51420F is similar to SAE 51420 except that elements have been added to improve its machinability.

f. SAE 51431 is a nickel-bearing chromium steel capable of being heat treated to a maximum useful hardness of about 42/44 RC. Its corrosion resistance is superior to that of the other hardenable grades such as SAE 51410, 51420, and 51440. It is magnetic in all conditions and used for aircraft bolting, cable terminals, bomb shackle parts, and other parts requiring a hardenable steel with high mechanical properties and superior corrosion resistance.

g. SAE 51440A is hardenable to a greater quenched hardness than SAE 51420 and has greater toughness than SAE 51440B or 51440C. It can be hardened to a maximum of about 56/59 RC. Maximum corrosion resistance is obtained only from a polished surface on fully hardened material. Magnetic in all conditions, this steel is used for cutlery, paint spray nozzles, and some types of bearings.

h. SAE 51440B is hardenable to a greater quenched hardness than SAE 51440A and has greater toughness than SAE 51440C. Maximum corrosion resistance is obtained only from a polished surface on fully hardened material. Depending upon carbon content, it can be hardened to 53/58 RC. It is magnetic in all conditions and used for balls and races.

i. SAE 51440C acquires on heat treatment the highest quenched hardness and greatest wear resistance of any corrosion or heat resistant steel. It can be hardened to 55/60 RC and is corrosion resistant only in the fully hardened and polished condition. It is magnetic in all conditions. This steel is used for diesel engine pump parts, instrument parts, crankshaft counterweight pins, valve trim, ball bearings, races, and other parts requiring a hard wear and corrosion resistant surface.

j. SAE 51440F is similar to SAE 51440C except that elements have been added to improve its machinability and nonseizing characteristics. This steel is used for carburetor parts.

k. SAE 51501 is used for its heat resistance, corrosion resistance, and good mechanical properties at elevated temperatures. It is produced with about 0.5% molybdenum to improve its toughness. It can be heat treated to various hardnesses depending on the carbon content. It is magnetic in all conditions. It is used in service up to about 650 °C (1200 °F). A 0.15% maximum carbon type is used for tubing in oil stills and heat-treat exchangers. High carbon types are used for valve stems, valves, and hot or cold work dies and mandrels. This steel is not a true stainless steel.

7.4 Stainless Ferritic Chromium Steels (Not Hardenable)—The third group contains more chromium and less carbon than the second group. Nickel, if present, is incidental. By virtue of this high-chromium and low-carbon content, several of these steels are ferritic at room and elevated temperatures. As they do not transform to austenite, they cannot be hardened by heat treatment and are known as ferritic stainless steels. Table 6 shows typical heat treatments for these steels.

TABLE 6—TYPICAL HEAT TREATMENTS FOR STAINLESS CHROMIUM STEELS

SAE Steels	AISI No.	Subcritical Ann. Temp., °C	Subcritical Ann. Temp., °F	Full Annealing Temperature(1), °F	Full Annealing Temperature(1), °F	Hardening Temp., °C	Hardening Temp., °F	Quenching(2) Medium
51409	—	—	—	885	1625	—	—	air
51410	410	705–730(3)	1300–1350(3)	815–900	1500–1650	925–1010	1700–1850	oil or air
51414	414	650–675(3)	1200–1250(3)	—	—	980–1040	1800–1900	oil or air
51416	416	705–730(3)	1300–1350(4)	815–900	1500–1650	925–1010	1700–1850	oil or air
51420	420	730–790(3)	1350–1450(3)	845–900	1550–1650	980–1040	1800–1900	oil or air
51420F(5)	—	730–790(3)	1350–1450(3)	845–900	1550–1650	980–1040	1800–1900	oil or air
51430	430	760–815(4)	1400–1500(4)	—	—	—	—	—
51430F(5)	—	675–760(4)	1250–1400(4)	—	—	—	—	—
51431	431	620–665(3)	1150–1225(3)	—	—	980–1065	1800–1950	oil or air
51434	—	760–870(4)	1400–1600(4)	—	—	—	—	—
51436	—	760–870(4)	1400–1600(4)	—	—	—	—	—
51440A(5)	440A	730–780(3)	1350–1440(3)	845–900	1550–1650	1010–1065	1850–1950	oil or air
51440B(5)	440B	730–780(3)	1350–1440(3)	845–900	1550–1650	1010–1065	1850–1950	oil or air
51440C(5)	440C	730–780(3)	1350–1440(3)	845–900	1550–1650	1010–1065	1850–1950	oil or air
51440F(5)	—	730–780(3)	1350–1440(3)	845–900	1550–1650	1010–1065	1850–1950	oil or air
51442	442	730–815(4)	1350–1500(4)	—	—	—	—	—
51446	446	790–870(3)	1450–1600(4)	—	—	—	—	—
51501	501	720–745(4)	1325–1375(4)	830–870	1525–1600	870–925	1600–1700	oil or air

1. Cool slowly in furnace.
2. All steels are tempered to desired hardness.
3. Usually air-cooled but may be furnace cooled.
4. Cool rapidly in air.
5. Suffixes A, B, and C denote three types of steel differing only in carbon content. Suffix F denotes a free machining steel.

a. SAE 51409 has excellent weldability and formability characteristics. Its corrosion resistance is superior to carbon and low-alloy steels but not as high as SAE 51430. It is not normally considered hardenable by cold working or heat treatment. Its ductility is slightly higher than SAE 51430, and it is magnetic. It is primarily used in muffler, manifold, catalytic converter, and exhaust pipe applications but is being used in an increasing number of other automotive applications such as filter bodies and thermostat components. This steel is the largest tonnage stainless presently used in automotive parts.

b. SAE 51430 has superior corrosion and heat resistance, as compared with SAE 51410. Its ductility is fair, but it is resistant to destructive oxidation up to about 815 °C (1500 °F). Magnetic in all conditions, this steel is used for parts requiring only a moderate draw, such as moldings, windshield wiper yokes, heat control valves, shafts and bushings, fasteners of all types, wire strainer screens, and fender guards.

c. SAE 51430F is similar to SAE 51430 except that elements have been added to improve its machinability and nonseizing characteristics. It is less amenable to both cold and hot work than SAE 51430 and is used for oil burner nozzles and other machined parts requiring good corrosion or heat resistance. This type of steel is not recommended for welding.

d. SAE 51434 is similar to SAE 51430 in ductility and heat resistance. It is magnetic in all conditions. More resistant to road salt attack than SAE 51430, it is used as trim and other exterior parts. A modification of SAE 51434 is SAE 51436, which has the ability to reduce a "roping" characteristic found in SAE 51430 and 51434 when the alloys are stretched. SAE 51436 is used in "stretch-bent" automobile trim applications.

e. SAE 51442 is somewhat superior in corrosion and heat resistance compared to SAE 51430. It has good resistance to oxidation up to 980 °C (1800 °F). This steel is magnetic in all conditions.

f. SAE 51446 has the maximum amount of chromium, consistent with commercial malleability. It is used primarily for the manufacture of parts that must resist high temperatures in service without scaling but which are not highly stressed. It resists destructive oxidation up to a temperature of about 1095 °C (2000 °F). This steel is used for glass seals, salt bath electrodes, thermocouple wells, combustion chambers, and other parts where resistance to oxidation is important but where the need to carry a load is negligible.

g. Type 466 is a 11.50% chromium ferritic stainless steel. By dual stabilizing with titanium and columbium, the alloy chemistry is balanced to provide a very low titanium content resulting in a significant reduction in objectionable titanium-related surface defects that are sometimes associated with titanium (only) stabilized Type 409 alloys. In some instances, weldability appears to be improved. The low titanium content in 466 alloy also improves brazing characteristics. The mechanical property and corrosion data indicate 466 alloy has the same general corrosion resistance and formability properties as Type 409. Like all ferritic stainless steels, this steel is highly resistant to stress corrosion cracking.

Straight chromium steels (16% or more) and chromium-nickel steels having 18% or more chromium are subject to development of the sigma phase when exposed to temperatures of 540 °C (1000 °F) or higher for extended time periods. This phase is an intermetallic compound that increases hardness, but decreases ductility, notch toughness, and corrosion resistance. Its presence can lead to service failure. This phase can be eliminated by heating to about 900 °C (1650 °F).

7.5 Precipitation Hardened Stainless Steels—Precipitation hardened stainless steels can be hardened through low temperature heat treatments and offer high strength in addition to excellent corrosion resistance. The martensitic group is most widely used and includes SAE 17400 and SAE 15500. The semiaustenite group was developed for increased formability before the hardening heat treatment and includes SAE 17700. All grades are available in sheet, strip, plate, bar, and wire.

a. SAE 17400 is a precipitation hardenable stainless steel that is used in a variety of applications such as valves, gears, aircraft fittings, pump shafts, and jet engine parts. Typical composition is 16% chromium, 4% nickel, 3% copper, and the balance iron. Niobium plus tantalum ranges from 0.15 to 0.45. Maximum strength is obtained after solution treating to 1040 °C (1900 °F), cooling to room temperature, reheating for 1 h at the precipitation temperature of 480 °C (900 °F), and cooling to room temperature. Higher precipitation temperatures may also be selected to obtain better ductility and toughness.

b. SAE 15500 is very similar to SAE 17400 in suggested heat treatment and properties. However, when the aerospace and nuclear industry require stringent cleanliness with excellent transverse mechanical properties, SAE 15500 is the choice because of the practice of remelting this steel in a vacuum or with a protective flux. Also, the SAE 15500 chemistry is adjusted to eliminate delta ferrite, which improves the transverse mechanical properties in any test location.

c. SAE 17700—For better fabricability in the solution-treated condition, SAE 17700 is offered with the ability to be precipitation hardened. Typical applications include aircraft skins, structural parts, jet engine parts, springs, diaphragms, bellows, fasteners, and whip antennae. For maximum strength, SAE 17700 can be used in the fully cold worked condition and precipitation heat-treated at 480 °C (900 °F) for 1 h and cooled to room temperature. Other heat treatments exist for solution annealed products that necessitate the forming characteristics of a 300 series stainless steel. Typical composition for this grade is 17% chromium, 7% nickel, and 1% aluminum.

d. SAE 15700 is a semiaustenitic, precipitation hardenable stainless steel that has similar mechanical properties and forming characteristics to type SAE 17700. The modified chemistry of 15% chromium, 7% nickel, 2.5% molybdenum, and 1% aluminum makes precipitation heat treating somewhat simpler along with better ductility in weldments. End uses include retaining rings, springs, diaphragms, bellows, fasteners, and instrument parts.

e. SAE 35000 is a semiaustenitic chromium-nickel-molybdenum stainless steel. SAE 35000 combines the corrosion resistance and formability characteristics of the austenitic stainless steels with the strengths of the martensitic stainless steels. Relatively low temperature heat treatments of this precipitation hardening stainless steel have eliminated many of the problems associated with normal heat treating procedures. While the primary hardening mechanism is the formation of martensite, from the proper control of the austenite to martensite transformation, tempering treatments furnish additional hardness and strength. The chemistry of this grade results in about 10% ferrite to be stable throughout processing.

f. SAE 35500 is a semiaustenitic chromium-nickel-molybdenum stainless steel. SAE 35500 combines the corrosion resistance and formability characteristics of the austenitic stainless steels with the strengths of the martensitic stainless steels. Relatively low-temperature heat treatments of this precipitation hardening stainless steel have eliminated many of the problems associated with normal heat treating procedures. While the primary hardening mechanism is the formation of martensite, with proper control of the austenite to martensite transformation, tempering treatments furnish additional hardness and strength. The ferrite phase is generally absent from this grade. This can result in a higher strength cold-rolled product.

7.6 Age Hardenable Martensitic Steels (Maraging)—The 18% nickel maraging steels belong to a loosely knit family of iron-base alloys that are strengthened by a combination of martensite formation followed by an aging treatment. Yield strengths up to and well beyond 2070 MPa (300 ksi) are available when these steels are in the aged condition.

a. SAE 93120 is a member of the 18% nickel-cobalt-molybdenum-titanium maraging martensitic steels that offer the best combination of mechanical properties and heat treatment. The titanium-aluminum or the cobalt-molybdenum-titanium contents of these steels serve as the hardening agents. Depending on composition and product form, strengths of 1380 to 2070 MPa (200 to 300 ksi) yield strength and 1450 to 2140 MPa (210 to 310 ksi) tensile strength, accompanied by 15 to 5% elongation, are possible with these alloys.

b. SAE 36200 is a chromium-nickel maraging steel. It contains sufficient chromium to exhibit the corrosion and oxidation resistance of the stainless steels. SAE 36200 is martensitic in the annealed condition with good toughness and ductility. Increased strength is achieved by low-temperature heat treatments.

7.7 Stainless Steels Possessing Special Machinability Features—This group represents proprietary modifications of standard SAE steels to provide steels of special machining characteristics in comparison to the standard free-machining counterparts. These steels are particularly suited for parts made in automatic screw machines. Table 7 shows typical heat treatments for these steels.

a. Type 203-EZ is a chromium-nickel-manganese free machining stainless steel. It is austenitic and does not respond to thermal treatments. This steel is nonmagnetic when annealed, but slightly magnetic when cold worked.

b. Types 303 Ma, 303 Cu, and 303 Plus X are modifications of SAE 30303. They are austenitic and do not respond to thermal treatments. These steels are nonmagnetic when annealed, but slightly magnetic when cold worked.

c. Type 416 Plus X is a modification of SAE 51416. This steel is martensitic and hardenable by thermal treatments to RC 40 minimum. It is magnetic in all conditions.

TABLE 7—TYPICAL HEAT TREATMENTS FOR WROUGHT STAINLESS STEELS OF SPECIAL MACHINABILITY

Proprietary Designation	Subcritical Annealing Temperature, °C	Subcritical Annealing Temperature, °F	Full Annealing Temperature, °C	Full Annealing Temperature, °F	Quenching Medium
203-EZ	—	—	1010–1120(1)	1850–2050(1)	Water or air
303 Ma	—	—	1010–1120(1)	1850–2050(1)	Water or air
303 Cu	—	—	1010–1120(1)	1850–2050(1)	Water or air
303 Plus X	—	—	1010–1120(1)	1850–2050(1)	Water or air
416 Plus X	705–730(2)	1300–1350(2)	845–900(3)	1550–1650(3)	—

1. Quench to produce full austenitic structure using water or air in accodance with thickness of section. Annealing temperatures given cover process and full annealing as already established and used by industry, the lower end of the range being used for process annealing.
2. Usually air-cooled but may be furnace cooled.
3. Cool slowly in the furnace.

8. Heat Treatments Applied to Steel

8.1 Normalizing—The normalizing process consists of:

a. Uniformly heating steel to a temperature high enough to obtain complete transformation to austenite.

b. Holding at the austenitizing temperature until the mass is of equal temperature throughout.

c. Air cooling, allowing free air circulation to give uniform cooling. Normalizing temperatures are dependent on the steel grade, while holding time at temperature will vary with the mass being heat treated. Hence, normalizing cycles and subsequent steel properties may vary considerably with steel grade, part size, individual furnace conditions, and cooling facilities.

Normalizing is generally performed to obtain desired mechanical properties but is also used for the following functions:

1. Modify and refine coarse as-rolled or forged structures.
2. Improve hardening characteristics by refining grain size and homogenizing microstructure.
3. Improve machining characteristics. This treatment is especially beneficial for 0.15 to 0.40% carbon steels.

8.2 Annealing—When the term "annealing" is applied without qualification, the term implies full annealing. Full annealing consists of austenitizing and then cooling uniformly and slowly, through the transformation range. In isothermal annealing, the heating is the same as used for a full anneal, but the steel is held for a given time at a constant temperature in the upper transformation range before being cooled at a uniform rate. This practice produces pearlite structure that greatly improves machinability of medium carbon steels. Spheroidizing is an annealing process where steel is slowly cooled to a point below the A1 transformation temperature, and under suitable conditions of temperature and time, produces a spheroidal or globular form of carbide in steel and is recommended prior to machining steels higher than 0.60% carbon.

Recrystallization annealing is another form of subcritical annealing. The part is heated to a temperature just below the A1 transformation temperature and held for a predetermined length of time. It is most effective on hardened or cold-worked steels that recrystallize readily to form new ferrite grains. The rate of softening increases rapidly as the temperature approaches the transformation temperature.

In addition to producing desired mechanical properties, improving machinability, and obtaining the desired microstructure, the various forms of annealing are frequently used to improve the cold-forming properties of steels.

8.3 Carbon Restoration—Carbon restoration or carbon correction is, in reality, a carburizing treatment for restoring carbon to the decarburized skin found on some grades of hot-rolled, cold-drawn, or cold-drawn and annealed steel products. The process was originally applied to medium carbon steels where substantial differences in carbon content can occur between the base metal and the decarburized zone. The intent is to adjust the carbon potential of the furnace atmosphere to the carbon content of the steel being treated.

Although carbon restoration can be applied to any product that the available equipment can accommodate, its usual application is to bars and rods in either coils or cut lengths. The carbon-restored product will approximate the mechanical properties of annealed bars or rods of the base carbon level. In any application, it is well to keep in mind that the surface condition of the carbon-restored product, with respect to seams, is the same as that of the hot-rolled or cold-drawn stock before the process started.

8.4 Case Hardening—In this report, case hardening refers to heat treatments utilizing gases or molten baths, and includes carburizing, nitriding, and carbonitriding.

Gas carburizing is accomplished by heating the work to austenitizing temperature and subjecting the hot steel to an atmosphere containing carbon monoxide and methane. The depth of case is determined by carburizing time, carburizing temperature, carbon potential of the atmosphere, and to some extent, the type of steel being carburized.

The time required to achieve a desired case depth can be significantly shortened by elevating the temperature well into the austenite range (980 to 1040 °C or 1800 to 1900 °F); however, temperature is usually reduced towards the end of the cycle to control carbon diffusion and to prevent cracking and excessive distortion. Also, undesirable grain growth can occur during high-temperature carburizing.

The most commonly used carburizing atmosphere is a mixture of endothermic carrier gas (a product resulting from the burning of natural gas and an insufficient amount of air for complete combustion) and a source of carbon such as natural gas or propane. Another carburizing atmosphere is produced by introducing a liquid hydrocarbon into nitrogen gas at high temperature. Vacuum carburizing involves removing air from the furnace chamber and then introducing the carburizing gas or agent under partial pressure.

Ion (or plasma) carburizing is a relatively new alternative to gas carburizing. The workpieces are placed in a vacuum chamber and the parts electrically isolated from the vessel walls. Application of a high voltage causes the treatment gas to become ionized. Under these conditions, the vessel wall acts as the anode and the work pieces act as the cathode. Positive ions of treatment gas bombard the workpiece, causing carbon to penetrate the surface. Selective carburizing can be accomplished by masking off portions of the workpiece from the bombarding action.

Liquid carburizing is accomplished by immersing the work in a molten salt bath containing sodium cyanide (NaCN) in an inert carrier salt. This process is performed at 900 to 955 °C (1650 to 1750 °F). At this temperature carbon from the cyanide is chemically active, while the nitrogen is inert. Disposal problems of these salts often make this process less attractive.

Gas carbonitriding introduces both carbon and nitrogen into the metal surface, producing a harder and more wear-resistant surface than can be accomplished by carburizing alone. Ammonia (NH_3) gas is introduced into the carburizing atmosphere. At high temperature, the ammonia gas breaks up and chemically active nitrogen gas forms iron nitrides at the steel surface. Carbonitriding is carried out at a lower temperatures and for shorter periods of time than carburizing, and less distortion is usually evident. Case depths of 0.075 to 0.75mm (0.003 to 0.03 in) are typical. Since nitrogen is also an austenite stabilizer, increased levels of retained austenite are possible.

Liquid carbonitriding (also known as cyaniding) involved immersion of the work in a molten bath containing NaCN and a carrier salt. The process differs from liquid carburizing in that it is carried out at a lower temperature (815 to 845 °C or 1500 to 1550 °F). At this temperature, both carbon and nitrogen from the cyanide are chemically active with the iron.

Gas nitriding is accomplished by introducing ammonia into the furnace at approximately 540 °C (1000 °F). At this temperature, the nitrogen available from the ammonia is chemically active with the steel, forming a very hard iron nitride white layer that is 0.0025 to 0.02 mm (0.0001 to 0.0008 in) thick at the surface. A hardened case is formed below this layer. Depending on time at temperature, this case may be as much as 0.3 to 0.4mm (0.012 to 0.016 in) thick. Liquid nitriding uses the same molten salt bath immersion process as liquid carburizing and carbonitriding, but at a temperature of only 510 to 565 °C (950 to 1050 °F).

Ion nitriding is analogous to ion carburizing. The process is performed in a vacuum furnace. High-voltage electrical energy ionizes the treatment gas and nitrogen ions bombard the surface of the workpiece.

The carburizing processes are completed by either direct quenching into a suitable liquid medium or cooling to room temperature, reheating, and quenching. Nitrided cases do not need quenching after the nitride operation. Since nitriding is performed at a much lower temperature and quenching is not required, distortion during nitriding is much less than with carburizing and hardening.

Carburizing is generally preferable to the other case hardening processes when a case having high strength and particularly high crushing load resistance is desired. When high resistance to wear is most important, a carbonitrided or nitrided steel surface is preferred.

8.5 Through Hardening—Carbon and alloy steel may be hardened by quenching from the austenitizing temperature. Generally, steels having 0.30% or more carbon are through hardened. Steels capable of being quenched to high hardness throughout their cross section are described as "through hardened."

The level of "as quenched" surface hardness is dependent on the carbon content, the quench intensity, and the quenching temperature. Hardnesses at various depths under the surface are also dependent on these factors plus the hardenability of the steel. Hardenability is determined by alloy content.

To prevent surface decarburization, a protective atmosphere having a carbon potential nearly equal to the carbon content of the work is commonly utilized in batch and continuous furnaces used for through hardening. Subsequent tempering is required to achieve desired hardness, ductility, and toughness.

8.6 Selective Heating and Hardening—Carbon and alloy steels may be subjected to selective hardening when a hard case and comparatively soft core are desired, or when only a portion of the steel surface is to be hardened. Hardening is accomplished by rapidly heating the area to be hardened to austenitizing temperature, then quenching rapidly before the heat can diffuse.

8.6.1 INDUCTION HARDENING—Selective heating is most commonly accomplished by means of an inductor that carries a high-frequency alternating current. Depending on the application, the frequency generally ranges from 60 to 500 000 Hz. Steel in the immediate vicinity of the inductor is heated rapidly by induced eddy currents. The inductive heating machine may be designed to cause the work to revolve or traverse past the inductor, so that a large surface can be heated by a relatively small inductor. In some induction heating setups, both the work and inductor remain stationary during the heating cycle. Relatively low-frequency current is used for deep heating, whereas high-frequency current is used for shallow heating. The area to be hardened is heated until the required depth of hardening reaches austenitizing temperature. The work is then quenched, either by flooding with, or immersing into, a quenching medium.

8.6.2 FLAME HARDENING—Selective heating can also be accomplished by a hot flame from one or a series of torch nozzles. Oxygen plus acetylene (or one of several commercially available torch heating gases) are used as the source of energy.

8.6.3 LASER AND E.B. HARDENING—Two relatively new, more sophisticated methods now coming into use for selective heating are the laser beam and the electron beam. In either case, the high energy beam is directed at the area to be heated. If the area is heated to a very shallow depth, the surface can be "self quenched" whereby the cold mass of the part causes the hot surface to cool very rapidly without any external quenching. If deeper depths are heated, conventional quenching methods must be employed.

Hardened parts can be selectively softened by any of these methods. The parts are simply heated to the required temperature and allowed to cool in air.

8.7 Deep Freezing—If a carburized or through hardened part contains a high level of retained austenite (greater than approximately 30%), surface hardnesses can be significantly increased by cooling the work to a temperature of −40 °C (−40 °F) or lower, thus converting nearly all retained austenite in the structure to hard martensite. It is often necessary to temper or retemper after deep freezing.

8.8 Tempering—Most "as quenched" carburized, through hardened, and selectively hardened steel is subjected to a tempering heat treatment to convert the very hard, brittle untempered martensite to a tempered condition that is softer and more ductile. Hardness reduction is dependent on tempering temperature, and on time at temperature, which can vary from a few seconds to several hours. Carburizing grade steels are usually tempered at 120 to 205 °C (250 to 400 °F), while steels having 0.30% or more carbon content are tempered at 370 to 595 °C (700 to 1100 °F), depending on the hardness level desired.

Some steels become brittle when tempered at 205 to 370°C (400 to 700 °F). Susceptibility to this condition, known as blue brittleness, should be investigated before a steel is tempered within this temperature range.

8.9 Austempering—This heat treatment is used when a combination of fairly high hardness (35 to 55 RC) and good toughness is essential. It is not used on steels having 0.40% or less carbon content, and is applicable only to steels and cast irons having certain time-temperature transformation characteristics.

The work is heated to austenitizing temperature and quenched very quickly in a salt or oil bath maintained at a temperature just above the MS (start of martensite transformation) temperature. The steel is held at this temperature for sufficient time to form a structure having a high percentage of hard, tough lower bainite and then cooled to room temperature.

8.10 Martempering and Marquenching—When freedom from distortion is important and some hardness reduction from that obtained by conventional quenching can be accepted, a steel part is quenched into hot oil or molten salt (at a temperature at or just below the MS temperature). This process, known as martempering, is not a replacement for tempering. Martempered parts are cooled to room temperature and then given a conventional tempering treatment. When martempering is applied to carburizing grade steels, it is sometimes referred to as marquenching.

8.11 Quenching—An important parameter in the determination of "as quenched" hardness for a steel part is the quench severity. The level of severity is dependent upon the quenching medium used, the quenchant temperature, the temperature of the steel being quenched, and the quenching pressure (rate at which the quenchant is supplied to the metal surface).

In order of increasing severity, commonly used liquid quenchants are molten salt, oil, soluble oil-water mix, polymer solutions, water brine, and caustic soda solution. It is usually desirable to obtain the greatest quench severity that can be used without subjecting the steel to cracking, objectionable distortion, or excessive stresses that cannot be overcome by subsequent tempering.

Some high-hardenability steels are quenched in forced air, or even in still air. Some tool steels can be quenched in fluidized beds of rapidly agitated small solid particles.

8.12 Stress Relieving—This operation consists of uniformly heating a part or structure to a temperature below the transformation temperature and holding for a predetermined length of time. The time must be long enough to equalize temperature throughout the part and followed by uniform cooling at a fairly slow rate, usually by air cooling. Stress relieving temperatures vary from 150 to 705 °C (300 to 1300 °F) depending on the type of steel being treated. (Temperatures above the transformation temperature will remove the effects of prior heat treatment.) This operation is used to relieve residual stresses that may have resulted from manufacturing processes such as cold working, welding, or heat treatment. No change in the basic microstructure is expected.

CASE HARDENABILITY OF CARBURIZED STEELS —SAE J1975 NOV1997

SAE Information Report

Report of the SAE Iron and Steel Technical Committee Division 8—Carbon And Alloy Steel Hardenability approved June 1991 and revi sed November 1997.

1. Scope—This SAE Information Report summarizes the characteristics of carburized steels and factors involved in controlling hardness, microstructure, and residual stress. Methods of determining case hardenability are reviewed, as well as methods to test for freedom from non-martensitic structures in the carburized case. Factors influencing case hardenability are also reviewed. Methods of predicting case hardenability are included, with examples of calculations for several standard carburizing steels. A bibliography is included in 2.2. The references provide more detailed information on the topics discussed in this document.

2. References

2.1 Applicable Publications—The following publications form a part of this specification to the extent specified herein. Unless otherwise indicated, the latest issue of SAE publications shall apply.

2.1.1 SAE PUBLICATIONS—Available from SAE, 400 Commonwealth Drive, Warrendale, PA 15096-0001.

SAE J403—Chemical Compositions of SAE Carbon Steels
SAE J404—Chemical Compositions of SAE Alloy Steels
SAE J406—Methods of Determining Hardenability of Steels
SAE J417—Hardness Tests and Hardness Number Conversions
SAE J1268—Hardenability Bands for Carbon and Alloy H Steels

2.2 Other Publications

1. R.F. Thomson, "Summary," *Fatigue Durability of Carburized Steel*, ASM International, Metals Park, Ohio, 1957, p. 110.
2. D.H. Breen, "Fundamentals of Gear Stress/Strength Relationships—Materials," SAE Technical Paper 841083, 1984.
3. J.M. Hodge and M.A. Orehoski, "Relationship Between Hardenability and Percentage of Martensite in Some Low Alloy Steels," Trans. AIME, 1946, Vol. 167, pp. 627–642.
4. M. Atkins, *Atlas of Continuous Cooling Transformation Diagrams for Engineering Steels*, ASM International and British Steel Corporation, 1980.
5. A. Rose and H. Hougardy, *Atlas zur Waermebehandlung der Stahle*, V.2, 1972, Max-Planck-Institut fuer Eisenforschung; Verlag Stahleisen m.b.H., P.O. Box 8229, D-4000, Dusseldorf, West Germany. Summarized in English by Rose and Hougardy in "Transformation Characteristics and Hardenability of Carburizing Steels," in the proceedings of the Symposium Transformation and Hardenability in Steels, Climax Molybdenum Co., 1967, pages 155-167.
6. C.A. Siebert, D.V. Doane and D.H. Breen, *The Hardenability of Steels—Concepts, Metallurgical Influences, and Industrial Applications*, ASM International, 1977, pp. 163–176.
7. "Modern carburized nickel alloy steels," Reference Book No. 11005, Nickel Development Institute, Toronto, Ontario, Canada M5H 3S6, 1990, pages 19-22.
8. A.E. Gurley and C.R. Hannewald, "Development and Applications of Iso-Hardness Diagrams," Metal Treating, V. 7, May-June 1956, p. 2.
9. J. A. Halgren and E.A. Solecki, "Case Hardenability of SAE 4028, 8620, 4620 and 4815 Steels," SAE Technical Paper 149A, 1960.
10. Atlas, *Hardenability of Carburized Steels*, Climax Molybdenum Co., 1960.
11. D.E. Diesburg, C. Kim and W. Fairhurst, "Microstructure and Residual Stress Effects on the Fracture of Case-Hardened Steels," Proceedings of *Heat Treatment '81*, The Metals Society, London, September, 1981.
12. R.F. Kern, Metal Progress, Oct. 1972, p. 172.
13. G.T. Eldis and Y.E. Smith, "Effect of Composition on Distance to First Bainite in Carburized Steels," Journal of Heat Treating, V. 2, No. 1, June 1981, pp. 62–72.
14. I.R. Kramer, S. Siegel and J.G. Brooks, "Factors for the Calculation of Hardenability," Trans. AIME, 1946, Vol. 167, p. 670.
15. C.F. Jatczak, "Hardenability in High Carbon Steels," Met. Trans., 1973, V. 4, p. 2272.
16. "New CCT Diagrams for Carburizing Steels," Molybdenum Mosaic, 1987, V. 10, No. 1, AMAX Metal Products, Bridgeville, PA, p. 11.
17. D.V. Doane, "Softening High Hardenability Steels for Machining and Cold Forming," Journal of Heat Treating, V. 6, No. 2, 1988, pp. 97–109.
18. R.J. Love, H.C. Allsopp and A.T. Weare, "The Influence of Carburizing Conditions and Heat Treatment on the Bending Fatigue Strength and Impact Strength of Gears Made from EN352 Steel," MIRA Report No. 19.59/7.
19. J.A. Burnett, "Prediction of Stresses Generated During the Heat Treating of Case Carburized Parts," *Residual Stresses for Designers and Metallurgists*, ASM International, 1981, pp. 51–69.
20. C. Kim, D.E. Diesburg and G.T. Eldis, "Effect of Residual Stress on Fatigue Fracture of Case-Hardened Steels—An Analytical Model," *Residual Stress Effects in Fatigue*, ASTM Special Technical Publication 776, 1982, pp. 224–234.

3. General—The typical carburized steel component can be modeled as a composite material with a high-hardness, carbon-rich surface layer on a lower carbon base that is lower in hardness but higher in toughness. The continuous nature of the transition between the high-carbon case and the low-carbon core, combined with the sequence of transformation events occurring throughout the component during quenching result in the development of a microstructural gradient and a favorable residual stress profile. These factors define the overall fatigue and fracture properties of the carburized component.

Failure modes of carburized components influence the choice of case depth and microstructure. To illustrate the nature of the stresses developed in a carburized component, and how they can be effectively used, Figure 1 shows the stresses in a carburized bar subjected to bending fatigue [1].[1] In this situation, the applied stress is highest at the surface and zero at the centerline. The hardness gradient of the carburized and hardened bar indicates the probable gradient in endurance limit (or fatigue limit) which is highest at the surface, and drops through the case-core interface to the lower fatigue limit of the core.

During quenching, the core material transforms first because its lower carbon content has a higher martensite-start temperature. The case material transforms somewhat later because its higher carbon content has a lower martensite-start temperature. Since the strength of the core resists the expansion of the case during its martensite transformation, compressive stresses develop in the case that are balanced by tensile stresses in the core. These residual stresses (curve A) add to, or subtract from, the inherent microstructural strength (curve B), resulting in the net effective fatigue limit (or endurance limit) shown by the dashed curve. Note that in this properly designed and loaded beam, the effective fatigue limit level is always greater than the applied stress. The diagram is over-simplified, of course, to demonstrate the principles involved.

Breen has discussed modes of failure in gears [2] and showed that the applied stresses at the root of the tooth decrease nonlinearly with depth. The high stress level at the surface is a result of the cantilever loading of the gear tooth, intensified by the stress concentration caused by the root radius and surface finish. Thus, for a carburized gear, it is quite important that the effective fatigue limit be as high as possible at the surface.

For failure at and below the contact or pitch line of a gear tooth, the applied stress curve is yet a different shape, as described in Breen's article [2], and illustrated in Figure 2. Hertzian stresses are greatest below the surface, the depth depending on the profile of the surfaces in contact. If the net fatigue limit curve, the critical strength curve B shown in the figure, coincides with the applied stress curve A at some depth X below the surface, e.g., at the case-core interface, then subcase (spalling) fatigue can occur. This failure mode emphasizes the need to provide adequate case depth and optimum microstructure at all carbon levels.

The ratio of the volume (or cross-sectional area) of case to core defines the magnitude of compressive stress at the surface. Thus, for a given part, the magnitude of the compressive stress in the case tends to decrease as the case depth increases. When the design is correct, the critical shear strength will remain above the applied stress curve.

3.1 Hardness versus Carbon Content—For a given carbon level there is a systematic relationship between hardness and structure in hardened steel, as shown in Figure 3, from the work of Hodge and Orehoski [3]. The curves not only show the differences due to microstructure, but also the variability in measurements. The spread in hardness at 99.9% martensite is due primarily to measurement errors; the greater spread at 50% martensite is attributable to the variability in the non-martensitic structure. Breen [2] has stated that to resist fatigue failure due to cyclic bending stresses at the root fillet of gears, the optimum case structure is a mixture of high carbon martensite and retained austenite, with enough martensite to assure a hardness of at least 57HRC. The microstructure in the core should comprise only martensite and bainite. For most alloy carburizing steels, transformation to at least 50% martensite assures that the balance of the structure is bainite [4,5].

1. Numbers in brackets are references cited in 2.2.

To maintain high case hardness, retained austenite must be restricted. Data from Rose and Hougardy [5] on microstructure and hardness of several carburized steels show that alloy content and alloy interactions influence the range of case carbon contents within which a suitable hardness and a martensite/austenite microstructure can be achieved.

3.2 Hardenability—A certain minimum hardenability is necessary to develop the required strength in a carburized part. The hardenability of the base composition governs the capability of developing high strength martensite in the core and in the medium carbon portion of the case. Hardenability in the high carbon region controls the capability of a steel to develop sufficient hardness and an appropriate microstructure at the case surface. The conventional Jominy end-quench test can provide much of the needed information, if case hardenability is considered as well as base, or core, hardenability.

For certain applications, shallow carburized cases may be employed to improve wear resistance under light to moderate load conditions. For such applications, high surface hardness is the important criterion. A fully martensitic structure at the surface provides highest hardness and best resistance to wear. Section size dictates the cooling rate that can be achieved at the surface, especially in parts which are oil quenched (Figure 7 of SAE J406). Cooling rate, expressed as distance from the quenched end of the Jominy hardenability bar, can define the hardenability required.

Hardenability requirements for carburized components are discussed in some detail in an ASM monograph [6], including consideration of section size in terms of "Jominy equivalent," carbon gradient, and surface oxidation. An example uses a gear to demonstrate the engineering approach to steel selection, and the steps involved in reaching a cost-effective choice of steel which meets design requirements. Processing requirements are also included.

4. Methods of Determining Case Hardenability—The end-quench method for determining hardenability is described in SAE J406. The method has been used to determine case as well as core hardenability of carburized steels. Figure 4 shows the core and case hardenability of a heat of SAE 4620 steel, containing nominally 0.2% C, 0.6% Mn, 1.8% Ni, and 0.25% Mo. A common criterion for evaluating the hardenability of a steel is the "ideal critical diameter, D_I." It is defined as the diameter of a bar which exhibits an acceptable microstructure when subjected to an "ideal" quench (a quench of infinite severity, defined in more detail in [6]). For carbon contents in the core and transition regions of a carburized steel, a microstructure of 50% martensite, balance bainite, is often chosen. This microstructure is characteristic of that found in the inflection region of the hardenability curve. This "50% martensite" criterion is indicated by the dashed line in Figure 4, and relates to the D_I for each carbon level. In the carburized case, however, a microstructure containing at least 90% martensite and retained austenite is considered necessary to resist fatigue failure. This "90% martensite" criterion is indicated by another dashed line in Figure 4, and relates to the D_I for case hardenability.

4.1 Jominy End-Quench Test—The test can be used to determine hardness at various carbon levels in the carburized case, as a function of cooling rate, expressed as the distance from the quenched end of the test bar. Figure 4 is one example. The method for determining case hardenability from Jominy end-quench bars is described in detail in Appendix A. Data showing case hardenability can be found in several references [7–10] presented either as standard hardenability curves or as isohardness diagrams.

4.2 Distance to First Appearance of Bainite in the Carburized Case—Data suggest that the as-quenched microstructure must be substantially free from bainite or pearlite to obtain the greatest resistance to impact [11]. The presence of very small amounts of bainite in the case has also been reported to reduce fatigue resistance [12]. Eldis and Smith reported the results of a detailed study of the occurrence of bainite in carburized end-quench hardenability specimens [13]. In the study, specimens of 81 alloys were carburized at 925 °C (1700 °F), cooled to 845 °C (1550 °F) and end-quenched. Companion bars were carburized to provide carbon gradient data. Flats were ground on the bars to a depth corresponding to 0.9% carbon in the case and hardness profiles were determined. Those flats were then metallographically polished, etched, and examined using quantitative metallographic techniques to determine the amount of bainite as a function of distance from the quenched end of the bar. The data for percent bainite were plotted and extrapolated to determine the "distance to first (appearance) of bainite" (DFB). Figure 5 shows a schematic diagram of the test technique.

Figure 6 shows data obtained for three steels, plotted on standard hardenability coordinates. It clearly illustrates that one cannot detect the presence of small amounts of bainite from hardness data. The results of the investigation [13] were subjected to multiple regression analysis to develop an empirical relationship for predicting DFB from composition. The regression equations appear below, and are valid at the 0.9% C level in the case for steels containing 0.5 to 1.1% Mn, 0 to 1.5% Ni, 0 to 1.0% Cr, and 0 to 0.5% Mo. Alloy contents are entered in weight percent:

$$\text{DFB (in millimeters from the quenched end)} = 54.7Mo^2 + 6.4Cr^2 - 76.1\,MoNi + 118.8\,MnMoNi + 106.1\,MnMoCr + 15.5MnNiCr + 52.9MoNiCr + 1.18 \quad \text{(Eq. 1)}$$

or

$$\text{DFB (in sixteenths of an inch from the quenched end)} = 34.5Mo^2 + 4.0Cr^2 - 47.9MoNi + 74.8MnMoNi + 66.9MnMoCr + 9.8MnNiCr + 33.3\,MoNiCr + 0.7 \quad \text{(Eq. 2)}$$

It is important to recognize that alloy interactions influence the presence of bainite in the carburized case. One should check these interactions when modifying a carburizing steel composition. The regression equations provide a convenient method of predicting the effect of changes in composition on DFB. They also can aid in the establishment of a minimum alloy content to assure a bainite-free microstructure in the carburized case.

5. Calculating Case Hardenability—D_I can be calculated using the general equation:

$$D_I = D_I^o(MF_{Si})(MN_{Mn})(MF_{Ni})(MF_{Cr})(MF_{Mo}) \quad \text{(Eq. 3)}$$

where:

$D_I{}^o$ is the base D_I for carbon (and grain size), as shown in Figure 7, and
MF_x is the multiplying factor for each alloying element, taken from a table or graph, such as Figure 8, or a specialized slide rule.

D_I can also be calculated using computer programs, which may include alloy interaction effects.

Core hardenability (expressed as 50% martensite D_I), case hardenability (expressed as 90% martensite D_I), and distance to first appearance of bainite (DFB) were calculated for several standard carburizing steels. For core hardenability, the method given in the Appendix of SAE J406 was used. The methods described in this document were used to calculate case D_I and DFB. For each steel, the midrange composition was selected for calculation purposes (assuming no residual elements), and 0.9% carbon was chosen for case D_I calculations (assuming a quench temperature of 925 °C, 1700 °F). The results are shown in Table 1. It is evident that one cannot assume that case hardenability or freedom from bainite will be proportional to core hardenability. The materials engineer must know the requirements for both case and core hardenability to provide a steel that can adequately meet both of these requirements.

5.1 Factors Influencing Case Hardenability—As shown in Figure 4, carbon is exceedingly influential in increasing both hardness and hardenability. This is also evident from data on the effect of carbon on hardenability multiplying factors (or D_I) as shown in Figure 7. Note the additional influence of austenitizing temperature, and the fact that there is an optimum carbon content at which the carbon effect is at a maximum.

The apparent loss of hardenability at carbon levels above 0.8% carbon at normal austenitizing temperatures is due to the formation of alloy carbides. At normal austenitizing temperatures these alloy carbides that form above 0.8% carbon do not fully redissolve, thus the benefit of the alloy elements tied up as carbides is lost. The hardenability effect of these alloy elements could be recovered if a higher austenitizing temperature was used. But such temperatures are not usually recommended for standard carburizing steels due to the adverse effects on grain growth, cracking, and distortion.

The curves in Figure 7 for 0.2 to 0.7% carbon are those of Kramer [14]; the curves for 0.6 to 1.1% carbon are those developed by Jatczak [15]. Alloy multiplying factors developed by Jatczak for carburized steels are shown in Figure 8. The alloy factors were developed for microstructures containing less than 10% pearlite or bainite.

6. Continuous-Cooling Transformation (CCT) Diagrams—Carbon content and microstructure resulting from transformation during heat treatment exert control over the properties of carburized steel. As shown in previous sections, the results of Jominy end-quench tests provide good hardness data, but only indirectly indicate microstructure. A more direct way of defining microstructure as a function of cooling characteristics is the continuous-cooling transformation (CCT) diagram. A partial CCT diagram for SAE 4815H steel is shown in Figure 9, from [16]. Note the time-temperature regions in which ferrite, pearlite, bainite, and martensite occur during cooling the steel from the austenitizing temperature at a series of controlled rates. Cooling at rates faster than those which intersect a region of higher temperature transformation will result in martensitic structures at room temperature.

In developing the CCT diagrams, hardness data are obtained from the as-cooled specimens. Vickers hardness values (using 10 kg load) are shown in circles at the end of the cooling curves. Cooling curves which intersect regions of ferrite, pearlite, or bainite formation show hardness values less than the maximum achieved with a completely martensitic structure. CCT diagrams are usually developed over a wide range of cooling rates, and thus can be used in the development of annealing heat treatments [17] to obtain specific hardness values or microstructures.

Diesburg and others [11] have pointed out that large variations in resistance to impact can be at least partially explained by the presence of bainite at the subsurface carbon levels in the carburized case. Therefore, data on the effect of carbon on transformation characteristics are useful in determining how to prevent the occurrence of undesirable microstructures.

CCT diagrams are available for several steels having the same base composition, but varying carbon contents corresponding to carbon levels attained during carburizing [4,5]. Figure 10 shows partial CCT diagrams (reported in the Diesburg reference [11]) for three such steel base compositions, and provides some insight into the transformation behavior during cooling after carburizing. Shown in the figure are transformation-start curves for various carbon levels, plus a range of cooling conditions encountered in parts of moderate section size. At the left end of each curve is the hardness (HV10) of the structure, predominantly martensite, formed at fast cooling rates. Steels of higher hardenability are required to eliminate formation of pearlite and bainite at intermediate carbon levels in the case. Note that with SAE 4620 steel, one can expect bainite near the carburized surface (the 0.8% C curve) at cooling rates encountered in quenching even moderate section sizes. Increasing the alloy content slightly can avoid such bainite transformation (as with the Mo-modified 4600 steel).

7. Related Parameters—In addition to hardness and microstructure, one needs to consider the effects of case depth and residual stress on the properties of carburized components. Case depth and case properties (hardness and residual stresses) can be developed to provide critical strength levels greater than the applied stress at all locations in the carburized part. The magnitude of residual stress, and thus the net effective bending fatigue strength (fatigue limit) of carburized steel, is influenced by case depth.

7.1 Case Depth—Experience has shown that once a case depth has been attained that is sufficient to (a) prevent case crushing, and (b) provide adequate fatigue life, there is nothing to be gained by further increasing case depth. In fact, some British work [18] shows that over-carburizing can decrease the fatigue limit of a part. That work also shows that higher fatigue limits can be achieved at higher quenching temperatures.

7.2 Residual Stress—The magnitude of residual stress is dependent on processing variables, such as case depth, but is also dependent on material variables, such as hardenability. Burnett [19] developed a method to predict the stresses generated during heat treatment of carburized parts. The method was based on extensive experimental data on thermal gradients, carbon gradients, and phase transformations, plus a knowledge of elastic-plastic behavior as a function of carbon content and temperature.

Kim and others [20] have shown that fatigue crack initiation and propagation in carburized steels are significantly delayed in the presence of residual compressive stresses. They also point out that surface oxidation can counteract the beneficial effect of residual stress.

TABLE 1—CORE AND CASE HARDENABILITY COMPARISON (DATA IN MILLIMETERS, WITH INCHES IN PARENTHESES)

Steel Grade[1]	Mid-range Composition wt. % C	Mid-range Composition wt. % Mn	Mid-range Compositionwt. % Si	Mid-range Compositionwt. % Cr	Mid-range Composition wt. % Ni	Mid-range Composition wt. % Mo	Core D_I [50% M]	Core D_I [90% M]	D_{FB} [J_D in 16ths]
1018	0.18	0.75	0.25	—		—	10	48	<1.5
							(0.4)	(1.9)	(<1)
4028H	0.27	0.80	0.25	—		0.25	28	86	5
							(1.1)	(3.4)	(3)
4118H	0.20	0.80	0.25	0.50		0.11	33	105	8
							(1.3)	(4.2)	(5)
4120H	0.20	1.05	0.25	0.50	—	0.18	46	145	14
							(1.8)	(5.8)	(9)
4121	0.21	0.88	0.25	0.55	—	0.25	48	157	19
							(1.9)	(6.2)	(12)
4130H	0.30	0.50	0.25	1.00	—	0.20	66	145	21
							(2.6)	(5.7)	(13)
4320H	0.20	0.55	0.25	0.50	1.75	0.25	56	225	27[2]
							(2.2)	(8.8)	(17[2])
5120H	0.20	0.80	0.25	0.80	—		33	100	5
							(1.3)	(4.0)	(3)
8620H	0.20	0.80	0.25	0.50	0.55	0.20	48	150	22
							(1.9)	(6.0)	(14)
8720H	0.20	0.80	0.25	0.50	0.55	0.25	51	175	27
							(2.0)	(6.9)	(17)
8822H	0.22	0.88	0.25	0.50	0.55	0.35	71	215	40
							(2.8)	(8.5)	(25)

1. SAE grades, from composition ranges given in SAE J403 (for carbon steel 1018), SAE J404 (for alloy steel 4121) and SAE J1268 (for H steels).
2. Note that nickel content falls outside the 0 to 1.5% Ni range of steels used in developing the regression equation.

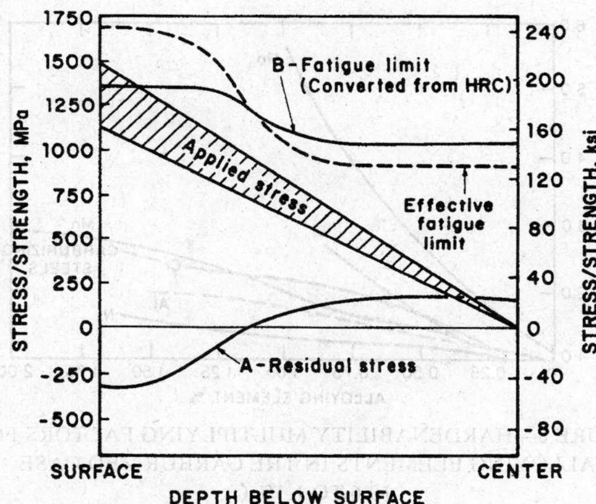

FIGURE 1—SCHEMATIC DIAGRAM OF STRESSES IN A CARBURIZED BAR, LOADED IN SIMPLE BENDING

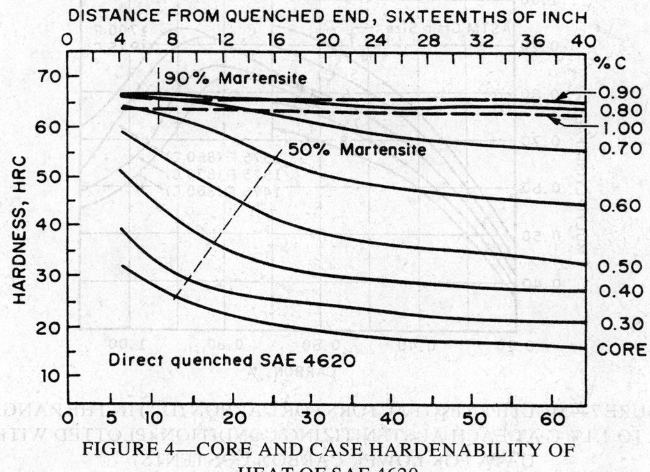

FIGURE 4—CORE AND CASE HARDENABILITY OF HEAT OF SAE 4620

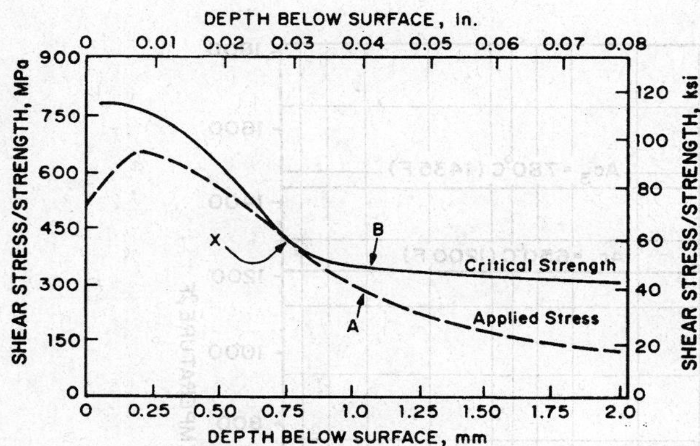

FIGURE 2—APPLIED STRESSES AT THE PITCH LINE OF A GEAR TOOTH REACH A MAXIMUM BELOW THE SURFACE AND THEN DECREASE. THE CRITICAL STRENGTH CURVE DEFINES THE NET FATIGUE LIMIT

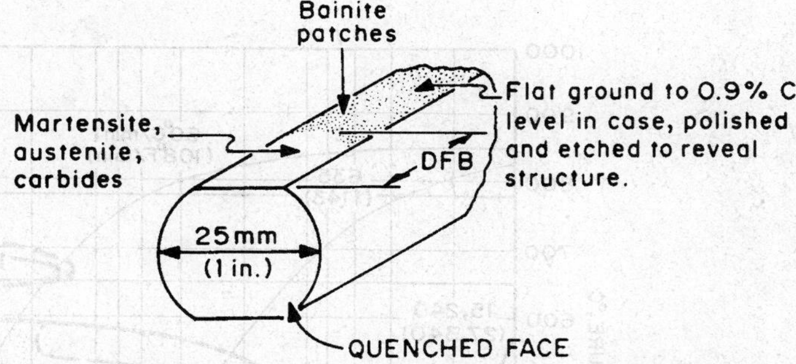

FIGURE 5—SKETCH OF A JOMINY END-QUENCH HARDENABILITY BAR SHOWING THE METHOD USED TO DETERMINE DISTANCE TO FIRST APPEARANCE OF BAINITE (DFB)

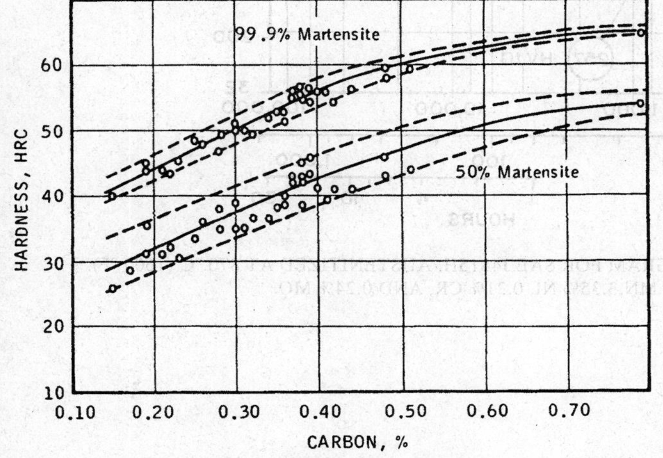

FIGURE 3—HARDNESS OF MARTENSITE PRODUCTS AS A FUNCTION OF CARBON CONTENT

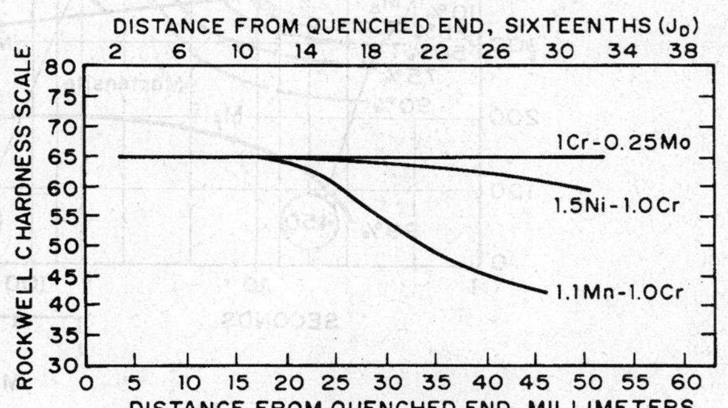

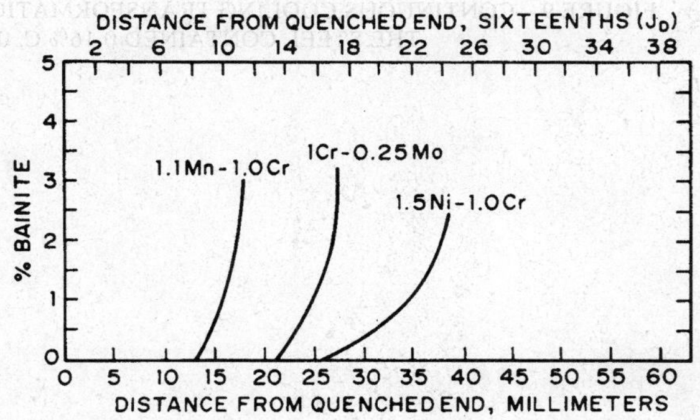

FIGURE 6—CASE HARDENABILITY DATA (UPPER DIAGRAM) AND CORRESPONDING BAINITE PROFILE DATA (LOWER DIAGRAM) FOR THREE STEELS

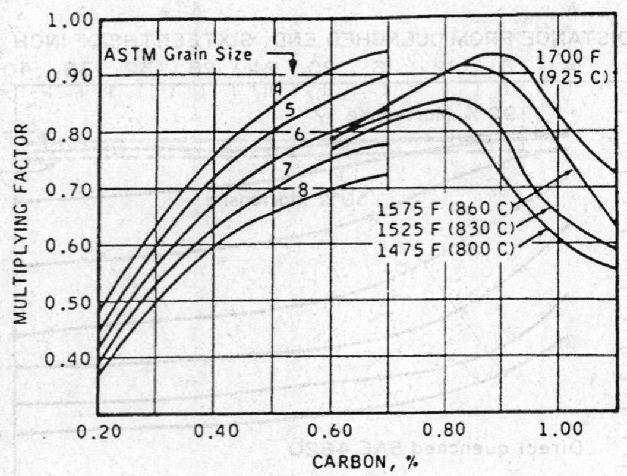

FIGURE 7—MULTIPLYING FACTORS FOR CARBON (D_I^0) IN THE RANGE 0.6 TO 1.1% C AT EACH AUSTENITIZING CONDITION (PLOTTED WITH DATA FOR LOWER CARBON CONTENTS)

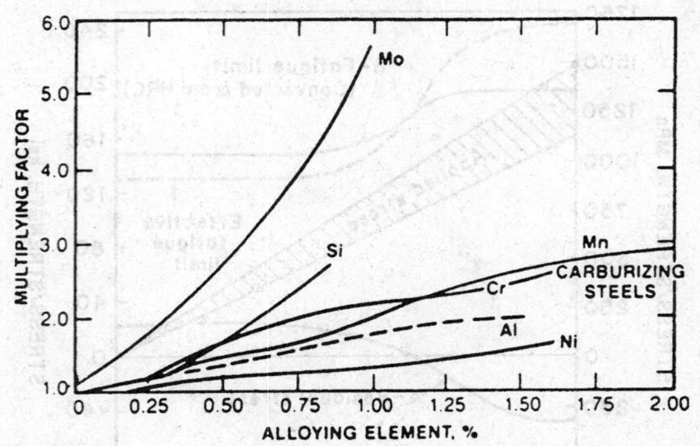

FIGURE 8—HARDENABILITY MULTIPLYING FACTORS FOR ALLOYING ELEMENTS IN THE CARBURIZED CASE (0.6 TO 1.1% C)

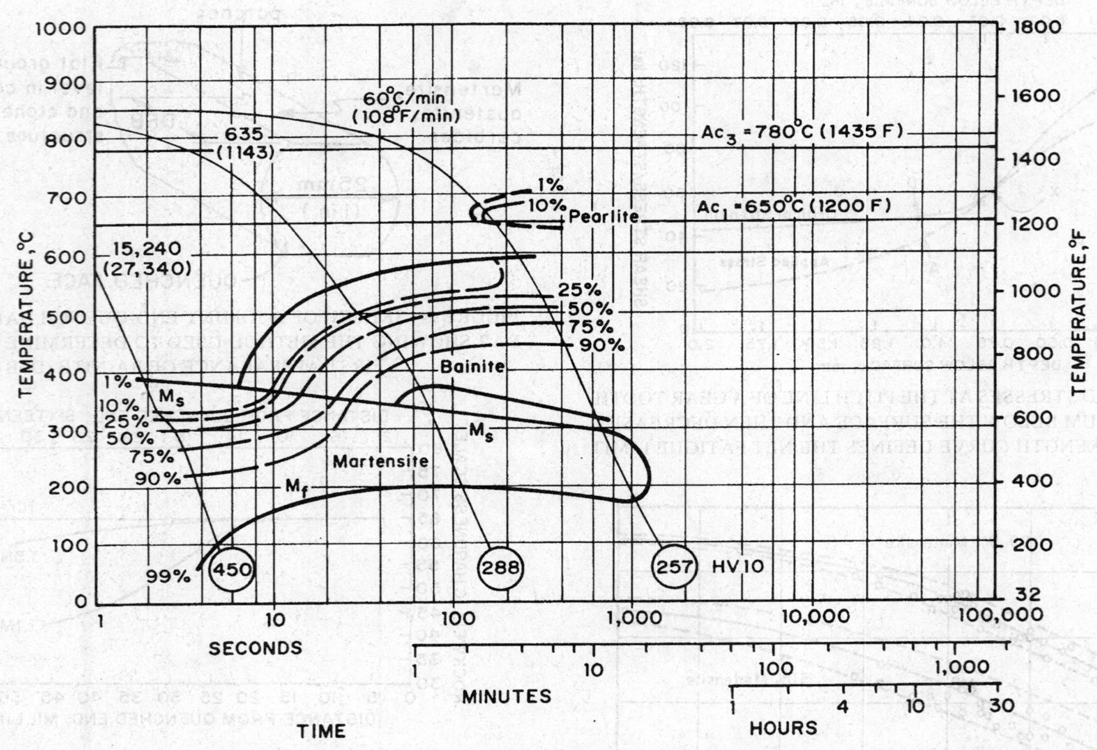

FIGURE 9—CONTINUOUS COOLING TRANSFORMATION (CCT) DIAGRAM FOR SAE J4815H, AUSTENITIZED AT 870 °C (1600 °F). THE STEEL CONTAINED 0.16% C, 0.24% SI, 0.63% MN,3.35% NI, 0.21% CR, AND 0.24% MO.

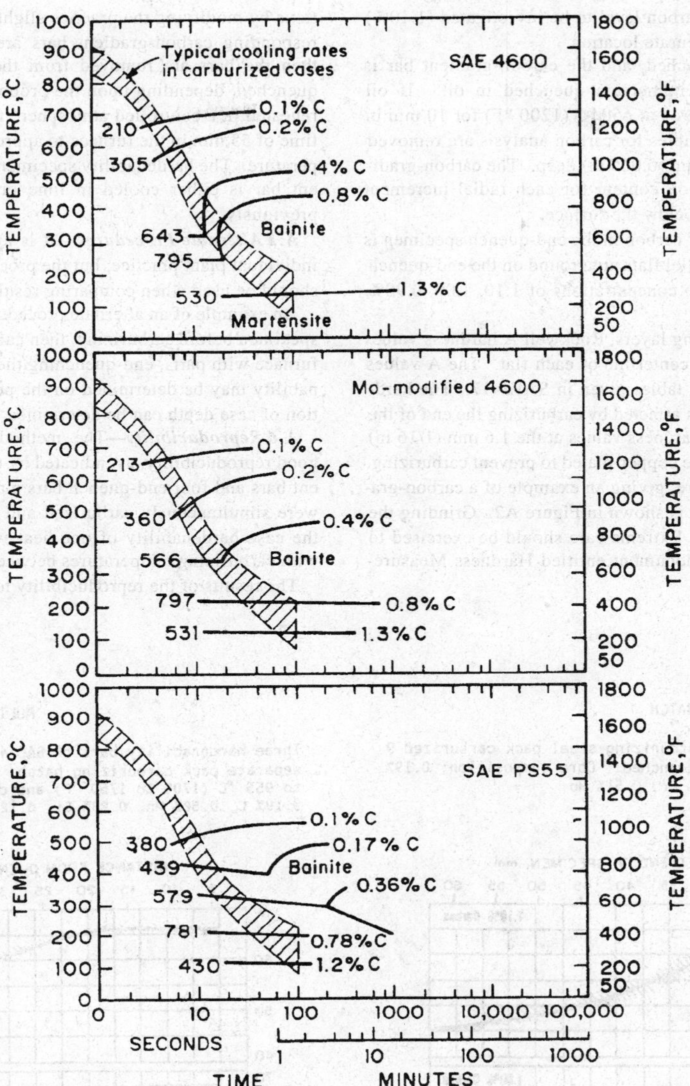

FIGURE 10—PARTIAL CCT DIAGRAMS FOR THREE CARBURIZING STEELS WITH FIVE LEVELS OF CARBON. MARTENSITIC HARDNESS VALUES (HV10), OR HARDNESS OF MARTENSITE-BAINITE AGGREGATE AT LOWEST CARBON CONTENTS, ARE SHOWN FOR EACH CARBON LEVEL. ALLOY CONTENTS ARE:
SAE 4600: 0.62% MN, 1.78% NI, 0.25% MO
MODIFIED 4600: 0.58% MN, 1.81% NI, 0.47% MO
SAE PS55: 0.89% MN, 1.74% NI, 0.60% CR, 0.74% MO

APPENDIX A
METHODS FOR DETERMINING CARBURIZED HARDENABILITY

A.1 Scope—This method prescribes procedures for determining the hardenability of steels after carburizing and for subsequently recording the results. It is of interest to note that such a procedure was used by Walter Jominy when he first introduced the end-quench test.

This Appendix formerly appeared as an appendix to SAE J406. With publication of J1975, it has been transferred to this document.

A.2 Test Procedure—The end-quench specimens and quenching and testing procedures, described in detail in SAE J406, are used. When evaluating the carburized hardenability characteristics of a steel, high-carbon-potential pack carburizing procedures are employed as described in Section A.3. Results using this practice have been reported previously.[2, 3]

A.3 Direct Quench—In the determination of case hardenability, a standard end-quench hardenability specimen and a carbon-gradient specimen, 25 mm diameter x 152 mm long (1 in x 6 in), prepared from the same bar, are simultaneously carburized in a covered alloy steel box for 9 h at 925 °C (1700 °F). The composition of the carburizing medium is to be: charcoal 50%, coke 30%, barium carbonate 12%, sodium carbonate 3%, calcium carbonate 3%, molasses binder 2%. An alternate barium-free carburizer is cited in the footnote.[4]

2. J. A. Halgren and E. A. Solecki, "Case Hardenability of SAE 4028, 8620, 4620, and 4815 Steels." SAE Transactions, Vol. 69 (1961), p. 662.
3. Atlas "Hardenability of Carburized Steels." New York: Climax Molybdenum Co., 1960.
4. Pack carburizer BF#21, a proprietary compound produced by Heatbath Corp., Springfield, MA 01101, is claimed to be barium-free and to provide suitably high carbon contents at the surface of the part or test bar.

All new carburizer is used for each batch to provide uniform carburizing conditions and to overcarburize so the highest carbon level to be investigated (1.10%) will be sufficiently subsurface to permit accurate location.

The hardenability specimen is end-quenched, and the carbon-gradient bar is either cooled in loose hydrated lime or immersion quenched in oil. If oil quenched, the carbon-gradient bar is tempered at 650 °C (1200 °F) for 10 min in lead or salt to soften it for machining. Samples for carbon analysis are removed by lathe turning in radial increments 0.13 mm (0.005 in) deep. The carbon-gradient curve is obtained by plotting the carbon content for each radial increment against the average depth of the increment below the surface.

On the assumption that the distribution of carbon in the end-quench specimen is the same as in the carbon-gradient bar, parallel flats are ground on the end-quench specimen to levels corresponding to carbon concentrations of 1.10, 1.00, 0.90% and, in some cases, lower carbon levels.

To minimize the effect of softer underlying layers, Rockwell A hardness values are determined with impressions along the centerline of each flat. The A values are converted to C values using conversion tables given in SAEJ417. The hardness value at the 1.6 mm (1/16 in) position is affected by carburizing the end of the bar, therefore this reading is discarded. If hardness values at the 1.6 mm (1/16 in) position are desired, the quenched end can be copper-plated to prevent carburizing.

A pictorial representation of the procedure, giving an example of a carbon-gradient curve, and the sequence of operations is shown in Figure A2. Grinding the end-quenched hardenability bar is critical. Extreme care should be exercised to avoid tempering. See the section of this document entitled Hardness Measurement.

A.4 Reheat and Quench—Steels may be tested under reheat and quench conditions by modifying the practice slightly. The end-quench specimens and the corresponding carbon-gradient bars are pack-carburized as described previously, then the bars are removed from the box and either cooled in still air or oil quenched, depending upon the proposed plant practice. The specimens are then reheated in a controlled atmosphere furnace held at 845 °C (1550 °F), for a total time of 55 min in the furnace to approximate the specified 30 min at furnace temperature. The hardenability specimen is then end-quenched and the carbon-gradient bar is either cooled in lime or oil quenched and tempered as described previously.

A.5 Alternate Procedures—It is apparent that the test can be tailored to suit individual plant practice, but the procedures described in the preceding paragraph should be used when comparing results with other laboratories.

An example of an alternate procedure would be to grind flats on the end-quench specimen before carburizing, then carburize the specimen in the same carburizing furnace with parts, end-quenching the specimen after carburizing. Surface hardenability may be determined on the pre-ground flats, and hardenability as a function of case depth can be determined by grinding flats to specified depths.

A.6 Reproducibility—The method described for direct quenching provides good reproducibility, as indicated by two tests. In the first test, four carbon-gradient bars and four end-quench bars machined from the same normalized bar stock were simultaneously carburized and sequentially quenched. In the second test, the case hardenability of one heat was determined on three separate occasions with carburizing temperatures between 925 and 955 °C (1700 and 1750 °F).

The results of the reproducibility tests are given in Figure A1.

SINGLE BATCH

Four hardenability bars of SAE 4419 carburizing steel pack carburized 9 h at 925 °C (1700 °F) and direct end quenched. Core composition: 0.19% C, 0.52% Mn, 0.23% Si, 0.12% Ni, 0.20% Cr, 0.51% Mo.

MULTIPLE BATCH

Three hardenability bars of SAE 4419 carburizing steel each run in a separate pack carburizing batch. Each batch pack carburized 9 h at 925 to 955 °C (1700 to 1750 °F) and direct quenched. Core composition: 0.19% C, 0.52% Mn, 0.23% Si, 0.12% Ni, 0.20% Cr, 0.51% Mo.

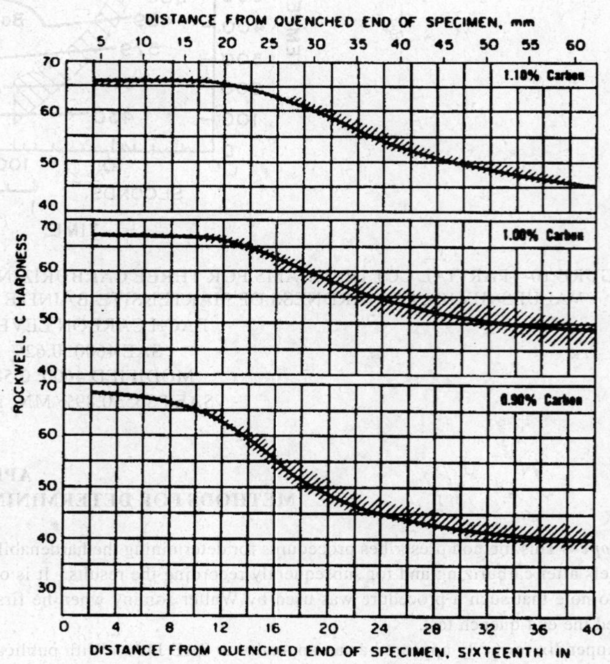

FIGURE A1—REPRODUCIBILITY OF CASE HARDENABILITY

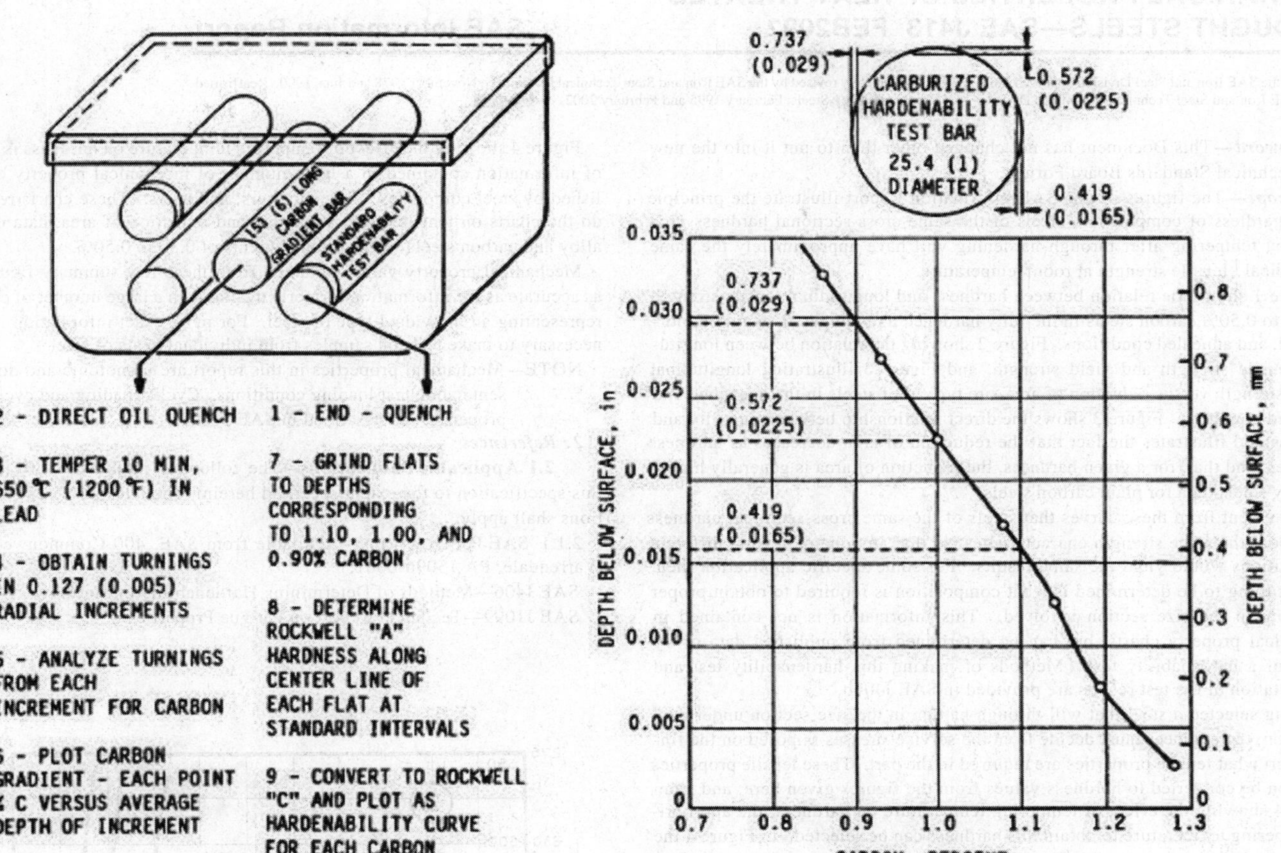
153 (6) LONG CARBON GRADIENT BAR
STANDARD HARDENABILITY TEST BAR
2 - DIRECT OIL QUENCH
1 - END - QUENCH
3 - TEMPER 10 MIN, 650 °C (1200 °F) IN LEAD
7 - GRIND FLATS TO DEPTHS CORRESPONDING TO 1.10, 1.00, AND 0.90% CARBON
4 - OBTAIN TURNINGS IN 0.127 (0.005) RADIAL INCREMENTS
8 - DETERMINE ROCKWELL "A" HARDNESS ALONG CENTER LINE OF EACH FLAT AT STANDARD INTERVALS
5 - ANALYZE TURNINGS FROM EACH INCREMENT FOR CARBON
6 - PLOT CARBON GRADIENT - EACH POINT % C VERSUS AVERAGE DEPTH OF INCREMENT
9 - CONVERT TO ROCKWELL "C" AND PLOT AS HARDENABILITY CURVE FOR EACH CARBON CONTENT
0.737 (0.029)
0.572 (0.0225)
CARBURIZED HARDENABILITY TEST BAR 25.4 (1) DIAMETER
0.419 (0.0165)
DEPTH BELOW SURFACE, in
DEPTH BELOW SURFACE, mm
CARBON, PERCENT
NOTE: DIMENSIONS ARE mm (in)

FIGURE A2—STANDARD CARBURIZING PROCEDURE, PACK CARBURIZE 9 H AT 925 °C (1700 °F)

MECHANICAL PROPERTIES OF HEAT TREATED WROUGHT STEELS—SAE J413 FEB2002

SAE Information Report

Report of the SAE Iron and Steel Division approved January 1932. Completely revised by the SAE Iron and Steel Technical Committee November 1978 and June 1990. Reaffirmed by the SAE Iron and Steel Technical Committee Division 1—Carbon and Alloy Steels, February 1995 and February 2002.

Foreword—This Document has not changed other than to put it into the new SAE Technical Standards Board Format.

1. Scope—The figures in this SAE Information Report illustrate the principle that, regardless of composition, steels of the same cross-sectional hardness produced by tempering after through hardening will have approximately the same longitudinal[1] tensile strength at room temperature.

Figure 1 shows the relation between hardness and longitudinal tensile strength of 0.30 to 0.50% carbon steels in the fully hardened and tempered, as rolled, normalized, and annealed conditions. Figure 2 showing the relation between longitudinal tensile strength and yield strength, and Figure 3 illustrating longitudinal tensile strength versus reduction of area, are typical of steels in the quenched and tempered condition. Figure 3 shows the direct relationship between ductility and hardness and illustrates the fact that the reduction of area decreases as hardness increases, and that, for a given hardness, the reduction of area is generally higher for alloy steels than for plain carbon steels.

It is evident from these curves that steels of the same cross-sectional hardness have about the same strength characteristics, so that any one of several different compositions would yield the same results. For some specific application then, the first thing to be determined is what composition is required to obtain proper hardening in the size section involved. This information is not contained in mechanical property charts, but can be determined from published data or by means of a hardenability test. Methods of making this hardenability test and interpretation of the test results are provided in SAE J406b.

Having selected a steel that will through harden in the size section under consideration, the engineer must decide from the service stresses imposed on the finished part what tensile properties are required in the part. These tensile properties may then be converted to hardness values from the figures given here; and from Figure 4 showing the effect of tempering temperature on hardness, the appropriate tempering temperature to obtain this hardness can be selected. In Figure 4 the curves are approximate values to be used as a guide. Carbon steels and lean alloy steels, when fully hardened, will fall slightly below the curves and strongly alloyed steels will fall slightly above the curves.

Figure 4 showing the effect of tempering temperature on hardness is a summary of information contained in a large number of mechanical property charts published by steel companies, alloy suppliers, and users. These charts represent, as do the charts on tensile, yield strengths, and reduction of area, data on all SAE alloy and carbon steels with carbon contents of 0.30 to 0.50%.

Mechanical property values obtained from these few summary figures will be as accurate as the information formerly available in a large number of charts, each representing an individual type of steel. For more exact information it would be necessary to make tests on samples from individual heats of steel.

NOTE—Mechanical properties in this report are monotonic and do not represent cyclic test loading conditions. Cyclic loading and cyclic material properties are described in SAE J1099.

2. References

2.1 Applicable Publications—The following publications form a part of this specification to the extent specified herein. The latest issue of SAE publications shall apply.

2.1.1 SAE PUBLICATIONS—Available from SAE, 400 Commonwealth Drive, Warrendale, PA 15096-0001.

SAE J406—Methods of Determining Hardenability of Steels

SAE J1099—Technical Report on Fatigue Properties

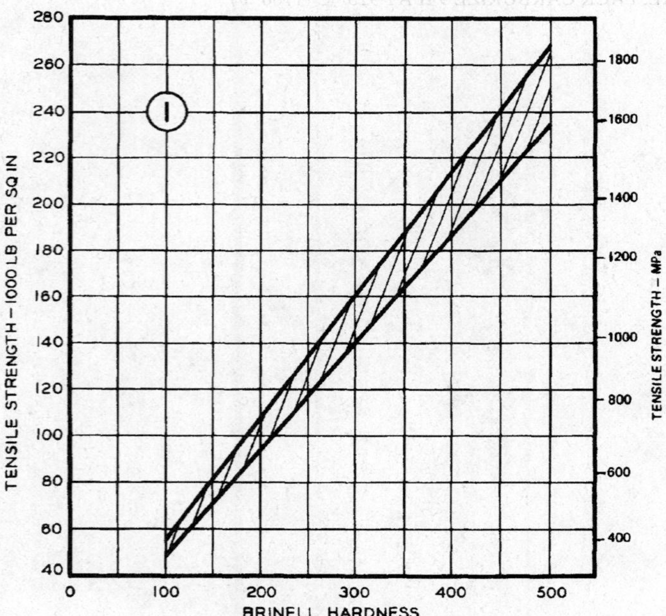

FIGURE 1—RELATIONSHIP BETWEEN HARDNESS AND LONGITUDINAL TENSILE STRENGTH OF 0.30 TO 0.50% CARBON STEELS

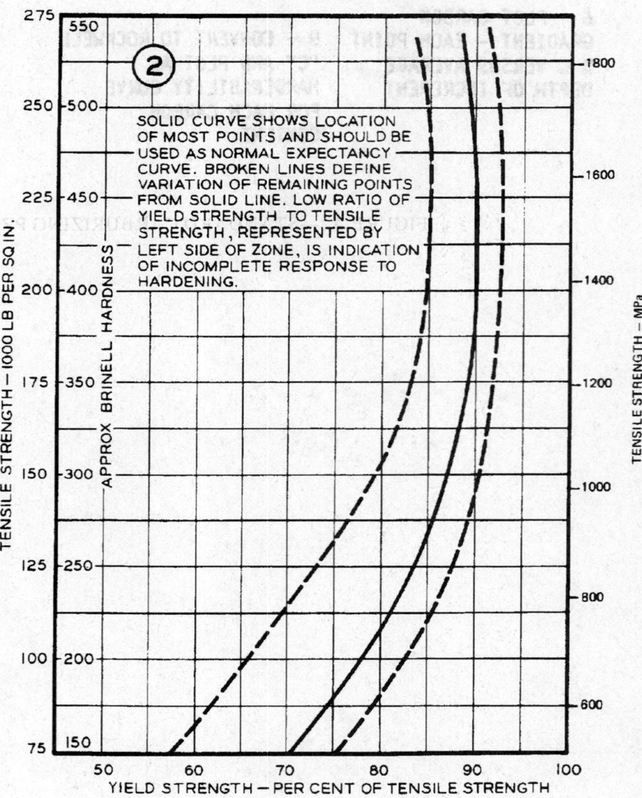

FIGURE 2—RELATIONSHIP BETWEEN LONGITUDINAL TENSILE STRENGTH AND YIELD STRENGTH FOR QUENCHED AND TEMPERED STEELS

1. Longitudinal means parallel to rolling direction.

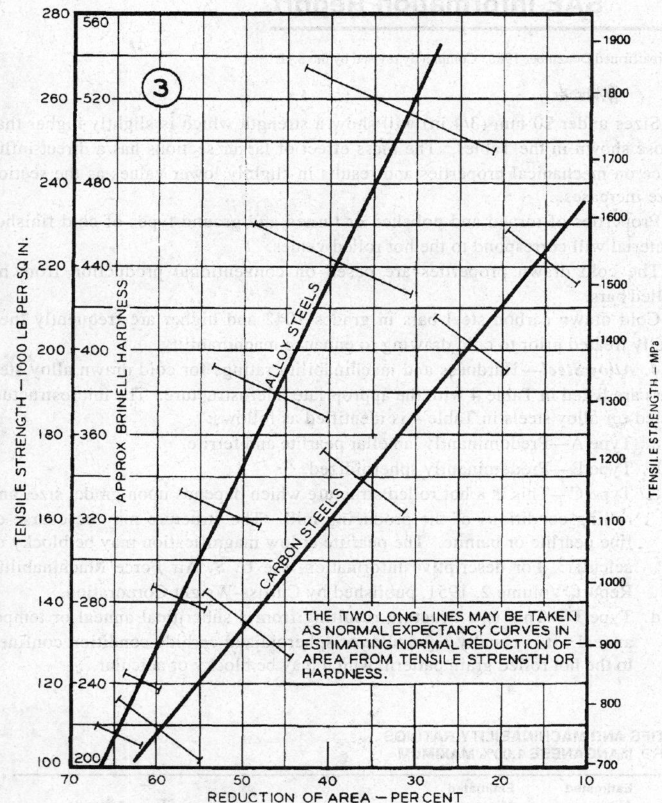

FIGURE 3—RELATIONSHIP OF LONGITUDINAL TENSILE STRENGTH TO REDUCTION OF AREA FOR QUENCHED AND TEMPERED STEELS

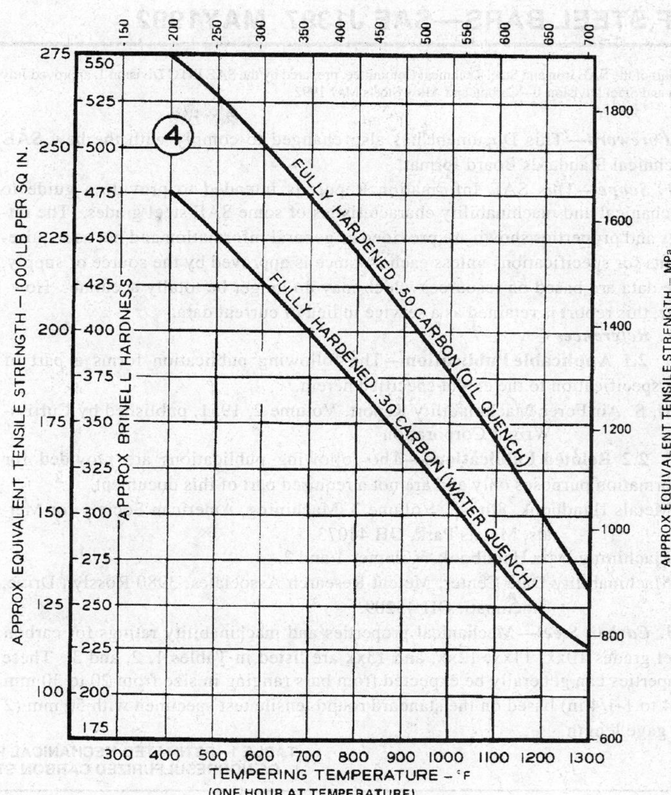

FIGURE 4—EFFECT OF TEMPERING TEMPERATURE ON THE HARDNESS OF STEEL

(R) ESTIMATED MECHANICAL PROPERTIES AND MACHINABILITY OF STEEL BARS—SAE J1397 MAY1992

SAE Information Report

Report of the SAE Iron and Steel Technical Committee, prepared by the SAE ISTC Division 1, approved July 1982 and reaffirmed December 1988. Completely revised by the SAE Iron and Steel Division 1—Carbon and Alloy Steels May 1992.

Foreword—This Document has also changed to comply with the new SAE Technical Standards Board format.

1. Scope—This SAE Information Report is intended to provide a guide to mechanical and machinability characteristics of some SAE steel grades. The ratings and properties shown are provided as general information and not as requirements for specifications unless each instance is approved by the source of supply. The data are based on resources which may no longer be totally accurate. However, this report is retained as a service in lieu of current data.

2. References

2.1 Applicable Publication—The following publication forms a part of this specification to the extent specified herein.

U. S. Air Force Machinability Report, Volume 2, 1951, published by Curtiss-Wright Corporation

2.2 Related Publications—The following publications are provided for information purposes only and are not a required part of this document.

Metals Handbook, 8th ed., Volume 3, Machining, American Society for Metals, Metals Park, OH 44073.

Machining Data Handbook, Volumes 1 and 2.

Machinability Data Center, Metcut Research Associates, 3980 Rosslyn Drive, Cincinnati, OH 45209.

3. Carbon Steel—Mechanical properties and machinability ratings for carbon steel grades 10xx, 11xx, 12xx, and 15xx are listed in Tables 1, 2, and 3. These properties can generally be expected from bars ranging in size from 20 to 30 mm (3/4 to 1-1/4 in) based on the standard round tensile test specimen with 50 mm (2 in) gage length.

Sizes under 20 mm (3/4 in) will show a strength which is slightly higher than those shown in the Tables. The mass effect of larger sections has a direct influence on mechanical properties and results in slightly lower values as the section size increases.

Properties of turned and polished or turned and ground types of cold finished material will correspond to the hot rolled values.

The cold drawn properties are based on conventional production from hot rolled bars.

Cold drawn carbon steel bars in grades 1042 and higher are frequently thermally treated prior to cold drawing to enhance machinability.

4. Alloy Steel—Hardness and machinability ratings for cold drawn alloy steel bars are listed in Table 4 with the appropriate microstructure. The microstructure listed for alloy steels in Table 4 is identified as follows:

a. Type A—Predominantly lamellar pearlite and ferrite.
b. Type B—Predominantly spheroidized.
c. Type C—This is a hot rolled structure which depends upon grade, size, and rolling conditions of the producing mill. The structure may be coarse or fine pearlite or bainite. The pearlite at low magnification may be blocky or acicular. For descriptive information, see U. S. Air Force Machinability Report, Volume 2, 1951, published by Curtiss-Wright Corporation.
d. Type D—This is a structure resulting from a subcritical anneal or temper anneal. It is usually a granular or spheroidized carbide condition confined to the hot rolled grain pattern, which may be blocky or acicular.

TABLE 1—ESTIMATED MECHANICAL PROPERTIES AND MACHINABILITY RATINGS OF NONRESULFURIZED CARBON STEEL BARS, MANGANESE 1.00% MAXIMUM

UNS No.	SAE and/or AISI No.	Type of Processing	Tensile Strength MPa	Tensile Strength psi	Estimated Minimum Values Yield Strength MPa	Estimated Minimum Values Yield Strength psi	Estimated Minimum Values Elongation in 2 in, %	Reduction in Area %	Brinell Hardness	Average Machinability Rating (Cold Drawn) 1212=100%
G10060	1006	Hot Rolled	300	43 000	170	24 000	30	55	86	
		Cold Drawn	330	48 000	280	41 000	20	45	95	50
G10080	1008	Hot Rolled	303	44 000	170	24 500	30	55	86	
		Cold Drawn	340	49 000	290	41 500	20	45	95	55
G10100	1010	Hot Rolled	320	47 000	180	26 000	28	50	95	
		Cold Drawn	370	53 000	300	44 000	20	40	105	55
G10120	1012	Hot Rolled	330	48 000	180	26 500	28	50	95	
		Cold Drawn	370	54 000	310	45 000	19	40	105	55
G10150	1015	Hot Rolled	340	50 000	190	27 500	28	50	101	
		Cold Drawn	390	56 000	320	47 000	18	40	111	60
G10160	1016	Hot Rolled	380	55 000	210	30 000	25	50	111	
		Cold Drawn	420	61 000	350	51 000	18	40	121	70
G10170	1017	Hot Rolled	370	53 000	200	29 000	26	50	105	
		Cold Drawn	410	59 000	340	49 000	18	40	116	65
G10180	1018	Hot Rolled	400	58 000	220	32 000	25	50	116	
		Cold Drawn	440	64 000	370	54 000	15	40	126	70
G10190	1019	Hot Rolled	410	59 000	220	32 500	25	50	116	
		Cold Drawn	460	66 000	380	55 000	15	40	131	70
G10200	1020	Hot Rolled	380	55 000	210	30 000	25	50	111	
		Cold Drawn	420	61 000	350	51 000	15	40	121	65
G10210	1021	Hot Rolled	420	61 000	230	33 000	24	48	116	
		Cold Drawn	470	68 000	390	57 000	15	40	131	70
G10220	1022	Hot Rolled	430	62 000	230	34 000	23	47	121	
		Cold Drawn	480	69 000	400	58 000	15	40	137	70
G10230	1023	Hot Rolled	370	56 000	210	31 000	25	50	111	
		Cold Drawn	430	62 000	360	52 500	15	40	121	65
G10250	1025	Hot Rolled	400	58 000	220	32 000	25	50	116	
		Cold Drawn	440	64 000	370	54 000	15	40	126	65
G10260	1026	Hot Rolled	440	64 000	240	35 000	24	49	126	
		Cold Drawn	490	71 000	410	60 000	15	40	143	75
G10300	1030	Hot Rolled	470	68 000	260	37 500	20	42	137	
		Cold Drawn	520	76 000	440	64 000	12	35	149	70

TABLE 1—ESTIMATED MECHANICAL PROPERTIES AND MACHINABILITY RATINGS OF NONRESULFURIZED CARBON STEEL BARS, MANGANESE 1.00% MAXIMUM (continued)

UNS No.	SAE and/or AISI No.	Type of Processing	Tensile Strength MPa	Tensile Strength psi	Estimated Minimum Values Yield Strength MPa	Estimated Minimum Values Yield Strength psi	Estimated Minimum Values Elongation in 2 in, %	Reduction in Area %	Brinell Hardness	Average Machinability Rating (Cold Drawn) 1212=100%
G10350	1035	Hot Rolled	500	72 000	270	39 500	18	40	143	
		Cold Drawn	550	80 000	460	67 000	12	35	163	65
G10370	1037	Hot Rolled	510	74 000	280	40 500	18	40	143	
		Cold Drawn	570	82 000	480	69 000	12	35	167	65
G10380	1038	Hot Rolled	520	75 000	280	41 000	18	40	149	
		Cold Drawn	570	83 000	480	70 000	12	35	163	65
G10390	1039	Hot Rolled	540	79 000	300	43 500	16	40	156	
		Cold Drawn	610	88 000	510	74 000	12	35	179	60
G10400	1040	Hot Rolled	520	76 000	290	42 000	18	40	149	
		Cold Drawn	590	85 000	490	71 000	12	35	170	60
G10420	1042	Hot Rolled	550	80 000	300	44 000	16	40	163	
		Cold Drawn	610	89 000	520	75 000	12	35	179	60
		NCD(1)	590	85 000	500	73 000	12	45	179	70
G10430	1043	Hot Rolled	570	82 000	310	45 000	16	40	163	
		Cold Drawn	630	91 000	530	77 000	12	35	179	60
		NCD(1)	600	87 000	520	75 000	12	45	179	70
G10440	1044	Hot Rolled	550	80 000	300	44 000	16	40	163	
G10450	1045	Hot Rolled	570	82 000	310	45 000	16	40	163	
		Cold Drawn	630	91 000	530	77 000	12	35	179	55
		ACD(2)	590	85 000	500	73 000	12	45	170	65
G10460	1046	Hot Rolled	590	85 000	320	47 000	15	40	170	
		Cold Drawn	650	94 000	540	79 000	12	35	187	55
		ACD(2)	620	90 000	520	75 000	12	45	179	65
G10490	1049	Hot Rolled	600	87 000	330	48 000	15	35	179	
		Cold Drawn	670	97 000	560	81 500	10	30	197	45
		ACD(2)	630	92 000	530	77 000	10	40	187	55
G10500	1050	Hot Rolled	620	90 000	340	49 500	15	35	179	
		Cold Drawn	690	100 000	580	84 000	10	30	197	45
		ACD(2)	660	95 000	550	80 000	10	40	189	55
G10550	1055	Hot Rolled	650	94 000	360	51 500	12	30	192	
		ACD(2)	660	96 000	560	81 000	10	40	197	55
G10600	1060	Hot Rolled	680	98 000	370	54 000	12	30	201	
		SACD(3)	620	90 000	480	70 000	10	45	183	60
G10640	1064	Hot Rolled	670	97 000	370	53 500	12	30	201	
		SACD(3)	610	89 000	480	69 000	10	45	183	60
G10650	1065	Hot Rolled	690	100 000	380	55 000	12	30	207	
		SACD(3)	630	92 000	490	71 000	10	45	187	60
G10700	1070	Hot Rolled	700	102 000	390	56 000	12	30	212	
		SACD(3)	640	93 000	500	72 000	10	45	192	55
G10740	1074	Hot Rolled	720	105 000	400	58 000	12	30	217	
		SACD(3)	650	94 500	500	73 000	10	40	192	55
G10780	1078	Hot Rolled	690	100 000	380	55 000	12	30	207	
		SACD(3)	650	94 000	500	72 500	10	40	192	55
G10800	1080	Hot Rolled	770	112 000	420	61 500	10	25	229	
		SACD(3)	680	98 000	520	75 000	10	40	192	45
G10840	1084	Hot Rolled	820	119 000	450	65 500	10	25	241	
		SACD(3)	690	100 000	530	77 000	10	40	192	45
G10850	1085	Hot Rolled	830	121 000	460	66 500	10	25	248	
		SACD(3)	690	100 500	540	78 000	10	40	192	45
G10860	1086	Hot Rolled	770	112 000	420	61 500	10	25	229	
		SACD(3)	670	97 000	510	74 000	10	40	192	45
G10900	1090	Hot Rolled	840	122 000	460	67 000	10	25	248	
		SACD(3)	700	101 000	540	78 000	10	40	197	45
G10950	1095	Hot Rolled	830	120 000	460	66 000	10	25	248	
		SACD(3)	680	99 000	520	76 000	10	40	197	45

1. NCD represents normalized cold drawn.
2. ACD represents annealed cold drawn.
3. SACD represents spheroidized annealed cold drawn.

5. Machinability—While it is recognized that the views regarding alloy steel machinability vary considerably, it is believed that the ratings contained in this report reflect current industry experience. The data on which the ratings were based were obtained by a detailed survey of both producers and users. The data summarize the combined experience of both groups. Various factors influence machinability and, therefore, results shown in Table 1 are average and may be affected to some degree by the amount of cold reduction, mechanical properties, grain size, microstructure, type of tooling, and machining operation(s) performed.

The machinability ratings listed are based on a value of 100% for SAE 1212 cold drawn steel. This value involves turning at a cutting speed of 55 m (180 surface feet) per minute for feeds up to 0.18 mm (0.007 in) per revolution and depths of cut up to 6.4 mm (0.250 in), using appropriate cutting fluids with high speed steel tools, SAE Grade T-1 (18-4-1) hardened to 63-65 HRC (SAE J437, J438).

Most low carbon alloy steels are machined in the as-rolled or as-rolled and cold drawn or cold finished condition. Higher carbon alloy steels and high hardenability low carbon steels, such as SAE 9310, may be conditioned for machining by a variety of heat treatments. Thermal treatments used to condition these steels for machining include subcritical annealing, annealing for softening to no specified structure, annealing to a specified structure such as lamellar pearlite or a percentage of lamellar pearlite and spheroidization, or to a fully spheroidized condition.

The structures imparted to the bars are evaluated in the machining operation by the tooling setup and the type of tool used. It is possible to use widely diverging hardnesses and structures with different tooling setups and obtain satisfactory results both as to finish and parts per hour.

TABLE 2—ESTIMATED MECHANICAL PROPERTIES AND MACHINABILITY RATINGS OF RESULFURIZED CARBON STEEL BARS[1]

UNS No.	SAE and/or AISI No.	Type of Processing	Tensile Strength MPa	Tensile Strength psi	Estimated Minimum Values Yield Strength MPa	Estimated Minimum Values Yield Strength psi	Estimated Minimum Values Elongation in 2 in, %	Reduction in Area %	Brinell Hardness	Average Machinability Rating (Cold Drawn) 1212=100%
G11080	1108	Hot Rolled	340	50 000	190	27 500	30	50	101	
		Cold Drawn	390	56 000	320	47 000	20	40	121	80
G11170	1117	Hot Rolled	430	62 000	230	34 000	23	47	121	
		Cold Drawn	480	69 000	400	58 000	15	40	137	90
G11320	1132	Hot Rolled	570	83 000	310	45 500	16	40	167	
		Cold Drawn	630	92 000	530	77 000	12	35	183	75
G11370	1137	Hot Rolled	610	88 000	330	48 000	15	35	179	
		Cold Drawn	680	98 000	570	82 000	10	30	197	70
G11400	1140	Hot Rolled	540	79 000	300	43 500	16	40	156	
		Cold Drawn	610	88 000	510	74 000	12	35	170	70
G11410	1141	Hot Rolled	650	94 000	360	51 500	15	35	187	
		Cold Drawn	720	105 100	610	88 000	10	30	212	70
G11440	1144	Hot Rolled	670	97 000	370	53 000	15	35	197	
		Cold Drawn	740	108 000	620	90 000	10	30	217	80
G11460	1146	Hot Rolled	590	85 000	320	47 000	15	40	170	
		Cold Drawn	650	94 000	550	80 000	12	35	187	70
G11510	1151	Hot Rolled	630	92 000	340	50 500	15	35	187	
		Cold Drawn	700	102 000	590	86 000	10	30	207	65
G12110	1211	Hot Rolled	380	55 000	230	33 000	25	45	121	
		Cold Drawn	520	75 000	400	58 000	10	35	163	95
G12120	1212	Hot Rolled	390	56 000	230	33 500	25	45	121	
		Cold Drawn	540	78 000	410	60 000	10	35	167	100
G12130	1213	Hot Rolled	390	56 000	230	33 500	25	45	121	
		Cold Drawn	540	78 000	410	60 000	10	35	167	135
G12144	12L14	Hot Rolled	390	57 000	230	34 000	22	45	121	
		Cold Drawn	540	78 000	410	60 000	10	35	163	160

1. All 1100 and 1200 series steels are rated on the basis of 0.10% maximum silicon or coarse grain melting practice.

TABLE 3—ESTIMATED MECHANICAL PROPERTIES AND MACHINABILITY RATINGS OF NONRESULFURIZED CARBON STEEL BARS, MANGANESE MAXIMUM OVER 1.00%

UNS No.	SAE and/or AISI No.	Type of Processing	Tensile Strength MPa	Tensile Strength psi	Estimated Minimum Values Yield Strength MPa	Estimated Minimum Values Yield Strength psi	Estimated Minimum Values Elongation in 2 in, %	Reduction in Area %	Brinell Hardness	Average Machinability Rating (Cold Drawn) 1212=100%
G15240	1524	Hot Rolled	510	74 000	280	41 000	20	42	149	
		Cold Drawn	570	82 000	480	69 000	12	35	163	60
G15270	1527	Hot Rolled	520	75 000	280	41 000	18	40	149	
		Cold Drawn	570	83 000	480	70 000	12	35	163	65
G15360	1536	Hot Rolled	570	83 000	310	45 500	16	40	163	
		Cold Drawn	630	92 000	530	77 500	12	35	187	55
G15410	1541	Hot Rolled	630	92 000	350	51 000	15	40	187	
		Cold Drawn	710	102 500	600	87 000	10	30	207	45
		ACD[1]	650	94 000	550	80 000	10	45	184	60
G15480	1548	Hot Rolled	660	96 000	370	53 000	14	33	197	
		Cold Drawn	730	106 500	620	89 500	10	28	217	45
		ACD[1]	640	93 500	540	78 500	10	35	192	50
G15520	1552	Hot Rolled	740	108 000	410	59 500	12	30	217	
		ACD[1]	680	98 000	570	83 000	10	40	193	50

1. ACD represents annealed cold drawn.

TABLE 4—MACHINABILITY OF ALLOY STEEL

UNS No.	AISI and/or SAE No.	Machinability Rating	Condition	Range of Typical Hardness HB	Microstructure Type[1]
G13300	1330	55	Annealed and Cold Drawn	179/235	A
G13350	1335	55	Annealed and Cold Drawn	179/235	A
G13400	1340	50	Annealed and Cold Drawn	183/241	A
G13450	1345	45	Annealed and Cold Drawn	183/241	A
G40230	4023	70	Cold Drawn	156/207	C
G40240	4024	75	Cold Drawn	156/207	C
G40270	4027	70	Annealed and Cold Drawn	167/212	A
G40280	4028	75	Annealed and Cold Drawn	167/212	A
G40320	4032	70	Annealed and Cold Drawn	174/217	A
G40370	4037	70	Annealed and Cold Drawn	174/217	A
G40420	4042	65	Annealed and Cold Drawn	179/229	A
G40470	4047	65	Annealed and Cold Drawn	179/229	A
G41180	4118	60	Cold Drawn	170/207	C
G41300	4130	70	Annealed and Cold Drawn	187/229	A
G41350	4135	70	Annealed and Cold Drawn	187/229	A
G41370	4137	70	Annealed and Cold Drawn	187/229	A
G41400	4140	65	Annealed and Cold Drawn	187/229	A
G41420	4142	65	Annealed and Cold Drawn	187/229	A
G41450	4145	60	Annealed and Cold Drawn	187/229	A
G41470	4147	60	Annealed and Cold Drawn	187/235	A
G41500	4150	55	Annealed and Cold Drawn	187/241	A, B
G41610	4161	50	Spheroidized and Cold Drawn	187/241	B, A
G43200	4320	60	Annealed and Cold Drawn	187/229	D, B, A
G43400	4340	50	Annealed and Cold Drawn	187/241	B, A
G43406	E4340	50	Annealed and Cold Drawn	187/241	B, A
G44220	4422	65	Cold Drawn	170/212	C
G44270	4427	65	Annealed and Cold Drawn	170/212	C
G46150	4615	65	Cold Drawn	174/223	C
G46170	4617	65	Cold Drawn	174/223	C
G46200	4620	65	Cold Drawn	183/229	C
G46260	4626	70	Cold Drawn	170/212	C
G47180	4718	60	Cold Drawn	187/229	C
G47200	4720	65	Cold Drawn	187/229	C
G48150	4815	50	Annealed and Cold Drawn	187/229	D, B
G48170	4817	50	Annealed and Cold Drawn	187/229	D, B
G48200	4820	50	Annealed and Cold Drawn	187/229	D, B
G50401	50B40	65	Annealed and Cold Drawn	174/223	A
G50441	50B44	65	Annealed and Cold Drawn	174/223	A
G50460	5046	60	Annealed and Cold Drawn	174/223	A
G50461	50B46	60	Annealed and Cold Drawn	174/223	A
G50501	50B50	55	Annealed and Cold Drawn	183/235	A
G50600	5060	55	Spheroidized Annealed and Cold Drawn	170/212	B
G50601	50B60	55	Spheroidized Annealed and Cold Drawn	170/212	B
G51150	5115	65	Cold Drawn	163/201	C
G51200	5120	70	Cold Drawn	163/201	C
G51300	5130	70	Annealed and Cold Drawn	174/212	A
G51320	5132	70	Annealed and Cold Drawn	174/212	A
G51350	5135	70	Annealed and Cold Drawn	179/217	A
G51400	5140	65	Annealed and Cold Drawn	179/217	A
G51470	5147	65	Annealed and Cold Drawn	179/229	A
G51500	5150	60	Annealed and Cold Drawn	183/235	A, B
G51550	5155	55	Annealed and Cold Drawn	183/235	A, B
G51600	5160	55	Spheroidized Annealed and Cold Drawn	179/217	B
G51601	51B60	55	Spheroidized Annealed and Cold Drawn	179/217	B
G50986	50100	40	Spheroidized Annealed and Cold Drawn	183/241	B
G51986	51100	40	Spheroidized Annealed and Cold Drawn	183/241	B
G52986	52100	40	Spheroidized Annealed and Cold Drawn	183/241	B
G61180	6118	60	Cold Drawn	179/217	C
G61500	6150	55	Annealed and Cold Drawn	183/241	B, A
G81150	8115	65	Cold Drawn	163/202	C
G81451	81B45	65	Annealed and Cold Drawn	179/223	A
G86150	8615	70	Cold Drawn	179/235	C
G86170	8617	70	Cold Drawn	179/235	C
G86200	8620	65	Cold Drawn	179/235	C
G86220	8622	65	Cold Drawn	179/235	C
G86250	8625	60	Annealed and Cold Drawn	179/223	A
G86270	8627	60	Annealed and Cold Drawn	179/223	A
G86300	8630	70	Annealed and Cold Drawn	179/229	A
G86370	8637	65	Annealed and Cold Drawn	179/229	A
G86400	8640	65	Annealed and Cold Drawn	184/229	A
G86420	8642	65	Annealed and Cold Drawn	184/229	A
G86450	8645	65	Annealed and Cold Drawn	184/235	A
G86451	86B45	65	Annealed and Cold Drawn	184/235	A
G86500	8650	60	Annealed and Cold Drawn	187/248	A, B
G86550	8655	55	Annealed and Cold Drawn	187/248	A, B
G86600	8660	55	Spheroidized Annealed and Cold Drawn	179/217	B
G87200	8720	65	Cold Drawn	179/235	C
G87400	8740	65	Annealed and Cold Drawn	184/235	A
G88220	8822	55	Cold Drawn	179/223	B
G92540	9254	45	Spheroidized Annealed and Cold Drawn	187/241	B
G92600	9260	40	Spheroidized Annealed and Cold Drawn	184/235	B
G93106	9310	50	Annealed and Cold Drawn	184/229	D
G94151	94B15	70	Cold Drawn	163/202	C
G94171	94B17	70	Cold Drawn	163/202	C
G94301	94B30	70	Annealed and Cold Drawn	170/223	A

1. (See section 3) for description of type.

LABORATORY MEASUREMENT OF THE COMPOSITE VIBRATION DAMPING PROPERTIES OF MATERIALS ON A SUPPORTING STEEL BAR—SAE J1637 FEB1993 SAE Recommended Practice

Report of the SAE Sound and Heat Insulation Materials Committee approved February 1993.

Foreword—This Document has not changed other than to put it into the new SAE Technical Standards Board Format.

*1. **Scope***—This SAE Recommended Practice describes a laboratory test procedure for measuring the vibration damping performance of a system consisting of a damping material bonded to a vibrating cantilevered steel bar. The bar is often called the Oberst bar (named after Dr. H. Oberst) and the test method is often called the Oberst Bar Test Method. Materials for damping treatments may include homogeneous materials, nonhomogeneous materials, or a combination of homogeneous, nonhomogeneous, and/or inelastic (such as aluminum foil) materials. These materials are commonly installed in transportation systems such as ground vehicles, marine products, and aircraft to reduce vibration at resonance, and thus reduce the noise radiation from the vibrating surface. However, the test method described herein was developed to rank order materials used in PASSENGER VEHICLE APPLICATIONS with steel sheet metal and may not be fully applicable to other situations.

Damping performance for most materials and systems varies as a function of both frequency and temperature. Accordingly, this test procedure includes provisions for measuring damping over a range of frequencies and temperatures found applicable to many transportation systems. The measured damping performance will be expressed in terms of composite loss factor, η_c, within the frequency range of approximately 100 to 1000 Hz, and over the useful temperature range for the given application. The term composite refers to the steel and damping material combination.

The test procedure described here is based on the method described in ASTM E 756. However, this SAE document differs from the ASTM E 756 method in that the SAE practice specifies the bar material, the bar size, and the mounting conditions of the test samples. This document provides a means of rank ordering damping materials according to their composite loss factor values from test samples that represent typical passenger vehicle applications.

The ASTM E 756 should be followed to determine the damping properties of materials alone, including loss factor η, Young's modulus E, and shear modulus G.

*2. **References***

2.1 Applicable Publications—The following publications form a part of this specification to the extent specified herein. The latest issue of SAE publications shall apply.

2.1.1 SAE PUBLICATION—Available from SAE, 400 Commonwealth Drive, Warrendale, PA 15096-0001.

SAE TSB 003—Rules for SAE Use of SI (Metric) Units

2.1.2 ANSI PUBLICATIONS—Available from ANSI, 11 West 42nd Street, New York, NY 10036-8002.

ANSI S1.1—Acoustical Terminology

ANSI S2.9—Nomenclature for Specifying Damping Properties of Materials

2.1.3 ASTM PUBLICATIONS—Available from ASTM, 100 Barr Harbor Drive, West Conshohocken, PA 19428-2959.

ASTM E 691—Conducting an Interlaboratory Study to Determine the Precision of a Test Method

ASTM E 756—Measuring Vibration—Damping Properties of Materials

2.1.4 DIN PUBLICATIONS—Available from DIN Deutsches Institute fur Normung, Burggrafengstrasse 6, Postfach 1107, D-1000 Berlin 30 Germany.

DIN 53 440—Testing of Plastics and Damped Laminated Systems; Bending Vibration Test

Teil 1—General Rudiments of Dynamic Elastic Properties of Bars and Strips

Teil 2—Determination of Complex Modulus of Elasticity

Teil 3—Determination of Dynamic-Elastic Values of Damped Laminated Systems

2.1.5 JASO PUBLICATION—Available from The Society of Automotive Engineers of Japan, Inc., 10-2, Goban-cho, Chiyoda-ku, Tokyo 102, Japan.

JASO M 329—Asphalt Sheet for Automobiles

*3. **Test Method***—The method is based on exciting the damped bar at various modes of vibration at a given temperature of interest, and obtaining the damping performance using the half-power bandwidth technique. In this technique, first the resonant frequency, f, at a given mode of the bar is measured. Next, the lower and upper frequencies (fl and f_u, respectively) are measured on the response curve on either side of the resonant frequency where the levels are 3 dB lower than the level at resonance (3 dB down points or half-power points). The difference of f_u and f_l in this case, is called the half-power bandwidth. This procedure is repeated for other modes of vibration and temperatures. The composite damping performance is given by Equation 1 (see Figure 1):

$$\eta_c = \frac{\Delta f}{f} \quad \text{(Eq. 1)}$$

where:

$\Delta f = f_u - f_l$
= frequency bandwidth, Hz
f = resonant frequency, Hz
η_c = composite loss factor at resonant frequency, f, dimensionless

*4. **Instrumentation***—The instrumentation to be used is as follows (see Figure 2 for a schematic of a typical set-up):

4.1 A bar mounting fixture (test fixture) that is heavy, rigid, and can provide adequate force at the clamped end of the bar to simulate the cantilever boundary conditions (clamped-free).

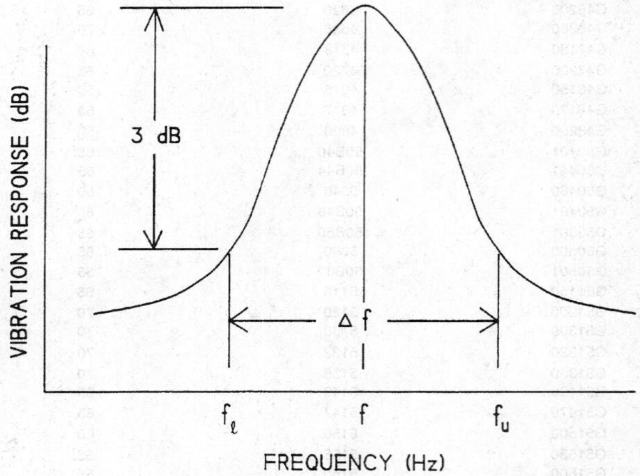

FIGURE 1—COMPOSITE DAMPING PERFORMANCE COMPUTATION

4.2 A temperature chamber so that the sample can be maintained at the appropriate temperature.

4.3 Two transducers with associated power supplies and signal conditioners—one applies the excitation force (called the excitation transducer or the exciter) and the other measures the response of the bar (called the pick-up transducer). The purpose is to measure only the damping of the test sample, without any additional damping from any other effects. Therefore, it is preferable that the pick-up transducer be a noncontacting type transducer. If a contacting type transducer is used as a pick-up transducer, extreme care should be taken to ensure that the transducer does not contribute to the damping of the test sample (i.e., overdamp the test sample). Refer to 7.2.2. The excitation transducer is generally a noncontacting type electromagnetic vibration exciter.

4.4 A signal generator that generates a sinusoidal or a random signal. The signal is applied to the excitation transducer by means of a power amplifier. The response of the bar will be measured using the pick-up transducer.

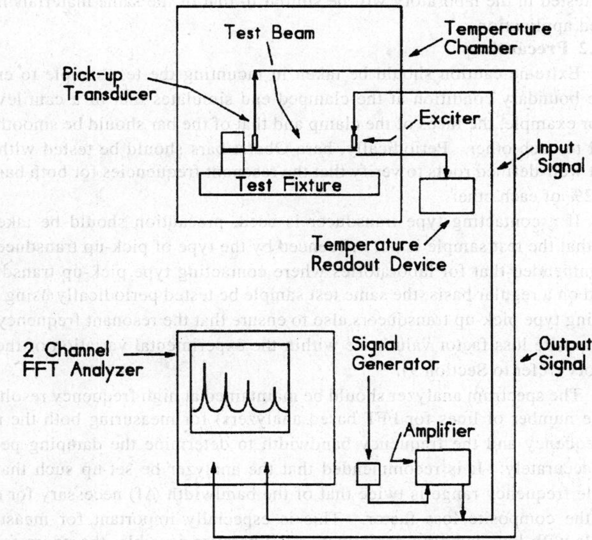

FIGURE 2—SCHEMATIC OF A TYPICAL TEST SET-UP FOR DAMPING PERFORMANCE EVALUATION

4.5 An analyzer or an analysis system capable of determining the transfer function between the excitation signal and the response signal. Examples include: a two-channel spectrum analyzer (e.g., based on Fast Fourier Transform algorithm) that is suitable for the signal, such as the random noise signal. Alternatively, a single channel system with separate excitation and response analysis systems can be used. However, efforts must be made to make the excitation force constant with frequency so that the response can be measured directly. The minimum amplitude precision of the measuring system should be 0.1 dB. The minimum frequency resolution of the measuring system should be 0.1 Hz.

5. Test Sample

5.1Test Bar—The test bar to be used is as follows:

5.1.1 The metal for the bare bar should be steel. Precision Ground Gage Stock (or also called Precision Ground Flat Stock) bars should be used as the Oberst bar for damping tests. Precision Ground Gage Stock bars are commercially available. Alternatively, the bare bar may be manufactured by machining a mild steel bar stock. A new bar should be used for each application.

5.1.2 The dimensions of the bar should be as follows (refer to Figure 3):

a. Mounted free length: 200 mm ± 0.5 mm
b. Total length: 225 mm
c. Thickness: 0.8 mm ± 0.03 mm
d. Width: 12.7 mm ± 0.03 mm

(Precision ground gage stock steel bars are commercially available at various lengths with 0.8 mm thickness and 12.7 mm width. Should the bars be manufactured by machining a mild steel bar stock, precautions should be taken to ensure that the two faces of the bar are parallel to each other and that the edges and the ends are square with the face of the bar.)

The modes of vibration of this size cantilevered steel bar (i.e., with free length of 200 mm) at 25 °C are generally calculated as follows:

Experience has been that measured values of mode-frequencies within 2% of the calculated values at 25 °C produce repeatable test results. Figure 4 shows the typical frequency response of a bare Oberst bar.

Mode 1 is usually not used for this measurement, primarily for the following reasons:

a. The bar and the fixture both tend to vibrate as a rigid body, thereby introducing error in measuring the composite loss factor.
b. The first mode is most sensitive to any error due to the static magnetic field of the transducers that may influence the vibration of the free end of the bar.

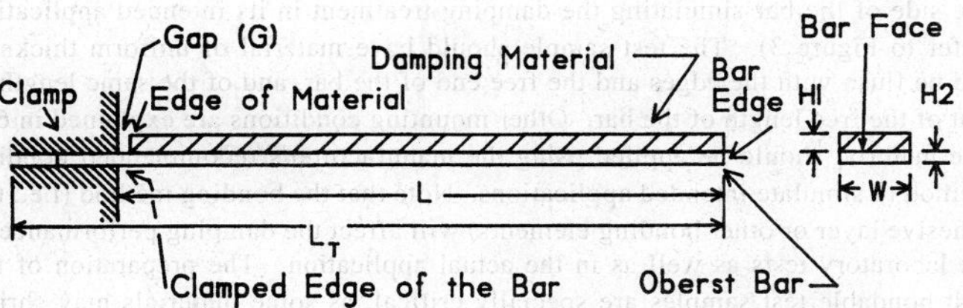

LEGEND:

L - Free length of the bar: 200 mm (This is also the length of the damping material)

L_T - Total length of the bar: 225 mm

Hl - Thickness of the damping material

H2 - Thickness of the bar: 0.8 mm

W - Width of the bar: 12.7 mm

NOTE:

The damping material should not touch the clamping mechanism or the test fixture. The gap (G) between the clamping device and the material should be less than or equal to 1 mm.

FIGURE 3—TEST SAMPLE FOR OBERST BAR

TABLE 1—(Using density of steel: 7840 kg/m³ Modulus of steel: 2.0 x 10¹¹ Pa)

Mode	Resonant Frequency (Hz)
2	102
3	286
4	561
5	927

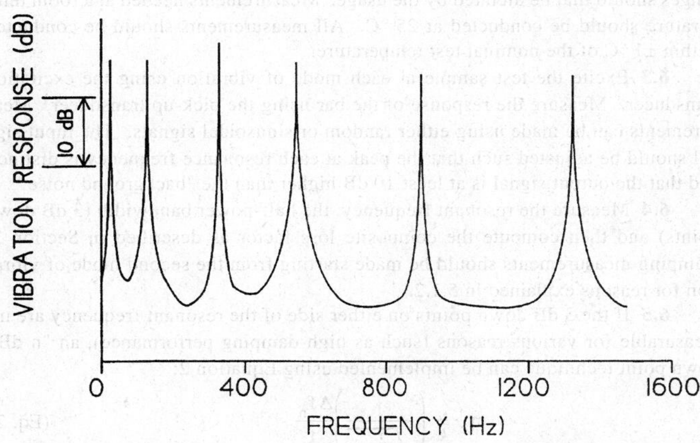

FIGURE 4—TYPICAL FREQUENCY RESPONSE OF A BARE BAR

5.1.3 Some laboratories employ a stepped increase in bar thickness (also called roots) at the clamped end of the test bars to mount the bar in a fixture. These are not required, provided proper boundary conditions can be simulated at the clamped end of the bar to represent a fixed support cantilever condition. However, note that interlaboratory and intralaboratory studies suggest that the range of the results obtained from test bars without roots is likely to vary more than that of the test bars with roots, unless proper care is taken to ensure that the free length is precise, the clamped edge is perpendicular to the face of the bar, and that the bar mounting fixture is rigid and massive.

5.2 Sample Preparation—The damping material should be attached to one side of the bar simulating the damping treatment in its intended application (refer to Figure 3). The test sample should have material of uniform thickness and be flush with the edges and the free end of the bar, and of the same length as that of the free length of the bar. Other mounting conditions are explained in 6.1. The material should be applied using the manufacturer's recommended bonding method to simulate intended applications. Note that the bonding method (i.e., the adhesive layer or other bonding elements) will affect the damping performance in the laboratory tests as well as in the actual application. The preparation of the heat bondable test samples are specially critical, as some materials may shrink and some materials may expand during the heat bonding process.

6. Procedure

6.1 Securely clamp the test sample in the test fixture to provide a sufficiently rigid mounting to simulate a cantilever bar condition. The test sample shall be mounted in the fixture with a free length of 200 mm and ensuring that the clamped edge is perpendicular to the face of the bar. The damping material should not touch the clamping mechanism or anything else associated with the test fixture. The gap between the clamping device and the edge of the damping material should be less than or equal to 1 mm, and yet maintain the tolerance of the mounted free length as mentioned in 5.1.2.

It is important to position the transducers at appropriate locations to obtain the best dynamic response and the optimal signal to noise ratio of the vibrating test sample. Generally, the transducers are located close to the clamped end of the bar and close to the free end of the bar. (The exciter and the pick-up transducers should be at least sufficient distance apart to reduce "cross-talk" effects between the two transducers. Cross-talk can be verified by removing the sample bar.) This will permit correct measurement of the damping performance. For noncontacting type transducers, the transducers may require positioning within 1 mm of the test sample.

6.2 Place the test fixture inside a temperature chamber so the damping performance can be evaluated at different temperatures. The temperature in the chamber may vary considerably depending on where the temperature is measured. Therefore, the temperature shall be monitored close to the test sample. This requirement is best fulfilled by monitoring the temperature on a separate bare steel bar located very close to, but not touching the test sample. Once the separate bare bar has reached the test temperature, allow the sample to soak at that temperature for at least 20 min to ensure that the test sample temperature has stabilized and is uniform everywhere in the sample.

It is recommended that the damping performance be measured at −20 °C, −5 °C, 10 °C, 25 °C, 40 °C, and 55 °C for materials that are formulated to be used in this temperature range. Measurements shall be conducted at other temperature ranges should that be dictated by the usage. Measurements needed at a room temperature should be conducted at 25 °C. All measurements should be conducted within ±1 °C of the nominal test temperature.

6.3 Excite the test sample at each mode of vibration using the excitation transducer. Measure the response of the bar using the pick-up transducer. Measurements can be made using either random or sinusoidal signals. The input signal should be adjusted such that the peak at each resonance frequency is distinct, and that the output signal is at least 10 dB higher than the "background noise."

6.4 Measure the resonant frequency, the half-power bandwidth (3 dB down points) and then compute the composite loss factor as described in Section 3. Damping measurements should be made starting from the second mode of vibration for reasons explained in 5.1.2.

6.5 If the 3 dB down points on either side of the resonant frequency are not measurable for various reasons (such as high damping performance), an "n dB" down point technique can be implemented using Equation 2:

$$\eta_c = \left(\frac{1}{\sqrt{x^2 - 1}}\right)\frac{\Delta f_n}{f} \quad \text{(Eq. 2)}$$

where:

$x = 10^{n/20}$
n = "n dB" down point
Δf_n = frequency bandwidth for "n dB" down point, Hz

6.6 The "n dB down point" technique should not be used if n is less than or equal to 0.5 dB. In such cases, or if the composite loss factor could not be computed for other reasons (such as double peak or overdamped test bar), this should be noted in the test report.

7. Assumptions and Precautions

7.1 Assumptions—The size of the steel bar is selected based on the following assumptions:

7.1.1 The frequency range (i.e., from 100 to 1000 Hz) where the damping performance is evaluated agrees with the frequency range of interest for the intended application.

7.1.2 The performance ranking of different materials (based on composite loss factor) tested in the laboratory will be similar to that of the same materials in the intended application.

7.2 Precautions

7.2.1 Extreme caution should be taken in mounting the test sample to ensure that the boundary condition at the clamped end simulates that of a cantilevered bar. For example, the faces of the clamp and that of the bar should be smooth and parallel to each other. Periodically, bare Oberst bars should be tested with and without well-defined roots to verify that the resonant frequencies for both bars are within 2% of each other.

7.2.2 If a contacting type transducer is used, precaution should be taken to ensure that the test sample is not influenced by the type of pick-up transducer. It is recommended that for laboratories where contacting type pick-up transducers are used on a regular basis, the same test sample be tested periodically using non-contacting type pick-up transducers also to ensure that the resonant frequency and the composite loss factor values are within the experimental variation of the test laboratory (refer to Section 9).

7.2.3 The spectrum analyzer should be maintained at high frequency resolution (i.e., the number of lines for FFT based analyzers) for measuring both the resonant frequency and the frequency bandwidth to determine the damping performance accurately. It is recommended that the analyzer be set-up such that the available frequency range is twice that of the bandwidth (Δf) necessary for computing the composite loss factor. This is especially important for measuring materials with low damping performance. Wherever possible, the zoom feature of the analyzer should be used for greater precision.

7.2.4 Damping measurements can be made using either manual or software-driven automated data acquisition systems. Extreme caution should be taken, especially for automated systems, to be able to identify "humps," double peaks, and/or other outlying data such as "spikes" in the response spectrum of each mode (refer to Figure 5). These occurrences should be noted in the test report, if they are used for damping calculations.

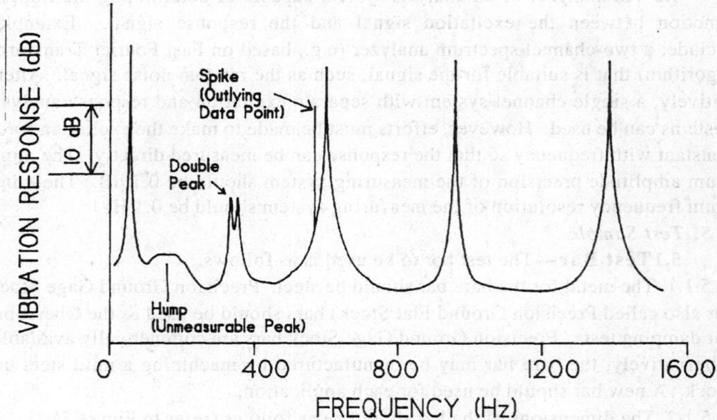

FIGURE 5—POSSIBLE FREQUENCY RESPONSE OF A DAMPED BAR

7.2.5 No single method of measuring damping performance may meet the needs of all users of damping materials. This document is a relatively simple approach for rank ordering materials. The potential user of this document must determine the level of sophistication required for the application. Those who require material properties such as loss factor η, Young's modulus E, shear modulus G, for predictive modeling or other reasons, are referred to ASTM E 756.

8. Report—The report shall include the following:

8.1 A description of the test procedure used for conducting the measurements shall be provided. Any deviations or exceptions taken from this test method shall be explicitly noted. The report should explicitly state that the measurements made and data reported are that of a damping material bonded to a steel Oberst bar, and that the damping performance is expressed in terms of "composite loss factor" (η_c).

8.2 The report shall provide a description of the damping material including thickness, density or specific gravity, bake condition, and/or any other pertinent data. The report shall state the size of the steel bar and identify any chemical treatment (e.g., E-coat) to the steel bar prior to the preparation of the test sample.

8.3 The report shall identify how the test sample was prepared (i.e., how the material and the bar were bonded together, e.g., pressure-sensitive adhesive, self-adhesion type material, baked-on, etc.). If the material and the steel bar were baked to prepare the test sample, the bake conditions (i.e., temperature and time) shall be stated.

8.4 The test temperatures, the modes of vibration, the resonant frequencies, and the composite loss factor values shall be reported in the test results.

If the measured temperatures varied beyond ±1 °C of the nominal test temperature, this shall be noted, and the measured temperature shall be reported.

The value of the resonant frequencies shall be reported as an integer (e.g., report 101 Hz and not 101.2 Hz).

The value of the composite loss factor shall be reported to the third decimal point (e.g., report 0.098, and not 0.0979).

If the vibration response of the test sample has double peaks that affect the measurements, or if the composite loss factor is computed based on "n dB down point" technique, this shall be stated in the report.

8.5 The test results shall be provided in tabular form, and wherever possible, in graphical form. Figures 6 and 7 illustrate recommended formats for presenting the test results in tabular and graphical forms, respectively. The graphical form of the data may also be presented as a function of temperature as illustrated in Figure 8.

Test Material:
Bake Condition:

Data of the Test Material:
Specific Gravity or Surface Weight:
Nominal Thickness:
Measured Thickness:

Test Bar Dimension - Oberst Bar: Free length 200 mm, thickness 0.8 mm, width 12.7 mm

Exception:

Test Temperature	Mode	Resonance Frequency (Hz)	Composite Loss Factor η_c
10°C	2	105	0.076
	3	310	0.069
	4	620	0.067
	5	1100	0.071
20°C (Figure 6)	2	101	0.108
	3	294	0.132
	4	592	0.152
	5	1015	0.168
40°C	2	96	0.097
	3	282	0.115
	4	563	0.120
	5	981	0.105

FIGURE 6—RESULTS OF OBERST BAR DAMPING TESTS

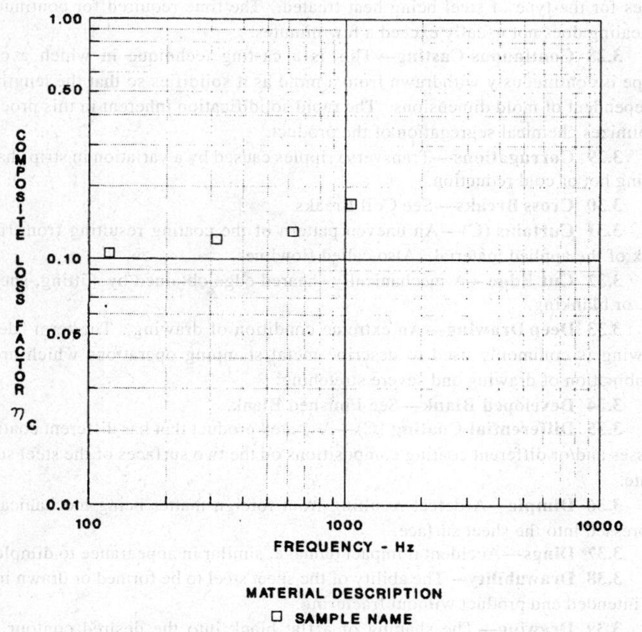

FIGURE 7—COMPOSITE LOSS FACTOR AT 25 °C FROM OBERST BAR DAMPING TESTS

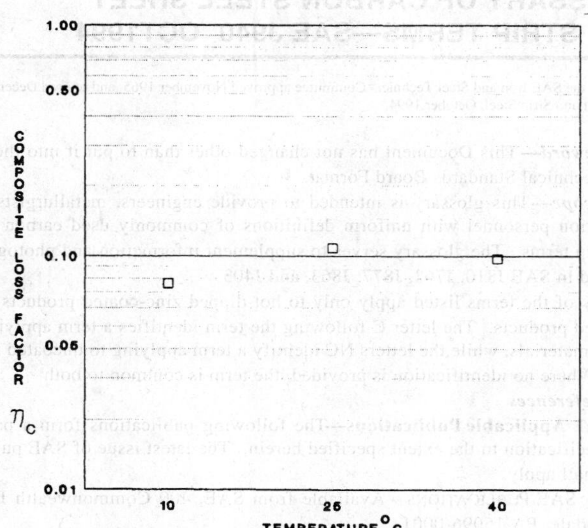

FIGURE 8—COMPOSITE LOSS FACTOR AT 2ND MODE FROM OBERST BAR DAMPING TESTS

9. Precision and Bias

9.1 Precision— The precision is based on 95% confidence limit.

An interlaboratory study was conducted according to ASTM E 691 to determine the laboratory precision of this test method and to express the test results in terms of the coefficient of variation. Based on this study, the coefficient of variation for the composite loss factor values for a laboratory test will be within 20%, provided all the precautions are followed as mentioned in Section 7. Coefficient of variation of 20% means the composite loss factor of a material (with nominal composite loss factor of 0.160) for a given mode at worst will vary from 0.144 to 0.176. The coefficient of variation for tests conducted between laboratories will be within 35% when all the precautions are taken. Coefficient of variation of 35% means the composite loss factor of a material (with nominal composite loss factor of 0.160) for a given mode at worst will vary from 0.132 to 0.188.

The general formula to compute the range of the composite loss factor is given by Equation 3:

$$\eta_c = \eta_c \pm (1/2)(cv/100)\eta_c \quad \text{(Eq. 3)}$$

where:

η_c = nominal composite loss factor
cv = coefficient of variation in percent

9.2 Bias— This method cannot provide any information on the bias of the measurements, except resonant frequencies of the bare bar.

10. General Comment— During interlaboratory tests, the test laboratories were asked to measure the damping performance of various test samples (including homogeneous and nonhomogeneous damping materials) with and without roots at different temperatures. The test laboratories used their own test procedures for determining composite loss factor using the half-power bandwidth technique and within the confines of certain guidelines established by the Vibration Damping Task Force of the SAE Sound and Heat Insulation Materials Committee. The purpose was to obtain the variation in test results due to different operators, different types of instrumentation used for measurements, different test procedures used, etc.

Data were obtained using contacting type and noncontacting type transducers as well as using manual and software-driven automated data acquisition systems. The study shows that the coefficient of variation for composite loss factors were in general high for tests conducted using bars without roots. On average, the coefficient of variation (95% confidence limit) for results within a laboratory and for results between laboratories were 37% and 53%, respectively. It was identified that a few measurements made the results worse for bars without roots. Once the results from these measurements were deleted (because they were obviously erroneous), the results from these measurements improved significantly as reported in 9.1.

GLOSSARY OF CARBON STEEL SHEET AND STRIP TERMS—SAE J940 OCT1994

SAE Information Report

Report of the SAE Iron and Steel Technical Committee approved November 1965, and revised December 1988. Revised by the SAE Iron and Steel Technical Committee Division 32—Sheet and Strip Steel, October 1994.

Foreword—This Document has not changed other than to put it into the new SAE Technical Standards Board Format.

1. Scope—This glossary is intended to provide engineers, metallurgists, and production personnel with uniform definitions of commonly used carbon sheet and strip terms. The glossary serves to supplement information and photographs reported in SAE J810, J763, J877, J863, and J403.

Many of the terms listed apply only to hot-dipped zinc-coated products or to uncoated products. The letter C following the term identifies a term applying to coated materials, while the letters NC identify a term applying to uncoated materials. Where no identification is provided, the term is common to both.

2. References

2.1 Applicable Publications—The following publications form a part of this specification to the extent specified herein. The latest issue of SAE publications shall apply.

2.1.1 SAE PUBLICATIONS—Available from SAE, 400 Commonwealth Drive, Warrendale, PA 15096-0001.

SAE J403—Chemical Compositions of SAE Carbon Steels
SAE J415—Definitions of Heat Treating Terms
SAE J448—Surface Texture
SAE J450—Use of Terms Yield Strength and Yield Point
SAE J763—Aging of Carbon Steel Sheet and Strip
SAE J810—Classification of Common Imperfections in Sheet Steel
SAE J863—Methods of Determining Plastic Deformation in Sheet Metal Stampings
SAE J877—Properties of Low Carbon Sheet Steel and Their Relationship to Formability

3. Definitions

3.1 Aging—A term applied to changes in physical and mechanical properties of low carbon steel that occur with the passage of time. (See SAE J763.)

3.2 Annealing Border (NC)—See Oxidized Surface. (See also SAE J810).

3.3 Annealing Stain (NC)—A discoloration on annealed material which may occur anywhere on the sheet (usually lighter than annealing border). It results from residue, or oxidation, during annealing.

3.4 Arc (C)—A narrow curved pencil-like line in the coating running transversely approximately 2 in from each edge of the strip.

3.5 Bake Hardenable Steels—Those steels that increase in strength while undergoing a paint-baking cycle.

3.6 Band Mark—An indentation caused by the packaging band resulting from external pressure on cut lengths or coils and may occur in handling, transit, and storing.

3.7 Batch Annealing—See Box Annealing.

3.8 Beads (C)—Small lumps in the coating surface. Particles of dross picked up in the coating or iron oxide particles embedded in the strip surface from the furnace hearth rolls. Also referred to as dross.

3.9 Black Spots (NC)—Carbonaceous deposits caused by tightly wound areas in a coil not being exposed to the circulating gases during open coil type annealing. This condition is aggravated by poor strip shape.

3.10 Blank—A flat piece of sheet steel produced in blanking dies or by shearing for an identified part. The blank is usually subjected to further press operations.

3.11 Blanking—Cutting desired shapes out of flat sheet.

3.12 Blister——A small raised area on the surface resulting from the expansion of gas concentrated at a subsurface inclusion or other imperfection. May occur as isolated spots, but often found in longitudinal streaks.

3.13 Box Annealing—The process of softening steel by heating coils or stacks of sheets slowly in a closed container, through which, in most cases, a controlled atmosphere is circulated to prevent oxidation during the heating and cooling cycle. The time required may vary from one to several days. (See SAE J415.)

3.14 Breaks—Creases or ridges usually in "untempered" or in aged material where the yield point has been exceeded. Depending on the origin of the break, it might be termed a crossbreak, a coil break, an edge break, a sticker break, etc. (See SAE J810.)

3.15 Bright Annealing (NC)—Annealing in a protective atmosphere to prevent discoloration of the surface.

3.16 Bright Finish (NC)—A high-quality finish produced on sheets by rolls which have been ground and polished. Suitable for electroplating.

3.17 Buckles—A series of waves in sheets which are ordinarily transverse to the direction of rolling. (See SAE J810.) In formed panels, "excess metal" in the form of wrinkles, kinks, or folds.

3.18 Buildup (C)—Localized lineal areas showing a difference in cross-sectional contour during coiling. Usually occurs on the edges of the strip.

3.19 Camber—Deviation from a straight edge, usually referring to the greatest deviation of the concave side edge of a sheet or strip from a straight line.

3.20 Capped Steel—This is a type of steel with characteristics similar to those of rimmed steels, but to a degree intermediate between those of rimmed and semikilled steels. It can be either mechanically capped or chemically capped when the ingot is cast, but in either case the full rimming action is stopped, resulting in a more uniform composition than rimmed steel.

3.21 Carbon Edge (NC)—Carbonaceous deposits in a wavy pattern along the edges or coil. (See also Snaky Edges.)

3.22 Chatter—A series of lines uniformly spaced appearing transverse to the rolling direction usually resulting from material being rolled on units having loose bearings. Results in a slight thickness variation where lines appear.

3.23 Checked Edges—Sawtooth edges seen after hot rolling and/or cold rollling. (See also Ragged Edge in SAE J810.)

3.24 Coil Breaks—Creases or ridges which appear as parallel lines across the direction of rolling and which generally extend across the width of the sheet. (See SAE J810.)

3.25 Coil Weld—A joint between two lengths of metal within a coil. (See SAE J810.)

3.26 Cold-Rolled Sheets (NC)—A product produced form a hot-rolled pickled oil which has been given substantial cold reduction at room temperature. The resulting product usually requires further processing to make it suitable for most common applications. The usual end product is characterized by improved surface, greater uniformity in thickness, and improved mechanical properties compared to hot-rolled sheet.

3.27 Continuous Annealing—The process of passing a strand or sheet through a controlled atmosphere furnace that has both heating and cooling zones. Temperatures, line speeds, and cooling rates are varied to obtain the desired properties for the type of steel being heat treated. The time required for continuous annealing does not usually exceed a few minutes.

3.28 Continuous Casting—This is a casting technique in which a cast shape is continuously withdrawn from a mold as it solidifies so that the length is independent of mold dimensions. The rapid solidification inherent in this process minimizes chemical segregation of the product.

3.29 Corrugations—Transverse ripples caused by a variation in strip shape during hot or cold reduction.

3.30 Cross Breaks—See Coil Breaks.

3.31 Curtains (C)—An uneven pattern of the coating resulting from runback of the applied material. Also called flowlines.

3.32 Cut Edge—A mechanically sheared edge obtained by slitting, shearing, or blanking.

3.33 Deep Drawing—An extreme condition of drawing. The term "deep drawing is commonly used to describe metal stamping operations which are a combination of drawing and severe stretching.

3.34 Developed Blank—See Finished Blank.

3.35 Differential Coating (C)—A coated product that has different coating masses and/or different coating compositions on the two surfaces of the steel substrate.

3.36 Dimple—A defect resulting from foreign matter being mechanically impressed into the sheet surface.

3.37 Dings—Accidental impact damage, similar in appearance to dimples.

3.38 Drawability—The ability of the sheet steel to be formed or drawn into the intended end product without fracturing.

3.39 Drawing—The shaping of a flat blank into the desired contour by causing the metal to flow over a draw ring and round a punch. The flow of metal is restrained by sufficient blank holder pressure to prevent buckling.

3.40 Drawing Lubricant (Drawing Compound)—A substance applied to minimize metal-to-metal contact between the sheet metal and the die. Proper application of the proper lubricant can improve flow characteristics of the metal and prevent scoring, galling, and pickup on the dies or part.

3.41 Dross (C)—The scum that develops in a molten galvanizing pot.

3.42 Ductility—The ability of a metal to be deformed plastically without fracturing. (See Formability.)

3.43 "E" Finish—This designation indicates that the material is to be used for an exposed part requiring a good painted surface. (See SAE J403.)

3.44 Earing (Scalloping)—The formation of scallops (ears or marked unevenness) around the top edge of a drawn cup caused by differences in the directional properties of the sheet metal used.

3.45 Edge Break (Side Strain)—See Edge Strain. (See also SAE J810.)

3.46 Edge Strain—Transverse strain lines or Lüder's Lines ranging from 1 to 12 inches in from the edges of the sheet. (See SAE J810.)

3.47 Electrogalvanizing (C)—The electroplating of zinc or zinc alloys upon iron or steel.

3.48 End Mark—A roll mark caused by the end of a sheet marking the roll during hot- or cold-rolling.

3.49 Entry Mark (Exit Mark)—A slight corrugation caused by the entry or exit rolls of a roller leveling unit.

3.50 Finished Blank (Developed Blank)—A blank that requires little or no trimming after being formed.

3.51 Flex Roll—The movable jump roll designed to push up against the sheet as it passes through the roller lever. The roll can be adjusted to produce varying amounts of deflection of the sheet up to the diameter of the roll.

3.52 Flex Rolling—Passing sheets through a flex roll unit to minimize yield point elongation so as to reduce the tendency for stretcher strains to appear in forming.

3.53 Floppers—Lines or ridges which are transverse to the direction of rolling and generally confined to the section midway between the edges of the coil as rolled. They are somewhat irregular and tend toward a flat arc shape. (See SAE J810.)

3.54 Flowlines (C)—An uneven pattern of the coating resulting from run-back of the applied material. Also called curtains.

3.55 Fluting—A series of sharp parallel kinks or creases occurring in the arc when sheet steel is rolled formed into a cylindrical shape. (See SAE J810.)

3.56 Formability—The degree to which a metal can be shaped through plastic deformation. (See Ductility.)

3.57 Forming—The shaping of sheet metal by bending, uniaxial stretching, biaxial stretching, compression, or by a combination thereof.

3.58 Friction Gouges or Scratches—A series of relatively short scratches variable in form or severity. (See SAE J810.)

3.59 Full Center—A "fullness" in the center portion of the sheet or strip.

3.60 Galling—Scratches caused by localized cold welding of particles to the tool during the forming operation.

3.61 Galvannealed Coating (C)—Galvannealed sheets are hot-dipped zinc-coated sheets which have been processed to produce a zinc-iron alloy coating. This product does not have a spangle and is suitable for painting after cleaning. The alloy produced lacks ductility and powdering of the coating can occur during forming.

3.62 Ghost Lines (NC) (Ghost Welt Lines)—Lines running parallel to the rolling direction that appear in a panel when it is stretched. These lines may not be evident unless panel has been sanded or painted. (Not to be confused with leveler lines.)

3.63 Handling Breaks—Irregular breaks caused by improper handling of sheets during processing. These breaks result from the bending or sagging of the sheets while being handled.

3.64 Healed Over Scratch (NC)—A scratch that occurred in an earlier mill operation and was partially masked in subsequent rolling. It may open up during forming. (See SAE J810.)

3.65 Hot-Rolled—Hot-rolled sheets are those that are reduced to required thickness at temperatures at which scale is formed and, therefore, carry hot mill oxide.

3.66 Hot-Rolled, Pickled—The hot-rolled product which has been pickled to remove the hot-mill oxide.

3.67 Impact or Recoil Line—The line on a drawn panel where a change in thickness occurs. Caused by: (a) the transfer of the panel from the die to the punch; (b) the reaction from the blank being pulled sharply through the draw ring (recoil); (c) the impact of the punch contacting the blank.

3.68 Inclusions—Nonmetallic materials in a solid metallic matrix.

3.69 Ironing—Thinning the walls of deep-drawn articles by reducing the clearance between punch and die.

3.70 Killed Steel—Steel deoxidized with certain deoxidizing elements, such as aluminum, silicon, etc. The term "killed" is used because such additions cause the steel to lie quietly in the mold during solidification. (See SAE J877.)

3.71 Laminations—Defects aligned parallel to the worked surface of the sheet resulting from the presence of inclusions. (See SAE J810.)

3.72 Loose Metal—Refers to an area in a formed panel that is not stiff enough to hold its shape, may be confused with Oil Canning.

3.73 Lüder's Lines—See Stretcher Strains.

3.74 Luster Finish (NC)—A finish produced on ground rolls suitable for decorative painting and plating with additional surface preparation after forming.

3.75 Matte Finish—The texture produced on sheets by rolls which have been finished to various degrees of roughness depending upon the end use.

3.76 Mechanical Properties—The properties of a material that reveal its elastic and plastic behavior when force is applied, for example, yield strength, ultimate strength, elongation, hardness, etc.

3.77 Mill Edge—The normal edge produced in hot rolling. This edge is customarily removed when hot-rolled sheets are further processed into cold-rolled sheets.

3.78 Minimized Spangle (C)—Minimized spangle galvanized sheet has very small spangles which are obtained by treating the galvanized sheet during the solidification of the zinc to restrict the normal zinc spangle formation.

3.79 Necking—Reducing the thickness of a sheet in a localized area by stretching.

3.80 Normalizing—Heating steel to a suitable temperature above the transformation range and then cooling in air to a temperature substantially below the transformation range. (See SAE J415.)

3.81 Offal—The material trimmed from blanks or formed panels.

3.82 Oil Can Oil (Oil Canning)—Refers to an area in a formed panel that when depressed slightly will recover its original contour after the depressing force is removed.

3.83 Orange Peel—A course textured or pebbly surface condition which becomes evident during forming. (See SAE J810.)

3.84 Oxide Border (NC)—See Oxidized Surface.

3.85 Oxidized Surface (NC)—Surface having a thin, tightly adhering (discolored from straw to blue) oxidized skin extending in from the edge of the coil or sheet. Sometimes called "Annealing Border." (See SAE J810.)

3.86 Physical Properties—The properties other than mechanical properties that pertain to the physics of a material; for example, density, electrical conductivity, thermal expansion, etc. Often improperly used to express mechanical properties.

3.87 Pickle Patch (NC)—A tightly adhering oxide or scale not removed during the pickling process. (See SAE J810.)

3.88 Pickle Stain (NC)—Discoloration present after pickling.

3.89 Pickling—The removal of surface oxides from sheets by chemical or electrochemical reaction.

3.90 Pickup—Metal particles adhering to a work roll or tool which cause a series of dents, scratches, or pits on a sheet or part.

3.91 Pinchers—Fernline ripples or creases usually diagonal to the rolling direction. (See SAE J810.)

3.92 Pipe—In sheets, it appears as a separation midway between the surfaces containing oxide inclusions. (See SAE J810.)

3.93 Pits—Small cavities in the surface of the sheet. (See SAE J810.)

3.94 Reel Breaks (Reel Kinks)—Transverse breaks or ridges on successive inner laps of a coil which are the result of crimping the lead end of the coil into a gripping segmented mandrel.

3.95 Ridge—A longitudinal line where the thickness of the metal is slightly greater than the thickness adjacent.

3.96 Rimmed Steel—A type of steel characterized by a gaseous effervescence when cooling in the mold. This results in a relatively pure iron outer rim. Rimmed steel is subject to aging. (See SAE J877.)

3.97 Roller Leveler—A series of small diameter staggered rolls used primarily to improve flatness and/or to remove yield point elongation.

3.98 Roller Leveler Breaks—Obvious transverse breaks usually 1/8 to 1/4 in apart caused by the sheet fluting during roller leveling. These will not be removed by stretching.

3.99 Roller Leveler Lines—Lines running transverse to the direction of leveling. These may be seen upon stoning or light sanding after leveling and before drawing. Moderate stretching will usually remove them.

3.100 Rosebuds (C)—Noted only on minimized spangle. Concentric rings of distorted coating, giving the effect of an opened rosebud.

3.101 Rough Developed Blank—A blank that will require trimming after being formed.

3.102 Saw Tooth Edge—See Checked Edges.

3.103 Scabs—Elongated patches of loosened metal which have been rolled into the surface of the sheet or strip.

3.104 Scale—Oxides of iron which form on the surface of hot steel.

3.105 Scoring—Marring or scratching of a formed part by metal pickup on the punch or die. (Also see Galling.)

3.106 Scratches—Lines caused by the abrasion of one surface against another during rolling, processing, or shipping.

3.107 Scribed Square Test—A method to determine the percent increase in unit area of selected regions of a formed panel. (See SAE J863.)

3.108 Seam Lines (C)—A continuous line of small beads.

3.109 Seams—Open, broken surface running in straight longitudinal lines caused by the presence of oxides near the surface of the sheet.

3.110 Segregation—The variation in chemical composition resulting from natural phenomena in the solidification of a steel ingot. The various elements of the steel having lowest freezing points are concentrated in parts of the ingot last to solidify.

3.111 Semikilled Steel—Steel that is partially deoxidized so that there is greater degree of gas evolution than in killed steel, but less than in capped or rimmed steel. The uniformity in composition lies between that of killed steel and rimmed steel.

3.112 Side Strain—See Edge Strain.

3.113 Skin Lamination—Subsurface separation which usually results in surface rupture. (See SAE J810.)

3.114 Skin Pass—See Temper Rolling.

3.115 Slivers—Surface ruptures somewhat similar in appearance to skin laminations, but usually more prominent. (See SAE J810.)

3.116 Smudge (NC)—A dark residue on the surface of sheet steel. (See Smut.)

3.117 Smut (NC)—A reaction product sometimes left on the surface of the sheet after pickling or annealing. (See Smudge.)

3.118 Snaky Edges (NC)—Carbonaceous deposits in a wavy pattern along the edges of the annealed strip. (See Carbon Edge.)

3.119 Spangle (C)—The characteristic crystalline form in which the hot dipped zinc coating solidifies on steel strip. (See SAE J1562.)

3.120 Spinning—The shaping of flat circular blanks by forcing the blank against a chuck or form block while it is rotating.

3.121 Springback—The tendency of metal to partially return to its original shape after cold forming.

3.122 Sticker Breaks (NC)—Arc-shaped breaks usually located near the middle of the sheet. (See SAE J810.)

3.123 Stiffness—The ability of a metal or shape to resist deflection.

3.124 Strain Hardening—An increase in hardness and strength caused by plastic deformation at temperatures lower than the recrystallization range. (See SAE J877.)

3.125 Strain Hardening Exponent—A measure of the rate of strain hardening. The constant 'n' in the expression. (See Equation 1.)

$$\sigma = K\varepsilon^n \qquad \text{(Eq. 1)}$$

where:

s =True Stress
K = Constant in the equation
ε = True strain
n = Strain hardening exponent

The 'n' value is a good measure of stretch formability. The higher the 'n' value, the better the stretch formability. (See SAE J877.)

3.126 Strain Ratio—This expressed as 'r' value. It is the ratio of width to thickness strain determined in uniform elongation portion of a tension test. It is a good measure of the crystallographic directionality of the material. It is also a good measure of deep drawability. The higher the 'r' value, the better the deep drawability. (See SAE J877.)

3.127 Stretchability—The ability of a metal to be stretched over a punch without splitting.

3.128 Stretch Forming—Shaping of a sheet or part, usually of uniform cross section by applying suitable tension or stretch and forming it around or over a die of the desired shape.

3.129 Stretching—The operation where the blank is stretched around the punch with no metal flow over the draw ring. The metal thickness is reduced.

3.130 Stretcher Leveling—Leveling where a piece of metal is gripped at each end and subjected to a stress higher than its yield strength to obtain a high degree of flatness. (Sometimes called patent leveling.)

3.131 Stretcher Strain (Lüder's Lines)—Irregular surface patterns of ridges and valleys which develop during forming. (See SAE J810.)

3.132 Surface Texture—The finish of the surface of sheet steel presently described by the roughness (peak) height in micro inches and the peaks per inch. (See Matte Finish and SAE J448.)

3.133 Synthetic Cold-Rolled (NC)—A hot-rolled pickled sheet given a sufficient final temper pass to impart a surface approximating that of cold-rolled steel.

3.134 Temper Rolling—Light cold rolling of sheet steel. This operation is performed to improve flatness, minimize the tendency to stretcher strain and flute, obtain the desired texture and mechanical properties.

3.135 Tensile Strength—The unit stress at the highest load reached during the tension test. (See SAE J877.)

3.136 Tiger Stripes (C)—Continuous bright lines in the rolling direction.

3.137 Total Elongation—Percent elongation measured after fracture in a tension test. (See SAE J877.)

3.138 Traverse Lines—Lines closely spaced across the full width of the sheet and running in the direction of rolling.

3.139 "U" Finish—This designation indicates that the material is to be used for an unexposed part for which surface finish is unimportant. (See SAE J403.)

3.140 Uniform Elongation (Uniform Strain E_u)—The percent elongation at the onset of necking, usually taken as the strain to maximum load in the tension test.

3.141 Vacuum Degassing—A process of refining liquid steel in which the liquid is exposed to a vacuum as part of a special refining technique for the purpose of removing impurities or for decarburizing the steel.

3.142 Work Hardening—Same as Strain Hardening.

3.143 Wrinkling—Small buckles which occur in drawing sheet metal as it passes over the drawing ring radius.

3.144 Yield Point—The stress beyond which the metal is permanently deformed. (See SAE J877 and J450.)

3.145 Yield Point Elongation—Percent elongation at the end of nonhomogeneous yielding in a tension test.

3.146 Yield/Tensile Ratio—The 0.2% yield strength divided by the tensile strength.

DEFINITIONS OF HEAT TREATING TERMS—SAE J415 JUL1995

SAE Information Report

Report of the SAE Iron and Steel Division approved June 1911. Thirteenth revision by the SAE Iron and Steel Technical Committee Division 12—Definitions of Terms on Heat Treatment of Metals, July 1995.

Foreword—This Document has not changed other than to put it into the new SAE Technical Standards Board Format.

1. Scope—(These definitions were prepared by the Joint Committee on Definitions of Terms Relating to Heat Treatment appointed by the American Society for Testing and Materials, The American Society for Metals, the American Foundrymen's Association, and the SAE.) This SAE revision emphasizes the terms used in heat treating ferrous alloys, but also includes for reference some non-ferrous definitions at the end of the document.

This glossary is not intended to be a specification, and it should not be interpreted as such. Since this is intended to be strictly a set of definitions, temperatures have been omitted purposely.

2. References

2.1 Applicable Publications—The following publications form a part of this specification to the extent specified herein. The latest issue of SAE publications shall apply.

2.1.1 SAE PUBLICATIONS—Available from SAE, 400 Commonwealth Drive, Warrendale, PA 15096-0001.

SAE J418—Grain Size Determination

SAE J763—Aging of Carbon Steel Sheet and Strip

SAE J940—Glossary of Carbon Steel Sheet and Strip Terms

3. Definitions

3.1 Ac_{cm}, Ac_1, Ac_3, Ac_4——Defined under Transformation Temperature.

3.2 Ae_{cm}, Ae_1, Ae_3, Ae_4——Defined under Transformation Temperature.

3.3 Age Hardening—Hardening by aging, usually after rapid cooling or cold working. See Aging.

3.4 Aging—A generic term denoting a time-temperature-dependent change in the properties of certain alloys. Except for strain aging and age softening, it is the result of precipitation from a solid solution of one or more compounds whose solubility decreases with decreasing temperature. For each alloy system susceptible to aging, there is a unique range of time-temperature combinations to which the system will respond. See also Age Hardening, Artificial Aging, Age Softening, Natural Aging, Overaging, Peak Aging, Precipitation Hardening, Precipitation Heat Treatment, Quench Aging, Strain Aging, and Underaging.

3.5 Annealing—A generic term denoting a treatment, consisting of heating at an appropriate rate to a suitable temperature, holding for an appropriate time, and cooling at a suitable rate. Used primarily to soften metallic materials, but also to simultaneously produce desired changes in other properties or in microstructure. The purpose of such changes may be, but is not confined to, one or more of: (a) improvement of machinability; (b) facilitation of cold work; (c) improvement of mechanical or electrical properties or increase in stability of dimensions.

The time-temperature cycles used vary widely in heating rate, maximum temperature attained, and in cooling rate employed, depending on the composition of the material, its condition, and the results desired. When applicable, the following more specific commercial process names should be used: Black Annealing, Blue Annealing, Box Annealing, Bright Annealing, Cycle Annealing, Flame Annealing, Full Annealing, Graphitizing, In-Process Annealing, Isothermal Annealing, Malleabilizing, Orientation Annealing, Process Annealing, Quench Annealing, and Spheroidizing. When the term is used without qualification full annealing is implied. Any process of annealing will usually reduce stresses, but when applied only for the relief of stress, the process is properly called stress relief annealing.

3.6 Artificial Aging—Aging above room temperature. See Aging and Precipitation Heat Treatment. Compare with Natural Aging.

3.7 Ausforming—Mechanically working an appropriate high hardenability steel after quenching from above the upper critical temperature to a temperature between the lower critical and the M_s temperature, and isothermally transforming or quenching to produce the desired properties.

3.8 Austempering—Quenching a ferrous alloy from a temperature above the transformation range, in a medium having a rate of heat extraction sufficient to prevent the formation of ferrite or pearlite, and then holding the alloy just above M_s until transformation to bainite is complete.

3.9 Austenitizing—Forming austenite by heating a ferrous alloy into the transformation range (partial austenitizing) or above the transformation range (complete austenitizing). When used without qualification, the term implies complete austenitizing.

3.10 Austentic Nitrocarburizing—A lower-temperature variant of carbonitriding, austenitic nitrocarburizing is applied to ferrous materials at typical processing temperatures of 676 °C to 774 °C (1250 °F to 1425 °F). The process involves the diffusion of nitrogen and carbon into the surface of the work piece and the formation of a thin white layer of epsilon carbonitrides. Subsurface microstructure includes martensite and bainite which improve the load carrying capability when compared to ferritic nitrocarburizing.

3.11 Baking—Heating to a low temperature usually to remove gases such as hydrogen. Aging may result from baking treatments.

3.12 Black Annealing—Box annealing or pot annealing ferrous alloy sheet, strip, or wire. See Box Annealing.

3.13 Blank Carburizing—Simulating the carburizing operation without introducing carbon. This is usually accomplished by using an inert material in place of the carburizing agent, or by applying a suitable protective coating to the ferrous alloy.

3.14 Blank Nitriding—Simulating the nitriding operation without introducing nitrogen. This is usually accomplished by using an inert material in place of the nitriding agent, or by applying a suitable protective coating to the ferrous alloy.

3.15 Blue Annealing—Heating hot-rolled ferrous sheet in an open furnace to a temperature within the transformation range and then cooling in air, in order to soften the metal, normally with the formation of a bluish oxide on the surface.

3.16 Bluing—Subjecting the scale free surface of a ferrous alloy to the action of air, steam, or other agents at a suitable temperature, thus forming a thin blue film of oxide and improving the appearance and resistance to corrosion and adhesive wear.

NOTE—This term is ordinarily applied to sheet, strip, or finished parts. It is used also to denote the heating of springs after fabrication, in order to improve their properties.

3.17 Box Annealing—Annealing a metal or alloy in a sealed container under conditions that minimize oxidation. In box annealing a ferrous alloy, the charge is usually heated slowly to a temperature below the transformation range, but sometimes above or within it, and is then cooled slowly; this process is also called "close annealing" or "pot annealing." See Black Annealing and SAE J940.

3.18 Bright Annealing—Annealing in a protective medium to prevent discoloration of the bright surface or to produce a bright surface.

3.19 Burning—Permanently damaging a metal or alloy by heating to cause either incipient melting or intergranular oxidation. See Overheating.

3.20 Carbon Potential—A measure of the ability of an environment containing active carbon to alter or maintain, under prescribed conditions, the carbon content of the steel exposed to it.

NOTE—In any particular environment, the carbon level attained will depend on such factors as temperature, time, and steel composition.

3.21 Carbon Restoration—Replacing the carbon lost in the surface layer from previous processing by adding carbon to this layer to substantially the original carbon level.

3.22 Carbonitriding—A case hardening process in which a suitable ferrous material is heated above the lower transformation temperature in a gaseous atmosphere of such composition as to cause simultaneous absorption of carbon and nitrogen by the surface and, by diffusion, create a concentration gradient. The process is completed by cooling at a rate which produces the desired properties in the workpiece.

3.23 Carburizing—A process in which an austenitized ferrous material is brought into contact with a carbonaceous atmosphere of sufficient carbon potential to cause absorption of carbon at the surface and, by diffusion, create a concentration gradient.

3.24 Case—In a ferrous alloy workpiece, the outer discrete layer whose composition has been altered by one of the processes of case hardening.

3.25 Case Hardening—A generic term covering several processes applicable to steel that change the chemical composition of the surface layer by absorption of carbon, nitrogen, or a mixture of the two and, by diffusion, create a concentration gradient. The processes commonly used are: carburizing and quench hardening, cyaniding, nitriding, and carbonitriding. The surface is characteristically harder than the subsurface material. The use of the applicable specific process name is preferred.

3.26 Cementation—The introduction of one or more elements into the outer portion of a metal object by means of diffusion at high temperature.

3.27 Close Annealing—See Box Annealing.

3.28 Cold Treatment—Exposing to suitable low temperatures (usually below −40 °C) for the purpose of obtaining desired conditions or properties, such as dimensional or microstructural stability. When the treatment involves the transformation of retained austenite, it is usually followed by a tempering treatment.

3.29 Conditioning Heat Treatmtnt—A preliminary heat treatment used to prepare a material for a desired reaction to a subsequent heat treatment. For the term to be meaningful, the treatment used must be specified.

3.30 Continuous Annealing—Process of passing a strand or sheet through a controlled atmosphere furnace that has both heating and cooling zones. Temperatures, line speeds, and cooling rates are varied to obtain the desired properties. Can also refer to a continuous heat treating process (e.g., belt furnaces.)

3.31 Controlled Cooling—Cooling from an elevated temperature in a predetermined manner, to avoid hardening, cracking, or internal damage, or to produce a desired microstructure or mechanical properties.

3.32 Core—(a) Surface Hardening: Interior portion of unaltered composition, or microstructure, or both, of a surface treated steel article. (b) Clad Products: The central portion of a multilayer composite metallic material.

3.33 Critical Cooling Rate—The minimum rate of continuous cooling to prevent undesirable transformations. For steel, unless otherwise specified, it is the minimum rate at which austenite must be continuously cooled to suppress transformations above the M_s temperature.

3.34 Critical Tempurature Range—Synonymous with Transformation range, which is preferred.

3.35 Cryogenic Treatments—Same as cold treatment only specifically related to temperatures at or below that of liquid nitrogen (−196 °C).

3.36 Cyaniding—A case hardening process in which a ferrous material is heated above the lower transformation range in a molten salt containing cyanide to cause simultaneous absorption of carbon and nitrogen at the surface and, by diffusion, create a concentration gradient. Quench hardening completes the process.

3.37 Cycle Annealing—An annealing process employing a predetermined and closely controlled time-temperature cycle to produce specific properties or microstructure.

3.38 Decarburation—The loss of carbon from the surface of a ferrous alloy usually as a result of heating in a medium that reacts with the carbon.

3.39 Die Quenching or Press Quenching—Rigidly fixturing a ferrous workpiece during quench hardening to minimize distortion produced by transformation of austenite.

3.40 Diferential Heating—Heating that intentionally produces a temperature gradient within an object such that, after cooling, a desired stress distribution or variation in properties is present within the object.

3.41 Diffusion Coating—Any process whereby a base metal or alloy is either: (a) coated with another metal or alloy and heated to a sufficient temperature in a suitable environment or (b) exposed to a gaseous or liquid medium containing the other metal or alloy, to cause diffusion of the coating or of the other metal or alloy into the base metal with resultant change in the composition and properties of its surface.

3.42 Direct Quenching—Quenching carburized parts directly from the carburizing or austenitizing temperature.

3.43 Double Aging—Employment of two different aging treatments to control the type of precipitate formed from a supersaturated alloy matrix in order to obtain the desired properties. The first aging treatment, sometimes referred to as intermediate or stabilizing, is usually carried out at a higher temperature than the second.

3.44 Double Tempering—A treatment in which quench hardened steel is given two complete tempering cycles at substantially the same temperature for the purpose of assuring completion of the tempering reaction and transformation of untransformed austenite, promoting stability of the resulting microstructure.

3.45 Drawing—A misnomer for Tempering.

3.46 Ductile Nitriding—See nitriding.

3.47 Ferritic Nitrocarburizing—A process applied to ferrous materials that involves the diffusion of nitrogen and carbon into the ferrite phase and the formation of thin white layer of epsilon carbonitrides. Low process temperatures (below 676 °C (1250 °F)) contribute to low distortion of the workpiece. Resultant properties of the process include improved adhesive wear properties (due to the thin white layer of epsilon carbonitrides), improved fatigue resistance, and improved corrosion resistance.

3.48 Ferritizing Anneal—A treatment given as-cast gray or ductile (nodular) iron to produce an essentially ferritic matrix. For the term to be meaningful, the final microstructure desired or the time-temperature cycle used must be specified.

3.49 Flame Annealing—Annealing in which the heat is applied directly by a flame.

3.50 Flame Hardening—A surface hardening process in which only the surface layer of a suitable workpiece is heated by a suitably intense flame to above the upper transformation temperature and immediately quenched.

3.51 Full Annealing—An imprecise term used to denote the annealing cycle required to produce minimum strength and hardness. For the term to be meaningful, the composition, starting condition of the material, and the time-temperature cycle used must be stated.

3.52 Grain Growth—An increase in the average size of the grains (see Notes 1 and 2) in polycrystalline metal, usually as a result of heating at elevated temperature.

NOTE 1—A grain is an individual crystal in a polycrystalline metal and includes twined regions and subgrains when present.

NOTE 2—Grain size is a measure of the mean diameter, area, or volume of all individual grains observed in a polycrystalline metal. In metals containing two or more phrases, the grain size refers to that of the matrix unless otherwise specified. For further information on grain size and its measurement, see SAE J418.

3.53 Graphitizing—Annealing a ferrous alloy in such a way that some or all of the carbon is precipitated as graphite.

3.54 Hardenability—The capacity of a ferrous alloy to transform partially or completely from austenite to some percentage of martensite at a given depth when cooled under some given condition.

3.55 Hardening—Increasing the hardness by suitable treatment, usually involving heating and cooling. When applicable, the following more specific terms should be used: Age Hardening, Case Hardening, Flame Hardening, Induction Hardening, Precipitation Hardening, Quench Hardening, and Surface Hardening.

3.56 Heat Treatment—Heating and cooling of metals and/or alloys in the solid state for the purpose of changing their physical and mechanical properties. Heating for the sole purpose of hot working is excluded from the meaning of this definition.

3.57 Homogenizing—Soaking at a temperature sufficient to improve chemical and structural uniformity, usually applied prior to mechanical working.

3.58 Hot-Cold Working—Mechanical deformation of austenitic and precipitation hardening alloys at a temperature just below the recrystallization range to increase the yield strength and hardness by either plastic deformation or precipitation hardening effects induced by plastic deformation or both. See Warm Working.

3.59 Hot Quenching—An imprecise term used to cover a variety of quenching procedures in which a quenching medium is maintained at a prescribed temperature usually above 70 °C (160 °F).

3.60 Induction Hardening—A surface hardening process in which only the surface layer of a suitable ferrous workpiece is heated by electrical induction to a temperature above the upper critical temperature and immediately quenched. Induction heating can also be used for hardening the entire cross section.

3.61 Induction Heating—Heating by combined electrical resistance and hysteresis losses induced by subjecting a metal to the varying magnetic field surrounding a coil carrying alternating current.

3.62 Intermediate Annealing—Annealing wrought metals at one or more stages during manufacture and before final thermal treatment.

3.63 Interrupted Aging—Aging at two or more temperatures, by steps, and cooling to room temperature after each step. See Aging and compare with Progressive Aging.

3.64 Interrupted Quenching—A quenching procedure in which the workpiece is removed from the first quench at a temperature substantially higher than that of the quenchant and is then subjected to a second quenching system having a different cooling rate than the first. See also Time Quenching.

3.65 Isothermal Annealing—Austenitizing a ferrous alloy and then cooling to and holding at a temperature at which austenite transforms to a relatively soft ferrite-carbide aggregate.

3.66 Isotermal Transformation—A solid state phase transformation at constant temperature.

3.67 Malleablizing—A process in which the as-cast malleable-type (white) iron is thermally treated for the purpose of converting most of all of the carbon in Fe_3C to graphite (temper carbon) to produce a family of products with improved ductility.

3.68 Maraging—A precipitation hardening treatment applied to a special group of iron base alloys to precipitate one or more intermetallic compounds in matrix of essentially low carbon martensite.

3.69 Marquenching—See martempering (b).

3.70 Martempering—(a) A hardening procedure in which an austenitized ferrous workpiece is quenched into an appropriate medium whose temperature is maintained substantially at the M_s of the workpiece, held in the medium until its temperature is uniform throughout but not long enough to permit bainite to form and then cooled in air. The treatment is frequently followed by tempering. (b) When the process is applied to carburized material, the part is quenched to a temperature below the core M_s but above the case M_s temperature. This variation of the process is frequently called marquenching.

3.71 Martensite Range—The temperature interval between M_s and M_f.

3.72 M_f—Defined under Transformation Temperature.

3.73 M_s—Defined under Transformation Temperature

3.74 Natural Aging—Spontaneous aging of a supersaturated solid solution at room temperature over time. See Aging and compare with Artificial Aging.

3.75 Nitriding—A case hardening process in which a ferrous-base material is heated to approximately the iron-nitrogen eutectoid temperature in either a gaseous or a liquid medium containing active nitrogen, thus causing absorption of nitrogen at the surface and, by diffusion, creating a concentration gradient. Within the capabilities of the particular material, slow cooling produces full hardness of the case.

In *conventional nitriding* a hardened and tempered alloy steel or tool steel is treated for sufficient time to produce highly saturated nitrides in the case.

In an important variation of the process, sometimes called *ductile nitriding*, applied to any ferrous-base material, the amount of active nitrogen and the time of exposure are so controlled as to produce a case of lower nitrogen content which, within the capabilities of the material, is fully hard on a microscale but lower in hardness on a macroscale and relatively ductile.

3.76 Normalizing—Heating a ferrous alloy to a suitable temperature above the transformation range and then cooling in air to a temperature substantially below the transformation range usually to improve machinability or impart specific mechanical properties.

3.77 Orientation Anneal—A final, high-temperature anneal applied principally to flat-rolled electrical steel to develop secondary grain growth and directionality of magnetic properties.

3.78 Overaging—Aging at any combination of time and temperature in excess of that required to obtain the optimum strength and hardness.

3.79 Overheating—Heating a metal or alloy to such a high temperature that its properties are impaired. When the original properties cannot be restored by further heat treating, by mechanical working, or by a combination of working and heat treating, the overheating is known as Burning.

3.80 Patenting—In wire making, a heat treatment applied to medium carbon or high carbon steel before the drawing of wire or between drafts. This process consists of heating to a temperature above the transformation range and then cooling to a temperature below Ae_1 in air or in a bath of molten lead or salt.

3.81 Peak Aging—Aging at whatever combination of time and temperature produces maximum strength or hardness. See Aging.

3.82 Postheating—Heating weldments immediately after welding, for tempering, for stress relieving, or for providing a controlled rate of cooling to prevent formation of a hard or brittle structure.

3.83 Pot Annealing—See Box Annealing.

3.84 Precipitation Hardening—Hardening caused by the precipitation of a constituent from a supersaturated solid solution. See also Age Hardening and Aging.

3.85 Precipitation Heat Treating—Artificial aging in which a constituent precipitates from a supersaturated solid solution. See Artificial Aging, Interrupted Aging, and Progressive Aging.

3.86 Preheating—(a) An imprecise term meaning heating to an appropriate temperature in preparation for mechanical work, for welding, or for further thermal treatment. (b) Heating to an appropriate temperature immediately prior to austenitizing when hardening high hardenability constructional steels, many of the tool steels, and heavy sections.

3.87 Process Annealing—An imprecise term used to denote various treatments used to improve workability. For the term to be meaningful, the condition of the material and the time-temperature cycle used must be stated.

3.88 Progressive Aging—Aging by increasing the temperature in steps or continuously during the aging cycle. See Aging and compare with Interrupted Aging and Step Aging.

3.89 Quench Aging—Natural or artificial aging of a ferrous material caused by the precipitation of an iron carbide or an iron nitride or a complex of both in alpha iron supersaturated with these compounds. Supersaturation is achieved by rapidly cooling the heated material.

3.90 Quench Annealing—Annealing an austenitic ferrous alloy by Solution Heat Treatment.

3.91 Quench Hardening—Hardening a suitable ferrous alloy by austenitizing and then cooling at a rate such that a substantial amount of austenite transforms to martensite.

3.92 Quenching—Rapid cooling. When applicable, the following more specific terms should be used: Direct Quenching, Fog Quenching, Hot Quenching, Interrupted Quenching, Selective Quenching, Spray Quenching, and Time Quenching.

3.93 Recrystallization—The formation of a new, strain-free grain structure from that existing in cold-worked metal, usually accomplished by heating.

3.94 Recrystallization Annealing—Annealing cold-worked metal to produce a new grain structure without phase change.

3.95 Recrystallization Temperature—The approximate minimum temperature at which complete recrystallization of a cold-worked metal occurs within a specified time, dependent upon the composition, microstructure, heating rate, and amount of prior cold work.

3.96 Reheating—An imprecise term denoting an additional heating applied between different mechanical operations or successive steps of the same operation or for hardening after carburizing.

3.97 Secondary Hardening—The hardening phenomenon that occurs during high temperature tempering of certain steels containing one or more specific carbide forming alloying elements. Up to an optimum combination of tempering time and temperature, the reaction results either in the retention of hardness or an actual increase in hardness.

3.98 Selective Carburizing—Carburizing only selected surfaces of a workpiece by preventing absorption of carbon by all other surfaces.

3.99 Selective Heating—Intentional heating of only certain portions of a workpiece.

3.100 Selective Quenching—Quenching only certain portions of a workpiece.

3.101 Shell Hardening—A surface hardening process in which a suitable steel workpiece, when heated through and quench hardened, develops a martensitic layer or shell that closely follows the contour of the piece and surrounds a core of essentially pearlitic transformation product. This result is accomplished by a proper balance between section size, steel hardenability, and severity of quench.

3.102 Slack Quenching—The incomplete hardening of steel due to quenching from the austenizing temperature at a rate slower than the critical cooling rate for the particular steel, resulting in the formation of one or more transformation products in addition to martensite.

3.103 Snap Temper—A precautionary interim stress-relieving treatment applied to high hardenability steels immediately after quenching to prevent cracking because of delay in tempering them at the prescribed higher temperature. It is also used prior to fixture tempering to prevent cracking.

3.104 Soaking—Holding at a selected temperature.

3.105 Solution Heat Treatment—Heating an alloy to a suitable temperature, holding at that temperature long enough to cause one or more constituents to enter into solid solution, and then cooling rapidly enough to hold these constituents in solution.

3.106 Soft Nitriding—A misnomer for ductile nitriding.

3.107 Spheroidizing—Heating and cooling to produce a spheroidal or globular form of carbide in steel. Spheroidizing methods frequently used are:

a. Prolong holding at a temperature just below Ae_1.

b. Heating and cooling alternately between temperatures that are just above and just below Ae_1.

c. Heating to a temperature above Ae_1 or Ae_3 and then cooling very slowly in the furnace or holding at a temperature just below Ae_1.

d. Cooling at a suitable rate from the minimum temperature at which all carbide is dissolved, to prevent the reformation of a carbide network and then reheating in accordance with Method a or b. (Applicable to hypereutectoid steel containing a carbide network.)

3.108 Spray Quenching—Quenching in a spray of liquid.

3.109 Stabilizing Treatment—A treatment applied for the purpose of stabilizing the dimensions of a workpiece or the structure of a material such as (a) before finishing to final dimensions, heating a workpiece to or somewhat beyond its operating temperature and then cooling to room temperature a sufficient number of times to insure stability of dimensions in service, (b) transforming retained austenite in those materials which retain substantial amounts when quench hardened (see cold treatment), (c) heating a solution treated austenitic stainless steel that contains controlled amounts of titanium or columbium plus tantalum to a temperature below the solution heat treating temperature to cause precipitation of finely divided, uniformly distributed carbides of those elements, thereby substantially reducing the amount of carbon available for the formation of chromium carbides in the grain boundaries upon subsequent exposure to temperatures in the sensitizing range.

3.110 Strain Aging—A change in mechanical properties of a ferrous material during (dynamic strain aging) or after (static strain aging) cold plastic strain. When tested in tension, strain-aged low-carbon sheet exhibits discontinuous yielding, a decrease in ductility, and an increase in yield strength and hardness without substantial change in tensile strength as compared with unaged sheet. Appropriate restraining (temper rolling) temporarily restores continuous yielding. See SAE J763.

3.111 Stress Relieving—Heating to a suitable temperature, holding long enough to reduce residual stresses and then cooling at a rate to minimize the development of new residual stresses.

NOTE—Stress relief may be accomplished by the application of other forms of energy, principally mechanical, either alone or in combination with thermal energy.

3.112 Subcritical Annealing—A process anneal performed at a temperature below Ac_1.

3.113 Surface Hardening—A generic term covering several processes applicable to a suitable ferrous alloy that produces by quench hardening only, a surface layer that is harder or more wear resistant than the core. There is no significant alteration of the chemical composition of the surface layer. The processes commonly used are induction hardening, flame hardening, and shell hardening. Use of the applicable specific process name is preferred.

3.114 Temper Brittleness—Brittleness that results when certain steels are held within, or are cooled slowly through, a certain range of temperature below the transformation range. The brittleness is manifested as an upward shift in ductile-to-brittle transition temperature in notched-bar impact tests, but only rarely produces a low value of reduction in area in a smooth-bar tension test of the embrittled material.

3.115 Tempering—(a) Reheating a quench hardened or normalized ferrous alloy to a temperature below the transformation range (Ac_1) and then cooling at any desired rate. (b) A term used in conjunction with a qualifying adjective to designate the relative properties of a particular metal or alloy induced by cold work or heat treatment, or both.

3.116 Time Quenching—Interrupted quenching in which the duration of holding in the quenching medium is controlled.

3.117 Transformation Ranges or Transformation Temperature Ranges—Those ranges of temperature within which austenite forms during heating and transforms during cooling. The two ranges are distinct, sometimes overlapping but never coinciding. The limiting temperatures of the ranges depend on the composition of the alloy and on the rate of change of temperature, particularly during cooling. See Transformation Temperature.

3.118 Transformation Temperature—The temperature at which a change in phase occurs. The term is sometimes used to denote the limiting temperature of a transformation range. The following symbols are used for iron and steels:

Ac_{cm}—In hypereutectoid steel, the temperature at which the solution of cementite in austenite is completed during heating.

Ac_1—The temperature at which transformation of ferrite to austenite begins during heating.

Ac_3—The temperature at which transformation of ferrite to austenite is completed during heating.

Ac_4—The temperature at which austenite transforms to delta ferrite during heating.

Ae_1, Ae_3, Ae_{cm}, Ae_4—The temperatures of phase changes in equilibrium.

Ar_{cm}—In hypereutectoid steel, the temperature at which precipitation of cementite starts during cooling.

Ar_1—The temperature at which transformation of austenite to ferrite or to ferrite plus cementite is completed during cooling.

Ar_3—The temperature at which austenite begins to transform to ferrite during cooling.

Ar_4—The temperature at which delta ferrite transforms to austenite during cooling.

M_s—The temperature at which transformation of austenite to martensite starts during cooling.

M_f—The temperature at which transformation of austenite to martensite is substantially completed during cooling.

NOTE—All these changes except the formation of martensite occur at lower temperatures during cooling than during heating, and depend on the rate of change of temperature and the kinetics of transformation.

3.119 Underaging—Aging at any combination of time and temperature insufficient to produce maximum strength to hardness.

NOTE—This treatment is used to improve workability in some precipitation hardening copper alloys.

3.120 Warm Working—Plastically deforming metal at a temperature above ambient (room) temperature but below the temperature at which the material undergoes recrystallization.

*4. **Nonferrous Definitions***—(Included for sake of completeness, but not updated in this revision.)

4.1 Age Softening Aluminum Alloys—Spontaneous decrease of strength and hardness which takes place at room temperature in certain strain hardened alloys.

4.2 Anneal To Temper Copper and Copper Alloys—A final anneal used to produce specified mechanical properties in a material.

4.3 Annealing Aluminum and Aluminum Alloys—Annealing cycles are designed to (a) remove part or all of the effects of cold working (recrystallization may or may not be involved); (b) cause substantially complete coalescence of precipitates from solid solution in relatively coarse form; or (c) both, depending on the composition and condition of the material. When the term is used without qualification, full annealing is implied. Specific process names in commercial use are: Final Annealing, Full Annealing, Intermediate Annealing, Partial Annealing, Recrystallization Annealing, and Stress Relief Annealing.

4.4 Annealing Copper and Copper Alloys—Depending on composition and condition, these materials are annealed by: (a) removal of the effects of cold work by recrystallization or recrystallization and grain growth; (b)substantially complete precipitation of the second phase in relatively coarse form in age (precipitation) hardened alloys; (c) solution heat treatment of age (precipitation) hardenable alloys; (d) relief of residual stress in castings. Specific process names in commercial use are: Final Annealing, Full Annealing, Light Annealing, Soft Annealing, Solution Annealing.

4.5Betatizing—Forming beta constituent by heating a nonferrous alloy into the temperature region in which the constituent forms.

4.6 Final Annealing—Nonferrous—An imprecise term used to denote the anneal used to prepare a material for shipment to the user.

4.7 Fog Quenching—Quenching in a mist with glycol or water.

4.8 Full Annealing—Aluminum and Aluminum Alloys—An imprecise term used to denote the annealing cycle required to produce minimum strength. For the term to be meaningful, the composition and condition of the material and the time temperature cycle used must be stated.

4.9 Intermediate Annealing—Aluminum and Aluminum Alloys—An imprecise term used to denote annealing of wrought products at one or more stages during processing but before final heat treatment. For the term to be meaningful, the type and condition of the material and the time-temperature cycle used must be stated.

4.10 Light Anneal Copper and Copper Alloys—An imprecise term used to indicate the formability of cold-rolled and annealed products. Its use is discouraged. The desired product is properly described as "Fully recrystallized; grain size 0.015 to 0.035 mm."

4.11 Partial Annealing—Aluminum and Aluminum Alloys—An imprecise term used to denote a treatment given cold-worked material to reduce the strength to a controlled level or to effect stress relief. To be meaningful, the type of material, the degree of cold work it had undergone and the time temperature cycle used must be stated.

4.12 Quench Hardening—Copper Alloys—Hardening suitable alloys by betatizing and quenching to develop a martensite-like structure.

4.13 Reheating Aluminum and Aluminum Alloys—Heating to hot working temperature. Improvement of chemical or structural uniformity is incidental.

4.14 Soft Anneal—Copper and Copper Alloys—An imprecise term used to indicate the formability of cold-rolled and annealed products. Its use is discouraged. The desired product is properly described as "Fully recrystallized; grain size 0.025 to 0.090 mm."

4.15 Solutionizing—Another name for solution heat treatment, used principally in copper beryllium technology.

4.16 Stabilizing Treatment—Aluminum and Aluminum Alloys—An imprecise term used to denote a treatment above room temperature but below the recrystallization temperature applied:

a. To cold worked materials of some nonheat-treatable alloy systems to reduce the tendency to age soften.

b. To some types of solution-treated artificial aging alloys in order to improve stability of mechanical properties and of dimensions. See Overaging.

c. To other types of solution-treated artificial aging alloys to control the size and distribution of the precipitate to improve resistance to intergranular corrosion or exfoliation corrosion and to stress corrosion cracking.

d. To still other types of age hardening alloys to reduce the tendency to age naturally.

4.17 Stop Aging—Aluminum Alloys—Employment of two different aging treatments to control the type of precipitate formed from a supersaturated alloy matrix in order to obtain the desired properties. The first aging treatment, sometimes referred to as intermediate or stabilizing, is usually carried out at a higher temperature than the second.

4.18 Tempering—Copper Alloys—Heating quench hardened material to a temperature below the solution treatment temperature to produce desired changes in properties.

3 Methods of Testing Steels

SURFACE HARDNESS TESTING WITH FILES —SAE J864 MAY1993

SAE Recommended Practice

Report of the SAE Iron and Steel Technical Committee approved June 1963, completely revised by the SAE Iron and Steel Technical Committee, Division 3, June 1984, and reaffirmed December 1988. Reaffirmed by the SAE Iron and Steel Technical Committee 3—Test Procedures May 1993.

Foreword—This Reaffirmed Document has been changed only to reflect the new SAE Technical Standards Board Format.

1. Scope—Hardness testing with files consists essentially of cutting or abrading the surface of metal parts, and approximating the hardness by the feel, or extent to which, the file bites into the surface. The term "file hard" means that the surface hardness of the parts tested is such that a new file of proven hardness will not cut the surface of the material being tested.

1.1 Application—This SAE Recommended Practice describes the technique of using a file for testing the surface hardness of miscellaneous iron and steel parts as designated by engineering specifications. In presenting this procedure, it is recognized that it is subjective and that it must be used with considerable judgment on the part of the operator. File hardness tests may be used when case depth is too shallow for conventional indentation hardness methods, to detect the presence of a soft surface condition on hardened or case-hardened parts, or to check the hardness of sintered parts that may not respond predictably to indentation hardness methods. The method is useful in production control.

2. References—There are no referenced publications specified herein.

3. Apparatus Required

3.1 Standard Files—Hand files meeting the following requirements:

a. 150 or 200 mm (6 or 8 in) pillar
b. No. 1 Swiss double cut
c. 26 cuts per cm (66 per in)
d. Hardness of File
   - 65 to 68 HRC designated No. 65
   - 61 to 63 HRC designated No. 62
   - 57 to 59 HRC designated No. 58
   - 54 to 56 HRC designated No. 55
   - 49 to 51 HRC designated No. 50
e. Chemical Composition
   - Carbon—1.20 to 1.40%
   - Manganese—0.20 to 0.40%
   - Phosphorus—0.40% max
   - Sulfur—0.05% max
   - Silicon—0.10 to 0.20%

3.2 Standard Prover—Standard steel or iron test pieces, 50 mm (2 in) dia and approximately 6 mm (1/4 in) thick, hardened and tempered to the hardness of the lower limit of each standard file range, are required for testing the standard files.

The prover shall be filed with a discarded test file to remove any hard or soft skin that will interfere with the accuracy of the test. Similar provers hardened to the ranges in Table 1 and above the medians can be used to prove the file will cut below and not above the designated file hardness.

Testing of files is performed by passing the test file across the 6 mm (1/4 in) thick face of the prover.

A 6 mm (1/4 in) prover is specified because at the higher hardnesses, the surface area contacted affects the cutting area considerably. Narrow areas can be cut more readily than wide areas due to the concentration of pressure that may be obtained.

3.3 Standard Test Pieces—Standard test pieces (of the same contour, steel or iron composition, and heat treatment) varying in hardness by small increments, with which the parts being inspected can be compared, are recommended. In the case of steels, each family of SAE steels, namely, 10XX, 20XX, 30XX, and the like should be used. They can be heat treated to compare with the operation, such as carburized, quenched, and temper or carbonitrided, quenched, and temper.

These pieces will enable the operator to learn, with fair accuracy, the feel of the file as it cuts, or does not cut, in relation to the Rockwell hardness.

TABLE 1—CHART OF FILES AND PROVERS

File No.	Standard Prover Hardness	Prover Cutting Hardness	Prover Noncutting Hardness
Untempered			
65	65 HRC	63 HRC	67 HRC
Tempered(1)			
62	61 HRC	60 HRC	64 HRC
58	57 HRC	56 HRC	60 HRC
55	54 HRC	53 HRC	57 HRC
50	49 HRC	48 HRC	52 HRC

1. Using tempered files below 65 HRC is less accurate and, therefore, more judgment on the part of the operator must be exercised as the hardness of the file decreases.

4. Surface Condition—In testing high surface hardnesses with a file, experience has shown that surface condition is important; very smoothly ground surfaces cannot be touched with a file as readily as surfaces that have been filed. Sometimes a testing file will cut a prover of a certain steel at, for example, 64 HRC, yet when the file is applied to a smoothly ground part made of the same steel and at the same hardness, the part feels harder. It is important when comparisons are made that the surface smoothness of the parts being tested be the same as the standard test piece. The standard test pieces can be made in a series of microfinish of 0.5, 1.5, 3.2, and 5 µm (20, 60, 125, and 200 µin).

On surfaces with a microfinish, the direction of the test filing across or parallel with the finish direction affects results. When filing, the direction of the file in relation to the microfinish should always be the same as the standard test piece.

5. Testing Hardness

5.1 Check file against standard prover.

5.2 Apply the file to the surface of the part being tested at such an angle that only a few teeth will engage the surface at once. Use slow, firm strokes in an effort to feel the manner in which the file cuts or does not cut. To prolong the life of the file, use as short a stroke as possible.

NOTE—To standardize pressure, attach specimen to a balance scale platform and measure the file effort against specimen in kilograms (pounds). Application should be between 4.5 and 5.5 kg (10 and 12 lb).

5.3 Compare the parts with a standard test piece with a known hardness range. This will assist in determining whether the part falls within the range specified by the engineering specifications. File hardness should not replace conventional methods where penetrators will not break through surface hardened areas.

NOTE—During the testing of a batch of parts, the files must not be allowed to become so dull as to cause difficulty in discriminating between parts within specification and those below specification. This can be prevented by frequent checking against the standard part or prover.

5.4 The hardness should be specified according to the Rockwell reading of the file as to the surface requirements of an iron or steel part. The designation should be "file hard - 65" for 65 HRC surface; "file hard - 62" for 62 HRC and so on.

6. Sources of Test Files

6.1 Simonds Cutting Tools, Newcomerstown, Ohio. Available through distributors in boxes of 10 files per hardness level.

6.2 Nicholson Files, Raleigh, North Carolina. Available in minimum quantities of 600.

HARDNESS TESTS AND HARDNESS NUMBER CONVERSIONS—SAE J417 DEC1983

SAE Information Report

Report of the SAE Iron and Steel Technical Committee, approved January 1946, third revision, Division 3, December 1983.

Foreword—This Document has not changed other than to put it into the new SAE Technical Standards Board Format.

*1. **Scope***—This report lists approximate hardness conversion values; test methods for Vickers Hardness, Brinell Hardness, Rockwell Hardness Rockwell Superficial Hardness, Shore Hardness; and information regarding surface preparation, specimen thickness, effect of curved surfaces, and recommendations for Rockwell surface hardness testing for case hardened parts.

The tables in this report give the approximate relationship of Vickers Brinell, Rockwell, and Scleroscope hardness values and corresponding approximate tensile strengths of steels. It is impossible to give exact relationships because of the inevitable influence of size, mass, composition, and method of heat treatment. Where more precise conversions are required, they should be developed specially for each steel composition, heat treatment, and part.

The accompanying conversion tables for steel hardness numbers are based on extensive tests on carbon and alloy steels, mostly in the heat treated condition, but have been found to be reliable on practically all constructional alloy steels and tool steels in the as-forged, annealed, normalized, and quenched and tempered conditions, provided they are homogeneous. Such special cases as high manganese steel, 18% chromium—8% nickel steel and other austenitic steels, and nickel base alloys, as well as constructional alloy steels and tool steels in the cold worked condition, may not conform to the relationships given with the same degree of accuracy as the steels for which the tables are intended.

All numbers in these tables given in bold face type were prepared jointly by the American Society for Testing and Materials, the American Society for Metals, and SAE from carefully checked data. The values given in regular face type were taken from the Army-Navy Approximate Hardness Tensile Strength Relationship of Carbon and Low Alloy Steels (ANQQ-H-201) published in the 1943 SAE Handbook, with only minor adjustments.

*2. **References***

2.1 Applicable Publications—The following publications form a part of this specification to the extent specified herein. Unless otherwise indicated, the latest version of SAE publications shall apply.

2.1.1 SAE Publication—Available from SAE, 400 Commonwealth Drive, Warrendale, PA 15096-0001.

SAE J423—Methods of Measuring Case Depth

ANQQ-H-201—Army-Navy Approximate hardness Tensile Strength Relationship of Carbon and Low Alloy Steels (published in the 1943 SAE Handbook)

2.1.2 ASTM Publication—Available from ASTM, 100 Barr Harbor Drive, West Conshohocken, PA 19428-2959.

ASTM E 10—Test Method for Brinell Hardness of Metallic Material

ASTM E 18—Test Methods for Rockwell Hardness and Rockwell Superficial Hardness of Metallic Materials

*3. **Use of Conversion Tables***—The conversions given in the accompanying Tables 1, 2, and 3 are recommended for use in converting the results of one form of hardness test to another only on flat surfaces and only when the specific test procedures and precautions outlined in the several hardness test methods are followed. Attention is called to the limitation in ASTM E 10 (Brinell Hardness Tests) on the use of the standard steel ball to hardness values less than 450 HB, and the use of a tungsten carbide ball to hardness values less than 630 HB. The Rockwell Superficial and Vickers Hardness tests require especially smooth surfaces for accurate results. In all tests, a specimen should be of sufficient thickness to avoid anvil effect—which thickness is roughly 10 times the depth of the indentation. It is important that conversions from Brinell Hardness to shallow impression type tests, such as Rockwell Superficial and Vickers Hardness tests, be made only on materials that are of uniform hardness to a depth at least 10 times that of the indentation. Such hardness conversions should not be made on surface hardened, coated, or decarburized surfaces. Although the Rockwell Hardness and the Rockwell Superficial Hardness values in the tables are given to tenths of a point in order to maintain exact relationships between the various scales, it is customary to report these values to the nearest point. Experience has shown that even under carefully controlled conditions, some deviations from the conversion relationships will occur.

The numbers given in parentheses in the tables are values beyond the practical range of usefulness of the type of' test under which they appear and have no strict application. They are included in the tables as a matter of information only, and should not be used for specifications.

*4. **Vickers Hardness (HV), Table I***—Vickers Hardness is determined by forcing a square base diamond pyramid having an apex angle of 136 deg into the test specimen under loads usually of 3-50 kg and measuring the diagonals of the recovered indentations. The Vickers Hardness is defined as the load per unit area of surface contact in kilograms per square millimeter as calculated from the average diagonal as follows:

$$HV = \frac{2L \sin\frac{a}{2}}{d^2} \quad \text{(Eq. 1)}$$

where:

HV = Vickers Hardness
d = length of average diagonal in millimeters
a = apex angle = 136 deg
L = load in kilograms

For further information on standard methods of Vickers Hardness Testing, refer to ASTM E 92-72.

*5. **Brinell Hardness—Tables 2 and 3***

5.1 Test Ball—The diameter of the ball shall be 10.00 ± 0.005 mm (0.3937 ± 0.0004 in). The load applied shall be 3000 kg (6614 lb) for at least 15 s on iron and steel. The standard ball is hardened steel; a tungsten carbide ball is used to test hard materials.

5.2 Test Impression—The average diameter of the impression shall be obtained from two measurements at right angles to each other, made with an instrument having a reading error not over 0.01 mm (0.0004 in).

5.3 Test Specimen—The surface of the specimen should be flat and reasonably free from scratches. The specimen shall be taken deep enough to represent the true composition of the material to be tested, and the test surface shall be maintained in a plane normal to the direction of the testing load.

5.4 Exceptions—This test should not be used on soft steels less than 10 mm (3/8 in) thick or on areas small enough to permit deflection of the edges of the specimen owing to the flow from the ball depression.

For further information on standard methods of Brinell Hardness testing, refer to ASTM E 10. For Brinell Hardness Numbers for Various Loads, see Table 3.

*6. **Rockwell Hardness—Table 4***

6.1 Principle of Test—The Rockwell Hardness tester is essentially a machine that measures hardness by determining the depth of penetration of a penetrator into the specimen under certain arbitrarily fixed conditions of test. The penetrator may be either a steel ball or a diamond sphero-conical penetrator. The hardness value as read from the dial (more recent testers incorporate digital readings) is an arbitrary number which is related to the depth of indentation, and since the scales are reversed, the number is higher the harder the material. A minor load of 10 kg is first applied which causes an initial penetration which sets the penetrator on the material and holds it in position. The dial is set at zero on the black figure scale and the major load is applied. After the major load is applied and removed, according to standard procedure, the reading is taken while the minor load is still in position.

6.2 Preparation of Surfaces—Concordant results are dependent on surface roughness being much less than the size of the impression. Surfaces that are ridged perceptibly to the eye by rough grinding or machining offer unequal support to the penetrator. The degree of surface preparation then depends, to some extent, on the requirements of testing, whether they be production or research.

6.3 Thickness of Specimens—The minimum allowable thickness of any specimen varies according to the hardness, the load applied, and the kind of test point or penetrator used. See Tables 2 and 3 of ASTM E 18 for selection of Rockwell scales for a given hardness and thickness of specimen.

TABLE 1—APPROXIMATE EQUIVALENT HARDNESS NUMBERS[a] FOR VICKERS HARDNESS NUMBERS (HV), FOR STEEL

Vickers Hardness No.	Brinell Hardness No. 10-mm Ball, 3000-kg Load[b]: Standard Ball	Brinell Hardness No. 10-mm Ball, 3000-kg Load[b]: Tungsten-Carbide Ball	Rockwell Hardness No.[b]: A-Scale, 60-kg Load, Brale Penetrator	Rockwell Hardness No.[b]: B-Scale, 100-kg Load, 1.6-mm (1/16-in) Dia Ball	Rockwell Hardness No.[b]: C-Scale, 150-kg Load, Brale Penetrator	Rockwell Hardness No.[b]: D-Scale, 100-kg Load, Brale Penetrator	Rockwell Superficial Hardness No., Superficial Brale Penetrator: 15-N Scale, 15-kg Load	Rockwell Superficial Hardness No., Superficial Brale Penetrator: 30-N Scale, 30-kg Load	Rockwell Superficial Hardness No., Superficial Brale Penetrator: 45-N Scale, 45-kg Load	Shore Scleroscope Hardness No.	Tensile Strength (Approximate) in MPa (1000 psi)	Vickers Hardness No.
Col. 1	Col. 2	Col. 3	Col. 4	Col. 5	Col. 6	Col. 7	Col. 8	Col. 9	Col. 10	Col. 11	Col. 12	Col. 13
940	—	—	85.6	—	68.0	76.9	93.2	84.4	75.4	97	—	940
920	—	—	85.3	—	67.5	76.5	93.0	84.0	74.8	96	—	920
900	—	—	85.0	—	67.0	76.1	92.9	83.6	74.2	95	—	900
880	—	(767)	84.7	—	66.4	75.7	92.7	83.1	73.6	93	—	880
860	—	(757)	84.4	—	65.9	75.3	92.5	82.7	73.1	92	—	860
840	—	(745)	84.1	—	65.3	74.8	92.3	82.2	72.2	91	—	840
820	—	(733)	83.8	—	64.7	74.3	92.1	81.7	71.8	90	—	820
800	—	(722)	83.4	—	64.0	73.8	91.8	81.1	71.0	88	—	800
780	—	(710)	83.0	—	63.3	73.3	91.5	80.4	70.2	87	—	780
760	—	(698)	82.6	—	62.5	72.6	91.2	79.7	69.4	86	—	760
740	—	(684)	82.2	—	61.8	72.1	91.0	79.1	68.6	84	—	740
720	—	(670)	81.8	—	61.0	71.5	90.7	78.4	67.7	83	—	720
700	—	(656)	81.3	—	60.1	70.8	90.3	77.6	66.7	81	—	700
690	—	(647)	81.1	—	59.7	70.5	90.1	77.2	66.2	—	—	690
680	—	(638)	80.8	—	59.2	70.1	89.8	76.8	65.7	80	—	680
670	—	630	80.6	—	58.8	69.8	89.7	76.4	65.3	—	—	670
660	—	620	80.3	—	58.3	69.4	89.5	75.9	64.7	79	—	660
650	—	611	80.0	—	57.8	69.0	89.2	75.5	64.1	—	—	650
640	—	601	79.8	—	57.3	68.7	89.0	75.1	63.5	77	—	640
630	—	591	79.5	—	56.8	68.3	88.8	74.6	63.0	—	—	630
620	—	582	79.2	—	56.3	67.9	88.5	74.2	62.4	75	—	620
610	—	573	78.9	—	55.7	67.5	88.2	73.6	61.7	—	—	610
600	—	564	78.6	—	55.2	67.0	88.0	73.2	61.2	74	—	600
590	—	554	78.4	—	54.7	66.7	87.8	72.7	60.5	—	2055 (298)	590
580	—	545	78.0	—	54.1	66.2	87.5	72.1	59.9	72	2020 (293)	580
570	—	535	77.8	—	53.6	65.8	87.2	71.7	59.3	—	1985 (288)	570
560	—	525	77.4	—	53.0	65.4	86.9	71.2	58.6	71	1950 (283)	560
550	(505)	517	77.0	—	52.3	64.8	86.6	70.5	57.8	—	1905 (276)	550
540	(496)	507	76.7	—	51.7	64.4	86.3	70.0	57.0	69	1860 (270)	540
530	(488)	497	76.4	—	51.1	63.9	86.0	69.5	56.2	—	1825 (265)	530
520	(480)	488	76.1	—	50.5	63.5	85.7	69.0	55.6	67	1795 (260)	520
510	(473)	479	75.7	—	49.8	62.9	85.4	68.3	54.7	—	1750 (254)	510
500	(465)	471	75.3	—	49.1	62.2	85.0	67.7	53.9	66	1705 (247)	500
490	(456)	460	74.9	—	48.4	61.6	84.7	67.1	53.1	—	1660 (241)	490
480	448	452	74.5	—	47.7	61.3	84.3	66.4	52.2	64	1620 (235)	480
470	441	442	74.1	—	46.9	60.7	83.9	65.7	51.3	—	1570 (228)	470
460	433	433	73.6	—	46.1	60.1	83.6	64.9	50.4	62	1530 (222)	460
450	425	425	73.3	—	45.3	59.4	83.2	64.3	49.4	—	1495 (217)	450
440	415	415	72.8	—	44.5	58.8	82.8	63.5	48.4	59	1460 (212)	440
430	405	405	72.3	—	43.6	58.2	82.3	62.7	47.4	—	1410 (205)	430
420	397	397	71.8	—	42.7	57.5	81.8	61.9	46.4	57	1370 (199)	420
410	388	388	71.4	—	41.8	56.8	81.4	61.1	45.3	—	1330 (193)	410
400	379	379	70.8	—	40.8	56.0	81.0	60.2	44.1	55	1290 (187)	400
390	369	369	70.3	—	39.8	55.2	80.3	59.3	42.9	—	1240 (180)	390
380	360	360	69.8	(110.0)	38.8	54.4	79.8	58.4	41.7	52	1205 (175)	380
370	350	350	69.2	—	37.7	53.6	79.2	57.4	40.4	—	1170 (170)	370
360	341	341	68.7	(109.0)	36.6	52.8	78.6	56.4	39.1	50	1130 (164)	360
350	331	331	68.1	—	35.5	51.9	78.0	55.4	37.8	—	1095 (159)	350
340	322	322	67.6	(108.0)	34.4	51.1	77.4	54.4	36.5	47	1070 (155)	340
330	313	313	67.0	—	33.3	50.2	76.8	53.6	35.2	—	1035 (150)	330
320	303	303	66.4	(107.0)	32.2	49.4	76.2	52.3	33.9	45	1005 (146)	320
310	294	294	65.8	—	31.0	48.4	75.6	51.3	32.5	—	980 (142)	310
300	284	284	65.2	(105.5)	29.8	47.5	74.9	50.2	31.1	42	950 (138)	300
295	280	280	64.8	—	29.2	47.1	74.6	49.7	30.4	—	935 (136)	295
290	275	275	64.5	(104.5)	28.5	46.5	74.2	49.0	29.5	41	915 (133)	290
285	270	270	64.2	—	27.8	46.0	73.8	48.4	28.7	—	905 (131)	285
280	265	265	63.8	(103.5)	27.1	45.3	73.4	47.8	27.9	40	890 (129)	280
275	261	261	63.5	—	26.4	44.9	73.0	47.2	27.1	—	875 (127)	275
270	256	256	63.1	(102.0)	25.6	44.3	72.6	46.4	26.2	38	855 (124)	270
265	252	252	62.7	—	24.8	43.7	72.1	45.7	25.2	—	840 (122)	265
260	247	247	62.4	(101.0)	24.0	43.1	71.6	45.0	24.3	37	825 (120)	260
255	243	243	62.0	—	23.1	42.2	71.1	44.2	23.2	—	805 (117)	255
250	238	238	61.6	99.5	22.2	41.7	70.6	43.4	22.2	36	795 (115)	250
245	233	233	61.2	—	21.3	41.1	70.1	42.5	21.1	—	780 (113)	245
240	228	228	60.7	98.1	20.3	40.3	69.6	41.7	19.9	34	765 (111)	240
230	219	219	—	96.7	(18.0)	—	—	—	—	33	730 (106)	230
220	209	209	—	95.0	(15.7)	—	—	—	—	32	695 (101)	220
210	200	200	—	93.4	(13.4)	—	—	—	—	30	670 (97)	210
200	190	190	—	91.5	(11.0)	—	—	—	—	29	635 (92)	200
190	181	181	—	89.5	(8.5)	—	—	—	—	28	605 (88)	190

(Table continued on next page)

TABLE 1—APPROXIMATE EQUIVALENT HARDNESS NUMBERS[a] FOR VICKERS HARDNESS NUMBERS (HV), FOR STEEL (continued)

	Brinell Hardness No. 10-mm Ball, 3000-kg Load[b]		Rockwell Hardness No.[b]				Rockwell Superficial Hardness No., Superficial Brale Penetrator					
Vickers Hardness No.	Standard Ball	Tungsten-Carbide Ball	A-Scale, 60-kg Load, Brale Penetrator	B-Scale, 100-kg Load, 1.6-mm (1/16-in) Dia Ball	C-Scale, 150-kg Load, Brale Penetrator	D-Scale, 100-kg Load, Brale Penetrator	15-N Scale, 15-kg Load	30-N Scale, 30-kg Load	45-N Scale, 45-kg Load	Shore Scleroscope Hardness No.	Tensile Strength (Approximate) in MPa (1000 psi)	Vickers Hardness No.
Col. 1	Col. 2	Col. 3	Col. 4	Col. 5	Col. 6	Col. 7	Col. 8	Col. 9	Col. 10	Col. 11	Col. 12	Col. 13
180	171	171	—	87.1	(6.0)	—	—	—	—	26	580 (84)	180
170	162	162	—	85.0	(3.0)	—	—	—	—	25	545 (79)	170
160	152	152	—	81.7	(0.0)	—	—	—	—	24	515 (75)	160
150	143	143	—	78.7	—	—	—	—	—	22	490 (71)	150
140	133	133	—	75.0	—	—	—	—	—	21	455 (66)	140
130	124	124	—	71.2	—	—	—	—	—	20	425 (62)	130
120	114	114	—	66.7	—	—	—	—	—	—	390 (57)	120
110	105	105	—	62.3	—	—	—	—	—	—	—	110
100	95	95	—	56.2	—	—	—	—	—	—	—	100
95	90	90	—	52.0	—	—	—	—	—	—	—	95
90	86	86	—	48.0	—	—	—	—	—	—	—	90
85	81	81	—	41.0	—	—	—	—	—	—	—	85

[a] The values in this table shown in **bold face type** correspond to the values shown in the corresponding joint SAE-ASM-ASTM Committee on Hardness Conversions as printed in ASTM E 140, Table 1.

[b] Values in ( ) are beyond normal range and are given for information only.

TABLE 2—APPROXIMATE EQUIVALENT HARDNESS NUMBERS[a] FOR BRINELL HARDNESS NUMBERS[b], FOR STEEL

	Brinell Hardness No.,[b] 10-mm Ball, 3000-kg Load			Rockwell Hardness No.[b]				Rockwell Superficial Hardness No. Superficial Brale Penetrator					
Brinell Indentation Dia, mm	Standard Ball	Tungsten-Carbide Ball	Vickers Hardness No.	A-Scale, 60-kg Load, Brale Penetrator	B-Scale, 100-kg Load 1.6-mm (1/16-in) Dia Ball	C-Scale, 150-kg Load Brale Penetrator	D-Scale, 100-kg Load Brale Penetrator	15-N Scale, 15-kg Load	30-N Scale, 30-kg Load	45-N Scale, 45-kg Load	Shore Scleroscope Hardness No.	Tensile Strength (Approximate) in MPa (1000 psi)	Brinell Indentation Dia, mm
Col. 1	Col. 2	Col. 3	Col. 4	Col. 5	Col. 6	Col. 7	Col. 8	Col. 9	Col. 10	Col. 11	Col. 12	Col. 13	Col. 14
—	—	—	940	85.6	—	68.0	76.9	93.2	84.4	75.4	97	—	—
—	—	—	920	85.3	—	67.5	76.5	93.0	84.0	74.8	96	—	—
—	—	—	900	85.0	—	67.0	76.1	92.9	83.6	74.2	95	—	—
—	—	(767)	880	84.7	—	66.4	75.7	92.7	83.1	73.6	93	—	—
—	—	(757)	860	84.4	—	65.9	75.3	92.5	82.7	73.1	92	—	—
2.25	—	(745)	840	84.1	—	65.3	74.8	92.3	82.2	72.2	91	—	2.25
—	—	(733)	820	83.8	—	64.7	74.3	92.1	81.7	71.8	90	—	—
—	—	(722)	800	83.4	—	64.0	73.8	91.8	81.1	71.0	88	—	—
2.30	—	(712)	—	—	—	—	—	—	—	—	—	—	2.30
—	—	(710)	780	83.0	—	63.3	73.3	91.5	80.4	70.2	87	—	—
—	—	(698)	760	82.6	—	62.5	72.6	91.2	79.7	69.4	86	—	—
—	—	(684)	740	82.2	—	61.8	72.1	91.0	79.1	68.6	—	—	—
2.35	—	(682)	**737**	**82.2**	—	**61.7**	**72.0**	**91.0**	**79.0**	**68.5**	84	—	**2.35**
—	—	(670)	720	81.8	—	61.0	71.5	90.7	78.4	67.7	83	—	—
—	—	(656)	700	81.3	—	60.1	70.8	90.3	77.6	66.7	—	—	—
2.40	—	(653)	**697**	**81.2**	—	**60.0**	**70.7**	**90.2**	**77.5**	**66.5**	81	—	**2.40**
—	—	(647)	690	81.1	—	59.7	70.5	90.1	77.2	66.2	—	—	—
—	—	(638)	680	80.8	—	59.2	70.1	89.8	76.8	65.7	80	—	—
—	—	630	670	80.6	—	58.8	69.8	89.7	76.4	65.3	—	—	—
2.45	—	**627**	**667**	**80.5**	—	**58.7**	**69.7**	**89.6**	**76.3**	**65.1**	79	—	**2.45**
2.50	—	—	**677**	**80.7**	—	**59.1**	**70.0**	**89.8**	**76.8**	**65.7**	—	—	**2.50**
	—	**601**	**640**	**79.8**	—	**57.3**	**68.7**	**89.0**	**75.1**	**63.5**	77	—	
2.55	—	—	**640**	**79.8**	—	**57.3**	**68.7**	**89.0**	**75.1**	**63.5**	—	—	**2.55**
	—	**578**	**615**	**79.1**	—	**56.0**	**67.7**	**88.4**	**73.9**	**62.1**	75	—	
2.60	—	—	**607**	**78.8**	—	**55.6**	**67.4**	**88.1**	**73.5**	**61.6**	—	—	**2.60**
	—	**555**	**591**	**78.4**	—	**54.7**	**66.7**	**87.8**	**72.7**	**60.6**	73	2055 (298)	
2.65	—	—	**579**	**78.0**	—	**54.0**	**66.1**	**87.5**	**72.0**	**59.8**	—	2015 (292)	**2.65**
	—	**534**	**569**	**77.8**	—	**53.5**	**65.8**	**87.2**	**71.6**	**59.2**	71	1985 (288)	
2.70	—	—	**553**	**77.1**	—	**52.5**	**65.0**	**86.7**	**70.7**	**58.0**	—	1915 (278)	**2.70**
	—	**514**	**547**	**76.9**	—	**52.1**	**64.7**	**86.5**	**70.3**	**57.6**	70	1890 (274)	
	(495)	—	**539**	**76.7**	—	**51.6**	**64.3**	**86.3**	**69.9**	**56.9**	—	1855 (269)	
2.75	—	—	**530**	**76.4**	—	**51.1**	**63.9**	**86.0**	**69.5**	**56.2**	—	1825 (265)	**2.75**
	—	**495**	**528**	**76.3**	—	**51.0**	**63.8**	**85.9**	**69.4**	**56.1**	68	1820 (264)	
	(477)	—	**516**	**75.9**	—	**50.3**	**63.2**	**85.6**	**68.7**	**55.2**	—	1780 (258)	
2.80	—	—	**508**	**75.6**	—	**49.6**	**62.7**	**85.3**	**68.2**	**54.5**	—	1740 (252)	**2.80**
	—	**477**	**508**	**75.6**	—	**49.6**	**62.7**	**85.3**	**68.2**	**54.5**	66	1740 (252)	

(Table continued on next page)

TABLE 2—APPROXIMATE EQUIVALENT HARDNESS NUMBERS[a] FOR BRINELL HARDNESS NUMBERS[b], FOR STEEL (continued)

	Brinell Hardness No.,[b] 10-mm Ball, 3000-kg Load			Rockwell Hardness No.[b]				Rockwell Superficial Hardness No. Superficial Brale Penetrator					
Brinell Indentation Dia, mm	**Standard Ball**	**Tungsten-Carbide Ball**	**Vickers Hardness No.**	**A-Scale, 60-kg Load, Brale Penetrator**	**B-Scale, 100-kg Load 1.6-mm (1/16-in) Dia Ball**	**C-Scale, 150-kg Load Brale Penetrator**	**D-Scale, 100-kg Load Brale Penetrator**	**15-N Scale, 15-kg Load**	**30-N Scale, 30-kg Load**	**45-N Scale, 45-kg Load**	**Shore Sclero-scope Hardness No.**	**Tensile Strength (Approximate) in MPa (1000 psi)**	**Brinell Indentation Dia, mm**
Col. 1	**Col. 2**	**Col. 3**	**Col. 4**	**Col. 5**	**Col. 6**	**Col. 7**	**Col. 8**	**Col. 9**	**Col. 10**	**Col. 11**	**Col. 12**	**Col. 13**	**Col. 14**
	(461)	—	495	75.1	—	48.8	61.9	84.9	67.4	53.5	—	1680 (244)	
2.85	—	—	491	74.9	—	48.5	61.7	84.7	67.2	53.2	—	1670 (242)	2.85
	—	461	491	74.9	—	48.5	61.7	84.7	67.2	53.2	65	1670 (242)	
	444	—	474	74.3	—	47.2	61.0	84.1	66.0	51.7	—	1595 (231)	
2.90	—	—	472	74.2	—	47.1	60.8	84.0	65.8	51.5	—	1585 (230)	2.90
	—	444	472	74.2	—	47.1	60.8	84.0	65.8	51.5	63	1585 (230)	
2.95	429	429	455	73.4	—	45.7	59.7	83.4	64.6	49.9	61	1510 (219)	2.95
3.00	415	415	440	72.8	—	44.5	58.8	82.8	63.5	48.4	59	1460 (212)	3.00
3.05	401	401	425	72.0	—	43.1	57.8	82.0	62.3	46.9	58	1390 (202)	3.05
3.10	388	388	410	71.4	—	41.8	56.8	81.4	61.1	45.3	56	1330 (193)	3.10
3.15	375	375	396	70.6	—	40.4	55.7	80.6	59.9	43.6	54	1270 (184)	3.15
3.20	363	363	383	70.0	—	39.1	54.6	80.0	58.7	42.0	52	1220 (177)	3.20
3.25	352	352	372	69.3	(110.0)	37.9	53.8	79.3	57.6	40.5	51	1180 (171)	3.25
3.30	341	341	360	68.7	(109.0)	36.6	52.8	78.6	56.4	39.1	50	1130 (164)	3.30
3.35	331	331	350	68.1	(108.5)	35.5	51.9	78.0	55.4	37.8	48	1095 (159)	3.35
3.40	321	321	339	67.5	(108.0)	34.3	51.0	77.3	54.3	36.4	47	1060 (154)	3.40
3.45	311	311	328	66.9	(107.5)	33.1	50.0	76.7	53.3	34.4	46	1025 (149)	3.45
3.50	302	302	319	66.3	(107.0)	32.1	49.3	76.1	52.2	33.8	45	1005 (146)	3.50
3.55	293	293	309	65.7	(106.0)	30.9	48.3	75.5	51.2	32.4	43	970 (141)	3.55
3.60	285	285	301	65.3	(105.5)	29.9	47.6	75.0	50.3	31.2	—	950 (138)	3.60
3.65	277	277	292	64.6	(104.5)	28.8	46.7	74.4	49.3	29.9	41	925 (134)	3.65
3.70	269	269	284	64.1	(104.0)	27.6	45.9	73.7	48.3	28.5	40	895 (130)	3.70
3.75	262	262	276	63.6	(103.0)	26.6	45.0	73.1	47.3	27.3	39	875 (127)	3.75
3.80	255	255	269	63.0	(102.0)	25.4	44.2	72.5	46.2	26.0	38	850 (123)	3.80
3.85	248	248	261	62.5	(101.0)	24.2	43.2	71.7	45.1	24.5	37	825 (120)	3.85
3.90	241	241	253	61.8	100.0	22.8	42.0	70.9	43.9	22.8	36	800 (116)	3.90
3.95	235	235	247	61.4	99.0	21.7	41.4	70.3	42.9	21.5	35	785 (114)	3.95
4.00	229	229	241	60.8	98.2	20.5	40.5	69.7	41.9	20.1	34	765 (111)	4.00
4.05	223	223	234	—	97.3	(18.8)	—	—	—	—	—	—	4.05
4.10	217	217	228	—	96.4	(17.5)	—	—	—	—	33	725 (105)	4.10
4.15	212	212	222	—	95.5	(16.0)	—	—	—	—		705 (102)	4.15
4.20	207	207	218	—	94.6	(15.2)	—	—	—	—	32	690 (100)	4.20
4.25	201	201	212	—	93.8	(13.8)	—	—	—	—	31	675 (98)	4.25
4.30	197	197	207	—	92.8	(12.7)	—	—	—	—	30	655 (95)	4.30
4.35	192	192	202	—	91.9	(11.5)	—	—	—	—	29	640 (93)	4.35
4.40	187	187	196	—	90.7	(10.0)	—	—	—	—	—	620 (90)	4.40
4.45	183	183	192	—	90.0	(9.0)	—	—	—	—	28	615 (89)	4.45
4.50	179	179	188	—	89.0	(8.0)	—	—	—	—	27	600 (87)	4.50
4.55	174	174	182	—	87.8	(6.4)	—	—	—	—	—	585 (85)	4.55
4.60	170	170	178	—	86.8	(5.4)	—	—	—	—	26	570 (83)	4.60
4.65	167	167	175	—	86.0	(4.4)	—	—	—	—	—	560 (81)	4.65
4.70	163	163	171	—	85.0	(3.3)	—	—	—	—	25	545 (79)	4.70
4.80	156	156	163	—	82.9	(0.9)	—	—	—	—	—	525 (76)	4.80
4.90	149	149	156	—	80.8	—	—	—	—	—	23	505 (73)	4.90
5.00	143	143	150	—	78.7	—	—	—	—	—	22	490 (71)	5.00
5.10	137	137	143	—	76.4	—	—	—	—	—	21	460 (67)	5.10
5.20	131	131	137	—	74.0	—	—	—	—	—	—	450 (65)	5.20
5.30	126	126	132	—	72.0	—	—	—	—	—	20	435 (63)	5.30
5.40	121	121	127	—	69.8	—	—	—	—	—	19	415 (60)	5.40
5.50	116	116	122	—	67.6	—	—	—	—	—	18	400 (58)	5.50
5.60	111	111	117	—	65.7	—	—	—	—	—	15	385 (56)	5.60

[a] This table corresponds to the table in ASM Metals Handbook, 8th Edition, Vol. 1, page 1235, and is included in this report for convenience. It has been modified to add metric equivalents for approximate tensile strength values, and to indicate Brinell hardness values that are beyond the recommended range for this test.

[b] Values in ( ) are beyond normal range and are given for information only.

TABLE 3—BRINELL HARDNESS NUMBERS (10 MM BALL DIAMETER)

Dia of In-den-ta-tion, mm	Loads, kg						Dia of In-den-ta-tion, mm	Loads, kg					
	500[a]	1000	1500	2000	2500	3000[b]		500[a]	1000	1500	2000	2500	3000[b]
2.00	158	316	473	632	788	945	4.25	33.6	67.2	101	134	167	201
2.05	150	300	450	600	750	899	4.30	32.8	65.6	98.5	131	164	197
2.10	143	286	428	572	714	856	4.35	32.0	64.0	96.0	128	160	192
2.15	136	272	409	544	681	817	4.40	31.2	62.4	93.5	125	156	187
2.20	130	260	390	520	650	780	4.45	30.5	61.0	91.5	122	153	183
2.25	124	248	373	496	621	745	4.50	29.8	59.6	89.5	119	149	179
2.30	119	238	356	476	593	712	4.55	29.1	58.2	87.0	116	145	174
2.35	114	228	341	456	568	682	4.60	28.4	56.8	85.0	114	142	170
2.40	109	218	327	436	545	653	4.65	27.8	55.6	83.5	111	139	167
2.45	104	208	314	416	522	627	4.70	27.1	54.2	81.5	108	136	163
2.50	100	200	301	400	500	601	4.75	26.5	53.0	79.5	106	133	159
2.55	96.3	193	289	385	482	578	4.80	25.9	51.8	78.0	104	130	156
2.60	92.6	185	278	370	462	555	4.85	25.4	50.8	76.0	102	127	152
2.65	89.0	178	267	356	445	534	4.90	24.8	49.6	74.5	99.2	124	149
2.70	85.7	171	257	343	429	514	4.95	24.3	48.6	73.0	97.2	122	146
2.75	82.6	165	248	330	413	495	5.00	23.8	47.6	71.5	95.2	119	143
2.80	79.6	159	239	318	398	477	5.05	23.3	46.6	70.0	93.2	117	140
2.85	76.8	154	231	307	384	461	5.10	22.8	45.6	68.5	91.2	114	137
2.90	74.1	148	222	296	371	444	5.15	22.3	44.6	67.0	89.2	112	134
2.95	71.5	143	215	286	358	429	5.20	21.8	43.6	65.5	87.2	109	131
3.00	69.1	138	208	276	346	415	5.25	21.4	42.8	64.0	85.6	107	128
3.05	66.8	134	201	267	334	401	5.30	20.9	41.8	63.0	83.6	105	126
3.10	64.6	129	194	258	324	388	5.35	20.5	41.0	61.5	82.0	103	123
3.15	62.5	125	188	250	313	375	5.40	20.1	40.2	60.5	80.4	101	121
3.20	60.5	121	182	242	303	363	5.45	19.7	39.4	59.0	78.8	98.5	118
3.25	58.6	117	176	234	293	352	5.50	19.3	38.6	58.0	77.2	96.5	116
3.30	56.8	114	171	227	284	341	5.55	18.9	37.8	57.0	75.6	95.0	114
3.35	55.1	110	166	220	276	331	5.60	18.6	37.2	55.5	74.4	92.5	111
3.40	53.4	107	161	214	267	321	5.65	18.2	36.4	54.5	72.8	90.8	109
3.45	51.8	104	156	207	259	311	5.70	17.8	35.6	53.5	71.2	89.2	107
3.50	50.3	101	151	201	252	302	5.75	17.5	35.0	52.5	70.0	87.5	105
3.55	48.9	97.8	147	196	244	293	5.80	17.2	34.4	51.5	68.8	85.8	103
3.60	47.5	95.0	143	190	238	285	5.85	16.8	33.6	50.5	67.2	84.2	101
3.65	46.1	92.2	139	184	231	277	5.90	16.5	33.0	49.6	66.0	82.5	99.2
3.70	44.9	89.8	135	180	225	269	5.95	16.2	32.4	48.7	64.8	81.2	97.3
3.75	43.6	87.2	131	174	218	262	6.00	15.9	31.8	47.8	63.6	79.5	95.5
3.80	42.4	84.8	128	170	212	255	6.05	15.6	31.2	46.9	62.4	78.0	93.7
3.85	41.3	82.6	124	165	207	248	6.10	15.3	30.6	46.0	61.2	76.7	92.0
3.90	40.2	80.4	121	161	201	241	6.15	15.1	30.2	45.2	60.4	75.3	90.3
3.95	39.1	78.2	118	156	196	235	6.20	14.8	29.6	44.4	59.2	73.8	88.7
4.00	38.1	76.2	115	152	191	229	6.25	14.5	29.0	43.6	58.0	72.6	87.1
4.05	37.1	74.2	112	148	186	223	6.30	14.2	28.4	42.8	56.8	71.3	85.5
4.10	36.2	72.4	109	145	181	217	6.35	14.0	28.0	42.0	56.0	70.0	84.0
4.15	35.3	70.6	106	141	177	212	6.40	13.7	27.4	41.3	54.8	68.8	82.5
4.20	34.4	68.8	104	138	172	207	6.45	13.5	27.0	40.5	54.0	67.5	81.0

Values in the table correspond to the formula:

$$HB = \frac{2P}{\pi D\left(D - \sqrt{D^2 - d^2}\right)}$$

[a] For 500 kg load and 10 mm ball:

$$HB = \frac{31.83}{10 - \sqrt{10 - d^2}}$$

[b] For 3000 kg load and 10 mm ball:

$$HB = \frac{191.0}{10 - \sqrt{10 - d^2}}$$

6.4 Curved Surfaces—Data for hardness tests on a highly curved surface should be accompanied by a statement of the radius of curvature. In testing small rounds, the effect of curvature can be eliminated by making a small flat spot on the specimen. See Tables 5 and 6 of ASTM E 18 for corrections for tests on cylindrical specimens.

6.5 Case Hardened Parts—The following information defines the minimum effective case depths which will allow the accurate determination of indentation surface hardness measurements for standard and superficial hardness tests. These practices are for fully hardened cases either as quenched or with low [approximately 175 °C (350 °F)] temperature temper. Tempering to lower hardness levels may require less indention load than described.

Effective case is defined as the depth to 50 HRC or its equivalent (see SAE J423). These practices will not avoid errors caused by surface metal of reduced hardness resulting from decarburization, retained austenite, grinding damage, etc. These recommendations may be used for all levels of core hardness.

It is recommended that surface hardness be specified and measured with a scale which has indentation loads no greater than the following:

Minimum Effective Case Depth on Parts	Scale
0.18 mm (0.007 in)	H R15N
0.25 mm (0.010 in)	H R30N
0.31 mm (0.012 in)	H R45N
0.38 mm (0.015 in)	H RA
0.46 mm (0.018 in)	H RD
0.53 mm (0.021 in)	H RC

6.6 Rockwell Scales—In the dial type tester, the black figures are used only for the diamond brale penetrator with various loads. Scale A applies when the major load is 60 kg, scale D when it is 100 kg, and scale C when the load is 150 kg. The red figures are used for readings obtained with ball penetrators regardless of size or magnitude of major load; scale B applies when the major load of 100 kg is applied to the 1.6-mm (1/16-in) steel ball penetrator. All data should be accompanied by a letter showing whether the values are on the A, B, C, or D scale.

6.7 Testing Cast Iron—Materials such as cast iron with graphite particles and some nonferrous materials whose crystalline aggregates are comparatively large, must be tested with a penetrator of sufficient size to overcome local or grain hardness in order to secure mass hardness.

6.8 Superficial Hardness Tester—The Rockwell Superficial Hardness tester utilizes the same principle as the regular Rockwell tester, but employs a light minor load of 3 kg and a light major load of 15, 30, or 45 kg in conjunction with a more sensitive depth measuring system. It is recommended for use on thin strip or sheet material, nitrided or lightly carburized pieces, finished pieces on which large test marks would be undesirable, areas near edges, extremely small parts or sections, and shapes that would collapse under the comparatively heavy test loads of the regular Rockwell tester. When the 120 deg diamond cone penetrator is used, readings are designated by the letter N prefixed by the major load (that is, 15-N, 30-N, or 45-N). Similarly, the letter T prefixed by the major load is applied to readings taken with the 1.6-mm (1-1/16-in) steel ball. Special penetrators for very soft metals or nonmetallic materials include 3.2-mm (1/8-in), 6.4-mm (1/4-in), and 12.7-mm (1/2-in) steel balls, designated by the letters W, X, and Y, respectively. In using the Rockwell Superficial Hardness tester, the general methods prescribed for the regular Rockwell tester should be observed.

For further information on standard methods of Rockwell hardness testing of metallic materials, refer to ASTM E 18.

7. ***Shore Hardness***—The Shore hardness number is the reading obtained on an arbitrary scale ranging from 0–120 by the rebound of a small diamond pointed hammer dropped from a fixed height. Two types of instruments are in common use, one in which the rebound is read directly on a vertical scale and the other on which the reading is registered by the instrument on a recording dial.

CAUTION—Shore (and other testers based on the rebound principle) readings are affected by variations in mass, form, surface, composition, and physical condition of different specimens being tested.

TABLE 4—APPROXIMATE EQUIVALENT HARDNESS NUMBERS[a] FOR ROCKWELL C HARDNESS NUMBERS, FOR STEEL

		Brinell Hardness No. 10-mm Ball, 3000-kg Load[b]		Rockwell Hardness No.[b]			Rockwell, Superficial Hardness No. Superficial Brale Penetrator					
Rockwell C-Scale Hardness No.[b]	Vickers Hardness No.	Standard Ball	Tungsten-Carbide Ball	A-Scale, 60-kg Load, Brale Penetrator	B-Scale, 100-kg Load, 1.6-mm (1/16-in) Dia Ball	D-Scale, 100-kg Load, Brale Penetrator	15-N Scale, 15-kg Load	30-N Scale, 30-kg Load	45-N Scale, 45-kg Load	Shore Scleroscope Hardness No.	Tensile Strength (Approximate) in Mpa (1000 psi)	Rockwell C-Scale Hardness No.[b]
Col. 1	Col. 2	Col. 3	Col. 4	Col. 5	Col. 6	Col. 7	Col. 8	Col. 9	Col. 10	Col. 11	Col. 12	Col. 13
68	**940**	—	—	**85.6**	—	**76.9**	**93.2**	**84.4**	**75.4**	97	—	**68**
67	**900**	—	—	**85.0**	—	**76.1**	**92.9**	**83.6**	**74.2**	95	—	**67**
66	**865**	—	—	**84.5**	—	**75.4**	**92.5**	**82.8**	**73.3**	92	—	**66**
65	**832**	—	(739)	**83.9**	—	**74.5**	**92.2**	**81.9**	**72.0**	91	—	**65**
64	**800**	—	(722)	**83.4**	—	**73.8**	**91.8**	**81.1**	**71.0**	88	—	**64**
63	**772**	—	(705)	**82.8**	—	**73.0**	**91.4**	**80.1**	**69.9**	87	—	**63**
62	**746**	—	(688)	**82.3**	—	**72.2**	**91.1**	**79.3**	**68.8**	85	—	**62**
61	**720**	—	(670)	**81.8**	—	**71.5**	**90.7**	**78.4**	**67.7**	83	—	**61**
60	**697**	—	(654)	**81.2**	—	**70.7**	**90.2**	**77.5**	**66.6**	81	—	**60**
59	**674**	—	(634)	**80.7**	—	**69.9**	**89.8**	**76.6**	**65.5**	80	—	**59**
58	**653**	—	**615**	**80.1**	—	**69.2**	**89.3**	**75.7**	**64.3**	78	—	**58**
57	**633**	—	**595**	**79.6**	—	**68.5**	**88.9**	**74.8**	**63.2**	76	—	**57**
56	**613**	—	**577**	**79.0**	—	**67.7**	**88.3**	**73.9**	**62.0**	75	—	**56**
55	**595**	—	**560**	**78.5**	—	**66.9**	**87.9**	**73.0**	**60.9**	74	2075 (301)	**55**
54	**577**	—	**543**	**78.0**	—	**66.1**	**87.4**	**72.0**	**59.8**	72	2015 (292)	**54**
53	**560**	—	**525**	**77.4**	—	**65.4**	**86.9**	**71.2**	**58.6**	71	1950 (283)	**53**
52	**544**	(500)	**512**	**76.8**	—	**64.6**	**86.4**	**70.2**	**57.4**	69	1880 (273)	**52**
51	**528**	(487)	**496**	**76.3**	—	**63.8**	**85.9**	**69.4**	**56.1**	68	1820 (264)	**51**
50	**513**	(475)	**481**	**75.9**	—	**63.1**	**85.5**	**68.5**	**55.0**	67	1760 (255)	**50**
49	**498**	(464)	**469**	**75.2**	—	**62.1**	**85.0**	**67.6**	**53.8**	66	1695 (246)	**49**
48	**484**	**451**	**455**	**74.7**	—	**61.4**	**84.5**	**66.7**	**52.5**	64	1635 (237)	**48**
47	**471**	**442**	**443**	**74.1**	—	**60.8**	**83.9**	**65.8**	**51.4**	63	1580 (229)	**47**
46	**458**	**432**	**432**	**73.6**	—	**60.0**	**83.5**	**64.8**	**50.3**	62	1530 (222)	**46**
45	**446**	**421**	**421**	**73.1**	—	**59.2**	**83.0**	**64.0**	**49.0**	60	1480 (215)	**45**
44	**434**	**409**	**409**	**72.5**	—	**58.5**	**82.5**	**63.1**	**47.8**	58	1435 (208)	**44**
43	**423**	**400**	**400**	**72.0**	—	**57.7**	**82.0**	**62.2**	**46.7**	57	1385 (201)	**43**
42	**412**	**390**	**390**	**71.5**	—	**56.9**	**81.5**	**61.3**	**45.5**	56	1340 (194)	**42**
41	**402**	**381**	**381**	**70.9**	—	**56.2**	**80.9**	**60.4**	**44.3**	55	1295 (188)	**41**
40	**392**	**371**	**371**	**70.4**	—	**55.4**	**80.4**	**59.5**	**43.1**	54	1250 (181)	**40**
39	**382**	**362**	**362**	**69.9**	—	**54.6**	**79.9**	**58.6**	**41.9**	52	1215 (176)	**39**
38	**372**	**353**	**353**	**69.4**	—	**53.8**	**79.4**	**57.7**	**40.8**	51	1180 (171)	**38**
37	**363**	**344**	**344**	**68.9**	—	**53.1**	**78.8**	**56.8**	**39.6**	50	1160 (168)	**37**
36	**354**	**336**	**336**	**68.4**	(109.0)	**52.3**	**78.3**	**55.9**	**38.4**	49	1115 (162)	**36**
35	**345**	**327**	**327**	**67.9**	(108.5)	**51.5**	**77.7**	**55.0**	**37.2**	48	1080 (157)	**35**
34	**336**	**319**	**319**	**67.4**	(108.0)	**50.8**	**77.2**	**54.2**	**36.1**	47	1055 (153)	**34**
33	**327**	**311**	**311**	**66.8**	(107.5)	**50.0**	**76.6**	**53.3**	**34.9**	46	1025 (149)	**33**
32	**318**	**301**	**301**	**66.3**	(107.0)	**49.2**	**76.1**	**52.1**	**33.7**	44	1000 (145)	**32**
31	**310**	**294**	**294**	**65.8**	(106.0)	**48.4**	**75.6**	**51.3**	**32.5**	43	980 (142)	**31**
30	**302**	**286**	**286**	**65.3**	(105.5)	**47.7**	**75.0**	**50.4**	**31.3**	42	950 (138)	**30**
29	**294**	**279**	**279**	**64.7**	(104.5)	**47.0**	**74.5**	**49.5**	**30.1**	41	930 (135)	**29**
28	**286**	**271**	**271**	**64.3**	(104.0)	**46.1**	**73.9**	**48.6**	**28.9**	41	910 (132)	**28**
27	**279**	**264**	**264**	**63.8**	(103.0)	**45.2**	**73.3**	**47.7**	**27.8**	40	880 (128)	**27**
26	**272**	**258**	**258**	**63.3**	(102.5)	**44.6**	**72.8**	**46.8**	**26.7**	38	860 (125)	**26**
25	**266**	**253**	**253**	**62.8**	(101.5)	**43.8**	**72.2**	**45.9**	**25.5**	38	840 (122)	**25**
24	**260**	**247**	**247**	**62.4**	(101.0)	**43.1**	**71.6**	**45.0**	**24.3**	37	825 (120)	**24**
23	**254**	**243**	**243**	**62.0**	100.0	**42.1**	**71.0**	**44.0**	**23.1**	36	805 (117)	**23**
22	**248**	**237**	**237**	**61.5**	99.0	**41.6**	**70.5**	**43.2**	**22.0**	35	785 (114)	**22**
21	**243**	**231**	**231**	**61.0**	98.5	**40.9**	**69.9**	**42.3**	**20.7**	35	770 (112)	**21**
20	**238**	**226**	**226**	**60.5**	97.8	**40.1**	**69.4**	**41.5**	**19.6**	34	760 (110)	**20**
(18)	230	219	219	—	96.7	—	—	—	—	33	730 (106)	(18)
(16)	222	212	212	—	95.5	—	—	—	—	32	705 (102)	(16)
(14)	213	203	203	—	93.9	—	—	—	—	31	675 (98)	(14)
(12)	204	194	194	—	92.3	—	—	—	—	29	650 (94)	(12)
(10)	196	187	187	—	90.7	—	—	—	—	28	620 (90)	(10)
(8)	188	179	179	—	89.5	—	—	—	—	27	600 (87)	(8)
(6)	180	171	171	—	87.1	—	—	—	—	26	580 (84)	(6)
(4)	173	165	165	—	85.5	—	—	—	—	25	550 (80)	(4)
(2)	166	158	158	—	83.5	—	—	—	—	24	530 (77)	(2)
(0)	160	152	152	—	81.7	—	—	—	—	24	515 (75)	(0)

ϕ [a] The values in this table shown in **bold face type** correspond to the values shown in the corresponding joint SAE-ASM-ASTM Committee on Hardness Conversions as printed in ASTM E 140, Table 1.

[b] Values in ( ) are beyond normal range and are given for information only.

METHODS OF MEASURING DECARBURIZATION—SAE J419 DEC1983

SAE Recommended Practice

Report of the SAE Iron and Steel Technical Committee approved May 1959, first revision, Division 3, December 1983.

Foreword—This Document has not changed other than to put it into the new SAE Technical Standards Board Format.

1. Scope—This report covers the recommended practice for the evaluation and measurement of decarburization in ferrous material. Included are definitions of types with charts and micrographs and methods most commonly used for the measurement of decarburization.

2. References

2.1 Applicable Publication—The following publication forms a part of this specification to the extent specified herein. Unless otherwise specified, the latest issue of SAE publications shall apply.

2.1.1 SAE PUBLICATION—Available from SAE, 400 Commonwealth Drive, Warrendale, PA 15096-0001

SAE J423—Methods of Measuring Case Depth

3. Definitions

3.1 Decarburization—Decarburization is the loss of carbon at the surface of commercial ferrous materials which have been heated for fabrication or when heated to modify mechanical properties.

3.2 Complete Decarburization—Complete loss of carbon as determined by examination.

3.3 Partial Decarburization—Any measurable loss of carbon content, less than complete, with respect to carbon level of base material.

3.4 Effective Decarburization—Any measurable loss of carbon content which results in mechanical properties below the minimum acceptable specifications for hardened material.

4. Types Of Decarburization—Three general types of decarburization may be prevalent in ferrous materials dependent on manner and degree of carbon loss from the material. Classifying decarburization into three types may aid in selecting the process necessary to utilize the material to meet a product specification. Accompanying photomicrographs are illustrations of typical conditions which may be encountered.

4.1 Type 1 Decarburization—Indicated by the curve and photomicrographs in Figure 1, covers that condition in which carbon free ferrite exists for a measurable distance below the surface. Underneath the ferrite will exist varying degrees of partial decarburization.

4.2 Type 2 Decarburization—Indicated by the curve and photomicrographs in Figure 2, covers that condition in which there is a loss of more than 50% of the base carbon at the surface but where no measurable depth of complete decarburization is evident.

4.3 Type 3 Decarburization—Indicated by the curve and photomicrographs in Figure 3, covers that condition where some loss of carbon at the surface is evident but to a degree less than 50% of the base carbon of the material.

4.3.1 Further subdividing of Type 3 Decarburization may be necessary for highly stressed members such as spring or high strength materials. In this category, the effective decarburization may be determined by microhardness testing for materials lower than 0.6% base carbon.

Chemical analysis procedures may be required when examining high carbon materials.

5. Methods Of Measuring Decarburization—The common methods used for the measurement of decarburization are:

a. microscopic;
b. hardness, including cross section microhardness traverse, longitudinal traverse, and file hardness; and
c. chemical analysis.

The accuracy of the method to be used is dependent on the degree of decarburization, microstructure, and base carbon content of the steel. The metallographic method is sufficiently accurate for most annealed and hot rolled materials, but inaccurate for small amounts of decarburization in high carbon (above 0.60%), high hardness steels. The hardness method is also insensitive in this latter case and recourse must be taken to chemical analysis.

The file method is often suitable for detecting decarburization of hardened materials during shop processing but not for accurate measurement.

It is fundamental that true measure of decarburization lies in chemical analysis for carbon content. This method is normally used only in research investigations or to check accuracy of other methods. With the possible exception of specialized electron microprobe analytical techniques, which are recommended when available, analysis is difficult and slow in application because of limitations of size and section of material. The method of procuring sample itself depends upon shape and hardness of test piece. Parts and/or test specimens too hard to machine should be tempered at 600 to 650 °C (1100 to 1200 °F) to permit machining of surface layers into chips for subsequent carbon analysis. Obviously, a sample which is annealed to permit milling of chips may be modified in its condition of decarburization. Standard methods for carbon determination are described in textbooks of analytical chemistry.

6. Microscopic Method

6.1 Specimen—The area to be examined should be cut at right angles to the surface. Samples are preferably taken when the material is in full annealed or in hot rolled condition. Other conditions, such as spheroidized annealed, hardened, or cold worked material, may be examined but care must be used in interpretation. For sections up to 13 mm (1/2 in), the entire cross section is normally mounted for examination. For larger sections, a specimen should be cut to include about 19 mm (3/4 in) of the surface to be examined. Corners of straight sided sections should not be included, since they are not considered representative.

6.2 Preparation—In mounting the specimen for grinding and polishing, protection from rounding the surface to be examined is essential. The specimen should be mounted in a clamp or in a plastic mount, the latter being the preferred method. An additional method of protection is to deposit (by electroless or electroplating) a metallic coating of 0.03–0.08 mm (0.001–0.003 in) on the specimen before mounting.

After mounting, the surface should be ground and polished in accordance with good metallographic practice.

Etching in a 3% nital (concentrated nitric acid in alcohol) is usually suitable for showing changes in microstructure caused by decarburization.

6.3 Measurement—Magnification for examination can be agreed on between purchaser and producer. However, it is recommended that 100X magnification be used. If the microscope is of a type with a ground glass screen, the extent of decarburization can be measured directly with a scale. If an eyepiece is used for measurement, it should be an appropriate type containing a cross hair or a scale.

7. Hardness Methods

7.1 Cross Section Microhardness Traverse

7.1.1 SPECIMEN—Sample to be checked should be cut at right angles to the surface. If cross section is too large, a portion of suitable size including surface to be checked should be cut before examination.

7.1.2 PREPARATION—The specimen shall be hardened by quenching from equipment under conditions which minimize further change in carbon distribution. The time at temperature should be minimized to avoid excessive carbon diffusion. In the case of finished parts, which have been previously quenched and tempered, no further treatment is necessary. For sections up to 13 mm (1/2 in), the entire cross section is normally mounted in plastic. After mounting, the surface should be ground and polished in accordance with good metallographic practice.

7.1.3 MEASUREMENT—A series of microhardness impressions made by pyramidal or Knoop indentors should be extended from the surface until the hardness of the base metal is obtained.

7.2 Longitudinal Traverse (Taper or Step Grind)

7.2.1 SPECIMEN—A specimen containing the surface on which decarburization is to be measured is prepared so that it can be manipulated on a superficial hardness tester.

7.2.2 PREPARATION—If the specimen is not in the hardened condition, it is recommended that it be hardened by quenching from heating equipment under conditions which avoid further change in carbon distribution.

For the taper grind specimen, a shallow taper is ground through the decarburized layer, see SAE Recommended Practice, Methods of Measuring Case Depth—SAE J423. The angle is chosen so that hardness readings spaced equal distances apart will represent the hardness at the desired increments below the surface. Unless special anvils are used on the hardness tester, a parallel section should be prepared so that indentations will be at right angles to the tapered surface.

For the step grind procedure, flats are ground at predetermined intervals below the original surface. These flats should have sufficient area to allow several hardness readings to be taken on each flat.

7.2.3 MEASUREMENT—A superficial hardness tester such as a Rockwell Superficial or Vickers Tester using a light load should be employed in making the hardness measurements. The depth of decarburization is defined as the distance measured from the nearest original surface to the point at which no increase in hardness is found.

7.3 File Method

7.3.1 SPECIMEN—A specimen of suitable size is obtained from the desired location.

7.3.2 PREPARATION—The specimen shall be hardened by quenching from heating equipment under conditions which avoid further decarburization.

7.3.3 MEASUREMENT—After hardening, the sample is filed. Base metals expected to harden to above 60 HRC and found to be file soft are probably decarburized. Decarburization of base metals that will not harden to 60 HRC cannot be detected by this method unless specially prepared files are used. The extent and severity of any decarburization detected by this method should be verified by either of the other two methods.

8. Chemical Analysis—Procedure is the same as SAE J423.

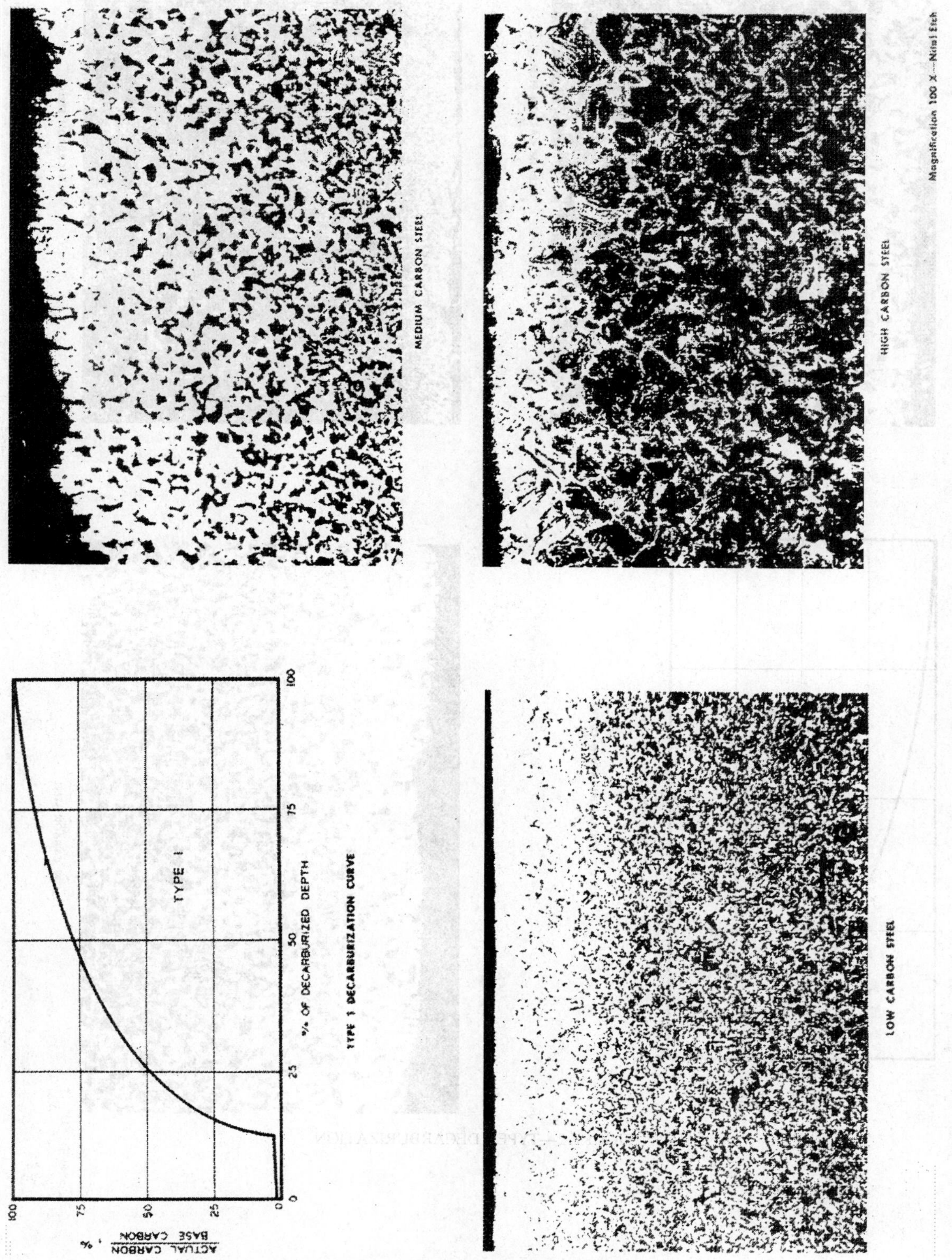

FIGURE 1—TYPE 1 DECARBURIZATION

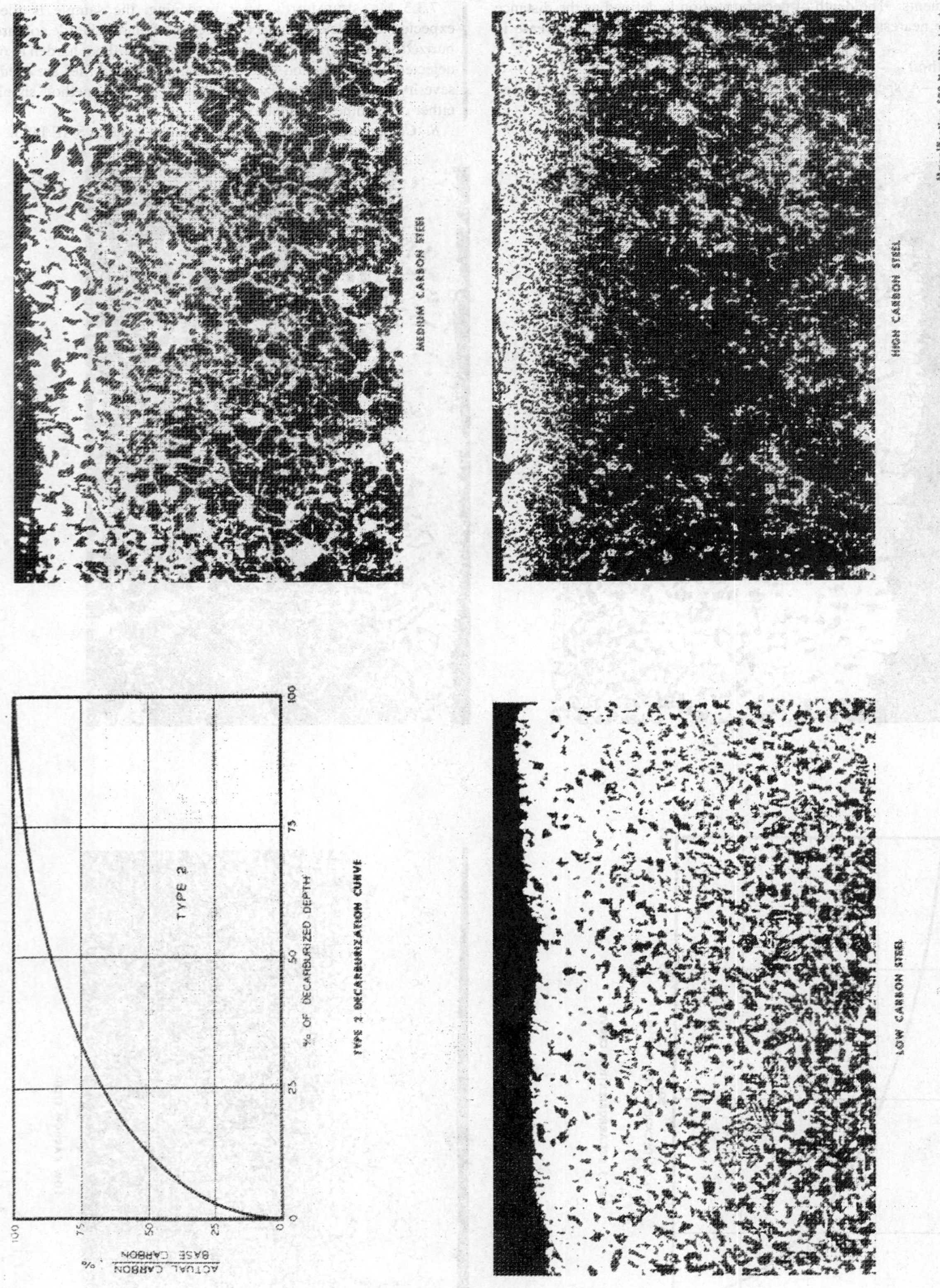

FIGURE 2—TYPE 2 DECARBURIZATION

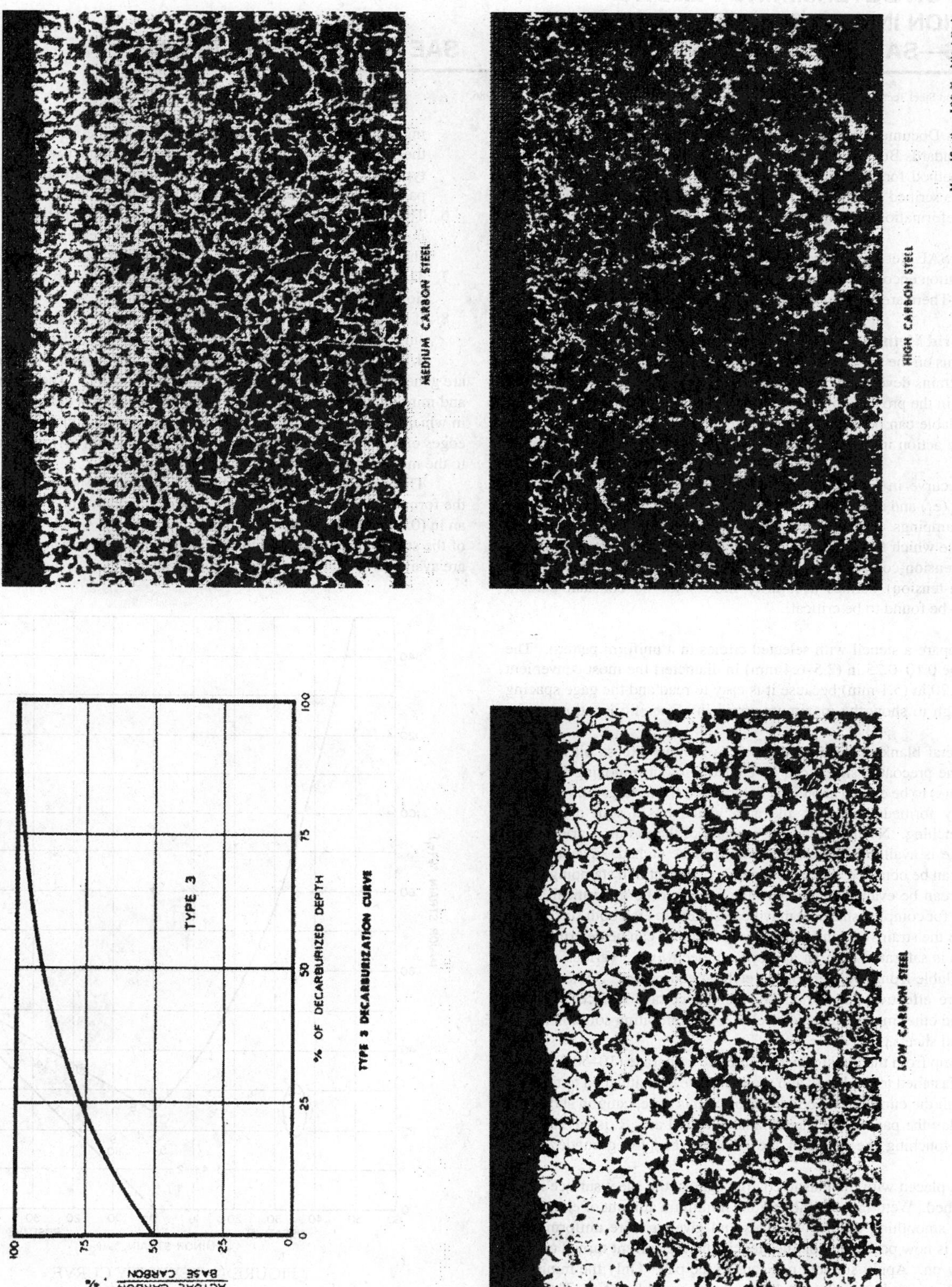

FIGURE 3—TYPE 3 DECARBURIZATION

METHODS FOR DETERMINING PLASTIC DEFORMATION IN SHEET METAL STAMPINGS—SAE J863 JUN1986

SAE Recommended Practice

Report of the SAE Iron and Steel Technical Committee approved June 1963, reaffirmed without change, June 1986.

Foreword—This Document has not changed other than to put it into the new SAE Technical Standards Board Format.

The preferred method for determining plastic strain is the circle grid and the severity curve. The scribed square and change in thickness methods may also be used to evaluate deformation during the forming of a flat sheet into the desired shape.

1. Scope—This SAE Recommended Practice describes methods for determining plastic deformation encountered in the forming or drawing of sheet steel.

2. References—There are no referenced publications specified herein.

3. Methods

3.1 Circle Grid Method—The test system employs electrochemically etched circle patterns on the surface of a sheet metal blank and a severity curve for the evaluation of strains developed by forming in press operations. It is useful in the laboratory and in the press room. Selection from the various steels which are commercially available can be done effectively by employing this technique. In addition, corrective action in die or part design to improve performance is often indicated.

The severity curve in Figure 1 has been developed from actual measurements of the major (e_1) and associated minor (e_2) strains found in critical areas of production type stampings. Strain combinations which locate below this curve are safe, while those which fall above the curve are critical. The left of zero portion of the curve (tension-compression) represents 25% change in unit area. The right side (tension-tension) defines a severity limit since no constant percent change in area will be found to be critical.

4. Procedure

1. Obtain or prepare a stencil with selected circles in a uniform pattern. The circles may be 0.10–0.25 in (2.5–6.4 mm) in diameter; the most convenient diameter is 0.20 in (5.1 mm) because it is easy to read and the gage spacing is short enough to show the maximum strain in a specific location on the part.
2. The sheet metal blanks should be cleaned to remove excess oil and dirt; however, some precoated sheets can be etched without removing the coating. The area(s) to be etched should be determined from observation of panels previously formed; generally, the area which has a split problem is selected for etching. Normally, the convex side of the radius is gridded. If sufficient time is available, the entire blank may be etched, since valuable information can be obtained about the movement of metal in stamping a part when strains can be evaluated in what may appear to be noncritical areas. Additionally, for complex shapes it may be desirable to etch both surfaces of blanks so that the strains which occur in reverse draws can be determined.
3. The etch pad is saturated with an appropriate electrolyte. Various electrolytes are available from suppliers of the etching equipment. Some electrolytes are more effective than others for etching certain surfaces, such as terne plate and other metallic coated steels. A rust inhibiting solution is preferred for steel sheets.
4. A ground clamp from the transformer of suitable amperage (10–50 A is usually used) is fastened to the blank and the second lead is attached to the etch pad. Although the current may be turned on at this time, caution should be taken not to lay the pad on the sheet blank as it will arc. It is advisable to refrain from touching the metal of the etch pad and the grounded sheet blank.
5. The stencil is placed with the plastic coating against the sheet surface in the area to be etched. Wetting the stencil with a minimum amount of electrolyte will assist in smoothing out the wrinkles and gives a more uniform etch. The etch pad is now positioned on the stencil and the current turned on, if it is not already on. Apply suitable pressure to the pad. Only the minimum time necessary to produce a clear etched pattern should be used. The etching time will vary with the amperage available from the power source and the stencil area, as well as the pad area in contact with the stencil. Rocker type etch pads give good prints and require less amperage than flat surfaced pads. Excessive current causes stencil damage.
6. The etching solution activates the surface of the metal and may cause rusting unless it is inhibited. After the desired area has been etched, the blank should be wiped or rinsed, dried, and neutralized.
7. The etched blank is now ready for forming. The lubricants and press conditions should simulate production situations.
8. If a sequence of operations is used in forming a part, it is desirable to etch sufficient blanks so that each operation can be studied.

4.1 Measurement of Strain After Forming—After forming, the circles are generally distorted into elliptical shapes (Figure 2). These ellipses have major and minor strain axes. The major strain (e_1) is always defined to be the direction in which the greatest positive strain has occurred without regard to original blank edges or the sheet rolling direction. The minor strain (e_2) is defined to be 90 deg to the major strain direction.

There are several methods for determining the major and minor strains of the formed panel. Typical tools are a pair of dividers and a scale ruled in 50ths of an in (0.5 mm). For sharp radii, a thin plastic scale, which can follow the contour of the stamping, can be used to determine the dimensions of the ellipses. (Scales are available to read the percent strain directly.)

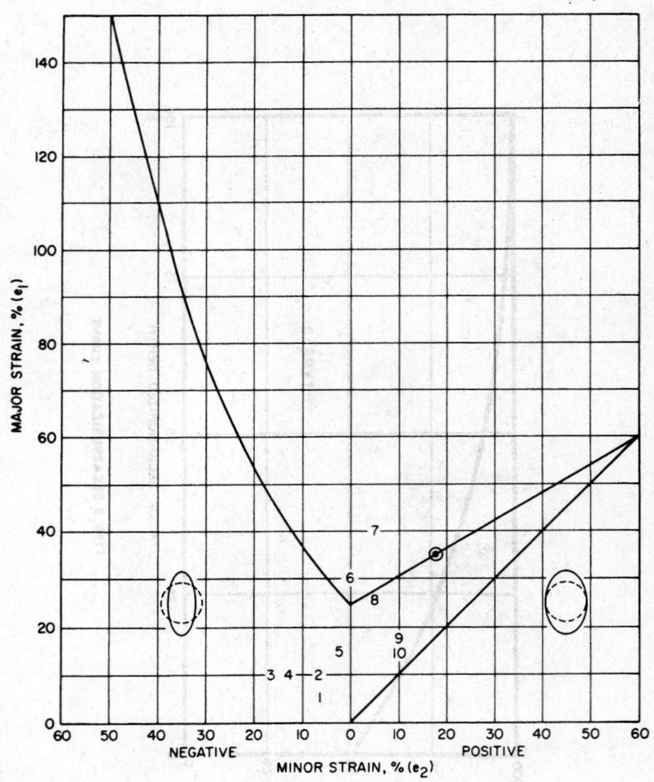

FIGURE 1—SEVERITY CURVE

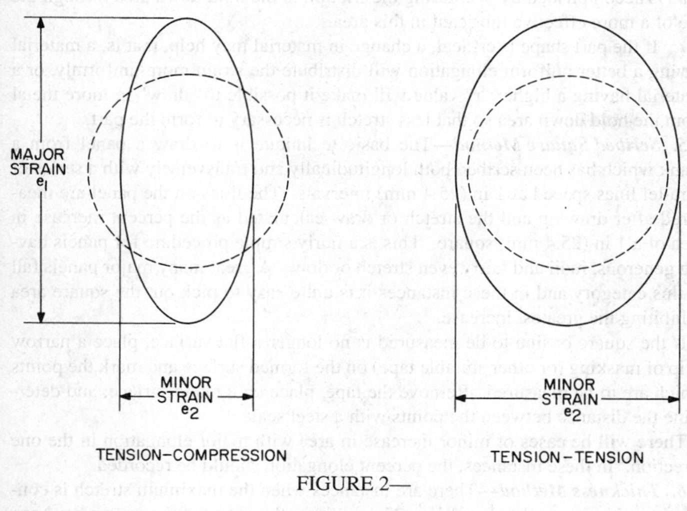

FIGURE 2—

4.2 Evaluation Of Strain Measurement—The e_1 strain is always positive while the e_2 strain may be zero, positive, or negative, as indicated on the severity curve chart (Figure 1). The maximum e_1 and associated e_2 values measured in critical areas on the formed part are plotted on the graph paper containing the severity curve by locating the point of intersection of the e_1, e_2 strains

If this point is on or below the severity curve, the strain should not cause breakage. Points further below the curve indicate that a less ductile material of a lower grade may be applied. Points above the severity curve show the fabrication has induced strains which could result in breakage. Therefore, in evaluations on stampings exhibiting high strains, efforts should be made to provide an e_1, e_2 strain combination which would lie on or below the severity curve. A different e_1, e_2 strain combination can be obtained through changes of one or more of the forming variables such as die conditions, lubricants, blank size, thickness, or material grade.

When attempting to change the relationship of e_1 and e_2 strains, it should be noted that on the severity curve the most severe condition for a given e_1 strain is at 0% e_2 strain. This means the metal works best when it is allowed to deform in two dimensions, e_1 and e_2, rather than being restricted in one dimension. A change in e_2 to decrease the severity can be made by changing one of the previously mentioned forming variables or the die design, for example, improving lubrication on the tension-tension side will increase e_2 and decrease the severity.

In addition to the severity curve, the e_1, e_2 strain measurements may be used to evaluate the material requirements on the basis of strain gradients, as illustrated in Figure 3, or by plotting contours of equivalent strain levels on the surface of the formed part. Even when the level of strain is relatively low, parts in which the e_1 strain is changing rapidly either in magnitude or direction over a short span on the surface may require more ductile grades of sheet metal, change in lubrication, or change in part design.

4.3 Example Of Major And Minor Strain Distribution—A formed panel (Figures 4 and 5), with a cross section as shown in Figure 3, is used to illustrate major and minor strain combinations. A plot of the major strain distribution is made by finding the ellipse with the largest major strain (circle 7 in Figure 3), corresponding to the fracture area shown in Figure 5, original contour, and measuring the major and minor strains in the row of ellipses running in the direction of the major strain. The solid dots (Figure 3), are the measured major strains for each ellipse. The x's are the critical major strains as determined from the severity curve at the corresponding minor strain (intersection of the measured minor strain and the severity curve, the numbers on Figure 1 are the major and minor (e_1, e_2) strains for the measured circles of 3).

Usually, a row of ellipses will suffice to determine the most severe strain distribution. The resulting strain distribution plot (Figure 3), illustrates both severity of strain compared to the critical strain limits and the concentration of the strain in the stamping. Steep strain gradients should be avoided because they are inherent fracture sites.

The lower picture in Figure 4 is a top view of the original contour shown in Figure 5. The final contour (upper picture) shows the line of dots indicating the row of ellipses measured for the strain evaluations. A corresponding row was measured on the original contour with the results as shown in Figure 3.

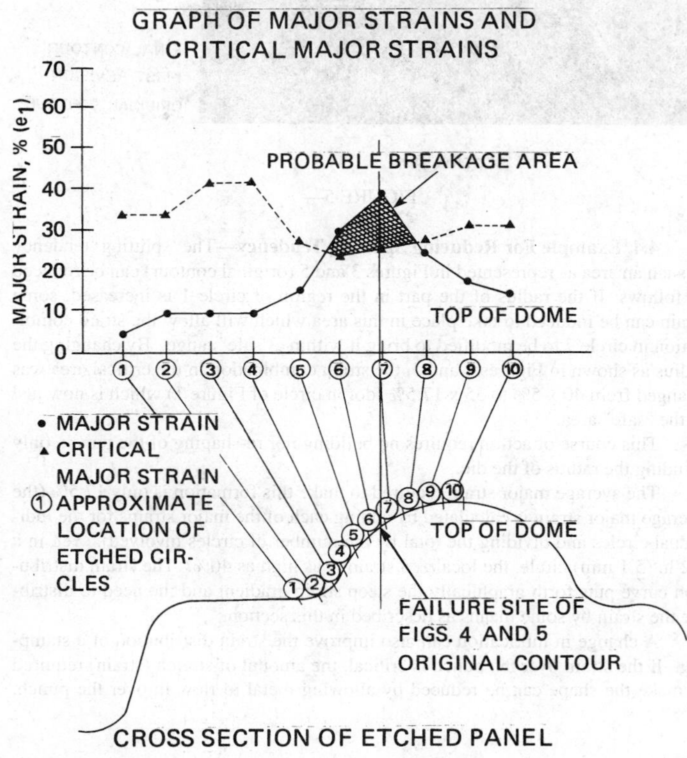

FIGURE 3—

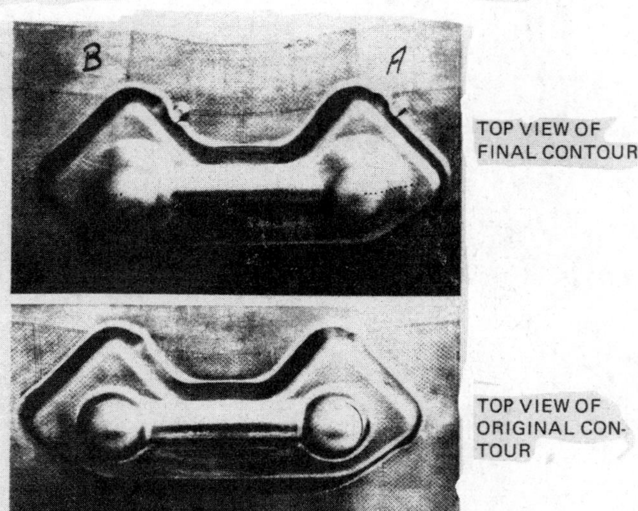

FIGURE 4—

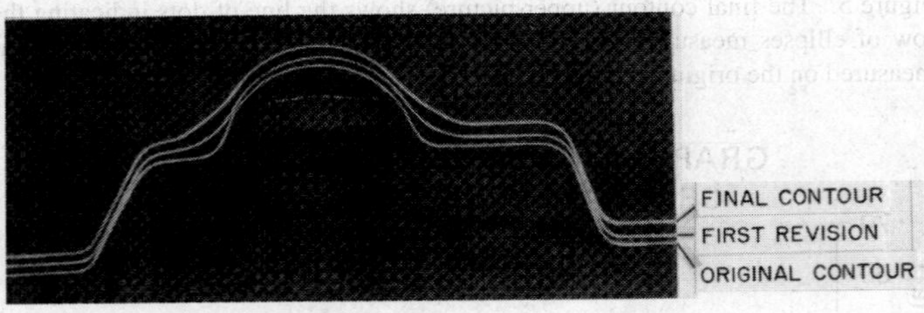

SECTION A-A

FIGURE 5—

4.4 Example For Reducing Splitting Tendency—The splitting tendency in such an area as represented in Figures 3 and 5 (original contour) can be reduced as follows: If the radius of the part in the region of circle 1 is increased, some strain can be induced to take place in this area which will allow the strain combination in circle 7 to be modified to bring it within a "safe" range. By changing the radius as shown in Figures 4 and 5, the strain combination in the critical area was changed from 40 x 5% to 35 x 17.5% (dot in circle of Figure 1) which is now just in the "safe" area.

This course of action requires no building nor re-shaping of the punch, only grinding the radius of the die.

The average major strain required to make this formation is only 17.5% (the average major strain is calculated by adding each of the major strains for the individual circles and dividing the total by the number of circles involved). Yet, in a 0.2 in (5.1 mm) circle, the localized strain is as high as 40%. The strain distribution curve puts forth graphically the steep strain gradient and the need to distribute the strain by some means as described in this section.

A change in lubrication can also improve the strain distribution of a stamping. If the strain over the punch is critical, the amount of stretch (strain) required to make the shape can be reduced by allowing metal to flow in over the punch. This is accomplished by decreasing the friction in the hold down area through the use of a more effective lubricant in this area.

If the part shape is critical, a change in material may help, that is, a material having a better uniform elongation will distribute the strain more uniformly, or a material having a higher "r" value will make it possible to "draw" in more metal from the hold down area so that less stretch is necessary to form the part.

5. Scribed Square Method—The basic technique is to draw a panel from a blank which has been scribed both longitudinally and transversely with a series of parallel lines spaced at 1 in (25.4 mm) intervals. The lines on the panel are measured after drawing and the stretch or draw calculated as the percent increase in area of a 1 in (25.4 mm) square. This is a fairly simple procedure for panels having generous, radii and fairly even stretch or draw. A great many major panels fall in this category and in these instances it is quite easy to pick out the square area exhibiting the greatest increase.

If the square or line to be measured is no longer a flat surface, place a narrow strip of masking (or other suitable tape) on the formed surface and mark the points which are to be measured. Remove the tape, place on a plane surface, and determine the distance between the points with a steel scale.

There will be cases of minor increase in area with major elongation in the one direction. In these instances, the percent elongation should be recorded.

6. Thickness Method—There are instances when the maximum stretch is confined to an area smaller than 1 in^2 (25.4 mm^2) or the shape of the square has been distorted irregularly, making measurement difficult and calculation inaccurate. When either of these conditions exists, an electronic thickness gage may be used at the area in question or this area may be sectioned and the decrease in metal thickness measured with a ball point micrometer. The increase in unit area can be calculated by dividing the original thickness by the final thickness.

EXAMPLE—Assuming the blank thickness to be 0.035 in (0.889 mm) and the final thickness to be 0.028 in (0.7112 mm), the increase in unit area would be 0.035/0.028 = 1.25 (0.7112/0.889 = 1.25) or 25% increase in unit area.

STANDARD SHEET STEEL THICKNESS AND TOLERANCES—SAE J1058 DEC1999

SAE Recommended Practice

Report of SAE Iron and Steel Technical Committee approved February 1976. Completely revised by the SAE Iron and Steel Technical Committee Division 32—Sheet and Strip Steel April 1991 and December 1999. Rationale statement available.

1. Scope—This SAE Recommended Practice provides an orderly series for designating the thickness of unocated and coated hot-rolled and cold-rolled sheet and strip. This document also provides methods for specifying thickness tolerances.

1.1 Requirements of industry permit leeway in the choice of thickness inAAS some instances, but it is recognized that for many applications, particularly the tonnage requirements of the mass production industries, thickness is normally determined by critical engineering design or manufacturing considerations. However, for general applications or where requirements permit some latitude in the selection of thickness, the preferred thickness given in Table 1 will facilitate interchangeability of different metals in design, reduce inventory, and increase the availability in warehouse stocks of thicknesses commonly required for general applications.

1.2 All of the thicknesses listed are not necessarily produced in all metals and grades. Producers or distributors must be consulted to determine availability of a particular thickness for a given metal product.

2. References

2.1 Applicable Publications—The following publications form a part of this specification to the extent specified herein. Unless otherwise indicated, the latest issue of SAE publications shall apply.

2.1.1 ASTM PUBLICATIONS—Available from ASTM, 100 Barr Harbor Drive, West Conshohocken, PA 19428-2959.

ASTM A 463-88—Steel Sheet, Cold-Rolled, Aluminum-Coated, Type 1 and Type 2

ASTM A 568-91—Steel Sheet, Carbon and High Strength, Low Alloy, Hot-Rolled and Cold-Rolled

ASTM A 591-91—Sheet Steel, Electrolytic Zinc-Coated, for LIght Coating Mass Applications

ASTM A 635-91—Steel Sheet and Strip, Heavy-Thickness Coils, Carbon, Hot-Rolled

ASTM A 792-85—Steel Sheet, Aluminum-Zinc Alloy-Coated by the Hot-Dip Process

ASTM A 924-94—Steel Sheet, Metallic Coated by the Hot Dip Process

2.2 Related Publications—The following publications are provided for information purposes only and are not a required part of this document.

2.2.1 SAE PUBLICATIONS—Available from SAE, 400 Commonwealth Drive, Warrendale, PA 15096-0001.

SAE J1562—Selection of Zinc and Zinc-Alloy (Hot Dipped an Electrodeposited) Coated Steel Sheet

SAE J2329—Categorization and Properties of Low Carbon Automotive Sheet Steels

SAE J2340—Categorization and Properties of Dent Resistant, High Strength, and Ultra High Strength Automotive Sheet Steels

2.2.2 ASTM PUBLICATIONS——Available from ASTM, 100 Barr Harbor Drive, West Conshohocken, PA 19428-2959.

ASTM A 525-91—Steel Sheet, Zinc Coated (Galvanized) by the Hot Dip Process

ASTM A 653-94—Steel Sheet, Zinc-Coated (Galvanized) or Zinc-Iron Alloy-Coated (Galvannealed) by the Hot Dip Process

ASTM A 879-92—Steel Sheet, Zinc Coated by the Electrolytic Process for Applications Requiring Designation of the Coating Mass on Each Surface

ASTM A 917-93—Steel Sheet, Coated by the Electrolytic Process for Applications Requiring Designation of the Coating Mass on Each Surface

2.2.3 ISO AND ANSI PUBLICATIONS—Available from ANSI, 11 West 42nd Street, New York, NY 10036-8002.

ISO 3574—Cold-reduced carbon steel sheet of commercial and drawing qualities

ANSI Z1.1

ANSI B32.3-1977

3. Specifying Thickness

3.1 Method I—Ordering to Minimum Thickness—This is the preferred method used today and is the most common because it provides the design engineer with a minimum thickness for design calculations and a specification system where they can select a minimum thickness without regard to tolerance due to ordered width. When material is ordered to minimum thickness, the tolerance is all plus as shown in Table 1.

3.2 Method II—Ordering to Nominal Thickness—Sheet steel can be ordered to specified nominal thickness with the tolerances shown in Table 1 being half over and half under the specified nominal thickness.

3.3 Location of Thickness Measurement—The specified thickness range will be maintained throughout the coil or sheet at all points not less than 25 mm from the edge.

4. Recommended Thickness and Thickness Tolerances

4.1 Recommended thickness and thickness tolerances for steel sheet for automotive applications are shown in Table 1. Thickness and tolerances for sizes or applications other than shown in Table 1 are covered by appropriate ASTM standards for each product.

5. Notes

5.1 Note 2—Thickness is measured at any point across the width not less than 25 mm in from a longitudinal edge. The width of the sheet is the dimension perpendicular to the sheet rolling direction.

5.2 Note 2—The thickness tolerance for a specified thickness also applies when sheet is specified to a nominal thickness except the tolerances are divided equally (and rounded up), over and under.

5.3 Note 3—Thickness tolerances shown for cold-rolled substrates are one half and those shown for hot-rolled substrates are three quarters of those shown in ASTM specifications.

5.4 Note 4—Thickness tolerances apply to widths produced by slitting from a wider sheet.

5.5 Note 5—Table 1 is based on the following:

Electrolyltic Zinc Coated:	ASTM A 51, Table 3
Hot Dip Zinc Coated:	ASTM A 924, Table 2
	ASTM A 568, Table 4
	ASTM A 635, Table 4
Hot Dip Aluminum Coated:	ASTM A 463, Table 3
Hot Dip Aluminum-Zinc Coated:	ASTM A 792, Table 6

TABLE 1: (METRIC)—PREFERRED THICKNESS AND THICKNESS TOLERANCES OF UNCOATED OR COATED STEEL SHEET WITH COLD-ROLLED OR HOT-ROLLED SUBSTRATES IN WIDTHS TO 1850 MM

Preferred Specified Thickness in mm	Total Thickness Tolerance - mm Cold-Rolled Substrate Uncoated and/or Electrogalvanized Coated Carbon Steel, HSS, HSLA, and Stainless Steel	Total Thickness Tolerance - mm Cold-Rolled Substrate Hot Dip Zinc, Aluminum Aluminum-Zinc, and Terne Coated Carbon Steel, HSS, HSLA, and Stainless Steel	Total Thickness Tolerance - mm Hot-Rolled Substrate Uncoated and Hot Dip and Electrogalvanized, Aluminum and Aluminum-Zinc Coated Carbon Steel	Total Thickness Tolerance - mm Hot-Rolled Substrate Uncoated and Hot Dip and Electrogalvanized, Aluminum and Aluminum-Zinc Coated HSS and HSLA Steel
0.50	0.06	0.10		
0.55	0.08	0.10		
0.60	0.08	0.10		
0.65	0.08	0.10		
0.70	0.08	0.10		
0.75	0.08	0.10		
0.80	0.08	0.10		
0.85	0.08	0.10		
0.90	0.08	0.10		
0.95	0.08	0.10		
1.00	0.08	0.10	0.08	0.10
1.05	0.10	0.12	0.10	0.12
1.10	0.10	0.12	0.10	0.12
1.20	0.10	0.12	0.10	0.12
1.40	0.10	0.12	0.10	0.12
1.50	0.10	0.12	0.10	0.12
1.60	0.12	0.14	0.14	0.16
1.70	0.12	0.14	0.18	0.20
1.80	0.12	0.14	0.22	0.26
1.90	0.12	0.14	0.22	0.26
2.00	0.12	0.20	0.22	0.26
2.10	0.12	0.20	0.26	0.30
2.20	0.12	0.20	0.26	0.30
2.30	0.12	0.20	0.26	0.30
2.40	0.12	0.20	0.26	0.30
2.50	0.12	0.20	0.26	0.30
2.60	0.14	0.22	0.30	0.38
2.80	0.14	0.22	0.30	0.38
3.00	0.14	0.22	0.30	0.38
3.20	0.14	0.22	0.30	0.38
3.40	0.14	0.22	0.30	0.38
3.50	0.14	0.22	0.30	0.38
3.60	0.14	0.22	0.30	0.38
3.80		0.22	0.30	0.38
4.00		0.22	0.30	0.38
4.20			0.30	0.38
4.50			0.30	0.38
4.80			0.34	0.38
5.00			0.34	0.38
5.50			0.34	0.38
5.80			0.34	0.38
6.00			0.34	0.38
6.50			0.34	0.38
7.00			0.34	0.38
7.50			0.34	0.38
8.00			0.38	0.38
9.00			0.38	0.38
10.00			0.40	0.40
11.00			0.40	0.40
12.00			0.40	0.40

CATEGORIZATION AND PROPERTIES OF DENT RESISTANT, HIGH STRENGTH, AND ULTRA HIGH STRENGTH AUTOMOTIVE SHEET STEEL—SAE J2340 OCT1999 SAE Recommended Practice

Report of the SAE Iron and Steel Technical Committee Division 32—Sheet and Strip Steel approved October 1999. Rationale statement available.

Foreword—The primary reason higher strength steels are used is because their yield and tensile strengths are higher than those of low-carbon sheet steel, which are described in SAE J2329. Higher strength steels are desirable for dent resistance, increased load bearing capability, better crash energy management, or for part mass reduction through a decrease in sheet metal thickness.

An increase in strength generally leads to reduced ductility or formability. Care must be taken in designing parts, tooling, and fabrication processes to obtain the greatest benefit from the higher strength sheet steels. Consultation in grade selection between user and steel producer is recommended to insure compatibility of the strength and forming characteristics.

Strength in these steels is achieved through chemical composition (alloying) and special processing. Special processing includes mechanical rolling techniques, temperature control in hot rolling, and time/temperature control in annealing of cold-reduced steel. Further or additional thermal treatment may modify the original mechanical properties.

1. Scope—This SAE Recommended Practice defines and establishes mechanical property ranges for seven grades of continuously cast high strength automotive sheet steels that can be formed, welded, assembled, and painted in automotive manufacturing processes. The grade of steel specified for an identified part should be based on part requirements (configuration and strength) as well as formability. Material selection should also take into consideration the amount of strain induced by forming and the impact strain has on the strength achieved in the finished part. These steels can be specified as hot-rolled sheet, cold-reduced sheet, uncoated, or coated by hot dipping, electroplating, or vapor deposition of zinc, aluminum, and organic compounds normally applied by coil coating. The grades and strength levels are achieved through chemical composition and special processing. Not all combinations of strength and coating types may be commercially available. Consult your steel supplier for details.

2. References

2.1 Applicable Publications—The following publications form a part of this specification to the extent specified herein. Unless otherwise indicated, the latest issue of SAE and ASTM publications shall apply.

2.1.1 SAE PUBLICATIONS—Available from SAE, 400 Commonwealth Drive, Warrendale, PA 15096-0001.

SAE J1058—Standard Sheet Thickness' and Tolerances

SAE J1562—Selection of Zinc and Zinc-Alloy (Hot Dipped and Electrodeposited) Coated Steel Sheet

SAE J2329—Categorization and Properties of Low Carbon Automotive Sheet Steels

2.1.2 ASTM PUBLICATIONS—Available from ASTM, 100 Barr Harbor Drive, West Conshohocken, PA 19428-2959.

ASTM A 370—Standard Test Methods and Definitions for Mechanical Testing of Steel Products

ASTM A 980—Standard Specification for Steel Sheet, Carbon, Ultra High Strength Cold Rolled

ASTM E 8M—Standard Test Methods of Tension of Metallic Materials

ASTM E 517—Standard Test Method for Plastic Strain Ratio r for Sheet Metal

ASTM E 646—Standard Test Method for Tensile Strain-Hardening Exponents (n value) of Metallic Sheet Materials

2.1.3 ANSI/AWS/SAE PUBLICATION—Available from ANSI, 11 West 42nd Street, New York, NY 10036-8002.

ANSI/AWS/SAE D8.8-97—A Specification for Automotive and Light Truck Component Weld Quality - Arc Welding

2.1.4 OTHER PUBLICATION

AZ-017-02-295 1.0C RI—Weld Quality Test Method Manual; Standardized Welding Test Method Task Force, Auto/Steel Partnership (A/SP)

2.2 Related Publications—The following publications are provided for information purposes only and are not a required part of this document.

2.2.1 SAE PUBLICATIONS—Available from SAE, 400 Commonwealth Drive, Warrendale, PA 15096-0001.

SAE J416—Tensile Test Specimens

SAE J810—Classifications of Common Imperfections in Sheet Steel

SAE J1392—Steel, High Strength, Hot Rolled Sheet and Strip, Cold Rolled Sheet, and Coated Sheet

SAE J2328—Selection and Specification of Steel Sheet, Hot Rolled, Cold Rolled, and Coated for Automotive Applications

2.2.2 ASTM PUBLICATIONS—Available from ASTM, 100 Barr Harbor Drive, West Conshohocken, PA 19428-2959.

ASTM A 463—Standard Specification for Cold Rolled Aluminum Coated Type 1 & Type 2 Steel Sheet

ASTM A 568—General Requirements for Carbon and High Strength, Low Alloy Steel Sheet

ASTM A 653—Steel Sheet, Zinc Coated (Galvanized) or Zinc-Iron Alloy Coated (Galvanneal) by the Hot-Dip Process

ASTM A 751—Standard Test Methods for Determining Chemical Composition of Steel Products

ASTM A 924—General Requirements for Steel Sheet Metallic Coated by the Hot Dip Process

2.2.3 ISO PUBLICATION—Available from ANSI, 11 West 42nd Street, New York, NY 10036-8002.

ISO 13887—Cold Reduced Steel Sheet of Higher Strength with Improved Formability

2.2.4 OTHER PUBLICATION

Steel Products Manual, Sheet Steel; Iron and Steel Society Publication, January 1988

3. General Information—This document defines seven grades of higher strength steel based on material type and processing. These strength grades are shown in Table 1.

TABLE 1—STEELS AND STRENGTH GRADES

Steel Description	Grade Type	Available Strength Grade - MPa
Dent Resistant Non-Bake-Hardenable	A	180, 210, 250, 280
Dent Resistant Bake-Hardenable	B	180, 210, 250, 280
High Strength Solution Strengthened	S	300, 340
High Strength Low Alloy	X & Y	300, 340, 380, 420, 490, 550
High Strength Recovery Annealed	R	490, 550, 700, 830
Ultra High Strength Dual Phase	DH & DL	500, 600, 700, 800, 950, 1000
Ultra High Strength Low Carbon Martensite	M	800, 900, 1000, 1100, 1200, 1300, 1400, 1500

4. Condition—Several conditions of hot-rolled and cold-reduced uncoated and coated sheet steels are used by the automotive stamping and assembly operations. The conditions of sheet steel are referred to by letter code that follows the class designation.

4.1 Cold-Reduced Uncoated and Metallic Coated Sheet Steel—Three conditions of sheet steel surface characteristics are produced.

4.1.1 Exposed (E) is intended for the most critical exposed applications where painted surface appearance is of primary importance. This surface condition of sheet steel will meet requirements for controlled surface texture, surface quality, and flatness.

4.1.2 Unexposed (U) is intended for unexposed applications and may also have special use where improved ductility over a temper rolled product is desired. Unexposed can be produced without temper rolling; this surface condition of sheet steel may be susceptible to exhibit coil breaks, fluting, and stretcher straining. Standard tolerances for flatness and surface texture are not applicable. In addition, surface imperfections can be more prevalent and severe than with exposed.

4.1.3 Semi Exposed (Z) is intended for non-critical exposed applications. This is typically a hot-dip galvanized temper-rolled product, see SAE J1562 for full explanation. Acceptability of surface characteristics or discontinuities shall be negotiated between user and supplier.

4.2 Hot-Rolled Uncoated and Metallic Coated Sheet Steel—Four conditions of hot-rolled sheet steel are available.

4.2.1 Condition P is an as hot-rolled coiled product, typically known as hot roll black band, which has not been pickled, oiled, temper rolled, side trimmed, rewound, or cut back to established thickness and width tolerances.

4.2.2 Condition W has been processed and is available in coils or cut lengths. This material may be susceptible to coil breaks and aging. Yield strength range classes apply only to material that has been cut back to established thickness and width tolerances. Processed coils may receive any or all of the processing steps listed in 4.2.1.

4.2.3 Condition N has been processed and is available in coils or cut lengths. This material possesses mechanical properties that do not deteriorate at room temperature, however, condition N material is susceptible to coil breaks.

4.2.4 Condition V has been processed and is available in coils or cut lengths. This material is free from coil breaks and its mechanical properties do not deteriorate at room temperature.

Some of the product characteristics available for each type of hot-rolled steel are listed in Table 2.

TABLE 2—PRODUCT CHARACTERISTICS OF HOT-ROLLED SAE J2340 STEEL

Condition	Freedom From Coil Breaks	Non Aging	Pickle and Oil(1)(2)	Cut Edge(1)(2)	Special Surface(1)(2)
P	No	No	n	n	n
W	No	No	a	a	n
N	No	Yes	a	a	n
V	Yes	Yes	a	a	a

1. a = available but not required
2. n = not available

5. *Steels and Strength Grades*

5.1 Dent Resistant Cold-Reduced Sheet Steels—There are two types of dent-resistant steel; non-bake-hardenable and bake-hardenable. Both are available in grades with minimum yield strengths from 180 MPa and higher. Both are available uncoated or coated.

Non-bake-hardenable, dent resistant steels achieve their final strength in the part through a combination of their initial yield strength and the work hardening imparted during forming. Bake-hardenable steels exhibit an additional increase in strength due to age hardening after forming which is accelerated by subsequent paint baking.

Although dent-resistant steels are not specified by chemistry, the following is provided for information purposes only. Both non-bake-hardenable and bake-hardenable dent resistant steels can be based on conventional low carbon steel (0.02 to 0.08% C), steel vacuum-degassed to very low carbon levels (<0.02% C), or interstitial-free (IF) steel. IF steel is vacuum degassed to ultra-low carbon levels (<0.01% C) and then any carbon remaining in solution is removed by adding titanium, niobium (columbium), or vanadium to form carbide precipitates. Solid solution strengthening elements such as phosphorous, manganese, or silicon may also be added to increase the as-received strength while not significantly reducing the material's work hardenability. A material's bake hardenability depends upon the amount of carbon remaining in solution, which is controlled through the steel chemistry and thermomechanical processing.

In this document, classification is based on minimum yield strength of the steel sheet and the strengthening that occurs during forming and paint baking. Classification of dent resistant steel is not based on chemistry.

5.1.1 TYPES AND MECHANICAL PROPERTY REQUIREMENTS—Mechanical property requirements of dent resistant cold-reduced uncoated and coated sheet steel grades are based on the minimum values of the following: As received yield strength (180, 210, 250, and 280 MPa), n value, tensile strength and the yield strength after strain (for non-bake-hardenable grades) or strain and bake (for bake-hardenable grades). These are the only mechanical requirements of this document for dent resistant cold-reduced uncoated and coated sheet steel grades (see Table 3). Typical mechanical properties of dent resistant cold-reduced uncoated and coated sheet steel grades are shown in Table A1 ("A" designates the Appendix).

5.1.1.1 Type A—This is a non-bake-hardenable dent resistant steel in which increase in yield strength due to work hardening results from strain imparted during forming. For the purpose of this document, a non-bake-hardenable dent resistant steel shall gain at least 35 MPa in yield strength (longitudinal direction) after a 2% tensile prestrain that represents the forming strain. This is considered the "strain hardening index" (SHI).

5.1.1.2 Type B—This is a bake-hardenable dent resistant steel in which increase in yield strength due to work hardening results from strain imparted during forming and an additional strengthening increment that occurs during the paint-baking process. For the purposes of this document, bake-hardenable dent resistant steels are defined as those products which possess a "bake hardening index" (BHI) (as shown in Figure A1). This is an increase in yield strength of at least 30 MPa in upper yield strength or 25 MPa based on lower yield point (longitudinal direction) after a 2% tensile strain and baking at 175 °C for 30 min (representing the paint-baking process). The total hardening response is the sum of the SHI and the BHI.

In order to help visualize the concept of the SHI and BHI, Figure A1 in the Appendix shows a portion of a stress strain curve and how these two characteristics are determined.

In practice, the magnitudes of the forming strain and the paint-baking temperature may be different than those designated for the purposes of this specification. Figures A2 and A3 in the Appendix describe their typical effects on the strain hardening and bake hardening increments.

5.1.2 SUB TYPE T—Sub Type T may be specified to denote an interstitial free dent resistant steel (Type A grades only). When interstitial free steel is used the tensile strength shall be 30 MPa higher than a non-interstitial free steel. Sub Type T steels shall be specified by the "T" designator (e.g., SAE J2340 - 180AT).

5.1.3 BASE METAL—Dent resistant steel furnished to this document shall be cold-reduced low carbon deoxidized steel made by basic oxygen, electric furnace, or other process which will produce a material which satisfies the requirements for the specific grade. This steel shall be continuously cast. The chemical composition shall be capable of achieving the desired mechanical and formability properties for the specified grade and type. For grades 180 and 210 using an interstitial free (IF) base metal having a carbon content less than 0.010, an effective boron addition of <0.001% may be required to minimize secondary work embrittlement (SWE) and to control grain growth during welding. The steel supplier shall define the chemical composition range that will be furnished on a production basis. The steel supplier shall not change the product/process without complying with the purchaser's supplier quality assurance requirements.

5.2 High Strength Solution Strengthened and High Strength Low Alloy (HSLA) Hot-Rolled and Cold-Reduced Sheet Steels and High Strength Recovery Annealed Cold-Reduced Sheet Steels—High strength, HSLA, and high strength recovery annealed categories include steel grades with minimum yield strengths in the range of 300 to 830 MPa. These sheet steels can be ordered and supplied as uncoated or coated.

TABLE 3—REQUIRED MINIMUM MECHANICAL PROPERTIES(1) OF DENT RESISTANT SHEET STEEL

SAE J2340 Grade Designation and Type	As Received Yield Strength(2) MPa	As Received Tensile Strength MPa	As Received n Value(3)	Yield Strength After 2% Strain MPa	Yield Strength After Strain and Bake MPa(4)
180 A	180	310	0.20	215	
180 B	180	300	0.19		245
210 A	210	330	0.19	245	
210 B	210	320	0.17		275
250 A	250	355	0.18	285	
250 B	250	345	0.16		315
280 A	280	375	0.16	315	
280 B	280	365	0.15		345

1. The mechanical property requirements shall be determined in longitudinal direction unless otherwise specified and shall be performed per Section 10.
2. Yield Strength is 0.2% offset or, in the presence of yield point elongation, lower yield point.
3. n value shall be calculated, per ASTM E 646, from 10 to 20% strain or to the end of uniform elongation when uniform elongation is less than 20%.
4. 2% tensile prestrain and baking at 175 °C for 30 min at temperature. The upper yield point is used for determination of yield strength. WIth lower yield point, requirement is 5 MPa lower.

Several different types of high strength steel based on chemistry can fall under this category. Solution strengthened high strength steels are those that contain additions of phosphorus, manganese, or silicon to conventional low carbon (e.g., 0.02 to 0.13% carbon) steels. HSLA steels have additions of carbide formers, such as, titanium, niobium (columbium), or vanadium made to conventional low carbon (0.02 to 0.13% carbon) steel. High strength recovery annealed steels have chemistries similar to the previous varieties of steels, but special annealing practices prevent recrystallization in the cold-rolled steel.

5.2.1 TYPES AND MECHANICAL PROPERTY REQUIREMENTS—Mechanical properties of these high strength sheet steels shall be measured in longitudinal direction unless otherwise specified and shall conform to the requirements for the grades specified in Tables 4 and 5. Classification is based on the minimum yield strength: 300 to 830 MPa. Several categories at each strength level are defined as follows:

5.2.1.1 Type S—High strength solution strengthened steels use carbon and manganese in combination with phosphorus or silicon (as solution strengtheners) to meet the minimum strength requirements. Carbon content is restricted to 0.13% maximum for improved formability and weldability. Phosphorus is restricted to a maximum of 0.100%. Sulfur is restricted to a maximum of 0.020%.

5.2.1.2 Type X—Typically referred to as HSLA steels, these high strength steels are alloyed with carbide and nitride forming elements, commonly niobium (columbium), titanium, and vanadium either singularly or in combination. These elements are used with carbon, manganese, phosphorus, and silicon to achieve the specified minimum yield strength. Carbon content is restricted to 0.13% maximum for improved formability and weldability. Phosphorus is restricted to a maximum of 0.060%. The specified minimum for niobium (columbium), titanium, or vanadium is 0.005%. Sulfur is restricted to a maximum of 0.015%. A spread of 70 MPa is specified between the required minima of the yield and tensile strengths.

5.2.1.3 Type Y—Same as Type X, except that a 100 MPa spread is specified between the required minima of the yield and tensile strengths.

5.2.1.4 Type R—High strength recovery annealed or stress-relief annealed steels achieve strengthening primarily through the presence of cold work. Alloying elements mentioned under Types S and X may also be added. Carbon is restricted to 0.13% maximum for improved formability and weldability. Phosphorus is restricted to a maximum of 0.100%. Sulfur is restricted to a maximum of 0.015%. These steels are best suited for bending and roll-forming applications since the mechanical properties are highly directional and ductility and formability are limited.

5.2.2 SUB TYPE F—Sub Type F may be specified to denote sulfide inclusion controlled. These steels are specified for forming applications and are generally used in unexposed applications only. Special steel making practice is used to control the shape or the volume fraction of manganese sulfide inclusions to improve edge stretching or bending in some applications. It is recommended that the producer and purchaser consult to determine the specific forming requirements prior to specifying Sub Type F. Sub Type F steels may be specified by the "F" designator (e.g., SAE J2340 - 340XF).

5.2.3 BASE METAL—High strength steel furnished to this document shall be a low carbon deoxidized steel made by basic oxygen, electric furnace, or other process which will produce a material which satisfies the requirements for the specific grade. This steel shall be continuously cast. The chemical composition shall be capable of achieving the desired mechanical and formability properties for the specified grade and type. The steel supplier shall define the chemical composition range that will be furnished on a production basis. The steel supplier shall not change the product/process without complying with the purchaser's supplier quality assurance requirements.

5.3 Ultra High Strength Cold-Rolled Steels; Dual Phase and Low Carbon Martensite—The Ultra High Strength Dual Phase and Low Carbon Martensite (LCM) categories include steel grades with minimum tensile strengths in the range of 500 to 1500 MPa. These sheet steels may be ordered and supplied as uncoated or coated. Contact your steel supplier to determine coating availability.

Special heat treating practices that involve quenching and tempering treatments are used to generate a martensite phase in the steel microstructure. The volume fraction and carbon content of the martensite phase determines the strength level. These steels are primarily alloyed with carbon and manganese. Boron may be added in some cases.

Specification of chemical limits for low carbon martensitic grades may be found in ASTM A 980.

5.3.1 TYPES AND MECHANICAL PROPERTY REQUIREMENTS—The mechanical property requirements of ultra high strength sheet steels are specified in Tables 6 and 7. Classification is based on the minimum tensile strength of the sheet steel: 500 to 1500 MPa. Typical mechanical properties of ultra high strength sheet steels are shown in Tables A2 and A3.

The formability and weldability characteristics of these ultra high strength steels shall be agreed upon between purchaser and supplier.

TABLE 4—REQUIRED MECHANICAL PROPERTIES(1) OF HIGH STRENGTH AND HSLA HOT-ROLLED AND COLD-REDUCED UNCOATED AND COATED SHEET STEEL(2)

SAE J2340 Grade Designation and Type	Yield Strength(3) MPa Minimum	Yield Strength(3) MPa Maximum	Tensile Strength MPa Minimum	% Total Elongation Min Cold-Reduced	% Total Elongation Min Hot-Rolled(4)
300 S	300	400	390	24	26
300 X	300	400	370	24	28
300 Y	300	400	400	21	25
340 S	340	440	440	22	24
340 X	340	440	410	22	25
340 Y	340	440	440	20	24
380 X	380	480	450	20	23
380 Y	380	480	480	18	22
420 X	420	520	490	18	22
420 Y	420	520	520	16	19
490 X	490	590	560	14	20
490 Y	490	590	590	12	19
550 X	550	680	620	12	18
550 Y	550	680	650	12	18

1. The mechanical property requirements shall be determined in longitudinal direction unless otherwise specified and shall be performed per Section 10.
2. Consultation between user and producer is recommended regarding the selection of specific steel grade and welding process optimization.
3. Yield strength is 0.2% offset or, in the presence of yield point elongation, lower yield point.
4. For thickness less than 2.5 mm, minimum percent elongation is permitted to be 2% less than the value shown.

TABLE 5—REQUIRED MECHANICAL PROPERTIES(1) OF HIGH STRENGTH RECOVERY ANNEALED COLD-REDUCED SHEET STEEL(2)

SAEJ2340 Grade Designation and Type	Yield Strength(3) MPa Minimum	Yield Strength(2) MPa Maximum	Tensile Strength MPa Minimum	% Total Elongation Minimum
490 R	490	590	500	13
550 R	550	650	560	10
700 R	700	800	710	8
830 R	830	960	860	2

1. The mechanical property requirements shall be determined in longitudinal direction unless otherwise specified and shall be performed per Section 10.
2. Consultation between user and producer is recommended regarding the selection of specific steel grade and welding process optimization.
3. Yield strength is 0.2% offset or, in the presence of yield point elongation, lower yield point.

TABLE 6—REQUIRED MECHANICAL PROPERTIES(1) OF ULTRA HIGH STRENGTH DUAL PHASE HOT-ROLLED AND COLD-REDUCED SHEET STEEL(2)

SAE J2340 Grade Designation and Type	Yield Strength MPa Minimum(3)	Tensile Strength MPa Minimum	% Total Elongation in 50 mm Minimum
500 DL	300	500	22
600 DH	500	600	14
600 DL1	350	600	16
600 DL2	280	600	20
700 DH	550	700	12
800 DL	500	800	8
950 DL	550	950	8
1000 DL	700	1000	5

1. The mechanical property requirements shall be determined in longitudinal direction unless otherwise specified and shall be performed per Section 10.
2. Consultation between user and producer is recommended regarding the selection of specific steel grade and welding process optimization.
3. Minimum yield strength can be waived upon agreement between user and supplier.

TABLE 7—REQUIRED MECHANICAL PROPERTIES[(1)] OF LOW CARBON MARTINSITE HOT-ROLLED AND COLD-REDUCED SHEET STEEL[(2)(3)]

SAE J2340 Grade Designation and Type	Yield Strength MPa Minimum[(4)]	Tensile Strength MPa Minimum
800M	600	800
900 M	750	900
1000 M	750	1000
1100 M	900	1100
1200 M	950	1200
1300 M	1050	1300
1400 M	1150	1400
1500 M	1200	1500

1. The mechanical property requirements shall be determined in longitudinal direction unless otherwise specified and shall be performed per Section 10.
2. Consultation between user and producer is recommended regarding the selection of specific steel grade and welding process optimization.
3. Minimum total elongation for all grades is 2%.
4. Minimum yield strength can be waived upon agreement between user and supplier.

5.3.1.1 Type DH/DL—The ultra high strength dual phase steel microstructure is comprised of ferrite and martensite, (dual phase), with the volume fraction of low-carbon martensite primarily determining the strength level. Two types of dual phase steels are available; a) a high yield ratio (ratio of YS/TS) product designated as DH in Table 6; and b) a low yield ratio product designated as DL in Table 6. For the purpose of this specification, products with yield ratios of 0.7 or lower are designated as DL and products with yield ratios greater than 0.7 are designated as DH.

5.3.1.2 Type M—In these fully martensitic ultra high strength sheet steels, carbon content determines the strength level. These steels have limited ductility.

5.3.2 BASE METAL—High strength steel furnished to this document shall be a low carbon deoxidized steel made by basic oxygen, electric furnace, or other process which will produce a material which satisfies the requirements for the specific grade. This steel shall be continuously cast. The chemical composition shall be capable of achieving the desired mechanical and formability properties for the specified grade and type. The steel supplier shall define the chemical composition range that will be furnished on a production basis. The steel supplier shall not change the product/process without complying with the purchaser's supplier quality assurance requirements.

6. Weldability—When the steel is used in welded applications, welding procedures shall be suitable for the steel chemistry and intended service. Unspecified chemical elements may be present. Limits on chemistry shall be as stated in Table 8. The sum Cu, Ni, Cr, and Mo shall not exceed 0.50% on heat analysis. When one or more of these elements are specified, the sum does not apply; in which case, only the individual limits on the remaining unspecified elements will apply.

TABLE 8—CHEMICAL LIMITS ON UNSPECIFIED ELEMENTS

Element	Maximum Weight Percent Allowed Type A, B, and R	Maximum Weight Percent Allowed Type S	Maximum Weight Percent Allowed Type X and Y	Maximum Weight Percent Allowed Type D and M
P	0.100[(1)]	0.100	0.060	0.020
S	0.015	0.020	0.015	0.015
Cu	0.200	0.200	0.200	0.200
Ni	0.200	0.200	0.200	0.200
Cr	0.150	0.150	0.150	0.150
Mo	0.060	0.060	0.060	0.060

1. Maximum phosphorus shall be less than 0.050 on grades 180A and 180B.

6.1 High Strength Steel—In welding high strength steels it is important to consider several factors usually not considered in welding lower strength steels; for example, welding process, welding parameters and, of course, material combinations. Integration of these types of considerations can result in a successful system of welding for HSS. Various welding methods (arc welding, resistance welding, laser welding and high frequency welding) all have unique advantages in welding specific sheet steel combinations. Considerations for production rate, heat input, weld metal dilution, weld location access, etc., may make one system more weldable than another system. For instance, an HSS that is problematic for spot welding may not exhibit the same difficulty in arc or high frequency welding. In fact, a low heat input resistance seam welding method has been successfully employed for commercial production of bumper beams with a 1300M grade. Considerations with respect to material combinations are important for those welding processes that solidify from a molten pool, or that are constrained by thickness ratio. In general, caution should be exercised in spot welding an HSS to itself because of possible weld metal interfacial fracture tendencies, but even a problematic HSS can be spot welded to a low carbon mild steel.

The resistance spot weldability requirements for low strength steels evaluate the operational robustness of the candidate steel. This often embodies measurements of current range and electrode wear (for galvanized coatings). The resistance spot weldability requirements for HSS may be similar to those of low strength steels with the added requirement for mechanical performance. The evaluation of mechanical performance alone may also be sufficient to assess weldability. End use requirements will determine required spot weld performance. These requirements may limit the current range and/or electrode life based on individual company weld quality specifications. For instance, fast quenching of the weld may damage the weld metal integrity causing interfacial fracture, or excessive weld heat input may cause metallurgical changes that soften the heat affected zone. Both of these conditions could result in a loss of joint strength. Incorporation of appropriate weld and temper cycles or modification of weld chemistry through selective dilution of the joint can lead to acceptable weld strength and thus ensure the retention of advantages to using HSS for weight reduction in automotive components.

Weld Quality Test Method Manual (AZ-017-02 295 1.0C RI) or AWS/ ANSI/SAE Standard D8.9-97, should be used as reference documents for further details. Note these standard test methods are intended for strength levels up to 420 MPa and modifications may be required for higher strength levels. Due to unique properties of HSS, selection of the weld process parameters should be determined in consultation with the steel supplier. It is recommended that product validation include production intent weld processes, preferably at the extremes of expected spot properties as determined by the laboratory studies.

Similar to resistance spot welding, the evaluation of other welding methods should take into account the appropriate operational robustness measures and the mechanical and/or fracture performance of the resulting weld quality. Weld performance, not absolute base material chemistry, is the important distinction between low and high strength steels. Since weldability requirements differ for different weld methods, it is difficult to summarize these requirements into a unified document. For example, ANSI/AWS/SAE Standard D8.8-97, may be used as a reference document for further details. Consultation is recommended between user and steel producer regarding the selection of specific steel grade as well as weld process optimization.

7. Cold Bending—High strength steels are frequently fabricated by cold bending. There are a multiplicity of inter-related factors which affect the ability of a given piece of steel to form over any given radius in shop practice. These factors include thickness, strength level, degree of restraint in bending, relationship to rolling direction, chemical composition, and microstructure. Table A4 lists those ratios which should be used as minimums for 90 degree bends in actual shop practice. It recognizes that "hard way" bending (bend axis parallel to rolling direction) is common in production and presupposes that reasonably good forming practices will be employed. Where design permits, users are encouraged to employ large radii that are shown in Table A4 for improved performance. Where the bend axis can be designed across the width ("easy way") of the sheet, or bends less than 90 degrees, slightly tighter radii can be employed. As the cold forming becomes progressively more difficult, that is, from a straight bend to a curved or offset bend to stretching or drawing, it is advisable that the producer and user consult to determine the special material, design, and tooling requirements of the application. The fabricator should be aware that steel may crack to some degree when bent on a sheared or burned edge. This is not to be considered to be the fault of the steel, but rather a function of the induced cold work or heat affected zone (HAZ).

8. Nomenclature and Suggested Ordering Practice

8.1 Specifying sheet steel on the engineering drawing under this document should include the following information to adequately describe the desired material:

a. Name of material being specified; such as electro-galvanized bake-hardenable steel.
b. SAE Recommended Practice number (SAE J2340).
c. Base metal type; hot rolled (HR) or cold reduced (CR).
d. Grade (four character identification which includes minimum yield strength and sheet steel product type).
e. Coating type and coating weight, if any. Indicate hot-dip or electro-galvanized zinc coating and coating weight. See SAE J1562 for detailed nomenclature.

f. Surface condition. Indicate exposed, E, unexposed, U; or semi exposed, Z, matte, or dull finish will be supplied unless otherwise specified.
g. Part thickness plus the tolerance.

8.2 Suggested ordering practice should include the specification from the engineering drawing plus the following additional information.

a. Application (show part identification and description).
b. Dimensions (thickness, tolerance, width, and length for cut lengths).
c. Condition (specify pickled if required, specify oiled or not oiled as required, specify chemical treatment for coated product if required).
d. Edges (must be specified for hot-rolled sheet and strip, that is, mill edge or cut edge).
e. Coil size and weight requirements (must include inside diameter, outside diameter, and maximum weight).
f. Cut length weight restrictions, that is, maximum weight of individual bundle.
g. Heat or cast analysis and mechanical property report (if required).

8.3 Typical specification and ordering descriptions are as follows:

a. Hot-dip galvanized dent resistant steel per SAE J2340 CR 180A HD70G70GZ, 1.00 mm min. +0.08 thick. Cold-reduced hot-dip galvanized dent resistant sheet for a semi-exposed application, cut edge, 1625 mm wide x coil.
b. Electro-galvanized bake-hardenable steel per SAE J2340 CR 250B EG70G70GE, 0.80 mm min. + 0.08 thick. Cold-reduced electro-galvanized bake-hardenable sheet for an exposed application, 1500 mm wide X 2540 mm.
c. High strength low alloy steel per SAE J2340 HR 340XU, 2.50 mm min +0.30 thick. Hot-rolled high strength low alloy sheet steel, pickled and oiled, unexposed surface, 1400 mm wide X coil.
d. Ultra high strength sheet steel per SAE J2340 CR 1300M, 1.20 mm min + 0.10 thick. Cold-reduced ultra high strength sheet steel, 1220 mm wide x coil.

*9. **Thickness Tolerances***—Tolerances for dimensions are shown in SAE J1058.

*10. **Tensile Samples***

10.1 Method

10.1.1 Samples should be flat and free of defects such as scores, wrinkles, die marks, etc.

10.1.2 For standard testing, one longitudinal 0 degree coupon is needed.

10.1.3 For r-Bar (r_m) testing, one longitudinal 0 degree, one diagonal 45 degrees and one transverse 90 degrees samples are required. r Bar (r_m) is a calculated number from individual r value tests.

10.1.4 Care should be taken to insure that the samples be cut exactly at 0 degree, 45 degrees, or 90 degrees to the coil rolling direction.

10.1.5 Tensile test shall be made with coating on.

10.2 Preparation of Samples

10.2.1 Method (ASTM E 8, E 517, E 646)

10.2.1.1 Samples must have all oils, lubricants, or dry films removed prior to measurement.

10.2.1.2 If base metal hardness is a desired value for correlation information, all coating must be removed from samples prior to testing.

10.2.1.3 Samples should be EDM (electrical discharge machining) cut if possible. If specimens are milled, preparation must be such that minimal cold work is imparted to the edges of the reduced section.

10.2.2 DIMENSIONS

10.2.2.1 Gage Length—50 mm ± 0.10 mm.

10.2.2.2 Width—12.50 mm ± 0.25 mm.

10.2.2.3 Parallelism

a. Standard Testing—Reduced section must be parallel to ±0.025 mm.
b. r value Testing—Reduced section must be parallel to ±0.013 mm.

10.2.2.4 Reduced section should be approximately 75 mm.

10.2.2.5 Overall length should be approximately 200 mm.

10.3 Measurements

10.3.1 EQUIPMENT

10.3.1.1 Use a digital measuring device capable of resolving to at least 0.013 mm.

10.3.1.2 Measuring device should be verified and documented with a test block or pin daily, before measurements are made.

10.3.1.3 Measuring device should be zeroed after each set of tests. If it does not return to zero, reset the device and re-measure the previous set of samples.

10.3.2 MEASUREMENT METHOD

10.3.2.1 Standard Testing—Measure narrowest width and thickness within the 50 mm gage marks.

10.3.2.2 r Value Testing—Measure at least three equally spaced width and thickness measurements across the 50 mm gage length. Average these for the initial dimensions. End gage mark must be at least 25 mm from grips.

10.4 Testing

10.4.1 TENSILE MACHINE OPERATING PARAMETERS—See Table 9.

TABLE 9—TENSILE MACHINE OPERATING PARAMETERS

	Crosshead Speed	Strain Rate
Ramp rate 1 (1)	3.0 mm/min	1.5 mm/min
Ramp rate 2(2) to determine r value	12.5 mm/min	6.2 mm/min
Ramp rate 2 for all standard tensile tests	25.0 mm/min	12.5 mm/min

1. Ramp rate 1 is prior to and through yield or YPE.
2. Ramp rate 2 is after yield or YPE (yield point elongation). Either crosshead speed control or strain rate control can be used; the method must be noted in test report results. Speed of testing greatly affects stress values, making uniformity critical.

10.4.2 Machine grips should cover at least 2/3 of the gripped section of the sample.

10.4.3 Stopping point for r value test measurement is 17% elongation.

10.4.4 n-value determination range is 10% to 20% elongation, or 10% - ultimate load if uniform elongation is less than 20%. Minimum 5 data pairs. Calculation per ASTM E 646 Part 10.

10.4.5 Tensile machine repeatability and reproducibility must be performed, and results documented as defined by the quality control procedures of the testing laboratory.

10.5 Calculation methods

10.5.1 Elongation can be determined by either the piece-fit method or computer generated through the extensometer. Whatever method is used must be stated in the lab report, because piece-fit elongation is generally higher than extensometer elongation. Elongation value is invalid if the specimen breaks within 6 mm of, or outside the gage marks.

10.5.2 Uniform elongation is defined as the elongation value measured at peak stress.

10.5.3 0.2% offset yield strength will be used for all samples without YPE. For samples with YPE, the yield strength at the lowest point of discontinuous yielding shall be reported, along with the percentage of YPE.

10.5.4 r Bar (r_m) Value = ($r_{90°}$ $r_{0°}$ + $2r_{45°}$)/4

10.5.5 Earing Tendency (Δr) = ($r_{90°}$ + $r_{0°}$ - $2r_{45°}$)/2

APPENDIX A
DENT RESISTANT STEELS
DATA ARE SHOWN IN THE APPENDIX FOR INFORMATION ONLY.

A.1 Dent Resistant Steels—See Table A1.

TABLE A1—TYPICAL MECHANICAL PROPERTIES(1) OF DENT RESISTANT COLD-REDUCED SHEET STEEL

SAE J2340 Grade and Type	As Received Properties Yield Strength(2) MPa	As Received Properties Tensile Strength MPa	As Received Properties Total Elongation %	As Received Properties n Value(3)	As Received Properties r_m Value(4)	Yield Strength after 2% Strain MPa	Upper Yield Strength After 2% Strain and Bake MPa(5)
180 A	200	350	40	0.22	1.7	235	
180 B	200	330	39	0.21	1.6		265
210 A	230	375	38	0.21	1.7	265	
210 B	230	350	37	0.19	1.5		295
250 A	270	400	36	0.20	1.5	305	
250 B	270	370	35	0.18	1.4		335
280 A	300	430	36	0.18	1.4	335	
280 B	300	410	35	0.17	1.1		365

1. The mechanical property requirements shall be determined in longitudinal direction unless otherwise specified and shall be performed per Section 10.
2. Yield Strength is 0.2% offset or, in the presence of yield point elongation, lower yield point.
3. n value shall be calculated, per ASTM E 646, from 10 to 20% strain or to the end of uniform elongation when uniform elongation is less than 20%.
4. r value shall be calculated, per ASTM E 517, at 17% strain, r_m calculation by $(r_0 + r_{90} + 2r_{45})/4$. The r_m value can be up to 0.2 lower for thickness greater than 1.4 mm and/or galvanneal products.
5. 2% tensile prestrain and baking at 175 °C for 30 min at temperature.

A.1.1 Determination of Strain-Hardening Index and Bake-Hardening Index—Bake-hardening steel strength shall be determined in specimens that have been prestrained 2% and baked at 175 °C for 30 min. Standard test specimens will be taken from unstrained and unbaked material in the longitudinal (rolling) direction per ASTM A 370. Referring to Figure A1, both the bake-hardening index (BHI) and the strain-hardening index (SHI) of the material can be determined as follows in Equation 1:

$$BHI = C - B \quad \text{(Eq. A1)}$$

where:

B = Flow stress at 2% prestrain
C = Yield strength (either upper or lower yield strength) after baking at 175 °C for 30 min.

$$SHI = B - A \quad \text{(Eq. A2)}$$

where:

A = Initial 0.2% offset yield strength
B = Flow stress at 2% prestrain

The original specimen area is used in calculation of all engineering strengths in this test (A, B, and C). The total increase in strength from the test is reported as BHI (BHI_U or BHI_L) + SHI.

For the purpose of part design, it may be desirable to predict yield strength at various locations on the finished part. The yield strength for 180B, 210B, 250B, and 280B shown in Table 3 is attained by straining 2% during forming followed by a paint cycle of 30 min at 175 °C. Figure A2 approximates the changes from this yield strength with varying amounts of prestrain.

The after strain and bake yield strengths given in Table 3 were initially developed with data derived from samples subjected to 2% strain followed by a 30-min bake at 175 °C. Figure A3 is presented to show the effect of lower paint bake temperatures following 2% strain on resulting typical yield strength values.

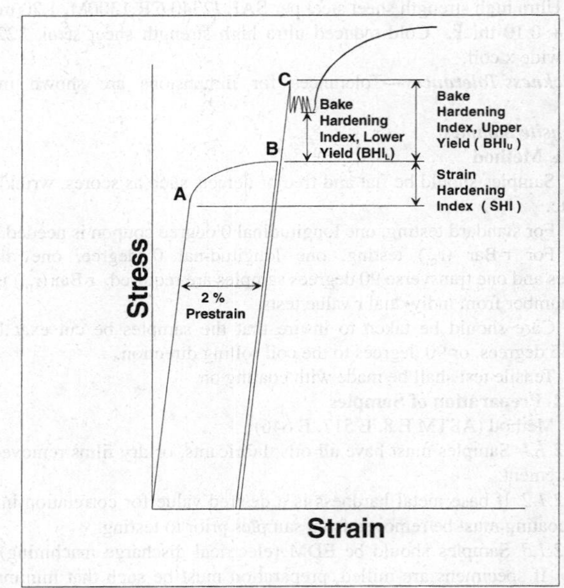

FIGURE A1—REPRESENTATION OF STRAIN-HARDENING AND BAKE-HARDENING INDEX

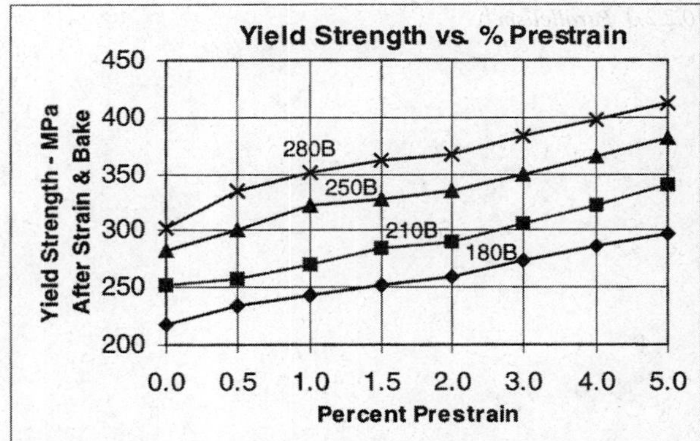

FIGURE A2—TYPICAL CHANGES TO YIELD STRENGTH WITH VARYING AMOUNTS OF PRESTRAIN

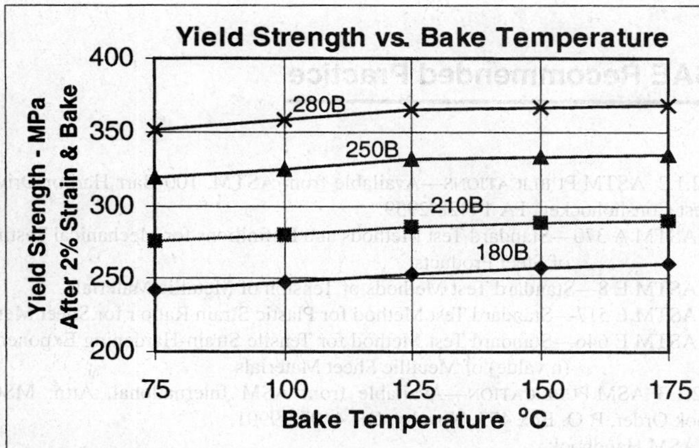

FIGURE A3—TYPICAL CHANGES TO YIELD STRENGTH WITH LOWER BAKE TEMPERATURES

A.2 Ultra High Strength Dual Phase Steels—See Table A2.

TABLE A2—TYPICAL MECHANICAL PROPERTIES(1) OF ULTRA HIGH STRENGTH DUAL PHASE HOT-ROLLED AND COLD-REDUCED SHEET STEEL

SAE J2340 Grade Designation and Type	Yield Strength MPa	Yield after 2% Strain and Bake MPa	Tensile Strength MPa	% Total Elongation in 50 mm	Bend Radii(2) r/t
500DL	340	480	550	28	.5 L & T
600DH	550	690	710	20	2 L & T
600DL1	390	560	650	22	.5 L & T
600DL2	340	490	660	27	.5 L & T
700DH	600	720	760	16	2 L & T
800DL	580	800	860	14	1 L & T
950DL	680	1030	1050	12	4 L & T
1000DL	810	1070	1070	9	3 L & T

1. The mechanical property requirements shall be determined in longitudinal direction unless otherwise specified and shall be performed per Section 10.
2. 90 degrees Bend test shall be conducted per ASTM A 370. Ratio of bend radius to thickness (T = transverse specimen and L = longitudinal specimen).

Forming limits studies are helpful in predicting the success of forming complex shapes. Roll forming processes are recommended. Stampings which require draws may be unsuccessful due to the limited flow of dual phase and martensitic microstructures. Spring back variation is much greater in dual phase and martensitic steel and should be considered in the part, tool, and weld fixture designs.

A.3 Ultra High Strength Martensitic Steels—See Table A3.

TABLE A3—TYPICAL MECHANICAL PROPERTIES(1) OF ULTRA HIGH STRENGTH LOW CARBON MARTENSITE COLD-REDUCED SHEET STEEL

SAE J2340 Grade Designation and Type	Yield Strength MPa	Tensile Strength MPa	% Total Elongation in 50 mm	Bend Radii(2) r/t
800M	N. A.(3)	N. A.	N. A.	N. A.
900M	900	1025	5	4 L & T
1000M	N. A.	N. A.	N. A.	N. A.
1100M	1030	1180	4	4 L & T
1200M	1140	1340	6	4 T & L
1300M	1200	1400	5	4 L & T
1400M	1260	1480	5	4 T & L
1500M	1350	1580	5	4 L & T

1. The mechanical property requirements shall be determined in longitudinal direction unless otherwise specified and shall be performed per Section 10.
2. 90 degrees Bend test shall be conducted per ASTM A 370. Ratio of bend radius to thickness (T = transverse specimen and L = longitudinal specimen).
3. N. A. - Information not available.

A.4 High Strength Solution Strengthened and HSLA Steels—See Table A4.

TABLE A4—TYPICAL INSIDE BEND RADII(1)(2)(3) HIGH STRENGTH AND HSLA, COLD-REDUCED AND HOT-ROLLED AND HIGH STRENGTH RECOVERY ANNEALED COLD-REDUCED UNCOATED AND COATED SHEET STEEL

SAE J2340 Grade Designation and Type	Cold-Reduced Bend Radius/ Thickness	Hot-Rolled Bend Radius/ Thickness
300 S, X, & Y	1/2 T	1 T
340 S, X, & Y	1/2 T & L	1 T & L
380 X & Y	1 T & L	1 T & L
420 X & Y	1 T & L	1 T & L
490 X & Y	2 T & L	2 T & L
550 X & Y	2 T & L	2 T & L
490 R	3 T & L	N. A.(4)
550 R	3 T & L	N. A.
700 R	4 T & L	N. A.
830 R	6 T & L	N. A.

1. 90 degrees Bend test shall be conducted per ASTM A 370. Ratio of bend radius to thickness (T = transverse specimen and L = longitudinal specimen).
2. The suggested minimum bending radius is based on the nominal rolled thickness, not the minimum ordered thickness.
3. For thicknesses over 4.50 mm, add 1/2 t to the radius shown in the Table.
4. N. A. - Information not available

CATEGORIZATION AND PROPERTIES OF LOW-CARBON AUTOMOTIVE SHEET STEELS —SAE J2329 MAY1997

SAE Recommended Practice

Report of the SAE Iron and Steel Technical Committee Division 32 - Sheet and Strip Steel, approved May 1997.

Foreword

a. **Categorization**—Mechanical property, surface quality, and manufacturing requirements for automotive sheet steels, together with improvements in steel manufacturing and processing techniques, have made earlier methods of categorizing sheet steel obsolete. Classification of steel quality by deoxidation process is no longer appropriate. Uniformity of material properties is of major importance. This SAE Recommended Practice furnishes a categorization procedure to aid in selecting low-carbon sheet steel for identified parts and fabrication processes.

It is necessary for both the steel user and producer to know the mechanical properties and the range in these properties. There is a wide variety of parts within the automotive industry, and different levels of specific mechanical properties, e.g., r_m value, n value, yield strength, and total elongation may be required for specific applications. With the recent advent of computer simulation of the steel deformation process during die design, it is vitally important that certain minimum levels of formability exist within a particular category or grade of steel. It is suggested that the steel user and steel supplier consult early in the part and die design process to determine specific grade requirements. In the past, yield strength has been chosen as a major discriminator of the categorization system since this property has meaning to both automotive and steel engineers, this document builds on that rationale but also addresses certain minimum elongation, n value and r_m value discriminators. In this document, low-carbon sheet steel is classified by 5 grade levels with yield strength, tensile strength, elongation, r_m value, and n value requirements. In addition, surface quality and/or aging characteristics are an important consideration. Thus, the categorization system is as follows:

1. The first two alphabetic characters will designate hot-rolled or cold-rolled method of manufacture.
2. The third numeric character defines grade based on yield strength range, minimum tensile strength, minimum percent elongation, minimum r_m value, and minimum n value.
3. The fourth alphabetic character classifies the steel type with regards to surface quality and/or aging character.
4. An optional fifth alphabetic character may restrict the carbon content to a minimum of 0.015%.

b. **Properties**—The mechanical properties of the substrate (ductility, work hardening, and plastic anisotropy) determine the ability of the steel to withstand strain in various modes of forming (such as stretching and deep drawing). Mechanical properties are important to the formability of uncoated and coated steels, both cold-rolled and hot-rolled. Compared with uncoated steel sheets, hot-dip and electroplated coated steels have different characteristics which may affect automotive manufacturing operations such as stamping, welding, and painting. Material related factors greatly influence the formability of coated sheets. Coating characteristics although less important to forming than the substrate, can have a significant influence on forming because the coating can affect metal flow over tool and die surfaces.

Definition of steel sheet properties is contained in Appendix A.

1. Scope—This SAE Recommended Practice establishes mechanical property ranges for low-carbon automotive hot-rolled sheet, cold-rolled sheet, and metallic-coated sheet steels. It also contains information that explains the different nomenclature used with these steels.

2. References

2.1 Applicable Publications—The following publications form a part of this specification to the extent specified herein. Unless otherwise indicated, the latest issue of SAE publications shall apply.

2.1.1 SAE PUBLICATIONS—Available from SAE, 400 Commonwealth Drive, Warrendale, PA 15096-0001.

SAE J416—Tensile Test Specimens

SAE J863—Methods for Determining Plastic Deformation in Sheet Metal Stampings

SAE J1392—Steel, High-Strength, Hot-Rolled Sheet and Strip, Cold-Rolled Sheet, and Coated Sheet

SAE J1562—Selection of Galvanized (Hot-Dipped and Electrodeposited) Steel Sheet

2.1.2 ASTM PUBLICATIONS—Available from ASTM, 100 Barr Harbor Drive, West Conshohocken, PA 19428-2959.

ASTM A 370—Standard Test Methods and Definitions for Mechanical Testing of Steel Products

ASTM E 8—Standard Test Methods of Tension of Metallic Materials

ASTM E 517—Standard Test Method for Plastic Strain Ratio r for Sheet Metal

ASTM E 646—Standard Test Method for Tensile Strain-Hardening Exponents (n value) of Metallic Sheet Materials

2.1.3 ASM PUBLICATION—Available from ASM International, Attn: MSC/Book Order, P. O. Box 473, Novelty, OH 44072-9901.

ASM Handbook

2.2 Related Publications—The following publications are provided for information purposes only and are not a required part of this document.

2.2.1 SAE PUBLICATIONS—Available from SAE, 400 Commonwealth Drive, Warrendale, PA 15096-0001.

SAE J810—Classifications of Common Imperfections in Sheet Steel

SAE J940—Glossary of Carbon Steel Thickness and Tolerances

SAE J1058—Standard Sheet Steel Thickness and Tolerances

2.2.2 ASTM PUBLICATIONS—Available from ASTM, 100 Barr Harbor Drive, West Conshohocken, PA 19428-2959.

ASTM A 366/A 366M—Specification for Steel, Sheet, Carbon, Cold-Rolled, Commercial Quality

ASTM A 568/A 568M—Specification for Steel, Sheet, Carbon, and High Strength, Low Alloy, Hot-Rolled and Cold-Rolled, General Requirements for

ASTM A 569/A 569M—Specification for Steel, Carbon (0.15 Maximum, Percent), Hot-Rolled Steel and Strip, Commercial Quality

ASTM A 619A/619M—Specification for Steel, Sheet, Carbon Cold-Rolled Drawing Quality

ASTM A 620/A 620M—Specification for Steel, Sheet, Carbon, Drawing Quality, Special Killed, Cold-Rolled

ASTM A 621/A 621M—Specification for Steel, Sheet and Strip, Carbon, Hot-Rolled, Drawing Quality

ASTM A 622/A 622M—Specification for Steel, Sheet and Strip, Carbon, Drawing Quality, Special Killed, Hot-Rolled

ASTM A 642/A 642M—Specification for Steel Sheet, Zinc-Coated (Galvanized by the Hot-Dip Process, Drawing Quality, Special Killed)

ASTM A 653/A 653M—Steel Sheet, Zinc Coated (Galvanized) or Zinc-Iron Alloy Coated (Galvannealed) by the Hot-Dip Process

ASTM A 924/A 924M—General Requirements for Steel Sheet, Metallic Coated by the Hot-Dip Process

2.2.3 OTHER PUBLICATION

Steel Products Manual, Sheet Steel; Iron and Steel Society Publication, January 1988

3. Grades—The specific grades are identified by a maximum of 5 characters. The first two characters will be letters defining method of manufacture of steel; HR for hot rolled and CR for cold rolled. The third character will consist of a single digit number defining the chemical and forming characteristics as specified in Tables 1 through 3. The fourth character, an alphabetic character, will define the type of steel as outlined in Section 4. An additional 5th suffix character, C, may be added if restriction to low-carbon steelmaking is desired by the purchaser. The single-digit number specifies the mechanical requirements for: yield and tensile strength in MPa, elongation %, r_m value, and n value.

Under certain circumstances particular parts may require steel properties that do not conform exactly to the specific grades defined herein. These deviations should be resolved through agreement between the steel user and the steel producer.

Cold-rolled and metallic-coated cold-rolled coated steels specified to a 180 MPa or greater minimum yield strength are considered high-strength steels.

Hot-rolled and metallic-coated hot-rolled steels specified to a 260 MPa or greater minimum yield strength are considered high-strength steels.

Titanium, Niobium, and other alloy elements can be used in combination, if fully stabilized product is required. Stabilization elements must be reported on chemical certification.

TABLE 1—COLD-ROLLED STEEL SHEET, COATED AND UNCOATED, MECHANICAL PROPERTIES(1)(2)

SAE J2329 Designation	Yield Strength (MPa) at 0.2% Offset	Tensile Strength (MPa) Minimum	Total % Elongation in 50 mm Minimum	r_m value(3) Min.	n Value(4) Min.
Grade 1	N/R	N/R	N/R	N/R	N/R
Grade 2	140 to 260	270	34	N/R	0.16
Grade 3	140 to 205	270	38	1.5	0.18
Grade 4	140 to 185	270	40	1.6	0.20
Grade 5	110 to 170	270	42	1.7	0.22

1. N/R = Not required.
2. ASTM A 370, Test parameters in all directions.
3. ASTM E 517, Parameter for r calculated at 17% strain, r_m calculation by $(r_0 + r_{90} + 2r_{45})/4$. The r_m value can be up to 0.2 lower for thickness greater than 1.4 mm and/or Galvanneal products.
4. ASTM E 646, n Value calculated from 10 to 20% strain or 10% to end of uniform elongation when uniform elongation is less than 20%.

TABLE 2—HOT-ROLLED STEEL SHEET, COATED AND UNCOATED, MECHANICAL PROPERTIES(1)(2)

SAE J2329 Designation	Yield Strength (MPa) at 0.2% Offset	Tensile Strength (MPa) Minimum	Total % Elongation in 50 mm Minimum	n Value(3) Min.
Grade 1	N/R	N/R	N/R	N/R
Grade 2	180 to 290	270	34	0.16
Grade 3	180 to 240	270	38	0.18

1. N/R = Not required.
2. ASTM A 370, Test parameters in all directions.
3. ASTM E 646, n Value calculated from 10 to 20% strain or 10% to end of uniform elongation when uniform elongation is less than 20%.

TABLE 3—HOT-ROLLED AND COLD-ROLLed STEEL SHEET, LOW CARBON, CHEMICAL COMPOSITION(1)

SAE J2329 Designation	Carbon % max(2)	Manganese Max. %	Phosphorus Max. %	Sulfur Max. %.	Aluminum Min. %
Grade 1	0.13	0.60	0.035	0.035	
Grade 2	0.10	0.50	0.035	0.030	0.020
Grade 3	0.10	0.50	0.030	0.030	0.020
Grade 4	0.08	0.40	0.025	0.025	0.020
Grade 5	0.02	0.30	0.025	0.025	0.020

1. Ladle or Heat Analysis
2. 0.015% Carbon minimum requirement if suffix C is used. C cannot be specified for Grade 5.

4. Types—There are several types of cold-rolled/coated steels and hot-rolled steels that result from differences in steel manufacturing processes and automotive stamping operations. The types of steels are referred to by letter code that follows the class designation.

4.1 Cold-Rolled and Metallic-Coated Cold-Rolled Sheet Steel—Two types of these steels are produced. These types are based on surface quality.

4.1.1 Type E is intended for the most critical exposed applications where surface appearance is of primary importance. This type of steel will meet requirements for controlled surface texture, surface quality, and flatness.

4.1.2 Type U is intended for unexposed applications and may also have special use where improved ductility over a temper-rolled product is desired. Type U can be produced without temper rolling; this type of steel may be expected to exhibit coil breaks, fluting, and stretcher straining. Standard tolerances for flatness and surface texture are not applicable. In addition, surface imperfections are more prevalent and severe than with Type E.

4.2 Hot-Rolled and Metallic-Coated Hot-Rolled Sheet Steel—Four types of hot-rolled steel are available.

4.2.1 Type R is an as-hot-rolled coiled product. Typically known as Hot Roll Black Band. Therefore, it has not been processed in any way; i.e., pickled, oiled, temper-rolled, side trimmed, rewound, or cut back to established thickness and width tolerances. Yield strength range classes apply only to material that has been cut back to established thickness and width tolerances. Processed coils may have had any or all of the processing steps listed in the previous paragraph performed subsequent to hot rolling. Ends of coils are cut back to established width and thickness tolerances.

4.2.2 Type F has been processed and is available in coils or cut lengths. This material is susceptible to coil breaks and aging.

4.2.3 Type N has been processed and is available in coils or cut lengths. This material is nonaging at room temperature but is susceptible to coil breaks.

4.2.4 Type M has been processed and is available in coils or cut lengths. This material is free from coil breaks and does not strain age at room temperature.

Some of the product characteristics available for each type of hot-rolled steel are listed in Table 4.

TABLE 4—PRODUCT CHARACTERISTICS OF HOT-ROLLED STEEL(1)

Type	Freedom from Coil Breaks	Non Aging	Pickle and Oil	Cut Edge	Special Surface
R	No	No	n	n	n
F	No	No	a	a	n
N	No	Yes	a	a	
M	Yes	Yes	a	a	a

1. a = available but not required; n = not available

5. Examples—As previously discussed, categorization is made by commodity, grade, and type.

CR2E: Cold-rolled sheet steel with chemical requirements of Table 3 – Grade 2, minimum mechanical properties as specified in Table 1 — Grade 2 and of critical exposed surface quality.

HR3MU: Hot-rolled sheet steel with chemical requirements of Table 3 — Grade 3, minimum mechanical properties as specified in Table 2 — Grade 3, unexposed, M product characteristics as specified in Table 4.

For metallic-coated sheet products, SAE J1562 is used to designate coatings of hot-dipped and electrodeposited zinc. SAE J1562 should be referenced for full explanation of the nomenclature and product characteristics.

CR4C EG60G60GE: Cold-rolled sheet steel with the chemical requirements of Table 3 — Grade 4, minimum mechanical properties as specified in Table 1 — Grade 4, critical exposed surface quality, 0.015% minimum carbon, and two side electrogalvanized coated to 60 g/m^2 each side.

HR2M 45A45AU: Hot-rolled sheet steel with the chemical requirements of Table 3 — Grade 2, minimum mechanical properties as specified in Table 2 — Grade 2, unexposed, M product characteristic as specified in Table 4, two side galvannealed coated to 45 g/m^2 each side.

6. Sampling Procedure—When questions arise as to steel meeting the minimum or maximum criteria, the following procedure applies. When tested as outlined in the following section, tests must fall within the ranges for the grade specified: otherwise the lift of blanks, cut lengths, or coil can be considered unacceptable.

7. Yield Strength Determination—The procedures given in SAE J416, ASTM E 8, and ASTM A 370 shall be followed in determining tensile properties. However, within these specifications latitude exists in determining yield strength/yield point. For this document, the following procedures apply.

7.1 Specimen Geometry—The 12.5 mm (0.5 in) wide sheet type specimen will be used. The width of the grip section will be 20 mm (3/4 in).

7.2 Speed of Testing—ASTM A 370—87c Section 11.4.1 applies with the addition that the speed change from a maximum of 1.6 mm (1/16 in) per minute per millimeter (inch) of gage length shall not be made until a minimum of 2% elongation is achieved.

7.3 Discontinuous Yielding—For material showing discontinuous yielding, the lower yield point shall be considered to be the yield strength. The lower yield point is defined as the lowest stress at which an increase in strain occurs without an increase in stress. For steels with continuous yielding, the 0.2% offset method shall be used to determine the yield strength.

APPENDIX A

A.1 Introduction—Problems associated with the evaluation of formability or deep drawability of sheet metals are complex and may be difficult to solve due to the number of variable involved. As long ago as 1940, the AISI Technical Committee on Sheet Steel reviewed this problem. Volume 1 of the Ninth Edition of the ASM Metals Handbook contains sections on "Low Carbon Steel Sheet and Strip" and "Formability of Steel Sheet" that provide suggestions to help evaluate parts and select materials. The purpose of this document is to summarize the sheet metal characteristics that are commonly used when attempting to predict the formability of sheet metal.

A.2 Tension Test—Data from tension tests can give a more complete measurement of formability, ASTM A 370 and ASTM E 8 describe testing procedures.

NOTE—Any taper in the width of the bar between the gage marks could affect the total elongation adversely.

A.2.1 Yield Strength—The measured strength depends on both the steel and the conditions under which the prepared specimen is loaded. This term is applicable to those materials having an engineering stress-strain diagram in the transition from elastic to plastic strain which is a smooth curve as well as to those which exhibit an upper yield point or sharp knee. In reporting yield strength, the method by which it was determined should be stated (0.2% offset method, 0.5% extension under load method, halt of the pointer or from a stress-strain diagram). See ASTM E 8 for a description of these methods.

In forming sheet metal, the upper yield point has to be overcome before any deformation occurs in the flat blank. Experience has indicated that when the upper yield point is high in relation to the lower yield and approaches the ultimate strength, the material will have a greater tendency to split than material which has an upper yield point only slightly higher than the lower yield point. A low yield strength is preferred when formability is the major consideration.

A.2.2 Tensile Strength—The strength at the highest load reached during the tension test is the tensile strength. It is calculated in psi or MPa units using the specimen cross-sectional area measured before testing.

A.2.3 Yield to Tensile Ratio—The yield strength divided by the tensile strength expressed as a decimal value is the elastic ratio. Steels with low yield to tensile ratios have a greater capacity for being formed due to the greater separation between the yield load and the ultimate load during which forming can take place.

A.2.4 Total Elongation—The total elongation is the percent increase of a gage length on the tension test specimen. For low-carbon sheet steel, a 50 mm (2 in) gage length and a 12.5 mm (0.5 in) gage width is normally used. Steels with a higher percent elongation will stretch further before failure. This elongation is a direct measure of ductility and represents an important consideration in evaluating formability. Caution must be used, however, in comparing elongation values since they depend on specimen preparation and testing procedure. Total elongation also may vary with sample orientation in relation to the sheet rolling direction.

A.2.5 Uniform Elongation—The amount of deformation that can occur before any measurable localized necking of the tension specimen starts, is known as uniform elongation. This is designated as e_u and will usually vary between 20 and 28% for low-carbon steel.

A.2.6 Yield Point Elongation—The yield point elongation indicates the intensity of stretcher strains that can develop in certain low-carbon steels in lightly formed areas. It is caused by interstitial elements such as carbon and nitrogen, or in the case of certain high-strength steels, a very fine grain size. The tendency to strain can be minimized by temper rolling at the producing mill. However, in grades subject to aging, the effect of temper rolling is only temporary and it is necessary for the user to properly roller level the sheet immediately before forming a shape. Sheet steels are available that will not exhibit yield point elongation.

A.2.7 Mechanical Properties—Mechanical properties have not been typically used in specifications unless special structural properties are required in the part, this has changed due to the process control methods now used by automotive manufacturing facilities. Due to the range of properties possible, the expected distribution can overlap among the various grades. The ranges are broader for hot-rolled sheets than for cold-rolled.

A.3 Special Tests of Formability—During the late 1960s, the new test methods more directly related to the actual mechanism of deformation began to be developed and accepted. These tests are used to obtain a more complete characterization of sheet steel formability.

A.3.1 Plastic Strain Ratio (r_m value)—This is a measure of a sheet metal's resistance to thinning as controlled by the crystallographic orientation of its structure, which is dependent on the chemistry and processing of the material. When a tensile test specimen from a sheet of ductile metal having isotropic mechanical properties is stretched 20%, the width and thickness will each contract 10%. This is essentially true for steel in the as-hot-rolled condition, or for a normalized low-carbon sheet steel. If the sheet has been cold reduced and annealed subcritically by conventional methods, it will have a degree of anisotropic mechanical properties. In that case, a tensile test specimen stretched 20% will exhibit a different amount of contraction in the thickness than in the width. The degree of anisotropy is measured by the plastic stain ratio, r. The procedure for determining r can be found in ASTM E 517. For anisotropic materials, the r value changes with test direction, and for convenience, it is measured in directions longitudinal (0 degrees), diagonal (45 degrees), and transverse (90 degrees) to the rolling direction. An average value, r_m, is usually reported.

Higher r values indicate greater resistance to thinning, and are directly related to an increased ability of the sheet to be formed by deep drawing.

The plastic strain ratio can also be measured by the MODUL-r method. This device measures Young's modulus from a vibrating beam. Small strips are blanked at 0, 45, and 90 degrees to the rolling direction to use as test samples. The MODUL-r employs a simple feed-back system called a Magnetostrictive oscillator, consisting of a measuring head, an amplifier, and an electronic counter. The measuring head consists of three coils that form the sample chamber. When a sample is inserted and the test button depressed, an alternating field is created by the current passing through the coil network, producing cyclical longitudinal expansion and contraction in the sample through a process called magnetostriction.

These vibrations match a characteristic velocity of sound for that particular sample, or resonant frequency. This frequency is displayed on the front of the unit and an empirical graph converts the readings to r_m and Dr values.

A.3.2 Strain Hardening Exponent (n value)—The strain hardening exponent, known as the n value, is defined as the exponent of the power law relationship of true stress (s) to true strain (e), $s = Ke^n$, where K is a strength coefficient. True stress and true strain are based on the instantaneous cross section area, rather than the initial area used for engineering stress and strain. Determination of n from load elongation curves is described in ASTM E 646. A higher n value indicates a capability for the metal to strain harden in areas that have been cold worked by deformation processes, and in turn cause further straining to occur in less cold worked areas. This capacity to transfer strain contributes to a better response to biaxial stretch deformation modes.

A.3.3 Strain Rate Hardening (m value)—The m value is a measure of the change of the flow stress as the rate of strain is changed. It becomes important beyond uniform elongation, when a tension tests specimen necks-down by a diffuse, and finally localized reduction of cross section prior to fracture. It is the strain rate sensitivity of the flow stress ( ) in the modified power law equation, $s = Ke^n \cdot m$. Since the m value is strain rate dependent, its determination requires loading control based on changes in the strain. In general, higher positive m values are desired. For low-carbon steels, the m value is positive and generally in the range of 0.006 to 0.012. Its significance is apparent in that is accounts for the total elongation being on the order of two times the uniform elongation for most low-carbon high-ductility sheet steels.

A.3.4 Cup Drawing Tests—Deep draw biaxial deformation cupping tests, in which metal is allowed to be drawn-in from the flange area of the test blank, are considered distinct from clamped flange stretch tests such as the previously described Ball Punch Deformation Test. Referring to the severity curve of SAE J863, these tests generally develop negative e_2 strains in the cup side wall near the flange.

A.3.4.1 SWIFT CUP—Either a flat bottomed or a round bottomed punch is used to draw a suitably lubricated circular blank into a straight walled cup shape of 50 mm (2 in) outside diameter over an approach radiused hold-down die. The punch diameter, die radius, and pressure are optimized for the gage and strength level of the sheet metal under test. Blanks of increasing diameter are tested until a diameter is reached with which the cup bottom is punched out rather than forming a straight-walled cylindrical cup shape. The reported value is the limiting draw ratio (LDR) determined by dividing the largest blank diameter that will make a straight-walled shape by the punch diameter. A value of 2 to 2.5 is generally expected for low-carbon sheet steel. The LDR has been found to correlate with the r value in that material with a higher r_m will form a cup from a larger blank. The round bottom swift cup is considered a combination stretch and deep-draw test.

A.3.4.2 FUKUI CONICAL CUP—The Fukui test does not employ a hold-down force on the flange. This eliminates a difficult to control variable. A 60-degree approach angle conical die is used to form a cup shape by a ball punch forcing a suitably lubricated circular blank into the die until the ball ruptures the conical form. The ball diameter and blank diameter depend on the thickness of the sheet metal being tested. For low-carbon steel, a 60-mm diameter blank is frequently used. A larger diameter tends to collapse in the circumference rather than form a cup. The base diameter of the formed cup is measured in as many directions as necessary to determine the average, usually longitudinal, diagonal, and transverse to the rolling direction. This value may be reported, or a reduction of blank diameter can be calculated for a percent diameter reduction value. Other modifications are possible, but the test has limited usefulness due to the small amount of material being tested. It has been found to relate to both r and n of low-carbon steel. Some of the more recently developed steels, such as the interstitial-free with extremely high r_m values, do not rupture in the Fukui cup test.

A.3.4.3HOLE EXPANSION TEST—There are several versions of this test. In one, a cup is made using a blank with a punched or machined hole in the center which is stretched to failure as the flange is securely clamped. The test is useful in evaluating edge tearing tendencies, as well as the sheet metal ductility. For heavier gage sheets, such as hot-rolled, a drilled and reamed hole of 13 mm (0.5 in) diameter is prepared and a 30-degree conical punch is forced into it until it ruptures. The ratio of the final diameter to the 13 mm (0.5 in) initial diameter is reported.

A.3.4.4LIMITING DOME HEIGHT—The most severe forming condition, as shown in the severity curve of SAE J863 DEC81, is when the e_2 strain is near 0% while the e_1 strain is high. The observed minimum e_1 strain develops between 0% and +5% e_2. This test is designed to duplicate this strain condition in a repeatable manner for comparison of sheet materials. A 102 mm (4 in) diameter punch acts against a 127 mm (5 in) wide strip of sheet metal that is securely clamped by a hold-down ring. The test value is the height of punch travel at the instant of local neck-down prior to fracture as determined by observation or by drop in punch load.

A.4 High-Strength Steels—It is possible to successfully form many complex parts using high-strength steels such as those described in SAE J1392. Their formability, however, tends to decrease with increasing yield strengths and/or hardness. Therefore consultation of producer and user regarding specific grade selection is recommended to insure compatibility of the strength and forming requirements.

A.5 Annealing Practices—Annealing of cold-rolled sheet steels is performed by either batch or continuous annealing practice. In batch annealing, multiple coils of sheet are placed under a cover with a reducing atmosphere and heated for a time period that may involve days. In contrast, in continuous annealing, sheet steel moves through the heating and cooling sections of a continuous processing line in a matter of minutes. The different heating and cooling profiles that characterize the two annealing practices result in different steel properties. In the case of conventional low-carbon steels (0.015% to 0.15 Carbon) batch annealed sheet steel can exhibit excellent formability and low yield strengths, this is generally not the case with continuous annealing. Alternatively, with ultra-low carbon interstitial free sheet steel (Carbon < 0.015%), excellent formability and very low yield strengths can be achieved with continuous anneal.

A.6 Aging—A term applied to changes in properties of conventional carbon steels that can occur with the passage of time. These changes include an increase in yield strength and a decrease in total elongation. Furthermore, yield point elongation can increase in temper-rolled steel, a manifestation of which is the presence of surface irregularities (also known as stretcher strains, Luders lines, or fluting) during forming; these may render the sheet unsuitable for use on exposed parts.

Aging results from the presence of interstitial nitrogen and carbon. In aluminum-killed steels, control of chemistry (Al, N) and processing generally precludes the phenomena called nitrogen aging. Aging can result from an excessive amount of interstitial carbon, as is the case for hot-dipped coated conventional low-carbon sheet steels that are in-line annealed. In bake hardenable steels, interstitial carbon is controlled under 20 ppm (parts per million) to prevent aging at ambient temperatures, yet still exhibit bake hardening characteristics.

Aging does not occur in fully stabilized or interstitial-free steels.

A.7 Coatings—Some metals and alloys are applied as a coating to steel substrates for corrosion protection. These coatings are most commonly produced by hot-dipping and electroplating.

A.7.1 Hot-Dip Coatings—In the most common method for pure zinc hot-dipped galvanizing, the sheet reaches one of two different temperature regions depending on the nature of the process and metallurgical properties required.

a. Low Temperatures of about 460 °C (860 °F) are attained when a flux-cleaned strip enters the molten zinc pot or when preheating is done to ensure that the sheet is at the same temperature as the molten zinc pot. These temperatures are usually used when the cold-rolled steel has been pre-batch annealed to obtain a soft, ductile structure that exhibits good formability. Hot-rolled steels can also be galvanized with this method.
b. High Temperatures of about 675 to 900 °C (1250 to 1650 °F) are employed to achieve in-line annealing and replace pre-batch annealing. Because of short duration annealing, higher temperatures, and rapid cooling rates, formability is lower and strength is higher compared with conventional batch annealed material, than conventional low-carbon steels (0.015% to 0.15% carbon). The heating during the hot-dipped galvanizing, and the associated rapid cooling, causes excess carbon to remain in solution in the steel. This carbon tends to reduce the formability of the steel compared with batch annealing. For this reason, post-heat treating at about 260 °C (500 °F) is often practiced to precipitate interstitial carbon and hence restore some of the formability. Alternatively, when ultra low carbon (<0.015% carbon) interstitial-free steels are used, post-heat treating is not necessary because the carbon is stabilized by alloying elements, and excellent formability is obtained.

Besides pure zinc (Zn), other coatings are used to provide specific advantages such as: improved paintability, spot weldability, resistance to high temperature, etc. These coatings include:

A.7.1.5 FREE ZINC COATING (ZN)—Commonly known as Hot-Dipped Galvanized with a minimum spangle or extra smooth finish.

A.7.1.6 ZINC-IRON ALLOY COATING (ZN-FE)—Commonly known as Galvanneal, the iron content is usually in the range of 9 to 12%. In galvannealing, the hot-dip galvanized sheet is heated in-line after emergence from the molten zinc pot by use of flame or induction heating. This heating allows inter-diffusion of iron from the substrate with zinc from the coating to form the zinc-iron alloy coating.

A.7.1.7 ZINC-55AL COATING—Commonly known as Galvalume.

A.7.1.8 ZINC-5AL COATING—Commonly known as Galfan.

A.7.1.9 LEAD TIN ALLOY (PB-SN) COATING—Commonly known as Terne.

A.7.1.10 ALUMINUM (AL) COATING—Type 1 is Aluminum-Silicon (5 to 11% Silicon) alloy coating. Type II is pure Aluminum.

A.7.2 Electroplated Coatings—The electroplating process is conducted slightly above normal room temperature. Commonly used electroplated coatings include Free Zinc (EG), Zinc-Nickel (Zn-Ni) and Zinc-Iron (Zn-Fe) single layer coatings, and two layer coatings such as Zn/Zn-Ni, Zn-Fe/Zn-Ni, and Zn-Cr/Zn-Ni. Consequently, the mechanical properties of electrogalvanized sheet are almost identical to incoming substrate, although some minor effects may occur because of in-line tension or bending.

A.7.3 Post-Coating Treatments—Can include mill applied rust preventative oils, dry film lubes, and phosphates.

A.8 Effects of Coatings on Formability—The formability of the coated steels depends both upon the properties of the substrate and the characteristics of the coating. In the case of EG coatings, the coated steel properties are similar to the substrate properties. For the Hot-Dip, Zn-Fe (Galvanneal) and Zn-Ni coatings, formability of the coated steel is lower than that of the substrate.

It must be recognized that sheet metal forming is a complex process involving interactions among the material being formed, the tooling, and the lubricants. While all are important, under certain circumstances one may overshadow the others. What may be found to work well for one material under one set of conditions may not work well for that same material on another part. For example, because of the material-tool-lubricant interactions, comparison between galvannealed and bare steel on soft prototype tooling using the same lubricant may result in the galvannealed steel exhibiting poorer forming performance than would be expected for hard production tooling. For such cases, the soft prototype tool trials may be misleading. It is suggested that different lubricants may be required for soft prototype tool and hard production tool conditions. Furthermore, because of these interactions, it may be more fruitful to use a different type of steel and/or coating for the prototype tool trials than will be used under production conditions.

A.9 Effects of Surface Characteristics on Formability—In general, experience has shown that the substrate properties are more important than those of the galvanized coatings. There are, of course, exceptions to this and there are applications where the surface characteristics of the galvanized coatings become very important. These surface characteristics can change the frictional behavior during the forming process. This is especially true for prototype or soft tool programs where results have shown that galvanized sheets behave differently from cold-rolled sheets, even when the substrate properties are similar. For example, it has been established that one of the primary reasons for the poorer performance of the galvannealed steels during tooling development is because there is an interaction between the galvannealed surface and the soft prototype tooling. This produces high-frictional forces that adversely affect formability. Also, the coating surface topography can determine to a great extent the ability of that coating to carry lubricant into the die forming operation. Accordingly, the surface characteristics can affect the material-tool-lubricant interactions.

Post-coating treatments may affect the surface characteristics of the coating and hence the formability of the electroplated or hot-dip sheet steel.

SELECTING AND SPECIFYING HOT AND COLD ROLLED STEEL SHEET AND STRIP—SAE J126 JUN1986

SAE Recommended Practice

Report of the SAE Iron and Steel Technical Committee approved September 1969, reaffirmed without change, June 1986.

Foreword—This Reaffirmed Document has been changed only to reflect the new SAE Technical Standards Board Format.

1. Scope—This SAE Recommended Practice outlines a procedure for selecting the proper specification for carbon steel sheet and strip which are purchased to make an identified part. Specifications considered are:

ASTM A109—Steel, Carbon, Cold Rolled Strip.

ASTM A569—Steel, Carbon (0.15 maximum percent), Hot Rolled Sheet, Commercial Quality (HRCQ).

ASTM A621—Steel, Sheet, Carbon, Hot Rolled, Drawing Quality (HRDQ).

ASTM A622—Steel, Sheet, Carbon, Hot Rolled, Drawing Quality, Special Killed (HRDQSK).

ASTM A568—Steel, Carbon and High-Strength Low-Alloy Hot Rolled Sheet, and Cold Rolled Sheet, General Requirements.

ASTM A366—Steel, Carbon, Cold Rolled Sheet, Commercial Quality (CRCQ).

ASTM A619—Steel, Sheet, Carbon, Cold Rolled, Drawing Quality (CRDQ).

ASTM A620—Steel, Sheet, Carbon, Cold Rolled, Drawing Quality, Special Killed (CRDQSK).

ASTM A749M—Steel, Carbon and High-Strength Low-Alloy, Hot Rolled Strip, General Requirements.

ASTM A635—Steel Sheet and Strip, Carbon, Hot Rolled Commercial Quality, Heavy Thickness Coils.

(Metric ASTM documents are designated by suffix M)

It also describes how codes or symbols for specifying certain characteristics may be used in electronic data processing systems. Characteristics covered are:

a. Hot or cold rolled.
b. Sheet or strip.
c. Severity of draw (quality of steel).
d. Surface condition (finish, etc.).
e. Edge condition.
f. Dimensions.

It is intended that other characteristics and part identification be covered by a supplement to the specification, as necessary.

2. References

2.1 Applicable Publications—The following publications form a part of the specification to the extent specified herein. Unless otherwise indicated the latest revision of SAE publications shall apply.

2.1.1 ASTM PUBLICATIONS—Available from ASTM, 100 Barr Harbor Drive, West Conshohocken, PA 19428-2959.

ASTM A109—Steel, Carbon, Cold Rolled Strip.

ASTM A569—Steel, Carbon (0.15 maximum percent), Hot Rolled Sheet, Commercial Quality (HRCQ).

ASTM A621—Steel, Sheet, Carbon, Hot Rolled, Drawing Quality (HRDQ).

ASTM A622—Steel, Sheet, Carbon, Hot Rolled, Drawing Quality, Special Killed (HRDQSK).

ASTM A568—Steel, Carbon and High-Strength Low-Alloy Hot Rolled Sheet, and Cold Rolled Sheet, General Requirements.

ASTM A366—Steel, Carbon, Cold Rolled Sheet, Commercial Quality (CRCQ).

ASTM A619—Steel, Sheet, Carbon, Cold Rolled, Drawing Quality (CRDQ).

ASTM A620—Steel, Sheet, Carbon, Cold Rolled, Drawing Quality, Special Killed (CRDQSK).

ASTM A749M—Steel, Carbon and High-Strength Low-Alloy, Hot Rolled Strip, General Requirements.

ASTM A635—Steel Sheet and Strip, Carbon, Hot Rolled Commercial Quality, Heavy Thickness Coils.

(Metric ASTM documents are designated by suffix M)

3. Procedure—Evaluate the part to determine the requirements for characteristics A-F, as follows:

3.1 A - Hot or Cold Rolled Product—Normally the finish or thickness of the metal required for a part will determine whether hot-rolled or cold-rolled product should be specified. (See Table 1A, Table 1B, and Table 4.)

3.2 B - Sheet or Strip—Principal factors to consider in determining whether sheet or strip should be specified are:

Size of part, or more specifically, size of flat steel required to develop part.

Thickness of metal required for the part.

Hot or cold rolled steel.

Selection and specification of temper for cold rolled strip. (See Table 3A, Table 3B.)

Equipment on which the metal will be handled and fabricated.

Steel industry product classification by size. (See Table 1A, Table 1B.)

TABLE 1A—STEEL SHEET OR STRIP PRODUCT CLASSIFICATION BY SIZE, METRIC UNITS

Product	Thickness, mm	Width, mm	Other Limitations	Specification Symbol (ASTM No.)
Hot Rolled Sheet	1.2–6.0	Over 300 thru 1200	Coils and Cut Lengths	A 569M, A 621M, or A 622M
	1.2–4.5	Over 1200		
	6.0–12.5	Over 300 thru 1200	Coils Only	A 635M
	4.5–12.5	Over 1200 thru 1800		
Hot Rolled Strip	1.2–5.0	Thru 200	Coils and Cut Lengths	A 569M, A 621M, or A 622M
	1.2–6.0	Over 200 thru 300		
	6.0–12.5	Over 200 thru 300	Coils Only	A 635M
Cold Rolled Sheet	0.35–2.0	Over 50 thru 300	See Note 1	A 366M, A 619M, or A 620M
	0.35 and Over	Over 300	See Note 2	
Cold Rolled Strip	Thru 6.0	Over 12 thru 600	See Note 3	A 109M

NOTE 1— Cold rolled sheet, coils, and cut lengths, slit from wider coils with cut edge (only), thicknesses 0.35–2.0 mm and carbon of 0.25% max by cast analysis.

NOTE 2— When no special edge or finish (other than matte, commercial bright, or luster) is required and/or single strand rolling of widths under 600 mm is not required.

NOTE 3— Widths 50–300 mm with thicknesses of 0.35–2.0 mm are classified as "sheet" when slit from wider coils, have a cut edge only, and carbon of 0.25% max by cast analysis.

TABLE 1B—STEEL SHEET OR STRIP PRODUCT CLASSIFICATION BY SIZE, INCH-POUND UNITS

Product	Thickness, in	Width, in	Other Limitations	Specification Symbol (ASTM No.)
Hot Rolled Sheet	0.045 thru 0.230	Over 12 thru 48	Coils and Cut Lengths	A 569, A 621, or A 622
	0.045 thru 0.180	Over 48		
	0.230 thru 0.500	Over 12 thru 48	Coils Only	A 635
	0.180 thru 0.500	Over 48 thru 72		
Hot Rolled Strip	0.045 thru 0.203	Thru 6	Coils and Cut Lengths	A 569, A 621, or A 622
	0.045 thru 0.229	Over 6 thru 12		
	0.230 thru 0.500	Over 8 thru 12	Coils Only	A 635
Cold Rolled Sheet	0.014 thru 0.082	Over 2 thru 12	See Note 1	A 366, A 619, or A 620
	Over 0.014	Over 12	See Note 2	
Cold Rolled Strip	Thru 0.250	Over 0.50 thru 23.9	See Note 3	A 109

NOTE 1— Cold rolled sheet, coils, and cut lengths, slit from wider coils with cut edge (only), thicknesses 0.014–0.082 in and carbon of 0.25% max by cast analysis.

NOTE 2— When no special edge or finish (other than matte, commercial bright, or luster) is required and/or single strand rolling of widths under 24 in is not required.

NOTE 3— Widths 2–12 in with thicknesses of 0.014–0.082 in are classified as "sheet" when slit from wider coils, have a cut edge only, and carbon of 0.25% max by cast analysis.

3.3 C - Selection of Sheet Steel for Formability—For Cold Rolled Carbon Sheet and Hot Rolled Carbon Sheet and Strip, three levels of formability or drawability (called quality in the steel industry) are available as indicated in the Scope. They are commonly referred to as CQ, DQ, and DQSK.

The following procedure is based on a Forming Severity Index (FSI) which has been developed through experience in production forming of sheet metal stampings. The procedure is recommended for determining the quality needed for a specific part and fabrication operation.

1. Form a sample or prototype part from a specimen of known quality of steel using the gridding procedure outlined in SAE J863. (For the most accurate description of the quality of steel used for the gridded blank, the mechanical properties of a sample taken from material adjacent to the blank used for the gridded part should be known. This can be from the same blank, or the sheet preceding or following the sheet to be gridded.) If the specimen fractures, form another sample from the next better quality of steel.
2. Measure the e_1 and e_2 strains as described in SAE J863. (This should be done on a sample part which has not fractured during forming.)

3. Calculate the Forming Severity Index (FSI), for the critical area or areas of the sample part, using the following formulae:

NOTE—The e_2 strain is the associated strain (minor) measured perpendicular to the major strain, e_1.

When the e_2 strain as measured on the grid in the maximum stretch area is 0 to +30%.

$$FSI = (0.6e_2 + 15 + 350t) - e_1 \quad \text{(Eq. 1)}$$

When the e_2 strain is 0 to −30% (biaxial tension compression forming).

$$FSI = (1.5e_2 + 15 + 350t) - e_1 \quad \text{(Eq. 2)}$$

where:

t = thickness of gridded panel in inches.
e_1 = major strain expressed as a percent (not a decimal value).
e_2 = minor strain expressed as a percent (not a decimal value).
The sign of e_2 is disregarded (an e_2 of −30 is expressed as 30 in the formula).

NOTE:

a. The thickness t in the above formulae is only a correction factor for calculation of the FSI. Material formability may not be dependent on the sheet metal thickness.
b. If t is expressed in millimeters, the multiplier will be 13.8 instead of 350.
c. The reliability of the equations for stock over 0.125 in or 3 mm has not been established.
d. The constant 15 in the above formulae can be modified by mutual consent of the supplier and user to provide the desired degree of risk of breakage. A constant of 15 approximates a safety factor of ten percentage of strain points for die, lubricant, press, and material variance of e_1 strain (major strain). A constant of 20 gives a safety factor of 5, and a constant of 10 gives a safety factor of 15.

4. Select the quality of steel sheet needed for the part from Table 2. When a change in material is indicated by Table 2, the selection should be verified using the new quality of sheet metal to form another sample part.

TABLE 2—SELECTION OF QUALITY OF STEEL SHEET AND STRIP BASED ON THE FORMING SEVERITY INDEX (FSI)

Quality of Steel Used for the Gridded Sample Panel	Quality Suggested When the Forming Severity Index is Within the Range Given Below			
	−20 to −11	−10 to −1	0 to +5	+6 and Greater
DQSK	DQSK (1) (2)	DQSK(2)	DQSK	DQ
DQ	DQSK(2)	DQSK	DQ	CQ
CQ	DQSK	DQ	CQ	CQ (3)

1. This indicates too much is being expected of the sheet metal, a part redesign or breakdown into separate components may be necessary in addition to the factors below.
2. This represents a part which is difficult to form, other factors, such as tools, design, drawing compound application, blank development, etc., should be considered to provide an adequate Forming Severity Index because further upgrading is not possible. (Premium quality grades of steel with a high plastic strain ratio (r_m) values may be necessary if the above factors cannot be modified to produce a more favorable Forming Severity Index.)
3. The part should have no forming problems and if further economics are desired, factors other than material quality should be investigated, such as, thickness reduction, drawing compound change, or simplified tooling. In the appropriate thickness range HR should be considered in place of CR.

5. After a sufficient production history has been obtained through the use of the SAE Recommended Practice J424, Determination of Breakage Allowance for Steel Sheets, the quality of steel being used should be reviewed. For a given part an unusually high scrap rate indicates either a tool, lubricant, or material quality selection problem. If material quality is found to be the problem, upgrading should be considered. Conversely, an unusually low scrap rate indicates a less expensive quality should be considered. SAE Recommended Practice J863 should be followed to determine the most beneficial material change.

EXAMPLE—In the case of 0.080 in or 2.00 mm thick sheet steel with e_1 strain of 33% and e_2 strain of +10%, the Forming Severity Index (FSI) would be:

$$FSI = \left[0.6(10) + \frac{(in)}{15} + 350(0.080)\right] - 33 \quad \text{(Eq. 3)}$$

$$FSI = 16$$

$$FSI = \left[0.6(10) + \frac{(mm)}{15} + 13.8(2.0)\right] - 33 \quad \text{(Eq. 4)}$$

$$FSI = 16$$

If the gridded panel was CRCQ steel, the FSI indicates the selection of a lower quality steel such as HRDQ (A621). Note that in cases such as this where the FSI is greater than +6 there are other factors than material which should be investigated to obtain the most economical production.

If the gridded panel was HRDQ, the indicated selection would be HRCQ (A569).

In the case of 0.036 in or 0.9 mm thick stock with an e_1 strain of 55% and an e_2 strain of −15%, the FSI would be:

$$FSI = \left[1.5(15) + \frac{(in)}{15} + 350(0.036)\right] - 55 \quad \text{(Eq. 5)}$$

$$FSI = -5$$

$$FSI = \left[1.5(15) + \frac{(mm)}{15} + 13.8(0.09)\right] - 55 \quad \text{(Eq. 6)}$$

$$FSI = -5$$

TABLE 3A—(INCH-POUND UNITS)--SELECTION AND SPECIFICATION OF THE AMOUNT OF TEMPER (COLD WORK) (APPLICABLE TO COLD ROLLED STEEL STRIP ONLY)

Requirement of Part (Relative to Hardness and Maximum Severity of Bend Involved in Forming the Part)					
Stock Thickness in		Rockwell Hardness		Bend Test Requirements	Temper of Strip Normally Required
Over	Thru	Min	Max (Approx.)		
0.070	--	B84	--	No bending in any direction.	No. 1 (Hard)
0.040	0.070	B90	--		
0.025	0.040	30T76.0	--		
--	0.025	15T90.0	--		
0.040	--	B70	B85(1)	Bend 90 deg across rolling direction around a radius equal to that of the metal thickness.(2)	No. 2 (Half-Hard)
0.025	0.040	30T63.5	30T73.5		
--	0.025	15T83.5	15T88.5		
0.040	--	B60	B75(1)	Bend 180 deg across rolling direction over one thickness of the strip and 90 deg in the direction of rolling around a radius equal to the thickness.	No. 3 (Quarter-Hard)(2)
0.025	0.040	30T56.5	30T67.0		
--	0.025	15T80.0	15T85.0		
0.040	--	--	B65(1)	Bend flat upon itself in any direction.	No. 4 (Skin Rolled)(3)
0.025	0.040	--	30T60.0		
--	0.025	--	15T82.0		
0.040	--	--	B55(1)	Bend flat upon itself in any direction.	No. 5 (Dead Soft)(3)
0.025	0.040	--	30T53.0		
--	0.025	--	15T78.5		

1. Rockwell hardness values apply to special killed steels and also rimmed or semi-killed steels at time of shipment only. Aging of these latter steels may result in slightly higher values when tested at a later date.
2. To bend across the rolling direction means that the crease formed by the bend shall be at right angles to the length of the strip. To bend along the rolling direction means that the crease formed by the bend shall be parallel with the length of the strip.
3. Number 4 and 5 tempers may sometimes be ordered with a carbon range of 0.15–0.25%. In each instance the maximum hardness requirement is established by agreement.

TABLE 3B—(METRIC UNITS)—SELECTION AND SPECIFICATION OF THE AMOUNT OF TEMPER (COLD WORK) (APPLICABLE TO COLD ROLLED STEEL STRIP ONLY)

Stock Thickness mm		Rockwell Hardness		Bend Test Requirements	Temper of Strip Normally Required
Over	Under	Min	Max (Approx.)		
1.8	--	B84	--	No bending in any direction.	No. 1 (Hard)
1.0	1.8	B90	--		
0.6	1.0	30T76.0	--		
--	0.6	15T90.0	--		
1.0	--	B70	B85[(1)]	Bend 90 deg across rolling direction around a radius equal to that of the metal thickness.[(2)]	No. 2 (Half-Hard)
0.6	1.0	30T63.5	30T73.5		
--	0.6	15T83.5	15T88.5		
1.0	--	B60	B75[(1)]	Bend 180 deg across rolling direction over one thickness of the strip and 90 deg in the direction of rolling around a radius equal to the thickness.[(2)]	No. 3 (Quarter-Hard)[(2)]
0.6	1.0	30T56.5	30T67.0		
--	0.6	15T80.0	15T85.0		
1.0	--	--	B65[(1)]	Bend flat upon itself in any direction.	No. 4 (Skin Rolled)[(3)]
0.6	1.0	--	30T60.0		
--	0.6	--	15T82.0		
1.0	--	--	B55[(1)]	Bend flat upon itself in any direction.	No. 5 (Dead Soft)[(3)]
0.6	1.0	--	30T53.0		
--	0.6	--	15T78.5		

1. Rockwell hardness values apply to special killed steels and also rimmed or semi-killed steels at time of shipment only. Aging of these latter steels may result in slightly higher values when tested at a later date.
2. To bend across the rolling direction means that the crease bend shall be at right angles to the length of the strip. To bend along the rolling direction means that the crease formed by the bend shall be parallel with the length of the strip.
3. Number 4 and 5 tempers may sometimes be ordered with a carbon range of 0.15-0.25%. In each instance the maximum hardness requirement is established by agreement.

If the gridded panel was CRCQ and trouble was being encountered in forming production parts, the indicated selection would be to upgrade to CRDQ (A619). If the gridded panel was CRDQ, the indicated selection would be to upgrade to CRDQSK (A620) and if the panel was CRDQSK some other changes may be required in the forming operations or in the design of the part (comments in Table 2).

3.4 D - Surface Condition (Finish, etc.)—Consider any surface conditions required for the part. Consult Table 4 for a description of surfaces applicable to the product selected in A, B, and C above. Designate surface, finish, coating, etc. by symbol shown.

3.5 E - Edge Condition—Consider any necessary edge conditions required for the part. Consult Table 5 for a description of edges applicable to the product selected in A, B, and C above. Designate the required edge condition by the symbol shown.

3.6 F - Dimensions—Consider all dimensions required for the part.

Refer to ASTM A568 for thickness tolerance tables.

Designate dimensions in the following order: thickness, width, and length. (Note: Use the symbol C for length of material purchased in coil form.) When the measuring unit is inches, all fractions thereof shall be expressed as decimals and not as common fractions (for example, 1.25 in, not 1-1/4 in). State the thickness to three decimal places and width and length to two decimal places.

When metric units are used for dimensions, the thickness, width, and length should be expressed in millimeters. State thickness to one decimal place and width and length in whole numbers.

EXAMPLE—

For cut length: 0.035 x 36.25 x 84.75 (in) 0.9 x 900 x 2153 (mm)

For coil length: 0.047 x 47.37 x C (in) 1.2 x 1200 x C(mm)

(These units are not intended to indicate conversion of inch to metric units.)

3.7 G—For a more complete explanation of industry nomenclature for Cold Rolled or Hot Rolled Steel Sheet, the AISI Steel Customer Communication Handbooks are recommended.

TABLE 4—SELECTION AND SPECIFICATION OF SURFACE CONDITION OF STEEL SHEET AND STRIP

Description of Surface	Surface Described Applicable To	Specification Symbol
Surface finish as normally used for unexposed automotive parts. Matte (dull) appearance. Normally annealed last.	Cold rolled sheet	U[a]
Surface finish as normally used for exposed automotive parts which require a good painted surface. Free from strain markings and fluting. Matte (dull) appearance. Temper rolled.	Cold rolled sheet	E[b]
Same as above, except commercial bright appearance.	Cold rolled sheet	B
Same as above, except luster appearance.	Cold rolled sheet	L
No. 1 or dull finish (no luster). Especially suitable for lacquer or paint adhesion. Facilitates drawing by reducing the contact friction between the die and the metal.	Cold rolled Strip	1
No. 2 or regular bright finish (moderately smooth). Suitable for many applications, but not generally applicable for parts to be plated, unless polished and buffed.	Cold rolled strip	2
No. 3 or best bright finish (relatively high luster). Particularly suitable for parts to be plated.	Cold rolled strip	3
As rolled or black (oxide or scale not removed).	Hot rolled sheet and strip	A
Pickled (scale removed), not oiled.	Hot rolled sheet and strip	P
Same as above, except oiled.	Hot rolled sheet and strip	O

[a]U - unexposed is presently also designated as Class 2, Cold Rolled Sheet.

[b]E - exposed is presently also designated as Class 1, Cold Rolled Sheet.

TABLE 5—SELECTION AND SPECIFICATION OF EDGE CONDITION OF STEEL SHEET AND STRIP

Description of Edge	Edge Described Applicable To	Specification Symbol
Cut Edge.	Cold rolled sheet	None required
No. 1 Edge is a prepared edge of a specified contour (round, square, or beveled) supplied when a very accurate width is required, or where the finish of the edge is required to be suitable for electroplating, or both.	Cold rolled strip	1
No. 2 Edge is a natural mill edge carried through the cold rolling from the hot rolled strip without additional processing of the edge.	Cold rolled strip	2
No. 3 Edge is an approximately square edge produced by slitting, on which the burr is not eliminated.	Cold rolled strip	3
No. 4 Edge is a rounded edge produced by edge rolling the natural edge of hot rolled strip or slit-edge strip. This edge is produced when the width tolerance and edge condition are not as exacting as for No. 1 Edge.	Cold rolled strip	4
No. 5 Edge is an approximately square edge produced by rolling or filing of a slit-edge to remove burr only.	Cold rolled strip	5
No. 6 Edge is a square edge produced by edge rolling the natural edge of hot rolled strip or slit-edge strip, where the width tolerance and finish required are not as exacting as for No. 1 Edge.	Cold rolled strip	6
Mill Edge.	Hot rolled sheet and strip	M
Cut Edge.	Hot rolled sheet and strip	C
Square Edge (square and smooth, corners slightly rounded). Produced by rolling through vertical edging rolls during the hot rolling operation.	Hot rolled strip	S

TABLE 6—SUMMARY OF AVAILABLE TYPES OF LOW CARBON STEEL SHEET AND STRIP

Product Name	"Quality" or Temper [1]	Applicable Basic Specification Number	Surface Finish, etc. Description		Surface Finish, etc. Symbol	Edge Description	Edge Symbol
		A 366	For exposed parts: Temper rolled	For unexposed parts: Annealed last			
Cold Rolled	Commercial quality						
Carbon Steel Sheet			Matte (dull)	--	E		See Note [2]
	Drawing quality	A 619	--	Matte (dull)	U	Cut	
			Commercial bright	--	B		
			Luster	--	L		
	Drawing quality, special killed	A 620					
Hot Rolled	Commercial quality	A 569					
Carbon Steel Sheet		A 635					
	Drawing quality	A 621	As rolled (black)		A	Mill	M
			Pickled - dry		P		
			Pickled and oiled		O	Cut	C
	Drawing quality, special killed	A 622					
Hot Rolled	Commercial quality	A 569					
Carbon Steel Strip						Mill	M
	Drawing quality	A 621	As rolled (black)		A		
			Pickled - dry		P	Square	S
			Pickled and oiled		O		
	Drawing quality, special killed	A 622				Cut	C
Cold Rolled							
Carbon Steel Strip	Temper[1]						
	Description						
	No. 1	A 109	Matte (dull)		1	Table 5	1
	No. 2		Regular bright		2		2
	No. 3		Best bright		3		3
	No. 4						4
	No. 5						5
							6

1. Temper designation applicable to cold rolled strip only, "quality" not applicable. (Metric ASTM documents are designated by suffix "M".)
2. No symbol necessary; cut edge is "standard".

(R) CLASSIFICATION OF COMMON IMPERFECTIONS IN SHEET STEEL—SAE J810 MAR1996

SAE Information Report

Report of the SAE Iron and Steel Technical Committee approved April 1956, completely revised June 1980, and reaffirmed March 1987. Completely revised by the SAE Iron and Steel Technical Committee Division32 - Sheet and Steel, MArch 1996.

Foreword—This Document has also changed to comply with the new SAE Technical Standards Board format.

1. Scope—Common or obvious surface imperfections, which sometimes occur in sheet steel, are normally visible to the naked eye before or after fabrication.

Illustrations and definitions of these imperfections are contained in this SAE Information Report. The identifying names are those commonly used throughout the steel industry. The imperfections identified include the major and most often encountered imperfections known to exist at this time. These imperfections are variable in appearance and severity. Extreme conditions have been selected in some instances in order to obtain suitable photographs.

Photographs are courtesy of the American Iron and Steel Institute, Kaiser Aluminum, LTV Steel, National Steel, The Budd Company.

2. References—There are no referenced publications specified herein.

3. Most Common Imperfections—(See Table 1.)

4. Steelmaking Imperfections—(See Table 2 and Figures 1 to 6.)

TABLE 1—COMMON IMPERFECTIONS ENCOUNTERED IN SHEET STEEL

Imperfections	Origin Steelmaking	Origin Rolling	Origin Processing	Origin Coating	Page No.
Blisters	X				3
Buckles		X			10
Camber			X		20
Chatter Marks		X			11
Coil Welds			X		21
Crown		X			12
Dross Stringers				X	30
Edge Breaks		X			13
Friction Digs			X		22
Ghost Lines	X				4
Healed-Over-Scratch		X			14
Holes	X				5
Line-Stop				X	31
Lüder Lines			X		23
Orange Peel			X		24
Oscillation			X		25
Pinchers		X			15
Pipe Lamination	X				6
Pits		X			16
Ragged-Edges	X		X		7
Reel-Breaks		X			14
Rolled-In Scale		X			18
Sliver	X				8
Speckled Rust			X		26
Sticker Breaks			X		27
Telescoping			X		28

This table lists alphabetically the most common imperfections encountered in sheet steel. They are classified according to the various manufacturing processes. The appropriate descriptions can be found in the following sections under:

a. Section 4—Steelmaking
b. Section 5—Rolling
c. Section 6—Processing
d. Section 7—Coating

TABLE 2—STEELMAKING IMPERFECTIONS

Steelmaking Imperfections	Similar Imperfections
Blisters	Pinhead Stringers
Ghost Lines	
Holes	
Pipe Lamination	Laminations
Ragged-Edges	Sawtooth Edges, Damaged Edges
Sliver	Scabs, Skin Laminations

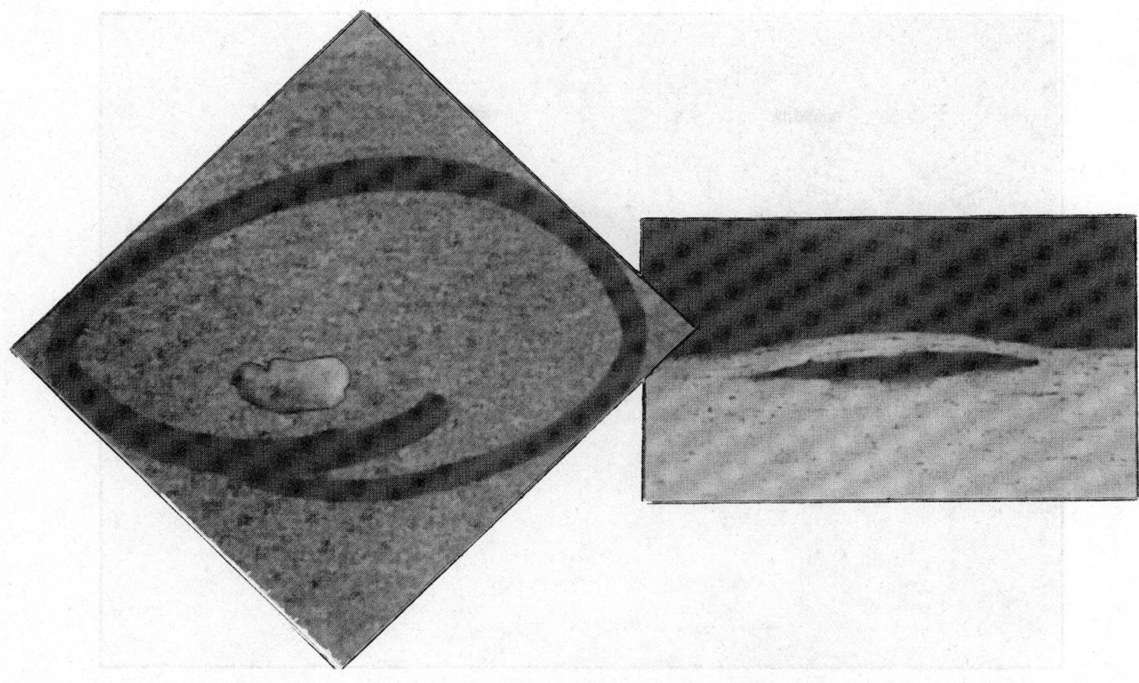

Description:	Blister is a small raised area on the steel surface. It may be an isolated spot or it may occur as longitudinal streaks.
Cause:	Blisters are caused by the expansion of gas concentrated at a subsurface inclusion.
Similar Imperfection:	Pinhead, Stringers

FIGURE 1—BLISTERS

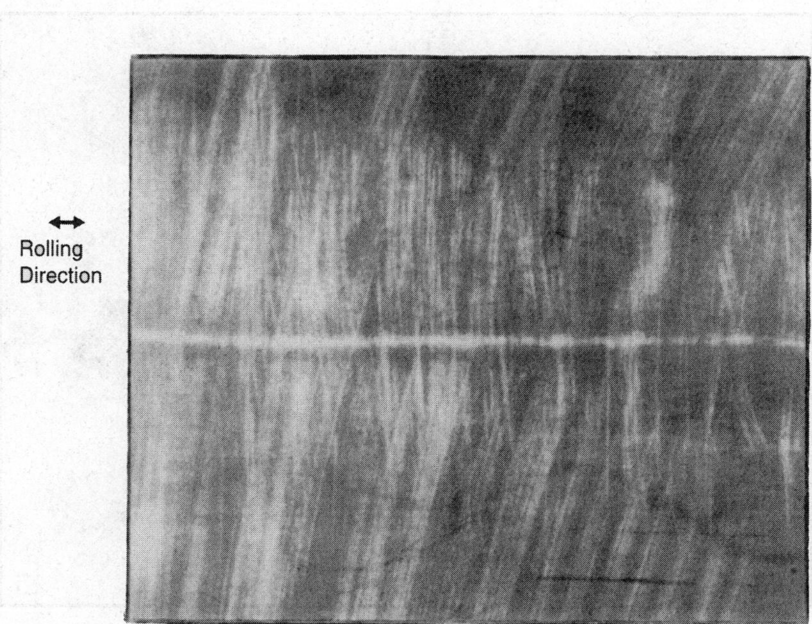

Description:	Ghost lines appear in a panel after it is formed. They may not be evident until the panel is drawn. These lines run parallel to the direction of rolling. Stoning brings out the ghost lines.
Cause:	Ghost lines are caused by improper deoxidation.

FIGURE 2—GHOST LINES

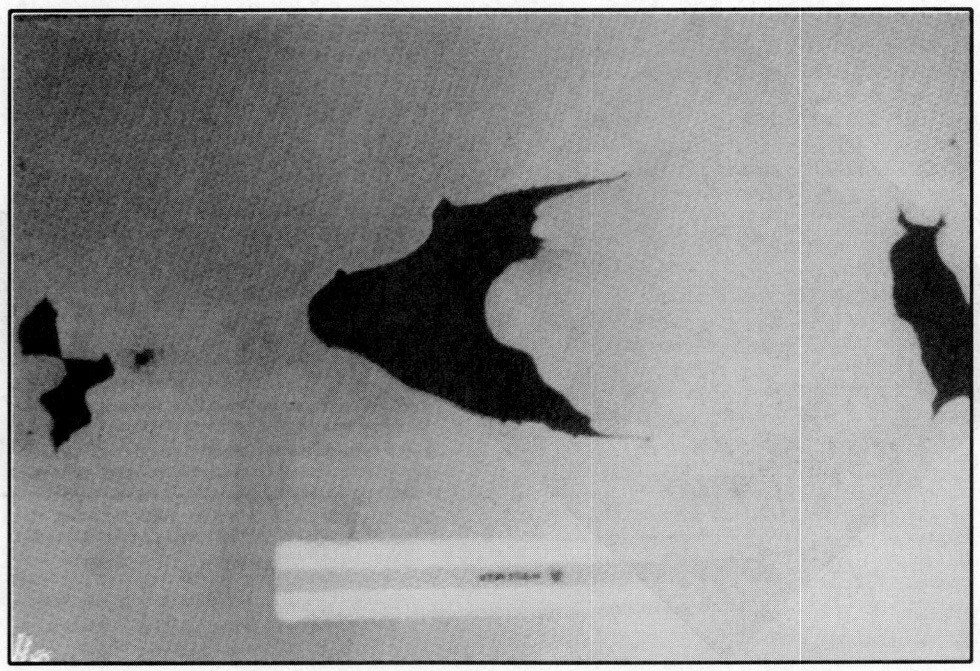

Description:	Holes are actual voids in the surface of the sheet. They are variable in severity.
Cause:	Holes result from skin laminations and pipe laminations which open up during rolling.

FIGURE 3—HOLES

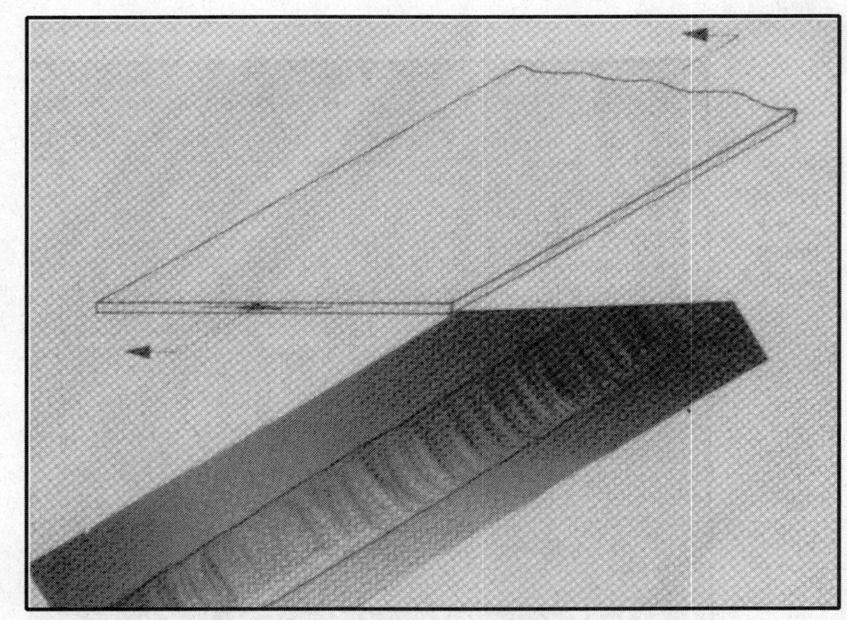

Description:	Pipe lamination is an internal imperfection running parallel to the rolling direction. It appears as a separation midway between the surfaces.
Cause:	Pipe lamination results from segregation and the presence of oxide inclusions.

FIGURE 4—PIPE LAMINATION

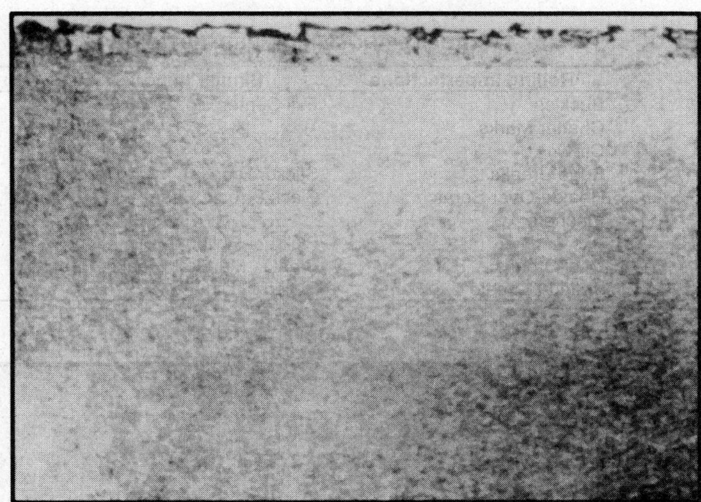

Description:	Ragged edge (sawtooth edge) is a serrated edge due to a slitting line burr that is work hardened and subsequently fractured or deformed during the rolling operation.
Cause:	Ragged edge can be originated by: • Wrong chemistry and bad heating practices • Poor slitting • Damage during annealing
Similar Imperfection:	Damaged Edge

FIGURE 5—RAGGED EDGES

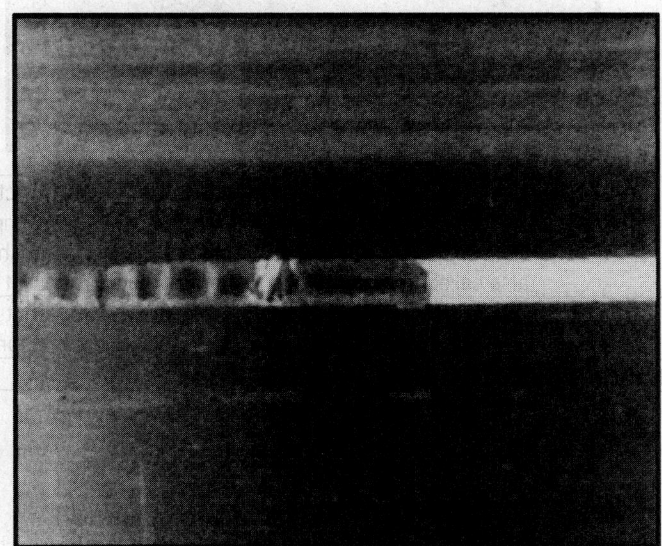

Description:	A sliver is a prominent surface rupture consisting of a very thin elongated piece of metal attached only by one end to the parent steel into whose surface it has been rolled. Slivers will vary in severity and frequency.
Cause:	• Improper composition (overoxidized, high sulfur) • Improper teeming (scabs) • Improper heating (burning) • Tearing of corners in early stages of rolling • Inadequate conditioning Slivers can also be generated mechanically.
Similar Imperfection:	Scab, Seam, Skin Lamination

FIGURE 6—SLIVER

5. Rolling Imperfections—(See Table 3 and Figures 7 to 15.)

TABLE 3—ROLLING IMPERFECTIONS

Rolling Imperfections	Similar Imperfections
Buckles	Full Center, Edge Wave
Chatter Marks	
Crown	
Edge Breaks	Sticker Breaks
Healed-Over-Scratch	Black Streak, Seam
Pinchers	
Pits	Pick-up, Rolled-in Dirt
Reel-Breaks	Breaks, Mandrel Breaks, Reel Kink
Rolled-In Scale	Rolled-in Dirt

Rolling Direction

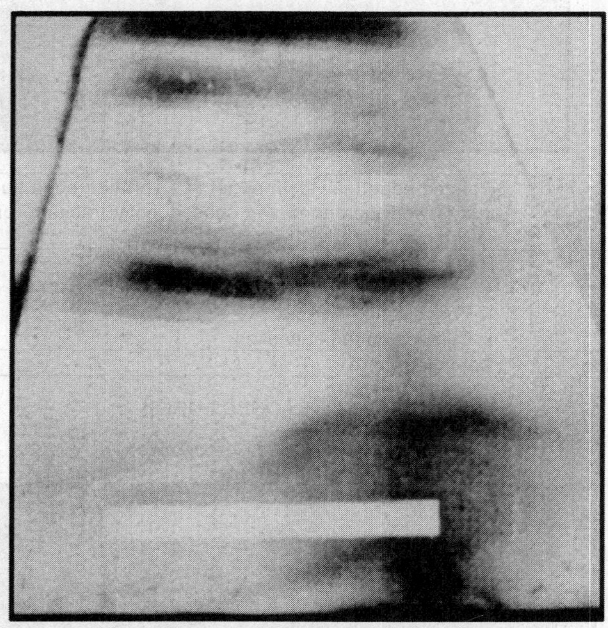

Description:	Buckles are a series of waves transverse to the direction of rolling. This condition varies in severity and frequency. The imperfection is called Center Buckle when it is located in the middle of the sheet, or Side Buckle (also called Quarter Buckle) when it is located near, but off, center.
Cause:	Buckles are caused by hardness variations of the hot rolled sheet due to uneven cooling of the steel or mill rolls, build-up, or poor rolling practice.
Similar Imperfection:	Full Center, Edge Wave

FIGURE 7—BUCKLES

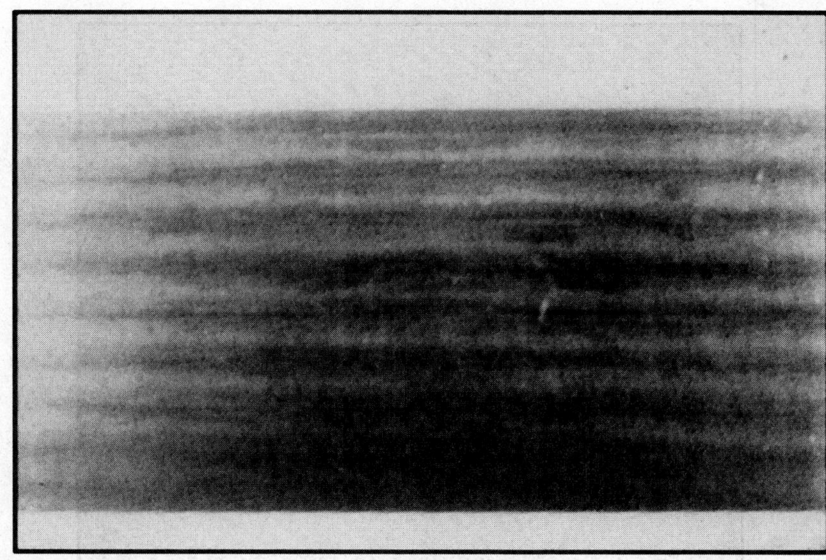

Description:	Intermittent surface distortion perpendicular to the direction of rolling (across the width). They may or may not be perceptible to the touch. They may appear as alternate bright and dull streaks. They can be highlighted by stoning.
Cause:	• Vibration during rolling • Lubricant failure causing fluctuation in the coefficient of friction between the roll face and the sheet surface • Improper tension between stands during rolling

FIGURE 8—CHATTER MARKS

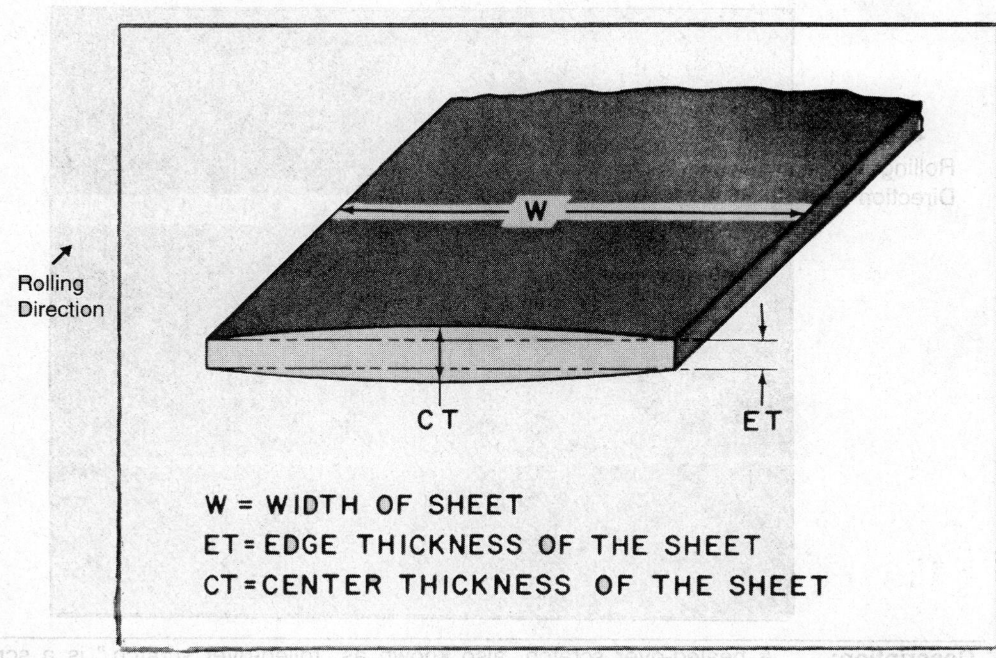

Rolling Direction

Description:	Crown exists when the thickness at the center of the sheet is greater than at the edges. Under normal conditions a flat rolled product will exhibit a crown. This condition is classified as an imperfection when the center thickness of the sheet exceeds the published thickness tolerances.
Cause:	Crown can be caused by the bending of the rolls, worn rolls, improperly ground rolls, or rolling practices.

FIGURE 9—CROWN

Rolling Direction

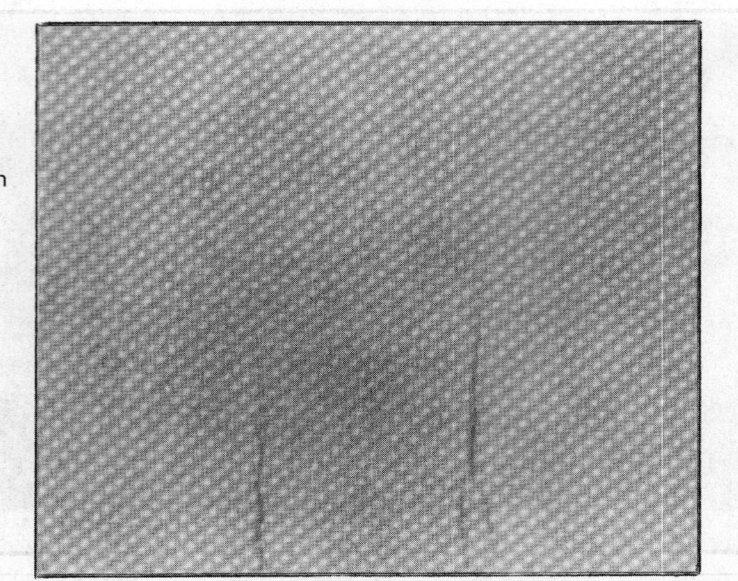

Description:	Edge breaks are short creases which extend in from the side edge of the temper rolled sheet.
Cause:	Edge breaks are found in steel where the extreme sheet edges are substantially thinner than the rest of the sheet and, therefore, are placed in tension during the temper rolling process.
Similar Imperfection:	Sticker Breaks

FIGURE 10—EDGE BREAKS

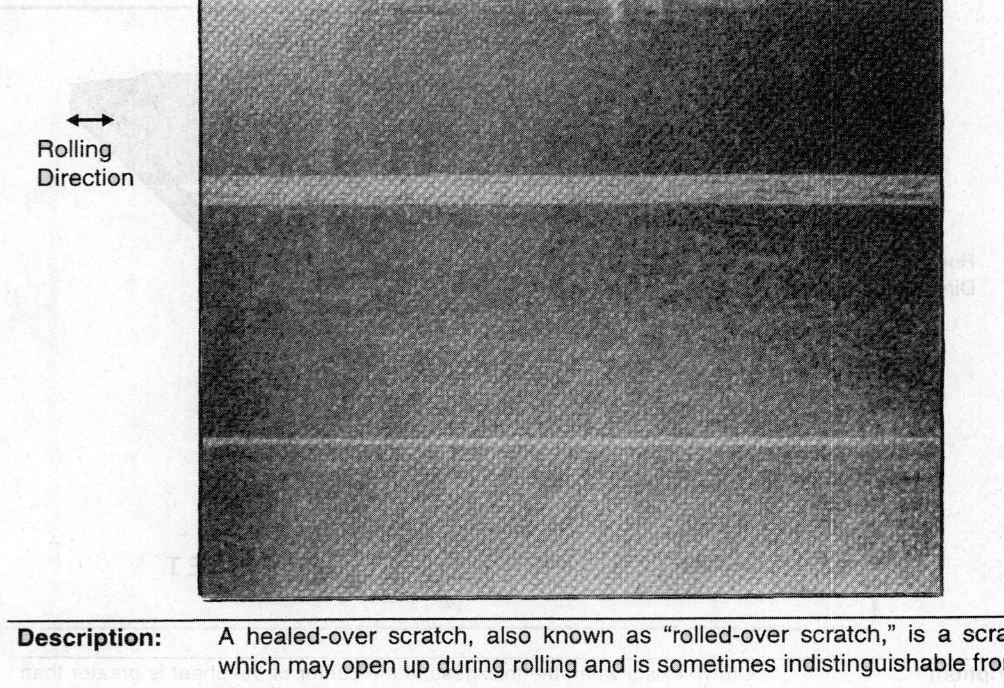

Description:	A healed-over scratch, also known as "rolled-over scratch," is a scratch which may open up during rolling and is sometimes indistinguishable from a seam.
Cause:	A scratch which originated in a previous mill operation and it has been partially masked in subsequent rolling.

FIGURE 11—HEALED-OVER SCRATCH

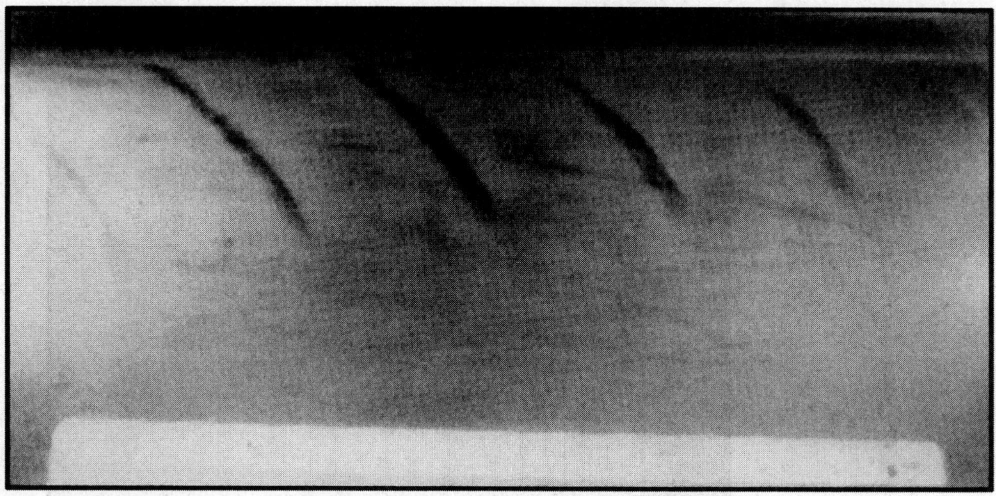

Description:	Pinchers (feathering) occur during temper rolling. They can be observed with the naked eye and usually they run diagonal to the direction of rolling.
Cause:	Pinchers may occur locally or across the width of the sheet. They are caused when the profile of the ingoing strip does not coincide with that of the "roll gap" during temper rolling (Ex: wavy strip).

FIGURE 12—PINCHERS

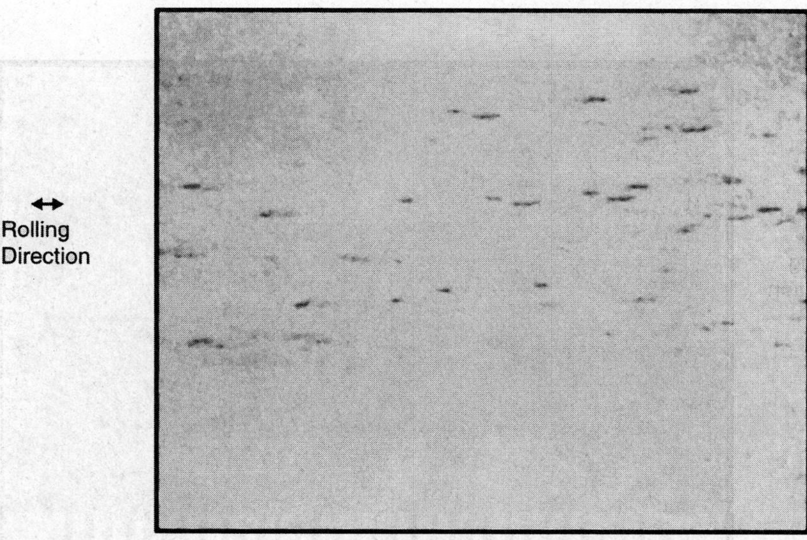

Description:	Pits are small cavities in the surface of the steel. Pits are randomly distributed indentations.
Cause:	• Pits can be caused by the temper mill rolls. Pits that repeat periodically are called Grease Pits. • Pits can be caused by picked-up sand from the box-type annealing furnaces. The sand is rolled into the surfaces and they appear as multiple small pits about 12 in from the edge; they are Sand Pits. • Pits can be caused by rolled-in scale which has been removed by pickling; they are called Scale Pits. • Pits can be caused by foreign particles or metal flakes, which are rolled into and fall out of the surface of the steel, they are called: Slug Pits.
Similar Imperfection:	Pick-Up, Rolled-In Dirt, Rolled-In Scale

FIGURE 13—PITS

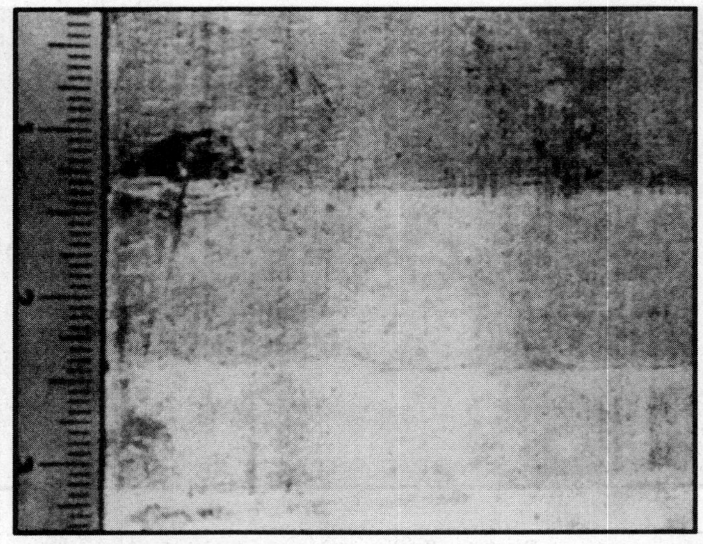

Description:	Reel breaks are transverse breaks or ridges on successive inner laps of a coil.
Cause:	Reel breaks originate when the lead end of the coil may not have been properly entered into the clamp. They are also caused by excessive tension during coiling.
Similar Imperfection:	Breaks, Mandrel Breaks, Reel Kink

FIGURE 14—REEL BREAKS

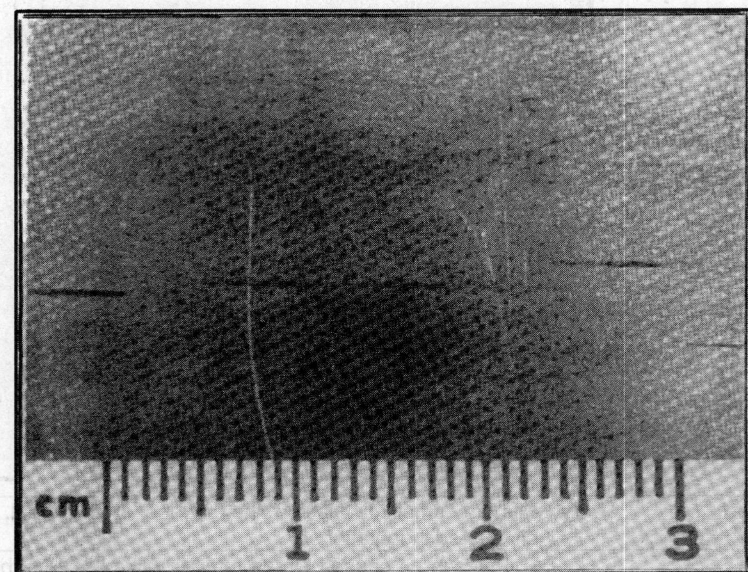

Description:	Rolled-in scale appears as dark streaks in the rolling direction.
Cause:	Rolled-in scale results when scale is partially rolled into the surface of the sheet. This condition can cause holes in certain products.

FIGURE 15—ROLLED-IN SCALE

6. Processing Imperfections—(See Table 4 and Figures 16 to 24.)

TABLE 4—PROCESSING IMPERFECTIONS

Processing Imperfections	Similar Imperfections
Camber	
Coil Welds	
Friction Digs	Gouges, Coil Digs
Lüder Lines	Stretcher Strains
Orange Peel	Alligator Skin
Oscillation	
Speckled Rust	Rust Patches, Pinpoint Rust
Sticker Breaks	Coil Breaks, Edge Breaks
Telescoping	

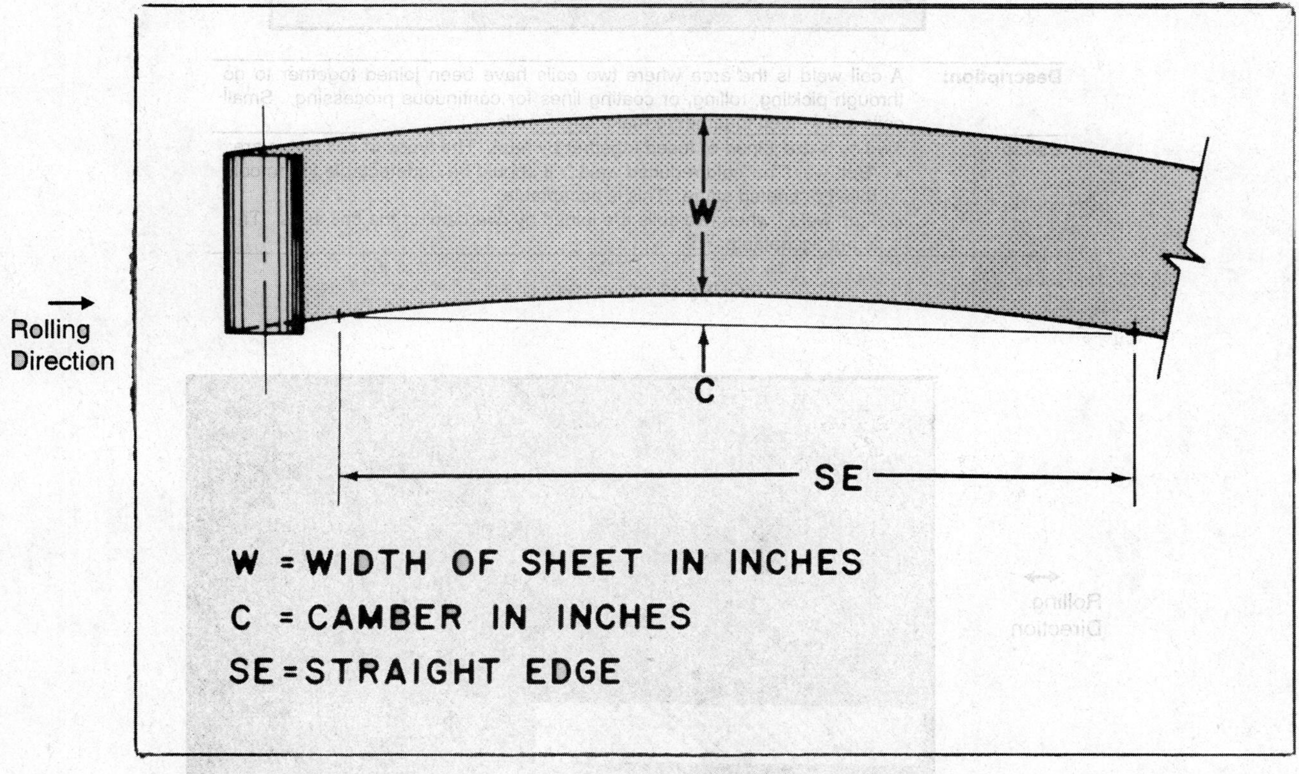

Description:	Camber is the deviation of a sheet edge from a straight line. It is measured as the greatest deviation of the concave edge of the sheet from a straight line.
Cause:	Camber is the result of bad slitting or is caused when the mill is off level when the sheet is rolled. Camber can also be caused by edge wave and center buckle.

FIGURE 16—CAMBER

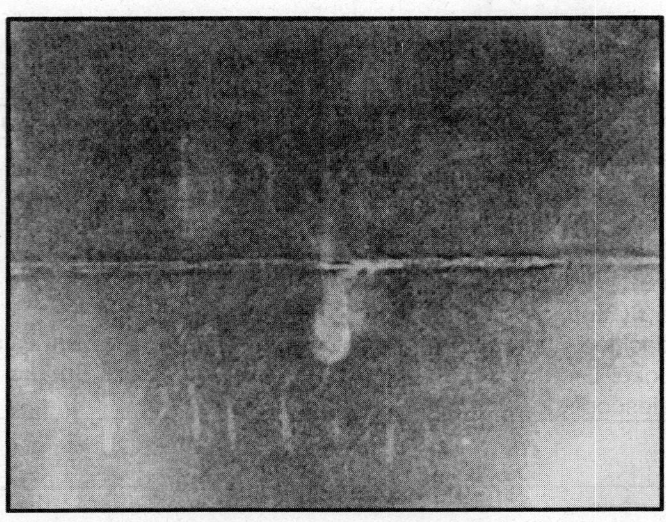

Description:	A coil weld is the area where two coils have been joined together to go through pickling, rolling, or coating lines for continuous processing. Small coils are welded together to make larger coils.
Cause:	Two coils are joined or fused together by heat. The types of coil welds are: • "Butt weld" or "cold reduced weld." It should be undetectable in the cold rolled or coated stage. This is acceptable. • "Lap weld," when two coils are joined by overlapping the coil ends. This is not acceptable.

FIGURE 17—COIL WELD

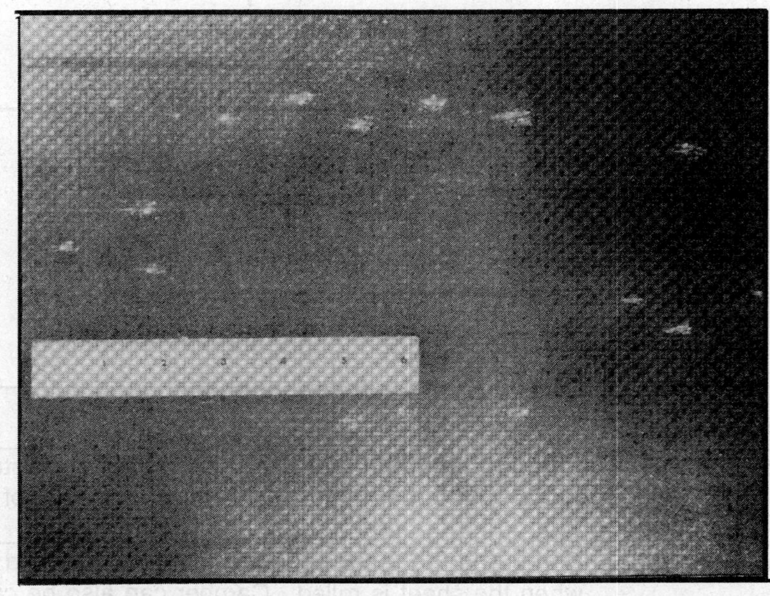

Description:	Friction digs are short scratches running in the longitudinal or diagonal direction. They are usually deeper than handling or mechanical scratches.
Cause:	Friction digs are caused by slippage of adjacent laps of a coil during uncoiling and coiling.

FIGURE 18—FRICTION DIGS

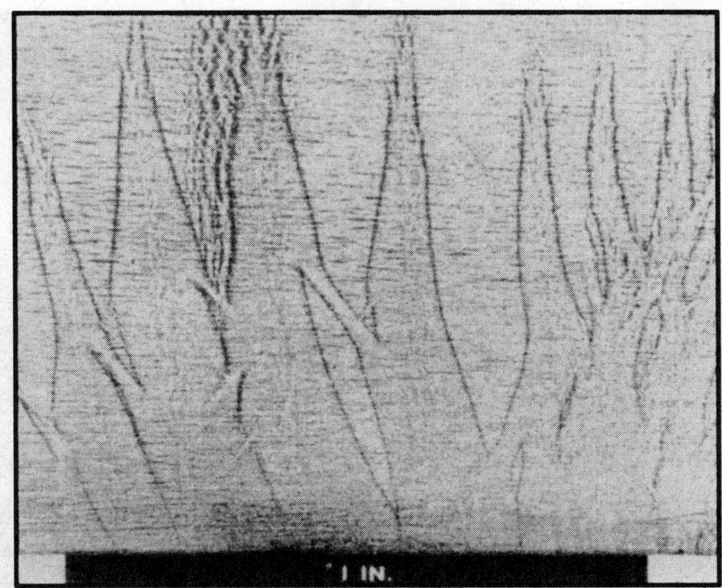

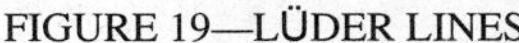

Description:	Lüder lines, also called stretcher strains, are lines which occur during forming. For exposed applications, they are objectionable, since they cause uneven, undulating surfaces.
Cause:	These lines are associated with the yield point. When the yield point is exceeded, nonuniform plastic deformation occurs. With increased stretching, these zones multiply and intersect each other, until the entire surface is covered with these type of lines.

FIGURE 19—LÜDER LINES

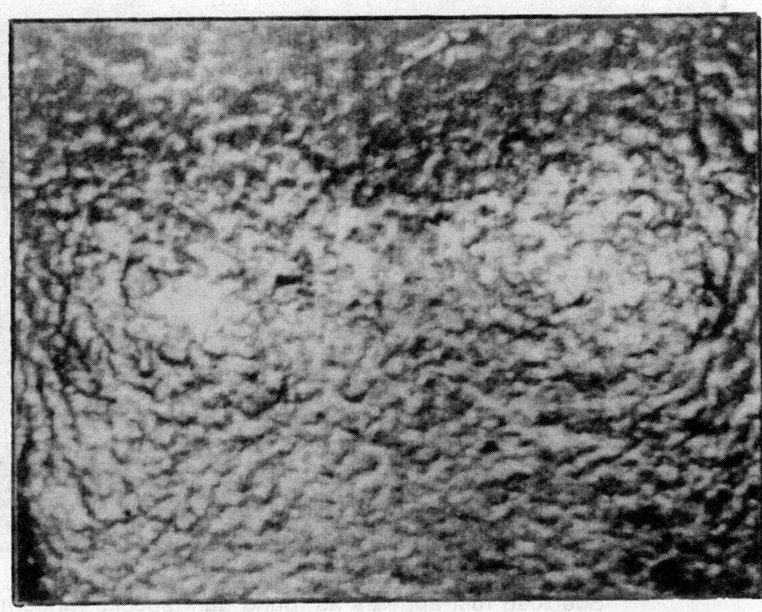

Description:	Orange peel is a rough surface in the form of a pebbly-grained pattern produced during forming (drawing operation) when the metal has a very coarse grain size and is stressed beyond its elastic limit. Also called alligator skin.
Cause:	Coarse grain structure occurs because of secondary recrystallization after deformation when annealing at high temperatures.

FIGURE 20—ORANGE PEEL

Description:	The wraps of the oscillated coil are wound unevenly, resulting in an intermittent telescoping condition throughout the coil.
Cause:	• Temporary loss of tension during coiling

FIGURE 21—OSCILLATION

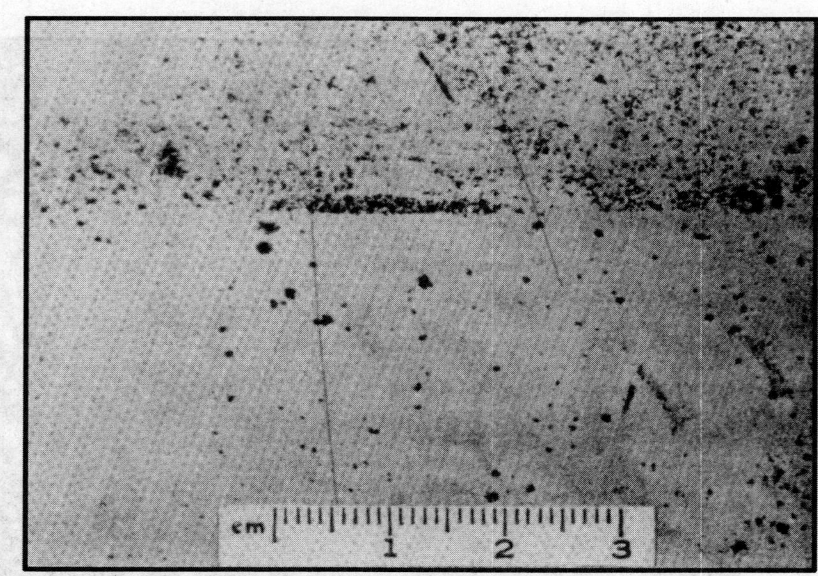

Description:	Speckled rust appears as round dark specks randomly distributed on the surface of the coil.
Cause:	Speckled rust is caused by high humidity or moisture spray.
Similar Imperfection:	Lineal Rust, Pin Point Rust, Rust Patches

FIGURE 22—SPECKLED RUST

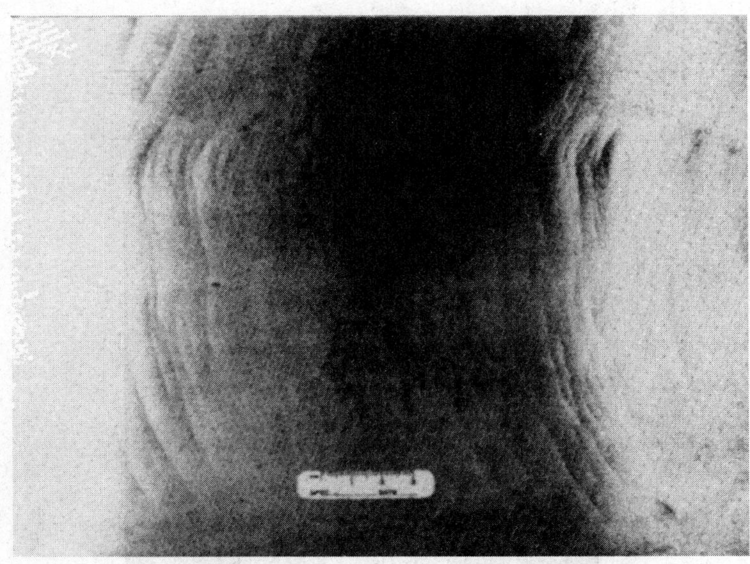

Description:	Sticker breaks are creases or ridges which appear as roughly arc-shaped lines running transverse to the direction of rolling and usually near the middle of the sheet.
Cause:	Sticker breaks are formed as a result of coil laps sticking together during uncoiling, because of: • Coils being too tightly wound prior to annealing • Surface too smooth • Annealing temperature too high • Damaged coils (bumped) prior to annealing
Similar Imperfection:	Coil Breaks, Edge Breaks

FIGURE 23—STICKER BREAKS

Description:	Telescoped coils are formed when transverse slipping of successive inner wraps of the coil occurred giving the formation of a cone between the inner wraps and the OD.
Cause:	• Wrap to wrap slippage during coiling • Uneven wrap in coiling and lateral travel during winding • Wrap too loosely

FIGURE 24—TELESCOPING

7. ***Coating Imperfections***—(See Table 5 and Figures 25 and 26.)

TABLE 5—COATING IMPERFECTIONS

Coating Imperfections	Similar Imperfections
Dross Stringers	Seam Line
Line-Stop	Bare Spots

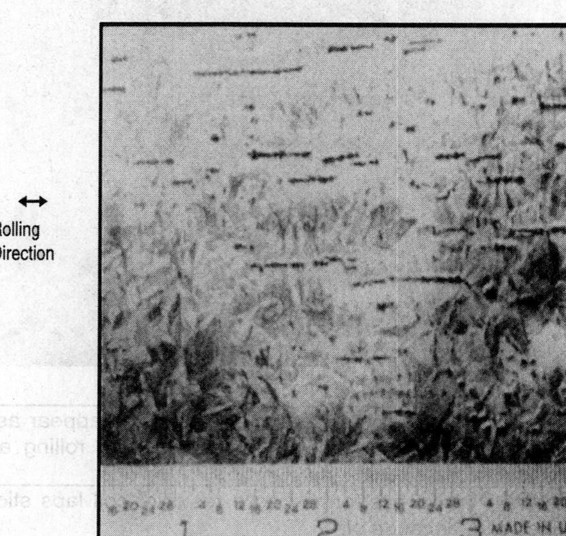

Description:	Dross stringers appear as raised lines in the rolling direction on the surface of "hot-dipped" galvanize and terne plate.
Cause:	Dross stringers are caused when the scum that floats on the surface of the molten metal is picked up by the steel strip and streaked onto the coating by the control knives as the strip exits from the bath.
Similar Imperfection:	Seam Line

FIGURE 25—DROSS STRINGERS

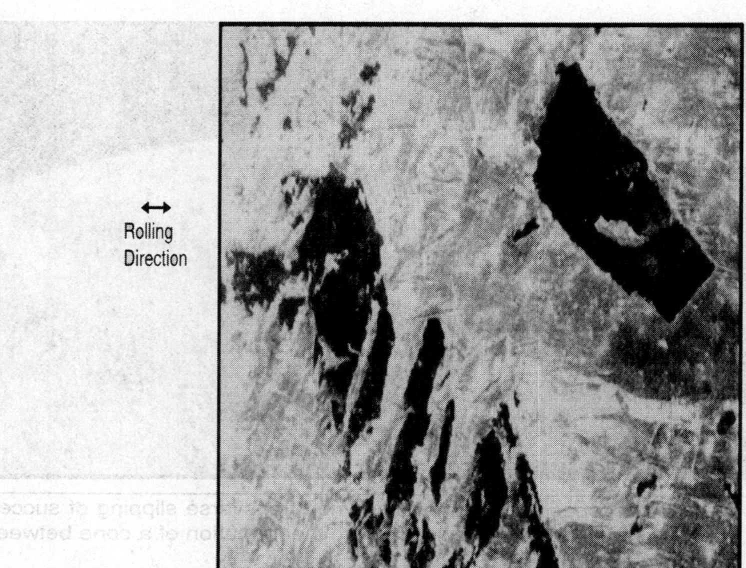

Description:	A line stop is an area on the surface of the steel where there is no coating (bare spots).
Cause:	A line stop is caused when the metal and fluxing agent are burned due to the operational shutdown of the "hot-dipped" coating line.

FIGURE 26—LINE STOP (HD COATED PRODUCTS)

BODY CORROSION—A COMPREHENSIVE INTRODUCTION—SAE J1617 NOV1993

SAE Information Report

Report of the SAE Automotive Corrosion and Prevention Committee Division 1-Body, approved November 1993.

Foreword—This Document has not changed other than to put it into the new SAE Technical Standards Board format.

1. Scope—The mechanism of automotive body corrosion is scientific, based on established laws of chemistry and physics. Yet there are many opinions related to the cause of body corrosion, not always based on scientific axioms. The purpose of this SAE Information Report is to present a basic understanding of the types of body corrosion, the factors that contribute to body corrosion, the testing procedures, evaluation of corrosion performance, and glossary of related terms.

1.1 Purpose—The purpose of this document is to provide a basic understanding of body corrosion as influenced by materials, environment, design, pretreatment and paint systems, and evaluation thereof. If the reader requires in-depth information on these subjects, additional reading material and personal contacts should be pursued with raw material, paint, chemical, and equipment suppliers.

2. References

2.1 Applicable Publications—The following publications form a part of the specification to the extent specified herein. Unless otherwise indicated the latest revision of SAE publications shall apply.

2.1.1 SAE PUBLICATION—Available from SAE, 400 Commonwealth Drive, Warrendale, PA 15096-0001.

SAE 892578—U.S. Automotive Corrosion Trends at 5 and 6 Years

2.1.2 OTHER PUBLICATIONS

1. Annual statistical report 1990, American Iron and Steel Institute, Washington, DC (1991), p. 25–27.
2. H. E. Townsend, "Coated Steel Sheets for Corrosion-Resistant Automobiles," Materials Performance, October 1991, p 60.; National Association of Corrosion Engineers, Corrosion '91, Paper # 91416, NACE, Houston, TX.
3. Y. Miyoshi, "State of the Art in Precoated Steel Sheet for Automotive Body Materials in Japan," ISIJ International, 31,1,1991, p1.
4. D. Quantin, D. Deparis, and J. C. Charbonnier, "Coated Steel Sheets for the Automotive Industry," Steel Technology International, 1990/1991, p245.
5. K. Yamoto, T. Ichida, and T. Irie, "Progress in Precoated Steel Sheets for Automotive Use," Kawasaki Steel Technical Report, #22, May 1990, p57.
6. "Cracking Down on Corrosion," American Iron and Steel Institute, Washington, 1991.
7. "Data on Aluminum Alloy Properties and Characteristics for Automotive Applications," The Aluminum Association, Washington, D.C., 4th Edition, February 1982.
8. "Registration Record of International Alloy Designations and Chemical Composition Limits for Wrought Aluminum and Wrought Aluminum Alloys," The Aluminum Association, Washington, D.C., April 1991.
9. "Aluminum Standards and Data, 1990," The Aluminum Association, Washington, D.C.
10. "Formability of ABS," Alcoa paper for SAE '93.
11. Aluminum: Properties and Physical Metallurgy, John E. Hatch ed., American Society for Metals, Metals Park, OH, 1984.
12. T. Komatsubara, T. Muramatsu, M. Matsuo; "Aluminum Alloy Rolled Sheet and Production Therefore," U.S. Patent No 4,838,958, June 13, 1989.
13. Metals Handbook Volume 13, Corrosion, American Society for Metals, Metals Park, OH, 1987.

3. Definitions

3.1 Acid—Acids can be defined in several ways. For many purposes it is sufficient to say that an acid is a hydrogen containing substance which dissociates on solution in water to produce one or more hydrogen ions. The Bronsted concept states that an acid is any compound that can furnish a proton. The more general Lewis definition of an acid is anything that can attach itself to something with an unshared pair of electrons.

3.2 Acidic—Anything having a pH that is less than 7 is considered acidic.

3.3 Acrylic—Resin polymerized from acrylic acid, methacrylic acid, esters of these acids, or acrylonitrile.

3.4 Active—A state in which a metal tends to corrode (opposite of passive).

3.5 Active Potential—The potential of a corroding metal.

3.6 Alkaline—For aqueous solutions, anything having a pH that is greater than 7 is considered alkaline.

3.7 Alkyd—Resin used in coatings. Reaction products of polyhydric alcohols and polybasic acids.

3.8 Alligatoring—Pronounced wide cracking over the entire surface of a coating having the appearance of alligator hide.

3.9 Aluminum Coated—Aluminum coated steel is produced by hot-dip coating cold-rolled sheet steel on continuous lines. It provides a material with the superior strength of steel and the surface properties of alumimum.

3.10 Aluminum-Zinc Coated—Aluminum-zinc alloy coated steel is produced by hot-dip coating cold-rolled sheet steel on continuous lines. It has the superior strength of steel and excellent corrosion resistance.

3.11 Anion—A negatively charged ion or radical (for example Cl^- or $SO_4^=$) which migrates toward the anode under the influence of a potential gradient.

3.12 Anode/Anodic—An electrode or portion of an electrode at which a net oxidation reaction occurs. This is the electrode, or area, that has the greater tendency to dissolve or corrode.

3.13 Anodic Coating—A coating that is anodic to the underlying substrate. Anodic coatings offer sacrificial protection to the substrate.

3.14 Anodic Inhibitor—A chemical substance or combination of substances that prevent or reduce the rate of the anodic or oxidation reaction by a physical, physico-chemical, or chemical action.

3.15 Anodic Potential—Electronegative potential.

3.16 Anodic Protection—A technique to reduce corrosion of a metal surface under some conditions by applying sufficient anodic current to it to cause its electrode potential to enter and remain in the passive region.

3.17 Anodizing—Oxide coating formed on a metal surface (generally, aluminum) by an electrolytic process.

3.18 Barrier Protection—A type of protection that relies on the coating preventing access of moisture or oxygen to the material being protected. Organic coatings often offer barrier protection to underlying substrates.

3.19 Base—Bases can be defined in several ways. For many purposes it is sufficient to say that a base is a substance which dissociates on solution in water to produce one or more hydroxyl ions. The Bronsted concept states that a base is any compound that can accept a proton. The more general Lewis definition of a base is anything that has an unshared pair of electrons.

3.20 Base Metal—A metal that is usually high in the Electromotive Force Series. Base metals have relatively poor corrosion resistance.

3.21 Basic—For aqueous solutions, anything having a pH that is greater than 7 is considered basic.

3.22 Bimetallic Corrosion—Corrosion resulting from dissimilar metal contact; galvanic corrosion.

3.23 Bituminous Coating—Coal tar or asphalt based coating.

3.24 Blister—A region of lifted paint typically caused by loss of adhesion within the paint system or between the paint and metal surface.

3.25 Block Coat/Blocking—Tie coat (adhesive) between noncompatible paints.

3.26 Blushing—Whitening and loss of gloss of a coating due to moisture; blooming.

3.27 Catalyst—A substance which alters the rate of a reaction by its presence and may be recovered unaltered in nature or amount at the end of the reaction.

3.28 Cathode—The electrode of an electrolytic cell at which reduction occurs. In corrosion processes, usually the area at which metal ions do not enter the solution. Typical cathodic processes are cations taking up electronsand being discharged, oxygen being reduced, and the reduction from a higher to a lower valence state.

3.29 Cathodic Coating—A coating that is cathodic to the underlying substrate.

3.30 Cathodic Corrosion—An unusual condition in which corrosion is accelerated at the cathode because the cathodic reaction creates an alkaline condition which is corrosive to certain metals (esp. with Al, Zn, Pb).

3.31 Cathodic Delamination—Type of corrosion damage caused by loss of adhesion between the paint finish and the metal.

3.32 Cathodic Inhibitor—A chemical substance or combination of substances that prevent or reduce the rate of cathodic or reduction reaction by a physical, physico-chemical, or chemical action.

3.33 Cathodic Potential—Electropositive potential.

3.34 Cathodic Protection—Reduction or elimination of corrosion by making the metal a cathode by means of impressed direct current or attachment to a sacrificial anode (usually Mg, Al, or Zn).

3.35 Cation—A positively charged ion or radical (for example Fe^{++} or NH_4^+) which migrates toward the cathode under the influence of a potential gradient.

3.36 Cavitation Corrosion—Cavitation Corrosion occurs on the low pressure side of propellers and pump impellers where interruption in smooth flow causes vapor bubbles to form. When these bubbles collapse, they can destroy any protective coating and remove minute particles of metal.

3.37 Cell—Electrochemical system consisting of an anode and a cathode immersed in an electrolyte. The anode and cathode may be separate metals or dissimilar areas on the same metal. When the electrodes are in electrical contact with each other, they develop a difference in potential which causes current to flow and produces corrosion at the anode. A cell involving an electrolyte in the corrosion process is referred to as an electrolytic cell.

3.38 Chalking—The development of loose removable powder at or just beneath a coating surface.

3.39 Checking—Surface cracking in a checkerboard-like pattern; this may be in a surface layer (coating) or on the metal surface itself.

3.40 Chemical Conversion Coating—A protective or decorative coating produced in situ by chemical reaction of a metal with a chosen environment.

3.41 Chromated—Parts treated with chromic acid to improve their corrosion resistance.

3.42 Clear Coat—A paint without pigment applied over a color basecoat to enhance the appearance and durability of the total paint system.

3.43 Concentration Cell—A cell involving an electrolyte and two identical electrodes, with the potential resulting from differences in the chemistry of the environments adjacent to the two electrodes.

3.44 Conductivity—The ability of a material to transfer heat or electricity. Copper is a good conductor of electricity.

3.45 Contact Corrosion—A term mostly used in Europe to describe galvanic corrosion between dissimilar metals.

3.46 Conversion Coating—An adherent reaction product layer on a metal surface formed by reaction with a suitable chemical; such as an iron phosphate film on iron developed by H_3PO_4.

3.47 Corrosion—The deterioration of a material, usually a metal, because of a reaction with its environment.

3.48 Corrosion Fatigue—Effect of the application of repeated or fluctuating stresses in a corrosive environment characterized by shorter life than would be encountered as a result of either the repeated or fluctuating stresses alone or the corrosive environment alone.

3.49 Corrosion Potential—The potential that a corroding metal exhibits under specific conditions of concentration, time, temperature, aeration, velocity, etc. Also called: rest potential, open circuit potential, freely corroding potential.

3.50 Corrosion Rate—The speed (usually an average) with which corrosion progresses (it may be linear for awhile); often expressed as though it was linear, in units of mdd (milligrams per square decimeter per day) for weight change, or mpy (mils per year) for thickness changes. Corrosion rates may be reported as: (a) A weight loss per area divided by the time (a milligram is 1/1000th of a gram) (there are 453.6 g/lb); and a decimeter is 3.937 in, or (b) The depth of metal corroded, divided by the time (a "mil" is 1/1000th of an inch).

3.51 Cosmetic Corrosion—Corrosion typically characterized by blistering and/or rusting that is aesthetically displeasing, but may not result in catastrophic failure of the item.

3.52 Couple—A cell developed in an electrolyte resulting from electrical contact between two dissimilar metals.

3.53 Cracking—Fracture of a metal in a brittle manner along a single or branched path.

3.54 Crazing—A network of checks or cracks appearing on a surface.

3.55 Creepback—The undercutting or the separation of paint from the substrate from an edge, damage site, or a scribe line.

3.56 Creep/Creepback—Time-dependent strain occurring under stress.

3.57 Crevice Corrosion—Localized corrosion resulting from the formation of a concentration cell in a crevice formed between a metal and a nonmetal, or between two metal surfaces.

3.58 Critical Humidity—The relative humidity above which the atmospheric corrosion rate of a given metal increases sharply.

3.59 Current—The "flow" of electricity expressed in amperes, milliamperes, and microamperes.

3.60 Current Density—The current per unit area; generally expressed as amps per sq cm.

3.61 Cyclic Testing—Accelerated testing and simulation of service conditions by the use of controlled alternating exposures to at least two corrosive environments, such as, salt or other chemical exposure, water immersion, temperature variations, humidity variations, ultraviolet (UV) light exposure, mud or clay contamination, gravel or shot blasting, and driving.

3.62 Deicing Salt—Salts, typically NaCl and/or $CaCl_2$, applied to highways to aid in seasonal deicing.

3.63 Deionized Water—Water that has had the charged species (Cl^-, Ca^{2+}, etc.) removed from it.

3.64 Deposit—A foreign substance, which comes from the environment, adhering to a surface of a material.

3.65 Deposit Attack—Corrosion occurring under or around a discontinuous deposit on a metallic surface.

3.66 Dew Point—Temperature at which condensation of water vapor from air occurs.

3.67 Differentially Zinc Coated—A sheet (usually steel) with a zinc coating of a different thickness on one side than on the other side.

3.68 Diffusion—The movement of one substance through another. Diffusion of contaminants into a paint system is often the cause of corrosion attack.

3.69 Direct Current—Electricity which flows in one direction at all times.

3.70 E Coat/ELPO—Common names for the electrocoating process.

3.71 Electrochemical—A chemical reaction which is driven by a difference in electrode potential from one site to another on the same or different parts.

3.72 Electrochemical Corrosion—Corrosion of metal caused by current flowing between anode and cathode areas in an electrolyte.

3.73 Electrochemical Potential—The partial derivative of the total electrochemical free energy of a constituent with respect to the number of moles of this constituent where all factors are kept constant.

3.74 Electrocoating—A method of coating a metal requiring the application of high voltages between an anode and a cathode in an electrolyte. Based upon the method of deposition, two types of electropaint have been developed: anodic and cathodic. Cathodic electrocoating is commonly used in the automotive industry.

3.75 Electrode—A conductor (usually a metal) through which current enters or leaves an electrolyte.

3.76 Electrode Potential—Voltage or potential of an electrode with respect to a reference half cell.

3.77 Electrodeposition—The deposition of a coating on an electrode by means of electrolysis.

3.78 Electrogalvanized—Steel containing a zinc coating produced by continuously electroplating zinc onto the steel surface.

3.79 Electrolysis—The chemical change in an electrolyte resulting from the passage of electricity.

3.80 Electrolyte—A chemical substance or mixture, usually liquid, containing ions which migrate in an electric field.

3.81 Electrolytic Cleaning—The process of degreasing or descaling a metal by making it an electrode in a suitable bath.

3.82 Electromotive Force—Force which causes a flow of current. Electromotive force is usually expressed in volts.

3.83 Electromotive Force Series/EMF Series—An orderly listing of elements according to their standard electrode potentials. (Hydrogen electrode is a reference point and is given the value of zero.)

3.84 Electroplated Coatings—Coatings applied in a low temperature continuous process where negatively charged steel sheet is passed between positively charged anodes. Metallic ions in an electrolyte bath are reduced and plated on the surface of the steel sheet forming the coating.

3.85 Embrittlement—Severe loss of ductility of a material due to a chemical or physical change.

3.86 Epoxy—Resin formed by the reaction of bisphenol and epichlorohydrin.

3.87 Erosion Corrosion—A corrosion reaction accelerated by the relative movement of a corrosive fluid and a metal surface.

3.88 Exfoliation Corrosion—Localized subsurface corrosion in zones parallel to the surface which result in thin layers of uncorroded metal resembling the pages of a book.

3.89 Filiform Corrosion—Corrosion which occurs under films in the form of randomly distributed hairlines.

3.90 Film—A thin surface layer that may or may not be visible.

3.91 Flash Coating—A very thin coating of paint or plating applied to provide limited corrosion protection or to improve the adhesion of subsequent coatings.

3.92 Fretting Corrosion—Deterioration at the interface between two contacting surfaces accelerated by relative motion between them of sufficient amplitude to produce slip.

3.93 Galvanic Cell—A cell consisting of two dissimilar metals in contact with each other and with a common electrolyte (sometimes refers to two similar metals in contact with each other but with dissimilar electrolytes; differences can be small and more specifically defined as a concentration cell).

3.94 Galvanic Corrosion—Corrosion associated with the current resulting from the electrical coupling of dissimilar electrodes in an electrolyte.

3.95 Galvanic Series—A list of metals arranged according to their relative corrosion potentials in some specific environment; sea water is often used.

3.96 Galvanized—Zinc coated sheet steel.

3.97 Galvanneal—Steel containing a zinc/iron alloy coating produced by either the hot-dip or electroplating process.

3.98 General Corrosion (see Uniform Corrosion)—Corrosion in a uniform manner.

3.99 Gravelometer—Machine used to cause consistent intentional paint damage to samples prior to or during laboratory corrosion testing. A gravelometer propels gravel or metal shot of a particular size and shape at the surface of a painted test specimen. The gravelometer is used to simulate the type of field paint damage caused by gravel or other road debris.

3.100 Heat Affected Zone (HAZ)—That portion of the base metal that was not melted during brazing, cutting, or welding, but whose microstructure and properties were altered by the heat of these processes.

3.101 Hem Flange—A method of joining two pieces of metal together in which the edge of one piece is folded tightly over the edge of the other.

3.102 Hot-Dip Coating—A continuous process of applying coatings to steel in which the steel is immersed in a molten bath of the coating material.

3.103 Holiday—Any discontinuity or bare spot in a coated surface.

3.104 Hot-Dip Galvanized—Steel containing a zinc coating produced by immersion of the steel in a molten zinc bath.

3.105 Impingement—Localized erosion-corrosion caused by turbulence or impinging flow at certain points. Also impact or road debris on surfaces.

3.106 Inhibitor—A chemical substance or combination of substances, which when present in the proper concentration and forms in the environment, prevents or reduces corrosion.

3.107 Inside-Out Corrosion—Corrosion that starts from the inside surface of a body panel and works outward.

3.108 Ion—An electrically charged atom or group of atoms.

3.109 Lamelar Corrosion (see Exfoliation)—Localized subsurface corrosion in zones parallel to the surface which results in thin layers of uncorroded metal resembling the pages of a book.

3.110 Local Cell—A galvanic cell resulting from inhomogeneities between areas on a metal surface in an electrolyte. The inhomogeneities may be of physical or chemical nature in either the metal or its environment.

3.111 Localized Corrosion—Corrosion resulting in differential attack across a metallic surface. Localized corrosion is typically of a cosmetic nature, but can lead to catastropic failure if a primary structural component is the site of severe attack.

3.112 Long Terne—Cold-rolled sheet steel coated on both sides with a lead-tin alloy by a continuous hot-dip process.

3.113 Metal Ion Concentration Cell—A galvanic cell caused by a difference in metal ion concentration at two locations on the same metal surface.

3.114 Metallizing—A process of coating a surface with a layer of metal; spraying, vacuum deposition, dipping, plasma jet, cementation, etc., are used.

3.115 Neutral—In aqueous solutions, a substance having a pH of 7 is considered neutral.

3.116 Neutralization—Hydrogen ions of an acid combined with hydroxyl ions of a base to form water ($H^+ + OH^- = HOH$).

3.117 Nickel Terne—Cold-rolled sheet steel electrolytically nickel flash plated and then coated on both sides with a lead-tin alloy by a continuous hot-dip process. Corrosion resistance is superior to standard long terne.

3.118 Noble/Noble Metal—A metal which is not very reactive, as silver, gold, and copper and may be found naturally in metallic form on earth.

3.119 Organic Coatings—Coatings, primarily paints, applied to metallic or other substrates typically to provide corrosion protection and to improve aesthetic characteristics of the material.

3.120 Outside-In Corrosion—Corrosion that starts from the outside surface of a body panel and works inward.

3.121 Oxidation—Loss of electrons by a constituent of a chemical reaction. The combination of oxygen with metal ions to form an oxide. Rust is iron oxide.

3.122 Passivation/Passive—A reduction of the anodic reaction rate of an electrode involved in electrochemical action such as corrosion.

3.123 Perforation Corrosion—Penetration of a panel due to corrosion. Perforation corrosion is usually associated with inside-out corrosion.

3.124 pH—A measure of the acidity or alkalinity of a solution. A value of seven is neutral; low numbers are acid, large numbers are alkaline. Strictly speaking, pH is the negative logarithm of the hydrogen ion concentration.

3.125 Phosphate Coatings—Protective coatings formed by reaction of a metallic substrate with an acidic phosphate containing solution. The primary role of the phosphate coating is to enhance adhesion of the primer (electrocoat or other) to the metal. Phosphate coatings are typically Zn, Fe, Zn-Ni, or Zn-Ni-Mn phosphates.

3.126 Pits—Localized corrosion of a metal surface, confined to a small area which takes the form of cavities.

3.127 Pitting—Highly localized corrosion resulting in deep penetration at only a few spots.

3.128 Pitting Corrosion—A type of perforation corrosion. Pitting corrosion is highly localized corrosion resulting in deep penetration at only a few spots.

3.129 Polarization—The deviation from the open circuit potential of an electrode resulting from the passage of current.

3.130 Polarization Curve—A plot of current density versus electrode potential for a specific electrode-electrolyte combination.

3.131 Polyester—Resin formed by condensation of polybasic and monobasic acids with polyhydric alcohols.

3.132 Potential—See electrochemical potential.

3.133 Poultice—An accumulation of mud, sand, salt, and other road debris on the interior surface joints of body panels and structural components.

3.134 Precoated—A material that has been coated prior to the manufacture of the ware or part.

3.135 Pretreatment—The treatment of a surface prior to the process of interest, for example: a phosphate coating is a pretreatment for electrocoat or painting.

3.136 Prime Coat—A first coat of paint applied to inhibit corrosion and/or improve adherence of the next coat.

3.137 Primer—Primer—First coat of paint applied to a surface. Formulated to have good bonding and wetting characteristics; may or may not contain inhibitive pigments.

3.138 Proving Ground Tests—Cyclical programs primarily conducted by the automotive companies to realistically evaluate the effects of corrosive elements on the performance of fully assembled vehicles. Proving Ground Tests often combine on-road and laboratory exposures.

3.139 Reaction Cell—A cell at which a chemical reaction is occurring. See "Cell."

3.140 Reduction—Gain of electrons by a constituent of a chemical reaction.

3.141 Relative Humidity—The ratio, expressed as a percentage, of the amount of water present in a given volume of air at a given temperature to the amount required to saturate the air at that temperature.

3.142 Rust—Corrosion product consisting primarily of hydrated iron oxide—a term properly applied only to iron and ferrous alloys.

3.143 Rust Proofing—The application of coatings intended to prevent or greatly reduce the formation of rust on steel parts.

3.144 Sacrificial Protection—Reduction of corrosion of a metal in an electrolyte by galvanically coupling it to a more anodic metal. A form of cathodic protection.

3.145 Saponification Corrosion—Formation of a soap by the reaction of corrosion products with some organic coatings.

3.146 Scab Corrosion—Cosmetic corrosion caused by break down of the surface protection system often proceeded by blisters.

3.147 Scribe—Intentional paint damage typically used for material evaluation during corrosion testing.

3.148 Sealers—Products applied to joints or seams to prevent the entry of moisture or contaminants. Paint coatings applied to prevent the undesirable interaction of a subsequent coating with a previous coating or to enhance adhesion or corrosion protection.

3.149 Selective Corrosion—The selective corrosion of certain alloying constituents from an alloy (as dezincification), or in an alloy (as internal oxidation).

3.150 Slushing Compound—A non-drying oil, grease, or similar organic compound which, when coated over a metal, affords at least temporary protection against corrosion.

3.151 Thermogalvanic Corrosion—Corrosion resulting from a galvanic cell caused primarily by a thermal gradient.

3.152 Throwing Power—The relationship between the current density at a point on the specimen and its distance from the counter electrode. The greater the ratio of the surface resistivity shown by the electrode reaction to the volume of resistivity of the electrolyte the better is the throwing power of the process.

3.153 Undercutting—See "Creepback."

3.154 Underfilm Corrosion—Corrosion which occurs under films in the form of randomly distributed hairlines (filiform corrosion).

3.155 Uniform Corrosion—Corrosion which appears on the surface of a part and is not associated with joints and is not pitting. See "Cosmetic Corrosion."

3.156 Voids—A term generally applied to paints to describe holidays, holes, and skips in the film. The term "void" is also used to describe shrinkage in castings or welds.

3.157 Wash Primer—A thin inhibiting paint usually chromate pigmented with a polyvinyl butyrate finder.

4. Historical Development—The automotive industry and its supply base have worked together to achieve many unique accomplishments. Some originated as new technology while others resulted from solving customer dissatisfactions. Increasing vehicle durability has been an ongoing customer satisfaction item for the automotive industry with varying degrees of emphasis since the automobile was invented.

4.1 Early Galvanized Applications and Electrocoat Priming—The use of galvanized steel for rocker panels in the late 1950s and early 1960s, and the introduction of electrocoat priming in the late 1960s were two of the most noteworthy and far reaching changes. The steel industry responded to the automotive industry's needs and worked on the development of a minimum spangle, two-side hot-dip galvanized sheet. The application of this product for rocker panels set the stage for other applications. Meanwhile, the chemical and paint industries also responded with the development of an immersion primer system which was supposed to infiltrate into all the hidden cavities and crevices to reduce perforation corrosion.

A "Catch 22" situation was developing since state and local highway departments were also trying to react to their "customers'" demand for better driving conditions and increased the usage of salt to deice the roadways of many northern states. This increased usage of salt accelerated the corrosion of the vehicle bodies.

The automotive industry was developing its own new corrosion problems with the sleek, finned styling associated with the late 1950 and 1960 vehicles. Thinner body materials were used to form these styling designs. These designs were found to be more difficult to assemble and protect with existing sealers, primers, and paints. Another new generation of materials was required.

Galvanized steel became more common, especially for unexposed areas that had been susceptible to poor durability. Minimum spangle hot-dip galvanized steel sheet was modified so that the spangle pattern was appropriate for use in exposed panel applications, such as cowl tops. New manufacturing equipment was necessary for spot welding. New pretreatment chemicals, compatible with zinc coatings, were developed.

Deicing salts continued to be used in increasing amounts in the northern snow belt areas and for dust control (replacing waste oil) for unpaved roads. This created an accelerating corrosion problem since the combination of heat, moisture, and salt resulted in very active galvanic cells with the car bodies being consumed in the salt electrolyte. Automotive engineers became aware of the acceleration of corrosion in many Canadian localities. Due to the severity of corrosion problems, Toronto, Montreal, and Nova Scotia became the "university" for corrosion engineers and the test site for automotive suppliers of precoated steel, pretreatment systems, primer, paint systems, and wax and sealant manufacturers.

New industries were initiated to fulfill the customer needs through aftermarket goods and services, such as undercoating and rust proofing. While it is easy to think of problems associated with perforation corrosion, this is not the only issue of body durability that was addressed. Cosmetic corrosion had been an issue with both the automotive industry and its customers. Changes in the type of primers, primer surfaces, and topcoats improved cosmetic durability. Development of new waxes to help protect these paint systems was similar to the development of undercoatings that increased underbody life. Paint systems also needed to withstand the effects of deicing salts as well as other environmental factors such as sunlight, industrial fall out, and acid rain.

Environmental factors continued to worsen over the years making the task of increasing vehicle body durability more complex and difficult. A tenfold, increase in the amount of deicing salts, occurred from 1955 to 1985. The complexity of this salt also increased with a mixture of NaCl and $CaCl_2$ being used, particularly in Canada for low-temperature deicing, and in other locations for year round dust control. Air pollution became more widespread and extended into many rural areas. These issues were not unique to the United States and Canada, but also existed in Europe and other countries. These environmental issues became a factor for automotive manufacturers that exported their products to other parts of the world.

As previously stated, new materials and primer systems were introduced in the 1960s. Vehicle undercoating was applied at both dealerships and specialty shops. Basic perforation corrosion warranties only covered 12 months or 12 000 miles (12/12 system). Dip primers were replaced by anodic electrocoat systems and finally by cathodic electrocoating systems. Changes in the manufacturing system occurred like the introduction of weldable zinc-rich primers applied prior to subassembly to improve perforation performance. New sealers and sound deadeners were introduced.

4.2 Technological Developments—Raw Materials, Components, Manufacturing—In the 1970s, an acceleration of new technological developments occurred in raw materials, components, and vehicle manufacturing. Steel processing changes include a higher percentage of aluminum killed steel for body panels and changes in annealing gas composition providing a cleaner surface and improved paint adhesion. Coil-coating technology and paints were developed that provided the automotive industry with a baked-on one-side coated steel product that was formable with good barrier protection, extending body panel durability. New technology was developed making one-side electroplated zinc sheet steel available for exposed body panels. Due to the added cost and limited availability, the use of this product was restricted to areas of high corrosion susceptibility. The combination of a two-side coated minimum spangled material for an inner panel combined with a one-side electroplated zinc material for an outer panel was believed to provide a vehicle designed for 5-year durability. Mechanical properties (forming) of hot-dip galvanized steel were improved, extending the use of more complex shapes. Aluminum and plastic made inroads into the material area for a multitude of reasons—weight savings, parts consolidation, styling and corrosion improvement. While aluminum was used for vehicle bodies in the 1950s for low-volume specialty vehicles, the application in the 1970s was primarily for weight savings. Corrosion improvement of the material was offset by the necessity to isolate it from the adjoining steel used on other body components. Some of these isolators were not well designed and eventually caused subsequent repairs. Processing of aluminum also created changes in manufacturing, such as new handling techniques, metal finishing practices, and welding techniques. Similarly, plastic components had to be handled and assembled or joined differently, and painted off-line. Some types of plastic/steel reinforced assemblies were required to withstand impact and required a flexible paint system that could match existing paint systems for color and weathering. Sheet molding compound parts required a unique sealer/primer which was typically applied by the supplier, off-line painted, and assembled to the finish painted vehicle.

Other materials developed and used in the 1970s include: expandable sealers and new types of waxes. Paint pretreatment systems were modified, stages added, and minimum timing requirements established. The types of top coats available expanded and some types of paints eliminated due to air pollution. Body panel and total vehicle design were impacted again with the shift to body immersion primer systems and the need for fluid entry and exit, as well as the sensitivity to current flow for electrocoat efficiency. Primer oven cure temperature and conductivity restricted the assembly of plastic components to post-paint operations. Exterior stone chip protection was added late in the 1970s although lower body design modifications were made earlier in an effort to minimize or eliminate stone chipping caused by new wide low profile tires. Other design changes affected outer body panel styling lines. Use of door edge guards and body side moldings increased clearance between portions of inner and outer panels and the location and size of drain holes. The trend in design was an increased awareness of the impact of design on vehicle body durability while improving "packaging" and exterior aerodynamics to meet fuel economy standards.

Another reason for the interest in improving body durability was the passage of legislation in Canada requiring 3-year body durability—no perforations. This government mandate was later incorporated into most manufacturers' warranties in the United States. Cosmetic warranties were extended from a typical 90-day coverage to a time period of up to 12/12 depending upon the manufacturer. As the 1980s arrived, the 3-year corrosion warranties continued to be increased with some government incentives, again initiated by Canada and followed in the U.S., for a 5-year perforation-free exterior body. This reflects the greater severity of the Canadian environment than the U.S., as explained in 3.1. U.S. automotive manufacturers decided to use the corrosion improvements as marketing tools, and therefore, offered somewhat different corrosion warranties on groups of vehicle lines. Perforation warranties varied from 3-year limited coverage to 6-year/ 100 000 miles. Cosmetic corrosion warranties also increased from limited time periods to 3-year coverage.

4.3 Further Technological Advances — Coated Sheet, Paint Systems, Design Changes—Technology changes in the 1980s included a wider range of one- and two-sided coated steel available in zinc and zinc alloy coating compositions of various thicknesses. The trend was from bare cold-rolled steel and the one-side zinc-rich coated paint product to two-side coated electroplated zinc. Current practice is that inner panels with any risk of corrosion (perforation or cosmetic) utilize some type of galvanized steel, usually a hot-dip galvanized coating. Some aluminum is still in use, but primarily for weight savings with precautions taken to preclude galvanic cells. Plastic has continued to replace steel with several all-plastic bodied vehicles being introduced. However, manufacturability and environmental issues have restricted wider use. Paint systems have continued to be modified. Electrocoat primer systems were modified to achieve higher filmbuilds while throwing power was studied to achieve more uniform coverage in box sections. Pretreatment systems were modified to achieve optimum phosphate coverage on a material mix that has a high percentage of zinc on the surfaces. Primed only surfaces have been nearly eliminated while water base color coat and clear coat were protecting the outer surfaces. Flexible bumper fascias with a more flexible paint system replaced most metal bumpers. And, flexible plastic skins are now commonly used as fairing to provide unique niche market aerodynamic designs. Tape stripes and other appliques provide other types of niche styling designs; however, these items are particularly susceptible to the cosmetic corrosion (deterioration) that displeases the customer. Exterior moldings and the attachment methods have also changed over the years. Many moldings have been adhesively bonded over the finished paint system. A variety of molding materials have been tried and used successfully ranging from traditional stainless steel, fastened with metal clips to weld studs, to other grades of unplated or plated stainless steel and fastened with plastic clips. A variety of plastic or rubber, black or color coordinated, moldings have and are still in use for body side protection along with plated zinc materials. The use of flush glass has eliminated many window moldings while other window moldings have been influenced by the desires of the designer for a uniform black appearance around the glass.

While the previous text provides limited insight into the changes in body material and paint system changes, limited data is available to qualify the accomplishments of the automotive industry and the supply base. Typically, each automotive manufacturer has developed its own accelerated corrosion tests for both cosmetic and perforation corrosion, all of which were correlated with the manufacturer's field and fleet survey data. Unfortunately, little of this data is ever shared with the manufacturers' supply base, much less the industry in general.

The Society of Automotive Engineers (SAE) Automotive Corrosion and Prevention Committee (ACAP) Division 1 Group has conducted three surveys of 5- and 6-year-old vehicles in 2 areas of Detroit to help establish a data base to monitor improvement in passenger car body durability. Two SAE papers have been published providing access to the field survey data of over 1200 vehicles. These surveys will be an ongoing project of this committee.

Results to date, as published in "Automotive Corrosion & Prevention Conference Proceedings" — P-228; Pages 185–198, or as "U.S. Automotive Corrosion Trends At 5 & 6 Years", SAE-892578 are shown in Table 1:

TABLE 1—DETROIT AREA FIELD SURVEY RESULTS (5- AND 6-YEAR-OLD CARS)

	Vehicle Years 1980–1	Vehicle Years 1982–3	Vehicle Years 1984–5
% of cars with a defect	86.1%	79.5%	59.0%
% of cars with blisters	60.8%	55.9%	33.5%
% of cars with surface rust	78.2%	76.1%	46.2%
% of cars with perforation	20.2%	7.6%	2.9%

Unfortunately, data from the Detroit area is not available for vehicles manufactured prior to 1980 and the readers will have to utilize other references or memory to try to make comparisons.

5. Types of Automotive Corrosion—General—Corrosion is the deterioration of a material because of a reaction with its environment. For example, in the case of a motor vehicle, the steel components, in the presence of water and salt (an electrolyte), combine with the oxygen in the air to produce rust. This process is predominantly electrochemical involving a transfer of electrons in an oxidation-reduction reaction.

The principals of electrochemical corrosion can be compared with the functioning of a dry cell battery which contains a graphite cathode (site of reduction) and a zinc anode (site of oxidation) in contact with a conductive solution (electrolyte). When the two electrodes (the positive and the negative) are connected with an electrically conductive material, current (electrons) will flow between them because of the difference in their oxidation-reduction (electrical) potentials. This current flow gradually consumes the anode.

The three essential parts of a corrosion cell are: (a) an anode, (b) a cathode, and (c) a conductive solution called an electrolyte. If any one part is missing, or if there is an interruption in the electrical path, current cannot flow and electrochemical corrosion cannot occur.

In general, two types of corrosion affect auto bodies: Corrosion that starts from the outside surface of a body panel and works inward, and that which starts from the inside and works outward. These are commonly referred to as OUTSIDE-IN CORROSION and INSIDE-OUT CORROSION. Outside-in corrosion, in its early stage, is often called COSMETIC CORROSION because its initial effects are generally a degradation of the appearance of the paint finish. Inside-out corrosion, on the other hand, is usually not visible until it has perforated the body panel. If unchecked, cosmetic corrosion can also lead to eventual perforation of the body panel; however, PERFORATION CORROSION is usually associated with inside-out corrosion.

Cosmetic Corrosion — There are several types of cosmetic corrosion. SCAB CORROSION, probably the most common form of cosmetic corrosion, is normally seen as surface blisters or scabs caused by a breakdown of the surface protection system. Scab corrosion can be affected by damage to the protective coating on the panel, such as stone chips or scratches.

Improper surface preparation or treatment of the metal prior to painting could cause a breakdown of the protective coating. This breakdown of the finish is sometimes caused by SAPONIFICATION. In saponification corrosion, a soap is formed by the reaction of corrosion products with some organic coatings. This reaction is accelerated by the presence of salt water and zinc compounds. The corrosion is formed at the interface of the metal panel and phosphate coating or the phosphate coating and prime coating interfaces. Under prolonged exposure to moisture, the adhesion between the metal substrate and the paint system is destroyed, and the paint forms blisters or simply peels off. While this type of failure can occur on almost any painted substrate, it is more common on painted galvanized steel. Saponification corrosion may occur if the galvanized surface is not properly treated prior to painting, and/or if the prime coat is not properly formulated for zinc-coated steel. Even when panels are properly processed, this type of corrosion is more commonly observed on repainted than original factory processed surfaces.

FILIFORM CORROSION is another form of finish degradation. It is identified by its hair or worm-like filaments. Filiform corrosion of body panels is usually associated with prolonged exposure to high humidity. It can initiate at damage sites or improperly prepared metal surfaces.

Cosmetic corrosion adjacent to trim or plated nameplates can be caused by various mechanism. GALVANIC CORROSION is one of the primary causes of this type of damage. Galvanic corrosion occurs when dissimilar metals are in electrical contact in the presence of an electrolyte. An electrical potential difference exists between the two metals and current flows. The more active material (less noble) is the anode, and the less active material is the cathode. The corrosion attack is more severe on the anodic material while the cathodic material is protected. Localized corrosion of an anodic region can result in perforation of a panel.

As an example, galvanic corrosion has been observed on panels at damage sites adjacent to stainless steel trim. At these sites, the less noble carbon steel of the body panel corrodes in deference to the more noble stainless steel of the trim. With the introduction of aluminum trim the condition is reversed. If any corrosion takes place, it is the aluminum trim that corrodes because aluminum is less noble than steel. This method lessens the degree of anodic corrosion observed in body panels, at trim areas.

However, this introduces a second mechanism of corrosion which is CATHODIC DELAMINATION. When cathodic delamination occurs, damage to the cathodic metal is caused by a loss of adhesion of the paint finish. Initially, paint blisters filled with water are formed on the cathodic metal (noble metal). The water, which becomes highly alkaline, due to the cathodic reaction, attacks the bonding mechanism of the paint system. Typically, corrosion of the metal surface does not take place until after the blisters are drained and the metal is exposed to the atmosphere. This type of corrosion is sometimes observed where galvanized steel panels join cold-rolled steel panels.

Perforation Corrosion — Inside-out corrosion, leading to perforation of the auto body, is destructive. When panel are perforated structural integrity may be compromised. At the very least, an expensive repair is in order. Perforation may be caused by several corrosion mechanisms. A common mechanism is CONCENTRATION CELL CORROSION. This is a condition in which local electrical potential differences arise between two areas of a metal surface exposed to different concentrations of dissolved ions in the same solution. Concentration cells are usually associated with crevices, recessed areas, or surface deposits, and can be broken down into different types. The type that most affects vehicle bodies is the METAL-ION CONCENTRATION CELL.

The metal-ion concentration cell is so often associated with crevices that it is commonly referred to as CREVICE CORROSION. When it occurs in association with deposits of road debris, it is sometimes called POULTICE INDUCED CORROSION. Crevice corrosion, although generally an inside-out mechanics, can cause corrosion damage to the outer body surface, as in corrosion at trim areas. However, the greatest damage caused by crevice corrosion is the inside-out corrosion associated with poultice formed by the accumulation of mud, sand, salt, and other road debris on the interior surface joints of body panels and structural components.

Pitting Corrosion — This is another type of perforation corrosion affecting vehicle bodies. It is more common on metals such as stainless steel and aluminum, but can occur on carbon steel panels. It usually involves an initiation and propagation stage, and normally attacks horizontal surfaces. Pits vary in size, and usually have well defined boundaries at their onset. The increase in depth usually proceeds at a faster rate than the increase in width.

6. Factors Affecting Corrosion

6.1 Environmental Factors Effecting the Corrosion of Automobile Bodies— There are many hostile forces in the environment that work on the automobile's new finish as soon as it leaves the assembly plant. The main elements needed for corrosion are moisture, oxygen, and chemical contaminants which form electrolytes. The automotive paint systems not only provide aesthetic appeal that's pleasing to the eye, but also act as barrier coatings to these harmful elements in order to prevent them from reaching the base auto body materials. However, most organic coatings are not completely impermeable and can be easily damaged. This permits chemical contaminates, moisture, and oxygen to reach and attack the body material. Damage to the paint film and subsequent corrosion of body materials can occur from several sources.

6.1.1 SUN DAMAGE—The ultraviolet portion of the sun's electromagnetic spectrum can do severe damage to an unprotected paint surface. The damage manifests itself in the form of checking, cracking, and chalking which reduces the paint's ability to act as a barrier. Many paints incorporate ultraviolet absorbers to help reduce this problem.

6.1.2 DEICING SALTS AND SEA AIR—Salts accelerate the corrosion process by increasing the electrical conductivity of the electrolyte and are present in different forms, depending on the geographic region. Locations in the "snow belt" necessitate the use of large quantities of deicing salt. Currently 10 million tons of sodium chloride (salt) per year are used in the U.S. for deicing. Calcium chloride is also used in regions where temperatures are consistently below –20 °C. Summertime finds calcium chloride used on suburban and rural dirt roads as a dust control agent due to its ability to retain moisture (hygroscopic). This characteristic increases the extent or probability of corrosion when calcium chloride is present. Salt-laden sea air in coastal environments is another source for electrolyte formation. Salt particles can travel as much as 10 miles inland and are constantly moistened by fog and dew.

6.1.3 ACID RAIN—Industrial areas not only have to contend with the use of deicing salts but also to the SO_2 and NO_x pollutants emitted with each year. The resulting acid deposition, including acid rain, snow, fog, dew, and dry deposits combined with the road deicing salts, cause an extremely corrosive environment for automobiles. These acids do not always fall on the areas where they originate. Storms and wind currents carry these components many miles from their source. There is a noted increase in the acidity of rainfall. For example, New York City's rain measured around pH 6.0 in the 1920s and pH 4.5 in the 1950s. Today, some storms drop rain as acidic as pH 3.0.

6.1.4 ROAD BLAST—Road blast from stones and sand not only damages paint but also creates dirt accumulation. Typical areas for poultice to form are inside wheel houses, box sections, and underbody components. This has a hygroscopic effect and allows for concentration of corrosive road salts and chemical pollutants, resulting in corrosion.

6.1.5 INDUSTRIAL FALLOUT—Industrial fallout can consist not only of the chemicals that cause acid rain, but also particulate matter such as soot and iron particles. These can serve as nucleation sites for the initiation of corrosion.

6.1.6 BIOLOGICAL FALLOUT—The damaging effects of tree sap, bird droppings, bug stains, and road tars should not be overlooked. Although not directly related to corrosion these organic substances can break down some paint polymers and reduce the paint's ability to protect the base body materials.

Field surveys have shown that the severest environments are in the Northeast and Midwest followed by industrial regions of the East Coast. The South and Gulf Coast regions are also quite corrosive. Measurements have shown that the most severe corrosion rates take place during parked periods. Condensation, combined with the hygroscopic effect of poultice and chemical pollutants, provides a moist corrosive surface every day, even when the car is not driven. The automotive corrosion engineer is faced with providing a barrier between these environmental factors and the automobile body. Success or failure is measured by how well the products perform in the field.

6.2 Design—The first step in reducing or preventing corrosion on an automotive product is to design it with corrosion prevention in mind. This means trying to design a product so the (a) water and contaminants are kept out of and away from it and (b) damage does not occur to the protective coatings.

Although all vehicles are designed with joints and seals to shed water, the bottoms of doors and quarter panels must have drain holes to allow egress of water and contaminants that will certainly enter some vehicles.

These same drain holes, plus larger holes in other areas, must be designed-in to allow full penetration of phosphate, rinse and electrocoat material in the spray and dip tanks described later (refer to 5.5.1.3). The holes also allow the plating action of the electrocoat to take place and total drainage of the materials.

Box sections in the underbody structure, such as crossmembers, as well as roof rails, are examples of other areas which must be designed to drain as completely as possible.

All areas of the floor pans must be channelled toward drain holes to afford as complete drainage as possible. It is necessary to have these holes for drainage of phosphate, rinse and electrocoat materials to prevent contamination of each succeeding bath and associated loss of materials, both of which are costly and affect quality. These holes are usually plugged to prevent the entry of road debris.

To prevent stone chipping damage, the sides of the vehicle should be as vertical as possible and avoid a large radius tuck-under. Offsetting the rocker panel, slightly wider than the doors, will protect the bottom edge of the doors and part of the curvature of the body-side from stone chipping. A robot or hand sprayed application of vinyl (usually textured) or urethane (usually smooth) to the rocker panels, lower doors, wheelhouse openings and some areas of the floor pans is standard. Less standard, but very effective, are designed-in stone shields or mud guards to the rear of the wheels.

On some vehicles, full plastic cladding and fairing on the body sides and full wraparound plastic bumpers greatly improve the stone-pecking resistance and subsequent corrosion resistance of the whole body.

6.3 Materials

6.3.1 COATED STEEL PRODUCTS—As mentioned in section 4.3, during the 1980s significant increases in the use of coated sheet products occurred. An 83% increase in North American shipments of all coated steel products occurred between 1982 and 1989 (Reference 1). The primary reason for this increase was the movement by the automotive industry toward coated sheet to combat corrosion.

Coated sheet steel is the term typically used to designate steel overlayed with a protective coating applied in a continuous process. These materials provide the traditional advantages of steel, such as strength and formability, with the cost-effective durability and corrosion resistance of the coatings. The corrosion resistance of coated steel products is afforded by the coatings which can be either barrier, sacrificial, and/or inhibitive coatings. Barrier coatings separate the steel from corrosive environments. A barrier coating owes its protective value to its own relative chemical inertness to the environment in which it is exposed. Sacrificial coatings offer electrochemical protection to the exposed steel surfaces. Sacrificial coatings are anodic with respect to the steel and in the presence of an electrolyte (e.g., moisture films, containing conductive ions) will tend to protect exposed steel surfaces at breaks in the coatings. It is important to note that the effectiveness of a sacrificial coating depends upon both the corrosive environment and the type and thickness of the coating. A coating that offers sacrificial protection in one environment may not do so in another. Inhibitive coatings contain substances that act to inhibit the corrosion of steel. Chromates are often added to coatings to act as inhibitors.

Coated sheet products are usually prepared by one of two techniques: hot-dipping or electroplating. The most commonly used commercial coated sheet products and the relevant processes of application are described in the next few pages. The reader is also referred to several recent review articles that describe coating microstructure, preparation and properties in further detail (References 2 to 6).

6.3.1.1 Hot-Dip Coated Steel Products—Hot-dip coated steel products are produced by a continuous process of immersing properly cleaned and annealed steel strip into a molten bath of the desired metal coating. The hot-dip process is the most cost-effective method of producing corrosion-resistant coatings on a steel substrate.

The principal types of hot-dip coated steel currently available are: zinc coated (galvanized), zinc-iron coated (galvanneal), aluminum coated, aluminum-zinc alloy coated (Galvalume®), and lead-tin alloy coated (terne). Characteristics of these products are described later in this section.

6.3.1.1.1 Galvanized Steel—Hot-dip galvanized steel (HDG) is produced by dipping the steel strip into a bath of molten zinc containing 0.1% to 0.2% aluminum. HDG steel may be produced with a wide range of coating weights depending on the automotive specification. Table 2 shows the minimum and maximum coating limits per side for a variety of coating classes typically used by car makers. The automotive industry has moved away from coating designations previously specified as oz/ft^2 to the international designation of g/m^2.

A variety of strength and formability levels are available ranging from commercial quality, drawing quality, deep drawing quality, extra deep drawing quality, as well as 35 ksi to 120 ksi minimum yield strength high strength low alloy galvanized.

TABLE 2—TYPICAL AUTOMOTIVE COATING WEIGHTS FOR HOT DIP GALVANIZED STEEL

Coating Designation	Minimum Check Limit Single Spot Test/Side (g/m^2)	Maximum Check Limit Single Spot Test/Side (g/m^2)
0G	0	0
20G	20	60
60G	60	110
70G	70	120
90G	90	140
98G	100	160
100G	100	140

NOTE 1— 60G0G refers to one side coated galvanized steel: 60 to 110 g/m^2 on one side and 0 g/m^2 on the other side.

NOTE 2— 100G100G refers to two side equally coated galvanized steel: 100 to 140 g/m^2 on each side.

NOTE 3— 90G70G refers to differentially coated galvanized steel: 90 to 140 g/m^2 on one side and 70 to 120 g/m^2 minimum on the other side.

NOTE 4— Some North American car makers have more restrictive limits than shown previously. Others have limits based on triple spot test measurements.

Zinc is anodic to steel under most exposure conditions and will offer sacrificial protection to exposed steel surfaces. Hence, zinc coatings will continue to offer protection to the base steel after the coating is penetrated by corrosion or mechanically damaged or at cut edges. Zinc coatings will protect steel at moderate temperatures, but zinc coated steels should not be used above 260 °C (500 °F).

Zinc-coated steels are subject to damage from humid storage stain caused by adverse storage or shipping conditions. The product may be rendered more resistant to humid storage stain by the application of a "ship out" oil. However, the protection afforded is temporary.

Zinc coatings are ductile and can be stamped, roll or brake formed, deep drawn, spun, or lock formed.

Zinc-coated steel can be welded by electric resistance, metal arc, laser and seam welding, although the processes must be adjusted to allow for the peculiarities of the material. Arc welding produces a zinc oxide vapor which requires ventilation. Resistance welding requires higher currents, higher pressures, and longer cycle times than for uncoated steel. Zinc-coated steel is readily solderable with low melting point solder.

Although zinc-coated steels are paintable with a variety of paints readily available from most paint suppliers, a conversion pretreatment (such as zinc phosphate) is required for good paint adhesion.

6.3.1.1.2 Hot-Dip Galvanneal—Zinc-iron alloy (galvanneal = GA) coatings are produced by heating zinc-coated strip during the continuous galvanizing operation immediately after hot dipping. Preparation of GA coatings begins by dipping the steel strip in a bath of molten zinc that also contains aluminum (0.1 to 0.2%) to control the extent of iron/zinc alloying. Coating weight is controlled by blowing off the excess zinc using air knives after the strip exits the bath. The strip is then reheated to start the diffusion of iron from the steel substrate into the zinc. The strip temperature is maintained to allow the iron to diffuse to the coating surface and then the strip is rapidly cooled to stop the diffusion process.

GA is a zinc-iron coating consisting of approximately 8 to 18% iron and the balance zinc. Unlike pure zinc coatings, which have a silver, reflective appearance, the GA coating has a dull grey color. The GA coating also "feels less smooth" due to its micro-porous surface. This micro porous surface can also result in retention of applied lubricants during subsequent cleaning processes. Although the bulk iron concentration in the coating is 8 to 12%, the coating typically contains several different zinc-iron phases ranging from 5 to 21% iron. The iron concentration and phase variations occur due to the diffusion process by which GA is made.

Zinc-iron coatings provide less sacrificial protection of exposed steel compared to free zinc coatings. Also, due to their iron content, the corrosion products of GA are reddish-brown whereas the corrosion products of free zinc coatings are white. However, alloying zinc with iron improves the corrosion resistance by lowering the corrosion rate of the coating.

Zinc-iron alloy coatings are also more weldable and offer better paint adhesion than free zinc coatings. They are, therefore, well suited for exterior skin panels, inner closure panels and structural components. However, GA coatings are more susceptible to coating adhesion problems, such as powdering and flaking, compared to HDG steel.

Typical coating weights of automotive GA are shown in Table 3. As with HDG coatings a variety of formable and high-strength grades are widely available.

6.3.1.1.3 Other Hot-Dip Coated Products—Other types of hot-dip coated steels are used in automotive applications other than body panels. These include aluminum-coated steel, aluminum-zinc alloy coated steel, and lead-tin coated steel.

Aluminum coated steel has enhanced high-temperature resistance over zinc or zinc/iron coated steel. It is well suited for making parts of the automotive exhaust system including intermediate pipes, mufflers, and tail pipes.

Aluminum-zinc alloy coated steel, Galvalume®, (55% aluminum, 43.5% zinc and 1.5% silicon) has automotive applications that are similar to those for aluminum coated steel, i.e., requiring high-temperature corrosion resistance. Typical applications include heat shields, gas tank shields, mufflers, and under hood parts.

Lead-tin (long-terne) coated steel has a lead alloy coating containing nominally 8% tin. It protects against corrosion in gas tanks, fuel lines, and brake lines and does not contaminate gasoline or brake fluid. Less active than the steel substrate, it does not provide galvanic protection if the coating is penetrated.

TABLE 3—TYPICAL AUTOMOTIVE COATING WEIGHTS FOR HOT DIP GALVANNEAL STEELS

Coating Designation	Minimum Check Limit Single Spot Test/Side (g/m^2)	Maximum Check Limit Single Spot Test/Side (g/m^2)
30A	30	60
40A	40	80
50A	45	90
60A	60	90

Some North American car makers have more restrictive limits than shown previously. Others have limits based on triple spot test measurements.

Nickel terne coated steel includes an electrolytic flash coating of nickel (1 to 1.5 g/m^2) underneath a conventional lead-tin coating for enhanced corrosion resistance. Applications are similar to long-terne described previously.

A variation of long-terne coated steel employs a subsequent prepainted organic coating on each surface for some fuel tanks. The outer surface has a zinc rich organic coating to provide added exterior corrosion protection, while the inner surface has an aluminum-rich organic coating to augment the lead-tin coating resistance to gasoline, and low concentrations of methanol and ethanol containing fuels.

6.3.1.1.4 Electroplated Steel Products—Electroplated coatings are applied in a low-temperature continuous process where negatively charged steel sheet is passed between positively charged anodes. Metallic ions in an electrolyte bath are reduced and plated on the surface of the steel sheet forming the coating. The bath composition, electrolyte velocity, current density, and temperature determine the chemistry and properties of the metallic/alloy coating applied to the steel sheet. The plating current and strip speed will determine the coating thickness. Electroplated coatings are particularly attractive to the automotive industry because of their uniform appearance, formability, weldability, and coating thickness control. Electroplated coatings can be applied to one or both sides of the steel sheet with equal or differential coating thicknesses on each side.

Electroplating lines are often identified or distinguished based on plating cell type or geometry, anode type, and/or electrolyte composition. In the US, one of three cell geometries: horizontal, vertical, or radial are commonly used. Electroplating lines can also be classified by the type of anode used: soluble or insoluble. The selection of anode type will depend on the electrolyte type, the cell design, and the desired coating. The final method of identifying electroplating lines is according to electrolyte composition. Electrolyte baths are usually sulfate based (typically used with insoluble anodes, but also used with soluble anodes) or chloride based (used only with soluble anodes).

6.3.1.1.4.1 Electroplated Zinc Coatings—Pure zinc electroplated coatings, electrozinc coatings (EZ), are the most commonly used coated sheet in the US for exposed body panels. Similar to HDG, the zinc coating is significantly anodic to the underlying steel and, therefore, galvanically protects the steel substrate from corrosion. Corrosion products on EZ and HDG are typically white zinc oxides, hydroxides, or carbonates and are often less objectionable to automotive customers compared to red iron corrosion products. The primary driving force for the widespread use of EZ over HDG for exposed panels is enhanced coating thickness uniformity and surface characteristics (2). EZ coating thicknesses range from 4 to 13 µm (20 to 90 g/m^2) per side. Typical specifications for EZ coating weight and tolerances are listed in Table 4.

TABLE 4—TYPICAL AUTOMOTIVE COATING WEIGHTS FOR ELECTROZINC COATINGS

Coating Designation Electrozinc Coatings	Minimum Check Limit Single Spot Test (g/m^2)	Maximum Check Limit Single Spot Test (g/m^2)
60G00G	60/0	70/0
60G60G	60/60	60/60
70G70G	70/70	80/80

6.3.1.1.5 Alloy Electroplated Coatings—Two primary electroplated alloy coatings, zinc-nickel (Zn-Ni) and zinc-iron (Zn-Fe), are of commercial importance in the automotive industry. Both galvanically protect steel (Note —Zn-Ni protection consists of a combined galvanic/barrier mechanism), similar to EZ, but have the added advantage of lower coating dissolution rates enabling similar coating lifetimes at lower coating weights. Zn-Ni coatings contain 10-14% Ni and are applied at coating thicknesses ranging from 3 to 6 µm (20 to 40 g/m^2). Zn-Ni coatings are used for exposed and unexposed panels because of their corrosion resistance, superior weldability (over EZ, HDG, and GA), and good formability. Zn-Fe electroplated coatings offer the good weldability of hot-dipped Zn-Fe coatings, and the surface appearance and coating uniformity of electroplated coatings. These coatings generally contain 8 to 18% iron and are applied at thicknesses up to 7 µm per side (50 g/m^2). Zn-Fe electroplated coatings are often used for exposed automotive panels where surface appearance and coating uniformity are critical areas of concern.

Enhancements of these alloy coatings are also commercially available. Zn-Ni composite coatings are prepared by applying a chromium pretreatment followed by a thin (1 to 2 g/m^2) silicate containing organic topcoat to the Zn-Ni surface. The organic coating is typically applied to one side of the Zn-Ni; the side that will be the interior of the final panel. This provides additional protection to the areas where phosphating and priming may be inadequate after assembly. The other side of the steel sheet will typically contain Zn-Ni, but can be uncoated. Perforation corrosion resistance is significantly enhanced in Zn-Ni composite coatings over conventional Zn-Ni coatings.

Plating of a thin iron-phosphorous (Fe-P) layer (2 g/m^2) or Fe-Zn (3 g/m^2) layer on the surface of Zn-Fe hot-dip or electroplated coatings is also used for automotive applications. The thin electroplated layer is designed to improve formability and reduce electrocoat cratering tendencies of the Zn-Fe alloy coating.

Typical coating weight specifications and tolerances for alloy electroplate coatings are listed in Table 5.

TABLE 5—TYPICAL AUTOMOTIVE COATING WEIGHTS FOR ALLOY ELECTROPLATED COATINGS

Coating Designation	Alloy Type	Minimum Check Limit Single Spot Test (g/m^2)	Maximum Check Limit Single Spot Test (g/m^2)
30N30N	ZnNi	30/30	40/40
20N20N	ZnNi	20/20	30/30
40A40AEL	ZnFe	40/40	55/55
45A45A	ZnFe	45/45	55/55

6.3.1.2 Summary—Usage of coated sheet products in the automotive industry has increased significantly over the last several years. This increase is largely due to the ability of coated products to provide superior corrosion protection in typical automotive environments. The selection of a specific coated sheet product for a specific application is usually based on a combination of factors. No one product is superior to the others in all areas. In addition to corrosion resistance, the factors that typically influence selection include: part design and application, formability, weldability, uniformity requirements (appearance, tolerances, etc.), and cost. Only after careful assessment of the requirements for the target application, can the best coated sheet product be selected.

6.3.2 ALUMINUM

6.3.2.1 Introduction—As fuel efficiency requirements for automobiles continue to increase, the need for lighter-weight materials becomes critical. This continued need for weight savings is the primary driving force for the implementation of more aluminum in automotive applications. Currently, aluminum body sheet is used commercially for a relatively small number of outer and/or inner body panels on passenger vehicles. However, many aluminum producers and auto makers have active, ongoing development programs. A significant increase in aluminum used for body panel applications is envisioned toward the latter 1990s.

Aluminum alloys have been used for various other automotive applications for many years. Examples include sheet products for coolant/heat exchange systems, sheet and extrusions for bumper systems, castings for power train applications, forgings, castings and sheet product for wheels, and many other applications in suspensions, brakes, engines, body, and chassis, etc. Given the theme of this document, the following discussion focuses on body sheet alloys specifically.

6.3.2.2 Alloys, Tempers, and Their Designations—A four-digit numerical system is used to identify wrought aluminum alloys. The alloys are categorized according to the major alloying element(s), and the first digit designates these major element(s). The three major alloy classes of interest to auto body sheet applications along with the major alloying elements are presented in Table 6. Table 7 lists a few representative alloys from each class. Depending on the alloy and application, the material is processed (thermally and/or mechanically) to produce desired properties. These basic processing paths are referred to by temper designations. A few tempers common to aluminum auto body sheet are given in Table 8.

TABLE 6—MAJOR ALLOYING ELEMENTS FOR SELECTED ALUMINUM ALLOY CLASSES

Alloy Class	Major Alloying Element(s)	Secondary Alloying Elements
2XXX	Cu	Mg, Si,
5XXX	Mg	Si, Cu, Mn
6XXX	Mg and Si	Cu, Mn

TABLE 7—CHEMICAL COMPOSITIONS OF REPRESENTATIVE ALUMINUM AUTO BODY ALLOYS

Alloy	Composition Si	Composition Fe	Composition Cu	Composition Mn	Composition Mg	Composition Cr	Composition Zn	Composition Ti
2XXX Type								
2008	0.5–0.8	0.4	0.7–1.1	0.3	0.25–0.5	0.1	0.25	0.1
2036	0.5	0.5	2.2–3.0	0.1–0.4	0.3–0.6	0.1	0.25	0.15
5XXX Type								
5030	0.25	0.4	0.5	0.2	3.5–5.0	0.2	0.1	0.1
5052	0.25	0.4	0.1	0.1	2.2–2.8	0.15–0.35	0.1	–
5182	0.2	0.35	0.15	0.2–0.5	4.0–5.0	0.1	0.25	0.1
6XXX Type								
6009	0.6–1.0	0.5	0.15–0.6	0.2–0.8	0.4–0.8	0.1	0.25	0.1
6016(5)	1.0–1.5	0.5	0.2	0.2	0.25–0.6	0.1	0.2	0.15
6111	0.7–1.1	0.4	0.5–0.9	0.15–0.45	0.5–1.0	0.1	0.15	0.1

Elemental compositions not listed as a range should be considered a maximum.

This is not intended as an exhaustive list. The reader is advised to consult References 7 to 10 for further information.

TABLE 8—SELECTED TEMPER DESIGNATIONS OF INTEREST FOR ALUMINUM AUTO BODY SHEET

Temper Designations	Definitions
T4	Solution Heat-Treated and Naturally Aged to a Substantially Stable Condition — This temper is common for precipitation hardened alloys, e.g., 2XXX, 6XXX, and selected 5XXX alloys (e.g., 5030).
T4	Plus Forming and Assembly in T4, Followed by Artificial Aging as a Paint Bake Result of Paint Bake Practices — This IS NOT AN OFFICIAL Aluminum Association TEMPER DESIGNATION. Other terms can be used as well (e.g., T4+assembly age). The key here is that this refers to a temper between T4 and maximum strength. For further discussion see T6 temper.
T6	Solution Heat-Treated and Artificially Aged (i.e., T4 plus aging)
	It is important to note a subtle difference between T6 and T4 + Paint Bake (T4 + PB). Note that technically, T4 + PB could be considered a T6 temper. However, it is a common (though not universal) practice in the aluminum industry to consider T6 as a Peak-Aged temper (e.g., maximum or near-maximum strength). T4+PB, on the other hand, is usually significantlyless than peak strength, due to the lower paint bake temperatures and times. The separate T6 and T4+PB tempers are provided here to inform the reader that caution must be used to clarify whether T6 or T4+PB is the temper resulting from a particular assembly process.
O	Annealed — Applies to wrought products which are annealed to obtain the lowest strength temper. This temper is common for nonheat-treatable 5XXX alloys (e.g., 5182).
HXX	Strain Hardened — Product is strain hardened (typically by cold-roll reduction), with or without supplementary thermal treatment to improve stability. This temper is used primarily for nonheat-treatable 5XXX alloys.
	The 2XXX and 6XXX series alloys are heat-treatable (or precipitation hardening) alloys. This implies that the alloys are given a thermal treatment sufficient to dissolve all or most alloying elements into solid solution (solution heat-treat), then quenched to room temperature to produce a supersaturated solid solution (T4 temper). Upon subsequent aging (thermal treatment at lower temperatures), precipitation occurs which influences properties (e.g., increase in strength). The 5XXX series alloys are characteristically nonheat-treatable. These alloys are frequently used in the fully annealed "O" temper, or in any number strain-hardened "HXX" tempers. Some newer 5XXX alloys, however (e.g., 5030), now require solution heat treatment and aging to achieve optimum properties. These are used in a T4 temper. For more extensive information on this topic, the reader is referred to References 7, 11, and 12.

6.3.2.3 Corrosion Behavior and Mechanical Properties—Aluminum alloys offer excellent resistance to general corrosion in a variety of environments. This is due to the presence of a thin oxide barrier layer (on the order of hundreds to thousands of angstroms) on the metal surface. Relative to cold-rolled steel (uncoated), the general corrosion resistance of aluminum alloys is far superior. Because of this, aluminum body sheet is utilized without the addition of metallic surface coating (e.g., galvanized steel) for anodic protection. Although aluminum alloys are highly resistant to general corrosion, localized corrosion due to local breakdown of the protective oxide film must be considered. Aluminum alloys can be susceptible to a number of forms of localized corrosion including pitting, intergranular corrosion and stress corrosion cracking. The presence of impurities such as sulfates and nitrates (common in acid rain) and chloride ions (e.g., road salts) can exacerbate the attack. Galvanic effects (e.g., from contact to steel parts) can also intensify the corrosion attack. The resistance of aluminum alloys to these various types of localized attack is highly dependent upon the alloy type and/or temper. A more thorough review of aluminum corrosion, specifically the influence of alloy type and temper, is presented in References 5 and 7.

In addition to corrosion performance two key properties for body sheet materials are formability and strength. Aluminum alloys offer a range of these properties depending on the needed application. In many applications, the mechanical properties of aluminum body sheet allow for a gage-for-gage substitution of aluminum for steel.

The 5XXX alloys typically have excellent formability in the annealed "O" temper. However, these alloys are frequently susceptible to the formation of Luder lines during forming. Also, the nonheat-treatable 5XXX series alloys offer lower strengths than their 2XXX and 6XXX counterparts. Due to this combination of lower strength and cosmetic defects, 5XXX-O alloys are frequently used for non-exterior applications that are not strength-critical. In applications where greater strengh is required from 5XXX alloys, strain hardened "HXX" tempers can be utilized; however, this increase in strength typically comes at the expense of formability. Although perhaps not as formable as the 5XXX-O temper alloys, the 2XXX and 6XXX alloys (and heat-treatable 5XXX alloys) offer relatively good formability in the T4 temper. Furthermore, Luder lines typically do not develop on these alloys. Upon aging, either as an intended processing step or as part of a paint-bake cycle, precipitation enhances the strength of these alloys. This combination of adequate T4 formability without Ludering and enhanced post-age strength makes these alloys excellent candidates for outer body panel applications.

The previous discussion is presented as a generic guideline of the properties of aluminum body sheet alloys. Specific cases may deviate from the generalizations presented. The reader is advised to consult the references provided for more detailed information regarding specific alloys of interest.

6.3.3 PLASTICS—There are many different types of plastics. A plastic is a high-molecular-weight polymer which is a long chain molecule containing thousands of repeating small molecular units (monomers). The long molecular chains of the polymer mainly consist of carbon atoms linked together. The type of simpler molecule (monomer) that a commercial polymer is synthesized from determines what kind of properties the polymer will exhibit. Examples of some of these monomer units are propylene which is used in thermoplastic olefin (TPO), bisphenol A which is used in polycarbonate (PC) and diphenylmethane 4,4′-diisocyanate which is used in polyurethane/urea. Many of the monomers for the polymers are derived from crude oil or natural gas. The many different types of monomers allows for the wide variety of plastics.

6.3.3.1 Thermoplastics and Thermosets—There are two main classes of plastics: thermoplastics and thermosets. Thermoplastics are stable high molecular weight polymers in the form of small pellets that are melted in order to form the shape of the structure they are being used to produce. Once the material cools, it becomes one continuous piece of plastic that is tough and can resist impact. However, if heated to a high enough temperature, it will soften and start to flow. Thermoplastic materials are very viscous when they are melted, therefore they must be molded under high pressure and sometimes it is difficult to mold large complex parts. Some typical automotive thermoplastics are polyesters, polycarbonate/polybutylene terephthalate (PC/PBT) and acrylonitrile-butadiene-styrene (ABS). Thermosets are reactive fluids and consist of prepolymers or monomers and a catalyst which initiates a reaction to build molecular weight and crosslink the polymer. The resulting three-dimensional network produces a polymer with excellent strength and chemical resistance. If heated to a high temperature, thermoset material will not melt. During the molding operation the materials first enter the mold as low-viscosity liquids. Therefore, thermosets can be molded with less pressure than a thermoplastic and readily fills the mold before curing. Some typical automotive thermosets are polyesters, polyurethanes/ureas and caprolactams. Some of the different kinds of polymers can either be a thermoplastic or a thermoset depending on how they are formulated. Thermosets tend to have a higher degree of crosslinking than a thermoplastic. Examples of polymers that can be both are polyesters, polyurethane/urea and nylon. Recent advances in polymer chemistry now allow chemists to blend two different thermoplastic polymers together that will result in a new polymer that has product attributes better than those of either component. This process is similar to making alloys from different metals. Most polymers are incompatible when mixed together; therefore, compatibilizers are added to produce super polymeric alloys. An example is the polymer blend of polyphenylene oxide (PPO)/nylon. A thermoplastic or thermoset plastic can encompass many different types of materials.

The two classes of plastics can either be composed of the pure polymer ("neat") or solid materials can be added to produce a filled or reinforced plastic. The solid material can be added along with the polymer components as they're being injected into the mold or the reinforcement can be placed in the mold and then the polymeric liquid forced into it. Solid materials are added to polymers for many different reasons, including cost reduction, improved dimensional stability, or increased stiffness and strength. Many different materials can be used, such as talc, calcium silicate (wollastonite), or other structural fibers or glass fiber mat. Besides fillers, the plastic can be pigmented with colorants and contain additives such as U.V. stabilizers, impact modifiers or lubricants. Therefore, a plastic material may be a mixture of a polymer with other materials.

There are many different ways to process a plastic mixture. The method used depends on the type of polymer made and the application. For thermoset material, one can use compression-molding, injection-molding, resin transfer molding (RTM), or reaction injection molding (RIM). With compression-molding, injection-molding and RTM, the filler is usually placed in the mold. The filler is usually mixed with one of the components in the RIM process. When thermoplastic material is used for exterior automotive applications, it is done mostly by injection molding. However, some parts can be made by blow molding or extruding. If fillers are used with a thermoplastic, they are usually incorporated into the thermoplastic. Whichever process is chosen, the plastic material can be made to produce many shapes and many surface finishes to fit different applications.

6.3.3.2 Automotive Applications of Plastics—Over the past several years the use of plastics in automotive applications has increased significantly. Plastics are used in the interior, on the exterior, and under the hood of the car. Plastics are a very good choice for exterior applications because they do not corrode and have excellent resistance to inorganic acids, bases and water solutions of most salts. Other attractive characteristics are the ability to easily produce aerodynamic, aesthetically-pleasing shapes and the ability to effect design changes quickly. Plastics can be used to form more intricate and consolidated parts than can be formed by metallic substrates. Manufacturing parts out of plastic can be more cost effective compared to metal when several different design types of a specific model are made at a moderate production volume. It is dependent on the exact process and material, but there is usually an economic advantage to use plastic when the annual production volume is lower than between 60 000 and 200 000 parts. Also, plastic can provide weight savings which allows for better gas mileage and durability and resistance to denting. A characteristic that determines how a plastic can be used is plastic's tendency to creep under a load at room temperature. Metal panels don't creep. Creep is a problem for plastic parts when they are used horizontally such as hoods or roofs, because under a load some plastic materials will warp with time. Therefore, exterior applications are separated into two groups, vertical panels such as bumper covers where creep is not a factor and horizontal panels such as roof panels. Two examples of plastic materials that have a very low creep modulus and therefore can be used for horizontal applications are sheet molding compound (SMC) and structural reaction injection molded polyurethane (SRIM). These two examples contain some type of fiber mat which helps to reduce the creep of the "neat" resin. Table 9 gives examples of exterior automotive parts and the plastic material that can be used to produce them. The major automotive exterior uses for plastics are front and rear fascias, bumper covers, and side molding trims. The major material used for those applications is polyurethane/urea reaction injection molding (RIM). Each plastic was chosen for its particular automotive application because it meets the performance required.

The decision as to what plastic should be used depends on the application and the physical properties of the plastic. Properties that are often important are coefficient of linear thermal expansion (CLTE), water absorption, and dimensional stability. These properties will indicate what needs to be done for the part to maintain a good fit at different conditions. Often the plastic part must have the same appearance as the metal part next to it. Therefore, the surface properties including distinctness of image (DOI) that can be obtained with a painted plastic material and how well the paint will coat such a material is important, because most exterior applications are painted. The painted fascia or bumper of U.S. cars must pass the 2.5 mph impact standard and the other exterior panels must resist denting or cracking. Therefore, to what degree the material can withstand impact can be another important consideration. The cost difference between two plastics may determine which one is used when their properties are similar. An increasingly important property for plastic materials is recyclability. Methods exist or are being developed to recycle most plastics at different points in their life span, thereby increasing their cost efficiency.

A comparison of the cost and physical properties of different automotive polymers is given in Table 10. The table shows that the polymers differ widely in their properties allowing them to fit into a broad range of applications. The properties and characteristics of plastics allow them to be used in automotive exterior applications to produce aerodynamic, light-weight, durable and corrosion-resistant parts.

TABLE 9—POLYMERS FOR AUTOMOTIVE APPLICATIONS

		TYPES OF PLASTIC									
EXTERIOR AUTOMOTIVE PARTS	**Millions of lb per year**	**Polyester TS**	**Polyester TP**	**PPO Nylon TP**	**Polyurethane Urea TS**	**PC ABS TP**	**ABS TP**	**Nylon TP**	**TPO TP**	**PC PBT TP**	**PVC TP**
Cowl Vent Grille	15.7	1.3	13.3				1.1				
Doors, Liftgate	27.5	27.5									
Door Side	20.6	17.9				2.7					
Fender Extenders	1.2	1						0.2			
Rear Fender	5.8	5.8									
Front Fender	6.7			6	0.7						
Front End Panel	20.1	18.1	2								
Hood	13.4	13.4									
Quarter Panel	6.1	4.2		1.9							
Rear End Panel	8.8	2.9			1.8		1.4	2.7			
Roof Panel	12.7	12.7									
Rear Spoiler	5.5	3.3		0.4	1.6			0.2			
Fascia/Bumper Cov.	158.4		2.4		86.8				43.8	25.4	
Side Molding Trim	56		2.5		7.6			0.9	17.3		27.7
TOTAL	358.5	108.1	20.2	8.3	98.5	2.7	2.5	4	61.1	25.4	27.7

The data used for this illustration is from 1992.

TS: thermoset; TP: thermoplastic; PPO: polyphenylene oxide; PC: polycarbonate; ABS: acrylonitrile-butadiene-styrene; TPO: thermoplastic olefin elastomer; PBT: polybutylene terephthalate; PVC: polyvinyl chloride

TABLE 10—POLYMERS FOR AUTOMOTIVE APPLICATIONS

PROPERTY	TYPES OF PLASTIC									
	Polyester TS	Polyester TP	PPO Nylon TP	Poly-urethane Urea TS	PC ABS TP	ABS TP	Nylon TP	TPO TP	PC PBT TP	PVC TP
COST/LB (w/o filler)	$0.85	$1.98	$2.36	$1.35	$2.00	$.134	$2.00	$0.85	$2.77	$0.40
DENSITY,lb/ft^3	120	78	69	72	72	67	81	54	76.5	81.1
REINFORCEMENT	50 % Glass	Unfilled	Unfilled	15% Glass	Unfilled	Unfilled	30% Glass (Unfilled)	Unfilled	Unfilled	Unfilled
FLEXURAL MODULUS, psi	1 900 000	120 000	310 000	58 000	420 500	350 000	1 000 000 (234 000)	100 700	300 000	400 000
FLEXURAL STRENGTH, psi	40 000	NA	NA	NA	10 440	11 000	30 000	NA	11 020	13 000
TENSILE STRENGTH, psi	21 000	5 260	8 000	2 900	6 500	6 200	29 000 (6 200)	2 288	7 200	6 200
ELONGATION, %	1.6%	480%	60%	109%	60%	36%	3% (90%)	234%	148%	115%
TEAR STRENGTH, pli	NA	NA	800	437	NA	NA	815	645	NA	NA
NOTCHED IZOD, ft-lb/in	23		4	5.5	10	4	3 (8)	8.4	15	8
-20 °F		4	2.5		8				8.5	
HEAT SAG										
6 in Overhang, 1 h @ 250 °F	NA	0.59		0.62	NA	NA	NA	0.66	NA	NA
6 in Overhang, 1 h @ 325 °F			0.25				(>2)			
DEFLECTION TEMPERATURE,										
66 psi, deg F		225	380	185	252			149	239	163
264 psi, deg F	>450		290	119	210	230	350	113	190	155
CLTE, X10-6 F	7.7		46	72	43	50	(49)	54	90	42
(74 to 176 °F)		92	60							

TS: thermoset; TP: thermoplastic; PPO: polyphenylene oxide; PC: polycarbonate; ABS: acrylonitrile-butadiene-styrene; TPO: thermoplastic olefin elastomer; PBT: polybutylene terephthalate; PVC: polyvinyl chloride; NA: data not available

6.4 Processing

6.4.1 Paint Systems

6.4.1.1 Introduction—The "body-in-white," as it is called after stamping and assembly, is made up of combinations of materials which carry a variety of contaminants into the paint shop. The materials often include bare steel, one-and/or two-sided galvanized steel (zinc, zinc-iron, and zinc-nickel), other metallic coated steels (aluminum, terne plate, and tin plate), prepainted steels like Zincrometal, aluminum, composites like SMC, plastics, sealers, adhesives, and deadeners. The contaminants often include mill oils, draw lubricants, corrosion preventives, welding residue, metal finishing grit and general manufacturing dirt. The best paint system will provide the best corrosion protection only if these contaminants are removed.

Improved corrosion durability and appearance are the direct result of pretreatment, primer, topcoat, and application process technology development. Because these technologies are changing rapidly, the following represents the generally accepted best paint processing practices at this time.

6.4.1.2 Pretreatment Area—The modern assembly plant typically has an automatic car wash type precleaning unit using either high-pressure rotating nozzles or rotating brushes to remove the bulk of the soil from the exterior of the body ahead of the automated in-line pretreatment stage. Often this operation is supplemented by manually wiping the body with cleaning solution to loosen stubborn soil from exterior area.

From this precleaning area, the body-in-white enters the automatic pretreatment stage. Industry consensus is that at least four of the stages in the pretreatment facility should be total immersion (clean, rinse, phosphate, and rinse). As the body-in-white passes through the pretreatment process it will be cleaned at least twice using alkaline compounds, rinsed at least twice, activated with a nucleating agent, treated by either a chromic acid or chromium-free solution, and finally rinsed several times with deionized water to produce a clean, phosphated body that is ready to be primed. Because the body-in-white typically contains a variety of materials, e.g., bare steel, galvanized steel with various coating compositions (zinc, zinc nickel, zinc iron, one-side and two-side), prepainted steel (zincrometal, etc.), aluminum coated steel, aluminum, and plastic (thermosets and thermoplastics), phosphating technology has changed to accommodate increased usage of these materials. Selection of the phosphate is dependent on the mix of materials and the phosphating process, i.e., immersion versus spray. The phosphate selection is important in regard to paint adherence and corrosion performance.

6.4.1.3 Electrocoat Prime System Area—After phosphating a typical car body moves to the primer application facility where it is immersed in a large tank containing water soluble electro-deposition primer. The primer is electrically deposited on the exterior and interior of the body by up to 350 V and 1400 amp of direct electrical current. The body is grounded and the prime solution charged by submerged anodes. The primer has a unique property in that it insulates as it is deposited, limiting the thickness and driving the coating process into remote areas of the body. The body remains in the tank usually 2 to 5 min depending on the specifics of the body, the solution and the facility. The final applied thickness of the primer varies from 15 to 41 µm (0.0006 to 0.0016 µin) depending on the requirements. As the primed body exits the electrodeposition tank it is subjected to an immersion water rinse and several thorough spray rinses to remove all unreacted primer and return it to the tank. The final rinsing is done using deionized water, which is usually counter flowed back through the line to conserve unused deionized water. The modern electro-deposition facility is supported by an extensive system of filters, heat exchangers and controls that result in primer usage efficiencies exceeding 96%.

After priming the car body enters a bake oven to cure the primer. Typical electro-deposition primer ovens operate to achieve metal temperatures of 149 °C to 162 °C (325 °F to 350 °F) for about 30 min. Because of this temperature certain plastic components must be assembled subsequent to electrocoating. After exiting the primer oven, the body moves to the sealing area.

6.4.1.4 Body Sealing Area—In the sealing area, many spot welded joints and die notches are sealed with vinyl, asphaltic or urethane compounds to provide a water- and dust-tight body. Most modern plants do most seam sealing with sealers that are applied by spraying through a spray nozzle directed by a robot for consistency and repeatability. Sealers that are in high-visibility areas are usually smoothed by hand wiping or skiving for better appearance. Often a derivative of a polyvinyl chloride sealer is used as an under-vehicle protective coating and may be sprayed in the wheel houses and on the underside of the floor pan. Many vehicles utilize sound-deadening pads applied to the interior of the passenger compartment and luggage compartment so that they will melt in place in the sealer oven which also provides some secondary sealing.

6.4.1.5 Special Primer Application Area—In most cases, the sealed body then moves into a spray booth where special primers are applied for a variety of reasons, as follows: Frequently, anti-chip plastisol urethane materials are applied to chip susceptible areas of the body, e.g., the lower body, the leading edge of the hood and roof.

In many plants where a lower thickness of electro-deposition primer is used, a 10 to 38 μm (0.0004 to 0.0015 μin) coat of primer-surfacer is applied to the entire exterior of the body as a foundation for the color top coats. A few plants use primer coats that are color keyed to the final top coat color to achieve full rich color while using less of the costly top coat materials which are difficult to control in thicker coatings.

The sealed and primed body now enters the primer/sealer oven where the primers and sealers are co-baked at 107 °C to 162 °C (250 °F to 350 °F) peak metal temperature for 30 to 50 min to cure them. After exiting the primer/sealer oven, the body usually goes to a sanding area for preparation for top coat application.

6.4.1.6 Sanding Area—In the sanding area, the body is closely examined for imperfections and/or dirt in the primer coat. Any noted imperfections are then smoothed out by sanding, either dry, moist, or wet. Dry sanding is sanding of defects with no lubricant, such as water or solvents. Dry sanding residue is removed by wiping with lint-free dustless tack rags. Moist sanding is done with sandpaper moistened in a container of water and the body wetted only locally. Wet sanding is done by wetting the entire body with water from a spray ring and sanding the wet body. Some manufacturers routinely wet or moist sand some exterior areas of the body to maximize the appearance. After the body has been sanded, it is rinsed off with deionized water to remove any residue and neutralize the body surface in preparation for the application of the color top coats. The body then goes through a short (approximately 20 min) oven to dry off the rinse water.

After the body leaves the dry-off oven, it is again examined for imperfections as it is wiped-off immediately before entering the top coat color application area. This wipe-off is done with tack rags designed to remove and contain all dirt and dust particles.

6.4.1.7 Color Top Coat Area—Virtually all modern assembly plants use thermoset acrylic, alkyd enamel, or urethane technology to top coat their bodies. Almost all use base coat/clear coat (BC/CC) enamels. A few use BC/CC for both metallic and solid colors. Others use BC/CC only for the metallic colors, and non-BC/CC alkyd or acrylic enamels for the solid colors. The base coat/clear coat system applies all the color in the first coats and immediately applies clear coats to provide depth and gloss. Conventional systems apply the color throughout the paint film. The BC/CC system used by most manufacturers uses solvent-borne base coat for the color coats followed by solvent-borne clear coats. Typical coating thicknesses are as follows:

a. Base coat — 13 to 40 μm (0.0007 to 0.0020 μin)
b. Conventional enamels — 25 to 64 μm (0.0010 to 0.0025 μin)

A few manufacturers are progressing to even newer technology which use water-borne color base coats with solvent-borne clear coats for better process control, enhanced appearance and minimized hydrocarbon emissions. In the near future, some colors will probably use a three coat system to produce striking color changes depending on the viewing angle. Some manufacturers use two component clear coats to provide improved appearance and coating durability. All these systems require essentially the same basic application methodology. Some variations will be noted as the top coat systems are described.

The color top-coat application area is often designated as an "ultra clean area" because special steps are taken to prevent any dirt from getting into the paint finish. This is often accomplished by totally enclosing the area, thoroughly filtering all the air and paint products into the area, having personnel dress in lint-free uniforms and enter through air-lock double doors which have a wet mat on the floor to remove any dirt from shoes, and maintaining a higher air pressure in the ultra clean area than in the surrounding plant.

Many modern assembly plants utilize a split line color application system in which the conveyor divides the production into two lines. Each operates at one half the plant line speed providing more time for paint application in the paint booths. In some plants, the solid colors go through one booth and the clear coat colors go through the other.

The color-base coat or solid-color enamel is applied to the body in an enclosed, controlled spray booth by either air atomized spray guns, electrostatic spray guns, high-speed electrostatic rotary atomizers, or any combination of the previous. Usually two coats of base coat (wet on wet) are required to achieve the necessary coverage and color density. However, in some circumstances, this can be accomplished with one coat. The final pass for a metallic color coat is typically made using an air atomized spray gun to provide the proper orientation to the metallic particles in the color coat. In many modern plants, the color coats are applied to the top and sides of the body by automatic spray machines. Areas inaccessible to the automatic sprayers are painted manually. In other plants the color coats are applied entirely by robotic systems to either a stationary body or a moving body on a conveyer. If this is a water-borne base coat operation, there is a covered heated flashoff area where the bulk of the water evaporates before the body passes into the clear coat booth.

6.4.1.8 Clear Top Coat Area—Clear coat is applied in a controlled spray booth with high-speed electrostatic rotary atomizers mounted on fixed carriers or handled by robots. Areas inaccessible to the automatic sprayers are painted manually. Those plants that do not clear-coat the solid colors either let the painted solid color bodies pass straight through the clear-coat booth or let them pass uncoated through the base-coat booth and apply the total color-coat in the clear-coat booth.

Three coat high fashion color systems require another color application booth between the base-coat booth and the clear coat booth with the appropriate flashoff time between each coat.

After the color and clear coats have been applied, the bodies enter the color-bake oven where they are baked at 107 °C to 126 °C for about 30 min. The painted bodies are closely examined for irregularities as they come out of the oven. They are either designated as "OK to ship" or require repair. The "OK to ship" bodies are sent through the anti-rust and deadener blackout booths to the trim shop for finishing. Bodies requiring repair move to a designated paint repair areas for paint touch-up and baking. Some bodies require two-tone treatment.

6.4.1.9 Two-Tone and Repair Areas—Those bodies that are designated as "two-tone" are directed to an area where they are prepared for the second color. Preparation for two-tone includes scuff sanding of the area to be painted, cleaning with tack rags to remove standing residue, and the area to be painted. The body moves into the two-tone-booth where it receives the second base coat and clear coat, and subsequent baking, the same as it received the first coat. As the body exits the oven, it is again examined and designated as either "OK to ship" or requiring repair.

Bodies classified as having a major defect are recycled back through a sanding area, receive hand-applied repair phosphate on any area where bare steel is exposed, pass through a prime booth, if needed, pass through color booths (base coat and clear coat) and a color bake oven. Bodies classified as having minor surface defects are sent to a finesse area where minor top coat defects can be removed without painting. In any case, repainted areas receive the same full-bake cycle and have the same durability as the original paint.

Electronic control and measurement systems are continually being improved to provide faster, better, and more accurate assessment and control of the paint application processes.

7. Corrosion Testing and Materials Evaluation

7.1 Introduction—Corrosion testing plays a key role in the evaluation of automotive designs and materials, including predictions concerning the performance of a product, fundamental and environmental studies, new product development, materials selection, quality control, and auditing.

There are a wide variety of corrosion tests published in the literature. This section provides a cursory look at corrosion testing and materials evaluation relevant to automotive body panel exposures. Corrosion tests are grouped in two categories: service testing which employs exposure to natural environmental conditions, and accelerated testing which uses simulated conditions to predict product performance. Automotive service in the northeastern US and eastern Canada snow belt region, where exposure is to road salts, and the southern US coastal region, where exposure is to high humidity and sea salts, are considered the most severely corrosive environments.

7.2 Service Testing

7.2.1 FIELD SURVEYS—Field surveys are the most reliable means to access corrosion performance, as they involve the inspection and evaluation of standard production and experimental vehicles exposed to natural environment, normal operating conditions, and time.

The types of field surveys include fleet vehicle surveys and random surveys. Corrosion examinations can range from a periodic evaluation of exterior body panels to the total destruction of vehicles for thorough evaluation of the entire body and structural members. In the past, field surveys have been used to monitor environmental performance of body panels, establish the location of problem areas or designs in a car, identify corrosion problems based on geographical consideration, and examine the corrosion mechanisms occurring in service.

Because corrosion rates vary with exposure conditions, it is important in field surveys to have a well-defined history of the driving climate, driving conditions, general maintenance schedule, and access to repair records to interpret the results. Often this type of information is available for fleet vehicle and special survey programs sponsored by the automotive companies, but not so in random surveys.

The advantages of a field survey are that the subjects are production vehicles exposed to actual consumer use. Data from these surveys help to establish correlation between customer usage and accelerated testing.

However, field surveys are expensive, and require long-term commitment, thus these tests are often limited to automotive company sponsorship. This test method cannot practically be used to evaluate new materials quickly, and requires extensive time to evaluate any changes made in automotive designs, materials, and other protective measures.

7.2.2 MOBILE COUPON TEST RACKS—The mobile coupon test rack is a scaled-down version of the field survey. In this test, panels of materials are attached to racks which are subsequently installed on vehicles or trailers exposed to regular driving conditions and subjected to regular inspections. This test is referred to as "undervehicle" testing when the racks are located underneath a vehicle. However, racks are also located on bumpers, truck trailers, car doors, etc. Panels of various sizes configurations and conditions (bare, phosphated and primed, full paint system) can be accommodated and materials often contain test defects, such as scribes, stone pecks, and induced deformations, prior to exposure.

This test is long-term and provides close simulation of actual service environment with the added advantage of being able to test a number of materials simultaneously in the same environment. The mobile test rack is also a valuable procedure for companies who do not have the resources to obtain field surveys or have access to proving ground facilities.

Test racks provide reliable in-service correlation at the particular mounting location and environment (accurate driving records are helpful to interpret results), but they do not provide the dynamic mechanical input available through total vehicle testing.

7.2.3 ATMOSPHERIC EXPOSURE—Atmospheric tests are static, long term exposure of materials to weathering conditions at a select geographic location. Common examples are southern seacoast and industrial pollutant fallout areas. Corrosion rates at these sites vary with the environment, such as pollutants, time of wetness, temperature, humidity, hours of sunshine, and seasonal variability.

Atmospheric exposure can be accelerated, and more closely targeted for automotive service exposures, by routinely spraying panels with salt solution to stimulate deicing salt environment and/or subjecting the panels to gravel impingement/stone pecking. These types of modifications to a standard outdoor exposure test provide improved correlation to in-service automotive conditions. Corrosion exposure sites are available worldwide and require little maintenance or expense. The atmospheric tests are lengthy, and do not take into account the dynamic effects encountered when operating a vehicle.

7.2.4 ACCELERATED LABORATORY TESTING—The objectives of accelerated laboratory testing are to:

a. Select corrosion conditions representative of in-service exposures
b. Produce laboratory corrosion without changing the mechanism of in-service corrosion failures
c. Develop reproducibility of test results
d. Establish a mean to correlate these results to expected in-service performance

Although these objectives are not fully being met, accelerated laboratory testing does provide a benchmark for comparison of one material to another, or for use in quality control of a given material.

7.2.5 ELECTROCHEMICAL—There are numerous electrochemical tests, which typically involve the measurement of corrosion potentials, electrochemical currents, and/or polarization curves of materials exposed to electrolyte solutions anticipated to represent in-service conditions. For instance, NaCl solutions are used to represent exposure to saline environment, such as sea side, or exposure to road deicing salts.

Electrochemical tests are theoretical in nature and require sophisticated equipment, the correct use of techniques, and relevant electrolytes for testing. The tests provide a quantitative value for corrosion rates. They are typically quick, inexpensive, highly automated, and easily reproducible. They provide a means to study a large number of parameters with relative ease. These tests are useful for providing an insight to corrosion reaction mechanisms; however, they are not easily correlated to in-service performance.

7.2.6 STATIC LABORATORY TESTING—Numerous static tests have been used over the years to evaluate corrosion resistance of materials. These tests include, but are not limited to: salt spray, humidity or water fog, water immersion, and sulfur dioxide or Kesternich. Static tests are intended to simulate industrial environments and evaluate the coating's performance.

In static tests, panels are exposed to a severely accelerated, constant environment and are evaluated periodically for corrosion performance, such as time-to-red-rust, percentage of red rust, paint blistering, and creep from scribe lines, which is a measure of paint lifting from an intentional scratch, and loss of adhesion.

Controversy surrounds the static accelerated tests regarding their ability to provide a valid test simulation for in-service vehicle corrosion environments, and their ability to predict field corrosion mechanism. Studies have shown that the salt spray test, probably the most widely used laboratory test, does not produce results representative of corrosion in actual service. In addition, there is a question as to whether these tests are reproducible on the basis of test-to-test and cabinet-to-cabinet.

However, the accelerated static tests are quick and easy with a large amount of historical data. At this time, they appear to be most valuable as a quality control tool to access performance rather than as a predictive tool regarding material's performance ranking in service.

7.2.7 CYCLIC LABORATORY TESTING—Cyclic laboratory tests have been developed to provide accelerated corrosion performance results with failures representative of those observed in service conditions. These tests provide for accelerated testing and simulation of service conditions by the use of controlled alternating exposures to at least two corrosive environments, such as, salt or other chemical exposure, water immersion, temperature variations, humidity variations, ultraviolet (UV) light exposure, mud or clay contamination, gravel or shot blasting, and drying. Panels employed in cyclic tests typically contain intentional paint damage such as a scribe-to-metal or abrasion to accelerate the corrosion process.

The cyclic test has the benefit of providing conditions more representative of in-service conditions than a static test while remaining in a laboratory setting. Results can be obtained quickly; typically established test procedures range from five to ten weeks, and testing methods can accommodate large amounts of samples.

Still, these tests are accelerated and results require knowledgeable interpretation for correlation to actual in-service performance. Also, of the numerous cycles tests that have been developed, many do not rank materials performance equivalently nor do they correlate well to field performance results. Standardization of testing procedures is needed in cyclic testing to limit the number of tests and provide correlation to in-service performance.

7.2.8 PROVING GROUNDS—The proving ground tests are cyclical programs conducted by the automotive companies to evaluate the effects of corrosive elements on the performance of fully assembled vehicles. They provide accelerated dynamic corrosion aging of prototype or production vehicles by cyclic exposure to in-service conditions. The cyclic schedules vary by automotive company, but typically involve both chemical and mechanical inputs and can include salt trough, salt spray, dirt and gravel road travel, dry and salt-wetted highway travel, grit trough, variable temperature, humidity exposure, mud trough, and drying.

These tests simulate field experience but still represent an accelerated test condition and require knowledgeable interpretation of results for comparison to field performance. They have been established as providing limited evaluation of cosmetic and exterior corrosion results, and perforation performance. Some tests are aimed mainly at cosmetic and exterior corrosion while other tests focus on perforation. In addition, they are extremely costly and lengthy tests, requiring from approximately 10 weeks to 2 years to complete.

7.2.9 EVALUATION METHODS—The basis of the performance ratings in most of these tests is visual examination of appearance changes, appearance at initiated damage sites, and measurement of various parameters, including:

a. Measurement of blistering or paint loss area
b. Time to initiation of rust
c. Thickness or weight change of metal
d. Pit depth measurement of the localized corrosion
e. Change in mechanical properties

To evaluate any result, the tester must determine the credibility of the tests and properly extrapolate these findings to useful service-related information.

LABORATORY CYCLIC CORROSION TEST—SAE J2334 DEC2003

SAE Standard

Report of the SAE Automotive Corrosion and Prevention Committee approved June 1998 and revised October 2002 and December 2003. Rationale statement available.

Foreword—This laboratory cyclic corrosion test procedure is based on a field-correlated Design of Experiment process conducted by the SAE Automotive Corrosion and Prevention Committee (SAE/ACAP) and the Auto/Steel Partnership (A/SP) Corrosion Task Force. Results from this test will provide excellent correlation to severe corrosive field environments with respect to cosmetic corrosion performance. For historical information on the development of this test, refer to 2.1.4.

A typical automotive paint system was used to develop this test. See 2.1.4, 1 to 5. If a different type of coating system is used, field correlation must be determined.

1. Scope—The SAE J2334 lab test procedure should be used when determining corrosion performance for a particular coating system, substrate, process, or design. Since it is a field-correlated test, it can be used as a validation tool as well as a development tool. If corrosion mechanisms other than cosmetic or general corrosion are to be examined using this test, field correlation must be established.

2. References

2.1 Applicable Publications—The following publications form a part of this specification to the extent specified herein. Unless otherwise indicated, the latest version of SAE publications shall apply.

2.1.1 SAE PUBLICATION—Available from SAE, 400 Commonwealth Drive, Warrendale, PA 15096-0001.

SAE J1563—Guidelines for Laboratory Cyclic Corrosion Test Procedures for Painted Automotive Parts

2.1.2 ASTM PUBLICATIONS—Available from ASTM, 100 Barr Harbor Drive, West Conshohocken, PA 19428-2959.

ASTM D 1193—Specification for Reagent Water

ASTM D 1654—Method for Evaluation of Painted or Coated Specimens Subjected to Corrosive Environments

ASTM D 1735—Practice for Testing Water Resistance of Coatings Using Water Fog Apparatus

ASTM D 2247—Practice for Testing Water Resistance of Coatings in 100% Relative Humidity

ASTM E 70-90—Test Method for pH of Aqueous Solutions with the Glass Electrode

ASTM G 1—Recommended Practice for Preparing, Cleaning, and Evaluating Corrosion Test Specimens

2.1.3 GENERAL MOTORS PUBLICATIONS—Available from Global Engineering Documents, 15 Inverness Way East, Englewood, CO 80112.

GM 9540P— Accelerated Corrosion Test

2.1.4 OTHER PUBLICATIONS

1. Townsend, H. E., "Development of an Improved Laboratory Corrosion Test by the Automotive and Steel Industries," in *Advanced Coatings Technology, Proceedings of the fourth Annual ESD Advanced Coatings Conference*, The Engineering Society, Ann Arbor, MI, 1994, pp. 29-49.
2. Roudabush, L.A., Townsend, H.E., and McCune, D.C., "Update on the Development of an Improved Cosmetic Corrosion Test by the Automotive and Steel Industries," *Automotive Corrosion and Prevention Conference Proceedings, P-268,* Society of Automotive Engineers, Warrendale, PA, 1993, pp. 53-63.
3. Townsend, H.E., "Accelerated Corrosion Testing: A Cooperative Effort by the Automotive and Steel Industries, " *Proceedings of the Symposium on Corrosion-Resistant Automotive Sheet Steels,* ASM Materials Congress, ASM International, Metals Park, OH, 1988, pp. 55-67.
4. Townsend, H.E., "Status of a Cooperative Effort by the Automotive and Steel Industries to Develop a Standard Accelerated Corrosion Test," *Automotive Corrosion and Prevention Conference Proceedings, P-228,* Society of Automotive Engineers, Warrendale, PA, 1989, pp. 133-145.
5. Townsend, H.E., Granata, R.D., McCune, D.C., Schumacher, W.A., and Neville, R.J., "Progress by the Automotive and Steel Industries Toward an Improved Laboratory Cosmetic Corrosion Test," *Automotive Corrosion and Prevention Conference Proceedings, P-250,* Society of Automotive Engineers, Warrendale, PA, 1991, pp. 73-97.
6. Stephens, M.L., "SAE ACAP Division 3 Project: Evaluation of Corrosion Test Methods," *Automotive Corrosion and Prevention Conference Proceedings, P-228,* Society of Automotive Engineers, Warrendale, PA, 1989, pp. 157-164.
7. Lutze, F.W., and Shaffer, R.J., "Accelerated Atmospheric Corrosion Testing of AISI Panels," *Automotive Corrosion and Prevention Conference Proceedings, P-250,* Society of Automotive Engineers, Warrendale, PA, 1991, pp. 115-127.
8. Petschel, M., "Statistical Evaluation of Accelerated Corrosion Tests and Correlation with Two-Year On-Vehicle Tests," *Automotive Corrosion and Prevention Conference Proceedings, P-250,* Society of Automotive Engineers, Warrendale, PA, 1991, pp. 179-203.
9. Davidson, D.D. and Schumacher, W.A., "An Evaluation and Analysis of Commonly Used Accelerated Cosmetic Corrosion Tests Using Direct Comparison with Actual Field Exposure," *Automotive Corrosion and Prevention Conference Proceedings, P-250,* Society of Automotive Engineers, Warrendale, PA, 1991, pp. 205-219.
10. Ostermiller, M.R., and Townsend, H.E., "On-Vehicle Cosmetic Corrosion Testing of Coated and Cold-Rolled Steel Sheet," *Automotive Corrosion and Prevention Conference Proceedings, P-268,* Society of Automotive Engineers, Warrendale, PA, 1993, pp. 65-83.
11. Granata, R.D. and Moussavi-Madani, M., "Characterization of Corrosion Products and Corrosion Mechanisms on Automotive Coated Steels Subjected to Field and Laboratory Exposure Tests," Leigh University Report to the ASP Corrosion Task Force, January 10, 1996.
12. ASTM E 691-92, "Standard Practice for Conducting an Interlaboratory Study to Determine the Precision of a Test Method."
13. ASTM E 177-90a, "Standard Practice for Use of the Terms Precision and Bias in ASTM Test Methods."
14. Townsend, H.E. and McCune D.C., "Round-Robin Evaluation of a New Standard Laboratory Test for Cosmetic Corrosion," *Automotive Corrosion and Prevention Conference Proceedings, SP-1265,* Society of Automotive Engineers, Warrendale ,PA, 1997, pp. 53-68.
15. H. E. Townsend, D. D. Davidson, and M. R. Ostermiller, "Development of Laboratory Corrosion Tests by the Automotive and Steel Industries of North America," *Proceedings of the Fourth International Conference on Zinc and Zinc-Alloy Coated Steel Sheet, Iron and Steel Institute of Japan, Tokyo, pp. 659-666* (1998).
16. F. W. Lutze, D. C. McCune, and K. A. Smith, "Development of and Interlaboratory Test Evaluation of a Laboratory Corrosion Tests by the Automotive and Steel Industries of North America," *24th Annual Conference of Future Of Coatings Under Study (FOCUS), Detroit Society for Coatings Technology, Troy Michigan, U.S.A.*, (4-1999).
17. F. W. Lutze, D. C. McCune, H. E. Townsend, K. A. Smith, R. J. Shaffer, L. S. Thompson, and H. D. Hilton, "The Effects of Temperature and Salt Concentration on the Speed of the SAE J2334 Cyclic Corrosion Test," *Proceedings of the European Corrosion Congress*, London (2000).
18. F. W. Lutze, D. C. McCune, J. R. Schaffer, K. A. Smith, L.S. Thompson, and H. E. Townsend, "Interlaboratory Testing to Evaluate improvements in the precision of the SAE J2334 Cyclic Corrosion Test," *Proceedings of the Fifth International Conference on Zinc and Zinc Alloy Coated Steel Sheet, Centre for Research in Metallurgy, Brussels Belgium* (June 2001).
19. SAE ACAP committee, presented by Cynthia L. Meade, "Update on the developments of the SAE J2334 laboratory Cyclic Corrosion Test", SAE International Congress 2003, SAE International, Detroit, MI, paper # 2003-01-1234.
20. SAE ACAP committee, presented by Larry S. Thompson, "Perforation Corrosion Performance of Autobody Steel Sheet in On-Vehicle and Accelerated Tests", SAE International Congress 2003, SAE International, Detroit, MI, paper # 2003-01-1238.
21. SAE SP-1770 - Advances in Coatings & Corrosion Prevention.

2.1.4.1 Reproducibility and Repeatability information concerning this test method is discussed in SAE Paper 970734. See Reference 14.

3. Definitions

3.1 Cosmetic Corrosion—Corrosion that occurs as a result of the breakdown or damage to a coating system. Typically, this type of corrosion does not impact function but does compromise appearance.

3.2 General Corrosion—Corrosion of a component that is typically bare (no organic coating). Corrosive attack is uniform in nature and distributed over "large" areas.

3.3 Scribe Creepback—Coating creepback resulting from corrosion and undercutting from the scribe line. A scribe is a controlled simulated damage site designed to represent a scratch or chip.

3.4 Corrosion Coupons—Samples of bare metals, that are used to monitor and compare the corrosivity of laboratory corrosion tests in terms of mass-loss.

3.5 Test Controls—Components (i.e., test panels, coupons, parts, etc.) which have been previously tested and/or correlated. They can be used to control the test conduct and compare the test results (also assist in evaluating reproducibility and repeatability).

4. Equipment and Test Materials

4.1 Test Cabinets—Test cabinet(s) with the ability to obtain and maintain the following environmental conditions (Reference SAE J1563, ASTM D 1735, and ASTM D 2247):

a. 50 °C ± 2 °C and 100% Relative Humidity—The 100% relative humidity wet-stage condition can be achieved by use of one of the three methods shown as follows. Whichever method is employed, test samples and controls are required to be visibly moist/wet.
   1. Wet-bottom method according to ASTM D 2247 – except that the temperature shall be 50 °C ± 2 °C.
   2. Water fog method according to ASTM D 1735, except that the collection rate is reduced from a range of 1.5 to 3 mL/h to 0.75 to 1.5 mL/h. The use of this method requires that the collection rates be documented.
   3. Steam (vapor) generator method.

NOTE—The majority of the development of this specification was performed using the Wet-bottom method of humidity generation. This method was used as the basis when comparing other methods of humidity generation as well as other variables.

b. 60 °C ± 2 °C and 50% Relative Humidity ±5%. Additional equipment will be required to maintain the 50% relative humidity condition.

Air circulation must be sufficient to prevent temperature stratification and allow drying of test parts during the dry-off portion of the test cycle.

Air circulation can be obtained through the use of a fan or forced air.

4.2 Salt Solution Application—The samples must be subject to an application of salt solution by use of one of the three methods shown as follows. Whichever method is employed, test samples and controls are required to be visibly moist/wet during the entire 15-minute interval of each test cycle.

0.5% NaCl
0.1% $CaCl_2$
0.075% $NaHCO_3$

a. Immersion Method—Test specimens are to be immersed in the salt solution for a 15-minute interval of each test cycle.

b. Spray Method—A periodic or continuous direct impingement spray of the salt solution over the 15-minute interval that ensures the test specimens are kept wet for the entire 15-minute interval. Avoid a high intensity (pressure) spray that may affect test results. (Note 5) Both direct solution displacement and atomized spray are suitable for this method.

c. Air Atomized Fog Method—Applications of the salt solution to the test specimens by a 15-minute exposure to atomized fog provided the fog collection rate is 2 to 4 mL/h instead of 1 to 2 mL/h (collection rate as defined in ASTM D 1735). The use of this method requires that the collection rates be documented.

NOTE 1—"Either the $CaCl_2$ or $NaHCO_3$ material must be dissolved separately in deionized water (Reference ASTM D 1193 Type IV) and then added to the solution of other materials. If all solid materials are added at the same time in a "dry" state, an insoluble precipitate may result. If a precipitate forms and a spray application is used to apply the solution, it may be necessary to remove the precipitate to avoid clogging of nozzles (i.e., filter or siphon solution). Any filter media used must be inert to the solution being used. A 20 to 100 micron cotton or nylon mesh filter would be suitable. Do not attempt to dissolve the precipitate by adding acid.

NOTE 2—Measure and record pH of the salt solution prior to the start of test and on a weekly basis thereafter (Reference ASTM E 70-90). Do not attempt to adjust the pH with any form of buffers.

NOTE 3—The majority of the development of this specification was performed using the immersion method of salt solution application. This method was used as the basis when comparing other methods of salt solution applications as well as other variables.

NOTE 4—A freshly prepared test solution will have a conductivity of 10 to 12 ms at 25 °C ± 2 °C. Measure and record the conductivity (in units of ms) of the salt solution after mixing, prior to the last amount being used, and as needed to ensure that the conductivity of the solution remains between 10 to 12 mS at 25 °C.

NOTE 5—Careful attention should be paid to the spray method to avoid a high intensity spray that may affect test results by removal of the corrosion product, removal of the coating or driving solution into the corrosion products.

It is recommended that the test solution be changed weekly and that agitation/stirring of the solution be done prior to the salt solution application.

5. Test Procedure

5.1 Test Cycle—The test cycle is outlined in Figure 1 (5 day/week – manual operation) and Figure 2 (7 day/week - automatic operation). It consists of three basic stages:

1. Humid Stage—50 °C and 100% humidity, 6 h in duration,
2. Salt Application Stage—15 min duration conducted at ambient conditions
3. Dry Stage—60 °C and 50% RH, 17 h and 45 min in duration

The test cycle is repeated daily. Fully automatic cabinets have the option of running during the weekends or programming in a dry stage soak for the weekends (typically it would be desired to run on weekends and holidays to complete the test sooner). An exception to this rule would be if comparisons to other laboratories who do not have fully automatic capabilities is desired (for manual operations, the weekend exposure is typically maintained at dry stage conditions unless 7 day operations are available). Total test duration and weekend conditions must be documented in the test results. If two or more laboratories will be conducting tests on similar parts, it is recommended that a constant/common weekend condition be defined before testing begins.

Ramp time between the salt application stage (2) and dry stage (3) are part of the dry stage time. Similarly, ramp time between the dry stage (3) and humid stage (1) are part of the humid stage. Ramp times should be documented for each test set-up.

For cosmetic corrosion evaluations of coatings susceptible to damage, test samples will be scribed prior to exposure (Reference ASTM D 1654). Scribe length should be a minimum of 50 mm. Scribe creepback measurements are to be taken at predetermined intervals depending on the level of corrosion resistance desired. Scribe orientation, on the specimen, must be specified and documented (for typical flat panel specimens, it is recommended that panels be oriented 15 degrees from the vertical such that no one panel shadows another and that the scribe line be made in a diagonal across the panel face).

5.2 Test Duration—Typically, SAE J2334 is conducted for a minimum of 60 cycles when evaluating coated products. Longer durations may be required to observe performance differences in the heavier weight metallic precoats. Different test durations may be appropriate based on other materials, corrosion mechanisms of interest, or past history.

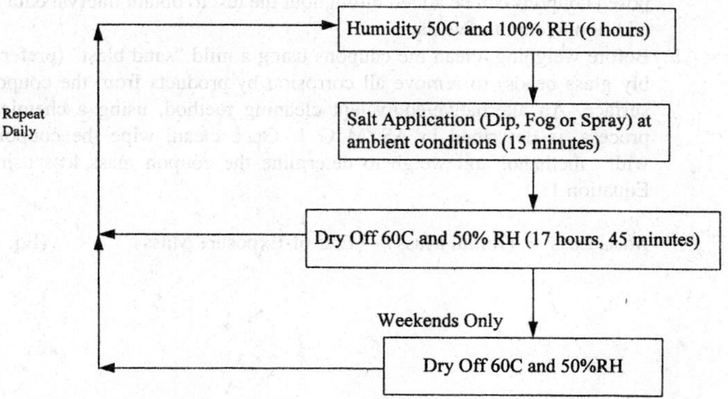

FIGURE 1—COSMETIC CORROSION LAB TEST CYCLES—5 DAY/WEEK—MANUAL OPERATION

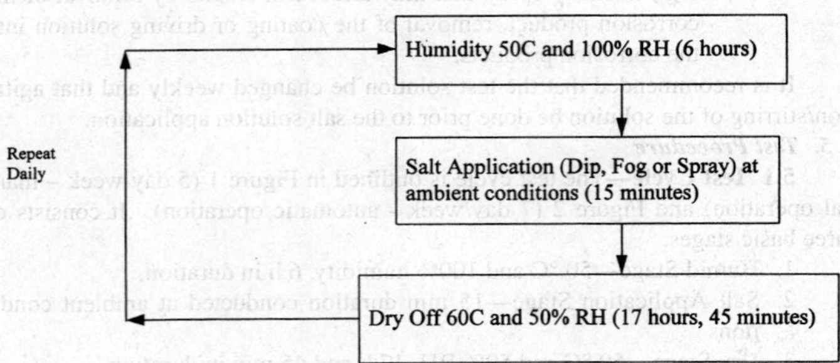

FIGURE 2—COSMETIC CORROSION LAB TEST CYCLES—7 DAY/WEEK—AUTOMATIC OPERATION

5.3 Coupon Monitoring—The testing process will be monitored with bare steel corrosion coupons.

a. Corrosion coupons generally consist of 25.4 mm by 50.8 mm pieces of bare sheet metal which serve to monitor the corrosivity of the test environment during the test. The sheet metal coupon will always include low-carbon cold rolled steel sheet (SAE 1006 to SAE 1010), and may also include other bare metals, such as zinc.

b. Each coupon shall be permanently identified by stamping a number onto the surface.

c. Corrosion coupons shall be thoroughly cleaned to remove all forming and storage oils/lubes with a commercially available degreaser followed by a methanol rinse. Then the mass in milligrams shall be recorded and retained for future reference.

d. The coupons shall be secured to an aluminum or nonmetallic coupon rack. The coupons shall be electrically isolated from the rack by using fasteners and washers made from a non-black plastic material, preferably nylon.

e. Allow a minimum 5 mm spacing between the coupons and the rack surface. All coupons shall be secured at a maximum 15 degrees from vertical and must not contact each other.

f. The coupon rack shall be placed in the general vicinity of the samples being tested, such that the coupons receive the same environmental exposure.

g. Coupons shall be removed and analyzed after a predetermined number of cycles throughout the test to monitor corrosion. To analyze coupons, remove 1 coupon from each end of the rack and prepare for weighing and mass loss determination. Insure enough coupons are exposed in the test so monitoring frequency can be accomplished. Additional unexposed coupons can be added throughout the test to obtain interval data in addition to cumulative data.

h. Before weighing, clean the coupons using a mild "sand blast" (preferably glass beads) to remove all corrosion by-products from the coupon surface. An alternative/equivalent cleaning method, using a chemical process, is described in ASTM G 1. Once clean, wipe the coupons with methanol and weigh to determine the coupon mass loss using Equation 1:

$$\text{Mass Loss} = (\text{Initial Mass}) - (\text{End-of-Exposure Mass}) \qquad \text{(Eq. 1)}$$

Corrosion losses may also be expressed in term of average corrosion rates from the mass loss, coupon area, test duration, and metal density by use of the calculation described in ASTM G 1.

6. Data Reporting

6.1 Coupons—Coupon mass loss values are to be recorded after each set of a predetermined number of cycles (typically, every 20 cycles). This will be a cumulative value. Additional unexposed coupons can be installed and removed after the next set of cycles to obtain interval coupon data if desired.

6.2 Test Samples—The test samples will have scribe creepback values or corrosion rate measurements recorded at predetermined intervals (typically, 20 cycles – in a rinsed only condition). At end-of-test two sets of creepback values will be recorded (if coated samples are to be evaluated) one set in a rinsed only condition and one set after the scrape and tape process (Reference 1989 SAE Automotive Corrosion and Prevention Conference P228, pages 144-5, see 2.1.4 (4)).

As a guideline, scribe creepback measurements of average, maximum, and minimum (total width) will be recorded.

6.2.1 BY DEFINITION

a. Total Width Creepback—A measurement of the distance between the unaffected paint film areas, in millimeters, on each side of the scribed line (measured across and perpendicular to the scribe line). (Loss of adhesion between paint film and substrate).

b. Average—The mean of a set of measurements of Total Width Creepback, at points spaced equidistant apart centered on the scribed line.

c. Maximum—A measurement of the Total Width Creepback at the point with the most extensive adhesion loss, discounting the areas at the ends of the scribed line.

d. Minimum—A measurement of the Total Width Creepback at the point with the least extensive adhesion loss, discounting the areas at the ends of the scribed line.

6.3 Test Equipment—Test equipment used shall be documented and include the following information:

If multiple cabinets are used to conduct the test, the following information must be recorded for each cabinet.

a. Cabinet Manufacturer/Model
b. Humidity
c. Temperature
d. Humidification Process
e. De-humidification Process
f. Heating Process
g. Cooling Process
h. Air Circulation Process
i. Size
j. Capacity
k. Calibration Process
l. Frequency of Calibration
m. Ramp Time Between Stages

6.3.1 SOLUTION INFORMATION:

a. Frequency of Salt Solution Changes (recommend weekly or sooner if contamination is a suspected concern)
b. Method of Salt Application
c. pH Measurement Method
d. If an Air Atomized Fog is chosen, then collection rates must be taken and documented.
e. Measure and record the conductivity (in units of ms) of the salt solution after mixing, prior to the last amount being used, and as needed to ensure that the conductivity of the solution remains within range. A freshly prepared test solution will have a conductivity of 10 to 12 ms at 25 °C ± 2 °C.

If a recorder is in use, a representative cycle profile should be submitted with test sample data. If a recorder is not in use, written documentation should be provided indicating typical steady-state conditions and the ramp times between steady-state conditions.

(8) PREVENTION OF CORROSION OF MOTOR VEHICLE BODY AND CHASSIS COMPONENTS—SAE J447 JUL1995 SAE Information Report

Report of the SAE ACAP Division 1—Body Corrosion approved January 1956, revised June 1981, an completely revised July 1995.

Foreword—Prevention of corrosion is an important design consideration for metals used in body and chassis components. In some cases, corrosion resistance may be the dominating factor governing the selection of material or process; in others, it will be secondary to manufacturing feasibility, appearance requirements, and availability. Means of preventing or retarding corrosion on specific parts may be important from the standpoint of assuring proper engineering function, contributing to service life, or producing and maintaining appearance. The designer should be familiar with the part that corrosion prevention plays in the selection of metal and/or treatment, so that the performance complies with the requirements.

With the use of salt for de-icing and dust control increasing at a rapid rate for the past decade, corrosion problems have been recognized as ones of primary importance. Components experiencing the most severe corrosion are those exposed to road splash thrown up by the wheels. Salt and mud poultices built up in these areas hold moisture in contact with the metal parts and extend the periods of wetness, which in turn accelerate deterioration by corrosion. The best way to prevent corrosion is to keep these critical surfaces free from prolonged contact with salt and mud. Therefore, the owner can help prevent corrosion by washing the vehicle, including the underbody, particularly during periods of high salt exposure.

This report is intended to provide information covering the corrosion preventive methods commonly used for both ferrous and nonferrous metals. The particular practices discussed are those considered typical within the automotive industry, but are believed applicable to parts and products for many other applications. Care has been taken to provide reliable data, but users should supplement this with their own experience and tests to be assured of satisfactory results for their own specific requirements. Optional methods may be equally suitable for typical classes of parts, and the choice may vary, with acceptable results. In some instances the preferred type of finish, coating, or treatment is indicated. Within the limits of whatever restrictions apply, after the selection is made, quality requirements are met by establishing suitable specifications, process controls, and acceptance tests.

The choice of corrosion preventive methods is greatly affected by the environmental and other conditions to which the part will be subjected in use, such as:

a. Moisture
b. Temperature
c. Salt
d. Galvanic Couples
e. Abrasion

The applicable conditions of service should be evaluated and protection provided in terms of the expected life of the part. Also, the part design may have an important effect on prevention of corrosion in severe environments and should be considered in relation to the materials and/or treatments and coatings. Trapped moisture, lack of ventilation, crevices, and other design details or effects of design may be significant.

In general, the corrosion preventive requirements of most automotive parts may be satisfied by a combination of the following:

a. Selection of material
b. Design considerations
c. Choice of protective treatments and/or coatings

The application of treatments or coatings to metal almost always requires some form of cleaning or other preparation for satisfactory results. Variations required for different coatings will be covered where they are considered important to the results obtained.

A general discussion of the methods, characteristics of materials, and specific applications is given in subsequent test.

TABLE OF CONTENTS

1. Scope—This SAE Information Report provides automotive engineers with the basic principles of corrosion, design guidelines to minimize corrosion, and a review of the various materials, treatments, and processes available to inhibit corrosion of both decorative and functional body and chassis components.

2. References

2.1 Applicable Publications—The following publications form a part of this specification to the extent specified herein. The latest issue of SAE publications shall apply.

2.1.1 SAE PUBLICATIONS—Available from SAE, 400 Commonwealth Drive, Warrendale, PA 15096-0001.

SAE Paper 912275—Proc. Automotive Corros. and Prevention Conference, Townsend, H. E., et al., 1991, p. 73

SAE Paper 912278—Lutze, F. and Shaffer, R. J., ibid., p. 115

SAE Paper 912283—Petschel, M., ibid., p. 179

SAE Paper 912284—Davidson, D. D. and Schumacher, W. A., ibid., p. 205

SAE Paper 912285—Roudabush, L. A. and Dorsett, T. E., ibid., p. 221

SAE Paper 912291—Roberto, O. E. and Hart, R. G., ibid., p. 289

SAE Paper 950375—Simpson, T.C., Bryant, A.W., Hook, G., Daley, R.A., Swinko, R.J., and Miller, R.W.

2.1.2 ASTM PUBLICATIONS—Available from ASTM, 100 Bar Harbor St., Philadelphia, PA 19103-1187.

ASTM B 110—Dielectric Strength

ASTM B 117—Test Method of Salt Spray (Fog) Testing

ASTM B 136—Stain Resistance

ASTM B 137—Coating Weight

ASTM B 177—Practice for Chromium Electroplating on Steel for Engineering Use

ASTM B 183—Practice for Preparation of Low Carbon Steel for Electroplating

ASTM B 200—Specification of Electrodeposited Coatings of Lead and Lead-Tin Alloys on Steel and Ferrous Alloys

ASTM B 242—Practice for Preparation of High-Carbon Steel for Electroplating

ASTM B 252—Practice for Preparation of Zinc Alloy Die Castings for Electroplating and Conversion Coating

ASTM B 253—Guide for Preparation of Aluminum Alloys for Electroplating

ASTM B 254—Practice for Preparation of and Electroplating on Stainless Steel

ASTM B 281—Practice for Preparation of Copper and Copper-Base Alloys for Electroplating and Conversion Coatings

ASTM B 320—Practice for Preparation of Iron Castings for Electroplating

ASTM B 322—Practice for Cleaning Metals Prior to Electroplating

ASTM B 368—Method for Copper-Accelerated Acitic Acid-Salt Fog Testing (CASS Test)

ASTM B 380—Methods for Corrosion Testing of Decorative Chromium Electroplating by the Corrodkote Procedure

ASTM B 456—Specification for Electrodeposited Coatings of Copper Plus Nickel Plus Chromium and Nickel Plus Chromium

ASTM B 487—Test Method for Measurement of Metal and Oxide Coating Thickness by Microscopal Examination of a Cross Section

ASTM B 499—Test Method for Measurement of Coating Thickness by the Magnetic Method: Nonmagnetic Coatings on Magnetic Basis Metals

ASTM B 504—Test Method for Measurement of Thickness of Metallic Coatings by the Coulometric Method

ASTM B 530—Method for Measurement of Coating Thickness by the Magnetic Method: Electrodeposited Nickel Coatings on Magnetic and Nonmagnetic Substrates

2.1.3 SME PUBLICATIONS—Available from SME, P.o. Box 930, 1 SME Drive, Dearborn, MI 48121.

2.1.3.1 SME Paper FC91-371 Jones, T.C., Proc. Finishing `91, 1991

2.1.3.2 Jones, T. C., The Finishing Line, SME, Third Quarter 1990, p. 1

2.1.3.3 User's Guide to Powder Coating, 2nd Edition," SME, 1987, Chapter 5, p. 55

2.1.4 OTHER PUBLICATIONS

2.1.4.1 Annual Statistical Report 1990, American Iron and Steel Institute, Washington, DC (1991), pp. 25–27

2.1.4.2 A. W. Bryant, L. M. Thompson, and W. C. Oldenburg, "U.S. Automotive Corrosion Trends at 5 and 6 Years," Automotive Corrosion and Prevention Conference Proceedings, P 228, L. Allegra, ed., Society of Automotive Engineers, Warrendale, PA (1989), p. 185

2.1.4.3 H. E. Gannon, ed., "The Making, Shaping, and Treating of Steel," 10th edition, United States Steel Corporation

2.1.4.4 H. E. Townsend, "Coated Steel Sheets for Corrosion-Resistant Automobiles," Materials Performance, October 1991, p. 60; National Association of Corrosion Engineers, Corrosion `91, Paper 91416, NACE, Houston, TX

2.1.4.5 Y. Miyoshi, "State of the Art in Precoated Steel Sheet for Automotive Body Materials in Japan," ISIJ International, 31, 1, 1991, p. 1

2.1.4.6 D. Quantin, D. Deparis, and J. C. Charbonnier, "Coated Steel Sheets for the Automotive Industry," Steel Technology International, 1990/1991, p. 245

2.1.4.7 K. Yamoto, T. Ichida, and T. Irie, "Progress in Precoated Steel Sheets for Automotive Use," Kawasaki Steel Technical Report, #22, May 1990, p. 57

2.1.4.8 "Cracking Down on Corrosion," American Iron and Steel Institute, Washington, DC, 1991

2.1.4.9 G. W. Bush, "Developments in the Continuous Galvanizing of Steel," Journal of Metals, August 1989, p. 34

2.1.4.10 L. W. Austin and J. H. Lindsay, "Continuous Steel Strip Electroplating," American Electroplaters and Surface Finishers Society Press, Orlando, FL, 1989

2.1.4.11 R. Baboian, "Causes and Effects of Corrosion Relating to Exterior Trim on Automobiles," Proceedings of the 2nd Automotive Corrosion and Prevention Conference, P-136, SAE, Warrendale, PA.

2.2 Related Publications—The following publications are provided for information purposes only and are not a required part of this document.

H. H. Uhlig, "Corrosion and Corrosion Control," New York, NY, John Wiley & Sons, Inc., 1963

U. R. Evans, "The Corrosion and Oxidation of Metals," London, England, Edward Arnold, Ltd., 1960

F. T. Laque and H. R. Copson, "Corrosion Resistance of Metals and Alloys," New York, NY, Reinhold Publishing Co., 1963

N. D. Tomoshov, "Theory of Corrosion and Protection of Metals," New York, NY, Macmillan, 1966

W. H. Ailor, Editor, "Handbook on Corrosion Testing and Evaluation," New York, NY, John Wiley & Sons, Inc., 1971

"NACE Basic Corrosion Course," Houston, TX, National Association of Corrosion Engineers, 1971

M. G. Fontana and N. D. Greene, "Corrosion Engineering," New York, NY, McGraw-Hill, 1967

"Localized Corrosion—Cause of Metal Failure," STP 516, Philadelphia, PA, American Society for Testing and materials, 1972

L. C. Rowe, "The Prevention of Galvanic Corrosion in Bimetallic Assemblies," SAE Paper 740101, presented at SAE Automotive Engineering Congress, Detroit, MI, 1974

H. P. Godard, W. P. Jepson, M. R. Bothwell, and R. L. Kane, "The Corrosion of Light Metals," New York, NY, John Wiley & Sons, Inc., 1976

H. Leidheiser, Jr., "The Corrosion of Copper, Tin, and Their Alloys," New York, NY, John Wiley & Sons, Inc., 1971

J. C. Hudson, "The Corrosion of Iron and Steel," New York, NY, Van Nostrand, 1940

H. H. Uhlig, Editor, "Corrosion Handbook," New York, NY, John Wiley & Sons, Inc., 1948

C. J. Slunder and W. K. Boyd, "Zinc: Its Corrosion Resistance," New York, NY, Zinc Institute, Inc., 1971

R. M. Burns and W. W. Bradley, "Protective Coatings for Metals," 2nd Ed., New York, NY, Reinhold Publishing Co., 1955

L. L. Sheir, "Corrosion," Parts I and II, New York, NY, John Wiley & Sons., Inc., 1963

L. C. Rowe, "The Application of Corrosion Principles to Engineering Design," SAE Paper 770292, presented at SAE Automotive Engineering Congress, Detroit, MI, 1977

M. Henthorne, "Corrosion—Causes and Control," reprinted from Chemical Engineering, Vol. 78, 5/17/71 to 4/3/72, New York, NY, McGraw-Hill, Inc., 1971–72

Anon., M/DE Special Report No. 202, "Corrosion," Materials in Design Engineering, 57, 85 (1963), January

H. Suss, "Stress Corrosion—Causes and Cures," Materials in Design Engineering, 61, 102 (1965), April

R. T. Knapp, J. W. Daily, and F. G. Hammitt, "Cavitation," McGraw-Hill, Inc., New York, NY, 1970

L. C. Rowe, "The Application of Corrosion Principles to Engineering Design," SAE Paper 770292 presented at SAE Automotive Engineering Congress, Detroit, MI, 1977

A. W. Bryant, "Designing Body Panels for Corrosion Prevention," SAE Paper 780916 presented at SAE Conference on Designing for Automotive Corrosion Prevention," Troy, MI, November 1978

Proceedings P-78, SAE Conference on Designing for Automotive Corrosion Prevention, November 1978

R. Dietz, "Design Characteristics and Constructional Features to Minimize Corrosion Sensitivity of Automobiles," NACE Paper 48 presented at NACE Corrosion 88, St. Louis, MO, March 1988

R. Baboian, "Automotive Corrosion and Protection," NACE International, Houston, TX, 1992.

R. Baboian, "Automotive Corrosion by Deicing Salts," NACE International, Houston TX, 1981.

R. Baboian, "Chemistry and Corrosivity of the Automotive Environment," in Designing for Corrosion Prevention, SAE, Warrendale, PA 1978.

R. Baboian, "Materials Degradation Caused by Acid Rain," American Chemical Society, Washington, DC 1986.

3. *Definitions*

3.1 Acid—Acids can be defined in several ways. For many purposes it is sufficient to say that an acid is a hydrogen containing substance which dissociates on solution in water to produce one or more hydrogen ions. The Bronsted concept states that an acid is any compound that can furnish a proton. The more general Lewis definition of an acid is anything that can attach itself to something with an unshared pair of electrons.

3.2 Acidic—For aqueous solutions, anything having a pH that is less than 7 is considered acidic.

3.3 Alkaline—For aqueous solutions, anything having a pH that is greater than 7 is considered alkaline.

3.4 Anodic Coating—A coating that is anodic to the underlying substrate. Anodic coatings offer sacrificial protection to the substrate.

3.5 Barrier Protection—A type of protection that relies on the coating preventing access of moisture or oxygen to the material being protected. Organic coatings often offer barrier protection to underlying substrates.

3.6 Base—Bases can be defined in several ways. For many purposes it is sufficient to say that a base is a substance which dissociates on solution in water to produce one or more hydroxyl ions. The Bronsted concept states that a base is any compound that can accept a proton. The more general Lewis definition of a base is anything that has an unshared pair of electrons.

3.7 Basic—For aqueous solutions, anything having a pH that is greater than 7 is considered basic.

3.8 Blister—A region of lifted paint typically caused by loss of adhesion within the paint system or between the paint and metal surface.

3.9 Cathodic Delamination—Type of corrosion damage caused by loss of adhesion between the paint finish and the metal.

3.10 Cathodic Coating—A coating that is cathodic to the underlying substrate.

3.11 Cavitation Corrosion—Cavitation Corrosion occurs on the low pressure side of propellers and pump impellers where interruption in smooth flow causes vapor bubbles to form. When these bubbles collapse, they can destroy any protective coating and remove minute particles of metal.

3.12 Chromated—Parts treated with chromic acid to improve their corrosion resistance.

3.13 Clearcoat—A paint without pigment applied over a color basecoat to enhance the appearance and durability of the total paint system.

3.14 Cosmetic Corrosion—Corrosion typically characterized by blistering and/or rusting that is aesthetically displeasing, but does not result in catastrophic failure of the item.

3.15 Creepback—The undercutting or the separation of paint from the substrate at an edge, damage site, or a scribe line.

3.16 Current—The "flow" of electricity expressed in amperes, milliamperes and microamperes.

3.17 Cyclic Testing—Accelerated testing and simulation of service conditions by the use of controlled alternating exposures to at least two corrosive environments, such as salt or other chemical exposure, water immersion, temperature variations, humidity variations, ultraviolet (UV) light exposure, mud or clay contamination, gravel or shot blasting, and driving.

3.18 Current Density—The current per unit area; generally expressed as amps per sq cm.

3.19 Deicing Salt—Salts, typically NaCl and/or $CaCl_2$, applied to highways to aid in seasonal deicing.

3.20 Deionized Water—Water that has had the charged species (Cl^-, Ca^{2+}, etc.) removed from it.

3.21 Diffusion—The movement of one substance through another. Diffusion of contaminants into a paint system is often the cause of corrosion attack.

3.22 Differentially Zinc Coated—A sheet (usually steel) with a zinc coating of a different thickness on one side than on the other side.

3.23 Dip-Spin—A process using a perforated basket in which parts are placed to be dipped into an organic/inorganic finish, spun to remove excess coating then normally placed in an oven to cure the finish.

3.24 Electrochemical Reaction—A chemical reaction which is driven by a difference in electrode potential from one site to another on the same or different parts.

3.25 Electrocoat, E-coat, ELPO—A coating for metals deposited by the application of high voltages between an anode and a cathode in an electrolyte. Cathodic electrocoating is commonly used in the automotive industry.

3.26 Electrogalvanized—Steel containing a zinc coating produced by continuously electroplating zinc onto the steel surface.

3.27 Electroplated Coatings—Coatings applied in a low temperature continuous process where negatively charged steel sheet is passed between positively charged anodes. Metallic ions in an electrolyte bath are reduced and plated on the surface of the steel sheet forming the coating.

3.28 Flash Coating—A very thin coating of paint or plating applied to provide limited corrosion protection or to improve the adhesion of subsequent coatings.

3.29 Hot Dip Galvanized—Steel containing a zinc coating produced by immersion of the steel in a molten zinc bath.

3.30 Galvanneal—Steel containing a zinc/iron alloy coating produced by the hot-dip process.

3.31 Gravelometer—Machine used to cause consistent intentional paint damage to samples prior to or during laboratory corrosion testing. A gravelometer propels gravel or metal shot of a particular size and shape at the surface of a painted test specimen. The gravelometer is used to simulate the type of field paint damage caused by gravel or other road debris.

3.32 Hem Flange—A method of joining two pieces of metal together in which the edge of one piece is folded tightly over the edge of the other.

3.33 Hot-Dip Coating—A continuous process of applying coatings to steel in which the steel is immersed in a molten bath of the material to be coated.

3.34 Inside-Out Corrosion—Corrosion that starts from the inside surface of a body panel and works outward.

3.35 Localized Corrosion—Corrosion resulting in differential attack across a metallic surface. Localized corrosion is typically of a cosmetic nature, but can lead to catastrophic failure if a primary structural component is the site of severe attack.

3.36 Neutral—In aqueous solutions, a substance having a pH of 7 is considered neutral.

3.37 Organic Coatings—Coatings, primarily paints, applied to metallic or other substrates typically to provide corrosion protection and to improve aesthetic characteristics of the material.

3.38 Outside-In Corrosion—Corrosion that starts from the outside surface of a body panel and works inward.

3.39 Perforation Corrosion—Penetration of a panel due to corrosion. Perforation corrosion is usually associated with inside-out corrosion.

3.40 Phosphate Coatings—Protective coatings formed by reaction of a metallic substrate with an acidic phosphate containing solution. The primary role of the phosphate coating is to enhance adhesion of the primer (electrocoat or other) to the metal. Phosphate coatings are typically Zn, Fe, Zn-Ni, or Zn-Ni-Mn phosphates.

3.41 Pitting Corrosion—A type of perforation corrosion. Pitting corrosion is highly localized corrosion resulting in deep penetration at only a few spots.

3.42 Potential—See electrochemical potential.

3.43 Poultice—An accumulation of mud, sand, salt, and other road debris on the interior surface joints of body panels and structural components.

3.44 Pre-coated—A material that has been coated prior to the manufacture of the ware or part.

3.45 Pre-treatment—The treatment of a surface prior to the process of interest, for example: a phosphate coating is a pre-treatment for electrocoat or painting.

3.46 Proving Ground Tests—Cyclical programs primarily conducted by the automotive companies to evaluate the effects of corrosive elements on the performance of fully assembled vehicles. Proving Ground Tests often combine on-road exposures with exposures in environmental chambers.

3.47 Reaction Cell—A cell at which a chemical reaction is occurring.

3.48 Rust Proofing—The application of coatings intended to prevent or greatly reduce the formation of rust on steel parts.

3.49 Saponification Corrosion—Formation of a soap by the reaction of corrosion products with some organic coatings.

3.50 Scab Corrosion—Cosmetic corrosion caused by break down of the surface protection system often proceeded by blisters.

3.51 Scribe—An intentional paint damage typically used for material evaluation during corrosion testing.

3.52 Sealers—Products applied to joints or seams to prevent the entry of moisture or contaminants. Paint coatings applied to prevent the undesirable interaction of a subsequent coating with a previous coating or to enhance adhesion or corrosion protection.

3.53 Undercutting—See Creepback

3.54 Uniform Corrosion—Corrosion which occurs uniformly on the surface of a part. Uniform corrosion is not associated with joints and is not pitting.

4. Chapter 1—Principles of Corrosion

4.1 Electrochemical Theory—Corrosion in the broad sense is accepted as the deterioration of any material because of a reaction with its environment, which means that materials such as plastics, ceramics, concrete, glass, and many others would be included in that definition. Most often, however, corrosion is associated with the deterioration of metals and alloys. The processes involved with corrosion of metals and alloys are predominantly electrochemical. An electrochemical process is one that involves a transfer of electrons in an oxidation-reduction reaction. Corrosion by direct chemical reaction (which does not involve a transfer of electrons) and hot corrosion (which involves high-temperature gases or molten salts) will not be discussed here.

The principle of electrochemical corrosion is the same as that involved with the functioning of a dry cell battery, which contains a graphite cathode[1] and a zinc anode in contact with a conductive solution (electrolyte). When the two electrodes are connected with an electrically conductive material, current will flow between them because of the difference in their oxidation-reduction (electrical) potentials. This current flow gradually destroys the anode. The degree of destruction depends upon the total amount of current flow. Faraday's law states it another way: "The mass of a substance liberated in an electrolytic cell is proportional to the quantity of electricity passing through the cell." These concepts of anode-cathode relationships and current flow are fundamental to understanding electrochemical corrosion.

The three essential parts of a corrosion cell are: (a) an anode, (b) a cathode, and (c) a conductive solution called an electrolyte. If any one part is missing, or if there is an interruption in the electrical path, current cannot flow and electrochemical corrosion cannot occur. Figure 1 shows how the current flows in a corroding system.

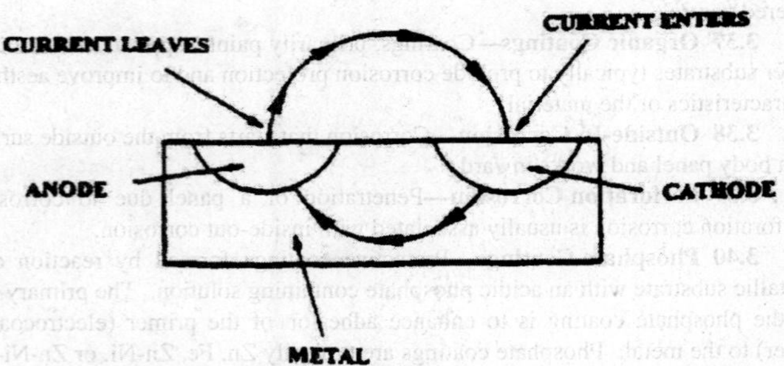

FIGURE 1—CURRENT FLOW IN A CORRODING SYSTEM

1. Because of convention, the graphite rod carries the "+" (positive) designation in the typical dry cell battery. Electrochemically, it is the cathode and carries the "–" (negative) designation.

When a metal corrodes, oxidation occurs at the anode, which loses electrons, and reduction occurs at the cathode, which gains electrons. The direction of flow of electrons is the opposite to the current flow. The reactions at the anode and cathode are called half-cell reactions, and both must occur for corrosion to occur. They can occur on the same metal surface or on separated metal surfaces, provided there is some form of metallic contact between the surfaces and they share a common electrolyte. Some typical half-cell reactions for the anodic process are shown as follows:

$$FE \rightarrow Fe^{++} + 2e \quad \text{(Eq. 1)}$$
$$Zn \rightarrow Zn^{++} + 2e$$
$$A1 \rightarrow A1^{++} + 3e$$

When iron corrodes, ferrous ions (Fe^{++}) are found at the anode by the oxidation of the iron metal. Eventually, they are further oxidized at ferric ions that combine with oxygen and water to form hydrated ferric oxide (rust). The electrons lost at the anode are transported to the cathode, which allows the reduction reaction to take place. Half-cell reactions for the cathode process vary with the environment and involve consumption of electrons as shown as follows:

Hydrogen Reduction (Evolution): $2H^{+} + 2e \rightarrow H_2 \leftarrow$ (Eq. 2)

Oxygen Reduction

Acid Solution: $O_2 + 4H^{+} + 4e \rightarrow 2H_2O$

Neutral and Alkaline Solution: $O_2 + 2H_2O + 4e \rightarrow 4OH$

Metal Ion Reduction: $Fe^{+3} + e \rightarrow Fe^{+2}$

Metal Deposition: $Zn^{+2} + 2e \rightarrow Zn$

Hydrogen evolution is a very common cathodic reaction in acid solutions, and oxygen reduction can occur in any solution in contact with air. Metal ion reduction and metal deposition are less commonly associated with the corrosion process, but may be found in chemical process systems.

General chemistry uses the principle of an electrochemical corrosion reaction to produce hydrogen gas, H_2. This occurs when zinc particles are added to dilute hydrochloric acid. The acid attacks the zinc metal forming zinc ions (Zn^{++}) and the zinc atom gives up two electrons (oxidation). This area becomes the anode. The electrolyte, dilute HCl, contains hydrogen ions (H^{+}) and chloride ions (Cl^{-}). The electrons leave the metal (this area becomes the cathode), are accepted by the hydrogen ions, and form a free hydrogen gas molecule (reduction). To complete the reaction, the zinc ion (Zn^{++}) joins with two chloride ions (Cl^{-}) and forms $ZnCl_2$. The complete chemical reaction is:

$$Zn + 2\,HCl \rightarrow ZnCl_2 + H_2 \quad \text{(Eq. 3)}$$
$$(Zn \rightarrow Zn^{++} + 2e)$$
$$(HCl \rightarrow H^{+} + Cl^{-})$$
$$2H^{+} + 2e \rightarrow H_2$$
$$Zn^{++} + 2\,Cl^{-} \rightarrow ZnCl_2 \uparrow$$

The previous concept is illustrated in Figure 2.

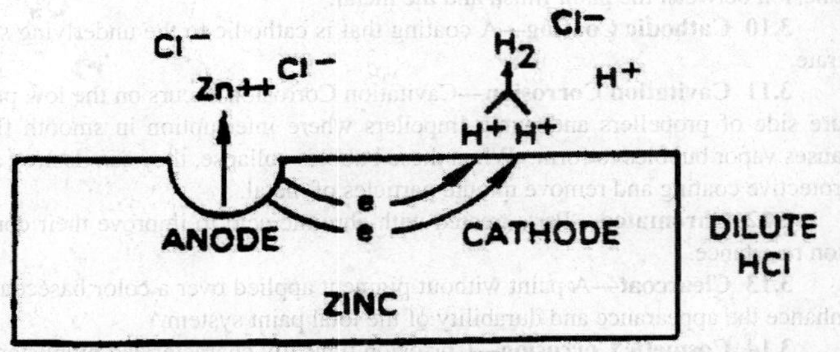

FIGURE 2—ANODIC AND CATHODIC REACTIONS WITH ZINC METAL IN DILUTE HYDROCHLORIC ACID

The possibility for corrosion to occur in a particular environment depends upon whether the free-energy change (ΔG) is negative in the following equation:

$$\Delta G + -nFE \quad \text{(Eq. 4)}$$

where:

n = Number of electrons involved
F = Faraday constant
E = Cell potential

The cell potential (E) is the difference between the equilibrium potentials of the cathodic and anodic half-cell reactions, and can be determined from half-cell potentials that were measured under standard conditions. A list of such potentials is shown in Table 1. An example of how to determine the feasibility of a reaction between aluminum and moist air is as follows:

E = the potential of the cathodic reaction minus the potential of the anodic reaction

$E(O_2/OH^-) - E\ (Al/AL{+}{+}{+})$

$E + 0.401 - (-1.662) = 2.063$

The cell potential for this reaction is positive, and when substituted in the free-energy equation, it is found that the reaction can occur because DG is negative.

In summary, corrosion occurs when metal atoms are oxidized at the anode and enter the solution as ions, leaving behind an excess of negatively charged electrons in the metal. Electrons flow through the metallic circuit to the cathode, where positively charged hydrogen ions at the cathode surface are reduced to hydrogen atoms which combine to form hydrogen gas. When this reaction does not occur readily, oxygen is reduced and it combines with hydrogen ions or with water. The corrosion rate is dependent upon the ease with which these reactions occur and the driving force, or potential difference, between anodic and cathodic sites.

The essential requirement for corrosion is that a potential difference exist between two sites which are joined by an electrolyte and by an electrical path. Corrosion prevention is simply a means of interfering with the continuity of the circuit. The degree of success is determined by the extent of the interference.

TABLE 1—STANDARD OXIDATION-REDUCTION (REDOX) POTENTIALS (25 °C, VOLTS VS. NORMAL HYDROGEN ELECTRODE)[1]

Element	Electrode Reaction	Redox Potential
Gold	$Au = Au^{+3} + 3e$	+1.498
Oxygen (acid media)	$O_2 + 4H^+ + 4e = 2H_2O$	+1.229
Palladium	$Pt = Pt^{+2} + 2e$	+1.2
Platinum	$Pd = Pd^{+2} + 2e$	+0.987
Mercury	$Hg = Hg^+ + e$	+0.799
Silver	$2Ag = Ag_2^{+2} + 2e$	+0.788
Iron (ferric)	$Fe^{+2} = Fe^{+3} + e$	+0.771
Oxygen (neutral or alkaline media)	$O_2 + 2H_2O + 4e = 4OH$	+0.401
Copper	$Cu = Cu^{+2} + 2e$	+0.337
Tin (stannic)	$Sn^{+2} = Sn^{+4} + 2e$	+0.15
Hydrogen	$H_2 = 2H^+ + 2e$	0.000
Lead	$Pb = Pb^{+2} + 2e$	−0.126
Tin (stannous)	$Sn = Sn^{+2} + 2e$	−0.136
Nickel	$Ni = Ni^{+2} + 2e$	−0.250
Cobalt	$Co = Co^{+2} + 2e$	−0.277
Cadmium	$Cd = Cd^{+2} + 2e$	−0.403
Iron (ferrous)	$Fe = Fe^{+2} + 2e$	−0.440
Chromium	$Cr = Cr^{+3} + 3e$	−0.744
Zinc	$Zn = Zn^{+2} + 2e$	−0.763
Aluminum	$Al = Al^{+3} + 3e$	−1.662
Magnesium	$Mg = Mg^{+2} + 2e$	−2.363
Sodium	$Na = Na^+ + e$	−2.714
Potassium	$K = K^+ + e$	−2.925

1. Electrode potential values are given and are invariant (e.g., $Zn = Zn^{+2} + 2e$ and $Zn^{+2} + 2e = Zn$ are identical and represent zinc in equilibrium with its ions with a potential of −0.763 V versus normal hydrogen electrode.)

4.2 Factors Affecting Corrosion Rate—Among some of the more common parameters that affect the corrosion rate for a given metal or alloy are: (a) the chemical composition of the electrolyte, (b) temperature, (c) relative humidity, (d) surface conditions, (e) metal stress, (f) galvanic effects, and (g) ratio of electrode areas.

The effect of the chemical composition of the electrolyte is associated mostly with salt concentration, pH, and the nature of the ions. For a solution to be corrosive, it must be conductive; that is, it must have sufficient ionic strength to pass a reasonable amount of current. The acidity or alkalinity of a solution affects different metals differently. Such metals as zinc, aluminum, lead, and tin are soluble in acids as well as alkalis, but are more soluble when the solution pH is either very high or very low. Other metals, such as nickel, copper, cobalt, chromium, manganese, cadmium, magnesium, and iron are soluble in acids, but are generally insoluble in alkalis. Certain ions, particularly chloride ions, are highly mobile and have the ability to penetrate oxide films on the metal surface, which can lead to localized corrosion. Also, the species of salts in the electrolyte will often determine whether the corrosion products formed on the surface are adherent and protective or whether they are loose and permeable to the solution, allowing corrosion to continue.

Increasing temperature generally increases reaction rates, but it can also affect corrosion through its effect on films. It may increase their solubility or otherwise change their nature to make them less protective, or it can change the solubility characteristics of certain products and cause a precipitate to form that is protective. Temperature differential may also create an anode/cathode relationship on a given piece of metal; the part at elevated temperature may be anodic to the part at the lower temperature.

Relative humidity can have a very dramatic effect on the corrosion of metals, and for certain metals there is such a thing as a critical relative humidity above which corrosion will proceed at an accelerated rate. For example, the critical relative humidity for iron, copper, nickel, and zinc generally falls between 50 and 70%.

A dirty surface often exerts a very strong influence on the initiation and rate of corrosion. For example, dirt, debris, and hygroscopic substances can absorb and retain moisture, and also create local anodes and cathodes on a surface, which can initiate and prolong corrosive attack. Topographical irregularities and metallurgical variations and inhomogeneities at the surface are potential sites for initiation of corrosion. Surface films, particularly if they are discontinuous, can contribute to corrosion. Corrosion products can be very voluminous, and may accelerate corrosion by absorbing and retaining moisture.

Stressed materials often corrode faster than unstressed materials, and those under tension will corrode sooner and at a higher rate than the same material under compressive stress.

Galvanic effects result from the coupling of dissimilar metals and are particularly devastating when the electromotive (driving) force, or potential difference, between the metals is large. In addition, there is an area effect to consider because the corrosion rate of the more anodic member of the couple will increase almost in direct proportion to the cathode-to-anode area ratio. The worst case is when a large cathode is connected to a small anode. Besides the obvious situation where dissimilar metals are coupled, many galvanic effects result from dissimilar surface conditions discussed previously.

4.3 Forms of Corrosion—The forms of corrosion are broadly classified as: (a) uniform, or general corrosion; and (b) localized corrosion. Uniform corrosion occurs over the entire surface at about the same rate, which varies depending on the environment. In acids or other aggressive solutions, the attack may be very rapid, while in ordinary air atmospheres, the attack may be slow because of the formation of protective corrosion deposits. Uniform corrosion normally does not cause metal failures as rapidly as localized corrosion, but it is detrimental to appearance. Localized corrosion affects smaller portions of the metal surface, but the rate of penetration of the affected area can often be very fast, perhaps hundreds to thousands of micrometers per year. Some metals are more susceptible to one form of localized corrosion than to another. This type of information should be known before selecting a material for a particular application. The following brief descriptions of various forms of localized corrosion serve only as an introduction. More extensive information may be obtained from the literature.

4.3.1 CONCENTRATION CELL CORROSION—One of the most serious causes of localized corrosion is the concentration cell. This is a condition in which a local potential difference arises between two areas of metal exposed to different concentrations of dissolved ions in the same solution. Concentration cells are usually associated with crevices, recessed areas, scale, or surface deposits. The two major types of cells are: (a) the differential-aeration cell, and (b) the metal-ion cell.

The differential-aeration cell is formed as a result of a difference in the concentration of dissolved oxygen in the solution to which two areas of metal are exposed. The area that is exposed to the higher oxygen concentration tends to be cathodic, and the area exposed to the lower oxygen concentration tends to become anodic. These variations in concentration occur because oxygen is readily replenished at exposed areas of metal but not in stagnant areas. A typical differential-aeration cell is shown in Figure 3.

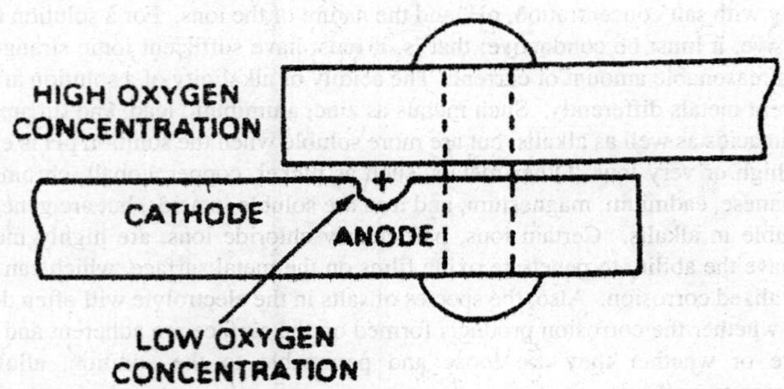

FIGURE 3—DIFFERENTIAL-AERATION CELL AT CREVICE FORMED WHEN TWO PARTS ARE BOLTED TOGETHER

A special case of the differential-aeration cell is called the active-passive cell. This type of cell is usually associated with metals, such as stainless steel, that require oxygen to retain their passivity. In the passive condition, these metals are very resistant to corrosion. If the film on the metal surface is damaged and cannot be reformed because of a lack of oxygen, the surface assumes a potential different from that of the surrounding passive surface, and a concentration cell is established. Because the anodic area is usually quite small, the attack can be very severe, developing deep pits in the surface. A typical example of this type of cell is that of attached trim molding. It is difficult for that area of aluminum or stainless steel in contact with painted body sheet metal to remain passive because air flow over it is slight, whereas the remainder of the molding surface is freely exposed to air, and it can remain passive. An active-passive cell is established between these two portions of the metal surface.

A metal-ion cell is formed when there is a variation in the concentration of metal ions at two different locations in a solution. Differences in metal-ion concentration result because open or exposed areas can have metal ions diffused or swept away more readily than when they are in stagnant areas. A difference of potential is found between these two locations, and current can flow. Corrosion occurs at the anode, which is the point where metal ions diffuse away from the surface. The area of attack in this case is opposite to that of the differential-aeration cell. An example of a metal-ion cell is shown in Figure 4.

Concentration cells can be set up by differences in temperature, agitation, illumination, liquid velocity, and other factors that affect solution homogeneity. This type of corrosion so often with crevices that it is frequently referred to as "crevice corrosion." When it occurs under deposits on the surface, it is sometimes called "poultice corrosion."

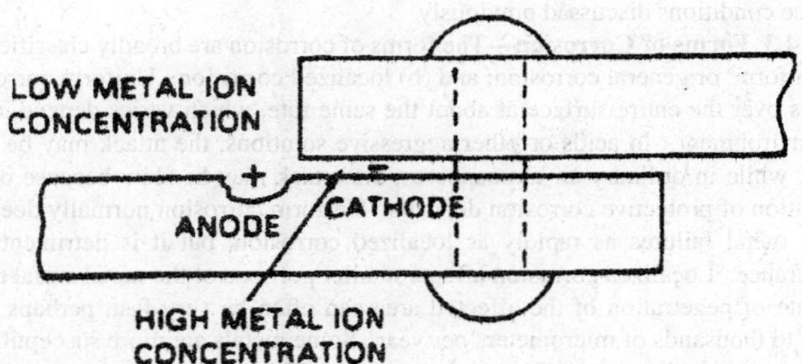

FIGURE 4—METAL-ION CONCENTRATION CELL AT CREVICE FORMED BETWEEN
TWO PIECES OF METAL BOLTED TOGETHER

4.3.1.1 Prevention

a. Use welded joints in preference to bolted or riveted joints.
b. Caulk or seal unavoidable crevices effectively, using durable and noncorrosive materials.
c. Minimize the contact between metal and plastics, fabrics, debris, etc.
d. Avoid contact with materials which are known to contain corrosive elements or which are hygroscopic, since they may accelerate the cell effect. (Stainless steel has pitted when in contact with insulation containing only a few parts per million of chloride ion.)
e. Avoid sharp corners, ledges, and pockets where debris can accumulate.

4.3.2 PITTING CORROSION—Pitting corrosion is a form of localized attack at a metal surface where small areas corrode preferentially. The rate of penetration is usually more rapid than it is in uniform corrosion. Some metals have a greater tendency to pit than others, but most metals will pit under some specific set of conditions. Metals such as aluminum or stainless steel, which form passive films, are especially susceptible to pitting corrosion.

Pitting should be considered a two-step process: one of initiation and the other of propagation. The exact cause of pit initiation is not well understood, but some differences must exist at the metal surface to account for the difference in potential which is necessary for corrosion to occur. Conditions which are usually associated with pitting are inhomogeneities in the metal surface, breaks in a protective film, deposits on a surface, and various kinds of imperfections. Pits vary greatly in size, depth of penetration, and frequency of occurrence. The increase in depth usually proceeds at a faster rate than the increase in width. Pits often have well-defined boundaries.

The environment has an important bearing on the initiation and growth of pits. Halides or halogen-containing ions contribute greatly to pitting; chlorides, bromides, and hypochlorites are considered to be the most aggressive. The chloride ion, for example, not only interferes with the formation of a protective film, but because of its size and mobility diffuses through weak points in the oxide film and enters into the corrosion reaction.

The auto-catalytic nature of a pit is responsible for its continued propagation at a fast rate. Chloride ions continue to migrate into the pit, and the solution within the pit becomes acidic. The acidity prevents the formation of a protective film, and the metal surface in the pit is kept in an active condition. As more metal ions are formed, more chloride ions diffuse into the pit, and the process continues.

4.3.2.1 Prevention

a. Use materials with alloying elements designed to minimize pitting susceptibility, for example, molybdenum in stainless steel.
b. Provide a surface as homogeneous as possible through proper cleaning, heat treating, and surface finishing.
c. Reduce exposure to aggressive ions by shielding the part, coating the part, or by reducing the concentration of these ions.
d. Increase the capability of the solution to make the metal passive. If the metal is immersed, use inhibitors or other additives.
e. Minimize the effects of external factors on the design features which lead to localized corrosion; for example, the effects of differential aeration on crevices.

4.3.3 GALVANIC CORROSION—This type of corrosion occurs when two dissimilar metals are coupled and exposed to an electrolyte. The intensity of the galvanic effect will be determined by the potential difference between the metals and the ratio of the cathode-to-anode areas mentioned earlier. The farther apart metals are in the electromotive series, the greater will be the accelerated corrosion of the least noble metals (anode).

The ratio of cathode surface area to anode surface area is important because it determines the current density on the anode surface. A large cathode area and a small anode area result in a high current density at the anode, whereas the reverse situation results in a low anode current density. In both cases the potential difference may be the same and the total current passing between two metals may be the same, but the rate of penetration is different because it is directly proportional to the current density. This effect, which is shown schematically in Figure 5, applies particularly to joints where rivets, screws, or bolts are used to join two pieces of metal together.

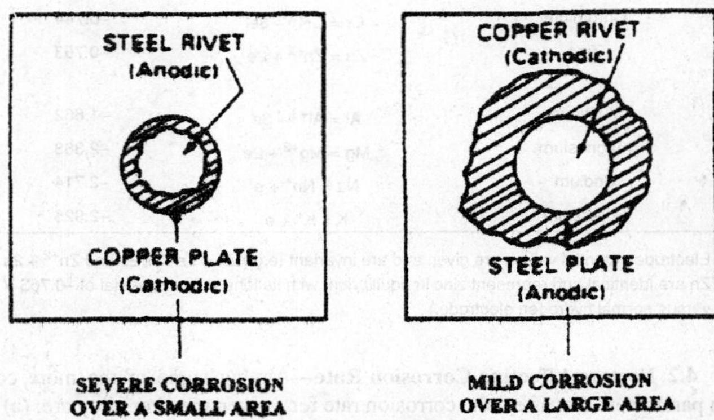

FIGURE 5—GALVANIC CORROSION BETWEEN STEEL AND COPPER
(CORROSION OF STEEL IS SEVERE WHEN CORROSION
IS CONCENTRATED ON A SMALL AREA)

Since the potential difference between two metals is so important to galvanic corrosion, a series, such as that shown in Table 2, is often used to estimate the likelihood of galvanic corrosion occurring and its magnitude. This series, based on a sea water environment, is at most a guide, since some variations are found in other environments. Ideally, a separate series should be determined for each environment, but this is hardly feasible. Alloys or metals which appear lower on the list corrode preferentially over those above them, when they are in galvanic contact. Metals are grouped together, and those in the same group should have little effect on each other.

TABLE 2—GALVANIC SERIES IN SEA WATER(1)

Reactivity	Material
Cathodic (Noble)	Platinum
	Gold
	Graphite
	Silver
	Stainless Steel, SAE Types 30310, 30316 (Passive)
	Stainless Steel, SAE Types 30301, 30304 (Passive)
	Titanium
	Stainless Steel, SAE Types 51410, 51430 (Passive)
	67Ni-33Cu Alloy (Monel)
	76Ni-16Cr-7Fe Alloy (Passive) (Inconel)
	Nickel (Passive)
	Silver Solder
	Bronze
	70-30 Cupro-Nickel
	Silicon Bronze
	Copper
	Brasses
	76Ni-16Cr-7Fe Alloy (Active) (Inconel)
	Nickel (Active)
	Manganese Bronze
	Muntz Metal
	Tin
	Lead
	Lead-Tin Solder
	Stainless Steel, SAE Types 30310, 30316 (Active)
	Stainless Steel, SAE Types 30301, 30304 (Active)
	Stainless Steel, Types 51410, 51430 (Active)
	Cast Iron
	Wrought Iron
	Mild Steel
	Aluminum 2024
	Cadmium
	Alclad Aluminum
	Aluminum 1100, 3003, 5052, 6053
	Galvanized Steel
	Zinc
Anodic (Active)	Magnesium Alloys
	Magnesium

1. Modified from "Corrosion Resistance of Metals and Alloys," LaQue and Copson, 2nd Edition.

4.3.3.1 Prevention

a. Avoid the use of combinations of metals which are widely separated in the galvanic series.
b. Avoid combinations where the area of the anodic metal is small compared with that of the cathodic metal. Use more noble metals for rivets, bolts, and fasteners.
c. Insulate joints of dissimilar metals when possible; even paint or plastic coatings will be helpful.
d. Paint or coat all surfaces when possible. Avoid painting only the anodic metal, since corrosion may be accelerated at imperfections or breaks in the coating.
e. Seal faying surfaces.
f. Apply metallic coatings to reduce the potential difference between dissimilar metals.
g. Avoid threaded connections if dissimilar metals that are far apart in the galvanic series must be used.
h. Increase the thickness of replaceable sections of less noble metal.
i. Attach sacrificial anodes such as zinc, magnesium, or aluminum to the metal to be protected, provided there is electrolytic contact.
j. Use chemical inhibitors in solutions if possible.

4.3.4 STRESS CORROSION—Stress corrosion of a metal occurs when the metal is under the combined influence of sustained tensile stress, either applied or residual, and corrosion. Damage usually appears as localized cracks. The attack may be intergranular, transgranular, or a combination of the two. The conditions for stress corrosion are:

a. A susceptible material
b. An appropriate environment
c. Stress
d. Time

An example of intergranular stress corrosion cracking is shown schematically in Figure 6.

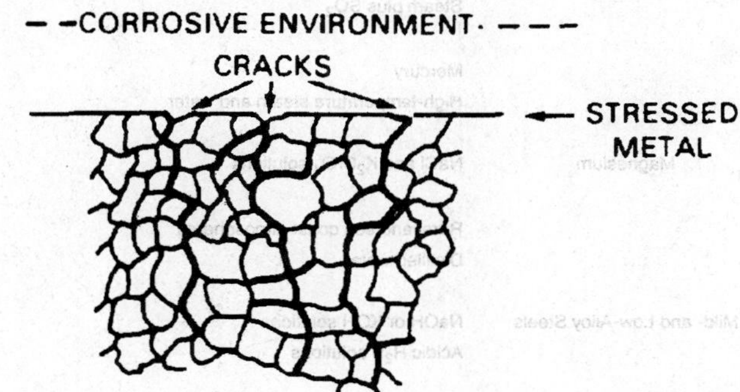

FIGURE 6—INTERGRANULAR STRESS CORROSION CRACKING

There is no known mechanism that explains all of the experimental evidence for stress corrosion. Three basic theories have been proposed: (a) electrochemical, (b) mechanical, and (c) surface energy. The electrochemical theory presumes the formation of fissures at grain boundaries because of either tensile stress or specific corrosion such as pitting or intergranular. Once the surface has been broken, the conditions are sufficient for accelerated corrosion, since film-free metal and grain boundaries are known to be anodic to film-covered metal and crystal faces, respectively. Regions of stress concentration develop after the onset of corrosion. When the stresses become sufficient, cracks develop and penetrate into the metal. Cracking stops when plastic deformation of metal, caused by strain and the cracking process, increases the energy necessary to propagate the crack. If a new film does not form over the freshly exposed metal, a new fissure starts at the notch of the crack by electrochemical corrosion, and the process is repeated.

The mechanical theory presumes that an electrochemical reaction may be necessary to initiate the crack, but mechanical effects are sufficient to propagate the crack. The surface energy theory is based on a lowering of surface energy by adsorption of specific ions. The reduction in atomic bond strength allows crack initiation and propagation to occur at abnormally low stresses.

Aging, heat treating, and tempering processes have an important bearing on the tendency of a material to crack; even slight variations in the hardness of a material have an effect on the stress level at which cracking occurs. A low concentration of certain impurities can increase the tendency of even pure metals to crack. The metallurgical condition of the metal is a determining factor in the susceptibility of the material to stress crack, but practically any material will undergo stress corrosion cracking under some condition of exposure. Some metals stress crack in very mild environments, while others require a more severe environment. Examples of various environments that produce corrosion of some of the common alloys are shown in Table 3.

Under some conditions the concentration of unfavorable species in the environment is increased at a localized area, or their effect is focused on sites that are susceptible to crack initiation. Some of these conditions are nucleate (surface) boiling, heat transfer, crevices, pits, cracks, voids, corrosion products, insulating materials, and splash zones. For example, water with only a few parts per billion of chloride can produce stress corrosion of sensitized stainless steel at pits; insulating materials with leachable chlorides at a concentration level as low as 2 or 3 ppm have caused cracking of stainless steel.

TABLE 3—ENVIRONMENTS WHICH HAVE SHOWN A TENDENCY TO PRODUCE STRESS CORROSION FOR CERTAIN MATERIALS[1]

Alloy	Environment
Aluminum	Solutions of NaCl with or without H_2O_2
	Sea water
	Air
Copper	Ammonia vapor and solutions
	Amines
	Air, steam
	Mercury and mercury salts
	KOH or NaOH solutions
Inconel and Monel	KOH or NaOH solutions
	Organic chlorides
	Steam plus SO_2
	Mercury
	High-temperature steam and water
Magnesium	NaCl and K_2CrO_4 solutions
	Rural and sea coast atmospheres
	Distilled water
Mild- and Low-Alloy Steels	NaOH or KOH solutions
	Acidic H_2S solutions
	Nitrate salts (Ca, NH_3, Na, and Ni)
	HCN solutions
	Chloride salts (Al, Mg, Ca)
Austenitic Stainless Steels	Pickling solutions (HCl, HNO_3, HF)
	Inorganic and organic chlorides
	KOH or NaOH solutions
	Sea water
	Steam condensate plus NH_3
	H_2S
	Sulfate solutions
Titanium	High temperature chloride
	HCl
	Chlorinated hydrocarbons
	NaCl solutions

1. Modified from "Stress Corrosion—Causes and Cures," H. Suss.

Although the environment has an important bearing on stress corrosion, its effects can be minimized by reducing stress concentrations and residual stresses which are introduced during fabrication of the material. Some of the factors that should be considered are: (a) discontinuities and sharp corners, (b) the effects of heat treatment, (c) galvanic couples and crevices that accelerate the effect of stress, (d) nonmetallic inclusions at or near the surface, (e) cold working without stress relief, (f) thermal gradients produced by quenching or welding, (g) welding defects, and (h) machining that leaves residual stresses.

4.3.4.1 Prevention

a. Substitute more corrosion-resistant materials for the stress-sensitive material when possible.
b. Design to minimize the factors that promote corrosion and residual or applied stresses. Avoid crevices, deep recesses, dissimilar metals, sharp corners, and notches.
c. Alter the metallurgical structure of the metal by aging or tempering.
d. Avoid designs that tend to concentrate specific effects or produce high thermal stresses.
e. Include stress-relieving treatments when residual stresses are likely to occur. (One of the most effective treatments is the introduction of a counter compressive layer at the surface by surface rolling or shot peening.)
f. Use protective coatings to reduce the incidence of stress corrosion; include organic as well as metallic coatings. (Coatings should be resistant to the environment and free of cracks or pores, since any opening in the coating might introduce a cracking problem that did not exist originally.)
g. Modify the environment by changing the pH or reducing the oxygen content.
h. Use inhibitors or cathodic protection, but only if appropriate for the conditions of use. (In case of cathodic protection, hydrogen is discharged, and it may increase the tendency for failure by hydrogen embrittlement.)

4.3.5 INTERGRANULAR CORROSION—Intergranular corrosion is the selective or localized attack of the grain boundaries or closely adjacent material without appreciable attack on the grain. An example of this type of corrosion is shown in Figure 7.

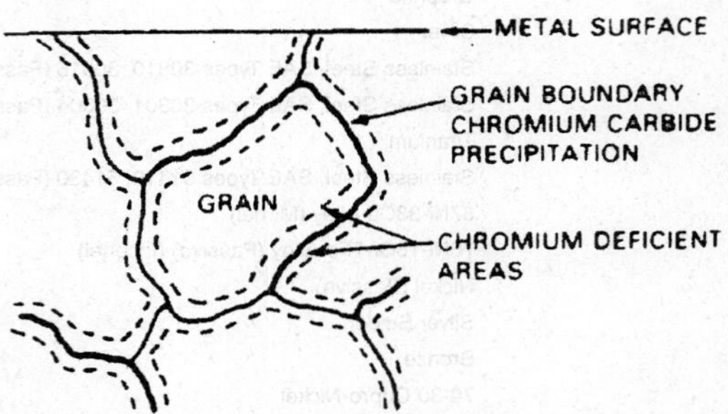

FIGURE 7—INTERGRANULAR CORROSION AT GRAIN BOUNDARIES DUE TO CHROMIUM DEFICIENCY

This type of corrosion is most often associated with austenitic stainless steels (e.g., SAE Type 30304). (Other alloys such as those of copper or nickel can be affected, too.) It appears to be related to the carbon content and perhaps to the nitrogen content. When stainless steel containing a significant concentration of carbon is heat treated in the sensitizing range of about 400 to 900 °C (750 to 1650 °F), carbon diffuses to the grain boundaries, where it combines preferentially with chromium to form chromium carbides. As a result, a small band of material on each side of the grain boundary becomes deficient in chromium. A potential difference is found between the chromium-deficient material in the grain boundaries and the grains. Since the grain boundaries represent a small surface area of anodic material compared with that of the grains, which are cathodic, the attack is usually accelerated.

Intergranular attack, often associated with arc welding, is sometimes referred to as "weld decay." It occurs some distance from the actual weld, because sensitizing temperatures are usually reached away from the weld. Spot welding is less susceptible to this effect because heating and cooling are more rapid, and hence there is less tendency for carbon diffusion to occur.

Several methods are used to prevent intergranular corrosion. The most obvious is the reduction of the carbon content (e.g., SAE Type 30304L). An alternative method is the addition of stabilizing elements, such as titanium (e.g., SAE Type 30321), columbium, or tantalum (e.g., SAE Type 30347). These elements have a higher affinity for carbon than does chromium, and chromium depletion is prevented. This type of corrosion can be prevented also by proper heat treatment. In the case of austenitic stainless steels, heat treatment in the temperature range of 1050 to 1100 °C (1920 to 2010 °F) is high enough above the sensitizing range to dissolve the carbides. This treatment is followed by rapid cooling to prevent the carbides from reforming. Ferritic stainless steels (e.g., SAE Type 51430) have a sensitizing range much above that of the austenitic steels, and they require heat treatment in a temperature range of 650 to 815 °C (1200 to 1500 °F), which is below the sensitizing range. When the problem cannot be avoided by any of these treatments, it is best to avoid the use of susceptible materials.

4.3.5.1 Prevention

a. Use stainless steel alloys with low carbon content.
b. Anneal the alloy at the proper temperature and follow with rapid quenching.
c. Use stainless steel alloys that contain stabilizing elements such as titanium, columbium, and tantalum.
d. Substitute an alloy that is less sensitive to intergranular corrosion.

4.3.6 EXFOLIATION CORROSION—This type of corrosion is considered to be a special form of intergranular attack in which delamination takes place parallel to the metal surface. Flakes of metal are peeled or pushed to the surface because of the internal stresses created by corrosion products. This form of corrosion is most common in rolled or extruded aluminum alloys in which grains are elongated or flattened. Susceptibility to exfoliation is associated with grain boundary precipitation and may be prevented by appropriate heat treatments.

4.3.7 DEZINCIFICATION (DEALLOYING)—Dezincification is a phenomenon associated with the preferential removal of zinc from brass alloys. It can be recognized by the pronounced copper color that appears, as opposed to the yellow color of brass. It may occur locally as a plug-type attack, penetrating the metal in a direction perpendicular to the surface, or as a layer type which affects broad areas of the surface. These two types are shown schematically in Figure 8.

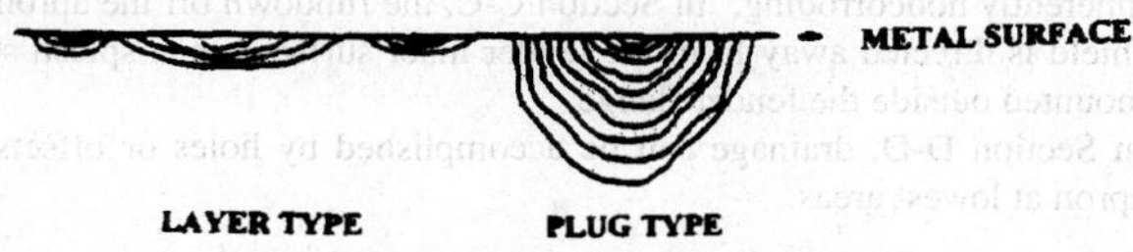

FIGURE 8—DEZINCIFICATION OF BRASS ALLOYS

Two possible mechanisms have been proposed for this type of attack: (a) the selective removal of zinc, leaving the copper behind, and (b) the dissolution of brass with the deposition of copper in the same area. In both types of attack, the metal is weakened as the result of the formation of a porous copper structure. The rate of attack increases with increasing temperature, increasing solution conductivity, decreasing solution flow and the accumulation of deposits on the metal surface. Dezincification is usually found to occur with brasses having a copper content below 85%. The plug type occurs more readily in low-zinc brasses and the layer type in high-zinc brasses. Dezincification can be avoided by using alloys which contain tin, antimony, or arsenic.

The effect of this type of corrosion is not much different from that of the graphitization of cast iron, where metal is preferentially removed and a porous mass of carbon is left behind. Similar types of corrosion are found with alloys of aluminum, cobalt, and nickel. In these cases it is referred to as dealuminification, etc.

4.3.7.1 Prevention

a. Use copper alloys with the copper content above 85%.
b. Use brasses alloyed with tin, arsenic, or antimony.
c. Avoid environments where the solution becomes stagnant and deposits can accumulate on the surface of the metal.

4.3.8 FRETTING CORROSION—This type of corrosion is defined as damage that occurs at the interface of two contacting surfaces, at least one of which is metal, when they are subject to minute slippage relative to each other. This condition may be caused by vibration or by continuous slippage between two surfaces. Fretting corrosion is sometimes referred to as wear or rubbing corrosion, chafing corrosion, or friction oxidation. It is usually characterized by discoloration, formation of debris, and formation of deep pits. Fatigue cracks may be initiated at these pits.

The mechanism of fretting corrosion is not well understood. It is assumed that asperities on one surface rub clean the opposite surface. The fresh surface becomes oxidized immediately, and the oxide is removed when the surface is rubbed again with the asperity. The formation and removal of oxides occur continuously, increasing the local stress because of their larger volume. Mechanical removal of metal particles is also a factor, since these particles can be converted to oxides which increase the amount of debris. Fretting corrosion requires the presence of oxygen but not moisture. In fact, moisture may function as a lubricant and reduce the rate of corrosion. Damage can increase with a decrease in temperature and with an increase in load.

This type of corrosion can occur whether relative motion is intended or not. Parts which are quite often affected are bolts, suspension springs, flanges, king pins of steering mechanisms, keyed shafts and gears, ball and roller bearings, flexible couplings, connecting rods, electrical relay contacts, and many other parts of vibrating equipment. Parts fail because of fatigue, loss of dimensional stability, and damage of the surface.

4.3.8.1 Prevention

a. Use a soft metal surface in contact with a hard metal surface; for example, tin, lead, or silver-coated metals in contact with steel.
b. Roughen the surface to increase friction and reduce slippage.
c. Increase the load to reduce relative motion. (If the load is not sufficient, damage can be increased.)
d. Use low-viscosity lubricants in combination with phosphate-treated surfaces. (Molybdenum sulfide also decreases damage until it is displaced from the surface.)
e. Increase the surface hardness of contacting metals.
f. Use one material with a low coefficient of friction, if possible.

4.3.9 CORROSION FATIGUE—Corrosion fatigue is the cracking of a metal that has been subjected to the combined action of corrosion and alternating or fluctuating tensile stress. The initiation of cracks is generally associated with crevices at the metal surface produced during cyclic stress. Sometimes corrosion pits are formed at the metal surface first and provide sites for cracks to initiate. Unlike stress corrosion cracking, corrosion fatigue can occur with almost any material that is susceptible to corrosion. The damage that results usually exceeds the total amount that would be caused by corrosion and fatigue acting separately.

Corrosion fatigue cracks are generally, but not always, transgranular. For example, corrosion fatigue is apparently intergranular in lead. Also, in certain cases, the cracks in steel will follow grain boundaries for short distances if the boundary directions are oriented in the right direction.

A large number of aqueous environments can cause corrosion fatigue. Steel, for example, is susceptible in fresh waters, sea water, condensates from combustion products, and miscellaneous chemical environments. Generally, the resistance of a metal to corrosion fatigue is linked more closely with its resistance to corrosion than with its high mechanical strength.

4.3.9.1 Prevention

a. Reduce stress by changing design.
b. Shot peen the surface, or otherwise introduce compressive stresses.
c. Improve corrosion resistance with metallic coatings, nitride coatings, or inhibited paint.
d. Use corrosion inhibitors or cathode protection when exposure is in a solution.

4.3.10 CAVITATION-CORROSION—Cavitation is the formation of cavities or vapor bubbles in a liquid. This phenomenon occurs when the pressure of the liquid falls below its vapor pressure at localized sites in a given system. The formation of bubbles is known as boiling when caused by a temperature rise at constant pressure, but is known as cavitation when caused by a pressure reduction at constant temperature. The damage due to cavitation is caused primarily by the high impact collapse or implosion of the bubbles at or near the metal surface. The pressures generated by the collapse of a cavity have been calculated in some cases to be thousands of pounds (kilopascals) per square centimeter. However, there are at least two factors that contribute to the ultimate deterioration of the metal. One is the mechanical factor, which must always be present, and the other is corrosion. The relationship between the mechanical and corrosion components of cavitation damage is complex, but it is generally recognized that the collapse of cavities at the metal surface can destroy protective oxide films, and thus permit fresh metal to react with the environment. Hence, corrosion can accelerate damage initiated by the collapse of cavities.

Cavitation damage occurs typically on water pumps and pump impellers, on trailing faces of propellers and water turbine blades, and on the water-cooled side of diesel engine cylinders. It has been shown that there is considerable variation in the susceptibility of different alloys to cavitation damage. This variation extends also to different alloys with the same base metal. Such factors as surface hardness, metallurgical history, chemical composition, and, of course the environment are important to this difference. Nevertheless, the following list of alloys is offered as a general guide (but not as a specific use recommendation) to the selection of resistant materials. The alloy types are listed in order of probable decrease in resistance to cavitation damage:

a. Stainless and high alloy steels
b. Low-carbon steels
c. Cast iron
d. Brasses and bronzes
e. Aluminum alloys

4.3.10.1 Prevention

a. Design to minimize cavitation
b. Select resistant materials
c. Use appropriate corrosion inhibitors in recirculating systems

5. Chapter 2—Design Considerations

5.1 Introduction—Design is a major factor in corrosion prevention, but by itself cannot permanently preclude corrosion. It can minimize or eliminate pockets and ledges which tend to trap road debris and salt. It can provide drainage to minimize water retention or, alternatively, provide access holes for the introduction of barrier coats such as paints, sealers, and waxes. Appropriate selection of materials in the design stage can minimize galvanic couples or provide insulators to break the galvanic couple. Design can minimize susceptibility to stone pecking, shield unavoidable pockets, and locate electrical components in positions remote from corrosive environments.

Design also has a great influence in the application of protective coatings because to adequately coat bare steel components, the area must be accessible.

The amount of access required is dependent on the material and application process chosen, but not to the extent that general guidelines cannot be developed or would not apply. The objective of this chapter is to suggest basic design guidelines.

5.2 General Design Guide—The design guidelines which follow are based on the fairly direct principles of (a) providing access paths for ingress and egress of protective coating materials and (b) preventing or reducing ingress of, and providing egress for, environmentally induced moisture and contaminants. The approach chosen is to show the application of this principle to major body components. In the process, areas of specific interest are highlighted.

5.2.1 HOOD ASSEMBLY—Figure 9 shows two basically different hood design approaches, the "hatch" hood, Section B-B, incorporating a grille opening panel (GOP), and the "conventional" hood, Section A-A, which does not utilize a GOP. For either approach the following aspects should be considered during the design process:

a. All horizontal surfaces should slope toward drain holes. See Section 5.2.7.
b. All primary drain holes should be located in the lowest outboard surfaces.
c. A flat is generally required on the inner panel to accommodate the latch mechanism. This area should be carefully reviewed to provide drainage and eliminate pockets.
d. In many cases, forming and/or appearance advantages are realized by use of a downstanding flange, for assembly of the hood inner and outer panels.

5.2.2 FENDER ASSEMBLY—Figure 10 reviews some components of a typical fender assembly. For all designs, a full inner liner or apron is desirable to protect front components (headlamp housing, side marker lamps, etc.) and rear structure (fender reinforcement, door hinges, etc.) from road splash and possible abrasion. General comments for all designs are as follows:

a. In Section A-A, the lower design is preferred since it generally allows a smaller metal-to-metal contact area.
b. In Section B-B, fender extension, if welded in place as part of the fender assembly, should allow access for coatings.
c. Section C-C shows various apron or splash shield approaches. If structurally possible, plastic is preferred for this component since this material is inherently noncorroding. In Section C-C, the rundown off the apron splash shield is directed away from the fender inner surface when splash shield is mounted outside the fender flange.
d. In Section D-D, drainage can be accomplished by holes or offsets in the apron at lowest areas.

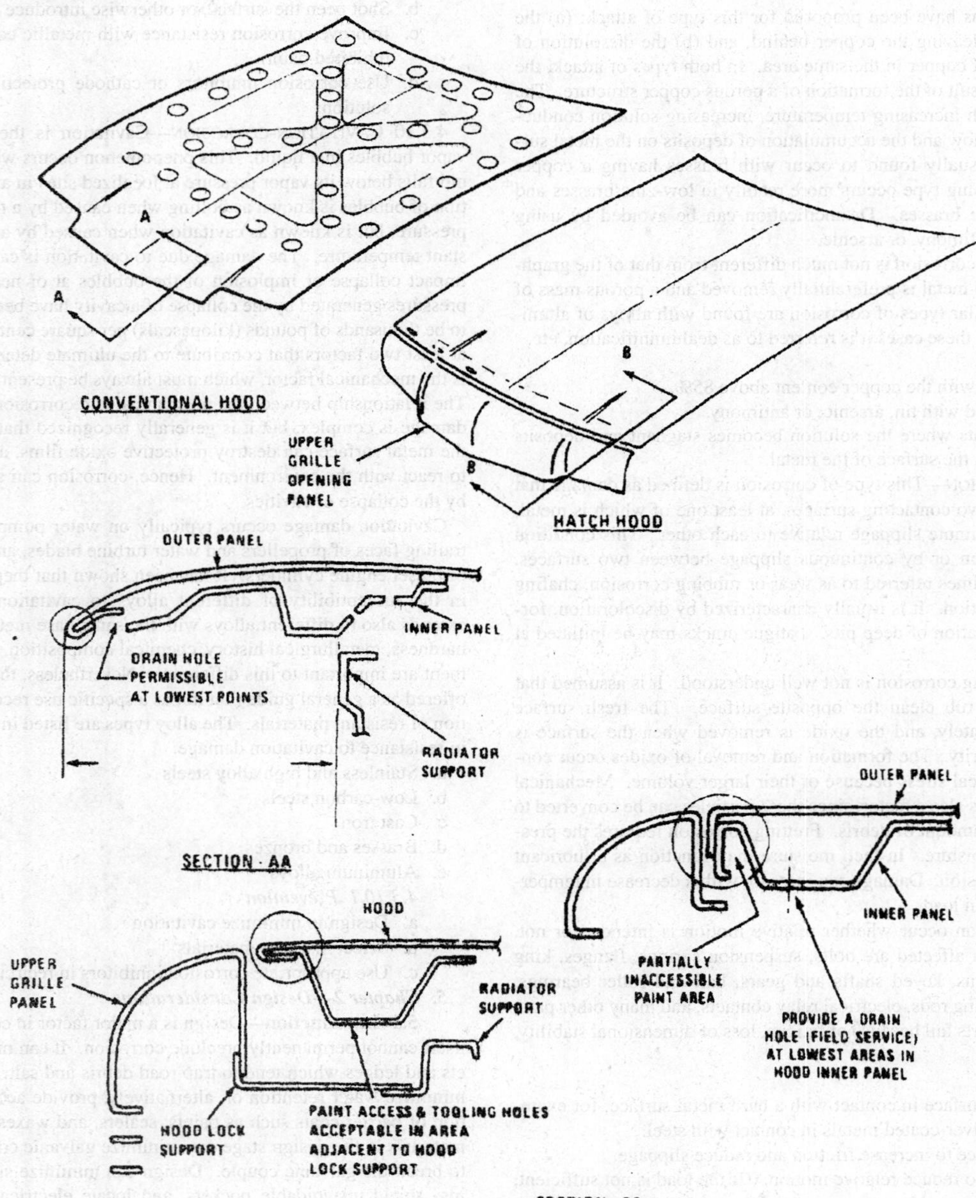

FIGURE 9—HOOD

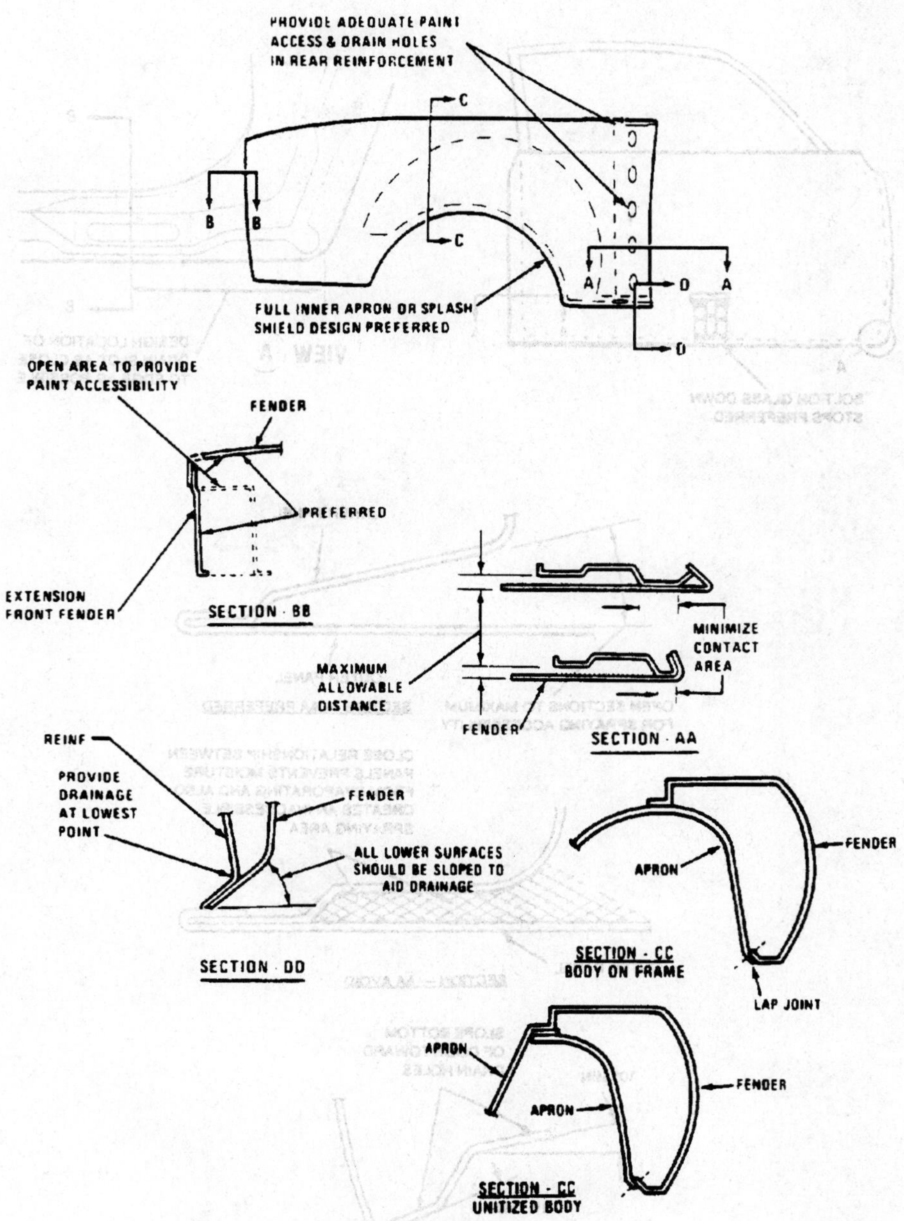

FIGURE 10—FENDER

5.2.3 Door Assembly—Figure 11 typifies door inner and outer panel assembly conditions. In the overall view, the use of bolt on glass down stops or other bracketry is stated as preferred to a welded component. This design is preferred since a bolted component can generally be installed after protective coatings have been applied. General comments are as follows:

a. Section A-A again calls for opening inner to outer panels as far as possible to allow access for protective coatings. This approach should be maintained along vertical edges. Along the leading edge, the inner panel will usually be pocketed outboard in the hinge mounting area. Although this is the typical situation, clearances should be maximized by careful review of hinge pillar, door inner panel, and hinge designs.
b. View A and Section B-B show drainage provisions for lowest forward and rearward areas. Note in View A that outer panel hem flange is locally reduced to achieve a lower drainage point.
c. Section B-B also highlights the previously stated rule of sloping horizontal surfaces toward drain points. This condition should be followed along the lower edge of the door inner panel (area "B").

5.2.4 Quarter Panel Assembly—Figure 12 shows a few typical construction areas in the quarter panel assembly. General comments are as follows:

a. The forward lower edge of the quarter panel generally joins to the rocker panel. This joint should be sloped at least 15 degrees from the horizontal to provide drainage, Section C-C. Should this not be possible, as is often the case, or if an even more undesirable channel is formed, Section C'-C', a hot melt sealer may be placed in the area and allowed to flow. This will raise the level to that of the drain hole and allow proper drainage.
b. Reinforcing ribs usually required on the wheelhouses would be indented inboard, as shown in Section B-B, to allow increased spacing between quarter and outer wheelhouse. As before, this enhances the ability to apply protective coatings. These ribs should also be designed to direct drainage toward drain holes in rocker and rear floor pan.
c. Section A-A (preferred) shows the use of locating tabs for the quarter panel on the wheelhouse outer as a means of increasing space between the two panels. This design, although requiring removal of the tabs after assembly, has the benefit of reducing metal-to-metal contact.

Due to the great variation in quarter panel designs at quarter to rocker joints, lower back panel or quarter extension, and upper back or "tulip" panel, specific sections are not shown. These areas should be designed, however, using the drainage and coating access principles shown for other areas/panels.

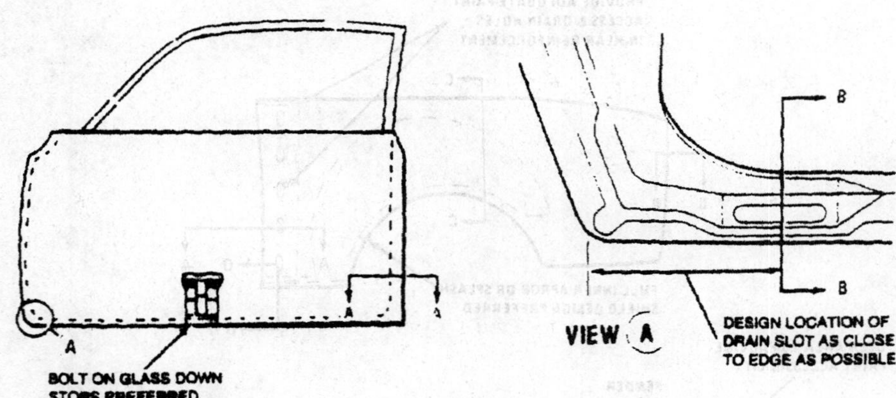
A
BOLT ON GLASS DOWN
STOPS PREFERRED
A
A
B
B
VIEW A
DESIGN LOCATION OF
DRAIN SLOT AS CLOSE
TO EDGE AS POSSIBLE

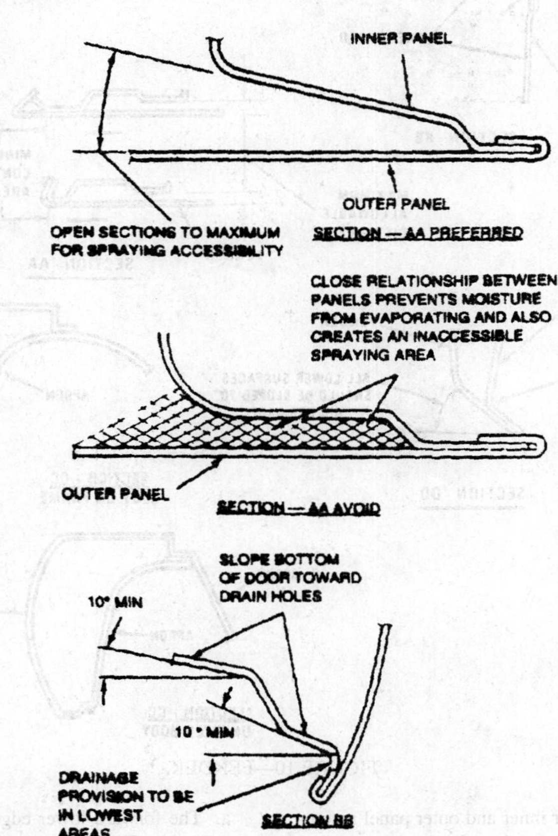
INNER PANEL
OUTER PANEL
OPEN SECTIONS TO MAXIMUM
FOR SPRAYING ACCESSIBILITY
SECTION — AA PREFERRED
CLOSE RELATIONSHIP BETWEEN
PANELS PREVENTS MOISTURE
FROM EVAPORATING AND ALSO
CREATES AN INACCESSIBLE
SPRAYING AREA
OUTER PANEL
SECTION — AA AVOID
SLOPE BOTTOM
OF DOOR TOWARD
DRAIN HOLES
10° MIN
10 ° MIN
DRAINAGE
PROVISION TO BE
IN LOWEST
AREAS
SECTION BB

FIGURE 11—DOOR

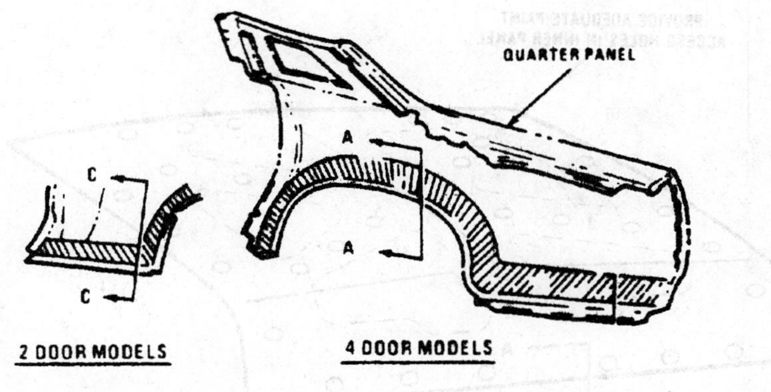

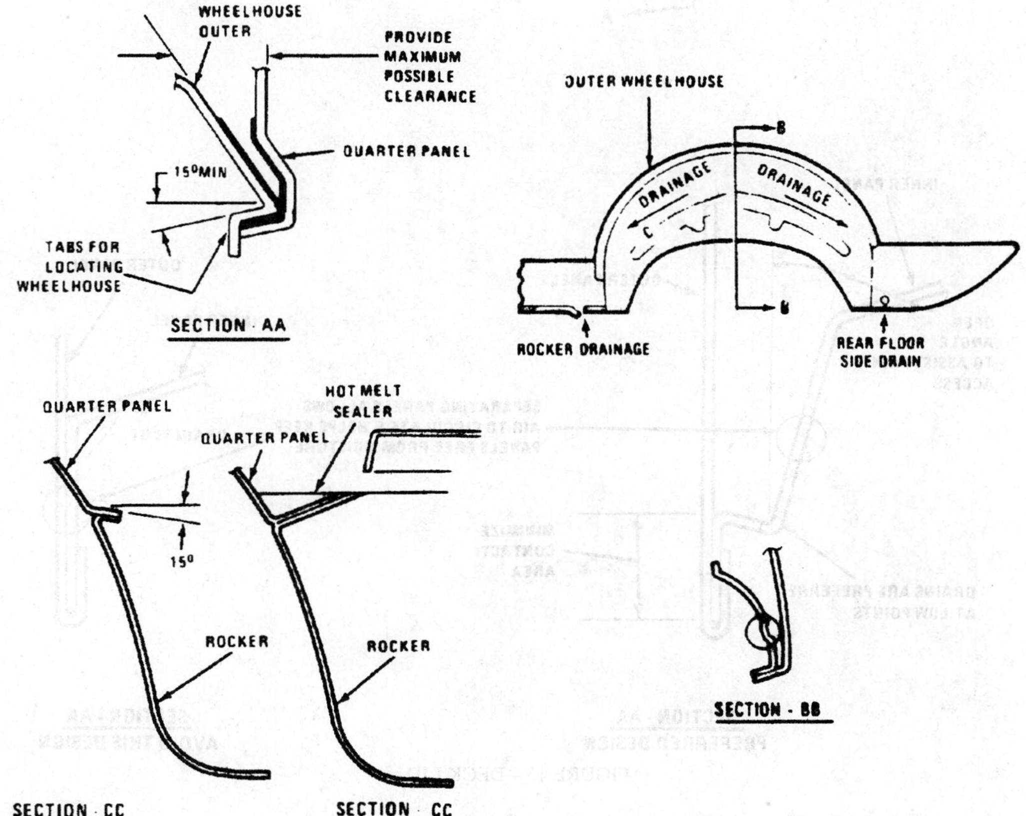

FIGURE 12—QUARTER PANEL ASSEMBLY

5.2.5 Deck Lid Assembly—Figure 13 shows a typical deck lid assembly. Many of the same conditions shown for hood panels (Figure 9) hold true for deck lids with the exception of assembly by downstanding flange. In this light, the inner panel should have adequate paint access holes and flutes, and horizontal surfaces should be sloped toward drainage areas. The generally unique area on the deck lid is the rearward vertical surface shown in Section A-A.

a. Section A-A (right hand) is occasionally used to accommodate appearance or other conditions. This is not the preferred approach due to generation of a high metal-to-metal contact area and inability to locate drain holes in lowest regions.
b. Section A-A, preferred, shows a different approach which maximizes coating access area and allows effective drainage locations. This design approach should be considered at the earliest possible stage since it will generally affect the lower back panel configuration.

5.2.6 Drainage—There are several aspects to consider regarding drainage from body sheet metal.

a. All parts must be designed with the drain holes necessary to provide adequate drainage of water and contaminants during a lifetime of field usage. The placement and design of these drain holes in many panels have been discussed under previous headings.
b. Figure 14 shows the drainage principle as it applies to location on the body. Joints should be "shingled" to reduce the possibility of moisture impinging directly into the lap as shown in the underbody section.
c. Where not possible to shingle an exposed joint, as in some wheel splash areas, one panel should be turned to protect the joint as shown in the wheelhouse section.
d. All drainage holes should be located in areas where contaminants and moisture will not be forced in when the vehicle is in forward motion. This condition is most critical in underbody areas such as the rocker panel and rear floor pan as shown in the field drain hole section.

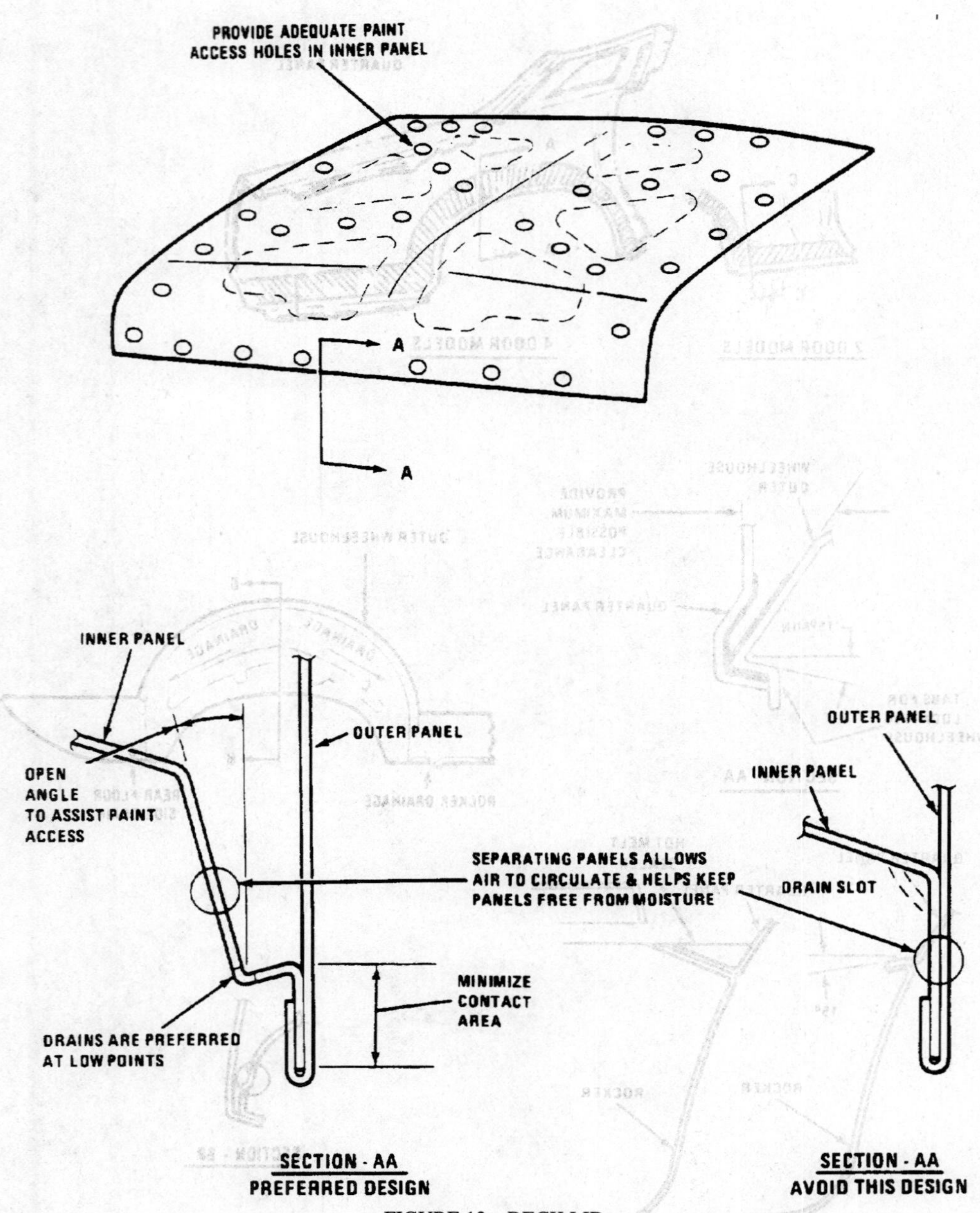
PROVIDE ADEQUATE PAINT ACCESS HOLES IN INNER PANEL
A
A
INNER PANEL
OUTER PANEL
OPEN ANGLE TO ASSIST PAINT ACCESS
SEPARATING PANELS ALLOWS AIR TO CIRCULATE & HELPS KEEP PANELS FREE FROM MOISTURE
MINIMIZE CONTACT AREA
DRAINS ARE PREFERRED AT LOW POINTS
SECTION - AA
PREFERRED DESIGN
OUTER PANEL
INNER PANEL
DRAIN SLOT
SECTION - AA
AVOID THIS DESIGN

FIGURE 13—DECK LID

Adequate drainage is also important during the cleaning, phosphating, and electrocoating of the sheet metal body in spray and dip systems.

a. Where possible all horizontal surfaces such as floor pans and package trays should be sloped toward drain holes by at least 3 degrees. Due to surface tension, large amounts of liquid will fail to drain off horizontal and nearly horizontal surfaces.
b. As many drain holes as possible should be used to avoid as much as possible the carryover of fluid from one tank to another. The loss of fluid from one tank is made even more costly by the need to filter it from the next tank. The use of drain holes that will require plugging must be balanced against the cost of plugging the holes.
c. Provision must be made for sufficient ingress and egress of fluids when entering and leaving the various tanks to avoid floating the body on entry or dragging heavy amounts of fluid out upon exiting.

5.2.7 ROCKER PANEL—Rocker panels should be designed outboard of the door lower hem to protect the bottom edge of the door from stone abrasion and dirt accumulation Figure 15. The lower surface of the rocker panel should be sloped toward drain holes.

5.2.8 ELECTROCOAT PRIMER ACCESS HOLES—The holes required to permit the electrocoat priming process to function properly fall into three categories although in most cases the holes will serve overlapping purposes.

a. Holes must be provided to allow the paint material to enter all box sections and closed off areas.
b. Additional holes sometimes must be provided to ensure that the electrical plating process of the paint takes place on all the surface area. Due to the Faraday cage effect the throwing power, the distance into a closed chamber that the plating will occur, may not cover all the surface area between two access holes. When this happens additional holes are needed near the uncoated areas to allow plating of all the surfaces. Figure 9, Figure 10, and Figure 13 for examples of multiple holes in inner panels and reinforcements to improve throwing power.
c. When a vehicle enters a dip tank there are some areas such as the wheelhouses that trap a bubble of air which prevents the fluid from contacting and, therefore, plating on the top surfaces. When this happens a small vent hole must be added to the top of the wheelhouse to relieve the air bubble. The hole must later be plugged. See the wheelhouse drawing in Figure 12.

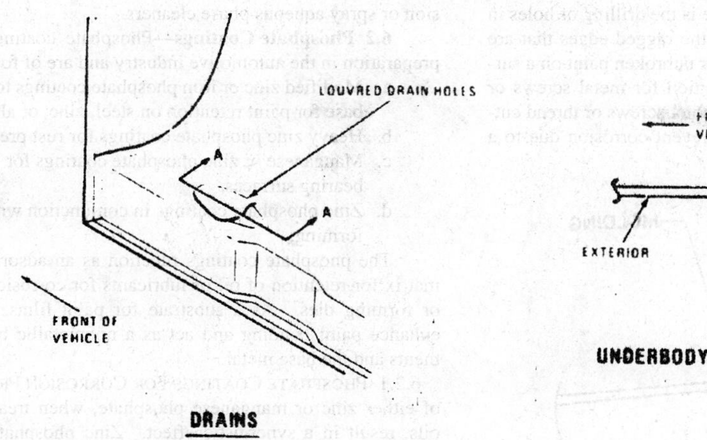

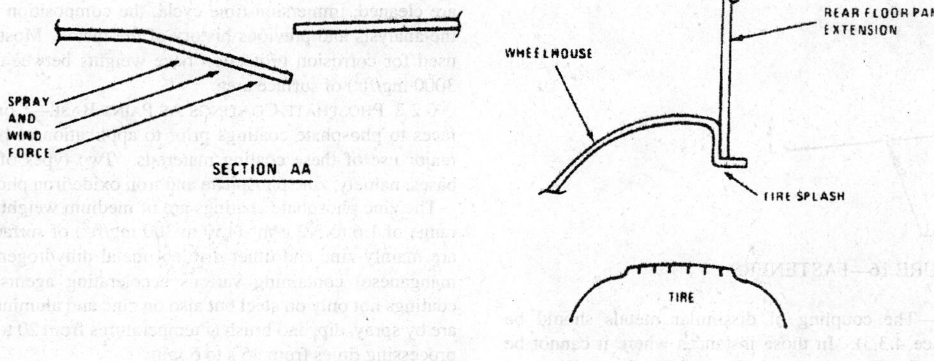

FIGURE 14—DRAINAGE

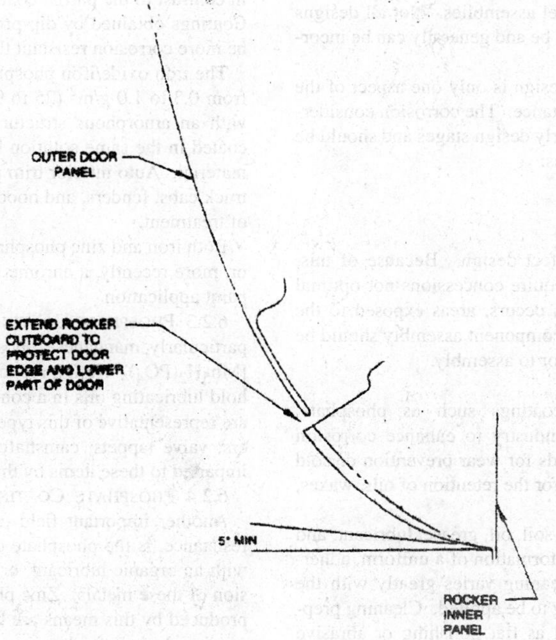

FIGURE 15—ROCKER PANEL

5.2.9 Fasteners—Sheet metal parts should be designed so that all holes for fasteners are stamped in the body panels. Less desirable is the drilling of holes in the body shop because of the metal chips created and the ragged edges that are hard to paint. These two methods do, however, allow for unbroken paint on a surface in conjunction with plastic inserts to act as insulation for metal screws or other nonmetallic fasteners Figure 16. The use of drill point screws or thread cutting screws must be avoided. These guidelines will prevent corrosion due to a broken paint surface.

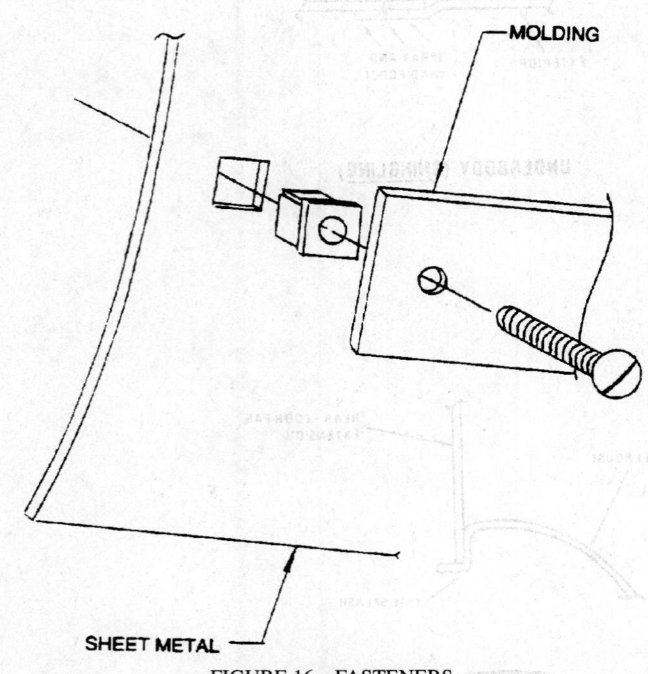

FIGURE 16—FASTENERS

5.2.10 Dissimilar Metals—The coupling of dissimilar metals should be avoided whenever possible. (See 4.3.3). In those instances where it cannot be avoided, steps must be taken to insulate the metals from each other. All metal molding and trim parts must be insulated from the painted sheet metal (unless bimetal trim is used), and the metal attachments should be insulated. Adhesive attachments for moldings and trim parts are preferred.

5.2.11 General Comments—Figures 9 through 16 show general application of desirable design conditions for major body panel assemblies. Not all designs are considered but the principle exemplified should be and generally can be incorporated in variations not discussed.

As suggested at the beginning of this chapter, design is only one aspect of the many considerations in maximizing corrosion resistance. The corrosion considerations reviewed should be considered during the early design stages and should be carefully balanced with other considerations such as:

a. Structural requirements
b. Manufacturing and assembly feasibility
c. Cost and weight objectives

It is seldom, if ever, possible to achieve a perfect design. Because of this, design considerations other than corrosion may require concessions not optimal for application of protective coatings. When this occurs, areas exposed to the external environment which are inaccessible after component assembly should be reviewed for application of protective materials prior to assembly.

6. Chapter 3—Chemical Conversion Coatings

6.1 Introduction—Chemical conversion coatings such as phosphate, oxide, or chromate are universally accepted in industry to enhance corrosion resistance. Phosphate coatings are also used as aids for wear prevention or cold forming, as a substitute for paints, and as matrices for the retention of oils, waxes, or lubricants.

Metal surfaces must be rendered free of shop soil, oil, grease, lubricant, and rust to provide a surface condition receptive to the formation of a uniform, adherent chemical film or coating. The method of cleaning varies greatly with the metal to be treated and the type of chemical coating to be applied. Cleaning preparation may vary from mechanical methods such as flat polishing or abrasive blasting to vapor or solvent degreasing through the more generally used immersion or spray aqueous phase cleaners.

6.2 Phosphate Coatings—Phosphate coatings are the most widely used preparation in the automotive industry and are of four basic types:

a. Modified zinc or iron phosphate coatings to produce a corrosion resistant base for paint retention on steel, zinc, or aluminum surfaces.
b. Heavy zinc phosphate coatings for rust preventive oil retention.
c. Manganese or zinc phosphate coatings for wear resistance or break-in on bearing surfaces.
d. Zinc phosphate coatings in conjunction with soap films as an aid to cold forming.

The phosphate coatings function as an adsorbative crystalline nonmetallic matrix for retention of oil or lubricants for corrosion resistance, wear resistance, or forming dies. As a substrate for paint films, the phosphate coatings may enhance paint bonding and act as a nonmetallic barrier between corrosive elements and the base metal.

6.2.1 Phosphate Coatings For Corrosion Protection—Heavy coatings of either zinc or manganese phosphate, when treated with corrosion inhibiting oils, result in a synergistic effect. Zinc phosphate and manganese phosphate, when oiled, are used to protect underparts of automobiles, such as nuts, bolts, brake pedal assemblies, accelerator levers, master cylinder plugs, accelerator brackets, hood latch yokes, hydraulic cylinder covers, etc.

All these heavy coatings are produced by immersing the cleaned articles in the hot processing solution for 5 to 15 min, depending on the bath chemistry. The weight of the coatings produced depends upon the manner in which the articles are cleaned, immersion time cycle, the composition of the processing bath, and the analysis and previous history of the metal. Most coatings, however, that are used for corrosion protection have weights between 8.6 and 32 g/m^2 (800 and 3000 mg/ft^2) of surface area.

6.2.2 Phosphate Coatings As Paint Base—Conversion of metallic surfaces to phosphate coatings prior to application of paint finishes constitutes the major use of these coating materials. Two types of coatings are used as paint bases, namely, zinc phosphate and iron oxide/iron phosphate.

The zinc phosphate coatings are of medium weight with coating weights in the range of 1.6 to 3.2 g/m^2 (150 to 300 mg/ft^2) of surface area. The solutions used are mainly zinc and other divalent metal dihydrogen phosphates (like nickel or manganese) containing various accelerating agents and producing phosphate coatings not only on steel but also on zinc and aluminum. Methods of application are by spray, dip, and brush at temperatures from 20 to 100 °C (70 to 210 °F) and processing times from 45 s to 5 min.

Automobile bodies and sheet metal parts are coated with a zinc phosphate coating prior to spray or electrophoretic painting. (Processing times generally vary from 45 s to 2 min with temperatures ranging from 45 to 60 °C (115 to 140 °F).) Dip treatment is preferred since inner surfaces of the bodies are phosphate coated in contrast to the partial coating (primarily exterior) achieved by spray treatment. Coatings obtained by dip processing generally have smaller crystals and tend to be more corrosion resistant than the larger crystals obtained by spray processing.

The iron oxide/iron phosphate coatings are relatively light in weight and range from 0.3 to 1.0 g/m^2 (25 to 90 mg/ft^2) of surface area. They are thin and dense, with an amorphous structure. Steel surfaces may be both spray cleaned and coated in the same solution by combining a synthetic detergent with the coating material. Auto interior trim parts such as instrument panels or steering posts and truck cabs, fenders, and hoods represent items that may be processed by this type of treatment.

Both iron and zinc phosphate coatings are usually given a chromium containing or, more recently, a chrome free rinse (post rinse) prior to final water rinses and paint application.

6.2.3 Phosphate Coatings For Wear Resistance—Phosphate coatings, particularly manganese phosphate, consisting mainly of the mineral hureaulite [$Mn_5H_2(PO_4)_4 \cdot 4H_2O$], reduce wear on bearing surfaces by acting as a medium to hold lubricating oils in a continuous film between moving metal parts. Parts that are representative of this type of application are pistons, piston rings, cylinder liners, valve tappets, camshaft, gears, and the like. Corrosion resistance is also imparted to these items by this heavy phosphate treatment.

6.2.4 Phosphate Coatings As An Aid In Cold Forming Of Metal—Another important field of application, although not primarily for corrosion resistance, is the phosphate coating of steel and aluminum, subsequently treated with an organic lubricant, or reactive soap, to aid in the cold forming and extrusion of these metals. Zinc phosphate is commonly used. Some automotive parts produced by this means are bumper bars and guards, tubing, truck wheels, transmission driveshafts, housing, piston pins, and gear blanks.

6.3 Oxides

6.3.1 Black Oxide On Steel—The black oxide type of surface treatments are used to produce an attractive black appearance on steel articles, with little increase in corrosion resistance. The oxide coating can be produced with slight dimensional change of the part being treated. This coating has a property of holding oils and waxes and may be suitable for a variety of applications, including bearings, gages, aircraft engine parts, and machine components. The coatings are used in the automotive field on spark plug shells, bolts and nuts, and bearing separators or retainers.

The most commonly used method of forming the coating is the alkali/nitrate method. The clean metal is immersed in a strong alkaline solution containing oxidizing agents and other additives, which at temperatures up to approximately 150 °C (300 °F), produces the blackening effect.

A lower temperature method for forming the black oxide uses a weak acid solution containing neutral nitrate salts and other additives. The clean metal part is immersed in an agitated solution at 100 to 105 °C (210 to 220 °F), and the coating formed is chemically equivalent to that using the hot alkaline solution.

6.3.2 Anodic Coatings On Aluminum—The purpose of anodizing is to produce an oxide coating on aluminum under controlled conditions to enhance the durability and/or appearance of the parts. Anodizing is applicable to wrought, cast, or extruded aluminum alloys. The following types of functional and decorative aluminum parts are often anodized:

a. Pistons and hydraulic cylinders
b. Automotive moldings
c. Bumpers and grilles

The electrolytic finish on aluminum, produced by an anodic treatment is a dense durable aluminum oxide which offers good abrasion and corrosion protection after proper sealing. These films possess excellent absorption qualities for paints, dyes, and electrolytic coloring processes which are often applied after anodizing but prior to sealing. When paint is applied to anodized aluminum, the seal is omitted unless the parts are used for decorative purposes.

After appropriate cleaning and/or bright dipping, the anodizing process is continued by making the aluminum the anode in an electrolyte that yields oxygen upon electrolysis.

Chromic and sulfuric acid anodizing processes are the most commonly used. The porous oxide film produced by either of these processes must be sealed by immersion in hot water, chromate, nickel acetate, or silicate solution to increase the barrier properties of the oxide. Combinations of these seals, such as nickel acetate followed by hot chromate or hot water [100 °C (210 °F) min], have gained increasing acceptance by the entire automotive industry for decorative parts. Anodic treatment of pure aluminum gives the best protection. Alloying constituents to aid in manufacturing and improve mechanical properties generally degrade the corrosion resistance of the coating.

All aluminum must be properly prepared to insure complete coverage and image clarity to the finished part. Recommended practices are detailed in the Aluminum Association publication "Designation System for Aluminum Finishes," Table 2, Chemical Finishes.

Various ASTM and automotive standards exist specifying various anodic thicknesses for specific service conditions or use. Descriptions of the anodic coatings are contained in Table 1 of ASTM B 580-73.

Coatings on the order of 8 µm (0.0003 µin) are generally specified for automotive exterior moldings and other decorative parts. Parts subsequently exposed to temperatures over 100 °C (210 °F) in various stages of assembly (paint repair ovens, etc.) have a tendency to craze. The thicker the anodic coating, the more pronounced the crazing.

The most common quality control tests are:

a. ASTM B 117—Salt Spray Test
b. ASTM B 136—Stain Resistance
c. ASTM B 137—Coating Weight
d. ASTM B 368—CASS Test
e. ASTM B 110—Dielectric Strength
f. ASTM B 487—Microscopical Thickness Measurements

Other tests could include the Acid Dissolution Test and Thickness Measurements by Light Section Microscope.

6.3.3 Oxide-chromate Coatings On Aluminum—Coatings for aluminum produced in short immersion or spray times have been developed for sheet, castings, forgings, and extruded and rolled structural forms.

These films produce good corrosion resistance for unpainted surfaces and are also bases for paint. The coatings which are thin and often iridescent, are formed at room temperature without electricity by spray, immersion, or brush application. These amorphous oxide/chromate films are flexible and can withstand moderate draws without trouble. There is no appreciable dimensional change in the article being treated. Coated metal parts can be both arc and spot welded.

6.4 Chromates

6.4.1 Chromate Coatings For Zinc And Cadmium—Chromate coatings aid in preparation of zinc and cadmium as bases for paint. Nonmetallic chromates prevent the metal from reacting chemically with the fatty acids in the paint vehicles. Chromate treatments are also used to retard "white rusting" of unpainted metal and to color the surface for decorative purposes.

Most of the commercial processes are applied by immersing the cleaned metal in the chromate bearing solution for a short time at room temperature. The gelatinous film that is deposited is a basic chromium chloride.

Chromate coatings tend to become harder and more adherent during rinsing and subsequent exposure to the environment. Films are thin, iridescent, and produce very little change in dimensions of the article treated. Abrasion resistance is usually low. Zinc die cast carburetors, lock cylinder assemblies, and fuel pumps illustrate automotive items that may be chromate treated.

6.5 Coatings for Magnesium—In general, two classes of treatment are used for preparation of magnesium alloy surfaces for painting: chemical treatments, class I; and anodic treatments, class II. The class II treatments are more protective. Generally, these coatings are applied to very clean surfaces.

Cleaning methods include mechanical (abrasive) treatments, solvent cleaning, alkaline solution treatments, and acid pickles not resulting in protective conversion coatings. Cleaned surfaces will withstand only mildly corrosive indoor exposure. When greater corrosion protection is desired, as in many outdoor environments, surface preparation by one of the conversion classes is necessary. ASTM D 1732 describes the treatments and methods available.

6.6 Evaluation Tests—Accelerated laboratory tests commonly used for evaluating chemical surface treatments are salt spray, humidity, cyclic corrosion, and water soak tests. Some of the ASTM test methods are given in Table 4.

TABLE 4—EVALUATION TESTS

Test Method	Specification
Salt Spray, 5% NaCl	ASTM B 117
5 or 20% NaCl	QQ-M-151[(1)]
Water Immersion	ASTM D 870
Conical Mandrel	ASTM D 522
Preparation of Steel Panels for Testing	ASTM D 609
Conducting Exterior Exposure Tests of Paint on Steel	ASTM D 1014
General Testing	TT-P-141-B[(1)]

1. Federal Specification

Proper chemical control of all surface treatment solutions and good maintenance of equipment are prerequisites to obtaining satisfactory results. Painted articles in particular should be evaluated for corrosion resistance on a frequent and regularly scheduled basis to detect both improper operation of the chemical surface treatment system and contamination of the coated surface prior to application of paint.

7. *Chapter 4—Organic Primers and Topcoats*

7.1 Introduction—Corrosion protection for metals is often obtained by the use of an organic coating or paint. This method of corrosion protection has been used from the beginning of recorded paint technology and the recognition of corrosion as a phenomenon of nature.

The basic components of a paint are resin, pigment, and usually a carrier or solvent. This technology has evolved from a simple mixture of materials found in nature, such as ores and natural gums or resins, to a complex chemistry of numerous specific pigments dispersed in synthetic polymers with a variety of solvents having carefully controlled properties.

Painting to control corrosion of metals is often done because it is a cost-effective method of achieving protection and may also provide decorative characteristics. Paint achieves corrosion protection primarily as a barrier coat. It prevents or retards the electrochemical reaction of corrosion by stopping or slowing down the charge transfer at the metal-solution interface. Specific resins provide properties of good adhesion to metal and good corrosion resistance under a variety of corrosive environments.

Examples of resin polymers are epoxies, epoxy esters, polyesters, alkyds, vinyls, acrylics, oils, and others. Usually the thicker the coating, the greater its corrosion resistant properties. Primers are normally applied at 10 to 30 µm. Additional coats can increase the total film thickness to 100 µ m or more, as needed.

A variety of pigments are also utilized to achieve corrosion resistance. Specific pigments such as the family of chromates, provide unique properties of corrosion inhibition. Others, such as molybdates, lead, or zinc-containing pigments also provide some corrosion-resistant characteristics when dispersed in the paint.

Some paints are formulated to be sacrificial coatings which contain pigments less "noble" in the galvanic series (Table 2) than the metal to be protected. Corrosion protection is obtained from the pigment, such as zinc metal, being electrochemically consumed as the sacrificial anode. This coating has a specific protective life related to the corrosive environment in which it is used.

There are a wide variety of paints which may provide corrosion protection for specific situations. The evaluation of these paints may require a complex, environmentally specific testing procedure. The most common accelerated noncyclic, QC type test for paints is the ASTM B 117 salt fog exposure. There are a variety of other more field relevant cycle tests which can be used [SAE Papers 912275, 912278, 912283, 912284, and 912285]. It is important that any accelerated test be related to intended end use.

Material selection is influenced by the method of application. Often the application method is as important with regard to cost and protection desired as the paint to be used. The variety of methods used and their characteristics are described to provide a basis for selecting a process to obtain the necessary paint properties.

Due to environmental restrictions, the use of water-borne coatings is increasing. With the addition of nonmetallic materials (e.g., plastics) as parts of automotive components and assemblies, lower cure temperatures 65 to 110 °C (150 to 230 °F) are desired.

Coating lines for body assemblies require a high degree of sophistication in the control of paint chemistry and application.

7.2 Spray Application—The application of organic primers and topcoats with the various types of spray equipment available is a proven and well-defined process. This equipment effectively acts upon a stream of paint, solvent or water-borne, and by various means disperses the paint into a cloud of finely divided particles. This cloud of atomized paint particles is then deposited on the intended surface forming a protective or decorative coating. Atomization is desirable to produce surface smoothness and, in the case of metallic topcoats, uniform metallic flake orientation.

Spray application provides considerable flexibility in processing methods and procedures. Some of the advantages are as follows:

a. A variety of shapes can be coated with reasonable uniformity.
b. Spraying is still the only practical method of applying the very popular metallic topcoat finishes. Good atomization of the paint stream and uniform application are essential to proper orientation of the metal flake.
c. In general, spray application provides greater latitude in the type of paint formulation that can be used. For example, it is very difficult or impractical to use dip application methods with highly pigmented products.
d. Spraying provides the opportunity to apply different products to accomplish very specific goals. Guide coat primer systems, primers of contrasting color applied wet-on-wet, are very common where subsequent sanding is done to signal the operator to stop prior to exposing the substrate.
e. High-fill primers for rough metal, corrosion-inhibiting primers for high-corrosion areas, and low-gloss black-out topcoats for special styling treatments provide further examples of instances where spray application is particularly appropriate.
f. Variations in paint thickness are possible as specific areas can be increased without the expense and problems associated with higher thicknesses all over.
g. The ability to change products quickly and at generally less expense is also an advantage associated with spray application. Spray systems usually utilize lower paint volumes than typical dip or flow-coat installations. Higher volumes can produce significant disposal costs should it become necessary to change products because of new technology, a change in processing requirements, or possibly a failure related to the paint formulation itself.
h. Many different substrate materials can be painted simultaneously by spraying.

A few drawbacks do exist with spray painting, as with any system, with the most important being:

a. Efficiency—When compared with most dip, flow coat, electrocoat, or autodeposition operations, the amount of coating actually being deposited in relation to the total amount used is lower with spray application. This is accounted for by the loss of overspray or the atomized paint particles that get blown beyond the work by the atomizing air. This can be controlled somewhat by electrostatic application equipment.
b. Health—Potential health hazards do exist since the spray principle requires the fine atomization of coating material. Inhalation of some of the paint ingredients could be harmful and should be controlled with the proper equipment and precautions.
c. Labor—Spraying is generally more labor intensive than other coating methods and requires some degree of operator skill. Automatic spray equipment reduces these requirements.
d. Application Control—The cost of controlling the spray environment can become considerable. The human element requires that high volumes of fresh air (for safety and health reasons) be supplied at a comfortable working temperature. Water-borne materials generally must be applied in a humidity-controlled atmosphere since very little can be done to change the evaporation rate. And finally, spray booth maintenance is a very important aspect of spray application. The cleaning of filters and exhaust stacks and the removal of waste overspray require close attention.

7.3 Dip Application—This process is a method of dipping the part into a bath of paint, draining the part, and force drying or baking the part. Dip coatings are used throughout industry for many primer and one-coat finishing systems.

The selection of a coating type and color is directly related to the end use intended for the finished part. Water-borne dip coatings provide fire resistance and desirable ecological properties. The use of a dip-coating system does affect properties of appearance, quality, cost, and other factors.

Some of the advantages are:

a. Simplicity—Minimal manpower and equipment for painting are required.
b. Low Cost—Paint utilization is relatively high on properly operated systems. Paint drippings are recovered and returned to the system.
c. Ease of Control—A minimally skilled operator can maintain proper solids, viscosity, and other factors to maintain acceptable application properties.
d. Good Coverage—A dipped part receives a complete coating, except for air bubbles or pockets, on all areas immersed in the paint.
e. Consistency—Each part coated receives an identical coating similar in appearance and film build; i.e., the process is not operator dependent.

Some disadvantages are:

a. Nonuniform Film Coating—The coating on a dipped part tends to be wedge-shaped with a thin film at the top and thicker at the bottom. There can also be flow lines or sags around any openings and a bead at the bottom of the part.
b. Part Design and Hanging—A part must be hung properly. Parts may trap and carry out paint or have air bubbles trapped in some inaccessible areas preventing paint from coating these areas. Some parts do not lend themselves to dip application.
c. Solvent Washing—Solvent evaporating from warmer areas may condense on colder areas "washing" the paint off the colder wall, leaving some areas unpainted. Oven curing increases this tendency.
d. Labor—Proper part hanging in loading and unloading may be labor-intensive.
e. Product Change—Changing product requires extensive cleaning and recharging of the tank or having multiple dip tanks with a relatively large paint inventory.
f. Flammability—Special fire protection is required for solvent-borne dip primers. Water-borne primers reduce this problem.
g. Foam—Solvent-borne paints usually have fewer foaming problems than water-borne paints. Foam can cause a flaw in the paint film which adversely affects appearance and quality.

Dip-spin application of organic coating is used primarily on smaller stampings and fasteners. Organic or inorganic/organic finished are applied over phosphated, plated, or mechanically cleaned surfaces. After application, the dip spin method is baked at temperatures ranging from 90 °C to over 315 °C (200 °F to over 600 °F). However, other colors are available and color matches can be obtained.

Organic/inorganic coatings have provided the newest generation of corrosion resistance performing in most cases better than electroplated/chromated finishes. Providing salt spray corrosion resistance (ASTM B 117) from 240 h to over 1000 h. They also provide excellent resistance to galvanic corrosion. Being less conductive, they can be coupled with stainless steel, aluminum, and carbon steel.

Coatings with PTFE (Polytetrafluorethylene) can act as a replacement for cadmium plated parts where required for lubricity and where range of torque must be controlled for clamp load.

Some advantages of the process are:

a. Excellent coating utilization (low cost) could be in the high 90's percent. Coating only goes onto product not into air spray.
b. Minimal manpower requirements.
c. Good part coverage, skilled operations can maintain the proper RPM's, viscosity and proper solids to attain the coatings acceptable application properties.
d. Some coating types can withstand operating temperatures up to 648 °C (1200 °F).

e. Can be applied to ferrous or nonferrous substrates.
f. Normally provide longer life corrosion resistance than standard electroplated parts.

Some disadvantages of the process are:

a. Most present coatings are solvent, not water-based.
b. Cannot throw coating into deep or blind holes.
c. When not applied properly, can fill fastener and stamping recesses and shallow holes.
d. Expensive to coat flat parts.

7.4 Flow Coat Application—Flow coating is an automatic operation in which the product to be painted is conveyed through a chamber equipped with low pressure nozzles that completely flood the product with paint. There is no atomization as with spray painting. This process is especially adapted to painting large articles which would require large dip tanks if finished by dipping and are of such shape that spray painting would not be practical because of high material losses.

Coatings that are formulated as flow-coat primers may be chemically similar to their spray- or dip-applied counterparts. They are normally modified to provide for better oxidation stability, improved flow, and increased hiding. The selection of a coating formulation is influenced by the environmental factors to be encountered during storage, the end use intended for the part, and coating cost.

Some disadvantages of the process are:

a. Good Paint Utilization—Material utilization can be as high as 97% depending on the product being flow coated. Since excess paint can be collected and reused, material utilization varies only slightly from product to product.
b. Versatility—Practically any type of part can be flow coated provided it can be properly drained.
c. Good Coverage—Since the parts are completely flooded with the coating material, a complete coating is obtained on all exposed surfaces.
d. Labor Savings—Manpower requirements are minimal for flow coating. The principal need is for loading and unloading. With automatic viscosity and make-up control, very little labor is needed to control the bath during operations.
e. Low Paint Inventory—The quantity of paint in use at any time is only about 10 to 15% of the bulk volume of material normally required for dipping the same quantity of work.
f. Minimal Health Hazard—As with other automatic coating processes, the exposure of personnel to a potentially hazardous environment is minimized because the coating is applied and cured in more or less isolated enclosures.

Some disadvantages of the process are:

a. Nonuniform Coating—Because of flow-out immediately following coating, film thicknesses will be somewhat heavier at the bottom of the product than at the top. However, as with dip coating, film thickness characteristics and appearance are very consistent within a given set of control parameters based on viscosity, total solids, solvent balance, paint temperature, and paint application pressure.
b. Part Configuration and Hanging—The method of hanging is important in obtaining proper coating on all surfaces. When parts are improperly hung, problems can occur from excessive paint carry-out or carry-in of pretreatment chemicals and from lack of proper flow-out. As a result, loading labor is critical.
c. Solvent Washing—Solvent evaporation from inner areas during flow-out may condense on adjacent cooler areas resulting in washing off the coating from the colder surface leaving the surface unpainted.
d. Foam—Foam can cause appearance and protection problems on parts. If the foam is not rapidly dissipated, cratering or film discontinuities will occur. Foaming is more prevalent in water-borne coating than in solvent-borne. Foaming can be controlled by a well-formulated paint containing defoaming agents.
e. Clean-Up and Maintenance—Clean-up and maintenance costs are generally higher with flow coating than with competing processes.

Following shutdowns, the flow-out tunnel must be flushed down, the flow coat piping, headers, nozzles, and heat exchangers must be flushed, and bath agitation must be started. Since a number of mechanical components are an integral part of the flow coating process, maintenance can be a significant portion of the operating costs.

7.5 Electrocoating—Electrocoating is a dipping process where the piece to be painted is immersed in a tank containing paint solids dispersed in water and then electrically energized with a direct current potential that causes almost water-free paint solids to deposit on an electrically conductive surface. For safety purposes, no one is allowed within the coating enclosure while the system is in operation.

Paints used in this process are electrically ionizable and can be formulated to deposit at either the anode or the cathode. Although a wide range of resins including alkyds, epoxies, polybutadienes, acrylics and polyesters have been used in electrocoat paint formulations, not all organic resins are currently used in this process. Pigment composition, size, and purity are critical. Water soluble organic solvents (e.g., the monoalkyl ether of ethylene glycol) and water insoluble solvents (e.g., naphtha) are used in electrocoat paints.

The electrocoat process is used to apply primers and single-coat enamels. Some of the advantages of using this process are:

a. The coating process is completely automatic.
b. A relatively uniform film can be obtained over all surfaces.
c. All sizes and shapes of parts can be coated in the same tank.
d. Paint drawaway from sharp edges during coating and baking is minimized.
e. The coating formed is usually free from runs, sags, and similar surface defects.
f. Compared to conventional spray or dip applications, the process is capable of providing improved coverage over hidden and recessed areas such as coach joints, automobile rocker panels, and structural steel sections.
g. The deposited coating is relatively free of solvents. Solvent washing is not a problem.
h. Through the use of ultrafiltration and reverse osmosis equipment, electrocoating can be made into a closed-loop system reducing pollution problems.
i. Paint utilization in this process approaches 100% of theoretical.

Some of the drawbacks of the electrocoat process are:

a. Facility and equipment costs are relatively high.
b. A large volume of paint is required.
c. Energy costs may be higher than on other processes.
d. Coverage is dependent on voltage, the length of the tank, and the speed of the conveyor.
e. Adequate access and drainage holes must be provided in parts for the paint and electrical energy to enter to allow the coating process to occur.
f. Maintenance of electrocoating tanks is important to ensure proper operating conditions.
g. "Cratering" can occur when painting some metals.
h. Thermal distortion of plastic components (of an assembly) can occur due to the (relatively) high cure temperature.

7.6 Autodeposition [SAE Paper 912291 and 2.1.3.1, 2.1.3.2]—Autodeposition is a coating process in which a combination organic-inorganic film is deposited on metal surfaces. Only four steps are usually employed, including cleaning, autodeposition coating, a final sealing rinse, and oven curing. This process precludes the need for a conventional phosphate pretreatment process prior to painting. Curing is achieved by standard convection ovens, infrared radiation, or by a heated "immersion cure" aqueous final rinse stage.

Coating occurs via a chemical oxidation-reduction reaction similar to those that occur in electroless plating of metals. The autodeposition painting bath comprises a 4 to 7% by weight dispersion of an organic latex emulsion, dilute (0.2%) hydrofluoric acid, and an oxidizing agent. In the autodeposition process, metallic iron is oxidized by the acid to the ferrous cation which dissolves into solution at the work surface. Subsequently, the metal cation coprecipitates with the anionically-stabilized organic latex onto the work surface. The coating reactions are not exothermic so that neither the solution nor the part to be coated are heated. A final reaction rinse is typically employed to impart additional corrosion resistance to the coating.

The autodeposited coating is uniform, usually 12 to 25 μm in thickness, low in gloss, and suitable for items requiring good corrosion protection.

Some advantages of this process are:

a. Few process stages are required, minimizing capital and floor space requirements.
b. No coating build-up on hangers.
c. The coating process relies on chemical reaction allowing coating of all hidden or recessed areas with even coverage.
d. Reduction in expended energy is realized by the elimination of the phosphate pretreatment process.
e. The coating does not pull away from sharp edges, coats evenly over machined surfaces (e.g., threaded fasteners) and is free from runs, sags, orange peel, and similar defects.
f. Very low maintenance is required.
g. The process is environmentally benign with low or no VOC emission and heavy metal effluent. No fire hazards are present.

Some of the drawbacks of the autodeposition process are:

a. Current applications are for ferrous and galvanized surfaces only.
b. The coating can exhibit some patterning and is topcoatable by only selected finishes.
c. Waste paint generation may be higher than some other coating systems unless an ion exchange reclamation unit is employed.
d. Color availability is limited at present.

7.7 Powder Coating—Powder coating is a process which has had recent developments of new coating materials and new application techniques. In this process, dry plastic powders are applied to a clean/treated surface. After application, the coated object is heated, fusing the powder into a smooth continuous film. Today, plastic powders are available representing a wide range of chemical types, coating properties, and colors. The most widely used types include acrylic, vinyl, epoxy, nylon, polyester, urethanes, and cellulosics. They are finely ground, free-flowing powders with generally higher molecular weight polymers than those used in solution finishes.

It is because of the high molecular weights that the coatings may be formulated to have good durability, toughness, and abrasion resistance. Powder coatings and the means of applying them offer some distinct advantages over conventional painting processes.

a. The most significant advantage, from an environmental point of view, is the elimination of organic solvent carriers. The powders are applied as 100% solids and are virtually free of pollutants.
b. The 100% solids nature of powder offers conservation advantages. The fact that the coating is a powder, means that the overspray can be collected, separated, and reused.
c. With powder, spray-coating efficiency is high; as much as 90% can be retained on the parts, especially if recovery of overspray is used. The complete coating can be applied with one coat as compared to the two to four coats often necessary with conventional systems. Smaller more compact spray areas can be used, saving space and energy.
d. Powder coating operations are much simpler. Unskilled labor can be used to apply these coatings. Many operations can be automated.

Some of the disadvantages of powder coatings are:

a. The majority of the exterior automotive topcoat colors sold in the U.S. today are metallic finishes. A special process is available in which metallic flakes are blended into the powder coating and sprayed onto a part; however, the clarity of the finish is not currently equal to that produced by the conventional basecoat/clearcoat paints. Powder suppliers must match existing standards or automotive styling must sell a different "metal appearance" to the public.
b. Color matching is more difficult to achieve initially and may be more difficult to correct in production.
c. High baking or high application temperatures are required for these materials.
d. Some parts with recessed areas may be difficult to coat electrostatically because of loss of electrical attraction to inner or recessed areas.
e. Equipment for spray-powder coating is relatively complex and expensive in order to provide color changing, powder recovery, and safety.
f. Film thickness control at low film build is difficult.

7.7.1 Powder Application Techniques [See 2.1.3.3]—Modern application techniques for applying powders fall into three basic categories: (a) Fluidized Powder Bed Process, (b) Electrostatic Fluidized Bed Process, and (c) Electrostatic Powder Spraying and other electrostatic application methods, including Discs and Powder Coating Tunnels.

7.7.1.1 Fluidized Powder Bed Process—The fluidized bed is essentially a chamber or box with a porous bottom through which air is introduced. When the flow rate of the air is properly adjusted, the powder behaves like a fluid. The object being coated is then preheated and immersed in the bed of fluidized powder. The heat causes the powder particles to adhere to the object. The powder is then fused into a smooth continuous coating in an oven. Coated parts can then be air-cooled or water-quenched. Film thicknesses, ranging from 254 to 1270 μm can be obtained. Low film thicknesses are not normally achieved as film thickness control is difficult.

7.7.1.2 Electrostatic Fluidized Bed Process—Electrostatic fluidized bed process combines features of both the fluidized bed process and the electrostatic spray process. The preheated or cold electrically grounded object is immersed into or suspended over a cloud of charged particles. The particles are post-heated in order to fuse them into a continuous film suitable for small parts.

7.7.1.3 Electrostatic Powder Spray Coating—In this process, the electrically conductive and grounded object is sprayed with charged, nonconducting powder particles. The charged particles are attracted to and cling to the substrate until the charge is dissipated (several days), thus allowing time for the particles to be oven-fused into a smooth continuous film. Coating thicknesses ranging from 25 to 126 μm are obtained. Control of low film thickness is difficult. A spray booth and collection system can recover all overspray. This powder can be separated and reused.

8. Chapter 5—Protective and Decorative Post-Applied Metallic Coatings

8.1 Introduction—Various types of metallic coatings can be applied to ferrous and nonferrous metallic and nonmetallic substrates after forming. These coatings are used to provide corrosion protection and/or a decorative appearance. Some coatings are chosen because they are anodic to the base material and offer sacrificial protection. Others offer barrier type protection. The choice of a particular coating material is dependent on the environment it is exposed to and the function it is to perform.

8.2 Application of Metallic Coatings—Metallic coatings can be applied by different processes. The most common method of application is electroplating. This process deposits coating material to the substrate metal (or conductive nonmetal) by applying an electrical potential between the part (cathode) and a suitable anode while immersed in an electrolyte. Mechanical plating is a process which uses finely divided metal powder. The powder is cold-welded to the part by tumbling the powder, the part, and a suitable media such as glass beads in an aqueous solution. Autocatalytic application is an electroless plating system where the metal coating is deposited on a part by way of a chemical reduction reaction in the presence of a catalyst. Hot-dip coating is a process where the part is immersed in the molten metallic coating material. The coating is usually of greater thickness than that produced by other processes.

The following are descriptions of the more common metallic coatings:

8.2.1 Zinc—A common corrosion-resistant coating used to protect metallic parts. Because of its position in the electromotive series, zinc offers sacrificial as well as barrier protection to iron and steel substrates. Zinc alloy coatings, such as zinc/nickel and zinc/iron, are gaining popularity for their improved corrosion resistance. Zinc coatings are most commonly deposited by electroplating. Mechanical plating is often used when parts may be subject to hydrogen embrittlement. Mechanical plating is limited to relatively small parts that can be tumbled. Zinc can also be applied by hot dipping. This process develops a coating thickness in excess of that of electro- or mechanical-plating. The appearance of a hot-dipped (galvanized) part is not as good as either electro- or mechanical-plated parts due to the increased thickness and spangle associated with this process. Zinc-coated parts are almost always used with a conversion coating applied after plating to retard the formation of white-corrosion product, or to act as a paint base.

8.2.2 Cadmium—This coating material is very similar in appearance and corrosion protection to zinc. It can be applied by electroplating and mechanical plating. It can be alloyed with other materials such as tin to increase its corrosion resistance. This is generally done by mixing the cadmium/tin powders for the mechanical process. Once popular and used interchangeably with zinc, cadmium is now becoming very scarce due to environmental concerns. Cadmium is considered very toxic and has been outlawed in some European countries. Because of its excellent predictable torque tension relationship, it is still used in critical fastener application and areas where its lubricity is necessary. Like zinc, cadmium is usually supplied with a chromate conversion coating applied after plating to retard the formation of white-corrosion product.

8.2.3 Lead—Lead is commonly applied to metals to provide protection from corrosive chemicals such as battery acid. It is also used in the fuel system on parts like metal filler neck tubes. However, lead is attacked by alcohol, and its use in alternate fuel systems must be controlled. Lead coatings are applied by the electroplating and hot-dipped methods. Lead coatings are barrier-type coatings, and offer no sacrificial protection to iron and steel parts.

8.2.4 Nickel/chromium—One of the most common metallic coating systems used in the automotive industry is copper/nickel/chromium or nickel/chromium in either bright, satin, or brushed finish. Because of their durability and appearance, these coatings are widely used on a variety of substrates to provide an attractive corrosion resistant metallic surface. Common substrates for these coatings include: steel (both low and high strength), aluminum, zinc, and plastic. While this coating offers barrier-type corrosion protection to the substrate, the different

8.2.4.1 Steel—After proper cleaning, parts are electroplated with a layer of copper (this step is optional in many specifications). A layer of semi-bright nickel is then applied followed by a layer of bright nickel. A very thin layer of chromium is then applied. The chromium layer is usually microdiscontinuous (microporous or microcracked). Pore count or crack density is closely controlled. Different methods are used to produce the microdiscontinuous chromium layer. The typical solutions used for the chromium layer are the hexavalent type. Due to environmental concerns, use of hexavalent chroumium salt baths may be eliminated or reduced.

8.2.4.2 Aluminum—There are two major pre-plate systems used to produce decorative chromium-plated aluminum parts. These are the Zincate and Alstan processes. Modifications of the processes are used by different platers. Modifications sometimes include a layer of electroless nickel after the pre-plate treatment. The remainder of the plating process is similar to that described for steel except the copper layer is required.

8.2.4.3 Plastic—Different types of plastic are being plated. Most end users have internal specifications governing the process and performance of the plated part. An initial pre-plate system is used to apply a conductive coating to the part. The remainder of the plating process is similar to that described for steel. As with the aluminum substrate, the copper layer is required for plated plastic parts.

8.2.4.4 Zinc—Many zinc parts are plated with decorative chromium. These include both die cast and wrought zinc substrates. The plating process is similar to that described for steel, except copper layer is required.

8.3 Hard Chromium—This electrodeposited coating is a hard, durable abrasion resistant finish. Smooth hard chromium surfaces have a very low coefficient of friction. Coating thicknesses vary depending on the intended use. Thin coatings are usually plated to size and buffed to remove microscopic roughness. Parts with thicker coatings are usually overplated, then ground to size.

8.4 Precious Metal—Gold and silver plating are sometimes used to coat such things as electrical contacts. Due to the high cost of the plating material, systems have been developed to selectively plate areas of a part. Many of the plated parts are supplied as part of module assemblies.

8.5 Specifications—The following is a list of specifications that deal with metallic coatings:

ASTM B 117—Test Method of Salt Spray (Fog) Testing
ASTM B 177—Practice for Chromium Electroplating on Steel for Engineering Use
ASTM B 183—Practice for Preparation of Low Carbon Steel for Electroplating
ASTM B 200—Specification of Electrodeposited Coatings of Lead and Lead-Tin Alloys on Steel and Ferrous Alloys
ASTM B 242—Practice for Preparation of High-Carbon Steel for Electroplating
ASTM B 252—Practice for Preparation of Zinc Alloy Die Castings for Electroplating and Conversion Coating
ASTM B 253—Guide for Preparation of Aluminum Alloys for Electroplating
ASTM B 254—Practice for Preparation of and Electroplating on Stainless Steel
ASTM B 281—Practice for Preparation of Copper and Copper-Base Alloys for Electroplating and Conversion Coatings
ASTM B 320—Practice for Preparation of Iron Castings for Electroplating
ASTM B 322—Practice for Cleaning Metals Prior to Electroplating
ASTM B 368—Method for Copper-Accelerated Acitic Acid-Salt Fog Testing (CASS Test)
ASTM B 380—Methods for Corrosion Testing of Decorative Chromium Electroplating by the Corrodkote Procedure
ASTM B 456—Specification for Electrodeposited Coatings of Copper Plus Nickel Plus Chromium and Nickel Plus Chromium
ASTM B 487—Test Method for Measurement of Metal and Oxide Coating Thickness by Microscopal Examination of a Cross Section
ASTM B 499—Test Method for Measurement of Coating Thickness by the Magnetic Method: Nonmagnetic Coatings on Magnetic Basis Metals
ASTM B 504—Test Method for Measurement of Thickness of Metallic Coatings by the Coulometric Method
ASTM B 530—Method for Measurement of Coating Thickness by the Magnetic Method: Electrodeposited Nickel Coatings on Magnetic and Nonmagnetic Substrates

9. Chapter 6—Coated Steels for Corrosion Resistance

9.1 Introduction—Coated-sheet steel typically refers to steel overlayed with a protective coating applied in a continuous process. These materials provide the traditional advantages of steel, such as strength and formability, with the cost-effective durability and corrosion resistance of the coatings.

With coated steel, the responsibility of applying the coatings is dealt with prior to the delivery of the steel. The cleaning and coating of the steel are the responsibility of the supplier. These coatings on steel are often applied with more efficiency and uniformity than is possible with post-applied coatings, and this can translate into lower "per part" costs. Another benefit to the user of coated sheet is minimization of environmental concerns over coating application. Although coated steel can be used without any additional coating, coated steel for automotive applications will typically receive an organic coating after assembly. This requires the same types of cleaning and/or chemical pretreatments as uncoated steel substrates to ensure good paint adhesion and field performance.

Coated steel may be especially useful for preventing "inside out" or perforation corrosion. Perforation corrosion in automotive bodies usually starts on the interior surfaces of the body panels. This often occurs on interior areas that are difficult, if not impossible, to coat after assembly. Coated steel also offers all the advantages of typical anti-corrosion systems: acting to increase the life and value of a product; allowing the use of thinner steels to reduce weight and increase fuel economy; and increasing vehicle safety by reducing corrosion damage to critical load bearing parts.

The use of coated steel products in the U.S. has increased dramatically over the last ten years. Figure 17 graphically represents an 83% increase in North American shipments of all coated steel products between 1982 and 1989 [2.1.4.1]. The primary reason for this increase was the movement by the automotive industry toward coated sheet to combat corrosion. During this period, a significant decrease in the incidence of automotive corrosion was also witnessed throughout the industry. Figure 18 shows the results of five SAE parking lot surveys of 5 and 6 year old cars with model years ranging from 1980 to 1989 and SAE Paper 950375. A significant decrease in both the number and severity of defects occurred during this period. Although design modifications, improved pretreatments, and paints also played a role in this decrease, the movement to coated sheet body panels is probably the key factor responsible for this decrease.

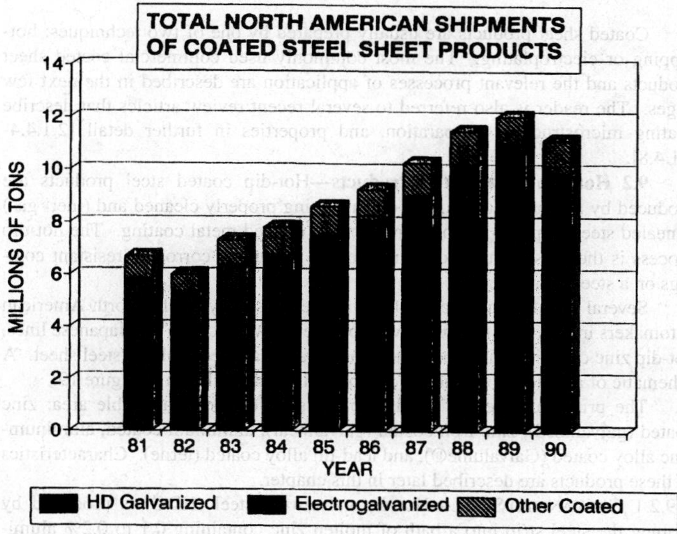

FIGURE 17—NORTH AMERICAN SHIPMENTS OF COATED STEEL SHEET PRODUCTS

The corrosion resistance of coated-steel products is afforded by the coatings which can be either barrier, sacrificial, and/or inhibitive coatings. Barrier coatings separate the steel from corrosive environments. A barrier coating owes its protective value to its own relative chemical inertness to the environment in which it is exposed.

Sacrificial coatings offer electrochemical protection to the exposed steel surfaces. When two pieces of dissimilar metal are electrically or galvanically coupled and exposed to an electrolyte, there is a flow of electrons between the metals accompanied by chemical reactions on their surfaces. The difference in the electrode potentials of the two metals produces the flow of electrons from the more active metal (the anode) to the less active metal (the cathode). This results in an accelerated rate of corrosion of the more active metal while corrosion of the less active metal is prevented. Sacrificial coatings are anodic with respect to steel and in the presence of an electrolyte (e.g., moisture films containing conductive ions) will tend to protect exposed steel surfaces at breaks in the coatings. It is important to note that the effectiveness of a sacrificial coating depends upon both the corrosive environment and the type and thickness of the coating. A coating that offers sacrificial protection in one environment may not do so in another. If there is no exposed base steel, sacrificial coatings act as barrier coatings, although such coatings are subject to chemical attack and oxidation in contrast with true barrier coatings. This is not a problem for coatings such as zinc, however, which has a corrosion rate that is approximately 1/10th that of iron in atmosphere.

Inhibitive coatings contain substances that act to inhibit the corrosion of steel. Chromates are often used for this purpose [2.1.4.3].

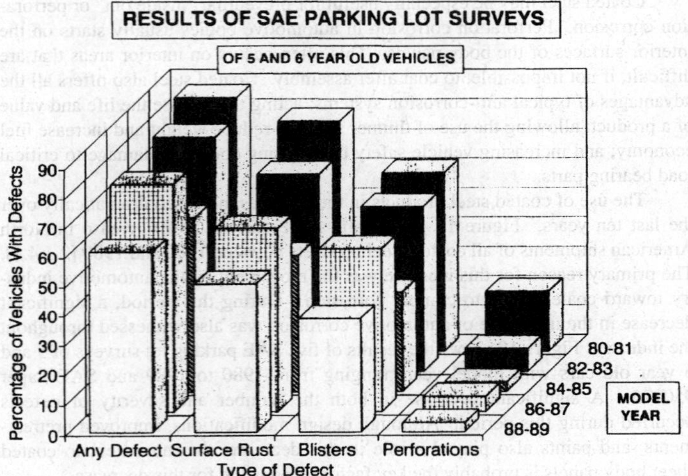

FIGURE 18—RESULTS OF SAE PARKING LOT SURVEYS

Coated sheet products are usually prepared by one of two techniques: hot-dipping or electroplating. The most commonly used commercial coated sheet products and the relevant processes of application are described in the next few pages. The reader is also referred to several recent review articles that describe coating microstructure, preparation, and properties in further detail [2.1.4.4-2.1.4.8].

9.2 Hot-Dip Coated Steel Products—Hot-dip coated steel products are produced by a continuous process of immersing properly cleaned and (inert gas) annealed steel strip into a molten bath of the desired metal coating. The hot-dip process is the most cost effective method of producing corrosion resistant coatings on a steel substrate.

Several new hot-dip coating facilities began supplying the North American automakers in 1993 and combined with planned new European and Japanese lines, hot-dip zinc capacity is increasing at a faster rate than electroplated steel sheet. A schematic of a typical continuous hot-dip coating line is shown in Figure 19.

The principal types of hot-dip coated steel currently available area: zinc coated (galvanized), zinc-iron coated (galvanneal), aluminum coated, aluminum-zinc alloy coated (Galvalume®), and lead-tin alloy coated (terne). Characteristics of these products are described later in this chapter.

9.2.1 GALVANIZED STEEL—Hot-dip galvanized steel (HDG) is produced by dipping the steel strip into a bath of molten zinc containing 0.1 to 0.2% aluminum. Although both, one- and two-side galvanized steel can be produced, the automotive industry predominantly uses two-side coated HDG for parts designated as hot-dip coated.

HDG may be produced with a wide range of coating weights depending on the automotive specification. Table 5 shows the minimum and maximum coating limits per side for a variety of coating classes typically used by car makers. The automotive industry is moving away from coating designations previously specified as oz/ft^2 to the international designation of g/m^2.

A variety of strength and formability levels are available ranging from commercial quality, drawing quality, deep-drawing quality, extra-deep drawing quality, as well as 240 to 825 MPa (35 to 120 ksi) minimum yield strength, high strength, low alloy galvanized.

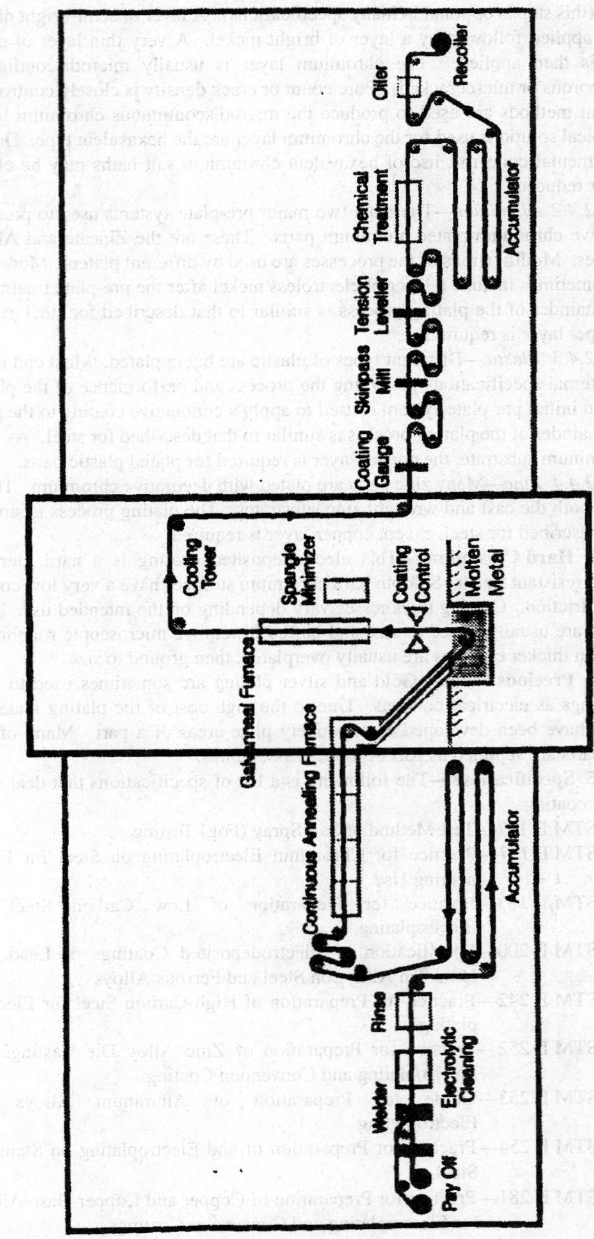

FIGURE 19—CONTINUOUS HOT-DIP LINE

Zinc is anodic to steel under most exposure conditions and will offer sacrificial protection to exposed steel surfaces. Hence, zinc coatings will continue to offer protection to the base steel after the coating is penetrated by corrosion or mechanically damaged or at cut edges. Zinc coatings will protect steel at moderate temperatures, but zinc-coated steels should not be used above 260 °C (500 °F).

Zinc-coated steels are subject to damage from humid storage stain caused by adverse storage or shipping conditions. The product may be rendered more resistant to humid storage stain by the application of a "ship-out" oil. However, the protection afforded is temporary.

Zinc coatings are ductile and can be stamped, roll or brake formed, deep drawn, spun, or lock formed.

Zinc-coated steel can be welded by electric resistance, metal arc, laser and seam welding, although the processes must be adjusted to allow for the peculiarities of the material. Arc welding produces a zinc oxide vapor which requires ventilation. Resistance welding requires higher currents, higher pressures, and longer cycle times than for uncoated steel. Zinc-coated steel is readily solderable with low melting point solder.

TABLE 5—TYPICAL AUTOMOTIVE COATING WEIGHTS FOR HOT-DIP GALVANIZED STEEL

Coating Designation	Minimum Check Limit Single Spot Test/Side (g/m2)	Maximum Check Limit Single Spot Test/Side (g/m2)
0G	0	0
20G	20	60
60G	60	110
70G	70	120
90G	90	140
98G	100	160
100G	100	140

NOTES

a.60G0G refers to one-side coated galvanized steel: 60 to 110 g/m^2 on one side and 0 g/m^2 on the other side.

b.100G100G refers to two-side equally coated galvanized steel: 100 to 140 g/m^2 on each side.

c.90G70G refers to differentially coated galvanized steel: 90 to 140 g/m^2 on one side and 70 to 120 g/m^2 minimum on the other side.

d.Some North American car makers have more restrictive limits than shown above. Others have limits based on triple spot test measurements.

Although zinc-coated steels are paintable with a variety of paints readily available from most paint suppliers, a conversion pretreatment (such as zinc phosphate) is required for good paint adhesion.

9.2.2 HOT-DIP GALVANNEAL—Zinc-iron alloy coatings (galvanneal = GA) are produced by heating zinc-coated strip during the continuous galvanizing operation immediately after hot dipping. Preparation of GA coatings begins by dipping the steel strip in a bath of molten zinc that also contains aluminum (0.1 to 0.2%) to control the extent of iron/zinc alloying. Coating weight is controlled by blowing off the excess zinc using air knives after the strip exits the bath. The strip is then reheated to start the diffusion of iron from the steel substrate into the zinc. The strip temperature is maintained to allow the iron to diffuse to the coating surface and then the strip is rapidly cooled to stop the diffusion process.

GA is a zinc-iron coating consisting of approximately 8 to 18% iron and the balance zinc. Unlike pure zinc coatings, which have a silver, reflective appearance, the GA coating has a dull grey color. The GA coating also "feels less smooth" due to its microporous surface. This microporous surface can also result in retention of applied lubricants during subsequent cleaning processes. Although the bulk iron concentration in the coating is 8 to 12%, the coating typically contains several different zinc-iron phases ranging from 5 to 21% iron. The iron concentration and phase variations occur due to the diffusion process by which GA is made.

Zinc-iron coatings provide less sacrificial protection of exposed steel compared to free zinc coatings. Also, due to their iron content, the corrosion products of GA are reddish-brown, whereas the corrosion products of free zinc coatings are white. However, alloying zinc with iron improves the corrosion resistance by lowering the corrosion rate of the coating.

Zinc-iron alloy coatings are also more weldable and offer better paint adhesion than free zinc coatings. They are, therefore, well suited for exterior skin panels, inner closure panels, and structural components. However, GA coatings are more susceptible to coating adhesion problems, such as powdering and flaking, compared to HDG steel.

Typical coating weights of automotive GA are shown in Table 6. As with HDG coatings, a variety of formable and high-strength grades are widely available.

TABLE 6—TYPICAL AUTOMOTIVE COATING WEIGHTS FOR HOT-DIP GALVANNEAL STEELS

Coating Designation	Minimum Check Limit Single Spot Test Side (g/m2)	Maximum Check Limit Single Spot Test/Side (g/m2)
30A	30	60
40A	40	80
50A	50	90
60A	60	90

NOTES

a. Some North American car makers have more restrictive limits than shown above. Others have limits based on triple spot test measurements.

Other types of hot-dip coated steels are used in automotive applications other than body panels. These include aluminum-coated steel, aluminum-zinc alloy-coated steel, and tern-coated steel.

9.2.3 ALUMINUM-COATED STEEL—Aluminum-coated steel is produced by dipping cleaned and inert gas annealed steel strip into a molten bath of aluminum alloy containing 8 to 12% silicon. Coating weight is typically 120 g/m^2 total both sides based on triple spot measurements.

The enhanced high temperature corrosion performance makes this product well suited for making parts of the automotive exhaust system including intermediate pipes, mufflers, and tail pipes.

9.2.4 ALUMINUM-ZINC ALLOY-COATED STEELS (GALVALUME®)—Aluminum-zinc alloy coated steel is also produced by dipping cleaned and inert gas annealed steel strip into a molten bath of aluminum alloy containing 55% aluminum, 43.5% zinc, and 1.5% silicon. The coating consists of an aluminum rich matrix with zinc rich interdendritic areas. Coating weight is typically 150 g/m^2 total both sides based on triple spot measurements.

Automotive applications for this product are similar to those for aluminum-coated steel; i.e., requiring high-temperature corrosion resistance. Typical applications include heat shields, gas tank shields, mufflers, and under hood parts.

9.2.5 TERNE-COATED STEEL—Long terne coated steel has a lead alloy coating containing nominally 8% tin. It protects against corrosion in gas tanks, fuel lines, and brake lines and does not contaminate gasoline or brake fluid. Less active than the steel substrate, it does not provide galvanic protection if the coating is penetrated.

Nickel terne-coated steel includes an electrolytic flash coating of nickel (1 to 1.5 g/m^2) underneath a conventional lead/tin coating for enhanced corrosion resistance. Applications are similar to long-terne described previously.

A variation of long-terne coated steel employs a subsequent prepainted organic coating on each surface for some fuel tanks. The outer surface has a zinc rich organic coating to provide added exterior corrosion protection, while the inner surface has an aluminum-rich organic coating to augment the lead/tin coating resistance to gasoline, and low concentrations of methanol and ethanol containing fuels.

9.3 Electroplated Steel Products—Electroplated coatings are applied in a low-temperature continuous process where negatively charged steel sheet is passed between positively charged anodes. Metallic ions in an electrolyte bath are reduced and plated on the surface of the steel sheet forming the coating. The bath composition, electrolyte velocity, current density, and temperature determine the chemistry and properties of the metallic/alloy coating applied to the steel sheet. The plating current and strip speed will determine the coating thickness. A schematic of an electroplating line is shown in Figure 20 [2.1.4.9–2.1.4.10]. Electroplated coatings are particularly attractive to the automotive industry because of their uniform appearance, formability, weldability, and coating thickness control. Electroplated coatings can be applied to one or both sides of the steel sheet with equal or differential coating thicknesses on each side.

Electroplating lines are often identified or distinguished based on plating cell type or geometry, anode type, and/or electrolyte composition. In the U.S., one of three cell geometries: horizontal, vertical, or radial are commonly used. Schematics of each of these cell types are shown in Figures 21 to 23 [2.1.4.9–2.1.4.10]. Electroplating lines can also be classified by the type of anode used: soluble or insoluble. The selection of anode type will depend on the electrolyte type, the cell design, and the desired coating. The final method of identifying electroplated lines is according to electrolyte composition. Electrolyte baths are usually sulfate based (typically used with insoluble anodes, but also used with soluble anodes) or chloride based (used only with soluble anodes).

9.3.1 ELECTROPLATED ZINC COATINGS—Pure zinc electroplated coatings, electrozinc coatings (EZ), are the most commonly used coated sheet in the U.S. for exposed body panels. Similar to HDG, the zinc coating is significantly anodic to the underlying steel and, therefore, galvanically protects the steel substrate from corrosion. Corrosion products on EZ and HDG are typically white zinc oxides, hydroxides, or carbonates and are often less objectionable to automotive customers compared to red iron corrosion products. The primary driving force for the widespread use of EZ over HDG for exposed panels is enhanced coating thickness uniformity and surface characteristics [2.1.4.4]. EZ coating thicknesses range from 4 to 13 μm (20 to 90 g/m^2) per side. Typical specifications for EZ coating weight and tolerances are listed in Table 7.

TABLE 7—TYPICAL AUTOMOTIVE COATING WEIGHTS FOR ELECTROZINC COATINGS

Coating Designation Electrozinc Coatings	Minimum Check Limit Single Spot Test (g/m2)	Maximum Check Limit Single Spot Test (g/m2)
60G00G	60/0	70/0
60G60G	60/60	60/60
70G70G	70/70	80/80

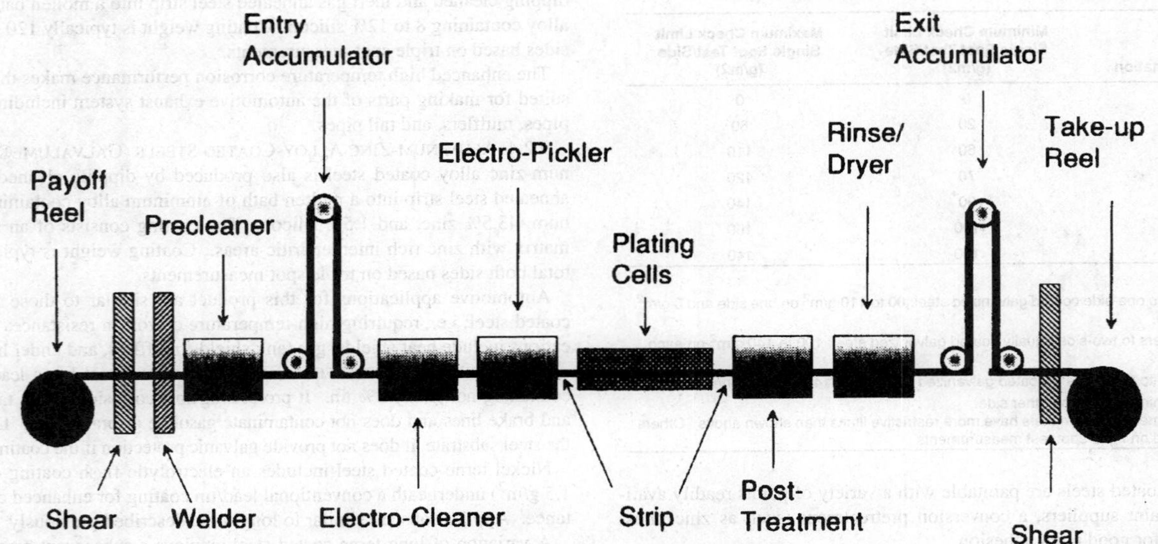

FIGURE 20—CONTINUOUS ELECTROPLATING LINE

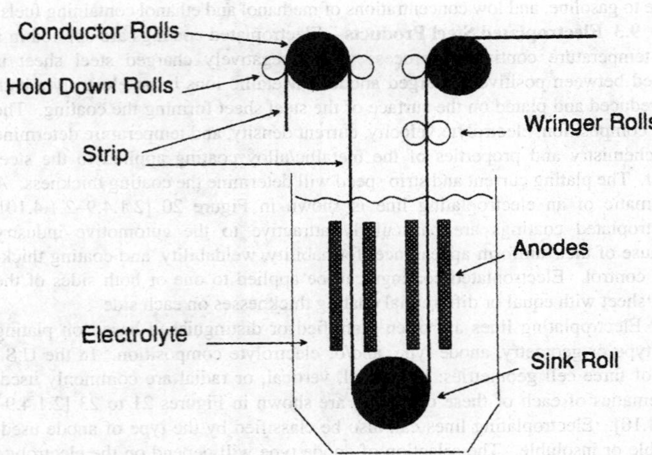

FIGURE 21—VERTICAL PLATING CELL

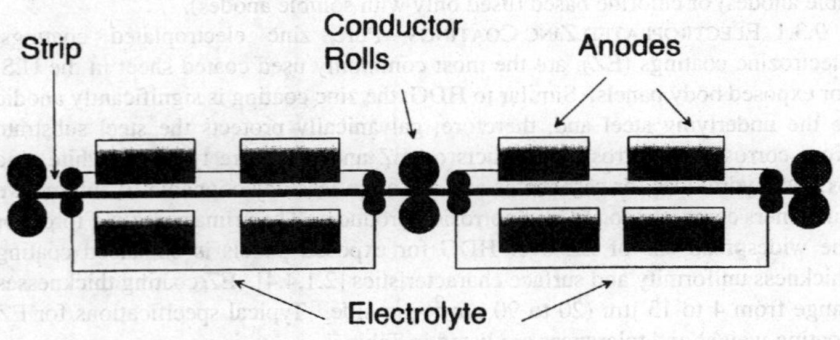

FIGURE 22—HORIZONTAL PLATING CELL

9.3.2 ALLOY ELECTROPLATED COATINGS—Two primary electroplated alloy coatings, zinc-nickel (Zn-Ni) and zinc-iron (Zn-Fe), are of commercial importance in the automotive industry. Both galvanically protect steel, similar to EZ, but have the added advantage of lower coating dissolution rates enabling similar coating lifetimes at lower coating weights. Zn-Ni coatings contain 10 to 14% Ni and are applied at coating thicknesses ranging from 3 to 6 µm (20 to 40 g/m^2). Zn-Ni coatings are used for exposed and unexposed panels because of their corrosion resistance, superior weldability (over EZ, HDG, and GA), and good formability. Zn-Fe electroplated coatings offer the good weldability of hot-dipped Zn-Fe coatings, and the surface appearance and coating uniformity of electroplated coatings. These coatings generally contain 8 to 18% iron and are applied at thicknesses up to 7 µm per side (50 g/m^2). Zn-Fe electroplated coatings are often used for exposed automotive panels where surface appearance and coating uniformity are critical areas of concern.

Enhancements of electroplated coatings are also commercially available. Composite coatings are prepared by applying a chromium pretreatment followed by a thin (1 to 2 g/m^2) silicate containing organic topcoat to the metallic coating surface. The organic coating is typically applied to one side of the material; the side that will be the interior of the final panel. This provides additional protection to the areas where phosphating and priming may be inadequate after assembly. The other side of the steel sheet will typically contain a metallic coating, but can be uncoated. Perforation corrosion resistance is significantly enhanced in composite coatings over conventional electroplated coatings. Weldability of composite coatings will be comparable or slightly poorer than electroplated coatings.

Plating of a thin iron-phosphorous (Fe-P) layer (2 g/m^2) or Fe-Zn (3 g/m^2) layer on the surface of Zn-Fe hot-dip or electroplated coatings is also used for automotive applications. The thin electroplated layer is designed to improve formability and reduce electrocoat cratering tendencies of the Zn-Fe alloy coating.

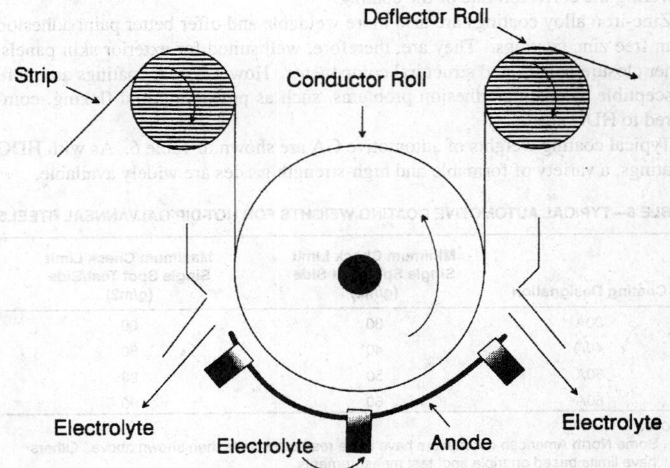

FIGURE 23—RADIAL PLATING CELL

Typical coating weight specifications and tolerances for alloy electroplate coatings are listed in Table 8.

TABLE 8—TYPICAL AUTOMOTIVE COATING WEIGHTS FOR ALLOY ELECTROPLATED COATINGS

Coating Designation	Alloy Type	Minimum Check Limit Single Spot Test (g/m^2)	Maximum Check Limit Single Spot Test (g/m^2)
30N30N	ZnNi	30/30	40/40
20N20N	ZnNi	20/20	30/30
40A40AEL	ZnFe	40/40	55/55
45A45A	ZnFe	45/45	55/55

9.4 Summary—Usage of coated sheet products in the automotive industry has increased significantly over the last several years. This increase is largely due to the ability of coated products to provide superior corrosion protection in typical automotive environments. The selection of a specific coated sheet product for a specific application is usually based on a combination of factors. No one product is superior to the others in all areas. In addition to corrosion resistance, the factors that typically influence coating selection include: part design and application, formability, weldability, uniformity requirements (appearance, tolerances, etc.), and cost. Only after careful assessment of the requirements for the target application, should be best coated sheet product be selected.

10. *Chapter 7—Rust Preventive Oils, Greases, and Coatings*

10.1 General Information—Rust preventive oils and greases form preservative coatings by dipping, spraying, brushing, roll coating, or electrostatic oiling as fluids or semifluids. They function as semipermanent barriers to moisture and oxygen and as vehicles for active inhibitors. They are usually easily removed and do not alter the surface characteristics of the item protected.

Film thickness increases as viscosity of the rust preventive is increased. Protective value and durability generally increase with increased film thickness. Ease of removal tends to improve with decreasing film thickness, except for the oxidizable or solvent cut-back thin film types.

Temporary usage is for protection of parts or coils in warehouse storage, or in manufacturing between machining operations, or during preassembly transit or storage. Duration of storage may range from one or two weeks to several months. Adhesives are frequently used to bond oily sheet metal during assembly operations. The oil used on sheet steel stock for storage and/or in transit corrosion protection should be evaluated for compatibility with the adhesives involved. Removal of the rust preventive may or may not be necessary before placing the part in use. Rust preventives meeting these extremes in requirement are readily available. Successful selection and performance then depend on accurate assessment of the parameters of the conditions of use.

Rust preventive coatings are generally intended for more permanent rust prevention of vehicle and/or component parts. Corrosion protection of these materials ranges up to 500 h salt spray exposure.

Economics of the choice of a material for a specific application are influenced by the cost of applying the rust preventive and the cost of placing the part in use as much as by the cost of the rust preventive material itself. Once the range of materials with the protective value capable of meeting the environmental requirement has been determined, the factors of cost of application and removal become decisive.

Wherever the volume and nature of parts to be protected will justify it, automatic application, either by itself or integrated into existing operations, gives the greatest potential for both minimum cost and maximum protection, by reason of optimum film control and coverage.

In Table 9 the various types of rust preventive oils and greases are classified and described by characteristics and usage. Rust preventive oils are much more commonly used than rust preventive greases. Typical uses of coatings for vehicle and component parts are outlined in 10.2.2.1.

10.2 Adhesives, Sealers, and Deadeners

10.2.1 ADHESIVES—These materials are used to temporarily or permanently adhere a wide variety of similar or dissimilar substrates. They may serve in a dual function, i.e., to bond and seal component parts against environmental conditions. Adhesives can be formulated to provide acceptable structural strength to replace welding or mechanical retention.

Adhesives intended for application prior to paint operations must be formulated to withstand the paint bake schedules without promoting corrosion.

Adhesives used to bond exterior ornamentation minimize or eliminate holes or weld studs necessary for mechanical attachment and thus reduce corrosion. Also, they provide a barrier against galvanic corrosion.

10.2.2 SEALERS—Asphaltic, rubber, vinyl, and hot melts modified with corrosion inhibitors are commonly used, and the selection for a specific application is dependent upon the intended process and environmental conditions. Asphaltic air dry or heat cure sealers are normally lower cost, exhibit poor paintability, and their use is restricted to nonvisible areas subject to low abrasion in service. Vinyl base, heat-curing sealers are normally applied prior to paint bake ovens, to yield good paintability, flexibility, and also abrasion resistance. Heat-expanding vinyl sealers are also used for sealer washers and dip-coated clips or brackets to prevent water entry and subsequent corrosion.

Wax compounds are widely used on exterior sheet metal screws to seal against water leaks and also to prevent corrosion in body ornamentation holes.

10.2.2.1 Typical Uses Of Rust Preventive Coatings

a. Battery terminal felt washer saturants
b. Chassis leaf springs
c. Standard parts which require a phosphate and oil finish
d. Ferrous metal surfaces for extended indoor or outdoor storage—non-paint staining
e. Underhood hardware (phosphate and oil)
f. Steel exhaust pipes which are stored for aftermarket use
g. Lever assemblies of starting motor drives
h. Bearing cups in rotors and hub and drum assemblies for front wheels
i. Front suspension control arms
j. Supplemental use on inner surfaces of doors, quarter panels, etc.
k. Dealer application—for underbody and interior areas subject to severe corrosion
l. Temporary use on parts to be assembled within the fluid-containing portion of a brake system component
m. Chassis components—overcoated with chassis enamel
n. Brake rotors and hubs during storage and shipment
o. Compressor valves for temporary protection
p. Weldable zinc-rich primer on fabricated sheet metal parts prior to assembly and weld operations

In addition to the required functional properties of a sealer, the determination and selection must include consideration of the process, safety, and industrial health and hygiene requirements.

Sealers may be furnished in liquid, paste, film, and solid form, and may be hand-applied, dip-coated, extruded, or spray applied with suitable equipment.

10.2.3 DEADENERS—These water emulsion or solvent cut-back asphaltic materials are used to change the frequency and amount of vibration of sheet metal surfaces. They are generally applied on interior, nonvisible surfaces. Spray applied deadeners generally provide abrasion and corrosion protection due to the exclusion of a corrosive atmosphere, however the corrosion protection is generally not as effective as sealers, and this is attributed to porosity, thin film application, and occasional lack of adherence.

In addition to the required functional properties of a deadener, the determination and selection must include consideration of the process, safety, industrial and health and hygiene requirements.

The typical uses of adhesives, sealers, and deadeners are outlined in 10.2.3.1 through 10.2.3.3.

10.2.3.1 Adhesive-Coated Tapes or Films

a. Provide stone pecking protection in wheelhouse areas
b. Prevent paint damage during installation of spare tire carrier assemblies
c. Provide stone pecking protection on lower exterior bodyside sheet metal

10.2.3.2 Sealers

a. Seal faying surfaces of metal joints to prevent corrosion
b. Seal edges of metal joints to prevent red rust bleedout onto painted exterior surfaces
c. Coat and/or seal components such as speed control sensor to prevent corrosion
d. Provide stone pecking protection on lower exterior bodyside sheet metal
e. Coat interior surfaces not accessible after assembly operations
f. Coat electrical connections in lamp sockets to prevent corrosion

10.2.3.3 Deadeners

a. Provide stone pecking protection in underbody areas

TABLE 9—TYPES OF RUST PREVENTIVE OILS AND GREASES

Class and Type	Description	Film Thickness, µm	Durability	Method of Application	Principal Uses
Grease	Oil thickened with soap or synthetic thickeners and containing polar organic inhibitors (for example, petroleum sulphonates or sulphated fatty oils) provide a heavy nonhardening film with self-healing properties.	380-2400	12–14 months outside	Brushing	Protection of rough or machined ferrous surfaces under severe conditions, but not including outside storage.
Oil Nondrying	Medium to heavy viscosity, nonhardening; contain active polar inhibitors to fortify the function of the oil in providing a barrier against moisture on the protected surface.	125-380	7–9 months inside storage	Brushing, spraying, cold dipping, electrostatic	Protection of ground or fine machined surfaces of parts for long term inside storage.
Fingerprint neutralizing	Very light viscosity, contain polar organic inhibitors, alcohols, and organic bases, which dissolve and suppress or neutralize salts and organic acids from handling.	Less than 25	2–3 weeks inside storage	Dipping or brushing	Protection of ground or fine machined surfaces of parts between machining operations or for limited preassembly storage.
Water displacing	Very light viscosity, contain wetting agents and polar compounds; function by displacement of moisture on the protected surface by the surface active agents, which then provide a moisture barrier.	Less than 25	2–3 weeks inside storage	Dipping or brushing	Protective of ground or fine machined surfaces which have been processed in emulsified compounds just prior to limited storage.
Dry Film Oxidizable	Drying oil modified with natural or synthetic resins and solvents; oxidation or polymerization of the oil after evaporation of the solvent builds a moisture-proof barrier.	25–125	18–24 months outside storage	Dipping, brushing, spraying	Protection of nonmachined surfaces of such parts as springs, linkages, and the like, against severe outside exposure.
Solvent cutback	Solution of wax or heavy asphaltic solids in solvent which evaporates to build dry to semi-dry film; may also contain active polar compounds.	50–250	18–24 months outside exposure	Dipping, brushing, or spraying	Protection of nonmachined surfaces under severe conditions, including unprotected outside storages.
Removable plastic	Synthetic resin; usually thermoplastic; capable of providing an effective moisture barrier.	25–125	24–36 months outside exposure	Hot dipping or hot contour forming	Protection of a wide variety of items, from perishable tools to delicate assemblies where positive protection against moisture must be combined with a high degree of resistance to mechanical damage by the film.
Water soluble	Compounded oils with emulsifiers and added polar compounds; after application as emulsion, water phase evaporates, leaving thin film of oil and inhibitors.	Less than 25	2–3 weeks inside storage (when used as an emulsion)	Dipping, spraying, brushing	Temporary protection of machined surfaces between operations or in limited preassembly storage.

PROVING GROUND VEHICLE CORROSION TESTING—SAE J1950 MAY1989

SAE Information Report

Report of the SAE Automotive Corrosion and Prevention Committee approved May 1989.

Foreword—This Document has not changed other than to put it into the new SAE Technical Standards Board Format.

1. Scope—The facilities used by domestic automotive manufacturers to provide accelerated corrosion aging of complete vehicles are described in general. The types of vehicles tested, general test methodology, and techniques used to determine test-to-field correlation are discussed. The different procedures used throughout the industry produce different results on various vehicle coatings, components, and systems. The key to successful interpretation of test results is a thorough understanding of the corrosion mechanisms involved and the effects of test limitations on these mechanisms.

1.1 Purpose—The purpose of this information report is to provide a general overview of some proving ground procedures and facilities used in the United States to evaluate the corrosion protection performance of vehicles. Because of limitations involved with any accelerated testing procedure, and despite the use of complete vehicles and attempts to make test environments all-inclusive, test results require knowledgeable interpretation.

Proving grounds are, in effect, large laboratories. As with different laboratory test procedures, different test techniques will produce different results. Consideration of the various techniques and analysis tools discussed in the following sections may give the reader an understanding of the environments that vehicles must be designed to survive and may aid in the further development of accelerated corrosion tests.

2. References

2.1 Related Publications—The following publications are provided for information purposes only and are not a required part of this document.

G. Hook; "The Historical Development of a Proving Ground Accelerated Corrosion Test." Presented at NACE Corrosion/80, March 1980, Chicago, IL.

R. Ericsson, S. Haagenrud, and J. Henriksen; "Simultaneous Measurements of Corrosiveness and Environment on Different Parts of the Automotive Body." Presented at NACE Corrosion/82, March 1982, Houston, Texas (Paper No. 260).

3. Locations Of Corrosion Testing Facilities—Although laboratory tests of vehicle components and systems are conducted at various locations within an automotive company and it may have more than one proving ground facility, each company performs proving ground corrosion tests at one location only. (As of this writing, although Chrysler and AMC have merged, they have not yet consolidated proving ground testing.) The locations of these facilities are shown in Figure 1. They are centered either in southeastern Michigan (GM and Chrysler) or in Arizona (Volkswagen of America, Navistar, American Motors Corporation, Ford).

Each testing location has certain advantages. Locations in Southeast Michigan have the advantage of being near to corporate design and engineering activities so communication of test information may be optimized. Persons responsible for system corrosion performance can easily view interim test results without extensive time or travel. Locations in Arizona have the advantage of fairly consistent weather, particularly humidity. Because ambient environment has a large effect on vehicle corrosion in Michigan, test corrosion rate differences on the order of 2:1 summer-to-winter have been observed if corrective measures are not used. Arizona's low relative humidity ensures that test vehicle corrosion occurs mainly under controlled conditions in temperature/humidity chambers.

4. Vehicles Tested—Various types of vehicles are proving ground tested by the automotive manufacturers. These include audit testing of production vehicles, validation testing of preproduction vehicles (prototype, pilot line, etc.), and development testing for evaluation of new designs, materials, coatings, assembly and processing techniques, etc. Vehicles tested include the full range of each manufacturer's product from subcompact cars to highway trucks and buses.

5. Test Methods And Facilities—Test methods used by the various manufacturers are often different in environmental content because each test evolved separately; thus, the final results are often different. The general test methods presently in use are as follows:

5.1 General Motors—Several different test schedules are used, each having a particular area of emphasis but all having similar corrosive inputs. The "full corrosion/durability" schedule requires approximately 10 months to complete and is intended to relate to 160 000 km (approximately 10 years) of severe customer service. Major test inputs are shown in Figure 2. Rather than driving a totally preset cycle, events are combined to provide proportional corrosion (chemical) and durability (mechanical) input fitting schedule needs. This test can be modified by removing some or most of the "mild" durability inputs while leaving corrosive inputs essentially unchanged. This allows testing to be completed more rapidly while not largely affecting general and cosmetic corrosion results. However, corrosion mechanisms, which are dependent upon stress cycles or other operation cycles, will not be accelerated as greatly. Because it is believed that durability inputs (such as operation on rough roads, brake applications, operation of electrical systems, etc.) can affect corrosion results, and vice versa, these two types of test content (durability and corrosion) usually are run concurrently on a vehicle. The fastest GM Proving Ground corrosion test, which contains only the most significant durability inputs, requires about ten weeks to complete.

General Motors' corrosion test inputs are intended to relate directly to metallic general corrosion, cosmetic corrosion, and functional corrosion of systems, assemblies, electrical connectors, etc. that occur in the field. Actual perforations of body panels usually are not produced within the time frame of these tests. However, these may be predicted with some confidence using metal thickness loss measurements and perforation acceleration factors known from past experience. Some uncertainty always exists because the test time required to cause deterioration of protective organic coatings is not always known.

The General Motors corrosion test environment consists of alternate exposure to a shallow salt splash road (5% NaCl in water), an exterior salt spray (5% NaCl in water), gravel roads (portions treated with calcium chloride), a grit trough (containing sand, clay, and coal cinders in deep water), and 8 h periods of elevated temperature and relative humidity (RH) (49 °C, 100% RH). Near the beginning of each test, the vehicle is driven through deep mud to provide poultice accumulation. (See Reference 1.)

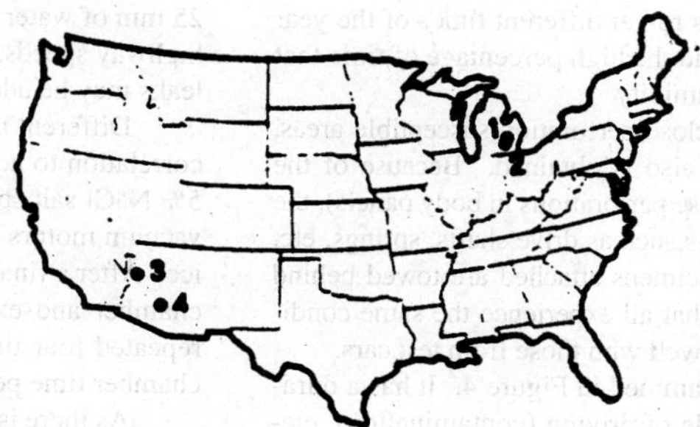

1. Milford, MI - General Motors
2. Chelsea, MI - Chrysler
3. Kingman, AZ - Ford
4. Phoenix, AZ - Navistar, American Motors, Volkswagen

FIGURE 1—PROVING GROUND CORROSION TESTING LOCATIONS

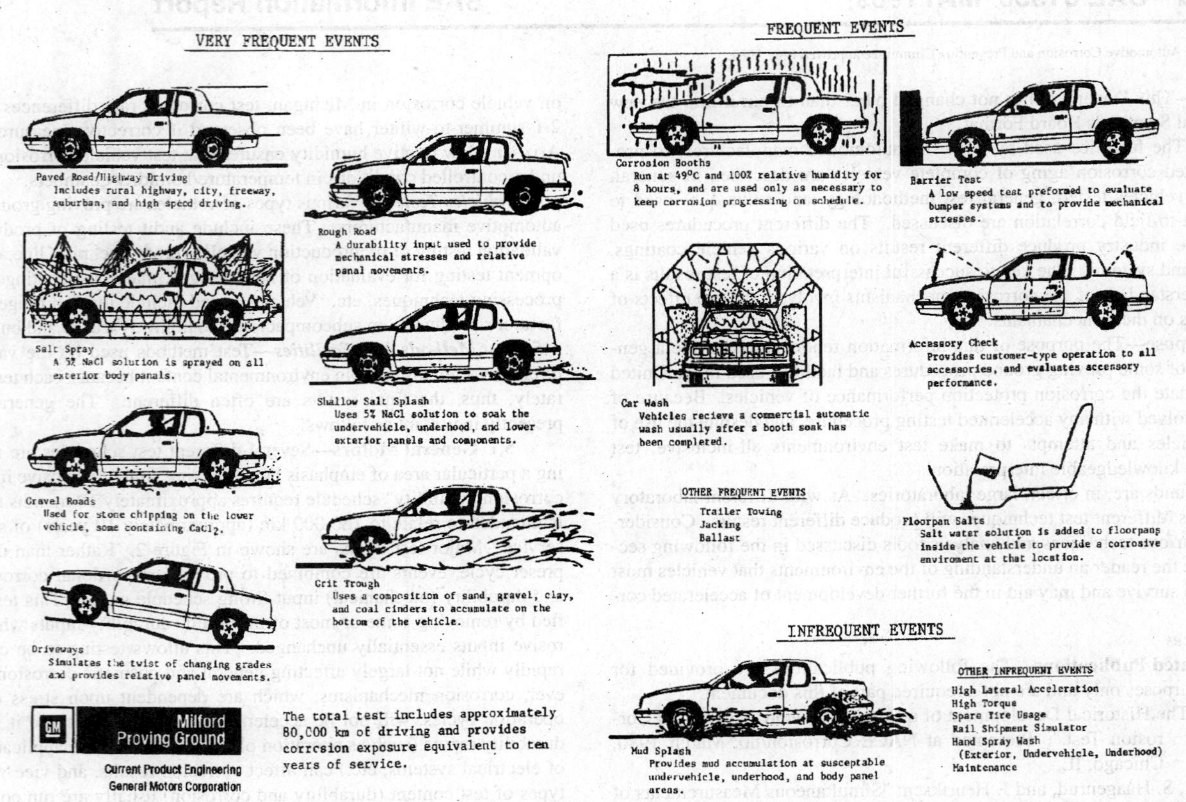

FIGURE 2—GENERAL MOTORS CORPORATION VEHICLE CORROSION TESTING

Test vehicle general corrosion exposure is monitored using bare steel coupons. Coupon weight loss is checked periodically throughout the test, and results are compared to test objectives (known general corrosion rates from field vehicles). To adjust for corrosion rate variations which might be caused by weather differences (for example, winter vs. summer testing) or test length (for example, full test or accelerated version), the number of exposures to 49°C/100% RH is varied while all other inputs remain constant.

5.2 Ford—The Ford corrosion test daily cycle is diagrammed in Figure 3. It includes 1.5 h of driving on dirt and gravel roads and a paved road onto which a thin layer of 5% salt solution is sprayed, and through a salt trough (5% NaCl), a salt spray (5% NaCl, 15 min total time), and a mud bath containing 4 parts NaCl to 1 part $CaCl_2$ for a total of 3% salt concentration in the mud. This is followed by 22.5 h in a humidity chamber at 49 °C/85% RH. This constitutes one cycle; five cycles per week are run and the vehicle is left in the humidity chamber on weekends and holidays. Total test duration is 100 cycles which approximates five years of severe field corrosion.

Minimal variation is observed among tests run at different times of the year due to minimal variation in Arizona's climate and the high percentage of time that vehicles spend in controlled temperature and humidity.

The Ford test is intended primarily to disclose perforation-susceptible areas, although some cosmetic corrosion information also is obtained. Because of the severe nature of the test environment (able to cause perforations in body panels), the test is not used to judge the performance of items such as drive shafts, springs, etc. In some cases, trailers with body panel test specimens attached are towed behind test vehicles. Specimens are rotated to ensure that all experience the same conditions. The results obtained in this way correlate well with those from test cars.

5.3 Chrysler—The Chrysler test is diagrammed in Figure 4. It has a duration of up to two years. It involves a 48 h cycle of driving (contamination), elevated temperature and humidity (38 °C, 100% relative humidity), and drying. Salt splash and spray are provided by a single facility using 0.5% NaCl, 0.5% $CaCl_2$, and 0.125% sodium metabisulfite.

Fifty test cycles are believed to correspond to 2.5-3.0 years of field exposure; tests frequently are run for several hundred cycles in order to evaluate long-term field exposure. Although good cosmetic corrosion results are obtained, some uncertainty exists in evaluating perforation corrosion. Slight differences in the environment have been found to cause relatively large differences in corrosion of bare steel coupons. Chrysler is considering the use of a controlled environment for drying periods. However, the fact that the test may last for two years should tend to minimize long-term test result differences, which might be caused by day-to-day weather variations.

5.4 Navistar—The Navistar test cycle, shown in Figure 5, is designed to indicate perforation corrosion susceptibility of medium and heavy-duty truck cabs. While the test track has facilities for stone pecking and salt and mud splash exposures, previous tests have shown these have little effect on a truck cab. The cab sits high enough off the road to normally avoid this environment. Also, these tests are extremely hard on chassis components which are not the subject of the cab corrosion test. In fact, chassis components are sometimes coated with rust inhibiting compounds or oils to extend their lives for possible use in additional tests.

Cabs are prepared in accordance with the test objectives. Blower motors are installed so that when in operation they will create a vacuum of approximately 25 mm of water inside the cab. This approximates the vehicle traveling in rain, at highway speeds, with the wing vents open. Panels may be scribed and intentional leaks may be added. Observation ports are installed in areas of interest.

Different test cycles have been tried, but the one which has shown the best correlation to actual field data in the shortest test time is alternate exposures to a 5% NaCl salt spray and a dirt road run at 30–35 mph. These are performed with vacuum motors to ensure penetration of the salt solution into every possible crevice. After a final exposure to the salt spray, the test truck is driven into a humidity chamber and exposed to a relative humdity of 100% at 38 °C. This cycle is repeated four times per week and includes an average of approximately 39 h of chamber time per cycle. Test duration is 100 cycles.

As there is little or no effect from stone pecking or other road hazards in this test, two cabs can be mounted on the same chassis. This reduces total test time and costs. Also, this is very helpful in comparing alternate materials or manufacturing processes as both cabs are exposed to exactly the same environment.

Navistar has recently closed their Phoenix test facility; future corrosion tests will be conducted at a new facility in Ft. Wayne, IN.

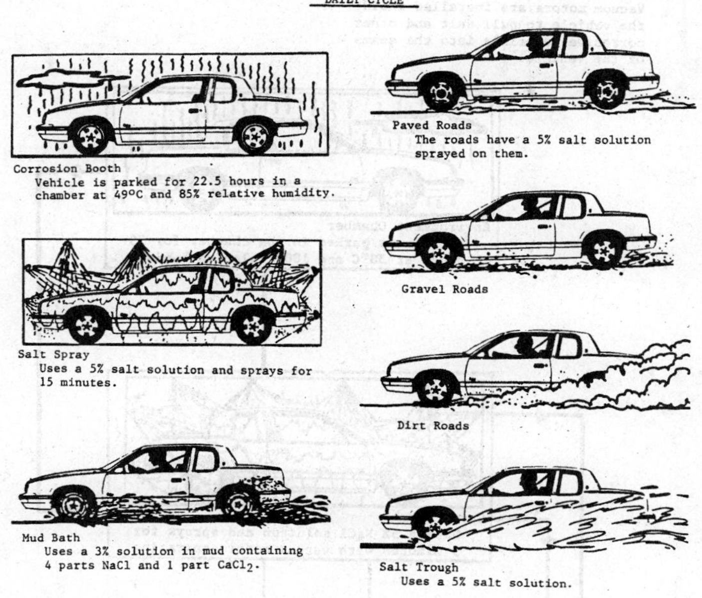

FORD MOTOR COMPANY
CORROSION TESTING CYCLE
DAILY CYCLE
Corrosion Booth
Vehicle is parked for 22.5 hours in a chamber at 49°C and 85% relative humidity.
Paved Roads
The roads have a 5% salt solution sprayed on them.
Salt Spray
Uses a 5% salt solution and sprays for 15 minutes.
Gravel Roads
Dirt Roads
Mud Bath
Uses a 3% solution in mud containing 4 parts NaCl and 1 part CaCl2.
Salt Trough
Uses a 5% salt solution.
Note: Test duration is 100 cyles and approximates five years of severe corrosion.

FIGURE 3—FORD MOTOR COMPANY CORROSION TESTING CYCLE

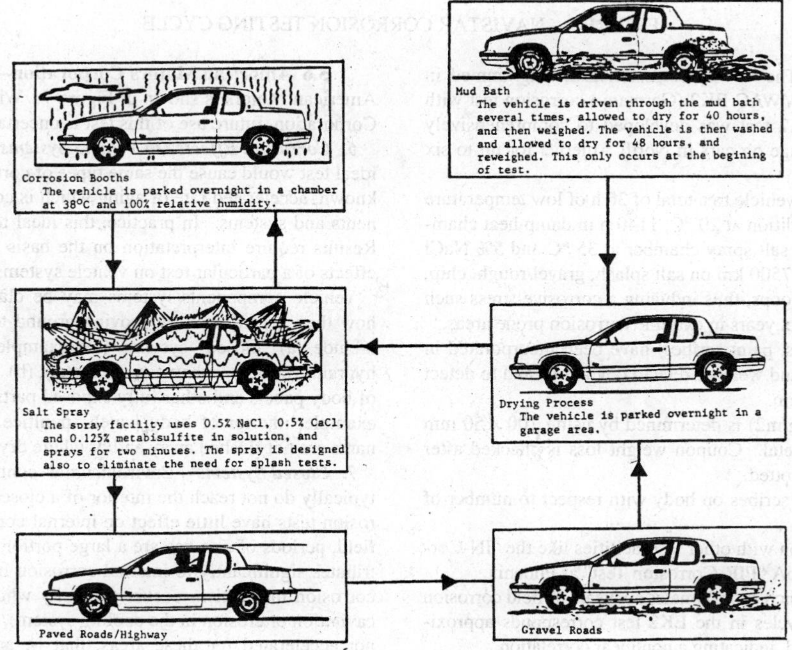

ACCELERATED CORROSION CYCLE
Mud Bath
The vehicle is driven through the mud bath several times, allowed to dry for 40 hours, and then weighed. The vehicle is then washed and allowed to dry for 48 hours, and reweighed. This only occurs at the begining of test.
Corrosion Booths
The vehicle is parked overnight in a chamber at 38°C and 100% relative humidity.
Salt Spray
The spray facility uses 0.5% NaCl, 0.5% CaCl, and 0.125% metabisulfite in solution, and sprays for two minutes. The spray is designed also to eliminate the need for splash tests.
Drying Process
The vehicle is parked overnight in a garage area.
Paved Roads/Highway
Gravel Roads
Note: 50 cycles approximates 2.5 to 3.0 years of corrosion.

FIGURE 4—CHRYSLER CORPORATION ACCELERATED CORROSION CYCLE

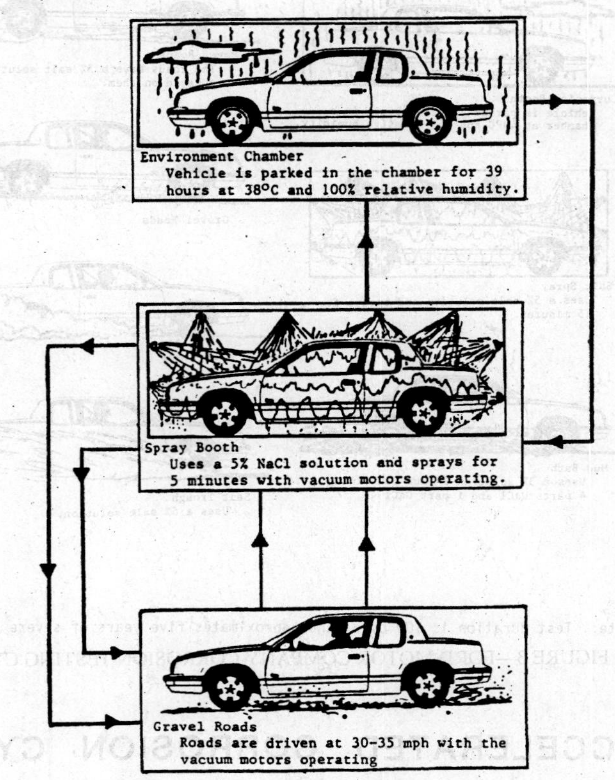
NAVISTAR
CORROSION TESTING CYCLE
Vacuum motors are installed inside the vehicle to pull salt and other corrosive materials into the seams of the vehicle.
Environment Chamber
Vehicle is parked in the chamber for 39 hours at 38°C and 100% relative humidity.
Spray Booth
Uses a 5% NaCl solution and sprays for 5 minutes with vacuum motors operating.
Gravel Roads
Roads are driven at 30-35 mph with the vacuum motors operating
Note: Cycle is repeated four times a week; test duration is 100 cycles.

FIGURE 5—NAVISTAR CORROSION TESTING CYCLE

5.5 Volkswagen of America—The VWoA corrosion test, diagrammed in Figure 6, is basically the same as the VWAG EK2 (Germany) corrosion test with minor variations. Essentially the EK2 test was developed to comprehensively simulate the extent of corrosion damage on cars in North America for up to six years.

The test consists of subjecting a vehicle to a total of 36 h of low temperature condition at –35 °C, 700 h of dry condition at 20 °C, 1140 h in damp heat chamber at 45/50 °C and 95% RH, 60 h in salt spray chamber at 35 °C and 5% NaCl salt spray plus road cycle of a total of 7500 km on salt splash, gravel/rough, chip, mud and accelerated durability track loops, thus inducing a corrosive stress such as would occur in cars in service for six years in extreme corrosion prone areas.

Two control systems (test panels, paint scribes) have been incorporated in the EK2 test to take care of seasonal and weather related deviations and to detect potential fluctuations in the paint system.

The average material loss rate (g/m2) is determined by using 100 x 50 mm panels made of body quality sheet metal. Coupon weight loss is checked after every ten cycles and the weight loss plotted.

Corrosion creepback from paint scribes on body with respect to number of cycles is also determined and plotted.

This yields a basis for comparison with other test facilities like the "IN-Corrosion Test" at Audi and with the VWoA "PIR-Corrosion Test" at Phoenix.

Total test duration is 60 cycles which approximates six years of field corrosion service in North America. Fifteen cycles in the EK2 test corresponds approximately to a three year period in the field, indicating a nonlinear correlation.

5.6 American Motors Corporation—The corrosion test schedule used by American Motors is shown in Figure 7. With the purchase of AMC by Chrysler Corporation, future use of this test is uncertain.

6. Corrosion Effects On Vehicle Systems (Results and Interpretation)—An ideal test would cause the same types of corrosion to occur as in the field and at a known, accelerated rate of aging which is consistent for all of a vehicle's components and systems. In practice, this ideal test does not appear to be achievable. Results require interpretation on the basis of experience and knowledge of the effects of a particular test on vehicle systems and/or corrosion mechanisms.

Vehicle components/systems may be classifield into categories according to how they are affected by proving ground test environments. Categories would include (a) "closed" systems (for example, the inside of the cooling system, hydraulic system, exhaust system, etc.), (b) "open" systems (for example, exterior of body panels and other fully exposed parts), and (c) "semi-closed" systems (for example, interior of body panels, poultice accumulation areas where contaminants are not flushed away and/or where drying is inhibited).

7. Closed Systems—Environmental contaminants (salt, dirt, humidity, etc.) typically do not reach the interior of a closed system; hence, proving ground corrosion tests have little effect on internal corrosion of this type of system. In the field, periods of non-use are a large portion of a vehicle's life, and this time contributes significantly to internal corrosion in closed systems. Unless an internal corrosion mechanism occurs primarily while a vehicle is being driven (such as cavitation or erosion in the cooling system), it should be assumed that corrosion is not accelerated for these areas; that is, an "accelerated" corrosion test which requires six months to complete provides only six months of corrosion aging of closed systems.

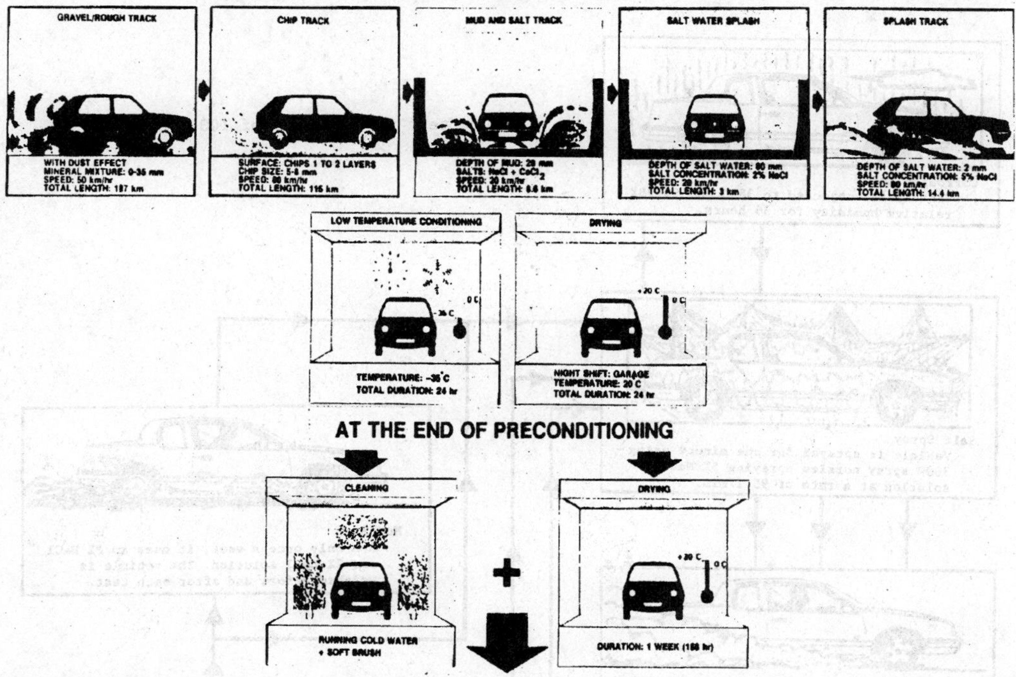

FIGURE 6A—VW CORROSION TEST PROCEDURE EK2 PRECONDITIONING (DURATION: FOUR DAYS)

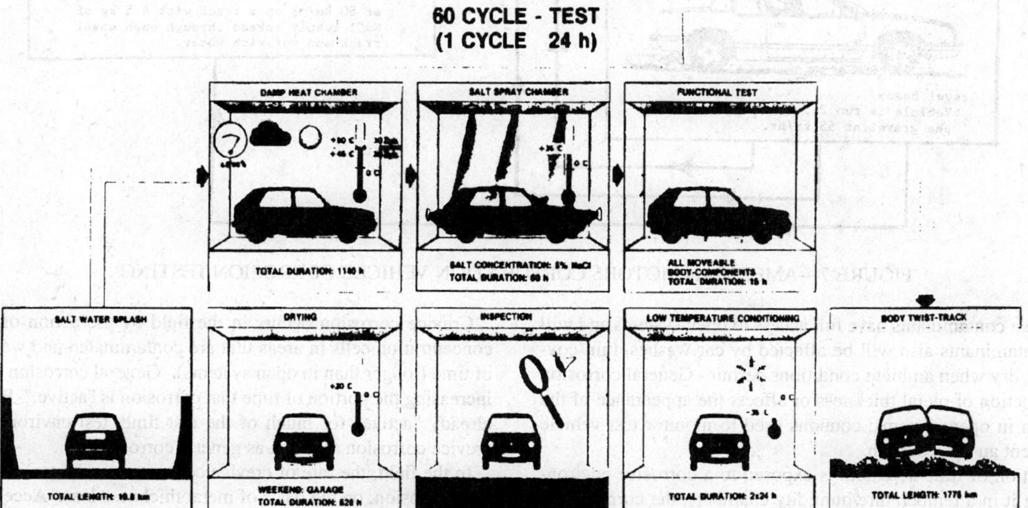

FIGURE 6B—VW CORROSION TEST PROCEDURE EK2 60 CYCLE—TEST (1 CYCLE 24 H)

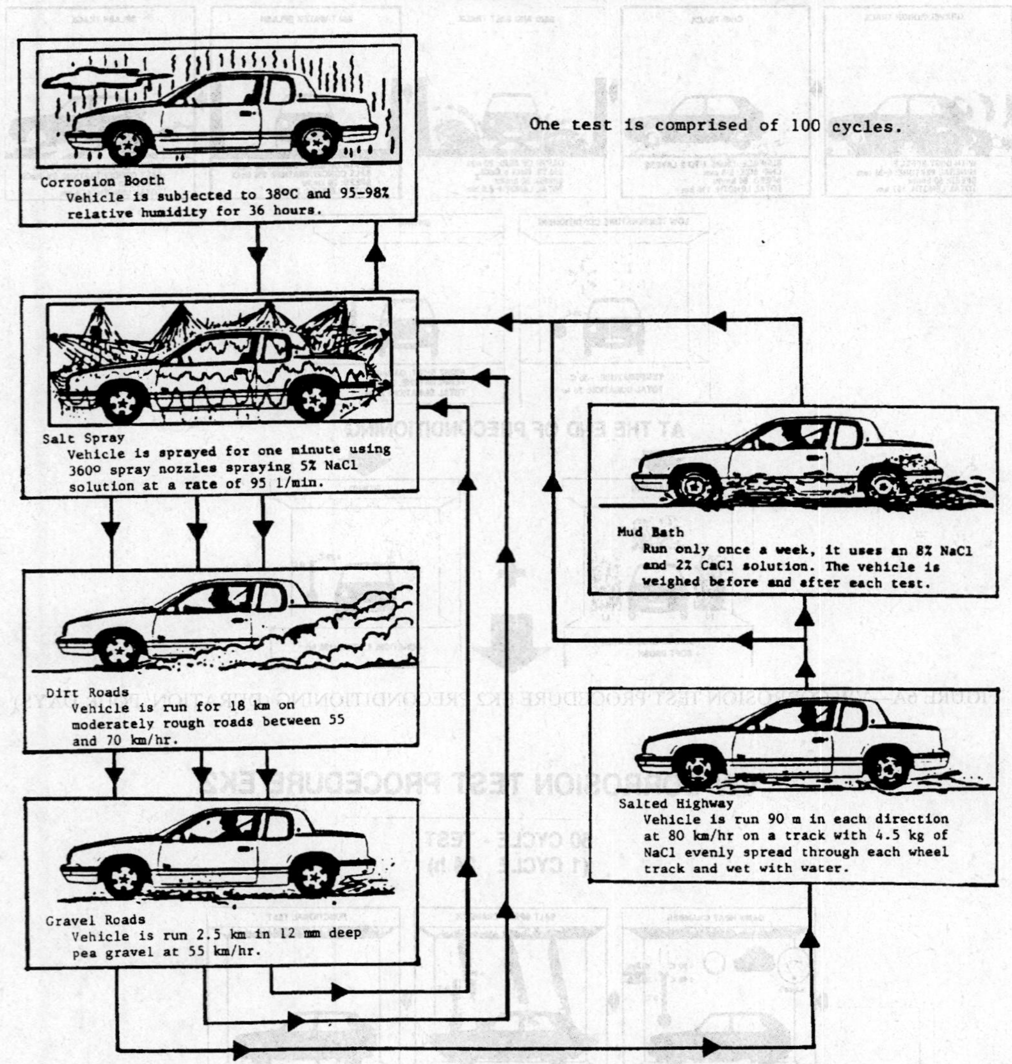

AMERICAN MOTORS CORPORATION
VEHICLE CORROSION TESTING
One test is comprised of 100 cycles.
Corrosion Booth
Vehicle is subjected to 38°C and 95-98% relative humidity for 36 hours.
Salt Spray
Vehicle is sprayed for one minute using 360° spray nozzles spraying 5% NaCl solution at a rate of 95 l/min.
Dirt Roads
Vehicle is run for 18 km on moderately rough roads between 55 and 70 km/hr.
Gravel Roads
Vehicle is run 2.5 km in 12 mm deep pea gravel at 55 km/hr.
Mud Bath
Run only once a week, it uses an 8% NaCl and 2% CaCl solution. The vehicle is weighed before and after each test.
Salted Highway
Vehicle is run 90 m in each direction at 80 km/hr on a track with 4.5 kg of NaCl evenly spread through each wheel track and wet with water.

FIGURE 7—AMERICAN MOTORS CORPORATION VEHICLE CORROSION TESTING

8. Open Systems—Test contaminants have full access to open systems and will be deposited there. Contaminants also will be affected by car washes, rain-covered roads, etc., and will dry when ambient conditions permit. General corrosion that causes uniform reduction of metal thickness or affects the appearance of the vehicle is most common in open systems; coupons used to monitor test vehicle corrosion usually represent an open system.

By increasing the portion of time a vehicle is exposed to a corrosive environment (that is, by placing it in a temperature/humidity chamber), the corrosion of open systems can be greatly accelerated. A full year of general corrosion in the field can be produced in as little as one week, an acceleration factor of 52:1. If the test contains reasonable contaminant levels, temperatures, wet/dry cycles, and durability inputs (vibration, stress, etc.), then there is some degree of confidence that general corrosion of steel coupons is indicative of general corrosion of a vehicle's bare metal components and of cosmetic corrosion at defects in coated surfaces.

9. Semi-closed Systems—These are areas where crevice corrosion is likely to occur and can cause metal perforation. Contaminants may have easy access to these areas or be somewhat restricted. Removal or drying of contaminants is difficult.

Crevice corrosion occurs in the field by the action of differential aeration or concentration cells in areas that are contaminated and wet for substantial periods of time (longer than in open systems). General corrosion is accelerated in tests by increasing the portion of time that corrosion is "active." Because crevice areas are already "active" for much of the test time, test environments do not accelerate crevice corrosion as much as general corrosion.

In the field, the rate of crevice corrosion can be ten or more times that of general corrosion, on the basis of metal thickness loss. Accelerated corrosion testing greatly decreases this ratio, and a knowledgeable interpretation of results is required. If a given test produces five "equivalent years" of general or cosmetic corrosion, the perforation "age" for this test will be less than five years. In this regard, the test procedures used by automotive manufacturers may produce different equivalence between one type of corrosion and another.

10. Salt Concentration Concerns—The amount of contaminants applied to a test vehicle can markedly affect the acceleration of different corrosion mechanisms. Consider the effect of salt concentration on general steel corrosion and on corrosion of sacrificial coatings or powered electrical connectors (Figure 8) from experiments performed at the General Motors Proving Ground. The general steel corrosion rate is limited by electrolyte oxygen solubility and ion mobility, and decreases as salt concentration increases (past about 3% NaCl). Sacrificial and electrical corrosion increase with increasing electrolyte conductivity (proportional to salt content). From Figure 8, it can be seen that a given amount of general corrosion could be provided by either of two salt concentrations, while only one concentration would provide the "correct" result for sacrificial/electrical corrosion. Vehicle tests must use proper contamination levels in order to provide confidence that consistent acceleration is provided to as many different corrosion mechanisms as possible.

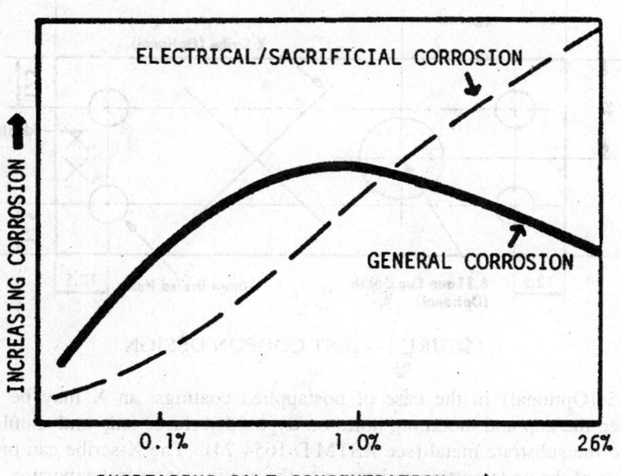

FIGURE 8—EFFECT OF SALT CONCENTRATION ON CORROSION RATES ALTERNATE SALT EXPOSURE (ATOMIZED SPRAY), HUMIDITY EXPOSURE (100% RH, 38 °C) AND DRYING (LABORATORY AMBIENT).

11. Proving Ground Test Limitations—If an experimental/new material performs worse on test than a field proven material, one can be fairly confident that it also will perform worse in the field. However, if the new material performs the same as or better than the old, its field performance cannot be predicted with complete confidence due to uncertain effects of test environments on the new material. (No test includes all possible types and combinations of field environments.) In this sense, unfamiliar or new materials cannot "pass" a proving ground test; the best they can do is "not fail."

Degradation of organic protective coatings is a significant item which generally is not accelerated by proving ground test environments to as great a degree as metallic corrosion. Yet organic coatings often are a major part of a corrosion protection system; they significantly affect an "incubation period" for crevice/perforation corrosion. As an example, asphalt-based deadeners which were used on some cars in the 1960's performed well on proving ground tests, but after some years in the field, they were found to have dried and cracked, possibly accelerating crevice corrosion.

12. Field-to-test Correlation—The success of any test procedure is determined by how well test results agree with field experience. In practice, this often is difficult to assess because (1) vehicles currently being tested may have different corrosion protection systems than vehicles which have been in the field for several years, and (2) test procedures may have been changed in an effort to make them more accelerated or realistic. Corrosion expertise and engineering judgment often must be used to estimate the degree of field-to-test correlation. Examples of techniques which have been and are being used by automotive manufacturers to define test procedures and determine their success are as follows:

a. Corrosion Coupons: Bare steel coupons have been used for many years, in many areas of the United States and Canada. They are attached to many different types of vehicles (taxis, police cars, customers' cars, etc.). These data have been used to determine test general corrosion objectives (targets for amount of general coupon corrosion at various points in a test) and to determine "severe" field corrosion areas (where coupons corrode fastest) to be used for fleets and/or field surveys. Field coupon studies have been expanded in some instances to include metals other than steel. Types of coupons used include those described in SAE J1293 as well as other configurations designed to provide galvanic and/or crevice corrosion.

b. Metal Thickness Measurements: Thickness measurements of bare steel components on randomly-selected field vehicles have been used to supplement coupon data. There is some uncertainty associated with this technique, however, because original (uncorroded) metal thickness usually is not precisely known. Body panel thickness measurements, using an ultrasonic thickness gauge, have been used to determine potential field perforation areas and corrosion rates in general.

c. Contaminant Measurements: The amount of salt deposited at various points on field vehicles has been measured by placing collectors on customers' cars, then periodically removing and analyzing the collectors for salt content. This technique has been used by at least one manufacturer to develop representative proving ground salt splash and spray facilities and exposure procedures. Techniques used by Volvo to measure several different environmental factors simultaneously have been described by Ericsson, et al. (See Reference 2.)

d. Paint Scribes: The paint is frequently scribed to bare metal on test vehicles, and occasionally on field fleet vehicles, in order to evaluate a system's resistance to undercutting corrosion. Special painted panels often are scribed and exposed on proving ground tests and in the field to compare paint systems' performance and to check field-to-test correlation. A major field-to-test difference which has been observed since the advent of electrophoretic primer paints concerns filiform corrosion. This type of underfilm corrosion, which occurs at relative humidity greater than about 70% but less than 95%, usually is not evident on test vehicles which are exposed to environmental chambers at 100% relative humidity.

e. Field Surveys: Surveys are conducted on randomly selected vehicles in snowbelt areas such as Detroit, Erie, Buffalo, Montreal, and in coastal areas such as Miami and Newfoundland. The purpose is not only to check test results and predictions but also to ensure that there are no problem areas undetected by testing. Surveys also are used to monitor environmental degradation of items which cannot be monitored on proving ground tests, such as paint dulling or discoloration of plastic. In surveying, it must be remembered that vehicle repainted areas or perforation repairs, if done well, may be almost indistinguishable from the original material. If undetected, repair areas can cause errors in survey results.

f. Fleets: Monitoring of field fleet vehicles serves essentially the same purposes as random field surveys. However, fleets may offer the advantage of many similar vehicles driven in similar environments (consistency of performance may be measured), access to repair records (can obtain information other than visual inspection), and the opportunity to install and monitor experimental components.

Fleets may be privately owned (taxi cabs, police, phone company, etc.) or may be owned by an automotive company and leased to a fleet operator.

13. Summary—Proving ground tests are one step in the overall vehicle design and validation process. They are not used to replace good engineering judgment and practice in concept and design but rather to augment this judgment. The tests themselves cannot replace competent personnel. The key to successful testing is a thorough understanding of corrosion mechanisms and environments and knowledge of the limitations of the test that is used.

14. Acknowledgement—The information concerning proving ground test methods and results (other than General Motors) was obtained from discussions with D. D. Walker of Ford, D. K. Kelley of Chrysler, F. E. Yanko of Navistar, J. Hamann of American Motors and V. Venugopal of Volkswagen. Their contributions are gratefully acknowledged.

(R) UNDERVEHICLE COUPON CORROSION TESTS—SAE J1293 JAN1990

SAE Recommended Practice

Report of the SAE Iron and Steel Technical committee, approved January 1980. Completely revised by the SAE ACAP Executive Committee January 1990.

Foreword—SAE J1293 was prepared as a recommended practice for evaluating the corrosion resistance of steel in an undervehicle deicing salt environment. This procedure recommended locating samples on the rear control arms of passenger vehicles. Due to the increasing use of unitized body designs, alternative sample mounting locations are needed. This revised procedure recommends the use of undervehicle corrosion coupon racks attached to the chassis frame of a straight truck or box truck (without a detachable trailer), which also enables a larger number of samples to be evaluated. This revision is based on techniques reported by Neville and de Souza (see ASM 8512-004).

1. Scope—This document is a road test procedure for comparing the corrosion resistance of both coated and uncoated sheet steels in an undervehicle deicing salt environment.

2. References

2.1 Applicable Publications—The following publications form a part of the specification to the extent specified herein. Unless otherwise indicated the lastest revision of SAE publications shall apply.

2.1.1 ASM PUBLICATION—Available from ATTN: MSC/Book Order, ASM International, PO Box 473, Novelty, OH 44072-9901.

R. J. Neville and K. M. de Souza, Undervehicle Corrosion Testing of Zinc and Zinc Alloy Coated Steels. American Society for Metals, Technical Paper Series No. 8512-004 (1985).

2.1.2 SAE PUBLICATION—Available from SAE, 400 Commonwealth Drive, Warrendale, PA 15096-0001.

R. J. Neville, Results of a Test for Undervehicle Corrosion Resistance (SAE Task Force, Iron and Steel Technical Committee, Division 32), SAE Paper 800144 (February 1980).

2.1.3 ASTM PUBLICATIONS—Available from ASTM, 100 Barr Harbor Drive, West Conshohocken, PA 19428-2959.

ANSI/ASTM E 643-78—Method of Conducting a Ball Punch Deformation Test for Metallic Sheet Material

ASTM D 1654-74—Evaluation of Painted or Coated Specimens Subjected to Corrosive Environments

ANSI/ASTM G 1-81—Standard Practice for Preparing, Cleaning and Evaluating Corrosion Test Specimens

ANSI/ASTM A 90-69—Tests for Weight of Coating on Zinc-Coated (Galvanized) Iron or Steel Articles

3. Background—A single result from one test material exposed on a given rack should not be compared to a single result from a test material exposed on another rack. A suggestion for an evaluation would be to use a minimum of two vehicles with random placement of the panels on each test rack and then averaging the results. However, the ranking of test materials from rack-to-rack should be similar.

The key features of this test are:

a. Measurement of steel substrate corrosion rather than coating failure.

b. Both exposed and crevice test conditions.

c. Realistic comparison of precoated and postapplied coated material.

The reliability and reproducibility of the test are demonstrated in ASM 8512-004 and SAE Paper 800144.

4. Method—The test method described herein should be followed carefully and any deviations reported, as they may influence the results.

4.1 Test Materials

4.1.1 New coatings should be evaluated using a standard coated steel for which sufficient data have been previously generated (i.e., hot dip galvanized steel). Low carbon mild steel (uncoated) may be included to indicate the severity of the test environment.

4.2 Test Coupon Preparation

4.2.1 Sample thickness is optional but should be similar in a given test where galvanic edge protection is a consideration. Steel coupons, 50 x 125 mm (2 x 5 in), can be sheared directly from prefinished sheet. Postapplied coatings are applied after test coupon assembly (See 4.3).

4.2.2 Prepare each test coupon as shown in Figure 1.

4.2.3 Identify coupons as shown in Figure 1 by XX.

4.2.4 (Optional) If sample thickness and mechanical properties are appropriate, a ball punch deformation test (see Reference 3) may be drawn so that the coupons nest properly as follows: ball diameter, 22.2 mm (7/8 in); upper die diameter, 25.4 mm (1.0 in); and depth, 6.35 mm (0.250 in). The cup provides an indication of leading surface abrasion and formability.

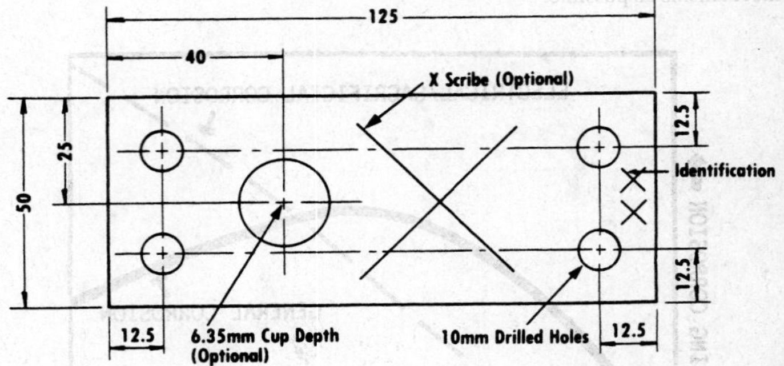

FIGURE 1—TEST COUPON DESIGN

4.2.5 (Optional) In the case of postapplied coatings, an X may be scribed between the cup and mounting holes on exposed surfaces only and should penetrate to the substrate metal (see ASTM D 1654-74). The X-scribe can provide a measure of the undercutting resistance of the coatings after test exposure.

4.2.6 (Optional) Bare steel coupon weights of precoated materials can be estimated by nondestructively measuring coating thickness and subtracting the weight calculated from this thickness (knowing coating density) from the total coupon weight.

Alternatively, a more accurate procedure is to evaluate the coating weight using a weigh-strip-weigh technique of an adjacent (scrap) piece of the precoated steel. This requires weighing of the sample, chemically removing the coating (See 5.4.4 and 5.5.3) and reweighing. The weight of the coating is then subtracted from the total (sample) coupon weight.

The base steel coupon weights of precoated materials should be recorded in milligrams.

4.2.7 (Optional) Weigh metallic coated coupons and record total coupon weight in milligrams. These data are required for coating weight loss determination when the steel substrate is not attacked during the exposure interval.

4.3 Test Coupon Assembly

4.3.1 Assemble the test coupons as shown in Figure 2 (one-sided coated steels) and Figure 3 (two-sided coated steels). To ensure that the perforation of the one-sided coated steels does not progress from the uncoated surface, the uncoated surface should be protected with an air-dry spray lacquer and electroplater's tape.

4.3.2 Use 10 mm I.D. x 15 mm O.D. x 0.25 mm thick polyethylene shims. For postapplied coatings, select a temperature resistance material, such as mica, to withstand the high temperature bake.

4.3.3 The 6.35 mm (1/4 in) I.D. Neoprene rubber grommets, selected to withstand paint bake temperatures, can be obtained from an electrical supply house. A typical assembly for the rubber grommet is given in Figure 4. The rubber grommets are necessary to isolate the test samples from the metal bolts.

4.3.4 Apply postapplied coatings to the coupon assembly after assembling the coupons as shown in Figures 2 or 3. It will be necessary to have longer bolts (secured by a nut) at one end of the assembly to hold the assembly together during postcoating. Another nut and washer would be necessary to secure the assembly to the support rack (Figures 2 and 3).

4.4 Test Rack Assembly

4.4.1 A typical test rack assembly is shown in Figure 5. This figure displays recommended sample spacing. Coupon assemblies can be cantilevered off of both sides of the support bar to increase the number of available test sites.

4.5 Test Rack Mounting

4.5.1 Select a vehicle with expected high driving frequency.

4.5.2 Mount the test rack on the straight truck chassis frame as shown in Figures 6a and 6b. The test racks should be located such that the coupons are horizontal, and are unlikely to receive mechanical damage. Avoid direct impingement of exhaust gases on the test coupons.

4.5.3 Record mounting date and odometer reading.

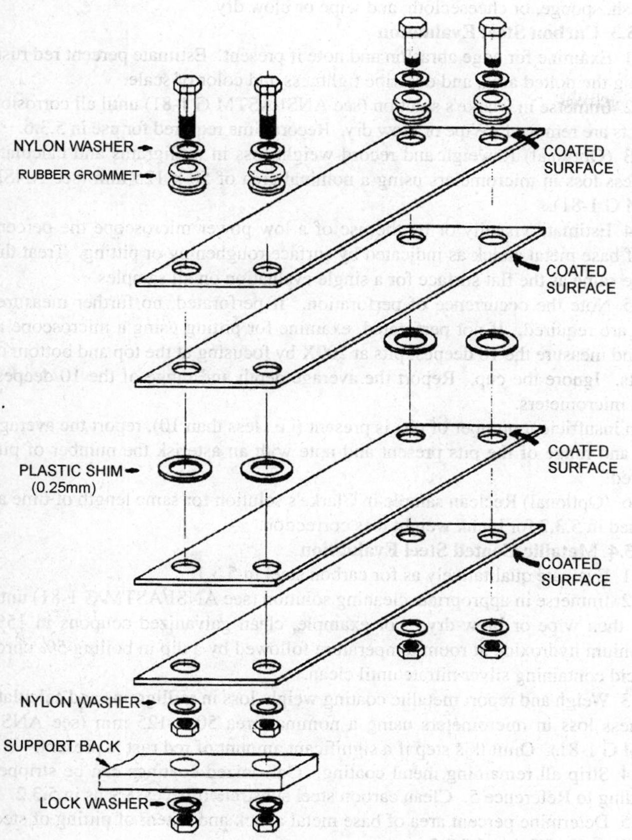

FIGURE 2—ONE-SIDED COATED STEELS COUPON ASSEMBLY

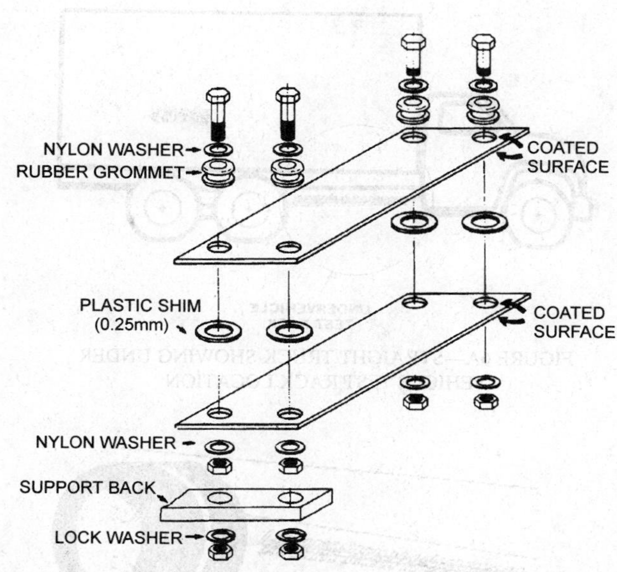

FIGURE 3—TWO-SIDED COATED STEELS COUPON ASSEMBLY

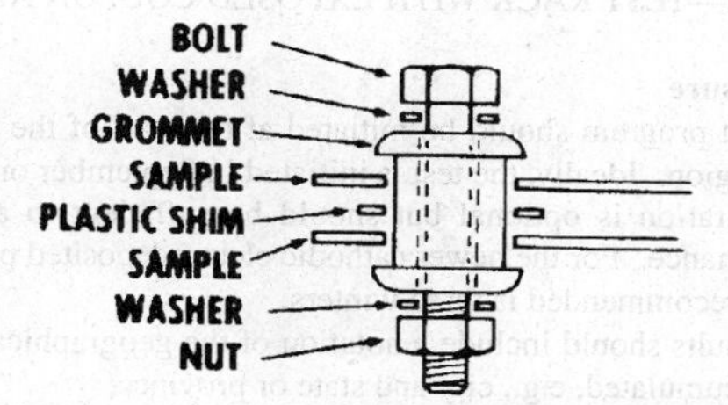

FIGURE 4—TYPICAL RUBBER GROMMET ASSEMBLY

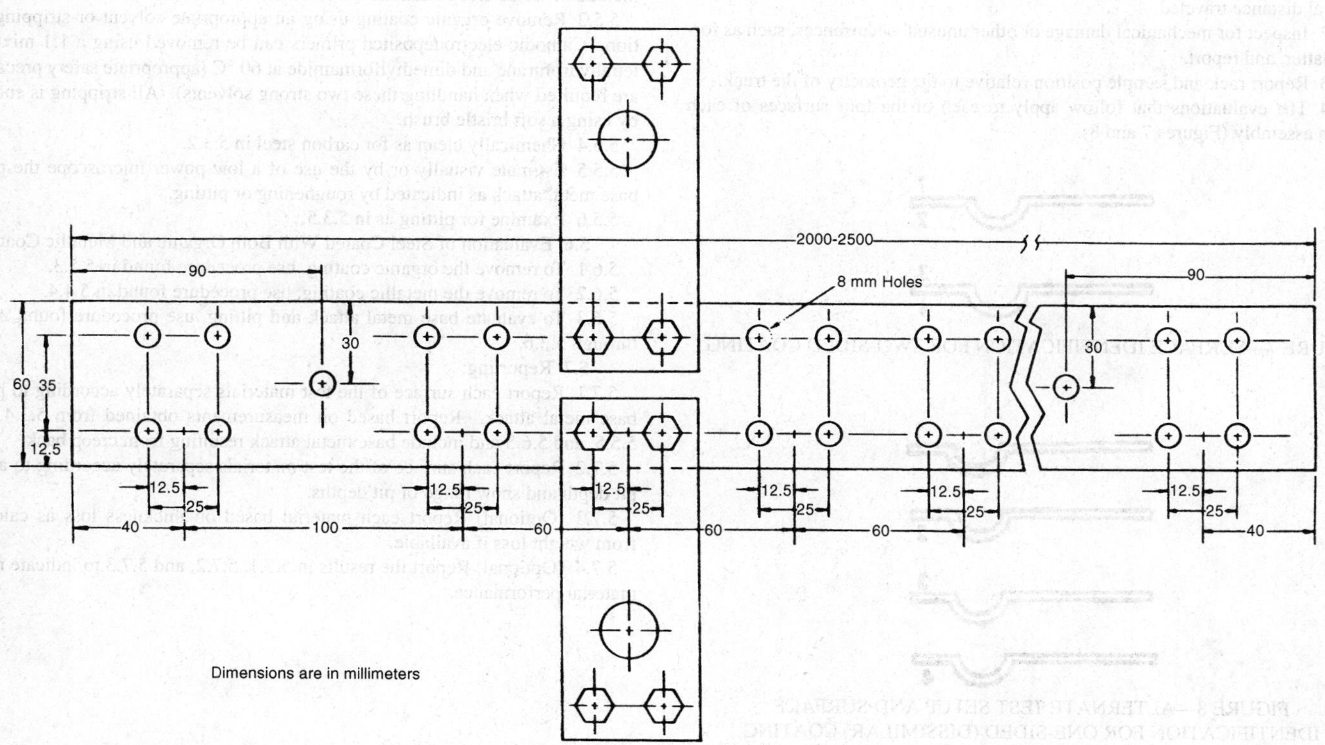

FIGURE 5—TYPICAL TEST RACK ASSEMBLY WITH TWO SAMPLES - TOP VIEW

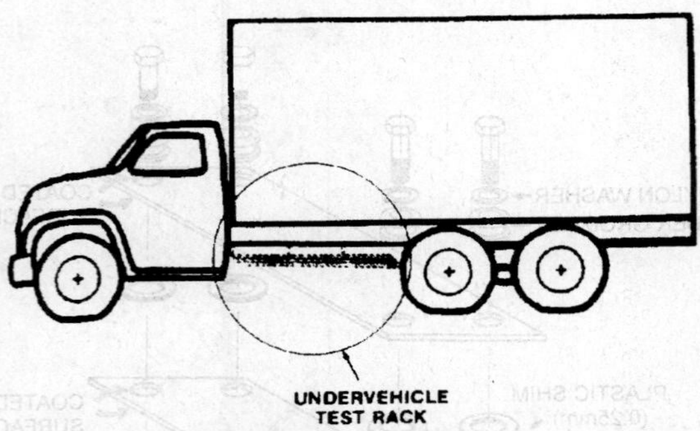

FIGURE 6A—STRAIGHT TRUCK SHOWING UNDER VEHICLE TEST RACK LOCATION

FIGURE 6B—TEST RACK WITH EXPOSED COUPON ASSEMBLIES

4.6 Exposure

4.6.1 The test program should be initiated at the start of the winter season in the snow belt region. Ideally, the test is initiated in September or October.

4.6.2 Test duration is optional but should be sufficient to allow ranking of material performance. For the newer cathodic electrodeposited primers, the minimum exposure recommended is three winters.

4.6.3 Test results should include a notation of the geographical area where the mileage was accumulated, e.g., city and state or province.

5. Evaluation

5.1 General Inspection Before Disassembly

5.1.1 Record removal date, calculate total exposure time on vehicle in days, and total distance traveled.

5.1.2 Inspect for mechanical damage or other unusual occurrences, such as foreign matter, and report.

5.1.3 Report rack and sample position relative to the geometry of the truck.

5.1.4 The evaluations that follow apply to each of the four surfaces of each coupon assembly (Figures 7 and 8).

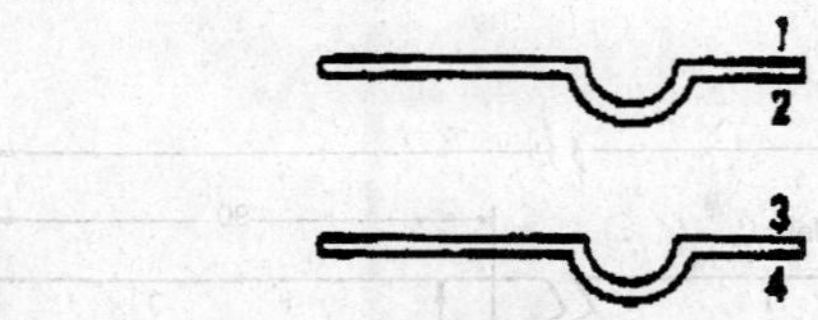

FIGURE 7—SURFACE IDENTIFICATION FOR TWO-SIDED COATING

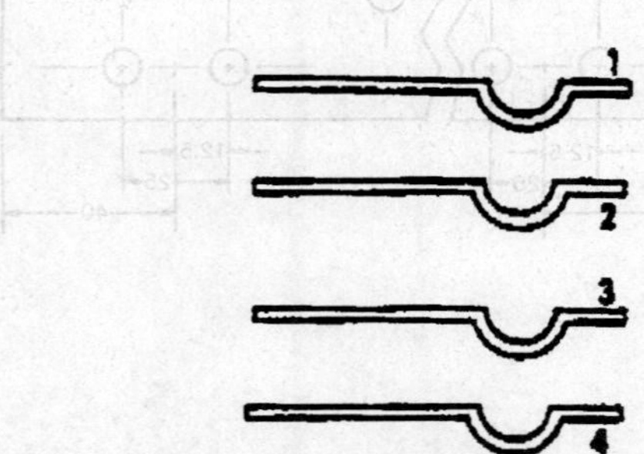

FIGURE 8—ALTERNATE TEST SETUP AND SURFACE IDENTIFICATION FOR ONE-SIDED (DISSIMILAR) COATING

5.2 Initial Cleaning—Wash each panel with warm water using a nonmetallic brush, sponge, or cheesecloth, and wipe or blow dry.

5.3 Carbon Steel Evaluation

5.3.1 Examine for edge abrasion and note if present. Estimate percent red rust, ignoring the bolted area, and describe tightness and color of scale.

5.3.2 Immerse in Clarke's solution (see ANSI/ASTM G 1-81) until all corrosion products are removed. Wipe or blow dry. Record time required for use in 5.3.6.

5.3.3 (Optional) Reweigh and record weight loss in milligrams and calculate thickness loss in micrometers using a nominal area of 50 x 125 mm (see ANSI/ASTM G 1-81).

5.3.4 Estimate visually or by the use of a low power microscope the percent area of base metal attack as indicated by surface roughening or pitting. Treat the cup the same as the flat surface for a single evaluation on all samples.

5.3.5 Note the occurrence of perforation. If perforated, no further measurements are required. If not perforated, examine for pitting using a microscope at 10X and measure the 10 deepest pits at 200X by focusing at the top and bottom of the pits. Ignore the cup. Report the average depth and range of the 10 deepest pits in micrometers.

If an insufficient number of pits is present (i.e., less than 10), report the average depth and range of the pits present and note with an asterisk the number of pits involved.

5.3.6 (Optional) Reclean sample in Clarke's solution for same length of time as recorded in 5.3.2 for blank weight loss correction.

5.4 Metallic Coated Steel Evaluation

5.4.1 Evaluate qualitatively as for carbon steel in 5.3.1.

5.4.2 Immerse in appropriate cleaning solution (see ANSI/ASTM G 1-81) until clean, then wipe or blow-dry. For example, clean galvanized coupons in 15% ammonium hydroxide at room temperature followed by a dip in boiling 5% chromic acid containing silver nitrate until clean.

5.4.3 Weigh and report metallic coating weight loss in milligrams and calculate thickness loss in micrometers using a nominal area 50 x 125 mm (see ANSI/ASTM G 1-81). Omit this step if a significant amount of red rust is present.

5.4.4 Strip all remaining metal coating. Galvanized coatings can be stripped according to Reference 5. Clean carbon steel substrate if necessary as in 5.3.2.

5.4.5 Determine percent area of base metal attack and extent of pitting of steel substrate as in 5.3.4 and 5.3.5.

5.5 Organic Coated Steel Evaluation

5.5.1 Evaluate qualitatively as for carbon steel in 5.3.1.

5.5.2 If the coating was scribed, measure total width of creep back from the scribe and record half of the maximum width in millimeters. Note, (but do not include in scribe creep back measurements), the presence of filiform corrosion.

5.5.3 Remove organic coating using an appropriate solvent or stripping solution. Cathodic electrodeposited primers can be removed using a 1:1 mixture of tetrahydrofurane and dimethylformamide at 60 °C (appropriate safety precautions are required when handling these two strong solvents). All stripping is enhanced by using a soft bristle brush.

5.5.4 Chemically clean as for carbon steel in 5.3.2.

5.5.5 Estimate visually or by the use of a low power microscope the percent base metal attack as indicated by roughening or pitting.

5.5.6 Examine for pitting as in 5.3.5.

5.6 Evaluation of Steel Coated With Both Organic and Metallic Coatings:

5.6.1 To remove the organic coating, use procedure found in 5.5.3.

5.6.2 To remove the metallic coating, use procedure found in 5.4.4.

5.6.3 To evaluate base metal attack and pitting, use procedure found in 5.3.2 through 5.3.6.

5.7 Reporting:

5.7.1 Report each surface of the test materials separately according to percent base metal attack. Report based on measurements obtained from 5.3.4, 5.4.5, 5.5.5, and 5.6.3 and include base metal attack resulting from creep back.

5.7.2 Report each surface of the test materials separately according to average pit depth and show range of pit depths.

5.7.3 (Optional) Report each material based on thickness loss as calculated from weight loss if available.

5.7.4 (Optional) Report the results in 5.7.1, 5.7.2, and 5.7.3 to indicate relative material performance.

GUIDELINES FOR LABORATORY CYCLIC CORROSION TEST PROCEDURES FOR PAINTED AUTOMOTIVE PARTS—SAE J1563 OCT1993

SAE Information Report

Report of the SAE AUtomotive Corrosion and Prevention Comimittee approved May 1987. Completely Irevised by the SAE Automotive Corrosion and Prevention Committee Division3 October 1993. Rationale statement available.

Foreword—This Document has not changed other than to put it into the new SAE Technical Standards Board Format.

In cyclic corrosion testing, test specimens are exposed to at least three different types of environmental conditions:

and cycled from one environment to another. Intentional paint film damage prior to testing, such as scribing or exposure to gravelometer, is usually an essential part of the test procedure. The cyclic tests make use of many types of environments, such as ASTM B 117 salt spray, immersion in a salt solution, or an exposure to hot and/or cold conditions. A humid environment or water immersion of the test specimens is included in most tests. In some cases, a thin layer of clay is applied to the specimen surface.

a. Corrosive Solutions
b. Wet Conditions
c. Dry Conditions

The diagram in Figure 1 is an example of a cyclic test which consists of three environment types:

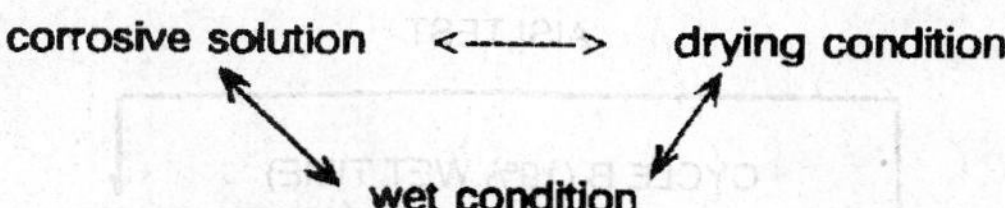

FIGURE 1—CYCLIC TEST ENVIRONMENT TYPES

1. Scope—These guidelines are intended for those engineers and scientists who evaluate the corrosion performance of painted automotive parts in laboratory cyclic tests. The guidelines are intended to help ensure that the results of the tests can be used to reach conclusions concerning the variables under study without being confounded by the test procedure itself. The guidelines also serve as a means to assist users of this type of test in obtaining good inter-laboratory agreement of results.

2. References

2.1 Applicable Publications—Many companies have their own accepted cyclic tests and the companies should be contacted for the one appropriate for the end use in question. SAE and AISI are engaged in a cooperative effort to develop a universal cyclic test for cosmetic corrosion. Progress in that direction is documented in the papers listed in 2.2.2 which were presented at the SAE Corrosion Conference in 1989 and 1991.

The following publications form a part of this specification to the extent specified herein. The latest issue of SAE publications shall apply.

2.1.1 SAE PUBLICATIONS—Available from SAE, 400 Commonwealth Drive, Warrendale, PA 15096-0001.

SAE J400—Test for Chip Resistance of Surface Coatings

2.1.2 ASTM PUBLICATIONS—Available from ASTM, .

ASTM B 117-90—Method of Salt Spray (Fog) Testing

ASTM D 1193-77 (1983)—Specification for Reagent Water

ASTM D 1654-79a (1984)—Method for Evaluation of Painted or Coated Specimens Subjected to Corrosive Environments

2.2 Related Publications—The following publications are provided for information purposes only and are not a required part of this document.

2.2.1 ASTM PUBLICATIONS—Available from ASTM, 100 Barr Harbor Drive, West Conshohocken, PA 19428-2959.

ASTM D 2247-87—Practice for Testing Water Resistance of Coatings in 100% Relative Humidity

ASTM D 2933-74 (986)—Test Method for Corrosion Resistance of Coated Steel Specimens (Cyclic Method)

2.2.2 OTHER PUBLICATIONS

M. L. Stephens, "SAE ACAP Division 3 Project: Evaluation of Corrosion Test Methods," Paper No. 892571, Automotive Corrosion and Prevention Conference Proceedings, P-228. Society of Automotive Engineers, Warrendale, PA (1989), pp. 157–164.

H. E. Townsend, "Status of a Cooperative Effort by the Automotive and Steel Industries to Develop a Standard Accelerated Corrosion Test," Paper No. 892569, ibid., pp. 133–145.

F. Blekkenhorst, "Hoogovens' Contribution to AISI Program "Accelerated Corrosion Testing: A Cooperative Effort by the Automotive and Steel Industries," Paper No. 892570, ibid., pp. 147–156.

M. Petschel, Jr., "SAE ACAP Division 3 Project: Evaluation of Corrosion Test Results and Correlation with Two-Year, On-Vehicle Field Results," Paper No. 912283, Automotive Corrosion and Prevention Conference Proceedings, P-250, Society of Automotive Engineers, Warrendale, PA (1991), pp. 179–203.

R. J. Neville, W.A. Schumacher, D. C. McCune, R. D. Granata and H.E. Townsend, "Progress by the Automotive and Steel Industries Toward an Improved Laboratory Cosmetic Corrosion Test," Paper No. 912275, ibid., pp. 73–98.

F. Blekkenhorst, "Further Developments Toward a Standard Accelerated Corrosion Test for Automotive Materials," Paper No. 912277, ibid., pp. 99–114.

D. D. Davidson and W. A. Schumacher, "An Evaluation and Analysis of Commonly Used Accelerated Cosmetic Corrosion Tests Using Direct Comparisons with Actual Field Exposure," Paper No. 912284, ibid., pp. 205–220.

3. History—In 1914 Mr. J. A. Capp proposed the use of neutral salt spray for the corrosion evaluation of protective coatings on ferrous surfaces. Over the last 70 years this neutral salt spray test was accepted as a standard method for testing painted automotive body panels. Although there have been many modifications and refinements to this test over the years, there is now general agreement that this test does not predict "real world" corrosion. As the demand for improved corrosion protection increased, engineers and scientists have developed cyclic testing procedures that more accurately predict the corrosion of materials used on vehicles.

4. Sample Preparation—Prior to testing, the type of specimen surface and the panel preparation should be agreed to by personnel involved, and should simulate actual production materials and conditions. The number of test specimens selected should be sufficient to ensure that the test results are statistically significant at some predetermined confidence level. Any unusual observations made during panel preparation should be recorded and reported as part of the test results.

In addition to the test specimens, control panels (panels of known performance in the test conducted) should be tested concurrently. It is preferred that control panels be provided which bracket the expected test panel performance. The controls will allow the normalization of test conditions during repeated running of the test and will also allow comparison of test results from different repeats of the test.

5. Paint Film Damage—The gravelometer or a scribing tool is used to provide damage to coating layers in cyclic testing. To assure consistent results, the procedure shown in SAE J400 should be followed when a gravelometer test is used. Scribing of test specimens should be agreed upon by the parties concerned. It is especially important that the scribe tool be agreed upon since scribe geometry can affect the results of the test.

It has been noted that a variance in scribe depth can affect the results of cyclic testing. This variation of test results due to scribe differences can be significant. For example, test results for galvanized steel specimen are known to fluctuate depending on scribing tool type and scribe depth. It is recommended that the scribe depth penetrate into the base metal. A microscopic investigation of scribe geometry can be used to characterize the scribe.

6. Control of Test Conditions—To assure consistency of results, the uniformity of the test conditions should be established on a periodic basis by placing identical test panels at various locations in the test equipment. If poor repeatability of results is observed, the test equipment should be brought up to the specification cited in the test procedure.

7. Test Equipment Variables and Precautions

a. Corrosive Environment Including Chloride
b. Ambient Environment
c. Non-ambient Environment
   1. High humidity environment
   2. High temperature environment
   3. Low temperature environment
d. Water Immersion
e. Surface Contamination

7.1 Corrosive Environment—This environment could include an aqueous solution of one or more of the following at various concentrations:

Sodium Chloride
Calcium Chloride
Calcium Bicarbonate
Sodium Bicarbonate
Sodium Sulfate
Sodium Metabisulfite
Sodium Nitrate
Calcium Carbonate
Magnesium Carbonate
Sodium Phosphate

a. Concentration: Typically Up to 5%
b. pH: 4 to 8
c. Temperature ±3 °C of the stated temperature for the cycle.

The solution may become contaminated with corrosion products. To assure consistent results, the solution should be monitored and changed on a regular basis.

7.2 Ambient Environment

a. Relative Humidity: Less than or equal to 50%

This ambient exposure condition should consist of an environment which is free of corrosive vapors, for example, acidic and alkaline fumes. Air movement should not be excessive. The ambient conditions should be monitored and recorded for each test.

7.3 Non-Ambient Environment—Non-ambient temperature and relative humidity control limits should be held to the following tolerances to achieve consistent results:

a. Temperature: ± 2 °C
b. Relative Humidity: ± 5%

The temperature and relative humidity should be monitored. It is suggested that automatic control systems be used.

7.4 Water Immersion—Distilled or deionized water should be used as make-up in this step (see ASTM D 1193). The container should be made of inert material. The immersion bath should be controlled to:

a. pH: 6 to 8
b. Relative Temperature: 24 °C ± 3 °C
c. Conductivity: < 50 µS/cm at 25 °C

To assure consistent results, the water should be changed on a regular basis.

7.5 Surface Contamination—When surface contamination of the painted test surface is used, care should be taken to assure that the contamination conforms to predetermined standards. Kaolin clay is suitable as a surface contaminant.

8. Test Procedure—Precautions

8.1 Racking—Panels should be racked so that there is no metal-to-metal contact between them. The racks used in any of the cycles should be constructed to have nonconductive contact surfaces. The angle of exposure and the panel orientation specified in the test should be followed for consistency and repeatability of test results.

8.2 Loading Level—To assist in obtaining good repeatability, test equipment should be loaded evenly to maintain good air flow during the test.

8.3 Test Interruptions—In situations where the test cycle has to be interrupted due to equipment malfunction or holiday breaks, the test panels should be stored under the least corrosive conditions available, for example, during a dry cycle or a freeze cycle. Preferably, test interruptions should not exceed 5 days but all interruptions and handling of panels should be reported.

8.4 Ramp Time—Transition between conditions is considered ramp time. Ramp time from condition to condition can be a critical factor affecting results. Depending on type of equipment used and cabinet loading, ramp time may vary and should be monitored and recorded.

9. Rating/Reporting

9.1 Panel Preparation for Rating—Conditions for panel rating vary. Panels may be rinsed, soaked, taped, blasted with air or scraped. Because paint systems differ in the rate of recovery of their physical properties after testing, agreed upon preparation methods should be conducted according to a specified sequence and time limit.

9.2 Rating—The rating system used to report the corrosion which occurs in a cycle test should be agreed upon prior to testing. ASTM D 1654 is an example of a possible system to be used. Corrosion within 6 mm of a cut edge should be disregarded unless otherwise agreed upon.

10. Recommendations—Test cycles for the tests which most successfully correlated with field results for cosmetic corrosion are shown in Figures 2 to 4. They may not be suitable for all material applications since the testing emphasized coated steels and was limited to cosmetic corrosion.

See references under 2.2.2 and AISI Corrosion Task Force.

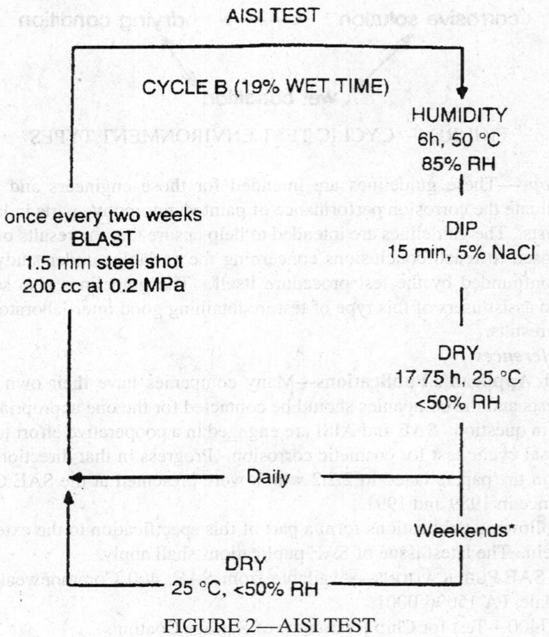

AISI TEST

CYCLE B (19% WET TIME)

HUMIDITY
6h, 50 °C
85% RH

once every two weeks
BLAST
1.5 mm steel shot
200 cc at 0.2 MPa

DIP
15 min, 5% NaCl

DRY
17.75 h, 25 °C
<50% RH

Daily

Weekends*

DRY
25 °C, <50% RH

FIGURE 2—AISI TEST

CCT – IV

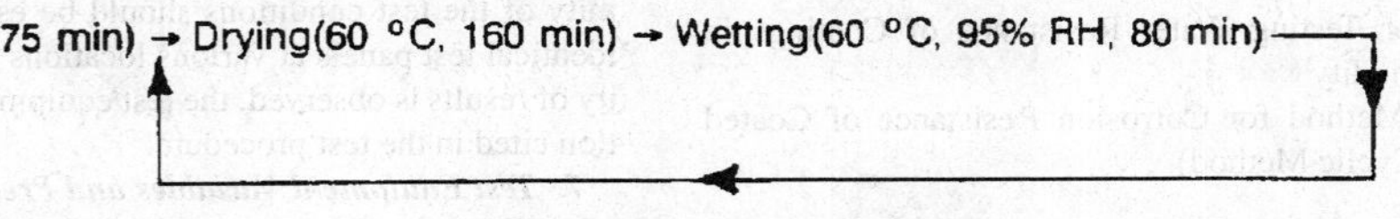
Salt spray(35°C, 10 min) → drying(60°C, 155 min) → wetting(60 °C, 95% RH,
75 min) → Drying(60 °C, 160 min) → Wetting(60 °C, 95% RH, 80 min)

Repeat Five Times

FIGURE 3—CCT-IV TEST

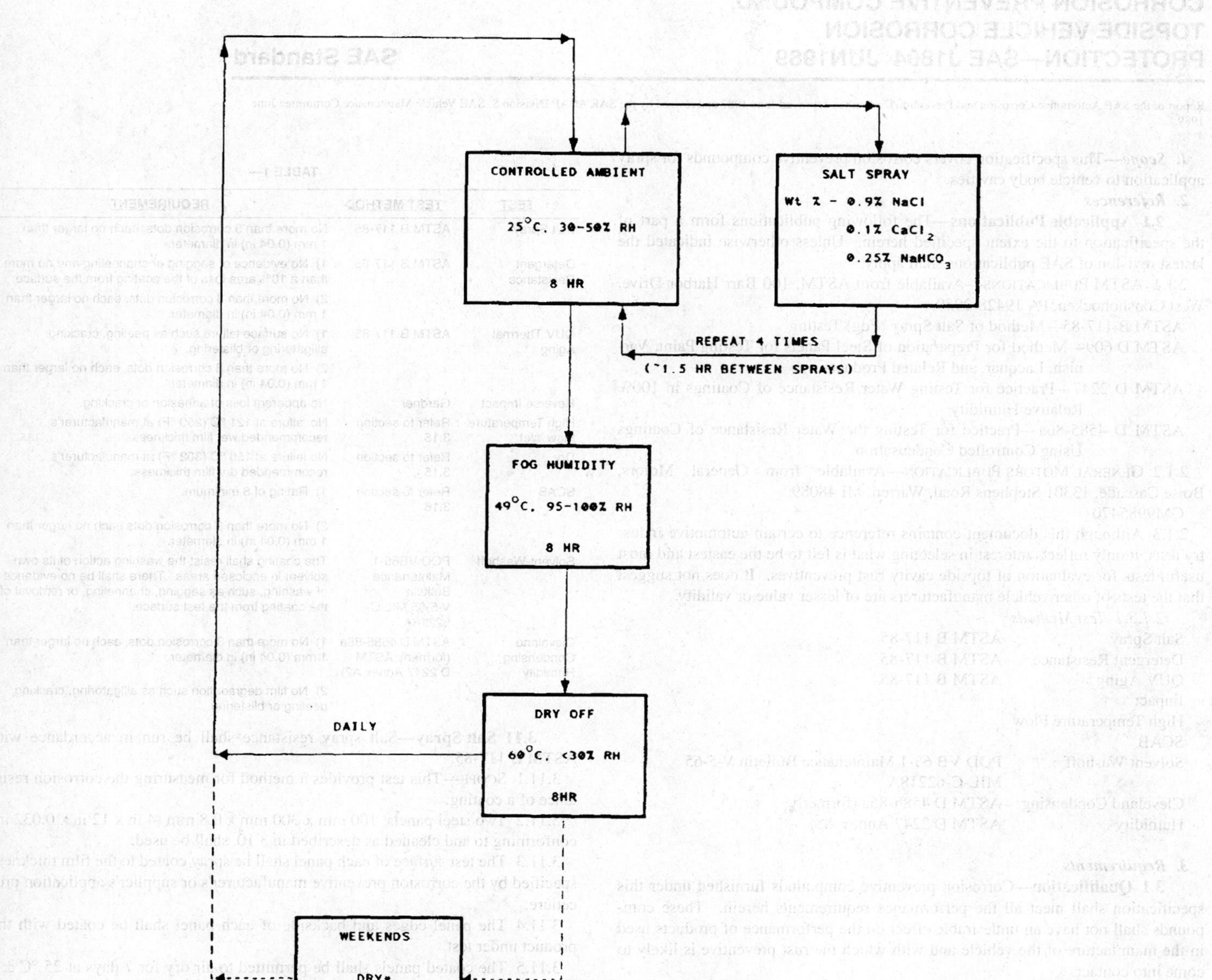

FIGURE 4—9540 P TEST (METHOD B)

CORROSION PREVENTIVE COMPOUND, TOPSIDE VEHICLE CORROSION PROTECTION—SAE J1804 JUN1989

SAE Standard

Report of the SAE Automotive Corrosion and Prevention Committee approved June 1987 and revised by the SAE ACAP Division S, SAE Vehicle Maintenance Committee June 1989.

1. Scope—This specification covers corrosion preventive compounds for spray application to vehicle body cavities.

2. References

2.1 Applicable Publications—The following publications form a part of the specification to the extent specified herein. Unless otherwise indicated the lastest revision of SAE publications shall apply.

2.1.1 ASTM PUBLICATIONS—Available from ASTM, 100 Barr Harbor Drive, West Conshohocken, PA 19428-2959.

ASTM B 117-85—Method of Salt Spray (Fog) Testing

ASTM D 609—Method for Preparation of Steel Panels for Testing Paint, Varnish, Lacquar, and Related Products

ASTM D 2247—Practice for Testing Water Resistance of Coatings in 100% Relative Humidity

ASTM D 4585-86a—Practice for Testing the Water Resistance of Coatings Using Controlled Condensation

2.1.2 GENERAL MOTORS PUBLICATION—Available from General Motors, Boise Cascade, 13301 Stephens Road, Warren, MI 48089.

GM9985470

2.1.3 Although this document contains reference to certain automotive industry tests, it only reflects interest in selecting what is felt to be the easiest and most useful tests for evaluation of topside cavity rust preventives. It does not suggest that the tests of other vehicle manufacturers are of lesser value or validity.

2.1.3.1 Test Methods

Salt Spray	ASTM B 117-85
Detergent Resistance	ASTM B 117-85
QUV Aging	ASTM B 117-85
Impact	
High Temperature Flow	
SCAB	
Solvent Washoff	POD VB 65-1 Maintenance Bulletin V-5-65 MIL-C-62218A
Cleveland Condensing Humidity	ASTM D 4585-86a (formerly ASTM D 2247 Annex A2)

3. Requirements

3.1 Qualification—Corrosion preventive compounds furnished under this specification shall meet all the performance requirements herein. These compounds shall not have an undesirable effect on the performance of products used in the manufacture of the vehicle and with which the rust preventive is likely to come into contact.

3.1.1 Any change in formulation shall necessitate requalification.

3.2 Material—The corrosion preventive compound may be a water based or solvent based product which is fluid, homogeneous, free from grit and abrasives, and non-toxic.

3.3 Film Characteristic—The corrosion preventive compound shall readily adhere to surfaces commonly encountered in underbody and inner body cavities of vehicles. The film shall not exhibit evidence of alligatoring, cracking, peeling, blistering, humidity condensate wash-off, or other degradation.

3.4 Color—None specified.

3.5 Sprayability and Low Temperature Fluidity—The rust preventive compound shall be sprayable from 10 to 38 °C (50 to 100 °F).

3.6 Condition in Container—The compound shall exhibit no settling, separation, skinning, or lumpiness.

3.7 Low Temperature Stability—The compound shall show no evidence of separation or nonhomogeneity at a temperature as low as –29 °C (–20 °F).

3.8 Manufacturer's recommended application procedure(s) shall ensure that the film thickness required for performance compliance with this specification be achieved in field application.

3.9 When tested as specified, the compound shall conform to the following requirements at the manufacturer's recommended film thickness for actual field application.

3.10 Panel Preparation—The panels used for evaluation of rust preventives against this specification shall conform to ASTM D 609-73, Type 1, and shall be prepared by Methods B or D according to that standard.

TABLE 1—

TEST	TEST METHOD	REQUIREMENT
Salt Spray	ASTM B 117-85	No more than 3 corrosion dots, each no larger than 1 mm (0.04 in) in diameter.
Detergent Resistance	ASTM B 117-85	1) No evidence of sagging or channeling and no more than a 10% area loss of the coating from the surface.
		2) No more than 3 corrosion dots, each no larger than 1 mm (0.04 in) in diameter.
QUV Thermal Aging	ASTM B 117-85	1) No surface failure such as peeling, cracking, alligatoring or blistering.
		2) No more than 3 corrosion dots, each no larger than 1 mm (0.04 in) in diameter.
Reverse Impact	Gardner	No apparent loss of adhesion or cracking.
High Temperature Flow Wet	Refer to section 3.15	No failure at 121 °C (250 °F) at manufacturer's recommended wet film thickness.
Dry	Refer to section 3.15	No failure at 150 °C (302 °F) at manufacturer's recommended dry film thickness.
SCAB	Refer to section 3.16	1) Rating of 8 minimum.
		2) No more than 3 corrosion dots each no larger than 1 mm (0.04 in) in diameter.
Solvent-Washoff	POD VB65-1 Maintenance Bulletin V-5-65 MIL-C-62218A	The coating shall resist the washing action of its own solvent in enclosed areas. There shall be no evidence of washing, such as sagging, channeling, or removal of the coating from the test surface.
Cleveland Condensing Humidity	ASTM D 4585-86a (formerly ASTM D 2247 Annex A2)	1) No more than 3 corrosion dots, each no larger than 1 mm (0.04 in) in diameter.
		2) No film degradation such as alligatoring, cracking, peeling or blistering.

3.11 Salt Spray—Salt spray resistance shall be run in accordance with ASTM B 117-85.

3.11.1 SCOPE—This test provides a method for measuring the corrosion resistance of a coating.

3.11.2 Two steel panels, 100 mm x 300 mm x 0.8 mm (4 in x 12 in x 0.032 in) conforming to and cleaned as described in 3.10, shall be used.

3.11.3 The test surface of each panel shall be spray coated to the film thickness specified by the corrosion preventive manufacturer's or supplier's application procedure.

3.11.4 The panel edges and backside of each panel shall be coated with the product under test.

3.11.5 The coated panels shall be permitted to air dry for 7 days at 25 °C ± 2 (77 °F ± 5).

3.11.6 The coated panels shall be unscribed, and exposed in salt spray for 1000 h as described in section 3.11.

3.11.7 After exposure, the coating shall be stripped from the panels using an appropriate solvent and the surface examined for compliance with the requirement in 3.9. Corrosion at the outer 6.35 mm (0.25 in) of the panel shall not be included in the panel rating.

3.12 Detergent Resistance

3.12.1 This test provides a method for measuring the resistance of the coating to removal by detergent wash and its ability to protect against corrosion after exposure to detergent washes.

3.12.2 Two steel panels as described in 3.11.2 shall be coated as described in 3.11.3 and 3.11.4 and conditioned as described in 3.11.5.

3.12.3 The coated panels shall be immersed in detergent solution at 50 °C (122 °F). (The detergent solution shall be composed of 2.5 g/L of DuPont #7 Car Wash Compound or Bordens Rain Dance Car Wash.) Rinse under spray nozzle (Spray Systems Co., Full Jet # 1/2 GG-25 or equivalent) at 50 °C (122 °F) water temperature, 70 kPa (10 psi) water pressure and 250 mm (10 in) distance between the spray nozzle and the panel per the following cycle:

Immersion - 5 min
Rinse - 1 min
Immersion - 10 min
Rinse - 2 min
Immersion - 10 min
Rinse - 2 min

3.12.4 Criteria for a pass shall be no evidence of sagging or channeling and no more than 10% loss of coating from the surface.

3.12.5 If the coated panels pass the detergent wash and rinse according to 3.12.4, they shall then be exposed in salt spray in accordance with ASTM B 117-85 for 168 h.

3.12.6 After salt spray exposure, the panels shall be evaluated for compliance in the same manner as in 3.11.7.

3.13 QUV Thermal Aging

3.13.1 SCOPE—This test provides a method to determine the resistance of the coating to oxidative degradation.

3.13.2 Two steel panels as described in 3.11.2 shall be coated as described in 3.11.3 and 3.11.4 and conditioned as described in 3.11.5. For the apparatus which cannot take 100 mm x 300 mm x 0.8 mm (4 in x 12 in x 0.032 in) panels, 75 mm x 300 mm x 0.8 mm (3 in x 12 in x 0.032 in) panels can be used.

3.13.3 The coated panels shall be exposed for 100 h in the QUV cabinet using the following cycle:

a. Ultraviolet lights "on"
Temperature : 50 °C (122 °F)
Time : 8 h

b. Ultraviolet lights "off"
100% Humidity (condensing)
Temperature : 46 °C (114.8 °F)
Time : 4 h
One cycle = 12 h of exposure

3.13.4 The cycle in 3.13.3 shall be repeated 8 times with the extra 4 h being ultraviolet exposure. Panel exposure shall always be started at the beginning of the ultraviolet light "on" portion of the cycle.

3.13.5 The criteria for passing the 100 h QUV exposure shall be no evidence of alligatoring, cracking, peeling, or blistering.

3.13.6 If the coated panels pass QUV exposure, they shall be exposed to salt spray in accordance with ASTM B 117-85 for 336 h.

3.13.7 After salt spray exposure, the panels shall be evaluated in the same manner as in 3.11.7.

3.14 Impact

3.14.1 SCOPE—This test provides a method to measure the adhesion of the coating to the substrate when subjected to impact at low temperature.

3.14.2 The apparatus used in this test is the Gardner Impact Tester or equivalent.

3.14.3 Two steel panels as described in 3.11.2 shall be coated as described in 3.11.3 and conditioned as described in 3.11.5.

3.14.4 The coated panels shall be conditioned at –29 °C (–20 °F) for 24 h. If possible, the Impact Tester shall also be conditioned at –29 °C (–20 °F).

3.14.5 The coated panels shall be impacted with a force of 2.3 J (20 in lb) on the uncoated side (reverse impact) of the panels. The impact test shall be carried out within 30 s after removal from the cold chamber.

3.14.6 The criteria for meeting the requirement of this specification shall be no cracking or loss of adhesion.

3.15 High Temperature Flow

3.15.1 SCOPE—This test provides a method to determine the high temperature flow resistance of wet and dry films of the rust preventive.

3.15.2 APPARATUS

3.15.2.1 Multinotch Applicator

3.15.2.1.1 The applicator is designed to lay down at least eight strips of coating of graduating thickness. The space between the strips shall be 1.6 mm (0.0625 in). A typical applicator of this type is a Leneta Antisag Meter or equivalent.

3.15.2.1.2 An applicator shall be chosen to draw down wet film thicknesses in the range recommended for application by the manufacturer or supplier.

3.15.2.2 Oven

3.15.2.2.1 A well ventilated, thermostatically controlled convection type oven shall be used. The oven shall be capable of being controlled through a temperature range of 20 °C ± 3 to 150 °C ± 3 (68 °F ± 5 to 302 °F ± 5).

3.15.2.3 Test panels shall conform to ASTM D 609 Type 1 as described in 3.11.2 and shall be cleaned with mineral spirits as described in ASTM D 609 Method D.

3.15.3 PROCEDURE

3.15.3.1 Application of Film

3.15.3.1.1 Sufficient rust preventive shall be applied by spatula or eyedropper at one edge of the test panel to cover the range of film thicknesses when applied by the multinotch applicator described in 3.15.2.11 and 3.15.2.1.2.

3.15.3.1.2 The multinotch applicator shall be drawn through the applied test material in one smooth movement such that the strips of rust preventive left on the panel shall be straight and without any waviness.

3.15.4 WET FILM PERFORMANCE

3.15.4.1 Immediately after the coating has been drawn down as in 3.15.3.1.1 and 3.15.3.1.2, the test panel shall be placed vertically such that the rust preventive strips are horizontal to the ground and with the thickest strip in the lowest position. The panel shall be left in this position for 5 min at 25 °C ± 3 (77 °F ± 5).

3.15.4.2 The test panel shall then be placed vertically in an oven as described in paragraph 3.15.2.2 at 121 °C ± 3 (250 °F ± 5) for 20 min. The thickest strip shall be in the lowest position.

3.15.4.3 Evaluation of Results—After removal of the test panel from the oven exposure described in 3.15.4.2, the strip of coating which sags or flows sufficiently to cross into the next thicker strip of coating shall be considered the thickness at which failure occurs. There shall be no failure at the manufacturer's or supplier's recommended wet film thickness.

3.15.5 DRY FILM PERFORMANCE

3.15.5.1 Immediately after the film has been applied and drawn-down, as in 3.15.3.1.1 and 3.15.3.1.2, the test panel shall be placed vertically such that the rust preventive strips are horizontal to the ground and with the thickest strip in the lowest position. The test panel shall be stored in this position for 7 days at 25 °C ± 3 (77 °F ± 5).

3.15.5.2 The test panel shall then be placed vertically in an oven as described in 3.15.2.2.1 at 150 °C ± 3 (300 °F ± 5) for 20 min. The thickest strip shall be in the lowest position.

3.15.5.3 Evaluation of Results—After removal of the panel from the oven exposure described in 3.15.5.2, the strip of coating which sags or flows sufficiently to cross into the next thicker coating shall be considered the thickness at which failure occurs. There shall be no failure at the manufacturer's or supplier's recommended dry film thickness.

3.16 SCAB Test

3.16.1 SCOPE—This test provides a method of measuring the corrosion resistance of a coating.

3.16.2 Two steel panels as described in 3.11.2 shall be coated as described in 3.11.3 and 3.11.4 and conditioned as described in 3.11.5.

3.16.3 After conditioning panel as described in 3.11.5 and prior to exposure, each test surface shall be diagonally scribed to 25 mm (1 in) from either corner. A straight edge shall be used to guide the scribing instrument, which can be a carbide tip scribe tool or a sharp knife. The scribe shall be made with sufficient pressure to cut completely through the coating and expose a bright line of bare metal.

3.16.4 Place the test panels with the 300 mm (12 in) dimension horizontal in a suitable wood or plastic rack. The rack shall hold panels at a 0 to 15 deg angle from the vertical and the panels shall be spaced a minimum of 13 mm (0.5 in) apart.

3.16.5 The racked panels shall be placed in test and the following procedures performed on a weekly basis.

a. Monday Only
— 1 h in a 60 °C ± 1 (140 °F ± 2) oven
— 30 min in a –23 °C (–10°F) cold cabinet
— 15 min immersion in 5% by weight sodium chloride solution
— 1 h 15 min drain at room temperature
— 21 h in a controlled humidity cabinet operating at 60°C ± 1 (140 °F ± 2) and 85% RH

b. Tuesday through Friday
— 15 min immersion in 5% by weight sodium chloride solution
— 1 h 15 min drain at room temperature
— 22 1/2 h in a controlled humidity cabinet operating at 60 °C ± 1 (140 °F ± 2) and 85% RH

c. Saturday/Sunday
— Samples remain in the humidity cabinet operating as above

3.16.6 The test panels shall be exposed to 30 cycles in the exposure described in 3.16.5. A + B + C constitutes 5 cycles.

3.16.7 After completion of the 30 cycles, the panels shall immediately be rinsed with warm flowing water not exceeding 38°C (100°F).

3.16.8 Within 15 min of removal from the exposure test, the test panel shall be air blown along the entire scribe line and any other points of indicated failure with a nozzle held lightly against and approximately 45 deg to the surface. The air supply shall be capable of obtaining an open line pressure of 550 kPa (80 psi) through a nozzle with a 3.0 mm (0.12 in) orifice. The length of hose between the nozzle and the air regulator shall be less than 3 m (10 ft) and it is recommended that the inside diameter of the hose shall be between 6 mm and 10 mm (0.25 in and 0.375 in).

3.16.9 EVALUATION

3.16.9.1 To evaluate the creepback, the distance between the unaffected coating on each side of the scribe line shall be measured to the nearest mm in several places. Each value shall be divided by two and then a mean value calculated. The number of measurements shall be dependent on the uniformity of corrosion creepback. A minimum rating of 8 shall constitute a pass using the following rating scale:

Rating	Corrosion Creepback (mm)
10	0
9	0 to less than 0.5
8	0.5 to less than 1.5
7	1.5 to less than 2.5
6	2.5 to less than 3.5
5	3.5 to less than 5.0
4	5.0 to less than 6.5
3	6.5 to less than 8.0
2	8.0 to less than 10.0
1	10.0 to less than 12.0
0	12.0 and greater

3.16.9.2 Field corrosion shall be evaluated in the same manner as in 3.11.7 and shall meet the same compliance requirement.

3.17 Solvent Washoff

3.17.1 SCOPE—To determine resistance of the coating to be washed off in enclosed areas by reflux action from its own solvent.

3.17.2 EQUIPMENT—An empty cylindrical, tin plated 0.946 L (1 qt) paint can shall be affixed, approximately centered, to the bottom or inside face of the cover for a cylindrical tin plated 3.785 L (1 gal) paint can. Joining may be by bolting or soldering. The bottom or seam closed end of the 0.946 L (1 qt) can shall be away from the 3.785 L (1 gal) cover plate. Two 25 mm (1 in) holes shall be drilled in the sides of the cylindrical, tin plated 3.785 L (1 gal) paint can:

1. one hole centered 63 mm (2.5 in) from the top edge of the can and
2. one hole centered 25 mm (1 in) from the bottom chime of the can and on the side opposite the upper hole. The upper half of the outer face of the 3.785 L (1 gal) can shall be insulated, leaving an opening over the 25 mm (1 in) hole.

3.17.3 TEST PROCEDURE—A wet film, meeting the manufacturer's or supplier's recommended application thickness, shall be sprayed-applied uniformly onto the entire outside face of the sides and bottom of an empty cylindrical, tin-plated 0.946 L (1 qt) paint can. The film shall not exceed a dry film thickness of 0.15 mm (0.006 in). The coated test piece shall be conditioned for 2 h at a temperature of 25 °C ± 3 (77 °F ± 5). At the end of this period, a 6.3 mm (0.25 in) layer of the test compound shall be poured into the bottom of the 3.785 L (1 gal) can and the 3.785 L (1 gal) can cover tightly affixed with the coated 0.946 L (1 qt) can test piece suspended inside the 3.785 L (1 gal) can. The entire test assembly shall be placed in an oven stabilized at 121 °C ± 3 (250 °F ± 5). After 15 min residence time in the oven maintained at 121 °C ± 3 (250 °F ± 5), the test assembly shall be removed from the oven and allowed to cool at room temperature for 15 min. The cover shall be removed from the 3.785 L (1 gal) can and the test piece withdrawn and inspected.

3.17.4 Criteria for a pass shall be in conformance with the requirement in 3.9.

3.18 Cleveland Condensing Humidity

3.18.1 SCOPE—This test provides a measure of the resistance of the coating to cyclic conditions of condensing humidity and dry-off.

3.18.2 EQUIPMENT—Cleveland Condensing Humidity Cabinet.

3.18.3 PANEL PREPARATION—Two steel panels as described in 3.11.2 shall be coated as described in 3.11.3 and 3.11.4 and conditioned as described in 3.11.5.

3.18.4 The panels shall be positioned in the cabinet in conformance with ASTM D 4585-86a (formerly ASTM D 2247 Annex A2).

3.18.4.1 The coated flat panels with straight and coated or taped edges shall be butted together with the test side facing down across the top of the cabinet. Properly installed, the panels will be in a slightly sloped position to return excess condensation to the water tank without running on other test panels.

3.18.5 CYCLIC TEST CONDITIONS—A cycle shall consist of 3 h of continuous condensation and 3 h of air dry-off. Four cycles shall be performed every 24 h.

3.18.6 CABINET CONDITIONS

3.18.6.1 The temperature of the saturated air during continuous condensation shall be 38 °C ± 1 (100 °F ± 2).

3.18.6.2 There shall be 100% relative humidity with continuous condensation on the test panels 50% of the time.

3.18.6.3 The cabinet shall be allowed to equilibrate to ambient conditions during the dry-off cycle(s).

3.18.7 The test panels shall be examined daily. If there is evidence of film degradation (for example, cracking, peeling, alligatoring, or blistering) prior to 1 000 h, the test shall be terminated and that point considered as the time to failure.

3.18.8 After a total of 1 000 h, the test panels shall be removed from test, allowed to stand for 24 h in an atmosphere of 25 °C ± 1 (77 °F ± 2) having a relative humidity of 50% ± 5.

3.18.9 The test panels shall be evaluated in the same manner as in 3.11.7.

Copies of POD Specification VB-65-1 Maintenance Bulletin V-5-65 can be obtained by writing to:

Director
Engineering and Facilities Division
Post Office Department
Washington, DC

CORROSION PREVENTIVE COMPOUND, UNDERBODY VEHICLE CORROSION PROTECTION—SAE J1959 SEP2003

SAE Standard

Report of the SAE Automotive Corrosion and Prevention Committee approved June 1989 and reaffirmed September 2003.

Foreword—This Document has not changed other than to put it into the new SAE Technical Standards Board Format.

1. Scope—This specification covers underbody corrosion preventive compounds for application to vehicle underbodies.

2. References

2.1 Applicable Publications—This document contains reference to certain automotive industry tests, it only reflects interest in selecting what is felt to be the easiest and most useful tests for evaluation of rust corrosion preventatives, and does not suggest that the tests of other vehicle manufacturers are of lesser value or validity.

2.1.1 SAE PUBLICATION—Available from SAE, 400 Commonwealth Drive, Warrendale, PA 15096-0001.

SAE J400 JAN85—Test for Chip Resistance of Surface Coatings

2.1.2 ASTM PUBLICATIONS—Available from ASTM, 100 Barr Harbor Drive, West Conshohocken, PA 19428-2959.

ASTM B 117-85—Method of Salt Spray (Fog) Testing

ASTM D 609—Method for Preparation of Steel Panels for Testing Paint, Varnish, Lacquer, and Related Products

ASTM D 1654—Method for Evaluation of Painted or Coated Specimens Subjected to Corrosive Environments

ASTM D 2243—Test Method for Freeze-Thaw Resistance of Latex and Emulsion Paints

ASTM D 4585-86a—Practice for Testing the Water Resistance of Coatings Using Controlled Condensation

2.1.3 FEDERAL AND MILITARY PUBLICATION—U. S. Government, DOD SSP, Subscription Service Division, Building 4D, 700 Robbins Avenue, Philadelphia, PA 19111-5094.

MIL-C-52218A—Corrosion Preventative Compound, Cold Application

3. Requirements

3.1 Qualification—Underbody corrosion preventive compounds furnished under this specification shall meet all the performance requirements herein. These compounds are likely to contact products used in the manufacture of the vehicle. These compounds shall not have an undesirable effect on the performance of the products.

3.1.1 Any change in formulation shall necessitate requalification.

3.2 Material—The corrosion preventive compound may be a water-based or solvent-based product which is fluid, homogeneous, free from extraneous grit and abrasives, and nontoxic.

3.3 Film Characteristic—The corrosion preventive compound shall readily adhere to surfaces commonly encountered in underbody of vehicles. The film shall not exhibit evidence of alligatoring, cracking, peeling, blistering, or other degradation.

3.4 Color—None specified.

3.5 Sprayability and Low Temperature Fluidity—The underbody corrosion preventive compound shall be sprayable from 10 – 38 °C (50 – 100 °F).

3.6 Condition in Container—The compound shall exhibit no settling, separation, skinning, or lumpiness.

3.7 Low Temperature Stability

3.7.1 The solvent-based compounds shall show no evidence of separation or nonhomogeneity at a temperature as low as –29 °C (–20 °F) according to MIL-C-62218A, 4.7.13.

3.7.2 The water-based compounds shall show no evidence of separation or nonhomogeneity after five freeze/thaw cycles according to ASTM D 2243.

3.8 Manufacturers' or suppliers' recommended application procedure(s) shall ensure that the film thickness required for performance compliance with this specification be achieved in field application.

3.9 When tested as specified, the compound shall conform to the following requirements at the manufacturers' recommended film thickness for actual field application:

TEST	TEST METHOD	REQUIREMENT
Salt Spray	ASTM B 117–85	1) No more than three corrosion dots, each no larger than 1 mm (0.04 in) in diameter. 2) Scribe rating of 8 per ASTM D 1654.
SCAB	Refer to 3.12	1) Rating of 8 minimum. 2) No more than three corrosion dots, each no larger than 1 mm (0.04 in) in diameter.
Cleveland Condensing Humidity	ASTM D 4585–86a (formerly D 2247–68)	1) No more than three corrosion dots, each no larger than 1 mm (0.04 in) in diameter. 2) No film degradation such as alligatoring, cracking, peeling or blistering.
Gravelometer/Salt Spray	SAE J400/ASTM B 117–85	1) Less than 5% face corrosion.

3.10 Panel Preparation—The panels used for evaluation of underbody corrosion preventives against this specification shall conform to ASTM D 609, Type 1, and shall be prepared by Methods B or D according to that standard.

3.11 Salt Spray—Salt spray resistance shall be run in accordance with ASTM B 117-85.

3.11.1 SCOPE—This test provides a method for measuring the corrosion resistance of a coating.

3.11.2 Two steel panels, 100 x 300 x 0.8 mm (4 x 12 x 0.032 in) conforming to and cleaned as described in 3.10, shall be used for each scribed and unscribed set.

3.11.3 The test surface of each panel shall be coated to the film thickness specified by the corrosion preventive manufacturers' or suppliers' application procedure.

3.11.4 The panel edges and backside of each panel shall be coated with the product under test.

3.11.5 The coated panels shall be permitted to air dry for seven days at 25 °C ± 2 (77 °F ± 5).

3.11.6 One set each of coated scribed and unscribed panels shall be exposed in salt spray for 1000 h as described in 3.11.

3.11.7 After exposure, the coating shall be stripped from the panels using an appropriate solvent and the surface examined for compliance with the requirement in 3.9. Corrosion at the outer 6.35 mm (0.25 in) of the panel shall not be included in the panel rating.

The test panels shall be evaluated in accordance with ASTM D 1654 and shall have a rating number of not less than 8 in both scribed and unscribed areas.

3.12 SCAB Test

3.12.1 SCOPE—This test provides a method of measuring the corrosion resistance of a coating.

3.12.2 Two steel panels as described in 3.11.2 shall be coated as described in 3.11.3 and 3.11.4 and conditioned as described in 3.11.5.

3.12.3 After conditioning panel as described in 3.11.5 and prior to exposure, each test surface shall be diagonally scribed to 25 mm (1 in) from either corner. A straight edge shall be used to guide the scribing instrument, which shall be a sharp knife, made with sufficient pressure to cut completely through the coating and actually cut into the metal, exposing a bright line of bare metal.

3.12.4 Place the test panels with the 300 mm (12 in) dimension horizontal in a suitable wood or plastic rack. The rack shall hold panels at a 0 – 15 deg angle from the vertical and the panels shall be spaced a minimum of 13 mm (0.5 in) apart.

3.12.5 The racked panels shall be placed in test and the following procedures performed on a weekly basis:

a. Monday Only
- 1 h in a 60 °C ± 1 (140 °F ± 2) oven
- 30 min in a –23 °C (–10 °F) cold cabinet
- 15 min immersion in 5% by weight sodium chloride solution
- 1 h 15 min drain at room temperature
- 21 h in a controlled humidity cabinet operating at 60 °C ± 1 (140 °F ± 2) and 85% RH

b. Tuesday through Friday
   - 15 min immersion in 5% by weight sodium chloride solution
   - 1 h 15 min drain at room temperature
   - 22 1/2 h in a controlled humidity cabinet operating at 60 °C ± 1 (140 °F ±2) and 85% RH

c. Saturday/Sunday
   - Samples remain in the humidity cabinet operating as above

3.12.6 The test panels shall be exposed to 30 cycles in the exposure described in 3.12.5. a + b + c constitutes five cycles.

3.12.7 After completion of the 30 cycles, the panels shall immediately be rinsed with warm flowing water not exceeding 38 °C (100 °F).

3.12.8 Within 15 min of removal from the exposure test, the test panel shall be air blown along the entire scribe line and any other points of indicated failure with a nozzle held lightly against and approximately 45 deg to the surface. The air supply shall be capable of obtaining an open line pressure of 550 kPa (80 lb/in^2) through a nozzle with a 3.0 mm (0.12 in) orifice. The length of hose between the nozzle and the air regulator shall be less than 3 m (10 ft) and it is recommended that the inside diameter of the hose shall be between 6 mm and 10 mm (0.25 and 0.375 in).

3.12.9 EVALUATION:

3.12.9.1 To evaluate the creepback, the distance between the unaffected coating on each side of the scribe line shall be measured to the nearest mm in several places. Each value shall be divided by two and then a mean value calculated. The number of measurements shall be dependent on the uniformity of corrosion creepback. A minimum rating of 8 shall constitute a pass using the following rating scale:

Rating	Corrosion Creepback (mm)
10	0
9	0 to less than 0.5
8	0.5 to less than 1.5
7	1.5 to less than 2.5
6	2.5 to less than 3.5
5	3.5 to less than 5.0
4	5.0 to less than 6.5
3	6.5 to less than 8.0
2	8.0 to less than 10.0
1	10.0 to less than 12.0
0	12.0 and greater

3.12.9.2 Field corrosion shall be evaluated in the same manner as in 3.11.7 and shall meet the same compliance requirement.

3.13 (Cleveland Condensing Humidity) or CCT

3.13.1 SCOPE—This test provides a measure of the resistance of the coating to cyclic conditions of condensing humidity and dry-off.

3.13.2 EQUIPMENT—Cleveland Condensing Humidity Cabinet.

3.13.3 PANEL PREPARATION—Two steel panels as described in 3.11.2 shall be coated as described in 3.11.3 and 3.11.4 and conditioned as described in 3.11.5.

3.13.4 The panels shall be positioned in the cabinet in conformance with ASTM D 4585-86a (formerly D 2247-68).

3.13.4.1 The coated flat panels with straight and coated or taped edges shall be butted together with the test side facing down across the top of the cabinet. Properly installed, the panels will be in a slightly sloped position to return excess condensation to the water tank without running onto the other test panels.

3.13.5 CYCLIC TEST CONDITIONS—A cycle shall consist of 3 h of continuous condensation and 3 h of air dry-off. Four cycles shall be performed every 24 h.

3.13.6 CABINET CONDITIONS

3.13.6.1 The temperature of the saturated air during continuous condensation shall be 38 °C ±1 (100 °F ±2).

3.13.6.2 There shall be 100% relative humidity with continuous condensation on test panels 50% of the time.

3.13.6.3 The cabinet shall be allowed to equilibriate to ambient conditions during the dry-off cycle(s).

3.13.7 The test panels shall be examined daily. If there is evidence of film degradation (for example, cracking, peeling, alligatoring, or blistering) prior to 1000 h, the test shall be terminated and that point considered as the time of failure.

3.13.8 After a total of 1000 h, the test panels shall be removed from test, allowed to stand for 24 h in an atmosphere of 25 °C ±1 (77 °F ±2) having a relative humidity of 50% ±5.

3.13.9 The test panels shall be evaluated in the same manner as in 3.11.7.

3.14 Gravelometer/Salt Spray Test—Gravelometer shall be run in accordance with SAE J400 and salt spray shall be run in accordance with ASTM B 117-85.

3.14.1 SCOPE—This test provides a method for measuring the corrosion resistance of a coating after it has been subjected to abrasion damage.

3.14.2 Run gravelometer test after conditioning panels 4 h at −30 °C. Age 24 h at room temperature, then subject to 336 h salt spray per ASTM B 117-85.

3.14.3 After testing, the panels shall exhibit less than 5% face corrosion after coating removal. Removal shall be in accordance with 3.11.7.

MICROSCOPIC DETERMINATION OF INCLUSIONS IN STEELS—SAE J422 DEC1983

SAE Recommended Practice

Report of the SAE Iron and Steel Division, approved January 1941, third revision by Division 3, approved by the SAE Iron and Steel Technical Committee December 1983.

Foreword—This Document has not changed other than to put it into the new SAE Technical Standards Board Format.

1. Scope—This recommended microscopic practice for evaluating the inclusion content in steel has been developed as a practical method of quantitatively determining the degree of cleanliness of steel. This method has been established as a reasonable control for steel mill operations and acceptance for production manufacturing. It has been widely accepted for carbon and alloy steel bars, billets, and slabs. Exceptions are resulfurized grades which are outside the limits of these photomicrographs and the high carbon bearing quality steels which are generally classified using ASTM E 45-60T, Method A, Jernkontoret Charts.

2. References—There are no referenced publications specified herein.

3. Preparation of Samples—This microscopic method is based on examination of specimens approximately 160 mm^2 (1/4 in^2) in area [10 x 19 mm (3/8 x 3/4 in)]. The exact dimensions are not of prime importance since the area examined represents an extremely small part of the bar, billet, or heat being evaluated. For bars 40 mm (1-1/2 in) and smaller, the face obtained by cutting from surface to center with the short dimension parallel to the rolling direction is polished and examined. If one-half the diameter is more than 25 mm (1 in), the specimen shall be taken midway between the outside and center. The manner of cutting a specimen from a 38 mm (1-1/2 in) round bar is shown in Fig. 1. A disk, 10 mm (3/8 in) in thickness should be sliced from the bar, the section indicated in Fig. 1 cut out of the disk and the shaded area polished parallel to the direction of rolling.

Bars and billets over 100–150 mm (4–6 in) are normally forged to 100 mm (4 in) square before specimens are obtained from a midway position as described above for bars over 50 mm (2 in). This is illustrated in Fig. 2. The area that shall be polished is shown shaded and extends 10 mm (3/8 in) parallel to the length of the bar or billet and 19 mm (3/4 in) in the longitudinal center plane normal to the longitudinal axis, so that the polished face is midway between the outside and center of the bar or billet.

It is generally desirable to facilitate polishing by hardening the specimen. Polishing may be done by any desired technique. One generally followed is:

Step 1—Grind.

Step 2—Rough polish, going successively from Nos. 240, 320, 400 grits and Nos. 0, 00, and 000 emery papers.

Step 3—Fine polish, employing some medium such as alumina or other powders having a uniform particle size of 0.3 µm to less than 0.1 µm.

Step 4—Wash in hot water and follow by rinsing in alcohol.

Polishing scratches in the direction of rolling tends to confuse the appearance of the specimen. It is of utmost importance that the polished surface not be pitted or the inclusions distorted.

The entire polished surface of the prepared specimen is examined at 100 diameters. The examination may be made using the eyepiece or by projecting the field on a ground glass screen. In practice, visual observation of the prepared sample is often used to locate critical areas for microscopic examination.

4. Classification—The inclusions observed are compared with the accompanying series of photomicrographs of oxides and silicates classified from 1 to 8 inclusive. The length of the field shown is represented as 1.1 mm (0.045 in), and the classification is based on length with consideration given to width in the photomicrographs over class 6. The maximum length of each type of inclusion oxide or silicate, is generally used to evaluate a specimen. The silicate photomicrographs are used for all slag or fluid type inclusions and the oxide photomicrographs for all oxide or hard type inclusions. For example, a specimen may be classified 5-0 (oxide) 4-S (silicate) to indicate that the longest oxide inclusion noted was comparable to photomicrograph 5 and the longest silicate inclusion noted was comparable to photomicrograph 4.

Modifications may be used such as suffix numerals to indicate the number of long inclusions noted or the exact length of a particular inclusion in thousandths of an inch when over the maximum length indicated by the photomicrographs.

In evaluating steel cleanliness it is important to recognize that the value obtained applies directly to that area being examined. For proper inclusion determination, adequate sampling is of prime importance. Inclusions vary from heat to heat, ingot to ingot, and in different portions of the same ingot product. The accompanying standard series of photomicrographs is designed for use in evaluating the severity of the most common types of inclusions and it should be recognized that they do not represent a complete metallographic study of steel cleanliness.

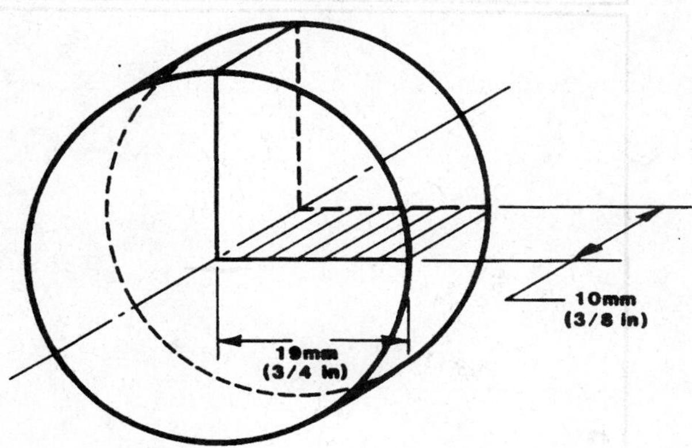

FIGURE 1—SPECIMEN FROM 33 mm (1-1/2 in) ROUND SECTION FOR MICROSCOPIC TEST

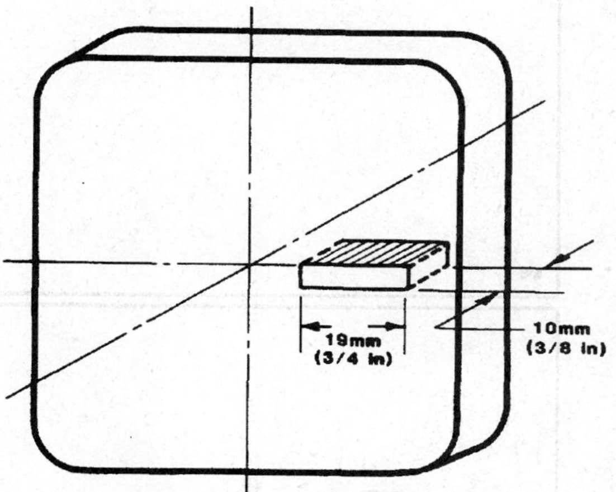

FIGURE 2—SPECIMEN FROM LARGE BAR OR BILLET FOR MICROSCOPIC TEST

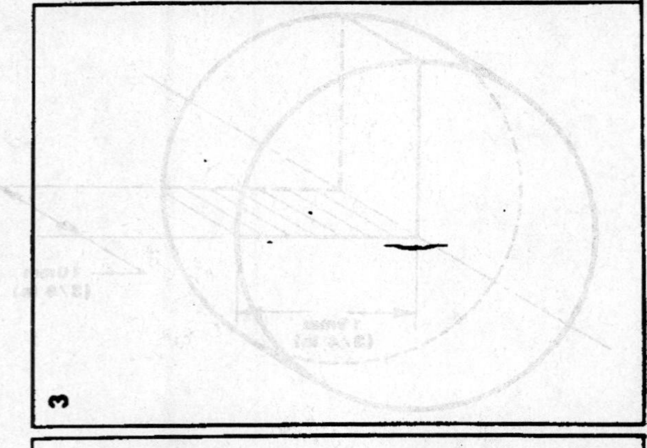

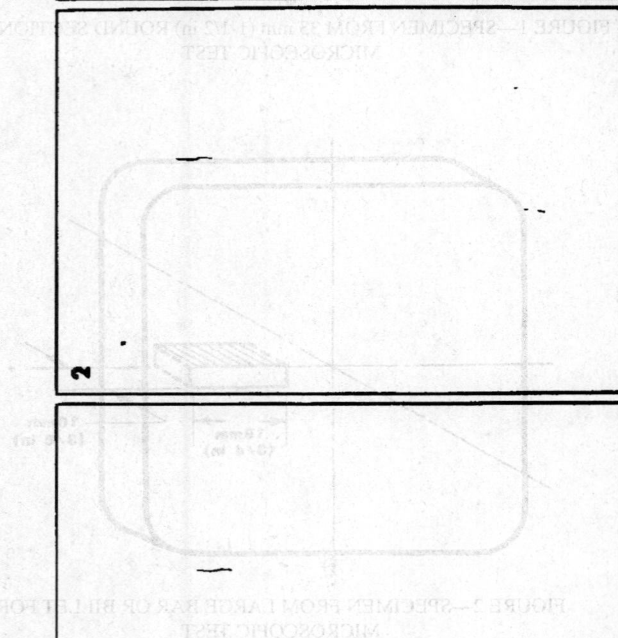

SILICATE INCLUSIONS
Magnification 100X

OXIDE INCLUSIONS

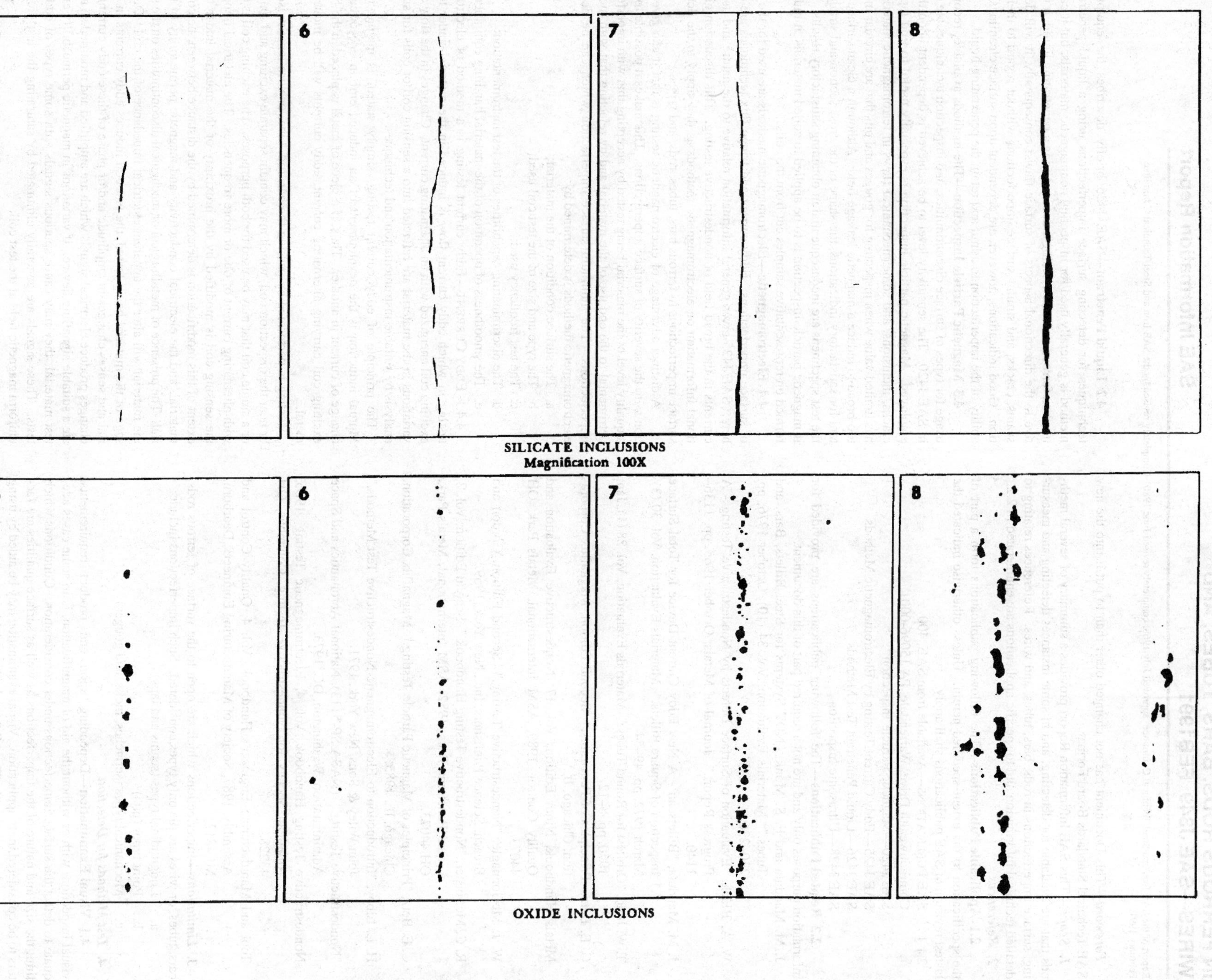

SILICATE INCLUSIONS
Magnification 100X

OXIDE INCLUSIONS

(R) DETECTION OF SURFACE IMPERFECTIONS IN FERROUS RODS, BARS, TUBES, AND WIRES—SAE J349 FEB1991

SAE Information Report

Report of the SAE Iron and Steel Technical Committee approved July 1968, completely revised June 1980. Completely revised by the SAE Iron and Steel Technical Committee February 1991.

Foreword—This Document has not changed other than to put it into the new SAE Technical Standards Board Format.

1. Scope—This SAE Information Report provides a summary of several methods that are available for detecting, and in some instances detecting and measuring, surface imperfections in rods, bars, tubes, and wires. References relating to detailed technical information and to specific applications are enumerated in 2.2.

2. References

2.1 Applicable Publications—The following publications form a part of the specification to the extent specified herein. Unless otherwise indicated the lastest revision of SAE publications shall apply.

2.1.1 SAE PUBLICATIONS—Available from SAE, 400 Commonwealth Drive, Warrendale, PA 15096-0001.

SAE J420—Magnetic Particle Inspection
SAE J425—Eddy Current Testing by Electromagnetic Methods
SAE J426—Liquid Penetrant Test Methods
SAE J428—Ultrasonic Inspection

2.2 Related Publications—The following publications are provided for information purposes only and are not a required part of this document.

J. M. Mandula and E. S. Monk, "NDT Systems for Steel Billets, Bars, and Tubes." Materials Evaluation, Vol. 34 (10), October 1976, pp. 230–236.

W. A. Black, "Evaluation of Surface Defects by Nondestructive Testing - A Progress Report." Journal of Metals, October 1965, pp. 1136–1140.

J. M. Mandula, "Billetscan - A New Eddy Current Device for Total Surface Inspection of Square Billets." Materials Evaluation, Vol. 30 (3), March 1972, pp. 49–54.

T. W. Judd, "Orbitest for Round Tubes." Materials Evaluation, Vol. 28 (1), Jan. 1970, pp. 8–12.

C. E. Betz, "Principles of Penetrants." Second Edition, Magnaflux Corporation, Chicago, IL.

Metals Handbook, Ninth Edition, Vol. 17, Nondestructive Evaluation and Quality Control, 1989, ASM International, Metals Park, OH 44073.

W. J. McGonnagle, "Nondestructive Testing." Second Edition, Gordon and Breach, Science Publishers, Inc., New York, 1969.

R. C. McMaster, "Nondestructive Testing Handbook." Second Edition, Vol. 2, Liquid Penetrant Tests, 1982, ASM International, Metals Park, OH 44073.

C. E. Betz, "Principles of Magnetic Particle Testing." Magnaflux Corporation, Chicago, IL, 1985.

H. L. Libby, "Introduction to Electromagnetic Nondestructive Test Methods." John Wiley & Sons, New York, 1971.

"Nondestructive Testing." (NASA SP-5113), National Aeronautics and Space Administration, Washington, DC, 1973.

Nondestructive Testing Handbook, Vol. 4, Electromagnetic Testing, 1986, American Society for Nondestructive Testing, Columbus, OH 43228.

Tool and Manufacturing Engineer's Handbook, Vol. 4, Quality Control and Assembly, 1987, Society of Manufacturing Engineers, Dearborn, MI 48121.

3. Limitations—Imperfections which are open to the surface of ferrous rods, bars, tubes, or wires are the only types considered. Such imperfections include:

a. Longitudinal types (seams and laps)
b. Point types (pits)
c. Mechanical types (scratches, nicks, and gouges)

4. Test Methods for Detection

4.1 Visual Examination—Depending upon end product requirements, visual inspection, with or without the aid of magnification, is in some cases adequate to detect the surface imperfections under consideration. Conditions which limit the size and nature of the imperfections as well as surface qualities are factors to be considered in its application. Visual examination may be aided by using surface preparations such as buffing, light grinding, pickling, or blast cleaning using a small particle grit or sand. Sometimes pickling is used in conjunction with blast cleaning.

4.2 Liquid Penetrant—SAE J426 briefly describes the equipment and techniques for detecting surface imperfections using a liquid penetrant. The method is generally used for inspecting nonmagnetic materials, but it can also be used on ferrous materials. Being a test involving a penetrating liquid, it is insensitive to the directional aspects of surface flaws; consequently, it will detect laps, seams, cracks, and similar surface imperfections without regard to their orientation. Good indications, however, are dependent upon surface cleanliness, and the ability of the imperfection to admit and retain the penetrating liquid.

4.3 Magnetic Particle Inspection—The methods available, recommended usage for types of surface discontinuities, and inspection techniques are described in SAE J420. The sensitivity level to be achieved is dependent upon the system employed. Magnetic particle inspection is especially useful to find laps, seams, cracks, inclusions, and some mechanical flaws in ferromagnetic materials, but it has limited value when inspecting for gouges and pits that are circular in nature or too broad to induce a magnetic leakage field. Although a clean surface is important for satisfactory indications, the shape of the cross section and straightness of the test specimens are inconsequential in obtaining satisfactory results. However, if magnetic particle inspection is to be applied to coiled materials, it must be performed on representative samples cut from the coils.

4.4 Electromagnetic—Electromagnetic methods are used for the detection of surface imperfections. Eddy current and fringe flux techniques are discussed here. SAE J425 gives general information relative to the nature and use of eddy currents in the broad field of nondestructive testing. This discussion gives additional information on electromagnetic methods as they apply to the detection of surface imperfections in ferrous bars, tubes, rods, and wires.

A distinct advantage of electromagnetic testing is that it can give information as to the severity of surface imperfections. This makes it possible to establish a quality level of the material being tested by accepting that with imperfection not detrimental to the end use of the material and by rejecting that with more severe imperfections. The minimum surface imperfection which can be detected by electromagnetic methods is determined by:

a. The surface condition of the material;
b. The type and size of the test coil used;
c. The test frequency used;
d. The discriminating capabilities of the test instrumentation;
e. The smoothness of operation of the material handling equipment.

4.4.1 EDDY CURRENT—Eddy current testing is a method of electromagnetic testing in which eddy current flow is induced in the material under test by an exciting coil energized with an alternating current. Changes in the flow caused by variations in the material are reflected into a sensing coil or coils for subsequent analysis by suitable instrumentation and techniques.

The principle of eddy current testing, simply stated, is mutual induction. Mutual induction is the development of an induced emf in one circuit by the change of current in another. Thus, if a piece of metal is placed in the field of an exciting coil carrying alternating current, eddy currents will be induced in the metal.

Testing is performed by passing the bar, rod, tube, or wire lengthwise through or near the inspection coil, which may contain separate exciting and sensing coils or a single coil that may be used for both purposes. The exciting coil is energized with alternating current of one or more frequencies. The electrical impedance of the sensing coil is modified by the proximity of the material under test. The extent of this modification is determined by the distance between the coil and the material, and the electrical conductivity and magnetic permeability of the material. The presence of metallurgical or mechanical discontinuities on the surface of the material will alter the apparent electrical impedance of the coil. During passage of the material being tested, the test coil induces eddy currents in the material and senses changes in amplitude and/or phase of these eddy currents. These changes produce electrical signals which are amplified and modified so as to actuate a suitable signalling device. If variations in magnetic permeability exist in the test material, they may cause spurious signals with some types of eddy current tests. These signals are generally eliminated by saturating the test piece with a uniform magnetic field at the test coil.

Two general coil types will be discussed here. One coil type is the encircling or feed-through type where the coil or coils are stationary while the material is fed through by means of a suitable transport mechanism. Either absolute or differential coil arrangements can be used. The differential coil arrangement is particularly sensitive to short imperfections such as pits, silvers, or nicks. Longitudinal imperfections, such as cracks or seams, may be indicated if they are variable. The absolute arrangement is sensitive to variables such as material properties, size, shape, and imperfections.

The other type is the probe coil. This type can be made to rotate around the material, or the coil can be held stationary while the material is rotated and traversed longitudinally in close proximity to the coil. The probe coil type is reliable and lends itself to mechanization of round product testing. The advantages are that no material saturation is necessary; that it is sensitive to continuous, uniform, longitudinal type imperfections; and that very shallow surface imperfections can be detected.

4.4.2 FRINGE FLUX—Fringe (or leakage) flux testing is a nondestructive method for detecting cracks and other discontinuities at or near the surface in ferromagnetic materials. The method consists of the following steps:

a. The part is magnetized immediately prior to or during the test to a proper level approaching saturation.
b. A flux sensor containing magnetic transducers is placed on the surface in the magnetized area.
c. The part or the magnetic flux sensor is moved progressively at a constant speed so the entire surface is scanned by the sensor.
d. Each magnetic transducer in the flux sensor is connected to an electronic console which amplifies, filters, and electronically processes the signals such that significant discontinuities are indicated (visually and audibly), then marked with paint or automatically removed from the production line, or both.

The fringe flux test is somewhat similar to a magnetic particle test with the flux sensor replacing the magnetic particles. It is somewhat similar to eddy current testing in the scanning and capability. The severity of the discontinuity can be estimated and a rejection level set with respect to the magnitude of the electromagnetic indication produced by the discontinuity.

If properly applied, this method is capable of detecting the presence and location of significant discontinuities such as pits, scabs, slivers, gouges, roll-ins, laps, seams, cracks, holes, and imperfections in welds.

4.5 Ultrasonic—Ultrasonic test methods, as described in SAE J428, can be used for the detection of surface discontinuities in bar and tube products. Various adaptations of the basic method are employed. The choice is influenced by factors such as cross-sectional area of the bar and the size and nature of the imperfections sought. Under proper conditions, ultrasonic waves can be propagated on and just below the surface of the bar. This test mode is particularly well suited to surface inspection. However, surface roughness and cleanliness must be controlled to prevent false determinations.

In general, ultrasonic inspection is limited to bars and wires greater than 2.5 mm (0.1 in) in diameter.

*5. **Methods of Measurement***—Electromagnetic (eddy current or fringe flux) and ultrasonic testing may be considered quantitative in that acceptance standards can be established, and the equipment set to reject materials having surface imperfections exceeding the predetermined acceptable conditions. Actual deviations from an acceptance standard can be interpreted quantitatively, after acquiring experience with the material being tested and gaining familiarity with the signal changes resulting from the type of imperfection or imperfections being investigated.

Only the surface length of an imperfection can usually be determined from liquid penetrant testing, magnetic particle testing, and visual examination and are usually interpreted qualitatively. However, some indication of the depth of surface discontinuities is sometimes possible on hot rolled products if a fluorescent powder is used when inspecting by the magnetic particle method (see Principles of Magnetic Particle Testing, p. 354).

Methods of actual depth measurement that are easy to use will either destroy the initial evidence or are a destructive test method. Those commonly used are as follows:

5.1 File or Grind and Inspect—Depth is often determined by merely filing or grinding the imperfection until it disappears visually. When using magnetic particle inspection, the material is ground or filed and then magnetic particle inspected again to determine if the imperfection is completely removed. The depth of the resulting groove to the point of complete removal of the discontinuity, can then be measured.

5.2 Macroexamination—Depth can be determined by cutting and grinding a section perpendicular to the direction of the imperfection and macroetching the sample. The depth is measured by a suitable means which could be a scale, Brinell glass, or low power microscope.

5.3 Microexamination—A very accurate method of measuring depth is by cutting and metallographically polishing a section perpendicular to the direction of the imperfection and measuring the depth microscopically.

5.4 Macroetching—If all conditions, including acid concentration, temperature, and time are controlled, a surface discontinuity of a section can be exaggerated by macroetching. The depth of the etched imperfection can be estimated and a rough approximation made of the original imperfection depth since the amount of material removed can be determined by measuring the cross section before and after etching. Subtracting this difference from the estimated depth of the etched surface imperfection gives the rough estimate.

METHODS OF MEASURING CASE DEPTH—SAE J423 FEB1998

SAE Standard

Report of the SAE Iron and Steel Technical Committee approved January 1950, third revision, Division 3, December 1983. Reaffirmed by the SAE Iron and Steel Technical Committee Division 3—Test Procedures February 1998. Rationale statement available.

Foreword—This Document has not changed other than to put it into the new SAE Technical Standards Board Format. References were added as Section 2. Definitions were changed to Section 3. All other section numbers have changed accordingly.

1. Scope—Case hardening may be defined as a process for hardening a ferrous material in such a manner that the surface layer, known as the case, is substantially harder than the remaining material, known as the core. The process embraces carburizing, nitriding, carbonitriding, cyaniding, induction, and flame hardening. In every instance, chemical composition, mechanical properties, or both are affected by such practice.

This testing procedure describes various methods for measuring the depth to which change has been made in either chemical composition or mechanical properties. Each procedure has its own area of application established through proved practice, and no single method is advocated for all purposes.

Methods employed for determining the depth of case are either chemical, mechanical, or visual, and the specimens or parts may be subjected to the described test either in the soft or hardened condition. The measured case depth may then be reported as either effective or total case depth on hardened specimens, and as total case depth on unhardened specimens.

It should be recognized that the relationship between case depths as determined by the different methods can vary extensively. Factors affecting this relationship include case characteristics, parent steel composition, quenching conditions, and others. It is not possible to predict, in some instances for example, effective case depth by chemical or visual means. It is important, therefore, that the method of case depth determination be carefully selected on the basis of specific requirements, consistent with economy.

2. References

2.1 Applicable Publication—The following publication forms a part of the specification to the extent specified herein. Unless otherwise indicated the latest revision of SAE publications shall apply.

2.1.1 ASM INTERNATIONAL PUBLICATION—Available from: ATTN: MSC/Book Order, ASM International, PO Box 473, Novelty, OH 44072-9901.

"The Application of M_sPoints to Case Depth Measurement," by E. S. Rowland and S. R. Lyle, ASM Transactions, Vol. 37 (1946) pp. 26–47.

3. Definitions

3.1 Effective Case Depth—The perpendicular distance from the surface of a hardened case to the furthest point where a specified level of hardness is maintained. The hardness criterion is 50 HRC normally, but see Table 1 under 5.1.

Effective case depth should always be determined on the part itself, or on samples or specimens having a heat-treated condition representative of the part under consideration.

3.2 Total Case Depth—The distance (measured perpendicularly) from the surface of the hardened or unhardened case to a point where differences in chemical or physical properties of the case and core no longer can be distinguished.

4. Chemical Methods

4.1 General—This method is generally applicable only to carburized cases, but may be used for cyanided or carbonitrided cases. The procedure consists in determining the carbon content (and nitrogen when applicable) at various depths below the surface of a test specimen. This method is considered the most accurate for measuring total case depth on carburized cases.

4.2 Procedure for Carburized Cases—Test specimens shall normally be of the same grade of steel as parts being carburized. Test specimens may be actual parts, rings, or bars and should be straight or otherwise suitable for accurate machining of surface layers into chips for subsequent carbon analysis.

Test specimens shall be carburized with parts or in a manner representative of the procedure to be used for parts in question. Care should be exercised to avoid distortion and decarburization in cooling test specimens after carburizing. In cases where parts and test specimens are quenched after carburizing, such specimens should be tempered at approximately 600 to 650 °C (1100 to 1200 °F) and straightened to 0.04 mm (0.0015 in) max total indicator reading (TIR) before machining is attempted. The time at temperature should be minimized to avoid excessive carbon diffusion.

Test specimens must have clean surfaces and shall be machined dry in increments of predetermined depth. The analysis of machined chips will then accurately reveal the depth of carbon penetration. Chosen increments usually vary between 0.05 and 0.25 mm (0.002 and 0.010 in) depending upon the accuracy desired and expected depth of case.

Chips from each increment shall be kept separate and analyzed individually for carbon content by an accepted method. Total case depth is considered to be the distance from the surface equivalent to the depth of the last increment of machining whose chips analyze to a carbon content 0.04% higher than that of the established carbon content of the core.

Specialized electron microprobe analyses on carefully prepared cross-sections represent an alternate procedure with potentially greater accuracy and speed, and is recommended when equipment is available.

5. Mechanical Methods

5.1 General. This method is considered to be one of the most useful and accurate of the case depth measuring methods. It can be effectively used on all types of hardened cases, and is the preferred method for determination of effective case depth. The use of this method requires the obtaining and recording of hardness values at known intervals through the case. For determination of effective case depth, the 50 HRC criterion is generally used. The sample or part is considered to be through hardened when the hardness level does not drop below the effective case depth hardness value. In some instances involving flame and induction hardened cases, it is desirable to use a lower hardness criterion. Suggested hardness levels are tabulated in Table 1 for various nominal carbon levels.

TABLE 1—CARBON CONTENT

Carbon Content	Effective Case Depth Hardness
0.28–0.32% C	35 HRC
0.33–0.42% C	40 HRC
0.43–0.52% C	45 HRC
0.53% and over	50 HRC

A plot of hardness versus depth from the surface will facilitate this reading. Figures 1, 2, 3, and 4 illustrate the recommended procedures.

Hardness testers which produce small, shallow impressions should be used for all of the following procedures, in order that the hardness values obtained will be representative of the surface or area being tested. Those testers which are used to produce Diamond Pyramid or Knoop Hardness Numbers are recommended, although testers using heavier loads, such as the Rockwell superficial, A or C scales, can be used in some instances on flame and induction hardened cases.

Considerable care should be exercised during preparation of samples for case depth determination by any of the mechanical methods, to insure against grinding or cutting burn. The use of an etchant for burn detection is recommended as a general precaution, because of the serious error which can be introduced by its presence.

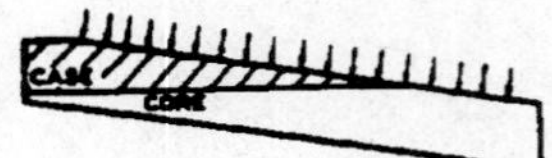

FIGURE 1—SPECIMEN FOR TAPER GRIND PROCEDURE

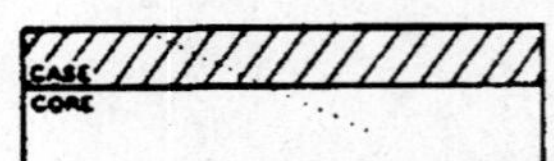

FIGURE 2—SPECIMEN FOR CROSS SECTION PROCEDURE

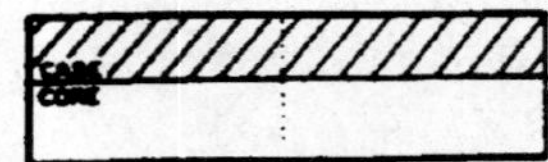

FIGURE 3—SPECIMEN FOR ALTERNATE CROSS SECTION PROCEDURE

FIGURE 4—SPECIMEN FOR STEP GRIND PROCEDURE

5.2 Hardness Traverse Procedure. Cut specimens perpendicular to hardened surface at critical location being careful to avoid any cutting or grinding practice which would affect the original hardness.

Grind and polish specimen. Surface finish of the area to be traversed shall be polished finely enough so the hardness impressions are unaffected—that is, the lighter the indentor load, the finer the polish necessary.

The procedure illustrated by Figure 2 is recommended for the measurement of light and medium cases. The alternate procedure illustrated in Figure 3 is recommended for medium and heavier cases.

The hardness traverse should be started far enough below the surface to ensure proper support from the metal between the center of the impression and the surface. Subsequent impressions are spaced far enough apart so as not to distort hardness values. The distance from the surface of the case to the center of the impression is measured on a calibrated optical instrument, micrometer stage, or other suitable means.

5.3 Taper Grind Procedure. This procedure, illustrated by Figure 1, is recommended for measurement of light and medium cases.

A shallow taper is ground through the case, and hardness measurements are made along the surface thus prepared. The angle is chosen so that readings, spaced equal distances apart, will represent the hardness at the desired increments below the surface of the case.

Unless special anvils are used, a parallel section should be prepared so that readings are taken at right angles to the surface. Care should be exercised in grinding to prevent tempering or rehardening.

5.4 Step Grind Procedure. This procedure illustrated by Figure 4 is recommended for measurement of medium and heavy cases.

It is essentially the same as the taper grind section method with the exception that hardness readings are made on steps which are known distances below the surface.

A variation in this procedure is the step grind method where two predetermined depths are ground to insure that the effective case depth is within specified limits.

6. Visual Methods

6.1 General. This method employs any visual procedure with or without the aid of magnification for reading the depth of case produced by any of the various processes. Samples may be prepared by combinations of fracturing, cutting, grinding, and polishing methods. Etching with a suitable reagent is normally required to produce a contrast between the case and core. Nital (concentrated nitric acid in alcohol) of various strengths is frequently used for this purpose.

6.2 Macroscopic. Magnification methods for determination of case depth measurement are recommended for routine process control, primarily because of the short time required for determinations, and the minimum of specialized equipment and trained personnel needed. They have the added advantage of being applicable to the measurement of all types of cases. However, the accuracy can be improved by correlation with other methods more in keeping with engineering specifications for the parts being processed. These methods are applied normally to hardened specimens, and while a variety of etchants may be employed with equal success, the following procedures are typical and widely used.

6.2.1 FRACTURE. Prepare product or sample by fracturing. Examine at a magnification not to exceed 20 diameters with no further preparation.

6.2.2 FRACTURE AND ETCH. Water quench product or samples directly from the carburizing temperature. Fracture and etch in 20% nitric acid in water for a time established to develop maximum contrast. Rinse in water and read while wet.

6.2.3 FRACTURE OR CUT, AND ROUGH GRIND. Prepare specimen by either fracturing, or cutting and rough grinding. Etch in 10% nital for a period of time established to provide a sharp line of demarcation between case and core. Examine at magnification not to exceed 20 diameters (Brinell glass) and read all the darkened area for approximate total case depth.

6.2.4 FRACTURE OR CUT, AND POLISH OR GRIND. Prepare specimen by fracturing or cutting. Polish or grind through No. 000 or finer metallographic emery paper or both. Etch in 5% nital for approximately 1 min. Rinse in two clean alcohol or water rinses. Examine at magnification not to exceed 20 diameters (Brinell glass) and read all of the darkened zone. After correlation, effective case depth can be determined by reading from external surface of specimen to a selected line of the darkened zone.

6.3 Microscopic. Microscopic methods are generally for laboratory determination and require a complete metallographic polish and an etch suitable for the material and the process. The examination is made most commonly at 100 diameters.

6.3.1 CARBURIZED CASES. The microscopic method may be used for laboratory determinations of total case and effective case depths in the hardened condition. When the specimen is annealed properly, the total case depth and the depth of the various zones—hypereutectoid, eutectoid, and hypoeutectoid—also can be determined quite precisely.[1]

1.For certain applications involving moderate to high hardenability alloy steels in the 0.4 to 0.8% carbon range, the M_s method of case depth determination to specific carbon level has been found to be effective. In this method, the specimen is austenitized at the time and temperature sufficient to more than take into solution the alloy and carbon at the desired level of measurement. It is then quenched into salt at the M_s temperature of the carbon level desired, held just long enough to temper the martensite at all lower carbon levels and water quenched. Subsequent polishing and etching disclose a sharp line of demarcation between tempered and untempered martensite, which can be read with a Brinell glass to a precision of 0.05 mm (0.002 in). Additional information on this technique can be obtained by reference to "The Application of M_s Points to Case Depth Measurement," by E. S. Rowland and S. R. Lyle, ASM Transactions, Vol. 37 (1946) pp. 26–47.

a. Hardened Condition
   1. Fracture or cut specimen at right angles to the surface.
   2. Prepare specimen for microscope and etch in 2 to 5% nital (concentrated nitric acid in alcohol).
   3. For effective case depth, read from surface to metallographic structures which have been shown to be equivalent to 50 HRC.
   4. For total case depth, read to the line of demarcation between the case and core. In alloy steels quenched from a high temperature, the line of demarcation is not sharp. Read all the darkened zone that indicates a difference in carbon from the uniform core structure.

b. Annealed Condition
   1. For specimens previously hardened or not cooled under controlled conditions.
   2. The specimen to be annealed may be protected by copper plate or any suitable means for preventing loss of carbon.
   3. Pack in a small, thin-wall container with a suitable material such as charcoal
   4. Place container in furnace at 40 to 80 °C (75 to 150 °F) above the upper critical temperature (Ac3) for the core. (Generally an annealing temperature of 870 to 925 °C (1600 to 1700 °F) is satisfactory.)
   5. Leave in furnace long enough for specimen to reach furnace temperature, but not for an excessive time at temperature, as carbon diffusion will increase total case depth.

c. Cooling Rates
   1. Carbon Steels—A satisfactory cooling rate is obtained by cooling the container in mica, lime, or other insulating material at a rate which will reduce the temperature to 430 °C (800 °F) in 2½ to 3 h. Cool as desired below 430 °C (800 °F).
   2. Alloy Steels—Slower cooling rates or isothermal transformations are required. If martensite is retained in the structure, better contrast after etching may be obtained by tempering the specimens at 540 to 600 °C (1000 to 1100 °F). Cool as desired after tempering.
   3. Section, prepare, and etch specimen as desired under 6.3.1, (a) Hardened Condition. Etching time is usually longer.
   4. For total case depth measurement, read the depth of carbon enrichment.
   5. For specimens cooled slowly after carburizing. If the production carburizing cycle provides the proper cooling rate, or the cooling rate is otherwise controlled as described for the annealed condition, specimens may be prepared and examined without reheating after carburizing. This is often possible when the parts are cooled in solid compound when the boxes are not too small.

6.3.2 CARBONITRIDED CASES. Carbonitrided cases are measured for total case depth in the hardened condition. High quenching temperatures, high alloy content of the steel, and high carbon content of the core decrease the accuracy of readings obtained by this method.

a. Section, prepare, etch, and read as described in 6.3.1, (a) Hardened Condition.

6.3.3 CYANIDED CASES. Cyanided cases are thin, and only the microscopic method is recommended for accurate case depth measurements. The usual cyanide case contains a light etching layer followed by a totally martensitic constituent, which in turn is followed by martensite with increasing networks of other constituents, depending on the type of steel which has been cyanided. Cyanided cases are read in the hardened condition only and results reported as total case depth.

a. Section, prepare, and etch specimen as described in 6.3.1, (a) Hardened Condition.
b. Read to the line of demarcation between the case and core.
c. (When a sharp line of demarcation does not exist, the use of a hardness test such as described under Mechanical Methods is recommended.)

6.3.4 NITRIDED CASES. The microscopic method is used chiefly in those situations where the available sample cannot readily be prepared for the more desirable hardness traverse method. It may be difficult to read the case depth because the nitride network gradually diminishes.

a. Section and prepare the specimen as described in Carburized Cases, (a) Hardened Condition.
b. Etch in 10% nital.
c. Read all darkened zone for total case depth.

6.3.5 FLAME OR INDUCTION HARDENED CASES. Since no chemical change occurs in flame or induction hardening, readings must be made in the hardened or hardened and tempered condition only. A procedure for reading effective case depth may be established by correlating microstructures with a hardness traverse method. A minimum hardness of 50 HRC is used commonly but some other point may be selected or required, for example, in lower carbon steels that do not reach 50 HRC when fully hardened. See Table 1. The microstructure at the selected location will differ depending on steel composition, prior treatment (annealed, heat treated, or other treatments) and on the hardness level chosen.

a. Section, prepare, and etch specimen as described in 6.3.1, (a) Hardened Condition.
b. For total case depth, read the entire zone containing structures hardened by the process.
c. For effective case depth, read to selected microstructure correlated with specified hardness.

(R) NONDESTRUCTIVE TESTS—SAE J358 FEB1991 SAE Information Report

Report of the SAE Iron and Steel Technical Committee approved September 1968, last revised June 1978: editorial change January 1980. Completely revised by the SAE Iron and Steel Technical Committee February 1991.

Foreword—This Document has also changed to comply the new SAE Technical Standards Board Format.

1. Scope—Nondestructive tests are those tests which detect factors related to the serviceability or quality of a part or material without limiting its usefulness. Material defects such as surface cracks, laps, pits, internal inclusions, bursts, shrink, seam, hot tears, and composition analysis can be detected. Sometimes their dimensions and exact location can be determined. Such tests can usually be made rapidly. Processing results such as hardness, case depth, wall thickness, ductility, decarburization, cracks, apparent tensile strength, grain size, and lack of weld penetration or fusion may be detectable and measurable. Service results such as corrosion and fatigue cracking may be detected and measured by nondestructive test methods. In many cases, imperfections can be automatically detected so that parts or materials can be classified.

The SAE Handbook describes the following nondestructive test methods:

SAE J359—Infrared
SAE J420—Magnetic Particle
SAE J425—Eddy Current
SAE J426—Liquid Penetrant
SAE J427—Penetrating Radiation
SAE J428—Ultrasonic
SAE J1242—Acoustic Emission
SAE J1267—Leakage Testing

Table 1 summarizes the principal features of most of these tests. In addition to the tests described, other nondestructive tests exist which are less well established, but whose use is expanding. Among these are microwave tests, holography, and sonic tests. Microwaves are used to locate defects in nonmetallic substances and to determine some physical characteristics of those materials. Optical holography uses coherent light from a laser beam to detect strains and defects in materials by means of three-dimensional imaging and interferometry techniques. Acoustical holography uses ultrasonic waves to image discontinuities in the interior of solids. Recent refinements in sonic testing permit more objective determination of the physical properties of cast iron. Complete information concerning each nondestructive test can be obtained from books listed in the bibliographies of the aforementioned reports.

Increasing consumer demand for product quality at reasonable cost has resulted in development of nondestructive tests which can be applied to materials and manufactured parts. Although a variety of complementary nondestructive methods is available, development time is generally required for application to specific materials or products. The effect of part contour, surface condition, heat treatment, composition variation, and other variables may limit the ability of certain tests to detect imperfections with desired accuracy.

Nondestructive tests properly applied to basic material can add greater assurance of performance to design strengths, thereby affecting material and manufacturing economy. In addition, parts can be tested after each basic operation which is critical to service performance of the finished part. In-process nondestructive tests can also serve as basic components of feedback process control systems since all tests are based upon measurements which do not damage the material or part being inspected.

2. References

2.1 Applicable Publications—The following publications form a part of the specification to the extent specified herein. Unless otherwise indicated the lastest revision of SAE publications shall apply.

2.1.1 SAE PUBLICATIONS—Available from SAE, 400 Commonwealth Drive, Warrendale, PA 15096-0001.

SAE J369—Infrared Testing
SAE J420—Magnetic Particle Inspection
SAE J425—Electromagnetic Testing by Eddy Current Methods
SAE J426—Liquid Penetrant Test Methods
SAE J427—Penetrating Radiation Inspection
SAE J428—Ultrasonic Inspection
SAE J1242—Acoustic Emission Test Methods
SAE J1267—Leakage Testing

TABLE 1—FEATURES OF NONDESTRUCTIVE TESTS

Method	Principle	Material	Applications	Advantages	Limitations
Magnetic particle (SAE J420)	Magnetic particles attracted by leakage flux at surface flaws of magnetic object and visual inspection.	Magnetic materials	Surface flaws such as cracks, laps, and seams. Some subsurface flaws.	Easy to interpret, fast, simple to perform	Parts must be relatively clean. Usually requires high current source. Parts sometimes must be demagnetized. Standards difficult to establish.
Electromagnetic (eddy current) (SAE J425)	Alternating current coil induces eddy currents in test object. Flaws and material properties affect flow of currents. Information derived from meter or cathode ray tube indications.	Metals	Material composition, structure, hardness changes, cracks, case depth, voids, large inclusions, tubing weld defects, laminations, coating thickness, porosity, and conductivity	Intimate contact between coil and material not required. Versatile. Special coils easily made. Fast operation: can be automated. Electric circuit design variations permit selective sensitivity and function. Sensitive to surface and near surface inhomogeneities.	Sensitive to many variables. Sensitivity varies with depth. Reference standards needed. Response often comparative.
Liquid penetrant (SAE J426)	Liquid penetrant is drawn into surface flaws by capillary action, then revealed by developer material to aid in visual inspection	Nonporous material, metals, plastics, glazed ceramics	Surface flaws such as cracks, porosity, pits, seams, and laps.	Simple to perform applicable to complex shapes, on site inspection.	Only surface flaws detected. Surfaces must be clean. Penetrant washes out of wide defects. Standards difficult to establish.
Penetrating Radiation (SAE J427)	General-Penetrating radiation is differentially absorbed by materials, depending upon thickness and type of material.	Most materials	Internal defects such as inclusions, porosity, shrink, hot tears, cracks, cold shuts, and coarse structure in cast metals; lack of fusion and penetration in welds. Detection of missing internal parts in an assembly.	More standards established than for other methods. Internal defects detected. Permanent film record. Automatic thickness gaging.	Health precautions necessary. Defect must be at least 2% of total section thickness. Film processing requires time, facilities, and care. Difficulty with complex shapes. Most costly non-destructive test method.
	X-ray source produces radiation electrically, by deceleration of electrons.			Versatile-energy adjustable. Fluoroscopy available. Image intensification available. Thickness up to 600 mm (24 in) of steel.	Electric power and water required. Equipment heavy and costly. Shielded area usually required.
	Gamma source produces radiation as a result of decay of radioactive material.			More portable than x-ray. Lower cost than x-ray. Thickness up to 250 mm (10 in) steel can be tested.	Government license required. Energy cannot be adjusted or turned off. Source must be replaced. Orientation affects the test.
	Neutron source produces radiation by nuclear reactors, accelerators, or decay of radioactive material.			Penetrates dense metals but is attenuated by light elements such as in water, plastics, and oil. Usable on radioactive objects.	Government license required. Less portable and more expensive than x-ray.
Ultrasonic (SAE J248)	Mechanical vibrational waves (frequency range 0.1 to 25 MHz) are introduced into a test object. This energy is reflected and scattered by inhomogeneities or becomes resonant. Information is interpreted from cathode ray tube or read from meter.	Metals, plastics, ceramics, glass, rubber, graphite, concrete	Inclusions, cracks, porosity, bursts, laminations, structure, lack of bond, thickness measurement, weld defects.	Variety of inspection elements and circuitry permits selective high sensitivity. High speed test. Can be automated and recorded. Penetrates up to 60 ft (18m) steel. Indicates flaw location. Access to only one surface usually needed.	Difficulty with complex shapes. Surface roughness may affect test. Defect orientation affects test. Comparative standards only. Requires couplant.
Infrared (SAE J359)	Electromagnetic radiation from test objects above a temperature of absolute zero is detected and correlated to quality. Information is displayed by meter, recorder, photograph, or CRT.	Most materials	Discontinuities that interrupt heat flow: flaws, voids, inclusions, lack of bond. Higher or lower than normal resistances in circuitry.	High sensitivity. One-sided inspection possible. Applicable to complex shapes and assemblies of dissimilar components. Active or passive specimens.	Emissivity variations in materials, coatings, and colors must be considered. In multilayer assemblies, hot spots can be hidden behind cool surface component. Relatively slow.
Acoustic Emission (SAE J1242)	Acoustic emission is a transient elastic wave generated by rapid release of energy from a localized source within a solid material. Rate and amplitude of high frequency (0.1 to 1 MHz) acoustic emissions are noted and correlated to structure or object characteristics.	Most soild materials	Determine or monitor integrity of structures such as weldments or castings.	Remote and continuous real time surveillance of structures is possible. Inaccessible flaws can be detected. Location of flaws can be determined. Permanent record can be made.	Part must be stressed. Nonpropagating flaws cannot be detected. Nonrelevant noise must be filtered out. Transducers must be placed upon the object.
Leakage Testing (SAE J1267)	Material flows across an interface at a leak site. Rate of flow is pressure, time, and leak size dependent. Detection of the trans interface migration is done in one of eight or more ways.	Totally independent of materials.	Any vessel containing a product at a pressure different from ambient or a vessel in which a pressure different from ambient can be created for evaluation.	Provides assurance that the vessel will retain contents as designed. Advantages vary for the individual methods.	Vary from method to method.

(R) INFRARED TESTING—SAE J359 FEB1991

SAE Information Report

Report of the SAE Steel Technical Committee approved July 1973, reaffirmed without change October 1976, editorial change June 1981.
Completely revised by the SAE Iron and Steel Technical Committee Februrary 1991.

Foreword—This Document has also changed to comply with the new SAE Technical Standards Board format.

1. Scope—The scope of this SAE Information Report is to provide general information relative to the nature and use of infrared techniques for nondestructive testing. The document is not intended to provide detailed technical information, but will serve as an introduction to the theory and capabilities of infrared testing and as a guide to more extensive references.

2. References

2.1 Related Publications—The following publications are provided for information purposes only and are not a required part of this document.

Metals Handbook, Vol. 17, 9th edition, 1989, "Thermal Inspection," pp. 396–404.

Tool and Manufacturing Engineers Handbook, Vol. 4, pp. 6–86 to 6–90, Engineers, Dearborn, MI 48121.

Kruse, McGlaucklin, McQuistan, Elements of Infrared Technology. New York: John Wiley & Sons, 1963.

Jamieson, McFee, Plass, Grube, Richards, Infrared Physics and Engineering, New York: McGraw-Hill Co., 1963.

Hackforth, Infrared Radiation. New York: McGraw-Hill Book Co., 1960.

William G. Hyzer, "Thermography," Research Development. February 1978, pp. 44–50.

W. D. Lawson and J. H. Sabey, "Infrared Techniques," Research Techniques in Nondestructive Testing, R. S. Sharpe, editor, Academic Press, 1970, pp. 443–479.

Transactions of the Infrared Sessions, SNT Convention, February 1965, Society for Nondestructive Testing, 914 Chicago, Ave., Evanston, Ill.

Riccardo Vanzetti, Practical Applications of Infrared Technology. New York: John Wiley & Sons, 1972.

Applied Optics, Vol. 7, No. 9 (September 1968). (Special edition on infrared containing 23 papers.)

P. Vogel, "Thermal Fingerprint." Army Research and Development News Magazine, May-Jun 1972.

3. General—Infrared (IR) nondestructive testing can be defined as a method by which objects (raw materials, in-process, or finished items) can be evaluated by detecting, displaying, and interpreting the infrared emissions which are a function of the physical, electrical, mechanical, and thermal properties that may generate a temperature differential or influence heat transfer. As an independent system, this relatively new method of testing bridges existing gaps in nondestructive testing technology and is useful in supplementing or verifying other methods. It is being successfully applied as a process control technique where it can monitor extremely high temperatures in minute areas, using either focused optics or optical fibers, and it can be coupled by feedback to automated systems. Its precise measurement lends itself to smelting of high purity materials. IR testing equipment now has a sufficiently broad production base to assure the availability of options to suit a particular problem or for versatile operations. IR testing has been used successfully in detecting delaminations in solid propellant missile motors, ply separations in automobile tires, and effectiveness of vacuum, batt, or foamed-in-place insulation; and it can detect flaws, voids, and lack of bond in welds and solder joints, castings, etc. It has found high acceptance in the form of various infrared "cameras" which produce in real-time, thermal images of items ranging in size from very large missiles to electronic microcircuits to display actual and potential defects.

4. Principle—Infrared testing is used to detect electromagnetic radiation with wavelengths between 0.7 and 100 µm. All objects at a temperature greater than absolute zero radiate infrared light. As the temperature of the object increases, the intensity and frequency of the infrared radiation increases. Thus, temperature can be measured by measuring the intensity of radiation. When the temperature of an object is high enough to radiate in the visible wavelengths of about 0.4 to 0.7 µm, ordinary photography will record shadings corresponding to localized heat changes. Upon cooling, the radition changes to the longer red wavelengths where visible detection of the light begins to fail, some photographic red films can still provide a record. Beyond this narrow threshold, detection of radiation is made possible by the use of infrared detectors and systems.

Infrared detectors fall into two general types:

a. Photodetectors which produce a signal from a semiconductor, the signal being proportional to the impinging radiation. These detectors include photoelectromagnetic, photovoltaic, and photoconductive types.
b. Thermal detectors, which undergo a physical change in response to thermal change. These detectors include thermistors, thermocouples, bolometers, oil film evaporation and radiometer types.

An infrared detector will generally include an optical system, a blackbody, electronic circuitry, and a visual display. The optical system will magnify and/or focus the object. The blackbody is a controlled temperature radiator which is used as a reference in measuring the infrared emissions from the object.

Systems can be selected for measuring temperatures as low as −150 °C to as high as desired: for detecting gradients as small as 0.05 °C; for focusing from 12.7 mm (1/2 in) to infinity; and with resolution as small as 0.0038 mm (0.00015).

5. Procedure—Most of the systems are portable and have external power requirements. Readout is rapid and the system, being remote from the specimens, is inherently nondestructive. However, a specimen could be energized or heated to destruction if so desired, while the system recorded points or elements of failure. Operation of most systems requires some training. Experience required for evaluation of the readout is dependent on the type of information desired; that is, common sense would allow the interpretation of the "Polaroid" display of a heat leak on a foundry furnace, while evaluation of the same display of relative temperatures of an electronic microcircuit taken by an infrared microscope would require a knowledge of the operating thermal characteristics of the components of the specimen.

In a more complex single specimen, such as a printed circuit board, a good knowledge is needed of the theory of heat transfer as well as the construction of the board. Lateral transfer of heat to another component functioning as a sink could mask a defect which would otherwise be indicated by an abnormal temperature.

Because infrared radiates in the same manner as visible light and because the detector measures the surface radiation, a defect in a multilayer specimen could be concealed behind a surface component at normal operating temperature. In evaluation of thermographs or thermoplots of complex specimens, consideration must be given to the wide variations in emissivity resulting from dissimilar materials, coatings, etc.

None of the foregoing present insurmountable problems. It would be expected that in production testing a good standard sample would be made available, then one of many techniques such as "flicker" comparison of thermographs, overlays, etc., would quickly distinguish between go and no-go.

MAGNETIC PARTICLE INSPECTION —SAE J420 MAR1991

SAE Information Report

Report of the SAE Iron and Steel Technical Committee approved June 1952, completely revised March 1981. Completely revised by the SAE Iron and Steel Technical Committee March 1991.

1. Scope—The scope of this SAE Information Report is to provide general information relative to the nature and use of magnetic particles for nondestructive testing. The document is not intended to provide detailed technical information, but will serve as an introduction to the theory and capabilities of magnetic particle testing, and as a guide to more extensive references.

2. References

2.1 Related Publications—The following publications are provided for information purposes only and are not a required part of this document.

2.1.1 SAE PUBLICATION—Available from SAE, 400 Commonwealth Drive, Warrendale, PA 15096-0001.

AMS 2640—Magnetic Particle Inspection, 1969.

2.1.2 ASM PUBLICATIONS—ATTN: MSC/Book Order, ASM International, PO Box 473, Novelty, OH 44072-9901.

Metals Handbook, Ninth Edition, Vol. 17, Nondestructive Evaluation and Quality Control, 1987.

Metals Handbook, Eighth Edition, Vol. 11, 1976, pp. 44–75.

2.1.3 ASTM PUBLICATIONS—Available from ASTM, 100 Barr Harbor Drive, West Conshohocken, PA 19428-2959

ASTM E 125—Reference Photographs for Magnetic Particle Indications on Ferrous Castings

ASTM E 269—Standard Definitions for Terms Relating to Magnetic Particle Inspection

ASTM E 709—Recommended Practice for Magnetic Particle Examination

2.1.4 OTHER PULICATIONS

Nondestructive Testing Handbook, Vol. 6, Magnetic Particle Testing, 1989, American Society for Nondestructive Testing, Columbus, OH 43228

C. E. Betz, "Principles of Magnetic Particle Testing," Magnaflux Corp., Chicago, IL, 1985

MIL-M-6867—Magnetic Inspection Units, Department of Defense

MIL-STD-1949—Inspection, Military Standard, Department of Defense

MIL-STD-410—Qualification of Inspection Personnel, Department of Defense

Programmed Instruction Handbook PI-4-3, Magnetic Particle Testing. Convair Div., General Dynamics Corp., 1967

SNT-TC-1A Nondestructive Testing and Certification, 1984, American Society for Nondestructive Testing, Columbus, OH 43228

Tool and Manufacturing Engineer's Handbook, Vol. 4, Quality Control and Assembly, 1987, Society of Manufacturing Engineers, Dearborn, MI 48121

3. General—Magnetic particle inspection is a nondestructive means of inspecting ferromagnetic materials such as iron and steel for discontinuities (cracks, seams, near surface inclusions) by the detection of leakage fields through the use of magnetic particles.

Magnetic particle inspection is an aid to visual inspection of objects. Surface or near surface discontinuities that might not be seen with the aid of optical magnification are regularly detected in manufacturing operations or maintenance. The process is not applicable to nonmagnetic materials. The usual basic steps in magnetic particle inspection of an object are: clean, magnetize, apply magnetic particles, inspect, and demagnetize. Post cleaning is frequently done. Magnetic particle inspection is a relatively simple procedure. It is most effective when the various factors, such as types of magnetization, current, particles, equipment, and method, are properly selected for the application.

4. Principle—The principle of magnetic particle inspection is the accumulation of particles due to magnetic flux leakage at discontinuities in a magnetized test object. The material subjected to the inspection is magnetized in a fashion which will produce north and south poles on opposite edges of a discontinuity. Finely divided magnetic particles are introduced into the flux leakage field between the poles, and are held there by the magnetic leakage flux. The visible accumulation of these particles is called an indication.

5. Procedure—A magnetic field is induced in the part to be tested by the application of an electric current through the part, or through a central conductor inserted through a hole in the part, or by means of a yoke, prods, or coil. The type of magnetization selected is determined primarily by the need to establish magnetic flux lines perpendicular to the direction of anticipated surface imperfections. Any discontinuity at or near the surface of the part will interrupt the magnetic flux induced in the part and a leakage field will be formed at the surface of the part. Magnetic particles in the vicinity of this leakage field will be attracted to it, forming a visible indication which, to experienced interpreters, expresses the characteristics of the discontinuity. Following the creation of the indication, the interpretation of the indication, and the evaluation of the discontinuity, the part is suitably demagnetized and, where required, cleaned.

Adequate light must be provided for the quick and sure detection of the indications of discontinuities. Lights should be adjusted to give broad highlights on finished machine parts. If fluorescent lighting is used, the tubes should be located transverse to the long axis of the parts being inspected. A nominal illumination level of 108 1x (100 ft-c) of white light should be present on the part surface in the case of nonfluorescent inspection. Personnel should have eyesight, corrected or uncorrected, capable of distant vision of 20/30 in at least one eye and should be able to read Jaeger Type No. 2 with both eyes at 305 mm (12 in).

An adequate source of long wave ultraviolet light (approximate 3650 Å, colloquially known as black light) must be provided for inspection when using the flourescent magnetic particle inspection method. A filtered high-pressure mercury vapor source is generally recommended. The emitted light should have an intensity of 97 1x (90 ft-c) at a 380 mm (15 in) distance from the source, or no less than 140 mW cm^2 (900 mW in^2) on the part surface. For detection of certain fine indications, illumination at the part surface may need to be as high as 270 1x (250 ft-c). Personnel vision requirements are the same as for nonfluorescent inspection, but in addition, visual acuity in the green-yellow spectrum must be satisfactory.

Demagnetization consists of removing objectionable residual magnetic fields from parts which have been subjected to magnetic particle inspection. This must be done to prevent the deflection of adjacent sensitive instruments and to prevent the attraction of small magnetic chips, or the like, which could cause damage to contacting surfaces. The most common type of demagnetization consists of drawing the magnetized part through a high intensity alternating current solenoid. Another type, often used on heavier parts, consists of passing an alternating current or reversing direct current through the part or through a surrounding solenoid, and then gradually reducing the current value to near zero. Demagnetization is sometimes effected in subsequent processing, such as heat treatment, or hot washing, of a part. Effectiveness of the demagnetizing is usually determined through use of inexpensive meters made for this purpose.

Irons and steels exhibit magnetic characteristics which vary with hardness and composition. Continuous magnetization during particle application is used on relatively soft steels since they usually do not retain sufficient magnetism to allow the use of the residual method. These steels are processed for inspection by introducing the magnetic particles into the leakage fields created at the discontinuities while the magnetizing force is present. Parts processed in this way are said to be processed by the continuous method. Use of the continuous method makes possible the successful inspection of irons and steels which do not retain sufficient magnetism for processing by the residual method. In addition to this, certain subsurface discontinuities are easily detected in both hardened and unhardened parts by this method when direct current magnetization is employed.

The residual magnetization test method may be applied to hardened steels, and other highly retentive materials, since they will retain magnetism after the force has been removed. These remaining magnetic fields will produce leakage fields adjacent to discontinuities strong enough to hold magnetic particles and produce indications. Parts processed through the use of these retained fields are said to be processed by the residual method. Use of the residual method often eliminates nonrelevant indications. It is especially useful for the detection of surface discontinuities in hardened parts. An adequate level of magnetization is required.

Wet particles used in suspension liquid usually consist of finely ground magnetic iron oxide. These particles are coated so they can be easily dispersed in a liquid vehicle. They are generally available in powder form having red or black nonfluorescent colors. They are also available coated with a material which fluoresces under long wave ultraviolet (black) light. Wet particles are commonly used in maintenance, process, and finish inspection of machine and engine parts. The wet process offers the advantage of ease of application of the particles, sensitivity in locating the finest discontinuities, and, especially with the fluorescent particle, rapid inspection rates.

Dry particles consist of finely divided magnetic material in powder form. These particles are coated so as to be easily conveyed by air to the part being inspected. They are generally available in many colors for maximum contrast with the test object. Dry particles are commonly used for the maintenance, process, and finish inspection of heavy weldments, heavy castings, and heavy forgings. Dry particles are superior for the inspection of very rough surfaces and for the location of subsurface discontinuities in rough castings, forgings, and weldments.

Circular magnetization consists of inducing a circular magnetic field in a part so that the magnetic lines of force take the form of concentric rings about the axis of the current. This is accomplished by passing the current directly through the part, or by passing the current through a conductor which passes through a hole in the part, sometimes by use of prods. The circular method is used chiefly to indicate discontinuities radiating from and parallel to the axis of the current flow.

Longitudinal magnetization consists of inducing a longitudinal magnetic field in a part by making it the core of a solenoid, such as placing it in a coil or by making it a link in a magnetic circuit through use of a yoke. In a part so magnetized, the lines of force will be parallel to the axis of the solenoid, and the part will exhibit the properties of a bar magnet. The longitudinal method is used to indicate discontinuities transverse or circumferential to the long axis of a part.

Moving field magnetization consists of inducing fields in a part in more than one direction almost simultaneously. The fields induced may be a combination of circular and longitudinal or may be a combination of either type. The moving field method may be used on many parts ordinarily requiring two or more distinct magnetization and inspection operations. The moving field method, because of the rapidly changing field directions, makes possible the location of all detectable discontinuities after only one processing. This may, in some cases, eliminate a great percentage of the time required for the inspection if the parts were processed by more conventional methods.

Alternating current magnetization is commonly used for moderately stressed parts in production and for the detection of fatigue discontinuities due to service. Alternating current magnetization is always equal to, and often superior to, direct current magnetization for the detection of surface discontinuities. Subsurface discontinuities are not revealed when alternating current is used. In moderately stressed parts, this greatly simplifies inspection.

Direct current magnetization is commonly used for highly stressed parts. It is able to disclose certain subsurface discontinuities in addition to surface discontinuities.

Half-wave direct current is commonly used in the inspection of heavy weldments, heavy castings, and heavy forgings, in conjunction with dry magnetic particles. Half-wave direct current is essentially a pulsating direct current. The pulsations impart mobility to the magnetic particles, thereby assisting in aligning them in the weaker leakage fields produced by subsurface discontinuities. Subsurface discontinuities are best revealed by the use of this type current.

) ELECTROMAGNETIC TESTING BY EDDY CURRENT METHODS—SAE J425 MAR1991

SAE Information Report

Report of the SAE Iron and Steel Technical Committee, approved June 1960, third revision March 1981. Completely revised by the SAE Iron and Steel Technical Committee March 1991.

This Document has not changed other than to put it into the new SAE Technical Standards Board Format.

1. Scope—The purpose of this SAE Information Report is to provide general information relative to the nature and use of eddy current techniques for nondestructive testing. The document is not intended to provide detailed technical information but to serve as an introduction to the principles and capabilities of eddy current testing, and as a guide to more extensive references listed in Section 2.

2. References

2.1 Related Publications—The following publications are provided for information purposes only and are not a required part of this document.

2.1.1 ASM PUBLICATION—ATTN: MSC/Book Order, ASM International, PO Box 473, Novelty, OH 44072-9901.

Metals Handbook, Eighth Edition, Vol. 11, 1976, pp. 75–93.

Metals Handbook, Ninth Edition, Vol. 17, Nondestructive Evaluation and Quality Control, 1989.

2.1.2 ASTM PUBLICATION—Available from ASTM, 100 Barr Harbor Drive, West Conshohocken, PA 19428-2959

ASTM Annual Standards, Part 11, Standards E 215, E 243, E 268, E 309, E 376, E 426, E 566, E 570, E 571, E 690.

2.1.3 OTHER PUBLICATIONS

Nondestructive Testing Handbook, Second Edition, Vol. 4, Electromagnetic Testing, 1986, American Society for Nondestructive Testing, Columbus, OH 43228

Programmed Instruction Handbooks, PI-4-5, Eddy Current Testing, 1971. Classroom Training Handbook, CT-6-5, Eddy Current Testing, 1971. The above prepared by General Dynamics and available from American Society for Nondestructive Testing.

Hugo L. Libby, Introduction to Electromagnetic Nondestructive Test Methods, New York: John Wiley and Sons, Inc., 1985

Tool and Manufacturing Engineer's Handbook, Vol. 4, Quality Control and Assembly, 1987, Society of Manufacturing Engineers, Dearborn, MI 48121

3. General—Eddy current testing is a method of electromagnetic testing which uses induced electrical currents to indicate or measure certain characteristics of electrically conducting bodies (ferrous and nonferrous). Applications are in one of three general categories: metal sorting, surface discontinuity detection, or thickness measurement. Under appropriate conditions and with proper instrumentation, eddy current testing has been used to:

a. Detect discontinuities such as seams, laps, slivers, scabs, pits, cracks, voids, inclusions, and cold shuts.
b. Sort for chemical composition on a qualitative basis.
c. Sort for physical properties such as hardness, case depth, and heat damage.
d. Measure conductivity and related properties.
e. Measure dimensions such as the thickness of metallic coatings, plating, cladding, wall thickness or outside diameter of tubing, corrosion depth, and wear.
f. Measure the thickness of nonmetals, when a metallic backing sheet can be employed.

4. Principle—Eddy currents are induced in a test piece by a time varying magnetic field generated by an alternating current flowing in a coil. The coil configuration may assume a wide variety of shapes, sizes, and arrangements. The coil may surround the test piece or may be placed on or near the surface.

Eddy currents are influenced by many characteristics of the metal: conductivity, magnetic permeability, geometry, mass, and homogeneity. This fact makes it possible to evaluate many different characteristics of the test piece with appropriate test procedures.

In electromagnetic testing, energy is dissipated in the test piece by two separate processes: magnetic hysteresis and eddy current flow. In magnetic materials, both effects are present. In nonmagnetic and magnetically saturated materials, the hysteresis effect is absent or suppressed; and the prevalent losses are due to eddy currents.

Saturation is a term used generally to describe the condition of a ferromagnetic material at its maximum value of magnetization. To provide saturation, a direct current magnetic field or a permanent magnet of sufficient strength is applied to bring the material to a point where the ratio force approaches unity.

In this condition, the material behaves as if it were nonmagnetic. Theoretically, magnetic saturation should not be necessary for nonferromagnetic material, but some nonmagnetic materials contain small amounts of ferromagnetic material which can generate electrical noise during testing. This noise can usually be eliminated by the use of a saturating field.

5. Procedure—The effect of the characteristics of the test piece on the eddy currents may be studied in a number of different ways. A characteristic to be studied is related to a change in the amplitude, distribution, or phase of the eddy currents, or some combination of these three. These changes are reflected as changes in the exciting coil or in auxiliary coils located to be sensitive to the eddy currents. These changes may be measured as voltage differences, current differences, phase differences, or changes in the impedance of the coil or coils.

The coils and the instrumentation can be arranged to measure a given characteristic directly, or they may be used as a comparator. In the latter case, the measurement is the difference between the characteristics of the test piece and a similar piece of known or acceptable characteristics. Such measurements can also be made to determine differences between various segments of the same test piece.

Even with the best instrumentation, it is sometimes difficult to separate effects of the characteristics to be measured from effects of other characteristics. The success of an eddy current test depends on:

a. Proper coil design and arrangement
b. Selection of the proper test frequency
c. Selection of the proper analysis circuit
d. Use of proper magnetic field strength
e. Optimization and maintenance of electromagnetic coupling between the coil and test piece
f. Selection of the most suitable stage in the manufacturing process for the inspection procedure

Eddy current effects are most pronounced near the surface, with sensitivity for detecting irregularities of composition or structure falling off as depth below the surface increases. Depth of eddy current penetration of an object decreases as test frequency increases. Ferromagnetic metals, such as steel, are generally tested with low frequencies in the range of 1 to 10 000 Hz (10 kHz). Nonmagnetic metals with higher conductivity, such as aluminum, are generally tested with frequencies around 100 kHz, while those with lower conductivity, such as titanium, are generally tested with frequencies in the range of 1 to 10 MHz. There are numerous exceptions to these generalities.

6. Test Coil Methods

6.1 Single Coil—In this method, a single coil is used. It may have one or more windings for excitation and detection. A winding is excited from an alternating current source within the test instrument. The amplitude and phase of the voltage across a winding is a function of the effect of the test piece on the coil.

6.2 Differential Coil—An arrangement where two separate detector coils are used to compare two different test pieces, or two different portions of the same test piece. A voltage appears at the output terminal of the coils when the effective permeability, conductivity, mass, geometry, or homogeneity of the metal in the two coils differ.

7. Method Of Analysis

7.1 Lumped Impedance—In the lumped impedance analysis, a single coil is employed. A characteristic of the test piece is correlated to the amplitude and phase of the coil voltage.

7.2 Impedance Plane Analysis

7.2.1 MAGNETIC PARAMETER AMPLITUDE—The single coil or the differential coil method may be employed in this analysis. The variation in amplitude and phase of the detector coil voltage is measured and plotted in an impedance plane. The coil parameters are correlated to a test piece characteristic. Some variation in chemistry and size can be tolerated in this system providing the proper test frequency is employed.

7.2.2 PHASE ANGLE ANALYSIS—A two-coil method is more suited to this type of analysis. The phase angle between the voltage at the driving coil and that at the detector coil is measured and related to a test piece characteristic.

8. Equipment—Eddy current test instrumentation with a wide range of test frequencies and associated coils and probes of various sizes are commercially available to meet the needs of many applications. One of the advantages of electromagnetic equipment is that it lends itself to automatic operations for regularly shaped parts. Electromagnetic equipment can be large, elaborate, and expensive when multiple stations and materials handling sections are included, such as are used on sheets and plates. Manual systems which are small, simple, and inexpensive are common in other instances, and are used with large or irregularly shaped objects.

The electronic apparatus energizes an encircling coil or probe with alternating currents of suitable frequency and amplitude and detects the electromagnetic response of the coil. Equipment may include a detector phase discriminator, filter circuits, modulation circuits, magnetic saturation devices, recorders, and signaling devices as required by the application.

The encircling or probe coil assembly is capable of inducing current in the part and sensing changes in the electric and magnetic characteristics of the part.

A mechanical device capable of passing a part (such as a tube) through the encircling coil or past the probe may be used. It generally operates at uniform speed with minimum vibration of the coil, probe, or part, and maintains the article to be inspected in proper register or concentricity with the probe or encircling coil. A mechanism capable of uniformly rotating or moving the part or the probe may be required.

An end effect suppression device, a means capable of suppressing the signals produced at the ends of tubes or bars, may be used.

Reference standards are generally required to relate eddy current measurements to test part characteristics, and to adjust the sensitivity of the electronic apparatus.

8.1 Typical Examples of Equipment Variations for Different Applications

8.1.1 Equipment using impedance plane analysis and operable over a range of test frequencies from 1 Hz to 10 kHz has been used to sort carbon steel mixtures involving different compositions and/or different heat treat conditions. A unique advantage of this instrument is that it is possible to quickly determine the optimum frequency for performing a given test. Similar equipment has been calibrated to indicate conductivity, hardness, case depth, and dimensions.

8.1.2 Equipment using a single coil to scan the surface has been used to detect and indicate the depth of seams, cracks, laps, slivers, and similar surface and near-surface imperfections in bars, rounds, billets, and tubular products. The sensitivity of this equipment depends on the surface conditions of the product under test. On a hot-rolled surface with thin, tightly adherent scale, seams as shallow as 0.25 mm (0.010 in) are reliably evaluated. Product with heavy or broken scale should be cleaned by grit blasting prior to testing. Under more favorable (smoother, less scale) surface conditions seams as shallow as 0.13 mm (0.005 in) have been evaluated. On polished (ground) surfaces, seams and cracks as shallow as 0.025 mm (0.001 in) have been detected.

8.1.3 Equipment using differential test coils has been used to detect imperfections in carbon steel tubular and bar products. Testing frequencies ranging from 400 Hz to over 20 kHz have been used. At the lowest testing frequencies, and with the use of magnetic saturation, defects have been reliably detected (OD, ID, or subsurface) in the wall of tubular products with wall thicknesses as great as 15.9 mm (0.62 in). When testing at frequencies as low as 400 Hz, the testing speed is limited to about 30.5 m/min (100 ft/min). When higher testing frequencies are used, the testing speed can be correspondingly increased. Higher testing frequencies can be used for testing product with thinner walls and higher resistivity.

8.1.4 Vector sensitive instruments operate on the impedance plane principle. The frequency range of these instruments is from 100 Hz to 6 MHz. This type of operation considers both the amplitude and phase of the eddy currents. This allows one to optimize the instrument response for a selected material variable, while minimizing response to another variable, such as probe spacing.

8.1.5 Multiple frequency eddy current instruments can test a product at several frequencies simultaneously or in rapid sequence. Unuseful signal variations due to overlapping responses, product geometry variations, and probe lift-off effects can be reduced significantly. Thus the resulting signal response is enhanced. Simultaneous multiple frequency tests are generally used to overcome probe lift-off effects in surface defect tests of nonferrous products. Sequential multiple frequency tests are generally used to sort ferrous products of similar composition, or to determine two characteristics, such as hardness and case depth, in a single test.

LEAKAGE TESTING—SAE J1267 DEC1988

SAE Information Report

Report of the SAE Iron and Steel Technical Committee approved May 1979, first revision, Division 25, June 1984; reaffirmed 1988.

Foreword—This Reaffirmed Document has not changed other than to put it into the new SAE Technical Standards Board Format.

1. Scope—This information report provides basic information on leakage testing, as applied to nondestructive testing, and affords the user sufficient information so that he may decide whether leakage testing methods apply to his particular need. Detailed references are listed in Section 2.

2. References

2.1 Applicable Publications—The Following Publications Form A Part Of The Specification To The Extent Specified Herein. Unless Otherwise Indicated The Lastest Revision Of SAE Publications Shall Apply.

2.1.1 SAE PUBLICATION—Available from SAE, 400 Commonwealth Drive, Warrendale, PA 15096-0001.

SAE J426—Liquid Penetrant Test Methods

2.2 Related Publications—The Following Publications Are Provided For Information Purposes Only And Are Not A Required Part Of This Document.

2.2.1 ASTM PUBLICATIONS—Available from ASTM, 100 Barr Harbor Drive, West Conshohocken, PA 19428-2959.

ASTM E 425—Standard Definitions of Terms Relating to Leak Testing

ASTM E 427—Recommended Practice for Testing for Leaks Using the Halogen Leak Detector (Alkali-Ion Diode)

ASTM E 432—Standard Recommended Guide for the Selection of a Leak Testing Method

ASTM E 479—Standard Recommended Guide for Preparation of a Leak Test Specification

ASTM E 493—Standard Test Methods for Leaks Using the Mass Spectrometer Leak Detector in the Inside-Out Testing Mode

ASTM E 498—Standard Methods of Testing for Leaks Using the Mass Spectrometer Leak Detector or Residual Gas Analyzer in Tracer Probe Mode

ASTM E 499—Standard Methods of Testing for Leaks Using the Mass Spectrometer Leak Detector in the Detector Probe Mode

ASTM E 515—Standard Methods of Testing for Leaks Using Bubble Emission Techniques

ASTM E 908—Standard Practice for Calibrating Gaseous Reference Leaks

2.3 Other Publications

Nondestructive Testing Handbook, Volume 1, "Leak Testing," 1982, American Society for Nondestructive Testing, Columbus, OH 43228.

J. W. Marr, Leakage Testing Handbook, 1968, NASA Cr-952, Jet Propulsion Laboratory, National Aeronautics and Space Administration, Washington, DC.

N. I. Sax, Dangerous Properties of Industrial Methods, 2nd Edition, 1963, Reinhold Publishing Corp., New York, NY.

J. W. Perry, Chemical Engineering Handbook, 3rd Edition, 1950, McGraw-Hill Book Co., New York, NY.

Metals Handbook, 8th Edition, Volume 11, 1976, pp. 260-270, American Society for Metals, Metals Park, OH 44073.

ASME Boiler and Pressure Vessel Code, latest addenda, American Society for Mechanical Engineers, New York, NY.

Qualification and Certification of Personnel, Recommended Practice SNT-TC-1A, Supplement G (Leak Testing), American Society for Nondestructive Testing, Columbus, OH 43228.

R. J. Roehrs, Leak Testing of Welded Vessels, 2nd Annual Symposium on Nondestructive Testing of Welds, sponsored by IITRI, Chicago, IL, 1967.

3. General—Leakage testing is a form of nondestructive testing capable of determining the existence of leak sites and, under proper conditions, measuring the quantity of material passing through these sites. The word leak means the hole through which fluid (liquid or gas) passes in either a pressurized or evacuated system, while leakage is the term used to connote the mass flow of fluid regardless of the size of the leak. Leakage rate is the quantity of fluid per unit time that flows through the leak at a given temperature as a result of a specified pressure difference across the leak. The ASTM accepted unit of leakage rate is standard cubic centimeters per second (std. cm^3/s), frequently referred to as atmosphere cubic centimeters per second (atm. cm^3/s). The SI terminology is Pascal cubic meters per second (Pa m^3/s). (1 Pa M^3/s = 10 atm. cm^3/s, approximately.)

There is no container in which a differential pressure exists (either pressurized or vacuum) that does not leak to some extent. Absolute leak tightness is an absolute impossibility. Any container must, therefore, have a maximum leakage rate specified. In considering the leakage rate that can be tolerated, one must decide whether the rate represents the total leakage from the system or the maximum leakage from a single leak. Additional factors to be considered include shelf life, product contained, toxicity, legal requirements, consequences of excessive leakage, cost of product, cost of testing, and customer requirements. Once a leakage rate has been specified then a leak test procedure describing the operating and test conditions needs to be detailed. Since leakage rate relates pressure, volume, and time, more than one set of procedural values can yield the same leakage rate. In general, the pressure used should reflect pressures that the item would see in service, however, this is not a requirement. In some isolated cases, using markedly different pressures can cause leaks to pass grossly different rates of fluid due to elastic deformation of the item being tested. Regardless of the type of leakage testing being done, safety considerations for the personnel performing these tests must be a paramount consideration.

4. Principles—There are eight or more primary methods which may be employed to detect, locate, and/or measure leakage. The following paragraphs identify these methods and describe their principles, as well as their capabilities and limitations.

4.1 Mass Loss and Pressure Change—These are two related methods. Traditionally, these are used for sizable leakage rates, and provide no information as to the leak site. Mass loss is calculated on the basis of change in mass at two times; accordingly, extremely accurate weighing is a requirement of this method. Pressure change methods operate in a similar fashion, except that a change in pressure is the signaling mechanism. Pressure change systems usually measure change of the gaseous systems. Since pressure is temperature dependent, the temperature of the system must either remain constant or be compensated for by use of ideal gas laws. Mass loss and pressure change methods, using most techniques, are time consuming and thus are limited in leakage testing applications.

Theoretically, these methods are very accurate if one has sufficient time to conduct the test.

4.2 Ultrasonic Leak Testing—This is a method valuable for detecting leakage great enough to produce turbulent flow. Turbulent flow in a gas occurs when the velocity approaches the speed of sound in that gas; this is approximately 10^{-1} to 10^{-2} std. cm^3/s. This method takes advantage of the fact that turbulent flow generates sound frequencies from audible upward to 60 kHz. In using only the ultrasonic component generated, fewer false signals are detected because there are fewer other sources of ambient ultrasound. Because of the highly directional nature of ultrasound, the leak can usually be accurately located. Output of ultrasonic leak detectors is an audible signal or a meter deflection, the strength of which is a function of the leak rate. Advantages of the ultrasonic method are that the equipment is simple to operate, it can be done with the probe removed from the leak, and it does not require any material which could clog a leak and require cleaning. Its primary disadvantage lies in its lack of sensitivity to small leakage rates (less than 10^{-2} std. cm^3/s).

4.3 Chemical Penetrant Leak Tests—These are incapable of providing leakage rate information, but do clearly point out sites for repair. Sensitivities are generally conceded to be in the range of 10^{-3} std. cm^3/s, although greater sensitivities have been achieved. Two basic forms of chemical penetrants are available, liquid tracers (quite similar to liquid penetrants, see SAE Information Report J426) and gaseous tracers. Hydrostatic testing with water alone is not a substitute for leakage testing.

4.3.1 LIQUID TRACERS—Liquid tracers are usually a solution of a tracer dye and a liquid in which it is soluble. It is essential to determine the coloring power of the tracer solution in the concentration being used as this relates to the sensitivity, as does the wettability of the tracer solution. As a general rule in white light systems, basic dyes work best in a water solution and solvent dyes are better suited to an oil based system. White light liquid tracer systems are generally inferior to fluorescent liquid tracer systems. This sensitivity inferiority is due, in part, to the increased visibility of fluorescent dyes, and the inherent contrast of the dyes to the near black background used in testing. By dissolving a fluorescent tracer in a volatile liquid, very small leaks can be found, because the liquid which evaporates leaves behind a concentrated dye which is more visible. Advantages of liquid tracers lie in their cost, sensitivity, and ease of use. Foremost among their disadvantages is that they use material which could temporarily clog a leak. Also, liquid tracers require cleaning of the parts after use and care in their application so as not to create false signals. In addition, one may experience occasional difficulty in tracing large leakages to their source due to liquid spread.

4.3.2 Gaseous Tracers—Gaseous tracers are gases which color indicating media, thereby denoting the location of a leak. The most widely used gas for this application is ammonia. Indicating media for ammonia gas are:

1. Phenolphthalein which turns from clear to pink.
2. Bromocresol purple which turns from a yellow-green to purple.
3. Bromothymol blue, which turns from yellow to blue.

Carbon dioxide gas can be used for leak testing with an indicating medium of sodium carbonate and phenolphthalein in an agar-agar solution. This bright red indicator will turn white at a leak site.

There is another medium, which is much less widely used, due to the inherent danger of its chemicals. Pressurizing a component with ammonia and then allowing hydrogen chloride to be brought near, will produce a white cloud of ammonium chloride vapor which is clearly visible. These gases are highly corrosive and dangerous to human tissue. Extreme care and a high level of ventilation are needed, as well as consideration for the safety of the personnel performing the test.

There is little difference in the level of sensitivity for gaseous tracers when compared to liquid tracers; both are typically at 10^{-3} std. cm^3/s. Rates as low as 10^{-6} std. cm^3/s have been reported for gaseous tracers. Primary among their advantages is their low cost of operation since no instrumentation is needed. Disadvantages are that some gases could corrode the test object, be hazardous to personnel, require cleanup, and clog leaks.

4.4 Bubble Leak Test—These methods are widely used. They possess sensitivities to a commercial range as small as 10^{-4} std. cm^3/s (10^{-2} is a practical value for an unskilled operator). In the laboratory, under ideal conditions with special combinations of liquid and gas, rates as low as 10^{-7} std. cm^3/s have been detected. The method operates on the basis of a differential pressure at a leak creating a flow of gas. This gas, upon escaping, will produce one or more bubbles in the test liquid. These bubbles mark the location of the leak and the frequency and size can be used to estimate the leakage rate.

Procedurally, the test object is fixtured and pressurized, and then the indicating liquid (not a soap or detergent solution) is brought into contact with the component. This precludes the liquid from temporarily blocking a small leak which could cause the acceptance of a leaking component. Precleaning of the test object is necessary because surface contaminants also may cause a temporary blockage of a leak. From a practical standpoint, any gas may be used to pressurize the object. Should air be used, it must be very clean, again to preclude temporary blockage of a leak. Shop air is generally too dirty, wet, and oily to use for leak testing.

Ample illumination must be provided to permit the inspector to be able to see a stream of bubbles; 1000 1m/m^2 (100 fc) is recommended as a minimum level.

Indication of leakage may be accomplished by the use of:

1. A liquid in which the test object is immersed.
2. A liquid film which produces bubbles when a leakage passes. (A vacuum box which surrounds the test area may be used to create the pressure differential.)

Liquids used in bubble testing must not corrode the object being tested. Frequently, it is desired to enhance the sensitivity of a bubble test. Enhancement can be done by increasing the time for testing or increasing the pressure. In some instances, neither of these approaches is practical. Changing the gas to one of a lower molecular weight and/or lowering the surface tension of the liquid will also enhance the sensitivity. Visual inspection should be conducted at distances less than 0.6 m (2 ft) for best results.

A vacuum box places an area to be tested under a sub-atmospheric pressure. A clear window through which observations are made and a liquid in which leakage appears are necessary for the vacuum box technique. When used (usually for welds in large vessels) adjacent testing locations must be overlapped to assure full coverage.

The advantages of bubble testing lie in its simplicity, cost, and relative sensitivity. Disadvantages include the need for cleanup, the fact that fine leaks may not be detected due to a lack of time, the possibility of clogging, and finally that bubble testing is a visual inspection, and as such, bubble testing is limited by the performance of an operator.

4.5 Thermal Conductivity Leak Testing—These methods have a minimum leakage rate detectability of 10^{-5} std. cm^3/s. They are based on the principle that certain gases have a markedly different thermal conductivity when compared to air. Equipment for this method consists of two heated filaments in a bridge circuit. One filament is cooled by air and the other by the test gas. Any differences unbalance the bridge and can be related to leakage. The two gases with the greatest difference in thermal conductivity are hydrogen and helium. Most thermal conductivity leak testing is done with argon, CO_2, neon, or R-12 (freon). Advantages include cost of equipment, reduced sensitivity to contaminants in the ambient atmosphere than other instrumented leak detectors, and simplicity of operation. Disadvantages include the limited gases which can be used.

4.6 Halogen-Based Leak Detectors—These use a halogen gas as the pressurizing medium and may take several forms, including the halide torch, the heated anode detector, and the electron capture detector. The upper limit of sensitivity is 10^{-9} std. cm^3/s. Halogen leak detector tests are normally not conducted using elemental halogens as a detector gas. Halogen leak detector tests are conducted using a chlorinated, fluorinated, or chlori-fluorinated hydrocarbon as the tracer gas.

Simplest and least expensive in the halogen family of leak detectors is the halide torch. It consists of a halide free source of gas, frequently acetylene, and a search tube to look for leaks, both of which feed a burner with a copper plate. In operation, the flame of the torch is blue when no halogens are present. The flame turns green when small leaks are detected, and turns violet when exposed to larger leaks. Search rates are approximately 6 mm (1/4 in)/s. Halide torches have a leakage detectability of 10^{-4} std. cm^3/s. Since torches generate toxic vapors they must be used only in areas with adequate ventilation and cannot be used in flammable environments.

Due to the widespread use of the heated anode halogen detector in the refrigeration industry, this instrumentation is the most widely used of the halogen leak detectors. Operationally, ions are emitted from a hot plate to a collector. These positive ions increase in proportion to the amount of halogen present. Sensitivities of 10^{-9} std. cm^3/s are obtainable. This detector has the advantages of high sensitivity, and the ability to operate in air. Its disadvantages include responding to halogen containing suspended particles from sources like cigarette smoke and chlorinated hydrocarbons used in cleaning compounds, and that the decomposed products are toxic and corrosive. Further, the anode operates at 900 °C (1650 °F) which makes it unusable in a flammable environment, and there is a need to recalibrate the unit regularly as the calibration changes with use.

The electron capture leak test method uses a non-electron capturing gas (argon or nitrogen) as a background gas. The electron capture test gas is ionized producing tritium. In operation, the halogens drawn through the sensor reduce the ion content which produces a current. This current is proportional to the amount of halogen. Electron capture is frequently used with sulphur hexafluoride as a tracer. Sensitivities of 10^{-10} std. cm^3/s or better have been achieved. Advantages include very good calibration sensitivity, the absence of a heated element, and non-production of toxic or corrosive gases. Cost is the primary disadvantage of this sytem.

One of the most sensitive types of leakage testing equipment is the mass spectrometer. Leakage rates of 10^{-11} std. cm^3/s are achievable under ideal conditions. This method is the most accurate form for vacuum testing. A mass spectrometer operates on the principle of sorting gaseous ions with respect to their molecular weight. In a helium mass spectrometer, baffles with slits allow He^+ ions to pass through to the detector while all other ions are blocked. The number of He^+ ions which arrive at the collector per unit time is a measure of the leakage rate. Rates are typically displayed on a calibrated meter. As in any tracer gas system, care should be exercised to keep false signals from being sensed and displayed as leakage. Grease, oil, rubber, and other materials can act as storage reservoirs for helium.

Sensitivity is usually considered to be the greatest advantage of the mass spectrometer, also the fact that it is not affected by background contamination (other than He) is a great asset. Using helium provides inherent safety when compared with other gases which are toxic.

Cost is the greatest disadvantage of the mass spectrometer; however, many thousands are currently in use.

5. Applications—Any attempt to list the more common products evaluated by these test methods would be cumbersome and fail to serve the user. Briefly, any product containing a pressure different from atmospheric can be leak tested. The decision to leak test or not to leak test should be based on economic considerations and applicable legal requirements.

With the capability to sense leakage rates to 10^{-11} std. cm^3/s, there is no reasonable leakage rate that cannot be detected using available leakage testing technology.

Table 1 is presented to give the reader a better understanding of leakage rates.

TABLE 1—COMPARISON OF LEAKAGE RATES

Leakage Rate (Std. cm^3/s)	Approximate Time to Fill	
	1 cm^3	1 in^3
10^{-1}	10 s	3 min
10^{-2}	2 min	27 min
10^{-3}	17 min	4 h
10^{-4}	3 h	2 days
10^{-5}	28 h	19 days
10^{-6}	12 days	6 months
10^{-7}	4 months	5 years
10^{-8}	3 years	52 years
10^{-9}	32 years	520 years
10^{-10}	320 years	5200 years
10^{-11}	3200 years	52 000 years

(R) LIQUID PENETRANT TEST METHODS—SAE J426 MAR1991

SAE Information Report

Report of the SAE Iron and Steel Technical Committee, approved June 1960, fourth revision by ISTC Division 25 June 1983 and reaffirmed December 1988. Completely revised by the SAE Iron and Steel Technical Committee March 1991.

Foreword—This Document has not changed other than to put it into the new SAE Technical Standards Board Format.

1. Scope—The scope of this SAE Information Report is to supply the user with sufficient information so that he may decide whether liquid penetrant test methods apply to his particular inspection problem. Detailed technical information can be obtained by referring to Section 2.

2. References

2.1 Related Publications—The following publications are provided for information purposes only and are not a required part of this document.

2.1.1 SAE PUBLICTIONS—Available from SAE, 400 Commonwealth Drive, Warrendale, PA 15096-0001.

SAE AMS 2645H—Fluorescent Penetrant Inspection, January 1, 1983
SAE AMS 2646C—Contrast Dye Penetrant Inspection, April 1, 1982
SAE AMS 3155B—Oil, Fluorescent Penetrant Solvent Soluble, November 1, 1970
SAE AMS 3156B—Oil Fluorescent Penetrant Water Base, November 1970
SAE AMS 3158A—Solution, Fluorescent Penetrant Water Base, July 1979

2.1.2 ASM PUBLICATION—ATTN: MSC/Book Order, ASM International, PO Box 473, Novelty, OH 44072-9901.

Metals Handbook, Ninth Edition, Vol. 17, pp. 71–88, Nondestructive Evaluation and Quality Control, 1989.
Metals Handbook, Eighth Edition, Volume 11, 1976, pp. 20–44.

2.1.3 ASTM PUBLICATIONS—Available from ASTM, 100 Barr Harbor Drive, West Conshohocken, PA 19428-2959

ASTM E 165—Method for Liquid Penetrant Inspection
ASTM E 270—Definitions of Terms Relating to Liquid Penetrant Inspection

2.1.4 OTHER PUBLICATIONS

C. E. Betz, "Principles of Penetrants," Magnaflux Corp., 1963
Nondestructive Testing Handbook, R. C. McMaster, ed., Columbus, OH 43228. American Society for Nondestructive Testing, Volume 2, "Liquid Penetrant Tests" Second Edition, 1982
Tool and Manufacturing Engineer's Handbook, Vol. 4, Quality Control and Assembly, 1987, Society of Manufacturing Engineers, Dearborn, MI 48121
MIL-I-6866B—(ASG), Inspection, Penetrant Method of
MIL-I-25135C—(ASG), Materials, Penetrant
Programmed Instruction Handbook PI-4-2, Convair Div., General Dynamics Corp., 1967
Recommended Practice SNT-TC-1A, Supplement D-Liquid Penetrant, Qualification and Certification of Personnel. American Society for Nondestructive Testing, Columbus, OH 43221

3. General—Liquid penetrant testing is a nondestructive inspection method suitable for the detection of very small discontinuities that are open to the surface of nonporous objects. It is generally used on materials such as metals, plastics, and ceramics. However, the magnetic particle method is generally preferred for ferromagnetic materials. Specific applications include detection of cold shuts, seams, shrinkage, porosity, cracks, and other imperfections which are open to the surface.

4. Principle—The liquid penetrant test method is based upon capillary action, using low surface tension liquids. The liquid penetrant is applied to the surface to be inspected by dipping, spraying, or brushing. The excess penetrant is removed and a developer is applied. The bleeding out of penetrant from the discontinuity into the developer yields indications which can be observed and evaluated. This is done under ultraviolet or white light, depending upon the type of liquid penetrant used - fluorescent or nonfluorescent (visible).

5. Procedure

a. Clean parts by washing, degreasing, or etching. (Paint or other surface coatings must first be removed.)
b. Apply penetrant to the surface to be inspected.
c. Allow adequate time for penetration.
d. Remove excess penetrant from the surface.
e. Dry the surface to be inspected. (Perform after the next step if a wet developer is used.)

NOTE—Excessive part temperatures can degrade penetrants.

f. Apply a developer when applicable. The developer is a material which acts like a blotter and draws penetrant from the defect. Dry or wet (aqueous or nonaqueous) developers are used.
g. Locate imperfections by observing penetrant bleed-out from the discontinuity.
h. Post clean parts. Remove residual penetrant and developer.

6. Characteristics—Penetrants are classified into two types. One type of penetrant employs fluorescent dyes to make surface imperfections visible under ultraviolet light. The other type of penetrant employs red nonfluorescent dyes which are visible under white light.

7. Method Of Penetrant Removal—The penetrants are further classified according to the method of excess penetrant removal:

7.1 Method A: Water Washable—The penetrants contain an emulsifier which makes them water washable.

7.2 Method B: Post Emulsified—These penetrants require that an emulsifier or remover (hydrophilic) be applied over the penetrants to make them water washable. Hence, they are called post-emulsifiable penetrants or remover penetrants.

7.3 Method C: Solvent Removable—These penetrants are mechanically removed by hand wiping with a final wipe with a solvent dampened cloth.

8. Penetrant Selection—Generally, there are several recognized sensitivity levels of penetrant performance relating primarily to the width of discontinuity that must be detected. Selection of the appropriate penetrant system (type method and sensitivity level) will be based on the following factors:

a. Surface roughness
b. Surface treatment
c. Size of discontinuity to be disclosed
d. Environment
e. Production required
f. Equipment available
g. Type of material to be inspected
h. Subsequent use of the part
i. Disposal restrictions
j. Cost
k. Others

Where minimal sensitivity with respect to size of discontinuities is needed, the color contrast or visible dye penetrants are usually employed and any of the three methods of penetrant removal listed in Section 7 can be used.

Fluorescent penetrants make discontinuities more discernible. Fluorescent penetrants may be selected for use with method A, B, or C. Three principal factors affect performance: the amount and brilliance of fluorescent dye that is contained within the penetrant material and the ability of the penetrant to be retained in the surface discontinuities after surface excess is removed.

Generally, Method A or B is preferred to Method C.

9. Developers—One of three types of developers is used to draw the penetrant from the discontinuities.

9.1 Dry developer consists of a dry, light-colored, powdery material. Dry developer is applied to the surface of the parts after removal of the excess penetrant and drying of the part. Dry developer is applied by immersing the parts in a tank containing powder, by brushing it on with a paintbrush (usually not a desirable technique), or by blowing the powder onto the surface of the part.

9.2 Aqueous wet developer consists of powdered material suspended in water. The use of the wet developers permits rapid coverage of a large number of parts or of parts that have complicated shapes. After application of the wet developer, usually by dipping, the part is dried and then inspected for penetrant indications.

9.3 Nonaqueous wet developer is a powder suspended in a suitable solvent and sprayed onto the surface of the dry part. The solvent evaporates quickly, leaving a fine coating of developer on the surface of the part. The nonaqueous wet developer produces very high sensitivity when inspecting parts with small, tight defects.

Selection of the type of development method or material used for an application is important to the achievement of reliable inspections. The three types of developers vary widely in the degree of enhancement of indications. Nonaqueous wet developer, aqueous wet developer, or dry powder may be preferred depending upon the application. Surface finish may affect the degree of enhancement of developers. An aqueous developer, either soluble or particulate, should not generally be used with water-washable penetrants.

R) PENETRATING RADIATION INSPECTION —SAE J427 MAR1991

SAE Information Report

Report of the SAE Iron and Steel Technical Committee, approved June 1960, third revision by ISTC Division 25 June 1983, and reaffirmed December 1988. Completely revised by the SAE Iron and Steel Technical Committee-Division 25-Nondestructive Test Methods March 1991.

Foreword—This Document has not changed other than to put it into the new SAE Technical Standards Board Format.

1. Scope—The purpose of this SAE Information Report is to provide basic information on penetrating radiation, as applied in the field of nondestructive testing, and to supply the user with sufficient information so that he may decide whether penetrating radiation methods apply to his particular inspection need. Detailed information references are listed in Section 2.

2. References

2.1 Applicable Publications—The following publications form a part of this specification to the extent specified herein. The latest issue of SAE publications shall apply.

2.1.1 ASTM PUBLICATIONS—Available from ASTM, 1916 Race Street, Philadelphia, PA 19103

ASTM E 94—Recommended Practice for Radiographic Testing

ASTM E 545—Standard Method for Determining Image Quality in Thermal Neutron Radiographic Testing

2.2 Related Publications—The following publications are provided for information purposes only and are not a required part of this document.

2.2.1 ASM PUBLICATION—ATTN: MSC/Book Order, ASM International, PO Box 473, Novelty, OH 44072-9901.

Metals Handbook, Vol. 17, 1989, pp. 295–357.

2.2.2 ASME PUBLICATION—Available from ASME, 345 East 47 Street, New York, NY 10017-2330.

"ASME Boiler and Pressure Vessel Code."

2.2.3 ASTM PUBLICATIONS—Available from ASTM, 100 Barr Harbor Drive, West Conshohocken, PA 19428-2959

ASTM E 142, "Controlling Quality of Radiographic Testing."

ASTM E 545 "Standard Method for Determining Image Quality in Thermal Neutron Radiographic Testing."

ASTM E 748 "Standard Practice for Thermal Neutron Radiography of Materials."

H. Berger, ed., "Practical Applications of Neutron Radiography and Gaging," ASTM STP 586.

2.2.4 OTHER PUBLICATIONS

Nondestructive Testing Handbook, Vol. 3, Radiography and Radiographic Testing, 1985, American Society for Nondestructive Testing, Columbus, OH 43228

Tool and Manufacturing Engineers Handbook, Vol. 4, Quality Control Assembly, 1987, Society of Manufacturing Engineers, Dearborn, MI 48121

"Radiography in Modern Industry." Eastman Kodak Co., Rochester, NY, 1969.

John R. Bradford, ed., "Radioisotopes in Industry." 1953.

R. C. McMaster, ed., Nondestructive Testing Handbook, Vol. I, Section 13–27, 1959. American Society of Nondestructive Testing, Columbus, OH 43321.

H. Berger, Neutron Radiography. New York: American Elsevier Publishing Co., 1965.

W. J. McGonnagle, Nondestructive Testing. New York: McGraw-Hill Book Co., 1961.

R. Halmshaw, ed., Industrial Radiology Techniques. New York: American Elsevier Publishing Co., 1971.

E. T. Clarke, "Gamma Radiography of Light Metals." Nondestructive Testing, Vol. 16, May-June 1958, p. 265.

"Qualification and Certification of Personnel." Recommended Practice No. SNT-TC-1A, Supplement A (Radiography), American Society for Nondestructive Testing, Columbus, OH 43328.

Justin G. Schneeman, Industrial X-Ray Interpretation. Evanston, IL: Intex Publishing Co., 1968.

"Radiographic Testing." Programmed Instruction Handbook PI-4–6, Convair Div., General Dynamics Corp., 1967.

AMS 2635 C "Radiographic Inspection." July 15, 1981.

"Military Standard Inspection—Radiographic." MIL-STD-453, U.S. Department of Defense.

M. R. Hawkesworth, ed., "Radiography with Neutrons," British Nuclear Energy Society, London, 1975."

Neutron Radiography Issue, Atomic Energy Review, Vol. 15, No. 2, International Atomic Energy Agency, Vienna, 1977.

3. General—Penetrating radiation is a versatile nondestructive test method used in modern industry. The use of penetrating x-rays, gamma rays, thermal neutrons, and other forms of radiation which do not affect the material being inspected, provide the basic information by which soundness can be determined. Radiography provides a permanent record on film of internal conditions. Fluoroscopy differs from radiography in that the radiation image is projected on a fluorescent screen or other readout monitor and is often observed visually in real time rather than recorded on a film. Systems are available that produce digitally reconstructed, photographic, or magnetically recorded displays. Penetrating radiation enables industry to monitor a variety of products for a number of types of imperfections. Objects inspected range in size from microminiature electronic parts to very large components in a wide range of manufactured forms (for example, castings, weldments, assemblies).

4. Principles—X-rays, gamma rays, and neutrons possess the capability of penetrating materials, even those that are opaque to light. In passing through matter, some of these rays are absorbed or scattered. Materials absorb x-rays and gamma rays in proportion to their mass. Neutron absorption, on the other hand, is not related proportionally to atomic number or mass; neighboring elements can differ in neutron absorption by factors of 100 or more. Differential absorption of the radiant energy passing through the object due to the presence of voids, discontinuities, or density variations caused by inhomogeneity or internal construction is recorded on radiographic film or observed directly by fluoroscopic methods. With acceptable conditions of technology and equipment, it is generally agreed that discontinuities can be detected which present to the axis of radiation a minimum dimension of 1 to 2% of the thickness of the object undergoing radiographic examination, or 2 to 6% for fluoroscopic examination. Two-dimensional imperfections, such as cracks and cold shuts, are not detectable unless they present an effective thickness difference of the above magnitude, or greater, and are in appropriate alignment with the beam of radiation.

5. Procedure

5.1 Radiographic Film Technique—A radiographic film is a photographic record produced by the passage of x-rays, gamma rays, or neutrons through an object onto a film. When film is exposed to a radiation source or light, an invisible change is produced in the film emulsion. The areas so exposed become dark when the film is immersed in a developing solution; the amount of darkening depends upon the degree of exposure. Image formation is usually enhanced through use of thin metal screens in intimate contact with the film. Lead screens are used in x-ray exposures made with energy above 100 kV and in gamma ray exposures. Screens are necessary for film detection of thermal neutrons. Gadolinium metal screens are normally used for direct-exposure techniques and indium metal screens are normally used for indirect-exposure techniques. The developing, fixing, and washing of exposed film may be done either manually or in an automatic film processor. The exposed, processed, and dried radiographic film is examined under transmitted light. Interpretation of the image is performed in accordance with established codes, specifications, or acceptance criteria.

The finished radiograph should be viewed under conditions which provide for the best visualization of detail combined with maximum comfort and minimum fatigue for the observer. A high-intensity illuminator with adjustable intensity is almost a necessity for optimum radiographic observation and interpretation. Penetrameters are used to indicate the image quality which exists in a radiograph. The type generally used in the United States is a small rectangular plate of the same material as the object being x-rayed. It is uniform in thickness (usually 2% of the object thickness) and has holes drilled through it. ASTM specifies hole diameters 1, 2, and 4 times the thickness of the penetrameter. Step, wire, and bead penetrameters are also used. (See ASTM E 94.) For neutron radiography, image quality indicators provide a measure of the relative exposure due to gamma rays, higher energy neutrons, and scattered neutrons. Additional image quality indicators are suggested to provide measures of contrast and resolution capability. (See ASTM E 545.)

5.1.1 ADVANTAGES—Film radiography provides a permanent, visible record of the internal condition of the subject. Preservation of films is a common practice in industry.

5.1.2 DISADVANTAGES—High cost is the chief objection to film radiography. One-half of the average inspection cost may be the radiographic film cost. X-ray paper products reduce this disadvantage when maximum performance capability is not required.

Inspection results are not available until radiographic film has been exposed, processed, and interpreted.

5.2 Fluoroscopic Inspection Technique—Fluoroscopy is the process of examining an object by direct or indirect observation of the fluorescence of a screen caused by radiation transmitted through an object. The arrangement of the x-ray source, object, and imaging plane is identical to that used in radiography. The fluorescent screen, image intensifier tube, television camera, and similar electronic imaging devices convert x-ray to visible light for further signal processing, operator interpretation, and recording.

5.2.1 ADVANTAGES—Production line inspection systems are available. These can result in low cost per part inspected and can meet the inspection requirements of high-volume production. Real-time image enhancement and interpretation are available in systems using television imaging.

5.2.2 DISADVANTAGES—The sensitivity of the fluoroscopic process is not usually as great as that of radiography, 2 to 6% being routine. The additional cost of producing a permanent record of the examination may be a disadvantage. For systems employing television imaging, however, magnetic recording can be used, photographs may be taken of the television image, or digital processing can be used for imaging and interpretation.

6. Application—The ability of high energy radiation to penetrate all engineering materials and the differential rates of absorption for different materials are responsible for the extensive use of this nondestructive inspection technique throughout industry. Accordingly, penetrating radiation inspection methods are extensively used for flaw detection in the following areas:

6.1 Castings—The widespread use of penetrating radiation methods for the inspection of castings results from the fact that most of the flaws and discontinuities inherent in ferrous and nonferrous castings can be readily detected by this inspection medium. Shrinkage, gas porosity, inclusions, hot tears, cracks, cold shuts, core shifts, and major surface irregularities may be detectable by radiographic or fluoroscopic inspection techniques. In addition, the following discontinuities which are peculiar to light metal (aluminum and magnesium) castings are detectable: gas holes, dross inclusions, segregation, microshrinkage, hydrogen porosity, microporosity, shrinkage, sponge, cold shuts, and other discontinuities common to light metal castings.

6.2 Weldments—Penetrating radiation inspection of weldments is a widely accepted procedure for the detection of internal discontinuities. It is used in the establishment of welding procedures to qualify welders and especially to control quality of welded joints in finished products. The following imperfections or discontinuities are detectable by radiography: porosity, cracks, incomplete penetration and fusion, inclusions, and other discontinuities common in welded joints.

6.3 Finished Assemblies—Penetrating radiation techniques are applicable to the inspection of fabricated assemblies relative to placement of internal components, such as electronic devices, mufflers, fuel tanks, bonded honeycomb, and tires. Electrical connections as well as the position of bolts and nuts in finished enclosures are frequently checked by radiography. Neutron radiography of assemblies provides a capability to verify proper placement of hydrogen-containing materials in metal assemblies. By this method rubber O-Rings, plastic parts, propellants, fluid levels, and similar materials can be visualized even when these objects are inside metallic containers.

6.4 Miscellaneous Applications—Occasional use is made of radiographic techniques in the inspection of forgings, powder metal parts, and of nonmetallic materials such as plastic, rubber, ceramic, and solid propellant. The limited use of this inspection medium for forgings is explained by the fact that forging defects are smaller in size and unsuitably oriented for reliable detection by radiography.

7. Equipment—There are a number of factors which affect the use of penetrating radiation to varying extents. These factors can be grouped into three general categories as follows:

a. Source of radiation
b. Object or material to be examined
c. Detecting or recording medium.

Sources for neutron radiography include nuclear reactors, accelerators, and radioactive isotopes. These sources can be moved (in a truck, for example) but most neutron radiographic inspection is done by bringing the inspection object to the source. Radiation sources for other types of radiography involve either x-ray generators or one of several radio isotopes. X-rays are produced when high-velocity electrons impinge upon target atoms. The energy of the x-radiation produced is a function of the velocity of the impinged electrons, which in turn is dependent upon the applied anode voltage (kV or MeV). The practical thickness range of steel which can be inspected by x-ray units is proportional to their radiation energy, as shown in Figure 1. The usefulness of Figure 1 can be extended to other materials by referring to Table 1, which gives equivalence factors for various other materials as compared to steel.

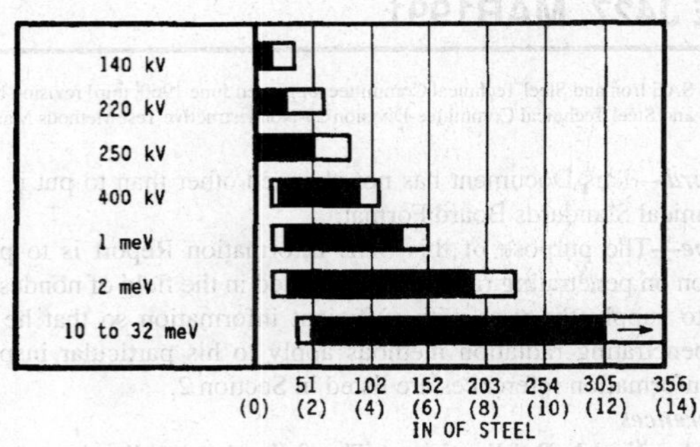

The shaded portions of the bar represent thickness where 1% sensitivity is obtained.
The unshaded portion at Bar ends represent 2% sensitivity.
NOTE—Dimensions are mm (inch)

FIGURE 1—APPROXIMATE PRACTICAL THICKNESS RANGES OF STEEL FOR VARIOUS X-RAY KILOVOLTAGES

Radiographic isotopes emit radiation at discrete energy levels. The approximate practical thickness range of the most commonly used radioisotopes for steel is included in Figure 2. The energy level of the gamma radiation for the two most commonly used isotopes determines the equivalence factor for materials other than steel (included in Figure 2). Table 1 can be utilized to approximate these equivalence factors by averaging the energy values for a given source and using the closest energy level column in the table.

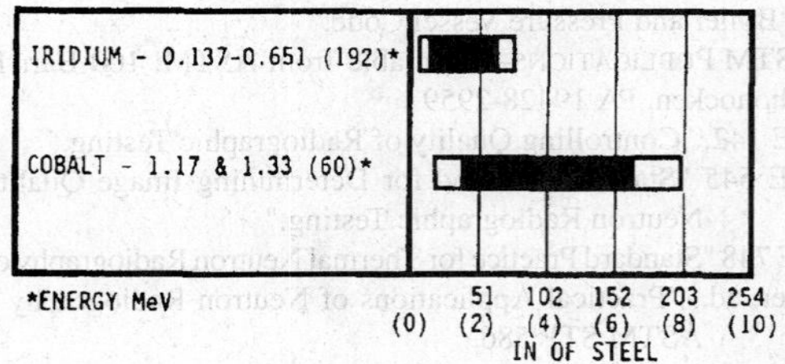

The shaded portions of the bar represent thickness where 1% sensitivity is obtained.
The unshaded portion at Bar ends represent 2% sensitivity.
NOTE—Dimensions are mm (inch)

FIGURE 2—APPROXIMATE PRACTICAL THICKNESS OF STEEL FOR VARIOUS RADIOACTIVE ISOTOPE SOURCES

TABLE 1—APPROXIMATE RADIOGRAPHIC EQUIVALENCE FACTORS FOR SEVERAL METALS IN RELATION TO STEEL (1) (ADAPTED FROM ASTM E 94)

Metal (2)	140 kV	220 kV	250 kV	400 kV	1 MeV	2 Mev
Aluminum (2.7)	0.083	0.24	0.24	--	--	--
Magnesium (1.7)	0.05	0.08	0.08	--	--	--
Steel (7.8)	1.0	1.0	1.0	1.0	1.0	1.0
Stainless (7.9)	1.0	1.0	1.0	1.0	1.0	1.0
Copper (8.9)	1.8	1.4	1.4	1.4	--	--
Zinc (7.1)	--	1.3	1.3	1.3	--	--
Brass (8.4)	--	1.3	1.3	1.3	1.2	--
Lead (11.3)	--	11.0	--	--	5.0	2.5

1. To determine upper practical limit for materials listed other than steel, divide the value given for steel by the proper equivalence factor. Table 1 may be extended to apply to radioisotopes by taking the average of the energy values given in Figure 2, and using the nearest size x-ray unit in the table.
2. Density is given in parentheses.

Other factors such as economics, flexibility, sensitivity, maintenance costs, and portability must of necessity be considered when deciding the type of unit to be used.

Generally, x-ray film is used as the detecting medium. Various types of film are commercially available. These differ in speed, grain, and contrast. The selection of a film is interrelated with the type and energy of the radiation, and the material and thickness of the object to be inspected. Factors such as sensitivity required and exposure time are also considerations. Industrial x-ray paper may be used as a detecting medium. Paper supported emulsions offer several advantages: lower material cost, increased processing speed, darkroom simplicity, and space savings. Consideration should be given to this process if maximum sensitivity and long periods of radiographic print storage are not required. Other detecting media are available, such as instant process film and xerographic processes.

Fluoroscopic systems are available for instantaneous radiographic inspections. The sensitivity of this type of inspecting medium is somewhat less than the photographic method.

*8. **Protection***—Personnel protection from all forms of radiation is an essential requirement in the use of penetrating radiation. It is a fact that scattered as well as direct rays have a biological and physical effect on all living matter. It is recommended (and is generally a legal requirement) that all persons operating or working near any source of radiation keep a record of the radiation dosage received weekly and at no time exceed the limits allowed by the Nuclear Regulatory Commission, or licensing state.

(R) ULTRASONIC INSPECTION—SAE J428 MAR1991 SAE Information Report

Report of the SAE Iron and Steel Technical Committee, approved June 1960, third revision by ISTC Division 25 June 1983. Completely revised by the SAE Iron and Steel Technical Committee Division 25 March 1991.

Foreword—This Document has not changed other than to put it into the new SAE Technical Standards Board Format.

1. Scope—The scope of this SAE Information report is to provide basic information on ultrasonics, as applied in the field of nondestructive inspection. References to detailed information are listed in Section 2.

2. References

2.1 Related Publications—The following publications are printed for information purposes only and are not a required part of this document.

2.1.1 SAE PUBLICATION—Available from SAE, 400 Commonwealth Drive, Warrendale, PA 15096-0001.

AMS 2631, Ultrasonic Inspection of Titanium Alloys, November, 1972..

2.1.2 ASM PUBLICATION—ATTN: MSC/Book Order, ASM International, PO Box 473, Novelty, OH 44072-9901.

Metals Handbook, Ninth Ed., Vol. 17, Nondestructive Evaluation and Quality Control, 1989.

2.1.3 OTHER PUBLICATIONS

Nondestructive Testing Handbook, Vol. 7, Ultrasonic Testing, 1990, American Society for Nondestructive Testing, Columbus, OH 43228

Tool and Manufacturing Engineers' Handbook, Vol. 4, Quality Control and Assembly, 1987, Society of Manufacturing Engineers, Dearborn, MI 48121

J. & H. Krautkramer, "Ultrasonic Testing of Materials." New York: Springer-Verlag, Third Edition, 1983

T. F. Hueter and R. H. Bolt, "Sonics" (Fifth Edition). New York: John Wiley & Sons, Inc., 1966.

R. Goldman, "Ultrasonic Technology." New York: Reinhold Publishing Corp., 1962.

J. Frederick, "Ultrasonic Engineering." New York: John Wiley & Sons, Inc., 1965.

R. C. McMaster, ed., "Nondestructive Testing Handbook," Vol. II, Section 43–50, 1959. American Society for Nondestructive Testing, Columbus, OH 43328

A. L. Phillips, ed., "Welding Handbook" (Sixth Edition), pp. 6.54-60. New York: American Welding Society, 1968.

3. General—Ultrasonic testing is a versatile nondestructive inspection method which is applicable to most solid materials, metallic or nonmetallic. Materials inspected include steel, aluminum, cast iron, concrete, rubber, glass, and plastics. Through these tests, surface and internal discontinuities such as laps, seams, voids, cracks, blow holes, inclusions, lack of bond, and porosity can be detected. Material thickness can be accurately measured from one side. Under certain conditions, materials at elevated temperatures can be inspected.

Totally automatic systems are in use in heavy industry. Location of defects can be marked on parts, or graphic recordings made of parts. Parts can be automatically removed from a processing line when defect severity exceeds established limits.

In many cases, the extent of discontinuities can be determined. The minimum size discontinuity which can be located by ultrasonics in a given application is determined by:

a. The sensitivity of the test equipment
   1. Physical characteristics of the transducer
   2. Gain/band width characteristics of the instrument
b. The material inspected
   1. Physical properties (modulus, grain size)
   2. Surface condition (i.e., rough, smooth, wavy, scaly, painted)
c. The test frequency used; in general, higher test frequencies permit detection of smaller discontinuities. Lower frequencies permit penetration of greater thickness of material, or of coarse grained material that cannot be inspected with the higher frequencies.
d. Orientation of discontinuity and its distance from the ultrasound entrant surface
e. Type of defect and acoustic impedance mismatch

In addition to discontinuity detection, ultrasonic energy is also used to gage the thickness of materials from one side. Yield or tensile strength of nodular cast irons can be estimated through its relationship to the velocity of ultrasonic energy in the metal.

4. Principles—Ultrasonic inspection is made possible by the ability of most solid materials to support the transmission of high frequency sound waves. This ability to support these mechanical vibrations varies for different materials, and depends upon certain physical properties of each material, such as density, modulus, grain structure, etc.

All ultrasonic tests involve introducing controlled ultrasonic energy into the object under test, and observing how the passage of sound is affected in transit. Any discontinuity in the material can reflect, disperse, or attenuate the energy. The ultrasonic energy used for testing is usually generated in short bursts or pulses by piezoelectric transducers driven by appropriate electronic circuitry. Test frequencies used are usually between 1 to 25 MHz, and the pulse repetition rates from a few hertz to thousands of hertz. Since air will not support these ultrasonic signals, a liquid such as water or oil is used to couple the energy from the transducer into the material under test. Ultrasonic transducers, often called search units, are typically less than 25 mm (1 in) in diameter. Thus, when inspecting large objects, it is necessary to scan the object with the transducer.

5. Types Of Tests

5.1 Pulse Echo—A pulse of ultrasonic energy is transmitted into the part. The time required for the reflected energy to return to the transducer is observed. A discontinuity is usually indicated by:

a. Reflections received from locations where no physical discontinuities (such as end faces, grooves, or holes) are known to exist
b. Loss of the reflection from the known physical discontinuity

5.1.1 ADVANTAGES

a. Single tranducer operation permits inspection with access to only one side of the material
b. The resolution and sensitivity of this method, in most applications, is superior to other ultrasonic methods

5.1.2 DISADVANTAGES—The minimum thickness of material which can be inspected is about 0.254 mm (0.01 in) with present-day equipment.

5.2 Through Testing—Either a pulsed or continuous beam of energy is coupled into the material from one transducer. A second transducer, placed in a position to receive the transmitted energy, receives the energy leaving the material. Changes in the amplitude of the received energy indicates discontinuities in the part.

5.2.1 ADVANTAGES

a. The energy passes through the part only one time, permitting this test to be used on materials difficult to penetrate
b. Very thin materials can be tested

5.2.2 DISADVANTAGES

a. Precision fixturing for two transducers and preparation of two test surfaces are required
b. The accuracy is usually less than in Pulse Echo testing
c. Depth of discontinuity cannot be determined

6. Procedure—Two techniques, contact testing and immersion testing, are used in ultrasonic inspection. In any application, the material under test should be cleaned to remove any loose particles or scale prior to inspection.

6.1 Contact Testing—The transducer is placed directly against the material under test. A film of liquid couplant (i.e., water, oil, glycerine) is required between them.

6.1.1 ADVANTAGES

a. Relatively low cost equipment
b. Portable battery operated equipment available
c. Good sound penetration
d. Surface defects can be detected by transmitting a surface wave along the outside contour of most parts. Results are a direct function of surface smoothness, improving with better surface.

6.1.2 DISADVANTAGES

a. A reasonably smooth surface finish is required
b. The energy cannot be readily focused to obtain increased resolution and sensitivity in a given area
c. Difficult to control shape and direction of beam
d. The transducer is subject to wear thus requiring replacement or wear/shoes in some applications
e. Sensitivity is variable, depending upon the efficiency of the coupling

6.2 Immersion Testing—The material to be inspected is placed in a reservoir of couplant liquid. The transducer is immersed in the reservoir and accurately positioned relative to the material under test. Water columns between the transducers and the test surface may also be used where immersion is undesirable.

6.2.1 ADVANTAGES

a. The energy can be focused or shaped for the part, permitting increased resolution and sensitivity
b. Immersion coupling facilitates the inspection of nonuniformly contoured parts
c. Better close-to-surface resolution than other ultrasonic techniques
d. Lends to automatic inspection and recording of results
e. Transducer wear is minimized
f. Test results are more repeatable

6.2.2 DISADVANTAGES

a. The requirement of immersing the sample
b. The necessity of accurate positioning of the material and transducer(s)
c. The sample (or object) size is limited by the size of the immersion reservoir
d. Equipment is expensive when compared to contact techniques

(R) ACOUSTIC EMISSION TEST METHODS —SAE J1242 MAR1991

SAE Information Report

Report of the SAE Iron and Steel Technical Committee, approved June 1978, first revision by ISTC Division 25 June 1983, and reaffirmed December 1988. Completely revised by the SAE Iron and Steel Technical Committee Division 25 March 1991.

1. Scope—The scope of this SAE Information Report is to supply the user with sufficient information so that he may decide whether acoustic emission test methods apply to his particular inspection problem. Detailed technical information can be obtained by referring to Section 2.

2. References

2.1 Related Publications—The following publications are provided for information purposes only and are not a required part of this document.

Nondestructive Testing Handbook, Vol. 5, Acoustic Emission Testing, 1987, American Society for Nondestructive Testing, Columbus, OH 43228.

Metals Handbook, Ninth Edition, Vol. 17, pp. 278–294, Nondestructive Evaluation and Quality Control, 1989, ASM International, Metals Park, OH 44073.

Tool and Manufacturing Engineers Handbook, Vol. 4, Quality Control and Assembly, 1987, Society of Manufacturing Engineers, Dearborn, MI 48121.

"Acoustic Emission," A Symposium presented December 7–8, 1971, at Bal Harbor, Florida. American Society for Testing and Materials, STP 505, (1972).

Monitoring Structural Integrity by Acoustic Emission, A Symposium presented at Fort Lauderdale, Florida, January 17–18, 1974. American Society for Testing and Materials, STP 571, (1975).

R. G. Liptai and D. O. Harris, "Acoustic Emission – An Introductory Review." Materials Research and Standards, Vol. 11, No. 3, March 1971, pp. 8–10.

C. R. Horak and A. F. Weyhreter, "Acoustic Emission System for Monitoring Components and Structures in a Severe Fatigue Noise Environment," Materials Evaluation, Vol. 35, No. 5, May 1977, pp. 59–63.

J. C. Spanner, "Acoustic Emission Techniques and Applications," Intex Publishing Co., 1974.

ASTM E 569, "Recommended Practice for Acoustic Emission Monitoring of Structures During Controlled Stimulation," American Society for Testing and Materials, Philadelphia, PA 19103.

ASTM E 610, "Definitions of Terms Relating to Acoustic Emission," American Society for Testing and Materials, Philadelphia, PA 19103.

3. General—Acoustic emission is defined as a transient elastic wave generated by the rapid release of energy from a localized source or sources within a material. The emission may be the result of any of several changes taking place in the material. A crack may be growing, the material may be undergoing permanent deformation, the internal structure may be changing due to heat treatment, or, in the case of composite materials, the fibers that strengthen the material may be breaking.

Some metals produce audible acoustic emission when they are bent. This is due to a deformation process called twinning. Tin, magnesium, and zinc show this effect. In tin this is known as "tin cry."

Acoustic emission technology is applicable to many nondestructive inspection problems. These include detection and growth monitoring of fatigue cracks and stress-corrosion cracking, in-process determination of weld quality, measurement of adhesive bond integrity, and in certain cases, the detection of loose parts in assembled components. Acoustic emission is particularly useful for monitoring the growth of a crack in order to give warning of impending failure, and to detect deformation. It is also useful for surveying very large volumes to locate emission sites. However, these sites often must be evaluated by supplementary methods.

3.1 There are several advantages of acoustic emission as a nondestructive test method when compared with more common methods such as radiography, ultrasonics, or magnetic particle techniques. Some of these are as follows:

a. It is capable of continuously monitoring a complete structure in real time.
b. It is very sensitive to the presence of active flaws when compared to other nondestructive test methods, but usually requires these other methods to characterize the flaws.
c. It can detect discontinuities that may be inaccessible to other nondestructive test methods.
d. It is suitable for use during proof testing in those structures that will be stressed sufficiently to produce local plastic deformation during the test.

3.2 Limitations of acoustic emission testing include:

a. Inactive nonpropagating flaws cannot be detected.
b. The significance of a detected source of emission cannot be assessed unambiguously.
c. As with many other nondestructive tests, acoustic emission tests are best used in conjunction with other nondestructive test methods, such as ultrasonics and radiography.
d. The part or system under test must be stressed by an external stimulus.

4. Principle—There are two types of acoustic emission: burst and continuous. The length of a single burst of emission is measured in microseconds. Continuous emission consists of a series of closely spaced noise peaks of random amplitude that occur without interruption. Burst emissions usually have a larger amplitude than continuous emissions.

A specimen must be stressed to generate acoustic emission. For a material with no active sources, emission usually occurs while the stress is increasing. When the stress stops increasing, the emission stops. For many materials, excluding composites, when the force is reapplied it must exceed the previous stress level before the specimen will emit again.

Most of the acoustic emission signals that are useful in nondestructive testing are usually of low amplitude and have frequencies that are above the audible range. Ordinarily they are between 100 kHz and 1 MHz, depending upon the application. Low frequencies are filtered out in order to avoid interference from unwanted sources of noise such as machines or electrical equipment. The maximum distance that the signals will travel in a structure and still be detectable depends on the type of material and on the range of frequencies in the signal. In steel pressure vessels, the acoustic emission caused by crack growth in welds can travel 10 m or more from the source of the emission to the transducer that is detecting it.

The location of a source of the emission is determined by triangulation methods. These are based on the differences in the times required for the signals to reach the various elements in an array of transducers.

5. Procedure—Specially designed transducers are used for detecting the acoustic emission in a test specimen or structure. These must be coupled to the test specimen with a suitable liquid or grease, or by means of an epoxy cement or other adhesive. The output of the transducer is amplified and the low frequencies filtered out. Processing of the signal is usually very desirable. The simplest method for monitoring an acoustic emission test is to electronically convert the high frequency acoustic emission signals to lower frequencies that can be heard with the human ear. The most common methods, however, use chart recorders or cathode ray oscilloscopes to display the test results. Magnetic tape is used for storing larger amounts of data for later processing or display. Specialized equipment for the detection and processing of acoustic emission signals is available from several manufacturers. Data processing as applied to acoustic emission tests is limited only by the creativity and sophistication of the user and the data processing facility.

DEFINITION FOR PARTICLE SIZE —SAE J391 JUL1981

SAE Recommended Practice

Report of the SAE Fatigue Design and Evaluation Committee, approved May 1969, reaffirmed without change July 1981.

Foreword—This Document has not changed other than to put it into the new SAE Technical Standards Board Format.

1. Scope—"Effective particle or domain size" is a phrase used in X-ray diffraction literature to describe the size of the coherent regions within a material which are diffracting. Coherency in this sense means diffracting as a unit. Small particle size causes X-ray line broadening and as such can be measured. It has been shown related to substructure as observed in transmission electron microscopy. Particle size is affected by hardening, cold working, and fatigue; conversely, there is increasing evidence that particle size, per se, affects both static and dynamic strength.

2. Definition

2.1 Effective Particle or Domain Size—as determined by diffraction, is a one-dimensional measure of the average size of essentially perfect regions within a material.

NOTE—Such regions are related to the substructure seen in transmission electron microscopy. Small particle size contributes to diffraction line broadening.

(R) DEFINITIONS FOR MACROSTRAIN AND MICROSTRAIN—SAE J932 AUG1985

SAE Recommended Practice

Report of the SAE Iron and Steel Technical Committee, approved July 1965, reaffirmed by the SAE Fatigue Design and Evaluation Committee, August 1985.

Foreword—This Document has also changed other to comply with the new SAE Technical Standards Board Format. References were added as Section 2.

1. Scope—In the analysis and measurement of residual stresses of materials, it has been noted that there are frequently differences in interpretation of the terms "macrostrain" and "microstrain." To assist communication among research personnel in this area, definitions for these two terms are suggested by the Fatigue Design and Evaluation Committee of SAE. Since "macrostress" is commonly computed from "macrostrain" in residual stress analysis, to be consistent, the definitions given are for "macrostrain" and "microstrain."

2. References—There are no referenced publications specified herein.

3. Definitions

3.1 Macrostrain—The mean or average strain measured from a finite control volume of material with a gage length or characteristic lineal dimension that is several orders of magnitude greater than the interatomic dimensions (or characteristic length of the material microstructure).

NOTE—Macrostrain can be measured by several methods, including electrical resistance strain gages and mechanical or optical extensometers. Elastic macrostrain can be measured by X-ray diffraction or other nondestructive techniques.

3.2 Microstrain—The strain measured from a finite control volume of material with a characteristic lineal dimension that is of the same order of magnitude as the materials interatomic distance.

NOTE—These are the strains that are "averaged" by the macrostrain measurement. Microstrain is not measurable with the commonly employed techniques used for macrostrain measurement, such as finite length foil resistant strain gages. Microstrain distribution is typically measured with x-ray diffraction techniques. The term "microstrain" is often used to signify the macrostrain multiplied by 10^6.

) POTENTIAL FAILURE MODE AND EFFECTS ANALYSIS IN DESIGN (DESIGN FMEA), POTENTIAL FAILURE MODE AND EFFECTS ANALYSIS IN MANUFACTURING AND ASSEMBLY PROCESSES (PROCESS FMEA), AND POTENTIAL FAILURE MODE AND EFFECTS ANALYSIS FOR MACHINERY (MACHINERY FMEA)—SAE J1739 AUG2002 SAE Recommended Practice

Report of the SAE J1739 Task Force approved July 1994 and completely revised by the SAE J1739 Task Force (2000) June 2000. Completely revised by the SAE Automotive Quality and Process Improvement Group.

1. Scope—**General Information**

1.1 Overview—This SAE Recommended Practice was jointly developed by DaimlerChrysler Corporation, Ford Motor Company, and General Motors Corporation.

This document introduces the topic of potential Failure Mode and Effects Analysis (FMEA) and gives general guidance in the application of the technique.

All FMEA's focus on the design, whether it be of the product, the process or the machinery used to build the product. An Applications Section (see Section 5) has been added to provide information on applying the FMEA technique to plant machinery and equipment using the Machinery FMEA (MFMEA).

1.2 Recommended Practice Format—For ease of use, this reference document presents the two basic types of FMEA (Design FMEA and Process FMEA) in their own separate sections. This document also contains an Applications Section (Section 5) which discusses in some detail how an FMEA is applied to Plant Machinery and Equipment (Machinery FMEA).

The Machinery FMEA (MFMEA) information has been provided due to the importance of Plant Machinery, Tooling, and Equipment functioning as intended in manufacturing and assembly plants. The use of the MFMEA, on Plant Machinery, Tooling, and Equipment, will assist with the identification of potential failure modes, so that design and processing alternatives can be considered, prior to finalizing the Plant Machinery, Tooling, and Equipment Designs.

It should be noted that this document is a recommended practice, and as such, each Team is free to use the guidelines listed herein in the manner which will be most effective for a given situation.

Figure 1 illustrates an approximate time line where the Design FMEA (DFMEA) for the product is started somewhat before the Process FMEA (PFMEA) for producing the product. Figure 1 shows that the Machinery FMEA (MFMEA) should be started at about the same time as the PFMEA. The "OEM Product Development Time Line" refers to the "Original Equipment Manufacturer's Time Line" which is used for the design, development, and production of the product. In some situations, all three FMEAs (i.e., DFMEA, PFMEA, and MFMEA) might be started at the same time. In general, the earlier that FMEAs are started, the better the chances of optimizing the various activities/designs/processes in a cost and time effective manner.

1.3 What is an FMEA?—An FMEA can be described as a systematic group of activities intended to: (a) recognize and evaluate the potential failure of a product/process and the effects of that failure, (b) identify actions that could eliminate or reduce the chance of the potential failure occurring, and (c) document the process. It is complementary to the process of defining what a design or process must do to satisfy the customer.

1.4 FMEA Implementation—Because of the general industry trend to continually improve products and processes whenever possible, using the FMEA as a disciplined technique to identify and help minimize potential concern is as important as ever. Studies of vehicle campaigns have shown that fully implemented FMEA programs could have prevented many of the campaigns.

One of the most important factors for the successful implementation of an FMEA program is timeliness. It is meant to be a "before-the-event" action, not an "after-the-fact" exercise. To achieve the greatest value, the FMEA must be done before a product or process failure mode has been incorporated into a product or process. Up front time spent properly completing an FMEA, when product/process changes can be most easily and inexpensively implemented, will minimize late change crises. An FMEA can reduce or eliminate the chance of implementing a preventive/corrective change which would create an even larger concern. Communication and coordination should occur between all types of FMEAs (i.e., Design - DFMEA, Process - PFMEA, and Machinery - MFMEA). (See Figure 1).

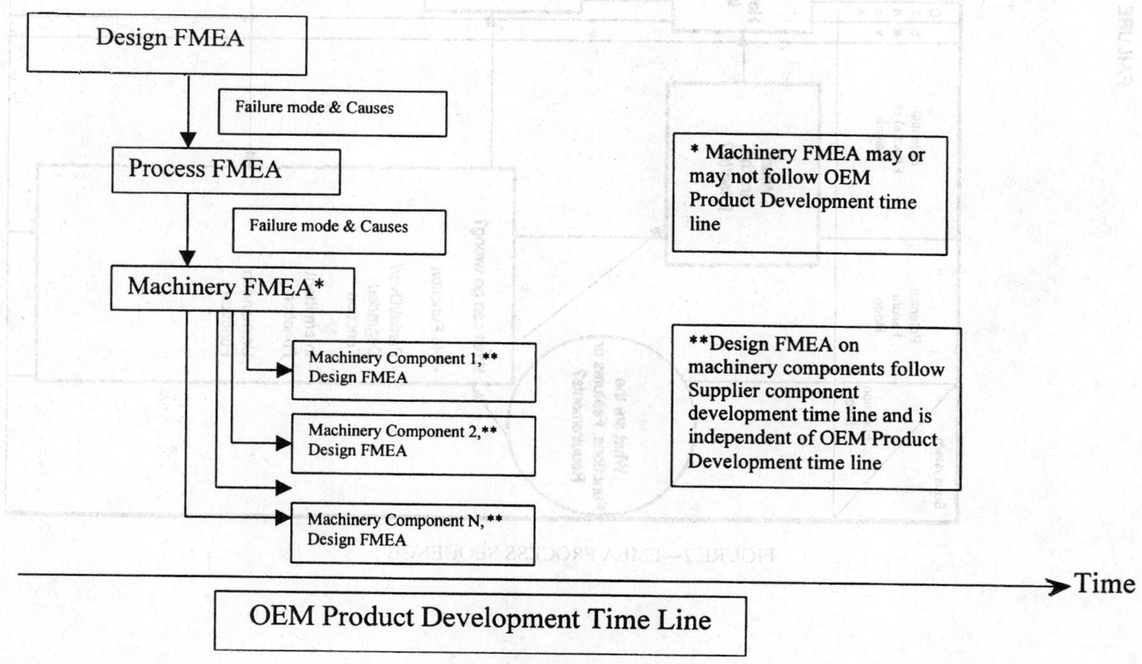

FIGURE 1—OEM PRODUCT DEVELOPMENT TIME LINE

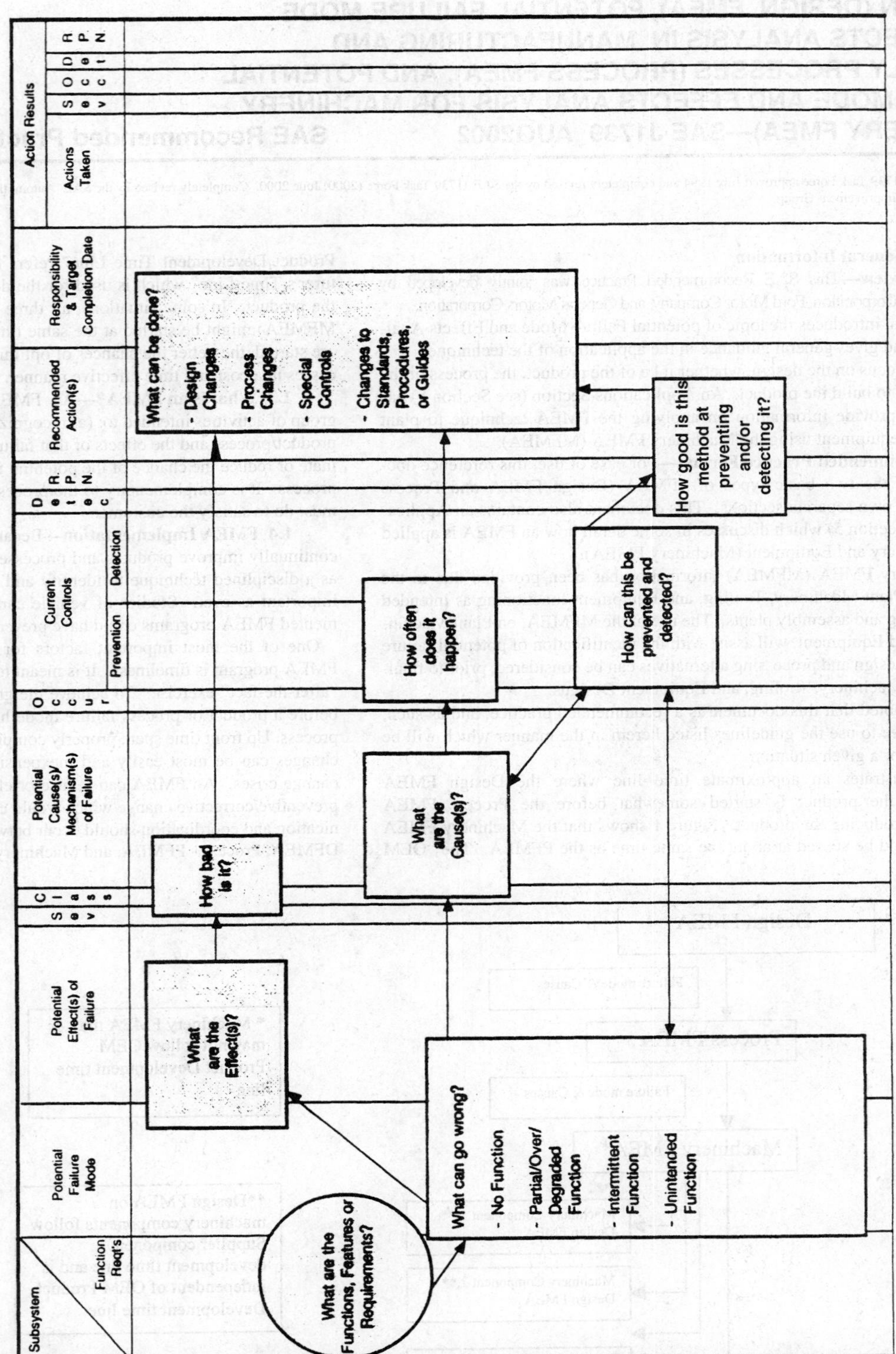

FIGURE 2—FMEA PROCESS SEQUENCE

POTENTIAL
FAILURE MODE AND EFFECTS ANALYSIS
(DESIGN FMEA)

___ System

___ Subsystem

___ Component ___

Model Year(s)/Program(s) ___

Core Team ___

Design Responsibility ___

Key Date ___

FMEA Number ___

Page ___ of ___

Prepared By ___

FMEA Date (Orig.) ___ (Rev.) ___

Item / Function	Potential Failure Mode	Potential Effect(s) of Failure	S e v	C l a s s	Potential Cause(s)/ Mechanism(s) of Failure	O c c u r	Current Design Controls Prevention	Current Design Controls Detection	D e t e c	R. P. N.	Recommended Action(s)	Responsibility & Target Completion Date	Action Results: Actions Taken	S e v	O c c	D e t	R. P. N.

FIGURE 3A—POTENTIAL FAILURE MODE AND EFFECTS ANALYSIS IN DESIGN (DFMEA)
– TWO COLUMNS, CURRENT DESIGN CONTROLS –

POTENTIAL
FAILURE MODE AND EFFECTS ANALYSIS IN DESIGN
(DESIGN FMEA)

____ System

____ Subsystem

____ Component ____________

Model Year(s)/Program(s) ____________

Core Team ____________

Design Responsibility ____________

Key Date ____________

FMEA Number ____________

Page ______ of ______

Prepared By ____________

FMEA Date (Orig.) ______ (Rev.) ______

Item / Function	Potential Failure Mode	Potential Effect(s) of Failure	Sev	Class	Potential Cause(s)/ Mechanism(s) of Failure	Occur	Current Design Controls — Prevention — Detection	Detec	R.P.N.	Recommended Action(s)	Responsibility & Target Completion Date	Action Results: Actions Taken	Sev	Occ	Det	R.P.N.

FIGURE 3B—POTENTIAL FAILURE MODE AND EFFECTS ANALYSIS IN DESIGN (DESIGN FMEA)
– ONE COLUMN, CURRENT DESIGN CONTROLS –

Figure 2 depicts the sequence in which an FMEA should be performed. It is not simply a case of filling out the column, but rather understanding the process in order to eliminate risk and plan the appropriate controls to ensure customer satisfaction.

There are three basic cases for which FMEA's are generated, each with a different scope or focus:

Case 1: New designs, new technology, or new process.
The scope of the FMEA is the complete design, technology, or process.

Case 2: Modifications to existing design or process (assumes there is a FMEA for the existing design or process).
The scope of the FMEA should focus on the modification to design or process, possible interactions due to the modification, and field history.

Case 3: Use of existing design or process in a new environment, location, or application (assumes there is an FMEA for the existing design or process).
The scope of the FMEA is the impact of the new environment or location on the existing design or process.

Although responsibility for the preparation of the FMEA is usually assigned to an individual, FMEA input should be a team effort. A team of knowledgeable individuals should be assembled (e.g., engineers with expertise in Design, Analysis/Testing, Manufacturing, Assembly, Service, Recycling, Quality, and Reliability). The FMEA is initiated by the engineer from the responsible activity, which can be the Original Equipment Manufacturer (i.e., produces the final product), a supplier, or a subcontractor.

It is not appropriate to compare the ratings of one team's FMEA with the ratings of another team's FMEA, even if the product/process appear to be identical, since each team's environment is unique and thus their respective individual ratings will be unique (i.e., the ratings are subjective).

A review of the FMEA document against FMEA quality objectives (see Appendix A and Appendix B) is recommended including a management review.

1.5 Follow-Up—The need for taking effective, preventive/corrective actions, with appropriate follow-up on those actions cannot be overemphasized. A thoroughly thought out and well developed FMEA will be of limited value without positive and effective preventive/corrective actions.

The responsible engineer is in charge of assuring that all recommended actions have been implemented or adequately addressed. The FMEA is a living document and should always reflect the latest level, as well as the latest relevant actions, including those occurring after the start of production.

The responsible engineer has several means of assuring that recommended actions are implemented. They include, but are not limited to the following:

a. Reviewing designs, processes, and/or machinery to ensure that recommended actions have been implemented
b. Review of engineering drawings, product/process specifications, and process flow,
c. Confirmation of incorporation of changes to design/assembly/manufacturing documentation, and
d. Review of Design/Process FMEAs, special FMEA applications such as Machinery FMEA and Build and Installation FMEA, Control Plans, and Operation Instructions.

2. References—There are no referenced publications specified herein.

3. Potential Failure Mode and Effects Analysis in Design (Design FMEA)

3.1 Introduction—A Design potential FMEA is an analytical technique utilized primarily by a Design-Responsible Engineer/Team as a means to ensure that, to the extent possible, potential failure modes and their associated causes/mechanisms have been considered and addressed. End items, along with every related system, subassembly, and component, should be evaluated. In its most rigorous form, an FMEA is a summary of the team's thoughts (including an analysis of items that could go wrong based on experience) as a component, subsystem, or system is designed. This systematic approach parallels, formalizes, and documents the mental disciplines that an engineer normally goes through in any design process.

The Design potential FMEA supports the design process in reducing the risk of failures (including unintended outcomes) by:

a. Aiding in the objective evaluation of the design, including functional requirements and design alternatives.
b. Evaluating the initial design for manufacturing, assembly, service, and recycling requirements.
c. Increasing the probability that potential failure modes and their effects on system and vehicle operation have been considered in the design/development process.
d. Providing additional information to aid in the planning of thorough and efficient design, development, and validation programs.
e. Developing a ranked list of potential failure modes according to their effect on the "customer," thus establishing a priority system for design improvements, development, and validation testing/analysis.
f. Providing an open issue format for recommending and tracking risk reducing actions.
g. Providing future reference (e.g., lessons learned), to aid in analyzing field concerns, evaluating design changes, and developing advanced designs.

3.1.1 CUSTOMER DEFINED—The definition of "CUSTOMER" for a Design potential FMEA is not only the "END USER," but also the design-responsible engineers/teams of the vehicle or higher level assemblies, and/or the manufacturing/process-responsible engineers in activities such as Manufacturing, Assembly, and Service.

3.1.2 TEAM EFFORT—During the initial Design potential FMEA process, the responsible engineer is expected to directly and actively involve representatives from all affected areas. These areas of expertise and responsibility should include, but are not limited to assembly, manufacturing, design, analysis/test, reliability, materials, quality, service, and suppliers, as well as the design area responsible for the next higher or lower assembly or system, sub-assembly or component. The FMEA should be a catalyst to stimulate the interchange of ideas between the functions affected and thus promote a team approach.

Unless the responsible engineer is experienced with FMEA and team facilitation, it is helpful to have an experienced FMEA Facilitator assist the team in its activities.

The Design FMEA is a living document and should:

a. Be initiated before or at design concept finalization,
b. Be continually updated as changes occur or additional information is obtained throughout the phases of product development, and
c. Be fundamentally completed before the production drawings are released for tooling.

Considering that manufacturing/assembly needs have been incorporated, the Design FMEA addresses the design intent and assumes the design will be manufactured/assembled to this intent. Potential failure modes and/or causes/mechanisms that can occur during the manufacturing or assembly process need not, but may, be included in a Design FMEA. When not included, their identification, effect, and control are covered by the Process FMEA.

The Design FMEA does not rely on process controls to overcome potential design weaknesses, but it does take the technical/physical limits of a manufacturing/assembly process into consideration, for example:

a. Necessary mold drafts
b. Limited surface finish
c. Assembling space/access for tooling
d. Limited hardenability of steels
e. Tolerances/process capability/performance

The Design FMEA can also take into consideration the technical/physical limits of product maintenance (service) and recycling, for example:

a. Tool access
b. Diagnostic capability
c. Material classification symbols (for recycling)

3.2 Development of a Design FMEA—The design responsible engineer has at his/her disposal a number of documents that will be useful in preparing the Design FMEA. The process begins by developing a listing of what the design is expected to do, and what it is expected not to do, i.e., the design intent. Customer wants and needs — as may be determined from sources such as Quality Function Deployment (QFD), Vehicle Requirements Documents, known product requirements and/or manufacturing/assembly/service/recycling requirements — should be incorporated. The better the definition of the desired characteristics, the easier it is to identify potential failure modes for preventive/corrective action.

A Design FMEA should begin with a block diagram, for the system, subsystem, and/or component being analyzed.

An example block diagram is shown in Appendix C. The block diagram can also indicate the flow of information, energy, force, fluid, etc. The objective is to understand the deliverables (input) to the block, the process (function) performed in the block, and the deliverables (output) from the block.

The diagram illustrates the primary relationship between the items covered in the analysis and establishes a logical order to the analysis. Copies of the diagrams used in FMEA preparation should accompany the FMEA.

In order to facilitate documentation of the analysis of potential failures and their consequences, a blank form is available in Appendix D.

An example of a completed form is contained in Appendix E, including numbered headings (1) – (22) for ease of reference to the following descriptions.

3.2.1 (1) FMEA NUMBER—Enter the FMEA document number, which may be used for tracking. (See Figure 3A or 3B.)

3.2.2 (2) SYSTEM, SUBSYSTEM, OR COMPONENT NAME AND NUMBER—Indicate the appropriate level of analysis and enter the name and number of the system, subsystem, or component being analyzed. The FMEA team must decide on what constitutes a system, subsystem, or component for their specific activities. The actual boundaries that divide a System, Subsystem, and Component are arbitrary and must be set by the FMEA team. Some descriptions are provided below and some examples are provided in Appendix F (See Figure 3A or 3B.)

3.2.2.1 System FMEA Scope—A system can be considered to be made up of various subsystems. These subsystems often have been designed by different teams. Some typical System FMEAs might cover the following systems: Chassis System, or Powertrain System, or Interior System, etc. Thus, the focus of the System FMEA is to ensure that all interfaces and interactions between the various subsystems that make up the system as well as interfaces to other vehicle systems and the customer are covered.

3.2.2.2 Subsystem FMEA Scope—A subsystem FMEA is generally a subset of a larger system. For example, the front suspension subsystem is a sub-set of the chassis system. Thus, the focus of the Subsystem FMEA is to ensure that all interfaces and interactions between the various components that make up the subsystem are covered in the Subsystem FMEA.

3.2.2.3 Component FMEA Scope—A component FMEA is generally an FMEA focused on the sub-set of a subsystem. For example, a strut is a component of the front suspension (which is a subsystem of the chassis system.)

3.2.3 (3) DESIGN RESPONSIBILITY—Enter the OEM, department, and group. Also include the supplier name if applicable. (See Figure 3A or 3B.)

3.2.4 (4) PREPARED BY—Enter the name, telephone number, and company of the engineer responsible for preparing the FMEA. (See Figure 3A or 3B.)

3.2.5 (5) MODEL YEAR(S)/PROGRAM(S)—Enter the intended model year(s) and program(s) that will utilize and/or be affected by the design being analyzed (if known). (See Figure 3A or 3B.)

3.2.6 (6) KEY DATE—Enter the initial FMEA due date, which should not exceed the scheduled production design release date. (See Figure 3A or 3B.)

3.2.7 (7) FMEA DATE—Enter the date the original FMEA was compiled, and the latest revision date. (See Figure 3A or 3B.)

3.2.8 (8) CORE TEAM—List the names of the responsible individuals and departments which have the authority to identify and/or perform tasks. (It is recommended that each team member's name, department, telephone number, address, etc., be included on a distribution list). (See Figure 3A or 3B.)

3.2.9 (9) ITEM/FUNCTION—Enter the name and other pertinent information (e.g., the number, the part class, etc.) of the item being analyzed. Use the nomenclature and show the design level as indicated on the engineering drawing. Prior to initial release (e.g., in the conceptual phases), experimental numbers should be used. (See Figure 3A or 3B.)

Enter, as concisely as possible, the function of the item being analyzed to meet the design intent. Include information (metrics/measurables) regarding the environment in which this system operates (e.g., define temperature, pressure, humidity ranges, design life). If the item has more than one function with different potential modes of failure, list all the functions separately.

3.2.10 (10) POTENTIAL FAILURE MODE—Potential Failure Mode is defined as the manner in which a component, subsystem, or system could potentially fail to meet or deliver the intended function described in the item/function column (i.e., intended function fails). The potential failure mode may also be the cause of a potential failure mode in a higher level subsystem, or system, or be the effect of one in a lower level component. (See Figure 3A or 3B.)

List each potential failure mode associated with the particular item and item function. The assumption is made that the failure could occur, but may not necessarily occur. A recommended starting point is a review of past things-gone-wrong, concerns, reports, and group brainstorming.

Potential failure modes that could only occur under certain operating conditions (i.e., hot, cold, dry, dusty, etc.) and under certain usage conditions (i.e., above average mileage, rough terrain, only city driving, etc.) should be considered.

Typical failure modes could be, but are not limited to:

cracked	deformed	loosened
leaking	sticking	oxidized
fractured	does not transmit torque	slips (does not hold full torque)
no support (structural)	inadequate support (structural)	harsh engagement
disengages too fast	inadequate signal	intermittent signal
no signal	EMC/RFI	drift

NOTE—Potential failure modes should be described in "physical" or technical terms, not as a symptom necessarily noticeable by the customer.

3.2.11 (11) POTENTIAL EFFECT(S) OF FAILURE—Potential Effects of Failure are defined as the effects of the failure mode on the function, as perceived by the customer. (See Figure 3A or 3B and 3.1.1)

Describe the effects of the failure in terms of what the customer might notice or experience, remembering that the customer may be an internal customer as well as the ultimate end user. State clearly if the function could impact safety or noncompliance to regulations. The effects should always be stated in terms of the specific system, subsystem, or component being analyzed. Remember that a hierarchical relationship exists between the component, subsystem, and system levels. For example, a part could fracture, which may cause the assembly to vibrate, resulting in an intermittent system operation. The intermittent system operation could cause performance to degrade, and ultimately lead to customer dissatisfaction. The intent is to forecast the failure effects, to the team's level of knowledge.

Typical failure effects could be, but are not limited to:

Noise	Rough	Leaks
Erratic Operation	Inoperative	Regulatory Non-Compliance
Poor Appearance	Unpleasant Odor	
Unstable	Operation Impaired	
Intermittent Operation	Thermal Event	

3.2.12 (12) SEVERITY (S)—Severity is the rank associated with the most serious effect for a given failure mode. Severity is a relative ranking, within the scope of the individual FMEA. A reduction in Severity Ranking index can be effected only through a design change. Severity should be estimated using Table 1 as a guideline.

3.2.12.1 Suggested Evaluation Criteria—The team should agree on an evaluation criteria and ranking system that is consistent, even if modified for individual product analysis. (See Table 1.)

NOTE 1—It is not recommended to modify criteria ranking values of 9 and 10. Failure Modes with rank Severity 1, should not be analyzed further.

NOTE 2—High Severity Rankings can sometimes be reduced by making design revisions that compensate or mitigate the resultant severity of failure. For example, "run flat tires" can mitigate the severity of a sudden tire blowout and "seat belts" can mitigate the severity of a vehicle crash.

TABLE 1—SUGGESTED DFMEA SEVERITY EVALUATION CRITERIA

Effect	Criteria: Severity of Effect	Ranking
Hazardous without warning	Very high severity ranking when a potential failure mode affects safe vehicle operation and/or involves noncompliance with government regulation without warning.	10
Hazardous with warning	Very high severity ranking when a potential failure mode affects safe vehicle operation and/or involves noncompliance with government regulation with warning.	9
Very High	Vehicle/item inoperable (loss of primary function).	8
High	Vehicle/Item operable, but at a reduced level of performance. Customer very dissatisfied.	7
Moderate	Vehicle/Item operable, but Comfort/Convenience item(s) inoperable. Customer dissatisfied.	6
Low	Vehicle/Item operable, but Comfort/Convenience item(s) operable at a reduced level of performance. Customer somewhat dissatisfied.	5
Very Low	Fit and Finish/Squeak and Rattle item does not conform. Defect noticed by most customers (greater than 75%).	4
Minor	Fit and Finish/Squeak and Rattle item does not conform. Defect noticed by 50% of customers.	3
Very Minor	Fit and Finish/Squeak and Rattle item does not conform. Defect noticed by discriminating customers (less than 25%).	2
None	No discernible effect.	1

3.2.13 (13) CLASSIFICATION—This column may be used to classify any special product characteristics (e.g., critical, key, major, significant) for components, subsystems, or systems that may require additional design or process controls. (See Figure 3A or 3B.)

This column may also be used to highlight high-priority failure modes for engineering assessment, if the Team finds this helpful, or if local management requires same.

Special Product or Process Characteristic symbols and their usage is directed by specific company policy and is not standardized in this document.

3.2.14 (14) POTENTIAL CAUSE(S)/MECHANISM(S) OF FAILURE—Potential Cause of Failure is defined as an indication of a design weakness, the consequence of which is the failure mode. (See Figure 3A or 3B.)

List, to the extent possible, every potential cause and/or failure mechanism for each failure mode. The cause/mechanism should be listed as concisely and completely as possible so that remedial efforts can be aimed at pertinent causes.

Typical failure causes may include, but are not limited to:

Incorrect Material Specified	Inadequate Design Life Assumption
Over-stressing	Insufficient Lubrication Capability
Inadequate Maintenance Instructions	Incorrect Algorithm
Improper Maintenance Instructions	Improper Software Specification
Improper Surface Finish Specification	Inadequate Travel Specification
Improper Friction Material Specified	Excessive Heat
Improper Tolerance Specified	

Typical failure mechanisms may include, but are not limited to:

Yield	Chemical Oxidation
Fatigue	Electromigration
Material Instability	
Creep	
Wear	
Corrosion	

3.2.15 (15) OCCURRENCE (O)—Occurrence is the likelihood that a specific cause/mechanism will occur during the design life. The likelihood of occurrence ranking number has a relative meaning rather than an absolute value. Preventing or controlling the causes/mechanisms of the failure mode through a design change or design process change (e.g., design checklist, design review, design guide) is the only way a reduction in the occurrence ranking can be effected. (See Figure 3A or 3B.)

Estimate the likelihood of occurrence of potential failure cause/mechanism on a "1" to "10" scale. In determining this estimate, questions such as the following should be considered:

a. What is the service history/field experience with similar components, subsystems, or systems?
b. Is component carryover or similar to a previous level component, subsystem, or system?
c. How significant are changes from a previous level component, subsystem, or system?
d. Is component radically different from a previous level component?
e. Is component completely new?
f. Has the component application changed?
g. What are the environmental changes?
h. Has an engineering analysis (e.g., reliability) been used to estimate the expected comparable occurrence rate for the application?
i. Have preventive controls been put in place?

A consistent occurrence ranking system should be used to ensure continuity. The occurrence ranking number is a relative rating within the scope of the FMEA and may not reflect the actual likelihood of occurrence.

3.2.15.1 Suggested Evaluation Criteria—The team should agree on an evaluation criteria and ranking system, which is consistent, even if modified for individual product analysis. (See Table 2.) Occurrence should be estimated using Table 2 as a guideline:

NOTE—The ranking value of 1 is reserved for "Remote: Failure Is unlikely".

3.2.16 (16) CURRENT DESIGN CONTROLS—List the prevention, design validation/verification (DV), or other activities which are completed or committed to and that will assure the design adequacy for the failure mode and/or cause/mechanism under consideration. Current controls (e.g., road testing, design reviews, fail/safe designs such as a pressure relief valve, mathematical studies, rig/lab testing, feasibility review, prototype tests, fleet testing) are those that have been or are being used with the same or similar designs. (See Figure 3A and 3B.) The Team should always be focused on improving design controls; for example, the creation of new system tests in the lab, or the creation of new system modeling algorithms, etc.

There are two types of Design Controls to consider:

a. Prevention: Prevent the cause/mechanism of failure or the failure mode from occurring, or reduce the rate of occurrence,
b. Detection: Detect the cause/mechanism of failure or the failure mode, either by analytical or physical methods, before the item is released to production.

TABLE 2—SUGGESTED DFMEA OCCURRENCE EVALUATION CRITERIA

Probability of Failure	Likely Failure Rates Over Design Life	Ranking
Very High: Persistent failures	≥100 per thousand vehicles/items	10
	50 per thousand vehicles/items	9
High: Frequent failures	20 per thousand vehicles/items	8
	10 per thousand vehicles/items	7
Moderate: Occasional failures	5 per thousand vehicles/items	6
	2 per thousand vehicles/items	5
	1 per thousand vehicles/items	4
Low: Relatively few failures	0.5 per thousand vehicles/items	3
	0.1 per thousand vehicles/items	2
Remote: Failure is unlikely	≤ 0.01 per thousand vehicles/items	1

The preferred approach is to first use prevention controls, if possible. The initial occurrence rankings will be affected by the prevention controls, provided they are integrated as part of the design intent. The initial detection rankings will be based on design controls that either detect the cause/mechanism of failure, or detect the failure mode.

The Design FMEA form in Figure 3A has two columns for the design controls (i.e., separate columns for Prevention Controls and Detection Controls) to assist the team in clearly distinguishing between these two types of design controls. This allows for a quick visual determination that both types of design controls have been considered. Use of this two-column form is the preferred approach. (See Figure 3A.)

NOTE—In the example included here, it is clear that the team has not identified any prevention controls. This could be due to prevention controls not having been used on the same or similar designs.

If a one-column (for design controls) form is used, then the following prefixes should be used. For prevention controls, place a 'P' before each prevention control listed. For detection controls, place a 'D' before each detection control listed. (See Figure 3B.)

Once the design controls have been identified, review all prevention controls to determine if any occurrence rankings need to be revised.

3.2.17 (17) DETECTION (D)—Detection is the rank associated with the best detection design control from the list in the previous column. Detection is a relative ranking, within the scope of the individual FMEA. In order to achieve a lower ranking, generally the planned design control (e.g., validation, and/or verification activities) has to be improved.

3.2.17.1 Suggested Evaluation Criteria—The team should agree on an evaluation criteria and ranking system, which is consistent, even if modified for individual product analysis. (See Table 3.)

TABLE 3—SUGGESTED DETECTION EVALUATION CRITERIA

Detection	Criteria: Likelihood of Detection by Design Control	Ranking
Absolute Uncertainty	Design Control will not and/or can not detect a potential cause/mechanism and subsequent failure mode; or there is no Design Control	10
Very Remote	Very remote chance the Design Control will detect a potential cause/mechanism and subsequent failure mode	9
Remote	Remote chance the Design Control will detect a potential cause/mechanism and subsequent failure mode	8
Very Low	Very Low chance the Design Control will detect a potential cause/mechanism and subsequent failure mode	7
Low	Low chance the Design Control will detect a potential cause/mechanism and subsequent failure mode.	6
Moderate	Moderate chance the Design Control will detect a potential cause/mechanism and subsequent failure mode.	5
Moderately High	Moderately High chance the Design Control will detect a potential cause/mechanism and subsequent failure mode.	4
High	High chance the Design Control will detect a potential cause/mechanism and subsequent failure mode.	3
Very High	Very High chance the Design Control will detect a potential cause/mechanism and subsequent failure mode.	2
Almost Certain	Design Control will almost certainly detect a potential cause/mechanism and subsequent failure mode.	1

3.2.17.2 It is best to have detection design controls in place as early as possible in the design development process.

NOTE—After making the Detection Ranking, the Team should review the Occurrence Ranking and ensure that the Occurrence Ranking is still appropriate

Detection should be estimated using Table 3 as a guideline:

NOTE—The ranking value of 1 is reserved for "almost certain."

3.2.18 (18) RISK PRIORITY NUMBER (RPN)—The Risk Priority Number is the product of the Severity (S), Occurrence (O), and Detection (D) ranking. (See Figure 3A or 3B.)

$$\text{RPN} = (\text{S}) \times (\text{O}) \times (\text{D}) \qquad \text{(Eq. 1)}$$

Within the scope of the individual FMEA, this value (between "1" and "1000") can be used to rank order the concerns in the design (e.g., in Pareto fashion).

3.2.19 (19) RECOMMENDED ACTION(S)—Engineering assessment for preventive/corrective action should be first directed at high severity, high RPN, and other items designated by the team. The intent of any recommended action is to reduce rankings, in the following preference order: severity, occurrence, and detection rankings. (See Figure 3A or 3B.)

In general practice when the severity is a "9" or "10", special attention must be given to assure that the risk is addressed through existing design controls or preventive/corrective action(s), regardless of the RPN. In all cases where the effect of an identified potential failure mode could be a hazard to the end-user, preventive/corrective actions should be considered to avoid the failure mode by eliminating, mitigating, or controlling the cause(s).

After special attention has been given to Severity Rankings of 9 or 10, the team then addresses other Failure Modes, with the intent of reducing Severity, then Occurrence, and then Detection.

Actions such as, but are not limited to, the following should be considered:

a. Revised Design Geometry and/or tolerances,
b. Revised Material Specification,
c. Design of experiments (particularly when multiple or interactive causes are present)/or other problem solving techniques, and
d. Revised Test Plan.

The primary objective of recommended actions is to reduce risks and increase customer satisfaction by improving the design.

Only a design revision can bring about a reduction in the severity ranking. A reduction in the occurrence ranking can be effected only by removing or controlling one or more of the causes/mechanisms of the failure mode through a design revision. An increase in design validation/verification actions will result in a reduction in the detection ranking only. Increasing the design validation/verification actions is a less desirable engineering action since it does not address the severity or occurrence of the failure mode.

If engineering assessment leads to no recommended actions for a specific failure mode/cause/control combination, indicate this by entering a "NONE" in this column.

3.2.20 (20) RESPONSIBILITY (FOR THE RECOMMENDED ACTION)—Enter the name of the organization and individual responsible for the recommended action and the target completion date. (See Figure 3A or 3B.)

3.2.21 (21) ACTIONS TAKEN—After an action has been implemented, enter a brief description of the actual action and effective date. (See Figure 3A or 3B.)

3.2.22 (22) REVISED RATINGS—After the preventive/corrective action has been identified, estimate and record the resulting severity, occurrence, and detection rankings. Calculate and record the resulting RPN. If no actions are taken, leave the related ranking columns blank. (See Figure 3A or 3B.)

All revised ratings should be reviewed. If further action is considered necessary, repeat the analysis. The focus should always be on continuous improvement.

3.2.23 FOLLOW-UP ACTIONS—See 1.5.

4. Potential Failure Mode and Effects Analysis in Manufacturing and Assembly Processes (Process FMEA)

4.1 Introduction—A Process potential FMEA is an analytical technique utilized by a Manufacturing/Assembly Responsible Engineer/Team as a means to assure that, to the extent possible, potential failure modes and their associated causes/mechanisms have been considered and addressed. In its most rigorous form, an FMEA is a summary of the engineer's/team's thoughts (including an analysis of items that could go wrong based on experience) as a process is developed. This systematic approach parallels and formalizes the mental discipline that an engineer normally goes through in any manufacturing planning process.

The Process potential FMEA:

a. Identifies the process functions and requirements,
b. Identifies potential product and process related failure modes,
c. Assesses the effects of the potential failures on the customer,
d. Identifies the potential manufacturing or assembly process causes and identifies process variables on which to focus controls for occurrence reduction or detection of the failure conditions,
e. Identifies process variables on which to focus process controls,
f. Develops a ranked list of potential failure modes, thus establishing a priority system for preventive/corrective action considerations, and
g. Documents the results of the manufacturing or assembly process.

4.1.1 CUSTOMER DEFINED—The definition of "CUSTOMER" for a Process potential FMEA should normally be seen as the "END USER." However, customer can also be a subsequent or downstream manufacturing or assembly operation, a service operation, as well as government regulations.

4.1.2 TEAM EFFORT—During the initial Process potential FMEA development, the responsible engineer is expected to directly and actively involve representatives from all affected areas. These areas should include, but are not limited to design, assembly, manufacturing, materials, quality, service, and suppliers, as well as the area responsible for the next assembly. The FMEA should be a catalyst to stimulate the interchange of ideas between the areas affected and thus promote a team approach.

Unless the responsible engineer is experienced with FMEA and team facilitation, it is helpful to have an experienced FMEA Facilitator assist the team in its activities.

The Process FMEA is a living document and should be initiated:

a. Before or at the feasibility stage,
b. Prior to tooling for production, and
c. Take into account all manufacturing operations, from individual components to assemblies.

The PFMEA should be addressed according to the 3 cases outlined in 1.4.

Early review and analysis of new or revised processes is promoted to anticipate, resolve, or monitor potential process concerns during the manufacturing planning stages of a new model or component program.

The Process FMEA assumes the product, as designed, will meet the design intent. Potential failure modes which can occur because of a design weakness may be included in a Process FMEA. Their effect and avoidance is covered by the Design FMEA.

The Process FMEA does not rely on product design changes to overcome weaknesses in the process. However, it does take into consideration a product's design characteristics relative to the planned manufacturing or assembly process to assure that, to the extent possible, the resultant product meets customer needs and expectations.

4.2 Development of a Process FMEA—The process-responsible engineer has at his or her disposal a number of documents that will be useful in preparing the Process FMEA. The FMEA begins by developing a listing of what the process is expected to do, and what it is expected not to do, i.e., the process intent.

The Process FMEA should begin with a flow chart of the general process. This flow chart should identify the product/process characteristics associated with each operation. Identification of some product effects from the corresponding Design FMEA, should be included, if available. Copies of the flow chart used in FMEA preparation should accompany the FMEA.

In order to facilitate documentation of the analysis of potential failures and their consequences, a Process FMEA form has been developed and is in Appendix G.

An example of a completed form is contained in Appendix H, including numbered headings (1) – (22) for ease of reference to the following descriptions.

4.2.1 (1) FMEA NUMBER—Enter the FMEA document number, which may be used for tracking. (See Figure 4A or 4B.)

4.2.2 (2) ITEM—Enter the name and number of the system, subsystem, or component, for which the process is being analyzed. (See Figure 4A or 4B.)

4.2.3 (3) PROCESS RESPONSIBILITY—Enter the OEM, department, and group. Also include the supplier name if known. (See Figure 4A or 4B.)

4.2.4 (4) PREPARED BY—Enter the name, telephone number, and company of the engineer responsible for preparing the FMEA. (See Figure 4A or 4B.)

4.2.5 (5) MODEL YEAR(S)/PROGRAM(S)—Enter the intended model year(s)/program(s) that will use and/or be affected by the design/process being analyzed (if known). (See Figure 4A or 4B.)

4.2.6 (6) KEY DATE—Enter the initial FMEA due date, which should not exceed the scheduled start of production date. (See Figure 4A or 4B.)

NOTE—In the case of a supplier, the initial FMEA due date should not exceed the customer required Production Part Approval Process (PPAP) submission date.

POTENTIAL
FAILURE MODE AND EFFECTS ANALYSIS
(PROCESS FMEA)

FMEA Number ______________

Page ________ of ________

Item ______________________ Process Responsibility ______________________ Prepared By ______________________

Model Year(s)/Program(s) ______________________ Key Date ______________________ FMEA Date (Orig.) ________ (Rev.) ________

Core Team ______________________

Process Function / Requirements	Potential Failure Mode	Potential Effect(s) of Failure	Sev	Class	Potential Cause(s)/ Mechanism(s) of Failure	Occur	Current Process Controls Prevention	Current Process Controls Detection	Detec	R.P.N.	Recommended Action(s)	Responsibility & Target Completion Date	Action Results				
													Actions Taken	Sev	Occ	Det	R.P.N.

FIGURE 4A—POTENTIAL FAILURE MODE AND EFFECTS ANALYSIS IN MANUFACTURING AND ASSEMBLY PROCESSES (PROCESS FMEA)
– TWO COLUMNS, CURRENT PROCESS CONTROLS –

POTENTIAL

FAILURE MODE AND EFFECTS ANALYSIS
IN MANUFACTURING AND ASSEMBLY PROCESSES
(PROCESS FMEA)

FMEA Number ____________

Page ______ of ______

Item ____________ Process Responsibility ____________ Prepared By ____________

Model Year(s)/Program(s) ____________ Key Date ____________ FMEA Date (Orig.) ______ (Rev.) ______

Core Team ____________

Process Function / Requirements	Potential Failure Mode	Potential Effect(s) of Failure	Sev	Class	Potential Cause(s)/ Mechanism(s) of Failure	Occur	Current Process Controls — Prevention — Detection	Detec	R.P.N.	Recommended Action(s)	Responsibility & Target Completion Date	Action Results: Actions Taken	Sev	Occ	Det	R.P.N.

FIGURE 4B—POTENTIAL FAILURE MODE AND EFFECTS ANALYSIS IN MANUFACTURING AND ASSEMBLY PROCESSES (PROCESS FMEA)
– ONE COLUMN, CURRENT PROCESS CONTROLS –

4.2.7 (7) FMEA Date—Enter the date the original FMEA was compiled, and the latest revision date. (See Figure 4A or 4B.)

4.2.8 (8) Core Team—List the names of the responsible individuals and departments which have the authority to identify and/or perform tasks. (It is recommended that each team member's name, department, telephone number, address, etc., be included on a distribution list.) (See Figure 4A or 4B.)

4.2.9 (9) Process Function/Requirements—Enter a simple description of the process or operation being analyzed (e.g., turning, drilling, tapping, welding, assembling). The team should review applicable performance, material, process, environmental, and safety standards. Indicate as concisely as possible the purpose of the process or operation being analyzed, including information about the design (metrics/measurables) describing the system, subsystem, or component. Where the process involves numerous operations (e.g., assembling) with different potential modes of failure, it may be desirable to list the operations as separate elements. (See Figure 4A or 4B.)

4.2.10 (10) Potential Failure Mode—Potential Failure Mode is defined as the manner in which the process could potentially fail to meet the process requirements and/or design intent as described in the process function/requirements column. It is a description of the nonconformance at that specific operation. It can be a cause associated with a potential failure mode in a subsequent (downstream) operation or an effect associated with a potential failure in a previous (upstream) operation. However, in preparation of the FMEA, the assumption may be made that the incoming part(s)/material(s) are correct. Exceptions can be made by the FMEA team where historical data indicates deficiencies in incoming part quality. (See Figure 4A or 4B.)

List each potential failure mode for the particular operation in terms of a component, subsystem, system, or process characteristic. Assume that the failure could occur, but may not necessarily occur. The process engineer/team should be able to pose and answer the following questions:

a. How can the process/part fail to meet specifications?
b. Regardless of engineering specifications, what would a customer (end user, subsequent operations, or service) consider objectionable?

Start by comparing similar processes and reviewing customer (end user and subsequent operation) claims relating to similar components. In addition, a knowledge of the design intent is necessary. Typical failure modes could be, but are not limited to:

Bent	Burred	Hole off-location
Cracked	Hole too shallow	Hole missing
Handling damage	Dirty	Hole too deep
Surface too rough	Deformed	Surface too smooth
Open Circuited	Short Circuited	Mis-labeled

NOTE—Potential failure modes should be described in "physical" or technical terms, not as a symptom noticeable by the customer.

4.2.11 (11) Potential Effect(s) of Failure—Potential Effects of Failure are defined as the effects of the failure mode on the customer(s). (See Figure 4A or 4B and 4.1.1.)

Describe the effects of the failure in terms of what the customer might notice or experience, remembering that the customer may be an internal customer as well as the ultimate end user. State clearly if the failure mode could impact safety or cause noncompliance to regulations. The customer(s) in this context could be the next operation, subsequent operations or locations, the dealer, and/or the vehicle owner. Each must be considered when assessing the potential effect of a failure.

For the End User, the effects should always be stated in terms of product or system performance, such as:

Noise	Rough	Erratic Operation	Excessive Effort
Inoperative	Unpleasant Odor	Unstable	Operation Impaired
Draft	Intermittent Operation	Poor Appearance	Leaks
Vehicle Control Impaired	Rework/Repairs	Customer Dissatisfaction	Scrap

If the customer is the next operation or subsequent operation(s)/location(s), the effects should be stated in terms of process/operation performance, such as:

Can not fasten	Does not fit	Can not bore/tap	Does not connect
Can not mount	Does not match	Can not face	Causes Excessive tool wear
Damages equipment	Endangers operator		

4.2.12 (12) Severity(s)—Severity is the rank associated with the most serious effect for a given failure mode. Severity is a relative ranking, within the scope of the individual FMEA. A reduction in Severity Ranking index can be effected through a design change to system, subsystem or component, or a redesign of the process. (See Figure 4A or 4B.)

If the customer affected by a failure mode is the manufacturing or assembly plant or the product user, assessing the severity may lie outside the immediate process engineer's/team's field of experience or knowledge. In these cases, the design FMEA, design engineer, and/or subsequent manufacturing or assembly plant process engineer, should be consulted.

4.2.12.1 Suggested Evaluation Criteria—The team should agree on an evaluation criteria and ranking system, which is consistent, even if modified for individual process analysis. (See Table 4.)

Severity should be estimated using Table 4 as a guideline:

NOTE—It is not recommended to modify criteria for ranking values of 9 and 10. Failure Modes with rank Severity 1, should not be analyzed further.

TABLE 4—SUGGESTED PFMEA SEVERITY EVALUATION CRITERIA

Effect	Criteria: Severity of Effect This ranking results when a potential failure mode results in a final customer and/or a manufacturing/assembly plant defect. The final customer should always be considered first. If both occur, use the higher of the two severities. (Customer Effect)	Criteria: Severity of Effect This ranking results when a potential failure mode results in a final customer and/or a manufacturing/assembly plant defect. The final customer should always be considered first. If both occur, use the higher of the two severities. (Manufacturing/Assembly Effect)	Ranking
Hazardous without warning	Very high severity ranking when a potential failure mode affects safe vehicle operation and/or involves noncompliance with government regulation without warning.	Or may endanger operator (machine or assembly) without warning.	10
Hazardous with warning	Very high severity ranking when a potential failure mode affects safe vehicle operation and/or involves noncompliance with government regulation with warning.	Or may endanger operator (machine or assembly) with warning.	9
Very High	Vehicle/item inoperable (loss of primary function).	Or 100% of product may have to be scrapped, or vehicle/item repaired in repair department with a repair time greater than one hour.	8
High	Vehicle/Item operable but at a reduced level of performance. Customer very dissatisfied.	Or product may have to be sorted and a portion (less than 100%) scrapped, or vehicle/item repaired in repair department with a repair time between half an hour and an hour.	7
Moderate	Vehicle/Item operable but Comfort/Convenience item(s) inoperable. Customer dissatisfied.	Or a portion (less than 100%) of the product may have to be scrapped with no sorting, or vehicle/item repaired in repair department with a repair time less than half an hour.	6
Low	Vehicle/Item operable but Comfort/Convenience item(s) operable at a reduced level of performance. Customer somewhat dissatisfied.	Or 100% of product may have to be reworked, or vehicle/item repaired off-line but does not go to repair department.	5
Very Low	Fit & finish/Squeak and rattle item does not conform. Defect noticed by most customers (greater than 75%).	Or the product may have to be sorted, with no scrap, and a portion (less than 100%) reworked.	4
Minor	Fit & finish/Squeak and rattle item does not conform. Defect noticed by 50% of customers.	Or a portion (less than 100%) of the product may have to be reworked, with no scrap, on-line but out-of-station.	3
Very Minor	Fit & finish/Squeak and rattle item does not conform. Defect noticed by discriminating customers (less than 25%).	Or a portion (less than 100%) of the product may have to be reworked, with no scrap, on-line but in-station.	2
None	No discernible effect.	Or slight inconvenience to operation or operator, or no effect.	1

4.2.13 (13) CLASSIFICATION—This column may be used to classify any special product or process characteristics (e.g., critical, key, major, significant) for components, subsystems, or systems that may require additional process controls. (See Figure 4A or 4B.)

This column may also be used to highlight high priority failure modes for engineering assessment.

If a classification is identified in the Process FMEA, notify the design responsible engineer since this may affect the engineering documents concerning control item identification.

Special Product or Process Characteristic symbols and their usage is directed by specific company policy and is not standardized in this document.

4.2.14 (14) POTENTIAL CAUSE(S)/MECHANISM(S) OF FAILURE—Potential Cause of Failure is defined as how the failure could occur, described in terms of something that can be corrected or can be controlled. (See Figure 4A or 4B.)

List, to the extent possible, every failure cause assignable to each potential failure mode. If a cause is exclusive to the failure mode, i.e., if correcting the cause has a direct impact on the failure mode, then this portion of the FMEA thought process is completed. Many causes, however, are not mutually exclusive, and to correct or control the cause, a design of experiments, for example, may be considered to determine which root causes are the major contributors and which can be most easily controlled. The causes should be described so that remedial efforts can be aimed at those causes which are pertinent. Typical failure causes may include, but are not limited to:

Improper torque - over, under	Improper weld - current, time, pressure
Inaccurate gauging	Improper heat treat - time, temperature
Inadequate gating/venting	Inadequate or no lubrication
Part missing or mislocated	Worn locator
Worn tool	Chip on locator
Broken tool	Improper machine setup
Improper programming	

Only specific errors or malfunctions (e.g., operator fails to install seal) should be listed; ambiguous phrases (e.g., operator error, machine malfunction) should not be used.

4.2.15 (15) OCCURRENCE (O)—Occurrence is the likelihood that a specific cause/mechanism of failure will occur. The likelihood of occurrence ranking number has a relative meaning rather than an absolute value. Preventing or controlling the causes/mechanisms of the failure mode through a design or process change is the only way a reduction in the occurrence ranking can be effected. (See Figure 4A or 4B.)

Estimate the likelihood of occurrence of potential failure cause/mechanism on a "1" to "10" scale.

A consistent occurrence ranking system should be used to ensure continuity. The occurrence ranking number is a relative rating within the scope of the FMEA and may not reflect the actual likelihood of occurrence.

The "Possible Failure Rates" are based on the number of failures which are anticipated during the process execution. If statistical data are available from a similar process, the data should be used to determine the occurrence ranking. In all other cases, a subjective assessment can be made by using the word descriptions in the left column of the table, along with any historical data available for similar processes.

4.2.15.1 Suggested Evaluation Criteria—The team should agree on an evaluation criteria and ranking system, that is consistent, even if modified for individual process analysis. (See Table 5.)

Occurrence should be estimated using the following table as a guideline:

NOTE—The ranking value of 1 is reserved for "Remote: Failure Is unlikely."

TABLE 5—SUGGESTED PFMEA OCCURRENCE EVALUATION CRITERIA

Probability	Likely Failure Rates[(1)]	Ranking
Very High: Persistent failures	≥100 per thousand pieces	10
	50 per thousand pieces	9
High: Frequent failures	20 per thousand pieces	8
	10 per thousand pieces	7
Moderate: Occasional failures	5 per thousand pieces	6
	2 per thousand pieces	5
	1 per thousand pieces	4
Low: Relatively few failures	0.5 per thousand pieces	3
	0.1 per thousand pieces	2
Remote: Failure is unlikely	≤ 0.01 per thousand pieces	1

1. For associated Ppk calculations and values, see Appendix M.

4.2.16 (16) CURRENT PROCESS CONTROLS—Current Process Controls are descriptions of the controls that either prevent to the extent possible the failure mode/cause from occurring or detect the failure mode or cause should it occur. These controls can be process controls such as error/mistake proofing or Statistical Process Control (SPC), or can be post-process evaluation. The evaluation may occur at the subject operation or at subsequent operations. (See Figure 4A or 4B.)

There are two types of Process Controls/features to consider:

a. Prevention: Prevent the cause/mechanism or failure mode/effect from occurring, or reduce their rate of occurrence
b. Detection: Detect the cause/mechanism or failure mode, and lead to corrective action(s)

The preferred approach is to first use prevention controls if possible. The initial occurrence rankings will be affected by the prevention controls provided they are integrated as part of the process intent. The initial rankings for detection will be based on process controls that either detect the cause/mechanism of failure, or detect the failure mode.

The Process FMEA form in Figure 4A has two columns for the process controls (i.e., separate columns for Prevention Controls and Detection Controls) to assist the team in clearly distinguishing between these two types of process controls. This allows for a quick visual determination that both types of process controls have been considered. Use of this two-column form is the preferred approach. (See Figure 4A.)

If a one-column (for process controls) form is used, then the following prefixes should be used. For prevention controls, place a 'P' before each prevention control listed. For detection controls, place a 'D' before each detection control listed. (See Figure 4B.)

Once the process controls have been identified, review all prevention controls to determine if any occurrence rankings need to be revised.

4.2.17 (17) DETECTION (D)—Detection is the rank associated with the best detection control listed in the process control column. Detection is a relative ranking, within the scope of the individual FMEA. In order to achieve a lower ranking, generally the planned process control has to be improved. (See Figure 4A or 4B.)

Assume the failure has occurred and then assess the capabilities of all "Current Process Controls" to prevent shipment of the part having this failure mode or defect. Do not automatically presume that the detection ranking is low because the occurrence is low (e.g., when Control Charts are used), but do assess the ability of the process controls to detect low frequency failure modes or prevent them from going further in the process.

Random quality checks are unlikely to detect the existence of an isolated defect and should not influence the detection ranking. Sampling done on a statistical basis is a valid detection control.

4.2.17.1 Suggested Evaluation Criteria—The team should agree on an evaluation criteria and ranking system, that is consistent, even if modified for individual product analysis. (See Table 6.)

Detection should be estimated using Table 6 as a guideline:

NOTE—The ranking value of 1 is reserved for "Controls certain to Detect."

4.2.18 (18) RISK PRIORITY NUMBER (RPN)—The Risk Priority Number is the product of the Severity (S), Occurrence (O), and Detection (D) ranking. (See Figure 4A or 4B.)

$$\text{RPN} = (S) \times (O) \times (D) \qquad \text{(Eq. 2)}$$

Within the scope of the individual FMEA, this value (between "1" and "1000") can be used to rank order the concerns in the process (e.g., in Pareto fashion).

4.2.19 (19) RECOMMENDED ACTION(S)—Engineering assessment for corrective action should be first directed at high severity, high RPN, and other items designated by the team. The intent of any recommended action is to reduce rankings, in the following preference order: severity, occurrence, and detection rankings. (See Figure 4A or 4B.)

In general practice when the severity is "9" or "10", special attention must be given to assure that the risk is addressed through existing design actions/controls or process preventive/corrective action(s), regardless of the RPN. In all cases where the effect of an identified potential failure mode could be a hazard to manufacturing/assembly personnel, preventive/corrective actions should be taken to avoid the failure mode by eliminating or controlling the cause(s), or appropriate operator protection should be specified.

TABLE 6—SUGGESTED PFMEA DETECTION EVALUATION CRITERIA

Detection	Criteria	Inspection Type A(1)	Inspection Type B(1)	Inspection Type C(1)	Suggested Range of Detection Methods	Ranking
Almost Impossible	Absolute certainty of non-detection			X	Cannot detect or is not checked.	10
Very Remote	Controls will probably not detect			X	Control is Achieved with indirect or random checks only.	9
Remote	Controls have poor chance of detection			X	Control is achieved with visual inspection only.	8
Very Low	Controls have poor chance of detection			X	Control is achieved with double visual inspection only.	7
Low	Controls may detect.		X	X	Control is achieved with charting methods, such as SPC {Statistical Process Control}	6
Moderate	Controls may detect		X		Control is based on variable gauging after parts have left the station, OR Go/No Go gauging performed on 100% of the parts after parts have left the station.	5
Moderately High	Controls have a good chance to detect	X	X		Error detection in subsequent operations, OR gauging performed on set-up and first-piece check (for set-up causes only).	4
High	Controls have a good chance to detect	X	X		Error detection in-station, OR error detection in subsequent operations by multiple layers of acceptance: supply, select, install, verify. Can not accept discrepant part.	3
Very High	Controls almost certain to detect.	X	X		Error detection in-station (automatic gauging with automatic stop feature). Can not pass discrepant part.	2
Certain	Controls certain to detect.	X			Discrepant parts can not be made because item has been error proofed by process/product design.	1

1. Inspection Types:
   A. Error Proofed
   B. Gauging
   C. Manual Inspection

NOTE—X's indicate the inspection type(s) used for a given rank.

After special attention has been given to Severity Rankings of 9 or 10, the team then addresses other Failure Modes, with the intent of reducing Severity, then Occurrence, and then Detection.

Actions such as, but not limited to, the following should be considered:

a. To reduce the probability of occurrence, process and/or design revisions are required. An action-oriented study of the process using statistical methods could be implemented with an ongoing feedback of information to the appropriate operations for continuous improvement and defect prevention.
b. Only a design and/or process revision can bring about a reduction in the severity ranking.
c. To increase the probability of detection, process and/or design revisions are required. A preferred method for generating possible process and/or design revisions, to increase the probability of detection, is Error/Mistake Proofing. Generally, improving detection controls is costly and ineffective for quality improvements. Increasing quality controls inspection frequency is not an effective preventive/corrective action and should only be utilized as a temporary measure, since permanent preventive/corrective action is required. In some cases, a design change to a specific part may be required to assist in the detection. Changes to the current control system may be implemented to increase this probability.
   Emphasis must, however, be placed on preventing defects (i.e., reducing the occurrence) rather than detecting them. An example would be the use of Statistical Process Control and process improvement rather than random quality checks or associated inspection.

If engineering assessment leads to no recommended actions for a specific failure mode/cause/control combination, indicate this by entering a "NONE" in this column.

4.2.20 (20) RESPONSIBILITY (FOR THE RECOMMENDED ACTION)—Enter the individual responsible for the recommended action, and the target completion date. (See Figure 4A or 4B.)

4.2.21 (21) ACTIONS TAKEN—After an action has been implemented, enter a brief description of the action and effective date. (See Figure 4A or 4B.)

4.2.22 (22) REVISED RATINGS—After the preventive/corrective action has been identified, estimate and record the resulting severity, occurrence, and detection rankings. Calculate and record the resulting RPN. If no actions are taken, leave the related ranking columns blank. (See Figure 4A or 4B.)

All revised ratings should be reviewed and if further action is considered necessary, repeat the analysis. The focus should always be on continuous improvement.

4.2.23 FOLLOW-UP ACTIONS—See 1.5.

5. Potential Failure Mode and Effects Analysis for Machinery (Machinery FMEA). An Application of Design FMEA to Plant Machinery, Tooling, and Equipment.

5.1 Introduction—Failure Mode and Effects Analysis concepts can be applied to machinery (the term machinery, as used throughout this text includes tooling and equipment) to reduce the probability that potential failure modes, related to machinery, will occur. The Machinery potential FMEA (MFMEA) supports the machinery design process from design development through design approval. The MFMEA is a thorough review of each step, or function, in the overall operation of the machinery. This section addresses the concepts used to develop an effective MFMEA, which is an application of a Design FMEA (Section 3) for Plant Machinery, Tooling, and Equipment.

This section on MFMEA includes unique "Machinery Tables" for Severity, Occurrence, and Detection Rankings.

It should be noted that a Process FMEA can also be applied to Machinery for the "Build/Installation Process." The information provided for Process FMEA (Section 4) can be used for the creation of "Build/Installation Process FMEA," but an application is not listed here-in. The Build/Installation Process FMEA should be initiated prior to the creation of any machinery that will be used for production. The MFMEA is a design output used to evaluate and improve the reliability, maintainability, and the durability of the machinery.

A Machinery potential FMEA (MFMEA) for plant machinery, tooling, and equipment is an analytical technique utilized primarily by a Machinery-Responsible Engineer/Team. The purpose of the FMEA is to assure that, to the extent possible, potential failure modes and their associated causes/mechanisms have been considered and addressed. In its most rigorous form, an FMEA is a summary of the team's thoughts (including analysis of items that could go wrong based on experience) as the machinery is designed. The systematic approach parallels, formalizes, and documents the mental disciplines that an engineer/team normally goes through in any design/development process.

Since the MFMEA should be used as an input to the machinery preventive maintenance program, and used to assist in the determination of machinery controls that will be used, it is impossible to develop an effective MFMEA without the plant machinery personnel and the various supplier field service activities represented on the team. The team (see 5.1.2) should also focus on improving the reliability, durability, maintainability, and availability of the machine while conducting the analysis.

The Machinery Potential FMEA supports the design process in reducing risk of failures by:

POTENTIAL
FAILURE MODE AND EFFECTS ANALYSIS
(MACHINERY FMEA)

____ System ____________________

____ Subsystem ____________________

____ Component ____________________ Design Responsibility ____________________

Program(s)/Plant(s) ____________ Key Date ____________________

Core Team: ____

FMEA Number ____________________

Page ________ of ________

Prepared By ____________________

FMEA Date (Orig.) ________ (Rev.) ________

Item / Function Req'ts	Potential Failure Mode	Potential Effect(s) of Failure	Sev	Class	Potential Cause(s)/ Mechanism(s) of Failure	Occur	Current Machinery Controls Prevention	Current Machinery Controls Detection	Detec	R. P. N.	Recommended Action(s)	Responsibility & Target Completion Date	Action Results: Actions Taken	S e v	O c c	D e t	R. P. N.

FIGURE 5A—MACHINERY FMEA FORM
–TWO COLUMN, CURRENT MACHINERY DESIGN CONTROLS –

POTENTIAL
FAILURE MODE AND EFFECTS ANALYSIS
(MACHINERY FMEA)

____ System ________________

____ Subsystem ________________

____ Component ________________

Program(s)/Plant(s) ________________

Core Team: ________________

Design Responsibility ________________

Key Date ________________

FMEA Number ________________

Page ________ of ________

Prepared By ________________

FMEA Date (Orig.) ________ (Rev.) ________

Item / Function Req'ts	Potential Failure Mode	Potential Effect(s) of Failure	Sev	Class	Potential Cause(s)/ Mechanism(s) of Failure	Occur	Current Machinery Controls —Prevention —Detection	Detec	R. P. N.	Recommended Action(s)	Responsibility & Target Completion Date	Action Results: Actions Taken	Sev	Occ	Det	R. P. N.

FIGURE 5B—MACHINERY FMEA FORM
– ONE COLUMN, CURRENT MACHINERY DESIGN CONTROLS –

a. Aiding in the objective evaluation of equipment functions and sequence of steps, design requirements, and design alternatives;
b. Increasing the probability that potential failure modes and their effects on the customer (see 5.1.1) and the "End User" have been considered in the design and development process;
c. Providing additional information to aid in the planning of thorough and efficient design, validation, and development programs, including the planning of an efficient and effective process for preventive maintenance;
d. Developing a ranked list of potential failure modes ranked according to their effect on the "customer", thus establishing a priority system for design improvements, development, and validation testing/analysis;
e. Providing future reference, e.g., lessons learned to aid in analyzing field concerns, evaluating design changes, and developing advanced machinery designs;
f. Improving the reliability and durability of the machinery, resulting in reduced life cycle costs;
g. Improving machinery maintainability, resulting in reduced mean time to repair; and,
h. Improving reliability, durability, and maintainability, resulting in increased availability.

When fully implemented, the MFMEA discipline can be performed on new, modified, or carry-over designs in new applications or environments. An engineer from the responsible design source should initiate the MFMEA process, which for a proprietary design, may be the supplier.

5.1.1 CUSTOMER DEFINED—The definition of "Customer" for a MFMEA is the manufacturing facility where the machinery is to be installed for production. The manufacturing facility includes plant engineers, maintenance, production, and other plant support personnel.

5.1.2 TEAM EFFORT—During the MFMEA process, the machinery-responsible engineer is expected to actively involve representatives from all affected areas. These areas should include, but are not limited to production, manufacturing engineering, safety, quality, suppliers, product engineering, and the "customer" of the machinery as described in 5.1.1. The MFMEA should be a catalyst to stimulate the interchange of ideas between activities affected and thus promote a team approach. In addition, for any commercial "Catalog" components, the responsible representative from the component supplier should be consulted as required.

Unless the responsible engineer is experienced with FMEA and team facilitation, it is helpful to have an experienced FMEA Facilitator assist the team in its activities.

The Machinery FMEA is a living document and should:

a. Be initiated during machinery design concept development,
b. Be continually updated as changes occur or additional information is obtained throughout the phases of machinery development, and
c. Should be completed before engineering release for construction.

The MFMEA analyzes functions, design requirements, needs, and assumes the machinery will be built to specification. The focus of the MFMEA is to eliminate potential failures by removing design weaknesses before the machinery is built as opposed to relying on machinery controls and/or preventive maintenance to reduce the occurrence of the failures.

5.2 Development of a Machinery FMEA—The machinery design responsible engineer has at his/her disposal a number of formal and informal documents that will be useful in the preparation of the Machinery FMEA. The process of preparing the MFMEA begins with the full understanding of what the machinery is expected to do or not to do, in a given environment, under stated conditions, and for a defined period of time. These expectations may be determined from sources such as the Reliability and Maintainability specification statement, design requirements, performance reports, preventive/corrective action reports, maintenance history, program objectives, and federal or local regulatory requirements.

Prior to beginning the MFMEA, the team should have at their disposal a minimum of:

a. Detailed description of the sequence of steps in the overall operation of the machinery,
b. Equipment literature,
c. Engineering drawings of the machinery, and,
d. Machinery reliability and maintainability information (estimated or actual).

A Machinery FMEA should begin by prioritizing the subsystem improvements necessary to meet the overall system expectations.

A Machinery FMEA should begin with a block diagram for the system or subsystem being analyzed. An example of the block diagram is shown in Appendix C.

In order to facilitate documentation of the Machinery FMEA, a form is available in Appendix I.

An example of a completed form is contained in Appendix K.

5.2.1 FMEA NUMBER—Enter the FMEA document number, which may be used for tracking. (See Figure 5A or 5B.)

5.2.2 MACHINERY/SYSTEM, SUBSYSTEM, OR COMPONENT NAME—Indicate the appropriate level of analysis and enter the name and identification number of the system, subsystem, or component being analyzed. The FMEA team members must decide on what constitutes a system, subsystem, or component for their specific activities. The actual boundaries that divide a system, subsystem, and component are arbitrary and must be set by the FMEA team. (See Figure 5A or 5B and Appendix F.)

5.2.2.1 System FMEA Scope—A system can be considered to be made up of various subsystems. These subsystems often have been designed by different teams. Some typical Machinery System FMEAs might cover the following systems: Underbody Welding System, or Chassis Decking/Marriage System, etc. Thus, the focus of the System FMEA is to ensure that all interfaces and interactions are covered among the various subsystems that make up the system.

5.2.2.2 Subsystem FMEA Scope—A Subsystem FMEA is generally a subset of a larger system. For example, the robots are a sub-set of the underbody welding system. Thus, the focus of the Machinery Subsystem FMEA is to ensure that all interfaces and interactions are covered among the various components that make up the subsystem.

5.2.2.3 Component FMEA Scope—A Component FMEA is generally an FMEA focused on the sub-set of a subsystem. For example, end-of-arm tooling (e.g., weld gun, sealer gun, gripper) is a component of the robot (which is a subsystem of the underbody welding system.)

5.2.3 DESIGN RESPONSIBILITY—Enter the OEM, department, group, and the supplier name as applicable. (See Figure 5A or 5B.)

5.2.4 PREPARED BY—Enter the name, telephone number, and the company of the engineer responsible for preparing the MFMEA document. (See Figure 5A or 5B.)

5.2.5 PROGRAM(S)/PLANT(S)—Enter the intended programs(s) and plant(s) that will utilize and/or be affected by the machinery being analyzed. (See Figure 5A or 5B.)

5.2.6 KEY DATE—Enter the initial MFMEA due date, which should not exceed the scheduled engineering release date for construction. (See Figure 5A or 5B.)

5.2.7 FMEA DATE—Enter the date the original MFMEA was compiled, and the latest revision date. (See Figure 5A or 5B.)

5.2.8 CORE TEAM—List the names of the responsible individuals and departments that have the authority to identify and/or perform tasks. (It is recommended that each team member's name, department, telephone number, address, etc., be included on the distribution list.) (See Figure 5A or 5B.)

5.2.9 ITEM/FUNCTION REQUIREMENTS—Enter the name of the item and enter a simple description of the step, or function, that is being analyzed. The team should review applicable performance, material, process, environmental, and safety standards. Indicate as concisely as possible the purpose/requirements of the step, or function, being analyzed, including information about the design (metrics/measurables) describing the system, subsystem or component.

If the subsystem has more than one function with different potential modes of failure, it may be desirable to list the functions as separate elements.

Performance Requirement Examples:

To pump sealant to panel at the rate of X cubic centimeters per minute
To pump coolant to work piece at not less than X gallons per minute
To achieve a torque of X N-m in Y seconds
To ramp up to X degree Celsius in Y seconds and maintain temperature for Z seconds
To transfer power from point A to point B
To move product X meters in Y minutes

5.2.10 POTENTIAL FAILURE MODE—Potential Failure Mode is defined as the manner in which the machinery could potentially fail to meet or deliver its intended function described in Item/Function Requirements column (i.e., intended function fails). (See Figure 5A or 5B.)

The potential failure mode is a description of the nonconformance at that specific step, or function. It can be a cause associated with a potential failure mode in a subsequent (downstream) step or an effect associated with a potential failure in a previous (upstream) step. However, in preparation of the MFMEA, the following assumptions should be made:

a. Incoming parts and materials are correct,
b. Machinery will be built, installed, adjusted, and maintained to specifications, and,
c. All preceding steps in the sequence of operations have been executed to specifications.

List each potential failure mode associated with the particular item and item function or step. The assumption is made that the failure could occur, but may not necessarily occur. A recommended starting point is a review of machinery supplier correction action reports, lessons learned documents (including end user and subsequent operations reports), machinery down time logs and group brainstorming.

Potential failure modes that could only occur under certain operating conditions (e.g., temperature extremes, high humidity, external shock/vibration) and under certain usage conditions (increased line rate) should be considered.

The machinery engineer/team should be able to pose and answer the following questions:

a. How can the machinery/sequence step fail to meet engineering specifications?
b. What could fail to meet customer (end user, subsequent steps of functions, or field service) expectations?

Typical failure modes, could be, but are not limited to:

Bent	Broken	Worn
Cracked	Warped	Short circuit
Dirty	Binding	Open circuit
Grounded		

5.2.11 POTENTIAL EFFECTS OF FAILURE—The effects should be stated in terms of a specific system, subsystem, or component being analyzed. Any impact of the failure mode on upstream and downstream processes should also be stated.

State clearly if the function could impact safety or noncompliance to regulations and if operators and safety are potentially affected. The effects should always be stated in terms of what the customer might notice or experience (see 5.1.1). List all effects and rank the most severe effect.

Typical failure effects could be, but are not limited to:

Machinery breakdowns	Increased cycle time
Degraded Output	Impaired performance
Inadequate torque	Loss of production during operation
Intermittent operation	Partial or complete loss of function
Excessive Noise	Excessive vibration
Excessive effort required	Lack of repeatability
Endangers operator/technician	Excessive backlash

5.2.12 SEVERITY—Severity is the rank associated with the most serious effect for a given failure mode. Severity is a relative ranking, within the scope of the individual FMEA.

A reduction in Severity Ranking index can be effected only through a machinery design change. Severity should be estimated using Table 7.

5.2.12.1 Suggested Evaluation Criteria—The team should agree on an evaluation criteria and ranking system, which is consistent, even if modified for an individual system. (See Table 7.)

NOTE—It is not recommended to modify criteria for ranking values of 9's and 10's. Failure Modes with a Severity rank of 1 should not be analyzed further.

TABLE 7—SUGGESTED SEVERITY EVALUATION CRITERIA

Effect	Severity of Effect	Ranking
Hazardous – Without Warning	Very high severity ranking – Affects operator, plant or maintenance personnel, safety, and/or affects non-compliance with government regulations, without warning.	10
Hazardous – With Warning	High severity ranking – Affects operator, plant or maintenance personnel, safety, and/or affects non-compliance with government regulations with warning.	9
Very High	Downtime of more than 8 h or the production of defective parts for more than 4 h.	8
High	Downtime of between 4 and 8 h or the production of defective parts for between 2 and 4 h.	7
Moderate	Downtime of between 1 and 4 h or the production of defective parts for between 1 and 2 h.	6
Low	Downtime of between 30 min and 1 h or the production of defective parts for up to 1 h.	5
Very Low	Downtime of between 10 and 30 min, but no production of defective parts.	4
Minor	Downtime of up to 10 min, but no production of defective parts	3
Very Minor	Process parameter variability not within specification limits. Adjustment or other process controls need to be taken during production. No downtime and no production of defective parts.	2
None	Process parameter variability within specification limits. Adjustment or other process controls can be done during normal maintenance	1

5.2.13 CLASSIFICATION—This column may be used to classify any special product characteristics (e.g., critical, key, major, significant) for components, subsystems, or systems that may require additional design or process controls. (See Figure 5A or 5B.)

This column may also be used to highlight high-priority failure modes for engineering assessment, if the Team finds this helpful, or if local management requires same.

Special Product or Process Characteristic symbols and their usage is directed by specific company policy and is not standardized in this document.

5.2.14 POTENTIAL CAUSES/MECHANISM'S OF FAILURE—Potential Cause of Failure is defined as an indication of a design weakness, the consequence of which is the failure mode. (See Figure 5A or 5B.)

List, to the extent possible, every potential cause and/or failure mechanism for each failure mode. The cause/mechanism should be listed as concisely and completely as possible so that remedial efforts can be aimed at pertinent causes.

Typical failure causes may include, but are not limited to:

Tool Drift	Contamination
Incorrect Material Specified	Inadequate Design Life Assumption
Over-stressing	Insufficient Lubrication Capability
Inadequate Maintenance Instructions	Incorrect Algorithm
Improper Maintenance Instructions	Improper Software Specification
Improper Surface Finish Specification	Inadequate Travel Specification
Improper Friction Material Specified	Excessive Heat
Improper Tolerance Specified	Worn Locator
Chip on Locator	

Typical failure mechanisms may include, but are not limited to:

Yield	Chemical Oxidation
Fatigue	Electromigration
Material Instability	Wear
Creep	Corrosion

5.2.15 (15) OCCURRENCE (O)—Occurrence is the likelihood that a potential cause/mechanism of failure will occur within a specific time period. Preventing or controlling the cause/mechanism of failure through a design change is the preferred way to reduce the occurrence ranking.

A consistent occurrence ranking system should be used to ensure continuity. The occurrence ranking number is a relative rating within the scope of the FMEA and may not reflect the actual likelihood of occurrence.

5.2.15.1 Suggested Evaluation Criteria—The team should agree on an evaluation criteria and ranking system that is consistent, even if modified for an individual system. (See Table 8). The following suggested criteria allows for the use of standard operating time or reliability as a means for determining the occurrence rankings.

a. Reliability is the probability that manufacturing machinery/equipment can perform continuously, without failure, for a specified interval of User's time when operating under stated conditions.
b. User's time is the span of time the machinery is required to run without failure (time, cycles, etc.). The User's time frame should be defined in terms of an operating pattern that is important to the user.

NOTE—The ranking value of 1 is reserved for "Failure occurs once in 25 000 hours of operation".

TABLE 8—SUGGESTED OCCURRENCE EVALUATION CRITERIA

Criteria: Possible Number of Failures within Hours of Operation	or	Criteria: Possible Number of Failures within Cycles of Operation	or	Criteria: The Reliability based on the Users Required Time	Ranking
1 in 1		1 in 90		R(t) <1%: MTBF is about 10% of the User's required time.	10
1 in 8		1 in 900		R(t) = 5%: MTBF is about 30% of User's required time	9
1 in 24		1 in 36000		R(t) = 19%: MTBF is about 60% of the User's required time.	8
1 in 80		1 in 90000		R(t) = 37%: MTBF is equal to the User's required time.	7
1 in 350		1 in 180000		R(t) = 61%: MTBF is 2 times greater than the User's required time. I	6
1 in 1000		1 in 270000		R(t) = 78%: MTBF is 4 times greater than the User's required time.	5
1 in 2500		1 in 360000		R(t) = 85%: MTBF is 6 times greater than the User's required time.	4
1 in 5000		1 in 540000		R(t) = 90%: MTBF is 10 times greater than the User's required time.	3
1 in 10 000		1 in 900000		R(t) = 95%: MTBF is 20 times greater than the User's required time.	2
1 in 25 000		1 in more than 900000 cycles		R(t) = 98%: MTBF is 50 times greater than the User's required time.	1

NOTE—The reliability values listed previously assume the machines have a constant failure rate and are repairable. See Appendix J for sample calculations for the occurrence table.

5.2.16 CURRENT MACHINERY CONTROLS—List the prevention, detection, design validation/verification (DV), or other activities that have been completed or committed to and that will assure the design adequacy for the failure mode and/or cause/mechanism under consideration. Current controls (e.g., design reviews, mathematical studies, feasibility review, prototype tests) are those that have been or are being used with the same or similar designs. The team should always be focused on improving design controls; for example, creating new system tests, or creating new system modeling algorithms, etc. There are two types of design controls to consider:

a. Prevention: Prevent the cause/mechanism of failure or the failure mode from occurring, or reduce their rate of occurrence.
b. Detection: Detect the cause/mechanism of failure or the failure mode, either by analytical or physical methods.

The preferred approach is to first use prevention controls, if possible. The initial occurrence rankings will be affected by the prevention controls provided they are integrated as part of the design intent. The initial rankings for detection will be based on design controls that either detect the cause/mechanism of failure, or detect the failure mode.

For example, consider a failure mode of "belt breaks". A detection control could be a sensor that detects the breakage and notifies through the use of an alarm or light that the belt has broken. A prevention control could be a sensor with a feedback system to an automatically adjustable pulley system that continuously adjusts the tension to prevent the belt from breaking, and thus, reduces the rate of occurrence of the belt breaking due to improper tension.

The Machinery FMEA form in this manual has two columns for the machinery controls (i.e., separate columns for Prevention Controls and Detection Controls) to assist the team in clearly distinguishing between these two types of machinery controls. This allows for a quick visual determination that both types of machinery controls have been considered. Use of this two-column form is the preferred approach. (See Figure 5A.)

If a one-column (for machinery controls) form is used, then the following prefixes should be used. For prevention controls, place a 'P' before each prevention control listed. For detection controls, place a 'D' before each detection control listed. Once the machinery controls have been identified, review all prevention controls to determine if any occurrence rankings need to be revised. (See Figure 5B.)

5.2.17 DETECTION—Detection is the rank associated with the best detection control listed in the machinery controls. Detection is a relative ranking, within the scope of the individual FMEA. In order to achieve a lower ranking, generally the planned machinery control has to be improved. (See Table 9.)

5.2.17.1 *Suggested Evaluation Criteria*—The team should agree on an evaluation criteria and ranking system that is consistent, even if modified for an individual system.

NOTE—The ranking value of 1 is reserved for "Almost Certain."

TABLE 9—SUGGESTED DETECTION EVALUATION CRITERIA

Detection	Criteria: Likelihood of Detection by Design and/or Machinery Control	Ranking
Almost Impossible	Design and/or Machinery Controls cannot detect a potential cause and subsequent failure, or there are no design or machinery controls.	10
Very Remote	Very remote chance that design and/or machinery controls will detect a potential cause and subsequent failure mode.	9
Remote	Remote chance that design and/or machinery controls will detect a potential cause and subsequent failure mode. Machinery control will provide indication of failure.	8
Very Low	Design and/or Machinery controls do not prevent the failure from occurring. Machinery controls will isolate the cause and subsequent failure mode after the failure has occurred.	7
Low	Low chance that design and/or machinery controls will detect a potential cause and subsequent failure mode. Machinery controls will provide an indicator of imminent failure.	6
Medium	Medium chance that design controls will detect a potential cause and subsequent failure mode. Machinery controls will prevent imminent failure.	5
Moderately High	Moderately high chance that design controls will detect a potential cause and subsequent failure mode. Machinery controls will prevent imminent failure.	4
High	High chance that design controls will detect a potential cause and subsequent failure mode. Machinery controls will prevent an imminent failure and isolate the cause.	3
Very High	Very high chance that design controls will detect a potential cause and subsequent failure mode. Machinery controls may not be required.	2
Almost Certain	Design controls almost certain to detect a potential cause and subsequent failure mode, machinery controls not required.	1

5.2.18 RISK PRIORITY NUMBER—The Risk Priority Number is the product of the Severity (S), Occurrence (O), and Detection (D) ranking. (See Figure 5A or 5B).

$$RPN = (S) \times (O) \times (D) \quad \text{(Eq. 3)}$$

Within the scope of the individual FMEA, this value (between "1" and "1000") can be used to rank order the concerns in the design (e.g., in Pareto fashion).

5.2.19 (19) RECOMMENDED ACTION(S)—Engineering assessment for corrective action should be first directed at high severity, high RPN, and other items designated by the team. The intent of any recommended action is to reduce rankings, in the following preference order: severity, occurrence, and detection rankings. (See Figure 5A or 5B.)

In general practice when the severity is a "9" or "10", special attention must be given to assure that the risk is addressed through existing design and/or machinery controls or preventative/corrective action(s), regardless of the RPN. In all cases where the effect of an identified potential failure mode could be a hazard to manufacturing/ assembly personnel, preventive/corrective actions should be taken to avoid the failure mode by eliminating or controlling the cause(s), or appropriate operator protection should be specified.

After special attention has been given to Severity(s) of 9 or 10, the team then addresses other Failure Modes, with the intent of reducing Severity, then Occurrence, and then Detection. The primary objective of recommended actions is to reduce risks, increase customer satisfaction, and improve the reliability, maintainability, and durability of the machine.

Only a design revision can bring about a reduction in the severity ranking. A reduction in the occurrence ranking can be effected only by removing or controlling one or more of the causes/mechanisms of the failure mode through a design revision. An increase in design validation/verification actions, machine controls, inspection, and/or preventive/predictive maintenance will result in a reduction in the detection ranking only. Increasing the design validation/verification actions is a less desirable engineering action since it does not address the severity or occurrence of the failure mode.

If engineering assessment leads to no recommended actions for a specific failure mode/cause/control combination, indicate this by entering a "NONE" in this column.

5.2.20 RESPONSIBILITY (FOR THE RECOMMENDED ACTION)—Enter the organization and individual responsible for the recommended action and its target completion date. (See Figure 5A or 5B.)

5.2.21 ACTIONS TAKEN—After an action has been implemented, enter a brief description of the actual action taken and its effective date. (See Figure 5A or 5B.)

5.2.22 REVISED RATINGS—After the preventive/corrective action has been identified, estimate and record the resulting severity, occurrence, and detection rankings. Calculate and record the resulting RPN. If no actions are taken, leave the related ranking columns blank. (See Figure 5A or 5B.)

All revised ratings should be reviewed and if further action is considered necessary, repeat the analysis. The focus should always be on continuous improvement.

5.2.23 FOLLOW-UP ACTIONS—See 1.5.

APPENDIX A
DESIGN FMEA QUALITY OBJECTIVES
NOTE: SPECIFIC PROGRAM REQUIREMENTS TAKE PRECEDENCE

1. DESIGN IMPROVEMENTS
   The FMEA drives Design Improvements as the primary objective.
2. High Risk Failure Modes
   The FMEA address all high risk Failure Modes, as identified by the FMEA team, with executable Action Plans. All other failure modes are considered.
3. A/D/V or DVP&R PLANS
   The Analysis/Development/Validation (A/D/V), and/or Design Verification Plan and Report (DVD&R) considers the failure modes from the Design FMEA.
4. Interfaces
   The FMEA scope includes integration and interface failure modes in both block diagram and analysis.
5. Lessons Learned
   The FMEA considers all major "lessons learned" (such as high warranty, campaigns, etc.) as input to failure mode identification.
6. Special or Key Characteristics
   The FMEA identifies appropriate Key Characteristics candidates, as input to the Key Characteristics selection process, if applicable due to company policy.
7. Timing
   The FMEA is completed during the "Window of Opportunity" where it could most efficiently impact the product design.
8. TEAM
   The right people participate as part of the FMEA team throughout the analysis, and are adequately trained in FMEA methods. As appropriate, a facilitator should be used.
9. Documentation
   The FMEA document is completely filled out "by the book", including "Action Taken" and new RPN values.
10. Time Usage
   Time spent by the FMEA team, as early as possible, is an effective and efficient use of time, with a value-added result. This assumes Recommended Actions are identified as required and the actions are implemented.

APPENDIX B
PROCESS FMEA QUALITY OBJECTIVES
NOTE: SPECIFIC PROGRAM REQUIREMENTS TAKE PRECEDENCE

1. PROCESS IMPROVEMENTS
   The FMEA drives Process Improvements as the primary objective, with an emphasis on Error/Mistake Proofing solutions.
2. HIGH RISK FAILURE MODES
   The FMEA addresses all high risk Failure Modes, as identified by the FMEA team, with executable Action Plans. All other failure modes are considered.
3. CONTROL PLANS
   The Pre-launch and Production Control Plans consider the failure modes from the Process FMEA.
4. INTEGRATION
   The Process FMEA is integrated and consistent with the Process Flow Diagram and the Process Control Plan. The Process FMEA considers the Design FMEA as part of its analysis.
5. LESSONS LEARNED
   The FMEA considers all major "lessons learned" (such as high warranty, campaigns, non-conforming product, customer complaints, etc.) as input to failure mode identification.
6. SPECIAL OR KEY CHARACTERISICS
   The FMEA identifies appropriate Key Characteristics candidates, as input to the Key Characteristics selection process, if applicable due to company policy.
7. TIMING
   The FMEA is completed during the "Window of Opportunity" where it could most efficiently impact the design of product or process.
8. TEAM
   The right people participate as part of the FMEA team throughout the analysis, and are adequately trained in FMEA methods. As appropriate, a facilitator should be utilized
9. DOCUMENTATION
   The FMEA document is completely filled out "by the book", including "Action Taken" and new RPN values.
10. TIME USAGE
   Time spent by the FMEA team, as early as possible, is an effective & efficient use of time, with a value-added result. This assumes Recommended Actions are identified as required and the actions are implemented.

APPENDIX C
DESIGN FMEA BLOCK DIAGRAM EXAMPLE

FAILURE MODE AND EFFECTS ANALYSIS (FMEA)
BLOCK DIAGRAM/ENVIRONMENTAL EXTREMES

SYSTEM NAME: FLASHLIGHT
YEAR VEHICLE PLATFORM: 1994 NEW PRODUCT
FMEA I.D. NUMBER: XXXI10D001

OPERATIONAL ENVIRONMENTAL EXTREMES

TEMPERATURE: -20 to 160 °F CORROSIVE: TEST SCHEDULE B VIBRATION: NOT APPLICABLE
SHOCK: 6 FOOT DROP FOREIGN MATERIAL: DUST HUMIDITY: 0 - 100% RH
FLAMMABILITY: (WHAT COMPONENT(S) ARE NEAR HEAT SOURCE(S)?
OTHER:

LETTERS = COMPONENTS
NUMBERS = ATTACHING METHODS
____ = ATTACHED/JOINED
----- = INTERFACING, NOT JOINED
= NOT INCLUDED IN THIS FMEA

The example below is a relational block diagram. Other types of block diagrams may be used by the FMEA Team to clarify the item(s) being considered in their analysis.

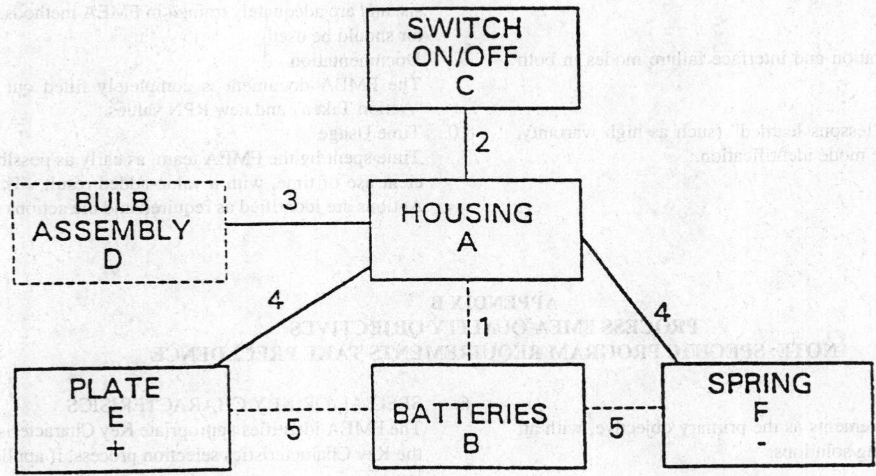

COMPONENTS
A. HOUSING
B. BATTERIES (2 D Cell)
C. ON/OFF SWITCH
D. BULB ASSEMBLY
E. PLATE
F. SPRING

ATTACHING METHOD
1. SLIP FIT
2. RIVETS
3. THREAD
4. SNAP FIT
5. COMPRESSIVE FIT

FIGURE C1—DESIGN FMEA BLOCK DIAGRAM EXAMPLE

APPENDIX D
STANDARD FORM FOR DESIGN FMEA

POTENTIAL
FAILURE MODE AND EFFECTS ANALYSIS
(DESIGN FMEA)

____ System

____ Subsystem

____ Component ____________________

Model Year(s)/Program(s) ____________________

Design Responsibility ____________________

Key Date ____________________

FMEA Number ____________________

Page ________ of ________

Prepared By ____________________

FMEA Date (Orig.) ________ (Rev.) ________

Core Team ____

Item / Function	Potential Failure Mode	Potential Effect(s) of Failure	Sev	Class	Potential Cause(s)/ Mechanism(s) of Failure	Occur	Current Design Controls Prevention	Current Design Controls Detection	Detec	R.P.N.	Recommended Action(s)	Responsibility & Target Completion Date	Action Results					
													Actions Taken	Sev	Occ	Det	R.P.N.

FIGURE D1—STANDARD FORM FOR DESIGN FMEA
– TWO COLUMNS, CURRENT DESIGN CONTROLS –

POTENTIAL FAILURE MODE AND EFFECTS ANALYSIS (DESIGN FMEA)

____ System

____ Subsystem

____ Component ____________________

Model Year(s)/Program(s) ____________________

Core Team ____________________

Design Responsibility ____________________

Key Date ____________________

FMEA Number ____________________

Page ________ of ________

Prepared By ____________________

FMEA Date (Orig.) ________ (Rev.) ________

Item / Function	Potential Failure Mode	Potential Effect(s) of Failure	Sev	Class	Potential Cause(s)/ Mechanism(s) of Failure	Occur	Current Design Controls – Prevention – Detection	Detec	R.P.N.	Recommended Action(s)	Responsibility & Target Completion Date	Action Results: Actions Taken	Sev	Occ	Det	R.P.N.

FIGURE D2—STANDARD FORM FOR DESIGN FMEA
– ONE COLUMN, CURRENT DESIGN CONTROLS –

APPENDIX E
DESIGN FMEA EXAMPLE

POTENTIAL
FAILURE MODE AND EFFECTS ANALYSIS
(DESIGN FMEA)

_____ System
_x_ Subsystem
_____ Component 01.03/Body Closures (2)
Model Year(s)/Program(s) 199X/Lion 4dr/Wagon (5)

Design Responsibility Body Engineering (3)
Key Date 9X 03 01 ER (6)

FMEA Number 1234 (1)
Page 1 of 1
Prepared By A. Tate - X6412- Body Engr (4)
FMEA Date (Orig.) 8X 03 22 (Rev.) 8X 07 14 (7)

Core Team T. Fender-Car Product Dev., Childers-Manufacturing, J. Ford-Assy Ops (Dalton, Fraser, Henley Assembly Plants) (8)

Item (9) Function	Potential Failure Mode (10)	Potential Effect(s) of Failure (11)	Sev (12)	Class	Potential Cause(s)/ Mechanism(s) of Failure (13) (14)	Occur	Current Design Controls Prevention (15) (16)	Current Design Controls Detection (16)	Detec (17)	R.P.N.	Recommended Action(s) (18) (19)	Responsibility & Target Completion Date (20)	Action Results: Actions Taken (21)	Sev	Occ	Det	R.P.N. (22)
Front Door L.H. H8HX-0000-A • Ingress to and egress from vehicle • Occupant protection from weather, noise, and side impact • Support anchorage for door hardware including mirror, hinges, latch and window regulator • Provide proper surface for appearance items - Paint and soft trim	Corroded interior lower door panels	Deteriorated life of door leading to: • Unsatisfactory appearance due to rust througH paint over time • Impaired function of interior door hardware	7		Upper edge of protective wax application specified for inner door panels is too low	6		Vehicle general durability test veh. T-118 T-109 T-301	7	294	Add laboratory accelerated corrosion testing	A Tate-Body Engrg 8X 09 30	Based on test results (Test No. 1481) upper edge spec raised 125mm	7	2	2	28
			7		Insufficient wax thickness specified	4		Vehicle general durability testing- as above	7	196	Add laboratory accelerated corrosion testing Conduct Design of Experiments (DOE) on wax thickness	Combine w/test for wax upper edge verification A Tate Body Engrg 9X 01 15	Test results (Test No. 1481) show specified thickness is adequate. DOE shows 25% variation in specified thickness is acceptable.	7	2	2	28
			7		Inappropriate wax formulation specified	2		Physical and Chem Lab test- Report No.1265	2	28	None						
			7		Entrapped air prevents wax from entering corner/edge access	5		Design aid investigation with non-functioning spray head	8	280	Add team evaluation using production spray equipment and specified wax	Body Engrg & Assy Ops 8X 11 15	Based on test, 3 additional vent holes provided in affected areas	7	1	3	21
			7		Insufficient room between panels for spray head access\	4		Drawing evaluation of spray head access	4	112	Add team evaluation using design aid buck and spray head	Body Engrg & Assy Ops 8X 09 15	Evaluation showed adequate access	7	1	1	7

SAMPLE

FIGURE E1—DESIGN FMEA

APPENDIX F
SYSTEM FMEA

F.1 Section 3.2.2 discusses the scope of System, Subsystem, and Component FMEA's. To help illustrate the meaning of these FMEA's, two examples have been constructed in Figure F1 (for Interfaces and Interactions) and in Figure F2 (for Item, Function, and Failure Modes).

EXAMPLE 1: Interfaces and Interactions

It is the responsibility of the FMEA Team to specify the scope of their respective FMEA's. The example in Figure F1 shows that the Team has specified Subsystems A, B, C, and D along with the surrounding environment as comprising the System that must be considered while completing the System FMEA.

INTERFACES: SUBSYSTEMS ARE DIRECTLY CONNECTED VIA INTERFACES.

In Figure F1, interfaces between subsystems are shown where Subsystem A touches (connects with) Subsystem B, B touches C, C touches D, A touches D, and B touches D. It should be noted that the Environment also touches each of the subsystems listed in Figure F1, which requires that the 'Environmental Interfaces' be considered when completing the FMEA.

NOTE—Each Subsystem FMEA should have its Interfaces included in its respective Subsystem FMEA.

INTERACTIONS: A CHANGE IN ONE SUBSYSTEM MIGHT CAUSE A CHANGE IN ANOTHER SUBSYSTEM.

In Figure F1, interactions between subsystems can occur between any of the interfacing systems (e.g., Subsystem A heats up resulting in Subsystem D and Subsystem B also gaining heat through the respective interfaces, as well as the Subsystem A giving off heat to the environment). Interactions might also occur between 'non-contacting' systems via transfer through the 'environment' (e.g., if the environment is composed of high humidity and Subsystems A and C are dissimilar metals separated by a non-metal composing Subsystem B, Subsystems A and C can still have an electrolytic reaction due to the moisture from the environment). Thus, interactions between non-contacting subsystems can be relatively difficult to predict, but are important and should be considered.

EXAMPLE 2: Items, Functions, and Failure Modes

Figure F2 (see next page) describes a method of showing the Items, Functions, and Failure Modes in a 'tree arrangement' that can assist the team in visualizing the System, Subsystems, and Components. At the System Level, the descriptions will tend to be much more general than for the Subsystems and Components (Components will usually have the most specific descriptions).

The 'tree arrangement' is arranged as follows for the System, Subsystem, and Components:

ITEM
Design Objectives (a statement of design objectives is often helpful)
--FUNCTION 1
  FAILURE MODE A
  FAILURE MODE B
  etc.....
--FUNCTION 2
  FAILURE MODE A
  FAILURE MODE B
  etc.....
-- etc.....

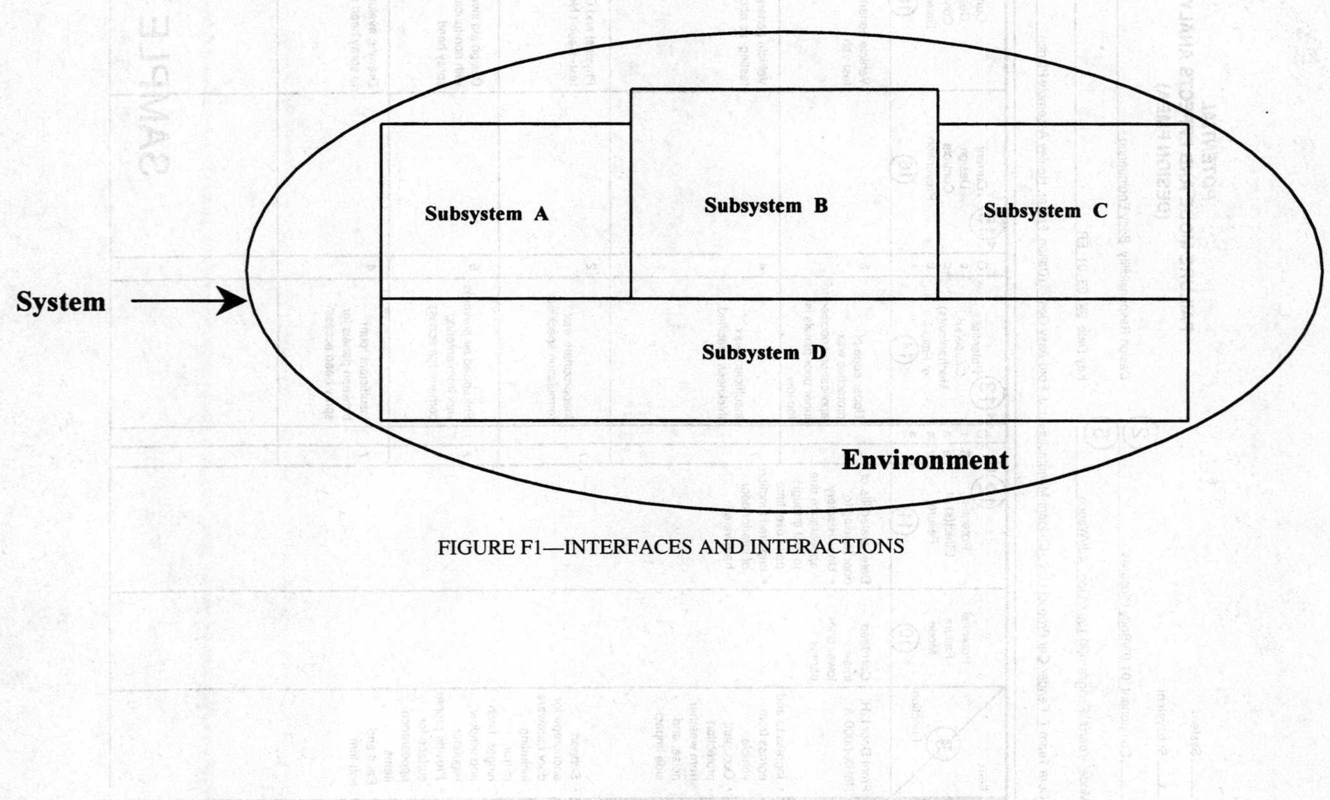

FIGURE F1—INTERFACES AND INTERACTIONS

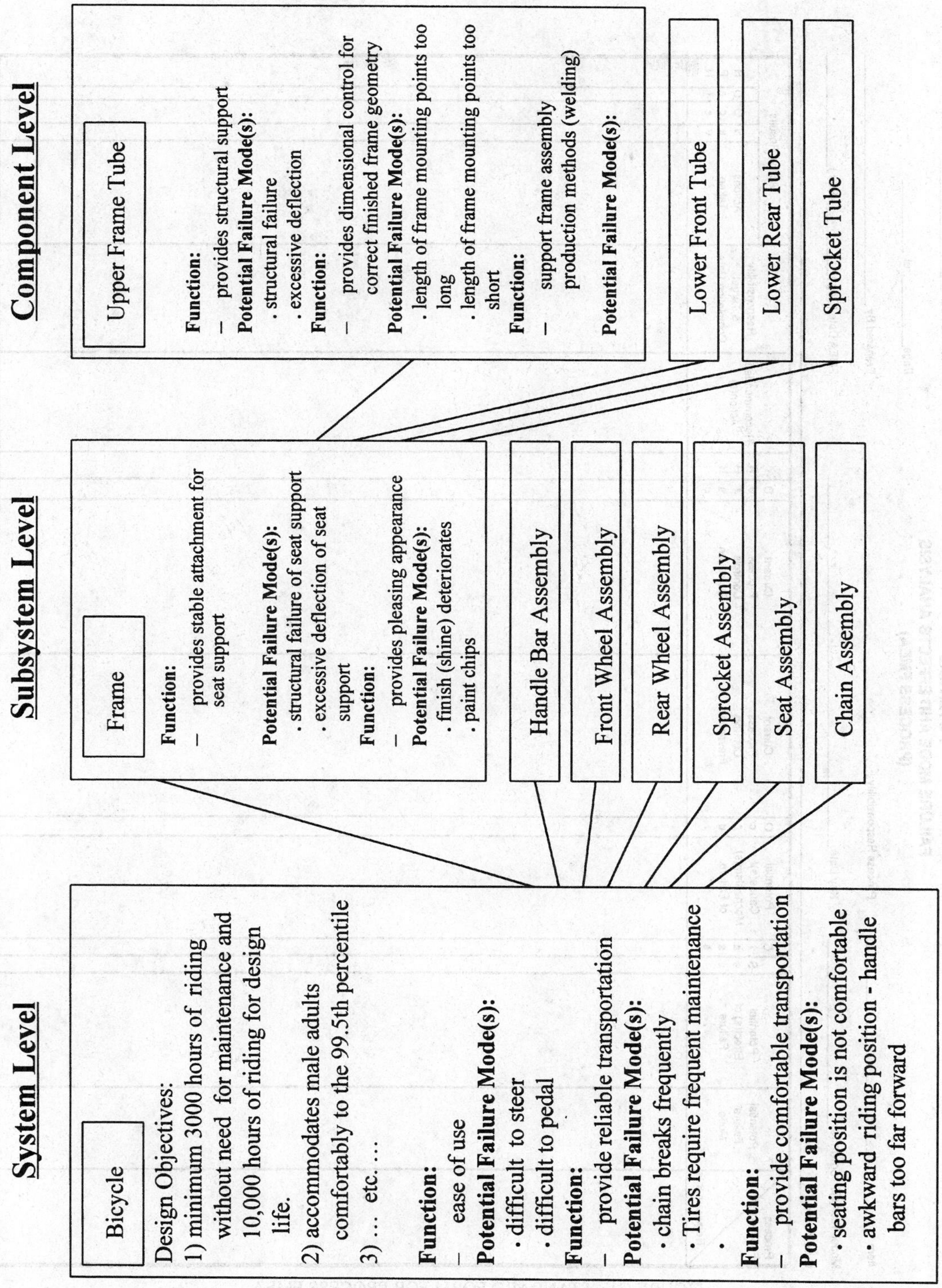

System Level

Bicycle

Design Objectives:

1) minimum 3000 hours of riding without need for maintenance and 10,000 hours of riding for design life.
2) accommodates male adults comfortably to the 99.5th percentile
3) … etc. …

Function:
– ease of use

Potential Failure Mode(s):
- difficult to steer
- difficult to pedal

Function:
– provide reliable transportation

Potential Failure Mode(s):
- chain breaks frequently
- Tires require frequent maintenance
-

Function:
– provide comfortable transportation

Potential Failure Mode(s):
- seating position is not comfortable
- awkward riding position - handle bars too far forward

Subsystem Level

Frame

Function:
– provides stable attachment for seat support

Potential Failure Mode(s):
. structural failure of seat support
. excessive deflection of seat support

Function:
– provides pleasing appearance

Potential Failure Mode(s):
. finish (shine) deteriorates
. paint chips

Handle Bar Assembly

Front Wheel Assembly

Rear Wheel Assembly

Sprocket Assembly

Seat Assembly

Chain Assembly

Component Level

Upper Frame Tube

Function:
– provides structural support

Potential Failure Mode(s):
. structural failure
. excessive deflection

Function:
– provides dimensional control for correct finished frame geometry

Potential Failure Mode(s):
. length of frame mounting points too long
. length of frame mounting points too short

Function:
– support frame assembly production methods (welding)

Potential Failure Mode(s):

Lower Front Tube

Lower Rear Tube

Sprocket Tube

FIGURE F2—ITEMS, FUNCTIONS, AND FAILURES

APPENDIX G
STANDARD FORM FOR PROCESS FMEA

POTENTIAL
FAILURE MODE AND EFFECTS ANALYSIS
(PROCESS FMEA)

FMEA Number ____________

Page ________ of ________

Item ____________ Process Responsibility ____________ Prepared By ____________

Model Year(s)/Program(s) ____________ Key Date ____________ FMEA Date (Orig.) ________ (Rev.) ________

Core Team ____________

Process Function / Requirements	Potential Failure Mode	Potential Effect(s) of Failure	Sev	Class	Potential Cause(s)/ Mechanism(s) of Failure	Occur	Current Process Controls Prevention	Current Process Controls Detection	Detec	R. P. N.	Recommended Action(s)	Responsibility & Target Completion Date	Action Results: Actions Taken	Sev	Occ	Det	R. P. N.

FIGURE G1—STANDARD FORM FOR PROCESS FMEA
– TWO COLUMN, CURRENT PROCESS CONTROLS –

POTENTIAL
FAILURE MODE AND EFFECTS ANALYSIS
(PROCESS FMEA)

Item ____________ Process Responsibility ____________ FMEA Number ____________

Page ______ of ______

Model Year(s)/Program(s) ____________ Key Date ____________ Prepared By ____________

Core Team ____________ FMEA Date (Orig.) ____________ (Rev.) ____________

Process Function / Requirements	Potential Failure Mode	Potential Effect(s) of Failure	Sev	Class	Potential Cause(s)/ Mechanism(s) of Failure	Occur	Current Process Controls –Prevention –Detection	Detec	R. P. N.	Recommended Action(s)	Responsibility & Target Completion Date	Action Results: Actions Taken	Sev	Occ	Det	R. P. N.

FIGURE G2—STANDARD FORM FOR PROCESS FMEA
– ONE COLUMN, CURRENT PROCESS CONTROLS –

APPENDIX H
PROCESS FMEA EXAMPLE

POTENTIAL
FAILURE MODE AND EFFECTS ANALYSIS
(PROCESS FMEA)

FMEA Number 1450 (1)

Page 1 of 1

Item Front Door L.H./H8HX-000-A (2)   Process Responsibility Body Engrg. (3)   Prepared By J. Ford - X6521 - Assy Ops (4)

Model Year(s)/Program(s) 199X/Lion 4dr/Wagon (5)   Key Date 9X 03 01 ER   9X 08 26 Job #1 (6)   FMEA Date (Orig.) 9X 05 17 (Rev.) 9X 11 06 (7)

Core Team A. Tate Body Engrg., J. Smith-OC, R. James-Production, J. Jones-Maintenance (8)

Process Function / Requirements (9)	Potential Failure Mode (10)	Potential Effect(s) of Failure (11)	Sev (12)	Class	Potential Cause(s)/ Mechanism(s) of Failure (14) (13)	Occur	Current Process Controls Prevention (16) (15)	Current Process Controls Detection (16) (17)	Detec	R.P.N.	Recommended Action(s) (19) (18)	Responsibility & Target Completion Date (20)	Action Results: Actions Taken (21)	Sev	Occ	Det	R.P.N. (22)
Manual application of wax inside door To cover inner door, lower surfaces at minimum wax thickness to retard corrosion	Insufficient wax coverage over specified surface	Deteriorated life of door leading to: • Unsatisfactory appearance due to rust through paint over time • Impaired function of interior doo hardware	7		Manually inserted spray head not inserted far enough	8		Visual check each hour-1/shift for film thickness (depth meter) and coverage	5	280	Add positive depth stop to sprayer	MFG Engrg 9X 10 15	Stop added, sprayer checked on line	7	2	5	70
											Automate spraying	Mfg Engrg 9X 12 15	Rejected due to complexity of different doors on same line				
			7		Spray heads clogged - Viscosity too high - Temperature too low - Pressure too low	5	Test spray pattern at start-up and after idle periods, and preventive maintenance program to clean heads	Visual check each hour-1/shift for film thickness (depth meter) and coverage	5	175	Use Design of Experiments (DOE) on viscosity vs. temperature vs. pressure	Mfg Engrg 9X 10 01	Temp and press limits were determined and limit controls have been installed - control charts show process is in control Cpk=1.85	7	1	5	35
			7		Spray head deformed due to impact	2	Preventive maintenance programs to maintain heads	Visual check each hour-1/shift for film thickness (depth meter) and coverage	5	70	None						
			7		Spray time insufficient	8		Operator instructions and lot sampling (10 doors / shift) to check for coverage of critical areas	7	392	Install spray timer	Maintenance 9X 09 15	Automatic spray timer installed - operator starts spray, timer controls shut-off control charts show process is in control Cpk=2.05	7	1	7	49

SAMPLE

FIGURE H1—PROCESS FMEA EXAMPLE

APPENDIX I
MACHINERY FMEA FORM

POTENTIAL
FAILURE MODE AND EFFECTS ANALYSIS
(MACHINERY FMEA)

System ______________ Subsystem ______________ Component ______________ Program(s)/Plant(s) ______________ Core Team ______________

Design Responsibility ______________ Key Date ______________

FMEA Number: ______________ Page ______ of ______ Prepared By: ______________ FMEA Date (Orig.) ______ (Rev.) ______

Item / Function Req'ts	Potential Failure Mode	Potential Effect(s) of Failure	Sev	Class	Potential Cause(s)/ Mechanism(s) of Failure	Occur	Current Machinery Controls Prevention	Current Machinery Controls Detection	Detec	RPN	Recommended Action(s)	Responsibility & Target Completion Date	Action Results: Actions Taken	Sev	Occ	Det	RPN

FIGURE I1—MACHINERY FMEA FORM
– TWO COLUMN, CURRENT MACHINERY DESIGN CONTROLS –

POTENTIAL
FAILURE MODE AND EFFECTS ANALYSIS
(MACHINERY FMEA)

____ System ______________________

____ Subsystem ______________________

____ Component ______________________

Program(s)/Plant(s) ______________________

Design Responsibility ______________________

Key Date ______________________

FMEA Number: ______________________

Page ________ of ________

Prepared By: ______________________

FMEA Date (Orig.) ________ (Rev.) ________

Core Team ______________________

Item / Function Req'ts	Potential Failure Mode	Potential Effect(s) of Failure	Sev	Class	Potential Cause(s)/ Mechanism(s) of Failure	Occur	Current Machinery Controls — Prevention — Detection	Detec	R. P. N.	Recommended Action(s)	Responsibility & Target Completion Date	Action Results: Actions Taken	Sev	Occ	Det	R. P. N.

FIGURE I2—MACHINERY FMEA FORM
– ONE COLUMN, CURRENT MACHINERY DESIGN CONTROLS –

APPENDIX J
MACHINERY FMEA OCCURRENCE TABLE CALCULATIONS

TABLE J1—OCCURRENCE TABLE CALCULATIONS

Failure Rate	MTBF	t (User's Time)	R(t)[1]	Implication
1 in 1	1	8	0.03%	MTBF is equal to about 10% of the user's time.
1 in 8	8	24	4.98%	MTBF is equal to about 30% of the user's time.
1 in 24	24	40	18.89%	MTBF is equal to about 60% of the user's time.
1 in 80	80	80	36.79%	MTBF is equal to the user's time.
1 in 350	350	200	60.65%	MTBF is about 2 times greater than the user's time.
1 in 1000	1000	250	77.88%	MTBF is about 4 times greater than the user's time.
1 in 2500	2500	400	85.21%	MTBF is about 6 times greater than the user's time.
1 in 5000	5000	500	90.48%	MTBF is about 10 times greater than the user's time.
1 in 10000	10000	500	95.12%	MTBF is about 20 times greater than the user's time.
1 in 25000	25000	500	98.02%	MTBF is about 50 times greater than the user's time.

1. $R(t) = e^{-t/mtbf}$

APPENDIX K
MACHINERY FMEA EXAMPLE

POTENTIAL
FAILURE MODE AND EFFECTS ANALYSIS
(MACHINERY FMEA)

___ System
X Subsystem Underbody Conveyor Line
___ Component
Program(s)/Plant(s) X10 / SA
Core Team Joe Doe, Mike Transfer, Bill Brakes, and Joe Company (O.E.M.)

Design Responsibility Joe Doe, Acme Enterprises (supplier)
Key Date 05 / 02 / 200X

FMEA Number MF 112
Page 1 of 1
Prepared By: Joe Doe
FMEA Date (Orig.) 02/02/200X (Rev.)

Item / Function Req'ts	Potential Failure Mode	Potential Effect(s) of Failure	Sev	Class	Potential Cause(s)/ Mechanism(s) of Failure	Occur	Current Machinery Controls Prevention	Current Machinery Controls Detection	Detec	RPN	Recommended Action(s)	Responsibility & Target Completion Date	Action Results: Actions Taken	Sev	Occ	Det	RPN
Main Underbody Conveyor drive unit	Conveyor drive chain breaks	Main underbody conveyor inoperable/Line down	7		Chain stretch due to wear resulting in chain breakage (MCBF = 180 000)	6	None	Maintenance program to detect chain wear and replace chain when wear limit reached in accordance with preventive maintenance procedure	6	252	Investigate automatic tensioner with feedback system (Prevention Control)	Machine Design Dept xx/xx/xx	Automatic tensioner with feedback system to notify plant personnel when system cannot maintain specified tension incorporated into Conveyor design	7	3	3	63
Transfer underbodies weighting 350 lbs at a speed of 60 min			7		Sprockets and chain not properly lubricated	6	Lubrication of chain and sprockets part of preventive maintenance	None	10	420	Investigate line alternative lubrication system	Machine Design Dept. xx/xx/xx	Automatic lubrication system incorporated into Conveyor design	7	2	2	28
			7		Pallet carrier loosens and jams Conveyor line resulting in chain breakage.	4	None	None	10	280	Investigate line shutdown system	Machine Design Dept. xx/xx/xx	Automatic line shutdown system and safety straps incorporated into Pallet design	7	3	2	42
Transfer underbodies at a consistent speed without jerking			7		Drive end or Follower sprocket loosen and "walks" on shaft	6		Maintenance program to detect loose Sprocket or Follower	6	252	Investigate alternative Sprocket-Shaft design interface.	Machine Design Dept. xx/xx/xx	Shaft redesigned with shoulder and locking Collar to prevent lateral movement of Sproket. Redesigned Shaft validated at 1 million cycles with load	7	2	2	28

SAMPLE

FIGURE K1—MACHINERY FMEA EXAMPLE

APPENDIX L
GLOSSARY

L.1 Glossary

L.1.1 Availability—A measure of the degree to which tooling and equipment is in an operable and committable state at any point in time. Specifically, the percent of time that tooling and equipment will be operable when needed.

L.1.2 Control Plans—The control plan provides the process monitoring and control methods that will be used to control characteristics.

L.1.3 Design Intent—List of what a given component/subsystem/system is expected to do or not to do.

L.1.4 Design Life—The time period (e.g., cycles, time, mileage) for which the design is intended to perform its requirements.

L.1.5 Design Validation/Verification (DV)—A program intended to assure that the design meets its requirements.

L.1.6 Design of Experiments (DOE)—Methods which identify factors that affect the mean and variation with minimum testing/experimentation.

L.1.7 Durability—Ability to perform intended function over the design life under normal use with specified maintenance, without significant deterioration.

L.1.8 Equipment—The portion of process machinery which is not specific to a component or sub-assembly (e.g., a sheet metal press).

L.1.9 Error/Mistake Proofing—Each O.E.M. may have their own unique definition for Error/Mistake Proofing. Confer with the O.E.M. for the appropriate definition.

L.1.10 Feature—A measurable product characteristic (e.g., radius, hardness) or a measurable process characteristic (e.g., insertion force, temperature).

L.1.11 Life Cycle—The sequence through which a product or machinery and equipment passes from conception through decommission.

L.1.12 Life Cycle Cost (LCC)—The sum of all cost factors incurred during the expected life of a product or machinery.

L.1.13 Machinery—Tooling and Equipment combined. A generic term for all hardware, (including necessary operational software) which performs a manufacturing process.

L.1.14 Maintainability—A characteristic of design, installation and operation, usually expressed as the probability that a machine can be retained in, or restored to, a specified operable condition within a specified interval of time when maintenance is performed in accordance with prescribed procedures.

L.1.15 Mean Time Between Failures (MTBF)—The average time between failure occurrences. The sum of the operating time of a machine divided by the total number of failures.

L.1.16 Mean Time To Repair (MTTR)—The average time required to restore machinery or equipment to specified conditions.

L.1.17 Pareto—A simple tool which can assist problem solving that involves ranking all potential problem areas.

L.1.18 Process—The combination of people, machines and equipment, raw materials, methods and environment that produces a given product or service.

L.1.19 Process Change—A change in processing concept which could alter the capability of the process to meet the design requirements or durability of the product.

L.1.20 Quality Function Deployment (QFD)—A structured method in which customer requirements are translated into appropriate technical requirements for each stage of product development and production.

L.1.21 Reliability—The probability that machinery and equipment can perform continuously, without failure, for a specified interval of time when operating under stated conditions.

L.1.22 Root Cause—The root cause is the reason for the primary non-conformance and is the item that requires change to achieve permanent preventive/corrective action.

L.1.23 Special Product Characteristic—A special product characteristic (e.g., critical, key, major, significant) is a product characteristic for which reasonably anticipated variation could significantly affect a product's safety or compliance with governmental standards or regulations, or is likely to significantly affect customer satisfaction with a product.

L.1.24 Special Process Characteristic—A special process characteristic (e.g., critical, key, major, significant) is a process characteristic for which variation must be controlled to some target value to ensure that variation in a process, or special product characteristic is maintained to its target value during manufacturing and assembly.

L.1.25 Tooling—The portion of process machinery which is specific to a component or sub-assembly (e.g., a sheet metal die).

L.1.26 Vehicle Campaigns—Recall of vehicles for rework or safety inspection.

APPENDIX M
OPTIONAL PFMEA OCCURRENCE EVALUATION CRITERIA WITH Ppk VALUES

TABLE M1—OPTIONAL PFMEA OCCURRENCE EVALUATION CRITERIA WITH Ppk VALUES

Probability	Likely Failure Rates	Ppk	Ranking
Very High; Persistent Failures	≥ 100 per thousand pieces	<0.55	10
	50 per thousand pieces	≥0.55	9
High; Frequent Failures	20 per thousand pieces	≥0.78	8
	10 per thousand pieces	≥0.86	7
Moderate; Occasional Failures	5 per thousand pieces	≥0.94	6
	2 per thousand pieces	≥1.00	5
	1 per thousand pieces	≥1.10	4
Low; Relatively Few Failures	0.5 per thousand pieces	≥1.20	3
	0.1 per thousand pieces	≥1.30	2
Remote; Failure is Unlikely	≤0.01 per thousand pieces	≥1.67	1

SAMPLE CALCULATION

Sample Calculation to determine Ppk value from a likely failure rate of 5 per thousand pieces.

$$\text{Defect rate} = \frac{5}{1000} = 0.005 \qquad \text{(Eq. M1)}$$

0.005 / 2 = 0.0025 for out-of-specifications, high or low.

Using a “Z” table, the associated “Z” value is 2.81 for a tail value of 0.0025.

1.

$$Z = \frac{SL - \bar{x}}{S} \qquad \text{(Eq. M2)}$$

where:

$\bar{x}$ = Average,
SL = Specifications Limits (upper and lower), and
S = Sample Standard Deviation

2.

$$Ppk = \frac{\min(SL\ upper - \bar{x},\ \bar{x} - SL\ lower)}{3S} \qquad \text{(Eq. M3)}$$

3. Substitute Z into Ppk equation.

4.

$$Ppk = \frac{Z}{3} = \frac{2.81}{3} = 0.9367 \cong 0.94 \qquad \text{(Eq. M4)}$$

NOTE— The previous Ppk values are to be used by the FMEA team as guidance to assist in determining an occurrence ranking when valid statistical data is available (e.g., requires a stable process). No other use of the previous Ppk values is intended. Do not mix “Failure Rate” values with “Ppk” values when making an occurrence evaluation. Choose one (e.g., either “Failure Rate” or “Ppk”) and use it consistently.

TECHNICAL REPORT ON LOW CYCLE FATIGUE PROPERTIES FERROUS AND NON-FERROUS MATERIALS—SAE J1099 AUG2002

SAE Information Report

Report of the SAE Fatigue Design and Evaluation Steering Committee approved February 1975 and completely revised June 1998. Revised by the SAE Material Properties Division Subcommittee of the SAE Fatigue Design and Evaluation Committee August 2002. Rationale statement available.

Foreword—Designing a component to avoid fatigue failure is one of the more important, yet difficult, tasks an engineer faces. Many factors are involved and the relationships between these factors are developed largely through empiricism. Fatigue failure is caused by repeated loading with the number of loading cycles to failure being dependent upon the load range.

Designing to avoid fatigue failure requires knowledge of the following:

a. The expected load-time history (the local strain-time and stress-time history at the most critical locations).
b. The geometry of the component and areas of stress concentration (geometrical, metallurgical, surface finish, manufacturing variability, etc.)
c. The nature of the environment in which the component is operated (wet, dry, corrosive, temperature, etc.)
d. The properties of the material as it exists in the finished component at the most critically stressed locations ("inherent" fatigue properties, residual stress effects, surface effects, sensitivity to corrosion, "cleanliness," variability, etc.)

Variability in fatigue life is another aspect of fatigue life evaluation and prediction that must be considered. This often calls for statistical analysis. Circumstances dictate the degree of sophistication required in all aspects of an evaluation or prediction.

1. Scope—Information that provides design guidance in avoiding fatigue failures is outlined in this SAE Information Report. Of necessity, this report is brief, but it does provide a basis for approaching complex fatigue problems. Information presented here can be used in preliminary design estimates of fatigue life, the selection of materials and the analysis of service load and/or strain data. The data presented are for the "low cycle" or strain-controlled methods for predicting fatigue behavior. Note that these methods may not be appropriate for materials with internal defects, such as cast irons, which exhibit different tension and compression stress-strain behavior.

2. References

2.1 Applicable Publications—The following publications form a part of the specification to the extent specified herein. Unless otherwise indicated, the latest revision of SAE publications shall apply.

1. Mitchell, M. R., Fundamentals of Modern Fatigue Analysis for Design, ASM, Vol. 19, Fatigue and Fracture, 1997.
2. Annual Book of ASTM Standards, Metals—Mechanical Testing: Elevated and Low Temperature Tests; Metallography, Standard E 606-80, "Constant-Amplitude Low-Cycle Fatigue Testing," Vol. 3.01, American Society for Testing and Materials, West Conshohocken, PA, 1996.
3. Dowling, N.E., Mechanical Behavior of Materials; Engineering Methods for Deformation, Fracture, and Fatigue, Prentice-Hall, 1993.
4. Chernenkoff, R.A., Editor, Fatigue Research and Applications, SP-1009, Society of Automotive Engineers, Warrendale, PA, 1993.
5. Rice, R. C., Editor, Fatigue Design Handbook (A-10), 1988, Society of Automotive Engineers, Inc., 400 Commonwealth Drive, Warrendale, PA 15096-0001.
6. Boardman, B. E., Crack Initiation Fatigue-Data, Analysis, Trends and Estimation, Proceeding of the SAE Fatigue Conference, P109, Society for Automotive Engineers, Warrendale, PA, 1982.
7. Wetzel, R. M., Editor, Fatigue Under Complex Loadings: Analysis and Experiments, AE-6, Society of Automotive Engineers, Warrendale, PA, 1977.
8. Bannantine, J., Comer, J., and Handrock, J., Fundamentals of Metal Fatigue Analysis, Prentice-Hall, 1989.
9. Multiaxial Fatigue; Analysis and Experiments, AE-14, Society of Automotive Engineers, Warrendale, PA, 1989.
10. Fuchs, H. O. and Stephens, R. I., Metal Fatigue in Engineering, John Wiley and Sons, 1980.
11. Bridgeman, P. W., Transactions of ASM, American Society for Metals, Vol. 32, p. 553, 1944; (also Dieter, G. E. Mechanical Metallurgy, McGraw-Hill Book Co., Inc., 1961, New York, NY, pp. 250-254.
12. Raske, D. T. and Morrow, JoDean, "Mechanics of Materials in Low Cycle Fatigue Testing, Manual on Low Cycle Fatigue Testing," ASTM STP 465, American Society for Testing and Materials, 1969, pp. 1-25.
13. Landgraf, R. W., Morrow, JoDean, and Endo, T., "Determination of the Cyclic Stress-Strain Curve," Journal of Materials, ASTM, Vol. 4, No. 1, March 1969, pp. 176-188.
14. Gallagher, J. P., "What the Designer Should Know About Fracture Mechanics Fundamentals," Paper 710151 presented at SAE Automotive Engineering Congress, Detroit, January 1971.
15. Sinclair, G. M., "What the Designer Should Know About Fracture Mechanics Testing," Paper 710152 presented at SAE Automotive Engineering Congress, January 1971.
16. Ripling, E. J., "How Fracture Mechanics Can Help the Designer," Paper 710153 presented at SAE Automotive Engineering Congress, Detroit, January 1971.
17. Campbell, J. E., Berry, W. E., and Fedderson, C. E., "Damage Tolerant Design Handbook," MCIC HB-01, Metal and Ceramics Information Center, Battelle Columbus Laboratories, Columbus, OH.
18. Jaske, C. E., Fedderson, C. E., Davies, K. B., Rice, R. C., "Analysis of Fatigue, Fatigue Crack Propagation and Fracture Data," NASA CR-132332, Battelle Columbus Laboratories, Columbus, OH, November 1973.
19. Moore, T. D., "Structural Alloys Handbook," Mechanical Properties Data Center, BelFour Stulen, Inc., Traverse City, MI.
20. Wolf, J., Brown, W. F., Jr., "Aerospace Structural Metals Handbook," Vol. 1-4, Mechanical Properties Data Center, BelFour Stulen, Inc., Traverse City, MI.
21. Raske, D. T., "Review of Methods for Relating the Fatigue Notch Factor to the Theoretical Stresss Concentration Factor, Simulation of the Fatigue Behavior of the Notch Root in Spectrum Loaded Notched Members," Chapter II, TAM Report No. 333--Department of Theoretical and Applied Mechanics, University of Illinois, Urbana, January 1970.
22. Topper, T. H., Wetzel, R. M. and Morrow, JoDean, "Neuber's Rule Applied to Fatigue of Notched Specimens," Journal of Materials, ASTM, Vol. 4, No. 1, March 1969, pp. 200-209.
23. Tucker, L. E., "A Procedure for Designing Against Fatigue Failure of Notched Parts," SAE Paper No. 720265, Society of Automotive Engineers, New York, NY 10001.
24. Dowling, N. E., "Fatigue Failure Predictions for Complicated Stress-Strain Histories," J. Materials, ASTM, March 1972; (see also: Fatigue Failure Predictions for Complicated Stress-Strain Histories. TAM Report No. 337, Theoretical and Applied Mechanics Dept., University of Illinois, Urbana, 1970.
25. Morrow, JoDean, "Cyclic Plastic Strain Energy and Fatigue of Metals," Internal Friction, Damping, and Cyclic Plasticity, ASTM STP 378, American Society for Testing and Materials, 1965, pp 45-87.
26. Miller, G. A., and Reemsnyder, H. S., "Strain-Cycle Fatigue of Sheet and Plate Steels I: Test Method Development and Data Presentation," SAE Paper No. 830175, 1983.
27. Annual Book of ASTM Standards, Metals—Mechanical Testing; Elevated and Low Temperature Tests; Metallography, Standard E 739-91, "Statistical Analysis of Linear or Linearized Stress-Life and Strain-Life Fatigue Data," Vol. 3.01, American Society for Testing and Materials, West Conshohocken, PA, 1995.

3. Material Property Tables—Tables 2 to 4 list the monotonic and cyclic stress-strain properties and the fatigue properties for selected materials. These tables are preceded by a brief introduction, definitions, discussion, and Table 1 which lists the abbreviations used in this document.

The majority of the properties listed in the Tables have been contributed by members of the SAE Fatigue, Design, and Evaluation Committee and are the property of SAE International, Warrendale, PA, 15096. Researchers are encouraged to contribute their data and may do so by contacting the Fatigue Design and Evaluation Committee through the SAE.

For several materials commonly used in the as-received condition, there are numerous data sets available. These have been reported as a single value or a range and are identified as to which data were involved. As defined, these properties are from specimens tested in ambient environments and, therefore, do not include such influences as environmental effects (wet or corrosive conditions, elevated temperature, etc.), surface roughness effects, mean stress effects, notch effects, etc.

There are many procedures for using this information for design purposes. They are too lengthy to be included in this report; however, there are a number of publications which discuss these procedures. Several key references [1-27] that discuss fatigue properties, methods for determining fatigue properties, and illustrate the use of these data for making design decision are listed in Section 2.

4. Monotonic Stress-Strain Properties

4.1 Monotonic stress-strain properties are generally determined by testing a smooth polished specimen under axial loading. The load, diameter and/or strain on the uniform test section is measured during the test in order to determine the materials stress-strain response as illustrated in Figures 1 and 2. Properties, most of which are discrete points on the stress-strain curve, can be defined to describe the behavior of a material.

4.2 Ultimate Tensile Strength (Su)—The engineering stress at maximum load. In a ductile material, it occurs at the onset of necking in the specimen.

$$S_u = P_{max}/A_o \quad \text{(Eq. 1)}$$

where:

P_{max} = maximum load
A_o = original cross sectional area

4.3 True Fracture Strength (σ_f)—The "true" tensile stress required to cause fracture.

$$\sigma_f = P_f/A_f \quad \text{(Eq. 2)}$$

where:

P_f = load at failure
A_f = minimum cross sectional area after failure

The value σ_f must be corrected for the effect of triaxial stress present due to necking. One such correction suggested by Bridgeman [11] is illustrated in Figure 3. In this figure, the ratio of the corrected value to the uncorrected value ($\sigma_f/(P_f/A_f)$) is plotted against true tensile strain.

4.4 Tensile Yield Strength (S_{ys}, σ_{ys})—The stress to cause a specified amount of inelastic strain, usually 0.2%. It is usually determined by constructing a line of slope E (modulus of elasticity) through 0.2% strain and zero stress. The stress where the constructed line intercepts the stress-strain curve is taken as the yield strength.

4.5 Percentage Reduction of Area (% RA)—The percentage of reduction in cross sectional area after fracture.

$$\%RA = 100(A_o - A_f/A_o) \quad \text{(Eq. 3)}$$

4.6 True Fracture Ductibility (ε_f)—The "true" plastic strain after fracture.

$$\varepsilon_f = \ln(A_o/A_f) = \ln(100/(100 - \%RA)) \quad \text{(Eq. 4)}$$

4.7 Monotonic Strain Hardening Exponent (n)—The power to which the "true" plastic strain must be raised to be directly proportional to the "true" stress. It is generally taken as the slope of log σ versus log ε_p plot as shown in Figure 2.

$$\sigma = K\varepsilon_p^{\ n} \quad \text{(Eq. 5)}$$

4.8 Monotonic Strength Coefficient (K)—The "true" stress at a "true" plastic strain of unity as shown in Figure 2. If the value of the true fracture ductility is less than 1.0, it is necessary to extrapolate. (see Equation 5).

4.8.1 Monotonic tension properties of a material can be classed into two groups, engineering stress-strain properties and "true" stress-strain properties. Engineering properties are associated with the original cross sectional area of the test specimen, and "true" values relate to actual area while the specimen is under load. The difference between "true" and engineering values is insignificant in the low strain region, less than or equal to 2% strain.

4.8.2 Until the test bar begins to locally neck, some simple relationships exist between engineering and "true" stress-strain values. Equation 6 gives the relationship between engineering and true strain.

$$\varepsilon = \ln(1 + e) \quad \text{(Eq. 6)}$$

where:

ε = "true" strain
e = engineering strain

Similarly, Equation 7 relates true stress to engineering stress.

$$\sigma = S(1 + e) \quad \text{(Eq. 7)}$$

where:

σ = "true" stress
S = engineering stress

These relationships do not apply after onset of necking.

4.8.2.1 A more detailed discussion and derivation of monotonic stress-strain properties can be found in ASTM STP 465 [12]. Figures 1 and 2 graphically illustrate a majority of these properties.

5. Cyclic Stress-Strain Properties

5.1 Cyclic stress-strain properties are determined by testing smooth polished specimens under axial cyclic strain control conditions. The cyclic stress-strain curve is defined as the locus of tips of stable "true" stress-strain hysteresis loops each obtained from a constant amplitude test specimen. A typical stable hysteresis loop is illustrated in Figure 4 and a set of stable loops with a cyclic stress-strain curve down through the loop tips is illustrated in Figure 5. As illustrated, the height of the loop from tip-to-tip is defined as the stress range. For completely reversed testing, one-half of the stress range is generally equal to the stress amplitude while one-half of the width from tip-to-tip is defined as the strain amplitude. Plastic strain amplitude is found by subtracting the elastic strain amplitude from the strain amplitude as indicated in Equations 8, 9, and 10.

$$\Delta\varepsilon_p/2 = \Delta\varepsilon/2 - \Delta\varepsilon_e/2 \quad \text{(Eq. 8)}$$

According to Hooke's law,

$$\Delta\varepsilon_e/2 = \Delta\sigma/2E \quad \text{(Eq. 9)}$$

where:

E = modulus of elasticity

$$\Delta\varepsilon_p/2 = \Delta\varepsilon/2 - \Delta\sigma/2E \quad \text{(Eq. 10)}$$

5.2 A more complete discussion of the cyclic stress-strain curve and other methods of obtaining the curve are given in STP 465 [12] and [4].

5.3 Cyclic Yield Strength (0.2% σ_{ys})—The stress to cause 0.2% inelastic strain as measured on a cyclic stress-strain curve. It is usually determined by constructing a line parallel to the slope of the cyclic stress-strain curve at zero stress through 0.2% strain. The stress where the constructed line intercepts the cyclic stress-strain curve is taken as the 0.2% cyclic yield strength.

5.4 Cyclic Strain Hardening Exponent (n')—The power to which "true" plastic strain amplitude must be raised to be directly proportional to "true" stress amplitude. It is taken as the slope of the log $\Delta\sigma/2$ versus log $\Delta\varepsilon_p/2$ plot, where $\Delta\sigma/2$ and $\Delta\varepsilon_p/2$ are measured from cyclically stable hysteresis loops.

$$(\Delta\sigma)/2 = K'(\Delta\varepsilon_p/2)^{n'} \quad \text{(Eq. 11)}$$

where:

$\Delta\varepsilon_p/2$ = "true" plastic strain amplitude

The line defined by this equation is illustrated in Figure 6.

5.5 Cyclic Strength Coefficient (K')—The "true" stress at a "true" plastic strain of unity in Equation 11. It may be necessary to extrapolate as indicated in Figure 6.

5.5.1 Stress-strain response of some materials can change significantly when subjected to inelastic strains such as can occur nominally or at notch roots due to cyclic loading. When fatigue failure occurs, particularly low cycle fatigue, such inelastic straining is present. Hence, the cyclic stress-strain curve best represents the materials stress-strain response rather than the monotonic stress-strain curve.

5.5.2 In many field test situations, it may be desirable to convert measured strains to stress in order to estimate fatigue life. The cyclic stress-strain curve can be described with an equation using the cyclic properties. Equation 10 can be rewritten by rearranging the terms as shown in Equation 12.

$$\Delta\varepsilon/2 = \Delta\sigma/2E + \Delta\varepsilon_p/2 \quad \text{(Eq. 12)}$$

Rearranging the terms in Equation 11 indicates the relationship between plastic strain amplitude and stress amplitude.

$$\Delta\varepsilon_p/2 = (\Delta\sigma/2K')^{1/n'} \quad \text{(Eq. 13)}$$

Substituting Equation 13 into Equation 12 yields an equation relating cyclic strain amplitude to cyclic stress amplitude in terms of the previously defined properties and the modulus of elasticity.

$$\Delta\varepsilon/2 = \Delta\sigma/2E + (\Delta\sigma/2K')^{1/n'} \quad \text{(Eq. 14)}$$

5.5.3 For a more detailed discussion see STP 465 [12].

6. Fatigue Properties

6.1 Fatigue resistance of materials can be described in terms of the number of constant amplitude stress or strain reversals required to cause failure. The properties defined in this section are determined on smooth polished axial specimens tested under strain control. Stress amplitude, elastic and plastic strain amplitude and total strain amplitude can each be plotted against reversals to failure. The plot of log "true" plastic strain amplitude and log "true" stress amplitude versus log reversals to failure are typically straight lines as illustrated in Figures 7 and 8. The intercept at one reversal and the slope of these straight lines can be described as fatigue parameters.

6.2 Fatigue Ductility Exponent (c)—The power to which the life in reversals, $2N_f$, is raised to be directly proportional to the "true" plastic strain amplitude. It is taken as the slope of the log $(\Delta\varepsilon_p/2)$ versus log $(2N_f)$ plot.

6.3 Fatigue Ductility Coefficient (ε_f')—The "true" plastic strain required to cause failure in one reversal. It is taken as the intercept of the log $(\Delta\varepsilon_p/2)$ versus log $(2N_f)$ plot at $2N_f = 1$.

6.4 Fatigue Strength Exponent (b)—The power to which life in reversals must be raised to be directly proportional to "true" stress amplitude. It is taken as the slope of the log $(\Delta\sigma/2)$ versus log $(2N_f)$ plot.

6.5 Fatigue Strength Coefficient (σ'_f)—The "true" stress required to cause failure in one reversal. It is taken as the intercept of the log $(\Delta\sigma/2)$ versus log $(2N_f)$ plot at $2N_f = 1$.

6.6 Transition Fatigue Life ($2N_t$)—The life where elastic and plastic components of the total strain are equal. It is the life at which the plastic and elastic strain-life lines cross.

6.7 A materials resistance to strain cycling can be considered as the summation of the elastic and plastic resistance as indicated by Equation 15.

$$\Delta\varepsilon/2 = (\Delta\varepsilon_e/2) + (\Delta\varepsilon_p/2) \quad \text{(Eq. 15)}$$

An equation of the "true" plastic strain-life relationship can be written in terms of the previous fatigue properties (Figure 8).

$$\Delta\varepsilon_p/2 = \varepsilon_f'(2N_f)^c \quad \text{(Eq. 16)}$$

where $2N_f$ is reversals to failure. The "true" elastic strain-life relationship is simply the stress-life relationship divided by the modulus of elasticity (Figure 7).

$$\Delta\varepsilon_e/2 = (\sigma_f'/E)(2N_f)^b \quad \text{(Eq. 17)}$$

Substituting Equations 16 and 17 into Equation 15 gives an equation between "true" strain amplitude and reversals to failure in terms of the fatigue parameters.

$$\Delta\varepsilon/2 = (\sigma_f'/E)(2N_f)^b + \varepsilon_f'(2N_f)^c \quad \text{(Eq. 18)}$$

Equation 18 is illustrated in Figure 9.

Specimen failure may be defined several ways. Current definitions include complete separation, a change in hysteresis loop shape, and one of several percentage drop in stress. For several materials, the choice can effect the results. ASTM E 606 [2] should be consulted for current practice.

Sample geometry may have an effect on the fatigue results due to differences in surface residual stress, surface condition, gage length, and shape. Consult ASTM E 606 [2] for current practice.

A statistical treatment of these properties can be useful when making comparisons between materials or between many of the variables within a material grade. Numerous attempts have been made to describe these properties such that statistical lower limits for a specification could be determined. As yet, this has been somewhat less than successful. A more complete treatment of the procedures and sources of potential error may be found in ASTM E 739.

Estimating these fatigue properties, in the absence of test data, is not recommended: but, it is recognized that there will be times when the practitioner will require data and none will be available. As a first estimate, one might consider using data from a similar material in a similar condition at the same hardness or strength. A summary of estimating procedures and their use in included in Reference 6.

TABLE 1—ABBREVIATIONS

Abbreviation	Full-Term
HR	Hot-Rolled
CC	Continuous Casting
IC	Ingot Casting
SH	Sheet
CR	Cold Rolled
CD	Cold Drawn
MOD	Modified
BA	Batch Annealed
GA	Galvannealed
HT	Heat Treated
HDG	Hot-Dip Galvanized
ANN	Annealed
Norm.	Normalized
Q&T	Quenched & Tempered
As-rec.	As Received
UTS	Ultimate Tensile Strength
RA	% Reduction in Area
K	Strength Coefficient
n	Strain Hardening Exponent
E	Modulus of Elasticity
σ_f'	Fatigue Strength Coefficient
b	Fatigue Strength Exponent
ε_f'	Fatigue Ductility Coefficient
c	Fatigue Ductility Exponent
K	Cyclic Strength Coefficient
n	Cyclic Strain Hardening Exponent

TABLE 2A—STEEL—MONOTONIC PROPERTIES

Material	Material Condition	Test Condition	BHN	Yield—0.2% (MPa)	UTS (MPa)	RA %	K (MPa)	n	E (GPa)
1004	HR,CC	As-rec.		287	378				
1004	HR,CC			472	490				
1005	HR,IC	As-rec.		226	321				
1005	HR,IC	As-rec.		234	356				
1005	HR,IC	As-rec.		245	323				
1005	HR,IC	As-rec.		267	359				
1008	HR,CC	As-rec.		252	363				
1008	HR,CC	As-rec.		273	399				
1008	HR,CC			381	392				
1008	HR,CC			424	433				
1008	HR,SH	As-rec.	86	234	331	77.5		0.190	207

TABLE 2A—STEEL—MONOTONIC PROPERTIES (continued)

Material	Material Condition	Test Condition	BHN	Yield—0.2% (MPa)	UTS (MPa)	RA %	K (MPa)	n	E (GPa)
1008	HR,SH	As-rec.	90	255	365	77.9		0.184	203
1010	HR,SH	As-rec.		200	331	80.4	534	0.185	203
1010	HR,SH	As-rec.							203
1010	HR,SH								203
1015	HR,SH	Norm.	80	228	414	68			207
1020	HR,SH	As-rec.	109	262	441	61.8	738	0.190	203
1020	CR,SH	As-rec.	108	255	393	64	400	0.072	186
1025	HR,SH	As-rec.		306	547	62.6	1142	0.281	207
1035	HR,Bar	As-rec.		443	641				
1035	HR,Bar	As-rec.		448	623				
1040	CD,Bar	As-rec.		637	759				
10V40	HR,Bar	As-rec.		572	802				
1045	CD	Annealed	225	517	752	44			
1045		Q&T	500	1689	1827	51		0.047	207
1045	HR,Bar	Q&T	595	1862	2241	41		0.071	207
1045	HR,Bar	Norm.	192	424	718	48			
1045	HR,Bar	HT	277	620	942	39			
1045	HR,Bar	HT	336	787	1322	21			
1045	HR,Bar	HT	410	865	1516	6			
1045	HR,Bar	HT	563	1636	2297	18			
1045	HR,Bar	HT	500	1729	1956	38.3	2352	0.041	207
1045	HR,Bar	HT	390	1275	1344	59		0.044	207
10B21		HT	318	999	1048	67.6	1295	0.054	197
10B21		HT	255	806	834				203
10B22		HT	255	806	834				203
15B27		HT	250	772	847	69		0.075	203
15B27		HT	264	854	916	66.5		0.065	203
94B30		HT	285	799	896	63	1378	0.062	200
HF 50	HR	As-rec.		342	416				
HF 50	HR	As-rec.		359	442				
HF 50	HR	As-rec.		361	441				
HF 50	HR	As-rec.		375	461				
HF 50	HR	As-rec.		383	448				
HF 50	HR	As-rec.		385	448				
HF 50	HR	As-rec.		403	479				
HF 50	HR	As-rec.		417	492				
HF 50	HR	As-rec.		428	474				
HF 60	HR	As-rec.		416	481				
HF 60	HR	As-rec.		431	479				
HF 60	HR	As-rec.		434	525				
HF 60	HR	As-rec.		456	534				
HF 60	HR	As-rec.		459	533				
HF 60	HR	As-rec.		466	558				
HF 70	HR	As-rec.		505	570				
HF 70	HR	As-rec.		521	628				
HF 80	HR	As-rec.		557	617				
HF 80	HR	As-rec.		569	697				
HF 80	HR	As-rec.		579	756				
HF 80	HR	As-rec.		580	654				
HF 80	HR	As-rec.		581	645				
HF 80	HR	As-rec.		585	635				
HF 80	HR	As-rec.		596	657				

TABLE 2A—STEEL—MONOTONIC PROPERTIES (continued)

Material	Material Condition	Test Condition	BHN	Yield—0.2% (MPa)	UTS (MPa)	RA %	K (MPa)	n	E (GPa)
HF 80	HR	As-rec.		605	681				
HF 80	HR	As-rec.		642	719				
HF 80	HR			710	711				
DDQ+	CR,BA	As-rec.		152	306				
DQSK	CR,BA	As-rec.		171	307				
HF 40	CR,BA	As-rec.		279	370				
HF 50	CR,BA	As-rec.		357	490				
HF 50	CR,BA	As-rec.		439	496				
50Y60T	CR,CA	As-rec.		417	554				
80Y90T	CR,CA	As-rec.		603	747				
DDQ+	GA	As-rec.		140	292				
DDQ+	HDG	As-rec.		179	303				
DDQ	HA	As-rec.		150	279				
DQSK	HDG	As-rec.		185	321				
CQ	HDG	As-rec.		314	352				
HF 60	HDG	As-rec.		424	501				
4130	HT		366	1358	1427	54.7			200
4130	HT		259	778	896	67.3			221
4140	HT		293	848	938		1303	0.094	207
4140	HT		475	1895	2033	20.0			200
4142	HT		400	1447	1551	47.0		0.032	200
4142	HT		450	1860	1929	37.0		0.016	200
4142	HT		380	1378	1413	48.0		0.051	207
4142	HT		670	1619	2446	6.0		0.136	200
4142	HT		450	1584	1757	42.0		0.043	207
4142	HT		475	1722	1929	35.0		0.048	207
4340	HT		409	1371	1468	38.1			200
4340	HT		275	834	1048				190
4340	HR		243	634	827	43.4			193
4340	HT			1102	1171	56	1358	0.036	207
5160	HT		430	1488	1584	39.7	1941	0.0463	203
5160	MOD			1565	1755				
51V45				1871	2108				
52100	HT		519	1922	2912	11.2			207
	Cast Steel								
0030	Cast		137	303	496	46			207
0050A	Cast		192	415	787	19			209
	Cast		174	402	583	26			209
	Cast		206	542	702				211
8630	Cast		305	985	1144	29			207

TABLE 2B—STEEL CYCLIC PROPERTIES

Material	Material Condition	Test Condition	BHN	σ_f' (MPa)	b	ε_f'	c	K′ (MPa)	n′	Data Points
1004	HR,CC	As-rec.		1159	–0.142	1.300	–0.649	781-x	0.180-x	
1004	HR,CC			1019	–0.124	1.450	–0.701	561-x	0.180-x	
1005	HR,IC	As-rec.		888	–0.137	0.280	–0.505	1208-x	0.260-x	
1005	HR,IC	As-rec.		878	–0.129	0.460	–0.536	834-x	0.200-x	
1005	HR,IC	As-rec.		1024	–0.151	0.290	–0.509	1254-x	0.270-x	
1005	HR,IC	As-rec.		776	–0.126	0.240	–0.466	626-x	0.170-x	
1008	HR,CC	As-rec.		1225	–0.143	0.350	–0.522	1706-x	0.240-x	
1008	HR,CC	As-rec.		1016	–0.136	0.210	–0.473	958-x	0.220-x	
1008	HR,CC			2012	–0.195	1.050		687-x	0.160-x	
1008	HR,CC			1069	–0.126	0.940		605-x	0.130-x	
1008	HR,SH	As-rec.	86	1124	–0.172	0.460	–0.543	1443-c	0.318-c	16
1008	HR,SH	As-rec.	90	1007	–0.159	0.500	–0.5402	1234-c	0.290-c	51
1010	HR,SH	As-rec.		499	–0.100	0.104	–0.408	867-c	0.244-c	18
1010	HR,SH	As-rec.		634	–0.109	0.145	–0.426	1040-c	0.256-c	39
1010	HR,SH			888	–0.148	0.408	–0.521	1145-c	0.284-c	51
1015	HR,SH	Norm.	80	884	–0.124	0.729	–0.581	945-c	0.213-c	31
1020	HR,SH	As-rec.	109	1384	–0.156	0.337	–0.485	1962-c	0.321-c	12
1020	CR,SH	As-rec.	108	697	–0.116	0.136	–0.405	1233-c	0.286-c	8
1025	HR,SH	As-rec.		934	–0.107	0.590	–0.520	1042-c	0.207-c	9
1035	HR,Bar	As-rec.		2034	–0.172	3.670	–0.860	865-x	0.140-x	
1035	HR,Bar	As-rec.		1491	–0.152	1.560	–0.729	838-x	0.090-x	
1040	CD,Bar	As-rec.		1311	–0.103	0.848	–0.612	915-x	0.131-x	
10V40	HR,Bar	As-rec.		1287	–0.092	0.316	–0.577	1371-x	0.150-x	
1045	CD	Annealed	225	916	–0.079	0.486	–0.520	1022-c	0.152-c	
1045		Q&T	500	2661	–0.093	0.196	–0.643	3371-c	0.145-c	9
1045	HR,Bar	Q&T	595	3294	–0.104	0.220	–0.868	3947-c	0.120-c	9
1045	HR,Bar	Norm.	192	1439	–0.127	0.525	–0.522	1401-c	0.212-c	
1045	HR,Bar	HT	277	2906	–0.161	0.786	–0.579	1770-c	0.191-c	
1045	HR,Bar	HT	336	3403	–0.151	0.458	–0.560	2066-c	0.165-c	
1045	HR,Bar	HT	410	4385	–0.167	0.491	–0.491	3048-c	0.208-c	
1045	HR,Bar	HT	563	5813	–0.154	1.379	–1.082	3083-c	0.075-c	
1045	HR,Bar	HT	500	2636	–0.086	0.210	–0.551	3366-c	0.157-c	9
1045	HR,Bar	HT	390	1785	–0.086	1.207	–0.825	1751-c	0.104-c	10
10B21		HT	318	1204	–0.063	3.709	–0.832	1089-c	0.076-c	8
10B21		HT	255	922	–0.063	2.377	–0.753	858-c	0.083-c	11
10B22		HT	255	841	–0.043	1.928	–0.738	809-c	0.058-c	11
15B27		HT	250	938	–0.057	1.689	–0.784	903-c	0.072-c	6
15B27		HT	264	1062	–0.059	1.575	–0.782	1026-c	0.075-c	6
HF 50	HR	As-rec.		112	–0.117	0.940	–0.676	694-x	0.132-x	
HF 50	HR	As-rec.		686	–0.074	0.337	–0.540	761-x	0.129-x	
HF 50	HR	As-rec.		732	–0.09	1.384	–0.703	684-x	0.124-x	
HF 50	HR	As-rec.		889	–0.055	0.345	–0.563	632-x	0.092-x	
HF 50	HR	As-rec.		959	–0.102	3.189	–0.794	745-x	0.116-x	
HF 50	HR	As-rec.		1088	–0.116	2.828	–0.790	785-x	0.127-x	
HF 50	HR	As-rec.		1000	–0.102	0.563	–0.622	1014-x	0.151-x	
HF 50	HR	As-rec.		1218	–0.118	1.932	–0.771	1056-x	0.147-x	
HF 50	HR	As-rec.		1378	–0.143	3.091	–0.807	694-x	0.110-x	
HF 60	HR	As-rec.		895	–0.091	0.967	–0.750	687-x	0.094-x	
HF 60	HR	As-rec.		1113	–0.109	0.754	–0.670	1029-x	0.143-x	
HF 60	HR	As-rec.		1074	–0.105	0.429	–0.598	1152-x	0.163-x	
HF 60	HR	As-rec.		913	–0.091	0.226	–0.552	1134-x	0.161-x	
HF 60	HR	As-rec.		744	–0.063	0.451	–0.598	792-x	0.103-x	
HF 60	HR	As-rec.		976	–0.88	1.007	–0.705	876-x	0.106-x	

NOTE— x = experimental—from raw data
c = calculated—$K' = \sigma_f'/(\varepsilon_f')^{n'}$—$n' = b/c$

TABLE 2B—STEEL CYCLIC PROPERTIES (continued)

Material	Material Condition	Test Condition	BHN	σ_f' (MPa)	b	ε_f'	c	K′ (MPa)	n′	Data Points
HF 70	HR	As-rec.		1461	–0.123	6.052	–0.904	937-x	0.101-x	
HF 70	HR	As-rec.		1230	–0.104	4.202	–0.843	1251-x	0.173-x	
HF 80	HR	As-rec.		1239	–0.108	1.053	–0.771	1125-x	0.122-x	
HF 80	HR	As-rec.		1428	–0.105	1.816	–0.861	1287-x	0.118-x	
HF 80	HR	As-rec.		2126	–0.152	3.217	–0.934	1389-x	0.133-x	
HF 80	HR	As-rec.		1145	–0.091	1.104	–0.717	1091-x	0.124-x	
HF 80	HR	As-rec.		1451	–0.113	5.289	–0.958	1122-x	0.170-x	
HF 80	HR	As-rec.		1379	–0.112	1.979	–0.820	984-x	0.100-x	
HF 80	HR	As-rec.		1512	–0.119	2.214	–0.826	981-x	0.096-x	
HF 80	HR	As-rec.		1818	–0.134	1.641	–0.830	1387-x	0.139-x	
HF 80	HR	As-rec.		2008	–0.131	7.185	–0.985	1285-x	0.115-x	
HF 80	HR	As-rec.		1704	–0.118	0.764	–0.670	1061-x	0.117-x	
DDQ+	CR,BA	As-rec.		607	–0.116	0.125	–0.437	832-x	0.234-x	
DQSK	CR,BA	As-rec.		591	–0.105	0.155	–0.450	694-x	0.196-x	
HF 40	CR,BA	As-rec.		753	–0.103	0.222	–0.477	596-x	0.134-x	
HF 50	CR,BA	As-rec.		536	–0.047	4.118	–0.883	481-x	0.049-x	
HF 50	CR,BA	As-rec.		571	–0.057	2.046	–0.787	516-x	0.64-x	
50Y60T	CR,CA	As-rec.		912	–0.095	0.127	–0.366	935-x	0.174-x	
80Y90T	CR,CA	As-rec.		2744	–0.173	0.448	–0.548	2221-x	0.267-x	
DDQ+	GA	As-rec.		430	–0.083	0.066	–0.430	641-x	0.201-x	
DDQ+	HDG	As-rec.		564	–0.103	0.122	–0.428	635-x	0.178-x	
DDQ	HA	As-rec.		545	–0.102	0.082	–0.388	1143-x	0.289-x	
DQSK	HDG	As-rec.		875	–0.134	0.142	–0.418	824-x	0.214-x	
CQ	HDG	As-rec.		561	–0.089	15.240	–0.956	419-x	0.088-x	
HF 60	HDG	As-rec.		572	–0.053	20.116	–0.810	531-x	0.068-x	
4130	HT		366	1655	–0.076	0.803	–0.672	1696-c	0.114-c	14
4130	HT		259	1261	–0.077	0.985	–0.648	1264-c	0.119-c	21
4140	HT		293	1163	–0.062	2.360	–0.765	1084-c	0.082-c	18
4140	HT		475	1832	–0.070	0.400	–0.867	1974-c	0.081-c	10
4142	HT		400	1787	–0.084	1.195	–0.859	1756-c	0.098-c	10
4142	HT		450	2079	–0.086	2.620	–0.972	1910-c	0.088-c	9
4142	HT		380	2143	–0.094	0.637	–0.761	2266-c	0.124-c	8
4142	HT		670	2549	–0.078	0.003	–0.436	7119-c	0.179-c	10
4142	HT		450	1937	–0.076	0.706	–0.869	1997-c	0.088-c	10
4142	HT		475	2161	–0.081	0.331	–0.854	2399-c	0.094-c	7
4340	HT		409	1879	–0.0859	0.640	–0.636	1996-c	0.135-c	14
4340	HT		275	1276	–0.075	1.224	–0.714	1249-c	0.105-c	6
4340	HR		243	1198	–0.095	0.522	–0.563	1337-c	0.168-c	11
4340	HT			1165	–0.058	5.492	–0.850	1037-c	0.069-c	10
5160	HT		430	2054	–0.081	1.571	–0.821	1964-c	0.099-c	24
5160	MOD			3553	–0.125	11.532	–1.095	2065-x	0.089-x	
51V45				4585	–0.150	35.560	–1.442	2799-x	0.090-x	
52100	HT		519	2709	–0.096	0.243	–0.642	3348-c	0.150-c	16
	Cast Steel									
0030	Cast		137	655	–0.083	0.280	–0.552	738-c	0.136-c	
0050A	Cast		192	1338	–0.127	0.300	–0.569	1165-c	0.171-c	
	Cast		174	869	–0.101	0.150	–0.514	896-c	0.141-c	
	Cast		206	1117	–0.101	0.780	–0.729	786-c	0.960-c	
8630	Cast		305	1936	–0.121	0.420	–0.693	1502-c	0.122-c	

NOTE— x = experimental—from raw data
c = calculated—$K' = \sigma_f'/(\varepsilon_f')^{n'}$—$n' = b/c$

TABLE 3A—STAINLESS STEEL AND LIGHT NONFERROUS ALLOYS— MONOTONIC PROPERTIES

Material	Material Condition	Test Condition	BHN	Yield—0.2% (MPa)	UTS (MPa)	RA %	K (MPa)	n	E (GPa)
	Stainless Steel								
304	CD		327	744	951	68.8			172
304	ANN	As-rec.		276	572				190
310	ANN	As-rec.		230	592				144
310	ANN		142	221	641	63.5			193
	Aluminum								
1100	T6		26	97		87.6			69
2014	T6		255	461	510	25			69
5086				217					72
5182	O			116	279	60	318	0.119	75
5456	H311		95	234	400	34.6			69
6009	T4			103	226	60	256	0.112	74
6009	T6			259	301	59	351	0.03	66
A356	T6	Cast	93	229	283	5.7	388	0.083	70
A356	T6	Cast	93	224	266	3	397	0.087	70
A356	T6	Cast	89	181	268	8.5			69
	Cast Aluminum MMC								
A356	T6	Cast		280	318	3	585	0.107	102
	Cast Magnesium								
AZ91E	T6	Cast		142	318	12.8	639	0.137	45

TABLE 3B—STAINLESS STEEL AND LIGHT NONFERROUS ALLOYS— CYCLIC PROPERTIES

Material	Material Condition	Test Condition	BHN	σ_f' (MPa)	b	ε_f'	c	K′ (MPa)	n′	Data Points
	Stainless Steel									
304	CD		327	2047	–0.112	0.554	–0.635	2270-x	0.176-c	11
304	ANN	As-rec.		1267	–0.139	0.174	–0.415	2275-c	0.334-c	8
310	ANN	As-rec.		1036	–0.140	0.334	–0.465	1442-c	0.302-c	8
310	ANN		142	1660	–0.155	0.553	–0.553	1960-c	0.281-c	15
	Aluminum									
1100	T6		26	166	–0.096	1.643	–0.669	154-c	0.144-c	12
2014	T6		255	1008	–0.114	1.418	–0.870	963-c	0.132-c	12
5086				491	–0.081	0.118	–0.578	662-c	0.139-c	7
5182	O			768	–0.114	0.293	–0.592	974-c	0.193-c	10
5456	H311		95	826	–0.115	1.076	–0.797	817-c	0.145-c	11
6009	T4			571	–0.0983	0.924	–0.794	577-c	0.124-c	11
6009	T6			588	–0.0957	0.561	–0.746	633-c	0.128-c	12
A356	T6	Cast	93	594	–0.124	0.027	–0.530	379-x	0.043-c	
A356	T6	Cast	93	502	–0.119	0.017	–0.544	383-x	0.050-c	
A356	T6	Cast	89	491	–0.087	0.063	–0.540	372-x	0.044-c	
	Cast Aluminum MMC									
A356	T6	Cast		520	–0.104	0.019	–0.717	925-c	0.155-c	
	Cast Magnesium									
AZ91E	T6	Cast		831	–0.148	0.089	–0.451	552-c	0.184-c	

NOTE— x = experimental—from raw data
c = calculated—$K' = \sigma_f'/(\varepsilon_f')^{n'}$—$n' = b/c$

**TABLE 4A—MISCELLANEOUS MATERIALS—
MONOTONIC PROPERTIES—LIMITED DATA
Caution—no long life data points**

Material	Material Condition	Test Condition	BHN	Yield—0.2% (MPa)	UTS (MPa)	RA %	K (MPa)	n	E (GPa)
1005	HR		86	236	356	81.2	617	0.214	207
1005	HR		86	245	323	68.9	536	0.191	207
1005	HR		86	225	321	73.4	549	0.207	207
1005	HR		86	267	359	70.2	602	0.19	207
1045		HT	450	1515	1584	55		0.041	207
4340		HT	350	1178	1240	57	1580	0.066	193
Maraging		HT	405	1482	1515	67		0.03	186
Maraging		HT	460	1791	1860	56		0.02	186
Maraging		HT		1903	1982				190
Maraging		HT	480	1929	1998	55		0.015	179
Copper				30	207				114
Incon 713		HT	336	813	1045				207
Incon 713		HT	344	788	928				207
Incon 718		Aged		1110	1304				204

Caution—no long life data points—10^2 to 10^5 data only

**TABLE 4B—MISCELLANEOUS MATERIALS—
CYCLIC PROPERTIES—LIMITED DATA**

Material	Material Condition	Test Condition	BHN	σ_f' (MPa)	b	ε_f'	c	K′ (MPa)	n′	Data Points
1005	HR		86	832	–0.122	0.450	–0.534	999-c	0.229-c	12
1005	HR		86	872	–0.134	0.271	–0.503	1234-c	0.266-c	7
1005	HR		86	829	–0.129	0.246	–0.492	1199-c	0.263-c	7
1005	HR		86	483	–0.079	0.215	–0.450	631-c	0.174-c	15
1045		HT	450	1728	–0.060	0.934	–0.819	1737-c	0.073-c	9
4340		HT	350	1917	–0.099	1.122	–0.720	1887-x	0.137-x	8
Maraging		HT	405	2156	–0.083	0.417	–0.682	2399-c	0.122-c	7
Maraging		HT	460	2851	–0.094	2.627	–0.992	2602-c	0.095-c	7
Maraging		HT		2742	–0.087	10.188	–1.006	2245-c	0.086-c	7
Maraging		HT	480	3113	–0.102	2.331	–0.968	2847-c	0.106-c	9
Copper				564	–0.141	0.483	–0.535	683-c	0.263-c	6
Incon 713		HT	336	1319	–0.075	0.052	–0.560	1962-c	0.134-c	5
Incon 713		HT	344	1294	–0.065	0.034	–0.521	1969-c	0.124-c	5
Incon 718		Aged		2295	–0.100	3.637	–0.894	1986-c	0.112-c	12

Caution—no long life data points—10^2 to 10^5 data only

NOTE— x = experimental—from raw data
c = calculated—$K' = \sigma_f'/(\varepsilon_f')^{n'}$—$n' = b/c$

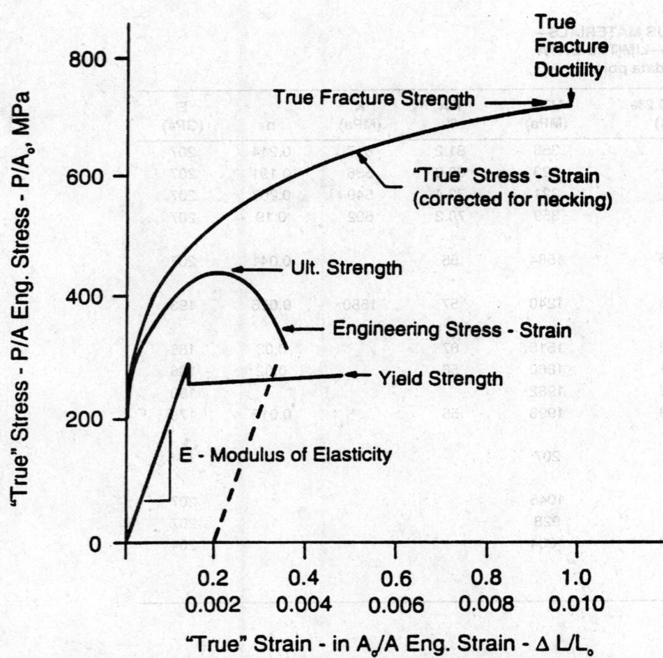

FIGURE 1—ENGINEERING AND "TRUE" STRESS-STRAIN PLOT

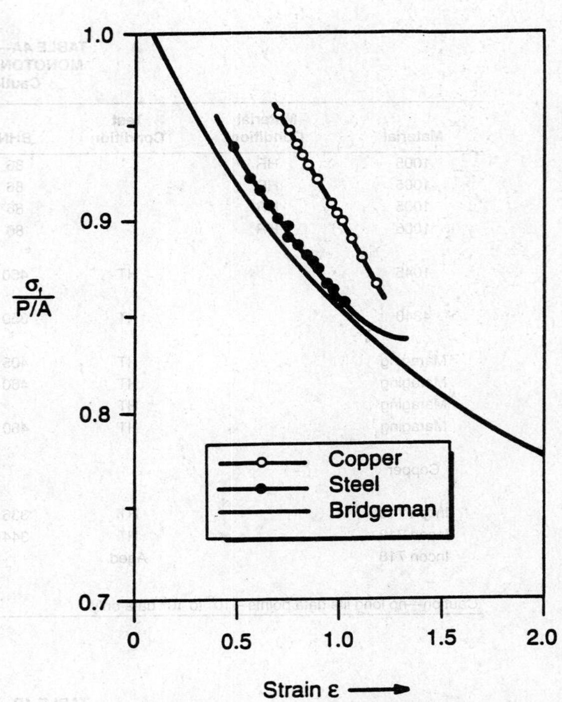

FIGURE 3—RELATIONSHIP BETWEEN BRIDGEMEN CORRECTION FACTOR, Σ_F/(P/A) AND "TRUE" TENSILE STRAIN

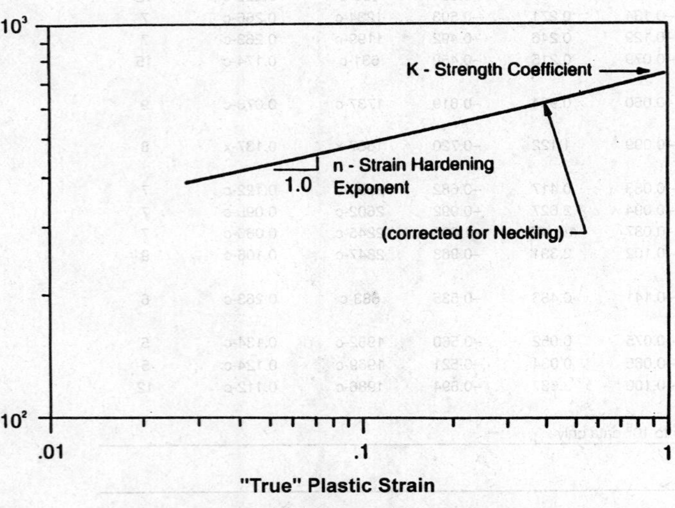

FIGURE 2—"TRUE" STRESS-PLASTIC STRAIN PLOT

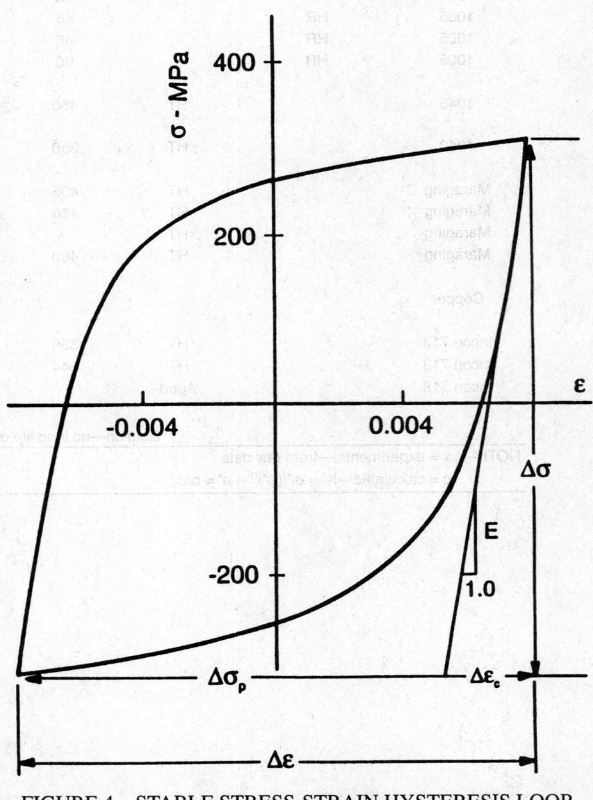

FIGURE 4—STABLE STRESS-STRAIN HYSTERESIS LOOP

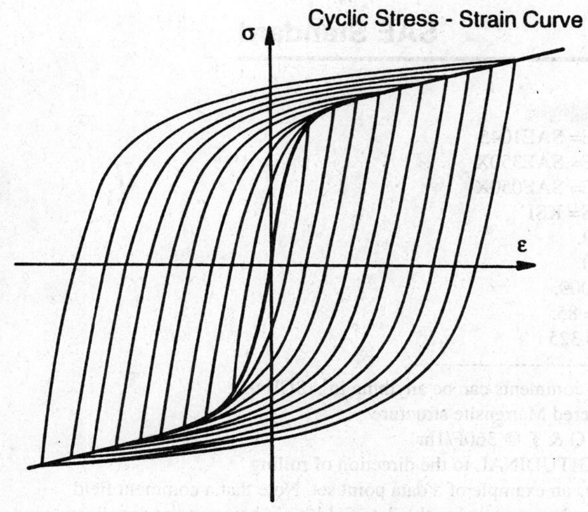

FIGURE 5—CYCLIC STRESS-STRAIN CURVE DRAWN THROUGH STABLE LOOP TIPS

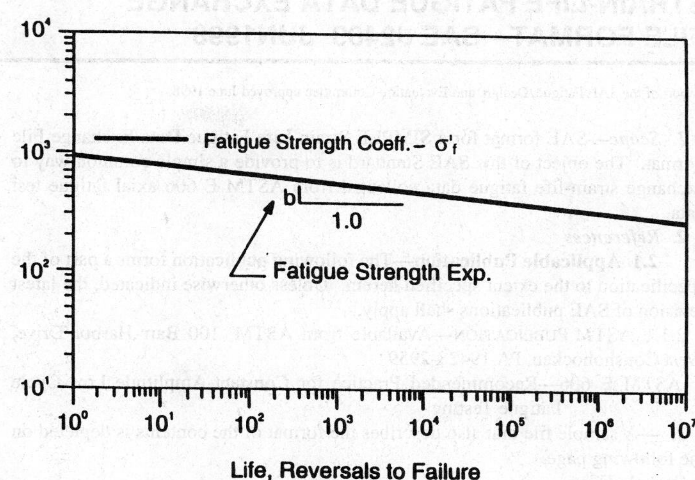

FIGURE 7—STRESS AMPLITUDE VERSUS REVERSALS TO FAILURE

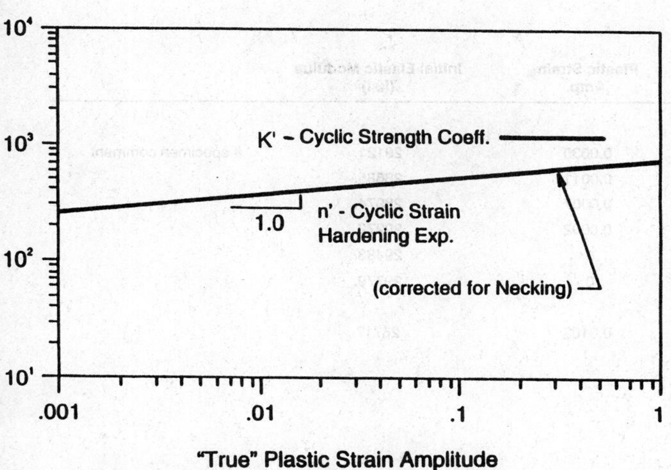

FIGURE 6—CYCLIC STRESS-PLASTIC STRAIN PLOT

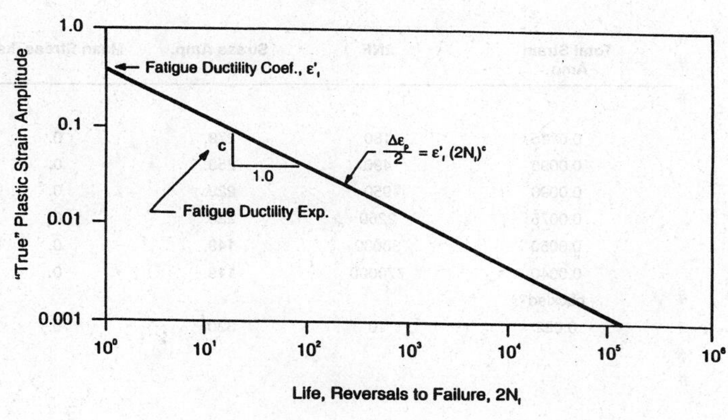

FIGURE 8—PLASTIC STRAIN AMPLITUDE VERSUS REVERSALS TO FAILURE

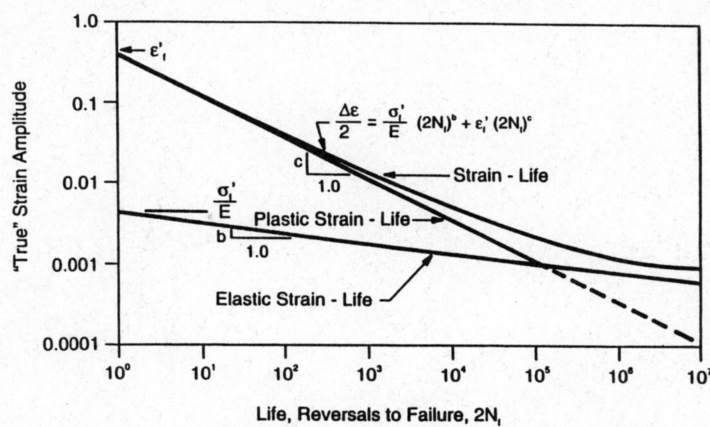

FIGURE 9—STRAIN AMPLITUDE VERSUS REVERSALS TO FAILURE

STRAIN-LIFE FATIGUE DATA EXCHANGE FILE FORMAT—SAE J2409 JUN1998

SAE Standard

Report of the SAE Fatigue, Design, and Evaluation Committee approved June 1998.

1. Scope—SAE format for a SIMPLE Strain-Life Fatigue Data Exchange File Format. The object of this SAE Standard is to provide a simple common way to exchange strain-life fatigue data collected from ASTM E 606 axial fatigue test data.

2. References

2.1 Applicable Publication—The following publication forms a part of the specification to the extent specified herein. Unless otherwise indicated, the latest revision of SAE publications shall apply.

2.1.1 ASTM PUBLICATION—Available from ASTM, 100 Barr Harbor Drive, West Conshohocken, PA 19428-2959.

ASTM E 606—Recommended Practice for Constant-Amplitude Low-Cycle Fatigue Testing

3. —A sample file that also describes the format of the contents is depicted on the following page.

Sample File:

```
# Any line that begins with a # sign is a comment line, or an identifier
# line.  Blank lines can also be inserted anywhere.
#--------------------------------
# Certain lines that begin with a #SYMBOL= VALUE  have special meanings
#  that can be decoded by the receiving program, e.g.:
#NAME= SAE1045
#NAME= SAE350X
#NAME= SAE050X
#UNITS= KSI
#Su= 89.
#Sy= 50.
#E= 30000.
#%RA= 85.
#BHN= 325
#--------------------------------
# Other comments can be anything in ASCII text
# Tempered Martensite structure
# Brine Q & T @ 360F/1hr
# LONGITUDINAL to the direction of rolling
# Here is an example of a data point set. Note that a comment field
#can also be appended to the data field, or in between the data lines.
#A data line is assumed to be any line that is not a blank or a comment
#line.  The data should contain one fatigue test per line, and on each
#line the fields are separated by one or more blanks.
```

#	Total Strain Amp	2NF	Stress Amp. (ksi)	Mean Stress (ksi)	Plastic Strain Amp.	Initial Elastic Modulus (ksi)	
#							
	0.0125	180	279.	0.	0.0030	29121.	# specimen comment
	0.0095	490	253.	0.	0.0011	28685.	
	0.0090	950	229.	0.	0.0007	28974.	
	0.0075	2260	220.	0.	0.0002	29272.	
	0.0050	38000	149.	0.	0.	29483.	
	0.0040	770000	119.	0.	0.	29779.	
#	buckled?:						
	0.022	10	320.	0.	0.0102	26717	
#							
#							

STANDARD RAINFLOW FILE FORMAT —SAE J2623 APR2002

SAE Standard

Report of the SAE Road Load Data Acquisition Subcommittee of the SAE Fatigue, Design and Evaluation Committee approved April 2002. Rationale statement available.

1. Scope—This SAE Standard provides a definition of a rainflow file format. This type of simple text file would contain all relevant information about the rainflow cycle content of a time history. Included information are Comments, Signal Range, Signal Mean, Number of Cycles, Signal Maximum, Signal Minimum.

Rainflow cycle counting has become the most accepted procedure for identifying material fatigue relevant cycles in complex variable amplitude load time histories. The cycle counting methods account for the effects of material plasticity and material memory of prior deformation, and the resulting compressed history information is used by durability analysts to estimate the effects of a given service or test history. Standardization of the rainflow counting methods output files, which is the format addressed by the present standard, is important for reliable information transfer between test and design groups, or different calculation software packages, and thus forms a critical step in the evaluation of components and vehicles. Further background information can be found in the SAE publication AE-10 cited in 2.1.1.

2. References

2.1 Applicable Publications—The following publications form a part of the specification to the extent specified herein. Unless otherwise indicated, the latest version of SAE publications shall apply.

2.1.1 SAE PUBLICATION—Available from SAE, 400 Commonwealth Drive, Warrendale, PA 15096-0001.

The following publication lists a computer program for rainflow cycle counting.

SAE AE-10—"Fatigue Design Handbook," 2nd edition 1988 pages 126-132.

2.1.2 ASTM PUBLICATION—Available from ASTM, 100 Barr Harbor Drive, West Conshohocken, PA 19428-2959.

The following publication defines how rainflow cycles are counted.

ASTM E 1045, 1996—Standard Practices for Cycle, Counting in Fatigue Analysis

3. Definitions—See ASTM E 1045.

4. Rationale—A standard rainflow file is proposed to facilitate easy exchange of information of the rainflow content of a time history. Various vendor specific formats exist, but this document would allow users to exchange information without the use of commercial file translators.

APPENDIX A
SAE STANDARD RAINFLOW TEXT FILE EXAMPLE

A.1 Standard Rainflow File—The first part of the file is a comment section like this section of text.

Anything can go in this section except the word **BEGIN** or **"#BEGIN"** at the front of a line. Users can add special flags, switches and operators if they wish, but no standards are set about what is in this comment section.

Examples of user specific comments:

#FileType= rainflow
#DataType= raw #"raw"= measured, as opposed to "fitted"
#This is a S A E STANDARD RAINFLOW DATA TEXT FILE
Examples of user specific program switches:
!MIDDLE OF BAND ZERO:0!
!UNITS/LEVEL:100!
sptv 1 5 25.0000
start T: 0 5700 22700
end T: 5600 22000 37000
.rain 800.000 -800.000
#Emod= 201000.

If you see text like this in a file supplied to you, it would be prudent to ask your supplier as to their meaning or intent. It is recommended that such flags, or switches not be or used in an SAE standard rainflow file if possible because they can mislead an inexperienced user. It is preferable that the data should be adjusted by the supplier program to reduce the reliance on switches.

A.1.1 End of Comments, Beginning of Data—The comment section is ended by the following line, after which the data follows:

#BEGIN DATA

A.1.2 Data Section—The data can be in any units for the signal, but must use CYCLES (rather than reversals) as the event counter. Numbers are to be read (and therefore can be written) in "free format", i.e.: separated by one or more blanks. Note that blank lines are allowed amongst the data lines. In normal practice the SIGNAL values will be read by computers into REAL (Floating Point) storage locations. CYCLES are generally expected to be INTEGERS, but some rainflow counting methods create fractional cycles, and in consequence give a cycle count such as "1050.5" for example. Thus the cycle numbers should be read as REAL*8 or DOUBLE PRECISION. The write format can be REAL OR INTEGER depending on the algorithm used to count the cycles. See Table A1:

TABLE A1—DATA COLUMN CODE

Col.1	Col.2	Col.3	Col.4	Col.5
Signal Range	Signal Mean	No. of Cycles	Signal Maximum	Signal Minimum

A.1.3 End of Data Section—No special delimiters are used as "End-of-File"(EOF); it is up to the reading program to detect the EOF by itself. (On some machines it may be wise to place an extra blank line as the last line, otherwise the last data line may not be read.)

A.1.4 Example of Data Section

```
#BEGIN  DATA
0.103E+04  232.  1   748.   -284.
826.       232.  1   645.   -181.
877.       258.  1   697.   -181.
51.6  -103.      17  -77.4  -129.

103. -77.4 5 -25.8 -129.
155. -51.6 3 25.8 -129.
206. -25.8 1 77.4 -129.
258. 0.305E-04 2 129. -129.
310. 25.8 3 181. -129.
361. 51.6 2 232. -129.
465. 103. 2 335. -129.


516. 129. 1 387. -129.
568. 155. 4 439. -129.
619. 181. 3 490. -129.
671. 206. 2 542. -129.
723. 232. 5 594. -129.
774. 258. 4 645. -129.
826. 284. 1 697. -129.
51.6 -51.6 61 -25.8 -77.4
103. -25.8 29 25.8 -77.4
155. 0. 27 77.4 -77.4
206. 25.8 23 129. -77.4
258. 51.6 6 181. -77.4
310. 77.4 8 232. -77.4
361. 103. 3 284. -77.4
413. 129. 7 335. -77.4
619. 232. 1 542. -77.4
671. 258. 2 594. -77.4
51.6 0. 287 25.8 -25.8
103. 25.8 125 77.4 -25.8
155. 51.6 61 129. -25.8
206. 77.4 14 181. -25.8
```

TEST PROCEDURES FOR AUTOMOTIVE STRUCTURAL COMPOSITE MATERIALS—SAE J2253 DEC1995

SAE Standard

Report of the SAE Composites Committee approved December 1995.

Foreword—This Document has not changed other than to put it into the new SAE Technical Standards Board Format.

TABLE OF CONTENTS

1. Scope—This SAE Standard is intended to serve as a guide for the collection of physical, mechanical, and thermal properties of fiber-reinforced polymer composite materials for automotive structural applications. This document attempts to utilize test methods applicable to the widest range of structural materials and processes without compromising the integrity of the data being sought. A summary of the material characterization is shown in Section 15.

2. References

2.1 Applicable Publications—The following publications form a part of the specification to the extent specified herein. Unless otherwise indicated the latest revision of SAE publications shall apply.

2.1.1 SAE PUBLICATION—Available from SAE, 400 Commonwealth Drive, Warrendale, PA 15096-0001.

SAE EA-2253—SDRP Data Reporting Program

2.1.2 ASTM PUBLICATIONS—Available from ASTM, 100 Barr Harbor Drive, West Conshohocken, PA 19428-2959.

ASTM D 618—Conditioning Plastics and Electrical Insulating Materials for Testing
ASTM D 638—Tensile Properties of Plastics
ASTM D 696—Coefficient of Linear Thermal Expansion of Plastics
ASTM D 792—Specific Gravity and Density of Plastics by Displacement
ASTM D 2584—Ignition Loss of Cured Reinforced Resins
ASTM D 3039—Tensile Properties of Fiber Composites
ASTM D 3410—Compression Properties of Fiber Composites
ASTM D 3417—Heats of Fusion and Crystallization of Polymers by Thermal Analysis
ASTM D 3593—Molecular Weight Averages and Distribution of Polymers by GPC Method
ASTM D 4065—Practice for Determining and Reporting Dynamic Mechanical Properties of Plastics
ASTM D 5083—Tensile Properties of Reinforced Thermosetting Plastics Using Straight Sided Specimens
ASTM D 5296—Molecular Weight Averages and Molecular Weight Distribution of Polystyrene by High Performance Size-Exclusion Chromatography
ASTM D 5379—Shear Properties of Composite Materials by the V-notched Beam Method

2.1.3 GENERAL MOTORS PUBLICATION—Available from Boise Cascade, 13301 Stephens Road, Warren, MI 48089.

GM Std 9077-P—Determination of Filler Content

2.1.4 CONFLICTS—In the event of a conflict between the text of this document and the references cited herein, the text of this document shall take precedence.

3. Definitions

3.1 Structural Polymer Composite—Automotive structural polymer composites are considered to be those having a tensile modulus greater than 7 GPa and a tensile strength greater than 100 MPa.

3.2 Planar Isotropic Composites—These materials are defined as being comprised of randomly oriented fibers that will result in properties that are nearly the same in all directions in-plane, but different in the thickness direction. Examples of such materials include liquid molded composites reinforced with continuous strand mats, chopped strand mats, or directed fiber preforms; random fiber sheet molded composites (SMC) and random fiber reinforced thermoplastic composites.

3.3 Orthotropic Composites—These materials do not have the same *x*, *y*, and *z* directional properties. Such materials include liquid molded composites reinforced with unidirectional and bidirectional stitched mats, woven fabrics, knitted fabrics, and directionally reinforced SMC and thermoplastic composites.

3.4 Special Reinforced Composites—Some reinforcements create different symmetry than planar isotropic or orthotropic reinforcements. Examples include some triaxial woven preforms, braided mats, or mixed lay-ups. Test specimen layout definition for these reinforcements is beyond the scope of this document. Sampling of these materials should be done with the prior approval of the customer.

3.5 Ambient Conditions—These are room temperature laboratory conditions, which are assumed to be 23 °C ± 2 °C and 50% ± 5% RH.

4. General Requirements

4.1 Calibrations—All measuring equipment for determining or controlling physical, mechanical, or thermal characteristics shall be calibrated and certified with traceability to the National Institute of Standards and Technology.

4.2 Equivalence—Any substitution of supposed equivalent items, where "or equivalent" is specified herein, must first be approved by the customer.

4.3 Responsibility for Quality—Unless otherwise specified, the supplier is responsible for all quality inspection and for meeting all of the test requirements specified herein. The supplier may use internal testing facilities or any other qualified test agencies.

4.4 Data Reporting—All physical, thermal, and mechanical data and information on the constituent materials and panel molding shall be submitted to the customer using the Supplemental Data Reporting Package (SDRP). All data requested herein shall be manually recorded onto the SDRP forms or entered into the electronic SDRP program for output and transmittal to the customer. Graphs or other requested traces shall also be packaged and sent with the SDRP to the customer.

The SDRP Data Reporting Program (EA-2253) available from SAE as a 3-1/2 in or a 5-1/4 in diskette, is a menu-driven program, which facilitates data entry and reporting using an IBM-compatible personal computer. This program is the preferred method for reporting data.

The SDRP reporting forms are found in Appendix A. These include a "Constituent Materials/Process Data Sheet" (A3-A5) for the raw materials and processing data. This form may be modified as required to provide additional relevant information.

5. Panel Fabrication

5.1 General Panel Requirements

5.1.1 NUMBER OF PANELS—Six panels shall be tested for any given material (a material is defined here as any particular combination of resin, reinforcement, and filler). Sufficient panels should be molded to assure that six panels are available after potential rejections cited in 5.1.4, 5.1.6, 5.3.2, or 5.4.2.

5.1.2 CONSTITUENT MATERIALS—All of the panels shall be from a single production lot of composite using single batches of resin, fiber, filler, and additives. The resin type, all matrix constituents and fibers used in molding are to be clearly defined. RECORD IN SDRP.

5.1.3 PREFORM/MOLD CHARGE LAY-UP—To allow for a direct comparison to be made among material systems, all plies shall be aligned in the same direction. Every ply in a given plaque shall also be the same reinforcement form and product code. Mixed lay-ups may be considered for submittal, but should be discussed with the customer prior to panel fabrication. If multiple plies are used, the plies must be aligned and directionally indicated. The number of plies must also be indicated. RECORD IN SDRP.

5.1.4 Panel Quality—Evidence of a flawed or an improperly prepared test panel shall be cause for discarding the panel prior to testing and fabrication of a replacement panel. Such causes include incorrect lay-up sequence, incorrect cure cycle, incorrect fiber content, fiber misalignment, nonfilling of mold cavity, blisters, excessive porosity, excessive void content, severe panel warpage, resin rich surfaces, thickness variation across the plaque, or compression of the preform towards the surface.

5.1.5 Panel Dimensions—Nominal panel dimensions shall be 610 mm x 610 mm.

5.1.6 Panel Thickness—Panel thickness shall be 3.2 mm ± 0.2 mm with maximum thickness run out of 0.2 mm.

5.2 Panel Molding—Molding conditions such as injection time, mold temperature, and postcure schedules must be reported. Reaction conditions for the material must be representative of conditions which would be utilized to mold an actual production part and should be reported in complete detail. Panels may be fixtured during postcure if warpage is likely to occur. RECORD IN SDRP.

5.2.1 Liquid Composite Molding—Thermoplastic or thermoset binders in the preform shall be "set" prior to molding. All panels shall be molded in a center-gated mold. Following the cure, care should be taken to avoid unnecessary flexing of the plaque during demolding. Postcure is permissible, but should be noted in the SDRP.

5.2.2 SMC Molding—The structural SMC molding charge must be prepared in a manner consistent with production molding practice. If the material will be used with 80% mold coverage, a similar coverage should be used in the fabrication of test plaques. Using 80% as an example, the charge should consist of one or more plies cut to a square configuration and placed over the central 430 mm x 430 mm area of the mold. The charge should be from properly matured material and should be thermally equilibrated to ambient temperature prior to molding. Following cure, care should be taken to avoid unnecessary flexing of the plaque during demolding. Postcure is permissible but should be noted in the SDRP.

5.2.3 Thermoplastic Compression Molding—Charge preparation and coverage should be similar to the procedure used for thermosetting SMC materials. Charge preheating should be done in a manner similar to actual production molding. Any process deviation used in charge preheating must be noted. Since the cooling rate and dwell time will influence the crystallinity level in some materials, care should be taken to reproduce the thermal cycle encountered in production. Any release agents used in component molding should also be used in plaque molding.

5.3 Orthotropic Composites

5.3.1 Fiber Orientation—The primary fiber direction of the preform or mold charge is defined as 0× and is depicted in Figure 1.

5.3.2 Fiber Content—The preferred fiber content for composites with orthotropic fiber orientation is 45% ± 2% by volume. See Section 14 for conversion between weight percent and volume percent. If this fiber content is not practical, alternative fiber contents of 35% ± 2% or 25% ± 2% by volume may be used. Consult with the customer if none of these fiber contents are acceptable.

5.4 Planar Isotropic Composites

5.4.1 Panel Test Orientation—For materials with a nominal planar isotropic fiber orientation, a processing parameter such as roll direction for continuous strand mat products or machine direction for SMC will be defined as 0× as depicted in Figure 1 and designated in the SDRP tables.

5.4.2 Fiber Content—The preferred fiber content for composites with planar isotropic fiber orientation is 25% ± 2% by volume. See Section 14 for conversion between weight percent and volume percent. If this fiber content is not practical, alternative fiber contents of 35% ± 2% or 45% ± 2% by volume may be used. Consult with the customer if none of these fiber contents are acceptable.

6. Material Sampling

6.1 Sampling Procedure—Specimens for physical, thermal, and mechanical tests shall be cut from the panels fabricated according to Section 5 using procedures described in Section 7.

6.2 Specimen Layout—Specific specimen locations for Planar Isotropic Fiber-Reinforced composites and Orthotropic Fiber-Reinforced composites are shown in Figure 1. Samples shall be cut and labeled per the codes indicated in Figure 1. This sample coding scheme is consistent with the SDRP. For liquid-molded panels, the center-gate area shall not be used and should be discarded. For all panels, the 25 mm trim areas shaded in Figure 1 shall not be used for specimen sampling and should be discarded.

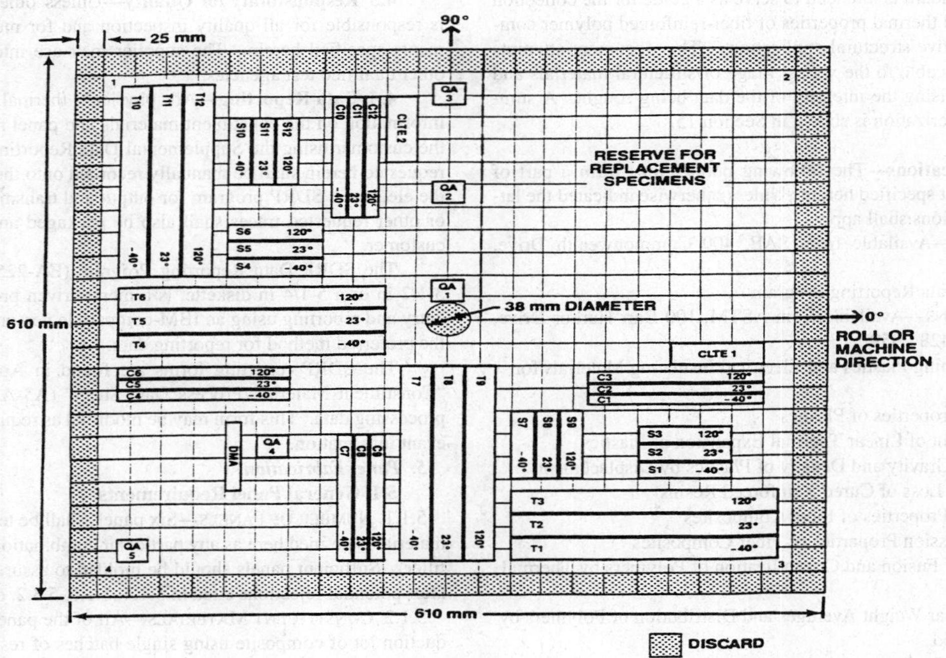

SPECIMEN LOCATION TEMPLATE

SPECIMEN DIMENSIONS

TENSILE (T)	**215 mm x 25 mm**	**COMPRESSION (C)**	**140 mm x 12.5 mm**
SHEAR (S)	**75 mm x 20 mm**	**CLTE**	**75 mm x 25 mm**
DMA	**65 mm x 10 mm**	**QA**	**25 mm x 25 mm**

FIGURE 1—SPECIMEN LOCATION

7. Specimen Preparation

7.1 General—The techniques described in this section are recommended requirements to ensure good quality test specimens produced in a consistent manner.

7.2 Rough Cutting—Rough cutting of specimens can be accomplished by machining operations by cutting pieces from the panel to a size approximating the specimen configuration. The specimen layout plan shown in Figure 1 shall be used for specimen location.

7.3 Surface Edge Finishing—Final surface edge preparation can be accomplished by surface grinding. The finish sanding should be done only in the direction of the length of the specimens and the sanding grit size should be 180 grit or finer. Sanding or grinding perpendicular to the length of the specimen may result in lower failure strengths because of high-stress concentrations at the scratch marks. No sanding is required, however, if specimens are cut with a diamond saw using a 180 grit or finer diamond blade and a minimum tip speed of 200 m/min. Water cooling of the saw blade is recommended for all materials, but is required for urethane materials.

7.4 Specimen Conditioning—All specimens shall be conditioned prior to testing per ASTM D 618, Method A. For tests at any temperature other than ambient, specimens shall be further conditioned at the test temperature for 30 min immediately prior to testing.

8. Physical Test Methods

8.1 General—It is desirable that the tests in 8.2 to 8.5 be performed on the same specimens. The specimen size for each test performed shall be 25 mm x 25 mm and shall be taken from the QA locations designated in Figure 1.

8.2 Specific Gravity—Specific gravity shall be determined in accordance with ASTM D 792. RECORD IN SDRP.

8.3 Resin Content—Resin content shall be determined in accordance with ASTM D 2584. See Section 14 for conversion between weight percent and volume percent. RECORD IN SDRP.

8.4 Filler Content—Filler content shall be determined in conjunction with ASTM D 2584. Appropriate procedures (for example, GM Engineering Standard—Materials and Process Procedure GM 9077-P) utilizing acid wash for calcium carbonate filler shall be used to determine the amount of particulate fillers in the composite. See Section 14 for conversion between weight percent and volume percent. RECORD IN SDRP.

8.5 Fiber Content—Fiber content shall be determined in accordance with ASTM D 2584. For reinforcements other than glass fiber, consult the customer. See Section 14 for conversion between weight percent and volume percent. RECORD IN SDRP.

8.6 Panel Thickness—Panel thickness uniformity shall be determined as follows:

a. Measure the thickness of each panel three separate times at each corner (25 mm from each edge) and at a region near the center of the panel (but away from the discarded gate region for liquid-molded panels).

b. Using all three measurements taken, report the average value for that region of the panel. RECORD IN SDRP.

8.7 Crystallinity—For semi-crystalline thermoplastic composites, heat of fusion and heat of crystallization shall be determined in accordance with ASTM D 3417. An appropriate sample shall be taken from an area near the DMA specimen as designated in Figure 1. A Differential Scanning Calorimeter (DSC) shall be used to determine the areas under crystallization exotherm and fusion endotherm. RECORD IN SDRP.

8.8 Molecular Weight—For thermoplastic composites, molecular weight averages and molecular weight distribution shall be determined in accordance with ASTM D 5296. The "universal calibration" principles outlined in ASTM D 3593 or a suitable monodisperse polymeric standard shall be used for calibrating the test equipment. An appropriate sample shall be taken from an area near the DMA specimen as designated in Figure 1. High Performance Size-Exclusion Chromatography (HPSEC) shall be used to determine number and weight average molecular weights and molecular weight distribution. RECORD IN SDRP.

9. Thermal Test Methods

9.1 General—Dynamic Mechanical Analysis (DMA) and Coefficient of Linear Thermal Expansion (CLTE) tests shall be conducted on each of the specimens labeled DMA and CLTE, respectively, in Figure 1.

9.2 DMA Test Method—Dynamic mechanical analysis testing shall be conducted in accordance with ASTM D 4065 with the following provisions or exceptions cited herein.

9.2.1 INSTRUMENTATION—A Rheometrics RDS II or TA System's (formerly Dupont's) 983 Dynamic Mechanical Analyzer or instrumentation which provides equivalent results shall be utilized. The instrument utilized in the evaluation shall be calibrated in accordance with the manufacturer's recommendations.

9.2.2 SAMPLE PREPARATION—Test specimen preparation procedures described in Section 7 shall be followed to ensure good quality specimens.

9.2.3 SAMPLE DIMENSIONS—Sample dimensions for the previously named instruments shall be at least 65 mm x 10 mm x 3.2 mm. Distance between the instrument clamps shall be at least 40 mm. Sample dimensions for testing with other instrumentation may be selected using ASTM D 4065 guidelines.

9.2.4 TEST TEMPERATURE RANGE—A temperature sweep shall be conducted from -50 °C to an upper limit temperature which shall be at least 40 °C above the material's glass transition or 200 °C, whichever is higher.

9.2.5 HEATING RATE—The heating rate shall be no greater than 5 °C/min (5 °C steps with 1 min equilibration for the previously named Rheometrics instrumentation).

9.2.6 FREQUENCY—The frequency shall be maintained at 1 Hz (6.28 radians/s) for fixed frequency instrumentation.

9.2.7 OTHER TEST PARAMETERS—Strain shall be maintained at a minimum value which allows the measured stress to exceed the lower limit of sensitivity of the transducer. Typical strain levels are 0.02 to 0.2%. When possible, an amplitude of 0.6 mm should be utilized with other fixed frequency instrumentation. Test parameters for resonant frequency experiments (e.g., sample length) should be adjusted so that an initial frequency of 30 Hz at 0.2 mm amplitude is obtained at the onset of the experiment.

9.2.8 GLASS TRANSITION TEMPERATURE—The glass transition temperature (Tg) shall be determined from the storage modulus data. A line is drawn tangent to the storage modulus plateau at temperatures below the transition and a second line is drawn tangent to the storage modulus curve beginning at the transition inflection point, which is approximately midway through the sigmoidal curve associated with the transition. The temperature at which these two tangent lines intersect is reported as the glass transition temperature (see Figure 2).

9.2.9 REPORT—The test report shall include measured transition temperatures and thermograms for either shear moduli (G', G", and tan δ) or flexural moduli (E', E", and tan δ) versus temperature. One specimen per panel shall be run. RECORD IN SDRP AND PROVIDE THERMOGRAMS.

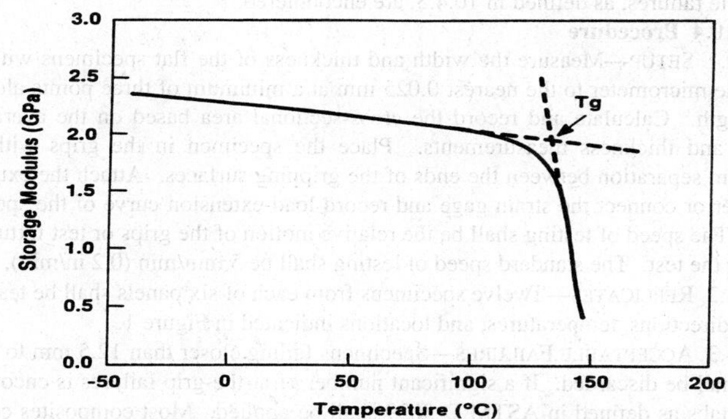

FIGURE 2—STORAGE MODULUS DIAGRAM

9.3 Coefficient of Linear Thermal Expansion (CLTE)

9.3.1 CLTE TESTING—Thermal expansion properties shall be measured in accordance with ASTM D 696 with the following provisions and exceptions cited herein.

9.3.2 INSTRUMENTATION—A fused-quartz dilatometer equipped with precise length measuring devices such as Linear Variable Differential Transformer (LVDT) shall be used to record change in length of the specimen as a function of temperature.

9.3.3 SAMPLE DIMENSIONS—The test specimen shall be of constant cross-section and the specimen size is 75 mm x 25 mm x 3.2 mm. Dimensional variation of specimen length shall be limited to 0.25 mm.

9.3.4 SAMPLE PREPARATION—Test specimen preparation procedures described in Section 7 shall be followed to ensure good quality specimens.

9.3.5 PROCEDURE—The CLTE shall be measured and/or reported over the following temperature ranges:

a. -30 to 30 °C

b. 30 to 80 °C

c. 80 to 125 °C

If the instrumentation allows, the change in length should be monitored continuously or in increments of 20 °C over the temperature range of the test.

9.3.6 REPORT—The CLTE shall be reported over the ranges a, b, and c. If the data can be obtained from the instrumentation, a table showing Δl/l values at 20 °C intervals should be provided. Use the specimen original length (l) at -30 °C as the "zero" point for Δl/l. RECORD IN SDRP AND PROVIDE TABULATED DATA.

10. Tensile Testing

10.1 General Description—Tensile testing shall be conducted in general accordance with ASTM D 3039 and ASTM D 5083 with the following provisions or exceptions cited herein. Mechanical properties determined shall include the following: tensile strength, modulus, strain to failure, Poisson's ratio, and energy to failure at -40 °C, 23 °C, and 120 °C. These tests shall be conducted on each of the appropriately labeled specimens in the numbers and directions indicated in Figure 1.

NOTE—If a material cannot be tested at 120 °C because it is too close to the resin Tg or exceeds the resin Tg, contact the customer to discuss an appropriate lower temperature.

10.2 Apparatus—Grips shall be self-aligning, so that the long axis of the specimen is aligned with the direction of the applied load through the centerline of the grip assembly. The specimen should not have any rotary motion which may induce slippage in the grips. Fine serrations on grip faces have been found to be effective for composite materials. A biaxial extensometer or strain gage accurate to 1% of the measured strain shall be used for measuring Poisson's ratio. Extensometer or strain gage attachment should not cause damage to the specimen surface.

10.3 Test Specimen

10.3.1 SPECIMEN DIMENSIONS—The test specimen shall be of constant cross-section and the specimen size is 215 mm x 25 mm x 3.2 mm for random fiber composites and 215 mm x 12.5 mm x 3.2 mm for 0 degree continuous fiber composites. Dimensional variation of specimen width shall be limited to ±0.15 mm. Measure samples to nearest 0.025 mm.

10.3.2 SPECIMEN PREPARATION—Test specimen preparation procedures described in Section 7 shall be followed to ensure good quality samples.

10.3.3 SPECIMEN TABBING—Tabbing of specimens is not required unless unacceptable failures, as defined in 10.4.3, are encountered.

10.4 Procedure

10.4.1 SETUP—Measure the width and thickness of the flat specimens with a suitable micrometer to the nearest 0.025 mm at a minimum of three points along its length. Calculate and record the cross-sectional area based on the average width and thickness measurements. Place the specimen in the grips with a 115 mm separation between the ends of the gripping surfaces. Attach the extensometer or connect the strain gage and record load-extension curve of the specimen. The speed of testing shall be the relative motion of the grips or test fixtures during the test. The standard speed of testing shall be 5 mm/min (0.2 in/min).

10.4.2 REPLICATES—Twelve specimens from each of six panels shall be tested in the directions, temperatures, and locations indicated in Figure 1.

10.4.3 ACCEPTABLE FAILURES—Specimens failing closer than 12.5 mm to the grip shall be discarded. If a significant number of at-the-grip failures is encountered, tabs as defined in ASTM D 3039 shall be applied. Most composites containing 0 degree continuous fibers will require tabbing.

10.5 Calculations—Determine the tensile strength, chord modulus, Poisson's ratio, and percent strain at failure using the standard procedures. The chord modulus shall be calculated using the 0.05% and 0.25% strain and corresponding stress values. Poisson's ratio shall be calculated using the 0.05% and 0.25% longitudinal strain and corresponding transverse strain values. The area under the stress-strain curve up to the point of failure (maximum stress) shall be determined and reported as the tensile energy to failure in units of MJ/m^3. If the energy-to-failure is not reported for a material, the customer will approximate this number as one-half the product of the stress at failure multiplied by the strain at failure. This approximation may result in an underestimation of the energy-at-failure.

10.6 Report—The report shall include the following:

a. Individual tensile strength values, average value, and standard deviation
b. Tensile (chord) moduli, average value, and standard deviation
c. Tensile strains to failure, average value, and standard deviation
d. Poisson's ratio, average value, and standard deviation
e. Tensile energies to failure, average value, and standard deviation
f. A representative example of the stress/strain or load/extension curve

RECORD IN SDRP AND PROVIDE CURVE.

10.7 Resin Tensile Properties—Determine the tensile strength, modulus, and strain to failure for the neat, cured resin in accordance with ASTM D 638. RECORD ON SDRP.

11. Compression Testing

11.1 General Description—Compression testing shall be conducted according to ASTM D 3410, Procedure B (IITRI method), with the exceptions and/or provisions cited herein. Mechanical tests shall include compressive strength at -40 °C, 23 °C, and 120 °C. Modulus, strain to failure, and energy to failure at these temperatures are optional. These tests shall be conducted on each of the labeled specimens in the numbers and directions indicated in Figure 1.

NOTE—If a material cannot be tested at 120 °C because it is too close to the resin Tg or exceeds the resin Tg, contact the customer to discuss an appropriate lower temperature.

11.2 Compression Test Fixture—Test fixture dimensions shall correspond to those found in ASTM D 3410, Procedure B for specimens 12.5 mm wide.

11.3 Test Specimen

11.3.1 SPECIMEN DIMENSIONS—The test specimen shall be 12.5 mm wide. All other necessary specimen dimensions are called out in ASTM D 3410, Procedure B for specimens 12.5 mm wide.

11.3.2 SPECIMEN PREPARATION—Test specimen preparation procedures described in Section 7 shall be followed to ensure good quality samples.

11.3.3 SPECIMEN TABBING—Untabbed specimens are permissible if failures occur within the center area of the sample and away from the edge of the grip. If required, specimen tabs as specified in ASTM D 3410 shall be applied prior to any environmental conditioning. However, specimen tabs are not required to be beveled as specified in ASTM D 3410. Tabs shall be applied to the specimens prior to final width dimension machining.

11.4 Procedure

11.4.1 SETUP—Measure the width and thickness of the compression specimens in the gage area to the nearest 0.025 mm. Calculate and record the cross-sectional area of the specimen. Particular care should be taken to properly align the specimen in the test fixture. Specimen shall be tested using a constant crosshead rate of 5 mm/min (0.2 in/min).

11.4.2 REPLICATES—Twelve specimens from each six panels shall be tested in the directions, temperatures, and locations indicated in Figure 1.

11.4.3 STRAIN MEASUREMENT—If performed, strain measurement may be taken by use of strain gages or extensometer. Any transducer used shall not in any way damage the surface of the specimen prior to or during the test.

11.4.4 CHORD MODULUS—When measured, modulus shall be collected using the chord modulus method, and shall be calculated using the 0.05 and 0.25% strain and corresponding stress values.

11.5 Calculations—Determine the compressive strength as well as the chord modulus and percent strain at failure when measured using standard procedures. The area under the stress-strain curve up to the point of failure (maximum stress) shall be determined and reported as the tensile energy to failure in units of MJ/m3. If the energy-to-failure is not reported for a material, the customer will approximate this number as one-half the product of the stress at failure multiplied by the strain at failure. This approximation may result in an underestimation of the energy-at-failure.

11.6 Report—The report shall include the following:

a. Individual compressive strengths, average value, and standard deviation
b. Compressive (chord) moduli, average value, and standard deviation (optional)
c. Compressive strains to failure, average value, and standard deviation (optional)
d. Compressive energies to failure, average value, and standard deviation (optional)
e. A representative example of the stress/strain or load/displacement curve (optional)

RECORD IN SDRP AND PROVIDE CURVE.

12. Shear Testing

12.1 General Description—Shear testing shall be conducted according to ASTM D 5379 (Iosipescu method) with the exceptions and/or provisions cited herein. Mechanical properties determined shall include: shear strength, modulus, and strain to failure at -40 °C, 23 °C, and 120 °C. These tests shall be conducted on each of the labeled specimens in the numbers and directions indicated in Figure 1.

NOTE—If a material cannot be tested at 120 °C because it is too close to the resin Tg or exceeds the resin Tg, contact the customer to discuss an appropriate lower temperature.

12.3 Test Specimen

12.3.1 SPECIMEN DIMENSIONS—Specimens shall nominally be 75 mm long, 20 mm wide, and 3.2 mm thick. Load bearing edges should be ground flat and parallel to within 0.05 mm using an abrasive wheel operating on a precision surface grinder as described in Section 7.

12.3.2 SPECIMEN PREPARATION—The prescribed notch angles and root radii should be ground in the specimens using diamond abrasive tooling on a precision surface grinder. Care must be taken to avoid delaminating specimens during notch grinding. Stacking and clamping specimens in the tool grinder vise have been found to be effective. The strain is to be measured using a strain gage rosette (for example, Micro - Measurements EA-06-062TV-350 or N2A series gages). Special care shall be taken in the mounting and alignment of the gages in order to avoid erroneous data collection. Appropriate gage excitation voltages shall also be used, and a sufficiently low voltage applied to prevent excessive resistive heating of the test sample. For elevated temperature gaging, refer to the strain gage manufacturer's literature for proper adhesive.

12.3.3 SPECIMEN TABBING—Untabbed specimens are permissible providing the specimens exhibit appropriate failure modes as defined in ASTM D 5379. The tabs shall be bonded to the specimen per the adhesive manufacturer's instructions prior to final machining and conditioning. The adhesive used shall be commercially available and capable of withstanding the load levels and temperatures of the test. Most random fiber composites will require tabbing.

12.4 Procedure

12.4.1 DIMENSIONS—Measure the thickness of the specimen to within 0.025 mm at three points. Determine the minimum distance between the notch tips. Calculate and record the cross-sectional area.

12.4.2 MOUNTING—Mount the specimen in the test fixture using a lift-up alignment tool to index on the lower specimen notch. Tighten the wedge clamps to hold the specimen firmly in place. These clamps need only be "finger tight." The purpose of the wedges is to prevent the specimen from rotating during a test. Excessive tightening of the wedge clamps is not necessary or desirable.

12.4.3 LOADING—The fixture is loaded in compression until the specimen fails. The loading rate shall be no greater than 5 mm/min (0.2 in/min).

12.4.4 REPLICATES—Twelve specimens from each of six panels shall be tested in the directions, temperatures, and locations indicated in Figure 1.

12.5 Calculation

12.5.1 SHEAR STRENGTH—Shear strength is calculated by dividing the applied load by the specimen cross-sectional area between the notches as shown in Equation 1:

$$\tau_{12} = P/wt \qquad \text{(Eq. 1)}$$

where:

τ_{12} = Shear strength
P = Applied load
w = Distance between the notches
t = Specimen thickness

Ultimate shear strength is not necessarily calculated from the maximum force attained during loading. During and after actual shear failure, the reinforcing fibers in a composite material may reorient, subsequently bearing some portion of the applied force in a tensile mode. This reorientation is more likely to occur in composites with matrix materials which are very nonlinear in shear, such as thermoplastic composites. The point at which this happens can usually be determined from a load (stress) versus displacement plot. The point at which the stress-displacement plot abruptly changes slope is the point at which shear failure occurred. Test results must thus be carefully examined.

NOTE—On the 0 degree unidirectional specimens a horizontal crack consistently develops at the notch root causing a small drop in the load-deflection curve. In determining shear strength for the 0 degree unidirectional specimen, this failure should not be taken as the shear failure of the specimen.

12.5.2 SHEAR MODULUS—Shear modulus is determined using the shear stress-strain curve. The shear strain is determined by Equation 2:

$$\gamma_{12} = |\varepsilon_{45} - \varepsilon_{-45}| \qquad \text{(Eq. 2)}$$

where:

γ_{12} is the total shear strain

ε_{45} and ε_{-45} are the strains measured by each gage

Shear modulus is then determined by Equation 3:

$$G_{12} = \tau_{12}/\gamma_{12} \qquad \text{(Eq. 3)}$$

The shear modulus shall be defined as a chord modulus using the 0.05 and 0.25% strain (γ_{12}) levels.

12.5.3 ASSESSING FAILURE MODES—The failure mode should be assessed for each failed test specimen to determine the validity of the failure mode. Failure should be through the test section. There should be no failures along the loaded portions of the specimen. Any failure which does not meet these conditions constitutes grounds for discounting the strength data measured by the test and additional tests shall be run. Acceptable and unacceptable failure modes are depicted in ASTM D 5379. Figure 3 presents typical load/deflection plots for several types of specimens.

12.6 Report—The report shall include the following:

a. Individual shear strengths, average value, and standard deviation
b. Shear (chord) moduli, average value, and standard deviation
c. A representative example of the stress/strain or load/extension curve

RECORD IN SDRP AND PROVIDE CURVE.

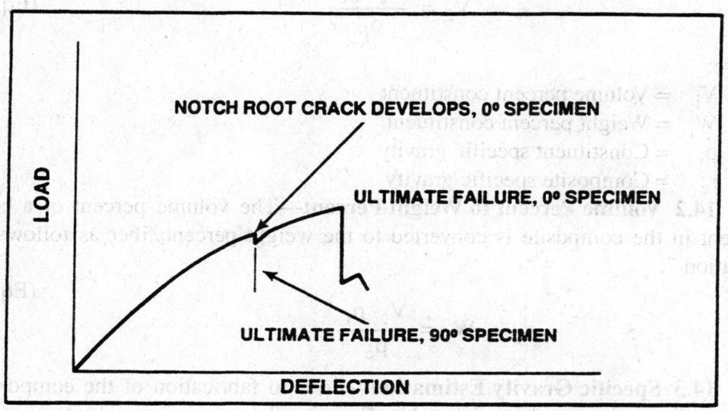

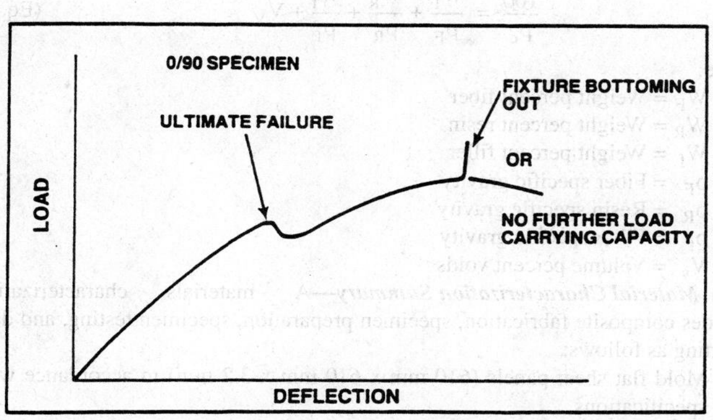

FIGURE 3—TYPICAL SHEAR LOAD-DEFLECTION CURVES

13. Statistical Analysis Methods

13.1 Mean Calculation—The arithmetic mean for a given set of data shall be calculated as follows in Equation 4:

$$\bar{x} = \frac{\sum_{i=1}^{n} x_i}{n} \qquad \text{(Eq. 4)}$$

where:

$\bar{x}$ = Arithmetic mean
x_i = Value of a single observation
n = Number of observations

13.2 Standard Deviation Calculation—The standard deviation for a given set of data shall be calculated as follows in Equation 5:

$$S = \sqrt{\frac{\left(\sum_{i=1}^{n} x_i^2 - n\bar{x}^2\right)}{(n-1)}} \qquad \text{(Eq. 5)}$$

where:

S = Standard deviation
$\bar{X}$ = Arithmetic mean
x_i = Value of a single observation
n = Number of observations

14. Constituent Content Conversions

14.1 Weight Percent to Volume Percent—The volume percent of a constituent (fiber, resin, or filler) in the composite is calculated from the weight percent of the constituent as follows in Equation 6:

$$V_i = \frac{W_i \cdot \rho_c}{\rho_i} \qquad \text{(Eq. 6)}$$

where:

V_i = Volume percent constituent
W_i = Weight percent constituent
ρ_i = Constituent specific gravity
r_c = Composite specific gravity

14.2 Volume Percent to Weight Percent—The volume percent of a constituent in the composite is converted to the weight percent fiber as follows in Equation 7:

$$W_i = \frac{V_i \cdot \rho_i}{\rho_c} \qquad \text{(Eq. 7)}$$

14.3 Specific Gravity Estimation—Prior to fabrication of the composite, its specific gravity may be estimated by Equation 8:

$$\frac{100}{\rho_c} = \frac{W_F}{\rho_F} + \frac{W_R}{\rho_R} + \frac{W_f}{\rho_f} + V_V \qquad \text{(Eq. 8)}$$

where:

W_F = Weight percent fiber
W_R = Weight percent resin
W_f = Weight percent filler
ρ_F = Fiber specific gravity
ρ_R = Resin specific gravity
ρ_f = Filler specific gravity
V_v = Volume percent voids

15. Material Characterization Summary—

A materials characterization includes composite fabrication, specimen preparation, specimen testing, and data reporting as follows:

a. Mold flat sheet panels (610 mm x 610 mm x 3.2 mm) in accordance with specifications.
b. Cut specimens from six panels per specified layout (Figure 1).
c. Assure that all panels meet thickness and fiber content standards and measure specific gravity. If any panel does not meet the standard, replace it with one that does.
d. Measure dynamic mechanical properties and assure acceptable material performance at 120 °C.
e. Determine coefficient of linear thermal expansion and measure mechanical properties (tensile, compression, shear) at -40 °C, 23 °C, 120 °C (Figure 4).
f. Enter constituent material descriptions, resin properties, molding information, panel dimensions, fiber content measurements, and test results into the computerized Supplemental Data Reporting Package (SDRP, Appendix B).
g. Send copy of the completed SDRP and requested graphs to the customer.

PROPERTY	MANUAL SECTION	TOTAL SPECIMENS REQUIRED
RESIN PROPERTIES		
TENSILE TESTS TENSILE STRENGTH TENSILE MODULUS TENSILE STRAIN TO FAILURE	ASTM D 638	5
THERMOPLASTIC RESIN PROPERTIES		
CRYSTALLINITY	8.7	6
MOLECULAR WEIGHT	8.8	6
COMPOSITE PROPERTIES		
DIMENSIONAL TESTS PANEL THICKNESS	8.6	N/A
PHYSICAL PROPERTIES TEST		30
SPECIFIC GRAVITY	8.2	
RESIN CONTENT	8.3	
FILLER CONTENT	8.4	
FIBER CONTENT	8.5	
THERMAL TESTS		
DMA TESTS[1]	9.2	6
CLTE 0°, 90°	9.3	12
TENSILE TESTS TENSILE STRENGTH 0°, 90° TENSILE MODULUS 0°, 90° POISSON'S RATIO 0°, 90° STRAIN TO FAILURE 0°, 90° ENERGY TO FAILURE 0°, 90°	10	72[2]
COMPRESSION TESTS[3] COMPRESSION STRENGTH 0°, 90° COMPRESSION MODULUS 0°, 90° STRAIN TO FAILURE 0°, 90° ENERGY TO FAILURE 0°, 90°	11	72[2]
SHEAR TESTS SHEAR STRENGTH 0°, 90° SHEAR MODULUS 0°, 90°	12	72[2]

FIGURE 4—CHARACTERIZATION TEST MATRIX—TEST MATRIX—PLANAR ISOTROPIC OR ORTHOTROPIC COMPOSITES—MINIMUM REQUIREMENT

APPENDIX A
SUPPLEMENTAL DATA REPORTING PACKAGE (SDRP)

Organization Supplying Data ____________________ Date ________

Composite Designation ____________________

CONSTITUENT MATERIALS

Fiber

Fiber Material Type ____________
Fiber Product Form ____________
Nominal Volume Fraction in Composite (%) ____________
Specific Gravity ____________
Manufacturer ____________
Trade Name ____________
Product Code ____________
Lot Number ____________
Chopped Fiber Length (mm) ____________
Roving/Yarn Yield (m/kg) ____________
Bundle Size/Splits ____________
Filament Diameter (microns) ____________
Chemical Size Description ____________
Chemical Size Amount (wt%) ____________
Binder Description ____________
Binder Amount (wt%) ____________

Mat/Fabric

Product Form ____________
Manufacturer ____________
Trade Name ____________
Product Code ____________
Lot Number ____________
Stitching Material ____________
Stitching Material Amount (wt%) ____________
Stitch Designation ____________
Area Weight (g/m2) ____________

Resin

Resin Type ____________
Nominal Volume Fraction in Composite (%) ____________
Specific Gravity (Cured) ____________
Manufacturer ____________
Trade Name ____________
Product Code ____________
Lot Number ____________
Viscosity (cp) ____________
Resin Composition ____________

FIGURE A1—CONSTITUENT MATERIALS/PROCESS DATA SHEET

Resin

Neat Polymer Glass Transition Temp. (°C) ______

Neat Polymer Mechanical Properties:

Tensile Strength (MPa) ______

Tensile Modulus (GPa) ______

Tensile Elongation (%) ______

Filler

Filler Type ______

Nominal Volume Fraction in Composite (%) ______

Specific Gravity ______

Manufacturer ______

Trade Name ______

Product Code ______

Lot Number ______

Particle Size ______

Surface Treatment ______

Cure System

Catalyst/Initiator(s) Concentration and Type:

Type ______

Concentration (%) ______

Supplier ______

Trade Name ______

Lot Number ______

Promoter(s) Concentration and Type:

Type ______

Concentration (%) ______

Supplier ______

Name ______

Lot Number ______

Accelerator:

Type ______

Concentration (%) ______

Supplier ______

Trade Name ______

Lot Number ______

Inhibitor:

Type ______

Concentration (%) ______

Supplier ______

Trade Name ______

Lot Number ______

Additional Constituents (each)

Material Type ______

Material Function ______

Nominal Volume Fraction in Composite (%) ______

Specific Gravity ______

Manufacturer ______

Trade Name ______

Product Code ______

Lot Number ______

Relevant Information ______

PROCESS

General

Molding Date ______

Molding Process ______

Mold Composition ______

Molding Detail

Mold Temperature (°C) ______

Mold Pressure (MPa) ______

Vacuum (Bars) ______

Fill Time/Mold Closure Time (sec) ______

Cure Time (sec) ______

Liquid Molding

Preform Construction ______

Number of Layers ______

Binder Type ______

Binder Conc. (wt%) ______

Preform Processing:

Procedure ______

Temperature (°C) ______

Time (sec) ______

Pressure (KPa) ______

Resin A/B Mix Ratio ______

Resin Injection Rate (Kg/min) ______

Resin Injection Pressure (MPa) ______

Resin Temperatures (°C)

A Side ______

B Side ______

Thermoplastic Composite

Resin Molecular Weight ______

Resin Crystallinity ______

Preheat Time (sec) ______

Preheat Temperature (°C) ______

Number of Plies ______

Mold Coverage (%) ______

SMC

Maturation Temperature (°C) ______

Maturation Time (hours) ______

Paste Viscosity at Molding (KPa·sec) ______

Number of Plies ______

Mold Coverage (%) ______

Postcure

Postcure temperature (°C) ______

Postcure Time (min) ______

Additional Parameters ______

FIGURE A1—CONSTITUENT MATERIALS/PROCESS DATA SHEET (CONTINUED)

Supplier__________ Date__________

Composite Designation__________

Fiber Content (% Vol) _____ Specific Gravity _____ Tg (°C) _____
Resin Content (% Vol) _____
Filler Content (% Vol) _____

0° DIRECTION PROPERTIES

Thermal

CLTE (1/°C x 10^{-6}) Ranges: A _____ B _____ C _____

MECHANICAL

		−40 °C		23 °C		120 °C*	
Tensile		AVG	STD DEV	AVG	STD DEV	AVG	STD DEV
STRENGTH	(MPa)						
MODULUS	(GPa)						
POISSON'S RATIO							
FAILURE STRAIN	(%)						
FAILURE ENERGY	(MJ/m³)						
Compressive							
STRENGTH	(MPa)						
MODULUS	(GPa)						
FAILURE STRAIN	(%)						
FAILURE ENERGY	(MJ/m³)						
Shear							
STRENGTH	(MPa)						
MODULUS	(GPa)						

*See 10.1 for alternative temperature testing.

FIGURE A2—MATERIAL PROPERTIES—0° DIRECTION SUMMARY SHEET

Supplier__________ Date__________

Composite Designation__________

Fiber Content (% Vol) _____ Specific Gravity _____ Tg (°C) _____
Resin Content (% Vol)
Filler Content (% Vol)

90° DIRECTION PROPERTIES

Thermal

CLTE (1/°C x 10^{-6}) Ranges: A _____ B _____ C _____

MECHANICAL

		−40 °C		23 °C		120 °C	
Tensile		AVG	STD DEV	AVG	STD DEV	AVG	STD DEV
STRENGTH	(MPa)						
MODULUS	(GPa)						
POISSON'S RATIO							
FAILURE STRAIN	(%)						
FAILURE ENERGY	(MJ/m³)						
Compressive							
STRENGTH	(MPa)						
MODULUS	(GPa)						
FAILURE STRAIN	(%)						
FAILURE ENERGY	(MJ/m³)						
Shear							
STRENGTH	(MPa)						
MODULUS	(GPa)						

FIGURE A3—MATERIAL PROPERTIES—90° DIRECTION SUMMARY SHEET

Supplier ____________________ Date ____________

Composite Designation ____________________

QA DATA							
		PLAQUE NUMBER					
SAMPLE	TEST	1	2	3	4	5	6
QA 1	FIBER % VOL						
	RESIN % VOL						
	FILLER % VOL						
	Sp. Gr.						
QA 2	FIBER % VOL						
	RESIN % VOL						
	FILLER % VOL						
	Sp. Gr.						
QA 3	FIBER % VOL						
	RESIN % VOL						
	FILLER % VOL						
	Sp. Gr.						
QA 4	FIBER % VOL						
	RESIN % VOL						
	FILLER % VOL						
	Sp. Gr.						
QA 5	FIBER % VOL						
	RESIN % VOL						
	FILLER % VOL						
	Sp. Gr.						

THERMOPLASTIC DATA						
	PLAQUE NUMBER					
TEST	1	2	3	4	5	6
CRYSTALLINITY %						
MOLECULAR WT X 10^5						

FIGURE A4—QA PROPERTIES DATA

THERMAL EXPANSION			UNITS = (1/°C x 10^{-6})				DMA UNITS = °C
SAMPLE NUMBER	CLTE1			CLTE 2			
TEMP. RANGE	A	B	C	A	B	C	Tg
PLAQUE 1							
PLAQUE 2							
PLAQUE 3							
PLAQUE 4							
PLAQUE 5							
PLAQUE 6							

FIGURE A5—THERMAL PROPERTIES DATA

Supplier____________________ Date__________

Composite Designation____________________

PANEL THICKNESS AVERAGE VALUES					UNITS = mm
REGION	CORNER #1	CORNER #2	CORNER #3	CORNER #4	CENTER
PLAQUE 1					
PLAQUE 2					
PLAQUE 3					
PLAQUE 4					
PLAQUE 5					
PLAQUE 6					

FIGURE A6—PANEL THICKNESS DATA

Supplier____________________ Date__________

Composite Designation____________________

0° TENSILE STRENGTH						UNITS = MPa
SAMPLE #1	T1	T2	T3	T4	T5	T6
PLAQUE 1						
PLAQUE 2						
PLAQUE 3						
PLAQUE 4						
PLAQUE 5						
PLAQUE 6						

90° TENSILE STRENGTH						UNITS = MPa
SAMPLE #1	T7	T8	T9	T10	T11	T12
PLAQUE 1						
PLAQUE 2						
PLAQUE 3						
PLAQUE 4						
PLAQUE 5						
PLAQUE 6						

FIGURE A7—MECHANICAL PROPERTIES DATA SHEET—TENSILE STRENGTH

Supplier__________ Date__________

Composite Designation__________

0° TENSILE MODULUS						UNITS = GPa
SAMPLE #1	T1	T2	T3	T4	T5	T6
PLAQUE 1						
PLAQUE 2						
PLAQUE 3						
PLAQUE 4						
PLAQUE 5						
PLAQUE 6						

90° TENSILE MODULUS						UNITS = GPa
SAMPLE #1	T7	T8	T9	T10	T11	T12
PLAQUE 1						
PLAQUE 2						
PLAQUE 3						
PLAQUE 4						
PLAQUE 5						
PLAQUE 6						

FIGURE A8—MECHANICAL PROPERTIES DATA SHEET—TENSILE MODULUS

Supplier__________ Date__________

Composite Designation__________

0° POISSON'S RATIO						
SAMPLE #1	T1	T2	T3	T4	T5	T6
PLAQUE 1						
PLAQUE 2						
PLAQUE 3						
PLAQUE 4						
PLAQUE 5						
PLAQUE 6						

90° POISSON'S RATIO						
SAMPLE #1	T7	T8	T9	T10	T11	T12
PLAQUE 1						
PLAQUE 2						
PLAQUE 3						
PLAQUE 4						
PLAQUE 5						
PLAQUE 6						

FIGURE A9—MECHANICAL PROPERTIES DATA SHEET—POISSON'S RATIO

Supplier________________________________ Date__________

Composite Designation________________________________

0° TENSILE STRAIN TO FAILURE						UNITS = %
SAMPLE #1	T1	T2	T3	T4	T5	T6
PLAQUE 1						
PLAQUE 2						
PLAQUE 3						
PLAQUE 4						
PLAQUE 5						
PLAQUE 6						

90° TENSILE STRAIN TO FAILURE						UNITS = %
SAMPLE #1	T7	T8	T9	T10	T11	T12
PLAQUE 1						
PLAQUE 2						
PLAQUE 3						
PLAQUE 4						
PLAQUE 5						
PLAQUE 6						

FIGURE A10—MECHANICAL PROPERTIES DATA SHEET—TENSILE STRAIN TO FAILURE

Supplier________________________________ Date__________

Composite Designation________________________________

0° TENSILE ENERGY TO FAILURE						UNITS = MJ/m^3
SAMPLE #1	T1	T2	T3	T4	T5	T6
PLAQUE 1						
PLAQUE 2						
PLAQUE 3						
PLAQUE 4						
PLAQUE 5						
PLAQUE 6						

90° TENSILE ENERGY TO FAILURE						UNITS = MJ/m^3
SAMPLE #1	T7	T8	T9	T10	T11	T12
PLAQUE 1						
PLAQUE 2						
PLAQUE 3						
PLAQUE 4						
PLAQUE 5						
PLAQUE 6						

FIGURE A11—MECHANICAL PROPERTIES DATA SHEET—TENSILE ENERGY TO FAILURE

Supplier______________________________ Date______________

Composite Designation______________________________

0° COMPRESSIVE STRENGTH						UNITS = MPa
SAMPLE #1	C1	C2	C3	C4	C5	C6
PLAQUE 1						
PLAQUE 2						
PLAQUE 3						
PLAQUE 4						
PLAQUE 5						
PLAQUE 6						

90° COMPRESSIVE STRENGTH						UNITS = MPa
SAMPLE #1	C7	C8	C9	C10	C11	C12
PLAQUE 1						
PLAQUE 2						
PLAQUE 3						
PLAQUE 4						
PLAQUE 5						
PLAQUE 6						

FIGURE A12—MECHANICAL PROPERTIES DATA SHEET—COMPRESSIVE STRENGTH

Supplier______________________________ Date______________

Composite Designation______________________________

0° COMPRESSIVE MODULUS						UNITS = GPa
SAMPLE #1	C1	C2	C3	C4	C5	C6
PLAQUE 1						
PLAQUE 2						
PLAQUE 3						
PLAQUE 4						
PLAQUE 5						
PLAQUE 6						

90° COMPRESSIVE MODULUS						UNITS = GPa
SAMPLE #1	C7	C8	C9	C10	C11	C12
PLAQUE 1						
PLAQUE 2						
PLAQUE 3						
PLAQUE 4						
PLAQUE 5						
PLAQUE 6						

FIGURE A13—MECHANICAL PROPERTIES DATA SHEET—COMPRESSIVE MODULUS

Supplier__________ Date__________

Composite Designation__________

0° COMPRESSIVE STRAIN TO FAILURE						UNITS = %
SAMPLE #1	C1	C2	C3	C4	C5	C6
PLAQUE 1						
PLAQUE 2						
PLAQUE 3						
PLAQUE 4						
PLAQUE 5						
PLAQUE 6						

90° COMPRESSIVE STRAIN TO FAILURE						UNITS = %
SAMPLE #1	C7	C8	C9	C10	C11	C12
PLAQUE 1						
PLAQUE 2						
PLAQUE 3						
PLAQUE 4						
PLAQUE 5						
PLAQUE 6						

FIGURE A14—MECHANICAL PROPERTIES DATA SHEET—COMPRESSIVE STRAIN TO FAILURE

Supplier__________ Date__________

Composite Designation__________

0° COMPRESSIVE ENERGY TO FAILURE						UNITS = MJ/m^3
SAMPLE #1	C1	C2	C3	C4	C5	C6
PLAQUE 1						
PLAQUE 2						
PLAQUE 3						
PLAQUE 4						
PLAQUE 5						
PLAQUE 6						

90° COMPRESSIVE ENERGY TO FAILURE						UNITS = MJ/m^3
SAMPLE #1	C7	C8	C9	C10	C11	C12
PLAQUE 1						
PLAQUE 2						
PLAQUE 3						
PLAQUE 4						
PLAQUE 5						
PLAQUE 6						

FIGURE A15—MECHANICAL PROPERTIES DATA SHEET—COMPRESSIVE ENERGY TO FAILURE

Supplier______________________________ Date____________________

Composite Designation______________________________

0° SHEAR STRENGTH				UNITS = MPa		
SAMPLE #1	S1	S2	S3	S4	S5	S6
PLAQUE 1						
PLAQUE 2						
PLAQUE 3						
PLAQUE 4						
PLAQUE 5						
PLAQUE 6						

90° SHEAR STRENGTH				UNITS = MPa		
SAMPLE #1	S7	S8	S9	S10	S11	S12
PLAQUE 1						
PLAQUE 2						
PLAQUE 3						
PLAQUE 4						
PLAQUE 5						
PLAQUE 6						

FIGURE A16—MECHANICAL PROPERTIES DATA SHEET—SHEAR STRENGTH

Supplier______________________________ Date____________________

Composite Designation______________________________

0° SHEAR MODULUS				UNITS = GPa		
SAMPLE #1	S1	S2	S3	S4	S5	S6
PLAQUE 1						
PLAQUE 2						
PLAQUE 3						
PLAQUE 4						
PLAQUE 5						
PLAQUE 6						

90° SHEAR MODULUS				UNITS = GPa		
SAMPLE #1	S7	S8	S9	S10	S11	S12
PLAQUE 1						
PLAQUE 2						
PLAQUE 3						
PLAQUE 4						
PLAQUE 5						
PLAQUE 6						

FIGURE A17—MECHANICAL PROPERTIES DATA SHEET—SHEAR MODULUS

APPENDIX B
SDRP DATA REPORTING PROGRAM

B.1 General—The Supplemental Data Reporting Package (SDRP) Data Reporting Program is available from SAE as Engineering Aid EA-2253 and has been designed to assist in the collection and reporting of test data. The program format mirrors the SDRP data tables, with the added benefits of providing a statistical summary function and an input/output capability for loading different materials and generating an output disk.

The SDRP program is not copy-protected or copyrighted, and replication of this program for internal distribution is encouraged. This program allows a user to generate an output disk to be returned to the customer. The diskette should be previously blank and formatted, and should be clearly labeled regarding what material(s) information it contains and the company submitting the data. This program is the preferred method for reporting data.

B.2 Setup—The SDRP program runs on PC DOS or MS DOS version 2.0 or later. This program requires the driver ANSI.SYS (part of DOS) which provides a standardized set of codes for cursor control. To use ANSI.SYS, the CONFIG.SYS must contain this line:

DEVICE = path \ ANSI.SYS, where "path" is the path of the driver.

The complete CONFIG.SYS file should look like this:

BUFFER = 20
FILES = 30
DEVICE = path \ ANSI.SYS, where "path" is the path of the driver.

NOTE—If your system does not have the file CONFIG.SYS, you must create it in the ROOT directory to include the lines described previously.

B.3 Installation

B.3.1 To install the SDRP on a hard disk, do the following:

1. Insert the SDRP diskette in drive A: and type:
   C:\> **A: <ENTER>**
   A:\> **INSTALL <Enter>**
   This creates a SDRP directory on the hard disk and copies all the modules to it.
2. Modify the file CONFIG.SYS, in the root directory to include:
   BUFFERS = 20
   FILES = 30
   DEVICE = path ANSI.SYS, where "path" is the path of the driver
3. Remove the SDRP diskette for driver A: and reboot the machine.
4. Change directory and start the SDRP program by typing:
   C:\> **CD\ SDRP <ENTER>**
   C:\ SDRP> **SDRP <ENTER>**

B.3.2 To execute the SDRP from drive A: (Note—Make sure to include the file CONFIG.SYS in the bootable disk), do the following:

1. Insert the SDRP diskette in the A: drive and type:
   C:\> **A: <ENTER>**
   A:\> **SDRP <ENTER>**
   This installation procedure is also described in "README.DOC," which may be accessed from DOS by entering:
   C:\> **README <ENTER>**

B.4 Running the SDRP Program—The execute the SDRP Data Reporting Program, define your default location as the designated SDRP directory and enter:

C:\> **SDRP <ENTER>**

This should bring up the SDRP main menu. At this point the system is ready for an operator to choose a menu item.

B.4.1 Main Menu—Depending on what screen or menu level, the user may select any menu option by depressing the indicated key for that menu. Press the [ESC] key to back up one screen level. If the user is in the main menu, [ESC] will terminate the program, and the user will be returned to DOS.

B.4.2 Help Screens—Whenever the user is in a Data Entry Screen, the [F1] key may be depressed for help. This help screen describes the function of every Hot Key displayed on the Data Entry Screen. To exit from the help screen back to the Data Entry Screen, press the [ESC] key.

B.4.3 Data Entry Screen—At this level, the user is ready to view and/or change data on the screen. The cursor initially will be flashing in the first data element of the screen. Use the following Hot Keys:

[INS]	This key allows the user to modify data displayed on the screen. When this key is pressed, the data previously displayed in that cell will be blanked out and the message "EDIT MODE" will be displayed. Using the arrow keys, the user may move to the desired data element and then enter the correct value. More data elements may be changed at this time in a similar manner. The [BACKSPACE] key may be used to correct mistyped values. The [INS] key is then depressed again to exit the EDIT MODE.
[F10]	Press this key to save new data to the directory file.
[ESC]	Press this key to back up one screen level. If the user has changed any data and did not perform a save, the system will prompt the user as to whether a save is desired. A "Y" response will execute the save function.
[TAB]	This key is accessible from some screens to enable a continuation page to be displayed.
[F1]	This key is used to display a help screen.

B.4.4 Error Messages—At the bottom of the screen, different error messages might be displayed whenever the user enters invalid data. Press [ENTER] to clear the message and to continue the program.

B.4.5 Data Files—There are a total of six data files in the SDRP package for each material system. These data files contain the data the user entered on the screen. The data files are:

BMAT_PRO.n	Constituent materials/process data
BQA_THER.n	QA/Thermal data
BPA_THCK.n	Panel thickness data
BTENSIL.n	Tensile data
BCOMPRES.n	Compression data
BSHEAR.n	Shear data

Where n is a sequentially assigned material file number.

B.4.6 Printing a Summary Report—The user can print a hard copy of the materials summary report. To do so, press P from the main menu, then a warning message will be displayed on the screen to set up the output device for printing. The system will then request "C" to confirm setup or "A" to abort.

B.4.7 Material File Utility—The user may access this function by selecting the File Utility Option from the main menu. The purpose of this function is to provide the user the flexibility to create a new or to modify an existing material file, convert the selected file to ASCII format, and to copy a material file(s) to a diskette. The user may use the following "Hot Keys" to access this function:

[F1]	Create a new material file
[F2]	Convert the selected file to ASCII format
[F3]	Copy the selected material file to floppy disk
[F4]	Load a specific material file
[PGUP]	Scroll viewing screen up
[PGDN]	Scroll viewing screen down
[ESC]	Exit to SDRP main menu

When the File Utility function is executed, a list of existing material files in the default directory will be displayed on the screen. The user may select any one of the displayed materials files for editing. Press [PGUP] or [PGDN] to view additional files if they exist. The SDRP program will automatically execute this function initially to prompt the user to select or create a new material file.

B.4.8 Exit to DOS—In order to terminate the SDRP Data Reporting Program and exit to DOS, press the [ESC] key from the main menu.

CATEGORIZATION AND PROPERTIES OF SAE COLD ROLLED STRIP STEELS—SAE J2392 MAR2003

SAE Recommended Practice

Report of the SAE Iron and Steel Technical Committee Division 32 approved March 2003.

1. Scope—This SAE recommended practice defines and establishes tolerances and attributes of cold rolled strip steels. Differences between cold rolled strip and cold rolled sheet products are discussed so that process designers can make informed material selection decisions.

1.1 Purpose—Cold rolled strip steels are produced to closer dimensional tolerances than cold rolled sheet steels. Cold rolled strip is commercially available over a wider range of thickness and chemical compositions. Cold rolled strip is also available with finishes, tempers and edges that differ from sheet products. Cold rolled strip steels are produced in sizes as follows in Table 1:

TABLE 1—DIMENSIONAL LIMITS FOR COLD ROLLED STRIP STEELS

Width, mm	Thickness, mm
12.5 to 600 mm	7.6 mm and under

Strip tolerance products are available in widths greater than 600 mm, however, these products are technically classified as sheet.

2. References

2.1 Applicable Publications—The following publications form a part of this specification to the extent specified herein. Unless otherwise specified, the latest issue of SAE and ASTM publications shall apply.

2.1.1 SAE PUBLICATIONS—Available from SAE, 400 Commonwealth Drive, Warrendale, PA 19103.

SAE J403—Chemical Compositions of SAE Carbon Steels
SAE J404—Chemical Compositions of SAE Alloy Steels
SAE J409—Product Analysis—Permissible Variations from Specified Chemical Analysis of a Heat or Cast of Steel
SAE J911—Surface Texture Measurement of Cold Rolled Sheet Steel
SAE J2329—Categorization and Properties of Low Carbon Automotive Sheet Steels

2.1.2 ASTM PUBLICATIONS—Available from ASTM, 100 Barr Harbor Drive, West Conshohocken, PA 19428-2959.

ASTM A109/A109M—Standard Specification for Steel, Strip, Carbon, Cold Rolled
ASTM E 430—Method for Measurement of Gloss of High Gloss Surfaces By Goniophotometry

2.2 Related Publications—The following publications are provided for information purposes only and are not a required part of this specification.

2.2.1 SAE PUBLICATIONS—Available from SAE, 400 Commonwealth Drive, Warrendale, PA 15096-0001.

SAE J1058—Standard Steel Sheet Thickness and Tolerances
SAE J1268—Hardenability Bands for Carbon and Alloy H Steels
SAE J2340—Categorization and Properties of Dent Resistant, High Strength, and Ultra High Strength Automotive Sheet Steel

2.2.2 ASTM PUBLICATIONS—Available from ASTM, 100 Barr Harbor Drive, West Conshohocken, PA 19428-2959.

ASTM A 682/A 682M—Standard Specification for Steel, Strip, High - Carbon, Cold - Rolled, Spring Quality, General Requirements For
ASTM A 684/A 684M—Standard Specification for Steel, Strip, High - Carbon, Cold Rolled

2.2.3 OTHER PUBLICATIONS—Available from ISS Book Sales, 410 Commonwealth Drive, Warrendale, PA 19103.

Steel Products Manual, Strip Steel; Carbon, High Strength Low Alloy, and Alloy; Iron and Steel Society Publication, February, 1995

3. Temper Designation

3.1 Low carbon cold rolled strip is often specified to standard tempers. Temper refers to the hardness, or strength of the steel. As hardness increases, formability decreases. In general, the degree of formability increases as the temper number increases, as indicated in Table 2.

3.2 Low carbon cold rolled strip is available in tempers other than standard by agreement between strip user and strip producer.

4. Chemical Composition

4.1 Cold rolled strip steels are produced from a wide range of hot band alloys. In general, cold rolled strip steel products may be produced from any grade of steel that is available for hot band substrate. With the exception of strip produced to standard tempers (hardness), other public specifications govern the applicable composition limits.

4.2 Low Carbon Steel Specified To Temper—When cold rolled strip is specified to a standard temper, chemical composition limits are given by Table 3.

TABLE 2—TEMPER DESIGNATORS: LOW CARBON COLD ROLLED STRIP STEELS

Temper Number	Temper Name	Thickness Under	Thickness Through	Hardness Minimum	Hardness Maximum	Approx. Tensile Strength (MPa)	Description
1	Hard	0.6		15T90	—	620 ± 70	Very hard and springy intended for flat work not requiring cold forming.
		1.0	0.6	30T76	—		
		1.8	1.0	B90	—		
		7.6	1.8	B84	—		
2	Half Hard	0.6		15T83.5	15T88.5	450 ± 70	Moderately hard and springy intended for limited bending defined as 90 degrees across the rolling direction around a radius equal to the thickness.
		1.0	0.6	30T63.5	30T73.5		
		7.6	1.0	B70	B85		
3	Quarter Hard	0.6	—	15T80	15T85	380 ± 70	Medium soft intended for limited amounts of bending, forming and drawing. May be bent 180 degrees across the rolling direction around a radius equal to the thickness.
		1.0	0.6	30T56	30T67		
		7.6	1.0	B60	B75		
4	Skin Rolled	0.6	—	—	15T82	330 ± 40	Soft and ductile intended for deep drawing. May be bent flat upon itself in any direction.
		1.0	0.6	—	30T60		
		7.6	1.0		B65		
5	Dead Soft	0.6	—	—	15T78.5	300 ± 40	Soft and ductile intended for deep drawing applications where stretcher straining and fluting is not objectionable.
		1.0	0.6		30T53		
		7.6	1.0		B55		

TABLE 3—HEAT ANALYSIS COMPOSITION—WT %

Element	Temper 1, 2, 3	Number 4, 5
Carbon, max.	0.25	0.15
Manganese, max.	0.60	0.60
Phosphorus, max.	0.025	0.025
Sulfur, max.	0.025	0.025

4.3 Carbon cold rolled strip steels are available in chemical compositions defined by SAE J403.

4.4 Alloy cold rolled strip steels are available in chemical compositions defined by SAE J404.

4.5 Cold rolled high strength low alloy strip steels are produced to chemical compositions defined by SAE J2340.

4.6 Fully stabilized cold rolled strip steels are available with chemical limits defined by SAE J2329, Grade 5.

4.7 Special chemical compositions and restricted versions of standard SAE grades are available subject to hot band substrate availability. Chemical analysis limits for these grades are defined by agreement between strip user and strip producer.

4.8 Permissible product analysis variations from specified ladle chemical analysis are defined in SAE J409.

5. *Thickness Tolerances*

5.1 Across the full range of nominal thickness, cold roll strip thickness tolerances range from 58% to 83% of the corresponding thickness tolerances for cold rolled sheet steels.

5.2 Standard cold rolled strip tolerances for carbon, alloy, high strength low alloy, fully stabilized and special alloy steels appear in Table 4.

5.3 Non standard tolerances, either wider or closer, may be specified subject to strip producer capabilities. Such tolerances are by agreement between strip user and strip producer.

TABLE 4—THICKNESS TOLERANCES OF COLD ROLLED STRIP STEELS[(1)]

Nominal Thickness (mm)	Width (mm) 12.5 to less than 300	Width (mm) 300 to less than 450	Width (mm) 450 to 600
6.40 - 7.60	0.080	0.090	0.100
4.00 - 6.39	0.065	0.080	0.090
3.20 - 3.99	0.055	0.070	0.080
1.80 - 3.19	0.045	0.055	0.070
1.00 - 1.79	0.035	0.045	0.060
0.75 - 0.99	0.030	0.040	0.050
0.50 - 0.74	0.025	0.035	0.040
0.38 - 0.49	0.020	0.025	0.030
0.25 - 0.37	0.013	0.020	0.025
<0.25	0.007	0.015	0.020

1. Measured 10 mm or more in from edge; and on narrower than 25 mm, at any place between edges. (plus and minus, mm)

6. *Edges and Width Tolerances*

6.1 Cold rolled strip may be specified with many different types of edge conditions produced by rolling, slitting or other mechanical means.

6.2 No. 1 Edge is a prepared edge of a specified contour (round or square), which is produced when a very accurate width is required, or when an edge condition suitable for electroplating is required, or both.

6.3 No. 2 Edge is a natural mill edge carried through the cold rolling from the hot rolled strip without additional processing of the edge.

6.4 No. 3 Edge is an approximately square edge produced by slitting on which the burr is not eliminated. This edge is most frequently specified for cold rolled strip steels.

6.5 No. 4 Edge is a rounded edge produced by edge rolling either the natural edge of hot rolled strip or slit strip edge. This edge is produced when the width tolerance and edge condition are not as exacting as for No. 1 edge.

6.6 No. 5 Edge is an approximately square edge produced from slit edge material on which the burr is eliminated usually by rolling or filing.

6.7 No. 6 Edge is a square edge produced by edge rolling the natural edge of hot rolled strip or slit edge strip. This edge is produced when the width tolerance and edge condition are not as exacting as for No. 1 edge.

6.8 Skived edges are custom shaped edges produced by mechanical edge shaving with special tools.

6.9 Some edges are not available over the entire range of cold rolled strip thickness and width.

6.10 Width tolerances for different edges are defined in ASTM A109/A109M.

7. *Finish*

7.1 Cold rolled strip steels are usually specified to one of the following finishes.

7.1.1 Number 1 or Matte (Dull) Finish is a finish without luster produced by rolling on rolls roughened by mechanical or other means. This finish is especially suitable for paint adhesion and may aid drawing by reducing contact friction between die and steel.

7.1.2 Number 2 or Regular Bright Finish is produced by rolling on moderately smooth rolls.

7.1.3 Number 2-1/2 or Better Bright finish is a smooth finish suitable for those plating applications where high luster is not required.

7.1.4 Number 3 or Best Bright finish is generally of high luster produced by special rolling practices, including the use of specially prepared rolls. It is the highest quality finish commonly produced and is particularly suited for bright plating. The production of this finish requires extreme care in processing and extensive inspection. Paper interleaving is frequently used for protection. In addition to the surface roughness values in Table 5, the user and producer may agree on goniophotometric measurement values (Rs/DI) as defined in ASTM E 430.

TABLE 5—TYPICAL SURFACE ROUGHNESS MEASUREMENT RANGES[(1)(2)(3)]

Surface	Microinches Maximum
Number 1 or Matte (Dull)	80 Ra
Number 2 or Regular Bright	20 Ra
Number 2-1/2 or Better Bright	10 Ra
Number 3 or Best Bright	4 Ra

1. Due to vagaries in measuring surface roughness, as well as the inherent variability in such rolled surfaces, these values are only typical, and values outside these ranges would not be considered unexpected.
2. Measured either parallel with or across the rolling direction.
3. Tested in accordance with SAE J911.

8. *High Carbon and Alloy Cold Rolled Strip Steels*

8.1 High carbon steels are those whose maximum specified carbon contents exceed 0.25 weight percent.

8.2 High carbon and alloy cold rolled strip steels are supplied as either untempered or as Hardened and Tempered. Untempered products are supplied as-produced; the end user will often heat treat the part after forming. Hardened and tempered strip is given a quench and temper heat treatment prior to shipment; the end user does not need to heat treat to achieve maximum strength.

8.3 Untempered high carbon and alloy cold rolled strip steels are supplied in four product types.

8.3.1 Spheroidized Annealed is intended for applications requiring maximum formability. It is normally produced to give the lowest maximum hardness for each carbon range. The microstructure of this type consists of spheroidal carbides in a matrix which is essentially free of pearlite.

8.3.2 Annealed is intended for applications requiring moderate cold forming. It is produced to a maximum hardness. The microstructure is mostly a spheroidal structure, but may contain some vestiges of pearlite.

8.3.3 Table 6 shows approximate relationships between steel grade and hardness for spheroidized annealed and annealed high carbon steels. Hardness limits for alloy steels are usually higher than the corresponding high carbon steel and are usually established by agreement between strip user and strip producer.

8.3.4 Full Hard high carbon and alloy strip steels are hard and springy steels intended for flat applications not requiring cold forming. Full hard is cold rolled, with or without preparatory treatment, to minimum hardness requirements. The prior treatment and amount of cold reduction are varied to produce hardness requirements as established by consumer and producer.

8.4 Hardened and Tempered Cold Rolled High Carbon and Alloy Strip

8.4.1 Hardened and tempered cold rolled high carbon steel strip is produced by continuously heat treating the metal resulting in very high strength and hardness.

8.4.2 Hardened and tempered cold rolled high carbon steel strip customarily has a carbon content over 0.55% and is commonly produced to meet a range of hardness as shown in Table 7. The minimum values for the ranges are normally higher than the maximum values obtainable by cold rolling.

The specified range to be agreed upon between consumer and supplier.

TABLE 6—APPROXIMATE RELATIONSHIP BETWEEN STEEL GRADE, ANNEALING TREATMENT AND HARDNESS FOR COLD ROLLED STRIP STEEL

	Grade	HR15T	HR30T	HRB
Annealed Steel				
	1035	86	68	78
	1045	87	70	80
	1050	87	71	82
	1055/1060	88	72	84
	1065	89	73	85
	1070	89	74	86
	1074	89	74	87
	1080	89	75	88
	1095	90	77	91
Spheriodized Annealed Steel				
	1035	85	66	75
	1045	86	68	77
	1050	86	69	79
	1055/1060	87	70	71
	1065	87	71	72
	1070	88	72	83
	1074	88	72	84
	1080	89	74	86
	1095	89	75	88

8.4.3 The hardness scale applicable to each thickness range is shown in Table 9. Although conversion tables for hardness numbers are available, it is recommended that the hardness be specified in the same scale that is to be used in testing. A hardness range is typically specified using a 3, 4 or 5 - point range, based on the scale to be used and as agreed between consumer and producer. In the check testing of hardened and tempered steel strip, a tolerance of a half HRc point below the minimum and above the maximum of the range specified is commonly allowed to compensate for normal differences in testing equipment.

8.4.4 Below a thickness of 0.2 mm., the HR15N test becomes inaccurate and the use of a tension test or microhardness test is recommended. The Diamond Pyramid Hardness (DPH) test, also known as Vickers, is typically specified for a stated indenter load using a 50 - point range. An ultimate tensile strength is usually specified with a 210 MPa range.

8.4.5 The desired mechanical properties for a given application are achieved by quenching and tempering to obtain the proper combination of hardness, toughness and formability. In the as-quenched condition, the steel lacks ductility and therefore is tempered using a lower temperature stress relief cycle. By varying the carbon and manganese content and the conditions of quenching and tempering, the required combination of strength, hardness, toughness and ductility can be produced.

8.4.6 The variation of hardness and ultimate tensile strength with carbon content and thicknesses for hardened and tempered cold rolled high carbon strip steel, heat treated to combinations of mechanical properties appropriate for spring applications, is shown in Tables 10A and 10B. Each ten point (0.10%) increase in carbon content is accompanied by an average increase of about two points HRc hardness and an equivalent increase in HR30N, HR15N, DPH, and ultimate tensile strength. The mechanical properties specified should be compatible with the fabricating requirements involved in making the part.

TABLE 7—HARDNESS RANGES[1]: HARDENED AND TEMPERED COLD ROLLED HIGH CARBON STEEL STRIP

Thickness, (mm)	Hardness Scale	Hardness Ranges (% Carbon 0.55 - 1.05)
Over 2.90 to 3.20 incl.	C	28 to 50
Over 2.50 to 2.90 incl.	C	29 to 51
Over 2.20 to 2.50 incl.	C	30 to 52
Over 1.80 to 2.20 incl.	C	31 to 53
Over 1.40 to 1.80 incl.	C	32 to 54
Over 0.90 to 1.40 incl.	C	33 to 55
Over 0.40 to 0.90 incl.	30N	53 to 73
Over 0.20 to 0.40 incl.	15N	80 to 87
Over 0.05 to 0.20[2] incl.	DPH	400 to 580

1. By common usage, a hardness range is the arithmetical difference between two limits (for example, HRc 42 to HRc 46 is a four point range). Typical range requirements appear in Table 8.
2. For thickness less than 0.200 mm, use of the tension test is recommended as an alternative to microhardness testing (DPH / Vickers).

TABLE 8—TYPICAL HARDNESS RANGES SPECIFIED FOR HARDENED AND TEMPERED COLD ROLLED HIGH CARBON STEEL STRIP

Hardness Scale	Specific Range
HRc	Any 4 points
HR30N	Any 4 points
HR15N	Any 3 points
DPH (Vickers)	Any 50 points

8.4.7 When the steel is heat treated, an oxide is formed on the surface on the strip. The type of oxide depends on the use of atmosphere within the tempering furnace and the temperature of the strip when it exits the tempering furnace and comes in contact with air. This oxide layer may be removed with the use of acid baths and surface treatment, such as buffing or grinding. The surface of the strip steel can be produced with any of the following finishes:

Black Tempered
Bright Tempered
Scaleless Tempered
Tempered and Polished
Tempered, Polished and Colored (typically Blue or Straw)

In addition to the finish, the surface roughness may also be critical for the application, and is typically specified with an RMS or Ra value in microns or micro-inches.

8.4.8 Hardened and tempered cold rolled high carbon strip steel is normally produced with a No. 1 edge that is a prepared edge of a specified contour (typically round or square). It is produced when a very accurate width is required or when fatigue / life cycle testing is a concern. Material can also be provided with a No. 3 slit edge or No. 5 deburred edge.

TABLE 9—HARDNESS SCALES FOR VARIOUS THICKNESSES: A GUIDE FOR SELECTION OF HARDNESS SCALES FOR HARDENED AND TEMPERED COLD ROLLED HIGH CARBON STEEL STRIP

Thickness mm	A Dial Reading	A C-Scale[1]	C Dial Reading	15N Dial Reading	15N C-Scale[1]	30N Dial Reading	30N C-Scale[1]	45N Dial Reading	45N C-Scale[1]
0.20	—	—	—	90	60	—	—	—	—
0.25	—	—	—	88	55	—	—	—	—
0.30	—	—	—	83	45	82	65	77	69.5
0.35	—	—	—	76	32	78.5	61	74	67
0.40	86	69	—	68	18	74	56	72	65
0.45	84	65	—	—	—	66	47	68	61
0.50	82	61.5	—	—	—	57	37	63	57
0.55	79	56	69	—	—	47	26	58	52.5
0.60	76	50	67	—	—	—	—	51	47
0.65	71	41	65	—	—	—	—	37	35
0.70	67	32	62	—	—	—	—	20	20.5
0.75	60	19	57	—	—	—	—	—	—
0.80	—	—	52	—	—	—	—	—	—
0.85	—	—	45	—	—	—	—	—	—
0.90	—	—	37	—	—	—	—	—	—
0.95	—	—	28	—	—	—	—	—	—
1.00	—	—	20	—	—	—	—	—	—

1. Approximate Hardness

TABLE 10A—APPROXIMATE RELATIONSHIP BETWEEN THICKNESS, CARBON CONTENT, HARDNESS, AND UTS OF HARDENED AND TEMPERED STRIP FOR SPRING APPLICATIONS

Thickness (mm)	0.55% Carbon Hardness	0.55% Carbon UTS MPa (ksi)	0.65% Carbon Hardness	0.65% Carbon UTS MPa (ksi)	0.75% Carbon Hardness	0.75% Carbon UTS MPa (ksi)
0.15(1)	450	1650 (240)	475	1760 (255)	500	1860 (270)
0.25(2)	82.8	1620 (235)	84.0	1720 (250)	85.0	1830 (265)
0.40(2)	82.6	1600 (232)	83.8	1700 (247)	84.6	1810 (262)
0.50(3)	62.8	1570 (228)	64.8	1670 (243)	66.3	1780 (258)
0.65(3)	62.5	1550 (225)	64.4	1650 (240)	68.0	1760 (255)
0.75(3)	62.2	1530 (222)	64.0	1630 (237)	65.8	1740 (252)
0.90(3)	62.0	1520 (220)	63.7	1620 (235)	65.5	1720 (250)
1.00(4)	42.5	1500 (218)	44.5	1600 (232)	46.5	1700 (247)
1.25(4)	42.0	1480 (215)	44.0	1590 (230)	46.0	1690 (245)
1.50(4)	41.5	1460 (212)	43.5	1560 (227)	45.5	1690 (242)
1.75(4)	41.0	1440 (209)	43.0	1540 (224)	45.0	1650 (239)
2.00(4)	40.7	1420 (206)	42.7	1520 (221)	44.7	1630 (236)
2.25(4)	40.3	1400 (203)	42.3	1500 (218)	44.3	1610 (233)
2.50(4)	40.0	1380 (200)	42.0	1480 (215)	44.0	1590 (230)
2.75(4)	39.6	1360 (197)	41.6	1460 (212)	43.6	1560 (227)
3.00(4)	39.2	1340 (194)	41.2	1440 (209)	43.2	1540 (224)

1. For thicknesses less then 0.200 mm, use of the tension test is recommended as an alternative to microhardness testing (DPH/Vickers).
2. 15N Hardness Scale
3. 30N Hardness Scale
4. C-Scale

TABLE 10B—APPROXIMATE RELATIONSHIP BETWEEN THICKNESS, CARBON CONTENT, HARDNESS, AND UTS OF HARDENED AND TEMPERED STRIP FOR SPRING APPLICATIONS

Thickness (mm)	0.85% Carbon Hardness	0.85% Carbon UTS MPa (ksi)	0.95% Carbon Hardness	0.95% Carbon UTS MPa (ksi)	1.05% Carbon Hardness	1.05% Carbon UTS MPa (ksi)
0.15(1)	525	1970 (285)	580	2100 (305)	595	2240 (325)
0.25(2)	86.0	1930 (280)	87.0	2070 (300)	88.0	2210 (320)
0.40(2)	65.8	1910 (277)	86.8	2040 (296)	87.8	2180 (316)
0.50(3)	68.3	1880 (273)	70.6	2010 (291)	71.7	2140 (311)
0.65(3)	68.0	1860 (270)	70.1	1980 (288)	71.4	2120 (308)
0.75(3)	67.8	1840 (267)	69.6	1960 (285)	71.2	2100 (305)
0.90(3)	67.5	1830 (265)	69.2	1940 (282)	71.0	2080 (302)
1.00(4)	48.5	1810 (262)	50.5	1920 (279)	52.5	2060 (299)
1.25(4)	48.0	1790 (260)	50.0	1900 (275)	52.0	2030 (294)
1.50(4)	47.5	1770 (257)	49.5	1870 (272)	51.5	2000 (290)
1.75(4)	47.0	1750 (254)	49.0	1850 (269)	51.0	1970 (286)
2.00(4)	46.7	1730 (251)	48.7	1830 (286)	50.7	1940 (282)
2.25(4)	46.3	1710 (248)	48.3	1810 (263)	50.3	1920 (278)
2.50(4)	46.0	1690 (245)	48.0	1790 (260)	50.0	1900 (275)
2.75(4)	45.6	1670 (242)	47.6	1770 (257)	49.6	1870 (272)
3.00(4)	45.2	1650 (239)	47.2	1750 (254)	49.2	1850 (269)

1. For thicknesses less then 0.200 mm, use of the tension test is recommended as an alternative to microhardness testing (DPH/Vickers).
2. 15N Hardness Scale
3. 30N Hardness Scale
4. C-Scale

STRAIN-LIFE OVERLOAD FATIGUE DATA FILE FORMAT—SAE J2649 DEC2003

SAE Recommended Practice

Report of the SAE Material Properties Division of the SAE Fatigue, Design and Evaluation Committee approved December 2003. Rationale statement available.

1. Scope—SAE data file format for exchanging controlled periodic overload data. The object of this SAE Standard is to provide a simple, common methodology for exchanging the data from periodic overload fatigue tests. These tests consist of a single large fatigue cycle followed by a larger number of smaller cycles. The overloads are fully reversed fatigue cycles while the smaller cycles share a common mean and amplitude.

2. Reference

2.1 Related Publication—The following publication is provided for information purposes only and is not a required part of this specification.

2.1.1 ASTM PUBLICATION—Available from ASTM, 100 Barr Harbor Drive, West Conshohocken, PA 19428-2959.

ASTM E 606-92 (1998)—Recommended Practice for Constant-Amplitude Low-Cycle Fatigue Testing

3. A sample file that defines the format of the contents is depicted in Figures 1a and 1b.

APPENDIX A
EXAMPLE STRAIN-LIFE OVERLOAD FATIGUE TEST DATA FILE

```
# Proposed Fatigue Design & Evaluation Comm. Standard Periodic Overload Test
# data file Format.
#
# ------------------------
# Any line that begins with a # sign is a comment line, or an identifier
# line.  Blank lines can also be inserted anywhere.  A comment can
# also appear at the end of a data line, or between data lines.
# ------------------------
# A data line is assumed to be any line that is not a blank or a comment line.
#
# Certain lines that begin with a #SYMBOL= VALUE, called tags, have special
# meanings that can be decoded by the receiving program.  Tag definitions
# are set out below.  Curly braces {} with comma delimited values
# indicate the different values that may be used with a tag.  Otherwise
# character or numeric fields are required.  The units on strain values
# are absolute (no percentages), and the stress units may be defined
# as below.  Tags should begin in the first column.
#
# Use one or more "SPACE" characters to separate tags, values, and data items.

#
# *** MANDATORY TAGS ***              ***    TAG Explanation  ***
#
#   #FileType= strain_life_overload  #    Define this file type
#
#   #DataType= {raw,fitted}          #    Experimental data are indicated with a "raw",
#                                         interpolated data with "fitted"
#
#   #NAME=                       # Unique material identifier.  Several of these tags may
#                                         be used in a single file.
#
#   #UNITS= {ksi,MPa}            # Define stress units used in the file. Not case sensitive.
#
#   #E=                          # Average First Loading Elastic Modulus as measured
#                                         from fatigue tests
#
#  **OPTIONAL SUGGESTED TAGS**
#
#   #Sy=                         # Monotonic 0.2% Offset Tensile Yield Stress
#
#   #Su=                         # Monotonic Tensile Ultimate Stress
#
#   #%RA=                        # percent reduction in area at failure in monotonic tensile test
#
#   #HB=                         # Hardness of material in the Brinell scale
#
#   #monotonic_K=                # strain hardening coefficient, K, for monotonic tensile test
#
#   #monotonic_n=                # strain hardening exponent, n, for monotonic tensile test
#
#   #LowerYield=                 # Lower yield stress (average value)
#
#   #FractureStrength=           # True Fracture Stress at fracture (monotonic tensile)
#
#   #FractureStrain=             # True Fracture Strain at fracture (monotonic tensile)
#
#   #MaterialForm=               # Raw form of material {e.g. plate, rod, bar, sheet, extrusion}
#
#   #SpecimenForm=               # Type of fatigue specimen {e.g. threaded_round,flat_dogbone}
#
#   #PlasticStrain={measured,calculated}   #  Plastic strain indicated in table was "measured"
#                                          # from S-e loop or "calculated" from stress.
#
#   #FailureDef=                 # Definition of failure {e.g. 5% load drop, complete separation, …}
#
# Items whichs don't appear in tags but should be included in descriptive comments
#   (such as this one) include material processing, microstructure, specimen
#   orientation and other issues discussed in ASTM E606.


#  **SAMPLE FILE **** :

#FileType= strain_life_overload       # strain life overload type standard file
#DataType= raw                        # "raw"= measured, as opposed to "fitted"


#NAME= SAE1045
#NAME= SAE350X
```

FIGURE 1A—EXAMPLE STRAIN-LIFE OVERLOAD FATIGUE TEST DATA FILE

```
#NAME= SAE050X

#UNITS= KSI
#Su= 100.
#Sy= 60.0
#E=  29500.
#%RA= 50.
#HB= 203
#XK= 200.
#Xn= 0.25
#LowerYield= 60.0
#FractureStrength= 250.
#FractureStrain= 0.60
#MaterialForm= bar
#SpecimenForm= round_dogbone
#PlasticStrain= measured

# General definitions of abbreviations
# SC =Small Cycle
# OL =OverLoad cycle
# e =engineering strain
# S =engineering stress
# Amp = stress/strain amplitude associated with cycle
# Mean = average value of quantity
# Plastic e = plastic strain associated with cycle
# initial modulus = initial elastic modulus from first cycle

# Specific meanings of labels:
# Fail Blocks - total number of block repetitions to failure (as defined by #FailureDef= )
# SC per block - number of small cycles per block (between overloads)
# CA-OL Life = Constant Amplitude life of the OverLoad cycle by itself

#Strains are to be reported in their native dimensionless units (mm/mm or in/in)
# Data for a single specimen appear on a single line
#   SC      Fail      SC     SC     SC      SC     SC           OL        CA-OL   OL    OL      OL    initial
#   e       Blocks    per    S      Mean    Mean   Plastic      e         Life    S     Mean  Plastic elastic
#  Amp                block  Amp    e       S      e Amp        Amp.      (Nf)    Amp   S       e Amp modulus
0.00075   4347.7   10000  20.0  0.00390  36.0  0.0000625  0.00500  10000   60.0  0.0  0.00270 28371.
0.0008    5000.0    5000  25.0  0.00380  34.0  0.0000500  0.00500  10000   60.0  0.0  0.00270 28593
0.0009    3000.1     500  27.0  0.00400  30.0  0.0000625  0.00500  10000.  60.0  0.0  0.00280 31395
0.0015    2000       100  36.0  0.00000   0.0  0.0002200  0.00550   7000   65.0  0.0  0.00325 27896.
0.002     1400.5     100  41.0  0.00000 -10.0  0.0005250  0.00500  10000   60.0  0.0  0.00280 30948
0.0025    1700        50  43.0  0.00250  20.0  0.0007500  0.00500  10000.  60.0  0.0  0.00280 29346 #buckled?

#no recorded stress data?:
0.00125   1300       250   0.0  0.00550   0.0  0.0001400  0.00650   5000   68.0  0.0  0.00400 27943

#Suspended test articles are denoted by a "#runout" appended to the dataline
0.00070   4347.7   50000  17.0  0.00390  36.0  0.000025   0.00500  10000   60.0  0.0  0.00270 29375.  #runout
```

FIGURE 1B—EXAMPLE STRAIN-LIFE OVERLOAD FATIGUE TEST DATA FILE (CONTINUED)

4 Steel Fasteners

MECHANICAL AND MATERIAL REQUIREMENTS FOR EXTERNALLY THREADED FASTENERS—SAE J429 JAN1999

SAE Standard

Report of the SAE Iron and Steel Technical Committee approved January 1949. Eleventh revision, SAE ISTC Division 29, August 1983. Completely revised by the SAE Fasteners Committee July 1997, and revised May 1998 and January 1999. Rationale statement available.

1. Scope—This SAE Standard covers the mechanical and material requirements for inch-series steel bolts, screws, studs, sems[1], and U-bolts[2] used in automotive and related industries in sizes to 1-1/2 in inclusive.

The term "stud" as referred to herein applies to a cylindrical rod of moderate length threaded on either one or both ends or throughout its entire length. It does not apply to headed, collared, or similar products which are more closely characterized by requirements shown herein for bolts.

1.1 The mechanical properties included in Table 1 were compiled at an ambient temperature of approximately 20°C (68 °F). These properties are valid within a temperature range which depends upon the material grade used and thermal and mechanical processing. Other properties such as fatigue behavior, corrosion resistance, impact properties, etc., are beyond the scope of this document and responsibility for ensuring the acceptability of the product for applications where conditions warrant consideration of these other properties must be borne by the end user.

2. References

2.1 Applicable Publications—The following publications form a part of the specification to the extent specified herein. Unless otherwise indicated, the latest revision of SAE publications shall apply.

2.1.1 SAE PUBLICATIONS—Available from SAE, 400 Commonwealth Drive, Warrendale, PA 15096-0001.

SAE J121—Decarburization in Hardened and Tempered Unified Threaded Fasteners
SAE J123—Surface Discontinuities on Bolts, Screws, and Studs
SAE J403—Chemical Compositions of SAE Carbon Steels
SAE J404—Chemical Composition of SAE Alloy Steels
SAEJ409—Product Analysis—Permissible Variations from Specified Chemical Analysis of a Heat or Cast of Steel
SAE J411—Carbon and Alloy Steels
SAE J417—Hardness Tests and Hardness Number Conversions
SAE J1061—Surface Discontinuities on General Application Bolts, Screws, and Studs
SAE J1086—Numbering Metals and Alloys
SAE J1268—Hardenability Bands for Carbon and Alloy H Steels

2.1.2 ASME PUBLICATION—Available from ASME, 22 Law Drive, Box 2300 Fairfield, NJ 07007-2300.

ASME B18.2.1—
ASME B18.18.1M—Inspection and Quality Assurance for General Purpose Fasteners

2.1.3 ASTM PUBLICATION—Available from ASTM, 100 Barr Harbor Drive, West Conshohocken, PA 19428-2959.

ASTM E 18—Test Methods for Rockwell Hardness and Rockwell Superficial Hardness of Metallic Materials

2.2 Related Publications—The following publications are provided for information purposes only and are not a required part of this document.

2.2.1 SAE PUBLICATION—Available from SAE, 400 Commonwealth Drive, Warrendale, PA 15096-0001.

SAE J995—Mechanical and Material Requirements for Steel Nuts

2.2.2 ASTM PUBLICATION—Available from ASTM, 100 Barr Harbor Drive, West Conshohocken, PA 19428-2959.

ASTMF1470—Guide for Fastener Sampling for Specified Mechanical Properties and Performance Inspection

3. Designations

3.1 Designation System—Grades are designated by numbers where increasing numbers represent increasing tensile strength, and by decimals of whole numbers where decimals represent variations at the same strength level. The grade designations are given in Table 1.

3.2 Grades—Bolts and screws are normally available only in Grades 1, 2, 5, 5.2, 8, and 8.2 (see Appendix A). Studs are normally available only in Grades 1, 2, 4, 5, 8, and 8.1. Grade 5.1 is applicable to sems which may be heat treated following assembly of the washer on the screw, and to products without assembled washer.

4. Materials and Processes

4.1 Steel Characteristics—All fasteners shall be made of steel conforming to the chemical composition requirements in Table 2 for each grade.

For the definition of carbon and alloy steels, see SAE J411. Refer to SAE J403, J404, J1086, or J1268 for the chemical composition limits of standard steel grades. Standard H grade steels are acceptable substitutes as are nonstandard steels which fit the definition of carbon and alloy steels in SAE J411. For Grades 5, 5.1, 5.2, 8, 8.1, and 8.2 the maximum content of bismuth selenium, tellurium, or lead shall be 0.02%.

Steel for Grades 8 and 8.2 fasteners shall be fine grained steel with sufficient hardenability to provide hardness equivalent to 90% minimum martensite at the center of a transverse section one diameter from the threaded end of the fastener after quenching. Minimum as-quenched hardness required for steels in the carbon range 0.15 to 0.55% is shown in Table 3.

4.2 Heading Practice—Methods other than upsetting and/or extrusion are permitted only by special agreement between purchaser and supplier.

Grade 1 bolts and screws shall be hot or cold headed, at option of the manufacturer.

Grades 2, 5, 5.2, 8, and 8.2 bolts and screws in sizes up to 3/4 in, inclusive, and in lengths up to 6 in, inclusive, shall be cold headed, except that by special agreement they may be hot headed. Larger sizes and longer lengths shall be hot or cold headed, at option of the manufacturer.

Grade 5.1 sems screws shall be cold headed.

4.3 Threading Practice—Grades 2, 5, 5.2, 8, and 8.2 bolts and screws in sizes up to 3/4 in, inclusive, and lengths up to 6 in, inclusive, shall be roll threaded, except by special agreement. Grade 5.1 sems shall be roll threaded. Threads of all sizes of Grade 1 bolts and screws, and Grades 2, 5, 5.2, 8, and 8.2 bolts and screws in sizes over 3/4 in and/or lengths longer than 6 in shall be rolled, cut, or ground, at option of the manufacturer. Threads of all grades and sizes of studs shall be rolled, cut, or ground, at option of the manufacturer.

1. Sems—Screw and washer assemblies
2. U-bolts covered by this SAE Standard are those used primarily in the suspension and related areas of vehicles. For specification purposes, this standard treats U-bolts as studs. Thus, wherever the word "studs" appears, "U-bolts" is also implied. (Designers should recognize that the "U" configuration may not sustain a load equivalent to two bolts or studs of the same size and grade; thus, actual load-carrying capacity of U-bolts should be determined by saddle load tests.)

TABLE 1—MECHANICAl REQUIREMENTS AND IDENTIFICATION MARKING FOR BOLTS, SCREWS, STUDS, SEMS, AND U-BOLTS[1]

Grade Designation	Products	Nominal Size Dia, In	Full Size Bolts, Screws, Studs Sems, Proof Load (Stress), psi	Full Size Bolts, Screws Studs, Sems, Tensile Strength (Stress) Min, psi	Machine Test Specimens of Bolts, Screws, and Studs Yield[2] Strength (Stress) Min, psi	Machine Test Specimens of Bolts, Screws, and Studs Tensile Strength (Stress) Min, psi	Machine Test Specimens of Bolts, Screws, and Studs Elongation[3] Min, %	Machine Test Specimens of Bolts, Screws, and Studs Reduction of Area Min, %	Surface Hardness Rockwell 30N Max	Core Hardness Rockwell Min	Core Hardness Rockwell Max	Grade Identification Marking[4]
1	Bolts, Screws, Studs	1/4 thru 1-1/2	33 000[5]	60 000	36 000[6]	60 000	18	35	—	B70	B100	None
2	Bolts, Screws, Studs	1/4 thru 3/4[7]	55 000[5]	74 000	57 000	74 000	18	35	—	B80	B100	
		Over 3/4 thru 1-1/2	33 000	60 000	36 000[6]	60 000	18	35	—	B70	B100	None
4	Studs	1/4 thru 1-1/2	65 000	115 000	100 000	115 000	10	35	—	C22	C32	None
5	Bolts, Screws, Studs	1/4 thru 1	85 000	120 000	92 000	120 000	14	35	54	C25	C34	
		Over 1 thru 1-1/2	74 000	105 000	81 000	105 000	14	35	50	C19	C30	
5.1[8]	Sems	No. 4 thru 5/8	85 000	120 000	—	—	—	—	59.5	C25	C40	
5.2	Bolts, Screws	1/4 thru 1	85 000	120 000	92 000	120 000	14	35	56	C26	C36	
8	Bolts, Screws, Studs	1/4 thru 1-1/2	120 000	150 000	130 000	150 000	12	35	58.6	C33	C39	
8.1	Studs	1/4 thru 1-1/2	120 000	150 000	130 000	150 000	10	35	58.6	C33	C39	None
8.2	Bolts, Screws	1/4 thru 1	120 000	150 000	130 000	150 000	10	35	58.6	C33	C39	

1. See footnote 2 of text.
2. Yield strength is stress at which a permanent set of 0.2% of gage length occurs.
3. See Table 8 for gage length.
4. Not applicable to studs or slotted and cross recess head products.
5. Proof load test: Requirements in these grades only apply to stress relieved products.
6. Yield point shall apply instead of yield strength at 0.2% offset.
7. Grade 2 requirements for sizes 1/4 through 3/4 in apply only to bolts and screws 6 in and shorter in length, and to studs of all lengths. For bolts and screws longer than 6 in, Grade 1 requirements shall apply.
8. Grade 5 material heat treated before assembly with a hardened washer is an acceptable substitute.

4.4 Heat Treatment Practice—Grades 1 and 2 bolts and studs need not be heat treated. Grades 1 and 2 cold headed carriage bolts and other bolts and screws with thin heads shall be stress relieved at 468 °C (875 °F) minimum. (Prior agreement with purchaser will be required if mechanical properties are affected). Additionally, when specified by purchaser, Grade 2 cold headed hex head bolts and screws shall be stress relieved at 468°C (875 °F) minimum. Grades 4 and 8.1 studs are manufactured from pretreated material and the studs, as manufactured, need no further heat treatment. Grades 5 and 5.2 bolts, screws, and studs shall be heat treated (fully austenitized), oil or water quenched, at option of manufacturer, and tempered at a minimum tempering temperature of 427 °C (800 °F). Grade 5.1 Sems shall be heat treated (fully austenitized), quenched, and tempered at a minimum tempering temperature of 343 °C (650 °F); quenchants whose principal constituent is water shall not be used, unless specifically approved by the user. Grade 8 bolts and screws and studs shall be heat treated (fully austenitized), oil quenched, and tempered at a minimum tempering temperature of 427 °C (800 °F). Grade 8.2 bolts and screws shall be heat treated (fully austenitized), quenched in oil or water, and tempered at a minimum temperature of 340 °C (650 °F).

Under no circumstances should heat treatment or carbon restoration be accomplished in the presence of nitrogen compounds, such as in carbonitriding or cyaniding.

4.5 Decarburization—Unless otherwise specified, Grades 5 and 5.2 bolts, screws, and studs shall conform to Class C, and Grades 8, 8.1, and 8.2 bolts, screws, and studs shall conform to Class B as described in SAEJ121.

4.6 Surface Discontinuities—Grades 5, 5.1, 5.2, 8, 8.1, and 8.2 bolts, screws, and studs in sizes up to 1 in inclusive, and lengths up to 6 in inclusive shall be in conformity with the requirements of SAE J1061.

When the engineering requirements of the application necessitate that surface discontinuities of bolts, screws, and studs should be more closely controlled, the purchaser shall specify the applicable limits in the original inquiry and purchase order. For certain fasteners, this may be done by reference to SAE J123.

5. Mechanical Requirements—Bolts, screws, studs, and sems shall be tested in accordance with the mechanical testing requirements for the applicable type, grade, size, and length of product as specified in Table 4 and shall meet the mechanical requirements specified for that product in Table 1.

In the case of U-bolts having thread length equal to 3D or longer, cut stud-like specimens from either leg of the "U" (utilizing the maximum available thread length) and test as shown for studs. Where thread length is less than 3D, test for hardness only as shown for "short studs." (Applicable mechanical tests are shown in Table 4 and shall meet requirements specified for that product in Table 1.)

6. Methods of Test

6.1 Hardness—The hardness of bolts, screws, studs, and sems shall be determined at mid-radius of a transverse section through the threaded portion of the product taken at a distance of one diameter from the end of the product. The reported hardness shall be the average of four hardness readings located at 90 degrees to one another. The preparation of test specimens and the performance of hardness tests shall be in conformity with the requirements of SAE J417.

To meet the requirements of Section 5, the hardness shall not exceed the maximum hardness specified in Table 1 for the applicable grade. In addition, as required in Section 5 and Table 4, the hardness shall not be less than the minimum hardness specified in Table 1 for the applicable grade.

TABLE 2—CHEMICAL COMPOSITION TEMPERING TEMPERATURE AND IDENTIFICATION FOR BOLTS, SCREWS, AND STUDS

Grade Desig- nation	Products	Nominal Size Dia, In	Material	Treatment	Product Chemical Analysis[(1)], (% by Weight) Carbon Min	Product Chemical Anaysis[(1)] (% by Weight) Carbon Max	Product Chemical Analysis[(1)] (% by Weight) Manganese Min	Product Chemical Analysis[(1)] (% by Weight) P Max	Product Chemical Analysis[(1)] (% by Weight) S Max	Product Chemical Analysis[(1)] (% by Weight) Boron) Min	Product Chemical Analysis[(1)] (% by Weight) Boron Max	Tempering Temperatur e °F (Min)	Grade Identification Marking
1	Bolts, Screws, Studs	1/4 thru 1-1/2	Low or Medium Carbon Steel	See 4.4		0.55		0.030	0.050			See 4.4	None
2	Bolts, Screws, Studs	1/4 thru 1-1/2	Low or Medium Carbon Steel	See 4.4	0.15	0.55		0.030	0.050[(2)]			See 4.4	None
4	Studs	1/4 thru 1-1/2	Medium Carbon Steel	Cold Drawn	0.28	0.55		0.030	0.13			See 4.4	None
5	Bolts, Screws, Studs	1/4 thru 1-1/2	Medium Carbon Steel[(3)]	Quenched Tempered	0.28	0.55		0.030	0.050[(4)]			427 °C (800 °F)	
5.1[(5)]	Sems	No. 4 thru 5/8	Low or Medium Carbon Steel[(3)]	Quenched & Tempered	0.15	0.30		0.030	0.050			340 °C (650 °F)	
5.2	Bolts, Screws	1/4 thru 1	Low Carbon Boron Steel	Quenched & Tempered	0.15	0.25	0.74	0.030	0.050	0.0005		427 °C (800 °F)	
8	Bolts, Screws, Studs	1/4 thru 1-1/2	Medium Carbon (6) Alloy Steel	Quenched & Tempered	0.28	0.55		0.030	0.050			427 °C (800 °F)	
8.1	Studs	1/4 thru 1-1/2	Medium Carbon Alloy or SAE1541 Steel	Elevated Temperature Drawn	0.28	0.55		0.030	0.040			427 °C (800 °F)	None
8.2	Bolts, Screws	1/4 thru 1	Low Carbon Boron Steel	Quenched & Tempered	0.15	0.25	0.74	0.030	0.050	0.0005		340 °C (650 °F)	

1. All values are for product analysis (percent by weight). For cast or heat analysis, use standard permissible variations as shown in SAE J409.
2. For studs only, sulfur content may be 0.33% maximum.
3. For Grades 5 and 5.1, fasteners, medium carbon boron or medium carbon alloy steels, as specified for Grades 8 fasteners, may also be used at the manufacturer's option.
4. For studs only, sulfur content may be 0.13% maximum.
5. Grade 5 material heat treated before assembly with a hardened washer is an acceptable substitute.
6. When agreed to by manufacturer and purchaser, medium carbon steel may be used for products 7/16 inch in nominal diameter and smaller and medium carbon boron steel may be used for products 1 inch in nominal diameter and smaller.

TABLE 3—CARBON CONTENT VERSUS MINIMUM AS-QUENCHED HARDNESS FOR 90% MARTENSITE

Carbon (%)	Hardness HRC
0.15 through 0.19	35
0.20 through 0.24	38
0.25 through 0.29	41
0.30 through 0.34	44
0.35 through 0.39	47
0.40 through 0.44	50
0.45 through 0.55	53

6.2 Surface Hardness—Tests to determine surface hardness conditions shall be conducted on the ends, hexagon flats, or unthreaded shanks which have been prepared by lightly grinding or polishing to insure accurate reproducible readings in accordance with SAE J417. Proper correction factors shall be used when hardness tests are made on curved surfaces, per ASTM E 18.

Depending on the location and individual surface upon which the test is conducted, some increase in hardness above that specified in Table 1, when measured on the Rockwell 30N scale, may occur for reasons other than carburization. To ensure that lots of products not considered acceptable for this cause are in fact carburized, the metallographic and hardness checking technique described in SAE J121 shall be used. In cases where carburization is not substantiated by SAE J121 testing, the parts shall be accepted.

In applying the SAE J121 procedure, a difference between Knoop and Rockwell 30N readings by conversion may occur. This difference is disregarded since the primary purpose of the Knoop traverse in SAE J121 is to establish the existence of carburization.

6.3 Referee Tempering Temperature Test—In a dispute concerning the tempering temperature, the following procedure shall be used for referee purposes. Conduct hardness test (6.1) on one or more bolts, screws, or studs from the lot; retemper the products at a temperature 6.7 °C (20 °F) less than the specified minimum tempering temperature for a minimum of 30 min per 1.0 in nominal diameter but not less than 30 min; repeat product hardness test. The difference between the mean hardness (before and after retempering) shall be no greater than two points Rockwell C. This is a referee test and not a mandatory requirement.

TABLE 4—MECHANICAL TESTING REQUIREMENTS FOR BOLTS, SCREWS, STUDS, AND SEMS

Product	Grade	Specified Minimum Ultimate Tensile Load "lb"	Length of Product(1)	Hardness(2) max	Hardness(1) Min	Tests Conducted Using Full Size Products(1) Proof Load	Tests Conducted Using Full Size Products(1) Wedge Tensile Strength	Tests Conducted Using Full Size Products(1) Axial Tensile Strength	Tests Conducted Using Machine Test Specimens(1) Yield Strength	Tests Conducted Using Machine Test Specimens(1) Axial Tensile Strength	Tests Conducted Using Machine Test Specimen(1) Elongation	Tests Conducted Using Machine Test Specimens(1) Reduction of Area	Surface Hardness max(3)	Decarburization in Threaded Section(2)
Short Bolts and Screws	1, 2.5, 5.2, 8, 8.2	All	Less than 2-1/2 D(4)	*	*	—	—	—	—	—		—	*	Option C
Special Head(5) Bolts and Screws	1, 2.5, 5.2, 8, 8.2	All	All	*	*	—	—	—	—	—	—	—	*	Option C
Square and Hex Bolts and Screws	1, 2.5, 5.2, 8, 8.2	100 000 and less	2-1/2D to 8D or 8 in, whichever is greater	*	—	Option C	*	—	—	—	—	—	*	Option C
			Over 8D or 8 in, whichever is greater, thru and including 12 in	*	—	Option C	*	—	Option B	Option B	Option B	Option B	*	Option C
			Over 12 in	*	—	Option C	Option A	—	Option B	Option B	Option B	Option B	*	Option C
		Over 100 000	2-1/2D and longer	*	—	Option C	Option A	—	Option B	Option B	Option B	Option B	*	Option C
All Other Bolts and Screws	1, 2.5, 5.2, 8, 8.2	100 000 and less	2-1/2 to 8D or 8 in, whichever is greater	*	—	Option C	—	*	—	—	—	—	*	Option C
			Over 8D or 8 in, whichever is greater	*	—	Option C	—	Option A	Option B	Option B	Option B	Option B	*	Option C
		Over 100 000	2-1/2D and longer	*	—	Option C	—	Option A	Option B	Option B	Option B	Option B	*	Option C
Short Studs	1, 2.4, 5, 8. 8.1	All	Less than 3D	*	*	—	—	—	—	—		—	*	Option C
All Other Studs	1, 2, 4, 5, 8, 8.1	100 000 and less	3D to 8D or 8 in, whichever is greater	*	—	Option C	*	—	—	—	—	—	*	Option C
			Over 8D or 8 in, whichever is greater	*	—	Option C	Option A	—	Option B	Option B	Option B	Option B	*	Option C
		Over 100 000	3D and longer	*	—	Option C	Option A	—	Option B	Option B	Option B	Option B	—	Option C
Short Bolts, Screws, and Sems	5.1	All	Less than 2-1/2D	*	*	—	—	—	—	—	—	—	*	Option C
Hex Head Bolts, Screws, and Sems	5.1	All	2-1/2D and longer	*	—	Opion C	*	—	—	—		—	*	Option C
Other Bolts, Screws, and Sems	5.1	All	2-1/2D and longer	*	—	Option C	—	*	—	—	—	—	*	Option C
Tests to be performed in accordance with paragraph				6.1	6.1	6.4	6.6	6.5	6.7	6.7	6.7	6.7	6.2	4.5

1. For purposes of Table 4 requirements, "length of product" is the nominal length including point chamfer as defined in ASME B18.2.1 and all special point products which shall be measured from the bearing surface to the crest of the last complete thread form.
2. Asterisks (*) denote mandatory tests. Where options are indicated, all Option A tests (which apply to full size products) or all Option B tests (which apply to machined specimens) shall be performed. Option C tests (which apply to full size products) are not mandatory unless specified in the original inquiry and purchase order. Option A and Option C tests shall be performed in case arbitration is necessary.
3. Surface hardness and decarburization requirements apply only to Grades 5, 5.1, 5.2, 8, 8.1, and 8.2.
4. D equals diameter of the product.
5. Special head bolts and screws are those with special configurations or with drilled heads which are weaker than the threaded section.

6.4 Proof Load—The proof load test consists of stressing the bolt, screw, stud, or sem with a specified load which the product must withstand without permanent set.

The overall length of the specimen shall be measured between conical or ball centers on the centerline of the specimen, using mating centers on the measuring anvils. The specimen shall be marked so that it can be placed in the measuring fixture in the same position for all measurements. The measurement instrument shall be capable of measurement to 0.0001 in. In the case of sems, the washer may be removed from the screw prior to assembly in the testing machine; however, for referee testing, the washer shall be removed. For bolts, screws, and sems, 3D or longer, the specimen shall be assembled in the fixture of the tensile machine so that six complete threads are exposed between the grips. This is obtained by freely running the nut or fixture to the thread runout of the specimen and then unscrewing the specimen six full turns. Short bolts, 2-1/2-3D in length, threaded to within 2-1/2 pitches of the bearing surface shall be assembled finger-tight in the fixture and unscrewed two full turns. When proof load testing studs, one end of the stud shall be assembled in a threaded fixture to the thread runout. For studs having unlike threads, this shall be the end with the finer pitch thread. The other end of the stud shall likewise be assembled in a threaded fixture, as previously mentioned for bolts. The bolt, screw, stud, or sem shall then be axially loaded to the proof load specified for the applicable size, thread series, and grade in Table 5, the load retained for a period of 10 s, the load removed, and the overall length again measured. The speed of testing, as determined with a free running cross head, shall not exceed 0.12 in/min.

To meet the requirements of Section 5, the length of the bolt, screw, stud, or sem after loading shall be the same as before loading within a tolerance of ±0.0005 in allowed for measurement error.

Variables, such as straightness and thread alignment (plus measurement error), may result in apparent elongation of the fasteners when the proof load is initially applied. In such cases, the fastener may be retested using a 3% greater load, and may be considered satisfactory if the length after this loading is the same as before this loading (within the 0.0005 in tolerance for measurement error).

6.5 Axial Tensile Strength—Following proof load testing, the same bolt, screw, stud, or sem shall be reassembled in the testing machine per 6.4 and axial loading applied until failure. Typical fixturing is illustrated in Figure 1. The speed of testing, as determined with a free running cross head, shall not exceed 1 in/min.

To meet the requirements of Section 5, the bolt, screw, stud, or sem shall not fracture before having withstood the minimum tensile load specified for the applicable size, thread series, and grade in Table 5. In addition for bolts, screws, and sems with regular style heads, the ultimate failure location shall occur in the body or threaded section and not at the junction of the head and shank. (See footnote 5 under Table 4.)

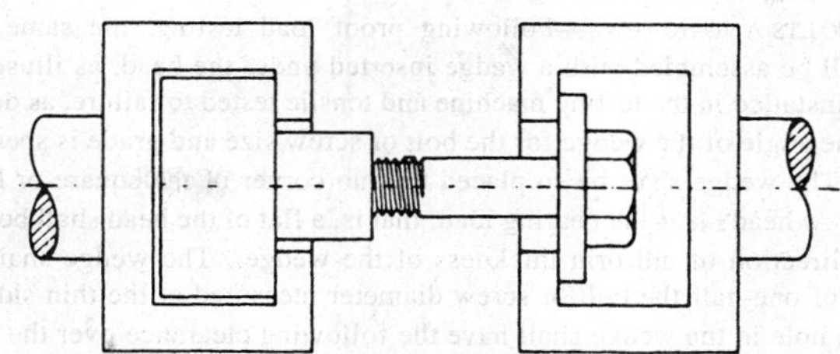

FIGURE 1—TENSILE TESTING OF FULL-SIZE BOLT OR SCREW

TABLE 5—PROOF LOAD AND TENSILE STRENGTH REQUIREMENTS(1)

	Stress Area, in^2	Grade 1 Proof Load, lb	Grade 1 Tensile Strength Min, lb	Grade 2 Proof Load, lb	Grade 2 Tensile Strength min, lb	Grade 4 Proof Load, lb	Grade 4 Tensile Strength Min, lb	Grades 5 and 5.2(2) Proof Load, lb	Grades 5 and 5.2(2) Tensile Strength Min, lb	Grade 5.1 Proof Load, lb	Grade 5.1 Tensile Strength Min, lb	Grades 8, 8.1, 8.2(2) Proof Load, lb	Grades 8 8.1, 8.2(2) Tensile Stregnth Min, lb
						Coarse Thread Series UNC							
No. 6-32	0.00909	—	—	—	—	—	—	—	—	750	1100	—	—
8-32	0.0140	—	—	—	—	—	—	—	—	1200	1700	—	—
10-24	0.0175	—	—	—	—	—	—	—	—	1500	2100	—	—
12-24	0.0242	—	—	—	—	—	—	—	—	2050	2900	—	—
1/4-20	0.0318	1050	1900	1750	2350	2050	3650	2700	3800	2700	3800	3800	4750
5/16-18	0.0524	1750	3150	2900	3900	3400	6000	4450	6300	4450	6300	6300	7850
3/8-16	0.0775	2550	4650	4250	5750	5050	8400	6600	9300	6600	9300	9300	11 600
7/16-14	0.1063	3500	6400	5850	7850	6900	12 200	9050	12 800	9050	12 800	12 800	15 900
1/2-13	0.1419	4700	8500	7800	10 500	9200	18 300	12 100	17 000	12 100	17 000	17 000	21 300
9/16-12	0.182	6000	10 900	10 000	13 500	11 800	20 900	15 500	21 800	15 500	21 800	21 800	27 300
5/8-11	0.226	7450	13 600	12 400	16 700	14 700	25 400	19 200	27 100	19 200	27 100	27 100	33 900
3/4-10	0.334	11 000	20 000	18 400	24 700	21 700	38 400	28 400	40 100	—	—	40 100	50 100
7/8-9	0.462	15 200	27 700	15 200	27 700	30 000	53 100	39 300	55 400	—	—	55 400	69 300
1 - 8	0.606	20 000	36 400	20 000	36 400	39 400	69 700	51 500	72 700	—	—	72 700	90 900
1-1/8-7	0.763	25 200	45 800	25 200	45 800	49 600	87 700	56 500	80 100	—	—	91 600	114 400
1-1/4-7	0.969	32 000	58 100	32 000	58 100	63 000	111 400	71 700	101 700	—	—	116 300	145 400
1-3/8-6	1.155	38 100	69 300	38 100	69 300	75 100	132 800	85 500	121 300	—	—	138 600	173 200
1-1/2-6	1.405	46 400	84 300	46 400	84 300	91 300	161 600	104 000	147 500	—	—	168 600	210 800
						Fine Thread Series UNF							
No. 6-40	0.01015	—	—	—	—	—	—	—	—	850	1200	—	—
8-36	0.01474	—	—	—	—	—	—	—	—	1250	1750	—	—
10-32	0.0200	—	—	—	—	—	—	—	—	1700	2400	—	—
12-28	0.0258	—	—	—	—	—	—	—	—	2200	3100	—	—
1/4-28	0.0364	1200	2200	2000	2700	2350	4200	3100	4350	3100	4350	4350	5450
5/16-24	0.0580	1900	3500	3200	4300	3750	6700	4900	6950	4900	6950	6950	8700
3/8-24	0.0878	2900	5250	4800	6500	5700	10 100	7450	10 500	7450	10 500	10 500	13 200
7/16-20	0.1187	3900	7100	6550	8800	7700	13 650	10 100	14 200	10 100	14 200	14 200	17 800
1/2-20	0.1599	5300	9600	8800	11 800	10 400	18 400	13 600	19 200	13 600	19 200	19 200	24 000
9/16-18	0.203	6700	12 200	11 200	15 000	13 200	23 300	17 300	24 400	17 300	24 400	24 400	30 400
5/8-18	0.256	8450	15 400	14 100	18 900	16 600	29 400	21 800	30 700	21 800	30 700	30 700	38 400
3/4-16	0.373	12 300	22 400	20 500	27 600	24 200	42 900	31 700	44 800			44 800	56 000
7/8-14	0.509	16 800	30 500	16 800	30 500	33 100	58 500	43 300	61 100			61 100	76 400
1 - 12	0.663	21 900	39 800	21 900	39 800	43 100	76 200	56 400	79 600			79 600	99 400
1- 14 UNS	0.679	22 400	40 700	22 400	40 700	44 100	78 100	57 700	81 500	—	—	81 500	101 900
1-1/8-12	0.856	28 200	51 400	28 200	51 400	55 600	98 400	63 300	89 900	—	—	102 700	128 400
1-1/4-12	1.073	35 400	64 400	35 400	64 400	69 700	123 400	79 400	112 700	—	—	128 800	161 000
1-3/8-12	1.315	43 400	78 900	43 400	78 900	85 500	151 200	97 300	138 100	—	—	157 800	197 200
1-1/2-12	1.581	52 200	94 900	52 200	94 900	102 800	181 800	117 000	166 000	—	—	189 700	237 200

1. Proof loads and tensile strengths are computed by multiplying the proof load stresses and tensile strength stresses given in Table 1 by the stress area of the thread. The stress area of sizes and thread series not included in Table 5 may be computed from the formula:

$$A_s = 0.7854\left[D - \frac{0.9743}{n}\right]^2 \qquad \text{(Eq. 1)}$$

where D equals nominal diameter in inches and n equals threads per inch.

2. Grades 5.2 and 8.2 applicable to sizes 1/4 through 1 in.

6.6 Wedge Tensile Strength

6.6.1 BOLTS AND SCREWS—Following proof load testing, the same bolt or screw shall be assembled with a wedge inserted under the head, as illustrated in Figure 2, installed in the testing machine and tensile tested to failure, as described in 6.5. The angle of the wedge for the bolt or screw size and grade is specified in Table 6. The wedge shall be so placed that no corner of the square or hexagon bolt or screw head takes the bearing load; that is, a flat of the head shall be aligned with the direction of uniform thickness of the wedge. The wedge shall have a thickness of one-half the bolt or screw diameter measured at the thin side of the hole. The hole in the wedge shall have the following clearance over the nominal size of the bolt or screw, and its top and bottom edges shall be rounded or chamfered 45 degrees to the dimensions in Table 7.

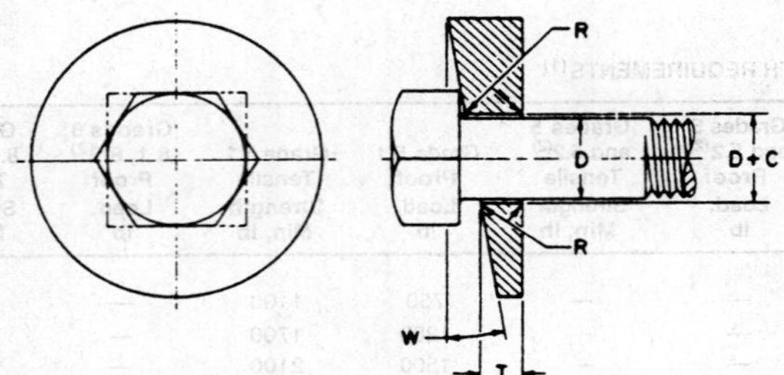

FIGURE 2—WEDGE TEST DETAILS—BOLTS AND SCREWS

TABLE 6—TENSILE TEST WEDGE ANGLES

Product	Grade	Nominal Size of Product, in	Wedge Angle deg
Bolts and Screws[1]	1,2	1/4 thru 1	10
		Over 1 to 1-1/2	6
	5, 5.2, 8, 8.2[2]	1/4 thru 1	10
	5, 8[2]	Over 1 to 1-1/2	6
Hex Head Sems	5.1	No. 6 thru 5/8	6
Studs	1, 2, 5, 8, 8.1	1/4 thru 3/4	6
		Over 3/4 to 1-1/2	4

1. For hex flange and hex washer head product, the wedge angle shall be 6 degrees.
2. For Grades 5, 5.2, 8, and 8.2 bolts and screws which are threaded 1 dia and closer to the underside of head, wedge angle shall be 6 degrees for sizes 1/4 through 3/4 in, and 4 degrees for sizes over 3/4 in.

Wedge tensile testing shall be limited to product with hexagon, square, hex flange, or twelve point flange heads. Product with other head styles and shaped shoulders or those with shoulders substantially larger in diameter than the nominal bolt body diameter, should be axial tensile tested.

To meet the requirement of Section 5, the bolt, screw, stud, or sems shall not fracture before having withstood the minimum tensile load specified for the applicable size, thread series, and grade in Table 5. In addition, the ultimate failure location shall occur in the body or threaded section and not at the junction of the head and shank. (See footnote 5 under Table 4.)

TABLE 7—WEDGE, CLEARANCE, AND CHAMFER DIMENSIONS

Nominal Bolt or Screw Size, in	Clearance in Hole, in	Radius or Depth of Chamfer, in
No. 6 thru 12	0.020	0.020
1/4 thru 1/2	0.030	0.030
9/16 thru 3/4	0.050	0.060
7/8 and 1	0.060	0.060
1-1/8 and 1-1/4	0.060	0.125
1-3/8 and 1-1/2	0.094	0.125

6.6.2 STUDS—Following proof load testing, the stud shall be assembled per 6.4 except with a threaded wedge, as illustrated in Figure 3. The angle of the wedge for the stud size and grade shall be as specified in Table 6. The stud shall be assembled in the testing machine and tensile tested to failure, as described in 6.5. The length of the threaded section of the wedge shall be equal to the diameter of the stud. To facilitate removal of the broken stud, the wedge shall be counterbored. The thickness of the wedge at the thin side of the hole shall equal the diameter of the stud plus the depth of counterbore. The supporting fixture, as shown in Figure 3, shall have hole clearance over the nominal size of the stud, and shall have its top and bottom edges rounded or chamfered to the same limits specified for the hardened wedge in 6.6.1.

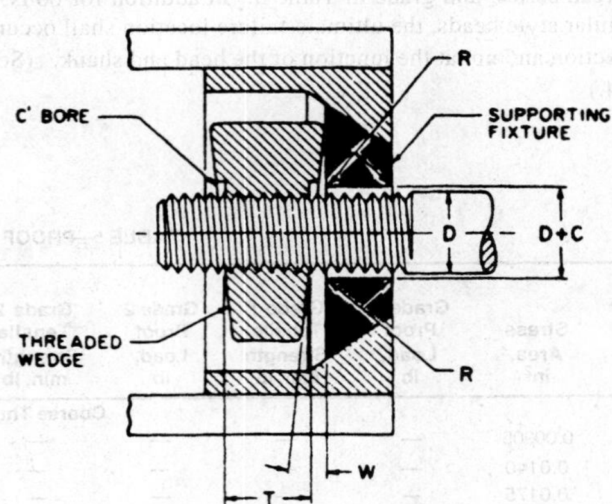

FIGURE 3—WEDGE TEST DETAILS—STUDS

To meet the requirements of Section 5, the stud shall not fracture before having withstood the minimum tensile load specified for the applicable size, thread series, and grade in Table 5.

6.7 Testing of Machined Test Specimens—Where bolts, screws, and studs cannot be tested in full size for proof load and tensile strength requirements, tests shall be conducted using test specimens machined from the bolt, screw, or stud.

For 1-1/2 in diameter bolts, screws, and studs, a standard 0.500 in round 2 in gage length test specimen shall be turned from the bolt, screw, or stud with the axis of the specimen located midway between the center and outside surface of the bolt, screw, or stud shank, as shown in Figure 4. Bolts, screws, and studs 3/4 through 1-3/8 in diameter shall have their shanks machined to the dimensions of a standard 0.500 in round 2 in gage length test specimen concentric with the axis of the bolt, screw, or stud, leaving the bolt or screw head and threaded sections intact, as shown in Figure 5 and Table 8. Bolts, screws, and studs 1/4 through 5/8 in diameter shall have their shanks machined to subsize specimens having dimensions shown in Figure 5 and Table 8.

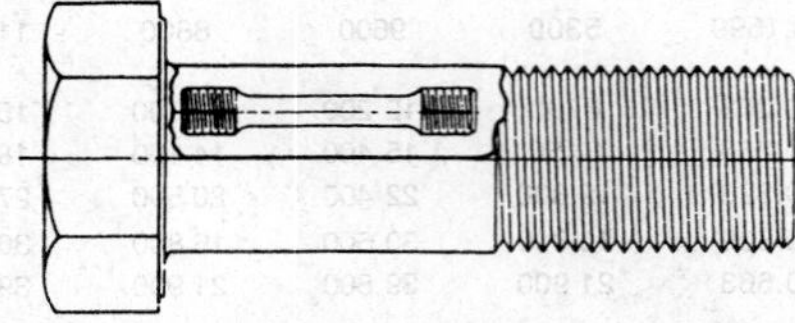

FIGURE 4—LOCATION OF STANDARD ROUNDS 2 IN GAGE LENGTH TENSILE TEST SPECIMEN WHEN TURNED FROM LARGE SIZE BOLTS OR SCREWS

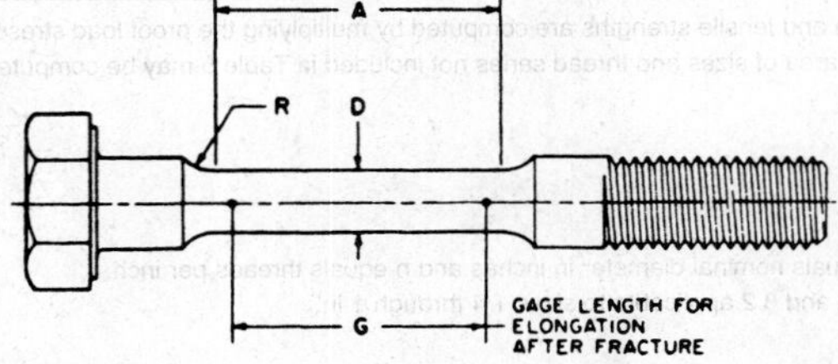

FIGURE 5—TENSILE TEST SPECIMEN FOR BOLTS OR SCREWS WITH TURNED DOWN SHANK

TABLE 8—DIMENSIONS OF MACHINED TEST SPECIMENS (SEE 6.7 AND FIGURE 5)

Nominal Dia of Product	Gage Length G	Dia Parallel Section D	Length Parallel Section, Min A	Fillet Radius, Min R
3/4 thru 1-1/2	2.000 ± 0.005	0.500 ± 0.010	2.25	0.38(1)
1/4 thru 5/8	1.400 ± 0.005	0.350 ± 0.007	1.75	0.25
	1.000 ± 0.005	0.250 ± 0.005	1.25	0.19

1. Minimum radius recommended 0.38 in; 0.12 minimum permitted.

The test specimen shall be tensile tested as described in 6.5, and the yield strength, tensile strength, elongation, and reduction of area determined.

To meet the requirements of Section 5 the test specimens must have a yield strength, tensile strength, elongation, and reduction of area equal to or greater than the values for those properties specified for the applicable product size and grade in Table 1.

6.8 Common Test Fixture Details—The grips of the tensile testing machine shall be self-aligning to avoid side thrust on the specimen.

The wedge shall have a minimum hardness of 45 HRC.

The hole in the fixture or washer used under the head of bolts and screws during proof load and tensile testing shall have the same clearance as that specified for wedges (6.6.1).

Wedges, nuts, and fixtures into which bolts, screws, and studs are threaded for proof load, tensile strength, and wedge tensile testing shall have threads which are of the same size, pitch, and tolerance class as the product being tested. (For standard products Class 3B tolerances are normally applicable.) For studs having interference fit threads, wedges shall be threaded to provide a finger-free fit.

7. Product Marking—Bolts and Screws—Internal drive screws of all sizes and other screws and bolts of sizes smaller than 1/4 in need not be marked. All other screws and bolts of sizes 1/4 in and larger shall be marked permanently and clearly to identify the strength grade and the manufacturer. The grade identification symbols shall be as shown in Table 1. Markings shall be located on the top of the head and may be either raised or depressed. For hex head products, the markings may be indented on the side of the head. Studs need not be marked.

Marking product with special heads weaker than the threads and product manufactured with a collar shall be at the option of the manufacturer. The end user of product used for decorative purposes shall have the option of waiving the requirement for marking and its location.

8. Test Requirements

8.1 Manufacturer's Responsibility—The requirements of this document are intended to be met by both special and standard fasteners which are generally produced in large volume for stock. During the manufacture of products to this specification, the manufacturer shall make periodic tests to ensure that the properties of the product are being maintained within the specified limits. Such tests shall be conducted in accordance with a planned program of control which shall include elements related to the selection of suitable material and to the product processing and testing practices. The test results shall be recorded.

8.2 Manufacturer's Test Reports—When requested in writing by the purchaser, the supplier shall furnish a copy of the manufacturer's test report certified to be a report of the results of the tests for the specific type, size, length, and grade of product for each lot of fasteners.

Additional tests of products in individual shipments are not normally contemplated.

8.2.1 SMALL LOT PROVISIONS—Where fasteners are produced to order in small quantities, 2000 pieces or less, having different lengths or cut to different lengths in subsequent operations, but made from the same mill heat of material of the same nominal diameter, head type or configuration, formed in a given machine and heat treated essentially together, they shall be considered a lot for test report purposes.

8.3 Purchaser's Options—If the purchaser requires that additional tests be performed by the manufacturer to determine that the properties of products in an individual shipment are within specified limits, or if the purchaser requires that a quality control program or particular sampling plan shall be used when determining the acceptability of a lot, or shipment of products, the purchaser shall specify the complete testing requirements, including sampling plan and basis of acceptance in the original inquiry and purchase order.

8.4 Quality Control—Fasteners manufactured in conformance with this document shall be furnished to the purchaser in accordance with ASME B18.18.1M unless otherwise specified by the purchaser. If verifiable in-process inspection is used, inspection sample size and reporting shall be in accordance with the applicable ASME, ASTM, or SAE quality system consensus standard.

8.5 Purchaser's Responsibility—When fasteners are to be used in conditions of an unusual nature and where corrosion, fatigue, or temperature is a consideration, it is desirable that a purchaser consult with the manufacturer regarding material choice.

While purchase users may have an awareness of product end use and environment, purchasers of product for resale or distribution may not. For this reason, it is suggested and recommended that purchase resellers give careful consideration when selecting alternative materials to be used in the manufacture of stocks for their inventories.

For the purpose of defining responsibility, this specification defines the responsible party to be the organization that supplies the fastener to the final purchaser. That organization should be able to certify that the fastener was manufactured, tested, and inspected in accordance with this specification, or some other related product specification and meets all of its requirements.

APPENDIX A

A.1 (Relative to 150 000 psi tensile strength bolts and screws produced from low carbon boron steels and designated as Grade 8.2.)

Users should recognize the difference in stress relaxation characteristics of various steels between the tempering temperature range of 340 °C (650 °F), minimum, specified for Grade 8.2 and 427 °C (800 °F), minimum, specified for Grade 8, when considering bolts and screws that may be exposed to such temperature range. The data available on elevated temperature properties of Grade 8.2 indicates that performance testing is desirable in applications where the operating temperature exceeds 260 °C (500 °F) (as may also be the case with Grade 8 fasteners).

MECHANICAL AND MATERIAL REQUIREMENTS FOR METRIC EXTERNALLY THREADED STEEL FASTENERS—SAE J1199 MAR2001

SAE Standard

Report of the SAE Iron and Steel Technical Committee approved February 1978. Revised by the ISTC Division 29 September 1983. Completely revised by the SAE Iron and Steel Committee December 1996. Revised by the SAE Fastener Committee March 2001. Rationale statement available.

1. Scope

1.1 This SAE Standard covers the mechanical and material requirements for eight property classes of steel, externally threaded metric fasteners in sizes M1.6 through M36, inclusive, and suitable for use in automotive and related applications.

1.2 Products included are bolts, screws, studs, U-bolts, preassembled screw and washer assemblies (sems), and products manufactured the same as sems except without washer.

1.3 Products not covered are tapping screws, thread-rolling screws, and self-drilling screws. Mechanical and material requirements for these products are covered in other SAE documents.

1.4 The term stud as referred to herein, applies to a cylindrical rod of moderate length, threaded on either one or both ends or throughout its entire length. It does not apply to headed, collared, or similar products which are more closely characterized by requirements shown herein for bolts.

1.5 For specification purposes, this document treats U-bolts as studs. Thus, wherever the word studs appears, U-bolts is also implied. U-bolts covered by this document are those used primarily in the suspension and related areas of vehicles. (Designers should recognize that the U configuration may not sustain a load equivalent to two bolts or studs of the same size and grade; thus actual load-carrying capacity of U-bolts should be determined by saddle load tests.)

2. References

2.1 Applicable Publications—The following publications form a part of this specification to the extent specified herein. Unless otherwise indicated, the latest issue of SAE publications shall apply.

2.1.1 SAE PUBLICATIONS—Available from SAE, 400 Commonwealth Drive, Warrendale, PA 15096-0001.

SAE J121M—Decarburization in Hardened and Tempered Metric Threaded Fasteners

SAE J123—Surface Discontinuities on Bolts, Screws, and Studs in Fatigue Applications

SAE J429—Mechanical and Material Requirements for Externally Threaded Fasteners

SAE J1061—Surface Discontinuities on General Application Bolts, Screws, and Studs

2.1.2 ASTM PUBLICATIONS—Available from ASTM, 100 Barr Harbor Drive, West Conshohocken, PA 19428-2959.

ASTM A 307—Specification for Carbon Steel Bolts and Studs, 60 000 psi Tensile

ASTMA354—Specification for Quenched and Tempered Alloy Steel Bolts, Studs, and Other Externally Threaded Fasteners

ASTM A 449—Specification for Quenched and Tempered Steel Bolts and Studs

ASTMF606M—Standard Test Methods for Determining the Mechanical Properties of Externally and Internally Threaded Fasteners, Washers, and Rivets

2.1.3 ASME PUBLICATION—Available from ASME, 345 East 47 Street, New York, NY 10017-2330.

ASME B18.2.1

3. Designations

3.1 Property classes are designated by numbers where increasing numbers generally represent increasing tensile strengths. The designation symbol consists of two parts:

a. The first numeral of a two-digit symbol or the first two numerals of a three-digit symbol approximates
1/100 of the minimum tensile strength in MPa.

b. The last numeral approximates 1/10 of the ratio expressed as a percentage between minimum yield stress and minimum tensile stress.

3.2 For specification purposes (on engineering drawings, purchase orders, etc.) all property class designations are used in combination with a single basic specification number as follows:

SAE J1199 (4.6)
SAE J1199 (4.8)
SAE J1199 (5.8)
SAE J1199 (8.8)
SAE J1199 (9.8)
SAE J1199 (10.9)

3.3 Property Classes

3.3.1 Machine screws are normally available only in classes 4.8 and 9.8; other bolts, screws, and studs are available in all classes within the specified product size limitations given in Tables 1A and 1B.

3.3.2 Screw and washer assemblies (sems) are covered by classes 4.8 and 9.8 and allowable deviations from normal 9.8 requirements are stated in footnotes throughout the document.

3.3.3 At the option of the manufacturer, class 5.8 may be supplied with either class 4.6 or 4.8 is ordered, and class 4.8 may be supplied when class 4.6 is ordered.

3.4 Conversion Guidance

3.4.1 For guidance purposes only, to assist designers in selecting a property class:

a. Class 4.6 is approximately equivalent to SAE J429, Grade 1 and ASTM A 307, Grade A.
b. Class 5.8 is approximately equivalent to SAE J429, Grade 2.
c. Class 8.8 is approximately equivalent to SAE J429, Grade 5, and ASTM A 449.
d. Class 9.8 has properties approximately 9% stronger than SAE J429, Grade 5, and ASTM A 449.
e. Class 10.9 is approximately equivalent to SAE J429, Grade 8, and ASTM A 354, Grade BD.

3.4.2 Note that class 8.8 is applicable to sizes above 16 mm, and class 9.8 is applicable to sizes 16 mm and smaller.

4. Materials and Processes

4.1 Steel Characteristics—Bolts, screws, and studs shall be made of steel conforming g to the description and chemical composition requirements specified in Table 2 for the applicable property class.

4.2 Heading Practice

4.2.1 Methods other than upsetting and/or extrusion are permitted only by special agreement between purchaser and manufacturer.

4.2.2 Class 4.6 may be hot or cold headed at option of the manufacturer.

4.2.3 Class 4.8, 5.8, 8.8, 9.8, and 10.9 bolts and screws in sizes up to M20 inclusive, and lengths up to 10 times the nominal product size or 150 mm, whichever is shorter, shall be cold headed, except that they may be hot headed by special agreement of the purchaser. Larger sizes and longer lengths may be cold or hot headed at option of the manufacturer.

4.3 Threading Practice—Class 4.8, 5.8, 8.8, 9.8, and 10.9 bolts and screws in sizes up to M20 inclusive, and lengths up to 150 mm inclusive, shall be roll threaded, except by special agreement. Threads of all sizes of class 4.6 bolts and screws and class 4.8, 5.8, 8.8, 9.8, and 10.9 bolts and screws in sizes over M20 and/or lengths longer than 150 mm, may be rolled, cut, or ground, at option of the manufacturer. Threads of all classes and sizes of studs may be rolled, cut, or ground at option of the manufacturer.

4.4 Heat Treatment Practice

4.4.1 Class 4.6 bolts and screws and class 4.6, 4.8, and 5.8 studs need not be heat treated. Class 4.8 and 5.8 bolts and screws shall be stress relieved if necessary to assure the soundness of the head to shank junction. When specified by the purchaser, class 5.8 bolts and screws shall be stress relieved at a minimum stress relief temperature of 470 °C. Where higher temperatures are necessary to relieve stresses in severely upset heads, mechanical requirements shall be agreed upon by manufacturer and purchaser.

4.4.2 Class 8.8 and 9.8 bolts, screws, and studs shall be heat treated, quenched in oil or water-base quenchant at the option of the manufacturer, and tempered at a minimum tempering temperature of 425 °C for class 8.8 and 410 °C for class 9.8. For class 9.8 screw and washer assemblies (sems), quenchants whose principal constituent is water shall NOT be used, and tempering temperature shall be no less than 340 °C. See also 4.4.5.

TABLE 1A—MECHANICAL REQUIREMENTS FOR BOLTS, SCREWS, AND STUDS

Property Class	Nominal Dia	Full Size Bolts, Screws, and Studs Proof Load (Stress) MPa(1)	Full Size Bolts, Screws, and Studs Tensile Strength (Stress) Min MPa(1)	Machined Test Specimens of Bolts, Screws, and Studs (Sizes Larger than M24) Yield Strength (Stress) Min(2) MPa	Machined Test Specimens of Bolts, Screws, and Studs (Sizes Larger Than M24) Tensile Strength (Stress) Min MPa	Machined Test Specimens of Bolts, Screws, and Studs (Sizes Larger Than M24) Elongation Min %	Machined Test Specimens of Bolts, Screws, and Studs (Sizes Larger than M24) Reduction of Area Min %
4.6	M5 thru M36	225	400	240(3)	400	22	35
4.8	M1.6 thru M16	310	420	—	—	—	—
5.8	M5 thru M24(4)	380	520	—	—	—	—
8.8	M17 thru M36	600	830	660	830	12	35
9.8	M1.6 thru M16(5)	650	900	—	—	—	—
10.9	M6 thru M36	830	1040	940	1040	9	35

1. Proof load and tensile strength values for full size products of each property class are given in Table 5.
2. Yield strength is stress at which a permanent set of 0.2% of gage length occurs.
3. Yield point shall apply instead of yield strength at 0.2% offset for class 4.6 products.
4. Class 5.8 requirements apply to bolts and screws with lengths 150 mm and shorter, and to studs of all lengths.
5. For class 9.8 screw and washer assemblies (sems), base metal hardness may be 25–40 HRC (270–390 HV) and surface hardness shall not exceed 60 HR30N. This requirement applicable also to products manufactured same as sems except without washer, sizes M1.6 thru M12.

TABLE 1B—MECHANICAL REQUIREMENTS FOR BOLTS, SCREWS, AND STUDS

Property Class	Nominal Dia	Surface Hardness Rockwell 30N Max	Product Hardness Rockwell Min(1)	Product Hardness Rockwell Max	Product Hardness Vickers Min(1)	Product Hardness Vickers Max
4.6	M5 thru M36	—	B67	B87	120	180
4.8	M1.6 thru M16	—	B71	B87	130	180
5.8	M5 thru M24(2)	—	B82	B95	160	220
8.8	M17 thru M36	(3)	C23	C34	254	336
9.8	M1.6 thru M16(4)	(3)	C27	C36	279	354
10.9	M6 thru M36	(3)	C33	C39	327	382

1. Minimum hardness requirement is waived if minimum tensile strength is met.
2. Class 5.8 requirements apply to bolts and screws with lengths 150 mm and shorter, and to studs of all lengths.
3. Surface hardness shall not exceed base metal hardness by more than 2 points (Rockwell C equivalent), and in the case of class 10.9 shall also not exceed 59 HR30N.
4. For class 9.8 screw and washer assemblies (sems), base metal hardness may be 25–40 HRC (270-390 HV) and surface hardness shall not exceed 60 HR30N. This requirement applicable also to products manufactured same as sems except without washer, sizes M1.6 thru M12.

TABLE 2—CHEMICAL COMPOSITION REQUIREMENTS PRODUCT ANALYSIS (% BY MASS)

Property Class	Description and Chemical Compositions
4.6 and 4.8	Manufacturer's Option— Low or medium carbon steels (for all sizes), within following limits: C 0.55 max, P 0.048 max, S 0.058 max
5.8	Manufacturer's Option— Low or medium carbon steels (for all sizes), within following limits: C 0.13 to 0.55, P 0.048 max, S 0.058 max For studs only, sulfur content may be 0.33 max
8.8	Manufacturer's Option— Medium carbon steels (for all sizes), within following limits: C 0.28 to 0.55, P 0.048 max, S 0.058 max For studs only, sulfur content may be 0.13 max Medium carbon alloy steels (for sizes over M24), within following limits: C 0.28 to 0.55, P 0.040 max, S 0.045 max When Authorized by Purchaser— Low carbon martensite steels (for sizes thru M20), within following limits: C 0.15 to 0.27, Mn 0.74 to 1.46, P 0.038 max, S 0.048 max, B 0.0005 to 0.003(1) Medium carbon boron steels (for sizes through M24), within following limits: C 0.25 to 0.40, Mn 0.74 min, P 0.048 max, S 0.058 max, B 0.0005 to 0.003(1)
9.8	Medium carbon steels (for all sizes), within following limits: C 0.28 to 0.55, P 0.048 max, S 0.058 max For studs only, sulfur content may be 0.13 max For screw and washer assemblies (sems) and for products manufactured same as sems except without washer, sizes thru M12 only, carbon content may be 0.15 to 0.40. See note 2, Table 6. When Authorized by Purchaser— Low carbon martensite steels (for sizes thru M20), within following limits: C 0.15 to 0.27, Mn 0.74 to 1.46, P 0.038 max, S 0.048 max, B 0.0005 to 0.003(1) Medium carbon boron steels (for sizes thru M24), within following limits: C 0.25 to 0.40, Mn 0.74 min, P 0.048 max, S 0.058 max, B 0.0005 to 0.003(1)
10.9	Manufacturer's Option— Medium carbon alloy steels (for all sizes), within following limits: C 0.28 to 0.55, P 0.040 max, S 0.045 max Fine grain Hardenability—47 min HRC(2) SAE 1541 or SAE 1541H (for sizes thru M12) Fine grain When Authorized by Purchaser— Carbon steels (for sizes thru M20); Fine grain Low carbon martensite steels (for sizes thru M20), within the following limits: C 0.15 to 0.27, Mn 0.74 to 1.46, P 0.038 max, S 0.048 max, B 0.0005 to 0.003(1) Hardenability—40 min HRC(2) Medium carbon boron steels (for sizes thru M24), within following limits: C 0.25 to 0.40, Mn 0.74 min, P 0.048 max, S 0.058 max, B 0.0005 to 0.003(1) Hardenability—47 min HRC(2)

1. Products made from low carbon martensite steels and medium carbon boron steels shall be identified as specified in Table 6, note 1.
2. Steels shall have hardenability that is capable of producing the minimum hardness (Rockwell C) shown at the center of a transverse section one nominal diameter from the threaded end of bolt, screw, or stud (after quenching).

4.4.3 Medium carbon alloy steel class 10.9 bolts, screws, and studs shall be heat treated, oil quenched, and tempered at a minimum tempering temperature of 425 °C. Low-carbon martensite steel class 10.9 bolts, screws, and studs shall be heat treated, quenched in oil or water-base quenchant at the option of the manufacturer, and tempered at a minimum tempering temperature of 340 °C. See also 4.4.5.

4.4.4 Under no circumstances should heat treatment or carbon restoration be accomplished in the presence of nitrogen compounds, such as carbonitriding or cyaniding.

4.4.5 Tempering Temperature Audit Test (for checking whether products have been tempered at specified temperature). Conduct hardness test (ASTM F 606M) on one or more bolts, screws, or studs; retemper the product(s) at a temperature 10 °C less than the specified minimum tempering temperature for 30 min; repeat product hardness test. The difference between the mean hardnesses (before and after retempering) shall be no greater than 2 points Rockwell C (approximately 20 Vicker points).

5. *Mechanical and Physical Properties*

5.1 Mechanical—Bolts, screws, and studs shall be tested in accordance with the mechanical testing requirements for the applicable type, property class, size, and length of product as specified in Tables 3A and 3B, and shall meet the mechanical requirements specified for that product in Tables 1A and 1B.

5.2 Decarburization—Unless otherwise specified, class 8.8 and 9.8 products shall conform to decarburization class 1/2H and Class 10.9 products shall conform to decarburization class 2/3H as specified in SAE J121M.

5.3 Surface Discontinuities

5.3.1 Bolts, screws, and studs of classes 8.8, 9.8, and 10.9 in sizes up to M24 inclusive, and lengths up to 150 mm inclusive, shall not have surface discontinuities exceeding the limits specified in SAE J1061.

Surface discontinuities for sizes and lengths of products not covered in the scope of SAE J1061 shall be within limits specified by purchaser.

5.3.2 When the engineering requirements of the application necessitate that surface discontinuities must be more closely controlled, the purchaser shall specify the applicable limits in the original inquiry and purchase order. For certain fasteners, this may be done by reference to SAE J123.

6. *Methods of Test*

6.1 General—Procedures for conducting the tests to determine the mechanical properties as specified in Tables 3A and 3B for the applicable product, property class, size, and length are given in ASTM F 606M. Tables 3A and 3B specifies the applicable test method to be followed when determining each mechanical property.

7. *Marking*

7.1 Bolts and Screws—Slotted and cross-recessed screws of all sizes and other screws and bolts of sizes smaller than M5 need not be marked. All other bolts and screws of sizes M5 and larger shall be marked permanently and clearly to identify the property class and the manufacturer. The property class symbols shall be as given in Table 6; the symbol for the manufacturer's identification shall be at his option. Markings shall be located on the top of the head of bolts and screws, and may be either raised or depressed at option of the manufacturer. Alternatively, for hex head products, the markings may be indented on the side of the head.

Property class marking shall conform to Table 7.

Metric bolts and screws shall not be marked with radial line symbols.

7.2 Studs—All studs of sizes M5 and larger shall be marked permanently and clearly to identify the property class. The symbols used shall be as given in Table 6. Markings shall be located on the extreme end of the stud, and may be raised or depressed at the option of the manufacturer. For studs with an interference fit thread, the markings shall be located at the nut end. Studs of sizes smaller than M12 may be marked using the property class symbols given in Table 6.

TABLE 3A—MECHANICAL TESTING REQUIREMENTS FOR BOLTS, SCREWS, AND STUDS

Product	Property Class	Specified Min Tensile Strength of Product (See Table 5) kN	Length of Product(1)	Product Hardness Max(2)	Product Hardness Min(2)	Surface Hardness (2)(3)	Tests Conducted Using Full Size Products Proof Load(2)	Tests Conducted Using Full Size Products Wedge Tensile Strength(2)(4)	Tests Conducted Using Full Size Products Axial Tensile Strength(2)
Short bolts and screws	all	all	less than 2-1/4D	•	•	•	—	—	—
Special head bolts and screws(5)	all	all	all	•	•	•	—	—	—
Hex bolts and screws(6)(7)	all	450 and less	2-1/4D to 8D or 200 mm, whichever is greater	•	—	•	°	•	—
	all	450 and less	Over 8 D or 200 mm, whichever is greater thru and incl 300 mm	•	—	•	°	•	—
	all	450 and less	over 300 mm	•	—	•	°	A	—
	all	over 450	2-1/4D and longer	•	—	•	°	A	—
All other bolts and screws	all	450 and less	2-1/4D to 8D or 200 mm, whichever is greater	•	—	•	°	—	•
	all	450 and less	over 8D or 200 mm, whichever is greater	•	—	•	°	—	A
	all	over 450	2-1/4D and longer	•	—	•	°	—	A
Short studs	all	all	less than 2-1/4D	•	•	•	—	—	—
All other studs	all	450 and less	2-1/4D to 8D or 200 mm, whichever is greater	•	—	•	°	•	—
	all	450 and less	over 8D or 200 mm, whichever is greater	•	—	•	°	A	—
	all	over 450	2-1/4D and longer	•	—	•	°	A	—
Tests to be conducted in accordance with paragraph				See ASTM F 606M 3.1	See ASTM F 606M 3.1	See ASTM F 606M 3.1	See ASTM F 606M 3.2	See ASTM F 606M 3.5	See ASTM F 606M 3.4

1. D equals nominal diameter of product. For purposes of Table 3 requirements, "length of product" is the nominal length including point chamfer as defined in ASME B18.2.1, and all special point products shall be measured from the bearing surface to the crest of the last complete thread form.
2. • denotes a mandatory test. For each product, all mandatory tests (•) shall be performed. In addition, either all tests denoted A (which apply to full size products) or all tests denoted B (which apply to machined test specimens) shall be performed; except optional B tests are not applicable to products M24 and smaller. ° denotes tests to be performed when specifically required in the original inquiry and purchase order. In case arbitration is necessary, both A tests and ° tests shall be performed. Dashes (—) indicate tests which are not required.
3. Surface hardness and decarburization requirements apply only to property classes 8.8, 9.8, and 10.9.
4. Tensile test wedge angles are specified in Table 4.
5. Special head bolts and screws are those with special configurations or with drilled heads which are weaker than the threaded section.
6. Includes flange, washer, and other hex head configurations which are not weaker than the threaded section.
7. Includes class 9.8 sems and 9.8 products manufactured same as sems except without washer (sizes M1.6 thru M12). For purposes of determining applicability of tensile testing, length of sems is the distance measured from the underside of bearing plane of the unflattened washer to the last full thread of the screw.

TABLE 3B—MECHANICAL TESTING REQUIREMENTS FOR BOLTS, SCREWS, AND STUDS

Product	Property Class	Specified Min Tensile Strength of Product (See Table 5) kN	Length of Product(1)	Tests Conducted Using Machined Test Specimens Yield Strength(2)	Tests Conducted Using Machined Test Specimens Tensile Strength(2)	Tests Conducted Using Machined Test Specimens Elongation(2)	Tests Conducted Using Machined Test Specimens Reduction of Area(2)	Decarburization in Threaded Section(2)(3)
Short bolts and screws	all	all	less than 2-1/4D	—	—	—	—	°
Special head bolts and screws (4)	all	all	all	—	—	—	—	°
Hex bolts and screws (5)(6)	all	450 and less	2-1/4D to 8D or 200 mm, whichever is greater	—	—	—	—	°
	all	450 and less	Over 8D or 200 mm, whichever is greater thru and incl 300 mm	—	—	—	—	°
	all	450 and less	over 300 mm	B	B	B	B	°
	all	over 450	2-1/4D and longer	B	B	B	B	°
All other bolts and screws	all	450 and less	2-1/4D to 8D or 200 mm, whichever is greater	—	—	—	—	°
	all	450 and less	over 8D or 200 mm, whichever is greater	B	B	B	B	°
	all	over 450	2-1/4D and longer	B	B	B	B	°
Short studs	all	all	less than 2-1/4D	—	—	—	—	°
All other studs	all	450 and less	2-1/4D to 8D or 200 mm, whichever is greater	—	—	—	—	°
	all	450 and less	over 8D or 200 mm, whichever is greater	B	B	B	B	°
	all	over 450	2-1/4D and longer	B	B	B	B	°
Tests to be conducted in accordance with paragraph				See ASTM F 606M 3.6	See ASTM F 606M 3.6	See ASTM F 606M 3.6	See ASTM F 606M 3.6	See SAE J121M See SAE J121M

1. D equals nominal diameter of product. For purposes of Table 3 requirements, "length of product" is the nominal length including point chamfer as defined in ASME B18.2.1, and all special point products shall be measured from the bearing surface to the crest of the last complete thread form.
2. • denotes a mandatory test. For each product, all mandatory tests (•) shall be performed. In addition, either all tests denoted A (which apply to full size products) or all tests denoted B (which apply to machined test specimens) shall be performed; except optional B tests are not applicable to products M24 and smaller. ° denotes tests to be performed when specifically required in the original inquiry and purchase order. In case arbitration is necessary, both A tests and ° tests shall be performed. Dashes (—) indicate tests which are not required.
3. Surface hardness and decarburization requirements apply only to property classes 8.8, 9.8, and 10.9.
4. Special head bolts and screws are those with special configurations or with drilled heads which are weaker than the threaded section.
5. Includes flange, washer, and other hex head configurations which are not weaker than the threaded section.
6. Includes class 9.8 sems and 9.8 products manufactured same as sems except without washer (sizes M1.6 thru M12). For purposes of determining applicability of tensile testing, length of sems is the distance measured from the underside of bearing plane of the unflattened washer to the last full thread of the screw.

TABLE 4—TENSILE TEST WEDGE ANGLES

Product	Property Class	Nominal Dia.	Wedge Angle Deg
Hex and hex washer head machine screws	4.8, 9.8	thru M10	6
Hex bolts and screws threaded 1D and closer to underside of head	8.8, 9.8, 10.9	thru M20	6
		over M20 to M36	4
Hex flange and hex washer head bolts and screws	4.6, 4.8, 5.8, 8.8, 9.8, 10.9	thru M36	6
All other hex bolts and screws	4.6, 4.8, 5.8, 8.8, 9.8, 10.9	thru M24	10
		over M24 to M36	6
Studs	all	thru M20	6
		over M20 to M36	4

TABLE 5A—PROOF LOAD AND TENSILE STRENGTH VALUES(1)

Nominal Thread Dia and Thread Pitch	Stress Area(2) mm^2	Class 4.6 Proof Load kN	Class 4.6 Tensile Strength Min kN	Class 4.8 Proof Load kN	Class 4.8 Tensile Strength Min kN	Class 5.8 Proof Load kN	Class 5.8 Tensile Strength Min kN
M1.6 x 0.35	1.27			0.39	0.53		
M2 x 0.4	2.07			0.64	0.87		
M2.5 x 0.45	3.39			1.05	1.42		
M3 x 0.5	5.03			1.56	2.11		
M3.5 x 0.6	6.78			2.10	2.85		
M4 x 0.7	8.78			2.72	3.69		
M5 x 0.8	14.2	3.20	5.68	4.40	5.96	5.40	7.38
M6 x 1	20.1	4.52	8.04	6.23	8.44	7.64	10.4
M8 x 1.25	36.6	8.24	14.6	11.3	15.4	13.9	19.0
M10 x 1.5	58.0	13.1	23.2	18.0	24.4	22.0	30.2
M12 x 1.75	84.3	19.0	33.7	26.1	35.4	32.0	43.8
M14 x 2	115	25.9	46.0	35.7	48.3	43.7	59.8
M16 x 2	157	35.3	62.8	48.7	65.9	59.7	81.6
M20 x 2.5	245	55.1	98.0			93.1	127
M24 x 3	353	79.4	141			134	184
M30 x 3.5	561	126	224				
M36 x 4	817	184	327				

1. Proof loads and tensile strengths are computed by multiplying the stresses given in Table 1 by the stress area of the thread.
2. Stress area = $0.7854\ (D—0.9382P)^2$ where D is nominal thread diameter in mm and P is thread pitch in mm.

TABLE 5B—PROOF LOAD AND TENSILE STRENGTH VALUES[1]

Nominal Thread Dia and Thread Pitch	Stress Area[2] mm²	Class 8.8 Proof Load kN	Class 8.8 Tensile Strength Min kN	Class 9.8 Proof Load kN	Class 9.8 Tensile Strength Min kN	Class 10.9 Proof Load kN	Class 10.9 Tensile Strength Min kN
M1.6 x 0.35	1.27			0.83	1.14		
M2 x 0.4	2.07			1.35	1.86		
M2.5 x 0.45	3.39			2.20	3.05		
M3 x 0.5	5.03			3.27	4.53		
M3.5 x 0.6	6.78			4.41	6.10		
M4 x 0.7	8.78			5.71	7.90		
M5 x 0.8	14.2			9.23	12.8	11.8	14.8
M6 x 1	20.1			13.1	18.1	16.7	20.9
M8 x 1.25	36.6			23.8	32.9	30.4	38.1
M10 x 1.5	58.0			37.7	52.2	48.1	60.3
M12 x 1.75	84.3			54.8	75.9	70.0	87.7
M14 x 2	115			74.8	104	95.4	120
M16 x 2	157			102	141	130	163
M20 x 2.5	245	147	203			203	255
M24 x 3	353	212	293			293	367
M30 x 3.5	561	337	466			466	583
M36 x 4	817	490	678			678	850

1. Proof loads and tensile strengths are computed by multiplying the stresses given in Table 1 by the stress area of the thread.
2. Stress area = $0.7854\,(D—0.9382P)^2$ where D is nominal thread diameter in mm and P is thread pitch in mm.

TABLE 6—PROPERTY CLASS IDENTIFICATION SYMBOLS

Property Class	Identification Symbol Bolts, Screws, and Studs Sizes M5 and Larger	Identification Symbol Optional for Studs Sizes M5 thru M11
4.6	4.6	
4.8	4.8	
5.8	5.8	
8.8[1]	8.8	°
9.8(1)[2]	9.8	+
10.9[1]	10.9	

1. Products made of low carbon martensite steel shall be additionally identified by underlining the numerals.
2. Products manufactured same as sems except without washer, from steel having optional carbon content permitted in Table 2, shall be additionally identified with an inverted T located between the numerals 9.8 as follows: 9^8.

TABLE 7—PROPERTY CLASS MARKING

Bolt or Screw Size mm	Height of Symbol mm
5 thru 6	1.5 min
8 thru 10	2.3 min
12 and 14	3.2 min
16 and larger	4.0 min

TORQUE-TENSION TIGHTENING FOR INCH SERIES FASTENERS—SAE J1701 MAR1999

SAE Information Report

Report of the SAE Fasteners Committee approved July 19961996-07 Rationale statement available.1999-03

Foreword—Fundamentally, threaded fasteners are required to create a clamping force or load on the assembled joint to prevent loosening. To accomplish this, a tensile loading is applied onto a bolt or screw by itself or by a nut tightened on the bolt or screw.

The axial stress in them produces a clamping force equal to the product of the proof-load stress, reduced by a design factor, and the core area of the bolt or screw.

Although clamping or tension load can be measured by load cells and strain gauges, these methods are impractical on the production line. The most practical methods of achieving control of joint clamp load involve torque control, tightening angle control, or combinations of torque and angle. In some cases, a torque versus angle yield method is utilized, particularly when tightening 5/8 in and larger fastener sizes. But measurement and assembly equipment is sensitive. Therefore, it becomes very important to understand the relationship between torque and tension.

1. Scope—This SAE Information Report is provided as an advisory guide. Individual application discretion is recommended. The content has been presented as accurately as possible, but responsibility for its application lies with the user. The document covers the variables in the torque-tension relationship: friction, materials, temperature, humidity, fastener and mating part finishes, surfaces, and the kind of wrenching employed.

Also described in this document is the torque management required to achieve correct fastener joint tightening.

The thread fit of fasteners must be in accordance with Class 2A for external and 2B for internal inch threads.

2. References

2.1 Related Publications—The following publications are provided for information purposes only and are not a required part of this document.

2.1.1 SAE PUBLICATIONS—Available from SAE, 400 Commonwealth Drive, Warrendale, PA 15096-0001.

SAE J174—Torque-Tension Test Procedures

SAE J995—Mechanical and Material Requirements for Steel Nuts

SAE J1648—Protective Coatings for Fasteners

3. Explanation of Tightening Terms

3.1 Torque is the product of force x lever arm length. It is the moment resistance of the fastener and its components to tightening, expressed in in-oz, in-lb, and ft-lb.

3.2 Turn Screw or Bolt and Turn Nut Terms describe which mating part is tightened. For turn screw, the head of the screw or bolt is turned against a panel into either a panel with a tapped thread or separate nut component.

For turn nut, the nut is threaded onto a screw or bolt and is tightened against the panel surface.

3.3 Clamping Load occurs when the screw or bolt is stretched when the fastener is tightened. It is equal and opposite to the tensile force developed in the screw or bolt and is expressed as pounds (lb).

3.4 Inertia is the tendency of a body to continue in motion after being subjected to a force in a specific direction until acted upon by an outside force. In tightening, friction between mating parts and bearing against panel or part surfaces is the major contributing outside force and has to be overcome. Inertia of the rotating power tool is another factor which must be considered.

4. Variables in the Relationship of Clamping Load to Applied Torque

4.1 Friction—The friction resistance torque is the most important of all of the variables. It has two components, the friction resistance of the applied nut fastener with respect to mating part threads, and the bearing surface against joint members. Increasing the clamping tension force on the screw or bolt increases the resistance to turning.

4.2 Fastener Materials—Characteristic properties of hardness and surface condition can contribute to friction variability thus affecting tightening torque to obtain the same clamping load.

4.2.1 Nonheat-treatable low-carbon stainless steels and other soft alloys cause increased friction resistance resulting in higher tightening torque for a given clamp load.

4.2.2 Hardened steel or hard alloy fasteners have a harder slippery surface reducing friction and thereby requiring lower tightening torque.

4.2.3 Special materials, rubber, plastics, etc., either as fabricated fasteners or attached to them, also affect torque if they contact the rubbing surfaces during the tightening.

4.3 Surface Conditions, such as coatings or effects of the environment applied to fasteners and bearing surfaces will affect tightening torque requirements for a given clamp load.

4.3.1 The roughness, coarseness, or abrasiveness of coatings will increase required torque.

4.3.2 Decreased friction due to the nature of the coating including oil, wax, teflon, or other lubricants will reduce required torque.

4.3.3 Interferences due to dirt, rust, burrs and galling, or seizing caused by soft coatings (zinc is an example) on fasteners, mating parts, and panels increases required torque.

4.3.4 Hardness of the fastener, its mating part, or the joint material will reduce required torque.

4.3.5 Temperature contraction, especially if the assembly tightening was made while warm, will reduce clamping load. If the fastener is at a higher temperature than the assembly, then the clamping load increases upon cooling. Adjustments to assembly torque must accommodate these conditions.

4.3.6 Humidity will cause reduced friction reducing required torque.

4.3.7 Joint relaxation can occur if joint material can deform under load and/or time. In such cases, special torque sequencing may be required.

4.4 Wrenching—The method of tightening has a profound influence on required torque.

4.4.1 The slow deliberate turning by hand wrenching allows the assembly to settle somewhat during tightening thus negating some of the effects of joint relaxation.

4.4.2 High air pressure or electric power tool fastener tightening involving rotation contribute to lower torque. The use of inertia lessens the affect of static friction, but can increase torsional loading of bolts or screws.

5. Torque Management—To determine how much hand or power tool torque should be applied to a fastener assembly or how much turn-of-the-nut tightening is required, consideration must be directed to the development of these methods.

5.1 Theoretical Calculations to Obtain Torque Guide

5.1.1 EMPIRICAL EQUATION

$$T = KDW \qquad \text{(Eq. 1)}$$

where:

T= Torque (in-lb, ft-lb)
D = Screw or bolt nominal size (in)
W = Screw or bolt tension (lb-oz)
K = Torque factor

5.1.2 The tension of the screw or bolt is calculated by multiplying the usable screw or bolt tensile strength by the tensile-stress core area of the screw or bolt. The nominal clamp load stress is assumed as 75% of proof load.

5.1.3 The torque factor is the critical parameter in Equation 1 influenced primarily by the frictional conditions along the thread flank and at the bearing surfaces.

The other influence on "K" is the relative resiliency of the fastener and joint material.

a. Therefore:

$$K = K_1 + K_2 + K_3 \qquad \text{(Eq. 2)}$$

where:

K_1 represents the torque factor wasted by friction on the bearing surface of the nut or bolt, approximately 50% of the total torque factor.

K_2 factor represents the wasted friction on the contact flanks of the threads, about 40% of the total "K".

K_3 factor represents the useful torque producing the bolt tension, about 10% of the total "K".

b. K is 0.15/0.20 when bolts, nuts, and washers of the fastener joint are clean and coated with a thin film of protective oil. When dirt, rust, and other defects of field storage and environmental exposure are present, K can be 0.25/0.40. Refer to Table 1 for torque K factors for other conditions.

TABLE 1—TORQUE FACTORS FOR SURFACE CONDITIONS OF MATING FASTENERS

Mating Parts	K
Dry, clean with thin film of oil	0.15/0.20
Additional lubricating coatings of oil, wax, or dissimilar plating or hard washer	0.10/0.15
Thread and head bearing surfaces covered with high-performance lubricants or with anti-seize compounds	can be as low as 0.05
Combinations of certain materials such as Austenite stainless steel screws/bolts and parts not lubricated or coated	can be as high as 0.35

5.2 Clamp load and torque calculations based on the aforementioned formula for dry and lubricated conditions are tabulated in Table 2.

5.3 Turn-of-the-Nut Method—The previous sections dwelled on tightening torque to produce clamping tension. The turn-of-the-nut method can produce satisfactory clamping when the joint is completely closed prior to the turn movement.

Since the basis for tightening threaded fasteners is screw or bolt tension, stretching the bolt by turning the nut a number of degrees clockwise after finger or snug tight will accomplish this. The bolt stretch is the degrees turned portion of the 360 degree pitch dimension. The number of degrees turned depends upon the strength of the bolt and the joint thickness.

This document has not elaborated on the method because it is not effective unless the joint is closed under the screw/bolt head or nut. Nevertheless, turn-of-the-nut is the most practical for 5/8 in and larger sizes.

5.4 Check procedure for correct tightening torque because assembly conditions such as mismatching components and pull-up tightening occur. The calculated guide torques previously discussed may overpower the fastener or its mating part causing failure to each other or both. Therefore, the following procedure on assimilated assemblies can be a practical method of establishing installation torque.

5.4.1 First determine the torque at which any of twelve or statistically determined number of fasteners selected from the same lot or their mating parts fail when they are applied by either hand or power tool wrenching to be used in production.

5.4.2 Average the twelve individual torques. Then apply 85% safety factor and repeat the previous with a new set of twelve fasteners until no failures occur.

5.4.3 Retest a new set of fasteners on the assemblies utilizing the design factor established torque to confirm installation is satisfactory or make minor adjustments until it is so.

TABLE 2—TORQUE-TENSION RELATIONSHIPS FOR SAE GRADES 2, 5, AND 8

Nominal Size and Threads/in	Stress Area (1) in²	Grade 2 Clamp Load lb	Grade 2 Torque Dry K = 0.2 in-lb	Grade 2 Torque Lub K = 0.15 in-lb	Grade 5 Clamp Load lb	Grade 5 Torque Dry K = 0.2 in-lb	Grade 5 Torque Lub K = 0.15 in-lb	Grade 8 Clamp Load lb	Grade 8 Torque Dry K = 0.2 in-lb	Grade 8 Torque Lub K = 0.15 in-lb
0.250-28	0.03637	1500	75.0	56.0	2319	116.0	87.0	3273	164	123
0.250-20	0.03182	1313	66.0	49.0	2029	101.0	76.0	2864	143	107
0.3125-24	0.05806	2395	150.0	112.0	3700	230.0	173.0	5225	327	245
0.3125-18	0.05243	2163	135.0	101.0	3342	209.0	157.0	4719	295	221
0.375-24	0.08783	3623	272.0	204.0	5600	420.0	315.0	7905	593	445
0.375-16	0.07749	3196	240.0	180.0	4940	370.0	278.0	6974	523	392
0.4375-20	0.11870	4896	428.0	321.0	7567	662.0	496.0	10683	935	700
0.4375-14	0.10630	4385	384.0	288.0	6777	593.0	445.0	9567	837	628
0.500-20	0.15995	6598	660.0	495.0	10197	1020.0	764.0	14396	1440	1080
0.500-13	0.14190	5853	585.0	439.0	9046	904.0	678.0	12771	1277	958
Nominal Size and Threads/in	**Stress Area (1) in²**	**Grade 2 Clamp Load lb**	**Grade 2 Torque Dry K = 0.2 ft-lb**	**Grade 2 Torque Lub K = 0.15 ft-lb**	**Grade 5 Clamp Load lb**	**Grade 5 Torque Dry K = 0.2 ft-lb**	**Grade 5 Torque Lub K = 0.15 ft-lb**	**Grade 8 Clamp Load lb**	**Grade 8 Torque Dry K = 0.2 ft-lb**	**Grade 8 Torque Lub K = 0.15 ft-lb**
0.5625-18	0.20298	8373	78	59	12940	121	91	18268	171	128
0.5625-12	0.18195	7505	70	53	11600	109	82	16376	154	115
0.625-18	0.25595	10558	110	82	16317	170	127	23036	240	180
0.625-11	0.22600	9322	97	73	14407	150	113	20340	212	159
0.750-16	0.37296	15385	192	144	23776	297	223	33566	420	315
0.750-10	0.33446	13796	172	129	21532	269	201	30101	376	282
1.000-12	0.66304	—	—	—	42269	704	528	59674	995	746
1.000-8	0.60574	—	—	—	38616	644	483	54517	909	681
Tensile Strength			74,000 psi			120,000 psi			150,000 psi	
Proof Load Stress			55,000 psi			85,000 psi			120,000 psi	

Caution—The previously listed torque and resulting tension are provided as an advisory guide. Individual application discretion is recommended. The content has been presented as accurately as possible, but responsibility for its application lies with the user.

Note 1—The stress area of threaded series not included in Table 2 may be computed from the equation:

$$A_S = 0.7854\left(D - 0.9743/n\right)^2 \quad \text{(Eq. 3)}$$

where:

A_s = Stress area in in²
D = Diameter in inches
n = Threads per inch

TORQUE-TENSION TIGHTENING FOR METRIC SERIES FASTENERS—SAE J1701M JUL1996

SAE Information Report

Report of the SAE Fasteners Committee approved July 1996.

Foreword—Fundamentally, threaded fasteners are required to create a clamping force or load on the assembled joint to prevent loosening. To accomplish this, a tensile loading is applied onto a bolt or screw by itself or by a nut tightened on the bolt or screw.

The axial stress in them produces a clamping force equal to the product of the proof-load stress, reduced by a design factor, and the core area of the bolt or screw.

Although clamping or tension load can be measured by load cells and strain gauges, these methods are impractical on the production line. The most practical methods of achieving control of joint clamp load involve torque control, angle (tightening) control, or combinations of torque and angle. In some cases, a torque versus angle yield method is utilized, particularly when tightening 16 mm and larger sizes. But measurement and assembly equipment is sensitive. Therefore, it becomes very important to understand the relationship between torque and tension.

1. Scope—This SAE Information Report is provided as an advisory guide. Individual application discretion is recommended. The content has been presented as accurately as possible, but responsibility for its application lies with the user. The document covers the variables in the torque-tension relationship: friction, materials, temperature, humidity, fastener and mating part finishes, surfaces, and the kind of wrenching employed.

Also described in this document is the torque management required to achieve correct fastener joint tightening.

The thread fit of fasteners must be in accordance with Class 6g for external and 6H for internal metric threads.

2. References

2.1 Related Publications—The following publications are provided for information purposes only and are not a required part of this document.

2.1.1 SAE PUBLICATIONS—Available from SAE, 400 Commonwealth Drive, Warrendale, PA 15096-0001.

SAE J174—Torque-Tension Test Procedures
SAE J1648—Protective Coatings for Fasteners

3. Explanation of Tightening Terms

3.1 Torque—Is the product of force x lever arm length. It is the moment resistance of the fastener and its components to tightening, expressed in newton-meters (N·m).

3.2 Turn Screw or Bolt and Turn Nut Terms—Describe which mating part is tightened. For turn screw, the head of the screw or bolt is turned against a panel into either a panel with a tapped thread or separate nut component.

For turn nut, the nut is threaded onto a screw or bolt and is tightened against the panel surface.

3.3 Clamping Load—Occurs when the screw or bolt is stretched when the fastener is tightened. It is equal and opposite to the tensile force developed in the screw or bolt and is expressed as newtons (N).

3.4 Inertia—Is the tendency of a body to continue in motion after being subjected to a force in a specific direction until acted upon by an outside force. In tightening, friction between mating parts and bearing against panel or part surfaces is the major contributing outside force and has to be overcome. Inertia of the rotating power tool is another factor which must be considered.

4. Variables in the Relationship of Clamping Load to Applied Torque

4.1 Friction—The friction resistance torque is the most important of all of the variables. It has two components, the friction resistance of the applied nut fastener with respect to mating part threads, and the bearing surface against joint members. Increasing the clamping tension force on the screw or bolt increases the friction resistance to turning.

4.2 Fastener Materials—Characteristic properties of hardness and surface condition can contribute to friction variability thus affecting tightening torque to obtain the same clamping load.

4.2.1 Nonheat-treatable low-carbon stainless steels and other soft alloys cause increased friction resistance resulting in higher tightening torque for a given clamp load.

4.2.2 Hardened steel or hard alloy fasteners have a harder slippery surface reducing friction and thereby requiring lower tightening torque.

4.2.3 Special materials, rubber, plastics, etc., either as fabricated fasteners or attached to them, also affect torque if they contact the rubbing surfaces during the tightening.

4.3 Surface Conditions, such as coatings or effects of the environment applied to fasteners and bearing surfaces will affect tightening torque requirements for a given clamp load.

4.3.1 The roughness, coarseness, or abrasiveness of coatings will increase torque required resistance.

4.3.2 Decreased friction due to the nature of the coating including oil, wax, teflon, or other lubricants will reduce torque required resistance.

4.3.3 Interferences due to dirt, rust, burrs and galling, or seizing caused by soft coatings (zinc is an example) on fasteners, mating parts, and panels increases torque resistance.

4.3.4 Hardness of the fastener, its mating part, or the joint material panel will reduce required torque.

4.3.5 Temperature contraction, especially if the assembly tightening was made while warm, will reduce clamping load. If the fastener is at a higher temperature than the assembly, then the clamping load increases upon cooling. Adjustments to assembly torque must accommodate these conditions.

4.3.6 Humidity will cause reduced friction and stickiness reducing required torque.

4.3.7 Joint relaxation can occur if joint material deforms under load and/or time. In such cases, special torque sequencing may be required.

4.4 Wrenching—The method of tightening has a profound influence on required torque.

4.4.1 The slow deliberate turning by hand wrenching allows the assembly to settle somewhat during tightening thus negating some of the effects of joint relaxation.

4.4.2 High air pressure or electric power tool fastener tightening involving rotation inertia and sudden stoppage contribute to lower torque. The use of inertia lessens the affect of static friction but can increase torsional loading of bolts or screws.

5. Torque Management—To determine how much hand or power tool torque should be applied to a fastener assembly or how much turn-of-the-nut tightening is required, consideration must be directed to the development of these methods.

5.1 Theoretical Calculations to Obtain Torque Guide

5.1.1 EMPIRICAL EQUATION

$$T = KDW \qquad \text{(Eq. 1)}$$

where:

T = Torque (N·m)
D = Screw or bolt nominal size (mm)
W = Screw or bolt tension (kN)
K = Torque factor

5.1.2 The tension of the screw or bolt is calculated by multiplying the usable screw or bolt tensile strength by the tensile-stress core area of the screw or bolt. The nominal clamp load stress is assumed as 75% of proof load stress.

5.1.3 The torque factor is the critical parameter in Equation 1 influenced primarily by the frictional conditions along the thread flank and at the bearing surfaces.

The other influence on "K" is the relative resiliency of the fastener and joint material.

a. Therefore:

$$K = K_1 + K_2 + K_3 \qquad \text{(Eq. 2)}$$

where:

K_1 represents the torque factor wasted by friction on the bearing surface of the nut or bolt, approximately 50% of the total torque factor.

K_2 factor represents the wasted friction on the contact flanks of the threads, about 40% of the total "K".

K_3 factor represents the useful torque producing the bolt tension, about 10% of the total "K".

b. K is 0.15/0.20 when bolts, nuts, and washers of the fastener joint are clean and coated with a thin film of protective oil.

When dirt, rust, and other defects of field storage and environmental exposure are present, K can be 0.25/0.40. Refer to Table 1 for torque K factors for other conditions.

TABLE 1—TORQUE FACTORS FOR SURFACE CONDITIONS OF MATING FASTENERS

Mating Parts	K
Dry, clean with thin film of oil	0.15/0.20
Additional lubricating coatings of oil, wax, or dissimilar plating or hard washer	0.10/0.15
Thread and head bearing surfaces covered with high-performance lubricants or with anti-seize compounds	can be as low as 0.05
Combinations of certain materials such as Austenite stainless steel screws/bolts and parts not lubricated or coated	can be as high as 0.35

5.2 Clamp load and torque calculations based on the Equation 2 formula for dry and lubricated conditions are tabulated in Table 2.

5.3 Turn-of-the-Nut Method—The previous sections dwelled on tightening torque to produce clamping tension. The turn-of-the-nut method can produce satisfactory clamping when the joint is completely closed prior to the turn movement.

Since the basis for tightening threaded fasteners is screw or bolt tension, stretching the bolt by turning the nut a number of degrees clockwise after finger or snug tight will accomplish this. The bolt stretch is the degrees turned portion of the 360 degree pitch dimension. The number of degrees turned depends upon the strength of the bolt and the joint thickness.

This document has not elaborated on the method because it is not effective unless the joint is closed under the bolt head or nut. Nevertheless, turn-of-the-nut is the most practical for M16 and larger fastener sizes.

5.4 Check procedure for correct tightening torque because assembly conditions such as mismatching components and pull-up tightening occur, the calculated guide torques previously discussed may overpower the fastener or its mating part causing failure to each other or both. Therefore, the following procedure on assimilated assemblies can be a practical method of establishing installation torque.

5.4.1 First determine the torque at which any of twelve or statistically determined number of fasteners selected from the same lot or their mating parts fail when they are applied by either hand or power tool wrenching to be used in production.

5.4.2 Average the twelve individual torques. Then apply 85% safety factor and repeat the previous with a new set of twelve fasteners until no failures occur.

5.4.3 Retest a new set of fasteners on the assemblies utilizing the design factor established torque to confirm installation is satisfactory or make minor adjustments until it is so.

TABLE 2—TORQUE-TENSION RELATIONSHIP FOR METRIC PROPERTY CLASSES

Major Diameter and Thread Pitch	Stress Area mm^2	Class 4.6 Clamp Load kN	Class 4.6 Torque Dry K = 0.2 N·m	Class 4.6 Torque Lub K = 0.15 N·m	Class 4.8 Clamp Load kN	Class 4.8 Torque Dry K = 0.2 N·m	Class 4.8 Torque Lub K = 0.15 N·m	Class 5.8 Clamp Load kN	Class 5.8 Torque Dry K = 0.2 N·m	Class 5.8 Torque Lub K = 0.15 N·m
3.0 x 0.5	5.03	0.85	0.50	0.40	1.17	0.70	0.50			
3.5 x 0.6	6.78	1.14	0.80	0.60	1.58	1.10	0.80			
4.0 x 0.7	8.78	1.48	1.20	0.90	2.04	1.60	1.20			
5.0 x 0.8	14.20	2.40	2.40	1.80	3.30	3.30	2.50	4.05	4.00	3.00
6.0 x 1.0	20.10	3.40	4.00	3.00	4.67	5.66	4.20	5.73	6.90	5.20
8.0 x 1.25	36.6	6.18	9.90	7.40	8.51	13.60	10.20	10.40	16.70	12.50
10.0 x 1.50	58.0	9.79	19.60	14.70	13.48	27.00	20.00	16.50	33.10	24.80
12.0 x 1.75	84.3	14.22	34.10	25.60	19.60	47.00	35.00	24.00	58.00	43.00
14.0 x 2.00	115.0	19.41	54.30	40.80	26.74	75.00	56.00	32.80	92.00	69.00
16.0 x 2.00	157.0									
20.0 x 2.50	245.0									
24.0 x 3.00	353.0									
30.0 x 3.50	561.0									
36.0 x 4.00	817.0									
Tensile Strength			400 MPa			420 MPa			520 MPa	
Proof Load Stress			225 MPa			310 MPa			380 MPa	

Major Diameter and Thread Pitch	Stress Area mm^2	Class 8.8 Clamp Load kN	Class 8.8 Torque Dry K = 0.2 N·m	Class 8.8 Torque Lub K = 0.15 N·m	Class 9.8 Clamp Load kN	Class 9.8 Torque Dry K = 0.2 N·m	Class 9.8 Torque Lub K = 0.15 N·m	Class 10.9 Clamp Load kN	Class 10.9 Torque Dry K = 0.2 N·m	Class 10.9 Torque Lub K = 0.15 N·m
3.5 x 0.6	6.78									
4.0 x 0.7	8.78									
5.0 x 0.8	14.20									
6.0 x 1.0	20.10									
8.0 x 1.25	36.6	16.50	26.40	19.80	17.80	28.50	21.40	22.80	36.50	27.30
10.0 x 1.50	58.0	26.10	52.20	39.20	28.30	56.60	42.40	36.10	72.20	54.20
12.0 x 1.75	84.3	37.90	91.00	68.00	41.10	99.00	74.00	52.50	126.00	94.00
14.0 x 2.00	115.0	51.80	145.00	109.00	56.10	157.00	118.00	71.60	200.00	150.00
16.0 x 2.00	157.0	70.60	226.00	170.00	76.50	245.00	184.00	97.70	313.00	235.00
20.0 x 2.50	245.0	110.20	441.00	331.00	119.40	478.00	358.00	152.50	610.00	458.00
24.0 x 3.00	353.0	158.90	762.00	572.00	172.10	826.00	620.00	220.00	1055.00	791.00
30.0 x 3.50	561.0	252.40	1515.00	1136.00	273.50	1641.00	1231.00	349.00	2095.00	1572.00
36.0 x 4.00	817.0	367.60	2647.00	1985.00	398.30	2868.00	2151.00	509.00	3662.00	2746.00
Tensile Strength			830 MPa			900 Pa			1040 Pa	
Proof Load Stress			600 MPa			650 Pa			830 Pa	

Caution—The previously listed torque and resulting tension are provided as an advisory guide. Individual application discretion is recommended. The content has been presented as accurately as possible, but responsibility for its application lies with the user.

Note 1—The stress area of threaded series not included in Table 2 may be computed from the equation:

$$As = 0.7854\ (D - 0.9382\ P)^2$$

where:

As = Stress area in mm^2

D = Diameter in mm

P = Pitch in mm

TENSION INDICATING WASHER TIGHTENING METHOD FOR FASTENERS—SAE J2486 MAY1999

SAE Standard

Report of the SAE Fasteners Committee approved May 1999.

Foreword—The fundamental function of mechanical fasteners is to create and maintain a prescribed tension (also known as clamping force or preload) in bolted joints. Bolted joints, which in practice attain the prescribed levels of tension after tightening (or tensioning) of the fasteners, are described as properly tensioned or preloaded. Original Equipment Manufacturers (OEMs) choose from a number of different assembly techniques to attain the tension that the responsible engineers expect or need for a given application. Such techniques provide tension to meet requirements that can be divided into three general categories:

a.A requirement that the tension be above a minimum prescribed level.

b.A requirement that the tension be above a minimum prescribed level and below a maximum prescribed level.

c.A requirement that the tension be within permissible limits of a prescribed target, wherein demonstrated control and statistical measures of dispersion from the target (or proximity to permissible limits) are used to determine acceptance.

Design engineers typically choose from among these three options depending upon the nature of the application, the service environment, production capabilities, installation costs, and other factors. Engineers will then specify procedures for installation of fasteners so, that required levels of tension are achieved. Success in achieving required tension depends upon the methods chosen and how well the manufacturer controls the extraneous variables which may impact the chosen method.

Attainment of at least a minimum level of tension is needed to resist vibration loosening, fatigue, joint slip into bearing, and other conditions which are potential forms of joint failure. Thus, the majority of mechanically fastened applications are intended to attain tensions above a prescribed minimum level. When properly designed and tensioned, a fastened joint is capable of withstanding anticipated service loads throughout the life-cycle of the finished product.

1. Scope

1.1 This SAE Recommended Practice covers installation and inspection methods for fasteners which are tensioned using Tension Indicating Washers (TIWs) as a means to ensure that adequate tension is developed in mechanically fastened joints. Figure 1 depicts a typical TIW, and Figure 2 depicts a fastener assembly with a TIW before and after tensioning.

1.2 This document describes practices for the use of TIWs which are typically produced for use with SAE J429 Grade 5 and Grade 8 fasteners or their metric counterparts, although the same principals hold true for bolted joints using other fasteners. Users are advised to contact a manufacturer for advice on use of these products before using them with special fasteners or applications.

1.3 This document defines and illustrates preferred installation and inspection methodologies. The contents of this document are presented as accurately as possible; however, responsibility for its application lies with the user.

2. References

2.1 Applicable Publications—The following publications form a part of this specification to the extent specified herein. Unless otherwise indicated, the latest issue of SAE publications shall apply.

2.1.1 SAE PUBLICATIONS—Available from SAE, 400 Commonwealth Drive, Warrendale, PA 15096-0001.

SAE J174—Torque-Tension Test Procedure for Steel Threaded Fasteners—Inch Series

SAE J174M—Torque-Tension Test Procedure for Steel Threaded Fasteners—Metric Series

SAE J429—Mechanical and Material Requirements for Externally Threaded Fasteners

SAE J1701—Torque-Tension Tightening for Inch Series Fasteners

SAE J1701M—Torque-Tension Tightening for Metric Series Fasteners

2.1.2 ASTM PUBLICATIONS—Available from ASTM, 100 Barr Harbor Drive, West Conshohocken, PA 19428-2959.

ASTM E 4—Practices for Force Verification in Testing Machines

ASTMF959—Standard Specification for Compressible-Washer-Type Direct Tension Indicators for Use with Structural Fasteners

2.1.3 IFI PUBLICATION—Available from Industrial Fasteners Institute, 1717 East 9th Street, Suite 1105, Cleveland, OH 44114-2879.

IFI Technical Data—Fastener Standards, 6th Edition

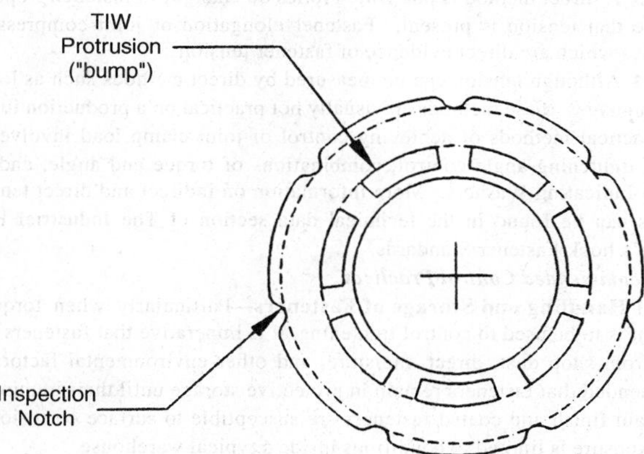

FIGURE 1—TENSION INDICATING WASHER (TIW)

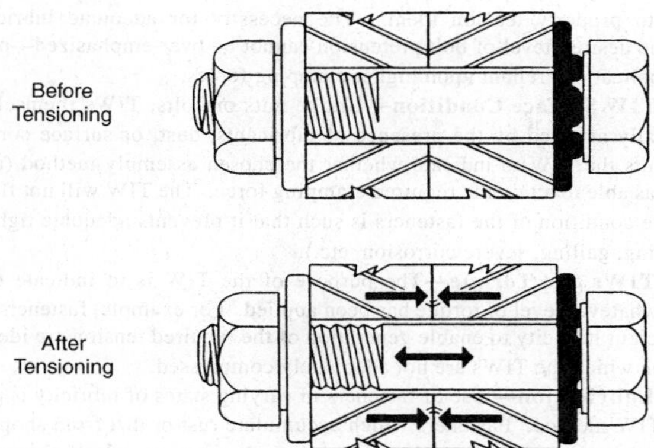

FIGURE 2—ASSEMBLY BEFORE AND AFTER TENSIONING

3. Definitions

3.1 Tension Indicating Washer (TIW)—A steel washer-shaped mechanical load cell with protrusions projecting from one face and corresponding pockets on the opposite face. It is used as a direct method to confirm a tension load in a fastener or bolted joint. Also known as a Direct Tension Indicator (DTI).

3.2 Torque—The product of force times lever arm length. With respect to fasteners, it is the moment resistance of the fastener and its components to turning, and is expressed as in-ozs, in-lbs, and ft-lbs, or newton-meters (Nm).

3.3 Tension—The force transmitted by fasteners into assembled parts after tightening. Also known as clamp load, clamping force, preload, or pretension. Expressed in pounds (lbs), thousands of pounds (kips), or kilonewtons (kN).

3.4 Tighten (Tightening)—The action of taking a fastener assembly into tension, usually by turning or torquing a bolt head or a nut. The action intended to induce tension, although efforts to attain tension are not synonymous or directly correlated with actually generating tension.

3.5 Snug—The condition of a mechanically fastened joint in which all of the mating materials are drawn into firm and near-continuous contact by application of some initial clamping force.

4. Tensioning Methods Overview

4.1 The design of mechanically fastened joints follows generally accepted engineering principals supported by empirical evidence. Installation or tensioning methods, play a significant role in determining whether design assumptions concerning required tension are met. There are two categories of tensioning methods: (a)indirect, and (2) direct.

4.2 An indirect method is one which relies on the correlation between tension and a related variable. The most common indirect method is torque, or more specifically, the control of input torque as a means to estimate attained tension. The torque method is indirect because torque is not a property of a tensioned fastener. Greater detail on torque-tensioning methods can be found in SAE J174/J174M and SAE J1701/J1701M.

4.3 A direct method is one which relies on changes in fastener properties as evidence that tension is present. Fastener elongation or joint compression are properties which are direct evidence of fastener tension.

4.4 Although tension can be measured by direct methods such as load cells or strain gauges, these methods are usually not practical on a production line. The most practical methods of achieving control of joint clamp load involve torque control, tightening angle control, combinations of torque and angle, and use of Tension Indicating Washers. More information on indirect and direct tensioning methods can be found in the technical data section of The Industrial Fastener Institute's book Fastener Standards.

5. Recommended Control Practices

5.1 Handling and Storage of Fasteners—Particularly when torque measurement is to be used to control tightening, it is imperative that fasteners be protected from shop dust, direct, moisture, and other environmental factors. It is recommended that fasteners remain in protective storage until their imminent use. Both plain finish and coated fasteners are susceptible to surface corrosion, even when exposure is limited to conditions inside a typical warehouse.

5.2 Fastener Surface Condition—Dry or rusty threads and bearing surfaces significantly increase the amount of torque required to tighten fasteners to a prescribed tension. Failure to protect fasteners from environmental factors may lead to inability to properly tension the fasteners, or torsional failures during attempts to properly tension them. The necessity for adequate lubricant to achieve the desired level of bolt pretension cannot be over-emphasized—particularly in applications reliant upon higher clamping forces.

5.3 TIW Surface Condition—Unlike nuts or bolts, TIWs themselves are not generally affected by the presence of lubricants, dust, or surface corrosion. This permits the TIW to indicate whether the chosen assembly method (usually torque) was able to attain the required clamping force. The TIW will not flatten if the surface condition of the fasteners is such that it prevents adequate tightening (e.g., seizing, galling, severe corrosion, etc.).

5.4 TIWs and Torque—The purpose of the TIW is to indicate the adequacy of whatever level of torque has been applied. For example, fasteners which lack sufficient lubricity to enable generation of the required tension are identified as those on which the TIWs are not adequately compressed.

5.5 Lubrication—Use of fasteners in varying states of lubricity is possible with the TIW method. Fasteners which accumulate rust or dirt from shop or job site conditions can be cleaned and lubricated prior to installation without adversely impacting the ability of the TIW to indicate clamp force. However, necessary precautions for "field lubricating" may need to be considered in order to avoid introduction of any unacceptable factor.

5.6 Bolt Holes—Users are advised to specify and control the acceptable characteristics of bolt holes. Such practice requires the establishment of accepted limits on bolt hole location, minimum and maximum permissible size, permissible limits on out-of-round, alignment, burrs, finish, and other variables. In order for fasteners (including TIWs) to function properly, control of these elements is necessary.

5.7 Bolt Lengths—Although rare, in some cases, the use of TIWs will require the use of slightly longer bolts due to the added thickness of the TIW within the grip of the joint. Bolts should project through nuts far enough such that at least one full and complete thread is "exposed" beyond the nut face. This maximizes the contact area between the mating surfaces of the nut and the bolt. A maximum of three full threads projecting beyond the nut face is often established to ensure that a sufficient number of threads remain in the "grip" of the joint, thus stabilizing performance and mechanical characteristics. Alternately, one can specify a minimum number of threads which must remain within the grip after tensioning.

*6. Installation Methods for TIWs—*This document recognizes four permissible methods for installation of fasteners using TIWs. When a particular method is not specified, selection shall be made by the party responsible for installation and tightening of the fasteners. Unless specified otherwise, the "normal" inspection method shall apply.

6.1 Method 1—Torque Tensioning/TIW Inspection—The most common method for the use of TIWs involves retaining the use of the OEM's current torque-tensioning practices and uses the TIW as an inspection device to point out those applications, occurrences, or pieces of installation equipment which for one reason or another did not attain the required tension. The following is a step-by-step procedure for using this method:

6.1.1 TIW-TORQUE TIGHTENING

a. Use normal specified and calibrated "torque-controlled" installation equipment.
b. There are four basic assembly configurations compatible with use of TIWs. (See Figure 3.) Fasteners are to be assembled in the normal manner, and whenever possible, TIWs are located under the head of each cap screw or bolt with the protrusions ("bumps") facing the head.
c. Set the equipment to operate at the specified or calibrated torque settings and operate it as normally required. Follow procedures for "snugging" or "stepping up" the level of torque in increments before final tensioning. For joints with fasteners in close proximity, follow normally prescribed tightening patterns.
d. Whenever possible, tightening shall be done from the end opposite from the TIWs. This enables inspection to verify that clamping force has been generated throughout the full length of the fasteners.
e. Continue tightening until the specified torque is applied, or on tools so equipped, until the torque-controlled shut-off occurs.
f. Follow tensioning with an appropriate inspection protocol selected from Section 8.

6.2 Method 2—Modified Turn-of-Nut/TIW Inspection—It is well established by research that the geometric method known as "turn-of-the-nut" can be used under controlled circumstances to reliably attain required clamping force. The method relies on attainment of a proper snug condition, followed by match-marking and a prescribed degree of turn thereafter.

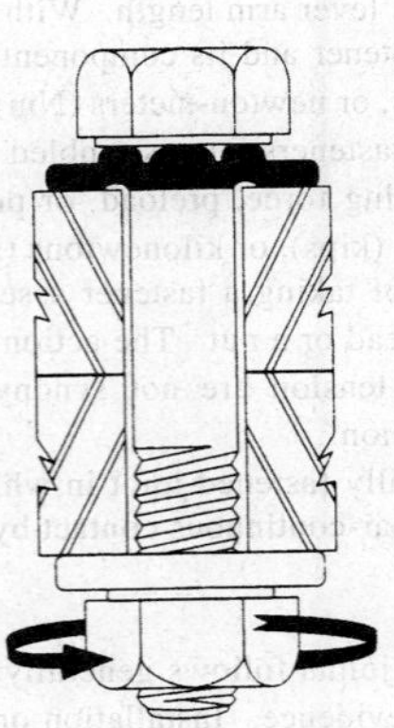
TIW under head, turn nut to tighten, bolt head held.

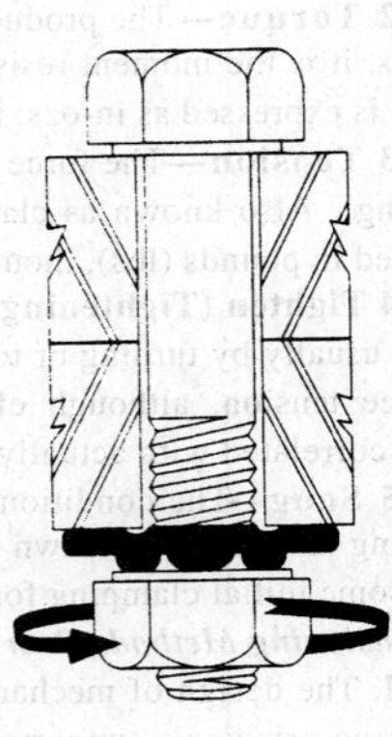
TIW under nut, turn nut to tighten, bolt head held.

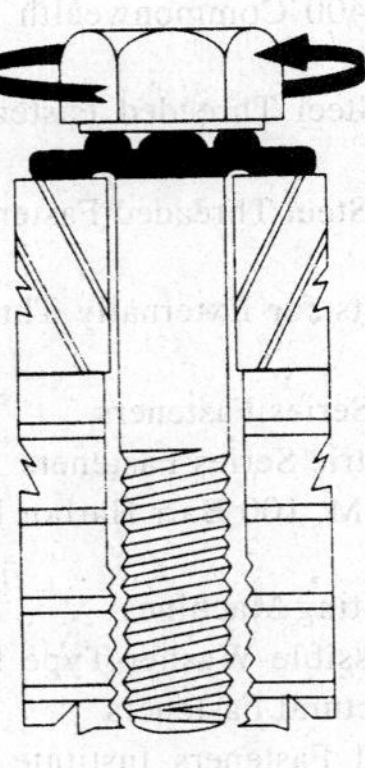
TIW under head, turn head to tighten into a tapped hole.

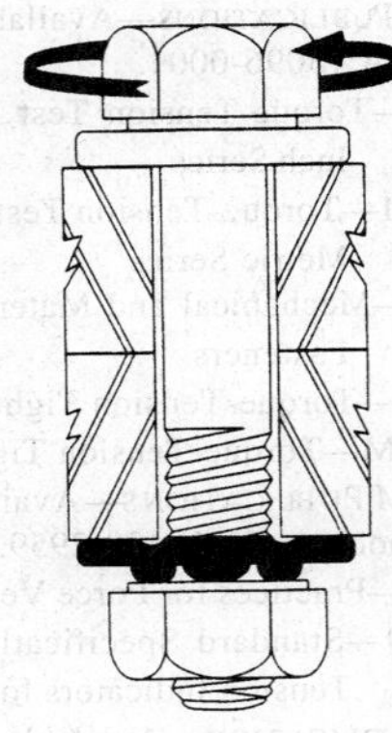
TIW under nut, turn head to tighten, nut held.

FIGURE 3—BASIC ASSEMBLY CONFIGURATION WITH TIW s

6.2.1 TIW-TURN-OF-NUT TIGHTENING

a. Use normal specified installation equipment.

b. Fasteners are to be assembled in the normal manner, and whenever possible, TIWs shall be located under the head of each cap screw or bolt with the protrusions ("bumps") facing the head.

c. Set the equipment to operate at the specified or calibrated torque settings and operate it as normally required for any torque controlled "snugging" or "stepping up" operations prior to final tensioning. For joints with fasteners in close proximity, follow normally prescribed tightening patterns.

d. Whenever possible, tightening shall be done from the end opposite from the TIWs. This enables inspection to verify that clamping force has been generated throughout the full length of the fasteners.

e. Previously published "degrees of turn" can not be used when TIWs are used, as it takes more "turn" when TIWs are present due to the compression of the TIW bumps during the turning (tightening) operation. Figure 4 depicts a comparison between the turn-tension relationship on 3/4 in SAE Grade 8 fasteners with and without TIWs. Appropriate "degree of turn" must be determined experimentally in the actual application using TIWs.

f. To determine an appropriate "degree of turn" experimentally, start by selecting an appropriate sample size for tests. Next, establish the "degree of turn' beyond the snug condition which is required to sufficiently flatten the TIWs such that the appropriate "no-go" feeler-gage can not be inserted. (See 7.1.) Add to the experimentally derived "degree of turn" a plus (+) tolerance to allow for practical limitations of equipment and operators.

g. Confirm that the experimentally derived "degree of turn" is satisfactory to meet the inspection requirements outlined in Section 8 in actual practice. Use of TIWs with the "turn-of-nut" method typically reduces the variation in clamp load normally attributed to the use of the "turn-of-nut" method alone. This is because TIWs change the slope of the "turn-tension" curve.

6.3 Method 3—Modified Torque-Angle/TIW Inspection—Among the most sophisticated installation methods known is "Torque-Angle" Tensioning. This method is based upon empirical evidence which correlates controllable indirect factors of torque and angle with known material responses to alignment, elastic tensioning, and yielding. Recent variants of this method store electronic "signatures" of how these variables interact, and provides control of the installation based on the information provided in these signatures.

6.3.1 TIW-TORQUE-ANGLE TIGHTENING

a. Use normal specified installation equipment.

b. Fasteners are to be assembled in the normal manner, and whenever possible, TIWs shall be located under the head of each cap screw or bolt with the protrusions ("bumps") facing the head.

c. Set the equipment to operate at the specified or calibrated torque settings and operate it as normally required for any torque controlled "snugging" or "stepping up" operations prior to final tensioning. For joints with fasteners in close proximity, follow normally prescribed tightening patterns.

d. Whenever possible, tightening shall be done from the end opposite from the TIWs. This enables inspection to verify that clamping force has been generated throughout the full length of the fasteners.

e. Previously prescribed "signatures" can not be used when TIWs are used, as the torque-turn/joint response relationship is different when TIWs are present due to the compression of the TIW bumps during the turning (tightening) operation. Appropriate "degree of turn" must be determined experimentally in the actual application using TIWs.

f. To create appropriate "signatures" experimentally, refer to the instructions provided by the manufacturer of the installation equipment.

g. Confirm that the experimentally derived "signature" is satisfactory to meet the inspection requirements outlined in Section 8.

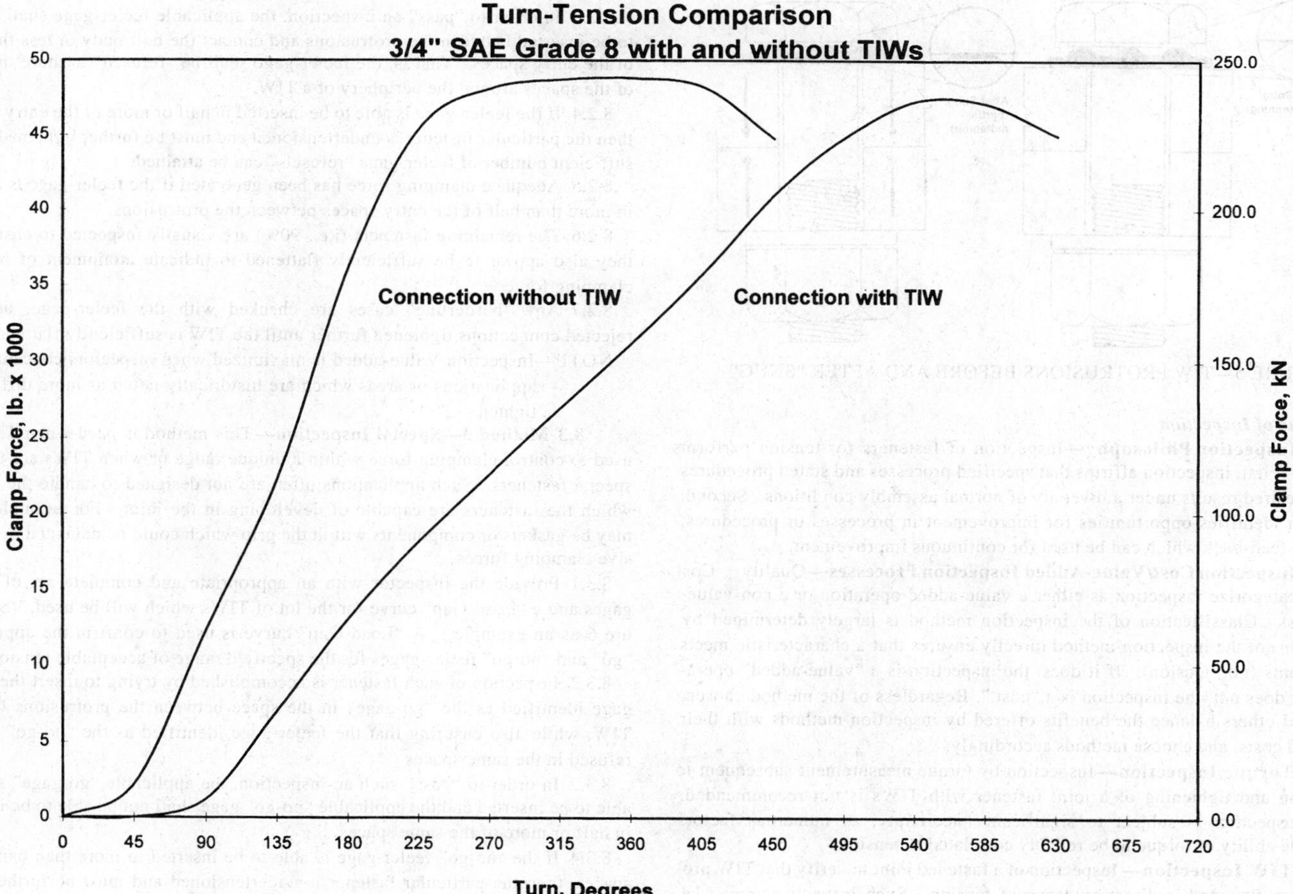

FIGURE 4—TENSION-TURN RELATIONSHIPS WITH AND WITHOUT TIW s

6.4 Method 4—Visual Control/TIW Inspection—A common method for the use of TIWs in maintenance or repair involves using readily available box or socket wrenches with simultaneous visual inspection of TIW compression. This method is used for example when OEM torque guidelines are not available, when calibrated torque wrenches are not available, when field conditions undermine the relied upon torque-tension relationship, or when normally prescribed tightening tools are obstructed from access to the bolted connection. The following is a typical step-by-step procedure for using this method.

6.4.1 VISUAL-TIW TIGHTENING

a. Use any appropriate wrench or driver of capable strength, (i.e., capable of delivering normally required levels of torque).
b. Fasteners are to be assembled in the normal manner, and whenever possible, TIWs shall be located under the head of each cap screw or bolt with the protrusions ("bumps") facing the head.
c. Follow normally prescribed tightening patterns. If none exist, start at the center or most rigid part of the connection, and continue to the outside or free edges.
d. Follow normal procedures for "snugging" or "stepping up" the tension in increments. The snug condition is attained in joints constructed with TIWs when initial partial flattening of the TIW protrusions has occurred. (See Figure 5.) This is sometimes called "flat-topping" the TIW, because the top of the normally convex protrusions just begin to flatten.
e. Whenever possible, tightening shall be done from the end opposite from the TIWs. This enables inspection to verify that clamping force has been generated throughout the full length of the fasteners.
f. Continue tightening until the gap between the TIW and the bolt or cap screw head is virtually flattened as judged by eye.
g. Follow tensioning with an appropriate inspection method selected from Section 8 to confirm visual judgment.

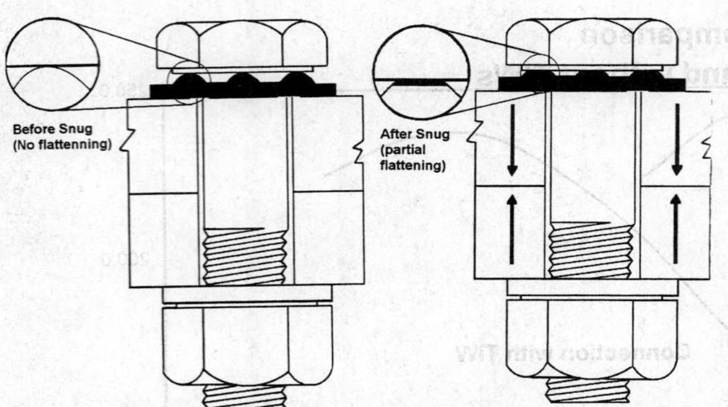

FIGURE 5—TIW PROTRUSIONS BEFORE AND AFTER "SNUG"

7. Value of Inspection

7.1 Inspection Philosophy—Inspection of fasteners for tension performs two roles. First, inspection affirms that specified processes and stated procedures achieve desired results under a diversity of normal assembly conditions. Second, inspection identifies opportunities for improvement in processes or procedures, providing feed-back which can be used for continuous improvement.

7.2 Inspection Cost/Value-Added Inspection Processes—Quality Cost Systems categorize inspection as either a value-added operation or a non-value-added cost. Classification of the inspection method is largely determined by whether or not the inspection method directly ensures that a characteristic meets requirements (i.e., tension). If it does, the inspection is a "value-added" operation. If it does not, the inspection is a "cost." Regardless of the method chosen, OEMs and others balance the benefits offered by inspection methods with their associated costs, and choose methods accordingly.

7.3 Torque Inspection—Inspection by torque measurement subsequent to installation and tightening of a joint fastener with TIWs is not recommended. Torque inspection is subject to significant uncertainty, as numerous factors impede the ability of torque to be reliably correlated to tension.

7.4 TIW Inspection—Inspection of a fastened joint to verify that TIW protrusions are flattened is direct evidence of tension. Such inspection may take place at any time subsequent to installation without reducing the validity of the inspection. Undertensioned fasteners can be identified by unflattened TIWs, which can be further tightened subsequent to installation to ensure that required tension is generated.

8. Inspection Methods

8.1 Method 1—Mandatory 100% Inspection—This is usually reserved for critical applications, previously identified troublesome applications, and for special purposes.

8.1.1 Provide the inspector with an appropriate feeler-gage, (e.g., 0.25 mm for metric product, 0.010 in for inch product.)

8.1.2 Inspection of each fastener is accomplished by trying to insert the feeler-gage in the space between the protrusions on each TIW. (See Figure 1.) Note that there are "Inspection Notches" around the periphery of each TIW to help indicate where insertion of the feeler-gage is to be attempted.

8.1.3 In order to "pass" an inspection, the applicable feeler-gage shall be able to be inserted between the protrusions and contact the bolt body in less than half of the entry spaces. That is, the feeler-gage shall be "refused" in more than half of the spaces around the periphery of a TIW.

8.1.4 If the feeler-gage is able to be inserted in half or more of the entry spaces, then the particular fastener is undertensioned and must be further tightened until a sufficient number of feeler-gage "refusals" can be attained.

8.1.5 Adequate clamping force has been generated if the feeler-gage is refused in more than half of the entry spaces between the protrusions.

8.2 Method 2—Normal Inspection—This is the most common method of inspection. It is used on a variety of applications and is chosen for its balance between cost and value-added. Normal Inspection entails inspection of a stated percentage of fasteners using a feeler-gage (usually 10%), followed by an overview visual inspection confirming that all other fasteners appear to be similarly flattened.

8.2.1 Provide the inspector with an appropriate feeler-gage, (e.g., 0.25 mm for metric product, 0.010 in for inch product.)

8.2.2 Inspection of the specified number of fasteners (i.e., 10%) is accomplished by trying to insert the feeler-gage in the space between the protrusions on each TIW. (See Figure 1.) "Inspection Notches" around the periphery of each TIW help indicate where insertion of the feeler-gage is to be attempted.

8.2.3 In order to "pass" an inspection, the applicable feeler-gage shall be able to be inserted between the protrusions and contact the bolt body in less than half of the entry spaces. That is, the feeler-gage shall be "refused" in more than half of the spaces around the periphery of a TIW.

8.2.4 If the feeler-gage is able to be inserted in half or more of the entry spaces, then the particular fastener is undertensioned and must be further tightened until a sufficient number of feeler-gage "refusals" can be attained.

8.2.5 Adequate clamping force has been generated if the feeler-gage is refused in more than half of the entry spaces between the protrusions.

8.2.6 The remaining fasteners (i.e., 90%) are visually inspected to ensure that they also appear to be sufficiently flattened to indicate attainment of required clamping force.

8.2.7 Any "borderline" cases are checked with the feeler-gage, and any rejected connections tightened further until the TIW is sufficiently flattened.

NOTE—Inspection Value-added is maximized when inspectors concentrate on applications or areas which are historically noted as more difficult to tighten.

8.3 Method 3—Special Inspection—This method is used when TIWs are used to control clamping force within a unique range or when TIWs are used on special fasteners. Such applications often are not designed to handle the tension which the fasteners are capable of developing in the joint. For example, there may be gaskets or components within the grip which could be damaged by excessive clamping forces.

8.3.1 Provide the inspector with an appropriate and complete set of feeler-gages and a "Load-Gap" curve for the lot of TIWs which will be used. (See Figure 6 as an example.) A "Load-Gap" curve is used to confirm the appropriate "go" and "no-go" feeler-gages for the specified range of acceptable tension.

8.3.2 Inspection of each fastener is accomplished by trying to insert the feeler-gage identified as the "go-gage" in the space between the protrusions on each TIW, while also ensuring that the feeler-gage identified as the "no-go" gage is refused in the same spaces.

8.3.3 In order to "pass" such an inspection, the applicable "go-gage" shall be able to be inserted and the applicable "no-go" gage shall not be able to be inserted in half or more of the same spaces.

8.3.4 If the "no-go" feeler-gage is able to be inserted in more than half of the spaces, then the particular fastener is undertensioned and must be further tightened until a sufficient number of "no-go" gage refusals is attained.

8.3.5 If the "go-gage" is not able to be inserted in more than half of the spaces, then the particular fastener is overtensioned and must be removed and replaced with a new fastener and a new TIW.

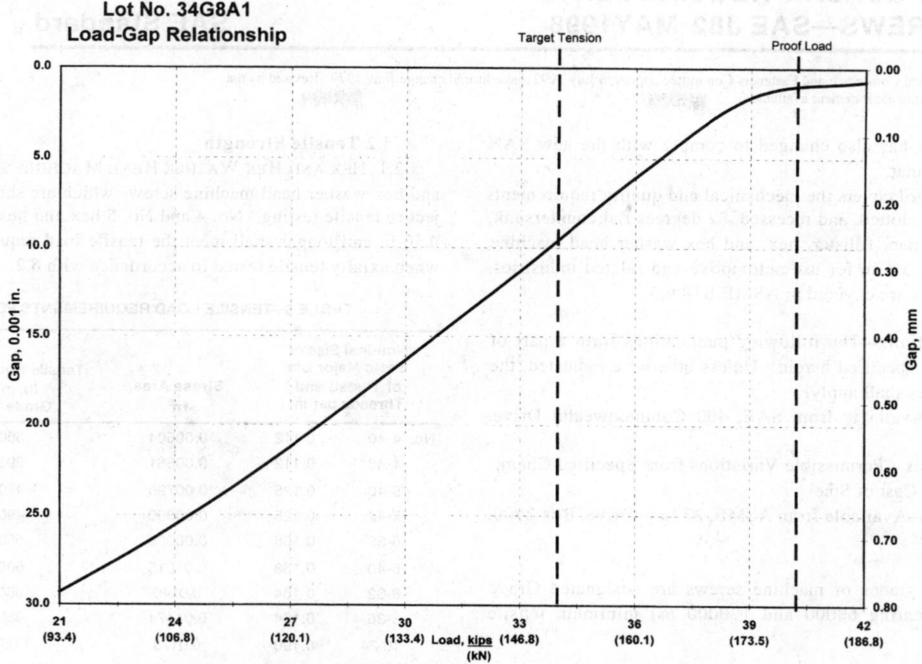

FIGURE 6—A TYPICAL LOAD-GAP CURVE

8.4 Optional and Supplemental Inspection Requirements

8.4.1 OPTIONAL INSPECTION MARKINGS—Some OEMs find it helpful to paint, mark, or otherwise indicate which connections have been inspected and passed. This is useful when tensioning and inspection occurs at a number of different points or times as on a production line.

8.4.2 OPTIONAL FOLLOW-UP INSPECTION—In some applications, joint relaxation in service is sufficient to cause concern over loss of tension. This relaxation results from the cumulative effects of fastener thread and bearing interface accommodation, extrusion of paints, gaskets, burrs, or other soft material within the joint, and other factors. In such cases, it is common to reinspect fastened joints after a specified time or service period. Lost clamping force due to relaxation can be re-gained through the application of sufficient torque energy to further flatten the TIWs. Any further flattening will require clamping force equal to or greater than that original attained. Alternately, for applications subject to severe relaxation (or safety critical applications) use of new TIWs ensures that clamping force is reattained.

9. Product Qualification Tests

9.1 Test Types—In general, there are two types of tests which provide useful information on the quality and usability of Tension Indicating Washer lots and the fastener lots on which they are to be used. The first general type of types are those conducted under laboratory conditions for the purpose of establishing the mechanical and performance characteristics of each lot. The second general type of tests include those conducted "in the field" for the purpose of establishing the compatibility and function of the TIWs with the fasteners on which they are to be used.

9.2 Laboratory Tests—As with all high-strength fasteners, control of material and mechanical properties is important to the function of TIWs. Therefore, manufacturers of TIWs perform tests on a lot by lot basis to confirm that each lot meets requirements. Further, as TIWs are used to measure tension or clamping force, and because they are used as a tool for acceptance of fastened joints, control of their mechanical properties is of particular significance. To confirm the suitability of TIW lots, samples from each lot are tested in a calibrated compression-load analyzer such as is found in Annex A1 of ASTM F 959. (See Figure 7.) Reports of such tests are routinely required with the purchase of TIWs. The equipment used in such tests shall be calibrated in accordance with ASTM E 4.

9.3 Field Tests—Devices such as Tension Calibrators are useful for verification that fastener assemblies (nut, bolt, washer, and TIW) are compatible and functioning as expected. Tension Calibrators are devices, which by measurement of hydraulic pressure, are able to determine clamp load or preload in fastener assemblies. Fasteners can be inserted in a Tension Calibrator, tightening effort (torque) exerted, and resulting clamp load or tension determined. They can also be used to "calibrate" torque-controlled installation tools. The accuracy of Tension Calibrators shall be confirmed through calibration by an accredited testing facility at least annually. It is recommended that Tension Calibrators be calibrated in accordance with ASTM E 4.

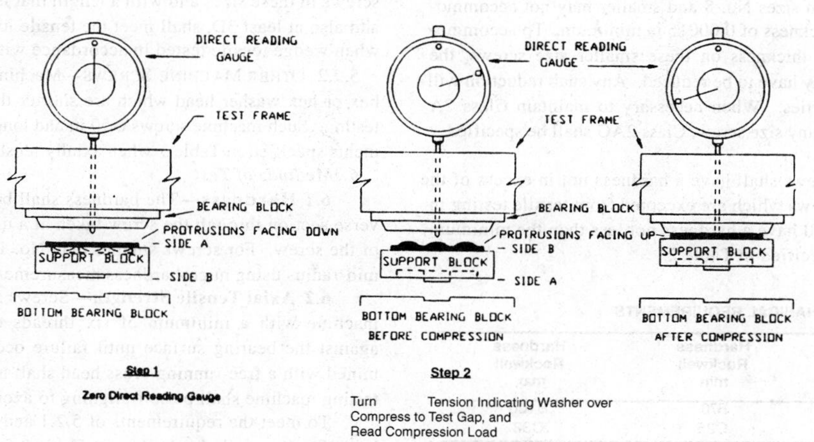

FIGURE 7—A COMPRESSION-LOAD ANALYZER

MECHANICAL AND QUALITY REQUIREMENTS FOR MACHINE SCREWS—SAE J82 MAY1998

SAE Standard

Report of the SAE Iron and Steel Technical Committee and Fasteners Committee approved July 1992 and editorial change June 1979. Revised by the SAE Fasteners Committee May 1998. Rationale statement available.

Foreword—This Document has also changed to comply with the new SAE Technical Standards Board format.

1. Scope—This SAE Standard covers the mechanical and quality requirements for two grades of carbon steel, slotted, and recessed, 82 degrees flat countersunk, 82 degrees oval countersunk, pan, fillister, hex, and hex washer head machine screws in sizes No. 4 through 3/4 in for use automotive and related industries. The dimensions of these screws are covered in ASME B18.6.3.

2. References

2.1 Applicable Publications—The following publications form a part of this specification to the extent specified herein. Unless otherwise indicated, the latest issue of SAE publications shall apply.

2.1.1 SAE PUBLICATION—Available from SAE, 400 Commonwealth Drive, Warrendale, PA 15096-0001.

SAE J409—Product Analysis—Permissible Variations from Specified Chemical Analysis of a Heat or Cast of Steel

2.1.2 ASME PUBLICATION—Available from ASME, 22 Law Drive, Box 2900, Fairfield, NJ 07007-2900.

ASME B18.6.3

3. Designations—The two grades of machine screws are designated Grade 60M and Grade 120M, indicating 60000 and 120000 psi minimum tensile strength, respectively.

4. Materials and Processes

4.1 Steel Characteristics—Machine screws shall be made of steel conforming to the description and chemical composition requirements specified in Table 1 for the applicable grade.

TABLE 1—CHEMICAL COMPOSITION REQUIREMENTS[1]

Grade	Material and Treatment	Element, % C min	Element, % C max	Element, % P, max	Element, % S, max
60M	Carbon steel	—	0.30	0.048	0.058
120M	Carbon steel, quenched and tempered	0.15	0.55	0.048	0.058

1. All values are for check analysis (percent by weight). For ladle analysis, use standard permissible variations as shown in SAE J409.

4.2 Heading Practice—Machine screws shall be cold headed and/or extruded, unless other methods are permitted by special agreement of the purchaser.

4.3 Threading Practice—Machine screws shall be roll threaded, except by special agreement of purchaser.

4.4 Heat Treatment Practice—Grade 60M machine screws need not be heat treated. When specified by purchaser, Grade 60M screws shall be stress relieved. Grade 120M machine screws shall be heat treated, oil or water quenched and tempered at a minimum tempering temperature of 343 °C (650 °F).

4.5 Finish—Unless otherwise specified, machine screws shall be supplied with a natural (as processed) finish unplated or uncoated. Plated and coated finishes shall be supplied in accordance with requirements of the purchaser.

NOTE—Class 2A allowance in sizes No. 8 and smaller may not accommodate a commercial thickness of 0.00015 in minimum. To accommodate this commercial thickness on these smaller size screws, the before-plating size may have to be reduced. Any such reduction will affect strength properties. When necessary to maintain Class 2A limits after plating of any size screw, Class 2AG shall be specified.

5. Mechanical Requirements

5.1 Hardness—Machine screws shall have a hardness not in excess of the maximum specified in Table 2. Screws which are excepted from tensile testing in accordance with 5.2.1 and 5.2.2 shall have a hardness not less than the minimum and not more than the maximum specified in Table 2.

TABLE 2—MECHANICAL REQUIREMENTS

Grade	Tensile Strength, min, psi	Hardness Rockwell min	Hardness Rockwell max
60M	60 000	B70	B100
120M	120 000	C25	C38

5.2 Tensile Strength

5.2.1 HEX AND HEX WASHER HEAD MACHINE SCREWS—No. 4 and No. 5 hex and hex washer head machine screws which are shorter than 0.50 in are not subject to tensile testing. No. 4 and No. 5 hex and hex washer head machine screws 0.50 in and longer shall meet the tensile load requirements specified in Table 3 when axially tensile tested in accordance with 6.2.

TABLE 3—TENSILE LOAD REQUIREMENTS FOR MACHINE SCREWS

Nominal Size or Basic Major Dia of Thread and Threads per in		Stress Area, in^2	Tensile Strength,[1] lb, min Grade 60M	Tensile strength,[1] lb, min Grade 120M
No. 4-40	0.112	0.00604	360	720
4-48	0.112	0.00661	390	780
5-40	0.125	0.00796	470	940
5-44	0.125	0.00830	490	980
6-32	0.138	0.00909	550	1 100
6-40	0.138	0.01015	600	1 200
8-32	0.164	0.0140	850	1 700
8-36	0.164	0.01474	880	1 750
10-24	0.190	0.0175	1 050	2 100
10-32	0.190	0.0200	1 200	2 400
12-24	0.216	0.0242	1 450	2 900
12-28	0.216	0.0258	1 550	3 100
1/4-20	0.250	0.0318	1 900	3 800
1/4-28	0.250	0.0364	2 200	4 350
No. 5/16-18	0.312	0.0524	3 150	6 300
5/16-24	0.312	0.0580	3 500	6 950
3/8-16	0.375	0.0775	4 650	9 300
3/8-24	0.375	0.0878	5 250	10 500
7/16-14	0.438	0.1063	6 400	12 800
7/16-20	0.438	0.1187	7 100	14 200
1/2-13	0.500	0.1419	8 500	17 000
1/2-20	0.500	0.1599	9 600	19 200
9/16-12	0.562	0.182	10 900	21 800
9/16-18	0.562	0.203	12 200	24 400
5/8-11	0.625	0.226	13 600	27 100
5/8-18	0.625	0.256	15 400	30 700
3/4-10	0.750	0.334	20 100	40 100
3/4-16	0.750	0.373	22 400	44 800

1. Tensile strength values for Grade 60M and Grade 120M are based on 60 000 and 120 000 psi, respectively.

Hex and hex washer head machine screws in sizes No. 6 to 3/4 in inclusive, which are shorter than either 0.50 in or 3D (where D is nominal screw size in inches) are not subject to tensile testing. Hex and hex washer head machine screws in these sizes and with a length that is both equal to or longer than 0.50 in, and also at least 3D, shall meet the tensile load requirements specified in Table 3 when wedge tensile tested in accordance with 6.3.

5.2.2 OTHER MACHINE SCREWS—Machine screws with head styles other than hex or hex washer head which are shorter than 0.50 in, are not subject to tensile testing. Such machine screws 0.50 in and longer shall meet the tensile load requirements specified in Table 3 when axially tensile tested in accordance with 6.2.

6. Methods of Test

6.1 Hardness—The hardness shall be determined at mid-radius of a transverse section through the screw taken at a distance of one diameter from the end of the screw. For screws smaller than No. 10 size, a referee test may be made at mid-radius using microhardness measurement techniques.

6.2 Axial Tensile Strength—Screws shall be assembled in a tensile testing machine with a minimum of six threads exposed, and an axial load applied against the bearing surface until failure occurs. The speed of testing as determined with a free-running cross head shall not exceed 1 in/min. The grips of the testing machine shall be self-aligning to avoid side thrust on the specimen.

To meet the requirements of 5.2.1 and 5.2.2, the load at failure shall not be less than the tensile load given in Table 3 for the applicable size and grade.

6.3 Wedge Tensile Strength—Screws shall be installed in a tensile testing machine with a 6 degrees wedge inserted under the head, as illustrated in Figure 1 and tensile tested to failure as described in 6.2. The wedge shall be so placed that no corner of the hexagon screw head takes the bearing load; that is, a flat of the head shall be aligned with the direction of uniform thickness of the wedge.

To meet the requirements of 5.2.1, the load at failure should not be less than the tensile load given in Table 3 for the applicable size and grade. In addition, failure shall occur in the body or threads with no fracture at the junction of the head and shank or failure due to any portion of the shank being pulled out of the head.

6.3.1 Wedge may be either circular or square. (See Figure 1.) Recommended outside dimension is 1.25 in for screw sizes No. 4 through No. 12 and 1.75 in for larger sizes. Thickness of wedge at thin size of hole shall be equivalent to one-half the nominal diameter of the screw but not less than 0.12 in. Hole shall be 0.020 in over the nominal diameter of the screw for sizes No. 4 through No. 12, 0.030 in over for sizes 1/4 through 1/2in, and 0.050 in over for sizes 9/16 through 3/4 in. Top and bottom edges of the hole shall be rounded or chamfered, with radius and depth of chamfer as follows: 0.020 in for sizes No. 4 through No. 12, 0.030 in for sizes 1/4 through 1/2 in, and 0.060 in for sizes 9/16 through 3/4 in. The wedge shall have a minimum hardness of Rockwell C45.

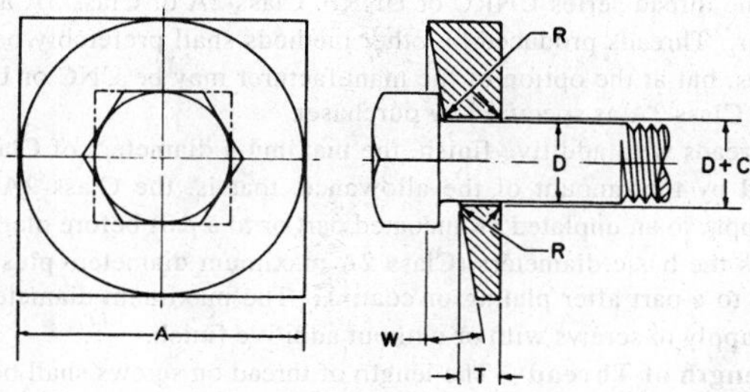

A = WEDGE OUTSIDE DIMENSIONS (SEE PARAGRAPH 6.3.1)
C = CLEARANCE HOLE (SEE PARAGRAPH 6.3.1)
D = DIAMETER OF SCREW
R = RADIUS OR CHAMFER (SEE PARAGRAPH 6.3.1)
T = THICKNESS AT THIN SIDE OF HOLE (SEE PARAGRAPH 6.3.1)
W = WEDGE ANGLE (6 DEG)

FIGURE 1—WEDGE TEST DETAILS

7. Marking—Machine screws need not be marked to identify grade or manufacturer.

8. Testing Requirements

8.1 Manufacturer's Responsibility—During the manufacture of machine screws to the requirements of this document, the manufacturer shall make periodic tests to ensure that the properties of the screw are being maintained within the specified limits. Such tests shall be conducted in accordance with a sampling plan, preferably the sampling plan given in Table 4.

Additional tests of screws in individual shipments are not normally contemplated. Unless otherwise agreed at time of original inquiry and purchase order, individual heats of steel need not be identified.

8.2 Purchaser's Options—If the purchaser requires that additional tests be performed by the manufacturer to determine that the properties of screws in an individual shipment are within specified limits, or if the purchaser requires that a specific (that shown in Table 4 or other) sampling plan shall be used when determining the acceptability of a lot or shipment of screws, or if the purchaser requires test data to be recorded and furnished, the purchaser shall specify the complete testing requirements, including sampling plan and basis of acceptance, in the original inquiry and purchase order.

TABLE 4—SAMPLING PLAN

Number of Pieces in Lot	Minimum Number of Specimens to be tested
50 and under	2
51 to 500	3
501 to 35 000	5
35 001 and over	8

8.3 General—An acceptable sampling plan is outlined in Table 4.

A lot, for purposes of selecting test specimens, shall consist of all screws offered for inspection and testing at one time that are of the same head style, grade, size, length, and thread series and are manufactured from the same heat or coil of steel and essentially at one time and under the same process conditions.

The same test specimen may be used for different tests wherever practical.

When tested in accordance with this sampling plan, a lot shall be subject to rejection if any of the test specimens fail to meet the applicable test requirements. If the failure of a test specimen is due to improper preparation of the specimen or to incorrect testing technique, the specimen shall be discarded and another specimen substituted.

FLANGED 12-POINT SCREWS—SAE J58 MAY98 SAE Standard

Report of the SAE Fasteners Committee approved September 1972, cancelled 1990, reissued August 1993 and reaffirmed May 1998.

1. Scope—Included in this SAE Standard are the detailed general and dimensional specifications applicable to flanged 12-point screws recognized as SAE Standard and intended for general use in automotive and other ground-based vehicles and industrial equipment. Also included is Appendix A, covering runout sleeve gages and gaging.

The inclusion of dimensional data in this standard is not intended to imply that all of the products described are stock production sizes. Consumers should consult manufacturers concerning availability of product.

2. References

2.1 Applicable Publications—The following publication forms a part of the specification to the extent specified herein. Unless otherwise indicated the latest revision of SAE publications shall apply.

2.1.1 SAE PUBLICATION—Available from SAE, 400 Commonwealth Drive, Warrendale, PA 15096-0001.

SAE J429—Mechanical and Material Requirements for Externally Threaded Fasteners

3. General Specifications—(See Figure 1.)

3.1 Dimensions—All dimensions in this document are in inches unless otherwise stated.

3.2 Options—Options, where specified, shall be at the discretion of the manufacturer unless otherwise agreed by manufacturer and purchaser.

3.3 Heads

3.3.1 HEAD HEIGHT—The head height shall be measured, parallel to the axis of screw, from the top of the head to the bearing surface of the flange.

3.3.2 TOP OF HEAD—The top of head may be full form or indented at the option of the manufacturer. If full form, the top of head shall be chamfered or rounded with the diameter of chamfer circle or start of rounding being equal to the specified maximum width across flats within a tolerance of –15%. If the top of head is indented, the periphery may be rounded.

3.3.3 CORNER FILL—The rounding due to lack of fill at all 12 corners of the head shall be reasonably uniform and the width across corners of the head shall be such that when a sharp ring, having an inside diameter equal to the T dimension and a thickness within the limits for A specified in Table 1, is placed on the top of the head, normal to the screw axis, the head may enter but shall not protrude through the gage.

3.3.4 WRENCHING HEIGHT—The wrenching height shall be measured, parallel to the axis of screw, from the intersection of the top contour of flange with any corner of head to the top of the head.

3.3.5 BEARING SURFACE—The outer periphery may be rounded or chamfered to the extent permitted by X, as measured on the bearing face. The plane of the bearing face shall be perpendicular to the axis of screw within the runout limit specified in Table 1. Measurement of runout shall be made as close to the periphery of bearing face as possible while the screw is held in a collet or other gripping device at a distance equal to one screw diameter from the underside of the head.

3.4 Underhead Fillets—For all lengths of screws, the form of the fillet shall be optional provided: it is tangent to the shank of the screw at a distance no greater than L_a from the underside of the head; it is tangent to the bearing surface within the limits of the basic screw diameter plus M max, and E min plus M min; and it is a smooth continuous curve having a bearing surface juncture radius no less than that specified in Table 1.

For reduced diameter body screws threaded full length, the minimum fillet extension, M min, may be reduced by an amount equivalent to one-half the difference between the basic screw diameter and the specified minimum pitch diameter of the thread.

3.5 Length

3.5.1 MEASUREMENT—The length of screw shall be measured, parallel to the axis of screw, from the bearing surface of the head to the extreme end of the shank.

3.5.2 TOLERANCE ON LENGTH—The tolerance on length shall be as tabulated in Table 2.

3.6 Body Diameter—On screws threaded full length, the diameter of the screw under the head shall not be less than the specified minimum pitch diameter of the thread.

3.7 Threads—Threads, when produced by roll threading, shall be Unified coarse or fine thread series UNRC or UNRF, Class 2A or Class 3A as specified by purchaser. Threads produced by other methods shall preferably be UNRC or UNRF series, but at the option of the manufacturer may be UNC or UNF series, Class 2A or Class 3A as specified by purchaser.

For threads with additive finish, the maximum diameters of Class 2A may be exceeded by the amount of the allowance, that is, the Class 2A maximum diameters apply to an unplated or uncoated part or to a part before plating or coating, whereas the basic diameters (Class 2A maximum diameters plus the allowance) apply to a part after plating or coating. The maximum diameters of Class 3A threads apply to screws with or without additive finish.

3.8 Length of Thread—The length of thread on screws shall be controlled by the grip gaging length L_G max and the body length L_B min as set forth in the following:

3.8.1 GRIP GAGING LENGTH—L_G max is the distance, measured parallel to the axis of screw, from the underside of head to the face of a noncounterbored or nonchamfered standard GO thread ring gage assembled by hand as far as the thread will permit. It represents the minimum design grip length and shall be used as the criterion for inspection and for determining thread availability when selecting screw lengths even though usable threads may extend beyond this point. Values for L_G max applicable to common nominal screw lengths are shown in Table 3.

For screws having nominal lengths which fall between those tabulated in Table 3, the L_G max value shown for the next shorter tabulated nominal length and respective screw size shall apply.

For screws having nominal lengths longer than those specified in Table 3 for the respective screw size, the L_G max value shall be determined by subtracting the L_T value in Table 1 from the nominal screw length.

For screws having shorter nominal lengths than those specified in Table 3 for the respective screw size, the complete (full form) thread, as measured with a thread ring gage, shall extend to within two threads (pitches) of the bearing face for sizes up to and including 5/8 in, and as close to the head as practicable for larger sizes.

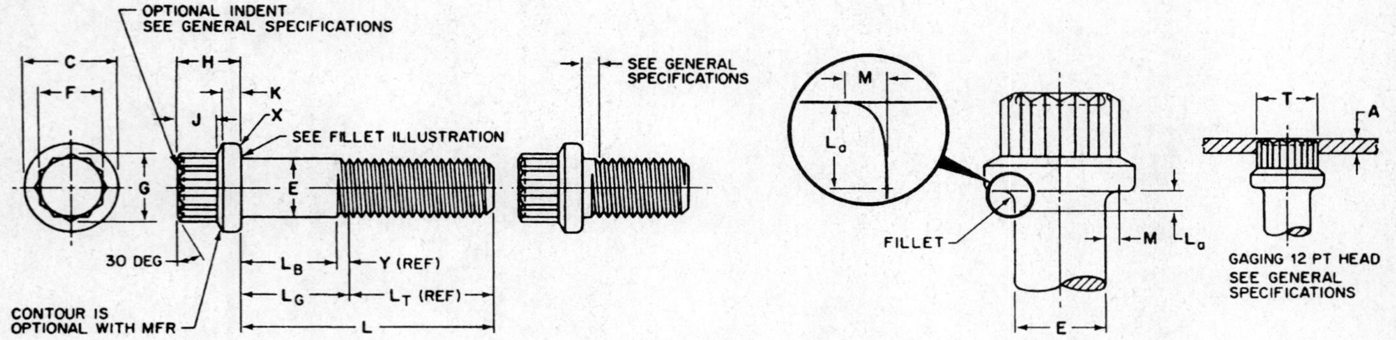

FIGURE 1—DIMENSIONS OF FLANGED 12-POINT SCREWS AND HEAD GAGING RINGS

TABLE 1—DIMENSIONS OF FLANGED 12-POINT SCREWS AND HEAD GAGING RINGS

Nominal Size[1] or Basic Screw Dia	Nominal Size[1] or Basic Screw Dia	E Body Dia Min (Max Equal to Basic Screw Dia)	C Flange Dia Max	C Flange Dia Min	F Width Across Flats Max	F Width Across Flags Min	G Width Across Corners Min	H Head Height Max	J Wrenching Height Min	K Flange Thickness Min	Runout of Bearing Surface FIM Max
1/4	0.2500	0.2435	0.375	0.365	0.252	0.244	0.278	0.260	0.15	0.058	0.007
5/16	0.3125	0.3053	0.469	0.457	0.315	0.306	0.348	0.312	0.18	0.074	0.008
3/8	0.3750	0.3678	0.562	0.550	0.377	0.368	0.420	0.375	0.21	0.095	0.010
7/16	0.4375	0.4294	0.656	0.642	0.438	0.429	0.489	0.438	0.26	0.109	0.011
1/2	0.5000	0.4919	0.750	0.735	0.502	0.493	0.562	0.500	0.29	0.129	0.013
9/16	0.5625	0.5538	0.844	0.828	0.564	0.555	0.633	0.563	0.33	0.145	0.015
5/8	0.6250	0.6163	0.938	0.921	0.627	0.618	0.705	0.625	0.36	0.166	0.016
3/4	0.7500	0.7406	1.125	1.107	0.752	0.743	0.847	0.750	0.44	0.200	0.020
7/8	0.8750	0.8647	1.312	1.293	0.877	0.866	0.987	0.875	0.51	0.234	0.023
1	1.0000	0.9886	1.500	1.479	1.003	0.991	1.130	1.000	0.60	0.268	0.026
1-1/8	1.1250	1.1086	1.688	1.665	1.128	1.115	1.271	1.125	0.66	0.310	0.029
1-1/4	1.2500	1.2336	1.875	1.852	1.253	1.240	1.414	1.250	0.73	0.350	0.033
1-3/8	1.3750	1.3568	2.062	2.038	1.378	1.365	1.556	1.375	0.80	0.392	0.036
1-1/2	1.5000	1.4818	2.250	2.224	1.503	1.489	1.697	1.500	0.87	0.433	0.039

Nominal Size[1] or Basic Screw Dia	Nominal Size[1] or Basic Screw Dia	M Fillet Extension Max	M Fillet Extension Min	L Fillet Length Max	Bearing Surface Juncture Radius Min	X Chamfer or Radius Max	A Gaging Ring Thickness Max	A Gaging Ring Thickness Min	T Gaging Ring Dia Max	T Gaging Ring Dia Min	L_T Thread Length Basic	Y Transition Thread Length Max
1/4	0.2500	0.014	0.009	0.087	0.007	0.020	0.0525	0.0522	0.2783	0.2780	1.000	0.25
5/16	0.3125	0.017	0.012	0.087	0.009	0.020	0.0600	0.0597	0.3483	0.3480	1.125	0.28
3/8	0.3750	0.020	0.015	0.087	0.012	0.020	0.0711	0.0708	0.4203	0.4200	1.250	0.31
7/16	0.4375	0.023	0.018	0.087	0.014	0.030	0.0840	0.0837	0.4893	0.4890	1.375	0.36
1/2	0.5000	0.026	0.020	0.087	0.016	0.030	0.0948	0.0945	0.5623	0.5620	1.500	0.38
9/16	0.5625	0.029	0.022	0.157	0.018	0.030	0.1071	0.1068	0.6333	0.6330	1.625	0.42
5/8	0.6250	0.032	0.024	0.157	0.021	0.040	0.1179	0.1176	0.7053	0.7050	1.750	0.46
3/4	0.7500	0.039	0.030	0.157	0.025	0.040	0.1416	0.1413	0.8473	0.8470	2.000	0.50
7/8	0.8750	0.044	0.034	0.227	0.031	0.040	0.1656	0.1653	0.9873	0.9870	2.250	0.56
1	1.0000	0.050	0.040	0.332	0.034	0.040	0.1893	0.1890	1.1303	1.1300	2.500	0.62
1-1/8	1.1250	0.055	0.045	0.332	0.039	0.050	0.2109	0.2106	1.2713	1.2710	2.750	0.71
1-1/4	1.2500	0.060	0.050	0.332	0.044	0.050	0.2331	0.2328	1.4143	1.4140	3.000	0.71
1-3/8	1.3750	0.065	0.055	0.332	0.048	0.050	0.2544	0.2541	1.5563	1.5560	3.250	0.83
1-1/2	1.5000	0.070	0.060	0.332	0.052	0.050	0.2763	0.2760	1.6973	1.6970	3.500	0.83

1. Where specifying nominal size in decimals, zeros preceding decimal and in fourth decimal place shall be omitted.
Additional requirements given in Section 3 shall apply.

TABLE 2—LENGTH TOLERANCE

Nominal Screw Length, in	Nominal Screw Size 0 thru 3/8	Nominal Screw Size 7/16 thru 3/4	Nominal Screw Size 7/8 thru 1-1/2
Up to 1, incl	–0.03	–0.03	–0.05
Over 1 to 2-1/2, incl	–0.04	–0.06	–0.10
Over 2-1/2 to 6, incl	–0.06	–0.08	–0.14
Over 6	–0.12	–0.12	–0.20

3.8.2 BODY LENGTH—L_B min is the distance, measured parallel to the axis of screw, from the underside of the head to the last scratch of thread or the top of extrusion angle. The minimum body length for any screw length shall be equal to the maximum grip length minus the transition thread length (L_B min = L_G max – Y max). It shall be used as a criterion for inspection.

3.8.3 BASIC THREAD LENGTH—L_T is a reference dimension, intended for calculation purposes only, which represents the distance from the extreme end of the screw to the last complete (full form) thread.

3.8.4 TRANSITION THREAD LENGTH—Y max is a reference dimension, intended for calculation purposes only, which represents the length of incomplete threads and the tolerance on grip length.

3.9 Point—The point shall be flat and chamfered from a diameter approximately 0.016 in below the minor diameter of the thread to produce a length of point equivalent to 1/2 to 1-1/2 threads (pitches).

3.10 Incomplete Thread Diameter—The major diameter of incomplete thread shall not exceed the actual major diameter of the full form thread.

3.11 Thread Runout—The total runout between thread, body, and head of screws shall be such that screw may be assembled for a minimum of two full turns into the threaded hole of a concentricity sleeve gage as shown in Appendix A.

3.12 Materials

3.12.1 STEEL—Suitable properties for steel screws are covered in SAE J429, Grades 2, 5, and 8, as specified by purchaser.

3.12.2 OTHER MATERIALS—Where specified, screws may be made from brass, corrosion resisting steel, or other materials as agreed upon by the manufacturer and purchaser.

3.13 Finish—Unless otherwise specified, screws shall be supplied plain (unplated or uncoated), as processed.

3.14 Workmanship—Screws shall be free from burrs, seams, laps, loose scale, and any defects that affect serviceability.

TABLE 3—MAXIMUM GRIP GAGING LENGTHS (La MAX) FOR FLANGED 12-POINT SCRWS—NOMINAL SIZ

Nominal Length[(1)]	1/4	5/16	3/8	7/16	1/2	9/16	5/8	3/4	7/8	1	1-1/8	1-1/4	1-3/8	1-1/2
1-1/2	0.500	—	—	—	—	—	—	—	—	—	—	—	—	—
1-3/4	0.500	0.625	0.500	—	—	—	—	—	—	—	—	—	—	—
2	1.000	0.625	0.500	0.625	—	—	—	—	—	—	—	—	—	—
2-1/4	1.000	1.125	1.000	0.625	0.750	0.750	—	—	—	—	—	—	—	—
2-1/2	1.500	1.125	1.000	1.125	0.750	0.750	0.750	—	—	—	—	—	—	—
2-3/4	1.500	1.625	1.500	1.125	0.750	0.750	0.750	—	—	—	—	—	—	—
3	2.000	1.625	1.500	1.625	1.500	1.500	0.750	1.000	—	—	—	—	—	—
3-1/4	2.000	2.125	2.000	1.625	1.500	1.500	1.500	1.000	1.000	—	—	—	—	—
3-1/2	2.500	2.125	2.000	2.125	1.500	1.500	1.500	1.000	1.000	1.000	—	—	—	—
3-3/4	2.500	2.625	2.500	2.125	2.250	2.250	1.500	1.000	1.000	1.000	1.000	—	—	—
4	3.000	2.625	2.500	2.625	2.250	2.250	2.250	2.000	1.000	1.000	1.000	1.000	—	—
4-1/4	3.000	3.125	3.000	2.625	2.250	2.250	2.250	2.000	2.000	1.000	1.000	1.000	1.000	—
4-1/2	3.500	3.125	3.000	3.125	3.000	3.000	2.250	2.000	2.000	2.000	1.000	1.000	1.000	1.000
4-3/4	3.500	3.625	3.500	3.125	3.000	3.000	3.000	2.000	2.000	2.000	2.000	1.000	1.000	1.000
5	4.000	3.625	3.500	3.625	3.000	3.000	3.000	3.000	2.000	2.000	2.000	2.000	1.000	1.000
5-1/4	—	4.125	4.000	3.625	3.750	3.750	3.000	3.000	3.000	2.000	2.000	2.000	2.000	1.000
5-1/2	—	4.125	4.000	4.125	3.750	3.750	3.750	3.000	3.000	3.000	2.000	2.000	2.000	2.000
5-3/4	—	4.625	4.500	4.125	3.750	3.750	3.750	3.000	3.000	3.000	3.000	2.000	2.000	2.000
6	—	4.625	4.500	4.625	4.500	4.500	3.750	4.000	3.000	3.000	3.000	3.000	2.000	2.000
6-1/4	—	5.125	5.000	4.625	4.500	4.500	4.500	4.000	4.000	3.000	3.000	3.000	3.000	2.000
6-1/2	—	5.125	5.000	5.125	4.500	4.500	4.500	4.000	4.000	4.000	3.000	3.000	3.000	3.000
6-3/4	—	—	5.500	5.125	5.250	5.250	4.500	4.000	4.000	4.000	4.000	3.000	3.000	3.000
7	—	—	5.500	5.625	5.250	5.250	5.250	5.000	4.000	4.000	4.000	4.000	3.000	3.000
7-1/4	—	—	6.000	5.625	5.250	5.250	5.250	5.000	5.000	4.000	4.000	4.000	4.000	3.000
7-1/2	—	—	—	6.125	6.000	6.000	5.250	5.000	5.000	5.000	4.000	4.000	4.000	4.000
7-3/4	—	—	—	6.125	6.000	6.000	6.000	5.000	5.000	5.000	5.000	4.000	4.000	4.000
8	—	—	—	6.625	6.000	6.750	6.000	6.000	5.000	5.000	5.000	5.000	4.000	4.000
8-1/2	—	—	—	7.125	7.000	6.750	6.750	6.000	6.000	6.000	5.000	5.000	5.000	4.000
9	—	—	—	7.625	7.000	7.750	6.750	7.000	6.000	6.000	6.000	5.000	5.000	5.000
9-1/2	—	—	—	—	8.000	7.750	7.750	7.000	7.000	7.000	6.000	6.000	5.000	5.000
10	—	—	—	—	8.000	9.25	7.750	8.000	7.000	7.000	7.000	6.000	6.000	5.000
11	—	—	—	—	—	10.25	9.25	9.000	8.000	8.000	7.000	7.000	6.000	6.000
12	—	—	—	—	—	—	10.25	10.000	9.000	9.000	8.000	7.000	7.000	6.000
13	—	—	—	—	—	—	—	11.000	10.000	10.000	9.000	8.000	7.000	7.000
14	—	—	—	—	—	—	—	12.000	11.000	11.000	10.000	9.000	8.000	7.000
15	—	—	—	—	—	—	—	13.000	12.000	12.000	11.000	10.000	9.000	8.000
16	—	—	—	—	—	—	—	—	13.000	13.000	12.000	11.000	10.000	9.000
17	—	—	—	—	—	—	—	—	14.000	14.000	13.000	12.000	11.000	10.000
18	—	—	—	—	—	—	—	—	15.000	15.000	14.000	13.000	12.000	11.000
19	—	—	—	—	—	—	—	—	—	16.000	15.000	14.000	13.000	12.000
20	—	—	—	—	—	—	—	—	—	17.000	16.000	15.000	14.000	13.000

1. For nominal screw lengths falling between tabulated lengths, and nominal lengths shorter than tabulated lengths, see 3.8.

APPENDIX A
THREAD RUNOUT SLEEVE GAGE

A.1 A gage capable of checking the head and thread eccentricity along with the bow of shank on screws is illustrated in Figure A1.

The gage construction incorporates three primary components: ring gage A, shank sleeve B_2, and head sleeve B_1. Shank sleeve length can be varied to accommodate different lengths of product and also diameters D_2 and D_1 can be varied depending upon the screw diameter and head size, respectively. Ring gage A and head sleeve B_1 are centered on the sleeve B_2 by means of the positioning plug shown below the gage proper and are secured in position by means of attachment screws C. The ring gage A is also set to Class 2B or 3B maximum pitch diameter as applicable.

Diameter D_1, of the head sleeve, equals the maximum flange diameter of the screw plus 0.031 in allowance. Diameter D_2, of the shank sleeve, equals the max screw diameter plus the runout allowance given below as a function of product length. The shank sleeve length L_2 should be such that entering face of gage A extends beyond the last thread of the product to be inspected.

Failure of the screw to enter the threads of gage or interference between the sides of hole D_1 or D_2 and the screw while engaging threads of the gage indicates excessive runout.

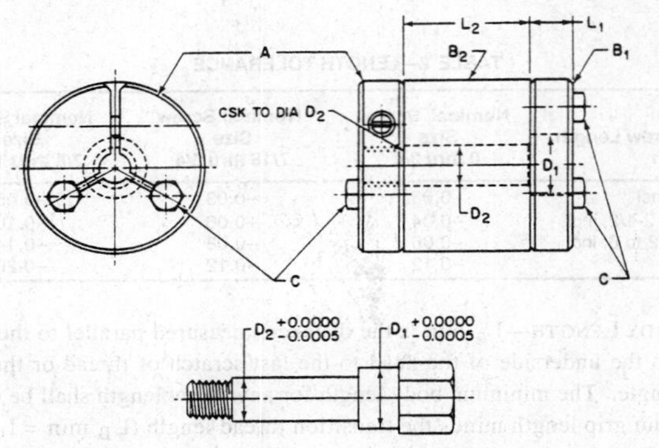

LEGEND

A —THREAD RING GAGE SET TO 2B OR 3B MAX PITCH DIAMETER, AS APPLICABLE
B_1—HEAD SLEEVE
B_2—SHANK SLEEVE
C —ATTACHMENT SCREWS
D_1—DIAMETER OF HOLE IN HEAD SLEEVE = MAX FLANGE DIAMETER OF SCREW PLUS 0.031 IN ALLOWANCE
D_2—DIAMETER OF HOLE IN SHANK SLEEVE = MAX SCREW DIAMETER PLUS 0.016 IN FOR LENGTHS UP TO 2 IN, INCL; 0.031 IN FOR LENGTHS OVER 2 TO 6 IN, INCL; AND 0.062 IN FOR LENGTHS OVER 6 IN
L_1—LENGTH OF HEAD SLEEVE = HEAD HEIGHT OF SCREW
L_2—LENGTH OF SHANK SLEEVE = LENGTH OF SCREW MINUS ONE SCREW DIAMETER

FIGURE A1—THREAD RUNOUT SLEEVE GAGE

MECHANICAL AND MATERIAL REQUIREMENTS FOR STEEL NUTS—SAE J995 JUL1999

SAE Standard

Report of the SAE Iron and Steel Technical Committee approved August 1967, revised September 1974, and editorial change June 1979. Completely revised by the SAE Fasteners Committee July 1999.

1. Scope—This SAE Standard covers the mechanical and material requirements for three grades of steel nuts suitable for use in automotive and related engineering applications, in sizes 1/4 to 1-1/2 in, inclusive, and with dimensions conforming with the requirements of the latest issue of ASME B18.2.2 or ASME B18.6.3, as applicable.

1.1 This document does not include limits for surface discontinuities. Where usage requires such control, limits may be specified separately. For sizes 1/4 through 1 in, this may be done by the statement: "Surface discontinuities shall not exceed the limits specified in SAE J122."

2. References

2.1 Applicable Publications—The following publications form a part of this specification to the extent specified herein. Unless otherwise indicated, the latest version shall apply.

2.1.1 SAE PUBLICATIONS—Available from SAE, 400 Commonwealth Drive, Warrendale, PA 15096-0001.

SAE J122—Surface Discontinuities on Nuts

SAEJ409—Product Analysis—Permissible Variations from Specified Chemical Analysis of a Heat or Cast of Steel

SAE J417—Hardness Test and Hardness Number Conversions

2.1.2 ASME PUBLICATIONS—Available from ASME, 22 Law Drive, Box 2900, Fairfield, NJ 07007-2900.

ASME B18.2.2—Square and Hex Nuts (Inch Series)

ASME B18.6.3—Machine Screws and Machine Screw Nuts

3. Designation—The three grades of nuts are designated Grades 2, 5, and 8.

4. Material—Nuts shall be made of steel conforming to the chemical composition limits specified in Table 1.

5. Mechanical Requirements

5.1 Proof Load—Nuts described in this document shall withstand the proof load stress specified in Table 2 for the nut grade, size, and thread series.

5.2 Hardness—Nuts shall have a hardness within the limits specified in Table 4.

6. Test Methods

6.1 Proof Load Test—The nut shall be assembled on a test bolt or on a hardened and threaded mandrel, as described in the following and illustrated in Figure 1. The specified proof load for the nut shall be applied against the nut in an axial direction. (See footnote 1 of Table 2 for method for computing the proof load in pounds for a nut.) The nut shall resist this load without failure by stripping or rupture, and shall be removable from the test bolt or mandrel by the fingers after the load is released.

NOTE—Occasionally it may be necessary to use a manual wrench or other means to start the nut in motion. Use of such means is permissible, providing the nut is removable by the fingers following an initial loosening of not more than one-half turn of the nut.

TABLE 1—CHEMICAL COMPOSITION REQUIREMENTS(1)

Nut Grade	C Max	Mn Min	P Max	S Max
2	0.47	—	0.12(2)	0.15(3)
5	0.55	0.30	0.05(4)(5)	0.15(3)(5)
8	0.55	0.30	0.04	0.05(6)

1. All values are for ladle analysis (percent by weight) and are subject to standard variations for check analysis as given in SAE J409.
2. Resulfurized and rephosphorized material is not subject to rejection based on check analysis for sulfur.
3. If agreed between purchaser and producer, sulfur content may be 0.23 max.
4. Phosphorus content may be 0.13 max for acid bessemer steel only.
5. If agreed between purchaser and producer, sulfur content may be 0.35 max and phosphorus content may be 0.12 max provided that manganese content is 0.70 min.
6. If agreed between purchaser and producer, sulfur content may be 0.33 max provided that manganese content is 1.35 min.

If the threads of the test bolt or mandrel are damaged during the test, the test shall be discarded.

Test bolts shall have threads conforming to Class 2A tolerances and shall have a yield strength in excess of the specified proof load of the nut being tested.

Mandrels shall have a minimum hardness of 45 HRC; and shall be threaded to Class 3A tolerance, except that the major diameter shall be the minimum major diameter with a tolerance of +0.002 in.

For referee purposes, the proof load test shall be conducted using a hardened mandrel.

6.2 Hardness Test—Rockwell hardness shall be determined on the top or bottom nut face halfway between the major diameter of the thread and one corner, or, if applicable, on a wrench face one-third of the distance from corner to the center of the wrench face. In preparing the surface, sufficient material shall be removed to assure elimination of any decarburization or other surface irregularities.

Hardness tests shall be conducted in accordance with SAE J417.

TABLE 2—PROOF LOAD REQUIREMENTS FOR NUTS(1)

Nut Grade Nut Size Thread Series Nut Type	2(2) 1/4 thru 1-1/2 UNC and 8UN Proof Load Stress, psi(1)	5 1/4 thru 1 UNC and 8UN Proof Load Stress, psi(1)	5 1/4 thru 1 UNF, 12 UN and Finer Proof Load Stress, psi(1)	5 Over 1 thru 1-1/2 UNC and 8UN Proof Load Stress, psi(1)	5 Over 1 thru 1-1/2 UNF, 12UN and Finer Proof Load Stress, psi(1)	8 1/4 thru 1-1/2 UNC and 8UN Proof Load Stress, psi(1)	8 1/4 thru 1-1/2 UNF, 12UN and Finer Proof Load Stress, psi(1)
Hex	—	120 000	109 000	105 000	94 000	150 000	150 000
Hex Flange	—	120 000	109 000	105 000	94 000	150 000	150 000
Hex Jam(3)	—	72 000	65 000	63 000	57 000	90 000	90 000
Heavy Hex Jam(3)	—	72 000	65 000	63 000	57 000	90 000	90 000
Hex Slotted(3)	—	96 000	87 000	84 000	75 000	120 000	120 000
Heavy Hex(3)	—	133 000	120 000	116 000	105 000	165 000	150 000
Hex Thick(3)	—	133 000	120 000	116 000	105 000	165 000	150 000
Heavy Hex Slotted(3)	—	105 000	96 000	92 000	84 000	132 000	120 000
Hex Thick Slotted(3)	—	105 000	96 000	92 000	84 000	132 000	120 000
Square(2)	90 000	—	—	—	—	—	—

1. The proof load in pounds for a nut is computed by multiplying the proof load stress, in psi (lbf/in^2), for the nut grade, size, thread series, and type, as shown in Table 2, and the stress area, in sq in (in^2), for the applicable size and thread series shown in Table 3. (See Appendix A, Table A1 for computed values for some products.)
2. Grade 2 is normally applicable to square nuts only, and square nuts are normally available in Grade 2 only.
3. Proof load stress values for hex jam, heavy hex jam, hex slotted, heavy hex, hex thick, heavy hex slotted, and hex thick slotted nuts are based on requirements for hex nuts. Primarily, each value is derived from the ratio of minimum thickness of the product involved to the minimum thickness of hex or square machine screw nuts and hex nuts (see ASME B18.2.2 and ASME B18.6.3) of the same size—and adjusted to compensate for differences in width across flats, width and depth of slots, and depth of countersink.

TABLE 3—TENSILE STRESS AREAS (TEST BOLT OR MANDREL)

Coarse Thread Series UNC Nominal Size and Threads Per Inch	Coarse Thread Series UNC Tensile Stress Area, sq in	Fine Thread Series UNF Nominal Size and Threads Per Inch	Fine Thread Series UNF Tensile Stress Area, sq in	8–Thread Series 8 UN Nominal Size and Threads Per Inch	8–Thread Series 8 UN Tensile Stress Area sq in
1/4 – 20	0.0318	1/4 – 28	0.0364	—	—
5/16 – 18	0.0524	5/16 – 24	0.0580	—	—
3/8 – 16	0.0775	3/8 – 24	0.0878	—	—
7/16 – 14	0.1063	7/16 – 20	0.1187	—	—
1/2 – 13	0.1419	1/2 – 20	0.1599	—	—
9/16 – 12	0.182	9/16 – 18	0.203	—	—
5/8 – 11	0.226	5/8 – 18	0.256	—	—
3/4 – 10	0.334	3/4 – 16	0.373	—	—
7/8 – 9	0.462	7/8 – 14	0.509	—	—
1 – 8	0.606	1 – 12	0.663	1 – 8	0.606
1-1/8 – 7	0.763	1-1/8 – 12	0.856	1-1/8 – 8	0.790
1-1/4 – 7	0.969	1-1/4 – 12	1.073	1-1/4 – 8	1.000
1-3/8 – 6	1.155	1-3/8 – 12	1.315	1-3/8 – 8	1.233
1-1/2 – 6	1.405	1-1/2 – 12	1.581	1-1/2 – 8	1.492

TABLE 4—HARDNESS REQUIREMENTS FOR NUTS

Nut Grade	Nominal Nut Size	Hardness
2	1/4 thru 1-1/2	32 HRC max
5	1/4 thru 1-1/2	32 HRC max
8	1/4 thru 5/8	24 – 32 HRC
8	Over 5/8 thru 1	26 – 34 HRC
8	Over 1 thru 1-1/2	26 – 36 HRC

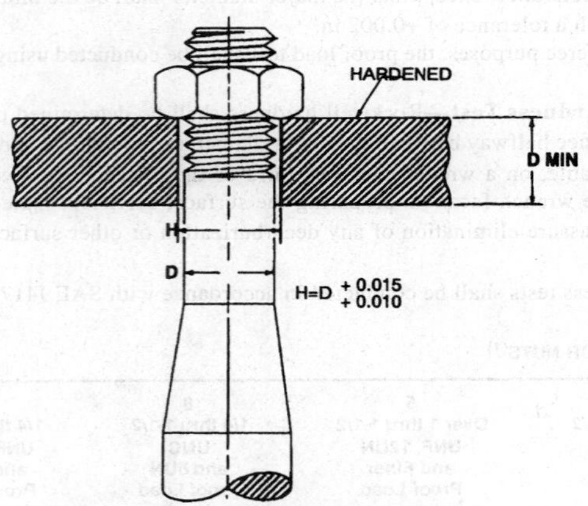

FIGURE 1—PROOF LOAD TEST

7. Marking—Three "styles" of grade marking are acceptable. Style A is applicable to all types and sizes of nuts. Style B is applicable to hex nuts of sizes 5/8 in and larger; but may be used for smaller sizes or other types of nuts only when authorized by the purchaser. Style C is applicable to nuts which are fabricated by cutting from hex bar.

Marking for source (manufacturer or private label distributor) identification shall be by the manufacturer's or private label distributor's mark.

Markings shall not project beyond the height or width across flats of the nuts. No more than 10% of the nut top surface area may be used for grade and source markings. In the case of double chamfer nuts, one face only is considered a top surface.

Style A marking shall be depressed on the top surface of the nut on a circular line or path approximately midway between hole diameter and hex flat diameter, or, for hex flange nuts at the supplier's option, raised or depressed on top of the flange, and shall consist of: a single circumferential line for Grade 2 nuts; two circumferential lines 120 degrees apart for Grade 5 nuts; and two circumferential lines 60 degrees apart for Grade 8 nuts. The circumferential lines shall conform to the following dimensions (inch, nominal): (See Table 5.)

TABLE 5—MARKING DIMENSIONS

Nut Size	Marking Lines[(1)] Width	Marking Lines(1) Length	Marking Line(1) Depth
1/4 and 5/16	0.015	0.05	0.010
3/8 thru 9/16	0.020	0.06	0.010
5/8 thru 7/8	0.030	0.08	0.010
1 and larger	0.030	0.12	0.010

1. For hex flange nuts, lines on the top of the flange may be up to two times the dimensions shown.

Style B marking shall be raised or depressed on the chamfer surface of the top of the nut corners, and shall consist of: one circumferential line on one corner for Grade 2 nuts; one circumferential line on each of two corners 120 degrees apart for grade 5 nuts; and one circumferential line on each of two corners 60 degrees apart for Grade 8 nuts.

Style C marking shall consist of notches at the hexagon corners, one notch at each corner for Grade 5 nuts, and two notches at each corner for Grade 8 nuts.

7.1 Grade 2 nuts are not required to be marked for grade or source identification, unless specified by the purchaser. If marked, Grade 2 nuts shall be marked with grade and source identification marks.

7.2 Grade 5 and Grade 8 hex and hex flange nuts, sizes 1/4 through 1-1/2, shall be marked for grade identification and for source identification. Grade 5 and Grade 8 hex jam, heavy hex jam, hex slotted, heavy hex slotted, hex thick slotted, hex thick, and heavy hex nuts are not required to be marked for grade or source identification, unless specified by the purchaser. If marked, Grade 5 and Grade 8 hex jam, heavy hex jam, hex slotted, heavy hex slotted, hex thick slotted, hex thick, and heavy hex nuts shall be marked with grade and source identification marks.

8. Testing Requirements

8.1 Manufacturer's Responsibility—During the manufacture of products to the requirements of this specification, the manufacturer shall make periodic tests to ensure that the properties of the product are being maintained within specified limits. For all Grade 8 nuts, and for Grade 5 hex and hex flange nuts, each lot shall be tested. Such tests shall be conducted in accordance with a sampling plan, preferably the sampling plan given in 8.3, and the test results shall be recorded in a test report. When requested in writing by the purchaser, the manufacturer shall furnish a copy of the test report certified to be a report of the results of the lot for Grade 8 nuts or Grade 5 hex or hex flange nuts, or, for other nuts, of the last completed set of tests for the specific type, size, and grade of product.

8.2 Purchaser's Options—If the purchaser requires that additional tests be performed by the manufacturer to determine that the properties of products in an individual lot or shipment are within specified limits, or if the purchaser requires that a sampling plan different from that given in 8.3 shall be used when determining the acceptability of a lot, or shipment, of products, the purchaser shall specify the complete testing requirements, including sampling plan and basis of acceptance, in the original inquiry and purchase order.

8.3 General—An acceptable sampling plan, with the acceptance criteria of zero nonconformances, is outlined in Table 6.

A lot, for purposes of selecting test specimens, shall consist of a quantity of nuts of one part number manufactured by the same production process from the same coil or heat number of steel and submitted for inspection and testing at one time.

The same test specimens may be used for different tests wherever practical.

If the failure of a test specimen is due to improper preparation of the specimen or to incorrect testing technique, the specimen shall be discarded and another specimen substituted.

TABLE 6—SAMPLING PLAN

Number of Pieces in Lot	Minimum Number of Specimens to be Tested
50 and under	2
51 to 500	3
501 to 35 000	5
35 001 to 250 000	8

APPENDIX A

A.1 See Table A1.

TABLE A1—PROOF LOAD FOR MISCELLANEOUS NUTS,(1) LBf (UNC THREADS ONLY)

Nominal Nut Size and Threads Per Inch	Square Nuts Grade 2	Hex and Hex Flange Nuts Grade 5	Hex and Hex Flange Nuts Grade 8	Hex Jam and Heavy Hex Jam Nuts Grade 5	Hex Jam and Heavy Hex Jam Nuts Grade 8	Hex Slotted Nuts Grade 5	Hex Slotted Nuts Grade 8	Heavy Hex and Hex Thick Nuts Grade 5	Heavy Hex and Hex Thick Nuts Grade 8	Heavy Hex Slotted and Hex Thick Slotted Nuts Grade 5	Heavy Hex Slotted and Hex Thick Slotted Nuts Grade 8
1/4 – 20	2 850	3 800	4 750	2 300	2 850	3 050	3 800	4 250	5 250	3 350	4 200
5/16 – 18	4 700	6 300	7 850	3 750	4 700	5 050	6 300	6 950	8 650	5 500	6 900
3/8 – 16	7 000	9 300	11 600	5 600	7 000	7 450	9 300	10 300	12 800	8 150	10 200
7/16 – 14	9 550	12 800	15 900	7 650	9 550	10 200	12 800	14 100	17 500	11 200	14 000
1/2 – 13	12 800	17 000	21 300	10 200	12 800	13 600	17 000	18 900	23 400	14 900	18 700
9/16 – 12	16 400	21 800	27 300	13 100	16 400	17 500	21 800	24 200	30 000	19 100	24 000
5/8 – 11	20 300	27 100	33 900	16 300	20 300	21 700	27 100	30 100	37 300	23 700	29 800
3/4 – 10	30 100	40 100	50 100	24 000	30 100	32 100	40 100	44 400	55 100	35 100	44 100
7/8 – 9	41 600	55 400	69 300	33 300	41 600	44 400	55 400	61 400	76 200	48 500	61 000
1 – 8	54 500	72 700	90 900	43 600	54 500	58 200	72 700	80 600	100 000	63 600	80 000
1-1/8 – 7	68 700	80 100	114 000	48 100	68 700	64 100	91 600	88 500	126 000	70 200	101 000
1-1/4 – 7	87 200	102 000	145 000	61 000	87 200	81 400	116 000	112 000	160 000	89 100	128 000
1-3/8 – 6	104 000	121 000	173 000	72 800	104 000	97 000	139 000	134 000	191 000	106 000	152 000
1-1/2 – 6	126 000	148 000	211 000	88 500	126 000	118 000	169 000	163 000	232 000	129 000	185 000

1. Computed according to Table 2, Footnote 1, using psi (lbf/in^2) values shown in Table 2.

(R) MECHANICAL AND MATERIAL REQUIREMENTS FOR WHEEL BOLTS—SAE J1102 FEB1995

SAE Standard

Report of the SAE Iron and Steel Technical Committee approved October 1974. Completely revised by the SAE Fasteners Committee February 1995.

Foreword—This Document has not changed other than to put it into the new SAE Technical Standards Board Format.

1. Scope—This SAE Standard covers the chemical, metallurgical, and mechanical requirements for two types of passenger car and truck wheel bolts, as follows:

a. Nonserrated shank bolts which are heat treated
b. Serrated shank bolts which are case hardened

2. References

2.1 Applicable Publications—The following publications form a part of this specification to the extent specified herein. The latest issue of SAE publications shall apply.

2.1.1 SAE PUBLICATIONS—Available from SAE, 400 Commonwealth Drive, Warrendale, PA 15096-0001.

SAE J121—Decarburization in Hardened and Tempered Unified Threaded Fasteners
SAE J417—Hardness Tests and Hardness Number Conversions
SAE J429—Mechanical and Material Requirements for Externally Threaded Fasteners
SAE J1061—Surface Discontinuities on General Application Bolts, Screws, and Studs

2.1.2 ASTM PUBLICATION—Available from ASTM, 100 Barr Harbor Drive, West Conshohocken, PA 19428-2959.

ASTME18—Test Methods for Rockwell Hardness and Rockwell Superficial Hardness of Metallic Materials

3. Materials and Processes

3.1 Steel Characteristics

3.1.1 Nonserrated bolts in sizes through 1.0 in diameter shall be made of killed steel with carbon content of 0.28 to 0.47, sulphur 0.058 max, and phosphorous 0.048 max.

3.1.2 Serrated bolts in sizes through 9/16 in diameter shall be made of SAE 1541 steel, fine grain.

3.1.3 Serrated bolts in sizes over 9/16 in diameter shall be made of a medium carbon alloy steel (carbon content 0.28 to 0.55), fine grain with hardenability that will produce a minimum hardness of Rockwell C47 at the center of a transverse section one diameter from the threaded end of the bolt after oil quenching.

3.1.4 The preceding analyses are product chemical analyses (percent by weight) and refer to individual determinations on uncarburized or core portion of bolts.

3.2 Heading Practice—Bolts in sizes through 3/4 in shall be cold headed. Larger sizes may be hot or cold headed, at the option of the manufacturer.

3.3 Threading Practice—All bolts, regardless of size, shall be roll threaded.

3.4 Heat Treatment Practice

3.4.1 NONSERRATED SHANK BOLTS

3.4.1.1 Bolts shall be heat treated, quenched in a liquid medium and tempered at a minimum tempering temperature of 425 °C (800 °F).

3.4.1.2 Bolts shall conform to Decarburization 1/2 H (as described in SAE J121), unless otherwise specified.

3.4.2 SERRATED SHANK BOLTS

3.4.2.1 Bolts shall be carburized in a nonnitriding atmosphere to a total depth of 0.004 to 0.012 in, oil quenched and tempered at a minimum tempering temperature of 450 °C (850 °F).

3.4.2.2 Case depth shall be measured on the body or head of the bolt.

3.5 Surface Discontinuities—Bolts in sizes up to 1.0 in diameter inclusive, and lengths up to 6.0 in inclusive shall not have surface discontinuities exceeding the limits specified in SAE J1061. Surface discontinuities for other sizes and lengths shall be within limits specified by the purchaser.

4. Mechanical and Performance Requirements

4.1 Proof Load—85 ksi

4.2 Axial Tensile Strength—120 ksi minimum

4.2.1 Bolts shall withstand the minimum tensile stress without breaking into separate parts.

4.2.2 For serrated shank bolts, a snug or press fit of the serrations to retaining fixture is recommended to minimize potential of fracture at the bolt head to shank junction.

4.3 Core Hardness—Rockwell C25-34.

4.4 Surface Hardness

4.4.1 NONSERRATED SHANK BOLTS

4.4.1.1 Bolts shall conform to the surface hardness requirements specified in SAE J429—grade 5.

4.4.2 SERRATED SHANK BOLTS

4.4.2.1 Bolts shall meet Rockwell hardness 15N 77 minimum.

4.5 Bend Test—Bolts shall withstand a 10 degree bend without breaking into separate parts.

4.6 Serration Test (Serrated Shank Bolts Only)—Bolts shall assemble in a test plate without visual evidence of surface stripping of the serrations. The serrations shall not peel such that they accumulate under the bolt head when the bolt is pressed into the specified test plate.

5. Test Methods

5.1 Proof Load—Same as defined in SAE J429.

5.2 Axial Tensile Strength—Same as defined in SAE J429.

5.3 Core Hardness—Same as defined in SAE J429.

5.4 Surface Hardness—Tests to determine surface hardness conditions shall be conducted on the ends, head, or unthreaded and nonserrated portion of the shanks which have been prepared by lightly grinding or polishing to ensure accurate reproducible readings in accordance with SAE J417. Proper correction factors shall be used when hardness tests are made on curved surfaces, per ASTM E 18.

5.5 Bend Test—The test bolt shall be threaded or clamped into a hardened block or other suitable device with three threads exposed. A force perpendicular to the centerline of the bolt shall be applied against the bolt head and continued until the bolt is permanently bent through 10 degrees.

5.6 Serration Test (Serrated Shank Bolts Only)—The test bolt shall be pressed into a hole in a steel plate or appropriate wheel hub or axle flange until the head is seated by applying an axial compression load to the head of the bolt. The bolt shall then be removed and visually examined for evidence of serration stripping. If a wheel hub or axle flange is used it shall be of the same material and hardness required for the part into which the bolt is normally assembled in production. If a plate is used, it shall be 0.5 in thick with a hardness of Brinell 269-285. The hole size shall be as specified by the purchaser; however, if not specified, the diameter shall be the average of the mean major and mean minor serration diameters.

5.7 Methods for Measuring Carburization—Two methods for measuring carburization are provided. The microscopic method is intended primarily for routine inspection purposes. The hardness method is intended primarily for referee purposes.

5.7.1 MICROSCOPIC METHOD

5.7.1.1 Specimens—Transverse sections taken through the head, shank, or unthreaded portion of the bolt, after all heat treating operations have been performed on the product.

5.7.1.2 Preparation

a. Mount specimen for grinding and polishing. Protection from rounding the surface to be examined is essential. The specimen should be mounted in a clamp or in a plastic mount, the latter being the preferred method.
b. After mounting, grind and polish the surface in accordance with good metallographic practice.
c. Etching in a 3% nital (concentrated nitric acid) or picral (saturated picric acid) is usually suitable for showing changes in microstructure for carburization, a darker shade of tempered martensite than that of the immediately adjacent base metal.

5.7.1.3 Measurement—Unless otherwise agreed on between purchaser and producer, examine at 100X magnification.

If the microscope is of a type with a ground glass screen, the extent of carburization can be measured directly with a scale. If an eye-piece is used for measurement, it should be an appropriate type containing a cross hair or a scale.

5.7.2 HARDNESS METHOD

5.7.2.1 Prepare specimens as outlined in 5.7.1.1 and 5.7.1.2, except the specimen is not to be etched.

5.7.2.2 Measurement—Unless otherwise agreed on between purchaser and producer, hardness measurements are made using a Knoop Indenter with a 500 g load or Vickers DPH with a 300 g load.

a. Determine the average base metal hardness from at least six readings. The initial indentation measurement shall be taken 0.040 in from the product outer surface and each subsequent measurement interval shall be 0.020 in moving towards the core of the specimen.

b. To determine total case depth, the first measurement shall be taken 0.002 in from the specimen outer surface and each subsequent hardness measurement shall be at 0.002 in intervals from the previous reading towards the core of the part. For accuracy, the measurements should be staggered to ensure sufficient indentation separation (Figure 1).

c. Total case depth shall be established from the average base metal hardness value to an intersecting line where a distinct increased hardness change occurs.

6. Marking

6.1 Nonserrated shank bolts shall be marked with three radial lines 120 degrees apart and manufacturer's identification marking.

6.2 Serrated shank bolts shall be marked with the specification number 1102, and manufacturer's identification marking.

6.3 Markings shall be located on the top of the head and may be either raised or depressed at the option of the manufacturer.

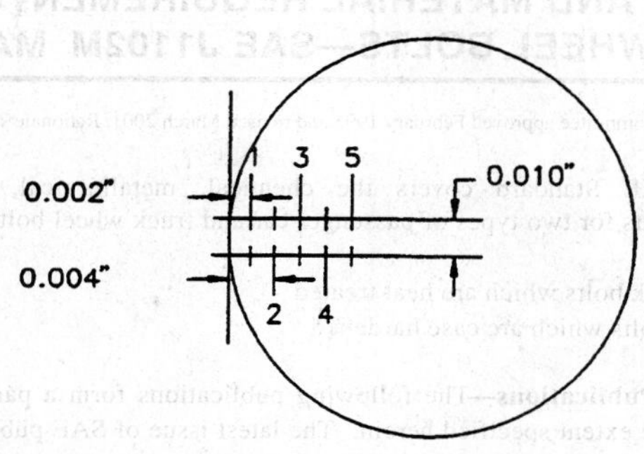

FIGURE 1—CASE DEPTH BY HARDNESS METHOD

MECHANICAL AND MATERIAL REQUIREMENTS FOR METRIC WHEEL BOLTS—SAE J1102M MAR2001 SAE Standard

Report of the SAE Fasteners Committee approved February 1995 and revised March 2001. Rationale statement available.

1. Scope—This SAE Standard covers the chemical, metallurgical, and mechanical requirements for two types of passenger car and truck wheel bolts, as follows:

a. Nonserrated shank bolts which are heat treated
b. Serrated shank bolts which are case hardened

2. References

2.1 Applicable Publications—The following publications form a part of this specification to the extent specified herein. The latest issue of SAE publications shall apply.

2.1.1 SAE PUBLICATIONS—Available from SAE, 400 Commonwealth Drive, Warrendale, PA 15096-0001.

SAE J121M—Decarburization in Hardened and Tempered Metric Threaded Fasteners

SAE J417—Hardness Tests and Hardness Number Conversions

SAE J1061—Surface Discontinuities on General Application Bolts, Screws, and Studs

2.1.2 ASTM PUBLICATION—Available from ASTM, 100 Barr Harbor Drive, West Conshohocken, PA 19428-2959.

ASTME18—Test Methods for Rockwell Hardness and Rockwell Superficial Hardness of Metallic Materials

ASTMF606M—Standard Test Methods for Determining the Mechanical Properties of Externally and Internally Threaded Fasteners, Washers, and Rivets.

2.1.3 ISO PUBLICATION—Available from ANSI, 25 West 43rd Street, New York, NY 10036-8002.

ISO 898-1—Mechanical properties of fasteners—Part 1: Bolts, screws and studs

3. Materials and Processes

3.1 Steel Characteristics

3.1.1 Nonserrated bolts shall be made of carbon killed steel conforming to ISO 898-1 for property class 8.8.

3.1.2 Serrated bolts in sizes through 14 mm diameter shall be made of SAE 1541 steel, fine grain.

3.1.3 Serrated bolts in sizes over 14 mm diameter shall be made of a medium carbon alloy steel (carbon content 0.28 to 0.55), fine grain with hardenability that will produce a minimum hardness of Rockwell C47 at the center of a transverse section one diameter from the threaded end of the bolt after oil quenching.

3.1.4 The preceding analyses are product chemical analyses (percent by weight) and refer to individual determinations on uncarburized or core portion of bolts.

3.2 Heading Practice—Bolts in sizes through 20 mm shall be cold headed. Larger sizes may be hot or cold headed, at the option of the manufacturer.

3.3 Threading Practice—All bolts, regardless of size, shall be roll threaded.

3.4 Heat Treatment Practice

3.4.1 NONSERRATED SHANK BOLTS

3.4.1.1 Bolts shall be heat treated, quenched in a liquid medium and tempered to a minimum tempering temperature of 425 °C.

3.4.1.2 Bolts shall conform to Decarburization 1/2 H (as described in SAE J121M), unless otherwise specified.

3.4.2 SERRATED SHANK BOLTS

3.4.2.1 Bolts shall be carburized in a nonnitriding atmosphere to a total depth of 0.10 to 0.30 mm, oil quenched and tempered at a minimum tempering temperature of 450 °C.

3.4.2.2 Case depth shall be measured on the body or head of the bolt.

3.5 Surface Discontinuities—Bolts in sizes up to 24 mm diameter inclusive, and lengths up to 150 mm inclusive, shall not have surface discontinuities exceeding the limits specified in SAE J1061. Surface discontinuities for other sizes and lengths shall be within limits specified by the purchaser.

4. Mechanical and Performance Requirements

4.1 Nonserrated Shank Bolts

4.1.1 Bolts shall conform to the latest revision of ISO 898-1 for property class 8.8.

4.2 Serrated Shank Bolts

4.2.1 PROOF LOAD—600 MPa

4.2.2 AXIAL TENSILE STRENGTH—830 MPa minimum

4.2.2.1 Bolts shall withstand the minimum tensile stress without breaking into separate parts.

4.2.2.2 For serrated shank bolts, a snug or press fit of the serrations to retaining fixture is recommended to minimize potential of fracture at the bolt head to shank junction.

4.2.3 CORE HARDNESS—Rockwell C25-34.

4.2.4 SURFACE HARDNESS—Bolts shall meet Rockwell hardness 15N 77 minimum.

4.2.5 BEND TEST—Bolts shall withstand a 10 degree bend without breaking into separate parts.

4.2.6 SERRATION TEST (SERRATED SHANK BOLTS ONLY)—Bolts shall assemble in a test plate without visual evidence of surface stripping of the serrations. The serrations shall not peel such that they accumulate under the bolt head when the bolt is pressed into the specified test plate.

5. Test Methods

5.1 Proof Load—Same as defined in ASTM F 606M 3.2.

5.2 Axial Tensile Strength—Same as defined in ASTM F 606M 3.4.

5.3 Core Hardness—Same as defined in ASTM F 606M 3.1.

5.4 Surface Hardness—Tests to determine surface hardness conditions shall be conducted on the ends, head, or unthreaded and nonserrated portion of the shanks which have been prepared by lightly grinding or polishing to ensure accurate reproducible readings in accordance with SAE J417. Proper correction factors shall be used when hardness tests are made on curved surfaces, per ASTM E 18.

5.5 Bend Test—The test bolt shall be threaded or clamped into a hardened block or other suitable device with three threads exposed. A force perpendicular to the centerline of the bolt shall be applied against the bolt head and continued until the bolt is permanently bent through 10 degrees.

5.6 Serration Test (Serrated Shank Bolts Only)—The test bolt shall be pressed into a hole in a steel plate or appropriate wheel hub or axle flange until the head is seated by applying an axial compression load to the head of the bolt. The bolt shall then be removed and visually examined for evidence of serration stripping. If a wheel hub or axle flange is used it shall be of the same material and hardness required for the part into which the bolt is normally assembled in production. If a plate is used, it shall be 12.7 mm thick with a hardness of Brinell 269-285. The hole size shall be as specified by the purchaser; however, if not specified, the diameter shall be the average of the mean major and mean minor serration diameters.

5.7 Methods for Measuring Carburization—Two methods for measuring carburization are provided. The microscopic method is intended primarily for routine inspection purposes. The hardness method is intended primarily for referee purposes.

5.7.1 MICROSCOPIC METHOD

5.7.1.1 Specimens—Transverse sections taken through the head, shank, or unthreaded portion of the bolt, after all heat treating operations have been performed on the product.

5.7.1.2 Preparation

a. Mount specimen for grinding and polishing. Protection from rounding the surface to be examined is essential. The specimen should be mounted in a clamp or in a plastic mount, the latter being the preferred method.
b. After mounting, grind and polish the surface in accordance with good metallographic practice.
c. Etching in a 3% nital (concentrated nitric acid) or picral (saturated picric acid) is usually suitable for showing changes in microstructure for carburization, a darker shade of tempered martensite than that of the immediately adjacent base metal.

5.7.1.3 Measurement—Unless otherwise agreed on between purchaser and producer, examine at 100X magnification.

If the microscope is of a type with a ground glass screen, the extent of carburization can be measured directly with a scale. If an eye-piece is used for measurement, it should be an appropriate type containing a cross hair or a scale.

5.7.2 HARDNESS METHOD

5.7.2.1 Prepare specimens as outlined in 5.7.1.1 and 5.7.1.2, except the specimen is not to be etched.

5.7.2.2 Measurement—Unless otherwise agreed on between purchaser and producer, hardness measurements are made using a Knoop indenter with a 500 g load or Vickers DPH with a 300 g load.

a. Determine the average base metal hardness from at least six readings. The initial indentation measurement shall be taken 1.0 mm from the product outer surface and each subsequent measurement interval shall be 0.5 mm moving towards the core of the specimen.
b. To determine total case depth, the first measurement shall be taken 0.05 mm from the specimen outer surface and each subsequent hardness measurement shall be at 0.05 mm intervals from the previous reading moving towards the core of the part. For accuracy, the measurements should be staggered to ensure sufficient indentation separation (Figure 1).
c. Total case depth shall be established from the average base metal hardness value to an intersecting line where a distinct increased hardness change occurs.

6. Marking

6.1 Nonserrated shank bolts shall be marked with numerical 8.8 and manufacturer's identification marking on the top of the head and the markings may be raised or depressed at the option of the manufacturer.

6.2 Serrated shank bolts shall be marked with 1102M and the manufacturer's identification marking.

6.2.1 Bolts shall be marked also with the letter "M" on the end of the bolt.

6.2.2 Manufacturer's identification mark and "1102M" numerical designation shall be located on the top of the head and the markings may be raised or depressed at the option of the manufacturer.

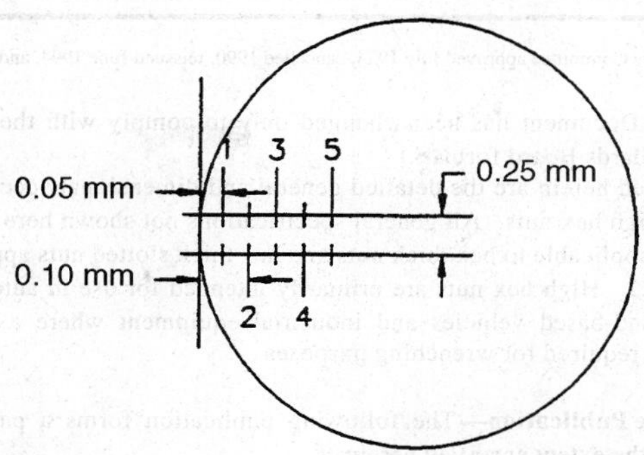

FIGURE 1—CASE DEPTH BY HARDNESS METHOD

HEXAGON HIGH NUTS—SAE J482 MAY1998 SAE Standard

Report of the SAE Fasteners Committee approved July 1924, cancelled 1990, reissued June 1994, and reaffirmed May 1998.

Foreword—This Document has been changed only to comply with the new SAE Technical Standards Board format.

1. Scope—Included herein are the detailed general and dimensional specifications applicable to high hex nuts. All general specifications not shown here shall conform with those applicable to hex thick nuts and hex thick slotted nuts appearing in ASME B18.2.2. High hex nuts are primarily intended for use in automotive and other ground-based vehicles and industrial equipment where a long length of hexagon is required for wrenching purposes.

2. References

2.1 Applicable Publication—The following publication forms a part of this specification to the extent specified herein.

2.1.1 ANSI/ASME PUBLICATION—Available from ASME, 22 Law Drive, Box 2900, Fairfield, NJ 07007-2900.

ANSI/ASME B18.2.2—Square and Hex Nuts—Inch Series

3. General Specifications

3.1 Threads

3.1.1 FORM AND TOLERANCE—Threads shall conform to unified Standard, Class 2B. See Table 1 and Figure 1.

3.1.2 SERIES—Threads shall be coarse (UNC) or fine (UNF) thread series.

3.1.3 COUNTERSINK—Tapped holes shall be countersunk (unless counterbore option is specified) on the bearing face or faces. The maximum countersink diameter shall be the thread basic (nominal) diameter plus 0.025 in for 3/8 size or smaller, and 1.06 times the basic major diameter for larger sizes. No part of the threaded portion shall extend beyond the bearing surface.

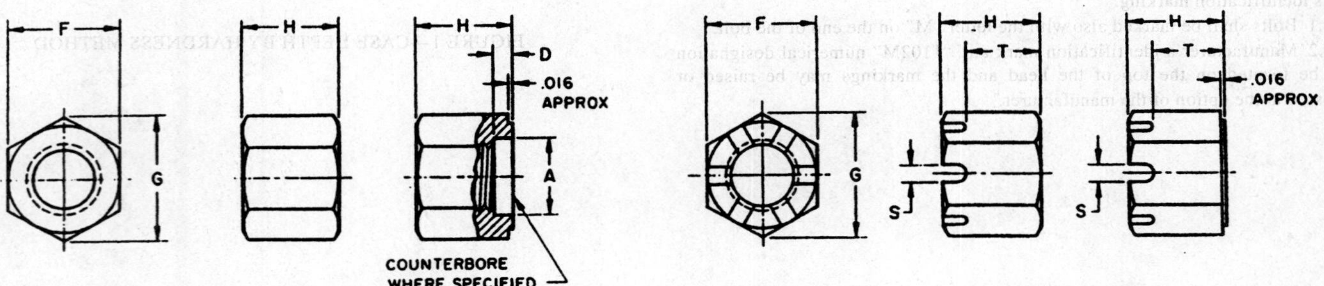

FIGURE 1—HEX HIGH AND HEX SLOTTED HIGH NUTS

TABLE 1—DIMENSIONS OF HEX HIGH AND HEX SLOTTED HIGH NUTS

Nominal Size[1] or Basic Major Dia of Thread	Width Across Flats F Basic	Width Across Flats F Max	Width Across Flats F Min	Width Across Corners G Max	Width Across Corners G Min	Thickness H Basic	Thickness H Max	Thickness H Min	Slot Width, S Min	Slot Width S Max	Unslotted Thickness, T Max	Unslotted Thickness, T Min	Counterbore (Optional) Dia A	Counterbore (Optional) Depth, D
1/4 (0.2500)	7/16	0.4375	0.428	0.505	0.488	3/8	0.382	0.368	0.07	0.10	0.29	0.27	0.266	0.062
5/16 (0.3125)	1/2	0.5000	0.489	0.577	0.557	29/64	0.461	0.445	0.09	0.12	0.37	0.35	0.328	0.078
3/8 (0.3750)	9/16	0.5625	0.551	0.650	0.628	1/2	0.509	0.491	0.12	0.15	0.38	0.36	0.391	0.094
7/16 (0.4375)	11/16	0.6875	0.675	0.794	0.768	39/64	0.619	0.599	0.12	0.15	0.46	0.44	0.453	0.109
1/2 (0.5000)	3/4	0.7500	0.736	0.866	0.840	21/32	0.667	0.645	0.15	0.18	0.51	0.49	0.516	0.125
9/16 (0.5625)	7/8	0.8750	0.861	1.010	0.982	49/64	0.778	0.754	0.15	0.18	0.59	0.57	0.594	0.141
5/8 (0.6250)	15/16	0.9375	0.922	1.083	1.051	27/32	0.857	0.831	0.18	0.24	0.63	0.61	0.656	0.156
3/4 (0.7500)	1-1/8	1.1250	1.088	1.299	1.240	1	1.015	0.985	0.18	0.24	0.76	0.73	0.781	0.188
7/8 (0.8750)	1-5/16	1.3125	1.269	1.516	1.447	1-5/32	1.172	1.140	0.18	0.24	0.92	0.89	0.906	0.219
1 (1.0000)	1-1/2	1.5000	1.450	1.732	1.653	1-5/16	1.330	1.294	0.24	0.30	1.05	1.01	1.031	0.250[1]
1-1/8 (1.1250)	1-11/16	1.6875	1.631	1.949	1.859	1-1/2	1.520	1.480	0.24	0.33	1.18	1.14	1.156	0.281
1-1/4 (1.2500)	1-7/8	1.8750	1.812	2.165	2.066	1-11/16	1.710	1.666	0.31	0.40	1.34	1.29	1.281	0.312

1. Where specifying nominal size in decimals, zeros in the fourth decimal place shall be omitted.

CROWN (BLIND, ACORN) NUTS—SAE J483 MAY1998SAE Recommended Practice

Report of the SAE Fasteners Committee approved January 1933, cancelled 1990, reissued September 1993, and revised May 1998. Rationale statement available.

1. Scope—Included in this SAE Recommended Practice are complete general and dimensional data for the high and low types of crown nuts recognized as SAE Standard. These nuts are primarily intended for application in automotive and other ground-based motor vehicles and industrial equipment to provide an ornamental or protective closure over end of bolts, studs, or screws.

2. References

2.1 Applicable Publication—The following publication forms a part of this specification to the extent specified herein. The latest issue of SAE publications shall apply.

2.1.1 SAE PUBLICATION—Available from SAE, 400 Commonwealth Drive, Warrendale, PA 15096-0001.

SAE J995—Mechanical and Material Requirements for Steel Nuts

3. General Specifications

3.1 Dimensions—All dimensions in this document are illustrated in Figure 1 and are expressed in inches in Table 1 unless otherwise stated.

3.2 Options—Options, where specified, shall be at the discretion of the manufacturer unless otherwise agreed by manufacturer and user.

3.3 Construction—Nuts may be either solid or of two-piece construction. The bearing surface shall be flat with chamfered corners or washer faced. The diameter of chamfer circle or washer face shall be equal to the maximum width across flats within a tolerance of −5%. The length of chamfer at hexagon corners shall be from 5 to 15% of the basic thread diameter. The surface of chamfer may be slightly convex or rounded.

3.4 Rounding at Corners—A rounding or lack of fill at junction of hex corners with chamfer shall be permissible, provided the minimum width across corners is reached and maintained beyond a distance equal to 17.5% of the basic thread diameter from the chamfered face and the junction of hexagon faces with crown fillet.

3.5 Taper of Sides—No transverse section through hexagon portion of nut between 25 and 75% of the actual hexagon thickness, as measured from the bearing face, shall be less than the minimum width across flats. The maximum width across flats shall not be exceeded except for milled-from-bar nonferrous nuts where the maximum (basic) width may conform with the commercial tolerances of the bar stock material.

3.6 Angularity of Bearing Surface—The bearing surface shall be at right angle to the axis of the tapped hole within 2 degrees for 1 in size or smaller, and within 1 degree for larger sizes. Therefore, the maximum total runout of bearing face shall equal the tangent of the angular deviation times the distance across flats.

3.7 Threads

3.7.1 FORM AND TOLERANCE—Threads shall conform to Unified Standard, Class 2B.

3.7.2 SERIES—Threads shall be coarse (UNC) or fine (UNF) thread series.

3.7.3 COUNTERSINK—The tapped hole shall be countersunk on the bearing face. The maximum countersink diameter shall be the thread basic (nominal) major diameter plus 0.025 in for 3/8 size or smaller, and 1.06 times the basic major diameter for larger sizes. No part of the threaded portion shall extend beyond the bearing surface.

3.8 Materials

3.8.1 STEEL—Suitable properties for steel nuts are covered in SAE J995.

3.8.2 OTHER MATERIALS—Other materials shall be as agreed upon by the manufacturer and user.

3.9 Finish

3.9.1 PLAIN—Unless otherwise specified, nuts shall be supplied plain (unplated or uncoated), as processed.

3.9.2 PLATED—Where plating is specified, the thickness or quality of plating shall be measured or tested on the side of the nut.

3.10 Defects—Nuts shall be free from burrs, seams, laps, loose scale, and any other defects that affect serviceability.

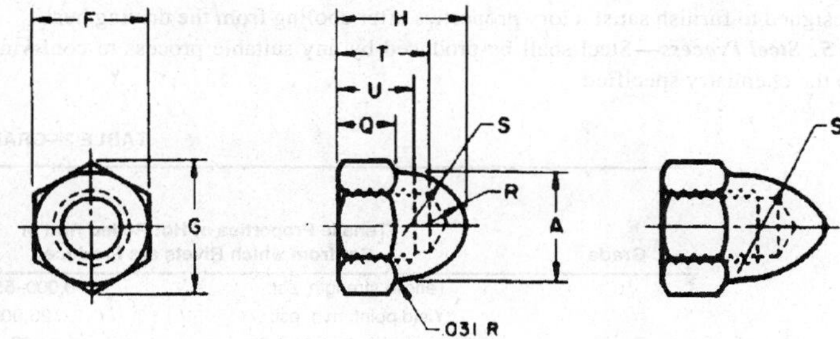

FIGURE 1—DIMENSIONS OF NUTS

TABLE 1—DIMENSIONS OF HIGH AND LOW CROWN NUTS

Nominal Size [1] or Basic Major Dia of Thread	Nominal Size [1] or Basic Major Dia of Thread	Width Across Flats F Max (Basic)	Width Across Flats F Max (Basic)	Width Across Flats F Min	Width Across Corners G Max	Width Across Corners G Min	Body Dia A	High Crown Over-all Height H	High Crown Hexagon Height Q	High Crown Nose Radius R	High Crown Body Radius S	High Crown Drill Depth T Max	High Crown Full Thread U Min	Low Crown Over-all Height H	Low Crown Hexagon Height Q	Low Crown Nose Radius R	Low Crown Body Radius S	Low Crown Drill Depth T Max	Low Crown Full Thread U Min
No. 6	0.1380	5/16	0.3125	0.302	0.361	0.344	0.30	0.42	0.17	0.05	0.25	0.28	0.19	0.34	0.16	0.08	0.17	0.25	0.16
No. 8	0.1640	5/16	0.3125	0.302	0.361	0.344	0.30	0.42	0.17	0.05	0.25	0.28	0.19	0.34	0.16	0.08	0.17	0.25	0.16
No. 10	0.1900	3/8	0.3750	0.362	0.433	0.413	0.36	0.52	0.20	0.06	0.30	0.34	0.25	0.41	0.19	0.09	0.22	0.28	0.19
No. 12	0.2160	3/8	0.3750	0.362	0.433	0.413	0.36	0.52	0.20	0.06	0.30	0.38	0.28	0.41	0.19	0.09	0.22	0.31	0.22
1/4	0.2500	7/16	0.4375	0.428	0.505	0.488	0.41	0.59	0.23	0.06	0.34	0.41	0.31	0.47	0.22	0.11	0.25	0.34	0.25
5/16	0.3125	1/2	0.5000	0.489	0.577	0.557	0.47	0.69	0.28	0.08	0.41	0.47	0.38	0.53	0.25	0.12	0.28	0.41	0.31
3/8	0.3750	9/16	0.5625	0.551	0.650	0.628	0.53	0.78	0.31	0.09	0.44	0.56	0.47	0.62	0.28	0.14	0.33	0.45	0.38
7/16	0.4375	5/8	0.6250	0.612	0.722	0.698	0.59	0.88	0.34	0.09	0.50	0.62	0.53	0.69	0.31	0.16	0.36	0.52	0.44
1/2	0.5000	3/4	0.7500	0.736	0.866	0.840	0.72	1.03	0.42	0.12	0.59	0.75	0.62	0.81	0.38	0.19	0.42	0.59	0.50
9/16	0.5625	7/8	0.8750	0.861	1.010	0.982	0.84	1.19	0.48	0.16	0.69	0.81	0.69	0.94	0.44	0.22	0.50	0.69	0.56
5/8	0.6250	15/16	0.9375	0.922	1.083	1.051	0.91	1.28	0.53	0.16	0.75	0.91	0.78	1.00	0.47	0.23	0.53	0.75	0.62
3/4	0.7500	1-1/16	1.0625	1.045	1.227	1.191	1.03	1.45	0.59	0.17	0.84	1.06	0.94	1.16	0.53	0.27	0.59	0.88	0.75
7/8	0.8750	1-1/4	1.2500	1.231	1.443	1.403	1.22	1.72	0.70	0.20	0.98	1.22	1.09	1.36	0.62	0.31	0.70	1.00	0.88
1	1.0000	1-7/16	1.4375	1.417	1.660	1.615	1.41	1.97	0.81	0.23	1.14	1.38	1.25	1.55	0.72	0.36	0.81	1.12	1.00
1-1/8	1.1250	1-5/8	1.6250	1.602	1.876	1.826	1.59	2.22	0.92	0.27	1.28	1.59	1.41	1.75	0.81	0.41	0.92	1.31	1.12
1-1/4	1.2500	1-13/16	1.8125	1.788	2.093	2.038	1.78	2.47	1.03	0.28	1.44	1.75	1.56	1.95	0.91	0.45	1.03	1.44	1.25

1. Where specifying nominal size in decimals, zeros in the fourth decimal place shall be omitted.

MECHANICAL AND CHEMICAL REQUIREMENTS FOR NONTHREADED FASTENERS CARBON STEEL SOLID RIVETS—SAE J430 MAY1998

SAE Recommended Practice

Report of the SAE Iron and Steel Technical Committe approved March 1960, reaffirmed without change October 1968, and reaffirmed May 1998.

Foreword—This Reaffirmed Document has been changed only to reflect the new SAE Technical Standards Board Format.

1. Scope—These specifications cover the mechanical and chemical requirements for carbon steel solid rivets used in automotive and other related industries.

2. References

2.1 Applicable Publication—The following publications form a part of the specification to the extent specified herein. Unless otherwise indicated the latest revision of SAE publications shall apply.

2.1.1 SAE PUBLICATION—Available from SAE, 400 Commonwealth Drive, Warrendale, PA 15096-0001.

SAE J417—Hardness Test and Hardness Number Conversions

3. Grouping—Rivets in Grades 0 and 1 fall in two groups; namely, those of small diameter—7/16 in and less, usually driven cold, and over 7/16 in usually driven hot. It is recommended that the rivets for cold driving in sizes over 7/16 in be ordered annealed.

4. General Data—Rivets for cold driving are specified so as to provide the necessary ductility for the application.

The properties of rivets intended for hot driving are not necessarily those found in the driven rivet. Therefore, the specifications for hot driven product are designed to furnish satisfactory properties after cooling from the driving heat.

5. Steel Process—Steel shall be produced by any suitable process to conform to the chemistry specified.

6. Quality—Surface shall be commercially free of injurious cracks and seams, and steel shall be free of injurious pipe and excessive segregation.

Annealed rivets for cold driving should be free of loose scale.

7. Number of Tests on Annealed Rivets

a. Samples shall be selected for hardness test from each lot of rivets as follows in Table 1:

TABLE 1—SAMPLES

Items in Lot	Number of Samples
to 800	3
801–8000	6
8001–22000	9
over 22000	15

b. All samples must meet the hardness requirements of the specification for acceptance, but retests are permitted as stated in paragraph C. Retests.

c. Retests—If any sample from the same lot fails to meet the specified requirement, double the number of samples shall be tested, in which case for acceptance all of the additional samples shall meet the specification (see Table 2):

TABLE 2—GRADES AND PROPERTIES

Grade	Tensile Properties of Hot Rolled Rod or Bar from which Rivets are Produced		Chemical Composition Ladle Analysis % Max	Heat Treatment of Rivets
0	Tensile strength, psi:	40,000–55,000	P —0.040	7/16 in dia and under are
	Yield point, min, psi:	23,000	S —0.050	furnished annealed to Rockwell B
	Elongation in 8 in, Min, %:	27		65 max(1)
1	Tensile strength, psi:	52,000–62,000	P —0.040	7/16 in dia and under are
	Yield point, Min, psi:	28,000	S —0.050	furnished annealed to Rockwell B
	Elongation in 8 in, Min, %:	24		85 max(1)
2(2)	Tensile strength, psi:	55,000–70,000	C —0.28	Not specified
	Yield point, Min, psi:	29,000	Mn—0.30—0.90	
	Elongation in 8 in., Min, %:	22	P —0.040	
			S —0.050	
			Si —0.25	
3(2)	Tensile strength, psi:	68,000–82,000	C —0.30	Not specified
	Yield point, Min, psi:	38,000	Mn—1.65	
	Elongation in 8 in, Min, %:	20	P —0.040	
			S —0.050	

1. Hardness to be taken in accordance with SAE Information Report, Hardness Tests and Hardness Number Conversions—SAE J417.
2. Grades 2 and 3 intended for hot driving only. The tensile requirements of grade 3 are met by heating to 1450 °F, holding at this temperature for not less than 30 min and cooling slowly in the furnace.

MECHANICAL AND QUALITY REQUIREMENTS FOR TAPPING SCREWS—SAE J933 MAY1998

SAE Recommended Practice

Report of the SAE Iron and Steel Technical Committee, approved July 1965, last revised September 1969, reaffirmed with editorial change June 1979, and revised May 1998.
Rationale statement available.

Foreword—This Document has also changed to comply with the new SAE Technical Standards Board Format. References were added as Section 2. All other section numbers have changed accordingly.

1. Scope

1.1 This SAE Recommended Practice covers the mechanical and quality requirements for steel tapping screws used in automotive and related industries. It does not apply to corrosion resistant (stainless) steel screws. (Dimensional requirements for most types of screws mentioned herein are covered in SAE J478.)

1.2 The primary objective of the specification is to insure that screws form or cut mating threads in materials of construction into which they are normally driven, without deforming their own thread and without breaking during assembly or service.

NOTE—Certain limitations on basic material and manufacturing processes have been incorporated because the size and configuration of the parts under consideration make them vulnerable to relatively small variations in chemistry, heat treatment, etc., and because experience has shown that in processing it is difficult to keep these variables consistently "in balance." Until improved performance tests are developed, these limitations will supplement the "performance" features of the specification.

2. References

2.1 Applicable Publication—The following publication forms a part of this specification to the extent specified herein. Unless otherwise indicated, the latest issue of SAE publications shall apply.

2.1.1 SAE PUBLICATION—Available from SAE, 400 Commonwealth Drive, Warrendale, PA 15096-0001.

SAE J423—Methods of Measuring Case Depth
SAE J478—Slotted and Recessed Head Screws

3. Performance Requirements

3.1 General—In cases where screws are plated subsequent to delivery to the purchaser (or where plating of screws is otherwise under the control of the purchaser), the screw producer is not responsible for failures due to plating. In such cases, additional screws from the same lot shall be stripped of plating, baked, lubricated with machine oil, and retested in the plain finish condition.

3.2 Drive Test for Types A, B, C, D, F, G, T, AB, and BP[1]—Sample screws (coated or uncoated, as received) shall, without deforming their own thread, form a mating thread in test plate described as follows until a thread of full diameter is completely through the test plate.

1. This test does not apply to Types BF, BG, and BT screws.

The test plate shall be made of low-carbon cold-rolled steel, having hardness of Rockwell B70-85 or equivalent, and thickness as specified in Table 1A. Test holes shall be drilled or punched and redrilled, or reamed, to ±0.001 in of nominal diameter specified in Table 1B for type and size screw being tested.

3.3 Torsional Strength Test—Shank of sample screw (coated or uncoated, as received) shall be securely clamped in a mating, split, blind-hole die (Figure 1) or other means, such that the clamped portion of the threads is not damaged and at least two full threads project above the clamping device and at least two full form threads exclusive of point, flute(s), or end slot are held within the clamping device. (A blind hole may be used in place of the clamping device, providing the hole depth is such as to insure that the breakage will occur beyond the point, or the full length of the flute(s) or end slot.) By means of a suitably calibrated torque measuring device, apply torque to the screw until failure occurs. The torque required to cause failure shall equal or exceed the minimum value shown in Table 2 for the type and size of screw being tested.

TABLE 1A—STANDARD TEST PLATE THICKNESSES AND HOLES SIZES FOR DRIVE TEST INSPECTION OF TAPPING SCREWS[(1)]—THICKNESS

Nominal Screw Size	Types AB, A, B, BP, and C Gage	Types AB, A, B, BP, and C Max	Types AB, A, B, BP, and C Min	Types D, F, G, and T Max	Types D, F, G, and T Min
2	18	0.0500	0.0460	0.0800	0.0760
3	18	0.0500	0.0460	0.0960	0.0920
4	18	0.0500	0.0460	0.1110	0.1070
5	18	0.0500	0.0460	0.1110	0.1070
6	14	0.0770	0.0730	0.1425	0.1385
7	14	0.0770	0.0730	—	—
8	14	0.0770	0.0730	0.1420	0.1380
10	1/8	0.1270	0.1230	0.1905	0.1845
12	1/8	0.1270	0.1230	0.1905	0.1845
14	1/8	0.1270	0.1230	—	—
1/4	3/16	0.1905	0.1845	0.2530	0.2470
16	3/16	0.1905	0.1845	—	—
18	3/16	0.1905	0.1845	—	—
5/16	3/16	0.1905	0.1845	0.3155	0.3095
20	3/16	0.1905	0.1845	—	—
24	3/16	0.1905	0.1845	—	—
3/8	3/16	0.1905	0.1845	0.3780	0.3720
7/16	3/16	0.1905	0.1845	—	—
1/2	3/16	0.1905	0.1845	—	—

1. Requirements shown in each column of Tables 1 and 2 are applicable also to screws which have thread-forming characteristics similar to the type(s) designated in the column heading.

TABLE 1B—STANDARD TEST PLATE THICKNESSES AND HOLES SIZES FOR DRIVE TEST INSPECTION OF TAPPING SCREWS[(1)]—HOLE SIZE

Nominal Screw Szie	Type A Drill Size	Type A Hole Dia	Types AB, B, and BP Drill Size	Types AB, B, and BP Hole Dia	Type C Coarse Thread Drill Size	Type C Coarse Thread Hole Dia	Type C Fine Thread Drill Size	Type C Fine Thread Hole Dia	Types D, F, G, and T Coarse Thread Drill Size	Types D, F, G, and T Coarse Thread Hole Dia	Types D, F, G, and T Fine Thread Drill Size	Types D, F, G, and T Fine Thread Hole Dia
2	No. 48	0.0760	No. 48	0.0760	No. 48	0.0760	No. 48	0.0760	No. 49	0.0730	—	—
3	No. 46	0.0810	No. 46	0.0810	No. 44	0.0860	No. 43	0.0890	No. 46	0.0810	—	—
4	No. 44	0.0860	No. 44	0.0860	No. 41	0.0960	No. 40	0.0980	No. 41	0.0960	—	—
5	No. 36	0.1065	No. 36	0.1065	No. 35	0.1100	No. 35	0.1100	No. 37	0.1040	—	—
6	No. 32	0.1160	No. 32	0.1160	No. 31	0.1200	1/8	0.1250	No. 31	0.1200	—	—
7	No. 30	0.1285	No. 30	0.1285	—	—	—	—	—	—	—	—
8	No. 29	0.1360	No. 29	0.1360	No. 27	0.1440	No. 26	0.1470	No. 26	0.1470	—	—
10	No. 21	0.1590	No. 21	0.1590	No. 19	0.1660	11/64	0.1719	No. 17	0.1730	No. 16	0.1770
12	3/16	0.1875	3/16	0.1875	No. 11	0.1910	No. 10	0.1935	No. 8	0.1990	—	—
14	5.5 mm	0.2165	—	—	—	—	—	—	—	—	—	—
1/4	—	—	5.5 mm	0.2165	7/32	0.2188	1	0.2280	1	0.2280	A	0.2340
16	B	0.2380	—	—	—	—	—	—	—	—	—	—
18	G	0.2610	—	—	—	—	—	—	—	—	—	—
5/16	—	—	1	0.2720	J	0.2770	L	0.2900	L	0.2900	M	0.2950
20	L	0.2900	—	—	—	—	—	—	—	—	—	—
24	11/32	0.3438	—	—	—	—	—	—	—	—	—	—
3/8	—	—	21/64	0.3281	R	0.3390	11/32	0.3438	T	0.3580	T	0.3580
7/16	—	—	13/32	0.4062	10 mm	0.3937	—	—	—	—	—	—
1/2	—	—	15/32	0.4688	29/64	0.4531	—	—	—	—	—	—

1. Requirements shown in each column of Tables 1 and 2 are applicable also to screws which have thread-forming characteristics similar to the type(s) designated in the column heading.

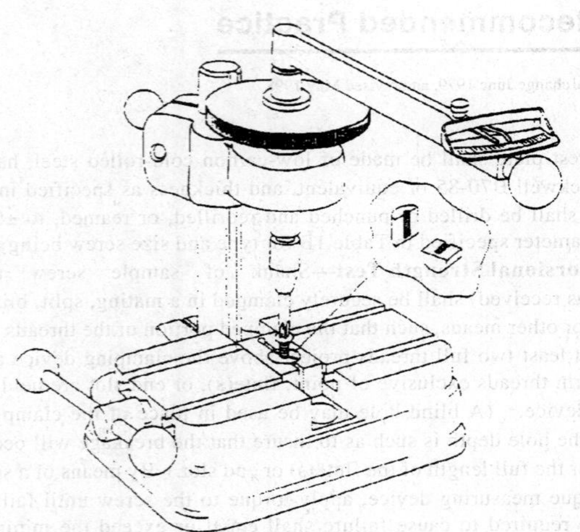

FIGURE 1—

TABLE 2—TORSIONAL STRENGTH REQUIREMENTS FOR TAPPING SCREWS[1] (MINIMUM TORSIONAL STRENGTH, lb-in)

Nominal Screw Size	Type A	Types AB, B, BF, BG, BP, and BT	Type C Coarse Thread	Type C Fine Thread	Types D, F, G, and T Coarse Thread	Types D, F, G, and T Fine Thread
2	4	4	5	6	5	6
3	9	9	9	10	9	10
4	12	13	13	15	13	15
5	18	18	18	20	18	20
6	24	24	23	27	23	27
7	30	30	—	—	—	—
8	39	39	42	47	42	47
10	48	56	56	74	56	74
12	83	88	93	108	93	108
14	125	—	—	—	—	—
1/4	—	142	140	179	140	179
16	152	—	—	—	—	—
18	196	—	—	—	—	—
5/16	—	290	306	370	306	370
20	250	—	—	—	—	—
24	492	—	—	—	—	—
3/8	—	590	560	710	560	710
7/16	—	—	—	—	—	—
1/2	—	—	—	—	—	—

1. Requirements shown in each column of Tables 1A, 1B, and 2 are applicable also to screws which have thread-forming characteristics similar to the type(s) designated in the column heading.

4. *Material and Processing Requirements*

4.1 Material—Screws shall be made from cold heading quality, killed steel wire, conforming to the composition limits shown in Table 3.

TABLE 3—

Tapping Screw Size (dia)	Analysis [1]	Chemical Composition, % by weight Carbon	Chemical Composition, % by weight Manganese
No. 4 and smaller	Ladle	0.13–0.25	0.60–1.65
	Check	0.11–0.27	0.57–1.71
No. 5 thru 1/2 in	Ladle	0.15–0.25	0.70–1.65
	Check	0.13–0.27	0.64–1.71

1. Ladle analyses are shown for informational purposes. Check analyses are mandatory and refer to individual determinations on uncarburized or core portion of screws.

4.2Heat Treatment—Shall be in carbonitriding or gas carburizing system. Screws shall be quenched in a liquid medium and then tempered by reheating to 650 °F min.

Cyaniding systems may be approved by a purchaser when the producer shows that a continuous flow (no batch) quenching process is employed which consistently produces uniform case and core.

4.3 Total Case Depth—Shall conform to the tabulation as shown in Table 4, as measured at thread flank midpoint between the crest and root:

TABLE 4—

Nominal Screw Size	Total Case Depth (in) Max.	Total Case Depth (in) Min
4 and 6	0.007	0.002
8 through 12	0.009	0.004
1/4 and larger	0.011	0.005

Case depth is to be checked in the hardened condition in accordance with SAE J423, 5.3.1, using a magnification of 100x. For referee purposes, the screws must meet all performance requirements as defined in Tables 1A, 1B, and 2, and the hardness at the maximum case depth shall not exceed 42 HRc when read with a microhardness instrument and a 500-g load converting the results to HRc. This is required to ensure that the total case does not exceed the maximum specified depth.

4.4 Surface Hardness After Tempering—Screws shall have a surface hardness equivalent to 45 HRc minimum. For the purpose of routine testing or a quick check, the surface hardness may be checked by the use of HR15N, knoop, or pyramid indentor. The method selected shall be dependent on the size of the product and testable area. The readings may be taken on the surface with light surface preparation. In the event that a hardness lower than specification is obtained, the Referee Method described as follows will prevail.

The hardness readings shall be taken 0.002 in below the surface of the screw using a microhardness instrument with a knoop or pyramid indentor and a 500-g load. In cases where the total depth of the case is 0.004 in or less, the reading may be taken 0.001 in below the surface of the screw using 100-g load.

For the purposes of measuring surface hardness and case depth, the readings will be taken on specimens which have been sectioned in a tolerance zone from true center to above center in order to ensure adequate support in the mounting media. When measuring the apparent major diameter on the sectioned metallographic specimen, the apparent major diameter shall be no less than 95% of the minimum major diameter permitted for the size of fastener being tested.

4.5 Core Hardness After Tempering—Shall be Rockwell C28-38[2], as determined at mid-radius of a transverse section through the screw taken at a distance sufficiently behind the point of the screw to be through the full minor diameter.

4.6 Microstructure—Shall show no band of free ferrite between case and core, as determined by metallographic examination.

5. *Testing Requirements*

5.1 The requirements of this specification shall be met in continuous mass production for stock, and the producer shall make sample inspections to insure that the product is controlled within the specified limits. Additional tests of individual shipments are not ordinarily contemplated. Individual heats of steel are not identified in the finished product, and testing on a heat basis is not feasible.

When specified on purchase order or engineering drawing, the manufacturer shall furnish a report certified to be the latest set of test results for the following tests for each stock size in each shipment: Core Hardness, Torsional Strength Test, and Drive Test (in case of self-drilling screws, both Drill and Drive Tests). Strength Test, and Drive Test.

Chemical and metallurgical tests (material analysis, surface hardness, case depth, metallographic examination of cross section) are not inspected frequently during normal processing, and consequently, such testing shall be considered as special and shall only be done by the manufacturer when specifically required in the original inquiry and purchase order.

5.2 When testing on a lot basis is specified, a lot shall consist of all screws of a single type, size, and length, manufactured under essentially the same conditions and submitted for inspection at one time. Unless otherwise agreed between purchaser and supplier the following number of tests shall be conducted to determine acceptance of each of the mechanical requirements (core hardness, torsional strength, and driving characteristics). (See Table 5.)

TABLE 5—

Lot Size (places)	No. of Tests	Lot Size (places)	No. of Tests
50 and less	2	501 to 35 000	5
51 to 500	3	Over 35 000	8

5.3 If failure of a test specimen is due to improper preparation of the specimen or to incorrect testing technique, the specimen shall be discarded and another specimen substituted.

2. Hardness shall not exceed maximum shown and preferably should be no higher than Rockwell C36 to insure against failure in assembly and service.

BOLT AND CAPSCREW SIZES FOR USE IN CONSTRUCTION AND INDUSTRIAL MACHINERY —SAE J370 MAY1998

SAE Recommended Practice

Report of the SAE Fasteners Committee approved November 1968, cancelled 1990, reissued June 1994, and reaffirmed May 1998.

Foreword—This Reaffirmed Document has been changed only to reflect the new SAE Technical Standards Board Format. The AMSE Documents were changed to 2.1.3.

1. Scope—This SAE Recommended Practice covers the use of preferred bolt and capscrew sizes, wherever applicable, on construction and industrial machinery to ease serviceability.

1.1 Purpose—Designers, in their efforts to determine the proper fastener for heavy equipment, sometimes overlook the practical aspects of serviceability. When a particular component requires frequent service, it is much faster and easier for the serviceman to work with common size, easily distinguished bolts, and capscrews which require a minimum of tools.

Section 4 lists eight diameters of recommended bolts and capscrews, some of which can be found in any hardware store, require only standard tools, are easy to distinguish, and at the same time cover proof loads from 1043 kg (2300 lb) on up at convenient intervals.

While some applications may require other sizes and/or fine threaded fasteners for greater camping forces and/or area restrictions, the convenience of UNC threads in the sizes indicated is preferred wherever possible.

2. References

2.1 Related Publications—The following publications are provided for information purposes only and are not a required part of this document. The latest issue of SAE publications shall apply.

2.1.1 SAE PUBLICATIONS—Available from SAE, 400 Commonwealth Drive, Warrendale, PA 15096-0001.

SAE J429—Mechanical and Material Requirements for Externally Threaded Fasteners

SAE J871—Hi Head Finished Hex Bolts

2.1.2 ANSI PUBLICATIONS—Available from ANSI, 11 West 42nd Street, New York, NY 10036-8002.

ANSI/ASME B18.2.2—Square and Hex Nuts—Inch Series

ANSI B18.6.1—Wood Screws (Inch Series)

ANSI B18.6.3—Slotted and Recessed Head Machine Screws and Machine Screw Nuts

ANSI B18.6.4—Screws, Tapping and Metallic Drive, Inch Series, Thread Forming and Cutting

2.1.3 AMSE PUBLICATIONS—Available from ASME, 345 East 47 Street, New York, NY 10017-2330.

ASME B18.2.1—Square and Hex Bolts and Screws—Inch Series

ASME B18.6.2—Slotted Head Cap Screws, Square Head Set Screws, and Slotted Headless Set Screws

3. Threads—Unified Coarse Thread Series (UNC).

4. Diameters—3/8, 1/2, 5/8, 7/8, 1, 1-1/8, 1-1/4.

a. Diameters above 1-1/4 in to increase in 1/4-in increments

b. Diameter deviations below 1/2-in decrease in 1/16-in increments

STEEL SELF-DRILLING TAPPING SCREWS—SAE J78 MAY1998

SAE Standard

Report of the SAE Iron and Steel Technical Committee and SAE Fasteners Committee approved July 1972, revised October 1973, reaffirmed June 1979, completely revised August 1996, and revised May 1998. Rationale statement available.

1. Scope

1.1 General—This SAE Standard covers the dimensional and general specifications, including performance requirements, for carbon steel self-drilling tapping screws suitable for use in general applications.

It is the objective of this document to insure that carbon steel self-drilling tapping screws, by meeting the mechanical and performance requirements specified, shall drill a hole and form or cut mating threads in materials into which they are driven without deforming their own thread and without breaking during assembly.

Appendix A is included to provide a recommended technique for measuring the case depth on the screws.

1.2 Screw Types and Application—The two types of self-drilling tapping screws covered by this document are designated and described as follows:

1.2.1 TYPE BSD—Type BSD screws shall have spaced threads with drill points of varying configuration, designated Style 2 and Style 3, designed to accommodate different panel thickness conditions as delineated in Section 6.

1.2.2 TYPE CSD—Type CSD screws shall have threads of machine screw diameter-pitch combinations approximating Unified Form with drill points of varying configuration, designated Style 2 and Style 3, designed to accommodate different panel thickness conditions as delineated in Section 6. Type CSD screws are not subject to thread gaging but shall meet dimensions specified in this document. They are intended for application where the use of a machine screw pitch thread is preferred over the spaced thread.

1.3 Head Types—The head types applicable to self-drilling tapping screws covered by this document shall include those specified in ANSI B18.6.4, except for slotted head and hex (nonwasher) head designs which are not recommended for self-drilling screws.

2. References

2.1 Applicable Publications—The following publications form a part of this specification to the extent specified herein. Unless otherwise indicated, the latest version of SAE publications shall apply.

2.1.1 SAE PUBLICATION—Available from SAE, 400 Commonwealth Drive, Warrendale, PA 15096-0001.

SAE J423—Methods of Measuring Case Depth

2.1.2 ANSI PUBLICATIONS—Available from ANSI, 11 West 42nd Street, New York, NY 10036-8002.

ANSI B18.6.4—Slotted and Recessed Head Topping Screws and Metallic Drive Screws

ANSI B18.22.1—Plain Washers

3. Dimensional Requirements

3.1 General Dimensions—Dimensions and general specifications applicable to heads, body, and screw length for Type BSD and Type CSD screws shall conform to those specified for Type B and Type C tapping screws, respectively, as specified in SAE J478 or ANSI B18.6.4, except as specified in 3.2 to 3.4.

3.2 Heads—The underside on all noncountersunk styles of heads on milled point self-drilling screws may be chamfered at the periphery of head in accordance with the dimensions specified in Figure 1 and Table 1.

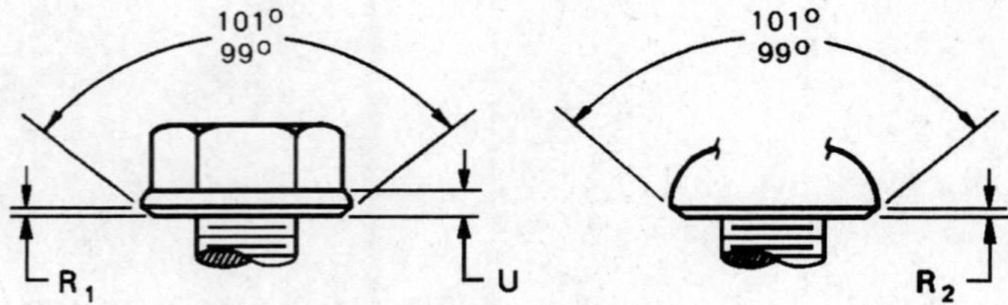

FIGURE 1—HEAD CHAMFERS ON MILLED POINT SCREWS

3.3 Eccentricity—Eccentricity is defined as one-half of the full or total indicator reading.

3.3.1 ECCENTRICITY OF HEX AND HEX WASHER HEADS—Hex and hex washer heads shall not be eccentric with the axis of screw by an amount equal to more than 4% of the basic screw diameter.

TABLE 1—HEAD CHAMFER DIMENSIONS FOR MILLED POINT SELF-DRILLING TAPPING SCREWS, in (Figure 1)

Nominal Screw Size	U Washer Thickness Max	U Washer Thickness Min	R_1 Chamfer Height Hex Washer Heads Ref	R_2 Chamfer Height Recessed Heads Ref
4	0.030	0.020	0.015	0.015
6	0.040	0.025	0.015	0.015
8	0.050	0.035	0.020	0.015
10	0.050	0.035	0.020	0.020
12	0.050	0.035	0.020	0.020
1/4	0.060	0.040	0.025	0.020

3.3.2 ECCENTRICITY OF RECESS—The recess in recessed head screws shall not be eccentric with the axis of screw by an amount equal to more than 4% of the basic screw diameter.

3.4 Length of Thread

3.4.1 TYPE BSD SCREWS—For screws of nominal lengths equal to or shorter than 1.50 in, the full form threads shall extend close to the head such that the specified minor diameter limits are maintained to within one pitch (thread), or closer if practicable, of the underside of the head. See Figure 2. For screws of nominal lengths longer than 1.50 in, the length of full form thread shall be as specified by the purchaser.

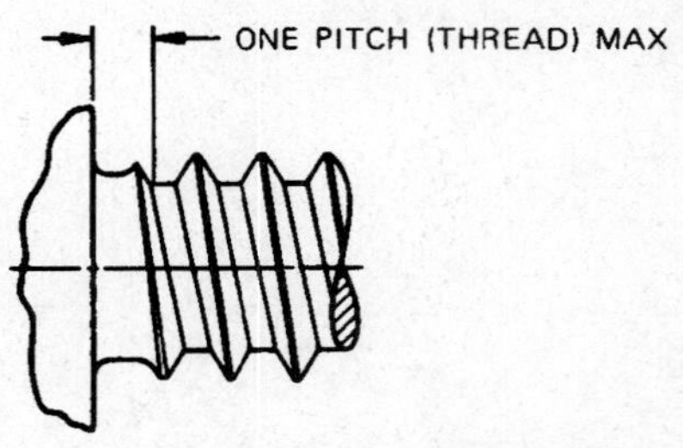

FIGURE 2—TYPE BSD THREAD FORM

3.4.2 TYPE CSD SCREWS—For screws of nominal lengths equal to or shorter than 1.50 in, the full form threads shall extend close to the head such that the specified major diameter limits are maintained to within two pitches (threads), or closer if practicable, of the underside of the head. See Figure 3. For screws of nominal lengths longer than 1.50 in, the length of full form thread shall be as specified by the purchaser.

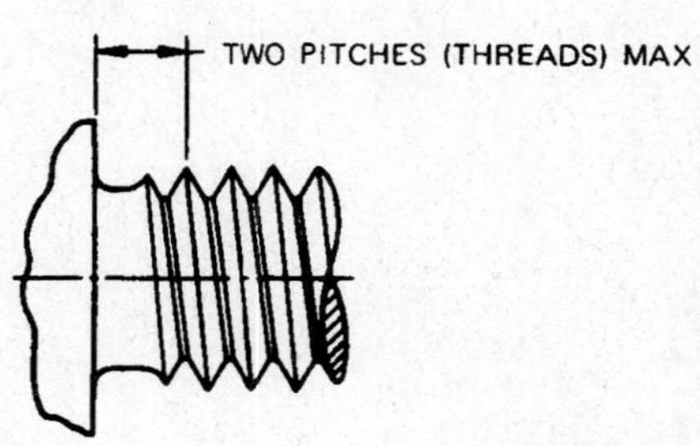

FIGURE 3—TYPE CSD THREAD FORM

3.5 Threads and Points—The threads and points applicable to screws covered by this document are generally described under 1.2. They shall conform to the dimensions specified in Tables 2A and 2B.

TABLE 2A—DIMENSIONS OF THREADS AND POINTS FOR TYPES BSD AND CSD SELF-DRILLING TAPPING SCREWS (Figure 4)(1)

Nominal Size(2) or Basic Screw Diameter	Type BSD Threads Per Inch	Type BSD D Major Diameter Max	Type BSD D Major Diameter Min	Type BSD d Minor Diameter Max	Type BSD d Minor Diameter Min	Type BSD Z(3) Protrusion Allowance (Ref) Style 2 Point	Type BSD Z(3) Protrusion Allowance (Ref) Style 3 Point	Type CSD Threads Per Inch	Type CSD D Major Diameter Max	Type CSD D Major Diameter Min	Type CSD Z(3) Protrusion Allowance (Ref) Style 2 Point	Type CSD Z(3) Protrusion Allowance (Ref) Style 3 Point
4 0.1120	24	0.114	0.110	0.086	0.082	0.163	—	40	0.1120	0.1072	0.130	—
6 0.1380	20	0.139	0.135	0.104	0.099	0.190	0.220	32	0.1380	0.1326	0.152	0.172
8 0.1640	18	0.166	0.161	0.122	0.116	0.211	0.251	32	0.1640	0.1586	0.162	0.202
10 0.1900	16	0.189	0.183	0.141	0.135	0.235	0.300	24	0.1900	0.1834	0.193	0.258
12 0.2160	14	0.215	0.209	0.164	0.157	0.283	0.353	24	0.2160	0.2094	0.223	0.293
1/4 0.2500	14	0.246	0.240	0.192	0.185	0.318	0.393	20	0.2500	0.2428	0.275	0.350

1. Drill portion of points may be milled and/or cold formed and details of point taper and flute design shall be optional withth he manufacturer, provided the screws meet the performance requirements specified in this document and are capable of drilling the maximum panel thicknesses shown in (see 5)Table 5 prior to thread pickup.
2. Where specifying nominal size in decimals, zeros preceding decimal and in fourth decimal place shall be omitted.
3. Protrusion allowance Z is the distnace, measured parallel to the axis of screw, from the extreme end of the point to the first full form thread beyond the point and encompasses the length of drill point and the tapered incomplete threads. It is intended for use in calculating the maximum effective design grip length Y on the screw in accordance with the following: Y = L min – z

TABLE 2B—DIMENSIONS OF THREADS AND POINTS FOR TYPES BSD AND CSD SELF-DRILLING TAPPING SCREWS (Figure 4)(1) (Continued)

Nominal Size(2) or Basic Screw Diameter	Types BSD and CSD L Minimum Practical Nominal Screw Lengths (Ref) Style 2 Points Formed 90 Deg Heads	Types BSD and CSD L Minimum Practical Nominal Screw Lengths (Ref) Style 2 Points Formed Csk Heads	Types BSD and CSD L Minimum Practical Nominal Screw Lengths (Ref) Style 2 Points Milled 90 Deg Heads	Types BSD and CSD L Minimum Practical Nominal Screw Lengths (Ref) Style 2 Points Milled Csk Heads	Types BSD and CSD L Minimum Practical Nominal Screw Lengths (Ref) Style 3 Points Formed 90 Deg Heads	Types BSD and CSD L Minimum Practical Nominal Screw Lengths (Ref) Style 3 Points Milled Csk Heads	Types BSD and CSD L Minimum Practical Nominal Screw Lengths (Ref) Style 3 Points Formed 90 Deg Heads	Types BSD and CSD L Minimum Practical Nominal Screw Lengths (Ref) Style 3 Points Milled Csk Heads
4 0.1120	5/16	3/8	3/8	7/16	—	—	—	—
6 0.1380	5/16	3/8	3/8	7/16	3/8	7/16	7/16	1/2
8 0.1640	3/8	7/16	7/16	1/2	7/16	1/2	1/2	9/16
10 0.1900	7/16	1/2	15/32	19/32	1/2	9/16	9/16	21/32
12 0.2160	1/2	5/8	17/32	21/32	1/2	5/8	21/32	25/32
1/4 0.2500	1/2	5/8	17/32	11/16	1/2	5/8	11/16	27/32

1. Drill portion of points may be milled and/or cold formed and details of point taper and flute design shall be optional witht he manufacturer, provided the screws meet the performance requirements specified in this document and are capable of drilling the maximum panel thicknesses shown in Table 5 prior to thread pickup.
2. Where specifying nominal size in decimals, zeros preceding decimal and in fourth decimal place shall be omitted.

4. Material and Process Requirements

4.1 Material and Chemistry—Screws shall be made from cold heading quality, killed steel wire conforming to the chemical composition in Table 3:

TABLE 3—CHEMICAL COMPOSITION—COMPOSITION LIMITS, % BY WEIGHT

Analysis(1)	Carbon Max	Carbon Min	Manganese Max	Manganese Min
Ladle	0.25	0.15	1.65	0.70
Check	0.27	0.13	1.71	0.64

1. Ladle analyses are shown for informational purposes. Check analyses are mandatory and refer to individual determinations on uncarburized or core portions of screws.

4.2 Heat Treatment—Screws shall be heat treated in a carbonitriding or gas-carburizing system. Cyaniding systems may be approved by the purchaser when it is shown that a continuous flow (no batch) quenching process which consistently produces uniform case and core hardnesses is employed.

4.2.1 TEMPERING TEMPERATURE—Minimum tempering temperature shall be 330 °C (625 °F).

When cyaniding systems are approved, the minimum tempering temperature shall be 232 °C (450 °F).

4.2.2 TOTAL CASE DEPTH—Screws shall have a total case depth conforming to the tabulation in Table 4.

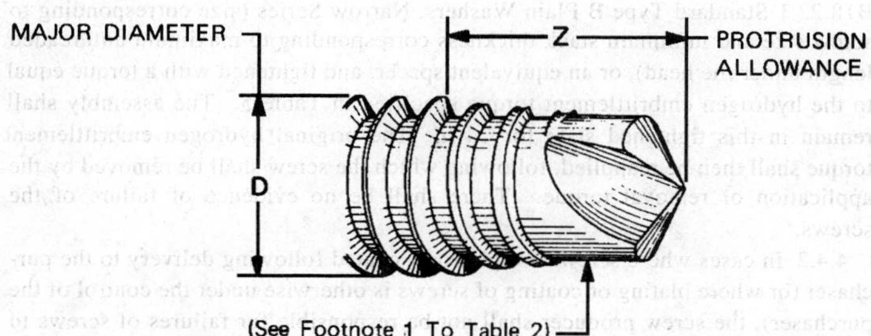

FIGURE 4—TYPICAL SELF-DRILLING TAPPING SCREW POINT

TABLE 4—TOTAL CASE DEPTH

Nominal Screw Size	Total Case Depth, in Max	Total Case Depth, in Min
4 and 6	0.007	0.002
8 through 12	0.009	0.004
1/4 and larger	0.011	0.005

Total case depth shall be measured at a midpoint between crest and root on the thread flank. The recommended technique for measuring case depth is given in Appendix A. Total case depth is the distance measured perpendicularly from the surface of a hardened case to a point where differences in chemical or physical properties of the case and core can no longer be distinguished (see SAE J423) or when the microhardness converted to HRC is 42.

4.2.3 SURFACE HARDNESS—Screws shall have a surface hardness equivalent to 50 to 56 HRC. For the purpose of the routine testing or a quick check, the surface hardness may be checked by the use of HR15N, knoop or pyramid identor. The method selected shall be dependent on the size of the product and testable area. The readings may be taken on the surface with light surface preparation. In the event that a hardness lower than specification is obtained, the Referee Method described as follows will prevail.

The hardness reading shall be taken 0.002 in below the surface of the screw using a microhardness instrument with a knoop or pyramid indentor and a 500-g load. In cases where the total case depth is 0.004in or less, the reading may be taken 0.001 in below the surface of the screw using 100-g load used.

For the purposes of measuring surface hardness and case depth, the readings will be taken on specimens which have been sectioned in a tolerance zone from true center to above center in order to ensure adequate support in the mounting media. When measuring the apparent major diameter on the sectioned metallographic specimen, the apparent major diameter shall be no less than 95% of the minimum major diameter permitted for the size of fastener being tested.

4.2.4 CORE HARDNESS—Screws shall have a core hardness equivalent to Rockwell C 32-40 when measured at mid-radius of a transverse section through the screw taken at a distance sufficiently behind the point of the screw to be through the full minor diameter.

4.3 Ductility—Heads of screws shall not separate completely from the shank when a permanent deformation of 5degrees is induced between the plane of the under head bearing surface and a plane normal to the axis of the screw, when tested in accordance with 4.3.1.

4.3.1 DUCTILITY TEST—The sample screw shall be inserted into a drilled hole in a hardened wedge block, or other suitable device, and an axial compressive (or impact) load applied against the top of the screw head. Loading shall be continued until the plane of the under head bearing surface is bent permanently through 5degrees with respect to a plane normal to the axis of the screw.

4.4 Finish—Unless otherwise specified, screws shall be supplied with a natural (as processed) finish, unplated or uncoated. Where corrosion preventive or decorative finishes are required, screws shall be plated or coated as specified by the user. However, where steel screws are plated or coated and subject to hydrogen embrittlement, they shall be suitably treated subsequent to the plating or coating operation to obviate such embrittlement. Cadmium or zinc electroplated screws shall be subjected to the hydrogen embrittlement test in 4.4.1.

4.4.1 HYDROGEN EMBRITTLEMENT TEST—Cadmium and zinc electroplated screws shall drill their own hole and form a thread in a steel test plate with a thickness equal to the maximum specified for the applicable screw type and size in Section 6. The head of the screw shall be seated against one or more ANSI B18.22.1 Standard Type B Plain Washers, Narrow Series (size corresponding to screw size and minimum stack thickness corresponding to maximum unthreaded length under the head), or an equivalent spacer, and tightened with a torque equal to the hydrogen embrittlement torque specified in Table 5. The assembly shall remain in this tightened state for 24 h. The original hydrogen embrittlement torque shall then be reapplied, following which the screw shall be removed by the application of removal torque. There shall be no evidence of failure of the screws.

4.4.2 In cases where screws are plated or coated following delivery to the purchaser (or where plating or coating of screws is otherwise under the control of the purchaser), the screw producer shall not be responsible for failures of screws to meet mechanical or performance requirements due to plating or coating. In such cases, additional screws from the same lot shall be stripped of plating or coating, baked, lubricated with machine oil, and retested in the natural finish.

5. Performance Requirements and Tests

5.1 Torsional Strength—Screws shall not fail with the application of a torque less than the torsional strength torque specified in Table 5, when tested in accordance with 5.1.1.

5.1.1 TORSIONAL STRENGTH TEST—The sample screw shall be securely clamped by suitable means (Figure 5) such that the threads in the clamped length are not damaged, and that at least two full threads project above the clamping device, and that at least two full threads exclusive of point, flutes, or thread cutting slot, are held within the clamping device. By means of a suitably calibrated torque measuring device, torque shall be applied to the screw until failure of the screw occurs. The torque required to cause failure shall be recorded as the torsional strength torque.

TABLE 5—MECHANICAL AND PERFORMANCE REQUIREMENTS FOR TYPES BSD AND CSD SELF-DRILLING TAPPING SCREWS

Nominal Screw Size	Minimum Torsional Strength lb-in Type BSD	Minimum Torsional Strength lb-in Type CSD	Hydrogen Embrittlement Test Torque, lb-in Cadmium Plated Screws Types BSD and CSD	Hydrogen Embrittlement Test Torque, lb-in Zinc Plated Screws Types BSD and CSD
4	14	14	10.5	12
6	24	24	18	20
8	42	48	36	41
10	61	65	49	55
12	92	100	72	85
1/4	150	156	114	132

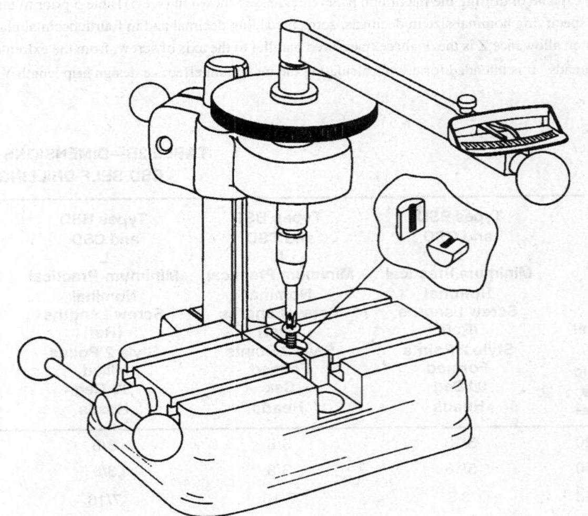

FIGURE 5—TYPICAL TORSIONAL STRENGTH TEST FIXTURE

5.2 Drill-Drive Test—Sample screws shall be selected at random from the lot and shall be used to drill holes and form or cut mating threads in a test plate. The time in seconds for the screw to drill and thread a hole completely through the test plate shall be recorded. The test plate material and thickness, and load applied against the screw during drilling and threading, and the other test conditions are specified in Table 6. Each screw shall be used to drill and thread only one hole. A typical drill drive test fixture is depicted in Figure 6.

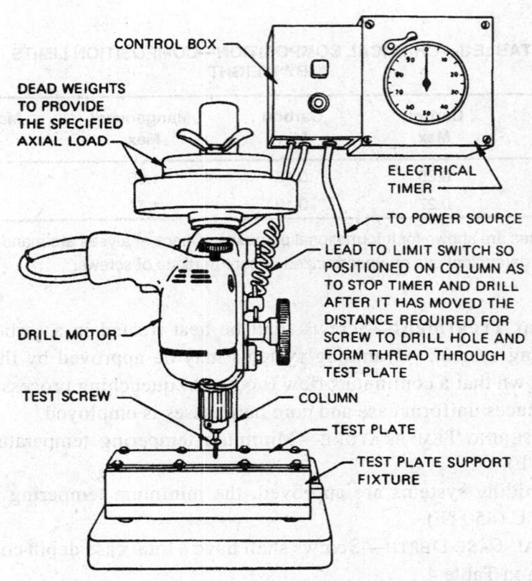

FIGURE 6—TYPICAL DRILL-DRIVE TEST FIXTURE

TABLE 6—DRILL-DRIVE TEST CONDITIONS AND REQUIREMENTS FOR TYPES BSD AND CSD SELF-DRILLING TAPPING SCREWS

Nominal Screw Size	Test Plate Thickness,[1] in Max	Test Plate Thickness,[1] in Min	Axial Loading,[2] lb A Max	Axial Loading,[2] lb B Max	Axial Loading,[2] lb C Max	Time to Drill and Form Thread,[3] s Max
4	0.068	0.062	25	30	40	2.0
6	0.068	0.062	30	35	45	2.5
8	0.068	0.062	30	35	45	3.0
10	0.068	0.062	35	40	50	3.5
12	0.068	0.062	45	50	60	4.0
1/4	0.068	0.062	45	50	60	5.0

1. Test plates shall be low carbon, cold rolled steel having a hardness of Rockwell B60-85.
2. Axial loads are varied to offset the detrimental effects on drilling capability created by finishes applied to screws in accordance with the following:
   Column A—Axial loads tabulated shall apply to plain, oiled, and commercial phosphate coating and cadmium and zinc platings up to 0.0003in thickness.
   Column B—Axial loads tabulated shall apply special electroplated finishes exceeding 0.0003 in thickness and to special coatings, such as thread sealing hot melts, etc.
   Column C—Axial loads tabulated shall apply to chromium finish.
3. Tool speed shall be 2500 rpm for screw sizes No. 4 through No. 10. Tool speed of 1800 rpm is recommended for screw sizes No. 12 and 1/4; however, 2500 rpm may be used provided care is exercised to minimize influence of high heat buildup due to surface speed.

The drill-drive test shall be conducted in accordance with the sampling plan in Table 7.

TABLE 7—SAMPLING PLAN

Lot Size[1]	Sample Size
Up to 5 000	6
5 001 to 15 000	12
15 001 to 50 000	18
50 001 and over	25

1. Lot size is defined as a quantity submitted for inspection.

If the actual time for each of the sample screws to drill and thread a hole does not exceed the maximum time specified in Section 6, the lot shall be acceptable. If one or more of the test times exceed the maximum specified in Table 6, a retest shall be made using twice the original sample size. The lot shall then be acceptable in accordance with Table 8.

TABLE 8—LOT ACCEPTANCE LIMITS

Sample Size	Slow Drive[1]	Excessive Drive[2]
12	1	0
24	1	0
36	2	1
50	3	1

1. A "slow drive" is defined as a screw having a drilling and threading time in excess of, but less than, twice the specified maximum.
2. An "excessive drive" is defined as a screw having a drilling and threading time twice the specified maximum or greater.

5.3 Drive to Failure Test—There shall be a satisfactory difference between starting torque and failure torque. The difference may be expressed as a ratio or range of torques.

(Test conditions and performance ratios or torque ranges are to be developed.)

5.4 Drill Hole Size—When desired to determine that the drill point does not drill an oversize hole that would cause a loss of thread engagement and result in premature stripping of the mating thread, a drill hole size test may be conducted in accordance with 5.4.1. The diameter of the hole drilled by the screw shall not exceed the point diameter of the test screw by more than 0.005 in.

5.4.1 DRILL HOLE SIZE TEST—The sample screw shall be inserted through a sleeve or collar (Figure 7) having an inside diameter of approximately 0.010 in greater than the major diameter of the screw. The length of sleeve or collar should be such that sufficient unthreaded point length extends through the sleeve or collar to drill a hole through the minimum thickness material specified in Table 6 without thread pickup. After the hole is drilled in the test plate, the screw shall be removed and the diameter of the drilled hole gaged.

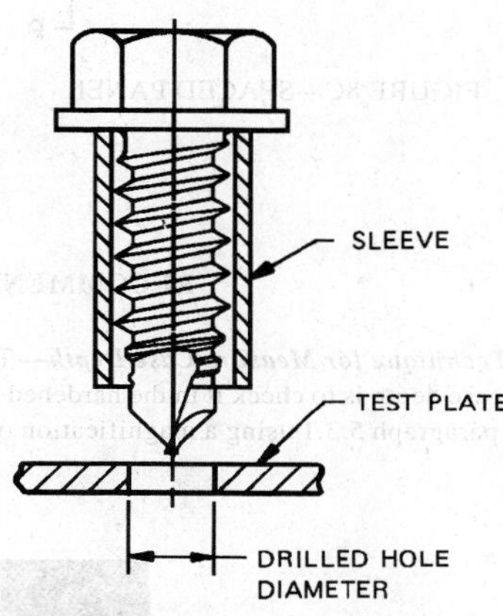

FIGURE 7—DRILL HOLE SIZE TEST

6. Screw Selection and Installation Considerations—Screw point style selection should be made on the basis of the recommended panel thicknesses specified in Table 9. For multipanel applications which exceed the thickness tabulated, clearance holes should be provided in the uppermost panel or panels to reduce the thickness to be drilled by the screw.

TABLE 9—SELF-DRILLING TAPPING SCREW SELECTION CHART

Screw Type	Point Style	Nominal Screw Size	p[1] Recommended Panel Thickness, in
BSD and CSD	2	4	0.080 Max
		6	0.090 Max
		8	0.100 Max
		10	0.110 Max
		12	0.140 Max
		1/4	0.175 Max
	3	6	0.090-0.110
		8	0.100-0.140
		10	0.110-0.175
		12	0.110-0.210
		1/4	0.110-0.210

1. If the panel to be drilled is comprised of two or more layers (see Figures 8B and 8C), the gap between the layers (which might consist of a sealing strip, airspace caused by warpage, etc., or just the separation caused by the pressure exerted by the driver) must be considered in determining the point style for the particular fastener. Using a self-drilling tapping screw as covered in this document in a multilayer application with an excessive gap could result in point breakage since the tapping in one layer begins before completion of the drilling of the other layers and since the advancement of the screw in the tapping operation is much faster than in the drilling operation.

FIGURE 8A—SINGLE PANEL

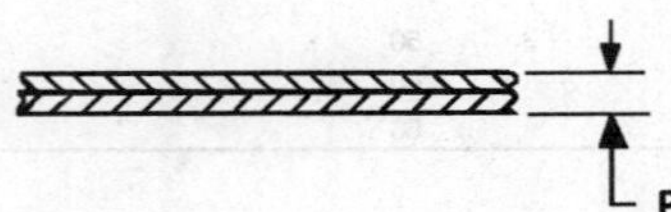

FIGURE 8B—DOUBLE PANEL

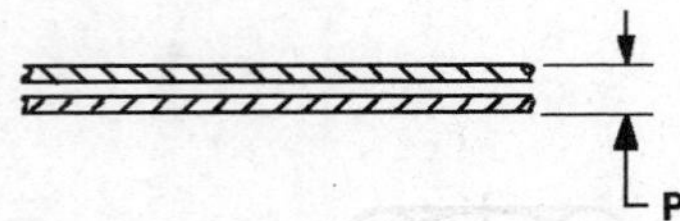

FIGURE 8C—SPACED PANEL

Driving tools which operate between 1800 and 3000 rpm are commonly used for self-drilling tapping screw applications.

Figure A1a illustrates comparisons between the structure of case and core produced by the method recommended herein and a regular quenched and tempered structure. Case depths were measured on each of three screws after carbonitriding and microhardness traverses were run. The same parts were then water-quenched from 777 °C (1430 °F) and case depths were again measured. Results of each method appear under the photographs.

6.1 Optional Head Marking—For the purpose of identifying self-drilling tapping screws in assembled components, the consumer, at his option, may specify identifying head markings. Heads of self-drilling tapping screws, when specified by the consumer, shall be marked as shown in Figure 9.

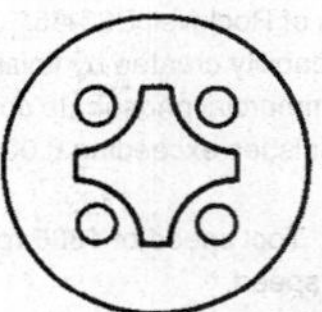
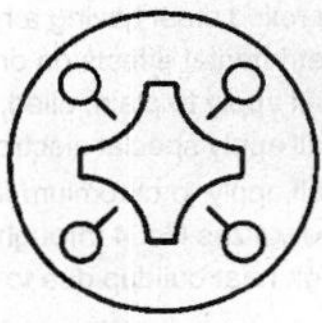
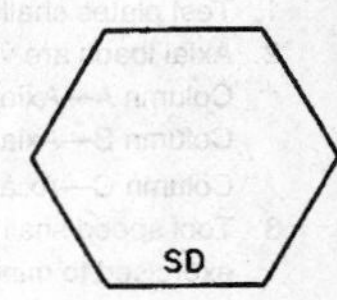

FIGURE 9—HEAD MARKING

APPENDIX A
RECOMMENDED TECHNIQUE FOR MEASURING CASE DEPTH

A.1 Recommended Technique for Measure Case Depth—The recommended method for measuring case depth is to check it in the hardened condition in accordance with SAE J423, paragraph 5.3.1 using a magnification of 100X.

A.2 Referee Procedures—Screws shall meet performance requirements and tests as defined by Section 5. Hardness at the maximum case depth as defined by 4.2.2 shall not exceed 42 RC when read with a microhardness instrument using a knoop or pyramid indentor and a 500-g load and converting to HRC. This is required to ensure that the total case does not exceed the maximum specified depth.

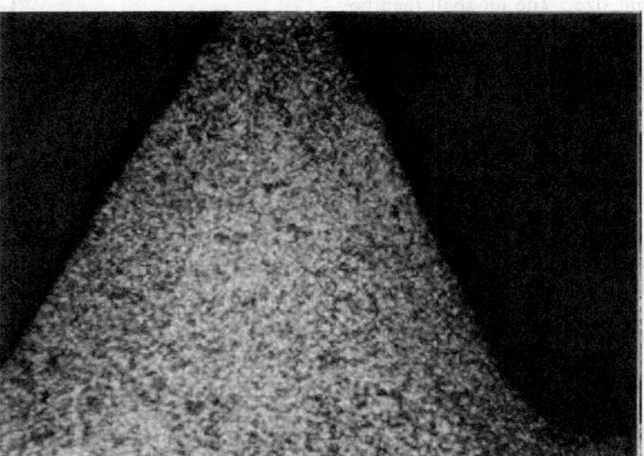

Structure of case and core after anneal at 1600 °F for 7 min, nital etch (100X)

FIGURE A1A—COMPARISON OF STRUCTURE

0.002 in case depth, water quench from 1430 °F, nital etch (100X)

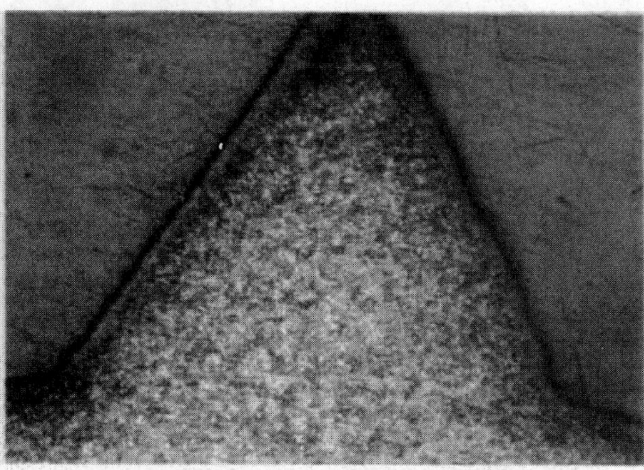

0.0015/0.002 in case depth, 0.002 in to Rc 45, all quenched and tempered, nital etch (100X)

FIGURE A1B—COMPARISON OF STRUCTURE (CONTINUED)

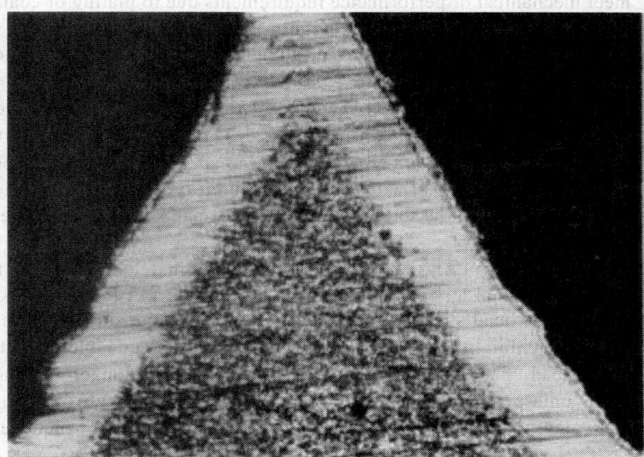

0.003 in case depth, water quench from 1430 °F, nital etch (100X)

0.0025/0.003 in case depth, 0.0025 in to Rc 45, oil quenched and tempered, nital etch (100X)

FIGURE A1C—COMPARISON OF STRUCTURE (CONTINUED)

0.005/0.0055 in case depth, water quench from 1430 °F, nital etch (100X)

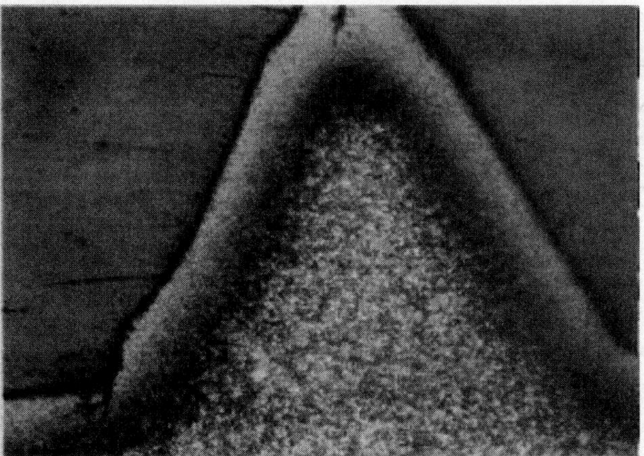

0.004/0.005 in case depth, 0.0045 in to Rc 45, oil quenched and tempered, nital etch (100X)

FIGURE A1D—COMPARISON OF STRUCTURE (CONTINUED)

THREAD ROLLING SCREWS—SAE J81 SEP1997 SAE Standard

The report of the Iron and Steel Technical Committee and Fasteners Committee, approved July 1972, editorial change June 1979. Revised by the SAE Fasteners Committee September 1997. Note: SAE J1237 is available for Metric Thread Rolling Screws.

Foreword—This Document has also changed to comply with the new SAE Technical Standards Board format.

1. Scope—This SAE Standard covers requirements for thread rolling screws suitable for use in general engineering applications. (It is intended that "thread rolling" screws have performance capabilities beyond those normally expected of other standard types of tapping screws.)

NOTE—The performance requirements covered in this document apply only to the combination of laboratory conditions described in the testing procedures. If other conditions are encountered in an actual service application (such as different materials, thicknesses, hole sizes, etc.), values shown herein for drive torque, torque-to-clamp load, and proof torque may require adjustment.

2. References

2.1 Applicable Publications—The following publications form a part of this specification to the extent specified herein. The latest issue of SAE publications shall apply.

2.1.1 SAE PUBLICATIONS—Available from SAE, 400 Commonwealth Drive, Warrendale, PA 15096-0001.

SAE J78—Steel Self-Drilling Tapping Screws
SAE J478—Slotted and Recessed Head Screws

2.1.2 ANSI PUBLICATIONS—Available from ANSI, 11 West 42nd Street, New York, NY 10036-8002.

ANSI B18.6.4—Slotted and Recessed Head Tapping Screws and Metallic Drive Screws

2.1.3 MILITARY PUBLICATIONS—Available from DODSSP, Subscription Services Desk, Building 4D, 700 Robins Avenue, Philadelphia, PA 19111-5094.

MIL-STD-105D

3. Requirements

3.1 Material and Process Requirements

3.1.1 MATERIAL AND CHEMISTRY—Screws shall be made from cold-heading quality, killed steel wire conforming to the following chemical composition requirements:

TABLE 1—COMPOSITION LIMITS, % BY WEIGHT

Analysis	Carbon Min	Carbon Max	Manganese Min	Manganese Max
Ladle	0.15	0.25	0.70	1.65
Check	0.13	0.27	0.64	1.71

3.1.2 HEAT TREATMENT—Screws shall be heat treated in a gas-carburizing system. Cyaniding systems may be approved by the purchaser when it is shown that a continuous flow (no batch) quenching process which consistently produces uniform case and core hardnesses is employed. Carbonitriding systems may also be used when approved by the purchaser.

3.1.3 TEMPERING TEMPERATURE—Minimum tempering temperature shall be 650 °F.

3.1.4 FINISH—Screws shall be cadmium or zinc plated with a coating thickness of 0.0002 to 0.0004 in, or have a phosphate and oil coating, as specified by the purchaser. At the option of the manufacturer, screws may be provided with an additional supplementary lubricant as necessary to meet the performance requirements.

Electroplated screws shall be baked within 1 h of plating at a temperature range of 375 °F to 450 °F for a minimum of 4 h at temperature.

In cases where screws are plated or coated following delivery to the purchaser (or where plating or coating of screws is otherwise under the control of the purchaser), the screw producer shall not be responsible for failures of the screw to meet mechanical or performance requirements due to plating or coating.

3.2 Dimensional Requirements

3.2.1 HEAD DIMENSIONS—Head dimensions shall conform to those specified in SAE J478 and ANSI B18.6.4.

3.2.2 THREAD AND POINT DIMENSIONS—Thread and point dimensions shall conform to the values shown in Table 2. Threads shall conform to a 60-degree basic thread form, but are not subject to thread gaging. Details of point configurations shall be optional with the manufacturer, provided all dimensions specified are maintained and the screws meet the performance requirements set forth in this document.

3.2.3 THREAD LENGTH—For screws of nominal lengths equal to or shorter than the nominal lengths tabulated in Table 3, the full form threads shall extend close to the head such that the specified thread major diameter limits are maintained to within two pitches (threads), or closer if practicable, from the underside of the head. See Figure 1. Screws of nominal lengths longer than those tabulated shall, unless otherwise specified, have a minimum length of full form thread equivalent to six times the basic screw diameter or 1.50 in, whichever is shorter.

TABLE 2—THREAD AND POINT DIMENSIONS OF THREAD ROLLING SCREWS

Nominal Screw Size and Threads per inch(1)	Major Diameter(2) max	Point Diameter(2) max	Dia of Circumscribing Circle(3) max	Circumscribing Circle (Point)(3) max	Point Length Max(4)	Point Length Min(5)	Min Practical Nominal Screw Lengths 90-degree Heads	Min Practical Nominal Screw Lengths Csk Heads
No. 2-56	0.086	—	0.088	0.070	0.062	0.036	5/32	3/16
3-48	0.099	—	0.101	0.081	0.073	0.042	3/16	7/32
4-40	0.112	0.086	0.115	0.090	0.088	0.050	3/16	1/4
5-40	0.125	0.099	0.128	0.103	0.088	0.050	7/32	1/4
6-32	0.138	0.106	0.141	0.111	0.109	0.062	1/4	5/16
8-32	0.164	0.132	0.167	0.137	0.109	0.062	1/4	11/32
10-24	0.190	0.147	0.194	0.153	0.146	0.083	5/16	13/32
1/4-20	0.250	0.198	0.255	0.206	0.175	0.100	13/32	1/2
5/16-18	0.313	0.255	0.318	0.264	0.194	0.111	15/32	5/8
3/8-16	0.375	0.310	0.281	0.320	0.219	0.125	9/16	23/32
7/16-14	0.438	0.361	0.445	0.375	0.250	0.143	21/32	13/16
1/2-13	0.500	0.416	0.508	0.433	0.269	0.154	23/32	7/9

1. Fine thread series screws are also available.
2. These dimensions are applicable to screw blanks prior to thread rolling and to types of screws where the periphery of the thread approximates a circle.
3. These dimensions are applicable to types of screws where some portions of the periphery of the thread are further from the screw axis than others (lobular, elliptical, tri-roundular, etc.).
4. These values are equal to 3.5 times the pitch distance rounded off to three decimal places.
5. These values are equal to 2 times the pitch distance rounded off to three decimal places.

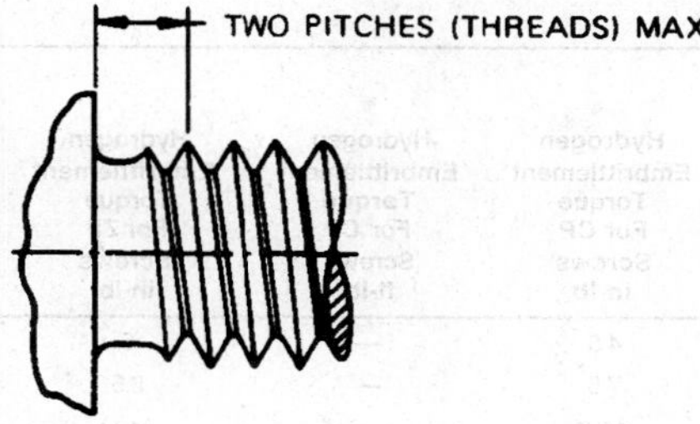

FIGURE 1—THREAD MAJOR DIAMETER LIMIT

TABLE 3—MINIMUM FULL FORM THREAD LENGTH

Nominal Screw Size	Nominal Screw Length	Full Form Thread Length (1) Min	Two Pitches Length(2) CoarseThread
2	5/8	0.52	0.036
3	5/8	0.59	0.042
4	3/4	0.67	0.050
5	7/8	0.75	0.050
6	7/8	0.83	0.062
8	1	0.98	0.062
10	1-1/4	1.14	0.083
1/4	1-1/2	1.50	0.100
5/16	1-1/2	1.50	0.111
3/8	1-1/2	1.50	0.125
7/16	1-1/2	1.50	0.143
1/2	1-1/2	1.50	0.154

1. Tabulated values through No. 10 size are 6 times the basic screw diameter, rounded off to two decimal places.
2. Values are tabulated for convenient reference.

3.3 Mechanical and Performance Requirements

3.3.1 HARDNESS

3.3.1.1 Core Hardness—Screws shall have a core hardness of Rockwell C28–38, when tested as specified in 4.1.

3.3.1.2 Case Hardness—Screws shall have a case hardness equivalent to Rockwell C45 minimum, when tested as specified in 4.2.

3.3.1.3 Total Case Depth—Screws shall have a total case depth conforming to the tabulation as shown in Table 4.

Total case depth shall be measured at a midpoint between crest and root on the thread flank. The recommended technique for measuring case depth is given in Appendix A of SAE J78. Total case depth is the distance measured perpendicularly from the surface of a hardened case to a point where differences in chemical or physical properties of the case and core no longer can be distinguished (see SAE J423) or when the microhardness converted to HRC is 42.

TABLE 4—TOTAL CASE DEPTH

Nominal Screw Size	Total Case Depth (Inches) Max	Total Case Depth (Inches) Min
4 and 6	0.007	0.002
8 through 12	0.009	0.004
1/4 and larger	0.011	0.005

3.3.2 TENSILE STRENGTH—Hex and hex washer head screws which have nominal lengths equal to or longer than 1/2 in or three times the nominal screw diameter, whichever is longer, shall have tensile strengths not less than those specified in Tables 5A and 5B, when tested in accordance with 4.4. Screws with shorter lengths or screws with other head styles are not subject to tensile testing.

3.3.3 TORSIONAL STRENGTH—Screws shall not fail with the application of a torque less than the torsional strength torque specified in Tables 5A and 5B, when tested in accordance with 4.5.

3.3.4 DRIVE TORQUE—Screws shall, without deforming their own thread, form a mating internal thread in a test plate with the application of a torque not exceeding the drive torque specified in Tables 5A and 5B for the applicable screw size and finish, when tested in accordance with 4.6.

3.3.5 TORQUE-TO-CLAMP LOAD—Hex and hex washer head screws, in sizes No. 6 and larger, shall develop the clamp load specified in Tables 5A and 5B with the application of a torque not exceeding the clamp load torque specified in Tables 5A and 5B for the applicable screw size and finish, when tested in accordance with 4.7. Smaller sizes of screws and screws with other head styles are not subject to torque-to-clamp load requirements.

3.3.6 PROOF TORQUE—Hex and hex washer head screws shall withstand without failure the proof torque and shall be capable of being removed from the test plate following application of the proof torque specified in (see 6) for the applicable screw size and finish, when tested in accordance with 4.7. Screws with other head styles are not subject to proof torque requirements.

TABLE 5A—MECHANICAL AND PERFORMANCE REQUIREMENTS FOR THREAD ROLLING SCREWS(1) (TENSILE STRENGTH, MIN LB)

Nominal Screw Size and Threads per Inch	Tensile Strength, Min lb	Torsional Strength Min In-Lb	Torsional Strength Min ft-lb	Drive Torque For PC and CP Screws Max In-Lb	Drive Torque For PC and CP Screws Max ft-Lb	Drive Torque For ZP Screws Max In-lb	Drive Torque For ZP Screws Max ft-lb
No. 2-56	500	6		4.5	—	6	
3-48	660	10	—	7.5	—	9.5	—
4-40	810	14	—	9	—	13	—
5-40	1 100	22	—	12	—	16	—
6-32	1 250	24	—	14	—	20	—
8-32	1 900	48	—	25	—	32	—
10-24	2 350	65	—	35	—	52	—
1/4-20	4 300	156	13	90	7.5	120	10
5/16-18	7 100	330	27.5	180	15	240	20
3/8-16	10 500	600	50	240	20	300	25
7/16-14	14 400	840	70	360	30	480	40
1/2-13	19 100	1080	90	540	45	660	55

Legend: CP—cadmium plated
ZP—zinc plated
PC—phosphate coated

1. Values shown in Tables 5A and 5B are intended for specification purposes and for acceptability of screws to the requirements of the specification. These values are not valid for use in design or assembly unless all conditions of the application are identical with those specified for the inspection tests.

TABLE 5B—MECHANICAL AND PERFORMANCE REQUIREMENTS FOR THREAD ROLLING SCREWS[1]
(CLAMP LOAD, LB)

Nominal Screw Size and Threads per Inch	Clamp Load, lb	Clamp Load Torque For PC and CP Screws Max in-lb	Clamp Load Torque For PC and CP Screws Max ft-lb	Clamp Load Torque For ZP Screws Max in-lb	Clamp Load Torque For ZP Screws Max ft-lb	Proof Torque For PC and CP Screws in-lb	Proof Torque For PC and CP Screws ft-lb	Proof Torque For ZP Screws in-lb	Proof Torque For ZP Screws ft-lb	Hydrogen Embrittlement Torque For CP Screws in-lb	Hydrogen Embrittlement Torque For CP Screws ft-lb	Hydrogen Embrittlement Torque For ZP Screws in-lb	Hydrogen Embrittlement Torque For CP Screws ft-lb
No. 2-56	—	—	—	—	—	7	—	8	—	4.5	—	5	—
3-48	—	—	—	—	—	12	—	13.5	—	7.5	—	8.5	—
4-40	—	—	—	—	—	17	—	19	—	10.5	—	12	—
5-40	—	—	—	—	—	25	—	28	—	17	—	19	—
6-32	460	19	—	25	—	28	—	33	—	18	—	20	—
8-32	700	37	—	48	—	50	—	57	—	36	—	41	—
10-24	900	55	—	68	—	68	—	77	—	49	—	55	—
1/4-20	1600	120	10	144	12	162	13.5	186	15.5	114	9.5	132	11
5/16-18	2600	252	21	312	26	342	28.5	372	31	252	21	276	23
3/8-16	4000	480	40	612	51	636	53	690	57.5	456	38	510	42.5
7/16-14	5400	744	62	900	75	888	74	960	80	630	52.5	720	60
1/2-13	7200	996	83	1140	95	1170	97.5	1260	105	816	68	930	77.5

Legend: CP—cadmium plated
ZP—zinc plated
PC—phosphate coated

1. Values shown in Table 5 are intended for specification purposes and for acceptability of screws to the requirements of the specification. These values are not valid for use in design or assembly unless all conditions of the application are identical with those specified for the inspection tests.

3.3.7 DUCTILITY—Heads of screws shall not separate from the shank when a permanent deformation of 7 degrees is induced between the plane of the under head bearing surface and a plane normal to the axis of the screw, when tested in accordance with 4.8.

3.3.8 HYDROGEN EMBRITTLEMENT—Cadmium- and zinc-electroplated screws shall withstand without failure the hydrogen embrittlement torque specified in Tables 5A and 5B for the applicable screw size and finish, when tested in accordance with 4.9.

4. Test Methods

4.1 Core Hardness—Core hardness shall be determined at mid-radius of a transverse section through the screw taken at a distance sufficiently behind the point of the screw to be through the full minor diameter.

4.2 Surface Hardness—Screws shall have a surface hardness equivalent to 45 HRC minimum. For the purpose of routine testing or a quick check, the surface hardness may be checked by the use of H515N, knoop or pyramid identor. The method selected shall be dependent on the size of the product and testable area. The readings may be taken on the surface with light surface preparation. In the event that a hardness lower than specification is obtained, the Reference Method described below will prevail.

The hardness readings shall be taken 0.002 in below the surface of the screw using a microhardness instrument with a knoop or pyramid identor and a 500-g load. Where the total depth of case is 0.004 in or less, the reading may be taken 0.001 in below the surface of the screw using a 100-g load.

For the purposes of measuring surface hardness and case depth, the readings will be taken on specimens which have been sectioned in a tolerance zone from true center to above center in order to ensure adequate support in the mounting media. When measuring the apparent major diameter on the sectioned metalographic specimen, the apparent major diameter shall be no less than 95% of the minimum major diameter permitted for the size of fastener being tested.

4.3 Case Depth—Case depth shall be measured at the midpoint between crest and root on the thread flank. A recommended technique for measuring case depth is given in the Appendix of SAE J78.

4.3.1 REFEREE PROCEDURE—All screws shall meet performance requirements and tests as defined by Section 4. Hardness at the maximum case depth as defined by 3.3.1.3 shall not exceed 42 HRC when read with a microhardness tester using a 500-g load and converting to HRC. This is required to ensure that the total case does not exceed the maximum specified depth.

4.4 Tensile Strength Test—Screws shall be assembled in a tensile testing machine with a minimum of six threads exposed, and an axial load applied against the under head bearing surface until screw failure occurs. The speed of testing as determined with a free-running cross head shall not exceed 1 in/min. The grips of the testing machine shall be self-aligning to avoid side thrust on the specimen. The tensile strength of the screw shall be the maximum load in pounds occurring coincident with or prior to screw fracture (that is, screw breakage into two or more parts).

4.5 Torsional Strength Test—The sample screw shall be securely clamped by suitable means (Figure 2) such that the threads in the clamped length are not damaged, and that at least two full threads project above the clamping device, and that at least two full threads exclusive of point (2 to 3 1/2 thread pitches) are held within the clamping device. A blind hole may be used in place of a threaded clamping device, provided the hole depths is such as to insure that breakage will occur beyond the point (2 to 3 1/2 thread pitches). By means of a suitably calibrated torque-measuring device, torque shall be applied to the screw until failure of the screw occurs. The torque required to cause failure shall be recorded as the torsional strength torque.

4.6 Drive Test—The sample screw shall be driven into the hole in a test plate (see 4.11) until an internal thread of full major diameter is formed completely through the full thickness of the plate or until the screw head comes into contact with the plate, whichever occurs first. Speed of driving shall not exceed 500 rpm. For referee purposes, speed of driving shall not exceed 30 rpm. The maximum torque occurring during the test shall be recorded as the drive torque.

4.7 Clamp Load and Proof Torque Test—The test shall be conducted using a load-indicating type washer, or other load-measuring device, capable of measuring the actual tension induced in the screw as the screw is tightened. The device shall be accurate within ±5% of the test clamp load to be induced in the screw.

Place plain washer, or equivalent punched or drilled steel strip (see 4.12), and then load-indicating-type washer (see 4.7) on sample screw and position this assembly for driving into prescribed hole in test plate (see 4.11). Drive the screw into the test plate until the screw is seated and continue tightening until a tensile load equal to the clamp load as specified in Table 5A and 5B is developed. Restrain plain washer from turning to prevent damage to load-indicating-type washer. The torque necessary to develop the clamp load shall be recorded as the clamp load torque.

Tightening shall be continued until a torque equal to the proof torque as specified in Tables 5A and 5B has been applied to the screw. The assembly shall remain in this tightened state for 10 s, following which the screw shall be removed from the test plate by the application of removal torque.

If convenient, the clamp load and proof torque test may be conducted in conjunction with the drive test.

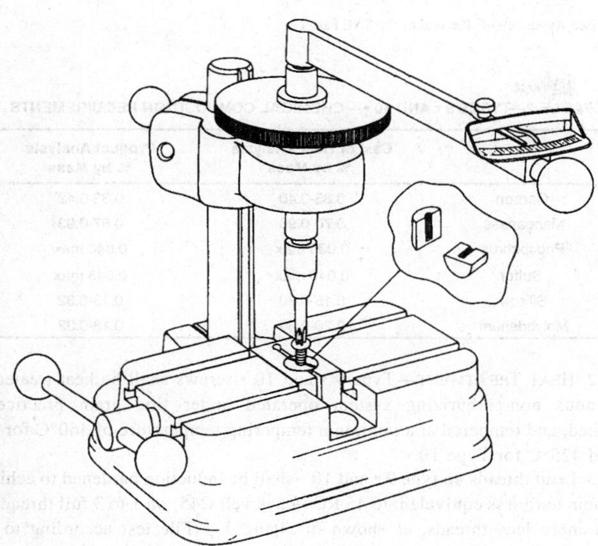

FIGURE 2—TYPICAL TORSIONAL STRENGTH TEST FIXTURE

4.8 Ductility Test—The sample screw shall be inserted into a hole in a hardened 7 degrees wedge block, or other suitable device, and an axial compressive load applied against the top of the screw head. The hole shall be 0.020 to 0.040 in larger than the nominal screw diameter. Loading shall be continued until the plane of the under head bearing surface of the protruding-type heads or the plane through the largest diameter of the head of countersunk-type heads is bent permanently through 7 degrees with respect to a plane normal to the axis of the screw.

4.9 Hydrogen Embrittlement Test—Screws shall be threaded into a tapped hole or free running nut (see 4.12) having thickness of at least 1.5 times the nominal screw size and tightened with a torque equal to the hydrogen embrittlement torque specified in Tables 5A and 5B for the applicable screw size and finish. Spacers should be used for screws with unthreaded shanks and may be used with other lengths providing full thread engagement is maintained within the test nut or tapped hole. The assembly shall remain in this tightened state for 24 h. The original hydrogen embrittlement torque shall then be reapplied, following which the screw shall be removed by the application of removal torque. Nuts may be hardened to permit reusability.

4.10 Torque Wrenches—Torque wrenches used in all tests shall be accurate within ±2% of the maximum of the specified torque range of the wrench.

Alternatively, a torque-sensing power device of equivalent accuracy may be used.

4.11 Test Plate—Test plates shall be low-carbon cold-rolled steel having a hardness of Rockwell B 70–85. Test plate thicknesses and hole sizes are given in Table 6. Test holes shall be drilled or punched and redrilled, or reamed, to ±0.001 in of the hole sizes specified in Table 6.

TABLE 6—TEST PLATE THICKNESSES AND HOLE SIZES FOR DRIVE CLAMP LOAD AND PROOF TORQUE TESTS(1)

Nominal Screw Size and Threads per Inch	Thickness, in Max	Thickness, in Min	Hole Dia, in
No. 2-56	0.1270	0.1230	0.075
3-48	0.1270	0.1230	0.087
4-40	0.1270	0.1230	0.098
5-40	0.1270	0.1230	0.110
6-32	0.1270	0.1230	0.120
8-32	0.1905	0.1845	0.147
10-24	0.1905	0.1845	0.166
1/4-20	0.2540	0.2460	0.219
5/16-18	0.3175	0.3075	0.277
3/8-16	0.3800	0.3700	0.339
7/16-14	0.4425	0.4325	0.394
1/2-13	0.5050	0.4950	0.456

1. Values shown in Table 6 are intended for specification purposes and for acceptability of screws to the requirements of the specification. These values are not valid for use in design or assembly unless all conditions of the application are identical with those specified for the inspection tests.

4.12 Under Head Bearing Test Surface—The surface condition of plain commercially available flat washers, free running nuts, and cold-rolled steel is normally suitable for tests specified in 4.6, 4.7, and 4.9. For referee purposes, however, the surface shall conform to 20 to 30 µin. (AA roughness range).

5. Inspection

5.1 Inspection Procedure—Screws shall be inspected to determine conformance with the requirements of this document. Inspection shall be performed in accordance with sampling plans given in MIL-STD-105D. Alternate inspection procedures may be specified by the purchaser on the purchase order or engineering drawing.

METRIC THREAD ROLLING SCREWS—SAE J1237 MAR2001 SAE Standard

Report of the SAE Iron and Steel Technical Committee approved June 1978, editorial change May 1979, and completely revised August 1996. Revised by the SAE Fastener Committee March 2001. Rationale statement available.

Foreword—This document has also changed to comply with the SAE Technical Standards Board format. The footnotes in the tables are listed consecutively.

1. Scope—This SAE Standard covers requirements for metric thread rolling screws suitable for use in general engineering applications.

1.1 Requirements for three material-process options are stated:

a. Screws (in sizes M2 x 0.4 thru M12 x 1.75) manufactured from low carbon steel, carburized, and tempered. These screws are designated SAE J1237 Type 2 •.

b. Screws (in sizes M2 x 0.4 thru M12 x 1.75) manufactured from medium carbon alloy steel, heat treated to achieve properties comparable to SAE J1199 class 9.8 screws, and additionally, with the point selectively hardened. These screws are designated SAE J1237 Type 9 •.

c. Screws (in sizes M5 x 0.8 thru M12 x 1.75) manufactured from medium carbon alloy steel, heat treated to achieve properties comparable to SAE J1199 class 10.9 screws, and additionally, with the point selectively hardened. These screws are designated SAE J1237 Type 10 •.

1.2 When SAE J1237 is specified without Type designation, either Type 2 • or Type 9 • may be supplied.

NOTE—The performance requirements covered in this document apply only to the combination of laboratory conditions described in the testing procedures. If other conditions are encountered in an actual service application (such as different materials, thicknesses, hole sizes, etc.), values shown herein for drive torque, torque-to-clamp load, and proof torque may require adjustment.

2. References

2.1 Applicable Publications—The following publications form a part of this specification to the extent specified herein. Unless otherwise specified, the latest issue of SAE publications shall apply.

2.1.1 SAE PUBLICATIONS—Available from SAE, 400 Commonwealth Drive, Warrendale, PA 15096-0001.

SAE J121—Decarburization in Hardened and Tempered Unified Threaded Fasteners

SAE J423—Methods of Measuring Case Depth

SAE J864—Surface Hardness Testing and Files

SAE J1199—Mechanical and Material Requirements for Metric Externally Threaded Steel Fasteners

2.1.2 ASTM PUBLICATION—Available from ASTM, 100 Barr Harbor Drive, West Conshohocken, PA 19428-2959.

ASTMF606M—Standard Test Methods for Determining the Mechanical Properties of Externally and Internally Threaded Fasteners, Washers, and Rivets

2.1.3 MILITARY DOCUMENT—Available from DODSSP, Subscription Services Desk, Building 4D, 700 Robbins Avenue, Philadelphia, PA 19111-5094.

MIL-STD-105D

3. Requirements

3.1 Material and Process Requirements—Type 2 •

3.1.1 MATERIAL AND CHEMISTRY—Type 2 • screws shall be made from cold heading quality, killed steel wire conforming to the chemical composition requirements in Table 1:

3.1.2 HEAT TREATMENT—Type 2 • screws shall be heat treated in a continuous carbonitriding or gas carburizing system. Cyaniding systems may be approved by the purchaser when it is shown that a continuous flow (no batch) quenching process which consistently produces uniform case and core hardnesses is employed.

3.1.3 TEMPERING TEMPERATURES—Minimum tempering temperatures shall be 340 °C.

3.2 Material and Process Requirements—Types 9 • and 10 •

3.2.1 MATERIAL AND CHEMISTRY—Unless otherwise specified by purchaser, Type 9 • and 10 • screws shall be made from cold heading quality, killed alloy steel wire conforming to the chemical composition requirements (SAE 4037) in Table 2:

TABLE 1—TYPE 2 •—CHEMICAL COMPOSITION REQUIREMENTS—COMPOSITION LIMITS(1), % BY MASS

Analysis	Carbon Min	Carbon Max	Manganese Min	Manganese Max
Cast or Heat	0.15	0.25	0.70	1.65
Product	0.13	0.27	0.64	1.71

1. Boron permitted in the range of 0.0005 to 0.003.

TABLE 2—TYPES 9 • AND 10 •—CHEMICAL COMPOSITION REQUIREMENTS

	Cast or Heat Analysis % by Mass	Product Analysis % by Mass
Carbon	0.35-0.40	0.33-0.42
Manganese	0.70-0.90	0.67-0.93
Phosphorus	0.035 max	0.040 max
Sulfur	0.040 max	0.045 max
Silicon	0.15-0.30	0.13-0.32
Molybdenum	0.20-0.30	0.18-0.32

3.2.2 HEAT TREATMENT—Type 9 • and 10 • screws shall be heat treated in a continuous non-carburizing system operated under fine grain practice, oil quenched, and tempered at a minimum tempering temperature of 460°C for Type 9 • and 425°C for Type 10 •.

3.2.3 Lead threads on type 9 • and 10 • shall be induction hardened to achieve a minimum hardness equivalent to 45 RC (Rockwell C45) on 1 to 3 full threads and one or more lead threads, as shown in Figure 1. (File test according to SAE J864.)

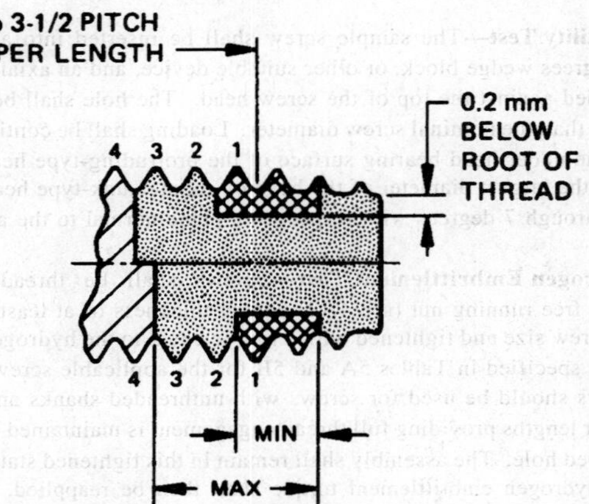

NOTE TO USER—When selecting length of Type 9 • and 10 • screws for any application, one objective should be location of the induction hardened zone beyond the nut anchorage, or a minimum of six full form threads in the threaded hole.

FIGURE 1—INDUCTION HARDENED LEAD THREADS

3.3 Finish—Screws shall be cadmium or zinc electroplated with a coating thickness of 5 to 10 µm, or have a zinc phosphate and oil coating as specified by the purchaser. Unless otherwise specified, screws may be provided with an additional supplementary lubricant as necessary to meet the performance requirements. Other finishes are available, however, and it is the intent of this document that the mechanical and performance requirements shall apply only to those screws having one of the three finishes specified previously. When other finishes are required, the purchaser and manufacturer may agree on performance values other than those of 3.7.

Electroplated screws shall be baked within the temperature range 190 to 230 °C within 1 h after plating to avoid hydrogen embrittlement. Parts must be maintained at temperature for 4 h.

In cases where screws are plated or coated following delivery to the purchaser (or where plating or coating of screws is otherwise under the control of the purchaser) the screw producer shall not be responsible for failures of the screw to meet mechanical or performance requirements due to plating or coating.

3.4 Dimensional Requirements

3.4.1 HEAD DIMENSIONS—Standard head styles for thread rolling screws are flat countersunk, oval countersunk, pan, hex, hex washer, and hex flange head. Flat countersunk, oval countersunk, and pan head screws are available slotted or with Type 1 or Type 1A cross recess drives. Head, slot, and cross recess dimensions shall be specified by purchaser.

3.4.2 THREAD AND POINT DIMENSIONS—Thread and point dimensions shall conform to those given in Table 3. Threads shall conform to a 60-degree basic thread form. Threads are not subject to thread gaging. Details of point configuration shall be optional with the manufacturer providing all specified dimensions are maintained and screws meet the performance requirements of this document.

3.4.3 THREAD LENGTH—For screws of nominal lengths within the ranges listed under column Y of Table 4, the full form threads shall extend close to the head such that the specified thread major diameter limits are maintained to within the respective Y distance from the underside of the head, or closer if practicable. See Figure 2. Screws of longer nominal lengths, unless otherwise specified by the purchaser, shall have a minimum length of full form thread as specified in column L_T.

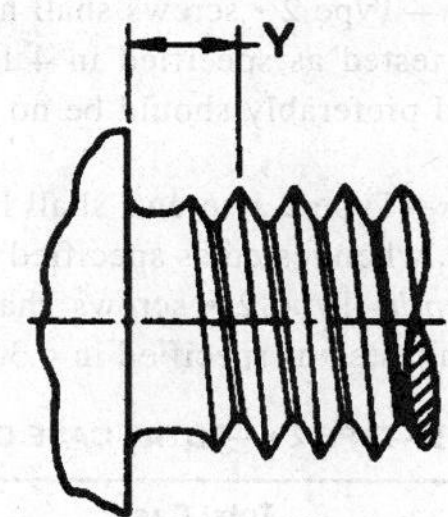

FIGURE 2—UNTHREADED LENGTH

TABLE 3—THREAD AND POINT DIMENSIONS OF THREAD ROLLING SCREWS(1)

Nominal Screw and Thread Pitch	Major Dia(2) Max	P Point Dia(2) Max	C Dia of Circumscribing Circle(3) Max	Cp Circumscribing Circle (Point)(3) Max	Point Length Max(4)	Point Length Min(5)	L Min Practical Nominal Screw Length Pan, Hex, Hex Washer Heads	L Min Practical Nominal Screw Length Flat and Oval Ctsk Heads
M2 x 0.4	2.00	1.6	—	—	1.4	0.8	4	5
M2.5 x 0.45	2.50	2.1	2.57	2.13	1.6	0.9	4	6
M3 x 0.5	3.00	2.5	3.07	2.58	1.8	1.0	5	8
M3.5 x 0.6	3.50	2.9	3.58	2.99	2.1	1.2	6	8
M4 x 0.7	4.00	3.4	4.08	3.40	2.4	1.4	8	10
M5 x 0.8	5.00	4.4	5.09	4.31	2.8	1.6	8	10
M6 x 1	6.00	5.3	6.10	5.12	3.5	2.0	10	12
M8 x 1.25	8.00	7.1	8.13	6.92	4.4	2.5	10	16
M10 x 1.5	10.00	9.0	10.15	8.69	5.2	3.0	13	16
M12 x 1.75	12.00	10.5	12.18	10.48	6.1	3.5	16	20

1. All dimensions are millimeters.
2. These dimensions are applicable to types of screws where periphery of the thread approximates a circle.
3. These dimensions are applicable to types of screws where some portions of the periphery of the thread are farther from the screw axis than others (lobular, triroundular, etc.).
4. These values are equal to 3.5 times the pitch distance rounded off to 1 decimal place.
5. These values are equal to 2 times the pitch distance rounded off to 1 decimal place.

TABLE 4—FULL FORM THREAD LENGTH AND UNTHREADED LENGTHS(1)

Nominal Screw Size and Thread Pitch	L_T Full Form Thread Length for Nominal Screw Lengths >Than	L_T Full Form Thread Length Min(2)	Y Unthreaded Length Under Head for Nominal Screw Lengths ≤Than	Y Unthreaded Length Under Head Max(3)	Y Unthreaded Length Under Head for Nominal Screw Lengths >Than	Y Unthreaded Length Under Head for Nominal Screw Lengths ≤Than	Y Unthreaded Length Under Head Max(4)
M2 x 0.4	16	12.0	6	0.40	6	16	0.8
M2.5 x 0.45	20	15.0	8	0.45	8	20	0.9
M3 x 0.5	25	18.0	9	0.50	9	25	1.0
M3.5 x 0.6	30	21.0	10	0.60	10	30	1.2
M4 x 0.7	35	24.0	12	0.70	12	35	1.4
M5 x 0.8	40	30.0	15	0.80	15	40	1.6
M6 x 1	45	38.0	18	1.00	18	45	2.0
M8 x 1.25	45	38.0	24	1.25	24	45	2.5
M10 x 1.5	45	38.0	30	1.50	30	45	3.0
M12 x 1.75	50	38.0	36	1.75	36	50	3.5

1. All dimensions are millimeters.
2. Tabulated values through 5 mm size are equal to 6 times basic screw diameter rounded to nearest millimeter.
3. Tabulated values are equal to 1 times thread pitch.
4. Tabulated values are equal to 2 times thread pitch.

3.5 Mechanical Requirements—Type 2 • Screws

3.5.1 HARDNESS

3.5.1.1 Core Hardness—Type 2 • screws shall have a core hardness of 28-38 RC (Rockwell C) when tested as specified in 4.1. Core hardness shall not exceed maximum shown and preferably should be no higher than 36 RC (Rockwell C) on electroplated parts.

3.5.1.2 Case Hardness—Type 2 • screws shall have a case hardness of 45 RC (Rockwell C), minimum, when tested as specified in 4.2.

3.5.1.3 Total Case Depth—Type 2 • screws shall have a total case depth conforming to Table 5, when tested as specified in 4.3.

TABLE 5—TYPE 2 •—TOTAL CASE DEPTH

Nominal Size	Total Case Depth, mm Min	Total Case Depth, mm Max
2 through 3.5	0.05	0.18
4 and 5	0.10	0.23
6 through 12	0.13	0.28

3.5.2 TENSILE STRENGTH—Type 2 • screws with hex head, hex washer head, and hex flange head, which have lengths equal to or longer than 12 mm or 3 times the nominal screw diameter, whichever is longer, shall have tensile strengths not less than those specified in Table 6, when tested in accordance with 4.4. Screws with shorter lengths or screws with other head styles which are weaker than the threaded section are not subject to tensile testing.

TABLE 6—MECHANICAL REQUIREMENTS FOR TYPE 2 • THREAD ROLLING SCREWS

Basic Dia and Thread Pitch (millimeters)	Min Tensile Strength kN	Min Torsional Strength N·m
M2 x 0.4	1.9	0.7
M2.5 x 0.45	3.15	1.2
M3 x 0.5	4.68	2.2
M3.5 x 0.6	6.3	3.5
M4 x 0.7	8.17	5.2
M5 x 0.8	13.2	10.5
M6 x 1	18.7	17.7
M8 x 1.25	34.0	43.0
M10 x 1.5	53.9	87.0
M12 x 1.75	78.4	152.0

3.5.3 TORSIONAL STRENGTH—Type 2 • screws shall not fail with the application of a torque less than the torsional strength torque specified in Table 6 when tested in accordance with 4.5.

3.5.4 DUCTILITY—Heads of screws shall not separate from the shank when a permanent deformation of 7 degrees is induced between the plane of the under head bearing surface and a plane normal to the axis of the screw, when tested in accordance with 4.8.

3.6 Mechanical Requirements—Type 9 • and 10 • Screws

3.6.1 Type 9 • and 10 • screws shall conform to the mechanical requirements specified in Table 7 when tested according to wedge tensile and hardness procedures published in ASTM F 606M.

TABLE 7—MECHANICAL REQUIREMENTS TYPE 9 • AND 10 • SCREWS

Type	Wedge Tensile Strength (Stress) MPa(1)(2)	Surface Hardness Rockwell 15N, max	Product Hardness Rockwell (3)
9 •	900 min	(4)	C27-36
10 •	1040 min	(4)	C33-39

1. Wedge tensile strength values for full size products are specified in Table 8. Wedge tensile strengths are applicable only to screws which have lengths equal to or longer than 12 mm or 3 times the nominal diameter, whichever is longer. Screws with shorter lengths or screws with head styles which are weaker than the threaded section are not subject to wedge tensile testing.
2. Tensile wedge angles: 6 degrees when screws are threaded one diameter or closer to the head; 10 degrees on all others.
3. Minimum product hardness values applicable to screws not subject to tensile tests, and these hardness requirements exclude induction hardened zone 3.2.3 (Figure 1).
4. Surface hardness shall not exceed product hardness by more 3 points Rockwell C equivalent, and in the case of Type 10 • shall also not exceed Rockwell 15N 80, except as noted in 3.2.3 (Figure 1).

TABLE 8—TENSILE STRENGTH VALUES—TYPE 9 • AND 10 • SCREWS

Nominal Thread Dia and Thread Pitch	Type 9 • Min Tensile Strength kN	Type 10 • Min Tensile Strength kN
M2 x 0.4	1.86	
M2.5 x 0.45	3.05	
M3 x 0.5	4.53	
M3.5 x 0.6	6.10	
M4 x 0.7	7.90	
M5 x 0.8	12.8	14.8
M6 x 1	18.1	20.9
M8 x 1.25	32.9	38.1
M10 x 1.5	52.2	60.3
M12 x 1.75	75.9	87.7

3.6.2 Type 9 • and 10 • screws shall conform to Class 3/4H decarburization limits as described in SAE J121.

3.6.3 DUCTILITY—Heads of screws shall not separate from the shank when a permanent deformation of 10degrees is induced between the plane of the under head bearing surface and a plane normal to the axis of the screw, when tested in accordance with 4.8.

3.7 Performance Requirements—Types 2 •, 9 •, and 10 •

3.7.1 DRIVE TORQUE—Screws shall, without deforming their own thread, form a mating internal thread in a test plate with the application of a torque not exceeding the drive torque specified in Table 9 for the applicable screw size and finish, when tested in accordance with 4.6.

3.7.2 TORQUE-TO-CLAMP LOAD—Screws subject to tensile test, M4 x 0.7 size and larger, shall develop the clamp load specified in Table 9 with the application of a torque not exceeding the clamp load torque specified in Table 9 for the applicable screw size and finish, when tested in accordance with 4.7. Smaller sizes of screws and screws not subject to tensile test are not subject to torque-to-clamp load requirements.

3.7.3 PROOF TORQUE—Screws with head styles subject to tensile test shall withstand without failure the proof torque and shall be capable of being removed from the test plate following application of the proof torque specified in Table 9 for the applicable screw size and finish, when tested in accordance with 4.7. Screws not subject to tensile test are not subject to proof torque requirements.

3.7.4 HYDROGEN EMBRITTLEMENT—Cadmium and zinc electroplated screws shall withstand without failure the hydrogen embrittlement torque specified in Table 9 for the applicable screw size and finish, when tested in accordance with 4.9.

4. Test Methods

4.1 Core Hardness—Core hardness shall be determined at mid-radius of a transverse section through the screw taken at a distance sufficiently behind the point of the screw to be through the full minor diameter.

4.2 Surface Hardness—Screws shall have a surface hardness of 45 HRC minimum. For the purpose of routine testing or a quick check, the surface hardness may be checked by the use of HR15N, knoop or pyramid indentor. The method selected shall be dependent on the size of the product and testable area. The readings may be taken on the surface with light surface preparation. In the event that a hardness lower than specification is obtained, the Referee Method described as follows will prevail.

The hardness readings shall be taken 0.051 mm below the surface of the screw using a microhardness instrument with a knoop or pyramid indentor and a 500-g load. In cases where the total depth of case is 0.10mm or less, the reading may be taken 0.025 mm below the surface and a 100-g load is used.

For the purposes of measuring surface hardness and case depth, the readings will be taken on specimens which have been sectioned in a tolerance zone from true center to above center in order to ensure adequate support in the mounting media. When measuring the apparent major diameter on the sectioned metalographic specimen, the apparent major diameter shall be no less than 95% of the minimum major diameter permitted for the size of fastener being tested.

TABLE 9—PERFORMANCE REQUIREMENTS—TYPES 2 •, 9 •, AND 10 •[1]

Basic Dia and Thread Pitch (millimeters)	Test Plate Thickness mm	Test Plate Pilot Hole Dia mm	Drive Torque for ZPC and CP SCrews max N·m	Drive Torque for ZP Screws max N·m	Clamp Load kN	Clamp Load Torque for ZPC and CP Screws max N·m	Clamp Load Torque for ZP Screws max N·m	Proof Torque for ZPC and CP Screws N·m	Proof Torque for ZP Screws N·m	Hydrogen Embrittlement Torque for CP Screws N·m	Hydrogen Embrittlement Torque for ZP Screws N·m
M2 x 0.4	3	1.77	0.4	0.6				0.6	0.7	0.4	0.5
M2.5 x 0.45	3	2.25	0.8	1.0				1.3	1.4	0.9	1.0
M3 x 0.5	3	2.7	1.3	1.7				2.4	2.5	1.7	1.9
M3.5 x 0.6	3	3.15	1.9	2.4				3.7	4.0	2.6	3.0
M4 x 0.7	5	3.6	2.6	3.4	3.1	4.2	4.8	5.4	5.8	3.8	4.4
M5 x 0.8	5	4.55	4.8	6.0	5.0	8.0	10.0	11.0	12.0	7.8	9.0
M6 x 1	6	5.4	7.5	9.2	6.9	15.0	16.0	19.0	20.0	13.0	15.0
M8 x 1.25	8	7.3	16.0	20.0	12.6	34.0	40.0	46.0	48.0	32.0	36.0
M10 x 1.5	10	9.2	28.0	35.0	20.0	68.0	81.0	92.0	96.0	65.0	74.0
M12 x 1.75	12	11.0	46.0	55.0	29.5	110.0	130.0	160.0	170.0	110.0	130.0

1. Values shown in Table 9 are intended for specification purposes and for determination of acceptability of screws to the requirements of this standard. These values are not valid for use in design or assembly unless all conditions of the application are identical with those specified for the inspection tests.

Legend: CP—Cadmium Electroplated
ZP—Zinc Electroplated
ZPC—Zinc Phosphate Coated—(Commonly known as Phosphate and oil)

4.3 Case Depth—Total case depth shall be measured at the midpoint between crest and root on the thread flank.

Total case depth to be checked in the hardened condition in accordance with SAE J423, Section 5.3.1 using a magnification of 100X. For referee purposes, ensure that the screws meet all performance requirements as defined in Tables 6 and 9, and that the hardness at the maximum case depth as defined in 4.3 does not exceed 42 HRC when read with a microhardness instrument using either a knoop or pyramid indentor and a 500-g load and converting to HRC. This is required to ensure that the total case does not exceed the maximum specified depth.

4.4 Tensile Strength Test—Screws shall be assembled in a tensile testing machine with a minimum of six threads exposed, and an axial load applied against the under head bearing surface until screw failure occurs. The speed of testing as determined with a free running cross head shall not exceed 25 mm/min. The grips of the testing machine shall be self-aligning to avoid side thrust on the specimen. The tensile strength of the screw shall be the maximum load in Newtons occurring coincident with or prior to screw fracture (such as, screw breakage into two or more parts).

4.5 Torsional Strength Test—The sample screw shall be securely clamped by suitable means (Figure 3) such that the threads in the clamped length are not damaged, and that at least two full threads project above the clamping device, and that at least two full threads exclusive of point (2 to 3.5 thread pitches) are held within the clamping device. A blind hole may be used in place of a threaded clamping device, provided the hole depth is such as to insure that breakage will occur beyond the point (2 to 3.5 thread pitches). By means of a suitably calibrated torque measuring device, torque shall be applied to the screw until failure of the screw occurs. The torque required to cause failure shall be recorded as the torsional strength torque.

4.6 Drive Test—The sample screw shall be driven into the hole in a test plate (4.6.1) until an internal thread of full major diameter is formed completely through the full thickness of the plate or until the screw head comes into contact with the plate, whichever occurs first. Speed of driving shall not exceed 500 rpm. For referee purposes, speed of driving shall not exceed 30 rpm. The maximum torque occurring during the test shall be recorded as the drive torque.

4.6.1 TEST PLATE—Test plates shall be low carbon cold rolled steel having a hardness of Rockwell B75-90. Test plate thicknesses and hole sizes are given in Table 9. Test holes shall be drilled or punched and redrilled, or reamed, to ±0.025 mm of the hole sizes specified in Table 9.

4.7 Clamp Load and Proof Torque Test—The test shall be conducted using a load indicating type washer, or other load measuring device, capable of measuring the actual tension induced in the screw as the screw is tightened. The device shall be accurate within ±5% of the test clamp load to be induced in the screw.

Assemble a plain washer, or equivalent punched or drilled steel strip as specified in 4.7.1, and then the load-indicating type washer on the sample screw and position this assembly for driving into the test plate (4.6.1). The screw shall be driven into the test plate until the screw is seated. Tightening shall be continued until a tensile load equal to the clamp load as specified in Table 9 is developed. Care shall be taken to prevent the under head bearing surface from turning during tightening. The torque necessary to develop the clamp load shall be recorded as the clamp load torque.

Tightening shall be continued until a torque equal to the proof torque as specified in Table 9 has been applied to the screw. The assembly shall remain in this tightened state for 10 s following which the screw shall be removed from the test plate by the application of removal torque.

If convenient, the clamp load and proof torque test may be conducted in conjunction with the drive test.

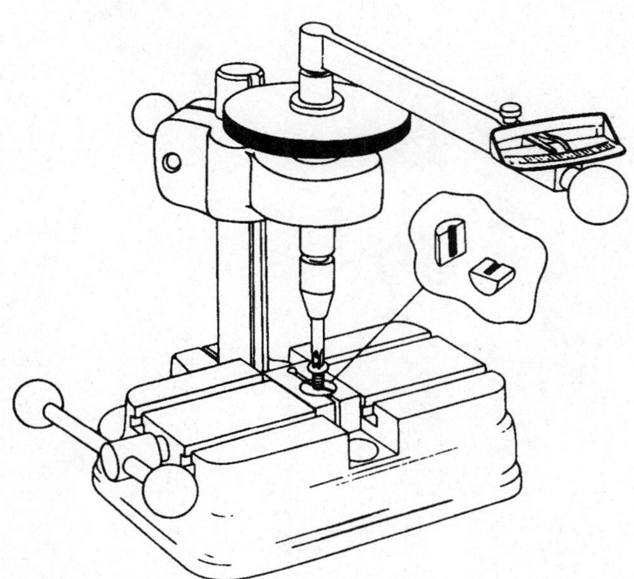

FIGURE 3—TYPICAL TORSIONAL STRENGTH TEST FIXTURE

4.7.1 UNDER HEAD BEARING TEST SURFACE—The surface condition of plain commercially available flat washers, free running nuts, and cold rolled steel is normally suitable for tests specified in 4.6, 4.7, and 4.9. For referee purposes, the surface shall conform to 0.50 to 0.75 μm (AA roughness range).

4.8 Ductility Test—The sample screw shall be inserted into a drilled hole in a hardened wedge block, or other suitable device, and an axial compressive load applied against the top of the screw head. The hole shall be 0.50 to 1.00 mm larger than the nominal screw diameter. Loading shall be continued until the plane of the under head bearing surface is bent permanently through the angle specified for the screw type with respect to a plane normal to the axis of the screw.

4.9 Hydrogen Embrittlement Test—Screws shall be threaded into a tapped hole or free running nut having thicknesses of at least 1.5 times the nominal screw size and tightened with a torque equal to the hydrogen embrittlement torque specified in Table 9 for the applicable screw size and finish. Spacers should be used for screws with unthreaded shanks and may be used with other lengths providing full thread engagement is maintained within the test nut or tapped hole. The assembly shall remain in this tightened state for 24 h. The original hydrogen embrittlement torque shall then be reapplied following which the screw shall be removed by the application of removal torque. Nuts may be hardened to permit reusability.

4.10 Torque Wrenches—Torque wrenches used in all tests shall be accurate within ±2% of the maximum of the specified torque range of the wrench.

Alternatively, a torque sensing power device of equivalent accuracy may be used.

5. Inspection

5.1 Inspection Procedure—Screws shall be inspected to determine conformance with the requirements of this document. Inspection shall be performed in accordance with sampling plans given in MIL-STD-105D. Alternate inspection procedures may be specified by the purchaser on the purchase order or engineering drawing.

6. Identification—The head identification markings in Table 10 may be specified as an option by the purchaser on hex or similar non-recessed or non-slotted head styles:

TABLE 10—IDENTIFICATION

Type	Identification Mark
2 •	2 •
9 •	9 •
10 •	10 •

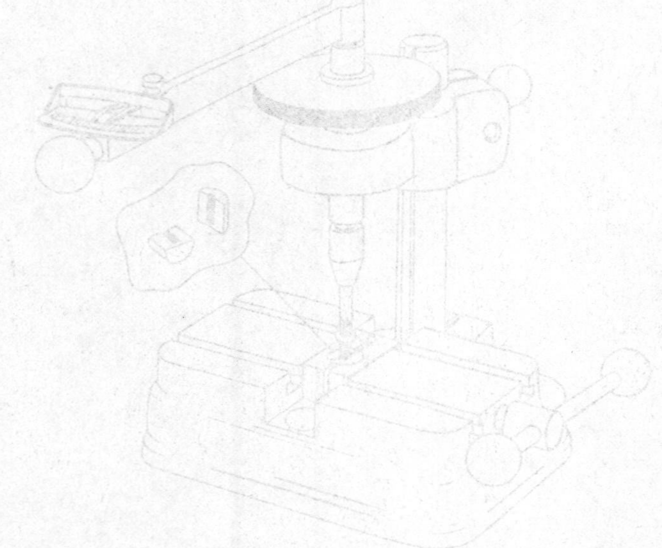

SURFACE DISCONTINUITIES ON GENERAL APPLICATION BOLTS, SCREWS, AND STUDS —SAE J1061 MAY1998

SAE Recommended Practice

Report of the Iron and Steel Technical Committee approved September 1973. Editorial change: metric products added July 1975. Reaffirmed by the SAE Fasteners Committee October 1992 and May 1998.

Foreword—This Reaffirmed Document has been changed only to reflect the new SAE Technical Standards Board format.

1. Scope—This SAE Recommended Practice defines, illustrates, and specifies allowable limits for various types of surface discontinuities that may occur during the manufacture and processing of bolts, screws, and studs in sizes through 24 mm or 1 in diameter inclusive with lengths to 150 mm or 6 in inclusive, having specified minimum tensile strengths of 900 MPa or 120 000 psi and greater, which are primarily intended for use in automotive assemblies.

1.1 The basic recommended practice does not include inspection sampling requirements. It is intended that the purchaser shall specify, in the original inquiry and purchase order, the inspection sampling requirements which the producer must satisfy to demonstrate the acceptability of bolts and screws with respect to surface discontinuities.

2. References

2.1 Applicable Publication—The following publications form a part of this specification to the extent specified herein.

2.1.1 ASTM PUBLICATION—Available from ASTM, 100 Barr Harbor Drive, West Conshohocken, PA 19428-2959.

ASTM E 3—Methods of Preparing Metallographic Specimens

3. Types of Surface Discontinuities—For the purpose of this document, surface discontinuities on bolts, screws, and studs are divided into nine "types", defined as follows:

3.1 Crack—A crack is a clean (crystalline) fracture passing through or across the grain boundaries without inclusion of foreign elements. Cracks are normally caused by overstressing the metal during forging or other forming operation, or during heat treatment. Where parts are subjected to significant reheating, cracks usually are discolored by scale.

3.1.1 QUENCH CRACKS—Quench cracks may occur during heat treatment due to excessively high thermal and transformation stresses. They usually traverse an irregular and erratic course on the surface of the fasteners. Typical quench cracks are shown in Figure 1.

3.1.2 FORGING CRACKS—Forging cracks may occur during the cutoff or forging operations and are located on the top of the heads of screws and bolts. Typical forging cracks are shown in Figure 2.

3.2 Seam—Seams are generally inherent in the raw material from which fasteners are manufactured. They are narrow, generally straight or smooth-curved line discontinuities, running longitudinally, on the shank and/or thread. Seams may extend onto the tops of the heads of circular head products as well as being present at the periphery of the head. Seams may also extend into the chamfer circle, washer face, and wrenching flats of hex head products. Typical seams are shown in Figure 3.

3.3 Burst—A burst is an open break in the metal (material). Bursts may occur on the flats or corners of the heads of bolts and screws, at the periphery of flanged or circular head products, or on the raised periphery of indented head bolts and screws. Typical bursts are shown in Figure 4.

3.4 Shear Burst—A shear burst is an open break in the metal, occurring most frequently at the periphery of products having circular or flanged heads and are generally located at approximately 45 degrees to the product axis. Shear bursts may also occur on the sides of hex head products. Typical discontinuities of this type are shown in Figure 4.

3.5 Void—A void is a shallow pocket or hollow on the surface of the bolt or screw due to nonfilling of metal during forging or upsetting. Typical voids are shown in Figure 5.

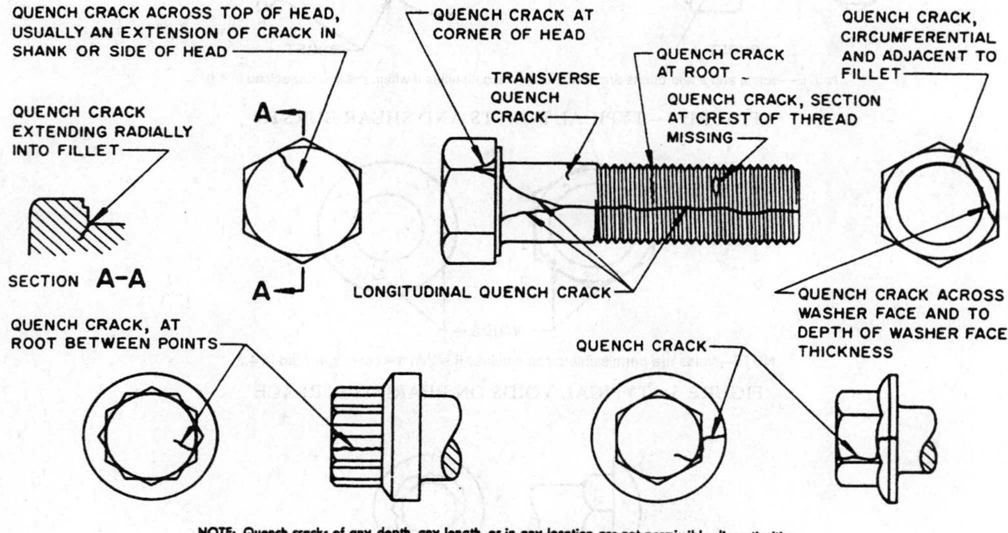

FIGURE 1—TYPICAL QUENCH CRACKS

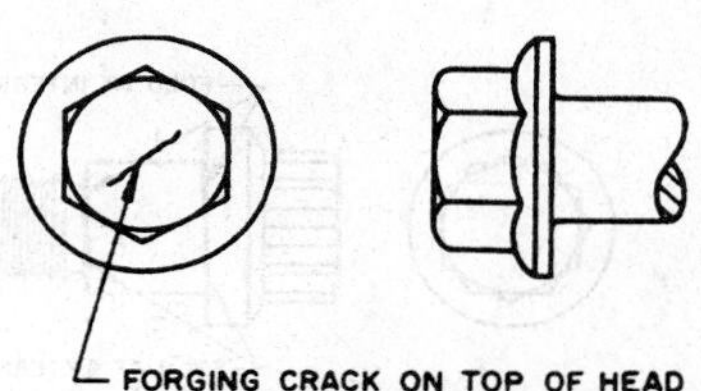

NOTE—Forging cracks are permissible discontinuities if with the limits specified in 4.4.

FIGURE 2—TYPICAL FORGING CRACKS

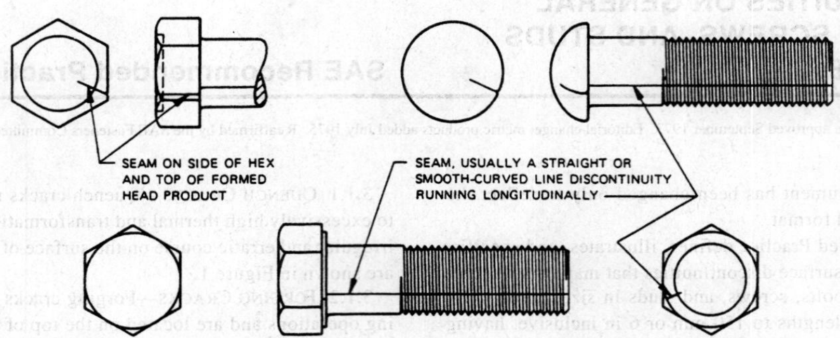

NOTE—Seams are permissible discontinuities if within the limits specified in 4.5.

FIGURE 3—TYPICAL SEAMS

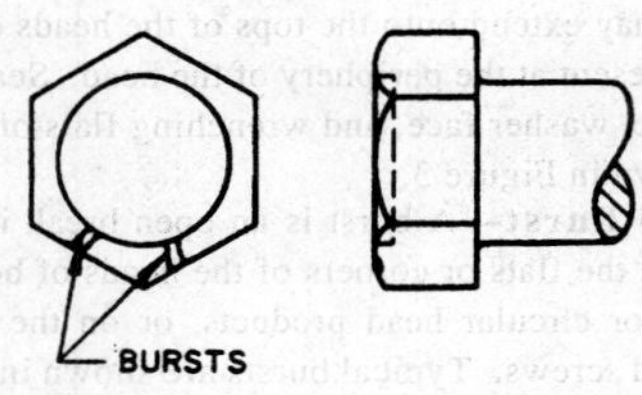

NOTE—Bursts in raised periphery of indented head bolts and screws are permissible discontinuities if within the limits specified in 4.6.3.

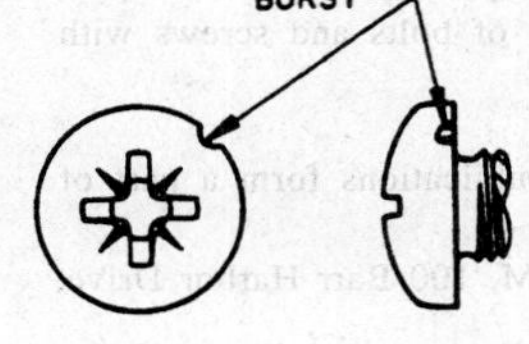

NOTE—Bursts in circular head products, with or without recess, are permissible discontinuities if within the limits specified in 4.6.2.

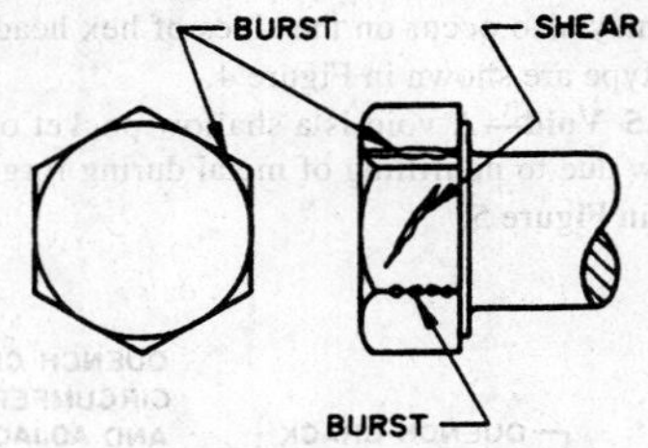

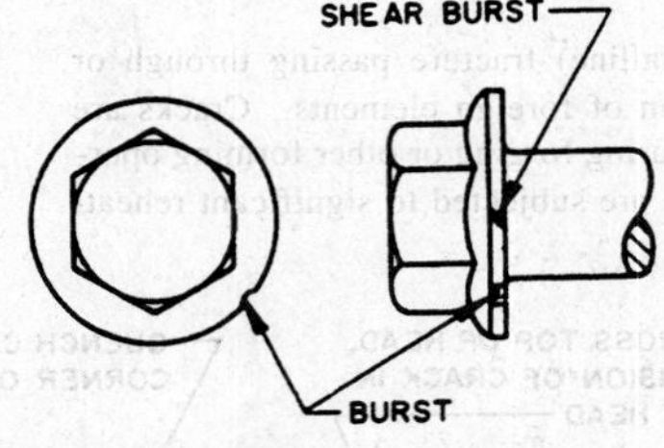

NOTE—Bursts and shear bursts are permissible discontinuities if within the limits specified in 4.6.

FIGURE 4—TYPICAL BURSTS AND SHEAR BURSTS

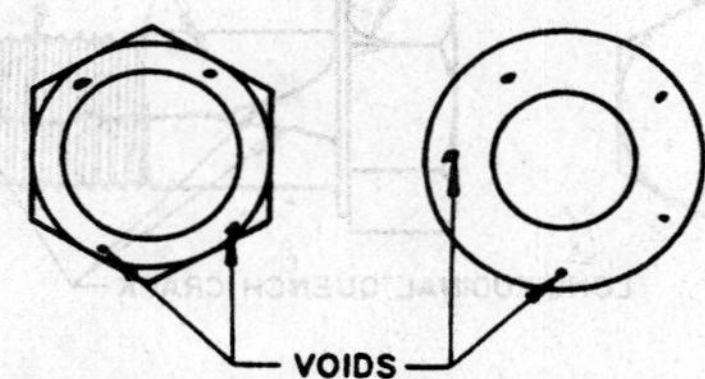

NOTE—Voids are permissible discontinuities if within the limits specified in 4.7.

FIGURE 5—TYPICAL VOIDS ON BEARING SURFACE

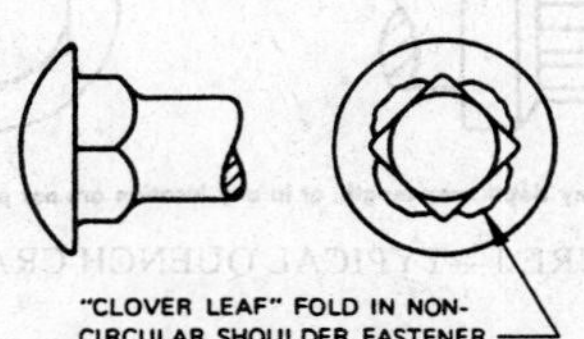

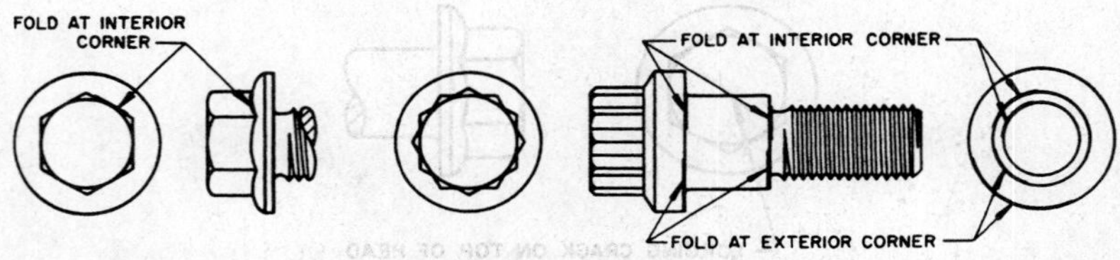

NOTE—Folds in interior corners at or below the bearing surface are non-permissible discontinuities. Folds at exterior corners are permissible discontinuities if within the limits specified in 4.3.

FIGURE 6—TYPICAL FOLDS

3.6 Fold—A fold is a doubling over of metal which may occur during the forging operation. Folds may occur at or near the intersection of diameter changes, and are especially prevalent with noncircular necks, shoulders, and heads. Typical folds are shown in Figure 6.

3.7 Tool Marks—Tool marks are longitudinal or circumferential grooves of shallow depth produced by the movement of manufacturing tools over the surface of the fastener. Typical tool marks are shown in Figure 7.

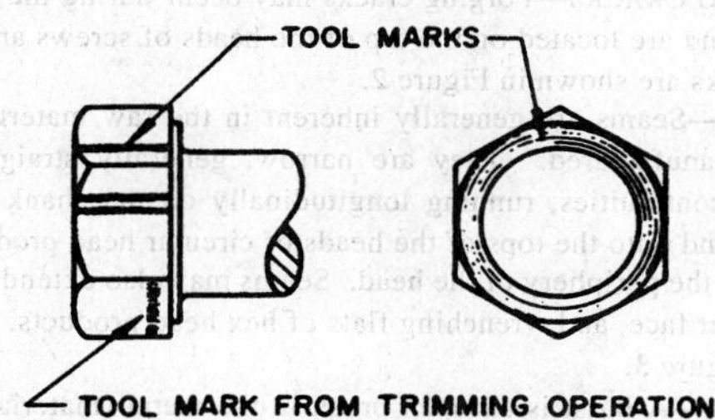

NOTE—Tool marks are permissible discontinuities if within the limits specified in 4.8.

FIGURE 7—TYPICAL TOOL MARKS

3.8 Nick or Gouge—A nick or gouge is an indentation on the surface of the fastener, produced by forceful abrasion or the impact of product coming into contact with other product or manufacturing equipment during manufacture.

4. Limits for Surface Discontinuities

4.1 Letter Definitions—Throughout the following requirements D designates the nominal size (basic major diameter of thread) of bolts, screws, and studs, except for bolts and screws with shoulders, in which case D designates the largest shoulder diameter. F designates the nominal flange diameter or head diameter of products having circular heads. For metric-series products, use millimeter; for inch-series products use inch.

4.2 Quench Cracks—Quench cracks of any depth, any length, or in any location, are not permitted. (See 3.1.1 and Figure 1.)

4.3 Folds—Folds located in internal corners at or below the bearing surface, for example, in the fillet at the junction of head and shank, are not permitted. (See 3.6 and Figure 6.)

4.4 Forging Cracks—Forging cracks on the top of heads of bolts and screws shall not exceed a length of 1 D or a width or depth of 0.040 D or 0.25 mm (0.010 in), whichever is greater.

4.5 Seams—Seams in the shanks of bolts, screws, and studs shall not exceed a depth of 0.030 D or 0.20 mm (0.008 in), whichever is greater. Seams extending into the heads and flanges of fasteners which do not open beyond the limits specified for bursts are acceptable. (See 3.2 and Figure 3.)

4.6 Bursts and Shear Bursts

4.6.1 No burst in the flats of hex bolts and screws shall extend into the top crown of head surface (chamfer circle) or the under head bearing surface. In addition, bursts occurring at the intersection of two wrenching flats shall not reduce the width across corners below the specified minimum.

4.6.2 Flanges of bolts and screws and peripheries of circular head products may have two or more bursts or shear bursts, providing that only one has a width greater than 0.040 F; in addition, this one burst shall not have a width exceeding 0.080 F.

4.6.3 Bursts in the raised periphery of indented head bolts and screws shall not exceed a width of 0.060 D or 0.40mm (0.015 in), whichever is greater, or have a depth extending into the indented portion. (See 3.3 and Figure 4.)

4.7 Voids on Bearing Surface—Voids on the bearing surface of bolts and screws shall not exceed a depth of 0.25mm (0.010 in), and the combined area of all voids shall not exceed 10% of the specified minimum area of the bearing surface. The method for determining area of voids shall be as agreed upon by purchaser and producer. (See 3.5 and Figure 5.)

4.8 Tool Marks—Tool marks on the bearing surface shall not exceed surface roughness measurement of 2.8 μm (110 μin) determined as the arithmetic average deviation from the mean surface. (See 3.7 and Figure 7.)

4.9 Nicks and Gouges—Nicks and gouges located in the threaded length shall not be of size and number which will interfere with assembly of the proper GO thread gage on the thread with the application of not more than 0.05 times DN·m (12 times D in-lb) of torque, where D is the nominal bolt, screw, or stud size in inches. The manufacturer shall exercise due care during the manufacture and handling of parts to minimize the number and magnitude of nicks and gouges.

5. Inspection Procedure—Bolts, screws, and studs shall be inspected. For referee purposes, unless otherwise specified by purchaser, inspection shall be in accordance with the procedures outlined in 5.1 and 5.2.

5.1 Visual Inspection—A representative sample with a size as given in Table 1 shall be picked at random from the lot. The sample shall be examined visually for quench cracks, bursts, shear bursts, forging cracks, folds, tool marks, seams, voids on the bearing surface, and nicks and gouges.

TABLE 1—SAMPLE SIZE FOR VISUAL AND SEAM INSPECTION

Lot Size	Sample Size Visual and Nondestructive Techniques	Sample Size Destructive Techniques
Up to 1 500, incl	15	2
1 501 to 5 000	25	3
5 001 to 15 000	50	5
15 001 to 50 000	75	8
50 001 and over	100	10

5.1.1 If any part is found with quench cracks or with folds at internal corners at or below the bearing surface, the lot shall be subject to rejection.

5.1.2 If any part is found with seams, bursts, shear bursts, forging cracks, tool marks, voids, or nicks and gouges which exceed the allowable limits as specified for the applicable type of discontinuity under Section 4, the lot shall be subject to rejection.

5.2 Seam Inspection—A representative sample with a size as given in Table 1 (if acceptable by visual inspection) shall then be examined for seams by deep (surface) acid etch or magnetic inspection techniques (Magna-glo, Magnaflux, eddy current, etc.). NOTE—Other examining procedures may be used providing they have an ability to detect discontinuities of the size specified in 4.5.

NOTE—During this inspection, attention should also be given to examining the product for indications showing transverse quench cracks or folds in internal corners as these discontinuities are sometimes not readily seen in visual examination.)

5.2.1 All parts showing indications which could be interpreted as seams shall be set aside. From this group, a secondary sample with a size as given in Table 2 shall be picked at random and each part in this sample sectioned through the shank perpendicular to the axis and etched for microscopic examination. The section should be through the unthreaded body adjacent to the thread runout. For bolts and screws which are threaded to the head, the section should be taken where the seam indication intersects the root of the thread at a distance of approximately 1 D from the underside of the head, where D is nominal size of bolt or screw. (A recommended procedure is outlined in ASTM E 3). If during the microscopic examination any part is found having a seam with a depth in excess of the limit specified in 4.5, the lot shall be subject to rejection.

TABLE 2—SAMPLE SIZE FOR MICROSCOPIC EXAMINATION OF PRODUCTS WITH SEAM INDICATIONS

Number of Products Showing Seam Indications	Sample Size
1	1
2 to 8	2
9 to 15	3
16 to 25	5
26 to 50	8
51 to 90	13
91 to 100	20

R) SURFACE DISCONTINUITIES ON BOLTS, SCREWS, AND STUDS IN FATIGUE APPLICATIONS—SAE J123 MAR1994

SAE Recommended Practice

Report of the SAE Iron and Steel Technical Committee approved September 1973 and revised June 1976. Completely revised by the SAE Fasteners Committee March 1994.

Foreword—This Document has not changed other than to put it into the new SAE Technical Standards Board Format.

1. Scope—This SAE Recommended Practice defines, illustrates, and specifies allowable limits for various types of surface discontinuities that may occur or become apparent during the manufacture and processing of bolts, screws, and studs which are primarily intended for use in automotive assemblies subjected to severe dynamic stresses and necessitating use of high strength fasteners having appropriate fatigue-resistant properties.

1.1 The basic document does not include inspection sampling requirements. It is intended that the purchaser shall specify, in the original inquiry and purchase order, the inspection sampling requirements which the producer must satisfy to demonstrate the acceptability of bolts and screws with respect to surface discontinuities. Appendix A outlines inspection sampling plans applicable when such requirements are not specified by the purchaser in the original inquiry, purchase order, or in related specifications.

1.2 When the provisions of this document are specified by the purchaser, the fastener manufacturer must significantly increase production controls including machine set up, blank diameters, die lubrication, in-process inspection requirements, and reduced production rate.

2. References

2.1 Applicable Publication—The following publication forms a part of this specification to the extent specified herein.

2.1.1 ASTM PUBLICATION—Available from ASTM, 100 Barr Harbor Drive, West Conshohocken, PA 19428-2959.

ASTM E 3—Methods of Preparing Metallographic Specimens

3. Types of Surface Discontinuities—For the purpose of this document, surface discontinuities on bolts, screws, and studs are divided into ten "types," defined as follows:

3.1 Crack—A crack is a clean (crystalline) fracture passing through or across the grain boundaries without inclusion of foreign elements. Cracks are normally caused by overstressing the metal during forging or other forming operation, or during heat treatment. Where parts are subjected to significant reheating, cracks usually are discolored by scale.

3.1.1 QUENCH CRACKS—Quench cracks may occur during heat treatment due to excessively high thermal and transformation stresses. They usually traverse an irregular and erratic course on the surface of the fastener. Typical quench cracks are shown in Figure 1.

3.1.2 FORGING CRACKS—Forging cracks may occur during the cutoff or forging operations and are located on the top of the heads of screws and bolts. Typical forging cracks are shown in Figure 2.

3.2 Seam—Seams are generally inherent in the raw material from which fasteners are manufactured. They are narrow, generally straight or smooth-curved line discontinuities, running longitudinally on the shank and/or thread. Seams may extend onto the tops of the heads of circular head products as well as being present at the periphery of the head. Seams may also extend into the chamfer circle, washer face, and wrenching flats of hex head products. Typical seams are shown in Figure 3.

3.3 Burst—A burst is an open break in the metal (material). Bursts may occur on the flats or corners of the heads of bolts and screws, at the periphery of flanged or circular head products, or on the raised periphery of indented head bolts and screws. Typical bursts are shown in Figure 4.

3.4 Shear Burst—A shear burst is an open break in the metal, occurring most frequently at the periphery of products having circular or flanged heads and are generally located at approximately 45 degrees to the product axis. Shear bursts may also occur on the sides of hex head products. Typical discontinuities of this type are shown in Figure 4.

3.5 Void—A void is a shallow pocket or hollow on the surface of the bolt or screw due to nonfilling of metal during forging or upsetting. Typical voids are shown in Figure 5.

3.6 Lap—A lap is a fold-over of metal in the threads of screws, bolts, and studs. If laps occur, they generally show a pattern of consistency between the product, that is, laps will be identically located and with the same direction of traverse between all product. Typical laps in external threads are shown in Figure 6A.

3.7 Fold—A fold is a doubling over of metal which may occur during the forging operation. Folds may occur at or near the intersection of diameter changes and are especially prevalent with noncircular necks, shoulders, and heads. Typical folds are shown in Figure 7.

3.8 Tool Marks—Tool marks are longitudinal or circumferential grooves of shallow depth produced by the movement of manufacturing tools over the surface of the fastener. Typical tool marks are shown in Figure 8.

3.9 Nick or Gouge—A nick or gouge is an indentation on the surface of the fastener, produced by forceful abrasion or the impact of product coming into contact with other product or manufacturing equipment during manufacture.

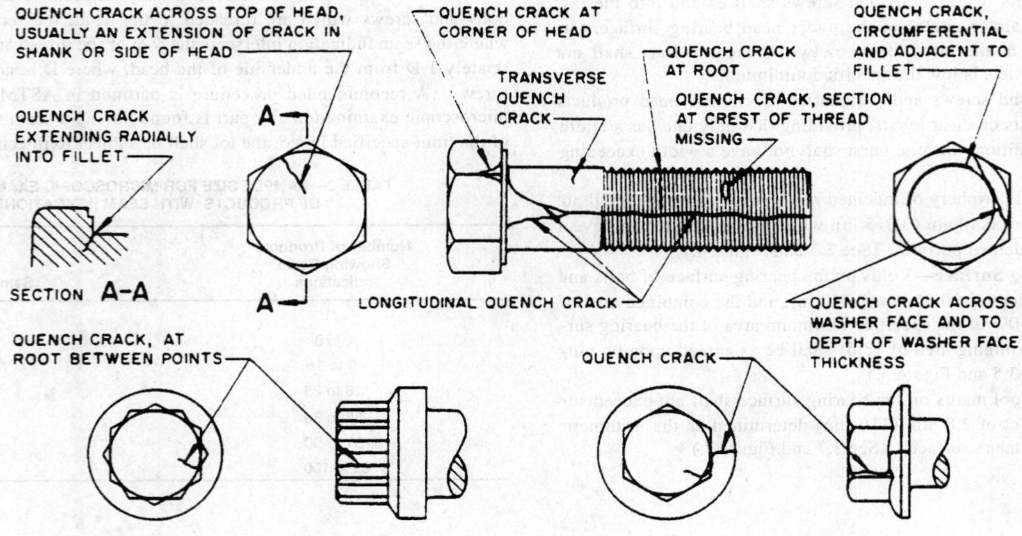

NOTE—Quench cracks of any depth, any length, or in any location are not permissible discontinuities.

FIGURE 1—TYPICAL QUENCH CRACKS

4. Limits for Surface Discontinuities

4.1 Letter Definitions—Throughout the following requirements, D designates the nominal size (basic major diameter of thread) of bolts, screws, and studs, except for bolts and screws with shoulders, in which case D designates the largest shoulder diameter. F designates the nominal flange diameter or head diameter of products having circular heads. For metric-series products, use millimeter; for inch-series products, use inch.

4.2 Quench Cracks—Quench cracks of any depth, any length, or in any location, are not permitted. (See 3.1.1 and Figure 1.)

4.3 Laps in Screw Threads—Laps of any depth and any length which (a) are present in the root of the screw thread, or (b) originate on the flank, traverse toward the interior, and extend in depth below the pitch line of the bolt, screw, or stud, or (c) originate below the pitch line on the pressure flank and traverse toward the major diameter, are not permitted. (This requirement is not applicable to tapping screws having spaced threads.) (See 3.6 and Figure 6A.) When approved by the purchaser, marks on threads caused by the serrations on thread rolling dies (see Figure 6B) shall be excluded from these requirements.

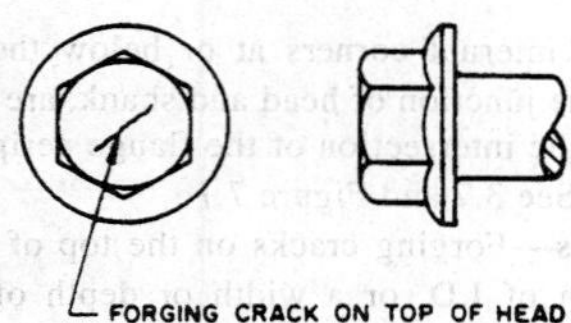

NOTE—Forging cracks are permissible discontinuities if within the limits specified in 4.5.

FIGURE 2—TYPICAL FORGING CRACKS

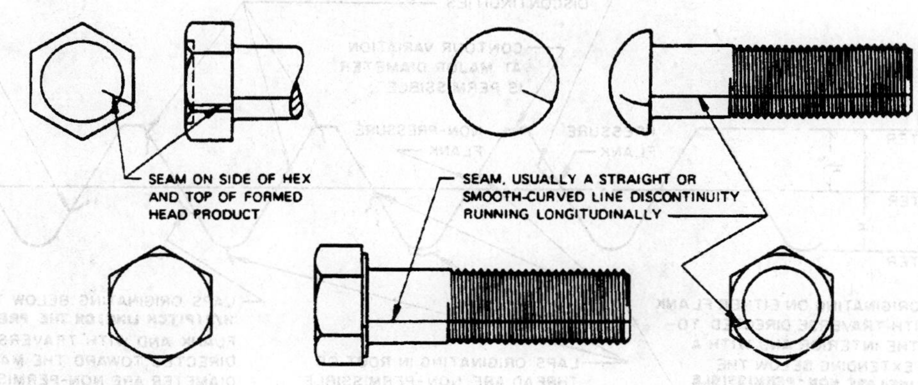

NOTE—Seams are permissible discontinuities if within the limits specified in 4.4.

FIGURE 3—TYPICAL SEAMS

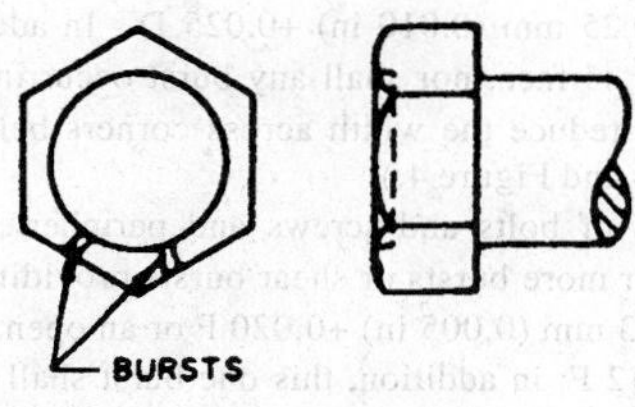

NOTE—Bursts in raised periphery of indented head bolts and screws are permissible discontinuities if within the limits specified in 4.7.3.

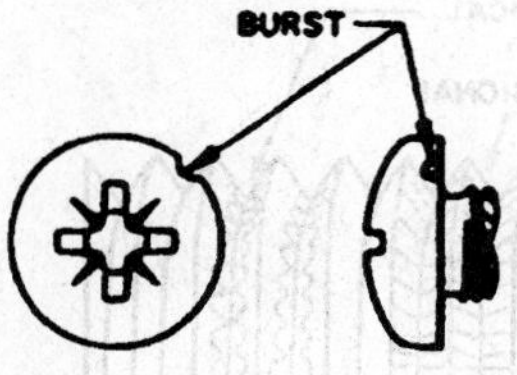

NOTE—Bursts in circular head products, with or without recess, are permissible discontinuities if within the limits specified in 4.7.2.

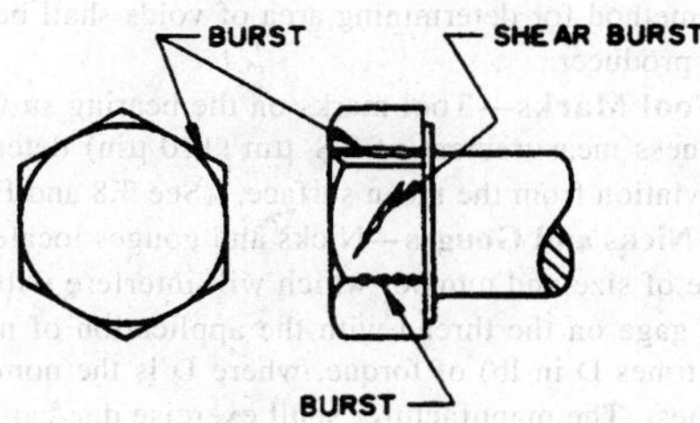

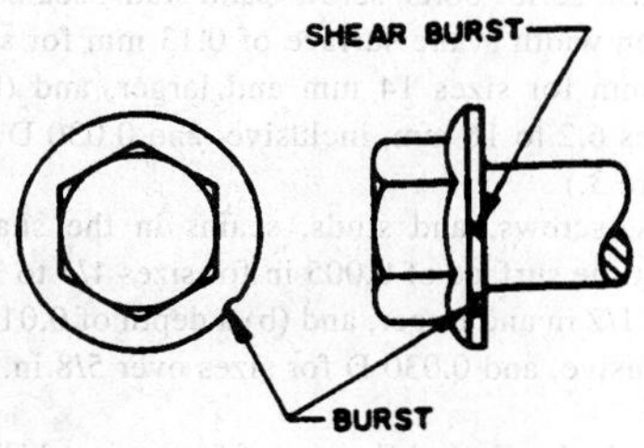

NOTE—Bursts and shear bursts are permissible discontinuities if within the limits specified in 4.7.

FIGURE 4—TYPICAL BURSTS AND SHEAR BURSTS

4.4 Folds

4.4.1 Folds located in internal corners at or below the bearing surface, for example, in the fillet at the junction of head and shank, are not permitted.

4.4.2 Folds located at the intersection of the flange periphery and bearing surface, are not permitted. (See 3.7 and Figure 7.)

4.5 Forging Cracks—Forging cracks on the top of head bolts and screws shall not exceed a length of I.D. or a width or depth of 0.20 mm (0.008 in) +0.010 D.

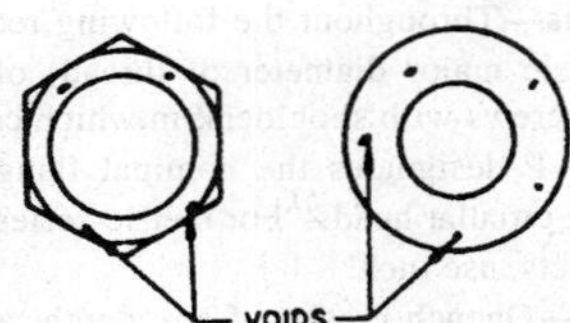

NOTE—Voids are permissible discontinuities if within the limits specified in 4.8.

FIGURE 5—TYPICAL VOIDS ON BEARING SURFACE

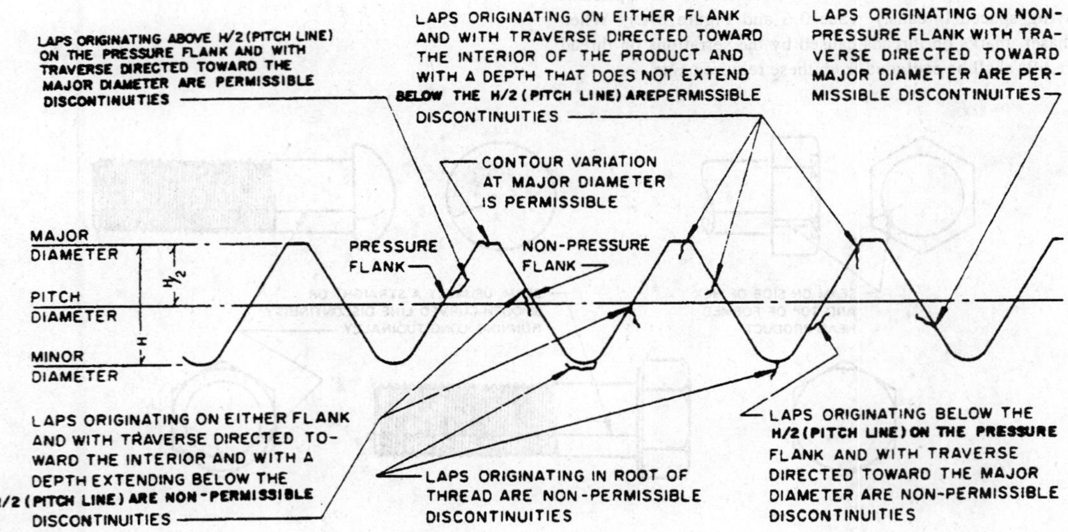

NOTE—These requirements apply to all bolts and screws except tapping screws with spaced threads.

FIGURE 6A—SURFACE DISCONTINUITIES IN EXTERNAL SCREW THREADS

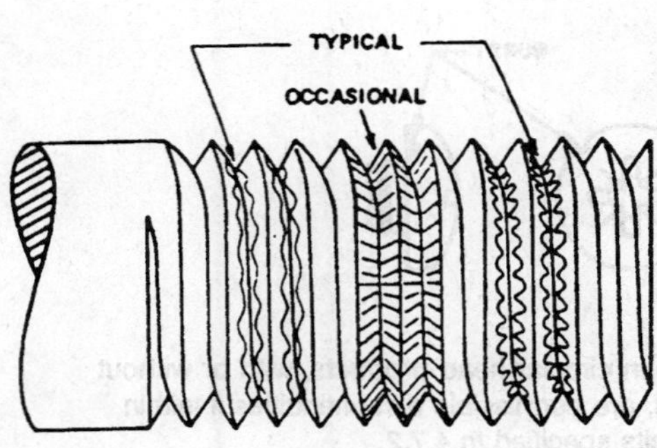

FIGURE 6B—STARTING SERRATION MARKS

4.6 Seams—For metric-series bolts, screws, and studs, seams in the shanks shall not exceed (a) an open width at the surface of 0.13 mm for sizes 6.3 to 12 mm, inclusive, and 0.25 mm for sizes 14 mm and larger, and (b) a depth of 0.015 D +0.10 mm for sizes 6.2 to 16 mm, inclusive, and 0.030 D for sizes over 16 mm. (See 3.2 and Figure 3.)

For inch-series bolts, screws, and studs, seams in the shanks shall not exceed (a) an open width at the surface of 0.005 in for sizes 1/4 to 7/16 in, inclusive, and 0.010 in for sizes 1/2 in and larger, and (b) a depth of 0.015 D +0.004 in for sizes 1/4 to 5/8 in, inclusive, and 0.030 D for sizes over 5/8 in. (See 3.2 and Figure 3.)

Seams extending into the heads and flanges of fasteners which do not open beyond the limits specified for bursts are acceptable.

4.7 Bursts and Shear Bursts

4.7.1 Bursts in the flats of hex bolts and screws shall not exceed a width or an open depth of 0.25 mm (0.010 in) +0.025 D. In addition, no burst shall extend into the bearing surface, nor shall any burst occurring at the intersection of two wrenching flats reduce the width across corners below the specified minimum. (See 3.3 and 3.4 and Figure 4.)

4.7.2 Flanges of bolts and screws and peripheries of circular head products may have two or more bursts or shear bursts providing that only one has a width greater than 0.13 mm (0.005 in) +0.020 F or an open depth greater than 0.08 mm (0.003 in) +0.012 F; in addition, this one burst shall not have a width exceeding 0.25 mm (0.010 in) +0.040 F or an open depth of 0.15 mm (0.006 in) +0.024 F.

4.7.3 Bursts in the raised periphery of indented head bolts and screws shall not exceed a width of 0.25 mm (0.010in) +0.020 D, or have a depth greater than the height of the raised periphery. (See 3.3 and Figure 4.)

4.8 Voids on Bearing Surface—Voids on the bearing surface of bolts and screws shall not exceed a depth of 0.25mm (0.010 in) and the combined area of all voids shall not exceed 5% of the specified minimum area of the bearing surface. The method for determining area of voids shall be as agreed upon by purchaser and producer.

4.9 Tool Marks—Tool marks on the bearing surface shall not exceed surface roughness measurement of 2.8 μm (110 μin) determined as the arithmetic average deviation from the mean surface. (See 3.8 and Figure 8).

4.10 Nicks and Gouges—Nicks and gouges located in the threaded length shall not be of size and number which will interfere with assembly of the proper GO thread gage on the thread with the application of not more than 0.06 times DN·m (12 times D in-lb) of torque, where D is the nominal bolt, screw, or stud size in inches. The manufacturer shall exercise due care during the manufacture and handling of parts to minimize the number and magnitude of nicks and gouges.

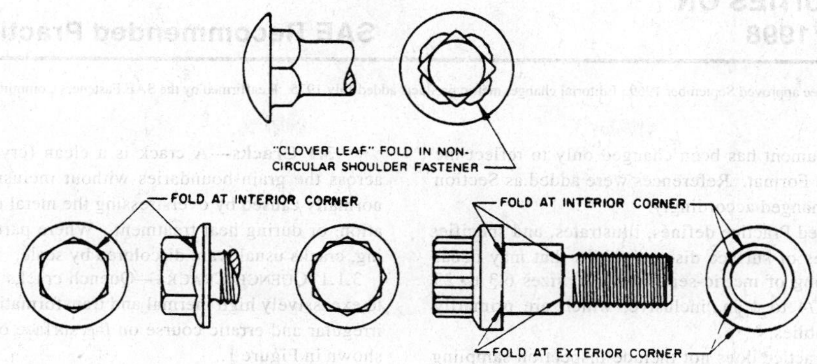

NOTE—Folds in interior corners at or below the bearing surface are not permissible discontinuities. Folds at exterior corners are permissible discontinuities if within the limits specified in 4.4.

FIGURE 7—TYPICAL FOLDS

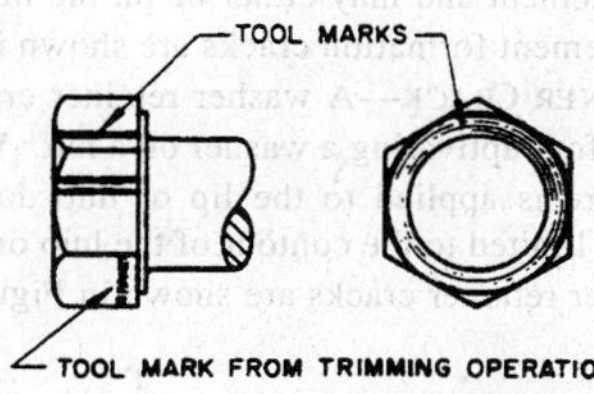

NOTE—Tool marks are permissible discontinuities if within the limits specified in 4.9.

FIGURE 8—TYPICAL TOOL MARKS

5. Inspection Procedure—Bolts, screws, and studs shall be inspected in accordance with the procedures outlined in 5.1 and 5.2, unless otherwise specified by purchaser.

5.1 Visual Inspection— A representative sample [1] shall be picked at random from the lot. The sample shall be examined visually for quench cracks, bursts, shear bursts, forging cracks, folds, tool marks, seams, voids on the bearing surface, and nicks and gouges.

5.1.1 If any part is found with quench cracks or with folds at internal corners at or below the bearing surface, the lot shall be subject to rejection.

5.1.2 If any part is found with seams, bursts, shear bursts, forging cracks, tool marks, voids, or nicks and gouges which exceed the allowable limits as specified for the applicable type of discontinuity under Section 4, the lot shall be subject to rejection.

5.2 Seam and Lap Inspection—The same sample (if acceptable by visual inspection) shall then be further examined for laps in threads and seams by deep (surface) acid etch.

NOTE—Other examining procedures may be used providing they have an equivalent ability to detect discontinuities of the size specified in 4.3 and 4.6.

5.2.1 All parts showing indications which could be interpreted as seams shall be set aside. From this group, a secondary sample [1] shall be picked at random and each part in this sample sectioned through the shank perpendicular to the axis and etched for microscopic examination. The section should be through the unthreaded body adjacent to the thread runout. For bolts and screws which are threaded to the head, the section should be taken where the seam indication intersects the root of the thread at a distance of approximately one D from the underside of the head, where D is nominal size of bolt or screw. (A recommended procedure is outlined in ASTM E 3.) If during the microscopic examination any part is found having a seam with a depth in excess of the limit specified in 4.6, the lot shall be subject to rejection.

5.2.2 LAPS IN SCREW THREADS—All products showing indications of laps in the threads shall be set aside. During this inspection, attention should also be given to examining the product for indications showing transverse quench cracks or folds in internal corners as these discontinuities are sometimes not readily seen in visual examination. From the products set aside, five specimens shall be selected at random, surface etched, and examined visually to determine that the pattern of laps is reasonably consistent between products. One of the five specimens shall be sectioned longitudinally on the centerline of the part and on a plane passing through the point at which any lap extends closest to the minor diameter of the thread and the section etched for microscopic examination. If during the microscopic examination any lap is found with a location and direction of traverse which classifies the lap as nonpermissible, the lot shall be subject to rejection.

1. See Appendix A.

APPENDIX A
SAMPLING PLAN

A.1 Scope—This Appendix outlines inspection sampling plans applicable when the purchaser has not specified a plan or plans in the original inquiry or purchase order, or in related specifications.

A.2 Sample size for inspection of surface discontinuities is as shown in Table A1:

TABLE A1—SAMPLE SIZE FOR INSPECTION OF SURFACE DISCONTINUITIES

Lot Size	Sample Size
Up to 1500 incl	15
1501 to 5000	25
5001 to 15 000	50
15 001 to 50 000	75
50 001 and over	100

A.3 Sample size for microscopic examination of products with seam indications is as shown in Table A2:

TABLE A2—SAMPLE SIZE FOR MICROSCOPIC EXAMINATION OF PRODUCTS WITH SEAM INDICATIONS

Number of Products Showing Seam Indications	Sample Size
1	1
2 to 8	2
9 to 15	3
16 to 25	5
26 to 50	8
51 to 90	13
91 to 100	20

SURFACE DISCONTINUITIES ON NUTS—SAE J122 MAY1998

SAE Recommended Practice

Report of SAE Iron and Steel Technical Committee approved September 1969. Editorial change; metric products added July 1975. Reaffirmed by the SAE Fasteners Committee May 1998.

Foreword—This Reaffirmed Document has been changed only to reflect the new SAE Technical Standards Board Format. References were added as Section 2. All other Section numbers have changed accordingly.

1. Scope—This SAE Recommended Practice defines, illustrates, and specifies allowable limits for the various types of surface discontinuities that may occur during the manufacture and processing of metric-series nuts, in sizes 6.3 to 25 mm and inch-series nuts in sizes 1/4 to 1 in, inclusive, which are primarily intended for use in automotive assemblies.

1.1 The basic recommended practice does not include inspection sampling requirements. It is intended that the purchaser shall specify in the original inquiry and purchase order the inspection sampling requirements which the producer must satisfy to demonstrate the acceptability of nuts with respect to surface discontinuities. Appendix A outlines inspection sampling plans applicable when such requirements are not specified by the purchaser in the original inquiry and purchase order.

2. References

2.1 Applicable Publication—The following publication forms a part of this specification to the extent specified herein. Unless otherwise indicated, the latest issue of SAE publications shall apply.

2.1.1 ASTM PUBLICATION—Available from ASTM, 100 Barr Harbor Drive, West Conshohocken, PA 19428-2959.

ASTM A 194—Steel Nuts for High Pressure and High Temperature Service

3. Types of Surface Discontinuities—For the purpose of this recommended practice, surface discontinuities on nuts are divided into 11 "types," defined as follows:

3.1 Cracks—A crack is a clean (crystalline) fracture passing through or across the grain boundaries without inclusion of foreign elements. Cracks are normally caused by overstressing the metal during forging or other forming operation, or during heat treatment. Where parts are subjected to significant reheating, cracks usually are discolored by scale.

3.1.1 QUENCH CRACKS—Quench cracks may occur during heat treatment due to excessively high thermal and transformation stresses. They usually traverse an irregular and erratic course on the surface of the nut. Typical quench cracks are shown in Figure 1.

3.1.2 FORGING CRACKS—Forging cracks may occur during the cutoff or forging operations and are located on the top and bottom face of the nut, and at the intersection of the face and flat. Typical forging cracks are shown in Figure 2.

3.1.3 LOCKING ELEMENT FORMATION CRACKS—These cracks may occur due to the application of pressure against the nut when introducing the locking element into prevailing torque nuts. Cracks of this type are usually located in the vicinity of the locking element and may either be on the internal or external surface. Typical locking element formation cracks are shown in Figure 3.

3.1.4 WASHER RETAINER CRACK—A washer retainer crack is an opening in a lip or hub of metal used for captivating a washer on a nut. Washer retainer cracks may occur when pressure is applied to the lip or hub during assembly of the washer. Such cracks are limited to the contour of the hub or lip used for retaining purposes. Typical washer retainer cracks are shown in Figure 5.

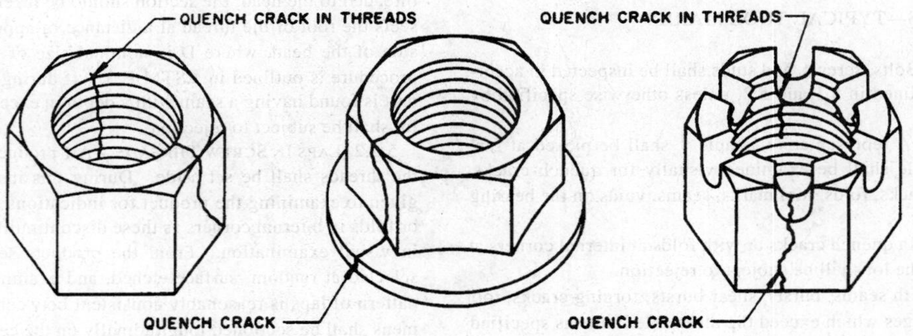

FIGURE 1—TYPICAL QUENCH CRACKS

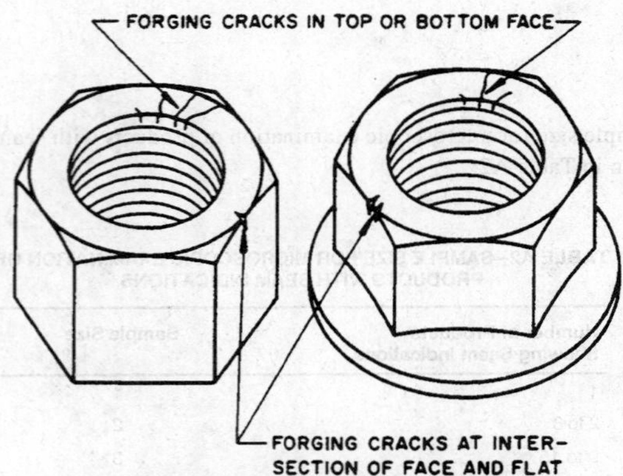

FIGURE 2—TYPICAL FORGING CRACKS

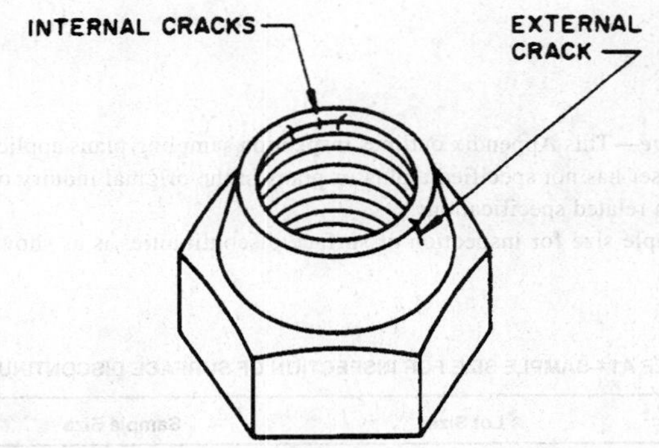

FIGURE 3—TYPICAL LOCKING ELEMENT FORMATION CRACKS ON PREVAILING-TORQUE NUTS

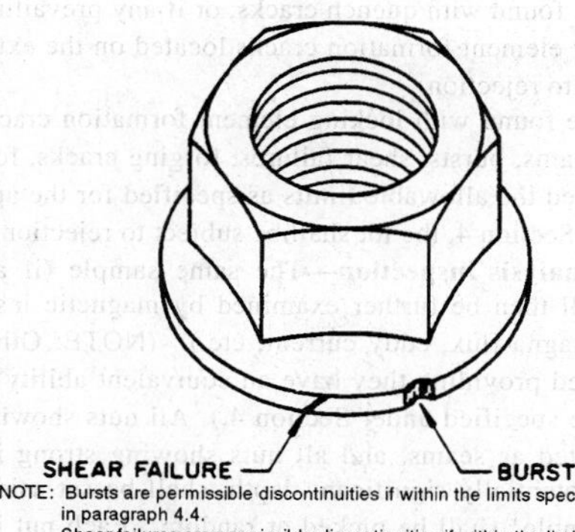

NOTE: Bursts are permissible discontinuities if within the limits specified in paragraph 4.4.
Shear failures are permissible discontinuities if within the limits specified in paragraph 4.5.

FIGURE 4—TYPICAL BURST AND SHEAR FAILURES ON FLANGED NUTS

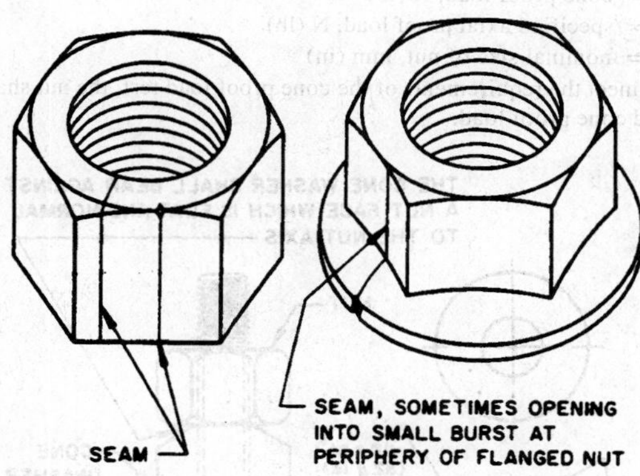

NOTE: Washer retainer cracks are permissible discontinuities.

FIGURE 5—TYPICAL WASHER RETAINER CRACKS

3.2 Seams—A seam is a narrow continuous discontinuity in the metal. Seams are generally inherent in the raw material from which the nut is made. Seams in nuts are usually straight or smooth curved line discontinuities running generally parallel to the nut axis. Typical seams are shown in Figure 6.

NOTE: Seams are permissible discontinuities only if within the limits specified in paragraph 4.3.1.

FIGURE 6—TYPICAL SEAMS

3.3 Bursts—A burst is an open break in the metal. Bursts may occur at the periphery of flanged nuts. A typical burst is shown in Figure 4.

3.4 Shear Failures—A shear failure is an open break in the metal, located at the periphery of flanged nuts and approximately at a 45 degree angle to the nut axis. Shear failures occur most frequently with flanged nuts and are due to overstressing the metal during forging. A typical shear failure is shown in Figure 4.

3.5 Folds—A fold is a doubling over of metal which may occur during the forging operation. Folds in nuts may occur at or near the intersection of diameter changes or on the top or bottom face of the nut. Typical folds are shown in Figure 7.

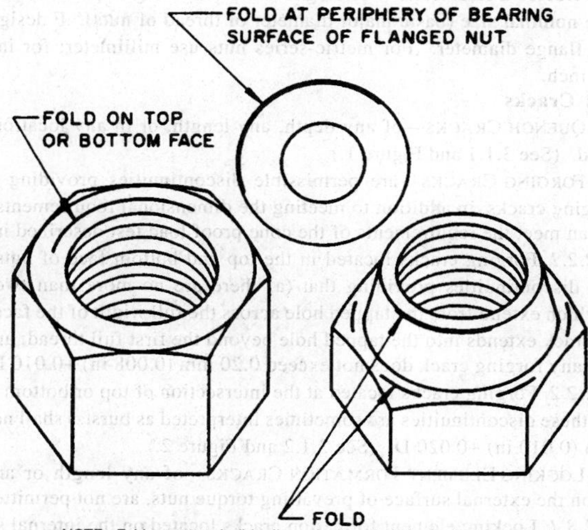

NOTE: Folds are permissible discontinuities if within the limits specified in paragraph 4.6.

FIGURE 7—TYPICAL FOLDS

3.6 Voids—A void is a shallow pocket or hollow on the surface of the nut due to nonfilling of metal during forging. Typical voids are shown in Figure 8.

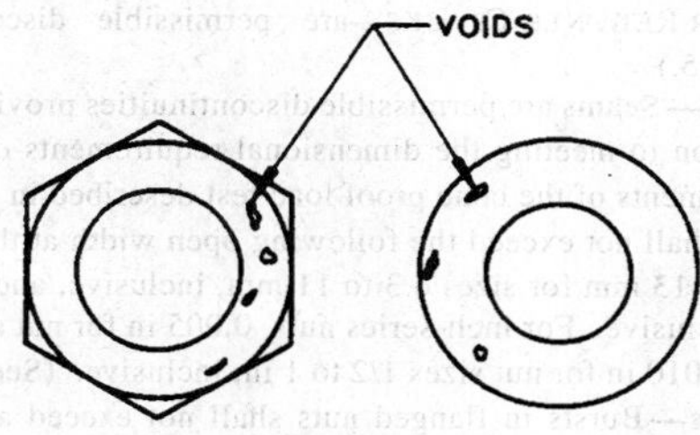

NOTE: Voids on the bearing surface of nuts are permissible if within the limits specified in paragraph 4.7.

FIGURE 8—TYPICAL VOIDS ON BEARING SURFACES

3.7 Tool Marks—Tool marks are longitudinal or circumferential grooves of shallow depth, produced by the movement of manufacturing tools over the surface of the nut. Typical tool marks are shown in Figure 9.

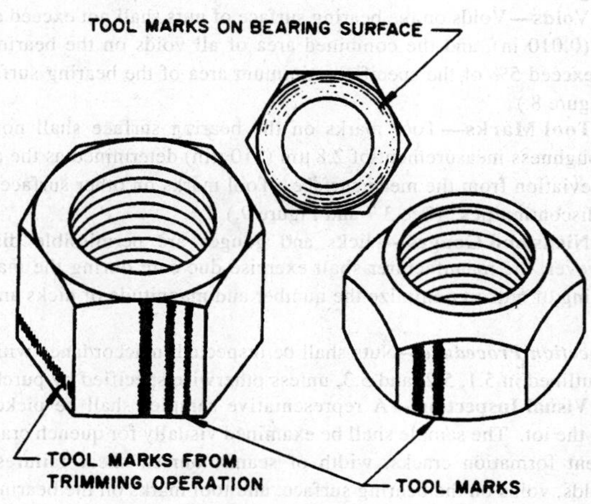

NOTE: Tool marks are permissible discontinuities if within the limits specified in paragraph 4.8.

FIGURE 9—TYPICAL TOOL MARKS

3.8 Nicks or Gouges—A nick or gouge is an indentation on the surface of a nut, produced by forceful abrasion or the impact of product coming into contact with other product or manufacturing equipment during manufacture.

4. Limits for Surface Discontinuities

4.1 Letter Definitions—Throughout the following requirements, D designates the nominal size (basic major diameter of thread of nuts). F designates the nominal flange diameter. For metric-series nuts use millimeter; for inch-series nuts use inch.

4.2 Cracks

4.2.1 QUENCH CRACKS—of any depth, any length, or in any location, are not permitted. (See 3.1.1 and Figure 1.)

4.2.2 FORGING CRACKS—are permissible discontinuities providing that nuts with forging cracks, in addition to meeting the dimensional requirements detailed below, can meet the requirements of the cone proof load test described in 5.3.

4.2.2.1 Forging cracks located in the top and bottom face of nuts are permissible discontinuities providing that (a) there are no more than two forging cracks which extend from the tapped hole across the full width of the faces; (b) no forging crack extends into the tapped hole beyond the first full thread; and (c) the width of any forging crack does not exceed 0.20 mm (0.008 in) +0.010 D.

4.2.2.2 Forging cracks located at the intersection of top or bottom face with the flat (these discontinuities are sometimes interpreted as bursts) shall not exceed 0.25 mm (0.010 in) +0.020 D. (See 3.1.2 and Figure 2.)

4.2.3 LOCKING ELEMENT FORMATION CRACKS—of any length or any depth, located on the external surface of prevailing torque nuts, are not permitted.

4.2.3.1 Locking element formation cracks located on the internal surface of prevailing torque nuts shall not exceed two thread pitches in length; shall not extend into the thread root; and the width of any crack shall not exceed the following: For metric-series nut, 0.18 mm for sizes 6.3 to 11 mm, inclusive, and 0.25 mm for sizes 12 to 25 mm, inclusive. For inch-series nuts, 0.007 in for sizes 1/4 to 7/16 in, inclusive, and 0.010 in for sizes 1/2 to 1 in, inclusive. (See 3.1.3 and Figure 3.)

4.2.4 WASHER RETAINER CRACKS—are permissible discontinuities. (See 3.1.4 and Figure 5.)

4.3 Seams—Seams are permissible discontinuities providing that nuts with seams, in addition to meeting the dimensional requirements detailed below, can meet the requirements of the cone proof load test described in 5.3.

4.3.1 Seams shall not exceed the following open width at the surface; for metric-series nuts, 0.13 mm for sizes 6.3 to 11 mm, inclusive, and 0.25 mm for sizes 12 to 25 mm, inclusive. For inch-series nuts, 0.005 in for nut sizes 1/4 to 7/16 in, inclusive, and 0.010 in for nut sizes 1/2 to 1 in, inclusive. (See 3.2 and Figure 6.)

4.4 Bursts—Bursts in flanged nuts shall not exceed a width of 0.13 mm (0.005 in) +0.020 F or an open depth of 0.08 mm (0.003 in) +0.012 F, except that one burst may have a width no greater than 0.25 mm (0.010 in) +0.040 F, or an open depth no greater than 0.15 mm (0.006 in) +0.024 F. (See 3.3 and Figure 4.)

4.5 Shear Failures—Shear failures on flanged nuts shall not exceed a width of 0.020 F or a depth of 0.030 F. (See 3.4 and Figure 4.)

4.6 Folds—Folds located at the intersection of the flange periphery and bearing surface of flanged nuts shall not project below the bearing surface. (See 3.5 and Figure 7.)

4.7 Voids—Voids on the bearing surface of nuts shall not exceed a depth of 0.25 mm (0.010 in), and the combined area of all voids on the bearing surface shall not exceed 5% of the specified minimum area of the bearing surface. (See 3.6 and Figure 8.)

4.8 Tool Marks—Tool marks on the bearing surface shall not exceed a surface roughness measurement of 2.8 μm (110 μin) determined as the arithmetic average deviation from the mean surface. Tool marks on other surfaces are permissible discontinuities. (See 3.7 and Figure 9.)

4.9 Nicks and Gouges—Nicks and gouges are permissible discontinuities; however, the manufacturer shall exercise due care during the manufacture and handling of nuts to minimize the number and magnitude of nicks and gouges. (See 3.8.)

5. Inspection Procedure—Nuts shall be inspected in accordance with the procedures outlined in 5.1, 5.2, and 5.3, unless otherwise specified by purchaser.

5.1 Visual Inspection—A representative sample[1] shall be picked at random from the lot. The sample shall be examined visually for quench cracks, locking element formation cracks, width of seams, bursts, shear failures, forging cracks, folds, voids on the bearing surface, and tool marks on the bearing surface.

1. See Appendix.

5.1.1 If any nuts are found with quench cracks, or if any prevailing torque nuts are found with locking element formation cracks located on the external surface, the lot shall be subject to rejection.

5.1.2 If any nuts are found with locking element formation cracks located on the internal surface, seams, bursts, shear failures, forging cracks, folds, voids, or tool marks which exceed the allowable limits as specified for the applicable type of discontinuity under Section 4, the lot shall be subject to rejection.

5.2 Magnetic Analysis Inspection—The same sample (if acceptable by visual inspection) shall then be further examined by magnetic inspection techniques (Magna-glo, Magna-flux, eddy current, etc.). (NOTE: Other examining procedures may be used providing they have an equivalent ability to detect discontinuities of the size specified under Section 4.) All nuts showing indications that could be interpreted as seams, and all nuts showing strong indications of forging cracks with potentially significant depth, shall be set aside. From this group a secondary sample[1] shall be picked at random. Each nut in this sample shall be cone proof load tested as outlined in 5.3. If any nut fails to meet the requirements of this test, the lot shall be subject to rejection.

5.3 Cone Proof Load Test—The purpose of the test[2] is to detect the presence of detrimental seams or forging cracks. The use of a conical washer and threaded mandrel, as illustrated in Figure 10, exaggerates the influence of such discontinuities on the load carrying ability of the nut by introducing a simultaneous dilation and stripping action on the nut.

5.3.1 The mandrel shall have a hardness of Rockwell C45 minimum. For metric-series nuts, the mandrel shall be threaded to class 5 g 6 g tolerances, except the minimum major diameter shall be the specified minimum major diameter for class 6 g, and the maximum major diameter shall be minimum major diameter plus 0.25 times the class 6 g major diameter tolerance; for inch-series nuts, the mandrel shall be threaded to Class 3A tolerance except that the major diameter shall be minimum major diameter with a tolerance of +0.002 in.

5.3.2 The cone washer shall have a hardness of Rockwell C57 minimum; a hole diameter equivalent to the nominal diameter of the mandrel, +0.05, –0 mm (+0.002, –0 in); and a flat contact point as follows: For metric-series nuts, 0.10–0.15 mm for sizes 6.3 through 12 mm, and 0.35–0.41 mm for sizes 14 through 25mm diameter; for inch-series nuts, 0.004–0.006 for sizes 1/4 through 1/2 in diameter, and 0.014–0.016 for sizes 1/2 through 1 in diameter.

5.3.3 The nut and the cone washer shall be assembled on mandrel, and the cone proof load for the nut shall be applied against the nut through the cone washer. The speed of testing, as determined with free running cross head, shall not exceed 3 mm/minute (0.125 in/minute). Loading shall be applied for 10 s the cone proof load of a nut shall be computed using the following formula:

$$PL_c = PL_a(1 - 0.3D) \qquad \text{(Eq. 1)}$$

where:

PL_c = cone proof load, N (lb)
PL_a = specified axial proof load, N (lb)
D = nominal size of nut, mm (in)

5.3.4 To meet the requirements of the cone proof load test, the nut shall support its specified cone proof load.

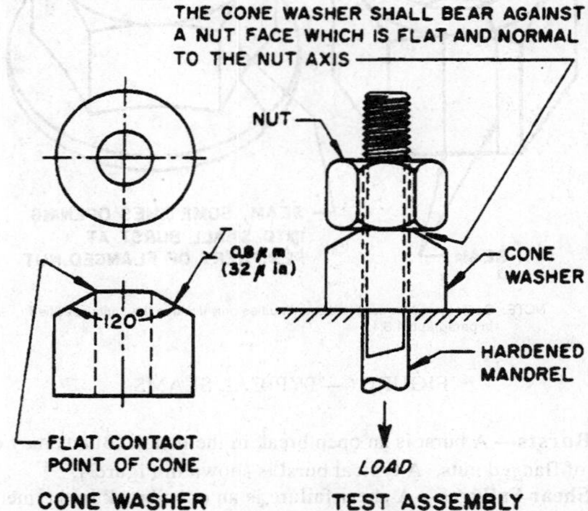

FIGURE 10—USE OF CONICAL WASHER AND THREADED MANDREL

2. Same as test specified in ASTM A 194, Steel Nuts for High Pressure and High Temperature Service.

APPENDIX A
SAMPLING PLAN

A.1 Scope—This appendix outlines inspection sampling plans applicable when the purchaser has not specified a plan or plans in the original inquiry or purchase order, or in related specifications.

A.2 Sample size for visual and magnetic analysis inspection of surface discontinuities is:

TABLE A1—SAMPLE SIZE FOR VISUAL AND MAGNETIC ANALYSIS INSPECTION OF SURFACE DISCONTINUITIES

Lot Size	Sample Size
Up to 1,500 include	15
1,501 to 5,000	25
5,001 to 15,000	50
15,001 to 50,000	75
50,001 and over	100

A.3 Sample size for cone proof load testing of products with seam and/or forging crack indications is:

TABLE A2—SAMPLE SIZE FOR CONE PROOF LOAD TESTING OF PRODUCTS WITH SEAM AND/OR FORGING CRACK INDICATIONS

Number of Products Showing Seam Indications	Sample Size
1	1
2 to 8	2
9 to 15	3
16 to 25	5
26 to 50	8
51 to 90	13
91 to 100	20

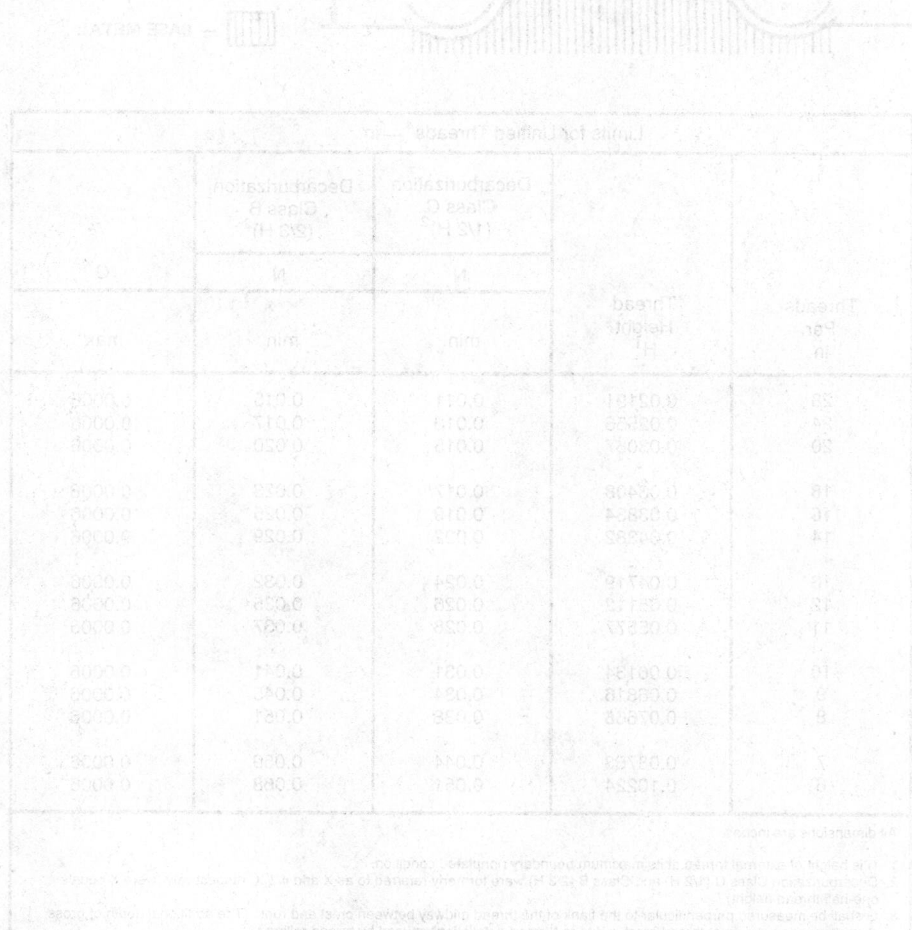

DECARBURIZATION IN HARDENED AND TEMPERED UNIFIED THREADED FASTENERS —SAE J121 APR1997

SAE Recommended Practice

1969-09 Rationale statement available.1997-04

Foreword—The changes to this document were made to comply with the new SAE Technical Standards Board format. They include making Definitions Section 3. All other section numbers have changed. Also Figure 2, measurement was changed from 0.0006 in to 0.005 in. This is the correct measurement.

1. Scope—This SAE Recommended Practice covers methods for measuring, classifying, and specifying decarburization in the threaded section of hardened and tempered steel bolts, screws, studs, and similar parts. It is not intended to cover products which are specifically carburized to achieve special properties.

2. References

2.1 Applicable Publications—The following publications form a part of this specification to the extent specified herein. Unless otherwise indicated, the latest issue of SAE publications shall apply.

2.1.1 SAE PUBLICATION—Available from SAE, 400 Commonwealth Drive, Warrendale, PA 15096-0001.

SAE J419—Methods of Measuring Decarburization

3. Definitions—According to SAE J419, "decarburization" is the loss of carbon at the surface of commercial ferrous materials which have been heated to facilitate fabrication or heated to modify mechanical properties. SAE J419 defines also "complete decarburization," "partial decarburization," and "effective decarburization," as related to unhardened steels. This document extends these definitions, as follows, to cover more specifically hardened and tempered steel bolts, screws, studs, and similar products.

3.1 Partial Decarburization—Decarburization with loss of carbon sufficient to cause a lighter shade of tempered martensite than that of the immediately adjacent base metal, when examined metallographically by the method outlined in 5.1, but insufficient carbon loss to show clearly defined ferrite grains. (The hardness traverse method, outlined in 5.2, is the referee method for determining that partial decarburization is not present at a point below that shown in Figure 1 for each classification.

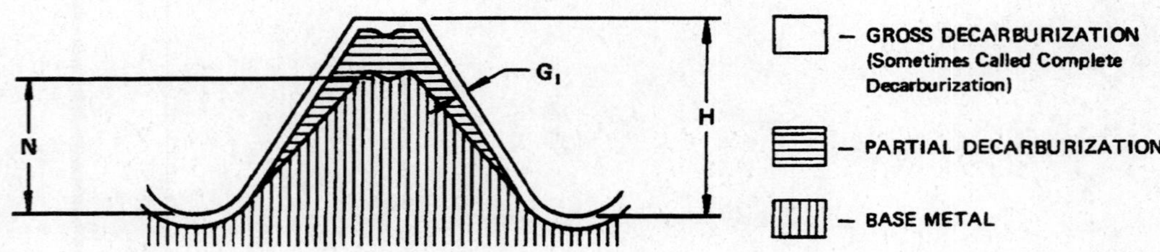

Limits for Unified Threads[4]— in				
		Decarburization Class C (1/2 H)[2]	Decarburization Class B (2/3 H)[2]	
		N	N	G[4]
Threads Per in	Thread Height H[1]	min	min	max
28	0.02191	0.011	0.015	0.0006
24	0.02556	0.013	0.017	0.0006
20	0.03067	0.015	0.020	0.0006
18	0.03408	0.017	0.023	0.0006
16	0.03834	0.019	0.025	0.0006
14	0.04382	0.022	0.029	0.0006
13	0.04719	0.024	0.032	0.0006
12	0.05112	0.026	0.035	0.0006
11	0.05577	0.028	0.037	0.0006
10	0.06134	0.031	0.041	0.0006
9	0.06816	0.034	0.045	0.0006
8	0.07668	0.038	0.051	0.0006
7	0.08763	0.044	0.059	0.0006
6	0.10224	0.051	0.068	0.0006

All dimensions are inches.

1. H is height of external thread at its maximum boundary nonplated condition.
2. Decarburization Class C (1/2 H) and Class B (2/3 H) were formerly referred to as X and 4/3 X, respectively (were X equals one-half thread height).
3. G shall be measured perpendicular to the flank of the thread midway between crest and root. (The additional depth of gross decarburization shown at thread crest is due to "thread enfoliation" caused by thread rolling.)
4. See Section 3 for limits applicable to other threaded products.

FIGURE 1—DECARBURIZATION LIMITS FOR COMMONLY USED ISO MODIFIED THREADS

3.2 Gross Decarburization—Decarburization with sufficient carbon loss to show only clearly-defined ferrite grains under metallographic examination by the method outlined in 5.1. This is sometimes called "Complete Decarburization."

3.3 Carbon Restoration—A process of restoring surface-carbon loss by heat-treating in an atmosphere furnace of properly controlled carbon potential. (This process is permitted but not recommended for threaded fasteners unless furnace atmosphere is adequately controlled.)

3.4 Carburization—A darker shade of tempered martensite than that of the immediately adjacent base metal, when examined metallographically by the method outlined in 5.1, and harder by at least 30 points (Knoop or Vickers DPH) than the hardness at root diameter when checked by the method outlined in 5.2. (The limits established by this document exclude this condition.)

3.5 Base-Metal Hardness—For purposes of this document, hardness at root diameter on a line bisecting the included angle of the thread (Position 1 in Figure 2) is considered "base-metal hardness."

4. Classes of Decarburization—This document establishes two classes of decarburization for inch-series threaded products. Each class is characterized by dimensional limits for decarburized zone, gross-decarburized zone, and/or base-carbon zone (as applied to longitudinal sections through the thread axis). Decarburization limits applicable to the more commonly used Unified Threads (in) are shown in Figure 1. Limits applicable to other threaded products are as follows:

a. For Class C (1/2 H)—N = 0.50 H; G = 0.0006 in
b. For Class B (2/3 H)—N = 0.67 H; G = 0.0006 in

NOTE—This document recognizes that the surface may vary in carbon content from the base-metal carbon content, and stipulates that this variation shall be either "partial decarburization" or "gross decarburization" or a "carbon-restored surface" to the extent allowed in Figure 1 for the different classes. "Carburization" is not permitted in the surface zone.

5. Methods for Measuring Decarburization—Two methods for measuring decarburization are provided. The microscopic method is intended primarily for routine inspection purposes. The hardness method is intended primarily for referee purposes. In the case of gross decarburization, however, only the microscopic method is applicable.

5.1 Microscopic Method[1]

5.1.1 SPECIMENS—Use longitudinal sections taken through the thread axis of the bolt, screw, or stud, after all heat-treating operations have been performed on the product. If specimens are prepared from surface-coated fasteners, care should be used when interpreting the substrate-coating interface.

5.1.2 PREPARATION

a. Mount specimen for grinding and polishing. Protection from rounding the surface to be examined is essential. The specimen should be mounted in a clamp or in a plastic mount, the latter being the preferred method.
b. After mounting, grind and polish the surface in accordance with good metallographic practice.
c. Etching in a 3% nital (concentrated nitric acid) or picral (saturated picric acid) is usually suitable for showing changes in microstructure caused by decarburization.

5.1.3 MEASUREMENT—Unless otherwise agreed on between purchaser and producer, examine at 100X magnification. Compare with Figure 1 and definitions in 3.1, 3.2, and 3.3.

If the microscope is of a type with a ground glass screen, the extent of decarburization can be measured directly with a scale. If an eye-piece is used for measurement, it should be an appropriate type containing a cross hair or a scale.

5.2 Hardness Method[2]

5.2.1 Prepare specimens as outlined in 5.1.1 and 5.1.2.

5.2.2 Determine hardness at three positions, as shown in Figure 2, using a Knoop indenter with a 500 g load or Vickers DPH with 300 g load.

5.2.3 Interpret hardness readings as follows:

a. A decrease of more than 30 hardness points from Position 1 to Position 2 indicates that the part does not conform to the classification specified.
b. An increase of more than 30 points between Position 1 and Position 3 is regarded as "carburization," and indicates that part does not conform to the classification specified.

NOTE—Careful differentiation must be made between an increase in hardness caused by carburization or by cold working the surface (such as form thread rolling).

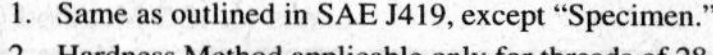

1. Same as outlined in SAE J419, except "Specimen."
2. Hardness Method applicable only for threads of 28 threads per inch and larger.

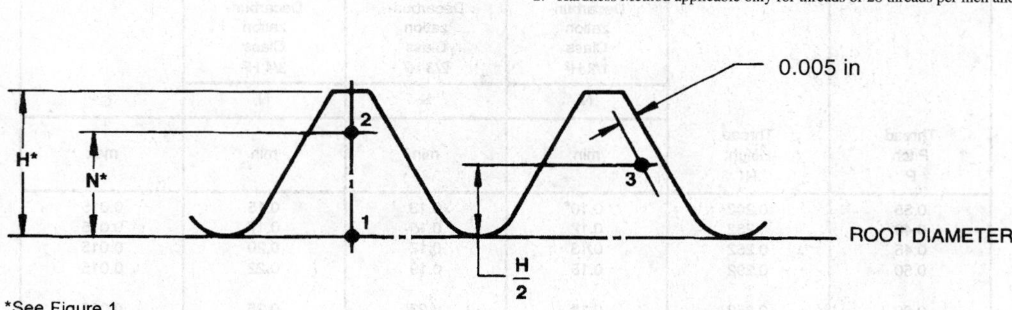

FIGURE 2—POSITIONS FOR DETERMINING HARDNESS

DECARBURIZATION IN HARDENED AND TEMPERED METRIC THREADED FASTENERS —SAE J121M APR97

SAE Recommended Practice

Report of the SAE Iron and Steel Technical Committee approved September 1969. Second revision, Division 29, August 1983. Completely revised by the SAE Fasteners Committee May 1994, and revised August 1996 and April 1997. Rationale statement available.

Foreword—The changes to this document were made to comply with the new SAE Technical Standards Board format. They include making Definitions Section 3. All other section numbers have changed. Also Figure 2, measurement was changed from 0.015 mm to 0.12 mm. This is the correct measurement.

1. Scope—This SAE Recommended Practice covers methods for measuring, classifying, and specifying decarburization in the threaded section of hardened and tempered steel bolts, screws, studs, and similar parts. It is not intended to cover products which are specifically carburized to achieve special properties.

2. References

2.1 Applicable Publications—The following publications form a part of this specification to the extent specified herein. Unless otherwise indicated, the latest issue of SAE publications shall apply.

2.1.1 SAE PUBLICATION—Available from SAE, 400 Commonwealth Drive, Warrendale, PA 15096-0001.

SAE J419—Methods of Measuring Decarburization

3. Definitions—According to SAE J419, "decarburization" is the loss of carbon at the surface of commercial ferrous materials which have been heated to facilitate fabrication or heated to modify mechanical properties. SAE J419 defines also "complete decarburization," "partial decarburization," and "effective decarburization," as related to unhardened steels. This document extends these definitions, as follows, to cover more specifically hardened and tempered steel bolts, screws, studs, and similar products.

3.1 Partial Decarburization—Decarburization with loss of carbon sufficient to cause a lighter shade of tempered martensite than that of the immediately adjacent base metal, when examined metallographically by the method outlined in 5.1, but insufficient carbon loss to show clearly defined ferrite graines. (The hardness traverse method, outlined in 5.2, is the referee method for determining that partial decarburization is not present at a point below that shown in Figure 1 for each classification.

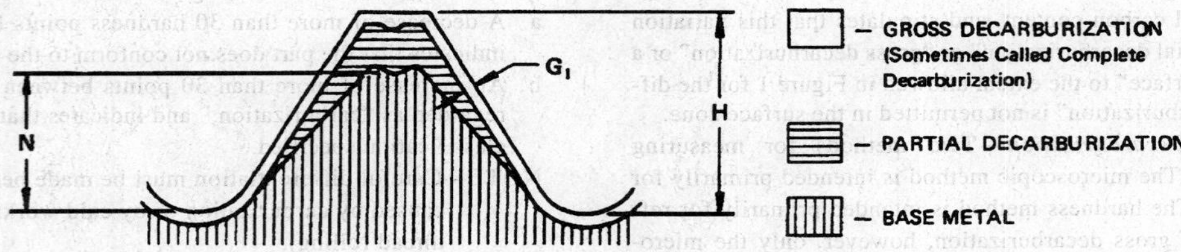

Limits for ISO Modified (OMFS) Metric Threads[4]—mm					
		Decarburization Class 1/2 H[2]	Decarburization Class 2/3 H[2]	Decarburization Class 3/4 H[2]	
		N	N	N	G[4]
Thread Pitch P	Thread Height H[1]	min	min	min	max
0.35	0.202	0.10	0.13	0.15	0.015
0.40	0.232	0.12	0.15	0.17	0.015
0.45	0.262	0.13	0.17	0.20	0.015
0.50	0.292	0.15	0.19	0.22	0.015
0.60	0.352	0.18	0.23	0.26	0.015
0.70	0.411	0.21	0.27	0.31	0.015
0.80	0.471	0.24	0.31	0.35	0.015
1.00	0.591	0.30	0.39	0.44	0.015
1.25	0.740	0.37	0.49	0.56	0.015
1.50	0.890	0.44	0.59	0.67	0.015
1.75	1.040	0.52	0.69	0.78	0.015
2.00	1.189	0.59	0.79	0.89	0.015
2.50	1.488	0.74	0.99	1.12	0.015
3.00	1.787	0.89	1.19	1.34	0.015
3.50	2.086	1.04	1.39	1.56	0.015
4.00	2.386	1.19	1.59	1.79	0.015

All dimensions are millimeters.

1. H is height of external thread at its maximum boundary nonplated condition.
2. Decarburization Class 1/2 H is commonly specified for Class 8.8 and Class 9.8 threaded fasteners; Class 2/3 H for Class 10.9 fasteners; Class 3/4 H for Class 12.9 fasteners.
3. G shall be measured perpendicular to the flank of the thread midway between crest and root. (The additional depth of gross decarburization shown at thread crest is due to "thread enfoliation" caused by thread rolling.)
4. See Section 3 for limits applicable to other threaded products.

FIGURE 1—DECARBURIZATION LIMITS FOR COMMONLY USED ISO MODIFIED THREADS

3.2 Gross Decarburization—Decarburization with sufficient carbon loss to show only clearly-defined ferrite grains under metallographic examination by the method outlined in 5.1. This is sometimes called "Complete Decarburization."

3.3 Carbon Restoration—A process of restoring surface-carbon loss by heat-treating in an atmosphere furnace of properly controlled carbon potential. (This process is permitted but not recommended for threaded fasteners unless furnace atmosphere is adequately controlled.)

3.4 Carburization—A darker shade of tempered martensite than that of the immediately adjacent base metal, when examined metallographically by the method outlined in 5.1, and harder by at least 30 points (Knoop or Vickers DPH) than the hardness at root diameter when checked by the method outlined in 5.2. (The limits established by this document exclude this condition.)

3.5 Base-Metal Hardness—For purposes of this document, hardness at root diameter on a line bisecting the included angle of the thread (Position 1 in Figure 2) is considered "base-metal hardness."

4. Classes of Decarburization—This document establishes three classes for SI (metric) series threaded products. Each class is characterized by dimensional limits for decarburized zone, gross-decarburized zone, and/or base-carbon zone (as applied to longitudinal sections through the thread axis). Decarburization limits applicable to the most commonly used ISO Modified Threads (mm) are shown in Figure 1. Limits applicable to other threaded products are as follows:

a. For Class 1/2 H—N = 0.50 H; G = 0.015 mm (0.0006 in) max
b. For Class 2/3 H—N = 0.67 H; G = 0.015 mm (0.0006 in) max
c. For Class 3/4 H—N = 0.75 H; G = 0.015 mm (0.0006 in) max

NOTE—This document recognizes that the surface may vary in carbon content from the base-metal carbon content, and stipulates that this variation shall be either "partial decarburization" or "gross decarburization" or a "carbon-restored surface" to the extent allowed in Figure 1 for the different classes. "Carburization" is not permitted in the surface zone.

5. Methods for Measuring Decarburization—Two methods for measuring decarburization are provided. The microscopic method is intended primarily for routine inspection purposes. The hardness method is intended primarily for referee purposes. In the case of gross decarburization, however, only the microscopic method is applicable.

5.1 Microscopic Method[1]

5.1.1 SPECIMENS—Use longitudinal sections taken through the thread axis of the bolt, screw, or stud, after all heat-treating operations have been performed on the product. If specimens are prepared from surface-coated fasteners, care should be used when interpreting the substrate-coating interface.

5.1.2 PREPARATION

a. Mount specimen for grinding and polishing. Protection from rounding the surface to be examined is essential. The specimen should be mounted in a clamp or in a plastic mount, the latter being the preferred method.
b. After mounting, grind and polish the surface in accordance with good metallographic practice.
c. Etching in a 3% nital (concentrated nitric acid) or picral (saturated picric acid) is usually suitable for showing changes in microstructure caused by decarburization.

5.1.3 MEASUREMENT—Unless otherwise agreed on between purchaser and producer, examine at 100X magnification. Compare with Figure 1 and definitions in 3.1, 3.2, and 3.3.

If the microscope is of a type with a ground glass screen, the extent of decarburization can be measured directly with a scale. If an eye-piece is used for measurement, it should be an appropriate type containing a cross hair or a scale.

5.2 Hardness Method[2]

5.2.1 Prepare specimens as outlined in 5.1.1 and 5.1.2.

5.2.2 Determine hardness at three positions, as shown in Figure 2, using a Knoop indenter with a 500 g load or Vickers DPH with 300 g load.

5.2.3 Interpret hardness readings as follows:

a. A decrease of more than 30 hardness points from Position 1 to Position 2 indicates that the part does not conform to the classification specified.
b. An increase of more than 30 points between Position 1 and Position 3 is regarded as "carburization," and indicates that part does not conform to the classification specified.

NOTE—Careful differentiation must be made between an increase in hardness caused by carburization or by cold working the surface (such as form thread rolling).

1. Same as outlined in SAE J419, except "Specimen."
2. Hardness Method applicable only for threads with pitches 1 mm and larger.

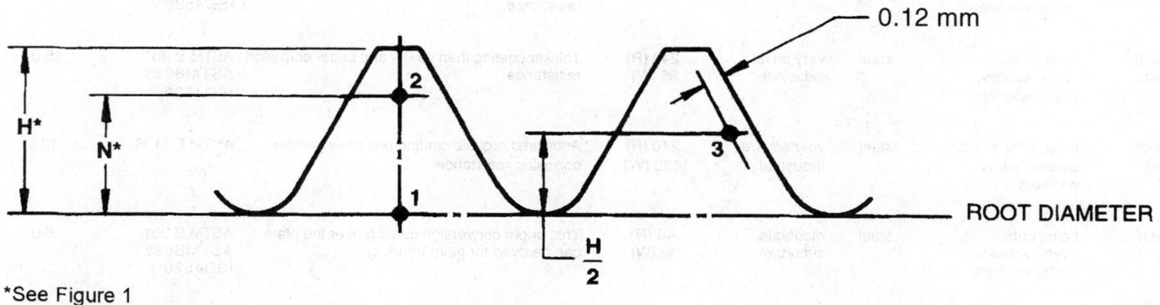

FIGURE 2—POSITIONS FOR DETERMINING HARDNESS

PROTECTIVE COATINGS FOR FASTENERS —SAE J1648 AUG1996

SAE Information Report

Report of the SAE Fasteners Committee approved August 1996.

Foreword—This Document has not changed other than to put it into the new SAE Technical Standards Board Format.

Protective coating finishes for fasteners not only enhance resistance to corrosion and appearance, but they are very important in the consideration of stresses developed and in the torque-tension tightening of the applied assembly. The effect of the coating on fastener torque-tension relationship is covered in a separate SAE Information Guide J1701.

1. Scope—This SAE Information Report is provided as an advisory guide. Careful discretion as to application is recommended. The content has been presented as accurately as possible, but responsibility for its application lies with the user. It covers finishes applied to fasteners and related topics, corrosion resistance, lubricity, electrical grounding, ultraviolet light, and embrittlement.

Table 1 lists these coatings and their properties so that finish selection can be reasonably made in accordance with known and anticipated fastener assembly applications.

Application of protective coatings will affect fastener dimensions. This is especially critical for the thread fit of mating parts because the pitch diameter increases by four times the coating thickness. Explanation is covered in Section 5.

TABLE 1—PROTECTIVE FINISHES FOR FASTENERS

Coat or Finish	For Use on Fastener	Surface	Corrosion Resistance(1) Environment Salt Spray Protection	Corrosion Resistance(1) Environment Salt Spray Hours Min	Description and Requirements	Specification Finish Reference	Thickness Micrometer µm	Temperature Resistance in Degrees
Nickel Electroplate	bolts, nuts, rivets, screws, studs, washers	steel	very mild indoor	2	Decorative silver appearance, good wear	ASTM F 871M	2.5	(204 °C)
Zinc Electroplate	bolts, nuts, rivets, screws, studs, washers	steel	moderate suburan sacrificial	32	Bright blue or white appearance. Smooth sacrificial.	ISO 2001	5.0	(177 °C)
Zinc Mechanical Plate	bolts, nuts, rivets, screws, studs, washers	steel	moderate suburban	48	Less susceptible to hydrogen embrittlement than electroplated zinc.	ASTM F 871M ASTMB633 ASTMB695	7.5	(149 °C)
Zinc Electroplate with Bright Chromate	bolts, nuts, rivets, screws, studs, washers	steel	moderate suburban	40 (R) 12 (W)	Thin bright conversion coating over the plate can be dyed for paint bonding.	ASTM B 201 ASTMB633 ISO4520	5.0	(120 °C)
Zinc Electroplate with Yellow Chromate	bolts, nuts, rivets, screws, studs, washers	steel	very severe industrial	144 (R) 72 (W)	Thicker conversion than clear with same characteristics and increased corrosion resistance.	ASTM B 201 ASTMB633 ISO4520	6.0	(120 °C)
Zinc Electroplate with Olive Drab Chromate	bolts, nuts, rivets, screws, studs, washers	steel	very severe industrial	240 (R) 96 (W)	Thicker coating than yellow and better corrosion resistance.	ASTM B 201 ASTMB633 ISO4520	5.0	(120 °C)
Zinc Electroplate with Chromate + Organic	bolts, nuts, rivets, screws, studs, washers	steel	very severe Industrial	240 (R) 120 (W)	Additional organic coating provokes greater corrosion resistance.	ASTM F 1136	13.0	(190 °C)
Zinc Mechanical with Bright Chromate	bolts, nuts, rivets, screws, studs, washers	steel	moderate suburban	40 (R) 12 (W)	Thin bright conversion coating over the plate can be dyed for paint bonding.	ASTM B 201 ASTMB695 ISO4520	5.0	(120 °C)
Zinc Mechanical with Yellow Chromate	bolts, nuts, rivets, screws, studs, washers	steel	Industrial	144 (R) 72 (W)	Thicker conversion than clear with same characteristics and increased corrosion resistance.	ASTM B 201 ASTMB695 ISO4520	5.0	(120 °C)
Zinc Mechanical with Olive Drab Chromate	bolts, nuts, rivets, screws, studs, washers	steel	very severe industrial	168 (R) 96 (W)	Thicker coating than yellow and better corrosion resistance.	ASTM B 201 ASTMB695 ISO 4520	5.0	(120 °C)
Zinc Mechanical with Chromate + Organic	bolts, nuts, rivets, screws, studs, washers	steel	very severe Industrial	336 (R) 100 (W)	Additional organic coating (cured) provides greater corrosion resistance.	ASTM F 1135	13.0	(190 °C)
Black Oxide + Oil	bolts, nuts, rivets, screws, studs, washers	steel	very mild Indoors	1	Porous thin; hydrogen embrittlement susceptible; oiling may be necessary.		2.5	(93 °C)
Brass Plate, Lacquered	bolts, nuts, rivets, screws, studs, washers	steel	very mild indoors	1	Decorative electroplated finish recommended for indoor use.	ASTM F 871M	2.5	(93 °C)
Chromium Electroplate	bolts, nuts, screws, studs, washers	steel and other metals	very mild indoors	2	Bright lustrous blue - white finish.	ASTM F 871M	7.5	(204 °C)

TABLE 1—PROTECTIVE FINISHES FOR FASTENERS (continued)

Coat or Finish	For Use on Fastener	Surface	Corrosion Resistance(1) Environment Salt Spray Protection	Corrosion Resistance(1) Environment Salt Spray Hours Min	Description and Requirements	Specification Finish Reference	Thickness Micrometer µm	Temperature Resistance in Degrees
Chromium Electroplate with Copper and Nickel Undercoat	bolts, nuts, rivets, screws, studs, washers	steel and other metals	very mild indoors	8	Surface is hard and abrasive resistant. Primarily for decorative use.	ASTM B 456 ISO1456	7.5	(260 °C)
Cadmium (Electroplate/ Mechanical Plate)	bolts, nuts, rivets, screws, studs, washers	steel	nonindustrial urban and marine applications	144	Bright silvery gray, dull gray, has lubricating (reduction of friction) property.	ASTM B 766 ASTM F 871M ASTM B 696 ISO 2082	5.0	(177 °C)
With Clear Chromate	bolts, nuts, rivets, screws, studs, washers	steel	nonindustrial urban and marine applications	192 (R) 12 (W)	Thin conversion coating base over the plate, bright, can be dyed for paint bonding.	ASTM B 201 ASTMB696 ASTMB766 ISO4520	5.0	(120 °C)
With Yellow Chromate	bolts, nuts, rivets, screws, studs, washers	steel	nonindustrial urban and marine applications	240 (R) 72 (W)	Thicker conversion coating than clear with same characteristics.	ASTM B 201 ASTM B 696 ASTM B 766 ISO 4520	5.0	(120 °C)
With Olive Drab Chromate	bolts, nuts, rivets, screws, studs, washers	steel	nonindustrial urban and marine	240 (R) 150 (W)	Thicker conversion coating than yellow with same characteristics.	ASTM B 201 ASTMB696 ASTMB766 ISO4520	5.0	(120 °C)
With Chromate + Organic Coating	bolts, nuts, rivets, screws, studs, washers	steel	nonindustrial urban and marine applications	336 (R) 216 (W)	Additional organic coating (cured) provides greater corrosion resistance.	ASTM F 1135	12.0	(190 °C)
Chromium/Zinc Inorganic	bolts, nuts, rivets, screws, studs, washers	steel	very severe industrial	240	Bright gray, an aqueous coating dispersion containing chromium in a proprietary organic. Zinc flake is dispensed evenly. The coating provoked encapsulating and sacrificial corrosion protection. Cannot be soldered or welded. Relatively hard and resistant to abrasion similar to cured paint finishes.	ASTM F 1136	6.2 - 13.0 g/m² 20.4 - 27.0	(260 °C)
With Sealant	bolts, nuts, rivets, screws, studs, washers	steel	very severe industrial	400	In addition to the previous the cured supplementary sealant may be clear or black and provokes greater corrosion resistance.	ASTM F 1136	6.2 - 13.0	(260 °C)
Copper Electroplate Lacquered	bolts, nuts, rivets, screws, studs, washers	steel	very mild indoors	1	Bright decorative electrically conductive.	ASTM F 871M	2.5	(93 °C)
Copper Flash Deposit (Immersion)	bolts, nuts, rivets, screws, studs, washers	steel	very, very mild indoors	0	Bright to dull electrically conductive.	—	1.2	(93 °C)
Zinc, Hot Dip, Mechanical Galvanize	bolts, nuts rivets, screws, studs, washers	steel	very severe industrial	950	Dull gray color, very thick deposit.	ASTM A 90 ASTMA153	42 min g/m² 305 500 avg. g/m² 300 avg.	(177 °C)
Solder, Electro	bolts, nuts rivets, screws, studs, washers	steel	very mild indoors	2	60% tin/40% lead coating bright sliver appearance excellent bond and solderability. Used primarily indoors.		3.8	(93 °C)
Phosphate, Zinc (bare)	bolts, nuts, rivets, screws, studs, washers	steel	none, serves as basis for paint and other supplementar y coatings	0	Light gray, crystalline, rough, powdery serves as base for supplementary coating.		11-16 g/m²	(120 °C)
Phosphate, Manganese (bare)	bolts, nuts, rivets, screws, studs, washers	steel	none, serves as basis for paint and other supplementar y coatings	0	Darker than zinc phosphate, finer crystalline.		11-16 g/m²	(120 °C)

TABLE 1—PROTECTIVE FINISHES FOR FASTENERS (continued)

Coat or Finish	For Use on Fastener	Surface	Corrosion Resistance[1] Environment Salt Spray Protection	Corrosion Resistance[1] Environment Salt Spray Hours Min	Description and Requirements	Specification Finish Reference	Thickness Micrometer μm	Temperature Resistance in Degrees
Phosphate, Zinc with Dry Lubricant	bolts, nuts, rivets, screws, studs, washers	steel	severe urban	48	Gray appearance.		11-16 g/m^2	(120 °C)
Phosphate, Zinc with Oil Wax	bolts, nuts, rivets, screws, studs, washers	steel	very severe industrial	168	Appearance varies from dark gray to black. Supplementary oil or wax enhances corrosion resistance.	ASTM F 1137	5.0	(120 °C)
Phosphate, Zinc with 1 Coat Paint + Organic	bolts, nuts, rivets, screws, studs, washers	steel	very severe industrial	144	Smooth, can be in different colors. Organic is a thin oil on top of the paint.		12.0	(190 °C)
Phosphate, Zinc with 2 Coat Paint + Organic	bolts, nuts, rivets, screws, studs, washers	steel	very severe industrial	240	Smooth, can be in different colors. Organic is a thin oil on top of the paint.		25.0	(190 °C)
Phosphate, Zinc with Zinc - Rich Resin Flake + Clear Organic Top Coat	bolts, nuts, rivets, screws, studs, washers	steel	very severe industrial	240	Gray metallic color, smooth	ASTM F 1137	15 - 25	(260 °C)
Phosphate, Zinc with Zinc - Rich Resin Powder + Clear Organic Top Coat	bolts, nuts, rivets, screws, studs, washers	steel	very severe industrial	400	Gray metallic color, smooth	ASTM F 1137	10 - 20	(260 °C)

1. Refer to Table 3 for service life values.

2. References

2.1 Applicable Publications—The following publications form a part of this specification to the extent specified herein. Unless otherwise specified, the latest issue of SAE publications shall apply.

2.1.1 SAE Publications—Available from SAE, 400 Commonwealth Drive, Warrendale, PA 15096-0001.

SAE J995—Mechanical and Material Requirements for Steel Nuts

SAE J1701—Torque-Tension Tightening for Fasteners

2.1.2 ASTM Publications—Available from ASTM, 100 Barr Harbor Drive, West Conshohocken, PA 19428-2959.

ASTMA90—Test Method for Weight of Coating on Zinc-Coated (Galvanized) Iron or Steel Articles

ASTMA153—Specification for Zinc Coating (Hot-Dip) on Iron and Steel Hardware

ASTMA239—Test Method for Locating the Thinnest Spot in a Zinc (Galvanized) Coating on Iron or Steel Articles by the Preece Test (Copper Sulfate Dip)

ASTMB117—Method of Salt Spray (Fog) Testing

ASTMB183—Preparation of Low Carbon Steel for Electroplating

ASTMB201—Practice for Testing Chromate Coatings on Zinc and Cadmium Surfaces

ASTMB242—Preparation of High Carbon Steel for Electroplating

ASTMB368—Method for Copper-Accelerated Acetic Acid-Salt Spray (Fog) Testing (CASS Test)

ASTMB456—Specification for Electrodeposited Coatings of Copper Plus Nickel Plus Chromium and Nickel Plus Chromium

ASTMB487—Method for Measurement of Metal and Oxide Coating Thicknesses by Microscopical Examination of a Cross Section

ASTMB499—Method for Measurement of Coating Thicknesses by the Magnetic Method: Nonmagnetic Coatings on Magnetic Basis Metals

ASTMB504—Method for Measurement of Thickness of Metallic Coatings by the Coulometric Method

ASTMB530—Method for Measurement of Coating Thicknesses by the Magnetic Method: Electrodeposited Nickel Coatings on Magnetic and Nonmagnetic Substrates

ASTMB633—Specification for Electrodeposited Coatings of Zinc on Iron and Steel

ASTMB695—Specification for Coatings of Zinc Mechanically Deposited on Iron and Steel

ASTMB696—Specification for Coatings of Cadmium Mechanically Deposited

ASTMB766—Specification for Electrodeposited Coatings of Cadmium

ASTMB839—Test Method for Residual Embrittlement in Metallic Coated Externally Threaded Fasteners and Rods

ASTMB849—Pre-Treatments of Iron and Steel for Reducing the Risk of Hydrogen Embrittlement

ASTMD450—Specification for Coal-Tar Pitch Used in Roofing, Dampproofing, and Waterproofing

ASTME376—Practice for Measuring Coating Thickness by Magnetic-Field or Eddy-Current (Electromagnetic) Test Methods

ASTMF606—Method for Conducting Tests to Determine the Mechanical Properties of Externally and Internally Threaded Fasteners

ASTMF871M—Specification for Electrodeposited Coatings on Threaded Components (Metric)

ASTMF1135—Specification for Cadmium or Zinc Chromate Organic Corrosion Protective Coating for Fasteners

ASTMF1136—Specification for Chromium/Zinc Corrosion Protective Coatings for Fasteners

ASTMF1137—Specification for Phosphate/Oil and Phosphate/Organic Corrosion Protective Coatings for Fasteners

2.1.3 ISO Publications—Available from ANSI, 11 West 42nd Street, New York, NY 10036-8002.

ISO 1456—Metallic coatings—Electrodeposited coatings of nickel plus chromium and of copper plus nickel plus chromium

ISO 2080—Metallic coatings—Electrodeposited coatings of zinc plus chromium and of copper plus nickel plus chromium

ISO 2082—Metallic coatings—Electroplated coatings of cadmium on iron or steel

ISO 4520—Chromate conversion coatings on electroplated zinc and cadmium coatings

ISO/DIS 9587—Pre-treatments of iron and steel for reducing the risk of hydrogen embrittlement

ISO/DIS 10587—Test method for residual embrittlement in metallic coated externally threaded fasteners and rods

3. General Requirements

3.1 Surface Condition Prior to Coating—The fasteners must be clean and free from rust, chips, scale, dirt, abrasives, excessive iron oxide, or other foreign materials. If protective lubricants or coatings are applied to prevent rusting in storage then they must not be tacky or difficult to remove in the cleaning process before finishing.

3.2 Cleaning

3.2.1 PRIOR TO ELECTROPLATING—Steel fasteners containing 0.35% or more carbon at the surface or heat treated to 32 HRC (320 HV) or higher hardness shall be cleaned per the requirements in ASTM B 242. Steel parts containing less than 0.35% carbon at the surface, or lower than 30 HRC (302 HV) in hardness shall be cleaned per instructions in ASTM B 183.

3.2.2 PRIOR TO MECHANICAL PLATING—The same procedures apply for the different steel carbon contents and hardnesses expressed for cleaning prior to electroplating, except electrolytic cleaning is not permitted and acids for treatment must be inhibited. Flash copper deposit must be applied by the immersion plating process.

3.2.3 PRIOR TO PHOSPHATING—Similarly, acids employed for cleaning or activation must be inhibited.

3.3 Brittleness—Fasteners shall be free from hydrogen embrittlement or other factors which may impart brittleness from the finishing processes. That includes cleaning, coating, and coating stripping. All heat treat operations including stress relief after cold forming, temper after quench, and hydrogen embrittlement relief must be completed before subsequent plating and phosphating.

Refer to ASTM B 839 (ISO/DIS 10587) for test method to determine if detrimental embrittlement remains in threaded fasteners. It includes three levels of confidence. ASTM B 849 (ISO/DIS 9587) contains eight standard stress relief treatments. Refer to 7.4 for additional test information.

3.3.1 ELECTROPLATED FASTENERS—Metal coatings are deposited electrically onto steel surfaces with evolvement of hydrogen which infiltrates into the grain boundaries.

Generally, high stressed fasteners containing 0.35% carbon or more cold worked or heat treated to hardness 32 HRC (320 HV) or higher must be baked within 1 h maximum after electroplating at a temperature of 205°C for 4 h at heat. Higher temperatures depending upon plate tolerance and/or longer times may be used to reduce risk of detrimental hydrogen embrittlement.

However, if verified by test data, some electroplated stressed steel fasteners with the previous hardness may be excluded from bake procedure because of the function of the special plating bath and their nonsusceptible microstructure for hydrogen infiltration and entrapment.

Hardened parts which have been tempered at less than 205 °C shall be baked within 1 h after plating to 150°C for 8 h at heat or longer as required.

It may be necessary to provide coatings other than electroplating for fasteners with a hardness above 40HRC (390 HV).

3.3.2 MECHANICAL PLATED OR PHOSPHATED FASTENERS—The mechanical plating process cold welds powdered zinc onto cleaned and immersion copper-plated steel surfaces by means of tumble peening with a nonmetallic media.

Mechanical plated parts with hardnesses of 32 HRC (320 HV) or higher must not be used for 48 h or be baked at 120 °C for 1 h minimum at heat within 4 h of processing.

Phosphated parts can become hydrogen embrittled due to the acidic condition of the chemical bath. However, this condition is relieved within 48 h because the crystalline coating is porous.

4. Fastener Coatings Description and Requirements—Finish selection is based on the desired tightened assembly application, the corrosion resistance, and appearance of the fastener.

4.1 Plain—The surface is without a coating or with a light protective oil film.

4.2 Copper—The finish is smooth, fine, and grained. It can be lustrous or dull. Thickness can vary from 2.5 μm or greater for electroplating and 1.2 μm for immersion plating.

4.3 Chromium—Chromium is a thin 0.025 μm hard, blue white chromium electroplate top coat applied to provide color, luster, and decorativeness. It is generally plated over substrates of a copper flash plus a corrosion resistant nickel totaling 7.5 μm thickness.

4.4 Nickel—The slight yellow or white bright color of this metal provides attractiveness for interior applications. Coatings for appearance only may be as thin as 2.5 μm. Coatings for corrosion resistance may be 5 μm or greater.

4.5 Phosphated/Organic Finishes—Phosphate is a conversion coating of fine or medium grain size crystals weighing 11 to 16 g/m^2 minimum. The zinc-phosphate type is primarily used as a base for supplementary coatings such as oil, wax, paint, or organic with dispersed zinc flake or dust. Another top sealant of oil, wax, or polymer may be applied over the paint.

NOTE—μm = micrometer

Manganese-phosphate, a more dense crystalline base, can be utilized also. Oil coatings on either type must be dry to touch as determined by Waterman #41 filter blot test.

4.6 Zinc—Zinc is another coating which can be applied, either electrically or mechanically onto steel fasteners, generally to 5 μm thickness. Corrosion products are very flocculent. Bright, yellow, and olive drab chromate conversion coatings are applied to deter this and to increase the corrosion resistance. However, chromates provide reduced zinc protection when subsequent heating exceeds 65 °C temperature.

4.6.1 HEAVIER—Thicker, 50 μm, zinc finishes applied by the hot-dip or mechanical galvanize processes offer greater corrosion resistance for better outdoor environment conditions. But fastener dimensions and threads must be made to allow for the thicker coating.

WARNING—Property Class 8.8 fasteners and greater can accommodate 5 to 7.5 μm coating thicknesses. However, if dimensions and threads are made to allow for thicker coatings, the undersized parts cannot be certified as conforming to the property class.

4.7 Chromium/Zinc/Organic—The chromium/zinc/organic gray colored finish is comprised of a dispersion of chromium and zinc flake or dust in a proprietary organic over which a clear or black polymer top coat is applied. The combination of organic seal and zinc sacrificial action retards corrosion.

5. The Effects of Finishes on Dimensions

5.1 Electroplating—It must be realized that deposition of the metal coating is not uniform on all areas of the fastener because of the following factors.

5.1.1 The "throwing" characteristics of electroplate bath deposit metal lightly in recessed areas as opposed to external areas.

5.1.2 The geometric design of the fastener:

a. Plating builds up at sharp corners.
b. Plated thickness is greater near ends and edges.
c. Plated thickness will be least in recessed areas.
d. External threads plating will be thickest at the apex tapering down to the root, causing a slight change in the thread's angle.
e. Internal threads, the opposite is true.
f. Plating builds up more rapidly at the mouth of the threaded hole of nuts rather than in the interior.
g. Coating the surface of the fastener increases its size and may cause fit problems with plated mating parts, particularly with threaded fasteners.

5.1.3 The operating conditions of the bath, chemical concentrations, temperature, and acidity/alkalinity.

5.1.4 Distribution of the parts to be plated, whether in rack or barrel bulk.

5.1.5 The current density, amperes/square meter, at which the plating takes place.

5.2 Mechanical Plating—Since coatings are cold welded onto surface areas they also are nonuniform because of the following factors.

5.2.1 The tumbling process burnishes edges and external surfaces making the plate thinner than in internal areas.

a. Plated thickness will be less on edges and corners.
b. Plated thickness will be greater in interior areas.
c. External threads plating will be thinner at the apex and tapering down to the thickest at the root.
d. Internal threads plating will be thicker varying to greatest in the root.
e. Plating will be thinner at the mouth of the threaded hole of nuts rather than the interior.
f. Greater chance of having thread fit problems with plated mating parts.

5.2.2 The geometric design of the fastener which will vary with the tumbling abrasion.

5.2.3 The operating conditions of proprietary chemical solution, concentration, and temperature.

5.2.4 The kind of media, size proportion, and ratio to parts to be plated.

5.2.5 Tumbler type, size, and speed.

5.3 Phosphate and Organic Coatings—Phosphating is deposited by direct chemical reaction with fastener steel surfaces. Therefore, the coating is uniform on internal and external areas. However, the following factors influence the quality of the deposit plus its supplementary organic coatings.

5.3.1 The type of phosphate bath material, zinc-phosphate, or manganese.

5.3.2 The coarse or fine size of phosphate crystals.

5.3.3 The operating conditions of the bath-temperature, chemical concentration, iron buildup, etc.

5.3.4 Type and concentration of oil supplementary coating.

5.3.5 Type, viscosity, and number of paint coatings.

5.3.6 Sealant top coat over the phosphate plus paint finishes.

5.4 Fastener Thread Fit—Coated mating parts with external and internal threads having minimum clearance between them can have fit problems.

5.4.1 The thread fit of fasteners before application of coatings must be in accordance with unified Class 2A for external and Class 2B for internal inch threads and 6g external and 6H internal metric threads.

5.4.2 Coating thicknesses up to 1/6 of the clearance allowance between Class 2A external (6g metric) and Class 2B internal (6H metric) can be applied without causing thread fit interference. However, consideration has to be given to the plating thickness process variations.

5.4.3 If the coating thickness is greater than 1/6 of the allowance, either the external thread has to be undercut or the internal thread has to be retapped to assure noninterference during assembly.

WARNING—If the external thread has to be undercut, or the internal thread retapped to assure noninterference during assembly, the overall thread proof load tensile strength will be reduced.

5.5 Functionality— Extra thick metallic coatings and thicker organics applied by dip-spinning or electro-disposition processes can cause other than thread fit assembly problems. It is important to recognize these before design finalization.

Possibly, they may be alleviated by reduced coating thickness to improve functionality, but at the expense of reduced corrosion resistance. The following examples illustrate the problems that may be encountered.

5.5.1 Parts sticking together or leaving a residue of oil or coating which hampers feeding systems and containers during handling, supply, and assembly.

5.5.2 Superfluous coating on fasteners preventing the driver tool from completing recess fits, as in the case of recess screw assemblies.

6. Corrosion Resistance

6.1 General Explanation— Corrosion occurs when water or moisture is present in the surrounding environment. This may be in the form of rain, dew, fog, ground water, condensation, or humidity. The rate of deterioration depends on other factors combining with the water and moisture in the environment, such as chemical concentrations from pollution, marine salt, spray electric currents, and dissimilar metals in contact with each other.

6.2 Types of Corrosion

6.2.1 Direct Chemical Attack—The environment may contain sulfur from industrial plants which expel these gases. The resulting sulfuric acid is very corrosive. The same thing applies to salt atmosphere from sea spray.

6.2.2 Electro Chemical Action—Metal fasteners may be subjected to and conduct stray electric currents caused by grounded electric power, generators, and welding equipment.

6.2.3 Galvanic Corrosion—Dissimilar metals in contact with each other in the presence of an electrolyte such as water causes a flow of current which deteriorates the anodic metal whether a coating or base material (for example, steel).

Refer to Figure 1, the galvanic series of metals and alloys. The upper end metals will sacrifice themselves to protect the adjacent. For example: cadmium or zinc coatings will be depleted to protect the base steel fastener. Metals at the lower end of the series serve to encapsulate thereby shutting out the environment.

Corroded End (anodic, or least noble)

Magnesium
Zinc
Aluminum 1100
Cadmium
Steel
Cast iron
18-8 Stainless
Tin
Nickel
Brasses
Copper
Bronzes
Titanium
Silver
Graphite
Gold
Platinum

Protected End (cathodic, or more noble)

FIGURE 1—GALVANIC SERIES OF METALS

6.2.4 Stress Corrosion Cracking—When fasteners are under either static or dynamic stresses, corrosion may cause cracking in the metal. Also, cyclic stresses from vibration oscillation or other flexing in combination with a corrosive environment will produce fatigue corrosion failures. They occur more readily in that environment than in the absence of the corrosive medium.

6.2.5 Pitting Corrosion—This phenomenon is caused by fast attack at small points on the surface while the rest of the surface is attacked hardly at all. The tops of bolt heads and nuts are subject to this corrosion. Remedy is thicker plating.

7. Test Methods for Evaluating Finishes on Fasteners

7.1 Definition of Significant Surfaces— Significant surfaces are all surfaces which are visible and that can be a source of corrosion in an assembly or where appearance is important.

7.2 Plating Thickness Measurements

7.2.1 Metallographic Tests—Copper, nickel, chromium, and zinc thicknesses can be determined by this so-called "umpire method." ASTM B 487, ASTM B 499, ASTM B 504, also ASTM B 530 for nickel only.

7.2.2 Electronic Depletion Test (Kocour)—The acidic removal of plating.

7.2.3 Acid Drop Test—Similar to 7.2.2 but number of drops/minute signifies thickness.

7.2.4 Magnetic Field or Eddy Current Test, ASTM E 376—Zinc organic (paint) thickness is measured by its resistance to current passing through to base steel.

7.2.5 Weight of Coating—Phosphate, hot-dip galvanize (ASTM A 90, A 153) average weight of coating is determined by weighing part, stripping off the coating and weighing again. It is expressed as weight/unit area.

7.2.6 Thinnest Coating Test—The copper sulfate dip test (Preece Test) ASTM A 239 determines the areas of least zinc coverage for hot-dip galvanize coating on steel.

7.3 Corrosion Tests

7.3.1 Salt Spray ASTM B 117

a. After a specified test time period one rust or corrosion spot, not larger than 0.016 mm diameter on the significant surface area is acceptable. On other surfaces corrosion must not exceed 2% of the area.
b. All zinc finishes without chromate treatment are evaluated for "red rust" failure.
c. Electroplated zinc finishes with chromate are rated for "white" corrosion products and ultimate "red rust."
d. Mechanical zinc finish with chromate evaluation permits "light haze" or "wisps" of whiteness, but no "red rust." A cancerous growth of corrosion products is unacceptable.

7.3.2 Corrodokote Test—Evaluation is the same as the salt spray test.

7.3.3 Cass Test (Copper Accelerated Acetic-Salt Spray, ASTM B 368)—No corrosion permitted on more than 2% of the significant area.

7.3.4 Service Life of the Protective Finish—The fastener is subjected to actual industrial, urban, suburban, marine, rural, and indoor environments over long periods of time so an average rate of deplating per annum can be determined. See Table 2. Refer to ASTM B 633 and ASTM B 695 for service life of zinc electroplate and mechanical plate.

7.4 Hydrogen Embrittlement Test— Discussion as to how this phenomenon occurs and how it must be relieved by baking is found in 3.3. Freedom from the existence of hydrogen embrittlement is determined by tightening the fasteners to critical stress conditions for a prescribed time period during which cracking may occur. Refer to ASTM F 606.

7.5 Electrical Grounding— Generally, chromate conversion coatings have a slight insulating effect on electrical grounding. Phosphate with organic coatings will also reduce electrical grounding.

7.6 Ultraviolet Light— Outdoor sunlight or special laboratory ultraviolet light tests are employed to determine freedom from their harmful effects on finishes.

TABLE 2—Zinc Coating Service Life Values

Atmosphere	Mean Corrosion Rate
Very severe (industrial)	5.6 µm/year
Severe (urban nonindustrial or marine)	1.5 µm/year
Moderate (suburban)	1.3 µm/year
Mild (rural)	0.8 µm/year
Very mild (indoors)	Less than 0.5 µm/year

HOLES IN BOLT AND SCREW SHANKS AND SLOTS IN NUTS FOR COTTER PINS—SAE J485 MAY1998

SAE Standard

Report of the SAE Fasteners Committee approved January 1956 and cancelled 1990. Reissued by the SAE Fasteners Committee January 1995 and reaffirmed May 1998.

1. Scope—SAE J485 specifies the recommended nominal diameters and locations of holes in bolt or screw shanks, and nominal widths and depths of slots in nuts, for use with the recommended sizes of inch-series cotter pins, as shown in Table 1.

2. References

2.1 Applicable Publications—The following publications form a part of this specification to the extent specified herein.

2.1.1 ASME PUBLICATIONS—Available from ASME, 22 Law Drive, Fairfield, NJ 07007-2900.

ASME B 18.2.2—Square and Hex Nuts (Inch Series)
ASME B 18.8.1—Clevis Pins and Cotter Pins (Inch Series)

TABLE 1—DIMENSIONS FOR COTTER PIN HOLES AND SLOTS (all dimensions are in inches)

Bolt, Screw, and Nut Nominal Size	Bolt, Screw, and Nut Nominal Size	Hole in Bolt or Screw Shank Dia(1)	Hole in Bolt or Screw Shank Distance, Extreme Point of Bolt or Screw to Hole Center(2)	Slot in Nut(3) Width (1)	Slot in Nut(3) Depth(4)	Cotter Pin(5) Nominal Size	Cotter Pin(5) Nominal Size	Cotter Pin(5) Min	Cotter Pin(5) Max
1/4	0.250	0.078	0.109	0.078	0.094	1/16	0.062	0.056	0.060
5/16	0.3125	0.094	0.109	0.094	0.094	5/64	0.078	0.072	0.076
3/8	0.375	0.109	0.141	0.125	0.125	3/32	0.094	0.086	0.090
7/16	0.4375	0.109	0.172	0.125	0.156	3/32	0.094	0.086	0.090
1/2	0.500	0.141	0.172	0.156	0.156	1/8	0.125	0.116	0.120
9/16	0.5625	0.141	0.203	0.156	0.188	1/8	0.125	0.116	0.120
5/8	0.625	0.172	0.234	0.188	0.219	5/32	0.156	0.146	0.150
3/4	0.750	0.172	0.266	0.188	0.250	5/32	0.156	0.146	0.150
7/8	0.875	0.172	0.281	0.188	0.250	5/32	0.156	0.146	0.150
1	1.000	0.203	0.312	0.250	0.281	3/16	0.188	0.172	0.176
1-1/8	1.125	0.203	0.391	0.250	0.344	3/16	0.188	0.172	0.176
1-1/4	1.250	0.234	0.406	0.312	0.375	7/32	0.219	0.202	0.207
1-3/8	1.375	0.234	0.438	0.312	0.375	7/32	0.219	0.202	0.207
1-1/2	1.500	0.266	0.484	0.375	0.438	1/4	0.250	0.220	0.225
1-5/8	1.625	0.266	0.484	0.375	0.438	1/4	0.250	0.220	0.225
1-3/4	1.750	0.312	0.547	0.438	0.500	5/16	0.312	0.275	0.280
1-7/8	1.875	0.312	0.547	0.438	0.562	5/16	0.312	0.275	0.280
2	2.000	0.312	0.641	0.438	0.562	5/16	0.312	0.275	0.280
2-1/4	2.250	0.312	0.641	0.438	0.562	5/16	0.312	0.275	0.280
2-1/2	2.500	0.375	0.750	0.562	0.688	3/8	0.375	0.329	0.335
2-3/4	2.750	0.375	0.750	0.562	0.688	3/8	0.375	0.329	0.335
3	3.000	0.500	0.750	0.625	0.750	1/2	0.500	0.467	0.473

1. Required tolerances are to be specified on the drawing.
2. This dimension is suggested to determine the distance from the cotter pin hole to the bearing face of the bolt or screw head. The drawing should specify the length, with required tolerances or limits, from the under head bearing face to the hole center.
3. See ASME B18.2.2 for dimensions of standard slotted hex nuts, slotted heavy hex nuts, or slotted hex thick nuts.
4. This dimension is suggested to determine the nut unslotted thickness, the distance from the nut bearing face to the bottom of the slots. The drawing should specify the nut unslotted thickness with required tolerances or limits.
5. See ASME B18.8.1 for dimensions of standard cotter pins.

SPRING NUTS—SAE J891 MAY1998 SAE Standard

Report of the Fasteners Committee approved August 1964 and revised June 1970. Completely revised by the Iron and Steel Technical Committee SC8—Carbon and Alloy Steel Hardenability June 1993. Revised by the SAE Fasteners Committee May 1998. Rationale statement available.

Foreword—This Document has also changed to comply with the new SAE Technical Standards Board format.

1. Scope—Included herein are complete general and dimensional specifications for metric and inch types of spring nuts recognized as SAE standard. These nuts are intended for general use where the engagement of a single thread on the mating screw is considered adequate for the application.

It should be noted that spring nuts having other configurations, dimensions, provisions for ground, etc., are available and manufacturers should be consulted.

2. References

2.1 Applicable Publications—The following publication forms a part of this specification to the extent specified herein.

2.1.1 ANSI PUBLICATIONS—Available from ANSI, 11 West 42nd Street, New York, NY 10036-8002.

ANSI B18.6.3—Slotted and Recessed Head Machine Screws and Machine Screw Nuts

ANSI B18.6.4—Screws, Tapping and Metallic Drive, Inch Series, Thread Forming and Cutting

2.1.2 ASME PUBLICATIONS—Available from ASME, 345 East 47 Street, New York, NY 10017-2330.

ASME B18.6.5M—Metric Thread Forming and Thread Cutting Tapping Screws

ASME B18.6.7M—Metric Machine Screws

3. General Specifications

3.1 Dimensional Tolerances—Dimensions and tolerances are given in both metric and inch units as designated. In many cases, the metric units have been rounded to reflect metric modules rather than being true soft conversions of the corresponding inch dimensions. Tolerances on dimensionns in Tables 1 to 9 and Figures 1 to 16 shall be ±0.25 mm (±0.010 in) unless otherwise specified.

3.2 Boss Detail—The detail of boss shall be such as to assemble readily and function satisfactorily with the specified screw and meet the performance requirements of this specification except as indicated otherwise.

Both the type "P" and "T" bosses are designed to function with all spaced threaded tapping screws in sizes 3.5 x 1.27 through 6.3 x 1.81 or (#6-20 through 1/4-14) with the exception of the type "T" boss of the 6.3 (1/4). The boss has been designed to perform satisfactorily with either a type AB or B tapping screw.

The sides of the Type P boss (see Figure 1) shall be formed to provide an opening conforming to the helix of the mating thread. The opening shall be round and equal to, or slightly larger than, the minor diameter of the mating thread.

The prongs of the Type T boss (see Figure 2) shall be formed to provide a circular opening conforming to the helix of the mating thread and, at the opening, the prongs shall be normal to the axis of the mating thread. The round portion of the opening shall be equal to, or slightly larger than, the minor diameter of the mating thread.

The size and formation of the helical opening (see Table 1) shall be such as to permit ready assembly of the specified screw or gage when inserted from the base of the boss at 90 degrees to the plane of the nut, or component thereof which contains the boss. For machine screw threads, basic GO thread plug gages shall be used to check assembly. For Type A and Type B pitch tapping screw threads, special gages conforming to the maximum limits of the screws may be used in place of the specified screws to check assembly.

3.3 Retaining Extrusion Detail—The size and configuration of the extrusion in the lower leg of "J" shape and "U" shape spring nuts shall be such that nuts will meet the performance requirements of this specification. The size and relative location of the hole and extrusion to the boss shall be such that when nut is assembled onto a test panel having minimum hole size, located at maximum edge distance, the extrusion will snap into the hole and permit the specified screw of maximum size (or special threaded plug gage, see Figure 3) to be assembled into the boss normal to the base of bass with interference at the extrusion or the sides of either hole. The screw or gage is to be entered into the boss until the head of the screw or shoulder on gage lightly contacts the bottom of the lower leg. The extrusion shall have a uniform shape and blend evenly from the specified height at point X into the upper surface of the lower leg at points Y and Y' as shown. The critical edges of the extrusion shall be free from burrs which would cause interference as spring nut is assembled to panel.

3.4 Material—Spring steel; SAE 1050 or higher carbon; suitably processed to meet the performance requirements of this specification.

3.5 Hardness—Hardness shall be as specified in Table 3.

3.6 Finish—Spring nuts are normally supplied with corrosion-resistant finish as specified by the purchaser. Nuts subjected to corrosion preventive treatment which might induce hydrogen embrittlement shall be baked or otherwise treated to obviate such embrittlement.

3.7 Workmanship—Spring nuts shall be free from cracks, burrs, splits, loose scale, or any other defects that might affect their serviceability.

3.8 Performance—Spring nuts shall perform in accordance with the requirements specified in Table 2 except as indicated otherwise.

3.9 Assembly Detail—The recommended design data pertaining to assembly of "J" shape and "U" shape spring nuts for guidance of users is presented in Tables 4 and 5. The proper method of assembling these corrosion-resistant nuts to panels is described as follows:

"J" shape nuts are assembled to panel by placing nut against the edge of the panel as shown opposite and rocking onto panel in the direction indicated by the arrow. See Figure 4A.

"U" shape nuts are assembled to panel by placing nut over edge of the panel as shown opposite and pushing onto the panel in the direction indicated by the arrow. See Figure 4B.

4. Tests and Test Fixtures for Evaluating Spring Nut Performance—Spring nuts shall be subjected to the following tests to determine conformance with the performance requirements specified in Table 2 except as indicated otherwise.

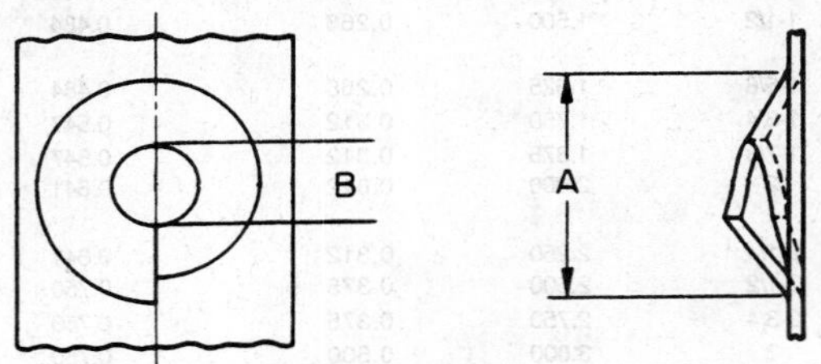

FIGURE 1—TYPE P BOSS

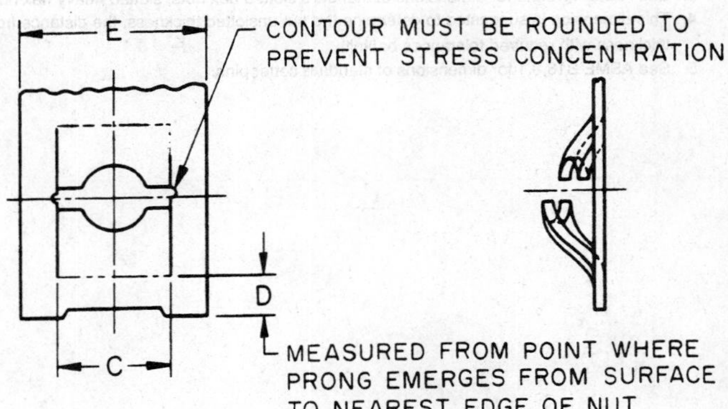

FIGURE 2—TYPE T BOSS

TABLE 1—DETAIL OF BOSSES

Screw Thread Type	Screw Nominal Size mm	Screw Nominal Size in	Type P Boss A Base Dia Ref mm	Type P Boss A Base Dia Ref in	Type P Boss B Hole Dia mm	Type P Boss B Hole Dia in	Type P Boss E Min Blank Width mm	Type P Boss E Min Blank Width in
Machine	M3.5 x 0.6	6-32	6.6	0.26	2.6	0.104	8.6	0.340
Machine	M4 x 0.7	8-32	5.8	0.23	3.3	0.130	10.3	0.406
Machine	M5 x 0.8	10-24	7.1	0.28	3.6	0.143	12.7	0.500
Machine		1/4-20	9.4	0.37	4.9	0.193	14.3	0.562
Tapping	3.5	#6	6.4	0.25	2.7	0.105	8.6	0.340
Tapping	4.2	#8	7.1	0.28	3.1	0.123	10.3	0.406
Tapping	4.8	#10	7.1	0.28	3.6	0.142	12.7	0.500
Tapping	6.3	1/4 #14	9.6	0.38	4.9	0.193	14.3	0.562

TABLE 1—DETAIL OF BOSSES (CONTINUED)

Screw Thread Type	Screw Nominal Size mm	Screw Nominal Size in	Type T Boss C Width of Shear Basic mm	Boss D Boss C Width of Shear Basic in	Type T Boss D(1) End of Slit to Edge Min mm	Type T Boss D(1) End of Slit to Edge Min in	Type T Boss E Min Blank Width mm	Type T Boss E Min Blank Width in
Machine	M3.5 x 0.6	6-32	4.0	0.157	1.3	0.050	8.0	0.312
Machine	M4 x 0.7	8-32	4.7	0.184	1.3	0.050	10.3	0.406
Machine	M5 x 0.8	10-24	5.3	0.210	1.3	0.050	9.5	0.375
Machine		1/4-20	6.9	0.270	2.3	0.090	12.7	0.500
Tapping	3.5	#6	4.0	0.157	1.3	0.050	8.0	0.312
Tapping	4.2	#8	4.7	0.184	1.5	0.060	10.3	0.406
Tapping	4.8	#10	5.3	0.210	2.0	0.080	12.7	0.500
Tapping	6.3	1/4 #14	6.9	0.270	2.3	0.090	14.3	0.562

1. The tabulated values are applicable to standard spring nuts only. This factor shall be sufficient to meet the performance requirements for torque, tensile strength, and vibration as set forth in Table 2.

TABLE 2—PERFORMANCE REQUIREMENTS FOR SPRING NUTS

Screw Thread Type	Screw Nominal Size mm	Screw Nominal Size in	Recommended Installation Torque-Max N·m	Recommended Installation Torque-Max lb-in	Clamp-Load at Recommended Installation Torque-Min kN	Clamp-Load at Recommended Installation Torque-Min lb	Destructive Torque Min N·m	Destructive Torque Min lb-in
Machine	M3.5 x 0.6	6-32	0.6	6	0.36	80	1.0	8
Machine	M4 x 0.7	8-32	1.0	8	0.44	100	1.2	10
Machine	M5 x 0.8	10-24	1.6	14	0.62	140	2.0	17
Machine		1/4-20	4.0	35	1.47	330	5.0	45
Tapping	3.5	#6	1.4	12	1.06	240	2.0	17
Types	4.2	#8	2.2	20	1.78	400	2.8	25
AB & B	4.8	#10	4.0	35	2.45	550	4.9	44
	6.3	#14-1/4	7.0	60	3.34	750	9.0	80

TABLE 2—PERFORMANCE REQUIREMENTS FOR SPRING NUTS (CONTINUED)

Screw Thread Type	Screw nominal Size mm	Screw Nominal Size in	Ultimate Tensile Strength Min Type P kN	Ultimate Tensile Strength Min Type P lb	Ultimate Tensile Strength Min Type T kN	Ultimate Tensile Strength Min Type T lb
Machine	M3.5 x 0.6	6-32	0.69	155	0.69	156
Machine	M4 x 0.7	8-32	0.89	200	0.84	189
Machine	M5 x 0.8	10-24	1.40	315	1.22	274
Machine		1/4-20	2.54	570	2.45	550
Tapping	3.5 x 1.3	#6-25	2.22	500	1.89	425
Types	4.2 x 1.4	#8-18	2.76	620	2.38	534
AB & B	4.8 x 1.6	#10-16	4.45	1000	2.99	672
	6.3 x 1.8	1/4-14	5.03	1130	5.15	1158

TABLE 3—FASTENER HARDNESS

Material Thickness mm	Material Thickness in	Rockwell Scale	Dial Reading	Conversion to Rockwell C Scale	Conversion to Vickers
up to 0.41	up to 0.016	15 N	80.4 to 85.5	40 to 50	390 to 515
0.43 to 0.61	0.017 to 0.024	30 N	59.5 to 68.5	40 to 50	390 to 515
0.64 to 0.99	0.025 to 0.039	45 N	43.1 to 55.0	40 to 50	390 to 515
1.02 and over	0.040 and over	C	40 to 50	40 to 50	390 to 515

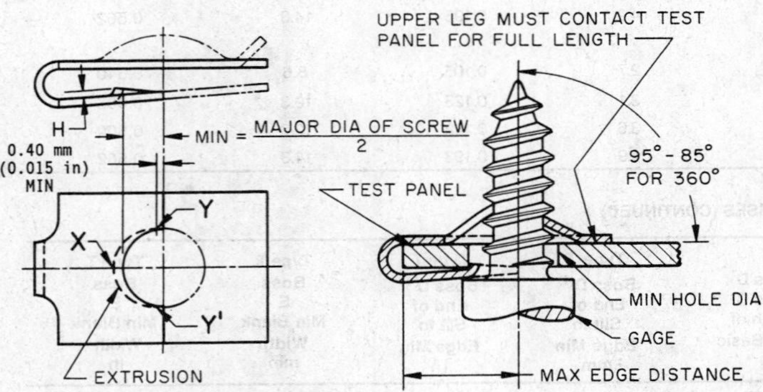

FIGURE 3—OPTIONAL EXTRUSION AND GAGING DETAIL

4.1 Test Plates and Screws for Tests—To assure uniformity of test results, the test plates and screws used for the tests shall conform to the following specifications.

Test plates shall have boundary dimensions and hole sizes as depicted in Figure 5. The thickness of test plates shall be equal to the mean of the specified panel range within a tolerance of ±0.03 mm (±0.001 in). The holes in test plates shall be located at the maximum edge distance specified for the particular spring nut within a tolerance of ±0.03 mm (±0.001 in). Test plates and panels shall have a minimum hardness of Rockwell C 50-54 (HV 515-580).

The screws used for test purposes shall conform to the specifications in ANSI B18.6.3 and B18.6.4 and ASME B18.6.5M and 18.6.7M for the respective sizes and types. They shall be Hexagon Head style and a length which is compatible with the test fixture, with a 72-h salt spray corrosion resistant phosphate finish (ASTM B 117).

4.2 Torque Tests—Spring nut samples shall be assembled with a test screw onto a test plate and tightened to the recommended installation torque. For wide-range design spring nuts, this test shall be performed with a device capable of measuring the clamp load developed and, when assembly is tightened to the recommended installation torque, the clamp load obtained shall not be less than the value tabulated.

Upon disassembly, the boss shall return to a position that will accept reentry of the test screw.

The spring nut, when reassembled and tightened on the test plate, shall not strip the threads on the screw nor fail the nut boss at less than the ultimate torque specified.

4.3 Tensile Tests—When the spring nut on a test plate is assembled to suitable back-up plates at the recommended installation torque and pulled in a tensile testing machine, the spring nut shall meet the ultimate strengths specified.

The ultimate strength shall be considered reached when the boss or the thread on the screw is destroyed. In performing tensile test, care should be taken to assure there is no interference between the screw and the holes in the plates. A typical tensile test fixture is illustrated in Figure 6.

4.4 Preassembly and Retention Test—The "J" shape and "U" shape spring nuts shall preassemble onto test panels of thickness equal to the two extremes of the panel ranges specified, having minimum holes, located at the maximum edge distance. The extrusion in the lower leg shall snap into the hole and when nuts are so assembled, a pull force of 13.3 N (3 lb) minimum applied parallel to the upper leg in line with the axis of the nut shall be required to remove the nut from the panel.

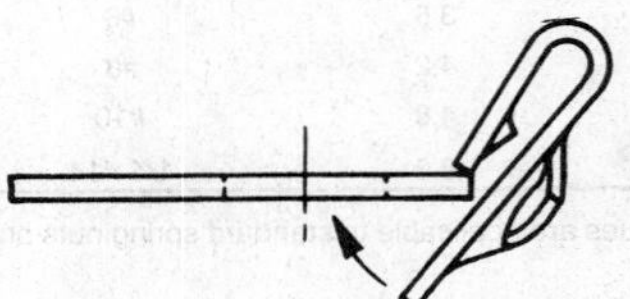

FIGURE 4A—J SHAPE NUTS

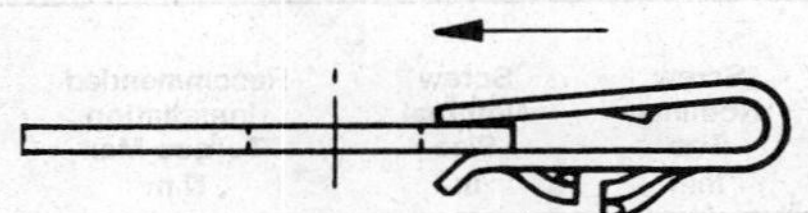

FIGURE 4B—U SHAPE NUTS

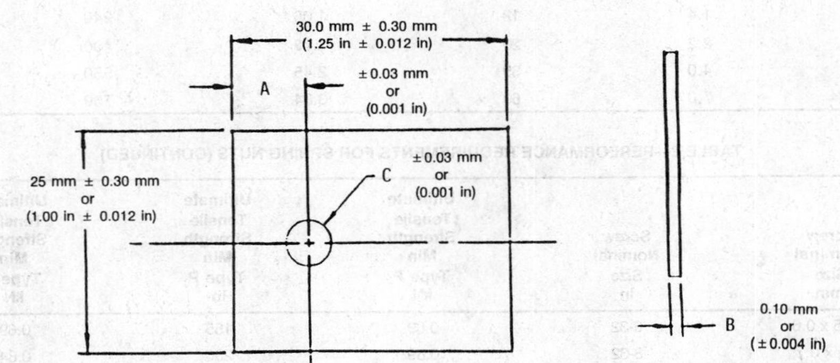

Machine and Tapping Screws Size mm	Machine and Tapping Screws Size in	A Edge to Center	B Plate Thickness	C Hole Dia mm	C Hole Dia in
3.5	#6	Equals Maximum	Equals Mean	6.35	0.250
4.2	#8	Edge Distance	of Panel Range	7.14	0.281
4.8	#10	Specified in	Specified in	7.92	0.312
6.3	#14-1/4	Assembly Data or on Part Drawing	Dimensional Tables	9.52	0.375

FIGURE 5—TEST PLATES

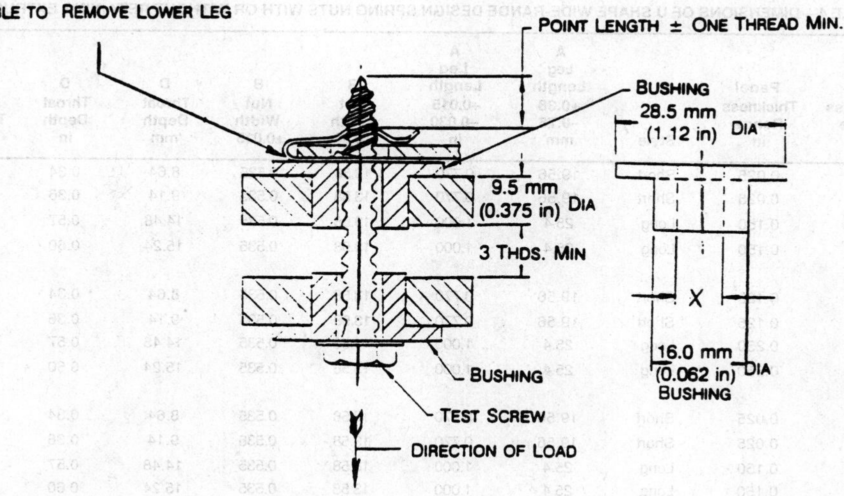

Tapping Screw Size mm	Machine and Tapping Screw Size in	X mm	X in
3.5	#6	4.0-4.5	0.157-0.177
4.2	#8	4.7-5.2	0.186-0.204
4.8	#10	5.3-5.8	0.208-0.228
6.3	1/4	6.8-7.3	0.268-0.287

FIGURE 6—TYPICAL TENSILE TEST FIXTURE

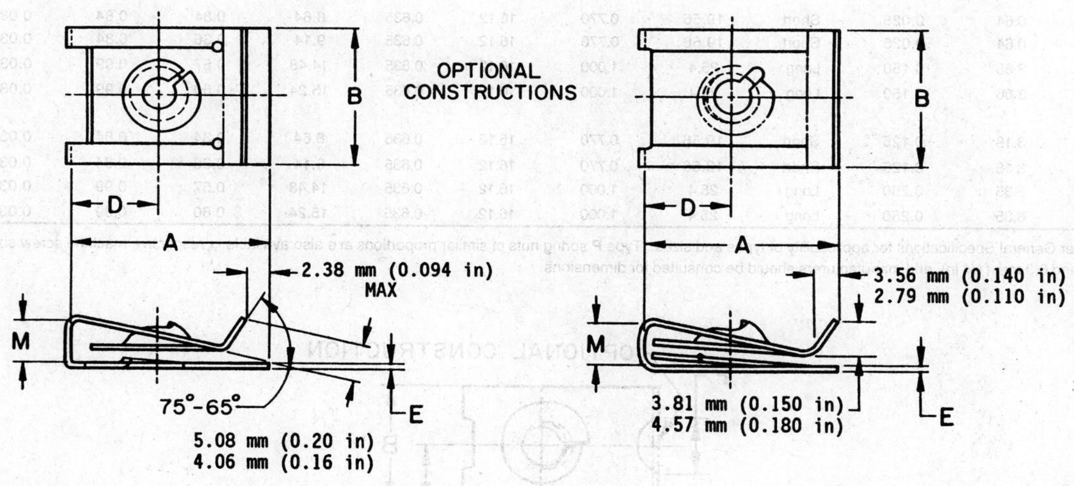

FIGURE 7—U SHAPE SHORT THREAD STYLE AND LONG THROAT STYLE

TABLE 4—DIMENSIONS OF U SHAPE WIDE-RANGE DESIGN SPRING NUTS WITH OR WITHOUT RETAINING EXTRUSION (FIGURE 7)

Tapping Screw Size[(1)] mm	Tapping Screw Size[(1)] in	Panel Thickness Range mm	Panel Thickness Range in	Style	A Leg Length +0.38 −0.76 mm	A Leg Length +0.015 −0.030 in	B Nut Width ±0.38	B Nut Width ±0.015	D Throat Depth mm	D Throat Depth in	E Stock Thickness mm	E Stock Thickness in	M Width at Fold mm	M Width at Fold in
3.5	#6	0.64	0.025	Short	19.56	0.770	13.58	0.535	8.64	0.34	0.46	0.018	3.81	0.150
3.5	#6	0.64	0.025	Short	19.56	0.770	13.58	0.535	9.14	0.36	0.46	0.018	3.81	0.150
3.5	#6	3.66	0.150	Long	25.4	1.000	13.58	0.535	14.48	0.57	0.68	0.027	4.04	0.190
3.5	#6	3.66	0.150	Long	25.4	1.000	13.58	0.535	15.24	0.60	0.68	0.027	4.04	0.190
3.5	#6	3.18	0.125	Short	19.56	0.770	13.58	0.535	8.64	0.34	0.46	0.018	6.60	0.260
3.5	#6	3.18	0.125	Short	19.56	0.770	13.58	0.535	9.14	0.36	0.46	0.018	6.60	0.260
3.5	#6	6.35	0.250	Long	25.4	1.000	13.58	0.535	14.48	0.57	0.68	0.027	7.11	0.280
3.5	#6	6.35	0.250	Long	25.4	1.000	13.58	0.535	15.24	0.60	0.68	0.027	7.11	0.280
4.2	#8	0.64	0.025	Short	19.56	0.770	13.58	0.535	8.64	0.34	0.58	0.023	3.81	0.150
4.2	#8	0.64	0.025	Short	19.56	0.770	13.58	0.535	9.14	0.36	0.58	0.023	3.81	0.150
4.2	#8	3.66	0.150	Long	25.4	1.000	13.58	0.535	14.48	0.57	0.76	0.030	4.04	0.190
4.2	#8	3.66	0.150	Long	25.4	1.000	13.58	0.535	15.24	0.60	0.76	0.030	4.04	0.190
4.2	#8	3.18	0.125	Short	19.56	0.770	13.58	0.535	8.64	0.34	0.58	0.023	6.60	0.260
4.2	#8	3.18	0.125	Short	19.56	0.770	13.58	0.535	9.14	0.36	0.58	0.023	6.60	0.260
4.2	#8	6.35	0.250	Long	25.4	1.000	13.58	0.535	14.48	0.57	0.76	0.030	7.11	0.280
4.2	#8	6.35	0.250	Long	25.4	1.000	13.58	0.535	15.24	0.60	0.76	0.030	7.11	0.280
4.8	#10	0.64	0.025	Short	19.56	0.770	16.12	0.635	8.64	0.34	0.71	0.028	3.81	0.150
4.8	#10	0.64	0.025	Short	19.56	0.770	16.12	0.635	9.14	0.36	0.71	0.028	3.81	0.150
4.8	#10	3.66	0.150	Long	25.4	1.000	16.12	0.635	14.48	0.57	0.88	0.035	4.04	0.190
4.8	#10	3.66	0.150	Long	25.4	1.000	16.12	0.635	15.24	0.60	0.88	0.035	4.04	0.190
4.8	#10	3.18	0.125	Short	19.56	0.770	16.12	0.635	8.64	0.34	0.71	0.028	6.60	0.260
4.8	#10	3.18	0.125	Short	19.56	0.770	16.12	0.635	9.14	0.36	0.71	0.028	6.60	0.260
4.8	#10	6.35	0.250	Long	25.4	1.000	16.12	0.635	14.48	0.57	0.88	0.035	7.11	0.280
4.8	#10	6.35	0.250	Long	25.4	1.000	16.12	0.635	15.24	0.60	0.88	0.035	7.11	0.280
6.3	1/4	0.64	0.025	Short	19.56	0.770	16.12	0.635	8.64	0.34	0.84	0.033	3.81	0.150
6.3	1/4	0.64	0.025	Short	19.56	0.770	16.12	0.635	9.14	0.36	0.84	0.033	3.81	0.150
6.3	1/4	3.66	0.150	Long	25.4	1.000	16.12	0.635	14.48	0.57	0.99	0.039	4.04	0.190
6.3	1/4	3.66	0.150	Long	25.4	1.000	16.12	0.635	15.24	0.60	0.99	0.039	4.04	0.190
6.3	1/4	3.18	0.125	Short	19.56	0.770	16.12	0.635	8.64	0.34	0.84	0.033	6.60	0.260
6.3	1/4	3.18	0.125	Short	19.56	0.770	16.12	0.635	9.14	0.36	0.84	0.033	6.60	0.260
6.3	1/4	6.35	0.250	Long	25.4	1.000	16.12	0.635	14.48	0.57	0.99	0.039	7.11	0.280
6.3	1/4	6.35	0.250	Long	25.4	1.000	16.12	0.635	15.24	0.60	0.99	0.039	7.11	0.280

1. See Boss Detail under General Specifications for applicability of types and sizes. Type P spring nuts of similar proportions are also available in respective machine screw sizes 3.5 mm (#6), 4.2 mm (#8), 4.8 mm (#10), and 6.3 mm (1/4 in), and manufacturers should be consulted for dimensions.

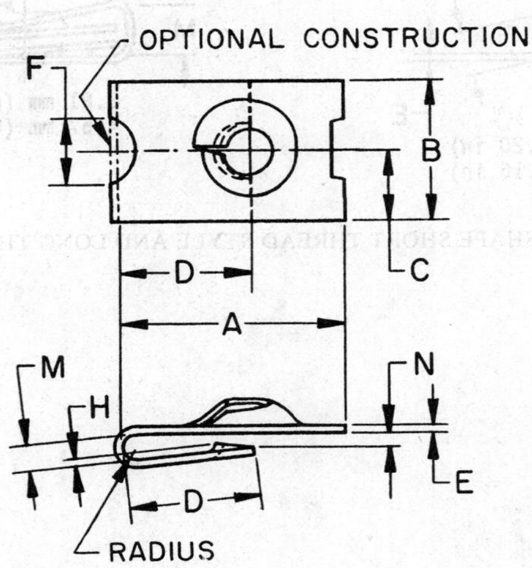

FIGURE 8—J SHAPE STYLE I—STANDARD, STYLE II—SHORT, AND STYLE III—LONG THROAT

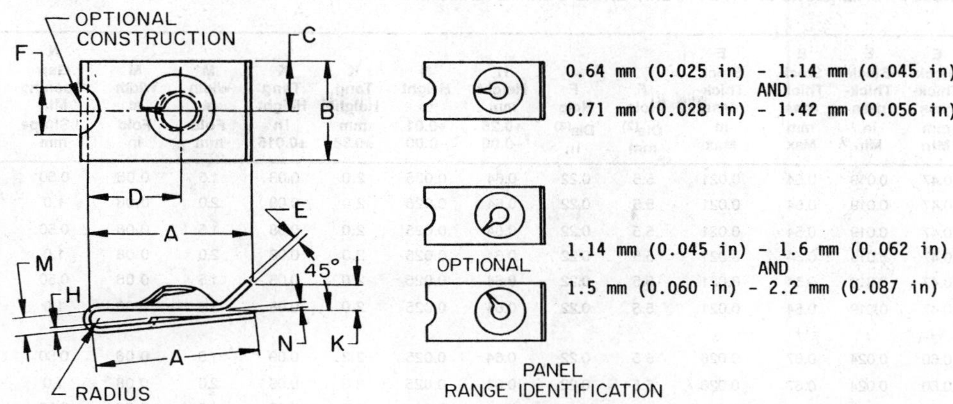

FIGURE 9—U SHAPE STYLE—STANDARD, STYLE II—SHORT, AND STYLE III—LONG THROAT

TABLE 5—DIMENSIONS OF TYPE P, J SHAPE, AND U SHAPE REGULAR DESIGN SPRING NUTS (FIGURES 8 AND 9)

Tapping Screw Size(1) mm	Tapping Screw Size(1) in	Panel Thickness Range mm	Panel Thickness Range in	Style	A Leg Length J Shape mm ±0.5	A Leg Length J Shape in ±0.02	A Leg Length U Shape mm ±0.5	A Leg Length U Shape in ±0.02	B Nut Width mm	B Nut Width in	C Edge to Center mm	C Edge to Center in	D Throat Depth mm ±0.5	D Throat Depth in ±0.02
3.5	#6	0.64–1.14	0.025–0.045	I	13.5	0.53	15.0	0.59	8.6	0.34	4.3	0.17	8.4	0.33
3.5	#6	1.14–1.6	0.045–0.062	I	13.5	0.53	15.0	0.59	8.6	0.34	4.3	0.17	8.4	0.33
3.5	#6	0.64–1.14	0.025–0.045	II	11.9	0.47	13.5	0.53	8.6	0.34	4.3	0.17	6.9	0.27
3.5	#6	1.14–1.6	0.045–0.062	II	11.9	0.47	13.5	0.53	8.6	0.34	4.3	0.17	6.9	0.27
3.5	#6	0.64–1.14	0.025–0.045	III	17.8	0.70	19.3	0.76	8.6	0.34	4.3	0.17	13.2	0.52
3.5	#6	1.14–1.6	0.045–0.062	III	17.8	0.70	19.3	0.76	8.6	0.34	4.3	0.17	13.2	0.52
4.2	#8	0.64–1.14	0.025–0.045	I	15.5	0.61	17.0	0.67	10.2	0.40	5.1	0.20	9.9	0.39
4.2	#8	1.14–1.6	0.045–0.062	I	15.5	0.61	17.0	0.67	10.2	0.40	5.1	0.20	9.9	0.39
4.2	#8	0.64–1.14	0.025–0.045	II	13.0	0.51	14.5	0.57	10.2	0.40	5.1	0.20	7.1	0.26
4.2	#8	1.14–1.6	0.045–0.062	II	13.0	0.51	14.5	0.57	10.2	0.40	5.1	0.20	7.1	0.26
4.2	#8	0.64–1.14	0.025–0.045	III	20.6	0.81	22.4	0.88	10.2	0.40	5.1	0.20	14.7	0.58
4.2	#8	1.14–1.6	0.045–0.062	III	20.6	0.81	22.4	0.88	10.2	0.40	5.1	0.20	14.7	0.58
4.8	#10	0.64–1.14	0.025–0.045	I	16.3	0.64	17.8	0.70	11.4	0.50	5.7	0.25	9.9	0.39
4.8	#10	1.14–1.6	0.045–0.062	I	16.3	0.64	17.8	0.70	11.4	0.50	5.7	0.25	9.9	0.39
4.8	#10	0.64–1.14	0.025–0.045	II	15.5	0.61	16.3	0.64	11.4	0.50	5.7	0.25	8.4	0.33
4.8	#10	1.14–1.6	0.045–0.062	II	15.5	0.61	16.3	0.64	11.4	0.50	5.7	0.25	8.4	0.33
4.8	#10	0.64–1.14	0.025–0.045	III	21.1	0.83	22.6	0.87	11.4	0.50	5.7	0.25	14.7	0.58
4.8	#10	1.14–1.6	0.045–0.062	III	21.1	0.83	22.6	0.87	11.4	0.50	5.7	0.25	14.7	0.58
6.3	1/4	0.71–1.42	0.028–0.056	I	20.3	0.80	21.8	0.86	14.2	0.56	7.1	0.28	11.9	0.47
6.3	1/4	1.5–2.2	0.06–0.087	I	20.3	0.80	21.8	0.86	14.2	0.56	7.1	0.28	11.9	0.47
6.3	1/4	0.71–1.42	0.028–0.056	III	27.7	1.09	28.4	1.16	14.2	0.56	7.1	0.28	18.3	0.72
6.3	1/4	1.5–2.2	0.06–0.087	III	27.7	1.09	28.4	1.16	14.2	0.56	7.1	0.28	18.3	0.72

1. See Boss Detail under General Specifications for applicability of types and sizes. Type P spring nut of similar proportions are also available in respective machine screw sizes 3.5 mm (#6), 4.2 mm (#8), 4.8 mm (#10), and 6.3 mm (1/4 in), and manufacturers should be consulted for dimensions.

TABLE 5—DIMENSIONS OF TYPE P, J SHAPE, AND U SHAPE REGULAR DESIGN SPRING NUTS (FIGURES 8 AND 9) (CONTINUED)

Tapping Screw Size[1] mm	Tapping Screw Size[1] in	Style	E Stock Thickness mm Min	E Stock Thickness in Min	E Stock Thickness mm Max	E Stock Thickness in Max	F Hole Dia[2] mm	F Hole Dia[2] in	H Height mm +0.25 −0.00	H Height in +0.01 −0.00	K Tang Height mm ±0.38	K Tang Height in ±0.015	M Width at Fold mm	M Width at Fold in	N Gap Opening Min J Shape mm	N Gap Opening Min J Shape in	N Gap Opening Max U Shape mm	N Gap Opening Max U Shape in
3.5	#6	I	0.47	0.019	0.54	0.021	5.5	0.22	0.64	0.025	2.0	0.08	1.5	0.06	0.50	0.02	0.50	0.02
3.5	#6	I	0.47	0.019	0.54	0.021	5.5	0.22	0.64	0.025	2.0	0.08	2.0	0.08	1.0	0.04	1.0	0.04
3.5	#6	II	0.47	0.019	0.54	0.021	5.5	0.22	0.64	0.025	2.0	0.08	1.5	0.06	0.50	0.02	0.50	0.02
3.5	#6	II	0.47	0.019	0.54	0.021	5.5	0.22	0.64	0.025	2.0	0.08	2.0	0.08	1.0	0.04	1.0	0.04
3.5	#6	III	0.47	0.019	0.54	0.021	5.5	0.22	0.64	0.025	2.0	0.08	1.5	0.06	0.50	0.02	0.50	0.02
3.5	#6	III	0.47	0.019	0.54	0.021	5.5	0.22	0.64	0.025	2.0	0.08	2.0	0.08	1.0	0.04	1.0	0.04
4.2	#8	I	0.60	0.024	0.67	0.026	5.5	0.22	0.64	0.025	2.3	0.09	1.5	0.06	0.50	0.02	0.50	0.02
4.2	#8	I	0.60	0.024	0.67	0.026	5.5	0.22	0.64	0.025	2.3	0.09	2.0	0.08	1.0	0.04	1.0	0.04
4.2	#8	II	0.60	0.024	0.67	0.026	5.5	0.22	0.64	0.025	2.3	0.09	1.5	0.06	0.50	0.02	0.50	0.02
4.2	#8	II	0.60	0.024	0.67	0.026	5.5	0.22	0.64	0.025	2.3	0.09	2.0	0.08	1.0	0.04	1.0	0.04
4.2	#8	III	0.60	0.024	0.67	0.026	5.5	0.22	0.64	0.025	2.3	0.09	1.5	0.06	0.50	0.02	0.50	0.02
4.2	#8	III	0.60	0.024	0.67	0.026	5.5	0.22	0.64	0.025	2.3	0.09	2.0	0.08	1.0	0.04	1.0	0.04
4.8	#10	I	0.70	0.028	0.82	0.032	5.5	0.22	0.64	0.025	2.3	0.09	1.5	0.06	0.50	0.02	0.50	0.02
4.8	#10	I	0.70	0.028	0.82	0.032	5.5	0.22	0.64	0.025	2.3	0.09	2.0	0.08	1.0	0.04	1.0	0.04
4.8	#10	II	0.70	0.028	0.82	0.032	5.5	0.22	0.64	0.025	2.3	0.09	1.5	0.06	0.50	0.02	0.50	0.02
4.8	#10	II	0.70	0.028	0.82	0.032	5.5	0.22	0.64	0.025	2.3	0.09	2.0	0.08	1.0	0.04	1.0	0.04
4.8	#10	III	0.70	0.028	0.82	0.032	5.5	0.22	0.64	0.025	2.3	0.09	1.5	0.06	0.50	0.02	0.50	0.02
4.8	#10	III	0.70	0.028	0.82	0.032	5.5	0.22	0.64	0.025	2.3	0.09	2.0	0.08	1.0	0.04	1.0	0.04
6.3	1/4	I	0.70	0.028	0.82	0.032	5.5	0.22	0.64	0.025	2.8	0.11	2.0	0.08	1.0	0.04	1.0	0.04
6.3	1/4	I	0.70	0.028	0.82	0.032	5.5	0.22	0.64	0.025	2.8	0.11	2.5	0.10	1.2	0.05	1.2	0.05
6.3	1/4	III	0.70	0.028	0.82	0.032	5.5	0.22	0.64	0.025	2.8	0.11	2.0	0.08	1.0	0.04	1.0	0.04
6.3	1/4	III	0.70	0.028	0.82	0.032	5.5	0.22	0.64	0.025	2.8	0.11	2.5	0.10	1.2	0.05	1.2	0.05

1. See Boss Detail under General Specifications for applicability of types and sizes. Type P spring nut of similar proportions are also available in respective machine screw sizes 3.5 mm (#6), 4.2 mm (#8), 4.8 mm (#10), and 6.3 mm (1/4 in), and manufacturers should be consulted for dimensions.
2. Diameter of hole punched in blank before forming.

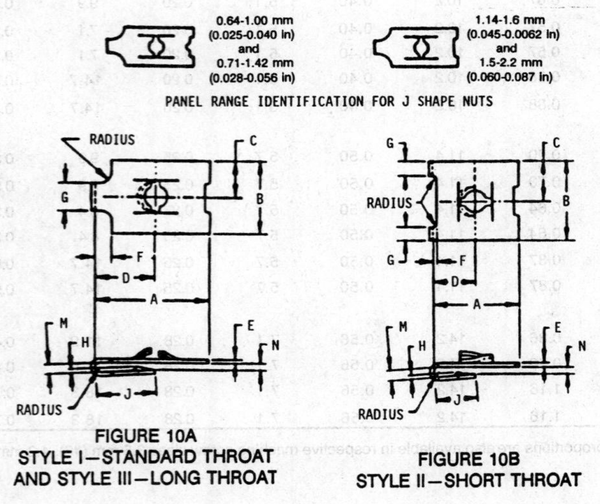

FIGURE 10A
STYLE I—STANDARD THROAT AND STYLE III—LONG THROAT

FIGURE 10B
STYLE II—SHORT THROAT

FIGURE 10—J SHAPE

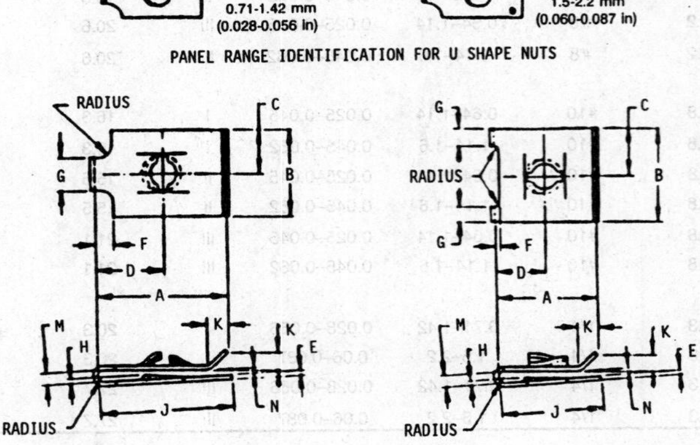

FIGURE 11A
STYLE I—STANDARD THROAT AND STYLE III—LONG THROAT

FIGURE 11B
STYLE II—SHORT THROAT

FIGURE 11—U SHAPE

TABLE 6—DIMENSIONS OF TYPE T, J SHAPE, AND U SHAPE REGULAR DESIGN SPRING NUTS (FIGURES 10A TO 10B)

Tapping Screw Size[1] mm	Tapping Screw Size[1] in	Panel Thick-ness range mm	Panel Thick-ness range in	Style	A Leg Length mm ±0.5	A Leg Length in ±0.02	B Nut Width mm	B Nut Width in	C Edge to Center mm	C Edge to Center in	D Throat Depth mm ±0.5	D Throat Depth in ±0.02	E Stock Thick-ness mm Min	E Stock Thick-ness mm Max	E Stock Thick-ness in Min	E Stock Thick-ness in Max
3.5	#6	0.64–1.14	0.025–0.045	I	16.3	0.64	7.9	0.312	4.0	0.156	8.6	0.34	0.027	0.023	0.69	0.58
3.5	#6	1.14–1.6	0.045–0.062	I	16.3	0.64	7.9	0.312	4.0	0.156	8.6	0.34	0.027	0.023	0.69	0.58
3.5	#6	0.64–1.14	0.025–0.045	II	12.2	0.48	12.7	0.50	6.4	0.25	6.7	0.26	0.027	0.023	0.69	0.58
3.5	#6	1.14–1.6	0.045–0.062	II	12.2	0.48	12.7	0.50	6.4	0.25	6.7	0.26	0.027	0.023	0.69	0.58
3.5	#6	0.64–1.14	0.025–0.045	III	20.1	0.81	7.9	0.312	4.0	0.156	13.0	0.51	0.027	0.023	0.69	0.58
3.5	#6	1.14–1.6	0.045–0.062	III	20.1	0.81	7.9	0.312	4.0	0.156	13.0	0.51	0.027	0.023	0.69	0.58
4.2	#8	0.64–1.14	0.025–0.045	I	17.3	0.68	10.3	0.406	5.2	0.203	9.4	0.37	0.03	0.026	0.76	0.66
4.2	#8	1.14–1.6	0.045–0.062	I	17.3	0.68	10.3	0.406	5.2	0.203	9.4	0.37	0.03	0.026	0.76	0.66
4.2	#8	0.64–1.14	0.025–0.045	II	13.2	0.52	12.7	0.50	6.4	0.25	6.6	0.26	0.03	0.026	0.76	0.66
4.2	#8	1.14–1.6	0.045–0.062	II	13.2	0.52	12.7	0.50	6.4	0.25	6.6	0.26	0.03	0.026	0.76	0.66
4.2	#8	0.64–1.14	0.025–0.045	III	21.8	0.86	10.3	0.406	5.2	0.203	14.0	0.55	0.03	0.026	0.76	0.66
4.2	#8	1.14–1.6	0.045–0.062	III	21.8	0.86	10.3	0.406	5.2	0.203	14.0	0.55	0.03	0.026	0.76	0.66
4.8	#10	0.64–1.14	0.025–0.045	I	19.3	0.76	12.7	0.50	6.4	0.25	10.7	0.42	0.033	0.029	0.84	0.74
4.8	#10	1.14–1.6	0.045–0.062	I	19.3	0.76	12.7	0.50	6.4	0.25	10.7	0.42	0.033	0.029	0.84	0.74
4.8	#10	0.64–1.14	0.025–0.045	II	14.5	0.57	15.9	0.625	7.9	0.312	7.8	0.31	0.033	0.029	0.84	0.74
4.8	#10	1.14–1.6	0.045–0.062	II	14.5	0.57	15.9	0.625	7.9	0.312	7.8	0.31	0.033	0.029	0.84	0.74
4.8	#10	0.64–1.14	0.025–0.045	III	24.4	0.96	12.7	0.50	6.4	0.25	15.5	0.61	0.033	0.029	0.84	0.74
4.8	#10	1.14–1.6	0.045–0.062	III	24.4	0.96	12.7	0.50	6.4	0.25	15.5	0.61	0.033	0.029	0.84	0.74
6.3	1/4	0.71–1.5	0.028–0.06	I	23.4	0.92	14.3	0.562	7.1	0.281	12.6	0.50	0.042	0.035	1.07	0.89
6.3	1/4	1.5–2.2	0.06–0.087	I	23.4	0.92	14.3	0.562	7.1	0.281	12.6	0.50	0.042	0.035	1.07	0.89
6.3	1/4	0.7–1.5	0.028–0.06	III	29.5	1.16	14.3	0.562	7.1	0.281	18.9	0.75	0.039	0.035	0.99	0.89
6.3	1/4	1.5–2.2	0.06–0.087	III	29.5	1.16	14.3	0.562	7.1	0.281	18.9	0.75	0.039	0.035	0.99	0.89

1. See Boss Detail under General Specifications for applicability of types and sizes. Type T spring nuts of similar proportions are also available in respective machine screw sizes 3.5 mm (#6), 4.2 mm (#8), 4.8 mm (#10), and 6.3 mm (1/4 in), and manufacturers should be consulted for dimensions.

TABLE 6—DIMENSIONS OF TYPE T, J SHAPE, AND U SHAPE REGULAR DESIGN SPRING NUTS (FIGURES 10A TO 10B) (CONTINUED)

Tapping Screw Size[1] mm	Tapping Screw Size[1] in	Style	F Notch Depth mm ±0.5	F Notch Depth in ±002	G Width mm ±0.5	G Width in ±0.02	H Height mm ±0.13	H Height in ±0.005	J Leg Length mm ±0.5	J Leg Length in ±0.02	K Tang mm ±0.5	K Tang in ±0.02	N Gap Opening J Shape mm Min	N Gap Opening J Shape in Min	N Gap Opening U Shape mm Max	N Gap Opening U Shape in Max
3.5	#6	I	2.0	0.08	2.8	0.11	0.5	0.02	8.9	0.35	2.0	0.08	0.5	0.02	0.5	0.02
3.5	#6	I	2.0	0.08	2.8	0.11	0.5	0.02	8.9	0.35	2.0	0.08	1.0	0.04	1.0	0.04
3.5	#6	II	0.5	0.02	2.3	0.09	0.5	0.02	6.6	0.26	2.0	0.08	0.5	0.02	0.5	0.02
3.5	#6	II	0.5	0.02	2.3	0.09	0.5	0.02	6.6	0.26	2.0	0.08	1.0	0.04	1.0	0.04
3.5	#6	III	6.2	0.24	3.6	0.14	0.5	0.02	13.0	0.51	2.0	0.08	0.5	0.02	0.5	0.02
3.5	#6	III	6.2	0.24	3.6	0.14	0.5	0.02	13.0	0.51	2.0	0.08	1.0	0.04	1.0	0.04
4.2	#8	I	2.3	0.09	4.6	0.18	0.64	0.025	9.4	0.37	2.3	0.09	0.5	0.02	0.5	0.02
4.2	#8	I	2.3	0.09	4.6	0.18	0.64	0.025	9.4	0.37	2.3	0.09	1.0	0.04	1.0	0.04
4.2	#8	II	0.5	0.20	2.3	0.09	0.64	0.025	6.9	0.27	2.3	0.09	0.5	0.02	0.5	0.02
4.2	#8	II	0.5	0.20	2.3	0.09	0.64	0.025	6.9	0.27	2.3	0.09	1.0	0.04	1.0	0.04
4.2	#8	III	6.9	0.27	4.6	0.18	0.64	0.025	14.2	0.56	2.3	0.09	0.5	0.02	0.5	0.02
4.2	#8	III	6.9	0.27	4.6	0.18	0.64	0.025	14.2	0.56	2.3	0.09	1.0	0.04	1.0	0.04
4.8	#10	I	2.8	0.11	3.1	0.12	0.64	0.025	10.7	0.42	2.3	0.09	0.5	0.02	0.5	0.02
4.8	#10	I	2.8	0.11	3.1	0.12	0.64	0.025	10.7	0.42	2.3	0.09	1.0	0.04	1.0	0.04
4.8	#10	II	0.5	0.02	3.3	0.13	0.64	0.025	7.9	0.31	2.3	0.09	0.5	0.02	0.5	0.02
4.8	#10	II	0.5	0.02	3.3	0.13	0.64	0.025	7.9	0.31	2.3	0.09	1.0	0.04	1.0	0.04
4.8	#10	III	6.4	0.25	4.3	0.17	0.64	0.025	15.5	0.61	2.3	0.09	0.5	0.02	0.5	0.02
4.8	#10	III	6.4	0.25	4.3	0.17	0.64	0.025	15.5	0.61	2.3	0.09	1.0	0.04	1.0	0.04
6.3	1/4	I	1.5	0.06	4.6	0.18	0.76	0.03	12.5	0.49	2.8	0.11	1.0	0.04	1.0	0.04
6.3	1/4	I	1.5	0.06	4.6	0.18	0.76	0.03	12.5	0.49	2.8	0.11	1.2	0.05	1.2	0.05
6.3	1/4	III	7.9	0.31	6.4	0.25	0.76	0.03	19.0	0.75	2.8	0.11	1.0	0.04	1.0	0.04
6.3	1/4	III	7.9	0.31	6.4	0.25	0.76	0.03	19.0	0.75	2.8	0.11	1.2	0.05	1.2	0.05

1. See Boss Detail under General Specifications for applicability of types and sizes. Type T spring nuts of similar proportions are also available in respective machine screw 3.5 mm (#6), 4.2 mm (#8), 4.8 mm (#10), and 6.3 mm (1/4 in), and manufacturers should be consulted for dimensions.

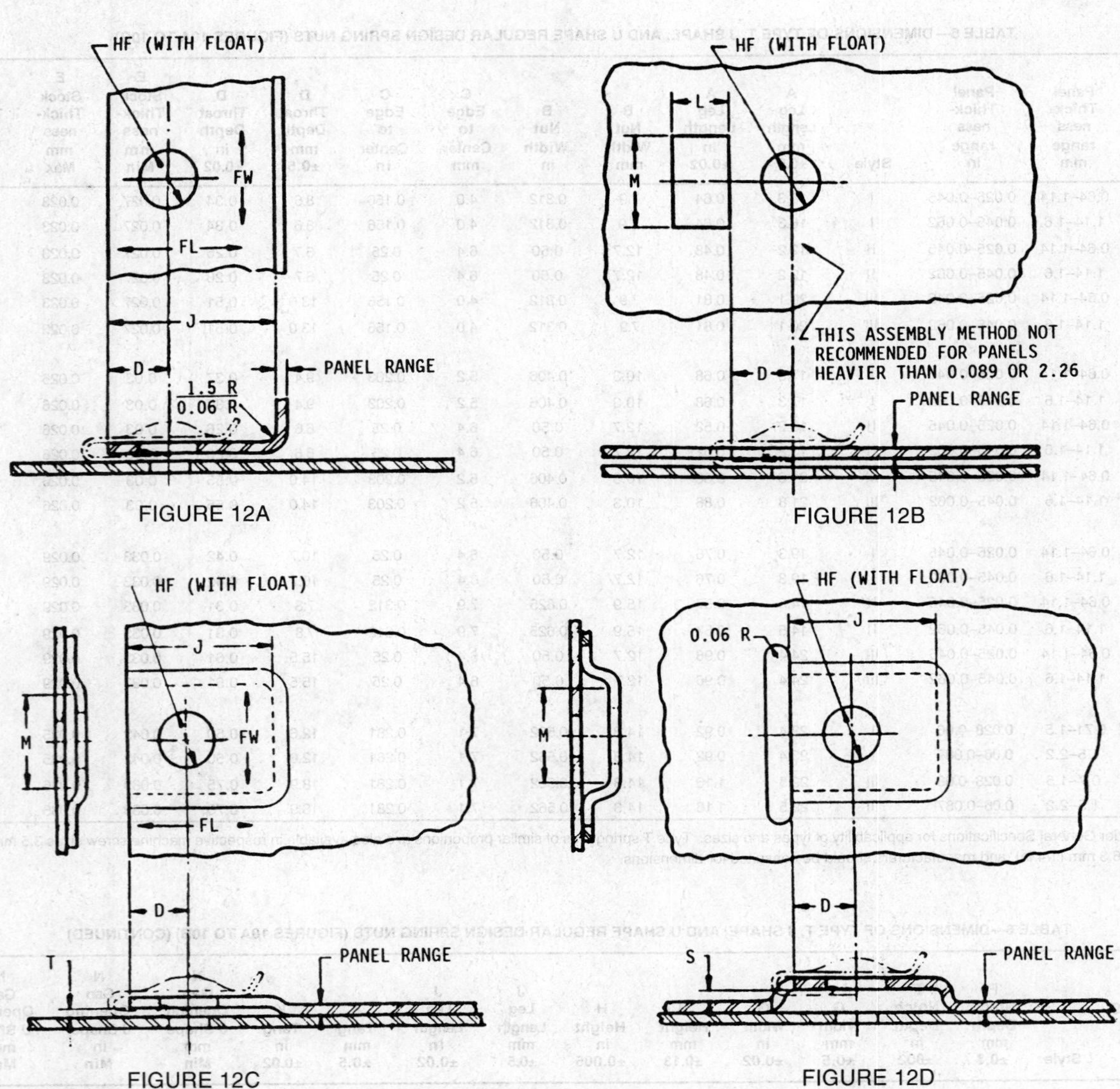

FIGURE 12—RECOMMENDED ASSEMBLY FOR WIDE-RANGE DESIGN SPRING NUTS

TABLE 7—RECOMMENDED ASSEMBLY DATA FOR WIDE-RANGE DESIGN SPRING NUTS[1] (FIGURES 12A TO 12D)

Tapping Screw Size mm	Tapping Screw Size in	Style	D mm ±0.5	D in ±0.02	HF Dia in ±0.13	HF Dia in ±0.005	J mm	J in	L Min mm	L Min in
3.5	#6	Short	6.4	0.25	6.4	0.25	19.8	0.78	6.4	0.25
3.5	#6	Long	12.2	0.48	6.4	0.25	25.6	1.01	6.4	0.25
4.2	#8	Short	6.4	0.25	7.1	0.28	19.8	0.78	8.6	0.34
4.2	#8	Long	12.2	0.48	7.1	0.28	25.6	1.01	8.6	0.34
4.8	#10	Short	6.4	0.25	7.9	0.31	19.8	0.78	10.9	0.43
4.8	#10	Long	12.2	0.48	7.9	0.31	25.6	1.01	10.9	0.43
6.3	1/4	Short	6.4	0.25	9.6	0.38	19.8	0.78	12.7	0.50
6.3	1/4	Long	12.2	0.48	9.6	0.38	25.6	1.01	12.7	0.50

1. These data are intended for design guidance only and are not to be considered a mandatory part of the document. The dimensions specified have been selected to accommodate the optional constructions of wide-range design spring nuts and both Type P and Type T regular design spring nuts, respectively, covered by the document. Tolerances on the nuts and tolerances entailed in the manufacturing processes used to emboss and punch the various assembly features were not considered in the derivation of these dimensions.

TABLE 7—RECOMMENDED ASSEMBLY DATA FOR WIDE-RANGE DESIGN SPRING NUTS (FIGURES 12A TO 12D) (CONTINUED)[1]

Tapping Screw Size mm	Tapping Screw Size in	Style	M Flat mm	M Flat in	S Min mm	S Min in	T Min mm	T Min in
3.5	#6	Short	16.0	0.63	1.6	0.65	0.6	0.027
3.5	#6	Long	16.0	0.63	1.6	0.65	0.6	0.027
4.2	#8	Short	16.0	0.63	1.6	0.65	0.8	0.03
4.2	#8	Long	16.0	0.63	1.6	0.65	0.8	0.03
4.8	#10	Short	18.5	0.73	1.6	0.65	0.9	0.035
4.8	#10	Long	18.5	0.73	1.6	0.65	0.9	0.035
6.3	1/4	Short	18.5	0.73	1.6	0.65	1.0	0.04
6.3	1/4	Long	18.5	0.73	1.6	0.65	1.0	0.04

1. These data are intended for design guidance only and are not to be considered a mandatory part of the document. The dimensions specified have been selected to accommodate the optional constructions of wide-range design spring nuts and both Type P and Type T regular design spring nuts, respectively, covered by the document. Tolerances on the nuts and tolerances entailed in the manufacturing processes used to emboss and punch the various assembly features were not considered in the derivation of these dimensions.

TABLE 8—RECOMMENDED ASSEMBLY DATA FOR TYPES P AND T, J SHAPE, AND U SHAPEREGULAR DESIGN SPRING NUTS [1] (FIGURES 12A TO 12D)

Tapping Size mm	Tapping Size in	Style	D mm ±0.5	D in ±0.02	HF Dia mm ±0.13	HF Dia in ±0.005	J mm	J in	L Min mm	L Min in
3.5	#6	I	6.4	0.25	6.4	0.25	17.5	0.69	5.6	0.22
3.5	#6	II	4.3	0.17	6.4	0.25	13.4	0.53	5.6	0.22
3.5	#6	III	10.6	0.42	6.4	0.25	22.4	0.88	5.6	0.22
4.2	#8	I	7.1	0.23	7.1	0.28	18.5	0.73	6.4	0.25
4.2	#8	II	4.6	0.18	7.1	0.28	14.9	0.59	6.4	0.25
4.2	#8	III	11.6	0.46	7.1	0.28	23.4	0.92	6.4	0.25
4.8	#10	I	7.6	0.30	7.9	0.31	20.6	0.81	7.9	0.31
4.8	#10	II	5.1	0.20	7.9	0.31	15.7	0.62	7.9	0.31
4.8	#10	III	12.2	0.48	7.9	0.31	25.4	1.00	7.9	0.31
6.3	#14 or 1/4	I	0.6	0.38	9.6	0.38	23.8	0.94	11.2	0.44
6.3	#14 or 1/4	III	15.7	0.62	9.6	0.38	29.7	1.17	11.2	0.44

1. These data are intended for design guidance only and are not to be considered a mandatory part of the document. The dimensions specified have been selected to accommodate the optional constructions of wide-range design spring nuts and both Type P and Type T regular design spring nuts, respectively, covered by the document. Tolerances on the nuts and tolerances entailed in the manufacturing processes used to emboss and punch the various assembly features were not considered in the derivation of these dimensions.

TABLE 8—RECOMMENDED ASSEMBLY DATA FOR TYPES P AND T, J SHAPE, AND U SHAPE REGULAR DESIGN SPRING NUTS (FIGURES 12A TO 12D) (CONTINUED)[1]

Tapping Size mm	Tapping Size in	Style	M Flat mm	M Flat in	S mm Min	S in Min	T mm Min	T in Min
3.5	#6	I	11.8	0.44	1.5	0.06	0.8	0.03
3.5	#6	II	14.9	0.59	1.5	0.06	0.8	0.03
3.5	#6	III	11.8	0.44	1.5	0.06	0.8	0.03
4.2	#8	I	12.7	0.50	1.5	0.06	0.8	0.033
4.2	#8	II	14.9	0.59	1.6	0.065	0.8	0.033
4.2	#8	III	12.7	0.50	1.6	0.065	0.8	0.033
4.8	#10	I	14.9	0.59	1.6	0.065	0.9	0.036
4.8	#10	II	18.2	0.72	1.6	0.065	0.9	0.036
4.8	#10	III	14.9	0.59	1.8	0.07	0.9	0.036
6.3	#14 or 1/4	I	16.8	0.66	2.2	0.085	1.1	0.042
6.3	#14 or 1/4	III	16.8	0.66	2.2	0.085	1.1	0.042

1. These data are intended for design guidance only and are not to be considered a mandatory part of the document. The dimensions specified have been selected to accommodate the optional constructions of wide-range design spring nuts and both Type P and Type T regular design spring nuts, respectively, covered by the document. Tolerances on the nuts and tolerances entailed in the manufacturing processes used to emboss and punch the various assembly features were not considered in the derivation of these dimensions.

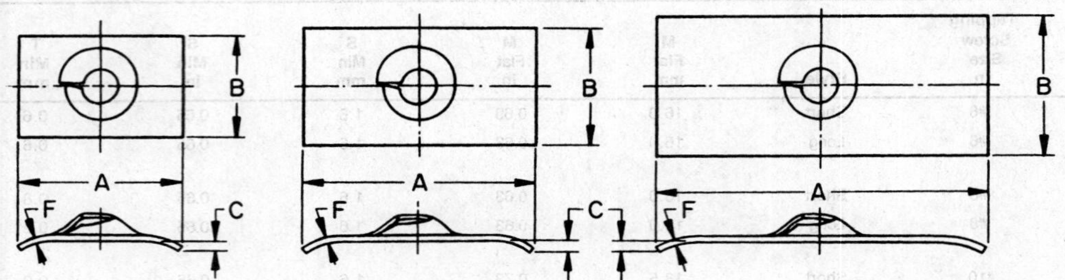

FIGURE 13—TYPE P SINGLE BOSS

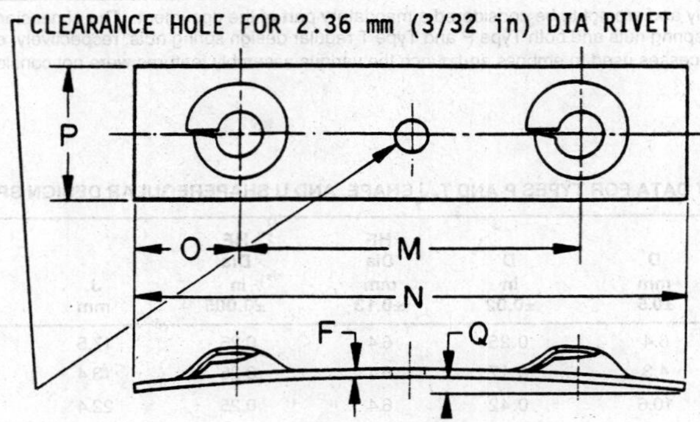

FIGURE 14—TYPE P TWIN BOSS

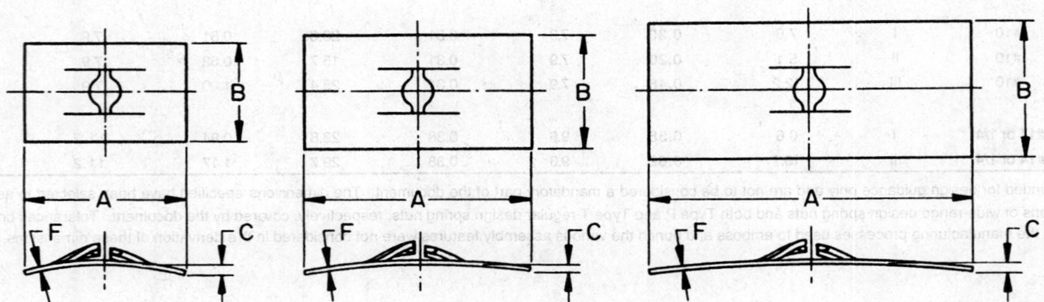

FIGURE 15—TYPE T SINGLE BOSS

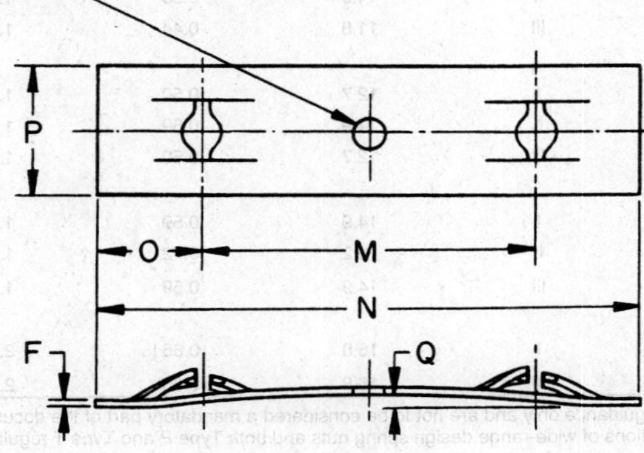

FIGURE 16—TYPE T TWIN BOSS

TABLE 9—DIMENSIONS OF TYPE P AND TYPE T FLAT SPRING NUTS[1][2] (FIGURES 13 TO 16)

Tapping Screw Size mm	Tapping Screw Size in	Single Boss Style	Single Boss A Nut Length mm ±0.50	Single Boss A Nut Length in ±0.02	Single Boss B Nut Width mm	Single Boss B Nut Width in	Single Boss C Arch Height mm Min	Single Boss C Arch Height in Min	Single Boss C Arch Height mm Max	Single Boss C Arch Height in Max	F Stock Thick-ness mm Min	F Stock Thick-ness in Min	F Stock Thick-ness mm Max	F Stock Thick-ness in Max
3.5	#6	I	12.7	0.50	7.90	0.312	0.50	0.02	1.02	0.04	0.48	0.019	0.66	0.026
3.5	#6	II	22.4	0.88	11.12	0.438	0.76	0.03	1.52	0.06	0.48	0.019	0.66	0.026
3.5	#6	III	35.0	1.38	13.48	0.531	0.25	0.01	1.27	0.05	0.48	0.019	0.66	0.026
4.2	#8	I	15.7	0.62	10.31	0.406	0.64	0.025	1.40	0.055	0.61	0.024	0.74	0.029
4.2	#8	II	22.4	0.88	11.91	0.469	0.89	0.035	1.65	0.065	0.61	0.024	0.74	0.029
4.2	#8	III	31.8	1.25	14.27	0.562	0.25	0.01	1.27	0.05	0.61	0.024	0.74	0.029
4.8	#10	I	19.1	0.75	12.70	0.500	0.89	0.035	1.65	0.065	0.71	0.028	0.84	0.033
4.8	#10	II	28.4	1.12	15.08	0.594	0.50	0.02	1.27	0.05	0.71	0.028	0.84	0.033
4.8	#10	III	35.0	1.38	17.48	0.688	1.02	0.04	2.03	0.08	0.71	0.028	0.84	0.033
6.3	#14 or 1/4	I	22.4	0.88	14.27	0.562	1.14	0.045	1.90	0.075	0.71	0.028	0.99	0.039
6.3	#14 or 1/4	II	26.9	1.06	5.88	0.625	0.50	0.02	1.27	0.05	0.71	0.028	0.99	0.039
6.3	#14 or 1/4	III	35.0	1.38	17.48	0.688	1.14	0.045	2.16	0.085	0.71	0.028	0.99	0.039

1. See Boss Detail under General Specifications for applicability of types and sizes.
2. The Type P nuts in this style will not meet the performance requirements in Table 2 due to the limitations on boss design imposed by the narrow width and the long length.

TABLE 9—DIMENSIONS OF TYPE P AND TYPE T FLAT SPRING NUTS (FIGURES 13 TO 16) (CONTINUED)[1]

Tapping Screw Size mm	Tapping Screw Size in	Twin Boss M Boss Center to Center mm	Twin Boss M Boss Center to Center in	Twin Boss N Nut Length mm ±0.50	Twin Boss N Nut Length in ±0.02	Twin Boss 0 End to Center mm	Twin Boss 0 End to Center in	Twin Boss P Nut Width mm	Twin Boss P Nut Width in	Twin Boss Q Arch Height mm Min	Twin Boss Q Arch Height in Min	Twin Boss Q Arch Height mm Max	Twin Boss Q Arch Height in Max
3.5	#6	12.70	0.500	28.4	1.12	7.90	0.312	9.52	0.375	0.12	0.005	1.14	0.045
3.5	#6	15.88	0.625	31.8	1.25	7.90	0.312	9.52	0.375	0.12	0.005	1.14	0.045
3.5	#6	19.05	0.750	35.1	1.38	7.90	0.312	9.52	0.375	0.12	0.005	1.14	0.045
3.5	#6	22.22	0.875	38.1	1.50	7.90	0.312	9.52	0.375	0.12	0.005	1.65	0.065
3.5	#6	25.4	1.000	41.1	1.62	7.90	0.312	9.52	0.375	0.12	0.005	1.65	0.065
4.2	#8	12.70	0.500	28.4	1.12	7.90	0.312	9.52	0.375	0.12	0.005	1.14	0.045
4.2	#8	15.88	0.625	31.8	1.25	7.90	0.312	9.52	0.375	0.12	0.005	1.14	0.045
4.2	#8	19.05	0.750	35.1	1.38	7.90	0.312	9.52	0.375	0.12	0.005	1.14	0.045
4.2	#8	22.22	0.875	38.1	1.50	7.90	0.312	9.52	0.375	0.12	0.005	1.65	0.065
4.2	#8	25.4	1.000	41.1	1.62	7.90	0.312	9.52	0.375	0.12	0.005	1.65	0.065
4.8	#10	12.70	0.500	28.4	1.12	7.90	0.312	9.52	0.500	0.12	0.005	1.14	0.045
4.8	#10	15.88	0.625	31.8	1.25	7.90	0.312	9.52	0.500	0.12	0.005	1.14	0.045
4.8	#10	19.05	0.750	35.1	1.38	7.90	0.312	9.52	0.500	0.12	0.005	1.14	0.045
4.8	#10	22.22	0.875	38.1	1.50	7.90	0.312	9.52	0.500	0.12	0.005	1.65	0.065
4.8	#10	25.4	1.000	41.1	1.62	7.90	0.312	9.52	0.500	0.12	0.005	1.65	0.065
6.3	#14 or 1/4	19.05	0.750	38.1	1.50	9.52	0.375	14.27	0.562	0.12	0.005	1.65	0.065
6.3	#14 or 1/4	22.22	0.875	41.1	1.62	9.52	0.375	14.27	0.562	0.12	0.005	1.65	0.065
6.3	#14 or 1/4	25.4	1.000	44.4	1.75	9.52	0.375	14.27	0.562	0.12	0.005	1.65	0.065

1. See Boss Detail under General Specifications for applicability of types and sizes.

PUSH-ON SPRING NUTS INCH SERIES—GENERAL SPECIFICATIONS—SAE J892 AUG1996

SAE Standard

Report of the SAE Fasteners Committee approved August 1964, revised June 1970, and completely revised August 1996.

Foreword—This Document has also changed to comply with the new SAE Technical Standards Board format.

1. Scope—Included herein are general, dimensional, and performance specifications for those types, styles, and sizes of steel stamped Push-On Spring Nuts recognized as SAE standard. These nuts are intended for general use where the engagement on the mating metal or plastic studs and in some cases screw or bolt threads is considered adequate for the fastening joint application. It should be noted that Push-On Spring Nuts having other characteristics and configurations are available and manufacturers should be consulted. For the metric equivalent of this document, see SAE J892M.

2. References

2.1 Applicable Publications—The following publication forms a part of this specification to the extent specified herein. Unless otherwise indicated, the latest version of SAE publications shall apply.

2.1.1 SAE PUBLICATION—Available from SAE, 400 Commonwealth Drive, Warrendale, PA 15096-0001.

SAE J892M—Push-On Spring Nuts Metric Series—General Specifications

3. Dimensional Tolerance—Tolerance on dimensions are in the tables.

4. Boss—Size and formation of boss and other detail shall be such as to assemble readily and function satisfactorily with the specified stud.

5. Material—Spring steel suitably processed to meet the hardness requirements of this specification.

6. Hardness—Hardness shall be as follows in Table 1:

TABLE 1—Hardness

Material Thickness	Rockwell Scale	Dial Reading	HR
Up to 0.016	15N	80.0-85.5	39-50
0.017 - 0.035	30N	58.0-68.5	39-50

7. Finish—Spring nuts are normally supplied with corrosion-resistant finish as specified by purchaser. Nuts subjected to corrosion preventive treatment which might induce hydrogen embrittlement shall be baked or otherwise treated to obviate such embrittlement.

8. Workmanship—Spring nuts shall be free from cracks, burrs, splits, loose scale, or any other defects which might affect their serviceability.

9. Application and Design—Where nut is to function only as a locking means (Figure 1, Table 2) Style 1 is recommended. Where greater area of load distribution is a requirement, i.e., nut is to function also as spanner washer, Style II is recommended. The Light Series are for use on plastic studs, the Medium Series are for use on soft metal studs, and the Heavy Series are for use on hardened metal or chromium plated studs. Tables 3 and 4 and Figures 2 and 3, Push-On Spring Nuts will be used likewise. Acorn types, closed and open top styles are shown in Table 5 and Figure 4. Note the restricted stud height is designated by rod penetration. Table 6 and Figures 5 and 6, Push-On Spring Bolt Retainers pertain to nuts applied onto screw and bolt threads. Blind push-on spring nut and stud requirements are listed in Tables 7 and 8 and Figures 7 and 8. The stud retained style must be preassembled onto the stud before inserting into a panel whereas the panel retained goes into the panel and then the stud is inserted.

10. Assembly Considerations—Since performance of push-on spring nuts is dependent upon the studs to which they are applied, it is essential that stud diameters and plating recommendations as set forth in Figure 9 and Table 9 be adhered to as closely as possible. The actual stud length is determined by adding the thickness of mating panel or panels "T" through which the stud protrudes to the factors tabulated under "C" (the minimum stud protrusion required for normal installation). It may be necessary to increase this factor to provide adequate stud protrusion where uncompressed materials or mismatch of trim contours are encountered. It should be noted by users desiring to standardize on stud designs that the studs applicable to self-threading stamped nuts may be utilized for push-on spring nuts where economics justify and the additional stud protrusion is not objectionable.

Heavy Series Nuts are used on round studs only. All other nuts in this document may be used on either round or "D" shaped studs. Nuts are used on round studs in applications where the assembly is permanent and on "D" shaped studs where disassembly is a consideration.

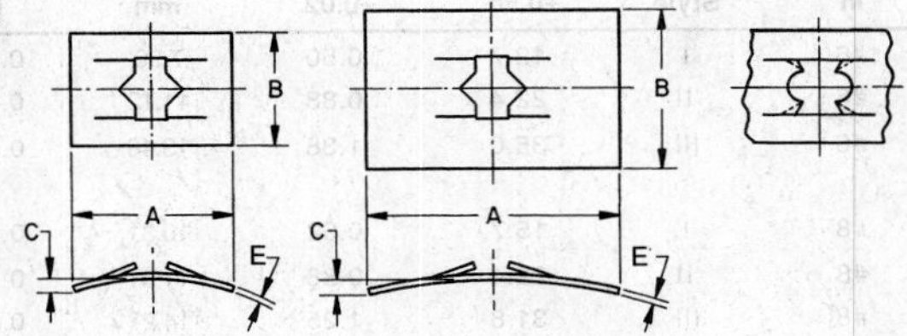

FIGURE 1A—STYLE 1 STANDARD

FIGURE 1B—STYLE II SPANNER

FIGURE 1C—HEAVY SERIES BOSS DESIGN SEE TABLE 3, NOTE 1

FIGURE 1—PUSH-ON SPRING NUTS—RECTANGULAR ARCHED

TABLE 2A—DIMENSIONS OF PUSH-ON SPRING NUTS (FIGURES 1A TO 1C)

Nominal[1] Stud Size in	Style	Series[2]	A Nut Length ±0.20 in	B Nut Width ±0.010 in	C Arch Height Max in	C Arch Height Min in	E Stock Thickness ±0.0015 in
1/16	I	Light	0.38	0.22	0.025	0.005	0.012
1/16	I	Medium	0.38	0.22	0.025	0.005	0.014
1/16	I	Heavy	0.38	0.22	0.025	0.005	0.017
1/16	II	Light	0.56	0.34	0.040	0.010	0.012
1/16	II	Medium	0.56	0.34	0.040	0.010	0.014
1/16	II	Heavy	0.56	0.34	0.040	0.010	0.017
3/32	I	Light	0.45	0.23	0.040	0.010	0.012
3/32	I	Medium	0.45	0.23	0.040	0.010	0.014
3/32	I	Heavy	0.45	0.23	0.040	0.010	0.017
3/32	II	Light	0.70	0.38	0.050	0.020	0.012
3/32	II	Medium	0.70	0.38	0.050	0.020	0.014
3/32	II	Heavy	0.70	0.38	0.050	0.020	0.017
1/8	I	Light	0.58	0.31	0.040	0.010	0.012
1/8	I	Medium	0.58	0.31	0.040	0.010	0.014
1/8	I	Heavy	0.58	0.31	0.040	0.010	0.017
1/8	II	Light	0.45	0.50	0.080	0.050	0.012
1/8	II	Medium	0.45	0.50	0.080	0.050	0.014
1/8	II	Heavy	0.45	0.50	0.080	0.050	0.017
5/32	I	Light	0.56	0.38	0.040	0.010	0.012
5/32	I	Medium	0.56	0.38	0.040	0.010	0.014
5/32	I	Heavy	0.56	0.38	0.040	0.010	0.017

1. See Table 9 for stud dimensions
2. See Section 9 Application and Design

TABLE 2B—DIMENSIONS OF PUSH-ON SPRING NUTS (CONTINUED)

Nominal[1] Stud Size in	Style	Series[2]	A Nut Length ±0.020 in	B Nut Width ±0.010 in	C Arch Height Max in	C Arch Height Min in	E Stock Thickness ±0.0015 in
5/32	II	Light	0.88	0.56	0.075	0.045	0.012
5/32	II	Medium	0.88	0.56	0.075	0.045	0.014
5/32	II	Heavy	0.88	0.56	0.075	0.045	0.017
3/16	I	Light	0.62	0.38	0.060	0.030	0.012
3/16	I	Medium	0.62	0.38	0.060	0.030	0.017
3/16	I	Heavy	0.62	0.38	0.060	0.030	0.020
3/16	II	Light	0.98	0.56	0.080	0.050	0.012
3/16	II	Medium	0.98	0.56	0.080	0.050	0.017
3/16	II	Heavy	0.98	0.56	0.080	0.050	0.020
7/32	I	Light	0.62	0.44	0.050	0.020	0.012
7/32	I	Medium	0.62	0.44	0.050	0.020	0.017
1/4	I	Light	0.62	0.44	0.050	0.020	0.012
1/4	I	Medium	0.62	0.44	0.050	0.020	0.017
1/4	I	Heavy	0.62	0.44	0.050	0.020	0.020
1/4	II	Light	0.98	0.62	0.095	0.065	0.012
1/4	II	Medium	0.98	0.62	0.095	0.065	0.017
1/4	II	Heavy	0.98	0.62	0.095	0.065	0.020
5/16	I	Light	0.69	0.50	0.060	0.030	0.014
5/16	I	Medium	0.69	0.50	0.060	0.030	0.020
3/8	I	Light	0.75	0.56	0.060	0.030	0.014
3/8	I	Medium	0.75	0.56	0.060	0.030	0.020

1. See Table 9 for stud dimensions
2. See Section 9 Application and Design

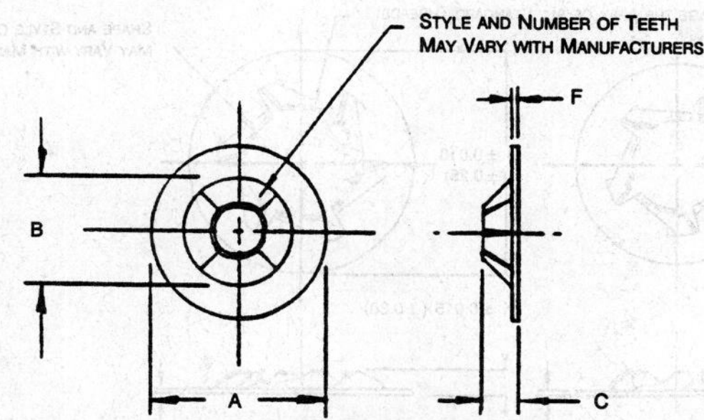

FIGURE 2—PUSH-ON SPRING NUTS—ROUND—FLAT

TABLE 3A—PUSH-ON SPRING NUTS—ROUND—FLAT (SEE FIGURE 2)

Nominal(1) Stud Dia in	Series	A Diameter ±0.005 in	B Tooth Base ±0.010 in	C Height ±0.007 in	E Metal Thickness ±0.0015 in
0.125	Light	0.375	0.228	0.045	0.010
0.125	Medium	0.375	0.228	0.052	0.013
0.156	Light	0.438	0.320	0.047	0.010
0.156	Medium	0.438	0.320	0.058	0.013
0.188	Light	0.438	0.320	0.051	0.010
0.188	Medium	0.438	0.320	0.059	0.015
0.219	Medium	0.531	0.338	0.017	0.017
—	Light	—	—	—	—
0.250	Light	0.531	0.338	0.057	0.012
0.250	Medium	0.531	0.338	0.066	0.017
0.312	Light	0.625	0.456	0.059	0.015
0.312	Medium	0.625	0.456	0.070	0.021
0.375	Light	0.750	0.546	0.061	0.017
0.375	Heavy	0.750	0.546	0.081	0.027
—	Light	—	—	—	—
—	Heavy	—	—	—	—
0.438	—	0.875	0.638	0.97	0.030
0.500	—	1.000	0.730	1.07	0.035

1. See Table 9 for stud dimensions

TABLE 3B—PUSH-ON SPRING NUTS—ROUND—FLAT (CONTINUED)

Nom(1) Stud Dia in	Series	D Teeth Inside Dia ±0.003 in	F Performance Force Requirements max. Push Onto Stud lb	F Performance Force Requirements min. Removal From Stud lb
0.125	Light	0.114	15	130
0.125	Medium	0.114	26	350
0.156	Light	0.140	15	60
0.156	Medium	0.140	25	180
0.188	Light	0.175	15	200
0.188	Medium	0.175	25	400
0.219	Medium	0.206	25	580
—	Light	—	—	—
0.250	Light	0.235	25	400
0.250	Medium	0.235	45	600
0.312	Light	0.295	40	650
0.312	Medium	0.295	60	900
0.375	Light	0.359	50	700
0.375	Heavy	0.359	85	1100
—	Light	—	—	—
—	Heavy	—	—	—
0.438	—	0.422	75	1500
0.50	—	0.482	160	2000

1. See Table 9 for stud dimensions

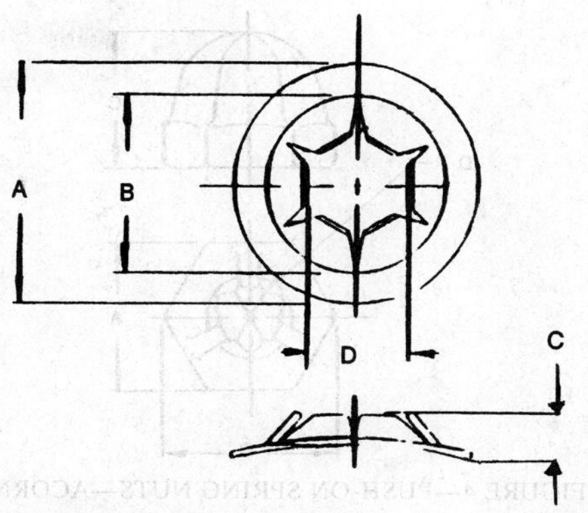

FIGURE 3—PUSH-ON SPRING NUTS—ROUND ARCHED

TABLE 4A—PUSH-ON SPRING NUTS—ROUND ARCHED (SEE FIGURE 3)

Nom(1) Stud Dia in	Series	A Diameter ±0.010 in	B Tooth Base Diameter ±0.010 in	C Height ±0.015 in	D Tooth Inside Dia ±0.003 in
0.125	Light	0.375	0.228	0.063	0.114
0.125	Medium	0.375	0.228	0.068	0.114
0.125	Heavy	0.375	0.228	0.072	0.114
0.156	Light	0.437	0.320	0.084	0.143
0.188	Light	0.437	0.320	0.087	0.175
0.188	Light	0.437	0.320	0.091	0.175
0.188	Medium	0.437	0.320	0.095	0.175
0.250	Light	0.531	0.388	0.095	0.235
0.250	Medium	0.531	0.388	0.103	0.235
0.312	Light	0.625	0.456	0.105	0.295
0.312	Medium	0.625	0.456	0.114	0.295
0.375	Light	0.750	0.546	0.095	0.359
0.375	Light	0.750	0.546	0.115	0.359
0.375	Medium	0.750	0.546	0.111	0.359

1. See Table 9 for stud dimensions

TABLE 4B—PUSH-ON SPRING NUTS—ROUND ARCHED (CONTINUED)

Nom(1) Stud Dia in	Series		E Metal Thickness ±0.0015 in	F Performance Force Required max. Push Onto Stud lb	F Performance Force Required min. Tension On Stud lb	F Performance Force Required min. Removal From Stud lb
0.125	Light	0.25	0.010	15	15	130
0.125	Medium	0.33	0.013	25	25	350
0.125	Heavy	0.43	0.017	55	80	400
0.156	Light	0.25	0.010	15	50	60
0.188	Light	—	0.010	15	50	100
0.188	Light	—	0.013	15	65	300
0.188	Medium	—	0.015	15	100	400
0.250	Light	0.30	0.012	25	60	400
0.250	Medium	0.43	0.017	30	115	600
0.312	Light	0.38	0.015	40	80	655
0.312	Medium	0.53	0.021	60	120	900
0.375	Light	—	0.017	55	110	700
0.375	Light	—	0.021	70	125	900
0.375	Medium	—	0.027	85	150	1160

1. See Table 9 for stud dimensions

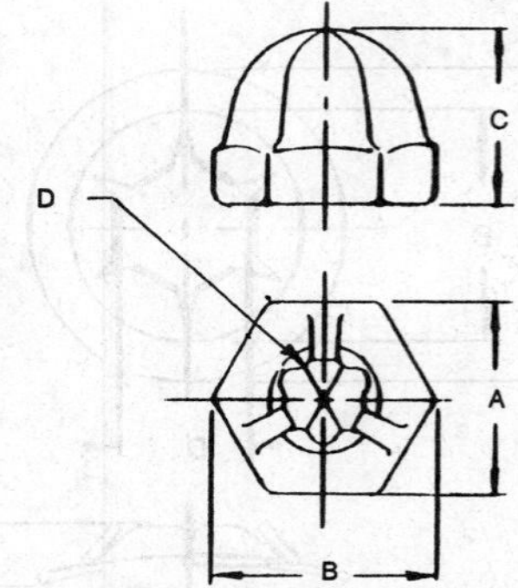

FIGURE 4—PUSH-ON SPRING NUTS—ACORN

TABLE 5A—PUSH-ON SPRING NUTS—ACORN (SEE FIGURE 4)

Nom[(1)] Stud Dia in	Top Style	A Hex in	B Across Hex Corners in	C Height in	D Tooth Inside Dia ±0.004 in
0.120	closed	0.312/0.306	0.361/0.348	0.271/0.251	0.113
0.120	open	0.312/0.306	0.361/0.348	0.245/0.225	0.113
0.148	closed	0.344/0.338	0.347/0.333	0.305/0.285	0.140
0.156	closed	0.344/0.338	0.347/0.333	0.305/0.285	0.148
0.188	closed	0.375/0.368	0.433/0.418	0.334/0.314	0.174
0.188	closed	0.437/0.429	0.505/0.488	0.390/0.370	0.174
0.188	open	0.437/0.429	0.505/0.488	0.320/0.300	0.174
0.250	closed	0.437/0.429	0.505/0.488	0.382/0.362	0.235
0.250	open	0.437/0.429	0.505/0.488	0.303/0.283	0.235
0.250	closed	0.562/0.553	0.650/0.627	0.494/0.474	0.235
0.250	open	0.562/0.553	0.650/0.627	0.405/0.385	0.235
0.312	closed	0.562/0.553	0.650/0.627	0.484/0.464	0.293
0.312	open	0.562/0.553	0.650/0.627	0.390/0.370	0.293

1. See Table 9 for stud dimensions

TABLE 5B—PUSH-ON SPRING NUTS—ACORN (CONTINUED)

Nom[(1)] Stud Dia in	Top Style	E Metal Thickness ±0.0015 in	F Rod Penetration in	G Performance Force Required Maximum Push On lb	G Performance Force Required Minimum Removal lb
0.120	closed	0.013	0.21/0.13	40	234
0.120	open	0.013	0.13 min	40	234
0.148	closed	0.017	0.24/0.13	30	329
0.156	closed	0.012	0.24/0.13	32	300
0.188	closed	0.015	0.26/0.16	40	70
0.188	closed	0.021	0.30/0.16	50	185
0.188	open	0.021	0.16 min	50	185
0.250	closed	0.017	0.28/0.19	45	120
0.250	open	0.017	0.19 min	45	120
0.250	closed	0.024	0.38/0.19	50	220
0.250	open	0.024	0.19 min	50	220
0.312	closed	0.020	0.36/0.22	55	200
0.312	open	0.020	0.22 min	55	200

1. See Table 9 for stud dimensions

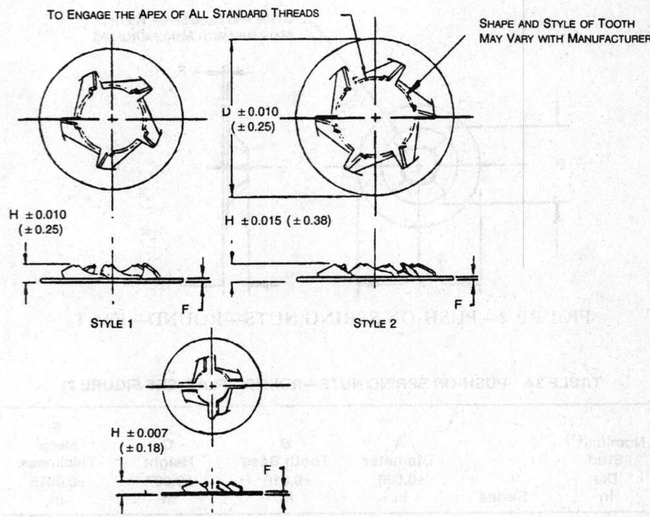

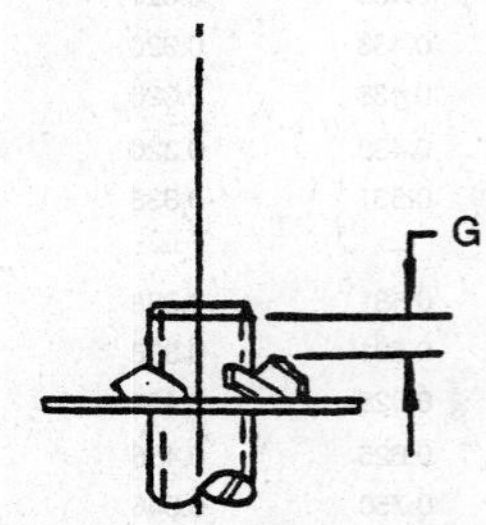

FIGURE 5—PUSH-ON SPRING BOLT RETAINER

FIGURE 6—PUSH-ON SPRING BOLT RETAINER

TABLE 6A—PUSH-ON SPRING BOLT RETAINER (SEE FIGURES 5 AND 6)

Machine Screw or Bolt[(1)] Dia in	Style	D Diameter ±0.010 in	H Height ±0.015 in	E Metal Thickness ±0.0015 in
#6	3	0.344	0.047	0.010
#8	3	0.375	0.049	0.010
#10	3	0.437	0.065	0.012
—	1	0.500	0.078	0.010
1/4	1	0.500	0.078	0.010
5/16	1	0.625	0.082	0.015
3/8	2	0.781	0.093	0.015
—	2	—	—	—
7/16	2	0.843	0.103	0.015
—	2	—	—	—
1/2	2	0.938	0.122	0.015
—	2	—	—	—

1. The impression will engage any pitch of thread UNC-UNF inch sizes for diameters shown.

TABLE 6B—PUSH-ON SPRING BOLT RETAINER (SEE FIGURES 5 AND 6) (CONTINUED)

Machine Screw or Bolt[(1)] Dia in	Style	G Minimum Bolt or Screw Protrusion in	F Performance Maximum Push-On Force lb	F Performance Minimum Removal Force lb
#6	3	0.140	3.8	9.0
#8	3	0.140	4.9	11.2
#10	3	0.156	5.6	14.6
—	1	0.188	5.6	20.2
1/4	1	0.188	5.6	20.2
5/16	1	0.218	6.7	22.5
3/8	2	0.218	6.7	33.7
—	2	—	6.7	33.7
7/16	2	0.250	6.7	56.2
—	2	—	6.7	67.2
1/2	2	0.250	6.7	67.2
—	2	—	6.7	67.2

1. The impression will engage any pitch of thread UNC-UNF inch sizes for diameters shown.

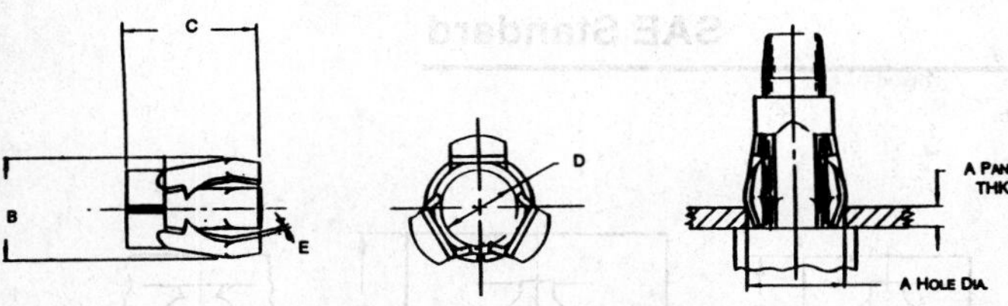

FIGURE 7—PUSH-ON SPRING NUTS—BLIND, STUD RETAINED STYLE

TABLE 7A—PUSH-ON SPRING NUTS—BLIND, STUD RETAINED STYLE (SEE FIGURE 7)

Nom[1] Stud Dia in	A Panel Hole Dia ±0.003 in	T Panel Thickness ±0.004 in	B Knee Dia ±0.010 in	C Length ±0.008 in	D Tooth Inside Dia ±0.008 in
0.094	0.139	0.040	0.162	0.265	0.074
0.094	0.139	0.055	0.162	0.280	0.074
0.094	0.139	0.070	0.162	0.296	0.074
0.125	0.187	0.040	0.205	0.280	0.103
0.125	0.187	0.055	0.205	0.296	0.103
0.125	0.187	0.070	0.205	0.312	0.103
0.156	0.218	0.070	0.238	0.328	0.136
0.188	0.249	0.040	0.275	0.312	0.169
0.188	0.249	0.070	0.275	0.344	0.169

1. See Table 9 for stud dimensions

TABLE 7B—PUSH-ON SPRING NUTS—BLIND, STUD RETAINED STYLE (CONTINUED)

Nom [1] Stud Dia in	E Metal Thickness ±0.0015 in	F Performance Force Required Maximum Push-On Fastener Onto Stud lb	F Performance Force Required Maximum Snap Assembly Into Panel lb	F Performance Force Required Minimum Remove Assembly From Panel lb
0.094	0.011	5	45	15
0.094	0.011	5	45	15
0.094	0.011	5	45	15
0.125	0.014	5	60	22
0.125	0.014	5	60	22
0.125	0.014	5	60	22
0.156	0.014	5	60	22
0.188	0.014	5	65	22
0.188	0.014	5	65	22

1. See Table 9 for stud dimensions

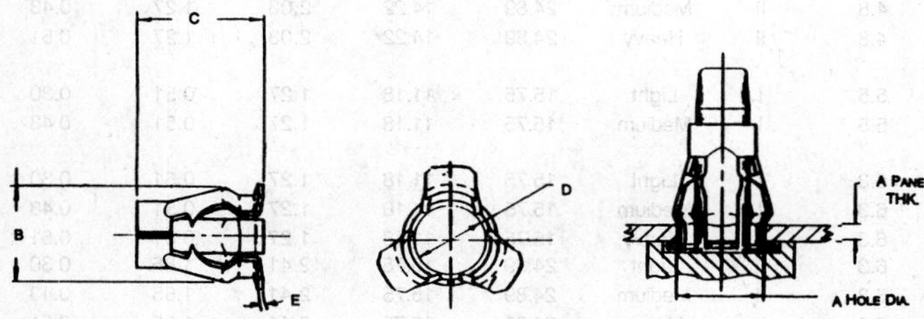

FIGURE 8—PUSH-ON SPRING NUTS—BLIND, PANEL RETAINED

TABLE 8A—PUSH-ON SPRING NUTS—BLIND, PANEL RETAINED (SEE FIGURE 8)

Nom[1] Stud Dia in	A Panel Hole Dia ±0.003 in	T Panel Thickness ±0.004 in	B Knee Dia ±0.010 in	C Length ±0.008 in	D Tooth Inside Dia ±0.008 in
0.094	0.139	0.040	0.178	0.275	0.07
0.125	0.187	0.040	0.234	0.290	0.106
0.188	0.249	0.040	0.297	0.325	0.160
0.188	0.249	0.027	0.297	0.312	0.160

1. See Table 9 for stud dimensions

TABLE 8B—PUSH-ON SPRING NUTS—BLIND, PANEL RETAINED (SEE FIGURE 8) (CONTINUED)

Nom[1] Stud Dia in	E Metal Thickness ±0.0015 in	F Performance Force Required Maximum Push Fastener into Panel lb	F Performance Force Maximum Push Stud into Assembly lb	F Performance Force Required Minimum Remove Studs From Panel lb
0.94	0.011	15	20	40
0.125	0.014	25	35	35
0.188	0.015	25	40	35
0.188	0.015	25	40	35

1. See Table 9 for stud dimensions

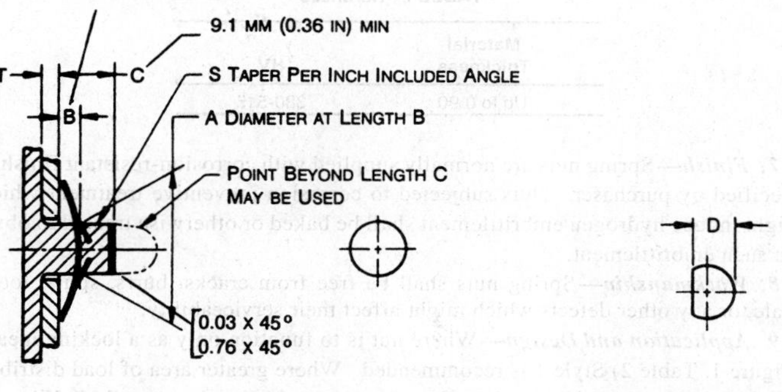

FIGURE 9A—ROUND STUD

FIGURE 9B—"D" SHAPED STUD

FIGURE 9—RECOMMENDED STUD DESIGN

TABLE 9—DIMENSIONS OF RECOMMENDED STUDS (FIGURES 9A AND 9B)

Nominal[1] Stud Diameter in	A[1] Stud Diameter Min in	A[1] Stud Diameter Max in	D Stud Width Min in	D Stud Width Max in	S Taper Max in
0.062	0.059	0.065	0.044	0.054	0.052
0.094	0.091	0.097	0.069	0.079	0.052
0.125	0.122	0.128	0.095	0.105	0.052
0.156	0.153	0.159	0.120	0.130	0.04
0.187	0.185	0.191	0.145	0.155	0.04
0.218	0.216	0.222	0.170	0.180	0.04
0.250	0.247	0.253	0.195	0.205	0.04
0.312	0.309	0.315	0.245	0.255	0.03
0.375	0.372	0.378	0.295	0.305	0.03
0.438	0.434	0.44	0.345	0.355	0.03
0.500	0.497	0.503	0.395	0.405	0.03

1. Diameter limits include thickness of plating on studs. Chromium or nickel plating is permissible only on studs to be used with Heavy Series Nuts and then it is recommended that plating thickness change length of die cast studs be held to within 0.0015 in wherever possible and that in no case should the plating thickness exceed 0.003 in.

PUSH-ON SPRING NUTS METRIC SERIES— GENERAL SPECIFICATIONS—SAE J892M AUG1996

SAE Standard

Report of the SAE Fasteners Committee approved August 1964, revised June 1970, and completely revised August 1996.

Foreword—This Document has also changed to comply with the new SAE Technical Standards Board format.

1. Scope—Included herein are general, dimensional, and performance specifications for those types, styles, and sizes of steel stamped Push-On Spring Nuts recognized as SAE standard. These nuts are intended for general use where the engagement on the mating metal or plastic studs and in some cases screw bolt threads is considered adequate for the fastening joint application. It should be noted that Push-On Spring Nuts having other characteristics and configurations are available and manufacturers should be consulted. For the inch equivalent of this document, see SAE J892.

2. References

2.1 Applicable Publication—The following publication forms a part of this specification to the extent specified herein unless otherwise specified. The latest issue of SAE publications shall apply.

2.1.1 SAE PUBLICATION—Available from SAE, 400 Commonwealth Drive, Warrendale, PA 15096-0001.

SAE J892—Push-On Spring Nuts Inch Series—General Specifications

3. Dimensional Tolerance—Tolerance on dimensions are in the tables.

4. Boss—Size and formation of boss and other detail shall be such as to assemble readily and function satisfactorily with the specified stud.

5. Material—Spring steel suitably processed to meet the hardness requirements of this specification.

6. Hardness—Hardness shall be as follows in Table 1:

TABLE 1—Hardness

Material Thickness	HV
Up to 0.90	380-515

7. Finish—Spring nuts are normally supplied with corrosion-resistant finish as specified by purchaser. Nuts subjected to corrosion preventive treatment which might induce hydrogen embrittlement shall be baked or otherwise treated to obviate such embrittlement.

8. Workmanship—Spring nuts shall be free from cracks, burrs, splits, loose scale, or any other defects which might affect their serviceability.

9. Application and Design—Where nut is to function only as a locking means (Figure 1, Table 2) Style 1 is recommended. Where greater area of load distribution is a requirement, i.e., nut is to function also as spanner washer, Style II is recommended. The Light Series are for use on plastic studs, the Medium Series are for use on soft metal studs, and the Heavy Series are for use on hardened metal or chromium plated studs. Tables 3 and 4 and Figures 2 and 3, Push-On Spring Nuts will be used likewise. Acorn types, closed and open top styles are shown in Table 5 and Figure 4. Note the restricted stud height is designated by rod penetration. Table 6 and Figures 5 and 6, Push-On Spring Bolt Retainers pertain to nuts applied onto screw and bolt threads. Blind push-on spring nut and stud requirements are listed in Tables 7 and 8 and Figures 7 and 8. The stud retained style must be preassembled onto the stud before inserting into a panel whereas the panel retained goes into the panel and then the stud is inserted.

10. Assembly Considerations—Since performance of push-on spring nuts is dependent upon the studs to which they are applied, it is essential that stud diameters and plating recommendations as set forth in Figure 9 and Table 9 be adhered to as closely as possible. The actual stud length is determined by adding the thickness of mating panel or panels "T" through which the stud protrudes to the factors tabulated under "C" (the minimum stud protrusion required for normal installation). It may be necessary to increase this factor to provide adequate stud protrusion where uncompressed materials or mismatch of trim contours are encountered. It should be noted by users desiring to standardize on stud designs that the studs applicable to self-threading stamped nuts may be utilized for push-on spring nuts where economics justify and the additional stud protrusion is not objectionable.

Heavy Series Nuts are used on round studs only. All other nuts in this document may be used on either round or "D" shaped studs. Nuts are used on round studs in applications where the assembly is permanent and on "D" shaped studs where disassembly is a consideration.

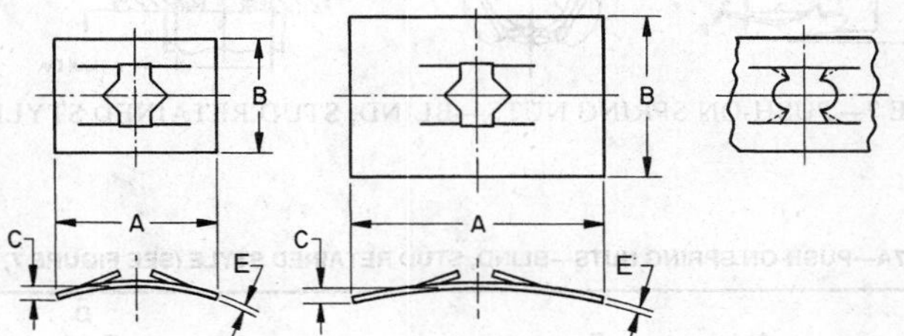

FIGURE 1A—STYLE 1 STANDARD

FIGURE 1B—STYLE II SPANNER

FIGURE 1C—HEAVY SERIES BOSS DESIGN SEE TABLE 3, NOTE 1

FIGURE 1—PUSH-ON SPRING NUTS—RECTANGULAR ARCHED

TABLE 2—DIMENSIONS OF PUSH-ON SPRING NUTS (FIGURES 1A TO 1C)

Nominal Stud[(1)] Size mm	Style	Series[(2)]	A Nut Length ±0.50 mm	B Nut Width ±0.25 mm	C Arch Height Max mm	C Arch Height Min mm	E Stock Thickness ±0.038 mm
1.6	I	Light	9.65	5.59	0.64	0.13	0.30
1.6	I	Medium	9.65	5.59	0.64	0.13	0.36
1.6	I	Heavy	9.65	5.59	0.64	0.13	0.43
1.6	II	Light	14.22	8.64	1.02	0.25	0.30
1.6	II	Medium	14.22	8.64	1.02	0.25	0.36
1.6	II	Heavy	14.22	8.64	1.02	0.25	0.43
2.4	I	Light	11.43	5.84	1.02	0.25	0.30
2.4	I	Medium	11.43	5.84	1.02	0.25	0.36
2.4	I	Heavy	11.43	5.84	1.02	0.25	0.43
2.4	II	Light	17.78	9.65	1.27	0.51	0.30
2.4	II	Medium	17.78	9.65	1.27	0.51	0.36
2.4	II	Heavy	17.78	9.65	1.27	0.51	0.43
3.2	I	Light	14.73	7.87	1.02	0.25	0.30
3.2	I	Medium	14.73	7.87	1.02	0.25	0.36
3.2	I	Heavy	14.73	7.87	1.02	0.25	0.43
3.2	II	Light	11.43	12.70	2.03	1.27	0.30
3.2	II	Medium	11.43	12.70	2.03	1.27	0.36
3.2	II	Heavy	11.43	12.70	2.03	1.27	0.43
4.0	I	Light	14.22	9.65	1.02	0.25	0.30
4.0	I	Medium	14.22	9.65	1.02	0.25	0.36
4.0	I	Heavy	14.22	9.65	1.02	0.25	0.43
4.0	II	Light	22.35	14.22	1.91	1.14	0.30
4.0	II	Medium	22.35	14.22	1.91	1.14	0.36
4.0	II	Heavy	22.35	14.22	1.91	1.14	0.43
4.8	I	Light	15.75	9.65	1.52	0.76	0.30
4.8	I	Medium	15.75	9.65	1.52	0.76	0.43
4.8	I	Heavy	15.75	9.65	1.52	0.76	0.51
4.8	II	Light	24.89	14.22	2.03	1.27	0.30
4.8	II	Medium	24.89	14.22	2.03	1.27	0.43
4.8	II	Heavy	24.89	14.22	2.03	1.27	0.51
5.5	I	Light	15.75	11.18	1.27	0.51	0.30
5.5	I	Medium	15.75	11.18	1.27	0.51	0.43
6.3	I	Light	15.75	11.18	1.27	0.51	0.30
6.3	I	Medium	15.75	11.18	1.27	0.51	0.43
6.3	I	Heavy	15.75	11.18	1.27	0.51	0.51
6.3	II	Light	24.89	15.75	2.41	1.65	0.30
6.3	II	Medium	24.89	15.75	2.41	1.65	0.43
6.3	II	Heavy	24.89	15.75	2.41	1.65	0.51
8.0	I	Light	17.53	12.70		0.76	0.36
8.0	I	Medium	17.53	12.70	1.52	0.76	0.51
9.5	I	Light	19.05	14.22	1.52	0.76	0.36
9.5	1	Medium	19.05	14.22	1.52	0.76	0.51

1. See Table 9 for stud dimensions
2. See Section 9 Application and Design

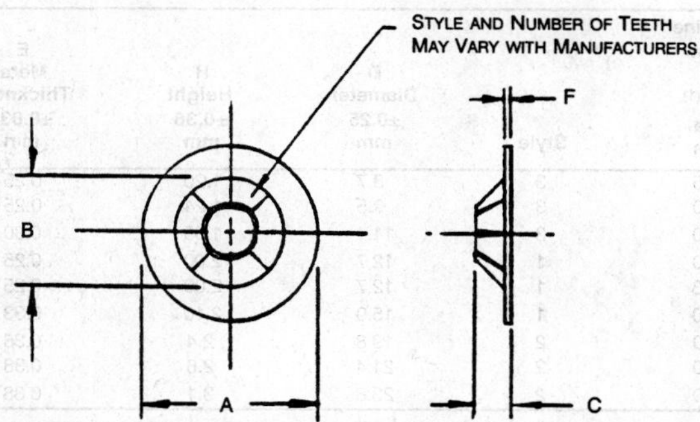

FIGURE 2—PUSH-ON SPRING NUTS—ROUND—FLAT

TABLE 3A—PUSH-ON SPRING NUTS—ROUND—FLAT (SEE FIGURE 2)

Nom[(1)] Stud Dia mm	Series	A Diameter ±0.13 mm	B Tooth Base ±0.25 mm	C Height ±0.18 mm	E Metal Thickness ±0.038 mm
3.2	Light	9.5	5.8	1.1	0.25
3.2	Medium	9.5	5.8	1.3	0.33
4.0	Light	11.1	8.1	1.2	0.25
4.0	Medium	11.1	8.1	1.5	0.33
—	Light	—	—	—	—
—	Medium	—	—	—	—
5.0	Light	11.1	8.1	1.3	0.25
5.0	Medium	11.1	8.1	1.5	0.38
—	Medium	—	—	—	—
6.0	Light	13.5	9.9	1.9	0.51
6.3	Light	13.5	8.6	1.5	0.30
6.3	Medium	13.5	8.6	1.7	0.43
8.0	Light	15.9	11.6	1.5	0.38
8.0	Medium	15.9	11.6	1.8	0.53
—	Light	—	—	—	—
—	Heavy	—	—	—	—
10.0	Light	19.0	13.9	1.4	0.43
10.0	Heavy	19.0	13.9	1.9	0.68
11.0	—	22.3	16.2	2.5	0.76
—	—	—	—	—	—
13.0	—	25.4	18.5	2.72	0.89

1. See Table 9 for stud dimensions

TABLE 3B—PUSH-ON SPRING NUTS—ROUND—FLAT

Nom[(1)] Stud Dia mm	Series	D Teeth Inside Dia ±0.08 mm	F Performance Force Requirements max. Push Onto Stud N	F Performance Force Requirements min. Removal From Stud N
3.2	Light	2.9	65	573
3.2	Medium	2.9	115	1544
4.0	Light	3.6	66	265
4.0	Medium	3.6	110	794
—	Light	—	—	—
—	Medium	—	—	—
5.0	Light	4.7	66	882
5.0	Medium	4.7	110	1764
—	Medium	—	—	—
6.0	Light	5.7	111	1780
6.3	Light	6.0	110	1764
6.3	Medium	6.0	198	2646
8.0	Light	7.5	176	2866
8.0	Medium	7.5	265	3969
—	Light	—	—	—
—	Heavy	—	—	—
10.0	Light	9.6	222	2892
10.0	Heavy	9.6	378	4895
11.0	—	10.7	331	6615
—	—	—	—	—
13.0	—	12.2	706	8820

1. See Table 9 for stud dimensions

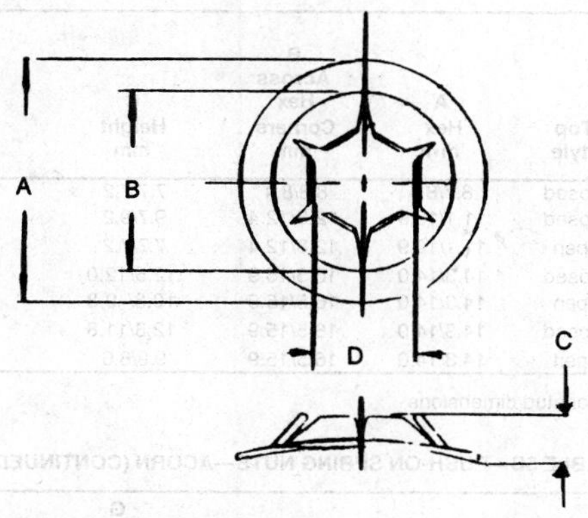

FIGURE 3—PUSH-ON SPRING NUTS—ROUND ARCHED

TABLE 4A—PUSH-ON SPRING NUTS—ROUND ARCHED (SEE FIGURE 3)

Nom[(1)] Stud Dia mm	Series	A Diameter ±0.25 mm	B Tooth Base Diameter ±0.25 mm	C Height ±0.38 mm	D Tooth Inside Dia ±0.08 mm
3.2	Light	9.5	5.8	1.6	2.9
3.2	Medium	9.5	5.8	1.7	2.9
3.2	Heavy	9.5	5.8	1.8	2.9
4.0	Light	11.0	8.1	2.1	3.6
6.3	Light	13.5	9.9	2.4	6.0
6.3	Medium	13.5	9.9	2.6	6.0
8.0	Light	15.9	11.6	2.7	7.5
8.0	Medium	15.9	11.6	2.9	7.5

1. See Table 9 for stud dimensions

TABLE 4B—PUSH-ON SPRING NUTS—ROUND ARCHED (CONTINUED)

Nom[(1)] Stud Dia mm	Series	E Metal Thickness ±0.38 mm	F Performance Force Required max. Push Onto Stud N	F Performance Force Required min. Tension On Stud N	F Performance Force Required min. Removal From Stud N
3.2	Light	0.25	66	66	573
3.2	Medium	0.33	110	110	1544
3.2	Heavy	0.43	243	353	1764
4.0	Light	0.25	66	220	265
6.3	Light	0.30	110	265	1764
6.3	Medium	0.43	132	507	2646
8.0	Light	0.38	178	353	2892
8.0	Medium	0.53	265	530	3969

1. See Table 9 for stud dimensions

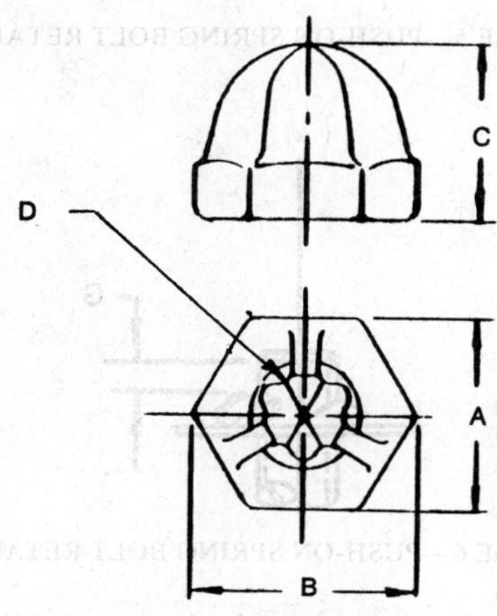

FIGURE 4—PUSH-ON SPRING NUTS—ACORN

TABLE 5A—PUSH-ON SPRING NUTS—ACORN (SEE FIGURE 4)

Nom (1) Stud Dia mm	Top Style	A Hex mm	B Across Hex Corners mm	C Height mm	D Tooth Inside Dia ±0.18 mm
4.0	closed	8.7/8.5	8.8/8.4	7.7/7.2	3.6
6.3	closed	11.1/10.9	12.8/12.4	9.7/9.2	6.0
6.3	open	11.1/10.9	12.8/12.4	7.7/7.2	6.0
6.3	closed	14.3/14.0	16.5/15.9	12.5/12.0	6.0
6.3	open	14.3/14.0	16.5/15.9	10.3/ 9.8	6.0
8.0	closed	14.3/14.0	16.5/15.9	12.3/11.8	7.4
8.0	open	14.3/14.0	16.5/15.9	9.9/8.6	7.4

1. See Table 9 for stud dimensions

TABLE 5B—PUSH-ON SPRING NUTS—ACORN (CONTINUED)

Nom(1) Stud Dia mm	Top Style	E Metal Thickness ±0.038 mm	F Rod Penetration mm	G Performance Force Required Maximum Push On N	G Performance Force Required Minimum Removal N
4.0	closed	0.30	6.1/3.3	141	1323
6.3	closed	0.43	7.1/4.8	198	529
6.3	open	0.43	4.8 min	198	529
6.3	closed	0.61	8.9/4.8	220	970
6.0	open	0.61	4.8 min	220	970
8.0	closed	0.51	9.1/5.6	243	882
8.0	open	0.51	5.6 min	243	882

1. See Table 9 for stud dimensions

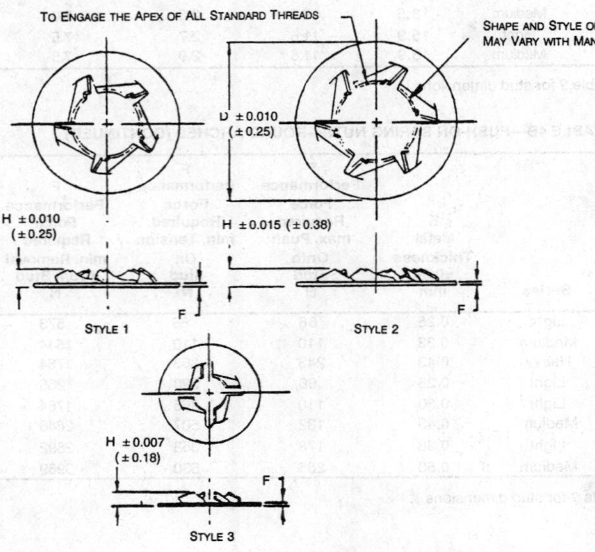

FIGURE 5—PUSH-ON SPRING BOLT RETAINER

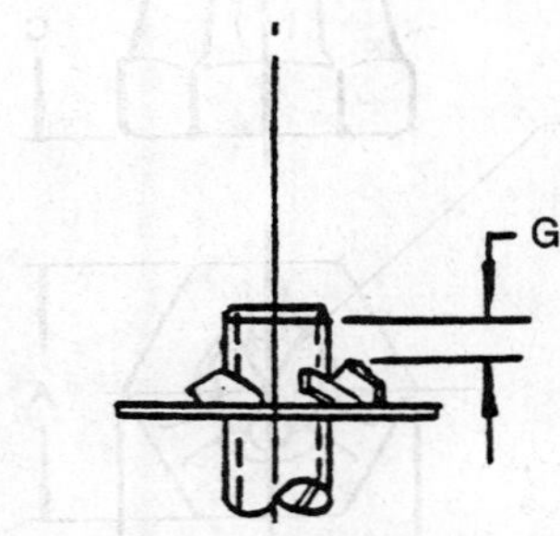

FIGURE 6—PUSH-ON SPRING BOLT RETAINER

TABLE 6A—PUSH-ON SPRING BOLT RETAINER (SEE FIGURES 5 AND 6)

Machine Screw or Bolt(1) Dia mm	Style	D Diameter ±0.25 mm	H Height ±0.38 mm	E Metal Thickness ±0.038 mm
3.5	3	8.7	1.20	0.25
4.0	3	9.5	1.24	0.25
5.0	3	11.1	1.65	0.30
6.0	1	12.7	2.00	0.25
6.3	1	12.7	2.00	0.25
8.0	1	15.9	2.10	0.33
10.0	2	19.8	2.4	0.38
12.0	2	21.4	2.6	0.38
14.0	2	23.8	3.1	0.38

1. The impression will engage any pitch of thread coarse and fine metric series for diameters shown.

TABLE 6B—PUSH-ON SPRING BOLT RETAINER (CONTINUED)

Machine Screw or Bolt(1) Dia mm	Style	G Minimum Bolt or Screw Protrusion mm	F Performance Maximum Push-On Force N	F Performance Minimum Removal Force N
3.5	3	3.6	17	40
4.0	3	3.6	22	50
5.0	3	4.0	25	65
6.0	1	4.8	25	90
6.3	1	4.8	25	90
8.0	1	5.6	30	100
10.0	2	5.0	30	150
12.0	2	6.0	30	300
14.0	2	6.0	30	300

1. The impression will engage any pitch of thread coarse and fine metric series for diameters shown.

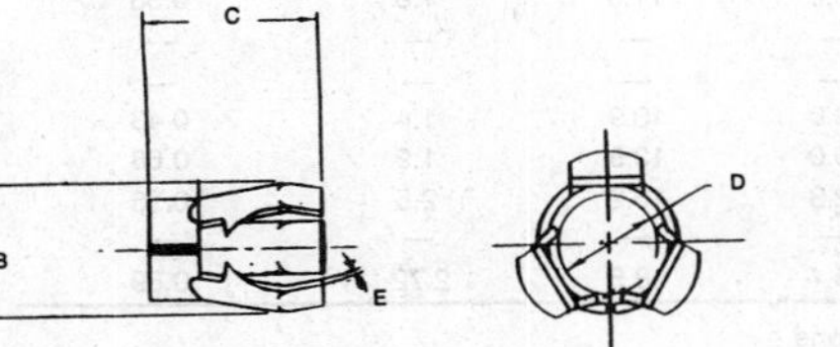

FIGURE 7—PUSH-ON SPRING NUTS—BLIND, STUD RETAINED STYLE

TABLE 7A—PUSH-ON SPRING NUTS—BLIND, STUD RETAINED STYLE (SEE FIGURE 7)

Nom(1) Stud Dia mm	A Panel Hole Dia ±0.08 mm	T Panel Thickness ±0.10 mm	B Knee Dia ±0.25 mm	C Length ±0.20 mm	D Tooth Inside Dia ±0.20 mm
3.2	4.75	1.02	5.21	7.11	2.6
3.2	4.75	1.40	5.21	7.52	2.6
3.2	4.75	1.78	5.21	7.92	2.6
4.0	5.5	1.78	6.05	8.33	3.4

1. See Table 9 for stud dimensions

TABLE 7B—PUSH-ON SPRING NUTS—BLIND, STUD RETAINED STYLE (CONTINUED)

Nom(1) Stud Dia mm	E Metal Thickness ±0.038 mm	F Performance Force Required Maximum Push-On Fastener Onto Stud N	F Performance Force Required Maximum Snap Assembly Into Panel N	F Performance Force Required Minimum Remove Assembly From Panel N
3.2	0.36	60	265	97
3.2	0.36	60	265	97
3.2	0.36	60	265	97
4.0	0.36	60	265	97

1. See Table 9 for stud dimensions

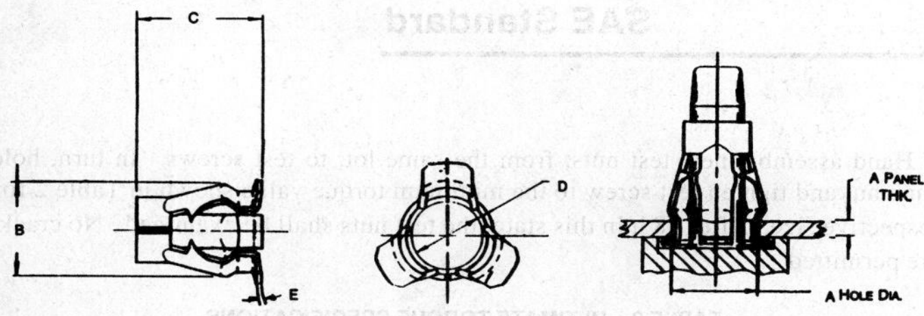

FIGURE 8—PUSH-ON SPRING NUTS—BLIND, PANEL RETAINED

TABLE 8A—PUSH-ON SPRING NUTS—BLIND, PANEL RETAINED (SEE FIGURE 8)

Nom[(1)] Stud Dia mm	A Panel Hole Dia ±0.08 mm	T Panel Thickness ±0.10 mm	B Knee Dia ±0.25 mm	C Length ±0.20 mm	D Tooth Inside Dia ±0.20 mm
3.2	4.75	1.02	5.94	7.37	2.7

1. See Table 9 for stud dimensions

TABLE 8B—PUSH-ON SPRING NUTS—BLIND, PANEL RETAINED (CONTINUED)

Nom[(1)] Stud Dia mm	E Metal Thickness ±0.038 mm	F Performance Force Required Maximum Push Fastener Into Panel N	F Performance Force Required Maximum Push Stud Into Assembly N	F Performance Force Required Minimum Remove Studs From Panel N
3.2	0.36	110	154	154

1. See Table 9 for stud dimensions

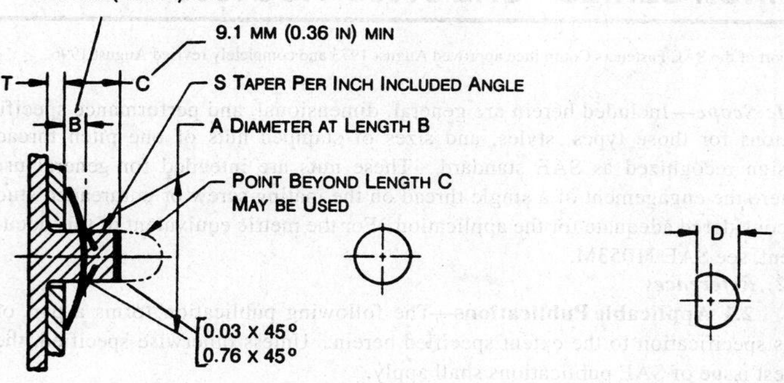

FIGURE 9A—ROUND STUD

FIGURE 9B—"D" SHAPED STUD

FIGURE 9—RECOMMENDED STUD DESIGN

TABLE 9—DIMENSIONS OF RECOMMENDED STUDS (FIGURES 9A AND 9B)

Nominal Stud Diameter mm	A[(1)] Stud Diameter Min mm	A[(1)] Stud Diameter Max mm	D Stud Width Min mm	D Stud Width Max mm	S Taper Max mm
1.6	1.5	1.6	1.1	1.4	0.05
2.4	2.3	2.5	1.8	2.0	0.05
3.2	3.1	3.2	2.4	2.7	0.05
4.0	3.9	4.0	3.0	3.3	0.04
4.8	4.7	4.8	3.7	3.9	0.04
5.0	4.9	5.1	3.9	4.1	0.04
5.5	5.5	5.6	4.3	4.6	0.04
6.3	6.3	6.4	5.0	5.2	0.04
8.0	7.8	8.0	6.2	6.5	0.03
9.5	9.4	9.6	7.5	7.8	0.03
10.0	9.9	10.1	8.2	8.5	0.03
11.1	11.0	11.2	8.8	9.0	0.03
12.7	12.6	12.8	10.0	10.3	0.03
13.0	12.9	13.1	10.3	10.6	0.03

1. Diameter limits include thickness of plating on studs. Chromium or nickel plating is permissible only on studs to be used with Heavy Series Nuts and then it is recommended that plating thickness change length of die cast studs be held to within 0.038 mm wherever and that in no case should the plating thickness exceed 0.076 mm.

STEEL STAMPED NUTS OF ONE PITCH THREAD DESIGN —INCH SERIES—SAE J1053 AUG1996

SAE Standard

Report of the SAE Fasteners Committee approved August 1973 and completely revised August 1996.

1. Scope—Included herein are general, dimensional, and performance specifications for those types, styles, and sizes of stamped nuts of one pitch thread design recognized as SAE standard. These nuts are intended for general use where the engagement of a single thread on the mating screw or unthreaded stud is considered adequate for the application. For the metric equivalent of this document, see SAE J1053M.

2. References

2.1 Applicable Publications—The following publication forms a part of this specification to the extent specified herein. Unless otherwise specified, the latest issue of SAE publications shall apply.

2.1.1 SAE PUBLICATION—Available from SAE, 400 Commonwealth Drive, Warrendale, PA 15096-0001.

SAE J1053M—Steel Stamped Nuts of One Pitch Thread Design—Metric Series

3. General Specifications

3.1 Dimensional Tolerance—Tolerance on dimensions are shown in Tables 1 to 12.

3.2 Miscellaneous Dimensions—Taper on the sides of hexagon portions of nuts (angle between one side and the axis of nut) shall not exceed 1 degree, the maximum limit specified being the largest dimension.

3.3 Thread Embossments

3.3.1 FORMED THREAD EMBOSSMENT—Detail of the thread engaging portion of formed thread type nuts shall be such as to permit nut to assemble readily with the specified screw and not strip or deform at the minimum torques shown in Table 2. The edges around the opening shall be spirally formed to conform to the helix of the mating thread and, as indicated on illustrations, the top or top and bottom corners on edges of holes shall be swaged to provide flats for bearing on flanks of the mating thread.

3.3.2 SELF-THREADING EMBOSSMENT—The configuration of self-threading embossment may vary with manufacturer; however, the detail and formation of embossment shall be such as to enable the nuts to cut and/or form threads on cast or wire studs, conforming to the recommended stud designs contained in 5.2, at or below the maximum driving torques shown in Table 3.

3.4 Material—Nuts shall be fabricated from carbon spring steel suitably processed to meet the performance requirements of this document.

3.5 Finish—Stamped nuts are normally supplied with finishes as specified by the purchaser. Nuts processed with supplemental finishes shall be suitably treated to obviate hydrogen embrittlement.

3.6 Workmanship—Stamped nuts shall be free from cracks, burrs, splits, loose scale, or any defects that might affect their serviceability.

4. Test Procedures and Performance Requirements

4.1 Formed Thread Embossment

4.1.1 ULTIMATE TORQUE TEST—Insert hardened steel (53 HRC min) unplated or uncoated test socket head cap screws of the respective size and 1.00 in length, Class 3A thread, as-received with light coating of oil, into holes in the test fixture. The test fixture is to consist of a hardened steel (58-62 HRC) bar, 1.00 x 0.25 x 18.00 in or equivalent, having 12 equally spaced test holes of the diameter given in Table 1 for respective size.

TABLE 1—TEST BAR HOLE SIZES, in

Nominal Screw and Nut Size	Hole Diameter Max	Hole Diameter Min	Nominal Screw and Nut Size	Hole Diameter Max	Hole Diameter Min
6-32	0.149	0.144	1/4-20	0.262	0.257
8-32	0.178	0.173	5/16-18	0.328	0.323
10-24	0.204	0.199	3/8-16	0.391	0.386

Hand assemble the test nuts to the test screws. In turn, hold each nut and tighten the test screw to the torque value shown in Table 2 for the respective size. The test shall be performed with a device capable of measuring the clamp load developed, and the load attained shall not be less than the minimum tension values specified in Table 2. After initial breakaway, the nuts must disassemble, by hand, from the test screws.

4.1.2 EMBRITTLEMENT TEST—Insert hardened steel (53 HRC min) unplated or uncoated test socket head cap screws of the respective size and 1.00 in length, Class 3A thread, as-received with light coating of oil, into holes in the test fixture described in 4.1.1.

Hand assemble new test nuts, from the same lot, to test screws. In turn, hold each nut and tighten test screw to the minimum torque value shown in Table 2 for respective size. After 48 h in this state, the test nuts shall be examined. No cracks are permitted.

TABLE 2—ULTIMATE TORQUE SPECIFICATIONS

Nominal Nut Size, in	Torque, lb-in Min	Tension, lb Min	Nominal Nut Size, in	Torque, lb-in Min	Tension, lb Min
6-32	8	120	1/4-20	27	340
8-32	12	150	5/16-18	32	450
10-24	17	220	3/8-16	40	480

4.1.3 SCREW THREAD DAMAGE APPRAISAL TEST—Insert 12 nonheat-treated, unplated or uncoated, steel screws of respective size and 25 mm length, into holes in the test fixture described in 4.1.1.

Hand assemble new test nuts, from the same lot, to test screws. In turn, hold each nut and tighten test screw to the torque value shown in Table 2 for the respective size. Remove nuts from screws and screws from test bar and examine threads on screws for visible damage. Continue test by assembling, with the fingers, untested nuts from same lot onto tested screws. The new nuts must pass over the area on the screw where the previously tested nut engaged the threads.

4.2 Self-Threading Embossment

4.2.1 STARTING EASE TEST—The test nut must start onto the chamfered end (0.003 x 45 degrees) of an unplated or uncoated cold-rolled steel (78-81 HR30T) rod of the diameter specified in Table 3, within one revolution of nut when applied with an appropriate socket affixed to a screwdriver handle.

TABLE 3—TORQUE AND RELATED TENSION SPECIFICATIONS

Nominal Stud or Test Rod Dia, in	Test Rod Dia, in Max	Test Rod Dia, in Min	Driving Torque, lb-in Max	Nut Flange Dia, in Basic	Test Torque, lb-in	Tension, lb Min
1/8	0.126	0.123	8	0.437	34	150
3/16	0.189	0.186	26	0.562	68	250
1/4	0.251	0.248	35	0.687	90	300

4.2.2 ULTIMATE TORQUE TEST—Insert a test rod (see 4.2.1) into a suitable holding device exposing the chamfered end to a height equivalent to the nut height plus 0.125 in or, for closed end nuts, equivalent to the wrenching height. Place an unplated or uncoated soft steel (78-82 HR30T) flat test plate on the exposed test rod. The test plate shall have a minimum thickness of 0.030 in, an inside diameter 0.031 in larger than the diameter of test rod, and shall be at least 1.00 in^2. A new test plate shall be used for each torque test. The test rod and assembled plate must be retained in a suitable clamping device to prevent rotation of the rod and plate and tilting of the plate. The test shall be performed with a device capable of measuring the clamp load developed.

Assemble test nut on the test rod with a suitable torque indicating device. The maximum driving torque shall be recorded and this shall not exceed the maximum driving torque values shown in Table 3 for the respective size. At the torque test values specified in Table 3, the minimum tension values indicated shall be achieved.

4.2.3 EMBRITTLEMENT TEST—Assemble new test nut from the same lot to test rod using test torques shown in Table 3 for respective size. After 48 h, inspect the assembled nut for cracks. No cracks are permitted.

5. Design Criteria

5.1 Formed Thread Embossment—To insure proper starting of formed thread type stamped nuts, the length of the mating externally threaded component shall be such that it will protrude beyond the embossment in nut a minimum distance equivalent to two pitches (threads), exclusive of the length of any chamfer or point provision, under limit stack conditions. Recommended minimum protrusion lengths beyond panels with no allowance for pointing are presented in Figure 1 and Table 4 for respective nut types.

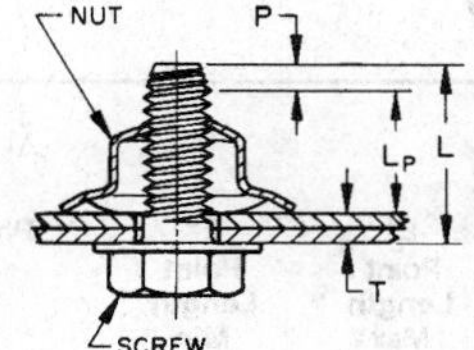

FIGURE 1A—FACETED FLANGE TYPE NUTS

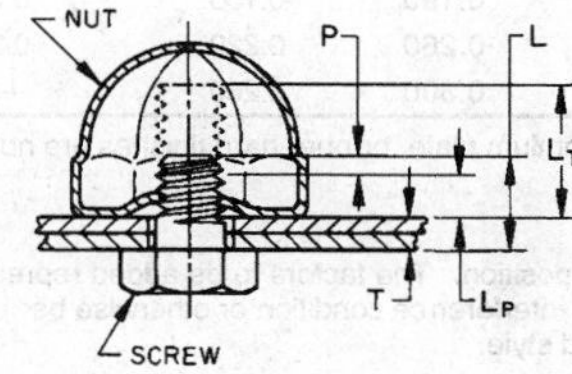

FIGURE 1B—ACORN OR REGULAR TYPE NUTS

$$L = L_P + T + P \qquad \text{(Eq. 1)}$$

where:

- L = Minimum length of screw or stud
- L_P = Minimum protrusion of full form thread length beyond panel (see Table 4 for respective nut types)
- L_T = Maximum protrusion of mating part beyond panel allowable for acorn type nuts (see Table 4)
- P = Length of point on screw or stud
- T = Maximum thickness of panel or panels to be assembled, including allowance, if necessary, to accommodate mismatch of surfaces, etc.

TABLE 4—PROTRUSION LENGTHS FOR FORMED THREAD TYPE STAMPED NUTS, in

Nominal Thread Size	L_P Protrusion of Threaded Length on Mating Part Beyond Panel Faceted Flange Type Min[1]	L_P Protrusion of Threaded Length on Mating Part Beyond Panel Acorn or Regular Types Min[2]	L_T Total Protrusion of Mating Part Beyond Panel Acorn Types Max[3]
6-32	0.29	0.13	0.21
8-32	0.29	0.13	0.24
10-24	0.33	0.16	0.25
1/4-20	0.40	0.19	0.28
5/16-18	0.44	0.22	0.36
3/8-16	—	0.23	0.34

[1]Values shown are applicable to nuts shown in Table 7. For sealer styles, add height of uncompressed sealer.
[2]Values shown are applicable to nuts shown in Tables 8 and 9, respectively.V
[3]Values shown apply to nuts shown in Table 8.
[4] There are no 3/8-16 washer faceted flange parts available at this time.

5.2 Self-Threading Embossment—To assure proper function and performance of self-threading types of stamped nuts and to provide flexibility for changing nut designs, it is essential that studs and clearance holes in mating panels be designed in conformance with the recommendations set forth in the following.

5.2.1 Stud Design—Studs which are integral features of die-cast components should comply as closely as possible with the recommendations presented in Figures 2 and 3 and Table 5. Studs fabricated from wire or rod shall be in accord with recommendations shown in Figures 4 and 5 and Table 5. Consideration should also be given to the recommendations for fillets, plating, and alignment which follow:

5.2.1.1 Fillets—The fillet at the junction of stud with die-casting base shall have as generous a radius as the design will permit, but not less than 0.010 in. Where the panel is to fit tight against the die casting, an annular relief groove should be provided in the die casting at base of stud to accommodate the fillet (see Figure 2) and the fillet radius should be made larger wherever the design will permit.

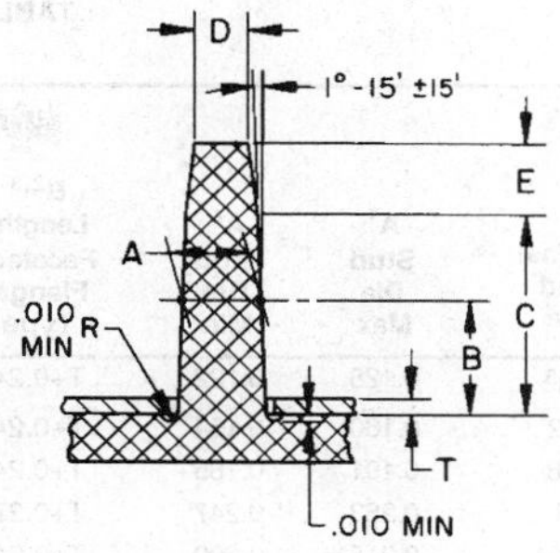

FIGURE 2—DIE CAST AND PLASTIC STUD

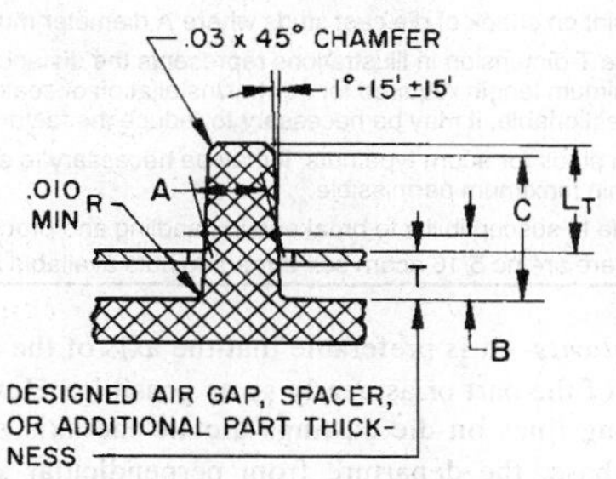

FIGURE 3—SHORT DIE CAST AND PLASTIC STUD

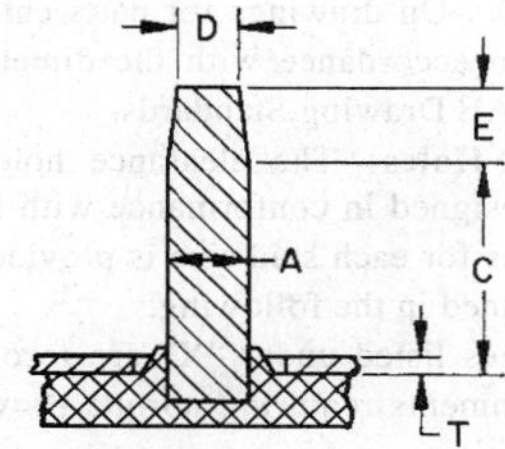

FIGURE 4A—WIRE OR ROD STUD

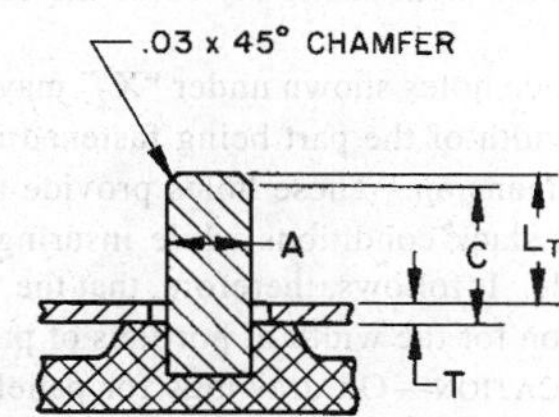

FIGURE 4B—SHORT WIRE OR ROD STUD

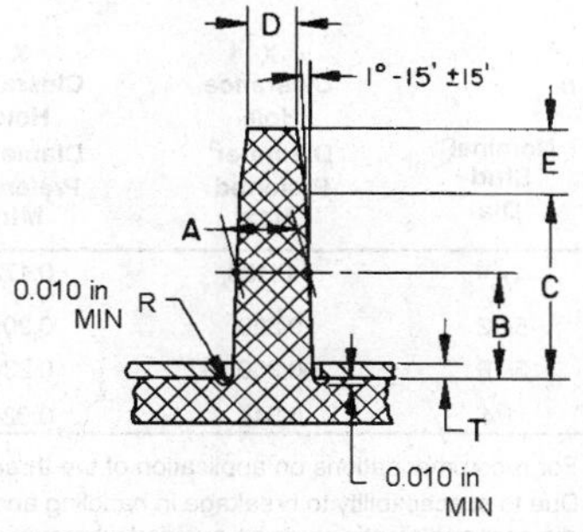

FIGURE 5—DIE CAST STEEL AND PLASTIC STUD

TABLE 5—RECOMMENDED DIMENSIONS OF STUDS FOR USE WITH SELF-THREADING TYPES OF SAMPLED NUTS, in

Nominal Stud Size	A[1] Stud Dia Max	A[1] Stud Dia Min	B[2,3] Length Faceted Flange Type	B[2,3] Length Acorn and Regular Types	C[3] Length Faceted Flange Type Min	C[3] Length Acorn and Regular Types Min	D[1] Point Dia ±0.005	E[4] Point Length Max	E[4] Point Length Min	L_T Stud Protrusion Acorn Type Max
1/8[5]	0.128	0.122	T+0.24	T+0.8	T+0.45	T+0.12	0.073	0.175	0.145	0.26
5/32	0.160	0.154	T+0.24	T+0.11	T+0.45	T+0.16	0.100	0.180	0.150	0.30
3/16	0.191	0.185	T+0.24	T+0.11	T+0.45	T+0.16	0.130	0.190	0.150	0.36
1/4	0.253	0.247	T+0.27	T+0.14	T+0.45	T+0.16	0.180	0.260	0.220	0.38
5/16	0.315	0.309	T+0.31	—6	T+0.45	—6	0.220	0.300	0.260	—6

[1] For plastic studs minimum and maximum diameters 0.05 in larger. Maximum plate per side 0.03 in0. Nickel, chromium plate, or other hard finishes are not recommended on steel studs

[2]Point on shank of die cast studs where A diameter must be within the specified limits.

[3]The T dimension in illustrations represents the distance from base of part to the bearing face of nut in the installed position. The factors to be added represent the minimum length required for normal installation of sealer styles of nuts. Where the factors specified would create an interference condition or otherwise be objectionable, it may be necessary to reduce the factor to that which is required for the respective nut size, type, and style.

[4]On studs for acorn type nuts, it may be necessary to shorten point or apply the chamfer specified for short studs in order to keep protrusion of stud beyond panel within maximum permissible.

[5]Due to susceptibility to breakage in handling and processing, it is recommended use of 1/8 and 5/32 in size die cast and plastic studs be avoided wherever possible.

[6]There are no 5/16 acorn self-threading nuts available at this time..

5.2.1.2 Angularity—It is preferable that the axis of the stud be kept perpendicular to the base of the part or as nearly so as possible. However, where design conditions or parting lines on die castings dictate the axis of stud must deviate from square with base, the departure from perpendicular shall not exceed 20 degrees. Similarly, where sufficient driver clearance cannot be provided in line with the stud axis, the angular deviation from axis should in no case exceed 15 degrees in order to insure the socket will have adequate engagement with the nut for assembly.

5.2.1.3 Stud Location—On drawings for parts entailing multiple studs, the studs should be located in accordance with the dimensioning and tolerancing practices set forth in the SAE Drawing Standards.

5.3 Panel Clearance Holes—The clearance holes in mating panels for stamped nuts should be designed in conformance with Figure 6 and Table 6. A selection of three hole sizes for each stud size is provided to best satisfy varying design conditions as explained in the following:

a. Preferred hole sizes listed under "X" are recommended and should be used for all attachments requiring normal provisions for clearance and adjustment.
b. Maximum clearance holes tabulated under "X_1" should be used only in applications where maximum adjustment capability is a requirement. These holes provide maximum clearance while assuring that the hole can effectively be sealed with sealer styles of the faceted flange type nuts contained herein.
c. Minimum clearance holes shown under "X_2" may necessarily have to be used where the width of the part being fastened is at or approaches the minimum "Z" dimension. These holes provide adequate clearance for studs under limit stack conditions while insuring that the fastened part will cover the hole. It follows, therefore, that the "Z" dimension shall be the design criterion for the width of portions of parts adjacent to studs.

5.3.1 PANEL HOLE LOCATION—On drawings for panels, multiple holes shall be located in a manner which is compatible with that used to position studs on the mating part.

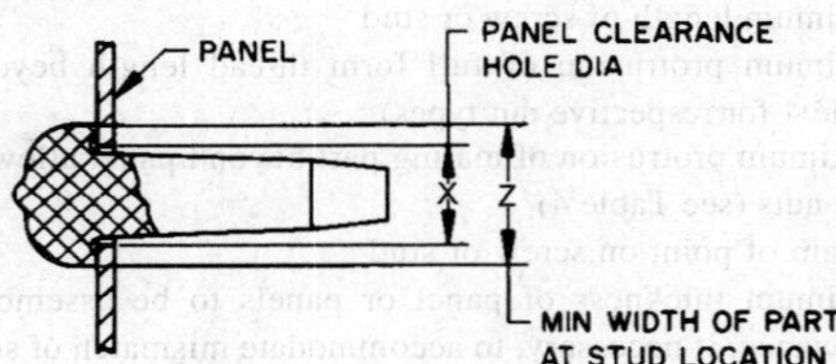

FIGURE 6—PANEL CLEARANCE HOLES

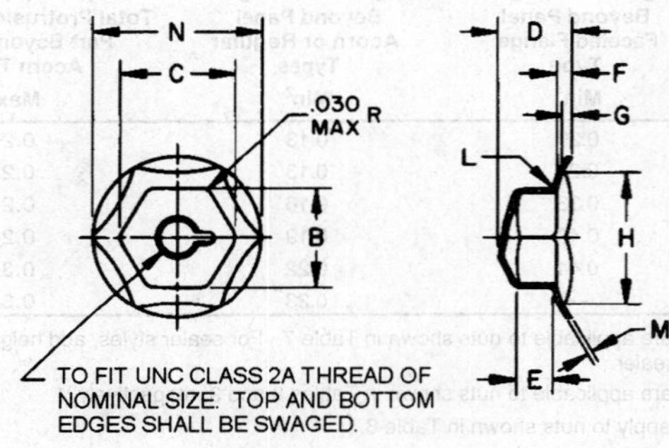

FIGURE 7—FORMED THREAD FACETED FLANGE TYPE STAMPED NUTS, in[1]

TABLE 6—PANEL CLEARANCE HOLES, in

Nominal Stud Dia	X Clearance Hole Diameter[1] Preferred Max	X Clearance Hole Diameter[1] Preferred Min	X_1 Clearance Hole Diameter[1] Maximum Clearance Max	X_1 Clearance Hole Diameter[1] Maximum Clearance Min	X_2 Clearance Hole Diameter[1] Minimum Clearance Max	X_2 Clearance Hole Diameter[1] Minimum Clearance Min	Z Part Width Min
1/8[2]	0.188	0.172	0.219	0.203	0.171	0.155	0.24
5/32	0.220	0.205	0.252	0.236	0.205	0.188	0.29
3/16	0.250	0.234	0.281	0.265	0.234	0.219	0.32
1/4	0.344	0.328	0.406	0.390	0.312	0.296	0.41

[1] For recommendations on application of the three choices offered, refer to 5.3.

[2] Due to susceptibility to breakage in handling and processing, it is recommended use of 1/8 and 5/32 mm size die cast and plastic studs be avoided wherever possible.

TABLE 7A—DIMENSIONS OF FORMED THREAD FACETED FLANGE TYPE STAMPED NUTS, in[1] (SEE FIGURE 7)

Nominal Size[2] or Basic Thread Dia	Threads Per In	B Hexagon Across Flats Max	B Hexagon Across Corners Min	C Hexagon Across Corners Max	C Hexagon Across Corners Min	D Overall Height Max	D Overall Height Min	E Height of Flat Min	F Depth to Radius Max	F Depth to Radius Min
6 0.1380	32	0.312	0.306	0.360	0.348	0.218	0.198	0.067	0.017	0.007
8 0.1640	32	0.343	0.337	0.396	0.382	0.225	0.205	0.072	0.018	0.008
10 0.1900	24	0.375	0.369	0.433	0.418	0.246	0.226	0.076	0.019	0.009
1/4 0.2500	20	0.437	0.430	0.505	0.488	0.302	0.282	0.090	0.047	0.035
5/16 0.3125	18	0.500	0.492	0.577	0.557	0.330	0.310	0.100	0.057	0.045

TABLE 7B—DIMENSIONS OF FORMED THREAD FACETED FLANGE TYPE STAMPED NUTS, in[1] (SEE FIGURE 7) (CONTINUED)

Nominal Size[2] or Basic Thread Dia	Thread Per in	G Dish Depth Max	G Dish Depth Min	H Dish Diameter Max	H Dish Diameter Min	L Fillet Radius Max	L Fillet Radius Min	M Stock Thickness Basic ±0.0015	N Flange Diameter Max	N Flange Diameter Min
6 0.1380	32	Equal to H	Equal to H	0.401	0.387	0.033	0.027	0.013	0.442	0.432
8 0.1640	32	Equal to H	Equal to H	0.429	0.415	0.035	0.029	0.014	0.474	0.464
10 0.1900	24	Equal to H	Equal to H	0.457	0.443	0.037	0.031	0.018	0.505	0.495
1/4 0.2500	20	0.043	0.033	0.572	0.552	0.039	0.033	0.021	0.692	0.682
5/16 0.3125	18	0.050	0.040	0.674	0.650	0.041	0.035	0.023	0.817	0.807

[1] Sealer styles are also available, consult nut manufacturers.

[2] Where specifying nominal size in decimals, zeros preceding decimal and in fourth decimal place shall be omitted.

For recommended assembly data refer to Design Criteria in Section 5. Additional requirements given in General Specifications in Section 3 shall apply.

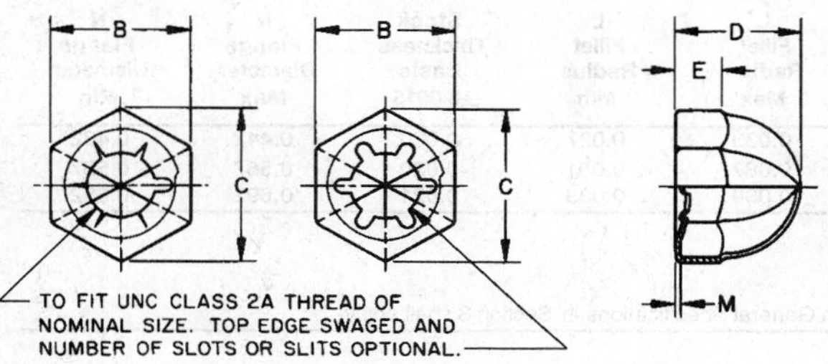

FIGURE 8—FORMED THREAD ACORN TYPE STAMPED NUTS

FIGURE 10—SELF-THREADING FACETED FLANGE TYPE STAMPED NUTS

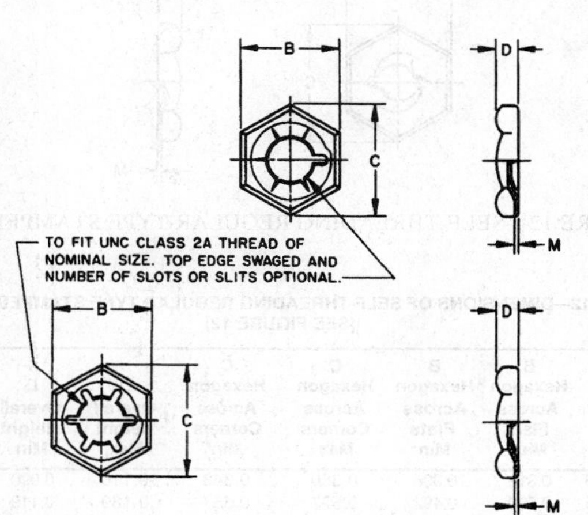

FIGURE 9—FORMED THREAD REGULAR TYPE STAMPED NUTS

TABLE 8—DIMENSIONS OF FORMED THREAD ACORN TYPE STAMPED NUTS, in

Nominal Size[1] or Basic Thread Dia	Threads Per in	B Hexagon Across Flats Max	B Hexagon Across Flats Min	C Hexagon Across Comers Max	C Hexagon Across Corners Min	D Overall Height ±0.010	E Height at Corner of Hexagon Min	M Stock Thickness Basic ±0.0015
6 0.1380	32	0.312	0.306	0.306	0.348	0.261	0.080	0.013
8 0.1640	32	0.343	0.337	0.397	0.383	0.297	0.094	0.013
10 0.1900	24	0.375	0.368	0.433	0.418	0.324	0.108	0.017
1/4 0.2500	20	0.437	0.429	0.505	0.488	0.380	0.122	0.021
5/16 0.3125	18	0.562	0.553	0.650	0.627	0.484	0.157	0.024
3/8 0.3750	16	0.562	0.553	0.650	0.627	0.474	0.157	0.020

[1] Where specifying nominal size in decimals, zeros preceding decimal and in fourth decimal place shall be omitted.

For recommended assembly data, refer to Design Criteria in Section 5. Additional requirements given in General Specifications in Section 3 shall apply.

TABLE 9—DIMENSIONS OF FORMED THREAD REGULAR TYPE STAMPED NUTS, in

Nominal Size[1] or Basic Thread Dia	Threads Per in	B Hexagon Across Flats Max	B Hexagon Across Flats Min	C Hexagon Across Corners Max	C Hexagon Across Corners Min	D Overall Height Max	D Overall Height Min	M Stock Thickness Basic ±0.0015
6 0.1380	32	0.312	0.305	0.341	0.348	0.102	0.082	0.013
8 0.1640	32	0.343	0.336	0.397	0.383	0.109	0.089	0.013
10 0.1900	24	0.375	0.348	0.433	0.418	0.113	0.095	0.017
1/4 0.2500	20	0.437	0.429	0.505	0.488	0.133	0.113	0.021
5/16 0.3125	18	0.500	0.492	0.578	0.558	0.144	0.124	0.021
3/8 0.3750	16	0.562	0.553	0.650	0.627	0.155	0.135	0.021

[1] Where specifying nominal size in decimals, zeros preceding decimal and in fourth decimal place shall be omitted.

For recommended assembly data, refer to Design Criteria in Section 5. Additional requirements given in General Specifications n Section 3 shall apply.

TABLE 10A—DIMENSIONS OF SELF-THREADING FACETED FLANGE TYPE STAMPED NUTS, in[1] (SEE FIGURE 10)

Nominal Size[1] or Basic Stud Dia	B Hexagon Across Flats Max	B Hexagon Across Flats Min	C Hexagon Across Corners Max	C Hexagon Across Corners Min	D Overall Height Max	D OverallHei ghtMin	E Height of Flat Min	E Depth to Radius Max	F Depth to Radius Min
1/8 0.125	0.312	0.034	0.360	0.348	0.199	0.179		0.017	0.007
3/16 0.188	0.375	0.366	0.433	0.418	0.239	0.219	0.078	0.037	0.025
1/4 0.250	0.437	0.428	0.505	0.488	0.273	0.253	0.090	0.047	0.035

TABLE 10B—DIMENSIONS OF SELF-THREADING FACETED FLANGE TYPE STAMPED NUTS, in[1] (SEE FIGURE 10) (CONTINUED)

Nominal Size[1] or Basic Stud Dia	G Dish Depth Max	G Dish Depth Min	H Dish Diameter Max	H Dish Diameter Min	K Corner Radius Max	L Fillet Radius Max	L Fillet Radius Min	M Stock Thickness Basic ±0.0015	N Flange Diameter Max	N Flange Diameter Min
1/8 0.125	Equal to H	Equal to H	0.401	0.387	0.035	0.033	0.027	0.020	0.442	0.432
3/16 0.188	0.036	0.026	0.468	0.448	0.037	0.037	0.031	0.020	0.567	0.557
1/4 0.250	0.043	0.033	0.572	0.552	0.043	0.039	0.033	0.021	0.692	0.682

[1] Sealer styles are also available, consult manufacturers.
[2] Where specifying nominal size in decimals, zeros preceding decimal shall be omitted.

For recommended assembly data refer to Design Criteria in Section 5. Additional requirements given in General Specifications in Section 3 shall apply.

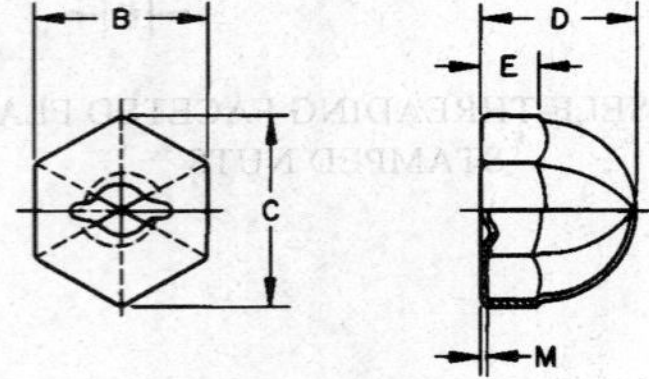

FIGURE 11—SELF-THREADING ACORN TYPE STAMPED NUTS

TABLE 11—DIMENSIONS OF SELF-THREADING ACORN TYPE STAMPED NUTS, in[1]

Nominal Size[2] or Basic Stud Dia	B Hexagon Across Flats Max	B Hexagon Across Flats Max	C Hexagon Across Corners Max	C Hexagon Across Corners Min	D Overall Height ±0.010	E Height at Corner of Hexagon Min	M Stock Thickness Basic ±0.0015
1/8 0.125	0.375	0.368	0.433	0.418	0.324	0.119	0.017
3/16 0.188	0.500	0.491	0.577	0.557	0.437	0.147	0.020
1/4 0.250	0.562	0.553	0.650	0.628	0.484	0.166	0.024

[1] Sealer Styles are also available, consult nut manufacturers.
[2] Where specifying nominal size in decimals, zeros preceding decimal shall be omitted.

For recommended assembly data, refer to Design Criteria in Section 5. Additional requirements given in General Specifications in Section 3 shall apply.

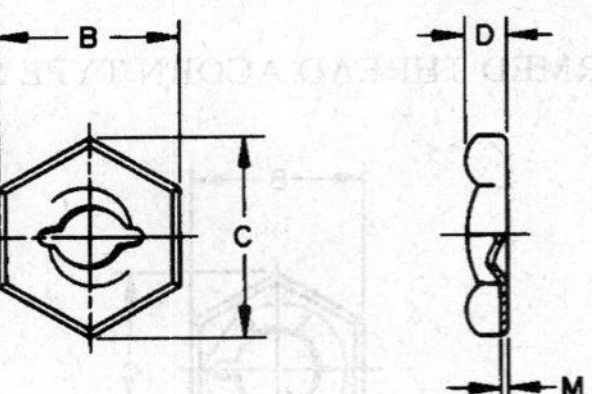

FIGURE 12—SELF-THREADING REGULAR TYPE STAMPED NUTS

TABLE 12—DIMENSIONS OF SELF-THREADING REGULAR TYPE STAMPED NUTS, in[1] (SEE FIGURE 12)

Nominal Size[2] or Basic Stud Dia	B Hexagon Across Flats Max	B Hexagon Across Flats Min	C Hexagon Across Corners Max	C Hexagon Across Corners Min	D Overall Height Max	D Overall Height Min	M Stock Thickness Basic ±0.0015
1/8 0.125	0.312	0.306	0.360	0.348	0.110	0.090	0.017
3/16 0.188	0.500	0.492	0.577	0.557	0.139	0.119	0.019
1/4 0.250	0.500	0.492	0.577	0.557	0.150	0.130	0.026

[1] Sealer Styles are also available, consult nut manufacturers.
[2] Where specifying nominal size in decimals, zeros preceding decimal shall be omitted.

For recommended assembly data refer to Design Criteria in Section 5. Additional requirements given in General Specifications in Section 3 shall apply.

STEEL STAMPED NUTS OF ONE PITCH THREAD DESIGN —METRIC SERIES—SAE J1053M AUG1996

SAE Standard

Report of the SAE Fasteners Committee approved August 1973 and completely revised August 1996.

1. Scope—Included herein are general, dimensional, and performance specifications for those types, styles, and sizes of stamped nuts of one pitch thread design recognized as SAE standard. These nuts are intended for general use where the engagement of a single thread on the mating screw or unthreaded stud is considered adequate for the application. For the inch equivalent of this document, see SAE J1053.

2. References

2.1 Applicable Publications—The following publication forms a part of this specification to the extent specified herein. Unless otherwise specified, the latest issue of SAE publications shall apply.

2.1.1 SAE PUBLICATION—Available from SAE, 400 Commonwealth Drive, Warrendale, PA 15096-0001.

SAE J1053 —Steel Stamped Nuts of One Pitch Thread Design—Inch Series

3. General Specifications

3.1 Dimensional Tolerance—Tolerance on dimensions are shown in Tables 1 to 12.

3.2 Miscellaneous Dimensions—Taper on the sides of hexagon portions of nuts (angle between one side and the axis of nut) shall not exceed 1 degree, the maximum limit specified being the largest dimension.

3.3 Thread Embossments

3.3.1 FORMED THREAD EMBOSSMENT—Detail of the thread engaging portion of formed thread type nuts shall be such as to permit nut to assemble readily with the specified screw and not strip or deform at the minimum torques shown in Table 2. The edges around the opening shall be spirally formed to conform to the helix of the mating thread and, as indicated on illustrations, the top or top and bottom corners on edges of holes shall be swaged to provide flats for bearing on flanks of the mating thread.

3.3.2 SELF-THREADING EMBOSSMENT—The configuration of self-threading embossment may vary with manufacturer; however, the detail and formation of embossment shall be such as to enable the nuts to cut and/or form threads on cast or wire studs, conforming to the recommended stud designs contained in 5.2, at or below the maximum driving torques shown in Table 3.

3.4 Material—Nuts shall be fabricated from carbon spring steel suitably processed to meet the performance requirements of this document.

3.5 Finish—Stamped nuts are normally supplied with finishes as specified by the purchaser. Nuts processed with supplemental finishes shall be suitably treated to obviate hydrogen embrittlement.

3.6 Workmanship—Stamped nuts shall be free from cracks, burrs, splits, loose scale, or any defects that might affect their serviceability.

4. Test Procedures and Performance Requirements

4.1 Formed Thread Embossment

4.1.1 ULTIMATE TORQUE TEST—Insert hardened steel (560 HV min) unplated or uncoated test socket head cap screws of the respective size and 25 mm length, Class 4g6g thread, as-received with light coating of oil, into holes in the test fixture. The test fixture is to consist of a hardened steel (653-746 HV) bar, 25 x 6 x 460 mm or equivalent, having 12 equally spaced test holes of the diameter given in Table 1 for respective size.

TABLE 1—TEST BAR HOLE SIZES, mm

Nominal Screws and Nut Size	Hole Diameter Max	Hole Diameter Min	Nominal Screw and Nut Size	Hole Diameter Max	Hole Diameter Min
M4 x 0.7	4.38	4.23	M8 x 1.25	8.41	8.28
M5 x 0.8	5.38	5.23	M10 x 1.50	10.41	10.28
M6 x 1.0	6.38	6.23	M12 x 1.75	12.41	12.28

Hand assemble the test nuts to the test screws. In turn, hold each nut and tighten the test screw to the torque value shown in Table 2 for the respective size. The test shall be performed with a device capable of measuring the clamp load developed, and the load attained shall not be less than the minimum tension values specified in Table 2. After initial breakaway, the nuts must disassemble, by hand, from the test screws.

4.1.2 EMBRITTLEMENT TEST—Insert hardened steel (560 HV min) unplated or uncoated test socket head cap screws of the respective size and 25 mm length, Class 4g6g thread, as-received with light coating of oil, into holes in the test fixture described in 4.1.1.

TABLE 2—ULTIMATE TORQUE SPECIFICATIONS

Nominal Nut Size	Torque, Nm Mn	Tension, N Mn	Nominal Nut Size	Torque, Nm Mn	Tension, N Mn
M4 x 0.7	1.13	550	M8 x 1.25	6.00	2000
M5 x 0.8	2.00	700	M10 x 1.50	9.00	2000
M6 x 1.0	4.00	1150	M12 x 1.75	18.00	3800

Hand assemble new test nuts, from the same lot, to test screws. In turn, hold each nut and tighten test screw to the minimum torque value shown in Table 2 for respective size. After 48 h in this state, the test nuts shall be examined. No cracks are permitted.

4.1.3 SCREW THREAD DAMAGE APPRAISAL TEST—Insert 12 nonheat-treated, unplated or uncoated, steel screws of respective size and 25 mm length, into holes in the test fixture described in 4.1.1.

Hand assemble new test nuts, from the same lot, to test screws. In turn, hold each nut and tighten test screw to the torque value shown in Table 2 for the respective size. Remove nuts from screws and screws from test bar and examine threads on screws for visible damage. Continue test by assembling, with the fingers, untested nuts from same lot onto tested screws. The new nuts must pass over the area on the screw where the previously tested nut engaged the threads.

4.2 Self-Threading Embossment

4.2.1 STARTING EASE TEST—The test nut must start onto the chamfered end (0.8 x 45 degrees) of an unplated or uncoated cold-rolled steel (195-230 HV) rod of the diameter specified in Table 3, within one revolution of nut when applied with an appropriate socket affixed to a screwdriver handle.

TABLE 3—TORQUE AND RELATED TENSION SPECIFICATIONS

Nominal Stud or Test Rod Dia, mm	Test Rod Dia, mm Max	Test Dia, mm Min	Driving Torque, N-m Max	Nut Flange Dia, mm Basic	Test Torque, N-m	Tension, N Min
3.2	3.23	3.15	0.90	14.00	4.00	530
4.0	4.03	3.95	2.60	15.00	5.10	890
5.0	5.03	4.95	2.60	15.00	6.80	1200
6.0	6.03	5.95	2.60	18.00	10.20	1270
6.3	6.33	6.25	2.60	18.00	10.70	1330
8.0	8.03	7.95	5.56	20.00	18.60	2000

4.2.2 ULTIMATE TORQUE TEST—Insert a test rod (see 4.2.1) into a suitable holding device exposing the chamfered end to a height equivalent to the nut height plus 3.0 mm or, for closed end nuts, equivalent to the wrenching height. Place an unplated or uncoated soft steel (195-230 HV) flat test plate on the exposed test rod. The test plate shall have a minimum thickness of 0.75 mm, an inside diameter 0.80 mm larger than the diameter of test rod, and shall be at least 645.2 mm^2. A new test plate shall be used for each torque test. The test rod and assembled plate must be retained in a suitable clamping device to prevent rotation of the rod and plate and tilting of the plate. The test shall be performed with a device capable of measuring the clamp load developed.

Assemble test nut on the test rod with a suitable torque indicating device. The maximum driving torque shall be recorded and this shall not exceed the maximum driving torque values shown in Table 3 for the respective size. At the torque test values specified in Table 3, the minimum tension values indicated shall be achieved.

4.2.3 EMBRITTLEMENT TEST—Assemble new test nut from the same lot to test rod using test torques shown in Table 3 for respective size. After 48 h, inspect the assembled nut for cracks. No cracks are permitted.

5. Design Criteria

5.1 Formed Thread Embossment—To insure proper starting of formed thread type stamped nuts, the length of the mating externally threaded component shall be such that it will protrude beyond the embossment in nut a minimum distance equivalent to two pitches (threads), exclusive of the length of any chamfer or point provision, under limit stack conditions. Recommended minimum protrusion lengths beyond panels with no allowance for pointing are presented in Figure 1 and Table 4 for respective nut types.

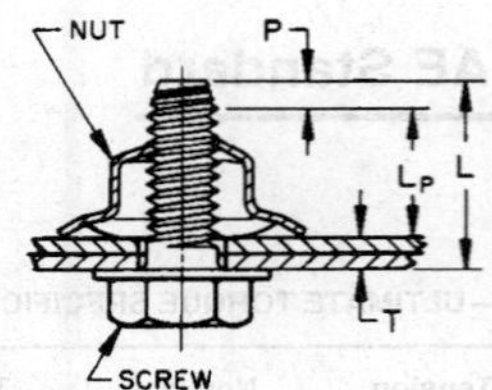

FIGURE 1A—FACETED FLANGE TYPE NUTS

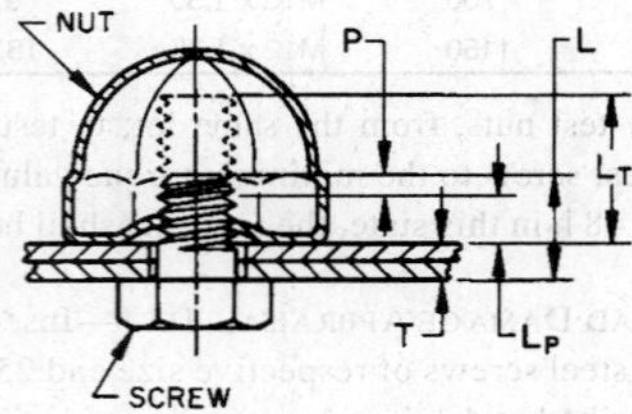

FIGURE 1B—ACORN OR REGULAR TYPE NUTS

$$L = L_P + T + P \quad \text{(Eq. 1)}$$

where:

L = Minimum length of screw or stud

L_P = Minimum protrusion of full form thread length beyond panel (see Table 4 for respective nut types)

L_T = Maximum protrusion of mating part beyond panel allowable for acorn type nuts (see Table 4)

P = Length of point on screw or stud

T = Maximum thickness of panel or panels to be assembled, including allowance, if necessary, to accomodate mismatch of surfaces, etc.

FIGURE 1—PROTUSION LENGTHS FOR FACETED FLANGE AND ACORN OR REGULAR TYPE NUTS

TABLE 4—PROTRUSION LENGTHS FOR FORMED THREAD TYPE STAMPED NUTS, mm

Nominal Thread Size	L_P Protrusion of Threaded Length on Mating Part Beyond Panel Faced Flange Type Min(1)	L_P Protrusion of Threaded Length on Mating Part Beyond Panel Faced Flange Type Min(2)	L_T Total Protrusion of Mating Part Beyond Panel Acorn Types Max(3)
M4 x 0.7	8.00	3.30	5.90
M5 x 0.8	9.00	3.60	6.30
M6 x 1.0	10.00	4.20	7.10
M8 x 1.25	11.00	5.00	9.10

1. Values shown are applicable to nuts shown in Table 7. For sealer styles, add height of uncompressed sealer.
2. Values shown are applicable to nuts shown in Tables 8 and 9, respectively.
3. Values shown apply to nuts shown in Table 8.

5.2 Self-Threading Embossment—To assure proper function and performance of self-threading types of stamped nuts and to provide flexibility for changing nut designs, it is essential that studs and clearance holes in mating panels be designed in conformance with the recommendations set forth in the following.

5.2.1 STUD DESIGN—Studs which are integral features of die-cast components should comply as closely as possible with the recommendations presented in Figures 2 and 3 and Table 5. Studs fabricated from wire or rod shall be in accord with recommendations shown in Figures 4 and 5 and Table 5. Consideration should also be given to the recommendations for fillets, plating, and alignment which follow:

5.2.1.1 Fillets—The fillet at the junction of stud with die-casting base shall have as generous a radius as the design will permit, but not less than 0.25 mm. Where the panel is to fit tight against the die casting, an annular relief groove should be provided in the die casting at base of stud to accommodate the fillet (see Figure 2) and the fillet radius should be made larger wherever the design will permit.

5.2.1.2 Angularity—It is preferable that the axis of the stud be kept perpendicular to the base of the part or as nearly so as possible. However, where design conditions or parting lines on die castings dictate the axis of stud must deviate from square with base, the departure from perpendicular shall not exceed 20 degrees. Similarly, where sufficient driver clearance cannot be provided in line with the stud axis, the angular deviation from axis should in no case exceed 15 degrees in order to insure the socket will have adequate engagement with the nut for assembly.

5.2.1.3 Stud Location—On drawings for parts entailing multiple studs, the studs should be located in accordance with the dimensioning and tolerancing practices set forth in the SAE Drawing Standards.

5.3 Panel Clearance Holes—The clearance holes in mating panels for stamped nuts should be designed in conformance with Figure 6 and Table 6. A selection of three hole sizes for each stud size is provided to best satisfy varying design conditions as explained in the following:

a. Preferred hole sizes listed under "X" are recommended and should be used for all attachments requiring normal provisions for clearance and adjustment.
b. Maximum clearance holes tabulated under "X_1" should be used only in applications where maximum adjustment capability is a requirement. These holes provide maximum clearance while assuring that the hole can effectively be sealed with sealer styles of the faceted flange type nuts contained herein.
c. Minimum clearance holes shown under "X_2" may necessarily have to be used where the width of the part being fastened is at or approaches the minimum "Z" dimension. These holes provide adequate clearance for studs under limit stack conditions while insuring that the fastened part will cover the hole. It follows, therefore, that the "Z" dimension shall be the design criterion for the width of portions of parts adjacent to studs.

5.3.1 PANEL HOLE LOCATION—On drawings for panels, multiple holes shall be located in a manner which is compatible with that used to position studs on the mating part.

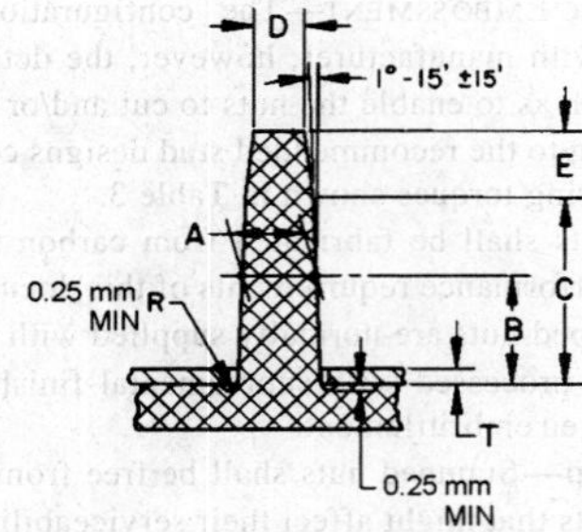

FIGURE 2—DIE CAST AND PLASTIC STUD

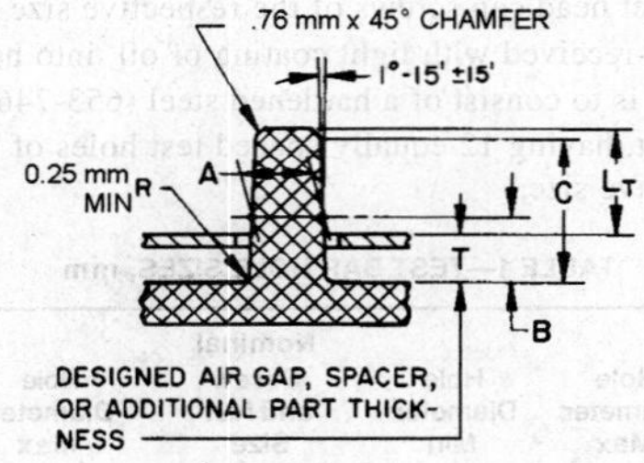

FIGURE 3—SHORT DIE CAST AND PLASTIC STUD

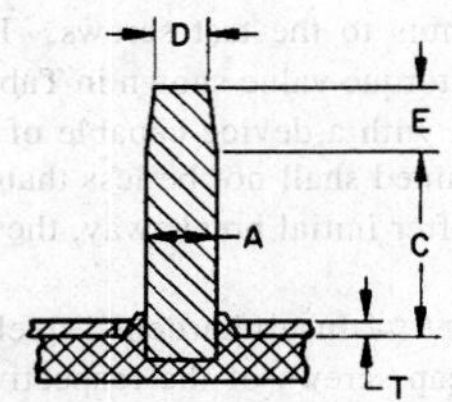

FIGURE 4A—WIRE OR ROD STUD

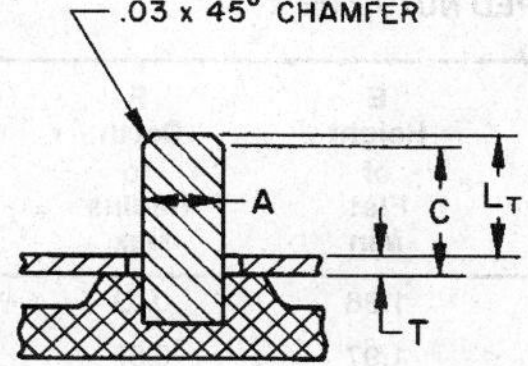

FIGURE 4B—SHORT WIRE OR ROD STUD

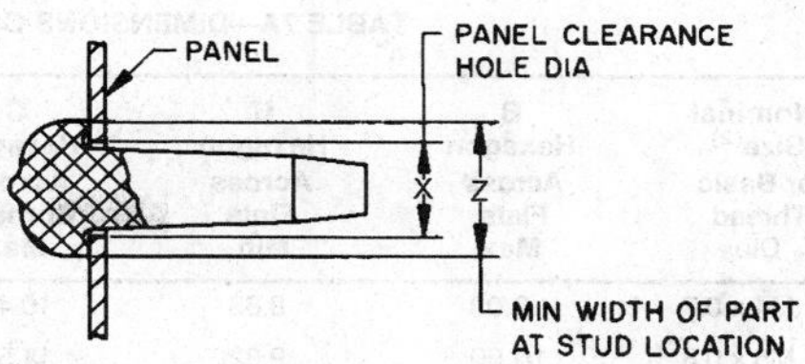

FIGURE 6—PANEL CLEARANCE HOLES

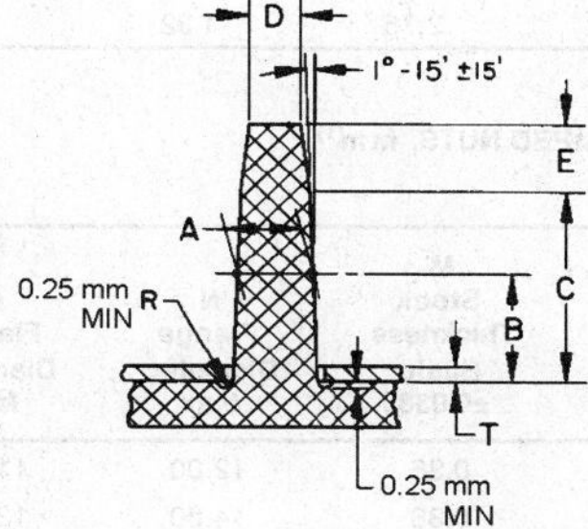

FIGURE 5—DIE CAST STEEL AND PLASTIC STUD

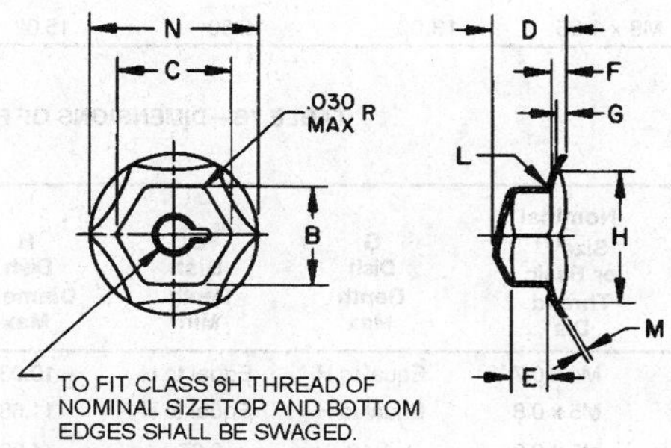

FIGURE 7—FORMED THREAD FACETED FLANGE TYPE STAMPED NUTS, mm

TABLE 5—RECOMMENDED DIMENSIONS OF STUDS FOR USE WITH SELF-THREADING TYPES OF STAMPED NUTS, mm

Nominal Stud Size	A(1) Stud Dia Max	A(1) Stud Dia Min	B(2)(3) Length Faceted Flange Type	B(2),(3) Length Acorn and Regular Types	C(3) Length Faceted Flange Type Min	C(3) Length Acorn and Regular Types Min	D(1) Point Dia Max	D(1) Point Dia Min	E(4) Point Length Max	E(4) Point Length Min	L_T Stud Protrusion Acorn Type Max
3.2	3.28	3.12	T+6.1	T+2.0	T+11.4	T+3.0	2.0	1.7	4.6	3.6	5.5
4.0	4.08	3.92	T+6.1	T+2.8	T+11.4	T+4.0	2.7	2.4	4.6	3.6	6.1
5.0	5.08	4.92	T+6.3	T+2.8	T+11.4	T+4.0	3.8	3.4	4.8	3.8	8.1
6.0	6.08	5.92	T+6.6	T+3.6	T+11.4	T+4.0	4.6	4.2	6.3	5.3	9.6
6.3	6.38	6.22	T+6.8	T+3.6	T+11.4	T+4.0	4.8	4.4	6.6	5.6	9.6
8.0	8.08	7.92	T+7.8	T+4.4	T+11.4	T+4.8	5.8	5.4	7.6	6.6	(6)

1. For plastic studs minimum and maximum diameters 0.38 mm larger. Maximum plate per side 0.08 mm. Nickel, chromium plate, or other hard finishes are not recommended on steel studs.
2. Point on shank of die cast studs where A diameter must be within the specified limits.
3. The T dimension in illustrations represents the distance from base of part to the bearing face of nut in the installed position. The factors to be added represent the minimum length required for normal installation of sealer styles of nuts. Where the factors specified would create an interference condition or otherwise be objectionable, it may be necessary to reduce the factor to that which is required for the respective nut size, type, and style.
4. On studs for acorn type ntus, it may be necessary to shorten point or apply the chamfer specified for short studs in order to keep protrusion of stud beyond panel within maximum permissible.
5. Due to susceptibility to breakage in handling and processing, it is recommended use of 3.2 and 4.0 mm size die cast and plastic studs be available wherever possible.
6. Not available at this time.

TABLE 6—PANEL CLEARANCE HOLES, mm

Nominal Stud Dia.	X Clearance Hole Diameter(1) Preferred Max	X Clearance Hole Diameter(1) Preferred Min	X_1 Clearance Hole Diameter(1) Maximum Clearance Max	X_1 Clearance Hole Diameter(1) Maximum Clearance Min	X_2 Clearance Hole Diameter(1) Minimum Clearance Max	X_2 Clearance Hole Diameter(1) Minimum Clearance Min	Z Part Width Min
3.2(2)	4.8	4.4	5.6	5.2	4.3	3.9	6.1
4.0(2)	5.6	5.2	6.4	6.0	5.2	4.8	7.4
5.0	6.6	6.2	7.4	7.0	6.2	5.8	8.4
6.0	8.4	8.0	10.0	9.6	7.6	7.2	10.1
6.3	8.7	8.3	10.3	9.9	7.9	7.5	10.4
8.0	10.4	10.0	12.0	11.6	9.6	9.2	12.1

1. For recommendations on application of the three choices offered, refer to 5.3.
2. Due to susceptibility to breakage in handling and processing, it is recommended use of 3.2 and 4.0 mm size die cast and plastic studs to be avoided wherever possible.

TABLE 7A—DIMENSIONS OF FORMED THREAD FACETED FLANGE TYPE STAMPED NUTS, mm[1]

Nominal Size[2] or Basic Thread Dia	B Hexagon Across Flats Max	B Hexagon Across Flats Min	C Hexagon Across Corners Max	C Hexagon Across Corners Min	D Overall Height Max	D Overall Height Min	E Height of Flat Min	F Depth to Radius Max	F Depth to Radius Min
M4 x 0.7	9.00	8.85	10.40	10.04	5.90	5.50	1.86	0.49	0.23
M5 x 0.8	10.00	9.82	11.55	11.15	6.20	5.70	1.97	0.57	0.27
M5 x 0.8	10.00	9.82	11.55	11.15	7.22	6.72	2.09	1.39	1.09
M5 x 0.8	10.00	9.82	11.55	11.15	7.92	7.52	2.21	1.90	1.60
M6 x 1.0	11.00	10.82	12.70	12.25	7.51	7.07	2.40	1.28	0.98
M6 x 1.0	11.00	10.82	12.70	12.25	8.56	8.06	2.58	2.08	1.78
M8 x 1.25	13.00	12.80	15.02	14.50	8.21	7.71	2.75	1.32	1.02

TABLE 7B—DIMENSIONS OF FORMED THREAD FACETED FLANGE TYPE STAMPED NUTS, mm[1] (CONTINUED)

Nominal Size[2] or Basic Thread Dia	G Dish Depth Max	G Dish Depth Min	H Dish Diameter Max	H Dish Diameter Min	L Fillet Radius Max	L Fillet Radius Min	M Stock Thickness Basic ±0.038	N Flange Diameter Max	N Flange Diameter Min
M4 x 0.7	Equal to H	Equal to H	10.03	9.53	0.90	0.74	0.36	12.00	11.75
M5 x 0.8	Equal to H	Equal to H	11.68	11.18	0.90	0.74	0.38	14.00	13.74
M5 x 0.8	1.13	0.87	14.92	14.42	0.90	0.74	0.38	18.00	17.75
M5 x 0.8	1.32	1.06	18.18	17.68	0.94	0.78	0.38	22.00	21.75
M6 x 1.0	1.13	0.87	14.92	14.42	0.94	0.78	0.43	18.00	17.75
M6 x 1.0	1.47	1.21	19.81	19.31	0.94	0.78	0.43	24.00	23.75
M8 x 1.25	1.24	0.98	16.55	16.05	0.94	0.78	0.53	20.00	19.75

1. Sealer styles are also available, consult nut manufacturers.
2. Where specifying nominal size in decimals, zeros preceding decimal and in fourth decimal place shall be omitted.

For recommended assembly data refer to Design Criteria in Section 5. Additional requirements given in General Specifications in Section 3 shall apply.

TABLE 8—DIMENSIONS OF FORMED THREAD ACORN TYPE STAMPED NUTS, mm

Nominal Size	Pitch	B Hexagon Across Flats Max	B Hexagon Across Flats Min	C Hexagon Across Corners Max	C Hexagon Across Corners Min	D Overall Height Max	D Overall Height Min	E Height at Cofrner of Hexagon Min	M Stock Thickness ±0.038
4.0	0.7	9.00	8.85	10.40	10.04	7.90	7.40	2.56	0.33
5.0	0.8	10.00	9.82	11.55	11.15	8.50	8.00	2.80	0.33
6.0	1.0	11.00	10.80	12.70	12.26	9.65	9.15	3.30	0.46
8.0	1.25	14.00	13.77	16.17	15.61	11.75	11.25	3.75	0.53

For recommended assembly data, refer to Design Criteria in Section 5. Additional requirements given in General Specifications in Section 3 shall apply.

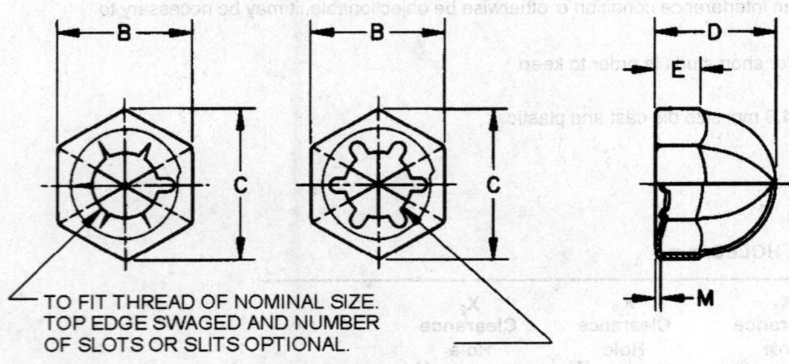

FIGURE 8—FORMED THREAD ACORN TYPE STAMPED NUTS

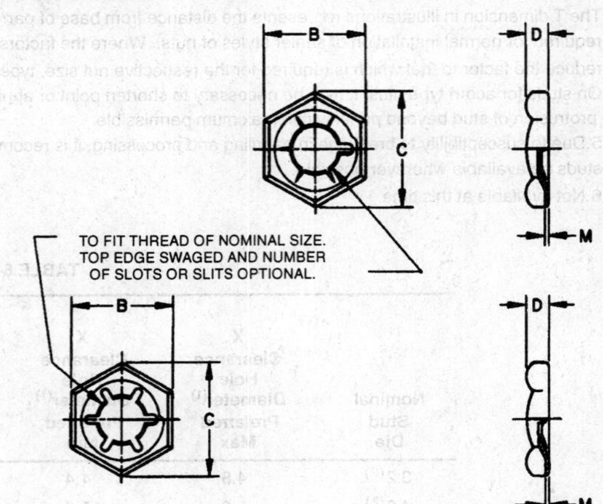

FIGURE 9—FORMED THREAD REGULAR TYPE STAMPED NUTS

TABLE 9—DIMENSIONS OF FORMED THREAD REGULAR TYPE STAMPED NUTS, mm

Nominal Size	Pitch	B Hexagon Across Flats Max	B Hexagon Across Flats Min	C Hexagon Across Corners Max	C Hexagon Across Corners Min	D Overall Height Max	D Overall Height Min	M Stock Thickness ±0.038
M4	0.70	9.00	8.82	10.40	10.04	2.81	2.31	0.36
M5	0.80	13.00	12.80	15.02	14.40	3.71	3.21	0.36
M6	1.00	11.00	10.80	12.70	12.26	3.30	2.80	0.46
M8	1.25	13.00	12.80	15.02	14.50	3.71	3.21	0.53
M10	1.50	15.00	14.80	17.32	16.72	4.07	3.57	0.55
M12	1.75	19.00	18.70	21.95	21.19	4.79	4.29	0.58
M14	2.00	24.00	23.64	27.72	26.76	5.69	5.19	0.84
M16	2.40	24.00	23.64	27.72	26.76	5.69	5.19	0.84
M20	3.00	30.00	29.65	34.65	33.45	6.72	6.32	0.97

For recommended assembly data, refer to Design Criteria in Section 5. Additional requirements given in General Specifications in Section 3 shall apply.

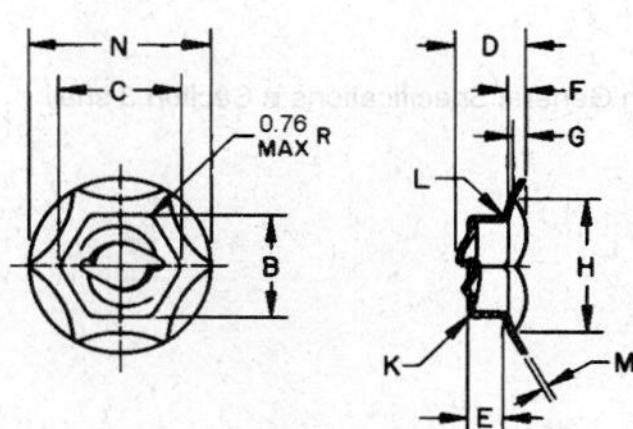

FIGURE 10—SELF-THREADING FACETED FLANGE TYPE STAMPED NUTS

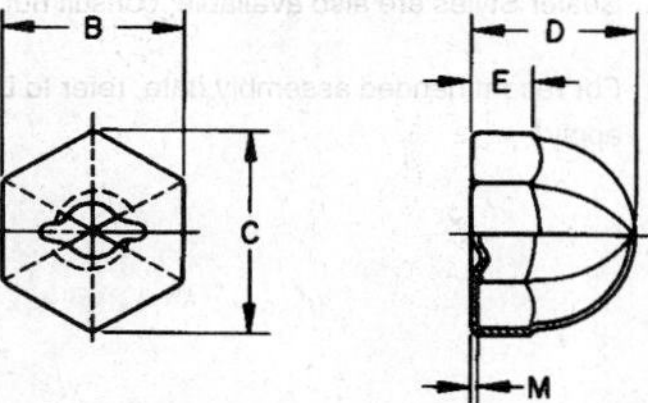

FIGURE 11—SELF-THREADING ACORN TYPE STAMPED NUTS

TABLE 10A—DIMENSIONS OF SELF-THREADING FACETED FLANGE TYPE STAMPED NUTS, mm[1]

Nominal[1] Size or Basic Stud Dia	B Hexagon Across Flats Max	B Hexagon Across Flats Min	C Hexagon Across Corners Max	C Hexagon Across Corners Min	D Overall Height Max	D Overall Height Min	E Height of Flat Min	F Depth to Radius Max	F Depth to Radius Min
3.2	8.00	7.80	9.24	8.92	5.03	4.53	1.70	0.46	0.20
3.2	8.00	7.80	9.24	8.92	5.57	5.07	1.79	0.91	0.61
4.0	9.00	8.77	10.40	10.04	6.08	5.58	1.95	1.07	0.82
5.0	10.00	9.77	11.55	11.15	6.10	5.60	2.00	0.98	0.68
5.0	10.00	9.77	11.55	11.15	6.60	6.10	2.09	1.39	1.09
5.0	10.00	9.77	11.55	11.15	7.09	6.59	2.18	1.79	1.49
6.0	11.00	10.77	12.70	12.26	6.60	6.10	2.31	0.60	0.30
6.0	11.00	10.77	12.70	12.26	7.43	7.03	2.40	1.27	0.97
6.3	11.00	10.77	12.70	12.26	6.48	5.98	2.31	0.60	0.30
6.3	11.00	10.77	12.70	12.26	7.89	7.39	2.49	1.68	1.38
6.3	11.00	10.77	12.70	12.26	8.37	7.87	2.58	2.08	1.78
6.3	11.00	10.77	12.70	12.26	7.31	6.91	2.40	1.27	0.97
8.0	13.00	12.80	15.02	14.50	8.10	7.60	2.75	1.32	1.02

1. Sealer styles are also available, consult manufacturers.

For recommended assembly data refer to Design Criteria in Section 5. Additional requirements given in General Specifications in Section 3 shall apply.

TABLE 10B— DIMENSIOINS OF SELF-THREADING FACETED FLANGE TYPE STAMPED NUTS, mm[1] (CONTINUED)

Nominal Size or Basic Stud Dia	G Dish Depth Max	G Dish Depth Min	H Dish Diameter Max	H Dish Diameter Min	K Corner Radius Max	L Filet Radius Max	L Fillet Radius Min	M Stock Thickness Basic ±0.038	N Flange Diameter Max	N Flange Diameter Min
3.2	Flat Flange—No Dish	Flat Flange—No Dish	Flat Flange—No Dish	Flat Flange—No Dish	0.89	0.86	0.70	0.51	11.00	10.75
3.2	0.78	0.52	12.08	11.58	0.89	0.86	0.70	0.51	14.00	14.75
4.0	Equal to H	Equal to H	12.40	12.05	0.94	0.95	0.79	0.51	15.00	14.75
5.0	Equal to H	Equal to H	12.47	11.97	0.95	0.96	0.80	0.51	15.00	14.75
5.0	1.13	0.87	14.92	14.42	0.95	0.96	0.80	0.51	18.00	17.75
5.0	1.30	1.04	17.37	16.87	0.95	0.96	0.80	0.51	21.00	20.75
6.0	Equal to H	Equal to H	13.75	13.25	1.09	0.99	0.83	0.53	15.00	14.75
6.0	1.13	0.87	14.98	14.48	1.09	0.99	0.83	0.53	18.00	17.75
6.3	Equal to H	Equal to H	13.75	13.25	1.09	0.99	0.83	0.53	15.00	14.75
6.3	1.29	1.03	17.36	16.86	1.09	0.99	0.83	0.53	21.00	20.75
6.3	1.47	1.21	19.81	19.31	1.09	0.99	0.83	0.53	24.00	23.75
6.3	1.13	0.87	14.98	14.48	1.09	0.99	0.83	0.53	18.00	17.75
8.0	1.28	0.90	16.55	16.05	1.14	0.88	1.04	0.58	20.00	19.75

1. Sealer styles are also available, consult nut manufacturers.

For recommended assembly data refer to Design Criteria in Section 5. Additional requirements given in General Specifications in Section 3 shall apply.

TABLE 11—DIMENSIONS OF SELF-THREADING ACORN TYPE STAMPED NUTS, mm[1]

Nominal Size or Basic Stud Dia	B Hexagon Across Flats Max	B Hexagon Across Flats Min	C Hexagon Across Corners Max	C Hexagon Across Corners Min	D Overall Height Max	D Overall Height Min	E Height at Corner of Hexagon Min	M Stock Thickness Basic ±0.038
3.2	8.00	7.85	9.24	8.92	6.97	6.47	2.36	0.43
3.2	10.00	9.82	11.55	11.15	8.60	8.10	2.80	0.43
3.2	11.00	10.80	12.70	12.26	9.70	9.20	3.30	0.43
4.0	9.00	8.85	10.40	10.04	8.01	7.51	2.54	0.43
5.0	11.00	10.80	12.70	12.26	9.80	9.30	3.30	0.53
5.0	13.00	12.77	15.02	14.50	11.35	10.85	3.70	0.51
5.0	14.00	13.77	16.17	15.61	11.75	11.25	3.75	0.51
6.3	14.00	13.77	16.17	15.61	11.90	11.40	3.75	0.61

1. Sealer Styles are also available, consult nut manufacturers.

For recommended assembly data, refer to Design Criteria in Section 5. Additional requirements given in General Specifications in Seciton 3 shall apply.

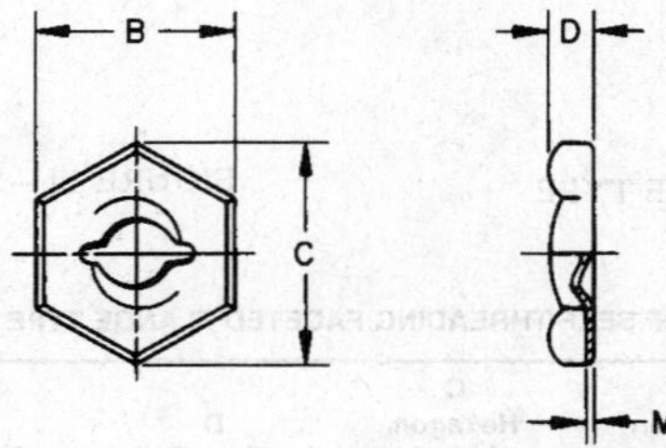

FIGURE 12—SELF-THREADING REGULAR TYPE STAMPED NUTS

TABLE 12—DIMENSIONS OF SELF-THREADING REGULAR TYPE STAMPED NUTS, mm[1]

Nominal Size or Basic Stud Dia	B Hexagon Across Flats Max	B Hexagon Across Flats Min	C Hexagon Across Corners Max	C Hexagon Across Corners Min	D Overall Height Max	D Overall Height Min	M Stock Thickness Basic ±0.038
3.2	7.00	6.85	8.09	7.81	2.50	2.24	0.38
3.2	8.00	7.85	9.24	8.92	2.90	2.40	0.43
4.0	9.00	8.82	10.40	10.04	3.00	2.50	0.43
5.0	10.00	9.83	11.55	11.15	3.00	2.50	0.48
5.0	13.00	12.80	15.02	14.50	3.60	3.10	0.48
6.3	13.00	12.80	15.02	14.50	3.65	3.15	0.64
8.0	16.00	15.80	18.48	17.84	4.06	3.56	0.53
10.0	17.00	16.80	19.64	18.96	4.95	4.45	0.66

1. Sealer Styles are also available, consult nut manufactuers.

For recommended assembly data refer to Design Criteria in Section5. Additional requirements given in General Specifications in Section 3 shall apply.

CONICAL SPRING WASHERS—SAE J773 MAY1998 SAE Standard

Report of the SAE Fasteners Committee approved June 1961, revised February 1976 and reaffirmed May 1998.

Foreword—This Document has been changed only to comply with the new SAE Technical Standards Board Format.

1. Scope—This SAE Standard covers dimensional, material, and general specifications and methods of test for two types of general purpose conical spring washers, designated type L and type H, for use as loose washers over screws and bolts, and also for use as pre-assembled washers in screw and washer assemblies.

1.1 Both the type L and type H washers are available in three washer series (narrow, regular and wide), having varied proportions designed to fulfill specific application requirements for load distribution.

1.2 Where so specified by the user, washers shall be supplied with peripheral teeth.

1.3 All sizes and types of washers specified in this standard are not necessarily stock production items. Users should consult with manufacturers concerning availability.

2. References

2.1 Applicable Publication—The following publication forms a part of the specification to the extent specified herein. Unless otherwise indicated the latest revision of SAE publications shall apply.

2.1.1 SAE PUBLICATION—Available from SAE, 400 Commonwealth Drive, Warrendale, PA 15096-0001.

SAEJ429—Mechanical and Material Requirements for Externally Threaded Fasteners

3. Designation—Washers shall be specified or designated as shown in the following example:

Washer, Conical, ½, SAE Type L, Wide

4. Use and Application—Type L washers are intended for use with screws and bolts equivalent to SAE Grade 1 and 2. Type H washers are intended for use with SAE Grade 5 or equivalent bolts or screws (SAE J429)

4.1 The desired installed position of this washer is as near flat as possible. The flattening will occur at a load equal to approximately 27 500 bolt psi for the Type L washer and 60 000 bolt psi for the Type H washer. The spring return will vary due to the compromises in washer diameter, thickness, and tolerances, which have been made to maintain this standard in a commercial category (see 8.1).

4.2 The relatively high supporting load and spring return makes this washer very effective where bolt tension may be subject to loss due to such factors as compensating for wear, thermal expansion, or compression set.

4.3 When used to span over-size clearance holes, it is recommended that (1) if the full periphery is supported, at least 70% of the washer annular area be bearing or (2) if the periphery is partially supported, as over a slot, the slot should be no wider than 1½ times the I.D. Narrow series should always be fully supported. Insufficient bearing will reduce spring return.

4.4 Washers with peripheral teeth are used for non-slip or positive electrical grounding purposes.

5. Dimensions—Dimensions of Type L and Type H conical spring washers are specified in Table 1.

5.1 Manufacturing Detail—Washers shall be symmetrical in shape. The radial section of the washer shall be flat to convex upward with flat preferred (see Figure 1). Unless otherwise specified by the user, the direction of blanking the outside diameter should permit the sharper edge to be on the underside of the washer. Washers shall be free from sharp edges, burrs, cracks, checks, embrittlement, loose scale, and all other defects that might affect their serviceability.

5.2 Assembly Detail—The inside diameters of washers for pre-assembly on unthreaded screw blanks shall be optional, but shall be such that the washer will be retained on the screw after thread rolling, but shall not bind on the screw shank before and during tightening of the assembly.

TABLE 1—DIMENSIONS OF CONICAL SPRING WASHERS, in (see FIGURE 1)

Nominal Screw or Bolt Size	Washer Series	A[1] ID Min	A[1] ID Max	B OD Max	B OD Min	Type L C Thickness Nom	Type L C Thickness Max	Type L C Thickness Min	Type L D Crown Height Min	Type L D Crown Height Max	Type H C^1 Thickness Nom	Type H C^1 Thickness Max	Type H C^1 Thickness Min	Type H D^1 Crown Height Min	Type H D^1 Crown Height Max
	Narrow			0.320	0.307	0.025	0.029	0.023	0.010	0.016	0.035	0.040	0.033	0.015	0.025
6	Regular	0.151	0.156	0.446	0.433	0.030	0.034	0.028	0.014	0.020	0.040	0.046	0.037	0.015	0.025
	Wide			0.570	0.557	0.030	0.034	0.028	0.021	0.031	0.040	0.046	0.037	0.019	0.029
	Narrow			0.383	0.370	0.035	0.040	0.033	0.010	0.016	0.040	0.046	0.037	0.015	0.025
8	Regular	0.183	0.188	0.508	0.495	0.035	0.040	0.033	0.020	0.030	0.045	0.050	0.042	0.016	0.026
	Wide			0.640	0.620	0.035	0.040	0.033	0.027	0.037	0.045	0.050	0.042	0.030	0.040
	Narrow			0.446	0.433	0.035	0.040	0.033	0.010	0.016	0.050	0.056	0.047	0.015	0.025
10	Regular	0.203	0.208	0.570	0.557	0.040	0.046	0.037	0.017	0.027	0.055	0.060	0.052	0.016	0.026
	Wide			0.765	0.743	0.040	0.046	0.037	0.026	0.036	0.055	0.060	0.052	0.024	0.034
	Narrow			0.446	0.433	0.040	0.046	0.037	0.011	0.017	0.055	0.060	0.052	0.015	0.025
12	Regular	0.230	0.240	0.640	0.620	0.040	0.046	0.037	0.023	0.033	0.055	0.060	0.052	0.016	0.026
	Wide			0.890	0.868	0.045	0.050	0.042	0.034	0.044	0.064	0.071	0.059	0.023	0.033
	Narrow			0.515	0.495	0.045	0.050	0.042	0.014	0.024	0.064	0.071	0.059	0.015	0.025
1/4	Regular	0.271	0.281	0.765	0.743	0.050	0.056	0.047	0.023	0.033	0.079	0.087	0.074	0.022	0.032
	Wide			1.015	0.993	0.055	0.060	0.052	0.030	0.040	0.079	0.087	0.074	0.029	0.039
	Narrow			0.640	0.620	0.055	0.060	0.052	0.016	0.026	0.079	0.087	0.074	0.016	0.026
5/16	Regular	0.334	0.344	0.890	0.868	0.064	0.071	0.059	0.031	0.041	0.095	0.103	0.090	0.019	0.029
	Wide			1.140	1.118	0.064	0.071	0.059	0.034	0.044	0.095	0.103	0.090	0.030	0.040
	Narrow			0.765	0.743	0.071	0.079	0.066	0.015	0.025	0.095	0.103	0.090	0.015	0.025
3/8	Regular	0.396	0.406	1.015	0.993	0.071	0.079	0.066	0.033	0.043	0.118	0.126	0.112	0.023	0.033
	Wide			1.265	1.243	0.079	0.087	0.074	0.037	0.047	0.118	0.126	0.112	0.035	0.045
	Narrow			0.890	0.868	0.079	0.087	0.074	0.018	0.028	0.128	0.136	0.122	0.016	0.026
7/16	Regular	0.470	0.480	1.140	1.118	0.095	0.103	0.090	0.031	0.041	0.128	0.136	0.122	0.028	0.038
	Wide			1.530	1.493	0.095	0.103	0.090	0.049	0.059	0.132	0.140	0.126	0.039	0.049
	Narrow			1.015	0.993	0.100	0.108	0.094	0.021	0.031	0.142	0.150	0.136	0.020	0.030
1/2	Regular	0.530	0.540	1.265	1.243	0.111	0.120	0.106	0.033	0.043	0.142	0.150	0.136	0.027	0.037
	Wide			1.780	1.743	0.111	0.120	0.106	0.052	0.062	0.152	0.160	0.146	0.042	0.052

1. Not applicable to washers assembled with screw blanks. See General Specifications.

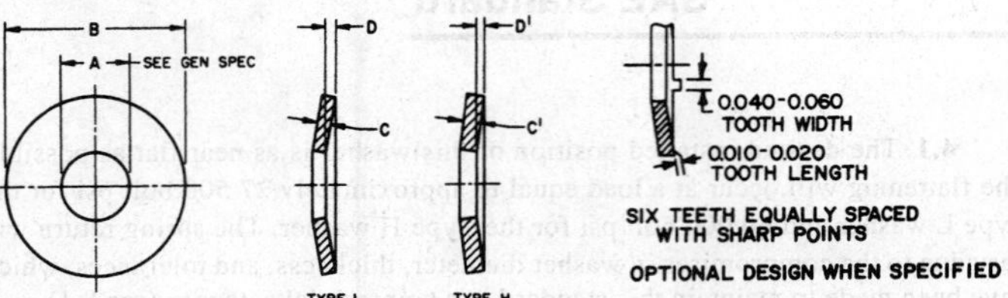

FIGURE 1—CONICAL SPRING WASHER DETAIL

6. Material and Hardness—Washers shall be made from SAE 1050 to 1065 carbon steel, fabricated and heat treated to a Rockwell hardness of 44-48 C scale (Rockwell hardness of C46-50 if austempering is used) or equivalent for loose washers, and 40-48 C scale or equivalent ibr pre-assembled washers, heat treated as an integral part of heat treated bolt or screw and washer assemblies. Washer hardness shall be checked by grinding or filing a flat spot on the top conical surface of the washer to rest on the anvil, with reading to be taken on the undisturbed inner face of the washer. If washer hardness, as obtained above, is not within specification, washers may be qualified by checking hardness on a cut-out section of the washer on which both sides have been ground. However, an excessive decarburized surface, especially on the lighter gage material, may be grounds for rejection if the performance of the washer is affected.

7. Finish—Electroplated washers or screw or bolt and washer assemblies shall be baked at 400 °F as soon as practicable after plating, in order to relieve hydrogen or acid embrittlement. If washers so treated fail to meet the prescribed tests, the baking time and/or the temperature shall be increased, but not to approach annealing temperature.

8. Tests

8.1 Recovery Test—The washers shall retain at least one-third their original crown height after flattening between two hardened plates and release. (Note: Conical washers which have a higher angle of elevation than covered by this standard are not expected to have the same percentage of recovery.)

8.2 Embrittlement Test—As a constant quality control check, a minimum of 12 pieces shall be taken from each batch after plating or final finishing operations and subjected to a load test sufficient to flatten washers for a minimum period of 24 h. Upon examination after testing, washers shall not exhibit cracks or fractures.

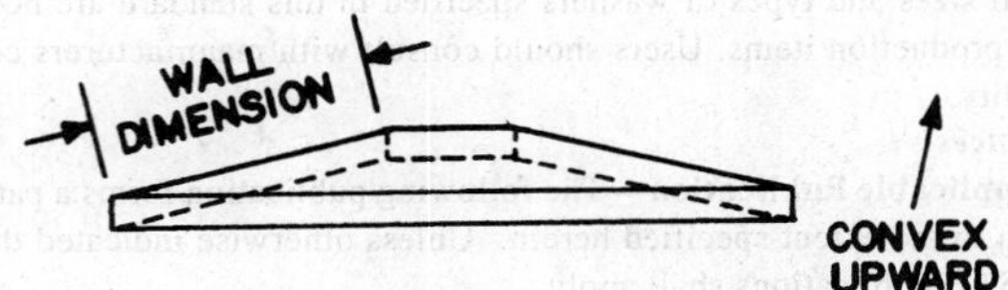

FIGURE 2—CONICAL SPRING WASHER ORIENTATION

NUT AND CONICAL SPRING WASHER ASSEMBLIES —SAE J238 MAY1998

SAE Standard

Report of the SAE Fasteners Committee approved August 1973 and reaffirmed May 1998.

Foreword—This Reaffirmed Document has been changed only to reflect the new SAE Technical Standards Board Format. References were added as Section 2. All other section numbers have changed.

1. Scope—This SAE Standard covers general, dimensional data, and methods of test for two types of general purpose nut and conical spring washer assemblies, designated Type LN and Type HN, intended for mass production and other operations where speed and convenience are paramount factors.

1.1 Both the Type LN and Type HN assemblies are available in three washer series (narrow, regular, and wide), having varied proportions designed to fulfill specific purposes of distributing the load over various areas, as shown in Table 1.

1.2 Where so specified by user, assemblies shall be supplied with toothed washers for nonslip or positive electrical grounding purposes. Toothed washers shall have six teeth, of proportions depicted in Figure 1, equally spaced on the outer periphery. Teeth shall have sharp edges.

1.3 The inclusion of dimensional data in this standard is not intended to imply that all of the products described are stock items. Users should consult with manufacturers concerning availability.

2. References

2.1 Applicable Publications—The following publications form a part of this specification to the extent specified herein. Unless otherwise indicated, the latest version of SAE publications shall apply.

SAE J429—Mechanical and Material Requirements for Externally Threaded Fasteners

SAE J995—Mechanical and Material Requirements for Steel Nuts

3. Designation—Nut and conical spring washer assemblies shall be specified or designated as shown in the following examples: 1/4-20 nut and conical spring washer assembly, Type LN, wide; No. 10-24 nut and toothed conical spring washer assembly, Type HN, regular. (Unless otherwise specified, threads will be furnished as Class UNC 2B.)

4. Identification—Assemblies for No. 10 and 1/4 in. nominal sizes are available in Types LN and HN. To identify the HN type in these sizes, parts should be finished in accordance with Section 8.

5. Use and Application—Type LN assemblies are intended for use with mating fasteners equivalent to SAE Grades 1 and 2, and Type HN assemblies are for use with mating fasteners equivalent to SAE Grade 5. (See SAE J429.)

5.1 In the installed position, it is desirable to have the washer compressed flat. Such flattening is designed to occur at a load in the bolt equivalent to approximately 27 500 psi for the Type LN assemblies and 60 000 psi for the Type HN assemblies.

5.2 The inclusion of dimensional data in this standard is not intended to imply that all of the products described are stock production items. Users should consult with manufacturers concerning availability.

6. Dimensions—All dimensions in this standard are in inches unless otherwise specified. Dimensions for both Type LN and Type HN assemblies are given in Table 1.

6.1 Nut Manufacturing Detail—The nut thickness specified in Table 1 is the overall distance, measured parallel to the axis of nut, from the top of nut to the surface which bears against top of washer. No transverse section through the nut between 25 and 75% of the actual nut thickness, as measured from the top of the nut, shall be less than the minimum width across flats. The maximum width across flats shall not be exceeded. Tops of nuts shall be flat. Corners on top and bottom of hexagon portion of nuts shall be chamfered to a diameter equal to the maximum width across flats within a tolerance of –15%. The length of chamfer at hexagon corners shall be 5–15% of the basic thread diameter. The surface of chamfer may be slightly convex or rounded. A rounding or lack of fill at the junction of hexagon corners with chamfer shall be permissible provided the minimum width across corners is reached and maintained beyond a distance equal to 17.5% of the basic thread diameter from the chamfered faces.

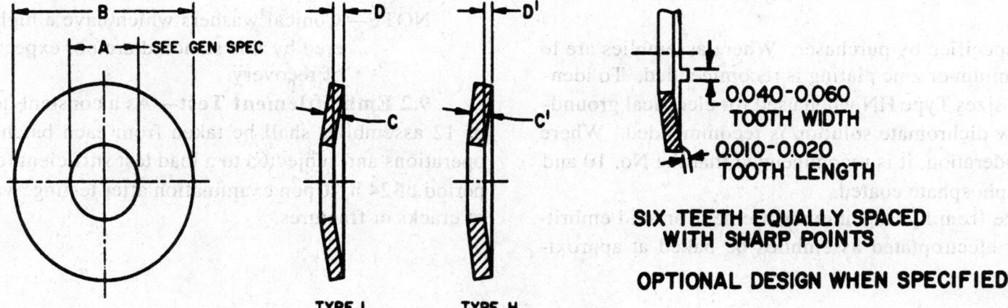

FIGURE 1—NUT AND CONICAL SPRING WASHER ASSEMBLY

6.1.1 TAPER OF SIDES OF HEX—Nut (angle between one side and the axis) shall not exceed 2 degrees, the specified width across flats being the largest dimension.

6.2 Washer Manufacturing Detail—The washers shall be symmetrical in shape and shall be tumbled (except toothed washers) or otherwise processed to remove sharp edge at top inner periphery prior to assembly to nuts.

6.2.1 A diametral section through the washer shall show the surface element to be straight, subject to the following tolerances (see Figure 2):

Wall Dimension	Tolerance (convex upward only), in
Up to 1/4	0.010
Over 1/4 to 1/2	0.015
Over 1/2	0.020

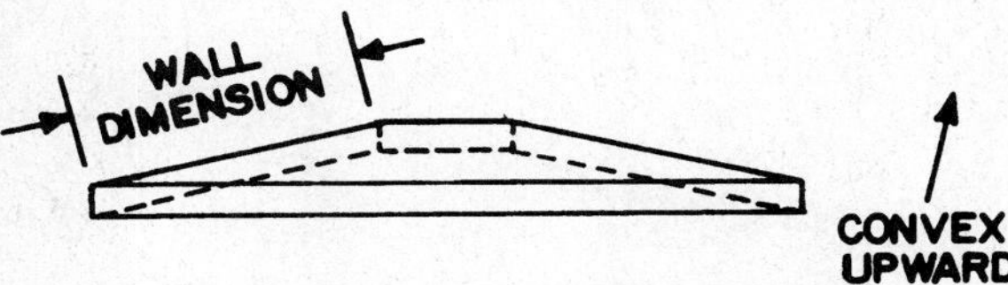

FIGURE 2—CONICAL WASHER TOLERANCE

6.3 Assembly Detail—The size and shape of the hole in washers and the collar on the nuts shall be such that washers after assembly to nuts—by spinning, swaging, or staking of collar—will be firmly retained on the nuts and yet be free to rotate at a torque not to exceed 5 lb-in. The length of the collar on the nuts shall be such as to be wholly contained within the thickness of the washer after the assembly operation. No protrusion of the collar beyond the washer in the retention area shall be permissible.

6.3.1 COLLAR CRACKS—Collar cracks may occur due to the application of pressure to the collar lip during assembly of the washer. Providing these cracks are limited to the contour of the collar, such cracks shall be permissible discontinuities and not considered cause for rejection of otherwise acceptable assemblies.

7. Material—Nut and washer components of assemblies shall be made from materials specified below:

7.1 Nuts shall be manufactured in accordance with SAE J995 (latest issue). Type LN shall be Grade 2 and Type HN shall be Grade 5.

7.2 Washers shall be made from SAE 1050 to 1065 carbon steel, fabricated and heat treated to a hardness of Rockwell C44-48 (or equivalent) and shall be capable of meeting the embrittlement tests set forth in 9.2. When the austempering process is used, washers shall be heat treated to a Rockwell C 46-50.

TABLE 1—DIMENSIONS OF NUT AND CONICAL SPRING WASHER ASSEMBLIES

Nom Size	Basic Major Dia of Thread	Thds per in	Types LN and HN Washer Series	Types LN and HN Washer OD E ±0.010	Types LN and HN Nut A Max	Types LN and HN Nut A Min	Types LN and HN Nut B Min	Types LN and HN Nut D Max	Types LN and HN Nut D Min	Type LN Nut C Max	Type LN Nut C Min	Type LN Washer F Max	Type LN Washer F Min	Type LN Washer G Max	Type LN Washer G Min	Type HN Nut C Max	Type HN Nut C Min	Type HN Washer F Max	Type HN Washer F Min	Type HN Washer G Max	Type HN Washer G Min
			Narrow	0.375								0.040	0.033	0.025	0.015						
No. 8	0.1540	32	Regular	0.500	0.343	0.332	0.378	0.236	0.232	0.130	0.117	0.040	0.033	0.025	0.015	—	—	—	—	—	—
			Wide	0.625								0.040	0.033	0.035	0.025						
			Narrow	0.438								0.040	0.033	0.025	0.015			0.043	0.037	0.025	0.015
No. 10	0.1900	24	Regular	0.562	0.375	0.365	0.413	0.274	0.270	0.130	0.117	0.040	0.033	0.025	0.015	0.207	0.187	0.051	0.042	0.025	0015
			Wide	0.750								0.046	0.037	0.030	0.020			0.056	0.047	0.030	0.020
			Narrow	0.625								0.051	0.042	0.025	0.015			0.065	0.055	0.025	0.015
1/4	0.2500	20	Regular	0.750	0.437	0.428	0.488	0.332	0.328	0.193	0.178	0.056	0.047	0.025	0.015	0.226	0.212	0.079	0.066	0.025	0.015
			Wide	1.000								0.065	0.055	0.030	0.025			0.087	0.074	0.030	0.020
			Narrow	0.750														0.079	0.066	0.025	0.015
5/16	0.3125	18	Regular	1.000	0.500	0.489	0.557	0.405	0.400	—	—	—	—	—	—	0.273	0.258	0.103	0.090	0.030	0.020
			Wide	1.125														0.103	0.090	0.032	0.022
			Narrow	1.000														0.103	0.090	0.025	0.015
3/8	0.3750	15	Regular	1.125	0.562	0.551	0.628	0.470	0.465	—	—	—	—	—	—	0.337	0.320	0.120	0.106	0.032	0.022
			Wide	1.250														0.120	0.106	0.035	0.025
			Narrow	1.125														0.126	0.112	0.027	0.017
7/16	0.4375	14	Regular	1.250	0.687	0.675	0.768	0.550	0.545	—	—	—	—	—	—	0.385	0.365	0.136	0.122	0.036	0.026
			Wide	1.500														0.136	0.122	0.036	0.026
			Narrow	1.250														0.140	0.126	0.027	0.017
1/2	0.5000	13	Regular	1.500	0.750	0.736	0.840	0.610	0.605	—	—	—	—	—	—	0.448	0.427	0.150	0.136	0.035	0.025
			Wide	1.750														0.150	0.136	0.035	0.025

When heat treatment takes place after assembly of the washer and nut, a hardness range of Rockwell C 40-48 is permitted. Washer hardness shall be checked by grinding or filing a flat spot on the top side of the washer to rest on the anvil with the reading to be taken on the undisturbed inner face of the washer. If washer hardness, as thus obtained, is not within specification, washers may be qualified by checking hardness on a cutout section of the washer on which both sides have been ground flat and parallel. Excessive decarburization which adversely affects the performance of the washer may be grounds for rejection of the assembly.

8. Finish—Finish shall be as specified by purchaser. Where assemblies are to be used for electrical ground, cadmium or zinc plating is recommended. To identify the No. 10 and 1/4 in nominal sizes Type HN when used for electrical grounding, surface treatment with yellow dichromate solution is recommended. Where electrical grounding is not a consideration, it is recommended that the No. 10 and 1/4 in nominal sizes Type HN be phosphate coated.

8.1 Assemblies shall be free from hydrogen embrittlement or acid embrittlement. It is recommended that electroplated assemblies be baked at approximately 400 °F for 3 h as soon as practicable after plating. If assemblies so treated fail to meet the test described in Section 9, the baking time and/or the baking temperature shall be increased.

9. Tests

9.1 Recovery Test—Conical washers shall not remain flat after deflection and release. The washers covered by this standard shall retain at least one-third the original minimum crown height after flattening between two hardened plates and release.

NOTE—Conical washers which have a higher angle of elevation than covered by this standard are not expected to have the same percentage of recovery.

9.2 Embrittlement Test—As a constant quality control check, a minimum of 12 assemblies shall be taken from each batch after plating or final finishing operations and subjected to a load test sufficient to flatten washers for a minimum period of 24 h. Upon examination after testing, washers shall not exhibit any sign of cracks or fractures.

TORQUE-TENSION TEST PROCEDURE FOR STEEL THREADED FASTENERS —INCH SERIES—SAE J174 MAY1998

SAE Recommended Practice

Report of the SAE Fasteners Committee approved June 1970, editorial change April 1971, completely revised August 1996, and reaffirmed May 1998.

Foreword—On some applications of threaded fasteners, it is desirable to control the amount of developed tension when a specific range of torque has been applied or the torque required to develop a specific range of tension. Accurate torque-tension relationships can be achieved only by uniquely defining and controlling the many related test parameters, such as: materials, their hardness and finish coatings, mating part interference fit, lubrication between both mated parts, the presence of foreign materials as rust, dust, and burrs, temperature and humidity, and whether the tightening is by hand or power tool turn nut or bolting wrenching.

1. Scope—This test procedure is intended to provide a quality control method for checking torque-tension characteristics of non-prevailing torque-type threaded steel fasteners 1/4 through 1 in nominal diameters. Realistically, torque-tension relationships for specific individual fastener assembly joints will vary due to the different joint parameters. Tests using actual joint components will be required to determine accurate torque-tension values for those conditions. For the metric version, see SAE J174M.

2. References

2.1 Applicable Publications—The following publications form a part of the specification to the extent specified herein. Unless otherwise indicated the latest revision of SAE publications shall apply.

2.1.1 SAE PUBLICATIONS—Available from SAE, 400 Commonwealth Drive, Warrendale, PA 15096-0001.

SAE J174M—Torque-Tension Test Procedure for Steel Threaded Fasteners—Metric Series

SAEJ429—Mechanical and Material Requirements for Externally Threaded Fasteners

SAEJ995—Mechanical and Material Requirements for Steel Nuts

2.1.2 ASTM PUBLICATIONS—Available from ASTM, 100 Barr Harbor Drive, West Conshohocken, PA 19428-2959.

ASTMB117—Method of Salt Spray (Fog) Testing

ASTMB487—Method for Measurement of Metal and Oxide Coating Thicknesses by Microscopical Examination of a Cross Section

3. Test Material

3.1Test Bolt—When evaluating nuts, test bolts conforming to SAE J429, grade 8 requirements shall be used. Threads shall gage to the same class of fit as the nuts. Threads on all bolts shall be produced by rolling.

Bolts shall be free from burrs, loose scale, and contamination. This test procedure can be applied to test bolts with different finish coatings. But to compare torque-tension bolt quality results, various lots, and/or manufacturers, the finish shall be zinc phosphate and oil, meeting a 72-h salt spray life when tested in accordance with ASTM B 117.

NOTE—The lubricant shall neither be added or removed from the test material. It shall be dry to the touch as determined by Waterman #41 filter blot test.

3.2 Test Washer—Washer shall conform to the dimensional, metallurgical, and finish requirements given in Table 1. (See also Figure 1.) Optionally, clipped washers or multihole plates or strips may be used providing they conform to the previous requirements.

TABLE 1—TEST WASHERS—WASHER DIMENSIONS—INCHES

Nominal Fastener Size	Inside Dia A[(1)] ±0.005	Outside Dia B ±0.010	Width D ±0.012	Thickness C Max	Thickness C Min
1/4	0.281	0.750	0.656	0.080	0.073
5/16	0.344	0.875	0.776	0.080	0.073
3/8	0.406	1.000	0.892	0.080	0.073
7/16	0.469	1.125	1.018	0.080	0.073
1/2	0.531	1.312	1.152	0.121	0.114
9/16	0.625	1.500	1.274	0.121	0.114
5/8	0.688	1.625	1.422	0.121	0.114
11/16	0.750	1.687	1.500	0.121	0.114
3/4	0.812	1.750	1.678	0.160	0.153
7/8	0.969	1.875	1.916	0.160	0.153
1	1.025	2.000	2.184	0.160	0.153

1. The washer ID is intended for use with hex bolts and all nuts. To accommodate other bolts with larger under head fillet radii, washer hole diameter shall be increased proportionally to allow bearing surface of bolt head to seat.

NOTES:

1. All dimensions are in inches.
2. Square washers are preferred. Use of round washers is acceptable during a transition period to exclusive use of square washers.
3. Material shall be carbon steel with a chemical composition of C, 0.48-0.60%; Mn, 0.60-1.50%; P, 0.035% max; and S, 0.045% max; quenched and tempered, with a surface hardness of 85-88, and a core hardness of 73-78 HR A.
4. Washers shall be electrodeposited zinc plated to a coating thickness of 0.0002 to 0.0004 in and shall be subjected to no additional surface treatment. As soon as practicable following plating, washers shall be baked or 1 h at 375 °F ± 25 °F. Plating thickness shall be checked in accordance with ASTM B 487 (Microscopic Test).
5. Washers shall be free from burrs and sharp edges.

3.3 Test Nut—When evaluating bolts, test nuts conforming to SAE J995, grade 8 requirements shall be used to evaluate bolts. Threads shall gage to the same class of fit as the bolt.

Nuts shall be free from burrs, loose scale, and contamination. Similar to test bolts, the test procedure can be applied to test nuts with different finish coatings. But to compare torque-tension nut quality results of various lots and/or manufacturers, the finish shall be zinc phosphate and oil, meeting a 72-h salt spray life when tested in accordance with ASTM B 117.

NOTE—The lubricant shall neither be added or removed from the test material. It shall be dry to the touch as determined by Waterman #41 filter blot paper test.

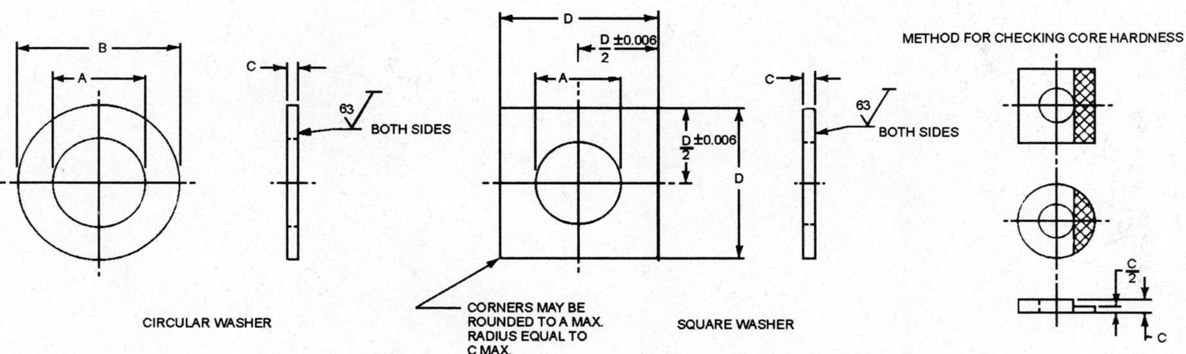

FIGURE 1—TEST WASHERS

4. Test Equipment

4.1 Tension-Measuring Device—The tension-measuring device shall be capable of measuring the axial tension induced in the bolt as it is tightened. The device shall be accurate within ±3% of the test load.

4.2 Torque-Measuring Device—The torque-measuring device shall have an accuracy within ±2% of a given torque reading.

4.3 Test Socket Wrench—A socket with a hexagon configuration is preferred, features shall be provided within the socket to prevent the socket from contacting either the test washer or the threaded end of the bolt.

4.4 Test Spacer (If Required)—The test spacer (used only for testing bolts) shall be placed under the nut. The spacer must be hardened to 52 HRC minimum and the faces shall be parallel to each other and perpendicular to the axis within 0.0005 in/in. The spacer hole diameter shall be equivalent to Table 1, dimension A, and minimum spacer wall thickness shall be equivalent to one-half the bolt diameter. A feature of preventing the nut and spacer from rotating shall be provided.

5. Test Method

5.1 Testing Bolt—The bolt, as received, shall be inserted in the tension-measuring device with the test washer placed under the bolt head. The test nut and spacer, if required, shall be assembled onto the bolt by turning the bolt head until the bolt is seated against the hardened washer. The test shall be such that a minimum of two threads protrude through the nut. The bolt shall then be continuously and uniformly tightened at a speed not to exceed 30 rpm with a torque-measuring device or equivalent means, until either the torque or the tension value, as required, is developed, at which time both torque and tension readings shall be recorded.

NOTE—The nut must not have engaged incomplete bolt threads.

During all tests, the test washer shall be prevented from turning and contacting bolt shank. A new bolt, nut, and washer shall be used for each test.

5.2 Testing Nut—To test a nut, the nut and bolt exchange positions and the previous procedure shall apply.

TORQUE-TENSION TEST PROCEDURE FOR STEEL THREADED FASTENERS—METRIC SERIES —SAE 174M MAY1998

SAE Recommended Practice

Report of the SAE Fasteners Committee approved June 1970, editorial change April 1971, completely revised August 1996, and reaffirmed May 1998.

Foreword—On some applications of threaded fasteners, it is desirable to control the amount of developed tension when a specific range of torque has been applied or the torque required to develop a specific range of tension. Accurate torque-tension relationships can be achieved only by uniquely defining and controlling the many related test parameters, such as: materials, their hardness and finish coatings, mating part interference fit, lubrication between both mated parts, the presence of foreign materials as rust, dust, and burrs, temperature and humidity, and whether the tightening is by hand or power tool turn nut or bolt wrenching.

1. Scope—This test procedure is intended to provide a quality control method for checking torque-tension characteristics of non-prevailing torque-type threaded steel fasteners 6 through 24 mm nominal diameters. Realistically, torque-tension relationships for specific individual fastener assembly joints will vary due to the different joint parameters. Tests using actual joint components will be required to determine accurate torque-tension values for those conditions. For the inch series version, see SAE J174.

2. References

2.1 Applicable Publications—The following publications form a part of this specification to the extent specified herein. Unless otherwise specified, the latest issue of SAE publications shall apply.

2.1.1 SAE PUBLICATIONS—Available from SAE, 400 Commonwealth Drive, Warrendale, PA 15096-0001.

SAE J174—Torque-Tension Test Procedure for Steel Threaded Fasteners—Inch Series

SAE J1199—Mechanical and Material Requirements for Metric Externally Threaded Steel Fasteners

2.1.2 ASTM PUBLICATION—Available from ASTM, 100 Barr Harbor Drive, West Conshohocken, PA 19428-2959.

ASTM A 563M—Specification for Carbon and Alloy Steel Nuts (Metric)

ASTM B 117—Method of Salt Spray (Fog) Testing

ASTMB487—Method for Measurement of Metal and Oxide Coating Thicknesses by Microscopical Examination of a Cross Section

3. Test Material

3.1 Test Bolt—When evaluating nuts, test bolts conforming to SAE J1199, property class 10.9 requirements shall be used. Threads shall gage to the same class of fit as the nuts. Threads on all bolts shall be produced by rolling.

Bolts shall be free from burrs, loose scale, and contamination. This test procedure can be applied to test bolts with different finish coatings. But to compare torque-tension bolt quality results, various lots, and/or manufacturers, the finish shall be zinc phosphate and oil, meeting a 72-h salt spray life when tested in accordance with ASTM B 117.

NOTE—The lubricant shall neither be added or removed from the test material. It shall be dry to the touch as determined by Waterman #41 filter blot test.

3.2 Test Washer—Washers shall conform to the dimensional, metallurgical, and finish requirements given in Table 1. (See also Figure 1.) Optionally, clipped washers or multihole plates or strips may be used providing they conform to the previous requirements.

TABLE 1—TEST WASHERS—WASHER DIMENSIONS—mm

Nominal Fastener Size	Inside Dia A[1]	Outside Dia B	Width D	Thickness C Max	Thickness C Min
M6	7.0/6.8	17.0/16.4	17.0/16.4	2.0	1.8
M8	9.4/9.2	20.0/19.4	20.0/19.4	2.0	1.8
M10	11.4/11.2	23.0/22.4	23.0/22.4	2.0	1.8
M12	13.9/13.7	29.6/29.0	29.6/29.0	3.1	2.9
M14	15.9/15.7	32.7/32.1	32.7/32.1	3.1	2.9
M16	18.0/17.8	36.4/35.8	36.4/35.8	3.1	2.9
M20	22.6/22.4	42.9/42.3	42.9/42.3	4.1	3.9
M24	26.6/26.4	55.8/55.2	55.8/55.2	4.1	3.0

1. The washer ID is intended for use with hex bolts and all nuts. To accommodate other bolts with larger under head fillet radii, washer hole diameter shall be increased proportionally to allow bearing surface of bolt head to seat.

NOTES

1. All dimensions are in millimeters.
2. Square washers are preferred. Use of round washers is acceptable during a transition period to exclusive use of square washers.
3. Material shall be carbon steel with a chemical composition of C, 0.48-0.60%; Mn, 0.60-1.50%; P, 0.035% max; and S, 0.045% max; quenched and tempered, with a surface hardness of 498-595 HV and a core hardness of 446-677 HV.
4. Washers shall be electrodeposited zinc plated to a coating thickness of 5 to 10 μm and shall be subjected to no additional surface treatment. As soon as practicable following plating, washers shall be baked for 1 h at 190 °C ± 15 °C. Plating thickness shall be checked in accordance with ASTM B 487 (Microscopic Test).
5. Washers shall be free from burrs and sharp edges.

3.3 Test Nut—When evaluating bolts, test nuts conforming to ASTM A 563M metric property class 10 requirements shall be used to evaluate bolts. Threads shall gage to the same class of fit as the bolts.

Nuts shall be free from burrs, loose scale, and contamination. Similar to test bolts, the test procedure can be applied to test nuts with different finish coatings. But to compare torque-tension nut quality results of various lots and/or manufacturers, the finish shall be zinc phosphate and oil, meeting a 72-h salt spray life when tested in accordance with ASTM B 117.

NOTE—The lubricant shall neither be added or removed from the test material. It shall be dry to the touch as determined by Waterman #41 filter blot paper test.

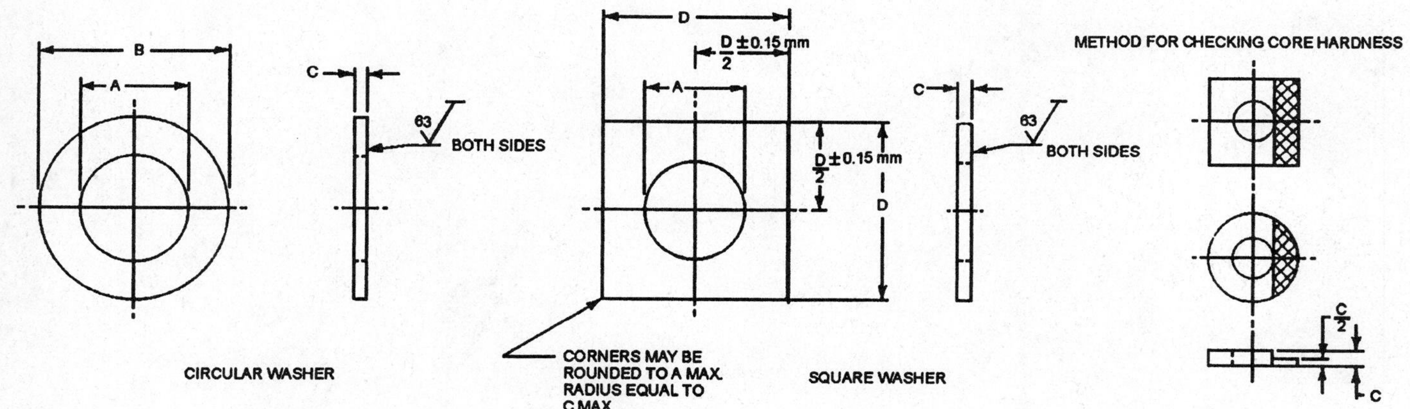

FIGURE 1—TEST WASHERS

4. Test Equipment

4.1 Tension-Measuring Device—The tension-measuring device shall be capable of measuring the axial tension induced in the bolt as it is tightened. The device shall be accurate within ±3% of the test load.

4.2 Torque-Measuring Device—The torque-measuring device shall have an accuracy within ±2% of a given torque reading.

4.3 Test Socket Wrench—A socket with a hexagon configuration is preferred, features shall be provided within the socket to prevent the socket from contacting either the test washer or the threaded end of the bolt.

4.4 Test Spacer (If Required)—The test spacer (used only for testing bolts) shall be placed under the nut. The spacer must be hardened to 545 HV minimum and the faces shall be parallel to each other and perpendicular to the axis within 0.0001 mm/mm. The spacer hole diameter shall be equivalent to Table 1, dimension A, and minimum spacer wall thickness shall be equivalent to one-half the bolt diameter. A feature of preventing the nut and spacer from rotating shall be provided.

5. Test Method

5.1 Testing Bolt —The bolt, as received, shall be inserted in the tension-measuring device with the test washer placed under the bolt head. The test nut and spacer, if required, shall be assembled onto the bolt by turning the bolt head until the bolt is seated against the hardened washer. The test shall be such that a minimum of two threads protrude through the nut. The bolt shall then be continuously and uniformly tightened at a speed not to exceed 30 rpm with a torque-measuring device or equivalent means, until either the torque or the tension value, as required, is developed, at which time both torque and tension readings shall be recorded.

NOTE—The nut must not have engaged incomplete bolt threads.

During all tests, the test washer shall be prevented from turning and contacting bolt shank. A new bolt, nut, and washer shall be used for each test.

5.2 Testing Nut—To test a nut, the nut and bolt exchange positions and the previous procedure shall apply.

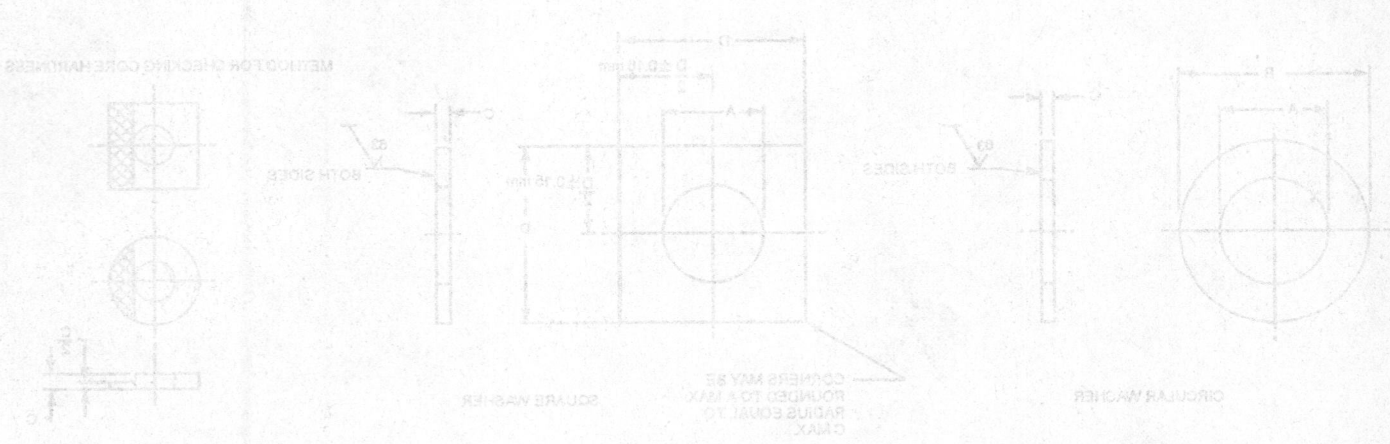

STRAIGHT PINS (SOLID)—SAE J495 JUN1964 SAE Standard

Report of the SAE Parts and Fittings Committee approved January 1957. Editorial change June 1964.

Foreword—This Document has also changed to comply with the new SAE Technical Standards Board format.

1. Scope—See Table 1 and Figure 1.

TABLE 1—DIMENSIONS OF STRAIGHT PINS, IN.[1]

A, Pin Dia Nominal	A, Pin Dia Max	A, Pin Dia Min	B Chamfer
0.062	0.0625	0.0605	0.015
0.094	0.0937	0.0917	0.015
0.109	0.1094	0.1074	0.015
0.125	0.1250	0.1230	0.015
0.156	0.1562	0.1542	0.015
0.188	0.1875	0.1855	0.015
0.219	0.2187	0.2167	0.015
0.250	0.2500	0.2480	0.015
0.312	0.3125	0.3095	0.030
0.375	0.3750	0.3720	0.030
0.438	0.4375	0.4345	0.030
0.500	0.500	0.4970	0.030

1. These pins must be straight and free from burrs or any other defects that will affect their serviceability.

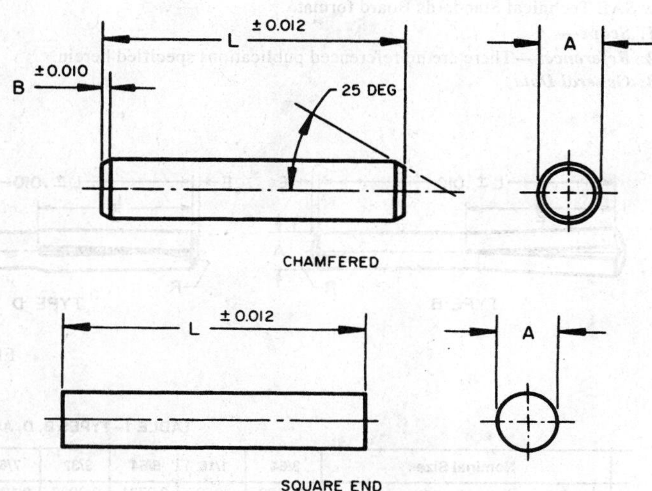

FIGURE 1—

2. References—There are no referenced publications specified herein.

GROOVED STRAIGHT PINS—SAE J494 JUN1964 SAE Standard

Report of the SAE Parts and Fittings Committee approved May 1955 and last revised May 1959. Editorial change June 1962. Reaffirmed without change June 1964.

Foreword—This Reaffirmed Document has been changed only to reflect the new SAE Technical Standards Board format.

1. Scope—

2. References—There are no referenced publications specified herein.

3. General Data

3.1 Material—Cold drawn SAE 1112 or 1113 steel, alloy steel, stainless steel or copper alloy as specified by purchaser.

3.2 Finishes—Unless otherwise specified, steel pins shall have a flash plate of cadmium or zinc for protection of pins in transit or storage.

3.3 Defects—Grooved Straight Pins must be free from burrs and all other defects that might affect their use and serviceability.

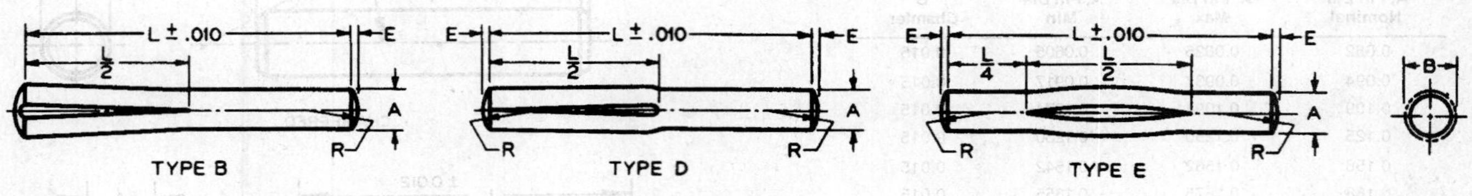

FIGURE 1—

TABLE 1—TYPES B, D, AND E GROOVED STRAIGHT PINS, IN.

Nominal Size	3/64	1/16	5/64	3/32	7/64	1/8	5/32	3/16	7/32	1/4	5/16	3/8	7/16	1/2
A Diameter, max	0.0469	0.0625	0.0781	0.0938	0.1094	0.1250	0.1563	0.1875	0.2188	0.2500	0.3125	0.3750	0.4375	0.5000
Diameter, min	0.0459	0.0615	0.0771	0.0928	0.1084	0.1230	0.1543	0.1855	0.2168	0.2480	0.3105	0.3730	0.4355	0.4980
Recommended Hole, max	0.0478	0.0640	0.0798	0.0956	0.1113	0.1271	0.1587	0.1903	0.2219	0.2534	0.3166	0.3797	0.4428	0.5060
Recommended Hole, min	0.0465	0.0625	0.0781	0.0938	0.1094	0.1250	0.1563	0.1875	0.2188	0.2500	0.3125	0.3750	0.4375	0.5000
Crown Height ±0.005	0.0000	0.0065	0.0087	0.0091	0.0110	0.0130	0.0170	0.0180	0.0220	0.0260	0.0340	0.0390	0.0470	0.0520
R Radius at Nom Crown Height, ±0.010	—	0.0781	0.0938	0.125	0.1406	0.1562	0.1875	0.2500	0.2812	0.3125	0.3750	0.4688	0.5312	0.6250
Length	**B Diameter, Max and Min Limits (Measured with Ring Gages)**													
1/4	0.052	0.069	0.085	0.102	0.118	0.136	—	—	—	—	—	—	—	—
	0.050	0.067	0.083	0.100	0.116	0.132	—	—	—	—	—	—	—	—
3/8	0.052	0.069	0.085	0.102	0.118	0.136	0.168	0.200	—	—	—	—	—	—
	0.050	0.067	0.083	0.100	0.116	0.132	0.164	0.196	—	—	—	—	—	—
1/2	0.052	0.069	0.085	0.102	0.118	0.136	0.168	0.200	0.232	0.265	—	—	—	—
	0.050	0.067	0.083	0.100	0.116	0.132	0.164	0.196	0.228	0.261	—	—	—	—
5/8	0.052	0.069	0.085	0.102	0.118	0.136	0.168	0.200	0.232	0.265	0.331	—	—	—
	0.050	0.067	0.083	0.100	0.116	0.132	0.164	0.196	0.228	0.261	0.327	—	—	—
3/4	—	0.069	0.085	0.102	0.118	0.136	0.168	0.200	0.232	0.265	0.331	0.396	—	—
	—	0.067	0.083	0.100	0.116	0.132	0.164	0.196	0.228	0.261	0.327	0.392	—	—
7/8	—	0.069	0.085	0.102	0.118	0.136	0.168	0.200	0.232	0.265	0.331	0.396	0.461	—
	—	0.067	0.083	0.100	0.116	0.132	0.164	0.196	0.228	0.261	0.327	0.392	0.457	—
1	—	0.069	0.085	0.102	0.118	0.136	0.168	0.200	0.232	0.265	0.331	0.396	0.461	0.527
	—	0.067	0.083	0.100	0.116	0.132	0.164	0.196	0.228	0.261	0.327	0.392	0.457	0.523
1-1/4	—	—	—	0.102	0.118	0.136	0.168	0.200	0.232	0.265	0.331	0.396	0.461	0.527
	—	—	—	0.100	0.116	0.132	0.164	0.196	0.228	0.261	0.327	0.392	0.457	0.523
1-1/2	—	—	—	—	—	0.136	0.168	0.200	0.232	0.265	0.331	0.396	0.461	0.527
	—	—	—	—	—	0.132	0.164	0.196	0.228	0.261	0.327	0.392	0.457	0.523
1-3/4	—	—	—	—	—	—	0.167	0.200	0.232	0.265	0.331	0.396	0.461	0.527
	—	—	—	—	—	—	0.163	0.196	0.228	0.261	0.327	0.392	0.457	0.523
2	—	—	—	—	—	—	0.167	0.200	0.232	0.265	0.331	0.396	0.461	0.527
	—	—	—	—	—	—	0.163	0.196	0.228	0.261	0.327	0.392	0.457	0.523
2-1/4	—	—	—	—	—	—	—	0.199	0.232	0.265	0.331	0.396	0.461	0.527
	—	—	—	—	—	—	—	0.195	0.228	0.261	0.327	0.392	0.457	0.523
2-1/2	—	—	—	—	—	—	—	—	0.232	0.265	0.331	0.396	0.461	0.527
	—	—	—	—	—	—	—	—	0.228	0.261	0.327	0.392	0.457	0.523

TABLE 1—TYPES B, D, AND E GROOVED STRAIGHT PINS, IN. (continued) (continued)

Nominal Size	3/64	1/16	5/64	3/32	7/64	1/8	5/32	3/16	7/32	1/4	5/16	3/8	7/16	1/2
2-3/4	—	—	—	—	—	—	—	—	0.231	0.264	0.331	0.396	0.461	0.527
	—	—	—	—	—	—	—	—	0.227	0.260	0.327	0.392	0.457	0.523
3	—	—	—	—	—	—	—	—	0.231	0.264	0.331	0.396	0.461	0.527
	—	—	—	—	—	—	—	—	0.227	0.260	0.327	0.392	0.457	0.523
3-1/4	—	—	—	—	—	—	—	—	—	0.264	0.330	0.395	0.461	0.527
	—	—	—	—	—	—	—	—	—	0.260	0.326	0.391	0.457	0.523
3-1/2	—	—	—	—	—	—	—	—	—	—	0.330	0.395	0.461	0.527
	—	—	—	—	—	—	—	—	—	—	0.326	0.391	0.456	0.523
3-3/4	—	—	—	—	—	—	—	—	—	—	—	0.395	0.460	0.527
	—	—	—	—	—	—	—	—	—	—	—	0.391	0.456	0.523
4	—	—	—	—	—	—	—	—	—	—	—	0.395	0.460	0.527
	—	—	—	—	—	—	—	—	—	—	—	0.391	0.456	0.523
4-1/4	—	—	—	—	—	—	—	—	—	—	—	0.395	0.460	0.526
	—	—	—	—	—	—	—	—	—	—	—	0.391	0.456	0.522
4-1/2	—	—	—	—	—	—	—	—	—	—	—	—	0.460	0.526
	—	—	—	—	—	—	—	—	—	—	—	—	0.456	0.522

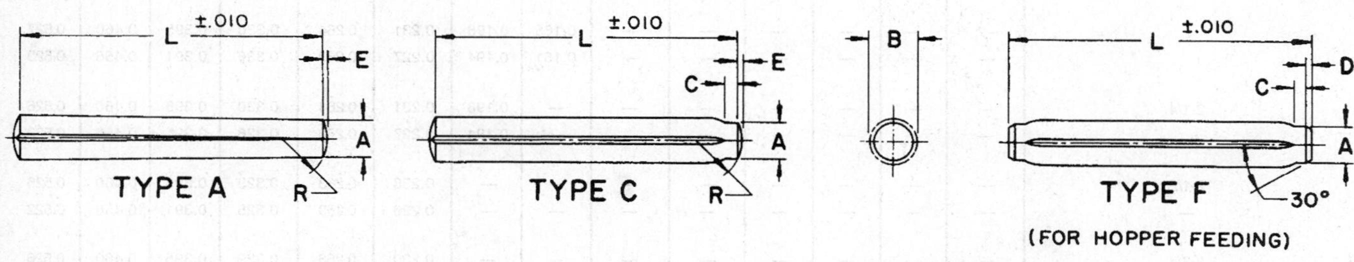

FIGURE 2—

TABLE 2—TYPES A, C, AND F GROOVED STRAIGHT PINS, IN.

	Nominal Size	3/64	1/16	5/64	3/32	7/64	1/8	5/32	3/16	7/32	1/4	5/16	3/8	7/16	1/2
A	Diameter, max	0.0469	0.0625	0.0781	0.0938	0.1094	0.1250	0.1563	0.1875	0.2188	0.2500	0.3125	0.3750	0.4375	0.5000
	Diameter, min	0.0459	0.0615	0.0771	0.0928	0.1084	0.1230	0.1543	0.1855	0.2168	0.2480	0.3105	0.3730	0.4355	0.4980
	Recommended Hole, max	0.0478	0.0640	0.0798	0.0956	0.1113	0.1271	0.1587	0.1903	0.2219	0.2534	0.3166	0.3797	0.4428	0.5060
	Recommended Hole, min	0.0465	0.0625	0.0781	0.0938	0.1094	0.1250	0.1563	0.1875	0.2188	0.2500	0.3125	0.3750	0.4375	0.5000
E	Crown Height ±0.005	0.0000	0.0065	0.0087	0.0091	0.0110	0.0130	0.0170	0.0180	0.0220	0.0260	0.0340	0.0390	0.0470	0.0520
R	Radius at Nom Crown Height, ±0.010	—	0.0781	0.0938	0.1250	0.1406	0.1562	0.1875	0.2500	0.2812	0.3125	0.3750	0.4688	0.5312	0.6250
C	Pilot Length	—	0.0312	0.0312	0.0312	0.0312	0.0312	0.0625	0.0625	0.0625	0.0625	0.0938	0.0938	0.0938	0.0938
D[(1)]	Chamfer Length (Type F Only)	—	0.0156	0.0156	0.0156	0.0156	0.0156	0.0312	0.0312	0.0312	0.0312	0.0469	0.0469	0.0469	0.0469
	Length	**B Diameter, Max and Min Limits (Measured with Ring Gages)**													
	1/8	0.052	—	—	—	—	—	—	—	—	—	—	—	—	—
		0.050	—	—	—	—	—	—	—	—	—	—	—	—	—
	3/16	0.052	—	—	—	—	—	—	—	—	—	—	—	—	—
		0.050	—	—	—	—	—	—	—	—	—	—	—	—	—
	1/4	0.052	0.069	0.085	0.102	0.118	0.136	—	—	—	—	—	—	—	—
		0.050	0.067	0.083	0.100	0.116	0.132	—	—	—	—	—	—	—	—
	3/8	0.052	0.069	0.085	0.102	0.118	0.136	0.168	0.200	—	—	—	—	—	—
		0.050	0.067	0.083	0.100	0.116	0.132	0.164	0.196	—	—	—	—	—	—
	1/2	0.052	0.069	0.085	0.102	0.118	0.136	0.168	0.200	0.232	0.265	—	—	—	—
		0.050	0.067	0.083	0.100	0.116	0.132	0.164	0.196	0.228	0.261	—	—	—	—

TABLE 2—TYPES A, C, AND F GROOVED STRAIGHT PINS, IN. (continued)

Nominal Size	3/64	1/16	5/64	3/32	7/64	1/8	5/32	3/16	7/32	1/4	5/16	3/8	7/16	1/2
5/8	0.052	0.069	0.085	0.102	0.118	0.136	0.168	0.200	0.232	0.265	0.331	—	—	—
	0.050	0.067	0.083	0.100	0.116	0.132	0.164	0.196	0.228	0.261	0.327	—	—	—
3/4	—	0.069	0.085	0.102	0.117	0.136	0.168	0.200	0.232	0.265	0.331	0.396	—	—
	—	0.067	0.083	0.100	0.115	0.132	0.164	0.196	0.228	0.261	0.327	0.392	—	—
7/8	—	0.069	0.085	0.102	0.117	0.135	0.167	0.200	0.232	0.265	0.331	0.396	0.461	—
	—	0.067	0.083	0.100	0.115	0.131	0.163	0.196	0.228	0.261	0.327	0.392	0.457	—
1	—	0.069	0.085	0.102	0.116	0.135	0.167	0.200	0.232	0.265	0.331	0.396	0.461	0.527
	—	0.067	0.083	0.100	0.114	0.131	0.163	0.196	0.228	0.261	0.327	0.392	0.457	0.523
1-1/4	—	—	—	0.102	0.116	0.134	0.166	0.199	0.232	0.265	0.331	0.396	0.461	0.527
	—	—	—	0.100	0.114	0.130	0.162	0.195	0.228	0.261	0.327	0.392	0.457	0.523
1-1/2	—	—	—	—	—	0.134	0.166	0.199	0.231	0.264	0.331	0.396	0.461	0.527
	—	—	—	—	—	0.130	0.162	0.195	0.227	0.260	0.327	0.392	0.457	0.523
1-3/4	—	—	—	—	—	—	0.165	0.199	0.231	0.264	0.330	0.395	0.461	0.527
	—	—	—	—	—	—	0.161	0.195	0.227	0.260	0.326	0.391	0.457	0.523
2	—	—	—	—	—	—	0.165	0.198	0.231	0.264	0.330	0.395	0.460	0.527
	—	—	—	—	—	—	0.161	0.194	0.227	0.260	0.326	0.391	0.456	0.523
2-1/4	—	—	—	—	—	—	—	0.198	0.231	0.264	0.330	0.395	0.460	0.526
	—	—	—	—	—	—	—	0.194	0.227	0.260	0.326	0.391	0.456	0.522
2-1/2	—	—	—	—	—	—	—	—	0.230	0.263	0.329	0.395	0.460	0.526
—	—	—	—	—	—	—	—	—	0.226	0.259	0.325	0.391	0.456	0.522
2-3/4	—	—	—	—	—	—	—	—	0.230	0.263	0.329	0.395	0.460	0.526
	—	—	—	—	—	—	—	—	0.226	0.259	0.325	0.391	0.456	0.522
3	—	—	—	—	—	—	—	—	0.229	0.262	0.329	0.394	0.459	0.525
	—	—	—	—	—	—	—	—	0.225	0.258	0.325	0.390	0.455	0.521
3-1/4	—	—	—	—	—	—	—	—	—	0.262	0.328	0.394	0.459	0.525
	—	—	—	—	—	—	—	—	—	0.258	0.324	0.390	0.455	0.521
3-1/2	—	—	—	—	—	—	—	—	—	—	0.328	0.393	0.458	0.524
—	—	—	—	—	—	—	—	—	—	—	0.324	0.389	0.454	0.520
3-3/4	—	—	—	—	—	—	—	—	—	—	—	0.393	0.458	0.524
—	—	—	—	—	—	—	—	—	—	—	—	0.389	0.454	0.520
4	—	—	—	—	—	—	—	—	—	—	—	0.392	0.457	0.523
—	—	—	—	—	—	—	—	—	—	—	—	0.388	0.453	0.519
4-1/4	—	—	—	—	—	—	—	—	—	—	—	0.392	0.457	0.523
—	—	—	—	—	—	—	—	—	—	—	—	0.388	0.453	0.519
4-1/2	—	—	—	—	—	—	—	—	—	—	—	—	0.456	0.522
—	—	—	—	—	—	—	—	—	—	—	—	—	0.452	0.518

1. On agreement between user and supplier a suitable radius may be substituted optionally for the chamfers on the ends of Type F pins for the 1/4 in. size and below.

SPRING TYPE STRAIGHT PINS—SAE J496 NOV1972 — SAE Standard

Report of the SAE Parts and Fittings Committee approved January 1957. Editorial change November 1972.

Foreword—This Document has also changed to comply with the new SAE Technical Standards Board format.

1. Scope

2. References—There are no referenced publications specified herein.

3. Length and Availability—Table 3, Practical Length Increments and Ranges, indicates spring pin sizes. Information on availability of individual lengths in the various types, weights, and materials may be obtained from suppliers.

The tolerance on length for coiled type spring pins shall be ±0.010 in. for sizes up to and including 5/16 in.; and ±0.015 in. for sizes larger than 5/16 in.

The tolerance on length for slotted type spring pins shall be in accordance with the following tabulation:

Length Range	3/16 to 1 Incl	Over 1 To 2 Incl	Over 2 To 3 Incl	Over 3 to to 4 Incl	Over 4 in
Tolerance On Length	±0.015	±0.020	±0.025	±0.030	±0.035

4. Surface Treatment—Where corrosion preventive treatment applied to carbon steel spring pins is such that it might produce hydrogen embrittlement, the spring pins shall be baked or treated in such a manner as to obviate such embrittlement.

5. Material and Hardness—Hardness shall be tested in the following manner: For slotted pins the readings shall be taken near the center of a longitudinal flat ground on the pin at right angles to the slot. Coiled pins shall be ground or cut in half along the longitudinal axis and the hardness readings shall be taken on the inside surface of the outer half coil. Table 2 designates materials and the proper Rockwell scale to be used for the various wall thickness ranges.

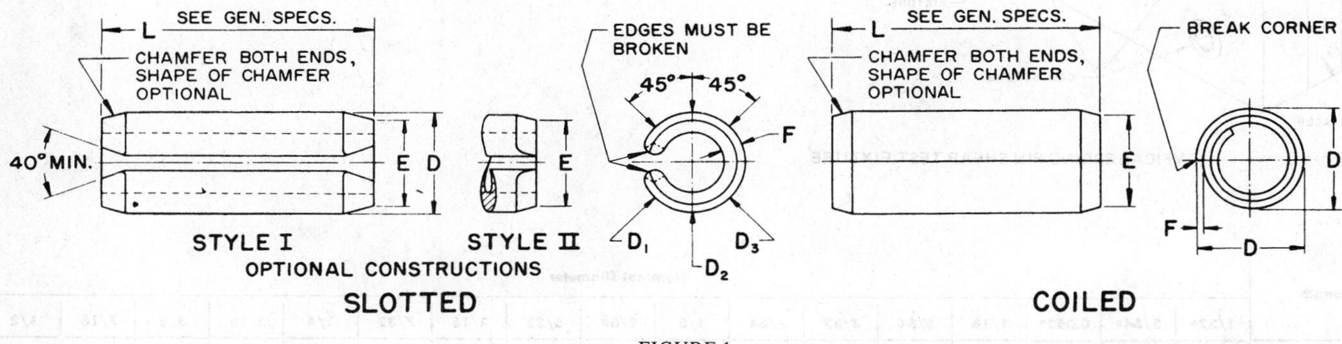

FIGURE 1—

TABLE 1—PIN DIMENSIONS

Nominal Pin Size	D[a] Slotted Series A[b] and B[b] Max	D Slotted Series A and B Min[c]	D Coiled Series A Max	D Coiled Series A Min	D Coiled Series B Max	D Coiled Series B Min	D Coiled Series C Max	D Coiled Series C Min	E Slotted and Coiled Series A, B, and C Max	F Slotted Series A Nominal	F Slotted Series B Style I Nominal	F Slotted Series B Style II Nominal	F Coiled Series A Nominal	F Coiled Series B Nominal	F Coiled Series C Nominal	Double Shear Strength (lb)[e] Slotted and Coiled Series A Min	Series B Min	Series C Min	Recommended Hole Size Slotted Series A and B Max	Slotted Series A and B Min	Coiled Series A, B, and C Max	Coiled Series A, B, and C Min
1/32	—	—	—	—	0.035	0.033	—	—	0.029[d]	—	—	—	—	0.003	—	—	75	—	—	—	0.0325	0.0310
3/64	—	—	—	—	0.052	0.049	—	—	0.045[d]	—	—	—	—	0.004	—	—	170	—	—	—	0.0485	0.0470
0.052	—	—	—	—	0.057	0.054	—	—	0.050[d]	—	—	—	—	0.004	—	—	230	—	—	—	0.0535	0.0520
1/16	0.069	0.066	0.070	0.066	0.071	0.067	0.072	0.067	0.059	0.012	—	0.006	0.007	0.005	0.003	425	300	160	0.065	0.062	0.065	0.061
5/64	0.086	0.083	0.086	0.082	0.087	0.083	0.088	0.083	0.075	0.018	—	0.008	0.007	0.005	0.003	650	480	260	0.081	0.078	0.081	0.077
3/32	0.103	0.099	0.103	0.098	0.104	0.099	0.105	0.099	0.091	0.022	0.012	0.012	0.010	0.007	0.005	1000	690	370	0.097	0.094	0.097	0.093
7/64	0.118	0.113	0.118	0.113	0.119	0.114	0.120	0.114	0.106	0.022	—	0.018	0.010	0.007	0.005	1410	940	510	0.112	0.109	0.112	0.108
1/8	0.135	0.131	0.136	0.130	0.137	0.131	0.138	0.131	0.122	0.028	0.012	0.018	0.014	0.010	0.007	1840	1000	660	0.129	0.125	0.129	0.124
9/64	0.149	0.145	0.151	0.145	0.152	0.146	0.153	0.146	0.136	0.028	—	0.022	0.014	0.010	0.007	2200	1550	830	0.141	0.140	0.144	0.139
5/32	0.167	0.162	0.168	0.161	0.170	0.163	0.171	0.163	0.152	0.032	0.018	0.022	0.017	0.011	0.007	2880	1750	1040	0.160	0.156	0.160	0.155
3/16	0.199	0.194	0.202	0.194	0.204	0.196	0.206	0.196	0.182	0.040	0.022	0.028	0.020	0.015	0.010	4140	2500	1500	0.192	0.187	0.192	0.185
7/32	0.232	0.226	0.235	0.226	0.238	0.229	0.240	0.229	0.214	0.048	0.028	0.032	0.024	0.017	0.011	5640	3760	2040	0.224	0.219	0.224	0.217
1/4	0.264	0.258	0.268	0.258	0.270	0.260	0.272	0.260	0.245	0.048	0.028	0.032	0.028	0.020	0.015	7360	4600	2660	0.256	0.250	0.256	0.248
5/16	0.328	0.321	0.340	0.327	0.341	0.327	0.342	0.327	0.306	0.062	—	0.040	0.032	0.024	0.017	11500	7670	4160	0.318	0.312	0.318	0.308
3/8	0.392	0.385	0.407	0.391	0.408	0.391	0.409	0.391	0.368	0.077	—	0.048	0.040	0.028	0.020	16580	11040	6000	0.382	0.375	0.382	0.368
7/16	0.456	0.448	0.475	0.457	0.476	0.457	0.478	0.457	0.430	0.077	—	0.048	0.047	0.036	0.024	20000	15020	8160	0.445	0.437	0.445	0.429
1/2	0.521	0.513	0.542	0.522	0.543	0.522	0.545	0.522	0.490	0.094	—	0.062	0.055	0.040	0.028	25800	19600	10640	0.510	0.500	0.510	0.490

[a] Maximum D shall be checked by a "GO" ring gage.
[b] Series designation applies to stock thickness, A being heaviest.
[c] Minimum D shall be the average of the D_1, D_2, and D_3 diameters.
[d] Series B coiled.
[e] Applies to pins made from SAE 1070 to 1095 steel and SAE 51410 or AISI 420 corrosion resistant steel. SAE 30302 stainless steel has a minimum shear strength equal to 85% of values shown for coiled pins.

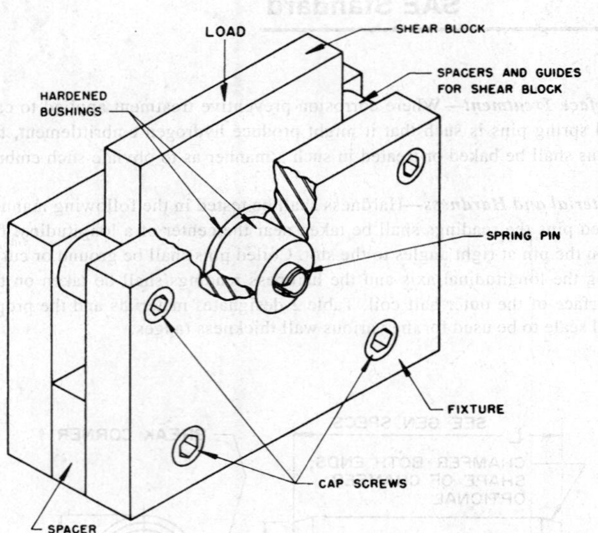

TYPICAL SPRING PIN SHEAR TEST FIXTURE

Wall Thickness Range		Over 0.001 to 0.010	Over 0.010 to 0.025	Over 0.025 to 0.050	Over 0.050 to 0.094
Rockwell Scale		Dph[a]-Tukon	15N	A	C
Pin Type	**Material**	**Hardness Reading**			
Slotted	SAE 1070–1095 Steel	458–562	83.6–87	73.6–78	46–53
	AISI 420 Corrosion Resistant Steel	413–545	82–86.6	72–77	43–52
Coiled	SAE 1070 Steel	393–515	80.4–85.5	70.4–75.9	40–50
	SAE 51410 or AISI 420 Corrosion Resistant Steel	393–515	80.4–85.5	70.4–75.9	40–50
	SAE 30302 Stainless Steel	—	—	—	—

[a] Diamond pyramidal hardness.

Length	Nominal Diameter																
	1/32[a]	3/64[a]	0.052[a]	1/16	5/64	3/32	7/64	1/8	9/64	5/32	3/16	7/32	1/4	5/16	3/8	7/16	1/2
1/8	X	X	X														
3/16	X	X	X	X	X												
1/4	X	X	X	X	X	X											
5/16	X	X	X	X	X	X											
3/8	X	X	X	X	X	X	X	X									
7/16	X	X	X	X	X	X	X	X	X								
1/2	X	X	X	X	X	X	X	X	X	X	X	X	X				
9/16	X	X	X	X	X	X	X	X	X	X	X	X	X				
5/8	X	X	X	X	X	X	X	X	X	X	X	X	X				
11/16				X	X	X	X	X	X	X	X	X	X				
3/4				X	X	X	X	X	X	X	X	X	X	X	X		
13/16				X	X	X	X	X	X	X	X	X	X	X	X		
7/8				X	X	X	X	X	X	X	X	X	X	X	X		
15/16				X	X	X	X	X	X	X	X	X	X	X	X		
1				X	X	X	X	X	X	X	X	X	X	X	X	X	
1-1/8					X	X	X	X	X	X	X	X	X	X	X	X	
1-1/4					X	X	X	X	X	X	X	X	X	X	X	X	X
1-3/8					X	X	X	X	X	X	X	X	X	X	X	X	X
1-1/2					X	X	X	X	X	X	X	X	X	X	X	X	X
1-5/8								X	X	X	X	X	X	X	X	X	X
1-3/4								X	X	X	X	X	X	X	X	X	X
1-7/8								X	X	X	X	X	X	X	X	X	X
2								X	X	X	X	X	X	X	X	X	X
2-1/4										X	X	X	X	X	X	X	X
2-1/2												X	X	X	X	X	X
2-3/4												X	X	X	X	X	X
3												X	X	X	X	X	X
3-1/4													X	X	X	X	X
3-1/2													X	X	X	X	X
3-3/4														X	X	X	X
4														X	X	X	X

[a] Coiled type only.

UNHARDENED GROUND DOWEL PINS—SAE J497 JUN1964 SAE Standard

Report of the SAE Parts and Fittings Committee approved January 1957. Editorial change June 1964.

Foreword—This Document has also changed to comply with the new SAE Technical Standards Board format.

1. Scope—See Table 1 and Figure 1.

TABLE 1—DIMENSIONS OF UNHARDENED GROUND DOWEL PINS, in.[1]

Nominal	Diameter, A Max	Diameter, A Min	Chamfer, B
0.062	0.0600	0.0595	0.015
0.094	0.0912	0.0907	0.015
0.109	0.1068	0.1063	0.015
0.125	0.1223	0.1218	0.015
0.156	0.1535	0.1530	0.015
0.188	0.1847	0.1842	0.015
0.219	0.2159	0.2154	0.015
0.250	0.2470	0.2465	0.015
0.312	0.3094	0.3089	0.030
0.375	0.3717	0.3712	0.030
0.438	0.4341	0.4336	0.030
0.500	0.4964	0.4959	0.030
0.625	0.6211	0.6206	0.045
0.750	0.7458	0.7453	0.045
0.875	0.8705	0.8700	0.060
1.000	0.9952	0.9947	0.060

1. Maximum diameters are graduated from 0.0005 on 0.0652 in. pins to 0.0028 on 1.000 in. pins under the minimum commercial bar stock sizes.

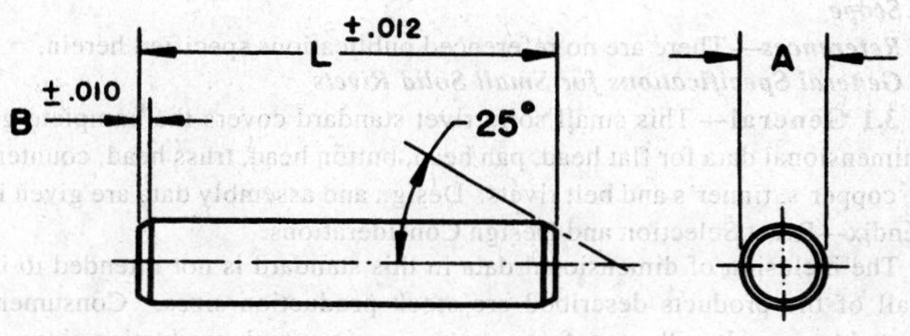

FIGURE 1—

2. References—There are no referenced publications specified herein.

RIVETS AND RIVETING—SAE J492 MAY1968 SAE Standard

Report of the SAE Parts and Fittings Division approved February 1928 and last revised by the SAE Fasteners Committee June 1961. Editorial change May 1968.

Foreword—This Document has also changed to comply with the new SAE Technical Standards Board format.

1. Scope

2. References—There are no referenced publications specified herein.

3. General Specifications for Small Solid Rivets

3.1 General—This small solid rivet standard covers the complete general and dimensional data for flat head, pan head, button head, truss head, countersunk head, copper's, tinner's and belt rivets. Design and assembly data are given in the Appendix—Rivet Selection and Design Considerations.

The inclusion of dimensional data in this standard is not intended to imply that all of the products described are stock production sizes. Consumers are requested to consult with manufacturers concerning stock production sizes.

3.2 Tolerances—The tolerances given on the dimensional tables are those for rivets made by the normal cold heading process. The tolerance for rivets made by the hot heading or forging process shall be as agreed upon between the purchaser and supplier.

3.3 Heads—Because the heads of these rivets are not machined or trimmed, the circumference may be slightly irregular and the edges may be rounded or flat.

3.4 Underhead Fillets—Rivets, other than countersunk type, shall be furnished with a definite fillet under the head but radius of fillet shall not exceed 10% of maximum shank diameter or 0.03 in., whichever is the smaller.

3.5 Material—Rivets shall be steel, copper, brass, aluminum, or other metals as specified by purchaser.

Suitable material for steel small solid rivets is covered by SAE Recommended Practice, Mechanical and Chemical Requirements for Non-threaded Fasteners—SAE J430.

Requirements of rivets made from other materials shall be as agreed upon between the purchaser and supplier.

3.6 Points—Unless otherwise specified, rivets shall have plain sheared ends. Ends shall be at right angles, within 2 deg, to the axis of the rivet and the end shall be reasonably flat, sufficient for the purpose of driving that end satisfactorily. When so specified, rivets with standard upset points are obtainable on lengths up to the maximum lengths shown in Table 1.

3.7 Workmanship—Rivets shall be free from surface seams, loose scale, and all other defects that might affect their serviceability.

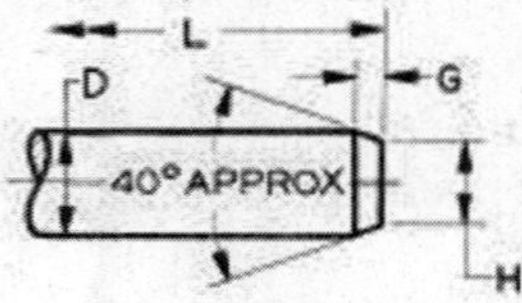

TABLE 1—DIMENSIONS OF STANDARD POINTS FOR SMALL SOLID RIVETS

Nominal Size or Basic Shank Dia	G Point Length Ref	H Point Dia Approx[1]	L Rivet Length Max
1/16 0.062	0.015	0.051	9/16
3/32 0.094	0.023	0.077	3/4
1/8 0.125	0.031	0.102	3/4
5/32 0.156	0.039	0.127	1
3/16 0.188	0.047	0.154	1
7/32 0.219	0.055	0.179	1-3/8
1/4 0.250	0.062	0.204	1-3/8
9/32 0.281	0.070	0.230	1-1/2
5/16 0.312	0.078	0.255	1-1/2
11/32 0.344	0.086	0.281	1-5/8
3/8 0.375	0.094	0.307	1-5/8
13/32 0.406	0.102	0.332	2
7/16 0.438	0.110	0.358	3

1. No standard tolerances are contemplated.

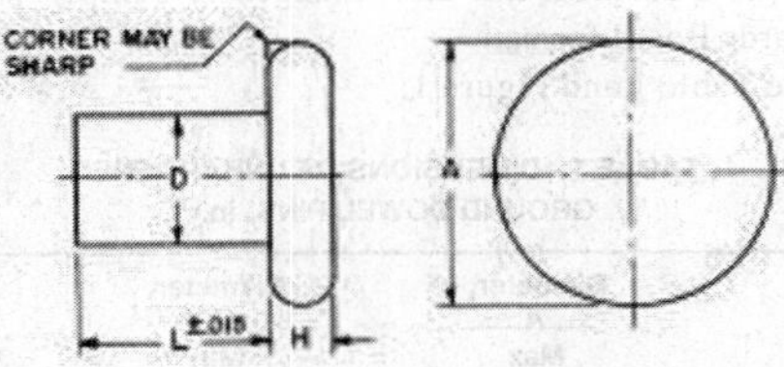

TABLE 2—FLAT HEAD RIVETS

Nominal Size or Basic Shank Dia	D Dia of Shank Max	D Dia of Shank Min	A Dia of Head Max	A Dia of Head Min	H Height of Head Max	H Height of Head Min
1/16 0.062	0.065	0.059	0.140	0.120	0.027	0.017
3/32 0.094	0.096	0.090	0.200	0.180	0.038	0.026
1/0 0.125	0.127	0.121	0.260	0.240	0.048	0.036
5/32 0.156	0.158	0.152	0.323	0.301	0.059	0.045
3/16 0.188	0.191	0.182	0.307	0.361	0.069	0.055
7/32 0.219	0.222	0.213	0.453	0.427	0.080	0.065
1/4 0.250	0.253	0.244	0.515	0.485	0.091	0.075
9/32 0.281	0.285	0.273	0.579	0.545	0.103	0.085
5/16 0.312	0.316	0.304	0.641	0.607	0.113	0.095
11/32 0.344	0.348	0.336	0.705	0.667	0.124	0.104
3/8 0.375	0.380	0.365	0.769	0.731	0.135	0.115
13/32 0.406	0.411	0.396	0.834	0.790	0.146	0.124
7/16 0.438	0.443	0.428	0.896	0.852	0.157	0.135

For dimensions and tolerances not secified above, see General Specifications.

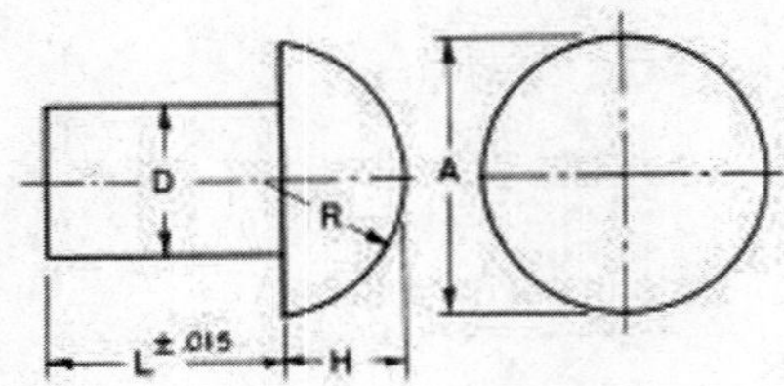

TABLE 3—BUTTON HEAD RIVETS

Nominal Size or Basic Shrink Dia	D Dia of Shank Max	D Dia of Shank Min	A Dia of Head Max	A Dia of Head Min	H Height of Head Max	H Height of Head Min	R Rad of Head Approx
1/16 0.062	0.065	0.059	0.122	0.102	0.052	0.042	0.055
3/32 0.094	0.096	0.090	0.182	0.162	0.077	0.065	0.084
1/8 0.125	0.127	0.121	0.235	0.215	0.100	0.088	0.111
5/32 0.156	0.158	0.152	0.290	0.268	0.124	0.110	0.138
3/16 0.188	0.191	0.182	0.348	0.322	0.147	0.133	0.166
7/32 0.219	0.222	0.213	0.405	0.379	0.172	0.158	0.195
1/4 0.250	0.253	0.244	0.460	0.430	0.196	0.180	0.221
9/32 0.281	0.285	0.273	0.518	0.484	0.220	0.202	0.249
5/16 0.312	0.316	0.304	0.572	0.538	0.243	0.225	0.276
11/32 0.344	0.348	0.336	0.630	0.592	0.267	0.247	0.304
3/8 0.375	0.380	0.365	0.684	0.646	0.291	0.271	0.332
13/32 0.406	0.411	0.396	0.743	0.699	0.316	0.294	0.358
7/16 0.438	0.443	0.428	0.798	0.754	0.339	0.317	0.387

For dimensions and tolerances not specified above, see General Specifications.

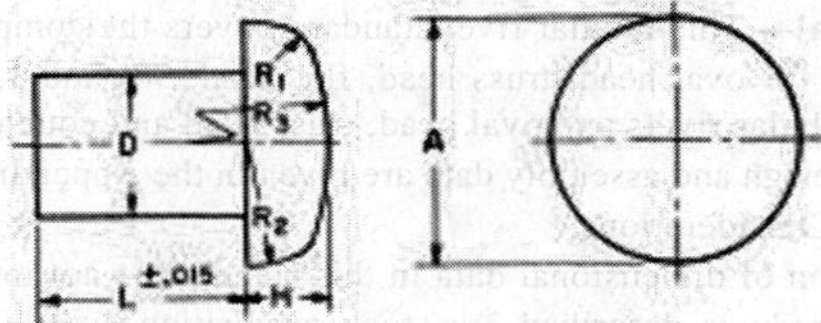

TABLE 4—PAN HEAD RIVETS

Nominal Size or Basic Shank Dia	D Dia of Shank Max	D Dia of Shank Min	A Dia of Head Max	A Dia of Head Min	H Height of Head Max	H Height of Head Min	Radii of Head R_1 Approx	Radii of Head R_2 Approx	Radii of Head R Approx
1/16 0.062	0.065	0.059	0.118	0.098	0.040	0.030	0.019	0.052	0.217
3/32 0.094	0.096	0.090	0.173	0.153	0.060	0.048	0.030	0.080	0.326
1/8 0.125	0.127	0.121	0.225	0.205	0.078	0.066	0.039	0.106	0.429
5/32 0.156	0.158	0.152	0.279	0.257	0.096	0.082	0.049	0.133	0.535
3/16 0.188	0.191	0.182	0.334	0.308	0.114	0.100	0.059	0.159	0.641
7/32 0.219	0.222	0.213	0.391	0.365	0.133	0.119	0.069	0.186	0.754
1/4 0.250	0.253	0.244	0.444	0.414	0.151	0.135	0.079	0.213	0.858
9/32 0.281	0.285	0.273	0.499	0.465	0.170	0.152	0.088	0.239	0.963
5/16 0.312	0.316	0.304	0.552	0.518	0.187	0.169	0.098	0.266	1.070
11/32 0.344	0.348	0.336	0.608	0.570	0.206	0.186	0.108	0.292	1.176
3/8 0.375	0.380	0.365	0.663	0.625	0.225	0.205	0.118	0.319	1.286
13/32 0.406	0.411	0.396	0.719	0.675	0.243	0.221	0.127	0.345	1.392
7/16 0.438	0.443	0.428	0.772	0.728	0.261	0.239	0.137	0.372	1.500

For dimensions and tolerances not specified above, see General Specifications.

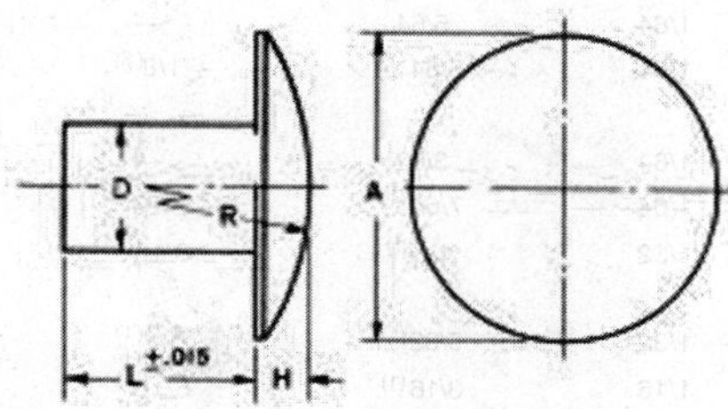

TABLE 5—TRUSS HEAD OR WAGON BOX RIVETS

Nominal Size or Basic Shank Dia	D Dia of Shank Max	D Dia of Shank Min	A Dia of Head Max	A Dia of Head Min	H Height of Head Max	H Height of Head Min	R Radius of Head Approx
3/32 0.094	0.096	0.090	0.226	0.206	0.038	0.026	0.239
1/8 0.125	0.127	0.121	0.297	0.277	0.048	0.036	0.314
5/32 0.156	0.158	0.152	0.368	0.348	0.059	0.045	0.392
3/16 0.188	0.191	0.182	0.442	0.422	0.069	0.055	0.470
7/32 0.219	0.222	0.213	0.515	0.495	0.080	0.066	0.555
1/4 0.250	0.253	0.244	0.590	0.560	0.091	0.075	0.628
9/32 0.281	0.285	0.273	0.661	0.631	0.103	0.085	0.706
5/16 0.312	0.316	0.304	0.732	0.702	0.113	0.095	0.784
11/32 0.344	0.348	0.336	0.806	0.776	0.124	0.104	0.862
3/8 0.375	0.380	0.365	0.878	0.848	0.135	0.115	0.942
13/32 0.406	0.411	0.396	0.949	0.919	0.145	0.123	0.128
7/16 0.438	0.443	0.428	1.020	0.990	0.157	0.135	1.098

For dimensions and tolerances not specified above, see General Specifications.

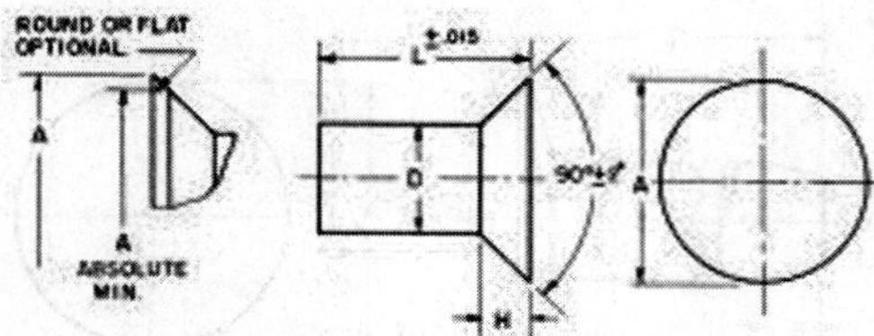

TABLE 6—COUNTERSUNK HEAD RIVETS

Nominal Size or Basic Shank Dia	D Dia of Shank Max	D Dia of Shank Min	A Dia of Head Max Sharp	A Dia of Head Abs Min	H[1] Height of Head
1/16 0.062	0.065	0.059	0.118	0.110	0.027
3/32 0.094	0.096	0.090	0.176	0.163	0.040
1/8 0.125	0.127	0.121	0.235	0.217	0.053
5/32 0.156	0.158	0.152	0.293	0.272	0.066
3/16 0.188	0.191	0.182	0.351	0.326	0.079
7/32 0.219	0.222	0.213	0.413	0.384	0.094
1/4 0.250	0.253	0.244	0.469	0.437	0.106
9/32 0.281	0.285	0.273	0.528	0.491	0.119
5/16 0.312	0.316	0.304	0.588	0.547	0.133
11/32 0.344	0.348	0.336	0.646	0.602	0.146
3/8 0.375	0.380	0.365	0.704	0.656	0.159
13/32 0.406	0.411	0.396	0.763	0.710	0.172
7/16 0.438	0.443	0.428	0.823	0.765	0.186

1. Height of head, H, is given for construction purposes only. Variations in this dimension are controlled by the diameters A and D and the included angle of the head.
For dimensions and tolerances not specified above, see General Specifications.

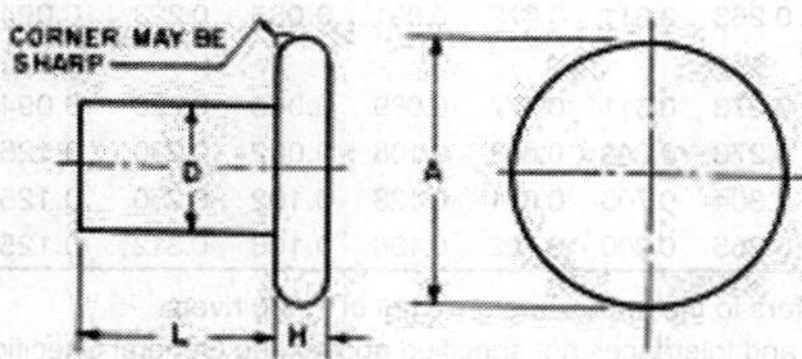

TABLE 7—TINNERS' RIVETS

Nominal Size[1]	D Dia of Shank Max	D Dia of Shank Min	A Dia of Head Max	A Dia of Head Min	H Height of Head Max	H Height of Head Min	Length Max	Length Min
6 oz	0.081	0.075	0.213	0.193	0.028	0.016	0.135	0.115
8 oz	0.091	0.085	0.225	0.205	0.036	0.024	0.166	0.146
10 oz	0.097	0.091	0.250	0.230	0.037	0.025	0.182	0.162
12 oz	0.107	0.101	0.265	0.245	0.037	0.025	0.198	0.178
14 oz	0.111	0.105	0.275	0.255	0.038	0.026	0.198	0.178
1 lb	0.113	0.107	0.285	0.265	0.040	0.028	0.213	0.193
1-1/4 lb	0.122	0.116	0.295	0.275	0.045	0.033	0.229	0.209
1-1/2 lb	0.132	0.126	0.316	0.294	0.046	0.034	0.244	0.224
1-3/4 lb	0.136	0.130	0.331	0.309	0.049	0.035	0.260	0.240
2 lb	0.146	0.140	0.341	0.319	0.050	0.036	0.276	0.256
2-1/2 lb	0.150	0.144	0.311	0.289	0.069	0.055	0.291	0.271
3 lb	0.163	0.154	0.329	0.303	0.073	0.059	0.323	0.303
3-1/2 lb	0.168	0.159	0.348	0.322	0.074	0.060	0.338	0.318
4 lb	0.179	0.170	0.368	0.342	0.076	0.062	0.354	0.334
5 lb	0.190	0.181	0.388	0.362	0.084	0.070	0.385	0.365
6 lb	0.206	0.197	0.419	0.393	0.090	0.076	0.401	0.381
7 lb	0.223	0.214	0.431	0.405	0.094	0.080	0.416	0.396
8 lb	0.227	0.218	0.475	0.445	0.101	0.085	0.448	0.428
9 lb	0.241	0.232	0.490	0.460	0.103	0.087	0.463	0.443
10 lb	0.241	0.232	0.505	0.475	0.104	0.088	0.479	0.459
12 lb	0.263	0.251	0.532	0.498	0.108	0.090	0.510	0.490
14 lb	0.288	0.276	0.577	0.543	0.113	0.095	0.525	0.505
16 lb	0.304	0.292	0.597	0.563	0.128	0.110	0.541	0.521
18 lb	0.347	0.335	0.706	0.668	0.156	0.136	0.603	0.583

1. Nominal size refers to the approximate weight of 1,000 rivets.
For dimensions and tolerances not specified above, see General Specifications.

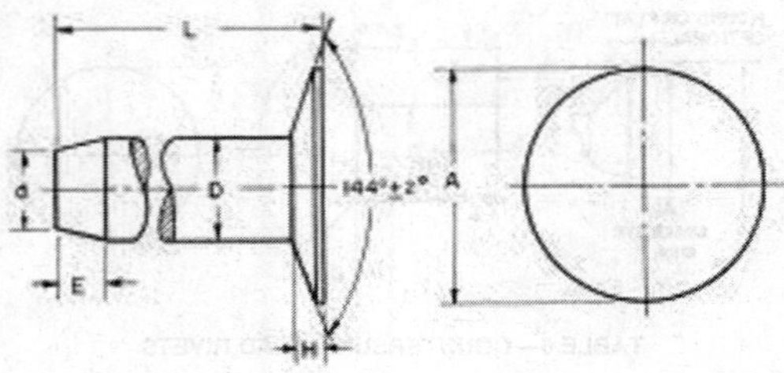

TABLE 8—COOPERS' RIVETS

Nominal Size(1)	D Dia of Shank Max	D Dia of Shank Min	A Dia of Head Max	A Dia of Head Min	H Height of Head Max	H Height of Head Min	Point d Dia Approx	Point E Length Approx	L Length Max	L Length Min
1 lb	0.111	0.105	0.291	0.271	0.045	0.031	Not Pointed		0.249	0.219
1-1/4	0.122	0.116	0.324	0.302	0.050	0.036	Not Pointed		0.285	0.255
1-1/2	0.132	0.126	0.324	0.302	0.050	0.036	Not Pointed		0.285	0.255
1-3/4	0.136	0.130	0.324	0.302	0.052	0.034	Not Pointed		0.318	0.284
2	0.142	0.136	0.355	0.333	0.056	0.038	Not Pointed		0.322	0.288
3	0.158	0.152	0.386	0.364	0.058	0.040	0.123	0.062	0.387	0.353
4	0.168	0.159	0.388	0.362	0.058	0.040	0.130	0.062	0.418	0.388
5	0.183	0.174	0.419	0.393	0.063	0.045	0.144	0.062	0.454	0.420
6	0.206	0.197	0.482	0.456	0.073	0.051	0.160	0.094	0.498	0.457
7	0.223	0.214	0.513	0.487	0.076	0.054	0.175	0.094	0.561	0.523
8	0.241	0.232	0.546	0.516	0.081	0.059	0.182	0.094	0.597	0.559
9	0.248	0.239	0.578	0.548	0.085	0.063	0.197	0.094	0.601	0.563
10	0.253	0.244	0.578	0.548	0.085	0.063	0.197	0.094	0.632	0.594
12	0.263	0.251	0.580	0.546	0.086	0.060	0.214	0.094	0.633	0.575
14	0.275	0.263	0.611	0.577	0.091	0.065	0.223	0.094	0.670	0.612
16	0.285	0.273	0.611	0.577	0.089	0.063	0.223	0.094	0.699	0.641
18	0.285	0.273	0.642	0.608	0.108	0.082	0.230	0.125	0.749	0.691
20	0.316	0.304	0.705	0.671	0.128	0.102	0.250	0.125	0.769	0.711
3/8	0.380	0.365	0.800	0.762	0.136	0.106	0.312	0.125	0.840	0.778

1. Nominal size refers to the approximate weight of 1,000 rivets.
For dimensions and tolerances not specified above, see General Specifications.

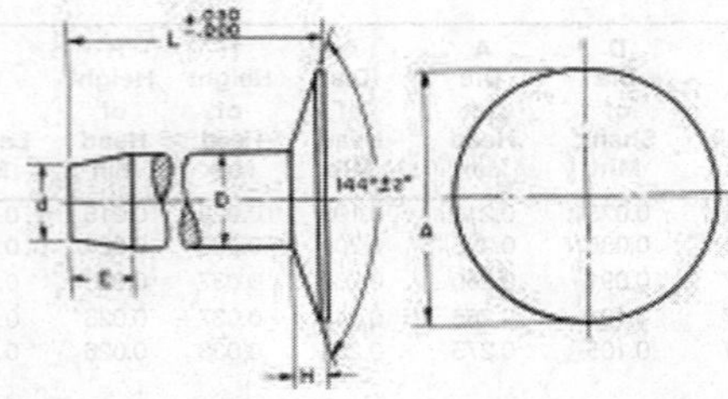

TABLE 9—BELT RIVETS

Nominal Size(1)	D Dia of Shank Max	D Dia of Shank Min	A Dia of Head Max	A Dia of Head Min	H Height of Head Max	H Height of Head Min	Point d Dia Approx	Point E Length Approx
14	0.085	0.079	0.260	0.240	0.042	0.030	0.065	0.078
13	0.097	0.091	0.322	0.302	0.051	0.039	0.073	0.078
12	0.111	0.105	0.353	0.333	0.054	0.040	0.083	0.078
11	0.122	0.116	0.383	0.363	0.059	0.045	0.097	0.078
10	0.136	0.130	0.417	0.395	0.065	0.047	0.109	0.094
9	0.150	0.144	0.448	0.426	0.069	0.051	0.122	0.094
8	0.167	0.161	0.481	0.455	0.072	0.054	0.135	0.094
7	0.183	0.174	0.513	0.487	0.075	0.056	0.151	0.125
6	0.206	0.197	0.606	0.580	0.090	0.068	0.165	0.125
5	0.223	0.214	0.700	0.674	0.105	0.083	0.185	0.125
4	0.241	0.232	0.921	0.893	0.138	0.116	0.204	0.141

1. Nominal size refers to the Stubs iron wirge gage number of the stock used in the shank of the rivet.
For dimensions and tolerances not specified above, see General Specifications.

4. General Specifications For Tubular Rivets

4.1 General—This tubular rivet standard covers the complete general and dimensional data for oval head, truss head, flat head, 90- and 120-deg countersunk head semitubular rivets and oval head, truss head and countersunk head full tubular rivets. Design and assembly data are given in the Appendix—Rivet Selection and Design Considerations.

The inclusion of dimensional data in this standard is not intended to imply that all of the products described are stock production sizes. Consumers are requested to consult with manufacturers concerning stock production sizes.

4.2 Heads—The bearing surface of flat, oval, and truss head rivets shall be at right angles to the axis of the body within 2 deg. Heads of all tubular rivets shall not be eccentric with the shank beyond a tolerance of 3% of the maximum head diameter. Because the heads are not machined or trimmed, the circumference may be slightly irregular and the edges rounded or flat.

4.3 Underhead Fillets—Rivets, other than countersunk type, shall be furnished with a definite fillet under the head but radius of fillet shall not exceed 10% of maximum shank diameter.

4.4 Material—Tubular rivets shall be low carbon steel, or brass, standard with manufacturer; or stainless steel, aluminum, copper, or other metals as agreed upon between the purchaser and supplier.

4.5 Length—Length of rivets shall be measured as indicated in the illustrations for each head style. Tubular rivets are available in length increments specified in Table 10.

Tolerance on length of tubular rivets shall be as specified in Table 11.

4.6 Workmanship—Tubular rivet end irregularities shall not be such that usability of the rivet is impaired. Rivets shall be free from surface seams, splits, and all other defects that might affect their serviceability.

TABLE 10—LENGTH INCREMENTS AND MINIMUM LENGTHS

Nominal Size	Length Increments	Min Lengths Right Angle Heads	Min Lengths 90 deg Csk Heads	Min Lengths 120 deg Csk Heads
1/16	1/64	1/16	—	—
5/64	1/64	5/64	—	—
3/32	1/64	5/64(1)	1/8(1)	7/64(1)
7/64	1/64	3/32	—	—
1/8	1/64	7/64(1)	11/64(1)	5/32(1)
9/64	1/32	1/8(1)	3/16(1)	3/16(1)
3/16	1/32	5/32(1)	1/4(1)	1/4(1)
7/32	1/16	3/16(1)	5/16(1)	9/32(1)
1/4	1/16	7/32(1)	11/32(1)	5/16(1)
5/16	1/16	1/4(1)	—	—

1. Hole depth to point of apex shall not exceed shank length for straight hole rivets of these lengths.

TABLE 11—TOLERANCES ON LENGTH

Nominal Size	Rivet Length To and Including 4 x Dia Tolerance	Rivet Length Over 4 Dia to and Including 8 x Dia Tolerance	Rivet Length Over 8 x Dia Tolerance
1/16	±0.007	±0.008	±0.010
5/64	±0.007	±0.008	±0.010
3/32	±0.007	±0.008	±0.010
7/64	±0.007	±0.008	±0.010
1/8	±0.007	±0.010	±0.015
9/64	±0.010	±0.012	±0.015
3/16	±0.010	±0.012	±0.015
7/32	±0.010	±0.015	±0.020
1/4	±0.010	±0.015	±0.020
5/16	±0.010	±0.015	±0.020

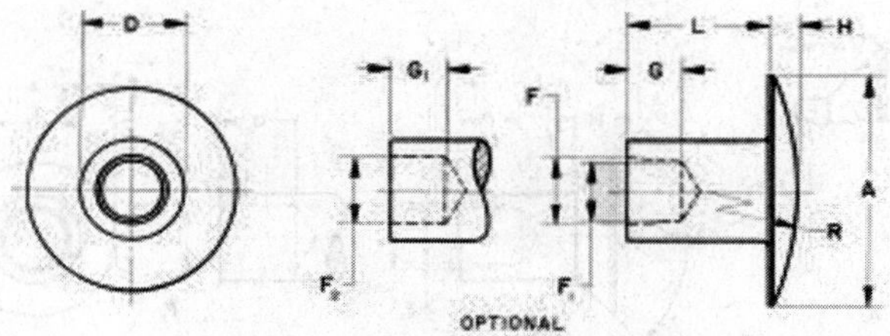

TABLE 12—DIMENSIONS OF OVAL HEAD SEMITUBULAR RIVETS

Nominal Size	D Dia of Shank Max	D Dia of Shank Min	A Dia of Head Max	A Dia of Head Min	H Height of Head Max	H Height of Head Min	Tapered Hole Dia F Max	Tapered Hole Dia F Min	Tapered Hole Dia F_1 Min	Tapered Hole G Depth Min	Straight Hole F_2 Dia Max	Straight Hole F_2 Dia Min	Straight Hole G_1 Depth Max	Straight Hole G_1 Depth Min	R Head Radius (Ref) Min
1/16	0.061	0.058	0.114	0.104	0.020	0.014	0.046	0.042	0.036	0.042	0.044	0.039	0.057	0.042	0.084
5/64	0.075	0.072	0.133	0.123	0.023	0.017	0.053	0.047	0.040	0.053	0.051	0.045	0.068	0.053	0.101
3/32	0.089	0.085	0.152	0.142	0.026	0.020	0.069	0.065	0.057	0.057	0.068	0.062	0.072	0.057	0.120
7/64	0.099	0.095	0.192	0.182	0.032	0.026	0.076	0.072	0.063	0.065	0.076	0.070	0.088	0.073	0.158
1/8	0.123	0.118	0.223	0.213	0.038	0.030	0.095	0.091	0.079	0.082	0.090	0.084	0.104	0.089	0.183
9/64	0.146	0.141	0.239	0.229	0.045	0.035	0.112	0.106	0.091	0.104	0.107	0.100	0.135	0.120	0.182
3/16	0.188	0.182	0.318	0.306	0.065	0.055	0.145	0.139	0.120	0.135	0.141	0.134	0.166	0.151	0.232
7/32	0.217	0.210	0.444	0.430	0.075	0.061	0.166	0.150	0.136	0.151	0.163	0.155	0.198	0.183	0.381
1/4	0.252	0.244	0.507	0.493	0.085	0.071	0.191	0.181	0.155	0.183	0.184	0.176	0.229	0.214	0.439
5/16	0.310	0.302	0.570	0.554	0.100	0.086	0.235	0.225	0.201	0.214	0.219	0.211	0.260	0.245	0.473

For dimensions and tolerances not specified above, see General Specifications.

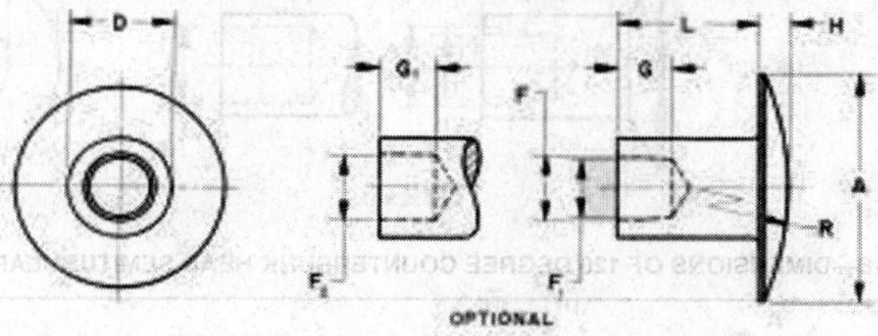

TABLE 13—DIMENSIONS OF TRUSS HEAD SEMITUBULAR RIVETS

Nominal Size	D Dia of Shank Max	D Dia of Shank Min	A Dia of Head Max	A Dia of Head Min	H Height of Head Max	H Height of Head Min	Tapered Hole Dia F Max	Tapered Hole Dia F Min	Tapered Hole Dia F_1 Min	Tapered Hole G Depth Min	Straight Hole F_2 Dia Max	Straight Hole F_2 Dia Min	Straight Hole G_1 Depth Max	Straight Hole G_1 Depth Min	R Head Radius (Ref) Min
1/16	0.061	0.058	0.130	0.120	0.020	0.014	0.046	0.042	0.036	0.042	0.044	0.039	0.057	0.042	0.110
3/32	0.089	0.085	0.192	0.182	0.026	0.020	0.069	0.065	0.057	0.057	0.068	0.062	0.072	0.057	0.189
1/8	0.123	0.118	0.286	0.276	0.038	0.030	0.095	0.091	0.079	0.082	0.090	0.084	0.104	0.089	0.300
9/64	0.146	0.141	0.318	0.306	0.045	0.035	0.112	0.106	0.091	0.104	0.107	0.100	0.135	0.120	0.313
3/16	0.188	0.182	0.381	0.369	0.065	0.055	0.145	0.139	0.120	0.135	0.141	0.134	0.166	0.151	0.324

For dimensions and tolerances not specified above, see General Specifications.

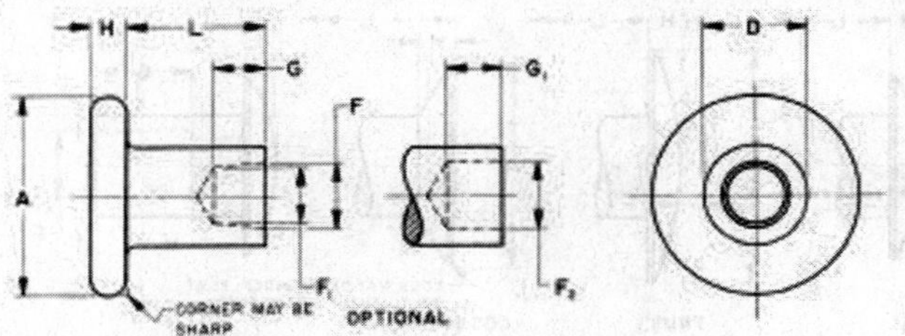

TABLE 14—DIMENSIONS OF FLAT HEAD SEMITUBULAR RIVETS

Nominal Size	D Dia of Shank Max	D Dia of Shank Min	A Dia of Head Max	A Dia of Head Min	H Height of Head Max	H Height of Head Min	Tapered Hole Dia F Max	Tapered Hole Dia F Min	Tapered Hole Dia F_1 Min	Tapered Hole G Depth Min	Straight Hole F_2 Dia Max	Straight Hole F_2 Dia Min	Straight Hole G_1 Depth Max	Straight Hole G_1 Depth Min
1/16	0.061	0.058	0.114	0.104	0.027	0.023	0.046	0.042	0.036	0.042	0.044	0.039	0.057	0.042
3/32	0.089	0.085	0.161	0.151	0.034	0.028	0.069	0.065	0.057	0.057	0.068	0.062	0.072	0.057
1/8	0.123	0.118	0.223	0.213	0.041	0.034	0.095	0.091	0.079	0.082	0.090	0.084	0.104	0.089
9/64	0.146	0.141	0.317	0.307	0.052	0.042	0.112	0.106	0.091	0.104	0.107	0.100	0.135	0.120
3/16	0.188	0.182	0.381	0.369	0.067	0.057	0.145	0.139	0.120	0.135	0.141	0.134	0.166	0.151
1/4	0.252	0.244	0.507	0.493	0.090	0.076	0.191	0.181	0.155	0.183	0.184	0.176	0.229	0.214

For dimensions and tolerances not specified above, see General Specifications.

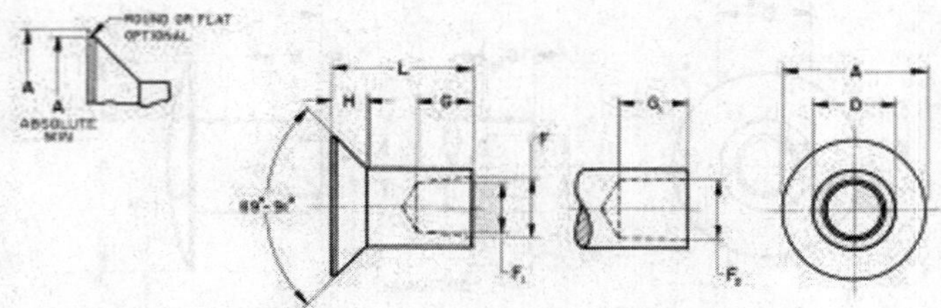

TABLE 15—DIMENSIONS OF 90 DEGREE COUNTERSUNK HEAD SEMITUBULAR RIVETS

Nominal Size	D Dia of Shank Max	A Dia of Shank Min	A Dia of Head Max Sharp	A Dia of Head Abs Sharp	H Height of Head Ref(1)	Tapered Hole Dia F Max	Tapered Hole Dia F Min	Tapered Hole Dia F_1 Min	Tapered Hole G Depth Min	Straight Hole F_2 Dia Max	Straight Hole F_2 Dia Min	Straight Hole G_1 Depth Max	Straight Hole G_1 Depth Min
3/32	0.089	0.085	0.176	0.163	0.045	0.069	0.065	0.057	0.057	0.068	0.062	0.072	0.057
1/8	0.123	0.118	0.235	0.217	0.057	0.095	0.091	0.079	0.082	0.090	0.084	0.104	0.089
9/64	0.146	0.141	0.270	0.250	0.060	0.112	0.106	0.091	0.104	0.107	0.100	0.135	0.120
3/16	0.188	0.182	0.351	0.326	0.083	0.145	0.139	0.120	0.135	0.141	0.134	0.166	0.151
7/32	0.217	0.210	0.413	0.384	0.100	0.166	0.158	0.136	0.151	0.163	0.155	0.198	0.183
1/4	0.252	0.244	0.469	0.437	0.112	0.191	0.181	0.155	0.183	0.184	0.176	0.229	0.214

1. Height of head, H, is given for reference purposes only. Variations in this dimension are controlled by diameters A and D and included angle of the head.
For dimensions and tolerances not specified above, see General Specifications.

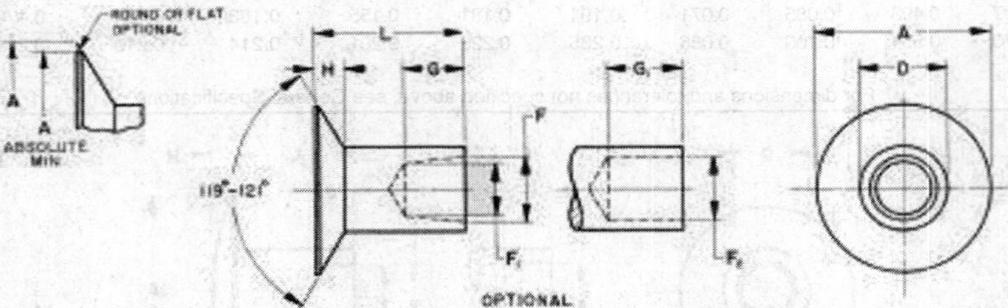

TABLE 16—DIMENSIONS OF 120 DEGREE COUNTERSUNK HEAD SEMITUBULAR RIVETS

Nominal Size	D Dia of Shank Max	D Dia of Shank Min	A Dia of Head Max Sharp	A Dia of Head Abs Min	H Height of Head Ref(1)	Tapered Hole Dia F Max	Tapered Hole Dia F Min	Tapered Hole Dia F_1 Min	Tapered Hole G Depth Min	Straight Hole F_2 Dia Max	Straight Hole F_2 Dia Min	Straight Hole G_1 Depth Max	Straight Hole G_1 Depth Min
3/32	0.089	0.085	0.223	0.203	0.041	0.069	0.065	0.057	0.057	0.068	0.062	0.072	0.057
1/8	0.123	0.118	0.271	0.245	0.045	0.095	0.091	0.079	0.082	0.090	0.084	0.104	0.089
9/64	0.146	0.141	0.337	0.307	0.057	0.112	0.106	0.091	0.104	0.107	0.100	0.135	0.120
3/16	0.188	0.182	0.404	0.369	0.065	0.145	0.139	0.120	0.135	0.141	0.134	0.166	0.151
7/32	0.217	0.210	0.472	0.430	0.077	0.166	0.158	0.136	0.151	0.163	0.155	0.198	0.183
1/4	0.252	0.244	0.540	0.493	0.087	0.191	0.181	0.155	0.183	0.184	0.176	0.299	0.214

1. Height of head, H, is given for reference purposes only. Variations in this dimension are controlled by diameters A and D and inlcuded angle of the head.
For dimensions and tolerances not specified above, see General Specifications.

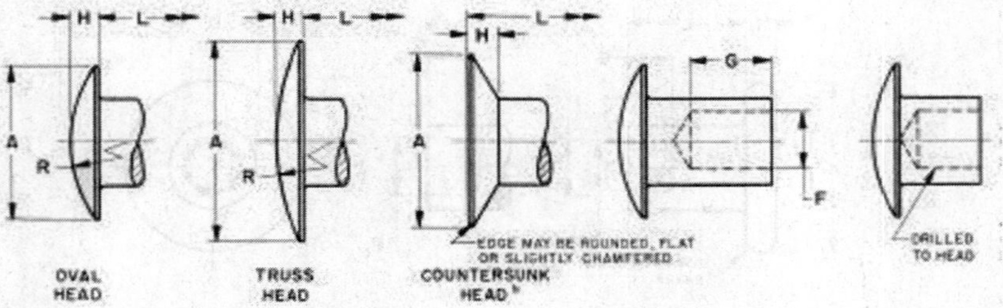

TABLE 17—DIMENSIONS OF FULL TUBULAR RIVETS

Head Style	Nominal Size	D Dia of Shank Max	D Dia of Shank Min	A Dia of Head Max	A Dia of Head Min	H Height of Head Max	H Height of Head Min	F Dia of Hole Max	F Dia of Hole Min	G Depth of Hole Min(1)	R Head Radius (Ref)
Oval	9/64	0.146	0.141	0.239	0.229	0.045	0.035	0.107	0.100	0.375	0.182
Truss	9/64	0.146	0.141	0.318	0.306	0.045	0.035	0.107	0.100	0.375	0.313
	3/16	0.188	0.182	0.381	0.369	0.065	0.055	0.141	0.134	0.375	0.324
Countersunk(2)	9/64	0.146	0.141	0.317	0.307	0.050	0.040	0.107	0.100	0.375	—
	3/16	0.188	0.182	0.381	0.369	0.060	0.048	0.141	0.134	0.375	—

1. Full tubular rivets having length of 3/8 or shorter shall be drilled to head.
2. Angle of head not specified since it is assumed this type of rivet would generally be used in soft materials and therefore form its own countersink.
For dimensions and tolerances not specified above, see General Specifications.

5. General Specifications For Split Rivets

5.1 General—This standard covers the complete general and dimensional data for oval head and countersunk head split rivets. Design and assembly data are given in the Appendix—Rivet Selection and Design Considerations.

5.2 Heads—The bearing surface of oval head split rivets shall be at right angles to the axis of the body within 2deg. Because the heads are not machined or trimmed, the circumference may be slightly irregular and the edges may be rounded or flat.

5.3 Material—Split rivets shall be low carbon steel, brass, or other metals as agreed upon between the purchaser and supplier.

5.4 Workmanship—Rivets shall be free from surface seams, and all other defects that might affect their serviceability.

5.5 Length—Rivet length shall be measured as indicated in the illustrations for each head style. Tolerance on length shall be as specified in Table 18.

TABLE 18—TOLERANCES ON LENGTH

Nominal Size	Rivet Length To and Including 4 x Dia Tolerance	Rivet Length Over 4 to and Including 8 x Dia Tolerance	Rivet Length Over 8 x Dia Tolerance
3/32	±0.0007	±0.008	±0.010
1/8	±0.007	±0.010	±0.015
9/64	±0.010	±0..012	±0.015
3/16	±0/010	±0.012	±0.015

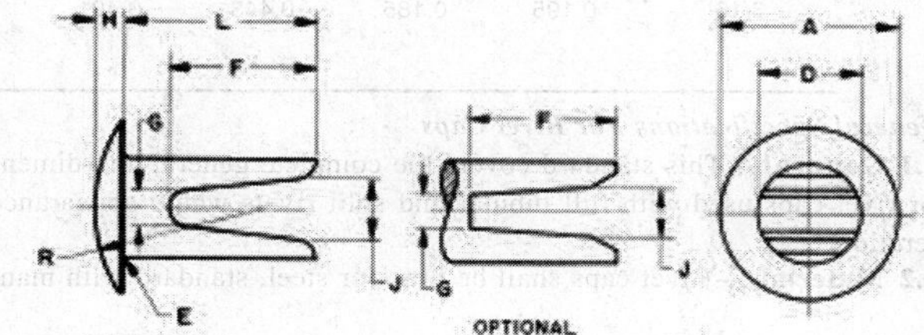

TABLE 19—DIMENSIONS OF OVAL HEAD SPLIT RIVETS

Nominal Size	D Dia of Shank Max	D Dia of Shank Min	A Dia of Head Max	A Dia of Head Min	H Height of Head Max	H Height of Head Min	E Radius of Fillet Max	R Radius of Head Ref	L[(1)] Length of Rivet	F Depth of Slot ±0.015	Width of Slot G ±0.005	Width of Slot J ±0.005
									3/16	0.156	0.030	0.037
									1/4	0.219	0.030	0.039
3/32	0.092	0.086	0.151	0.141	0.027	0.019	0.010	0.130	5/16	0.250	0.030	0.039
									3/8 and over	0.312	0.030	0.039
									3/16	0.156	0.040	0.047
									1/4	0.219	0.040	0.052
1/8	0.122	0.114	0.223	0.213	0.037	0.027	0.014	0.210	5/16	0.266	0.040	0.057
									3/8 and over	0.312	0.040	0.057
									3/16	0.156	0.050	0.060
									1/4	0.219	0.050	0.073
9/64	0.152	0.144	0.317	0.307	0.049	0.037	0.018	0.304	5/16	0.281	0.050	0.078
									3/8	0.328	0.050	0.081
									7/16	0.344	0.050	0.083
									1/2 and over	0.391	0.052	0.077
									1/4	0.219	0.065	0.120
									5/16	0.281	0.065	0.125
3/16	0.195	0.185	0.350	0.338	0.064	0.050	0.022	0.300	3/8	0.312	0.065	0.127
									7/16	0.375	0.065	0.130
									1/2 and over	0.437	0.068	0.133

1. Lengths over those tabulated shall be in increments of 1/16 in.
For dimensions and tolerances not specified above, see General Specifications.

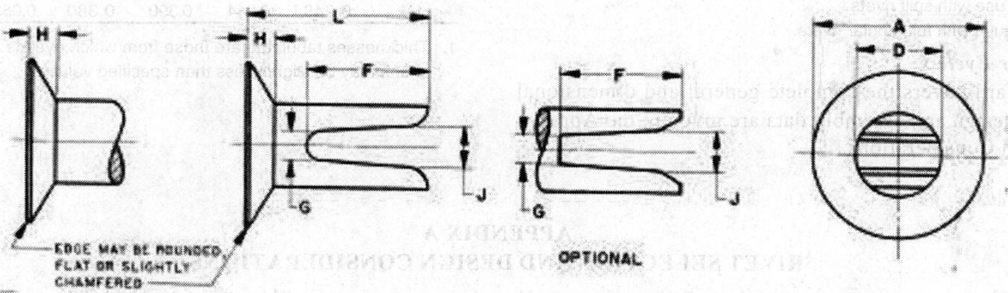

TABLE 20—DIMENSIONS OF COUNTERSUNK HEAD SPLIT RIVETS

Nominal Size	D Dia of Shank Max	D Dia of Shank Min	A Dia of Head Max	A Dia of Head Min	H Height of Head Max	H Height of Head Min	L Length of Rivet	F Depth of Slot ±0.016	Width of Slot G ±0.005	Width of Slot J ±0.005
							1/4	0.156	0.040	0.047
1/8	0.122	0.114	0.223	0.213	0.036	0.026	5/16	0.219	0.040	0.052
							3/8	0.281	0.040	0.057
							7/16 and over	0.312	0.040	0.057
							1/4	0.156	0.050	0.060
							5/16	0.219	0.050	0.073
							3/8	0.281	0.050	0.078
			0.317	0.307	0.053	0.043	7/16	0.328	0.050	0.081
							1/2	0.344	0.050	0.083
9/64	0.152	0.144					9/16 and over	0.391	0.052	0.077
							1/4	0.156	0.050	0.060

TABLE 20—DIMENSIONS OF COUNTERSUNK HEAD SPLIT RIVETS (continued)

Nominal Size	D Dia of Shank Max	D Dia of Shank Min	A Dia of Head Max	A Dia of Head Min	H Height of Head Max	H Height of Head Min	L Length of Rivet	F Depth of Slot ±0.016	Width of Slot G ±0.005	Width of Slot J ±0.005
							5/16	0.219	0.050	0.073
			0.380	0.370	0.062	0.052	3/8	0.281	0.050	0.078
							7/16	0.328	0.050	0.081
							1/2	0.344	0.050	0.083
							9/16 and over	0.391	0.052	0.077
							5/16	0.219	0.065	0.120
							3/8	0.281	0.065	0.125
3/16	0.195	0.185	0.443	0.431	0.061	0.051	7/16	0.312	0.065	0.127
							1/2	0.375	0.065	0.130
							9/16 and over	0.437	0.068	0.133

6. General Specifications For Rivet Caps

6.1 General—This standard covers the complete general and dimensional data for rivet caps used with full tubular and split rivets where appearance is a consideration.

6.2 Materials—Rivet caps shall be brass or steel, standard with manufacturer.

6.3 Workmanship—Rivet caps shall be free from all defects that might affect their serviceability.

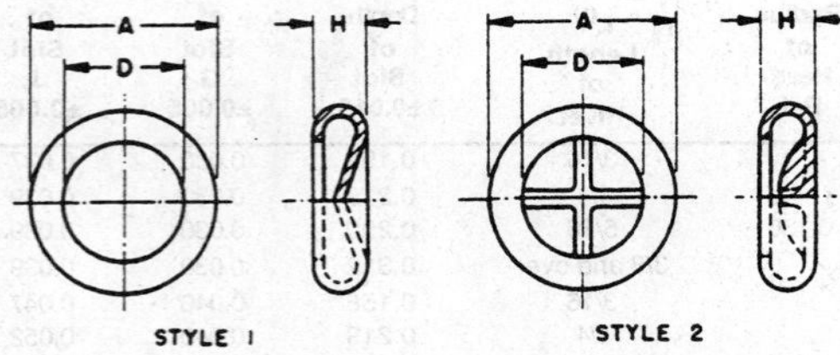

TABLE 21—DIMENSIONS OF RIVET CAPS

Style	D Dia of Hole Max	D Dia of Hole Min	A Outside Dia Max	A Outside Dia Min	H Height Max	H Height Min
	0.233	0.203	0.288	0.258	0.098	0.068
1(1)	0.233	0.203	0.311	0.299	0.098	0.068
	0.233	0.203	0.358	0.346	0.098	0.068
2(2)	0.233	0.203	0.350	0.320	0.098	0.068
	0.281	0.251	0.442	0.412	0.129	0.099

1. Style 1 rivet caps are designed for use with split rivets.
2. Style 2 rivet cpas are designed for use with full tubular rivets.

7. General Specifications For Eyelets

7.1 General—This standard covers the complete general and dimensional data for rolled flange eyelets. Design and assembly data are given in the Appendix—Rivet Selection and Design Considerations.

7.2 Flanges—Flanges of eyelets shall not be eccentric with the shank by more than 0.0075 in.

7.3 Material—Eyelets shall be brass, steel, or aluminum, standard with manufacturer.

7.4 Length—Length of eyelets shall be measured as indicated in the illustration. They are available in length increments of 1/32 in. between the limits specified in Table 22.

7.5 Workmanship—Eyelet end irregularities shall not be such that usability of the eyelet is impaired. Eyelets shall be free from surface seams, splits, and all other defects that might affect their serviceability.

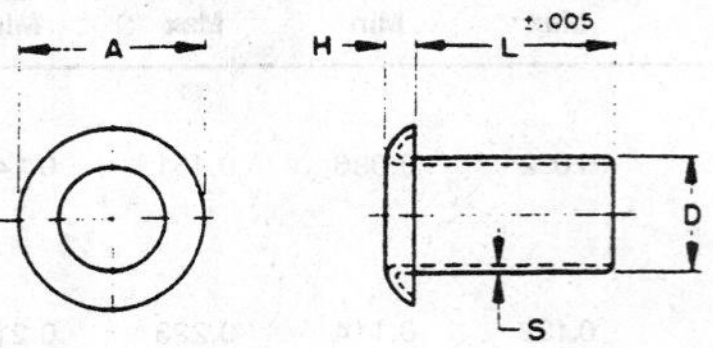

TABLE 22—DIMENSIONS OF EYELETS

Nominal Size	D Dia of Shank Max	D Dia of Shank Min	A Dia of Flange Max	A Dia of Flange Min	H Height of Flange Max	S(1) Material Thickness	L Available Lengths Max	L Available Lengths Min
1/16	0.061	0.057	0.110	0.100	0.025	0.007	7/32	1/16
3/32	0.091	0.087	0.155	0.145	0.030	0.009	5/16	3/32
1/8	0.123	0.119	0.205	0.195	0.035	0.0095	11/32	3/32
5/32	0.154	0.150	0.250	0.240	0.040	0.010	11/32	3/32
3/16	0.185	0.181	0.295	0.285	0.045	0.0105	7/16	3/32
7/32	0.217	0.213	0.345	0.335	0.050	0.011	3/8	3/32
1/4	0.248	0.244	0.390	0.380	0.055	0.011	13/32	3/32

1. Thicknesses tabulated are those from which eyelets are fabricated; therefore, thickness at shank may be slightly less than specified values.

APPENDIX A
RIVET SELECTION AND DESIGN CONSIDERATIONS

A.1 General—This appendix is a guide intended to aid the user in the proper selection and application of rivets as a fastening means. It consists of general information on the advantages of riveting, various methods of riveting, selection of rivets and design considerations.

A.2 Advantages of Riveting—Riveting as a means of fastening is popular because of its simplicity, dependability, and low cost. Where the parts to be assembled do not normally need to be disassembled and, in the case of tubular, semi-tubular and split rivets, the tensile and fatigue strength of the joinings made are not critical, riveting has many advantages. Some of the more outstanding of these are:

1. Metallic rivets are almost universally made by cold heading in high speed headers, and this makes a rivet a very economical fastener.
2. Investment in assembly equipment is low.
3. Maintenance costs of assembly equipment are low.
4. Rate of assembly is high and due to its simplicity, riveting lends itself to automation.
5. A minimum of skill is required to perform the operation.
6. Metallic or nonmetallic materials, or combinations thereof may be joined.
7. Rivets can be produced in a great variety of metals, ranging from low carbon steel to precious metals such as silver or gold.
8. Rivets may be used, not only as fasteners, but as functional components, such as pivots, electrical contacts, spacers, or supports.
9. Riveting normally requires no supplementary parts such as plain washers, lock washers, nuts, or safety wiring, nor are additional operations required such as assembly of nuts or locking devices as in the case of threaded fasteners.
10. Except for tubular, semitubular and split rivets, the rivet, when driven, usually fills the hole and prevents shifting of the parts joined.

A.3 Methods of Riveting—Riveting operations are performed by a number of methods, some of which are applicable only to particular types of rivets. The most commonly used methods are as follows:

A.3.1 Impact—This method employs a header die which strikes repetitive blows thus forming a head while the preformed end of the rivet is backed up with a tool called a buck or bucking bar. The header die may also be rotated while striking the repetitive blows. In machine riveting the buck is usually a part of the holding fixture. The method is applicable to solid rivets driven either hot or cold. Hot riveting is usually confined to large rivets used for structural purposes, while cold riveting is the method generally used for industrial applications on manufactured products. During the riveting operation the rivet material is displaced outward and downward into contact with the sides of the hole in which it is being assembled. The remainder of the material at rivet end forms the head. Upsetting of the shank can be controlled by using the proper impact force. See Figure A1.

A.3.2 Squeeze—As its name implies, this method consists of applying steady pressure with a formed header die while the preformed end of rivet is backed up with a buck which may be made a part of the holding fixture. This method is applicable to solid rivets driven hot or cold. As in the case of impact riveting, the rivet material is displaced outward and downward into contact with the sides of the hole in which it is being assembled. The remainder of the material forms the head. See Figure A2.

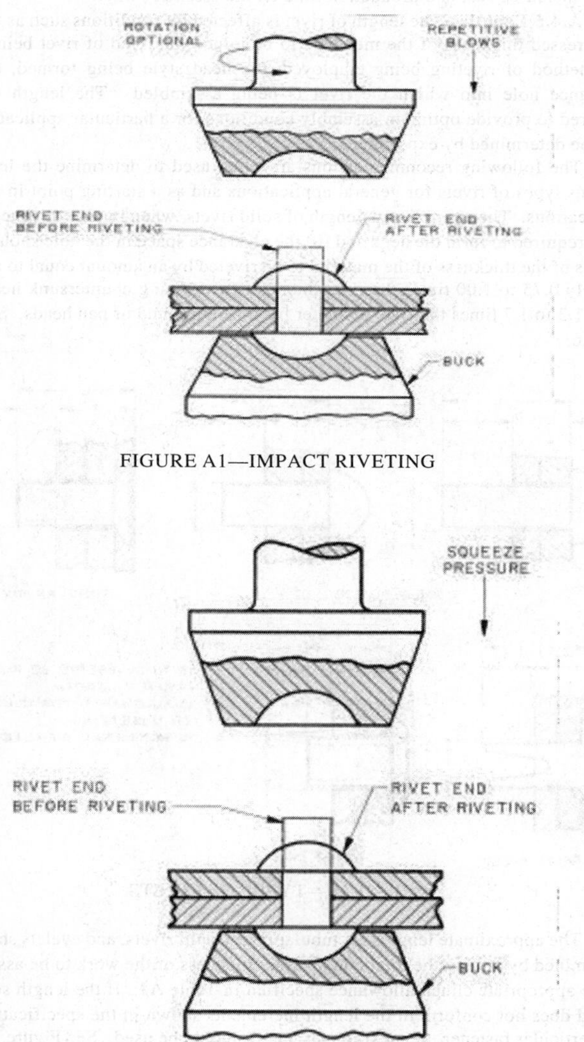

FIGURE A1—IMPACT RIVETING

FIGURE A2—SQUEEZE RIVETING

A.3.3 Clinch—This method of riveting involves forming the hollow end of tubular rivets and eyelets or prongs of split rivets back against the material being fastened and, depending on the shape and extent of the forming, is referred to as roll clinching, star or corrugated clinching, or scored clinching. See Figure A3. Roll clinching is accomplished by applying pressure with a formed header die, commonly called anvil, which turns or rolls the tubular shank or prongs of the rivet outward and over to bring it into contact with the part being assembled and is the method generally used to rivet semitubular and full tubular rivets and eyelets when used in metals or other hard materials. Star or corrugated clinching is accomplished by applying pressure with a formed header die which first splits or splays the tubular shank of the rivet and then turns or rolls the splayed portions outward and over to bring it into contact with the parts being assembled and is the method generally used to rivet full tubular rivets or eyelets when used in soft or resilient materials. When the splayed portions are actually turned back into the material being fastened, the method is often referred to as scored clinching. Where a finished appearance on both sides of the assembly is desirable, tubular and split rivets may be clinched into rivet caps designed for the purpose.

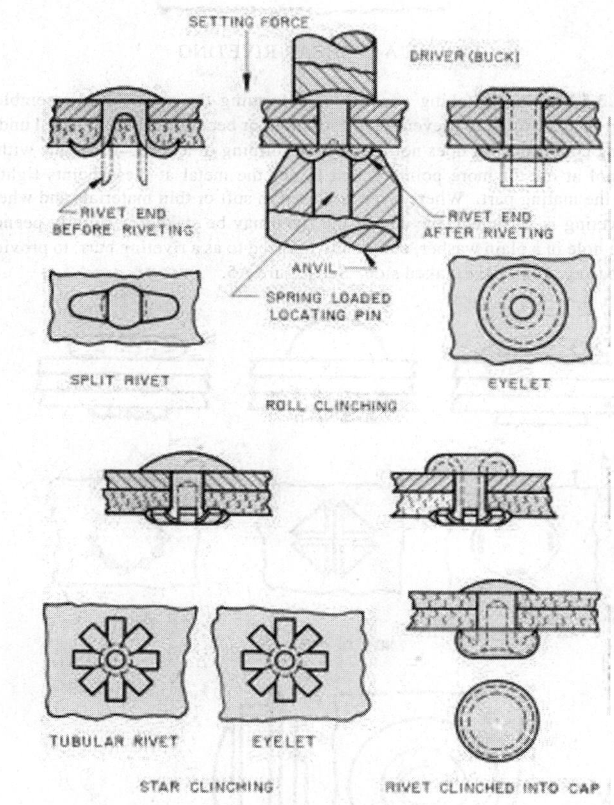

FIGURE A3—CLINCH RIVETING

A.3.4 Shear—This method of riveting is accomplished by the use of a circular shear tool resembling a hollow punch. The method is applicable to solid rivets and the operating is performed cold. With the rivet properly bucked the tool having a hollow portion smaller than the rivet shank shears an annulus of material from the shank and with squeeze pressure upsets or displaces it into a flat annular head formed around the stub portion of the shank left by the hollow in the tool. The annular head is in contact with the part being assembled. The shearing action terminates flush with the top of the head thus leaving the head integral with the shank. See Figure A4.

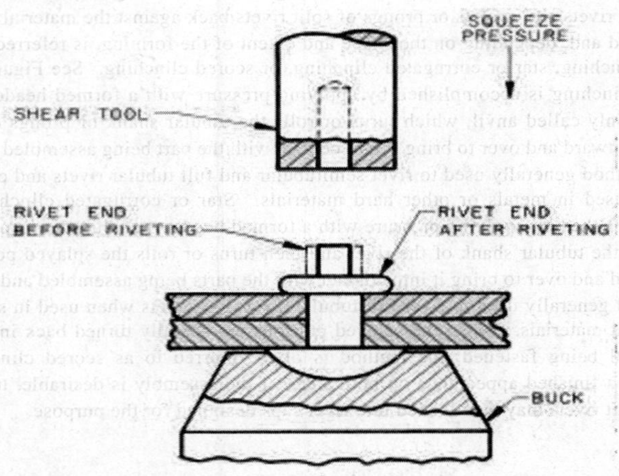

FIGURE A4—SHEAR RIVETING

A.3.5 Staking—Staking consists of deforming the material of assembled rivets in such a way as to prevent their loosening or becoming disassembled under operating conditions. It does not include the forming of a head. It is done with a sharp tool at one or more points which forces the metal at these points tightly against the mating part. Where rivets are used in soft or thin materials and where light riveting is sufficient, the end of the rivet may be staked or slightly peened over the hole in a plain washer, commonly referred to as a riveting burr, to provide more bearing area on the staked side. See Figure A5.

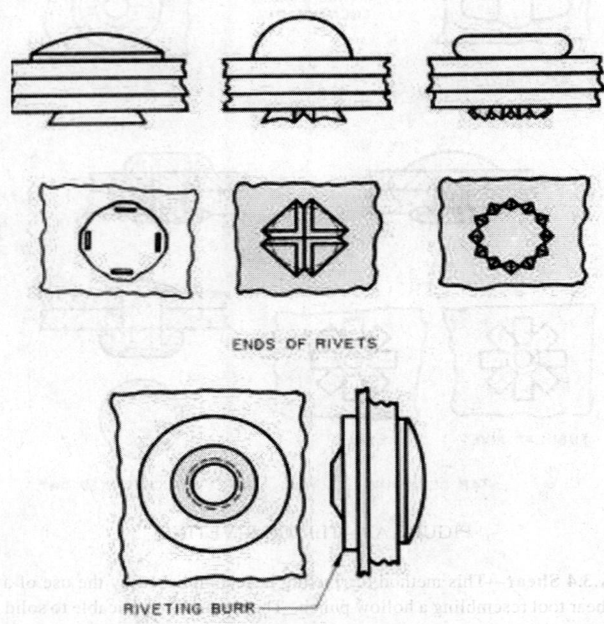

FIGURE A5—STAKING

A.4 Rivet Selection

A.4.1 Requirement Considerations—With the wide variety of rivet types available, no fixed rule can be established to cover the selection of a type best suited for a given application. Generally, however, solid rivets are indicated for maximum strength while semitubular are preferred where cost is a prime factor and tensile or fatigue strength is not as critical. Full tubular rivets can, in some cases, be used with materials such as plastic, leather, canvas fabric, and wood in which the rivet under pressure pierces its own hole. The deep hole allows the slugs of pierced material to compress inside the rivet thereby exposing the required rivet material for clinching. Split rivets are also used extensively in soft materials such as those mentioned herein. The prongs pierce their own holes and are then clinched to effect the assembly. Split rivets may be used in the self-piercing and fastening of light gage metal as well. Semitubular rivets may also be used in the self-piercing and fastening of light metal wherever the appearance of the clinch is not important. Self-piercing riveting is economical and lends itself to high speed assembly operations.

A.4.2 Strength—A rivet is primarily strong only in shear. When set it is not stressed in tension. Thus, the designer must select the rivet size and material which will provide the necessary shear resistance needed in the application.

A.4.3 Diameter—The shear strength of a rivet is a direct function of the diameter so it is important to select a diameter which will provide the necessary shear strength.

A.4.4 Head Design—The type of head specified will, of necessity, be dictated by the requirements of the application such as clearance, appearance, bearing area, and so forth. Round, truss, oval, flat, pan, and similar head styles with flat bearing surfaces provide good holding power at minimum cost. The use of flat head rivets where appearance is not a consideration minimizes tooling and production problems. Countersunk head rivets should be employed only where a flush surface is required since the countersinking or dimpling of parts to be fastened increases cost and production time on the assembly line.

A.4.5 Length—The length of rivet is affected by conditions such as the total compressed thickness of the members to be joined, the kind of rivet being used, the method of riveting being employed, the head style being formed, and the clearance hole into which the rivet is being assembled. The length of rivet required to provide optimum assembly conditions for a particular application can best be determined by experiment.

The following recommendations are often used to determine the length of various types of rivets for general applications and as a starting point in specific applications. The approximate length of solid rivets, when impact or squeeze riveted, required to form the head and fill the clearance space in the hole should be in excess of the thickness of the material to be riveted by an amount equal to approximately 0.75 to 1.00 times the rivet diameter for forming countersunk heads and from 1.3 to 1.7 times the rivet diameter for forming round or pan heads. See Figure A6.

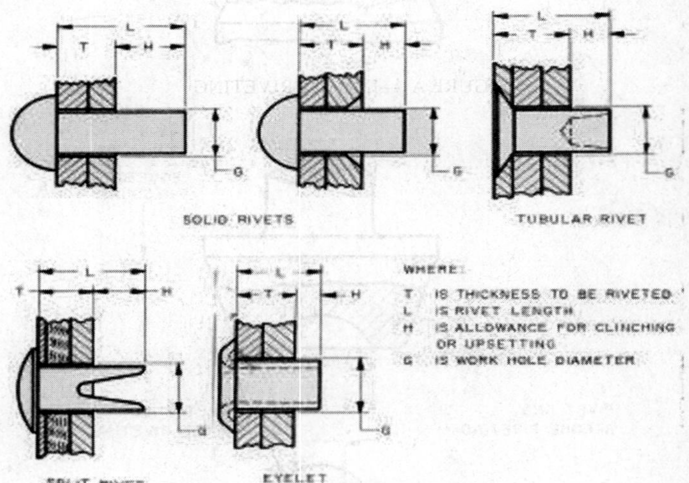

FIGURE A6—TYPES OF RIVETS

The approximate lengths for tubular rivets, split rivets, and eyelets should be determined by adding the total compressed thickness of the work to be assembled to the appropriate clinch allowance specified in Table A1. If the length so determined does not conform to the length increments shown in the specifications for the particular fastener, the next longer length should be used. See Figure A6.

TABLE A1—RECOMMENDED CINCH ALLOWANCES FOR TUBULAR AND SPLIT RIVETS AND EYELETS

Nominal Size	Clinch Allowances Semitubular Rivets(1)	Clinch Allowances Full Tubular Rivets(2)	Clinch Allowances Split Rivets	Clinch Allowances Eyelets(1)
1/16	0.034	—	—	0.043
5/64	0.041			
3/32	0.048	—	0.078	0.048
7/64	0.059	—	—	—
1/8	0.074	—	0.094	0.048
9/64	0.088	0.125	0.0125	—
5/32	—	—	—	0.053
3/16	0.122	0.188	0.141	0.053
7/32	0.141	—	—	0.058
1/4	0.162	—	—	0.058
5/16	0.202	—	—	—

1. For rolled cinch.
2. For star or corrugated clinch, where roll clinch is desired, use semitubular values.

A.5 Design Considerations—After the design of rivet to be used has been determined which includes diameter, type of head, material, and other factors, the designer must then establish other related features of the design of the assembly.

A.5.1 Spacing—Where more than one rivet is indicated, the spacing between rivets must be such that there is sufficient room for the driving tools. Also a minimum pitch of 3 times the rivet diameter should be provided. For thin sheets it is recommended that the pitch be not greater than 24 times the thickness of the sheet. For functional strength consideration the strength afforded by the portion of metal between rivet holes should be determined and compared with the shear and bearing strength of the rivets.

A.5.2 Edge Distance—Failure of the metal between the rivet hole and the edge of the sheet, where solid rivets are used, can be prevented by maintaining an edge distance of 1½ times the hole diameter for hot driven rivets and 2 times the hole diameter for cold driven rivets.

Clinching of tubular rivets exerts little radial force on the sides of the hole compared to the driving of solid rivets. The edge distance, where tubular rivets are used, can, therefore, be less than the values given herein. It can, in most applications, be dictated by the strength of the material and the load to be applied on the riveted joint. The small amount of radial force need be considered only where fastening very brittle materials such as ceramics and some plastics.

A.5.3 Accessibility—When using standard rivets, it is necessary to have both the preformed and driven head ends of the rivet accessible so that both the forming die and the buck may be properly used. Sufficient space should be provided to permit the use of power or manually operated rivet sets and bucks.

A.5.4 Hole Size—Holes should be held as close to the rivet shank diameter as possible and still permit easy and rapid assembly. Possible misalignment of holes must be considered in establishing hole sizes. Holes that are too large may result in buckling of the rivet shank or other detrimental effect when the rivet is being driven. The most suitable hole size for a given application can best be determined by experiment.

A general rule often applied to determine the hole size for solid rivets is to provide a clearance of from 0.003 to 0.008 over the maximum shank diameter of the rivet. The clearance can be increased to 0.015 where necessary for rivets ¼ in. and under and to 0.030 for rivets over ¼ in. in size. These increases, however, often result in poor riveting especially in applications requiring long grip lengths.

A general rule often applied to determine the preformed hole size for tubular rivets is to allow approximately 7% of the maximum shank diameter of the rivet for clearance. Recommended hole size values for these fasteners are given in Table A2. See Figure A6.

A.5.5 Countersinking—Where the rivet heads on one or both sides of a riveted assembly must be flush with the surface, rivets with countersunk heads are used and the hole is countersunk to conform with the size and contour of the heads.

A.5.6 Dimpling—Dimpling involves the deformation of a sheet surface by pressure to form a countersunk recess on the one side and a corresponding projecting cone on the other. In the case of 2 or more sheets to be joined by riveting the dimpling is done on each sheet. When assembled the nesting of the dimples and projecting cones provides a large shear area and the rivet merely serves as a compression anchor to keep the dimples in contact. A relatively thin sheet may also be dimpled to match a countersunk recess in a thick sheet or manufactured part. Dimpling may be produced by a die set or by pressure exerted on the rivet head.

TABLE A2—RECOMMENDED WORK HOLE DIAMETERS FOR TUBULAR AND SPLIT RIVETS AND EYELETS

Nominal Size	Tubular Rivets Hole Dia(1)	Tubular Rivets Drill Size	Split Rivets Hole Dia(1)	Split Rivets Drill Size	Eyelets Hole Dia	Eyelets Drill Size
1/16	0.064	No. 52	—	—	0.063	No. 52
5/64	0.081	No. 46	—	—	—	—
3/32	0.094	3/32	0.093	No. 42	0.093	No. 42
7/64	0.104	No. 37	—	—	—	—
1/8	0.129	No. 30	0.128	No. 30	0.125	1/8
9/64	0.152	No. 24	0.154	No. 23	—	—
5/32	—	—	—	—	0.156	5/32
3/16	0.196	No. 9	0.199	No. 8	0.188	No. 12
7/32	0.228	No. 1	—	—	0.219	7/32
1/4	0.261	G	—	—	0.250	1/4
5/16	0.328	21/64	—	—	—	—

1. Applicable to full tubular and split rivets only where one of the parts to be assembled is prepunched or drilled.

BLIND RIVETS—BREAK MANDREL TYPE—SAE J1200 MAY98 SAE Standard

Report of the Fasteners Committee approved July 1977. Reaffirmed by the SAE Fasteners Committee May 1998. Rationale statement available.

Foreword—This Document has not changed other than to put it into the new SAE Technical Standards Board Format. According to this format, Scope is Section 1, References is Section 2, and Definitions is Section 3. Metric is now the primary unit followed by English units in parentheses.

1. Scope—This SAE Standard establishes the dimensional, mechanical, and performance requirements of inch and metric break mandrel blind rivets suitable for use in joining the component parts of an assembly.

2. References—There are no referenced publications specified herein.

3. Definitions

3.1 Blind Rivet—A blind rivet is a blind fastener which has a self-contained mechanical, chemical, or other feature which permits the formation of an upset on the blind end of the rivet and expansion of the rivet shank during rivet setting to join the component parts of an assembly.

3.2 Break Mandrel Blind Rivet—Break mandrel blind rivets are pull mandrel-type blind rivets, where during the setting operation the mandrel is pulled into or against the rivet body and breaks at or near the junction of the mandrel shank and its upset end.

4. General Specifications

4.1 Designations—These rivets are designated by styles and grades as described below in addition to size, length, and finish.

4.1.1 RIVET STYLES—The two basic styles of break mandrel blind rivets are designated as protruding head and flush head. Protruding head rivets are available in two styles designated as regular head and large head. Flush head rivets are available in the 120 degrees countersunk head.

4.1.2 RIVET GRADES—The material combination of break mandrel blind rivets are designated as grades, with each material combination representing a different combination of rivet body material and mandrel material as given in Table 1.

TABLE 1—GRADES OF BREAK MANDREL BLIND RIVETS

Grade Designation	Rivet Body Material	Mandrel Material
10	Aluminum Alloy 5050	Aluminum Alloy 7178 or 2024
11	Aluminum Alloy 5052	Aluminum Alloy 7178 or 2024
16	Aluminum Alloy 5154	Carbon Steel
18	Aluminum Alloy 5052	Carbon Steel
19	Aluminum Alloy 5056	Carbon Steel
20	Copper alloy No. 110	Carbon Steel
30	Low Carbon Steel	Carbon Steel
40	Nickel-Copper Alloy (Monel)	Carbon Steel
50	Stainless Steel (300 Series)	Carbon Steel
51	Stainless Steel (300 Series)	Stainless Steel (300 Series)

4.2 Dimensions and Tolerances—The design of break mandrel type blind rivets shall be in accordance with the practice of the manufacturer providing the dimensions shown in Section 7 are maintained and rivets meet the mechanical and performance requirements of this standard. Tolerance on dimensions in tables, not designated otherwise, shall be 0.25 mm (±0.010 in).

4.3 Materials—Rivet bodies and mandrels shall be made of the material specified for the grade in Table 1. When the specific material analysis is not given, the analysis shall be selected by the manufacturer and shall be such to assure that rivets meet the mechanical and performance requirements specified under Section 5.

4.4 Finishes—Grade 30 rivet bodies are either zinc or cadmium plated with a minimum plating thickness of 0.004mm (0.00015 in). Rivet bodies of all other grades are furnished plain (bare metal), unless otherwise specified. Because mandrels are discarded following rivet setting, mandrels of all materials may be furnished plain or with a protective coating at the option of the manufacturer, unless otherwise specified.

5. Mechanical and Performance Requirements

5.1 Shear Strength—Rivets, except those described in 5.2.1, shall have ultimate shear loads not less than the minimum ultimate shear loads specified for the applicable size and grade given in Tables 2A and 2B, when tested in accordance with 6.1.

5.2 Tensile Strength—Rivets, except those described in 5.2.1, shall have ultimate tensile loads not less than the minimum ultimate tensile loads specified for the applicable size and grade given in Tables 3A and 3B when tested in accordance with 6.2.

5.2.1 Grade 20 rivet is not subject to either shear or tensile testing. For all other grades, protruding head rivets with specified maximum grip lengths shorter than 1.0 times the nominal rivet diameter, and flush head rivets with specified maximum grip lengths shorter than 1.5 times the nominal rivet diameter shall not be subject to either shear or tensile testing.

5.3 Mandrel Break Load—While the rivet is being set, the axially applied load necessary to break the mandrel shall be within the limits specified for the applicable rivet size and grade in Tables 4A and 4B when tested in accordance with 6.3.

5.4 Mandrel Retention—The mandrel shall be retained within the rivet body such that a force in excess of 8.9N (2lb) is required to reduce the mandrel protrusion to its specified minimum.

TABLE 2A—ULTIMATE SHEAR LOADS OF BREAK MANDREL BLIND RIVETS

Nominal Rivet Size mm	Ultimate Shear Load(1) (Force) Min/N				
	Grades 10, 11, & 18	Grades 16 & 19	Grade 30	Grade 40	Grades 50 & 51
2.4	310	400	580	890	1020
3.2	530	760	1160	1560	1870
4.0	850	1160	1650	2450	2890
4.8	1160	1690	2400	3560	4230
6.3	2050	3110	4450	6230	7560

1. Grade 20 rivet is not subject to shear testing.

TABLE 2B—ULTIMATE SHEAR LOADS OF BREAK MANDREL BLIND RIVETS

Nominal Rivet Size or Basic Shank Dia	Ultimate Shear Load(1) (Force) Min, lb				
	Grades 10, 11, & 18	Grades 16 & 19	Grade 30	Grade 40	Grades 50 & 51
3/32 0.0938	70	90	130	200	230
1/8 0.1250	120	170	260	350	420
5/32 0.1562	190	260	370	550	650
3/16 0.1875	260	380	540	800	950
1/4 0.2500	460	700	1000	1400	1700

1. Grade 20 rivet is not subject to shear testing.

TABLE 3A—ULTIMATE TENSILE LOADS OF BREAK MANDREL BLIND RIVETS

Nominal Rivet Size mm	Ultimate Tensile Load(1) (Force) Min/N				
	Grades 10, 11, & 18	Grades 16 & 19	Grade 30	Grade 40	Grades 50 & 51
2.4	360	530	760	1110	1250
3.2	670	980	1380	2000	2360
4.0	1020	1560	2090	3110	3650
4.8	1420	2220	3020	4450	5340
6.3	2490	4090	5520	8230	9340

1. Grade 20 rivet is not subject to tensile testing.

TABLE 3B—ULTIMATE TENSILE LOADS OF BREAK MANDREL BLIND RIVETS

Nominal Rivet Size or Basic Shank Dia	Ultimate Tensile Load(1) (Force) Min, lb				
	Grades 10, 11, & 18	Grades 16 & 19	Grades 30	Grade 40	Grades 50 & 51
3/32 0.0938	80	120	170	250	280
1/8 0.1250	150	220	310	450	530
5/32 0.1562	230	350	470	700	820
3/16 0.1875	320	500	680	1000	1200
1/4 0.2500	560	920	1240	1850	2100

1. Grade 20 rivet is not subject to tensile testing.

TABLE 4A—MANDREL BREAK LOADS OF BREAK MANDREL BLIND RIVETS

Nominal Rivet Size or Basic Shank Dia mm	Limit	Mandrel Break Load[1] N						
		Grades 10 & 11	Grades 16, 18, & 19	Grade 20	Grade 30	Grade 40	Grade 50	Grade 51
2.4	Min	620	780	780	1160	1330	1330	1330
2.4	Max	1070	1220	1220	1600	2000	2220	2220
3.2	Min	1110	1780	1780	2670	2890	2890	2890
3.2	Max	1780	2670	2670	3560	3780	4230	4230
4.0	Min	1890	2670	2670	3340	4230	5120	5120
4.0	Max	2670	3780	3780	4450	5340	6450	6450
4.8	Min	2780	3340	3340	5120	6450	6230	6230
4.8	Max	3670	4670	4670	6450	7780	8450	8450
6.3	Min	4890	6450	6450	8670	11 100	13 300	13 300
6.3	Max	6230	8230	8230	10 500	12 900	16 000	16 000

1. Mandrel break load is defined as the load in Newtons necessary to break the mandrel when setting break mandrel types of pull mandrel blind rivets.

TABLE 4B—MANDREL BREAK LOADS OF BREAK MANDREL BLIND RIVETS

Nominal Rivet Size or Basic Shank Dia	Limit	Mandrel Break Load[1] lb						
		Grades 10 & 11	Grades 16, 18, & 19	Grade 20	Grade 30	Grade 40	Grade 50	Grade 51
3/32 0.0938	Min	140	175	175	260	300	300	300
3/32 0.0938	Max	240	275	275	360	450	500	500
1/8 0.1250	Min	250	400	400	600	650	650	650
1/8 0.1250	Max	400	600	600	800	850	950	950
5/32 0.1562	Min	425	600	600	750	950	1150	1150
5/32 0.1562	Max	600	850	850	1000	1200	1450	1450
3/16 0.1875	Min	625	750	750	1150	1450	1400	1400
3/16 0.1875	Max	825	1050	1050	1450	1750	1900	1900
1/4 0.2500	Min	1100	1450	1450	1950	2500	3000	3000
1/4 0.2500	Max	1400	1850	1850	2350	2900	3600	3600

1. Mandrel break load is defined as the load in pounds necessary to break the mandrel when setting break mandrel types of pull mandrel blind rivets.

5.5 Blind Head Formation— The axially applied load necessary to upset the end of the rivet body, that is, form the blind side head, shall not exceed 80% of the actual mandrel break load, when tested in accordance with 6.3.

6. Test Methods

6.1 Shear Test—The test shall be comprised of loading a single lap joint assembled with one rivet so that the direction of applied load induces transverse shear against the rivet body. The test specimen shall be mounted in a tensile testing machine capable of applying load at a controllable rate. The grips shall be self-aligning and care shall be taken when mounting the specimen to assure that the load will be transmitted in a straight line through the test rivet.

The specimen shall be loaded at a speed of testing as determined with a free running cross head not less than 7.6 mm (0.3 in) nor greater than 13.0 mm (0.5 in)/min. Loading shall be continued until failure of the rivet occurs.

The maximum load in pounds or Newtons applied to the specimen coincident with or prior to rivet failure shall be recorded as the ultimate shear strength of the rivet.

The test specimen shall be comprised of two plates, of equal nominal thickness, axially aligned and assembled into a single lap joint with the test rivet, as shown in Figure 1 and Tables 5A and 5B. The design of test plates may be modified to include holes for shear testing two or more rivets using the same plates. Such holes shall be located on the longitudinal centerline of the plate, and center distances between adjacent holes shall be at least 4 times the diameter of the larger test hole. Ends of plates may be drilled for pin-type mounting in testing machine. Plates shall be alloy steel, quenched and tempered to a hardness of Rockwell C46-50.

The test rivet shall be set with a setting tool standard for that type of rivet and in accordance with the setting procedures recommended by the rivet manufacturer.

TABLE 5A—DIMENSIONS OF TEST PLATES, mm (FIGURES 1, 2, AND 3)

Nominal Rivet Size or Basic Shank Dia	G Shear and Tensile Test Plate Hole		G_1 Break Mandrel Test Restraining Plate Hole Dia	S End to Center Length	T Shear and Tensile Test Plate Thickness Protruding Head Styles	T_2 Shear and Tensile Test Plate Thickness Flush Head Styles
	Max	Min	Basic (1)	Min(2)	Min(3)	Min(4)
2.4	2.54	2.49	1.70	9.6	1.2	1.8
3.2	3.35	3.30	2.18	12.8	1.6	2.4
4.0	4.16	4.11	2.66	16.0	2.0	3.0
4.8	4.98	4.93	3.15	19.2	2.4	3.6
6.3	6.60	6.55	4.09	25.2	3.2	4.7

1. Values shown are equal to nominal mandrel diameter plus 0.25 mm.
2. Values shown are equal to 4 times basic shank diameter of rivet.
3. Minimum values shown are equal to 0.50 times basic shank diameter of rivet. Maximum thickness shall not exceed 0.50 times maximum grip length specified for applicable rivet in Table 8A.
4. Minimum values shown are equal to 0.75 times basic shank diameter of rivet. Maximum thickness shall not exceed 0.50 times maximum grip length specified for applicable rivet in Table 8A.
5. The protusion diameter of the mandrel (W diameter), including the point burr, shall be less than basic G1 plate hole diameter.

TABLE 5B—DIMENSIONS OF TEST PLATES, in (SEE FIGURES 1, 2, AND 3)

Nominal Rivet Size or Basic Shank Dia	G Shear and Tensile Test Plate Hole Dia		G_1 Break Mandrel Test Restraining Plate Hole Dia	S End to Center Length	T Shear and Tensile Test Plate Thickness Protruding Head Styles	T_1 Shear and Tensile Test Plate Thickness Flush Head Styles
	Max	Min	Basic(1)	Min(2)	Min(3)	Min(4)
3/32 0.0938	0.100	0.098	0.067	0.375	0.047	0.056
1/8 0.1250	0.132	0.130	0.086	0.500	0.062	0.093
5/32 0.1562	0.164	0.162	0.105	0.625	0.078	0.117
3/16 0.1875	0.196	0.194	0.125	0.750	0.094	0.141
1/4 0.2500	0.260	0.258	0.161	1.000	0.125	0.188

1. Values shown are equal to nominal mandrel diameter plus 0.010 in.
2. Values shown are equal to 4 times basic shank diameter of rivet.
3. Minimum values shown are equal to 0.50 times basic shank diameter of rivet. Maximum thickness shall not exceed 0.50 times maximum grip length specified for applicable rivet in Table 8B.
4. Minimum values shown are equal to 0.75 basic shank diameter of rivet. Maximum thickness shall not exceed 0.50 times maximum grip length specified for applicable rivet in Table 8B.
5. The protusion diameter of the mandrel (W diameter), including the point burr, shall be less than basic G1 plate hole diameter.

6.2 Tensile Test—The test shall be comprised of separating two plates of a joint assembled with one blind rivet. the test rivet shall be installed in a test fixture, as depicted in Figure 2 and Tables 5A and 5B, or another comparable arrangement if an alternate test fixture is used, and the fixture placed between the compression heads of a testing machine. For referee purposes the test fixture shown in Figure 2 shall be used. Care shall be exercised to locate the fixture at the center of the piston when hydraulic testing machines are used. Load shall be applied to the joint at a speed of testing, as determined with a free running cross head, not less than 7.6 mm (0.3 in) nor greater than 13.0 mm (0.5 in)/min. Loading shall be continued to failure with failure occurring when the rivet body fractures or is pulled through one of the plates. The maximum load in pounds (Newtons) applied to the joint coincident with or prior to rivet failure shall be recorded as the ultimate strength of the rivet.

The test specimen shall be comprised of two plates of equal nominal thickness, aligned and assembled into a joint with the test rivet. The plates shall be of alloy steel, quenched, and tempered to a hardness of Rockwell C46-50.

The test rivet shall be set with a setting tool which is standard for that type of rivet and in accordance with the setting procedures recommended by the rivet manufacturer.

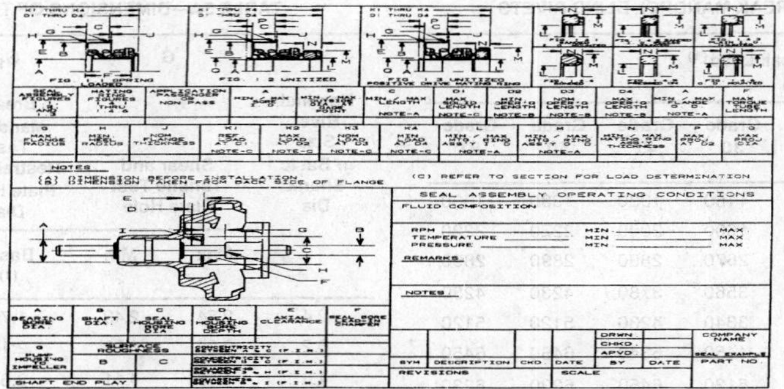

FIGURE 1—TEST SPECIMENS FOR SHEAR TESTING BREAK MANDREL BLIND RIVETS

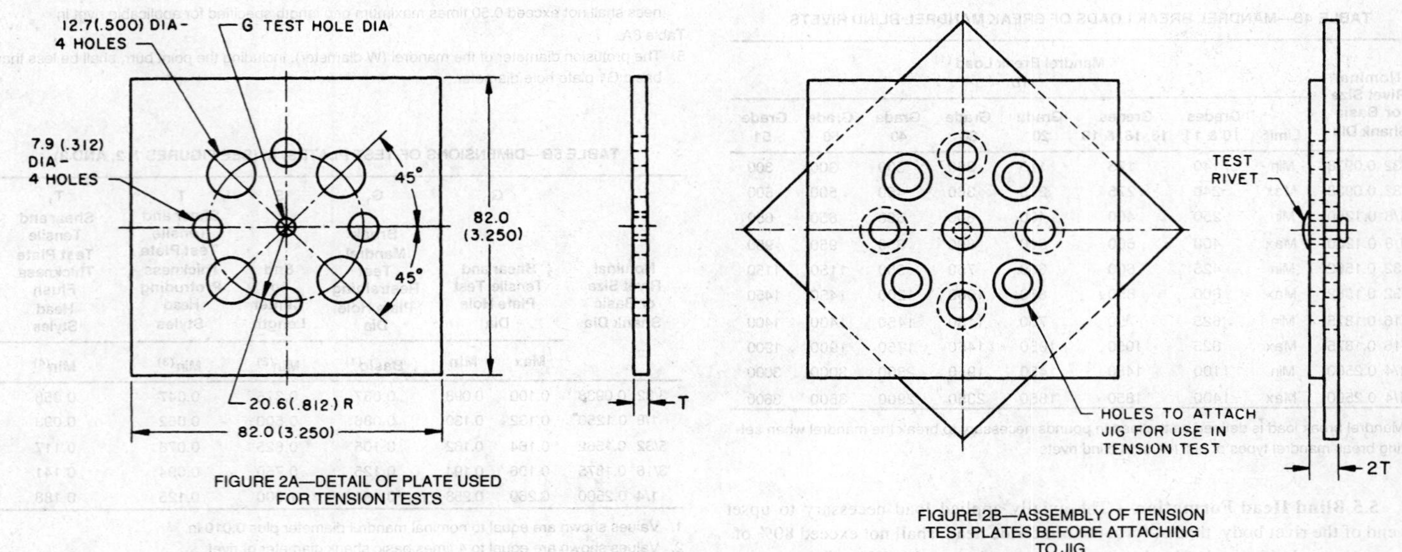

FIGURE 2A—DETAIL OF PLATE USED FOR TENSION TESTS

FIGURE 2B—ASSEMBLY OF TENSION TEST PLATES BEFORE ATTACHING TO JIG

FIGURE 2—TEST FIXTURES FOR TENSILE TESTING BREAK MANDREL BLIND RIVETS

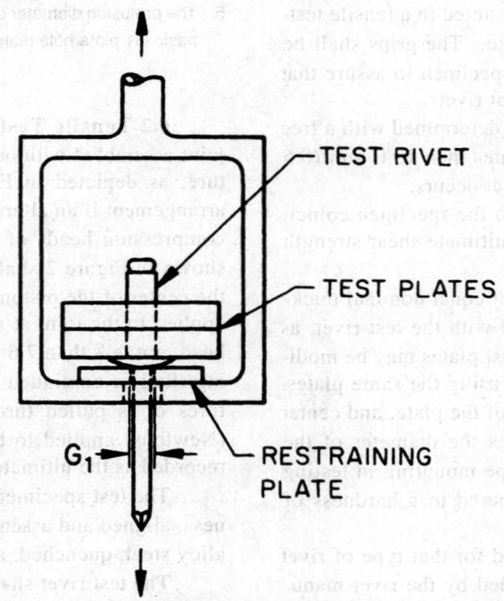

FIGURE 3—TEST FIXTURE FOR TESTING MANDREL BREAK LOADS AND BLIND HEAD FORMATION

6.3 Mandrel Break Load and Blind Head Formation Test—The test rivet shall be installed in a test plate(s), and the assembly mounted in the fixture of a tensile testing machine. A suggested test fixture is illustrated in Figure 3. Load shall be applied axially to the mandrel. The load at which it is visually observed that the rivet body end is upset or otherwise deformed to form a head on the blind side, shall be recorded as the blind head formation load. (Note: The blind head formation load is a load applied to the mandrel sufficient to pull the mandrel head into the rivet body and initiate an expansion of the length of rivet body projecting beyond the blind side surface of the joined parts. When the formation of the blind side upset occurs there will normally be a period of tensile machine cross head travel with little or no increase in applied load.) Loading shall be continued until the mandrel breaks, and the maximum load occurring coincident with or prior to failure shall be recorded as the mandrel break load.

The test plate(s) may be of any material capable of supporting the test load without permanent deformation. Thickness of test plate(s) shall be as close as practical to the maximum of the grip range of the test rivet as specified in Tables 8A and 8B. The hole in the test plate(s) shall conform to the recommended hole size given for the rivet size in Tables 8A and 8B.

The restraining plate shall be alloy steel, quenched, and tempered to a hardness of Rockwell C42-46. The hole in the plate shall conform to G diameter as specified in Tables 5A and 5B.

7. *Inspection*—Break mandrel blind rivets shall be inspected to determine conformance with dimensional, mechanical, and performance requirements. Inspection procedures shall be as specified by the purchaser on the purchase order or engineering drawings.

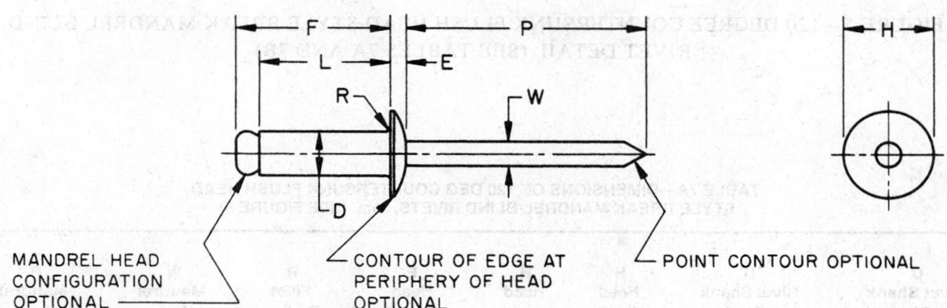

FIGURE 4—REGULAR AND LARGE PROTRUDING HEAD STYLE MANDREL BLIND RIVET DETAIL (SEE TABLES 6A AND 6B)

TABLE 6A—DIMENSIONS OF REGULAR AND LARGE PROTRUDING HEAD STYLE BREAK MANDREL BLIND RIVETS, mm (SEE FIGURE 4)

Nominal Rivet Size or Basic Shank Dia	D Rivet Shank Dia Max	D Rivet Shank Dia Min	H Style 1– Regular Head Head Dia Max	H Style 1– Regular Head Head Dia Min	E Style 1– Regular Head Head Height Max	H Style 2– Large Head Head Dia Max	H Style 2– Large Head Head Dia Min	E Style 2– Large Head Head Height Max	R Fillet Radius(1) Max	W Mandrel Dia Nom	P Mandrel Protrusion Min	F Blind Side Protrusion(2) Max
2.4	2.44	2.29	5.03	4.52	0.81	7.44	6.83	1.02	0.4	1.45	25.0	L + 2.5
3.2	3.25	3.10	6.65	6.05	1.02	9.91	9.14	1.65	0.5	1.93	25.0	L + 3.0
4.0	4.04	3.89	8.33	7.52	1.27	12.40	11.38	1.90	0.5	2.41	27.0	L + 3.5
4.8	4.85	4.65	10.01	9.04	1.52	16.51	15.24	2.34	0.7	2.90	27.0	L + 4.0
6.3	6.48	6.25	13.33	12.07	2.03	19.81	18.29	2.72	0.8	3.84	31.0	L + 4.5

1. The junction of head and shank shall have a fillet with a max radius as shown. For Grade 40, 50, and 51 rivets, the max fillet radius for 4.8 mm rivets shall be 0.9 mm and for 6.3 mm rivets shall be 1.5 mm.
2. When computing the blind side protrusion (F), the max length of rivet (L) as given in Table 8A for the applicable grip shall be used. Minimum blind side clearance may be calculated by subtracting the actual grip (G), (that is, total thickness of the material to be joined), from the specified blind side protrusion (F). (Example: To join two plates, each 2.5 mm thick, with a 4.0 mm rivet, a 10.8 mm length rivet would be used. Minimum blind side clearance necessary to permit proper rivet setting would be L + 3.5 mm - G, which is 10.8 mm + 3.5 mm – 5.0 mm, and equals 9.3 mm).

For application data see Table 8A.
Additional requirements given in General Specifications shall apply.

TABLE 6B—DIMENSIONS OF REGULAR AND LARGE PROTRUDING HEAD STYLE BREAK MANDREL BLIND RIVETS, in (SEE TABLE 4)

Nominal Rivet Size(1) or Basic Shank Dia	D Rivet Shank Dia Max	D Rivet Shank Dia Min	H Style 1– Regular Head Head Dia Max	H Style 1– Regular Head Head Dia Min	E Style 1– Regular Head Head Height Max	H Style 2– Large Head Head Dia Max	H Style 2– Large Head Head Dia Min	E Style 2– Large Head Head Height Max	R Fillet Radius(2) Max	W Mandrel Dia Nom	P Mandrel Protrusion Min	F Blind Side Protrusion(3) Max
3/32 0.0938	0.096	0.090	0.198	0.178	0.032	0.293	0.269	0.040	0.015	0.057	1.00	L + 0.100
1/8 0.1250	0.128	0.122	0.262	0.238	0.040	0.390	0.360	0.065	0.020	0.076	1.00	L + 0.120
5/32 0.1562	0.159	0.153	0.328	0.296	0.050	0.488	0.448	0.075	0.020	0.095	1.06	L + 0.140
3/16 0.1875	0.191	0.183	0.394	0.356	0.060	0.650	0.600	0.092	0.025	0.114	1.06	L + 0.160
1/4 0.2500	0.255	0.246	0.525	0.475	0.080	0.780	0.720	0.107	0.030	0.151	1.25	L + 0.180

1. Where specifying nominal size in decimals, zeros preceding decimal and in fourth decimal place shall be omitted.
2. The junction of head and shank shall have a fillet with a max radius as shown. For Grade 40, 50, and 51 rivets, the max fillet radius for 3/16 in rivets shall be 0.035 in and for 1/4 in rivets shall be 0.060 in.
3. When computing the blind side protrusion (F), the max length of rivet (L), as given in Table 8B for the applicable grip shall be used. Minimum blind side clearance may be calculated by subtracting the actual grip (G), (that is, total thickness of the material to be joined), from the specified blind side protrusion(F). (Example: To join two plates, each 0.100 in thick, with a 5/32 in rivet, a 0.425 length rivet would be used. Minimum blind side clearance necessary to permit proper rivet setting would be L + 0.140 in - G, which is 0.425 in + 0.140 in – 0.200 in, and equals 0.365 in).

For application data see Table 8B.
Additional requirements given in General Specifications shall apply.

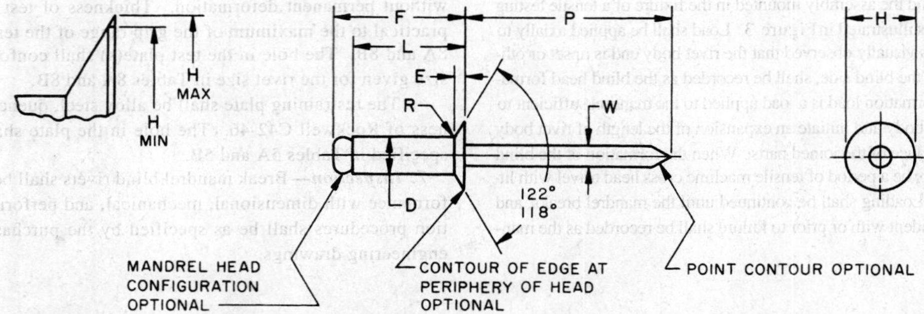

FIGURE 5—120 DEGREE COUNTERSUNK FLUSH HEAD STYLE BREAK MANDREL BLIND RIVET DETAIL (SEE TABLES 7A AND 7B)

TABLE 7A—DIMENSIONS OF 120 DEG COUNTERSUNK FLUSH HEAD STYLE BREAK MANDREL BLIND RIVETS, mm (SEE FIGURE 5)

Nominal Rivet Size or Basic Shank Dia	D Rivet Shank Dia Max	D Rivet Shank Dia Min	H Head Dia(1) Max	H Head Dia(1) Min	E Head Height(2) Ref	R Fillet Radius Max	W Mandrel Dia Nom	P Mandrel Protrusion Min	F Blind Side Protrusion(3) Max
2.4	2.44	2.29	4.75	4.09	0.69	0.5	1.45	25.0	L + 2.5
3.2	3.25	3.10	5.92	5.26	0.79	0.7	1.93	25.0	L + 3.0
4.0	4.04	3.89	7.47	6.81	1.02	0.8	2.41	27.0	L + 3.5
4.8	4.85	4.65	9.17	8.51	1.27	0.9	2.90	27.0	L + 4.0

1. Max head diameter is calculated on nominal rivet diameter and nominal head angle extended to sharp corner. Min head diameter is absolute.
2. Head height is given for reference purposes only. Variations in this dimension are controlled by the diameters (H) and (D) and the included angle of the head.
3. When computing the blind side protrusion (F), the max length of rivet (L), as given in Table 8A for the applicable grip shall be used. Minimum blind side clearance may be calculated by subtracting the actual grip (G), (that is, total thickness of the material to be joined), from the specified blind side protrusion (F). (Example: To join two plates, each 4.7 mm thick, with a 4.8 mm rivet, a 14.6mm length rivet would be used. Minimum blind side clearance necessary to permit proper rivet setting would be L + 4.0 mm – G, which is 14.6 mm + 4.0 mm – 9.4 mm which equals 9.2 mm).

For application data see Table 8A.
Additional requirements given in General Specifications shall apply.

TABLE 7B—DIMENSIONS OF 120 DEG COUNTERSUNK FLUSH HEAD STYLE BREAK MANDREL BLIND RIVETS, in (SEE FIGURE 5)

Nominal Rivet Size(1) or Basic Shank Dia	D Rivet Shank Dia Max	D Rivet Shank Dia Min	H Head Dia(2) Max	H Head Dia(2) Min	E Head Height(3) Ref	R Fillet Radius Max	W Mandrel Dia Nom	P Mandrel Protrusion Min	F Blind Side Protrusion(4) Max
3/32 0.0938	0.096	0.090	0.187	0.161	0.027	0.020	0.057	1.00	L + 0.100
1/8 0.1250	0.128	0.122	0.233	0.207	0.031	0.025	0.076	1.00	L + 0.120
5/32 0.1562	0.159	0.153	0.294	0.268	0.040	0.030	0.095	1.06	L + 0.140
3/16 0.1875	0.191	0.183	0.361	0.335	0.050	0.035	0.114	1.06	L + 0.160

1. Where specifying nominal size in decimals, zeros preceding decimal and in fourth decimal place shall be omitted.
2. Max head diameter is calculated on nominal rivet diameter and nominal head angle extended to sharp corner. Min head diameter is absolute.
3. Head height is given for reference purposes only. Variations in this dimension are controlled by the diameters (H) and (D) and the included angle of the head.
4. When computing the blind side protrusion (F), the max length of rivet (L), as given in Table 8B for the applicable grip shall be used. Minimum blind side clearance may be calculated by subtracting the actual grip (G), (such as, total thickness of the material to be joined), from the specified blind side protrusion (F). (Example: To join two plates, each 0.187 in thick, with a 3/16 in rivet, a 0.575 length rivet would be used. Minimum blind side clearance necessary to permit proper rivet setting would be L + 0.160 in – G, which is 0.575 in + 0.160 in – 0.374 in which equals 0.361 in).

For application data see Table 8B.
Additional requirements given in General Specifications shall apply.

TABLE 8A—APPLICATION DATA FOR PROTRUDING HEAD AND FLUSH HEAD STYLE BREAK MANDREL BLIND RIVETS,mm

Nominal Rivet Size or Basic Shank Dia	Recommended Hole Size Drill Size[(1)]	Recommended Hole Size Hole Dia Max	Recommended Hole Size Hole Dia Min	Grip Range For Protruding Style Heads	Grip Range for Flush Style Heads	L Rivet Length[(2)] Max
2.4	2.5	2.54	2.46	0.5–3.2	2.0–3.2	6.4
				Over 3.2–6.4	Over 3.2–6.4	9.5
				Over 6.4–9.5	—	12.7
3.2	3.3	3.38	3.28	0.5–1.6	—	5.4
				Over 1.6–3.2	2.3–3.2	7.0
				Over 3.2–4.8	Over 3.2–4.8	8.6
				Over 4.8–6.4	Over 4.8–6.4	10.2
				Over 6.4–7.9	Over 6.4–7.9	11.7
				Over 7.9–9.5	Over 7.9–9.5	13.4
				Over 9.5–12.7	Over 9.5–12.7	16.5
				Over 12.7–15.9	—	19.7
4.0	4.1	4.16	4.06	0.5–3.2	—	7.6
				Over 3.2–4.8	3.0–4.8	9.2
				Over 4.8–6.4	Over 4.8–6.4	10.8
				Over 6.4–9.5	Over 6.4–9.5	14.0
				Over 9.5–12.7	Over 9.5–12.7	17.2
				Over 12.7–15.9	—	20.3
4.8	4.9	4.98	4.88	0.5–3.2	—	8.3
				Over 3.2–4.8	3.8–4.8	9.8
				Over 4.8–6.4	Over 4.8–6.4	11.5
				Over 6.4–9.5	Over 6.4–9.5	14.6
				Over 9.5–12.7	Over 9.5–12.7	17.8
				Over 12.7–15.9	Over 12.7–15.9	21.0
				Over 15.9–19.1	—	24.2
				Over 19.1–22.2	—	27.3
				Over 22.2–25.4	—	30.5
				Over 25.4–28.6	—	33.7
6.3	6.5	6.63	6.53	0.5–3.2	—	9.5
				Over 3.2–6.4	—	12.7
				Over 6.4–9.5	—	15.9
				Over 9.5–12.7	—	19.1
				Over 12.7–15.9	—	22.2
				Over 15.9–19.1	—	25.4
				Over 19.1–22.2	—	28.6
				Over 22.2–25.4	—	31.8
				Over 25.4–28.6	—	34.9
				Over 28.6–31.8	—	38.1

1. Recommended drill sizes are those which normally produce holes within the specified hole size limits.
2. Where blind side clearances permit and it is economically feasible, rivets of the next longer length than those recommended for a given grip may be substituted to limit the number of different inventory items.

TABLE 8B—APPLICATION DATA FOR PROTRUDING HEAD AND FLUSH HEAD STYLE BREAK MANDREL BLIND RIVETS, in

Nominal Rivet Size or Basic Shank Dia	Recommended Hole Size Drill Size[(1)]	Recommended Hole Size Hole Dia Max	Recommended Hole Size Hole Dia Min	Grip Range For Protruding Style Heads	Grip Range for Flush Style Heads	L Rivet Length[(2)] Max
3/32 0.0938	No. 41	0.100	0.097	0.020–0.125	0.079–0.125	0.250
				0.126–0.250	0.126–0.250	0.375
				0.251–0.375	—	0.500
1/8 0.1250	No. 30	0.133	0.129	0.020–0.062	—	0.212
				0.063–0.125	0.092–0.125	0.275
				0.126–0.187	0.126–0.187	0.37
				0.188–0.250	0.188–0.250	0.400
				0.251–0.312	0.251–0.312	0.462
				0.313–0.375	0.313–0.375	0.525
				0.376–0.500	0.376–0.500	0.650
				0.501–0.625	—	0.775
5/32 0.1562	No. 20	0.164	0.160	0.020–0.125	—	0.300
				0.126–0.187	0.120–0.187	0.362
				0.188–0.250	0.188–0.250	0.425
				0.251–0.375	0.251–0.375	0.550
				0.376–0.500	0.376–0.500	0.675
				0.501–0.625	—	0.800
3/16 0.1875	No. 11	0.196	0.192	0.020–0.125	—	0.325
				0.126–0.187	0.151–0.187	0.387
				0.188–0.250	0.188–0.250	0.450
				0.251–0.375	0.251–0.375	0.575
				0.376–0.500	0.376–0.500	0.700
				0.501–0.625	0.501–0.625	0.825
				0.626–0.750	—	0.950
				0.751–0.875	—	1.075
				0.876–1.000	—	1.200
				1.001–1.125	—	1.325
1/4 0.2500	F	0.261	0.257	0.020–0.125	—	0.375
				0.126–0.250	—	0.500
				0.251–0.375	—	0.625
				0.376–0.500	—	0.750
				0.501–0.625	—	0.875
				0.626–0.750	—	1.000
				0.751–0.875	—	1.125
				0.876–1.000	—	1.250
				1.001–1.125	—	1.375
				1.126–1.250	—	1.500

1. Recommended drill sizes are those which normally produce holes within the specified hole size limits.
2. Where blind side clearances permit and it is economically feasible, rivets of the next longer length than those recommended for a given grip may be substituted to limit the number of different inventory items.

5 Spring Wire and Springs

STAINLESS STEEL 17-7 PH SPRING WIRE AND SPRINGS—SAE J217 JUL94

SAE Recommended Practice

Report of the SAE Iron and Steel Technical Committee approved November 1970 and reaffirmed December 1988. Completely revised by the SAE Iron and Steel Technical Committee Division 17—Spring Wire, July 1994.

Foreword—This Document has not changed other than to put it into the new SAE Technical Standards Board Format.

1. Scope—This SAE Recommended Practice covers a high-quality corrosion-resisting steel wire, cold drawn, formed, and heat treated to produce uniform mechanical properties. It is magnetic in all conditions. It is intended for the manufacture of springs and wire forms that are to be heat treated after forming to enhance the spring properties. This document also covers processing requirements of the springs and forms fabricated from this wire.

2. References

2.1 Applicable Publications—The following publications form a part of this specification to the extent specified herein.

2.1.1 ASTM PUBLICATIONS—Available from ASTM, 1916 Race Street, Philadelphia, PA 19103-1187.

ASTM A 313—Specification for Chromium Nickel Stainless and Heat-Resisting Steel Spring Wire
ASTM A 555—Special-Quality Ball and Roller Bearing Steel
ASTM A 555M—Special-Quality Ball and Roller Bearing Steel, Metric

3. Wire

3.1 The wire shall conform to ASTM A 313 Type 631 Condition CH 900 and ASTM A 555/A 555M.

3.2 Cleaning—Prior to heat treating, the samples will be cleaned to remove all drawing lubricants and metallic or nonmetallic coating by immersing the wire sample in 15 to 25% nitric acid at room temperature for 5 min followed by a thorough water wash.

3.3 Surface Condition—The surface of wire specimens shall be prepared in accordance with 4.3. The prepared specimens shall have a surface free from injurious imperfections, such as seams, pits, die scratches, and other defects which will impair the serviceability of the part.

4. Springs

4.1 Surface Condition—The surface conditions on the springs shall be as described for the wire, except certain instances where shot peening might be used. In addition, there shall be no excessive coiling marks, nicks, or gouges which would impair the serviceability of the part. When springs are shot peened, the surface appearance will be altered. Because of a resulting decrease in the spring resistance to relaxation, shot peening is permitted only when agreed upon by the purchaser. After shot peening, the springs shall be stress relieved at 230 to 260 °C (450 to 500 °F) for a minimum of 30 min at heat.

4.2 Forming—All forming shall be done on the wire in the as-drawn condition.

4.3 Cleaning and Passivation—Springs made from this wire must be cleaned and passivated after coiling to insure maximum corrosion resistance of the stainless steel. All metallic coatings must be removed prior to heat treatment. One procedure is as follows:

a. Remove drawing compounds from the wire surface by a 5 min dip in alkaline cleaner at approximately 90 °C (190 °F), followed by a water rinse.
b. Remove metallic and most nonmetallic coatings from the wire surface and passivate the surface by immersing parts in a nitric acid solution of 15 to 25% at 60 to 70 °C (140 to 160 °F) for 5 min or until clean. Follow with a water rinse.

4.4 After Passivating—Springs and forms made from this wire must be heated at 477 to 488 °C (890 to 900 °F) for 1 h and air cooled. No forming should be done to the wire or parts after heat treating.

STAINLESS STEEL, SAE 30302, SPRING WIRE AND SPRINGS—SAE J230 JUN94

SAE Recommended Practice

Report of the SAE Iron and Steel Technical Committee approved February 1971 and reaffirmed December 1988. Completely revised by the SAE Iron and Steel Technical Committee Division 17—Spring Wire, June 1994.

Foreword—This Document has not changed other than to put it into the new SAE Technical Standards Board Format.

*1. **Scope***—This SAE Recommended Practice covers a high-strength corrosion-resisting steel wire, uniform in mechanical properties, intended for the manufacture of springs and wire forms. It also covers processing requirements of springs and forms fabricated from this wire.

*2. **References***

2.1 Applicable Publications—The following publications form a part of the specification to the extent specified herein.

2.1.1 ASTM PUBLICATIONS—Available from ASTM, 100 Barr Harbor Drive, West Conshohocken, PA 19428-2959.

ASTM A 313—Specification for Chromium-Nickel Stainless and Heat-Resisting Steel Spring Wire

ASTM A 555—Specification for General Requirements for Stainless and Heat-Resisting Steel Wire and Wire Rods

ASTM A 555M—Specification for General Requirements for Stainless and Heat-Resisting Steel Wire and Wire Rods (Metric)

*3. **Wire***

3.1 The wire shall conform to ASTM A 313 Type 302 Class 1 and ASTM A 555/A 555M.

3.2 Welds—Each unit shall be a continuous length with welds being permitted before final drawing. Welds are not permitted at finished size except by negotiation between manufacturer and user.

3.3 Surface Condition—Surface of the wire shall be free from injurious imperfections, such as seams, pits, die scratches, and other defects which will impair the serviceability of the part. (Visually examine at 10X magnification.)

*4. **Springs***

4.1 Surface Condition—The surface condition of the finished parts shall be as described for the wire, except in certain instances where shot peening might be used. In addition, there shall be no excessive coiling marks, nicks, or gouges which would impair the serviceability of the part. When the springs are shot peened, the surface appearance will be altered. Because of a resulting decrease in the spring resistance to relaxation, shot peening is permitted only when agreed upon by the purchaser. After shot peening, the springs shall be stress relieved at 230 to 260 °C (450 to 500 °F) for a minimum of 30 min at heat.

4.2 Lead Removal—Lead coatings shall be removed from springs prior to stress relieving when a temperature of 290 °C (550 °F) or above is required.

4.3 Cleaning and Passivation—Springs made from this wire must be cleaned and passivated after coiling to insure maximum corrosion resistance of the stainless steel. All metallic coatings must be removed prior to heat treatment. One procedure is as follows:

a. Remove drawing compounds from the wire surface by a 5 min dip in alkaline cleaner at approximately 90 °C (190 °F) followed by a water rinse.

b. Remove metallic and most nonmetallic coatings from the wire surface and passivate the surface by immersing parts in a nitric acid solution of 15 to 25% at 60 to 70 °C (140 to 160 °F) for 5 min or until clean. Follow with a water rinse.

4.4 Heat Treatment—Springs made from this wire are normally stress relieved for a minimum of 30 min. Typical temperatures are 290 to 320 °C (550 to 600 °F). It should be recognized that other than typical stress relieving temperatures may be used or omitted completely, depending upon the spring design and application.

6 Ferrous Castings

AUTOMOTIVE GRAY IRON CASTINGS—SAE J431 DEC2000 SAE Standard

Report of the SAE Iron and Steel Division approved January 1935. Completely revised by the SAE Iron and Steel Technical Committee August 1979. Completely revised by the SAE Iron and Steel Executive Committee March 1993, and revised August 1996. Completely revised by the SAE Iron and Steel Technical Committee Division 9—Automotive Iron and Steel Castings of the SAE Iron and Steel Executive Committee December 2000. Rationale statement available.

1. Scope—This SAE Standard covers the hardness, tensile strength, and microstructure and special requirements of gray iron sand molded castings used in the automotive and allied industries. Specific requirements are provided for hardness of castings. Test bar tensile strength/Brinell hardness (t/h) ratio requirements are provided to establish a consistent tensile strength-hardness relationship for each grade to facilitate prediction and control of tensile strength in castings. Provision is made for specification of special additional requirements of gray iron automotive castings where needed for particular applications and service conditions.

NOTE—This document was revised in 1993 to provide grade specific t/h control. In 1999 the document was revised to make SI metric units primary. To better align the grading system with long established production methods and grades produced, the previous system of grading by fixed combinations of tensile strength and hardness was changed in 1999 to a system of grading by variable combinations of test bar t/h ratio and casting hardness grades. The number of hardness grades was increased relative to the number of previously available ranges to facilitate centering of casting mean hardness in the specification range so that dependence of cost optimization on controlling near the low or high sides of specification ranges is minimized.

2. References

2.1 Applicable Publications—The following publications form a part of this specification to the extent specified herein. Unless otherwise indicated, the latest issue of SAE publications shall apply.

2.1.1 SAE PUBLICATION—Available from SAE, 400 Commonwealth Drive, Warrendale, PA 15096-0001.

SAE J417—Hardness Tests and Hardness Number Conversions

2.1.2 ASTM PUBLICATIONS—Available from ASTM, 100 Barr Harbor Drive, West Conshohocken, PA 19428-2959.

ASTM A 48—Specification for Gray Iron Castings

ASTM A 247—Recommended Practice for Evaluating the Microstructure of Graphite in Iron Castings

ASTM A 438—Transverse Testing of Gray Cast Iron

ASTM E 10—Test for Brinell Hardness of Metallic Materials

ASTM E 562—Determining Volume Fraction by Systematic Manual Point Count

2.2 Related Publications—The following publications are provided for information purposes only and are not a required part of this document. Additional information concerning gray iron castings, their properties, and use can be obtained from:

1. Metals Handbook, Vol. 1, 10th Edition, ASM International, Materials Park, OH
2. Cast Metals Handbook, American Foundrymen's Society, Des Plaines, IL
3. 1981 Iron Castings Handbook, Iron Castings Society, Inc., Cleveland, OH
4. H.D. Angus, "Physical and Engineering Properties of Cast Iron," British Cast Iron Research Association, Birmingham, England, 2nd Edition, 1976
5. "Gray, Ductile, and Malleable Iron Castings Current Capabilities," STP-455, American Society for Testing and Materials, 100 Barr Harbor Drive, West Conshohocken, PA 19428-2959
6. G.N.J. Gilbert, "Engineering Data on Grey Cast Iron," BCIRA (1977), Alvechurch, Birmingham, England
7. "Tables for Normal Tolerance Limits, Sampling Plans and Screening," R.E. Odeh and D.B. Owen, Marcel Dekker, Inc., New York and Basel, 1980
8. "Fatigue Properties of Gray Cast Iron," L.E. Tucker and D.R. Olberts, SAE Paper 690471

3. Grade definition and Designation.

3.1 Iron Grade—Gray iron grades, defined by their minimum test bar t/h ratio, are designated by the letter G followed by a number equaling the defining minimum test bar t/h ratio multiplied by 100. The units used for this purpose are MPa for both tensile strength and hardness. The t/h ratio is dimensionless.

EXAMPLE—G10 designates a gray iron having minimum test bar t/h = 0.100.

3.2 Hardness Grade—Hardness grades, defined by minimum hardness exhibited in castings, are designated by the letter H followed by a number equaling the minimum casting hardness divided by 100. The casting hardness unit used for this purpose is the MPa.

EXAMPLE—H18 designates minimum casting hardness of 1800 MPa.

3.3 Casting Grade—SAE gray iron casting grades are defined and designated by combining the iron grade and the hardness grade designations.

EXAMPLE—G10H18 designates iron in castings with minimum test bar t/h of 0.100 MPa/MPa and minimum casting hardness of 1800 MPa.

3.4 Special Requirements—Special requirements, defined for special applications, are designated by a lowercase suffix letter placed at the end of the casting grade designation.

EXAMPLE—11H20b designates iron meeting special requirements of special service brakedrums.

3.5 Equivalency and Conversion—Equivalency information for engineering purposes, between this and other standards, is provided in A.4.1, A.4.6, and A.4.7. Grades of this document can have multiple equivalents with grades of previous SAE and most other standards as exemplified by grades G3000 and G4000. Determination of current grade equivalent for castings established in production under previous SAE or other documents, shall be by the producer, in accordance with 5.5.3, based on historical or current test data from the established process, and reported to and approved by the purchaser. When the producer does not have access to the applicable historical data, grade determination shall be based on samples provided by producer and approved by purchaser.

4. Grades

4.1 Iron Grades—Iron grades and their t/h lower limit requirements are shown in Table 1.

TABLE 1—IRON GRADES

Grade	Test Bar t/h Ratio Lower Limit[1] MPa/MPa[2]	Test Bar t/h Ratio Lower Limit(1) psi/HB[3][4]
G7	0.070	100
G9	0.090	128
G10	0.100	142
G11	0.110	156
G12	0.120	171
G13	0.130	185

1. Statistically defined
2. Both tensile and hardness in MPA units
3. For reference only. The MPa/MPa SI metric values are primary. See Section 1.
4. Units of HB are kgf per mm^2.

4.2 Hardness Grades—Hardness grades and their required lower hardness limits are shown in Table 2.

TABLE 2—HARDNESS GRADES

Grade	Casting Hardness Lower Limit[1] MPa[2]	Casting Hardness Lower Limit[1] HB[3]
H10	1000	102
H11	1100	112
H12	1200	122
H13	1300	133
H14	1400	143
H15	1500	153
H16	1600	163
H17	1700	173
H18	1800	184
H19	1900	194
H20	2000	204
H21	2100	214
H22	2200	224
H23	2300	235
H24	2400	245

1. Statistically Defined.
2. Hardness in MPa = HB multiplied by 9.80665.
3. Units of HB are kgf per mm^2.

4.3 Special Requirements—Special additional requirements for particular applications and service conditions and their lower case letter designators are shown in Table 3. Special additional requirements shall not change test bar t/h ratio or casting hardness requirements.

TABLE 3—SPECIAL REQUIREMENTS

Designator	Application	Requirements
a	Brake Drums and Discs and Clutch Plates for Special Service	1. Total Carbon 3.4% minimum. 2. Microstructure: Lamellar Pearlite. Ferrite < 15%[1]
b	Brake Drums and Discs and Clutch Plates for Special Service	1. Total Carbon 3.4% minimum. 2. Microstructure: Lamellar Pearlite. Ferrite or carbide < 5%(1)
c	Brake Drums and Discs and Clutch Plates for Special Service	1. Total Carbon 3.5% minimum. 2. Microstructure: Lamellar Pearlite. Ferrite or carbide < 5%(1)
d	Alloy Hardenable Gray Iron Automotive Camshafts[2]	1. Chromium shall be 0.85 to 1.50%[3] 2. Molybdenum shall be 0.40 to 0.60%(3) 3. Microstructure of cam nose: Extending to 45 degrees on both sides of cam nose centerline and to minimum depth of 3.2 mm from the surface shall consist of primary carbide (cellular and/or acicular) and graphite in a matrix of fine pearlite. 4. The amount of carbide in the cams and method of checking shall be specified by the purchaser. 5. Casting Hardness check location shall be on a bearing surface.

1. See ASTM E 562.
2. As-cast requirements. Camshafts may be flame or induction hardened to specified hardness and depth on cam surfaces.
3. Ranges for specific castings shall be within the ranges shown.

4.4 Casting Grades—Combination of iron grade, hardness grade, and special requirement designation, if any, defines casting grade. A partial list of casting grades in common production and use, identified as reference grades and considered standard, is given in Table 4 with current and previous SAE designations. Other combinations of iron grade and hardness grade which are established in production and use or become so in the course of application development, or in accordance with 3.5 and 5.5.3, are also considered standard.

TABLE 4—REFERENCE GRADES[1]

SAE Casting Grade	Previous SAE Designation[2]
G9H12	G1800
G9H17	G2500
G10H18	G3000
G11H18	G3000
G11H20	G3500
G12H21	G4000
G13H19	G4000
G7H16 c	G1800 h[3]
G9H17 a	G2500 a
G10H21 c	G3500 c
G11H20 b	G3500 b
G11H24 d	G4000 d

1. Established in production and use and having near equivalents with previous SAE designations.
2. Equivalency based on tensile strength in 30 mm diameter test bars. See Table A4.
3. The h suffix was previously used to designate both t/h and carbon requirements for this grade.

NOTE—For castings successfully established in production and use under previous designations, the current SAE casting grade shall be determined by the producer and approved by the purchaser (see 3.5).

5. Tensile Strength to Hardness Ratio, Hardness, and Casting Tensile Strength

5.1 Tensile strength values for the t/h ratio determination shall be obtained as shown in Figure 1 from separately cast 30 mm test bars (type "B") in accordance with ASTM A 48 except sampling frequency shall be as needed for statistical analysis to determine conformance of t/h ratio with requirements of this document. Test specimens shall be at room temperature, defined as between 10 and 35 °C, during tensile testing.

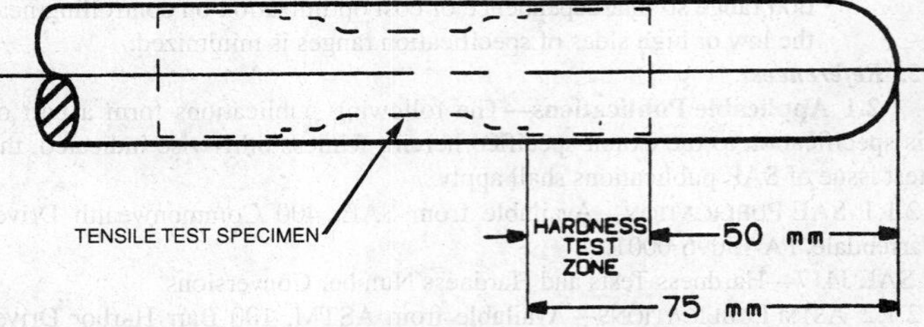

FIGURE 1—TEST BAR HARDNESS LONGITUDINAL TEST ZONE IN RELATION TO TENSILE SPECIMEN

5.2 Test bar hardness for the t/h ratio determination shall be taken on the tensile test bar between bar center and midpoint of the as-cast radius, and between 50 and 75 mm from the as-cast bar end as shown in Figures 1 and 2.

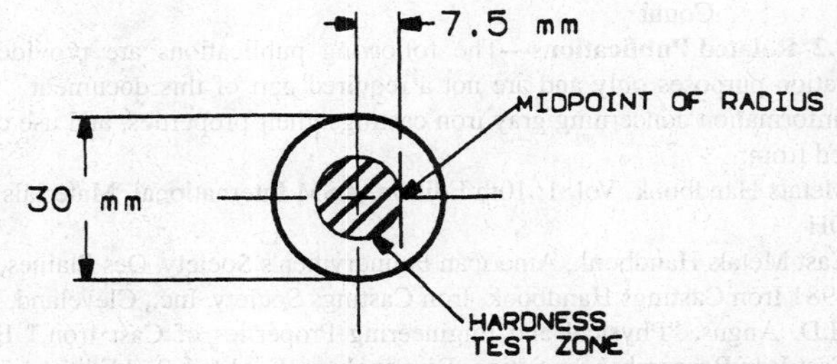

FIGURE 2—TEST BAR HARDNESS RADIAL TEST ZONE

5.3 Brinell Hardness is considered standard for test bars and production castings and shall be determined according to ASTM E 10 after sufficient material has been removed from the casting surface to insure representative hardness readings. The 10 mm ball and 3000 kgf load shall be used unless physically precluded by specimen dimensions as given in ASTM E 10. Test specimens shall be at room temperature, defined as between 10 and 35 °C, during hardness testing.

5.3.1 When a hardness test other than the Brinell test with 10 mm ball and 3000 kgf load must be used, conversion to the 3000 kgf 10 mm ball equivalent shall be by applicable conversion table in SAE J417 or by on-site calibration using Standard Brinell Bars.

5.4 A non-destructive casting hardness test location on the casting for monitoring conformance to grade limits shall be established by agreement between purchaser and producer or determined by producer. It should be readily accessible for convenience in performing the test to ensure adequate quantity, consistency, and accuracy of accumulated data for statistical validity in service of general variance control. Targeting of hardness measurement at service function related locations shall not be considered a requirement unless specified in accordance with 5.4.1.

5.4.1 In special cases, casting hardness at particular casting locations considered critical by the designer but difficult to access or requiring casting destruction may be specified by the purchaser with producer agreement. In such cases, hardness grade conformance may be established directly by hardness readings so obtained or indirectly by hardness readings at an accessible location using an agreed method of correlation.

5.5 The foundry shall exercise the necessary controls and inspection techniques to ensure compliance with the specified hardness and t/h ratio minimums. When samples exhibit normal variance patterns, conformance with grade requirements for t/h and casting hardness shall be determined by long term analysis of production samples using Normal Curve statistical methods. For sample sizes less than 30, the lower limit shall be taken as 3 standard deviations below the mean. For sample sizes larger than 30, the lower limits for t/h and casting hardness control may be optionally taken as the lower 3 standard deviation limit or the lower 99% population limit of the one-sided normal distribution at 95% confidence calculated by the confidence interval method (see A.1.5).

5.5.1 Test bar samples to confirm test bar t/h ratio conformance shall be random samples. Frequency of sampling may be specified by purchaser or determined by producer. Minimum frequency per grade shall be 1 per 8 h shift. Sample period may be any time interval or accumulation of time intervals in which the targeted mean t/h of producer's process control specifications is unchanged.

5.5.2 Casting samples to confirm casting hardness conformance shall be random samples. Frequency of sampling may be specified by purchaser or determined by producer. Minimum frequency shall be the least of 5 per 8 h shift or 100% of production. Sample period may be any time interval or accumulation of time intervals during which the targeted mean casting hardness of producer's process control specifications is unchanged.

5.5.3 Parts successfully established in production and use under previous SAE or other Standards shall be reclassified under this document, without change in mean test bar t/h or mean casting hardness, by appropriate selection of iron grade from Table 1, casting hardness grade from Table 2, and casting hardness range under 5.6.

5.5.4 Casting t/h data obtained by casting hardness tests as described in 5.4 or 5.4.1 and casting tensile tests as described in 5.7, shall be considered informational only and shall not be used for grade conformance assessment.

5.5.5 When casting hardness and/or test bar t/h variance patterns have too much skewness or otherwise do not support Normal Curve methods of analysis, an alternate method shall be established by agreement of purchaser and producer which achieves population limit control equivalent to that described in 5.5.

5.6 Casting hardness range may be specified by the purchaser to provide a non-statistical upper limit for machinability control. The standard range shall be 600 MPa or 60 HB, taken above the required grade minimum, and this shall be the assumed range when not specified. Purchasers shall not specify narrower ranges than this without prior agreement of the producer. Producers shall not exceed this range without prior agreement of the purchaser.

5.7 A minimum value for tensile strength determined by destructive testing at specified locations in castings may be specified as an additional, part number specific, conformance requirement by agreement between purchaser and producer on the applicable lower limit and statistical definition, sampling rate,and any special testing methods required. The agreed minimum shall be obtained with a standard grade as defined in this document. Information for estimating and experimentally determining the tensile minimum which can be expected for a given grade at specific locations in castings for purposes of design and development is given in Section A.4.

5.8 A statistical lower limit for tensile/hardness ratio determined by destructive testing at specified locations in castings may be specified as an additional, part number specific, conformance requirement by agreement between purchaser and producer on the applicable lower limit and statistical definition, sampling rate, and any special testing methods required. The agreed minimum shall be obtained with a standard grade as defined in this document. Information for estimating and experimentally determining the tensile/hardness ratio minimum which can be expected for a given grade at specific locations in castings for purposes of design and development is given in Section A.4.

6. Heat Treatment

6.1 Castings of hardness grades H10 through H17 may be annealed to meet hardness requirements. Castings of grades H21 through H24 may be quenched and tempered to meet hardness requirements.

6.2 Appropriate heat treatment for removal of residual stresses, or to improve machinability or wear resistance, may be specified. Heat treated castings must meet hardness requirements of the grade.

7. Microstructure

7.1 Unless otherwise specified, gray iron covered by this document shall be substantially free of primary cementite and/or massive steadite and shall consist of flake graphite in a matrix of ferrite or pearlite or mixtures thereof.

7.2 Unless otherwise specified, the graphite structure shall be primarily type A in accordance with ASTM A 247.

8. Castings for Special Applications with Controlled Composition and Microstructure

8.1 Heavy-Duty Brake Drums and Clutch Plates

8.1.1 These castings are considered as special cases and are covered in Tables 3 and 4.

8.2 Alloy Iron Automotive Camshafts

8.2.1 These castings are considered as special cases and are covered in Table 3 and 4.

9. General Requirements

9.1 Castings furnished to this document shall be representative of good foundry practice and shall conform to dimensions and tolerances specified on the casting drawing.

9.2 Approval by purchaser of location on the casting and method to be used is required for any casting repair.

9.3 Additional casting requirements such as vendor identification, other casting information, and special testing may be agreed upon by purchaser and supplier. These should appear as product specifications on the casting or part drawing.

APPENDIX A

Information in the Appendix is for reference only and does not constitute requirements.

A.1 Definition and Control of Gray Iron

A.1.1 Gray iron is a cast iron in which the graphite is present in flake form instead of nodules or spheroids as in malleable or ductile iron. Because its graphite has this flake structure, gray iron exhibits much greater sensitivity of mechanical properties to carbon content than malleable or ductile. As in malleable and ductile, the metallic matrix in which the graphite of gray iron resides is normally either eutectoid or hypo-eutectoid silicon steel with a working range of hardness of about 150 to 600 HB (1.5 to 6 GPa). In special cases, the matrix may be martensitic or hyper-eutectoidal with working hardness up to about 800 HB (8 GPa)

A.1.2 Gray iron naturally divides into a family or series of grades having different tensile strength to hardness (t/h) ratios uniformly regulated by eutectic graphite content up to the eutectic composition as shown in Figure A1 with carbon equivalent(CE) as the graphite parameter. Decline in t/h ratio continues as CE increases above the eutectic, but at a much smaller and less predictable rate. Constant t/h lines of this figure are essentially lines of constant graphite effect on mechanical properties. Properties sensitive to both graphite and matrix, such as bulk tensile strength and bulk hardness, vary in constant proportionality to each other and to their matrix counterparts—matrix tensile strength and matrix hardness—along constant t/h lines. Elastic modulus and damping capacity vary mainly only with graphite and are therefore highly constant along the constant t/h lines. Since these lines are also lines of constant eutectic graphite and CE, the most important castability parameters, they are logical grade lines for foundry control as well as for mechanical property control.

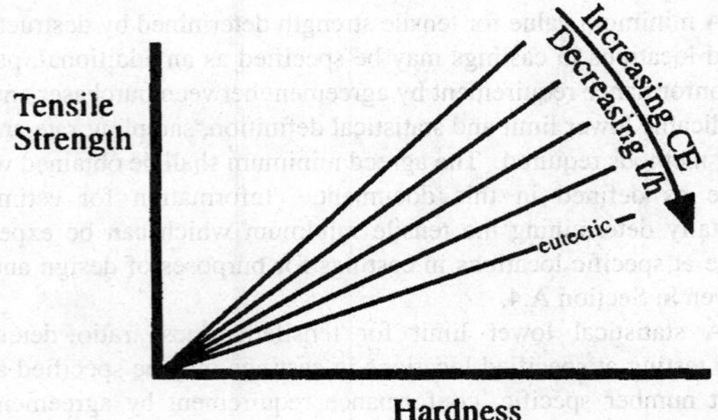

FIGURE A1—CHARACTERISTIC t/h RATIOS OF GRAY IRONS

A.1.3 Specification control of gray iron, since it is a composite material, requires joint classification by at least two property parameters of which one should be mainly graphite microstructure related and the other mainly a function of the matrix microstructure. Limited effectiveness of control by a single bulk property is illustrated in Figures A2 and A3. Figure A2 exemplifies grading by tensile strength alone—any given grade so defined is seen to traverse a wide range of possible hardness minimums. Likewise, in Figure A3, hardness is used as a single defining property and a wide range of possibilities exists for the tensile minimum. In both cases, t/h ratio and therefore, elastic modulus, damping capacity and castability are undefined. Figure A4 illustrates improved control obtainable by jointly specifying two property parameters. In this example, t/h ratio and hardness are the joint control parameters. A tensile minimum is now defined and, in general, all properties including castability are effectively controlled.

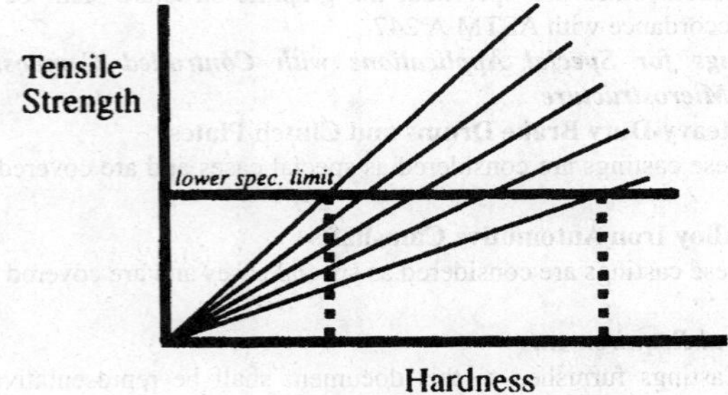

FIGURE A2—GRADING BY TENSILE

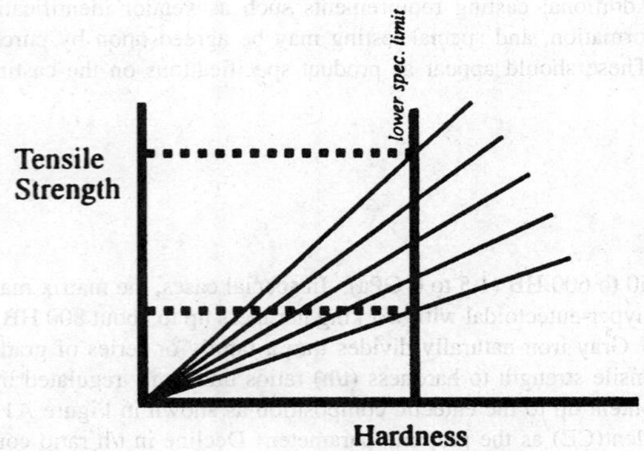

FIGURE A3—GRADING BY HARDNESS

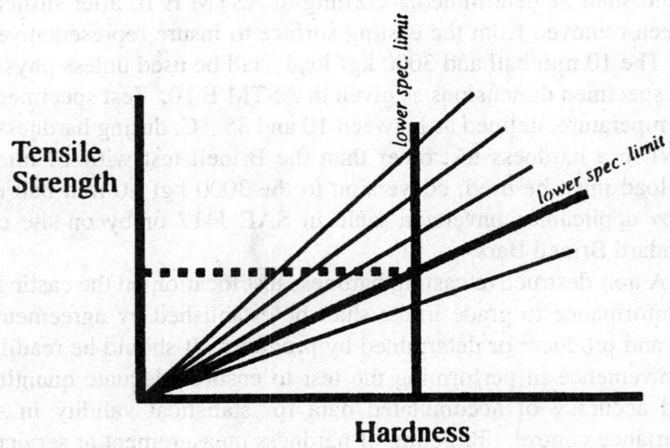

FIGURE A4—GRADING BY t/h RATIO AND HARDNESS

A.1.4 The control parameters used to classify gray iron in this document are test bar t/h ratio and casting hardness, selected because they meet the criteria cited in A.1.3 and are well established, widely used tests. The t/h ratio in this document is dimensionless, reflecting long established practice in the metric countries, where identical units have historically been used for both tensile strength and hardness. Hardness units will be in kg/mm^2 when reported as HB and are multiplied by g = 9.80665 to convert to MPa and form the dimensionless ratio with tensile strength in MPa units. For a number of purposes, it is useful to know the matrix hardness. Examples of its use are -- process control of the hardness property, simplification of bivariate statistical analysis of hardness and tensile strength, and engineering selection of iron grade for best wear resistance or fatigue life in strain limited loading. The matrix hardness can be estimated with sufficient accuracy for most purposes from the bulk hardness and t/h ratio with the relation:

$$H_{matrix} = H_{bulk}/[1 - k^*(1 - t/h\ ratio/0.35)] \qquad \text{(Eq. A1)}$$

in which k is a graphite structure related constant with a usual range in sand cast gray iron of 0.60 to 0.65.

A.1.5 With continuous production processes used for automotive casting production conformance to specification control limits can be assessed by analysis of periodic samples using the Confidence Interval method. This method predicts population limits of parent production in standard deviation units, at various confidence levels, as multiples of the sample standard deviation measured from the sample mean. Tabulations of such multipliers versus sample size are widely published (one of many possible references is given in 2.2). The curve of Figure A5 is a plot of such a tabulation showing how the multiplier typically varies with sample size. The curve of Figure A5 is drawn for 99% population limits of a one-sided normal distribution at 95% confidence. For a sample size of about 300 bars, the –2.5 sigma limit of the sample would be the 99% population limit for the parent production.

A.2 Chemical Composition

A.2.1 Typical base composition ranges generally employed for the iron grades are shown in Table A1. The base composition does not include alloys such as Cu, Cr, Mo, Ni, or others which may be added for hardness or t/h control, or to meet mandatory composition limits of special irons given in Table 3 of the main body of this document.

A.2.2 Typical base composition ranges may vary for specific grades depending on casting section size or metallurgical factors such as trace element content, or to satisfy mandatory composition requirements of special irons as given in Table 3.

A.2.3 Typical composition ranges including typical alloy content for camshaft iron, grade G11H24d, are shown in Table A2.

A.3 Microstructure

A.3.1 The as-cast microstructure of gray iron covered by this document consists of a mixture of flake graphite in a matrix consisting of ferrite, ferrite and pearlite, or pearlite, as described in Table A3. The quantity of flake graphite and size of the flakes vary with iron grade. The amount and fineness of pearlite vary with the hardness grade. The pearlite is usually lamellar but may be partially spheroidal in slowly cooled sections or where heat treatment has been applied.

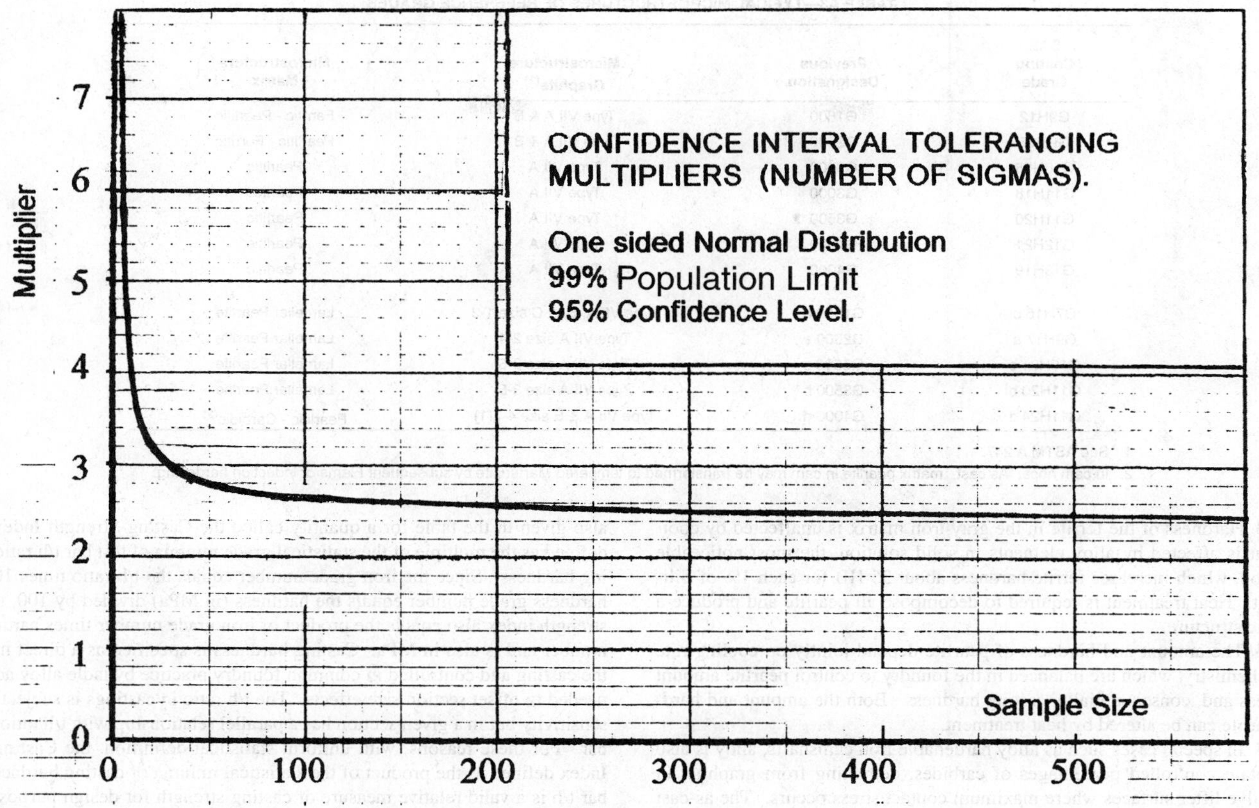

FIGURE A5—CONFIDENCE INTERVAL TOLERANCING MULTIPLIERS (NUMBER OF SIGMAS)

TABLE A1—TYPICAL BASE COMPOSITIONS

Iron Grade	Previous Designation	Carbon	Silicon	Manganese	Sulfur Max.	Phosphorus max	C. E.[1] (Approx.)
G7	G1800h	3.50 - 3.70	2.30 - 2.80	0.60 - 0.90	0.14	0.25	4.35 - 4.55
G9	G2500	3.40 - 3.65	2.10 - 2.50	0.60 - 0.90	0.12	0.25	4.15 - 4.40
G10	G3000	3.35 - 3.60	1.90 - 2.30	0.60 - 0.90	0.12	0.20	4.05 - 4.30
G11	G3000	3.30 - 3.55	1.90 - 2.20	0.60 - 0.90	0.12	0.10	4.00 - 4.25
G12	G3500	3.25 - 3.50	1.90 - 2.20	0.60 - 0.90	0.12	0.10	3.95 - 4.20
G13	G4000	3.15 - 3.40	1.80 - 2.10	0.70 - 1.00	0.12	0.08	3.80 - 4.05

1. C. E. (Carbon Equivalent) = %C + (1/3) %Si.

TABLE A2—TYPICAL CHEMICAL COMPOSITION OF ALLOY GRAY IRON AUTOMOTIVE CAMSHAFTS, GRADE G11H24d (PREVIOUS 4000d)

Constituent	Wt %
Total Carbon	3.10 to 3.60
Silicon	1.95 to 2.40
Manganese	0.60 to 0.90
Phosphorus	0.10 max
Sulfur	0.15 max
Chromium	0.85 to 1.50
Molybdenum	0.40 to 0.60
Nickel	0.20 to 0.45
Copper	Residual

A.3.2 The size and distribution of graphite flakes in gray iron depend upon chemistry, liquid metal treatment (inoculation), and cooling rate during solidification. The primary, but not sole, chemical determinant is carbon equivalent, defined as C+Si/3.

A.3.2.1 Alloying elements used for pearlite hardness control have small but non-negligible effects on graphite size. Since some elements operate as coarsening and others as refining agents, combinations can be used for a neutral effect.

A.3.2.2 When alloying elements are used to produce a mixed structure of primary carbide and graphite, as in the cams of alloy hardenable gray iron automotive camshafts, eutectic graphite is reduced and significant flake refinement results.

A.3.2.3 The graphite microstructure of gray iron cannot be changed by heat treatment.

TABLE A3—TYPICAL MICROSTRUCTURES OF REFERENCE GRADES

SAE Casting Grade	Previous Designation	Microstructure Graphite[1]	Microstructure Matrix
G9H12	G1800	Type VII A & B	Ferritic - Pearlitic
G9H17	G2500	Type VII A & B	Pearlitic - Ferritic
G10H18	G3000	Type VII A	Pearlitic
G11H18	G3000	Type VII A	Pearlitic
G11H20	G3500	Type VII A	Pearlitic
G12H21	G4000	Type VII A	Pearlitic
G13H19	G4000	Type VII A	Pearlitic
G7H16 c	G1800 h	Type VII A, B, & C size 1-3	Lamellar Pearlite
G9H17 a	G2500 a	Type VII A size 2-4	Lamellar Pearlite
G10H21 c	G3500 c	Type VII A size 3-5	Lamellar Pearlite
G11H20 b	G3500 b	Type VII A size 3-5	Lamellar Pearlite
G11H24 d	G4000 d	Type VII A & E size 4-7(1)	Pearlitic - Carbidic[2]

1. See ASTM A 247.
2. In cam nose. As cast. matrix pearlite in cam may be transformed to tempered Martensite by subsequent Flame or induction hardening.

A.3.3 Hardness of the ferrite in the gray iron matrix is unaffected by cooling rate but is affected by alloy elements in solid solution, the most noticeable being silicon, which increases ferrite hardness about 35 HB for each 1% of Silicon present. Heat treatment is required to decompose all pearlite and produce a fully ferritic structure.

A.3.4 The amount and hardness of pearlite depend jointly on cooling rate and alloy chemistry, which are balanced in the foundry to control pearlite amount and hardness and, consequentially, casting hardness. Both the amount and hardness of pearlite can be altered by heat treatment.

A.3.5 In special cases such as alloy hardenable iron camshafts, alloy is also used to obtain controlled percentages of carbides, detracting from graphite, in cam and valve lifter surfaces where maximum contact stress occurs. The as-cast matrix structure in these cases is pearlite; in the contact surfaces, the matrix is transformed to tempered martensite by surface heat treatment.

A.3.6 Gray iron castings can be through-hardened by liquid quenching or selectively surface-hardened by either flame or induction methods.

A.4 Mechanical Properties of Castings For Design

A.4.1 The calculated tensile strength minima shown in Table A4 for 30 mm diameter test bars assume Normal Curve statistics with foundry industry typical variance levels and are in good agreement with typical production data. Values are also given in the table for a quantity called the Casting Strength Index which is defined as the multiple of the statistical grade minima of test bar t/h ratio and casting hardness. Since the iron grade number equals the t/h ratio times 100 and the hardness grade number equals the hardness (in MPa) divided by 100, the casting strength index also equals the product of iron grade number times hardness grade number and is also in MPa. Casting hardness is specified as a direct measure on the casting and controlled in common foundry practice by ladle alloy additions as needed to offset section size effects. The t/h ratio in castings is subject to section sensitivity but in a given section has a parallel relationship with t/h ratio in the test bar. For these reasons, with uniform statistical definition, the Casting Strength Index defined as the product of the statistical minima of casting hardness and test bar t/h is a valid relative measure of casting strength for design purposes. When section sensitivity of the t/h ratio is quantitatively known, this index can also be used to make a first working estimate of the absolute value of casting tensile strength. Both test bar tensile strength and Casting Strength Index values can be used to determine tensile equivalency with iron graded by other specifications and to optimize SAE grade choice.

A.4.1.1 Method of defining Casting Strength Index as minimum casting hardness multiplied by minimum test bar t/h and its relationship to the statistical limits of tensile strength and hardness are shown graphically in Figure A6.

TABLE A4—TENSILE STRENGTH CHARACTERISTICS AND TENSILE EQUIVALENTS OFSAE REFERENCE GRADES[1]

SAE Casting Grades	Former SAE Grades[2]	Non-SAE Tensile Grades[3] SI	Non-SAE Tensile Grades[3] Inch-lb	Theoretical Tensile Strength Minimums of SAE Casting Grades Casting Strength Index[4] MPa	Theoretical Tensile Strength Minimums of SAE Casting Grades Casting Strength Index[4] ksi	Theoretical Tensile Strength Minimums of SAE Casting Grades 30 mm Dia. Test Bars[5] MPa	Theoretical Tensile Strength Minimums of SAE Casting Grades 30 mm Dia. Test Bars[5] ksi
G9H12	G1800			108	15.7	124	18.0
G9H17	G2500	175	25	153	22.2	170	24.6
G10H18	G3000	200	30	180	26.1	198	28.7
G11H18	G3000	225	30	198	28.7	217	31.5
G11H20	G3500	250	35	220	31.9	239	34.7
G12H21	G4000	275	40	252	36.5	272	39.4
G13H19	G4000	275	40	247	35.8	268	38.9
G7H16 c	G1800 h[6]			112	16.2	127	18.4
G9H17 a	G2500 a	175	25	153	22.2	170	24.6
G10H21 c	G3500 c	225	35	210	30.5	228	33.1
G11H20 b	G3500 b	250	35	220	31.9	239	34.7
G11H24 d	G4000 d	275	40	264	38.3	284	41.2

1. Established in production and use and having near equivalents in previous SAE standards and test bar tensile strength equivalents in other standards.
2. Former SAE grades having near equivalence with t/h and hardness requirements, and theoretical test bar tensile strength minimums of the current SAE casting grades.
3. Grades of standards based solely on test bar tensile strength such as ASTM A 48 and 48 M, ISO 185, EN 1561, and others, having near equivalence with theoretical test bar tensile strength minimums of the current SAE casting grades.
4. Multiple of test bar t/h ratio and casting hardness minimum of the current SAE casting grade. Numerically equal to multiple of iron number multiplied by casting hardness grade number.
5. 99% population lower limit of SAE casting grade at 95% confidence, one-sided normal distribution, 300 bar sample ($-2.5\ \sigma$). Hardness and t/h minimums at $-3\ \sigma$, hardness range 500 MPa, t/h range 0.35 for iron grades 7 to 11 and 0.30 for iron grades 12 to 13.
6. The h suffix was previously used to designate both t/h and carbon requirements of this grade.

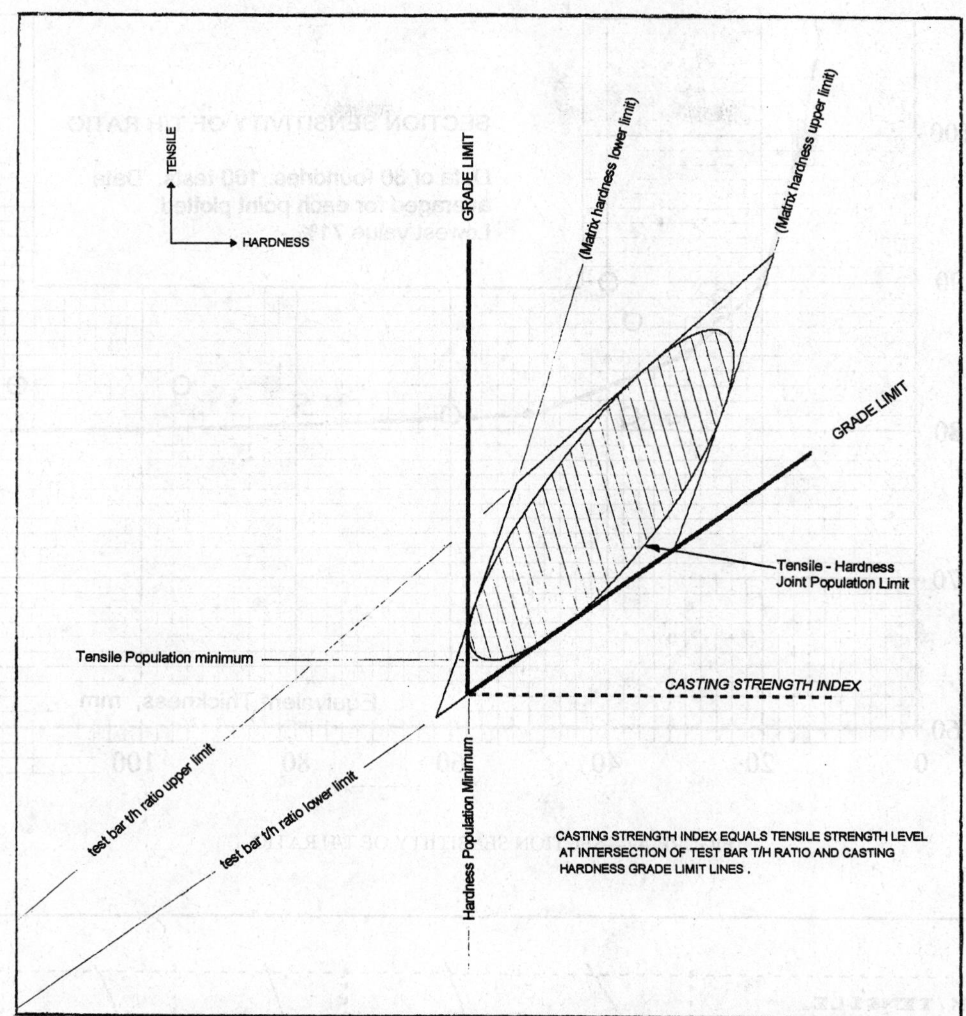

FIGURE A6—METHOD OF DEFINING CASTING STRENGTH INDEX

A.4.2 Tensile to hardness ratio (t/h) of cast iron is determined by graphite structure and is an independent parameter quantifying the effect of graphite structure on mechanical properties. In gray iron the dominant structural aspect affecting t/h ratio is comprised of the length, width and quantity of graphite flakes. The primary process control parameter determining this aspect is carbon equivalent. However, inoculation practice, alloy content and solidification time as controlled by casting thickness are important secondary factors. Although the solidification time or thickness effect is sometimes neutralized by the metallurgical factors, resulting in little or no decline, decline of t/h ratio as thickness increases is more typical. Average results of tests showing such decline, up to 100 mm equivalent wall thickness, have indicated t/h ratio does not usually decline to less than about 80% of the value obtained in the standard 30 mm diameter test bar (approximately 15 mm equivalent thickness). The curve of Figure A7, drawn from data of such tests, gives t/h in thickness up to 100 mm as a percentage of the 30 mm diameter test bar (15 mm equivalent thickness) value and is linearized between points for convenient use in estimating t/h, in various section thicknesses, from the 30 mm test bar value. Figure A7 can be used to make working estimates subject to experimental confirmation in castings. Microporosity, though rare in gray iron, can occur in underfed sections and is an issue in t/h ratio control. It is difficult to assess by microsopic examination but can be detected by means of density measurements.

A.4.3 Since the probability of minimum t/h ratio and minimum hardness occurring simultaneously in a casting is less than the probability of either occurring alone, the minimum tensile limit given by their product; i.e., the Casting Strength Index defined in A.4.1 and Figure A6, is always conservatively low. This is illustrated in Figure A8 with a typical data plot. The Casting Strength Index can be determined as a statistical limit by a bivariate normal analysis or estimated with sufficient accuracy for equivalency evaluations as about 20% farther from the tensile mean, measured in Sigma (standard deviation) units, than the control limit used for casting hardness and test bar t/h ratio; e.g., about $-3\text{-}1/2\ \sigma$ when the casting hardness and test bar t/h minima are at $-3\ \sigma$, or $-3\ \sigma$ when test bar t/h and casting hardness are at $-2\text{-}1/2\ \sigma$. Without correction for section thickness effect on the t/h property, this conservative margin may diminish when casting section thickness increases above 15 mm thickness; it will also tend to diminish if for any reason distributions become skewed with truncation or data concentration on the low side, or when metallurgical control ranges become either very small or very large (coefficient of variance for hardness or t/h ratio less then about 2% or greater than about 6%).

A.4.4 When casting design is developed primarily by simulated service testing of prototypes correlated by the Casting Strength Index defined in A.4.1 as a relative measure, standard 30 mm test bars should always be poured with the prototype castings so that the actual test bar t/h ratio and casting hardness product of the prototype castings is known in relation to the specification minimum as represented by the Casting Strength Index.

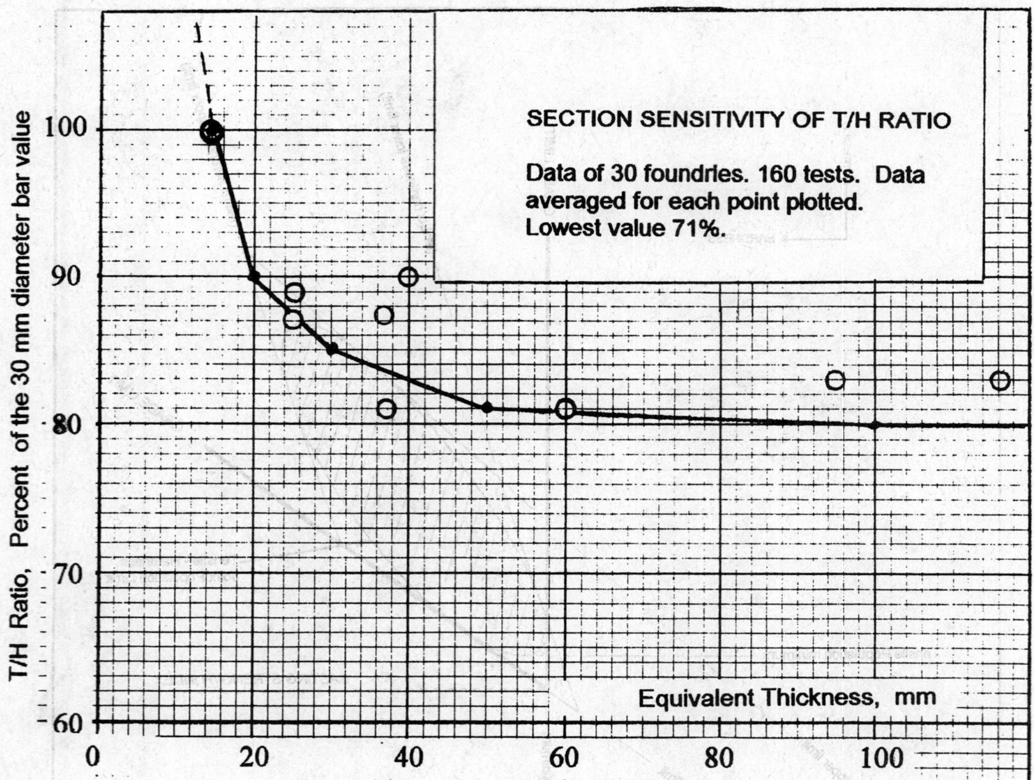

FIGURE A7—SECTION SENSITIITY OF T/H RATIO

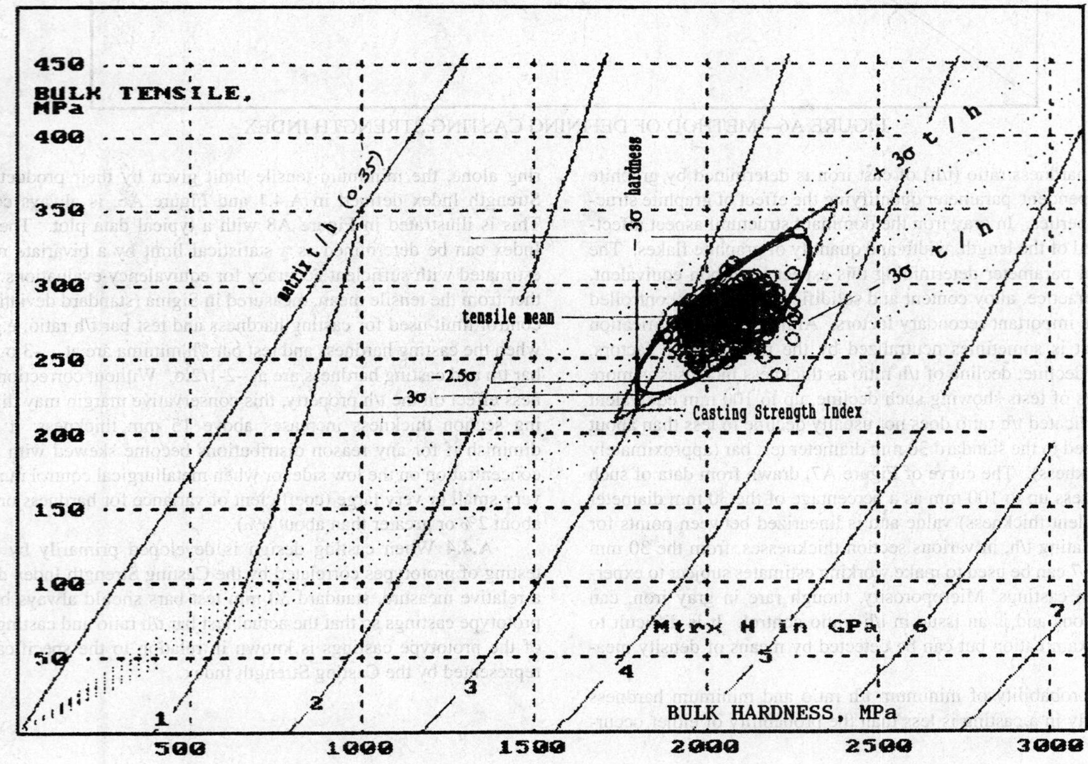

FIGURE A8—BIVARIATE FIELD FOR G12H18 WITH DATA APPROXIMATING THIS GRADE

A.4.5 When casting design is based primarily on the absolute value of casting tensile strength, destructive testing of castings is required of prototypes during development and of production samples for ongoing control. The casting strength index defined in A.4.1 can however be used as a first working estimate of tensile strength by correcting for thickness effect on t/h as shown in the example of A.4.7. The equivalent thickness can be estimated by geometric analysis and the relation that equivalent thickness equals volume/surface ratio multiplied by two or from solidification time, measured by thermocouple placement in prototype or production castings, and the Chvorinov relationship which gives equivalent thickness in mm equal to the square root of solidification time in seconds for cast iron in sand molds.

A.4.6 Equivalency between grades of this document and previous SAE grades can be determined from Table A4. Test bar tensile strength equivalency between grades of this and non-SAE tensile based standards can also be determined from Table A4. For casting grade optimization at constant tensile strength the casting strength index, as given in Table A4 or estimated from other limits or data in accordance with A.4.3 can be used. For example, if needed for a complex shape, G9H20 would provide higher castability than G10H18 with the same strength, since casting strength index for both is 180 MPa.

A.4.7 Equivalency between SAE grades of this document and grades classified by casting tensile strength according to section thickness can be assessed by correcting for section sensitivity of t/h ratio as given in Figure A7, which gives t/h ratio in various sections as a percentage of the t/h ratio in 15 mm thickness or 30 mm diameter. When statistical limits are not given or insufficient data is available for statistical analysis, the equivalent SAE grade will be that having the product of casting hardness multiplied by the corrected test bar t/h ratio equaling or exceeding the tensile strength requirements of the grade and section size being assessed. For example, SAE G13H19, with t/h corrected to section thickness of 50 mm, will ,in accordance with Figure A7, have estimated minimum t/h ratio in the 50 mm section of 80% of 0.13, or 0.105; the corrected product of t/h multiplied by casting hardness will be 0.105 x 1900 = 199.5 MPa, and equivalency is indicated with a grade requiring 200 MPa minimum in a 50 mm section thickness. In this case, use of the low ($-3.5\ \sigma$ value) is made to compensate for uncertainty of the statistically unknown case and for the small error introduced by the simplifying step of applying the 80% factor to the minimum instead of average t/h.

A.4.8 Transverse Strength—Table A5 provides estimates of transverse strength and deflection as obtained for 30 mm diameter test bars broken under centered transverse loading with a span of 457.2 mm (18 in) between supports. The test is usually performed on the as-cast bar without machining. The test is standardized under ASTM A 438. The values shown in Table A5 are carried forward from previous versions of SAE J431 and are typical of results long reported in the literature for unmachined sand cast bars and used in standards. This test is now rarely used and the data has mainly historical significance. Use of this test for any new application should be based on new data obtained for the grade of iron used.

A.5 Application of Gray Iron Castings

A.5.1 Typical applications of both the regular and special reference grades given in Table 4 are shown in Table A6. Iron grade combinations considered standard are not limited to these reference grades.

TABLE A5—ESTIMATED MINIMUMS FOR TRANSVERSE STRENGTH

SAE Casting Grade	Previous Designation	Transverse Strength, Minimum kN (lb)	Transverse Deflection Minimum mm (in)
G9H12	G1800	7.65 (1720)	3.6 (0.14)
G9H17	G2500	8.90 (2000)	4.3 (0.17)
G10H18	G3000	9.79 (2200)	5.1 (0.20)
G11H18	G3000	9.79 (2200)	5.1 (0.20)
G11H20	G3500	10.90 (2450)	6.1 (0.24)
G11H21	G4000	11.56 (2600)	6.9 (0.27)
G13H19	G4000	11.56 (2600)	6.9 (0.27)
G7H16 c	G1800 h	7.65 (1720)	3.6 (0.14)
G9H17 a	G2500 a	8.90 (2000)	4.3 (0.17)
G10H21 c	G3500 c	10.68 (2400)	6.1 (0.24)
G11H20 b	G3500 b	10.68 (2400)	6.1 (0.24)
G11H24 d	G4000 d	11.56 (2600)	6.9 (0.27)

TABLE A6—TYPICAL AUTOMOTIVE APPLICATIONS OF GRAY IRON REFERENCE GRADES

SAE Grade	Previous Designation	General Data
G9H12	G1800	Miscellaneous soft castings (as cast or annealed) with relatively low strength requirements. Exhaust manifolds, alloyed or unalloyed. Annealed as necessary to prevent growth cracking in service due to heat.
G9H17	G2500	Small cylinder blocks, cylinder heads, air cooled cylinders, pistons, clutchplates, oil pump bodies, transmission cases, gear boxes, clutch housings, light-duty brake drums.
G10H18	G3000	Passenger car and light-duty truck cylinder blocks and heads, flywheels, differential carrier castings, pistons, medium-duty brake drums and discs, clutch plates, hydraulic castings, and refrigerant compressor castings.
G11H18	G3000	Same general uses as G10H18 with suitability for larger section sizes or where tensile strength or duty requirements are higher.
G11H20	G3500	Medium and heavy-duty truck and tractor diesel cylinder blocks and heads, heavy flywheels, transmission cases, axle housings, and miscellaneous heavy gear boxes.
G12H21	G4000	Extra heavy-duty diesel engine cylinder heads, liners, and pistons.
G13H19	G4000	Large heavy-duty diesel engine and construction equipment castings. Heavy-duty hydraulic castings.
G7H16 c	G1800 h	Brake drums and discs where very high damping capacity is required.
G9H17 a	G2500 a	Brake drums and clutch plates for moderate service requirements and where high carbon iron is desired to minimize heat checking.
G10H21 c	G3500 c	Extra heavy-duty service brake drums.
G11H20 b	G3500 b	Brake drums and clutch plates for heavy-duty service where high carbon and high hardness are both required to minimize heat checking and provide higher strength.
G11H24 d	G4000 d	Alloy hardenable iron automotive engine camshafts.

A.5.2 The castability, thermal conductivity, and vibration damping capacity of gray iron all relate closely and directly with its largely graphitic carbon content and, therefore, vary inversely with iron grade as numerically defined in this document. Machinability and wear resistance are more influenced by hardness which is controlled more by matrix hardness than by graphite content. Tensile strength is directly proportional with both iron and hardness grades and can be regulated with either one. Since castability is constant with iron grade, it is often more practical to obtain a needed strength increment by using alloy ladle additions to change the hardness grade rather than to change the iron grade. Iron grade can also be changed by ladle alloy additions which change the size of graphite flakes rather than the quantity. This has an intermediate effect on castability that is often more tolerable and therefore less limiting of design freedom than changing iron grade by changing carbon equivalent.

A.5.3 With grade differentiation by t/h ratio comparative fatigue behavior of different grades of gray iron differs with the type of loading; i.e., whether strain limited or stress limited. In the case of strain limited cyclic loading, fatigue life ("strain life," in this case) tends to be mainly controlled by matrix strength and ductility and shows little variation with t/h ratio. This means that changing iron grade as defined in this document without altering matrix metallurgy, for example by changing only carbon equivalent, will not significantly change strain life even though there is substantial change in t/h ratio and tensile strength. This behavior is shown in reference 8 (see 2.2). For this reason, when service loads are strain limited, the lower t/h iron grades are often more optimum because of their better castability and also because, with a given matrix hardness, the lower t/h grades have a lower ratio of bulk hardness to matrix hardness and hence better machinability at a given strain life. The usual way of increasing matrix hardness -- by pearlite refining alloy additions -- also increases matrix ductility. Examples of strain limited loads are temperature gradient induced loads as in brake drums and water jacketed combustion chambers, and secondary loads carried by gray iron parts incorporated in structures with stronger components as the primary load carrying members and determinants of strain. However, fatigue life of gray iron parts subjected to stress limited loads is influenced by both t/h ratio and matrix hardness, and maximum fatigue life ("stress life") in these cases occurs in the highest t/h and hardness grades. Typical examples of castings subject to stress controlled loading are engine blocks and hydraulic castings.

A.6 Special Applications of Gray Iron

A.6.1 Heavy-Duty Brake Drums and Clutch Plates—Automotive brake drums and clutch plates for heavy-duty service are considered special cases. Mandatory minimum limits for carbon content and matrix microstructure requirements are given in Table 3. Typical base chemistry is given in Table A1. Alloy is normally used to meet casting hardness requirements of grades G10H21c and G11H20b.

A.6.2 Alloy Hardenable Iron Automotive Camshafts—Alloy hardenable automotive camshafts are also considered as special cases. Mandatory alloy content and microstuctural requirements are given in Table 3. Typical base chemistry is shown in Table A1. Typical overall composition ranges are given in Table A2.

A.6.2.1 In casting hardenable iron for camshafts, the aim is to obtain a suitable microstructure in critical locations of the casting and balance the composition to obtain response to induction or flame hardening. These depend not only on the chemistry of the iron but also on the equivalent thickness and details of the melting and liquid metal processes. In making a given casting, it is normal practice to adjust the chemistry to narrow limits within the ranges of Table A2.

A.6.2.2 The cam and bearing surfaces are critical performance areas of automotive camshafts. Carbide content and metallurgical response to flame or induction hardening of the cams in terms of hardness, depth, and area covered are specified for each part number. Requisite hardness results both from the Martensite produced by hardening and the presence of eutectic carbides, which approximately equal the martensite in hardness and contribute to bulk hardness both by their own hardness and by reducing eutectic graphite content. Apart from their contribution to hardness, some minimum limit on carbide content in the cams is also usually necessary for a scuff resistant surface topography.

AUTOMOTIVE DUCTILE (NODULAR) IRON CASTINGS—SAE J434 JUN86

SAE Standard

Report of the SAE Iron and Steel Technical Committee approved September 1956 and last revised June 1986.

1. Scope—This SAE Standard covers the hardness and microstructure requirements for ductile iron castings used in automotive and allied industries. Castings may be specified in the as-cast or heat treated condition.

The Appendix provides general information on the application of ductile iron castings and their chemical composition to meet hardness microstructure and other properties needed for particular service conditions. The mechanical properties in the Appendix are provided for design purposes.

2. References

2.1 Applicable Publications—The following publications form a part of the specification to the extent specified herein. Unless otherwise indicated, the latest revision of SAE publications shall apply

2.1.1 ASTM PUBLICATION—Available from ASTM, 100 Barr Harbor Drive, West Conshohocken, PA 19428-2959

ASTM E10—Test for Brinell Hardness of Metallic Materials

STP-455—Gray, Ductile, and Malleable Iron Castings Current Capabilities

2.1.2 OTHER PUBLICATION

Metals Handbook, Vol. 1, 2, and 5, 8th Edition, American Society for Metals, Metals Park, OH

Gray and Ductile Iron Castings Handbook, Gray and Ductile Iron Founder Society, Cleveland, OH

H. D. Angus, Physical Engineering Properties of Cast Iron, British Cast Iron Research Association, Birmingham, England

3. Grades—The specified grades, hardness range, and metallurgical description are shown in Table 1.

TABLE 1—GRADES OF DUCTILE IRON

Grade	Casting Hardness Range	Description
D4018	170 HB max or as agreed (4.6 BID, min)	Ferritic
D4512	156–217 HB or as agreed (4.80–4.10 BID)	Ferritic-pearlitic
D5506	187–255 HB or as agreed (4.4–3.8 BID)	Ferritic-pearlitic
D7003	241–302 HB or as agreed (3.90–3.50 BID)	Pearlitic
DQ&T	Range specific	Martensitic

NOTE— Brinell impression diameter (BID) is the diameter in millimeters (mm) of the impression of a 10 mm ball at 3000 kg load.

4. Hardness

4.1 The area or areas on the castings where hardness is to be checked should be established by agreement between supplier and purchaser.

4.2 The foundry shall exercise the necessary controls and inspection techniques to insure compliance with the specified hardness range. Brinell hardness shall be determined according to ASTM E 10, Test for Brinell Hardness of Metallic Materials, after sufficient material has been removed from the casting surface to insure representative hardness readings. The 10 mm ball and 3000 kg load shall be used unless otherwise agreed upon.

5. Heat Treatment

5.1 Unless otherwise specified, castings may be heat treated to the appropriate hardness range.

5.2 Appropriate heat treatment for removal of residual stresses, or to improve machinability may be specified by agreement between supplier and purchaser.

6. Microstructure—The graphite component of the microstructure shall consist of at least 80% spheroidal graphite conforming to Types I and II in Figure 1. The matrix microstructure shall consist of either ferrite, ferrite and pearlite, pearlite, tempered pearlite, or tempered martensite or a combination of these. The microstructure shall be substantially free of primary cementite.

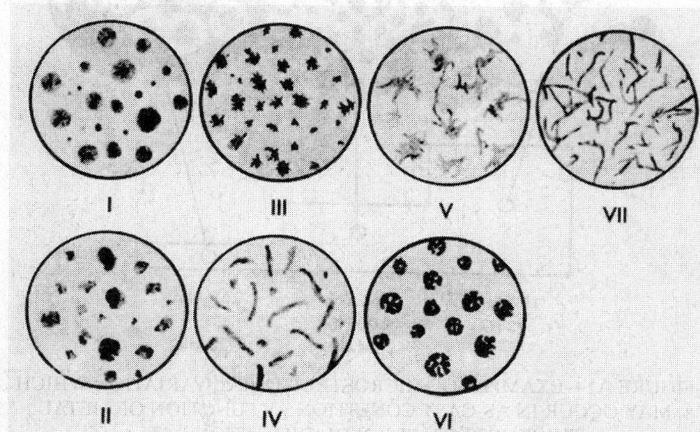

FIGURE 1—CLASSIFICATION OF GRAPHITE SHAPE IN CAST IRONS (FROM ASTM A 247)

7. Quality Assurance—Sampling plans are a matter of agreement between supplier and purchaser. The supplier shall employ adequate equipment and controls to insure that parts conform to the agreed upon requirements.

8. General

8.1 Castings furnished to this standard shall be representative of good foundry practice and shall conform to dimensions and tolerances specified on the casting drawing.

8.2 Minor imperfections usually not associated with the structural functioning may occur in castings. These imperfections are often repairable; however, repairs should be made only in areas and by methods approved by the purchaser.

8.3 Additional casting requirements, such as vendor identification, other casting information, and special tesing, may be agreed upon by the purchaser and supplier. These should appear as additional product requirements on the casting drawing.

APPENDIX A
DUCTILE (NODULAR) IRON
(A material description not a part of the standard)

A.1 Definition And Classification—Ductile (nodular) iron, also known as spheroidal graphite iron, is cast iron in which the graphite is present as spheroids, instead of flakes as in gray iron or temper carbon nodules as in malleable iron.

Ductile iron castings may be used in the as-cast condition, or may be heat treated.

A.2 Chemical Composition—The typical chemical composition of unalloyed iron generally conforms to the following ranges:

Total carbon	3.20–4.10%
Silicon	1.80–3.00%
Manganese	0.10–1.00%
Phosphorus	0.015–0.10%
Sulfur	0.005–0.035%

Individual foundries will produce to narrower ranges than those shown. The spheroidal graphite structure is produced by alloying the molten iron with small amounts of one or more elements such as magnesium or cerium.

A.3 Microstructure

A.3.1 The microstructure of the various grades of ductile iron consists of spheroidal graphite in a matrix of either ferrite, pearlite, tempered pearlite, tempered martensite, or certain combinations of these. The relative amounts of each of these constituents is dependent upon the grade of material specified, casting design as it affects cooling rate, and heat treatments, if any.

A.3.2 The matrix microstructure of as-cast ductile iron depends to a great extent on the solidification rate and cooling rate of the casting, as shown in Figure A1. If a section solidifies rapidly, especially sections of 0.25 in (6 mm) or less, an appreciable amount of carbide may be present in the casting. If a section cools slowly, as in a massive, heavy casting, a largely ferritic matrix may result.

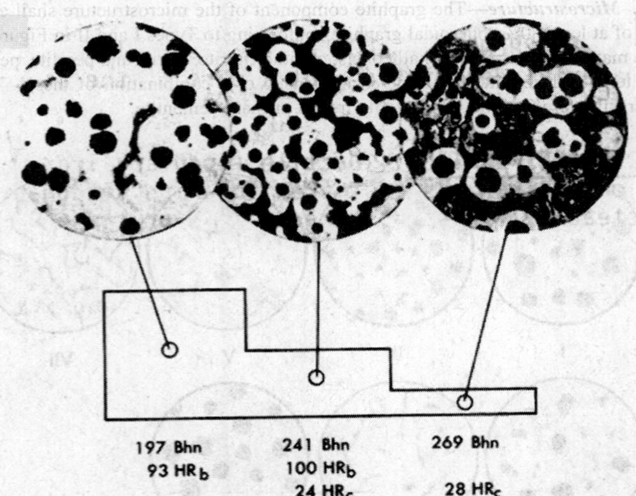

FIGURE A1—EXAMPLE OF MICROSTRUCTURAL VARIATION WHICH MAY OCCUR IN AS-CAST CONDITION AS FUNCTION OF METAL THICKNESS (THAT IS, SOLIDIFICATION RATE)

A.3.3 Alloying elements can also alter the microstructure usually resulting in increased amounts of pearlite. Large variations in structure can be eliminated or minimized by modifying the casting design or the runner system or both, or by controlled cooling, or any combination of these. Primary carbides, and/or pearlite can be decomposed by appropriate heat treatments.

A.3.4 A rim may occur on heat treated castings consisting of a graphite-free layer sometimes containing more or less combined carbon than the underlying material.

A.3.5 Typical microstructure of the grades of ductile iron are as follows:

D4018 is annealed ferritic ductile iron. The annealing time and temperature cycle is such that primary carbides, if present in the as-cast structure, are decomposed, and the resulting matrix is ferritic as shown in Figure A2.

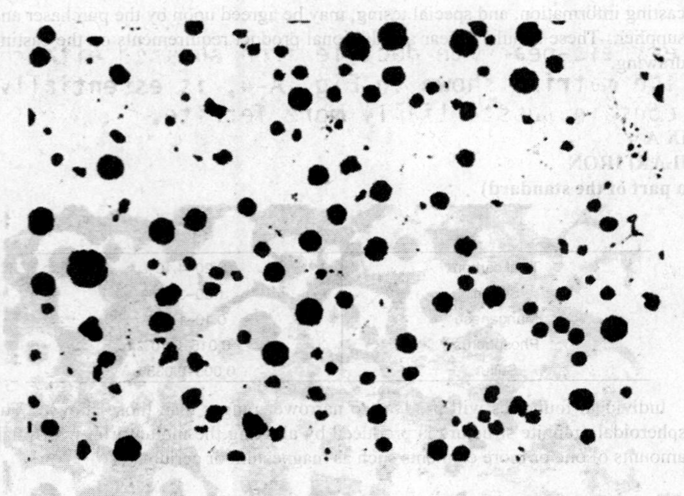

FIGURE A2—D4018, APPROXIMATE 156 HB (100X) TYPICAL MICROSTRUCTURES

D4512 is ferritic ductile iron supplied either as cast or heat treated. The matrix, shown in Figure A3, is essentially ferrite but this grade can contain pearlite, depending on the section size.

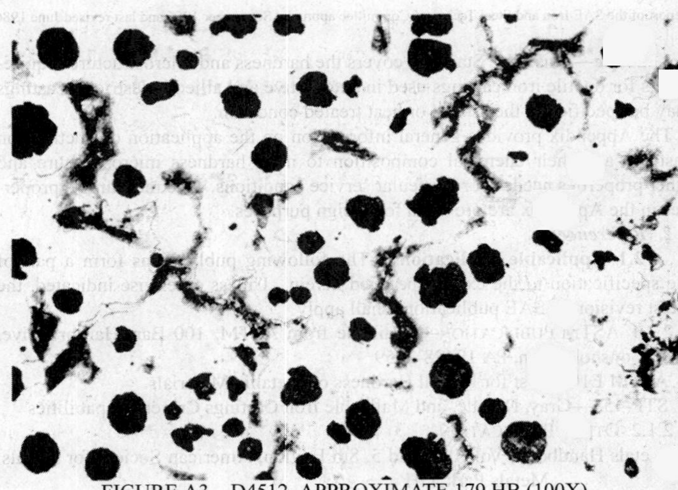

FIGURE A3—D4512, APPROXIMATE 179 HB (100X) TYPICAL MICROSTRUCTURES

D5506 is ferritic-pearlite ductile iron suppied either as-cast or heat treated. The matrix, shown in Figure A4, is essentially pearlite. This grade may contain substantially more ferrite.

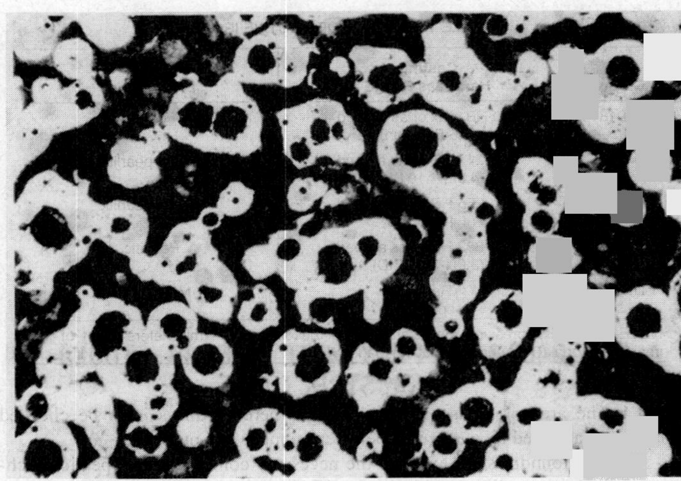

FIGURE A4—D5506, APPROXIMATE 235 HB (100X) TYPICAL MICROSTRUCTURES

D7003 (not shown) is generally air or liquid quenched and tempered to a specified hardness range. The resulting matrix is tempered pearlite or tempered martensite. Time and temperature before hardening can be such that primary carbides are decomposed.

DQ&T is a liquid quenched and tempered grade. The resulting matrix is tempered martensite. The Brinell hardness range is a matter of agreement between supplier and purchaser.

A.4 Mechanical Properties

A.4.1 The mechanical properties listed in Table A1 are intended as guidelines; but, since properties may vary with location in a given casting, the suitability of a particular metal for an intended use is best determined by laboratory or service tests.

A.4.2 The mechanical properties will vary with the microstructure which, especially in the as-cast condition, is dependent on section size as well as chemical composition and some foundry processes.

A.4.3 For optimum mechanical properties in the quenched and tempered grade, section size for unalloyed iron should generally not exceed 3/4 in (19 mm) to insure a uniform, through-hardened structure.

TABLE A1—TYPICAL MECHANICAL PROPERTIES FOR DUCTILE IRONS[1]

Grade	Hardness Range[2]	Description	Tensile Strength, psi (MPa)	Yield Strength 0.2% Off-set, psi (MPa)	Elongation, % In 2 In	Modulus of Elasticity, 10^6 psi (GPa)
D4018	170 HB max (4.6 BID min)	Ferritic	60,000 (414)	40,000 (276)	18	22 (152)
D4512	156–217 HB (4.80–4.10 BID)	Ferritic-pearlitic	65,000 (448)	45,000 (310)	12	22 (152)
D5506	187–255 HB (4.4–3.8 BID)	Ferritic-pearlitic	80,000 (552)	55,000 (379)	6	22 (152)
D7003	241–302 HB (3.9-3.5 BID)	Pearlitic	100,000 (689)	70,000 (483)	3	22 (152)
DQ&T	Range specified by agreement	Martensitic	A wide variety of desirable properties will result from liquid quenching and tempering			22 (152)

1. These properties were obtained on separately cast test bars and may vary in various sections of a casting depending on composition and cooling rate.
2. Brinell impression diameter (BID) is the diameter in millimeters (mm) of the impression of a 10 mm ball at 3000 kg load.

A.5 Typical Applications

A.5.1 D4018 is used in moderately stressed parts requiring high ductility and good machinability, such as automotive suspension parts.

A.5.2 D4512 is used for moderately stressed parts where machinability is less important, such as differential cases and carriers.

A.5.3 D5506 is used for more highly stressed parts, such as automotive crankshafts.

A.5.4 D7003 is used where high strength and/or improved wear resistance are required and where selective hardening is to be employed.

A.5.5 DQ&T is used where the uniformity of a heat treated material is required to control the range of mechanical properties or machinability.

A.6 Additional Information

a. Metals Handbook, Vol. 1, 2, and 5, 8th Edition, American Society for Metals, Metals Park, OH.
b. Gray and Ductile Iron Castings Handbook, Gray and Ductile Iron Founders Society, Cleveland, OH.
c. H. D. Angus, Physical Engineering Properties of Cast Iron, British Cast Iron Research Association, Birmingham, England.
d. STP-455—Gray, Ductile, and Malleable Iron Castings Current Capabilities, American Society for Testing and Materials, 100 Barr Harbor Drive, West Conshohocken, PA 19428-2959.

AUTOMOTIVE DUCTILE IRON CASTINGS FOR HIGH TEMPERATURE APPLICATIONS—SAE J2582 DEC2001

SAE Standard

Report of the SAE Iron and Steel Division 9—Automotive Iron and Steel Castings of the SAE Iron and Steel Technical Committee approved December 2001. Rationale statement available.

1. Scope—This SAE Standard covers the hardness, chemical analysis and microstructural requirements for ductile iron castings intended for high temperature service in automotive and allied industries. Commonly known as SiMo ductile iron, typical applications are in piston-engine exhaust manifolds and turbocharger parts. Castings may be specified in the as-cast or heat treated condition.

For design purposes, the Appendix provides general information on the application of high temperature ductile iron castings, their processing conditions, chemical composition, mechanical properties and microstructure.

2. References

2.1 Applicable Publications—The following publications form a part of this specification to the extent specified herein. Unless otherwise specified, the latest issue of SAE publications shall apply.

2.1.1 SAE PUBLICATIONS—Available from SAE, 400 Commonwealth Drive, Warrendale, PA 15096-0001.

SAE J417—Hardness Tests and Hardness Number Conversions
SAE J434—Automotive Ductile (Nodular) Iron Castings

2.1.2 ASTM PUBLICATIONS—Available from ASTM, 100 Barr Harbor Drive, West Conshohocken, PA 19428-2959.

ASTM A 247—Test Method for Evaluating the Microstructure of Graphite in Iron Castings
ASTM A 439—Austenitic Ductile Iron Castings
ASTM A 536—Standard Specification for Ductile Iron Castings
ASTM E 10—Test Method for Brinell Hardness of Metallic Material
ASTM E 351—Chemical Analysis of Cast Iron - All Types
ASTM E 1999—Analysis of Cast Iron by Optical Emission Spectrometry

2.2 Related Publications—The following publications are provided for information purposes only and are not a required part of this document.

2.2.1 SAE PUBLICATION—Available from SAE, 400 Commonwealth Drive, Warrendale, PA 15096-0001.

SAE J2515—High Temperature Materials for Exhaust Manifolds [See especially the comprehensive bibliography therein.]

2.2.2 ASM PUBLICATIONS—Available from ATTN: MSC/Book Order, ASM International, PO Box 473, Novelty, OH 44072-9901.

Metals Handbook, Vol. 1 & 15, 10th Ed. 1990 & 1988. ASM International, Materials Park, OH,
J.R. Davis (ed.); ASM Specialty Handbook - Cast Irons, 1996. ASM International, Materials Park, OH

2.2.3 ASTM PUBLICATIONS—Available from ASTM, 100 Barr Harbor Drive, West Conshohocken, PA 19428-2959.

STP-455—Gray, Ductile, and Malleable Iron Castings Current Capabilities

2.2.4 IRON CASTING PUBLICATIONS

Iron Castings Handbook, 2nd edition, 1981. Iron Castings Society, Cleveland, OH.

2.2.5 OTHER PUBLICATIONS

H.D. Angus; Cast Iron: Physical and Engineering Properties, 2nd Ed. 1976. BCIRA, Birmingham, UK
R. Eliott; Cast Iron Technology, 1988. Butterworth & Co., London, UK
Data Handbook for Ductile Cast Irons, 1997. Castings Development Centre, Sheffield, UK

3. Grades—The specified grades, chemical analysis requirements and casting hardness ranges are shown in Table 1.

TABLE 1—GRADES OF HIGH TEMPERATURE DUCTILE IRON

GRADE	Casting Hardness, HB	Silicon, %	Molybdenum, %
1	187 - 241	3.50 - 4.50	0.50 maximum
2	187 - 241	3.50 - 4.50	0.51- 0.70
3	196 - 269	3.50 - 4.50	0.71 - 1.00

4. Hardness

4.1 The area or areas on the castings where hardness is to be controlled and the hardness test method or methods to be used shall be established by agreement between the foundry and the purchaser.

4.2 The foundry shall exercise the necessary controls and inspection techniques to insure compliance with the specified casting hardness ranges. Brinell hardness shall be determined in accordance with ASTM E 10 after sufficient material has been removed from the casting surface to insure representative hardness readings. The 10 mm ball and 3000 kgf load for 10 s shall be used unless otherwise specified. Where agreed, other hardness test methods shall be in accordance with both SAE J417 and the applicable ASTM Test Methods.

5. Chemical composition

5.1 The concentrations of the elements silicon and molybdenum shall be controlled as specified in Table 1. Non-mandatory ranges typical for some other elements are found in the Appendix on Table A1.

5.2 Chemical composition shall be determined from samples representative of the castings and in accordance with applicable portions of ASTM E 1999, ASTM E 351, or other applicable ASTM Test Methods.

5.3 The chemical composition of high temperature ductile iron is such that the nil-ductility transition temperature is commonly at or above room temperature. Accordingly, and unlike general-purpose ductile iron castings, these castings may exhibit brittle fracture behavior if roughly handled.

6. Microstructure

6.1 The graphite component of the microstructure shall consist of at least 80% spheroidal graphite nodules conforming to Types I and II in Figure 1 as determined in accordance with ASTM A 247.

6.2 The matrix component shall consist of a mixture of ferrite and no more than 25% pearlite. Carbides, where present, may not exceed 5%.

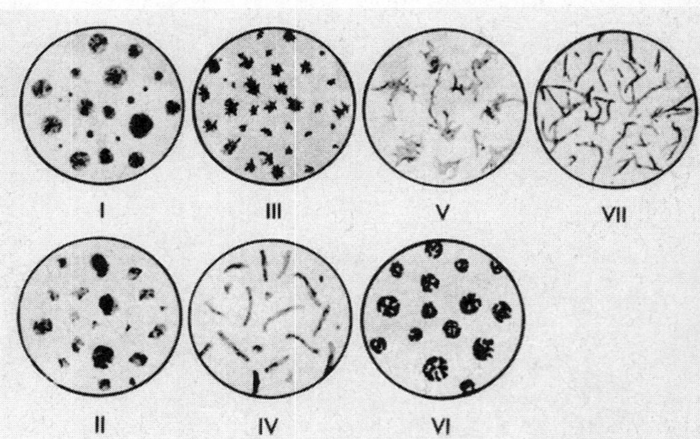

FIGURE 1—CLASSIFICATION OF GRAPHITE SHAPE IN CAST IRONS (FROM ASTM A 247)

7. Heat treatment—By documented agreement between the foundry and the purchaser, heat treatment of high temperature ductile iron castings is permitted provided the requirements for the grade are met.

8. Quality Assurance—Sampling plans are a matter of agreement between foundry and purchaser. The foundry shall employ adequate equipment and controls to ensure that the castings conform to the mandatory requirements of this standard and to any other agreements made by the parties.

9. General

9.1 Castings furnished to this standard shall be representative of good foundry practice and shall conform to dimensions and tolerances specified on the applicable drawing or engineering data base.

9.2 Minor imperfections usually not associated with structural function may occur in castings. These imperfections are often repairable; however, repairs shall be made only in those areas and by those methods agreed between the foundry and the purchaser.

9.3 Additional casting requirements, such as foundry identification, other casting information and special testing, may be agreed upon by the foundry and the purchaser.

APPENDIX A
HIGH TEMPERATURE DUCTILE IRON
(A MATERIAL DESCRIPTION NOT A PART OF THIS DOCUMENT)

A.1 Definition and Classification—High temperature ductile iron is a ductile (or nodular or spheroidal graphite) iron alloyed for applications where resistance to elevated temperature effects is an important material property.

High temperature ductile iron castings may be used in the as-cast condition or, as agreed between the foundry and the purchaser, it may be heat treated.

A.2 Hardness—Many applications of high temperature ductile iron are in predominantly thin section (<6 mm) castings for which the standard 10 mm ball/3000 kgf Brinell Hardness Test is inappropriate. Users of this document should consider carefully which alternative hardness test methods will be employed and at which point or points on the casting the hardness measurement will be made.

A.3 Chemical Composition—Other chemical elements of interest, not covered in Table 1 are shown in Table A1. The ranges are illustrative only and individual foundries will typically hold ranges significantly narrower than those indicated in Table A1. Other elements, notably copper, nickel, cerium and other rare earth metals, may also be present.

TABLE A1—TYPICAL COMPOSITION

Element	Typical ranges, %
Carbon	3.30 - 3.80
Manganese	0.10 - 0.50
Phosphorus	0.050 max
Sulfur	0.035 max
Magnesium[1]	0.025 - 0.060

1. Cerium and other rare earth elements may be substituted for a portion of the magnesium.

A more extensive discussion of ductile iron composition can be found in the Appendix to SAE J434.

A.4 Microstructure

A.4.1 The microstructure of high temperature ductile iron consists of spheroidal graphite nodules in a matrix composed of ferrite and, in substantially lesser amounts, pearlite. The actual amount of pearlite present in a given casting section will depend upon the grade of material specified, the effective cooling rate experienced by that section, the details of the chemical composition and heat treatments, if any.

A.4.2 Depending on the grade of material chosen and other influences as described above in A.4.1, minor amounts of carbide may be present at eutectic cell boundaries. These are often a complex mix of iron and molybdenum carbides which can be decomposed, completely or partially, by appropriate heat treatment.

A.4.3 Where employed, other alloying elements may influence the relative amounts of ferrite, pearlite and carbide present in the microstructure.

A.4.4 Iron castings, especially those that have been heat treated, commonly exhibit a shallow (approximately 1 mm thick) surface zone or rim that differs in composition and microstructure from the underlying material. This zone may be depleted in carbon content and may contain, depending on specific conditions, more (or less) pearlite than the bulk of the material.

A.5 Mechanical Properties

A.5.1 The mechanical properties expected in the various grades of high temperature ductile iron when poured into separate, standard test coupons (in accordance with ASTM A 536) are shown in Table A2. Test results obtained from sections cut from castings can be expected to vary, i.e., be greater or less, depending upon casting geometry and the actual cooling rate experienced by the section.

A.5.2 Since properties vary with location in a given casting, the suitability of a particular material or grade in a given application is best determined by laboratory or service tests.

A.6 Typical Applications

A.6.1 High temperature ductile iron fills a niche between general-purpose ductile irons, as in SAE J434 and heavily-alloyed austenitic ductile iron, ASTM A 439. Applications include exhaust manifolds, turbocharger parts and other castings where a modest resistance to elevated temperature is required.

A.6.2 For the most part, resistance to high temperature effects, i.e., scaling, growth and heat-checking, is conferred by the presence of elevated levels of silicon and molybdenum. So as a general rule, Grade 1 will be specified for the least demanding applications, Grade 3 for the most demanding and Grade 2 for intermediate ones.

TABLE A2—TYPICAL MECHANICAL PROPERTIES

Grade	Hardness HB	Tensile Strength MPa	Tensile Strength ksi	Yield Strength MPa	Yield Strength ksi	% Elongation	Young's Modulus GPa	Young's Modulus Mpsi
1	187 - 241	450	65	275	40	8	152	22
2	187 - 241	485	70	380	55	6	152	22
3	197 - 269	515	75	415	60	4	152	22

AUTOMOTIVE COMPACTED GRAPHITE IRON CASTINGS—SAE J1887 JUL2002

SAE Standard

Report of the SAE Metals Technical Committee Division 9—Automotive Iron and Steel Castings of the SAE Metals Technical Committee approved July 2002.

1. Scope

1.1 This SAE Standard covers the mechanical and physical requirements for Compacted Graphite Iron (CGI) castings used in automotive and allied industries. Requirements in this document include:

a. Tensile Strength
b. Yield Strength
c. Elongation
d. Graphite Morphology

1.2 Appendix A provides general information on application of this material along with additional data on mechanical and physical properties not specified but useful as a design reference. Appendix B provides a Compacted Graphite Iron Percent Nodularity Rating Chart not specified but useful as a visual reference.

2. References

2.1 Applicable Publications—The following publications form a part of this specification to the extent specified herein.

2.1.1 ASTM PUBLICATIONS—Available from ASTM, 100 Barr Harbor Drive, West Conshohocken, PA 19428-2959.

ASTM A 247—Test Method for Evaluating the Microstructure of Graphite in Iron Castings

ASTM E 8M—Test Methods for Tension Testing of Metallic Materials (Metric)

ASTM E 9—Test Methods of Compression Testing of Metallic Materials at Room Temperature

ASTM E 10—Test Method for Brinell Hardness of Metallic Materials

ASTM E 21—Test Methods for Elevated Temperature Tension Tests of Metallic Materials

ASTM E 132—Standard Test Method for Poisson's Ratio at Room Temperature

2.2 Related Publications—The following publications are provided for information purposes only and are not a required part of this specification.

2.2.1 SAE PUBLICATIONS—Available from SAE, 400 Commonwealth Drive, Warrendale, PA 15096-0001.

I.C.H. Hughes and J. Powell, "Compacted Graphite Irons – High Quality Engineering Materials in the Cast Iron Family," SAE Paper 840772, 1984.

S. Dawson, I. Hollinger, M. Robbins, J. Daeth, U. Reuter and H. Schultz, "The Effect of Metallurgical Variables on the Machinability of Compacted graphite Iron," SAE Technical Paper Series 2001-01-0409, March 2001.

2.2.2 OTHER

E. Nechtelberger, H. Puhr, J.B. van Nesselrode and A. Nakayasu, "Cast Iron with Vermicular/Compacted Graphite – State of the Art," International Foundry Congress, Chicago, Illinois, April 1983.

D.M. Stefanescu and C.R. Loper, "Recent Progress in the Compacted/Vermicular Graphite Cast Iron Field," Giesserei-Prax., No. 5.

S. Dawson, I. Hollinger and P. Smiles, "The Mechanical and Physical properties of Compacted Graphite Iron," Global Powertrain Congress, Detroit, October 1998

3. Grades

3.1 The specified grades, minimum mechanical properties and microstructure requirements, are shown in Table 1.

4. Hardness

4.1 The hardness ranges provided in Table 1 are guidelines only.

4.2 The area or areas on the casting where hardness may be checked should be established by agreement between the manufacturer and the purchaser.

4.3 Brinell hardness shall be determined according to ASTM E 10, Test for Brinell Hardness of Metallic Materials, after sufficient material has been removed from the casting to ensure representative hardness readings. A 10 mm ball, 3000 kg load and 10 second delay time shall be used unless otherwise agreed upon.

5. Heat Treatment

5.1 Appropriate heat treatment to obtain minimum mechanical properties, remove residual stresses, or improve machinability may only be performed by agreement between the manufacturer and the purchaser.

6. Microstructure

6.1 The metallographic examination of Graphite Morphology shall be performed in the specified critical region of the casting, test lug from the casting or separately cast test coupon or cast test bar as agreed between the manufacturer and the purchaser.

6.2 Compacted graphite iron shall be examined metallographically for the specified graphite morphology. The microstructure shall contain the specified percentage of graphite nodules, Types I and II (reference Plate 1, Graphite Form Types of ASTM A 247). The percentage of nodular graphite can be determined by manual particle count, semiautomatic or automatic image analysis or chart comparison techniques as agreed between the manufacturer and the purchaser. The remaining graphite particles shall be in the compacted graphite shape, Type IV. Flake graphite, Type VII is not permitted.

6.3 The matrix microstructure shall consist of ferrite, pearlite or a combination of these and be substantially free of primary cementite.

7. Quality Assurance

7.1 It is the responsibility of the manufacturer to demonstrate process capability. The specimen(s) used to do so shall be of a configuration and from a location agreed upon between the manufacturer and the purchaser.

7.2 Sampling plans shall be agreed between the manufacturer and the purchaser. The manufacturer shall employ adequate controls to ensure that parts conform to the agreed upon requirements.

7.3 Non-destructive methods may be utilized to assess graphite morphology when correlation to microstructure has been established and agreed between the manufacturer and the purchaser.

8. General

8.1 Castings furnished to this document shall be representative of good foundry practice and shall conform to the dimensions and tolerances specified on the casting drawing.

8.2 Minor imperfections usually not associated with the structural functioning may occur in castings. These imperfections are often repairable, however, repairs should be made only in areas and by methods approved by the purchaser.

8.3 The manufacturer and the purchaser may agree upon additional casting requirements, such as manufacturer identification, other casting information and special testing. These should appear as additional product requirements on the casting drawing.

TABLE 1—MINIMUM MECHANICAL PROPERTIES AND MICROSTRUCTURE FOR COMPACTED GRAPHITE IRON(1)

Grade(2)	Typical Hardness Range	Minimum Tensile Strength MPa	Minimum Tensile Strength ksi	Minimum 0.2% Yield Strength MPa	Minimum 0.2% Yield Strength ksi	Minimum % Elongation	Typical Matrix Microstructure	Graphite Morphology % Nodularity(3)
C250	121-179 HB	250	36.3	175	25.4	3.0	Ferritic	<20
C300HN	131-189 HB	300	43.5	175	25.4	3.0	Ferritic	20-50
C300	143-207 HB	300	43.5	210	30.5	2.5	Ferritic / Pearlitic	<20
C350	163-229 HB	350	50.8	245	35.5	2.0	Ferritic / Pearlitic	<20
C400	197-255 HB	400	58.0	280	40.6	1.5	Pearlitic / Ferritic	<20
C450	207-269 HB	450	65.3	315	45.7	1.0	Pearlitic	<20
C500HN	207-269 HB	500	72.5	315	45.7	1.5	Pearlitic	20-50

1. Refer to 7.1
2. "HN" denotes "High Nodularity". These grades are characterized by having 20 to 50% nodularity while conventional CGI is characterized by having less than 20% nodularity.
3. Refer to 6.1

APPENDIX A
COMPACTED GRAPHITE IRON
(MATERIAL DESCRIPTION NOT A PART OF THE STANDARD REQUIREMENTS)

A.1 Material Description

A.1.1 The graphite particles in Compacted Graphite Iron (Figure A1) appear as individual 'worm-shaped' or vermicular particles. The particles are elongated and randomly oriented as in gray iron, however they are shorter and thicker, and have rounded edges. While the compacted graphite particles appear vermicular when viewed in two dimensions, deep-etched SEM micrographs show that the individual 'worms' are connected to their nearest neighbors within the eutectic cell. This complex coral-like graphite morphology, together with the rounded edges and irregular bumpy surfaces, results in strong adhesion between the graphite and the matrix. The compacted graphite morphology inhibits the initiation and growth of cracks and is the source of the improved mechanical properties relative to gray iron.

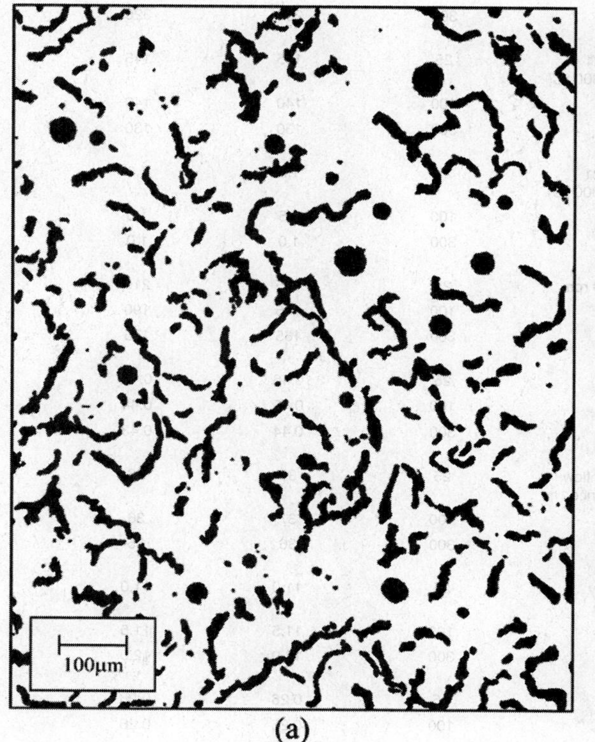

(a)

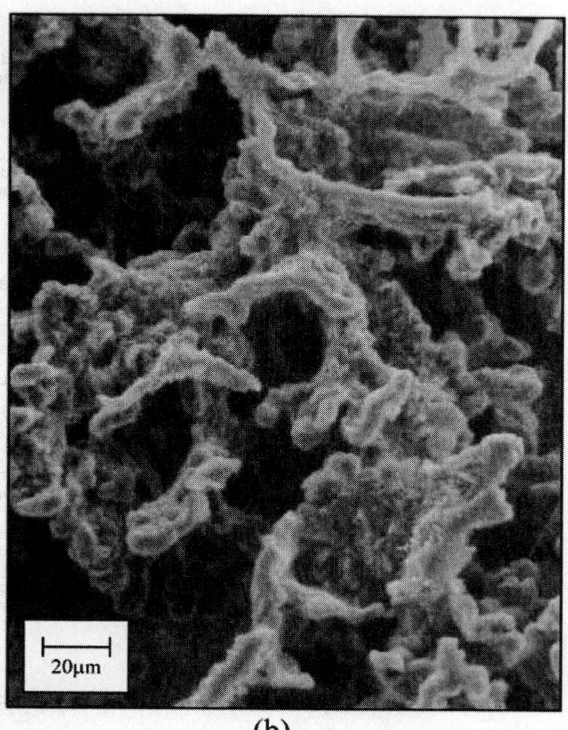

(b)

FIGURE A1—COMPACTED GRAPHITE IRON VIEWED (A) ON A TWO-DIMENSIONAL PLANE-OF-POLISH (10% NODULARITY CGI) AND (B) WITH A SCANNING ELECTRON MICROSCOPE AFTER DEEP-ETCHING.

A.2 Commercial Production Methods

A.2.1 The compacted graphite morphology is achieved by the addition of certain modifying elements to a low sulfur base iron prior to casting. Similar to ductile iron, most commercial compacted graphite iron is produced by the addition of magnesium, alone or in combination with rare earth elements such as cerium, that have a similar modifying effect on the graphite. Conventional CGI (<20% nodularity) is stable over a range of approximately 0.008% magnesium. Process control is most critical at the low end of this range. CGI is separated from gray iron by an abrupt transition of only about 0.001% magnesium. If the magnesium content is insufficient, flake-type graphite will form causing an immediate 20-30% decrease in mechanical properties. Magnesium contents above the stable range promote higher percent nodularity. Higher percent nodularity (20-50%) provides modest increases in mechanical properties with simultaneous reductions in the thermal conductivity, castability and machinability of CGI.

A.2.2 Control of the compacted graphite structure within the conventional nodularity range can be achieved by the addition of titanium, which inhibits graphite nodule formation. The addition of titanium allows higher magnesium contents to be used thus safely avoiding flake-type graphite formation while restricting the natural tendency to higher percent nodularity. Titanium additions, however, may reduce the machinability of CGI (See A.5.8.)

A.2.3 The compacted graphite structure has also been achieved without the aid of titanium by close control of the modifying elements as defined above and/or thermal analysis measurements of the iron prior to casting. Thermal analysis methods accurately assess the solidification characteristics of a small sample of iron that are then applied to the bulk iron to insure it is cast within the desired nodularity range. The titanium-free production processes are better suited for high volume castings that require extensive machining.

A.3 Material Properties Summary

A.3.1 The material properties of compacted graphite iron are intermediate to those of gray and ductile iron. CGI has better strength and stiffness than gray iron and better castability, machinability and thermal conductivity than ductile iron, making it ideal for components with simultaneous mechanical and thermal loading. The relative properties of gray, compacted graphite and ductile iron are provided in Table A1.

TABLE A1—RELATIVE PROPERTIES OF PEARLITIC GRAY, COMPACTED, AND DUCTILE IRONS

Property	Gray Iron	CGI	Ductile Iron
Tensile Strength	55	100	155
0.2% Yield Strength	—	100	155
Elastic Modulus	75	100	110
Elongation	0	100	200
R-B Fatigue	55	100	125
Hardness	85	100	115
Thermal Conductivity	130	100	75
Damping Capacity	285	100	65

An overview of the mechanical and physical properties of CGI is provided in Table A2.

TABLE A2—MECHANICAL AND PHYSICAL PROPERTIES OF CGI

Property	Test Method	Temp. (°C)	70% Pearlite	100% Pearlite
Ultimate Tensile Strength (MPa)	ASTM E 8M (25 °C) ASTM E 21 (100 °C and 300 °C)	25	420	450
		100	415	430
		300	375	410
0.2% Yield Strength (MPa)	ASTM E 8M and E 21 ASTM E 21 (100 °C and 300 °C)	25	315	370
		100	295	335
		300	284	320
Elastic Modulus (GPa)	ASTM E 8M and E 21 ASTM E 21 (100 °C and 300 °C)	25	145	145
		100	140	140
		300	130	130
Elongation (%)	ASTM E 8M and E 21 ASTM E 21 (100 °C and 300 °C)	25	1.5	1.0
		100	1.5	1.0
		300	1.0	1.0
Unnotched Fatigue Limit (MPa)	Rotating-Bending, 3000 rpm	25	195	210
		100	185	190
		300	165	175
Endurance Ratio	Fatigue Limit/UTS	25	0.46	0.44
		100	0.45	0.44
		300	0.44	0.43
Thermal Conductivity (W/m-°C)	Comparative axial heat flow Electrolytic iron reference	25	37	36
		100	37	36
		300	36	35
Thermal Expansion Coefficient (µm/m-°C)	Pushrod dilatometry Platinum reference	25	11.0	11.0
		100	11.5	11.5
		300	12.0	12.0
Poisson's Ratio	ASTM E 132	25	0.26	0.26
		100	0.26	0.26
		300	0.27	0.27
0.2% Compressive Yield (MPa)	ASTM E 9 (medium length)	25	400	430
		400	300	370
Density (g/cc)	Displacement (750x25x25) mm	25	7.0-7.1	7.0-7.1
Brinell Hardness (BHN)	10mm diameter ball, 3000 kg load	25	183-235	192-255

A.4 Factors Influencing Material Properties

A.4.1 Graphite Morphology—Compacted graphite irons rarely consist of only compacted graphite particles. CGI typically contains a specified amount of nodular graphite. Within the range of 0 to 50% nodularity, increasing nodularity has a positive influence on the mechanical properties. However, as percent nodularity increases, the material's physical and operational properties, such as its castability, thermal conductivity, damping capacity and machinability, can be significantly reduced. Appendix B provides CGI microstructures rated by percent nodularity for comparative evaluations.

Flake-type graphite morphologies cannot be tolerated in CGI specified areas. Flake-type 'patches' may form in CGI due to under-treatment or fading of magnesium and result in significant reductions in the mechanical properties. The influence of graphite morphology on the tensile and yield strengths of pearlitic CGI is shown in Figure A2.

A.4.2 Matrix Structure—CGI solidifies with a ferritizing tendency similar to ductile irons. Pearlitic matrix structures can readily be obtained by alloying with conventional stabilizers such as copper and tin, although antimony, arsenic, chromium, manganese, molybdenum and vanadium have also been used. The influence of percent pearlite on the tensile and yield strengths of CGI is provided in Figure A3.

The use of pearlite stabilizers in compacted graphite iron results in 10 to 15% higher hardness (Brinell) than for gray irons with similar matrix structures. Thus, a 70% pearlitic CGI has approximately the same hardness as fully pearlitic gray iron.

A.4.3 CGI Composition—The carbon content and thus carbon equivalent (CE) of cast irons influences the size, shape and number of graphite particles. As such, CE is an important factor in determining mechanical and physical properties. In order to optimize castability it is generally beneficial to increase the carbon equivalent toward eutectic solidification. The strength of CGI decreases only slightly with increasing carbon equivalent. The relative loss of strength in CGI is more similar to ductile iron and significantly less than that of gray iron. A typical CGI composition is provided in Table A3.

TABLE A3—TYPICAL CGI COMPOSITION

Carbon Equivalent	Carbon	Silicon	Sulfur	Manganese	Phosphorus
4.20-4.60%	3.5-3.8%	2.0-2.6%	<0.025%	0.20-0.50%	<0.050%

Similar to gray and ductile irons, compacted graphite irons can be alloyed with a wide range of elements to optimize properties for a given application. Specific examples include Cr-Mo alloying for heavy-duty diesel engine cylinder heads, Si-Mo alloying for exhaust manifolds and P-B alloying for cylinder liners.

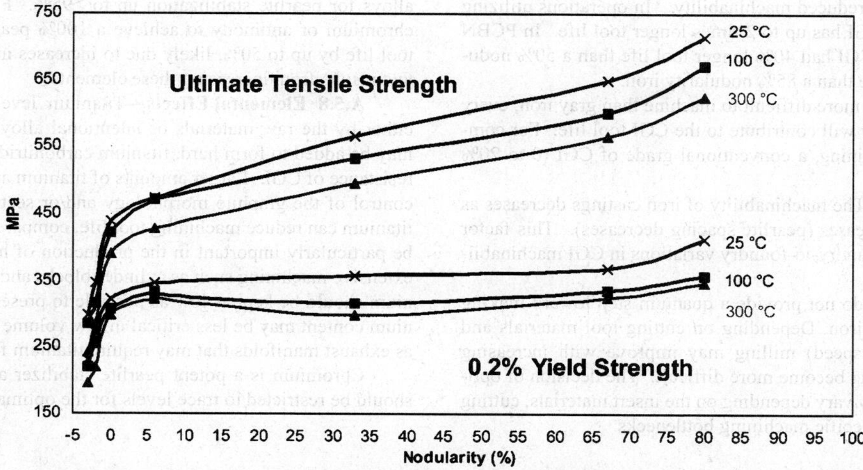

FIGURE A2—ULTIMATE TENSILE STRENGTH AND 0.2% YIELD STRENGTH OF 85 TO 100% PEARLITIC CAST IRONS AS A FUNCTION OF NODULARITY AND TEMPERATURE

NOTE—Negative % nodularity refers to the percent of the microstructure containing flake graphite wherein –5% represents a fully flake structure.

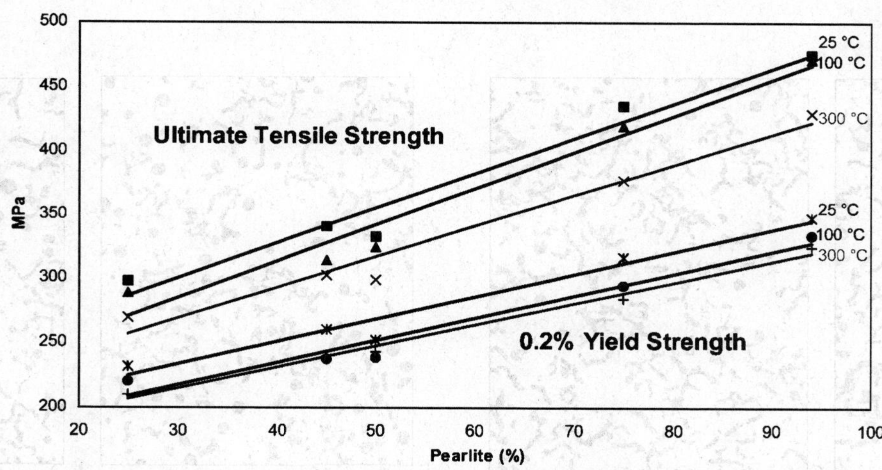

FIGURE A3—ULTIMATE TENSILE STRENGTH AND 0.2% YIELD STRENGTH OF 0 TO 10% NODULARITY CGI AS A FUNCTION OF PEARLITE CONTENT AND TEMPERATURE

A.4.4 Section Sensitivity—The CGI microstructure is sensitive to changes in section thickness or, more specifically, to changes in solidification cooling rates. The solidification and cooling rates of CGI castings are primarily governed by section thickness, however, the local casting modulus (surface area-to-volume ratio) and the preheating of sand caused by flow-through of molten metal must also be considered. Within a casting, higher cooling rates promote the formation of smaller and more nodular graphite particles and finer pearlite. For example, depending on the production process, CGI containing 10% percent nodularity in thick sections (≥6mm) may simultaneously contain 30 to 60% nodularity in thin walls (≤4mm). The changes that can occur in the microstructure influence the mechanical and physical properties. Table A4 summarizes the typical increase in mechanical and physical properties of pearlitic CGI (at 25 °C) as a function of percent nodularity.

Section sensitivity can be reduced with changes in the iron chemistry, such as the addition of titanium. Although such actions can be taken to reduce the section sensitivity, in many cases the differential cooling rates can be advantageous. In engine blocks, for example, the higher percent nodularity in thin-wall areas such as the water jacket and crankcase housings and ribs provide increased strength and stiffness to the benefit of the product.

A.5 Machinability—The machinability of CGI is intermediate between that of gray iron and ductile iron. Specific machining results depend on the microstructure, the machining operation and the machining parameters (cutting speed, feed rate, insert material and insert geometry).

TABLE A4—MECHANICAL AND PHYSICAL PROPERTIES OF PEARLITIC CAST IRONS

Material Property	Percent Nodularity 10	Percent Nodularity 30	Percent Nodularity 50	Percent Nodularity 70	Percent Nodularity 90
Tensile Strength (MPa)	450	520	590	640	700
0.2% Yield Strength (MPa)	370	390	410	440	490
Fatigue Limit (MPa)	210	220	230	240	255
Elastic Modulus (GPa)	145	150	155	155	160
Elongation (%)	1-2	1-3	2-4	2-5	3-6
Thermal Expansion (µm/m-°C)	11.0	11.0	11.0	11.5	12.0
Thermal Conductivity (W/m-°C)	37	33	31	30	28

A.5.5 Effects of Graphite Shape—As the graphite changes from a flake to compacted morphology the increase in strength and the change from a brittle to a ductile fracture mode predominate in the reduced machinability of CGI. These effects dilute and/or mask the potential contribution of other factors. Relative to gray iron, tool life reductions of 50% in carbide tooling operations to >80% in PCBN turning operations have been observed. The inability to alter the compacted graphite shape without sacrificing the material properties limits the ability to improve the machinability of the CGI itself. For example, a CGI structure containing patches of flake graphite provides approximately 30% longer tool life than normal CGI, however the flake patch structure results in reduced mechanical properties.

Increasing percent nodularity from conventional CGI to the typical ductile iron ranges also results in further reduced machinability. In operations utilizing carbide tooling, low nodularity CGI has up to 2 times longer tool life. In PCBN turning studies, a 5% nodularity CGI had 40% longer tool life than a 50% nodularity iron and 3.5 times longer life than a 85% nodularity iron.

Given that CGI is inherently more difficult to machine than gray iron, every effort to reduce percent nodularity will contribute to the CGI tool life. For components requiring extensive machining, a conventional grade of CGI (0 to 20% nodularity) should be selected.

A.5.6 Effects of Pearlite—The machinability of iron castings decreases as the Fe_3C (cementite) content increases (pearlite spacing decreases). This factor may predominate in explaining foundry-to-foundry variations in CGI machinability.

Changes in pearlite content do not provide a quantum step toward making CGI machinability equal to gray iron. Depending on cutting tool materials and machining conditions (feed and speed) milling may improve with increasing pearlite while turning and/or boring become more difficult. The decision of optimal pearlite content will ultimately vary depending on the insert materials, cutting speeds and the need to alleviate specific machining bottlenecks.

A.5.7 Effects of Alloying Elements—Copper and tin are the preferred alloys for pearlite stabilization up to >95%. Further alloying with manganese, chromium or antimony to achieve a 100% pearlitic microstructure may reduce tool life by up to 50%, likely due to increases in the Fe_3C content of the pearlite that results from increasing these elements.

A.5.8 Elemental Effects—Titanium levels in cast irons are determined either by the raw materials or intentional alloying. Small amounts of titanium may be added to form hard, titanium carbonitride inclusions to improve the wear resistance of CGI. Larger amounts of titanium are sometimes used to assist in the control of the graphite morphology and/or section sensitivity. The presence of titanium can reduce machining tool life, compared to titanium-free CGI. This can be particularly important in the production of high volume castings that require extensive machining such as cylinder blocks and heads. In these applications titanium should be kept as low as possible to preserve CGI machinability. The titanium content may be less critical in low volume or lesser-machined castings such as exhaust manifolds that may require titanium for microstructure control.

Chromium is a potent pearlite stabilizer and carbide promoter in CGI. It should be restricted to trace levels for the optimal machining of CGI.

APPENDIX B
COMPACTED GRAPHITE IRON PERCENT NODULARITY RATING CHART (MATERIAL DESCRIPTION NOT A PART OF THE STANDARD REQUIREMENTS)

B.1 See Figures B1 and B2.

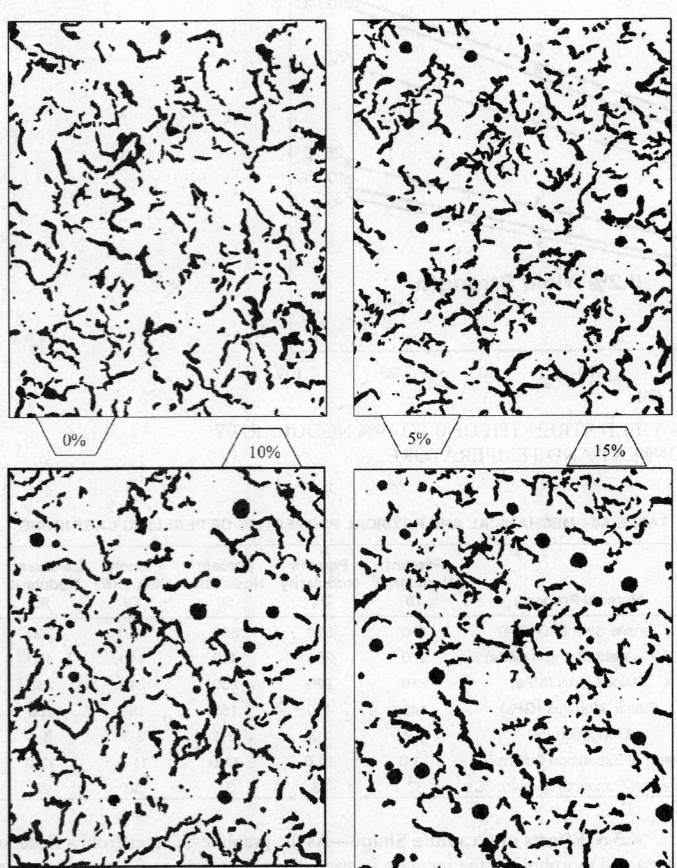

FIGURE B1—COMPACTED GRAPHITE IRON PERCENT NODULARITY RATING CHART (MATERIAL DESCRIPTION NOT A PART OF THE STANDARD REQUIREMENTS)

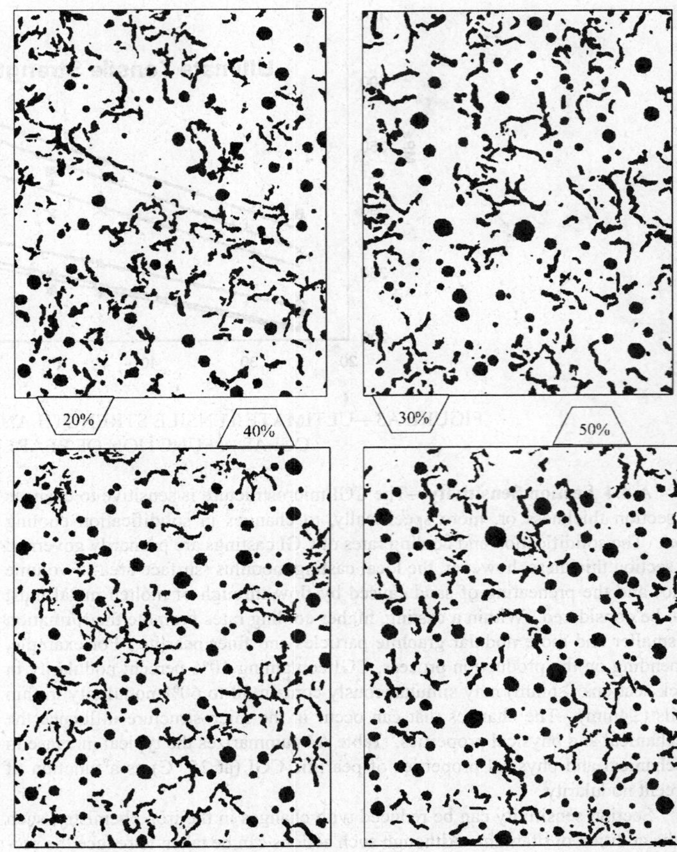

FIGURE B2—COMPACTED GRAPHITE IRON PERCENT NODULARITY RATING CHART (MATERIAL DESCRIPTION NOT A PART OF THIS DOCUMENT)

ELEVATED TEMPERATURE PROPERTIES OF CAST IRONS—SAE J125 MAY88

SAE Information Report

Report of the SAE Iron and Steel Technical Committee approved September 1969 and reaffirmed May 1988. This document is currently under revision.

Foreword—This Document has not changed other than to put it into the new SAE Technical Standards Board format.

This document is currently under revision.

1. Scope—The purpose of this SAE Information Report is to provide automotive engineers and designers with a concise statement of the basic characteristics of cast iron under elevated temperature conditions. As such, the report concentrates on general statements regarding these properties with limited illustrative data, anticipating that those who may be interested in more detail will want to use the bibliography provided at the conclusion of the report.

2. References

2.1 Related Publications—The following publications are provided for information purposes only and are not a required part of this document.

2.1.1 OTHER PUBLICATIONS

1. "Mechanical Properties of Metals and Alloys." U.S. Dept. of Commerce Circular C-447, National Bureau of Standards, 1943.
2. Kattus and McPherson, "Properties of Cast Iron at Elevated Temperatures." ASTM Special Technical Publication No. 248.
3. Malleable Iron Casting Handbook. Malleable Founders Society, 1960.
4. Gray Iron Castings Handbook. Gray Iron Founders' Society, Inc., 1958.
5. Cast Metals Handbook. American Foundrymens Society, 1957.
6. Colin J. Smithell, "Metals Reference Book." Washington Butterworths, 1962.
7. Metals Handbook, 8th Edition. American Society for Metals, 1961.
8. "Engineering Properties of Ductile Ni-Resist Austenitic Irons." International Nickel Co., 1955.
9. Schelleng and Eash, "Effect of Composition on the Elevated-Temperature Properties of Ductile Iron." Proceedings of ASTM, Vol. 57, 1957.
10. Greene and Sefing, "Cast Irons in High Temperature Service." Corrosion, Vol. 11, No. 7, July 1955.
11. Turnbull and Wallace, "Molybdenum Effect on Gray Iron Elevated Temperature Properties." Transactions AFS, Vol. 67, 1959.
12. F. B. Foley, "Mechanical Properties at Temperature of Ductile Cast Iron." Preprint No. 55-A-204, ASME, 1955.
13. Engineering Properties of Ni-Resist Ductile Irons." International Nickel Co., 1958.
14. Elevated Temperature Properties of Ductile Cast Irons." ASM Transactions, Vol. 47, 1955.
15. Scholz, Doane, and Timmons, "Effects of Molybdenum on Stability and High Temperature Properties of Pearlitic Malleable Iron." AFS Transactions, Vol. 63, 1955.
16. D. A. Pearson, "Stress-Rupture and Elongation of Malleable Iron at Elevated Temperatures." AFS Transactions, Vol. 74, 1966.
17. W. L. Collins, "Fatigue and Static Load Tests of an Austenitic Cast Iron at Elevated Temperatures." ASTM Proceedings, Vol. 48, 1948.

3. Introduction—Cast irons, like steels and other metals, lose strength as operating temperatures increase. Composition is of importance not only because of its effect on the basic properties of materials at elevated temperatures, but also because in cast irons it influences growth resulting from oxidation and microstructural changes. Irons may be used in most atmospheres at temperatures up to 750 °F without growth being a serious factor. Beyond 900 °F graphitization can cause growth and above 1200 °F internal oxidation can cause growth unless sufficient alloy is present to prevent it.

Deterioration of properties at high temperatures is in general time-dependent as well as temperature-dependent. Even at temperatures where strength has been greatly reduced, many useful hours of life can be obtained from a structure if proper allowances are made in the initial design. Where applications involve sustained stress at high temperature, the most valuable information for the designer is the creep rate at the temperature and stress involved. However, creep rate data generally involve long time tests and as a consequence complete information has not been generated for all materials under all conditions. Instead, it has been the practice for many years to compare materials in shorter duration tests. Such tests are called stress-to-rupture tests or more simply stress-rupture tests. These are conducted in the temperature ranges of interest but usually at much greater loads than any realistic design. In general, materials showing superior stress-rupture life have the lowest creep rates. This type of information has been used primarily for material development work. It can be used by the designer, however, to select better material on a comparison basis.

Several types of iron are included in this section to show trends; they are representative of broad classes of irons used commercially, and for which thermal data are available in the literature.

4. Effect of Elevated Temperature on Mechanical Properties

4.1 Tensile Strength—The tensile strength of ferrous materials generally shows small changes from room temperature up to 600–800 °F, at higher temperature the strengths usually fall rather rapidly. The presence of alloying elements which affect the stability of the higher strength microstructures tends to delay this effect or raise the temperature at which rapid loss of strength occurs. In some ferrous alloys, changes in microstructure occur at temperatures between room temperature and 800 °F which may cause small changes in strength and, in fact, may cause reversals in the strength versus temperature curve. In Figure 1, examples of tensile strength versus temperature for some typical cast irons are illustrated in comparison with the behavior of low carbon steel. Generally, the changes in structure which occur over this temperature range are associated with tempering after hardening. These changes are irreversible.

4.2 Stress Rupture Properties—Where metals are required to sustain loads over long periods of time at elevated temperatures, the stress-rupture test is used as an indication of the relative load-carrying ability at the test temperature.

The material is stressed in tension under a constant load at a constant temperature and the time that it takes the sample to rupture under these conditions is recorded. Separate samples of the material are stressed under a number of different loads at the same temperature and the rupture times are plotted against load to give a stress-rupture curve for the material. Typical stress-rupture curves for a number of SAE cast irons and alloyed irons at 800 °F are plotted in Figure 2. Stress-rupture curves for these and other cast irons at 1000 °F are plotted in Figure 3, which includes a stress-rupture curve for low carbon wrought steel for comparison.

TABLE 1—CHEMICAL COMPOSITION FOR CAST IRONS SHOWN IN FIGURES 1–7

Material	Alloying, %								
	T.C.	C	Si	Mn	P	S	Cr	Ni	Mo	Mg
Alloy gray cast iron (ASTM A 48, No. 60) (2) [1]	3.06	—	1.79	0.70	0.04	0.09	0.61	0.04	0.84	—
Alloy gray cast iron (SAE G4500) (2)	3.31	—	1.56	0.68	0.19	0.114	0.08	0.08	0.73	—
Gray cast iron SAE G4000 (2)	3.27	—	1.74	0.72	0.26	0.156	0.08	0.15	0.07	—
Ferritic malleable (3) (Creep and stress rupture data)	2.16 2.29	—	1.01 1.17	0.29 0.38	0.11 0.148	0.074 0.095	0.017 0.000	—	—	—
Pearlitic malleable (3)	2.27 2.29	—	1.01 1.15	0.89 0.75	0.135 0.110	0.098 0.086	0.019 0.000	—	—	—
Ferritic malleable (3) (Elevated temperature tensile strength data)	2.30 2.33	—	0.98 1.05	0.30 0.34	0.162 0.168	0.078 0.084	—	—	—	—
Gray cast iron SAE G4500 (4)	2.84	—	1.52	1.05	0.07	0.124	0.31	0.20	—	—
Ferritic ductile iron (4)	3.7	—	2.6	0.40	—	—	—	1.0	—	—
Low carbon steel (7)	—	0.08 0.20	0.25	0.30 0.80	0.045	0.060	—	—	—	—
Austenitic ductile + Cr and Mo (9)	2.38	—	1.99	0.62	—	—	3.05	30.18	0.95	0.13
Austenitic ductile + Cr (9)	2.98	—	2.20	1.15	—	—	2.36	20.48	—	0.085
Ferritic ductile iron (4)	3.64	—	2.66	0.46	0.032	0.014	—	0.66	—	0.076
Austenitic cast iron (17)	2.63	—	2.14	1.23	0.16	0.059	2.09	14.9	—	—

1. Parenthetical numbers indicate source of data in 2.2.

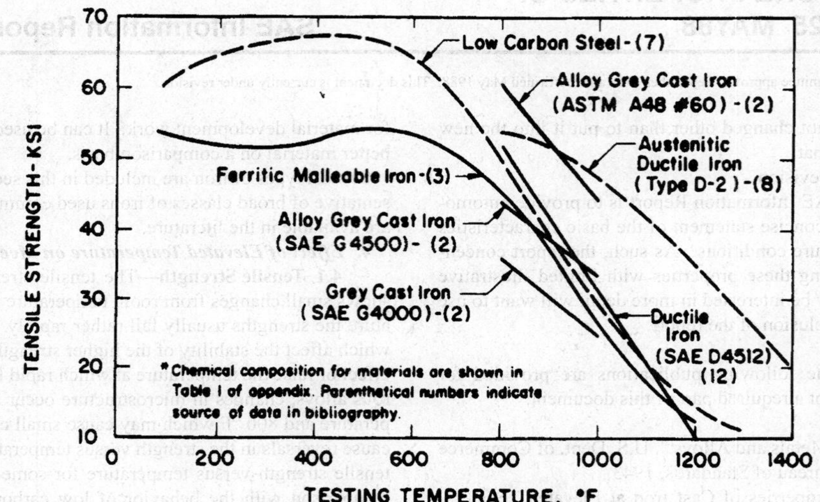

FIGURE 1—ELEVATED TEMPERATURE TENSILE STRENGTH

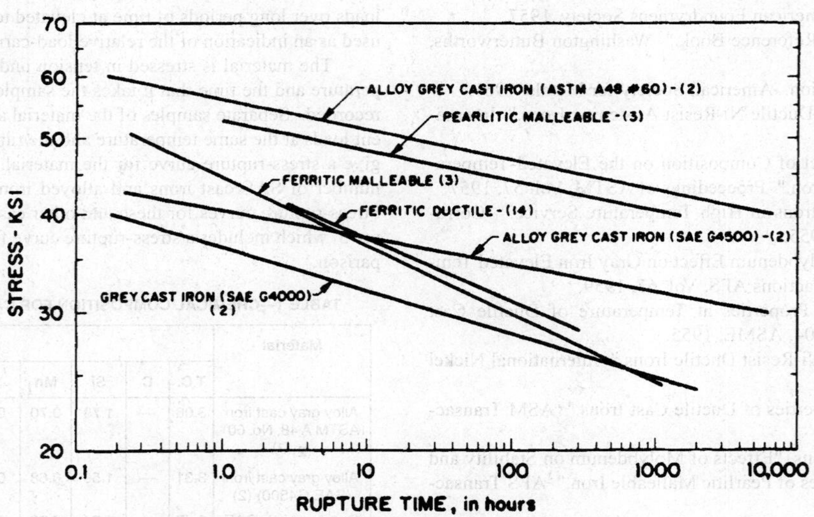

FIGURE 2—STRESS RUPTURE PROPERTIES OF CAST IRONS AT 800 °F

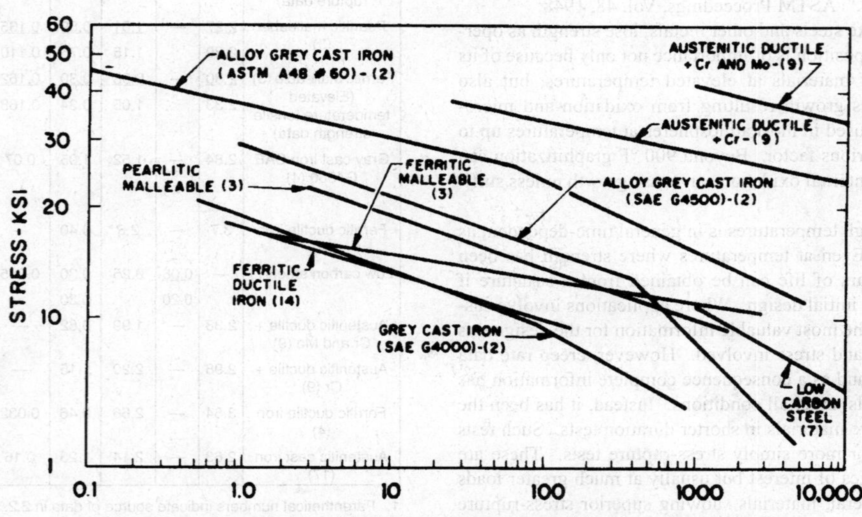

FIGURE 3—STRESS RUPTURE PROPERTIES OF CAST IRONS AT 1000 °F

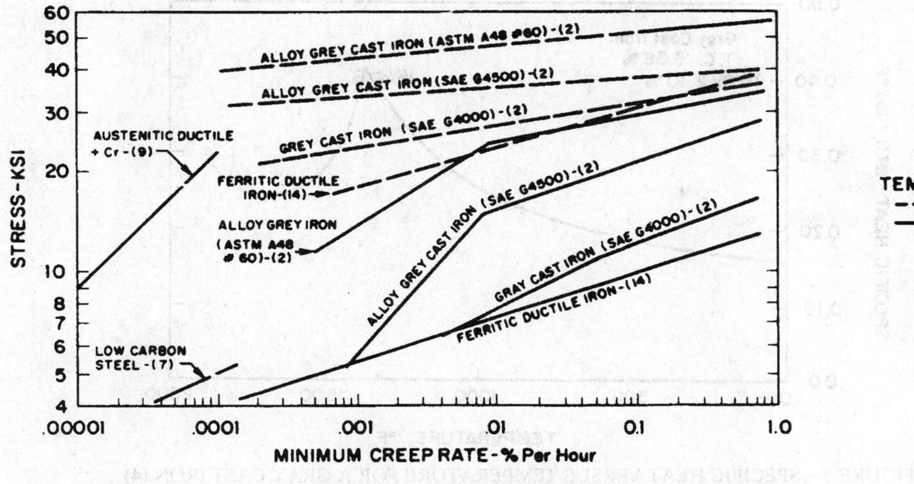

FIGURE 4—CREEP PROPERTIES OF CAST IRONS

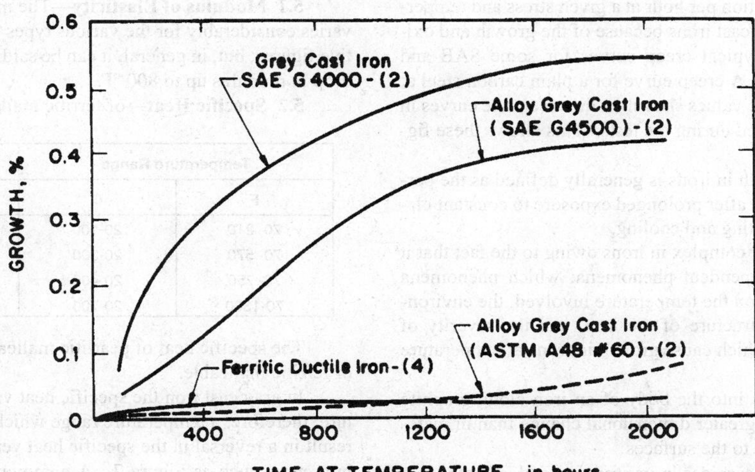

FIGURE 5—CAST IRON GROWTH AT 1000 °F

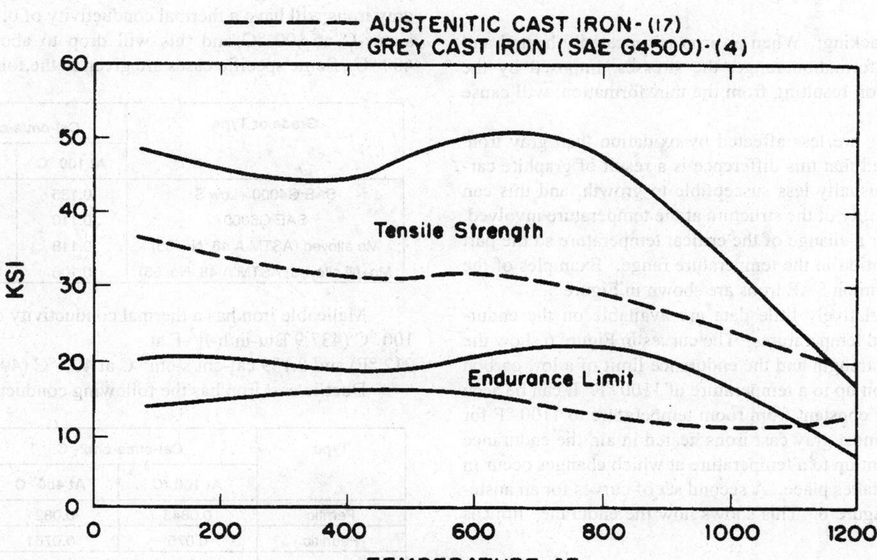

FIGURE 6—EFFECT OF TEMPERATURE ON STRENGTH AND ENDURANCE LIMIT

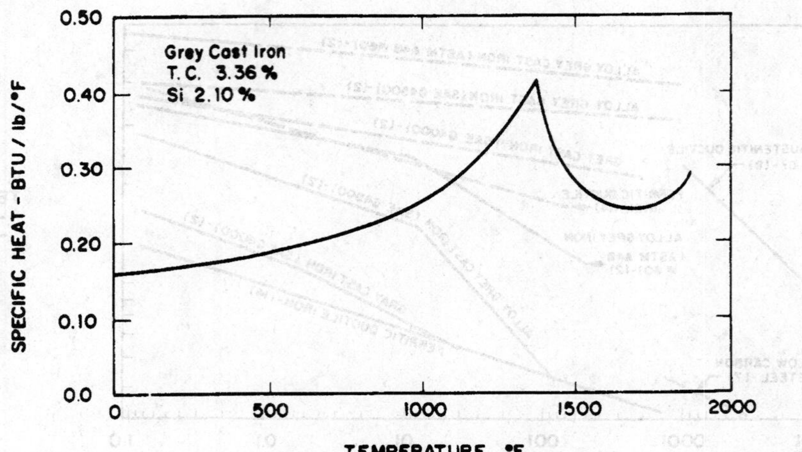

FIGURE 7—SPECIFIC HEAT VERSUS TEMPERATURE FOR A GRAY CAST IRON (4)

4.3 Creep Properties of Irons—Another important temperature effect on cast irons is the effect of creep or elongation per hour at a given stress and temperature. These tests are difficult to run on cast irons because of the growth and oxidation phenomena. Figure 4 shows typical creep curves for some SAE and alloyed cast irons at 800 ° and 1000 °F. A creep curve for a plain carbon steel at 1000 °F is included for comparison. The values shown on the creep rate curves in Figure 4 include any growth that occurred during the tests. This allows these figures to be used as design parameters.

4.4 Growth of Cast Iron—Growth in irons is generally defined as the permanent increase in volume which occurs after prolonged exposure to constant elevated temperatures or after repeated heating and cooling.

The mechanism of growth is rather complex in irons owing to the fact that it results from several different and independent phenomena; which phenomena occur in any given case is dependent upon the temperature involved, the environment, the chemical composition and structure of the iron, and the severity of cycling, if any. The main phenomena which cause growth in irons at temperature are as follows:

1. Oxidation: This may progress into the body of an iron along graphite flakes or cracks, resulting in a greater dimensional change than in materials where oxidation is limited to the surfaces.
2. Graphitization: If the iron has carbides in its structure and is heated to a temperature which will decompose the carbide structures (this temperature will vary considerably with chemistry), the resulting ferrite and graphite will occupy considerably greater volume than the original carbide.
3. Crazing or Thermal Cracking: When an iron is repeatedly heated and cooled through a transformation range, the stresses, imposed by the expansion and contraction resulting from the transformation, will cause crazing.

Ductile and malleable irons are less affected by oxidation than gray iron. Some investigators have indicated that this difference is a result of graphite carbon shapes. Alloyed irons are usually less susceptible to growth, and this can either be due to an increased stability of the structure at the temperature involved, improved oxidation resistance, or a change of the critical temperature so the part does not experience a transformation in the temperature range. Examples of the growth experienced by some common SAE irons are shown in Figure 5.

4.5 Endurance Limit—Relatively little data are available on the endurance limit of cast irons at elevated temperatures. The curves in Figure 6 show the relationship between the tensile strength and the endurance limit of a low carbon equivalent low alloy gray cast iron up to a temperature of 1100 °F. It can be seen that the endurance ratio is nearly constant from room temperature to 1100 °F for this iron. It is probable that for most gray cast irons heated in air, the endurance ratio would remain nearly constant up to a temperature at which changes occur in the structure or severe oxidation takes place. A second set of curves for an austenitic gray iron are included in Figure 6. This shows how the endurance limit is affected by structure.

5. Effect of Temperature on Physical Properties

5.1 Modulus of Elasticity—The modulus of elasticity at room temperature varies considerably for the various types of iron. It is difficult to give representative figures; but, in general, it can be said that the cast irons do not show a marked drop in modulus up to 800 °F.

5.2 Specific Heat—of ferritic malleable iron:

Temperature Range		Mean Specific Heat	
F	C	Btu/lb-F	Cal/g-C
70- 210	20-100	0.122	0.122
70- 570	20-300	0.128	0.128
70- 750	20-400	0.139	0.139
70-1300	20-700	0.159	0.159

The specific heat of pearlitic malleable iron is substantially the same as that of ferritic malleable.

In gray cast iron the specific heat varies with the temperature and the structure; therefore, a temperature range which causes a change in microstructure may result in a reversal in the specific heat versus temperature curve which will result in a curve such as Figure 7. A commonly used figure for average cast irons is 0.13 cal/g-C.

5.3 Thermal Conductivity—The thermal conductivity of gray cast iron varies considerably with both temperature and composition. Most plain and alloy gray irons will have a thermal conductivity of 0.10 to 0.135 cal-cm/s-cm^2-C at 100 °C and this will drop to about 0.09-0.115 cal-cm/s-cm^{2}C at 400 °C. Some specific cases are given in the following table:

Grade or Type	Cal-cm/s-cm^2-C		Btu-in/h-ft^2-F	
	At 100 °C	At 400 °C	at 212 °C	at 750 °F
SAE G4000 +Low S	0.135	0.114	391.5	330.6
SAE G5000	0.110	0.100	319	290
Mo alloyed (ASTM A 48, No. 55)	0.118	0.108	342.2	313.2
Mo+Ni alloyed (ASTM A 48, No. 55)	0.106	0.097	307.4	281.3

Malleable iron has a thermal conductivity of about 0.151 cal-cm/s-cm^2-C at 100 °C (437.9 Btu-in/h-ft^2-F at 212 °F) and 0.139 cal-cm/s-cm^2-C at 400 °C (403.1 Btu-in/h-ft^2-F at 750 °F).

Ductile cast iron has the following conductivity.

Type	Cal-cm/s-cm2-°C		Btu-in/h-ft2-°F	
	At 100 °C	At 400 °C	At 212 °F	At 750 °F
Ferritic	0.0845	0.0821	239.3	238.1
Pearlitic	0.075	0.0761	217.5	220.7
Austenitic	At Room Temperature 0.032		At Room Temperature 92.8	

5.4 Average Coefficient of Expansion—The coefficient of expansion of cast irons varies with temperature, and to a lesser degree with alloy content and structure or heat treatment. The following table gives values commonly used:

Type of Iron	Mean Coefficient of Linear Expansion	
	cm/c-°C 0-500 °C	in/in°F 32-932 °F
Gray iron	12.96×10^{-6}	7.2×10^{-6}
Ferritic malleable	11.88×10^{-6}	6.6×10^{-6}
Pearlitic malleable	13.5×10^{-6}	7.5×10^{-6}
	20-200 °C	68-392 °F
Ferritic ductile	$11.85–12.65 \times 10^{-6}$	$6.6–7.0 \times 10^{-6}$
Pearlitic ductile	$11.7 – 11.85 \times 10^{-6}$	$6.5–6.6 \times 10^{-6}$
Austenitic ductile	$3.98–18.9 \times 19^{-6}$	$2.2–10.5 \times 10^{-6}$

6. Bibliography

1. "Mechanical Properties of Metals and Alloys." U.S. Dept. of Commerce Circular C-447, National Bureau of Standards, 1943.
2. Kattus and McPherson, "Properties of Cast Iron at Elevated Temperatures." ASTM Special Technical Publication No. 248.
3. Malleable Iron Casting Handbook. Malleable Founders Society, 1960.
4. Gray Iron Castings Handbook. Gray Iron Founders' Society, Inc., 1958.
5. Cast Metals Handbook. American Foundrymens Society, 1957.
6. Colin J. Smithell, "Metals Reference Book." Washington Butterworths, 1962.
7. Metals Handbook, 8th Edition. American Society for Metals, 1961.
8. "Engineering Properties of Ductile Ni-Resist Austenitic Irons." International Nickel Co., 1955.
9. Schelleng and Eash, "Effect of Composition on the Elevated-Temperature Properties of Ductile Iron." Proceedings of ASTM, Vol. 57, 1957.
10. Greene and Sefing, "Cast Irons in High Temperature Service." Corrosion, Vol. 11, No. 7, July 1955.
11. Turnbull and Wallace, "Molybdenum Effect on Gray Iron Elevated Temperature Properties." Transactions AFS, Vol. 67, 1959.
12. F. B. Foley, "Mechanical Properties at Temperature of Ductile Cast Iron." Preprint No. 55-A-204, ASME, 1955.
13. Engineering Properties of Ni-Resist Ductile Irons." International Nickel Co., 1958.
14. Elevated Temperature Properties of Ductile Cast Irons." ASM Transactions, Vol. 47, 1955.
15. Scholz, Doane, and Timmons, "Effects of Molybdenum on Stability and High Temperature Properties of Pearlitic Malleable Iron." AFS Transactions, Vol 63, 1955.
16. D. A. Pearson, "Stress-Rupture and Elongation of Malleable Iron at Elevated Temperatures." AFS Transactions, Vol. 74, 1966.
17. W. L. Collins, "Fatigue and Static Load Tests of an Austenitic Cast Iron at Elevated Temperatures." ASTM Proceedings, Vol. 48, 1948.

(R) AUTOMOTIVE STEEL CASTINGS—SAE J435 OCT2002 SAE Standard

Report of the SAE Iron and Steel Technical Committee, approved October 1946, last revised July 1974. Completely revised by the SAE Iron and Steel Technical Committee Division 9—Automotive Iron and Steel Castings. Rationale statement available.

1. Scope—This SAE Standard defines the specifications for steel castings used in the automotive and allied industries.

2. References

2.1 Applicable Publications—The following publications form a part of the standard to the extent specified herein. Unless otherwise indicated the latest revision of SAE publications shall apply.

2.1.1 ASTM PUBLICATIONS—Available from ASTM, 100 Barr Harbor Drive, West Conshohocken, PA 19428-2959.

ASTM A 781/A 781M—Standard Specification for Castings, Steel and Alloy, Common Requirements, for General Industrial Use

ASTM A 370—Methods and Definitions for Mechanical Testing of Steel Products

ASTM A 802/A 802M—Standard Practice for Steel Castings, Surface Acceptance Standards, Visual Examination

ASTM A 488—Standard Practice for Steel Castings, Welding, Qualifications of Procedures and Personnel

ASTM A 781—Standard Specification for Castings, Steel and Alloy, Common Requirements, for General Industrial Use

ASTM E 1030—Standard Test Method for Radiographic Examination of Metallic Castings

ASTM E 446—Reference Radiographs for Steel Castings Up to 2 in. (51 mm) in Thickness

2.1.2 MSS PUBLICATIONS—Available from Manufacturers Standardization Society of the Valve and Fittings Industry, Inc., 127 Park Street, N.E., Vienna, Virginia 22180.

MSS SP-55—Quality Standard for Steel Castings for Valves, Flanges and Fittings and Other Piping Components – Visual Method

3. General Conditions for Delivery

3.1 Material furnished to this specification shall conform to the requirements of specifications ASTM A781/A781M, including any supplementary requirements that are indicated in the order.

4. Chemical Composition

4.1 The composition shall comply with the requirements of Table 1.

4.2 When not specified in Table 1 the content of carbon, manganese, silicon, and alloying elements may, by agreement, be prescribed by the purchaser. If not specified, the content may be selected by the manufacturer to obtain the required mechanical properties or hardenability.

5. Heat Treatment—All castings shall be supplied in the heat treated condition. The heat treatment procedure may be specified by the purchaser in a written agreement with the supplier. Unless otherwise specified, the supplier may choose to heat treat the castings by one or more of the following processes; annealing, normalizing, normalizing and tempering or quenching and tempering.

In the event of a change in the heat treatment procedure the requirements of Section 6 must be met.

6. Mechanical Properties

6.1 Mechanical testing from separately cast test bars shall be carried out in accordance with ASTM A370.

The mechanical properties shall comply with the requirements of Table 1. The test bars shall be heat treated in production furnaces. Test bars shall be heat treated to the same procedure as the castings they represent.

6.2 Product Testing—Subject to agreement between the purchaser and supplier, test bars may be taken from the castings. The location and the required mechanical properties are subject to agreement between the purchaser and supplier.

7. Frequency of Testing

7.1 Following the satisfactory achievement of the required mechanical properties of ten consecutive heats from any one grade, succeeding heats from the same grades may be qualified by hardness testing providing they fall within the range of compositions of the original 10 heats. The castings in each heat will be accepted by hardness testing of one test bar from each heat.

If the purchaser wishes to substitute complete mechanical testing then supplementary requirement 10.1 should be specified.

7.2 Retests—If any specimen shows defective machining, or exhibits flaws, it may be discarded and another substituted from the same heat.

8. Inspection

8.1 Minor discontinuities—The surface of the casting shall be free of adhering sand, scale, cracks and hot tears as determined by visual examination. Other surface discontinuities shall meet the visual acceptance standards specified in the order. Practice ASTM A 802/A 802M or other visual standards such as MSS SP-55 may be used to define acceptable surface discontinuities and finish. Unacceptable visual surface discontinuities shall be removed and their removal verified by visual examination of the resultant cavities.

8.2 Peening, plugging and impregnating of castings are not allowed.

8.3 Marking—The manufacturer's name or identification mark and the pattern number shall be cast or stamped on all castings. When further specified, the heat numbers or serial numbers shall be marked on the individual castings.

8.4 Inspection by the Purchaser—The manufacturer shall afford the purchaser's inspector all reasonable facilities necessary to satisfy him that the material is being produced and supplied in accordance with this specification. Foundry inspection by the purchaser shall not interfere with the manufacturer's operations`. All tests and inspections (except product analysis) shall be made at the place of manufacture unless otherwise agreed to.

8.5 Rejection and Rehearing—Requirements for rejections and rehearing shall be agreed between the purchaser and supplier.

TABLE 1—CHEMICAL AND MECHANICAL TEST REQUIREMENTS FROM SEPARATELY CAST TEST BARS

Grade New	Grade Old	Composition, (wt%)(1) C	Composition, (wt%)(1) Mn	Composition, (wt%)(1) Si	Composition, (wt%)(1) P	Composition, (wt%)(1) S	Mechanical Properties(2) Tensile Strength MPa	Mechanical Properties(2) Tensile Strength (ksi)	Mechanical Properties(2) Yield Strength MPa	Mechanical Properties(2) Yield Strength (ksi)	Mechanical Properties(2) El %	Mechanical Properties(2) R in A %	Mechanical Properties(2) HBW
0000	0022	0.12	0.50–0.90	0.60	0.40	0.045	—	—	—	—	—	—	187 max
415	0025	0.25	0.75(3)	0.80	0.040	0.045	415	(60)	205	(30)	22	30	187 max
450	0030	0.30	0.70(3)	0.80	0.040	0.045	450	(65)	240	(35)	24	35	131–187
585	0050A	0.40–0.50	0.50–0.90	0.80	0.040	0.045	585	(85)	310	(45)	16	24	170–229
690	0050B	0.40–0.50	0.50–0.90	0.80	0.040	0.045	690	(100)	485	(70)	10	15	207–255
550	080	—	—	—	0.040	0.045	550	(80)	345	(50)	22	35	163–207
620	090	—	—	—	0.040	0.045	620	(90)	415	(60)	20	40	187–241
725	0105	—	—	—	0.040	0.045	725	(105)	585	(85)	17	35	217–248
830	0120	—	—	—	0.040	0.045	830	(120)	655	(95)	14	30	248–311
1035	0150	—	—	—	0.040	0.045	1035	(150)	860	(125)	9	22	311–363
1205	0175	—	—	—	0.040	0.045	1205	(175)	1000	(145)	6	21	363–415

1. Single values are maxima.
2. Unless otherwise indicated single values are minima.
3. For each reduction of 0.01% below the specified maximum carbon content an increase of 0.04% manganese above the specified maximum will be permitted to a maximum of 1%.

9. Welding—Welding may be carried out by the producer. The welder and procedure must be qualified to the requirements of ASTM A 488. Welds shall be subject to the same inspection standards as the casting.

10. Supplementary Requirements—The following supplementary requirements may be specified at the time of the inquiry and order.

10.1 The castings in each heat will be accepted from one mechanical test specimen.

10.2 Limits for unspecified elements and the methods of analysis for them shall be as agreed upon by the supplier and purchaser.

10.3 Details of the following supplementary requirements may be found in ASTM A781/A781M.

10.3.1 Proof Testing
10.3.2 Destructive Tests
10.3.3 Radiographic Examination
10.3.4 Ultrasonic Examination
10.3.5 Magnetic Particle Examination

The acceptance standards for radiography, ultrasonic, magnetic particle examination, and destructive testing shall be agreed upon by the purchaser and supplier at the time of the enquiry and order.

APPENDIX A
A BRIEF GUIDE ON THE USE OF STEEL CASTING SPECIFICATIONS

A.1 Introduction—A steel casting like any other manufactured item, is purchased to fill a predetermined role. The necessary attributes of the casting such as strength, toughness, corrosion resistance, heat resistance, soundness and dimensional tolerances are dictated by the user. These characteristics are based on the conditions which will be encountered in service. These requirements must be clearly and accurately stated with nothing taken for granted.

These specifications can be found in a number of places, e.g., ASTM, ASME, ISO, SAE, and proprietary sources.

It is very important not to over specify as this may result in higher costs and longer lead times. It is equally wrong to under specify, leaving requirements vague or too broad will usually lead to the foundry supplying castings to a different quality level than that expected by the user. For example, stating that the castings shall be radiographed in accordance with ASTM E 1030 with acceptance levels stated in ASTM E 446 is not helpful. It is good that ASTM standards have been referenced but the acceptance standard has not been defined. This situation at best can lead to delays in determining from the customer which acceptance level he requires and at worst can lead the foundry to supply castings which may have been required at severity level 2 but may have been supplied at level 4. It is important that the term "commercial quality" not be used, it tends to be vague and will only lead to problems.

A.2 General—The specifications issued by ASTM, ASME, ISO, and SAE will contain such requirements as;

a. Chemical composition
b. Mechanical properties
c. Physical properties
d. Processes
e. Procedures
f. Testing and examination requirements
g. Surface roughness and integrity
h. Internal soundness

ASTM and ISO provide the most complete coverage of these requirements for steel castings where the specifications from other organizations may be used in combination with ASTM or ISO to provide some particular attributes for particular markets.

A.3 Conflicting Requirements—One of the most troubling situations that may arise is that of conflicting requirements. Some of the most common instances are;

a. The minimum tensile properties of the material specification and the hardness range given on the drawing do not correspond.
b. The material specification, the casting drawing and/or the purchase order have incompatible requirements.
c. The drawing revision number in the inquiry is not same as that referenced in the purchase order.
d. The enquiry and the purchase order have different NDE or other processing requirements.
e. Acceptance standards are not clearly defined.
f. A third-party inspector invokes requirements differing from those furnished to the foundry by the casting buyer.

AUTOMOTIVE AUSTEMPERED DUCTILE (NODULAR) IRON CASTINGS (ADI)—SAE J2477 MAR2003

SAE Standard

Report of the SAE Metals Technical Committee Division 9—Automotive Iron and Steel Castings approved March 2003.

1. Scope—This SAE Standard covers the mechanical and physical property requirements for Austempered Ductile Iron (ADI) castings used in automotive and allied industries. Specifically covered are:

a. Hardness
b. Tensile Strength
c. Yield Strength
d. Elongation
e. Modulus of Elasticity
f. Impact Energy
g. Microstructure

In this document SI units are primary and in-lb units are derived. Appendix A provides general information and related resources on the microstructural, chemical and heat treatment requirements to meet the mechanical properties needed for ADI in particular service conditions and applications.

2. References

2.1 Applicable Publications—The following publications form a part of this specification to the extent specified herein.

2.1.1 ASTM PUBLICATIONS—Available from ASTM, 100 Barr Harbor Drive, West Conshohocken, PA 19428-2959.

ASTM A 247—Standard Test Method for Evaluating the Microstructure of Graphite in Iron Castings

ASTM A 536—Standard Specification for Ductile Iron Castings

ASTM E 10—Standard Test Method for Brinell Hardness of Metallic Materials

ASTM E 23—Standard Test Methods for Notched Bar Impact Testing of Metallic Materials

ASTM E 111—Standard Test Method for Young's Modulus, Tangent Modulus and Chord Modulus

2.2 Related Publications—The following publications are provided for information purposes only and are not a required part of this specification.

2.2.1 ASM PUBLICATIONS—ATTN: MSC/Book Order, ASM International, PO Box 473, Novelty, OH 44072-9901.

ASM Metals Handbook, Vol. 1 Properties and Specifications. Iron and Steel. Ninth Edition, ASM International 1996 Materials Park, OH 44073-0002.

ASM Specialty Handbook, Cast Irons. ASM International 1996 Materials Park, OH 44073-0002.

2.2.2 OTHER PUBLICATIONS

1st International Conference on Austempered Ductile Iron: Your Means to Improved Performance, Productivity and Cost. American Society for Metals Highway/Off-Highway Vehicles Committee Materials systems and Design Division. April 2-4, 1984 Chicago, IL. ASM International, Materials Park, OH 44073-0002.

2nd International Conference on Austempered Ductile Iron: Your Means to Improved Performance, Productivity and Cost. Sponsored by ASME – Gear Research Institute, ASME – Design Division, AMAX, Inc. March 17-19, 1986, Ann Arbor, MI. ASME – Gear Research Institute c/o Pennsylvania State Univeristy, Applied Research Laboratory, P.O. Box 30, State College, PA 16804-0030.

www.ductile.org/didata Chapter IV- Austempered Ductile Iron (Ductile Iron Society (US) website)

3. Grades—The specified grades, hardness and mechanical properties are shown in Table 1.

4. Hardness

4.1 The area or areas on the castings where hardness is to be checked shall be established by agreement between the manufacturer and purchaser.

4.2 The foundry shall exercise the necessary controls and inspection techniques to insure compliance with the specified hardness range for the application. Brinell hardness shall be determined according to ASTM E 10 Test for Brinell Hardness of Metallic Materials, after sufficient material has been removed from the casting surface to insure representative hardness readings. The 10 mm ball and 3000 kg load shall be used unless otherwise specified and agreed upon.

5. Heat treatment

5.1 Castings produced in accordance with this document shall be heat treated by an austempering process consisting of heating the castings to a fully austenitic condition, then holding for a time sufficient to saturate the austenite with carbon, then cooling (at a rate sufficient to avoid the formation of pearlite) to a temperature above the martensite start temperature (Ms), and isothermally transforming the matrix structure for a time sufficient to produce the desired properties. This process shall produce a microstructure that is substantially ausferrite (acicular ferrite and austenite).

5.2 Appropriate heat treatment for removal of residual stresses, or to improve machinability shall be specified by agreement between the manufacturer and the purchaser.

5.3 Re-austempering of components or any deviation from the established heat treating process is permissible only with the expressed approval of the casting purchaser.

TABLE 1—MINIMUM MECHANICAL PROPERTIES FOR AUSTEMPERED DUCTILE IRON

Grade	Hardness HBN (dia. in mm) (MPa)	Tensile Strength (1)(2) MPa	Tensile Strength (1)(2) ksi	Yield Strength (1)(2) MPa	Yield Stength (1)(2) ksi	% Elongation Elasticity(1)(2)	Modulus of Elasticity(1)(2)(3) GPa	Modulus of Elasticity(1)(2)(3) psi	Impact Energy(4) Joules	Impact Energy(4) ft-lb
AD 900	269-341: (3.70-3.30) (2640-3340)	900	130	650	90	9	148	21.5×10^6	100	75
AD1050	302-375: (3.50-3.15) (2690-3680)	1050	150	750	110	7	148	21.5×10^6	80	60
AD1200	341-444: (3.30-2.90) (3340-4350)	1200	175	850	125	4	148	21.5×10^6	60	45
AD1400	388-477: (3.10-2.80) (3800-4680)	1400	200	1100	155	2	148	21.5×10^6	35	25
AD1600	402-512: (3.05-2.70) (3940-5020)	1600	230	1300	185	1	148	21.5×10^6	20	15

1. Applied to equivalent thickness of up to 64 mm (2.5 in). For equivalent thickness greater than 64 mm (2.5 in), the mechanical properties will be mutually agreed upon by the manufacturer and the purchaser.
2. The property requirements in this standard are based on separately cast test bars. Casting properties and microstructure may vary due to chemistry, section size, cooling rates and other parameters. It is desired that the test bars be designed to reflect the properties of the castings they represent. The casting process for the test bars shall be agreed upon between the manufacturer and purchaser. Refer to ASTM A 536.
3. The Young's Modulus (E) was determined by the procedure defined in ASTM E 111.
4. Values obtained using unnotched Charpy bars tested at 22 °C ± 2 °C (72 °F ± 4 °F). The values in the table are the average of the three highest of four tested samples. For details of Charpy test refer to ASTM Impact Test (ASTM E 23).

*6. **Microstructure***

6.1 The graphite component of the microstructure shall consist of at least 80% spheroidal graphite conforming to Types I and II per ASTM A 247.

6.2 The cooling rate within some sections may not be sufficient to avoid the formation of pearlite or other high temperature transformation products. In such cases, the maximum acceptable quantities of these microconstituents and the location(s) within the casting may be established by agreement between the heat treater, the manufacturer and the purchaser.

6.3 Minor amounts of martensite may be present in the microstructure of Grades 1400 and 1600. Acceptable quantities of martensite may be established by agreement between the heat treater, the manufacturer and the purchaser.

6.4 The microstructure shall be substantially free of undesirable microconstituents, the details of which are agreed upon between the heat treater, the manufacturer and the purchaser.

*7. **Quality Assurance***—It is the responsibility of the manufacturer to demonstrate process capability. The specimen(s) used to do so shall be of a configuration and from a location agreed upon between the manufacturer and the purchaser. Sampling plans shall be agreed upon between the heat treater, the manufacturer and the purchaser. The manufacturer shall employ adequate controls to ensure that the parts conform to the agreed upon requirements.

*8. **General***

8.1 Castings furnished to this standard shall be representative of good foundry practice and shall conform to dimensions and tolerances specified on the casting drawing.

8.2 Minor surface discontinuities usually not associated with the structural functioning may occur in castings. These imperfections are often repairable; however, repairs should be made only in areas and by methods approved by the purchaser. Welding repair is not acceptable after Austempering.

8.3 Additional casting requirements, such as vendor identification, other casting information, and special testing, may be agreed upon by the purchaser and the supplier. These should appear as additional product requirements on the casting drawing.

APPENDIX A
AUSTEMPERED DUCTILE (NODULAR) IRON
(A material description not a part of the document)

A.1 Definition and Classification—Austempered Ductile Iron (ADI) is produced by heat-treating Ductile (Nodular) Iron using the austempering Process, (as exemplified in A.5), a specialized, isothermal heat treatment. When compared to conventional ductile iron, ADI can have over twice the strength for a given level of ductility. ADI can have fatigue strength comparable to that of cast and forged steels and that strength can be greatly enhanced by subsequent grinding, fillet rolling or shot peening. Although the first commercial application of ADI did not occur until 1972, the material has found applications in virtually every industrial market segment. Its principal attribute is its ability to replace steel forgings, castings and weldments at equal or lesser weight and at a reduced cost. It is also typically much less costly than aluminum and, with its high strength-to-weight ratio it has replaced cast aluminum parts at equal weight in some automotive applications.

The ausferrite matrix in ADI undergoes a strain transformation hardening when exposed to a high normal force. That effect makes machining of ADI challenging, but knowledge of this effect allows the machinist to adjust the feeds, speeds and tool angles to adequately compensate. This same strain transformation hardening is what gives ADI wear resistance better than its bulk hardness would indicate.

Other attributes of the material include, good noise dampening, fracture toughness and low temperature properties, and reasonable stiffness.

A.2 Suggested Foundry Requirements for Ductile Iron that is to be Austempered (ADI)—ADI can be produced successfully from ductile iron castings with a wide range of chemistries and configurations. Although there is no optimum recipe for ADI castings, those produced to the following parameters have been shown to yield excellent results.

A.2.1 Casting Quality—The castings should be free of non-metallic inclusions, carbides, shrink and dross. Proper purchasing, storage and use of charge materials will minimize the occurrence of carbides and gas defects. Proper molding control will minimize surface defects and other sub-surface discontinuities. The castings should be properly gated and poured using consistent and effective treatment and inoculation techniques to yield shrink free castings. Any of the aforementioned non-conforming conditions will reduce the "toughness" of an ADI component (even if adequate for conventional ductile). The following are recommended as a minimum:

Nodule Count 100 / mm^2
Nodularity 85%

A.2.2 Carbon Equivalent—The carbon equivalent (CE) can be approximated by the relationship:

CE = %C + 1/3 (%Si). It should be controlled as follows in Table A1.

TABLE A1—SUGGESTED CARBON EQUIVALENT RANGES FOR VARIOUS SECTION SIZES

Section Size	CE Range
0-13 mm (0-1/2 in)	4.4 – 4.6
13-51 mm (½ in-2 in)	4.3 – 4.6
Over 51 mm (2 in)	4.3 – 4.5

A.2.3 Chemistry Control—Good ductile iron practice should prevail for ductile iron that is to be austempered. Alloying elements such as Mo, Cu and Ni should be added only when additional hardenability is required for heavier sections. This increased "hardenability" is required only to avoid the formation of pearlite during quenching. Ultimately the amount of alloying required, (if any), will be a function of the alloys in one's base metal, the part configuration and the austempering process used. The proper alloy configuration should be determined jointly by the foundry and the heat-treating source. Addition of the aforementioned alloys when not required does not enhance the properties of ADI but merely adds to the cost of the iron. Composition guidelines are recommended below in Tables A2 and A3:

TABLE A2—SUGGESTED TARGETS AND CONTROL RANGES FOR INTENTIONALLY ADDED ELEMENTS

Intentionally Added Elements	Suggested Target	Typical Control Range
C Carbon	3.6%	±0.20%
Si Silicon	2.5%	±0.20%
Mg Magnesium	(%S x 0.76) + 0.025%	±0.005%
Mn Manganese(1)	0.30%	±0.05%
Cu Copper	0.80% maximum (only as needed)	±0.05%
Ni Nickel	2.00% maximum (only as needed)	±0.10%
Mo Molybdenum	0.30% max. (only as needed)	±0.03%

1. Up to a section size of approximately 13 mm (0.51 in), Mn targets as high as 0.60% can be used successfully. In section sizes over 13 mm (0.51 in) (or in the presence of Mo or other carbide formers) the Mn target should be reduced to 0.35% or less to minimize the formation of cell boundary carbides which may negatively affect component machinability and ductility.

TABLE A3—SUGGESTED MAXIMUMS AND CONTROL RANGES FOR TRACE AND TRAMP ELEMENTS

Trace or Tramp Elements	Suggested Target (or maximum)	Typical Control Range
Sn Tin	0.02% maximum	±0.003%
Sb Antimony	0.002% maximum	±0.0003%
P Phosphorus	0.04% maximum	
S Sulfur	0.02% maximum	
O Oxygen	50 ppm maximum	
Cr Chromium	0.10% maximum	
Ti Titanium	0.040% maximum	
V Vanadium	0.10% maximum	
Al Aluminum	0.050% maximum	
As Arsenic	0.020% maximum	
Bi Bismuth	0.002% maximum	
B Boron	0.002% maximum	
Cd Cadmium	0.005% maximum	
Pb Lead	0.002% maximum	
Se Selenium	0.030% maximum	
Te Tellurium	0.020% maximum	

Other "nodulizing elements", (like, calcium, strontium, barium, yttrium, lanthanum and cerium), should be present only to the extent that they are used to replace Mg in nodulization. In any case, the amount of residual Mg plus the amounts of these elements should not exceed 0.06%. Carbide forming elements (such as Cr, Ti, V, etc.) tend to be additive in effect with Mn and/or Mo and one should be aware of this in alloy design to avoid the formation of carbides in the casting.

A.2.4 Prior Microstructure—The time required to saturate the matrix with carbon during austenitizing and the growth of the casting during austempering will be affected by the pearlite/ferrite ratio of the casting prior to heat treatment. A consistent pearlite/ferrite ratio is particularly important if the castings are machined prior to austempering. A consistent pearlite/ferrite ratio in the casting prior to austenitizing will result in consistent growth during austempering.

A.2.5 Thermal Behavior of ADI—The designer should be aware that the coefficient of thermal expansion for ADI can be 5 to 20% greater than that of steel or ductile iron (depending on the grade of ADI selected). This increased thermal expansion must be addressed in close tolerance designs that will see significant temperature fluctuations in service.

Furthermore, the ausferrite microstructure is generally stable to very low temperatures but, in elevated temperature service, will eventually exhibit a lowering of properties if continually operated at temperatures approaching the temperature at which the casting was austempered.

The preceding guidelines have been prepared as useful parameters for production. Good ADI can, and is, being produced from ductile iron not meeting these criteria, however, these criteria represent sound, commercial practices known to produce good results. They do not constitute a guarantee of final properties.

A.3 Microstructure

A.3.1 The microstructure of the various grades of ADI consists of spheroidal graphite in a matrix of carbon stabilized austenite and acicular ferrite – otherwise known as ausferrite. (See Figures A1 to A5).

A.3.2 The different grades of ADI are dependent upon the quench temperature of the heat treatment. The quench temperature affects the formation of the ausferrite matrix.

A.3.3 The following figures show typical microstructures of each grade of ADI.

A.4 Mechanical Properties

A.4.1 The mechanical properties are shown in Table 1. Since properties may vary with location on a given casting, the suitability of a particular material/process combination for an intended use is best determined by laboratory or service tests.

A.4.2 The mechanical properties are dependent on the Austempering process and may be marginally affected by section size.

A.4.3 For optimum mechanical properties, section size for unalloyed iron generally should not exceed 16 mm (0.63 in) to ensure a uniform, through hardened structure. Section sizes above 16 mm (0.63 in)may require additional alloying for through hardening. (Typical alloys added for increased hardenability include Cu, Ni and Mo.)

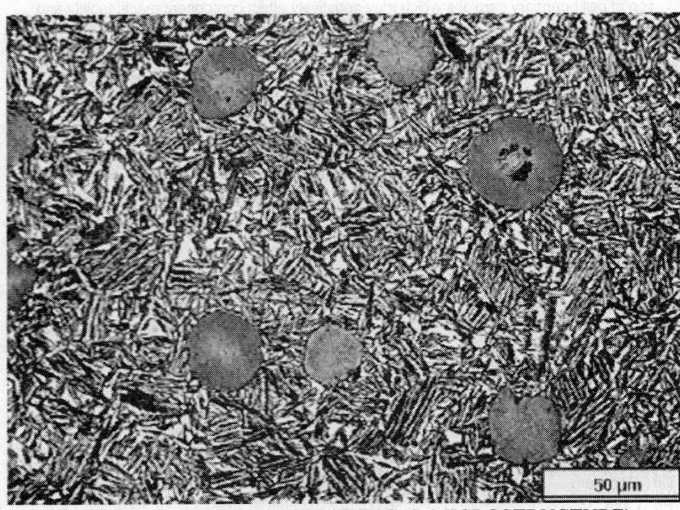

FIGURE A1—GRADE AD900 (TYPICAL MICROSTRUCTURE)

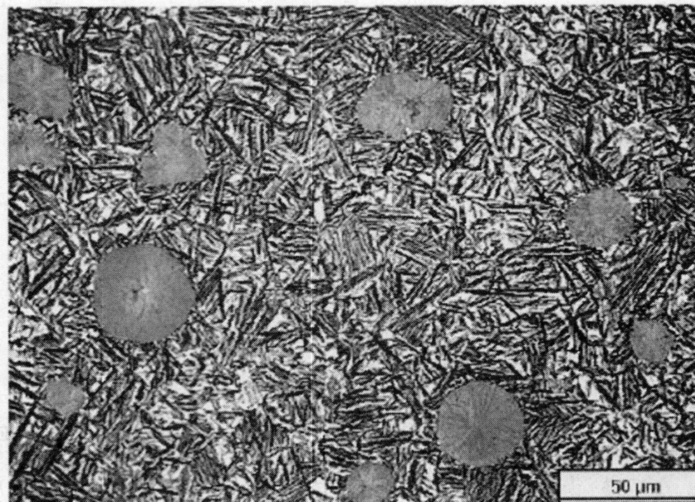

FIGURE A2—GRADE AD1050 (TYPICAL MICROSTRUCTURE)

FIGURE A3—GRADE AD1200 (TYPICAL MICROSTRUCTURE)

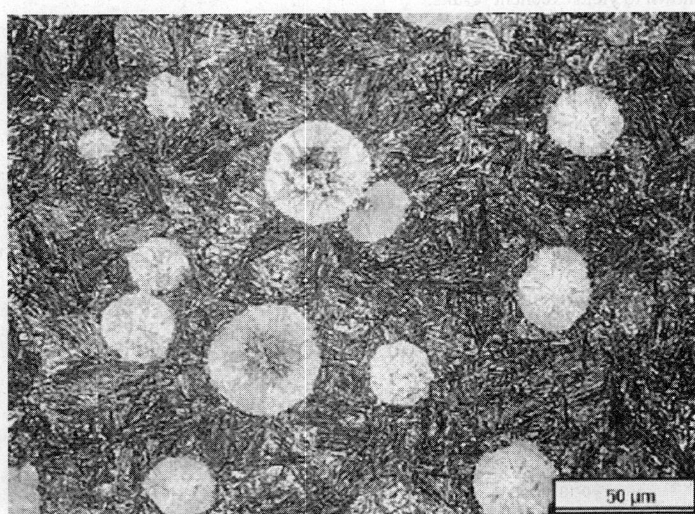

FIGURE A4—GRADE AD1400 (TYPICAL MICROSTRUCTURE)

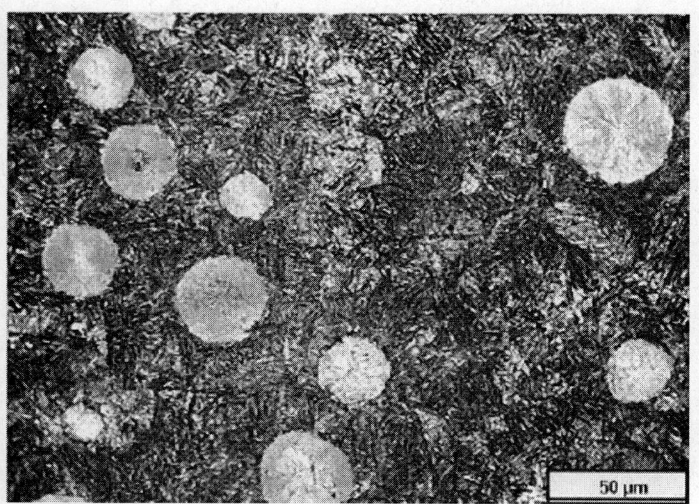

FIGURE A5—GRADE AD1600 (TYPICAL MICROSTRUCTURE)

A.5 Heat Treatment Process—Figure A6 shows a typical austempering process. (The actual temperatures and times suitable for a specific application would have to be determined based on the chemical composition, the component configuration and the strength grade desired).

A.5.1 A-B—Heat to appropriate austenitizing temperature.

A.5.2 B-C—Hold to saturate the austenite with carbon.

A.5.3 C-D—Quench rapidly enough to avoid the formation of pearlite, to a temperature above the martensite start temperature (Ms).

A.5.4 D-E—Austemper for a time sufficient to produce the desired ausferrite properties.

A.5.5 E-F—Cool to room temperature.

A.6 Typical Applications

A.6.1 AD900 is used in moderately stressed parts requiring high ductility and bending fatigue strength, and good machinability. AD900 also has very good low temperature properties.

A.6.2 AD1050 is used for moderately stressed parts requiring high ductility and bending fatigue strength, and good machinability. AD1050 has the best low temperature properties of all the grades.

A.6.3 AD1200 is used for a combination of fatigue strength, impact strength and wear resistance.

A.6.4 AD1400 is used where high strength and/or improved wear resistance are required.

A.6.5 AD1600 is used where high yield and contact strength, and/or improved wear resistance are required.

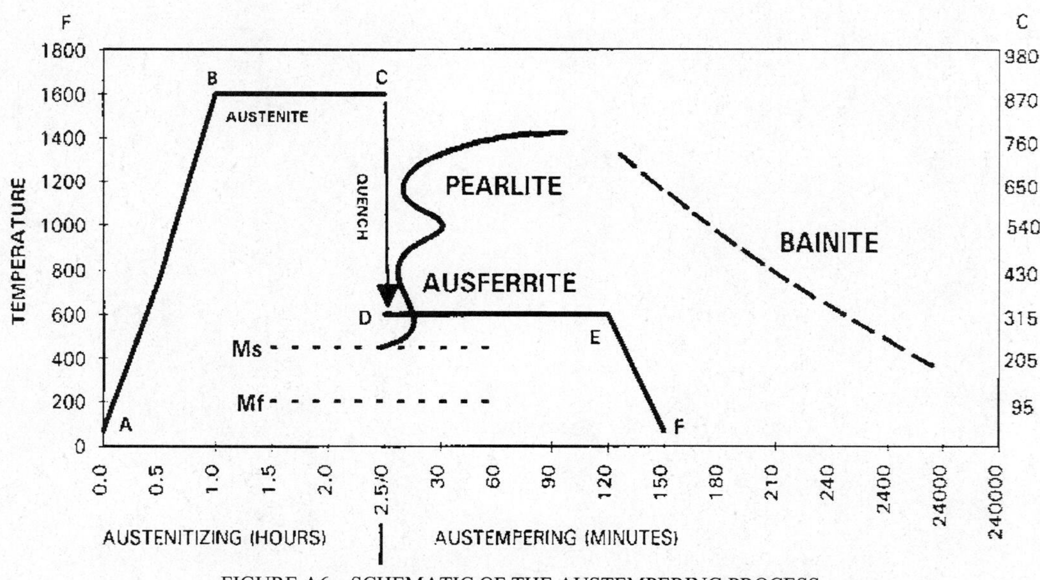

FIGURE A6—SCHEMATIC OF THE AUSTEMPERING PROCESS

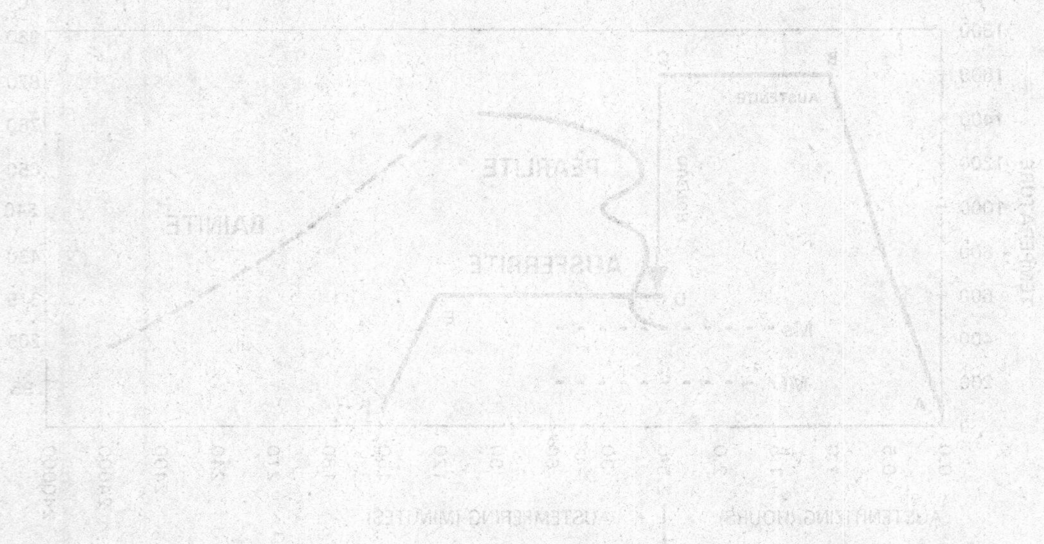

7 Tool and Die Steels

TOOL AND DIE STEELS—SAE J438b MAY1970

SAE Standard

Report of the SAE Iron and Steel Technical Committee approved January 1949 and last revised May 1970.

Foreword—This Document has also changed to comply with the new SAE Technical Standards Board format.

1. Scope—This standard covers the identification, classification, and chemical composition of tool and die steels for use by engineers, metallurgists, tool designers, tool room supervisors, heat treaters, and tool makers.

2. References—There are no referenced publications specified herein.

3. Definitions—Tool and die steels are defined as certain carbon or alloy steels, capable of being hardened and tempered. They are usually melted in electric furnaces and produced to meet special requirements. They may be used in certain hand tools, precision gages, or in mechanical fixtures for cutting, shaping, forming, and blanking of materials at either cold or elevated temperatures.

This definition is not intended to include that type of tonnage production open hearth steel used in the manufacture of ordinary mechanics' hand tools, nor steel used in the manufacture of such products as hammers, picks, files, hollow drill steel, mining bits and cutters, large rolling mill rolls, and low alloy medium carbon forging die blocks. These exceptions are stated as a matter of guidance only and are not inclusive.

4. Identification and Classification of Tool Steels—This method of identification and classification of tools steels was designed to follow the most commonly used and generally accepted terminology of tool steel types of classes. It includes such basic principles as method of quenching, applications, special characteristic, and steels for particular industries. The method is believed to be as simplified as possible and aims to avoid complications in details composition or metallurgical specifications. The method provides appropriate symbols for generally accepted types of tool steel. It also provides for the addition of new products as they may be developed. See Table 1.

The present commonly used tool steels have been grouped into 6 major headings and each commonly accepted group of tool steels under these headings has been assigned an alphabetical letter symbol. Each major group identified by a letter symbol may contain a number of individual types of tool steels. These types are identified by a suffix number which follows the letter symbol. For water hardening tool steels this number suffix consists of three digits, the last two digits representing the approximate mean of the carbon content in tenths of one percent. To the above may be added after a dash (-) a suffix to further designate the grade and hardenability of W1 steels. (Examples: W110-2R would indicate a Grade 2 with regular hardenability. W110-3 would indicate a Grade 3 not controlled for hardenability.)

Water Hardening Tool Steels: W
Shock Resisting Tool Steels: S
Cold Work Tool Steels:O–Oil Hardening Types
A–Medium Alloy Air Hardening Types
D–High Carbon High Chromium Types
Hot Work Tool Steels:H–H1-H19 incl–Chromium Base Types
H20-H39 incl–Tungsten Base Types
H40-H59 incl–Molybdenum Base Types
High Speed Tool Steels:T–Tungsten Base Types
M–Molybdenum Base Types
Special Purpose Tools Steels: L–Low Alloy Type

The chemical composition[1] of each type is given only as a representative type analysis. The carbon content is shown only in those cases where it is considered an identifying element to the steel.

5. Standards for Austenitic Grain Size of Tool and Die Steels—It is recommended that the following method be used for the determination of austenitic grain size of hardened tool steels:

The Shepherd Penetration Fracture Test—This test is used to determine hardenability and fracture grain size on tool and die steels. It is generally applied to carbon tool steels. To perform the test, a sample is machined to ¾ in diameter x 3 in long and pretreated by holding at 1600 F for 30 min and quenching in oil, followed by a retreatment by holding for 30 min at 1450 F, then quenching in brine. The specimen is notched midway and fractured by impact.

The penetration of hardening is measured in 64ths of an inch on half of the fractured sample after grinding and etching lightly in hot 50% hydrochloric acid solution.

The grain size is judged by comparing the surface of the fracture of the hardened case with Shepherd fracture grain size standards.

1. In cooperation with the American Iron and Steel Institute.

TABLE 1—CHEMICAL COMPOSITIONS OF TOOL AND DIE STEELS[1]

SAE Steel Designation	C	Mn	Si	Cr	V	W	Mo	Co
Water Hardening Tool Steels								
W108[2]	0.70–0.85	—[2]	—[2]	—[2]	—	—	—	—
W109[2]	0.85–0.95	—[2]	—[2]	—[2]	—	—	—	—
W110[2]	0.95–1.10	—[2]	—[2]	—[2]	—	—	—	—
W112[2]	1.10–1.30	—[2]	—[2]	—[2]	—	—	—	—
W209	0.85–0.95	—[2]	—[2]	—[2]	0.15–0.35	—	—	—
W210	0.95–1.10	—[2]	—[2]	—[2]	0.15–0.35	—	—	—
W310	0.95–1.10	—[2]	—[2]	—[2]	0.35–0.50	—	—	—
Shock Resisting Tool Steels								
S1—Chromium-Tungsten	0.45–0.55	0.20–0.40	0.25–0.45[3]	1.25–1.75	0.15–0.30	1.00–3.00	0.40[4]	—
S2—Silicon-Molybdenum	0.45–0.55	0.30–0.50	0.80–1.20	—	0.25[4]	—	0.40–0.60	—
S5—Silicon-Manganese	0.50–0.60	0.60–0.90	1.80–2.20	0.30[4]	0.25[4]	—	0.30–0.50	—

TABLE 1—CHEMICAL COMPOSITIONS OF TOOL AND DIE STEELS[1] (continued)

SAE Steel Designation	C	Mn	Si	Cr	V	W	Mo	Co
Cold Work Tool Steels								
Oil Hardening Types								
O1—Low Manganese	0.85–0.95	1.00–1.30	0.20–0.40	0.40–0.60	0.20[4]	0.40–0.60	—	—
O2—High Manganese	0.85–0.95	1.40–1.80	0.20–0.40	0.35[4]	0.20[4]	—	0.30[4]	—
O6—Molybdenum Graphitic	1.35–1.55	0.30–1.00	0.80–1.20	—	—	—	0.20–0.30	—
Medium Alloy Air Hardening Types								
A2—5% Chromium Air Hard	0.95–1.05	0.45–0.75	0.20–0.40	4.75–5.50	0.40[4]	—	0.90–1.40	—
High Carbon-High Chromium Types								
D2—High Carbon-High Chromium (Air)	1.40–1.60	0.30–0.50	0.30–0.50	11.00–13.00	0.80[4]	—	0.70–1.20	0.60[4]
D3—High Carbon-High Chromium (Oil)	2.00–2.35	0.24–0.45[3]	0.25–0.45	11.00–13.00	0.80[4]	0.75[4]	0.80[4]	—
D5—High Carbon-High Chromium (Cobalt)	1.40–1.60	0.30–0.50	0.30–0.50	11.00–13.00	0.80[4]	—	0.70–1.20	2.50–3.50
D7—High Carbon-High Chromium-High Vanadium	2.15–2.50	0.30–0.50	0.30–0.50	11.50–13.50	3.80–4.40	—	0.70–1.20	—
Hot Work Tool Steels								
Chromium Base Types								
H11—Chromium-Molybdenum-V	0.30–0.40	0.20–0.40	0.80–1.20	4.75–5.50	0.30–0.50	—	1.25–1.75	—
H12—Chromium-Molybdenum-Tungsten	0.30–0.40	0.20–0.40	0.80–1.20	4.75–5.50	0.10–0.50	1.00–1.70	1.25–1.75	—
H13—Chromium-Molybdenum-VV	0.30–0.40	0.20–0.40	0.80–1.20	4.75–5.50	0.80–1.20	—	1.25–1.75	—
Tungsten Base Types								
H21—Tungsten	0.30–0.40	0.20–0.40	0.15–0.30	3.00–3.75	0.30–0.50	8.75–10.00	—	—
High Speed Tool Steels								
Tungsten Base Types								
T1—Tungsten 18-4-1	0.65–0.75	0.20–0.40	0.20–0.40	3.75–4.50	0.90–1.30	17.25–18.75	—	—
T2—Tungsten 18-4-2	0.75–0.85	0.20–0.40	0.20–0.40	3.75–4.50	1.80–2.40	17.50–19.00	0.70–1.00	—
T4—Cobalt-Tungsten 18-4-1-5	0.70–0.80	0.20–0.40	0.20–0.40	3.75–4.50	0.80–1.20	17.25–18.75	0.70–1.00	4.25–5.75
T5—Cobalt-Tungsten 18-4-2-8	0.75–0.85	0.20–0.40	0.20–0.40	3.75–4.50	1.80–2.40	17.50–19.00	0.70–1.00	7.00–9.00
T8—Cobalt-Tungsten 14-4-2-5	0.75–0.85	0.20–0.40	0.20–0.40	3.75–4.50	1.80–2.40	13.25–14.75	0.70–1.00	4.25–5.75
Molybdenum Base Types								
M1—Molybdenum 8-2-1	0.75–0.85	0.20–0.40	0.20–0.40	3.75–4.50	0.90–1.30	1.15–1.85	7.75–9.25	—
M2—Molybdenum-Tungsten 6-6-2	0.78–0.88	0.20–0.40	0.20–0.40	3.75–4.50	1.60–2.20	5.50–6.75	4.50–5.50	—
M3—Molybdenum-Tungsten 6-6-3	1.00–1.25	0.20–0.40	0.20–0.40	3.75–4.50	2.25–3.25	5.50–6.75	4.75–6.25	—
M4—Molybdenum-Tungsten 6-6-4	1.25–1.40	0.20–0.40	0.20–0.40	4.00–4.75	3.90–4.50	5.25–6.50	4.50–5.50	—
Special Purpose Tool Steels								
Low Alloy Types								
L6—Nickel-Chromium[5]	0.65–0.75	0.55–0.85[3]	0.20–0.40	0.65–0.85	0.25[4]	—	0.25[4]	—
L7—Chromium	0.95–1.05	0.25–0.45	0.20–0.40	1.25–1.75	—	—	0.30–0.50	—

1. These compositions are not intended for forging die steels.
2. Water hardening steels listed herein are usually available in four grades or qualities as follows:
   Special (Grade 1)—The highest quality water hardening carbon tool steel, controlled for hardenability, chemistry held to closest limits, and subject to most rigid tests to insure maximum uniformity in performance.
   Extra (Grade 2)—A high quality water hardening carbon tool steel, controlled for hardenability, subject to tests to insure good service for general application.
   Standard (Grade 3)—A good quality water hardening carbon tool steel, not controlled for hardenability, recommended for application where some latitude with respect to uniformity is permissible.
   Commercial (Grade 4)—A commercial quality water hardening carbon tool steel, not controlled for hardenability, not subject to special tests.
   On Special and Extra Grades, limits on manganese, silicon, and chromium are not generally required in lieu of the following Shepherd hardenability limits:

	0.70–0.85 C and 0.85–0.95 C		0.95–1.10 C and 1.10–1.30 C	
	Hardenability, 64ths In. Penetration	Fracture Grain Size, min	Hardenability, 64ths In. Penetration	Fracture Grain Size, min
Shallow.......................	10 max	8	8 max	9
Regular.......................	9 to 13	8	7 to 11	9
Deep...........................	12 min	8	10 to 16	8

   On Standard and Commercial Grades, the following limits on composition are generally required:

	Mn	Si	Cr
Standard, max	0.35	0.35	0.15
Commercial, max	0.35	0.35	0.20

   Total of manganese, silicon, and chromium not to exceed 0.75%.
3. May be present in percentages other than shown.
4. Optional element. Steels have found satisfactory application either with or without the element present.
5. Nickel content 1.25–1.75.

SELECTION AND HEAT TREATMENT OF TOOL AND DIE STEELS—SAE J437a APR70

SAE Information Report

Report of the SAE Iron and Steel Technical Committee approved January 1949 and last revised May 1969. Editorial change April 1970.

Foreword—This Document has not changed other than to put it into the new SAE Technical Standards Board Format.

1. Scope—The information in this report covers data relating to SAE J438, Tool and Die Steels, and is intended as a guide to the selection of the steel best suited for the intended purpose and to provide recommended heat treatments and other data pertinent to their use.

Specific requirements as to physical properties are not included because the majority of tool and die steels are either worked or given special heat treatments by the purchaser. The purchaser may or may not elect to use the accompanying data for specification purposes.

2. References

2.1 Applicable Publication—The following publication forms a part of the specification to the extent specified herein. Unless otherwise indicated the lastest revision of SAE publications shall apply.

2.1.1 SAE PUBLICATION—Available from SAE, 400 Commonwealth Drive, Warrendale, PA 15096-0001.

SAE J438—Tool and Die Steels

2.1.2 ASM PUBLICATION—ATTN: MSC/Book Order, ASM International, PO Box 473, Novelty, OH 44072-9901.

ASM Handbook—1948 Edition, pp. 658-659

3. The Selection of Tool and Die Steels[1]—Simplification of the problems connected with the selection of tool steels has long been an aim of both producers and consumers. This article is restricted to a discussion of the general principles involved in selection and will include a tabulation of the metallurgical characteristics of the principal tool steel types as an aid in selection. A correlation of these metallurgical characteristics with the requirements of the tool in operation should form the basis of a sound approach to the selection of a steel for any application. Table 1.

Practical experience indicates that in the majority of instances the choice is not limited to a single type of tool steel or even to a particular family of tool steels for a workable solution to an individual tooling problem. Because it is desirable to select the steel that will give the most economical overall performance, the tool life obtained with each steel under consideration should be judged by weighing such factors as expected productivity, ease of fabrication, and cost.

The majority of tool steel applications can be divided into a small number of groups or types of operations: cutting, shearing, forming, drawing, extrusion, rolling, and battering. Cutting tools include drills, taps, broaches, hobs, lathe tools, and the like. Shearing tools include shears, blanking and trimming dies, punches, and such. Forming tools include draw, forging, cold heading, and die casting dies. Battering tools include chisels and all forms of tools involving heavy shock. Many of these classifications can be further divided into cold and hot working tools.

For each of these groups, certain metallurgical characteristics are of utmost importance. Most cutting tools require high hardness, high resistance to the softening effect of heat, and high wear resistance. Shearing tools require high wear resistance combined with fair toughness, and these characteristics must be properly balanced depending on the tool design, thickness of stock being sheared, and temperature of the shearing operation. Forming tools must possess high wear resistance or high toughness and high strength, and many require maximum resistance to heat softening. In battering tools high toughness is most important.

Hardness, strength, toughness, wear resistance, and resistance to heat softening are, therefore, prime selective factors for tool steel applications. Many other properties must be seriously considered in individual applications; these include permissible distortion in hardening, permissible surface decarburization, hardenability or depth of hardness desired, resistance to heat checking, machinability and grindability, as well as heat treating requirements, including temperatures, atmospheres, and equipment.

Table 1 lists those properties which merit special consideration when selecting steels for any application, from the list shown. For compositions of these steels, Table 1 of SAE J438.

Table 2 is presented as an aid in the relative evaluation of those properties which must be considered for the proper heat treatment of the steels.

1. Condensed from the ASM Handbook, 1948 edition, pp. 658–659, with the permission of the American Society for Metals.

4. Relation of Design to Heat Treatment—The design bears, in many ways, upon the serviceability of the tool or machine part, and unsatisfactory performance may frequently be traced directly to faulty design. This discussion is concerned only with design as it affects the heat treating operation and, through the heat treatment, the serviceability of the finished part. It is the purpose of this discussion to bring about a better mutual understanding between the designer and the steel treater so that faulty design which may cause cracking or distorting during heat treating can be avoided.

The fundamental principles of good design from a heat treatment standpoint are quite simple. Heat treated steel has a certain strength depending upon the analysis of the steel, the quality of the metal, and the heat treatment which it has received. When subjected to a combination of forces its ultimate strength, the steel cracks or fails. There are 2 types of force combining to break steel, which are:

a. The internal stress set up during fabrication and heat treatment of the tool.

b. The external force of service.

Sometimes the internal stresses alone exceed the strength of the metal, and the parts crack in hardening. Again, the internal stresses may equal 90% or more of the total strength, in which case failure will develop in service under relatively light loads. It therefore appears that the useful strength of a part decreases in proportion as the internal stresses increase.

Internal stresses arise from many causes, but the most serious by far are those developed by differential cooling resulting from quenching. This differential cooling is largely a function of the size and shape of the piece being quenched; in other words, the design. Here, then, is the relation of design to heat treatment, and the basic principle of successful design is to plan shapes which allow the piece to cool as uniformly as possible during quenching.

Some shapes are almost impossible to harden because of the abruptness in the change of sections, but a certain latitude in design is recognized when using an oil hardening or air hardening steel.

Errors in design reach further than merely affecting the internal stress of hardening. A sharp angle serves to concentrate greatly the stresses of service. The design of the part may be entirely responsible for concentrating the service stresses at a point already weakened by internal stresses produced during hardening.

Reducing all the foregoing to a single statement, a part is properly designed from the standpoint of heat treatment when the entire piece may be heated and cooled at approximately the same rate during the heat treating operation. Perfection in this regard is unattainable because, even in a sphere, the surface cools more rapidly than the interior. The designer should, however, attempt to so shape his parts that they will heat and cool as uniformly as possible. The greater the temperature difference between any two points on a given part during quenching and the closer these two points are together, the greater will be the internal stress and, therefore, the poorer the design.

The principles described in this article are illustrated in Figure 1.

5. Heat Treat Data—The thermal treatments listed in Table 3 cover the generally used treatments for the forging, normalizing, and annealing of tool and die steels.

The thermal treatments listed in Table 2, under selection, cover the usual ranges of temperature for hardening and tempering tool and die steels.

The information listed in Tables 2 and 3 is not intended for specification because of the need for altering treatments for specific applications.

6. Allowance for Machining of Tool Steel Bars[2]—Tool and die steels should be ordered oversize with sufficient material to be removed from all surfaces by machining or grinding to allow for:

a. Surface decarburization.

b. Surface defects such as slivers, seams, laps, scale marks, and the like.

c. Undersize tolerance as given in Tables 6, 7, 8, and 9.

Table 4 lists the minimum allowance per side over finish size for machining or grinding rounds, squares, hexagons, and octagons.

Polished or ground tool steel quality round drill rod is free from decarburization or any surface defects requiring surface removal.

2. In cooperation with the American Iron and Steel Institute.

TABLE 1—COMPARISON OF TOOL STEELS ON BASIS OF PROPERTIES AFFECTING SELECTION

SAE Steel Designation	Nondeforming Properties	Safety in Hardening	Depth of Hardening (1)	Toughness	Resistance to Softening Effect of Heat	Wear Resistance	Machinability
Water Hardening Tool Steels							
W108	Poor	Fair	Shallow	Good(2)	Poor	Fair	Best
W109	Poor	Fair	Shallow	Good(2)	Poor	Fair	Best
W110	Poor	Fair	Shallow	Good(2)	Poor	Good	Best
W112	Poor	Fair	Shallow	Good(2)	Poor	Good	Best
W209	Poor	Fair	Shallow	Good	Poor	Fair	Best
W210	Poor	Fair	Shallow	Good	Poor	Good	Best
W310	Poor	Fair	Shallow	Good	Poor	Good	Best
Shock Resisting Tool Steels							
S1—Chromium-Tungsten	Fair	Good	Medium	Good	Fair	Fair	Fair
S2—Silicon-Molybdenum	W Poor(3)	W Poor(3)	Medium	Best	Fair	Fair	Good
	O Fair(3)	O Good(3)					
S5—Silicon-Manganese	W Poor(3)	W Poor(3)	Medium	Best	Fair	Fair	Fair
	O Fair(3)	O Good(3)					
Cold Work Tool Steels							
Oil Hardening Types							
O1—Low Manganese	Good	Good	Medium	Fair	Poor	Good	Good
O2—High Manganese	Good	Good	Medium	Fair	Poor	Good	Good
O6—Molybdenum Graphitic	Fair	Good	Medium	Fair	Poor	Good	Best
Medium Alloy Air Hardening Types							
A2—5% Chromium Air Hard	Best	Best	Deep	Fair	Fair	Good	Fair
High Carbon-High Chromium Types							
D2—High Carbon-High Chromium (Air)	Best	Best	Deep	Fair	Fair	Best	Poor
D3—High Carbon-High Chromium (Oil)	Good	Good	Deep	Poor	Fair	Best	Poor
D5—High Carbon-High Chromium-Cobalt	Best	Best	Deep	Fair	Fair	Best	Poor
D7—High Carbon-High Chromium-High Vanadium	Best	Best	Deep	Poor	Fair	Best	Poor
Hot Work Tool Steels							
Chromium Base Types							
H11—Chromium-Molybdenum-V	Good	Good	Deep	Good	Good	Fair	Fair
H12—Chromium-Molybdenum-Tungsten	Good	Good	Deep	Good	Good	Fair	Fair
H13—Chromium-Molybdenum-VV	Good	Good	Deep	Good	Good	Fair	Fair
Tungsten Base Types							
H21—Tungsten	Good	Good	Deep	Good	Good	Fair	Fair
High Speed Tool Steels							
Tungsten Base Types							
T1—Tungsten 18-4-1	Good	Good	Deep	Poor	Good	Good	Fair
T2—Tungsten 18-4-2	Good	Good	Deep	Poor	Good	Good	Fair
T4—Cobalt-Tungsten 18-4-1-5	Good	Fair	Deep	Poor	Best	Good	Fair
T5—Cobalt-Tungsten 18-4-2-8	Good	Fair	Deep	Poor	Best	Good	Fair
T8—Cobalt-Tungsten 14-4-2-5	Good	Fair	Deep	Poor	Best	Good	Fair
Molybdenum Base Types							
M1—Molybdenum 8-2-1	Good	Fair	Deep	Poor	Good	Good	Fair
M2—Molybdenum-Tungsten 6-6-2	Good	Fair	Deep	Poor	Good	Good	Fair
M3—Molybdenum-Tungsten 6-6-3	Good	Fair	Deep	Poor	Good	Best	Fair
M4—Molybdenum-Tungsten 6-6-4	Good	Fair	Deep	Poor	Good	Best	Fair
Special Purpose Tool Steels							
Low Alloy Types							
L6—Nickel-Chromium	Fair	Good	Medium	Fair	Poor	Fair	Fair
L7—Chromium	Fair	Good	Medium	Fair	Poor	Good	Fair

1. These are intended to emphasize major differences between the groups of steels and do not account for the minor differences in depths of hardening that exist between steels of the same group. This is particularly true of the Water Hardening W Steels which are frequently furnished with varying degrees of hardenability as listed in Table 1.
2. Toughness decreases somewhat with increasing depth of hardening.
3. W as shown here indicates water quench. O as shown here indicates oil quench.

TABLE 2—APPROXIMATE COMPARISON OF TOOL AND DIE STEELS ON BASIS OF SOME HEAT TREATING CHARACTERISTICS

SAE Steel Designation	Quench Medium	Preheat Temperature, F	Hardening Temperature Range, (1) F	Hardness after Quenching, Rockwell C	Tempering Temperature Range, (1) F	Hardness after Tempering, Rockwell C	Decarburization (Prevention of During Heat Treatment)
Water Hardening Tool Steel							
W108	Water	—(2)	1420–1450	65–67	350–525	65-56	—(3)
W109	Water	—(2)	1420–1450	65–67	350–525	65-56	—(3)
W110	Water	—(2)	1420–1450	65–67	350–525	65-56	—(3)
W112	Water	—(2)	1420–1500	65–67	350–525	65-56	—(3)
W209	Water	—(2)	1420–1500	65–67	350–525	65-56	—(3)
W210	Water	—(2)	1420–1500	65–67	350–525	65-56	—(3)
W310	Water	—(2)	1420–1500	65–67	350–525	65-56	—(3)
Shock Resisting Tool Steels							
S1—Chromium-Tungsten	Oil	1200–1300	1650–1800	57–59	300–1000	57-45	—(4)
S2—Silicon-Molybdenum	Water	—(2)	1550–1575	60–62	300–500	60-54	—e
	Oil	—(2)	1600–1625	58–60	300–500	58-54	—e
S5—Silicon-Manganese	Water	—(2)	1550–1600	60–62	300–650	60-54	—e
	Oil	—(2)	1600–1675	58–60	300–650	58-54	—e
Cold Work Tool Steels							
Oil Hardening Types							
O1—Low Manganese	Oil	—(2)	1450–1500	63–65	300–800	62-50	—e
O2—High Manganese	Oil	—(2)	1420–1450	63–65	375–500	62-57	—e
O6—Molybdenum Graphitic	Oil	—(2)	1450–1500	63–65	300–800	63-50	—e
Medium Alloy Air Hardening Types							
A2—5% Chromium Air Hard	Air	1200–1300	1725–1775	61–63	400–700	60-57	—(4)
High Carbon-High Chromium Types							
D2—High Carbon-High Chromium	Air	1200–1300	1800–1875	61–63	400–700	60-58	—(4)
D3—High Carbon-High Chromium	Oil	1200–1300	1750–1800	62–64	400–700	62-58	—(4)
D5—High Carbon-High Chromium-Cobalt	Air	1200–1300	1800–1875	60–62	400–700	59-57	—(4)
D7—High Carbon-High Chromium-High Vanadium	Air	1200–1300	1850–1950	63–65	300–500	65-63	—(4)
					850–1000	62-58	
Hot Work Tool Steels							
Chromium Base Types							
H11—Chromium-Molybdenum-Y	Air	1450–1500	1825–1875	53–55	1000–1100	51-43	—(4)
H12—Chromium-Molybdenum-Tungsten	Oil, Air	1450–1500	1800–1900	53–55	1000–1100	51-43	—(4)
H13—Chromium-Molybdenum-VV	Air	1400–1450	1825–1875	53–55	1000–1100	51-43	—(4)
Tungsten Base Types							
H21—Tungsten	Oil, Air	1500–1550	2100–2150	50–52	950–1150	50-47	—(4)
High Speed Tool Steels							
Tungsten Base Types							
T1—Tungsten 18-4-1	Oil, Air, Salt	1500–1550	2300–2375	63–65	1025–1100	65-63	—(4)
T2—Tungsten 18-4-2	Oil, Air, Salt	1500–1550	2300–2375	63–65	1025–1100	65-63	—(4)
T4—Cobalt-Tungsten 18-4-1-5	Oil, Air, Salt	1500–1550	2300–2375	63–65	1025–1100	65-63	—(4)
T5—Cobalt-Tungsten 18-4-2-8	Oil, Air, Salt	1500–1550	2300–2400	63–65	1050–1100	65-63	—(4)
T8—Cobalt-Tungsten 14-4-2-5	Oil, Air, Salt	1500–1550	2300–2375	63–65	1025–1100	65-63	—(4)
Molybdenum Base Types							
M1—Molybdenum 8-2-1	Oil, Air, Salt	1400–1500	2150–2250	63–65	1025–1050	65-63	—(4)
M2—Molybdenum-Tungsten 6-6-2	Oil, Air, Salt	1450–1500	2175–2250	63–65	1025–1075	65-63	—(4)
M3—Molybdenum-Tungsten 6-6-3	Oil, Air, Salt	1450–1500	2150–2225	63–65	1025–1075	65-63	—(4)
M4—Molybdenum-Tungsten 6-6-4	Oil, Air, Salt	1450–1500	2150–2225	63–65	1025–1075	65-63	—(4)
Special Purpose Tool Steels							
Low Alloy Types							
L6—Nickel-Chromium	Oil	—(2)	1500–1600	62–64	400–800	62-48	—(3)
L7—Chromium	Oil	—(2)	1525–1550	63–65	350–500	62-60	—(3)

1. The purpose of these columns is to show the usual ranges of temperature employed in hardening and tempering and is not to be used as a specification.
2. For large tools and tools having intricate sections, preheating at 1050 to 1200 °F is recommended.
3. Use moderately oxidizing atmosphere in fumace or a suitable neutral salt bath.
4. Use protective pack from which volatile matter has been removed, carefully balanced neutral salt bath, or atmosphere controlled furnaces. In the latter case, the furnace atmosphere should be in equilibrium with the carbon content of the steel being treated. Furnace atmosphere dew point is considered a reliable method for measuring and controlling this equilibrium.

TABLE 3—FORGING, NORMALIZING, AND ANNEALING TREATMENTS OF TOOL AND DIE STEELS

SAE Steel Designation [1]	Forging [2]			Normalizing [3]		Annealing [4]			
	Heat Slowly to	Start Forging at	Do Not Forge below	Heat Slowly to	Hold at	Temperature	Maximum Rate of Cooling, F/hr	Approximate Brinell Hardness	Approximate Rockwell B
Water Hardening Tool Steels									
W108	1450	1800–1950	1500	1450	1500	1400–1450	75	159–202	84–94
W109	1450	1800–1950	1500	1450	1500	1375–1425	75	159–202	84–94
W110	1450	1800–1900	1500	1450	1550	1400–1450	75	159–202	84–94
W112	1450	1800–1900	1500	1450	1625	1400–1450	75	159–202	84–94
W209	1450	1800–1950	1500	1450	1500	1375–1425	75	159–202	84–94
W210	1450	1800–1900	1500	1450	1550	1400–1450	75	159–202	84–94
W310	1450	1800–1900	1500	1450	1550	1400–1450	75	159–202	84–94
Shock Resisting Tool Steels									
S1—Chromium-Tungsten	1500	1800–2000	1600	Do not normalize		1450–1500	50	192–235	92–99
S2—Silicon-Molybdenum	1500	1900–2100	1600	1500	1650	1400–1450	50	192–229	92–98
S5—Silicon-Manganese	1500	1900–2050	1600	1500	1600	1400–1450	50	192–229	92–98
Cold Work Tool Steels									
Oil Hardening Types									
O1—Low Manganese	1500	1750–1900	1550	1500	1600	1425–1475	50	183–212	90–96
O2—High Manganese	1500	1750–1900	1550	1500	1550	1375–1425	50	183–212	90–96
O6—Molybdenum Graphitic	1500	1750–1900	1500	1500	1625	1425–1475	20	183–217	90–96
Medium Alloy Air Hardening Types									
A2—5% Chromium Air Hard	1600	1850–2000	1650	Do not normalize		1550–1600	40	202–229	94–98
High Carbon-High Chromium Types									
D2—High Carbon-High Chromium (Air)	1650	1850–2000	1650	Do not normalize		1600–1650	40	207–255	95–192
D3—High Carbon-High Chromium (Oil)	1650	1850–2000	1650	Do not normalize		1600–1650	50	212–255	96–102
D5—High Carbon-High Chromium-Cobalt	1600	1850–2000	1650	Do not normalize		1600–1650	40	207–255	95–102
D7—High Carbon-High Chromium-High Vanadium	1650	2050–2125	1800	Do not normalize		1600–1650	50	235–262	99–103
Hot Work Tool Steels									
Chromium Base Types									
H11—Chromium-Molybdenum-V	1650	1950–2100	1650	Do not normalize		1550–1600	50	192–229	92–98
H12—Chromium-Molybdenum-Tungsten	1650	1950–2100	1650	Do not normalize		1600–1650	50	192–229	92–98
H13—Chromium-Molybdenum-VV	1650	1950–2100	1650	Do not normalize		1550–1600	50	192–229	92–98
Tungsten Base Types									
H21—Tungsten	1600	2000–2150	1650	Do not normalize		1600–1650	50	202–235	94–99
High Speed Tool Steels									
Tungsten Base Types									
T1—Tungsten 18-4-1	1600	1950–2100	1750	Do not normalize		1600–1650	50	217–255	96–102
T2—Tungsten 18-4-2	1600	2000–2150	1750	Do not normalize		1600–1650	50	223–255	97–102
T4—Cobalt-Tungsten 18-4-1-5	1600	2000–2150	1750	Do not normalize		1600–1650	50	229–255	98–102
T5—Cobalt-Tungsten 18-4-2-8	1600	2000–2150	1800	Do not normalize		1600–1650	50	248–293	102–106
T8—Cobalt-Tungsten 14-4-2-5	1600	2000–2150	1750	Do not normalize		1600–1650	50	229–255	98–102
Molybdenum Base Types									
M1—Molybdenum 8-2-1	1500	1900–2050	1700	Do not normalize		1525–1600	50	207–248	95–102
M2—Molybdenum-Tungsten 6-6-2	1500	1950–2100	1700	Do not normalize		1550–1625	50	217–248	96–102
M3—Molybdenum-Tungsten 6-6-3	1500	2000–2150	1700	Do not normalize		1550–1625	50	223–255	97–102
M4—Molybdenum-Tungsten 6-6-4	1500	2000–2150	1700	Do not normalize		1550–1625	50	229–255	98–102
Special Purpose Tool Steels									
Low Alloy Types									
L6—Nickel-Chromium	1500	1800–2000	1600	1550	1650	1400–1450	50	183–212	90–96
L7—Chromium	1500	1800–2000	1550	1550	1650	1450–1500	50	174–212	88–96

1. These tool and die steels are the same as those listed in Table 1 of this report.
2. The temperature at which to start forging is given as a range, the higher side of which should be used for large sections and heavy or rapid reductions and the lower side for smaller sections and lighter reductions. As the alloy content of the steel increases, the time of soaking at forging temperature increases proportionately. Likewise, as the alloy content increases, it becomes more necessary to cool slowly from the forging temperature. With very high alloy steels, such as high speed or air hardening steels, this slow cooling is imperative in order to prevent cracking and to leave the steel in a semisoft condition. Either furnace cooling or burying in an insulating medium, such as lime, mica, or silocel, is satisfactory.
3. The length of time the steel is held after being uniformly heated through at the normalizing temperature, varies from about 15 min for a small section to about 1 hr for large sizes. Cooling from the normalizing temperature is done in still air. The purpose of normalizing after forging is to refine the grain structure and to produce a uniform structure throughout the forging. Normalizing should not be confused with low temperature (about 1200 F) annealing used for the relief of residual stresses resulting from heavy machining, bending, and forming.
4. The annealing temperature is given as a range, the upper limit of which should be used for large sections. The length of time the steel is held after being uniformly heated through at the annealing temperature varies from about 1 hr for light sections and small furnace charges of carbon or low alloy steel to about 4 hr for heavy sections and large furnace charges of high alloy steel.

For information on the forging and heat treating of tool steels, see ASM Handbook, 1948 edition, pp.653-655.

TABLE 4—MINIMUM ALLOWANCES FOR MACHINING AND MAXIMUM DECARBURIZATION LIMITS (ROUNDS, HEXAGONS, AND OCTAGONS)[1]

Ordered Size, in.	Minimum Allowance Per Side for Machining Prior to Heat Treatment, in.			
	Hot Rolled	Forged	Rounds Rough Turned	Cold Drawn
Up to 0.5, incl	0.016	—	—	0.016
Over 0.5 to 1, incl	0.031	—	—	0.031
Over 1 to 2, incl	0.048	0.072	—	0.048
Over 2 to 3, incl	0.063	0.094	0.020	0.063
Over 3 to 4, incl	0.088	0.120	0.024	0.088
Over 4 to 5, incl	0.112	0.145	0.032	—
Over 5 to 6, incl	0.150	0.170	0.040	—
Over 6 to 8, incl	0.200	0.200	0.048	—
Over 8	—	0.200	0.072	—
Maximum Decarburization Limits				
80% of above allowances per side				

1. Rounds 1/4 in. and over of high speed steel are normally furnished free of scale and decarburization.

TABLE 5A—SIZE TOLERANCES FOR HOT ROLLED BARS (ROUNDS,[1] SQUARES, OCTAGONS, QUARTER OCTAGONS, HEXAGONS)

Specified Sizes, in.	Size Tolerances, in.	
	Under	Over
To 0.5, incl	0.005	0.012
Over 0.5 to 1, incl	0.005	0.016
Over 1 to 1.5, incl	0.006	0.020
Over 1.5 to 2, incl	0.008	0.025
Over 2 to 2.5, incl	0.010	0.030
Over 2.5 to 3, incl	0.010	0.040
Over 3 to 4, incl	0.012	0.050
Over 4 to 5.5, incl	0.015	0.060
Over 5.5 to 6.5, incl	0.018	0.100
Over 6.5 to 8, incl	0.020	0.150

1. For high speed steel rounds free of scale and decarburization, Table 4.

TABLE 5B—WIDTH AND THICKNESS TOLERANCES FOR HOT ROLLED FLATS

Specified Widths, in.	Width Tolerances, in.	
	Under	Over
To 1, incl	0.016	0.031
Over 1 to 3, incl	0.031	0.047
Over 3 to 5, incl	0.047	0.063
Over 5	0.063	0.094

Specified Widths, in.	Thickness Tolerances for Thicknesses Given, in.							
	To 0.25 Incl		Over 0.25 to 0.5, Incl		Over 0.5 to 1, Incl		Over 1 to 2, Incl	
	Under	Over	Under	Over	Under	Over	Under	Over
To 1, incl	0.006	0.010	0.008	0.012	0.010	0.016	—	—
Over 1 to 2, incl	0.006	0.014	0.008	0.016	0.010	0.020	0.020	0.024
Over 2 to 3, incl	0.006	0.018	0.008	0.020	0.010	0.024	0.020	0.027
Over 3 to 4, incl	0.008	0.020	0.010	0.022	0.013	0.024	0.024	0.030
Over 4 to 5, incl	0.010	0.020	0.012	0.024	0.015	0.030	0.027	0.035
Over 5 to 6, incl	0.012	0.020	0.014	0.030	0.018	0.030	0.030	0.035

TABLE 6A—WIDTH AND TOLERANCES FOR FORGED FLATS

Specified Widths, in.	Width Tolerances, in.	
	Under	Over
Over 1 to 3, incl	0.031	0.078
Over 3 to 5, incl	0.062	0.125
Over 5 to 7, incl	0.125	0.187
Over 7	0.187	0.312

Specified Width, in.	Thickness Tolerances for Thicknesses Given, in.									
	To 1, Incl		Over 1 to 3, Incl		Over 3 to 5, Incl		Over 5 to 7, Incl		Over 7, Incl	
	Under	Over	Under	Over	Under	Over	Under	Over	Under	Over
Over 1 to 3, incl	0.016	0.031	0.031	0.078	—	—	—	—	—	—
Over 3 to 5, incl	0.031	0.062	0.047	0.094	0.062	0.125	—	—	—	—
Over 5 to 7, incl	0.047	0.094	0.062	0.125	0.078	0.156	0.125	0.187	—	—
Over 7	0.062	0.125	0.078	0.156	0.094	0.187	0.156	0.219	0.187	0.312

TABLE 6B—SIZE TOLERANCES FOR FORGED BARS (ROUNDS, SQUARES, OCTAGONS, HEXAGONS)[1]

Specified Sizes, in.	Width Tolerances, in.	
	Under	Over
Over 1 to 2, incl	0.030	0.060
Over 2 to 3, incl	0.030	0.080
Over 3 to 5, incl	0.060	0.125
Over 5 to 7, incl	0.125	0.187
Over 7	0.187	0.312

1. Refer to Table 4 for diameter tolerances on rounds of high speed steels free of scale and decarburization.

TABLE 7—SIZE TOLERANCES FOR COLD DRAWN BARS

Rounds, Octagons, Quarter Octagons, and Hexagons		Squares and Flats	
Size Range, in.	Tolerance, ± in.	Size Range, in.	Tolerance, ± in.
0.25 to 0.50, excl	0.002	0.25 to 0.75, incl	0.002
0.50 to 1, excl	0.0025	Over 0.75 to 1.50, incl	0.003
1 to 2.75, incl	0.003	Over 1.50	0.004

TABLE 8—DIAMETER TOLERANCES FOR CENTERLESS GROUND BARS (ROUND)

Diameter Range, in.	Tolerance, in.	
	Under	Over
0.25 to 0.50, excl	0.0015	0.0015
0.50 to 3.0625, excl	0.002	0.002

TABLE 9A—SIZE TOLERANCE FOR DRILL ROD ROUNDS (POLISHED OR GROUND)

Size Range, in.	Standard Manufacturing Tolerance, ± in.	Closer Tolerance, ± in.
Up to 0.124, incl	0.0003	0.0002
0.125 to 0.499, incl	0.0005	0.00025
0.500 to 1.500, incl	0.001	0.0005

TABLE 9B—SIZE TOLERANCES FOR DRILL ROD SHAPES OTHER THAN ROUNDS (COLD DRAWN)

Size Range, in.	Tolerance, ± in.
Up to 0.25, excl	0.0005
0.25 to 0.75, excl	0.001
0.75 to 1, incl	0.0015

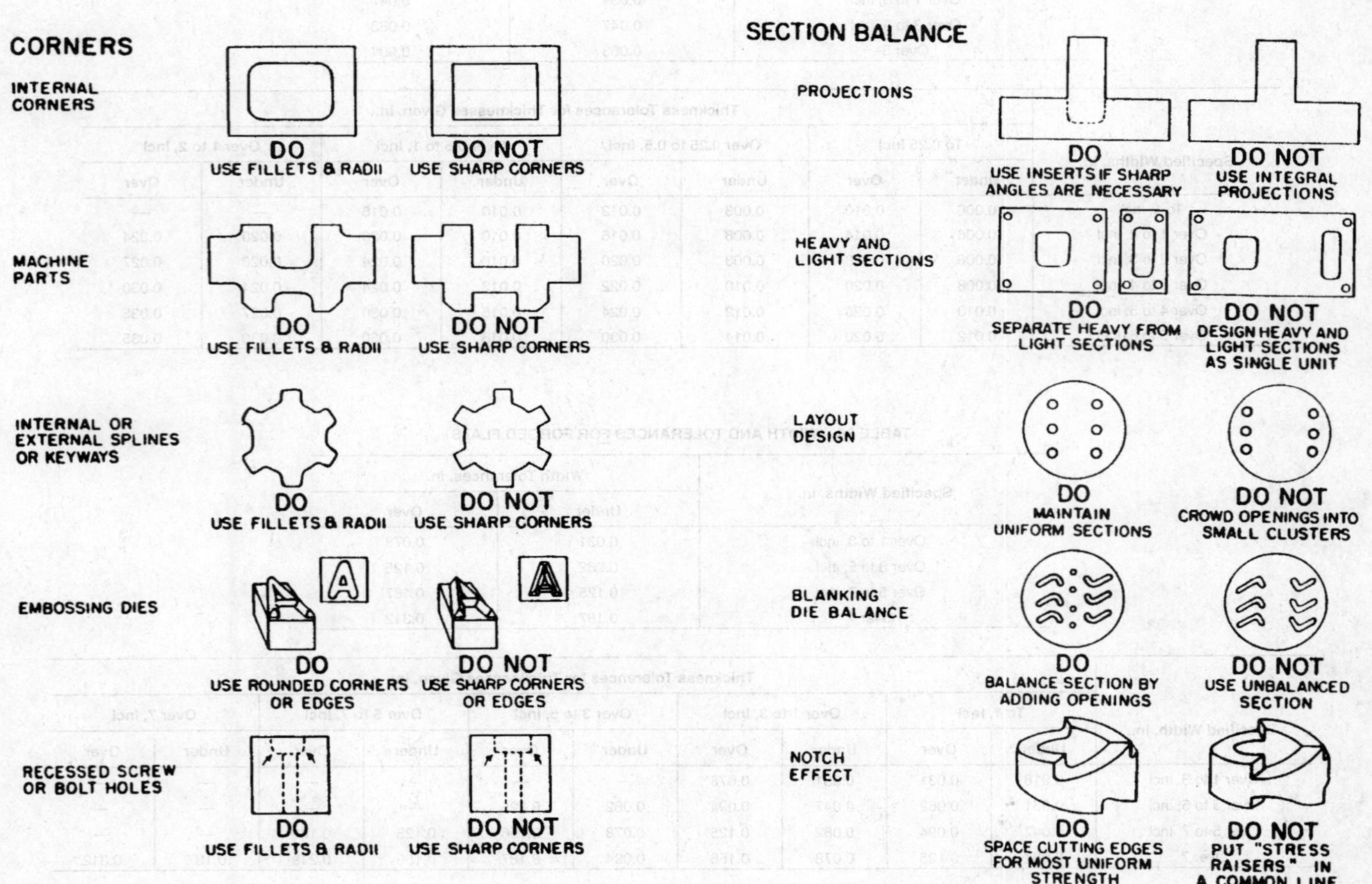

FIGURE 1—TOOL AND DIE DESIGN TIPS (TO REDUCE BREAKAGE IN HEAT TREATING)

SINTERED CARBIDE TOOLS—SAE J439a FEB77 SAE Recommended Practice

Report of the SAE Iron and Steel Technical Committee approved April 1956 and last revised April 1969. Editorial change February 1977.

Foreword—This Document has also changed to comply with the new SAE Technical Standards Board format.

1. Scope—This recommended practice covers methods for measuring or evaluating five properties or characteristics of sintered carbide which contribute significantly to the performance of sintered carbide tools. These properties are: hardness, specific gravity, apparent porosity, structure, and grain size. They are covered under separate headings below.

2. References—There are no referenced publications specified herein.

3. Hardness

3.1 General—The Rockwell hardness tester provides a simple, rapid, and reliable means of measuring the hardness of sintered carbide tools. A hardness value is easily obtained, but is subject to error if precautionary measures are not taken in making this test. Hardness determinations, therefore, shall be made according to the requirements outlined below and in ASTM E 18, Methods of Test for Rockwell Hardness and Rockwell Superficial Hardness of Metallic Materials.

3.2 Apparatus

a. Rockwell hardness testing machine with 60 kg load and diamond brale penetrator for use with the A scale[1].
b. Two tungsten carbide test blocks with a hardness of 90.0 and 92.0 Rockwell A (RA) respectively.

3.3 Material - Sample—Preparation of the surface of the specimen prior to making the hardness test is of major importance. It is recommended that a finish equivalent to that produced with a 220 grit diamond grinding wheel be obtained on the surface which is to be checked for hardness. Because of the shallow penetration of the diamond penetrator used in making this test, the surface being tested for hardness must be parallel to the surface opposite of that being tested. Both surfaces must be smooth and devoid of any bulge or other irregularity affecting parallelism. If these two surfaces are only slightly out of parallel, an error will be obtained in the hardness reading.

It is important that the Rockwell hardness testing machine is located in such a manner and area that it is free from vibration while hardness tests are being performed. Vibration is detected by the bounding effect transmitted through the needle of the indicator after the major load has been applied.

3.4 Procedure—The hardness test shall be made using the RA scale. This reading is obtained by observing the deflection of the needle pointer on the black scale with a 60 kg load and the diamond brale penetrator.[1]

Before making the hardness test on the carbide material, the Rockwell testing machine shall be checked for accuracy, using a tungsten carbide test block of known hardness. Two check blocks of different hardness values are recommended to assure accurate hardness readings over the general range of hardness of the common grades of sintered carbides. The check blocks should have a hardness of 90.0 and 92.0 RA respectively. The check block having the hardness closest to the expected hardness of the carbide material to be checked shall be selected for calibrating the Rockwell tester. The average of five readings should check within ±0.2 of a hardness number. If the Rockwell tester varies appreciably from the hardness number of the test block, the dial of the machine must be adjusted so that the correct reading is obtained. The amount of variation is noted and this correction plus or minus is applied when taking the hardness reading on the specimens of sintered carbide being tested. This dial adjustment will be made just before the major load is applied. With careful manipulations, hardness readings can be accurately duplicated when the hardness tester is calibrated in this manner.

4. Specific Gravity

4.1 General—The specific gravity of sintered carbide tool materials shall be determined by the immersion method, using as a basis the difference in weight of the carbide in air and in water.

4.2 Apparatus

a. A standard analytical balance of 200 g capacity and 0.1 mg sensitivity at full load.
b. A 150- or 250-ml beaker, depending upon the size of the carbide specimen.
c. Small diameter nonferrous wire.
d. Thermometer 0–100 °C for room temperatures capable of being read to nearest 0.5 °C.

4.3 Materials

a. The specimen shall be surface ground all over with a 100 grit diamond wheel before testing.
b. Distilled water.

4.4 Procedure

a. Weigh the specimen, to the nearest 0.5 mg.
b. Support a beaker of distilled water[2] over the pan of the balance by a suitable bridge. Water level should be high enough to cover the specimen by at least 1/4 in.
c. Suspend the specimen and the wire from the beam hook, placing the specimen in the water, and weigh to the nearest 0.5 mg.
d. Remover the specimen from the wire and weigh the wire alone in water. Subtract this weight from the total weight found in step c.
e. Observe the temperature of the water to the nearest 1.0 °C.

4.5 Calculations

W_a = Weight of Specimen in Air
W_w = Weight of Specimen in Water
D = Relative Density of Water at Test Temperature (Density relative to that of Water at 4 °C)

$$\text{Specific Gravity} = \frac{W_a \times D}{W_a - W_w} \qquad \text{(Eq. 1)}$$

5. Apparent Porosity, Structure, And Grain Size

5.1 General—Apparent porosity, structure, and grain size shall be evaluated by metallographic examination, as outlined below.

Apparent porosity is the term applied to the inherent porosity, non-metallic inclusions, and uncombined carbon as observed in the microstructure of the properly prepared surface of sintered carbides.

Structure refers to the type and distribution of the metal carbides and binder material observed in the microstructure of the properly prepared surface of sintered carbides.

Grain size is the term applied to the predominating particle sizes, in microns, of the metal carbides observed in the microstructure.

5.2 Sample Preparation—Select a specimen approximately 1/2 in. square from the area of particular interest of the sample to be tested. Sectioning should be done with a diamond cutoff wheel. Mount unwieldy specimens in hard bakelite or its equivalent, then grind as follows:

a. Rough grind using a green silicon carbide wheel.
b. Fine grind using a 320 grit diamond wheel running at a speed of approximately 5500 surface fpm.

Samples should be polished using the ordinary metallographic polishing equipment. Impregnate a paper polishing disc, properly attached to the bronze disc of the polishing lap, with a light (SAE 10) oil. Apply diamond paste to the oiled paper and work it in with the fingertip. At least two polishing laps should be used in the following order:

a. A diamond lap using a 10 µm maximum diamond powder.
b. A diamond lap using a 1 µm maximum diamond powder.

Hold the specimen 1-3 in. from the center of the lap running at approximately 1150 rpm. Considerable pressure should be exerted on the specimen while polishing in intervals of approximately 10 sec. Rotating the specimen 90 deg between each interval is recommended. (CAUTION: Light pressure and too much polishing may cause pitting of the specimen.)

Polishing is ineffective when the specimen is above approximately 150 °F; therefore, polishing time should be carefully watched to keep the temperature of the specimen below this point. Extreme cleanliness is necessary to prevent contamination of the diamond laps. The specimen should be washed thoroughly with a suitable solvent after each polishing operation.

1. It is recommended that a diamond brale especially selected for use with the Rockwell "A" scale be used for this type of testing. This type of penetrator is of higher quality, free from chips and other imperfections, and should be specified for Rockwell "A" scale use. Slowing down of the rate of speed at which the major load is applied during testing will aid in increasing the life of the diamond brale. This change in load application does not affect the accuracy of the hardness reading. The use of the superficial scale is not recommended for hardness testing of sintered carbides unless extreme care is exercised with regard to parallelism and smoothness during surface preparation of the specimen.

2. Care should be used to see that no air bubbles are present on the sample after immersion, and that the wire twist on the sample is completely submerged. Several drops of a suitable wetting agent will aid in eliminating air bubbles.

5.3 Apparent Porosity Evaluation—After the prescribed sample preparation, the sample shall be examined in the unetched condition at a magnification of 200X.

A porosity rating shall be made by comparing the observed field with the porosity charts of Figures 1–3.

The rating charts depict both the type of porosity, designated alphabetically, and the quantity of porosity, designated numerically. Type A classifies porosity sizes under 10 μm in diameter; Type B classifies porosity sizes between 10 and 40 μm in diameter; Type C classifies cluster porosity or that developed by the presence of uncombined carbon, and is considered the type most detrimental to tool performance.

5.4 Structure Evaluation—After the prescribed sample preparation the sample shall be etched and examined at a magnification of 1500X. The etchant shall consist of a fresh solution having equal parts of 10% potassium hydroxide and 10% potassium ferricyanide. The sample shall be immersed in the etchant for 2 minutes, then rinsed with water and the polished surface swabbed with wet cotton. A second immersion for approximately another 2 minutes shall be made to delineate the structure. The sample shall then be washed with water and dried with alcohol and air to prevent staining. Examination of the prepared surface shall be made with a metallographic microscope utilizing an oil immersion objective. Figures 4A and 4B are typical photomicrographs of tungsten carbide (WC) with 6% cobalt and 13% cobalt, respectively. Figures 4C and 4D are typical photomicrographs of tungsten carbide (WC) plus solid solution carbide (WC-TiC-TaC) with 4.5% cobalt and 11% cobalt, respectively. The tungsten carbide particles are angular and gray in appearance, the solid solution particles, where present, are rounded and usually darker gray, and the cobalt binder appears white. The abnormal "eta phase" carbide is not depicted by the photomicrographs. It is a brittle, carbon deficient carbide detrimental to tool performance but is readily detected as a very rapid etching, black constituent.

The data provided by this test are an excellent indicator for identifying a particular producer's product and its uniformity.

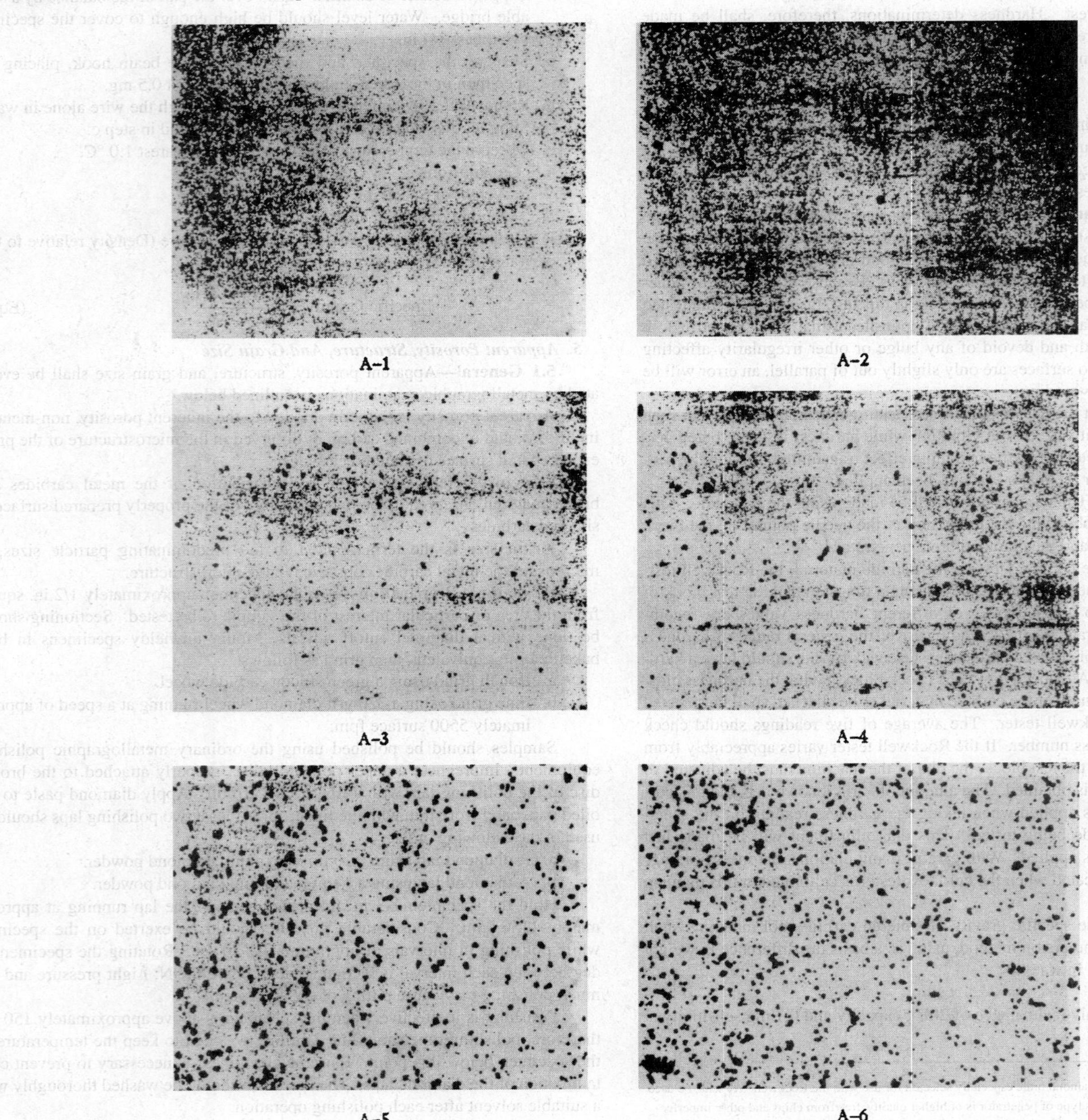

FIGURE 1—TYPE A - APPARENT POROSITY MICROSTRUCTURE OF CEMENTED CARBIDES (X200) (B 276)

5.5 Grain Size Evaluation—Sample preparation, etching technique, and equipment shall be the same as described for structure evaluation.

The grain size shall be determined by comparing representative areas of the observed sample field with the carbide grain size chart (Figure 5). This chart illustrates the relationship of particle sizes from 1 to 10 μm as observed at a magnification of 1500X.

The grain size rating shall consist of a sequence of numbers such as 231. Each number refers to a carbide particle size range; that is a "1" includes all particles which are 1 μm or finer, a "2" includes all particles over 1 through 2 μm, a "3" includes all particles over 2 through 3 μm, etc., as illustrated by the carbide grain size chart. The sequence of the numbers shall be in the order of the sample area they represent, with the first number representing the greatest area. A minimum of 80% of the representative sample area shall be included in the rating.

Grain size and distribution has considerable influence on the mechanical properties of sintered carbide. Thus, materials having similar composition but different grain size and distribution may have very different performance characteristics.

FIGURE 2—TYPE B - APPARENT POROSITY MICROSTRUCTURE OF CEMENTED CARBIDES (X200) (B 276)

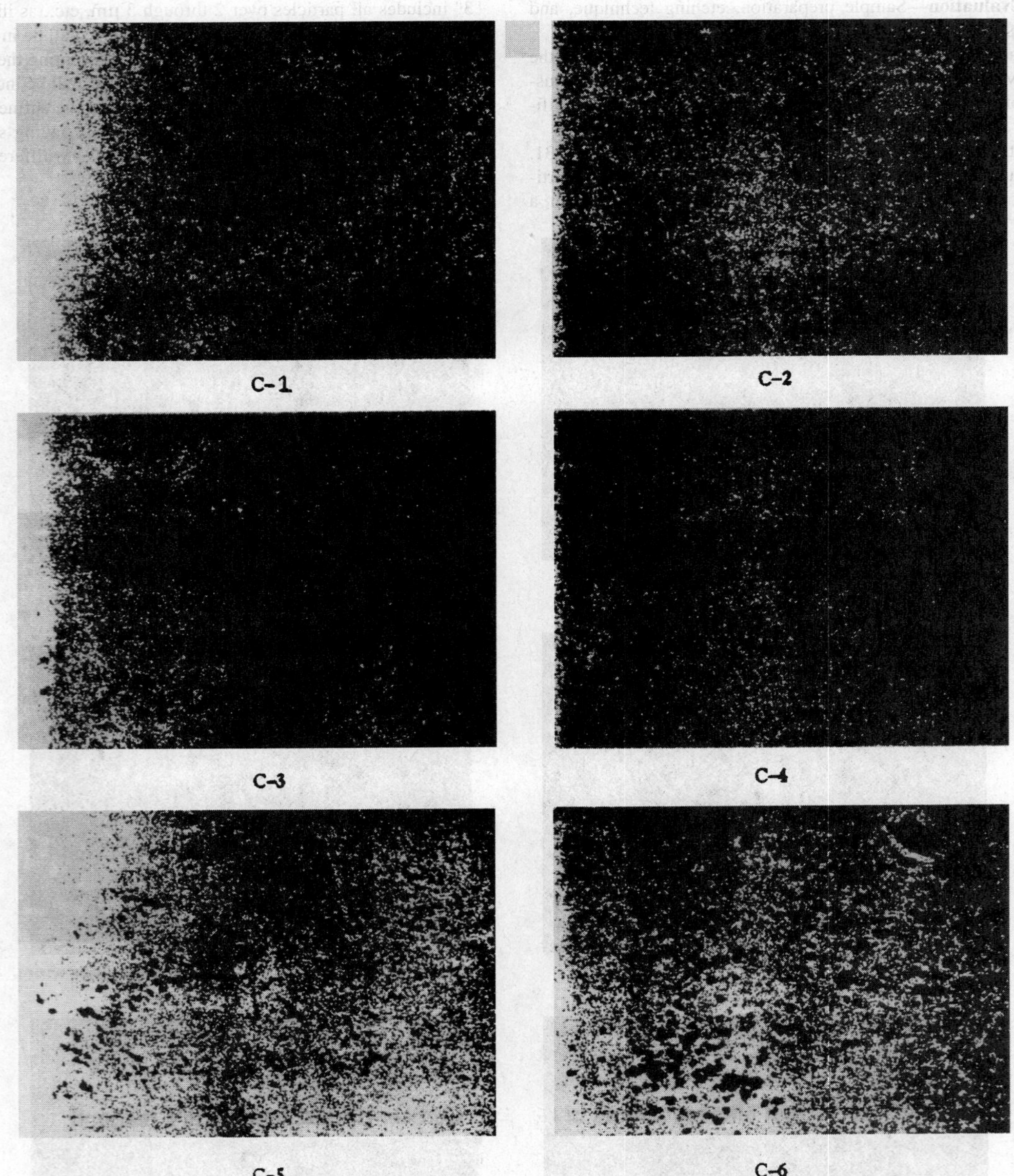

FIGURE 3—TYPE C - APPARENT POROSITY MICROSTRUCTURE OF CEMENTED CARBIDS (X200) (B 276)

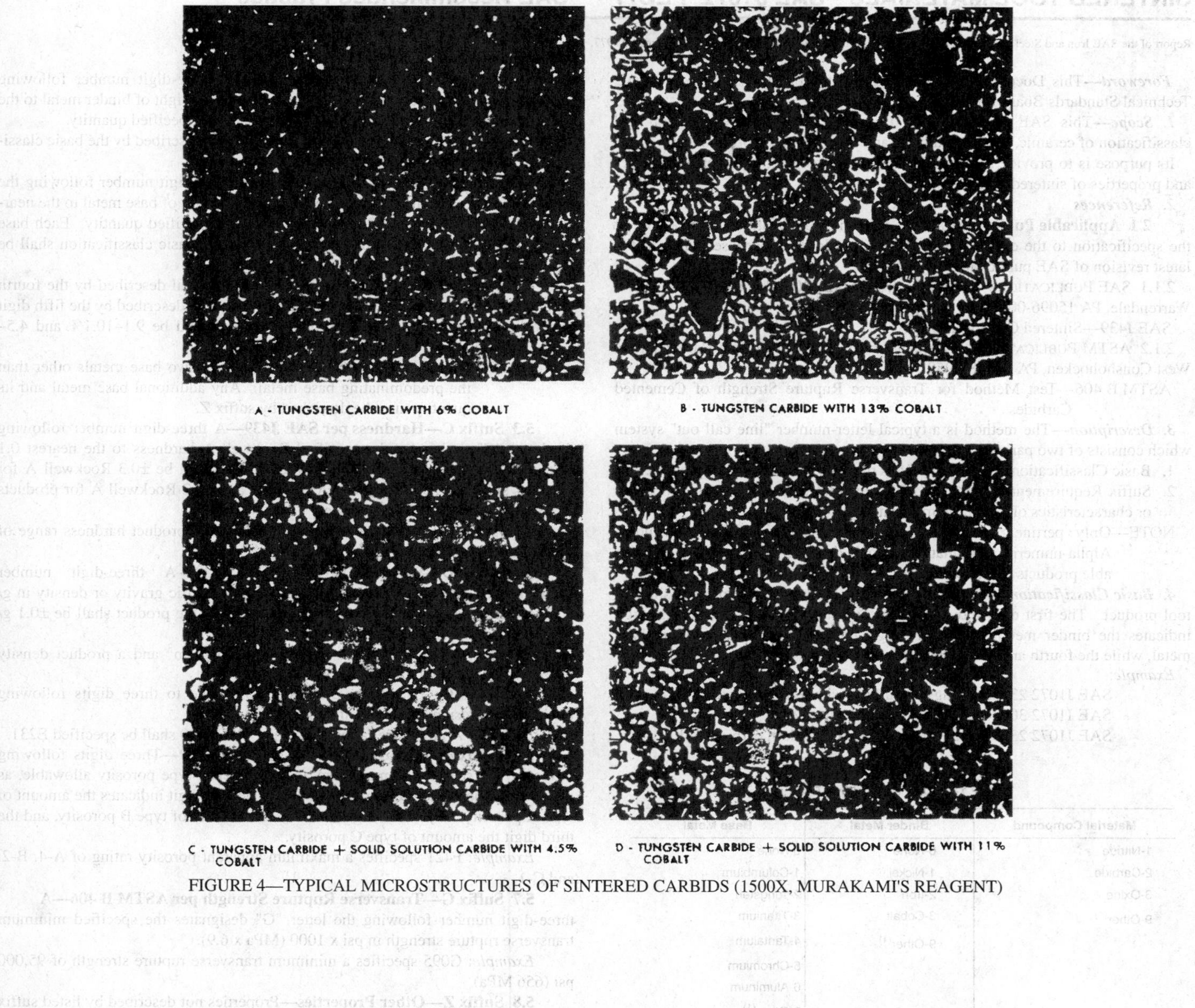

FIGURE 4—TYPICAL MICROSTRUCTURES OF SINTERED CARBIDS (1500X, MURAKAMI'S REAGENT)

(R) SINTERED TOOL MATERIALS—SAE J1072 FEB77 SAE Recommended Practice

Report of the SAE Iron and Steel Technical Committee approved January 1974. Editorial change February 1977.

Foreword—This Document has also changed to comply with the new SAE Technical Standards Board Format.

1. Scope—This SAE Recommended Practice covers the identification and classification of ceramic, sintered carbide, and other cermet tool products.

Its purpose is to provide a standard method for designating the characteristics and properties of sintered tool materials.

2. References

2.1 Applicable Publications—The following publications form a part of the specification to the extent specified herein. Unless otherwise indicated the latest revision of SAE publications shall apply.

2.1.1 SAE PUBLICATIONS—Available from SAE, 400 Commonwealth Drive, Warrendale, PA 15096-0001.

SAE J439—Sintered Carbide Tools

2.1.2 ASTM PUBLICATIONS—Available from ASTM, 100 Barr Harbor Drive, West Conshohocken, PA 19428-2959.

ASTM B 406—Test Method for Transverse Rupture Strength of Cemented Carbides

3. Description—The method is a typical letter-number "line call out" system which consists of two parts:

1. Basic Classification—which identifies the type of sintered tool product.
2. Suffix Requirements—which provide quantitative values for the properties or characteristics of a specific material.

NOTE—Only pertinent properties or characteristics should be included. Alpha-numeric combinations which describe commercially unavailable products must be avoided.

4. Basic Classification—A sequence of five digits is used to type each sintered tool product. The first digit indicates the type of compound. The second digit indicates the binder metal. The third digit indicates the *predominating* base metal, while the fourth and fifth digits indicate *other* base metals. See Table 1.

Example:

SAE J1072 23200—tungsten carbide with a cobalt binder
SAE J1072 30600—aluminum oxide ceramic
SAE J1072 23234—tungsten, titanium, tantalum carbide with a cobalt binder

TABLE 1—BASIC CLASSIFICATION

Material Compound	Binder Metal	Base Metal
1-Nitride	0-None	0-None
2-Carbide	1-Nickel	1-Columbium
3-Oxide	2-Iron	2-Tungsten
9-Other(1)	3-Cobalt	3-Titanium
	9-Other(1)	4-Tantalum
		5-Chromium
		6-Aluminum
		9-Other(1)

1. Shall be described by suffix Z.

5. Suffix Requirements—A letter designating the property or characteristic to be specified is followed by numbers which designate the level of the property or characteristic. (Note: Suffix Z shall be used to describe any property or characteristic for which an appropriate suffix letter has not been assigned.)

5.1 Suffix A—Binder Metal Quantity—A three-digit number following the letter "A" designates the specified percentage by weight of binder metal to the nearest 0.1%. The product range shall be ±5% of the specified quantity.

Example: A045 specifies 4.5% of binder metal described by the basic classification or a product range of 4.3–4.7%.

5.2 Suffix B—Base Metal Quantity—A three-digit number following the letter "B" designates the specified percentage by weight of base metal to the nearest 0.1%. The product range shall be ±5% of the specified quantity. Each base metal described by the fourth and fifth digits of the basic classification shall be included.

Example: B096B047 specifies 9.6% of base metal described by the fourth digit of the basic classification and 4.7% of base metal described by the fifth digit of the basic classification. The product ranges would be 9.1–10.1% and 4.5–4.9%, respectively.

NOTE—The Basic Classification provides for two base metals other than the predominating base metal. Any additional base metal and its quantity must be described by suffix Z.

5.3 Suffix C—Hardness per SAE J439—A three-digit number following the letter "C" designates the specified Rockwell A hardness to the nearest 0.1 Rockwell A. The hardness range of the product shall be ±0.3 Rockwell A for products specified 89.9 Rockwell A or softer and ±0.2 Rockwell A for products specified 90.0 Rockwell A or harder.

Example: C922 specifies 92.2 Rockwell A or a product hardness range of 92.0–92.4 Rockwell A.

5.4 Suffix D—Specific Gravity per SAE J439—A three-digit number following the letter "D" designates the specified specific gravity or density in g/cm^3 to the nearest 0.1 g/cm^3. The density range of the product shall be ±0.1 g/cm^3 from that specified.

Example: D126 specifies a density of 12.6 g/cm^3 and a product density range of 12.5–12.7 g/cm^3.

5.5 Suffix E—Grain Size per SAE J439—One to three digits following the letter "E" designate the specified grain size.

Example: A grain size rating of 231 per SAE J439 shall be specified E231.

5.6 Suffix F—Apparent Porosity per SAE J439—Three digits following the letter "F" specify the maximum amount of each type porosity allowable, as depicted by the photographs of SAE J439. The first digit indicates the amount of type A porosity, the second digit indicates the amount of type B porosity, and the third digit the amount of type C porosity.

Example: F421 specifies a maximum apparent porosity rating of A-4, B-2, and C-1.

5.7 Suffix G—Transverse Rupture Strength per ASTM B 406—A three-digit number following the letter "G" designates the specified minimum transverse rupture strength in psi x 1000 (MPa x 6.9).

Example: G095 specifies a minimum transverse rupture strength of 95,000 psi (656 MPa).

5.8 Suffix Z—Other Properties—Properties not described by listed suffix designations and those which require more explicit description shall be written out.

Examples:

Z1—thermal expansion from room temperature to 1500 °F (816 °C) shall be 3.46×10^{-6}/°F (6.23×10^{-6}/°C).

Z2—titanium carbide coated.

8 Ferrous Materials

SINTERED POWDER METAL PARTS: FERROUS—SAE J471d AUG1973

SAE Standard

Report of the SAE Nonferrous Metals Division approved January 1939, revised by Nonferrous Metals Committee June 1966, and last revised by the SAE Iron and Steel Technical Committee August 1973.

1. Scope—Powder metal (P/M) parts are manufactured by pressing metal powders to the required shape in a precision die and sintering to produce metallurgical bonds between the particles, thus generating the appropriate mechanical properties. The shape and mechanical properties of the part may be subsequently modified by repressing or by conventional methods such. as machining and/or heat treating.

While powder metallurgy embraces a number of fields wherein metal powders may be used as raw materials, this standard is concerned primarily with information relating to mechanical components and bearings produced from iron-base materials.

2. References—There are no referenced publications specified herein.

3. Bearings—Powder metal bearings are classified broadly in two groups: ferrous and nonferrous. While much of the basic information is common to both types, this standard is concerned only with the former. Information relating to copper- and aluminum-base materials is under development.

3.1 Chemical Composition—The chemical composition shall be determined on an oil-free basis and shall conform to the limits set out in Table 1. The analysis shall be performed in accordance with ASTM procedure, or any other approved method agreed upon by the manufacturer and the purchaser.

Subject to agreement between purchaser and manufacturer metallographic estimates of combined carbon values may be used.

In cases of disagreement in respect of composition, samples shall be submitted to independent umpire analysis.

3.2 Physical and Mechanical Properties—A most important characteristic of oil impregnated sintered bearings is their property of self-lubrication resulting from the internal oil reservoir created by the interconnected pore structure. The quantity of oil available is thus directly proportional to the pore volume of the bearing. The mechanical strength of bearings of the same composition produced under similar manufacturing conditions is inversely proportional to the pore volume. Although a tensile bar pressed and sintered under the same conditions as the bearing is sometimes used to evaluate materials, the generally accepted test is a radial crush test in which the load required to break the bearing is related to its physical dimensions via a constant, K, specified for each material.

3.2.1 DENSITY—The density of the bearing, fully impregnated with lubricant (see Appendix B), shall conform to the limits set out in Table 1. If in one bearing the variation of density from any one section to any other is less than 0.3 g/CM3, the density of the bearing as a whole shall fall within the limits prescribed in Table 1. If this point-to-point variation exceeds 0.3 g/CM3, the manufacturer and purchaser shall agree upon a critical section of the part in which the density requirements of the specification must be fulfilled.

3.2.2 OIL CONTENT—The oil content of the bearing shall not be less than that specified in Table 1. (See Appendix B.)

3.2.3 RADIAL CRUSHING STRENGTH—Radial crushing strength (see Appendix A) shall not be less than the value calculated as follows:

$$P = \frac{KLT^2}{D - T} \quad \text{(Eq. 1)}$$

where:

P = radial crushing load, lb (N)
D = outside diameter of bearing, in. (nini)
T = wall thickness of bearing, in. (mm)
L = length of bearing, in. (mm)
K = strength constant shown in Table I

3.2.4 PERMISSIBLE LOADS—In calculating permissible loads, the operating conditions, housing conditions, and construction should be considered. Permissible bearing loads for various operating conditions are shown in Table 2. These are intended only as a general guide.

Certain conditions will increase the permissible loads, such as additional lubrication, pressure lubrication, hardening of the shaft, loads of short duration.

Certain conditions will tend to reduce the load-carrying capacity of bearings regardless of type or make: continued start-stop operation, oscillating and reciprocating motion, extremely high or low temperatures; excessively close or loose bearing clearances; deflection or misalignment of shaft; dust, grit, corrosive fumes, or poor shaft finish.

3.3 Dimensional Characteristics

3.3.1 TOLERANCES—Dimensional tolerances allowed shall conform to the limits prescribed in Tables 3 and 4, unless otherwise agreed between supplier and purchaser.

3.3.2 RECOMMENDED PRESS FITS—Plain cylindrical journal bearings are commonly installed by press fitting the bearing into a housing using an insertion arbor. For housings rigid enough to withstand the press fit without appreciable distortion and for bearings with wall thickness approximately one-eighth of the bearing outside diameter, the press fits shown in Table 5 are recommended.

3.3.3 RUNNING CLEARANCES— Proper running clearances for sintered bearings depend to a great extent upon the particular application. Therefore, only minimum recommended clearances are listed in Table 6. It is assumed that ground steel shafting will be used and that all bearings will be oil impregnated.

TABLE 1—PROPERTIES OF FERROUS P/M BEARINGS

SAE No.	Density, g/cm³	Chemical Composition, % Cu	Chemical Composition, % C	Chemical Composition, % Others	Chemical Composition, % Fe	Minimum Oil Content by Volume, %	Strength Constant psi	Strength Constant MPa
850	5.7-6.1	—	0.25 max	2.0 max	Bal	18	25,000	172
851	5.7-6.1	—	0.25-0.60	2.0 max	Bal	18	30,000	207
862	5.8-6.2	7-11	0.30 max	2.0 max	Bal	18	40,000	276
863	5.8-6.2	18-22	0.30 max	2.0 max	Bal	18	40,000	276

TABLE 2—PERMISSIBLE BEARING LOADS

Shaft Velocity ft/min	Shaft Velocity m/min	Permissible Loads SAE 850/851 psi	Permissible Loads SAE 850/851 MPa	Permissible Loads SAE 862/863 psi	Permissible Loads SAE 862/863 MPa
Static (0)	0	7500	52	15,000	103
Slow and intermittent (25)	7.6	3600	25	8,000	55
50-100	15.2-30.4	1800	12	3,000	21
100-150	30.4-45.7	450	3.1	700	4.8
150-200	45.7-61	300	2.1	400	2.8
Over 200	61	225	1.6	300	2.1

For shaft velocities in excess of 200 ft/min (61 m/min), the permissible load may be calculated as follows:

P = 50,000/V

where:

P = safe load per square inch of projected area, psi
V = shaft velocity, ft/min
P = 105/V

or:

P = safe load per square metre of projected area, MPa
V = shaft velocity, m/min

TABLE 3—COMMERCIAL DIMENSIONAL TOLERANCES

Note: This table is intented for bearings with a 3:1 maximum length to inside diameter ratio and a 20:1 maximum length to wall thickness ratio. Bearings having greater ratios than these are not covered by the table.

Inside Diameter and Outside Diameter in	Inside Diameter and Outside Diameter mm	Total Diameter Tolerance(1) Inside Diameter in	Total Diameter Tolerance(1) Inside Diameter mm	Total Diameter Tolerance(1) Outside Diameter in	Total Diameter Tolerance(1) Outside Diameter mm
Up to 0.760	Up to 19.31	0.001	0.025	0.001	0.025
0.761 to 1.510	19.32 to 38.36	0.0015	0.025	0.0015	0.04
1.511 to 2.510	38.37 to 63.76	0.002	0.05	0.002	0.05
2.511 to 3.010	63.77 to 76.46	0.003	0.08	0.002	0.05
3.011 to 4.010	76.47 to 101.86	0.004	0.10	0.004	0.10
4.011 to 5.010	101.87 to 127.26	0.005	0.13	0.005	0.13
5.011 to 6.010	127.27 to 152.65	0.006	0.15	0.006	0.15

1. Total tolerance on the inside diameter and outside diameter is a minus tolerance only.

Length in	Length mm	Total Length Tolernace(1) in	Total Length Tolerance(1) mm
Up to 1.495	Up to 37.97	0.010	0.25
1.496 to 1.990	37.98 to 50.54	0.015	0.38
1.991 to 2.990	50.55 to 75.96	0.020	0.51
2.991 to 4.985	75.97 to 126.61	0.030	0.76

1. Total tolerance is split into plus and minus.

Outside Diameter in	Outside Diameter mm	Wall Thickness, max in	Wall Thickness, max mm	Concentricity Tolerance(1) in	Concentricity Tolerance(1) mm
Up to 1.510	Up to 38.36	Up to 0.355	9.02	0.003	0.08
1.511 to 2.010	38.37 to 51.06	Up to 0.505	12.83	0.004	0.10
2.011 to 4.010	51.07 to 101.86	Up to 1.010	25.65	0.005	0.13
4.011 to 5.010	101.87 to 127.26	Up to 1.510	38.35	0.006	0.15
5.011 to 6.010	127.27 to 152.65	Up to 2.010	51.05	0.007	0.18

1. Total indicator reading.

TABLE 4—FLANGE AND THRUST BEARINGS DIAMETER AND THICKNESS TOLERANCES(1)

Flange Bearings, Flange Diameter Tolerances

Diameter Range		Standard		Special	
in	mm	in	mm	in	mm
0 to 1-1/2	0 to 38	±0.005	±0.13	±0.0025	±0.06
Over 1-1/2 to 3	39 to 76	±0.010	±0.25	±0.005	±0.13
Over 3 to 6	77 to 152	±0.025	±0.64	±0.010	±0.25

1. Standard and special tolerances are specified for diameters, thickness, and parallelism. Special tolerances should not be specified unless required since they require additional or secondary operations and, therefore, are costlier.

Flange Bearings, Flange Thickness Tolerances

Diameter Range		Standard		Special	
in	mm	in	mm	in	mm
0 to 1-1/2	0 to 38	±0.005	±0.13	±0.025	±0.06
Over 1-1/2 to 3	39 to 76	±0.010	±0.25	±0.007	±0.18
Over 3 to 6	77 to 152	±0.015	±0.38	±0.010	±0.25

Thrust Bearings (1/4 in (6.35 mm) Thickness, max), Thickness Tolerances, All Diameters(1)

Standard		Special	
in	mm	in	mm
±0.005	±0.13	±0.0025	±0.06

1. Outside diameter tolerances same as for flange bearings.

Parallelism on Faces, max

Diameter Range		Standard		Special	
in	mm	in	mm	in	mm
0 to 1-1/2	0 to 38	0.005	0.13	0.003	0.03
Over 1-1/2 to 3	39 to 76	0.007	0.18	0.005	0.13
Over 3 to 6	77 to 152	0.010	0.25	0.007	0.18

TABLE 5—RECOMMENDED PRESS FITS

Outside Diameter Bearing		Press Fit			
		Min		Max	
in	mm	in	mm	in	mm
Up to 0.760	Up to 19.31	0.001	0.025	0.003	0.03
0.761 to 1.510	19.32 to 38.36	0.0015	0.04	0.004	0.10
1.511 to 2.510	38.37 to 63.76	0.002	0.05	0.005	0.13
2.511 to 3.010	63.77 to 76.45	0.002	0.05	0.006	0.15
Over 3.010	Over 76.45	0.002	0.05	0.007	0.18

TABLE 6—RUNNING CLEARANCES

Shaft Size		Total Clearance, min	
in	mm	in	mm
Up to 0.760	Up to 19.31	0.0005	0.01
0.761 to 1.510	19.32 to 38.36	0.001	0.025
1.511 to 2.510	38.37 to 63.76	0.0015	0.04
Over 2,510	Over 63.76	0.002	0.05

4. *Mechanical Components*

4.1 General Information—This section of the standard relates to mechanical or structural components such as cams, gears, levers, shock absorber parts, transmission parts, etc., which are produced by powder metallurgy methods. Many of these parts are used in the "as-sintered" or "as-sized" condition; however, in a large number of applications, additional processing of the parts is required. Additional processes include machining, heat treatment, sealing, or surface treatments, These notes are intended to provide a general guide on the application and use of some of these processes.

4.1.1 HEAT TREATMENT—P/M parts are porous and thus provide more surface area in any metal/gas reactions proceeding during heat treatment. In any given set of heat treating circumstances, the depth of carburization or decarburization will increase with decreasing density. Provided that the proper care is taken to maintain the appropriate carbon potential, carbonbearing iron-base P/M parts can be heat treated by conventional quenchhardening methods. It should be noted that the porous material will, on cooling, absorb some of the quench medium, perhaps resulting in some minor problems during tempering or further treatment.

The absorption of fluids by the porous materials usually precludes the use of liquid salt bath treatments.

4.1.2 STEAM TREATMENT—This process consists of heating ferrous parts to 1000-1100 °F (540-600 °C) and subjecting them to superheated steam under pressure. A layer of black iron oxide is formed on all external and internal (interconnected porosity) surfaces. This oxide layer improves wear resistance, surface hardness, compressive strength and, under some conditions, corrosion resistance. The presence of oxide within the pores tends to close these channels, reducing the volume of interconnected porosity and providing a measure of pressure tightness. Steam treatment usually results in a decrease in impact resistance. It should also be noted that oxidation can lead to the generation of internal stresses with a general degradation of mechanical properties.

4.1.3 PLATING—P/M parts can be electroplated by conventional techniques providing certain precautions are taken to prevent the absorption of the plating solution into the porous body. Trapped electrolyte will eventually exude, causing corrosion and flaking of the plate. The degree of surface preparation required is governed by the part density. Infiltrated parts and parts with a density in excess of 7.0 g/CM3 can be plated by procedures normally employed for wrought materials. At lower densities the parts must be scaled by resin impregnation if the plating is to be deposited from a liquid electrolyte. Certain types of mechanical plating can be applied to porous materials without difficulty.

4.1.4 INFILTRATION—Infiltration is a process in which the residual interconnected porosity in an iron-base P/M part is filled with a metal of lower melting point. The infiltrant, normally copper or a copper-base alloy, is placed in contact with the part and the two are heated above the melting point of the infiltrant. In the liquid state the infiltrant is drawn into the interconnected porosity of the part by capillary action. The major disadvantage of the process is that it may result in some loss of dimensional accuracy.

The process has the following advantages:

a. Improved mechanical properties. Higher tensile strength and hardness values, together with improved impact and fatigue resistance, are obtained as a result of infiltrating the part.
b. Elimination of porosity. The sealing effect resulting from the filling of interconnected porosity eliminates problems associated with electrolyte entrapment in plating or gas permeation in heat treatment. Infiltrated parts can usually be used in most applications requiring pressure tightness.

4.1.5 IMPREGNATION—Impregnat ion is the process of filling the pores of a part with oil or a plastic resin. Oil is used primarily for self-lubricating parts or bearings; plastic resins may be used

a. To effect pressure tightness.
b. To seal porosity as a pretreatment prior to plating.
c. To provide an uninterrupted surface for machining. Impregnation improves tool life and surface finish.

Two basic techniques are in use for oil impregnation:

a. The parts are immersed in hot oil for a period varying between 30 min and several hours depending upon the size, shape, and type of part.
b. The parts are immersed in oil under vacuum in some suitable vessel.

The latter method ensures the removal of air pockets from within the component.

In the case of plastic impregnation, only the vacuum technique is employed.

4.1.6 MACHINING—It is not possible to give many useful rules or principles for the machining of P/M materials because of the diversity of materials, machining techniques, and objectives. In general, the machining characteristics of P/M materials are different from those of wrought materials of similar hardness or composition. It is obvious that a machining operation may close surface porosity and hence interfere with the intended function of a bearing surface. If possible, machining operations should be carried out dry since coolants may be retained in the pores subsequently leading to corrosion or act as an adulterant to the impregnating lubricant. Wet machining can be used without difficulty on infiltrated or impregnated parts. It is necessary to examine each individual application in detail to devise the optimum method and conditions for machining.

4.2 Properties

4.2.1 CHEMICAL COMPOSITION—The chemical composition shall be determined on an oil-free basis and shall conform to the limits prescribed in Table 7. The analysis shall be carried out in accordance with ASTM procedure or by any approved method agreed upon by the manufacturer and purchaser.

Subject to agreement between purchaser and manufacturer, metallographic estimates of combined carbon values may be used.

In cases of disagreement in respect of composition, samples must be submitted to independent umpire analysis.

4.2.2 DENSITY—In structural parts of complex shape, there may be variation in density from one section of the part to another. If this variation is less than 0.3 g/CM^3, the overall density of the part as a whole shall fall within the limits prescribed in Table 7. If the variation exceeds 0.3 g/CM^3, the manufacturer and purchaser shall agree upon a critical section of the part in which the density requirements of the specification must be fulfilled. This critical section would ordinarily be that at which the stresses are highest.

Density shall be determined on a dry basis, that is, on the unimpregnated component. (See Appendix B.)

4.2.3 OTHER MECHANICAL PROPERTIES—The properties given in Table 7 are typical of materials within the specified density ranges and properly sintered.

Most P/M parts are too small to allow tensile bars to be cut from the actual component; thus, it is a common practice for the manufacturer and purchaser to agree upon an empirical acceptance test based upon the conditions of service of the part. This test may be an axial or radial crushing test, an impact test in which a weight is allowed to fall a specific distance onto a specified area of the part, a bending test, etc. The method of carrying out this test must be agreed upon, including the method of holding the specimen, the rate of application of the load, etc. Hardness tests are often used in conjunction with tests of this type. The actual metal hardness may be obscured by the collapse of the pore structure under the localized load of such a test. Consequently, it is usually impossible to correlate hardness measurements carried out by different methods as is often possible in wrought materials. In general, a particular hardness specification for a part should be developed by agreement of the supplier and customer. The familiar Rockwell scales such as B, C, and 15T are used to advantage.

The hardness values obtained for porous sintered materials on any scale should not be compared with the hardness readings yielded by wrought metals of similar composition because of the "pore effect" on hardness readings obtained on sintered materials and discussed earlier in this passage.

TABLE 7—PROPERTIES OF STRUCTURAL COMPONENTS

SAE No.	Grade	Class	Type	Chemical Composition, %					Density g/cm^3	Ultimate Yield Strength (typical)		Yield Strength in Compression (typical)		Ultimate Yield Strength After Heat Treatment (typical)	
				C	Cu	Ni	Others	Fe		psi	MPa	psi	MPa	psi	MPa
853	1	1	1	0.25 max	—	—	2.0 max	Bal	5.6-6.0	16,000	110	12,000	83	—	
853	1	1	2						6.0-6.4	20,000	138	17,000	117	—	
853	1	1	3						6.4-6.8	26,000	179	20,000	138	—	
853	1	1	4						6.8-7.2	30,000	207	25,000	172	—	
853	1	1	5						7.2 min	40,000	276	30,000	207	—	
853	2	2	1	0.25-0.60	—	—	2.0 max	Bal	5.6-6.0	20,000	138	18,000	124	30,000	207
853	2	2	2						6.0-60.4	26,000	179	22,000	152	40,000	276
853	2	2	3						6.4-6.8	34,000	234	24,000	166	50,000	345
853	2	2	4						6.8-7.2	50,000	345	35,000	241	70,000	483
853	2	2	5						7.2 min	60,000	414	42,000	290	80,000	552
853	3	3	1	0.60-0.90	—	—	2.0 max	Bal	5.6-6.0	26,000	179	22,000	152	40,000	276
853	3	3	2						6.0-6.4	34,000	234	26,000	179	50,000	345
853	3	3	3						6.4-6.8	40,000	276	28,000	193	64,000	441
853	3	3	4						6.8-7.2	60,000	414	42,000	290	80,000	552
853	3	3	5						7.2 min						
864	1	3	1	0.60-0.90	1-3	—	2.0 max	Bal	5.6-6.0	30,000	207	—	—	40,000	276
864	1	3	2						6.0-6.4	41,000	283	—	—	49,000	338
864	1	3	3						6.4-6.8	58,000	400	—	—	89,000	614
864	1	3	4						6.8-7.2	76,000	524	—	—	124,000	955
864	1	3	5						7.2 min	105,000	724	—	—	154,000	1062
864	2	3	1	0.60-0.90	3-6	—	2.0 max	Bal	5.6-6.0	34,000	234	—	—	45,000	310
864	2	3	2						6.0-6.4	48,000	331	—	—	54,000	372
864	2	3	3						6.4-6.8	68,000	469	—	—	92,000	634
864	3	3	1	0.60-0.90	6-11	—	2.0 max	Bal	5.6-6.0	36,000	248	—	—	—	—
864	3	3	2						6.0-6.4	51,000	352	—	—	—	—
864	4	3	1	0.60-0.90	18-22	—	2.0 max	Bal	5.6-6.0	33,000	228	—	—	—	—
864	4	3	2						6.0-6.4	47,000	324	—	—	—	—
	1	1	3	0.3 max	2.5 max	1-3	2.0 max	Bal	6.4-6.8	28,000	193	—	—	—	—
	1	1	4						6.8-7.2	38,000	262	—	—	—	—
	1	1	5						7.2 min	45,000	310	—	—	—	—
	1	2	3	0.3-0.6	2.5 max	1-3	2.0 max	Bal	6.4-6.8	37,000	255	—	—	82,000	565
	1	2	4						6.8-7.2	50,000	345	—	—	110,000	689
	1	2	5						7.2 min	61,000	421	—	—	134,000	924
	1	3	3	0.6-0.9	2.5 max	1-3	2.0 max	Bal	6.4-6.8	48,000	331	—	—	100,000	689
	1	3	4						6.8-7.2	65,000	448	—	—	135,000	931
	1	3	5						7.2 min	79,000	545	—	—	160,000	1103
	2	1	3	0.3 max	2.0 max	3-5.5	2.0 max	Bal	6.4-6.8	36,000	248	—	—	—	—
	2	1	4						6.8-7.2	49,000	338	—	—	—	—
	2	1	5						7.2 min	58,000	400	—	—	—	—
	2	2	3	0.3-0.6	2.0 max	3-5.5	2.0 max	Bal	6.4-6.8	45,000	310	—	—	112,000	772
	2	2	4						6.8-7.2	62,000	428	—	—	154,000	1062
	2	2	5						7.2 min	74,000	510	—	—	180,000	1241
	2	3	3	0.6-0.9	2.0 max	3-5.5	2.0 max	Bal	6.4-6.8	57,000	393	—	—	—	—
	2	3	4						6.8-7.2	77,000	531	—	—	—	—
	2	3	5						7.2 min	93,000	641	—	—	—	—
Infiltrated Materials															
870				0.25 max	15-25	—	4.5	Bal	7.1 min	65,000	448	70,000	483	—	—
872				0.6-0.9	15.25	—	4.5	Bal	7.1 min	85,000	586	90,000	621	120,000	827

NOTE—All properties given above are typical of materials produced from elemental powder mixes as distinct from prealloyed powders.

APPENDIX A
RADIAL CRUSHING STRENGTH

Radial crushing strength shall be determined by compressing the test specimen between two flat- surfaces at a no load speed of 0.1 in./min (2.54 mm/min), the direction of the load being normal to the longitudinal axis of the specimen. The point at which the load drops due to the first crack shall be considered the crushing strength.

In the case of flanged bearings, the flange shall be cut off and the two parts tested separately. Each section shall meet the minimum requirement as calculated by the formula given in paragraph 1.2.3.

APPENDIX B
DENSITY AND OIL CONTENT OF SINTERED STRUCTURAL PARTS AND OIL-IMPREGNATED BEARINGS

B.1 Scope—This appendix covers test procedures for determining the density and oil content of sintered structural parts and bearings.

B.2 Preparation of Test Specimens

B.2.1 Weight—The specimen weight must be a minimum of 2.0 g. Several specimens can be used to reach the minimum weight.

B.2.2 Impregnation—Either of the following two methods may be used to impregnate the test specimen for the purpose of determining weights of oil-impregnated specimens in air, B, or in water, C; however, the vacuum method is preferred.

B.2.2.1 Reduce the pressure over the specimen immersed in oil held at room temperature to not more than 2 in. (50.8 mm) of mercury pressure for 30 min by a suitable evacuating method, after which permit the pressure to increase to atmospheric pressure and the specimen to remain immersed in oil at room temperature and atmospheric pressure for 10 min.

B.2.2.2 Immerse the specimen for at least 4 h in oil (viscosity of approximately 200 sus at 100 °F (46 $\mu m^2/s$ at 38 °C)), held at a temperature of 180 ± 10 °F (82 ± 5 °C), and then cool to room temperature by immersion in oil at room temperature.

B.2.3 Oil Removal—Samples which are delivered to the purchaser with oil shall be freed from lubricant for determining weight A by extracting the lubricant in Soxhlet apparatus of suitable size using toluol or petroleum ether as a solvent. After extraction, the residual solvent shall be removed by heating samples for I h at 250 °F (120 °C). Alternate extraction and drying shall be continued until the dry weight in air is constant to 0.1%.

NOTE—A practical and fast method of oil removal is to heat the specimen in a reducing atmosphere in the temperature range of 1400-1600 °F (760-871 °C). This method, which is in close agreement with the Soxhlet apparatus, can be used if agreed upon by both parties.

B.3 Procedure

B.3.1 Using an analytical balance, obtain the dry and impregnated weights of the test specimen in air. These are weights A and B, respectively. These, and all subsequent weighings, should be to the nearest 0.001 g.

B.3.2 Select a fine wire, less than 0.010in. (2.54mm) in diameter, for supporting the specimen in a beaker of distilled water when suspended from the beam hook of the balance. A wetting agent (in the amount of 0.1-0.2% by weight) is to be used to reduce the effects of surface tension.

B.3.3 Support the beaker of water over the pan of the balance, using a suitable bridge.

B.3.4 Twist the wire around the specimen and suspend it from the bram hook so that the specimen is completely immersed in the water. The water should cover the specimen by at least 1/4 in. (6 mm), and the wire twist should be completely submerged. Care must be taken to ensure that no air bubbles adhere to the specimen or to the wire.

B.3.5 Weigh the specimen and wire in water. This is weight C.

B.3.6 Remove the specimen and reweigh the wire in water, immersed to the same point as before. This is weight E.

B.3.7 For interconnected porosity determinations, measure the temperature during the test to the nearest whole degree and determine the specific gravity of the impregnant, which is S.

B.4 Calculation

B.4.1 The density of structural parts shall be calculated as follows:

$$D = \frac{A}{B - C + E} = \frac{A}{B - (C - E)} \qquad \text{(Eq. B1)}$$

where:

D = density, g/CM^3
A = weight in air of the oil-free specimen, g
B = weight in air of the oil-impregnated specimen, g
C = weight of the oil-impregnated specimen and wire in water, g
E = weight of wire, g

B.4.2 The wet density of bearings supplied fully impregnated with lubricant shall be calculated as follows:

$$DB = \frac{B}{B - C + E} \qquad \text{(Eq. B2)}$$

where:

D = density, g/cm^3
B = weight of oil-impregnated specimen, g
C = weight of oil-impregnated specimen and wire in water, g
E = weight of wire in water, g

B.4.3 The interconnected porosity or oil content by volume shall be calculated as follows:

$$P = B - \frac{A}{(B - C + E) \times S} \times 100 = \frac{B - A}{(B - (C + E)) \times S} \times 100 \qquad \text{(Eq. B3)}$$

where:

P = oil content by volume, %
A = weight in air of oil-free specimen, g
B = weight in air of oil-impregnated specimen, g
C = weight of oil-impregnated sample immersed in water, g
E = weight of wire in water, g
S = specific gravity of impregnant at the temperature of test

For faster results, the alternate procedure given below gives a close approximation of density. In cases of dispute, however, the foregoing procedure should be used.

B.4.4 Alternate Procedure—Weigh the part in air, then coat the entire part with an air-drying transparent acrylic lacquer. The part is subsequently weighed again in air, then in water.

Density is calculated as follows:

$$D = \frac{A}{B - C} \qquad \text{(Eq. B4)}$$

where:

A = weight of the original part in air, g
B = weight of the part in air after coating with lacquer, g
C = weight of the part immersed in water after coating with lacquer, g
D = density, g/cm^3

NOTE—The foregoing methods give the density of the part in relation to the density of water at the testing temperature, that is, specific gravity. Although it is common practice to assume density and specific gravity to be equal, this is in fact not true since the maximum density of pure water is 0.999972 g/cm^3 at 39.16 °F (3.98 °C) and decreases with increasing temperature.

The resulting error increases to 0.5% above 90 °F (32 °C) and to 2.5% at 210 °F (99 °C). It is therefore suggested that the test temperature be held below 80 °F (26 °C) in order to minimize the error.

SHOT PEENING—SAE J2441 AUG2000 — SAE Standard

Report of the SAE Fatigue, Design, and Evaluation Committee August 2000. Rationale statement available.

1. Scope

1.1 Form—This SAE Standard covers the engineering requirements for peening surfaces of parts by impingement of metallic shot, glass beads, or ceramic shot.

1.2 Application—To induce residual compressive stress in surface layers of parts, thereby increasing fatigue strength and resistance to stress-corrosion cracking.

2. References

2.1 Applicable Publications—The following publications form a part of this specification to the extent specified herein. Unless otherwise indicated, the latest issue of SAE publications shall apply. The applicable issue of other publications shall be the latest revision.

2.1.1 SAE PUBLICATIONS—Available from SAE, 400 Commonwealth Drive, Warrendale, PA 15096-0001.

SAE J441—Cut Wire Shot
SAE J442—Test Strip, Holder, and Gage for Shot Peening
SAE J443—Procedures for Using Standard Shot Peening Test Strip
SAE J444—Cast Shot and Grit Size Specifications Peening and Cleaning
SAE J445—Metallic Shot and Grit Mechanical Testing
SAE J827—High-Carbon Cast-Steel Shot
SAE J1173—Size Classification and Characteristics of Glass Beads for Peening
SAE J1830—Ceramic
SAE J2175—Specifications for Low Carbon Cast Steel Shot
SAE J2277—Shot Peening Coverage

2.1.2 ASTM PUBLICATIONS—Available from ASTM, 100 Barr Harbor Drive West Conshohocken, PA 19428-2959.

ASTM E 18—Rockwell Hardness and Rockwell Superficial Hardness of Metallic Materials
ASTM E 11—Standard Specification for Wire Cloth and Sieves for Testing Purposes

3. Technical Requirements

3.1 Material

3.1.1 MEDIA—As received peening media shall conform to the requirements of SAE J441, J444, J827, J2175, J1173, and J1830.

3.1.1.1 Metallic shot may be used for peening to intensities requiring use of "N," "A," and "C" Almen test strips.

3.1.1.2 Glass beads may be used for peening to intensities requiring use of the "N" test strip.

3.1.1.3 Ceramic shot may be used for peening to both "A" and "N" intensities.

3.1.2 MEDIA MAINTENANCE

3.1.2.1 Media uniformity shall be in accordance with Table 1. Inspection shall be conducted in accordance with 4.3.3.

3.2 Equipment

3.2.1 PEENING MACHINE

3.2.1.1 Pneumatic and centrifugal machines shall be used to peen parts. Peening streams should have an angle of impingement of 45 to 85 degrees to the areas to be peened. Air pressure or wheel speeds shall be adjusted to yield designated intensities.

3.2.1.2 The peening machine shall provide means of propelling, at a controlled rate, dry metallic shot by air pressure or centrifugal force, or propelling dry or wet glass beads or ceramic shot by air pressure, against the work, and means of uniformly moving the work through the shot or bead stream in either translation, rotation, or both as required. The nozzles and/or the work shall be held and moved mechanically unless purchaser permits manual movement.

3.2.1.3 Unless otherwise specified, equipment for dry peening with either shot or beads should include a separator for size control and contaminant removal. The separator should provide means for removal of fine, broken or defective shot or beads during peening.

3.2.1.4 Each machine shall be qualified for each part number. Either a scrap piece or representative fixture shall be fitted with sufficient test strip holders oriented essentially in the same manner, with the same surrounding features-as the part, to represent the actual designated surface. A saturation curve shall be established for each test strip location. Saturation shall be determined using SAE J443. The test strip fixture employed shall be used to verify specified intensity with every batch of parts during peening as required by 4.1.2.

TABLE 1—SIZE UNIFORMITY REQUIREMENTS OF MEDIA IN MACHINE

Cast Shot Sizes - J444	Cut Wire Sizes - J441	Glass Bead Sizes - SAE J1173	Ceramic Shot Sizes - SAE J1830	0.5% Maximum (by weight) Retained on US Sieve(1) Size mm (in)	Maximum 20% (by Weight) Passing US Sieve(1) Size mm (in)
S930	—	GB 280	—	4.00 (0.157)	2.36 (0.0937)
S780	—	GB 235	—	3.35 (0.132)	2.00 (0.0787)
S660	—	GB 200	—	2.80 (0.110)	1.70 (0.0661)
S550	SCW/CW-62	GB 170	—	2.36 (0.0937)	1.40 (0.0555)
S460	SCW/CW-54	GB 140	—	2.00 (0.0787)	1.18 (0.0469)
S390	SCW/CW-47	GB 120	—	1.70 (0.0661)	1.00 (0.0394)
S330	SCW/CW-41	GB 100	Z 850	1.40 (0.0555)	0.850 (0.0331)
—	SCW/CW-35	—	—	1.18 (0.0469)	0.710 (0.0278)
S280	SCW/CW-32	GB 85	—	1.18 (0.0469)	0.710 (0.0278)
S230	SCW/CW-28	GB 70	Z 600	1.00 (0.0394)	0.600 (0.0234)
—	SCW/CW-23	GB 60	—	0.850 (0.0331)	0.500 (0.0197)
S170	SCW/CW-20	GB 50	Z 425	0.710 (0.0278)	0.425 (0.0165)
—	SCW/CW-17	GB 40	—	0.600 (0.0234)	0.355 (0.0139)
S110	SCW/CW-14	GB 35	Z 300	0.500 (0.0197)	0.300 (0.0117)
—	—	GB 30	—	0.425 (0.0165)	0.250 (0.0098)
—	—	GB 25	Z 210	0.355 (0.0139)	0.212 (0.0083)
—	—	GB 20	—	0.300 (0.0117)	0.180 (0.0070)
S70	AWC-12	—	—	0.425 (0.0165)	0.180 (0.0070)
—	—	GB 18	Z 150	0.250 (0.0098)	0.150 (0.0059)
—	—	GB 15	—	0.212 (0.0083)	0.125 (0.0049)
—	—	GB 12	—	0.180 (0.0070)	0.106 (0.0041)
—	—	GB 10	—	0.150 (0.0059)	0.090 (0.0035)
—	—	GB 9	—	0.125 (0.0049)	0.075 (0.0029)
—	—	GB 8	—	0.106 (0.0041)	0.063 (0.0025)
—	—	GB 6	—	0.090 (0.0035)	0.053 (0.0021)

1. Test Sieve specified in ASTM E 11.

3.2.2 Test Strip, Holder and Gage—Shall conform to SAE J442 and utilized per SAE J443.

3.2.2.1 In locations where standard test strips cannot be placed to accurately reflect the peening intensity, shaded test strips (as defined in SAE J442) may be used. The response of shaded strips shall be correlated to a standard unshaded strip.

3.3 Preparation

3.3.1 Preparation of Parts—Parts shall be free of grease, dirt, oil, corrosion, and corrosion-preventive coatings such as anodic coatings, plating, and paint. Areas of the part or workpiece, which are designated to be free from any shot peening marks, shall be suitably masked or otherwise handled to protect such surfaces from the peening stream.

3.3.1.1 Parts shall be suitably mounted and masked as required for peening. Parts shall be free from externally applied loads or forces during shot peening other than normal fixturing in supported areas. Parts to be stress peened shall be loaded in suitable fixturing designed to apply specified pre-peening stresses.

3.4 Procedure

3.4.1 Parts shall be peened on all areas specified on the engineering drawing.

3.4.2 The phrase "peening optional" shall mean that peening on areas so indicated is optional and may have complete, partial, or no coverage.

3.5 Post Peening Treatment

3.5.1 After peening and removal of protective masks, shot or beads and fragments shall be removed from surfaces of parts by a method which will not damage surfaces.

3.5.2 Straightening of peened parts is prohibited, unless otherwise specified.

3.5.3 Subsequent processing for metal removal, such as honing, lapping, or polishing, shall be performed only when specified on the engineering drawing.

3.5.4 Parts shall be protected from corrosion until protective coating or packaging is completed. The method of protection shall be as specified by the responsible authority.

3.6 Properties

3.6.1 Coverage—Surfaces, which have been peened, shall show complete coverage as defined in SAE J2277.

3.6.2 Intensity—Peening intensity shall be as specified on the engineering drawing, determined in accordance with SAE J443.

3.7 Tolerances—Unless otherwise specified, variation from the specified (minimum) peening intensity shall be –0, +40% to the nearest unit, but in no case less than 0.08 mm (0.003 in). Thus, a specified peening intensity of 0.15 mm (0.006 inches) A, denotes an arc height of 0.15 to 0.23 mm (0.006 to 0.009 in) on the "A" specimen and a specified peening intensity of 0.36 N denotes an arc height of 0.36 to 0.51 mm (0.014 to 0.020 in) on the "N" specimen. Unless otherwise specified, the variation in boundaries of areas to be peened, when limited, shall be –0 to +3.18 mm (–0 to +0.125 in).

4. Quality Assurance Provisions

4.1 Sampling and Testing—A lot shall be all parts in a production run that are peened in one setup of the machine using the same test piece fixture and the same peening parameters and in increments of not more than eight hours of machine operation.

4.1.1 Coverage and Appearance—Each manually peened part and representative parts from each lot of mechanically peened parts shall be inspected for coverage and appearance by one of the following methods defined in SAE J2277.

4.1.2 Intensity Verification

4.1.2.1 At least one Almen strip shall be used to confirm intensity, at each location, at the beginning and end of each lot, and shall be within the tolerance specification on the drawing.

4.1.2.2 For a continuous production operation, the intensity shall be determined:

When the size or type of media in the machine is changed
At least every 8 h for metallic shot
At least every 2 h for nonmetallic shot

4.1.3 Media Maintenance

4.1.3.1 At least one determination for shot size and uniformity shall be made when the size or type of media in the machine is changed, every 8 h of continuous machine operation with metallic shot, and every 2 h for nonmetallic shot.

4.1.3.2 Shape—It is permissible for a maximum of 10% of the particles in a representative sample to be broken.

4.1.3.3 For Wet Bead Peening—The entire slurry shall be changed often enough that the peening intensity under any given set of parameters remains within established limits for that set of parameters. Fresh beads may be added only once between changes of the entire slurry to maintain the peening intensity.

4.2 Approval

4.2.1 The supplier quality system to insure compliance to this specification shall be approved by the responsible authority before parts for production use are supplied.

4.2.2 The supplier shall establish, for each part number, parameters for the critical items of processing which will produce acceptable peened parts; these shall constitute the approved peening procedures and shall be used for peening production parts (quality plan).

4.2.2.1 Parameters for the critical items of processing include, but are not limited to, the following:

Type of machine (pneumatic or centrifugal)
Number of nozzles or wheels
Size of nozzles or wheels
Nozzle or control cage and wheel position
Air pressure or wheel speed in rpm
Media, hardness size and material
Speed of work movement in translation and rotation
Placement of test strips in relation to the work
Time to peen part
Media metering orifice or flow rate setting
Centrifugal Machine - Flow Rate and/or ammeter reading
Required test strip type
Holding and masking fixture
Intensity
Percent Coverage
Control program reference number (if applicable)

4.2.2.1.1 Any of the previous items of processing for which parameters are considered proprietary by the processing vendor may be assigned a code designation. Each variation in such parameters shall be assigned a modified code designation.

4.3 Test Methods

4.3.1 Coverage—Shall be determined in accordance with SAE J2277.

4.3.2 Intensity—Shall be determined in accordance with SAE J443.

4.3.3 Media Uniformity—Shall be determined using the sampling and sieving procedures defined in SAE J444.

4.4 Certification of Conformance—The processing supplier shall furnish with each shipment, if required, a report stating that the parts have been processed and tested in accordance with specified requirements and that they conform to the technical requirements. This report shall include the purchase order number, lot number, part number, serial numbers (if assigned), number of parts, supplier's procedure number.

5. Preparation for Delivery

5.1 Peened parts shall be handled and packaged to ensure that the required physical characteristics and properties of the peened parts are preserved.

5.2 Packages of peened parts shall be prepared for shipment in accordance with commercial practice and in compliance with applicable rules and regulations pertaining to the handling, packaging, and transportation of the parts to ensure carrier acceptance and safe delivery.

6. Acknowledgment—A supplier shall mention this specification number and its revision letter in all quotations and when acknowledging purchase orders.

7. Rejections—Parts on which peening does not conform to this specification, or to modifications authorized by purchaser, will be subject to rejection.

8. Notes

8.1 Information recommended for the Engineering Drawing:

8.1.1 A note specifying shot peening in accordance with SAE J2441.

8.1.2 Defined peening conditions such as areas to be peened, type of media and size, Almen intensity, location of Almen intensity verification, if required, wet peening, areas to be masked, and areas where peening is optional.

8.1.3 When it is impractical to mask or otherwise protect areas designated to be free from shot peening marks, sufficient stock to be provided in these areas for subsequent removal of affected material for compliance with dimensional requirements of the applicable drawing.

8.1.4 All heat treatment to meet requirements for mechanical properties should be completed prior to peening.

8.1.4.1 When such processing is performed, it should be controlled such that surface temperatures should not be so high as to reduce stresses imposed by peening or to adversely affect the mechanical properties of the material. Examples of temperature limits (maximum temperature including tolerance) are shown in Table 2.

TABLE 2—MAXIMUM TEMPERATURE LIMITS FOR PEENED PARTS

Alloy	Maximum Temperature
Low-alloy Steels	246 °C (475 °F)
Corrosion-Resistant Steels	399 °C (750 °F)
Aluminum Alloys	93 °C (200 °F)
Titanium Alloys	246 °C (475 °F)
Magnesium Alloys	93 °C (200 °F)
Nickel and Cobalt Alloys	538 °C (1000 °F)

8.1.5 All machining of areas to be peened should be completed, all fillets should be properly formed, all burrs should be removed, and edges and corners to be peened should be rounded.

8.1.6 When magnetic particle or fluorescent penetrant inspection is required, parts should be subjected to such inspection before being peened.

8.1.7 Areas specified not to be peened may either be masked from the peening stream or they may be peened if subsequent machining operations remove the effects of peening on such areas.

8.1.8 Metal removal after peening will be allowed as approved by the responsible authority.

8.1.9 Aluminum alloy, magnesium alloy, corrosion-resistant alloy, and titanium alloy parts, which have been steel shot peened with carbon steel media, may require cleaning by suitable methods to remove iron contaminants.

8.1.10 If fillet radii on parts are required to be peened, the shot or bead size used should be such that the shot or bead nominal diameter is not greater than one-half the smallest nominal fillet radius to be peened, except that the nominal diameter of the shot need not be smaller than 0.18 mm (0.007 in) and the nominal diameter of beads need not be smaller than 0.05 mm (0.002 in). If the shot or beads must pass through recesses or apertures to peen required surfaces, the nominal diameter of the shot or beads should be not greater than 25% of the width of the opening, except that the limitations as to minimum shot and bead size specified previously for peening fillets should also apply.

8.1.11 When peening with cut wire shot, edges of shot will be prerounded.

8.1.12 The hardness of the peening media should be approximately equal to, or harder than the hardness of the peened part.

8.2 Key Words—Metallic shot, glass shot, ceramic shot, surface stress, shot peening, shot peening intensity, coverage, saturation, fatigue strength, stress corrosion cracking.

CUT WIRE SHOT—SAE J441 JUN93

SAE Recommended Practice

Report of the SAE Iron and Steel Technical Committee approved January 1952 and revised by the SAE Mechanical Prestressing Subcommittee of the SAE Fatigue, Design, and Evaluation Committee May 1987. Completely revised by the SAE Surface Enhancement Committee of the SAE Fatigue, Design, and Evaluation Division June 1993.

1. Scope—This SAE Recommended Practice is considered to be tentative and is subject to modification to meet new developments or requirements. It is offered as a guide in the selection and use of cut wire shot.

2. References

2.1 Applicable Publications—The following publications form a part of this specification to the extent specified herein.

2.1.1 ASTM PUBLICATIONS—Available from ASTM, 100 Barr Harbor Drive, West Conshohocken, PA 19428-2959.

ASTM A 370—Test Methods and Definitions for Mechanical Testing of Steel Products

ASTM E 384—Test Method for Microhardness of Materials

3. Description—Cut wire shot shall be the product of carbon steel wire or stainless wire Type 302, 304, Condition B, Spring Temper, cut into the form of cylinders with lengths approximately equal to the wire diameter. Conditioned cut wire shot with edges prerounded shall be required for shot peening applications.

4. Classification—All cut wire shot shall be identified according to the wire size from which it is obtained. It shall be identified by the prefix letters CW meaning cut steel wire or SCW meaning stainless cut wire. This designation shall be followed by a two-digit suffix number equivalent to the mean diameter, in inches, of the wire from which the shot is produced times 1000 Table 1.

5. Chemical Composition—The chemical composition shall conform to the following specifications:

5.1 Carbon Steel

Carbon: 0.45 to 0.85
Manganese: 0.30 to 1.30
Phosphorus: 0.040 max
Sulphur: 0.050 max
Silicon: 0.15 to 0.35

TABLE 1—WIRE DIAMETER USED FOR CUT WIRE SHOT

Shot Size	Mean Wire Diameter (mm)	Mean Wire Diameter (in)
SCW/CW-62	1.6	0.062
SCW/CW-54	1.4	0.054
SCW/CW-47	1.2	0.047
SCW/CW-41	1.0	0.041
SCW/CW-35	0.9	0.035
SCW/CW-32	0.8	0.032
SCW/CW-28	0.7	0.028
SCW/CW-23	0.6	0.023
SCW/CW-20	0.5	0.020
SCW/CW-17	0.45	0.017
SCW/CW-14	0.35	0.014
SCW/CW-12	0.30	0.012

5.2 Stainless Steel

Carbon: 0.15 max
Manganese: 2.00 max
Phosphorus: 0.045 max
Sulphur: 0.030 max
Silicon: 1.00 max
Chromium: 17.00 to 20.00
Nickel: 8.00 to 10.50

6. Tensile Properties—Shot shall be made from wire conforming to the tensile strengths shown in Table 2. In order to meet purchaser specified hardness requirements, other tensile strengths may be permitted.

7. Hardness—Carbon steel cut wire particles shall have a minimum hardness of 426 KHN (42 HRC). Stainless cut wire shot shall have a minimum hardness of 466 KHN (45 HRC). The hardness shall be determined per ASTM E 384 and using a 500 gf load for sizes CW-28 and finer or a 1000 gf load for sizes larger than CW-28. Other microhardness test methods may be used as long as a reliable hardness conversion can be obtained by calibrating various machines against known standards. Approximate conversions to Rockwell C Hardness Numbers (HRC) from Knoop Hardness Numbers (KHN) are obtained from ASTM A 370. Other hardness values can be specified by the purchaser.

8. Size Classification—Cut wire shot shall be made from wire of the diameters shown in Table 1. The weight of random as-cut particles shall be within the limits of Table 3. The weight of random conditioned particles shall be within the limits of Table 4. Shot sizes varying from those shown are available and may be obtained by arrangement between shot manufacturer and purchaser.

TABLE 2—TENSILE PROPERTIES OF CUT WIRE SHOT

Shot Size (mm)	Shot Size (in)	Tensile Strength Carbon Steel Wire MPa	Tensile Strength Carbon Steel Wire (ksi)	Tensile Strength Stainless Steel Wire MPa	Tensile Strength Stainless Steel Wire (ksi)
1.6	SCW/CW-62	1630/1880	(237/272)	1758/1965	(255/285)
1.4	SCW/CW-54	1680/1920	(243/279)	1793/1999	(260/290)
1.2	SCW/CW-47	1710/1970	(248/286)	1806/2013	(262/292)
1.0	SCW/CW-41	1760/2020	(255/293)	1855/2062	(269/299)
0.9	SCW/CW-35	1800/2080	(261/301)	1882/2089	(273/303)
0.8	SCW/CW-32	1830/2110	(266/306)	1910/2117	(277/307)
0.7	SCW/CW-28	1870/2140	(271/311)	1972/2179	(286/316)
0.6	SCW/CW-23	1920/2200	(279/319)	2013/2220	(292/322)
0.5	SCW/CW-20	1950/2230	(283/323)	2068/2275	(300/330)
0.45	SCW/CW-17	1980/2250	(287/327)	2095/2300	(304/334)
0.35	SCW/CW-14	2010/2280	(291/331)	2135/2341	(310/340)
0.30	SCW/CW-12	2030/2300	(294/334)	2165/2370	(314/344)

TABLE 3—WEIGHT LIMITS FOR AS-CUT PARTICLES

Shot Size (mm)	Shot Size (in)	Weight of 50 Random Pieces (grams)
1.6	SCW/CW-62	1.090 – 1.330
1.4	SCW/CW-54	0.720 – 0.880
1.2	SCW/CW-47	0.480 – 0.580
1.0	SCW/CW-41	0.310 – 0.390
0.9	SCW/CW-35	0.200 – 0.240
0.8	SCW/CW-32	0.140 – 0.180
0.7	SCW/CW-28	0.100 – 0.120
0.6	SCW/CW-23	0.050 – 0.070
0.5	SCW/CW-20	0.040 – 0.050
		Weight of 100 Random Pieces (grams)
0.45	SCW/CW-17	0.040 – 0.060
0.35	SCW/CW-14	0.020 – 0.040
0.30	SCW/CW-12	0.010 – 0.025

TABLE 4—WEIGHT LIMITS FOR CONDITIONED CUT WIRE SHOT

Shot Size (mm)	Shot Size (in)	Weight of 50 Random Pieces (grams)
1.6	SCW/CW-62	1.040 – 1.260
1.4	SCW/CW-54	0.680 – 0.840
1.2	SCW/CW-47	0.460 – 0.550
1.0	SCW/CW-41	0.290 – 0.370
0.9	SCW/CW-35	0.190 – 0.230
0.8	SCW/CW-32	0.130 – 0.170
0.7	SCW/CW-28	0.095 – 0.115
0.6	SCW/CW-23	0.045 – 0.065
0.5	SCW/CW-20	0.040 – 0.050
		Weight of 100 Random Pieces (grams)
0.45	SCW/CW-17	0.035 – 0.055
0.35	SCW/CW-14	0.020 – 0.040
0.30	SCW/CW-12	0.010 – 0.025

9. Inspection Procedure—Shot particles to be checked for hardness are to be mounted, ground, and polished to the centerline.

10. Soundness—As-cut shot particles shall be free of shear cracks and laps and shall not contain excessive seams or burns. Conditioned particles shall be free of shear cracks and shall not contain excessive seams.

11. Packaging—This material shall be packaged to prevent loss during shipping and storage.

(R) TEST STRIP, HOLDER, AND GAGE FOR SHOT PEENING—SAE J442 DEC2001

SAE Standard

Report of the SAE Iron and Steel Technical Committee approved January 1952. Revised by the SAE Fatigue Design and Evaluation Steering Committee November 1977. Editorial change August 1979. Completely revised by the SAE Surface Enhancement Division of the SAE Fatigue, Design, and Evaluation Committee January 1995 and revised December 2001. Rationale statement available.

1. Scope—This SAE Standard defines requirements for equipment/supplies to be used in measuring shot peening intensity. Guidelines for the use of these articles (test strip, holding fixture, and gage) are also included.

2. References

2.1 Related Publications—The following publications are provided for information purposes only and are not a required part of this specification. The latest issue of SAE publications shall apply.

2.1.1 SAE PUBLICATION—Available from SAE, 400 Commonwealth Drive, Warrendale, PA 15096-0001.

SAE J443—Procedures for Using Standard Shot Peening Test Strip

SAE AMS-S-13165—Shot Peening of Metal Parts

2.1.2 ASTM PUBLICATION—Available from ASTM, 100 Barr Harbor Drive, West Conshohocken, PA 19428-2959.

ASTM E 18—Standard Test Method for Rockwell Hardness and Rockwell Superficial Hardness of Metallic Materials

3. Outline of Method of Control—The control of a peening machine operation is primarily a matter of the control of the properties of a stream of shot in relation to the work being peened. The basis of measurement of these properties is as follows:

If a flat piece of steel (the test strip) is clamped to a solid block (the test strip holder) and then exposed to a stream of shot, it will be curved upon removal from the block. The curvature is due to residual compressive stresses induced by the shot impacts, causing the peened face to be convex. The curvature serves as a means of measuring the effect of the shot stream. The degree of the curvature depends upon the properties of the shot stream, the properties and mounting of the test strip, and the exposure condition.

3.1 Properties

3.1.1 SHOT STREAM—The properties of the shot stream are: shot material (includes chemical and physical characteristics), size, shape, velocity, directional consistency, and shot flow rate.

3.1.2 TEST STRIP—The properties of the test strip are: material (includes chemical and physical properties), hardness, physical dimensions, and the extent of any internal stresses. The properties of the test strip mounting are flatness, rigidity, and the location and force of the holding means.

3.1.3 EXPOSURE—The properties of exposure to the blast stream are length of time, angle of impact, and the degree of uniformity and consistency of the geometric relationship between the shot stream and test strip.

3.2 Standards—Based on these principles, the SAE has adopted the following standards: test strips, holding block, and gage. Specifications for these parts, the method of use, and a standard designation are presented herein.

4. Specifications of Intensity Measuring Equipment

4.1 Test Strips and Holding Fixture—Standard test strips, N, A, and C are shown in Figure 1 and test strip holder is shown in Figure 2. The approximate relationships between readings of test strips N, A, and C (for conditions of identical blast and exposure) are as follows:

C strip reading x 3.5 = A strip reading
A strip reading x 3.0 = N strip reading

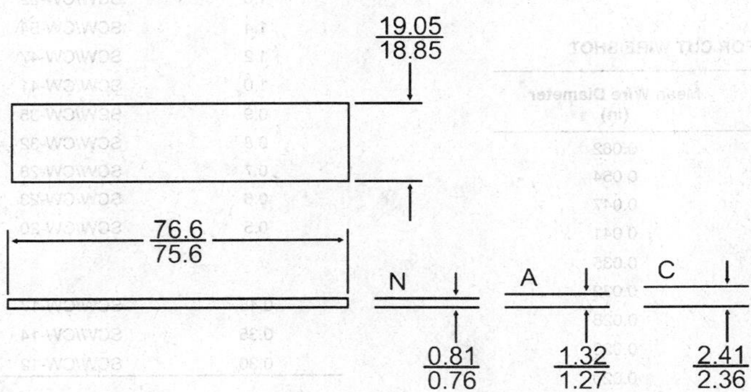

Flatness: Measured as the reading on the Almen gage for each strip type is as follows:

N - .025
A - .025
C - .038

Material: SAE 1070 cold rolled spring steel.

Edge Type: Number 1 round.

Finish: Plain tempered, all burrs removed.

Heat Treatment: All strips must be uniformly hardened and tempered at a minimum temperature of 371 degrees C (700 degrees F) to produce tempered martensite having a hardness, as measured on the surface, of HRC 44-50 (HRA 72.5-76.0 for the "N" strip).

Surface Carbon: Strips shall be free from alteration of surface carbon to the degree that any difference in average hardness between the surface and subsurface shall not exceed two points as measured on the Rockwell 30-N scale. The average of at least four readings in each region should be used to make the comparison. Any such determinations must be made on strips which have not been shot peened, and will preclude other use of a strip so tested. Surface hardness readings that are less than subsurface readings indicate evidence of decarburization. Surface readings which are higher than corresponding subsurface values indicate carburization.

Example:

If the average surface hardness is 62.5 on the Rockwell 30-N scale and, after careful grinding, a region below the surface is found to be 64.0 on the Rockwell 30-N scale - the strip is acceptable. If the subsurface reading had been 65.0 on the Rockwell 30-N scale, the difference (2.5 points) being over two points constitutes grounds for rejection.

FIGURE 1—TEST STRIP SPECIFICATIONS

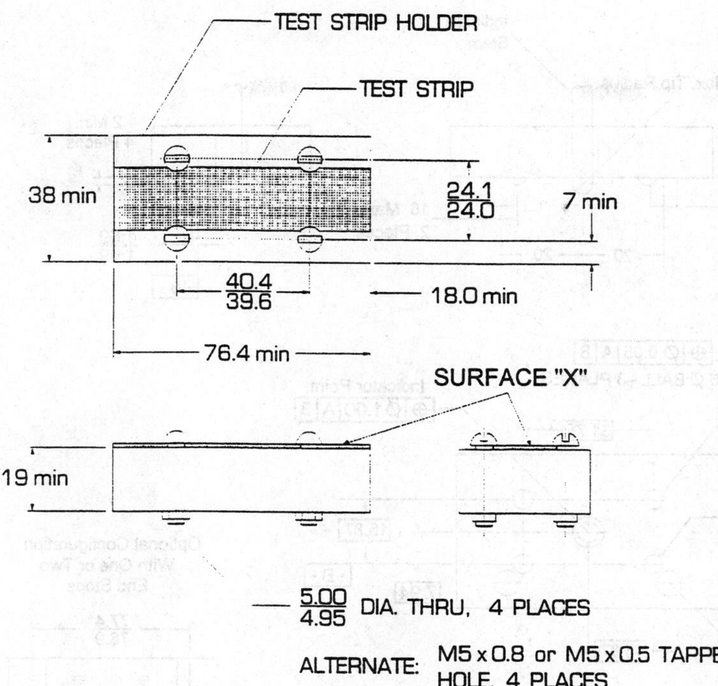

Recommended Material for Test Strip Holder - Any alloy or carbon steel, hardened to 57 HRC for a minimum depth of 0.7 mm. Alternate materials and thicknesses may be used when their wear and deformation characteristics do not adversely affect the performance of the test strip.

Use M5 socket head button or pan head screws and hex or square nuts

Alternate: Use screws only in tapped holes.

FIGURE 2—ASSEMBLED TEST STRIP AND HOLDER

4.2 Gage—The gage (Almen gage) for determining the curvature of the test strip must incorporate the elements shown in Figure 3. Curvature of the test strip is determined by a measurement of the height of the combined longitudinal and transverse arc across standard chords. This arc height is obtained by measuring the displacement of a central point on the nonpeened surface from the plane of four balls forming the corners of a particular rectangle. To use this gage, the test strip is located so that the indicator spindle bears against the center of the NON-PEENED surface, one long edge of the strip bearing against the two back stops. The test strip is then centered by placing the ends even with the edges of the base, or by resting the ends against built-in end stop(s).

5. Designation Standard of Intensity Measurement

5.1 Primary Standard—The standard designation of intensity measurement includes the gage reading and the test strip used. It may be explained by the example shown in Figure 4:

5.2 Transition Standard—Gages utilizing the inch-pound system (English units) may be encountered during the period of transition to SI. The designation of intensity measurement in this temporary alternate is explained in the example shown in Figure 5:

6. Maintenance, Calibration and Use

6.1 Test Strips—After removal from the test strip holder, test strips should not be replaced, re-used, or shot peened for any additional time.

6.2 Holding Fixture—The test strip contact area of the holding fixture shall be checked for flatness on a periodic basis. Flatness of the test strip contact area shall not exceed 0.1 mm. In addition to a dimensional check for flatness, holding fixtures shall be checked visually for the following characteristics:

a. Burrs or raised material that can be caused by damage or excessive peening (particularly on the holding fixture end faces).
b. Particles of shot or beads that could become trapped under the test strip during installation.
c. Damage to threads that may prevent one or more screws from adequately holding the test strip in place.

6.3 Gage—Locating balls and indicator tip shall be checked periodically for wear. Any visual signs of wear shall be cause for repair of the gage such that new round surfaces are in contact with the test strip. The indicator shall be calibrated periodically over the range used for measuring test strips. The calibration tolerance for the indicator shall not exceed 0.005 mm. The use of calibration blocks, either flat, curved, or equipped with steps, is recommended.

7. Notes

7.1 Superseded Gage Designation—Two types of gages were formerly used to measure the arc height of test strips. The number 1 gage, which is obsolete, employed two knife edges to support the test strip; the number 2 gage (developed in 1943) uses four balls to locate the test strip in relation to the indicator stem. Some engineering criteria may continue to show the numeral "2" after the test strip letter, designating the use of a number 2 gage. This designation (such as A2) is neither required nor recommended. The gage defined by this SAE Standard uses the same locating scheme as the number 2 gage, and therefore will yield an equivalent reading.

7.2 Superseded Intensity Designation—The prior "dimensionless" value relating to the number of graduations read on the dial indicator has been discontinued in favor of direct reading in millimeters (inches).

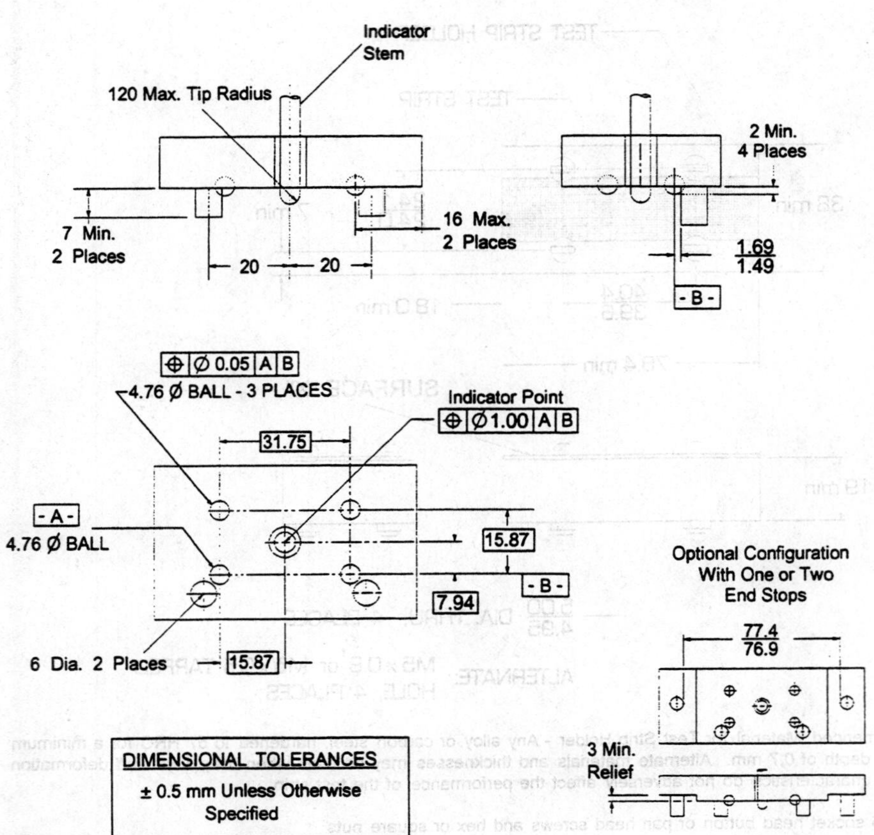

Notes:

1. **Four, 4.76 mm diameter, precision balls are installed in the test strip locating base. Balls must be in the same plane (perpendicular to the indicator stem) within .05 mm.**
2. **Digital or analog indicator must have .0025 mm graduations (maximum).**

FIGURE 3—ALMEN GAGE

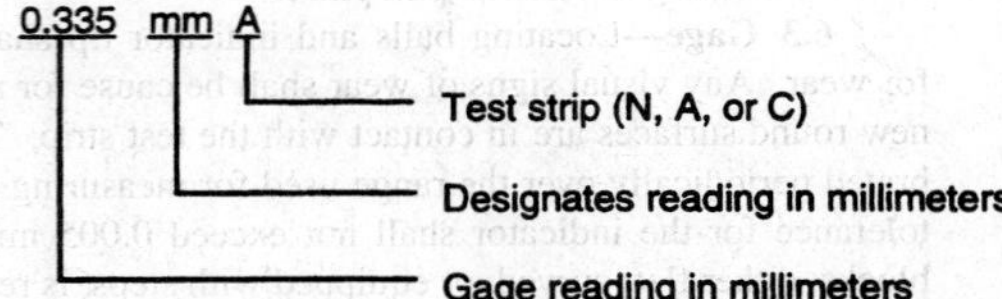

This example signifies that the Almen Gage reading of the peened Almen A test strip as measured on the gage is 0.335 mm.

FIGURE 4—EXAMPLE OF STANDARD DESIGNATION OF INTENSITY MEASUREMENT

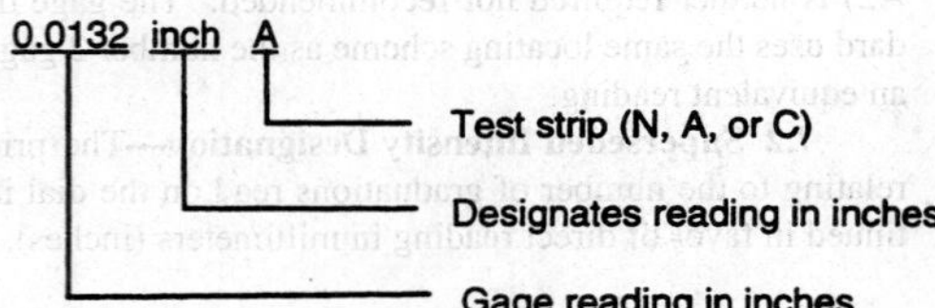

This example signifies that the Almen Gage reading of the peened A Strip as measured on the gage is 0.0132 inch.

FIGURE 5—EXAMPLE OF DESIGNATION OF INTENSITY MEASUREMENT IN TEMPORARY ALTERNATE

PROCEDURES FOR USING STANDARD SHOT PEENING TEST STRIP—SAE J443 JAN2003

SAE Recommended Practice

Report of the SAE Iron and Steel Technical Committee, approved January 1952, completely revised by the SAE Fatigue, Design and Evaluation Committee January 1984. Completey revised by the SAE Surface Enhancement Division of the SAE Fatigue, Design, and Evaluation Committee January 2003. Rationale statement available.

TABLE OF CONTENTS

1. Scope—This SAE Recommended Practice provides uniform procedures for using the standard shot peening test strips reported in SAE J442. Standard test strips are used to establish saturation, determine intensity, monitor repeatability of the shot peening machine operations, and can be used to predict a desired result on a part. It is recommended that the standard test strip A be used for intensities that produce arc heights of 0.10 mm A (0.004 inch A) to 0.60 mm A (0.024 inch A). For intensities below 0.10 mm A (0.004 inch A), the standard N strip is recommended, and for intensities above 0.60 mm A (0.024 inch A), the standard C strip is recommended.

The process of shot peening, in common with many other processes, cannot at present be adequately controlled by nondestructive inspection of the peened parts, therefore, it is necessary to control the process itself to achieve consistent, reliable results.

2. References

2.1 Applicable Publications—The following publications form a part of this specification to the extent specified herein. Unless otherwise indicated, the latest version of SAE publications shall apply.

2.1.1 SAE PUBLICATIONS—Available from SAE, 400 Commonwealth Drive, Warrendale, PA 15096-0001.

SAE J442—Test Strip, Holder and Gage for Shot Peening
SAE J2277—Shot Peening Coverage

3. Peening Intensity—Intensity is expressed as the arc height of a shot peened test strip at saturation. The intensity is a function of the mass of the shot, its hardness, its velocity and its angle of impingement on the peened surface of the strip to the shot stream.

4. Saturation—A plot of peening time versus arc height is used to define saturation. By peening a series of test strips, using increasingly longer peening times, with all other conditions maintained constant, and plotting the series of points on a graph of exposure time versus arc height, a curve will develop. These points define a curve with a general shape as shown in Figure 1.

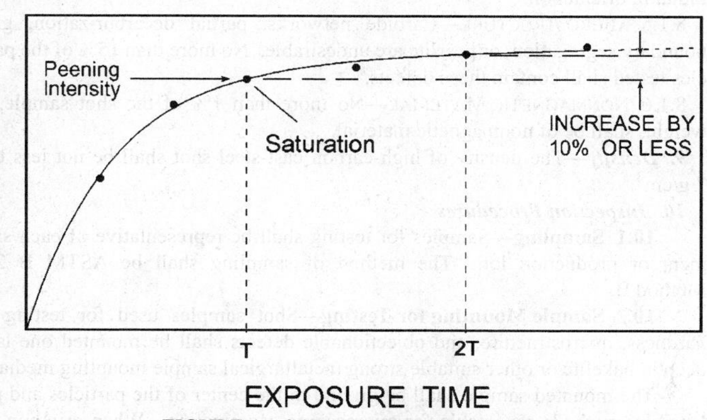

FIGURE 1—SATURATION CURVE

Saturation has been attained when the "knee" of the curve is passed and increasingly longer periods of peening time are required for a measurable increase in test strip arc height. The location of the knee, saturation point shown in Figure 1, can be defined as the first point on the curve beyond which the arc height increases by 10% or less when the peening time is doubled.

5. Procedure Based on Arc Height Versus Exposure Time Relationship

General—Prior to use, the zero position of the gage shall be checked with a flat calibration block (see SAE J442) and, if necessary, adjusted. Test strips should also be checked for flatness prior to use, in accordance with SAE J442. Pre-peen out of flatness measurements may be used to compensate raw arc height readings.

5.1 Fasten the test strip tightly and centrally to the test strip holder, avoiding entrapment of any foreign material - such as media.

5.2 Expose surface "X" (SAE J442) of the test strip to the peening stream to be measured. Record the time of exposure or its equivalent.

5.3 Remove the test strip from the holder and measure the arc height on the Almen gage, ensuring that the indicator stem contacts the unpeened face of the test strip.

5.4 Using different exposure times, repeat steps 1, 2, and 3 sufficiently (minimum of 4 test strips) to determine a curve similar to Figure 1.

5.5 Peening intensity is determined by interpreting the curve. Intensity is the value of the arc height at time T, which increases by no more than 10% when the exposure time is doubled - time 2T. The graph shall be constructed by using a minimum of four points other than zero.

NOTE—Test strip readings are "arc height," not "intensity." Therefore, exposing a single test strip will not reveal intensity. Intensity can only be determined by the procedure outlined previously.

5.6 Test strips peened at time T and greater shall exhibit uniform coverage. This requirement ensures that portions of surface "X" (as defined in SAE J442), exclusive of hold down screws, have not been shielded from the peening stream. It should be noted that part coverage time can not be associated with test strip saturation time (see SAE J2277 for part coverage).

6. Production Setup Procedure—Intensity Measurement—The procedure to be used in making a production setup in which a setting of the machine is to be determined for a desired intensity may be described as follows:

6.1 Provide fixture which supports the test strip(s) in a manner to simulate the selected surfaces of the part to be peened. Test blocks (see SAE J442) shall be mounted on the fixture to duplicate the angle and location of these areas. Setup shall be qualified by placing the test strip setup fixture in the machine in the same orientation to the shot stream that the part will be exposed during processing. Air pressure or wheel speed shall be adjusted to yield designated intensities. Nozzle positions or wheel cages should be set so that the shot stream(s) have an angle of impingement between 45 and 85 degrees to the test strip surface.

6.2 Intensity shall be determined by exposing individual test strips at each location in the test strip fixture for increasing periods of time and plotting the results from each location on a saturation curve (see Figure 1). Re-use of test strips is not permitted.

6.3 If the intensity measurement obtained from the curve does not fall within the specified tolerance, changes to the machine settings or shot characteristics not specified by the responsible authority are permissible. Steps 6.1 and 6.2 shall be repeated until the intensity falls within the specified tolerance.

7. Process Control of Intensity—When the machine settings are found that yield an intensity that falls within the specified tolerance, a means of process verification and control shall be implemented. Confirmation readings shall be taken at a frequency determined to be appropriate to assure consistent peening intensity. Confirmation of peening intensity is accomplished by shot peening a test strip at the time T, as determined in the previously established saturation curve. The arc height of this test strip shall fall within the intensity tolerance specified for the part.

(R) HIGH-CARBON CAST-STEEL SHOT—SAE J827 SEP1996

SAE Recommended Practice

Report of the SAE Iron and Steel Technical Committee approved June 1962. Reaffirmed with editorial change January 1969. Completely revised by the SAE Fatigue, Design, and Evaluation Committee March 1990. Completely revised by the SAE Surface Enhancement Division of the SAE Fatigue, Design, and Evaluation Committee July 1994 and September 1996.

1. Scope—This SAE Recommended Practice describes chemical composition and physical characteristic requirements for high-carbon cast-steel shot to be used for shot peening or blast cleaning operations.

2. References

2.1 Applicable Publications—The following publications form a part of this specification to the extent specified herein. The latest issue of SAE, ASTM, and ISO publications shall apply.

2.1.1 SAE PUBLICATIONS—Available from SAE, 400 Commonwealth Drive, Warrendale, PA 15096-0001.

SAE J444—Cast Shot and Grit Size Specifications for Peening and Cleaning

SAE J445—Metallic Shot and Grit Mechanical Testing

2.1.2 ASTM PUBLICATIONS—Available from ASTM, 100 Barr Harbor Drive, West Conshohocken, PA 19428-2959.

ASTM B 215, Method B—Methods of Sampling Finished Lots of Metal Powders

ASTM E 140—Hardness Conversion Tables for Metals (Relationship Between Brinell Hardness, Vickers Hardness, Rockwell Hardness, Rockwell Superficial Hardness, and Knoop Hardness)

ASTM E 384—Test Method for Microhardness of Materials

2.2 Related Publications—The following publications are provided for information purposes only and are not a required part of this document.

2.2.1 ISO PUBLICATIONS—Available from ANSI, 11 West 42nd Street, New York, NY 10036-8002.

ISO 11124 Part 3—High-carbon cast-sheet steel shot and grit

ISO 11125 Part 1—Preparation of steel substrates before application of paints and related products—Test methods for metallic abrasives—Part 1: Sampling

ISO 11125 Part 2—Preparation of steel substrates before application of paints and related products—Test methods for metallic abrasives—Part 2: Determination of particle size distribution

ISO 11125 Part 3—Preparation of steel substrates before application of paints and related products—Test methods for metallic abrasives—Part 3: Determination of hardness

ISO 11125 Part 4—Preparation of steel substrates before application of paints and related products—Test methods for metallic abrasives—Part 4: Determination of apparent density

ISO 11125 Part 5—Preparation of steel substrates before application of paints and related products—Test methods for metallic abrasives—Part 5: Determination of percentage defective particles and microstructure

ISO 11125 Part 6—Preparation of steel substrates before application of paints and related products—Test methods for metallic abrasives—Part 6: Determination of foreign matter

ISO 11125 Part 7—Preparation of steel substrates before application of paints and related products—Test methods for metallic abrasives—Part 7: Determination of moisture

3. Description—High-carbon cast-steel shot is obtained by atomizing molten steel. The shot is heat treated and screened to produce a range of sizes from HCS S70 to HCS S1320 or larger as described in SAE J444. Other sizes are available.

4. Size Classification—Cast-steel shot shall be identified by HCS S for shot, followed by three numbers representing the size in ten thousandths of inches, in accordance with SAE J444.

EXAMPLE—HCS330 indicates a cast-steel shot identified by a nominal sieve opening of 050 mm (0.0331 in).

5. Chemical Composition—The finished shot shall have the chemical composition shown in Table 1:

TABLE 1—CHEMICAL COMPOSITION

Element	Weight Percent
Carbon	0.80 – 1.2%
Manganese	
HCS S70 to HCS S110	0.35 – 1.2%
HCS S170	0.5 – 1.2%
HCS S230 and up	0.6 – 1.2%
Silicon	0.4% minimum
Sulfur	0.050% maximum
Phosphorous	0.050% maximum

6. Hardness

6.1 Standard Hardness—The hardness of 90% of all shot particles shall be within the range of 40 to 51 HRC.

6.2 Special Hardnesses—Shot for peening and blast cleaning is manufactured from 40 to 65 HRC. The user may specify a range to suit the application. The minimum hardness range that can be specified is 7 points HRC.

7. Microstructure—The microstructure of high-carbon cast-steel shot shall be uniform martensite, tempered to a degree consistent with the hardness range, with fine, well distributed carbides, if any.

8. General Appearance—High-carbon cast-steel shot is generally spherical and shall have no more than 20% of the particles with objectionable characteristics. Any one particle tested that has more than one different defect, shall only be counted once.

8.1 Objectionable Characteristics

8.1.1 PARTICLE SHAPE—No more than 5% of the particles in a shot sample shall be elongated. An elongated particle is one whose length is in excess of twice the maximum particle width.

8.1.2 VOIDS—No more than 10% of the particles in a sample shall contain objectionable voids. Such a void is a smooth-surfaced, internal hole whose cross-sectional area is larger than 10% of the cross-section area of the particle.

8.1.3 SHRINKAGE—No more than 10% of the particles in a sample shall contain objectionable shrinkage. Such a shrinkage is an internal cavity with an irregular dendritic surface whose area is larger than 40% of the particle area.

8.1.4 CRACKS—No more than 15% of the particles in a shot sample shall contain objectionable cracks. Such a crack is a linear discontinuity longer than three times its width, longer than 20% of the shortest cross section of the particle, and radial in orientation.

8.1.5 MICROSTRUCTURE—Carbide networks, partial decarburization, grain boundary segregation, or pearlite are undesirable. No more than 15% of the particles tested shall contain these defects.

8.1.6 NONMAGNETIC MATERIAL—No more than 1% of the shot sample, by weight, shall be of nonmagnetic material.

9. Density—The density of high-carbon cast-steel shot shall be not less than 7 g/cm^3.

10. Inspection Procedures

10.1 Sampling—Samples for testing shall be representative of each shipment or production lot. The method of sampling shall be ASTM B 215, Method B.

10.2 Sample Mounting for Testing—Shot samples used for testing for hardness, microstructure, and objectionable defects shall be mounted one layer deep in bakelite or other suitable strong metallurgical sample mounting media.

The mounted sample shall be ground to the center of the particles and polished by methods acceptable for microscopic examination. When grinding and polishing the sample, care must be taken not to overheat the sample and affect microstructure and/or hardness.

10.3 Hardness Testing—Hardness measurements shall be taken at the half radius on a minimum of 10 particles in the mounted samples.

The hardness shall be determined by using ASTM E 384 and using a 500 g load for sizes HCS S280 and finer, and 500 or 1000 g load for sizes HCS S330 and larger. Other microhardness test methods may be used as long as a reliable hardness conversion can be obtained by calibrating the test machine against known standards. Approximate conversion to Rockwell C Hardness Numbers can be obtained from ASTM 140 and from manufacturers of hardness testers.

10.4 Microstructure—The mounted and polished sample shall be etched with 2% Nital or other suitable etchant and examined at approximately 500X magnification.

10.5 Objectionable Characteristics—Objectionable characteristics shall be examined at 10X magnification. A minimum of 50 particles contained in the mount shall be evaluated.

10.6 Density—Density shall be determined by placing 50 mL of water or alcohol in a 100 mL graduate, adding 100 g of shot and recording the increase in volume. Dividing 100 g by the volume increase will give the density in g/cm^3. A pycnometer method may be used for more critical density measurements.

10.7 Nonmagnetic Material—A hand magnet will be used to separate the magnetic shot from the nonmagnetic contaminants. The nonmagnetic contaminants shall be weighed and their percentage of the original sample weight calculated.

10.8 Chemical Analysis—Any suitable ASTM Analytical procedure for steel may be used to test chemical composition.

10.9 Mechanical Tests—See SAE J445 for methods of checking uniformity of shipments of shot.

SPECIFICATIONS FOR LOW CARBON CAST STEEL SHOT—SAE J2175 JUN91

SAE Recommended Practice

Report of the SAE Surface Enhancement Subcommittee of the SAE Fatigue, Design, and Evaluation Executive Committee approved June 1991.

Foreword—This Document has not changed other than to put it into the new SAE Technical Standards Board Format.

1. Scope—This SAE Recommended Practice describes chemical analysis, hardness, microstructure, and physical characteristic requirements for low carbon cast steel shot to be used for shot peening or blast cleaning operations.

2. References

2.1 Applicable Publications—The following publications form a part of this specification to the extent specified herein. The latest issue of SAE publications shall apply.

2.1.1 SAE PUBLICATIONS—Available from SAE, 400 Commonwealth Drive, Warrendale, PA 15096-0001.

SAE J444—Cast Shot and Grit Size Specifications for Peening and Cleaning
SAE J445—Metallic Shot and Grit Mechanical Testing

2.1.2 ASTM PUBLICATIONS—Available from ASTM, 100 Barr Harbor Drive, West Conshohocken, PA 19428-2959.

ASTM A 370—Test Methods and Definitions for Mechanical Testing of Steel Products
ASTM E 384—Practice for Safeguarding Against Warpage and Distortion During Hot-Dip Galvanizing of Steel Assemblies

3. Description—Low carbon cast steel shot is the product obtained by atomizing and rapidly solidifying particles of molten steel in a controlled range of sizes. These shot particles are then screened to produce a range of sizes from LCS-70 to LCS-1320 or larger as described in SAE J444.

4. Classification—Low carbon cast steel shot shall be identified by LCS followed by the numbers representing the nominal size in ten thousandths of inches, in accordance with SAE J444, i.e., LCS-460.

5. Chemical Composition—The finished low carbon steel shot shall have the following chemical composition as listed in Table 1:

TABLE 1—CHEMICAL COMPOSITION

Low Carbon Steel Shot	Chemical Composition
Carbon	0.10 to 0.15%
Silicon	0.10 to 0.25%
Manganese	1.20 to 1.50%
Aluminum	0.05 to 0.15%
Phosphorus	0.035% maximum
Sulfur	0.035% maximum

6. Hardness—The hardness of 90% of all shot particles tested shall be within the range of 400 to 540 KHN (40 to 50 Rockwell C).

7. Microstructure—The microstructure of low carbon cast steel shot shall be an intermediate structure (bainite), a mechanical mixture of ferrite and cementite particles with random feather-like appearance (upper bainite) and accicular (lower bainite) with few or no free carbides, (see 8.1.5).

8. General Appearance—The low carbon steel shot shall be as spherical as commercially possible and no more than 20% of the shot particles shall have objectionable defects. Any one particle tested that has several different defects will only be counted once in the total. Notwithstanding the allowable percentages listed as follows, no more than a total of 20% objectionable particles are allowed.

8.1 Objectionable Defects

8.1.1 PARTICLE SHAPE—No more than 5% of the particles in a shot sample shall be elongated. An elongated particle is one whose length is in excess of twice the maximum particle width.

8.1.2 VOIDS—No more than 10% of the particles in a sample shall contain voids. A void is a smooth surfaced internal hole and must be greater than 10% of the particle to be considered harmful and counted as a void.

8.1.3 SHRINKAGE—No more than 10% of the particles in a sample shall contain shrinkage. A shrinkage area is an internal cavity with an irregular dendritic surface, and must be greater than 40% of the particle area to be considered harmful.

8.1.4 CRACKS—No more than 5% of the particles in a shot sample shall contain cracks. A crack is a linear discontinuity whose length is greater than three (3) times its width and its length is greater than 20% of the diameter or shortest dimension of the particle and radial in orientation.

8.1.5 MICROSTRUCTURE—Carbide networks, partial decarburization, and grain boundary segregation are undesirable. No more than 15% of the particles tested shall have these defects.

8.1.6 NONMAGNETIC MATERIAL—No more than 1% of the shot sample, by weight, shall be nonmagnetic material.

9. Density—The density of low carbon cast steel shot shall be not less than 7 g/cc.

10. Mechanical Tests—To conform with revised SAE J445.

11. Inspection Procedures

11.1 Sampling—Samples for chemical analysis, hardness, microstructure, density, objectionable defects, and mechanical testing shall be carefully obtained to be representative of each shipment of production lot.

11.2 Sample Mounting for Testing—Shot samples used for testing for hardness, microstructure, and objectionable defects shall be mounted one layer deep in bakelite or other suitable strong metallurgical sample mounting media.

The mounted sample shall be ground to the center of the particle and polished by acceptable methods for examination using a microscope. When grinding and polishing the sample, care must be taken not to overheat the sample and affect microstructure and/or hardness.

11.3 Hardness Testing—Hardness measurements shall be taken at the half radius on a minimum of ten (10) randomly selected particles in the mounted sample.

The hardness shall be determined by using ASTM E 384 and using a 500 gf load for sizes LCS-280 and finer and 500 or 1000 gf load for sizes LCS-330 and larger. Other microhardness test methods may be used as long as a reliable hardness conversion can be obtained by calibrating various machines against known standards. Approximate conversions to Rockwell C hardness numbers are obtained from ASTM A 370.

11.4 Microstructures—The mounted and polished sample shall be etched with 2% Nital and examined at approximately 500X magnification.

11.5 Objectionable Defects—Objectionable defects shall be measured using a microscope with a 10X magnification. All of the particles contained in the mount shall be evaluated.

11.6 Density—Density shall be determined by placing 50 ml of ethanol or methanol in a 100 ml graduate, adding 100 g of shot and recording the increase in volume. Dividing 100 g by the volume increase will give the density in grams per cubic centimeter (cc). A pycnometer method may be used for more critical density measurements.

11.7 Nonmagnetic Material—A hand magnet shall be used to separate the magnetic shot from the nonmagetic contaminants. The nonmagetic contaminants shall be weighed and the percentage of the original sample weight calculated.

11.8 Chemical Analysis—Any suitable ASTM analytical procedure for steel may be used to test chemical analysis.

CAST SHOT AND GRIT SIZE SPECIFICATIONS FOR PEENING AND CLEANING—SAE J444 MAY93 SAE Recommended Practice

Report of the SAE Production Division approved January 1946. Revised by the SAE Mechanical Prestressing of Metals Division November 1976. Reaffirmed with change by the SAE Fatigue, Design, and Evaluation Steering Committee August 1984. Completely revised by the SAE Fatigue, Design, and Evaluation Committee May 1993.

1. Scope—This SAE Recommended Practice pertains to blast cleaning and shot peening and provides for standard cast shot and grit size numbers. For shot, this number corresponds with the opening of the nominal test sieve, in ten thousandths of inches[1], preceded by an S. For grit, this number corresponds with the sieve designation of the nominal test sieve with the prefix G added. These sieves are in accordance with ASTM E 11.

The accompanying shot and grit classifications and size designations were formulated by representatives of shot and grit suppliers, equipment manufacturers, and automotive users.

2. References

2.1 Applicable Publication—The following publication forms a part of this specification to the extent specified herein.

2.1.1 ASTM PUBLICATION—Available from ASTM, 100 Barr Harbor Drive, West Conshohocken, PA 19428-2959.

ASTM E 11—Standard Specifications for Wire Cloth Sieves for Testing Purposes

2.2 Related Publications—The following publications are provided for information purposes only and are not a required part of this document. The latest issue of SAE publications shall apply.

2.2.1 SAE PUBLICATIONS—Available from SAE, 400 Commonwealth Drive, Warrendale, PA 15096-0001.

SAE J445—Metallic Shot and Grit Mechanical Testing—For Information on Shot Durability Determination

SAE J827—Cast Steel Shot—For Information on Composition and Shapes

SAE J1993—Cast Steel Grit—For Information on Composition and Shapes

SAE J2175—Low Carbon Steel Shot—For Information on Composition and Shapes

3. Testing Procedure—Sieve Analysis

3.1 Equipment

3.1.1 A rotating and tapping type of testing machine shall be used.

3.1.1.1 The shaking speed shall be 275 to 295 rpm.

3.1.1.2 The taps per minute shall be 145 to 160 when tapping machines are used.

3.2 Sieves

3.2.1 The testing sieves shall be in accordance with ASTM E 11. They shall be of the 203 mm (8 in) diameter series, of either 25 mm (1 in) or 51 mm (2 in) height.

3.3 Procedure

3.3.1 A 100 g sample of the shot or grit shall be obtained from a representative quantity.

3.3.2 The sample shall be placed on the top sieve of a stack of three or four sieves, depending on media and size (Figures 1 and 2). Nest the selected sieves and fit a pan to the bottom sieve.

3.3.3 The sample shall be run in the testing machine for 5 min ± 5 s for sizes using sieve designation 35 or coarser and 10 min ± 5 s for sizes using sieve designation finer than 35.

3.3.4 The stack of sieves shall be removed from the testing machine and the percentage of total weight shall be recorded for the media remaining on each sieve.

3.4 Any alternate method agreed upon by the supplier and the user which gives equivalent results will be acceptable.

1. Example: S-550 indicates a cast steel shot identified by a nominal sieve opening of 0.0555 in.

CAST SHOT SPECIFICATIONS FOR SHOT PEENING OR BLAST CLEANING

Sieve Designation	Nominal Sieve Opening	Test Sieve Opening Size and Designation With Maximum and Minimum Cumulative Percentages Allowed on Corresponding Test Sieves SAE Shot Number													
	(in)	S1320	S1110	S930	S780	S660	S550	S460	S390	S330	S280	S230	S170	S110	S70
4	(0.187)	All Pass	—	—	—	—	—	—	—	—	—	—	—	—	—
5	(0.157)	—	All Pass	—	—	—	—	—	—	—	—	—	—	—	—
6	(0.132)	90% min	—	All Pass	—	—	—	—	—	—	—	—	—	—	—
7	(0.111)	97% min	90% min	—	All Pass	—	—	—	—	—	—	—	—	—	—
8	(0.0937)	—	97% min	90% min	—	All Pass	—	—	—	—	—	—	—	—	—
10	(0.0787)	—	—	97% min	85% min	—	All Pass	All Pass	—	—	—	—	—	—	—
12	(0.0661)	—	—	—	97% min	85% min	—	5% max	All Pass	—	—	—	—	—	—
14	(0.0555)	—	—	—	—	97% min	85% min	—	5% max	All Pass	—	—	—	—	—
16	(0.0469)	—	—	—	—	—	97% min	85% min	—	5% max	All Pass	—	—	—	—
18	(0.0394)	—	—	—	—	—	—	96% min	85% min	—	5% max	All Pass	—	—	—
20	(0.0331)	—	—	—	—	—	—	—	96% min	85% min	—	10% max	All Pass	—	—
25	(0.0278)	—	—	—	—	—	—	—	—	96% min	85% min	—	10% max	—	—
30	(0.0234)	—	—	—	—	—	—	—	—	—	96% min	85% min	—	All Pass	—
35	(0.0197)	—	—	—	—	—	—	—	—	—	—	97% min	—	10% max	—
40	(0.0165)	—	—	—	—	—	—	—	—	—	—	—	85% min	—	All Pass
45	(0.0139)	—	—	—	—	—	—	—	—	—	—	—	97% min	—	10% max
50	(0.0117)	—	—	—	—	—	—	—	—	—	—	—	—	80% min	—
80	(0.0070)	—	—	—	—	—	—	—	—	—	—	—	—	90% min	80% min
120	(0.0049)	—	—	—	—	—	—	—	—	—	—	—	—	—	90% min
200	(0.0029)	—	—	—	—	—	—	—	—	—	—	—	—	—	—

…nds to ISO Recommendations

FIGURE 1—CAST SHOT SPECIFICATIONS FOR SHOT PEENING OR BLAST CLEANING

CAST GRIT SPECIFICATIONS FOR BLAST CLEANING

Sieve Opening Standard	Sieve Desig-nation	Nominal Sieve Opening	Test Sieve Opening Size and Designation With Maximum and Minimum Cumulative Percentages Allowed on Corresponding Test Sieves SAE Grit Number											
(mm[1])		(in)	G10	G12	G14	G16	G18	G25	G40	G50	G80	G120	G200	G32
4.75	4	(0.187)	–	–	–	–	–	–	–	–	–	–	–	–
4.00	5	(0.157)	–	–	–	–	–	–	–	–	–	–	–	–
3.35	6	(0.132)	–	–	–	–	–	–	–	–	–	–	–	–
2.80	7	(0.111)	All Pass	–	–	–	–	–	–	–	–	–	–	–
2.36	8	(0.0937)	–	All Pass	–	–	–	–	–	–	–	–	–	–
2.00	10	(0.0787)	80%	–	All Pass	–	–	–	–	–	–	–	–	–
1.70	12	(0.0661)	90%	80%	–	All Pass	–	–	–	–	–	–	–	–
1.40	14	(0.0555)	–	90%	80%	–	All Pass	–	–	–	–	–	–	–
1.18	16	(0.0469)	–	–	90%	75%	–	All Pass	–	–	–	–	–	–
1.00	18	(0.0394)	–	–	–	85%	75%	–	All Pass	–	–	–	–	–
0.850	20	(0.0331)	–	–	–	–	–	–	–	–	–	–	–	–
0.710	25	(0.0278)	–	–	–	–	85%	70%	–	All Pass	–	–	–	–
0.600	30	(0.0234)	–	–	–	–	–	–	–	–	–	–	–	–
0.500	35	(0.0197)	–	–	–	–	–	–	–	–	–	–	–	–
0.425	40	(0.0165)	–	–	–	–	–	80%	70%	–	All Pass	–	–	–
0.355	45	(0.0139)	–	–	–	–	–	–	–	–	–	–	–	–
0.300	50	(0.0117)	–	–	–	–	–	–	80%	65%	–	All Pass	–	–
0.180	80	(0.0070)	–	–	–	–	–	–	–	75%	65%	–	All Pass	–
0.125	120	(0.0049)	–	–	–	–	–	–	–	–	75%	60%	–	All Pa
0.075	200	(0.0029)	–	–	–	–	–	–	–	–	–	70%	55%	–
0.045	325	(0.0017)	–	–	–	–	–	–	–	–	–	–	65%	20%

[1] Corresponds to ISO Recommendations

FIGURE 2—CAST GRIT SPECIFICATIONS FOR BLAST CLEANING

METALLIC SHOT AND GRIT MECHANICAL TESTING—SAE J445 APR96

SAE Information Report

Report of the SAE Iron and Steel Technical Committee approved January 1957, revised June 1962, and reaffirmed August 1984. Completely revised by the SAE Surface Enhancement Subcommittee of the SAE Fatigue, Design, and Evaluation Committee April 1996.

Foreword—This Document has not changed other than to put it into the new SAE Technical Standards Board Format.

Shot testing machines differ in detail, but are alike in the fundamental principle that a sample of shot is subjected to repeated impacts on a target. The percentage of breakdown is readily determined by means of a screen analysis. These data can be used to check the uniformity of shipments or to determine the relative fatigue life. The results obtained from testing machines are not intended to be used in establishing consumption or cost in production machines because of other considerations not duplicated in the laboratory. However, the machines can be used to test incoming shot for consistency and comparative life with previous shipments of the same type of shot from the same manufacturer under laboratory conditions. Some machines can be fitted with standard test strips[1] to measure energy transfer.

NOTE—Shot particles may be subject to multiple impacts in a test machine. The target material of test machines are made of hard steel to resist wear during testing. Hard shot is more elastic than soft shot. Due to these considerations and their influence on shot failure, care must be exercised when analyzing results from this accelerated, laboratory testing.

1. Scope—This SAE Information Report is intended to provide users and producers of metallic shot and grit[2] with general information on methods of mechanically testing metal shot in the laboratory.

2. References

2.1 Applicable Publications—The following publications form a part of this specification to the extent specified herein. Unless otherwise specified, the latest issue of SAE publications shall apply.

2.1.1 SAE PUBLICATIONS—Available from SAE, 400 Commonwealth Drive, Warrendale, PA 15096-0001.

SAE J442—Test Strip, Holder, and Gage for Shot Peening

SAE J443—Procedures for Using Standard Shot Peening Test Strip

2.1.2 ASTM PUBLICATION—Available from ASTM, 100 Barr Harbor Drive, West Conshohocken, PA 19428-2959.

ASTM B 215—Methods of Sampling Finished Lots of Metal Powders

3. Sampling—Samples for testing shall be representative of each shipment or production lot. The method of sampling shall be ASTM B 215, Method B.

4. Calibration—Because results can be influenced by the condition of a test machine, the machine must be recalibrated according to the machine manufacturer's recommendation. This may be accomplished by reserving an adequate amount of shot of known life, and comparing the results obtained on tests with that of the "standard shot." The machine must be repaired or adjusted as necessary when off-standard conditions are observed.

5. Examples of Test Procedures

5.1 Average Life by Measurement of the Area Under the Breakdown Curve—If a representative sample of shot is observed as it is broken down in a testing machine, and the percent of the sample retained on a control sieve is plotted against the number of cycles, on rectangular coordinate paper, a breakdown curve typical of the shot is obtained. The control sieve aperture should be approximately equal to the removal size in the blast operation. The area under this curve is a measure of the average number of cycles required to reduce the size of the shot particles which pass through the control sieve. This average number of cycles, commonly referred to as the average life of the shot, is a complete evaluation of the life of the shot under the conditions of the test.

5.1.1 EXAMPLE PROCEDURE

a. Place 50 to 100 g of the sample to be tested into the test machine.
b. Run until about 20% passes through the control sieve.
c. Screen, weigh, and plot the percent retained on the control sieve against the number of cycles, using rectangular coordinate paper.
d. Return the sample retained on the control sieve to the machine and continue running.
e. Repeat steps (c) and (d) at intervals dictated by the rapidity of breakdown of the sample, until less than 5% of the sample is retained on the control sieve.
f. Draw the breakdown curve, extrapolating to 0% at the end of the next test interval. The breakdown curve, using the data from the following example, with trapezoids inscribed, is shown in Figure 1.
g. Measure the area under the breakdown curve. For example, use a planimeter or sum the areas of the individual trapezoids inscribed under the breakdown curve. Record the value as average life, in cycles.

5.1.1.1 Example

a. Initial Charge—100 g of S660
b. Control Sieve Opening—600 µm
c. Test Intervals—500 cycles

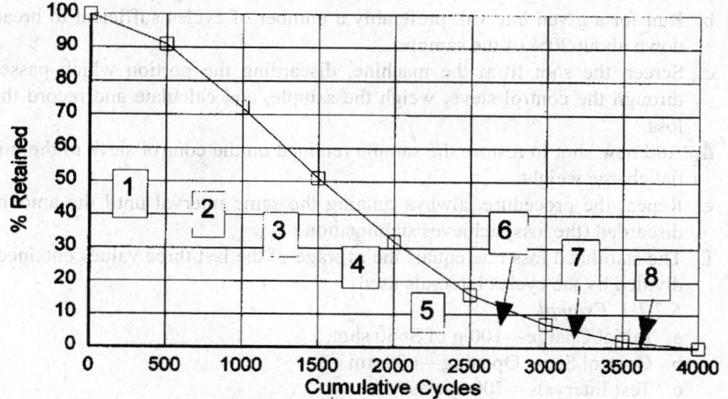

FIGURE 1—BREAKDOWN CURVE S660 SHOT TRAPEZOIDS INSCRIBED AND NUMBERED

5.1.1.2 Breakdown Data—(See Table 1.)

TABLE 1—BREAKDOWN DATA FOR EXAMPLE

Cumulative Cycles	% Retained on Control Sieve
0	100
500	91
1000	72
1500	51
2000	32
2500	16
3000	7
3500	2
4000	0

The area of a trapezoid is determined by multiplying the average height by the base. The area of trapezoid 1 is calculated as follows:

$$\text{Average height} = (100\% + 91\%) \text{ divided by } 2 = 95\% \quad \text{(Eq. 1)}$$

where:

the base = 500 cycles
Area = 95.5% x 500 cycles = 47 750% cycles

The calculations of areas of all the trapezoids are shown in Table 2.

TABLE 2—CALCULATION OF THE AREA UNDER THE BREAKDOWN CURVE AS THE SUM OF THE AREAS OF TRAPEZOIDS INSCRIBED UNDER THE BREAKDOWN CURVE

Trapezoid No.	1	2	3	4	5	6	7	8
Height 1, %	100	91	72	51	32	16	7	2
Height 2, %	91	72	51	32	16	7	2	0
Avg. Height, %	95.5	81.5	61.5	41.5	24	11.5	4.5	1
Base, cycles	500	500	500	500	500	500	500	500
Area, % cycles	47 750	40 750	30 750	20 750	12 000	5750	2250	500

NOTES

Sum of areas 160 500 % cycles

The average life = 160 500 % impacts divided by 100% =1605 cycles.

1. See SAE J442 and SAE J443.
2. Shot and grit will be hereafter referred to as shot.

5.2 Stabilized Loss Method—A sample of shot is run in a test machine for a given number of cycles. The sample is then screened to remove particles which pass through a control sieve. The control sieve aperture should approximately equal the removal size in the blast operation. New shot is added to replace the amount removed. Repeat the procedure, always running the same number of cycles until the amount discarded (the loss) achieves stabilization. The stabilized loss data can be used to compute the average life of the sample.

NOTE—The loss pattern, when each loss is plotted against test cycles, may go through several peaks and valleys before true stabilization occurs. Initial samples should be tested through sufficient test cycles to insure that the sample loss rate has truly stabilized. Stabilization occurs when three consecutive losses vary by less than 0.50% of the initial charge weight.

5.2.1 EXAMPLE PROCEDURE

a. Place 50 to 100 g of the shot to be tested into the testing machine.
b. Run for a given interval, preferably a number of cycles sufficient to break down about 20% of the sample.
c. Screen the shot from the machine, discarding the portion which passes through the control sieve, weigh the sample, and calculate and record the loss.
d. Add new shot to restore the sample retained on the control sieve to the initial charge weight.
e. Repeat the procedure, always running the same interval until the amount discarded (the loss) achieves stabilization.
f. The stabilized loss rate equals the average of the last three values obtained, divided by the cycles intervals used.

5.2.1.1 Example

a. Initial Charge—100 g of S660 shot
b. Control Sieve Opening—600 µm
c. Test Intervals—500 cycles

5.2.1.2 Breakdown Cycles—(See Table 3.)

TABLE 3—BREAKDOWN CYCLES

Cumulative Cycles	Grams Lost
500	9.0
1000	19.8
1500	24.5
2000	26.9
2500	28.9
3000	27.1
3500	27.2
4000	26.9

$$\text{Stabilized loss} = (27.1\text{ g} + 27.2 + 26.9\text{ g})/3 = 27.06\text{ g} \qquad \text{(Eq. 2)}$$

where:

Stabilized loss rate = 27.06 g/500 cycles = 0.0541 g/cycle

Final weight equals initial weight minus stabilized loss = 100 g – 27.06 g = 72.94 g

NOTE—The average life, in this example, is calculated as follows: Average life equals the average number of grams in machine, divided by the stabilized loss rate, in g/cycle, both at stabilized.

The average number of grams in the machine at stabilization equals the average of the initial weight and final weight:

(100 + 72.94) g, divided by 2 = 86.47 g

Average life = (86.47 g)/(0.0541 g/cycles) = 1599 cycles

5.3 100% Replacement Method—A sample of shot is run in a test machine for a given number of cycles. The sample is then screened to remove particles which pass through a control sieve. The control sieve aperture should approximately equal the removal size in the blast operation. New shot is added to replace the amount removed. Repeat the procedure until an amount equal to or greater than the initial charge has been added.

5.3.1 EXAMPLE PROCEDURE

a. Place 50 to 100 g of the shot to be tested into the testing machine.
b. Run for a given interval, preferably a number of cycles sufficient to break down about 20% of the sample.
c. Screen the shot from the machine, discarding the portion which passes through the control sieve, weigh the sample, and record the grams (%) retained.
d. Add new shot to restore the sample retained on the control sieve to the initial charge weight.
e. Repeat (a) to (d), always running the same interval, until the cumulative % discarded (the loss), is equal to or greater than the initial charge weight.
f. Determine the number of cycles at which 100% replacement has occurred, by interpolation, using Equation 3:

$$\text{100\% replacement value (in cycles)} = \text{total cycles} - (\text{interval}/\text{\% last loss})(\text{cumulative \% loss} - 100\%) \qquad \text{(Eq. 3)}$$

5.3.1.1 Example—(See Table 4.)

a. S660—Cast steel shot
b. Control Sieve Opening—425 µm
c. Test Intervals—500 cycles

TABLE 4—BREAKDOWN CYCLES

Accumulative Cycles	Individual % Remaining	Individual % Loss	Cumulative % Loss
500	87.7	12.2	12.2
1000	84.0	16.0	28.2
1500	82.4	17.6	45.8
2000	80.9	19.1	64.9
2500	80.5	19.5	84.4
3000	81.0	19.0	103.4

100% replacement value = 3000 – (500/19.0) (103.4 – 100%) = 2911 cycles

5.4 Transmitted Energy Arc Height Test—The purpose of this test is to evaluate the consistency of the transmission of the kinetic energy of the moving shot particles into useful energy to the work surface. Some shot testing machines are designed to locate a standard test strip in the particle blast stream inside the machine. The use of the standard test strips to monitor shot peening intensities (energy transformation) is discussed in SAE J442, J443, and other references on shot peening. The standard test strip curvature developed when the strip is impacted by the shot being tested can be used as a measure of the energy transmitted to the strip by the shot being tested.

5.4.1 EXAMPLE PROCEDURE

a. Using a sample splitter, carefully split the operating mix of used shot from the last interval in 5.2, or from 5.3, to obtain a sample of 50.0 g ± 0.1 g.
b. Place the sample from (a) into the test machine.
c. Place a standard test strip in the test machine fastened to the test strip holder per SAE J442.
d. Peen the standard test strip for 40 cycles.

NOTE—40 cycles may not represent standard test strip saturation for all shot sizes. It may be necessary to develop a full saturation curve, per SAE J442, to fully understand the performance of the shot being tested.

e. Remove the standard test strip and measure the arc height of the strip per SAE J442.
f. The results indicate transmitted energy for the given exposure time. Compare results with results obtained on previous shipments of production lots of the same material. If the arc height is equal to or greater than that achieved using the reference material, the shot is acceptable. If not, the shot is subject to further testing.

HIGH-CARBON CAST-STEEL GRIT—SAE J1993 SEP1996

SAE Recommended Practice

Report of the SAE Fatigue, Design, and Evaluation Committee approved March 1993. Completely revised by the SAE Surface Enhancement Division of the SAE Fatigue, Design, and Evaluation Committee, September 1996.

1. Scope—This SAE Recommended Practice describes the chemical composition, and physical characteristic requirements for high-carbon cast-steel grit, to be used for blast cleaning and etching operations.

2. References

2.1 Applicable Publications—The following publications form a part of this specification to the extent specified herein. Unless otherwise indicated, the latest issue of SAE publications shall apply.

2.1.1 SAE PUBLICATION—Available from SAE, 400 Commonwealth Drive, Warrendale, PA 15096-0001.

SAE J444—Cast Shot and Grit Size Specifications for Peening and Cleaning

SAE J445—Metallic Shot and Grit Mechanical Testing

2.1.2 ASTM PUBLICATIONS—Available from ASTM, 100 Barr Harbor Drive, West Conshohocken, PA 19428-2959.

ASTM B 215—Method B—Methods of Sampling Finished Lots of Metal Powders

ASTM E 140—Hardness Conversion Tables for Metals (Relationship Between Brinell Hardness, Vickers Hardness, Rockwell Hardness, Rockwell Superficial Hardness, and Knoop Hardness)

ASTM E 384—Test Methods for Microhardness of Materials

2.1.3 ISO PUBLICATIONS—Available from ANSI, 11 West 42nd Street, New York, NY 10036-8002.

ISO 11124 Part 3—High-carbon cast-steel shot and grit

ISO 11125 Part 1—Preparation of steel substrates before application of paints and related products—Test methods for metallic abrasives—Part 1: Sampling

ISO 11125 Part 2—Preparation of steel substrates before application of paints and related products—Test methods for metallic abrasives—Part 2: Determination of particle size distribution

ISO 11125 Part 3—Preparation of steel substrates before application of paints and related products—Test methods for metallic abrasives—Part 3: Determination of hardness

ISO 11125 Part 4—Preparation of steel substrates before application of paints and related products—Test methods for metallic abrasives—Part 4: Determination of apparent density

ISO 11125 Part 5—Preparation of steel substrates before application of paints and related products—Test methods for metallic abrasives—Part 5: Determination of percentage defective particles and microstructure

ISO 11125 Part 6—Preparation of steel substrates before application of paints and related products—Test methods for metallic abrasives—Part 6: Determination of foreign matter

ISO 11125 Part 7—Preparation of steel substrates before application of paints and related products—Test methods for metallic abrasives—Part 7: Determination of moisture

3. Description—High-carbon cast-steel grit is the product obtained by crushing heat-treated high-carbon cast-steel shot. The resulting angular particles are screened to a range of sizes from G10 to G325 as described in SAE J444.

4. Size Classification and Hardness Identification

4.1 High-carbon cast-steel grit will be identified by HCS G, followed by a number which represents the sieve designation, in accordance with SAE J444, followed by a letter designating the grit hardness range. See the example following 6.3 for the full grit designation.

5. Chemical Composition

a. Carbon—0.80 to 1.20%
b. Manganese—0.60 to 1.20%
c. Silicon—0.40% minimum
d. Sulphur—0.05% maximum
e. Phosphorus—0.05% maximum

6. Hardness

6.1 The four standard hardness ranges for high-carbon cast-steel grit are as follows:

a. HCS G([1])S—The hardness range shall be 40 to 51 HRC
b. HCS G([1])M—The hardness range shall be 47 to 56 HRC
c. HCS G([1])L—The hardness range shall be 54 to 61 HRC
d. HCS G([1])H—The hardness shall be 60 HRC minimum

6.2 90% of the hardness readings shall be within the specified range. For HCS G([1])H, 90% of the readings shall be 60 HRC or higher.

6.3 Special Hardness—Other hardnesses may be specified by the user. The minimum hardness range that can be specified is 7 points HRC.

EXAMPLE—HCS G25S indicates a high-carbon cast-steel grit meeting the G25 requirements in SAE J444, with a hardness designation of S (40 to 51 HRC).

7. Microstructure—The microstructure of high-carbon cast-steel grit shall consist of martensite, tempered to a degree consistent with the hardness, with fine, well distributed carbides, if any. Some retained austenite may be observed in H hardness grit.

8. General Appearance—The cast-steel grit shall be as angular as commercially possible. A total of no more than 40% of the grit particles shall have objectionable characteristics or contain more than 1% by weight of nonmetallic material. Any one particle tested that has more than one objectionable characteristic will only be counted once in the total. Notwithstanding the allowable percentages listed as follows, no more than a total of 40% objectionable particles are allowed.

8.1 Objectionable Characteristics

8.1.1 PARTICLE SHAPE—For the hard steel grits, HCS G([1])L, HCS G([1])H, there shall be no more than 5% round or half round particles. For the soft steel grits, HCS G([1])S and HCS G([1])M, there shall be no more than 10% round or half round particles.

8.1.2 SHRINKAGE—No more than 10% of the particles in the sample shall contain shrinkage. Shrinkage is an internal cavity with irregular dendritic surface, greater in area than 40% of the pellet area.

8.1.3 CRACKS—No more than 40% of the particles examined shall contain major cracks. A major crack is defined as a linear discontinuity whose length is greater than three times its width and is radial in direction.

8.1.4 MICROSTRUCTURE—Carbide networks, grain boundary segregation, decarburization, and high-temperature transformation products such as pearlite are undesirable. No more than 15% of the particles tested shall contain these defects.

9. Density—The density of the cast steel grit shall not be less than 7.3 g/cm^3.

10. Inspection Procedures

10.1 Sampling—Samples for testing shall be representative of each shipment or production lot. The method of sampling shall be ASTM B 215 Method B.

10.2 Sample Mounting for Testing—Grit samples used for testing for hardness, microstructure, and objectionable defects shall be mounted one layer deep in bakelite or other suitable strong metallurgical sample mounting media.

The mounted sample shall be ground to the center of the partical and polished using methods acceptable for microscopic examination. When grinding and polishing the sample, care must be taken not to overheat the sample and affect microstructure and/or hardness.

10.3 Chemical Analysis—Any suitable ASTM analytical procedure for steel may be used to test chemical composition.

10.4 Hardness Testing—Hardness measurements shall be taken on any sound area of a particle, preferably halfway between the center and the edge, on a minimum of ten particles in the mounted specimen. The hardness shall be determined in accordance with ASTM E 384 or equivalent microhardness testing methods. For G-80 and smaller grit, a load of 100 g shall be used. For G-50 and G-40, grit a load of 500 g shall be used. For grit larger than G-40, the load may be either 500 or 1000 g. Conversion to approximate Rockwell C numbers may be obtained from ASTM E 140 and manufacturers of hardness testers.

10.5 Microstructure—The mounted and polished specimen shall be etched with a suitable etchant and examined at a magnification of approximately 500 diameters.

10.6 Shrinkage and Cracks—Shrinkage and cracks shall be determined using a magnification of ten diameters.

10.7 Density—Density shall be determined by placing 50 mL of water or alcohol in a 100 mL graduate, adding 100 g of shot and recording the increase in volume. Dividing 100 g by the volume increase will give the density in g/cm^3. A pycnometer method may be used for more critical density measurements.

10.8 Mechanical Tests—See SAE J445 for methods of checking uniformity of shipments of grits.

1. Grit size designation from SAE J444.

SAE MANUAL ON BLAST CLEANING —SAE J792a JUN1968

SAE Information Report

Report of the SAE Iron and Steel Technical Committee approved July 1954 and last revised June 1968. Formerly HS 124.

Foreword—This Document has not changed other than to put it into the new SAE Technical Standards Board Format

This report on blast cleaning is a companion to the SAE report on Shot Peening. It is intended to help engineers, management, and shop personnel to increase their knowledge of the process. The information contained herein has been submitted and edited by a group that has had extensive and varied experience with blast cleaning and whose recommendations merit consideration.

1. Scope—Blast cleaning may be defined as a secondary manufacturing process in which a suitable stream of solid particles is propelled with sufficient velocity against a work surface to cause a cleaning or abrading action when it comes in contact with the workpiece.

As indicated in the definition, blast cleaning may be employed for a variety of purposes. Ordinarily, it is considered as a method for removing sand from castings, burrs or scale from forgings, mill products, or heat treated parts; to promote machinability, and to minimize the possibility of interference in actual operation. In addition to this use, blast cleaning also produces an excellent surface for industrial coatings. All these objectives are often accomplished in the one operation.

1.1 History—The cleaning problem of removing sand and scale has always been associated with the casting, forging, and heat treating of metal. As recently as the beginning of the twentieth century, foundrymen considered the chisel, hammer, dull file, and wire brush the chief weapons for attacking this problem. Hand tools were gradually augmented by "rattling" or tumbling methods.

Pressure blasting was first introduced in 1870 by Gen. Benjamin Chew Tilghman. He discovered that metals, stone, and glass could be shaded or etched by jets of sand. He took out patents covering pressure blasting with sand driven by compressed air, steam, and water; with sand struck by a paddle wheel, thrown centrifugally, or dropped from a height through a tube. Thus, General Tilghman advanced the principles upon which modern blast cleaning is based.[1]

Tilghman's first commercial machine used a steam blast as a method of propelling the sand. This proved to have several disadvantages. The steam moistened the sand, necessitating a drying operation. It also tended to hide the work, break glass objects, and rust metals. As a result, Tilghman changed to a tank-type compressed air machine, which proved more successful.

Other men and companies entered the blast cleaning equipment field. A natural development was the blasting machine in which sand could be refilled during operation. This was accomplished by pouring sand through a standpipe of sufficient height to overcome tank pressure.

Cabinets and barrels featuring pressure air blasting nozzles were advertised in magazines in 1895. That same year W. W. Sly introduced the exhaust tumbling barrel, which also increased the dust removal problem. This was partially solved by the first cloth screen dust arrester patented in 1897.

Many industries recognized the superior surface quality of castings, forgings, heat treated parts, etc., cleaned by blast cleaning. However, the high operational cost and low productivity of the process at that time limited its use to the cleaning of large castings or products where high quality was necessary regardless of cost.

An old leanto in back of the plant comprised the up-to-date blast cleaning department of 1915. A blower fan provided the ventilation. Wooden walls which splintered were soon replaced by steel sheets. The sand blasting distorted the sheets and cut the nails. Brick was used next and proved more durable. However, the silica dust produced was harmful to the operator.

In 1917 humane sand blast rooms were developed in which the operator stayed out of the blast zone. Downdraft ventilation, rubber-lined steel walls, and better lighting all served to improve the sand blasting operation.

A new phase of development took place with the introduction of metallic abrasives in the 1920's. Acceptance was slow, due to the availability and low first cost of sand. Industry soon recognized the improvement in the quality of the finish and the lower cost, through increased durability of the shot. Improvements in reclaiming the metal abrasive eventually won over most of industry. One of the chief benefits—savings in storage space and handling—was not appreciated until some years after the adoption of metal abrasives.

The development of metallic abrasives began with the use of chilled cast iron shot. The comparatively short shot life of chilled cast iron lead to the development of malleabilized and annealed cast iron shot. Next to be introduced into the metallic abrasive field was cast steel shot and more recently cut wire shot. Although these latest shot have a higher initial cost than the iron shot, their life is much greater. In many instances, they have proved to be more economical than the iron shot. These newer shot demand that the blasting equipment be operated to minimize shot losses.

As more companies produced metallic abrasives, more and more name and classification systems were used. This resulted in the need for standardization of abrasive classification for the entire blasting industry. A big step in this direction was taken in 1943 when a group of shot producers, users, and equipment manufacturers met in Detroit and formed the Shotpeening Committee of the SAE. This committee established size and nomenclature standards for shot and grit (SAE Handbook). Also, the committee has worked, and is still working, on a standard testing procedure for the endurance and wear of metallic abrasives.

With the introduction and acceptance of metallic abrasives, the blast cleaning suppliers were able to offer industry their next big improvement—the use of centrifugal force for blast cleaning. Here the abrasive is thrown by a revolving wheel, which propels the abrasive mechanically. The idea was first proposed in the 19th century but abandoned. The large volume of sand that even the smallest machines required, plus the excessive wear of sand on metals, made its use prohibitive. In 1933 the American Foundry Equipment Co. demonstrated at Benton Harbor, Mich., the use of a barrel-type machine using a wheel to propel the abrasive. Later, the Pangborn Corp. introduced a similar unit at Detroit, and another was introduced by the W. W. Sly Mfg. Co. in Cleveland. Among later improvements was the construction by the Cargill Detroit Co. of operatorless single-purpose equipment to provide process control on certain high production parts.

Mechanization of blasting equipment, metallic abrasives, and the use of centrifugal force led to the development of more high productive cleaning equipment to meet growing production demands. The improved blasting equipment developed includes the tumble type batch cabinets, continuous monorail cabinets, rotating tables, and the latest development—the continuous barrel type.

In the field of general cleaning the centrifugal or airless type is by far the most popular means of metallic abrasive propulsion. However, in the case of specialized or precision cleaning, air propulsion of metallic abrasives is more adaptable because of its ease of control and great flexibility. As parts become more complex in size and shape, specialized cleaning becomes more and more necessary.

Work in the development of abrasives, blasting equipment, processes, and standization goes on. The blast cleaning history has closely paralleled that of mass production. The blast cleaning industry has made many valuable contributions to the industrial growth of America, and will continue to do so.

1.2 Present Status—The present trend of blast cleaning, with few exceptions, is to use the continuous-barrel type of equipment with centrifugal blast wheels for all small castings that can be handled as bulk material. The use of the continuous-monorail type of blast cabinet equipment with centrifugal abrasive propulsion for large castings and forgings is very extensive. These two types of equipment are fast replacing the old pressure blast equipment. The centrifugal type of blast equipment has proved more economical per ton of cleaned castings than the previously used pressure blast equipment, with few exceptions. An exception to the preceding statement is the specific specialized type of pressure blast equipment on a part that has internal pockets and on which it is necessary to direct the blast stream at a small area that cannot be reached with the widely used centrifugal-type equipment.

The present trend in ferrous metal blasting abrasives is toward material having superior breakdown resistance. The result of this progressive change is a lower cost per ton of cleaned castings with reduced abrasive material breakdown provided adequate auxiliary equipment can be installed adjacent to the blast cleaning machine to salvage the blast material that otherwise would be carried out in pockets of the cleaned work and lost.

1.3 Secondary Effects

1.3.1 COMBINED CLEANING AND PEENING—Combined cleaning and peening is applicable to parts where it is necessary to remove scale, provided there is no subsequent heat treatment. Parts that are being treated in this manner include automotive connecting rods, axleshafts, and steering knuckles. However, on parts such as axleshafts and steering knuckles, which require machining in critical areas, some of the effectiveness of the peening is lost.

Parts with small surface imperfections may be improved by lessening the effect of the stress-raisers during the cleaning operation.

1. See "Modern Blast Cleaning and Ventilation," by C.A. Reams, Cleveland, Ohio: Penton Publishing Co., 1939.

Some controversy exists on the question of the inspection of blast cleaned parts. It is thought by some that small defects, ordinarily brought out by pickling, will be obscured by the blasting operation. Others claim that these small defects are made less detrimental by the peening action of the cleaning operation. Some surface defects may be concealed to the extent that an inspection other than visual may be necessary.

1.3.2 USE AS AN INSPECTION TOOL—Blasting is applied to facilitate inspection of selectively hardened parts; this blasting often serves as a cleaning operation as well. The inspection of chilled iron parts and decarburized areas on hardened parts is made easier by blasting. It is also possible by blasting to show leaks in masked areas after carburizing and hardening.

2. References

2.1 Applicable Publications—The following publications form a part of the specification to the extent specified herein. Unless otherwise indicated the lastest revision of SAE publications shall apply.

2.1.1 SAE PUBLICATIONS—Available from SAE 400 Commonwealth Drive, Warrendale, PA 15096-0001.

SAE J441—Cut Wire Shot
SAE J444—Cast Shot and Grit Size Specifications for Peening and Cleaning
SAE J827—Cast Steel Shot
SAE Handbook

2.1.2 OTHER PUBLICATIONS

"Modern Blast Cleaning and Ventilation," C.A. Reams, Cleveland, Ohio, Penton Publishing Company, 1939
"Simplified Practic Recommendation 118-50—Abrasive Grain Sizes," U.S. Department of Commerce Bulletin, June 1, 1950
"Hyrdo-Finish and Hydro Sandblast," W.I. Gladfelter, Pangborn Corporation
"Fine Particle Blasting or MicroBlast Fluid Honing and Finishing," E.E. Hawkinson, MicroBlast Manufacturing Corporation
"Fine Particle Blasting—A.P. Neuman and V.W. Nichols, Vapor Blast Manufacturing Company

3. Blast Cleaning Machines—Blast cleaning machines have any or all of the following components: abrasive propelling mechanism; cabinet or enclosure; abrasive cycling and regenerative system; work holding mechanism; load and unload mechanism; and controls.

Abrasive blasting equipment is generally divided into air blast units, airless blast units, and wet blasting machines, according to the method of propelling the abrasive. Air blasting and airless blasting machines are dry processes for general cleaning, while wet blasting is usually restricted to the cleaning and finishing of precision parts requiring special finishes or cleaning action.

3.1 Air Blasting Machines—In air blast equipment the abrasive material is forced by compressed air through a small orifice or nozzle (Figure 1). The abrasive stream takes the shape of a small cone and asserts its effect over a small area. The two advantages of air blasting are its flexibility in cleaning specific areas with a highly concentrated blast pattern and its ability to use both metallic and nonmetallic abrasives. The narrow, coneshape stream of abrasive is ideal for cleaning interior cavities, blind holes, and narrow recesses and localized areas of castings, forgings, and heat treated parts.

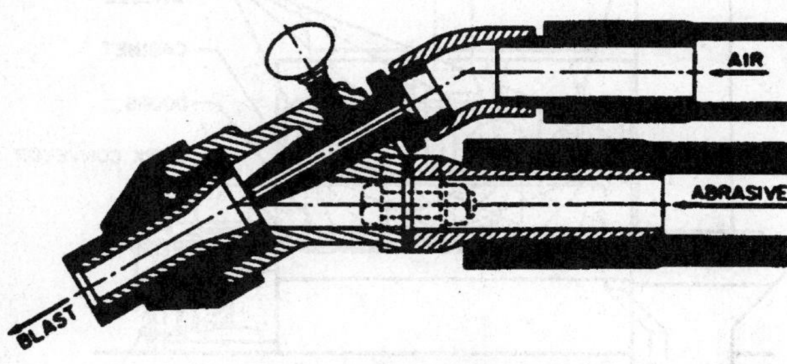

FIGURE 1—INDUCTION NOZZLE

Air blast cabinets are either of the suction feed, gravity feed, or direct pressure types, with the pressure type giving the more powerful blast, which is desirable for removing burned-in sand, heavy scale, etc. The most common form of air blast equipment is that in which the blasting nozzle is manipulated by an operator, who may be located outside or inside the blasting cabinet.

In the large air blast rooms (Figure 2) the operator, in special apparel, manipulates a flexible air blast nozzle to clean large and intricate parts that, because of their size, must remain stationary.

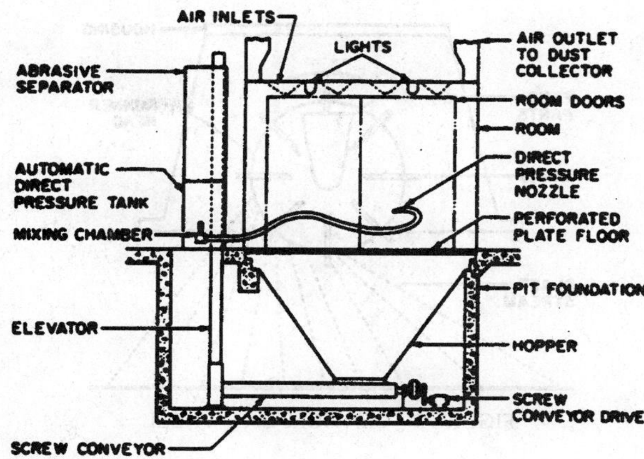

FIGURE 2—HAND BLAST ROOM

In the smaller so-called hand blast cabinet (Figure 3) the operator reaches through the cabinet and manipulates the nozzle and/or the work while viewing his progress through a suitably protected glass window.

Manual cabines, due to their flexibility, are generally used when only a few pieces or work constitute the entire production of that item. For cleaning high production items, single-purpose air blast machines are used, whereby the parts are automatically located in proper relation to the nozzles, blasted, and ejected into storage boxes and onto conveyor lines. These machines are able to use automatic loading devices and are able to operate without an operator.

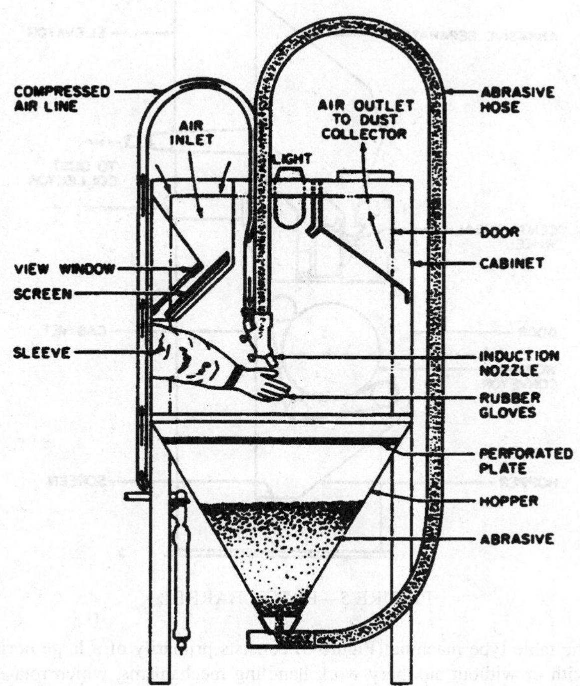

FIGURE 3—INDUCTION CABINET

3.2 Airless Blasting Machines—In airless blasting machines the abrasive material is thrown at the work by means of centrifugal force imparted by one or more rotating wheels located strategically within the cabinet or enclosure (Figure 4). The abrasive forms an elongated, cone-shaped pattern covering a large area and the operator remains outside the machine during the blasting cycle. For large volume, general-purpose cleaning operations, these machines, with their large blast patterns, are ideally suited. The units are built with work handling mechanisms to handle the parts in such a manner that the surfaces requiring cleaning will, at one time or another in their passage through the machine, be exposed to the blast pattern.

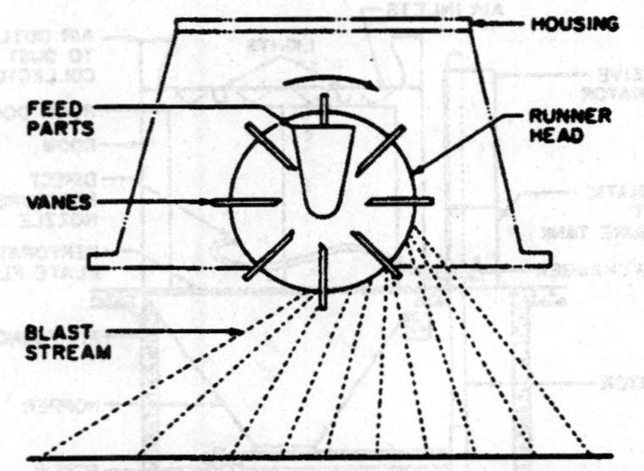

FIGURE 4—CENTRIFUGAL WHEEL

The number of wheel units required and their positioning in any cabinet are influenced by the combination of size, shape, and weight of the work to be cleaned plus the condition of the work and the production required. The most common airless blast machines used for general cleaning are the single-wheel units propelling a fixed downward pattern upon work carried before this pattern and are classified as batch type cleaning machines and continuous-table-type blast cleaning machines.

In the batch type units (Figure 5) the parts are loaded into the machine in one batch in a barrel or in a depressed cavity developed in a large endless type of flight conveyor completely enclosed. When the batch has been cleaned, the machine is opened and the parts ejected.

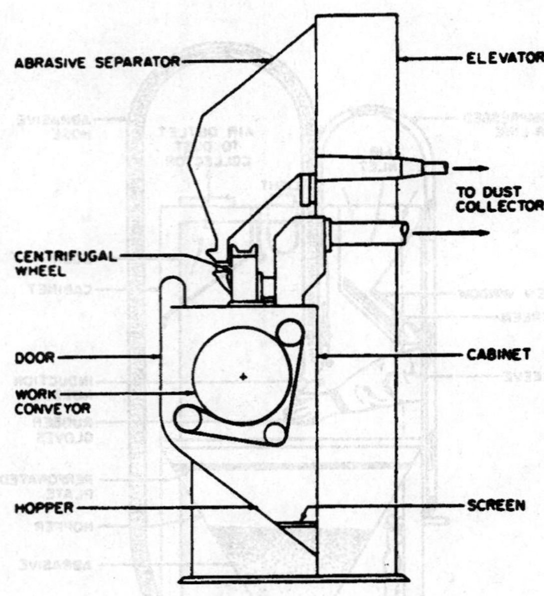

FIGURE 5—BATCH BARREL

The table type machine (Figure 6) consists primarily of a large horizontal table, with or without auxiliary work handling mechanisms, which rotates in a merry-go-round fashion. A portion of the table is opened to the operator allowing him to load and unload parts continuously; the other portion of the table is enclosed and houses the shot blast pattern.

Multiple-wheel machines (Figure 7) are more adaptable to high-production parts and utilize various types of conveyors to pass the parts through their multiple-blast patterns.

3.3 Wet Blasting Machines—In wet blasting equipment very fine mesh abrasives in water suspension are propelled at high velocity. These very fine abrasives react upon the surface of the parts in such a manner as to leave a very fine and especially smooth surface, such as is desirable on precision parts, where details must not be altered, and on parts requiring specially prepared and smooth surfaces.

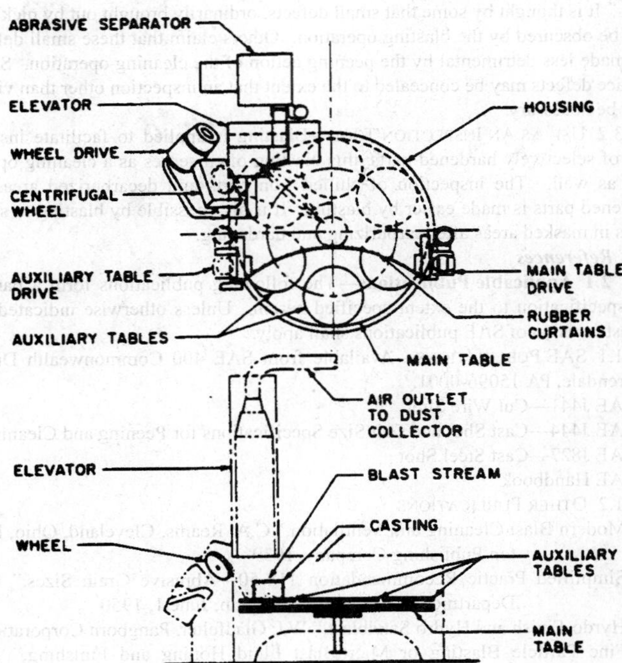

FIGURE 6—TABLE TYPE MACHINE

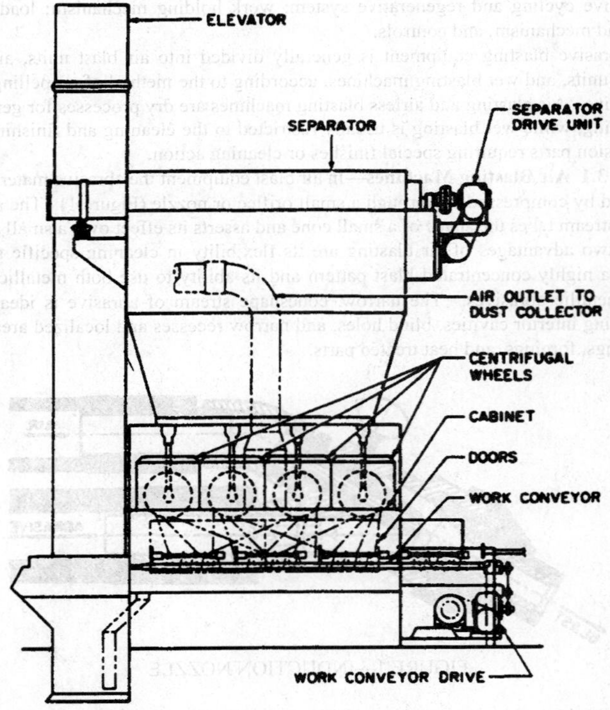

FIGURE 7—MULTIPLE-WHEEL MACHINE

The abrasive is kept in suspension in water by means of an agitator. This slurry is blasted against the work by the use of compressed air and nozzles similar to air blasting. An added component of this type of equipment is a rinse to remove the adhering abrasive.

The common wet blasting machine (Figure 8) is a manually operated hand cabinet. For high production, specialized parts, automatic machines are used in which the work is automatically loaded and unloaded from the unit.

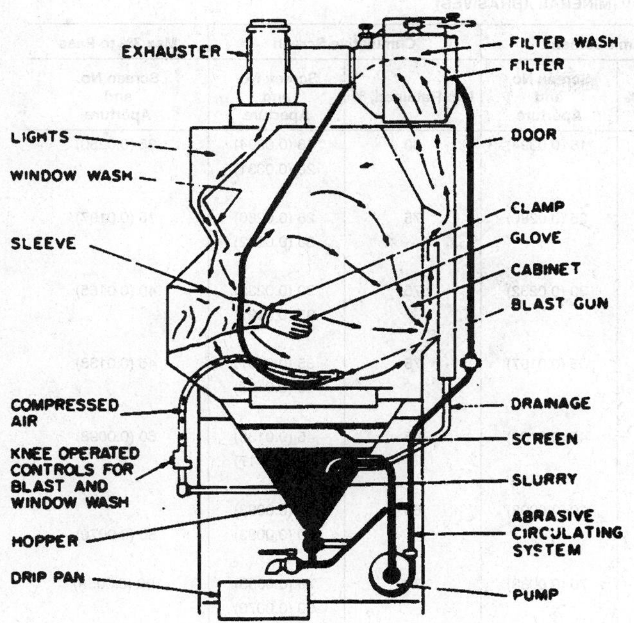

FIGURE 8—SCHEMATIC OF EQUIPMENT FOR WET BLASTING WITH FINE PARTICLES. (DETAIL ARRANGEMENT VARIES AMONG MANUFACTURERS.)

3.3.1 CABINETS OR ENCLOSURES—On blast cleaning equipment, since these enclose the blast stream and its rebound, they are subjected to high abrasive wearing conditions. They are constructed of steel and in critical areas are lined with special steel plates and abrasive resistant rubber to withstand this service. The cabinets are the basic structural components of the machine and generally support the other components.

3.3.2 ABRASIVE CYCLING SYSTEM—This is necessary to return the spent abrasive from the lowest point of the machine back to the abrasive propelling device. In most cases ordinary materials handling devices accomplish this task.

Somewhere in the abrasive cycle a separator, or regenerator, is used to remove broken down abrasive and other foreign material from the blast stream. (See discussion in paragraph 6.1.) A dust collection and exhaust system is operated in conjunction with the abrasive handling system.

3.3.3 WORK HOLDING MECHANISMS—These are designed to present the areas requiring cleaning to the blast stream. The features required of these mechanisms are a minimum of moving parts in the blast stream, ability to withstand abrasive conditions, and simplicity. The load and unload mechanisms used in certain blast equipment are generally confined to batch cleaning machines and are simple, general-purpose materials handling units.

For specialized blasting, automatic devices are becoming more prevalent for the handling of individual parts.

3.4 The Machine Controls—In most cases the machine controls are standard electrical and pneumatic devices manipulated by the operator as required. When the machine is used for repetitive tasks these controls are made to function automatically. Special attention is paid to these controls to eliminate the entrance of fine abrasive material which is always present around these machines.

4. Media—Types and Specifications

4.1 Ferrous Abrasives

4.1.1 CAST IRON SHOT—Cast iron shot is made from cupola melted iron generally containing over 21/2% carbon. It is atomized into random sizes and quenched in water to produce ball shaped particles of white cast iron, having a hardness of approximately Rockwell C 65. The random sizes are screened into standard SAE sizes. Cast iron grit is made by crushing cast iron shot and is available in standard SAE sizes. (See SAE J444.)

4.1.2 MALLEABLE IRON SHOT AND GRIT—Malleable iron shot and grit are made by heat treating cast iron shot or grit to reduce the hardness and increase the resistance to fracture. They are available in the standard SAE sizes of shot and grit.

4.1.3 CAST STEEL SHOT—Cast steel shot is high carbon steel, melted in an electric furnace, atomized into random sizes and quenched in water to produce ball shaped particles. It is heat treated and tempered to a uniform martensitic structure of various hardness. It is available in standard SAE sizes. See SAE J827.[2]

4.1.4 CUT STEEL WIRE SHOT—Cut steel wire shot is the product of cold drawn carbon steel wire cut into the form of cylinders with lengths approximately equal to wire diameter. It is available in standard SAE sizes. (See SAE J444 and J441.)

4.2 Nonferrous Abrasives—Nonferrous metallic abrasives are usually used on non-ferrous or stainless steel parts where ferrous shot or grit might cause a contamination problem or an objectionable color. They are generally limited in use and availability, but include copper, aluminum, stainless steel, and zinc. They are available as cut wire, cast or by-product.

4.3 Mineral Abrasives—Mineral abrasives consist of sand, crushed rock, garnet, pumice, and emery. Most of the blasting sands are found in rock formation and are crushed and screened in various sizes for different uses. By far the largest volume of abrasives used lie in this classification, as approximately 500,000 tons of blast sand and 100,000 tons of ground rock and sandstone are used annually in the United States. The use of garnet, pumice, and emery for blast cleaning is very limited. Blast sand and ground rock products are usually available as shown in Tables 1 and 2.

TABLE 1—APPROXIMATE SIEVE ANALYSIS, % (MINERAL ABRASIVES)

	Grade 1	Grade 2	Grade 3	Grade 4	Grade 7	Grade 7 Special	Grade 10
	Retained on						
No. 8 sq Mesh	0.0	0.0	0.0	0.0	1.0	1.0	8.0
No. 10 sq Mesh	0.0	0.0	0.0	0.0	10.0	12.5	40.0
No. 14 sq Mesh	0.0	0.0	25.0	36.0	45.0	47.0	37.0
No. 20 sq Mesh	0.0	5.0	49.0	51.0	32.0	36.0	12.0
No. 30 sq Mesh	1.5	43.0	23.0	11.0	10.0	3.5	1.5
No. 50 sq Mesh	78.5	48.0	3.0	2.0	2.0	0.0	1.5
Passing:							
No. 50 sq Mesh	20.0	4.0	0.0	0.0	0.0	0.0	0.0

Principal uses of the grades are as follows:
Grade No. 1: Blasting soft metal castings, such as aluminum, aircraft and where a "satin" finish is desired.
Grad No. 2: Blasting soft metal castings, for pointing, aircraft, etc.
Grade No. 3: Blasting castings, for enameling, lettering marble, etc.
Grade No. 4: Blasting for metallizing.
Grade No. 7: Blasting for metallizing, general cleaning of scale, castings, etc.
Grade No. 7 (Special): Blasting for metallizing, general cleaning of scale, castings, etc.
Grade No. 10: Heavy blasting, such as removing paint from tank cars, etc., and where air pressure is 110 psi or more.

The synthetic mineral abrasives include silicon carbide and aluminum oxide and, as the name implies, are man-made in electric furnaces. They are crushed and screened to produce the required sizes. To this may be added glass shot or beads which are manufactured of optical crown glass, soda lime type. They are resistant to atmospheric moisture, dilute acids and alkalis, and are annealed in the spherical shape for stress equalization to reduce wear and fracture. Glass bead size ranges from 0.0005 in and larger.

4.4 Vegetable Abrasives—Vegetable abrasives include such items as wheat grains, ground corncobs, crushed nut hulls such as walnut or hickory, fruit pits and so forth. These materials are often referred to as "soft grit" and are used in special purpose cleaning and deburring, where the surface must not be marred. Examples of such applications are the cleaning of aircraft, automobile, and diesel pistons, electric motor armatures, and pump impellers.

2. SAE J827, Cast Steel Shot. SAE Handbook, published by Society of Automotive Engineers, Inc.

TABLE 2—SCREENING SPECIFICATIONS[1] (MINERAL ABRASIVES)

	High Limit Screen		Control Screen		Low Limit Screen		Cumulative Screen		Max 3% to Pass
No.	Max Retained, %	Screen No. and Aperture	Max Retained, %	Screen No. and Aperture	Min Retained, %	Screen No. and Aperture	Min Retained, %	Screen No. and Aperture	Screen No. and Aperture
20	0	14 (0.0555)	15	16 (0.0469)	45	18 (0.0394)	80	18 (0.0394) 20 (0.0331)	25 (0.0280)
24	0	14 (0.0469)	20	20 (0.0331)	45	25 (0.0280)	75	25 (0.0280) 30 (0.0232)	35 (0.0197)
30	0	18 (0.0394)	20	25 (0.0289)	45	30 (0.0232)	75	30 (0.0232) 35 (0.0197)	40 (0.0165)
36	0	20 (0.0331)	20	30 (0.0232)	45	35 (0.0197)	75	35 (0.0197) 40 (0.0165)	45 (0.0138)
46	0	30 (0.0232)	30	40 (0.0165)	45	45 (0.0138)	65	45 (0.0138) 50 (0.0117)	60 (0.0098)
60	0	40 (0.0165)	30	50 (0.0117)	45	60 (0.0098)	65	60 (0.0098) 70 (0.0083)	80 (0.0070)
70	0	45 (0.0138)	15	60 (0.0098)	45	70 (0.0083)	70	70 (0.0083) 80 (0.0070)	100 (0.0059)
80	0	50 (0.0117)	15	70 (0.0083)	40	80 (0.0070)	70	80 (0.0070) 100 (0.0059)	120 (0.0049)
90	0	60 (0.0098)	15	80 (0.0070)	40	100 (0.0059)	70	100 (0.0059) 120 (0.0049)	140 (0.0041)
100	0	70 (0.0083)	15	100 (0.0059)	40	120 (0.0049)	65	120 (0.0049) 140 (0.0041)	200 (0.0029)
120	0	80 (0.0070)	15	120 (0.0049)	30	140 (0.0041)	60	140 (0.0041) 170 (0.0035)	230 (0.0024)
150	0	100 (0.0059)	15	140 (0.0041)	40	170 (0.0035) 200 (0.0029)	75	170 (0.0035) 200 (0.0029) 230 (0.0024)	270 (0.0021)
180	0	120 (0.0049)	15	170 (0.0035)	40	200 (0.0029) 230 (0.0024)	65	200 (0.0029) 230 (0.0024) 270 (0.0021)	—
220	0	140 (0.0041)	15	200 (0.0029)	40	230 (0.0024) 270 (0.0021)	60	230 (0.0024) 270 (0.0021) 325 (0.0017)	—
249	0	170 (0.0035)	5	200 (0.0029)	8	230 (0.0024) 270 (0.0021)	38	230 (0.0024) 270 (0.0021) 325 (0.0017)	—

1. From U.S. Dept. of Commerce Bulletin dated June 1, 1950, "Simplified Practice Recommendation 118-50—Abrasive Grain Sizes."

5. Recommended Practices

5.1 Oxide and Scale Type—Castings, forgings, hot rolled shapes, etc., may be classified into three general groups according to the type of scale or oxide to be removed:

5.1.1 GROUP A—HEAVY SCALE—Examples of this group are as follows:

a. Steel castings.
b. Alloy forgings—heat treated and annealed.
c. Large hot-rolled shapes.
d. Certain heat treated gray iron castings.
e. Miscellaneous parts for surface effect.

5.1.2 GROUP B—MEDIUM SCALE—Examples are as follows:

a. Carbon steel forgings.
b. Miscellaneous gray iron castings.
c. Miscellaneous malleable castings.
d. Light section—hot-rolled shapes and sheet.

5.1.3 GROUP C—LIGHT SCALES, OXIDES, AND CARBURIZING SMUTS—Examples are as follows:

a. Heat treated finished parts.
b. Nonferrous castings.
c. Miscellaneous parts for surface effect.

After a part is classified into its proper group, the next step should be the selection of the size of grit or shot to be used. This selection will depend upon a number of conditions and may require considerable experimentation. To clean effectively, it is necessary to use a grit or shot with sufficient impact to break the scale quickly and yet be small enough for adequate coverage. The coverage factor is particularly important when castings with deep or partially accessible cavities are being cleaned. It may be necessary, in some cases, to blend two or more different sizes to obtain the necessary stabilization of sizes in the machine, especially when using slow breakdown type of abrasives.

A general guide or starting point for selecting abrasive size can be determined through the use of the impact intensity versus wheel speed chart (Figure 9). Group A materials may require 0.006-0.014 ft-lb impact intensity; Group B may require 0.001-0.006 ft-lb; and Group C may require up to 0.001 ft-lb. Therefore, the selection of abrasive size will depend upon the wheel speed, as shown by Figure 9.

For example, a steel casting in Group A would probably require an abrasive size between 0.042 and 0.057 with a wheel speed of 2250 rpm. The abrasive size referred to in Figure 9 is, of course, the stabilized size in the machine as screened from a sample taken at the nozzle or hopper discharge chute.

PARTICLE SIZE	NUMBER OF PARTICLES PER LB
0.020	852,000
0.030	252,000
0.040	106,000
0.050	54,000
0.060	31,000

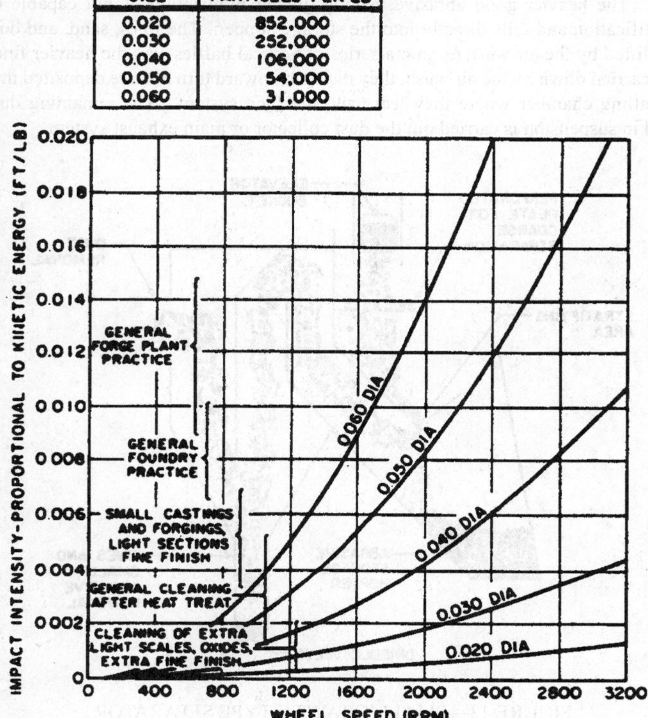

FIGURE 9—IMPACT INTENSITY VERSUS WHEEL SPEEDS FOR VARIOUS SIZE PARTICLES, 19.5 in. DIA STANDARD WHEEL

5.2 Cleaning Practices—The following general cleaning practices are recommended:

5.2.1 The cleaning machine should always be loaded to full capacity in order for the pattern to give proper coverage and to prevent excessive wear on the machine barrel or conveyor.

5.2.2 The frequency of exposure of the parts being cleaned to the abrasive spray is an important factor in minimizing the cleaning cycle time. It is recommended that the action of the parts be investigated, especially in barrel-type machines, and necessary steps be taken to reduce sliding action and to increase tumbling action. In some cases welding steel bars on the barrel or conveyor flights will be sufficient.

5.2.3 Abrasive losses through carry-out can be minimized by tumbling the parts for a predetermined time in batch-type machines, by vibrating parts over a screen in some cases, and by turning by hand or mechanically on the monorail-type machine.

5.2.4 Adjustment and periodic inspection of the blast gate on a gravity-type separator can be facilitated by installing a small spring-mounted screen and air vibrator under the dribble valve to determine effectiveness of the suction in removing the fines from the abrasive without removing useful abrasives. A discharge chute to collect abrasive not passing through the screen can be employed to return the usable material to the cleaning machine.

5.2.5 It is recommended that a production test procedure be established. This procedure will vary somewhat depending upon the type of material being used, type of machine being cleaned, and individual plant practices. However, the data form shown as Figure 10 and the following methods of accumulating and evaluating data may aid in setting up a procedure:

Type Machine ________ Equipment No. ________

Number of Wheels ________ Wheel Speed ________ Wheel Diameter ________

Type of Parts Cleaned ________

Type of Abrasive ________ Abrasive Size ________

Abrasive Source ________ Abrasive Cost/Ton ________

Date	Total Wheel Hours	Cumulative Wheel Hours	Pounds of Abrasive	Cumulative Pounds of Abrasive	Cumulative Abrasive Cost	Cumulative Maintenance Cost

FIGURE 10—PRODUCTION TEST OF ABRASIVE—DATA SHEET

a. The machine wheel hours on an airless blast machine can be accurately determined by installing a time meter on one wheel of the machine. The recorded time must then be multiplied by the number of wheels operating on the machine to determine the total machine wheel hours. A suggested method of wiring is give in Figure 11.

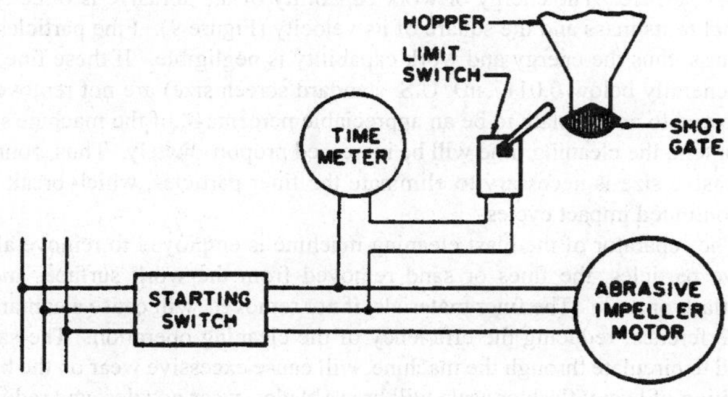

FIGURE 11—WHEEL TIMER

b. An abrasive consumption curve shows graphically not only the abrasive usage rate per wheel hour at any time but also the point at which an abrasive reaches a stabilized condition in the machine. Abrasive cost figures and screen analysis should be based on data obtained beyond the point of stabilization.

Any radical change in the slope of the curve during a test is an indication of excessive abrasive losses, negligence in maintaining the proper abrasive level in the machine, lack of recording new abrasive additions, or defective wheel hour timer circuit. See Figure 12.

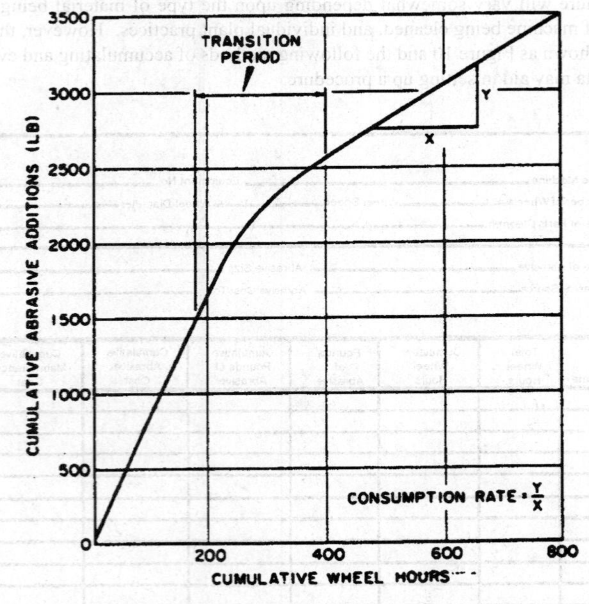

FIGURE 12—ABRASIVE CONSUMPTION CURVE

c. Monthly operating cost figures and/or curves can be generated to show comparative costs of abrasives, maintenance materials, maintenance labor, and productive labor. They can be based on either wheel hours or tons of material cleaned. It must be remembered that two abrasives can be compared economically only if all the direct costs are added into the total operating cost.

6. Production Procedures

6.1 Control of Abrasive Spray Pattern—When setting up a new machine, and periodically during its use, the abrasive spray pattern should be checked. This is done by placing a suitable piece of sheet steel at the same height and in the same position as the work to be cleaned and exposing to the shot blast for a few seconds. Remove and examine the sheet. If the centerline of the shot pattern, as shown on the sheet steel, is not in the center of the work, shift the work location or adjust wheel or nozzle alignment.

6.2 Control of Abrasive Size—Cleaning in a blast cleaning machine is accomplished when sufficient abrasive particles having high velocity impinge on the work surface. The energy or work capability of the abrasive is directly proportional to its mass and the square of its velocity (Figure 9). Fine particles have little mass, thus the energy and work capability is negligible. If these fine particles (generally below 0.0117 in. U.S. standard screen size) are not removed but are allowed to accumulate to be an appreciable percentage of the machine's abrasive content, the cleaning time will be increased proportionately. Thus, control of the abrasive size is necessary to eliminate the finer particles, which break down from continued impact cycles.

The separator of the blast cleaning machine is employed to remove all fine abrasive particles, the fines or sand removed from the work surface, and any heavy flash or scale. The finer materials, if not removed, will cause a contaminating interference, reducing the efficiency of the cleaning operation. The sand, if allowed to circulate through the machine, will cause excessive wear on the blades. Circulation of heavy flash or scale will break blades, wear nozzles, and reduce the life of the machine.

The gravity type separation principle is generally employed in all mechanical type blasting equipment. An air wash or suction from the exhaust system removes the fines, sand, and dust, as this material and the good abrasive fall over the edge of stratifying plates. This type of separator is adjustable so that any size particle can be removed. This adjustment is generally effected by increasing or decreasing the velocity of the air wash by opening or closing baffle plates in the separator exhaust line system.

When adjusting, it is good practice to make a screen analysis of the abrasive as well as the rejected fines. The level of separation should be high enough to remove all fines or sand from the abrasive, and yet low enough so that good abrasive particles (above 0.0117 in. U.S. standard screen size) are not removed from the machine.

In the gravity type system, the abrasive and fines or scale from the work are elevated from a hopper located below the cleaning chamber to the separator above. Coarse separation or the removal of large flash or scale takes place when the elevator bucket content is passed through a perforated plate or screen.

In cases where a greater amount of coarse separation is necessary, a perforated revolving drum replaces the holed plate. The abrasive, fines, or small scale, falls through the drum, while the larger flash or scale carries through to a discharge duct.

After the coarse separation, the abrasive, fines, sand, etc. fall into the fine separating chamber. In one system (Figure 13), this material, after being dispersed by the perforated drum or plate, falls onto an inclined plate. The abrasive, fines, sand, etc. are carried by gravity down the plate and fall over the edge. At this point, the air wash furnished by the exhaust system stratifies the finer material. The heavier good abrasive, having greater momentum, is not capable of stratification and falls directly into the storage hopper. The fines, sand, and dust are lifted by the air wash up into a series of vertical baffles. As the heavier fines are carried down by the air wash, they resist an upward turn and are deposited into a settling chamber where they leave the machine system. The remaining dust held in suspension is carried out the dust collector or main exhaust system.

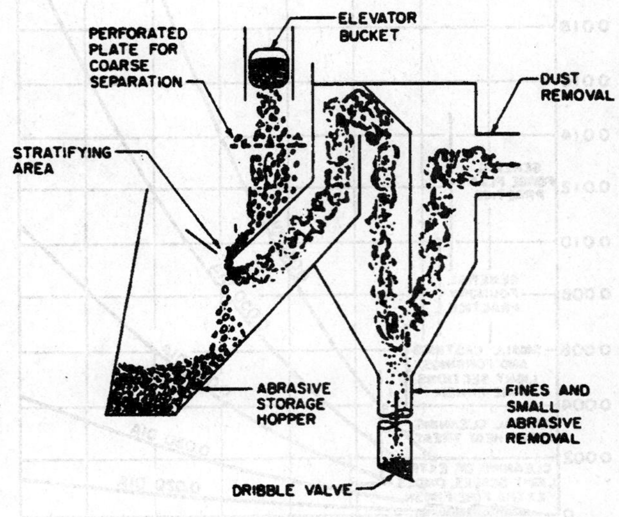

FIGURE 13—SMALL GRAVITY TYPE SEPARATOR

In a second type of gravity system (Figure 14), coarse separation is again effected by a perforated rotating drum or plate. In the fine separation chamber, the material passing through the coarse separator is evenly distributed when it falls through a perforated inclined plate. After being distributed, the particles fall over the edge of a second inclined plate where they become stratified. The material is then conveyed via air and gravity down another incline. As the particles fall over the edge of this plate, the heavier, good particles, having greater momentum, resist the air wash and fall directly into the abrasive storage hopper. The heavier fines are partially turned by the air wash and are deposited into a fines refuse discharge duct. An adjustable skimmer can be regulated to insure that all fines are removed.

Removal of larger or smaller particles is accomplished by adjusting the baffling in the exhaust ducts. The dust collector or main exhaust system (accommodating several machines) draws air from within the machine, causing an air vacuum, which has a dual purpose, that is, to furnish the suction or air wash in the separator to cause stratification of the finer particles and to ventilate the cleaning chamber. Figure 15. Baffles B and C are used to balance the total amount of air removed by the dust collector blower or main exhaust system. Closing baffle C will reduce the air velocity in the separator, but increase the velocity of the cleaning chamber draft. Reducing the air velocity in the separator (closing baffle C) will cause the removal of smaller particles. Increasing the air velocity (opening baffle C) will cause the removal of larger particles. Baffles B or C should never be closed more than halfway, for this will cause abnormal wear on the piping and elbows. If this becomes necessary, baffle A should be closed, reducing the total velocity.

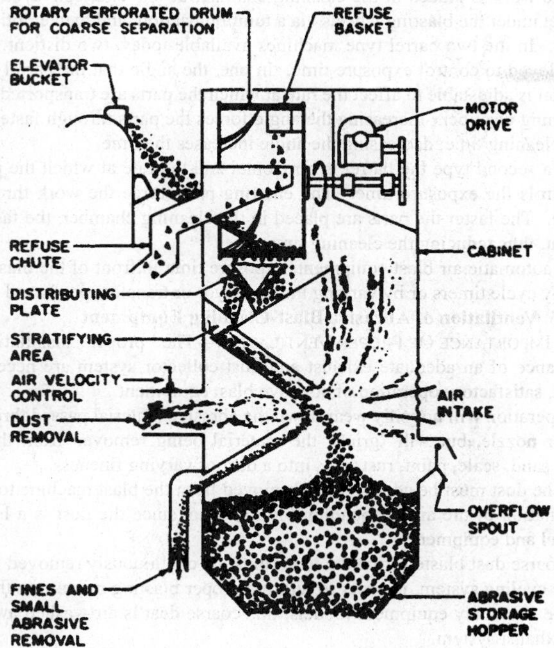

FIGURE 14—LARGE GRAVITY TYPE SEPARATOR

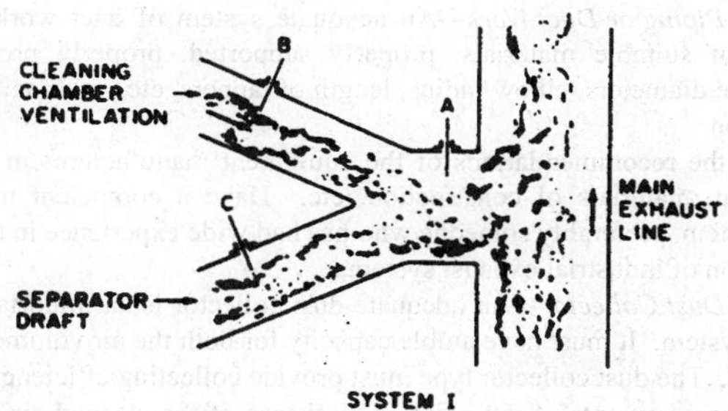

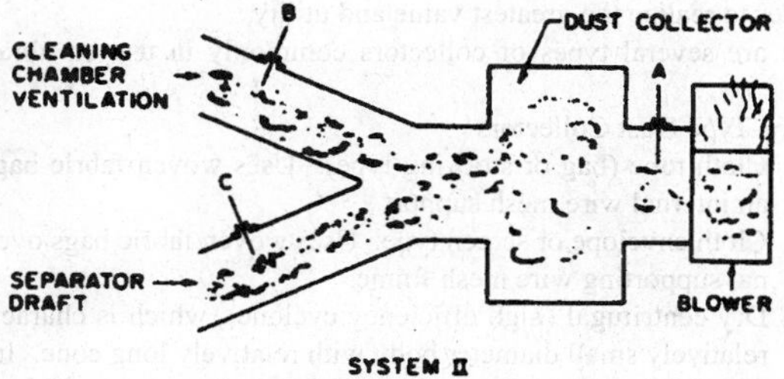

FIGURE 15—SCHEMATIC DRAWING OF PNEUMATIC SYSTEM FOR BLAST CLEANING EQUIPMENT

In large-production cleaning installations, greater quantities of abrasive must be separated. In many cases, the same separator is used but in series of one, two, three, etc. One type of multiple-wheel separator employs a rotating table and centrifugal force to distribute the abrasive, fines, sand, etc. evenly over the outer edge of the table where stratification takes place. The good abrasive falls directly into the storage hopper, while the removal of the fines and dust takes place inside a series of internal vertical cylindrical baffles. The air exhaust line is connected to the inner cylindrical baffle (Figure 16). Control of the abrasive size in these larger separators is again effected by adjusting the baffles located in the exhaust lines.

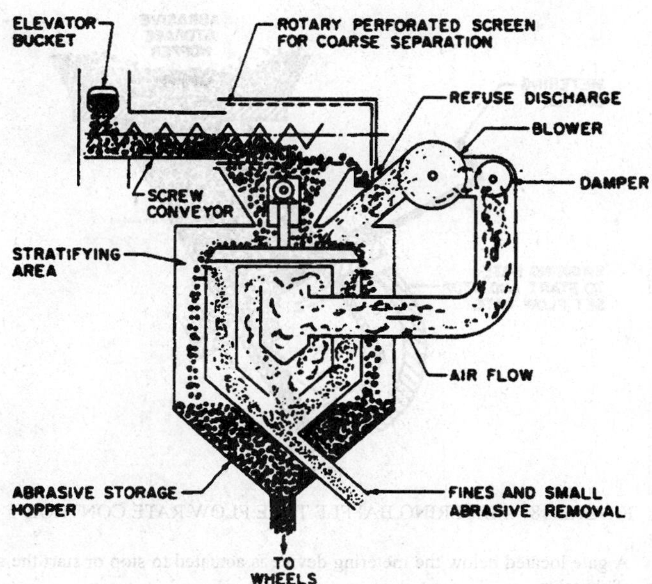

FIGURE 16—ROTARY TYPE SEPARATOR

6.3 Control of Abrasive Flow Rate—Cleaning of the work surface is accomplished by particle impact and by having sufficient particles impinge on the work surface—or sufficient coverage. The impact is influenced by the particle size and its velocity. Coverage is influenced by the overall particle size distribution and by the flow rate. Thus, control of the flow rate is necessary to maintain coverage. Increasing the flow rate will offer greater coverage and tend to reduce the cleaning time.

The rate at which a wheel can throw abrasive is largely dependent on the horsepower rating of the motor that rotates the wheel. Equipment having a 15-hp motor and 191/2 in wheel rotating at 2250 rpm will throw a maximum of approximately 350–400 lb of abrasive per minute. A 25 hp motor with a 191/2 in wheel having a larger wheel opening and rotating at 2250 rpm is capable of throwing 600–650 lb/min. Greater flow rates require larger motors, higher-capacity elevators, etc.

In air blast equipment, the abrasive flow is dependent upon nozzle size and rate of flow.

Control of the flow rate is accomplished by controlling the aperture through which the abrasive must pass. A larger opening will allow a greater amount of abrasive flow, while a smaller opening will reduce the rate.

To change the flow rate of a machine using an orifice plate, a complete plate having a larger or smaller opening must replace the one in use. Figure 17. With the adjustable metering device, the opening can be changed by moving the baffle plate in or out. Figure 18.

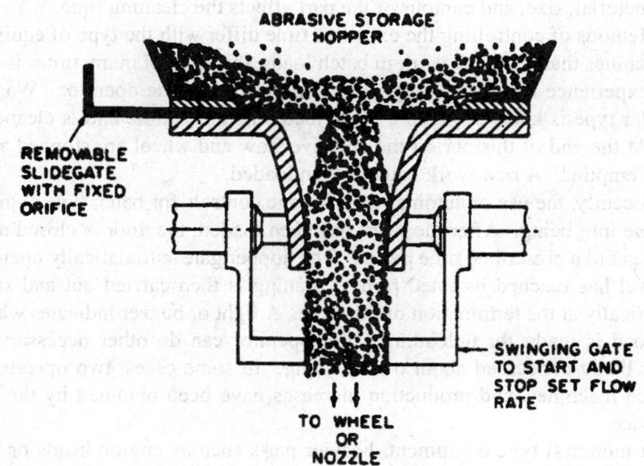

FIGURE 17—ORIFICE TYPE FLOW RATE CONTROL

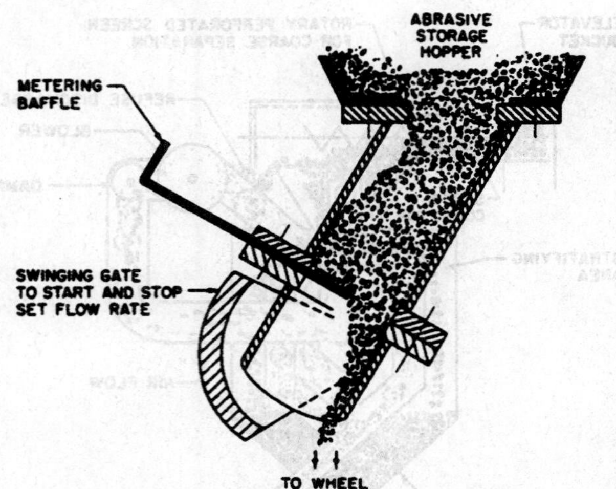

FIGURE 18—METERING BAFFLE TYPE FLOW RATE CONTROL

A gate located below the metering device is actuated to stop or start the set flow of abrasive.

In smaller equipment, where the storage hopper head pressure is not great, an orifice or metering device is not always employed. The flow rate is controlled by merely opening the hopper gate partially or fully. A partially opened gate reduces the rate of flow of the abrasive by diminishing the size of opening at this point.

On a wheel type machine, the motor ampere reading varies with the load on the motor wheel or the abrasive flow rate. The ampere reading then becomes a means of determining the flow rate, once a calibration is made.

A recommended method of determining an unknown flow rate is as follows: catch the abrasive that would normally pass through the control orifice receptacle for a period of 15 s. Weigh this abrasive. Multiplying this weight by a factor of 4 will give the weight in terms of pounds per minute.

6.4 Control of Exposure Time—Overcleaning of the work surface is a costly and unnecessary operation. Exposing the work surface to a blast stream for longer periods of time than necessary results in reduced productivity as well as increased abrasive, maintenance, and labor costs per piece. Underexposure, which allows sand or scale to remain on the work surface, is detrimental to tool life and consequently increases the perishable tool costs in the machine shop. Control then becomes necessary to insure that the work is cleaned properly but without excessive over-exposure.

When cleaning castings, exposure times vary with the size and contour of the work. Smaller parts, which tend to pack close together while being tumbled, or parts with deep cavities generally take a longer cleaning cycle than large, bulky parts. There are some cleaning time differences encountered between castings of the same type, varying pouring temperatures being the cause. High temperatures cause the sand to burn in and become more difficult to remove, necessitating a longer cleaning time. When cleaning forgings, the type of heat treat scale as well as the material, size, and contour of the part affects the cleaning time.

Methods of controlling the exposure time differ with the type of equipment. For machines that clean the work in batch loads, this control many times is left up to the experience of the cleaning room supervisor and the operator. Work of a particular type is known to take a prescribed amount of time and is cleaned that long. At the end of this period the abrasive flow and wheel are stopped and the work is emptied. A new work batch is then loaded.

Recently, the use of automatic cycle time controls for batch type equipment has come into being. After the work has been loaded, the door is closed and the timer is set to a prescribed time period. The hopper gate automatically opens after the wheel has reached its rated rpm. Cleaning is then carried out and stopped automatically at the termination of this time. A light or buzzer indicates when the batch load is ready for unloading. The operator can do other necessary work without being concerned about overcleaning. In some cases, two operators can run three machines, and production increases have been obtained by the use of this device.

In monorail type equipment, heavier parts such as engine heads or blocks are hung onto a monorail hook and carried in front of several blast cleaning wheels. Exposure time is controlled by varying the speed at which the monorail conveys the parts through the machine. In the continuous barrel type of equipment, the work is placed in the cleaning chamber at one end, conveyed through the barrel under the blasting wheels via a tumbling action, and then emptied at the exit end. In the two barrel type machines available today, two distict methods are employed to control exposure time. In one, the angle that the barrel is to the horizontal is adjustable to affect the rate at which the parts are transported through the cleaning chamber. Increasing the angle forces the parts through faster, reducing the cleaning time; decreasing the angle increases the time.

In a second type the barrel is horizontal and the rate at which the parts are fed controls the exposure time. The entering parts force the work through the machine. The faster the parts are placed in the cleaning chamber, the faster they come out, thus reducing the cleaning time.

In automatic air blast equipment, exposure time in front of the blast is controlled by cycle timers or by varying the conveyor or transfer speeds and feeds.

6.5 Ventilation of Abrasive Blast-Cleaning Equipment

6.5.1 IMPORTANCE OF PROPER VENTILATION—The proper installation and maintenance of an adequate exhaust and dust collector system are necessary to efficient, satisfactory operation of abrasive blast equipment.

The operation will not only wear down the abrasive material passed through the wheel or nozzle, but will "grind" the material being removed from the work, whether sand, scale, paint, rust, etc., into a dust of varying fineness.

The fine dust must be continuously removed from the blast machine to prevent contamination of the air surrounding the machine, since the dust is a hazard to personnel and equipment.

The coarse dust blasted from the work must be continuously removed from the abrasive cycling system, in order to return a proper blasting mixture to the wheel or nozzle. In many equipment models, this coarse dust is air-washed away only by the exhaust system.

Dust slows down the cleaning action, increases the length of cleaning cycle, discolors the work, and greatly increases wear.

6.5.2 ELEMENTS OF AN EXHAUST SYSTEM—An exhaust or ventilation system consists of:

6.5.2.1 Piping or Duct Work—An adequate system of duct work must be constructed of suitable materials, properly supported, properly proportioned regarding pipe diameters, elbow radius, length of tappers, etc., and maintained in good condition.

Follow the recommendations of the equipment manufacturer in regard to system design, materials of construction, etc. Have a competent metalsmith install the system, preferably someone who has had wide experience in the design and installation of industrial exhaust systems.

6.5.2.2 Dust Collector—An adequate dust collector is an important part of the exhaust system. It must have ample capacity for both the air volume and dust load involved. The dust collector type must provide collecting efficiency in keeping with the requirements of the point of discharge of the cleaned air. The unit must be operated and serviced in accordance with manufacturers' recommendations in order to realize the greatest value and utility.

There are several types of collectors commonly in use on abrasive blast equipment:

a. Dry-Type Dust Collectors
   1. Cloth tube (bag or stocking type). Uses woven fabric bags without an internal wire mesh support.
   2. Cloth envelope or screen type. Uses woven fabric bags over an internal supporting wire mesh frame.
   3. Dry centrifugal (high efficiency cyclone), which is characterized by relatively small diameter body with relatively long cone. It often has a small constant unit capacity and is usually employed in multiples.
   4. Dry centrifugal ("common" cyclone), which is characterized by relatively large-diameter body with short or medium cone length. Usually, a single unit is employed, with size varying according to capacity required.
   5. Dry dynamic (combination exhauster-collector), which is usually used with trap or precleaner to catch bulk of extremely coarse dust.

b. Wet-Type Dust Collectors
   1. Wet centrifugal, usually in the form of a tower with multiple stages of baffles to provide increased area of wet surfaces for impingement and a tortuous path for the dusty air.
   2. Wet orifice type employing specially shaped passages for the concurrent flow of air and water, plus baffles for impingement. Some models employ power-driven rolls or drums for water.
   3. Wet dynamic type (combination exhauster-collector) often employing a primary chamber for the settling of coarse dust and the storage of collected sludge.

Collector types (a3), (b1), and (b2) must be operated at rated capacity for maximum efficiency. It is wise to provide a gated stub in the pipeline to such a collector to provide make-up air, if necessary.

A central exhaust system serving several machines, possibly of different types, is often used successfully. However, an individual exhaust system for each blast machine is recommended as being a more flexible arrangement.

6.5.2.3 Exhaust Fan and Necessary Drive Equipment—The exhaust fan is the third main component of an exhaust system. There is a limited number of proper types of exhausters. These are: small cast iron or large steel plate "planning mill" exhausters, and large steel plate backward pitched blade exhausters with load limiting characteristics. Less satisfactory types are the propeller fan, "axial" flow fan, and so-called ventilating (low pressure) fans used in comfort air conditioning systems.

The exhaust fan casing and rotor must be whole, and suitably balanced. The rotor must revolve in the right direction (blade tips moving in the same direction as the path of air coming from the outlet) and the rotor must be located from side to side in the casing, according to manufacturer's recommendation. The drive must operate with minimum slippage. Direct-connected fans are seldom used. A V-belt drive with overhung sheave is the popular type of drive.

6.5.3 ADJUSTMENT OF AN EXHAUST SYSTEM—An abrasive blast exhaust system should be adjusted so that the machine surroundings are visibly clean during the blasting cycle, and so that the abrasive is nearly free from fines and dust. However, this condition may never be achieved if the machine dust seals, etc., are not in a first class condition. It is also possible to process work so abnormally dirty as to be beyond the capacity of the abrasive separator and any reasonable size of exhaust system.

6.5.3.1 Abrasive Separators—There are three basic types of abrasive separators used on blast equipment. These are as follows: gravity separator, closed-cycle gravity separator, and rotary separator. Their function is to airwash useless fines and dust from the abrasive stream after they have been spent against the work. The basic operation of the three types is the same: the abrasive is cascaded in a spreadout stream or curtain over the end of an inclined shed plate. Air is exhausted through this stream into a duct under this shed plate. An expansion chamber within the separator settles out a coarse fraction of the sand or scale. This is discharged through a dribble (airlock) valve, and flexible tubing, to a floor box. In the gravity separator, all the exhausted air passes to the exhaust system. In the closed-cycle gravity and rotary separators (having an integral exhaust fan independent of the ventilating system) the air is returned to the separator, except for a controllable fraction, which is bypassed into the exhaust system. The separators with integral fans will remove coarse contaminants, with a fixed airflow, independent of the exhaust system. The bypass into the exhaust system reduces the recycling fine dust to a satisfactory level.

An uneven or discontinuous curtain of abrasive over the shed plate will upset the separator operation. With a proper curtain, the separator blast gate (gravity separator) should be opened to the point of carrying over a detectable amount of full sized shot or grit, then backed off slightly. A proper blasting mixture will include fractions of smaller-than-full-size new abrasive, up to the fifth smaller commercial size. However, it is false economy to try to hold the bulk of finer metallic particles in the stream. The fraction settled out in the separator expansion should be thrown away, or used in an operation requiring smaller abrasive. It should not be returned to the same machine. If it is necessary to return it to the same machine to economize on abrasion, the separator is improperly adjusted. If the discharge of the settled material is dusty, open the adjustable sleeve on the dribble valve just enough to offset this condition.

6.5.3.2 Abrasive Elevators—The blast gate in the duct from the elevator should be opened only enough to prevent escape of dust into the room.

6.5.3.3 Abrasive Blasting Chamber—There are three general types of exhaust arrangements for blast machines. These are:

a. Baffled outlet on top of the machine (self draining into the top of the cabinet) with the exhaust duct leading to the line-size abrasive trap installed in the horizontal run of the exhaust duct, the trap located to drain back into the machine through the dribble (airlock) valve and the flexible hose.
b. Tapered outlet (nonbaffled) on top of the machine with the exhaust duct leading to the oversize abrasive trap located as above.
c. Expansion box (usually internal) large enough to eliminate the need of auxiliary traps or baffles. The duct from the top of the expansion leads directly to the dust collector.

If abrasive traps are used, and if the internal baffle is adjustable, the bottom of the baffle should be one-fourth the diameter of the trap pipe opening above the bottom of the opening or collar. If an oversize trap is used, the inlet connection must be a long taper from pipe diameter to trap diameter. An identical taper should be used on the trap outlet, if space is available. The blast gate(s) should be open enough to provide clean surroundings during the blasting cycle. All trap reclaim should be returned to the machine.

6.5.3.4 Blast Gates—Standard slide type blast gates are usually used in all branch exhaust lines from blast equipment. These gates should always be as remote from the machine collar as possible, should never be located between machine collar and abrasive trap, and should always be installed with the slide travel horizontal. Usually, these branch gates are used only for balancing the exhaust between the various branch pipes. If closed more than halfway, abnormal wear on piping and elbows will result. They should never be used for throttling an abnormal capacity system. Either throttle the fan inlet or outlet or a separate collector system, or install a throttle gate in the machine main duct at its junction with the large main of a central exhaust system.

6.5.4 CARE OF A CLOTH-TYPE COLLECTOR—These instructions are necessarily brief and are recommended unless they conflict with the directions supplied by the manufacturer:

6.5.4.1 Care—Daily Attention

a. Hoppers should be emptied daily when the exhaust fan is not operating. Shaker devices should be operated before emptying the hoppers, not after. Make sure that the hoppers are clean; do not presume that the hoppers are empty just because dust stops flowing. Make sure that the hopper vales are closed after emptying, before the exhauster is started again.
b. Shaker devices should be operated every 4 h if possible, for about 21/2 min, when the exhaust fan is not operating. If your collector is equipped with an automatic shaker timer, the shakers will operate each time the exhauster is shut off; after an automatic time delay to allow the exhauster to coast to a stop. If you should start the exhauster before the automatic cycle is completed, the shaking will stop instantly, and the timer will reset for the next cycle.

If your collector is equipped with a draft gage indicating draft loss through the cloth, then, as a general rule, when the draft gage shows 2 in differential pressure through the bags (one side of the manometer to the clean air side and the other to the dirty air side), it is time to operate the shaker devices.

6.5.4.2 Lubrication—The fan and shaker device should be lubricated once a month (where lubrication fittings are provided), under normal service, with a good ball-bearing grease. The fan and shaker motors should be lubricated according to the maker's instructions, or according to your shop practice.

6.5.4.3 General Attention—It is well to inspect the interior of the collector at regular intervals, watching for worn bags or envelopes, and to check on the mechanical condition of the shaker device. Baffle plates should be replaced when worn appreciably.

6.5.5 CONCLUSION—The exhaust and collector system for an abrasive blast machine is necessary to achieve the maximum production, minimum costs and best quality of work.

Proper care of the exhaust and collector system is less expensive and provides more satisfaction than haphazard care.

*7. **Inspection***—Inspection for cleanliness of castings or forgings is a rather undefinable procedure. Cleanliness in itself is a relative matter, and the degree of cleanliness desired for a certain piece of work is reasonably indeterminate and not readily specified. However, before one can inspect, he must have some specification and idea of the actual requirements. This information is usually supplied by the process department or the division that will perform the next operation on the parts. There is no generalized specification that can be applied to suit any or all conditions.

The best and most widely used means of inspection for cleanliness of any type of work is visual inspection. Here, the inspector observes the surface conditions of the casting or forging or other type of work to see if they meet the established requirements. If the workpiece is a casting, visual inspection would consist of looking for sand on the critical areas or perhaps on all surfaces, depending on the nature of the end use. In intricate castings with considerable core work, it is sometimes possible to be lenient on the complete removal of sand from the hard-to-get-at-places, provided such leniency does not affect the final usage of the casting.

Certain methods of inspection are used other than visual observation. One of these is the scratch test. A chisel or sharp instrument is used to scratch a critical area of a casting to determine if the sand has been completely removed. Burned-in sand will appear as a white mark as the sharp instrument scratches over it, while the metal will appear in the normal dark color.

Another test used on ferrous castings or forgings or other types of work is the copper sulphate test. Here, a concentrated solution of copper sulphate in water is applied with an eye dropper or small brush to the surface of the work. Scale that has not been removed from the work will appear black, while a clean area will "plate-out" copper color. This test is rather widely used.

Another test commonly used for gray iron sand castings (especially bathtubs and other sanitary ware) is the heating up of the casting to a cherry red temperature and then allowing the casting to cool—this procedure is called "burning-in." Here, any sand that is left on the surface will appear very light gray, while the remainder of the casting will be black. This clearly indicates the amount of sand on the surface of the casting.

Other requirements for inspection may include surface roughness and type of etch. In castings (both ferrous and nonferrous), as well as forgings and roll-steel products, there are many instances where the surface roughness of the final cleaned product is of considerable importance. This is defined by the requirements of the parts in question, and it is a good idea to have a comparator sample to use. This specimen would be a sample of the type of surface desired that will permit visual inspection to see if it has been attained. Considerable care and judgment should be exercised in preparing the comparator so that it will properly serve its purpose. If the surface condition is of little or no importance, this should be disregarded.

It is important to remember that any inspection is no better than the inspector performing the operation, and he can only do a good job if he has a thorough knowledge of the requirements.

8. Maintenance of Blast Cleaning Equipment—Maintenance in manufacturing plants consists of keeping equipment in condition for efficient plant operation. In blast cleaning, maintenance costs may amount to one-third the total cost of the operation. Preventive maintenance is recommended on this equipment.

Some of the important items that should be checked regularly are as follows:

1. Any abrasive that has spilled or accumulated around the machine should be cleaned up and returned to use.
2. Keep the machine loaded so that this loading will protect exposed parts and reduce the wear on them. If the loading is not continuous the abrasive should be shut off.
3. Proper abrasive flow must be maintained for the type of abrasive used, and abrasives must be kept free of any particles which might clog the regular flow.
4. Set up cleaning cycles, whenever possible, so that the parts are not run longer than necessary.
5. The abrasive should be added at regular intervals and in relation to the amount of fines rejected. Keep the abrasive supply hopper full.
6. In wheel type equipment the blades should be checked regularly and replacements made so as not to cause the wheel to become unbalanced.
7. Ventilating and dust systems must be properly adjusted for good operation. When dust is not controlled it will create hazardous working conditions, possibly damage other equipment in the vicinity and reduce the cleaning efficiency of the machine. The exhaust system should be finely adjusted so that all the dust is removed but none of the abrasive is carried out.
8. The shell of the machine should be kept tight to prevent loss of abrasive and damage to other parts.
9. An inspection chart can be kept on the job to remind those responsible what attention should be given to the machine regularly.

9. Testing of Shot Life in the Laboratory—During the past few years, there has been a good deal of work done on the problem of life testing of shot particles. This work covers not only the mechanics of testing, but the pooling of ideas of various users, so as to establish a common understanding and a common language as regards shot testing.

It is generally agreed that breaking the shot up by subjecting it to repeated impacts under its own momentum gives results most likely to correlate with service performance. Accordingly, drop-hammer impact tests, ball mill tests, crushing tests, etc., are regarded as unsatisfactory.

Testing machines, devices to subject the shot particles to impacts due to their own momentum, have been developed and are described later.

It is the purpose of this section to describe how these machines may be used.

All these machines have a means of accelerating the shot particles to velocities likely to be encountered in service, (about 200 fps), and some sort of target, which the shot particles strike. The sample to be tested, therefore, is repeatedly accelerated to some velocity and subjected to the impact of striking a target. The number of times that the shot particle can be subjected to such punishment before failure is the value that is measured.

What constitutes failure is a question that is answered by definition. Needless to say, this definition has gradually changed and is still subject to debate. Its importance, however, is not great unless comparative data with other laboratories are intended.

The punishment that a particular single shot particle can endure before failure is easy enough to determine. One would simply count the number of times that this particular particle could be subjected to a given number of impacts without failure. In this case, however, we are confronted with a sample that has hundreds or even thousands of particles. So it is necessary to determine the average life of the group of particles.

The procedure usually follows this pattern:

1. A sample that is as nearly representative of the whole as possible is obtained.
2. This sample is put through standard sieves and separated into the various sizes.
3. A sample of 100 gr is taken from the sieve holding the largest proportion of the original sample.
4. This 100 gr is then put into the shot tester. As it passes through the tester, it is subjected to several impacts. In the case of the American Wheelabrator machine or the Pangborn machine, the sample is collected in a cup after making one pass. It is then hoisted, either mechanically or manually, to the feeding funnel and introduced for the second pass, etc. The number of passes is counted. In the case of the Alloy Metal Abrasive machine, the repetition of blows is automatic and is proportional to time. The number of passes is counted.
5. After a predetermined number of passes or time, the sample is removed from the tester and screened, using screens with selected opening sizes. The selection of screen opening size depends upon the definition of failure. Since shot is used mainly for blast cleaning purposes and shotpeening purposes, we use the following definitions of failure:
   a. For blast cleaning, the shot particles are considered broken when they pass through a screen with an opening of 0.0117 in, (No. 50 U.S. standard sieve), for shot of sizes SAE 230 and over. For the smaller sizes of shot, a screen with an opening of 0.0049 in, (No. 120 U.S. standard), is used. The choice is made because some production machines discard material when such degree of smallness is reached.
   b. For shotpeening, the particles are considered broken when they pass through a screen with an opening next in line smaller in the U.S. standards than the sieve that held the material at the beginning of the test. For example, suppose the 100 gr sample to be tested was held initially on a sieve with an opening of 0.033 in; then the sieve to be used for measuring the breakdown would be one with an opening of 0.028 in. The choice of this definition of broken material for peening is based on the premise that full sized and uniform particles are wanted in a controlled peening operation, though it is acknowledged that this is sometimes impractical.

   If shot testing is to be done with some particular production machine in mind, the definition of failure, and hence the size of "breakdown" screen used in the test, should correspond with the size of the material being discarded as useless by the machine.
6. The data obtained from the sieve analysis are plotted on a chart such as Figure 19, which shows the per cent broken versus the life in passes or time.
7. Repeating the testing and separation of broken particles from the good particles, as many points as desired can be obtained to establish this curve.

Now comes the question of how this curve should be interpreted. We want an expression for the average life, because shot is fed into the production machine on the basis of average life. For a true value of the average life, this curve must be established accurately and completely—that is, until all the particles are failed (see peening breakdown curve, Figure 19). From the curve, one can see that some of the particles are weak and break down quickly, while others last a long time. To find the average life, it is necessary to add up the individual lives of all the particles and to divide by the total number of particles. This can be done by measuring the area under the curve and dividing by the height of the diagram.

Since curves for different shot materials are quite similar in nature, an approximation of the average life can be obtained by determining the life at the point where 55% of the sample is broken.[3] The value of 55% was established experimentally by measuring a number of typical diagrams.

To continue, there are definite liberties which can be taken, deviating from what has been said. For example, for testing incoming shipments of material, it would only be necessary to run the sample for some predetermined number of passes and measure the percentage of shot that is still good, provided that the selected number of passes is near the 55% breakdown point. A specification can be readily set up for this type of inspection.

---

3. From SAE Iron and Steel Technical Committee, Division 20.

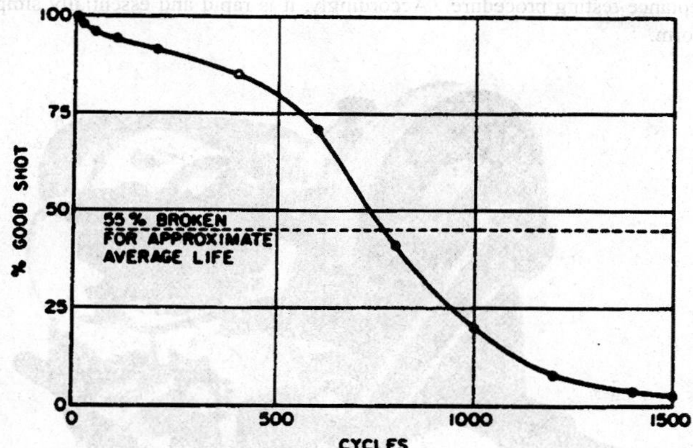

FIGURE 19—TYPICAL BREAKDOWN CURVE

It is not to be construed that these life tests tell the whole story about the performance of shot in blast cleaning operations. Proper consideration must be given to hardness. No specific tests have been devised to measure the influence of hardness on cleaning ability because no one knows how to measure cleaning ability. However, there have been experiences in the field that indicate the importance of hardness. When malleablized iron shot first made its appearance, there was some dissatisfaction with its performance as a cleaning medium because it did not knock the material off that was to be removed. A similar experience was had with the early cast steel shot. It can be appreciated that, in order to break or cut the scale from the surface, the stress at the instant of contact must be great enough to exceed the breaking strength. If a particle flattens out when it hits the work surface, it cannot produce the same stress as a particle that stays reasonably sharp. Long fatigue life can be obtained with relatively soft material, but its cleaning ability is also low. A compromise, then, must be made between the life and the hardness. Good results seem to be obtained with shot of "spring" hardness.

9.1 Shot Testing Machines—As a result of committee activities directed toward establishing a common testing procedure for shot quality, there are at present four testing machines. These are described here in the order in which they appeared.

9.1.1 AMERICAN WHEELABRATOR SHOT TESTER—The shot tester developed and used at American Wheelabrator and Equipment Corp. consists of a centrifugal wheel 4 5/16 in. in diameter. The wheel is driven by a 1/2-hp electric motor by means of an adjustable-speed belt drive. The wheel speed is adjustable between 5000 and 10,000 rpm in order to obtain the influence of wheel speed on the life of shot. The handle at the rear of the tester is attached to an adjusting screw for selecting the desired speed.

Surrounding the wheel is a specially designed, hardened-steel target. This target is provided with internal teeth, somewhat like an internal gear. Figure 20 shows a cross section of the wheel and target. The teeth of the target are inclined at a helix angle of 15 deg for the purpose of deflecting the shot into the hopper below, to prevent rebound of shot back into the wheel.

9.1.2 PANGBORN EV-1 SHOT TESTER—The Pangborn shot tester (Figure 21) is a small laboratory machine developed for the purpose of comparing different types of abrasive by means of a breakdown test.

It is a vertical type of tester with a centrifugal wheel 4-1/2 in. in diameter mounted on a vertical spindle, which runs on ball bearings. The wheel rotates counterclockwise (when looking into the wheel from the top of the machine).

The speed of the wheel is adjustable from 0–10,500 rpm. At 9315 rpm the abrasive is propelled at a speed equal to that of a standard 19-1/2 in wheel running at a standard speed of 2150 rpm.

The drive for the wheel is mounted in the bottom of the cast-aluminum housing of the machine. The blasting compartment, which is lined with rubber, is in the top.

The blasting compartment has a bottom, which slopes 45 deg into an outlet spout, on the end of which is inserted the receptacle receiving the abrasive after it has passed through the wheel.

A 1/3 hp, 12,000 rpm Universal motor drives the wheel. It is located directly under the spindle and connected to it by a flexible coupling. A pickup unit, driven from the vertical spindle through a belt, is also mounted in the bottom of the housing. This pickup unit registers the speed of the wheel on a speed indicator mounted on the front of the machine.

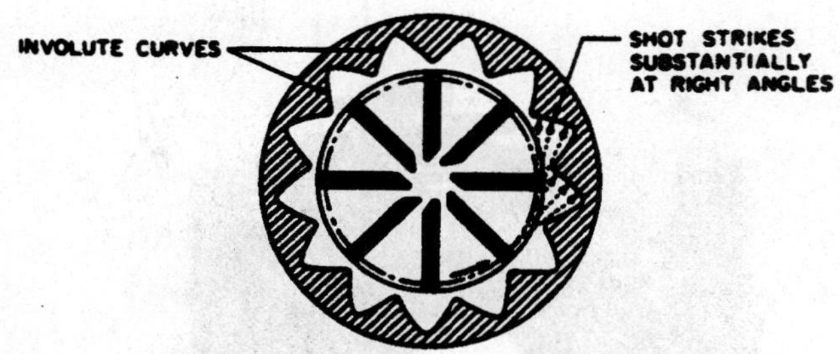

FIGURE 20—SHOT TESTER—WHEEL AND TARGET

A hinged cover, mounted on the top of the housing, allows access to the blasting compartment. The anvil is mounted on the bottom side of this hinged cover and has a 17-1/2 deg angle surface on which the shot, hurled from the wheel, is impacted.

Mounted on the outside and in the center of the hinged cover is a cone-shape receptable with a removable orifice in the bottom for feeding the abrasive uniformly to the center of the wheel.

Several instruments and controls are mounted on the front of the machine: a speed indicator for registering the speed of the wheel, a voltage controller for adjusting the speed of the wheel, a counter for registering the number of passes of shot or abrasive through the machine, an on and off switch for starting and stopping the motor, and a fuse to protect the motor.

The machine is equipped with an extension cord, which can be plugged into any 110 V light circuit.

9.1.3 ALLOY METAL ABRASIVE CO. SHOT TESTER—This machine was developed to give accurate breakdown results and do the job automatically and obtain accurate results in a comparatively short time. It has a recycling device that returns the material to the beater wheel, which is used for accelerating the shot against an anvil. This machine is shown in Figures 22 and 23; it operates automatically. The shot particles are accelerated by means of a belt-driven wheel, and the axis of rotation is horizontal. The target is inclined at a slight angle to the direction of discharge from the beater wheel. This anvil is driven by a separate motor by means of a belt and rotates about the same axis as the beater.

The Alloy Metal Abrasive shot tester machine has the following features:

9.1.3.1 All the small broken down material is removed from the machine by an air circulating device.

9.1.3.2 The machine approximates the same conditions as are experienced in the commercial blasting machine.

9.1.3.3 It has a positive feed control, which automatically passes the material through a definite cycle without variations.

9.1.3.4 The machine is powered to maintain constant speed, which discharges the shot at approximately 200 fps, which corresponds to the same velocity as experienced in the commercial blasting machine.

9.1.3.5 This machine will make a complete and accurate breakdown test in a comparatively short time, even for long life materials.

9.1.3.6 The machine is equipped with a counter register, which records the number of material passes through the machine.

9.1.3.7 The operation other than charging and discharging the material is automatic.

9.1.3.8 The charging and discharging the material from the machine requires only the removal of a rubber plug.

9.1.3.9 The machine will operate under normal conditions for many months without altering the test results.

9.1.3.10 The energy delivered by throwing 100 g at 200 fps, 25 times/min, approximates 60 ft-lb/s. This machine is powered with a 1/2 hp, 110 V motor.

9.1.3.11 The machine is hand portable and equipped with attached handles for easy carrying.

9.1.3.12 The approximate machine time required for the test of a 100 g sample broken down to a 0.010 size is as follows:

a. Hard iron: 7 min.
b. Steel: 60 min.

For a 50 g sample, the machine speed can be increased from 7000 rpm spindle speed to 10,000, and the time required reduced to one-half, which shows machine breakdown time for:

a. Hard iron: 3-1/2 min.
b. Steel: 30 min.

FIGURE 21—PANGBORN SHOT TESTER

9.1.3.13 This machine minimizes all the variables that are experienced when attempting to make the test in commercial blasting equipment.

9.2 Shot Acceptance Testing Method—The following shot testing method was developed by Division XX, Mechanical Prestressing of Metals, of the SAE Iron and Steel Technical Committee as a means of measuring the relative quality of shot materials used for blast cleaning and shotpeening. In this test, the particles are subjected to repeated impact in a manner similar to that in production shotpeening and blast cleaning machines, and the resulting failure of the shot particles is similar in nature. In actual shotpeening and blast cleaning machines, however, there are many additional factors that influence the useful life of these materials—hence, this property alone should not be considered as the sole criterion of the utility of any particular shot material.

The test is primarily designed to serve as one of the tests in a more general acceptance testing procedure. Accordingly, it is rapid and essentially simple to perform.

FIGURE 22—ALLOY METAL ABRASIVE CO. SHOT TESTER

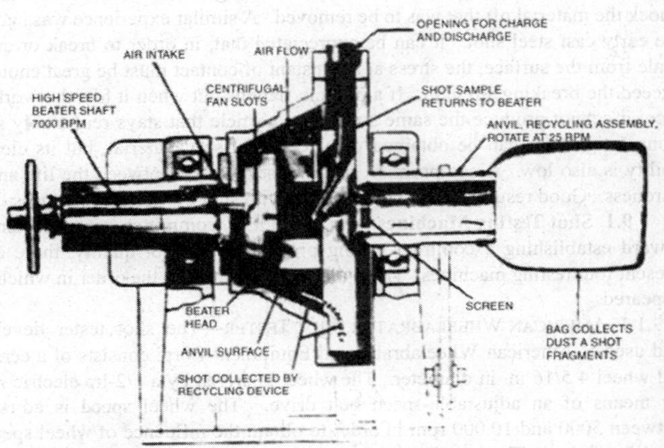

FIGURE 23—ALLOY METAL ABRASIVE CO. SHOT TESTER

10. Measuring Shot Blasting Machine Efficiency—A test method has been developed to aid in the evaluation of the operation of blast machine when using the various shot on the market today. The test is based on the measure of shot consumption versus time, tonnage cleaned, or wheel hours. The significant figures are pounds of shot consumed per hour of operation, pounds per ton cleaned, pounds per wheel hour; or the reciprocals of these figures. At the same time that shot consumption is being recorded, the amount of maintenance is usually recorded. Maintenance variations with different shots are as important, costwise, as shot consumption variations.

The test method has been designed to show the rate of shot consumption versus the previously mentioned units as a plotted curve. This graphically plotted curve, under ideal cleaning conditions, is a straight line. The usual curve measured under normal operating conditions with normal variables, etc., gives an excellent approximation of a straight line with the daily and weekly variables being evident; this feature being desirable in that the variables are apparent as to when they occur. The steps involved in developing such a curve are as follows:

1. Record each addition of shot by recording the weight of the addition and the operating hours since the last addition. If shot is added every day, record daily shot additions and daily hours of operation. This is simplified if an elapsed-time recording clock is connected to the shotblast equipment so that the clock operates when the machine operates. Clock readings taken when shot is added will show hours of operation between additions.
2. On a computation sheet accumulate the daily shot additions and the elapsed times, so that the latest figure in each column shows the total shot added since the test began, and the total hours of operation since the test began.

3. On graph paper, plot these accumulated shot totals versus the respective accumulated hours of operation. This will generate a rate curve. Dips and jumps in the curve indicate the effects of machine conditions, operating personnel, etc. The "straightness" of this rate curve generally indicates that the test is accurate. The idiosyncrasies that cause the curve to veer show up as soon as they occur and also show to what extent they alter the rate of shot consumption. Because one knows when they happen they can be quickly and effectively dealt with.

Figure 24 shows a typical methods test. This test was run on a 5-wheel cabinet cleaning complex, large, cored gray-iron castings. The manner in which this machine was operated involved the use of an inventory of 20 tons of shot in and about the machine. As you will note from the curve, it took approximately 20 tons of addition of new material before the old shot has been completely "flushed" and the effect of the new was felt. Within a week after the "turn" the lower usage of the new material was evident. The minor dips and curves show mainly the inaccuracy of the operator in judging the amount of shot necessary to add. The major jump at 600 h was due to the addition of a second shift on the cleaning operation. The work of the second shift was stacked until the next day and in that stack was a considerable amount of carryout. This carryout is all reclaimed and will be returned to the system when this type of two-shift operation ceases. You will note that the new rate of shot consumption continues after this large jump.

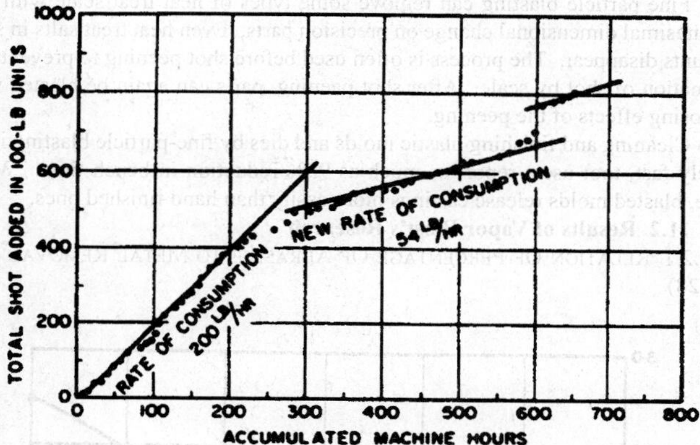

FIGURE 24—TYPICAL METHODS TEST

Figure 25 shows the operating curve of two identical shot peening machines operating side by side on different shots. The machines are 2-wheel automatic conveyor machines. These curves show that shot breaks down at a definite rate, regardless of operating disturbances. Rate of breakdown A is constant regardless of the two gaps where no record was made of shot additions. These gaps are so wide that if no shot had been added, as it appears, the machine would have exhausted itself and ceased to operate. Rate B is the effect of a new shipment of the same type of shot that was used during rate A. Rate C is from the second machine, which used a premium shot. The erratic behavior of the beginning of the curve was due to the shot stabilizing and the flushing of the previous shot. The jump just before rate C starts was due to an arbitrary raising of the shot level in the equipment. The level was arbitrarily raised again by 400 lb midway along the rate C line.

Figure 26 shows the comparison of operating features using four different shots in the same machine. A batch type airless blast machine was used to clean miscellaneous forgings.

This was a straightforward, easily and quickly determined test, using various sizes of shot, and consumption rates for cleaning a variety of forgings. On the shot C curve around 180 h there was a quick rise in shot consumption. Upon inspection of the equipment a large leak was found. The leak was plugged and the shot reclaimed. The next point fell on the curve where it belonged.

Figure 27 shows the cost per ton cleaned when using four shots whose rates where shown by Figure 26. During the time the four shots were run tabulations were kept on the amount of material cleaned, the amount of maintenance on the machine, and the cleaning rates of the shots. It was then an easy matter to gather the cost per ton cleaned.

These four illustrations and the data shown by each are an accurate representation of the operating conditions of these machines. None of the tests took an extremely long time to show the change in costs due to a change in shot. This test method can be used to show the effects of change in wheel speed, change in shot size, change in materials handling techniques, etc. It is not limited to showing effects of change in shot only.

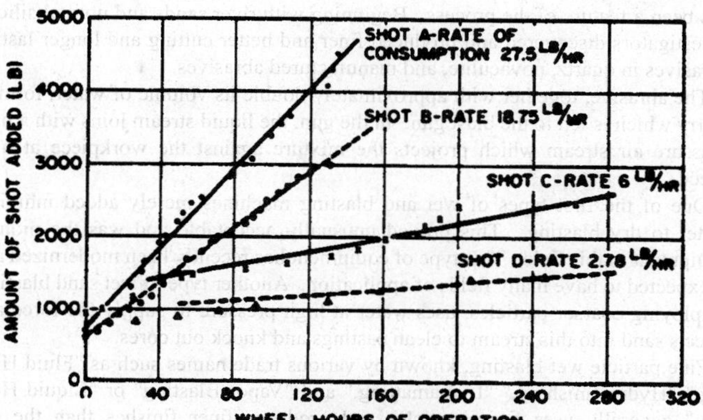

FIGURE 25—CURVE OF IDENTICAL SHOT PEENING MACHINES OPERATING ON DIFFERENT SHOTS

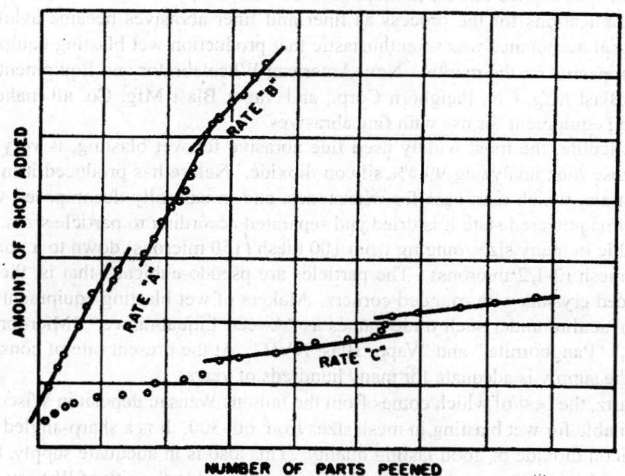

FIGURE 26—COMPARISON OF OPERATING FEATURES OF 4 DIFFERENT SHOTS

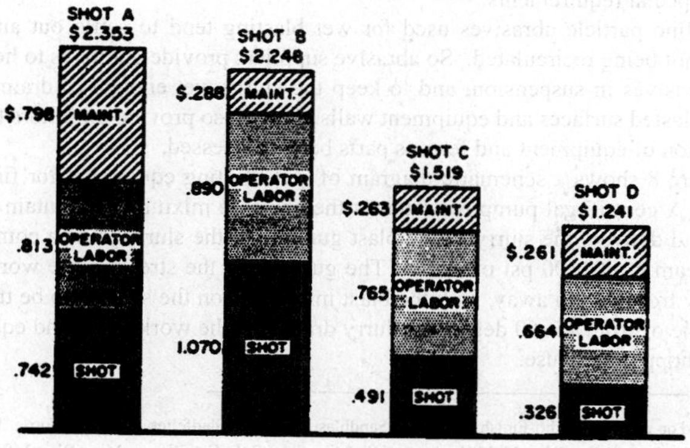

FIGURE 27—COST PER TON USING VARIOUS SHOTS

***11. Wet Blasting with Fine Particles*[4]**—Blasting with fine particles suspended in a liquid has become an important process in cleaning and producing better finishes on many products these days. The functional finishes produced by this process have aided in the development of improved tool performance, better lubrication, better plate adherence, and improvements in many processing techniques.

The development of a wide range of compositions, types, and sizes of abrasive has been a feature of the process. Beginning with river sands and normal silicas, investigators discovered and produced finer and better cutting and longer lasting abrasives in quartz, novaculite, and manufactured abrasives.

The abrasive, together with approximately double its volume of water, forms a slurry which is fed to the blast gun. In the gun, the liquid stream joins with a high pressure air stream which projects the mixture against the workpiece at high speed.

One of the first types of wet and blasting machines merely added inhibited water to dry blasting. This proved unusually acceptable and was the pioneer equipment in this field. This type of equipment has recently been modernized and is expected to have many fields of application. Another type of wet sand blasting, employing coarser particles, uses water at high pressure to supply the force and injects sand into this stream to clean castings and knock out cores.

Fine particle wet blasting, known by various trade names such as "Fluid Honing," "Hydro finishing," "Liquamatting," and "Vapor Blasting" or "Liquid Honing," generally uses finer particles and produces finer finishes than the dry blasting process.

The art of blasting, both wet and dry, dates back into the 1800's. Fresh impetus was given wet blasting with fine particles in 1934 by A. H. Eppler, who pioneered in the development of special equipment for this purpose. Working with C. T. Strauss, who owned Arkansas mines of novaculite, Eppler found new and valuable applications for the process as finer and finer abrasives became available. Industrial acceptance was so enthusiastic that production wet blasting equipment soon appeared on the market. Now American Wheelabrator and Equipment Co., MicroBlast Mfg. Co., Pangborn Corp., and Vapor Blast Mfg. Co. all make wet blasting equipment for use with fine abrasives.

Novaculite, the most widely used fine abrasive for wet blasting, is very hard quartzose rock analyzing 99.4% silicon dioxide. Nature has produced it in very firm strata, which man uses for whetstones, and in naturally decomposed veins. From this powered state it is dried and separated according to particle sizes. It is available in many sizes ranging from 100 mesh (150 microns) down to a nominal 5000 mesh (2-1/2 microns). The particles are pseudo-cubical—that is, they are six-faced crystals with rounded corners. Makers of wet blasting equipment market novaculite under such trade names as "Aweco Liquabrasive," "Microbrasive MNH," "Pangbornite," and "Vapor Blast NVB." At the present rate of consumption, the supply is adequate for many hundreds of years.

Quartz, the best of which comes from the famous Wausau deposit in Wisconsin, is available for wet blasting in mesh sizes from 60–300. It is a sharp-angled crystal silicon dioxide of good lasting quality. This also is in adequate supply, being so plentiful that the owners donated half of the deposit to the city of Wausau, Wisconsin, to make the famous Rib Hill recreation grounds and Ski Hill.

Other natural siliceous abrasives, made from pulverized silicas and river sands, are also used in wet blasting and are in ample supply. Manufactured abrasives such as aluminum oxide and silicon carbide are also used for fast cutting and other special requirements.

All fine particle abrasives used for wet blasting tend to settle out and pack, when not being recirculated. So abrasive suppliers provide additives to help keep the abrasives in suspension, and to keep the slurry wet enough to drain rapidly from blasted surfaces and equipment walls. They also provide inhibitors to retard corrosion of equipment and ferrous parts being processed.

Figure 8 shows a schematic diagram of wet blasting equipment for fine abrasives. A centrifugal pump recirculates the abrasive mixture to maintain suspension and delivers the slurry to the blast gun. Here the slurry joins a compressed air stream at 80–100 psi pressure. The gun shoots the stream a the work piece, usually from 1–3 in away, with the blast impinging on the surface to be treated at an angle of from 45–60 deg. The slurry drains off the work piece and equipment to the hopper for reuse.

4. Based on papers, "Hydro-Finish and Hydro Sandblast," by W. I. Gladfelter, Pangborn Corp.; "Fine Particle Blasting or MicroBlast Fluid Honing and Finishing," by E. E. Hawkinson, MicroBlast Mfg. Corp.; and "Fine Particle Blasting—Wet," by A. P. Neumann and V. W. Nichols, Vapor Blast Mfg. Co. These papers were presented at a meeting of Division 20—Shotpeening, Hot Springs, Va., Sept. 25, 1952. Division 20 is a part of the SAE Iron and Steel Technical Committee. Article reprinted from SAE Journal, October, 1953.

The operator manipulates the gun and work piece through armholes in the front of the machine with gloved hands. To keep his vision port or window clear from abrasive-laden fog, he presses a knee control which activates a clear water spray. The filter in the exhaust system is also spray washed to keep it functioning at good performance levels. To start or stop the blast and to control the air pressure, the operator presses another knee valve.

Machines have been built using several differing techniques, such as air agitation for abrasive suspension and venturi action for delivery of slurry to gun, but pumps have proved more efficient and economical for both purposes.

Delivery of the slurry to the gun under pressure (from pressurized tank or by pressure pumping) has been employed with success for spray head nozzles, long nozzles, small diameter nozzles, and for other special guns. Although design and function of manual machines has been pretty well standardized, many special machines for unusual and high production uses are continually being designed, developed, and built.

Users can procure fine particle machines with tracks, turntables, rotating devices, multiple gun manifolds, special guns for angle or lance blasting, gun oscillating mechanisms, and automatic rubber lined tumbling barrels.

11.1 Applications—Fine particle blasting guns benefit a great variety of products. They are used to clean off heat treat scale and corrosion, remove fine burrs, blend tool marks, smooth turbine blades; produce special lustrous or frosted finishes, and make micro-rough surfaces.

Fine particle blasting can remove some types of heat treat scale with only infinitesimal dimensional change on precision parts. Even heat treat salts in small amounts disappear. The process is often used before shot peening to prevent contamination of shot by scale. After shot peening, parts can again be blasted without losing effects of the peening.

Cleaning and finishing plastic molds and dies by fine-particle blasting is relatively fast, too; users report as much as 95% reduction in bench time. What's more, blasted molds release castings more easily than hand finished ones.

11.2 Results of Vapor Blast's Research

11.2.1 RELATION OF PERCENTAGE OF ABRASIVE TO METAL REMOVAL (FIGURE 28)

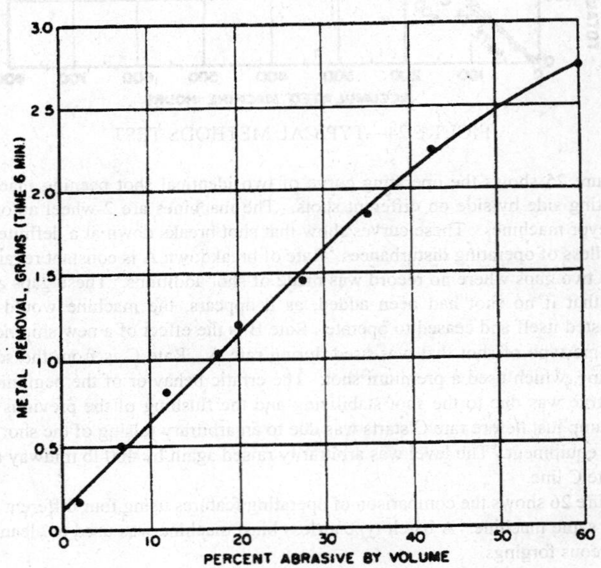

FIGURE 28—RELATION OF PERCENTAGE OF ABRASIVE TO METAL REMOVAL

11.2.1.1 Conditions—Duration of blasting, 6 min; angle of impingement, 90 deg; work-to-gun distance, 2 in; material used, SAE 1010; air pressure, 80 psi; type of gun used, V-B angle gun; diameter of nozzle, 1/2 in; diameter of air jet, 1/4 in.

11.2.1.2 Conclusions—An increase in the volume of abrasive, in the water-abrasive mixture, increases the cutting action of the blast.

A 68%-by-volume mixture was obtained before excessive settling occurred. This was decided to be the stopping point from the practical standpoint of using field equipment.

The data obtained show a straight-line relation between the amount of metal removed and the percentage of abrasive used up to 43% abrasive by volume. Any further increase in the amount of abrasive used causes the slope of the curve to decrease. This flattening of the curve could be credited to the settling of the abrasive. At these high percentages, the total amount of abrasive in the machine was not circulating properly.

11.2.2 Effects Of Cutting Angle On Weight Removal (Figure 29)

11.2.2.1 Conditions—Duration of blasting, 3 min; angle of impingement, 90 deg; work-to-gun distance, 2 in; material treated, SAE 1010; air pressure, 85 psi, type of gun used, V-B angle gun; diameter of nozzle, 1/2 in; diameter of air jet, 1/4 in.

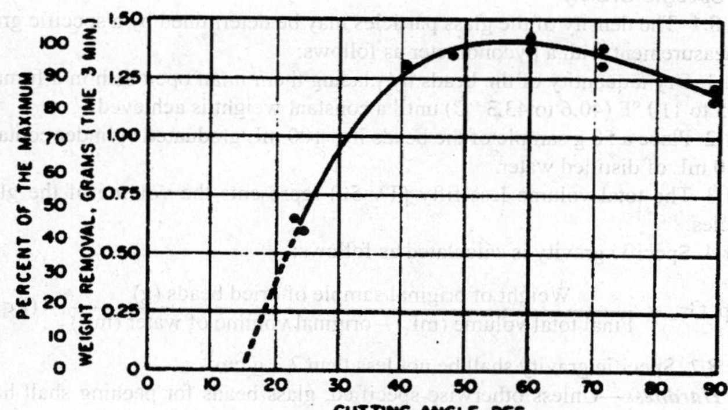

FIGURE 29—EFFECTS OF CUTTING ANGLE ON WEIGHT REMOVAL

11.2.2.2 Conclusions—Cutting action increases gradually as the cutting angle decreases from 90 to 60 deg.

This increase can probably be accounted for by two facts:

a. The rebound effect is reduced as the cutting angle approaches 60 deg.
b. There is more scouring and less peening action as the angle is decreased to 60 deg.

Angles more acute than 60 deg gave a decided decrease in cutting, and the slope of the curve at angles less than 60 deg is great. At these lower angles, the blast has a wearing action which is much slower in metal removal rates than the cutting or scouring type action obtained near 60 deg.

11.2.3 Relation Of Cutting Action To Air Pressure (Figure 30)

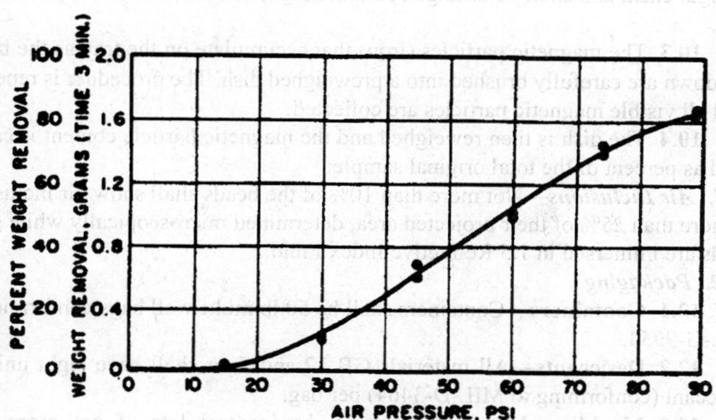

FIGURE 30—RELATION OF CUTTING ACTION TO AIR PRESSURE

11.2.3.1 Conditions—Duration of blasting, 3 min; angle of impingement, 90 deg; work-to-gun distance, 2 in; material treated, SAE 1010; air pressure, 85 psi; type of gun used, V-B angle gun; diameter of nozzle, 1/2 in; diameter of air jet, 1/4 in.

11.2.3.2 Conclusions—Between 30 and 75 psi the cutting action is almost directly proportional to air pressure.

At low pressure the kinetic energy of the particles is not sufficient to stress the surface of the steel beyond the failure point; hence the action is more wearing than cutting. Above 75 psi, a slight tapering off in the increase in cutting action was noted.

11.2.4 Effect Of Gun Distance On Weight Removal (Figure 31)

11.2.4.1 Conditions—Duration of blasting, 6 min; angle of blast impingement, 90 deg; material treated, SAE 1010; air pressure, 85 psi; type of gun, brass angle gun; diameter of nozzle, 1/2 in; diameter of air jet, 1/4 in.

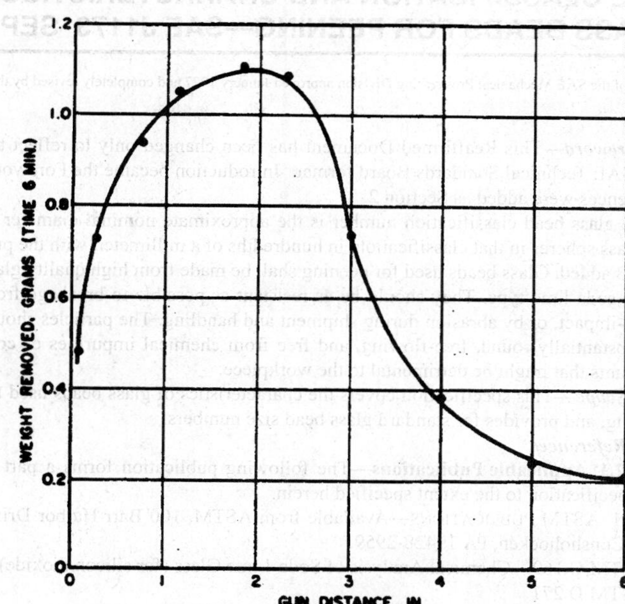

FIGURE 31—EFFECT OF GUN DISTANCE ON WEIGHT REMOVAL

11.2.4.2 Conclusions—No cutting action exists at distances less than 3/32 in. Optimum gun distance from the work is from 1.2-2.5 in.

At distances closer than 3/32 in, the back pressure reflected from the plate to the gun is sufficient to restrict flow of slurry. This rebound effect causes a rapid decrease in cutting action as the distance decreases. The cutting action falls off rapidly as the distance is increased beyond 2 in, but not proportionally to the square of the distance. Figure 31 would, of course, vary with changes in nozzle design. (Experiments have been performed only with a standard B-20 type brass angle gun.)

11.2.5 Air Required For Various Air Jet Diameters At Different Pressures (Figure 32)

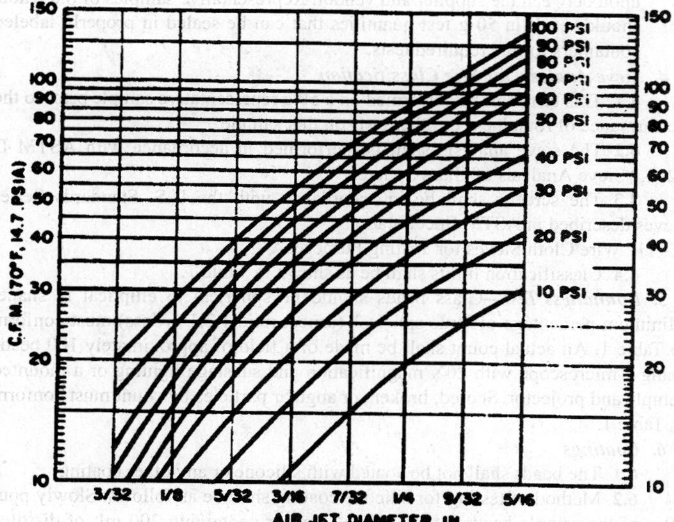

FIGURE 32—CFM OF AIR REQUIRED FOR VARIOUS AIR JET DIAMETERS AT DIFFERENT PRESSURES

11.2.5.1 Conditions—Type of gun used, V-B gun; abrasive used, 140 mesh, 40% by volume; air-measuring device, Fischer and Porter flowmeters; readings taken with slurry running through gun.

11.2.5.2 Conclusions—Air flow required is dependent on the abrasive flow, especially when the abrasive is under pressure greater than 3 psi.

SIZE CLASSIFICATION AND CHARACTERISTICS OF GLASS BEADS FOR PEENING—SAE J1173 SEP1988 SAE Recommended Practice

Report of the SAE Mechanical Prestressing Division approved January 1977 and completely revised by the SAE Fatigue, Design, and Evaluation Technical Committee September 1988.

Foreword—This Reaffirmed Document has been changed only to reflect the new SAE Technical Standards Board format. Introduction became the Foreword. References were added as Section 2.

The glass bead classification number is the approximate nominal diameter of the glass spheres in that classification, in hundredths of a millimeter, with the prefix GB added. Glass beads used for peening shall be made from high quality glass of the soda-lime type. They should be as resistant as possible to breakage from shock-impact, or by abrasion during shipment and handling. The particles should be substantially round, free-flowing, and free from chemical impurities or contaminants that might be detrimental to the workpiece.

1. Scope—This specification covers the characteristics of glass beads used for peening, and provides for standard glass bead size numbers.

2. References

2.1 Applicable Publications—The following publication forms a part of this specification to the extent specified herein.

2.1.1 ASTM PUBLICATIONS—Available from ASTM, 100 Barr Harbor Drive, West Conshohocken, PA 19428-2959.

ASTM C 169—Chemical Analysis of Soda-Lime Glass (for silicon dioxide)
ASTM D 271
ASTM D 1241—Sieve Analysis of Glass Spheres
ASTM E 11—Wire Cloth Sieves for Testing Purposes

2.1.2 FEDERAL AND MILITARY PUBLICATIONS—Available from U.S. Government, DOD SSP, Subscription Service Division, Building 4D, 700 Robbins Avenue, Philadelphia, PA 19111-5094.

MIL-D-3464
MIL-G-9954

3. Selection of Sample—A representative sample of the shipment shall be selected for evaluation. This can be accomplished by:

a. Splitting the entire large quantity by repeated passes through the sample reducer (16:1/1:1) splitter as described in ASTM D 271, or
b. Randomly selecting a number of containers equal to the nearest integer of the cube root of the total number of containers in the entire large quantity. Selected containers can then be reduced, as in (a) above, in order to obtain a representative sample. Other sampling techniques may be used if agreed upon between the supplier and vendor. Representative samples of the whole should result in 50 g test quantities that can be sealed in properly labeled containers for the required tests.

4. Sieve Analysis for Size Classification

4.1 This test shall be performed on a 50 g representative sample prior to the performance of roundness or other tests on that sample.

4.2 The sieve analysis shall be performed in accordance with ASTM D 1241, "Sieve Analysis of Glass Spheres."

4.3 The screens shall be in accordance with the U.S. Standards Series sieves described in ASTM Specification E- 11 "Wire Cloth Sieves for Testing Purposes."

4.4 Classification limits shall be as shown in Table 1.

5. Roundness Test—Glass beads should be spherical to elliptical in shape. Minimum percentage of "true spheres" (aspect ratio 1.2:1 or less) must conform to Table 1. An actual count shall be made of a field of approximately 100 beads using a microscope with 20X magnification and substage lighting or a mounted sample and projector. Scored, broken, or angular particles by count must conform to Table 1.

6. Coatings

6.1 The beads shall not be coated with silicone or any other coating.

6.2 Method of testing for silicone coating shall be as follows: Slowly pour 50 g of the sample beads into a 250 mL beaker containing 200 mL of distilled water. A small number of beads floating on the water is acceptable, but no coagulation (which is an indication of silicone coating) is permitted.

7. Composition

7.1 Silica content shall not be less than 67% in order to provide the highest chemical stability.

7.2 The method of analysis for silica shall be in accordance with ASTM C 169, "Chemical Analysis of Soda-Lime Glass (for silicon dioxide)."

8. Specific Gravity

8.1 The density of the glass particles may be determined by a specific gravity measurement with a pyconometer as follows:

8.1.1 Dry a quantity of the beads by placing them in an open dish in a furnace at 105 to 110 °F (40.6 to 43.3 °C) until a constant weight is achieved.

8.1.2 Place a 50 g sample of the beads in a 100 mL graduated cylinder containing 50 mL of distilled water.

8.1.3 The total volume less fifty (TV-50) represents the volume of the glass particles.

8.1.4 Specific gravity is calculated as follows:

$$\text{Sp. Gr.} = \frac{\text{Weight of original sample of dried beads (g)}}{\text{Final total volume (mL)} - \text{original volume of water (mL)}} \quad \text{(Eq. 1)}$$

8.2 Specific gravity shall be not less than 2.3 g/cm^3.

9. Hardness—Unless otherwise specified, glass beads for peening shall have the following hardness:

480 to 550 KHN (100gf)
458 to 528 DPH (50gf)
(for reference only approximately 48 to 50 HR$_c$)

10. Free Iron Content

10.1 Magnetic particles shall not exceed 0.1% of the original sample, by weight.

10.2 Iron particle content is determined by slowly sprinkling 1500 g of the sample bead material on an inclined aluminum tray that is 1.6 mm (0.62 in) deep x 152 mm (6 in) wide x 305 mm (12 in) long. The tray is supported by a nonmagnetic frame so that it is inclined with a 152 mm (6 in) rise from end to end (30 degrees from horizontal). Four 25 x 25 x 152 mm (1 x 1 x 6 in) barmagnets are positioned against the under surface and crosswise of the inclined tray about the middle of its length. Magnets shall be of not less than 10 000 Gauss magnetic strength each, and shall be arranged so that magnetic north and south poles alternate.

10.3 The magnetic particles (iron) that accumulate on the tray as the beads roll down are carefully brushed into a preweighed dish. The procedure is repeated until all visible magnetic particles are collected.

10.4 The dish is then reweighed and the magnetic particle content is calculated as percent of the total original sample.

11. Air Inclusions—Not more than 10% of the beads shall show air inclusions of more than 25% of their projected area, determined microscopically while glass beads are immersed in 1.5 Refractive Index Fluid.

12. Packaging

12.1 Containers—Containers shall be 50 lb multi-wall bags conforming to MIL-G-9954.

12.2 Desiccants—All materials GB 12 and finer shall have eight units of desiccant (conforming to MIL-D-3464) per bag.

12.3 Marking—Manufacturing will use control lots of not more than 1000 kg or 2200 lb. Lot numbers must be stamped on each bag, and sieve analysis record must be available on request from the manufacturer for two years after shipment.

TABLE 1—GLASS BEADS FOR PEENING—SIZES

	Nominal Sizes			SIEVE SIZE (mm)				(1) MIN %	(2) MAX %
DESIGNATION(3)(4)	mm	in	MESH	MAX TRACE RETAINS	MAX 5% RETAINS	MAX 10% PASS	MAX 5% PASS	TRUE SPHERES	SHARP PARTICLES
GB 280*	3.350/2.360	0.132/0.094	6/8	4.000	3.350	2.360	2.000	70	0.5
235*	2.800/2.000	0.111/0.079	7/10	3.350	2.800	2.000	1.700	75	0.5
200*	2.360/1.700	0.094/0.066	8/12	2.800	2.360	1.700	1.400	80	0.5
170*	2.000/1.400	0.079/0.056	10/14	2.360	2.000	1.400	1.180	80	0.5
140*	1.700/1.180	0.066/0.047	12/16	2.000	1.700	1.180	1.000	80	0.5
120*	1.400/1.000	0.056/0.039	14/18	1.700	1.400	1.000	0.850	80	0.5
100	1.180/0.850	0.047/0.0331	16/20	1.400	1.180	0.850	0.600	65	3.0
85*	1.000/0.710	0.039/0.0278	18/25	1.180	1.000	0.710	0.425	65	3.0
70	0.850/0.600	0.0331/0.0234	20/30	1.000	0.850	0.600	0.355	65	3.0
60*	0.710/0.500	0.0278/0.0197	25/35	0.850	0.710	0.500	0.300	70	3.0
50	0.600/0.425	0.0234/0.0165	30/40	0.710	0.600	0.425	0.250	70	3.0
40*	0.500/0.355	0.0197/0.0139	35/45	0.600	0.500	0.355	0.212	70	3.0
35	0.425/0.300	0.0165/0.0117	40/50	0.500	0.425	0.300	0.212	70	3.0
30*	0.355/0.250	0.0139/0.0098	45/60	0.425	0.355	0.250	0.180	70	3.0
25	0.300/0.212	0.0117/0.0083	50/70	0.355	0.300	0.212	0.150	80	3.0
20	0.250/0.180	0.0098/0.0070	60/80	0.300	0.250	0.180	0.125	80	3.0
18	0.212/0.150	0.0083/0.0059	70/100	0.250	0.212	0.150	0.106	80	3.0
15	0.180/0.125	0.0070/0.0049	80/120	0.212	0.180	0.125	0.090	80	3.0
12	0.150/0.106	0.0059/0.0041	100/140	0.180	0.150	0.106	0.063	90	3.0
10	0.125/0.090	0.0049/0.0035	120/170	0.150	0.125	0.090	0.053	90	3.0
9	0.106/0.075	0.0041/0.0029	140/200	0.125	0.106	0.075	0.045	90	3.0
8	0.090/0.063	0.0035/0.0025	170/230	0.106	0.090	0.063	0.038	90	3.0
6	0.075/0.053	0.0029/0.0021	200/270	0.090	0.075	0.053	0.038	90	3.0

1. A "true sphere" is defined as a spheroid with an aspect ratio (ratio of maximum to minimum diameter) of 1.2 or less.
2. "Sharp particles" are scored beads, broken beads, or angular glass particles with unfired edges.
3. Designation number is mean bead diameter mm x 100.
4. "*" indicates sizes added to SAE J1173, January 1977 list.

SIZE CLASSIFICATION AND CHARACTERISTICS OF CERAMIC SHOT FOR PEENING —SAE J1830 MAY87

SAE Recommended Practice

Report of the SAE Mechanical Prestressing Subcommittee of the SAE Fatigue, Design, and Evaluation Committee approved May 1987.

Foreword—This Document has not changed other than to put it into the new SAE Technical Standards Board Format.

1. Scope—This specification covers characteristics for chemistry, microstructure, density, hardness, size, shape and appearance of zirconium oxide based ceramic shot, suitable for peening surfaces of parts by impingement.

2. References

2.1 Applicable Publications—The following publication forms a part of the specification to the extent specified herein.

2.1.1 ASTM PUBLICATION—Available from ASTM, 100 Barr Harbor Drive, West Conshohocken, PA 19428-2959.

ASTM E 11-70—Specification for Wire-Cloth Sieves for Testing Purposes

3. Chemistry—This specification includes the nominal chemistry of zirconium oxide based ceramic shot and the amount of free iron particles.

3.1 Oxide Analysis—Ceramic shot shall be manufactured from zirconium oxide and silica. The main constituents shall be:

- Zirconium Oxide 60 to 70 weight per cent
- Silica 28 to 33 weight per cent
- Alumina less than 10 weight per cent

The total of other constituent contents shall not exceed 3 weight per cent. Analysis method is X-Ray Fluorescence or any other method acceptable to purchaser.

3.2 Free Iron Content—The free iron content of the ceramic shot sample shall not exceed 0.10 weight per cent. It is determined by slowly sprinkling 500 g of the sample ceramic bead shot on an inclined aluminum tray that is 1.6 mm (0.062 in) deep by 152 mm (6 in) wide by 305 mm (12 in) long. The tray is supported by a nonmagnetic frame so that it is inclined with a 152 mm (6 in) rise from end to end, (30 degrees from horizontal). Four 25 x 25 x 152 mm (1 x 1 x 6 in) bar magnets are positioned against the under surface and crosswise to the inclined tray about the middle of its length. Magnets shall be not less than 10 000 Gauss magnetic field each and arranged so that the magnetic north and south poles alternate. The magnetic particles (iron) that accumulate on the tray as the beads roll down are carefully brushed into a preweighed dish. The procedure is repeated with the same 500 g sample until all visible magnetic particles are collected. The dish is then reweighed and the magnetic particle content is calculated as a percentage of the total original sample.

4. Microstructure—Ceramic shot are manufactured by electric fusion of oxides to form a closely bonded internal structure of a crystalline zirconia phase within an amorphous silica phase.

5. Specific Gravity—This characteristic is closely related to chemical analysis. It ranges between 3.60 and 3.95 g/cm^3.

Specific gravity is measured at 31 °C by a pycnometric method.

6. Hardness—Unless otherwise specified, the ceramic shot shall have the following hardness:

623-785 DPH (1Kgf)
or 660-812 KHN (500 gf)
(for reference only approximately 57–63 HRC)

7. Size—Unless otherwise specified, the ceramic shot shall conform to Table I.

7.1 Testing—This is conducted by screening a 250 g sample with sieves conforming to ASTM E 11–70.

8. Shape—Sphericity and roundness are measured by an actual counting of a one layer field of a minimum of 200 ceramic beads, at a magnification of 20X.

8.1 Sphericity—It refers to the ratio of short to long axes of the hypothetical ellipse that would contain the actual image of the ceramic bead as seen through a microscope. Unless otherwise specified, Table I gives the maximal number of ceramic shot having a sphericity less than 0.5 and the minimum percentage of ceramic shot having a sphericity of 0.8 and greater.

8.2 Roundness—It refers to the relative angularity of grain corners, the ceramic shot having round and smooth surfaces. Scored, broken or angular particles are those that would present sharp or angular surfaces when impacted, causing metal removal or unsatisfactory or irregular finishes. An actual count shall be made of a field of 1 cm^2 at a 20X magnification. Maximum number of permissable broken or angular beads is shown on column 11 of Table I. This number shall never exceed 3%.

9. Appearance—Ceramic shot is constant in color, free flowing, free of defects and free of foreign matter.

10. Quality Assurance—Ceramic shot quality is checked by lots of 1,000 kg maximum. A representative sample of the shipped lot shall be tested for conformance to all requirements of this specification. Lot number and this specification number shall be marked on each container unit. All control data will be available from manufacturer on request for two (2) years after shipment.

TABLE 1—CERAMIC SHOT FOR PEENING - SIZES

									(7)	(8)
	NOMINAL SIZES			SIEVE SIZE (mm)						
DESIGNATION	MM	IN	MESH	MAX 0.5% RETAINS	MAX 5% RETAINS	MAX 10% PASS	MAX 3% PASS	MIN % OF SHOT W/ SPHERICITY 0.8 & ABOVE	MAX NO. OF BEADS PER SQUARE CM. WITH SPHERICITY BELOW 0.5	MAX NO. BROKENOR ANGULARBEADS PERSQUARE CM.
Z 850	0.850/1.180	0.033/0.046	16/20	1.400	1.180	0.850	0.710	65	4	2
Z 600	0.600/0.850	0.024/0.033	20/30	1.000	0.850	0.600	0.425	65	8	4
Z 425	0.425/0.600	0.017/0.024	30/40	0.710	0.600	0.425	0.300	70	14	8
Z 300	0.300/0.425	0.011/0.017	40/50	0.500	0.425	0.300	0.250	70	27	15
Z 210	0.210/0.300	0.008/0.011	50/70	0.355	0.300	0.212	0.180	80	45	20
Z 150	0.150/0.210	0.006/0.008	70/100	0.250	0.212	0.150	0.125	80	300	65

SURFACE ROLLING AND OTHER METHODS FOR MECHANICAL PRESTRESSING OF METALS —SAE J811 AUG81

SAE Information Report

Report of the SAE Iron and Steel Technical Committee approved June 1962, editorial change August 1981. Formerly HS-03.

1. Scope

2. References

2.1 Applicable Publications—The following publications form a part of the specification to the extent specified herein. Unless otherwise indicated the lastest revision of SAE publications shall apply.

1. Butz, G. A., and Lyst, J. O., "Improvements in Fatigue Resistance of Aluminum Alloys by Mechanical Surface Prestressing." Paper presented at 1961 Western Metals Congress (ASTM).
2. Gadd, C. W., Anderson, J. O., and Martin, D., "Some Factors Affecting the Fatigue Strength of Steel Members," SAE Transactions, Vol. 63, 1955.
3. Kudryavtsev, I. V., "The Influence of Internal Stresses on the Fatigue Endurance of Steel," Proceedings of the International Conference on Fatigue of Metals, Institution of Mechanical Engineers, London; ASME. New York, 1956.
4. Atkin, R. L., and Mezoff, J. G., "Development and Testing of Magnesium Alloy Wheels." Paper presented at Third Sagamore Ordnance Materials Research Conference, December 1956, Syracuse University Research Institute.
5. Lessels, J. M., Strength and Resistance of Metals, New York: John Wiley and Sons, Inc., 1954.
6. Cohen, B., "Effect of Shot Peening Prior to Chromium Plating on the Fatigue Strength of High Strength Steel," WADC Technical Note 57–178, ASTIA Document #AD 130821, 1975.
7. Sigwart, H., "Influence of Residual Stresses on the Fatigue Limit," Proceedings of the International Conference on Fatigue of Metals, Institution of Mechanical Engineers, London; ASME. New York, 1956.
8. Dugdale, D. S., "Effect of Residual Stress on Fatigue Strength," The Welding Journal, January 1959.
9. Grover, H. J., Gordon, S. A., and Jackson, L. P., Fatigue of Metals and Structures, Prepared for Bureau of Aeronautics, Department of the Navy, Nav Aer OO-25-534, 1954.
10. Brodrick, R. F., "Protective Shot Peening of Propellers—Residual Peening Stresses," WADC Technical Report 55–56, Part I, June 1955.
11. Horger, O. J., "Cold Working," Section 6.9, ASME Handbook, Metals Engineering—Design, McGraw-Hill, 1953.
12. Hertz, H., Journal of Mathematics (Crelles' Journal), Vol. 92, 1881.
13. Hertz, H., Gesammelte Werke, Vol. 1, p. 155, Leipzig, 1895.
14. Belajef, N. M., "On the Problem of Contact Stresses," Bulletin, Institute of Engineers of Ways and Communication, St. Petersburg, 1917. Memoirs on Theory of Structures, St. Petersburg, 1924.
15. Thomas, H. R., and Hoersch, V. A., "Stresses Due to the Pressure of One Elastic Solid Upon Another," University of Illinois Experimental Station Bulletin No. 212, Vol. 27, No. 46, July 15, 1930.
16. Lundberg, G., and Odqvist, F. K. G., Proc. Ingeniors Vetenskapa Akad., No. 116, Stockholm, 1932.
17. Horger, O. J., "Stressing Axles and Other Railroad Equipment by Cold Rolling," Surface Stressing of Metals, American Society for Metals, pp. 85–142, Cleveland, Ohio, 1947.
18. Way, S., Discussion of paper by R. E. Peterson and A. M. Wahl in Journal of Applied Mechanics, Vol. 2, No. 2, June, 1935, pp. A-69-71.
19. Horger, O. J., "Effect of Surface Rolling on the Fatigue Strength of Steel," Journal of Applied Mechanics, Transactions, A.S.M.E., Vol. 57, December, 1935, pp. A-128-136.
20. Love, R. J., "Cold Rolled Fillets," Engineering, August 8, 1952.
21. Ford Motor Company; Manufacturing Research Office.
22. General Motors Corporation (Patent #2,357,515).
23. Industrial Metal Products Corporation.
24. International Harvester Company (Patent #2,841,861).
25. Madison Industries, Inc.
26. "Shot Peening and Other Surface Working Processes," Supplement to Metals Handbook, Metal Progress, (ASM), July 15, 1954, pp. 104–108.
27. Almen, J. O., Mattson, R. O., and Fonda, H. E., Report on "Surface Rolling Treatment."
28. The Foote-Burt Company, Schraner Division.
29. Timken Roller Bearing Company, "Cold Rolling of Axle Fillets."
30. Almen, J. O., "Fatigue Durability of Prestressed Screw Threads," Product Engineering, April, 1951.
31. Cogsdill Tool Products, Inc.
32. Stewart, W. C., and Ellinghausen, H. C., "Examination and Test of Failed Port Tail Shaft, USS Norfolk (DL-1)," U.S. Naval Engr. Exp. Station, R&D Report, 040007AZ(2) NSM-000-003, December 5, 1955.
33. Dugdale, D. S., "Stress-Strain Cycles of Large Amplitude," J. Mech. Phys. Solids, 1959, Vol. 7, pp. 135–142. Pergaman Press, London, England.
34. Fuchs, H. O., "Shot-Peening Effects and Specifications," ASTM Spec. Tech. Pub. No. 196, pp. 22–32. Philadelphia, 1958.
35. Phillips, A., "Improvement of Fatigue Life of Aircraft Components by Coining," published by ASME, 1961. Paper 61-AV-35.
36. Almen, J. O., "Fatigue Loss and Gain by Electroplating," Product Engineering, Vol. 22, No. 6, June, 1951.
37. Grossman, Nicholas, "Effect of Shot Peening on the Brittle Transition Temperature," Metal Progress, p. 352. September, 1950.
38. Water, K. T., "Production Methods for Cold Working Joints Subjected to Fretting for Improvement of Fatigue Strength," Preprint Paper No. 75, ASTM, San Francisco Meeting, 1959.
39. SAE, Shot Peening Manual, SP-84, New York, 1952.
40. Timoshenko, S., and Goodier, J. N., Theory of Elasticity, 2nd Ed. New York, McGraw-Hill, 1951.
41. Timoshenko, S., Strength of Materials, 2nd Ed., Part II: Advanced Theory and Problems. New York: McGraw-Hill 1941.
42. Mattson, R. L., and Roberts, J. G., "Effect of Residual Stresses Induced by Strain Peening Upon Fatigue Strength." Internal Stresses and Fatigue in Metals. Amsterdam, Elsevier, 1958.
43. Fuchs, H. O., and Mattson, R. L., "Measurement of Residual Stresses in Torsion Bar Springs," Proceedings, SESA, Vol. 4, No. 1, 1946.
44. Almen, J. O., "Fatigue Failures are Tensile Failures," Product Engineering. McGraw-Hill Publishing Co., March, 1951.
45. Machine Design, Penton Publishing Co., October 20, 1958.
46. Harper, W. A., "Explosive Hardening of Steel Proves Out in Field Service," Iron Age, Vol. 185, No. 4, Feb. 4, 1960, p. 85.
47. Dermott, R. G., "Progress in Explosive Forming," Metal Progress. November 1959.
48. Courtesy of L. G. Johnson. Research Laboratories, General Motors Corp. Unpublished.
49. Thum, A., and Bruder, E., "Shape and Fatigue Strength of Rod Eyes and Similar Constructional Parts," Deutsche Kraftfahrtforschung, No. 20, 1939, pp. 1–10.
50. Design News, Dec. 8, 1958.
51. Wise, S., "Work-Hardening Bolt Holes in Rail Ends," The Railway Gazette, April 29, 1960, pp. 511–512.
52. "One Ball, No Errors," Machine Design. Penton Publishing Co., February, 1958.
53. Almen, J. O., "Brittle Structural Failures with Emphasis on Welded Ships," Product Engineering. April 1953.
54. Burnheim, H. "Surface Pressing of Notched Test Specimens Consisting of Cr-Mn-V Steel VCV 100," Luftfahrtforschung, Vol. 20, No. 1, January 20, 1943.
55. Coombs, A. G. H., Sherratt, F., and Pope, J. A., "An Analysis of the Effects of Shot-Peening Upon the Fatigue Strength of hardened and Tempered Spring Steel." Proceedings of the International Conference on Fatigue of Metals, Institution of Mechanical Engineers, London; American Institute of Mechanical Engineers, New York, 1956. London, William Clowes and Sons, 1956.
56. Courtesy H. R. Neifert, Timken Roller Bearing Co.
57. Courtesy G. F. Butz, Aluminum Co. of America.
58. Courtesy C. W. Cable, Boeing Aircraft Co.

2.2 Related Publications—The following publications are provided for information purposes only and are not a required part of this document.

Rosenthal, D., Sines, G., and Zizicas, G., "The Effect of Residual Compression on Fatigue," Welding J., Research Suppl., Vol. 28, 1949.

Rosenthal, D., and Sines, G., "Effect of Residual Stress on the Fatigue Strength of Notched Specimens," Proc. ASTM, Vol. 51, 1951.

Norton, J. T., Rosenthal, D., and Maloof, S. B., "X-Ray Diffraction Study of the Effect of Residual Compression on Fatigue of Notched Specimens." Welding J., Research Suppl. 1946.

Surface Stressing of Metals, American Society for Metals, Cleveland, 1947; H. F. Moore, "The Problem Defined;" W. M. Murray, "Measurement of Surface Stresses;" J. O. Almen, "Fatigue of Metals as Influenced by Design and Internal Stresses;" O. J. Horger, "Stressing Axles and Other Railroad Equipment by Cold Rolling;" P. R. Kosting, "Progressive Stress-Damage."

Almen, J. O., "Fatigue Weakness of Surfaces," Product Engineering. McGraw-Hill Publishing Co., November 1950.

Almen, J. O., "Torsional Fatigue Failures," Part I, Product Engineering, McGraw-Hill Publishing Co. September 1951.

Almen, J. O., "Torsional Fatigue Failures," Part II, Product Engineering, McGraw-Hill Publishing Co. March 1952.

Almen, J. O., "Residual Compressive Stress Strengthens Brittle Materials," Product Engineering. McGraw-Hill Publishing Co., July 1953.

Mattson, R. L., and Almen, J. O., "Effect of Shot Blasting on the Mechanical Properties of Steel," (NA-115), Final Report OSRD, 3274, 4825, 6647. Washington, 1945.

Green, W. B., "How Processing Affects Bolt Fatigue Strength," Machine Design. Penton Publishing Co., December 1947.

Weibull, W., "The Effect of Decarburization and Other Factors on the Fatigue Strength of Roll-Threaded Aircraft Bolts," SAAB TN 4, Svenska Aeroplan Aktiebolaget. Linkoping, Sweden, July 1952.

Buckwalter, T. V., and Horger, O. J., "Investigation of Fatigue Strength of Axles, Press-Fits, Surface Rolling, and Effect of Size," Transactions of the American Society for Metals, Vol. 25, March 1937, p. 229.

Horger, O. J., and Maulbetsch, J. L., "Increasing the Fatigue Strength of Press-Fitted Axle Assemblies by Surface Rolling," Journal of Applied Mechanics, September 1936, pp. A-91 to A-98.

Horger, O. J., Buckwalter, T. V., and Neifert, H. R., "Fatigue Strength of 5-1/4 in. Diameter Shafts as Related to Design of Large Parts," Journal of Applied Mechanics, September 1945, pp. A-149 to A-155.

Horger, O. J., and Cantley, W. I., "Design of Crankpins for Locomotives," Transactions ASME, Vol. 68, 1946, pp. A-17 to A-33.

Horger, O. J., "Residual Stress." Handbook of Experimental Stress Analysis, John Wiley & Sons, Inc., New York, 1950.

Horger, O. J., "Influence of Fretting Corrosion on the Fatigue Strength of Fitted Members," Symposium and Fretting Corrosion, Special Technical Publication No. 144, ATM, 1953, pp. 40–51.

Horger, O. J., and Lipson, C., "Automotive Rear Axles and Means of Improving Their Fatigue Resistance," ASTM Spec. Tech. Publ. 72, "Symposium on Testing of Parts and Assemblies," Philadelphia, 1947.

Horger O. J., "Stresses Imposed by Processing," SAE Quart. Trans. Vol. 5, No. 3, pp. 393–403, July 1951.

Horger, O. J., and Neifert, H. R., "Effect of Surface Conditions on Fatigue Properties," Surface Treatment of Metals, ASTM, 1941.

Horger, O. J., and Neifert, H. R., "Fretting Corrosion of Large Shafts as Influenced by Surface Treatments," Symposium on Large Fatigue Testing Machines and Their Results, Special Technical Publication No. 216, ASTM, 1957, pp. 81–95.

Horger, O. J., and Neifert, H. R., "Correlation of Residual Stresses with Fatigue Strength of Machine Elements and Related Phenomena," Residual Stresses in Metals and Metal Construction. Reinhold Publishing Corp., New York, 1954, pp. 219–253.

Neifert, H. R., and Robinson, J. H., "Further Results from the Society's Investigation of Tailshaft Failures," Transactions, Society of Naval Architects and Marine Engineers, Vol. 63, 1955, pp. 495–550.

Fuchs, H. O., "Trapped Stresses," Machine Design. Penton Publishing Co., July 1948.

Fuchs, H. O., "Techniques of Surface Stressing to Avoid Fatigue," Metal Fatigue, edited by G. Sines and J. L. Waisman, University of California Engineering Extension Series. McGraw-Hill Book Co., Inc., 1959.

Dolan, T. J., "Basic Concepts of Fatigue Damage in Metals," op. cit.

Peterson, R. E., "Fatigue Cracks and Fracture Surfaces—Mechanics of Development and Visual Appearance," op. cit.

Shook, L. L., Jr., and Long, C. L., "Surface Cold Rolling of Marine Propeller Shafting." paper presented December 6, 1957, to the Hampton Roads Section, The Society of Naval Architects and Marine Engineers.

Egger, Walter, and Diamond, Gerald X., "Fillet Rolling," Machine Design. Penton Publishing Co., January 5, 1961.

Garwood, M. F., ZurBurg, H. H., and Erickson, M. A., "Correlation of Laboratory Tests and Service Performance," Interpretation of Tests and Correlation with Service, ASM, 1950.

Love, R. J., and Waistall, D. N., "The Improvement in the Bending Fatigue Strength of Production Crankshafts by Cold Rolling," Report No. 1954/2, published by the Motor Industry Research Association, Lindley, Warwickshire, England. 1954.

Love, R. J., "Fatigue in Automobiles," Proceedings of the International Conference on Fatigue of Metals, Institution of Mechanical Engineers, London; ASME, New York; 1956.

Siebel, E., and Gaier, M., "The Influence of Surface Roughness on the Fatigue Strength of Steels and Non-Ferrous Alloys," translated in The Engineers' Digest. March 1957.

Bibliography on Residual Stress (SP-125), and Supplement I (SP-167), SAE.

Evaluation of Methods for Measurement of Residual Stress, (HS 147), SAE.

Horger, O. J., "Cold Working," ASME Handbook Metals Engineering-Design, 2nd edition, O. J. Horger, ed. McGraw-Hill, 1964, pp. 264–267.

Metals Handbook, Vol. 3, 8th edition, "Roller Burnishing," pp. 105–107, "Thread Rolling," pp. 130–145.

3. Applications of Mechanical Prestressing (by George A. Butz)

3.1 Introduction—The word "prestressing" implies that a stress is applied prior to service. For the purposes of this discussion this is true, but insufficient, definition. It must be extended to say, by virtue of a localized pressure on the surface of a part, that the surface of the part in the vicinity is stressed in tension beyond its elastic limit. When the pressure is removed, the surface elements tend to retain part of the total deformation experienced under pressure. Since this is resisted by subsurface layers which did not exceed the elastic limit, the surface and adjacent layers are left in a state of compressive residual stress.

The two most widely used methods of mechanical prestressing probably are surface rolling and shot peening. Since the process of shot peening has been rather widely discussed in previously published literature, the greater part of this manual is concerned with surface rolling and its theory, load specification, tooling, control, and effects. Methods briefly considered include hammer peening, cold pressing, and treatment of small holes with balls or tapered pins. The general aims of this manual are:

a. To give the reader a general understanding as to what mechanical prestressing is and whether it may be expected to help him with his product.
b. To help him choose a process.
c. To help him get started in tool design and preparation of test samples. At this stage of development of the art, the optimum prestressing conditions and degree of performance improvement should be established by objective and destructive tests, unless one has ample previous experience on similar materials and products.

Mechanical prestressing methods affect the surface layers of a part in at least three ways, the relative amounts being affected by the process and the material:

a. Compressive residual stresses.
b. Cold work or strain hardening.
c. Surface geometry or finish.

It is usually quite difficult to assess the individual contributions of these effects on the improvement in performance attained. The consensus, however, is that the compressive residual stress is the most potent of the three. These effects are discussed in later sections of this report.

While mechanical prestressing methods are now used in many various industries, most of their development and application has occurred in the transportation industry. This might be attributable to the intense competition which fosters development work, continually driving toward the attainment of maximum strength in minimum space and weight with low-cost alloys and processing. In meeting these goals, prestressing methods have made some of their most impressive accomplishments. The following list of parts is not intended to be comprehensive, but rather gives an idea as to the variety of parts where worthwhile gains in performance have been obtained:

a. Aircraft—Propellers, engine parts, wheels.
b. Marine—Propeller shafts, engine crankshafts.
c. Automotive—Coil and leaf springs, torsion bars, front axle spindles, crankshafts, wheels.
d. Railroad—Car axles.

Significant increases in performance have been obtained by prestressing techniques. Under certain conditions, the fatigue strength of specimens has been more than doubled (3). [1] Improvements of this order are not possible in all fatigue situations, nor in all materials. Furthermore, where they are possible, the optimum prestressing conditions must be worked out by objective performance tests. Once these are established and production specifications are set up, the processing engineer must insist that these specifications be met on every piece processed. Mechanical prestressing is unique because there are no simple, nondestructive, or even destructive, tests which can be routinely used to check whether a particular part has been properly prestressed, although certain laboratory methods can be used to measure residual stress. One must inspect the process rather than the part. Even then, subsequent processing steps can reduce or cancel the benefits obtained. These steps could include honing or other finishing, straightening, overheating, and so forth.

3.2 Improving Fatigue Resistance—An overwhelming majority of prestressing applications are aimed at improving performance under fatigue loading conditions (cyclic stressing). A detailed discussion of the relative contributions of residual stresses, strain hardening, and surface smoothness to fatigue resistance is beyond the scope and intent of this report. Although it is admittedly oversimplified, acceptance of the premises that initial fatigue cracking is associated with stresses in surface layers and that fatigue cracks are propagated by tensile mean stresses will lead to at least a qualitative understanding of the role of prestressing.

The fatigue situations in which prestressing might be considered may be divided into four arbitrary classes as follows:

a. "Normal" Conditions—No high stress gradients, no surface degradation from processing or service.
b. "Designed" Stress Concentrations—Fillets, grooves, transverse holes, and so on.
c. Surface Degradation From Service and Environments—Corrosion, fretting, wear, mechanical abuse (nicks, gouges, and related misuses).
d. Negative Effects of Fabricating Processes—Machining, grinding, unfavorable heat treatment, plating, anodizing, straightening, and so forth.

The data in Table 1 is illustrative of all these classes. Rolling increased the strength of the smooth specimen by 21%. The harmful effect of a sharp notch was cancelled when the specimens were rolled before notching. Exposure to a corrosive medium before testing reduced the strength of a machined specimen to 69% of the baseline. Companion specimens, which were rolled before exposure, not only exceeded the base line, but were equal to those which were rolled, stored, and tested in laboratory atmosphere. An overbending (intended to simulate a straightening operation), in which the smooth specimen was statically loaded in the test machine to a total strain of 2.5%, left a very undesirable situation on the side of the specimen which was in compression under the static load. The fatigue strength was reduced to 55% of the baseline, a more harmful effect than was caused by the sharp notch. Although the strength of a similarly bent specimen was raised 73% by rolling, it was not brought back to the baseline.

TABLE 1—RELATIVE IMPROVEMENTS IN FATIGUE STRENGTH OF A HIGH STRENGTH ALUMINUM ALLOY PROVIDED BY A PARTICULAR SURFACE ROLLING, 1.5 IN. DIA. SPECIMENS IN REVERSED BENDING (1)

Treatment Specimen	1,000,000 Cycle Strength, % of "As Machined"	Improvement Due to Rolling, %
As Machined	100	
As Machined + Roll	121	21
As Machined + Notch (0.020 in. deep)	61	
Roll + Notch (0.020 in. deep)	105	71
As Machined + Corrosion	69	—
Roll + Corrosion	122	77
As Machined + Overbent	55	—
Overbent + Roll	95	73

1. Numbers in parentheses in text and tables refer to references at end of report.

Table 2 shows how the bending fatigue strengths of steel crankshafts and specimens with fillets were increased by rolling. Increases of 19% for the mild steel specimens and of 25% for the alloy steel crankshaft were noted. A computed maximum contact pressure of 400,000 psi was used in rolling the specimens of mild steel.

TABLE 2—IMPROVEMENTS IN FATIGUE STRENGTH OF STEEL: (A) SPECIMEN OF 1.5 IN DIA WITH 3/8 IN FILLETS AND (B) CRANKSHAFT FOR 4 1/4 × 5 IN DIESEL WITH 0.145 IN FILLETS. EACH TESTED IN REVERSED BENDING (2)

Results From	Steel	Max Fillet Stress (ksi) For 1,000,000 Cycle Life Not Rolled	Max Fillet Stress (ksi) For 1,000,000 Cycle Life Rolled	Improvement Due to Rolling, %
Specimen (A)	UNS No. G10430			
	SAE/AISI 1043			
	(Normalized)	42.0	50.0	19
Crankshaft (B)	UNS No. G41400			
	SAE/AISI 4140			
	(300–340 Bhn)	55.0	69.0	25

Another case history is illustrated by Table 3. Mild steel shafts were first tested as normal type (rotating bending) fatigue specimens, where it was established that 20% higher strength was obtained by rolling. Specimens were then tested while held in a bushing where fretting was undoubtedly present at the maximum stress area. The effect was to drop the strength of the ground specimen to less than half of those tested in more conventional fashion. The fatigue strength in this environment was doubled by rolling. This almost brought the strength back to that of the original ground specimen, tested without bushing.

TABLE 3—ENDURANCE LIMIT OF NO. 45 STEEL (0.48% C, TENSILE STRENGTH = 92,500 psi) (3)

Test Specimen	Fatigue Limit (ksi)	Strength Improvement Over Ground Specimen, %
Conventional Rotating Beam:		
Ground	39.0	—
Rolled	45.7	20
0.69 in dia Cylindrical, Tested as Cantilever Beam Held in Steel Bushing, Causing Fretting Corrosion:		
Ground	18.0	
Rolled	36.2	101
Rolled + Light Grind	37.2	106

A comprehensive study of surface rolling was made by Atkin and Mezoff (4). It is concerned with the effect of rolling on magnesium alloys and the development of a prestressed magnesium wheel for military use. Some of the results are summarized in Table 4. Markedly different degrees of improvements were indicated for the three alloys tested, ranging from 8–77%. No obvious pattern is established relating the relative degree of improvements from rolling when loaded under complete reversal and zero-to-tension.

TABLE 4—FATIGUE STRENGTH OF MAGNESIUM ALLOY TEST SPECIMENS, 1.0 IN DIA WITH 5/16 IN RADIUS: TESTED IN REVERSED AND UNI-DIRECTIONAL BENDING (4)

Magnesium Alloy UNS No.	Magnesium Alloy SAE No.	Loading	1,000,000 Cycle Fatigue Strength As Machined	1,000,000 Cycle Fatigue Strength Rolled	Improvement Due to Rolling, %
M16600 (ZK60A)	524-F	Reversal	±18.7	±22.7	22
	(Wrought)	O-Tension	25.4	27.5	8
M11800 (AZ80A)	523-F	Reversal	—	±25.7	—
	(Wrought)	O-Tension	21.0	30.5	45
M11810 (AZ81A)	505-T4	Reversal	±11.5	±19.0	65
	(Cast)	O-Tension	13.0	23.0	77

In this same reference, the improvement in fatigue life of actual wheels is also reported, as shown in Table 5. It is characteristic of this product and test method that fretting and other surface damage may occur at high-stress regions. This test showed that the life of a particular wheel design could be extended more than ten times by surface rolling. Because of prestress due to tire inflation, the stress ratio in the critical regions would be positive, i.e., from one level of tension to another. The specific amounts of improvement quoted are only intended as representative figures. The actual amount possible in a given situation can vary widely in response to many effects including specimen type, stress level, rolling techniques, and others.

TABLE 5—LIFE OF 20 × 7.50 MAGNESIUM WHEEL, CAST SAE 505-T4 [UNS M11810 (AZ81A)]; UNDER ROLL TEST WITH INFLATED TIRE AT 8,000 LB LOAD (4)

Wheel Description	Life Cycles (Single Specimen)	Location of Fracture
Not Rolled	326,000	Bead seat radius of fixed flange
Bead Seat Rolled	2,018,000	Gutter cracks, bead seat OK
Bead Seat and Gutter Rolled	3,946,000	Wheel OK—Test halted

In summation, these examples show that fatigue strength can be improved by important—but widely varying—degrees with prestressing methods. While worthwhile increases are observed on smooth or mildly filleted specimens, the most impressive accomplishments are in protection against rather superficial surface damage, typified by corrosion, fretting, or shallow notches. This type of damage can be surprisingly effective in reducing fatigue strength of engineering structures where the surface is not prestressed.

3.3 Other Users for Prestressing—Stress corrosion cracking is a mode of failure that is influenced by surface stress, environment, and time. A prerequisite to the start and growth of these cracks is the presence of tensile stresses on the surface. Stress corrosion has been observed in many metals, including copper, lead, stainless steel, iron, brass, magnesium, aluminum, and zinc. It has usually been associated with residual or assembly stresses. Since it is strictly a surface phenomenon in its early stages and is entirely dependent upon the presence of tensile stresses of considerable magnitude, considerable protection is offered by appropriate prestressing. The major factor in this protection is certainly the introduction of compressive residual surface stress.

There are uses of prestressing techniques for reasons other than, or supplemental to, strength improvement. These, however, are usually so specific in terms of interest and material that they will be only briefly described here. The following list is typical of some of these possible uses:

3.3.1 SURFACE HARDENING—When materials subject to work hardening are mechanically prestressed, the surface layers may be significantly hardened. This may be useful in enhancing resistance to wear or other surface damage.

3.3.2 SURFACE FINISHING—The "characterizing" of the surface obtained when prestressed is often a useful engineering property. Surface rolling frequently produces a surface so smooth that subsequent grinding or other finishing steps may not be needed. Ball burnishing and some of the techniques used on holes (bearingizing, ballizing, taper plugs, and so on) can produce quite smooth surfaces.

3.3.3 CONTOUR FORMING—An example of this is the use of rollers or racks to produce strong, accurate threads and splines. Another use of rollers is to form fillets to a desired contour.

3.3.4 SIZING—Some of the methods, under certain conditions, may perform a useful sizing function. Bearingizing and ballizing are examples of this use.

3.3.5 SURFACE QUALITY CHECK—All the methods for mechanical prestressing depend on the yield strength of the metal being exceeded, usually by a high, localized pressure. Certain types of metallurgical flaws at, or near, the surface may be rendered obvious because of local spalling when subjected to this high stress. Thus, in a limited sense, the prestressing also acts as a proof test of the surface layers.

3.4 Choosing a Prestressing Process—There are many situations where either shot peening or rolling may be feasible to prestress and a choice is to be made between them. In this situation, there are several factors to be considered:

3.4.1 GEOMETRY OF AREA TO BE PRESTRESSED—There are almost no limitations on the shape of areas that may be shot peened, with the exception of small deep holes or slots. Rolling, on the other hand, can usually be applied only to surfaces of revolution.

3.4.2 RESIDUAL STRESS DISTRIBUTION—The depth of residual compression that can be set up by rolling is considerably greater than that set up by shot peening, although the surface compressive stress appears to be about the same for both. While there are little available data comparing fatigue strength of identical specimens prestressed by these two methods, one would expect that the potential for improvement by rolling would equal, and probably exceed, that of shot peening.

3.4.3 CHARACTER OF SURFACE FINISH—Shot peening will produce a surface whose roughness is generally dependent on the material hardness, shot size, and peening intensity. Rolling generally produces a much smoother surface than shot peening.

3.4.4 COST—There are very little available data to support specific statements here. On large or complex areas, shot peening will usually be cheaper, while on smaller areas of simple shape, rolling may be more favorable. A factor that enters the cost situation is the large capital investment required for an efficient shot peening machine, while rolling can be done in common machine tools with a modest tooling investment, unless highly automated equipment is desirable. Parts often require masking before peening and cleaning afterwards. Regardless of the comparison of these two methods, neither are expensive when compared to other methods of precision finishing.

3.5 Limitations and Precautions—There are examples available showing that significant benefits are possible through prestressing practices. As with all potent techniques, certain ground rules must be observed and basic limitations recognized, or trouble may be encountered. In this section, some of these features will be discussed briefly.

3.6 Introduction of Prestress—Perhaps the most obvious precaution here is that all the sensitive area of the part must be covered by prestressing. The operation should cover enough area for its boundaries to be in moderately stressed zones, and all of the intended area must be properly covered.

The size of the part needs to be considered in specifying rolling conditions. The volume of metal which has not been plastically deformed by the working must be at least several times as great as that which has been plastically deformed. This is necessary to insure that appropriate surface compression stresses are introduced without unduly high internal balancing stresses of a tensile nature.

Since the introduction of prestresses depends on a nonuniform plastic action, in general, the dimensions of a part will change when prestressed. In addition to this stress effect, there may be an apparent change in size as a result of change in the geometrical character of the surface. This would be a "lowering" effect when a rough surface is smoothed by rolling, or a "raising" effect when a smooth surface is peened with large shot or a peening tool. Generally, none of these effects are large, but if fits or alignments must be precise, they should be considered.

One of the more subtle limitations on mechanical prestressing is that there is no convenient and practical method for inspecting the work produced. One must concentrate on control of the process. If this is not done diligently, there is the risk of more or less prestressing intensity than intended. If on the low side, the improvement that was counted on may not be obtained. If on the high side, some materials actually may be harmed, with or without apparent visual indication of this damage.

3.6.1 MAINTENANCE OF PRESTRESSES—Once prestresses have been properly introduced, they obviously must be kept present during service. Subsequent processing or unusual service conditions must not cancel the benefits. Machining may cut away some of, or all, the compressive layer. Sufficient exposure to elevated temperature may relax residual stresses. Straightening or stretching operations may reduce or neutralize the deliberately introduced prestresses. Analogous effects may be present in service environments which may jeopardize the effect that prestressing should have on performance.

3.6.2 FUNDAMENTAL LIMITATIONS—One must recognize that the improvements in some particular mechanical property of a part which may be obtained through prestressing may lead to a change in some other property. The compressive surface prestresses are invariably balanced by tensile stresses below the surface. This internally balanced stress system may result in a lowered elastic limit or creep resistance. Under certain conditions, the fatigue resistance may actually be reduced. Examples of this could be small diameter rolled parts tested under axial loading or a relatively thin wall tube rolled externally and tested with fluctuating internal pressure.

The excellent protection against surface abuse under fatigue loading that prestressing gives obviously is limited in the sense that abuse exceeding some depth will be just as harmful, whether the part was prestressed or not. The relationship of this depth to the intensity of working, and knowledge of whether there is any notch depth where the part's fatigue resistance is actually harmed by prior prestressing, are points on which little evidence is available, but which should be useful fields of research.

There are other properties where, in general, little or no improvement is expected. Static tensile strength is one of these. Since this is the origin of the fatigue curve, the improvements should be related in some increasing proportion with increased cycles. Part rigidity or stability are generally considered insensitive to prestressing, as is impact strength. The latter property, however, may bear investigating for sensitive materials.

3.7 Specific Characteristics of Various Materials—In the illustrations used earlier in this chapter, an attempt was made to show responses of a variety of metals. Mechanical prestressing methods (other than shot peening) have been applied to the following materials, with at least some degree of success: wrought steel, at hardness levels ranging up to Rockwell C 45; gray, malleable, and nodular cast iron; cast and wrought aluminum; and cast and wrought magnesium. This list is not intended to be exclusive of other materials.

Optimum prestressing intensities and specific peculiarities of these materials are matters on which little or no published information is available. Certain materials show that a rather well defined optimum prestressing intensity leads to maximum improvement. Others have shown the same order of improvement over widely varying intensities. Some have shown good results with surfaces which were considerably degraded by the prestressing operation, based on visual observation. Others have shown an actual loss in fatigue strength with surfaces which, under casual observation, had an excellent appearance. Since all these observations were based on specific, individual tests, it seems unwise to attempt to generalize the results. As stated earlier, the choice of a prestressing method and intensity should be based on objective tests of the part under consideration, or previous experience with similar parts under similar load conditions.

4. Theory of Surface Rolling for Fatigue Improvement (by C. W. Cable)

4.1 Introduction—Proper application of controlled surface rolling is an effective method for improvement of fatigue performance. This chapter will discuss the reasons for this improvement and note some necessary conditions associated with the typical residual stress systems obtained from surface rolling. For simplicity, the discussion of residual stress distribution is confined to a two-dimensional presentation of unidirectional stresses. The actual application of this theory to a particular part would necessarily include a stress analysis suitable and adequate for that part. It will also be shown that, while local plastic deformation must occur during rolling to obtain necessary prestressing, the combined residual and applied stresses obtained in service should be within the elastic region; any yielding will change the residual stress system.

4.2 Effects of Surface Rolling—There are three principal changes caused by surface rolling to the part:

a. The surface finish is obviously "rolled," "roller burnished," and so on.
b. Surface layers of material are strain hardened or cold worked.
c. Surface layers are plastically deformed during rolling with the result that residual stresses are produced.

Each of these effects can influence fatigue performance. A great deal of work has been done to investigate the relationship of these factors especially with shot peening. The reader is referred to the references for a more complete review of data on this subject. [2]

It has been commonly accepted for many years that a smoother surface finish will result in fatigue improvement due to the reduced extent of minute surface imperfections. Also commonly accepted is the fact that fatigue failures usually originate at vulnerable stressed surface areas. Accordingly, we may expect that the finer surface finish produced by rolling will contribute to fatigue improvement.

In considering the effects of cold working the surface layers on fatigue performance, it has been shown that, within limits, both tensile strength and fatigue limit are increased by increasing amounts of cold work. The fatigue limit, however, does not increase in proportion to the increase in tensile strength, i.e.: the endurance ratio is reduced. Excessive cold working can even result in a decrease in fatigue strength (5). Since surface rolling actually changes the surface layers of material by cold working, we may expect this to affect the fatigue performance of the part.

These effects are generally considered to be secondary in importance to the effects of residual compressive stresses. It has been shown that heating of shot peened surfaces will reduce fatigue performance, even though hardness and surface finish were not significantly affected (6). Sigwart has reported fatigue improvement by residual surface compressive stresses obtained by quenching (7). Horger has noted that fatigue cracks were initiated at a rolled surface, but that the cracks then progressed at a slower rate than in comparable specimens which were not rolled (11).

2. Numbers in parentheses in text and tables refer to references at end of report.

4.3 Residual Stresses—For the purposes of this discussion, only the simple case of uniaxial stress in a two-dimensional section is illustrated. The necessary extension of the principles outlined herein to more complex analysis can be carried out consistently with the stress analysis required for the particular part. The discussion also assumes that we are dealing with a piece of homogeneous material, i.e., microstresses are not considered here.

Consider a round bar section longitudinally as shown in Figure 1. It has a known or assumed residual stress distribution near the surface as indicated by the heavy line showing the stress distribution across the section. By application of two basic principles of statics requiring equilibrium of forces and of moments, for any transverse section through Figure 1, it can be stated that:

a. The sum of the axial tensile and compressive forces must be equal to zero. If Section A-A, Figure 1, were taken from a flat plate, the areas bounded by the curve and the zero stress line on the compression side would equal the area on the tension side.
b. The opposing moments must be equal so that the sum of these moments equals zero.

The stress distribution curve is shown completed by the light line in a typical shape conforming to these principles. Note that these do not define the intensity of the unknown stresses or their distribution; the exact shape of the curve is not yet determined. It does provide insight, however, into the problems and also accents a very significant point: whenever there is a given prestressed region, as at a surface, there must also be a balancing region of opposite residual stress, usually of different intensity.

Figure 2 shows the same bar as in Figure 1 except that it has been bored out. Note that the tensile stress has been increased, also the compressive stress has been reduced. Further, careful measurement will show that the bar is longer.

Figure 3 shows a narrow strip cut from the tubular section of Figure 2. The strip is bowed, similar to the familiar Almen strip used in shot peening. The compressive stress has been further reduced, but a compressive stress at the opposite surface has also been produced with this relaxation. The necessary moment and force equilibrium has been maintained.

In other words, prestressing means that the part has been mechanically processed so that it contains a desired residual stress distribution which must be balanced both as to forces and moments. The exact distribution is related to process and material.

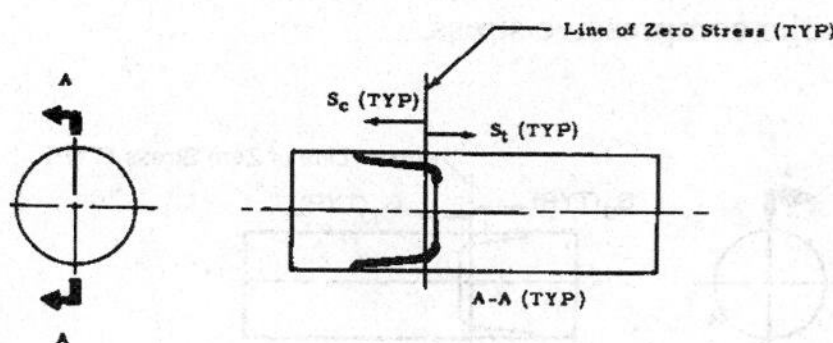

FIGURE 1—LONGITUDINALLY SECTIONED ROUND BAR

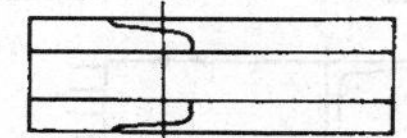

FIGURE 2—LONGITUDINALLY SECTIONED ROUND BAR, BORED OUT

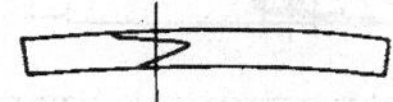

FIGURE 3—STRIP CUT FROM LONGITUDINALLY SECTIONED ROUND BAR, BORED OUT

The previous paragraphs have assumed a part with an existing desired residual stress distribution. To illustrate how the desired stress distribution was accomplished, assume there is a piece of uniform homogeneous material completely free from residual stresses. When, by definition, any loads are applied which produce only elastic stresses, the part will return to its original condition upon release of these loads. Further, if subjected to an assumed uniform plastic deformation, the shape will be altered, but no residual stresses will be produced. Therefore, to produce residual stresses by mechanical means in a part consisting of one piece of a uniform homogeneous material, nonuniform plastic deformation is necessary. This may be accomplished by locally deforming the surface by rolling, or other processes.

The most significant point is that previous local nonuniform plastic deformation has produced the present condition of static residual stress equilibrium. When known or determined, these stresses may be treated by proper application of the theory of elasticity. Local plastic deformation has been illustrated by Sigwart, using, as one example, the displacement and yielding of material under a Brinell ball (7). Essentially, high local contact stresses produce local biaxial tensile yielding at the surface of the part when the deforming load is applied. When this load is released, the yielded material will have been effectively stretched or spread out. The normal complete recovery of the adjacent unyielded material from its elastic deformation is then prevented. An equilibrium condition results where the yielded material is restrained in a biaxial residual compressive stress state by the unyielded material which is essentially in a residual tensile stress state.

In the preceding section it has been stated that a desirable residual stress distribution would improve fatigue performance. How this occurs will now be considered.

Figure 4A again shows a typical assumed residual stress distribution with surface layers in residual compression. It has been shown that mechanical prestressing is obtained by plastic deformation of a local area of initially uniform material and that the theory of elasticity must be applicable to the prestressed part. If an external load is then applied to the part to obtain a given uniform load stress as in axial tension or a nonuniform stress as in bending the applied load stresses and the residual stresses are additive algebraically. This rule holds true as long as the stresses remain below the elastic limit at all locations; when unloaded the part will elastically return to its original condition with residual stresses unchanged.

Superimposing an applied load tensile stress of less than the residual compressive stress allows the material to remain in compression; Figure 4B shows a slight increase so that an applied tensile stress greater than the residual compressive stress will cause the surface layer to be in tension, as in Figure 4C. The core material will have a final tensile stress greater than the applied tensile stress. Where applied load compressive stress is superimposed on an existing residual compressive stress layer the resultant compressive stress is increased, as in Figure 4D. The allowable applied compressive stress, therefore, may be reduced, even though the yield strength of the strain hardened surface layers will usually be significantly increased by rolling. Figure 4E shows the effect of a residual stress distribution upon stress range when exposed to cyclic tensile and compressive applied load stresses. The vulnerable surface layers under these conditions are exposed only to cyclic compressive stress.

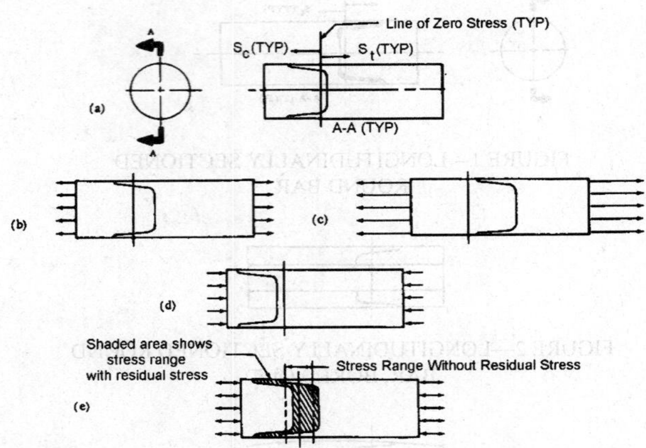

FIGURE 4—EFFECTS OF RESIDUAL STRESS DISTRIBUTION

The effects of geometric stress concentrations such as grooves, oil holes, fillets, and so on, must be considered both in compression and in tension to arrive at the resultant stress at any location. If the material yield strength is exceeded by the resultant stress, the residual stress will be changed after release of the applied load. For example: if an applied load compressive stress equal to 0.3 of the yield strength is added to a local residual stress of 0.5 of the yield strength in the presence of a stress concentration with a factor of 2.5, the calculated local resultant stress in compression equals 0.5 + (0.3 × 2.5) or 1.25 the yield strength. Obviously, local yielding must occur. Note that the actual local residual stress intensity value of 0.5 yield strength was used in this calculation and that this may be greater than the average residual stress at the surface away from the stress concentration depending upon the relative size of the stress concentration and the extent of the residual stress field.

Dugdale, in recent work, has shown some significant effects on fatigue performance obtained by prestressing machined notched bars. Compression preloading resulted in a reduction of fatigue performance (8). This may be explained as follows: it can be shown that a sufficiently large compression load applied to a notched bar would result in yielding at the notch. Upon release of the load, the root of the notch would be in residual tension. Such a residual tension stress at the notch would cause a reduction in fatigue life.

4.4 Fatigue—In fatigue loading one is concerned with the effects of variable loads of less than the critical static loads on structural integrity, part performance, or service life. The actual loads may be uniform alternating loads or may be applied in a random manner and sequence. It is most important that any experimental or analytical techniques simulate or duplicate actual service conditions as closely as practical, if reliable design decisions are to be based on the results of using these techniques. Actual service is still the best proof of a satisfactory design. For most experimental work a uniform, essentially sinusoidal, alternating load is used. The mean stress may be zero, compression, or tension. The rotating beam test gives a zero mean stress.

A local surface residual compressive stress will affect only the resultant local mean stress; obviously it can have no effect on the amplitude of the alternating stress. Any improvement in fatigue performance due to residual stress, therefore, must come from a reduction of the mean tension stress at the surface. A Goodman diagram, Figure 5A (9), has often been used to illustrate in a general manner the relative effects of mean and alternating stresses on the fatigue limit. Note that the reduction of the mean tensile stress allows an increase in the alternating stress, and, therefore, with a given alternating stress, reduction of the mean stress will improve fatigue performance. Experimental data has indicated that this general relationship is true; however, the exact linearity indicated by the Goodman diagram is not obtained. Figure 5B (9) shows a modified Goodman diagram with a plot of typical fatigue life data. Figure 5C (9) illustrates another method used for plotting such data. It is seen that a reduction of the mean stress should increase the fatigue life. The reader is referred to the work of Grover, Dolan, and others for a more thorough review (9).

For the purposes of illustration in this discussion, assume a fatigue loaded specimen with a known surface defect or crack of significant depth as shown in Figure 6. It is easily seen with this idealized defect that the specimen can transmit compressive stresses across the crack without difficulty. A tensile stress, however, will cause the crack to act as an extremely effective stress concentration. Plastic deformation will occur at the tip of the crack, with the crack necessarily extending deeper into the material; repeated cyclic loading will continue this damage until a critical cracksize is reached and failure occurs. By reducing the local surface tensile stress in the vicinity of the defect, the damage per cycle will be reduced and longer fatigue life will be obtained.

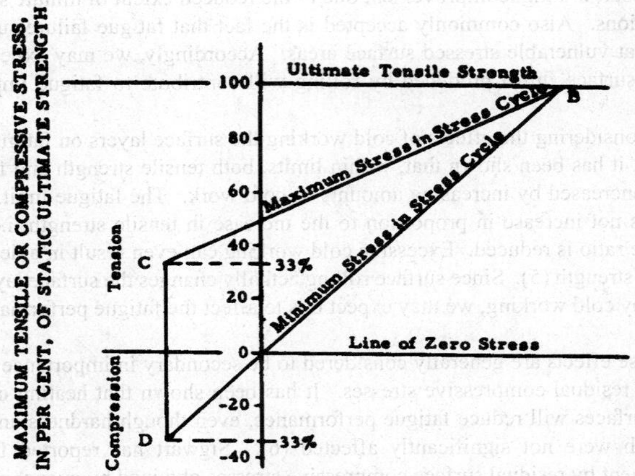

FIGURE 5A—GOODMAN DIAGRAM (9)

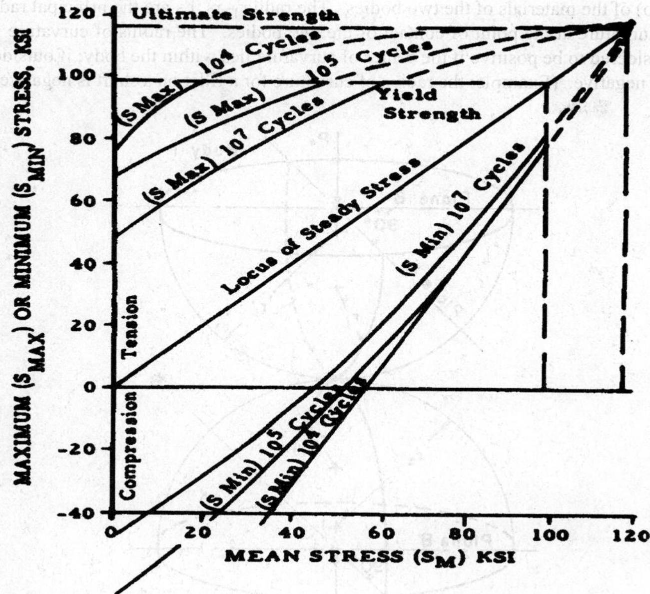

FIGURE 5B—MODIFIED GOODMAN DIAGRAM (9)

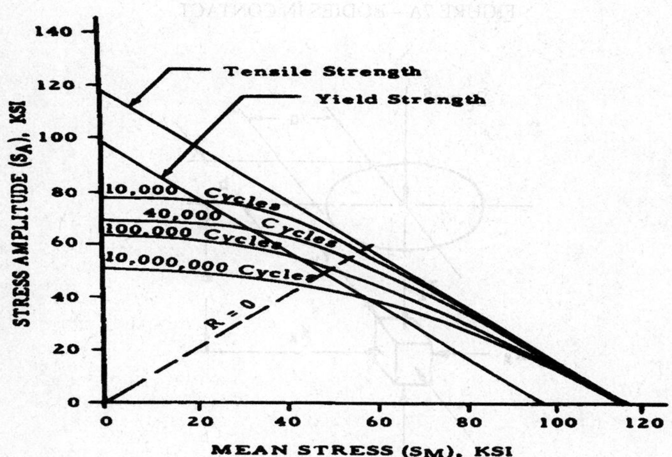

FIGURE 5C—EFFECT OF COMBINED AND STEADY STRESS ON FATIGUE STRENGTH

4.5 Limitations of Theory—The previous sections have assumed that the material used was capable of sufficient local plastic deformation during the rolling process to produce an adequately rolled surface without deleterious effects on the material. It was also assumed that elastic behavior was obtained at stress level less than the yield strength of the material. Further assumptions have been made that the material was originally free from residual stresses and that thermal or other processes have not been introduced in the system.

If the ductile capacity of the material is questionable so that there is the possibility of surface defects being initiated, a metallurgical examination is definitely indicated. Even when this condition exists, some improvement may be possible if the depth of the deepest defect is less than the depth of the maximum compressive stress; however, the danger here lies in the possibility of defects extending beyond the compressive layer so that rapid failure could result.

Yield strength is an arbitrary definition of a measurable amount of nonelastic behavior for many materials, such as 0.2% offset on a load-strain curve. The elastic behavior and yield strength of strain hardened material will be improved over the original material. It follows that the foregoing references to yield strength should be considered in this light with due allowance for the actual elastic behavior of the original and of the strain hardened material.

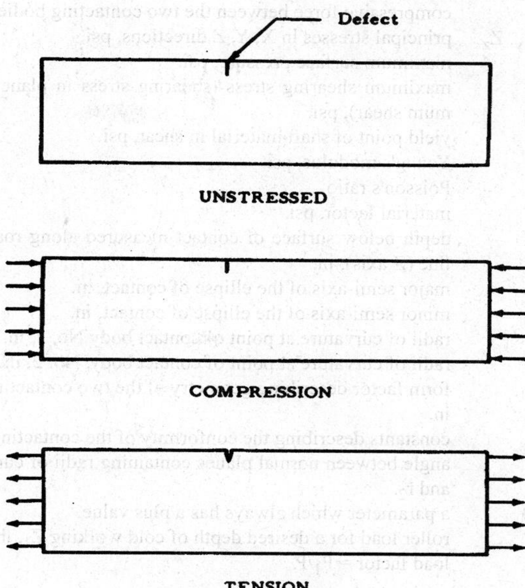

FIGURE 6—EFFECTS OF VARIOUS TYPES OF STRESS UPON KNOWN SURFACE DEFECT

The existence of residual stresses prior to surface rolling complicates the picture, particularly if these are present at a greater depth than the surface rolled layer. Surface rolling, however, can improve such parts, especially where a thin surface layer is in residual tension.

It should be noted that elevated temperature exposure may result in creep or relaxation of residual stresses or loss of residual stress by lowering of the yield strength. Similarly, severe temperature gradients and differential expansion may alter or relieve residual stresses. In other words, subsequent processing and service conditions should be examined to insure that the prestressed condition will be retained.

The actual maximum intensity of the residual compressive stress will vary with processing controls, but, for heavy rolling of ductile material, it may be expected to slightly exceed the yield strength of the original material. Residual stresses of this magnitude have been reported for shot peening by Brodrick (10), and Horger has noted residual compressive stresses of over 100,000 psi longitudinal and 46,000 psi tangential from surface rolling of normalized and tempered SAE 1050 steel (11). Far more information is available on fatigue improvement than actual residual stress data.

4.6 Conclusion—Surface rolling may be expected to improve fatigue performance when properly applied to suitable parts and materials. The process improves the surface finish, work hardens the surface layers, and imposes a residual compressive stress on these surface layers. Of these three effects, fatigue improvement is attributed principally to the super-imposition of a residual stress system upon the expected applied load stress system. Thus, the local mean tensile stress at the vulnerable surface of the part is either reduced or reversed so that the mean stress is actually in compression.

5. Calculations for the Surface Rolling Process (by H. R. Neifert)

5.1 Introduction—Successful application of the surface rolling process requires that the load on the roller be of sufficient magnitude to cause plastic deformation in the surface material of the work piece. Plastic deformation is obtained when the stress produced by the roller exceeds the elastic limit of the material being rolled. The depth beneath the surface to which the rolling is effective is dependent upon the geometrical shape of the roller and work piece, the materials involved, and the roller load. These factors can be related by mathematical analyses which permit a determination of required roller loading based either on the maximum compression in the contact area or on the shearing stress beneath the contact area.

The mathematical analysis assumes that the stresses produced in the contacting bodies are within the elastic range of the material. Experience, however, has indicated that the theory may be extended into the plastic stress range with reasonable accuracy for the practical application discussed herein.

LIST OF SYMBOLS

P	compressive force between the two contacting bodies, lb.
X_x, Y_y, Z_z	principal stresses in X, Y, Z directions, psi.
S_c	maximum surface pressure, psi.
S_s	maximum shearing stress (shearing stress in plane of maximum shear), psi.
S_{s1}	yield point of shaft material in shear, psi.
E	Young's modulus, psi.
μ	Poisson's ratio.
K	material factor, psi.
Z	depth below surface of contact measured along road centerline (Z axis), in.
a	major semi-axis of the ellipse of contact, in.
b	minor semi-axis of the ellipse of contact, in.
r_1, r'_1	radii of curvature at point of contact body No. 1, in.
r_2, r'_2	radii of curvature at point of contact body, No. 2, in.
δ	form factor describing geometry of the two contacting bodies, in.
α, β	constants describing the conformity of the contacting bodies.
φ	angle between normal planes containing radii of curvature, r_1 and r_2.
Cos θ	a parameter which always has a plus value.
P_1	roller load for a desired depth of cold working Z_1, lb.
m	load factor = P_1/P.
e	eccentricity of contact ellipse, $\frac{b}{a}$ or $\frac{B}{\alpha}$
PMP_c	hardness, Rockwell "C" scale

5.2 Mathematical Analysis for Determination of Stress in the Contact Area—When two bodies in contact are forced together by an external force, as in Figure 7A, stresses are induced in both bodies beneath the area of contact. The three principal stresses, X_x, Y_y, Z_z (Figure 7B) are maximum at the contacting surface and decrease as Z, the depth beneath the surface, increases. The problem of evaluating the stresses in the surface of the contacting bodies was solved by H. Hertz (12, 13) [3]. This work was later extended (14, 15, 16) so that stresses beneath the area of contact could be calculated. The magnitude of the subsurface stresses along the load centerline for a typical contact area is shown in Figure 8. The use of the subsurface shearing stress in the computation of roller load will be discussed later in this chapter.

The maximum pressure between the two bodies, which acts at the center of the elliptical contact area, can be calculated from the equation:

$$S_c = \frac{3}{2}\frac{P}{\pi ab} \qquad \text{(Eq. 1)}$$

as indicated in Figure 7B.

It must be emphasized that the semi-axes of the pressure ellipse, a and b, are the projected semi-axes and are not measured along the curvature of the pressure surface.

In the general case of compression of two bodies, where the surface of contact is an ellipse, the semi-axes are given by the equations:

$$a = \alpha\sqrt[3]{P\frac{\delta}{K}};\; b = \beta\sqrt[3]{P\frac{\delta}{K}} \qquad \text{(Eq. 2)}$$

The form factor, δ, describing the geometry of the two contacting bodies, and the material factor, K, are given by the expressions:

$$\delta = \frac{4}{\frac{1}{r_1}+\frac{1}{r_2}+\frac{1}{r'_1}+\frac{1}{r'_2}} \qquad \text{(Eq. 3)}$$

$$K = \frac{8}{3}\frac{E_1E_2}{E_2\left(1-\mu_1^2\right)+E_1\left(1-\mu_2^2\right)} \qquad \text{(Eq. 4)}$$

3. Numbers in parentheses in text and tables refer to references at end of report.

where E_1,μ_1 and E_2,μ_2 are elastic constants (Young's modulus and Poisson's ratio) of the materials of the two bodies. The radii r_1, r_2, r'_2 are the principal radii of curvature at the point of contact of the two bodies. The radius of curvature is considered to be positive if the center of curvature lies within the body; if outside, it is negative. (Example: the radius of curvature for a fillet on a shaft is negative.)

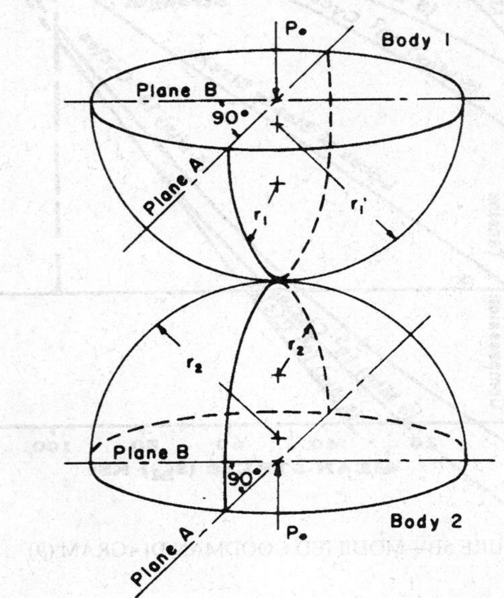

FIGURE 7A—BODIES IN CONTACT

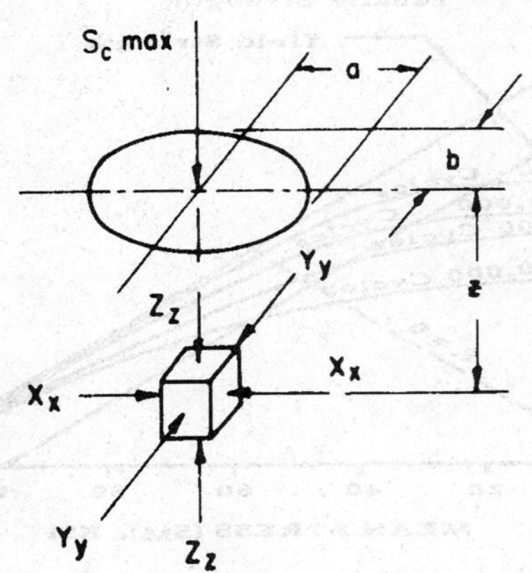

FIGURE 7B—AN ELLIPTICAL AREA OF CONTACT OF TWO BODIES AND PRINCIPAL STRESSES ACTING ON AN ELEMENT BENEATH THE CENTER OF CONTACT

In addition, planes A and B should be chosen so that plane A contains r_1 and r_2 and:

$$\frac{1}{r_1}+\frac{1}{r_2} > \frac{1}{r'_1}+\frac{1}{r'_2}$$

This is necessary to obtain positive values of Cos θ in Equations (5) and (6).

Plane A then determines the direction of the semi-minor axis of the pressure area and plane B the direction of the semi-major axis of the pressure area.

The values of α and β are given in Figure 9 as a function of Cos θ where

$$\cos\theta = \pm\frac{\delta}{4}\left[\left(\frac{1}{r_1}-\frac{1}{r'_1}\right)^2+\left(\frac{1}{r_2}\pm\frac{1}{r'_2}\right)^2+2\left(\frac{1}{r_1}-\frac{1}{r'_1}\right)\left(\frac{1}{r_2}-\frac{1}{r'_2}\right)\cos 2\phi\right]^{1/2} \qquad \text{(Eq. 5)}$$

and where θ is an angle between normal planes containing radii of curvature r_1 and r_2. Cos θ is merely a parameter and the plus value is always used.

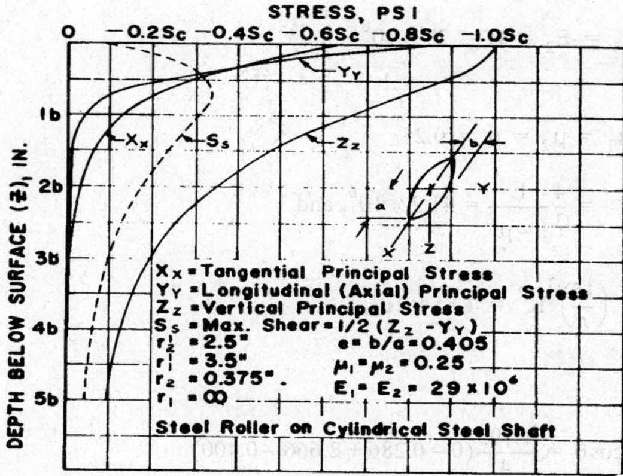

FIGURE 8—MAGNITUDE OF PRINCIPAL STRESSES AND MAXIMUM SHEARING STRESS ALONG LOAD CENTERLINE

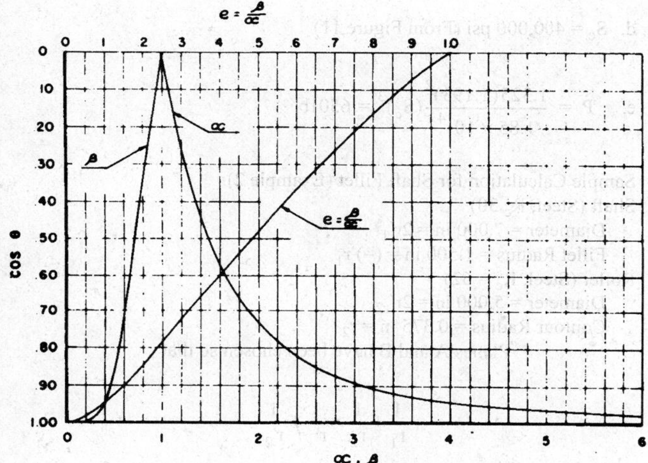

FIGURE 9—CURVES SHOWING VARIATION OF AB AND E WITH COS θ

The angle θ will usually be 0 deg when performing a surface rolling operation, since the axes of rotation of both bodies are generally in the same plane. Cos 2 θ is then equal to 1 and Equation (5) may be written in the simplified form.

$$\cos\theta = \frac{\delta}{4}\left(\frac{1}{r_1} - \frac{1}{r'_1} + \frac{1}{r_2} - \frac{1}{r'_2}\right) \quad \text{(Eq. 6)}$$

The ratio of $\frac{P}{(S_c)^3}$ can be written from Equation (1) as follows:

$$\frac{P}{(S_c)^3} = \frac{(\alpha\beta)^3}{\left(\frac{1.5}{\pi}\right)^3} \frac{\delta^2}{K^2} \quad \text{(Eq. 7)}$$

5.3 Determination of Roller Load Using Known S_c—Roller loads for surface rolling of parts and materials for which S_c has previously been determined may be computed using Equations (3), (4), (6), and (7). These equations are usually used in applications of surface rolling where the depth of working desired is only in the order of several thousandths of an inch, similar to that produced by shot peening.

The computation procedure may be briefly outlined as follows:

a. Calculate δ from Equation (3).
b. Calculate K from Equation (4). Values of K for several materials are given in Table 6.
c. Calculate Cosine θ from Equation (5) or (6) and read value of $(\alpha\beta)^3$ from Figure 10.
d. Determine required or desired S_c by test, or use values recommended in Table 7 or Figure 11.
e. Put these values into Equation (7), and solve for roller load P.

TABLE 6—ELASTIC CONSTANTS AND MATERIAL FACTORS FOR VARIOUS METALS ROLLED WITH STEEL ROLLER

Metal	Young's Modulus E, psi	Poisson's Ratio μ	K, psi	$\left(\frac{1.5}{\pi}\right)^3 K^2$
Steel	29×10^6	0.25	41.2×10^6	1.85×10^{14}
Aluminum	10×10^6	0.36	22.3×10^6	5.41×10^{13}
Magnesium	6.4×10^6	0.28	15.3×10^6	2.55×10^{13}

TABLE 7—VALUES OF S_c FOR SEVERAL MATERIALS (USED SUCCESSFULLY IN SPECIFIC CASES)

Material	psi	Source
Aluminum (Wrought)	362,000	G. A. Butz, Aluminum Company of America
Magnesium Alloy	258,000	R. L. Atkin and J. G. Mezoff (4)
Steel, R_c 30	400,000	J. O. Almen, also Figure 11 for steels of various hardness

TABLE 8—TABULATION OF α, β, e AND $(\alpha\beta)^3$ FOR VARIOUS VALUES OF θ AND COS θ (PLOTTED IN FIGureS 9 AND 10)

θ	Cos θ	α	β	$\left(\frac{\beta}{\alpha}\right)$	$(\alpha\beta)^3$
0	1.0000	∞	0	0	∞
10	0.9848	6.612	0.319	0.0483	9.383
20	0.9397	3.778	0.408	0.1080	3.662
30	0.8660	2.731	0.493	0.1805	2.441
35	0.8192	2.397	0.530	0.2211	2.050
40	0.7660	2.136	0.567	0.2655	1.776
45	0.7071	1.926	0.604	0.3136	1.574
50	0.6428	1.754	0.641	0.3655	1.421
55	0.5736	1.611	0.678	0.4209	1.303
60	0.5000	1.486	0.717	0.4825	1.210
65	0.4226	1.378	0.759	0.5508	1.144
70	0.3420	1.284	0.802	0.6246	1.092
75	0.2588	1.202	0.846	0.7038	1.052
80	0.1736	1.128	0.893	0.7917	1.022
85	0.0872	1.061	0.944	0.8897	1.005
90	0	1.000	1.000	1.0000	1.000

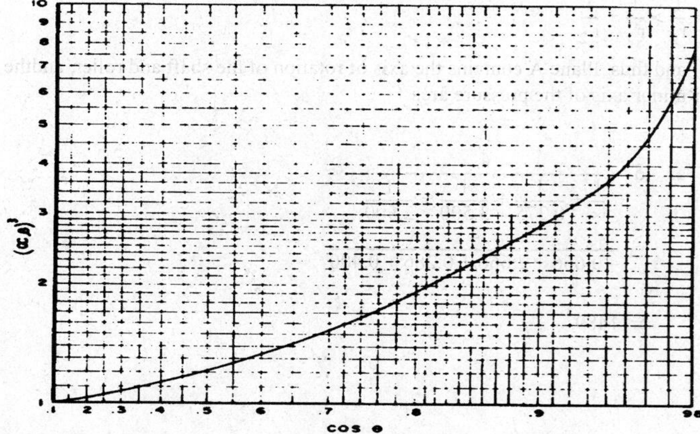

FIGURE 10—CURVES SHOWING VARIATION OF $(AB)^3$ WITH COS θ

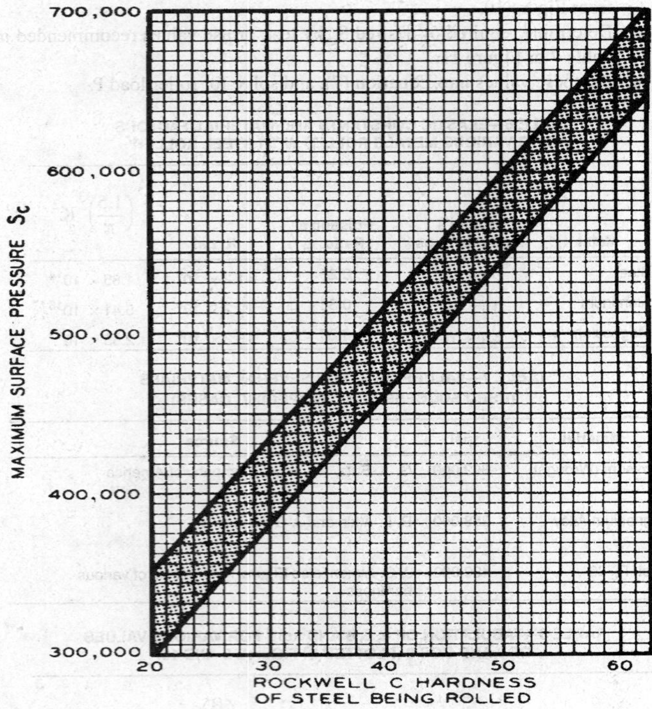

FIGURE 11—SUGGESTED S_C FOR STEEL OF VARIOUS HARDNESS (J. O. ALMEN)

For practical purposes, two assumptions are made in the application of these formulas. It will be noted that as the roller moves up a fillet, the radius of curvature of that fillet is constantly increasing. However, this change in radius, although numerically relatively great, has little effect on the value P/S_c^3. Consequently, this slight difference in value is assumed to be nonexistent. This same assumption is also applied to the roller when it is brought in contact with the surface at some angle other than 90 deg.

Sample Calculation for Cylindrical Shaft (Example 1):

Shaft (Steel, R_c 30)

Diameter = 7.000 in = $2r'_1$

Contour Radius = $\infty = r_1$

Roller (Steel, R_c 62)

Diameter = 5.000 in = $2r'_2$

Contour Radius = 0.375 in = r_2

Planes A and B have been chosen so that

$$\frac{1}{r_1} + \frac{1}{r_2} > \frac{1}{r'_1} + \frac{1}{r'_2}$$

and thus, Plane A contains the axis of rotation of the shaft and roller, andthe semi-minor axis of the pressure area.

a. $$\delta = \frac{4}{\frac{1}{\infty} + \frac{1}{0.375} + \frac{1}{3.500} + \frac{1}{2.500}} = \frac{4}{-0.666 + 2.666 + 0.286 + 0.400} = 1489$$

b. K, for steel roller and steel shaft, where:

$$E_1 = E_2 = E = 29 \times 10^6$$

$$\mu_1 = \mu_2 = \mu = 0.25$$

$$= \frac{4}{3}\frac{E}{1-\mu^2} = 41.2 \times 10^6, \text{ and}$$

$$\left(\frac{15}{\pi}\right)^3 K^2 = 1.85 \times 10^{14}$$

c. $$\cos\theta = \frac{1.193}{4}(0 - 0.286 + 2.666 - 0.400) = 0.592$$

$$(\alpha\beta)^3 = 1.325 \text{ (From Figure 10)}$$

d. S_c = 400,000 psi (From Figure 11)

e. $$P = \frac{1.325(1.193)^2}{1.85 \times 10^{14}}(S_c)^3 = 650\text{lb}$$

Sample Calculation for Shaft Fillet (Example 2):

Shaft (Steel, R_c 30)

Diameter = 7.000 in = $2r'_1$

Fillet Radius = 1.500 in = (–) r_1

Roller (Steel, R_c = 62)

Diameter = 5.000 in = $2r'_{r2}$

Contour Radius = 0.375 in = r_2

Planes A and B have been chosen so that

$$\frac{1}{r_1} + \frac{1}{r_2} > \frac{1}{r'_1} + \frac{1}{r'_2}$$

and again Plane A contains the axis of rotation of the shaft and roller, and the semi-minor axis of the pressure ellipse.

a. $$\delta = \frac{4}{-\frac{1}{1.5} + \frac{1}{0.375} + \frac{1}{3.500} + \frac{1}{2.500}} = \frac{4}{-0.666 + 2.666 + 0.286 + 0.400} = 1.489$$

b. $\left(\frac{15}{\pi}\right)^3 K^2 = 1.85 \times 10^{14}$ (Same as Example 1)

c. $$\cos\theta = \frac{1.489}{4}(-0.666 + 0.286 + 2.666 - 0.400) = 0.489$$

$$(\alpha\beta)^3 = 1.20 \text{ (From Figure 10)}$$

d. S_c = 400,000 psi (Same as Example 1)

e. $$P = \frac{1.20(1.489)^2}{1.85 \times 10^{14}}(S_c)^3 = 920\text{lb}$$

5.4 Mathematical Analysis for Determining and Relating Subsurface

Stresses—In the application of surface rolling to large shafts and various heavy walled steel parts, the possibility of shape distortion is not as critical as with parts of light section. Consequently, it has often been found desirable to surface roll heavy parts at roller loads which will produce plastic working to a much greater depth than the superficial rolling performed on parts of light section. Where such heavy pressures have been used on steel shafting, it is believed that the improvement in fatigue resistance obtained is the maximum that can be developed for the material by the surface rolling process. This contention pertains in particular to shafting having fitted members, such as railroad axles, marine shafting, and so on. For example press-fitted assemblies, using a 91/2 in. dia SAE 1050 normalized and tempered shaft surface rolled to an effective depth of 1/2 in., have shown a resistance to fatigue failure over twice that of assemblies not so rolled (17).

When surface rolling for deep penetration has been applied to such large parts, it has been found convenient to determine the roller load by a different approach than previously described using the maximum contact pressure S_c. The method used was suggested by S. Way (18) and relates roller load to the yield strength of the material being rolled and the desired depth of penetration.

When the pressure area is circular, b = a, and the "eccentricity" of the ellipse of contact e = b/a = 1. For $E_1 = E_2$ and $\mu_1 = \mu_2$, the principal stresses Z_z, X_x, and X_y are given by the equations:

$$Z_z = \frac{2aE}{\pi\delta(1-\mu^2)}\left[\frac{a^2}{a^2+Z^2}\right] \quad \text{(Eq. 8)}$$

$$X_x = Y_y = \frac{2aE}{\pi\delta(1-\mu^2)}\left[\frac{a^2}{a^2+Z^2} - (1+\mu)\left(1-\frac{Z}{a}\cot^{-1}\frac{Z}{a}\right)\right] \quad \text{(Eq. 9)}$$

These are stresses along the load centerline (Z axis), and Z is the depth below the surface of contact in inches. The maximum shearing stress at any point along the load centerline is equal to one-half the principal stress difference, and is then found from:

$$S_s = \frac{1}{2}(Z_z - Y_y) \quad \text{(Eq. 10)}$$

Substituting Equations (8) and (9) into Equation (10):

$$S_s = \frac{aE}{2\pi\delta(1-\mu^2)}\left[\frac{3a^2}{a^2+Z^2} - 2(1+\mu)\left(1-\frac{Z}{a}\cot^{-1}\frac{Z}{a}\right)\right] \quad \text{(Eq. 11)}$$

Now if various values of depth below the surface are assigned to Z a shear stress curve as shown in Figure 12 is obtained. The maximum for this curve occurs at Z = 0.467a. Similarly, curves may be obtained for other values of eccentricity "e". The family of curves plotted in Figure 12 can be used to permit development of a semigraphical solution for determining roller loads.

The semi-axis of a circular contact area as obtained from Equation (2) is:

$$a = \sqrt[3]{\frac{3P\delta(1-\mu^2)}{4E}} \qquad \alpha = 1 \qquad K = \frac{4E}{3(1-\mu^2)}$$

For E = 29 × 10^6, μ = 0.25 and P = 1000 lb,

$$\alpha = 0.02895\sqrt[3]{\delta}$$

For some other load $P_1 = P_M = 1000$ m,

$$a_1 = 0.02895\sqrt[3]{\delta m}, \qquad \text{or } a_1 = a\sqrt[3]{m} \quad \text{(Eq. 12)}$$

We may also set up the proportion, $\frac{Z}{a} = 0.467 = \frac{Z_1}{a}$

$$\text{Then, } \frac{Z_1}{a\sqrt[3]{m}} = \frac{Z}{a}, \text{ and } Z_1 = Z\sqrt[3]{m} \quad \text{(Eq. 13)}$$

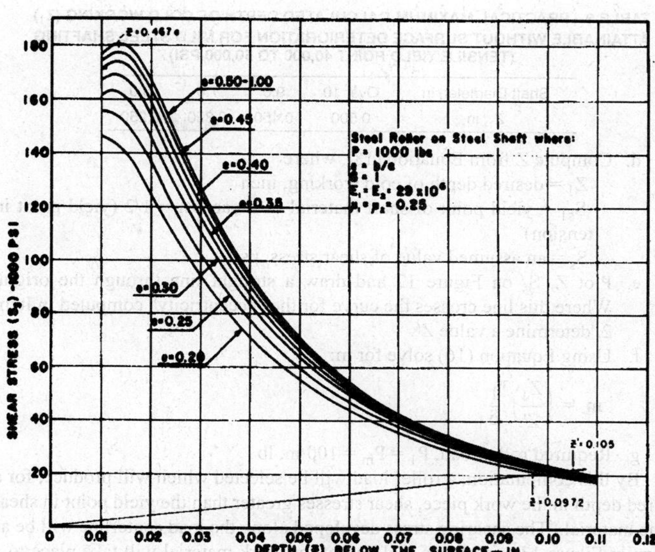

FIGURE 12—MAXIMUM SHEAR STRESS AT VARIOUS DEPTHS ALONG LOAD CENTERLINE

Finally, to obtain the shear stress S_s for the Load P_1, substitute into Equation (11) the values for a_1 and Z_1 from Equations (12) and (13):

$$S_{s_1} = \frac{a\sqrt[3]{m}E}{2\pi\delta(1-u)^2}\left[\frac{3(a\sqrt[3]{m})^2}{(a\sqrt[3]{m})^2+(Z\sqrt[3]{m})^2} - 2(1+\mu)\left(1+\frac{Z\sqrt[3]{m}}{a\sqrt[3]{m}}\cot^{-1}\frac{Z\sqrt[3]{m}}{a\sqrt[3]{m}}\right)\right] \quad \text{(Eq. 14)}$$

Comparing Equations (11) and (14) we observe that:

$$S_{s_1} = S_s\sqrt[3]{m} \quad \text{(Eq. 15)}$$

The relationships derived in Equations (13) and (15) are for circular contact where $e = \frac{b}{a} = 1$. For elliptical areas it can be similarly derived that:

$$Z_1 = Z\sqrt[3]{\delta m} \quad \text{(Eq. 16)}$$

$$S_{s_1} = S_{s3}\sqrt{\frac{m}{\delta^2}} \quad \text{(Eq. 17)}$$

$$Z = \frac{Z_1 S_s}{\delta S_{s_1}} \quad \text{(Eq. 18)}$$

This equation represents a straight line through the origin of Figure 12.

5.5 Determination of Roller Load for a Specific Depth of Plastic Working—Roller loads for surface rolling to a specific depth of penetration may now be computed by using Equations (16) and (18) and Figure 12. This method is usually used in applications where the depth of plastic working required for maximum fatigue resistance has been determined by previous testing, and is of some considerable magnitude.

The computation procedure may be briefly outlined as follows:

a. Compute δ from Equation (3).
b. Calculate Cos θ from Equation (5) or (6) and read the "eccentricity" e from Figure 9.
c. Determine desired depth of cold working from previous testing of particular material, or select from Table 9.

TABLE 9—PRACTICAL MAXIMUM CALCULATED DEPTH OF COLD WORKING (Z_1) ATTAINABLE WITHOUT SURFACE DETERIORATION FOR MILD STEEL SHAFTING (TENSILE YIELD POINT 40,000 TO 50,000 PSI)

Shaft Diameter, in	Over 10	9.0	7.0	5.0
Z_1, in	0.500	0.450	0.350	0.250

d. Compute Z from Equation (18), where
   Z_1 = desired depth of cold working, inch
   S_{s1} = yield point of shaft material in shear, psi = 1/2 (yield point in tension)
   S_s = an assumed value of shear stress, psi
e. Plot Z, S_s on Figure 12 and draw a straight line through the origin. Where this line crosses the curve for the "eccentricity" computed in Item 2, determine a value Z′.
f. Using Equation (16) solve for m:

$$m = \left(\frac{Z_1}{Z'}\right)^3 \frac{1}{\delta}$$

g. Required roller load, $P_1 = P_m$ = 100 m, lb

By this computation, a roller load will be selected which will produce, for a desired depth in the work piece, shear stresses greater than the yield point in shear of the material. The shearing stress developed along the load centerline will be as shown in Figure 13 and plastic yielding of the work material will take place to a depth Z_1.

This table is based on experience developed with 91/2 in dia press-fitted assemblies discussed by Horger (17), where fatigue resistance to fracture within the press fit was increased over 100% by surface rolling. A value of Z_1 equal to 5% of the shaft diameter has been found to be a good rule of thumb for applying a similar degree of surface rolling to mild steel shafting up to 10 in dia. For larger shaft sizes, surface deterioration limits the depth of rolling to less than 5% of shaft diameter.

Unpublished information developed by Horger and Neifert on similar 5 3/16 in dia shaft assemblies shows that surface rolling to a depth of 0.100 in will increase resistance to fracture by 50%. No curvature has been established relating fatigue resistance of such large assemblies with depth of cold working up to the practical maximum attainable. This example and others in the literature indicate that an appreciable increase in fatigue resistance is obtainable with a penetration less than maximum.

Although resistance to fatigue fracture is greatly increased by surface rolling, the stress level at which fatigue cracks initiate in press-fitted assemblies is little influenced. The effect of the compressive stress layer in retarding the propagation of fatigue cracks has been shown by Horger (17). Figure 22.

Sample Calculation for Cylindrical Shaft (Example 3)
Shaft (Steel, R_c 30)
Shaft (Steel, Y.P. = 50,000 psi)
   Diameter = 9,500 in = $2r'_1$
Contour Radius = ∞ = r_1
Roller (Steel, R_c = 62)
   Diameter = 10.000 in = $2r'_2$
Contour Radius = 1.500 in = r_2
Planes A and B have been chosen so that

$$\frac{1}{r_1} + \frac{1}{r_2} > \frac{1}{r'_1} + \frac{1}{r'_2}$$

and thus, Plane A contains the axis of rotation of the shaft and roller, and the semi-minor axis of the elliptical contact area.

1. $\delta = \dfrac{4}{\frac{1}{\infty} + \frac{1}{1.500} + \frac{1}{4.750} + \frac{1}{5.00}}$

   $= \dfrac{4}{0 + 0.666 + 0.211 + 0.200}$

   $= 3.71$

2. $\cos\theta = \dfrac{3.71}{4}(0 - 0.211 + 0.666 - 0.200)$

   $= 0.237$

   e = 0.74 (from Figure 9)

3. Z_1 = 0.450 in (Determined by fatigue test (17))

4. $Z = \dfrac{0.450(20,000)}{3.71(50,000/2)} = 0.0972\,\text{in}$

5. Plot Z, S_s (0.0972; 20,000) on Figure 12, and draw a straight line through this point and the origin. This line crosses the curve for e = 0.74 at Z^1 = 0.105 in.

6. $m = \left(\dfrac{0.450}{0.105}\right)^3 \dfrac{1}{3.71} = 21.3$

7. P_1 = 1000 m = 21,300 lb

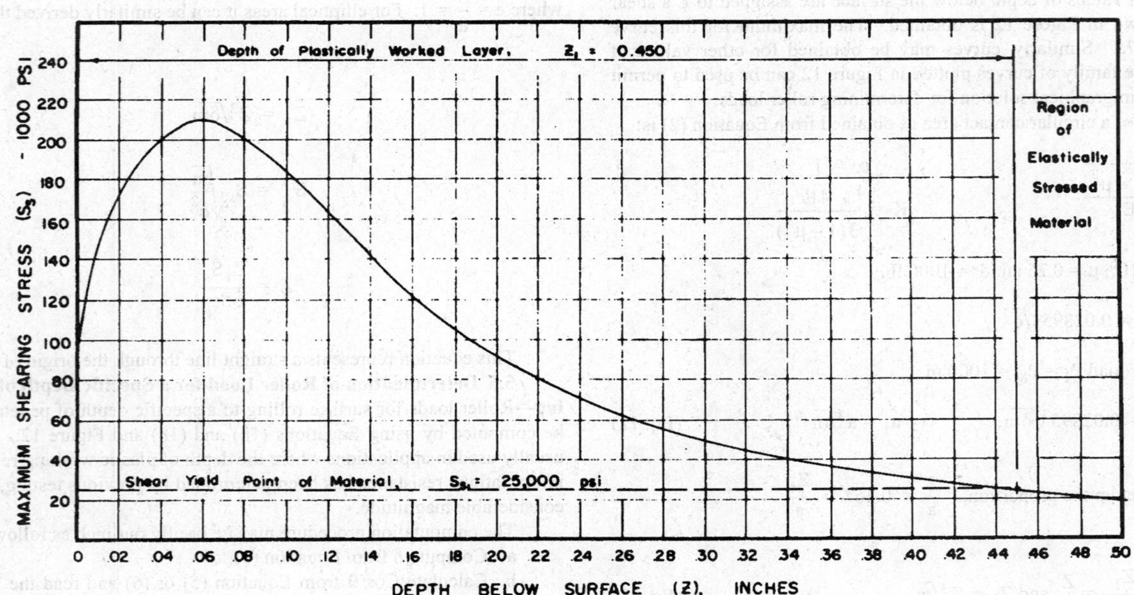

FIGURE 13—MAXIMUM SHEARING STRESS ALONG LOAD CENTER-LINE COMPUTED FOR SHAFT AND ROLLER OF EXAMPLE 3

If the maximum surface pressure, S_c, is computed for this example from Equation (1) a value of 650,000 psi is obtained. This will emphasize the order of magnitude of surface pressure developed in the deep rolling of heavy sections as compared with that used on parts of light section.

In surface rolling large shafts made from steel forgings having a yield point of 50,000 psi, experience has indicated that deterioration of the shaft surface will occur if the surface stress exceeds a value slightly above 650,000 psi. This surface deterioration is evidenced by the appearance of metallic flakes in the lubricant, as well as a scaly finish on the shaft surface. Such surface condition imposes a limitation on the magnitude of surface stress that can be used on each particular material, and can be used as an experimental criterion for determining maximum roller load in lieu of calculation.

5.6 Feed of Roller Along Shaft—Two factors must be considered in determining the optimum feed at which the roller should traverse the work. The rate should be slow enough to permit uniform working of the surface, but not so slow that the time consumed would make the surface rolling operation more costly than necessary.

As previously described, the contact area between the roller and work piece is generally an ellipse having semi-axes a and b, Figure 7B. It has been found by test that a feed rate equal to the half-width of contact in the plane of roller traverse will provide satisfactory coverage on steel shafts (19). The roller feed can therefore be determined from the equations for the semi-axes of the ellipse of contact:

$$a = \alpha \sqrt[3]{P\frac{\delta}{K}};\; b = \beta \sqrt[3]{P\frac{\delta}{K}}$$

In computing roller feed, the necessity for proper selection of planes A and B should again be emphasized. If planes A and B have been so chosen that:

$$\frac{1}{r_1} + \frac{1}{r_2} > \frac{1}{r'_1} + \frac{1}{r'_2}$$

plane A then determines the direction of the semi-minor axis of the pressure area and plane B the direction of the semi-major axis of the pressure area. If plane A contains the axis of rotation of the work piece, the maximum allowable feed will be:

$$b = \beta \sqrt[3]{P\frac{\delta}{K}} \text{(in/rev of work)}$$

If plane B contains the axis of rotation of the work piece, the maximum allowable feed will be:

$$a = \alpha \sqrt[3]{P\frac{\delta}{K}} \text{(in/rev of work)}$$

The ratio:

$$\frac{\text{Length of semi-axis in plane of roller traverse (in)}}{\text{Roller feed (in)}} = 1$$

may not be the optimum feed rate for all materials. Developmental work performed in connection with surface rolling of magnesium alloy wheels indicated that maximum improvement in fatigue strength was obtained when the above ratio was 10:1 (4).

Numerical computation of the feed rate, in addition to assuring proper coverage, can be useful in estimating the time required for a specific rolling operation. In production rolling of parts, the time factor could influence the selection of roller geometry as well as load.

Sample Calculation for Cylindrical Shaft of Example 1:

Plane A contains the axis of rotation of the work piece, so the maximum allowable feed will be:

$$b = \beta \sqrt[3]{P\frac{\delta}{K}}$$

For Cos θ = 0.592, β = 0.66 (from Figure 9)

Substituting values for P, δ and K previously determined in Example 1,

$$b = 0.666 \sqrt[3]{650\left(\frac{1.193}{41.2 \times 10^{06}}\right)}$$

$$= 0.017 \text{ in/rev}$$

The feed for rolling the fillet in Example 2 would be similarly calculated.

5.7 Experimental Verification of Depth of Cold Working—The mathematical analysis discussed in this chapter for computation of surface and subsurface stresses is theoretically correct only for loads which produce stresses within the elastic limits of the material of the contacting bodies. This fact has been recognized in extending the use of the formulas to computation of roller loads where the stresses are within the plastic range.

In the surface rolling of large mild steel forgings where roller load has been computed for a specific depth of working, the error between aim depth and actual depth obtained has not been unreasonable. This is shown by a typical example in Figure 14 where a hardness exploration on a transverse section indicated evidence of cold working to a depth of 0.500 in, whereas the aim depth was 0.450 in.

Thus, although these formulas are for stresses in the elastic range, they provide a convenient tool for relating rolling conditions of an unknown geometry to one which is known.

6. *Tooling for Surface Rolling (by A. E. Di Gregorio and W. J. Fuhrman)*

6.1 Introduction—The design and application of rollers and related tooling for refining and prestressing the surfaces of fillets, threads, and bearings or journals, thereby increasing fatigue life, will be reviewed in this chapter.

This material has been gathered from many large companies (21, 22, 24, 28, 29)[4] which have conducted original development work, and should be of value to engineers who desire to initiate experimental programs to determine the benefits that can be derived relative to their own products.

Quite notably, job shop and toolroom techniques in surface rolling have laid the groundwork for many of our current production accomplishments in this field—and with virtually identical and satisfactory results. For these reasons the basic and simpler rolling procedures, their history and advantages, are presented as an introduction to the production type tooling and machines presently employed for rolling of external cylindrical surfaces and fillets of shafts.

6.2 History—The principal application of surface rolling to increase fatigue qualities is on fillets and plain or threaded peripheries of shafts subjected to torsional and/or bending loads. In surface rolling, a suitably shaped hardened steel roller under a special load is forced into the fillet or against the periphery while the shaft is rotating for a predetermined number of revolutions, sufficient to smoothen the surface by plastic flow (26). (See Chapter 2 for a more complete discussion of the reasons for fatigue strengthening.)

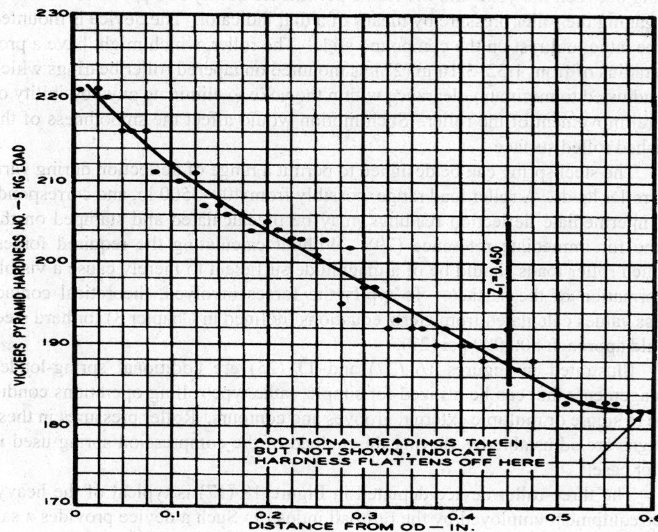

FIGURE 14—HARDNESS GRADIENT AT SURFACE OF 9 1/2 IN DIA CRANKPIN FORGING

4. Numbers in parentheses in text and tables refer to references at end of report.

As early as 1929, the beneficial effect in the prestressing of machined parts (29) through surface working by pressure rolling was realized by the railroad equipment industry in their manufacture of heavy, highly stressed components such as axle shafts and crankpins. Since that time, because of the large increase in fatigue resistance obtainable, surface rolling of critical sections has also been widely acclaimed and accepted for production applications in the automotive field.

Experience through the years has indicated that the success of surface rolling is contingent upon the proper design of rollers mainly, and, particularly if increased hardness and fatigue life is to be realized, upon roller pressures sufficiently great to cold work the material to an adequate depth. For example, portions of heavy railroad axles and crankpins are surface rolled under pressures that produce a cold-worked depth of 1/2 in or more (17). Although such operations will be discussed in the text, our interests will be concentrated mainly upon improving fatigue endurance through the superficial effects resulting from the compressive residual stress and the refinement of either machining or grinding imperfections, or both.

6.3 Simple Roller Devices—Rolling the periphery of straight external cylindrical surfaces on an experimental or toolroom basis is normally performed on a lathe or similar equipment. The rolling operation essentially consists of forcing a hardened steel roller under a predetermined load, applied by gravity, spring, air, or fluid pressure against the revolving part and applying a transverse feed to effect a sufficient overlap of the roller track, thus producing a cold-worked condition and a leveling off of tool marks to produce an improved bearing surface.

(See Chapter 3). Determined by such factors as roller shape, pressure, feed, lubricant, and mechanical condition of equipment, almost any degree of surface finish may be obtained by surface rolling. Although, in most cases, fine surface finishes are required to resist wear on bearings and journals, the fatigue resistance of rolled members is generally not dependent upon the degree of smoothness of the resulting surface (17). This is particularly true in deep-worked rolling conducted by the railroad industry. In contrast to this phenomenon, fatigue resistance of turned, polished, ground, or other types of machine-finished parts is largely influenced by both direction and irregularities of finish. In fact, polishing and fine finishes are not necessary from the standpoint of fatigue strength if the surface is to be rolled. When rolling, it is more essential to obtain an adequate cold working of the surface layers to the proper depth rather than to obtain a low microinch finish (17). A brief description of several special roller fixtures that can be applied to experimental type surface rolling on a lathe follows.

Figure 15 depicts a relatively simple device, wherein a precalibrated scale is employed to facilitate known and identical roller forces upon a succession of parts (29). As denoted, the tool steel roller, hardened to Rockwell C 62–65, is contained in a suitable yoke which in turn is hinged to a frame. The integral steel spring between the yoke and the frame permits flexibility and provides a method for gaging the roller pressure by means of a dial indicator. The device is mounted in the lathe tool rest on the compound slide. The roller, which might have a profile radius of from 1/32–3/16 in (27), is mounted on tapered roller bearings which are adjusted to minimum clearance within the yoke to eliminate any possibility of lateral movement of the roller. Such motion would affect the smoothness of the finished rolled surface.

The steel spring can be designed to permit a range of deflection during various roller loads. A roller load range, possibly from 400–3500 lb, and corresponding intermediate deflection readings, may be precalculated and stamped on the frame for immediate reference (29). Without calculating the required forces, applied roller loads should be of a magnitude sufficient to merely cause a visible deformation of the surface. To typify the forces involved, theoretical contact stress values calculated from Hertz equations (defined in Chapter 3) for hard steel would approach 800,000 psi (27).

Illustrated in Figures 16 (27) and 17 (25) are additional spring-loaded arrangements that can be utilized for simple, lathe type rolling operations conducive to single or multiple external grooves and contours. Roller pressures in these designs are adjustable by varying the preload of the compression spring used in either case.

The three-roller device depicted in Figure 18 (17) is typical of the heavy-duty equipment employed by the railroad industry. Such a device provides a satisfactory mechanical arrangement for applying a known pressure on cylindrical shafts. The reaction from the rolling pressure is taken through the closed frame supporting the rollers and is not transferred to the lathe centers as would be done with a single roller. The entire frame is permitted to float on the front and rear carriage supports on the lathe; the carriage feeds the rolling device along the shaft as though thread were being cut. This device has been designed to roll 6–15 in dia shafts by reversing and changing eccentric bushings on the spindles supporting the individual rollers. The top of the cradle opens so that a shaft may be loaded between the lathe centers without disturbing the rolling device. Two rollers have a relatively sharp contour radius of 11/2 in (each applying 18,500 lb while a third roller has a 5 in contour radius (applied at 21,000 lb). The former gives depth of work hardening and the latter a smooth finish (17).

When applied to 9 1/2 in dia shafts in the region where a press-fitted gear, pulley, or wheel is to be applied, the endurance limit against breakage in the fitted part is at least doubled. Depending on surface finish before rolling, a hardness penetration of about 7/8 in can be obtained with only 0.001-0.003 in reduction in shaft diameter. The depth of hardness penetration is determined by roller shape, size, pressure, and yield point of the shaft material and will, therefore, vary for each application (29).

Turned threads may be rolled in the root area to induce compressive residual stress and to improve fatigue strength. Small bolts and screws are rolled with a hand tool, Figure 19. The bolt is held with one hand and the tool is revolved with the other. Larger members are rolled with a lathe tool, Figure 20. The tool shank is a load-calibrated spring which is held in the tool post. Cross-sections of the roller and thread, Figure 21, indicate roller and thread geometry: A with no load on the thread, B with a roller force of 40 lb on the thread, and C the approximate areas of residual compressive stressed material at the thread roots. Resulting fatigue improvement is shown in Figure 22 for the three series of connecting rod bolts used in aircraft engines (30).

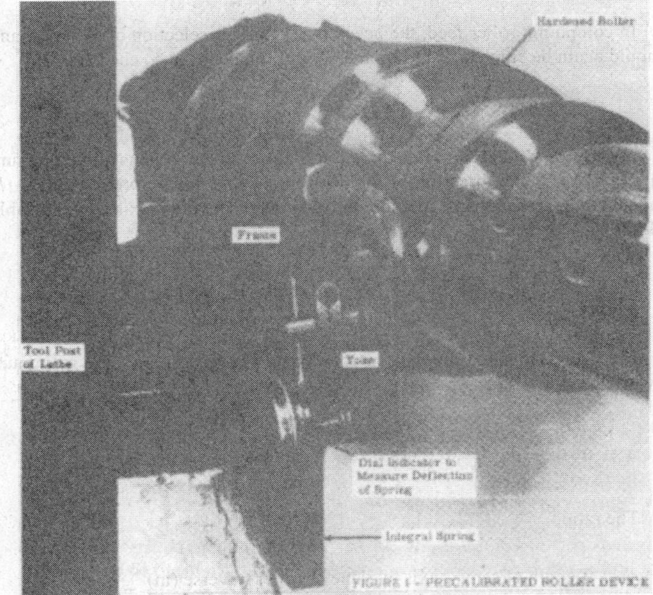

FIGURE 15—PRECALIBRATED ROLLER DEVICE

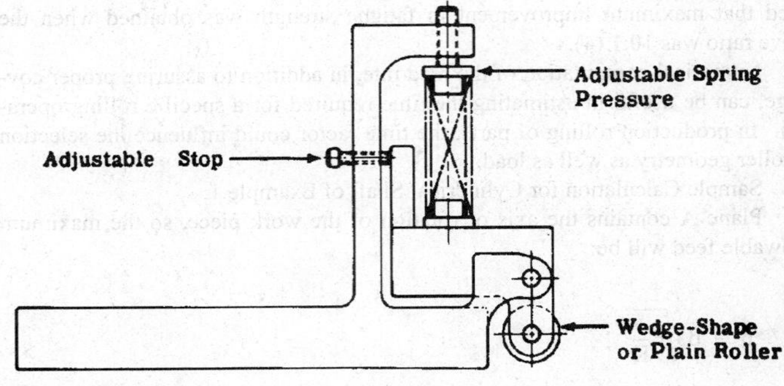

FIGURE 16—TYPICAL FIXTURE FOR ROLLING FILLETS OR EXTERNAL CYLINDRICAL SURFACES

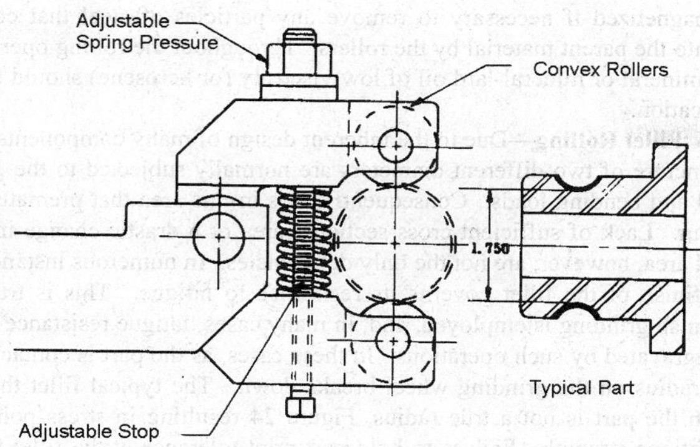

FIGURE 17—SPECIAL FIXTURE FOR ROLLING EXTERNAL GROOVES AND CONTOURS

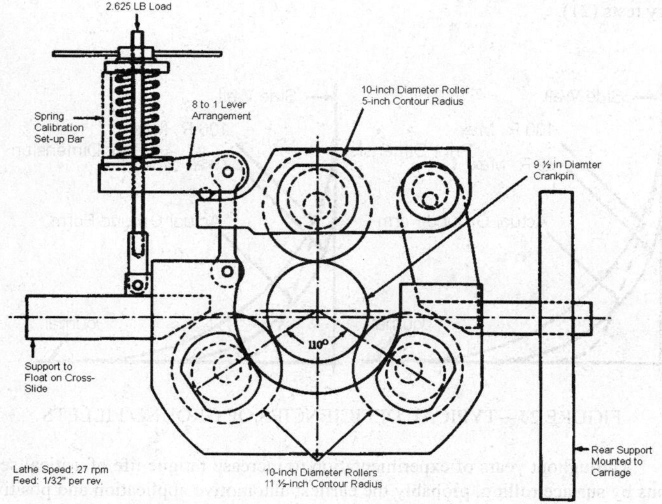

FIGURE 18—ROLLER DEVICE FOR HEAVY DUTY RAILROAD EQUIPMENT

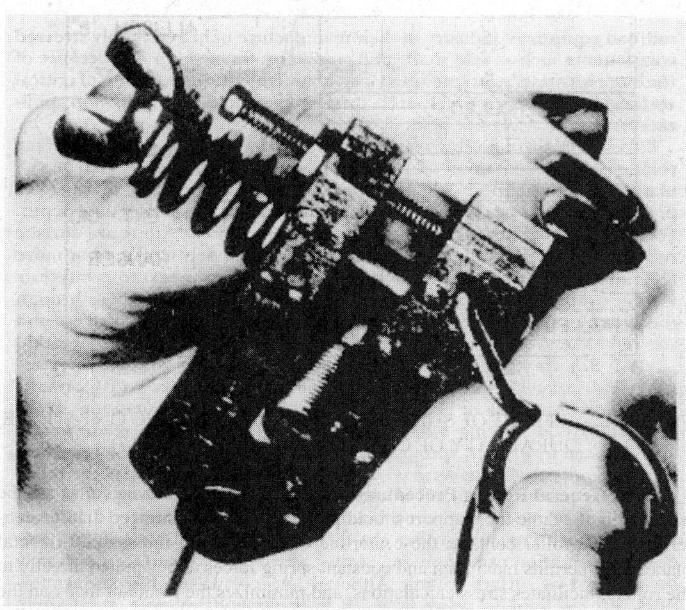

FIGURE 19—HAND TOOL FOR SUPERFICIAL ROLLING OF SCREW THREADS IN SMALL BOLTS AND SCREWS (30)

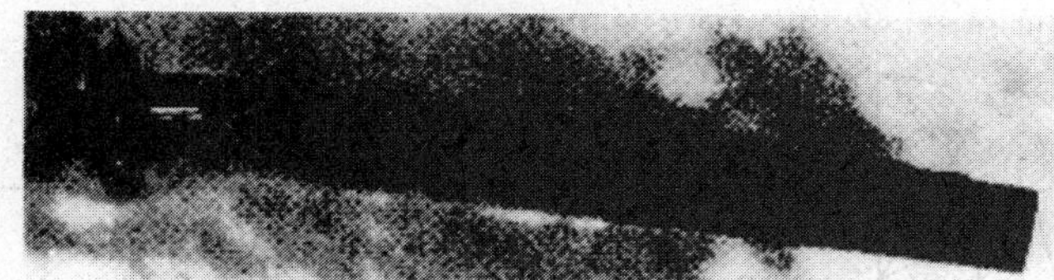

FIGURE 20—LATHE TOOL FOR SUPERFICIAL ROLLING OF COARSE SCREW THREADS IN WHICH SHANK SERVES AS LOAD CONTROL SPRING

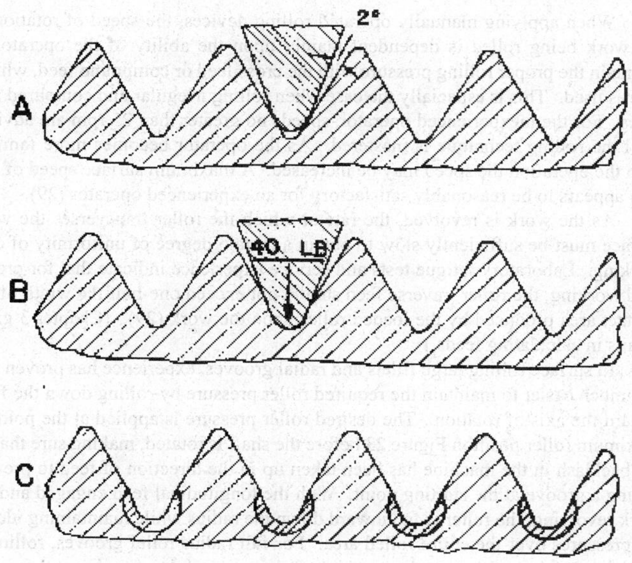

FIGURE 21—ROLLER FOR SUPERFICIALLY ROLLING SCREW THREADS IS DESIGNED TO COMPRESSIVELY STRESS METAL AT ROOT SECTION OF THREAD (30)

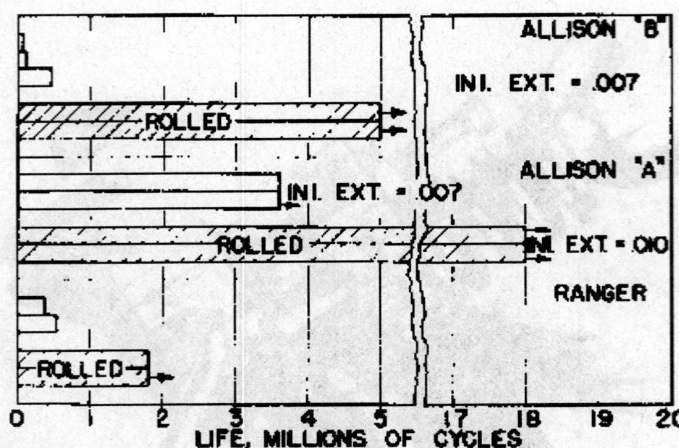

FIGURE 22—EFFECT OF SUPERFICIAL THREAD ROLLING ON FATIGUE DURABILITY OF CONNECTING ROD BOLTS (17)

6.4 General Rolling Procedures—The various roller devices that can be mounted in the lathe tool support should preferably be so positioned that the centerline of the roller contacts the centerline of the work on the same horizontal plane. This permits maximum and constant spring forces to be applied directly to the rollers, facilitates stress calculations, and minimizes the resultant loads on the fixture and machine. When rolling large fillets and radial relief grooves, the roller is inclined to the work at an angle equal to approximately half the angle between the tangency point and the maximum position of rolling as depicted in Figure 23. On cylindrical or tapered surfaces the roller may be fed straight into the work (29).

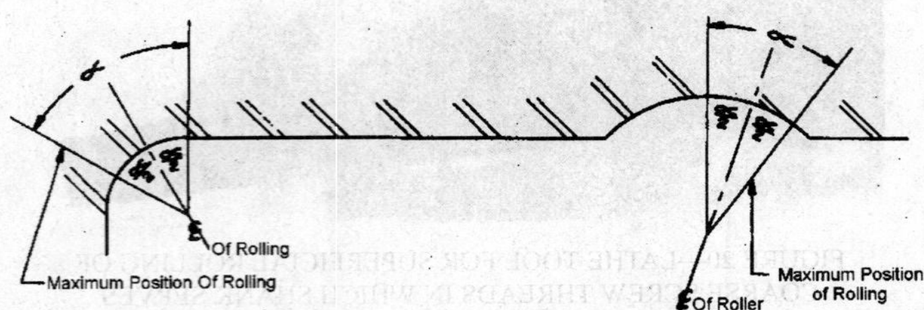

FIGURE 23—TYPICAL ROLLER POSITIONS FOR ROLLING FILLETS AND RELIEF GROOVES

When applying manually operated rolling devices, the speed of rotation of the work being rolled is dependent mainly upon the ability of the operator to maintain the proper rolling pressure with the cross feed or compound feed, whichever is used. This is especially the case when rolling irregular and contoured surfaces. For the inexperienced operator, speeds no greater than 25 rpm are advised until the rolling technique is mastered. As the operator becomes more familiar with the operation the speed may be increased. A maximum surface speed of 100 fpm appears to be reasonably satisfactory for an experienced operator (29).

As the work is revolved, the rate at which the roller transverses the work surface must be sufficiently slow to obtain a certain degree of uniformity of cold working. Laboratory fatigue tests and service experience indicate that for proper cold working, the roller traverse feed should not exceed one-half the width of the contact area produced by the loaded roller upon the work (29). (Chapter 3 gives details in calculating feeds.)

In surface rolling large fillets and radial grooves, experience has proven that it is much easier to maintain the required roller pressure by rolling down the fillet toward the axis of rotation. The desired roller pressure is applied at the point of maximum roller position Figure 23 before the shaft is rotated, making sure that all the backlash in the machine has been taken up in the direction of feed to prevent rolling a groove at the starting point. With the longitudinal feed engaged and the work revolving, the roller is fed inward down the radius while maintaining identical pressures over the entire rolled area. For full radius relief grooves, rolling is initiated at either of the outermost points and continued down and past the center of radius on the root diameter. An identical procedure is followed on the reverse radius of the groove, again rolling past center to insure a completely rolled root diameter (29).

Prior to the actual rolling operation, the part should be thoroughly cleaned and demagnetized if necessary to remove any particles of steel that could be forced into the parent material by the rollers. Throughout the rolling operation, a straight mineral or mineral-lard oil of low viscosity (or kerosene) should be used for lubrication.

6.5 Fillet Rolling—Due to the inherent design of many components, fillets at the juncture of two different diameters are normally subjected to the greatest torsional and bending loads. Consequently, it is in this area that premature failures occur. Lack of sufficient cross-sectional area or a drastic change in cross-sectional area, however, are not the only deficiencies. In numerous instances, the surface finish of the fillet governs its resistance to fatigue. This is true even where finish grinding is employed, and, in many cases, fatigue resistance is definitely aggravated by such operations. In these cases, as the part is contacted, the dressed radius on the grinding wheel breaks down. The typical fillet then produced on the part is not a true radius, Figure 24 resulting in stress points that reduce fatigue strength. Failure to hold part print tolerance at the fillet through grinding is common throughout the automotive industry, and is probably most serious on crankshaft bearings. Rolling the critical fillets results in work-hardening of the surface to a depth of approximately 0.0001 in without the apparent tear marks produced by abrasive methods. An approximate 115% increase in fatigue strength of nodular iron crankshafts is substantiated by actual engine and laboratory tests (21).

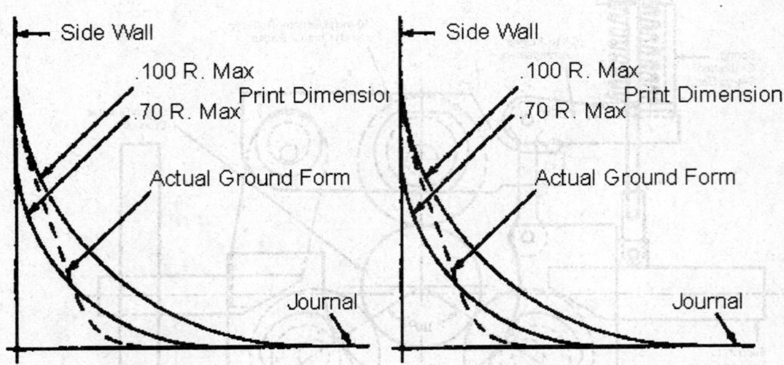

FIGURE 24—TYPICAL DEFICIENCIES OF GROUND FILLETS

Throughout years of experimentation to increase fatigue life of critical sections by surface rolling, probably the earliest automotive application and positive results were achieved by fillet rolling the highly stressed areas on the pin and main bearings of gray iron engine crankshafts. Here, cold rolling of fillets by means of steel balls increased the limiting stress 60% for reverse bending and 80% for "one-way" loading as compared to machined and ground fillets (20). In this method, as depicted in Figure 25 (20), three hardened steel balls are equally spaced around the fillet and held in place by a split loading ring having an internal 45 deg chamfer. With two of these rings assembled on the crank-pin, it is possible to roll both fillets at the same time, the ring being loaded endwise by a simple device containing four coil springs compressed by a screw attachment. This device can be easily rotated by hand during the actual rolling operation which is comprised of only several revolutions. To produce a small but detectable deformation of the fillet, typical loads applied to the rings are approximately one ton (20). A deformation of about 0.003 in in the fillet results, and, consequently, a work-hardened surface of very smooth and truly circular form. A small ridge of metal is normally raised at the junction of fillet and journal (possibly 0.0005 in) (20). To alleviate this condition, roller pressures should be maintained at a minimum and allowances made in the mating product component to insure that this slight ridge does not become an interference point (21). Although this simple method of fillet rolling can be quite successful, it often induces deformation and failure of the relatively small balls. Because of the geometry, the balls afford no practical solution for their retention and control, which is particularly essential for production applications.

As indicated, the success of surface rolling is mainly contingent on the design of the roller. This is true particularly in rolling smaller fillets. Although relatively large fillets and relief grooves can be experimentally hand followed on a lathe, as has been discussed, it is the smaller fillets (3/8 in and below) which primarily concern the critical strength areas normally encountered in highly stressed crankshafts, front wheel spindles, and the like.

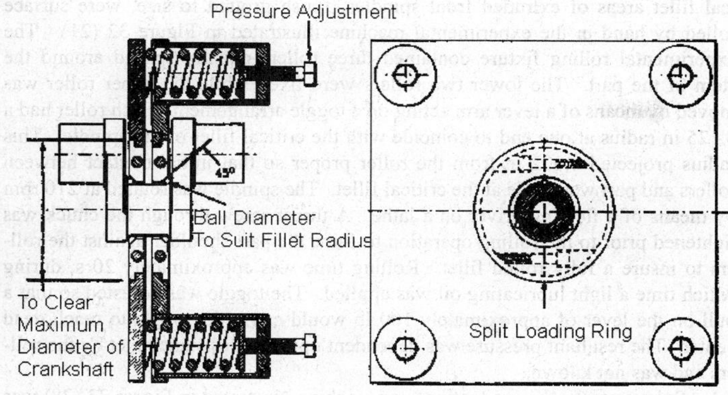

FIGURE 25—BALL DEVICE TO ROLL CRANKSHAFT FILLETS

For rolling concentric fillets such as on main bearings of crankshafts, toolroom methods employing spring loaded devices for use on lathes Figure 16 can likewise be applied to fillet rolling except that special rollers are recommended; these being fed into the corner fillet at 45 deg or at a position bisecting the shoulder-to-axis angle. No feed is necessary for these fillets.

The roller mounting and method of generating and maintaining the required force vary considerably with different users. The roller is usually pressed lightly onto a pin which rotates in bushings mounted in the holder. Sufficient side clearance is given to the roller so that it can slide laterally and center itself in the fillet (26).

Currently, two types of rollers are in commercial use for rolling small fillets.

Plain Fillet Roller—A plain type roller, as illustrated in Figure 26, (26), is used effectively for fillets having a radius of 1/32 in or less. The roller periphery has a radius at the low limit of the fillet radius tolerance, which generates, by plastic flow, a new shaft radius conforming to the roller periphery. An applied force of less than 100 lb is usually sufficient for this small radius, and greatly simplifies both the roller and shaft mounting. Very few shaft revolutions are required to obtain the maximum effect; in one application 10 revolutions of the shaft are sufficient. Plain rollers of oil-hardening tool steel machined to approximate the dimensions noted in Figure 26 and hardened to Rockwell C 62–65 have served for several thousand pieces at a negligible replacement cost (26).

Wedge Roller—It would be most desirable if all fillet rolling could be accomplished with a plain roller by making the radius on the roller periphery larger as the radius of the shaft fillet is increased. However, above 1/32 in fillets, the required force on the roller would rapidly reach high values where the roller and shaft mountings as well as the means of generating the required force become quite complex (26). (The normal manufacturing variation in fillet radius is also an important part in this same problem.) Through extensive studies, the wedge type roller (Figure 27), was developed (22). (C. W. Jackman, U.S. Patent #2,357,515.) This unique roller design offers a vast improvement. It can roll large fillets with a relatively small applied force and at the same time is unaffected by the normal manufacturing variations in fillet radii (26).

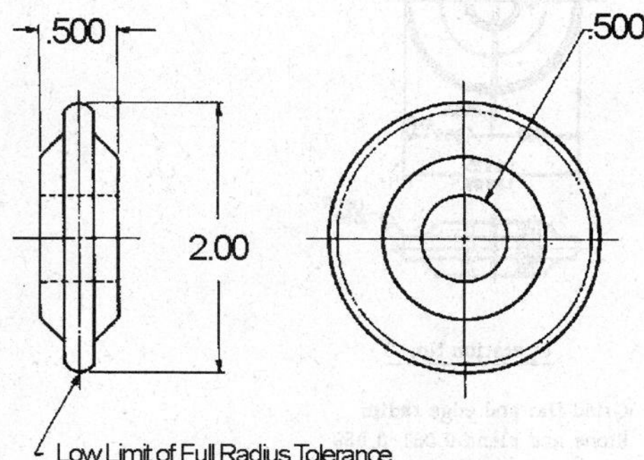

FIGURE 26—PLAIN FILLET ROLLER AND APPROXIMATE DIMENSIONS

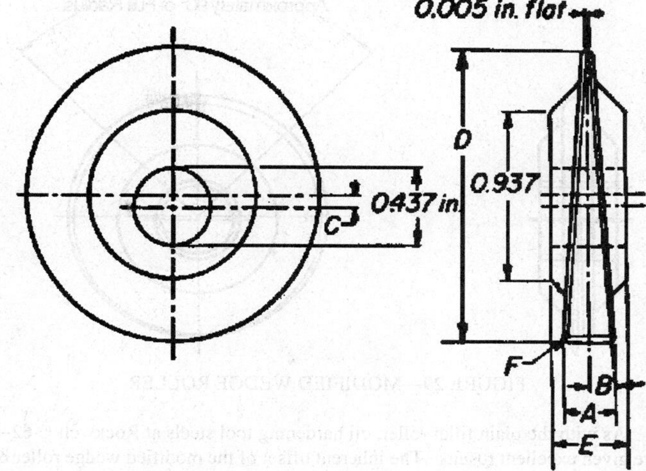

FIGURE 27—WEDGE-SHAPE FILLET ROLLER

On the wedge-type roller, the wide portion of the wedge rolls the extremities of the fillet while the narrower area of the wedge works the center, as shown in the two detail sketches in Figure 28 (26). The other points on the wedge contact the intermediate points in the fillet. Because the various points of contact between roller and fillet are virtually identical in area, the applied forces are equalized about the periphery of the roller. As the shaft rotates, the center of the roller with respect to the work never changes, but the roller edges ride up and down on each side of the fillet in a sort of kneading action (26). Since the relation of the diameter of the roller and diameter of the surfaces on which it works is varied with respect to each other, each point of the roller surface applies a different condition to each point of the fillet surface throughout the operation, and the entire fillet surface is rolled completely and uniformly.

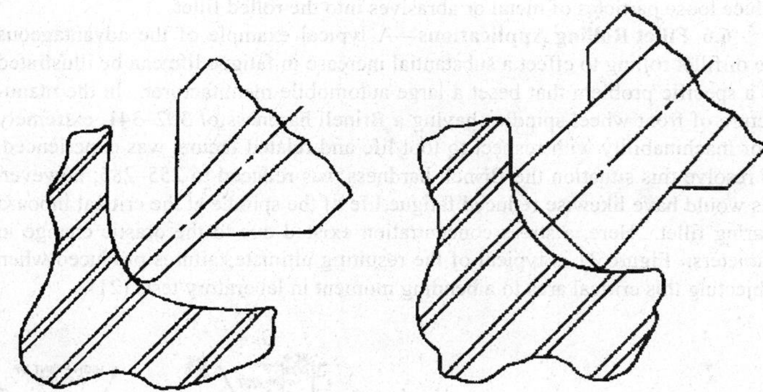

FIGURE 28—ACTION OF WEDGE-SHAPE ROLLER ON FILLET

The dimensions shown in Figure 27 are recommended for rolling shaft radii of different sizes. When selecting or designing a roller diameter, it is important that the roller speed be nonsynchronous with the work speed so as to distribute the work roller contact. It is desirable, therefore, to have the circumference of the roller such that it is not a multiple of the circumference of the work. This suitable difference in circumferences will give a hunting action to insure proper rolling of the fillet.

A modified version of the described wedge-shaped roller design has been developed (28). This concept not only adds considerably to the quality of the rolled fillet, but provides a definite simplification for its manufacture on toolroom equipment. On this type of roller, the narrowest section of the wedge is ground to a full radius approximately 0.010 in under the low manufacturing limit of the fillet to be rolled. This full radius is carried symmetrically on the periphery of the roller for approximately 90 deg as illustrated in Figure 29.

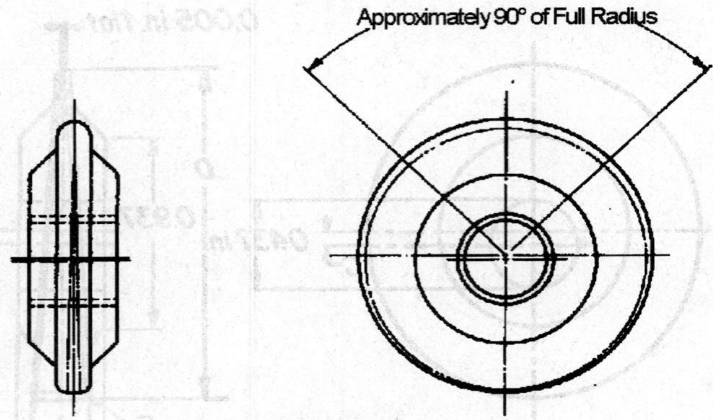
Approximately 90° of Full Radius

FIGURE 29—MODIFIED WEDGE ROLLER

As with the plain fillet roller, oil hardening tool steels at Rockwell C 62–65 have given excellent results. The inherent offset of the modified wedge roller can be machined and ground by toolroom methods consistent with the typical operational process illustrated in Figure 30. A special cam grinding machine highly expedites the cam generations of the wedge-type roller (28).

Experience has proven that the speed of the work while the rollers are in contact is immaterial. More cycles are required to roll a fillet with the wedge roller than with a plain roller. While using a single wedge roller, 200–600 rotations of the part is common, however, the use of multiple rollers simultaneously engaged will reduce the rotation requirements accordingly. Applied roller pressures of 60–200 lb (26), and a theoretical compressive shear stress of approximately 650,000 psi (28) of contact are also typical.

Normally, at comparable fillet radii, life of the wedge roller is less than for plain rollers because of the longer rolling time; however, wedge rollers have endured 15,000–20,000 pieces (26). Replacement cost is, therefore, negligible.

A light oil is especially necessary for lubrication while fillet rolling with the wedge roller. And, as a general rule for all types of surface rolling applications, rolling should not be combined with metal removing operations which inherently induce loose particles of metal or abrasives into the rolled fillet.

6.6 Fillet Rolling Applications—A typical example of the advantageous use of fillet rolling to effect a substantial increase in fatigue life can be illustrated by a specific problem that beset a large automobile manufacturer. In the manufacture of front wheel spindles having a Brinell hardness of 302–341, extremely poor machinability with respect to tool life and related factors was experienced. To resolve this situation the Brinell hardness was reduced to 255–285; however, this would have likewise reduced fatigue life of the spindle at the critical inboard bearing fillet. Here, a stress concentration existed due to the drastic change in diameters. Figure 31 is typical of the resulting ultimate failures produced when subjecting this critical area to a bending moment in laboratory tests (21).

To maintain comparable fatigue endurance at the reduced hardness, the critical fillet areas of extruded front spindles, finish ground to size, were surface rolled by hand in the experimental machine illustrated in Figure 32 (21). The experimental rolling fixture contained three rollers equally spaced around the stem of the part. The lower two rollers were fixed while the upper roller was moved by means of a lever arm acting on a toggle arrangement. Each roller had a 0.125 in radius at one end to coincide with the critical fillet of the spindle. This radius projected 0.002 in from the roller proper so that initial contact between rollers and part was made at the critical fillet. The spindle was rotated at 210 rpm by means of a floating driver on a lathe. A thrust screw through the chuck was tightened prior to the rolling operation to force the part shoulder against the rollers to insure a fully rolled fillet. Rolling time was approximately 20 s, during which time a light lubricating oil was applied. The toggle was adjusted so that a pull on the lever of approximately 100 lb would cause the toggle to reach dead center. The resultant pressure was dependent upon the resistance met by the rollers and was not known.

Subsequently, the production type machine illustrated in Figure 33 (28) was installed for fillet rolling front wheel spindles. Here, mounted to the machine base, is a motorized head, the spindle of which accepts a center and drive plate to locate and rotate the part at 400 rpm. Opposing the head is a hydraulically operated tailstock to support the shaft end of the part. Between the head and tailstock are two hydraulically operated slides positioned horizontally 45 deg to the center of the part; one forward and one rearward of the rotational axis. Each cylinder, at 400 psi, feeds and withdraws a wedge-type roller to the fillet. Semiautomatic controls actuate the tailstock center, initiate rotation of the spindle, and simultaneously feed the two fillet rollers to the work. After a predetermined rolling cycle, which in this case is 15–17 s, the rollers retract and the machine stops for unloading. A light oil is used for lubrication during the rolling operation. Replacement of rollers is required only after 15,000–20,000 pieces. A production rate of 127 pieces/h is maintained.

Where multiple fillets are involved or the rotation of the fillets is not concentric with the central axis of the shaft, such as on the main and pin bearings of crankshafts, a unique tooling problem is encountered (26).

As a toolroom method for accomplishing such rolling of crankshaft fillets, the device pictured in Figure 34 has been experimentally employed (24). This is comprised basically of a yoke containing two sets of two plain rollers positioned to float in the radius of opposing bearing fillets. The yoke is mounted to the carriage of a lathe in such a manner as to allow lateral float to compensate for the throw of the pin bearings. Opposing the two sets of fillet rollers is a support roller which remains in parallel contact with the bearing to be rolled. It is against this roller that the adjustable spring pressure is applied to force the rolers into the fillets. Use of this design is inherently limited to the width of the bearings which are to be fillet rolled. Inadequate width would not allow sufficient space for the two rollers. Because of the variable direction in which the rollers are presented to the fillet, plain rollers in place of the preferred wedge-type rollers become a necessity.

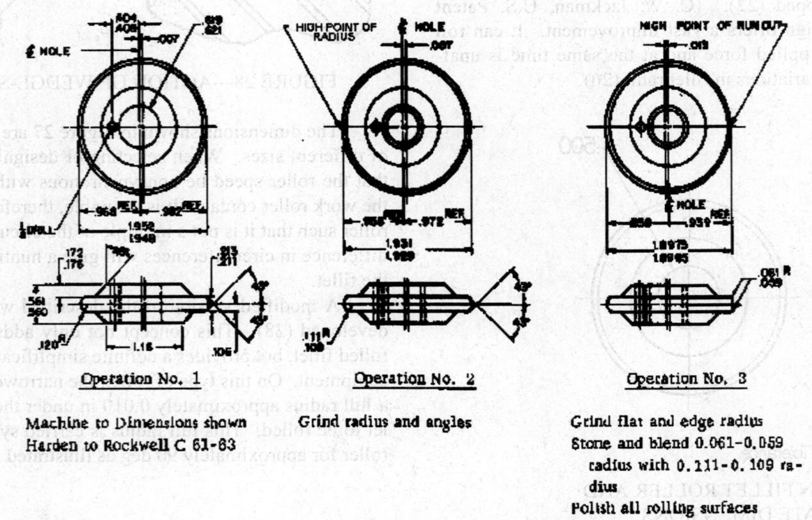
HIGH POINT OF RADIUS
HOLE
HIGH POINT OF RUN OUT
Operation No. 1
Machine to Dimensions shown
Harden to Rockwell C 61-63
Operation No. 2
Grind radius and angles
Operation No. 3
Grind flat and edge radius
Stone and blend 0.061-0.059 radius with 0.111-0.109 radius
Polish all rolling surfaces

FIGURE 30—TYPICAL PROCESS TO MANUFACTURE MODIFIED WEDGE-SHAPE ROLLER

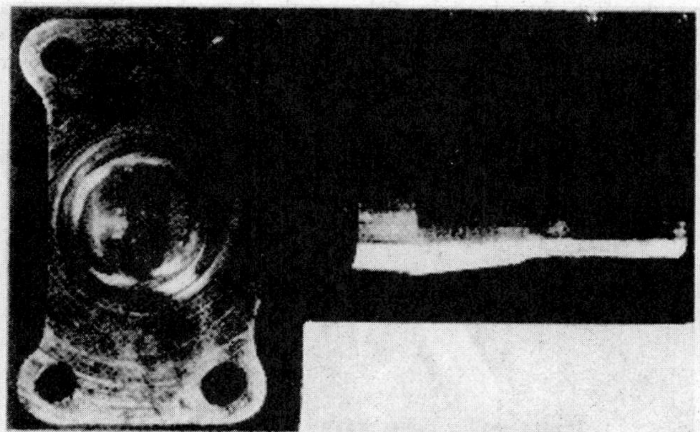

FIGURE 31—TYPICAL ULTIMATE FAILURE INDUCED BY DRASTIC CHANGE IN CROSS-SECTIONAL AREA

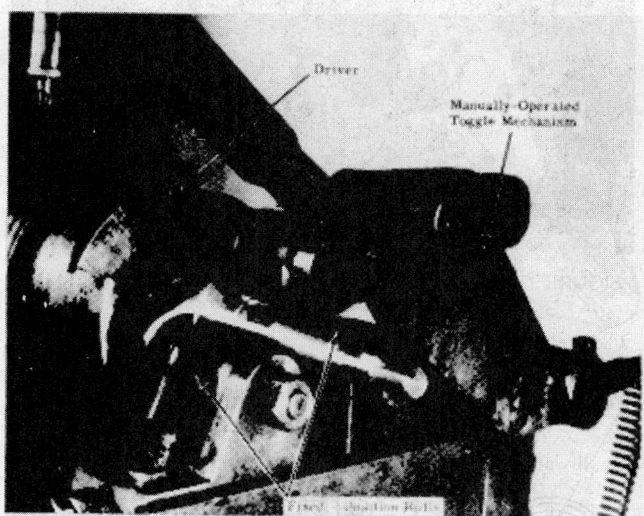

FIGURE 32—EXPERIMENTAL DEVICE USED FOR FILLET ROLLING FRONT SPINDLES

FIGURE 33—PRODUCTION MACHINE FOR FILLET ROLLING FRONT SPINDLES

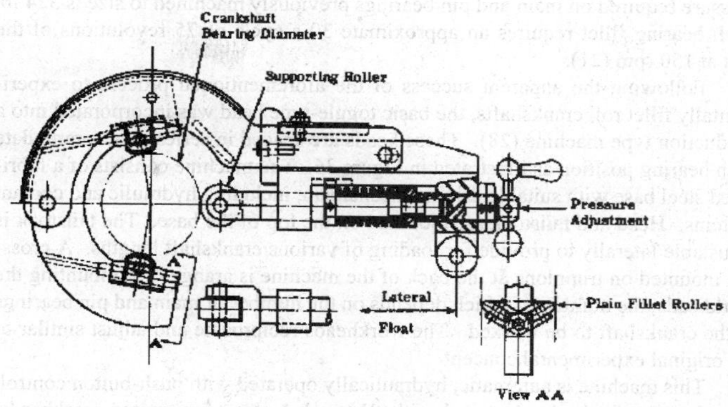

FIGURE 34—EXPERIMENTAL DEVICE TO ROLL CRANKSHAFT FILLETS

To provide an experimental means of fillet rolling with wedge rollers or toolroom type equipment which would eventually serve as a basis for adaptation to production, the toggle-type arrangement depicted in Figure 35 was devised (28). It is mounted to a crossarm attached to the carriage of a lathe and actuated through a 2.7:1 mechanical advantage by hydraulic pressure. This action scissors two opposing roller shoes against the main and pin bearing diameters of the crankshaft. The inherent design permits the entire head to reciprocate vertically to compensate for the throw of the crankpins. Being mounted to the carriage, the head is also adjustable laterally to allow for flexibility with various crankshaft designs for which rollers and shoes are special. Each of the opposing roller shoes carries two wedge rollers mounted at a 45 deg angle to the line of the crankshaft bearings and so arranged that when the shoes are close around the crankshaft bearings, the four rollers in each pair are diametrically opposed. All rollers are permitted to float laterally to compensate for crankshaft bearing tolerances.

Roller pressures are applied by means of a hydraulic cylinder incorporated within the head, through connecting rod and toggle linkage to claming fingers which support the roller shoes. This pressure is adjustable to suit whatever conditions require, and remains constant after the correct amount of pressure is determined.

In order to achieve proper results from this operation, it is first necessary machine all fillets of a crankshaft to the limits specified on the part print, not to exceed plus or minus 0.018. The wedge rollers are generated for a specific size fillet, and any variation beyond these limits will defeat the defect of the operation (21).

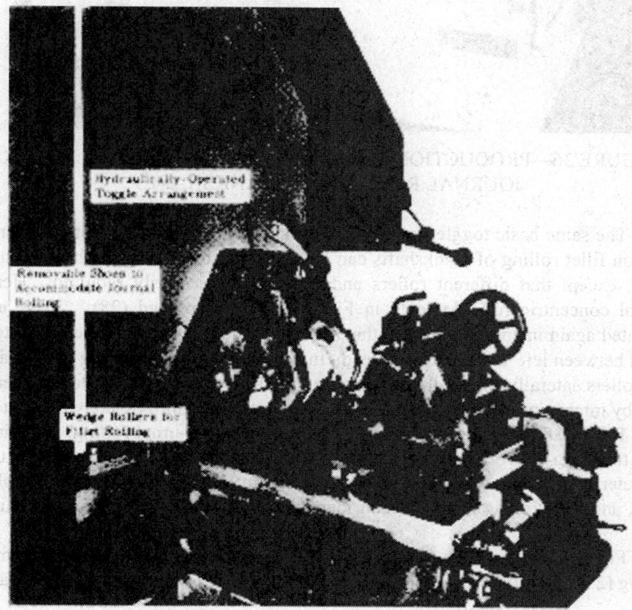

FIGURE 35—ADJUSTABLE DEVICE FOR EXPERIMENTAL ROLLING OF CRANKSHAFT FILLETS AND JOURNALS

Employing such an arrangement to roll fillets of 0.110–0.120 in radii, roll pressure required on main and pin bearings previously machined to size is 324 lb. Each bearing fillet requires an approximate 30 s cycle or 75 revolutions of the part at 150 rpm (21).

Following the apparent success of the aforementioned process to experimentally fillet roll crankshafts, the basic toggle-type head was incorporated into a production type machine (28). These heads are spaced in series to accommodate each bearing position as illustrated in Figure 36. The machine consists of a fabricated steel base with suitable driving mechanism, including hydraulic and coolant systems. Head and tailstock are mounted on the top of the base. The tailstock is adjustable laterally to provide for loading of various crankshaft lengths. A crossrail mounted on trunnions at the back of the machine is aranged for mounting the workheads, the number of which depends on the number of main and pin bearings of the crankshaft to be worked. The workheads reciprocate and adjust similar to the original experimental concept.

This machine is automatic, hydraulically operated with push-button control. The operator loads the part and with the push button, lowers the workheads. Roller shoes automatically close on each crankshaft bearing. After the operator pushes the button to start the machine, it operates for a predetermined time and automatically stops. The cycle reverses for unloading and reloading. Actual pressures and speeds simulate the experimental version. Time for the simultaneous rolling of all fillets is approximately 30 s.

6.7 Journal Rolling Crankshafts—As a means of eliminating the lapping operation of crankshaft bearing diameters and its inherently high cost, while maintaining comparable surface finishes and at the same time increasing fatigue strength and wear qualities through superficial hardening, rolling of the journals has proven beneficial (21).

FIGURE 36—PRODUCTION MACHINE ADAPTABLE FOR FILLET OR JOURNAL ROLLING OF CRANKSHAFTS

The same basic toggle-type equipment used for both experimental and production fillet rolling of crankshafts can be employed for rolling the bearing surfaces, except that different rollers and shoes are necessarily required. Here, helical concentric rolls depicted in Figure 37 are employed (28). These are mounted again in special shoes so that, circumferentially, the roller helix is alternated between left- and right-hand lead. In contact with the revolving crankshaft, the rollers laterally knead the high points of the surface into the lower areas, thereby improving the finish of the ground surface from approximately 25-12 μin, rms. Figure 38 illustrates typical roller dimensions for journal rolling. To minimize the roller-to-work contact area and, thereby, the required working forces, the diameter of the rolls should be as small as practicable. Applied forces, revolutions, and time requirements remain identical to the basic fillet rolling machine (28).

Figure 39 indicates a variation to the toggle-type arrangement for journal rolling (23). Results here are identically successful in rolling crankshaft journals. In this machine the crankshaft is loaded between centers and on two fixed rolls to support two of the main bearings. Subsequently, the mechanical crank-operated head, synchronized in rotation with the throw of the pin bearings, lowers and allows two opposing and predeterminately spaced rollers at each position to straddle the bearing diameter as indicated in Figure 40.

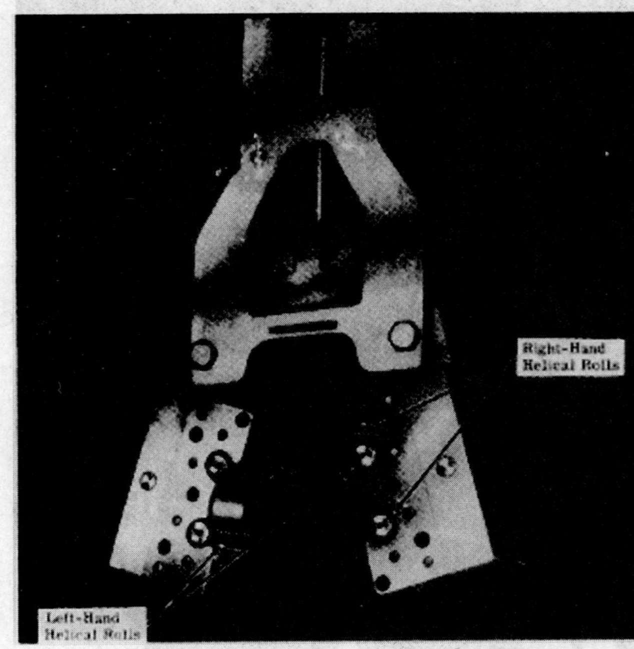

FIGURE 37—WORK HEAD TO SURFACE ROLL CRANKSHAFT JOURNALS

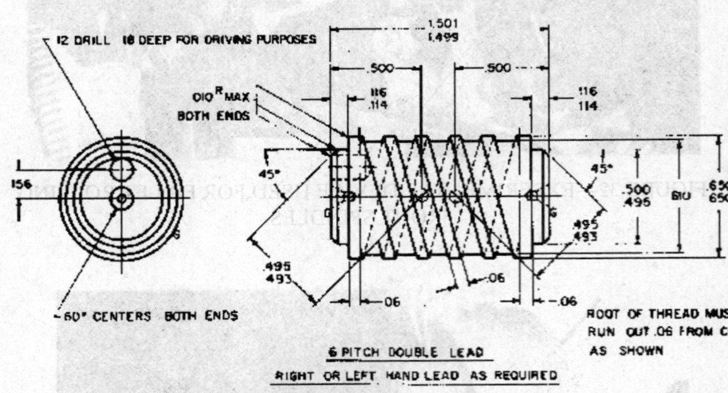

FIGURE 38—DIMENSIONS OF TYPICAL JOURNAL ROLLER

6.8 Conclusion—The tooling, methods, and results as outlined in this chapter are representative of experimental work and actual production applications. In each instance, however, the final results were governed by such factors as roller design, product design, material, and material hardness. It remains, therefore, the responsibility of the engineer to evaluate the data as it pertains to the specific problem at hand; each case is peculiar to itself.

7. Control and Inspection (by D. J. Wulpi)

7.1 Introduction—The reliability of a part is usually dependent upon the necessity for making the production parts at least as good as the preproduction parts that were tested in the engineering phase of development. Many manufacturing processes lend themselves to fairly accurate inspection after processing; others make such subtle changes in the part that inspection is difficult. Mechanical prestressing processes are in the latter category, for the most potent strengthening factors—compressive residual surface stresses—are very elusive and difficult to evaluate properly.

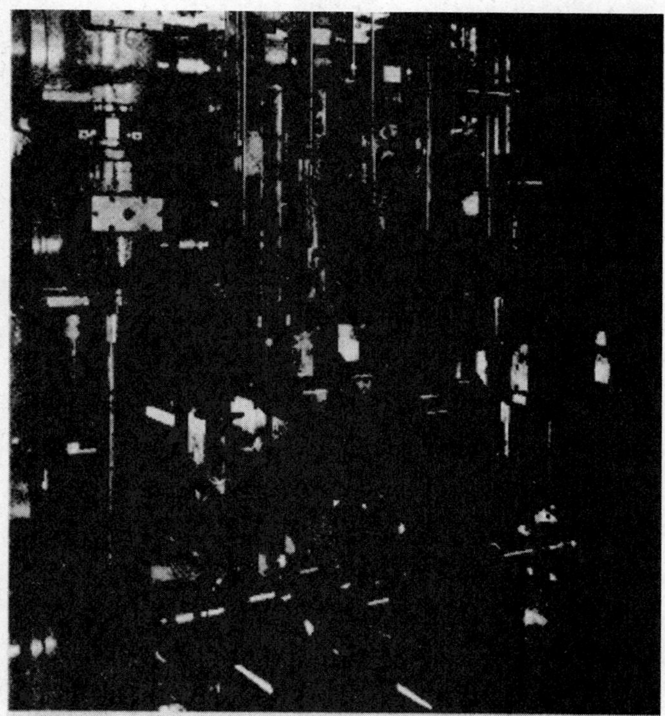

FIGURE 39—PRODUCTION MACHINE FOR JOURNAL ROLLING CRANKSHAFTS

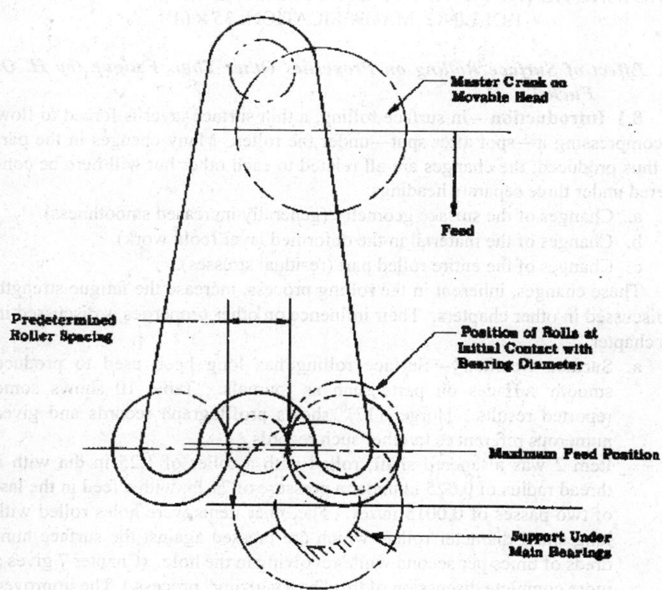

FIGURE 40—PRINCIPAL OF IMPCO SURFACE ROLLING MACHINE

7.2 Control—Since it is difficult to inspect finish rolled parts, the most practical method for consistently obtaining desired properties in production is to maintain close control of the rolling procedure and also to make frequent fatigue tests of the finished parts. Although usually not critical, the roller load and geometry should be kept fairly constant. With respect to the part, the hardness and prior surface finish may be expected to change the fatigue strength if they are allowed to vary widely. When rolling metals where relatively little plastic deformation is expected, the surface should be free from deep tool marks, so that the roller will contact the surface as intended. If there are "steps" or deep tool marks in a surface, prior to rolling, they may well result in improperly finished parts of relatively low fatigue strength. During the rolling process, the part and the rollers must be free from foreign matter such as dirt, chips, and so on.

7.3 Surface Finish—Although there is little direct evidence, the surface finish on a part, prior to surface rolling, apparently is not critical to fatigue strength, provided the entire surface in the zone subject to high service fatigue stress is plastically deformed. For this reason, higher rolling pressures must be used with hard materials and rough surfaces than are necessary for softer, smoother parts. It is believed that prior surface finish is more critical when little plastic deformation is involved than when a greater degree of plastic deformation takes place. Prior surface finish should be held constant for given rolling conditions if relatively close final dimensional tolerances are necessary, as for a shaft in a press fit (56).[5]

7.4 Nondestructive Inspection—As previously mentioned, control of the rolling process is important because of the difficulty of inspection of the finished part. At the present time, apparently, there is no commercial device for nondestructive inspection of rolled surfaces. Some experimental work has been done, primarily with X-rays and electro-magnetic induction, or "eddy current" testers, but no devices are commercially available as yet. In these tests, both of which detect changes due to plastic deformation, the X-ray instruments measure variations in the crystallographic structure of the metal, while the electromagnetic induction, or "eddy current", devices measure changes in electrical and magnetic properties of magnetic materials. It is hoped that commercial instruments will become available for nondestructive inspection of rolled surfaces.

There are, however, some simple methods for assuring that a part has been surface rolled and, to a certain extent, how well it has been rolled. A stripe of paint, ink, or similar material may be applied to the surface to be rolled and to the adjacent surface (57). Inspection will readily indicate whether or not rolling has been performed over the stripe because of the different appearance of the stripe in the rolled and nonrolled zones. For critical parts which have previously been subjected to magnetic, dye penetrant, ultrasonic, or other critical inspection controls, it is recommended that use of such controls be continued, with inspection both before and after rolling. Once a reliable process control procedure has been established for the rolling operation and performance reliability of the rolled parts confirmed, the necessity for the use of such critical inspection controls can be reevaluated (58).

A properly rolled surface should have a smooth appearance, but may be either bright or dull in luster. No tool marks from prior machining should be evident. Change in dimension may sometimes be used as a control, but this is influenced to a large degree by the flattening of tool marks.

7.5 Destructive Inspection—The metallurgical effects of rolling can be detected in different ways with different metals. If the effective rolling is sufficiently deep on a metal subject to work hardening, the increase in hardness may be detected by microhardness traverse. Where the rolled zone is shallow, however, metallurgical inspection is quite difficult. Figure 14 of Chapter 3 shows the hardness gradient formed by very heavy pressure on 9 1/2 in dia normalized carbon steel shaft (56). The vertical line at the 0.450 in depth indicates the depth of work hardening calculated by the method outlined in Chapter 3. Excellent correlation is usually obtained when a microhardness traverse is used on steel to check this method of calculation (56).

Metallographic examination can frequently be used to measure the depth of cold working. In ferrous metals, however, it is sometimes difficult to distinguish this deformed layer by metallographic means. In some nonferrous metals the effect is readily observed: in aluminum by recrystallization following solution treatment, Figure 41 (57); in magnesium by twinning within the grains, Figure 42 (4).

5. Numbers in parentheses in text, tables, and figure titles refer to references at end of report.

FIGURE 41—SAE AA 2014 AND UNS A92014-T6 ALUMINUM (WROUGHT) AFTER SURFACE ROLLING. SPECIMENS REHEATED TO SOLUTION TEMPERATURE AND QUENCHED IN COLD WATER. MAGNIFICATION: 45 × (57)

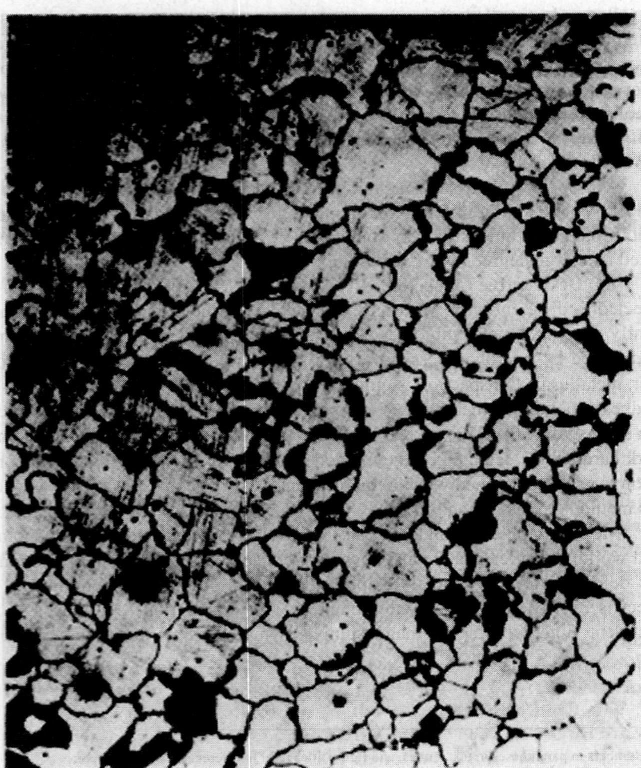

FIGURE 42A—SAE 505 AND UNS M11810-T4 MAGNESIUM (CAST) SHOWING STRUCTURE PRIOR TO SURFACE ROLLING. MAGNIFICATION: 35 × (4)

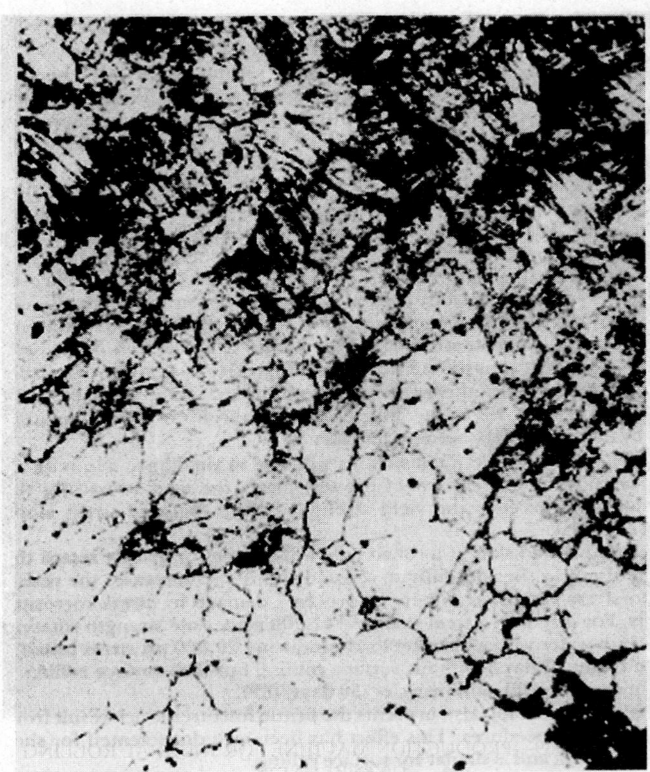

FIGURE 42B—SAE 505 AND UNS M11810-T4 MAGNESIUM (CAST) SHOWING HEAVILY TWINNED STRUCTURE NEAR SURFACE AFTER ROLLING. MAGNIFICATION: 35 × (4)

8. *Effect of Surface Rolling on Properties Other Than Fatigue (by H. O. Fuchs)*

8.1 Introduction—In surface rolling, a thin surface layer is forced to flow by compressing it—spot after spot—under the roller. Many changes in the part are thus produced; the changes are all related to each other but will here be considered under three separate headings:

a. Changes of the surface geometry (generally increased smoothness).
b. Changes of the material in the deformed layer (cold work).
c. Changes of the entire rolled part (residual stresses).

These changes, inherent in the rolling process, increase the fatigue strength as discussed in other chapters. Their influence on other properties is discussed in this chapter.

a. Surface Geometry—Surface rolling has long been used to produce smooth surfaces on parts such as journals. Table 10 shows some reported results. Horger (17)[6] shows profilograph records and gives numerous references to other such records.

   Item 2 was a tapered shaft, rolled with a roller of 1.25 in dia with a thread radius of 0.025 in under a pressure of 71 lb, with a feed in the last of two passes of 0.0015 in/rev. The other items were holes rolled with long small diameter rollers which are pressed against the surface hundreds of times per second while revolving in the hole. (Chapter 7 gives a more complete discussion of this "bearingizing" process.) The improved surface finish was accompanied by an increase in hole diameter of the order of 0.0005 in. Reduction of 0.002 in by surface rolling a 9 1/2 in dia rolled steel shaft was reported (17).

b. The Cold Worked Layer—Many materials change in hardness when they are forced to flow. "Work hardening" is often observed; work softening of previously work hardened material has also been reported (33).

   Table 11 lists hardness readings for the surface rolling hole specimens for which surface finish was given in Table 10 and for shafts of 0.50% carbon steel with 96,000 psi tensile strength.

6. Numbers in parentheses in text, tables, and figure titles refer to references at end of report.

Other changes also occur in metals which have been forced to flow; grains change shape; transformation or precipitation may be promoted; the modulus of elasticity of hard steel may temporarily be decreased by cold deformation to about 90% of its original value; magnetic properties may be improved; grains may coalesce on recrystallization (this may be used for destructive inspection).

c. The Entire Rolled Part—Surface rolling sets up compressive stresses in the plastically deformed skin which are balanced by tensile stresses in the core of parts. These stresses have a profound influence on the behavior of the part. Their beneficial effect on fatigue is treated in other chapters of this manual and will not be covered in this chapter.

TABLE 10—

Item	Material	Hardness Before Rolling, Brinnel	Finish Before Rolling, μ in	Finish After rolling, μ in	Reference
1	Steel, AISI B1112	195	120	6	(31)
2	Steel Alloy No. 4	290 (141,000 UTS)	20 to 35	12 to 16	(32)
3	Stainless Steel SAE 51416 UNS 514600	210	90	8	(31)
4	Cast Iron	185	200	15	(31)
5	Brass	116	80	10	(31)
6	Aluminum, SAE AA2017-T4 UNS A92017	102	150	5	(31)

TABLE 11—

Material	Hardness Below Skin, Brinell	Hardness at Surface, Brinell	Thickness of Hard Skin, in	Reference
Steel AISI B1112	195	240	0.015	(31)
Stainless Steel, SAE 51416 and UNS 541600	210	273	0.004	(31)
Cast Iron	185	260	—	—
Brass	116	155	0.013	(31)
Aluminum, SAE AA2017-T4 and UNS A92017	102	122	0.005	(31)
Steel, 0.50% Carbon	170	220	0.500	(17)

If the depth of the compressed layer is excessive relative to the section size, the tensile stresses in the core may reach high values and eventually lead to failure in the core of hollow parts. It should be understood that this is a rare condition. In unusual parts the core has so much more section area than the skin that tensile stresses remain quite low. In the absence of specific tests it is suggested that the compressively stressed skin should have a cross section area of no more than 20% of the total cross section.[7] This will hold the tensile stress in the core down to about 10% of the peak compressive stress near the surface. (If more precise tests are not available one might estimate that the depth of the compressed layer, or the thickness of the compressed skin, is roughly equal to the width of the indentation made by the roller (34). (See also Chapter 3.)

In a tensile test the residual stresses will lead to yielding at a lower load stress because, in some areas of the test piece, the load stress plus the residual stress exceeds the yield strength before the load stress alone would exceed it.

The compressed skin of a rolled part will prevent or greatly retard the growth of cracks. Besides fatigue resistance this also increases the resistance to stress corrosion greatly or prevents damage by stress corrosion entirely. For instance, a steel shaft of 141,000 psi tensile strength rotating in brackish water with a bending load producing 20,000 psi stress lasted 3 million cycles (2 days) without surface rolling, but with surface rolling it lasted more than 100 million cycles (50 days) (32).

Surface compression also prevents the brittle fractures which result from many plating procedures. This effect has been well documented for shot peening (6, 36), and is similar for surface rolling.

Similarly, the effect of surface compression in extending the range of ductile behavior of steel to lower temperatures (37) may safely be expected if surface rolling is used as the means of producing the compression.

7. Or a depth of no more than 5% of the diameter.

The harmful effects of fretting in promoting fracture are also prevented or greatly delayed by surface rolling. Increases in endurance strength under fretting conditions have been reported and are shown in Table 12.

Where pinhole porosity is a problem as in some parts which must be plated or must hold pressure, the surface compression induced by surface rolling can be used to close surface pores and cracks.

TABLE 12—

Permissible Stress, psi Without Rolling	Permissible Stress, psi With Rolling	Reference
20,000	60,000	(32)
11,000	22,000	(17)
800	3,200	(38)

9. *Other Methods for Mechanical Prestressing (by J. G. Roberts)*

9.1 Introduction—Mechanical prestressing of structural members by shot peening (39) and surface rolling have been described previously. Other methods for mechanical prestressing may be classified according to the initial cause of the prestress, as shown below.

- Yielding of Material
  - Surface Yielding
    - Presetting
    - Shock Hardening
  - Subsurface Yielding
    - Bearingizing
    - Ballizing
    - Hammer Peening
    - Strain Peening
    - Stress-Relief Grooving
- Interference of Assembled Parts
  - Press Fitting
- Miscellaneous
  - Stamping
  - Polishing

NOTE—Other than shot peening and surface rolling.

Each of the methods herein, with the exception of press fitting, causes residual stress by yielding (40)[8] of material at or near the surface.[9] Consequently, some material ductility is always required. In fact, the more ductility the material possesses the better it is suited for prestressing. Virtually all structural engineering metals and alloys have some ductility and may, therefore, be mechanically prestressed. In addition to generating residual stresses, the localized plastic deformations cause some materials to strain harden. This, too, can have a beneficial effect. Of course surface finish is altered by many of the prestressing methods. Depending upon the initial surface finish and/or the prestressing method and its severity, the prestressing can smoothen, roughen, or leave unaltered the initial surface finish. In describing the prestressing methods listed in Table 13 particular attention will be directed at the resulting residual stress, strain hardening, and surface finish. Some of the examples used to describe these methods will illustrate only the strain hardening or some other characteristic of the prestressing. Residual stress will, however, always be induced.

9.2 Presetting—One of the simplest methods for increasing fatigue strength of a part that will be service loaded in only one direction is to statically stress the structural member in the same direction it is loaded in service to a fixed maximum load or strain that exceeds the elastic limit. The fixed load or strain is usually held for a short time. Upon release of the load the member will have a residual stress distribution which will permit the same (initial) load to be subsequently carried elastically. As a result of the yielding, the member will also be permanently deformed. Material strain hardening is not required.[10]

The presetting of leaf spring specimens is an illustration, Figure 43 (42). Here, one-directional bending endurance limit is increased from 90,000 psi to 130,000 psi. All of this increase is attributable to the compressive residual stress induced by presetting the SAE 5160 steel. Torsion bars (43) and Belleville springs (44) furnish other examples of parts that have been preset.

8. Numbers in parentheses in text, tables, and figure titles refer to references at end of report.
9. For a general mathematical description of how residual stresses may occur as a result of plastic deformation, see (40) Initial Stresses, p. 425.
10. For a description of residual stresses produced by inelastic bending, i.e., presetting, see (41), p. 375

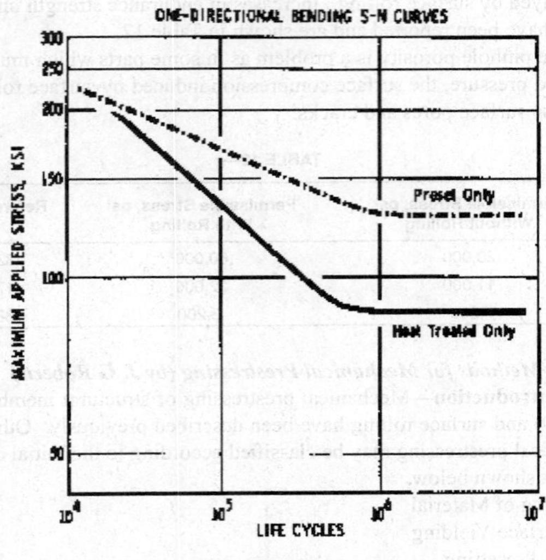

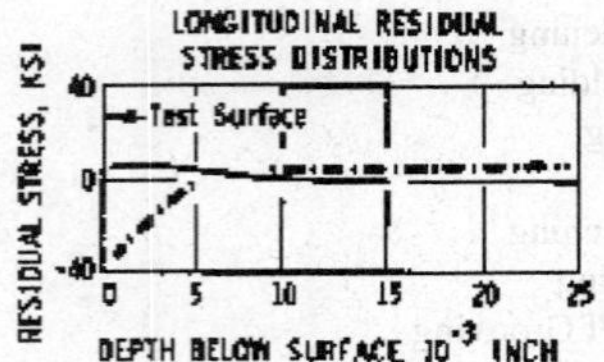

TEST SURFACE ROUGHNESS AND HARDNESS VALUES

TEST GROUP	SURFACE ROUGHNESS	HARDNESS ROCKWELL "C"
Preset Only	7-12	48
Heat Treated Only	10-25	47

FIGURE 43—RESIDUAL STRESS INDUCED BY PRESETTING LEAF SPRING SPECIMENS AND RESULTING FATIGUE PERFORMANCE (42)

Rectangular cross section beams can be preset to a greater extent than I-beams.[11] Residual stresses caused by presetting circular shafts[12] by one-directional torque and by presetting thick cylinders by internal pressure[13] are given by Timoshenko.

9.3 Shock Hardening—High velocity stress waves[14] can cause plastic deformations which induce residual stresses; however, judging from the experience reported in the literature, it appears that it is used primarily on materials that strain harden appreciably. The surface finish may be unaltered by the stress wave.

Railroad switch frogs, Figure 44, have been hardened by high velocity stress waves generated by sheet explosive (45). Five times its former useful life (20 versus 4 years) is expected for this application. Photomicrographs show plastic flow of the crystal structure that results in the hardness increase shown in Figure 45 (45). The penetration of the hardened layer extends to about 1 in, which is considerably deeper penetration than is usually found for other prestressing methods. Residual stress data were not reported, but it would appear that a considerable portion of the increased life is due to the strain hardening of the surface layer. Also, surface finish is apparently not altered greatly. Austenitic manganese steels, weldments, and castings have also been hardened by this method (46).

Fatigue S-N curves of explosively formed materials indicate that the high velocity stress waves do not always increase fatigue strength (47). Difficult-to-form aircraft materials such as 8% Mn-Ti have better fatigue strength in the annealed condition than in the annealed and hardened (by shock hardening) condition.

11. See Timoshenko (41), p. 371
12. See Timoshenko (41), p. 383.
13. See Timoshenko (41), p. 389.
14. For a mathematical description of how such waves are generated, see (40), p. 438.

FIGURE 44—SHOCK HARDENING OF RAILROAD-SWITCH FROGS (45)

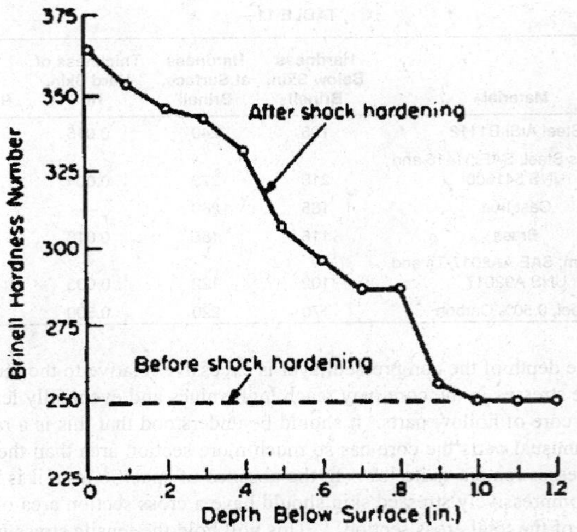

FIGURE 45—HARDNESS INDUCED Y SHOCK HARDENING RAILROAD-SWITCH FROGS (45)

9.4 Elastic Contact Stresses—Before describing the prestressing methods which are initially caused by subsurface yielding (see Table 13) of the material it is instructive to briefly review the maximum stresses caused by static loading of a ball on a flat plate. In Figure 46 [15] the three normal stresses along the normal (Oz) to the center of the circular contact area are shown. Distance below the contact circle is shown (vertical scale) in terms of a, the radius of the circle of contact, and the stresses, which are compressive, are shown (horizontal scale) in terms of the maximum compressive stress q_o. The latter is usually referred to as the "Hertz" stress. It occurs at the center of the contact area. The maximum shearing stress occurs at a depth of 0.5a and is equal to 0.31 q_o, which is almost 2 1/3 times the maximum tensile stress (0.133 q_o), which occurs at the boundary of the circle of contact. Ductile steels first yield at the point of maximum shearing stress. Since the depth at which the material first yields affects the penetration of the residual stress, it is useful to express the radius of the contact circle in terms of q_o and R, the radius of the sphere. For steel, $a = 2.86\, q_o R/E$. Thus, the distance below the surface at which yielding first occurs varies directly with both q_o and R, and inversely with E, the modulus of elasticity in tension.

15. From (40), p. 376.

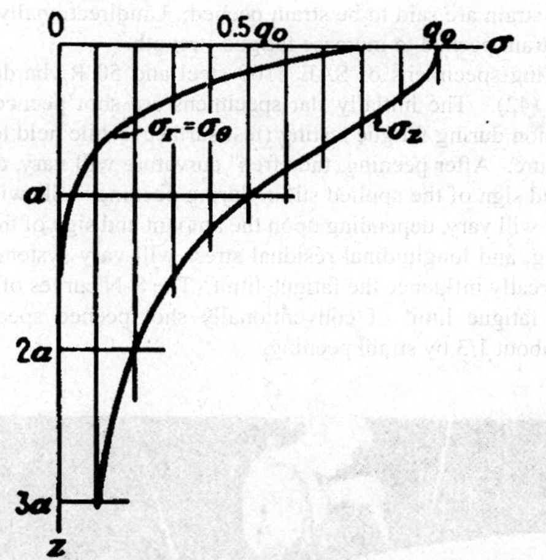

FIGURE 46—COMPRESSIVE CONTACT STRESSES ALONG PROJECTED LOAD AXIS FOR A BALL PRESSED AGAINST A FLAT PLATE (40)

After considerable yielding has taken place, Figure 47 (48), the elastic stresses are altered by the plastic flow and the computations are no longer valid. They do provide, however, a rational means for studying the penetration and the amount of yielding.

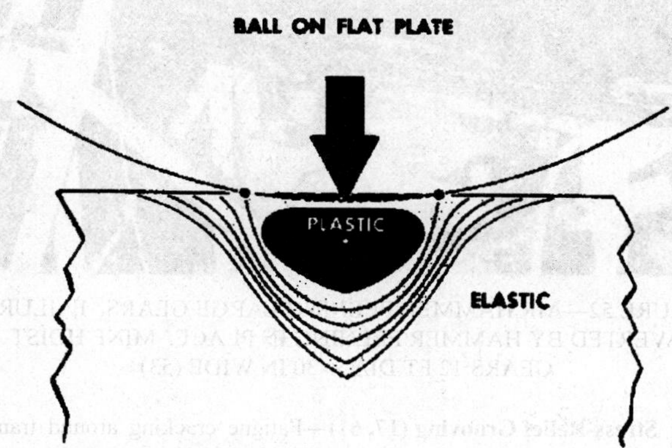

FIGURE 47—CALCULATED PLASTIC REGION IN FLAT PLATE (48)

9.5 Bearingizing—Rapid blows of rollers against the bearing surface for the purpose of strain hardening the material and/or surface finishing the bore is known as "bearingizing." A tool similar to that shown in Figure 48 (17, 49) is usually used for this purpose. The bores of the link rod shown in Figure 49 (17, 49) were rolled with such a tool with the resulting fatigue improvements shown.

A cutaway view of a "through" tool is shown in Figure 50 (50). As high points on a cam come up behind a series of rollers they deliver an outward radial blow to peen the work surface.

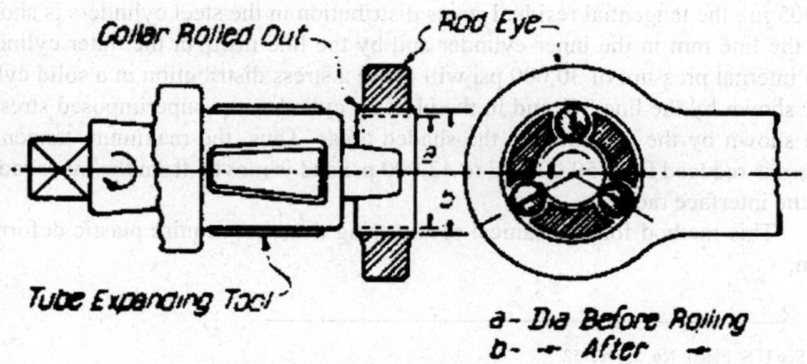

FIGURE 48—BEARINGIZING TOOL (17, 49)

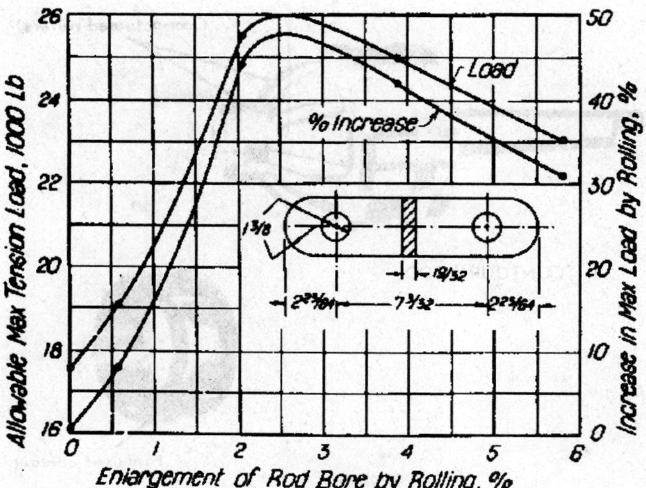

FIGURE 49—FATIGUE IMPROVEMENT IN LINK ROD BY BEARINGIZING (11, 12)

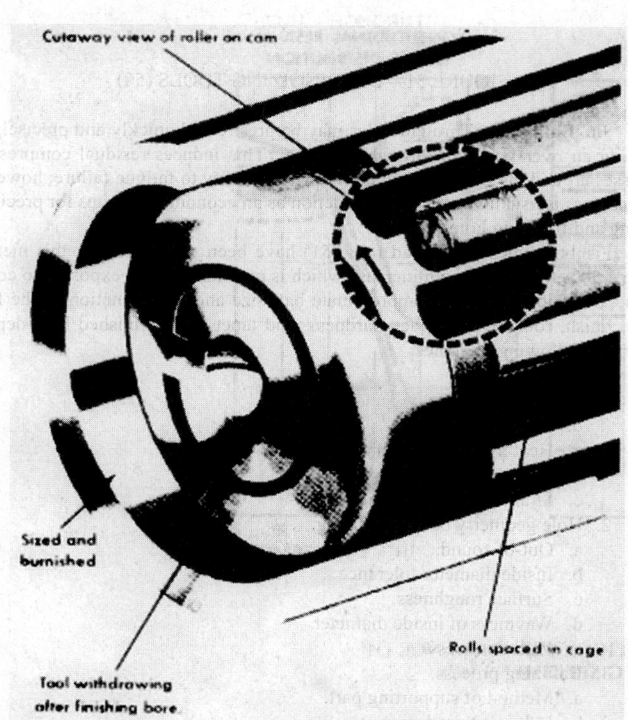

FIGURE 50—BEARINGIZING "THROUGH" TOOL (50)

Overall views of a "contour" tool and a "through" tool are shown in Figure 51 (50).

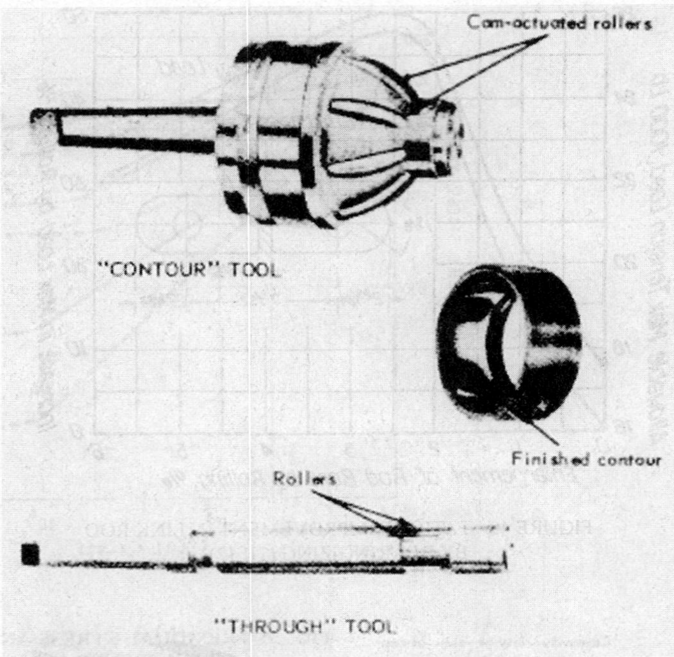

FIGURE 51—BEARINGIZING TOOLS (50)

9.6 Ballizing—Through holes may be prestressed quickly and precisely by forcing an oversized ball through the hole. This induces residual compressive stresses around the hole and reduces the vulnerability to fatigue failure; however, the process is usually applied in production as an economical means for precision sizing and finishing holes.

Fishbolt holes in railroad rails (51) have been prestressed by this method with a 50% fatigue strength increase which is maintained after exposure to corrosion. Selection (52) of the approximate ball size and determination of the final size, finish, roundness, surface hardness, and taper of the finished hole depend upon the following variables:

1. Material.
   a. Hardness.
   b. Ductility.
   c. Heat treatment history.
   d. Cold working history.
   e. Strain hardening properties.
2. Hole geometry before ballizing.
   a. Out-of-round.
   b. Inside diameter tolerance.
   c. Surface roughness.
   d. Waviness of inside diameter.
   e. Wall thickness.
3. Ballizing process.
   a. Method of supporting part.
   b. Lubricant used.
   c. Interference fit between ball and hole.

The experimental method is usually used in arriving at the desired characteristics of the finished hole.

9.7 Hammer Peening—Large parts may be conveniently and inexpensively prestressed by peening with a large radius tool (frequently 1 in). In this way greater penetration or depth of the prestressed layer may be obtained. Large gear teeth, Figure 52, have been prestressed in this manner to offset fatigue failure (53). An air hammer tool is fitted with a spherical-tipped hammer made of hardened (Rockwell C 60 +_ tool steel. Air pressure drives the hammer into the work for a distance determined by the porting of the driving piston. Usual air pressures are in the range from 35–70 psi and resulting impact rate ranges from 35–7 impacts/s. Hammer tip radius is determined by depth of penetration desired, part shape, and material ductility. For a given air pressure, small tip radii tend to increase depth of penetration.

9.8 Strain Peening[16]—Structural members that are shot peened while held at some fixed strain are said to be strain peened. Unidirectionally stressed members may be strain peened to increase fatigue strength.

Leaf spring specimens of SAE 5160 steel and 50 R_c hardness have been strain peened (42). The initially flat specimens are shot peened[17] on the face loaded in tension during fatigue testing (test surface) while held to a fixed longitudinal curvature. After peening, the "free" curvature will vary, depending upon the amount and sign of the applied strain during peening. Likewise, longitudinal residual stress will vary, depending upon the amount and sign of the applied strain during peening, and longitudinal residual stress will vary systematically, Figure 53, and will greatly influence the fatigue limit. The S-N curves of Figure 53 indicate that the fatigue limit of conventionally shot peened specimens may be increased by about 1/3 by strain peening.

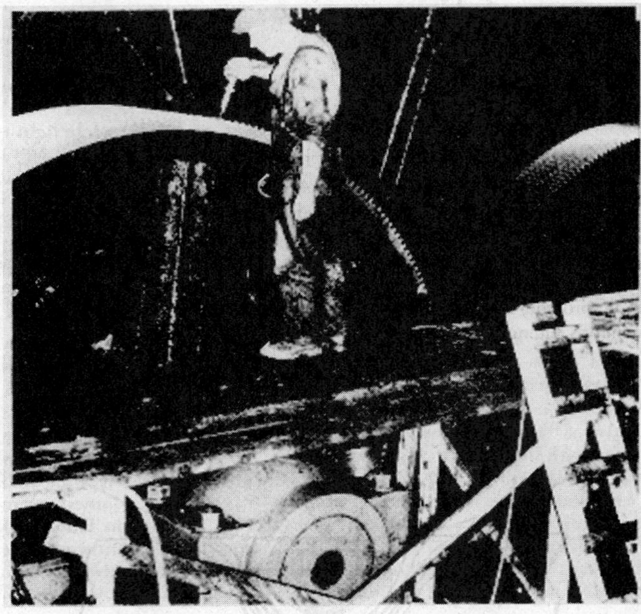

FIGURE 52—AIR HAMMER PEENING LARGE GEARS. FAILURE AVERTED BY HAMMER PEENING IN PLACE. MINE HOIST GEARS 12 FT DIA × 30 IN WIDE (53)

9.9 Stress-Relief Grooving (17, 61)—Fatigue cracking around transverse oil holes of crank pins may be offset or eliminated by stamping stress-relief grooves around the hole, Figure 54 (17). Steel specimens (SAE 1050 and UNS G10500) with a yield strength of 50,200 psi and a tensile strength of 92,000 psi and having the dimensions shown in Figure 54 were stamped with the apparatus shown. The rotating bending endurance limit was increased from 15,500 psi for the shaft without grooves to over 20,000 psi with stamped grooves, or an increase of over 35%. Coined grooves around holes may also be used to strengthen the holes in fatigue (35).

9.10 Press Fitting—Press fits and shrink fits are well known methods for holding tube assemblies together. Such interference fits also give rise to elastic stresses which may be beneficial. This is illustrated by an example (41). If in Figure 55, the radii a, b, c are 2, 4, and 6 in, respectively, and the interference is 0.005 in., the tangential residual stress distribution in the steel cylinders is shown by the line mm in the inner cylinder and by the line m_1n_1 in the outer cylinder. An internal pressure of 30,000 psi will cause a stress distribution in a solid cylinder shown by the line SS, and in the built up cylinder, the superimposed stresses are shown by the ordinates to the shaded area. Thus, the maximum tangential stress is reduced from 50,000 psi to 42,000 psi and is moved from the inner radius of the interface radius.

This method for mechanical prestressing does not require plastic deformation.

---

16. See U.S. Patent No. 2,608,752.
17. Chilled iron shot, 0.006 C Almen intensity, full visual coverage.

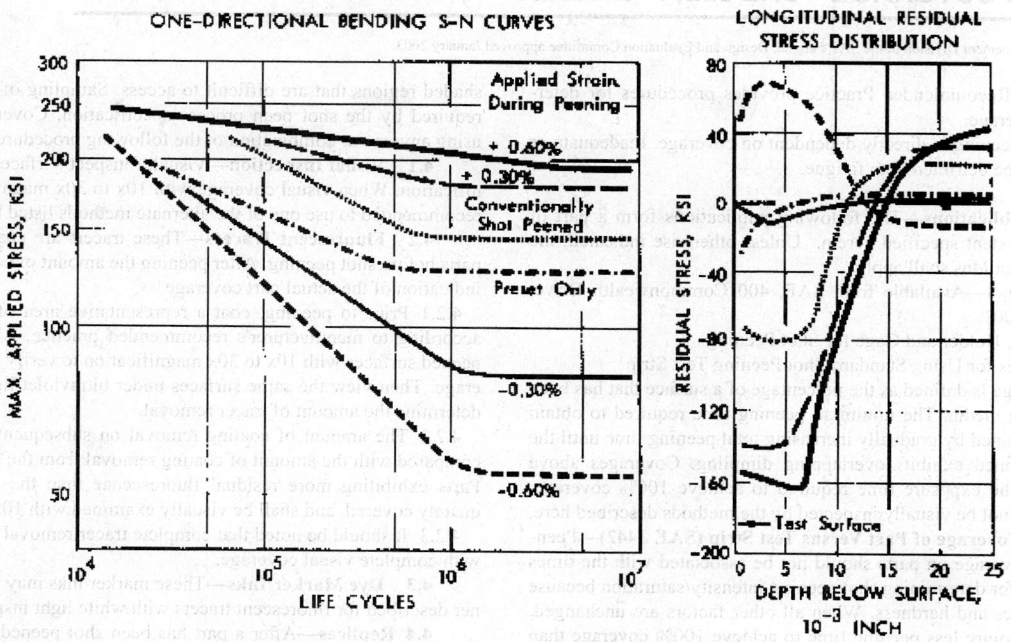

FIGURE 53—RESIDUAL STRESS AND FATIGUE PERFORMANCE OF STRAIN PEENED LEAF SPRING SPECIMENS (42)

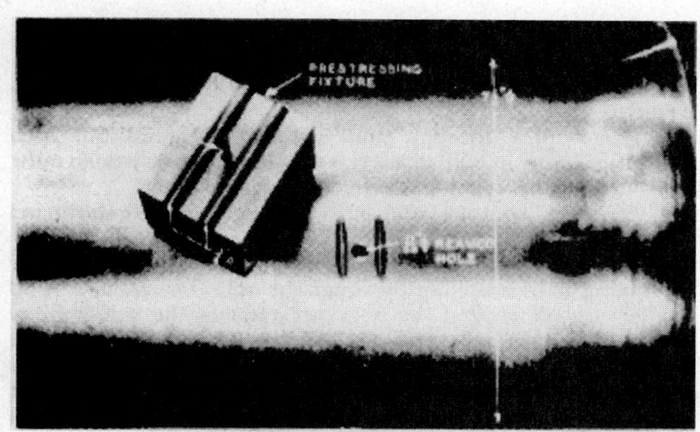

FIGURE 54—STRESS-RELIEF GROOVING

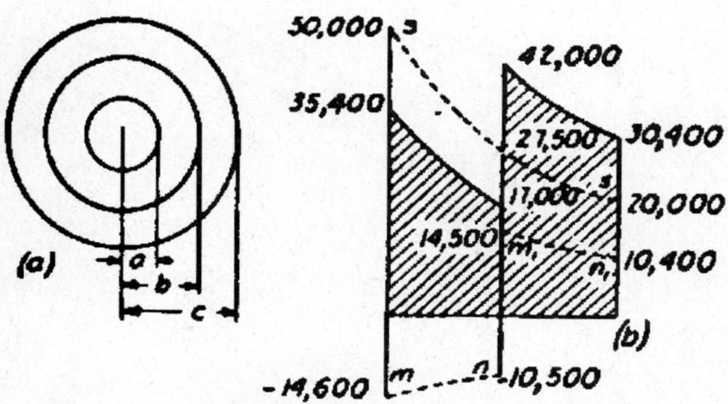

FIGURE 55—PRESS FIT ASSEMBLY CROSS SECTION (A) AND (B) TANGENTIAL STRESSES (41)

9.11 Stamping—This method for prestressing involves cold stamping the edges of holes, Figure 56 (17), Burnheim (54) found that steel plates of the shape shown in Figure 56 could be stamped at the hole edges to increase the reversed bending fatigue limit up to 44% by using the conical pin stamp and loading shown in the lower right portion of Figure 56. The conical stamp and loadings shown at the lower left resulting in fatigue limit improvements of from 25–33%. The Cr Mn V steel plates (yield strength 88,200 psi) with the hole unstamped had a 34,100 psi fatigue limit.

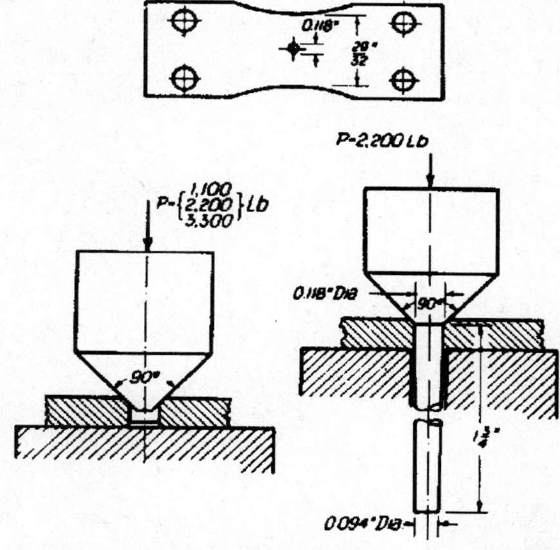

FIGURE 56—TOOLS FOR STAMPING HOLE EDGES (17, 54)

9.12 Polishing—Mechanically polished surfaces can cause fatigue strength improvements by reducing the stress concentrations and by prestressing the surface. Coombs' (55) reversed bending fatigue tests of shot peened leaf-spring steel indicate that hand polishing to a 7 µin finish causes about 20% increase in fatigue limit.

SHOT PEENING COVERAGE—SAE J2277 JAN2003 SAE Recommended Practice

Report of the SAE Surface Enhancement Division of the SAE Fatigue, Design and Evaluation Committee approved January 2003.

1. Scope—This SAE Recommended Practice provides procedures for determining shot peening coverage.

Effectiveness of shot peening is directly dependent on coverage. Inadequate or excessive coverage may be detrimental to fatigue.

2. References

2.1 Applicable Publications—The following publications form a part of the specification to the extent specified herein. Unless otherwise indicated, the latest issue of SAE publications shall apply.

2.1.1 SAE PUBLICATIONS—Available from SAE, 400 Commonwealth Drive, Warrendale, PA 15096-0001.

SAE J442—Test Strip, Holder and Gage for Shot Peening

SAE J443—Procedures for Using Standard Shot Peening Test Strip

3. Coverage—Coverage is defined as the percentage of a surface that has been impacted by the peening media. The minimum peening time required to obtain 100% coverage is determined by gradually increasing total peening time until the entire surface being peened exhibits overlapping dimpling. Coverages above 100% are multiples of the exposure time required to achieve 100% coverage. Coverage over 100% cannot be visually inspected by the methods described here.

3.1 Variation in Coverage of Part Versus Test Strip (SAE J442)—Peening time to reach full coverage on parts should not be associated with the times referenced in SAE J443 for determining shot peening intensity/saturation because of the parts' varied shapes and hardness. When all other factors are unchanged, soft surfaces typically require less peening time to achieve 100% coverage than hard surfaces, since the size of each impression in soft surfaces is larger.

4. Coverage Determination—Coverage determination shall be performed on representative areas of the peened surfaces. These areas shall include recesses and shaded regions that are difficult to access. Sampling of peened parts shall be as required by the shot peen process specification. Coverage may be determined using any one or combination of the following procedures:

4.1 Visual Inspection—Visually inspect surfaces using 10x to 30x magnification. When visual coverage with 10x to 30x magnification is not clear, it is recommended to use one of the alternate methods listed below.

4.2 Fluorescent Tracers—These tracers are coatings that are applied to parts before shot peening. After peening the amount of coating removal is a visual indication of the actual part coverage.

4.2.1 Prior to peening, coat a representative area of a part or sample piece according to manufacturer's recommended practice. After peening, inspect the peened surfaces with 10x to 30x magnification to verify the required level of coverage. Then view the same surfaces under ultraviolet light in a darkened area to determine the amount of tracer removal.

4.2.2 The amount of coating removal on subsequently peened parts shall be compared with the amount of coating removal from the sample prepared in 4.2.1. Parts exhibiting more residual fluorescence than the sample piece are inadequately covered, and shall be visually examined with 10x to 30x magnification.

4.2.3 It should be noted that complete tracer removal may or may not coincide with complete visual coverage.

4.3 Dye Marker Inks—These marker inks may be used in the same manner described for fluorescent tracers with white light inspection.

4.4 Replicas—After a part has been shot peened, a replica of the surface can be made. This replica can be projected on a screen and compared to other replicas, having various known degrees of coverage.

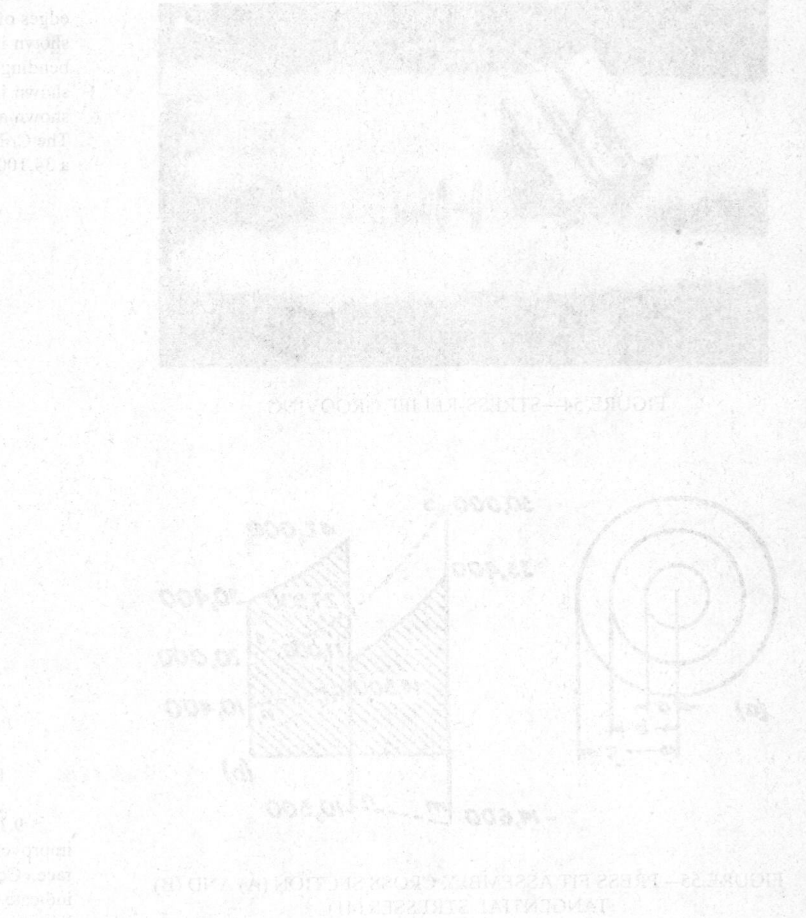

LIQUEFIED NATURAL GAS (LNG) VEHICLE METERING AND DISPENSING SYSTEMS—SAE J2645 MAR2003

SAE Recommended Practice

Report of the SAE Truck and Bus Alternative Fuels Subcommittee of the SAE Truck and Bus Chassis and Powertrain Committee approved March 2003.

TABLE OF CONTENTS

1. Scope—This SAE Recommended Practice applies to Liquefied Natural Gas Vehicle Fuel. The purpose of this document is to provide information on issues that are important to consider regarding LNG metering and dispensing systems.

2. References

2.1 Applicable Publications—The following publications form a part of this specification to the extent specified herein. Unless otherwise specified, the latest issue of each publication applies.

2.1.1 NIST PUBLICATION—Available from the National Institute of Standards and Technology, US Department of Commerce, Gaithersburg, MD 20899-2350, Phone 301-975-3058, www.nist.gov.

NIST Handbook 44—Specifications, Tolerances, and other Technical Requirements for Weighing and Measuring Devices

2.1.2 NFPA PUBLICATIONS—Available from the National Fire Protection Association, 1 Batterymarch Park, P.O. Box 9101, Quincy, MA 02269-9101, 1-800-344-3555 or http://catalog.nfpa.org.

NFPA 52—Compressed Natural Gas (CNG) Vehicular Fuel Systems Code

NFPA 57—Liquefied Natural Gas (LNG) Vehicular Fuel Systems Code

NFPA 59A—Standard for the Production, Storage, and Handling of Liquefied Natural Gas (LNG)

2.2 Related Publications—The following publications are provided for information purposes only and are not a required part of the document.

2.2.1 STATE OF CALIFORNIA PUBLICATIONS—Available on the web at http://www.dir.ca.gov/Title8/sub1.html.

California Code of Regulations (CCR), Title 8, Industrial Regulations, Article 7, Compressed and Liquefied Natural Gas Systems

2.2.2 NFPA PUBLICATIONS—Available from the National Fire Protection Association, 1 Batterymarch Park, P.O. Box 9101, Quincy, MA 02269-9101, 1-800-344-3555 or http://catalog.nfpa.org.

NFPA 30—Flammable and Combustible Liquids Code

NFPA 30A—Code for Motor Fuel Dispensing Facilities and Repair Garages

NFPA 70—National Electrical Code

NFPA 72—National Fire Alarm Code

NFPA 79—Electrical Standard for Industrial Machinery

NFPA 497—Classification of Flammable Liquids, Gases, or Vapors and of Hazardous Locations for Electrical Installations in Chemical Process Areas

3. Definitions—Definition 3.1 is taken from NFPA 52 (Compressed Natural Gas [CNG] Vehicular Fuel Systems Code). Definitions 3.2 to 3.4, 3.7 to 3.10, and 3.14 are taken from NIST Handbook 44 (Specifications, Tolerances, and Other Technical Requirements for Weighing and Measuring Devices), Appendix D. Definitions 3.5 and 3.11 are based on Handbook 44 definitions.

3.1 Authority Having Jurisdiction—The organization, office, or individual responsible for approving equipment, an installation, or a procedure.

3.2 Contract Sale—A sale where there is a written agreement stating the price as either a fixed price, a price above cost, or an adjustment from the posted price.

3.3 Cryogenic Liquids—Fluids with a normal boiling point below –153 °C (–243 °F).

3.4 Direct Sale—A sale in which both parties in the transaction are present when the quantity is being determined. An unattended automated or customer-operated weighing or measuring system is considered to represent the device/business owner in transactions involving an unattended device.

3.5 Dispenser—A device designed for the measurement and delivery of fluids used as fuel.

3.6 Liquefied Natural Gas (LNG)—A cryogenic liquid, produced by reducing the temperature of natural gas to about –162 °C (–260 °F) at atmospheric pressure.

3.7 Mass Flow Meter—A device that measures the mass of a product flowing through the system. The mass measurement may be determined directly from the effects of mass on the sensing unit or may be inferred by measuring the properties of the product, such as the volume, density, temperature, or pressure, and displaying the quantity in mass units.

3.8 NBP—Normal boiling point of a cryogenic liquid at 101.325 kPa (14.696 psi absolute).

3.9 NTP—Normal temperature of 21 °C (70 °F) and pressure of 101.325 kPa (14.696 psi absolute) respectively.

3.10 Point of Sale System—An assembly of elements including a weighing or measuring element, an indicating element, and a recording element (and may also be equipped with a "scanner") used to complete a direct sales transaction.

3.11 Retail Device—A device used for:

a. Single deliveries of less than 378 L (100 gal) or
b. Retail deliveries of motor fuels to individual vehicles.

3.12 Saturation Pressure—The point at which temperature and pressure of a liquid-vapor system are in equilibrium or the pressure at which the liquid will automatically boil. Raise the temperature, and the pressure will rise, lower the pressure and the temperature will fall. As a commonplace example, water will boil at 100 °C (212 °F) at sea level, but will boil at roughly 94 °C (202 °F) in Denver, where there is less air pressure. If a liquid is artificially pressurized, as in a pressure cooker, it will boil at a higher temperature than when in an open pot. Accurate control of the saturation pressure of dispensed LNG may be important because most LNG vehicle systems presently in use rely on this pressure to drive fuel to the engine.

3.13 Two-Phase Flow—A condition where the liquid is not in a compressed liquid state, but contains some percentage of gas entrained in the flowing liquid.

3.14 Wholesale Device—Any device other than a retail device (see 3.11).

4. Cryogenic Issues—There are challenges to accurately measure LNG. The most critical are addressed in succeeding sections. Note that these issues are interrelated.

4.1 Heat—Cryogenic liquids, under pressure, will gain heat unless the temperature can be kept at equilibrium. This heat transfer can be minimized, but not eliminated. Heat gain or loss will affect liquid density.

4.2 Saturation Pressure—Accurate control of the saturation pressure of dispensed LNG may be important because most LNG vehicle systems presently in use rely on this pressure to drive fuel to the engine. It is difficult to accurately measure the saturation pressure for flowing LNG.

4.3 Density—The density of LNG varies with saturation pressure. At higher saturation pressures (higher boiling points), LNG is less dense. This means that 3.79 liters (one gallon) of LNG at –154 °C (–246 °F) weighs 1.56 kg (3.44 lb) (and automatically boils at 170.3 kPa [24.7 psia]), and at –129 °C (–200 °F) it weighs 1.40 kg (3.08 lb) (and automatically boils at 790.8 kPa [114.7 psia]). Depending on the technology, a dispensing system must be capable of making corrections for density changes related to temperature, pressure and/or composition.

4.4 LNG Composition—Due to variance in feedstock, liquefaction methods, and LNG storage, the LNG's composition (chemical makeup) may vary. The variation of composition of LNG may change density and can thereby cause measurement errors.

4.5 Sub-Cooling—Cryogenic fluids are generally contained in pressure vessels. It is possible to artificially pressurize these vessels, without changing the temperature or the saturation of the liquid, by adding vapor to the top of the vessel. Under these conditions, the liquid is considered to be "sub-cooled." Pumping the fluid at a higher pressure has this same effect. Either method serves to suppress boiling of the liquid.

5. Dispensing System Issues—There are many issues outside of the measuring transducers themselves that affect measurement accuracy. Following are the main things to consider in avoiding measurement inaccuracy.

5.1 Hose Volume Corrections—Design consideration should be given to how the dispensing system will account for the amount of liquid or gas downstream of the meter installation. The dispenser may be designed to incorporate a liquid recirculating feature, a hose draining system or other methods to achieve a controlled condition.

5.2 Two-Phase Flow—Flowing LNG is subject to boiling as heat is added or pressure is reduced during its path from the storage tank to the vehicle system. Depending on the piping configuration, a combination of both vapor and liquid may occur in the system. This is especially true during the initiation of the dispensing process. Most meters experience errors due to two-phase flow. An accurate LNG dispensing system may require a means to detect and correct for the presence of two-phase flow.

5.3 Temperature Effects—Temperature changes may affect the dimensions and material properties of the dispensing system and metering device. Temperature will also impact the density of LNG. Dispensing systems should take these effects into account by design, calibration or correction techniques, if necessary.

5.4 Pressure Effects—Changes in pressure within the dispensing system itself (pressure drop) may cause two-phase flow, as well as density changes. Dispensing systems should take these effects into account by design, calibration or correction techniques, if necessary.

5.5 Composition Compensation—LNG is a mixture consisting primarily of Methane, Ethane, Propane, Butane, and Nitrogen. Composition depends on the feedstock and liquefaction methods. As such, the density of LNG can vary depending upon its composition. Chemical composition corrections should be considered in the metering system design.

5.6 Diversion of Measured Flow—In systems subject to metrological control or custody transfer, no means shall be provided by which any measured liquid can be diverted from the measuring chamber of the device or the discharge line therefrom, except that a manually controlled outlet that may be opened for purging or draining the measuring system shall be permitted. Effective means shall be provided to prevent the passage of liquid through any such outlet during normal operation of the device and to indicate clearly and unmistakably when the valve controls are so set as to permit passage of liquid through such outlet. (This requirement is taken from NIST Handbook 44, Section 3.34 - Cryogenic Liquid-Measuring Devices, S.3.1).

5.7 Vapor Equalization Line—A vapor equalization line shall not be used during a metered delivery unless the quantity of vapor displaced from the buyer's tank to the seller's tank is deducted from the metered quantity. (This requirement is taken from NIST Handbook 44, Section 3.38 - Carbon Dioxide Liquid-Measuring Devices, UR.2.3).

6. Dispensing System Selection—When selecting an LNG dispenser, the operation of the fleet(s) it serves should be considered. Refueling frequency, accuracy and metrological requirements should help guide the user.

6.1 Private Stations—For these stations, where metering is for internal accounting purposes, and fueling accuracy to each vehicle is not critical, a relatively simple metering system can be used. Typically these systems may have an accuracy of ±2.0 to 5.0%, but can be specified to meet each user's requirements. These devices are typically not subject to weights and measures approvals or requirements.

6.2 Public (Retail) Stations—If the station is accessible to the public, fleets, government vehicles, or other LNG users, and fuel is dispensed as a retail sale, or dispensed under a fleet or price contract, this type of system is subject to metrological control. More stringent accuracy and metrological requirements are required for this type of dispensing system. These systems typically have a minimum accuracy requirement of ±1.5%.

6.3 Refueling Frequency

6.3.1 ALL VEHICLES FUEL DURING THE SAME "FUELING WINDOW"—A fleet operator has all vehicles returned to the refueling station at same time. In this case the dispensing system may not require a dispenser cool down between each fill event. Potential losses in time and product associated with stabilizing a metering system become less important.

6.3.2 INTERMITTENT FUELING—The system will be used randomly throughout the day; the dispenser must be stabilized each time to safeguard dispensing accuracy. Potential losses in time and product to perform multiple stabilizing cycles during the day may affect the economics of the station.

7. Measurement Device Types—There are many types of measurement devices. This document cannot list all of the varying types and it does not intend to limit LNG measurement to the devices listed in 7.1 to 7.3.

7.1 Volumetric—These devices measure the volume (liters, gallons, etc.) which passes through a pipe. There are many different technologies available, employing varying measurement techniques to ascertain the volume flow through the pipe. Common technologies are turbine, vortex and orifice meters.

7.2 Mass—These devices directly measure the mass (kilograms, pounds, etc.) which passes through a pipe. Two common technologies are the coriolis and straight tube mass meter systems.

7.3 Inferred Mass—These devices use varying techniques to determine the inferred mass flow through a pipe. Inferred mass means that the density is inferred through the use of ancillary devices such as temperature and/or pressure sensors, densitometers, etc. These devices typically measure volumetric flow and apply correction factors based on flowing density or composition to determine the mass flowing through a pipe. Devices measuring inferred mass are typically defined as devices that do not measure mass directly.

8. LNG Dispenser/Meter—Table 1 that follows gives broad guidelines on the type of metering and dispensing system that may be required for particular applications. For comparison purposes, meters can be divided into three classes as a function of utility and accuracy. The three classes can be defined as follows;

C – Non-metered

B – Metered – No metrological control.

A – Metered – Metrologically controlled

Note that any facility may upgrade to a higher class meter.

TABLE 1—GUIDELINES ON METERING AND DISPENSING SYSTEMS

Metering Class	Required Accuracy	Density Compensation	Process Controls	Typical Application
C	Not applicable	Not applicable	User defined	Private station or demonstration project
B	Nominal <±2.5% by volume or mass	User defined	Diversion of metered flow: Allowed Audit trail security: Not needed Two phase flow mitigation: Not needed	Private stations. Internal accounting purposes/Not for use for billing or contract sales, whether public or private
A	±1.5% type acceptance tolerance ±2.5% maintenance tolerance	Automatic temperature, pressure, density and composition correction, as required.	Diversion of metered flow: Not allowed Audit trail security: Required Two phase flow mitigation: Required General compliance with Handbook 44	Public stations with retail or contract sales. Public, private or government fleets and vehicles.

9. Safe Operation

9.1 General—Procedures to safely operate a dispenser should be posted in a readily visible location at the dispenser. These instructions should include reference to the proper personal protective gear for safe LNG dispensing. "No smoking" signs and flammability notices should be posted as required by NFPA guidelines. Local fire codes should be observed. The relevant safety requirements of the National Fire Protection Association's - Liquefied Natural Gas (LNG) Vehicular Fuel Systems Code (NFPA 57) and Standard for the Production, Storage, and Handling of Liquefied Natural Gas (LNG) (NFPA 59A) should apply. Pictographs and bilingual (English/Spanish) written instructions for dispensing facilities are recommended. Those involved in LNG fueling operations should be in close contact with the Authority Having Jurisdiction (AHJ) concerning safety matters.

9.2 Hose Breakaway—The dispenser should be protected from developing an uncontrolled spill in the event of a vehicle drive away without un-coupling the dispensing hose.

9.3 Connectors—The fueling connector should safely accommodate the pressurized nature of the fuel and be rated for the cryogenic temperature.

9.4 Grounding—When the fuel coupling and related piping cannot be demonstrated to provide static electric grounding, static electric ground clamps should be provided. Clamps should be at each location where transfer of LNG takes place, if grounding through the fuel coupling and related piping cannot be demonstrated.

9.5 Venting—Vehicle tank venting should be incorporated into stations providing dispensing capabilities. Vented gas should be directed to a safe location (consistent with NFPA 57, Table 5-12.1) or returned to the bulk storage tank. Grounding clamps should be provided at venting points for vehicle grounding if coupling and related piping cannot be demonstrated to provide static electricity grounding. Unconnected vehicles being vented must always be grounded before venting.

10. Dispenser Display—Metrological testing of LNG is presently done in mass units, therefore such units should be displayed during testing and calibration. In addition, dispenser displays may be in volumetric units (such as gallons or liters) at NBP (normal boiling point).

9 Ferrous and Nonferrous—General

USE OF TERMS YIELD STRENGTH AND YIELD POINT—SAE J450 FEB2002 SAE Recommended Practice

Report of the SAE Nonferrous Metals Committee and the SAE Iron and Steel technical Committee approved June 9160. First revised by the SAE Iron and Steel Technical Committee, Divisions 1 and 32, June 1984. Completely revised by the SAE Iron and Steel Technical Committee Division 1—Carbon and Alloy Steels, June 1991, and reaffirmed March 1996 and February 2002.

1. Scope—The purpose of this SAE Recommended Practice is to describe the terms yield strength and yield point. Included are definitions for both terms and recommendations for their use and application.

2. References

2.1 Applicable Publications—The following publications form a part of this specification to the extent specified herein.

2.1.1 ASTM PUBLICATIONS—Available from ASTM, 100 Barr Harbor Drive, West Conshohocken, PA 19428-2959.

ASTM A 370—Standard Test Methods and Definitions for Mechanical Testing of Steel Products

ASTM E 6—Standard Terminology Relating to Methods of Mechanical Testing

ASTM E 8—Standard Test Methods of Tension Testing of Metallic Materials

3. Definitions

3.1 Yield Strength—The stress at which a material exhibits a specified limiting deviation from the proportionality of stress to strain. At the point of limiting deviation, the yield strength is expressed in units of stress and is referenced to a particular strain. The units of stress and strain should be defined as either engineering stress and strain or true stress and strain. The deviation may be measured either by the Offset method or by the Extension Under Load method as described in ASTM E 8. The method of measurement must be stated when reporting yield strength. The term is applicable to materials whose stress-strain diagram in the area of transition from elastic to plastic strain is a smooth curve, as well as to those which yield discontinuously and whose stress strain diagrams exhibit an upper yield point or sharp knee.

3.2 Yield Point—A special case of yield strength applicable where yielding occurs discontinuously. An upper and sometimes a lower value can be determined. The upper yield point is defined as the first stress in the material, at which an increase in strain occurs without an increase in stress. The lower yield point is defined as the lowest point between the first stress and the onset of continuous plastic behavior, at which an increase in strain occurs without an increase in stress.

Since in their commercial form, only ferrous metals exhibit this phenomenon and then only under some circumstances, it follows that the term yield point has only limited application to the results of tensile testing of ferrous metals and is not applicable to the testing of nonferrous metals.

4. Recommended Usage

4.1 Nonferrous Metals—Only the term yield strength is applicable. Specifications and test reports must always state the method of test and limiting values of strain.

4.2 Ferrous Metals—Yield strength is the general term and it is applicable to stress-strain curves of both the smooth, rounded type, and the type characteristic of discontinuous yielding. When reporting yield strength, the method of test and limiting values of strain must be stated.

Strictly interpreted, the term "yield point" is intended for application only in those cases in which the material exhibits the unique characteristics defined previously under yield point. If only a single value of yield point is reported, it should be indicated whether it is the upper or lower yield point. There are some specifications which prescribe a yield point for materials which have smooth stress-strain curves. In such cases, use of the term yield point should be discouraged. However a practical substitute for yield point would be a yield strength value obtained through any of the recommended methods described in ASTM E 8.

For a more detailed discussion of the terms involved and a description of the applicable methods of test refer to the following:

ASTM A 370—Standard Test Methods and Definitions for Mechanical Testing of Steel Products

ASTM E 6—Standard Terminology Relating to Methods of Mechanical Testing

ASTM E 8—Standard Test Methods of Tension Testing of Metallic Materials

(R) SURFACE ROUGHNESS AND PEAK COUNT MEASUREMENT OF COLD-ROLLED STEEL SHEET—SAE J911 MAR98

SAE Recommended Practice

Report of the SAE Iron and Steel Technical Committee approved January 1965 and reaffirmed June 1986. Completely revised by the SAE Iron and Steel Technical Committee Division 32—Sheet and Strip Steel March 1998.

1. Scope

1.1 This SAE Recommended Practice describes a method for measuring Roughness Average (R_a) and Peak Count (PC) of the surface of cold-rolled steel sheet.

1.2 The method includes a system for equipment configuration, calibration, and procedures for determining average surface roughness, R_a (µm or µin), and average peak count, PC (peaks per cm or peaks per inch) on cold-rolled steel sheet surfaces.

2. References

2.1 Applicable Publication—The following publication forms a part of the specification to the extent specified herein.

2.1.1 ASME PUBLICATION—Available from ASME, 345 East 47 Street, New York, NY 10017-2330.

ASME B46.1-1995—Surface Texture

3. Definitions

3.1 Roughness Average—The surface roughness average (R_a) shall be reported in micrometers (µm) as the arithmetical average of the absolute deviations from the median line, Figure 1, established within the limits of the filtered roughness profile.

Surface roughess consists of the finer irregularities in the surface texture which usually include those irregularities which result from the inherent action of the production process. These are considered to include texture characteristics transferred to the sheet surface from the roll surface during cold rolling, and which are within the limits of the roughness-width cutoff.

3.1.1 ROUGHNESS CUTOFF—The roughness cutoff is the electrical response characteristic of the roughness filter of the measuring instrument. Selection of this cutoff limits the spacings of the surface irregularities to be included in the assessment of roughness average. The standard value of the roughness cutoff is 0.8 mm (nominally 0.03 in).

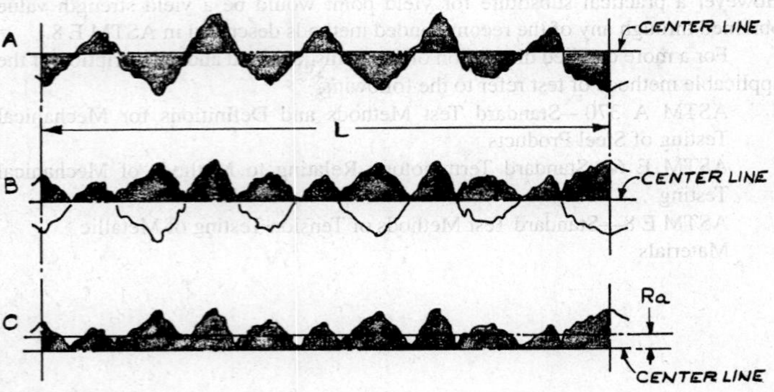

FIGURE 1—REPRESENTATION OF AVERAGE ROUGHNESS (Ra)

3.1.2 ROUGHNESS PROFILE—The roughness profile is the basis for measurement of all roughness-related surface properties, irrespective of whether an actual graphical recording is made of it or not. The roughness profile is a plot of the amplitude of the roughness irregularities along the scan length, and is obtained from the raw (unfiltered) profile signal by means of instrument filtering.

3.2 Peak—A surface irregularity wherein the roughness profile intersects consecutively a lower and upper boundary line. The boundary lines are located parallel and equidistant from the roughness profile mean line. The vertical distance between these boundary lines is termed the peak count level.

3.2.1 PEAK COUNT LEVEL—The vertical distance in micrometers (or microinch) between the boundary lines described in the definition of "Peak", (see Figure 2). The standard value for the peak count level is 1.25 µm (50 µin).

3.2.2 PEAK COUNT—The peak count (PC) is the number of peaks per unit length (peaks/cm or peaks/in).

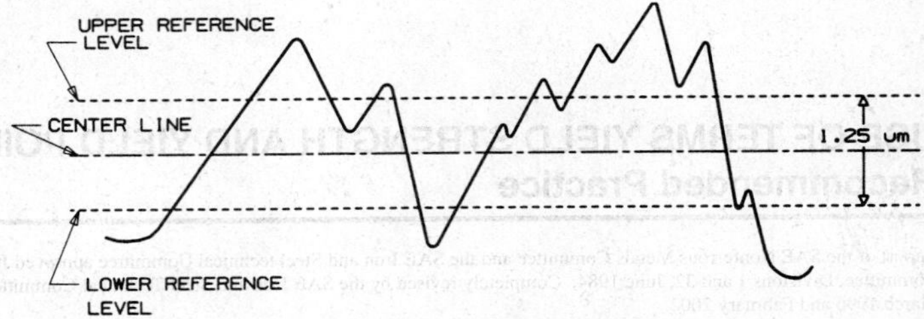

FIGURE 2—PEAK COUNTING

4. Equipment, Test Conditions, and Materials

4.1 A stylus type surface roughness and peak counting instrument (profilometer) or equivalent.

4.2 The instrument shall comply with specifications for stylus type instruments as detailed in section 4.4 of the American National Standard: ASME B46.1-1995; namely:

a. The nominal stylus radius shall be 10 µm (400 µin) or smaller.
b. The static stylus force (for a 10 µm stylus) shall not exceed 0.016 N at any point within the displacement range of the stylus, and the minimum stylus force shall be sufficient to maintain contact with the surface. (The maximum recommended stylus force will be lower for a smaller stylus radius; as tabulated in section 3.3.5.2 of ASME B46.1-1995).
c. The response of the filter used to process the profile signal (or the profile data) shall comply with the attenuation characteristics and limits stated in section 9.4 (of ASME B46.1-1995).

4.3 The instrument shall be calibrated in terms of average roughness (R_a) using a precision reference specimen having a nominal R_a value in the measurement range (typically 0.25 to 2.5 µm or 10 to 100 µin, for cold-rolled steel surfaces).

4.4 The standard filter cutoff length for average roughness and peak count measurements on cold-rolled steel sheet surfaces shall be 0.8 mm (nominally 0.03 in).

4.5 The standard value for the peak count level shall be 1.25 µm (50 µin).

4.6 The standard value for the traverse length (measurement length) shall be 7 times the filter cutoff length for "integrated roughness profilometers." Integrated roughness profilometers (recommended for use here) compute the roughness properties from a stored electrical waveform representing the profile upon completion of a surface scan over the traverse length. Most modern profilometers are of this type. Continuously averaging profilometers continuously compute, update, and display roughness properties as the stylus scans the traverse length. Use of these profilometers adds more constraints on the instrument's response time, speed, and indicated device characteristics (sections 4.4.3 and 4.4.4 of ASME B46.1-1995).

4.7 The instrument shall exclude from assessment, a short segment of the traverse length at either end to ensure that mechanical and electrical transients at the beginning and end of the profile are excluded from the measurement. The segment length shall be no longer than one cutoff length to ensure that at least five cutoff lengths are used for assessment.

4.8 Sample material selected for measurement shall be representative of the material as produced. The area tested should be at least 50 mm (2 in) from the coil edge. Samples for sheet examination shall be identified as to rolling direction, suitably flat, and the sample size large enough to run the tests. (A convenient size is 150 mm (6 in) long, and 100 mm (4 in) wide, with the longer dimension parallel to the direction of rolling.)

5. Test Procedure

5.1 Preparation—The following items should be inspected to insure proper operation of the measuring equipment:

a. Prepare the instrument for use according to the manufacturer's instructions.
b. Set the traverse length to 5.6 mm (nominally 0.21 in) for an integrated roughness profilometer, or 28 mm (nominally 1.05 in) for a continuously averaging profilometer. (Longer traversing lengths for either type of profilometers are permissible.)

c. Set the cutoff length to 0.8 mm (nominally 0.03 in).
d. Set the peak count level to 1.25 μm (50 μin).
e. Check the suitability of location. The suitability of location can be checked by observing the roughness reading obtained on a smooth piece of flat glass. A reading or 0.05 μm (2 μin) or less indicates the location is suitably vibration free.
f. Allow ample warm-up time after powering-up the instrument and before performing measurements.
g. Inspect the test sample to ensure it is free from burrs, scratches, and foreign particles. Deburr, identify a scratch-free test location, and wipe with a soft lint-free cloth if necessary.

5.2 Calibration—To achieve the greatest uniformity between instruments on sheet surface texture measurements, the instrument must be calibrated prior to use. Frequency of calibrations and calibration procedure should be performed based on manufacturer's instructions/recommendations of the individual equipment used, and on the pattern of use (heavy use of the instrument might necessitate more frequent calibrations). The guidelines outlined in 5.2.1 (of this document) for Calibration measurements shall apply when specific manufacturer's instructions are absent or when such instructions are inferior to those of 5.2.1.

5.2.1 CALIBRATION MEASUREMENTS—After preparation as described in 5.1, calibration measurements on the precision reference specimen shall be made to establish satisfactory operation of the instrument. The calibration reading for average roughness (R_a) should be obtained from an average of **ten** readings taken on the reference specimen. The instrument should be set up to obtain the readings in the direction (see Section 6, note (b)) indicated on the precision reference specimen (usually two parallel arrows), and should be fairly distributed over the designated measurement area (usually a rectangle enclosed by the two parallel arrows). If the average of the ten measurements on the precision reference specimen differs by more than 5% of the assigned value, instrument adjustment and recalibration (as described previously) are in order. Instrument adjustments should be performed following manufacturer's instructions.

5.3 Sample Roughness Average (R_a) and Peak Count (PC) Measurements—Sheet sample roughness average and peak count should be obtained from a calculated average of ten readings (see exception as follows) obtained in the following manner. Five readings are taken parallel to the direction of rolling of the sheet sample and approximately 2 mm (0.1 in) apart. The sheet metal sample is then rotated 90 degrees and five additional measurements are taken perpendicular to the rolling direction (i.e., the transverse direction). An average of the ten readings obtained in this manner is calculated, recorded, and reported along with test equipment identification and test operating variables.

Exception—The number of measurements per direction can be dropped from five to one, if an integrated roughness profilometer is used in conjunction with longer traverse lengths (35 times the cutoff length). In this case, the roughness average and peak count are based on the average of two measurements (one in the rolling direction and one in the transverse direction) rather than ten.

6. Additional Recommendations/Remarks—In addition to the test conditions, procedures, and requirements described in this SAE Recommended Practice, the following recommendations and remarks are in order:

a. Stylus damage and wear should be periodically checked following manufacturer's instructions.
b. The ten calibration measurements on the precision reference specimen should be performed in the same directions which were used to determine the assigned value for the specimen. A single-headed arrow on the reference specimen usually indicates that all of the readings were obtained in the direction of the arrow. A double-headed arrow indicates that half of the readings were obtained in the direction parallel to the arrow and the remaining half were obtained in the opposite direction (by rotating the specimen 180 degrees). When using a specimen of the latter type to check calibration, five of the calibration measurements should be performed parallel to the arrow; and the remaining five measurements should be performed after the specimen is rotated by 180 degrees.
c. Where additional surface properties are of interest (for example: maximum peak-to-valley height, or waviness average), the traverse length and the number of measurements per direction shall be the larger of the requirements listed here and those required to measure the additional surface properties.
d. This document may be extended to include coated steel sheet, provided that skidless instruments are used, or, in the case of a skidded instrument, that the skid does not glide over the region where measurements are taken. This is to ensure that measurements are not affected by possible damage to the coating surface as a result of contact with the skid (skid forces are generally large enough to deform the soft coating surface).
e. Although this document is designed around the use of contacting stylus instruments, the document may be extended to include non-contacting profilometers provided that such profilometers possess the same sensitivity and resolution levels as stylus profilometers. Stylus force limitations would not be applicable for non-contacting type instruments.

SURFACE TEXTURE—SAE J448a JUN1963

SAE Standard

Report of the SAE Surface Finish Committee approved March 1949 and last revised June 1963. Conforms in general with American Standard for Surface Texture, ASA B46. 1-1962.

Foreword—This Document has also changed to comply with the new SAE Technical Standards Board Format.

1. Scope—This SAE Standard is concerned with the geometrical irregularities of surfaces of solid materials. It establishes definite classifications for various degrees of roughness and waviness and for several varieties of lay. It also provides a set of symbols for use on drawings, and in specifications, reports, and the like. The ranges for roughness and waviness are divided into a number of steps, and the general types of lay are established by type characteristics.

This standard does not define what degrees of surface roughness and waviness or what type of lay are suitable for any specific purpose. It does not specify the means by which any degree of such irregularities may be obtained or produced. Neither is it concerned with the other surface qualities such as luster, appearance, color, corrosion resistance, wear resistance, hardness, microstructure, and absorption characteristics any of which may be governing considerations in specific applications.

Surfaces, in general, are very complex in character. Although the height, width, length, shape, and direction of surface irregularities may all be of practical importance in specific applications, this standard deals only with their height, width, and direction.

2. References

2.1 Applicable Publications—The following publications form a part of the specification to the extent specified herein. Unless otherwise indicated the lastest revision of SAE publications shall apply.

2.1.1 SAE PUBLICATIONS—Available from SAE, 400 Commonwealth Drive, Warrendale, PA 15096-0001.

SAE J449—Surface Texture Control

SAE Aerospace-Automotive Drawing Standard on Surface Texture—Roughness, Waviness, and Lay

2.1.2 OTHER PUBLICATION

ASA B46.1—1962

3. Definitions—(See Figure 1.)

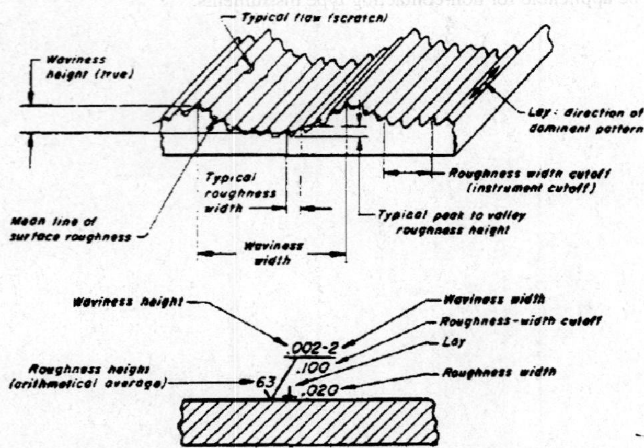

FIGURE 1—MEANING OF EACH PART OF SYMBOL DEFINED

3.1 Surface Texture—Repetitive or random deviations from the nominal surface which form the pattern of the surface. Surface texture includes roughness, waviness, lay, and flaws.

3.2 Surface—The surface of an object is the boundary which separates that object from another object, substance, or space. Surfaces with which this standard is concerned shall be those requiring control of roughness or other surface characteristics.

3.2.1 NOMINAL SURFACE—Nominal surface is the intended surface contour, the shape and extent of which is usually shown and dimensioned on a drawing or descriptive specification.

3.2.2 MEASURED SURFACE—The measured surface is a representation of the surface obtained by instrumentation or other means.

3.3 Profile—The profile is the contour of a surface in a plane perpendicular to the surface, unless some other angle is specified.

3.3.1 NOMINAL PROFILE—The nominal profile is the profile disregarding surface texture.

3.3.2 MEASURED PROFILE—The measured profile is a representation of the profile obtained by instrumental or other means. (See Figure 2.)

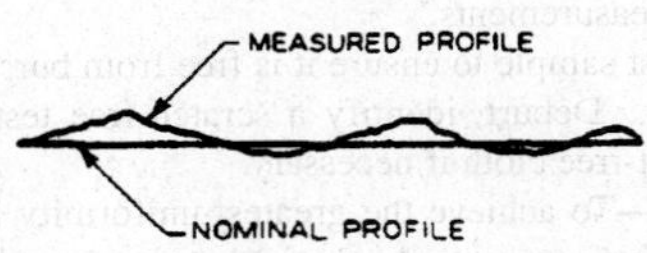

FIGURE 2—MEASURED PROFILE

3.4 Centerline (Roughness)—The centerline is the line about which roughness is measured and is a line parallel to the general direction of the profile within the limits of the roughness—width cutoff, such that the sums of the areas contained between it and those parts of the profile which lie on the either side of it are equal.[1]

3.5 Microinch—One millionth of a linear inch (0.000001 in.). This is the unit of height for roughness. Microinches may be abbreviated as Mu in.

3.6 Roughness—Roughness consists of the finer irregularities in the surface texture usually including those irregularities which result from the inherent action of the production process. These are considered to include traverse feed marks and other irregularities within the limits of the roughness—width cutoff. (See Figure 1.)

3.7 Waviness—Waviness is the usually widely spaced component of surface texture and is generally of wider spacing than the roughness—width cutoff. Waviness may result from such factors as machine or work reflections, vibration, chatter, heat treatment, or warping strains. Roughness may be considered as superposed on a wavy surface. Their directions are not necessarily related.

3.8 Lay—The direction of the predominant surface pattern, ordinarily determined by the production method used.

3.9 Flaws—Flaws are irregularities which occur at one place or at relatively infrequent or widely varying intervals in a surface. Flaws include such defects as cracks, blow holes, checks, ridges, and scratches. Unless otherwise specified, the effect of flaws shall not be included in the roughness height measurements.

4. Precision Reference Specimens—Surface roughness designation by this standard is based on instrument readings of surfaces to be rated in comparison with those of precision reference specimens having known roughness values and having a wide distribution of replicas. Surfaces described in the specifications for these specimens are designed primarily to serve for calibration of instruments used for measuring surface roughness height. They are not intended to have the appearance or characteristics of commonly produced surfaces, nor are they intended for use in visual or tactual comparisons.

Specifications are given for surface contour, material, accuracy, uniformity, and rating that will be satisfactory for the purpose.

4.1 Surface Contour—The normal surface profile of precision reference specimens of roughness height shall consist of a series of isosceles triangles having included angles of 150 deg. Such a profile is shown in Figure 3.

A departure from this triangular profile is permitted at the bottom of the grooves, provided that the deviated portion does not exceed 0.000130 in. in width and that there shall be no solid material at any point beyond a line corresponding to a flat of this width. This departure shall not affect the portion above this flat, which portion shall meet the allowed tolerance for accuracy.

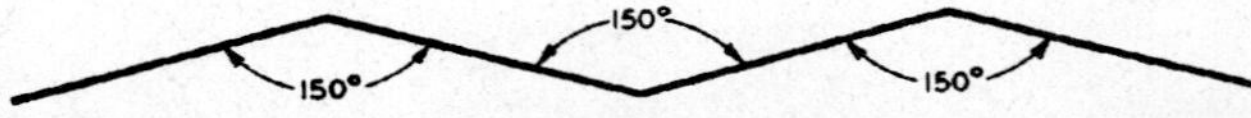

FIGURE 3—SURFACE PROFILE OF PRECISION REFERENCE SPECIMEN

4.2 Material—The material from which precision reference specimens are made shall be such that repeated measurements on these specimens can be made without significant loss of accuracy.

4.3 Accuracy—Average roughness values of precision reference specimens shall not vary from the designated value by more than ±1 Mu in. or ±3%, whichever is the larger. The average spacing of the grooves of precision reference specimens shall be within 2% or 20 Mu in. (whichever is the smaller) of the theoretical spacing corresponding to the nominal roughness height.

1. Centerline, as defined above, is also known mathematically as the median line.

4.4 Uniformity—The average deviation of roughness height of individual grooves of any precision reference specimen shall not exceed 4% of the total roughness height. The average deviation of the groove spacings on a given precision reference specimen shall not exceed 3% of the average spacing.

4.5 Rating—Precision reference specimens shall be rated for roughness height and roughness width as provided in the section on Recommended Values of Roughness and Waviness of this Standard. With tracer type instruments having a finite tracer tip radius, it is impossible to bottom the ideally sharp grooves as described for the ideal triangular profile. Accordingly, the proper reading of a tracer type instrument on the precision reference specimens will depend on the tracer tip radius. Ratings of the specimens for checking the calibration of such instruments shall be supplied with the specimens.[2]

5. Specification and Rating

5.1 Roughness Height Rating—The height of the roughness shall be specified in microinches as the arithmetical average of the absolute deviations from the mean surface. This value will be identified as a roughness number; for example, 16 means that the surface has an arithmetical average absolute deviation from the mean surface of 16 Mu in.[3]

5.2 Roughness Width Rating—The maximum permissible spacing of repetitive units of the dominant surface pattern. It may be specified in inches adjacent to the lay symbol. Irregularities having spacings up to and including the maximum specified are rated as roughness width and are to be included in the measurement of roughness height. When no maximum dimension is specified, spacings up to and including the width of the irregularities due to machine feed are rated as roughness width and are to be included in the measurement of roughness height.

5.3 Roughness—Width Cutoff—The greatest spacing of repetitive surface irregularities to be included in the measurement of average roundness height. Roughness—width cutoff is rated in inches. Roughness—width cutoff must always be greater than the roughness width in order to obtain the total roughness height rating.

Standard roughness—width cutoff values (inches) are:

0.003 0.010 0.030 0.100 0.300 1.000

When no value is specified, the value 0.030 is assumed. Refer to SAE J449, Surface Texture Control.

5.4 Waviness Height Rating—Waviness heights may be specified directly in inches as the vertical distance from peaks to valleys of waves.

5.5 Waviness Width Rating—Waviness widths may be specified directly in inches as the distance from peak to peak of the waves.

5.6 Lay Specifications—The lay of a surface shall be specified by the lay symbol indicating direction of dominant visible surface marks.

6. Measurement or Evaluation—For compliance with specified ratings, surfaces are to be evaluated by comparison with specified reference standards or by direct instrument measurements as described below.

6.1 Roughness—Roughness height values may be measured by any acceptable method, for instance, sight, feel, or instrument. For routine measurements, comparison may be made with a master surface that satisfactorily meets the requirements of the surface being measured. In making comparisons care should be exercised to avoids errors due to differences in material, contour, and type of operation represented by the reference surface and the work.

In using instruments for comparison or for direct measurement, care should be exercised to insure that the specified quality or characteristics of the surface is measured.[4]

Roughness measurements, unless otherwise specified, are taken in the direction which gives the maximum value of the reading normally across the lay.

6.2 Waviness—Waviness values for height and width may be measured by any suitable device for linear measurement.

7. Recommended Values of Roughness and Waviness—The use of only one number shall indicate the maximum value of either the height or the width of irregularities. Any less degree shall be satisfactory. When two numbers are used, they shall specify the maximum and minimum permissible values.

SAE Roughness Height Values, Mu in.

	3	8	20	50	125	320	800
	4	10	25	63	160	400	1000
1	5	13	32	80	200	500	
2	6	16	40	100	250	600	

2. See also Appendix C in ASA B46.1-1962.
3. Instruments calibrated in rms (root mean square) average will read approximately 11% higher on a given surface than those calibrated for arithmetic average (aa).
4. See ASA B46.1-1962 for instrument specifications.

SAE Waviness Height Values, in.

0.00002	0.00008	0.0003	0.001	0.005	0.015
0.00003	0.0001	0.0005	0.002	0.008	0.020
0.00005	0.0002	0.0008	0.003	0.010	0.030

8. Surface Symbol—The symbol used to designate surface irregularities is the check mark and extension as shown in Figure 4.

The point of the symbol may be on the line indicating the surface, on a witness line, or on a leader pointing to the surface. The long leg and extension shall preferably be to the right and erect, as the drawing is read. For preferred proportions see SAE Aerospace-Automotive Drawing Standard on Surface Texture—Roughness, Waviness, and Lay.

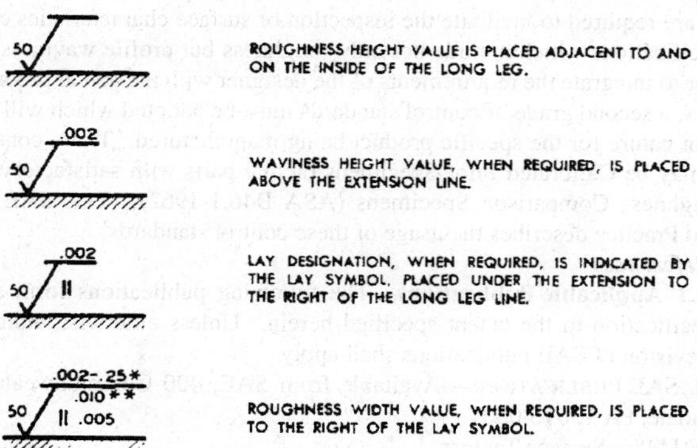
50
ROUGHNESS HEIGHT VALUE IS PLACED ADJACENT TO AND ON THE INSIDE OF THE LONG LEG.
.002
50
WAVINESS HEIGHT VALUE, WHEN REQUIRED, IS PLACED ABOVE THE EXTENSION LINE.
.002
50
WAVINESS HEIGHT VALUE, WHEN REQUIRED, IS PLACED ABOVE THE EXTENSION LINE.
LAY DESIGNATION, WHEN REQUIRED, IS INDICATED BY THE LAY SYMBOL, PLACED UNDER THE EXTENSION TO THE RIGHT OF THE LONG LEG LINE.
.002-.25*
.010**
50
.005
ROUGHNESS WIDTH VALUE, WHEN REQUIRED, IS PLACED TO THE RIGHT OF THE LAY SYMBOL.
* WHEN WAVINESS WIDTH VALUE IS REQUIRED, THE VALUE MAY BE PLACED TO THE RIGHT OF THE WAVINESS HEIGHT VALUE.
** ROUGHNESS WIDTH CUTOFF VALUE, WHEN REQUIRED, IS PLACED IMMEDIATELY BELOW THE RIGHT-HAND EXTENSION.

FIGURE 4—SURFACE SYMBOL

9. Symbol Indicating Direction of Lay—A lay symbol used with a surface symbol shall specify the direction of the visible pattern of the marks on the surface. (See Figure 5.)

Typical examples would be the use of the symbols, as in Figures 6 and 7, to express the given specifications.[5]

|| PARALLEL TO THE SURFACE BOUNDARY LINE INDICATED BY THE SYMBOL. EXAMPLE: PARALLEL SHAPING, END VIEW OF TURN AND OD GRIND.

⊥ PERPENDICULAR TO THE SURFACE BOUNDARY LINE INDICATED BY THE SYMBOL. EXAMPLE: END VIEW OF SHAPING, LONGITUDINAL VIEW OF TURN AND OD GRIND.

X ANGULAR IN BOTH DIRECTIONS TO THE SURFACE BOUNDARY LINE INDICATED BY THE SYMBOL. EXAMPLE: SIDE WHEEL GRIND, HONE, AND TRAVERSED END MILL.

M MULTIDIRECTIONAL. EXAMPLE: LAP, SUPERFINISH.

C APPROXIMATELY CIRCULAR RELATIVE TO THE CENTER OF THE SURFACE INDICATED BY THE SYMBOL. EXAMPLE: FACING.

R APPROXIMATELY RADIAL RELATIVE TO THE CENTER OF THE SURFACE INDICATED BY THE SYMBOL.

FIGURE 5—SYMBOLS INDICATING DIRECTION OF LAY

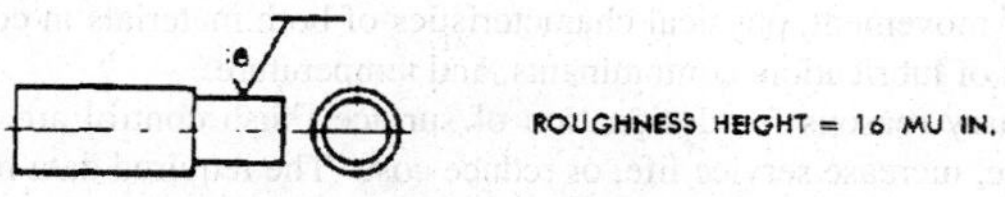
16
ROUGHNESS HEIGHT = 16 MU IN.

FIGURE 6—SPECIMEN APPLICATION

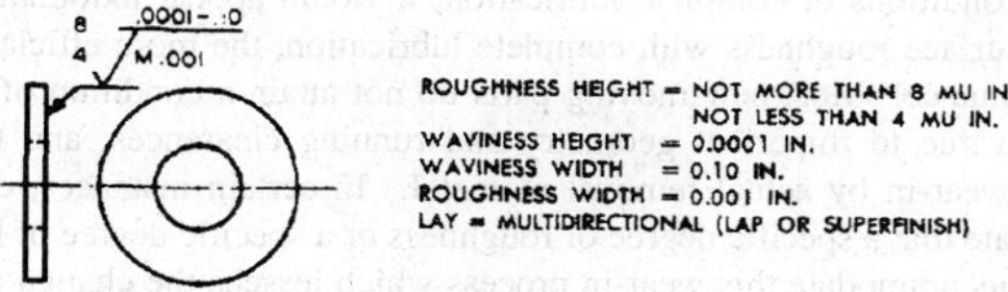
.0001-.10
8
4
M .001
ROUGHNESS HEIGHT – NOT MORE THAN 8 MU IN. NOT LESS THAN 4 MU IN.
WAVINESS HEIGHT = 0.0001 IN.
WAVINESS WIDTH = 0.10 IN.
ROUGHNESS WIDTH = 0.001 IN.
LAY = MULTIDIRECTIONAL (LAP OR SUPERFINISH)

FIGURE 7—SPECIMEN APPLICATION

5. For more complete discussion of application, see SAE Aerospace-Automotive Drawing Standard on Surface Texture—Roughness, Waviness, and Lay.

SURFACE TEXTURE CONTROL —SAE J449a JUN1963

SAE Recommended Practice

Report of the SAE Surface Finish Committee approved January 1953 and last revised June 1963. Conforms to Precision Reference Specimens of American Standard for Surface Texture, ASA B46. 1-1962.

Foreword—This Document has also changed to reflect the new SAE Technical Standards Board Format.

1. Scope—SAE J448, Surface Texture, has been set up for precision reference specimens using a controlled surface profile to obtain reproducible roughness values. These specimens are for instrument calibration. Appropriate symbols for roughness, waviness, and lay have also been standardized (ASA B46.1-1962 and SAE J448).

For production control, especially from one geographical location to another, means are required to facilitate the inspection of surface characteristics called for by specifications which include not only roughness but profile waviness and lay. In order to integrate the requirements of the designer with the actual production of surfaces, a second grade of control standards must be adopted which will be functional in nature for the specific product being manufactured. These control standards may be Calibrated Pilot Specimens (actual parts with satisfactory texture) or Roughness Comparison Specimens (ASA B46.1-1962). This SAE Recommended Practice describes the usage of these control standards.

2. References

2.1 Applicable Publications—The following publications form a part of the specification to the extent specified herein. Unless otherwise indicated the latest revision of SAE publications shall apply.

2.1.1 SAE PUBLICATIONS—Available from SAE, 400 Commonwealth Drive, Warrendale, PA 15096-0001.

SAE J448—Surface Texture

SAE Aerospace-Automotive Drawing Standards

2.1.2 OTHER PUBLICATION

ASA B46.1-1962

3. Roughness Comparison Specimens—In order to comply with a specific type of lay with required roughness and waviness values, a number of roughness machined comparison specimens are available commercially. These specimens are intended to have the appearance and feel of typical machine surfaces and are made to cover both a range of roughness and a variety of methods of surface preparation.

Roughness comparison specimens are well adapted for use by designers and draftsmen to relate numerical specifications of surface roughness and lay to general experience of appearance and texture of machined surfaces. They may also be used for visual and tactual comparison with production surfaces. Care should be taken when comparing specimens that the effect of shape, curvature, material, lay, and spectral characteristics do not produce misleading results. Samples of specific parts are usually the best control specimens.

4. Designation of Surface Texture—Surface texture should be specified for production parts only on those surfaces which must be under functional control. For all other surfaces the finish resulting from the machining method required to obtain dimensional accuracy is generally satisfactory, unless the appearance of the surface is of prime concern.

The recommended degree of functional roughness, direction of lay, and waviness for any specific surface cannot be accurately foretold because of many factors influencing optimum performance in any one application. The choice of surface characteristics will be determined by such factors as loading, speed and direction of movement, physical characteristics of both materials in contact, type and amount of lubrication, contaminants, and temperature.

The primary reasons for designation of surface finish control are to improve performance, increase service life, or reduce cost. The required data for this control comes from past experience of field service or experimental results. All significant variables should be considered when establishing test methods and analyzing results.

Under conditions of complete lubrication, it would appear axiomatic that the finer the surface roughness with complete lubrication, the more efficient will be the performance. Most new moving parts do not attain a condition of complete lubrication due to imperfect geometry and running clearances, and they must therefore wear-in by actual removal of metal. In certain instances, experience may indicate that a specific degree of roughness or a specific degree of lay is necessary to accommodate this wear-in process which lessens the change of galling, seizure, or excessive wear.

The surface chosen for a specific application will be determined by its required function and a compromise made between sufficient roughness to allow proper wearing-in and resulting smoothness for expected service life. In certain cases, a roughness number in itself may not adequately define the character of the surface found by experience to give the best results. Special reference samples may be made to give manufacturing, inspection, and engineering samples for comparison with the manufactured parts. In general, with lower dimensional tolerances and better manufacturing practices, with adequate lubrication and compatible surfaces, finer finishes would be expected to give optimum results. Frequently, cases where surfaces are not compatible, such as hardened parts running together, a certain degree of roughness or character of surface may assist lubrication in obtaining satisfactory wear-in. However, where hardened parts run against soft materials, the hardened parts must have a fine finish to avoid distress on the soft parts.

Typical normal ranges of surface roughness applications on functional parts are shown in Figure 1. Specific applications may require finer or coarse roughness values than those indicated, especially for gears and bearings.

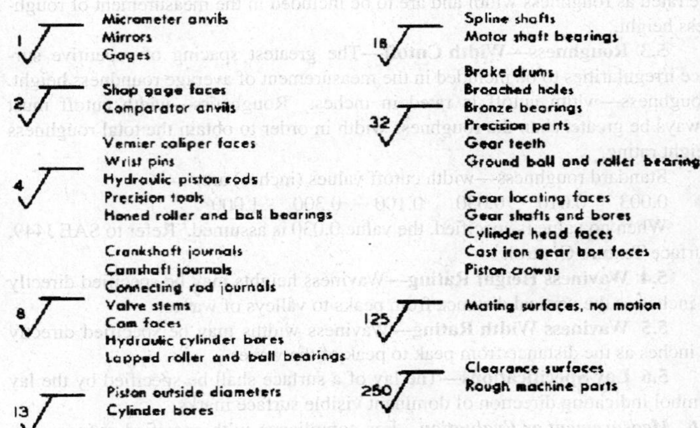

FIGURE 1—TYPICAL VALUES OF SURFACE ROUGHNESS FINISHES

The designation of surface texture requirements on drawings should conform with SAE J448, and with the Surface Texture section of the SAE Aerospace-Automotive Drawing Standards. The designer should be sure that those surfaces calling for control are of sufficient importance to warrant the expenditure of time and money necessary for this control. Profuse and loose usage of controlled finishes, where not essential, detracts from the emphasis that should be given to important surfaces. Where properly used, designation and control of a surface in accordance with SAE J448, can eliminate such confusion and many rejects.

5. Production of Required Surface Texture—Unless service or experimental results have indicated that only one process method will give completely satisfactory performance, the method of machining to obtain the desired finish should be left to the discretion of the processing shop supervisory staff. They will have more intimate knowledge of the desirable machines to produce economical parts under required schedules. It is important, therefore, that production engineers and master mechanics become thoroughly familiar with surface texture as defined and rated by SAE J448.

Figure 2 is a reproduction from the section on Surface Texture in the SAE Aerospace-Automotive Drawing Standards, and it shows typical surface roughness values obtained by various production methods. This chart indicates surface roughness values up to 2000 Mu in., although in automotive practice controlled surfaces rarely exceed 100 Mu in. roughness. Fine surface finishes may require more operations and greater care in production; but if quantities are large, special tooling with honing, lapping, or high speed grinding can produce better finishes more economically than with older methods of production.

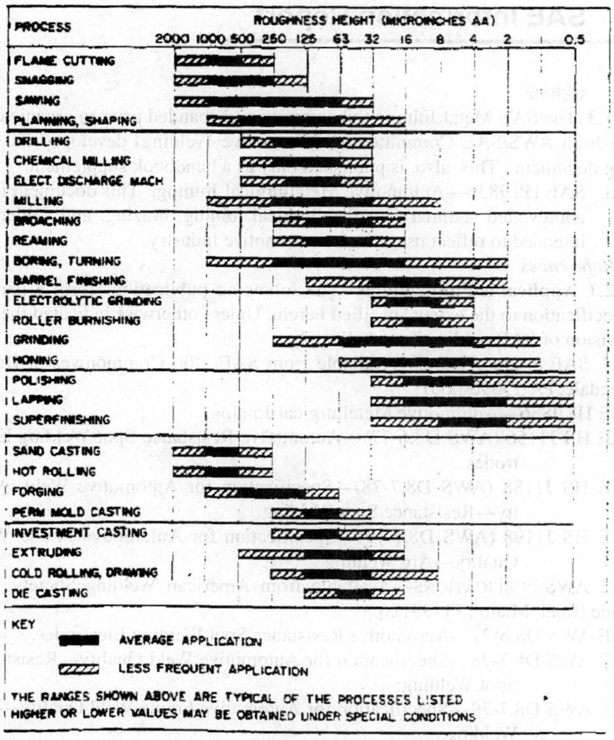

PROCESS | ROUGHNESS HEIGHT (MICROINCHES AA)
2000 1000 500 250 125 63 32 16 8 4 2 1 0.5

FLAME CUTTING
SNAGGING
SAWING
PLANNING, SHAPING
DRILLING
CHEMICAL MILLING
ELECT. DISCHARGE MACH
MILLING
BROACHING
REAMING
BORING, TURNING
BARREL FINISHING
ELECTROLYTIC GRINDING
ROLLER BURNISHING
GRINDING
HONING
POLISHING
LAPPING
SUPERFINISHING
SAND CASTING
HOT ROLLING
FORGING
PERM MOLD CASTING
INVESTMENT CASTING
EXTRUDING
COLD ROLLING, DRAWING
DIE CASTING

KEY
AVERAGE APPLICATION
LESS FREQUENT APPLICATION

THE RANGES SHOWN ABOVE ARE TYPICAL OF THE PROCESSES LISTED
HIGHER OR LOWER VALUES MAY BE OBTAINED UNDER SPECIAL CONDITIONS

FIGURE 2—SURFACE ROUGHNESS AVAILABLE BY COMMON PRODUCTION METHODS

6. Inspection and Control—A specific surface roughness depends on reproducible production techniques. The surface in question may be inspected by use of instruments or by visual or tactual comparison. Instruments should be calibrated by use of precision reference specimens. Approved pilot specimens or replicas may be used for comparison with the surface in question. Instruments may be used as a final check of the pilot specimen with the production machined surface. Roughness comparison specimens may be used for visual or tactual control but are not recommended for instrument comparison with manufactured part.

Production machined surfaces are composed of irregular peaks and valleys having a variety of grooves, angles, and variable roughness widths. The precision reference specimens have uniform roughness heights, groove angles, widths. Instruments readings will, therefore, reflect the effect of the irregular production surface character so that the readings will be relative rather than absolute.

The geometry of the precision reference specimens being uniform, instruments may be checked for worn or chipped stylus points by a comparison of corrected readings for two widely separated reference surfaces. The correction factors and methods of checking instrument accuracy are available in the literature accompanying the reference specimens. These factors are required because of the specific stylus tip radius used on the instrument. It is impossible to contact the bottom of the grooves, so this factor is comparatively small for coarse surfaces but large for fine ones.

Readings of stylus tip instruments are also affected by the roughness width because of low and high frequency response limits beyond which the instrument will not give reliable readings. In some instances the roughness width or wave length will be specified on the drawing, therefore requiring that the instrument have a definite width cutoff value. If no width is specified, it is necessary that the frequency response of the instrument does not limit its sensitivity to any significant roughness of the surface to be inspected; that is, that the significant roughness width is not greater or smaller than the instrument is capable of measuring and that the frequency response is correct for the roughness width range being measured. Technical data on roughness width cutoff of instruments is available from the various instrument manufacturers.

When continuously averaging stylus type instruments are used, the length of trace (sampling length) used should be not less than 20 times the roughness width cutoff value. For instruments having meters which indicate integrated roughness over a fixed length of trace, the sampling length shall preferably be at least five times the roughness width cutoff value.

Where the continuously-averaging type instrument is used, it is not necessary for the traversing length to be traversed continuously in one direction provided that the time required to reverse the direction of trace is short compared to the time the tracer is in motion. For this type of operation, the minimum length of travel shall be not less than five times the roughness-width cutoff. Where surfaces are not large enough to permit the recommended minimum traversing length, the readings may not be the actual roughness of a surface but may be useful for comparative purposes.

For proper surface control of production parts, the process should be completely specified and should include depth of cut, cutting speed, feed, grit size, lubricant, and so forth. Selection of process methods should be based on surface inspection of production specimens. Production may be controlled at the machine by visual, tactual, or instrument comparison of production pieces with sample specimens. If control is required at more than one station, sample specimens may be cut into the required number of pieces; or if a large quantity is required, electroformed or plastic reference specimens may be satisfactorily employed in many instances.

Final inspection of the production pieces may be by visual, tactual, or instrument comparison with the sample specimen or by instrument comparison with the precision reference specimen depending on the roughness variation allowed and on past experience with surfaces for a similar function. For disputed surfaces, instruments calibrated with the precision reference specimens should be used. A 100% inspection for all parts is necessary only for highly critical surfaces where failure to meet the surface requirements might result in costly delays. Normal sampling inspection should prove adequate for most production parts.

The thoroughness of surface roughness inspection should depend on the judgment of the inspector. He should take into account the roughness value tolerances allowed and the physical proportions of the surface.

Instrument readings are subject to the skill of interpretation of the inspector. Readings of stylus tip instruments fluctuate because of the roughness irregularities of a machined surface. All meters are damped to minimize acute fluctuations; nevertheless, extremely high and low momentary readings do occur. The reading which should be recorded as representing the roughness value of the surface should be a mean reading around which the needle tends to dwell or fluctuate under a small amplitude. Occasional extreme fluctuations represent flaws or defects rather than average surface conditions and should not be used in determining average roughness. If in the opinion of the inspector, the extreme fluctuations are too frequent, indicating excessive lack of uniformity in the surface, the manufacturing cause, such as loading of cutting edges, overheating, too rapid feeds, should be investigated.

7. Steps for Control of Surface Texture—The following outline summarizes briefly the steps necessary for proper control of surface texture. Some of these steps may be eliminated as experience is gained in the requirements for specific surface applications.

7.1 Establish need for control by:

a. Field experience.
b. Improvement of design.
c. Past experience with similar designs.

7.2 Experimental steps:

a. Designate tentative degrees of texture.
b. Trial manufacture.
c. Performance tests.
d. Choose most desirable texture.

7.3 Designate texture on drawing.

7.4 Processing steps:

a. Specify processing methods.
b. Prepare pilot specimen.
c. Obtain engineering approval.
d. Produce in quantity.

7.5 Inspection procedures at machines or final inspection, or both (usually only one procedure is followed for a given surface):

a. Instrument calibration and comparison with:
   1. Precision reference specimens.
b. Instrument comparison with:
   1. Calibrated pilot specimens.
c. Visual and tactual comparison with one of the following:
   1. Calibrated pilot specimens.
   2. Replicas of calibrated pilot specimens.
   3. Roughness comparison specimens.

7.6 Correct processing when irregular texture is detected.

7.7 Revise texture requirements if field service records indicate need.

WELDING, BRAZING, AND SOLDERING—MATERIALS AND PRACTICES—SAE J1147 JUN1983 SAE Information Report

Report of the AWS/SAE Joint Committee on Automotive Welding, approved July 1976, last revised June 1983.

Foreword—This Document has also changed to comply with the new SAE Technical Standards Board Format.

1. Scope—The Joint AWS/SAE Committee on Automotive Welding was organized on January 16, 1974, for the primary purpose of facilitating the development and publication of various documents related to the selection, specification, testing, and use of welding materials and practices, particularly for the automotive and related industries. A secondary purpose is the dissemination of technical information.

1.1 SAE participation in this activity is intended to insure that the needs and thinking of the industries mentioned are adequately considered prior to publication of selected Standards, Recommended Practices, and Information Reports. To this end, such documents are subject to the approval of the SAE General Materials Council, as well as the Joint AWS/SAE Committee and the AWS Board of Directions.

1.2 Docuemnts which are approved by the Council are printed as separate sheets or booklets, with both AWS D number and SAE HS J number identifications. They are not published in the SAE Handbook. SAE numbered items approved to date for listing in this Information Report are:

a. SAE HS J1156 (AWS D8.6-77—Automotive Resistance Spot Welding Electrods. THis document recommends a "standard" for spot welding electrodes sutiable foruse by smaller suppliers to the automotive industry. Typical electrode cap "standards" of the major autombile manufacturers are included for information purposes.
b. SAE HS J1188 (AWS D8.7-78)—Specification for Automotive Weld Quality—Resistance Spot Welding.
c. SAE HS J1196 (AWS D8.8-79)—Specification for Automotive Frame Weld Quality—Arc Welding.

1.3 The SAE Metal Joining Subcommittee (disbanded prior to organization of the Joint AWS/SAE Committee on Automotive Welding) developed the following document. This, also, is published only as a handbook supplement.

a. SAE HS J836—Automotive Metallurgical Joining. This document is an abbreviated summary of metallurgical joining, brazing, and soldering, intended to reflect usage in the automotive industry.

2. References

2.1 Applicable Publications—The following publications form a part of the specification to the extent specified herein. Unless otherwise indicated the latest revision of SAE publications shall apply.

2.1.1 SAE PUBLICATIONS—Available from SAE, 400 Commonwealth Drive, Warrendale, PA 15096-0001.

SAE HS J836—Automotive Metallurgical Joining.
SAE HS J1156 (AWS D8.6-77)—Automotive Resistance Spot Welding Electrodes.
SAE HS J1188 (AWS D8.7-78)—Specification for Automotive Weld Quality—Resistance Spot Welding.
SAE HS J1198 (AWS D8.7-79)—Specification for Automotive Frame Weld Quality—Arc Welding.

2.1.2 AWS PUBLICATIONS—Available from American Welding Society, 550 LeJeune Road, Miami, FL 33126.

SAE AWS D8.6-77—Automotive Resistance Spot Welding Electrodes.
SAE AWS D8.7-78—Specification for Automotive Weld Quality—Resistance Spot Welding.
SAE AWS D8.7-79—Specification for Automotive Frame Weld Quality—Arc Welding.

AUTOMOTIVE METALLURGICAL JOINING—SAE J836 OCT1970

SAE Information Report

Report of the SAE Nonferrous Metals Committee and SAE Iron and Steel Technical Committee approved June 1962 and last revised by the SAE Nonferrous Metals Committee October 1970. Formerly HS J836a.

Foreword—This Document has also changed to comply with the new SAE Technical Standards Board format.

1. Scope—This report is an abbreviated summary of metallurgical joining by welding, brazing, and soldering. It is generally intended to reflect current usage in the automotive industry; however, it does include some of the more recently developed processes. More comprehensive coverage of materials, processing details, and equipment required may be found in the Welding Handbook, Soldering Manual, and other publications of the American Welding Society and the American Society for Testing and Materials. AWS Automotive Welding Committee publications on Recommended Practices are particularly recommended for the design or product engineer.

This report is not intended to cover mechanical joining such as rivets or screw fasteners, or chemical joining processes such as adhesive joining.

1.1 Classification of Welding Processes—Current welding practices utilize a great variety of other welding processes not covered in the scope of this report. The AWS has classified all these processes in their Master Chart of Welding Processes (Figure 1).

1.2 Standard Welding Symbols

1.2.1 With the advancement of welding technology, more welding variables and controls are being continuously added to the manufacturing requirements of weldments. These may include:

1.2.1.1 Dimensional requirements of welds (size, length, pitch, number of welds, etc.).

1.2.1.2 Integrity requirements, such as shear strength for resistance welds, depth of penetration, etc.

1.2.1.3 Performance requirements of welds and welded joints. These may include:

1.2.1.3.1 Dimensional requirements (joint preparation, root opening, etc.).

1.2.1.3.2 Process requirements (series, direct, indirect, over and under welding, and process designations).

1.2.1.3.3 Other requirements such as weld all around, field weld, etc.

1.2.2 Symbols provide a universal means of communicating the above referenced information from the product designer to the process man without the risk of misinterpretation. Internationally accepted process and weldment symbols are shown in Figure 2.

1.3 Automotive Welding Applications—Certain welding processes have made further inroads in the area of automotive welding than others. This fact is caused not only by their greater adaptability to perform automotive welds, but also by keeping up with high production requirements at lower costs. At the present time the following processes are being used extensively:

a. Resistance welding processes.
b. Arc welding processes.
c. Brazing and soldering.
d. Special process.

2. References

2.1 Applicable Publications—The following publications form a part of the specification to the extent specified herein. Unless otherwise indicated the lastest revision of SAE publications shall apply.

2.1.1 AMERICAN WELDING SOCIETY PUBLICATIONS—AVAILABLE FROM??

American Welding Society Welding Handbook, Fifth Edition, Section 2, Chapter 30, p. 30.1.
American Welding Society Welding Handbook, Fifth Edition, Section 5, Chapter 90, p. 90.18.
Resistance Welder Manufacturers Association Manual.
American Welding Society Welding Handbook, Fifth Edition, Section 2, Chapters 30 and 32.
Resistance Welding Manual (RWMA), Third Edition, Chapter 4, p. 52.
American Welding Society Welding Handbook, Fifth Edition, Section 2, Chapter 30.
Recommended Practices for Automotive Welding Design D8.4-61.
American Welding Society Welding Handbook, Fifth Edition, Section 2, Chapter 31.
Resistance Welding Manual (RWMA), Third Edition, Chapter 5, p. 67.
American Welding Society Welding Handbook, Fifth Edition, Section 2, Chapter 31.
Resistance Welding Manual (RWMA), Third Edition, Chapter 5, p. 67.
American Welding Society Welding Handbook, Fifth Edition, Chapter 31.
Resistance Welding Manual (RWMA), Chapter 9, p. 111.
American Welding Society Welding Handbook, Fifth Edition, Section 2, Chapter 35 (1964).
W. C. Rudd, "High Frequency Resistance Welding." Welding Journal, Vol. 36, July 1957, pp. 703–707.
"Modern Joining Processes," Chapter 5, p. 51. American Welding Society (1966).
American Welding Society Welding Handbook, Fifth Edition, Section 2, Chapter 25.
American Welding Society Welding Handbook, Fifth Edition, Section 2, Chapter 28.
American Welding Society Welding Handbook, Fifth Edition, Section 2, Chapter 27.
American Welding Society Recommended Practices for Automotive Welding Design D8.4-61.
American Welding Society Welding Handbook, Fifth Edition, Section 2, Chapter 29.
American Welding Society Welding Handbook, Fifth Edition, Section 3, Chapter 54.
American Welding Society Welding Handbook, Fifth Edition, Section 3, Chapter 52.
American Welding Society Welding Handbook, Fifth Edition, Section 3, Chapter 56.
American Welding Society Welding Handbook, Fifth Edition, Section 3, Chapter 49.
American Welding Society Soldering Manual, First Edition, 1959.

2.1.2 SAE PUBLICATION—Available from SAE, 400 Commonwealth Drive, Warrendale, PA 15096-0001.

Solders—SAE J473, Table 1.

2.1.3 ASTM PUBLICATION—Available from ASTM, 100 Barr Harbor Drive, West Conshohocken, PA 19428-2959.

ASTM solder classifications are given in Tables 44.3 and 44.4 of the Welding Handbook, American Welding Society, Fifth Edition, Section 3.

3. Resistance Welding Processes—Resistance welding is a group of welding processes wherein coalescence is produced by the heat obtained from resistance of the work to the flow of electric current in a circuit of which the work is a part and by the application of pressure. It differs somewhat from other forms of welding in that no extraneous materials, such as filler rods, fluxes, etc., are utilized; thus the metallography of the weld is not complicated by the addition of materials and the cost of consumable material is nonexistent.

The Master Chart of Welding Processes classifies six basic resistance welding processes; however, the great majority of metal joining is accomplished by the first three of the listed processes. These processes are:

1. Resistance-spot welding.
2. Resistance-seam and roll spot welding.
3. Projection welding.
4. Flash welding.
5. Upset welding.
6. Percussion welding.

Each of the processes described develops the heat of fusion by the resistance offered to short time flow of low-voltage, high-density electric current. Force is always applied before, during, and after the application of current to assure a continuous electrical circuit and to forge the heated parts together.

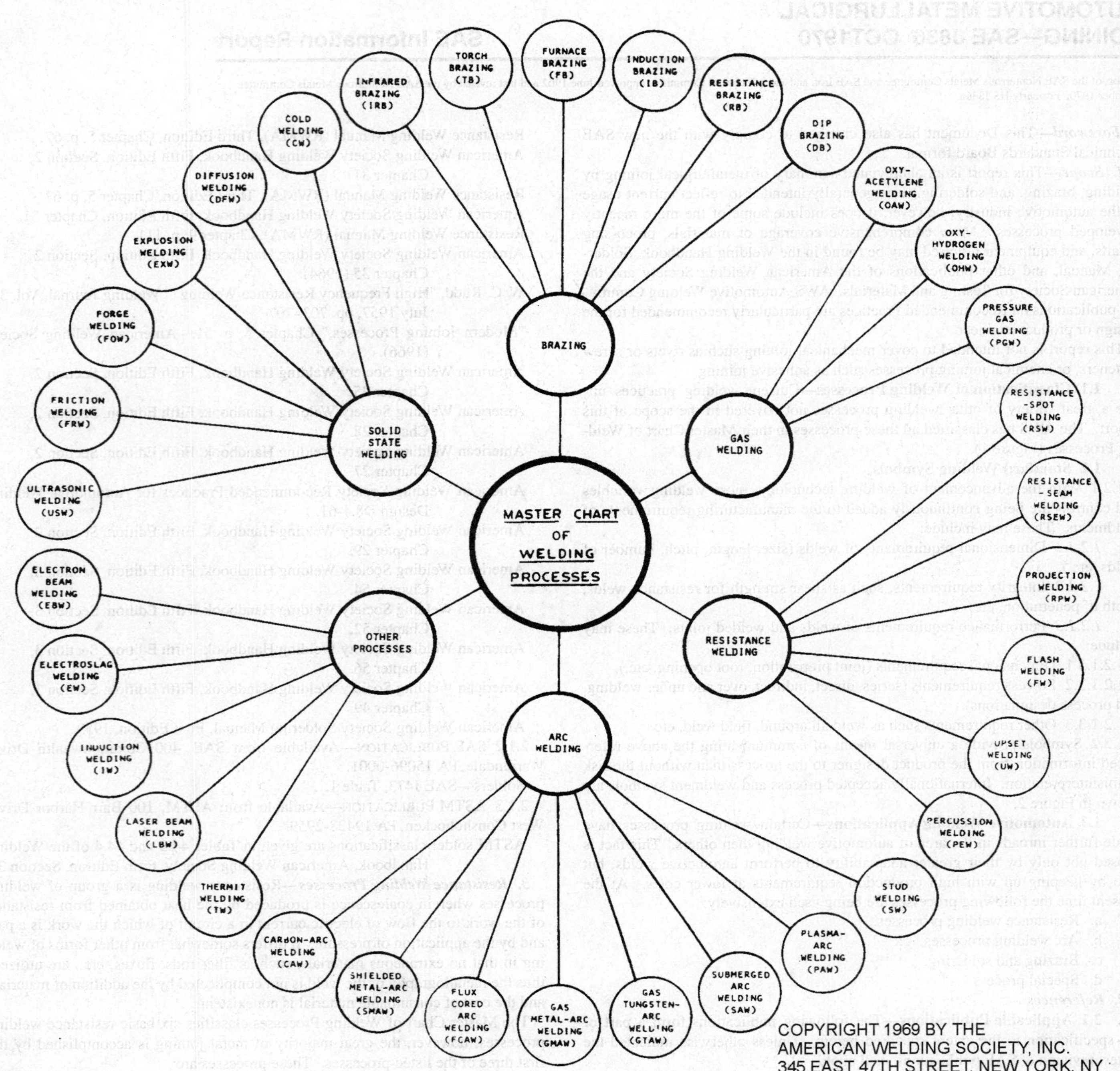

FIGURE 1—AMERICAN WELDING SOCIETY MASTER CHART OF WELDING PROCESSES (REPRINTED BY PERMISSION OF AMERICAN WELDING SOCIETY)

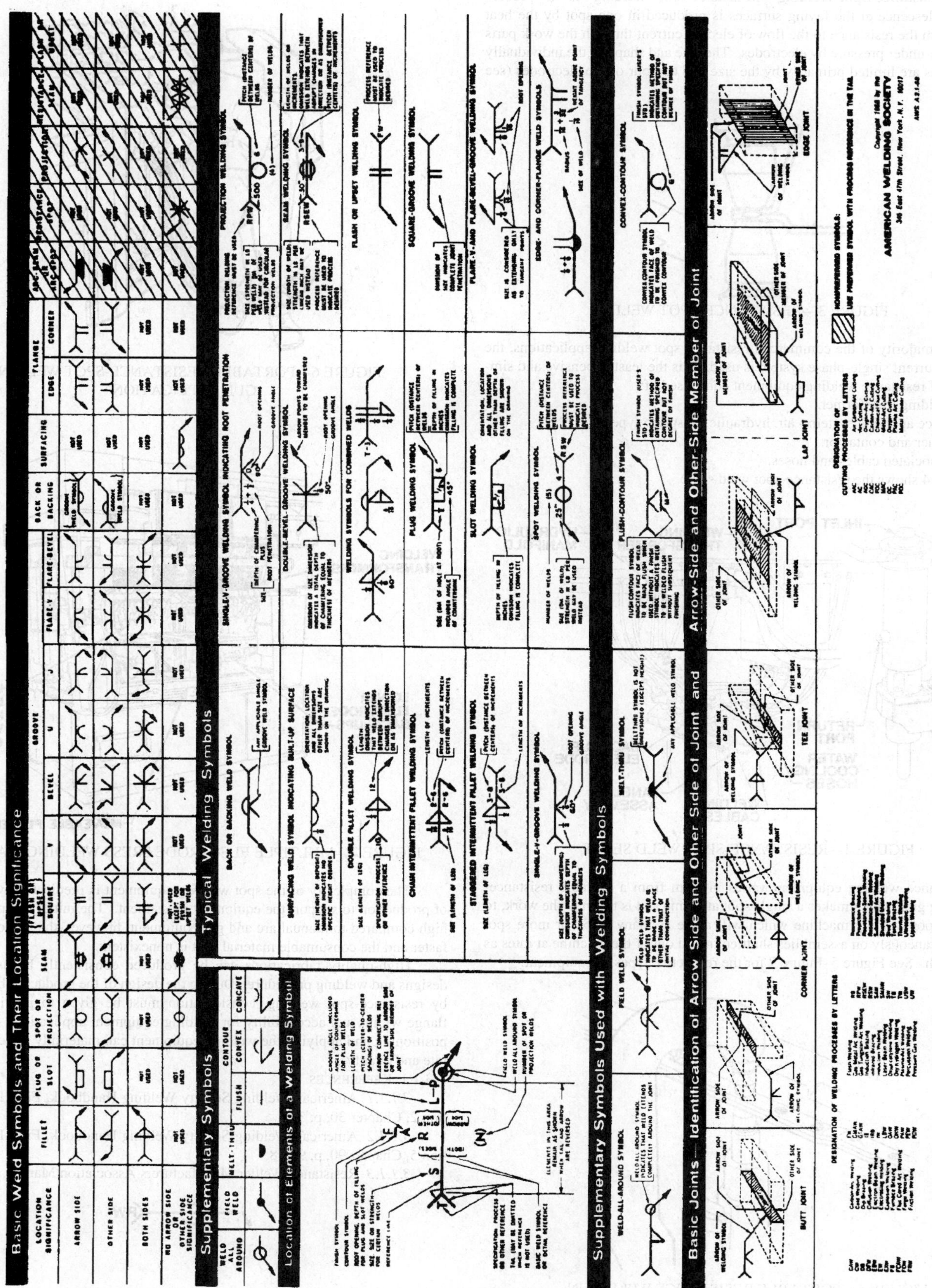

FIGURE 2—AMERICAN WELDING SOCIETY STANDARD WELDING SYMBOLS
(REPRINTED BY PERMISSION OF AMERICAN WELDING SOCIETY)

3.1 Resistance-Spot Welding—Resistance-spot welding is a process wherein coalescence at the faying surfaces is produced in one spot by the heat obtained from the resistance to the flow of electric current through the work parts held together under pressure by electrodes. The size and shape of the individually formed welds are limited primarily by the size and contour of the electrodes (see Figure 3).

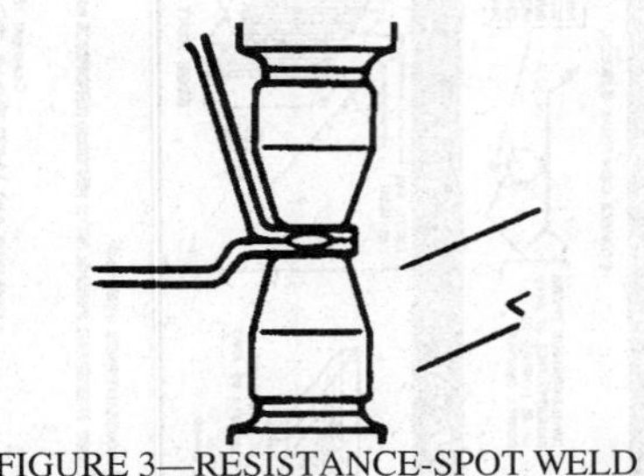

FIGURE 3—RESISTANCE-SPOT WELD

In the majority of the commercial resistance-spot welding applications, the alternating current single-phase system is used. It is the least expensive and simplest form of resistance welding equipment comprised of:

1. Welding transformer.
2. Force applying system - air, hydraulic, or spring type.
3. Timer and contactor.
4. Associated cables and hoses.

Figure 4 shows the resistance-spot weld setup.

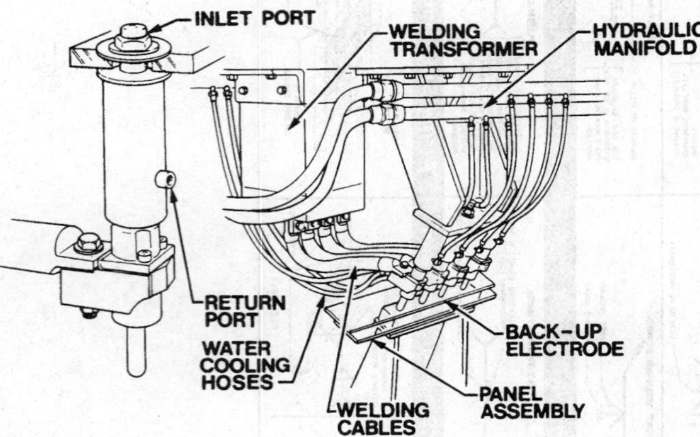

FIGURE 4—RESISTANCE-SPOT WELD SETUP

Resistance welding equipment varies in form from a portable resistance-spot welding gun, which makes a single spot at a time and is taken to the work, to a multiple spot welding machine which will make as many as 50 or more spot welds simultaneously on assemblies shuttled in and out of the machine at rates as high as 600/h. See Figure 5–Figure 7 for the respective types of equipment.

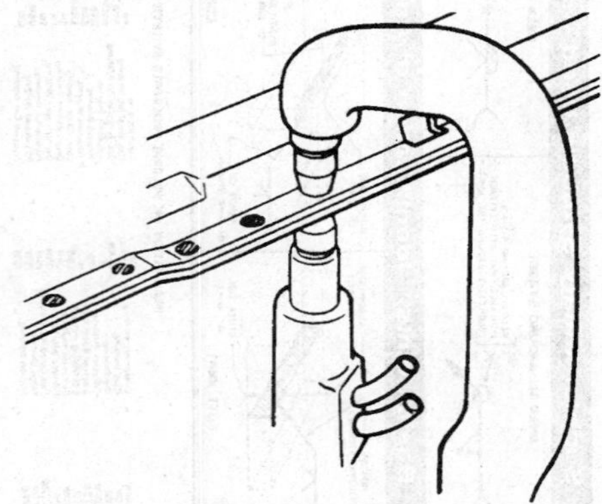

FIGURE 5—PORTABLE RESISTANCE WELD GUN

FIGURE 6—PORTABLE RESISTANCE-SPOT WELDING GUN APPLICATION

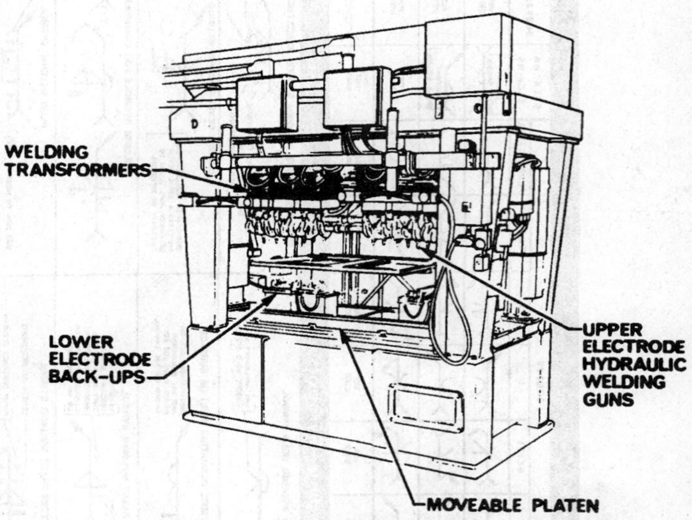

FIGURE 7—MULTIPLE ELECTRODE PRESS WELDING MACHINE

The complexity of the spot welding equipment is predicated by the volume of production to support the equipment investment. The initial equipment cost is high compared to manual arc and gas equipment; however, the rate of welding is faster and the consumable material cost is nonexistent.

High-quality fabrications can be produced consistently by use of proper designs and welding procedure. During the design of the product to be assembled by resistance-spot welding, consideration must be given to provide adequate flange widths and accessibility for welding equipment application. Difficulty in positioning and applying the welding equipment can materially affect production rate and quality.

3.1.1 References

3.1.1.1 American Welding Society Welding Handbook, Fifth Edition, Section 2, Chapter 30, p. 30.1.

3.1.1.2 American Welding Society Welding Handbook, Fifth Edition, Section 5, Chapter 90, p. 90.18.

3.1.1.3 Resistance Welder Manufacturers Association Manual.

3.2 Roll-Resistance Spot Welding—Roll-spot welding consists of making a series of separated spot welds in a row by means of one or two rotating, circular electrodes without retracting the electrodes or removing the welding force between spots. The principles described for conventional spot welding apply also to this process. The weld spacing is obtained and accurately maintained by proper adjustment of electrode speed and current off-time using conventional seam welding equipment. In the case of roll-resistance spot welding utilizing continuous motion, welding times are usually held to lower levels than that used for conventional spot welding, thus requiring higher magnitudes of current. Due to the continuous electrode travel the welds tend to be of an elongated nugget.

Roll-spot welding is usually accomplished on thicknesses up to 1/8 in with continuous motion of the wheel electrodes driven at a constant speed. For heavier thicknesses of 3/16 in and above, an intermittent motion is suggested. In this method, the work stops during the time required to make each individual weld and is automatically advanced the proper distance for the next weldment. This sequence is continued for the full length of the joint.

RSEW

3.3 Resistance-Seam Welding—Seam welding is a resistance welding process wherein coalescence is produced by the heat obtained from resistance to the flow of electric current through the work parts held together under pressure by circular electrodes. The resultant weld is a series of overlapping spot welds made progressively along a joint by rotating the electrodes.

Seam welding is usually applied to two types of joint designs - lap and flanged-lap. Variations of the standard seam weld principle are mash seam weld, foil-butt seam weld, and butt seam weld. For the respective characteristics of each variety, (see 3.3.1)see Section 3.3.1.

Roll-spot welding is used where precise spacing between welds is desired, as in welding the roof panel at the gutter area on an automobile body. Seam welding to produce a liquid and gas tight joint is used to fabricate automobile gas tanks, buckets, mufflers, water tanks, thin wall piping, etc. Mash seam welding and foil-butt seam welds are used where surface finishing is required after the joining process as there is a minimum of material required to be removed - applied to refrigerator and appliance cabinets and limited automotive outer panel fabrications. The butt seam weld is used for non-structural type joints, examples of which are found in toy and automobile horn fabrication.

Figures 8 and 9 show equipment concepts of a standard seam welder and a schematic of a roll-spot welder, respectively.

FIGURE 8—RESISTANCE SEAM WELDING MACHINE

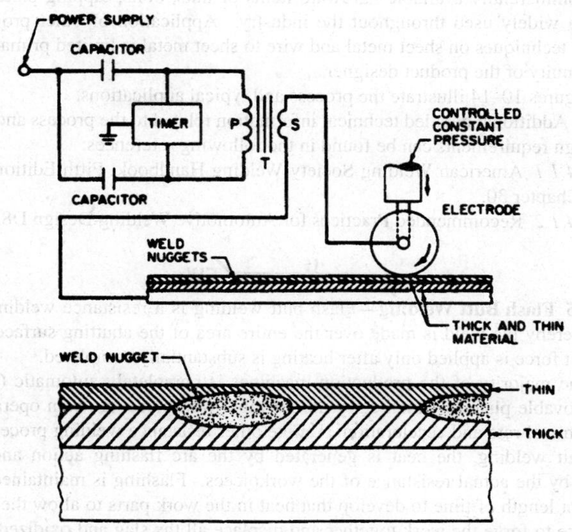

FIGURE 9—ROLL RESISTANCE-SPOT WELDING MACHINE

3.3.1 Additional information can be found on seam-resistance and roll-resistance spot welding and the variation of the process in the following references:

3.3.1.1 American Welding Society Welding Handbook, Fifth Edition, Section 2, Chapters 30 and 32.

3.3.1.2 Resistance Welding Manual (RWMA), Third Edition, Chapter 4, p. 52.

3.4 Projection Welding—Projection welding is a resistance welding process wherein coalescence is produced by the heat obtained from resistance to the flow of electric current through the work parts held together under pressure by electrodes. The resulting welds are localized at predetermined points by the design of the parts to be welded. The localization is usually accomplished by projections, embossments, or intersections.

Projection welding is a modification of the spot welding process. The concentration of the welding current and force is made by projections prepared in the workpiece rather than by the size and shape of the welding electrode. Normally, the projections are formed in the heavier of the two light metal pieces to be joined and in the case of dissimilar metal in the piece with higher electrical conductivity.

Projections can be produced by means of drawing with a punch and die, cold heading, coining, machining, shearing, and using natural projections as is the case with cross wire welding.

Advantages of projection welding which determine where the process can be best applied are:

1. More welds per unit area.
2. Improved surface marring condition.
3. Join difficult metal thickness combinations.
4. Increase output.
5. Less flange width requirement.
6. Consistent location of weld spots.
7. Longer electrode life.
8. Surface conditions less critical.
9. Allows joining components of irregular shapes (weld bolts, nuts, and tapping plates).

There are also factors which can be considered disadvantages:

1. Projections must be provided, which may mean an extra operation.
2. Projection dimensions must be maintained, so die maintenance is required.
3. Electrodes must be maintained although electrode life is longer.
4. Nugget size is limited by projection size.
5. High-capacity equipment required when making multiple simultaneous welds.
6. Limited generally to single-plane welding.
7. Poor condition and unfavorable characteristics of welding machine relative to impact and inertia will adversely affect the weld structural quality.

Commercially available hardware items of nuts, bolts, tapping plates, and pads are widely used throughout the industry. Application of other projection welding techniques on sheet metal and wire to sheet metal is limited primarily by the ingenuity of the product designer.

Figures 10–14 illustrate the process and typical applications.

3.4.1 Additional detailed technical information related to the process and product design requirements can be found in the following references:

3.4.1.1 American Welding Society Welding Handbook, Fifth Edition, Section 2, Chapter 30.

3.4.1.2 Recommended Practices for Automotive Welding Design D8.4–61.

3.5 Flash Butt Welding—Flash butt welding is a resistance welding process whereby the weld is made over the entire area of the abutting surfaces, and the upset force is applied only after heating is substantially completed.

The majority of the production machines is completely automatic (Figure 15). Movable platens, which carry the movable workpiece, are cam operated to control travel rate and acceleration. Unlike other resistance welding processes in flash butt welding, the heat is generated by the arc flashing action and only slightly by the actual resistance of the workpieces. Flashing is maintained for a sufficient length of time to develop that heat in the work parts to allow the upsetting force to forge the work together and displace all the slag and oxidized material from the joint's faying surface. This displaced metal is referred to as flash and usually is required to be removed by a grinding or cutting procedure.

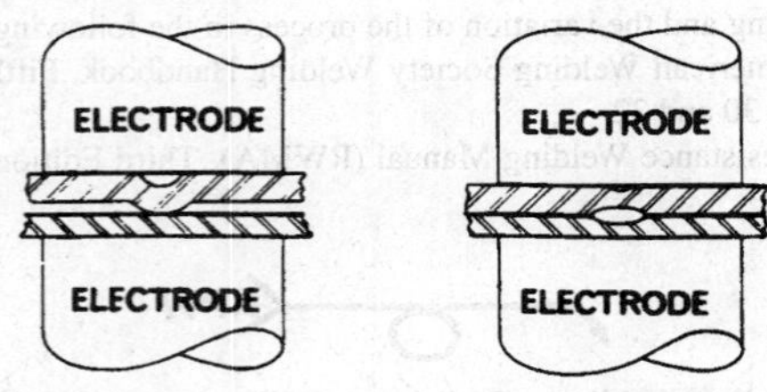

FIGURE 10A—DEFINITION OF PROJECTION WELDING. PROJECTION WELDING IS A METHOD OF RESISTANCE WELDING BY WHICH THE CURRENT FLOW AND HEATING DURING WELDING ARE LOCALIZED AT A PREDETERMINED POINT BY THE DESIGN OF THE PARTS BEING WELDED.

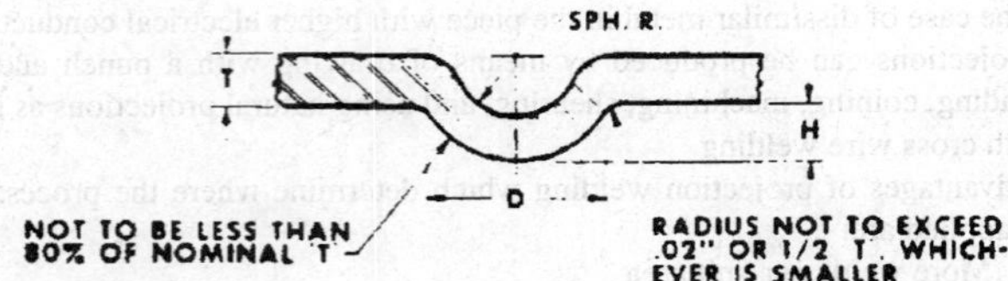

'D' REPRESENTS THE DIAMETER OF THE HOLE IN THE DIE AND THE RADIUS REFERRED TO IS THE ROUNDED EDGE OF THE HOLE

EMBOSSED SHEET THICKNESS	PROJECTION DIAMETER 'D'
.030	.105
.035 .041	.120
.047 .054	.135
.059 .067	.150
.075 .089	.170
.105 .120 .125	.190
.194 .209	.250

THINNER SHEET THICKNESS	PROJECTION HEIGHT 'H'
.030	.030
.035 .041	.035
.047 .054	.040
.059 .067	.045
.075 .089	.050
.105 .120 .125	.055
.194 .209	.070

FIGURE 10B—PROJECTION WELDING EMBOSSMENTS

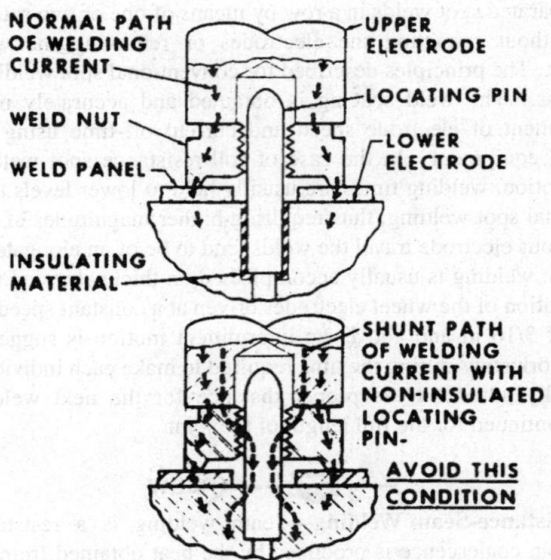

FIGURE 10C—PROJECTION WELD NUT SETUP

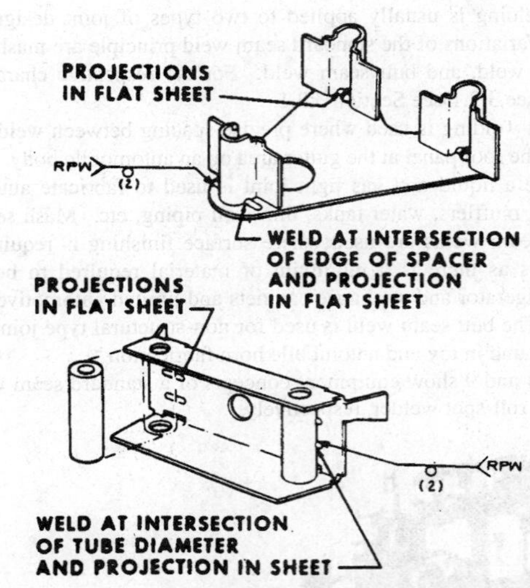

FIGURE 11—TUBES AND IRREGULAR SHAPES

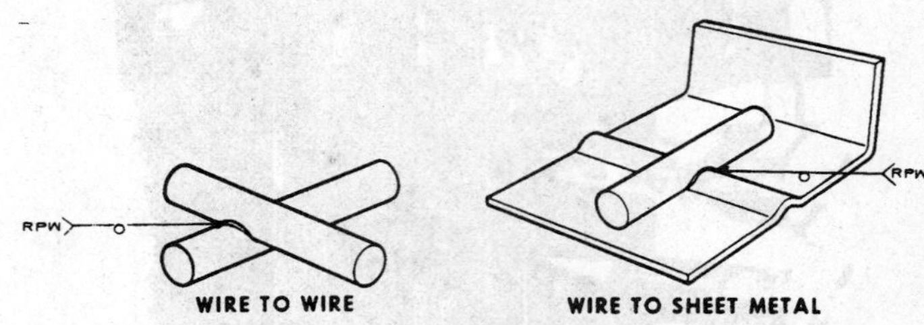

FIGURE 12—CROSS WIRE WELDING

Typical applications are on bar and rod products (Figure 16), starter ring gear for automotive production, low carbon drill shanks to tool steel drill points, etc.

3.5.1 Additional references are:

3.5.1.1 American Welding Society Welding Handbook, Fifth Edition, Section 2, Chapter 31.

3.5.1.2 Resistance Welding Manual (RWMA), Third Edition, Chapter 5, p. 67.

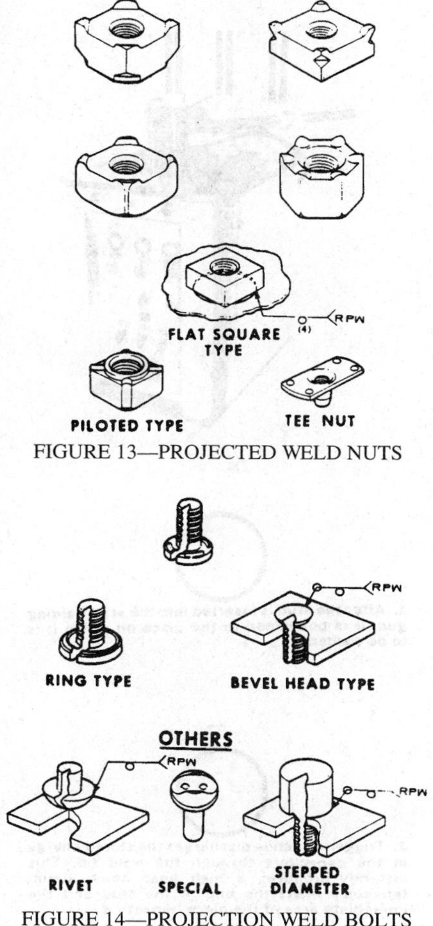

FIGURE 13—PROJECTED WELD NUTS

FIGURE 14—PROJECTION WELD BOLTS

3.6 Upset Butt Welding—Upset butt welding is a resistance welding process wherein coalescence is produced simultaneously over the entire area of abutting surfaces or progressively along a joint by the heat obtained from resistance to the flow of electric current through the area of contact of the abutting surfaces. Force is applied before heating is started and is maintained throughout the heating period.

Upset butt welding was the earliest form of resistance welding. This type of butt welding has no flash and results in a smooth and symmetrical upset section. The upset butt weld is of lower strength, quality, and uniformity as compared to flash butt welding. This is primarily due to any dirt, rust, scale, or other foreign matter on the abutting surfaces that will remain imbedded in the weld.

Principal applications of upset butt welding are wire products, pipes, and tubular members.

3.6.1 Additional references are:

3.6.1.1 American Welding Society Welding Handbook, Fifth Edition, Section 2, Chapter 31.

3.6.1.2 Resistance Welding Manual (RWMA), Third Edition, Chapter 5, p. 67.

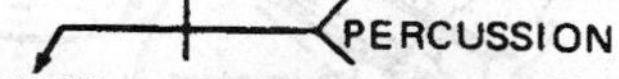

3.7 Percussion Welding—Percussion welding is defined as a resistance welding process wherein coalescence is produced simultaneously over the entire area of abutting surfaces, by heat obtained from an arc produced by a rapid discharge of electrical energy with force percussively applied during or immediately following the electrical discharge.

All percussive processes are confined to butt-welded joints. The total area that can be joined is limited to approximately 1/2 sq in, as larger areas present a problem in obtaining uniform distribution of the arcing over the entire area.

In general, this process is suitable for joining rod and tube forms to each other, or to a flat surface. The heat-affected zone is only 0.010 in deep with this process; therefore, the abutting surfaces must be finished accurately and maintained parallel to each other. See Figure 17 for equipment and operation references.

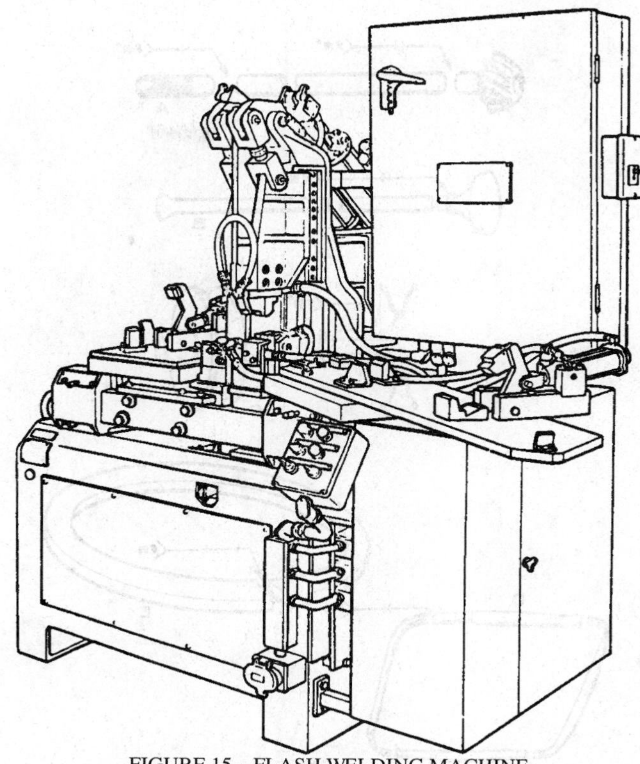

FIGURE 15—FLASH WELDING MACHINE

3.7.1 Additional information can be found in:

3.7.1.1 American Welding Society Welding Handbook, Fifth Edition, Chapter 31.

3.7.1.2 Resistance Welding Manual (RWMA), Chapter 9, p. 111.

3.8 High-Frequency Resistance Welding—(No Symbol)—High-frequency resistance welding is a welding process wherein coalescence is produced by the heat obtained from the resistance of the work to the flow of an induced high-frequency electric current, with or without the application of pressure.

High-frequency resistance welding is one of the newer welding processes utilizing alternating current frequency ranges of 10–450 kc. The currents flow mainly on or near the surface of metals, and heat is generated only in the section of the metal carrying the current, resulting in a skin heating effect. The higher the current frequency, the more pronounced is the skin effect. The output of the power source is connected directly to the work to be heated by means of contact electrodes. The contacts are placed on each side of two abutting electrodes. The edges touch at one end and the rest of the joint is open to form a "V." The current flows from one contact along the edge of the "V" to its root and completes the circuit by returning along the opposite edge to the second contact. The skin effect produces localized high-intensity heating on the surface, so that welding temperature is reached as pressure is applied to the root of the "V." Heat and pressure form an upset weld, and the upset is controlled by beveling and/or a trim operation. Diagrammatic sketches of high-frequency welding are shown in Figures 18 and 19.

3.8.1 Advantages

3.8.1.1 Applicable to a variety of metals and to a combination of dissimilar metals.

3.8.1.2 High welding speeds, up to 1000 ft/min on light-gage materials.

3.8.1.3 Applicable to highly automated fabrication lines.

3.8.1.4 A high-efficiency process which operates from a balanced 3-phase system.

3.8.1.5 Produces high-quality welds requiring no additional filler metal.

3.8.1.6 Narrow heat affected zone due to localized heating.

3.8.2 Disadvantages

3.8.2.1 Higher equipment and installation costs, as compared to arc welding processes.

3.8.2.2 Requires skilled personnel for setup and maintenance.

3.8.2.3 Requires trimming or planishing of upset.

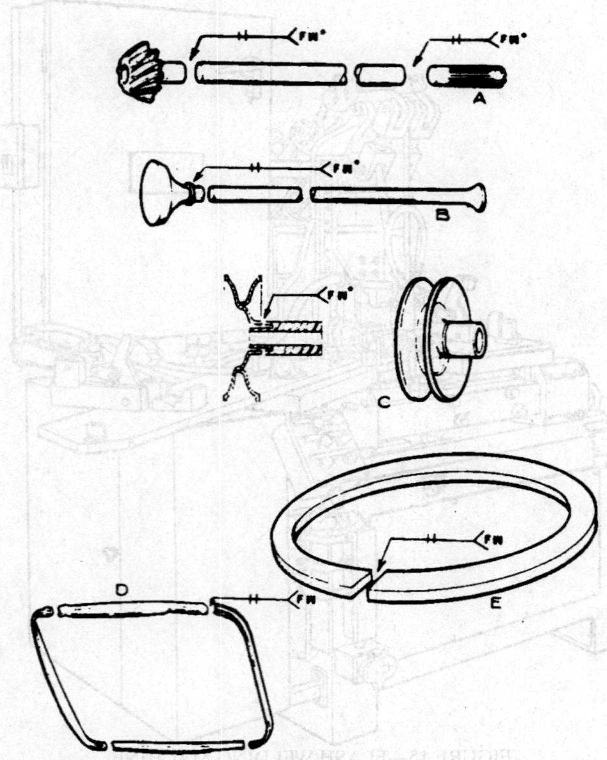

*FLASH WELD JOINT.

FIGURE 16—AUTOMOTIVE APPLICATIONS DESIGNED WITH GOOD FLASH BUTT WELDING FEATURES

(A) DRIVE SHAFT - PINION, SPLINE, AND SHAFT ARE MADE AS SEPARATE UNITS TO FACILITATE MACHINING, AND THEN FLASH BUTT WELDED TO MAKE COMPLETE DRIVE SHAFT.

(B) VALVE - HEAD IS MADE OF SPECIAL HEAT RESISTING ALLOY AND IS FLASH BUTT WELDED TO SHANK.

(C) PULLEY - STAMPING ASSEMBLY IS FLASH BUTT WELDED TO MACHINED PART, REPLACING MACHINED CASTING.

(D) DOOR FRAME - FOUR SMALL STAMPINGS ARE FLASH BUTT WELDED TO MAKE A COMPLETE FRAME, AVOIDING INTRICATE SINGLE STAMPING.

(E) RING GEAR BLANK - ROLLED STEEL STRIP IS FORMED AND FLASH BUTT WELDED, REPLACING FORGING.

3.8.3 APPLICATIONS

3.8.3.1 Tube mills.

3.8.3.2 Structural shapes such as Is, Ts, channels, and box sections.

3.8.3.3 Butt welds in tubing and pipes.

3.8.4 REFERENCES

3.8.4.1 American Welding Society Welding Handbook, Fifth Edition, Section 2, Chapter 35 (1964).

3.8.4.2 W. C. Rudd, "High Frequency Resistance Welding." Welding Journal, Vol. 36, July 1957, pp. 703–707.

3.8.4.3 "Modern Joining Processes," Chapter 5, p. 51. American Welding Society (1966).

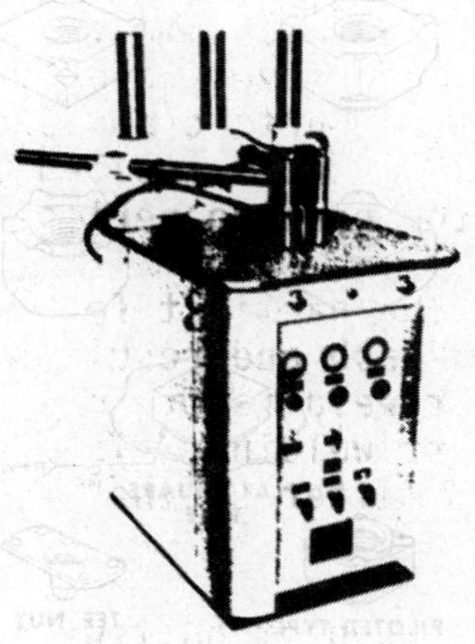

1. After the stud is inserted into the stud welding gun, it is positioned to the piece on which it is to be welded.

2. Triggering action discharges the stored energy in the capacitors through the weld tip. This instantly produces a high heat which simultaneously melts the end of the stud and the immediate area of the piece beneath it.

3. The automatic gun action then forces the stud to the piece. The bond is now complete. The entire weld cycle is less than 6/1000's of a second.

FIGURE 17—PERCUSSION WELDING MACHINE AND SEQUENCE OF OPERATION

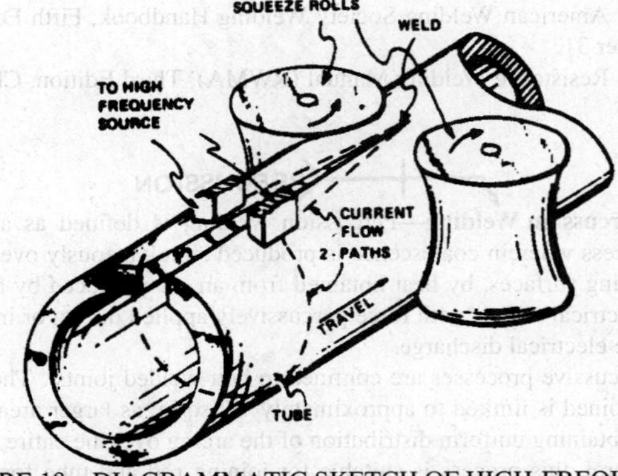

FIGURE 18—DIAGRAMMATIC SKETCH OF HIGH-FREQUENCY RESISTANCE WELDING EQUIPMENT FOR TUBE WELDING (COURTESY: THERMATOOL DIV., AMF CO.)

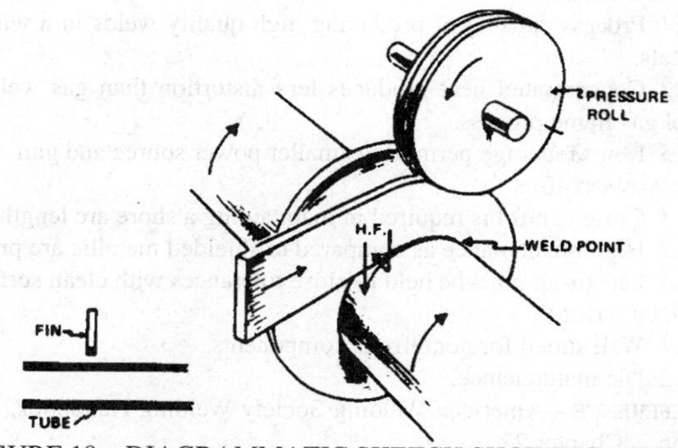

FIGURE 19—DIAGRAMMATIC SKETCH SHOWING METHOD OF WELDING SPIRAL FINS TO TUBE WITH HIGH-FREQUENCY RESISTANCE WELDING PROCESS (COURTESY: THERMATOOL DIV., AMF CO.)

4. Arc Welding—Arc welding is a term applied to a group of welding processes wherein coalescence is produced by heating with an electric arc or arcs, with or without the application of pressure and with or without the use of filler metal. The original arc welding processes, originated in the 1880s, utilized carbon or unshielded bare metal electrodes, manually held and guided along the desired path to produce a welded joint. Since that time, many advances and improvements have been made. Arc welding processes currently in common usage within the automotive industry include:

1. Shielded metal-arc welding (coated electrode) (Figure 20).
2. Submerged arc welding (Figure 21).
3. Gas tungsten-arc welding (Figure 22).
4. Gas metal-arc welding (Figure 23).
5. Stud welding.
6. Flux-cored arc welding.
7. Arc spot welding.

The various arc welding processes have evolved from advances in electrode, from advances in shielding methods and materials to protect the fusion zone and deposited metal from atmospheric contamination, or from specialized uses. Further descriptions of these arc welding processes are as follows:

4.1 Shielded Metal Arc Welding (SMAW)—This is the name of the process wherein heating is obtained from an arc between a covered metal electrode and the work. The decomposition of the electrode covering, at arc temperatures, provides a shielding atmosphere. Filler metal is obtained from the melted electrode. Commonly referred to as manual stick electrode arc welding, this process was for years by far the foremost welding process.

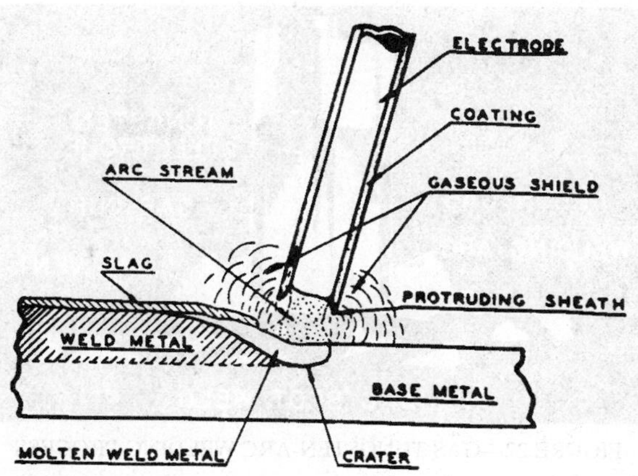

FIGURE 20—SHIELDED METAL-ARC WELDING (COATED ELECTRODE) PROCESS

4.1.1 Advantages

4.1.1.1 Simple, rugged equipment available.

4.1.1.2 Very flexible and portable equipment, either electric or gas engine power, can be used.

4.1.1.3 Electrodes commercially available for most weldable ferrous materials and many nonferrous metals. This is particularly true with the new materials coming on the market.

4.1.2 Disadvantages

4.1.2.1 Requires considerable operator skill.

4.1.2.2 Difficult to automate due to coating on electrode.

4.1.3 Applications

4.1.3.1 Frame and chassis components.

4.1.3.2 Casting repair.

4.1.3.3 Equipment, tooling, construction, and maintenance.

4.1.3.4 Die construction and repair.

4.1.3.5 Equipment maintenance.

4.1.4 Reference—American Welding Society Welding Handbook, Fifth Edition, Section 2, Chapter 25.

FIGURE 21—CUTAWAY VIEW OF SUBMERGED ARC WELDING PROCESS (COURTESY: LINDE AIR PRODUCTS UNIONMELT WELDING HANDBOOK, 1953)

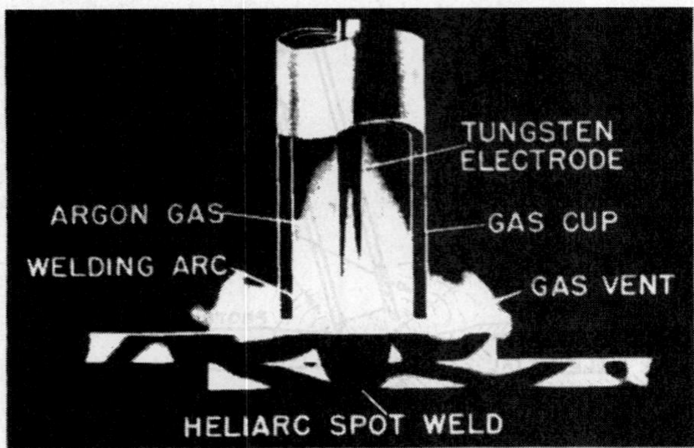

FIGURE 22—GAS TUNGSTEN-ARC WELDING PROCESS

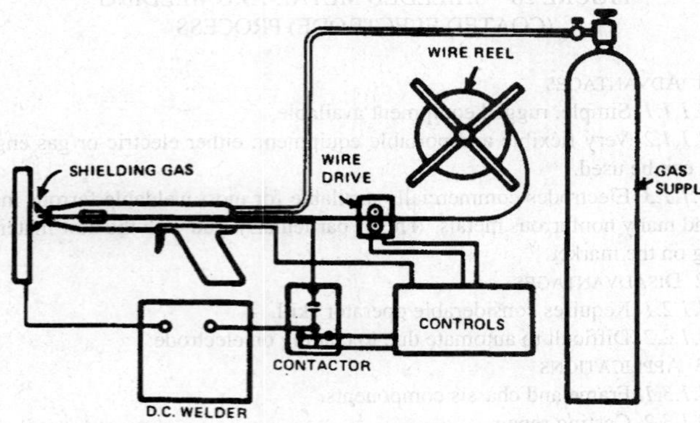

FIGURE 23—GAS METAL-ARC WELDING PROCESS

4.2 Submerged Arc Welding (SAW)—A welding process in which an arc between a bare consumable electrode and the work provides the heat for welding with shielding being provided by a blanket of granular fusible material on the work. Normally this process is considered for automatic applications using high currents, high-duty cycle, and multiple work on heavy weldments. Some light-gage applications have been successful, but for the most part this type of joining has shifted to the newer gas metal-arc welding or flux-cored arc welding processes, particularly for 0.125 in thick and under.

4.2.1 ADVANTAGES

4.2.1.1 Flux can hold weld metal in position on light-gage horizontal welds with base metal in the vertical plane.

4.2.1.2 Smooth external bead contour gives excellent appearance.

4.2.1.3 Uses coil stock electrode - minimum waste.

4.2.1.4 Can have very high deposition rates.

4.2.2 DISADVANTAGES

4.2.2.1 Abrasive flux difficult to contain causing equipment wear, especially material handling and housekeeping problems.

4.2.2.2 Separate flux presents handling problems both before welding and after the weld is completed.

4.2.3 APPLICATIONS

4.2.3.1 Chassis components.

4.2.3.2 Transmission components.

4.2.4 REFERENCE—American Welding Society Welding Handbook, Fifth Edition, Section 2, Chapter 28.

4.3 Gas Tungsten-Arc Welding (GTAW)—The necessary heat for gas tungsten-arc welding is produced by an arc between a nonconsumable electrode (usually tungsten or tungsten alloy) and the work. The heated weld zone, molten metal, and electrode are shielded by an inert gas. If additional filler metal is required over and above the melted workpiece, it is supplied by inserting filler rods into the weld zone. The process is adaptable to both manual and automatic equipment. Due to the partial rectification of the current flow in an arc between tungsten and the commonly used nonferrous base metals and the differences in types of current flow and surface cleaning, care should be exercised in the selection of equipment between direct and alternating current types and shielding gas to insure obtaining the ones best suited for the application.

4.3.1 ADVANTAGES

4.3.1.1 Process capable of producing high-quality welds in a wide variety of base metals.

4.3.1.2 Concentrated heat produces less distortion than gas welding with oxygen-fuel gas flame process.

4.3.1.3 Low amperage permitting smaller power source and gun.

4.3.2 DISADVANTAGES

4.3.2.1 Close control is required in maintaining a shore arc length.

4.3.2.2 High maintenance as compared to shielded metallic arc processes.

4.3.2.3 Part fit-up must be held to close tolerances with clean surfaces.

4.3.3 APPLICATIONS

4.3.3.1 Well suited for nonferrous components.

4.3.3.2 Die maintenance.

4.3.4 REFERENCE—American Welding Society Welding Handbook, Fifth Edition, Section 2, Chapter 27.

4.4 Gas Metal-Arc Welding (GMAW)—The necessary heat for gas metal-arc welding is produced by an arc between a consumable metal electrode and the work. The arc and weld puddle are shielded by an externally supplied gas, gas mixture, or, on rare occasion, by a mixture of gas and flux. The electrode feed is always mechanically driven. The process is used considerably with both operator guided (semiautomatic) and mechanically guided (automatic) torches. Since its introduction (about 1950) the process has grown very rapidly. The most common shielding gases are argon, carbon dioxide, helium, and their mixtures. Small amounts of oxygen are sometimes added to improve arc stability.

4.4.1 ADVANTAGES

4.4.1.1 No electrode loss such as unused stubs by using electrode in coils.

4.4.1.2 Little or no cleaning of deposit required.

4.4.1.3 Adaptable to wide range of metal thicknesses.

4.4.1.4 High deposition with deep penetration.

4.4.2 DISADVANTAGES

4.4.2.1 Higher maintenance than shielded metallic arc processes.

4.4.2.2 Air currents may disrupt gas shield.

4.4.2.3 Spatter may block shielding gas especially in out-of-position work.

4.4.3 APPLICATIONS

4.4.3.1 Frames.

4.4.3.2 Chassis components.

4.4.3.3 Body sheet metal joints with fine wire type.

4.4.3.4 Ferrous or nonferrous components.

4.4.4 REFERENCE—American Welding Society Welding Handbook, Fifth Edition, Section 2, Chapter 27.

4.5 Flux-Cored Arc Welding (FCAW)—This is an arc welding process wherein coalescence is produced by an electric arc between a consumable metal electrode and the work with shielding primarily obtained from a flux contained within the electrode. Additional shielding may or may not be obtained from an externally supplied gas or gas mixture. The discovery or development of flux-cored electrodes and the ability to make them commercially has brought this process into being. Best used on 0.0625 in material or heavier.

4.5.1 ADVANTAGES

4.5.1.1 Can be used without shielding gas.

4.5.1.2 High deposition rate produced.

4.5.1.3 Adaptable to both automatic and semiautomatic use with coiled electrode.

4.5.1.4 Less prone to undercutting than solid wire type.

4.5.1.5 Good for out-of-position work.

4.5.2 DISADVANTAGES

4.5.2.1 Material cost.

4.5.2.2 Possibility of having irregular flux core without detection.

4.5.3 APPLICATIONS

4.5.3.1 Drive shaft assembly.

4.5.3.2 Control arm.

4.5.3.3 Differential housing.

4.5.3.4 Frame assemblies used on 0.060 or heavier material.

4.6 Arc-Spot Welding—An arc welding method where coalescence at the faying surfaces is produced in one spot by heating with an electric arc between either a consumable or nonconsumable electrode and the work. The weld is made with or without preparing a hole in upper member. Shielding gas or flux may or may not be used. Any of the arc welding processes previously described may be used to perform arc-spot welding. However, the gas tungsten arc or gas metal arc processes are most often adopted. An arc timer control is added to conventional equipment to produce an arc-spot welding machine.

4.6.1 ADVANTAGES

4.6.1.1 Access to only one side of joint required.

4.6.1.2 Minimum operator skill required.

4.6.1.3 Applicable to wide range of thicknesses.

4.6.1.4 Nominal equipment cost.

4.6.2 DISADVANTAGES

4.6.2.1 Very good fit-up and clean materials are required to get good quality welds with gas tungsten-arc process.

4.6.2.2 Limited in positions welding can be performed because gravity will cause run-out of molten metal.

4.6.2.3 Equipment maintenance.

4.6.3 APPLICATIONS

4.6.3.1 Ferrous and nonferrous assemblies.

4.6.3.2 Truck and tractor frame components.

4.6.4 REFERENCE—American Welding Society Recommended Practices for Automotive Welding Design D8.4–61.

4.7 Stud Welding (SW)—Stud welding is an arc welding process wherein coalescence is produced by heating with an electric arc between a metal stud and the workpiece to heat the stud end and work surface before they are brought together under plunge force. Shielding may or may not be obtained by flux tipped studs, ceramic ferrules, or shielding gas, depending on size and material.

4.7.1 ADVANTAGES

4.7.1.1 Minimum operator skill required.

4.7.1.2 Can be automated for high-speed operation.

4.7.2 DISADVANTAGES

4.7.2.1 Complexity can cause it to be high-maintenance item.

4.7.2.2 Stud costs may be high.

4.7.3 APPLICATIONS

4.7.3.1 Trim and hardware attachment to bodies and fenders.

4.7.3.2 Ferrous and nonferrous components and some combinations.

4.7.4 REFERENCE—American Welding Society Welding Handbook, Fifth Edition, Section 2, Chapter 29.

5. Special Welding Processes

5.1 Electron Beam Welding—Electron beam welding is a process wherein coalescence is produced by the heat obtained from a concentrated beam composed primarily of high-velocity electrons impinging upon the surfaces to be joined. Electron beam welding is done in three modes:

1. Hard vacuum (see Figure 24).
2. Soft or partial vacuum.
3. Out-of-chamber or atmosphere welding.

Further descriptions of these three modes follow:

5.2 Hard Vacuum—This mode of welding is done in a chamber usually evacuated to a vacuum level of 1 x 10^{-4} Torr or 0.1 micron Hg.

5.2.1 ADVANTAGES

5.2.1.1 Has the ability to make welds with extremely high depth-to-width ratio; that is, a 1/6 in wide butt weld in a 1/2 in thick plate.

5.2.1.2 Approximation of true parallelism of the weld sides (minimum of "V" shape) to minimize distortion.

5.2.1.3 Welds created with a minimum of energy and therefore, minimal heat-affected zones.

5.2.1.4 Extremely small-diameter heat source.

5.2.1.5 High welding speeds.

5.2.1.6 Purity of vacuum melt metals.

5.2.1.7 Permits welding of refractory or highly active materials such as molybdenum, tantalum, tungsten, etc.

5.2.2 DISADVANTAGES

5.2.2.1 High equipment cost.

5.2.2.2 Parts to be welded must be housed in a vacuum chamber; the evacuation time can be long depending on chamber size.

5.2.2.3 Weld joint must fit within thousandths of an inch.

5.2.3 APPLICATIONS

5.2.3.1 Cluster gears.

5.2.3.2 Any precision part where maximum weld integrity is necessary.

5.2.3.3 Aerospace components.

5.2.4 REFERENCE—American Welding Society Welding Handbook, Fifth Edition, Section 3, Chapter 54.

5.3 Soft or Partial Vacuum—This mode of welding is usually done in a small chamber specifically designed to fit around the weldment with a minimum of clearance. As a result, a minimum of atmosphere must be evacuated.

The vacuum level is usually 50 microns Hg or 5 x 10^{-2} Torr.

5.3.1 ADVANTAGES

5.3.1.1 For all practical purposes, all of the advantages listed for "hard vacuum" welding apply with the possible exception of the ability to weld the refractory or highly active metals.

5.3.1.2 Evacuation time is reduced to seconds rather than minutes, thereby increasing production output.

5.3.2 DISADVANTAGES

5.3.2.1 High equipment cost.

5.3.2.2 Weld joint must fit within thousandths of an inch.

5.3.3 APPLICATIONS

5.3.3.1 Cluster gears.

5.3.3.2 Any precision weldment where maximum weld integrity is required.

5.3.3.3 Any precision weldment where premachining and/or preheat treatment is of prime consideration.

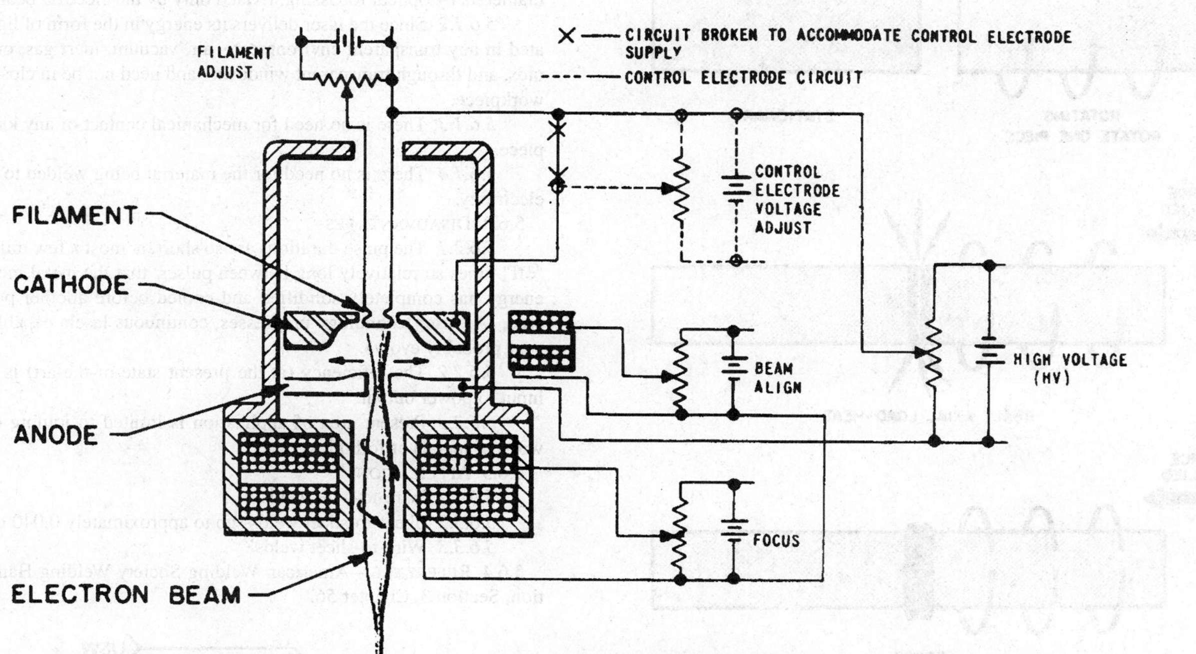

FIGURE 24—ELECTRON BEAM GUN AND ASSOCIATED CONTROLS (COURTESY: SCIAKY BROTHERS, INC.)

5.4 Out-of Chamber Welding—This mode of welding is a rather specialized version. The description "out-of-chamber" can be misleading in that it infers no vacuum is required. This is not completely true. The weldment is accomplished at atmospheric pressure; however, the equipment incorporates, by necessity, a pressure gradient from the gun to the workpiece which includes both a "hard" and a "soft" vacuum.

5.4.1 ADVANTAGES

5.4.1.1 The need and expense of a vacuum-tight welding chamber are eliminated.

5.4.1.2 Because of the nonvacuum environment, tooling problems are reduced.

5.4.2 DISADVANTAGES

5.4.2.1 The high depth-to-width ratio of the weld configuration is reduced almost to that obtained with "GTAW" welding.

5.4.2.2 Maximum gun-to-workpiece distance is reduced from 30–50 in to 1/2 in. This severely limits the area of application due to mechanical interference.

5.4.2.3 At the present state-of-the-art, approximately 150 kV appears to be the minimum practical operating voltage. At this level, significant levels of x-ray radiation and ozone are present, necessitating shielding and ventilation far beyond what is required in the other two modes.

5.4.3 APPLICATIONS

5.4.3.1 Tube mills.

5.4.3.2 Transmission and/or differential housings.

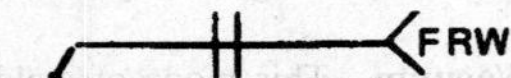

5.5 Friction Welding—Friction welding is a solid-state welding process wherein coalescence is produced by the heat obtained from mechanically induced sliding motion between rubbing surfaces. The work parts are held together under pressure.

A common scheme for friction welding is one in which two cylindrical bars (Figure 25) are axially aligned, one of which is rotated while the other is held stationary. The angular speed of the rotating member and the axial force at the rubbing ends of the bars are regulated so as to develop sufficient frictional heat and metal displacement for welding.

5.5.1 ADVANTAGES

5.5.1.1 Welds a wide variety of dissimilar materials and cross sections. Exception—most cast irons do not lend themselves to this process due to low coefficient of friction.

5.5.1.2 Produces welds of excellent quality at very high rates.

5.5.1.3 Weld zone is wrought structure rather than cast due to push out of molten metal during the welding process.

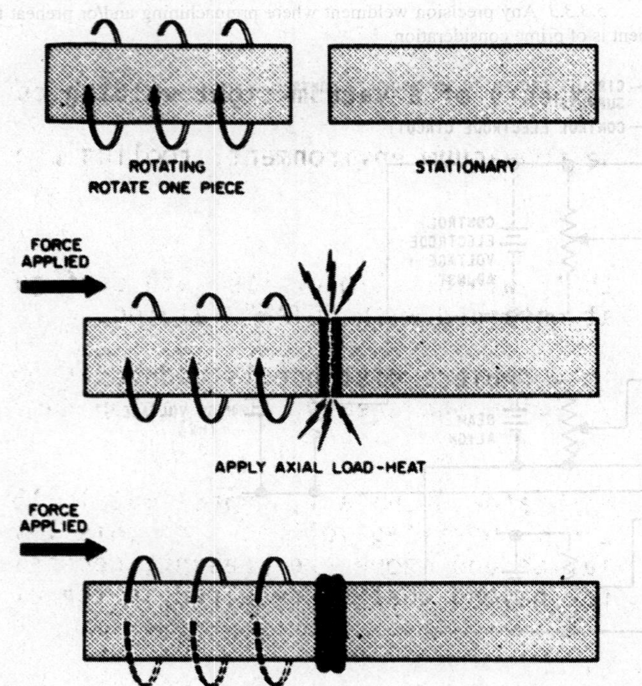

FIGURE 25—FRICTION WELDING

5.5.1.4 Weld zone is very narrow with nearly parallel sides. This keeps shrinkage stresses in one plane.

5.5.1.5 Heat-affected zone is usually very narrow by comparison to arc welding processes.

5.5.1.6 Rugged equipment readily available.

5.5.1.7 Process is fully automatic, keeping operator skill requirement to a minimum.

5.5.1.8 Very little if any joint preparation required.

5.5.1.9 Low maintenance.

5.5.2 DISADVANTAGES

5.5.2.1 High equipment cost.

5.5.2.2 One member of joint should be rotationally symmetrical. It is virtually impossible to maintain rotational orientation from one member to another across the face of the joint.

5.5.2.3 Premachining concept of fabrication is possible to only a limited degree, due to the problem of maintaining concentricity across the joint. This varies tremendously depending on the type of material being welded and the total cross-sectional area of joint.

5.5.3 APPLICATIONS

5.5.3.1 Worm gears to rod.

5.5.3.2 Valve stems to valve head.

5.5.3.3 Alloy steel tool joints to drill pipe for oil wells.

5.5.3.4 Copper circuit breaker assemblies.

5.5.3.5 Sprocket gears to hubs.

5.5.3.6 Some combinations of nonferrous materials to ferrous materials.

5.5.4 REFERENCE—American Welding Society Welding Handbook, Fifth Edition, Section 3, Chapter 52.

5.6 Laser Beam Welding (LBW)—A welding process wherein coalescence is produced by the heat obtained from the application of a concentrated coherent light beam impinging upon the surfaces to be joined.

A laser is a device which produces a concentrated coherent light beam through the manipulation and control of energy exchanges in solid-state transparent media. Welding may be accomplished by causing this light beam to impinge upon the surfaces to be joined.

Solid-state lasers are based on transparent single crystals or vitreous substances which contain small concentrations of transition elements. The transition element atoms can be excited to various levels upon exposure to intense optical radiation. As with other welding processes, the amount of metal melted depends upon the intensity and total energy transferred by the laser beam.

5.6.1 ADVANTAGES

5.6.1.1 The high-intensity beam can be focused to extremely small spot diameters by optical focussing, rivaled only by the electron beam.

5.6.1.2 Since the laser delivers its energy in the form of light, it can be operated in any transparent environment - air, vacuum, inert gas, or even certain liquids, and through transparent windows - and need not be in close proximity to the workpiece.

5.6.1.3 There is no need for mechanical contact of any kind with the workpiece.

5.6.1.4 There is no need for the material being welded to be a conductor of electricity.

5.6.2 DISADVANTAGES

5.6.2.1 The pulse durations are so short, at most a few milliseconds, and the "off" times so relatively long between pulses, that the metal melted by a pulse of energy has completely solidified and cooled before another pulse can be delivered. As laser technology progresses, continuous lasers capable of welding will very probably evolve.

5.6.2.2 The efficiency (at the present state-of-the-art) is quite low; power input to power output.

5.6.2.3 Present area of application is limited to joining of small diameter wires of metals of foil thicknesses.

5.6.3 APPLICATIONS

5.6.3.1 Wire-to-wire welds.

5.6.3.2 Sheet-to-sheet welds (up to approximately 0.040 thickness).

5.6.3.3 Wire-to-sheet welds.

5.6.4 REFERENCE—American Welding Society Welding Handbook, Fifth Edition, Section 3, Chapter 56.

5.7 Ultrasonic Welding—Ultrasonic welding is a process for joining similar and dissimilar metals by the introduction of high-frequency vibratory energy into the overlapping metals in the area to be joined. No fluxes or filler metals are used, no electrical current passes through the weld metal, and usually no heat is applied. The workpieces (Figure 26) are clamped together under moderately low static force, and ultrasonic energy is transmitted into the intended weld area. A sound metallurgical bond is produced without arc or melting of the weld metal and without the cast structure associated with melting. There is minor thickness deformation.

5.7.1 ADVANTAGES

5.7.1.1 Permits welding of many metals and alloys and combinations thereof.

5.7.1.2 Permits welding of certain joints with geometrical configurations that are difficult or impossible to join by other techniques.

5.7.1.3 Eliminates cast structure of weld.

5.7.1.4 Heat input is so low that most side effects of heating produced by other techniques are minimized or eliminated.

5.7.1.5 Power requirements are very low compared to other welding processes.

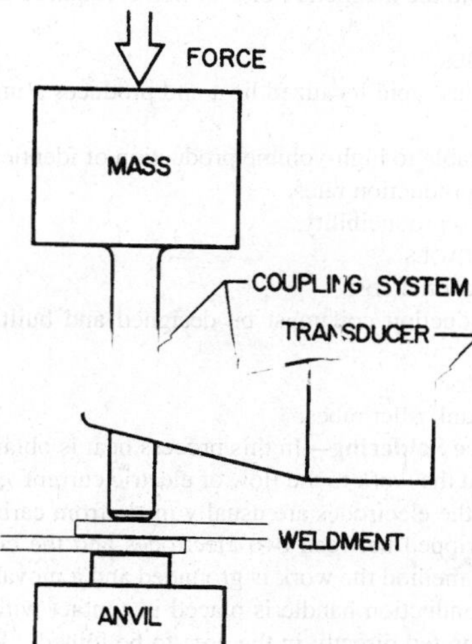

FIGURE 26—SCHEMATIC OF ULTRASONIC PROCESS

5.7.2 DISADVANTAGES

5.7.2.1 Is limited in metal thicknesses the process can handle. Maximum thickness is approximately 0.10 in. Some metals may be limited to as low as 0.015-0.040 in. There appears to be no lower limit; foils as thin as 0.00017 in have been welded.

5.7.2.2 Tip sticking, that is, tip welding itself to the part, can be troublesome.

5.7.2.3 Design requirements make accessibility to odd shaped joints limited compared to resistance welding.

5.7.3 APPLICATIONS

5.7.3.1 Electronic components.

5.7.3.2 Fine wires and thin foils.

5.7.3.3 Encapsulating materials that are heat sensitive such as pyrotechnics, explosives, reactive chemicals, and pharmaceuticals.

5.7.4 REFERENCE—American Welding Society Welding Handbook, Fifth Edition, Section 3, Chapter 49.

*6. **Brazing***—Brazing is a term applied to a group of welding processes wherein coalescence is produced by heating to a suitable temperature above 800 °F and by using a nonferrous filler metal, having a melting point below that to the base metals. The filler metal is distributed between the closely fitted surfaces of the joint by capillary attraction. Some of the most commonly used brazing processes in the automotive industry are:

1. Gas torch brazing.
2. Induction brazing.
3. Furnace brazing.
4. Salt bath brazing.

Descriptions of each of these processes along with their advantages, disadvantages, and some established applications follow.

6.1 Gas Torch Brazing—In this process the heat for brazing is supplied by a gas flame. It is one of the oldest and most widely used methods of heating for brazing. The variety of torches and combustion gases available makes this a versatile process. Highest flame temperatures are attained with acetylene and lower temperatures with propane, butane, natural gas, and manufactured gas, roughly in the order given. Any fuel gas burned with oxygen will give the highest temperature possible with that gas. Selection of a torch for brazing is controlled by the size, mass, and configuration of the parts to be joined. In most cases a flux is required. Filler metal may be hand fed or preplaced.

6.1.1 ADVANTAGES

6.1.1.1 It is simple and requires low capital investment.

6.1.1.2 It is especially adaptable to the brazing of parts of unequal mass or where a variety or limited number of parts are to be joined.

6.1.1.3 Adaptable to automation.

6.1.2 DISADVANTAGES

6.1.2.1 Possibility of distortion.

6.1.2.2 Produces oxidation in the heated area.

6.1.2.3 Requires adequate ventilation.

6.1.2.4 When a flux is used, removal is necessary to prevent corrosive action.

6.1.3 APPLICATIONS

6.1.3.1 Automotive air conditioning plumbing.

6.1.3.2 Accelerator linkage.

6.1.3.3 Marine manifolds.

6.1.3.4 Power steering pump oil reservoir.

6.2 Induction Brazing—In induction brazing heat is created by the resistance of the material being brazed to the flow of induced high-frequency eddy currents. A water-cooled induction coil is designed to follow the configuration of the joint to be brazed. The work is placed in or near the coil, and does not form a part of the electric circuit. A heat balance may be obtained in joints with varying cross section by adjusting the distance between the coil and the work. Sufficient time should be allowed to permit the brazing alloy to flow where required. Filler metal is preplaced in, or near, the joint. A flux is usually necessary. In special cases an atmosphere is introduced precluding the use of a flux.

6.2.1 ADVANTAGES

6.2.1.1 Lends itself particularly to large-scale production of identical joints.

6.2.1.2 Minimum oxidation of adjacent surfaces.

6.2.1.3 Provides a rapid localized heat permitting high production rates.

6.2.1.4 Good reproducibility.

6.2.2 DISADVANTAGES

6.2.2.1 High capital cost.

6.2.2.2 Joint design must be relatively simple.

6.2.2.3 An induction coil must be designed and built for each individual joint.

6.2.3 APPLICATIONS

6.2.3.1 Attachment of truck fuel tank filler tubes.

6.2.3.2 Attachment of steering column gearshift lever.

6.3 Furnace Brazing—In furnace brazing the heat source may be gas, oil, or electric. Adequate controls for regulation of temperature and atmosphere are required. This method also depends on setting up a cycle producing good results for a given type of work. When the heating cycle has been established for a given part, it may not produce satisfactory results with lighter or more massive parts. Assemblies should be designed to be self-fixturing or to require a minimum of fixturing. Intricate shapes are difficult to hold, and it is uneconomical to heat massive fixtures. When a protective atmosphere is used, fluxing of the joint is not normally required. Filler metal is preplaced in, or adjacent to, the joint.

6.3.1 ADVANTAGES

6.3.1.1 Most economical when large quantities of small or medium-sized parts are to be brazed.

6.3.1.2 Many components of an assembly may be joined at one time.

6.3.1.3 When a protective atmosphere is used, the as-brazed parts are free of scale and flux.

6.3.1.4 Adaptable to automation.

6.3.2 DISADVANTAGES

6.3.2.1 Not economical for low-volume production.

6.3.2.2 High capital cost.

6.3.2.3 Not practical to braze assemblies which vary appreciably in mass with the same furnace cycle.

6.3.3 APPLICATIONS

6.3.3.1 Torque converter impeller and turbine.

6.3.3.2 Power steering oil reservoir.

6.3.3.3 Fuel pump.

6.3.3.4 Oil pump suction tube.

6.3.3.5 Power steering pump pulley.

7. Soldering—Soldering is defined as a joining process wherein coalescence is produced by heating, generally below 800 °F, and by using a nonferrous filler metal that has a melting point below that of the base metal. The filler metal is distributed between the properly fitted parts by capillary attraction.

A variety of equipment and procedures may be used to supply the requirements to produce satisfactory soldered joints. The processes most commonly used in the automotive industry include:

1. Iron soldering.
2. Torch soldering.
3. Dip soldering.
4. Induction soldering.
5. Resistance soldering.
6. Oven soldering.
7. Ultrasonic soldering.
8. Abrasion soldering.

Descriptions of each of these processes along with their advantages, disadvantages, and some established applications follow.

7.1 Soldering Iron—The traditional soldering tool is the soldering iron, usually a copper bit heated either electrically or by a flame. Its function is to store heat, to heat the part to be soldered, to store molten solder, to convey molten solder, and to withdraw surplus molten solder. Electrically heated irons are more convenient for use in manual, high-speed repetitive operations.

7.1.1 ADVANTAGES

7.1.1.1 It is simple and requires a low capital investment.

7.1.1.2 Adaptable for use in a wide variety of applications.

7.1.1.3 Localized heat minimizes damaging adjacent insulation in electrical work.

7.1.2 DISADVANTAGES

7.1.2.1 Requires constant bit maintenance.

7.1.2.2 Limited to joints accessible to the bit.

7.1.3 APPLICATIONS—Applications for the use of the soldering iron are usually confined to the making of electrical connections.

7.2 Torch Soldering—Lower flame temperatures are used for torch soldering as compared with torch brazing. City gas burned with air is most commonly used. Higher temperature flames, such as that obtained with oxyacetylene, may be used under controlled automated conditions where a high rate of production is required. Soldering torches are available in a wide range of sizes from those which produce a needle point flame to those which emit a wide harsh flame, such as used in the applications of body solder. As in other soldering processes, the parts to be soldered must be clean. Filler metal may be fed by hand or preplaced. A flux is usually required.

7.2.1 ADVANTAGES

7.2.1.1 Adaptable to automation.

7.2.1.2 Wide range of heat output.

7.2.1.3 Economical.

7.2.1.4 Portability.

7.2.2 DISADVANTAGES

7.2.2.1 Open flame is objectionable in some environments.

7.2.2.2 Work tends to become discolored due to oxidation.

7.2.2.3 Probability of distortion.

7.2.3 APPLICATIONS

7.2.3.1 Filling exposed seams and dents on car bodies.

7.2.3.2 Application of plumbing fittings to fuel tanks and radiators.

7.2.3.3 Leak-tight seams in tank floats, tube fittings, etc.

7.3 Dip Soldering—In this process a pot of molten solder, heated electrically or by flame, supplies both the heat and the solder necessary to complete the joint. Prior to dipping into the solder the surfaces to be joined must be cleaned and fluxed. They also must be held stationary in relationship to each other during the soldering operation and until the deposited solder has completely solidified. Solder pots may vary in size from a few pounds to several tons. They should be large enough so that at a given rate of production the units being dipped will not appreciably lower the temperature of the solder bath.

7.3.1 ADVANTAGES

7.3.1.1 Numerous joints in an assembly can be soldered at one time.

7.3.1.2 Economical process.

7.3.1.3 Can be automated.

7.3.1.4 Can be used for solder coating parts for corrosion protection as well as joining.

7.3.2 DISADVANTAGES

7.3.2.1 All components of the assembly which are to be immersed in the solder bath must be able to withstand the bath temperature.

7.3.2.2 The solder bath level must be maintained and kept free of dross.

7.3.2.3 Jigs and fixtures are required.

7.3.2.4 Parts must be free of moisture to avoid explosions due to the formation of steam pockets in the molten solder.

7.3.3 APPLICATIONS

7.3.3.1 Soldering of cellular radiator and heater cores.

7.3.3.2 Coating of fuel tank filler tubes.

7.3.3.3 Joining terminals to stranded wire for battery cables.

7.3.3.4 Wiring harness and attaching electrical components to printed circuit boards.

7.4 Induction Soldering—To be induction heated the material must be an electrical conductor. Heat is obtained by resistance of the material to the flow of an induced eddy current. The part to be soldered is placed in, or near, a water cooled induction coil which must be designed for each joint configuration. In joining dissimilar metals or parts which differ in mass, heat input may be controlled by adjusting the coil to work distance. Locating fixtures in the vicinity of the coil are made of nonconductive materials to prevent heating from the induced current resulting from the magnetic field. A flux is required and the solder is usually preplaced.

7.4.1 ADVANTAGES

7.4.1.1 Supplies rapid localized heat and produces a minimum area of oxidation.

7.4.1.2 Adaptable to high-volume production of identical joints.

7.4.1.3 High production rates.

7.4.1.4 Good reproducibility.

7.4.2 DISADVANTAGES

7.4.2.1 High capital cost.

7.4.2.2 An induction coil must be designed and built for each particular joint.

7.4.3 APPLICATIONS

7.4.3.1 Fuel tank filler tubes.

7.5 Resistance Soldering—In this process heat is obtained from resistance of the electrodes and the work to the flow of electric current. A low-voltage transformer is used and the electrodes are usually made from carbon. In one application, the work is gripped between two electrodes and the current is applied for heating. In another method the work is grounded and a movable carbon electrode mounted in a nonconduction handle is placed in contact with the area to be soldered. Heat is generated directly in the area to be joined. The solder is usually hand fed. A flux is required.

7.5.1 ADVANTAGES

7.5.1.1 Fast localized heat.

7.5.1.2 Can be used to solder lap joints.

7.5.1.3 Minimum oxidation of work.

7.5.2 DISADVANTAGES

7.5.2.1 In general, the electrode cannot be tinned to permit storing of the solder, as with the soldering iron, so the solder must be fed directly into the joint.

7.5.2.2 Joint must be accessible to the electrode.

7.5.3 APPLICATIONS

7.5.3.1 Soldering joints in bus bars and other electrical connections.

7.6 Oven Soldering—The oven may be heated by gas or electricity and should be equipped with adequate temperature controls to assure consistently good results. For volume production the parts are moved through the oven on a conveyor. Proper clamping fixtures are very important, since the assembly is moving before and during solidification of the solder. Failure to fixture properly may result in poor joints, since solder has low strength near its solidus temperature and fails very easily when disturbed. It is often advantageous to accelerate the cooling of parts on removal from the oven in order to reduce the length of time the solder is near the solidus temperature. The assembly must be cleaned and fluxed prior to soldering.

7.6.1 ADVANTAGES

7.6.1.1 Adaptable to the joining of complex assemblies containing numerous joints.

7.6.1.2 Suitable for volume production.

7.6.2 DISADVANTAGES

7.6.2.1 High capital cost.

7.6.2.2 Requires jigs and fixtures.

7.6.2.3 All components of the assembly must be able to withstand the heat of the oven.

7.6.3 APPLICATIONS

7.6.3.1 Major automotive application is the soldering of radiator and heater cores.

7.7 Ultrasonic Soldering—This is a recently developed process and is used, primarily, for the soldering of aluminum. It is finding some use, however, on other metals such as silicon and germanium. The equipment used consists of an electronic ultrasonic generator and a transducer to which a soldering bit is connected. Electrical energy is transmitted to the transducer where it is transformed into mechanical energy. In practice, a small amount of solder is melted on the surface of the work. The energized bit is inserted in the solder pool producing ultrasonic vibrations resulting in the removal of the surface oxide barrier and wetting of the solder to the underlying aluminum producing a metallurgical bond. This process is also used for dip soldering, in which case the energized bit is immersed in the solder pot.

7.7.1 ADVANTAGES

7.7.1.1 No flux required.

7.7.2 DISADVANTAGES

7.7.2.1 Small capacity of the units.

7.7.2.2 Direct soldering of lap or crimp joints is not practical.

7.7.2.3 Supplemental heat usually required.

7.7.3 APPLICATIONS

7.7.3.1 Soldering of aluminum pigtail splices to coil windings and to fasten electrical ground terminals to aluminum face plates.

7.8 Abrasion Soldering—The solder is applied by mechanically abrasing the metal surface in the presence of molten solder. As the surface oxide is removed, the base metal is exposed to the wetting action of the solder. The abrasion tools generally used are fiberglass brushes, stainless steel brushes, stainless steel wool, or the solder bar itself. This process is used, primarily, on aluminum.

7.8.1 ADVANTAGES

7.8.1.1 No flux required.

7.8.2 DISADVANTAGES

7.8.2.1 Direct soldering of lap or crimp joints is not practical.

7.8.3 APPLICATIONS

7.8.3.1 On aluminum, when use of a flux cannot be tolerated.

7.9 References

7.9.1 American Welding Society Soldering Manual, First Edition, 1959.

7.9.2 Solders - SAE J473, Table 1.

7.9.3 ASTM solder classifications are given in Tables 44.3 and 44.4 of the Welding Handbook, American Welding Society, Fifth Edition, Section 3.

ABRASIVE WEAR—SAE J965 AUG66

SAE Information Report

Report of the SAE Iron and Steel Technical Committee approved August 1966. Formerly HS J965.

Foreword—This Document has not changed other than to put it into the new SAE Technical Standards Board Format.

1. Scope—An enormous economic loss, as well as a waste of natural resources, is incurred world-wide as a result of wear of components and tools. Any effort expended in an attempt to reduce this loss is indeed worthwhile. The purpose of this SAE Information Report is to present the current state of knowledge of abrasive wear. This report, therefore, covers wear, or the undesired removal of metal by mechanical action, caused by abrasive particles in contact with the surface. It does not concern metal-to-metal wear or wear in the presence of an abrasive free lubricant.

Abrasive wear occurs when hard particles, such as rocks, sand, or fragments of certain hard metals, slide or roll under pressure across a surface. This action tends to cut grooves across the metal surface, much like a cutting tool.

Abrasive wear is of considerable importance in any part moving in relation to an abrasive. Tools in contact with the ground, such as plows, cultivators, scraper and bulldozer blades, are intended to operate in abrasives. Machines for processing ores such as crushers and for grinding of natural minerals such as ball mills are also subjected to abrasive wear. Contact with abrasives by many other machinery components may not be a normal circumstance, but, since it may inadvertently occur, must be considered.

Increased hardness usually increases wear resistance but also increases brittleness, which can cause fracture of the tool in rocky soils. Thus, the selection of a suitable material for use in a variety of abrasive conditions is necessarily a compromise between wear and brittle fracture resistance.

This report presents present day information on the fundamentals, testing methods and specific solutions for abrasive wear problems. The limited information reflects the current lack of knowledge on this subject. However, it is a starting point. Further work is necessary to develop general design information.

Abrasive Wear—The removal of material from a surface by mechanical action of abrasive (hard) particles in contact with the surface.

Classifications—The following are arbitrary classifications of abrasive wear based on observed conditions(1): [1]

Gouging Abrasion—The result of this type of abrasive wear is the removal of large particles from a metal surface. Worn surfaces show heavy gouges.

High Stress Grinding Abrasion—This type of abrasive wear occurs during the progressive fragmentation or grinding of the abrasive which was initially of small size and takes place on the surfaces employed to grind the abrasive. The wear is believed to be caused by concentrated compressive stress at the point of abrasive contact and to result from plastic flowing and fatiguing of ductile constituents and cracking of hard constituents of the metal surface. The use of the words "high stress" in this classification is intended to imply that the crushing strength of the abrasive is exceeded.

Low Stress Scratching Abrasion or Erosion—The result of this type of abrasive wear is scratching of the metal surface, and the scratches are usually minute. The stress imposed on the abrasive particle does not exceed the crushing strength of the abrasive.

2. References

2.1 Related Publications—The following publications are provided for information purposes only and are not a required part of this document.

1. M. Spindel, "A New Method of Testing Railroad Materials for Wear Resistance." Brutcher Trans. No. 1662, Trans. from Zeitschrift VDI, Vol. 66 (1922), p. 1071–1072.
2. M. Suzuki, "An Investigation of Abrasion in Carbon Steels," ASME Mechanical Engineers Journal. Vol. 30, (December 1927), p. 559–626.
3. J. M. Blake, "Wear Testing of Various Types of Steel," Proc. A.S.T.M. Vol. 28, Part II, (1928), p. 341–355.
4. J. M. Blake, W. H. Parker, J. H. Hall, and H. J. French, "Wear Testing of Various Metals," Iron Age, Vol. 122, (July 17, 1928), p. 141–142.
5. H. J. French, "Abrasion Testing," Metallurgist (Supp. to Engineer.), (March 30, 1928), p. 45.
6. M. Finck, "Wear Oxidation, a New Component of Wear", Trans. A.S.M., Vol. 18, (1930), p. 1026–1034.
7. T. Klingenstein, "Influence of Structure and Composition of Cast Iron on Abrasive Strength with Special Regard for Phosphorus Content," Mitteilungen aus den Ferschungsanstalten, Vol. 1, (Sept. 1930), p. 18–24.
8. S. J. Rosenberg, "The Resistance of Steels to Abrasion by Sand," U.S. Bureau of Standards Research, Vol. 5, No. 3, (Sept 1930), p. 533–574.
9. L. Jordon, "Wear of Metals," Mechanical Engineer, Vol. 53, (Sept. 1931), p. 644–650.
10. S. A. Main, "Resistance to Abrasion in Relation to Hardness," Inst. of Mechanical Engineers, Proc., Vol. 121, (1931), p. 523–532.
11. S. J. Rosenberg and H. K. Herchmen, "Wear of Metals," Metals and Alloys, V.2, (Feb. 1931), p. 52–56.
12. S. J. Rosenberg, "How Carbon Content and Heat Treatment Can Affect Wear Resistance," Iron Age, Vol. 128, (Nov. 26, 1931), p. 1366–1367.
13. S. Saito, "Study of Abrasion," Tahoku Imperial University Science Reports, Vol. 20, (October 1931), p. 560–573. (In English).
14. H. W. Swift, "Some Tests of Inter-Metallic Abrasions," Engineering, Vol. 131, (June 19, 1931), p. 783–785.
15. C. R. Weiss, "Relative Wear of Metals Due to Abrasion," Iron Age, Vol. 129, (May 1932), p. 1166–1167 and 1180.
16. R. J. Piersol, "Measurement of Abrasive Hardness of Metallic Surfaces," Metal Cleaning and Finishing, Vol. 5, (August 1933), p. 321–325.
17. J. S. Vanick, "An Improved Nickel-Chromium Hardened Chilled Cast Iron," Trans. A.I.M.E., Vol. 105, Iron and Steel Div., (1933), p. 53–76.
18. O. W. Ellis, J.RR. Gordon, and G. S. Farnham, "Wear Resistance of White Cast Iron," Foundry Trade J., Vol. 53, (December 19, 1935), p. 449–452.
19. A. Kissock, "A Wear Resistant Steel," Climax Molybdenum Co., N.Y.C.
20. A. H. Dieker and J. O. Everhart, "Wearing Properties of Some Metals in Clay Plant Operation," Ohio State U. of Engineering Exp. St. Bull., No. 97, (November 1937).
21. O. W. Ellis, "Wear Tests on Ferrous Alloys", Foundry Trade J., Vol. 57, (July 8, 1937), p. 23–26 and 29.
22. H. W. Gillett, "Considerations Involved in the Wear Testing of Metals," A.S.T.M. Paper, from Symposium of Wear of Metals, Phil., 1937.
23. P. S. Lane, "Some Experiences With Wear Testing", A.F.S. Preprint No. 37-1, 1937.
24. "Symposium of Wear of Metals", published by the A.S.T.M., Phila., Pa., 1937.
25. W. L. Howes, "Considerations of Mill Liners," A.I.M.E. T.P. 1795, Mining Techn., March 1945.
26. C. E. Berry, "Wear-Resistance Tests on Domestic Materials for Pebble-Mill Linings," A.I.M.E. T.P. 1948, Mining Techn., March 1946.
27. Garms and Stevens, "Ball Wear and Functioning of the Ball Load in a Fine-grinding Ball Mill", A.I.M.E. T.P. 1984, Mining Techn., March 1946.
28. Southmayd, "Installation and Performance of Sand Pumps", A.I.M.E. T.P. 1978, Mining Techn., March 1946.
29. H. S. Avery, "Hard Surfacing by Fusion Welding," American Brake Shoe Co., New York, 1947.
30. "Field Experience with Abrasion," Mining and Metallurgy, October 1948, p. 559–562.
31. R. D. Haworth, Jr., "Effect of Welding Practice on Abrasion Resistance of Hard Facings", Iron Age, Vol. 162, (October 17, 1948), p. 83–87.
32. "Wear of Metals", chapter in A.S.M. Metals Handbook, 1948 ed., p. 216–222.
33. H. S. Avery, "Austenitic Manganese Steel," American Brake Shoe Co., New York City, 1949.
34. H. S. Avery, "The Metallurgical Background for Welding Austenitic Manganese Steel," American Brake Shoe Co., New York City, 1949.
35. H. S. Avery, "Discussion of Abrasion Resistance of Metals," Trans. A.S.M., Vol. 41, (1949), p. 854–860.
36. P. Grodzinski and W. R. J. Jacobson, "Apparatus for Testing the Wear and Abrasion Resistance of Hard Materials," British Patent BP 665, 429, (Nov. 28, 1949).
37. T. E. Norman and C. M. Loeb, Jr., "Wear Tests on Grinding Balls," Trans. A.I.M.E. (Mineral Beneficiation Div.) Vol. 183, (1949), p. 330–360.
38. Abrasion Resistant High Chromium Iron, booklet by Electro Metallurgical Division of Union Carbide and Carbon Corp., 1950.
39. H. S. Avery, "Hot Hardness of Hard Facing Alloys", Welding Journal, Vol. 29, 1950, p. 552–578.
40. F. P. Bowden and D. Tabor, "The Friction and Lubrication of Solids," Clarendon Press, Oxford, 1950.

1. Numbers in parentheses designate References—see Section 2.1, Applicable Publications.

41. J. T. Burwell, Jr., ed., "Mechanical Wear," A.S.M., Cleveland, 1950.

42. T. A. Jagger, "Abrasion Hardness," Hawaiian Volcano Research Assn., Honolulu, T. H. (5th Special Report, Hawaiian Volcano Observatory and U.S. Geological Survey.) 1950.

43. E. N. Maslov, "Friction Coefficient in Sliding and Scratching (Abrasion) of Metals," Zhurn Tekhn Fiz, Vol. 20, (July, 1950), p. 888–891.

44. N. G. Neuweiler, "The Phenomenon of Wear; A Practical Device for Testing Abrasion," Microtechnic, (English Ed.), Vol. 4, (Sept.-Oct. 1950), p. 283–287.

45. D. E. Nordquist and J. E. Moeller, "Relative Wear Rates of Various Diameter Grinding Balls in Production Mills," Trans, A.I.M.E., V. 177, 1950, p. 712–714 (Mining Engineering, Vol. 187, 1950, p. 714-714).

46. M. Riddigough, "Hardfacing v. Abrasion," Welding, Vol. 18. (March 1950), p. 109–111.

47. H. W. Wagner, "New Concepts of Abrasive Properties as Affecting Grinding Performance", Mechanical Engineering, Vol. 72, (1950), p. 225–226.

48. "Varying Hardness of Ore Slows Carbide Drilling," Anon., Engrg. and Mining J., Vol. 152 (8), (August 1951), p. 73.

49. H. L. Alling, "Abrasion of 9 Minerals of Sand Size in Ball Mills", Am. Journ. Sci., Vol. 249 (8), (August 1951), p. 569–590.

50. H. S. Avery, "Hard Facing Alloys for Steel Mill Use," Iron and Steel Engr., V. XXVIII(IX), (1951), p. 81–106.

51. H. S. Avery, "Some Characteristics of Composite Tungsten Carbide Weld Deposits", Welding Journal, Vol. 30 (2), (February 1951), p. 88–160.

52. J. T. Burwell, "Wear Tests and Service Performance," from A.S.M. Interpretation of Tests and Correlation with Service, (1951), p. 88–140.

53. P. Dinechert, "Abrasion and Polishing, Friction and Wear," Microtechnic (English Ed.), Vol. 5, (Sept-Oct. 1951), p. 225–232.

54. J. Mackenzie, "The Abrasion Resistance of Refractory Bricks," Trans. Brit. Ceram. Soc., Vol. 50 (4), (April, 1951), p. 145–174.

55. J. C. Outwater and M. C. Shaw, "Surface Temperatures in Grinding," A.S.M.E. Paper No. 51-SA-10 (June 1951).

56. L. P. Tarasov, "Grindability of Tool Steels," A.S.M. Trans., Vol. 43, 1951, p. 1144–1168.

57. H. S. Avery, "Hard Facing for Impact," Welding J. Vol. 31 (2), (1952), p. 116–143.

58. H. S. Avery, "Selecting Hard Facing Materials to Resist Impact, Heat, Friction, Abrasion," Product Engineering, Vol. 23, (March 1952), p. 154–159.

59. H. S. Avery and H. J. Cahpin, "Hard Facing Alloys of the Chromium Carbide Type," Welding J., Vol. 31 (10), (1952), p. 917–930.

60. G. E. Dunlap and J. A. Fellows, "Ferrous Castings for Abrasion Resistance," American Brake Shoe Co., 1952.

61. R. P. Agarwala and H. Wilman, "Deformation of Iron Crystals by Unidirectional Abrasion," J.I.S.I., Vol. 179, (1955), p. 124–131.

62. R. E. Blair, "Physical Properties of Mine Rock, Part III," U.S. Bur. Mines Rept. Invest. 5130, June 1955; "Part I", by Windes, S.L., R.I. 4459, March, 1949; "Part II", by Windes, S.L., R.I. 4727, September 1950.

63. T. W. Norman, "Wear Resistant Steel Castings for the Mining Industry," Climax Molybdenum Co., New York City.

64. W. A. Stauffer, "Wear of Metals by Sand Erosion", Metal Progress, Vol. 69, (January 1956), p. 102–107.

65. "White Iron with Molybdenum Has improved Wear Resistance," Materials in Design Engineering, Vol. 46 (August 1957), p. 144–145.

66. C. M. Allen, "Alleviating Abrasive Wear in Ceramic Industry Handling Equipment," Wear, Vol 1, (December, 1957) p. 232–238.

67. J. Dearden and J. D. Swindale, "Effect of Alternate Corrosion and Abrasion on Some Ferrous Metals," J.I.S.I., Vol. 185 (February 1957), p. 227–234.

68. F. T. Barwell, "Wear of Metals," Wear, Vol., 1, (February, 1958), p. 317–332.

69. C. Lipson and L. V. Colwell, ed., "Engineering Approach to Surface Damage," U. of Michigan Summer Conference Course, 1958.

70. T. E. Norman, "Factors Influencing the Resistance of Steel Castings to High Stress Abrasion," A.F.S. Trans., Vol. 66, (1958), p. 187–196.

71. L. Roseanu and B. Preotescu, "A Qualitative Separation of Wear Factors," Engineers Digest, Vol. 19, (March 1958) p. 102–105.

72. R. Davies, "Friction and Wear," Elseview Publishing Co., Amsterdam, Holland, 1959.

73. H. R. Letner, "Stress Effects of Abrasive Tumbling", Trans. A.S.M., Vol. 51, (1959), p. 402–420.

74. P. M. L'vov, "Calculation of Resistance to Abrasive Wear," Russian Engineering J. (July 1959), p. 32–35. (Translation PERA).

75. T. E. Norman, A. Solomon and D. V. Doane, "Martensitic White Irons for Abrasion-Resistant Castings," Trans. A.F.S., Vol. 67, (1959), p. 242–256.

76. R. B. Whitelaw, "Ni-Hard v. Abrasion," Inst. of Br. Foundrymen, Australian Branch (Victoria), Convention Proc., Vol. 10 (1959), p. 57–75.

77. "Fretting Corrosion and Abrasive Wear," Report of the Director, National Engineering Laboratory, (1959), p. 12–13.

78. "Amsco Manganese Steel (Wear and Abrasion Resisting Steel)," Alloy Digest SA 105, (October, 1960).

79. "New Wear Resistant Steel is Easy to Heat Treat," Steel, Vol. 146, (January 18, 1960), p. 100–101.

80. D. R. Miller, "Some Recent Developments in Friction and Abrasion," Australian Inst. of Metals J., Vol. 6, (November 1961), p. 263–269.

81. Selwood, A., "The Abrasion of Materials by Carborundum Paper," Wear, Vol. 4, (July and August 1961), p. 311–318.

82. D. G. Sopwith, L. Grunberg and K. H. R. Wright, "Studies of Abrasive Wear Resistance," Engineering, Vol. 191, (April 14, 1961), p. 546–547.

83. "The Selection of Steel for Wear Resistance," A.S.M. Metals Handbook, 8th ed., 1961, p. 244–257.

84. H. T. Angus, "The Use of Cast Iron Under Conditions of Abrasive, Dry and Lubricated Wear," BCIRA Journal, Vol. 10, No. 1, (1962), p. 80–103.

85. R. T. Spurr and T. P. Newcomb, "The Friction and Wear of Various Materials Sliding Against Unlubricated Surfaces of Different Types and Degrees of Roughness," Proc. Conf. on Lub. and Wear, Inst. of Mech. Engrs., London, 1957, p. 269.

86. G. V. Toporov, "The Influence of Structure on the Abrasive Wear of Cast Iron", Friction and Wear in Machinery, Vol. 12, A.S.M.E., N.Y. (1960), p. 39.

87. M. M. Krushchov, and M. A. Babichev, "Resistance to Abrasive Wear of Structurally Inhomogeneous Materials," Friction and Wear in Machinery, Vol. 12, A.S.M.E., N.Y., (1960), p. 5.

88. L. E. Val'dma, "The Wear of Metals in the Presence of a Non-Renewable Layer of Abrasive," Friction and Wear in Machinery, Vol. 13, A.S.M.E., N.Y., 1961, p. 17.

89. P. J. Alison and H. Wilman, "The Different Behavior of Hexagonal and Cubic Metals in their Friction, Wear and Work Hardening During Abrasion," Brit. J. Apply. Phys., Vol. 15, No. 3, (March 1964), p. 281.

90. M. Akhter, "A Bibliography of Abrasive Wear (with Abstracts)," NEL Report No. 123, National Engineering Laboratory, Glasgow, Scotland, December 1963.

91. M. M. Kruschov and M. A. Babichev, "Resistance to Abrasive Wear and Physical Properties of Materials," A.S.M.E. Paper presented at ASME-ASLE International Lubrication Conference, Washington, D.C., (October 15, 1964), A.S.M.E. Paper No. 64-LUB-31.

92. C. Lipson and L. V. Colwell (ed.), Handbook of Mechanical Wear, University of Michigan Press, Ann Arbor, Mich., 1961.

93. W. W. Fraser, "Abrasion-Resistant Alloys," Canadian Mining and Metallurgical Bulletin, Vol. 57, No. 628 (August 1964), p. 867–869.

3. Fundamentals of Abrasive Wear Phenomena—The action of a hard particle on a surface under the influence of a force which is oblique to the surface is generally referred to as abrasive wear. The interaction between the particle (of high crushing strength), and the surface is very much like the interaction between a cutting tool and a work-piece in machining. In the case of a ductile material, a continuous particle is removed from the surface by each cutting abrasive particle. In the case of a brittle material, many particles are removed during a single encounter by an abrasive particle. The parameters, which are important in metal cutting, should also be important in abrasive wear. However, as in machine shop grinding, it is difficult to state precisely the geometry of the cutting faces of the abrasive particle due to their random shape. This is a statistics problem.

Abrasive wear differs from adhesive wear (2, 3, 4) which occurs between two surfaces. In adhesive wear, the contacting asperities on adjacent surfaces weld, and the resulting interaction can lead to the removal of material from the surfaces. However, in the case of abrasive wear, material is removed from the surfaces, as indicated above, by the cutting action of abrasive particles. The hardness of the abrasive particle must exceed that of the abraded surface in order for cutting to occur. In the case when the crushing strength of the abrasive is exceeded, the method of material removal may be somewhat different than by the simple cutting action.

3.1 Mechanisms of Abrasive Wear—The force component which is normal to the surface and is acting on the hard particle causes penetration of the surface by the particle. That force component which is parallel to the surface causes relative tangential motion to occur between the particle and the surface. This results in shearing, plowing, or chipping of the surface which leaves the surface grooved. For ductile surfaces and hard particles which have sharp edged faces shearing occurs. This shearing is in the form of a continuous metal-cutting-like chip which removes material from the surface. Particles which have smooth edged or rounded faces tend to merely plow a ductile surface. During plowing, the surface material is pushed transversely to the direction of the particle motion to form a groove. Most of the displaced material piles up along the groove edges rather than being removed from the surface. In the case of a brittle material, the groove is formed by crack propagation and subsequent chipping out of surface material.

The severity of the wear by this mechanism for a given material and abrasive will greatly depend on the magnitude of the acting forces. When the forces are low (low stress), the wear rate per abrasive particle will also be low. In this case, this mechanism is sometimes referred to as scratching when fixed particles or loose particles are involved. In the machine shop, this type of abrasion is referred to as polishing. It is referred to as erosion when flowing loose particles are attacking a single surface. During erosion, the overall wear rate can be high if the flow rate of the abrasive particles is high. When the magnitude of the acting forces is higher, the wear rate per abrasive particle will be higher, and the mechanism is referred to as gouging when either fixed particles or loose particles are involved. When loose particles are present between two sliding surfaces (entrapped loose particles), this type of abrasion is referred to as lapping in the machine shop. This lapping or three body loose particle wear is less efficient than two body fixed particle wear because the loose particles tend to roll without cutting about 90% of the time (5). If the stress applied to the abrasive is so high as to exceed its crushing strength, then this type of abrasion is referred to as grinding abrasion. Here the abrasive is being ground up and was initially of a small size. This high stress grinding abrasion should not be confused with machine shop grinding which is classified as gouging abrasion.

When crushing of the abrasive occurs as in grinding abrasion, the mechanism of material removal may be somewhat different from the simple cutting mechanism. The abrasive may have little opportunity to roll or cut before crushing occurs, and the major effect on the abraded surface would then be due to the concentrated compressive stress at the point of abrasive contact. For a surface of ductile material, the surface will be displaced plastically by the abrasive in the manner of an indentation hardness impression. With many closely spaced impressions, the displaced material may flow back and forth, to fail eventually by fatigue. There is also the possibility of some cutting action by the rupturing abrasive with the cutting force being supplied by the elastic energy stored in the compressed abrasive particle. For a surface of a hard material, little plastic displacement will occur. Wear in this situation may occur as a result of brittle cracking (chipping) of the surface material. There is also the possibility of subsurface cracking due to fatigue under repeated stressing, as occurs in the spalling of ball bearing races.

3.2 Analytical Approaches to Abrasive Wear—The same underlying ideas are involved in all types of abrasive wear, except perhaps when the abrasive particle is crushed. Penetration of the surface and subsequent grooving of the surface by the abrasive particle occurs. When the abrasive is crushed, grooving of the surface may not occur, however penetration of the surface does occur. The appearance of the wear fragments and wear surface will vary depending on the ductility of the surface material and on the configuration of the particle.

The means by which the force is applied to the abrasive particle can be divided into two categories:

1. The direct mechanical application of force by the surfaces in the case of entrapped loose particles or by the abrasive bond and the surface in the case of fixed abrasives.
2. The kinetic application of force resulting from the kinetic energy of a flowing abrasive particle as it encounters a surface.

The first category of force application is experienced in gouging abrasion, grinding abrasion and scratching abrasion. The second category is experienced in erosion abrasion, and pertains to the handling of the abrasives in pneumatic or liquid systems, sand blasting or dust erosion of compressor blades in gas turbines. The second category of force application is probably not as common as the first. However, it will be considered here, since a fair amount of analytical work has been carried out for this case. There is a distinctly different analytical expression for abrasive wear for each category of force application. These analytical expressions will now be discussed.

3.2.1 THEORY OF ABRASIVE WEAR WITH DIRECT MECHANICAL APPLICATION OF FORCE TO ABRASIVE PARTICLE—A number of authors have investigated this type of wear (5–12). There is general agreement among authors that simplified theory results in the following expression for volume wear rate per unit length of sliding (q):

$$q = \frac{dQ}{d\ell} \propto \frac{W}{p} \qquad \text{(Eq. 1)}$$

where:

Q = Volume swept out by abrasive
ℓ = Sliding distance
W = Load
p = Hardness of surface material

Note that if q_t is the time rate of wear, then $q_t = q\,v$ where v is the velocity of sliding. Figure 1 shows an idealized picture of this type of wear.

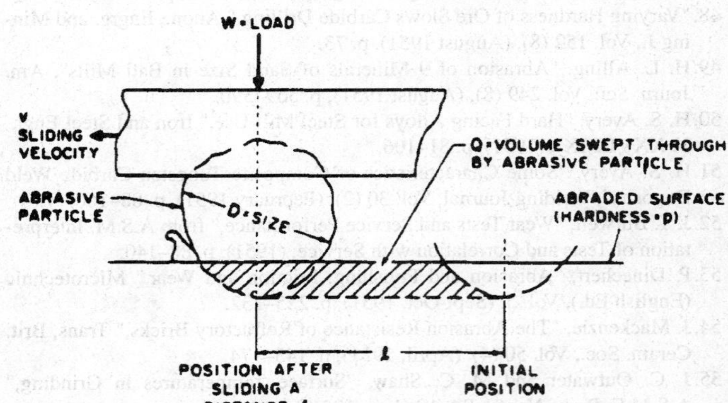

FIGURE 1—IDEALIZED PICTURE OF ABRASIVE WEAR WITH DIRECT MECHANICAL APPLICATION OF FORCE TO ABRASIVE PARTICLE

Equation 1 assumes that the abrasive particles are harder than the surface being abraded and that the abrasive particle is rigid, that is, it is not crushed. Equation 1 is valid for abrasive particle size, D, greater than 70 µm. For D less than this q also depends on D. Under this condition with fixed particles, clogging occurs and with loose particles, the wear fragments become of comparable size as the abrasive particles. The ratio of abrasive particles which cut to those which do not cut will also be of importance. The particle shape is another parameter which can be of significance, but which Equation 1 does not include. Equation 1 applies to annealed metals. The wear resistance (1/q) of heat treated steels is a function of their elastic limit, as well as of their hardness. However, in this case the wear resistance varies as low fractional powers of these parameters. Fatigue of the surface may also be of importance. For brittle materials, higher wear rates can occur due to the possibility of the formation of wear fragments having a total volume greater than the volume swept through by the abrasive particle (5, 8). However, brittle materials do tend to follow the relationship of Equation 1 even though higher wear rates are encountered (13). The presence of water vapor in the atmosphere or of a lubricating fluid on the abraded surface can increase the wear rate, apparently by flushing wear debris from the system and, hence, increasing the effectiveness of the abrading action. Rabinowicz (14) discusses this effect, as well as some of the other limitations of Equation 1 mentioned above, in his informative book on friction and wear.

Equation 1 is not necessarily valid for grinding abrasion, that is, when small abrasive particles are being crushed. A theoretical expression for the wear rate of the abraded surface for this case is not presently available. Grinding abrasion is common in ball and rod milling.

In ball milling the abrasive being ground is caught between adjacent balls or between ball and liner, and the ball weight crushes the hard particles (1). While impact may occur in ball mills, it is not the important crushing force (1). Grinding can be produced without impact. In fact, the most efficient ball mills are those which only roll and tumble the balls. Since the abrasive may have little opportunity to cut before it is crushed, the abraded surfaces are seen to be subjected merely to repetitive concentrated compressive stress over a period of time. The abraded surface therefore experiences attack similar to that which it would be subjected during sand blasting with the blast directed perpendicular to the surface. This is substantiated, as will be seen later in this report, by the fact that there seems to be a correlation between sand blasting wear results and ball mill wear results.

Bitter (19, 20), whose work will be discussed in more detail later on in this report, indicates that no cutting wear should occur during sand blasting at a 90 deg impingement angle. He also states that frequent repetition of elastic impact should not cause wear, apart from impossible fatigue damage. If, however, during collision the elastic limit is exceeded, plastic deformation sets in at the place of maximum stress; the repeated collisions of a large number of particles will form a plastically deformed surface layer. The resulting deformation hardening increases the elastic limit, and upon further plastic deformation, this limit will eventually become equal to the maximum strength of the material. It has then become relatively hard and brittle and can no longer be plastically deformed. If, subsequently, upon increasing the load, the elastic limit of the material is exceeded, the surface is destroyed and fragments of it are removed. Therefore, an initially ductile material will wear by means of the mechanism associated with the abrasive wear of brittle materials. Bitter refers to this type of wear as "deformation wear." Equation 3, further on in this report, gives the expression for volume worn by this mechanism in brittle materials. Equation 3 and Bitter's work are for the case of impact between the abrasive and the surface, however ball milling involves no impact. Therefore Equation 3 does not apply to grinding abrasion, but it seems feasible that the fundamental abrasion mechanism for this case could very well be "deformation wear" mechanism. This would be a good starting point in developing a theory for grinding abrasion. Development of such a theory is beyond the scope of this report, since only the current state of knowledge of abrasive wear is being presented.

3.2.2 THEORY OF ABRASIVE WEAR WITH KINETIC APPLICATION OF FORCE TO ABRASIVE PARTICLE (EROSION)—Under this abrasive wear condition, the kinetic energy of the particle is dissipated on a ductile surface in plastic work which causes indentation or shearing of the surface. In the case of indentation, layer-like exfoliations are extruded from the surface (15). In the case of shearing, material is gouged out of the surfaces. On brittle materials, the kinetic energy of the particle is dissipated in crack propagation which causes chipping of the surface.

The volume Q removed, from a ductile surface due to a mass M of angular abrasive particles having a velocity V, is given by Equation 2 (16–18).

$$Q \propto \frac{MV^2}{p} f(\alpha) \qquad \text{(Eq. 2)}$$

where:

V = Particle approach velocity

α = Particle impingement angle measured relative to the abraded surface

$f(\alpha) = (\sin 2\alpha - 3\sin^2\alpha)$ .... for $\alpha \le 18.5$ deg

$f(\alpha) = \cos^2\alpha$ .... for $\alpha \ge 18.5$ deg

Note that if M is replaced by the time rate of M then Q becomes q_t, that is the time rate of wear. Figure 2 shows an idealized picture of this type of wear. A more recent treatment for this type of wear is available which takes into account the elastic properties of the abrasive particles and the abraded surface (19).

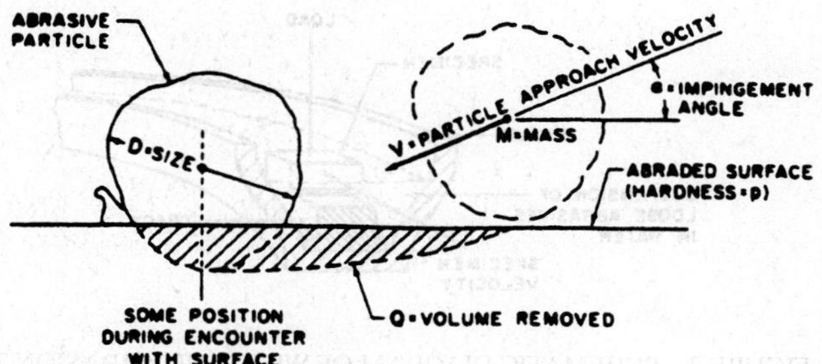

FIGURE 2—IDEALIZED PICTURE OF ABRASIVE WEAR WITH KINETIC APPLICATION OF FORCE TO ABRASIVE PARTICLE (EROSION)

The volume removed from a brittle surface under similar impact conditions, but not necessarily restricted to angular particles, is given by Equation 3 (20).

$$Q \propto \frac{M(V\sin\alpha - K)^2}{e} \qquad \text{(Eq. 3)}$$

where:

$$K \propto p_e^{5/2}\left(\frac{1}{D}\right)^{1/2}\left[\frac{1-\mu_1}{E_1} + \frac{1-\mu_2}{E_2}\right] \qquad \text{(Eq. 4)}$$

$$e \propto \frac{p_e^2}{E_2}$$

where:

p_e = Elastic limit

μ = Poisson's ratio

E = Modulus of elasticity

Subscripts 1 and 2 refer to the particle and surface, respectively

K = Velocity of impact at which the elastic limit is just reached

e = Energy needed to remove one unit volume of material from the surface

Equation 3 assumes that the particle penetrates into the surface to a depth only a fraction of its own diameter. For sharp edged particles, the resulting K value will be smaller. At high velocities large fragments may be broken from the surface, resulting in a lower value of e.

Equation 2 predicts reasonably well the trends for silicon carbide abrasives on SAE 1020 steel and for silica dust on SAE 1050 steel. However, it underestimates Q at high α angles (16, 18). Recently, this error has been found to be due to the lack of accounting for the elastic properties of the abrasive particles and the abraded surface (19). The erosion of glass by steel shot is in good agreement with Equation 3 (20). These expressions do not take into account fatiguing of the surface which may be of importance.

3.3 Conclusions—The fundamentals of abrasive wear are by no means thoroughly understood at present. Certain parameters have been found to be of significance. Others are still to be determined. Phenomena, such as the variation of wear resistance of steel with heat treatment, are still not explained. A fundamental expression for wear during grinding abrasion is still to be developed.

4. Testing for Abrasive Wear Resistance—It has been said often, and it bears repeating that "there is no universal wear test" and this applies as well to wear by abrasion from extraneous materials. Laboratory wear tests can only be considered as preliminary screening devices and can be misleading unless reasonable attempts are made to simulate service conditions with respect to:

1. Hardness and particle size of controlling abrasive (generally, the harder material in a mixture on Moh's scale of mineral hardnesses).
2. Unit pressures between abrasive particles and wearing surface.
3. Speed and direction of movement of abrasive in relation to the wearing surface.

Accordingly, wear tests must be rather specific but, considering the difficulty in obtaining reliable field test experience, can be very useful in defining characteristics desired in a material for service and in assigning orders of merit prior to field testing.

A wear test should have proven reliability as measured by reproducibility of results expressed in quantitative terms. Standardization of a wear test is invariably a time consuming and expensive procedure, and, to insure that the test does not deviate from the "norm," it is advisable to include a standard material as a control. The most useful wear tests have been those where the statistical variation in weight loss of the control material is well within the limits that indicate that the test process is in control. Unfortunately, when a significant change is made in a test procedure, such as hardness or particle size of the abrasive or unit pressure, the reproducibility of the test cannot be assumed and must be reestablished.

Abrasive wear at a significant rate requires an abrasive in the true sense (a material that is harder than the machinery part) and stress. Also, particle size and sharpness are extremely important with wear increasing generally with particle size. Abrasive wear is a tolling phenomenon with the size of the furrows across the wearing face controlled by the size, shape and hardness of the abrasive particle and the unit pressure. The relative wear rate of plow shares in loam versus sandy soils is a primary example. Actually, common structural steel is not worn at a significant rate by materials much under 4 on Moh's scale of hardness (400 Brinell approximately), and this includes minerals such as marble, dolomite, calcite, gypsum, talc and many other complex minerals and synthetic materials. Quartz (sand) is the most common damaging mineral because of its hardness, its angularity, providing sharp points, its strength and its frequent occurrence. Table 2 gives typical hardnesses of common minerals and other materials.

For purposes of this discussion abrasive wear can be classified in three categories.

1. Gouging abrasion is exemplified by the teeth of a power shovel worn in handling boulders of hard aggregate. The most extreme example is the loading of taconite from a blasted quarry face. Performance is related to the necessity for compromise between weight loss and structural failure by fracture. The same mechanism is controlling in the wear of crusher parts. Therefore, this type of service requires materials of high fracture toughness such as austenitic manganese and quenched and tempered medium carbon alloy steels.
2. High stress grinding abrasion, generally by relatively fine particles at high unit pressures, is represented most commonly in industrial practice by the grinding of natural minerals or manufactured products in ball and rod mills. In this case, resistance to impact forces is less important and relatively hard and brittle materials of low but measurable fracture toughness, such as Ni-Cr white iron and high carbon steels, can be used in many installations.

TABLE 1—TYPICAL HARDNESS OF MINERALS, STEEL PHASES AND OTHER MATERIALS[1]

Material	Mohs Scale	Knoop Microhardness (typical)
Talc	1	20
Gypsum	2	40
Calcite	3	130
Fluorite	4	175
Apatite	5	435
Orthoclase	6	620
Quartz	7	840
Topaz	8	1330
Corundum	9	2020
Diamond	10	7575
Silicon carbide		2585
Glass		455
Plastics		25
Magnetite		575
Bituminous coal		35
Garnet		1360
Flint		820
Emery		1400
Feldspare		550
Ferrite		235
Martensite- 0.30% carbon		555
- 0.40% carbon		710
- 0.60% carbon		800
Austenitic manganese steel		305
- fully work hardened		645
Iron carbide		1025
Chromium carbide		1735
Molybdenum carbide		1800
Tungsten carbide		2080
Vanadium carbide		2660
Titanium carbide		2955
Hard chromium electroplate		975

1. References
E. J. Dunwell and W. J. McDonald, "Metals Engineering Quarterly", May, 1965.
R. Unger, "Metals Progress", July, 1965.
L. P. Tarasov, "Metals Process", December, 1948.
L. D. Latva, "Metals Progress", October and November 1962.
C. B. Brodie, "ASM Trans.", Vol. 33 (1944).
"Norton Electrochemicals...Gifts of the Firebird", Norton Co.
N. W. Thibault and H. L. Nyquist, "ASM Trans.", Vol. 38, (1947).

3. Low stress scratching abrasion or erosion categorizes the handling of fine abrasive materials in pneumatic systems or the wear of a plow share in sandy or loam soil devoid of rocks. In this type of service, matrix characteristics are generally less important and the hardness and volume of the hard phase (carbides) is likely to be controlling. Therefore, materials of negligible fracture toughness such as martensitic white irons and carbide composites can be used.

4.1 Laboratory Test Methods

4.1.1 GOUGING ABRASION—John Howe Hall was the first to study this type of wear by locating a jaw crusher of modest size (perhaps a ton an hour feed) at the mine face. In these early days, the test crusher was not too different in size from the production size and much useful data on heat treatment and composition effects in austenitic manganese steel were developed.

Trials with small jaw crushers have demonstrated flow of surface in tough materials and fracture of carbides in white irons as is experienced with large crushers. At test device consisting of a 6-8 in diameter roll crusher, with the feed restricted to two protruding rings, has been suggested. One ring would involve the unknown and the second, a standard or control material. Feed could involve the mineral or abrasive of greatest interest at the maximum size feasible for the relatively small crusher. Such small devices could serve only as a rough screening device with respect to probable behavior in large production crushers.

Avery (21) has suggested that a fixed abrasive grinding wheel test, for which reproducibility and general ranking of materials has been established, is useful to simulate gouging wear, but the important requirement of toughness for service parts has prevented the development of correlative performance data over a wide range of materials. The fixed abrasive concept differs substantially from service in that surface work hardening is minimized, and the matrix cannot be differentially worn as would be the case with loose abrasive acting on a heterogeneous structure such as white cast iron. Other investigators feel that the bond of the fixed abrasive is a variable which is best avoided.

Most alloy development work for this type of wear service during the past ten years has involved direct field tests of dipper teeth and crusher parts in production equipment. Notably, a great amount of testing has been performed by those companies mining taconite in Michigan and Minnesota. There appears to be no laboratory procedure that can be recommended at the present time for evaluating gouging wear and no experiment work is known to be in progress.

4.1.2 HIGH STRESS GRINDING ABRASION—This type of service, typified by ball and rod mill operations, involves fine particles and high unit pressure, since the abrasive particles are being crushed. The operations are generally conducted in the presence of water, although some dry grinding (some cement operations) is performed. Since 1935 a wet sand abrasion test machine to simulate this type of service has been in operation in one particular laboratory and has been described on several occasions (22). The correlation with service performance in ball mills has been well established (23). Many hundreds of tests have been run on this equipment in the intervening years and test reproducibility has been proven.

For the last 10–12 years, one particular company has used production ball mills as a test medium by running tests on oversized (4 and 5 in) balls with the production ball load (24). After a suitable period, the balls are removed, weighed, measured and wear rates calculated. In these tests, relative wear rates of potential liner materials are assessed and experimental liner materials procured, if judged sufficiently promising with respect to wear rate, toughness and economics.

The "wet sand abrasion test" is the only well validated wear test simulating grinding abrasion that has been described in the literature in recent years and no alternate methods are known to be under development. (See Figure 3.) In this test, washed and carefully sized (AFS No. 50), sand is used and is replaced at regular intervals as it is reduced in size. A standard material is always run on one arm of the machine with the experimental material on the other. Relative weight losses determine the "abrasion factor."

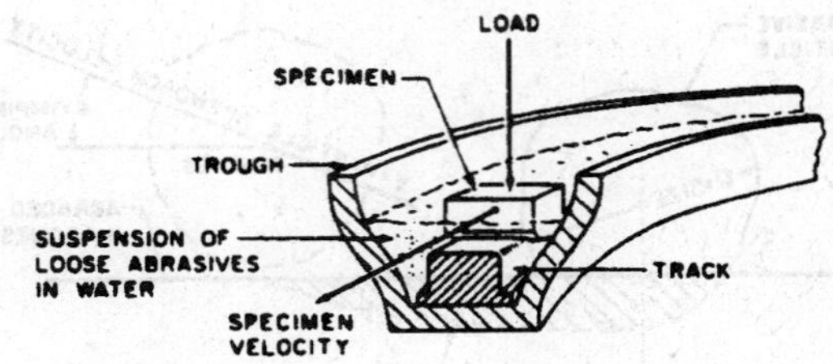

FIGURE 3—SCHEMATIC DIAGRAM OF WET SAND ABRASION TEST

The wear of grinding balls in wet and dry grinding of cement and in wet grinding of taconite has been studied by Battelle Memorial Institute. Because the relative wear of balls may vary from one ball-milling operation to another, depending upon the size of the mill, sizes of balls employed, nature of the material being milled, and possibly other factors, evaluation of balls in full scale operations is recommended. This has been done at Battelle (25) by irradiating experimental balls in a research reactor. The weighed and irradiated balls were placed in production mills for suitable periods of time, then separated from the unirradiated balls by means of a Geiger counter. The balls were reweighed to determine the amount of wear.

4.1.3 LOW STRESS SCRATCHING ABRASION—For this type of service simulating the pneumatic flow of solids or the flow of abrasives suspended in liquids in piping systems and approaching most closely the wear of plow shares, Haworth has probably developed the most successful device (26). Avery has improved on this device which has come to be known as the "Dry Sand Erosion Test" and has published results describing the test and comparing materials in this and the grinding abrasion test in the ASM book, "Surface Protection Against Wear and Corrosion" (27). One particular company has also used this general device successfully in evaluating carbon and low alloy steels (28). Reasonably good correlation was shown with field tests on plow shares and mold boards.

In the test device a rubber wheel in utilized to cushion the abrasive and reduce the interface pressure. Abrasive is fed continuously to the interface between the slowly revolving wheel and the specimen which is dead weight loaded to give a constant unit pressure. The test as modified by Avery is limited to abrasive size and shape that will flow freely from a calibrated orifice. (See Figure 4.) Finer abrasives could be utilized in a slurry, but special precautions would be necessary to insure that the volume of abrasive passing over the interface per unit time is controlled closely.

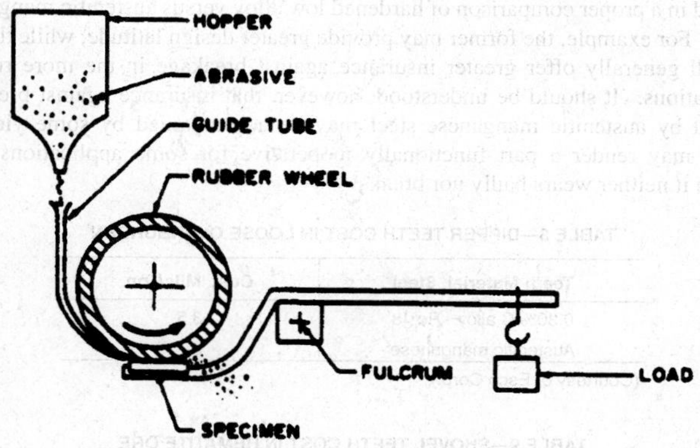

FIGURE 4—SCHEMATIC DIAGRAM OF DRY SAND EROSION TEST

Escher-Wyss, the Swiss manufacturer of hydraulic turbine equipment, has standardized a test to simulate the action of abrasive particles in the feed water powering turbines. The specimens are cylindrical and arranged around the periphery of a wheel which is rotated at relatively high speed in a slurry of the abrasive in water.

Higher unit pressures in pneumatic devices can be achieved, if the abrasive impacts the wearing surface at high velocities as in a sand blast device. By arranging a series of specimens on a slowly rotating wheel in front of a blast nozzle, useful data can be achieved, but rankings of materials do not agree with the "Dry Sand Erosion Test" described above. Rather because of the high unit pressures, the rankings resemble more closely those shown by the "Wet Sand Abrasion Test" which breaks down the abrasive because of high interface pressure.

4.2 Conclusions—Only a few validated wear test devices are in use today to provide in the laboratory a preliminary engineering judgment as to the new or modified materials deserving consideration for field test in various wear applications. Generally, the laboratory test devices do not impose the impact, tensile and bending stresses of many service applications and knowledge of mechanical properties is necessary therefore to minimize failures by fracture. Furthermore, in attempting to accelerate laboratory tests, the generation of elevated temperatures is a potential hazard. This should be avoided, unless it occurs in the ultimate applications, as the relative abrasion resistance of steels and irons may significantly shift with increasing temperature.

5. Solutions to Abrasive Wear Problems—Industrial wear problems could be solved quite simply by the use of laboratory wear data if it were not for two problem areas which cannot be ignored. These problem areas are discussed below:

1. High hardness materials, which are most resistant to abrasive wear, are prone to brittle fracture when used in highly stressed parts. Thus, cutting edges and track shoes are hardened to a value which is a compromise between best wear life and greatest breakage resistance.
2. Variations in rock, ore and soil conditions from one geographic area to another often upsets carefully conducted field wear study results. The best material for a rocky location will frequently be the poorest material when used in sand or loose abrasive soil.

The first problem area mentioned above will be of concern to every manufacturer some of the time. In manufacturing heavy duty equipment, it is impossible to avoid having some wear parts which are highly stressed. The highly competitive nature of the earthmoving industry forces manufacturers to use high strength materials. Bending loads imposed upon wear parts render them particularly sensitive to brittle fracture.

The second problem area mentioned above will be of concern only to manufacturers who operate on a worldwide or nation-wide basis. Manufacturers developing equipment for one particular ore body or some regional application are usually not greatly troubled with wide variations in abrasiveness of the ore or earth handled. This is especially true if the equipment is stationary or of such a size as to prohibit easy movement from one site to another. Small, highly mobile earthmoving equipment will be used by contractors on locations of widely differing geological nature. The manufacturers of such equipment are faced with the need to compromise their material and hardness selection with respect both to failure by fracture and to suitability for the widest variation in abrasive conditions. Thus, the existence of this second problem area tends to favor small manufacturers who operate only in well defined regional areas. Such small manufacturers, however, find themselves prisoners of the area for which they have developed a special material to combat local wear conditions. Small manufacturers, desiring to serve an increasing market by growth, are ultimately forced to use materials and hardnesses which are suitable for a wide spectrum of wear conditions.

5.1 Influence of Design of Parts Upon Wear Life—Design of wear resistant parts frequently centers around the problem of finding enough space for a thick wear surface. The equipment must be designed to work efficiently even after a considerable loss of metal from the abraded surface. The tolerable extent of abrasive wear may fall into distinct categories. This limit of wear in many machinery components may be on the order of 0.005 in whereas sacrificial wear of up to 5 in may be tolerable in a large gyratory crusher mantle. This distinction has obvious implications of design, material selection, economics and manufacturing feasibility. Design for maximum wear life will also frequently need to be compromised by the need of a part for good breakage resistance as well.

Results of field tests of track shoe grouser wear at Phoenix, Arizona are given in Table 2 and illustrate the need for compromise between maximum wear resistance and maximum strength. With a given steel at three different hardness levels, the highest hardness, (Rc 58) resulted in the lowest wear rate in caliche. This caliche is cemented material in which the aggregate is largely granite. The superior wear life is offset by the increasing percentage of failures by breaking which frequently plaques parts made at extremely high hardness.

TABLE 2—TRACK SHOE GROUSER WEAR AND BREAKAGE IN CALICHE
(ShoE Material—SAE 1049 Steel)

Hardness R_c	790 h Wear Loss, in	Broken, %
23	1-1/4	3.0
54	7/8	5.0
58	5/8	25.0

(Courtesy of Caterpillar Tractor Co.)

5.2 Influence of Different Soil Conditions Upon Wear—The higher hardness which reduced wear to about half that obtained on a Rc 23 shoe, as indicated in Table 2, cannot always be depended upon to produce this effect as illustrated in Table 3 by four sets of identical shoes tested in four different locations. Hardening track shoes to Rc 45 about tripled the life of shoes at Rc 23 in the state of Washington, but produced no significant benefit when tested at Navajo, Arizona.

TABLE 3—TRACK SHOE LIFE AT VARIOUS LOCATIONS
(ShoE Material—SAE 1040 Steel)

Hardness R_c	Life, h	Improvement, %	Location
23	550		Iron Range,
45	1560	184	Minnesota
23	2050		Oroville,
45	6130	199	Washington
23	1240		Climax,
45	1670	34.7	Colorado
23	1450		Navajo,
45	1485	2.4	Arizona

(Courtesy of Caterpillar Tractor Co.)

Another illustration of the influence of soil conditions is shown in Table 4 and is the application of a 0.30% carbon martensitic alloy steel for trunion and chain pins on a dragline bucket. The sharper rock fragments and fines from blasting wore out pins in about 40% of the time required to wear out the same steel, when more rounded "weathered rock and debris" were handled.

TABLE 4—DRAGLINE BUCKET TRUNION AND CHAIN PIN LIFE IN DIFFERENT ROCK (Pin Material—0.30% C Alloy Steel)

Hardness, R_c	Earthmoved	Wear Life, wks	Improvement
30	Blasted rock	6	
30	Weathered rock and debris	15	150

(Courtesy of Bucyrus-Erie Co.)

Even more dramatic changes in wear life are reported when both soil and moisture content of the earth are changed. When handling dry placermaterial with a 3 cu yd drag bucket, austenitic manganese steel bucket lip and a cast alloy steel lip each handled about 3 million cu yd of material before replacement. On river operation, however, the results were as shown in Table 5. These two materials which showed identical life in dry operation showed a five times different life when wet material of finer consistency was handled. A possible explanation would be that the conditions in river dredging were not conducive to work hardening of the austenitic manganese steel, probably the river material consisted mostly of silt, sand, and the like, which would not provide gouging. Only by "on the site" testing in a wide variety of soil conditions, can the most successful compromise material and hardness be achieved.

TABLE 5—DRAG BUCKET LIP LIFE IN RIVER DREDGING SERVICE

Lip Material	Earthmoved	Wear Life, cu yd	Improvement, %
Austenitic manganese steel	River dredging	330,000	
0.30% C alloy steel - R_c 30	River dredging	1,650,000	400

(Courtesy of Bucyrus-Erie Co.)

Data in Table 6 for shovel points used in different ores and slag show a similar trend for 0.30% C-Mn-Cr-Mo steel hardened to Rc 50 and austenitic manganese steel. When the material handled by the shovel is changed from blasted ore to iron ore, the advantage of the quenched and tempered material switches from 45% improvement to 900% improvement. However, a different iron ore showed only 87% improvement for the quenched and tempered steel.

TABLE 6—SHOVEL POINT LIFE IN DIFFERENT ORES AND SLAG

Point Material, Steel	Type Ore	Life	Improvement, %
Austenitic manganese	Iron ore	160 truck loads	
0.30% C-Mn-Cr-Mo (1)	Iron ore	1650 truck loads	900
Austenitic manganese	Iron ore	54,200 tons	
0.30% C-Mn-Cr-Mo(1)	Iron ore	101,700 tons	87
Austenitic manganese	Copper ore	46,000 tons	
0.30% C-Mn-Cr-Mo(1)	Copper ore	131,000 tons	185
Austenitic manganese	Blasted ore	1250 tons	
0.30% C-Mn-Cr-Mo(1)	Blasted ore	1825 tons	45
Austenitic manganese	Slag	9500 tons	
0.30% C-Mn-Cr-Mo(1)	Slag	24,000 tons	152

(Courtesy of American Steel Foundries)

1. Nominal composition: 0.30 C, 1.65 Mn, 0.85 Cr, 0.50 Mo plus boron and rare earths.

In contrast with large differences in wear life between martensitic steel and austenitic manganese steel shown above, rotary bars used to crush mildly sintered silicon carbide show, in Table 7, little difference in wear under this highly abrasive condition. Under such severe abrasive conditions even higher hardness does not help with the steel rotary bars.

TABLE 7—ROTARY BAR WEAR WHILE CRUSHING MILDLY SINTERED SILICON CARBIDE

Bar Material, Steel	Dimensional Wear, %
0.30% C alloy - Rc 48	36
SAE 4140, cold drawn - Rc 35	33
Austenitic manganese	38

(Courtesy of Esco Corp.)

The costs of using martensitic alloy steel and austenitic manganese steel for dipper teeth working in loose overburden are illustrated in Table 8. Although the cost advantage of the martensitic steel was moderate on the basis of abrasive wear, it was noted that the lower yield strength of the austenitic manganese steel led to greater wear on other components and lower working efficiency for the machine. The cost advantage of martensitic steel was lost when hematite ore was loaded with shovel teeth of the same two steels as shown in Table 9. Hematite ore resulted in an advantage for austenitic manganese steel over martensitic steel; presumably this reflects better work hardening conditions that prevailed for the cases cited in Tables 6 and 8. While this report is concerned exclusively with abrasion resistance, it is to be clearly recognized that this is not the only factor to be considered in a proper comparison of hardened low alloy versus austenitic manganese steels. For example, the former may provide greater design latitude, while the latter will generally offer greater insurance against breakage in the more rugged applications. It should be understood, however, that insurance against breaking offered by austenitic manganese steel may be accompanied by some yielding which may render a part functionally inoperative for some applications even though it neither wears badly nor breaks.

TABLE 8—DIPPER TEETH COST IN LOOSE OVERBURDEN

Teeth Material, Steel	Cost, Mils/Ton
0.30% C alloy - Rc 48	3.5
Austenitic manganese	3.7

(Courtesy of Esco Corp.)

TABLE 9—SHOVEL TEETH COST IN HEMATITE ORE

Teeth Material, Steel	Earthmoved	Cost, Mils/Ton
0.30% C alloy - Rc 48	Hematite ore	4.4
Austenitic manganese	Hematite ore	2.7

(Courtesy of Esco Corp.)

A different type of service, crusher wear plates, showed the wear rates given in Table 10. Another type of service, liners for chutes, gave the results shown in Table 11. It is noteworthy that in the two different chute liner tests, the quenched and tempered cast low alloy steel showed as little as 0.3% advantage to as much as 130% advantage in life over austenitic manganese steel.

TABLE 10—CRUSHER WEAR PLATE LIFE FOR REFRACTORY MATERIAL

Plate Material	Life, Shifts	Improvement, %
Gray Iron	3	
Ni-Cr white iron	7	133
0.30% C-Mn-Cr-Mo steel	9	200

(Courtesy of American Steel Foundries)

TABLE 11—CHUTE LINER LIFE FOR TACONITE ORE

Liner Material, Steel	Life, Tons	Improvement, %
(Test 1)		
Austenitic manganese	177,000	
0.30% C-Mn-Cr-Mo	400,000	130
(Test 2)		
Austenitic manganese	129,800	
0.30% C-Mn-Cr-Mo	130,200	0.3

(Courtesy of American Steel Foundries)

The relative wear of balls used to grind molybdenite ore is tabulated in Table 12 for three different materials (29). Ball mill liners of the same materials showed a similar ratio of wear.

TABLE 12—BALL AND LINER WEAR DURING BALL MILLING OF MOLYBDENITE ORE

Ball and Linear Material, Steel	Hardness R_c (worn surface)	Relative Wear 5 in Balls	Relative Wear Mill Liners
1% C martensitic alloy	56	100	100
1% C pearlitic alloy	40	127	122–127
Austenitic manganese	50	140	140–145

(Courtesy of Climax Molybdenum Co.)

Taconite ore wear results for austenitic manganese and hardened low alloy steels as dipper points are given in Table 13.

TABLE 13—DIPPER POINT LIFE FOR TACONITE ORE

Point Material, Steel	Life	Improvement, %
Austenitic manganese	250 loads	
0.30% C-Mn-Cr-Mo	820 loads	240

(Courtesy of American Steel Foundries)

Test data on water quenched and tempered SAE 1049 steel track shoes versus austenitic manganese steel track shoes at the Minnesota iron range are shown in Table 14. This test location showed 180–280% improvement for austenitic manganese steel over SAE 1049 steel at Rc 49. A change in design to two grousers per shoe brought the wear life of the quenched and tempered steel shoe up to the life of austenitic manganese steel. However, the double grouser shoe was considered inadequately self cleaning in certain types of mud and potentially more dangerous than the single grouser shoe.

TABLE 14—TRACK SHOE LIFE AT MINNESOTA IRON RANGE

Shoe Material, Steel	Hardness R_c	Left Side Wear Life, h	Right Side Wear Life, h	Improvement, %
SAE 1049	49	415	650	
Austenitic manganese	30	1592	1804	180 to 280
SAE 1049 (double grouser)	49	1647		

(Courtesy of Caterpillar Tractor Co.)

The foregoing data show wide variations in service life, depending upon specific service conditions, and tend to confuse the individual whose job it is to select a superior wear resistant material for a wide variety of earthmoving conditions.

5.3 Hardened Versus Unhardened Steels—The continued use of unhardened steel of 0.60–0.90% carbon for cutting edges indicates that there are types of service where an essentially pearlitic structure results in adequate wear life. However, wear tests in two Texas locations on hardened and unhardened 0.20% carbon steel for root plow service show, in Table 15, the desirability of hardening for this type of service.

TABLE 15—ROOT PLOW WEAR AT TEXAS LOCATIONS
(Plow Material—SAE 1020 Steel)

Hardness, R_c	Wear, oz/h	Improvement, %
10	0.084	
35	0.036	133
10	0.060	
35	0.033	81

(Courtesy of Caterpillar Tractor Co.)

Table 16 shows the results of side by side ripper tip tests near Phoenix, Arizona. There were significant reductions in wear rates for moderate hardness increases. Wear alone may not be the basis for removing a tip from service. Blunted tips which fail to penetrate will be removed from service long before destruction by wear reduces their usefulness. The quite uniform percentage wear reduction shown in Table 16 indicates a high degree of uniformity of the ripped material on this job.

TABLE 16—RIPPER TIP WEAR AT ARIZONA LOCATION

Tip Material, Steel	Hardness, R_c	Weight Loss in 5 h, lb	Improvement, %
SAE 8645	39	6 3/4	
0.30% C-Mn-Cr-Mo	52	5 1/4	28
SAE 8645	37	8 1/2	
0.30% C-Mn-Cr-Mo	51	6 1/2	31
SAE 8645	39	10 3/4	
0.30% C-Mn-Cr-Mo	50	8	35

(Courtesy of Caterpillar Co.)

Improved life obtained on parts by flame hardening, induction surface hardening, or hard surfacing are effective, but difficult to evaluate because of the dual wear rate obtained before and after the harder layer is removed. Scraper blades are compared in the through hardened versus flame hardened condition as shown in Table 17. Hard facing with weld deposit by users of equipment is frequently used as a means of restoring local areas which concentrated wear has destroyed preferentially.

TABLE 17—SCRAPER BLADE LIFE

Blade Material, Steel	Life, h
0.30% C - Rc 48	179
0.60% C, flame hardened	123

(Courtesy of Esco Corp.)

5.4 Summary—Keeping both the danger of breakage and the wide variety of soil conditions in mind, a manufacturer building mobile equipment for worldwide application will probably find that hardened steel represents the best compromise for ground engaging tools. Each manufacturer has a favored steel, hardness depth and case and core hardness ranges which his experience indicates is best for most applications.

Builders of crushers, rod mills and large stationary equipment can become much more specialized in selecting a material which will give best wear life under some specific local condition. For these applications austenitic manganese steel, various hard facing alloys, white iron, and sometimes even unhardened steel or gray iron may prove to have the longest life, or prove the most economical.

Far too little study has been given the abrading materials which are responsible for wear. The compactness of an aggregate, sharpness of fragmented particles, scratch hardness (Mohs) of the minerals making up a mixture, moisture content and many factors contribute to an unexpectedly wide scatter of results under what are thought to be controlled field tests. Because of the large variety of soils, ores and abrasive material which must be cheaply moved in large tonnages, a continuing search for improved wide spectrum tools is desirable. High hardness tools possessing good toughness have been the major goal of earthmovers in the past. For the future, an additional need can be seen on the horizon. Modern machines possess the power to operate at loads and speeds which generate considerable local surface heat. Loss of the hardness by tempering due to heat generated in service is on one manifestation of the heat problem. White martensitic layers are now developed in the surfaces with increasing frequency. These untempered martensite areas are more brittle than the tempered martensitic structures produced by heat treatment. As a result, fine craze cracks may develop in a ground engaging tool surface and lead to early fracture. The superior tools of the future will be required to work at elevated temperatures without loss of hardness or susceptibility to brittle failure. Despite the severe demands which will be made upon earthmoving tools in the future, the enormous usage of ground engaging tools dictates that only low cost materials are likely to be attractive for the broad spectrum jobs in the future.

The information given here presents some solutions to specific abrasive wear problems which have been encountered. General design information on this subject has not presently been developed. There is a need for more controlled testing in which the influence of the various parameters are studied. In this way, correlations can be established between the pertinent parameters and the abrasive wear resistance of materials. Furthermore, the materials can then be ranked with regard to their wear resistance as well as their mechanical properties. This information would be most helpful to the designer.

NONFERROUS METALS

10 Nonferrous Metals

ALUMINUM ALLOYS - FUNDAMENTALS —SAE J451 JAN1989

SAE Information Report

Report of the SAE Nonferrous Metals Division approved January 1934 and last revised by the SAE Nonferrous Metals Committee June 1971. Editorial change March 1976. Reaffirmed by the SAE Wrought Aluminum Committee January 1989.

Foreword—This Document has not changed other than to put it into the new SAE Technical Standards Board Format.

1. Scope

1.1 Purpose—This information report is intended to give general data on the properties of aluminum and information on working, joining, forming, machining, finishing, and heat treating of aluminum.

2. References

2.1 Applicable Publication—The following publication forms a part of the specification to the extent specified herein. Unless otherwise indicated the latest revision of SAE publications shall apply.

2.1.1 SAE PUBLICATION—Available from SAE, 400 Commonwealth Drive, Warrendale, PA 15096-0001.

SAE J454 AUG87—General Data on Wrought Aluminum Alloys

3. Properties—Commercially pure aluminum is a face-centered cubic metal with a specific gravity of about 2.71 (0.098 lb/in^3), a thermal conductivity of about 0.52 cgs units (at 25°C), and a melting point of approximately 1215 °F. Its coefficient of thermal expansion (approximately 0.000013 per °F) is about twice that of steel or cast iron and about one-third greater than that of copper or brass. The electrical conductivity of pure aluminum is about 62% of the International Annealed Copper Standard. In the form of cast test bars, the commercially pure metal has a typical tensile strength of 14 000 psi and a typical elongation of 30% in 2 in, while sheet in the annealed temper has a typical tensile strength of about 13 000 psi and a typical elongation of about 45% in 2 in. The modulus of elasticity, for all practical purposes, is 10 000 000 psi. The commercially pure metal and many of its alloys are highly resistant to atmospheric corrosion and to attack by many chemicals, with the notable exception of strong alkalis. Because it is so high in the electrochemical series, however, it is subject to galvanic attack if coupled with metals such as the copper alloys in the presence of an electrolyte.

4. Alloying Elements—Additions of alloying elements usually increase the specific gravity (silicon and magnesium lower it), decrease the electrical and thermal conductivity and the melting point, increase the strength, and have a rather slight effect on the coefficient of thermal expansion and the modulus of elasticity. Some alloying elements, alone or in combination, produce alloys that respond to heat treatment. The addition of alloying elements can increase or decrease corrosion resistance, depending on the alloying element, heat treatment, and service environment. Aluminum alloys which are adversely affected by such additions are often protected by metallurgical cladding with a sacrificial alloy. The alloying elements commonly used in this country are copper, silicon, magnesium, manganese, and zinc.

5. Working And Heat Treating—Aluminum and its commercial alloys, being rather ductile materials, can be hot or cold worked into most of the common manufactured forms. The commercially pure metal and some of the alloys are not heat treatable compositions, and attain their strengths either by virtue of the alloy content or because of strain hardening resulting from cold work. The strength of many of the alloys, however, can be further increased by suitable heat treatments.

The response of an aluminum alloy to heat treatment depends on the presence of one or more alloying elements substantially more soluble in aluminum at temperatures of about 900 – 1000°F than at room temperature. By heating the material for a sufficient time at the proper solution treating temperature, the alloying elements are substantially dissolved by the aluminum; and by quenching rapidly from the solution treating temperature, the elements are retained in solid solution. Longer heating times are required for castings than for wrought products, and for heavy as compared to light sections. Alloys which are susceptible to intergranular corrosion should be quickly quenched after solution heat treatment to prevent reprecipitation along grain boundaries.

Certain of the heat treatable alloys, notably the so-called duralumin (Cu, Mg, Si) type alloys, age harden considerably at room temperature within a few days after quenching; the others, although they harden slowly at room temperature, must be heated to about 300°F for a few hours to attain their maximum strengths. With a few exceptions, most alloys which age harden substantially at room temperature can be made to develop even greater strength by a precipitation treatment at 300 – 500°F. It is generally agreed that precipitation treatments or age hardening result from lattice strains and the precipitation of alloying elements or compounds from the supersaturated solid solution in the form of minute particles. Recent studies indicate that the strengthening of heat treatable aluminum alloy by aging is due to both the uniform dispersion of a finely dispensed submicroscopic precipitate and the distortion of the lattice structure by these particles before they reach a visible size. It is believed that these particles, because of their critical size and location in the crystal structure, impede or prevent slip and thus increase the strength of the metal. Because of this phenomenon, these aging treatments are normally referred to as precipitation treatments. Room temperature aging, on the other hand, is believed to be the result of zone hardening. In this connection, it is interesting to note that the better workability of the as-quenched material can be retained in those alloys which age at room temperature by the simple expedient of storing the quenched material at about 0°F.

The effects of either cold work or heat treatment on the strength and workability of the materials can be removed by annealing at temperatures of about 600 – 800°F, depending on the alloy and temper. It must be remembered, however, that the strength of a non-heat treatable alloy can be regained, after annealing, only by the introduction of additional cold work.

6. Joining—Aluminum and its alloys can be joined by fusion welding, resistance welding, soldering, brazing, and adhesive bonding. The choice of process is dependent on alloy composition, material thickness, joint configuration, and expected service environment. The inert gas shielded metal arc process (MIG) and inert gas shielded tungsten arc process (TIG) are the most widely used fusion welding processes. Oxygas and coated electrode welding techniques are sometimes used, but the fluxes required with these processes, if not completely removed after welding, can promote corrosion. Brazing techniques now in common use include torch, dip, and furnace brazing.

All aluminum alloys can be joined by one or more of the available processes. Heat treated aluminum alloys (like the ferrous base alloys) are subject to reductions in strength after welding. Heat treating after welding will restore most of the prewelded mechanical properties. Work hardened aluminum alloys provide good as-welded mechanical properties and are used for applications such as storage tanks, boats, ships, and railroad cars.

7. Forming—Aluminum and its alloys can be formed hot or cold with considerable ease, although the bend radii for cold forming and the allowance for springback must be increased as the strength of the material increases. For severe forming, very deep drawing, or spinning, the annealed (0) temper usually is employed; while for the less drastic operations, the intermediate, cold-worked temper (H12, H22, H32; or H14, H24, or H34), or the T3 or T4 type temper immediately after quenching usually is selected. The full hard (H18, H28, or H38) or the heat treated and aged (T6) tempers are not usually used where more than slight forming is required. Heat treatable alloys, however, can often be formed in the annealed or the as-quenched tempers and subsequently heat treated to the desired temper.

8. Machining—The aluminum alloys can generally be machined easily, if suitable practices and proper tools are used. Substantial tonnages of aluminum alloy rods and bars are regularly used for making screw-machine products.

9. Finishing And Coating—The aluminum alloys can be given a wide variety of mechanical, chemical, electrochemical, or paint finishes. The more common mechanical finishes include sand or grit blasting, scratch brushing, and buffing, while the chemical finishes may be a simple dip coating or an etching treatment. The possibility of generating an explosive mixture of finely powdered metal and air should be borne in mind in connection with mechanical finishing operations. Paint coatings may be either a clear lacquer or a pigmented coating and may be applied to secure either decoration or protection, or both. Paint adhesion is generally enhanced by the application of chemical conversion coatings prior to painting. Electroplating, although not extensively practiced in the past, is now gaining increased commercial use.

Anodic coatings can be produced to provide good protection against corrosion and are also good bases for subsequent paint coatings. These coatings can be dyed, and they make possible a variety of colored surfaces suitable for many decorative applications. Their hard, wear resistant surfaces are made use of in many applications.

The appearance of automotive bright anodized trim parts produced from 5252 or the 5X57 type sheet or a 6463 extrusion is dependent upon the alloy, the temper, the finishing procedure, the aluminum producers' controls of their fabrication procedures, and the metal handling and forming techniques used. Strength requirements and formability considerations generally dictate alloy selections. Variations of temper within the bright sheet trim alloys offer further opportunity to adjust mechanical and formability properties. However, the relationship between alloy, temper, and appearance must be given careful consideration. Alloy 5457-0, widely used, has excellent formability associated with the annealed temper. It offers a good and acceptable finish for many decorative trim parts, but lacks the image clarity or brightness of the less workable strain hardened tempers, such as the H25 and H28 tempers of all 5X57 type automotive trim alloys. Alloy 5657, when supplied in a modified strain hardened temper to achieve a higher minimum elongation, may have formability and finishing capabilities intermediate between the annealed and H25 tempers. Partially recrystallized structures, which may be experienced when material is produced to significantly higher minimum elongation requirements than those specified herein for the H25 temper, may give, under some conditions, an undesirable appearance after forming and finishing. Adequate control of finishing procedures is required to provide the highly lustrous and good image clarity possible using the 5X57 type decorative aluminum trim alloys. "Out-of-control" finishing procedures used after forming can produce trim parts having an unfavorable appearance or corrosion resistance. Improper handling and forming techniques can also contribute to an undesirable appearance (scratches, gouges, strains, etc.) of the final automotive trim part.

To simplify presentation of information about the aluminum alloys, the materials have been grouped under the general headings of casting alloys and wrought alloys. Generally speaking, a given composition is not used commercially for both wrought and cast products, and the casting alloys usually contain a somewhat greater total alloy content than the wrought alloys. When yield strength is specified, it is that stress at which the stress-strain curve deviates 0.2% from the modulus line (normally referred to as 0.2% offset).

Additional information on aluminum alloys and commercially available forms can be found in SAE J454.

ALLOY AND TEMPER DESIGNATION SYSTEMS FOR ALUMINUM—SAE J993 JAN1989

SAE Standard

Report of the SAE Nonferrous Metals Committee approved July 1967 and last revised September 1973. Conforms to American National Standard H35.1-1972. Reaffirmed January 1989.

Foreword—This Document has not changed other than to put it into the new SAE Technical Standards Board Format.

*1. **Scope***—This standard provides systems for designating wrought aluminum and wrought aluminum alloys, aluminum and aluminum alloys in the form of castings and foundry ingot, and the tempers in which aluminum and aluminum alloy wrought products and aluminum alloy castings are produced.

*2. **References***—There are no referenced publications specified herein.

*3. **Wrought Aluminum and Aluminum Alloy Designation System (See 6.1)***—A system of four-digit numerical designations is used to identify wrought aluminum and wrought aluminum alloys. The first digit indicates the alloy group as shown in Table 1. The last two digits identify the aluminum alloy or indicate the aluminum purity. The second digit indicates modifications of the original alloy or impurity limits.

3.1 Aluminum—In the 1xxx group for minimum aluminum purities of 99.00% and greater, the last two of the four digits in the designation indicate the minimum aluminum percentage (Note 5.2). These digits are the same as the two digits to the right of the decimal point in the minimum aluminum percentage when it is expressed to the nearest 0.01%. The second digit in the designation indicates modifications in impurity limits. If the second digit in the designation is zero, it indicates that there is no special control on individual impurities; integers 1 through 9, which are assigned consecutively as needed, indicate special control of one or more individual impurities or alloying elements.

TABLE 1—DESIGNATION SYSTEM FOR WROUGHT ALUMINUM AND ALUMINUM ALLOY

Composition	Alloy No.
Aluminum, 99.0% min and greater	1xxx
Aluminum alloys grouped by major alloying element (1) (2)(3)	
Copper	2xxx
Manganese	3xxx
Silicon	4xxx
Magnesium	5xxx
Magnesium and silicon	6xxx
Zinc	7xxx
Other element	8xxx
Unused series	9xxx

1. For codification purposes, an alloying element is any element which is intentionally added for any purpose other than grain refinement and for which minimum and maximum limits are specified.
2. Standard limits for alloying elements and impurities are expressed to the following places:
   Less than 1/1000%0.000X
   1/1000 up to 1/100%0.00X
   1/100 up to 1/10%
   Unalloyed aluminum mode by a refining process0.0XX
   Alloys and unalloyed aluminum not made by a refining process0.0X
   1/10 through 1/2% 0.XX
   Over 1/2%0.X, X.X, etc.
3. Standard limits for alloying elements and impurities are expressed in the following sequence: silicon; iron; copper; manganese; magnesium; chromium; nickel; zinc (Note 1); titanium; other elements (each); other elements (Total); aluminum (Note 2).

   Additional specified elements having limits are inserted in alphabetical order of their chemical symbols between zinc and titanium, or are specified in footnotes.
   Aluminum is specified as minimum for unalloyed aluminum, and as a remainder for aluminum alloys.

3.2 Aluminum Alloy—In the 2xxx through 8xxx alloy groups, the last two of the four digits in the designation have no special significance but serve only to identify the different aluminum alloys in the group. The second digit in the alloy designation indicates alloy modifications (See 6.3). If the second digit in the designation is zero, it indicates the original alloy; integers 1 through 9, which are assigned consecutively, indicate alloy modifications.

3.3 Experimental Alloys—Experimental alloys are also designated in accordance with this system, but they are indicated by the prefix X. The prefix is dropped when the alloy is no longer experimental. During development and before they are designated as experimental, new alloys are identified by serial numbers assigned by their originators. Use of the serial number is discontinued when the X number is assigned.

3.4 National Variations—National variations (see 6.4) of wrought aluminum and wrought aluminum alloys registered by another country in accordance with this system are identified by a serial letter (see Section 5) before the numerical designation.

*4. **Cast Aluminum And Aluminum Alloy Designation System [1] (See 6.1)***—A system of four-digit numerical designations is used to identify aluminum and aluminum alloys in the form of castings and foundry ingot. The first digit indicates the alloy group, as shown in Table 2. The second two digits identify the aluminum alloy or indicate the aluminum purity. The last digit, which is separated from the others by a decimal point, indicates the product form, that is, castings or ingot. A modification of the original alloy or impurity limits is indicated by a serial letter (see 6.6) before the numerical designation.

TABLE 2—DESIGNATION SYSTEM FOR CAST ALUMINUM AND ALUMINUM ALLOY

Composition	Alloy No.
Aluminum, 99.00% min and greater	1xx.x
Aluminum alloy group by major alloying element (1) (2)(3)	
Copper	2xx.x
Silicon, with added copper and/or magnesium	3xx.x
Silicon	4xx.x
Magnesium	5xx.x
Zinc	7xx.x
Tin	8xx.x
Other element	9xx.x
Unused series	6xx.x

1. For codification purposes, an alloying element is any element which is intentionally added for any purpose other than grain refinement and for which minimum and maximum limits are specified.
2. Standard limits for alloying elements and impurities are expressed to the following places:
   Less than 1/1000% 0.000X
   1/1000 up to 1/100% 0.00X
   1/100 up to 1/10%
   Unalloyed aluminum made by a refining process 0.0XX
   Alloys and unalloyed aluminum not made by a refining process 0.0X
   1/10 through 1/2% 0.XX
   Over 1/2% 0.X, X.X, etc.
3. Standard limits for alloying elements and impurities are expressed in the following sequence: silicon; iron; copper; manganese; magnesium; chromium; nickel; zinc (see Note 1); titanium; other elements (each); other elements (Total); aluminum (see Note 2).

   Additional specified elements having limits are inserted in alphabetical order of their chemical symbols between zinc and titanium, or are specified in footnotes.
   Aluminum is specified as minimum for unalloyed aluminum, and as a remainder for aluminum alloys.

4.1 Aluminum Castings and Ingot—In the 1xx.x group for minimum aluminum purities of 99.00% and greater, the second two of the four digits in the designation indicate the minimum aluminum percentage (see 6.2). These digits are the same as the two digits to the right of the decimal point in the minimum aluminum percentage when it is expressed to the nearest 0.01%. The last digit, which is to the right of the decimal point, indicates the product form: 1xx.0 indicates castings, and 1xx.1 indicates ingot. Special control of one or more individual elements other than aluminum is indicated by a serial letter (see 6.6) before the numerical designation.

1. The castings and ingot alloy designation system described herein is not currently in use for some SAE cast aluminum alloys. It is applicable to Aluminum Association (AA) and American National Standards Institute (ANSI), and other, specification systems. Although the chemical composition limits shown in most SAE reports conform to the limits shown for comparable castings and ingots covered in AA and ANSI publications, the designation system described herein is not currently used in SAE Standards and Information Reports.

4.2 Aluminum Alloy Castings and Ingot—In the 2xx.x through 9xx.x alloy groups, the second two of the four digits in the designation have no special significance but serve only to identify the different aluminum alloys in the group. The last digit, which is to the right of the decimal point, indicates the product form: xxx.0 indicates castings, xxx.1 indicates ingot which has chemical composition limits conforming to 3.2.1, and xxx.2 indicates ingot which has chemical composition limits that differ but fall within the limits for xxx.1 ingot. Alloy modifications (Note 5.3) are indicated by a serial letter (see 6.9) before the numerical designation.

4.2.1 Limits for alloying elements and impurities for xxx.1 ingot are the same as for the alloy in the form of castings, except for the limits noted in Table 3.

4.3 Experimental Alloys—Experimental alloys are also designated in accordance with this system, but they are indicated by the prefix X. The prefix is dropped when the alloy is no longer experimental. During development and before they are designated as experimental, new alloys are identified by serial numbers assigned by their originators. Use of the serial number is discontinued when the X number is assigned.

TABLE 3—

Element, %	For Castings	For Ingot
Iron, max	Sand and permanent mold:	
	Up thru 0.15	0.03 less than castings
	Over 0.15 thru 0.25	0.05 less than castings
	Over 0.25 thru 0.6	0.10 less than castings
	Over 0.6 thru 1.0	0.2 less than castings
	Over 1.0	0.3 less than castings
	Die	
	Up thru 1.3	0.3 less than castings
	Over 1.3	1.1 maximum
Magnesium, min	All	
	Less than 0.50	0.05 more than castings (1)
	0.5 and greater	0.1 more than castings(1)
Zinc, max	Die	
	Over 0.25 thru 0.6	0.10 less than castings
	Over 0.6	0.1 less than castings

1. Applicable only when the specified magnesium range for castings is greater than 0.15%.

5. Temper Designation System—The temper designation system is used for all forms of wrought and cast aluminum and aluminum alloys except ingot. It is based on the sequences of basic treatments used to produce the various tempers. The temper designation follows the alloy designation, the two being separated by a hyphen. Basic temper designations consist of letters. Subdivisions of the basic tempers, where required, are indicated by one or more digits following the letter. These designate specific sequences of basic treatments; but, only operations recognized as significantly influencing the characteristics of the product are indicated. Should some other variation of the same sequence of basic operations be applied to the same alloy, resulting in different characteristics, then additional digits are added to the designation.

5.1 Basic Temper Designations

F As Fabricated—Applies to the products of shaping processes in which no special control over thermal conditions or strain-hardening is employed. For wrought products, there are no mechanical property limits.

O Annealed (Wrought Products Only)—Applies to wrought products which are fully annealed to obtain the lowest strength condition.

H Strain Hardened (Wrought Products Only)—Applies to products which have their strength increased by strain-hardening, with or without supplementary thermal treatments to produce some reduction in strength. The H is always followed by two or more digits.

W Solution Heat-Treated—An unstable temper applicable only to alloys which spontaneously age at room temperature after solution heat-treatment. This designation is specific only when the period of natural aging is indicated; for example, W 1/2 hour.

T Thermally Treated to Produce Stable Tempers Other Than F, O, or H—Applies to products which are thermally treated, with or without supplementary strain-hardening, to produce stable tempers. The T is always followed by one or more digits.

5.2 Subdivisions of Basic Tempers

5.2.1 SUBDIVISIONS OF H TEMPER: STRAIN HARDENED

5.2.1.1 The first digit following the H indicates the specific combination of basic operations, as follows:

H1 Strain Hardened Only—Applies to products which are strain hardened to obtain the desired strength without supplementary thermal treatment. The number following this designation indicates the degree of strain hardening.

H2 Strain Hardened and Partially Annealed—Applies to products which are strain hardened more than the desired final amount and then reduced in strength to the desired level by partial annealing. For alloys that age soften at room temperature, the H2 tempers have the same minimum ultimate tensile strength as the corresponding H3 tempers. For other alloys, the H2 tempers have the same minimum ultimate tensile strength as the corresponding H1 tempers and slightly higher elongation. The number following this designation indicates the degree of strain hardening remaining after the product has been partially annealed.

H3 Strain Hardened and Stabilized—Applies to products which are strain hardened and whose mechanical properties are stabilized by a low-temperature thermal treatment which results in slightly lowered tensile strength and improved ductility. This designation is applicable only to those alloys which, unless stabilized, gradually age soften at room temperature. The number following this designation indicates the degree of strain hardening before the stabilization treatment.

5.2.1.2 The digit following the designations H1, H2, and H3 indicates the degree of strain hardening. Numeral 8 has been assigned to indicate tempers having an ultimate tensile strength equivalent to that achieved by a cold reduction (temperature during reduction not to exceed 120°F (49°C)) of approximately 75% following a full anneal. Tempers between 0 (annealed) and 8 are designated by numerals 1 through 7. Material having an ultimate tensile strength about midway between that of the 0 temper and that of the 8 temper is designated by the numeral 4; about midway between the 0 and 4 tempers by the numeral 2; and about midway between the 4 and 8 tempers by the numeral 6. Numeral 9 designates tempers whose minimum ultimate tensile strength exceeds that of the 8 temper by 2.0 ksi (14 MPa) or more. For two-digit H tempers whose second digit is odd, the standard limits for ultimate tensile strength are exactly midway between those of the adjacent two-digit H tempers whose second digits are even.

NOTE—For alloys which cannot be cold reduced, an amount sufficient to establish an ultimate tensile strength applicable to the 8 temper (75% cold reduction after full anneal), the 6 temper tensile strength may be established by a cold reduction of approximately 55% following a full anneal, or the 4 temper tensile strength may be established by a cold reduction of approximately 35% after a full anneal.

5.2.1.3 The third digit (Note 10), when used, indicates a variation of a two-digit temper. It is used when the degree of control of temper or the mechanical properties are different from, but close to, those for the two-digit H temper designation to which it is added, or when some other characteristic is significantly affected. (See Appendix for three-digit H tempers.)

NOTE—The minimum ultimate tensile strength of a three-digit H temper is at least as close to that of the corresponding two-digit H temper as it is to the adjacent two-digit H tempers.

5.2.2 SUBDIVISIONS OF T TEMPER: THERMALLY TREATED

5.2.2.1 Numerals 1 through 10 following the T indicate specific sequences of basic treatments, as follows (see 6.8):

T1 Cooled From an Elevated Temperature Shaping Process and Naturally Aged to a Substantially Stable Condition—Applies to products for which the rate of cooling from an elevated temperature shaping process, such as casting or extrusion, is such that their strength is increased by room temperature aging.

T2 Annealed (Cast Products Only)—Applies to cast products which are annealed to improve ductility and dimensional stability.

T3 Solution Heat Treated and Then Cold Worked—Applies to products which are cold worked to improve strength, or in which the effect of cold work in flattening or straightening is recognized in mechanical property limits.

T4 Solution Heat Treated and Naturally Aged to a Substantially Stable Condition—Applies to products which are not cold worked after solution heat treatment, or in which the effect of cold work in flattening or straightening may not be recognized in mechanical property limits.

T5 Cooled From an Elevated Temperature Shaping Process and Then Artificially Aged—Applies to products which are cooled from an elevated temperature shaping process, such as casting or extrusion, and then artificially aged to improve mechanical properties or dimensional stability or both.

T6 Solution Heat Treated and Then Artificially Aged—Applies to products which are not cold worked after solution heat treatment, or in which the effect of cold work in flattening or straightening may not be recognized in mechanical property limits.

T7 Solution Heat Treated and Then Stabilized—Applies to products which are stabilized to carry them beyond the point of maximum strength to provide control of some special characteristics.

T8 Solution Heat Treated, Cold Worked, and Then Artificially Aged—Applies to products which are cold worked to improve strength, or in which the effect of cold work in flattening or straightening is recognized in mechanical property limits.

T9 Solution Heat Treated, Artificially Aged, and Then Cold Worked—Applies to products which are cold worked to improve strength.

T10 Cooled From an Elevated Temperature Shaping Process, Artificially Aged, and Then Cold Worked—Applies to products which are artificially aged after cooling from an elevated temperature shaping process, such as casting or extrusion, and then cold worked to improve strength further.

5.2.2.2 Additional digits (see 6.9), the first of which shall not be zero, may be added to designations T1 through T10 to indicate a variation in treatment which significantly alters the characteristics of the product. (See Appendix for specific additional digits for T tempers.)

6. Notes

6.1 Producers of wrought aluminum and wrought aluminum alloys, and aluminum and aluminum alloy castings and foundry ingot, may register chemical composition limits and designations conforming to this standard with the Aluminum Association (AA) provided the aluminum or aluminum alloy is offered for sale; the complete chemical composition limits are registered; and the composition is significantly different from that of any aluminum or aluminum alloy for which a numerical designation already has been assigned. A numerical designation assigned in conformance with this standard should be used only to indicate an aluminum or aluminum alloy having chemical composition limits identical to those registered with AA for that aluminum or aluminum alloy.

6.2 The aluminum content for unalloyed aluminum made by a refining process is the difference between 100.000% and the sum of all other metallic elements present in amounts of 0.0010% or more each, expressed to the third decimal; for unalloyed aluminum not made by a refining process, it is the difference between 100.00% and the sum of all other metallic elements present in amounts of 0.010% or more each, expressed to the second decimal.

6.3 A modification of the original alloy is limited to any one or a combination of the following:

a. Change of not more than the following amounts in the arithmetic mean of the limits for an alloying element:

TABLE 4—

Arithmetic Mean of Limits for Alloying Elements in Original alloy, &	Maximum Change, %
Up thru 1.0	0.15
Over 1.0 thru 2.0	0.20
Over 2.0 thru 3.0	0.25
Over 3.0 thru 4.0	0.30
Over 4.0 thru 5.0	0.35
Over 5.0 thru 6.0	0.40
Over 6.0	0.50

To determine compliance when limits are specified for a combination of two or more elements in one alloy composition, the mean of such a combination should be compared to the sum of the mean values of the same individual elements, or any combination thereof, in another alloy composition.

b. Addition or deletion of not more than one alloying element with limits having an arithmetic mean of not more than 0.30%.

c. Substitution of one alloying element for another element serving the same purpose.

d. Change in limits for impurities.

e. Change in limits for grain refining elements.

f. Distinctive iron or silicon limits, or both, reflecting high purity base metal.

An alloy shall not be registered as a modification if it meets the requirements for a national variation.

6.4 A national variation has composition limits which are similar but not identical to those registered by another country, with differences such as:

a. Differences in the arithmetic mean of limits for alloying elements not exceeding the following amounts:

TABLE 5—

Arithmetic Mean of Limits for Alloying Elements in Original Alloy or Modification, %	Maximum Difference,%
Up thru 1.0	0.15
Over 1.0 thru 2.0	0.20
Over 2.0 thru 3.0	0.25
Over 3.0 thru 4.0	0.30
Over 4.0 thru 5.0	0.35
Over 5.0 thru 6.0	0.40
Over 6.0	0.50

To determine compliance when limits are specified for a combination of two or more elements in one alloy composition, the mean of such a combination should be compared to the sum of the mean values of the same individual elements, or any combination thereof, in another alloy composition.

b. Substitution of one alloying element for another element serving the same purpose.

c. Different limits on impurities except for low iron. Low iron, reflecting high purity base metal, should be considered an alloy modification. See 6.3 (see 6.3) (f).

d. Different limits on grain refining elements.

e. Inclusion of a minimum limit for iron or silicon, or both.

Wrought aluminum and wrought aluminum alloys meeting these requirements shall not be registered as a new alloy or alloy modification.

6.5 The serial letters are assigned internationally in alphabetical sequence starting with A but omitting I, O, and Q.

6.6 The serial letters are assigned in alphabetical sequence starting with A but omitting I, O, Q, and X, the X being reserved for experimental alloys.

6.7 Numerals 1 through 9 may be arbitrarily assigned as the third digit and registered with AA for an alloy and product to indicate a variation of a two-digit H temper provided the temper is used or is available for use by more than one user, mechanical property limits are registered, the characteristics of the temper are significantly different from those of all other tempers which have the same sequence of basic treatments and for which designations already have been assigned for the same alloy and product, and the following are also registered if characteristics other than mechanical properties are considered significant: a. test methods and limits for the characteristics, or b. the specific practices used to produce the temper. Zero has been assigned to indicate variations negotiated between the manufacturer and purchaser which are not used widely enough to justify registration.

6.8 A period of natural aging at room temperature may occur between or after the operations listed for tempers T3 through T10. Control of this period is exercised when it is metallurgically important.

6.9 Additional digits may be arbitrarily assigned and registered with AA for an alloy and product to indicate a variation of tempers T1 through T10 provided the temper is used or is available for use by more than one user; mechanical property limits are registered; the characteristics of the temper are significantly different from those of all other tempers which have the same sequence of basic treatments and for which designations already have been assigned for the same alloy and product. The following are also registered if characteristics other than mechanical properties are considered significant: a. test methods and limits for the characteristics, or b. the specific practices used to provide the temper. Variations in treatment which do not alter the characteristics of the product are considered alternate treatments for which additional digits are not assigned.

APPENDIX A

A.1 Three-digit H Tempers

A.1.1 The following three-digit H temper designations have been assigned for wrought products in all alloys:

H111 Applies to products which are strain hardened less than the amount required for a controlled H11 temper.

H112 Applies to products which acquire some temper from shaping processes not having special control over the amount of strain hardening or thermal treatment, but for which there are mechanical property limits.

A.1.2 The following three-digit H temper designations have been assigned for wrought products in alloys containing over a nominal 4% magnesium.

H311 Applies to products which are strain hardened less than the amount required for a controlled H31 temper.

H321 Applies to products which are strain hardened less than the amount required for a controlled H32 temper.

H323 Applies to products which are specially fabricated to have acceptable
H343 resistance to stress corrosion cracking.

A.1.3 The following three-digit H temper designations have been assigned for:

TABLE A1—

Patterned or Embossed Sheet	Fabricated from
H114	O temper
H124, H224, H324	H11, H21, H31 temper, respectively
H134, H234, H334	H12, H22, H32 temper, respectively
H144, H244, H344	H13, H23, H33 temper, respectively
H154, H254, H354	H14, H24, H34 temper, respectively
H164, H264, H364	H15, H25, H35 temper, respectively
H174, H274, H374	H16, H26, H36 temper, respectively
H184, H284, H384	H17, H27, H37 temper, respectively
H194, H294, H394	H18, H28, H38 temper, respectively
H195, H295, H395	H19, H29, H39 temper, respectively

A.2 Additional Digits For T Tempers

A.2.1 The following specific additional digits have been assigned for stress-relieved tempers of wrought products:

T51 Stress Relieved by Stretching—Applies to the following products when stretched the indicated amounts after solution heat treatment or cooling from an elevated temperature shaping process.

TABLE A2—

Product	Stretch, Permanent Set, %
Plate	1.5-3
Rod, bar, shapes extruded tube	1-3
Drawn tube	0.5-3

Applies directly to plate and rolled or cold-finished rod and bar. These products receive no further straightening after stretching.

Applies to extruded rod, bar, shapes, and tube and to drawn tube when designated as follows:

T510 Products that receive no further straightening after stretching.

T511 Products that may receive minor straightening after stretching to comply with standard tolerances.

T52 Stress Relieved by Compressing—Applies to products which are stress relieved by compressing after solution heat treatment, or cooling from an elevated temperature shaping process to produce a permanent set of 1-5%.

T54 Stress Relieved by Combined Stretching and Compressing—Applies to die forgings which are stress relieved by restriking cold in the finish die.

A.2.2 The following temper designations have been assigned for wrought products heat treated from O to F temper to demonstrate response to heat-treatment.

T42 Solution Heat Treated From the O or F Temper—To demonstrate response to heat treatment, and naturally aged to a substantially stable condition.

T62 Solution Heat Treated From the O or F Temper—To demonstrate response to heat treatment, and artificially aged.

Temper designations T42 and T62 may also be applied to wrought products heat treated from any temper by the user when such heat treatment results in the mechanical properties applicable to these tempers.

GENERAL INFORMATION—CHEMICAL COMPOSITIONS, MECHANICAL AND PHYSICAL PROPERTIES OF SAE ALUMINUM CASTING ALLOYS—SAE J452 DEC2003

SAE Information Report

Report of the SAE Nonferrous Metals Division, approved January 1934, completely revised by the SAE Nonferrous Metals Committee June 1983 and reaffirmed by the SAE Cast Aluminum Committee January 1989 and revised December 2003.

Foreword—This Document has not changed other than to put it into the new SAE Technical Standards Board Format.

1. Scope—The SAE Standards for aluminum casting alloys cover a wide range of castings for general and special use, but do not include all the alloys in commercial use. Over the years, aluminum alloys have been identified by many numbering systems as shown in Table 1. Presently, SAE is recommending the use of the UNS Numbering System to identify these materials. The castings are made principally by sand cast, permanent mold, or die cast methods; however, shell molding, investment casting, plaster cast, and other less common foundry methods may also be used. If the alloys listed do not have the desired characteristics, it is recommended that the manufacturers of aluminum castings be consulted.

2. References

2.1 Applicable Publications—The following publications form a part of the specification to the extent specified herein. Unless otherwise indicated the lastest revision of SAE publications shall apply.

2.1.1 ASTM PUBLICATIONS—Available from ASTM, 100 Barr Harbor Drive, West Conshohocken, PA 19428-2959.

ASTM E 29—Practice for Using Significant Digits in Test Data to Determine Conformance with Specifications

ASTM E 34—Test Method for Chemical Analysis of Aluminum and Aluminum Alloys

ASTM E 117—Method for Spectrographic Analysis of Pig Lead by the Point-to-Plane Technique

ASTM B 557—Methods of Tension Testing Wrought and Cast Aluminum and Magnesium Alloy Products

3. Casting Types—General—There are two general types of cast aluminum alloys: nonheat treatable and heat treatable. The nonheat treatable alloys normally are used in the as-cast condition (F), but may be annealed—temper designation (O)—to relieve casting stresses or to reduce the possibility of distortion during machining.

The heat treatable alloys usually are used in a heat treated condition because of the increased strengths resulting from the heat treatment. These treatments generally consist of a high temperature solution treatment, followed by quenching in water, and a low temperature aging treatment (T6).

TABLE 1—TYPICAL USES OF SAE ALUMINUM CASTING ALLOYS AND SIMILAR SPECIFICATIONS

Alloy Designations			Type of Casting [1]	Similar Specifications			Typical Uses and General Data
UNS	ANSI	Former SAE		ASTM	Federal	AMS	
A02010	201.0	382	S PM	B26 —	— —	— 4229	Very high strength at room and elevated temperature; good impact strength and ductility; high cost premium casting alloy.
A02060	206.0	—	S PM	— —	— —	4237 —	High tensile and yield strength with moderate ductility; good fracture toughness in T4 temper, structural parts for automotive and aerospace applications.
A02080	208.0	380	S PM	B26 B108	QQ-A-601 —	— —	Manifolds, valve bodies, and similar castings requiring pressure tightness.
A02220	222.0	34	S PM	B26 B108	QQ-A-601 QQ-A-596	— —	Primarily a piston alloy, but also used for aircooled cylinder heads and valve tappet guides.
A02420	242.0	39	S PM	B26 B108	QQ-A-601 QQ-A-596	4222 —	Used primarily for aircooled cylinder heads, but also for pistons in high performance gasoline engines.
A02950	295.0	38	S	B26	QQ-A-601	4231	General structural castings requiring high strength and shock resistance.
A02960	296.0	—	PM	B108	QQ-A-596	4282	Modification of alloy 295.0 for use in permanent molds.
A03190	319.0	326	S PM	B26 B108	QQ-A-601 QQ-A-596	— —	General purpose low-cost alloy; good foundry characteristics.
A23190	B319.0	329	S PM	— —	— —	— —	General purpose alloy similar to 319.0, but with lower ductility and improved machinability.
A03280	328.0	327	S	B26	QQ-A-601	—	Similar to alloys 355.0 and 356.0, but lower ductility.
A03320	332.0	332	PM	B108	QQ-A-596	—	Primarily used for automotive and compressor pistons.
A03330	333.0	331	PM	B108	QQ-A-596	—	General purpose low-cost permanent mold alloy used for engine parts, motor housings, flywheel housings, and regulator parts.
A03360	336.0	321	PM	B108	QQ-A-596	—	Piston alloy having low expansion.
A03390	339.0	334	PM	—	—	—	Piston alloy.
A03540	354.0	—	PM	B108 B686	— —	— —	High strength premium quality casting alloy.
A03550	355.0	322	S PM	B26 B108 — — —	QQ-A-601 QQ-A-596 — — —	4210 4212 4214 4280 4281	General use where high strength, medium ductility, and pressure tightness are required, such as pump bodies and liquid-cooled cylinder heads.
A33550	C355.0	335	S PM	B26 B108 B686	QQ-A-601 QQ-A-596 —	4215 — —	Similar to alloy 355.0, but has greater ductility.
A03560	356.0	323	S PM	B26 B108 —	QQ-A-601 QQ-A-596 —	4217 4284 4286	For intricate castings requiring good strength and ductility.
A13560	A356.0	336	S PM	B26 B108 B686	QQ-A-601 QQ-A-596 —	4218 — —	Similar to alloy 356.0, but has greater ductility.
A03570	357.0	—	S PM	— B108	— QQ-A-596	— —	Similar to alloy A357.0, but has greater ductility.

TABLE 1—TYPICAL USES OF SAE ALUMINUM CASTING ALLOYS AND SIMILAR SPECIFICATIONS (continued)

Alloy Designations			Type of Casting [1]	Similar Specifications			Typical Uses and General Data
UNS	ANSI	Former SAE		ASTM	Federal	AMS	
			S	—	—	4219	
A13570	A357.0	—	PM	B108	—	—	High strength structural alloy with good ductility.
				B686			
			S	—	—		
A03590	359.0	—	PM	B108	—	—	High strength structural alloy with good ductility.
A03600	360.0	—	D	B85	—	—	Very good casting characteristics; good corrosion resistance; used in place of alloy 413 where higher mechanical properties are required.
A13600	A360.0	309	D	B85	QQ-A-591	4290	Excellent casting characteristics; suited for use in thin-walled or intricate castings produced in cold-chamber casting machine; high corrosion resistance; slightly higher mechanical properties than alloy 360.0.
A03800	380.0	308	D	B85	QQ-A-591	—	Similar to alloy A380.0, but suitable for use in either cold-chamber or gooseneck machines.
A13800	A380.0	306	D	B85	QQ-A-591	4291	Good casting characteristics and fair resistance to corrosion; not especially suited for thin sections; limited to cold-chamber machines.
A03830	383.0	383	D	B85	QQ-A-591	—	Similar to alloy 380.0, but with improved castability.
A03840	384.0	303	D	B85	QQ-A-591	—	General purpose alloy with high fluidity; used for thin-walled castings or castings with large areas.
A03900	390.0	—	D	—	—	—	High wear resistance; used for cylinder blocks, transmission pump and air compressor housings, small engine crankcases, and air conditioner pistons.
			S	—	—	—	
A13900	A390.0	—	PM	—	—	—	Similar to 390.0, but formulated for sand and permanent mold casting.
A23900	B390.0	—	D	—	—	—	Similar to alloy 390.0.
A04130	413	—	D	B85	—	—	Good for large thin-wall die castings, difficult to machine and finish.
A14130	A413.0	305	D	B85	QQ-A-591	—	High corrosion resistance; excellent castability; used for complicated castings with thin sections, also difficult to machine and finish.
			S	B26	QQ-A-601	—	
A24430	B443.0	35	PM	B108	QQ-A-596	—	Used for intricate castings having thin sections; good corrosion resistance; fair strength and good ductility.
A34430	C443.0	304	D	B85	QQ-A-591	—	Good casting characteristics and resistance to corrosion.
A14440	A444.0	—	S	—	—	—	Good castability; excellent ductility for impact absorption; used for bridge railing posts and turbocharger compressor housings.
A05140	514.0	320	S	B26	QQ-A-601	—	Moderate strength; very high corrosion resistance.
A05200	520.0	324	S	B26	QQ-A-601	4240	High strength structural alloy; requires special foundry and heat treat practice; susceptible to stress corrosion failure.
A05350	535.0	—	S	B26	QQ-A-601	—	Excellent shock and corrosion resistance, dimensional stability, and machinability; used in computer components, frame sections, optical equipment, and applications where stress rupture is a factor.
			S	B26	QQ-A-601	—	
A07050	705.0	311	PM	B108	QQ-A-596	—	High strength general purpose alloy; excellent machinability and dimensional stability; high corrosion resistance; can be anodized.
			S	B26	QQ-A-601	—	
A07070	707.0	312	PM	B108	QQ-A-596	—	Similar to alloy 705.0, but higher strength and lower ductility.
A07100	710.0	313	S	B26	QQ-A-601	—	High strength general purpose alloy similar to alloys 705.0 and 707.0; easily polished.
A07120	712.0	310	S	B26	QQ-A-601	—	General purpose structural castings developing strengths equivalent to alloy 295.0 without requiring heat treatment, but casting characteristics slightly poorer than alloy 295.0.
A07130	713.0	315	S	B26	QQ-A-601	—	Similar to alloy 710.0.
			PM	B108	QQ-A-596	—	

1. S—sand cast; PM—permanent mold; D—die cast.

By aging the solution treated castings at higher temperature to a T7 condition, a product having more stable properties in service at elevated temperatures and less likely to distort during machining is obtained. Occasionally, the artificial aging treatment is omitted and the castings are used in the quenched and naturally aged condition (T4); at other times (especially in castings to be used at elevated temperatures) the solution treatment is omitted and the castings are merely stabilized or aged (T5). This type of thermal treatment provides a limited form of stress relief. Various combinations of properties can be secured by adjusting the thermal treatments, but only the commonly used conditions form a part of the specification.

4. Casting Type And Alloys—Selection—More liberal as-cast dimensional tolerances are employed for sand castings than for permanent mold or die castings. Overall wall thickness and finish stock allowance are usually greater than for permanent mold or die casting. The process has the capability of producing parts with good internal soundness. Newly developed automated high-pressure sand molding methods allow large volume production of sand castings. (Timing to get a new part into production is favorable due to lower tooling time requirements for sand equipment in comparison to the time required for hard molds and dies.)

Permanent mold castings can be cast to close tolerances. For the same chemical composition, they have slightly higher mechanical properties than sand castings. Disposable cores can be used to form both internal or external cavities having pockets or undercuts that will not draw with metal cores. This type casting is called semi-permanent mold. The process has the capability of allowing castings with good internal soundness to be produced.

Semi and permanent mold parts are generally produced by one of two methods: gravity, in which metal is poured into the mold, or low pressure, in which metal is forced into the mold from a sealed furnace by low-pressure air.

The use of die castings for high-volume production of automotive parts has found wide application in this industry. Die castings can be held to much closer tolerances than either sand or permanent mold. The process will permit thinner overall wall thickness and lesser amounts of finish stock thus resulting in a lower weight part. Some holes can be cast within the limitations of the design and part orientation in the die. The surface of die castings is smooth if dies are well maintained, but sometimes can deteriorate with extensive die usage. When surface finishing is required, this characteristic can be advantageous from a cost standpoint.

The uniformity of dimensions, lower weight, and lesser finish stock permits lower costs of finish machining operations. This, coupled with lower as-cast weight, removal of gating with trim dies, high productivity casting rates, and use in the as-cast condition, usually results in die castings having very favorable costs in comparison to parts made by other processes even though tooling costs are more expensive.

Although test bar values for die cast alloys are, in general, high in tensile and yield due to their having been cast with a high chill rate, a lack of internal soundness of castings made from the alloy can result in lower property levels. Injection of metal under high pressures through thin gates which may cause inclusions, solidification phenomena, and actual casting design features unfavorable to producing sound areas, can result in internal defects that reduce considerably the property level of actual parts from that of test bar values. It is extremely important that the producer and the user of die castings cooperate very closely in the design, planning, and try out stages to obtain satisfactory quality in die-cast parts.

5. Pattern Design—In the design of patterns for the production of aluminum alloy sand castings, a shrinkage is usually allowed Table 2A and may vary slightly depending upon the form and size of the casting. Producers of castings should also be consulted concerning the design of the pattern so that the best results may be obtained with the alloy to be used. The information provided in Table 2 is based on a study made by the American Foundrymen's Society.

6. Chemical Compositions—Chemical analysis shall be made in accordance with ASTM E 34, Standard Methods for Chemical Analysis of Aluminum and Aluminum Base Alloys, or any other approved method agreed upon by the manufacturer and the purchaser. The analysis may be made spectrographically, provided that, in case of dispute, the results secured by the ASTM E 34 methods shall be the basis for acceptance.

For purposes of determining conformance to limits indicated in Table 3, an observed or a calculated value obtained from analysis is rounded off to the nearest unit in the last right-hand place of figures used in expressing the specified limit in accordance with the rounding method of ASTM E 29, Recommended Practices for Indicating Which Places of Figures are to be Considered Significant in Specifying Limiting Values.

7. Mechanical And Physical Properties—The typical physical properties of SAE casting alloys are shown in Table 4. The specified mechanical properties shown in this SAE Information Report are the values that should be obtained from standard test specimens, separately cast under conditions that duplicate, as closely as possible, the conditions of solidification of the casting, and tested without machining, except to adapt the ends to the grips of the testing equipment. The specified properties for sand casting alloys Table 5 are for 1/2 in (12.7 mm) diameter standard test bars cast without chills in green sand molds, and the specified properties for the permanent mold alloys Table 6 are for 1/2 in (12.7 mm) diameter standard test bars cast in a permanent mold. The typical tensile properties given for die casting alloys Table 7 are for 1/4 in (6.4 mm) diameter standard die cast test bars as shown in ASTM B 557, Methods of Tension Testing Wrought and Cast Aluminum and Magnesium Alloy Products.

TABLE 2A—SAE ALUMINUM ALLOY CHARACTERISTICS

Alloy Designations			Foundry Characteristics(1)						
			Type of Casting	Pattern Shrinkage Allowance (2)		Resistance to Hot Cracking(3)	Pressure Tightness	Fluidity(4)	Solidification Shrinkage Tendency(5)
UNS	ANSI	SAE		in/ft	%				
A02010	201.0	382	S	5/32	1.30	4	3	3	4
			PM	(2)	(2)	4	3	3	4
A02060	206.0	—	S	5/32	1.30	4	3	3	4
			PM	(2)	(2)	4	3	3	4
A02080	208:0	380	S	5/32	1.30	4	3	3	3
			PM	(2)	(2)	4	3	3	3
A02220	222.0	34	S	5/32	1.30	3	3	3	3
			PM	(2)	(2)	4	4	3	4
A02420	242.0	39	S	5/32	1.30	4	3	3	4
			PM	(2)	(2)	4	4	3	4
A02950	295.0	38	S	5/32	1.30	4	4	3	3
A02960	296.0	—	PM	(2)	(2)	4	3	3	3
A03190	319.0	326	S	5/32	1.30	2	2	2	2
			PM	(2)	(2)	2	2	2	3
A23190	B319.0	329	S	5/32	1.30	2	2	2	2
			PM	(2)	(2)	2	2	2	2
A03280	328.0	327	S	5/32	1.30	1	1	1	1
A03320	332.0	332	PM	(2)	(2)	1	2	1	2
A03330	333.0	331	PM	(2)	(2)	2	2	1	3
A03360	336.0	321	PM	(2)	(2)	1	2	1	3
A03390	339.0	334	PM	(2)	(2)	1	2	1	2
A03540	354.0	—	PM	(2)	(2)	2	1	1	3
A03550	355.0	322	S	5/32	1.30	1	1	1	1
			PM	(2)	(2)	1	1	2	2
A33550	C355.0	335	S	5/32	1.30	1	1	1	1
			PM	(2)	(2)	1	1	2	2
A03560	356.0	323	S	5/32	1.30	1	1	1	1
			PM	(2)	(2)	1	1	2	1
A13560	A356.0	336	S	5/32	1.30	1	1	1	1
			PM	(2)	(2)	1	1	2	1
A03570	357.0	—	S	5/32	1.30	1	1	1	1
			PM	(2)	(2)	1	1	2	1
A13570	A357.0	—	S	5/32	1.30	1	1	1	1
			PM	(2)	(2)	1	1	2	1
A03590	359.0	—	S	5/32	1.30	2	2	1	2
			PM	(2)	(2)	2	2	2	2
A03600	360.0	—	D	(2)	(2)	1	1	1	—
A13600	A360.0	309	D	(2)	(2)	1	1	1	—
A03800	380.0	308	D	(2)	(2)	1	1	1	—
A13800	A380.0	306	D	(2)	(2)	1	1	1	—
A03830	383.0	383	D	(2)	(2)	1	1	1	—
A03840	384.0	—	D	(2)	(2)	1	1	1	—
A03900	390.0	—	D	(2)	(2)	3	3	1	—

TABLE 2A—SAE ALUMINUM ALLOY CHARACTERISTICS (continued)

Alloy Designations			Foundry Characteristics(1)						
			Type of Casting	Pattern Shrinkage Allowance (2)		Resistance to Hot Cracking(3)	Pressure Tightness	Fluidity(4)	Solidification Shrinkage Tendency(5)
UNS	ANSI	SAE		in/ft	%				
A13900	A390.0	—	S	5/32	1.30	3	3	1	3
			PM	(2)	(2)	3	3	1	3
A23900	B390.0	—	D	(2)	(2)	3	3	1	—
A04130	413.0	—	D	(2)	(2)	1	2	1	—
A14130	A413.0	305	D			1	2	1	—
A24430	B443.0	35	S	5/32	1.30	1	1	1	1
			PM	(2)	(2)	1	1	1	2
A34430	C443.0	304	D	(2)	(2)	2	3	3	—
A14440	A444.0	—	S	5/32	1.30	4	4	5	—
A05140	514.0	320	S	5/32	1.30	4	5	5	5
A05200	520.0	324	S	1/10	0.83	4	5	4	5
A05350	535.0	—	S	1/10	0.83	3	5	3	4
A07050	705.0	311	S	3/16	1.56	5	3	4	4
A07050	705.0	311	PM	(2)	(2)	5	4	4	5
A07070	707.0	312	S	3/16	1.56	5	3	4	4
			PM	(2)	(2)	5	4	4	5
A07100	710.0	313	S	3/16	1.56	5	3	4	4
A07120	712.0	310	S	3/16	1.56	5	3	4	4
A07130	713.0	315	S	3/16	1.56	5	3	4	4
			PM	(2)	(2)	5	4	4	5

1. 1 indicates best of group; 5 indicates poorest of group.
2. Not applicable to permanent mold and die castings. Allowances are for average sand castings. Shrinkage requirements will vary with intricacy of design and dimensions.
3. Ability of alloy to withstand contraction stresses while cooling through hot-short or brittle temperature range.
4. Ability of liquid alloy to flow readily in mold and fill thin sections.
5. Decrease in volume accompanying freezing of alloy and measure of amount of compensating feed metal required in form of risers.

NOTE: Type of casting: S—sand cast; PM—permanent mold; D—die cast.

TABLE 2B—SAE ALUMINUM ALLOY CHARACTERISTICS

Alloy		Other Characteristics									
UNS	ANSI	Normally Heat Treated	Resistance to Corrosion(1)	Machining(2)	Polishing(3)	Electroplating(4)	Anodized Appearance(5)	Chemical Oxide Coating(6) (Protection)	Strength at Elevated Temperature(7)	Suitability for Welding(8)	Suitability for Brazing(9)
A02010	201.0	Yes	4	1	1	1	2	2	1	4	No
A02060	206.0	Yes	4	1	1	1	2	2	1	4	No
A02080	208.0	Yes	4	3	2	1	3	2	2	4	No
A02220	222.0	Yes	4	1	2	1	3	4	1	4	No
A02420	242.0	Yes	4	2	2	1	3	4	1	4	No
A02950	295.0	Yes	3	2	2	1	2	3	3	3	No
A02960	296.0	Yes	4	3	4	2	4	3	3	2	No
A03190	319.0	Yes	3	3	4	2	4	3	3	2	No
A23190	8319.0	Yes	3	3	4	2	4	3	3	2	No
A03280	328.0	Yes	3	4	5	2	4	2	2	2	No
A03320	332.0	Aged Only	3	3	4	3	5	3	3	2	No
A03330	333.0	Yes	3	2	3	2	4	3	2	3	No
A03360	336.0	Yes	3	4	5	4	5	2	2	2	No
A03390	339.0	Aged Only	3	3	4	3	5	3	3	2	No
A03540	354.0	Yes	3	4	4	2	4	3	2	3	No
A03550	355.0	Yes	3	3	3	1	4	2	2	2	No
A33550	C355.0	Yes	3	3	3	2	4	2	2	2	No
A03560	356.0	Yes	2	4	3	2	4	2	3	1	No
A13560	A356.0	Yes	2	3	3	1	4	2	3	1	No
A03570	357.0	Yes	2	3	3	1	4	2	3	1	No
A13570	A357.0	Yes	2	3	3	1	4	2	3	1	No
A03590	359.0	Yes	2	4	4	2	4	2	2	1	No
A03600	360.0	No	2	4	4	2	4	3	2	3	No
A13600	A360.0	No	3	3	3	1	4	3	2	3	No
A03800	380.0	No	4	3	3	1	4	5	2	4	No
A13800	A380.0	No	4	3	3	1	4	5	2	4	No
A03830	383.0	No	4	3	3	1	4	5	2	4	No
A03840	384.0	No	4	3	3	1	4	5	3	4	No

Note: Type of casting: S—sand cast; PM—permanent mold; D—die cast.

TABLE 2B—SAE ALUMINUM ALLOY CHARACTERISTICS (continued)

Alloy		Other Characteristics										
UNS	ANSI	Normally Heat Treated	Resistance to Corrosion(1)	Machining(2)	Polishing(3)	Electroplating(4)	Anodized Appearance(5)	Chemical Oxide Coating(6) (Protection)	Strength at Elevated Temperature(7)	Suitability for Welding(8)	Suitability for Brazing(9)
A03900	390.0	No	3	4	3	—	5	—	1	4	No
A13900	A390.0	Yes	3	4	3	—	5	—	1	4	No
A23900	B390.0	No	3	4	3	—	5	—	1	4	No
A04130	413.0	No	2	4	5	3	5	3	3	3	No
A14130	A413.0	No	3	4	5	3	5	3	3	3	No
A24430	B443.0	No	3	5	5	2	5	3	3	3	No
A34430	C443.0	No	2	5	5	2	5	2	4	1	Ltd.
A14440	A444.0	No	2	4	4	—	4	3	5	1	No
A05140	514.0	No	1	1	1	5	4	2	3	1	No
A05200	520.0	Yes	1	1	1	4	1	1	2	4	No
A05350	535.0	Opt	1	1	1	—	1	1	— (10)	5	No
A07050	705.0	Aged Only	2	1	1	3	1	1	3	4	No
A07070	707.0	Yes	2	1	1	3	2	2	5	4	Yes
A07100	710.0	Aged only	2	1	1	2	2	2	5	4	Yes
A07120	712.0	Aged Only	2	1	1	2	2	3	5	4	Yes
A07130	713.0	Aged Only	2	1	1	2	2	3	5	4	Yes

Note: Type of casting: S—sand cast; PM—permanent mold; D—die cast.

1. Based on alloy resistance in 5% salt spray test (ASTM B117).
2. Composite rating based on ease of cutting, chip characteristics, quality of finishing, and tool life. Ratings, in the case of heat treatable alloys, based on T6 temper. Other tempers, particularly the annealed temper, may have lower rating.
3. Composite rating based on ease and speed of polishing and quality of finish provided by typical polishing procedure.
4. Ability of casting to take and hold on electroplate applied by present standard methods.
5. Rated on lightness of color, brightness, and uniformity of clear anodized coating applied in sulfuric acid electrolyte.
6. Rated on combined resistance of coating and base alloy to corrosion.
7. Rating based on tensile and yield strengths of temperature up to 500°F (260°C), after prolonged heating at testing temperatures.
8. Based on ability of material to be fusion welded with filler rod of same alloy.
9. Refers to suitability of alloy to withstand brazing temperatures without excessive distortion or melting.
10. Not recommended for service at temperatures exceeding 200 °F (93 °C).

TABLE 3—CHEMICAL COMPOSITIONS OF SAE ALUMINUM CASTING ALLOYS (1)

UNS	ANSI Designation	Former SAE	Product(2)	Si	Fe	Cu	Mn	Mg	Cr	Ni	Zn	Sn	Ti	Others Each	Others Total
A02010	201.0	382	S,PM	0.10	0.15	4.0–5.2	0.20–0.50	0.15–0.55	—	—	—	—	0.15–0.35	0.05(3)	0.10
A02060	206.0	—	S,PM	0.10	0.15	4.2–5.0	0.20–0.50	0.15–0.35	—	0.05	0.10	0.05	0.15–0.30	0.05	0.15
A02080	208.0	—	S,PM	2.5–3.5	1.2	3.5–4.5	0.50	0.10	—	0.35	1.0	—	0.25	—	0.50
A02220	222.0	34	S,PM	2.0	1.5	9.2–10.7	0.50	0.15–0.35	—	0.50	0.8	—	0.25	—	0.35
A02420	242.0	39	S,PM	0.7	1.0	3.5–4.5	0.35	1.2–1.8	0.25	1.7–2.3	0.35	—	0.25	0.05	0.15
A02950	295.0	38	S	0.7–1.5	1.0	4.0–5.0	0.35	0.03	—	—	0.35	—	0.25	0.05	0.15
A02960	296.0	380	PM	2.0–3.0	1.2	4.0–5.0	0.35	0.05	—	0.35	0.50	—	0.25	—	0.35
A03190	319.0	326	S,PM	5.5–6.5	1.0	3.0–4.0	0.50	0.10	—	0.35	1.0	—	0.25	—	0.50
A23190	B319.0	329	S,PM	5.5–6.5	1.2	3.0–4.0	0.8	0.10–0.50	—	0.50	1.0	—	0.25	—	0.50
A03280	328.0	327	S	7.5–8.5	1.0	1.0–2.0	0.20–0.6	0.20–0.6	0.35	0.25	1.5	—	0.25	—	0.50
A03320	332.0	332	PM	8.5–10.5	1.2	2.0–4.0	0.50	0.50–1.5	—	0.50	1.0	—	0.25	—	0.50
A03330	333.0	331	PM	8.0–10.0	1.0	3.0–4.0	0.50	0.05–0.50	—	0.50	1.0	—	0.25	—	0.50
A03360	336.0	321	PM	11.0–13.0	1.2	0.50–1.5	0.35	0.7–1.3	—	2.0–3.0	0.35	—	0.25	0.05	—
A03390	339.0(4)	334	PM	11.0–13.0	1.2	1.5–3.0	0.50	0.5–1.5	—	0.5–1.5	1.0	—	0.25	—	0.50
A03540	354.0	—	PM	8.6–9.4	0.20	1.6–2.0	0.10	0.40-0.6	—	—	0.10	—	0.20	0.05	0.15
A03550	355.0	322	S,PM	4.5–5.5	0.6(5)	1.0–1.5	0.50(5)	0.40-0.6	0.25	—	0.35	—	0.25	0.05	0.15
A33550	C355.0	335	S,PM	4.5–5.5	0.20	1.0–1.5	0.10	0.40-0.6	—	—	0.10	—	0.20	0.05	0.15
A03560	356.0	323	S,PM	6.5–7.5	0.6(5)	0.25	0.35(5)	0.20–0.45	—	—	0.35	—	0.25	0.05	0.15
A13560	A356.0	336	S,PM	6.5–7.5	0.20	0.20	0.10	0.25–0.45	—	—	0.10	—	0.20	0.05	0.15
A03570	357.0	—	S,PM	6.5–7.5	0.15	0.05	0.03	0.45-0.6	—	—	0.05	—	0.20	0.05	0.15
A13570	A357.0	—	S,PM	6.5–7.5	0.20	0.20	0.10	0.40–0.7	—	—	0.10	—	0.04–0.20	0.05(6)	0.15
A03590	359.0	—	S,PM	8.5–9.5	0.20	0.20	0.10	0.50-0.7	—	—	0.10	—	0.20	0.05	0.15
A03600	360.0	—	D	9.0–10.0	2.0	0.6	0.35	0.40-0.6	—	0.50	0.50	0.15	—	—	0.25
A13500	A360.0	309	D	9.0–10.0	1.3	0.6	0.35	0.40-0.6	—	0.50	0.50	0.15	—	—	0.25
A03800	380.0	308	D	7.5–9.5	2.0	3.0–4.0	0.50	0.10	—	0.50	3.0	0.35	—	—	0.50
A13800	A380.0	306	D	7.5–9.5	1.3	3.0–4.0	0.50	0.10	—	0.50	3.0	0.35	—	—	0.50

TABLE 3—CHEMICAL COMPOSITIONS OF SAE ALUMINUM CASTING ALLOYS [1] (continued)

UNS	ANSI Designation	Former SAE	Product[2]	Si	Fe	Cu	Mn	Mg	Cr	Ni	Zn	Sn	Ti	Others Each	Others Total
A03830	383.0	383	D	9.5–11.5	1.3	2.0–3.0	0.50	0.10	—	0.30	3.0	0.15	—	—	0.50
A03840	384.0	303	D	10.5–12.0	1.3	3.0–4.5	0.50	0.10	—	0.50	3.0	0.35	—	—	0.50
A03900	390.0	—	D	16.0–18.0	1.3	4.0–5.0	0.10	0.45–0.65	—	—	0.10	—	0.20	0.10	0.20
A13900	A390.0	—	S,PM	16.0–18.0	0.50	4.0–5.0	0.10	0.45–0.65	—	—	0.10	—	0.20	0.10	0.20
A23900	B390.0	—	D	16.0–18.0	1.3	4.0–5.0	0.50	0.45–0.65	—	0.10	1.5	—	0.20	0.10	0.20
A04130	413.0	—	D	11.0–13.0	2.0	1.0	0.35	0.10	—	0.50	0.50	0.15	—	—	0.25
A14130	A413.0	305	D	11.0–13.0	1.3	1.0	0.35	0.10	—	0.50	0.50	0.15	—	—	0.25
A24430	B443.0	35[7]	S,PM	4.5–6.0	0.8	0.15	0.35	0.05	—	—	0.35	—	0.25	0.05	0.15
A34430	C443.0	304	D	4.5–6.0	2.0	0.6	0.35	0.10	—	0.50	0.50	0.15	—	—	0.25
A14440	A444.0	I—	S	6.5–7.5	0.20	0.10	0.10	0.05	—	—	0.10	—	0.20	0.05	0.15
A05140	514.0	320	S	0.35	0.50	0.15	0.35	3.5–4.5	—	—	0.15	0.15	0.25	0.05	0.15
A05200	520.0	324	S	0.25	0.30	0.25	0.15	9.5–10.6	—	—	0.15	—	0.25	0.05	0.15
A05350	535.0	—	S	0.15	0.15	0.05	0.10–0.25	6.2–7.5	—	—	—	—	0.10–0.25	0.05[8]	0.15
A07050	705.0	311	S,PM	0.20	0.8	0.20	0.40–0.6	1.4–1.8	0.20–0.40	—	2.7–3.3	—	0.25	0.05	0.15
A07070	707.0	312	S,PM	0.20	0.8	0.20	0.40-0.6	1.8–2.4	0.20–0.40	—	4.0–4.5	—	0.25	0.05	0.15
A07100	710.0	313	S	0.15	0.50	0.35–0.65	0.05	0.6–0.8	—	—	6.0–7.0	—	0.25	0.05	0.15
A07120	712.0	310	S	0.30	0.50	0.25	0.10	0.50–0.65	0.40-0.6	—	5.0–6.5	—	0.15–0.25	0.05	0.20
A07130	713.0	315	S,PM	0.25	1.1	0.4–1.0	0.6	0.20–0.50	0.35	—	7.0–8.0	—	0.25	0.10	0.25

1. Values are maximum except where indicated as a range. Aluminum is the remainder.
2. S—sand cast; PM—permanent mold; D—die cast.
3. Also contains 0.40–1.0% silver.
4. Composition limits differ slightly from those previously listed for former SAE alloy 334.
5. If iron exceeds 0.45%, manganese content shall not be less than one-half the iron content.
6. Also contains 0.04–0.07% beryllium.
7. Former SAE 35 similar to B443.0. Actual former SAE 35 was alloy 443.0 which has been replaced in commercial use by alloy B443.0.
8. Also contains 0.003–0.007% beryllium, 0.002 max. % boron.

TABLE 4—TYPICAL PHYSICAL PROPERTIES OF SAE CASTING ALLOYS

Alloy UNS	Alloy ANSI	Temper	Density lb/in^2	Density kg/m^2	Approximate Melting Range[1] °F	Approximate Melting Range[1] °C	Elec. Cond. % IACS	Therm. Cond. W/(m · K)	Coeff. of Thermal Expan., x 10^{-6} 68–212 °F per °F	20–100 °C per °C	68–572 °F per °F	20–300 °C per °C
A02010	201.0	T6	0.101	2800	995–1200	535–650	30	121	10.7	19.3	13.7	24.7
		T7	0.101	2800	995–1200	535–650	30	121	10.7	19.3	13.7	24.7
A02060	206.0	T4	0.101	2800	1010–1200	542–650		121	10.7	19.3	—	—
A02080	208.0	F	0.101	2800	970–1160	521–627	31	125	12.4	22.3	13.4	24.1
		T4	0.101	2800	970–1160	521–627	—	—	12.4	22.3	13.4	24.1
		T55	0.101	2800	970–1160	521–627	—	—	12.4	22.3	13.4	24.1
		T6	0.101	2800	970–1160	521–627	—	—	12.4	22.3	13.4	24.1
		T7	0.101	2800	970–1160	521–627	—	—	12.4	22.3	13.4	24.1
A02220	222.0	0	0.107	2960	965–1155	518–624	—	—	12.3	22.1	13.1	23.6
		T551	0.107	2960	965–1155	518–624	—	—	12.3	22.1	13.1	23.6
		T61	0.107	2960	965–1155	518–624	33	130	12.3	22.1	13.1	23.6
		T65	0.107	2960	965–1155	518–624	—	—	12.3	22.1	13.1	23.6
A02420	242.0	0	0.102	2820	990–1175	532–635	—	—	12.6	22.7	13.6	24.5
		T571[2]	0.102	2820	990–1175	532–635	34	134	12.6	22.7	13.6	24.5
		T61	0.102	2820	990–1175	532–635	—	—	12.6	22.7	13.6	24.5
		T77	0.102	2820	990–1175	532–635	38	151	12.6	22.7	13.6	24.5
A02950	295.0	T4	0.102	2820	970–1190	521–643	—	138	12.7	22.9	13.8	24.8
		T6	0.102	2820	970–1190	521–643	35	138	12.7	22.9	13.8	24.8
		T62	0.102	2820	970–1190	521–643	—	138	12.7	22.9	13.8	24.8
		T7	0.102	2820	970–1190	521–643	—	—	12.7	22.9	13.8	24.8
A02960	296.0	T4	0.101	2800	970–1170	521–632	—	130	12.2	22.0	13.3	23.9
		T6[2]	0.101	2800	970–1170	521–632	33	130	12.2	22.0	13.3	23.9
		T7	0.101	2800	970–1170	521–632	—	—	12.2	22.0	13.3	23.9
A03190	319.0	F	0.101	2800	960–1120	516–604	27	109	11.9	21.4	12.7	22.9
		T5	0.101	2800	960–1120	516–604	—	—	11.9	21.4	12.7	22.9
		T6	0.101	2800	960–1120	516–604	—	—	11.9	21.4	12.7	22.9
		T61	0.101	2800	960–1120	516–604	—	—	11.9	21.4	12.7	22.9
A23190	B319.0	T5	—	—	—	—	—	—	—	—	—	—
		T6	—	—	—	—	—	—	—	—	—	—

TABLE 4—TYPICAL PHYSICAL PROPERTIES OF SAE CASTING ALLOYS (continued)

Alloy			Density		Approximate Melting Range[1]		Elec. Cond.	Therm. Cond.	Coeff. of Thermal Expan., x 10^{-6}			
UNS	ANSI	Temper	lb/in^2	kg/m^2	°F	°C	% IACS	W/(m · K)	68–212 °F per °F	20–100 °C per °C	68–572 °F per °F	20–300 °C per °C
A03280	328.0	F	0.098	2720	1025–1105	552–596	30	121	11.9	21.4	12.9	23.2
		T6	0.098	2720	1025–1105	552–596	—	—	11.9	21.4	12.9	23.2
A03320	332.0	T5[2]	0.100	2770	970–1080	521–582	26	104	11.5	20.7	12.4	22.3
		F[2]	0.100	2770	960–1085	516–585	26	104	11.4	20.5	12.4	22.3
A03330	333.0	T5[2]	0.100	2770	960–1085	516–585	29	117	11.4	20.5	12.4	22.3
		T6[2]	0.100	2770	960–1085	516–585	29	117	11.4	20.5	12.4	22.3
		T7[2]	0.100	2770	960–1085	516–585	35	138	11.4	20.5	12.4	22.3
A03360	336.0	T551[2]	0.098	2720	1000–1050	538–566	29	117	11.0	19.8	12.0	21.6
		T65	0.098	2720	1000–1050	538–566	—	—	11.0	19.8	12.0	21.6
A03390	339.0	T551[2]	0.098	2720	—	—	—	117	—	—	—	—
A03540	354.0	T61	0.098	2720	1000–1105	538–596	32	125	11.6	20.9	12.7	22.9
A03550	355.0	T51	0.098	2720	1015–1150	546–621	43	167	12.4	22.3	13.7	24.7
		T6	0.098	2720	1015–1150	546–621	36	142	12.4	22.3	13.7	24.7
		T62[2]	0.098	2720	1015–1150	546–621	36	142	12.4	22.3	13.7	24.7
		T7	0.098	2720	1015–1150	546–621	42	163	12.4	22.3	13.7	24.7
		T71	0.098	2720	1015–1150	546–621	39	151	12.4	22.3	13.7	24.7
A33550	C355.0	T6	0.098	2720	1015–1150	546–621	36	142	12.4	22.3	13.7	24.7
		T61	0.098	2720	1015–1150	546–621	37	146	12.4	22.3	13.7	24.7
A03560	356.0	F	0.097	2685	1035–1135	557–613	—	—	11.9	21.4	12.9	23.2
		T51	0.097	2685	1035–1135	557–613	43	167	11.9	21.4	12.9	23.2
		T6	0.097	2685	1035–1135	557–613	39	151	11.9	21.4	12.9	23.2
		T7	0.097	2685	1035–1135	557–613	40	155	11.9	21.4	12.9	23.2
		T71	0.097	2685	1035–1135	557–613	—	—	11.9	21.4	12.9	23.2
A13560	A356.0	T6	0.097	2685	1035–1135	557–613	—	—	11.9	21.4	12.9	23.2
		T61	0.097	2685	1035–1135	557–613	39	151	11.9	21.4	12.9	23.2
		T7	0.097	2685	1035–1135	557–613	—	—	11.9	21.4	12.9	23.2
		T71	0.097	2685	1035–1135	557–613	—	—	11.9	21.4	12.9	23.2
A03570	357.0	T6	0.097	2685	1035–1135	557–613	39	151	11.9	21.4	12.9	23.2
A13570	A357.0	T61	0.097	2685	1035–1135	557–613	39	151	11.9	21.4	12.9	23.2
A03590	359.0	T61	0.097	2685	1045–1115	563–602	35	138	11.6	20.9	12.7	22.9
A03600	360.0	F	0.095	2630	1035–1105	557–596	—	—	12.2[3]	22.0[3]	—	—
A13600	A360.0	F	0.095	2630	1035–1105	557–596	29	113	12.2[3]	22.0[3]	—	—
A03800	380.0	F	0.098	2720	1000–1100	538–593	23	96	12.1[3]	21.8[3]	—	—
A13830	A380.0	F	0.098	2720	1000–1100	538–593	—	100	—	—	—	—
A03830	383.0	F	0.098	2720	960–1080	516–582	23	96	11.7[3]	21.1[3]	—	—
A03840	384.0	F	0.098	2720	960–1080	516–582	23	96	11.7[3]	21.1[3]	—	—
A03900	390.0	F	—	—	—	—	—	—	—	—	—	—
A13900	A390.0	T5	0.099	2740	945–1200	507–649	25	134	10.0	18.0	—	—
		T6	0.099	2740	945–1200	507–649	—	—	10.0	18.0	—	—
		T7	0.099	2740	945–1200	507–649	—	—	10.0	18.0	—	—
A23900	B390.0	F	—	—	—	—	—	—	—	—	—	—
A04130	413.0	F	0.096	2660	1065–1080	574–582	—	—	11.9[3]	21.4[3]	—	—
A14130	A413.0	F	0.096	2660	1065–1080	574–582	31	121	11.9[3]	21.4[3]	—	—
A24430	B443.0	F	0.097	2685	1065–1170	574–632	37	146	12.3	22.1	13.4	24.1
A34430	C443.0	F	0.097	2685	1065–1170	574–632	37	142	12.9[3]	23.2[3]	—	—
A14440	A444.0	F	0.095	2635	1065–1145	574–618	41	159	12.1	21.8	13.2	23.8
A05140	514.0	F	0.096	2660	1085–1185	585–640	35	138	13.4	24.1	14.5	26.1
A05200	520.0	T4	0.093	2570	840–1120	449–604	21	88	13.7	24.7	14.8	26.6
A05350	535.0	F	0.095	2635	1020–1165	548–629	23	96	13.1	23.6	14.8	26.6
A07050	705.0	T5	0.100	2770	1105–1180	596–638	25	104	13.1	23.6	14.3	25.7
A07070	707.0	T5	0.100	2770	1085–1165	585–629	25	104	13.2	23.8	14.4	25.9
		T7	0.100	2770	1085–1165	585–629	—	—	13.2	23.8	14.4	25.9
A07100	710.0	T5	0.102	2820	1105–1195	596–646	35	138	13.4	24.1	14.6	26.3
A07120	712.0	T5	0.101	2800	1135–1200	613–649	35	138	13.7	24.7	14.8[4]	26.6[4]
A07130	713.0	T5	0.102	2810	1100–1180	593–638	30	121	13.4[4]	24.1[4]	14.6[4]	26.3[4]

1. The Approximate Melting Range data shown is a practical parameter of the alloy—not concise values. Normal and common composition and process variations can cause deviations from the values given.
2. Chill cast samples; all other samples cast in green sand molds.
3. For die cast alloys, data valid for temperature range of 68–392 °F (20–200 °C).
4. Estimated value.

TABLE 5—MECHANICAL PROPERTY LIMITS OF SAE SAND CASTING ALLOYS[1]

Alloy			Min. Tensile Strength		Min. Yield Strength (0.2% offset)			
UNS	ANSI	Temper	ksi	MPa	ksi	MPa	Elongation % Min. in 4D	Brinell Hardness[2] (500 kg)
A02010	201.0	T6	60.0	415	50.0	345	5.0	115–145
		T7	60.0	415	50.0	345	3.0	115–145
A02060	206.0	T4	40.0	275	24.0	165	8.0	—
A02080	208.0	F	19.0	130	12.0	85	1.5	40–70
		T55	21.0	145	—	—	—	—
A02220	222.0	0	23.0	160	—	—	—	—
		T61	30.0	205	—	—	—	100–130
A02420	242.0	0	23.0	160	—	—	—	—
		T571	29.0	200	—	—	—	—
		T61	32.0	220	20.0	140	—	90–120
		T77	24.0	165	13.0	90	1.0	—
A02950	295.0	T4	29.0	200	13.0	90	6.0	45–75
		T6	32.0	220	20.0	140	3.0	60–90
		T62	36.0	250	28.0	195	—	80–110
		T7	29.0	200	16.0	110	3.0	55–85
A03190	319.0	F	23.0	160	13.0	90	1.5	55–85
		T5	25.0	170	—	—	—	—
		T6	31.0	215	20.0	140	1.5	65–95
A23190	8319.0	T5	26.0[3]	180[3]	—	—	—	—
		T6	32.0[3]	220[3]	21.0[3]	145[3]	1.0[3]	70–100[3]
A03280	328.0	F	25.0	170	14.0	95	1.0	45–75
		T6	34.0	235	21.0	145	1.0	65–95
A03550	355.0	T51	25.0	170	18.0	125	—	50–80
		T6	32.0	220	20.0	140	2.0	65–95
		T7	35.0	240	—	—	—	—
		T71	30.0	205	22.0	150	—	60–90
A33550	C355.0	T6	36.0	250	25.0	170	2.5	—
		T61	36.0[3]	250[3]	30.0[3]	205[3]	1.0[3]	70–100[3]
A03560	356.0	F	19.0	130	—	—	2.0	40–70
		T51	23.0	160	16.0	110	—	45–75
		T6	30.0	205	20.0	140	3.0	55–85
		T7	31.0	215	29.0	200	—	60–90
		T71	25.0	170	18.0	125	3.0	45–75
A13560	A356.0	T6	34.0	235	24.0	165	3.5	55–85
		T7	32.0[3]	220[3]	30[3]	205[3]	—	—
		T71	26.0[3]	180[3]	19.0[3]	130[3]	4.0[3]	—
A03570	357.0	T6[4]	—	—	—	—	—	—
A13570	A357.0	T6[4]	—	—	—	—	—	—
A03590	359.0	T61[4]	—	—	—	—	—	—
A13900	A390.0	F	26.0[3]	180[3]	26.0[3]	180[3]	—	85–115[3]
		T5	26.0[3]	180[3]	26.0[3]	180[3]	—	85–115[3]
		T6	40.0[3]	275[3]	40.0[3]	275[3]	—	125–155[3]
		T7	36.0[3]	250[3]	36.0[3]	250[3]	—	100–130[3]
B24430	B443.0	F	17.0	115	6.0	40	3.0	25–55
A14440	A444.0	F	18.0[3]	125[3]	7.0[3]	50[3]	8.0[3]	35–65[3]
A05140	514.0	F	22.0	150	9.0	60	6.0	35–65
A05200	520.0	T4	42.0	290	22.0	150	12.0	60–90
A05350	535.0	F	35.0	240	18.0	125	9.0	60–90
A07050	705.0	T5	30.0	205	17.0	115	5.0	50–80
A07070	707.0	T5	33.0	230	22.0	150	2.0	60–90
		T7	37.0	255	30.0	205	1.0	65–95
A07100	710.0	T5	32.0	220	20.0	140	2.0	60–90
A07120	712.0	T5	34.0	235	25.0	170	4.0	60–90
A07130	713.0	T5	32.0	220	22.0	150	3.0	60–90

1. Values represent properties obtained from 0.500 in diameter separately cast test bars as depicted in Fig. 8 of ASTM B 557, cast in green sand molds, and tested in accordance with the procedures of ASTM B 557.
2. Hardness values are given for information only; not required for acceptance.
3. Preliminary value.
4. Mechanical properties for these alloys are dependent on casting process and heat treat procedures set for individual casting requirements. These alloys have generally been used in premium quality application, and process techniques have not been standardized. Consult individual foundry for applicable property limits.

TABLE 6—MECHANICAL PROPERTY LIMITS OF SAE PERMANENT MOLD CASTING ALLOYS[1]

Alloy			Min. Tensile Strength		Min. Yield Strength (0.2% offset)		Elongation	Brinell
UNS	ANSI	Temper	ksi	MPa	ksi	MPa	Min % in 4D	Hardness[2] (500 kg)
A02010	201.0	T6	60.0	415	50.0	345	5.0	115–145
		T7	60.0	415	50.0	345	3.0	115–145
A02060	206.0	T4	40.0[3]	275[3]	24.0[3]	165[3]	8.0[3]	—
		T4	33.0	230	15.0	105	4.5	60–90
A02080	208.0	T6	35.0	240	22.0	150	2.0	75–105
		T7	33.0	230	16.0	110	3.0	65–95
A02220	222.0	T551	30.0	205	—	—	—	100–130
		T65	40.0	275	—	—	—	125–155
A02420		0	24.0[3]	165[3]	—	—	—	—
	242.0	T571	34.0	235	—	—	—	90–120
		T61	40.0	275	—	—	—	95–125
		T4	33.0	230	15.0	105	4.5	60–90
A02960	296.0	T6	35.0	240	—	—	2.0	75–105
		T7	33.0	230	16.0	110	3.0	65–95
		F	28.0	195	14.0	95	1.5	70–100
A03190	319.0	T6	34.0	235	—	—	2.0	75–105
		T61	40.0	275	24.0	165	1.0	80–110
A23190	B319.0	F	29.0[3]	200[3]	15.0[3]	105[3]	1.0[3]	80–110[3]
		T6	36.0[3]	250[3]	—	—	1.0[3]	90–120[3]
A03320	332.0	T5	31.0	215	—	—	—	90–120
		F	28.0	195	—	—	—	65–100
A03330	333.0	T5	30.0	205	—	—	—	70–105
		T6	35.0	240	—	—	—	85–115
		T7	31.0	215	—	—	—	75–105
A03360	336.0	T551	31.0	215	—	—	—	90–120
		T65	40.0	275	—	—	—	110–140
A03390	339.0	T551	31.0	215	—	—	—	—
A03540	354.0	T61	48.0	330	37.0	255	3.0	—
		T51	27.0	185	—	—	—	60–90
		T6	37.0	255	—	—	1.5	75–105
A03550	355.0	T62	42.0	290	—	—	—	90–120
		T7	36.0	250	—	—	—	70–100
		T71	34.0	235	27.0	185	—	65–95
A33550	C355.0	T61	40.0	275	30.0	205	3.0	75–105
		F	21.0	145	—	—	3.0	40–70
		T51	25.0	170	—	—	—	55–85
A03560	356.0	T6	33.0	230	22.0	150	3.0	65–95
		T7	25.0	170	—	—	3.0	60–90
		T71	25.0	170	—	—	3.0	60–90
A13560	A356.0	T6	33.0[3]	230[3]	22.0[3]	150[3]	5.0[3]	65–95
		T61	37.0	255	26.0	180	5.0	70–100
A03570	357.0	T6	45.0	310	—	—	3.0	75–105
A13570	A357.0	T61	45.0	310	36.0	250	3.0	85–115
A03590	359.0	T61	45.0	310	34.0	235	4.0	75–105
		F	29.0[3]	200[3]	29.0[3]	200[3]	—	95–125[3]
A13900	A390.0	T5	29.0[3]	200[3]	29.0[3]	200[3]	—	95–125[3]
		T6	45.0[3]	310[3]	45.0[3]	310[3]	—	130–160[3]
		T7	38.0[3]	260[3]	38.0[3]	260[3]	—	105–135[3]
A24430	B443.0	F	21.0	145	6.0	40	2.5	30–60
A07050	705.0	T5	37.0	255	17.0	115	10.0	55–85
A07070	707.0	T5	42.0	290	25.0	170	4.0	80–110
		T7	45.0	310	35.0	240	3.0	80–110
A07130	713.0	T5	32.0	220	22.0	150	4.0	60–90

1. Values represent properties obtained from 0.500 in diameter separately cast test bars as depicted in Fig. 8 of ASTM B 557, cast in iron permanent molds, and tested in accordance with the procedures of ASTM B 557.
2. Hardness values are given for information only; not required for acceptance.
3. Preliminary value.

TABLE 7—TYPICAL MECHANICAL PROPERTIES OF SAE DIE CASTING ALLOYS[1]

Alloy		Tensile Strength		Yield Strength (0.2% offset)		Elongation in 4D
UNS	ANSI	ksi	MPa	ksi	MPa	
A03600	360.0	44.0	300	25.0	170	2.5
A13600	A360.0	46.0	315	24.0	165	3.5
A03800	380.0	46.0	315	23.0	160	2.5
A13800	A380.0	47.0	325	23.0	160	3.5
A03830	383.0	45.0	310	22.0	150	3.5
A03840	384.0	48.0	330	24.0	165	2.5
A03900	390.0	41.0	285	35.0	240	1.0
A13900	B390.0	46.0	315	36.0	250	—
A04130	413.0	43.0	295	21.0	145	2.5
A14130	A413.0	42.0	290	19.0	130	3.5
A34430	C443.0	33.0	230	14.0	95	9.0

1. It must be thoroughly understood that the above values were obtained from die-cast test specimens depicted in Figure 13 of ASTM B 557, cast in a test bar die, and tested according to the procedures of ASTM B 557. Specimens cut from commercial die cast parts should not be compared to the above data.

The properties obtained from test specimens machined from castings will vary, depending upon the location from which the bar is taken. Specimens taken from thin sections may have properties higher than those of separately cast test bars, while specimens taken from heavy sections or from locations near gates or risers may show lower properties. These relations are not peculiar to aluminum alloy castings but are the same in the castings of other metals. In general, when test bars machined from a casting are used as the basis for acceptance or rejection, the mechanical properties of these test bars cut from the castings shall be agreed upon between the purchaser and supplier.

The separately cast test specimen serves as a control of the metal quality, and in the case of heat treated alloys, serves also as a control of the heat treatment process, hence such test bars must be heat treated with the castings they represent. Factors of safety used in design cover the variations of commercial castings from the properties specified for the alloy which are based on tests of separately cast test specimens.

8. Temper Designation System—The temper designation system used for cast aluminum alloys is based on the treatment used to produce the temper. There are three major designations for aluminum castings: F, O, and T. These are defined as follows:

F—As Cast—Applies to castings as they are removed from the mold, with no subsequent thermal treatment to enhance or alter properties.

O—Annealed—Applies to castings that are thermally treated to obtain complete strain relief. This treatment provides the most ductile and most dimensionally stable condition, but it is also the weakest and softest state of the alloy.

T—Thermally Treated or Heat Treated—Applies to castings that are thermally treated to produce stable tempers other than F or "as cast." The T is always followed by one or more digits that further define the specific treatment used. In each case, the first digit after T gives the basic type of treatment used. When more than one treatment of a basic type is used, the modifications of the initial basic treatment are identified by a second or sometimes a third digit; for example, T5 is the treatment for an alloy. T51 would be a newer modification of the T5 treatment. T52 might be a second modification, etc.

The subdivisions of T temper or the basic types of heat treatment used on castings and their identification are listed and defined as follows:

T4—Solution Heat Treated, Quenched, and Naturally Aged Castings—Typically, a solution heat treatment consists of heating to a temperature somewhat below the melting temperature of the alloy for an extended period of time. This allows dispersion, solutionizing, or homogenizing of the alloy to remove constituent segregation normal in the "as solidified" condition of the alloy. In this manner, subsequent controlled precipitation of the constituents produces an evenly distributed hardening or strengthening of the alloy. This precipitation or aging may occur with heating to slightly elevated temperatures as artificial aging or it may occur with time only at room temperature. This is called natural aging. In some alloys, natural aging reaches a desirable or stable condition 3 to 14 days after quenching from the solution heat treatment temperatures. The modification numbers for T4 usually indicate variations in quenching media.

T5—"As-Cast" Castings Given an Artificial Age Only—Applies to castings that have been cooled from the pouring temperature and given an artificial age without a prior solution heat treatment. This is to improve mechanical properties or dimensional stability or both. Also, T5 temper is used to avoid possible distortion due to solutionizing and quenching treatments.

T6—Solution Heat Treated, Quenched, and Then Artificially Aged—This T6 treatment of castings is to improve mechanical properties, dimensional stability, or both.

T7—Solution Heat Treated, Quenched, and Then Stabilized—Applies to castings which are stabilized to an aging condition beyond the point of maximum strength to provide control of some special characteristic or enable use of the part at temperatures higher than the lower T6 aging temperature.

Table 8 for typical thermal treatments applied to aluminum casting alloys.

NOTE—Special timing conditions between thermal treatments are often required to obtain optimum results; for example, a period of natural aging at room temperature may be required after solution heat treatment and before aging or stabilizing. Also, after solution heat treatment, rapid quenching is often needed to produce the required mechanical properties. (Time lapse of not more than 10 s before entry into the quenching medium is usually considered desirable.)

TABLE 8—TYPICAL THERMAL TREATMENTS

Alloy			Sand Castings						Permanent Mold Castings					
			Solution Heat Treatment[1]			Precipitation Heat Treatment			Solution Heat Treatment[1]			Precipitation Heat Treatment		
			Temperature			Temperature			Temperature			Temperature		
UNS	ANSI	Temper	±10 °F	±6 °C	Hours	±10 °F	±6 °C	Hours	±10 °F	±6 °C	Hours	±10 °F	±6 °C	Hours
A02010	201.0	T6	980[2]	527[2]	14–20	310[3]	154[3]	20	980[2]	527[2]	14–20	310[3]	154[3]	20
		T7	980[2]	527[2]	14–20	370[3]	188[3]	5	980[2]	527[2]	14–20	370[3]	188[3]	5
A02060	206.0	T4	980[2]	527[2]	14–20	—	—	—	980[2]	527[2]	14–20	—	—	—
A02080	208.0	T4	—	—	—	—	—	—	940	504	4–12	—	—	—
		T55	—	—	—	310	154	16	—	—	—	—	—	—
		T6	—	—	—	—	—	—	940	504	4–12	310	154	2–5
		T7	—	—	—	—	—	—	940	504	4–12	500	260	4–6

TABLE 8—TYPICAL THERMAL TREATMENTS (continued)

Alloy			Sand Castings						Permanent Mold Castings					
			Solution Heat Treatment(1)			Precipitation Heat Treatment			Solution Heat Treatment(1)			Precipitation Heat Treatment		
			Temperature			Temperature			Temperature			Temperature		
UNS	ANSI	Temper	±10 °F	±6 °C	Hours	±10 °F	±6 °C	Hours	±10 °F	±6 °C	Hours	±10 °F	±6 °C	Hours
		0(4)	—	—	—	—	—	—	—	—	—	—	—	—
A02220	222.0	T551	—	—	—	—	—	—	—	—	—	340	171	16–22
		T61	950	510	8–12	310	154	10–12	—	—	—	—	—	—
		T65	—	—	—	—	—	—	950	510	4–12	340	171	7–9
		0	—	—	—	650	343	3	—	—	—	650	343	3
		T571	—	—	—	400	204	8	—	—	—	340	171	22–26
A02420	242.0	T61	960(5)	516	6–12	450	232	1–3	960(5)	516	4–12	400	204	3–5
		T77	960(5)	515	6	650	342	2 min	—	—	—	—	—	—
		T4	960	516	12	—	—	—	—	—	—	—	—	—
		T6	960	516	12	310	154	3–6	—	—	—	—	—	—
A02950	295.0	T62	960	516	12	310	154	12–24	—	—	—	—	—	—
		T7	960	516	12	500	260	4–6	—	—	—	—	—	—
		T4	—	—	—	—	—	—	950	510	8	—	—	—
A02960	296.0	T6	—	—	—	—	—	—	950	510	8	310	154	3–8
		T7	—	—	—	—	—	—	950	510	8	500	260	4–6
		T5	—	—	—	400	204	8	—	—	—	—	—	—
A03190	319.0	T6	940	504	6–12	310	154	2–5	940	504	4–12	310	154	2–5
		T61	—	—	—	—	—	—	940	504	4–12	310	154	8–12
A23190	B319.0	T5	—	—	—	400	204	8						
		T6	940	504	6–12	310	154	2–5	940	504	4–12	310	154	2–5
A03280	328.0	T6	960	516	8–12	310	154	2–5	—	—	—	—	—	—
A03320	332.0	T5	—	—	—	—	—	—	—	—	—	400	204	7–9
		T5	—	—	—	—	—	—	—	—	—	400	204	7–9
A03330	333.0	T6	—	—	—	—	—	—	940	504	6–12	310	154	2–5
		T7	—	—	—	—	—	—	940	504	6–12	500	260	4–6
A03360	336.0	T551	—	—	—	—	—	—	—	—	—	400	204	7–9
		T65	—	—	—	—	—	—	960	516	8	400	204	7–9
A03390	339.0	T551	—	—	—	—	—	—	—	—	—	400	204	8–12
A03540	354.0(6)	T61	—	—	—	—	—	—	980	527	10–12	310 (7)	154(7)	10–12
		T51	—	—	—	440	227	7–9	—	—	—	440	227	7–9
		T6	980	527	8–12	310	154	3–5	980	527	4–12	310	154	2–5
A03350	355.0	T62	—	—	—	—	—	—	980	527	4–12	340	171	14–18
		T7	527	980	8–12	440	227	3–5	980	527	4–12	440	227	3–9
		T71	980	527	8–12	475	246	4–6	980	527	4–12	475	246	3–6
A33550	C355.0(8)	T6	980	527	12	310(7)	154(7)	3–5	—	—	—	—	—	—
		T61	980	527	12	310(7)	154(7)	10–12	980	527	6–12	310(7)	154(7)	10–12
		T51	—	—	—	440	227	7–9	—	—	—	440	227	7–9
A03560	356.0	T6	1000	538	8–12	310	154	3–5	1000	538	4–12	310	154	2–5
		T7	1000	538	8-12	400	204	3–5	1000	538	4–12	440	227	7–9
		T71	1000	538	8–12	475	246	2–4	1000	538	4–12	475	246	3–6
		T6	1000	538	12	310(7)	154(7)	2–5	1000	538	6–12	310(7)	154(7)	2–5
A13560	A356.0[8]	T61	—	—	—	—	—	—	1000	538	6–12	310(7)	154(7)	6–12
		T7	1000	538	12	440(7)	227(7)	8	—	—	—	—	—	—
		T71	1000	538	12	475(7)	246(7)	3	—	—	—	—	—	—
A03570	357.0	T6	1000	538	12	350	177	6						
A13570	A357.0[8]	T61	1000	538	12	310	154	8–10	1000	538	10	310	154	8
A03590	359.0[8]	T61	1000	538	10–14	310	154	10–12	1000	538	10–14	310	154	10–12
		T5	—	—	—	450	232	8	—	—	—	450	232	8
A13900	A390.0	T6	925	496	8–12	350	177	8	925	496	6–12	350	177	8
		T7	925	496	8–12	450	232	8	925	496	6–12	450	232	8
A05200	520.0	T4(9)	810	432	16–18	—	—	—	—	—	—	—	—	—
A07050	705.0	T5	—	—	—	210	99	8	—	—	—	210	99	10
A07070	707.0	T5	—	—	—	210	99	8	—	—	—	210	99	8
		T7	990	532	8–16	350	177	4–10	990	532	8–10	350	177	4–10
A07100	710.0	T5	—	—	—	R.T.	R.T.	21(4)	—	—	—	—	—	—
A07120	712.0	T5	—	—	—	315(10)	157	6–8	—	—	—	—	—	—
A07130	713.0	T5	—	—	—	250(10)	121	16	—	—	—	250(10)	121	16

1. Quench in water at 150–212 °F (65–100 °C) except as noted.
2. Step solution heat treat 2 h at 950 °F (510 °C) prior to 980 °F (527 °C) temperature to avoid eutectic meeting.
3. Hold at room temperature for 12–24 h between solution and precipitation heat treatments.
4. Use air blast quench.
5. For these alloys, mechanical properties are often specified in critical casting locations. Precipitation heat treat temperatures and times may be widely altered to achieve specified casting properties.
6. Hold at room temperature for 8 h minimum between solution and precipitation heat treatments.
7. Quench in water at 150–212°F (65–100°C) for controlled time of 10–20 s only, then cool in still air outside the furnance.
8. Stress relieve for dimensional stability as follows: (1) Hold at 775 ± 25 °F (413 ± 14 °C) for 5 h. Then (2) furnace cool to 650 °F (343 °C) for 2 or more h. Then (3) furnace cool to 450 °F (232 °C) for not more than 1/2 h. Then (4) furnace cool to 250 °F (121 °C) for approximately 2 h. Then (5) cool to room temperature in still air outside the furnance.
9. For these alloys, mechanical properties are often specified in critical casting locations. Precipitation heat treat temperatures and times may be widely altered to achieve specified casting properties.
10. May be held at room temperature for 21 days in lieu of precipitation heat treatment.

WROUGHT ALUMINUM APPLICATIONS GUIDELINES—SAE J1434 JAN1989

SAE Information Report

Report of the SAE Nonferrous Metals Committee approved June 1983 and reaffirmed January 1989.

Foreword—This Reaffirmed Document has not changed other than to put it into the new SAE Technical Standards Board Format.

1. Scope—This report approaches the material selection process from the designer's viewpoint. Information is presented in a format designed to guide the user through a series of decision-making steps. "Applications criteria" along with engineering and manufacturing data are emphasized to enable the merits of aluminum for specific applications to be evaluated and the appropriate alloys and tempers to be chosen.

2. References

2.1 Applicable Publications

2.1.1 SAE PUBLICATION—Available from SAE, 400 Commonwealth Drive, Warrendale, PA 15096-0001.

SAE J399—Anodized Aluminum Automotive Parts

3. General Characteristics—In summary, aluminum is a suitable material for automotive applications. Its performance is a function of the degree to which its characteristics - which are different from steel - are recognized and taken into account in the design, fabrication, and assembly operations.

3.1 Strength—Typical property characteristics are illustrated in Figures 1 and 2. Commercially pure aluminum has tensile yield and ultimate strengths of about 50 MPa (7 ksi) and 90 MPa (13 ksi). Values approaching 500 MPa (73 ksi) and 600 MPa (87 ksi) can be obtained with a combination of the following:

a. Working the metal, as by cold rolling and forming.
b. Alloying aluminum with small percentages of one or more other metals such as manganese, silicon, copper, magnesium, or zinc.
c. Heat treatment and aging, as in the case of heat-treatable alloys. As a general rule, there is a reduction in elongation as yield and ultimate strengths of an aluminum alloy are increased by cold work or heat treatment. For alloys having a tensile yield strength of 500 MPa (73 ksi), elongations vary from 8–12%.

The strength and modulus of aluminum and its alloys decrease at elevated temperatures, although some alloys retain good strength at temperatures up to 200–260°C (400–500°F). At sub-zero temperatures, however, their strength increases without loss of ductility so that aluminum is a particularly useful metal for low-temperature applications.

3.2 Fatigue—Components subjected to repeated loads should be carefully checked for the possibility of fatigue failure. Aluminum does not exhibit well-defined endurance limits. Typically, the endurance limits published for aluminum alloys are based on 500 million cycles. More data are being generated at 10 million cycles.

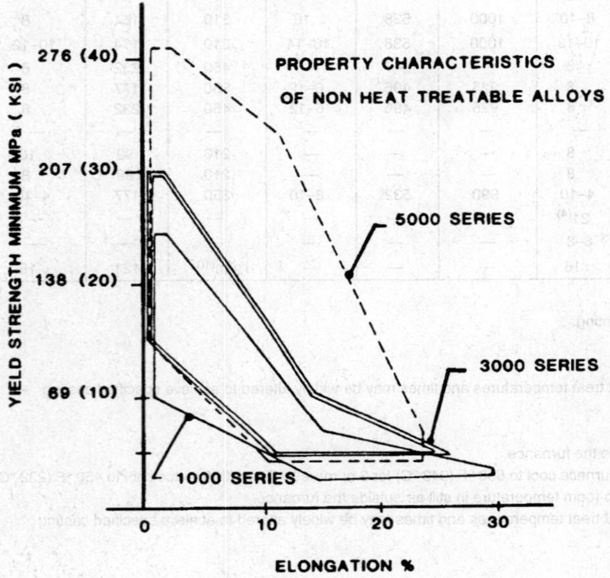

FIGURE 1—

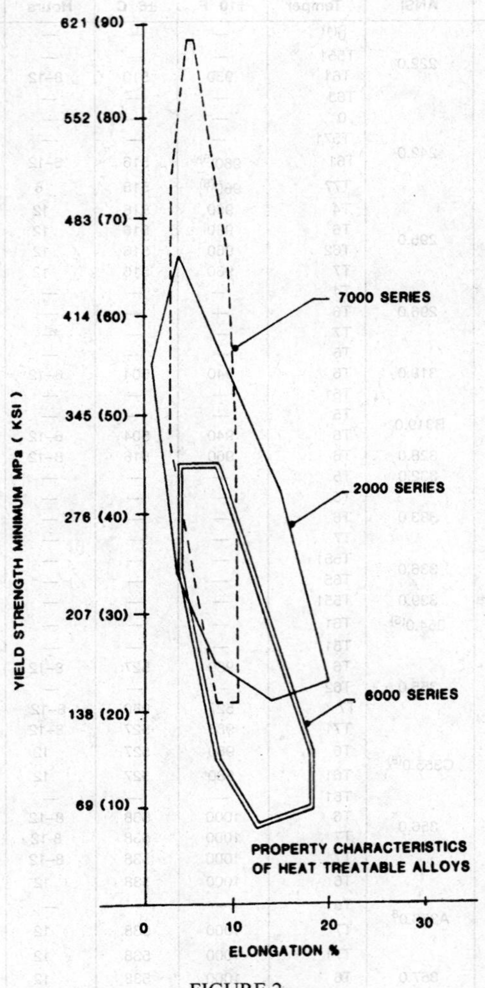

FIGURE 2—

Limited strain control life data are also available. An S/N curve representing the design condition is required to take full advantage of an aluminum alloy when designing for fatigue. Connections, joints, holes, or other features that cause stress concentrations are areas subject to fatigue, especially with aluminum alloys. Careful design can reduce concentrations in highly stressed areas, thereby making the most efficient use of the material. All changes between different cross sections within a component should be gradual, as smooth transitions produce an improvement in the fatigue life of a component. In the assessment of fatigue, it is invaluable to compare available test data for joints similar to those of interest.

3.3 Corrosion Resistance—Aluminum alloys are known for their excellent atmospheric and road salt corrosion resistance, which results from the tightly adherent natural oxide film present on the surface. In many instances, aluminum alloys can be exposed to industrial and seacoast environment with no protection; others may require a protective coating at least on faying surfaces. In situations where crevices and pockets allow accumulation of mud and road salts and at junctions with dissimilar metals (galvanic couples), the corrosion protection of the natural oxide is insufficient and severe corrosion damage can occur. The former conditions should be avoided where possible in the design stage (for example, elimination of shelves, incorporation of drain holes, etc.). The elimination of the latter galvanic joints is extremely difficult or impossible in most ground transportation applications and various combinations of coatings and insulation techniques must be utilized.

Certain alloys, especially those containing over 3% magnesium and magnesium/zinc can be susceptible to stress corrosion cracking. This susceptibility must be considered in design and testing and care should be exercised in selecting appropriate alloys and tempers when designing structural members from these alloys.

3.4 Finishing—Aluminum needs no protective coatings for many applications. In many instances, the surface finish supplied is entirely adequate without further finishing. Where the plain aluminum surface does not suffice, or where decoration or additional protection is required, a wide variety of surface finishes such as chemical, electrochemical, and paint finishes may be applied.

Chemical conversion coatings are available for additional corrosion protection. They also provide an excellent base for paint. Electroplating procedures have been developed to give aluminum an attractive, durable finish. Anodic coatings are used for both decorative and functional applications. Hardcoat anodized aluminum surfaces can provide wear resistance similar to case-hardened steel. Vitreous enamels have also been developed for aluminum.

3.5 Fabrication—Aluminum can be cast, stamped, drawn, extruded, forged, spun, roll formed, and cold impacted. Typical aluminum body-sheet alloys are not as formable as low-carbon steel, but are comparable to high-strength low-alloy steels. Aluminum can be fabricated on conventional press lines with modifications in tooling, lubrication, and handling. Formability considerations should be taken into account in the initial design phase.

3.6 Machinability—The high speed with which many aluminum alloys may be machined is an important factor in determining the manufacturing cost of aluminum parts. Aluminum may be turned, milled, bored, or machined at the maximum speeds of which most machines are capable. An example of this is aluminum rod and bar employed in the high speed manufacture of parts by automatic screw machines.

3.7 Joining—Aluminum may be resistance welded, arc welded, brazed, soldered, and adhesive bonded. It may also be joined by mechanical systems such as hemming, riveting, clinching, pierce riveting, bolting, and stitching. Resistance welding, clinching, and riveting may be combined with adhesives for improved strength and fatigue life. Resistance spot welding, for high-speed production applications, is in the developmental phase.

3.8 Electrical Conductivity—Electrical conductor grades of aluminum have 62% of the current carrying capacity of copper in equal volumes. These grades of aluminum have equal current carrying capacity at 1/2 the weight of copper. The high electrical conductivity property has led to the widespread use of aluminum in electromagnetic radiation shielding.

3.9 Magnetic Properties—Aluminum is nonmagnetic if sufficiently free from paramagnetic impurities such as iron. This property has led to the use of aluminum in sensitive mechanical and electronic devices.

3.10 Thermal Conductivity—The high thermal conductivity of aluminum has led to its extensive use in radiators, heat exchangers, heat sinks, and other devices that involve the transfer of thermal energy.

3.11 Reflectivity—Aluminum is an excellent reflector of radiant energy through the entire range of wavelengths, from ultraviolet through the visible spectrum and infrared heat waves. It is used for heat shields. It also reflects electromagnetic wavelengths in the radio and radar range. Aluminum has a light reflectivity of over 80% which has led to its wide use in automotive trim, reflectors, and in lighting fixtures.

4. Alloy and Temper Designation Systems

4.1 The Metallurgy of Aluminum—This section is intended to give the automotive designer a brief overview of the different types of alloys available and an indication of the effects of alloying elements. The numerical alloy designation system adopted by the aluminum industry is based on the principal alloying elements in each class of alloy.

In high-purity form, aluminum is soft and ductile. Most automotive uses, however, require greater strength than pure aluminum offers. This is achieved in aluminum first by the addition of other elements which singly, or in combination, impart strength to the metal to produce various alloys. Further strengthening is possible by heat treatment and cold work.

4.1.1 NON-HEAT-TREATABLE ALLOYS—The initial strength of alloys in this group depends on the hardening effect provided by manganese, silicon, iron, and magnesium, singly, or in various combinations. The non-heat-treatable alloys are usually designated as the 1000, 3000, 4000, or 5000 series. Further, strengthening is achieved by various degrees of cold working, denoted by the "H" series of tempers. Alloys containing appreciable amounts of magnesium, when supplied in strain-hardened tempers, are usually given a final elevated-temperature treatment called stabilizing to insure stability of properties.

4.1.2 HEAT-TREATABLE ALLOYS—The initial strength of alloys in this group is enhanced by the addition of alloying elements such as copper, magnesium, zinc, and silicon. These alloys are designated as the 2000, 6000, or 7000 series. It is possible to subject them to thermal treatments which will impart pronounced strengthening, denoted by the "T" series of tempers.

The first step, called heat treatment or solution heat treatment, is an elevated-temperature process designed to put the soluble element or elements in solid solution. This is followed by rapid quenching, usually in water.

At room or elevated temperature, the alloys are not stable after quenching and precipitation of the constituents from the super-saturated solution begins. After a period of several days at room temperature, termed aging or room-temperature precipitation, the alloy is considerably stronger. Many alloys approach a stable condition at room temperature, but some alloys, particularly those containing zinc magnesium or zinc with magnesium and copper, continue to age harden for long periods of time at room temperature.

By heating for a controlled time at slightly elevated temperatures, further strengthening is possible and properties are stabilized. This process is called artificial aging or precipitation hardening. By the proper combination of solution heat treatment, quenching, cold working, and artificial aging, the highest strengths are obtained.

4.1.3 ANNEALING CHARACTERISTICS—All wrought aluminum alloys are available in annealed form. In addition, it may be desirable to anneal an alloy from any other initial temper, after working, or between successive stages of working such as in deep drawing.

4.2 Alloy Designation System and Effect of Alloying Elements

4.2.1 1000 SERIES—Aluminum of 99% or higher purity. This series has many applications especially in the electrical and chemical fields and is characterized by excellent corrosion resistance, high thermal and electrical conductivity, low mechanical properties, and excellent workability. Moderate increases in strength may be obtained by strain hardening. Iron and silicon are the major impurities.

4.2.2 2000 SERIES—Copper is the principal alloying element in this group. These alloys require solution heat treatment to obtain optimum properties. The heat-treated condition has mechanical properties that are similar to, and sometimes exceed, those of mild steel. In some instances, artificial aging is employed to further increase the mechanical properties. This treatment increases yield strength, with attendant loss in elongation; its effect on ultimate tensile strength is not as great.

4.2.3 3000 SERIES—Manganese up to 1.5% is the major alloying element in this group of work-hardenable alloys. One of these is the alloy 3003 which is widely used as a general-purpose alloy for low to moderate strength applications requiring good workability.

4.2.4 4000 SERIES—The major alloying element of this group is silicon, which can be added in sufficient quantities to cause substantial lowering of the melting point without producing brittleness in the resulting alloys. For this reason, aluminum-silicon alloys are used in welding wire and as brazing alloys where a lower melting point than that of the parent metal is required. Alloys in this series are non-heat-treatable. When used in welding heat-treatable alloys, they will pick up some of the alloying constituents of the latter and so respond to heat treatment to a limited extent.

4.2.5 5000 SERIES—Magnesium is one of the most effective and widely used alloying elements for aluminum. When it is used as the major alloying element or with manganese, the result is a moderate to high strength non-heat-treatable alloy. Alloys in this series possess good welding and low temperature characteristics and good resistance to corrosion in marine atmosphere. Certain limitations should be placed on the amount of cold work and service temperatures for the higher magnesium content alloys (alloys with over 3% magnesium) to avoid susceptibility to intergranular forms of corrosion.

4.2.6 6000 SERIES—Alloys in this group contain silicon and magnesium and are heat-treatable.

The magnesium-silicon (magnesium-silicide) alloys possess good formability and corrosion resistance, with medium strength. Alloys in this heat-treatable group may be formed in the solution heat-treated condition and then artificially aged to attain optimum properties.

4.2.7 7000 SERIES—Zinc is the major alloying element in this group which is usually coupled with a smaller percentage of magnesium resulting in heat-treatable alloys of very high strength. Usually other elements such as copper and chromium can be added in small quantities.

4.2.8 8000 SERIES—This series is used for wrought alloys where the principal alloying element is not covered within the preceding series. Thus, a number of different and generally very specialized alloys are included in the series. The series includes alloys where iron is the principal alloying addition, which are general purpose and high strength fin stock alloys.

4.3 Temper Designation System—The temper designation system is used for all forms of wrought and cast aluminum alloys except ingot. It is based on the sequences of basic treatments used to produce the various tempers. The temper designation follows the alloy designation, the two being separated by a hyphen. Basic temper designations consist of letters. Subdivisions of the basic tempers, where required, are indicated by one or more digits following the letter. These designate specific sequences of basic treatments, but only operations recognized as significantly influencing the characteristics of the product are indicated. Should some other variation of the same sequence of basic operations be applied to the same alloy, resulting in different characteristics, then additional digits are added to the designation.

4.3.1 BASIC TEMPER DESIGNATION

F-as fabricated - Applies to the products of shaping processes in which no special control over thermal conditions or strain hardening is employed. For wrought products, there are no mechanical property limits.

O-annealed - Applies to wrought products which are annealed to obtain the lowest strength temper, and to cast products which are annealed to improve ductility and dimensional stability. The O may be followed by a digit other than zero.

H-strain-hardened (wrought products only) - Applies to products which have their own strength increased by strain hardening with or without supplementary thermal treatments to produce some reduction in strength. The H is always followed by two or more digits.

W-solution heat-treated - An unstable temper, applicable only to alloys which spontaneously age at room temperature after solution heat treatment. This designation is specific only when the period of natural aging is indicated; for example: W 1/2 h.

T-thermally treated to produce stable tempers other than F, O, or H - Applies to products which are thermally treated, with or without supplementary strain hardening, to produce stable tempers. The T is always followed by one or more digits.

4.3.1.1 Subdivision of H Temper: Strain-Hardened—The first digit following the H indicates the specific combination of basic operations, as follows:

H1-Strain-hardened only. Applies to products which are strain-hardened to obtain the desired strength without supplementary thermal treatment. The number following this designation indicates the degree of strain hardening.

H2-Strain-hardened and partially-annealed. Applies to products which are strain-hardened more than the desired final amount and then reduced in strength to the desired level by partial annealing. For alloys that age soften at room temperature, the H2 tempers have the same minimum ultimate tensile strength as the corresponding H3 tempers. For other alloys, the H2 tempers have the same minimum ultimate tensile strength as the corresponding H1 tempers and slightly higher elongation. The number following this designation indicates the degree of strain hardening remaining after the product has been partially-annealed.

H3-Strain-hardened and stabilized. Applies to products which are strain-hardened and whose mechanical properties are stabilized by a low temperature thermal treatment which results in slightly lowered tensile strength and improved ductility. This designation is applicable only to those alloys which, unless stabilized, gradually age soften at room temperature. The number following this designation indicates the degree of strain hardening after the stabilization treatment.

The digit following the designation H1, H2, and H3 indicates the degree of strain hardening. Numeral 8 has been assigned to indicate tempers having an ultimate tensile strength equivalent to that achieved by a cold reduction [temperature during reduction not to exceed 93°C (120°F)] of approximately 75% following a full anneal. Tempers between 0 (annealed) and 8 are designated by numerals 1–7. Material having an ultimate tensile strength about midway between that of the 0 temper and that of the 8 temper is designated by the numeral 4; about midway between 0 and 4 tempers by the numeral 2; and about midway between 4 and 8 tempers by the numeral 6. Numeral 9 designates tempers whose minimum ultimate tensile strength exceeds that of the 8 temper by 14 MPa (2.0 ksi) or more. For two-digit H tempers whose second digit is odd, the standard limits for ultimate tensile strength are exactly midway between those of the adjacent two digit H tempers whose second digits are even.

NOTE—For alloys, which cannot be cold reduced an amount sufficient to establish an ultimate tensile strength applicable to the 8 temper (75% cold reduction after full anneal), the 6 temper tensile strength may be established by a cold reduction of approximately 55% following a full anneal, or the 4 temper tensile strength may be established by a cold reduction of approximately 35% after a full anneal.

The third digit,[1] when used, indicates a variation of a two-digit temper. It is used when the degree of control of temper or the mechanical properties are different from, but close to, those for the two-digit H temper designation to which it is added, or when some other characteristic is significantly affected. [1] for three-digit H tempers.

NOTE—The minimum ultimate tensile strength of a three-digit H temper is at least as close to that of the corresponding two-digit H temper as it is to the adjacent two-digit H tempers.

4.3.1.2 Subdivision of T Temper: Thermally-Treated—Numerals 1–10 following the T indicate specific sequences of basic treatments, as follows: [2]

T1-Cooled from an elevated-temperature shaping process and naturally-aged to a substantially stable condition. Applies to products which are not cold-worked after cooling from an elevated-temperature shaping process, or in which the effect of cold work in flattening or straightening may not be recognized in mechanical property limits.

T2-Cooled from an elevated-temperature shaping process, cold-worked, and naturally-aged to a substantially stable condition. Applies to products which are cold-worked to improve strength after cooling from an elevated-temperature shaping process, or in which the effect of cold work in flattening or straightening is recognized in mechanical property limits.

T3-Solution heat-treated, [3] cold-worked, and naturally-aged to a substantially stable condition. Applies to products which are cold-worked to improve strength after solution heat-treatment, or in which the effect of cold work in flattening or straightening is recognized in mechanical property limits.

T4-Solution heat-treated[3] and naturally-aged to a substantially stable condition. Applies to products which are not cold-worked after solution heat-treatment, or in which the effect of cold work in flattening or straightening may not be recognized in mechanical property limits.

T5-Cooled from an elevated-temperature shaping process and then artificially-aged. Applies to products which are not cold-worked after cooling from an elevated-temperature shaping process, or in which the effect of cold work in flattening or straightening may not be recognized in mechanical property limits.

T6-Solution heat-treated[3] and then artificially-aged. Applies to products which are not cold-worked after solution heat-treatment, or in which the effect of cold work in flattening or straightening may not be recognized in mechanical property limits.

T7-Solution heat-treated[3] and overaged/stabilized. Applies to wrought products which are artificially aged after solution heat treatment to carry them beyond the point of maximum strength to provide control of some special characteristics.

T8-Solution heat-treated,[3] cold-worked, and then artificially-aged. Applies to products which are cold-worked to improve strength, or in which the effect of cold work in flattening or straightening is recognized in mechanical property limits.

T9-Solution heat-treated,[3] artificially-aged, and then cold-worked. Applies to products which are cold-worked to improve strength.

T10-Cooled from an elevated-temperature shaping process, cold-worked, and then artificially-aged. Applies to products which are cold-worked to improve strength, or in which the effect of cold work in flattening or straightening is recognized in mechanical property limits.

Additional digits,[4] the first of which shall not be zero, may be added to designations T1–T10 to indicate a variation in treatment which significantly alters

1. Numerals 1–9 may be arbitrarily assigned as the third digit and registered with The Aluminum Association for an alloy and product to indicate a variation of a two-digit H temper provided: (1) the temper is used or is available for use by more than one user, (2) mechanical property limits are registered, (3) the characteristics of the temper are significantly different from those of all other tempers which have the same sequence of basic treatments and for which designations already have been assigned for the same alloy and product, and (4) the following are also registered if characteristics other than mechanical properties are considered significant: (a) test methods and limits for the characteristics, or (b) the specific practices used to produce the temper. Zero has been assigned to indicate variations negotiated between the manufacturer and purchaser, which are not used widely enough to justify registration.
2. A period of natural aging at room temperature may occur between or after the operations listed for the T tempers. Control of this period is exercised when it is metallurgically important.
3. Solution heat treatment is achieved by heating cast or wrought products to a suitable temperature, holding at that temperature long enough to allow constituents to enter into solid solution, and cooling rapidly enough to hold the constituents in solution. Some 6000 series alloys attain the same specified mechanical properties whether furnace solution heat-treated or cooled from an elevated-temperature shaping process at a rate rapid enough to hold constituents in solution. In such cases the temper designations T3, T4, T6, T7, T8, and T9 are used to apply to either process and are appropriate designations.
4. Additional digits may be arbitrarily assigned and registered with the Aluminum Association for an alloy and product to indicate a variation of tempers T1-T10 provided: (1) the temper is used or is available for use by more than one user, (2) mechanical property limits are registered, (3) the characteristics of the temper are significantly different from those of all other tempers which have the same sequence of basic treatments and for which designations already have been assigned for the same alloy and product, and (4) the following are also registered if characteristics other than mechanical properties are considered significant: (a) test methods and limits for the characteristics, or (b) the specific practices used to produce the temper. Variations in treatment which do not alter the characteristics of the product are considered alternate treatments for which additional digits are not assigned.

the characteristics of the product. (See Footnote 4 for specific additional digits for T tempers.)

4.3.1.3 Variations of 0 Temper: Annealed—A digit following the 0, when used, indicates a product in the annealed condition having special characteristics.

5. Relative Features of Various Product Forms

5.1 Aluminum Sheet and Plate—Sheet is a rolled product having a thickness between 0.15 and 6.30 mm and is available in widths to approximately 2600 mm in coil or cut length form. It may be clad with other aluminum alloys for special finishes, corrosion protection, or brazing.

A variety of surface textures and patterns are available. Plate is a product thicker than 6.30 mm and is available in widths over 5 m. Some forms of plate may be cast rather than rolled as in tool and jig plate.

5.2 Foil—Foil is a rolled product less than 0.15 mm in thickness. It may be made in a variety of alloys for purposes such as electronic capacitors, fin stock for heat exchangers (some fin alloys are available which are anodic to the tubing used, giving corrosion protection), laminated packaging materials, reflective insulation, and plastic encapsulated foil trim.

5.3 Wire, Rod, and Bar—Wire, rod, and bar products are made by a sequence of rolling and drawing operations or less commonly by the extrusion process. Wire can be round, square, hexagonal, or rectangular in cross section. It is, by definition, 10 mm or less in diameter or the greatest perpendicular distance between parallel faces.

Rod is any round section over 10 mm in diameter. Bar is any section other than round with the greatest perpendicular distance between parallel faces being over 10 mm. Screw machine stock is rod, bar, or wire supplied in solid or hollow form and chamfered on the ends for automatic screw machines. A greater range of tempers in the non-heat-treatable alloys is available by rolling and drawing.

5.4 Extrusions—Extruded products are produced by forcing (hot, but not molten) metal through an orifice having a shape of the desired cross section. Complex structural shapes and beams having wide, thick flanges, and thin webs for efficient material utilization can be extruded. Irregular shapes having channels or slots for mating parts can be produced.

Sizes can range from rails for model railroads to aircraft wing spars weighing 100 kg/m of length.

Designers have found that the advantages of closer dimensional control and elimination of subsequent machining operations have warranted the use of extrusions in their designs.

5.5 Tube and Pipe—Tube and pipe are produced by extrusion, welding, or cold drawing. Round, square, rectangular, and oval shapes are available. Selection of the process is based on tolerance and straightness requirements. Tubing can be supplied in coils or straight lengths.

5.6 Forgings—Aluminum alloy forgings are produced on conventional hammer equipment and on hydraulic and mechanical presses. Forgings are applicable for brackets, support members, and connectors to other structural members where high strength, fatigue life, and good ductility are required. Die forgings are made in sizes from air-conditioning compressor connecting rods to parts covering over 4 m^2 and weighing 1500 kg.

5.7 Impact Extrusions—The primary advantage of an impact extrusion is that it can be made into a closed-end tube or cylinder. The tube section may have a variety of shapes, one or both ends open, internal web, or a heavy end with bosses suitable for further machining.

Impact extrusions are made from cast, blanked, or sawn slugs. Examples include: electronic condensor cans, air-conditioning receivers/dehydrator, and accumulator bodies.

5.8 Electrical Conductors—Aluminum conductors are available in a variety of forms, from wire to large bus bars. The natural oxide film on aluminum is a dielectric. Special joining techniques are required.

5.9 Roll-Bond—The product form "roll-bond" is aluminum sheets or plates containing continuous passages through which gases or liquids can flow. It is made by metallurgically bonding two sheet panels together after first silk-screening a specific pattern of nonbonding ink onto one of the adjoining surfaces. After roll-bonding the two sheets together, the nonbonded inked pattern is inflated to become the desired tube circuit. The most common application of roll-bond sheet panels is for household refrigerator evaporators but it can be used in many other heat exchanger applications such as condensers, tube circuits, accumulators, or in other fields where patterned, hollow plate sections are desired.

6. Influence of Aluminum Properties on Part Design and Fabrication—The analytical basis and procedure used in the design of an aluminum structural component are no different from those used for any other material. An engineer must recognize that the selection of aluminum requires an understanding of the material's physical and mechanical properties, as well as its fabrication characteristics. This will lead to an optimum design for a given set of loading and performance conditions, that is, the lightest weight structural component that is cost and performance effective.

6.1 Mechanical Properties

6.1.1 MODULUS—Young's modulus for aluminum, which varies slightly with alloy composition, is 69 000 MPa (10 x 10^6 psi). The shear or torsional modulus is 26 000 MPa (3.8 x 10^6 psi).

These values are approximately one-third of those for steel. (See Table 1.)

TABLE 1—MODULUS OF ELASTICITY OF SELECTED METALS

	Modulus of Elasticity	
Material	**MPa**	**psi x 10^6**
Magnesium	45 000	6.5
Aluminum	69 000	10
Copper	110 000	16
Carbon Steel	200 000	30

For a given design, modulus of elasticity determines the stiffness of a component. The modulus of aluminum (as compared to steel) may require that, where stiffness is important, a component be designed so that its geometric properties (moment of inertia, section modulus, end constraint, etc.) compensate for aluminum's lower modulus.

The elastic moduli must be considered when designing structures in which stiffness or deflection is important. The stiffness can be increased by a combination of increased thicknesses and sections, decreased spans, and improved joining techniques. For a simple beam loaded at its midpoint, the stiffness is proportional to the elastic modulus and moment of inertia and inversely proportional to the cube of the span.

$$\text{Stiffness} = \frac{\text{Load}}{\text{Deflection}} = \frac{\text{constant} \times \text{elastic modulus} \times \text{moment of inertia}}{(\text{span})^3} \quad \text{(Eq. 1)}$$

The most efficient method for increasing stiffness is by decreasing the span. Equal stiffness can be obtained with an aluminum span 70% that of a steel span. This is particularly applicable to outer panels, because inner panel structures can be designed to maintain the desired stiffness of an outer panel. As an example, in the original design of a steel hood, a large portion in the center of the outer panel may not have been reinforced, resulting in excessive deflection when using aluminum. However, a shallow web may be provided in the inner panel to contact the outer, which, coupled with adhesives, can effectively increase the stiffness of this section by several orders of magnitude; thereby reducing deflections to less than those for the original steel hood.

The deflection of an aluminum panel that has been substituted thickness-for-thickness for the steel panel, may be reduced by a factor of 2.8 by shortening the effective beam length by 50%. Flat fender panels often are reinforced with internal channel shapes. The use of an adhesive at the midpoint can effectively cut the "beam" length by a factor of two.

The next most efficient technique is to increase the depth of a section. For equal resistance to deflection of flat sheet panels, the thickness of the aluminum would need to be nearly 44% greater than a steel part, but the aluminum panel would weigh about 50% that of the steel panel. For structural shapes, such as channels and I-beams, increased resistance to deflection can be achieved most effectively by increasing the depth and the area of the flanges.

Lastly, if both span and depth changes are limited, the section shape can be modified. Increasing the width of the section, or the use of extrusions to redistribute material to the flanges as much as possible, improves stiffness without adding metal or increasing weight. Extrusion permits the use of thick flanges and thin webs for maximum strength and minimum deflection for a beam in a given space.

A designer should critically study the need for imposing stiffness limitations on parts because there will be a weight penalty when designing for stiffness rather than strength. In conclusion, where clearances permit and dies are designed for aluminum panels, equivalent deflection performance may be achieved in formed sheet members. For flat external panels, undesirable deflections may be greatly reduced by using an adhesive between the panel and existing reinforcements or by permitting metal to remain in large openings in inner panels so that additional spots of adhesive may be applied. Aluminum may then be used in thicknesses equal to steel, for a maximum weight saving at a minimum cost.

The natural frequency of vibration (flutter) of a part is a function of its mass-to-modulus ratio, and is, therefore, the same for aluminum and steel parts of the same geometry and thickness.

6.1.2 TENSILE—Structural aluminum alloys have yield strengths ranging from 35–500 MPa (5–73 ksi). Automotive aluminum alloys have yield strengths from 125–380 MPa (18–55 ksi) and ultimate tensile strengths from 205–410 MPa (30–60 ksi). In many cases, the alloys are formed in a low-strength temper and then artificially aged to maximum properties.

The high strength-to-weight ratio of the medium- to high-strength aluminum alloys makes them very efficient in crash energy management systems.

6.1.3 FATIGUE—Aluminum alloys do not exhibit a fatigue limit or stress level below which the fatigue life becomes essentially unlimited. Accordingly, their fatigue strengths must be specified for a certain number of cycles, commonly 10^6, 10^7, or rotation bending fatigue data, 5 x 10^8 cycles.

Typical values for automotive alloys tested in bending are in the range 110–165 MPa (16–24 ksi) at 10^6 cycles and 95–145 MPa (14–21 ksi) at 5 x 10^8 cycles.

These fatigue properties are slightly lower than those for low-carbon steel, which has a fatigue limit of 140–175 MPa (20–25 ksi). Particular care must, therefore, be taken in designing aluminum structures subject to fatigue stresses to avoid stress raisers such as notches, sudden changes in section, and heavy machining marks or other manufacturing or service damage and to ensure that good joining practices are used.

6.1.4 ELONGATION—Aluminum automotive alloys have elongations prior to forming of 20–25%, in comparison with about 40% for draw quality steel. This limits the depths of draw, sharpness of bend, and draw radii and other forming characteristics of aluminum and also the amount of service deformation it can withstand. Elongation is an important characteristic but many other properties must also be determined for a complete analysis of formability.

6.2 Physical Properties

6.2.1 DENSITY—A property of aluminum that makes it attractive to the designer is its light weight. It has a density of 2.65–2.85 x 10^3 kg/m^3 (0.096–0.103 lb/in^3), resulting in a high strength-to-weight ratio. For example, weight savings of 50–75% have been achieved in bumpers, hoods, and rear deck lids with strength performance equivalent to steel. The values are approximately one-third of those for steel. (See Table 2.)

The use of a single kilogram (pound) of aluminum in an auto part produces a primary (direct) weight saving of one to two kilograms (pounds) on the average, depending on product form and application, when substituted for traditional ferrous automotive materials. In addition, this weight saving encourages redesign, allowing use of a lighter supporting structure and reduced power requirements for comparable performance, saving at least an additional 50–100% of the direct or primary weight savings in the form of secondary savings.

TABLE 2—APPROXIMATE DENSITY OF SELECTED METALS

Material	Density	
	kg/m^3	lb/in^3
Magnesium	1700	0.06
Aluminum	2700	0.10
Zinc	7100	0.26
Carbon Steel	7900	0.28
Copper	9000	0.32

6.2.2 THERMAL CONDUCTIVITY—Aluminum has a high thermal conductivity. Alloy 1100, for example, has a value of 222 W/(m·K) [128 Btu/(h)(ft^2) (°F/ft)]. Table 3. Aluminum, therefore, is used to transfer thermal energy from one medium to another for either heating or cooling. Examples include tubing and sheet for heat exchangers in automotive airconditioning systems and aluminum radiators. Brazing alloys have the same thermal conductivity as the sheet and tubing being joined. Underhood heat sensitive electronic components are often housed in extruded housings with integral heat dissipating fins. Aluminum's high thermal conductivity combined with its high electrical conductivity also affects the welding procedures used for aluminum compared for those used for steel. (See 3.8, Electrical Conductivity.)

TABLE 3—THERMAL CONDUCTIVITY

Material	Btu/(h)(ft^2)(°F/ft)	W/(m·K)
Aluminum	128	222
Brass	87	151
Bronze	17	29.4
Cast Iron	27.6	47.8
Copper	227	393
Steel	26.2	45.3
Zinc	65	112.5

Finally, the coefficient of linear expansion for aluminum is approximately twice that of steel. Coefficients 100 K^{-1} (in/in/100°F) are shown in Table 4. It should be noted that, if fully restrained, the stress resulting from thermal expansion in an aluminum component is less than the stress in a ferrous component, because the modulus of elasticity of aluminum is only one-third that of steel.

TABLE 4—COEFFICIENT OF LINEAR EXPANSION

Material	in/in/100°F	100 K^{-1}
Aluminum	0.00128	0.002304
Copper	0.00093	0.001674
Iron	0.00059	0.001062
Steel	0.00067	0.001206

6.2.3 ELECTRICAL—Aluminum is one of the two common metals having electrical conductivity high enough for use as an electric conductor. The conductivity of electrical conductor grade aluminum (SAE-UNS A1350) is about 62% of the International Annealed Copper Standard. However, because aluminum has less than one-third the specific gravity of copper, an aluminum conductor of equivalent conductivity will weigh approximately one-half that of a copper conductor. Special treatment is required at joining surfaces because the natural oxide on aluminum is a nonconductor.

The high conductivity of aluminum means that spot welding equipment - along with power generation, distribution, and control - designed to join steel automotive components and assemblies - must be revised or redesigned to suit aluminum. This has been done successfully to produce low-volume automotive body applications, such as truck cabs. Work is still underway to develop processes to join consistently high volume passenger car assemblies by spot welding.

6.2.4 EMISSIVITY—The capacity of a material to emit radiant energy can be expressed by its emissivity ratio. This is the ratio of emissive power to that of a black body at the same temperature. Emissivity ratios for various materials are given in Table 5.

To be most effective, exposed metal surfaces of aluminum must face an air space to be in the bare condition and have no applied coating.

TABLE 5—EMISSIVITY RATIOS (1)

Aluminum (alloy 1100)	0.09	(commercial sheet)
	0.20	(heavily oxidized)
Copper (electrolytic)	0.072	(commercial shiny)
Iron (cast)	0.435	(freshly turned)
(wrought)	0.94	(heavily oxidized)
Steel (mild)	0.12	(cleaned)
Zinc (cast)	0.05	(polished)
(galvanized)	0.23	(fairly bright)
Paints (white enamel)	0.91	(on rough plate)
(flat black lacquer)	0.96	
(aluminum lacquer)	0.39	(on rough plate)

1. Source: ASHRAE Handbook of Fundamentals.

6.2.5 REFLECTIVITY—Aluminum reflects radiant energy through the entire range of wavelengths - from ultraviolet through the visible spectrum to infrared and heat waves. It also reflects electromagnetic wavelengths in the radio and radar range.

Because aluminum has a light reflectivity value of over 80%, several wrought alloys are used in auto trim and lighting fixtures.

6.2.6 MAGNETIC—Aluminum is nonmagnetic. This property makes aluminum useful in electronic applications where various components must be shielded from electromagnetic disturbances that would upset their operation.

This property also means that in warehousing, transport, fabrication, and assembly operations, magnetic devices employed to handle ferrous materials will require modification.

6.2.7 ACOUSTIC PROPERTIES—The influence of aluminum on the acoustical characteristics of a vehicle is governed by the design and shape of the component or assembly, rather than the material used. In terms of noise resulting from vibration, theoretically there should be no difference between identical aluminum and steel components, since the frequency of vibration is the same. On the other hand, if shielding governs, the component made from the metal with the lesser mass should allow more noise penetration. Nevertheless, because design is the key, passenger cars employing aluminum extensively for such items as body panels and engines are as quiet or quieter than their ferrous counterparts.

6.2.8 MELTING RANGE—The melting range for aluminum and its alloys is from 657°C (1215°F) for 99.5% pure aluminum to 477°C (890°F) for an Al-Zn-Mg alloy (AA7075). The melting range for various automotive materials is shown in Table 6.

TABLE 6—MELTING RANGE COMPARISON

Al (99.5% purity)	657°C (1215°F)
Al-Zn-Mg (AA7075)	477°C (890°F)
Mg alloys	490–610°C (914–1130°F)
Cu alloys	880–1180°C (1616–2156°F)
Zn alloys	380–442°C (716–828°F)
Steel	1400–1540°C (2250–2800°F)

6.3 Corrosion—Aluminum alloys currently specified for automotive applications have moderate to excellent resistance to corrosion. Because there are differences in corrosion resistance, the properties of the individual alloys should be considered for each application. Corrosion will usually not undercut protective and decorative coatings on aluminum even when the paint is scratched. If bright-finished products are required, anodizing enhances corrosion resistance.

Designs that provide crevices and "shelves" that could collect mud and debris that will form a poultice should be avoided, particularly where galvanic corrosion may occur.

Galvanic corrosion may be encountered where aluminum is coupled to steel or other dissimilar metals in the presence of an electrolyte. Corrosion of this type usually can be reduced or eliminated by taking the following precautions:

1. Keep electrolyte out of the joint. Sealants can be placed in hemmed joints or bolted connections.
2. Apply protective or inhibitive coatings of metallic or inorganic materials on the cathodic member or both of the materials prior to joining.
3. Provide some other satisfactory barrier between the two materials.
4. Proper design, such as avoiding crevices, can minimize corrosion in most cases.
5. Replace bare steel with galvanized or aluminized steel. Stress corrosion cracking and exfoliation corrosion can be encountered in certain alloys, especially the heat-treatable Al-Zn-Mg alloys. However, these effects can be overcome by the proper control of microstructure and heat-treatment practice. Al-Mg alloys with magnesium levels about 3% can also be susceptible to stress corrosion but this can be controlled by appropriate thermal-mechanical practice.

6.4 Fabrication

6.4.1 GENERAL—Aluminum sheet alloys can be successfully formed into automotive components on a high-volume basis utilizing existing press line equipment. High-volume production has been accomplished by understanding and properly managing the effects which material characteristics, tool design, tool finish, part shape, lubrication, and press setup have upon the overall forming process.

Key differences in the forming characteristics of drawing quality steel and aluminum are:

1. Strain distribution capabilities for aluminum are lower; intermediate forming steps may be required.
2. Forming limit diagram values and limiting strains are lower for aluminum.
3. Total elongation is lower for aluminum.
4. Drawing of typical shallow drawn auto body panels will be equal if tools are made using aluminum design guidelines.
5. Stretchability is less for aluminum.
6. Spring back is greater for aluminum, but overcrown can be built into the initial draw die to compensate for the difference.
7. Bending and hemming capabilities are less for the aluminum outer panel alloys, that is, 2036-T4, 6010-T4; therefore, rope hemming is recommended to prevent cracking.
8. Aluminum heat-treated body sheet may be supplied dry and has a natural thin oxide film. Light overall lubrication on both sides of the blank to be formed is preferred and supplemental binder lubrication may be required.

For successful volume production forming of aluminum sheet components:

1. Design the part to be compatible with the forming limitations of the specified alloy.
2. Design the draw tools to control metal flow into the die while minimizing stretch.
3. Apply a good lubricant evenly to both sides of the blank.
4. Use grid strain analysis techniques in conjunction with forming limit diagrams for the alloys involved during development of aluminum components and the production tools.

6.4.2 FORMABILITY TESTING—A large number of testing techniques are being used in an effort to predict the formability of sheet materials. Each technique has its advantages, but none correlate completely between the laboratory and press shop performance.

A description of an alloy's forming characteristics includes: the measurement of tensile and yield strength, uniform and total elongation, reduction in area, the strain hardening exponent "n", the plastic strain ratio "r", the strain rate sensitivity exponent "m", cup testing, tensile/yield ratio, and the development of forming limit diagrams and strain distribution capabilities.

The plastic strain ratio "r" is a measure of a metal's resistance to thinning. Higher "r" values indicate greater formability in a drawing operation. The values may vary with rolling direction and are generally lower for aluminum sheet than for steel.

The strain hardening exponent "n" reflects how well the metal distributes strain. It establishes relative performance in a stretching process. A high "n" value is desirable and values for aluminum and steel body sheet are similar.

The strain rate hardening exponent "m" may be positive or negative. Metals with positive values, such as steel, exhibit an increasing ability to strain harden as the strain rate increases. Those materials with negative values (many aluminum alloys) have a greater tendency towards localized necking as the strain rate increases. Metals with similar "n" values but differently directed "m" values, may demonstrate different results in stretching operations.

Uniform elongation is the limit of plastic strain which precedes localized necking. Total elongation is the strain to fracture and is related to gauge length. Elongation alone is not a reliable indicator of actual forming characteristics.

6.4.3 APPLICATION OF GRID STRAIN ANALYSIS—Grid strain analysis is a technique for effectively identifying, evaluating, and solving forming difficulties. The technique provides a record of the strains introduced during forming by the deformation of preprinted circles on the blank surface. The major and minor strains for deformed circles of interest may then be plotted on the forming limit diagram of the alloy involved (Schematic Forming Limit Diagram, Figure 3). Three features are important in a complete grid strain analysis. The first two are the strain state and the limiting strain. The third is the distribution of strain around the area where the peak strains occur. The peak strain levels provide a measure of total forming severity while strain distribution evaluates the efficiency of the forming operation. Since there is little control over the shape or level of the Forming Limit Diagram for a given material, a study of the strain distribution offers the only opportunity for controlling the process. The shape of the deformed circles identifies the specific forming process (strain state, Figure 4a) active at a failure location. Plotting the major and minor strains for circles on the selected strain path on the strain distribution plot (Figure 4b) establishes the critically strained regions and the maximum allowable strain level for a given location. Changes in material, tooling or part design, and lubrication can be made to lower peak strains or modify the strain distribution.

6.4.4 PART AND TOOL DESIGN GUIDELINES—The design of tooling to form sheet metal parts is covered extensively in the literature.[5] There are unique guidelines to insure satisfactory parts and shape control for aluminum. When followed for aluminum, they may enable the tooling to make excellent steel parts, but the reverse, is often not true.

5. 780141 - Forming High Strength Bumpers from Aluminum Sheet - Manufacturing sequences, part and tooling guidelines for forming bumpers are discussed.
780392 - Interrelation Between Part and Die Design for Aluminum Auto Body Panels - Guidelines for forming aluminum auto body panels have been developed for use by part and forming tool designers. Full size proof die and production die tryout programs were conducted to establish part design, forming, tool, and process parameters.
800931 - Reducing the Cost of Aluminum Body Panels - The design of parts to control stiffness and deflection while maintaining shape control in high visibility parts is discussed.
810122 - Aluminum Sheet Bumpers - Alloy selection, relative weight, design, forming, finishing, and corrosion are discussed.

SCHEMATIC FORMING LIMIT DIAGRAM

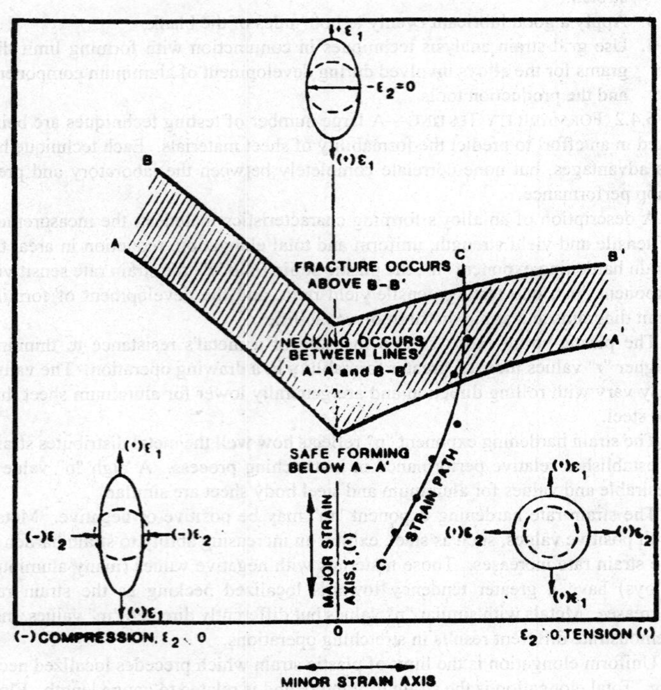

FIGURE 3—

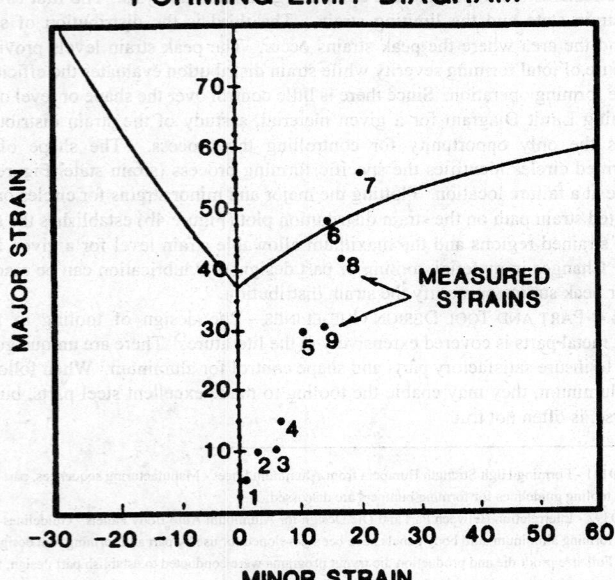

FIGURE 4A—

STRAIN DISTRIBUTION PLOT

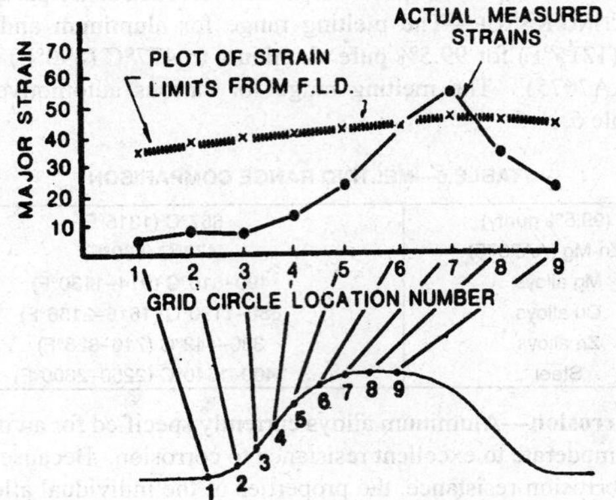

STRETCH - FORMED PART

STRAIN DISTRIBUTION SURVEY OF STRETCH - FORMED PART

FIGURE 4B—

6.4.5 Process Considerations

6.4.5.1 Tool Materials—A combination of hardened-steel tools with highly-polished forming surfaces and fully-lubricated blanks permit satisfactory production of aluminum panels with a minimum of tool maintenance. Excessive heat buildup or metal pickup can be avoided by using the proper die material, adequate maintenance, and suitable lubricants. Table 7 lists some of the die materials being used.

TABLE 7—A PARTIAL LIST OF SUGGESTED DIE MATERIALS

Application	Part Produced	Die Material	Die Hardness "C"
Blanking dies	Up to 2.29 mm (0.090 in) thick	SAE 1060	58–60
	Over 2.29 mm (0.090 in)	Type S7 tool steel	58–60
Draw dies	Most parts	Chromium-molybdenum alloy cast iron with D2, D5, or D7 tool steel inserts	60–65
Trim dies	Most parts	Composite sections: SAE 1020 base and SAE 1060 cutting edges	58–60
Flanging dies	From 0.58–1.91 mm (0.023–0.75 in) thick with straight flanges up to 25.4 mm (1 in) each	Type O tool steel	59–60
	Same Gauge range but with curved flanges, flanges over 25.4 mm (1 in) wide	Type D7 tool steel	64–65
	All parts over 1.91 mm (0.075 in) thick	Type T15 tool steel	64–66
Hemming dies	All parts	Type W110 tool steel, D2	60–63

Experience has shown that the finish of hardened-tool surfaces in sliding contact with aluminum, such as panel and die radii and binderline surfaces, should be polished and maintained to a 4–8 μin (rms) finish. Hardened and polished tool steel inserts should be used in key locations in cast iron drawn tools to improve wear resistance and minimize metal pickup.

6.4.5.2 Blanking and Shearing—A clean-cut blank edge free of burrs and slivers is essential to damage free forming. Suggested punch clearances for the aluminum body sheet alloys are shown in Table 8. The ordinary shearing forces encountered in blanking operations can be estimated by multiplying the area to be cut (thickness x perimeter) by the shear strength of the material. The ultimate shear strength of aluminum alloys is approximately equal to 60% of the ultimate tensile strength.

TABLE 8—SUGGESTED BLANKING/PIERCING AND SHEARING CLEARANCES [1]

Alloy/Temper	Blank/Pierce	Shear
5182-O, 6009-T4, 6010-T4, 2036-T4	8–12% x t [2]/Side	8–12% x t/Side
7021-O, 7029-O	15–20% x t/Side	20–25% x t/Side
7129-F-O		
7029-F	15–20% x t/Side	15% x t/Side
5454-O	7–10% x t/Side	7–10% x t/Side

1. Assumes sharp tooling.
2. t = Metal thickness.

6.4.5.3 Lubrication—The use of good lubrication is important in all aluminum forming operations. The lubricant must maintain film strength under high pressure at the draw radius, be nontoxic, nonstaining, easily removed, and be compatible with welding, adhesive bonding, and paint pre-cleaning operations to follow.

Aluminum sheet is normally supplied without lubricant in contrast to conventional steel. Good results are being obtained in production by roller coating lubricant to both sides of the sheet before forming. Occasionally, additional lubricants may have to be added at secondary operations.

6.4.5.4 Stretch Stamping—Stretch stamping is a sheet forming sequence in which the blank is clamped in lock bead tooling, prestretched over a punch to establish positive strains, and, finally, embossed to achieve part contours in mating tools. This process has the advantage of reducing blank size, maintaining shape control, reducing surface damage (visible surface up), and eliminating forming marks by reducing buckles and skid lines.

6.4.5.5 Hemming/Bending/Downflanging—The 90 deg bending and downflanging characteristics and the 180 deg hemming capabilities of the aluminum body sheet alloys are summarized in Table 9. In some instances, the inside radius for 90 deg bends for a straight downflange are sharper than the inside bend radius recommended for downflanges that will be formed into hemmed joints. The higher strength body sheet alloys require a roped hem. Schematic tool design for the rope hem is shown in Figure 5a.

6.4.5.6 Hole Flanging/Stretch Flanging—Hole flanging capabilities of aluminum body sheet are significantly influenced by tooling design and edge preparation. Flange lengths comparable to those obtained with steel can be produced through the use of specially designed pressure backup tooling. Splits occur in flanges when conventional piercing and flanging tools are used. Schematic representation of the tooling and its sequential operation are shown in Figures 6 and 6a. Hole flange guidelines using pressure backup tooling are shown in Table 10.

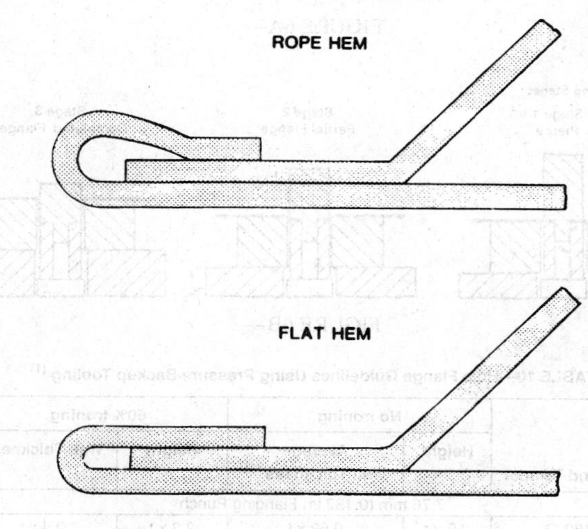

FIGURE 5A—

Rope Hem Tool Design for 6010-T4 and 2036-T4

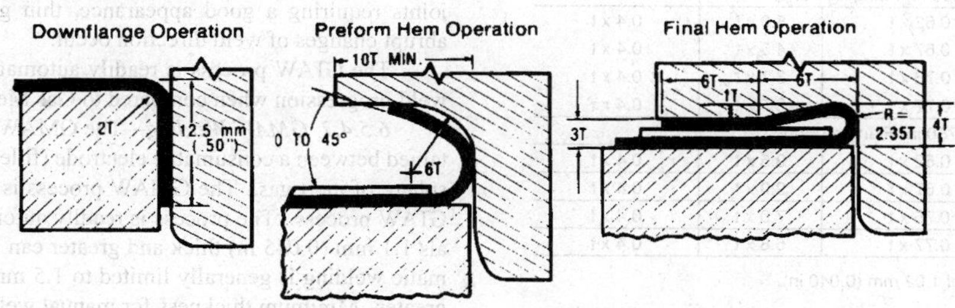

FIGURE 5B—

TABLE 9—RELATIVE FORMABILITY CHARACTERISTICS - BODY SHEET ALLOYS

		Bend Radii				Stretchability			
		90 deg Downflange	180 deg Hem			Plane Strain		Biaxial Strain	
Alloy	Gauge (mm)	As Received	cw [1]	DF [2]	Type	Strain (%)	Depth (mm)	Strain (%)	Depth (mm)
5182-O	0.7–1.2	1/2t [3]	1/2t	1t	Flat	20/5	23	40/35	33
6009-T4	0.7–1.2	1/2t	1/2t	1t	Flat	20/5	20	30/30	30
2036-T4	0.7–1.2	1t	1t	1-1/2t	Roped	20/5	21	25/25	30
6010-T4	0.7–1.2	1t	1t	1-1/2t	Roped	20/5	20	30/25	29
6009-T4	1.6		3/4t			25/5	29	35/35	37
	3.1		1-1/4t	—		25/5	30	40/40	38
6010-T4	1.6		1-1/2t		—	25/5	29	30/30	30
	3.1		2t	—		25/5	30	30/30	32

1. Cold-worked (cw) from forming operation.
2. Downflange (DF) radii.
3. Metal thickness (t).

Tooling for Flanging Operation

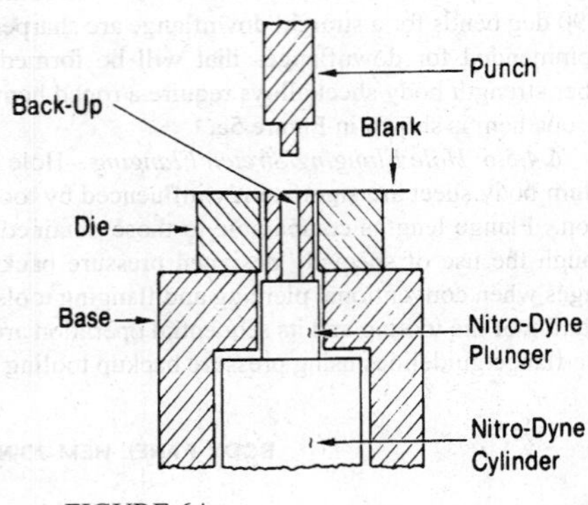

FIGURE 6A—

Hole Flanging Stages

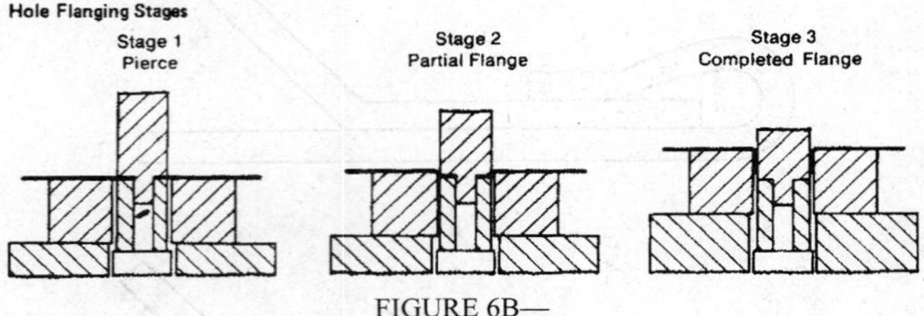

FIGURE 6B—

TABLE 10—Hole Flange Guidelines Using Pressure Backup Tooling (1)

Alloy and Temper	No Ironing		60% Ironing	
	Height	Average Wall Thickness (2)	Height	Wall Thickness
7.76 mm (0.187 in) Flanging Punch				
5182-O	2.0 x t	0.62 x t	2.8 x t	0.4 x t
6009-T4	1.7 x t	0.67 x t	2.4 x t	0.4 x t
2036-T4	1.2 x t	0.75 x t	1.8 x t	0.4 x t
6010-T4	1.1 x t	0.77 x t	1.7 x t	0.4 x t
8.89 mm (0.350 in) Flanging Punch				
5182-O	3.5 x t	0.62 x t	5.0 x t	0.4 x t
6009-T4	3.2 x t	0.67 x t	4.5 x t	0.4 x t
2036-T4	2.5 x t	0.76 x t	3.7 x t	0.4 x t
6010-T4	2.2. x t	0.77 x t	3.5 x t	0.4 x t
19.05 mm (0.750 in) Flanging Punch				
5182-O	7.2 x t	0.62 x t	9.5 x t	0.4 x t
6009-T4	6.0 x t	0.67 x t	9.0 x t	0.4 x t
2036-T4	4.7 x t	0.75 x t	7.0 x t	0.4 x t
6010-T4	4.5 x t	0.77 x t	6.8 x t	0.4 x t

1. Based on original metal thickness, t, of 1.02 mm (0.040 in).
2. Flange wall is slightly tapered.

6.5 Joining—Aluminum can be joined by most of the processes used to join steel such as resistance welding, fusion welding, mechanical fastening, adhesive bonding, and weldbonding.

6.5.1 RESISTANCE WELDING—Most series of aluminum alloys can be resistance welded. The 7000 series is an exception because many alloys of this series develop inferior mechanical properties and resistance to corrosion in the weld zone and should not be resistance- or fusion-welded.

The inherent characteristics of aluminum and its alloys require procedures which differ from the conventional methods used for carbon and stainless steels. The shear and peel strength and fatigue life of resistance spot welds in aluminum are approximately 50% of those of the same nugget size in low-carbon steel of the same gage.

Aluminum combines instantaneously with oxygen in the atmosphere to produce an aluminum oxide coating. This shortens the tip life of electrodes through pick-up of aluminum oxide, which results in a considerably shorter life for electrodes than when they are used in spot welding steel.

In addition, the oxide has a rather high and occasionally erratic electrical resistance which, in turn, affects the amount of heat produced during resistance welding. This can result in a wide variation in weld strength. Improved resistance welding results can be achieved by chemical cleaning and by mechanical abrasion to produce uniform low-resistance oxide surfaces.

Since aluminum has high electrical and thermal conductivity, about two to three times the amount of current and about one-quarter the welding time are needed compared to steel spot welding.

Welds should not be too closely spaced. While the amount of the current that is shunted depends on material thickness and the surface resistance of the faying surface, weld spacing is the principal controlling factor. Poor part fit up and the effects of too little overlap and edge distance, reduce weld strength and electrode life. For example, welds made on the edge or very close to the edge, have reduced strength and may cause a weld blowout, which normally requires an electrode change. Poor fit up conditions reduce effective weld pressure also leading to excessive weld heat and possible blow-outs.

6.5.2 FLASH WELDING - ADVANTAGES AND LIMITATIONS—Flash welding of aluminum is a high-volume production process that is suitable for making butt and miter joints between two workpieces of similar cross-sectional shape. Most aluminum alloys can be welded and no filler metal is required. The process is capable of producing welds that have strength equal to the base metal in some alloys. Flash welding can be used to produce assemblies that otherwise would require more costly forgings or castings. Dissimilar metals can also be welded using this process.

Cross sections up to 127 mm^2 (5 in^2) of aluminum can be joined by flash welding. Aluminum thicknesses below 12.7 mm (0.050 in) are difficult to flash weld and should be avoided. Machines for flash welding aluminum require much larger transformer capacity than is needed for steel. They also require a more precise control, a faster upset velocity, and good alignment of surfaces to be joined.

6.5.3 STUD WELDING—Stud welding is a specialized type of flash welding in which an aluminum stud is attached endwise to an aluminum surface. The stud can be a bolt, screw, rivet, or similar device. Two different systems are used for stud welding.

1. Capacitor discharge which is a very rapid flash weld. With this system, studs can be welded to sheet as thin as 0.5 mm (0.020 in) when proper back-ups are used.
2. DC shielded arc stud welding which is similar to gas metal arc welding (GMAW).

The minimum aluminum thickness limitation is 2.0 mm (0.080 in) when proper backups are used.

6.5.4 ARC WELDING

6.5.4.1 GTAW Welding—This is a joining method where an electric arc is maintained between a nonconsumable, tungsten type electrode and the workpiece in an atmosphere of inert gas. The most popular uses for this process are for weld joints requiring a good appearance, thin gauge welding, and for joints where abrupt changes of weld direction occur.

The GTAW process is readily automated. Its greatest deterrent is the slow weld progression when compared to Gas Metal Arc Welding (GMAW).

6.5.4.2 GMAW Welding—The GMAW process utilizes an electric arc maintained between a consumable electrode (filler wire) and the workpiece in an atmosphere of inert gas. The GMAW process is faster and more economical than the GTAW process. The process is readily automated, and used extensively. Materials 1.1 mm (0.045 in) thick and greater can be welded automatically. Semi-automatic welding is generally limited to 1.5 mm (0.060 in) material thicknesses and greater. Minimum thickness for manual welding is 0.9 mm (0.035 in).

6.5.4.3 Butt Welding—Butt welds have good appearance, better fatigue life than lap or fillet welds, use less base material, and are easy to design. They require more accurate alignment, fit up, and either tacking or fixturing. In material 4.8 mm (0.19 in) or thicker, edge preparation or back chipping may be required. A weld pass may be required on the root side of plate.

6.5.4.4 Fillet Welding—Fillet welds generally do not require any edge preparation of the weld joint. Continuous fillet welds have better fatigue life than do intermittent fillet welds and often cost less to produce due to the labor involved in stopping and restarting the arc. Continuous weldments are easier to automate than intermittent welds. The shear strength of fillet welds depends on the filler metal alloy rather than the base material.

6.5.4.5 GMAW or MIG Spot Welding—This is an adaptation of the basic GMAW process. The same equipment and principles are used except the controls are modified to control weld duration.

6.5.5 ADHESIVE BONDING—Adhesive bonded joints can have a number of advantages:

1. Loads are more evenly distributed and stress concentrations minimized. As a result, under certain conditions, longer fatigue life can be obtained with bonded joints than with spot welds or mechanical fasteners.
2. Adhesive bonded joints tend to dampen vibrations.

3. Dissimilar materials with different coefficients of thermal expansion can be joined with adhesives having specially selected flexibility characteristics.
4. In contrast to metal fusion joining processes, metals of different thickness can be easily assembled at room or low-elevated temperatures.
5. Large areas may be joined with a weight reduction often realized.
6. Electrically conductive or insulative joints may be provided depending on the properties of the adhesive materials employed.
7. Adhesive bonding is the only method of continuous joining for metals to nonmetals.
8. The elimination of drilling or tapping operations and protruding fasteners permits the design and production of good looking, versatile joints.

The part to be bonded should be designed for adhesive bonding. Inferior results often occur if adhesive bonding is substituted in a section designed for welding or mechanical joining. The strength requirements of the joint should be calculated and a determination made that adequate bond strength is available. Though adhesives can often be selected to resist particular stresses, such as tensile, compression, shear, peel, or cleavage, it is usually best to design in shear or compression. Peel and cleavage should be avoided wherever possible. The same basic design criteria previously used for steel can be used for aluminum as long as the particular strength properties of the alloy are used in design calculations.

When bonding any kind of assembly, the actual adhesive bonding step is only one part of an overall joining system. The automotive designer must consider joint design, surface condition of the parts to be bonded, adhesive selection, compatibility with lubricants used, ability of the adhesive to withstand the cleaning and painting operation, satisfactory curing of the adhesive during the painting operation, and final joint performance in the service environment. Any program which will utilize an adhesively bonded part, should contain analyses of all of these factors.

6.5.6 WELDBONDING—Weldbonding is a process which produces a joint by using a combination of resistance spot welding and adhesive bonding. The joint can be made by: (a) resistance spot welding through an uncured adhesive, (b) flowing an adhesive by capillary action into the bond area after resistance spot welding, or (c) by applying a film adhesive which has holes cut into it and resistance spot welding through these holes. Method (a) is the most applicable for joining auto body assemblies.

Weldbonding offers better resistance to peel forces than from spot welding alone. Fatigue life and durability are improved over that obtained with spot welding or mechanical fasteners alone. The adhesive acts as a partial seal at the joints to provide better corrosion protection and gives a tighter body construction.

Disadvantages primarily involve the problem associated with being able to make good welds through an adhesive and the need to prevent contamination of visible metal surfaces and the electrodes by the adhesive.

Depending on the adhesive properties, the weldbond can have a joint strength that is less than, equal to, or more than the adhesive bond alone. If an adhesive has very high shear strength, the addition of a spot weld acts only as an attachment fixture and imparts little to structural strength. The increased pressure of the spot weld on the adhesive bond may aid in adhesive wetting which could give better durability.

If an adhesive has a lower order of shear strength, the addition of a spot weld can improve overall joint strength. If an adhesive has poor elevated temperature properties, it can undergo heat deterioration during spot welding.

6.5.7 MECHANICAL FASTENING

6.5.7.1 Mechanical Clinching—Mechanical clinching offers a strong alternative to spot welding of aluminum panels. Three spoke joints exhibit tensile and peel properties similar to spot welds. Power requirements at rates up to 250 clinches per minute are minimal. Another advantage is its lack of sensitivity to metal surface composition or the alloy being used.

Fatigue performance is good, equal to, or superior to spot-welded joints. Clinch type mechanical lock joints, with aluminum-to-aluminum or aluminum-to-steel are used for joining hood outers to hood inners, seat back assemblies, and other body components. The technique is preferred to the use of screws or bolts because no fastener holes are required. Lineup problems are minimized.

6.5.7.2 Riveting—Riveting has been used extensively and is still being used in the fabrication of truck cabs and trailers. Riveting procedures are well-defined and equipment costs are low. High-speed automatic punch riveters are available which can set rivets at a rate similar to spot welding.

6.5.7.3 Mechanical Fasteners Plus Adhesives—Adhesives can be used with rivets, clinch joints, staples, etc. to improve overall strength properties. The combination joining method produces characteristics similar to weld-bonded joints. Since mechanical fasteners do not use heat, one need not worry about heat deterioration of the adhesive as in weld bonding. All body sheet alloys exhibit similar joining characteristics when joined by a combination of mechanical fasteners and adhesives. Generally, because of a larger area being joined and a more even distribution of load, both shear strength and fatigue strength are improved over the use of mechanical fasteners alone.

6.5.8 ELECTRON BEAM WELDING—Some advantages of vacuum EBW for aluminum include:

a. Ability to make welds that are deeper, narrower, and less tapered than conventional arc welds.
b. Total heat input much lower than gas tungsten arc (GTAW) or gas metal arc (GMAW) welds and consequently a smaller heat affected zone.

The vacuum chamber offers a high purity welding environment that results in freedom from impurities in the weld and permits high welding speeds. Deep, narrow, single pass welds can be made in heavy sections with or without filler additions.

Some limitations are:

a. Work has to be done in a vacuum chamber, which somewhat limits high-volume production except on small parts.
b. Some problems exist in the life of the emission system in welding guns. Either a special welding technique or a cosmetic pass is necessary to eliminate undercut and surface roughness.
c. Materials to be welded must be almost surgically clean.

6.5.9 LASER WELDING—The laser is a relatively new process that is developing rapidly in to a high volume production process for welding and cutting of metals.

The laser beam, unlike the electron beam, can be projected 6 m (20 ft) or more in air with no loss in power, and no vacuum chamber is needed.

The ease of beam transmission and directional control permits multi-station operation. Nearly 100% duty cycle is possible by switching the beam from station to station.

The high-power, high-speed operation produces a narrow heat-affected zone that minimizes loss of metal properties and provides relatively low distortion of the workpiece.

The process is easily automated and requires miminum operator attention.

The high-power density of the laser permits welding speeds considerably higher than other commercially available welding processes.

No filler metal is necessary, but may be used on crack-sensitive alloys. X-rays are not generated by the laser beam, and shielding can be accomplished using only plexiglass. Aluminum may be welded with as little as 1000 W.

Some disadvantages are:

1. Most of the multi-kilowatt laser systems operate at about 10–20% efficiency for converting electrical power into a focused infrared laser beam.
2. Precise fit up (a fit up tolerance of 15% of material thickness is desirable) is necessary on butt and lap joints for good weld quality.
3. The high cost of laser beam equipment.
4. Special precautions are necessary to make porosity-free welds in aluminum.

6.5.10 ULTRASONIC WELDING—The majority of aluminum alloys whether heat-treatable or non-heat treatabke and in thicknesses up to 2.54 mm (0.1 in) can be ultrasonically welded (solid-state bonded, that is, no cast structures). Many of these can also be joined to other metals such as copper and stainless steel. Weld time for spot welding is 0.5–1 s and seam welds have reportedly been made at weld travel speeds up to 2 ms^{-1} (400 fpm).

6.6 Finishing Aluminum—The variety of processes by which aluminum can be finished are possibly the greatest for any metal. However, in comparison to some metals which rely on an applied coating for corrosion protection, aluminum is being used with no applied finish. Where coating is required, organic, inorganic vitreous, and laminated coatings can be readily applied to aluminum using available technology.

Aluminum components with no protective finish are used for underhood applications such as: air-conditioning components, transmission housings, steering and suspension components, and parts for brake and exhaust systems.

Body sheet parts (hoods, deck lids, and interior trim) that require an organic paint finish can be cleaned, painted, and baked using the same processes used for steel and can be intermixed with steel during production. Specifications are available from a wide number of suppliers of finishing equipment and paint.

Bright extruded or sheet metal parts such as trim, wheel covers, and bumper face bars are normally bright anodized. This process is unique to aluminum. Anodizing is used to enhance corrosion resistance, wear resistance, and appearance and can also be used to provide a variety of colors. (See SAE J399, Anodized Aluminum Automotive Parts.)

Generally speaking, anodizing is more cost effective than chrome plating. However, the latter process has also been developed and used in production of aluminum bumpers.

(R) GENERAL DATA ON WROUGHT ALUMINUM ALLOYS—SAE J454 FEB1991

SAE Information Report

Report of the SAE Nonferrous Metals Division approved June 1911 and completely revised by the SAE Nonferrous Metals Committee August 1987. Completely revised by the SAE Wrought Aluminum Committee February 1991.

Foreword—This Document has not changed other than to put it into the new SAE Technical Standards Board Format.

1. Scope—The SAE Standards for wrought aluminum alloys cover materials with a considerable range of properties and other characteristics, but do not include all of the commercially available materials. If none of the materials listed in Tables 1 through 7 provides the characteristics required by a particular application, users may find it helpful to consult with the suppliers of aluminum alloy products. See companion document, SAE J1434.

2. References

2.1 Applicable Publications—The following publications form a part of this specification to the extent specified herein. The latest issue of SAE publications shall apply.

2.1.1 SAE PUBLICATIONS—Available from SAE, 400 Commonwealth Drive, Warrendale, PA 15096-0001.

SAE J1434—Wrought Aluminum Applications Guidelines

2.1.2 ASTM PUBLICATIONS—Available from ASTM, 100 Barr Harbor Drive, West Conshohocken, PA 19428-2959.

ASTM B 557M—Method of Tension Testing Wrought and Cast Aluminum- and Magnesium-Alloy Products (Metric)

ASTM E 29—Practice for Using Significant Digits in Test Data to Determine Conformance with Specifications

TABLE 1—ALLOY, TEMPER AND PRODUCT FORM USED IN AUTOMOTIVE APPLICATIONS

Application	Alloy and Temper(1)	Product Form
Body Sheet, Panels		
Body Panels	2036-T4	Sheet
	2038-T4	Sheet
	5052-0, H32, H34	Sheet
	5182-0, O2(2)	Sheet
	6010-T4, T6	Sheet
	6111-T4, T6	Sheet
Interior Panels, Components	3004-0, H32	Sheet
	5052-0, H32, H34	Sheet
	5182-0, O2(2)	Sheet
	6009-T4, T62	Sheet
Bumper Components(3)		
Reinforcements	6061-T4, T6	Sheet, Extrusions
Face Bar, Reinforcements	6009-T4, T6(4)	Sheet
	7021-T61(4)	Sheet
	7029-T5,T6 (5)(4)	Sheet, Extrusions
	7116-T5(4)	Extrusions
	7129-T6(4)	Extrusions

TABLE 1—ALLOY, TEMPER AND PRODUCT FORM USED IN AUTOMOTIVE APPLICATIONS (continued)

Application	Alloy and Temper(1)	Product Form
Structural & Weldable	5083-H111, H112, H116, H321	Sheet, Plate, Extrusions
	5086-H32, H34, H111	Sheet, Plate, Extrusions, Tube
	5182-0, O2(2)	Sheet
	5454-0, H32, H34, H111	Sheet, Plate, Extrusions, Tube
	6009-T4, T62	Sheet
	6061-T4, T6, T651	Sheet, Plate, Extrusions, Forgings, Structural Shapes, Tube, Rod, Bar
General Purpose	3003-H14, H24	Sheet
	3004-0, H32	Sheet
	5052-0, H32, H34	Sheet
	5454-0, H32, H34	Sheet, Plate, Extrusions, Tube
	6061-T4, T6, T651	Sheet, Plate, Extrusions, Forgings, Structural Shapes, Tube, Rod, Bar
	6463-T521(5)	Extrusions
	6063-T1, T5, T6	Extrusions, Tube
Trim		
Name Plates, Appliques	1100-0	Sheet
	3002-0	Sheet
	5005-0	Sheet
Strength Paramount	5252-H2X(6)	Sheet
	5457-H3X(6)	Sheet
Brightness Paramount	5657-H2X(6)	Sheet
Wheels(7), Fabricated	5454-0, H32, H34 H111, H112	Sheet, Plate, Extrusions
Fasteners (Mechanical)	2017-T4	Rivet and Cold Heading Wire and Rod
	2024-T4	
	2117-T4	
	6053-T61	
	6061-T4	
Heat Exchangers	A wide variety of alloys and tempers are currently specified or under consideration for heat-exchangers.	

1. Only the commonly used tempers are listed for the alloys shown. Other tempers of these alloys are available. For temper definitions, see SAE J1434.
2. Registered temper for a material which reduces incidence of stretcher strain.
3. Normally supplied with mill finish for bumper components if anodized or chrome plated finish is not required.
4. Suitable for bright dip and anodizing.
5. Suitable for chrome plating.
6. A wide variety of tempers are available to meet specific customer requirements. Normally a 2X temper is supplied.
7. Aluminum automotive wheels are also produced by the casting process.

TABLE 2A—TYPICAL MECHANICAL PROPERTIES AND COMPARATIVE CHARACTERISTICS

	Typical Mechanical Properties[1][2]						Resistance to Corrosion		Comparative Characteristics					
	Tension			Shear	Fatigue	Modulus						Weldability[3]		
	Strength		Elongation											
Alloy and Temper[4]	Ultimate MPa	Yield 0.2% Offset MPa	percent in 50 mm (1.60 mm Thick Speci-men)	Ultimate Shear Strength MPa	Endurance Limit MPa	Modulus[5] of Elasticity MPa x 10°	General[6]	Stress[7] corrosion Cracking	Toughness[8]	Workability[9] cold	Machability[9]	Gas	Arc	Resistance spot and Seam
1100-0	90	35	35	60	35[10]	69	A	A		A	E	A	A	B
2017-T4	425	275	20[11]	260	125[10]	75	D	C		C	B	N/A	N/A	N/A
2024-T4	470	325	20	285	140[10]	73	D	C		C	B	N/A	N/A	N/A
2036-T4	340	195	24	205	125[12]	71	C	A2[13]	A	B	C	—	B	B
2038-T4	325	170	25	205	125[12]	71	C	A2[13]		B	C	—	B	B
2117-T4	295	165	24[11]	195	95[10]	71	C	A		B	C	N/A	N/A	N/A
3002-0	95	40	33	70		69	A	A		A	E	A	A	B
3003-H14,H24	150	145	8	95	60[10]	69	A	A		B	D	A	A	A
3004-0	180	70	20	110	95[10]	69	A	A	B	A	D	B	A	B
-H32	215	170	10	115	105[10]	69	A	A		B	D	B	A	A
5005-0	125	40	25	75		69	A	A		A	E	A	A	B
5052-0	195	90	25	125	110[10]	70	A	A	A	A	D	A	A	B
-H32	230	195	12	140	115[10]	70	A	A		B	D	A	A	A
-H34	260	215	10	145	125[10]	70	A	A	B	B	C	A	A	A
5083-H321,H116	315	230	14[11]		160[10]	71	A	B		C	D	C	A	A
5086-H32	290	205	12			71	A	A		B	D	C	A	A
-H34	325	255	10	185		71	A	B		B	C	C	A	A
-H112	270	130	14			71	A	A		A	D	C	A	B
5182-0	275	130	21	165	140[12]	71	A-B	A2[14]		A	D	C	A	B
-02	270	125	23			71	A-B	A2[14]		A	D	C	A	B
5252-H25	235	170	11	145		69	A	A		B	C	A	A	A
5454-0	250	115	22	160		70	A	A	A	A	D	C	A	B
-H32	275	205	10	165		70	A	A		B	D	C	A	A
-H34	305	240	10	180		70	A	A	B	B	C	C	A	A
5457-H25	180	160	12	110		69	A	A		A	E	A	A	B
5657-H25	160	140	12	95		69	A	A		B	D	A	A	A
6009-T4	220	125	25	150	115[12]	69	B	A2	A	A	C	A	A	A
6010-T4	290	165	24	195	125[12]	69	B	A2	A	B	C	A	A	A
6053-T61						69	A	A	—	—	C	N/A	N/A	N/A
6061-T4	240	145	22	165	95[10]	69	B	B	A	B	C	A	A	A
-T6,T651	310	275	12	205	95[10]	69	B	A	B	C	C	A	A	A
6063-T1	150	90	20	95	60[10]	69	A	A		B	D	A	A	A
-T5	185	145	12	115	70[10]	69	A	A		B	C	A	A	A
-T6	240	215	12	150	70[10]	69	A	A		C	C	A	A	A
6111-T1	290	160	26		69	69	B	A2	A	B	C	A	A	B
6463-T52	185	145	12	115		69	A	A		B	C	A	A	A
7021-T61	430	380	13		140[10]	71	B	A2[15]						
7029-T5,T6	430	380	15	270		70	B	A2[15]						
7116-T5	360	315	16				B	A1[15]		C				
7129-T6	430	380	15	270	145[16]	70	B	A2[15]						

:

1. Typical properties are not guaranteed since in most cases they are averages for various sizes, product forms, and methods of manufacture and may not be exactly representative of any particular product or size. These data are intended only as a basis for comparing alloys and tempers and should not be specified as engineering requirements or used for design purposes.
2. The indicated typical mechanical properties for all except the 0 temper material are higher than the specified minimum properties. For 0 temper products, typical ultimate and yield values are slightly lower than specified (maximum) values.
3. Ratings A through D for weldability are relative ratings as follows:
   A —Generally weldable by all commercial procedures and methods.
   B —Weldable with special techniques.
   C —Limited weldability due to crack sensitivity, loss in corrosion resistance, loss in mechanical properties.
   D —No commonly used welding methods have been developed.
   N/A—Rating not applicable for end use application requirements, that is, rivets.
4. Only the commonly used tempers are listed for the alloys shown. Other tempers of these alloys are available.
5. Average of tension and compression modulii. Compression modulus is about 2% greater than tension modulus.
6. General corrosion ratings are based on exposures to sodum chloride solution by intermittent spraying or immersion. Ratings A through D are relative ratings in decreasing order of merit. The ratings do not necessarily imply acceptable performance in the intended application.

7. Stress-corrosion cracking ratings are basedon service experience and on laboratory tests of specimens exposed to the 35% sodum chloride alternate immersion test for 2XXX, 6XXX, and copper containing 7XXX series alloys and total immersion in boiling sodum chloride solution for 96 h for copper free 7XXX series alloys.
   A —No known instance of failure in service or in laboratory tests.
   A2—Insufficient service experience; no known instance of failure in laboratory tests.
   B —No known instance of failure in service; limited failures in laboratory service.
   B2—Insufficient service experience; limited failures in laboratory service.
   C —Service failures with sustained tension stress acting in short transverse direction relative to grain structure; limited failures in laboratory tests of long transverse specimens.
   D —Limited service failures with sustained longitudinal or long transverse stress.
8. Toughness ratings are based upon Kahn Tear Test of 1.60 mm thick sheet specimens in both longitudinal and transverse directions. This data is based on a limited number of tests and should be used for general comparisons only.
   Ratings A—over 175 000 Nm/m^2
   B—over 140 000 thru 175 000 Nm/m^2
   C—over 105 000 thru 140 000 Nm/m^2
   D—0 through 105 000 Nm/m^2
9. Ratings A through D for workability (cold) and A through E for machinability are relative ratings in decreasing order of merit.
10. Based upon 500 000 000 cycles of completely reversed stress using the RR Moore type of machine and specimen.
11. Elongation in 50 mm apply for thicknesses up through 12.50 mm and in 5D (5.65√A) for thicknesses over 12.50 mm where D and A are the diameter and cross-sectional area of the specimen. Values for elongations in 5D (5.65√A) are shown in brackets.
12. Based upon a single series of tests, 10 000 000 cycles sheet flexural specimens.
13. This rating would be B 2 for material exposed to elevated temperatures.
14. This rating may be different for material held at elevated temperatures for long periods.
15. Improved resistance to stress corrosion cracking can be realized by using controlled quenching and artificial aging practices in heat-treatable 7XXX aluminum alloys.
16. Based upon 50 000 000 cycles in a single series of tests using the RR Moore type of machine and specimen.

TABLE 2B—MECHANICAL PROPERTY LIMITS(1)(2)

Alloy and Temper	Product Form	Specified(3) Thickness or Diameter over mm	Specified(3) Thickness or Diameter thru mm	Area mm^2 thru	Tensile Strength(4) Ultimate min MPa	Tensile Strength(4) Ultimate max MPa	Tensile Strength(4) Yield min 0.2% Offset MPa	Elongation(5) % in 50 mm min
1100-0	Sheet	0.15	0.32		75	105	25	15
		0.32	0.63		75	105	25	17
		0.63	1.20		75	105	25	22
		1.20	6.30		75	105	25	30
2017-T4	Rivet and Cold Heading Wire and Rod	1.60	25.00		380		220	(10)
2024-T4	Rivet and Cold Heading Wire and Rod	1.60	25.00		425		275	(9)
2036-T4	Sheet	0.63	3.20		290		160	20
2038-T4	Sheet	0.63	1.80		275		140	20
2117-T4	Rivet and Cold Heading Wire and Rod	1.60	25.00		260		125	(10)
3002-0	Sheet	0.63	0.80		75	110	20	20
		0.80	1.20		75	110	20	23
		1.20	1.60		75	110	20	25
3003-H14,24	Sheet	0.20	0.32		140	180	115	1
		0.32	0.63		140	180	115	2
		0.63	1.20		140	180	115	3
		1.20	6.30		140	180	115	5
3004-0	Sheet	0.15	0.32		150	200	60	9
		0.32	0.63		150	200	60	12
		0.63	1.20		150	200	60	15
		1.20	6.30		150	200	60	18
-H32	Sheet	0.40	0.63		190	240	145	1
		0.63	1.20		190	240	145	3
		1.20	6.30		190	240	145	5
5005-0	Sheet	0.15	0.32		105	145	35	12
		0.32	0.63		105	145	35	16
		0.63	1.20		105	145	35	19
		1.20	6.30		105	145	35	21
5052-0	Sheet	0.15	0.32		170	215	65	13
		0.32	0.63		170	215	65	15
		0.63	1.20		170	215	65	17
		1.20	6.30		170	215	65	19
-H32	Sheet	0.40	0.63		215	265	160	4
		0.63	1.20		215	265	160	5
		1.20	6.30		215	265	160	7
5052-H34	Sheet	0.20	0.32		235	285	180	3
		0.32	0.63		235	285	180	3
		0.63	1.20		235	285	180	4
		1.20	6.30		235	285	180	6
5083-H112	Plate	6.30	12.50		275		125	12
-H321	Sheet & Plate	4.00	12.50		305	385	215 (6)	12
-H116	Sheet & Plate	1.60	12.50		305		215	10
-H111	Extrusions		130.00		275		165	12
-H112	Extrusions		130.00	20 000	270		110	12
5086-H32	Sheet & Plate	0.50	0.63		275	325	195	6
		0.63	1.20		275	325	195	6
		1.20	6.30		275	325	195	8
		6.30	50.00		275	325	195	12(10)

Notes:

TABLE 2B—MECHANICAL PROPERTY LIMITS[1][2] (continued)

Alloy and Temper	Product Form	Specified[3] Thickness or Diameter over mm	Specified[3] Thickness or Diameter thru mm	Area mm^2 thru	Tensile Strength[4] Ultimate min MPa	Tensile Strength[4] Ultimate max MPa	Tensile Strength[4] Yield min 0.2% Offset MPa	Elongation[5] % in 50 mm min
5086-H34	Sheet & Plate	0.20	0.32		300	350	235	4
		0.32	0.63		300	350	235	4
		0.63	1.20		300	350	235	5
		1.20	6.30		300	350	235	6
		6.30	25.00		300	350	235	10(9)
5086-H112	Extrusions		130.00	20 000	240		95	12
	Tubing	All	All	20 000	240		95	12
5182-0	Sheet	0.63	3.20		255	325	110	18
-02	Sheet	0.63	3.20		250	315	110	18
5252-H25	Sheet	0.63	2.50		215	270		9
5454-0	Sheet & Plate	0.50	0.63		215	285	85	12
		0.63	1.20		215	285	85	13
		1.20	6.30		215	285	85	16
		6.30	80.00		215	285	85	18(16)
-H32	Sheet & Plate	0.50	0.63		250	305	180	5
		0.63	1.20		250	305	180	6
		1.20	6.30		250	305	180	8
		6.30	50.00		250	305	180	12(10)
5454-H34	Sheet & Plate	0.50	0.63		270	325	200	4
		0.63	1.20		270	325	200	5
		1.20	6.30		270	325	200	6
		6.30	25.00		270	325	200	10(9)
5454-0	Extrusions		130.00	20 000	215	285	85	14
-H111	Extrusions		130.00	20 000	230		130	12
5454-0	Tube	All	All	20 000	215	285	85	14
-H111	Tube	All	All	20 000	230		130	12
5457-H-25	Sheet	0.75	2.50		160	215		7
5657-H25	Sheet	0.63	2.50		140	195		8
6009-T4	Sheet	0.50	1.80		185		105	21
		1.80	3.20		165		90	21
6009-T62	Sheet	0.50	1.80		270		235	9
6010-T4	Sheet	0.50	1.80		240		140	20
6010-T62		0.50	1.80		340		310	8
6053-T61	Rivet and Cold Heading Wire and Rod	1.60	25.00		205		135	(12)
6061-T4	Sheet	0.15	0.20		205		110	10
		0.20	0.25		205		110	12
		0.25	0.50		205		110	14
		0.50	6.30		205		110	16
6061-T6	Sheet	0.15	0.20		290		240	4
		0.20	0.25		290		240	6
		0.25	0.50		290		240	8
		0.50	6.30		290		240	10
6061-T651	Plate	6.30	12.50		290		240	10
		12.50	25.00		290		240	(8)
		25.00	50.00		290		240	(7)
6061-T4	Extrusions & Tube	All	All	All	180		110	16
6061-T6	Extrusions & Tube		6.30	All	260		240	8
		6.30		All	260		240	10
6061-T6	Rivet and Cold Heading Wire and Rod	1.60	25.00		290		240	(9)
6061-T6	Forgings Extension (Die Forgings)		100.00		260		240	7(6)[7]
								5(4)[8]
6063-T1	Extrusions & Tube		12.50	All	115		60	12
		12.50	25.00	All	110		55	
6063-T5	Extrusions & Tube		12.50	All	150		110	8
		12.50	25.00	All	145		105	
6063-T6	Extrusions & Tube		3.20	All	205		170	8
		3.20	25.00	All	205		170	10
6111-T4	Sheet	0.50	1.80		275		140	22
6111-T6	Sheet	0.50	1.80		320		275	10
6463-T521	Extrusions		25.00		150		95	8(7)
7021-T61	Sheet	1.60	6.30		380		345	8
7029-T5,T6	Extrusions	2.50	6.30		380		340	10
	Sheet							
7116-T5	Extrusions	3.20	12.50		330		290	8
7129-T5,T6	Extrusions		6.30		380		340	9

Notes:

1. Tensile property limits are based on producer analysis of data accumulated from standard production material which has been sampled and tested using standard procedures as detailed in the Quality Control Section of "Aluminum Standards and Data" published by The Aluminum Association Inc. The limits are established after sufficient test data has been accumulated to adequately determine the form of the frequency distribution curve and to provide a reliable estimate of the population mean and standard deviation. In most instances, the distribution is normal in form and properties are based on the results of a minimum of 100 tests from at least 10 different lots of material. The limits are subsequently established at levels at which 99% of the material is expected to conform at a confidence level of 0.95.

2. Ultimate Shearing Strength for Rivet and Cold Heading Wire & Rod

Alloy and Temper	Ultimate Shearing Strength min, MPa
2017-T4	225
2024-T4	255
2117-T4	180
6053-T6	135
6061-T6	170

3. Thicknesses shown are provided as a guide to the designer and should not be used for ordering purposes. Consult material supplier for details.
4. Tensile values are determined in accordance with ASTM B557M "Method of Tension Testing Aluminum and Magnesium Alloys."
5. Elongations in 50 mm apply for thicknesses up through 12.50 mm and in 5D (5.65√A) for thicknesses over 12.50 mm where D and A are the diameter and cross-sectional area of the specimen. Values for elongations in 5D (5.65√A) are shown in brackets.
6. Yield Maximum = 295 MPa for Alloy 5083-H321 Sheet and Plate
   = 180 MPa for Alloy 6463-T521 Extrusions
7. Specimen from forging axis parallel to direction of grain flow.
8. Specimen from forging axis not parallel to direction of grain flow.

TABLE 3—CHEMICAL COMPOSITION LIMITS[(1)(2)]

AA Number	UNS Number	Si	Fe	Cu	Mn	Mg	Cr	Zn		Ti	Other[(3)] Each	Other[(3)] Total [(4)]	Aluminum[(5)] Min
1100	A91100	0.95	Si + Fe	0.05–0.20	0.05	—	—	0.10	—	—	0.05	0.15	99.00
2017	A92017	0.20–0.8	0.7	3.5–4.5	0.40–1.0	0.40–0.8	0.10	0.25	—	0.15	0.05	0.15	Remainder
2024	A92024	0.50	0.50	3.8–4.9	0.30–0.9	1.2–1.8	0.10	0.25	—	0.15	0.05	0.15	
2036	A92036	0.50	0.50	2.2–3.0	0.10–0.40	0.30–0.6	0.10	0.25	—	0.15	0.05	0.15	
2038	A92038	0.50–1.3	0.6	0.8–1.8	0.10–0.40	0.40–1.0	0.20	0.50	0.05V–0.05Ga	0.15	0.05	0.15	
2117	A92117	0.8	0.7	2.2–3.0	0.20	0.20–0.50	0.10	0.25	—	—	0.05	0.15	
3002	A93002	0.08	0.10	0.15	0.05–0.25	0.05–0.20	—	0.05	0.05V	0.03	0.03	0.10	
3003	A93003	0.6	0.7	0.05–0.20	1.0–1.5	—	—	0.10	—	—	0.05	0.15	
3004	A93004	0.30	0.7	0.25	1.0–1.5	0.8–1.3	—	0.25	—	—	0.05	0.15	
5005	A95005	0.30	0.7	0.20	0.20	0.50–1.1	0.10	0.25	—	—	0.05	0.15	
5052	A95052	0.25	0.40	0.10	0.10	2.2–2.8	0.15–0.35	0.10	—	—	0.05	0.15	
5083	A95083	0.40	0.40	0.10	0.40–1.0	4.0–4.9	0.05–0.25	0.25	—	0.15	0.05	0.15	
5086	A95086	0.40	0.50	0.10	0.20–0.7	3.5–4.5	0.05–0.25	0.25	—	0.15	0.05	0.15	
5182	A95182	0.20	0.35	0.15	0.20–0.50	4.0–5.0	0.10	0.25	—	0.10	0.05	0.15	
5252	A95252	0.08	0.10	0.10	0.10	2.2–2.8	—	0.05	0.05V	—	0.03	0.10	
5454	A95454	0.25	0.40	0.10	0.50–1.0	2.4–3.0	0.05–0.20	0.25	—	0.20	0.05	0.15	
5457	A95457	0.08	0.10	0.20	0.15–0.45	0.8–1.2	—	0.05	0.05V	—	0.03	0.10	
5657	A95657	0.08	0.10	0.10	0.03	0.6–1.0	—	0.05	0.05V–0.03Ga	—	0.02	0.05	
6009	A96009	0.6–1.0	0.50	0.15–0.6	0.20–0.8	0.40–0.8	0.10	0.25	—	0.10	0.05	0.15	
6010	A96010	0.8–1.2	0.50	0.15–0.6	0.20–0.8	0.6–1.0	0.10	0.25	—	0.10	0.05	0.15	
6053	A96053	(6)	0.35	0.10	—	1.1–1.4	0.15–0.35	0.10	—	—	0.05	0.15	
6061	A96061	0.40–0.8	0.7	0.15–0.40	0.15	0.8–1.2	0.04–0.35	0.25	—	0.15	0.05	0.15	
6063	A96063	0.20–0.6	0.35	0.10	0.10	0.45–0.9	0.10	0.10	—	0.10	0.05	0.15	
6111	A96111	0.7–1.1	0.40	0.50–0.9	0.15–0.45	0.50–1.0	0.10	0.15	—	0.10	0.05	0.15	
6463	A96463	0.20–0.6	0.15	0.20	0.05	0.45–0.9	—	0.05	—	—	0.05	0.15	
7021	A97021	0.25	0.40	0.25	0.10	1.2–1.8	0.05	5.0–6.0	0.08–0.18Zr	0.10	0.05	0.15	
7029	A97029	0.10	0.12	0.50–0.9	0.03	1.3–2.0	—	4.2–5.2	0.05V	0.05	0.03	0.10	
7116	A97116	0.15	0.30	0.50–1.1	0.05	0.8–1.4	—	4.2–5.2	0.05v–0.03Ga	0.05	0.05	0.15	
7129	A97129	0.15	0.30	0.50–0.9	0.10	1.3–2.0	0.10	4.2–5.2	0.05V–0.03Ga	0.05	0.05	0.15	

1. Composition in percent maximum unless shown as a range.
2. For purposes of determining conformance to these limits, an observed value or a calculated value obtained from analysis is rounded off to the nearest unit in the last right-hand place of figures used in expressing the specified limit in accordance with the rounding-off method of ASTM E 29.
3. Analysis is required for elements other than aluminum for which specific limits are shown. Analysis for other elements is made when their presence is suspected to be, or in the course of routine analysis is indicated to be, in excess of the specified limits.
4. Other elements total is the sum of those other metallic elements 0.010 or more, each expressed to the second decimal before determining the sum.
5. The aluminum content for unalloyed aluminum not made by a refining process is the difference between 100.0% and the sum of all other metallic elements present in amounts of 0.010% or more each expressed to the second decimal before determing the sum.
6. 45% to 65% of actual Mg.

TABLE 4—TYPICAL HEAT TREATMENTS FOR ALUMINUM ALLOY MILL PRODUCTS(1)

Alloy	Product	Solution Heat(2) Treatment Metal(3) Temperature °C	Solution Heat(2) Treatment Temper Designation	Precipitation Heat Treatment Metal(3) Temperature °C	Precipitation Heat Treatment Approx.(4) Time at Temperature Hours	Precipitation Heat Treatment Temper Designation
2036	Sheet	(5)	T4			
2038	Sheet	(5)	T4			
6009	Sheet	(5)	T4	200–210°	1	T6(6)
6010	Sheet	(5)	T4	200–210°	1	T6(6)
6061	Sheet	515–550	T4	155–165	18	T6
	Plate	515–550	T451	155–165	18	T651
	Extrusions, Tube, Rod, Bar Forgings	515–550(7)	T4	170–180	8	T6
6063	Extrusions, Tube	(7)	T1	175–185(8)	3	T5
		515–525(7)	T4	170–180(9)	8	T6
6111	Sheet	(5)	T4	200–210	1	T6
6463	Extrusions	(7)	T1	175–185(8)	1	T5
		515–525	T4	170–180(9)	8	T6
7021	Sheet	395–405(10)	W	(11)	(11)	T61
7029	Extrusions	480–520(12)	W	(13)	(13)	T5,T6
7116	Extrusions	425–540	W	(14)	(14)	T5
7129	Extrusions	480–520	S	(13)	(13)	T5,T6

Notes:

1. The times and temperatures shown are typical for various forms, sizes and methods of manufacture and may not exactly describe the optimum treatment for a specific item.
2. Material should be quenched in water or by high velocity fans from the solution heat-treating temperature as rapidly as possible and with minimum delay after removal from the furnace. Unless otherwise indicated, when material is quenched by total immersion in water, the water should be at room temperature and suitably cooled to remain below 35 °C during the quench cycle. The use of high velocity, high volume jets of cold water is also effective for some material.
3. The metal temperature should be attained as rapidly as possible. When a temperature range exceeding 10 °C is shown, a temperature range of 10 degrees within the listed range should be selected and maintained during the time at temperature.
4. The time at temperature will depend on the time required for load to reach temperature. The times shown are based on rapid heating with soaking time measured from the time the load reaches the 10 °C range listed or selected.
5. These alloys are supplied in the solution heat-treated condition. For optimum properties, subsequent re-heat treatment is not recommended.
6. Mechanical properties of material will meet tensile property limits of T6 temper as specified in Table 2B.
7. By suitable control of extrusion temperature, product may be quenched directly from extrusion press to provide specified properties for this temper. Some products may be adequately quenched in air blast at room temperature.
8. An alternate treatment comprised of 1 to 2 h at 200 to 210 °C may be used.
9. An alternate treatment comprised of 6 h at 175 to 185 °C may be used.
10. Quenched at a minimum average cooling rate of 35 °C/s as measured over the range 385 to 205 °C.
11. A minimum of 8 h at room temperature followed by 2 h at 95 to 105 °C plus 4 h at 155 to 165 °C.
12. 10 minute soak at temperature followed by cold water quench.
13. 5 h at 95 to 105 °C plus 5 h at 155 to 165 °C.
14. 5 h at 95 to 105 °C plus 5 h at 160 to 170 °C.

TABLE 5—TYPICAL PHYSICAL PROPERTIES[1]

Average [2] Coefficient of Thermal Expansion 20 to 100 °C Per °C	Average[2] Coefficient of Thermal Expansion 20 to 100 °C Per °C	Approx. [3][4] Melting Range °C	Temper	Thermal Conductivity at 25 °C W/mK	Electrical[5] Conductivity at 20 °C (68 °F) Equal Volume	Electrical[5] Conductivity at 20 °C (68 °F) Equal Mass	Electrical Resistivity at 20 °C Ohm mm/m	Density 10 kg/m
1100	23.6	640–655	0	222	59	194	0.029	2.71
2036	23.4	555–650	T4	159	41	135	0.042	2.75
2038	23.4	555–650	T4	155	40	132	0.043	2.73
3002								2.70
3003	23.2	640–655	H14	159	41	134	0.042	2.73
3004	23.9	630–655	All	163	42	137	0.042	2.72
5005	23.8	630–655	All	201	52	172	0.033	2.70
5052	23.8	605–650	All	138	35	116	0.050	2.68
5083	23.8	580–640	0	117	29	98	0.059	2.66
5086	23.8	585–640	All	126	31	104	0.056	2.66
5182	24.1	575–640	All	121	31	110	0.056	2.65
5252	23.8	605–650	All	138	35	116	0.050	2.67
5454	23.6	600–640	0	134	34	113	0.050	2.69
			H38	134	34	113	0.050	
5457	23.8	630–655	All	176	46	153	0.037	2.69
6009	23.4	605–650	All	167	44	144	0.039	2.71
6010	23.2	585–650	All	151	39	128	0.044	2.71
6061	23.6	580–650	T4	155	40	132	0.043	2.70
			T6	167	43	142	0.040	
6063	23.4	615–655	T1	193	50	165	0.034	2.70
			T5	209	55	181	0.031	2.70
			T6	201	53	175	0.032	2.70
6111	23.4	585–650	T4	154	40	131	0.043	2.71
			T6	174	45	147	0.038	2.71
6463	23.4	615–655	T5	209	55	181	0.031	2.69
			T6	201	53	175	0.032	2.69
7021	22.8	595–645	T61	176	43	135	0.040	2.78
7029	22.8	585–645	T5,T6	163	42	133	0.041	2.77
7116	23.4	600–645	T5	176	46	148	0.037	2.78
7129	22.8	585–615	T5,T6	163	42	133	0.041	2.78

Notes:

1. Typical properties are not guaranteed since in most cases they are averages for various sizes, product forms, and methods of manufacture and may not be exactly representative of any particular product or size. These data are intended only as a basis for comparing alloys and tempers and should not be specified as engineering requirements or used for design purposes.
2. Coefficient to be multiplied by 10^{-6}. Example: $23.6 \times 10^{-6} = 0.0000236$.
3. Melting ranges shown apply to wrought products of 6 mm or greater thickness.
4. Based on typical composition of the indicated alloy.
5. IACS—International Annealed Copper Standard.

TABLE 6—TYPICAL TENSILE PROPERTIES AT VARIOUS TEMPERATURES[1]
(NOT FOR DESIGN PURPOSES)

The following typical properties are not guaranteed since in most cases they are averages for various sizes, product forms, and methods of manufacture and may not be exactly representative of any particular product or size. These data are intended only as a basis for comparing alloys and tempers and should not be specified as engineering requirements or used for design purposes.

Alloy and Temper	Temper-ature °F	Temper-ature °C	Tensile Strength Ultimate ksi	Tensile Strength Ultimate MPa	Tensile Strength Yield[2] ksi	Tensile Strength Yield[2] MPa	Elon-gation in 2 in, %
1100-0	−320	−196	25	172	6	41	50
	−112	−80	15	103	5.5	38	43
	−18	−28	14	97	5	34	40
	75	24	13	90	5	34	40
	212	100	10	69	4.6	32	45
	300	149	8	55	4.2	29	55
	400	204	6	41	3.5	24	65
	500	260	4	28	2.6	18	75
	600	316	2.9	20	2	14	80
	700	371	2.1	14	1.6	11	85
1100-H14	−320	−196	30	207	20	138	45
	−112	−80	20	138	18	124	24
	−18	−28	19	131	17	117	20
	75	24	18	124	17	117	20
	212	100	16	110	15	103	20
	300	149	14	97	12	83	23
	400	204	10	69	7.5	52	26
	500	260	4	28	2.6	18	75
	600	316	2.9	20	2	14	80
	700	371	2.1	14	1.6	11	85
1100-H18	−320	−196	34	234	26	179	30
	−112	−80	26	179	23	158	16
	−18	−28	25	172	23	158	15
	75	24	24	165	22	152	15
	212	100	21	145	19	131	15
	300	149	18	124	14	97	20
	400	204	6	41	3.5	24	65
	500	260	4	28	2.6	18	75
	600	316	2.9	20	2	14	80
	700	371	2.1	14	1.6	11	85
2011-T3	75	24	55	379	43	296	15
	212	110	47	324	34	234	16
	300	149	23	193	19	131	25
	400	204	16	110	11	76	35
	500	260	6.5	45	3.8	26	45
	600	316	3.1	21	1.8	12	90
	700	371	2.3	16	1.4	10	125
2014-T6, -T651	−320	−196	84	579	72	496	14
	−112	−80	74	510	65	448	13
	−18	−28	72	496	62	427	13
	75	24	70	482	60	414	13
	212	100	63	434	57	393	15
	300	149	40	275	35	241	20
	400	204	16	110	13	90	38
	500	260	9.5	66	7.5	52	52
	600	316	6.5	45	5	34	65
	700	371	4.3	30	3.5	24	72
2017-T4, -T451	−320	−196	80	551	53	365	28
	−112	−80	65	448	42	290	24
	−18	−28	64	441	41	283	23
	75	24	62	427	40	276	22
	212	100	57	393	39	269	18
	300	149	40	276	30	207	15
	400	204	16	110	13	90	35
	500	260	9	62	7.5	52	45
	600	316	6	41	5	34	65
	700	371	4.3	30	3.5	24	70

TABLE 6—TYPICAL TENSILE PROPERTIES AT VARIOUS TEMPERATURES[1]
(NOT FOR DESIGN PURPOSES) (continued)

The following typical properties are not guaranteed since in most cases they are averages for various sizes, product forms, and methods of manufacture and may not be exactly representative of any particular product or size. These data are intended only as a basis for comparing alloys and tempers and should not be specified as engineering requirements or used for design purposes.

Alloy and Temper	Temper-ature °F	Temper-ature °C	Tensile Strength Ultimate ksi	Tensile Strength Ultimate MPa	Tensile Strength Yield[2] ksi	Tensile Strength Yield[2] MPa	Elon-gation in 2 in, %
2024-T3	−320	−196	85	586	62	427	18
(sheet)	−112	−80	73	503	52	358	17
	−18	−28	72	496	51	352	17
	75	24	70	482	50	345	17
	212	100	66	455	48	331	16
	300	149	55	379	45	310	11
	400	204	27	186	20	138	23
	500	260	11	76	9	62	55
	600	316	7.5	52	6	41	75
	700	371	5	34	4	28	100
2024-T4, -T351	−320	−196	84	579	61	420	19
(plate)	−112	−80	71	490	49	338	19
	−18	−28	69	476	47	324	19
	75	24	68	469	47	324	19
	212	100	63	434	45	310	19
	300	149	45	310	36	248	17
	400	204	26	179	19	131	27
	500	260	11	76	9	62	55
	600	316	7.5	52	6	41	75
	700	371	5	34	4	28	100
2024-T6, -T651	−320	−196	84	579	68	469	11
	−112	−80	72	496	59	408	10
	−18	−28	70	483	58	400	10
	75	24	69	476	57	393	10
	212	100	65	448	54	372	10
	300	149	45	310	36	248	17
	400	204	26	179	19	131	27
	500	260	11	76	9	62	55
	600	316	7.5	52	6	41	75
	700	371	5	34	4	28	100
2024-T81, -T851	−320	−196	85	586	78	538	8
	−112	−80	74	510	69	476	7
	−18	−28	73	503	68	469	7
	75	24	70	482	65	448	7
	212	100	66	455	62	427	8
	300	149	55	379	49	338	11
	400	204	27	186	20	138	23
	500	260	11	76	9	62	55
	600	316	7.5	52	6	41	75
	700	371	5	34	4	28	100
2024-T861 [3]	−320	−196	92	634	85	586	5
	−112	−80	81	558	77	531	5
	−18	−28	78	538	74	510	5
	75	24	75	517	71	490	5
	212	100	70	483	67	462	6
	300	149	54	372	48	331	11
	400	204	21	145	17	117	28
	500	260	11	76	9	62	55
	600	316	7.5	52	6	41	75
	700	371	5	34	4	28	100
2117-T4	−320	−196	56	386	33	228	30
	−112	−80	45	310	25	172	29
	−18	−28	44	303	24	165	28
	75	24	43	296	24	165	27
	212	100	36	248	21	145	16
	300	149	30	207	17	117	20
	400	204	16	110	12	83	35
	500	260	7.5	52	5.5	38	55
	600	316	4.7	32	3.3	23	80
	700	371	2.9	20	2	14	110

TABLE 6—TYPICAL TENSILE PROPERTIES AT VARIOUS TEMPERATURES[1]
(NOT FOR DESIGN PURPOSES) (continued)

The following typical properties are not guaranteed since in most cases they are averages for various sizes, product forms, and methods of manufacture and may not be exactly representative of any particular product or size. These data are intended only as a basis for comparing alloys and tempers and should not be specified as engineering requirements or used for design purposes.

Alloy and Temper	Temperature °F	Temperature °C	Tensile Strength Ultimate ksi	Tensile Strength Ultimate MPa	Tensile Strength Yield[2] ksi	Tensile Strength Yield[2] MPa	Elongation in 2 in, %
2618-T61	–320	–196	78	538	61	420	12
	–112	–80	67	462	55	379	11
	–18	–28	64	441	54	372	10
	75	24	64	441	54	372	10
	212	100	62	427	54	372	10
	300	149	50	345	44	303	14
	400	204	32	221	26	179	24
	500	260	13	90	9	62	50
	600	316	7.5	52	4.5	31	80
	700	371	5	34	3.5	24	120
3003-0	–320	–196	33	227	8.5	59	46
	–112	–80	20	138	7	48	42
	–18	–28	17	117	6.5	45	41
	75	24	16	110	6	41	40
	212	100	13	90	5.5	38	43
	300	149	11	76	5	34	47
	400	204	8.5	59	4.3	30	60
	500	260	6	41	3.4	23	65
	600	316	4	28	2.4	16	70
	700	371	2.8	19	1.8	14	70
3003-H14	–320	–196	35	241	25	172	30
	–112	–80	24	165	22	152	18
	–18	–28	22	152	21	145	16
	75	24	22	152	21	145	16
	212	100	21	145	19	131	16
	300	149	18	124	16	110	16
	400	204	14	96	9	62	20
	500	260	7.5	52	4	28	60
	600	316	4	28	2.4	16	70
	700	371	2.8	19	1.8	12	70
3003-H18	–320	–196	41	283	33	228	23
	–112	–80	32	221	29	200	11
	–18	–28	30	207	28	193	10
	75	24	29	200	27	186	10
	212	100	26	179	21	145	10
	300	149	23	158	16	110	11
	400	204	14	96	9	62	18
	500	260	7.5	52	4	28	60
	600	316	4	28	2.4	16	70
	700	371	2.8	19	1.8	12	70
3004-0	–320	–196	42	290	13	90	38
	–112	–80	28	193	11	76	30
	–18	–28	26	179	10	69	26
	75	24	26	179	10	69	25
	212	100	26	179	10	69	25
	300	149	22	152	10	69	35
	400	204	14	96	9.5	66	55
	500	260	10	69	7.5	52	70
	600	316	7.5	52	5	34	80
	700	371	5	34	3	21	90
3004-H34	–320	–196	52	358	34	234	26
	–112	–80	38	262	30	207	16
	–18	–28	36	248	29	200	13
	75	24	35	241	29	200	12
	212	100	34	234	29	200	13
	300	149	28	193	25	172	22
	400	204	21	145	15	103	35
	500	260	14	96	7.5	52	55
	600	316	7.5	52	5	34	80
	700	371	5	34	3	21	90

TABLE 6—TYPICAL TENSILE PROPERTIES AT VARIOUS TEMPERATURES[1]
(NOT FOR DESIGN PURPOSES) (continued)

The following typical properties are not guaranteed since in most cases they are averages for various sizes, product forms, and methods of manufacture and may not be exactly representative of any particular product or size. These data are intended only as a basis for comparing alloys and tempers and should not be specified as engineering requirements or used for design purposes.

Alloy and Temper	Temperature °F	Temperature °C	Tensile Strength Ultimate ksi	Tensile Strength Ultimate MPa	Tensile Strength Yield[2] ksi	Tensile Strength Yield[2] MPa	Elongation in 2 in, %
3004-H38	–320	–196	58	400	43	296	20
	–112	–80	44	303	38	262	10
	–18	–28	42	290	36	248	7
	75	24	41	283	36	248	6
	212	100	40	276	36	248	7
	300	149	31	214	27	186	15
	400	204	22	152	15	103	30
	500	260	12	83	7.5	52	50
	600	316	7.5	52	5	34	80
	700	371	5	34	3	21	90
4032-T6	–320	–196	66	455	48	331	11
	–112	–80	58	400	46	317	10
	–18	–28	56	386	46	317	9
	75	24	55	379	46	317	9
	212	100	50	345	44	303	9
	300	149	37	255	33	228	9
	400	204	13	90	9	62	30
	500	260	8	55	5.5	28	50
	600	316	5	34	3.2	22	70
	700	371	3.4	23	2	14	90
5050-0	–320	–196	37	255	10	69	—
	–112	–80	22	152	8.5	59	—
	–18	–28	21	145	8	55	—
	75	24	21	145	8	55	—
	212	100	21	145	8	55	—
	300	149	19	131	8	55	—
	400	204	14	96	7.5	52	—
	500	260	9	62	6	41	—
	600	316	6	41	4.2	29	—
	700	371	3.9	27	2.6	18	—
5050-H34	–320	–196	44	303	30	207	—
	–112	–80	30	207	25	172	—
	–18	–28	28	193	24	165	—
	75	24	28	193	24	165	—
	212	100	28	193	24	165	—
	300	149	25	172	22	152	—
	400	204	14	96	7.5	52	—
	500	260	9	62	6	41	—
	600	316	6	41	4.2	29	—
	700	371	3.9	27	2.6	18	—
5050-H38	–320	–196	46	317	36	248	—
	–112	–80	34	234	30	207	—
	–18	–28	32	221	29	200	—
	75	24	32	221	29	200	—
	212	100	31	214	29	200	—
	300	149	27	186	25	172	—
	400	204	14	96	7.5	52	—
	500	260	9	62	6	41	—
	600	316	6	41	4.2	29	—
	700	371	3.9	27	2.6	18	—
5052-0	–320	–196	44	303	16	110	46
	–112	–80	29	200	13	90	35
	–18	–28	28	193	13	90	32
	75	24	28	193	13	90	30
	212	100	28	193	13	90	36
	300	149	23	158	13	90	50
	400	204	17	117	11	76	60
	500	260	12	83	7.5	52	80
	600	316	7.5	52	5.5	38	110
	700	371	5	34	3.1	21	130

TABLE 6—TYPICAL TENSILE PROPERTIES AT VARIOUS TEMPERATURES[1]
(NOT FOR DESIGN PURPOSES) (continued)

The following typical properties are not guaranteed since in most cases they are averages for various sizes, product forms, and methods of manufacture and may not be exactly representative of any particular product or size. These data are intended only as a basis for comparing alloys and tempers and should not be specified as engineering requirements or used for design purposes.

Alloy and Temper	Temperature °F	Temperature °C	Tensile Strength Ultimate ksi	Tensile Strength Ultimate MPa	Tensile Strength Yield[2] ksi	Tensile Strength Yield[2] MPa	Elongation in 2 in, %
5052-H34	−320	−196	55	379	36	248	28
	−112	−80	40	276	32	221	21
	−18	−28	38	262	31	214	18
	75	24	38	262	31	214	16
	212	100	38	262	31	214	18
	300	149	30	207	27	186	27
	400	204	24	165	15	103	45
	500	260	12	83	7.5	52	80
	600	316	7.5	52	5.5	38	110
	700	371	5	34	3.1	21	130
5052-H38	−320	−196	60	414	44	303	25
	−112	−80	44	303	38	262	18
	−18	−28	42	290	37	255	15
	75	24	42	290	37	255	14
	212	100	40	276	36	248	16
	300	149	34	234	28	193	24
	400	204	25	172	15	103	45
	500	260	12	83	7.5	52	80
	600	316	7.5	52	5.5	38	110
	700	371	5	34	3.1	21	130
5083-0	−320	−196	59	407	24	165	36
	−112	−80	43	296	21	145	30
	−18	−28	42	290	21	145	27
	75	24	42	29-	21	145	25
	212	100	40	276	21	145	36
	300	149	31	214	19	131	50
	400	204	22	152	17	117	60
	500	260	17	117	11	76	80
	600	316	11	76	7.5	52	110
	700	371	6	41	4.2	29	130
5086-0	−320	−196	55	379	19	131	46
	−112	−80	39	269	17	117	35
	−18	−28	38	262	17	117	32
	75	24	38	262	17	117	30
	212	100	38	262	17	117	36
	300	149	29	200	16	110	50
	400	204	22	152	15	103	60
	500	260	17	117	11	76	80
	600	316	11	76	7.5	52	110
	700	371	6	41	4.2	29	130
5154-0	−320	−196	52	358	19	131	46
	−112	−80	36	248	17	117	35
	−18	−28	35	241	17	117	32
	75	24	35	241	17	117	30
	212	100	35	241	17	117	36
	300	149	29	200	16	110	50
	400	204	22	152	15	103	60
	500	260	17	117	11	76	80
	600	316	11	76	7.5	52	110
	700	371	6	41	4.2	29	130
5454-0	−320	−196	54	372	19	131	39
	−112	−80	37	255	17	117	30
	−18	−28	36	248	17	117	27
	75	24	36	248	17	117	25
	212	100	36	248	17	117	31
	300	149	29	200	16	110	50
	400	204	22	152	15	103	60
	500	260	17	117	11	76	80
	600	316	11	76	7.5	52	110
	700	371	6	41	4.2	29	130

TABLE 6—TYPICAL TENSILE PROPERTIES AT VARIOUS TEMPERATURES[1]
(NOT FOR DESIGN PURPOSES) (continued)

The following typical properties are not guaranteed since in most cases they are averages for various sizes, product forms, and methods of manufacture and may not be exactly representative of any particular product or size. These data are intended only as a basis for comparing alloys and tempers and should not be specified as engineering requirements or used for design purposes.

Alloy and Temper	Temperature °F	Temperature °C	Tensile Strength Ultimate ksi	Tensile Strength Ultimate MPa	Tensile Strength Yield[2] ksi	Tensile Strength Yield[2] MPa	Elongation in 2 in, %
5454-H32	−320	−196	59	407	36	248	32
	−112	−80	42	290	31	214	23
	−18	−28	41	283	30	207	20
	75	24	40	276	30	207	18
	212	100	39	269	29	200	20
	300	149	32	221	26	179	37
	400	204	25	172	19	131	45
	500	260	17	117	11	76	80
	600	316	11	76	7.5	52	110
	700	371	6	41	4.2	29	130
5454-H34	−320	−196	63	434	41	283	30
	−112	−80	46	317	36	248	21
	−18	−28	44	303	35	241	18
	75	24	44	303	35	241	16
	212	100	43	296	34	234	18
	300	149	34	234	28	193	32
	400	204	26	179	19	131	45
	500	260	17	117	11	76	80
	600	316	11	76	7.5	52	110
	700	371	6	41	4.2	29	130
5456-0	−320	−196	62	427	26	179	32
	−112	−80	46	317	23	158	25
	−18	−28	45	310	23	158	22
	75	24	45	310	23	158	20
	212	100	42	290	22	152	31
	300	149	31	214	20	137	50
	400	204	22	152	17	117	60
	500	260	17	117	11	76	80
	600	316	11	76	7.5	52	110
	700	371	6	41	4.2	29	130
6053-T6, -T651	75	24	37	255	32	221	13
	212	100	32	221	28	193	13
	300	149	25	172	24	165	13
	400	204	13	90	12	83	25
	500	260	5.5	38	4	28	70
	600	316	4	28	2.7	19	80
	700	371	2.9	20	2	14	90
6061-T6, -T651	−320	−196	60	414	47	324	22
	−112	−80	49	338	42	290	18
	−18	−28	47	324	41	283	17
	75	24	45	310	40	276	17
	212	100	42	290	38	262	18
	300	149	34	234	31	214	20
	400	204	19	131	15	103	28
	500	260	7.5	52	5	34	60
	600	316	4.6	32	2.7	19	85
	700	371	3	21	1.8	12	95
6063-T1	−320	−196	34	234	16	110	44
	−112	−80	26	179	15	103	36
	−18	−28	24	165	14	96	34
	75	24	22	152	13	90	33
	212	100	22	152	14	96	18
	300	149	21	145	15	103	20
	400	204	9	62	6.5	45	40
	500	260	4.5	31	3.5	24	75
	600	316	3.2	22	2.5	17	80
	700	371	2.3	16	2	14	105

TABLE 6—TYPICAL TENSILE PROPERTIES AT VARIOUS TEMPERATURES[1] (NOT FOR DESIGN PURPOSES) (continued)

The following typical properties are not guaranteed since in most cases they are averages for various sizes, product forms, and methods of manufacture and may not be exactly representative of any particular product or size. These data are intended only as a basis for comparing alloys and tempers and should not be specified as engineering requirements or used for design purposes.

Alloy and Temper	Temper-ature °F	Temper-ature °C	Tensile Strength Ultimate ksi	Tensile Strength Ultimate MPa	Tensile Strength Yield[2] ksi	Tensile Yield[2] MPa	Elon-gation in 2 in, %
6063–T5	−320	−196	37	255	24	165	28
	−112	−80	29	200	22	152	24
	−18	−28	28	193	22	152	23
	75	24	27	186	21	145	22
	212	100	24	165	20	138	18
	300	149	20	138	18	124	20
	400	204	9	62	6.5	45	40
	500	260	4.5	31	3.5	24	75
	600	316	3.2	22	2.5	17	80
	700	371	2.3	16	2	14	105
6063-T6	−320	−196	47	324	36	248	24
	−112	−80	38	262	33	228	20
	−18	−28	36	248	32	221	19
	75	24	35	241	31	214	18
	212	100	31	214	28	193	15
	300	149	21	145	20	138	20
	400	204	9	62	6.5	45	40
	500	260	4.5	31	3.5	24	75
	600	316	3.3	23	2.5	17	80
	700	371	2.3	16	2	14	105
6151–T6	−320	−196	57	393	50	345	20
	−112	−80	50	345	46	317	17
	−18	−28	49	338	45	310	17
	75	24	48	331	43	296	17
	212	100	43	296	40	276	17
	300	149	28	193	27	186	20
	400	204	14	96	12	83	30
	500	260	6.5	45	5	103	50
	600	316	5	34	3.9	27	43
	700	371	4	28	3.2	22	35
6262-T651	−320	−196	60	414	47	324	22
	−112	−80	49	338	42	290	18
	−18	−28	47	324	41	283	17
	75	24	45	310	40	276	17
	212	100	42	290	38	262	18
	300	149	34	234	31	214	20
6262-T9	−320	−196	74	510	67	462	14
	−112	−80	62	427	58	400	10
	−18	−28	60	414	56	386	10
	75	24	58	400	55	379	10
	212	100	53	365	52	358	10
	300	149	38	262	37	255	14
	400	204	15	103	13	90	34
	500	260	8.5	59	6	41	48
	600	316	4.6	32	2.7	19	85
	700	371	3	21	1.8	12	95
7075-T6, -T651	−320	−196	102	703	92	634	9
	−112	−80	90	620	79	545	11
	−18	−28	86	523	75	517	11
	75	24	83	572	73	503	11
	212	100	70	483	65	448	14
	300	149	31	214	27	186	30
	400	204	16	110	13	90	55
	500	260	11	76	9	62	65
	600	316	8	55	6.5	45	70
	700	371	6	41	4.6	32	70

TABLE 6—TYPICAL TENSILE PROPERTIES AT VARIOUS TEMPERATURES[1] (NOT FOR DESIGN PURPOSES) (continued)

The following typical properties are not guaranteed since in most cases they are averages for various sizes, product forms, and methods of manufacture and may not be exactly representative of any particular product or size. These data are intended only as a basis for comparing alloys and tempers and should not be specified as engineering requirements or used for design purposes.

Alloy and Temper	Temper-ature °F	Temper-ature °C	Tensile Strength Ultimate ksi	Tensile Strength Ultimate MPa	Tensile Strength Yield[2] ksi	Tensile Strength Yield[2] MPa	Elon-gation in 2 in, %
7075-T73, -T7351	−320	−196	92	634	72	496	14
	−112	−80	79	545	67	492	14
	−18	−28	76	524	65	448	13
	75	24	73	503	63	434	13
	212	100	63	434	58	400	15
	300	149	31	214	27	186	30
	400	204	16	110	13	90	55
	500	260	11	76	9	62	65
	600	316	8	55	6.5	45	70
	700	371	6	41	4.6	32	70

1. These data are based on a limited amount of testing and represent the lowest strength during 10 000 h of exposure at testing temperature under no load; stress applied at 34 MPa (5000 psi/min) to yield strength and then at strain rate of 1.3 mm/mm/min (0.05 in/in/min) to failure. Under some conditions of temperature and time, the application of heat will adversely affect certain other properties of some alloys.
2. Offset equals 0.2%.
3. Temper T861 was formerly designated T86.

TABLE 7—NOMINAL CHEMICAL COMPOSITION—WROUGHT ALLOYS PERCENT OF ALLOYING ELEMENTS—ALUMINUM AND NORMAL IMPURITIES CONSTITUTE REMAINDER

The following values are shown as a basis for general comparison of alloys and are not guaranteed. The information in this table does not include the Alclad materials.

Alloy	Si	Cu	Mn	Mg	Cr	Ni	Zn	Pb	Bi
1050	—	—	99.50% min aluminum	99.50% min aluminum	99.50% min aluminum	—	—	—	—
1060	—	—	99.60% min aluminum	99.60% min aluminum	99.60% min aluminum	—	—	—	—
1100	—	0.12	99.00% min aluminum	99.00% min aluminum	99.00% min aluminum	—	—	—	—
1145	—	—	99.45% min aluminum	99.45% min aluminum	99.45% min aluminum	—	—	—	—
1175	—	—	99.75% min aluminum	99.75% min aluminum	99.75% min aluminum	—	—	—	—
1200	—	—	99.00% min aluminum	99.00% min aluminum	99.00% min aluminum	—	—	—	—
1230	—	—	99.30% min aluminum	99.30% min aluminum	99.30% min aluminum	—	—	—	—
1235	—	—	99.35% min aluminum	99.35% min aluminum	99.35% min aluminum	—	—	—	—
1345	—	—	99.45% min aluminum	99.45% min aluminum	99.45% min aluminum	—	—	—	—
1350	—	—	99.50% min aluminum	99.50% min aluminum	99.50% min aluminum	—	—	—	—
2011	—	5.5	—	—	—	—	—	0.40	0.40
2014	0.8	4.4	0.8	0.50	—	—	—	—	—
2017	0.5	4.0	0.7	0.6	—	—	—	—	—
2018	—	4.0	—	0.7	—	2.0	—	—	—
2024	—	4.4	0.6	1.5	—	—	—	—	—
2117	—	2.6	—	0.35	—	—	—	—	—
2124	—	4.4	0.6	1.5	—	—	—	—	—
2618[1]	0.18	2.3	—	1.6	—	1.0	—	—	—
3003	—	0.12	1.2	—	—	—	—	—	—
3004	—	—	1.2	1.0	—	—	—	—	—
3005	—	—	1.2	0.40	—	—	—	—	—
3105	—	—	0.6	0.50	—	—	—	—	—
4032	12.2	0.9	—	1.1	—	0.9	—	—	—
4043	5.2	—	—	—	—	—	—	—	—
4045	10.0	—	—	—	—	—	—	—	—
4343	7.5	—	—	—	—	—	—	—	—
5005	—	—	—	0.8	—	—	—	—	—
5050	—	—	—	1.4	—	—	—	—	—
5052	—	—	—	2.5	0.25	—	—	—	—
5056	—	—	0.12	5.1	0.12	—	—	—	—
5083	—	—	0.7	4.45	0.15	—	—	—	—
5086	—	—	0.45	4.0	0.15	—	—	—	—
5154	—	—	—	3.5	0.25	—	—	—	—
5252	—	—	—	2.5	—	—	—	—	—
5356[2]	—	—	0.12	5.0	0.12	—	—	—	—
5454	—	—	0.8	2.7	0.12	—	—	—	—

TABLE 7—NOMINAL CHEMICAL COMPOSITION—WROUGHT ALLOYS PERCENT OF ALLOYING ELEMENTS—ALUMINUM AND NORMAL IMPURITIES CONSTITUTE REMAINDER (continued)

The following values are shown as a basis for general comparison of alloys and are not guaranteed. The information in this table does not include the Alclad materials.

Alloy	Si	Cu	Mn	Mg	Cr	Ni	Zn	Pb	Bi
5456	—	—	0.8	5.1	0.12	—	—	—	—
5457	—	—	0.30	1.0	—	—	—	—	—
5657	—	—	—	0.8	—	—	—	—	—
6003	0.7	—	—	1.2	—	—	—	—	—
6053	0.7	—	—	1.3	0.25	—	—	—	—
6061	0.6	0.27	—	1.0	0.20	—	—	—	—
6063	0.40	—	—	0.7	—	—	—	—	—
6151	0.9	—	—	0.6	0.25	—	—	—	—
6253	—	—	—	1.2	0.25	—	2.0	—	—
6262	0.6	0.27	—	1.0	0.09	—	—	0.55	0.55
6463	0.40	—	—	0.7	—	—	—	—	—
6951	0.30	0.25	—	0.6	—	—	—	—	—
7072	—	—	—	—	—	—	1.0	—	—
7075	—	1.6	—	2.5	0.30	—	5.6	—	—

1. Iron, 1.1%; Titanium 0.07%
2. Titanium, 0.13%

CHEMICAL COMPOSITIONS, MECHANICAL PROPERTY LIMITS, AND DIMENSIONALTOLERANCES OF SAE WROUGHT ALUMINUM ALLOYS—SAE J457 FEB1991

SAE Standard

Report of the SAE Nonferrous Metals Division approved June 1911, last revised, SAE Nonferrous Metals Committee, May 1972, reaffirmed without change August 1985. Completely revised by the SAE Wrought Aluminum Committee February 1991.

1. Scope—This SAE Standard for wrought aluminum alloys provides sources of chemical and mechanical property data for a considerable range of alloys with varying properties, structures, and applications.

2. References

2.1 Applicable Publications—The following publications form a part of this specification to the extent specified herein. The latest issue of SAE publications shall apply.

2.1.1 SAE PUBLICATIONS—Available from SAE, 400 Commonwealth Drive, Warrendale, PA 15096-0001.

SAE J454—General Data on Wrought Aluminum Alloys
SAE J993—Alloy and Temper Designation Systems for Aluminum

2.1.2 ANSI PUBLICATIONS—Available from ANSI, 11 West 42nd Street, New York, NY 10036.

ANSI H35.1—Alloy and Temper Designation Systems for Aluminum
ANSI H35.2—Dimensional Tolerances for Aluminum Mill Products

2.1.3 ASTM PUBLICATIONS—Available from ASTM, 1916 Race Street, Philadelphia, PA 19103.

ASTM B 209—Specification for Aluminum-Alloy Sheet and Plate
ASTM B 210—Specification for Aluminum-Alloy Drawn Seamless Tubes
ASTM B 211—Specification for Aluminum-Alloy Bars, Rods, and Wire
ASTM B 221—Specification for Aluminum-Alloy Extruded Bars, Rods, Shapes, and Tubes
ASTM B 234—Specification for Aluminum-Alloy Drawn Seamless Tubes for Condensers and Heat Exchangers
ASTM B 236—Specification for Aluminum Bar for Electrical Purposes (Bus Bar)
ASTM B 241—Specification for Aluminum-Alloy Seamless Pipe and Seamless Extruded Tube
ASTM B 247—Specification for Aluminum-Alloy Die and Hand Forgings
ASTM B 308—Specification for Aluminum-Alloy Standard Structural Shapes, Rolled or Extruded

3. Specification of Wrought Aluminum Alloys—The Aluminum Association publishes a manual entitled Aluminum Standards and Data which includes the specified limits registered for the chemical composition and mechanical properties of standard aluminum alloys commercially available in the wrought product forms shown in Tables 2 and 3 of SAE J454.

NOTE—The Aluminum Association Inc. standards may be obtained at no cost to users of aluminum from The Aluminum Association, 900 19th Street, N.W., Washington, DC 20006.

4. Chemical Composition Limits—The chemical composition limits for each wrought aluminum alloy are registered in accordance with the designation system presented in ANSI H35.1 and SAE J993. The chemical composition limits are tabulated by alloy and are the same for all wrought product forms in which the alloy is available. In addition, the tabulation is by alloy components in the case of alclad sheet, plate, and tubular products.

5. Mechanical Property Limits—The specified mechanical property limits are established for each wrought product; that is, sheet, plate, drawn tube, extruded shapes, pipe and extruded tube, rolled shapes, rod, bar, wire, and die forgings.

6. Dimensional Tolerances—The dimensional tolerances to which aluminum alloy mill products are commercially produced are in accordance with the latest revision of the ANSI H35.2. For sizes outside commercial limits, the tolerance shall be as agreed upon by the supplier and purchaser.

7. Standards for Chemical Composition and Mechanical Property Limits—The American Society for Testing and Materials Standards and American National Standards in Table 1 contain the specified chemical composition limits, mechanical property limits, and material designations for each of the wrought products listed:

TABLE 1—STANDARDS FOR CHEMICAL COMPOSITION AND MECHANICAL PROPERTY LIMITS

	Title
ASTM B 209	Specification for Aluminum-Alloy Sheet and Plate
ASTM B 210	Specification for Aluminum-Alloy Drawn Seamless Tubes
ASTM B 211	Specification for Aluminum-Alloy Bars, Rods, and Wire
ASTM B 221	Specification for Aluminum-Alloy Extruded Bars, Rods, Shapes, and Tubes
ASTM B 234	Specification for Aluminum-Alloy Drawn Seamless Tubes for Condensers and Heat Exchangers
ASTM B 236	Specification for Aluminum Bar for Electrical Purposes (Bus Bar)
ASTM B 241	Specification for Aluminum-Alloy Seamless Pipe and Seamless Extruded Tube
ASTM B 247	Specification for Aluminum-Alloy Die and Hand Forgings
ASTM B 308	Specification for Aluminum-Alloy Standard Structural Shapes, Rolled or Extruded
ANSI H35.1	Alloy and Temper Designation Systems for Aluminum
ANSI H35.2	Dimensional Tolerances for Aluminum Mill Products

ANODIZED ALUMINUM AUTOMOTIVE PARTS —SAE J399 FEB1985

SAE Information Report

Report of the SAE Nonferrous Metals Committee, approved June 1969, last revised April 1976, reaffirmed without change, SAE Automotive Bright Trim Committee, February 1985.

1. Scope—Automotive parts can be fabricated from either coiled sheet, flat sheet or extruded shapes. Alloy selection is governed by finish requirements, forming characteristics, and mechanical properties.

Bright anodizing alloys 5657 and 5252[1] sheet provide a high luster and are preferred for trim which can be formed from an intermediate temper, such as H25. Bright anodizing alloy 5457 is used for parts which require high elongation and a fully annealed ("0") temper. Alloy 6463 is a medium strength bright anodizing extrusion alloy; Alloy X7016 is a high strength bright anodizing extrusion alloy primarily suited for bumper applications.

To satisfy anti-glare requirements for certain trim applications, sheet alloy 5205 and extrusion alloy 6063 are capable of providing the desired low-gloss anodized finish.

Bright anodizing alloys require control of the chemical composition of the alloy to enhance response to chemical brightening and to result in the formation of anodic coatings that are essentially transparent. Additionally, aluminum producers employ fabricating practices to minimize other metallurgical factors that adversely affect response to bright anodizing procedures. For non-heat-treatable alloys, a highly fragmented grain structure is preferred. Fully annealed, recrystallized grain structures are not optimum for bright anodizing. Where high elongations are required with intermediate tempers, fabricating practices are selected to minimize grain recrystallization.

Another factor to be considered for trim application is the type of mill surface finish that is required. When the metal working treatments do not mar the mill produced surface appreciably, the smooth, bright rolled, "automotive trim" surface is desirable since it often eliminates the need for expensive mechanical buffing operations. Where trim fabricating procedures might be expected to damage a bright-rolled surface, duller mill finishes can be used and parts are buffed after forming. Bright rolled mill surfaces occasionally are protected with a removable tape or water soluble film.

Selection of anodic coating required to protect aluminum parts is influenced by the required corrosion performance and appearance characteristics. Generally, anodic coatings 0.0003–0.0005 in (0.0076–0.0127 mm) thick are used for exterior trim application. Thinner anodic coatings 0.0001–0.0003 in (0.0025–0.0076 mm) are sufficient for interior trim components. Anodic coatings can be dyed to impart color, painted, or inlaid with vinyl or other plastics for aesthetic and/or functional purposes.

The Aluminum Association's "Designation System for Finishes" is a recommended guide to assist in specifying anodic coatings for automotive trim.

The American Society for Testing and Materials (ASTM) offers several test methods which are commonly used as the basis for many user specifications. These are:

ASTM B110—Dielectric Strength of Anodically coated Aluminum
ASTM B457—Measuring Impedance of Anodic Coatings of Aluminum
ASTM B244—Measuring Thickness of Anodic Coatings on Aluminum with Eddy Current Instruments
ASTM B136—Resistance of Anodically Coated Aluminum to Staining by Dyes
ASTM B137—Weight of Coating on Anodically Coated Aluminum
ASTM B368—Copper-Accelerated Acetic Acid Salt Spray (Fog) Testing (CASS Test)
ASTM B538—Fact (Ford Anodized Aluminum Corrosion Test) Testing
ASTM B580—Guide to the Specification of Anodic Oxide Coatings on Aluminum
ASTM 429—Measurement and Calculation of Reflecting Characteristics of Metallic Surfaces Using Integrating Sphere Instruments
ASTM E430—Measurement of Gloss of High Gloss Metal Surfaces Using Abridged Goniophotometer or Goniophotometer

2. References

2.1 Applicable Publications—The following publications form a part of this specification to the extent specified herein.

2.1.1 ASTM PUBLICATIONS—Available from ASTM, 100 Barr Harbor Drive, West Conshohocken, PA 19428-2959

ASTM B110—Dielectric Strength of Anodically coated Aluminum
ASTM B457—Measuring Impedance of Anodic Coatings of Aluminum
ASTM B244—Measuring Thickness of Anodic Coatings on Aluminum with Eddy Current Instruments
ASTM B136—Resistance of Anodically Coated Aluminum to Staining by Dyes
ASTM B137—Weight of Coating on Anodically Coated Aluminum
ASTM B368—Copper-Accelerated Acetic Acid Salt Spray (Fog) Testing (CASS Test)
ASTM B538—Fact (Ford Anodized Aluminum Corrosion Test) Testing
ASTM B580—Guide to the Specification of Anodic Oxide Coatings on Aluminum
ASTM 429—Measurement and Calculation of Reflecting Characteristics of Metallic Surfaces Using Integrating Sphere Instruments
ASTM E430—Measurement of Gloss of High Gloss Metal Surfaces Using Abridged Goniophotometer or Goniophotometer

1. Details of alloy numbers shown are published in Aluminum Association Standards.

DECORATIVE ANODIZING SPECIFICATION FOR AUTOMOTIVE APPLICATIONS—SAE J1974 JUN1993 SAE Recommended Practice

Report of the SAE Decorative Anodizing Subcommittee of the SAE Bright Trim Executive Committee approved June 1993. Rationale statement available.

Forword—This Document has not changed other than to put it into the new SAE Technical Standards Board Format.

This SAE Recommended Practice is aimed at ensuring high-quality products of anodized aluminum automotive components in terms of durability and appearance. Decorative sulfuric acid anodizing has been well developed over the last several decades in the aluminum industry. Exterior and interior performance demonstrated that parts processed to this document meet long-term durability requirements.

Since the treatment of processing variables is outside the scope of this document, it is important for applicators of this coating to develop an intimate knowledge of their process, and control all parameters that affect the quality of the end product. The use of techniques such as statistical process control (SPC), capability studies, design of experiments, process optimization, etc., are critical to produce material of consistently high quality.

1. Scope

1.1 Form—Detailed in this SAE Recommended Practice are interior and exterior bright or electrolytically colored anodized aluminum automotive components in the form of seat trim, dashboard, window or side body mouldings, bumpers, wheels, rocker panel, etc.

1.2 Application—This document defines performance requirements for bright or electrolytically colored anodized aluminum finishes including interior and exterior applications. The automotive parts can be fabricated from bare coiled sheet, flat sheet, or extruded shapes. Preanodized coiled sheet may be applicable for selected applications. Alloy selection is governed by finish requirements, forming characteristics, and mechanical properties.

2. References

2.1 Applicable Publications—The following ASTM methods form a part of this specification to the extent specified herein. The latest version of the single copy document shall apply.

2.1.1 ASTM PUBLICATIONS—Available from ASTM, 100 Barr Harbor Drive, West Conshohocken, PA 19428-2959.

ASTM B 137—Measurement of Weight of Coating on Anodically Coated Aluminum

ASTM B 368—Copper-Accelerated Acetic Acid-Salt Spray (Fog) Testing (CASS Test)

ASTM B 487—Measurement of Metal and Oxide Thicknesses by Microscopical Examination of a Cross Section

ASTM B 680—Seal Quality of Anodic Coatings on Aluminum by Acid Dissolution

ASTM B 681—Measurement of Thickness of Anodic Coatings on Aluminum and of Other Transparent Coatings on ASTM Opaque Surfaces, Using the Light-Section Microscope

ASTM D 2197—Standard Test Method for Adhesion of Organic Coatings by Scrape Adhesion

ASTM E 430—Measurement of Gloss of High Gloss Surfaces by Goniophotometry

ASTM G 23—Operating Light-Exposure Apparatus (Carbon-Arc Type) With and Without Water for Exposure of Nonmetallic Materials

3. Definitions

3.1 Gloss—Degree to which a surface simulates a perfect mirror in its capacity to reflect light.

3.2 Haze—Diffuse scattering of reflected light in directions adjacent to the direction of specular or mirror reflection.

3.3 Pickup—A mixture of aluminum fines, lubricant, and aluminum oxide generated from roll coating during the deformation process.

3.4 Significant Surfaces—These are defined as surfaces that are visible when the finished component is assembled onto the vehicle and is observed in normal viewing position. Nonvisible surfaces, when designated by the customer, are significant.

3.5 Stringers—Usually a mixture of magnesium and aluminum oxides that results from inadequate molten metal treatment.

3.6 Symbols and Abbreviations

µm — Micrometer or micron
mil — 0.001 Inch
g/m^2 — Grams per Square Meter
mg/dm^2 — Milligrams per Square Decimeter
g/cm^3 — Grams per Cubic Centimeter
MJ/m^2 — Megajoules per Square Meter
°F — degrees Fahrenheit
°C — degrees Celsius
ASTM — American Society for Testing and Materials
A.D.T. — Acid Dissolution Test
CASS — Copper Acidified Salt Spray

4. Technical Requirements

4.1 Quality

4.1.1 SUBSTRATE PREPARATION—The substrate surface finish can affect the anodized appearance. Suitable precautions in forming, cleaning, and chemical brightening must be taken to assure a satisfactorily finished part.

4.1.2 SURFACE APPEARANCE—Samples representing typical production parts should be used to define the appearance levels established by automotive companies in cooperation with anodizers and aluminum companies.

Anodized surfaces shall have the following general physical appearance:

a. Free of physical defects such as scratches, etc.
b. Acceptable levels of stringers, pickup, etc.
c. Color, gloss, and haze requirements as per master samples

4.2 Tolerances

4.2.1 COATING THICKNESS/WEIGHT—For automotive bright trim components, the most critical requirement is anodic coating thickness/weight. The coating thickness/weight has a direct impact on the appearance and durability. Thinner coatings generally give brighter appearance but less durability as compared to thicker coatings. Field exposure has shown that properly applied clear finishes provide durability while maintaining acceptable appearance. Despite the lack of similar long-term field service experience, the black electrolytic finish appears to provide adequate durability based on several years of experience.

The anodizing thickness/weights listed in Table 1 shall be met on all areas of the significant surfaces.

TABLE 1—MINIMUM COATING THICKNESS AND WEIGHT REQUIREMENT FOR CLEAR AND ELECTROLYTIC BLACK FINISHES

	Thickness(1) (Min) Exterior	Thickness(1) (Min) Interior	Coating Weight(2) (Min) Exterior	Coating Weight(2) (Min) Interior
Clear Finish	7.5 µm (0.3 mil)	2.5 µm (0.1 mil)	20 g/m^2	6 g/m^2
Electrolytic Black (Tin or Nickel Base)	15.0 µm(3) (0.6 mil)	7.5 µm(3) (0.3 mil)	40 g/m^2 (4)	20 g/m^2 (4)
Electrolytic Black (Cobalt Base)	7.5 µm(3) (5) (0.3 mil)	7.5 µm(3) (0.3 mil)	20 g/m^2 (4)	20 g/m^2 (4)

1. Coating Thickness—ASTM B 681; ASTM B 487
2. Coating Weight—ASTM B 137
3. Thicker coatings may be needed to meet requirements of color and gloss.
4. Coating weight should be determined on an equivalent clear sealed coating prior to electrolytic coloring.
5. Coating thickness requirements for bumper application using 7029 alloy, using a Cobalt based electrolyte must minimum of 15.0 µm (0.60 mil).

4.2.2 SEAL QUALITY—TEST METHOD—ASTM B 680—The Acid Dissolution Test (A.D.T.) is based on the concept that the resistance to dissolution of the anodic coating in the phosphoric-chromic acid solution is indicative of the effectiveness of the sealing operation. The amount of anodic coating dissolved is expressed as a mass in mg/dm^2 or in an A.D.T. "rating" unit independent of coating thickness. In the automobile industry in North America, the A.D.T. "rating" unit is widely used. The maximum value for the "rating" unit is 6.0, which is equivalent to 20 mg/dm^2 based on a coating density of 2.62 g/cm^3.

The formulas used to determine the units, as well as interrelationship of the A.D.T. units for various coating thicknesses, are presented in Appendix A and B, respectively.

The following Acid Dissolution Test (A.D.T.) requirements must be met to achieve acceptable field durability:

a. Clear Finish — 20 mg/dm^2 max (6 rating)
b. Electrolytic Black — 20 mg/dm^2 max (6 rating)

4.2.3 ACCELERATED CORROSION — TEST METHOD — ASTM B 368—The CASS test shall be carried out in strict accordance with ASTM B 368. Collection rates, ph, and specific gravity should preferably be run with every CASS test cycle.

The copper accelerated acetic acid salt spray or CASS test is presently the most widely used accelerated corrosion test in the automotive industry. The CASS test is not used to predict the number of years a part may last in service, but rather to evaluate the integrity of the metal finish. The CASS test does not have an exact correlation to years of corrosion protection in service. Failure to pass the test may be regarded as a probable indication of early failure in service.

The corrosion rating listed in Table 2 is required to maintain the high quality standards of the automotive industry and achieve acceptable field durability:

TABLE 2—CORROSION RATING REQUIREMENT FOR CLEAR AND ELECTROLYTIC BLACK FINISHES

	Exterior	Interior
Clear Finish	no pitting or corrosion after 6 h	N/A
Electrolytic Black	no pitting or corrosion after 6 h	N/A

4.2.4 OPTICAL PROPERTIES—The glossy appearance (brightness) of a high gloss metal finish can be determined in accordance with ASTM E 430. Acceptable levels of optical properties are to be established by automotive companies in cooperation with anodizers and aluminum suppliers. Master samples with representative optical properties are recommended for comparison.

4.2.5 NEW ALLOYS AND/OR NEW PROCESSES—Additional tests have been suggested to qualify new alloys and/or new finishing processes for automotive applications of decorative anodized products.

4.2.5.1 Scratch Resistance—ASTM D 2197 (suggested apparatus is Pacific Balanced Beam Scrape-Adhesion and Mar Tester, Model SG-8101)—For information purposes, some typical scratch widths on an anodized surface using a 500 g weight with loop stylus SG-8102 are as follows:

a. AA-5657-H25 is 500 to 600 µm
b. AA-5252-H25 is 400 to 500 µm
c. AA-7029-T6 is 200 to 300 µm

4.2.5.2 Heat—Finish should not craze or show signs of physical damage at a metal temperature up to 90 °C (194 °F).

4.2.5.3 Weatherometer — ASTM G 23 — Method 3 (Carbon-Arc Type)—Finish should not turn yellow, change color, fade, or show signs of chalking after 1000 h exposure at a black panel temperature of 63 °C (145 °F).

4.2.5.4 Outdoor Exposure (Exterior) — Direct Weathering in Florida—Samples to be exposed 5 degrees off horizontal facing south. Sample(s) will be examined at intervals 175 000 langleys (or 7322 MJ/m^2 or approximately 12 months) and 350 000 langleys (or 14 644 MJ/m^2 or approximately 24 months). No corrosion, color change, or color fading is allowed.

4.2.5.5 Outdoor Exposure (Interior) — Under Glass Exposure in Florida—Samples to be exposed under glass at 5 degrees off horizontal facing south. Sample(s) will be examined at intervals 175 000 langleys (or 7322 MJ/m^2 or approximately 12 months) and 350 000 langleys (or 14 644 MJ/m^2 or approximately 24 months). No corrosion, color change, or color fading is allowed.

APPENDIX A
FORMULAS USED FOR CALCULATIONS

A.1 A.D.T. results in:

$$mg/dm^2 = \frac{W_1 - W_2}{A_1} \quad \text{(Eq. A1)}$$

$$mg/in^2 = \frac{W_1 - W_2}{A_2} \quad \text{(Eq. A2)}$$

$$\% = \frac{W_1 - W_2}{W_1 - W_3} \times 100\% \quad \text{(Eq. A3)}$$

$$\text{A.D.T. Rating Unit} = \frac{W_1 - W_2}{W_1 - W_3} \times 200T^{(1)}; \frac{W_1 - W_2}{A_2} \times 4.65^{(2)} \quad \text{(Eq. A4)}$$

where:

W_1 - W_2 = weight of coating, in mg, dissolved in chromic-phosphoric acid solution as per ASTM B 680
W_1 - W_3 = total coating weight, in mg, as per ASTM B 137
A_1 = area of test specimen in dm^2
A_2 = area of test specimen in in^2
T = coating thickness in mils

NOTE 1—As specified in G.M. FBTM 55-46; FORD FLTM BQ 7—2; Chrysler LP 461A-241

NOTE 2—As specified in Chrysler LP 461A-241 (alternate procedure)

APPENDIX B
INTERRELATIONSHP OF A.D.T. UNITS FOR VARIOUS COATING THICKNESSES

B.1 See Table B1.

TABLE B1—INTERRELATIONSHIP OF A.D.T. UNITS FOR VARIOUS COATING THICKNESSES

Coating Type	Thickness (µm)	Thickness (mil)	Acid Dissolution Test Results (mg/dm^2)	Acid Dissolution Test Results (mg/in^2)	Acid Dissolution Test Results (%)	Acid Dissolution Test Results (rating)
Archit. Class I	18	0.7	40	2.6	8.5	12.0
Auto Black Ext.	15	0.6	40	2.6	10.2	12.0
Archit. Class II	10	0.4	40	2.6	15.3	12.0
Auto Clear Ext. Auto Black Int.	7.5	0.3	40	2.6	19.6	12.0
Auto Clear Int.	2.5	0.1	40	2.6	61.1	12.0
Archit. Class I	18	0.7	20	1.3	4.25	6.0
Auto Black Ext.	15	0.6	20	1.3	5.1	6.0
Archit. Class II	10	0.4	20	1.3	7.65	6.0
Auto Clear Int. Auto Black Int.	7.5	0.3	20	1.3	9.8	6.0
Auto Clear Int.	2.5	0.1	20	1.3	30.6	6.0
Archit. Class I	18	0.7	28.3	1.8	6.0	8.4
Auto Black Ext.	15	0.6	23.6	1.5	6.0	7.2
Archit. Class II	10	0.4	15.7	1.0	6.0	4.8
Auto Clear Ext. Auto Black Int.	7.5	0.3	11.8	0.8	6.0	3.6
Auto Clear Int.	2.5	0.1	3.9	0.3	6.0	1.2

NOTE— The mg/dm^2 and % numbers have been calculated based on ASTM B 680, and the ratings have been calculated based on Chrysler LP-461A-241 and G.M. FBTM 55-46. A value of 2.62 g/cm^3 has been used for the density of the anodic coating for conversion between weight per unit area and percent.

PILOT BEARINGS FOR TRUCK AND BUS APPLICATIONS—SAE J1731 JUN2001

SAE Recommended Practice

Report of the SAE Truck and Bus Clutch Subcommittee of the SAE Truck and Bus Powertrain Committee, approved June 1995. Revised by the SAE Truck and Bus Clutch Subcommittee of the SAE Truck and Bus Powertrain Committee June 2001.

1. Scope—This SAE Recommended Practice describes STANDARD-DUTY and EXTREME-DUTY Pilot Bearing requirements and sizes for class 6, 7, and 8 on-highway trucks and buses that use diesel engines and manual transmissions. The recommendations may apply to a wide range of other pilot-bearing applications, such as agricultural, industrial, and construction equipment.

1.1 Purpose—This document establishes standards for pilot-bearing construction, tolerances, installation dimensions, and operating characteristics. It is intended to standardize installation dimensions for engine and transmission manufacturers, and identify minimum operating characteristics to ensure satisfactory bearing life in pilot-bearing application environment.

2. References—There are no referenced publications specified herein.

3. General Information—This document applies to Pilot Bearings used to locate and support the transmission input shaft to the engine crankshaft rotational center. These bearings are usually located in the engine flywheel, and the pilot diameter of the transmission input shaft slides into them upon installation of the transmission to the engine.

Pilot Bearings described in this document are Conrad type ball bearings and generally conform to normal ball bearing construction and dimensioning practices, except as specified in this document.

The maximum operating temperatures shown in this document reflect temperature ratings for the various materials involved. It is generally agreed that peak temperatures will be short-term events related to duty cycle. Normal continuous operating temperatures will be significantly lower. Continuous operation at maximum temperature rating may result in shortened bearing life. Consult bearing manufacturer for application approval.

3.1 Standard-Duty Pilot Bearings—STANDARD-DUTY Pilot Bearings are recommended for applications where the maximum bearing temperature will not exceed 149 °C (300 °F).

3.2 Extreme-Duty Pilot Bearings

3.2.1 EXTREME-DUTY Pilot Bearings are recommended for applications where maximum bearing temperatures exceed 149 °C (300 °F) but do not exceed 200 °C (392 °F).

3.2.2 EXTREME-DUTY Pilot Bearings are suitable for use for standard-duty applications.

3.3 Operating Characteristics

3.3.1 OPERATING TEMPERATURE—Standard-Duty Pilot Bearings will operate in a temperature range of –40 to +149 °C (–40 to +300 °F). Extreme-Duty Pilot Bearings will operate in a temperature range of –40 to 200 °C (–40 to 392 °F). All materials shall be capable of operation throughout these respective temperature ranges, and be compatible with each other within these temperature ranges.

Extreme-Duty Pilot Bearings will require special heat stabilization of the steel elements to ensure compatibility with the higher operating temperature.

3.3.2 BEARING INTERNAL CLEARANCE—All Pilot Bearings shall have a C5 internal clearance to ensure that no preload exists within the bearing throughout the temperature range and dimensional fits.

3.3.3 SEALING—It is required that pilot bearings be sealed on both sides to prevent the ingestion of contaminants and to provide retention of the bearing lubricant. The seals must be capable of operating effectively throughout the established temperature ranges and must be compatible with the lubricant. It is generally accepted that fluorocarbon (Viton) seals, or equivalent, are required for both Standard-Duty and Extreme-Duty applications.

3.3.4 BEARING LUBRICANT—The pilot bearing should be permanently lubricated with a grease that is capable of operating throughout the required temperature range, and is compatible with the oil seal materials.

Premium-quality, high-temperature, petroleum-based lubricants may be satisfactory for Standard-Duty Pilot Bearings. Extreme-Duty Pilot Bearings require synthetic-based grease due to their higher operating temperature requirements.

The bearing shall be packed with a sufficient quantity of appropriate lubricant to ensure adequate lubrication, but shall not be overfilled to the point that lubricant will migrate out of the bearing or overcome the seals. It is generally accepted that a 30% fill of the actual sealed volume of the bearing is desired.

3.3.5 MAXIMUM ROTATING TORQUE—All pilot bearings require that the maximum torque to rotate the outer race relative to the inner race not exceed 0.20 N·m (1.77 in-lb).

Torque shall be measured at ambient temperature 22 °C ± 6 °C (72 °F ± 11 °F) while rotating the inner race at 600 RPM with the outer race restrained. Bearing should be operated at 600 RPM for 20 min prior to measurement of maximum torque. Test should be run with no radial load, and with no interference fit to the test fixture that would influence internal bearing clearance.

3.4 Pilot-Bearing Sizes and Tolerances—See Figure 1.

BASIC BEARING SIZE	PILOT BEARING WIDTH mm (in)	PILOT SHAFT O.D. mm (in)	PILOT BEARING I.D. mm (in)	PILOT BEARING O.D. mm (in)	FLYWHEEL BORE * I.D. mm (in)
6205	15.000/ 14.880 (0.5906/ 0.5858)	24.9859/ 24.9733 (0.9837/ 0.9832)	25.000/ 24.990 (0.9843/ 0.9839)	52.000/ 51.987 (2.0472/ 2.0467	51.986/ 51.956 (2.0467/ 2.0455)
6206	16.000/ 15.880 (0.6299/ 0.6252)	29.984/ 29.972 (1.1805/ 1.1800)	30.000/ 29.990 (1.1811/ 1.1807)	62.000/ 61.987 (2.4409/ 2.4404)	61.986/ 61.956 (2.4404/ 2.4392)
6305	17.000/ 16.880 (0.6693/ 0.6646)	24.986/ 24.973 (0.9837/ 0.9832)	25.000/ 24.990 (0.9843/ 0.9839)	62.000/ 61.987 (2.4409/ 2.4404)	61.986/ 61.956 (2.4404/ 2.4392)
6306	19.000/ 18.880 (0.7480/ 0.7433)	29.984/ 29.972 (1.1805/ 1.1800)	30.000/ 29.990 (1.1811/ 1.1807)	72.000/ 71.987 (2.8346/ 2.8341)	71.986/ 71.956 (2.8341/ 2.8329)

* **Flywheel bore size is in the installed condition with the fasteners torqued to engine manufacturer's specification.**
Flywheel manufacturers may process to different dimension to ensure compliance in the installed condition.

FIGURE 1—PILOT-BEARING SIZES AND TOLERANCES

BEARING BUSHING ALLOYS CHEMICAL COMPOSITION OF SAE BEARING AND BUSHING ALLOYS—SAE J460 OCT1991 SAE Standard

Report of the SAE Nonferrous Metals Division approved June 1911. Editorial change July 1974. Revised by the SAE Nonferrous Metals Committee October 1974. Editorial change April 1978. Revised by the SAE Bearings and Bushings Committee October 1991.

Foreword—This Document has not changed other than to put it into the new SAE Technical Standards Board Format.

1. Scope—Compositions apply to the finished bearing or bearing lining, not necessarily to the alloy at an intermediate processing stage. All values not given as ranges are maxima. (See Tables 1 through 5.)

2. References—There are no referenced publications specified herein.

TABLE 1—LEAD AND TIN-BASED ALLOYS

	SAE 12 ISO SnSb8Cu4	SAE 13 ISO PbSb10Sn6	SAE 14 ISO PbSb15Sn10	SAE 15 ISO PbSb1As	SAE 16[1] —	SAE 17
Pb	0.50[2]	Remainder	Remainder	Remainder	Remainder	0.50
Sn	Remainder	5.0–7.0	9.0–11.0	0.9–1.7	3.5–4.7	Remainder
Sb	7.0–8.0	9.0–11.0	14.0–16.0	13.5–15.5	3.0–4.5	7.5–9.0
Cu	3.0–4.0	0.7	0.7	0.7	0.4	3.0–4.0
Cd	—	0.05	0.05	0.02	0.05	1.0–1.5
As	0.10	0.25	0.6	0.8–1.2	0.6	0.10
Al	0.005	0.005	0.005	0.005	0.005	0.005
Bi	0.08	0.10	0.10	0.10	0.10	0.08
Fe	0.10	0.10	0.10	0.10	0.10	0.10
Zn	0.005	0.005	0.005	0.005	0.005	0.005
Total Others	0.20	0.20	0.20	0.20	0.40	0.20[3][4]

1. SAE 16 is cast into and on a porous sintered matrix, usually copper nickel or lead bronze, bonded to steel. For crankshaft bearings, the surface layer is 0.025 to 0.125 mm (0.001 to 0.005 in) in thickness.
2. ISO SnSb8Cu4 has 0.35 max. Pb.
3. A version of this alloy has 0.2 to 0.5 Ni.
4. A version of this alloy has 0.01 to 0.1 Cr.

TABLE 2—LEAD-BASED OVERLAYS

	SAE 191 ISO PbSn10	SAE 192 ISO PbSn10Cu2	SAE 193 —	SAE 194 ISO PbIn7
Pb	Remainder	Remainder	Remainder	Remainder
Sn	8.0–12.0	8.0–12.0	16.0–20.0	—
In	—	—		5.0–10.0
Cu	—	1.0–3.0	1.0–3.0	
Total Others	0.5	0.5	0.5	0.5

TABLE 3—COPPER-BASED ALLOYS—STEEL BACKED

	SAE 48 ISO CuPb30	SAE 49 ISO CuPb24Sn	SAE 485 —	SAE 792[1] ISO CuPb10Sn10	SAE 793 —	SAE 794[1] ISO CuPb24Sn4
Cu	Remainder	Remainder	Remainder	Remainder	Remainder	Remainder
Pb	26.0–33.0	21.0–27.0[2]	36.0–58.0	9.0–11.0	7.0–9.0	21.0–25.0[3]
Sn	0.50[4]	0.6–2.0[5]	1.0–8.0	9.0–11.0	3.5–4.5	3.0–4.0[3]
Fe	0.7	0.7	0.5	0.7	0.7	0.7
Ni	0.50	0.50	—	0.50	0.50	0.50
P	0.10	0.10	—	0.10	0.10	0.10
Sb	0.50	0.50	—	0.50	0.50	0.50
Zn	0.50	0.50	—	0.50[6]	0.50[7]	0.50[7]
Total Others	0.50	0.50	1.0	0.50	0.50	0.50

1. SAE 792 now covers both cast and sintered versions of CuPb10Sn10 and SAE 794 covers both cast and sintered versions of CuPb24Sn4. The SAE 797 and SAE 799 designations for the sintered versions have been eliminated.
2. ISO CuPb24Sn has 19.0 to 27.0 Pb.
3. ISO CuPb24Sn4 has 19.0 to 27.0 Pb and 3.0 to 4.5 Sn.
4. A version of this alloy has 1.3 max. Sn
5. A version of this alloy has 2.8 max. Sn.
6. A version of this alloy has 0.8 max. Zn.
7. A version of this alloy has 3.0 max. Zn.

TABLE 4—COPPER-BASED ALLOYS—CAST ALLOYS NOT BONDED TO STEEL

	UNS C98400	UNS C98200	SAE 791 UNS C83520	UNS C93700	UNS C93720	UNS C94330	SAE 795 UNS C83420
Cu	Remainder(1)	Remainder(1)	Remainder(1)	78.0–82.0(1)	83.0 min.(1)	68.5–75.5(1)	88.0–92.0(1)
Pb	26.0–33.0	21.0–27.0	3.5–4.5	8.0–11.0	7.0–9.0	21.0–25.0	0.50
Sn	0.50	0.6–2.0	3.5–4.5	9.0–11.0	3.5–4.5	3.0–4.0	0.25–0.7
Fe	0.7	0.7	0.30	0.7	0.7	0.7	0.10
Ni (incl Co)	0.50	0.50	1.0(1)	0.50(1)	0.50(1)	0.5	
P	0.10	0.10		0.10(2)	0.10(2)	0.10(2)	
Sb	0.50	0.50	0.25	0.50	0.50	0.50	—
Zn	0.50	0.50	1.5–4.0	0.8	4.0	3.0	Remainder
Ag	1.5	—	—	—	—	—	
Si	—	—	—	0.005	—	—	
S	—	—	—	0.08	—	—	
Al	—	—	—	0.005	—	—	
Cu + Sum of Named Elements	99.5 min.	99.5 min.	99.8 min.	99.0 min.	99.0 min.	99.0 min.	99.3 min.
Approx. SAE Equivalent	SAE 48	SAE 49	—	SAE 792	SAE 793	SAE 794	—

1. In determining copper min., copper may be calculated as Cu + Ni.
2. For continuous castings, phosphorus shall be 1.5% max.

TABLE 5—ALUMINUM-BASED ALLOYS

	SAE 770 ISO AlSn6Cu	SAE 780 —	SAE 781 ISO AlSi4Cd	SAE 782 ISO AlCd3CuNi	SAE 783 ISO AlSn20Cu	SAE 784 ISO AlSi11CU	SAE 785 ISO AlZn5Si2CuPb	SAE 786 ISO AlSn40	SAE 787	SAE 788
Al	Remainder	Remainder	Remainder	Remainder	Remainder	Remainder	Remainder	Remainder	Remainder	Remainder
Sn	5.5–7.0	5.5–7.0	—	—	17.5–22.5	0.20	0.20	37–42	0.4–2.0	10.0–14.0
Cd	—	—	0.8–1.4	2.7–3.5	—	—	—	—	—	—
Si	0.7	1.0–2.0	3.5–4.5	0.30(1)	0.50(2)	10.0–12.0	1.0–2.0(3)	0.3	3.5–4.5	1.8–3.5(4)
Cu	0.7–1.3	0.7–1.3	0.05–0.15	1.0–1.5(1)	0.7–1.3	1.7–1.3	0.7–1.3	0.35–0.7	0.5–2.0(5)	0.4–1.2(4)
Ni	0.7–1.3(6)	0.20–0.7	—	0.7–1.3	0.10	0.10	0.20	0.10	—	0.10
Zn	—	—	—	—	—	—	4.5–5.5(3)	—	—	—
Pb			—				0. 7–1.3	—	4.0–10.5(5)	1.0–2.4(4)
Mg	—	—	0.05–0.20(7)	—	—	—	—	—	—(5)	—
Mn	0.10(6)	0.10	0.10	1.2–1.6(1)	0.10(2)	0.10	0.10	0.10	—(5)	0.10
Fe	0.7	0.7	0.35	0.30(1)	0.50(2)	0.30	0.30	0.30	0.50	0.35
Cr	—	—	—	—	—	—	—	—	—	0.25
Sb	—	—	—	—	—	—	—	—	—	0.45
Sr	—	—	—	—	—	—	—	—	—	0.30
Ti	0.10(6)	0.10	0.10	0.10	0.10	0.10	0.10	0.10	0.10	0.10
Total Others	0.30	0.15	0.25	0.15	0.15(2)	0.30	0.30	0.30	0.30	0.30

1. ISO AlCd3CuNi has 0.7 to 1.3 Cu, 0.7 max. Si, 0.7 max. Mn, 0.7 max. Fe, 1.0 max. Si + Fe + Mn.
2. ISO AlSn20Cu has 0.7 max. Si, 0.7 max. Mn, 0.7 max. Fe, 1.0 max. Si + Fe, 1.0 max. Si + Fe + Mn, 0.5 max. total others.
3. A version of this alloy has 3.0 to 4.0 Zn, 2.5 to 3.5 Si.
4. A version of this alloy has 3.5 to 5.0 Si, 1.8 to 2.1 Cu and no lead.
5. A version of this alloy has 0.05 to 0.15 Cu, 0.05 to 0.15 Mg, 0.20 to 0.40 Mn.
6. ISO AlSn6Cu has no lower limit to Ni, 0.7 max. Mn, 0.2 max. Ti, 1.0 max Si + Fe + Mn.
7. ISO AlSi4Cd has no Mg, 0.2 max. Mn, 0.2 max. Ti.

(R) BEARING AND BUSHING ALLOYS—SAE J459 OCT1991 SAE Information Report

Report of the SAE Nonferrous Metals Committee approved February 1947 and revised August 1966. Editorial change July 1974. Completely revised by the SAE Bearings and Bushings Committee October 1991.

Foreword—This Document has not changed other than to put it into the new SAE Technical Standards Board Format.

1. Scope—The bearing performance of steel backed half bearings, bushings, and washers is dependent on the properties and thickness of the lining alloy, the strength and dimensional stability of the steel backing (usually SAE 1010) and the strength of the bond between the lining alloy and the backing. This SAE Information Report is primarily concerned with the properties of the lining alloys used in automotive applications, in particular, the crankshaft bearings of the internal combustion engine.

2. References—There are no referenced publications specified herein.

3. Factors Affecting the Choice of Crankshaft Bearing Alloy—The choice of alloy for the main and connecting rod bearings of an engine depends on the conditions in the hydrodynamic film separating the bearing surface from the crankshaft. If the dynamic load applied to the bearing through the oil film is high, fatigue strength of the bearing alloy will be the prime consideration. If the thickness of the oil film is low or at times incomplete, compatibility, or the ability to withstand occasional rubbing contact with the crankshaft, will become the most important property; the related property of dirt embeddability becomes particularly important if strict attention to cleanliness is not observed during engine assembly or maintenance. Cavitation of the oil film, which may arise from rapid movement of the journal across the bearing clearance or from other causes, requires that the bearing alloy be resistant to erosion by the collapsing vapor bubbles. Both fatigue strength and cavitation erosion resistance are broadly related to alloy hardness; generally, the harder the alloy the stronger and more cavitation erosion resistant it will be. Dirt embeddability and compatibility, on the other hand, are inversely related to alloy hardness; generally, the softer the alloy the better will these surface properties be.

The correct choice of alloy for a particular engine is that which offers the optimum compromise among these opposing requirements.

Corrosion and wear resistance are other important properties of engine bearing alloys. Corrosion resistance is necessary if engine temperatures are high and there is a danger of oil degradation and the appearance of an acidic component. Wear resistance is required if the crankshaft surface roughness is comparable to the oil film thickness. The choice of crankshaft finishing procedure has become particularly critical with the adoption of nodular iron crankshafts.

Characteristics and applications of typical bearing and bushing alloys are outlined in Table 1.

4. Tin- and Lead-Based Babbitts—The bearing alloys with the longest history are the tin and lead-based babbitts. These soft materials have excellent compatibility and dirt embeddability, but fall short of the fatigue strength requirements of present day automotive engines. There are, however, many bushing applications, and the alloys are still used in the crankshaft bearings of some slow speed marine diesel engines. Corrosion resistance is generally good, although the tin-based alloy can suffer from tin oxide corrosion in water contaminated oils, and the lead-based alloys are subject to corrosion in acidic oils. A version of lead-based babbitt in which the alloy is infiltrated into a steel backed porous copper-based matrix was widely used for many years as a crankshaft bearing, but is nowadays mainly found in camshaft bushings.

5. Copper-Lead Alloys—The copper-lead alloys are stronger than the babbitts, and are used in many automotive and heavy-duty engines.

The metallurgical structure of the copper-lead crankshaft bearing alloys consists of a fine distribution of interconnected lead islands in a copper-tin matrix. The higher the tin content, the stronger the matrix, and the higher the fatigue strength of the bearing. The metallurgical processes consist of lining steel strip continuously either by casting the alloy directly onto the steel, or by first atomizing the alloy and subsequently sintering the powder to the steel backing. Some large bearings are produced by centrifugal or gravity casting onto a preformed steel backing.

The lead content of most of the copper-lead crankshaft bearing alloys in current use is in the range of 14 to 27%. Alloys with lead contents of 40% or more have fallen into disuse, largely because of the introduction of lead free fuel, and a tendency for engine oils to become more corrosive in service. The lead phase of copper-lead alloys is subject to corrosion by oils which have become acidic during high temperature engine operation.

Almost all copper-lead crankshaft bearings are protected against corrosion by a thin overlay of lead-based alloy electrodeposited on the bearing surface. Lead-tin (PbSn10), lead-tin-copper (PbSn10Cu2), and lead-indium (PbIn7) are the three most common alloys. Lead-tin-indium overlays have been adopted in certain Japanese engines. The function of the tin or indium is to make the overlay resistant to corrosive attack by the engine oil as well as to increase fatigue and wear resistance. In the case of the tin-containing overlays, a thin nickel barrier is commonly incorporated between the overlay and the copper-lead to minimize the loss of tin which would otherwise occur through tin diffusion into the copper-lead at engine operating temperature.

The overlay also performs an important function by providing the bearing with a degree of conformability—the ability to conform to misalignment or imperfect crankshaft geometry. It also has good compatibility and dirt embeddability and allows the harder tin-containing copper-leads to be used with reduced risk of seizure. The overlay has a much lower fatigue strength than the underlying copper-lead, and thickness is usually kept between 0.02 and 0.03 mm to minimize fatigue damage.

6. Aluminum Alloys—The aluminum engine bearing family covers a wide range of alloys which are used both with and without overlay. Reticular tin-aluminum (AlSn20Cu1) is widely used in Europe as an automotive crankshaft bearing alloy. It is not usually overlay plated, but is sometimes given a thin tin flash for improved running-in. The alloy offers a good combination of strength and surface properties, but has insufficient fatigue strength for heavy-duty diesel applications. A softer version containing 40% tin is used in some slow speed marine diesel engines. Recently lower tin versions of aluminum-tin with 2 to 4% silicon for improved wear resistance against nodular iron crankshafts have been adopted in Europe and Japan. In the USA the equivalent alloys commonly used unplated in passenger car engines are two versions of aluminum-lead. Both alloys have 4 to 10% lead, and 4% silicon. A minor tin addition prevents corrosion of the lead phase.

Of the overlay plated aluminum alloys the most popular is aluminum-silicon-cadmium AlSi4Cd1, widely used in the USA in automotive applications. An aluminum-cadmium alloy AlCd3Mn1Cu1Ni1 is found in heavy-duty diesel applications. The high silicon alloy AlSi11Cu1 and an aluminum-zinc alloy AlZn5Si2CuPb are also intended for heavy-duty applications.

The overlays used on aluminum are lead-tin and lead-tin-copper with a thin interlayer of nickel or copper incorporated for electrochemical process reasons rather than as a diffusion barrier.

The aluminum alloys as a class have excellent corrosion resistance, but may prove more prone to cavitation erosion than the equivalent copper-lead alloy.

The aluminum alloys are bonded to steel by either hot or cold roll bonding. All are continuously cast and rolled to bonding thickness, except for one of the aluminum-lead alloys which is produced as strip by a powder metallurgy process and subsequently roll bonded.

7. Bushings and Washers—Automotive automatic transmissions use a number of steel backed bushings and thrust washers, lined with one or another of the copper or aluminum-based alloys described in Sections 5 and 6. The piston pin or small end bushing of both automotive and heavy-duty engines carries heavy dynamic loads and is generally lined with a low lead, high tin copper alloy CuPb10Sn10. The hardness of the alloy and the poor lubrication conditions require that the pin surface be hard and have a fine surface finish. Bushings wrapped from wrought bronze strip CuSn4Pb4Zn3 are occasionally used in this application and, together with bronze thrust washers, in some transmission applications.

Bronze bushings machined from continuously cast rod and tube are no longer used in engine or transmission applications, but may be found in agricultural and earthmoving equipment.

TABLE 1—BEARING AND BUSHING ALLOYS: SUMMARY OF CHARACTERISTICS AND APPLICATIONS

SAE No.	ISO Designation	Characteristics	Applications
A. Tin- and Lead-Based Alloys:			
12	SnSb8Cu4	Excellent compatibility, conformability and dirt embeddability; good corrosion resistance and cavitation erosion resistance; poor fatigue strength and temperature capability.	Marine diesel crankshaft bearings, steam turbine journal and thrust bearings, electric motor bushings.
13 14 15	PbSb10Sn6 PbSb15Sn10 PbSb15As	Excellent conformability and dirt embeddability; good compatibility, fair corrosion resistance; poor cavitation erosion resistance, fatigue strength and temperature capability. SAE 14 and 15 have higher load carrying ability than SAE 13.	Camshaft, transmission, and steering pump bushings.
16	—	Similar to SAE 13 to 15 but with improved fatigue strength.	Camshaft bushings, some less heavily loaded crankshaft bearings.
B. Copper-Based Alloys:			
48 49 794 (1)	CuPb30 CuPb24Sn CuPb24Sn4	Good fatigue strength and cavitation erosion resistance, increasing with increasing tin content. Overlay plating is required for corrosion resistance, compatibility and conformability in crankshaft bearing applications.	Main and connecting rod bearings, with overlay; transmission and hydraulic pump bushings.
792[1] 793[1]	CuPb10Sn10 —	Very good fatigue strength, load carrying capacity and wear resistance; fair corrosion resistance; poor compatibility and conformability.	Piston pin (small end), rocker arm and steering knuckle bushings; wear plates.
485		Fair fatigue strength; fair compatibility and conformability; fair embeddability; fair corrosion resistance.	Camshaft bushings and other applications requiring higher fatigue strength than tin- or lead-based alloys.
C. Aluminum-Based Alloys:			
786	AlSn40	Good conformability, dirt embeddability, compatibility and corrosion resistance, poor fatigue strength and cavitation erosion resistance but stronger than babbitt at engine operating temperature.	Cross head bearings in marine diesel engines, generally with lead-tin overlay.
783 787	AlSn20Cu —	Good compatibility, dirt embeddability and corrosion resistance; fair fatigue and cavitation erosion resistance.	Crankshaft bearings in passenger car engines. Does not require an overlay, although SAE 783 is often tin flashed.
788		SAE 787 and 788 have better fatigue strength and better wear resistance against nodular iron crankshafts than SAE 783.	
770 780 781	AlSn6Cu — AlSi4Cd	Good corrosion resistance; fair to good compatibility, conformability, dirt embeddability, fatigue strength, and cavitation erosion resistance.	Crankshaft bearings in passenger car and heavy-duty engines, with overlay. Camshaft and transmission bushings, crankshaft thrust washers.
782	AlCd3CuNi		
784 785	AlSi11Cu AlZn5Si2CuPb	Good corrosion resistance, fatigue strength, and cavitation erosion resistance; fair compatibility; poor conformability and dirt embeddability.	Crankshaft bearings for heavy-duty engines, with overlay.

1. These copper-lead alloy designations have been consolidated to reflect alloy chemistry regardless of method of manufacture.
SAE 792 has been combined with SAE 797.
SAE 793 has been combined with SAE 798.
SAE 794 has been combined with SAE 799.

WROUGHT AND CAST COPPER ALLOYS—SAE J461 DEC2002 SAE Standard

Report of the SAE Nonferrous Metals Division, approved January 1934, last revised by the SAE Nonferrous Metals Committee March 1976, reaffirmed with editorial change September 1981 and editorial change December 2002. Rationale statement available.

1. Scope—For convenience, this SAE Information Report is presented in two parts as shown below. To avoid repetition, however, data applicable to both wrought and cast alloys is included only in Part 1.

Part I—Wrought Copper and Copper Alloys

- Types of Copper (Table 1)
- General Characteristics (Table 3)
- Electrical Conductivity
- Thermal Conductivity
- General Mechanical Properties (Table 10)
- Yield Strength
- Fatigue Strength
- Physical Properties (Table 2)
- General Fabricating Properties (Table 3)
- Formability
- Bending
- Hot Forming
- Machinability
- Joining
- Surface Finishing
- Color
- Corrosion Resistance
- Effect of Temperature
- Typical Uses (Table 3)

Part II—Cast Copper Alloys

- Types of Casting Alloys
- Effects of Alloy Elements and Impurities
- General Characteristics (Table 11)
- Physical Properties (Table 12)
- Typical Uses (Table 11)

2. References

2.1 Applicable Publications—The following publications form a part of this specification to the extent specified herein. Unless otherwise indicated, the latest version of SAE publications shall apply.

2.1.1 SAE PUBLICATION—Available from SAE, 400 Commonwealth Drive, Warrendale, PA 15096-0001.

SAE J463—Wrought Copper and Copper Alloys

2.1.2 ASTM PUBLICATIONS—Available from ASTM, 100 Barr Harbor Drive, West Conshohocken, PA 19428-2959.

ASTM B 3—Specification for Soft or Annealed Copper Wire
ASTM B 16—Specification for Free-Cutting Brass Rod, Bar, and Shapes for Use in Screw Machines
ASTM B 21—Specification for Naval Brass Rod, Bar, and Shapes
ASTM B 36—Specification for Brass Plate, Sheet, Strip, and Rolled Bar
ASTM B 68—Specification for Seamless Copper Tube, Bright Annealed
ASTM B 75—Specification for Seamless Copper Tube
ASTM B 97—Specification for Copper-Silicon Alloy Plate, Sheet, Strip, and Rolled Bar for General Purposes
ASTM B 98—Specification for Copper-Silicon Alloy Rod, Bar, and Shapes
ASTM B 103—Specification for Phosphor Bronze Plate, Sheet, Strip, and Rolled Bar
ASTM B 111—Specification for Copper and Copper-Alloy Seamless Condenser Tubes and Ferrule Stock
ASTM B 121—Specification for Leaded Brass Plate, Sheet, Strip, and Rolled Bar
ASTM B 122—Specification for Copper-Nickel-Tin Alloy, Copper-Nickel-Zinc Alloy (Nickel Silfer) and Copper-Nickel Alloy Plate, Sheet, Strip, and Rolled Bar
ASTM B 133—Specification for Copper Rod, Bar, and Shapes
ASTM B 134—Specification for Brass Wire
ASTM B 135—Specification for Seamless Brass Tube
ASTM B 138—Specification for Manganese Bronze Rod, Bar, and Shapes
ASTM B 139—Specification for Phosphor Bronze Rod, Bar, and Shapes
ASTM B 150—Specification for Aluminum Bronze Rod, Bar, and Shapes
ASTM B 151—Specification for Copper-Nickel-Zinc Alloy (Nickel Silver) and Copper-Nickel Rod and Bar
ASTM B 152—Specification for Copper Sheet, Strip, Plate and Rolled Bar
ASTM B 154—Method of Mercurous Nitrate Test for Copper and Copper Alloys
ASTM B 159—Specification for Phosphor Bronze Wire
ASTM B 169—Specification for Aluminum Bronze Plate, Sheet, Strip, and Rolled Bar
ASTM B 171—Specification for Copper-Alloy Condenser Tube Plates
ASTM B 194—Specification for Copper-Beryllium Alloy Plate, Sheet, Strip, and Rolled Bar
ASTM B 196—Specification for Copper-Beryllium Alloy Rod and Bar
ASTM B 280—Specification for Seamless Copper Tube for Air Conditioning and Refrigeration Field Service
ASTM B 283—Specification for Copper and Copper-Alloy Die Forgings (Hot-Pressed)
ASTM B 301—Specification for Free-Cutting Copper Rod and Bar
ASTM B 441—Specification for Copper-Cobalt-Beryllium and Copper-Nickel-Beryllium Rod and Bar
ASTM B 453—Specification for Copper-Zinc-Lead Alloy (Leaded-Brass) Rod
ASTM B 534—Specification for Copper-Cobalt-Beryllium Alloy and Copper-Nickel-Beryllium Alloy Plate, Sheet, Strip, and Rolled Bar

3. Part I—wrought Copper and Copper Alloys—Factors influencing the uses of wrought copper and copper alloys concern electrical conductivity, thermal conductivity, machinability, formability, fatigue characteristics, strength, corrosion resistance, the ease with which alloys can be joined, and the fact that these materials are nonmagnetic. Copper and its alloys also have a wide range of rich, pleasing colors. The only other metal with such distinctive coloring is gold. These materials are all easily finished by buffing, scratch brushing, plating or chemically coloring, or clear protective coating systems.

When it is desired to improve one or more of the important properties of copper, alloying often solves the problem. A wide range of alloys, therefore, has been developed and commercially employed, such as the high copper alloys, brasses, leaded brasses, tin bronzes, heat treatable alloys, copper-nickel alloys, nickel silvers, and special bronzes.

The various types of copper and the principal alloys are listed in Tables I and 3, along with information describing composition, fabricating properties, and applications.

3.1 Types of Wrought Copper—Copper UNS Nos. C11000, C11100, C11300, C11400, C11500, and C11600[1] are either electrolytically or fire-refined, cast in the form of refinery shapes, containing a controlled amount of oxygen for the purpose of obtaining a level set on the top of the casting. It generally contains 0.01–0.04% oxygen, which exists as a coppercuprous oxide eutectic surrounding the crystals of copper. Within these limits, the oxygen has only a very slight effect on the electrical, mechanical, and physical properties of copper. Because of the oxidizing effect of oxygen on impurities, its presence in copper indicates a reduction or elimination of certain impurities which would otherwise have adverse effects on conductivity.

Copper UNS No. C10200 is electrolytically refined and specially produced to be free from cuprous oxide although it is made without the use of residual metallic or metalloidal deoxidizers. Because of its freedom from residual deoxidizers, it has high electrical conductivity.

Copper UNS Nos. C12000 and C12200 are cast in the form of refinery shapes, free from cuprous oxide, produced through the use of metallic or metalloidal deoxidizers. Because it is necessary to use some excess of reducing agent, the electrical and thermal conductivity of the copper is lowered, and this fact should be considered when high conductivity is needed.

Copper UNS Nos. C10200, C12000 and C12200 possess only slightly different mechanical properties from the C11XXX types. They differ little in respect to tensile strength when cold worked to similar extents, but do have somewhat higher ductility and also are not normally subject to hydrogen embrittlement.

3.2 Electrical Conductivity—The greatest single area of use for copper itself results from the high electrical conductivity of the metal. The combination of the property of high electrical conductivity with ease of forming and high corrosion resistance makes copper the preferred material for current-carrying members. The conductivity of copper for electrical conductors is 101% IACS (see Table 2) in the annealed or soft condition. The tensile strength of the soft copper, 220 MPa (32 ksi) can be increased to 345/380 MPa (50/55 ksi) by cold rolling, in which condition the electrical conductivity is decreased to about 97%. Heating such copper above 200 °C for an extended period of time will soften it to a tensile strength of 205/240 MPa (30/35 ksi).

1. Since the nomenclature used in the nonferrous metals trade is not always consistent, copper and copper base alloys are referenced by specification numbers described in SAE J463.

TABLE 1—GENERAL INFORMATION—NAME, NOMINAL COMPOSITION, AND COMPARABLE STANDARDS OF WROUGHT COPPER ALLOYS

Copper or Copper Alloy UNS No.[a]	Name[b]	Nominal Composition Percent by Weight		SAE No.	ASTM Standard No.[c]	Former SAE No.
		Cu	Other			
C10200	Oxygen free copper (OF)	99.9	—	CA102	B75, B152, B280	—
C11000	Electrolytic tough pitch copper (ETP)	99.9	—	CA110	B3, B133, B152, B283	71, 83
C11100	Electrolytic tough pitch, anneal resistant copper	99.9	(Trace elements)	CA111	—	71
C11300	Tough pitch copper with Ag (STP)	99.9	0.03 Ag	CA113	B152	71
C11400	Tough pitch copper with Ag (STP)	99.9	0.04 Ag	CA114	B152	71
C11500	Tough pitch copper with Ag (STP)	99.9	0.06 Ag	CA115	B152	—
C11600	Tough pitch copper with Ag (STP)	99.9	0.09 Ag	CA116	B152	71
C12000	Phosphorus deoxidized copper (DLP)	99.9	0.0008 P	CA120	B68, B75, B152, B280	75
C12200	Phosphorus deoxidized copper (DHP)	99.9	0.02 P	CA122	B68, B75, B152, B280	—
C14500	Phosphorus deoxidized tellurium copper (DPTE)	99.5	0.5 Te, 0.008 P	CA145	B283, B301	—
C14700	Sulfur bearing copper	99.7	0.3 S	CA147	B301	—
C15000	Zirconium copper	99.8	0.15 Zn	CA150	B301	—
C16200	Cadmium copper	99.0	1 Cd	CA162		—
C17000	Beryllium copper	98.0	1.7 Be	CA170	B194	—
C17200	Beryllium copper	98.0	1.9 Be	CA172	B194, B196	—
C17500	Beryllium copper	97.0	0.5 Be, 2.5 Co	CA175	B441, B534	—
C17600	Beryllium copper	97.0	0.4 Be, 1.5 Co, 1 Ag	CA176	B441	—
C18400	Chromium copper	99.0	0.8 Cr	CA184		—
C18700	Leaded copper	99.0	1 Pb	CA187	B301	—
C19200	High copper alloy	99.0	1 Fe, 0.03 P	CA192	B111	—
C21000	Gilding, 95%	95.0	5 Zn	CA210	B36	—
C22000	Commercial bronze, 90%	90.0	10 Zn	CA220	B36, B135	—
C23000	Red brass, 85%	85.0	15 Zn	CA230	B36, B135	74D, 79A
C24000	Low brass, 80%	80.0	20 Zn	CA240	B36	79B
C26000	Cartridge brass, 70%	70.0	30 Zn	CA260	B36, B134 B135	70A, 74C, 80A
C26800	Yellow brass, 66%	66.0	34 Zn	CA268	B36	70C
C27000	Yellow brass, 65%	65.0	35 Zn	CA270	B134	80B
C33000	Low leaded brass, (tube)	66.0	34 Zn, 0.5 Pb	CA330	B135	74B
C33100	Leaded brass	66.0	33 Zn, 1 Pb	CA331		
C34200	High leaded brass	65.0	33 Zn, 2 Pb	CA342	B121	
C34500	Leaded brass	63.0	35 Zn, 2 Pb	CA345	B453	
C35000	Medium leaded brass, 62%	63.0	36 Zn, 1 Pb	CA350	B121, B453	
C36000	Free cutting brass	62.0	35 Zn, 3 Pb	CA360	B16	72
C37700	Forging brass	60.0	38 Zn, 2 Pb	CA377	B283	88
C46400	Naval brass, unhibited	60.0	39 Zn, 0.8 Sn	CA464	B21, B283	73
C46500	Naval brass, arsenical	60.0	40 Zn, 0.5 As	CA465		
C46600	Naval brass, antimonial	60.0	40 Zn, 0.5 Sb	CA466		
C46700	Naval brass, phosphorized	60.0	40 Zn, 0.5 P	CA467		
C51000	Phosphor bronze, 5% A	95.0	5 Sn, 0.2 P	CA510	B103, B139, B159	77A, 81
C51100	Phosphor bronze	96.0	4 Sn, 0.2 P	CA511	B103	
C52100	Phosphor bronze, 8% C	92.0	8 Sn, 0.2 P	CA521	B103	77C
C52400	Phosphor bronze, 10% D	90.0	10 Sn, 0.2 P	CA524	B103	
C54400	Phosphor bronze, B-2	88.0	4 Sn, 4 Zn, 4 Pb	CA544	B103, B139	—
C60800	Aluminum bronze	95.0	5 Al	CA608	B111	
C61400	Aluminum bronze, D	91.0	7 Al, 2 Fe	CA614	B150, B169	701D
C61800	Aluminum bronze	89.0	10 Al, 1 Fe	CA618		
C62300	Aluminum bronze	88.0	9 Al, 3 Fe	CA623	B150, B283	701B
C62400	Aluminum bronze	86.0	11 Al, 3 Fe	CA624		701B
C63000	Aluminum bronze	82.0	10 Al, 3 Fe, 5 Ni	CA630	B150, B283	701C
C64200	Aluminum silicon bronze	91.0	7 Al, 2 Si	CA642	B150, B283	
C65500	High silicon bronze, A	97.0	3 Si	CA655	B97, B98, B283	—

(Table continued on next page)

TABLE 1—GENERAL INFORMATION—NAME, NOMINAL COMPOSITION, AND COMPARABLE STANDARDS OF WROUGHT COPPER ALLOYS (CONTINUED)

Copper or Copper Alloy UNS No.[a]	Name[b]	Nominal Composition Percent by Weight		SAE No.	ASTM Standard No.[c]	Former SAE No.
		Cu	Other			
C67000	Manganese bronze, B	65.0	24 Zn, 4 Mn, 4 Al, 3 Fe	CA670	B138	—
C67300	Manganese bronze	60.0	34 Zn, 3 Mn, 2 Pb, 1 Si	CA673		—
C67400	Manganese bronze	58.0	37 Zn, 3 Mn, 1 Al, 1 Si	CA674		—
C67500	Manganese bronze, A	58.0	40 Zn, 0.3 Mn, 1 Fe, 1 Sn	CA675	B138	—
C70600	Copper nickel, 10%	90.0	10 Ni	CA706	B111, B171	—
C71000	Copper nickel, 20%	80.0	20 Ni	CA710	B111, B122	—
C71500	Copper nickel, 30%	70.0	30 Ni	CA715	B111, B122, B171	—
C75200	Nickel silver, 65–18	65.0	18 Ni, 17 Zn	CA752	B122, B151	—
C77000	Nickel silver, 55–18	55.0	18 Ni, 27 Zn	CA770	B122, B151	—

[a] Unified numbering system.
[b] Alloy names are shown for information only, and should not be used. Use the appropriate designation only. (Example: Copper Alloy UNS No. C21000 Copper Alloy).
[c] ASTM Standard numbers listed are only those forms or shapes covered in the specification for wrought copper or copper alloy.

TABLE 2A—TYPICAL PHYSICAL PROPERTIES OF WROUGHT COPPER ALLOYS

Metric (SI) Units

Copper or Copper Alloy UNS No.	Melting Point °C		Density g/cm³ at 20°C	Coefficient of Thermal Expansion/°C × 10^{-5}			Thermal Conductivity W/m · K	Electrical Resistivity nΩ · m[a]	Specific Heat J/kg · K	Modulus GPa	
	Liquidus	Solidus		20–100°C	20–200°C	20–300°C				Elastic	Rigid
C10200	1083	—	8.94	1.70	1.73	1.77	391	17.1	385	117	44
C11000	1083	1065	8.91	1.70	1.73	1.77	391	17.1	385	117	44
C11100	1083	1065	8.91	1.70	1.73	1.77	388	17.2	385	117	44
C11300	1082	—	8.91	1.70	1.73	1.77	388	17.2	385	117	44
C11400	1082	—	8.91	1.70	1.73	1.77	388	17.2	385	117	44
C11500	1082	—	8.91	1.70	1.73	1.77	388	17.2	385	117	44
C11600	1082	—	8.91	1.70	1.73	1.77	388	17.2	385	117	44
C12000	1083	—	8.94	1.70	1.73	1.77	386	17.6	385	117	44
C12200	1083	—	8.94	1.70	1.73	1.77	339	20.3	385	117	44
C14500	1075	1051[b]	8.94	1.71	1.74	1.78	355	18.6	385	117	44
C14700	1076	1067	8.94	1.70	1.73	1.77	374	18.1	385	117	44
C15000	1080	980	8.89	1.63	1.80	2.01	367[d]	18.6[d]	385	117	44
C16200	1076	1030	8.89	1.70	1.73	1.77	360	19.2	385	117	44
C17000	980	865	8.26	1.67	1.70	1.78	118	76.8	420	131	50
C17200	980	865	8.26	1.67	1.70	1.78	118	76.8	420	131	50
C17500	1075	1070	8.75		1.76	—	234	37.9	420	124	47
C17600	1054	1010	8.75	—	—	—	—	31.6	—	124	47
C18400	1075	1070	8.89	1.76	—	—	324[d]	21.6[d]	385	131	50
C18700	1080	953[c]	8.94	—	—	1.76	377	17.9	385	117	44
C19200	1084	—	8.87	1.62	—	—	216	34.5	385	117	44
C21000	1065	1050	8.86		—	1.81	234	30.8	377	117	44
C22000	1045	1020	8.80	—	—	1.84	189	39.2	377	117	44
C23000	1025	990	8.75	—	—	1.87	159	46.6	377	117	44
C24000	1000	965	8.67	—	—	1.91	140	53.9	377	110	41
C26000	955	915	8.53	—	—	1.99	121	61.6	377	110	41
C26800	930	905	8.47	—	—	2.03	116	63.9	377	103	39
C27000	930	905	8.47		—	2.03	116	63.9	377	103	39
C33000	940	905	8.50		—	2.02	116	66.3	377	103	39
C33100	940	905	8.50		—	2.02	116	66.3	377	103	39
C34200	910	885	8.47		—	2.02	116	66.3	377	103	39
C34500	915	885	8.45		—	2.03	119	66.3	377	69	—
C35000	915	895	8.47		—	2.03	116	66.3	377	97	37
C36000	900	885	8.50	—	—	2.05	116	66.3	377	97	37
C37700	895	880	8.44	—	—	2.07	119	63.9	377	103	39
C46400	900	885	8.41	—	—	2.12	116	66.3	377	103	39
C46500	900	885	8.41	—	—	2.12	116	66.3	377	103	39
C46600	900	885	8.41	—	—	2.12	116	66.3	377	103	39
C46700	900	885	8.41	—	—	2.12	116	66.3	377	103	39
C51000	1050	950	8.86	—	—	1.78	69	115.0	377	110	41
C51100	1060	975	8.86	—	—	1.78	83	87.0	377	110	41
C52100	1020	880	8.80	—	—	1.82	62	133.0	377	110	41
C52400	1000	845	8.78	—	—	1.84	50	157.0	377	110	41
C54400	1000	930	8.89		—	1.73	87	90.7	377	103	39
C60800	1063	1050	8.17		—	1.81	80	100.0	377	121	46
C61300	1045	1040	7.89	—	—	1.62	67	123.0	377	117	44
C61400	1045	1040	7.89		—	1.62	67	123.0	377	117	44
C61800	1045	1040	7.53	—	—	1.62	64	133.0	377	117	44
C62300	1045	1040	7.66		—	1.62	61	144.0	377	117	44
C62400	1040	1025	7.45	—	—	1.92	54	144.0	377	117	44
C63000	1054	1035	7.58	—	—	1.62	38	192.0	377	117	44
C64200	1005	985	7.69	—	—	1.81	45	186.0	377	110	41
C65500	1025	970	8.53	—	—	1.80	36	246.0	377	103	39
C67000	930	905	7.81	—	—	2.00	24	75.0	—	103	39
C67300	890	845	8.28	—	—	2.00	—	75.0	—	103	39
C67400	885	865	8.08	—	—	2.00	100	75.0	377	97	37
C67500	890	865	8.36	—	—	2.12	106	71.8	377	103	39
C70600	1150	1100	8.94	—	—	1.71	45	191.0	377	124	47
C71000	1200	1150	8.94	—	—	1.64	36	266.0	377	138	52
C71500	1240	1170	8.94	—	—	1.62	29	375.0	377	152	57
C75200	1110	1070	8.73	—	—	1.62	33	287.0	377	124	47
C77000	1055		8.70	—	—	1.67	29	314.0	377	124	47

[a] See Table 2B for percent IACS electrical conductivity.
[b] Small amounts of tellurium-rich constituent remains liquid down to 490°C.
[c] Small amounts of lead-rich constituent remains liquid down to 325°C.
[d] After precipitation-hardening treatment.

TABLE 2B—TYPICAL PHYSICAL PROPERTIES OF WROUGHT COPPER ALLOYS

Copper or Copper Alloy UNS No.	Melting Point, °F		Customary Units									
	Liquidus	Solidus	Density[a]	Coefficient of Thermal Expansion[b] 68–212°F	68–392°F	68–572°F	Thermal Conductivity[c]	Electrical Resistivity[d]	Electrical Conductivity[e]	Thermal Capacity[f]	Modulus Elastic[g]	Rigid[h]
C10200	1981	—	.323	9.4	9.6	9.8	226	10.3	101	.092	17	6.4
C11000	1981	1949	.322	9.4	9.6	9.8	226	10.3	101	.092	17	6.4
C11100	1981	—	.322	9.4	9.6	9.8	224	10.3	101	.092	17	6.4
C11300	1981	—	.322	9.4	9.6	9.8	224	10.3	100	.092	17	6.4
C11400	1981	—	.322	9.4	9.6	9.8	224	10.4	100	.092	17	6.4
C11500	1981	—	.322	9.4	9.6	9.8	224	10.4	100	.092	17	6.4
C11600	1981	—	.322	9.4	9.6	9.8	224	10.4	99	.092	17	6.4
C12000	1981	—	.323	9.4	9.6	9.8	223	10.7	97	.092	17	6.4
C12200	1981	—	.323	9.4	9.5	9.8	196	12.2	85	.092	17	6.4
C14500	1960	1931[i]	.323	9.4	9.6	9.8	205	10.9	95	.092	17	6.4
C14700	1970	1953	.323	9.4	9.6	9.8	216	10.9	95	.092	17	6.4
C15000	1979	—	.323	9.4	9.6	9.8	212[k]	11.2[k]	93[k]	.092	17	6.4
C16200	1969	—	.321	9.4	9.6	9.8	208	11.9	87	.092	17	6.4
C17000	1800	1600	.298	9.3	9.4	9.9	—	47.2	22	—	19	7.3
C17200	1800	1600	.298	9.3	9.4	9.9	—	47.2	22	.100	19	7.3
C17500	1955	1885	.316	—	9.8	—	—	23.1	45	—	18	6.8
C17600	1930	1850	.316	—	9.8	—	—	19.0	50	—	18	6.8
C18400	1967	—	.321	9.4	9.6	9.8	187[k]	13.0[k]	80[k]	.092	19	7.2
C18700	1976	1947[j]	.323	9.4	9.6	9.8	218	10.6	98	.092	17	6.4
C19200	1983	—	.320	9.0	—	—	125	20.8	50	.092	17	6.4
C21000	1950	1920	.320	—	—	10.0	135	18.5	00	.090	17	6.4
C22000	1910	1870	.318	—	—	10.2	109	23.6	44	.090	17	6.4
C23000	1880	1810	.316	—	—	10.4	92	28.0	37	.090	17	6.4
C24000	1830	1770	.313	—	—	10.6	81	32.4	32	.090	16	6.0
C26000	1750	1680	.308	—	—	11.1	70	37.0	28	.090	16	6.0
C26800	1710	1660	.306	—	—	11.3	67	38.4	27	.090	15	5.6
C27000	1710	1660	.306	—	—	11.3	67	38.4	27	.090	15	5.6
C33000	1720	1660	.307	—	—	11.2	67	39.9	26	.090	15	5.6
C33100	1720	1660	.307	—	—	11.2	67	39.9	26	.090	15	5.6
C34200	1670	1630	.306	—	—	11.3	67	39.9	26	.090	15	5.6
C34500	1650	1625	.305	—	—	11.4	69	39.9	26	—	10	—
C35000	1650	1630	.305	—	—	11.4	67	39.9	26	.090	14	5.3
C36000	1650	1630	.307	—	—	11.4	67	39.9	26	.090	14	5.3
C37700	1640	1620	.305	—	—	11.5	69	38.4	27	.090	15	5.6
C46400	1650	1630	.304	—	—	11.8	67	39.9	26	.090	15	5.6
C46500	1650	1630	.304	—	—	11.8	67	39.9	26	.090	15	5.6
C46600	1650	1630	.304	—	—	11.8	67	39.9	26	.090	15	5.6
C46700	1650	1630	.304	—	—	11.8	67	39.9	26	.090	15	5.6
C51000	1920	1750	.320	—	—	9.9	40	69.1	15	.090	16	6.0
C51100	1945	1785	.320	—	—	9.9	48	52.0	20	.090	16	6.0
C52100	1880	1620	.318	—	—	10.1	36	79.8	13	.090	16	6.0
C52400	1830	1550	.317	—	—	10.2	29	94.3	11	.090	16	6.0
C54400	1830	1700	.321	—	—	9.6	50	54.6	19	.090	15	5.6
C60800	1945	1920	.295	—	—	10.0	46	60.0	17	.090	17.5	6.6
C61300	1915	1905	.285	—	—	9.0	39	74.1	14	.090	17	6.4
C61400	1915	1905	.285	—	—	9.0	39	74.1	14	.090	17	6.4
C61800	1910	1900	.274	—	—	9.0	37	79.8	13	—	17	—
C62300	1910	1890	.274	—	9.0	9.4	31	79.8	13	—	16	—
C62400	1910	1895	.274	—	9.0	9.2	34	79.8	13		16	—
C63000	1930	1890	.274	—	9.0	9.4	22	138.0	8	.090	17	6.4
C64200	1840	1800	.278	—	—	10.0	26	113.0	8	.090	16	6.0
C65500	1880	1780	.308	—	—	10.0	21	148.0	7	.090	15	5.6
C67000	1710	1665	.282	—	—	11.0	14	86.4	12	—	15	
C67300	1620	1555	.299	—	—	11.0	—	86.4	12	—	15	—
C67400	1625	1550	.292	—	—	11.0	58	86.4	12	—	14	—
C67500	1630	1590	.302	—	—	11.8	61	43.2	24	.090	15	5.6
C70600	2100	2010	.323	—	—	9.5	26	115.0	9	.090	18	6.8
C71000	2192	2066	.323	—	—	9.1	21	160.0	6	.090	20	7.5
C71500	2260	2140	.323	—	—	9.0	17	225.0	5	.090	22	8.3
C75200	2030	1960	.316	—	—	9.0	19	173.0	6	.090	18	6.8
C77000	1930	—	.314	—	—	9.3	17	189.0	6	.090	18	6.8

[a] lb/in^3 at 68°F. See Table 2A for specific gravity (g/cm^3 at 20°C).
[b] Per F at temperature range indicated (multiply factor given by 10^{-6}).
[c] Btu/ft^2/ft h F at 68°F.
[d] (Annealed) ohms (circular mil/ft) at 68°F.
[e] (Annealed) percent IACS at 68°F (volume basis).
[f] (Specific heat) Btu/lb/F at 68°F.
[g] (Tension) psi (multiply factor given by 10^6).
[h] Psi (multiply factor given by 10^6).
[i] Small amount of tellurium-rich constituent remains liquid down to 1575°F.
[j] Small amount of lead-rich constituent remains liquid down to 619°F.
[k] After precipitation-hardening heat treatment.

TABLE 3—FABRICATION PROPERTIES, OTHER CHARACTERISTICS AND TYPICAL USES (CONTINUED)

Copper or Copper Alloy UNS No.	Approximate Relative Suitability For Being, Worked[a]		Best Temperature For Hot Working, °C	Approximate Relative Suitability[a] For Being Joined By									Machinability[c]	Type of Chip[b]	Typical Uses	Characteristics
										Resistance Welding						
	Cold	Hot		Soldering	Brazing	Oxyacetylene Welding	Carbon Arc Welding	Gas Shielded Arc Welding	Coated Metal Arc Welding	Spot	Seam	Butt				
C21000	E	G	760–870	E	E	G	F	G	NR	NR	NR	G	20	L	Emblems, vitreous enamel base, ornamental trim and jewelry.	Copper Alloy UNS Nos. C21000, C22000 and C23000 are generally reddish in color, soft and malleable, higher annealing point than copper and slightly stronger and similar in corrosion resistance. Good for drawing and forming. Resistance to dezincification and season cracking is excellent.
C22000	E	G	760–870	E	E	G	F	G	NR	NR	NR	G	20	L	Emblems, vitreous enamel base, ornamental trim, jewelry, expansion plugs, valve parts, escutcheon fasteners and spring clips.	
C23000	E	G	790–900	E	E	G	F	G	NR	F	NR	G	30	L	Radiator parts, heat exchanger tubes, tube bends.	
C24000	E	F	815–900	E	E	G	F	G	NR	F	NR	G	30	L	Bellows and water temperature switch housing, flexible hose, pump lines.	Color is light golden, strength and ductility continue to increase.
C26000	E	F	730–845	E	E	G	F	F	NR	G	NR	G	30	L	Radiator tanks and lockseam tubes, header plates, reflectors, lamp bases, terminals, ground straps, baffles, ammeter shells and speedometer counterweights, washers, wheel covers, trim, carburetor parts.	Color is brass yellow. Greatest ductility of the copper-zinc series. Strength is higher than any of the preceding copper-zinc alloys.
C26800	E	NR	—	E	E	G	F	F	NR	G	NR	G	30	L	Radiator cores and tanks, lamp fixtures, socket shells, eyelets, fasteners and grommets, hinges, locks, pins, rivets, screws and springs.	Strength increases and ductility decreases, but is still very good.
C27000	E	NR	—	E	E	G	F	F	NR	G	NR	G	30	L		
C33000	E	NR	—	E	G	F	F	F	NR	F	NR	F	60	M	Tube carburetor parts, oil cooler tube, radiator and ornamental work, pump and power cylinders and liners.	Provides some degree of machinability, together with moderate cold working properties.
C33100	E	NR	—	E	G	NR	NR	NR	NR	NR	NR	F	70	M	Keys.	Intended for blanking, piercing, and machining.
C34200	E	NR	—	E	G	NR	NR	NR	NR	NR	NR	F	90	S	Clock plates and nuts, clock and watch backs, keys, gears and wheels.	Provides increased machinability with moderate cold working properties.
C34500	F	F	705–790	E	G	NR	NR	NR	NR	NR	NR	F	90	S	Screw machine parts requiring roll threads, knurls or staking operations.	Best combination of machinability and cold working properties.
C35000	F	NR	—	E	G	NR	NR	NR	NR	NR	NR	F	70	M	Keys.	Intended for blanking, piercing, and machining.
C36000	NR	F	709–790	E	G	NR	NR	NR	NR	NR	NR	F	100	S	Automatic screw machine parts and carburetor, magneto parts, radiator drums and other fittings, plugs, inserts, gears, pinions, locks.	The standard free cutting brass and its machinability has become the standard by which other alloys are rated.
C37700	NR	E	650–815	E	G	NR	NR	NR	NR	NR	NR	F	80	S	Forgings and pressings of all kinds. Headings, air conditioning tube fittings, convertible top hardware (latches, hinges, etc.) forged valve bodies.	Excellent hot working properties and widely used as forging rod. At ordinary temperatures it is strong, hard and free cutting.
C46400	F	E	650–815	E	E	G	F	F	NR	G	F	G	30	L	Aircraft turnbuckle barrels and balls, cold headed parts, forgings, screw machine parts, marine hardware, condenser plates, welding rod, nozzles and fittings.	Excellent hot and fair cold working properties of somewhat higher strength, good salt water corrosion resistance.
C46500	F	E	650–815	E	E	G	F	F	NR	G	F	G	30	L		
C46600	F	E	650–815	E	E	G	F	F	NR	G	F	G	30	L		
C46700	F	E	650–815	E	E	G	F	F	NR	G	F	G	30	L		
C51000	E	NR	—	E	E	F	G	G	F	G	F	E	20	L	Springs, bearings, clips, contacts, switch parts, diaphragms, welding rod, thermostats, bellows, clutch disks, lock washers, fasteners.	C51000 and C52100 have a remarkable combination of strength, ductility and resilience, and fatigue resistance.
C51100	E	NR	—	E	E	F	G	G	F	G	F	E	20	L		
C52100	G	NR	—	E	E	F	G	G	F	G	F	E	20	L	Springs, clips, contacts, terminal wire and bushings, diaphragms and bellows.	
C52400	G	NR	—	E	E	F	G	G	F	G	F	E	20	L		
C54400	G	NR	—	E	G	NR	NR	NR	NR	NR	NR	F	80	S	Bearings, bushings, gears, pinions, shafts, thrust washers, valve parts.	Free cutting, good cold working properties also suitable for blanking, forming and bending.
C60800	G	F	790–870	F	F	NR	—	G	G	G	G	G	20	—	Condenser, evaporator and heat exchanger tubes, ferrules.	

(Table continued on next page)

TABLE 3—FABRICATION PROPERTIES, OTHER CHARACTERISTICS AND TYPICAL USES (CONTINUED)

Copper or Copper Alloy UNS No.	Approximate Relative Suitability For Being Worked[a]		Best Temperature For Hot Working, °C	Approximate Relative Suitability[a] For Being Joined By									Machinability[c]	Type of Chip[b]	Typical Uses	Characteristics
										Resistance Welding						
	Cold	Hot		Soldering	Brazing	Oxyacetylene Welding	Carbon Arc Welding	Gas Shielded Arc Welding	Coated Metal Arc Welding	Spot	Seam	Butt				
C21000	E	G	760–870	E	E	G	F	G	NR	NR	NR	G	20	L	Emblems, vitreous enamel base, ornamental trim and jewelry.	Copper Alloy UNS Nos. C21000, C22000 and C23000 are generally reddish in color, soft and malleable, higher annealing point than copper and slightly stronger and similar in corrosion resistance. Good for drawing and forming. Resistance to dezincification and season cracking is excellent.
C22000	E	G	760–870	E	E	G	F	G	NR	NR	NR	G	20	L	Emblems, vitreous enamel base, ornamental trim, jewelry, expansion plugs, valve parts, escutcheon fasteners and spring clips.	
C23000	E	G	790–900	E	E	G	F	G	NR	F	NR	G	30	L	Radiator parts, heat exchanger tubes, tube bends.	
C24000	E	F	815–900	E	E	G	F	G	NR	F	NR	G	30	L	Bellows and water temperature switch housing, flexible hose, pump lines.	Color is light golden, strength and ductility continue to increase.
C26000	E	F	730–845	E	E	G	F	F	NR	G	NR	G	30	L	Radiator tanks and lockseam tubes, header plates, reflectors, lamp bases, terminals, ground straps, baffles, ammeter shells and speedometer counterweights, washers, wheel covers, trim, carburetor parts.	Color is brass yellow. Greatest ductility of the copper-zinc series. Strength is higher than any of the preceding copper-zinc alloys.
C26800	E	NR	—	E	E	G	F	F	NR	G	NR	G	30	L	Radiator cores and tanks, lamp fixtures, socket shells, eyelets, fasteners and grommets, hinges, locks, pins, rivets, screws and springs.	Strength increases and ductility decreases, but is still very good.
C27000	E	NR	—	E	E	G	F	F	NR	G	NR	G	30	L		
C33000	E	NR	—	E	G	F	F	F	NR	F	NR	F	60	M	Tube carburetor parts, oil cooler tube, radiator and ornamental work, pump and power cylinders and liners.	Provides some degree of machinability, together with moderate cold working properties.
C33100	E	NR	—	E	G	NR	NR	NR	NR	NR	NR	F	70	M	Keys.	Intended for blanking, piercing, and machining.
C34200	E	NR	—	E	G	NR	NR	NR	NR	NR	NR	F	90	S	Clock plates and nuts, clock and watch backs, keys, gears and wheels.	Provides increased machinability with moderate cold working properties.
C34500	F	F	705–790	E	G	NR	NR	NR	NR	NR	NR	F	90	S	Screw machine parts requiring roll threads, knurls or staking operations.	Best combination of machinability and cold working properties.
C35000	F	NR	—	E	G	NR	NR	NR	NR	NR	NR	F	70	M	Keys.	Intended for blanking, piercing, and machining.
C36000	NR	F	709–790	E	G	NR	NR	NR	NR	NR	NR	F	100	S	Automatic screw machine parts and carburetor, magneto parts, radiator drums and other fittings, plugs, inserts, gears, pinions, locks.	The standard free cutting brass and its machinability has become the standard by which other alloys are rated.
C37700	NR	E	650–815	E	G	NR	NR	NR	NR	NR	NR	F	80	S	Forgings and pressings of all kinds. Headings, air conditioning tube fittings, convertible top hardware (latches, hinges, etc.) forged valve bodies.	Excellent hot working properties and widely used as forging rod. At ordinary temperatures it is strong, hard and free cutting.
C46400	F	E	650–815	E	E	G	F	F	NR	G	F	G	30	L	Aircraft turnbuckle barrels and balls, cold headed parts, forgings, screw machine parts, marine hardware, condenser plates, welding rod, nozzles and fittings.	Excellent hot and fair cold working properties of somewhat higher strength, good salt water corrosion resistance.
C46500	F	E	650–815	E	E	G	F	F	NR	G	F	G	30	L		
C46600	F	E	650–815	E	E	G	F	F	NR	G	F	G	30	L		
C46700	F	E	650–815	E	E	G	F	F	NR	G	F	G	30	L		
C51000	E	NR	—	E	E	F	G	G	F	G	F	E	20	L	Springs, bearings, clips, contacts, switch parts, diaphragms, welding rod, thermostats, bellows, clutch disks, lock washers, fasteners.	C51000 and C52100 have a remarkable combination of strength, ductility and resilience, and fatigue resistance.
C51100	E	NR	—	E	E	F	G	G	F	G	F	E	20	L		
C52100	G	NR	—	E	E	F	G	G	F	G	F	E	20	L	Springs, clips, contacts, terminal wire and bushings, diaphragms and bellows.	
C52400	G	NR	—	E	E	F	G	G	F	G	F	E	20	L		
C54400	G	NR	—	E	G	NR	NR	NR	NR	NR	NR	F	80	S	Bearings, bushings, gears, pinions, shafts, thrust washers, valve parts.	Free cutting, good cold working properties also suitable for blanking, forming and bending.
C60800	G	F	790–870	F	F	NR	—	G	G	G	G	G	20	—	Condenser, evaporator and heat exchanger tubes, ferrules.	

(Table continued on next page)

TABLE 3—FABRICATION PROPERTIES, OTHER CHARACTERISTICS AND TYPICAL USES (CONTINUED)

Copper or Copper Alloy UNS No.	Approximate Relative Suitability For Being Worked[a]		Best Temperature For Hot Working, °C	Approximate Relative Suitability[a] For Being Joined By						Resistance Welding			Machinability[c]	Type of Chip[b]	Typical Uses	Characteristics
	Cold	Hot		Soldering	Brazing	Oxyacetylene Welding	Carbon Arc Welding	Gas Shielded Arc Welding	Coated Metal Arc Welding	Spot	Seam	Butt				
C61300	G	G	785–925	F	F	NR	G	See Note d	G	G	G	G	20	L	Gibs, wear strips, gears, bushings, nuts, bolts and threaded members.	Good cold working properties and corrosion resistance. High strength and ductility.
C61400	G	G	785–925	F	F	NR	G	See Note d	G	G	G	G	20	L	Gibs, wear strips, gears, bushings, nuts, bolts and threaded members.	Good cold working properties and corrosion resistance. High strength and ductility.
C61800	F	G	760–885	F	G	NR	—	G	G	G	G	G	40	—	Bushings, bearings, corrosion applications, welding rod.	
C62300	F	G	730–815	F	F	NR	G	See Note d	G	G	G	G	30	L	Valve guides, spark plug inserts, gears, valve seat inserts, oil plugs and shifter forks.	Good hot working properties; high strength retained well at elevated temperatures; acid and oxidation resistant.
C62400	NR	E	720–775	F	F	NR	G	See Note d	G	G	G	G	30	L	Valve guides, spark plug inserts, gears, valve seat inserts, oil plugs, shifter forks, wear strips, ball bearings and hydraulic valve components.	Excellent hot working, poor cold working properties; heat treated for high mechanical properties.
C63000	NR	G	705–760	F	F	NR	G	See Note d	G	G	G	G	20	L	Retractable landing gear, propeller gears, large valve seat inserts, spacer bearings, high pressure pump components.	Very high mechanical properties in the heat treated condition; difficult to cold work; good hot working properties, excellent corrosion resistance.
C64200	NR	E	705–760	F	F	NR	—	F	F	F	F	F	60	—	Valve stems, gears, bolts, nuts, valve bodies and components.	Free machining, high strength, high corrosion resistance.
C65500	E	E	705–760	G	E	G	G	E	F	E	E	E	30	L	Hydraulic pressure lines, bolts, clamps, piston rings, rivets and shafting.	Relatively high strength, marked ductility and capability for being both hot and cold worked and joined by all procedures. Excellent corrosion resistance.
C67000	NR	E	565–745	NR	F	NR	NR	See Note d	G	G	F	G	30	S	Diesel injector nozzles; high pressure hydraulic applications, cams, pistons and other components involving high mechanical loads and sliding contact.	High strength and good wear resistant properties.
C67300	F	E	625–745	NR	G	NR	NR	NR	NR	NR	NR	F	70	S	Forged water pump impellers; gears, axial piston pump components, bushings and bearings.	Hot forgeable free cutting alloy having fairly high strength and good corrosion resistant properties.
C67400	F	E	565–745	NR	F	NR	NR	See Note d	G	G	F	G	30	L	Connecting rods, transmission synchronizing stop ring, door striker plates, shifter shoes, differential idler pins, forged water pump impellers, axial piston pump parts, bushings and bearings.	Hot forgeable; high strength alloy with good wear resistant properties and good corrosion resistance.
C67500	NR	E	625–790	E	E	G	F	F	NR	G	F	G	30	L	Clutch disks, pump rods, shafting, balls, valve stems and bodies.	Strong, rigid and abrasion resistant; adopted to hot forging and pressing, hot-heading and upsetting.
C70600	G	G	760–980	E	E	F	NR	E	G	G	G	E	20	L	Condenser and heat exchanger tubes.	Used where requirements are severe. Strong, tough and very resistant to general corrosion as well as stress corrosion cracking; also serviceable at higher temperatures than copper and brasses. Well suited for condenser and heat exchanger tube.
C71000	G	G	760–980	E	E	G	NR	E	E	E	E	E	20	L	Condenser and heat exchanger tubes, ferrules.	Copper Alloy UNS Nos. C71000 and C71500 are used where requirements are severe. Strong, tough and very resistant to general corrosion as well as stress corrosion cracking; also; serviceable at higher temperatures than copper and brasses. Well suited for condenser and heat exchanger tube.
C71500	G	G	925–1035	E	E	G	NR	E	E	E	E	E	20	L	Automatic oil coolers, heat exchanger tube.	
C75200	E	NR	—	E	E	G	NR	F	NR	G	F	G	20	L	Rivets, screws, name plates, radio dials, etching stock, trim.	Copper Alloy UNS Nos. C75200 and C77000 are manufactured in a wide range of nickel contents. Higher the nickel the more silver white the alloy. 65% copper alloys have good cold working properties and are used for cold drawing, spinning, forming and stamping. The lower copper content alloys (55% Cu) are used for spring application.
C77000	G	NR	—	E	E	G	NR	F	NR	G	F	G	30	L	Springs, resistance wire.	

[a] E = Excellent; G = Good; F = Fair; NR = Not Recommended.
[b] S = Short; M = Medium; L = Long.
[c] Approximate relative machinability rating (Free Cutting Brass = 100).
[d] Consumable electrode excellent. Tungsten are good, with AC preferred.

Silver is added to copper to increase its resistance to softening at elevated temperature without decreasing the electrical conductivity. Cold worked silver-bearing copper (see Table 4) can be heated to about 350 °C for short periods of time without appreciable softening, and is less susceptible to creep rupture in highly stressed situations. Rolling mill practice and amount of silver have an effect upon the softening of such materials.

TABLE 4—TYPICAL SOFTENING TEMPERATURE

Copper UNS No.	Temperature °C
C11000	230
C10200	280
C11400	315
C12200	340
C11100	355

Cadmium added in small amounts (0.10%) to copper results in an alloy having superior resistance to softening at temperatures used in forming automotive radiators. Resistance to softening is retained even after the application of large amounts of cold work. The application of this material permits higher strength solders to be used and allows for the increase of soldering temperature range to a point not feasible with other high conductivity materials. Electrical and thermal conductivities are not appreciably different than for silver bearing copper.

Figure I illustrates the softening characteristics of electrolytic copper and silver bearing and cadmium bearing copper alloys in terms of tensile strength for the times and temperatures indicated.

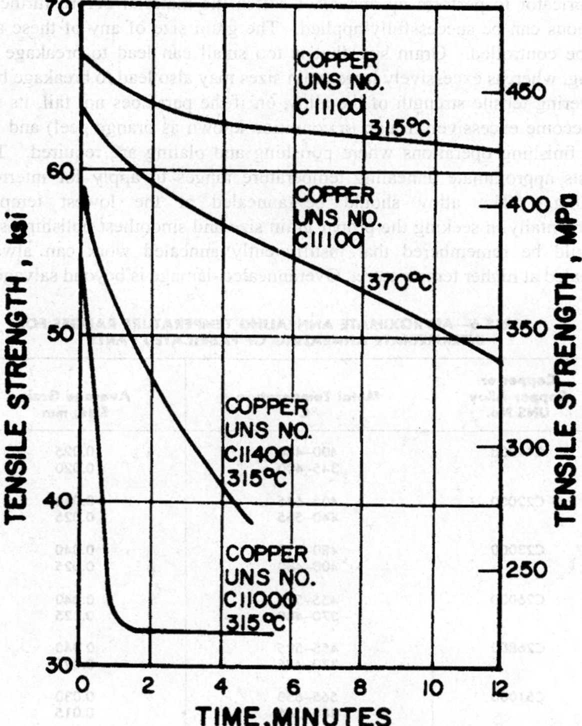

FIGURE 1—SOFTENING CHARACTERISTICS OF THREE COPPERS

The 0.85% silver-bearing alloy is the best, of the three commonly available alloys, to resist creep rupture. The silver-bearing coppers find use in radiator construction where the material is subjected to slightly elevated temperature during soldering operations, also for commutators which are baked to set mica between the copper segments. Copper must no be softened by these treatments.

To prevent embrittlement which takes place with copper should be specified if the material is to be heated much above 425 °C in an atmosphere of reducing gases such as hydrogen. Embrittlement results from the action of the reducing gases with the copper oxide normally present in all C11XXX types.

The addition of chromium to copper produces an alloy with a combination of high tensile strength (485 MPa [70 ksi]) and electrical conductivity (80% IACS). Copper Alloy UNS No. C18400 has the ability to retain its mechanical properties and wear resistance to a high degree at elevated temperatures. The copper chromium alloys have found considerable use as fabricated into welding tips and seam welding wheels. Zirconium bearing copper (Copper Alloy UNS No. C 15000) is also finding wide use in high temperature-high strength applications.

Heat treated beryllium bearing copper alloys having tensile strength up to 1345 MPa (195 ksi) and fatigue strengths up to 345 MPa (50 ksi are available; however, a drop in electrical conductivity to about 50% and high cost must be considered. Where repetitive or cycling operation must be performed, such properties have made application of these alloy economical.

Conducting contacts, springs or other stressed parts that are manufactured by forming may employ chromium or beryllium bearing coppers. The parts are formed by cold working and then strengthened by heat treatment.

The high degree of ductility and toughness of commercially pure copper usually make it unsuited for cutting or machining operations. Copper with lead, tellurium and sulfur were developed to combine the properties of copper with improved machinability. Parts that must be formed by extensive machining and be highly conductive are made from the free machining coppers. Tellurium copper has a 95% electrical conductivity and a machinability rating of 80–90. Sulfur bearing copper has a 95% IACS electrical conductivity and the same machinability rating, whereas lead copper has an electrical conductivity of 98% IACS and a machinability rating of 80. The machinability rating for copper is 20.

Where higher tensile strength 620 MPa (90 ksi) is required along wit good machinability (60) and lower electrical conductivity (10%) can be tolerated, aluminum silicon alloys may be used to advantage.

For applications requiring good fatigue properties, the nickel-silver phosphor, or beryllium alloys will serve. These alloys, however, have relatively low electrical conductivity ranging from 5 to 50%.

Copper UNS No. C12000 is also a good choice in the selection of conductor to be used where creep strength is to be considered, as may be the case when the material is to operate at slightly elevated temperature.

3.3 Thermal Conductivity—For the alpha solid solutions of copper alloys at least, the thermal conductivity is a nearly linear function of the electrical conductivity multiplied by the absolute temperature. Good conductor of electricity are also good conductors of heat and poor conductors of electricity are poor conductors of heat.

When high thermal conductivity is of principal importance, the same considerations given electrical conductivity apply.

3.4 Mechanical Properties—Except for the heat treatable alloys, strength is determined mainly by composition and degree of cold work. Mechanical properties of the most important alloys are to be found in Table 10.

Copper and copper alloys containing aluminum, silicon, tin, iron, an manganese, in various combinations and concentrations, are much stronger by virtue of their chemistry than the other coppers or alloys. For heavy sections or parts requiring high strength, inherently stronger alloy should be specified. For lighter or smaller sections which can be made adequately from stronger tempers, other alloys are successful. For example, the tensile strength of Copper Alloy UNS No. C26000 used in the production of radiator tanks can be increased by adjusting the rolling mill procedure from 310 to 365 MPa (45 to 53 ksi) without a harmful reduction in ductility. Similarly Copper Alloy UNS No. C26000 strip 0.11 mm (.0045 in) intended for fabrication into lockseam tube, used in radiator construction, is available in an annealed temper having a tensile strength of about 440 MPa (64 ksi) and an elongation of 32% in 50 mm (2 in). This represents an 18.5% increase in tensile strength without any sacrifice of ductility, compared to material produced by rolled-to-temper methods

The tensile strength of the copper-zinc series of alloys, the most widely used group in the industry, increases in general for any specific temper as the copper content decreases. The alloys also are characterized by extremely high ductility, excellent forming characteristics and ease of finishing. The relationship of the increase of properties with zinc content is shown in Figure 2.

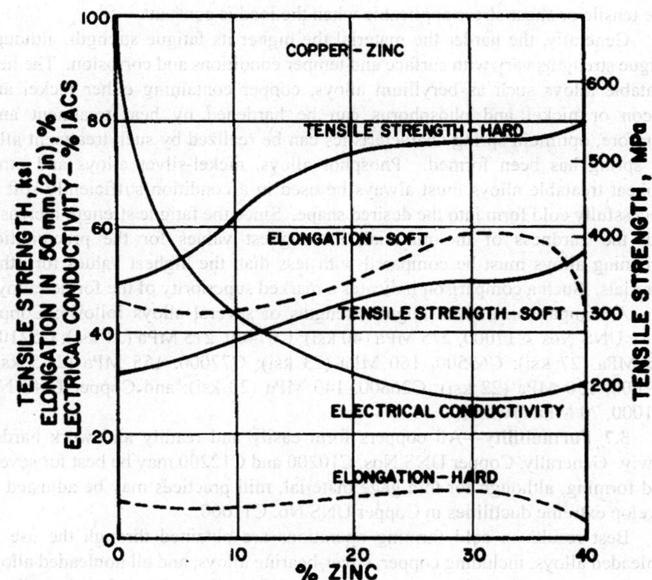

FIGURE 2—RELATIONSHIP OF INCREASE OF PROPERTIES

WITH ZINC CONTENT

A series of heat treatable alloys are commercially available and have strength as high as 1380 MPa (200 ksi). These alloys are produced with carefully controlled compositions and contain such elements as chromium, beryllium, nickel, phosphorus and silicon. The attractive diversity of properties obtainable in heat treatable copper alloys can be observed in Table 10.

The copper zirconium alloy (Copper UNS No. C15000) might be included in this group because it does respond to heat treatment; however, its strength is developed primarily through the application of cold working. Heat treatment primarily restores high electrical conductivity and ductility and increases surface hardness. The alloy has found use in the production of welding tips and wheels, stud bases for rectifiers, commutators for motors and electrical switch parts.

One outstanding characteristic of the heat treatable alloys is that they may be formed into articles, such as complex springs, while in the soft or partially work hardened state, and the mechanical properties subsequently improved to their maximum by heat treatment.

3.5 Yield Strength—Yield strength is the stress at which a material exhibits a specified limiting deviation of strain. Ordinarily the yield strength of copper and copper alloys is taken at 0.5% extension under load (strain) although for some design purposes values taken at 0.1 or 0.2% offset may be used.

Where residual stresses, due to forming, approach or exceed the yield strength, stress corrosion cracking may occur. Also, stresses may reach levels high enough to cause elastic drift in springs. In either case, it may be advisable to apply a low temperature, stress relieving treatment. Suggested temperatures for accomplishing a stress relief are listed in Table 5.

TABLE 5—TYPICAL THERMAL STRESS RELIEVING TREATMENTS

Copper Alloy UNS No.	Temperature °C	Time, h
C24000	260	1
C26000	260	1
C26800		
C27000	245	1
C51000	190	1
C71500	480	1

The tendency of a formed part to stress crack can be determined by the application of ASTM B 154, Method of Mercurous Nitrate Test for Copper and Copper Alloys. The effectiveness of thermal stress relieving treatment can be judged by the same test.

3.6 Fatigue Strength—Materials subjected to alternating tensile and compressive stress, or shear stress alternating in direction, will fail by "fatigue" fracture at much lower values for maximum stress than if subjected to steady loads. The same effect applies, but to a lesser degree if the stresses are constant in direction but vary in magnitude. Springs, diaphragms, bellows, flexible hose and similar applications are frequently exposed to such conditions, and when this is the case, the maximum stress used in design calculations must be less than the safe tensile or shear stress applicable when the load is constant.

Generally, the harder the material the higher its fatigue strength, although fatigue strengths vary with surface and temper conditions and corrosion. The heat treatable alloys such as beryllium alloys, copper containing either nickel and silicon or nickel and phosphorus can be hardened by heat treatment and, therefore, optimum spring characteristics can be realized by such treatment after the spring has been formed. Phosphor alloys, nickel-silver alloys and other nonheat treatable alloys must always be used in a condition sufficiently soft to successfully cold form into the desired shape. Since the fatigue strength increases with the hardness of the material, the highest values for the precipitation hardening alloys must be compared with less than the highest values for other materials. Such a comparison indicates a marked superiority of the former alloys.

A comparison of the fatigue strengths of several alloys follows: Copper Alloy UNS Nos. C17000, 275 MPa (40 ksi); C67400, 215 MPa (31 ksi); C52100, 185 MPa (27 ksi); C65500, 160 MPa (23 ksi); C77000, 155 MPa (22.5 ksi); C51000, 150 MPa (22 ksi); C26800, 140 MPa (20 ksi); and Copper UNS No. C11000, 70 MPa (10 ksi).

3.7 Formability—All coppers form easily and readily and work harden slowly. Generally, Copper UNS Nos. C10200 and C12200 may be best for severe cold forming, although for thin gage material, mill practices may be adjusted to develop extreme ductilities in Copper UNS No. C11000.

Best results in cold forming operations are obtained through the use of nonleaded alloys, including copper, silver-bearing alloys, and all nonleaded alloys containing more than 63% copper. Included in this list are the phosphor alloys, nickel-silver alloys (65–18) nickel alloys, and the age hardenable alloys in the solution treated condition. Some of the age hardenable alloys have excellent ductility even after fully heat treated and are capable of being cold formed to a high degree.

Copper Alloy UNS No. C26000 is the most widely used for operations such as cold drawing, upsetting, stamping, and bending. Copper Alloy UNS Nos. C23000, C22000, and C21000 are not as strong as Copper Alloy UNS No. C26000 but harden at a slower rate when cold worked, thereby allowing successive operations without intermediate annealing.

Forming operations such as deep drawing, eyelet work, coining, flanging, spinning, or similar cold working, all require annealed material usually ordered by specifying grain size. Care should be exercised to specify the grain size most suitable for the part to be made. Depending upon the severity of the cold forming operation during the production of a specific part, it is sometimes necessary for the fabricator to perform an anneal or soften the material before further press operations can be successfully applied. The grain size of any of these anneals must be controlled. Grain size that is too small can lead to breakage during forming, whereas excessively large grain sizes may also lead to breakage because of lowering tensile strength of the alloy, or, if the part does not fail, its surface may become excessively rough (a condition known as orange peel) and require costly finishing operations where polishing and plating are required. Table 6 suggests approximate annealing temperature ranges to apply for intermediate annealing. The alloy should be annealed at the lowest temperature experimentally in seeking the proper grain size and smoothest polishing surface. It should be remembered that insufficiently annealed work can always be reannealed at higher temperature. Overannealed damage is beyond salvage.

TABLE 6—APPROXIMATE ANNEALING TEMPERATURE RANGES FOR INTERMEDIATE ANNEALING OF FABRICATED PARTS

Copper or Copper Alloy UNS No.	Metal Temperature °C	Average Grain Size, mm
C11000	400–480 345–400	0.025 0.020
C22000	405–635 440–565	0.040 0.025
C23000	480–610 400–480	0.040 0.025
C26000	455–595 370–480	0.040 0.025
C26800	455–595 370–455	0.040 0.025
C51000	565–650 480–565	0.030 0.015
C75200	595–705 480–620	0.035 0.020

Currently the trend is toward the use of thinner gages of strip for fabrication purposes. Reduction of grain size to less than 0.010 mm makes available material of sufficient strength to withstand deeper drawing without intermediate annealing processes.

Coining operations demand metal of large grain size for maximum sharpness of impression. Cold upsetting, particularly of screws, rivets and bolts should be performed on metal lightly cold drawn to develop some strength in unsupported sections to resist bending as the parts are being fabricated.

Where machining is an important factor in making the finished part and cold forming is part of the fabricating process, leaded alloys in light drawn tempers are logical choices. The presence of lead results in easier machining. Control of the lead content and temper allows the alloy to be cold worked as, for example, in thread rolling.

Table 3 lists cold workability ratings for various alloys. The ratings are arbitrary for their approximate relative suitability for being cold worked; the ratings being excellent, good, fair, or not recommended. It must be realized that such arbitrary ratings cannot be too precise, due to the multiplicity of cold working operations that must be considered. Operations taken into account in assigning the ratings include drawing, forming, stamping, spinning, bending, and heading. The ratings given take into account not only the relative power required to cold work the alloy, but also the amount of deformation which is possible without fracture.

3.8 Bending—Bending is often the controlling factor in selection of temper for strip products. For a particular alloy and thickness, the harder the temper the more generous the bending radius must be for successful bending. Bending characteristics of strip are more favorable when the axis of the bend is at a right angle to the rolling direction. Bending problems may be prevented when sharp or difficult bends must be made in more than one direction by designing the bending tools to accommodate blanks cut on some axis other than parallel to the direction of rolling. Table 7 recommends radii for forming 90 deg bends in respect to rolling direction, gage and temper for various alloys.

TABLE 7—RECOMMENDED RADII FOR FORMING 90 DEG BENDS

Copper or Copper Alloy UNS No.	Temper	Thickness		Minimum Radius of Bends: Bend Perpendicular To Rolling Direction		Bend At 45 Deg To Rolling Direction		Bend Parallel To Rolling Direction	
		mm	in	mm	in	mm	in	mm	in
C11000	Half Hard	0.50	.020	Sharp		Sharp		1.6	.06
	Extra Hard			1.2	.05	1.2	.05	1.6	.06
C17200	Annealed	0.10	.004					0.4	.02
	Quarter Hard							0.4	.02
	Half Hard							0.8	.03
	Hard							0.8	.03
	Annealed	0.25	.010					1.2	.05
	Quarter Hard							1.6	.06
	Half Hard							2.4	.09
	Hard							4.0	.16
	Annealed	0.50	.020					2.8	.11
	Quarter Hard							3.2	.12
	Half Hard							4.8	.19
	Hard							8.0	.31
C23000	Soft	0.13/ 1.60	.005/ .063	Sharp		Sharp		Sharp	
	Half Hard	0.50/ 1.30	.020/ .050	Sharp		Sharp		Sharp	
	Hard	0.65	.025	Sharp		0.4	.02	1.2	.05
		1.00	.040	0.4	.02	.12	.05	1.6	.06
		1.60	.063	1.2	.05	2.4	.09	3.2	.12
	Extra Hard	0.30	.012	0.4	.02	1.2	.05	1.6	.06
		0.65	.025	0.8	.03	1.6	.06	3.2	.12
		1.00	.040	1.6	.06	3.2	.12	4.8	.19
	Spring	0.30	.012	1.2	.05	2.4	0.9	4.8	.19
		0.65	.025	1.6	.06	4.8	.19	6.4	.25
		1.00	.040	2.4	.09	6.4	.25	>6.4	>.25
C24000	Hard	0.50	.020	Sharp		0.8	.03	1.2	.05
	Spring	0.50	.020	1.6	.06	4.8	.19	6.4	.25
C26000	Half Hard	0.13/ 0.80	.005/ .032	Sharp		Sharp		Sharp	
		0.81/ 1.30	.033/ .050	Sharp		Sharp		0.4	.02
	Hard	1.31/ 0.48	.005/ .019	Sharp		0.4	.02	0.8	.03
		0.65	.025	0.4	.02	0.8	.03	1.6	.06
		1.00	.040	0.8	.03	1.6	.06	2.4	.09
		1.60	.063	1.6	.06	3.2	.12	4.8	.19
	Extra Hard	0.40	.106	0.8	.03	1.6	.06	3.2	.12
		0.65	.025	1.6	.06	2.4	.09	4.8	.19
		1.00	.040	2.4	.09	3.2	.12	6.4	.25
	Spring	0.25	.010	1.6	.06	3.2	.12	4.8	.19
		0.65	.025	2.4	.09	4.8	.19	>6.4	>.25
		1.00	.040	3.2	.12	>6.4	>.25	>6.4	>.25
	Extra Spring	0.25	.010	1.6	.06	3.2	.12	6.4	.25
		0.65	.025	2.4	.09	>6.4	>.25	>6.4	>.25
		1.00	.040	3.2	.12	>6.4	>.25	>6.4	>.25
C26800	Half Hard	0.13/ 0.80	.005/ .032	Sharp		Sharp		Sharp	
		0.81/ 1.30	.033/ .050	Sharp		Sharp		0.4	.02
	Hard	0.13/ 0.30	.005/ .012	Sharp		0.4	.02	0.8	.03
		1.00	.040	0.8	.03	1.6	.06	2.4	.09
		1.60	.063	1.6	.06	3.2	.12	4.8	.19
C51000	Half Hard	0.50/ 0.80	.020/ .032	Sharp		Sharp		0.4	.02
	Hard	1.00	.040	1.2	.05	2.4	.09	4.8	.19
	Extra Hard	1.00	.040	1.6	.06	3.2	.12	6.4	.25
	Spring	0.30	.012	0.8	.03	1.6	.06	4.8	.19
		0.65	.025	1.6	.06	3.2	.12	6.4	.25
		1.00	.040	2.4	.09	4.8	.19	>6.4	>.25
	Extra Spring	0.30	.012	1.2	.05	2.4	.09	6.4	.25
		0.50	.020	2.4	.09	4.8	.19	>6.4	>.25
C52100	Half Hard	0.13/ 0.48	.005/ .019	Sharp		Sharp		0.4	.02
	Hard	0.50	.020	0.4	.02	1.2	.05	2.4	.09
		1.00	.040	1.2	.05	2.4	.09	4.8	.19
		1.60	.063	2.4	.09	4.8	.19	>6.4	>.25
	Extra Hard	1.00	.040	2.4	.09	4.8	.19	>6.4	>.25
	Spring	1.00	.040	3.2	.12	6.4	.25	>6.4	>.25
	Extra Spring	1.60	.063	6.4	.25	>6.4	>.25	>6.4	>.25
C75200	Half Hard	1.00	.040			0.4	.02	0.8	.03
	Hard	1.00	.040	1.6	.06	1.6	.06	1.6	.06
	Extra Hard	1.00	.040	3.2	.12	3.2	.12	4.8	.19
	Spring	1.00	.040	4.0	.16	4.8	.19	5.6	.22
	Extra Spring	1.00	.040	4.0	.16	5.6	.22	6.4	.25

3.9 Hot Forming—Copper and a series of copper alloys lend themselves well to production by hot forming, die-pressed forging and extrusion. Where sufficient support is not provided by the tooling during hot working operations, the higher leaded alloys become susceptible to cracking.

Alloys specified for hot forming include many coppers, zinc alloys containing 58–63% copper, tin alloys, aluminum alloys, silicon alloys, and nickel-silver alloys. Table 8 lists the relative forgeability of the various alloys and takes into account such variables as pressure, die wear, and hot plasticity.

TABLE 8—RELATIVE FORGEABILITY RATING OF TYPICAL ALLOYS AS HOT PRESSED

Copper or Copper Alloy UNS No.	Relative Forgeability Rating
C11000	65
C12200	65
C37700	100
C46400	85
C67500	80
C65500	40
C63700	70
C62400	75
C67400	90

3.10 Machinability—The addition of lead to copper alloys greatly improves their machinability. The greater the amount of lead, the easier the alloy machines or cuts. Lead also improves the blanking quality in strip alloys by reducing their ductility, thereby providing a sharp, clean shear.

Lead does not dissolve in copper or its alloys and is finely dispersed throughout the alloy. During a cutting operation the presence of lead produces short or broken chips which are easily flushed away by lubricants. Excellent finishes can be attained with the use of proper tools and feeds, and machining rates are frequently as high as maximum machine capabilities. Screw machines often utilize speeds as high as 10,000 rpm producing parts from free cutting zinc alloy rod. The Copper Base Alloy Rod Handbook, published by the Copper Development Association (CDA), is recommended for information on tool shapes, feeds, speeds, and so forth.

Ordinarily, half hard Copper Alloy UNS No. C36000 containing about 3.25% lead is preferred for machining. For knurling or thread rolling operations demanding greater ductility, softer or lower leaded alloys should be specified.

Lead, tellurium, or sulfur added to copper combine the properties of pure copper with improved machinability, and all three alloys may be used where the basic properties of copper itself are required. Lead is insoluble in the copper and both tellurium and sulfur form insoluble compounds with copper thereby acting much in the same manner as lead in producing chips during machining operations. Table 3 lists the arbitrary relative machinability rating of many alloys. The numerical rating is a reasonable indication of the amount of power required for any given type and degree of cutting operation, and tool life will be found to vary in proportion to such a rating. The type of chip also plays an important part, for in certain operations almost any type of chip can be tolerated; whereas in others, for example deep drilling, box milling and tapping, long stringy chips may cause scoring of the stack and tool breakage. The table also lists the type of chip expected for each alloy by designating with the letters L, M, or S, indicating that the chips are long, medium, or short.

3.11 Joining—Copper and most of its alloys are readily joined by soldering and brazing and by most of the commonly used welding processes. Table 3 indicates the approximate relative suitability of alloys for being joined by various processes. The choice of method depends on shape of the work, composition of the metal, and the end use of the product. Thus, where welded joints of maximum strength are required, it is necessary to use Copper UNS Nos. C10200, C12000, C12200 or C14500 instead of the C11XXX types. Arc welding of zinc-bearing alloys is hampered by the vaporization of zinc; so, 'if oxyacetylene welding is not feasible, the parts are designed for brazing or soldering. On aluminum alloys, soldering is impossible, and brazing is difficult because interfering oxides form even under very active fluxes; oxyacetylene welding is also impossible because of interfering oxides; therefore, arc welding processes are the only practicable joining methods. Brazing and soldering are the preferred methods for joining leaded alloys, because welding develops increasing porosity and cracking as lead content increases.

Methods most commonly used are:

3.11.1 Resistance Welding—Applicable on all nonleaded alloys. Flash butt welding successful on all. Spot and seam welding practicable on those with conductivities below 30%. Copper-silicon and copper-nickel alloys are the most weldable and coppers are the least weldable.

3.11.2 Gas Shielded Are Welding—Widely employed on all. Silicon and aluminum alloys are readily welded by these processes. So are the nickel alloys if done with the specially alloyed filler metal developed for these processes.

3.11.3 Coated Metal Arc Welding—Excellent where good flux-coated electrodes are available, as for the nickel alloys. Coated electrodes are also available for aluminum and phosphor alloys. Process is not suitable for copper because of high heat requirements.

3.11.4 CARBON ARC WELDING—Less costly than gas shielded arc welding and produces good results on silicon alloys. Also useful for welding copper with silicon or phosphor alloy rods.

3.11.5 OXYACETYLENE WELDING—Good results on deoxidized copper using specialty alloyed welding rods, and on silicon alloys. Excellent to zinc alloys if low fuming rods are used. Not suitable for aluminum alloys

3.11.6 BRAZING—Generally useful with either silver alloys or phosphorus alloys. Latter are less costly. They are also considered self-fluxing on copper but best results require use of flux. Phosphorus alloys are often used to join the 90–10 nickel alloy but are not recommended to use on alloys with higher nickel contents. Tough pitch coppers are readily "gassed" and embrittled by exposure to hydrogen at high temperatures therefore they are not suitable for parts to be furnace brazed in hydrogen bearing atmospheres, and they cannot be safely brazed by flame processes if heating time is prolonged. Special fluxes are available to help in brazing of aluminum alloys.

3.11.7 SOLDERING—Readily done on all copper base metals except the aluminum alloys. Suitable fluxes are not available for use on these alloys.

3.12 Effect of Temperature—Copper and its alloys are not harmed b temperatures as low as –185 °C, rather, a gain in mechanical properties is noticed with decreasing temperature.

Most copper alloys do not find application above 200 °C since, dependent upon the amount of cold work applied during fabrication, most of the alloys soften between 200 and 425 °C. Further, oxidation also must be considered above these temperatures.

3.13 Color—Copper alloys are the only large tonnage metals that have a wide red and yellow color range. Red and pink for the copper rich materials, gold shades for Copper Alloy UNS Nos. C21000, C22000 and C23000 although sometimes these alloys are also a pleasing red because of the formation of a superficial copper oxide on the surface. The series of alloys becomes more yellow at 80% copper, 20% zinc (Copper Alloy UNS No. C24000) and develop the familiar yellow at the 70–30 (Copper Alloy UNS No. C26000) composition. The color reverses at about 55% copper, 45% zinc.

3.14 Surface Finishing—A number of types of mechanical finishes and treatments can be applied rather easily to the copper alloys. Among these are deburring, bright rolling, ball burnishing, wheel polishing and buffing belt polishing, scratch brushing, and sand blasting.

The highest luster that can be produced on copper alloys is by the combination of wheel polishing and buffing. Both manually operated and automatic buffing equipment together with an assortment of polishing and buffing wheels are available to accomplish this job.

Copper Alloy UNS No. C26000 lends itself extremely well to finishing such as just described and because of this and its excellent corrosion resistance, is often used for such items as automobile wheel covers or hub caps.

The ease with which a part can be polished can depend upon surface roughness termed orange peel which can develop on cold drawn parts if the base stock before forming has a grain size over 0.050 turn and the forming operation is severe. The degree of orange peel depends upon grain size and degree of forming. Therefore, when surface finish is important after the forming of a given part, attention must be directed to the grain size of the starting stock or to parts given an intermediate anneal in the fabrication sequence. Table 9 is a guide to specifying annealed tempers for strip in relation to type of operation being performed, gage of the material, and grain size.

Copper alloys in general offer a noncorroding surface for electroplating. A base electroplate of copper is usually not necessary under nickel or chromium used as decorative electroplates. Therefore, copper alloys, in general, allow thinner plates of such metals as tin, nickel, chromium, or silver, than do other metals.

Fused enamels are applied on Copper Alloy UNS Nos. C21000, C22000 and C23000 with very beautiful effects. Alloys containing much more than 7% zinc should not be used with transparent enamels as cloudiness or color change can result.

Tarnishing or discoloration of copper alloys may be retarded and, in many cases, delayed indefinitely by application of a lacquer selected with consideration to the service environment in which the object is to exist.

There are literally hundreds of transparent coatings which can be applied to copper articles. Perhaps in no other unit process of metal finishing is such a wide variety of materials available for use.

Lacquer or protective coating systems, which have very effectively protected the surface of copper alloys for both interior and exterior exposure for a number of years, have been developed and time tested.

TABLE 9—ANNEALED TEMPERS OF STRIP NOMINAL GRAIN SIZE, mm

Copper Alloy UNS No.	Thickness				Type of Operation			
	mm		in		Eyelet Type Forming	Deep Drawing, Spinning	Embossing, Severe Forming	Coining, Extremely Severe Drawing
	Over	Thru	Over	Thru				
C24000,	—	0.50	—	.020	0.015	0.025	0.035	—
C26000,	0.50	1.30	.020	.050	0.025	0.035	0.050	0.050
and	1.30	2.30	.050	.090	0.035	0.050	0.070	0.070
C26800	2.30	4.60	.090	.180	0.050	0.070	0.070	0.120
	4.60	—	.180	—	0.070	0.120	0.120	0.120
C21000,	—	0.50	—	.020	0.015	0.025	0.025	—
C22000,	0.50	1.30	.020	.050	0.025	0.035	0.050	0.050
and	1.30	4.60	.050	.180	0.035	0.035	0.050	0.050
C23000	4.60	—	.180	—	0.035	0.050	0.050	0.070
C10200,	—	0.50	—	.020	0.015	0.025	0.025	—
C11000,	0.50	1.30	.020	.050	0.015	0.025	0.025	0.035
C11300 thru	1.30	4.60	.050	.180	0.015	0.025	0.035	0.035
C12000, and C12200	4.60	—	.180	—	0.025	0.035	0.035	0.035

3.15 Corrosion Resistance—Copper and copper alloys have been extensively and successfully used for many years in a variety of corrosive conditions. Copper is highly resistant to the effects of atmosphere, naturally occurring fresh and salt waters, alkaline solutions (except those containing ammonia) and many organic chemicals. The severity of oxidizing conditions controls its behavior in acidic media. Many salt solutions are successfully handled. Sulfur and its sulfide compounds do combine with copper to produce copper sulfide as a corrosion product. As the zinc content of the copper alloys is increased over 15%, resistance to corrosion from sulfide compounds is markedly increased. This fact is important when radiator materials are selected for possible use on farm equipment that might come into contact with insecticide sprays that contain sulfur.

The commercial copper alloys vary widely in chemical composition; therefore, there is considerable variation in their resistance to corrosion. Many of the alloying elements improve corrosion resistance of the parent metal as well as enhance its mechanical properties.

Extensive use indicates the suitability and, often, superiority of copper and its alloys for many applications, including the following broad classifications: atmospheric exposures, such as hardware, building fronts, automotive radiators, and hub caps; fresh water supply lines, including those buried in soil; sea water applications; heat exchanges; and industrial and chemical plant equipment handling a variety of products.

TABLE 10A—TYPICAL MECHANICAL PROPERTIES OF WROUGHT COPPER AND COPPER ALLOYS

Metric (SI) Units

Copper or Copper Alloy UNS No.	Form	Temper	Size Section, mm	Tensile Strength, MPa	Yield Strength, 0.5% Ext Under Load, MPa	Elongation in 50 mm, %	Reduction of Area, %	Hardness			Shear Strength, MPa	Fatigue Strength	
								RF	RB	R30T.		MPa	Million Cycles
C10200 C11000 C11100 C11300 C11400 C11500 C11600 C12000 C12200	Plate, Sheet, Strip, and Rolled Bar	Soft Anneal	1.0	220	70	45	—	40	—	—	150	—	—
		Deep-Drawing Anneal	1.0	235	75	45	—	45	—	—	160	75	100
		Light Cold Rolled	1.0	250	195	30	—	60	10	25	170	—	—
		1/2 Hard	1.0	290	250	14	—	84	40	50	180	90	100
		Hard	1.0	345	310	6	—	90	50	57	195	90	100
		Spring	1.0	380	345	4	—	94	60	63	200	90	100
		Extra Spring	1.0	385	365	4	—	95	62	64	200	—	—
		Hot Rolled	1.0	235	70	45	—	45	—	—	160	—	—
		Hot Rolled and Annealed	1.0	230	70	45	—	42	—	—	150	—	—
C10200 C11000 C12000 C12200	Rod, Bar and Shapes	Soft Anneal	25.0	220	70	55	70	40	—	—	150	—	—
		Hard	6.0[g]	380	345	10	—	94	60	—	260	—	—
			25.0[g]	330	305	16	55	87	47	—	185	17	300
			50.0[g]	310	275	20	—	85	45	—	180	—	—
			12.0[h]	330	305	16	—	87	47	—	185	—	—
			12.0[i]	275	220	30	—	—	35	—	180	—	—
C10200 C12000 C12200	Tube	Soft Anneal	25.0 × 1.6	220	70	45	—	40	—	—	150	75[a]	20
		Light Anneal	25.0 × 1.6	235	75	45	—	45	—	—	160	—	—
		Light Drawn	25.0 × 1.6	275	220	25	—	77	35	45	180	95[a]	20
		Drawn	25.0 × 1.6	275	220	25	—	77	35	45	—	—	—
		Hard Drawn	25.0 × 1.6	380	345	8	—	95	60	63	200	130[a]	20
			50.0 × 1.6	380	345	8	—	95	60	63	—	—	—
			100.0 × 1.6	380	345	8	—	95	60	63	—	—	—
C10200 C11000	Wire	Annealed	2.0	240	—	35[f]	—	—	—	—	165	—	—
C14500 and C14700	Rod	1/2 Hard	6.0	295	260	20	—	—	38	—	170	—	—
			25.0	290	250	25	—	—	38	—	165	—	—
			50.0	285	240	25	—	—	35	—	165	—	—
		Hard	6.0	365	330	10	—	—	52	—	200	—	—
			25.0	330	290	15	—	—	50	—	185	—	—

(Table continued on next page)

TABLE 10A—TYPICAL MECHANICAL PROPERTIES OF WROUGHT COPPER AND COPPER ALLOYS (CONTINUED)

Metric (SI) Units

Copper or Copper Alloy UNS No.	Form	Temper	Size Section, mm	Tensile Strength, MPa	Yield Strength, 0.5% Ext Under Load, MPa	Elongation in 50 mm, %	Reduction of Area, %	Hardness			Shear Strength, MPa	Fatigue Strength	
								RF	RB	R30T		MPa	Million Cycles
C15000	Rod (Round Only)	Drawn and Heat Treated	25.0	415	345	12	—	—	67	—	—	195	100
C16200	Rod (Round Only)	Drawn	25.0	450	345	25	—	—	70	—	—	—	—
			50.0	415	240	30	—	—	65	—	—	—	—
			75.0	380	170	35	—	—	60	—	—	—	—
	Bar (Square and Rectangular) and Rod (Hexagonal)	Drawn	25.0	450	345	25	—	—	70	—	—	—	—
			Over 25.0	380	240	30	—	—	65	—	—	—	—
	Forging	As Forged	25.0	450	—	25	—	—	60	—	—	—	—
			50.0	380	—	30	—	—	55	—	—	—	—
			Over 50.0	380	—	30	—	—	55	—	—	—	—
C17000	Strip	A Soft[d]	—	475	220[j]	48	—	—	62	56	—	—	—
		1/4 Hard[d]	—	565	485[j]	22	—	—	79	68	—	—	—
		1/2 Hard[d]	—	635	565[j]	15	—	—	92	76	—	—	—
		Hard[d]	—	760	715[j]	5	—	—	99	81	—	—	—
									RC	R30N			
		AT (3h at 315°C)[k]	—	1140	1000[j]	3	—	—	36	56	—	260	100
		1/4 HT (2h at 315°C)[k]	—	1185	1035[j]	2	—	—	37	57	—	275	100
		1/2 HT (2h at 315°C)[k]	—	1255	1105[j]	1	—	—	38	58	—	290	100
		HT (2h at 315°C)[k]	—	1310	1170[j]	1	—	—	40	60	—	295	100
		AM[l]	—	745	565[j]	20	—	—	20	40	—	—	—
		1/4 HM[l]	—	815	635[j]	17	—	—	24	44	—	—	—
		1/2 HM[l]	—	850	725[j]	14	—	—	28	48	—	—	—
		HM[l]	—	985	840[j]	11	—	—	32	52	—	—	—
		XHM[l]	—	1160	1020[j]	4	—	—	34	54	—	—	—
C17200	Strip	A (Soft)[d]	—	475	220[j]	48	—	—	62	56	—	—	—
		1/4 Hard[d]	—	565	485[j]	22	—	—	79	68	—	—	—
		1/2 Hard[d]	—	635	550[j]	15	—	—	92	76	—	—	—
		Hard[d]	—	760	715[j]	5	—	—	99	81	—	—	—
									RC	R30N			
		AT (3h at 315°C)[k]	—	1230	1070[j]	6	—	—	38	58	—	260	100
		1/4 H (2h at 315°C)[k]	—	1295	1140[j]	4	—	—	40	60	—	275	100
		1/2 H (2h at 315°C)[k]	—	1365	1205[j]	3	—	—	42	62	—	295	100
		HT (2h at 315°C)[k]	—	1390	1240[j]	2	—	—	43	63	—	305	100
									RB	R30T			
	Rod and Bar	A (Soft)[d]	—	495	170[j]	48	—	—	62	—	—	—	—
		1/2 Hard[d]	Under 25.0	760	620[j]	15	—	—	96	—	—	—	—
		1/2 Hard[d]	Over 25.0	690	620[j]	15	—	—	96	—	—	—	—
									RC				
		AT (3h at 315°C)[k]	—	1230	1105[j]	6	—	—	38	—	—	345	100
		1/2 HT (2h at 315°C)[k]	Under 25.0	1380	1255[j]	4	—	—	42	—	—	350	100
		1/2 HT (2h at 315°C)[k]	Over 25.0	1325	1205[j]	4	—	—	42	—	—	350	100
									RB				
C17500	Strip and Plate	A (Soft)[d]	—	310	170[j]	28	—	—	32	37	—	—	—
		1/2 Hard[d]	—	470	385[j]	8	—	—	70	64	—	—	—
		Hard[d]	—	540	485[j]	5	—	—	83	72	—	—	—
		AT (3h at 480°C)[k]	—	760	620[j]	12	—	—	96	80	—	230	100
		1/2 HT (2h at 480°C)[k]	—	825	745[j]	8	—	—	98	81	—	240	100
		HT (2h at 480°C)[k]	—	825	745[j]	8	—	—	98	81	—	240	100

(Table continued on next page)

TABLE 10A—TYPICAL MECHANICAL PROPERTIES OF WROUGHT COPPER AND COPPER ALLOYS (CONTINUED)

Metric (SI) Units

Copper or Copper Alloy UNS No.	Form	Temper	Size Section, mm	Tensile Strength, MPa	Yield Strength, 0.5% Ext Under Load, MPa	Elongation in 50 mm, %	Reduction of Area, %	Hardness			Shear Strength, MPa	Fatigue Strength	
								RF	RB	R30T		MPa	Million Cycles
C17500 C17600	Rod, Bar Shapes and Tubing	A (Soft)[d]	—	310	170[j]	28	—	—	35	—	—	—	—
		1/2 Hard[d]	—	495	450[j]	12	—	—	68	—	—	—	—
		AT (3h at 480°C)[k]	—	760	620[j]	18	—	—	96	—	—	275	100
		1/2 HT (2h at 480°C)[k]	—	825	760[j]	14	—	—	98	—	—	275	100
C18400	Round Rod	Drawn	25.0	485	—	20	—	—	80	—	—	—	—
			50.0	450	—	20	—	—	75	—	—	—	—
			75.0	415	—	20	—	—	70	—	—	—	—
	Rod (Hexagonal) and Bar	Drawn	25.0	485	—	20	—	—	75	—	—	—	—
			Over 25.0	415	—	20	—	—	70	—	—	—	—
	Forgings	As Forged	25.0	485	—	20	—	—	80	—	—	—	—
			50.0	415	—	20	—	—	75	—	—	—	—
			Over 50.0	415	—	20	—	—	70	—	—	—	—
C18700	Rod	Hard	6.0	415	380	10	—	—	55	—	220	—	—
			12.0	380	345	11	—	—	50	—	205	—	—
			18.0	365	330	12	—	—	50	—	200	—	—
			25.0	350	315	14	—	—	50	—	195	—	—
C19200	Tube	A (Soft)	48.0 × 2.4	255	80	40	—	—	—	—	—	—	—
		Light Drawn	4.8 × 0.8	290	215	3	—	—	—	—	—	—	—
C21000	Plate, Sheet, Strip and Rolled Bar[e]	Annealed											
		0.050 mm	1.0	235	70	45	—	46	—	—	185	—	—
		0.035 mm	1.0	240	75	45	—	52	—	4	195	—	—
		0.025 mm	1.0	250	85	43	—	56	—	9	200	—	—
		0.015 mm	1.0	260	95	42	—	60	—	15	205	—	—
		1/4 Hard	1.0	290	220	25	—	—	38	44	220	—	—
		1/2 Hard	1.0	330	275	12	—	—	52	54	235	—	—
		3/4 Hard	1.0	350	310	8	—	—	59	58	240	—	—
		Hard	1.0	385	345	5	—	—	64	60	255	—	—
		Extra Hard	1.0	420	380	4	—	—	70	64	270	—	—
		Springs	1.0	440	400	4	—	—	73	66	275	—	—
		Extra Spring	1.0	450	—	—	—	—	74	68	—	—	—
C22000	Plate, Sheet Strip and Rolled Bar[e]	Annealed											
		0.050 mm	1.0	255	70	45	—	53	—	6	195	—	—
		0.035 mm	1.0	260	85	45	—	57	—	12	205	—	—
		0.025 mm	1.0	270	95	44	—	60	—	16	215	—	—
		0.015 mm	1.0	285	105	42	—	65	—	26	220	—	—
		1/4 Hard	1.0	310	240	25	—	—	42	44	230	—	—
		1/2 Hard	1.0	360	310	11	—	—	58	56	240	—	—
		3/4 Hard	1.0	395	345	8	—	—	67	63	250	—	—
		Hard	1.0	420	370	5	—	—	70	63	260	—	—
		Extra Hard	1.0	460	400	4	—	—	75	67	275	—	—
		Spring	1.0	495	425	3	—	—	78	69	275	145	15
		Extra Spring	1.0	525	—	—	—	—	82	73	290	—	—
	Tube	Soft Anneal	25.0 × 1.6	260	70	52	—	55	—	10	—	—	—
		Light Anneal	25.0 × 1.6	285	105	42	—	65	—	35	—	—	—
		Drawn (General Purpose)	25.0 × 1.6	310	240	25	—	—	50	50	—	—	—
		Hard Drawn	25.0 × 1.6	415	365	6	—	—	69	62	—	—	—

(Table continued on next page)

TABLE 10A—TYPICAL MECHANICAL PROPERTIES OF WROUGHT COPPER AND COPPER ALLOYS (CONTINUED)

Metric (SI) Units

Copper or Copper Alloy UNS No.	Form	Temper	Size Section, mm	Tensile Strength, MPa	Yield Strength, 0.5% Ext Under Load, MPa	Elongation in 50 mm, %	Reduction of Area, %	Hardness			Shear Strength, MPa	Fatigue Strength	
								RF	RB	R30T		MPa	Million Cycles
C23000	Sheet and Strip	Annealed											
		0.070 mm	1.0	270	70	48	—	56	—	10	215	—	—
		0.050 mm	1.0	275	85	47	—	59	—	14	215	—	—
		0.035 mm	1.0	285	95	46	—	63	—	22	215	—	—
		0.025 mm	1.0	295	110	44	—	66	—	28	220	—	—
		0.015 mm	1.0	310	125	42	—	71	—	38	230	—	—
		1/4 Hard	1.0	345	270	25	—	—	55	54	240	—	—
		1/2 Hard	1.0	395	340	12	—	—	65	60	255	—	—
		3/4 Hard	1.0	425	360	8	—	—	73	67	270	—	—
		Hard	1.0	495	395	5	—	—	77	68	290	—	—
		Extra Hard	1.0	540	420	4	—	—	83	72	305	—	—
		Spring	1.0	580	435	3	—	—	86	74	315	—	—
		Extra Spring	1.0	595	—	—	—	—	88	77	—	—	—
	Tube	Soft Anneal	25.0 × 1.6	275	85	55	—	60	—	15	—	—	—
		Light Anneal	25.0 × 1.6	305	125	45	—	71	—	38	—	—	—
		Light Drawn	25.0 × 1.6	345	275	30	—	—	55	54	—	—	—
		Drawn (General Purpose)	25.0 × 1.6	385	315	25	—	—	62	60	—	—	—
		Hard Drawn	25.0 × 1.6	455	400	8	—	—	77	68	—	—	—
C24000	Sheet and Strip	Annealed											
		0.070 mm	1.0	290	85	52	—	57	—	8	—	—	—
		0.050 mm	1.0	305	95	50	—	61	—	16	220	—	—
		0.035 mm	1.0	315	105	48	—	66	—	28	—	—	—
		0.025 mm	1.0	330	115	47	—	69	—	32	—	—	—
		0.015 mm	1.0	345	140	46	—	75	—	42	230	—	—
		1/4 Hard	1.0	365	275	30	—	—	55	54	250	—	—
		1/2 Hard	1.0	420	345	18	—	—	70	64	270	—	—
		3/4 Hard	1.0	455	370	12	—	—	76	68	285	—	—
		Hard	1.0	510	405	7	—	—	82	71	295	—	—
		Extra Hard	1.0	570	425	5	—	—	87	75	310	—	—
		Spring	1.0	625	450	3	—	—	91	77	330	165	20
		Extra Spring	1.0	640	—	—	—	—	92	78	—	—	—
C26000	Plate, Sheet, Strip, Rolled Bar and Wire*	Annealed											
		0.120 mm	1.0	305	75	66	—	54	—	11	—	90	100
		0.070 mm	1.0	315	95	65	—	58	—	15	220	90	100
		0.050 mm	1.0	325	105	62	—	64	—	26	—	—	—
		0.035 mm	1.0	340	115	57	—	68	—	31	235	95	100
		0.025 mm	1.0	350	130	55	—	72	—	36	—	—	—
		0.015 mm	1.0	365	150	54	—	78	—	43	240	105	100
		1/4 Hard	1.0	370	275	43	—	—	55	54	250	—	—
		1/2 Hard	1.0	425	360	23	—	—	70	65	275	125	100
		3/4 Hard	1.0	475	395	15	—	—	79	70	290	—	—
		Hard	1.0	525	435	8	—	—	82	73	305	145	100
		Extra Hard	1.0	595	450	5	—	—	88	76	315	—	—
		Spring	1.0	650	450	3	—	—	91	77	330	160	100
		Extra Spring	1.0	695	450	3	—	—	93	78	—	—	—

(Table continued on next page)

TABLE 10A—TYPICAL MECHANICAL PROPERTIES OF WROUGHT COPPER AND COPPER ALLOYS (CONTINUED)

Metric (SI) Units

Copper or Copper Alloy UNS No.	Form	Temper	Size Section, mm	Tensile Strength, MPa	Yield Strength, 0.5% Ext Under Load, MPa	Elongation in 50 mm, %	Reduction of Area, %	Hardness			Shear Strength, MPa	Fatigue Strength	
								RF	RB	R30T		MPa	Million Cycles
C26000 continued	Tube	Soft Anneal	25.0 × 1.6	325	105	65	—	64	—	26	—	—	—
		Light Anneal	25.0 × 1.6	360	140	55	—	75	—	40	—	—	—
		Hard Drawn	25.0 × 1.6	540	440	8	—	—	82	73	—	—	—
C26800	Plate, Sheet, Strip and Rolled Bar[e]	Annealed											
		0.120 mm	1.0	—	—	—	—	56	—	5	—	—	—
		0.070 mm	1.0	315	95	65	—	58	—	15	220	80	100
		0.050 mm	1.0	325	105	62	—	64	—	26	230	105	100
		0.035 mm	1.0	340	115	57	—	68	—	31	235	—	—
		0.025 mm	1.0	350	130	55	—	72	—	36	240	—	—
		0.015 mm	1.0	365	150	54	—	78	—	43	240	—	—
		1/4 Hard	1.0	370	275	43	—	—	55	54	250	—	—
		1/2 Hard	1.0	420	345	23	—	—	70	65	275	—	—
		3/4 Hard	1.0	460	380	15	—	—	77	69	285	—	—
	Plate, Sheet, Strip and Rolled Bar[e]	Hard	1.0	510	415	8	—	—	80	70	295	95	100
		Extra Hard	1.0	585	425	5	—	—	87	74	310	—	—
		Spring	1.0	625	425	3	—	—	90	76	325	140	100
		Extra Spring	1.0	655	—	—	—	—	92	78	—	140	100
C27000	Wire	Annealed											
		0.035 mm	2.0	345	—	60	—	—	—	—	235	—	—
		1/8 Hard	2.0	400	—	35	—	—	—	—	260	—	—
		1/4 Hard	2.0	485	—	20	—	—	—	—	290	150[a]	300
		1/2 Hard	2.0	605	—	15	—	—	—	—	315	—	—
		3/4 Hard	2.0	690	—	12	—	—	—	—	345	—	—
		Hard	2.0	760	—	8	—	—	—	—	380	—	—
		Extra Hard	2.0	825	—	4	—	—	—	—	400	—	—
		Spring	2.0	835	—	3	—	—	—	—	415	—	—
C33000 and C33100	Tube	Soft Anneal	25.0 × 1.6	325	105	60	—	64	—	26	—	—	—
		Light Anneal	25.0 × 1.6	360	140	50	—	75	—	37	—	—	—
		Hard Drawn	25.0 × 1.6	515	415	7	—	—	80	69	—	—	—
C34200 C35000	Plate, Sheet, Strip and Rolled Bar	Annealed											
		0.035 mm	1.0	340	115	52	—	68	—	31	235	—	—
		1/4 Hard	1.0	370	275	38	—	—	55	54	250	—	—
		1/2 Hard	1.0	420	345	20	—	—	70	65	275	—	—
		Hard	1.0	510	415	7	—	—	80	69	295	—	—
		Extra Hard	1.0	585	425	5	—	—	87	74	310	—	—
C34500 C35000	Rod	1/2 Hard	12.0	395	205	20	—	—	68	—	250	—	—
			25.0	380	205	25	—	—	68	—	240	—	—
			50.0	345	170	30	—	—	65	—	220	—	—
C36000	Rod	Soft	25.0	340	125	53	58	68	—	—	205	—	—
		1/2 Hard	6.0	470	360	18	48	—	80	—	260	—	—
			25.0	400	310	25	50	—	78	—	235	—	—
			50.0	380	305	32	52	—	75	—	220	{140[b] {95[b]	100 300
		Hard	3.0	585	345	—	—	—	—	—	—	—	—
			6.0	515	275	5[c]	—	—	—	—	—	—	—
			18.0	485	240	10[c]	—	—	—	—	—	—	—

(Table continued on next page)

TABLE 10A—TYPICAL MECHANICAL PROPERTIES OF WROUGHT COPPER AND COPPER ALLOYS (CONTINUED)

Metric (SI) Units

Copper or Copper Alloy UNS No.	Form	Temper	Size Section, mm	Tensile Strength, MPa	Yield Strength, 0.5% Ext Under Load, MPa	Elongation in 50 mm, %	Reduction of Area, %	Hardness			Shear Strength, MPa	Fatigue Strength	
								RF	RB	R30T		MPa	Million Cycles
C36000 continued	Flat Products	Soft	25.0 × 150.0	330	140	25[c]	—	—	—	—	205	—	—
			Over 25.0 × 150.0	310	125	30[c]	—	—	—	—	195	—	—
		1/2 Hard	6.0 × 25.0	385	310	20[c]	—	—	62	—	230	—	—
			12.0 × 150.0	345	205	20[c]	—	—	—	—	205	—	—
			50.0 × 50.0	340	205	25[c]	—	—	—	—	205	—	—
			50.0 × 150.0	310	170	25[c]	—	—	—	—	185	—	—
			Over 50.0 × 100.0	310	170	25[c]	—	—	—	—	185	—	—
C37700	Die Forgings	As Extruded	1.0	360	140	45[c]	65	78	—	—	—	—	—
		As Forged	4 kg	400	160	40[c]	—	—	—	—	—	—	—
C46400	Rod and Bar	Soft	6.0	400	185	45	60	—	56	—	275	—	—
C46500			25.0	395	170	47	60	—	56	—	275	—	—
C46600			50.0	385	170	47	60	—	55	—	275	—	—
C46700			Over 50.0	375	150	—	—	—	—	—	—	—	—
		1/2 Hard or Light Annealed	6.0	435	205	40	55	—	60	—	290	—	—
			25.0	435	205	40	55	—	60	—	290	—	—
			50.0	425	195	43	55	—	60	—	290	—	—
			75.0	395	180	—	—	—	—	—	—	—	—
			Over 75.0	395	165	—	—	—	—	—	—	—	—
		Hard	6.0	550	395	20	45	—	85	—	310	—	—
			25.0	515	365	20	45	—	82	—	305	—	—
			50.0	460	275	35	50	—	75	—	295	—	—
	Shapes	As Extruded	—	400	170	40	—	—	—	—	275	—	—
C51000	Sheet and Strip	Annealed											
		0.050 mm	1.0	325	130	64	—	73	26	—	250	—	—
		0.035 mm	1.0	340	140	58	—	75	28	—	255	—	—
		0.025 mm	1.0	345	145	52	—	77	30	—	260	—	—
		0.015 mm	1.0	365	150	50	—	79	34	—	275	—	—
		1/2 Hard	1.0	470	380	28	—	—	78	69	340	—	—
		Hard	1.0	560	515	10	—	—	87	75	—	170	100
		Extra Hard	1.0	635	550	6	—	—	93	78	—	—	—
		Spring	1.0	690	550	4	—	—	95	79	—	150	100
		Extra Spring	1.0	740	550	3	—	—	97	80	—	—	—
	Rod	Hard	12.0	515	450	25	—	—	80	—	370	—	—
			25.0	485	400	25	—	—	78	—	345	200	300
	Wire	Soft, 0.035 mm	2.0	345	140	58	—	—	38	—	—	—	—
		1/4 Hard	2.0	470	415	24	—	—	49	—	—	—	—
		1/2 Hard	2.0	585	550	8	—	—	—	—	—	—	—
		Hard	2.0	760	—	5	—	—	—	—	—	185	100
		Extra Hard	2.0	895	—	3	—	—	—	—	—	205	100
		Spring	2.0	905	—	2	—	—	—	—	—	—	—
C51100	Sheet and Strip	Annealed											
C54400		0.050 mm	1.0	315	—	48	—	70	—	—	—	—	—
		0.035 mm	1.0	330	—	47	—	73	—	—	—	—	—
		0.025 mm	1.0	345	—	46	—	75	—	—	—	—	—
		0.015 mm	1.0	350	—	46	—	76	—	—	—	—	—
		1/2 Hard	1.0	425	370	19	—	—	70	65	—	—	—
		Hard	1.0	550	510	7	—	—	86	74	—	—	—
		Extra Hard	1.0	635	—	4	—	—	91	78	—	—	—
		Spring	1.0	675	550	3	—	—	93	79	—	—	—
		Extra Spring	1.0	710	550	2	—	—	95	80	—	—	—

(Table continued on next page)

TABLE 10A—TYPICAL MECHANICAL PROPERTIES OF WROUGHT COPPER AND COPPER ALLOYS (CONTINUED)

Metric (SI) Units

Copper or Copper Alloy UNS No.	Form	Temper	Size Section, mm	Tensile Strength, MPa	Yield Strength, 0.5% Ext Under Load, MPa	Elongation in 50 mm, %	Reduction of Area, %	Hardness			Shear Strength, MPa	Fatigue Strength	
								RF	RB	R30T		MPa	Million Cycles
C52100	Sheet and Strip	Soft	1.0	475	165	63	—	82	50	—	—	—	—
		1/2 Hard	1.0	525	380	32	—	—	84	73	350	—	—
		Hard	1.0	640	495	10	—	—	93	78	—	150	100
		Extra Hard	1.0	730	550	4	—	—	96	80	—	—	—
		Spring	1.0	770	—	3	—	—	98	81	—	—	—
		Extra Spring	1.0	825	—	2	—	—	100	82	—	—	—
C52400	Sheet and Strip	Soft 0.035 mm	1.0	455	195	68	—	—	55	—	—	—	—
		1/2 Hard	1.0	570	—	32	—	—	92	—	—	—	—
		Hard	1.0	690	—	13	—	—	97	—	—	—	—
		Extra Hard	1.0	795	—	7	—	—	100	—	—	—	—
		Spring	1.0	840	—	4	—	—	101	—	—	—	—
		Extra Spring	1.0	845	—	3	—	—	103	—	—	—	—
C54400	Sheet and Strip	See C51100											
	Rod	Hard	12.0 25.0	515 470	435 385	15 20	— —	— —	83 80	— —	— —	— —	— —
	Flat Products	Hard	8.0 18.0	415 380	310 240	20 25	— —	— —	70 —	— —	— —	— —	— —
C60800	Tube	Annealed	25.0 × 1.6	415	185	—	—	77	—	—	—	—	—
C61300	Plate, Sheet, Strip and Rolled Bar	Soft	3.0 8.0 12.0 25.0	560 550 540 525	310 275 240 230	40 40 42 45	35 35 40 40	— — — —	84 83 82 81	— — — —	310 290 275 275	205 195 180 170	100 100 100 100
	Rod and Bar	—	12.0 25.0 50.0	585 565 550	345 310 275	35 35 35	55 55 60	— — —	91 90 88	— — —	330 310 275	— — —	— — —
C61400	Plate, Sheet, Strip and Rolled Bar	Soft	3.0 8.0 12.0 25.0	560 550 540 525	310 275 240 230	40 40 42 45	35 35 40 40	— — — —	84 83 82 81	— — — —	310 290 275 275	205 195 180 170	100 100 100 100
		Hard	3.0 8.0 12.0 25.0	615 585 550 540	415 400 370 310	32 35 38 40	— — — —	— — — —	87 86 85 84	— — — —	345 330 275 260	— — — —	— — — —
	Rod and Bar	—	12.0 25.0 50.0	585 565 550	310 275 240	35 35 35	55 55 60	— — —	91 90 88	— — —	330 310 275	— — —	— — —
C61800	Rod	1/2 Hard	25.0 50.0 75.0	585 570 550	295 270 270	23[c] 25[c] 28[c]	— — —	— — —	88 88 88	— — —	325 310 295	195 195 180	100 100 100
									BHN (1000 kg)				
C62300	Rod and Bar	Drawn	12.0 25.0 75.0	655 635 620	415 380 310	15[c] 20[c] 25[c]	— — —		180 — —		— — —	— — —	— — —
	Shapes	—	—	585	230	25[c]	—		170		—	—	—
	Forgings	As Forged	Thru 40.0 Over 40.0	585 565	230 215	25[c] 30[c]	— —		140 —		— —	— —	— —
									BHN (3000 kg)				

(Table continued on next page)

TABLE 10A—TYPICAL MECHANICAL PROPERTIES OF WROUGHT COPPER AND COPPER ALLOYS (CONTINUED)

Metric (SI) Units

Copper or Copper Alloy UNS No.	Form	Temper	Size Section, mm	Tensile Strength, MPa	Yield Strength, 0.5% Ext Under Load, MPa	Elongation in 50 mm, %	Reduction of Area, %	Hardness			Shear Strength, MPa	Fatigue Strength	
								RF	RB	R30T		MPa	Million Cycles
C62400	Rod	As Extruded	All Sizes	655	345	12[c]			200		—	—	—
	Forgings	As Forged	—	655	345	12[c]			200		—	—	—
	Forgings	Hardened and H_2O Quenched	—	655	345	—			265		—	—	—
		Hardened, H_2O Quenched and Tempered	—	690	—	12[c]			210		—	—	—
C63000	Rod and Bar	Annealed	25.0	725	415	12[c]	—	—	100	—	—	—	—
			50.0	655	345	15[c]	—	—	—	—	—	—	—
			100.0	620	310	17[c]	—	—	—	—	—	—	—
	Shapes	As Extruded	All Sizes	620	310	17[c]	—	—	—	—	—	—	—
C64200	Rod and Bar	Drawn	18.0	705	470	22[c]	—	—	94	—	405	345	100
			40.0	640	415	26[c]	—	—	90	—	—	—	—
C65500	Plate, Sheet, Strip and Rolled Bar[e]	Annealed											
		0.070 mm	1.0	385	145	63	—	76	40	—	290	—	—
		0.040 mm	1.0	415	170	60	—	85	62	—	295	110	100
		1/4 Hard	1.0	470	240	30	—	—	75	67	325	—	—
		1/2 Hard	1.0	540	310	17	—	—	87	75	345	—	—
		Hard	1.0	650	400	8	—	—	93	78	395	160	100
		Extra Hard	1.0	715	415	6	—	—	96	80	415	—	—
		Spring	1.0	760	425	4	—	—	97	81	435	—	—
		Hot Rolled	1.0	435	170	—	—	—	—	—	—	—	—
		Hot Rolled and Cold Rolled Finish	1.0	450	205	—	—	—	70	—	—	—	—
	Rod, Bar and Shapes	Soft 0.050 mm	25.0	400	150	60	80	—	60	—	295	130	300
		1/4 Hard	—	415	170	55	—	—	—	—	—	—	—
		1/2 Hard	25.0	540	310	35	65	—	85	—	360	—	—
		Hard	12.0	670	—	—	—	—	—	—	—	230	300
			25.0	635	380	22	62	—	90	—	400	—	—
		Extra Hard	25.0	745	415	13	60	—	95	—	425	—	—
	Rod	Soft	—	400	150	50	—	—	60	—	295	—	—
		Hard	25.0	485	275	25	—	—	—	—	345	—	—
			40.0	450	240	30	—	—	—	—	—	—	—
			75.0	415	195	30	—	—	—	—	—	—	—
C67000	Rod and Bar	Soft	All Sizes	620	345	20	—	—	—	—	—	—	—
		1/2 Hard	All Sizes	770	460	13	—	—	—	—	—	—	—
		Hard	All Sizes	815	485	12	—	—	—	—	—	—	—
	Forgings	Soft	—	620	345	20	—	—	—	—	—	—	—
		1/2 Hard	—	770	460	13	—	—	—	—	—	—	—
		Hard	—	815	485	12	—	—	—	—	—	—	—
C67300	Rod and Bar	As Extruded	All Sizes	485	275	25	—	—	70	—	—	—	—
		Soft	All Sizes	450	240	25	—	—	60	—	—	—	—
		1/2 Hard[g]	25.0	495	360	18	—	—	82	—	—	215	100
			75.0	485	345	22	—	—	80	—	—	215	100
			Over 75.0	485	310	25	—	—	75	—	—	—	—
		1/2 Hard[h]	All Sizes	485	310	25	—	—	75	—	—	—	—
		Hard[g]	25.0	550	415	15	—	—	86	—	—	—	—
			50.0	495	345	19	—	—	84	—	—	—	—

(Table continued on next page)

TABLE 10A—TYPICAL MECHANICAL PROPERTIES OF WROUGHT COPPER AND COPPER ALLOYS (CONTINUED)

Metric (SI) Units

Copper or Copper Alloy UNS No.	Form	Temper	Size Section, mm	Tensile Strength, MPa	Yield Strength, 0.5% Ext Under Load, MPa	Elongation in 50 mm, %	Reduction of Area, %	Hardness			Shear Strength, MPa	Fatigue Strength	
								RF	RB	R30T		MPa	Million Cycles
C67300 continued	Shapes	As Extruded	All Sizes	485	275	25	—	—	70	—	—	—	—
	Forgings	As Forged	—	485	275	25	—	—	70	—	—	—	—
		Forged and Heat Treated	—	515	310	20	—	—	85	—	—	—	—
C67400	Rod and Bar	As Extruded	All Sizes	505	260	16	—	—	80	—	—	—	—
		Extruded and Drawn	25.0	675	425	15	—	—	90	—	—	215	100
			50.0	635	385	18	—	—	88	—	—	—	—
			75.0	605	345	22	—	—	85	—	—	—	—
	Shapes	As Extruded	All Sizes	505	260	16	—	—	80	—	—	—	—
	Forgings	As Forged	—	470	235	18	—	—	75	—	—	—	—
C67500	Rod and Bar	Soft	25.0	450	205	33	—	—	65	—	290	—	—
		1/2 Hard	25.0	530	310	23	—	—	83	—	325	—	—
			50.0	495	290	27	—	—	77	—	305	—	—
			65.0	485	240	30	—	—	—	—	—	—	—
		Hard	25.0	590	415	10	—	—	90	—	330	—	—
			40.0	550	380	12	—	—	—	—	—	—	—
			65.0	515	345	15	—	—	—	—	—	—	—
	Shapes	Soft	—	450	205	33	—	—	65	—	290	—	—
C70600	Condenser Tube Plate	—	25.0	290	125	35	—	—	15	—	—	—	—
	Tube	Annealed	25.0 × 1.6	305	110	42	—	65	15	26	—	—	—
		Light Drawn	25.0 × 1.6	415	395	10	—	100	72	70	—	—	—
C71000	Tube	Annealed	25.0 × 1.6	345	150	45	—	—	35	—	—	—	—
		Annealed 0.035 mm	1.0	305	95	37	—	72	27	34	—	—	—
		0.015 mm	1.0	325	115	38	—	83	47	48	—	—	—
		1/4 Hard	1.0	380	—	—	—	—	59	56	—	—	—
		1/2 Hard	1.0	435	395	7	—	—	71	64	—	—	—
		Hard	1.0	505	—	—	—	—	80	70	—	—	—
		Extra Hard	1.0	540	—	—	—	—	83	72	—	—	—
		Spring	1.0	565	—	—	—	—	85	73	—	—	—
C71500	Condenser Tube Plate	—	25.0	380	140	45	—	—	35	—	—	—	—
	Tube	Annealed	25.0 × 1.6	415	170	45	—	80	45	—	—	—	—
		Drawn and Stress Relieved	25.0 × 1.6	515	380	20	—	—	—	—	—	—	—
	Plate, Sheet, Strip and Rolled Bar[a]	Annealed 0.035 mm	1.0	310	190	45	—	78	34	39	—	—	—
		0.015 mm	1.0	415	150	40	—	84	50	49	—	—	—
		1/4 Hard	1.0	450	345	20	—	—	74	66	—	—	—
		1/2 Hard	1.0	505	470	12	—	—	81	71	—	—	—
		Hard	1.0	565	510	4	—	—	86	74	—	—	—
		Extra Hard	1.0	595	545	2	—	—	88	75	—	—	—
		Spring	1.0	615	565	2	—	—	89	76	—	—	—

(Table continued on next page)

TABLE 10A—TYPICAL MECHANICAL PROPERTIES OF WROUGHT COPPER AND COPPER ALLOYS (CONTINUED)

Metric (SI) Units

Copper or Copper Alloy UNS No.	Form	Temper	Size Section, mm	Tensile Strength, MPa	Yield Strength, 0.5% Ext Under Load, MPa	Elongation in 50 mm, %	Reduction of Area, %	Hardness			Shear Strength, MPa	Fatigue Strength	
								RF	RB	R30T		MPa	Million Cycles
C75200	Plate, Sheet, Strip and Rolled Bar	Annealed											
		0.035 mm	1.0	400	170	40	—	85	40	47	—	—	—
		0.015 mm	1.0	415	205	32	—	90	55	55	—	—	—
		1/4 Hard	1.0	450	345	20	—	—	73	65	—	—	—
		1/2 Hard	1.0	510	425	8	—	—	83	72	—	—	—
		Hard	1.0	535	510	3	—	—	87	75	—	—	—
		Extra Hard	1.0	635	—	—	—	—	91	77	—	—	—
		Spring	1.0	660	—	—	—	—	93	78	—	—	—
	Rod and Bar	Annealed											
		0.035 mm	12.0	385	170	42	—	—	—	—	—	—	—
		0.015 mm	12.0	400	180	35	—	—	—	—	—	—	—
		1/4 Hard	12.0	485	415	20	—	—	78	—	—	—	—
		Hard	6.0[g]	620	515	10	—	—	—	—	—	—	—
			12.0[g]	550	470	12	—	—	—	—	—	—	—
			25.0	515	425	15	—	—	—	—	—	160	300
			Over 25.0[g]	485	380	20	—	—	—	—	—	—	—
C77000	Plate, Sheet, Strip and Rolled Bar	Annealed											
		0.035 mm	1.0	415	185	40	—	90	55	49	—	110	100
		0.015 mm	1.0	—	—	—	—	91	60	56	—	—	—
								RG					
		1/4 Hard	1.0	540	—	—	—	43	79	69	—	—	—
		1/2 Hard	1.0	600	—	—	—	60	87	75	—	—	—
		Hard	1.0	690	585	3	—	72	91	77	—	145	100
		Extra Hard	1.0	745	620	2	—	77	96	80	—	—	—
		Spring	1.0	795	—	2	—	80	99	81	—	—	—
	Rod and Bar	Annealed											
		0.035 mm	12.0	415	185	45	—	—	—	—	—	—	—
		1/4 Hard	12.0[m]	585	—	—	—	—	—	—	—	—	—
		Hard	6.0[g]	690	—	—	—	—	—	—	—	—	—
			12.0[g]	620	—	—	—	—	—	—	—	—	—
			25.0	585	—	—	—	—	—	—	—	—	—
			Over 25.0[g]	550	—	—	—	—	—	—	—	—	—

[a] Rotating beam tests on rod.
[b] Independent rotating beam tests, diameter of test sections 8.89 mm.
[c] Elongation in 4X diameter or thickness of specimen.
[d] Capable of being hardened by further heat treatment.
[e] Plate generally available in only annealed, 1/4 hard, and 1/2 hard.
[f] Elongation in 250 mm.
[g] Rods only.
[h] Bars only.
[i] Shapes only.
[j] Yield strength measured at 0.2% offset.
[k] After heat treatment.
[l] Mill heat treated.
[m] Rounds only.

TABLE 10B—TYPICAL MECHANICAL PROPERTIES OF WROUGHT COPPER AND COPPER ALLOYS

Customary Units

Copper or Copper Alloy UNS No.	Form	Temper	Size Section, in	Tensile Strength, ksi	Yield Strength, 0.5% Ext Under Load, ksi	Elongation in 2 in, %	Reduction of Area, %	Hardness			Shear Strength, ksi	Fatigue Strength	
								RF	RB	R30T		ksi	Million Cycles
C10200 C11000 C11100 C11300 C11400 C11500 C11600 C12000 C12200	Plate, Sheet, Strip, and Rolled Bar	Soft, Anneal	0.04	32	10	45	—	40	—	—	22	—	—
		Deep Drawing Anneal	0.04	34	11	45	—	45	—	—	23	11	100
		Light Cold Rolled	0.04	36	28	30	—	60	10	25	25	—	
		1/2 Hard	0.04	42	36	14	—	84	40	50	26	13	100
		Hard	0.04	50	45	6	—	90	50	57	28	13	100
		Spring	0.04	55	50	4	—	94	60	63	29	14	100
		Extra Spring	0.04	57	53	4	—	95	62	64	29	—	—
		Hot Rolled	0.04	34	10	45	—	45	—	—	23	—	—
		Hot Rolled and Annealed	0.04	33	10	45	—	42	—	—	22	—	—
C10200 C11000 C12000 C12200	Rod, Bar and Shapes	Soft Anneal	1.0	32	10	55	70	40	—	—	22	—	—
		Hard	0.25[g]	55	50	10	—	94	60	—	29	—	—
			1.00[g]	48	44	16	55	87	47	—	27	17	300
			2.00[g]	45	40	20	—	85	45	—	26	—	—
			0.50[h]	48	44	16	—	87	47	—	27	—	—
			0.50[i]	40	32	30	—	—	35	—	28	—	—
C10200 C12000 C12200	Tube	Soft Anneal	1 × 0.06	32	10	45	—	40	—	—	22	11[a]	20
		Light Anneal	1 × 0.06	34	11	45	—	45	—	—	23	—	—
		Light Drawn	1 × 0.06	40	32	25	—	77	35	45	26	14[a]	20
		Drawn	1 × 0.06	40	32	25	—	77	35	45	—	—	—
		Hard Drawn	1 × 0.06	55	50	8	—	95	60	63	29	19[a]	20
			1 × 0.06	55	50	8	—	95	60	63	—	—	—
			1 × 0.06	55	50	8	—	95	60	63	—	—	—
C10200 C11000	Wire	Annealed	0.08	35	—	35[f]	—	—	—		24	—	—
C14500 and C14700	Rod	1/2 Hard	0.25	43	38	20	—	—	38	—	25	—	—
			1.00	42	36	25	—	—	38	—	24	—	—
			2.00	41	35	25	—	—	35	—	24	—	—
		Hard	0.25	53	48	10	—	—	52	—	29	—	—
			1.00	48	42	15	—	—	50	—	27	—	—
C15000	Round Rod	Drawn and Heat Treated	1.00	60	50	12	—	—	67	—	—	28	100
C16200	Round Rod	Drawn	1.00	65	50	25	—	—	70	—	—	—	—
			2.00	60	35	30	—	—	65	—	—	—	—
			3.00	55	25	35	—	—	60	—	—	—	—
	Bar (Square and Rectangular) and Rod (Hexagonal)	Drawn	1.00	65	50	25	—	—	70	—	—	—	—
			Over 1.00	55	35	30	—	—	65	—	—	—	—
	Forging	As Forged	1.00	65	—	25	—	—	60	—	—	—	—
			2.00	55	—	30	—	—	55	—	—	—	—
			Over 2.00	55	—	30	—	—	55	—	—	—	—
C17000	Strip	A Soft[d]	—	69	32[j]	48	—	—	62	56	—	—	—
		1/4 Hard[d]	—	82	70[j]	22	—	—	79	68	—	—	—
		1/2 Hard[d]	—	92	82[j]	15	—	—	92	76	—	—	—
		Hard[d]	—	110	104[j]	5	—	—	99	81	—	—	—
									RC	R30N			
		AT (3 h at 600°F)[k]	—	165	145[j]	3	—	—	36	56	—	38	100
		1/4 HT (2 h at 600°F)[k]	—	172	150[j]	2	—	—	37	57	—	40	100
		1/2 HT (2 h at 600°F)[k]	—	182	160[j]	1	—	—	38	58	—	42	100
		HT (2 h at 600°F)[k]	—	190	170[j]	1	—	—	40	60	—	43	100
		AM[l]	—	108	82[j]	20	—	—	20	40	—	—	—
		1/4 HM[l]	—	118	92[j]	17	—	—	24	44	—	—	—

(Table continued on next page)

TABLE 10B—TYPICAL MECHANICAL PROPERTIES OF WROUGHT COPPER AND COPPER ALLOYS (CONTINUED)

Customary Units

Copper or Copper Alloy UNS No.	Form	Temper	Size Section, in	Tensile Strength, ksi	Yield Strength, 0.5% Ext Under Load, ksi	Elongation in 2 in, %	Reduction of Area, %	Hardness			Shear Strength, ksi	Fatigue Strength	
								RF	RB	R30T		ksi	Million Cycles
C17000 continued		1/2 HM[l]	—	123	105[j]	14	—	—	28	48	—	—	—
		HM[l]	—	143	122[j]	11	—	—	32	52	—	—	—
		XHM[l]	—	168	148[j]	4	—	—	34	54	—	—	—
C17200	Strip	A (Soft)[d]	—	69	32[j]	48	—	—	62	56	—	—	—
		1/4 Hard[d]	—	82	70[j]	22	—	—	79	68	—	—	—
		1/2 Hard[d]	—	92	82[j]	15	—	—	92	76	—	—	—
		Hard[d]	—	110	104[j]	5	—	—	99	81	—	—	—
									RC	R30N			
		AT (3 h at 600°F)[k]	—	178	155[j]	6	—	—	38	58	—	38	100
		1/4 H (2 h at 600°F)[k]	—	188	165[j]	4	—	—	40	60	—	40	100
		1/2 H (2 h at 600°F)[k]	—	198	175[j]	3	—	—	42	62	—	43	100
		HT (2 h at 600°F)[k]	—	202	180[j]	2	—	—	43	63	—	44	100
									RB	R30T			
	Rod and Bar	A (Soft)[d]	—	72	25[j]	48	—	—	62	—	—	—	—
		1/2 Hard[d]	Under 1.00	110	90[j]	15	—	—	96	—	—	—	—
		1/2 Hard[d]	Over 1.00	100	90[j]	15	—	—	96	—	—	—	—
									RC				
		AT (3 h at 600°F)[k]	—	178	160[j]	6	—	—	38	—	—	50	100
		1/2 HT (2 h at 600°F)[k]	Under 1.00	200	182[j]	4	—	—	42	—	—	51	100
		1/2 HT (2 h at 600°F)[k]	Over 1.00	192	175[j]	4	—	—	42	—	—	51	100
									RB				
C17500	Strip and Plate	A (Soft)[d]	—	45	25[j]	28	—	—	32	37	—	—	—
		1/2 Hard[d]	—	68	56[j]	8	—	—	70	64	—	—	—
		Hard[d]	—	78	70[j]	5	—	—	83	72	—	—	—
		AT (3 h at 900°F)[k]	—	110	90[j]	12	—	—	96	80	—	33	100
		1/2 HT (2 h at 900°F)[k]	—	120	108[j]	8	—	—	98	81	—	35	100
		HT (2 h at 900°F)[k]	—	120	108[j]	8	—	—	98	81	—	35	100
C17500 C17600	Rod, Bar Shapes and Tubing	A (Soft)[d]	—	45	25[j]	28	—	—	35	—	—	—	—
		1/2 Hard[d]	—	72	65[j]	12	—	—	68	—	—	—	—
		AT (3 h at 900°F)[k]	—	110	90[j]	18	—	—	96	—	—	40	100
		1/2 HT (2 h at 900°F)[k]	—	120	110[j]	14	—	—	98	—	—	40	100
C18400	Round Rod	Drawn	1.00	70	—	20	—	—	80	—	—	—	—
			2.00	65	—	20	—	—	75	—	—	—	—
			3.00	60	—	20	—	—	70	—	—	—	—
	Rod (Hexagonal) and Bar	Drawn	1.00	70	—	20	—	—	75	—	—	—	—
			Over 1.00	60	—	20	—	—	70	—	—	—	—
	Forgings	As Forged	1.00	70	—	20	—	—	80	—	—	—	—
			2.00	60	—	20	—	—	75	—	—	—	—
			Over 2.00	60	—	20	—	—	70	—	—	—	—
C18700	Rod	Hard	0.25	60	55	10	—	—	55	—	32	—	—
			0.50	55	50	11	—	—	50	—	30	—	—
			0.75	53	48	12	—	—	50	—	29	—	—
			1.00	51	46	14	—	—	50	—	28	—	—
C19200	Tube	A (Soft)	1.88 × 0.09	37	12	40	—	—	—	—	—	—	—
		Light Drawn	1.88 × 0.09	42	31	3	—	—	—	—	—	—	—
C21000	Plate, Sheet, Strip and Rolled Bar[e]	Annealed											
		0.050 mm	0.04	34	10	45	—	46	—	—	27	—	—
		0.035 mm	0.04	35	11	45	—	52	—	4	28	—	—
		0.025 mm	0.04	36	12	43	—	56	—	9	29	—	—
		0.015 mm	0.04	38	14	42	—	60	—	15	30	—	—
		1/4 Hard	0.04	42	32	25	—	—	38	44	32	—	—

(Table continued on next page)

TABLE 10B—TYPICAL MECHANICAL PROPERTIES OF WROUGHT COPPER AND COPPER ALLOYS (CONTINUED)

Customary Units

Copper or Copper Alloy UNS No.	Form	Temper	Size Section, in	Tensile Strength, ksi	Yield Strength, 0.5% Ext Under Load, ksi	Elongation in 2 in, %	Reduction of Area, %	Hardness			Shear Strength, ksi	Fatigue Strength	
								RF	RB	R30T		ksi	Million Cycles
C21000 continued		1/2 Hard	0.04	48	40	12	—	—	52	54	34	—	—
		3/4 Hard	0.04	51	45	8	—	—	59	58	35	—	—
		Hard	0.04	56	50	5	—	—	64	60	37	—	—
		Extra Hard	0.04	61	55	4	—	—	70	64	39	—	—
		Springs	0.04	64	58	4	—	—	73	66	40	—	—
		Extra Spring	0.04	65	—	—	—	—	74	68	—	—	—
C22000	Plate, Sheet Strip and Rolled Bar[a]	Annealed 0.050 mm 0.035 mm 0.025 mm 0.015 mm	 0.04 0.04 0.04 0.04	 37 38 39 41	 10 12 14 15	 45 45 44 42	 — — — —	 53 57 60 65	 — — — —	 6 12 16 26	 28 30 31 32	 — — — —	 — — — —
		1/4 Hard	0.04	45	35	25	—	—	42	44	33	—	—
		1/2 Hard	0.04	52	45	11	—	—	58	56	35	—	—
		3/4 Hard	0.04	57	50	8	—	—	67	63	36	—	—
		Hard	0.04	61	54	5	—	—	70	63	38	—	—
		Extra Hard	0.04	67	58	4	—	—	75	67	40	—	—
		Spring	0.04	72	62	3	—	—	78	69	42	21	15
		Extra Spring	0.04	76	—	—	—	—	82	73	—	—	—
	Tube	Soft Anneal	1 × 0.06	38	10	52	—	55	—	10	—	—	—
		Light Anneal	1 × 0.06	41	15	42	—	65	—	35	—	—	—
		Drawn (General Purpose)	1 × 0.06	45	35	25	—	—	50	50	—	—	—
		Hard Drawn	1 × 0.06	60	53	6	—	—	69	62	—	—	—
C23000	Sheet and Strip	Annealed 0.070 mm 0.050 mm 0.035 mm 0.025 mm 0.015 mm	 0.04 0.04 0.04 0.04 0.04	 39 40 41 43 45	 10 12 14 16 18	 48 47 46 44 42	 — — — — —	 56 59 63 66 71	 — — — — —	 10 14 22 28 38	 — — — — —	 — — — — —	 — — — — —
		1/4 Hard	0.04	50	39	25	—	—	55	54	—	—	—
		1/2 Hard	0.04	57	49	12	—	—	65	60	—	—	—
		3/4 Hard	0.04	62	52	8	—	—	73	67	—	—	—
		Hard	0.04	70	57	5	—	—	77	68	—	—	—
		Extra Hard	0.04	78	61	4	—	—	83	72	44	—	—
		Spring	0.04	84	63	3	—	—	86	74	46	—	—
		Extra Spring	0.04	86	—	—	—	—	88	77	—	—	—
	Tube	Soft Anneal	1 × 0.06	40	12	55	—	60	—	15	—	—	—
		Light Anneal	1 × 0.06	44	18	45	—	71	—	38	—	—	—
		Light Drawn	1 × 0.06	50	40	30	—	—	55	54	—	—	—
		Drawn (General Purpose)	1 × 0.06	56	46	25	—	—	62	60	—	—	—
		Hard Drawn	1 × 0.06	70	58	8	—	—	77	68	—	—	—

(Table continued on next page)

TABLE 10B—TYPICAL MECHANICAL PROPERTIES OF WROUGHT COPPER AND COPPER ALLOYS (CONTINUED)

Customary Units

Copper or Copper Alloy UNS No.	Form	Temper	Size Section, in	Tensile Strength, ksi	Yield Strength, 0.5% Ext Under Load, ksi	Elongation in 2 in, %	Reduction of Area, %	Hardness			Shear Strength, ksi	Fatigue Strength	
								RF	RB	R30T		ksi	Million Cycles
C24000	Sheet and Strip	Annealed											
		0.070 mm	0.04	42	12	52	—	57	—	8	—	—	—
		0.050 mm	0.04	44	14	50	—	61	—	16	32	—	—
		0.035 mm	0.04	46	15	48	—	66	—	28	—	—	—
		0.025 mm	0.04	48	17	47	—	69	—	32	—	—	—
		0.015 mm	0.04	50	20	46	—	75	—	42	33	—	—
		1/4 Hard	0.04	53	40	30	—	—	55	54	36	—	—
		1/2 Hard	0.04	61	50	18	—	—	70	64	39	—	—
		3/4 Hard	0.04	66	54	12	—	—	76	68	41	—	—
		Hard	0.04	74	59	7	—	—	82	71	43	—	—
		Extra Hard	0.04	83	62	5	—	—	87	75	45	—	—
		Spring	0.04	91	65	3	—	—	91	77	48	24	20
		Extra Spring	0.04	93	—	—	—	—	92	78	—	—	—
C26000	Plate, Sheet, Strip, Rolled Bar and Wire[a]	Annealed											
		0.120 mm	0.04	44	11	66	—	54	—	11	—	13	100
		0.070 mm	0.04	46	14	65	—	58	—	15	32	13	100
		0.050 mm	0.04	47	15	62	—	64	—	26	—	—	—
		0.035 mm	0.04	49	17	57	—	68	—	31	34	14	100
		0.025 mm	0.04	51	19	55	—	72	—	36	—	—	—
		0.015 mm	0.04	53	22	54	—	78	—	43	35	15	100
		1/4 Hard	0.04	54	40	43	—	—	55	54	36	—	—
		1/2 Hard	0.04	62	52	23	—	—	70	65	40	18	100
		3/4 Hard	0.04	69	57	15	—	—	79	70	42	—	—
		Hard	0.04	76	63	8	—	—	82	73	44	21	100
		Extra Hard	0.04	86	65	5	—	—	88	76	46	—	—
		Spring	0.04	94	65	3	—	—	91	77	48	23	100
		Extra Spring	0.04	99	65	3	—	—	93	78	—	—	—
	Tube	Soft Anneal	1 × 0.06	42	15	65	—	64	—	26	—	—	—
		Light Anneal	1 × 0.06	57	20	55	—	75	—	40	—	—	—
		Hard Drawn	1 × 0.06	78	64	8	—	—	82	73	—	—	—
C26800	Plate, Sheet, Strip and Rolled Bar[a]	Annealed											
		0.120 mm	0.04	—	—	—	—	56	—	5	—	—	—
		0.070 mm	0.04	46	14	65	—	58	—	15	32	12	100
		0.050 mm	0.04	47	15	62	—	64	—	26	33	15	100
		0.035 mm	0.04	49	17	57	—	68	—	31	34	—	—
		0.025 mm	0.04	51	19	55	—	72	—	36	35	—	—
		0.015 mm	0.04	53	22	54	—	78	—	43	35	—	—
		1/4 Hard	0.04	54	40	43	—	—	55	54	35	—	—
		1/2 Hard	0.04	61	50	23	—	—	70	65	40	—	—
		3/4 Hard	0.04	67	55	15	—	—	77	69	41	—	—
		Hard	0.04	74	60	8	—	—	80	70	43	14	100
		Extra Hard	0.04	85	62	5	—	—	87	74	45	—	—
		Spring	0.04	91	62	3	—	—	90	76	47	20	100
		Extra Spring	0.04	95	—	—	—	—	92	78	—	20	100

(Table continued on next page)

TABLE 10B—TYPICAL MECHANICAL PROPERTIES OF WROUGHT COPPER AND COPPER ALLOYS (CONTINUED)

Customary Units

Copper or Copper Alloy UNS No.	Form	Temper	Size Section, in	Tensile Strength, ksi	Yield Strength, 0.5% Ext Under Load, ksi	Elongation in 2 in, %	Reduction of Area, %	Hardness RF	Hardness RB	Hardness R30T	Shear Strength, ksi	Fatigue Strength ksi	Fatigue Strength Million Cycles
C27000	Wire	Annealed 0.035 mm	0.08	50	—	60	—	—	—	—	34	—	—
		1/8 Hard	0.08	58	—	35	—	—	—	—	38	—	—
		1/4 Hard	0.08	70	—	20	—	—	—	—	42	22[a]	300
		1/2 Hard	0.08	88	—	15	—	—	—	—	46	—	—
		3/4 Hard	0.08	100	—	12	—	—	—	—	50	—	—
		Hard	0.08	110	—	8	—	—	—	—	55	—	—
		Extra Hard	0.08	120	—	4	—	—	—	—	58	—	—
		Spring	0.08	128	—	3	—	—	—	—	60	—	—
C33000 and C33100	Tube	Soft Anneal	1 × 0.06	47	15	60	—	64	—	26	—	—	—
		Light Anneal	1 × 0.06	52	20	50	—	75	—	37	—	—	—
		Hard Drawn	1 × 0.06	75	60	7	—	—	80	69	—	—	—
C34200 C35000	Plate, Sheet, Strip and Rolled Bar	Annealed 0.035 mm	0.04	49	17	52	—	68	—	31	34	—	—
		1/4 Hard	0.04	54	40	38	—	—	55	54	36	—	—
		1/2 Hard	0.04	61	50	20	—	—	70	65	40	—	—
		Hard	0.04	74	60	7	—	—	80	69	43	—	—
		Extra Hard	0.04	85	62	5	—	—	87	74	45	—	—
C34500 C35000	Rod	1/2 Hard	0.50	57	30	20	—	—	68	—	36	—	—
			1.00	55	30	25	—	—	68	—	35	—	—
			2.00	50	25	30	—	—	65	—	32	—	—
C36000	Rod	Soft	1.00	49	18	53	58	68	—	—	30	—	—
		1/2 Hard	0.25	68	52	18	48	—	80	—	38	—	—
			1.00	58	45	25	50	—	78	—	34	—	—
			2.00	55	44	32	52	—	75	—	32	20[b] 14[b]	100 300
		Hard	0.12	85	50	—	—	—	—	—	—	—	—
			0.25	75	40	5[c]	—	—	—	—	—	—	—
			0.75	70	35	10[c]	—	—	—	—	—	—	—
	Flat Products	Soft	1 × 6	48	20	25[c]	—	—	—	—	30	—	—
			Over 1 × 6	45	18	30[c]	—	—	—	—	28	—	—
		1/2 Hard	0.25 × 1	56	45	20[c]	—	—	62	—	33	—	—
			0.50 × 6	50	30	20[c]	—	—	—	—	30	—	—
			2.00 × 2	50	30	25[c]	—	—	—	—	30	—	—
			2.00 × 6	45	25	25[c]	—	—	—	—	27	—	—
			Over 2.00 × 4	45	25	25[c]	—	—	—	—	27	—	—
C37700	Die Forgings	As Extruded	0.04	52	20	45[c]	65	78	—	—	—	—	—
		As Forged	2 lbs	58	23	40[c]	—	—	—	—	—	—	—
C46400 C46500 C46600 C46700	Rod and Bar	Soft	0.25	58	27	45	60	—	56	—	40	—	—
			1.00	57	25	47	60	—	56	—	40	—	—
			2.00	56	25	47	60	—	55	—	40	—	—
			Over 2.00	54	22	—	—	—	—	—	—	—	—
		1/2 Hard or Light Annealed	0.25	63	30	40	55	—	60	—	42	—	—
			1.00	63	30	40	55	—	60	—	42	—	—
			2.00	62	28	43	55	—	60	—	42	—	—
			3.00	57	26	—	—	—	—	—	—	—	—
			Over 3.00	57	24	—	—	—	—	—	—	—	—
		Hard	0.25	80	57	20	45	—	85	—	45	—	—
			1.00	75	53	20	45	—	82	—	44	—	—
			2.00	67	40	35	50	—	75	—	43	—	—
	Shapes	As Extruded	—	58	25	40	—	—	—	—	40	—	—
C51000	Sheet and Strip	Annealed 0.050 mm	0.04	47	19	64	—	73	26	—	36	—	—
		0.035 mm	0.04	49	20	58	—	75	28	—	37	—	—
		0.025 mm	0.04	50	21	52	—	77	30	—	38	—	—
		0.015 mm	0.04	53	22	50	—	79	34	—	40	—	—
		1/2 Hard	0.04	68	55	28	—	—	78	69	49	—	—

(Table continued on next page)

TABLE 10B—TYPICAL MECHANICAL PROPERTIES OF WROUGHT COPPER AND COPPER ALLOYS (CONTINUED)

Customary Units

Copper or Copper Alloy UNS No.	Form	Temper	Size Section, in	Tensile Strength, ksi	Yield Strength, 0.5% Ext Under Load, ksi	Elongation in 2 in, %	Reduction of Area, %	Hardness			Shear Strength, ksi	Fatigue Strength	
								RF	RB	R30T		ksi	Million Cycles
C51000 continued		Hard	0.04	81	75	10	—	—	87	75	—	25	100
		Extra Hard	0.04	92	80	6	—	—	93	78	—	—	—
		Spring	0.04	100	80	4	—	—	95	79	—	22	100
		Extra Spring	0.04	107	80	3	—	—	97	80	—	—	—
	Rod	Hard	0.50 1.00	75 70	65 58	25 25	— —	— —	80 78	— —	54 50	— 29	— 300
	Wire	Soft, 0.035 mm	0.08	50	20	58	—	—	38	—	—	—	—
		1/4 Hard 1/2 Hard Hard	0.08 0.08 0.08	68 85 110	60 80 —	24 8 5	— — —	— — —	49 — —	— — —	— — —	— — 27	— — 100
		Extra Hard Spring	0.08 0.08	130 140	— —	3 2	— —	— —	— —	— —	— —	30 —	100 —
C51100 C54400	Sheet and Strip	Annealed 0.050 mm 0.035 mm 0.025 mm 0.015 mm	 0.04 0.04 0.04 0.04	 46 48 50 51	 — — — —	 48 47 46 46	 — — — —	 70 73 75 76	 — — — —	 — — — —	 — — — —	 — — — —	 — — — —
		1/2 Hard	0.04	62	54	19	—	—	70	65	—	—	—
		Hard	0.04	80	74	7	—	—	86	74	—	—	—
		Extra Hard	0.04	92	—	4	—	—	91	78	—	—	—
		Spring	0.04	98	80	3	—	—	93	79	—	—	—
		Extra Spring	0.04	103	80	2	—	—	95	80	—	—	—
C52100	Sheet and Strip	Soft	0.04	60	24	63	—	82	50	—	—	—	—
		1/2 Hard	0.04	76	55	32	—	—	84	73	51	—	—
		Hard	0.04	93	72	10	—	—	93	78	—	22	100
		Extra Hard	0.04	106	80	4	—	—	96	80	—	—	—
		Spring	0.04	112	—	3	—	—	98	81	—	—	—
		Extra Spring	0.04	120	—	2	—	—	100	82	—	—	—
C52400	Sheet and Strip	Soft, 0.035 mm	0.04	66	28	68	—	—	55	—	—	—	—
		1/2 Hard	0.04	83	—	32	—	—	92	—	—	—	—
		Hard	0.04	100	—	13	—	—	97	—	—	—	—
		Extra Hard	0.04	115	—	7	—	—	100	—	—	—	—
		Spring	0.04	122	—	4	—	—	101	—	—	—	—
		Extra Spring	0.04	128	—	3	—	—	103	—	—	—	—
C54400	Sheet and Strip	See C51100											
	Rod	Hard	0.50 1.00	75 68	63 57	15 20	— —	— —	83 80	— —	— —	— —	— —
	Flat Products	Hard	0.38 0.75	60 55	45 35	20 25	— —	— —	70 —	— —	— —	— —	— —
C60800	Tube	Annealed	1 × 0.06	60	27	—	—	77	—	—	—	—	—

(Table continued on next page)

TABLE 10B—TYPICAL MECHANICAL PROPERTIES OF WROUGHT COPPER AND COPPER ALLOYS (CONTINUED)

Customary Units

Copper or Copper Alloy UNS No.	Form	Temper	Size Section, in	Tensile Strength, ksi	Yield Strength, 0.5% Ext Under Load, ksi	Elongation in 2 in, %	Reduction of Area, %	Hardness			Shear Strength, ksi	Fatigue Strength	
								RF	RB	R30T		ksi	Million Cycles
C61300	Plate, Sheet, Strip and Rolled Bar	Soft	0.12	82	45	40	35	—	84	—	45	30	100
			0.31	80	40	40	35	—	83	—	42	28	100
			0.50	78	35	42	40	—	82	—	40	26	100
			1.00	76	33	45	40	—	81	—	40	25	100
	Rod and Bar	—	0.50	85	50	35	55	—	91	—	48	—	—
			1.00	82	48	35	55	—	90	—	45	—	—
			2.00	80	40	35	60	—	88	—	40	—	—
C61400	Plate, Sheet, Strip and Rolled Bar	Soft	0.12	82	45	40	35	—	84	—	45	30	100
			0.31	80	40	40	35	—	83	—	42	28	100
			0.50	78	35	42	40	—	82	—	40	26	100
			1.00	76	33	45	40	—	81	—	40	25	100
		Hard	0.12	89	60	32	—	—	87	—	50	—	—
			0.31	85	58	35	—	—	86	—	48	—	—
			0.50	80	54	38	—	—	85	—	40	—	—
			1.00	78	45	40	—	—	84	—	38	—	—
	Rod and Bar	—	0.50	85	45	35	55	—	91	—	48	—	—
			1.00	82	40	35	55	—	90	—	45	—	—
			2.00	80	35	35	60	—	88	—	40	—	—
C61800	Rod	1/2 Hard	1.00	85	42	23[c]	—	—	88	—	47	28	100
			2.00	82	39	25[c]	—	—	88	—	45	28	100
			3.00	80	39	28[c]	—	—	88	—	43	26	100
									BHN(1000kg)				
C62300	Rod and Bar	Drawn	0.50	95	60	15[c]	—		180		—	—	—
			1.00	92	55	20[c]	—		—		—	—	—
			3.00	90	45	25[c]	—		—		—	—	—
	Shapes	—	—	85	33	25[c]	—		170		—	—	—
	Forgings	As Forged	Thru 1.5	85	33	25[c]	—		140		—	—	—
			Over 1.5	82	31	30[c]	—		—		—	—	—
									BHN(3000 kg)				
C62400	Rod	As Extruded	All Sizes	95	50	12[c]	—		200		—	—	—
	Forgings	As Forged	—	95	50	12[c]	—		200		—	—	—
		Hardened and H_2O Quenched	—	—	—	—	—		265		—	—	—
		Hardened, H_2O Quenched and Tempered	—	100	—	12[c]	—		210		—	—	—
C63000	Rod and Bar	Annealed	1.00	105	60	12[c]	—	—	100		—	—	—
			2.00	95	50	15[c]	—	—	—		—	—	—
			4.00	90	45	17[c]	—	—	—		—	—	—
	Shapes	As Extruded	All Sizes	90	45	17[c]	—	—	—	—	—	—	—
C64200	Rod and Bar	Drawn	0.75	102	68	22[c]	—	—	94	—	59	50	100
			1.50	93	60	26[c]	—	—	90	—	—	—	—
C65500	Plate, Sheet, Strip and Rolled Bar[e]	Annealed 0.070 mm	0.04	56	21	63	—	76	40	—	42	—	—
		0.040 mm	0.04	60	25	60	—	85	62	—	43	16	100
		1/4 Hard	0.04	68	35	30	—	—	75	67	47	—	—
		1/2 Hard	0.04	78	45	17	—	—	87	75	50	—	—
		Hard	0.04	94	58	8	—	—	93	78	57	23	100
		Extra Hard	0.04	104	60	6	—	—	96	80	60	—	—
		Spring	0.04	110	62	4	—	—	97	81	63	—	—
		Hot Rolled	0.04	63	25	—	—	—	—	—	—	—	—
		Hot Rolled and Cold Rolled Finish	0.04	65	30	—	—	—	70	—	—	—	—

(Table continued on next page)

TABLE 10B—TYPICAL MECHANICAL PROPERTIES OF WROUGHT COPPER AND COPPER ALLOYS (CONTINUED)

Customary Units													
Copper or Copper Alloy UNS No.	Form	Temper	Size Section, in	Tensile Strength, ksi	Yield Strength, 0.5% Ext Under Load, ksi	Elongation in 2 in, %	Reduction of Area, %	Hardness			Shear Strength, ksi	Fatigue Strength	
								RF	RB	R30T		ksi	Million Cycles
C65500 continued	Rod, Bar and Shapes	Soft, 0.050 mm	1.00	58	22	60	80	—	60	—	43	19	300
		1/4 Hard	—	60	25	55	—	—	—	—	—	—	—
		1/2 Hard	1.00	78	45	35	65	—	85	—	52	—	—
		Hard	0.50	97	—	—	—	—	—	—	—	34	300
			1.00	92	55	22	62	—	90	—	58	—	—
		Extra Hard	1.00	108	60	13	60	—	95	—	62	—	—
	Rod	Soft	—	58	22	50	—	—	60	—	43	—	—
		Hard	1.00	70	40	25	—	—	—	—	50	—	—
			1.50	65	35	30	—	—	—	—	—	—	—
			3.00	60	28	30	—	—	—	—	—	—	—
C67000	Rod and Bar	Soft	All Sizes	90	50	20	—	—	—	—	—	—	—
		1/2 Hard	All Sizes	112	67	13	—	—	—	—	—	—	—
		Hard	All Sizes	118	70	12	—	—	—	—	—	—	—
	Forgings	Soft	—	90	50	20	—	—	—	—	—	—	—
		1/2 Hard	—	112	67	13	—	—	—	—	—	—	—
		Hard	—	118	70	12	—	—	—	—	—	—	—
C67300	Rod and Bar	As Extruded	All Sizes	70	40	25	—	—	70	—	—	—	—
		Soft	All Sizes	65	35	25	—	—	60	—	—	—	—
		1/2 Hard[g]	1.00	72	52	18	—	—	82	—	—	31	100
			3.00	70	50	22	—	—	80	—	—	31	100
			Over 3.00	70	45	25	—	—	75	—	—	—	—
		1/2 Hard[h]	All Sizes	70	45	25	—	—	75	—	—	—	—
		Hard[g]	1.00	80	60	15	—	—	86	—	—	—	—
			2.00	72	50	19	—	—	84	—	—	—	—
	Shapes	As Extruded	All Sizes	70	40	25	—	—	70	—	—	—	—
	Forgings	As Forged	—	70	40	25	—	—	70	—	—	—	—
		Forged and Heat Treated	—	75	45	20	—	—	85	—	—	—	—
C67400	Rod and Bar	As Extruded	All Sizes	73	38	16	—	—	80	—	—	—	—
		Extruded and Drawn	1.00	98	62	15	—	—	90	—	—	31	100
			2.00	92	56	18	—	—	88	—	—	—	—
			3.00	88	50	22	—	—	85	—	—	—	—
	Shapes	As Extruded	All Sizes	73	38	16	—	—	80	—	—	—	—
	Forgings	As Forged	—	68	34	18	—	—	75	—	—	—	—
C67500	Rod and Bar	Soft	1.00	65	30	33	—	—	65	—	42	—	—
		1/2 Hard	1.00	77	45	23	—	—	83	—	47	—	—
			2.00	72	42	27	—	—	77	—	44	—	—
			2.50	70	35	30	—	—	—	—	—	—	—
		Hard	1.00	84	60	10	—	—	90	—	48	—	—
			1.50	80	55	12	—	—	—	—	—	—	—
			2.50	75	50	15	—	—	—	—	—	—	—
	Shapes	Soft	—	65	30	33	—	—	65	—	42	—	—
C70600	Condenser Tube Plate	—	1.00	42	18	35	—	—	15	—	—	—	—
	Tube	Annealed	1 × 0.06	44	16	42	—	65	15	26	—	—	—
		Light Drawn	1 × 0.06	60	57	10	—	110	72	70	—	—	—

(Table continued on next page)

TABLE 10B—TYPICAL MECHANICAL PROPERTIES OF WROUGHT COPPER AND COPPER ALLOYS (CONTINUED)

Customary Units

Copper or Copper Alloy UNS No.	Form	Temper	Size Section, in	Tensile Strength, ksi	Yield Strength, 0.5% Ext Under Load, ksi	Elongation in 2 in, %	Reduction of Area, %	Hardness RF	Hardness RB	Hardness R30T	Shear Strength, ksi	Fatigue Strength ksi	Fatigue Strength Million Cycles
C71000	Tube	Annealed	1 × 0.06	50	22	45	—	—	35		—	—	—
	Plate, Sheet, Strip and Rolled Bar[e]	Annealed											
		0.035 mm	0.04	44	14	37	—	72	27	34	—	—	—
		0.015 mm	0.04	47	17	38	—	83	47	48	—	—	—
		1/4 Hard	0.04	55	—	—	—	—	59	56	—	—	—
		1/2 Hard	0.04	63	57	7	—	—	71	64	—	—	—
		Hard	0.04	73	—	—	—	—	80	70	—	—	—
		Extra Hard	0.04	78	—	—	—	—	83	72	—	—	—
		Spring	0.04	82	—	—			85	73			
C71500	Condenser Tube Plate	—	1.00	55	20	45	—	—	35				
	Tube	Annealed	1 × 0.06	60	25	45	—	80	45	—	—	—	—
		Drawn and Stress Relieved	1 × 0.06	75	55	20	—	—	—	—	—	—	—
	Plate, Sheet, Strip and Rolled Bar[e]	Annealed											
		0.035 mm	0.04	54	20	45	—	78	34	39	—	—	—
		0.015 mm	0.04	60	22	40		84	50	49			
		1/4 Hard	0.04	65	50	20	—	—	74	66	—	—	—
		1/2 Hard	0.04	73	68	12	—	—	81	71	—	—	—
		Hard	0.04	82	74	4	—	—	86	74	—	—	—
		Extra Hard	0.04	86	79	2	—	—	88	75	—	—	—
	Plate, Sheet, Strip and Rolled Bar[e]	Spring	0.04	89	82	2	—	—	89	76	—	—	—
C75200	Plate, Sheet, Strip and Rolled Bar	Annealed											
		0.035 mm	0.04	58	25	40		85	40	47	—	—	—
		0.015 mm	0.04	60	30	32		90	55	55			
		1/4 Hard	0.04	65	50	20	—	—	73	65	—	—	—
		1/2 Hard	0.04	74	62	8	—	—	83	72	—	—	—
		Hard	0.04	85	74	3	—	—	87	75	—	—	—
		Extra Hard	0.04	92	—	—	—	—	91	77	—	—	—
		Spring	0.04	96	—	—			93	78	—	—	—
	Rod and Bar	Annealed											
		0.035 mm	0.50	56	25	42	—	—	—	—	—	—	—
		0.015 mm	0.50	58	26	35	—	—	—	—	—	—	—
		1/4 Hard	0.50	70	60	20		78					
		Hard	0.25[g]	90	75	10	—	—	—	—	—	—	—
			0.50[g]	80	68	12	—	—	—	—	—	—	—
			1.00	75	62	15	—	—	—	—	—	23	300
			Over 1.00[g]	70	55	20	—	—	—	—	—	—	—
C77000	Plate, Sheet, Strip and Rolled Bar	Annealed											
		0.035 mm	0.04	60	27	40	—	90	55	49	—	16	100
		0.015 mm	0.04	—	—	—	—	91	60	56	—	—	—
								RG					
		1/4 Hard	0.04	78	—	—	—	43	79	69	—	—	—
		1/2 Hard	0.04	87	—	—	—	60	87	75	—	—	—
		Hard	0.04	100	85	3	—	72	91	77	—	21	100
		Extra Hard	0.04	108	90	2	—	77	96	80	—	—	—
		Spring	0.04	115	—	2	—	80	99	81	—	—	—

(Table continued on next page)

TABLE 10B—TYPICAL MECHANICAL PROPERTIES OF WROUGHT COPPER AND COPPER ALLOYS (CONTINUED)

Customary Units

Copper or Copper Alloy UNS No.	Form	Temper	Size Section, in	Tensile Strength, ksi	Yield Strength, 0.5% Ext Under Load, ksi	Elongation in 2 in, %	Reduction of Area, %	Hardness RF	Hardness RB	Hardness R30T	Shear Strength, ksi	Fatigue Strength ksi	Fatigue Strength Million Cycles
C77000 continued	Rod and Bar	Annealed 0.035 mm	0.50	60	27	45	—	—	—	—	—	—	—
		1/4 Hard	0.50[m]	85	—	—	—	—	—	—	—	—	—
		Hard	0.25[g]	100	—	—	—	—	—	—	—	—	—
			0.50[g]	90	—	—	—	—	—	—	—	—	—
			1.00[g]	85	—	—	—	—	—	—	—	—	—
			Over 1.00[g]	80	—	—	—	—	—	—	—	—	—

[a] Rotating beam tests on rod.
[b] Independent rotating beam tests, diameter of test sections 0.350 in.
[c] Elongation in 4X diameter or thickness of specimen.
[d] Capable of being hardened by further heat treatment.
[e] Plate generally available in only annealed, 1/4 hard, and 1/2 hard.
[f] Elongation in 10 in.
[g] Rods only.
[h] Bars only.
[i] Shapes only.
[j] Yield strength measured at 0.2% offset.
[k] After heat treatment.
[l] Mill heat treated.
[m] Round only.

4. Part II—Cast Copper Alloys

4.1 General—The cast copper base alloys consist of a relatively few families or alloy types which have become standard through the years because of their excellent attributes for particular applications. Within each alloy type, many commercial modifications exist. Those most commonly use by the automotive and related industries are shown in Table 11 with the general characteristics and typical uses of each. Table 12 lists the typical physical properties of these same alloys.

4.2 Types of Cast Alloys

4.2.1 **Tin bronzes** are predominantly copper plus tin. Variations containing up to 4% of zinc and 2% lead have been used for pumps handling sea water, some acids, salt solution, and oils. Excellent worm gears are made from tin bronze containing 8% or more tin. Up to 2% nickel may be added for other types of gears. An alloy of 88 Cu, 5 Sn, 5 Ni, 2 Z is heat treatable to provide higher strength. (Typical properties: 585 MPa [85 ksi] tensile strength, 415 MPa [60 ksi] yield strength, 8% elongation and Brinell 185.)

4.2.2 **High lead tin bronzes** are produced by adding lead to amount equal to or more than the tin content. These are used for bearing applications where a combination of wear resistance and good anti-friction properties are desired.

4.2.3 **Lead red brasses** are alloys of copper, tin, lead, and zinc. They are the most widely used of all cast copper alloys and are satisfactory for a great many applications, including water pumps, small gears, fittings and valve bodies.

4.2.4 **Aluminum bronzes** (alloys of copper, aluminum, iron, and, in some modifications, nickel) are used extensively for structural applications. Their excellent resistance to corrosion leads to their use in sulfide bearing environments and sea water. Some aluminum bronzes may be heat treated to quite high strength. (Typical properties: 725 MPa [105 ksi] tensile strength, 415 MPa [60 ksi] yield strength, 5% elongation and Brinell 220).

4.2.5 **Leaded yellow brasses**, containing copper, lead, and more than 20% zinc, are inexpensive free machining general purpose alloys.

4.2.6 **High tensile brasses**, also known as manganese bronzes, are alloys of copper, aluminum, manganese, iron, and zinc. They are higher in strength than most of the cast copper alloys. In addition, they are readily cast and possess fairly good corrosion resistance.

4.2.7 **Special purpose alloys** with exceptional corrosion resistance include silicon bronze, silicon brass and copper-nickel.

4.3 Effect of Alloying Elements and Impurities

4.3.1 ZINC—Added to copper as a predominating alloying constituent in amounts of 5–40%, to form alloys known as brasses. These group are called leaded red and semired, silicon, yellow, and high strength yellow brasses. Zinc imparts strength. It is completely soluble in copper, forming solid solution except in such cases as in high strength yellow brasses it which a duplex type of structure is obtained. Smaller amounts of zinc up to 5% are used in tin bronzes to tighten up the structure and aid it producing sound castings for pressure work. Zinc is not considered very detrimental impurity in most alloys. However, it is generally kept to below 5% in bearing bronzes because large amounts would tend to impair bearing qualities.

4.3.2 TIN—Added to copper in amounts of 5–20% to form a series of alloys known as tin bronzes and leaded tin bronzes. While the copper-tin constitution diagram shows that it is possible to have approximately 16% tin in solid solution at 520 °C, the presence of a hard constituent (alpha-delta copper tin eutectoid) develops in the range of 6–8% tin because of deviation from true equilibrium conditions. The tin strengthens and hardens copper, making it tough and resistant to wear and increases its corrosion resistance. Smaller amounts of tin are used in leaded red and semired brasses for increasing the strength of such general utility alloys. Tin is not generally harmful as an impurity except in high tensile manganese bronze, where it is limited to 0.2%. It is generally felt that in this alloy, tin lowers the strength and ductility.

4.3.3 LEAD—Added alone to copper in large amounts of around 35% for automotive bearings and agricultural and aircraft gear pumps. In practically all other cases, it is added to copper base alloys as an additional alloying element. Small amounts of lead up to 1.5% increase machinability without important decreases in strength. Larger amounts of 5–25% increase machinability greatly, and, in tin-containing alloys, increase antifrictional qualities, however, with reduction of strength.

4.3.4 ALUMINUM—Added to copper as a predominating alloying constituent to form a series of high strength alloys known as aluminum bronzes. It is soluble in copper to the extent of about 9.5%. It is added to high strength yellow brasses in varying amounts, being a very necessary part of the high tensile alloy. Aluminum, when present as an impurity, has very detrimental effects upon high leaded bronzes, causing lead sweating and unsoundness during solidification. It is also considered detrimental in the nonleaded tin bronzes, causing unsoundness.

4.3.5 IRON—Added to copper alloys as a strengthening constituent for silicon, aluminum, and manganese bronzes. It combines with aluminum or manganese or both to form hard compounds. These compounds imbed themselves into the matrix to give the alloys wear resistance. Iron, when present as an impurity, is not desirable since it forms hard spots and is detrimental to machining.

4.3.6 PHOSPHORUS—Added to copper and copper alloys principally as a deoxidizer. It is added to bronzes in greater amounts than necessary for purely deoxidization considerations to improve hardness and wear resistance, particularly in chill mold castings.

4.3.7 NICKEL—Added to bronzes as an alloying constituent for refining the grain and toughening the alloy. It is also used in amounts up to 15% for nickel brasses to displace that amount of zinc. In this alloy, it promotes strength, corrosion resistance, and whiteness. Nickel is added to some of the high tin gear bronzes to provide improved wear characteristics. When present as an impurity, it does not have detrimental effects; and most specifications permit approximately 1%.

4.3.8 SILICON—Added to copper as an alloying constituent to form copper-silicon alloys. These alloys have high corrosion resistance, high strength, and toughness. Small amounts of silicon are used as deoxidizing elements. When silicon is present as an impurity, it is extremely detrimental in leaded tin bronzes, promoting unsoundness and lead sweating.

TABLE 11—CHARACTERISTICS AND USES OF CAST COPPER ALLOYS

Copper Alloy UNS No.[a]	SAE No.	Former SAE No.	ASTM Standard No.	Former ASTM Standard No.	Former Name[b]	General Characteristics	Typical Uses
C83600	CA836	40	B271, B505, B584	B145	Leaded red brass	General utility alloys with reasonable corrosion resistance and strength. Good casting and machining properties. Hydrostatic tightness.	Water pump fittings, valve bodies, and general plumbing hardware. Copper Alloy UNS No. C83600 used for bearing backs.
C83800	CA838	—	B271, B505, B584	B145	Leaded red brass		
C85200	CA852	—	B271, B584	B146	Leaded yellow brass	Inexpensive, good machining casting alloy.	Radiator parts, fittings for water-cooling systems, and battery terminals.
C85400	CA854	41	B271, B584	B146	Leaded yellow brass		
C85800	CA858	—	B176	—	Brass die castings	General purpose low-cost yellow brass alloy with good machining and soldering characteristics.	Plumbing hardware, lock mechanisms, window hardware, gear shift forks, bevel gears.
C87800	CA878	—	B176	—	Brass die castings	Higher in mechanical strength, hardness, and wear resistance than Copper Alloy UNS Nos. C85800 and C87900, but is more difficult to machine. It is used only for highest strength and wear resistance.	
C87900	CA879	—	B176	—	Brass die castings	General purpose alloy with higher strength than Copper Alloy UNS No. C87800. It is somewhat easier to die cast, but slightly more difficult to machine.	
C86200	CA862	430A	B271, B505, B584	B147	High strength yellow brass	Excellent strength, corrosion resistance, and casting properties.	Brackets, shafts, gears, and structural applications.
C86300	CA863	430B	B271, B505, B584	B147	High strength yellow brass		
C86500	CA865	43	B271, B505, B584	B147	High strength yellow brass		
C87200	CA872	—	B271, B584	B198	Silicon bronze	Good strength, toughness, and corrosion resistance. Good casting qualities.	Pump parts, gears, and shafts.
C87400	CA874	—	B271, B585	B198	Silicon brass		
C87500	CA875	—	B271, B584	B198	Silicon brass		
C90300	CA903	620	B271, B505, B584	B143	Tin bronze	Hard, strong, tough, resistant to wear, fine grained. Good machinability and corrosion resistant to sea water.	Worm wheels, gears, bushings for heavy loads and low speeds, zinc-containing alloys for pressure castings. Good resistance to pounding.
C90500	CA905	62	B271, B505, B584	B143	Tin bronze		
C90700	CA907	65	B505, B584	—	Phosphor bronze		
C92200	CA922	622	B271, B505, B584	B143	Leaded tin bronze		
C92300	CA923	—	B271, B505, B584	B143	Leaded tin bronze		
C92500	CA925	640	B505, B584	—	Nickel phosphor bronze		
C92700	CA927	63	B505, B584	—	Leaded tin bronze		
C92900	CA929	—	B427, B505	—	Leaded nickel tin bronze		
C93200	CA932	660	B271, B505, B584	B144	High leaded tin bronze	Excellent antifriction qualities and castings and machining properties. Resistant to wear. Antifriction qualities increase with lead content. Corrosion resistant.	Copper Alloy UNS No. C93200—General bearing and bushing applications. Copper Alloy UNS No. C93500—High speeds and light loads on bearing backs. Copper Alloy UNS No. C93700—High speeds and heavy loads.
C93500	CA935	66	B271, B505, B584	B144	High leaded tin bronze		
C93700	CA937	64	B271, B505, B584	B144	High leaded tin bronze		
C93800	CA938	67	B271, B505, B584	B144	High leaded tin bronze		Copper Alloy UNS No. C93800—General service bearing material for moderate pressures and high speeds. Copper Alloy UNS No. C94300—Light to moderate loads and high speeds.
C94300	CA943	—	B271, B505, B584	B144	High leaded tin bronze		
C94700	CA947	—	B505, B584	B292	Nickel tin bronze	High strength constructural castings. Easy to cast Hydrostatic tightness. Bearing applications. Corrosion and wear resistant. Copper Alloy UNS No. C94700 is heat treatable.	Worm gears, valve stems and nuts, impellers, screw conveyors, roller bearing cages, and railway electrification hardware.
C94800	CA948	—	B505, B584	B292	Leaded nickel tin bronze		
C95200	CA952	68a	B148, B271, B505	—	Aluminum bronze	Good strength. Wear and corrosion resistant. Copper Alloy UNS Nos. C95300, C95400, C95500 and C95800 are heat treatable.	Gears, worm wheels, valve guides and seats, and structural applications.
C95300	CA953	68b	B148, B271, B505	—	Aluminum bronze		
C95400	CA954	—	B148, B271, B505	—	Aluminum bronze		
C95500	CA955	—	B148, B271, B505	—	Aluminum bronze		
C95800	CA958	—	B148, B271, B505	—	Nickel aluminum bronze		
C96200	CA962	—	B369	—	Copper nickel	Good corrosion resistance and toughness. Low-temperature strength.	Pipe couplings, coastal powerplants, air conditioning, and saline water corrosion.

[a] Unified Numbering System.
[b] Alloy names are shown for information only, and should not be used. Use appropriate designation only. (Example: Copper Alloy UNS No. C87800 Copper Alloy.)

4.3.9 BERYLLIUM—Added to copper together with small amounts of cobalt or nickel as an alloying constituent to form a series of precipitation hardenable beryllium-copper alloys. When hardened, these are the strongest of the known copper alloys. They are used for plastic molds, resistance welding electrodes, welding gun components and nonsparking tools. Beryllium, though rarely present as an impurity, has the effect of increasing fluidity and decreasing electrical conductivity in most of the copper alloys

4.3.10 MANGANESE—Used primarily as an alloying constituent for high strength alloy brasses, where it forms compounds with other alloying elements such as iron and aluminum. It is also used, to some extent for deoxidizing. It is not considered very detrimental as an impurity.

4.3.11 CHROMIUM—Added to copper as an alloying constituent to produce a precipitation-hardening type alloy, which in the heat treated condition, has mechanical properties far exceeding that of copper at a slight sacrifice of the electrical conductivity. Heat treatment develops a nominal hardness of 120 Brinell and a nominal electrical conductivity of 80% IACS. The alloy in the heat treated condition is useful for resistance welding electrodes where high electrical conductivity coupled with strength and hardness values superior to copper are desired. Chromium is generally not present as an impurity.

4.3.12 ANTIMONY—Rarely added to copper alloys. When present as an impurity, it is not considered very detrimental in amounts up to 0.5%. If present in greater amounts, it does tend to decrease physical properties.

TABLE 12A—TYPICAL PHYSICAL PROPERTIES OF CAST COPPER ALLOYS (METRIC [SI] UNITS)[a]

Copper Alloy UNS No.	Melting Point °C		Density g/cm³ at 20°C	Coefficient of Thermal Expansion per °C × 10⁻⁵	Thermal Conductivity W/(m · K)	Electrical Resistivity[b] nΩ · m	Modulus of Elasticity GPa
	Liquidus	Solidus		20–200°C			
C83600	1010	855	8.83	1.80	72	115.0	96
C83800	1005	844	8.60	1.80	73	115.0	90
C85200	941	927	8.50	2.07	84	96.2	76
C85400	940	927	8.45	2.02	88	88.5	83
C85800	899	871	8.40	2.16	—	86.2	103
C86200	941	899	7.58	2.16	35	227.3	103
C86300	923	885	7.84	2.16	35	217.4	97
C86500	880	862	8.30	2.03	87	78.1	103
C87200	971	860	8.40	1.66	28	285.7	103
C87400	916	821	8.27	1.96	28	256.4	103
C87500	916	821	8.27	1.96	28	256.4	103
C87800	916	821	8.27	1.96	28	256.4	138
C87900	926	899	8.50	2.16	—	114.9	103
C90300	1000	854	8.70	1.80	75	144.9	103
C90500	999	854	8.72	1.98	75	156.3	103
C90700	1000	832	8.78	1.84	71	178.6	97
C92200	988	825	8.65	1.80	70	120.5	97
C92300	1000	854	8.80	1.80	75	142.9	97
C92500	1000	854	8.85	1.80	—	—	90
C92700	982	848	8.80	1.82	47	156.3	90
C92900	1030	857	8.79	1.71	58	188.7	97
C93200	977	854	8.93	1.80	58	142.9	97
C93500	1000	844	8.87	1.80	71	113.6	100
C93700	928	762	8.95	1.85	47	169.5	76
C93800	943	854	9.25	1.85	52	151.5	69
C94300	954	899	9.29	1.80	63	188.7	76
C94700	1027	904	8.80	1.98	54	142.9	103
C94700 (HT)	1027	904	8.80	1.98	59	113.6	103
C94800	1027	904	8.80	1.98	39	142.9	103
C95200	1045	1042	7.64	1.62	50	156.3	103
C95300	1045	1040	7.53	1.62	63	—	110
C95300 (HT)	1045	1040	7.53	1.62	63	133.3	103
C95400	1037	1027	7.45	1.62	59	—	107
C95400 (HT)	1037	1027	7.45	1.66	59	133.3	110
C95500	1054	1038	7.53	1.62	42	—	110
C95500 (HT)	1054	1038	7.53	1.62	42	204.1	117
C95800	1063	1043	7.64	1.62	36	243.9	114
C96200	1149	1099	8.94	1.71	45	156.3	124

[a] Specific heat, for all alloys listed is 377 J/kg · K except for the following: Copper Alloy UNS No. C95400 and C95500: 420 J/kg · K C95800: 440 J/kg · K.

[b] See Table 12B for % IACS Electrical Conductivity.

TABLE 12B—TYPICAL PHYSICAL PROPERTIES OF CAST COPPER ALLOYS (CUSTOMARY UNITS)

Copper Alloy UNS No.	Melting Point °F Liquidus	Melting Point °F Solidus	Density lb/in³	Specific Gravity	Coefficient of Thermal Expansion 10⁶ in/in/°F (20–400°F)	Thermal Conductivity % of Cu[a]	Electrical Conductivity % IACS[b]	Modulus of Elasticity 10⁶ psi
C83600	1840	1570	0.318	8.83	10.0	18	15	14
C83800	1840	1550	0.312	8.60	10.0	18	15	13
C85200	1725	1700	0.307	8.50	11.5	21	18	11
C85400	1725	1700	0.305	8.45	11.2	23	20	12
C85800	1650	1600	0.305	8.40	12.0	—	20	15
C86200	1725	1650	0.288	7.85	12.0	9	8	15
C86300	1690	1625	0.283	7.84	12.0	9	8	14
C86500	1620	1585	0.301	8.30	11.3	22	22	15
C87200	1780	1580	0.302	8.40	9.2	7	6	15
C87400	1680	1510	0.300	8.27	10.9	7	7	15
C87500	1680	1510	0.300	8.27	10.9	7	7	15
C87800	1680	1510	0.300	8.27	10.9	7	7	20
C87900	1700	1650	0.308	8.50	12.0	—	15	15
C90300	1830	1570	0.318	8.70	10.0	19	12	15
C90500	1830	1570	0.315	8.72	11.0	19	11	15
C90700	1830	1528	0.317	8.78	10.2	19	10	14
C92200	1810	1520	0.312	8.65	10.0	18	14	14
C92300	1830	1570	0.317	8.80	10.0	19	12	14
C92500	1830	1570	0.317	8.85	10.0	—	11	13
C92700	1800	1550	0.317	8.80	10.1	12	11	13
C92900	1880	1575	0.320	8.79	9.5	15	9	14
C93200	1800	1570	0.322	8.93	10.0	15	12	14
C93500	1830	1570	0.320	8.87	10.0	18	15	14.5
C93700	1705	1400	0.320	8.95	10.3	12	10	11
C93800	1730	1570	0.334	9.25	10.3	13	12	10
C94300	1750	1650	0.336	9.29	10.0	16	9	11
C94700	1880	1660	0.320	8.80	11.0	14	12	15
C94700 (HT)	1880	1660	0.320	8.80	11.0	15	15	15
C94800	1880	1660	0.320	8.80	11.0	10	12	15
C95200	1913	1907	0.276	7.64	9.0	13	11	15
C95300	1913	1904	0.272	7.53	9.0	16	15	16
C95300 (HT)	1913	1904	0.272	7.53	9.0	16	13	15
C95400	1900	1880	0.269	7.45	9.0	15	13	15.5
C95400 (HT)	1900	1880	0.269	7.45	9.2	15	12	16
C95500	1930	1900	0.272	7.53	9.0	11	8.5	16
C95500 (HT)	1930	1900	0.272	7.53	9.0	11	8	17
C95800	1940	1910	0.276	7.64	9.0	9	7	16.5
C96200	2100	2010	0.323	8.94	9.5	11	11	18

[a] Cu = 226 Btu/ft²/ft/h/F at 68°F.
[b] International Annealed Copper Standard.

(R) CAST COPPER ALLOYS—SAE J462 SEP1981 — SAE Standard

Report of the SAE Nonferrous Metals Division approved June 1911, last revised by the SAE Nonferrous Metals Committee May 1976, reaffirmed with editorial change September 1981.

Foreword—This Document has also changed to with the new SAE Technical Standards Board Format. References have been added as Section 2.

1. Scope—This standard prescribes the chemical and mechanical requirements for a wide range of copper base casting alloys used in the automotive industry. It is not intended to cover ingot. (ASTM B30 is suggested for this purpose.)

2. References

2.1 Applicable Publications—The following publications form a part of the specification to the extent specified herein. Unless otherwise indicated the latest revision of SAE publications shall apply.

2.1.1 SAE PUBLICATION—Available from SAE, 400 Commonwealth Drive, Warrendale, PA 15096-0001.

SAE J461—Wrought and Cast Copper Alloys

2.1.2 ASTM PUBLICATIONS—Available from ASTM, 100 Barr Harbor Drive, West Conshohocken, PA 19428-2959.

ASTM B30—Specification for Copper-Base Alloys in Ingot Form
ASTM B148—Specification for Aluminum-Bronze Castings
ASTM B176—Specification for Copper Alloy Die Castings
ASTM B208—Practice for Preparing Tension Test Specimens for Copper-Base Alloys for Sand, Permanent Mold, Centrifugal, and Continuous Castings
ASTM B271—Specification for Copper-Base Alloy Centrifugal Castings
ASTM B369—Specification for Copper-Nickel Alloy Castings
ASTM B427—Specification for Gear Bronze Alloy Castings
ASTM B505—Specification for Copper-Base Alloy Continuous Castings
ASTM B584—Specification for Copper Alloy Sand Castings for General Applications

3. Chemical and Mechanical Properties—The chemical composition and mechanical properties of products identified by UNS designations shall conform to the limits shown in Tables 1 and 2. Chemical analyses obtained by use of instruments, such as spectrograph, x-ray, and atomic absorption, the copper (%) may be reported as "calculated by difference." Mechanical property values are applicable to standard specimens (Sand Cast ASTM B208, Centrifugal Cast ASTM B271, Continuous Cast ASTM B505) cast under production conditions used for casting the part(s) identified by the UNS designation. Samples for chemical analysis should be taken from test bars where practical to do so.

4. Workmanship—Castings shall be of uniform quality, free from blowholes, porosity, hard spots, shrinkage defects or cracks, or other injurious defects.

TABLE 1—CHEMICAL COMPOSITION OF CAST COPPER ALLOYS(1)

Copper Alloy UNS NO.(2)	Cu(3)	Sn	Pb	Zn(3)	Fe	Sb	Ni (Incl. Co)	Mn	As	S	P	Al	Si
C83600	84.0-86.0(4)	4.0-6.0	4.0-6.0	4.0-6.0	0.30	0.25	1.0(4)	—	—	0.08	0.05(5)	0.005	0.005
C83800	82.0-83.8(4)	3.3-4.2	5.0-7.0	5.0-8.0	0.30	0.25	1.0(4)	—	—	0.08	0.03(5)	0.005	0.005
C85200	70.0-74.0	0.7-2.0	1.5-3.8	20.0-27.0	0.6	0.20	1.0	—	—	0.05	0.02	0.005	0.05
C85400	65.0-70.0	0.50-1.5	1.5-3.8	24.0-32.0	0.7	—	1.0	—	—	—	—	0.35	0.05
C85800	57.0 min(6)	1.5	1.5	31.0-34.0	0.50	0.05	0.50	0.25	0.05	0.05	0.01	0.50	0.25
C86200	60.0-66.0	0.20	0.20	22.0-28.0	2.0-4.0	—	1.0	2.5-5.0	—	—	—	3.0-4.9	—
C86300	60.0-66.0	0.20	0.20	22.0-28.0	2.0-4.0	—	1.0	2.5-5.0	—	—	—	5.0-7.5	—
C86500	55.0-60.0	1.0	0.40	36.0-42.0	0.40-2.0	—	1.0	0.10-1.5	—	—	—	0.50-1.5	—
C87200	89.0 min(6)	1.0	0.50	5.0	2.5	—	—	1.5	—	—	—	1.5	1.0-5.0
C87400	79.0 min(6)	—	1.0	12.0-16.0	—	—	—	—	—	—	—	0.8	2.5-4.0
C87500	79.0 min(6)	—	0.50	12.0-16.0	—	—	—	—	—	—	—	0.5	3.0-5.0
C87800(7)	80.0 min(8)	0.25	0.15	12.0-16.0	0.15	0.05	0.20	0.15	0.05	0.05	0.01	0.15	3.8-4.2
C87900	63.0 min(6)	0.25	0.25	30.0-60.0	0.40	0.05	0.50	0.15	0.05	0.05	0.01	0.15	0.8-1.2
C90300	86.0-89.0	7.5-9.0	0.30	3.0-5.0	0.20	0.20	1.0(4)	—	—	0.05	0.05(5)	0.005	0.005
C90500	86.0-89.0(4)	9.0-11.0	0.30	1.0-3.0	0.20	0.20	1.0(4)	—	—	0.05	0.05(5)	0.005	0.005
C90700	88.0-90.0(9)	10.0-12.0	0.50	0.50	0.15	0.20	0.50	—	—	0.05	0.30(5)	0.005	0.005
C92200	86.0-90.0(4)	5.5-6.5	1.0-2.0	3.0-5.0	0.25	0.25	1.0(4)	—	—	0.05	0.05(5)	0.005	0.005
C92300	85.0-89.0(4)	7.5-9.0	0.30-1.0	2.5-5.0	0.25	0.25	1.0(4)	—	—	0.05	0.05(5)	0.005	0.005
C92500	85.0-88.0	10.0-12.0	1.0-1.5	0.50	0.30	0.25	0.8-1.5	—	—	0.05	0.30(5)	0.005	0.005
C92700	86.0-89.0	9.0-11.0	1.0-2.5	0.7	0.20	0.25	1.0	—	—	0.05	0.25(5)	0.005	0.005
C92900	82.0-86.0(9)	9.0-11.0	2.0-3.2	0.25	0.20	0.25	2.8-4.0	—	—	0.05	0.50(5)	0.005	0.005
C93200	81.0-85.0(4)	6.3-7.5	6.0-8.0	2.0-4.0	0.20	0.35	1.0(4)	—	—	0.08	0.15(5)	0.005	0.005
C93500	83.0-86.0(4)	4.3-6.0	8.0-11.0	2.0	0.20	0.30	1.0(4)	—	—	0.08	0.05(5)	0.005	0.005
C93700	78.0-82.0(4)	9.0-11.0	8.0-11.0	0.8	0.15(10)	0.55	1.0(4)	—	—	0.08	0.15(5)	0.005	0.005
C93800	75.0-79.0(4)	6.3-7.5	13.0-16.0	0.8	0.15	0.8	1.0(4)	—	—	0.08	0.05(5)	0.005	0.005
C94300	68.5-73.5(4)	4.5-6.0	22.0-25.0	0.8	0.15	0.8	1.0(4)	—	—	0.08	0.05(5)	0.005	0.005
C94700	85.0-90.0	4.5-6.0	0.10(11)	1.0-2.5	0.25	0.15	4.5-6.0	0.20	—	0.05	0.05	0.005	0.005
C94800	84.0-89.0	4.5-6.0	0.30-1.0	1.0-2.5	0.25	0.15	4.5-6.0	0.20	—	0.05	0.05	0.005	0.005
C95200	86.0 min(12)	—	—	—	2.5-4.0	—	—	—	—	—	—	8.5-9.5	—
C95300	86.0 min(12)	—	—	—	0.8-1.5	—	—	—	—	—	—	9.0-11.0	—
C95400	83.0 min(6)	—	—	—	3.0-5.0	—	2.5	0.50	—	—	—	10.0-11.5	—

TABLE 1—CHEMICAL COMPOSITION OF CAST COPPER ALLOYS[1] (continued)

Copper Alloy UNS NO.[2]	Cu[3]	Sn	Pb	Zn[3]	Fe	Sb	Ni (Incl. Co)	Mn	As	S	P	Al	Si
C95500	78.0 min[6]	—		—	3.0-5.0	—	3.0-5.0	3.5	—	—	—	10.0-11.5	—
C95800	79.0 min[6]	—	0.03	—	3.5-4.5[13]	—	4.0-5.0[13]	0.8-1.5	—	—	—	8.5-9.5	0.10
										Nb	C		
C96200	84.5-87.0	—	0.03	—	1.0-1.8	—	9.0-11.0	1.5	—	1.0	0.15	—	0.30

NOTE 1— These specification limits do not preclude the possible presence of other unnamed elements. However, analysis shall regularly be made only for the minor elements listed in the table plus all major elements except one. The major element which is not analyzed shall be determined by difference between the sum of those elements analyzed and 100%. By agreement between producer and consumer, analysis may be required and limits established for elements not specified.

NOTE 2—For welding grades, lead may not exceed 0.01%.

1. Percent by mass (weight); maximum, unless shown as a range or minimum.
2. Unified Numbering System. For cross reference to SAE, former SAE, ASTM, former ASTM, and former trade names, see SAE Information Report for Wrought and Cast Copper Alloys, SAE J461.
3. In reporting chemical analyses by the use of instruments such as spectrograph, X-ray and atomic absorption, copper may be indicated as "remainder." In reporting chemical analyses obtained by wet methods, zinc may be indicated as "remainder" on those alloys with over 2% zinc.
4. In determining copper minimum, copper may be calculated at Cu + Ni.
5. For continuous castings, phosphorus shall be 1.5% maximum
6. Total named elements shall be 99.5% minimum.
7. Magnesium requirement is 0.01% maximum.
8. Total named elements shall be 99.8% minimum.
9. Cu + Sn + Pb + Ni + P shall be 99.5% minimum
10. The iron shall be 0.35% maximum when used for steel backed bearings
11. The mechanical properties of C94700 (heat treated) may not be attained if the lead content exceeds 0.01%.
12. Total named elements shall be 99.0% minimum.
13. Iron content shall not exceed nickel content.

TABLE 2—MECHANICAL PROPERTIES OF CAST COPPER ALLOYS

Copper Alloy UNS NO.[1]	SAE Suffix[2][3]	ASTM Standard No.	Casting Method[3][4] and Condition	Tensile Strength, min MPa	Tensile Strength, min ksi	Yield Strength, min MPa 0.5% Ext. Under Load	Yield Strength, min ksi 0.5% Ext. Under Load	Elongation min, % in 50 mm (2 in)
C83600	A	B271, B584	Sand, Centrifugal	205	30	95	14	20
C83600	B	B505	Continuous	250	36	130	19	15
C83600	C		Continuous	345	50	170	15	12
C83800	A	B271, B584	Sand, Centrifugal	205	30	90	13	20
C83800	B	B505	Continuous	205	30	95	15	16
C85200		B271, B584	Sand, Centrifugal	240	35	85	12	25
C85400		B271, B584	Sand, Centrifugal	205	30	75	11	20
						0.2% Offset		
C85800		B176	Die[5]	380	55	205	30	15
C86200		B271, B505, B584	Sand, Centrifugal, Cont.	620	90	310	45	18
C86300	A	B271, B584	Sand, Centrifugal	760	110	415	60	12
C86300	B	B505	Continuous	760	110	425	62	14
C86500	A	B271, B584	Sand, Centrifugal	450	65	170	25	20
C86500	B	B505	Continuous	485	70	170	25	25
						0.5% Ext. Under Load		
C87200		B271, B584	Sand, Centrifugal	310	45	125	18	20
C87400		B271, B584	Sand, Centrifugal	345	50	145	21	18
C87500		B271, B584	Sand, Centrifugal	415	60	165	24	16
						0.2% Offset		
C87800		B176	Die[5]	585	85	345	50	25
C87900		B176	Die[5]	485	70	240	35	25
						0.5% Ext. Under Load		
C90300	A	B271, B584	Sand, Centrifugal	275	40	125	18	20
C90300	B	B505	Continuous	305	44	150	22	18
C90500	A	B271, B584	Sand, Centrifugal	275	40	125	18	20
C90500	B	B505	Continuous	305	44	170	25	10
C90700	A		Sand	240	35	125	18	10
C90700	B	B505	Continuous	275	40	170	25	10
C92200	A	B271, B584	Sand, Centrifugal	235	34	110	16	24
C92200	B	B505	Continuous	260	38	130	19	18
C92300	A	B271, B584	Sand, Centrifugal	250	36	110	16	18
C92300	B	B505	Continuous	275	40	130	19	16
C92500	A		Sand	240	35	125	18	10
C92500	B	B505	Continuous	275	40	165	24	10
C92700	A		Sand	240	35	125	18	10

TABLE 2—MECHANICAL PROPERTIES OF CAST COPPER ALLOYS (continued)

Copper Alloy UNS NO.[1]	SAE Suffix[2][3]	ASTM Standard No.	Casting Method[3][4] and Condition	Tensile Strength, min MPa	Tensile Strength, min ksi	Yield Strength, min MPa 0.5% Ext. Under Load	Yield Strength, min ksi 0.5% Ext. Under Load	Elongation min, % in 50 mm (2 in)
C92700	B	B505	Continuous	260	38	140	20	8
C92900		B427, B505	Sand, Continuous	310	45	170	25	8
C93200	A	B271, B584	Sand, Centrifugal	205	30	95	14	15
C93200	B	B505	Continuous	240	35	140	20	10
C93500	A	B271, B584	Sand, Centrifugal	195	28	85	12	15
C93500	B	B505	Continuous	205	30	110	16	12
C93700	A	B271, B584	Sand, Centrifugal	205	30	85	12	15
C93700	B	B505	Continuous	240	35	140	20	6
C93700	C		Continuous	275	40	170	25	6
C93800	A	B271, B584	Sand, Centrifugal	180	26	95	14	12
C93800	B	B505	Continuous	170	25	110	16	5
C94300	A	B271, B584	Sand, Centrifugal	145	21	—	—	10
C94300	B	B505	Continuous	145	21	95	15	7
C94700	A	B505, B584	Sand, Continuous	310	45	140	20	25
C94700	B	B505, B584	Sand, Continuous (HT)	515	75	345	50	5
C94800		B505, B584	Sand, Continuous	275	40	140	20	20
C95200	A	B148, B271	Sand, Centrifugal	450	65	170	25	20
C95200	B	B505	Continuous	470	68	180	26	20
C95300	A	B148, B271	Sand, Centrifugal	450	65	170	25	20
C95300	B	B505	Continuous	485	70	180	26	25
C95300	C	B148, B271, B505	Sand, Centrifugal, Cont.(HT)	550	80	275	40	12
C95400	A	B148, B271	Sand, Centrifugal	515	75	205	30	12
C95400	B	B505	Continuous	585	85	220	32	12
C95400	C	B148, B271	Sand, Centrifugal (HT)	620	90	310	45	6
C95400	D	B505	Continuous (HT)	655	95	310	45	10
C95500	A	B148, B271	Sand, Centrifugal	620	90	275	40	6
C95500	B	B505	Continuous	655	95	290	42	10
C95500	C	B148, B271	Sand, Centrifugal (HT)	760	110	415	60	5
C95500	D	B505	Continuous (HT)	760	110	425	62	8
C95800	A	B148, B271	Send, Centrifugal	585	85	240	35	15
C95800	B	B505	Continuous(3)	620	90	260	38	18
C96200		B369	Sand	310	45	170	25	20

1. UNIFIED NUMBERING SYSTEM. For cross reference to SAE, former SAE, former ASTM, and Former trade names, see SAE Information Report for Wrought and Cast Copper Alloys, SAE J461.
2. Suffix symbols may be specified to distinguish between two or more sets of mechanical properties, heat treatment, conditions, etc. as applicable.
3. Most commonly used method of casting is shown for each alloy. However, unless the purchaser specifies the method of casting or the mechanical properties by supplement to the UNS number, the supplier may use any method which will develop the properties indicated.
4. All alloys listed are in the "as cast" condition except those designated as heat treated (HT) and copper alloy UNS No. C95800 which is temper annealed.
5. Mechanical properties shown for die castings are typical, not minimum.

WROUGHT COPPER AND COPPER ALLOYS —SAE 463 DEC2002

SAE Standard

Report of the SAE Nonferrous Metals Division approved June 1911, last revised by the SAE Nonferrous Metals Committee June 1976, reaffirmed with editorial change September 1981 and editorial change December 2002. Rationale statement available.

1. Scope—This standard[1] describes the chemical, mechanical, and dimensional requirements for a wide range of wrought copper and copper alloys used in the automotive and related industries.

1.1 Wrought forms covered by this standard include sheet, strip, bar, plate, rod, wire, tube, and shapes; however, form required must be specified by purchaser.

2. References

2.1 Applicable Publications—The following publications form a part of this specification to the extent specified herein.

2.1.1 ASTM PUBLICATIONS—Available from ASTM, 100 Barr Harbor Drive, West Conshohocken, PA 19428-2959.

ASTM B248—Specification for General Requirements for Wrought Copper and Copper-Alloy Plate, Sheet, Strip, and Rolled Bar

ASTM B249—Specificaiton for General Requirements for Wrought Copper and Copper-Alloy Rod, Bar, and Shapes

ASTM B250—Specification for General Requirements for Wrought Copper-Alloy Wire

ASTM B251—Specification for General Requirements for Wrought Copper-Alloy Wire

3. Chemical and Mechanical Properties—The chemical composition of products identified by the UNS designations shall conform to the limits shown in Table 1. Mechanical properties shall conform to limits shown in Table 2A (metric(si) units) or 2B (customary units).

3.1 Products shall be of uniform quality and free from defects (such as desegregation, pipes, nonmetallic inclusions, cracks, seams, laps, buckles, and die or roll marks) detrimental to their appearance, fabrication and/or performance in service.

3.2 Both inside and outside surfaces of tubing shall be clean and smooth.

3.3 Forgings shall not be brazed, soldered, welded, or ground to hide defects or to salvage defective products, unles specifically approved by the purchaser.

3.4 Necessary brazes in soft annealed copper wire shall be in accordance with best commercial practice.

4. Testing—Unless otherwise specified all properties stated herein are based on latest methods of test published in the ASTM Standards.

5. Dimensional Tolerances—Standard forms of products identified by the UNS designations shall conform to the dimensions specified by the purchaser, within the tolerance limits shown in Tables 4 - 11, the "key" for which is Table 3, "Index to Standard Product Tolerance Tables." Specified dimensions not covered by these tables shall be within the tolerance limits shown in ASTM B248 (plate, sheet, strip, and rolled bar), ATM B249 (rod, bar, and shapes), ASTM B250 (wire), and ASTM B251 (pipe and tube). (Note: the terms "refractory" and "nonrefractory" used in Table 3 are common in the copper industry, the first applying to alloys which, because of their hardness on abrasiveness, require dimensional tolerances greater than those established for nonrefractory alloys.)

1. If none of the alloys listed herein include the characteristics required for a particular application, users are encouraged to consider alloy specifications listed in CDA Publication "Standards Handbook for Copper Alloy Wrought Mill Products," published by the Copper Development Association, 405 Lexington Avenue, New York, NY 10017, before creating specifications of their own.

TABLE 1—CHEMICAL COMPOSITIONS OF WROUGHT COPPER ALLOYS [a]

Copper Alloy UNS No.[b]	% by Weight, Maximum (Except where otherwise noted)											
	Cu	Fe	Zn	Pb	Sn	Mn	Ni	Al	Si	P	Be	Other Named Elements
C10200[c]	99.9 min	—	—	—	—	—	—	—	—	—	—	—
C11000[c]	99.9 min	—	—	—	—	—	—	—	—	—	—	—
C11100[c]	99.9 min	—	—	—	—	—	—	—	—	—	—	See Note d
C11300[c,e]	99.9 min[f]	—	—	—	—	—	—	—	—	—	—	Ag, .027 min (8)[g]
C11400[c,e]	99.9 min[f]	—	—	—	—	—	—	—	—	—	—	Ag, .034 min (10)[g]
C11500[c,e]	99.9 min[f]	—	—	—	—	—	—	—	—	—	—	Ag, .054 min (16)[g]
C11600[c,e]	99.9 min[f]	—	—	—	—	—	—	—	—	—	—	Ag, .085 min (25)[g]
C12000	99.9 min	—	—	—	—	—	—	—	—	.004–.012	—	—
C12200[h]	99.9 min	—	—	—	—	—	—	—	—	.015–.040	—	—
C14500[i]	99.9 min[j]	—	—	—	—	—	—	—	—	.004–.012[k]	—	Te, .40–.60
C14700	99.9 min[l]	—	—	—	—	—	—	—	—	—	—	S, .2–.5
C15000	99.8 min	—	—	—	—	—	—	—	—	—	—	Zr, .10–20
C16200	99.8 min	.02	—	—	—	—	—	—	—	—	—	Cd, .7–1.2
C17000	99.5 min[m]	Note n	—	—	—	—	Note n	—	—	—	1.6–1.8	Co[n]
C17200	99.5 min[m]	Note n	—	—	—	—	Note n	—	—	—	1.8–2.0	Co[n]
C17500	99.5 min[m]	.10	—	—	—	—	—	—	—	—	.40–.70	Co, 2.4–2.7
C17600	99.5 min[m]	—	—	—	—	—	—	—	—	—	.25–.50	Co, 1.4–1.7 Ag, .9–1.1
C18400	99.8 min[o]	.15	.70	—	—	—	—	—	.10	.05	—	As, .005 Cr, .40–1.2 Li, .05 Ca, .005
C18700	99.9 min[o]	—	—	.8–1.5	—	—	—	—	—	—	—	—
C19200	98.7 min	.8–1.2	—	—	—	—	—	—	—	.01–.04	—	—
C21000	94.0–96.0	.05	rem	.05	—	—	—	—	—	—	—	—
C22000	89.0–91.0	.05	rem	.05	—	—	—	—	—	—	—	—
C23000	84.0–86.0[p]	.05	rem	.05[p]	—	—	—	—	—	—	—	—
C24000	78.5–81.5	.05	rem	.05	—	—	—	—	—	—	—	—
C26000	68.5–71.5	.05	rem	.07	—	—	—	—	—	—	—	—
C26800	64.0–68.5	.05	rem	.15	—	—	—	—	—	—	—	—
C27000	63.0–68.5	.07	rem	.10	—	—	—	—	—	—	—	—
C33000	65.0–68.0	.07	rem	.20–.8[q]	—	—	—	—	—	—	—	—
C33100	65.0–68.0	.06	rem	.70–1.2	—	—	—	—	—	—	—	—
C34200	62.5–66.5	.10	rem	1.5–2.5	—	—	—	—	—	—	—	—
C34500	62.0–64.0	.10	rem	1.5–2.8	—	—	—	—	—	—	—	—
C35000	59.0–64.0[r]	.10	rem	.8–1.4	—	—	—	—	—	—	—	—
C36000	60.0–63.0	.35	rem	2.5–3.7	—	—	—	—	—	—	—	—
C37700	58.0–62.0	.30	rem	1.5–2.5	—	—	—	—	—	—	—	—
C46400	59.0–62.0	.10	rem	.20	.50–1.0	—	—	—	—	—	—	—
C46500	59.0–62.0	.10	rem	.20	.50–1.0	—	—	—	—	—	—	As, .02–.10

ϕ

ed. **TABLE 1—CHEMICAL COMPOSITIONS OF WROUGHT COPPER ALLOYS[a] (CONTINUED)**

Copper Alloy UNS No.[b]	% by Weight, Maximum (Except where otherwise noted)											
	Cu	Fe	Zn	Pb	Sn	Mn	Ni (incl. Co)	Al	Si	P	Be	Other Named Elements
C46600	59.0–62.0	.10	rem	.20	.50–1.0	—	—	—	—	—	—	Sb, .02–.10
C46700	59.0–62.0	.10	rem	.20	.50–1.0	—	—	—		0.2–.10	—	—
C51000	99.5 min[s]	.10	.30	.05	4.2–5.8	—	—	—	—	.03–.35	—	—
C51100	99.5 min[s]	.10	.30	.05	3.5–4.9	—	—	—	—	.03–.35	—	—
C52100	99.5 min[s]	.10	.20	.05	7.0–9.0	—	—	—	—	.03–.35	—	—
C52400	99.5 min[s]	.10	.20	.05	9.0–11.0	—	—	—	—	.03–.35	—	—
C54400	99.5 min[t]	.10	1.5–4.5	3.5–4.5	3.5–4.5	—	—	—	—	.01–.50	—	—
C60800	88.8–92.5[f]	.10	—	.10	—	—	—	5.0–6.5	—	—		As, .2–.35
C61300	88.5–91.5[f]	2.0–3.0	.05	.01	—	.15	—	6.0–7.5	—	.015		See Note v
C61400	88.0–92.5[f]	1.5–3.5	.20	.10	—	1.0	—	6.0–8.0	—	.015	—	—
C61800	86.9–91.0[f]	.50–1.5	.02	.02	—	—	—	8.5–11.0	.10	—		—
C62300	82.2–89.5[f]	2.0–4.0	—	—	.60	.50	1.0	8.5–11.0	.25	—	—	—
C62400	82.8–88.0[f]	2.0–4.5	—	—	.20	.30	—	10.0–11.5	.25	—		—
C63000	78.0–85.0[f]	2.0–4.0	.30	—	.20	1.5	4.0–5.5	9.0–11.0	.25	—	—	—
C64200	88.2–92.2[f]	.30	.50	.05	.20	.10	.25	6.3–7.6	1.5–2.2	—	—	As, .15
C65500	rem[f]	.8	1.5	.05	—	.50–1.3	.60	—	2.8–3.8	—		—
C67000	63.0–68.0	2.0–4.0	rem	.20	.50	2.5–5.0	—	3.0–6.0	—	—	—	—
C67300	58.0–63.0	.50	rem	.4–3.0	.30	2.0–3.5	.25	.25	.50–1.5	—		—
C67400	57.0–60.0	.35	rem	.50	.30	2.0–3.5	.25	.50–2.0	.50–1.5	—	—	—
C67500	57.0–60.0	.8–2.0	rem	.20	.50–1.5	.05–.50	—	.25	—	—		—
C70600	99.5 min[o]	1.0–1.8	1.0[u]	.05[u]	—	1.0	9.0–11.0	—	—	—		See Note u
C71000	99.5 min[o]	1.0	1.0	.05	—	1.0	19.0–23.0	—		—	—	—
C71500	99.5 min[o]	.40–.70	1.0[u]	.05[u]	—	1.0	29.0–33.0	—	—	—		See Note u
C75200	63.0–68.5	.25	rem	.10	—	.50	16.5–19.5	—	—	—		—
C77000	53.5–56.5	.25	rem	.10	—	.50	16.5–19.5	—	—	—	—	—

ϕ [a] These specification limits do not preclude the possible presence of other unnamed elements. However, analysis shall regularly be made only for the minor elements listed in the table, plus all major elements except one. The major element which is not analyzed shall be determined by difference between the sum of those elements analyzed and 100%. By agreement between manufacturer and purchaser, analysis may be required and limits established for elements not specified.

[b] Unified Numbering System. For cross reference to SAE, Former SAE, ASTM, and Former Trade Names, see SAE J461.

[c] These are high conductivity coppers which have in the annealed condition a minimum conductivity of 100% IACS.

[d] Small amounts of Cd or other elements may be added by agreement to improve resistance to softening at elevated temperatures.

[e] This includes Low Resistance Lake Copper and Electrolytic Copper.

[f] This includes Cu + Ag.

ϕ [g] Figures in parentheses are troy ounces per avoirdupois ton.

[h] This includes Oxygen-Free Copper which contains P in an amount agreed upon.

[i] This includes Oxygen-Free Tellurium Bearing Copper which contains P in an amount agreed upon.

ϕ [j] This includes Cu + Ag + Te.

[k] Other deoxidizers may be used as agreed upon, in which case P need not be present.

[l] This includes Cu +Ag + S.

ϕ [m] The value of Cu is exclusive of Ag.

[n] Ni + Co, 0.20% min.
Ni + Fe, + Co, 0.6% max.

[o] This includes copper plus elements with specified limits. Copper alloy UNS Nos. C70600 (CA706), Cu + Ag, 86.5% min and C71500 (CA715), Cu + Ag, 65% min. Specific limits are defined as any numerical values, whether maximum only, minimum only or ranges. *ed.*

ϕ [p] For pipe and tube, the Cu limit may be 83.0% minimum and the Pb 0.06% max.

[q] For tube over 5 in O.D., the Pb may be less than 0.20%.

[r] Copper 61.0% min for rod.

[s] This includes Cu + Sn + P.

[t] This includes Cu + Sn + P + Pb + Zn.

[u] When the product is for welding applications and so specified by the purchaser, Zn shall be 0.50% max, Pb 0.02% max, P 0.02% max, S 0.02% max, and C 0.05% max.

[v] When the product is for welding applications and so specified by the purchaser, Cr, Cd, and Zr shall each be 0.05% max. *ed.*

ed. TABLE 2A—MINIMUM MECHANICAL PROPERTIES OF WROUGHT COPPER ALLOYS

Metric (SI) Units

Copper or Copper Alloy UNS No.[cc]	Form	Temper	Size Section, mm Over/Thru		Tensile Strength, MPa Min	Tensile Strength, MPa Max	Yield Strength, Min MPa 0.5% Ext Under Load	Elongation, Min %[c] In 4 × Dia or Thickness of Specimen	Hardness Min	Hardness Max	Hardness Min	Hardness Max	Grain Size, mm Min	Grain Size, mm Max
									RF[b]		R30T[b]			
C10200 C11000 C11100 C11300 C11400 C11500 C11600 C12000 C12200	Plate, Sheet, Strip, and Rolled Bar	Soft Anneal	—		—	—	—	—	—	65	—	—	Note a	—
		Deep-Drawing Anneal	—		—	—	—	—	30	75	—	—	Note a	0.050
		Light Cold Rolled	—		220	275	—	—	40	82	—	49	—	—
		1/2 Hard[r]	—		225	315	—	—	77	80	43	57	—	—
		Hard[r]	—		285	360	—	—	86	93	54	62	—	—
		Spring[r]	—		345	400	—	—	91	97	60	66	—	—
		Extra Spring[r]	—		360	—	—	—	92	—	61	—	—	—
		Hot Rolled	—		205	260	—	—	—	75	—	41	—	—
		Hot Rolled and Annealed	—		205	260	—	—	—	65	—	31	—	—
					Type B Matl[u]			Type B[u]	Type A[s,u]					
C10200 C11000 C12000 C12200	Rod, Bar and Shapes	Soft Anneal	All Sizes[m]		—	255	—	25	—	65	—	—	—	—
		Hard	—/6.5[w]		345	—	—	—	68	95	—	—	—	—
			6.5/9.5[w]		310	—	—	10	68	95	—	—	—	—
			9.5/25[w]		275	—	—	12	68	95	—	—	—	—
			25/50[w]		240	—	—	15	68	95	—	—	—	—
			50/75[w]		230	—	—	15	68	95	—	—	—	—
			4.8/9.5[x]		290	—	—	12	68	95	—	—	—	—
			9.5/13[x]		275	—	—	12	68	95	—	—	—	—
			13/50[x]		230	—	—	15	68	95	—	—	—	—
			50/100[x]		220	—	—	15	68	95	—	—	—	—
			All Sizes[y]		220	—	—	15	—	—	—	—	—	—
			OD	Wall				In 50 mm			R15T[d]			
C10200 C12000 C12200	Tube	Soft Anneal	All Sizes	0.4/0.9	—	—	—	40[e]	—	—	—	60	0.040	—
			All Sizes	0.9/—	—	—	—	—	—	50[d]	—	—	0.040	—
		Light Anneal	All Sizes	0.4/0.9	—	—	—	—	—	—	—	65	—	0.040
			All Sizes	0.9/—	—	—	—	—	—	55[d]	—	—	—	0.040
											R30T[d]			
		Light Drawn	All Sizes	All Sizes	250	325	—	—	—	—	30	60	—	—
		Drawn	All Sizes	All Sizes	250	—	—	—	—	—	30	—	—	—
		Hard Drawn	—/25	0.5/3.0	310	—	—	—	—	—	55	—	—	—
			25/50	0.4/4.5	310	—	—	—	—	—	55	—	—	—
			50/100	1.5/6.5	310	—	—	—	—	—	55	—	—	—
			Size Section, mm Over/Thru					In 250 mm	RF[b]		R30T[b]			
C10200 C11000	Wire	Annealed	0.08/0.25					15	—	—	—	—	—	—
			0.25/0.50					20	—	—	—	—	—	—
			0.50/2.5				—	25	—	—	—	—	—	—
			2.5/7.5				—	30	—	—	—	—	—	—
			7.5/12				—	35	—	—	—	—	—	—
								In 4 × Dia						
C14500	Rod	1/2Hard[f]	1.6/6.5		260	—	205	8	—	—	—	—	—	—
			6.5/65		260	—	205	12	—	—	—	—	—	—
		Hard	1.6/6.5		330	—	275	4	—	—	—	—	—	—
			6.5/30		305	—	260	8	—	—	—	—	—	—
			30/50		275	—	240	8	—	—	—	—	—	—
C14700	Rod	1/2 Hard[f]	1.6/6.5			—	205	8	—	—	—	—	—	—
			6.5/65			—	205	12	—	—	—	—	—	—
		Hard[g]	1.6/6.5			—	275	4	—	—	—	—	—	—
			6.5/30			—	260	8	—	—	—	—	—	—
			30/50			—	240	8	—	—	—	—	—	—
C15000	Round Rod													

ed. TABLE 2A—MINIMUM MECHANICAL PROPERTIES OF WROUGHT COPPER ALLOYS (CONTINUED)

Metric (SI) Units

Copper or Copper Alloy UNS No.[e]	Form	Temper	Size Section, mm Over/Thru	Tensile Strength, MPa Min	Tensile Strength, MPa Max	Yield Strength, Min MPa 0.5% Ext Under Load	Elongation, Min %[c] in 50 mm	Hardness Min	Hardness Max	Hardness Min	Hardness Max	Grain Size, mm Min	Grain Size, mm Max
				Type B Mat'l[u]				RB		R30T[b]			
C16200	Round Rod	Drawn	—/25 25/50 50/75	415 380 345	— — —	— — —	20 25 25	65 60 55	— — —	— — —	— — —	— — —	— — —
	Square, Rectangular and Hex Rod and Bar	Drawn	—/25 25/—	415 345	— —	— —	20 20	55 50	— —	— —	— —	— —	— —
	Forging	As Forged	—/25 25/—	415 345	— —	— —	20 25	55 55	— —	— —	— —	— —	— —
						0.2% Offset	in 50 mm[n]	RB[o,q]		R30T[p,q]		Elec Cond % IACS Min	Heat Treat h at 315°C
C17000	Strip	A Soft[l]	All Sizes	415	540	—	35	45	78	46	67	17	—
		1/4 Hard[l] 1/2 Hard[l] Hard[l]	All Sizes All Sizes All Sizes	515 585 690	605 690 825	— — —	10 5 2	68 88 96	90 96 102	62 74 79	75 79 83	16 15 15	— — —
								RC[o,q]		R30N[p,q]			
		AT[y] 1/4 HT[y] 1/2 HT[y] HT[y]	All Sizes All Sizes All Sizes All Sizes	1035 1100 1170 1240	— — — —	885 930 1000 1070	3 2.5 1 1	33 35 37 39	— — — —	53 55 56 59	— — — —	22 22 22 22	3 2 2 2
		AM[z]	All Sizes	690	795	485 min 655 max	18	18	23	37	44	23	—
		1/4 HM[z]	All Sizes	760	860	550 min 725 max	15	21	26	42	47	23	—
		1/2 HM[z]	All Sizes	830	930	655 min 795 max	12	25	30	46	50	24	—
		HM[z]	All Sizes	930	1030	760 min 930 max	9	30	35	50	55	25	—
		XHM[z]	All Sizes	1100	1200	930 min 1100 max	2	32	36	52	56	24	—
								RB[o,q]		R30T[p,q]			
C17200	Strip	A (Soft)[l]	All Sizes	415	535	—	35	45	78	46	67	17	—
		1/4 Hard[l] 1/2 Hard[l] Hard[l]	All Sizes All Sizes All Sizes	515 585 690	605 690 825	— — —	10 5 2	68 88 96	90 96 102	62 74 79	75 79 83	16 15 15	— — —
								RC[o,q]		R30N[p,q]			
		AT[y]	All Sizes	1140	1350	—	—	36	—	56	—	22	3
		1/4 Hard[y] 1/2 Hard[y] HT[y]	All Sizes All Sizes All Sizes	1200 1770 1310	1410 1480 1520	— — —	— — —	38 39 40	— — —	58 59 60	— — —	22 22 22	2 2 2
								RB[o,q]					
	Rod and Bar	A (Soft)[l]	All Sizes	415	585	—	—	45	85	—	—	17	—
		Hard[l]	—/9.5 9.5/25 25/—	655 620 585	895 825 795	— — —	— — —	92 91 88	103 102 104	— — —	— — —	15 15 15	— — —
								RC[o,q]					
		AT[y]	All Sizes	1140	1310	—	—	36	40	—	—	22	3
		HT[y]	—/9.5 9.5/25 25/—	1280 1240 1200	1480 1450 1410	— — —	— — —	39 38 37	45 44 43	— — —	— — —	22 22 22	3 2 2

ed. TABLE 2A—MINIMUM MECHANICAL PROPERTIES OF WROUGHT COPPER ALLOYS (CONTINUED)

Metric (SI) Units

Copper or Copper Alloy UNS No.[aa]	Form	Temper	Size Section, mm Over/Thru	Tensile Strength, MPa Min	Tensile Strength, MPa Max	Yield Strength, Min MPa 0.2% Offset	Elongation, Min %[c] in 50 mm	Hardness Min	Hardness Max	Hardness Min	Hardness Max	Elec Cond, %IACS Min	Heat Treat h at 315°C
								RB[o,q]		R30T[p,q]			
C17500	Strip and Plate	A (Soft)[1]	All Sizes	—	380	140 min 205 max	20	20	45	29	45	20	—
C17500	Strip and Plate	1/2 Hard[1]	All Sizes	415	515	345 min 485 max	5	65	76	60	67	25	—
C17500	Strip and Plate	Hard[1]	All Sizes	485	585	415 min 550 max	2	78	88	69	75	25	—
C17500	Strip and Plate	AT[y]	All Sizes	690	825	550 min 690 max	8	92	100	77	82	45	—
C17500	Strip and Plate	1/2 HT[y] HT[y]	All Sizes	760	895	655 min 825 max	5	95	102	79	83	48	—
C17500	Hot Worked Sizes, Forgings	A (Soft)[1]	All Sizes	—	380	140 min 205 max	20	20	45	—	—	20	—
C17500	Hot Worked Sizes, Forgings	AT[y]	All Sizes	690	825	550 min 690 max	10	92	100	—	—	45	—
C17500 C17600	Rod, Bar Shapes and Tubing	A (Soft)[1]	All Sizes	240	380	140 min 205 max	20	25	45	—	—	20	—
C17500 C17600	Rod, Bar Shapes and Tubing	1/2 Hard	All Sizes	450	585	380 min 515 max	10	60	75	—	—	20	—
C17500 C17600	Rod, Bar Shapes and Tubing	AT[y]	All Sizes	690	825	550 min 690 max	10	92	100	—	—	45	—
C17500 C17600	Rod, Bar Shapes and Tubing	1/2 HT[y]	All Sizes	760	895	690 min 825 max	8	92	102	—	—	48	—
						0.5% Ext Under Load		**RB**		**R30T[b]**		**Grain Size, mm Min**	**Grain Size, mm Max**
C18400	Rod (Round Only)	Drawn	—/25 25/50 50/75	450 415 380	— — —	— — —	15 15 15	75 70 65	— — —	— — —	— — —	— — —	— — —
C18400	Rod (Hexagonal) and Bar	Drawn	—/25 25/—	450 380	— —	— —	15 15	70 65	— —	— —	— —	— —	— —
C18400	Forgings	As Forged	—/25 25/50 50/—	450 380 380	— — —	— — —	15 15 15	72 70 65	— — —	— — —	— — —	— — —	— — —
C18700	Rod	1/2 Hard[ff]	1.6/6.5 6.5/65	260 260	— —	205 205	8 12	— —	— —	— —	— —	— —	— —
C18700	Rod	Hard	1.6/6.5 6.5/30 30/50	330 305 275	— — —	275 260 240	4 8 8	— — —	— — —	— — —	— — —	— — —	— — —
C19200	Tube	A (Soft) Light Drawn	All Sizes All Sizes	260 275	— —	80 240	— —	— —	— —	— —	— —	— —	— —
								RF[b]					
C21000	Plate, Sheet, Strip and Rolled Bar[1]	Annealed 0.050 mm 0.035 mm 0.025 mm 0.015 mm	— — — —	— — — —	— — — —	— — — —	— — — —	40 47 50 54	52 54 61 65	— — 1 7	4 7 17 23	0.035 0.025 0.015 Note 1	0.090 0.050 0.035 0.025
								RB[b]					
C21000	Plate, Sheet, Strip and Rolled Bar[1]	1/4 Hard	0.50/0.90 0.90/— 0.30/0.70 0.70/—	255	325	—	—	20 24 — —	48 52 — —	— — 34 37	— — 51 54	— — — —	— — — —

(Table continued on next page)

ed. TABLE 2A—MINIMUM MECHANICAL PROPERTIES OF WROUGHT COPPER ALLOYS (CONTINUED)

Copper or Copper Alloy UNS No.[a,e]	Form	Temper	Size Section, mm	Tensile Strength, MPa		Yield Strength, Min MPa	Elongation, Min %[c]	Hardness				Grain Size, mm	
			Over/Thru	Min	Max	0.5% Ext Under Load	In 50 mm	Min	Max	Min	Max	Min	Max
								RB[b]		R30T[b]			
Metric (SI) Units													
C21000	Plate, Sheet, Strip and Rolled Bar[d]	1/2 Hard	0.50/0.90 0.90/— 0.30/0.70 0.70/—	290	360	—	—	40 44 — —	56 60 — —	— — 46 48	— — 57 59	— — — —	— — — —
		3/4 Hard	0.50/0.90 0.90/—	315	385	—	—	50 53	61 64	— —	— —	— —	— —
							In 4 × Dia or Thickness of Specimen						
		3/4 Hard	0.30/0.70 0.70/—	315	385	—	—	— —	— —	52 54	60 62	— —	— —
		Hard	0.50/0.90 0.90/— 0.30/0.70 0.70/—	345	405	—	—	57 60 — —	64 67 — —	— — 57 59	— — 62 64	— — — —	— — — —
		Extra Hard	0.50/0.90 0.90/— 0.30/0.70 0.70/—	385	440	—	—	64 66 — —	70 72 — —	— — 62 63	— — 66 67	— — — —	— — — —
		Spring	0.50/0.90 0.90/— 0.30/0.70 0.70/—	415	470	—	—	68 70 — —	73 75 — —	— — 64 65	— — 68 69	— — — —	— — — —
		Extra Spring	0.50/0.90 0.90/— 0.30/0.70 0.70/—	420	475	—	—	69 71 — —	74 76 — —	— — 65 66	— — 69 70	— — — —	— — — —
								RF[b]					
C22000	Plate, Sheet, Strip and Rolled Bar[d]	Annealed 0.050 mm 0.035 mm 0.025 mm 0.015 mm	— — — —	— — — —	— — — —	— — — —	— — — —	50 54 58 62	60 64 70 75	1 7 13 19	16 21 31 39	0.035 0.025 0.015 Note 1	0.090 0.050 0.035 0.025
								RB[b]					
		1/4 Hard	0.50/0.90 0.90/— 0.30/0.70 0.70/—	275	345	—	—	27 31 — —	52 56 — —	— — 38 41	— — 53 56	— — — —	— — — —
		1/2 Hard	0.50/0.90 0.90/— 0.30/0.70 0.70/—	325	395	—	—	50 53 — —	63 66 — —	— — 52 54	— — 61 63	— — — —	— — — —
		3/4 Hard	0.50/0.90 0.90/— 0.30/0.70 0.70/—	360	425	—	—	59 62 — —	68 71 — —	— — 58 60	— — 64 66	— — — —	— — — —
		Hard	0.50/0.90 0.90/— 0.30/0.70 0.70/—	395	455	—	—	65 68 — —	72 75 — —	— — 62 64	— — 66 68	— — — —	— — — —
		Extra Hard	0.50/0.90 0.90/— 0.30/0.70 0.70/—	440	495	—	—	72 74 — —	77 79 — —	— — 67 68	— — 71 72	— — — —	— — — —
		Spring	0.50/0.90 0.90/— 0.30/0.70 0.70/—	475	530	—	—	76 78 — —	79 81 — —	— — 70 71	— — 72 73	— — — —	— — — —
		Extra Spring	0.50/0.90 0.90/— 0.30/0.70 0.70/—	495	550	—	—	78 80 — —	81 83 — —	— — 71 72	— — 73 74	— — — —	— — — —

ed. TABLE 2A—MINIMUM MECHANICAL PROPERTIES OF WROUGHT COPPER ALLOYS (CONTINUED)

Metric (SI) Units

Copper or Copper Alloy UNS No.[a,a]	Form	Temper	Size Section, mm Over/Thru	Tensile Strength, MPa Min	Tensile Strength, MPa Max	Yield Strength, Min MPa 0.5% Ext Under Load	Elongation, Min %[c] In 4 × Dia or Thickness of Specimen	Hardness Min	Hardness Max	Hardness Min	Hardness Max	Grain Size, mm Min	Grain Size, mm Max
			Wall Thickness					RF[b]		R30T[b]			
C22000	Tube	Soft Anneal	—/1.1	—	—	—	—	—	—	—	30	0.025	0.060
			1.1/—	—	—	—	—	—	70	—	—	0.025	0.060
		Light Anneal	—/1.1	—	—	—	—	—	—	—	37	Note a	0.035
			1.1/—	—	—	—	—	—	78	—	—	Note a	0.035
		Drawn (General Purpose)	All Sizes	275	—	—	—	—	—	38	—	—	—
			OD / Wall										
		Hard Drawn	—/100 / 0.5/6.5	360	—	—	—	—	—	55	—	—	—
			Size Section, mm Over/Thru										
C23000	Sheet and Strip	Annealed 0.070 mm	—	—	—	—	—	53	60	6	16	0.050	0.100
		0.050 mm	—	—	—	—	—	56	63	10	20	0.035	0.070
		0.035 mm	—	—	—	—	—	58	66	13	24	0.025	0.050
		0.025 mm	—	—	—	—	—	60	72	16	34	0.015	0.035
		0.015 mm	—	—	—	—	—	62	79	19	48	Note a	0.025
								RB[b]					
		1/4 Hard	0.50/0.90	305	370	—	—	33	58	—	—	—	—
			0.90/—					37	62	—	—	—	—
			0.30/0.70					—	—	42	57	—	—
			0.70/—					—	—	45	60	—	—
		1/2 Hard	0.50/0.90	350	420	—	—	56	68	—	—	—	—
			0.90/—					59	71	—	—	—	—
			0.30/0.70					—	—	56	64	—	—
			0.70/—					—	—	58	66	—	—
		3/4 Hard	0.50/0.90	395	460	—	—	66	73	—	—	—	—
			0.90/—					69	76	—	—	—	—
			0.30/0.70					—	—	63	68	—	—
			0.70/—					—	—	65	70	—	—
		Hard	0.50/0.90	435	495	—	—	72	78	—	—	—	—
			0.90/—					74	80	—	—	—	—
			0.30/0.70					—	—	67	71	—	—
			0.70/—					—	—	68	72	—	—
		Extra Hard	0.50/0.90	495	550	—	—	78	83	—	—	—	—
		Extra Hard	0.90/—	495	550	—	—	80	85	—	—	—	—
			0.30/0.70					—	—	70	74	—	—
			0.70/—					—	—	71	75	—	—
		Spring	0.50/0.90	540	595	—	—	82	85	—	—	—	—
			0.90/—					84	87	—	—	—	—
			0.30/0.70					—	—	74	76	—	—
			0.70/—					—	—	75	77	—	—
		Extra Spring	0.50/0.90	565	620	—	—	84	87	—	—	—	—
			0.90/—					86	89	—	—	—	—
			0.30/0.70					—	—	75	77	—	—
			0.70/—					—	—	76	78	—	—
			Wall Thickness					RF[d]		R30T[d]			
	Tube	Soft Anneal	—/1.1	—	—	—	—	—	—	—	36	0.025	0.060
			1.1/—	—	—	—	—	—	75	—	—	0.025	0.060
		Light Anneal	—/1.1	—	—	—	—	—	—	—	39	Note a	0.035
			1.1/—	—	—	—	—	—	85	—	—	Note a	0.035
		Light Drawn[e]	All Sizes	305	400	—	—	—	—	43	75	—	—
		Drawn (General Purpose)	All Sizes	305	—	—	—	—	—	43	—	—	—

ed. TABLE 2A—MINIMUM MECHANICAL PROPERTIES OF WROUGHT COPPER ALLOYS (CONTINUED)

Metric (SI) Units

Copper or Copper Alloy UNS No.[c,e]	Form	Temper	Size Section, mm		Tensile Strength, MPa		Yield Strength, Min MPa	Elongation, Min %[c]	Hardness				Grain Size, mm	
			Over/Thru		Min	Max	0.5% Ext Under Load	In 4 × Dia or Thickness of Specimen	Min	Max	Min	Max	Min	Max
			OD	Wall					RF[b]		R30T[d]			
C23000	Tube	Hard Drawn	—/109	0.5/6.5	395	—	—	—	—	—	65	—	—	—
			Size Section, mm Over/Thru											
C24000	Sheet and Strip	Annealed												
		0.070 mm	—		—	—	—	—	53	64	2	21	0.050	0.120
		0.050 mm	—		—	—	—	—	57	67	8	27	0.035	0.070
		0.035 mm	—		—	—	—	—	61	72	16	35	0.025	0.050
		0.025 mm	—		—	—	—	—	63	77	20	42	0.015	0.035
		0.015 mm	—		—	—	—	—	66	83	25	50	Note a	0.025
									RB[b]					
		1/4 Hard	0.50/0.90		330	400	—	—	38	61	—	—	—	—
			0.90/—						42	65	—	—	—	—
			0.30/0.70						—	—	42	57	—	—
			0.70/—						—	—	45	60	—	—
		1/2 Hard	0.50/0.90		380	450	—	—	59	70	—	—	—	—
			0.90/—						62	73	—	—	—	—
			0.30/0.70						—	—	56	64	—	—
			0.70/—						—	—	58	66	—	—
		3/4 Hard	0.50/0.90		420	490	—	—	69	76	—	—	—	—
			0.90/—						72	79	—	—	—	—
			0.30/0.70						—	—	63	68	—	—
			0.70/—						—	—	65	70	—	—
		Hard	0.50/0.90		470	530	—	—	76	82	—	—	—	—
			0.90/—						78	84	—	—	—	—
			0.30/0.70						—	—	68	72	—	—
			0.70/—						—	—	69	73	—	—
		Extra Hard	0.50/0.90		540	600	—	—	83	87	—	—	—	—
			0.90/—						85	89	—	—	—	—
			0.30/0.70						—	—	72	75	—	—
			0.70/—						—	—	73	76	—	—
		Spring	0.50/0.90		565	640	—	—	87	90	—	—	—	—
			0.90/—						89	92	—	—	—	—
			0.30/0.70						—	—	75	77	—	—
			0.70/—						—	—	76	78	—	—
		Extra Spring	0.50/0.90		615	670	—	—	88	91	—	—	—	—
			0.90/—						90	93	—	—	—	—
			0.30/0.70						—	—	76	78	—	—
			0.70/—						—	—	77	79	—	—
									RF[d]					
C26000	Plate[f], Sheet, Strip, Rolled Bar and Wire	Annealed												
		0.120 mm	—		—	—	—	—	50	62	—	21	0.070	—
		0.070 mm	—		—	—	—	—	52	67	3	27	0.050	0.120
		0.050 mm	—		—	—	—	—	61	73	20	35	0.035	0.070
		0.035 mm	—		—	—	—	—	65	76	25	38	0.025	0.050
		0.025 mm	—		—	—	—	—	67	79	27	42	0.015	0.035
		0.015 mm	—		—	—	—	—	72	85	33	50	Note 1	0.025
									RB[b]					
		1/4 Hard	0.50/0.90		340	405	—	—	40	61	—	—	—	—
			0.90/—						44	65	—	—	—	—
			0.30/0.70						—	—	43	57	—	—
			0.70/—						—	—	46	60	—	—
		1/2 Hard	0.50/0.90		395	460	—	—	60	74	—	—	—	—
			0.90/—						63	77	—	—	—	—
			0.30/0.70						—	—	56	66	—	—
			0.70/—						—	—	58	68	—	—
		3/4 Hard	0.50/0.90		440	510	—	—	72	70	—	—	—	—
			0.90/—						75	82	—	—	—	—
			0.30/0.70						—	—	65	70	—	—
			0.70/—						—	—	67	72	—	—

ed. TABLE 2A—MINIMUM MECHANICAL PROPERTIES OF WROUGHT COPPER ALLOYS (CONTINUED)

Copper or Copper Alloy UNS No.[a,e]	Form	Temper	Size Section, mm Over/Thru	Tensile Strength, MPa Min	Tensile Strength, MPa Max	Yield Strength, Min MPa 0.5% Ext Under Load	Elongation, Min %[c] In 4 × Dia or Thickness of Specimen	Hardness Min	Hardness Max	Hardness Min	Hardness Max	Grain Size, mm Min	Grain Size, mm Max
				Metric (SI) Units				RB[b]		R30T[d]			
C26000	Plate[f], Sheet, Strip, Rolled Bar and Wire	Hard	0.50/0.90 0.90/— 0.30/0.70 0.70/—	490	560	—	—	70 81 — —	84 86 — —	— — 70 71	— — 73 74	— — — —	— — — —
		Extra Hard	0.50/0.90 0.90/— 0.30/0.70 0.70/—	570	635	—	—	85 87 — —	89 91 — —	— — 74 75	— — 76 77	— — — —	— — — —
		Spring	0.50/0.90 0.90/— 0.30/0.70 0.70/—	625	690	—	—	89 90 — —	92 93 — —	— — 76 76	— — 78 78	— — — —	— — — —
		Extra Spring	0.50/0.90 0.90/— 0.30/0.70 0.70/—	655	715	—	—	91 92 — —	94 95 — —	— — 77 77	— — 79 79	— — — —	— — — —
	Tube		Wall Thickness					RF[b]					
		Soft Anneal	—/0.75 0.75/—	— —	— —	— —	—	— —	— 80	— —	40 —	0.025 0.025	0.060 0.060
		Light Anneal	—/0.75 0.75/—	— —	— —	— —	—	— —	— 90	— —	60 —	Note a Note a	0.035 0.035
		Drawn (General Purpose)	All Sizes	370	—	—	—	—	—	53	—	—	—
		Hard Drawn	OD —/100; Wall 0.5/6.5	455	—	—	—	—	—	70	—	—	—
			Size Section, mm Over/Thru					RF[d]		R30T[b]			
C26800	Plate[f], Sheet, Strip and Rolled Bar	Annealed 0.120 mm 0.070 mm 0.050 mm 0.035 mm 0.025 mm 0.015 mm	— — — — — —	— — — — — —	— — — — — —	— — — — — —	— — — — — —	50 52 61 65 67 72	62 67 73 76 79 85	— 3 20 25 27 33	21 27 35 38 42 50	0.070 0.050 0.035 0.025 0.015 Note a	— 0.120 0.070 0.050 0.035 0.025
								RB[b]					
		1/4 Hard	0.50/0.90 0.90/— 0.30/0.70 0.70/—	340	405	—	—	40 44 — —	61 65 — —	— — 43 46	— — 57 60	— — — —	— — — —
		1/2 Hard	0.50/0.90 0.90/— 0.30/0.70 0.70/—	380	450	—	—	57 60 — —	71 74 — —	— — 54 56	— — 64 66	— — — —	— — — —
		3/4 Hard	0.50/0.90 0.90/— 0.30/0.70 0.70/—	425	495	—	—	70 73 — —	77 80 — —	— — 65 67	— — 69 71	— — — —	— — — —
		Hard	0.50/0.90 0.90/— 0.30/0.70 0.70/—	470	540	—	—	76 78 — —	82 84 — —	— — 68 69	— — 72 73	— — — —	— — — —
								RF[b]					
		Extra Hard	0.50/0.90 0.90/— 0.30/0.70 0.70/—	545	615	—	—	83 85 — —	87 90 — —	— — 73 74	— — 75 76	— — — —	— — — —

TABLE 2A—MINIMUM MECHANICAL PROPERTIES OF WROUGHT COPPER ALLOYS (CONTINUED)

Metric (SI) Units

Copper or Copper Alloy UNS No.[c,e]	Form	Temper	Size Section, mm Over/Thru	Tensile Strength, MPa Min	Tensile Strength, MPa Max	Yield Strength, Min MPa 0.5% Ext Under Load	Elongation, Min %[c] In 4 × Dia or Thickness of Specimen	Hardness Min	Hardness Max	Hardness Min	Hardness Max	Grain Size, mm Min	Grain Size, mm Max
								RF[b]		R30T[b]			
C26800	Plate[f], Sheet, Strip and Rolled Bar	Spring	0.50/0.90 0.90/— 0.30/0.70 0.70/—	595	655	—	—	87 89 — —	90 92 — —	— — 75 76	— — 77 78	— — — —	— — — —
		Extra Spring	0.50/0.90 0.90/— 0.30/0.70 0.70/—	620	685	—	—	88 90 — —	91 93 — —	— — 76 77	— — 78 79	— — — —	— — — —
C27000	Wire	Annealed 0.100 mm 0.070 mm 0.050 mm 0.035 mm 0.025 mm 0.015 mm	 — — — — — —	 — — — — — —	 — — — — — —	 — — — — — —	 — — — — — —	 — — — — — —	 — — — — — —	 — — — — — —	 — — — — — —	 0.070 0.050 0.035 0.025 0.015 Note a	 — 0.100 0.070 0.050 0.035 0.025
		1/8 Hard 1/4 Hard 1/2 Hard 3/4 Hard Hard[h] Extra Hard[i]	— — — — — —	345 425 545 635 705 795	450 530 650 740 805 890	— — — — — —	— — — — — —	— — — — — —	— — — — — —	— — — — — —	— — — — — —	— — — — — —	— — — — — —
		Spring[j]	—	825	—	—	—	—	—	—	—	—	—
			Wall Thickness							R30T[d]			
C33000	Tube	Soft Anneal	—/0.75 0.75/—	— —	— —	—	— —	— —	— 80	— —	40 —	0.025 0.025	0.060 0.060
		Light Anneal	—/0.75 0.70/—	— —	— —	—	— —	— —	— 90	— —	60 —	Note a Note a	0.035 0.035
		Drawn (General Purpose)	All Sizes	370	—	—	—	—	—	53	—	—	—
			OD / Wall					RB[b]					
		Hard Drawn[g]	—/100 / 0.50/6.5	455	—	—	—	—	—	70	—	—	—
			Wall Thickness					RF[d]					
C33100	Tube	Soft Anneal	—/0.75 0.75/—	— —	— —	—	— —	— —	— 80	— —	40 —	0.025 0.025	0.060 0.060
		Light Anneal	—/0.75 0.75/—	— —	— —	—	— —	— —	— 90	— —	60 —	Note a Note a	0.035 0.035
		Drawn (General Purpose)	All Sizes	370	—	—	—	—	—	53	—	—	—
			OD / Wall										
		Hard Drawn	—/100 / 0.50/6.5	455	—	—	—	—	—	70	—	—	—
			Over/Thru					RF[b]		R30T[b]			
C34200 C35000	Plate, Sheet, Strip and Rolled Bar	Annealed 0.070 mm 0.050 mm 0.035 mm 0.025 mm	 All Sizes All Sizes All Sizes All Sizes	 — — — —	 — — — —	 — — — —	 — — — —	 54 61 65 67	 67 73 76 79	 12 20 25 27	 27 35 38 42	 0.050 0.035 0.025 0.015	 0.100 0.070 0.050 0.035
								RB[b]					
		1/4 Hard 1/2 Hard Hard Extra Hard	All Sizes All Sizes All Sizes All Sizes	340 380 470 545	405 450 540 615	— — — —	— — — —	40 57 76 83	65 74 84 89	43 54 68 73	60 66 73 76	— — — —	— — — —
C34500 C35000	Rod	Soft	—/12.5 12.5/25 25/50	315 305 275	— — —	110 105 105	20 25 30	— — —	— 45 45	— — —	— — —	— — —	— — —

ed. TABLE 2A—MINIMUM MECHANICAL PROPERTIES OF WROUGHT COPPER ALLOYS (CONTINUED)

Metric (SI) Units

Copper or Copper Alloy UNS No.[a]	Form	Temper	Size Section, mm: Over/Thru (Thickness)	Size Section, mm: Width	Tensile Strength, MPa: Min	Tensile Strength, MPa: Max	Yield Strength, Min MPa: 0.5% Ext Under Load	Elongation, Min %[c]: In 4 × Dia or Thickness of Specimen	Hardness RB[b]: Min	Hardness RB[b]: Max	Hardness R30T[b]: Min	Hardness R30T[b]: Max	Grain Size, mm: Min	Grain Size, mm: Max
C34500 C35000	Rod	1/4 Hard	—/12.5		360	—	170	10	50	75	—	—	—	—
			12.5/25		345	—	140	15	40	70	—	—	—	—
			25/50		290	—	105	20	35	65	—	—	—	—
		1/2 Hard	—/12.5		395	—	170	7	60	80	—	—	—	—
			12.5/25		380	—	170	10	55	75	—	—	—	—
			25/50		345	—	140	15	40	70	—	—	—	—
C36000	Rod	Soft	—/25		330	—	140	15	—	—	—	—	—	—
			25/50		305	—	125	20	—	—	—	—	—	—
			50/—		275	—	105	25	—	—	—	—	—	—
		1/2 Hard	—/12.5		395	—	170	7	—	—	—	—	—	—
			12.5/25		380	—	170	10	—	—	—	—	—	—
			25/50		345	—	140	15	—	—	—	—	—	—
			50/100		310	—	105	20	—	—	—	—	—	—
			100/—		275	—	105	20	—	—	—	—	—	—
		Hard	1.5/5.0		550	—	310	—	—	—	—	—	—	—
			5.0/12.5		480	—	240	4	—	—	—	—	—	—
			12.5/20		450	—	205	6	—	—	—	—	—	—
			Thickness	Width										
	Flat Products	Soft	—/25	—/150	305	—	125	20	—	—	—	—	—	—
			25/—	—/150	275	—	105	25	—	—	—	—	—	—
		1/2 Hard	—/12.5	—/25	345	—	170	10	—	—	—	—	—	—
			—/12.5	25/150	310	—	115	15	—	—	—	—	—	—
			12.5/50	—/50	310	—	115	20	—	—	—	—	—	—
			12.5/50	50/150	275	—	105	20	—	—	—	—	—	—
			50/—	50/100	275	—	105	20	—	—	—	—	—	—
			Over/Thru											
C37700	Die Forgings	As Forged	—/38		345	—	125	25	—	—	—	—	—	—
			38/—		315	—	105	50	—	—	—	—	—	—
C46400 C46500 C46600 C46700	Rod and Bar	Soft	—/25		370	—	140	30	—	—	—	—	—	—
			25/50		360	—	140	30	—	—	—	—	—	—
			50/—		345	—	140	30	—	—	—	—	—	—
		1/4 Hard or Light Annealed	—/12.5		415	—	185	22	—	—	—	—	—	—
			12.5/25		415	—	185	25	—	—	—	—	—	—
			25/50		400	—	180	25	—	—	—	—	—	—
			50/75		270	—	170	25	—	—	—	—	—	—
			75/100		270	—	150	27	—	—	—	—	—	—
			100/—		270	—	150	30	—	—	—	—	—	—
		Hard	—/25		460	—	310	13	—	—	—	—	—	—
			25/50		425	—	255	18	—	—	—	—	—	—
	Shapes	As Extruded	All Sizes		360	—	140	30	—	—	—	—	—	—
C51000	Sheet and Strip	Soft	1.0/—		295	400	—	—	16	64	—	—	—	—
			0.75/—						—	—	32	59	—	—
			0.50/1.0						12	60	—	—	—	—
			0.25/0.75						—	—	24	53	—	—
		1/2 Hard	1.0/—		400	505	—	—	64	85	—	—	—	—
			0.75/—						—	—	59	73	—	—
			0.50/1.0						60	82	—	—	—	—
			0.25/0.75						—	—	53	69	—	—
		Hard	1.0/—		525	625	—	—	86	93	—	—	—	—
			0.75/—						—	—	73	78	—	—
			0.50/1.0						84	91	—	—	—	—
			0.25/0.75						—	—	71	75	—	—
		Extra Hard	1.0/—		605	710	—	—	92	96	—	—	—	—
			0.75/—						—	—	77	81	—	—
			0.50/1.0						89	95	—	—	—	—
			0.25/0.75						—	—	74	78	—	—
		Spring	1.0/—		655	760	—	—	94	98	—	—	—	—
			0.75/—						—	—	79	82	—	—
			0.50/1.0						92	97	—	—	—	—
			0.25/0.75						—	—	76	80	—	—

ed. TABLE 2A—MINIMUM MECHANICAL PROPERTIES OF WROUGHT COPPER ALLOYS (CONTINUED)

Metric (SI) Units

Copper or Copper Alloy UNS No.[aa]	Form	Temper	Size Section, mm	Tensile Strength, MPa		Yield Strength, Min MPa	Elongation, Min %[c]	Hardness				Grain Size, mm	
			Over/Thru	Min	Max	0.5% Ext Under Load	In 4 × Dia or Thickness of Specimen	Min	Max	Min	Max	Min	Max
								RB[b]		R30T[b]			
C51000	Sheet and Strip	Extra Spring	1.0/—	690	785	—	—	95	99	—	—	—	—
			0.75/—					—	—	80	83	—	—
			0.50/1.0					94*	98	—	—	—	—
			0.25/0.75					—	—	77	81	—	—
	Rod	Soft	—/6.5	275	400	—	—	—	—	—	—	—	—
		Hard	—/6.5	550	885	—	—	—	—	—	—	—	—
			6.5/12.5	485	—	—	13	—	—	—	—	—	—
			12.5/25	415	—	—	15	—	—	—	—	—	—
			25/—	380	—	—	18	—	—	—	—	—	—
			6.5/9.5	415	—	—	10	—	—	—	—	—	—
			9.5/—	380	—	—	15	—	—	—	—	—	—
		Spring	—/0.65[aa]	860	—	—	—	—	—	—	—	—	—
		Spring	0.65/1.6[aa]	795	—	—	—	—	—	—	—	—	—
			1.6/3.2[aa]	760	—	—	—	—	—	—	—	—	—
			3.2/6.5[aa]	725	—	—	3.5	—	—	—	—	—	—
			6.5/9.5[aa]	690	—	—	5.0	—	—	—	—	—	—
			9.5/12.5[aa]	620	—	—	9.0	—	—	—	—	—	—
	Wire for General Purposes	Soft	—	295	400	—	—	—	—	—	—	—	—
		1/4 Hard	—	415	525	—	—	—	—	—	—	—	—
		1/2 Hard	—	550	670	—	—	—	—	—	—	—	—
		3/4 Hard	—	660	795	—	—	—	—	—	—	—	—
		Hard	—	745	885	—	—	—	—	—	—	—	—
	Wire for Spring Purposes						In 50 mm						
		—	—/0.65	1000	—	—	—	—	—	—	—	—	—
		—	0.65/1.6	930	—	—	—	—	—	—	—	—	—
		—	1.6/3.2	845	—	—	—	—	—	—	—	—	—
		—	3.2/6.5	860	—	—		—	—	—	—	—	—
		—	6.5/9.5	825	—	—	5.0	—	—	—	—	—	—
		—	9.5/12.5	720	—	—	9.0	—	—	—	—	—	—
C51100 C54400	Sheet and Strip	Soft	1.0/—	275	380	—	—	7	50	—	—	—	—
			0.75/—					—	—	24	50	—	—
			0.50/1.0					0	45	—	—	—	—
			0.25/0.75					—	—	16	46	—	—
		1/2 Hard	1.0/—	380	485	—	—	60	81	—	—	—	—
			0.75/—					—	—	57	73	—	—
			0.50/1.0					53	78	—	—	—	—
			0.25/0.75					—	—	52	71	—	—
		Hard	1.0/—	495	600	—	—	82	90	—	—	—	—
			0.75/—					—	—	71	77	—	—
			0.50/1.0					80	88	—	—	—	—
			0.25/0.75					—	—	69	75	—	—
		Extra Hard	1.0/—	580	685	—	—	88	94	—	—	—	—
			0.75/—					—	—	75	80	—	—
			0.50/1.0					86	92	—	—	—	—
			0.25/0.75					—	—	73	78	—	—
		Spring	1.0/—	625	725	—	—	90	96	—	—	—	—
			0.75/—					—	—	77	81	—	—
			0.50/1.0					88	94	—	—	—	—
			0.25/0.75					—	—	75	79	—	—
		Extra Spring	1.0/—	660	750	—	—	92	97	—	—	—	—
			0.75/—					—	—	78	82	—	—
			0.50/1.0					89	94	—	—	—	—
			0.25/0.75					—	—	76	80	—	—
C52100	Sheet and Strip	Soft	1.0/—	365	460	—	—	29	70	—	—	—	—
			0.75/—					—	—	38	68	—	—
							In 4 × Dia or Thickness of Specimen						
		Soft	0.50/1.0	365	460	—	—	20	66	—	—	—	—
			0.25/0.75					—	—	27	62	—	—

ed. TABLE 2A—MINIMUM MECHANICAL PROPERTIES OF WROUGHT COPPER ALLOYS (CONTINUED)

Copper or Copper Alloy UNS No.[cc]	Form	Temper	Metric (SI) Units: Size Section, mm Over/Thru	Tensile Strength, MPa Min	Tensile Strength, MPa Max	Yield Strength, Min MPa 0.5% Ext Under Load	Elongation, Min %[c] In 4 × Dia or Thickness of Specimen	Hardness RB[b] Min	Hardness RB[b] Max	Hardness R30T[b] Min	Hardness R30T[b] Max	Grain Size, mm Min	Grain Size, mm Max
C52100	Sheet and Strip	1/2 Hard	1.0/—	475	580	—	—	76	91	—	—	—	—
			0.75/—					—	—	67	78	—	—
			0.50/1.0					69	88	—	—	—	—
			0.25/0.75					—	—	63	75	—	—
		Hard	1.0/—	585	690	—	—	91	97	—	—	—	—
			0.75/—					—	—	76	81	—	—
			0.50/1.0					89	95	—	—	—	—
			0.25/0.75					—	—	73	80	—	—
		Extra Hard	1.0/—	670	770	—	—	95	100	—	—	—	—
			0.75/—					—	—	78	83	—	—
			0.50/1.0					93	98	—	—	—	—
			0.25/0.75					—	—	77	82	—	—
		Spring	1.0/—	725	820	—	—	97	102	—	—	—	—
			0.75/—					—	—	79	84	—	—
			0.50/1.0					95	100	—	—	—	—
			0.25/0.75					—	—	78	83	—	—
		Extra Spring	1.0/—	760	840	—	—	98	103	—	—	—	—
			0.75/—					—	—	80	84	—	—
			0.50/1.0					96	101	—	—	—	—
			0.25/0.75					—	—	79	83	—	—
C52400	Sheet and Strip	Soft	1.0/—	400	505	—	—	35	75	—	—	—	—
			0.75/—					—	—	40	78	—	—
			0.50/1.0					25	—	71	—	—	—
			0.25/0.75					—	—	29	84	—	—
		1/2 Hard	1.0/—	525	625	—	—	78	95	—	—	—	—
			0.75/—					—	—	67	80	—	—
			0.50/1.0					74	93	—	—	—	—
			0.25/0.75					—	—	63	77	—	—
		Hard	1.0/—	650	750	—	—	94	101	—	—	—	—
			0.75/—					—	—	78	82	—	—
			0.50/1.0					92	100	—	—	—	—
			0.25/0.75					—	—	75	81	—	—
		Extra Hard	1.0/—	740	840	—	—	93	103	—	—	—	—
			0.75/—					—	—	80	84	—	—
			0.50/1.0					97	102	—	—	—	—
			0.25/0.75					—	—	79	83	—	—
		Spring	1.0/—	795	890	—	—	99	104	—	—	—	—
			0.75/—					—	—	81	85	—	—
			0.50/1.0					98	103	—	—	—	—
			0.25/0.75					—	—	80	84	—	—
		Extra Spring	1.0/—	825	915	—	—	100	105	—	—	—	—
			0.75/—					—	—	82	86	—	—
		Extra Spring	0.50/1.0	825	915	—	—	99	104	—	—	—	—
			0.25/0.75					—	—	81	85	—	—
C54400	Sheet and Strip	See C51100											
	Rod	Hard	1.5/6.5[bb]	450	—	—	8	—	—	—	—	—	—
			6.5/12.5[bb]	415	—	—	10	—	—	—	—	—	—
			12.5/25[bb]	380	—	—	12	—	—	—	—	—	—
			25/—[bb]	345	—	—	15	—	—	—	—	—	—
	Flat Products	Hard	6.5/9.5[cc]	380	—	—	10	—	—	—	—	—	—
			9.5/—[cc]	345	—	—	15	—	—	—	—	—	—
C60800	Tube	Annealed	All Sizes	345	—	130	—	—	—	—	—	0.010	0.045
C61300	Plate[t], Sheet, Strip and Rolled Bar		Thickness / Width				In 50 mm			BHN 1000 kg			
		Soft	—/12.5 / All	515	—	255	35	—	—	—	—	—	—
			12.5/50 / All	495	—	210	35	—	—	—	—	—	—
			50/125 / All	450	—	195	35	—	—	—	—	—	—

ed. TABLE 2A—MINIMUM MECHANICAL PROPERTIES OF WROUGHT COPPER ALLOYS (CONTINUED)

Copper or Copper Alloy UNS No.[ee]	Form	Temper	Size Section, mm Over/Thru		Tensile Strength, MPa Min	Tensile Strength, MPa Max	Yield Strength, Min MPa 0.5% Ext Under Load	Elongation, Min %[c] In 4 × Dia or Thickness of Specimen	Hardness Min	Hardness Max	Hardness Min	Hardness Max	Grain Size, mm Min	Grain Size, mm Max
Metric (SI) Units														
			Thickness	Width				In 50 mm	RB[b]		BHN 1000 kg			
C61400	Plate[t], Sheet, Strip and Rolled Bar	Soft	—/12.5	All	495	—	220	35	—	—	—	—	—	—
			12.5/50	All	485	—	205	35	—	—	—	—	—	—
			50/125	All	450	—	195	35	—	—	—	—	—	—
		Hard	—/12.5	All	550	—	310	25	—	—	—	—	—	—
			12.5/25	All	485	—	275	30	—	—	—	—	—	—
C61300	Rod and Bar	—	—/12.5		550	—	345	30	—	—	—	—	—	—
			12.5/25		515	—	310	30	—	—	—	—	—	—
			25/50		495	—	275	30	—	—	—	—	—	—
			50/75		485	—	240	30	—	—	—	—	—	—
									RB[b]		BHN 1000 kg			
C61400	Rod and Bar	—	—/12.5		550	—	275	30	—	—	—	—	—	—
			12.5/25		515	—	240	30	—	—	—	—	—	—
			25/50		485	—	220	30	—	—	—	—	—	—
			50/75		485	—	205	30	—	—	—	—	—	—
C61800	Rod	1/2 Hard	—/75		—	—	—	—	—	—	—	—	—	—
C62300	Rod and Bar	Drawn	—/12.5		620	—	310	12	90	—	155	—	—	—
			12.5/25		605	—	305	15	—	—	—	—	—	—
			25/—		580	—	275	15	—	—	—	—	—	—
			50/25		525	—	255	20	—	—	—	—	—	—
			75/—		515	—	205	20	—	—	—	—	—	—
	Shapes	—	All Sizes		—	—	205	20	—	—	—	—	—	—
											3000 kg			
	Forgings	As Forged	—/38		515	—	205	20	—	—	—	—	—	—
			38/—		495	—	195	25	—	—	—	—	—	—
C62400	Rod	As Extruded	All Sizes		550	—	310	7.0	—	—	175	—	—	—
	Forgings	As Forged	—		550	—	310	7.0	—	—	175	—	—	—
		Hardened and H_2O Quenched	—		—	—	—	—	—	—	240	—	—	—
		Hardened, H_2O Quenched and Tempered	—		600	—	—	8.0	—	—	179	—	—	—
											R30T[b]			
C63000	Rod and Bar	Annealed	12.5/25		690	—	345	5	—	—	—	—	—	—
			25/50		620	—	310	6	—	—	—	—	—	—
			50/100		585	—	295	10	—	—	—	—	—	—
	Shapes	As Extruded	All Sizes		585	—	295	10	—	—	—	—	—	—
C64200	Rod and Bar	Drawn	—/12.5		620	—	310	9	—	—	—	—	—	—
			12.5/25		585	—	310	12	—	—	—	—	—	—
			25/50		550	—	290	12	—	—	—	—	—	—
			50/75		515	—	240	15	—	—	—	—	—	—
											RF[b]			
C65500	Plate[t], Sheet, Strip and Rolled Bar	Annealed 0.070 mm	—		360	400	—	—	—	—	70	82	0.050	0.110
		Annealed 0.040 mm	—		380	440	—	—	—	—	76	93	Note 1	0.055
		1/4 Hard	—		425	495	—	—	65	60	—	—	—	—
		1/2 Hard[k]	—		490	560	—	—	79	91	—	—	—	—
		Hard[k]	—		600	670	—	—	88	96	—	—	—	—
		Extra Hard[k]	—		685	745	—	—	93	98	—	—	—	—
		Spring[k]	—		725	780	—	—	94	99	—	—	—	—

ed. TABLE 2A—MINIMUM MECHANICAL PROPERTIES OF WROUGHT COPPER ALLOYS (CONTINUED)

Metric (SI) Units

Copper or Copper Alloy UNS No.[ee]	Form	Temper	Size Section, mm Over/Thru	Tensile Strength, MPa Min	Tensile Strength, MPa Max	Yield Strength, Min MPa 0.5% Ext Under Load	Elongation, Min %[c] In 4 × Dia or Thickness of Specimen	Hardness Min	Hardness Max	Hardness Min	Hardness Max	Grain Size, mm Min	Grain Size, mm Max
								RB[b]		RF[b]			
C65500	Plate[t], Sheet, Strip and Rolled Bar	Hot Rolled	—	380	495	—	—	—	—	72	—	—	—
		Hot Rolled and Cold Rolled Finish	—	400	495	—	—	60	80	—	—	—	—
										R30T[b]			
	Rod, Bar and Shapes	Soft	All Forms and Sizes	360	—	105	35	—	—	—	—	—	—
		1/4 Hard	All Forms and Sizes	380	—	165	25	—	—	—	—	—	—
		1/2 Hard	—/50[dd]	485	—	260	17	—	—	—	—	—	—
		Hard	—/6.5[dd]	585	—	345	8	—	—	—	—	—	—
			6.5/38[dd]	585	—	345	13	—	—	—	—	—	—
		Extra Hard	—/12.5[w]	690	—	380	7	—	—	—	—	—	—
	Rod	Soft	All Sizes	360	—	105	35	—	—	—	—	—	—
		Hard	—/25	450	—	265	20	—	—	—	—	—	—
			25/38	415	—	205	25	—	—	—	—	—	—
			38/75	380	—	165	27	—	—	—	—	—	—
C67000	Rod and Bar	Soft	All Sizes	585	—	310	10[v]	—	—	—	—	—	—
		1/2 Hard	All Sizes	725	—	415	7[v]	—	—	—	—	—	—
		Hard	All Sizes	795	—	470	5[v]	—	—	—	—	—	—
	Forgings	Soft	—	585	—	310	10	—	—	—	—	—	—
		1/2 Hard	—	675	—	345	7	—	—	—	—	—	—
		Hard	—	690	—	380	5	—	—	—	—	—	—
C67300	Rod and Bar	As Extruded	All Sizes	360	—	170	20	60	—	—	—	—	—
		Soft	All Sizes	360	—	170	20	50	—	—	—	—	—
		1/2 Hard[w]	—/25	450	—	275	12	70	—	—	—	—	—
			25/75	400	—	240	15	70	—	—	—	—	—
			75/—	360	—	205	18	65	—	—	—	—	—
		1/2 Hard[x]	All Sizes	415	—	205	20	70	—	—	—	—	—
		Hard[w]	—/25	485	—	345	10	70	—	—	—	—	—
			25/50	425	—	290	15	70	—	—	—	—	—
	Shapes	As Extruded	All Sizes	360	—	170	20	60	—	—	—	—	—
	Forgings	As Forged	—	360	—	170	20	60	—	—	—	—	—
		Forged and Heat Treated	—	475	—	240	12	70	—	—	—	—	—
C67400	Rod and Bar	As Extruded	All Sizes	485	—	235	12	75	—	—	—	—	—
		Extruded and Drawn	—/25	540	—	275	8	84	—	—	—	—	—
			25/50	515	—	275	10	80	—	—	—	—	—
			50/75	485	—	250	12	78	—	—	—	—	—
	Shapes	As Extruded	All Sizes	485	—	235	12	75	—	—	—	—	—
	Forgings	As Forged	—	450	—	205	15	75	—	—	—	—	—
C67500	Rod	Soft	All Sizes	380	—	150	20	—	—	—	—	—	—
		1/2 Hard	—/25	495	—	250	13	—	—	—	—	—	—
			25/65	485	—	240	15	—	—	—	—	—	—
			65/—	450	—	220	17	—	—	—	—	—	—
		Hard	—/25	550	—	385	8	—	—	—	—	—	—
			25/38	525	—	360	10	—	—	—	—	—	—
			38/65	505	—	330	12	—	—	—	—	—	—
			65/—	470	—	310	16	—	—	—	—	—	—

ed. TABLE 2A—MINIMUM MECHANICAL PROPERTIES OF WROUGHT COPPER ALLOYS (CONTINUED)

Metric (SI) Units

Copper or Copper Alloy UNS No.[aa]	Form	Temper	Size Section, mm Over/Thru	Tensile Strength, MPa Min	Tensile Strength, MPa Max	Yield Strength, Min MPa 0.5% Ext Under Load	Elongation, Min %[c] In 4 × Dia or Thickness of Specimen		Hardness Min	Hardness Max	Hardness Min	Hardness Max	Grain Size, mm Min	Grain Size, mm Max
									RB[b]		R30T[b]			
C67500	Bar	Soft	All Sizes	380	—	150	20		—	—	—	—	—	—
		1/2 Hard	—/25	495	—	250	13		—	—	—	—	—	—
			25/65	485	—	240	15		—	—	—	—	—	—
			65/—	450	—	220	17		—	—	—	—	—	—
		Hard	—/25	550	—	385	8		—	—	—	—	—	—
			25/65	525	—	360	12		—	—	—	—	—	—
			65/—	505	—	330	16		—	—	—	—	—	—
	Shapes	Soft	All Sizes	470	—	310	20		—	—	—	—	—	—
							In 50 mm							
C70600	Condenser Tube Plate	—	—/65	275	—	105	30		—	—	—	—	—	—
	Tube	Annealed	—	275	—	105	—		—	—	—	—	—	—
		Light Drawn	—	310	—	240	—		—	—	—	—	—	—
							Hardness Min	Hardness Max						
							RF[b]							
C71000	Tube	Annealed	—	310	—	110	—	—	—	—	—	—	—	—
	Plate[f], Sheet, Strip and Rolled Bar	Annealed												
		0.035 mm	—	—	—	—	67	76	18	35	28	40	0.025	0.050
		0.015 mm	—	—	—	—	76	90	35	58	40	55	Note a	0.020
		1/4 Hard	—	325	435	—	—	—	45	72	46	65	—	—
		1/2 Hard	—	385	485	—	—	—	64	78	59	69	—	—
		Hard	—	460	545	—	—	—	76	84	67	73	—	—
		Extra Hard	—	495	580	—	—	—	79	87	69	75	—	—
		Spring	—	525	600	—	—	—	82	88	71	75	—	—
							Elongation, Min % In 50 mm							
C71500	Condenser Tube Plate	—	—/65	345	—	140	35		—	—	—	—	—	—
			65/125	310	—	125	35		—	—	—	—	—	—
	Tube	Annealed	—	360	—	125	—		—	—	—	—	—	—
		Drawn and Stress Relieved	—/1.2 Wall	495	—	345	12		—	—	—	—	—	—
			1.2/— Wall	495	—	345	15		—	—	—	—	—	—
							Hardness Min	Hardness Max						
							RF[b]							
	Plate[f], Sheet, Strip and Rolled Bar	Annealed												
		0.035 mm	—	—		—	70	85	23	45	31	46	0.025	0.050
		0.015 mm	—	—	—	—	74	93	37	63	40	58	Note a	0.025
		1/4 Hard	—	400	485	—	—	—	67	81	61	71	—	—
		1/2 Hard	—	455	550	—	—	—	76	85	67	74	—	—
		Hard	—	515	605	—	—	—	83	89	72	76	—	—
		Extra Hard	—	550	635	—	—	—	85	91	73	77	—	—
		Spring	—	580	650	—	—	—	87	91	74	77	—	—

ϕ *ed.* **TABLE 2A—MINIMUM MECHANICAL PROPERTIES OF WROUGHT COPPER ALLOYS (CONTINUED)**

Metric (SI) Units

Copper or Copper Alloy UNS No.[ee]	Form	Temper	Size Section, mm	Tensile Strength, MPa		Yield Strength, Min MPa	Hardness						Grain Size, mm	
			Over/Thru	Min	Max	0.5% Ext Under Load	Min	Max	Min	Max	Min	Max	Min	Max
							RF[b]		RB[b]		R30T[b]			
C75200	Plate[t], Sheet, Strip and Rolled Bar	Annealed												
		0.070 mm	—	—	—	—	70	80	25	40	32	43	0.050	0.100
		0.035 mm	—	—	—	—	75	88	35	55	40	53	0.025	0.050
		0.015 mm	—	—	—	—	83	93	45	70	46	64	Note a	0.025
		1/4 Hard	—	400	495	—	—	—	50	75	49	67	—	—
		1/2 Hard	—	455	550	—	—	—	68	82	62	72	—	—
		Hard	—	540	625	—	—	—	80	90	70	76	—	—
		Extra Hard	—	595	675	—	—	—	87	94	74	79	—	—
		Spring	—	620	695	—	—	—	89	96	75	80	—	—
	Rod and Bar	Annealed												
		0.070 mm	—	—	—	—	—	—	—	—	—	—	0.050	0.100
		0.035 mm	—	—	—	—	—	—	—	—	—	—	0.025	0.050
		0.015 mm	—	—	—	—	—	—	—	—	—	—	—	0.030
		1/4 Hard	0.50/12.5[y]	415	550	—	—	—	—	—	—	—	—	—
		Hard	0.5/6.5[w]	550	690	—	—	—	—	—	—	—	—	—
			6.5/12.5[w]	480	620	—	—	—	—	—	—	—	—	—
			12.5/25[w]	450	555	—	—	—	—	—	—	—	—	—
			25/—[w]	415	550	—	—	—	—	—	—	—	—	—
			All Sizes[x]	470	605	—	—	—	—	—	—	—	—	—
C77000	Plate[t], Sheet, Strip and Rolled Bar	Annealed												
		0.070 mm	—	—	—	—	72	83	29	45	35	46	0.050	0.100
		0.035 mm	—	—	—	—	76	91	37	60	41	57	0.025	0.050
		0.015 mm	—	—	—	—	84	98	47	73	47	65	Note a	0.025
							RG[b]							
		1/4 Hard	—	475	600	—	23	62	70	88	63	75	—	—
		1/2 Hard	—	540	655	—	51	69	81	92	71	78	—	—
		Hard	—	635	740	—	67	76	90	96	76	80	—	—
		Extra Hard	—	705	795	—	73	80	95	99	79	82	—	—
		Spring	—	745	825	—	77	83	97	100	80	—	—	—
	Rod and Bar	Annealed												
		0.070 mm	—	—	—	—	—	—	—	—	—	—	0.050	0.100
		0.035 mm	—	—	—	—	—	—	—	—	—	—	0.025	0.050
		0.015 mm	—	—	—	—	—	—	—	—	—	—	—	0.030
		1/4 Hard	0.50/12.5[y]	515	655	—	—	—	—	—	—	—	—	—
		Hard	0.50/6.5[w]	620	700	—	—	—	—	—	—	—	—	—
			0.50/6.5[w]	550	690	—	—	—	—	—	—	—	—	—
			12.5/25[w]	515	655	—	—	—	—	—	—	—	—	—
			25/—[w]	485	620	—	—	—	—	—	—	—	—	—
			All Sizes[x]	515	655	—	—	—	—	—	—	—	—	—

[a] Although no minimum grain size is required, this material must be fully recrystallized.

[b] Values are approximate. F and B scales for metal 0.50 mm and over in thickness. 30T scale for metal 0.30 mm and over in thickness. (0.40 mm for annealed material to ASTM B36 and B122).

[c] In any case, a minimum gage length of 25 mm shall be used.

[d] Hardness values shall apply only to tubes having a wall thickness of 0.40 mm or over for annealed temper and 0.50 mm or over for drawn temper (0.30 mm for drawn temper to ASTM B135), to round tubes having an inside diameter of 8.0 mm or over, and to rectangular, including square, tubes having an inside major distance between parallel surfaces of 4.8 mm or over. For all other tubes, no Rockwell values shall apply. Hardness tests shall be made on the inside surface of the tube. When suitable equipment is not available for determining the specified hardness, other Rockwell scales and values may be specified, subject to agreement between purchaser and supplier.

[e] 3.2 to 22.0 mm outside diameter 0.75 to 1.1 mm wall.

[f] Generally available in round, hexagonal, and octagonal.

[g] Normally available in round only.

[h] Not generally available in sizes over 12.5 mm in diameter.

[i] Not generally available in sizes over 9.5 mm in diameter. Square and rectangular wire not generally available.

[j] Not generally available in sizes over 6.5 mm in diameter. Square and rectangular wire not generally available.

[k] Commercially supplied only as strip. Manufacturer should be consulted for sheet or plate.

[l] Capable of being hardened by further heat treatment.

[m] Rods and bars.

[n] Applicable to material 0.10 mm and over.

[o] Applicable to material 0.80 mm and over.

[p] Applicable to material 0.40 mm and over.

[q] When stated on contract or order, tension test shall be waived provided the strip meets the hardness requirement. In case of dispute, tension test shall be the basis for acceptance.

[r] Commonly supplied only as strip.

[s] 6.5 mm and over.

[t] Plate generally available only in annealed, quarter hard, and half hard.

[u] Type A material to listed hardness limits supplied unless otherwise specified.

[v] Cold finished.

[w] Rods only.

[x] Bars only.

[y] After heat treatment.

[z] After mill heat treatment.

[aa] Rounds only.

[bb] Rounds and hexagons.

[cc] Squares and rectangles.

[dd] Rods and square bars.

[ee] Unified Number System. For cross reference to SAE, former SAE, ASTM and former trade names, see SAE J461.

ed. TABLE 2B—MINIMUM MECHANICAL PROPERTIES OF WROUGHT COPPER ALLOYS (CONTINUED)

Customary Units

Copper or Copper Alloy UNS No.[ee]	Form	Temper	Size Section, in Over/Thru	Tensile Strength, ksi Min	Tensile Strength, ksi Max	Yield Strength, Min ksi 0.5% Ext Under Load	Elongation, Min %[c] In 2 in	Hardness Min	Hardness Max	Hardness Min	Hardness Max	Grain Size, mm Min	Grain Size, mm Max
				Type B Matl[u]				RB		R30T[b]			
C16200	Rod (Round Only)	Drawn	—/1.0	60	—	—	20	65	—	—	—	—	—
			1.0/2.0	55	—	—	25	60	—	—	—	—	—
			2.0/3.0	50	—	—	25	55	—	—	—	—	—
	Bar (Square and Rectangular) and Rod (Hexagonal)	Drawn	—/1.0 Thick	60	—	—	20	55	—	—	—	—	—
			1.0/— Thick	50	—	—	25	50	—	—	—	—	—
	Forging	As Forged	—/1.0 Thick	60	—	—	20	55	—	—	—	—	—
			1.0/— Thick	50	—	—	25	50	—	—	—	—	—
						0.2% Offset	In 2 in[n]	RB[o,q]		R30T[p,q]		Elec Cond, % IACS Min	Heat Treat h at 600°F
C17000	Strip	A (Soft)[l]	All Sizes	60	78	—	35	45	78	46	67	17	—
		1/4 Hard[l]	All Sizes	75	88	—	10	68	90	62	75	16	—
		1/2 Hard[l]	All Sizes	85	100	—	5	88	96	74	79	15	—
		Hard[l]	All Sizes	100	120	—	2	96	102	79	83	15	—
								RC[o,q]		R30N[p,q]			
		AT[y]	All Sizes	150	—	130 min	3	33	—	53	—	22	3
		1/4 HT[y]	All Sizes	160	—	135 mm	2.5	35	—	55	—	22	2
		1/2 HT[y]	All Sizes	170	—	145 min	1	37	—	56	—	22	2
		HT[y]	All Sizes	180	—	155 mm	1	39	—	59	—	22	2
		AM[z]	All Sizes	100	115	70 min 95 max	18	18	23	37	44	23	—
		1/4 HM[z]	All Sizes	110	125	80 min 105 max	15	21	26	42	47	23	—
		1/2 HM[z]	All Sizes	120	135	95 min 115 max	12	25	30	46	50	24	—
		HM[z]	All Sizes	135	150	110 min 135 max	9	30	35	50	55	25	—
		XHM[z]	All Sizes	160	175	135 min 160 max	2	32	36	52	56	24	—
								RB[o,q]		R30T[p,q]			
C17200	Strip	A (Soft)[l]	All Sizes	60	78	—	35	45	78	46	67	17	—
		1/4 Hard[l]	All Sizes	75	88	—	10	68	90	62	75	16	—
		1/2 Hard[l]	All Sizes	85	100	—	5	88	96	74	79	15	—
		Hard[l]	All Sizes	100	120	—	5	96	102	79	83	15	—
								RC[o,q]		R30N[p,q]			
		AT[y]	All Sizes	165	195	—	—	36	—	56	—	22	3
		1/4 HT[y]	All Sizes	175	205	—	—	38	—	58	—	22	2
		1/2 HT[y]	All Sizes	185	215	—	—	39	—	59	—	22	2
		HT[y]	All Sizes	195	220	—	—	40	—	60	—	22	2
								RB[o,q]					
	Rod and Bar	A (Soft)[l]	All Sizes	60	85	—	—	45	85	—	—	17	—
		Hard[l]	—/.375	95	130	—	—	92	103	—	—	15	—
			.375/1.0	90	120	—	—	91	102	—	—	15	—
			1.0/—	85	115	—	—	88	104	—	—	15	—
								RC[o,q]					
		AT[y]	All Sizes	165	190	—	—	36	40	—	—	22	3

ed. TABLE 2B—MINIMUM MECHANICAL PROPERTIES OF WROUGHT COPPER ALLOYS (CONTINUED)

Customary Units

Copper or Copper Alloy UNS No.[ce]	Form	Temper	Size Section, in	Tensile Strength, ksi		Yield Strength, Min ksi	Elongation, Min %[c]	Hardness				Elec Cond, % IACS	Heat Treat h at 600°F
			Over/Thru	Min	Max	0.2% Offset	In 2 in[n]	Min	Max	Min	Max	Min	
				Type B Mat'l[u]				RC[o,q]		R30N[p,q]			
C17200	Rod and Bar	HT[y]	—/.375 .375/1.0 1.0/—	185 180 175	215 210 205	— — —	— — —	39 38 37	45 44 43	— — —	— — —	22 22 22	3 2 2
				Min	Max		In 2 in	RB[o,q]		R30T[p,q]			
C17500	Strip and Plate	A (Soft)[l]	All Sizes	—	55	20 min 30 max	20	20	45	29	45	20	—
		1/2 Hard[l]	All Sizes	60	75	50 min 70 max	5	65	76	60	67	25	—
		Hard[l]	All Sizes	70	85	60 min 80 max	2	78	88	69	75	25	—
		AT[y]	All Sizes	100	120	80 min 100 max	8	92	100	77	82	45	—
		1/2 HT[y]	All Sizes	110	130	95 min 120 max	5	95	102	79	83	48	—
		HT[y]	All Sizes	110	130	95 min 120 max	5	95	102	79	83	48	—
	Hot Worked Sizes, Forgings	A (Soft)[l]	All Sizes	—	55	20 min 30 max	20	20	45	—	—	20	—
		AT[y]	All Sizes	100	120	80 min 100 max	10	92	100	—	—	45	—
										R30T[o,q]			
C17500 C17600	Rod, Bar Shapes and Tubing	A (Soft)[l]	All Sizes	35	55	20 min 30 max	20	25	45	—	—	20	—
		1/2 Hard	All Sizes	65	85	55 min 75 max	10	60	75	—	—	20	—
		AT[y]	All Sizes	100	120	80 min 100 max	10	92	100	—	—	45	—
		1/2 HT[y]	All Sizes	110	130	100 min 120 max	8	92	102	—	—	48	—
						0.5% Ext Under Load		RB		R30T[b]		Grain Size, mm Min	Grain Size, mm Max
C18400	Round Rod	Drawn	—/1.0 1.0/2.0 2.0/3.0	65 60 55	— — —	— — —	15 15 15	75 70 65	— — —	— — —	— — —	— — —	— — —
	Rod (Hexagonal) and Bars	Drawn	—/1.0 Thick 1.0/— Thick	65 55	— —	— —	15 15	70 65	— —	— —	— —	— —	— —
	Forgings	As Forged	—/1.0 1.0/2.0 2.0/—	65 55 55	— — —	— — —	15 15 15	72 70 65	— — —	— — —	— — —	— — —	— — —
C18700	Rod	1/2 Hard[f]	.062/.250 .250/2.625	38 38	— —	30 30	8 12	— —	— —	— —	— —	— —	— —
		Hard	.062/.250 .250/1.250 1.250/2.000	48 44 40	— — —	40 38 35	4 8 8	— — —	— — —	— — —	— — —	— — —	— — —
C19200	Tube	A (Soft) Light Drawn	All Sizes All Sizes	38 40	— —	12 35	— —	— —	— —	— —	— —	— —	— —

TABLE 2B—MINIMUM MECHANICAL PROPERTIES OF WROUGHT COPPER ALLOYS (CONTINUED)

Customary Units													
Copper or Copper Alloy UNS No.[a]	Form	Temper	Size Section, in	Tensile Strength, ksi		Yield Strength, Min ksi	Elongation, Min %[c]	Hardness				Grain Size, mm	
			Over/Thru	Min	Max	0.5% Ext Under Load	In 2 in	Min	Max	Min	Max	Min	Max
								RF[b]		R30T[b]			
C21000	Plate, Sheet, Strip and Rolled Bar[d]	Annealed 0.050 mm	—	—	—	—	—	40	52	—	4	0.035	0.090
		0.035 mm	—	—	—	—	—	47	54	—	7	0.025	0.050
		0.025 mm	—	—	—	—	—	50	61	1	17	0.015	0.035
		0.015 mm	—	—	—	—	—	54	65	7	23	Note a	0.025
								RB[b]					
		1/4 Hard	.019/.036	37	47	—	—	20	48	—	—	—	
			.036/—					24	52	—	—	—	
			.011/.028					—	—	34	51	—	
			.028/—					—	—	37	54	—	
		1/2 Hard	.019/.036	42	52	—	—	40	56	—	—	—	—
			.036/—					44	60	—	—	—	—
			.011/.028					—	—	46	57	—	—
			.028/—					—	—	48	59	—	—
		3/4 Hard	.019/.036	46	56	—	—	50	61	—	—	—	—
			.036/—					53	64	—	—	—	—
							In 4 × Dia or Thickness of Specimen						
		3/4 Hard	.011/.028	46	56	—	—	—	—	52	60		
			.028/—					—	—	54	62		
		Hard	.019/.036	50	59	—	—	57	64	—	—	—	—
			.036/—					60	67	—	—	—	—
			.011/.028					—	—	57	62	—	—
			.028/—					—	—	59	64	—	—
		Extra Hard	.019/.036	56	64	—	—	64	70	—	—	—	—
			.036/—					66	72	—	—	—	—
			.011/.028					—	—	62	66	—	—
			.028/—					—	—	63	67	—	—
		Spring	.019/.036	60	68	—	—	68	73	—	—	—	—
			.036/—					70	75	—	—	—	—
			.011/.028					—	—	64	68	—	—
			.028/—					—	—	65	69	—	—
		Extra Spring	.019/.036	61	69	—	—	69	74	—	—	—	—
			.036/—					71	76	—	—	—	—
			.011/.028					—	—	65	69	—	—
			.028/—					—	—	66	70	—	—
								RF[b]					
C22000	Plate, Sheet, Strip and Rolled Bar[d]	Annealed 0.050 mm	—	—	—	—	—	50	60	1	16	0.035	0.090
		0.035 mm	—	—	—	—	—	54	64	7	21	0.025	0.050
		0.025 mm	—	—	—	—	—	58	70	13	31	0.015	0.035
		0.015 mm	—	—	—	—	—	62	75	19	39	Note a	0.025
								RB[b]					
		1/4 Hard	.019/.036	40	50	—	—	27	52	—	—	—	—
			.036/—					31	56	—	—	—	—
			.011/.028					—	—	38	53	—	—
			.028/—					—	—	41	56	—	—
		1/2 Hard	.019/.036	47	57	—	—	50	63	—	—	—	—
			.036/—					53	66	—	—	—	—
			.011/.028					—	—	52	61	—	—
			.028/—					—	—	54	63	—	—
		3/4 Hard	.019/.036	52	62	—	—	59	68	—	—	—	—
			.036/—					62	71	—	—	—	—
			.011/.028					—	—	58	64	—	—
			.028/—					—	—	60	66	—	—
		Hard	.019/.036	57	66	—	—	65	72	—	—	—	—
			.036/—					68	75	—	—	—	—
			.011/.028					—	—	62	66	—	—
			.028/—					—	—	64	68	—	—

ed. TABLE 2B—MINIMUM MECHANICAL PROPERTIES OF WROUGHT COPPER ALLOYS (CONTINUED)

Customary Units

Copper or Copper Alloy UNS No.[ee]	Form	Temper	Size Section, in Over/Thru		Tensile Strength, ksi Min	Tensile Strength, ksi Max	Yield Strength, Min ksi 0.5% Ext Under Load	Elongation, Min %[c] In 4 × Dia or Thickness of Specimen	Hardness Min	Hardness Max	Hardness Min	Hardness Max	Grain Size, mm Min	Grain Size, mm Max
									RF[b]		R30T[b]			
C10200 C11000 C11100 C11300 C11400 C11500 C11600 C12000 C12200	Plate, Sheet, Strip and Rolled Bar	Soft Anneal	—		—	—	—	—	—	65	—	—	Note a	—
		Deep-Drawing Anneal	—		—	—	—	—	30	75	—	—	Note a	0.050
		Light Cold Rolled	—		32	40	—	—	40	82	—	49	—	—
		1/2 Hard[r]	—		37	46	—	—	77	89	43	57	—	—
		Hard[r]	—		43	52	—	—	86	93	54	62	—	—
		Spring[r]	—		50	58	—	—	91	97	60	66	—	—
		Extra Spring[r]	—		52	—	—	—	92	—	61	—	—	—
		Hot Rolled	—		30	38	—	—	—	75	—	41	—	—
		Hot Rolled and Annealed	—		30	38	—	—	—	65	—	31	—	—
					Type B Matl[w]			Type B[u]	Type A[a,u]					
C10200 C11000 C12000 C12200	Rod, Bar and Shapes	Soft Anneal	All Sizes[m]		—	37	—	25	—	65	—	—	—	—
		Hard	—/.250[w]		50	—	—	—	68	95	—	—	—	—
			.250/.375[w]		45	—	—	10	68	95	—	—	—	—
			.375/1.0[w]		40	—	—	12	68	95	—	—	—	—
			1.0/2.0[w]		35	—	—	15	68	95	—	—	—	—
			2.0/3.0[w]		33	—	—	15	68	95	—	—	—	—
			.188/.375[x]		42	—	—	12	68	95	—	—	—	—
			.375/.500[x]		40	—	—	12	68	95	—	—	—	—
			.500/2.0[x]		33	—	—	15	68	95	—	—	—	—
			2.0/4.0[x]		32	—	—	15	68	95	—	—	—	—
			All Sizes[y]		32	—	—	15	—	—	—	—	—	—
			OD	Wall				In 2 in			R15T[d]			
C10200 C12000 C12200	Tube	Soft Anneal	All Sizes	.014/.034	30	—	—	40[e]	—	—	—	60	0.040	—
			All Sizes	.034/—	—	—	—	—	—	50[d]	—	—	0.040	—
		Light Anneal	All Sizes	.014/.034	—	—	—	—	—	—	—	65	—	0.040
			All Sizes	.034/—	—	—	—	—	—	55[d]	—	—	—	0.040
											R30T[d]			
		Light Drawn	All Sizes	All Sizes	36	47	—	—	—	—	30	60	—	—
		Drawn	All Sizes	All Sizes	36	—	—	—	—	—	30	—	—	—
		Hard Drawn	—/1.0	.019/.120	45	—	—	—	—	—	55	—	—	—
			1.0/2.0	.034/.180	45	—	—	—	—	—	55	—	—	—
			2.0/4.0	.059/.250	45	—	—	—	—	—	55	—	—	—
			Size Section, in					In 10 in	RF[b]		R30T[b]			
C10200 C11000	Wire	Annealed	.0029/.0100 dia		—	—	—	15	—	—	—	—	—	—
			.0100/.0201 dia		—	—	—	20	—	—	—	—	—	—
			.0201/.1019 dia		—	—	—	25	—	—	—	—	—	—
			.1019/.2893 dia		—	—	—	30	—	—	—	—	—	—
			.2893/.4600 dia		—	—	—	35	—	—	—	—	—	—
								In 4 × Dia						
C14500	Rod	1/2 Hard[f]	.062/.250		38	—	30	8	—	—	—	—	—	—
			.250/2.625		38	—	30	12	—	—	—	—	—	—
		Hard	.062/.250		48	—	40	4	—	—	—	—	—	—
			.250/1.250		44	—	38	8	—	—	—	—	—	—
			1.250/2.000		40	—	35	8	—	—	—	—	—	—
C14700	Rod	1/2 Hard[f]	.062/.250		38	—	30	8	—	—	—	—	—	—
			.250/2.625		38	—	30	12	—	—	—	—	—	—
		Hard[g]	.062/.250		48	—	40	4	—	—	—	—	—	—
			.250/1.250		44	—	38	8	—	—	—	—	—	—
			1.250/2.000		40	—	35	8	—	—	—	—	—	—
C15000	Round Rod													

ed. TABLE 2B—MINIMUM MECHANICAL PROPERTIES OF WROUGHT COPPER ALLOYS (CONTINUED)

Customary Units

Copper or Copper Alloy UNS No.[aa]	Form	Temper	Size Section, in Over/Thru	Tensile Strength, ksi Min	Tensile Strength, ksi Max	Yield Strength, Min ksi 0.5% Ext Under Load	Elongation, Min %[c] In 4 × Dia or Thickness of Specimen	Hardness Min	Hardness Max	Hardness Min	Hardness Max	Grain Size, mm Min	Grain Size, mm Max
								RB[b]		R30T[b]			
C22000	Plate, Sheet, Strip and Rolled Bars[t]	Extra Hard	.019/.036 .036/— .011/.028 .028/—	64	72	—	—	72 74 — —	77 79 — —	— — 67 68	— — 71 72	— — — —	— — — —
		Spring	.019/.036 .036/— .011/.028 .028/—	69	77	—	—	76 78 — —	79 81 — —	— — 70 71	— — 72 73	— — — —	— — — —
		Extra Spring	.019/.036 .036/— .011/.028 .028/—	72	80	—	—	78 80 — —	81 83 — —	— — 71 72	— — 73 74	— — — —	— — — —
			Wall Thickness					RF[b]					
	Tube	Soft Anneal	—/.045 .045/—	— —	— —	— —	— —	— —	— 70	— —	30 —	0.025 0.025	0.060 0.060
		Light Anneal	—/.045 .045/—	— —	— —	— —	— —	— —	— 78	— —	37 —	Note a Note a	0.035 0.035
		Drawn (General Purpose)	All Sizes	40	—	—	—	—	—	38	—	—	—
			OD / Wall										
		Hard Drawn	—/4.0 / .019/.250	52	—	—	—	—	—	55	—	—	—
			Size Section, in										
C23000	Sheet and Strip	Annealed 0.070 mm 0.050 mm 0.035 mm 0.025 mm 0.015 mm	— — — — —	— — — — —	— — — — —	— — — — —	— — — — —	53 56 58 60 62	60 63 66 72 79	6 10 13 16 19	16 20 24 34 48	0.050 0.035 0.025 0.015 Note a	0.100 0.070 0.050 0.035 0.025
								RB[b]					
		1/4 Hard	.019/.036 .036/— .011/.028 .028/—	44	54	—	—	33 37 — —	58 62 — —	— — 42 45	— — 57 60	— — — —	— — — —
		1/2 Hard	.019/.036 .036/— .011/.028 .028/—	51	61	—	—	56 59 — —	68 71 — —	— — 56 58	— — 64 66	— — — —	— — — —
		3/4 Hard	.019/.036 .036/— .011/.028 .028/—	57	67	—	—	66 69 — —	73 76 — —	— — 63 65	— — 68 70	— — — —	— — — —
		Hard	.019/.036 .036/— .011/.028 .028/—	63	72	—	—	72 74 — —	78 80 — —	— — 67 68	— — 71 72	— — — —	— — — —
		Extra Hard	.019/.036 .036/—	72	80	—	—	78 80	83 85	— —	— —	— —	— —
		Extra Hard	.011/.028 .028/—	72	80	—	—	— —	— —	70 71	74 75	— —	— —
		Spring	.019/.036 .036/— .011/.028 .028/—	78	86	—	—	82 84 — —	85 87 — —	— — 74 75	— — 76 77	— — — —	— — — —
		Extra Spring	.019/.036 .036/— .011/.028 .028/—	82	90	—	—	84 86 — —	87 89 — —	— — 75 76	— — 77 78	— — — —	— — — —

ed. TABLE 2B—MINIMUM MECHANICAL PROPERTIES OF WROUGHT COPPER ALLOYS (CONTINUED)

Customary Units

Copper or Copper Alloy UNS No.[a,a]	Form	Temper	Size Section, in	Tensile Strength, ksi		Yield Strength, Min ksi	Elongation, Min %[c]	Hardness				Grain Size, mm	
			Over/Thru	Min	Max	0.5% Ext Under Load	In 4 × Dia or Thickness of Specimen	Min	Max	Min	Max	Min	Max
			Wall Thickness					RF[d]		R30T[d]			
C23000	Tube	Soft Anneal	—/.045 .045/—	— —	— —	— —	— —	— —	— 75	— —	36 —	0.025 0.025	0.060 0.060
		Light Anneal	—/.045 .045/—	— —	— —	— —	— —	— —	— 85	— —	39 —	Note a Note a	0.035 0.035
		Light Drawn[E]	All Sizes	44	58	—	—	—	—	43	75	—	—
		Drawn (General Purpose)	All Sizes	44	—	—	—	—	—	43	—	—	—
			OD / Wall					RF[b]					
		Hard Drawn	—/1.0 .019/.120 1.0/2.0 .034/.180 2.0/4.0 .059/.250	57	—	—	—	— — —	— — —	65 65 65	— — —	— — —	— — —
			Size Section, in										
C24000	Sheet and Strip	Annealed 0.070 mm 0.050 mm 0.035 mm 0.025 mm 0.015 mm	 — — — — —	 — — — — —	 — — — — —	 — — — — —	 — — — — —	 53 57 61 63 66	 64 67 72 77 83	 2 8 16 20 25	 21 27 35 42 50	 0.050 0.035 0.025 0.015 Note a	 0.120 0.070 0.050 0.035 0.025
								RB[b]					
		1/4 Hard	.019/.036 .036/— .011/.028 .028/—	48	58	—	—	38 42 — —	61 65 — —	— — 42 45	— — 57 60	— — — —	— — — —
		1/2 Hard	.019/.036 .036/— .011/.028 .028/—	55	65	—	—	59 62 — —	70 73 — —	— — 56 58	— — 64 66	— — — —	— — — —
		3/4 Hard	.019/.036 .036/— .011/.028 .028/—	61	71	—	—	69 72 — —	76 79 — —	— — 63 65	— — 68 70	— — — —	— — — —
		Hard	.019/.036	68	77	—	—	76	82	—	—	—	—
		Hard	.036/— .011/.028 .028/—	68	77	—	—	78 — —	84 — —	— 68 69	— 72 73	— — —	— — —
		Extra Hard	.019/.036 .036/— .011/.028 .028/—	78	87	—	—	83 85 — —	87 89 — —	— — 72 73	— — 75 76	— — — —	— — — —
		Spring	.019/.036 .036/— .011/.028 .028/—	85	93	—	—	87 89 — —	90 92 — —	— — 75 76	— — 77 78	— — — —	— — — —
		Extra Spring	.019/.036 .036/— .011/.028 .028/—	89	97	—	—	88 90 — —	91 93 — —	— — 76 77	— — 78 79	— — — —	— — — —
								RF[d]					
C26000	Plate,[t] Sheet, Strip, Rolled Bar and Wire	Annealed 0.120 mm 0.070 mm 0.050 mm 0.035 mm 0.025 mm 0.015 mm	 — — — — — —	 — — — — — —	 — — — — — —	 — — — — — —	 — — — — — —	 50 52 61 65 67 72	 62 67 73 76 79 85	 — 3 20 25 27 33	 21 27 35 38 42 50	 0.070 0.050 0.035 0.025 0.015 Note a	 — 0.120 0.070 0.050 0.035 0.025

(Table continued on next page)

ed. TABLE 2B—MINIMUM MECHANICAL PROPERTIES OF WROUGHT COPPER ALLOYS (CONTINUED)

Customary Units

Copper or Copper Alloy UNS No.[ce]	Form	Temper	Size Section, in Over/Thru	Tensile Strength, ksi Min	Tensile Strength, ksi Max	Yield Strength, Min ksi 0.5% Ext Under Load	Elongation, Min %[c] In 4 × Dia or Thickness of Specimen	Hardness Min	Hardness Max	Hardness Min	Hardness Max	Grain Size, mm Min	Grain Size, mm Max
								RB[b]		R30T[d]			
C26000	Plate,[t] Sheet, Strip, Rolled Bar and Wire	1/4 Hard	.019/.036 .036/— .011/.028 .028/—	49	59	—	—	40 44 — —	61 65 — —	— — 43 46	— — 57 60	—	—
		1/2 Hard	.019/.036 .036/— .011/.028 .028/—	57	67	—	—	60 63 — —	74 77 — —	— — 56 58	— — 66 68	—	—
		3/4 Hard	.019/.036 .036/— .011/.028 .028/—	64	74	—	—	72 75 — —	79 82 — —	— — 65 67	— — 70 72	—	—
		Hard	.019/.036 .036/— .011/.028 .028/—	71	81	—	—	79 81 — —	84 86 — —	— — 70 71	— — 73 74	—	—
		Extra Hard	.019/.036 .036/— .011/.028 .028/—	83	92	—	—	85 87 — —	89 91 — —	— — 74 75	— — 76 77	—	—
		Spring	.019/.036	91	100	—	—	89	92	—	—	—	—
		Spring	.036/— .011/.028 .028/—	91	100	—	—	90 — —	93 — —	— 76 76	— 78 78	—	—
		Extra Spring	.019/.036 .036/— .011/.028 .028/—	95	104	—	—	91 92 — —	94 95 — —	— — 77 77	— — 79 79	—	—
			Wall Thickness					RF[b]					
	Tube	Soft Anneal	—/.030 .030/—	— —	— —	— —	— —	— —	— 80	— —	40 —	0.025 0.025	0.060 0.060
		Light Anneal	—/.030 .030/—	— —	— —	— —	— —	— —	— 90	— —	60 —	Note a Note a	0.035 0.035
		Drawn (General Purpose)	All Sizes	54	—	—	—	—	—	53	—	—	—
			OD **Wall**										
		Hard Drawn	—/4.0 .019/.250	66	—	—	—	—	—	70	—	—	—
			Size Section, in					RF[d]		R30T[b]			
C26800	Plate,[t] Sheet, Strip and Rolled Bar	Annealed 0.120 mm 0.070 mm 0.050 mm 0.035 mm 0.025 mm 0.015 mm	— — — — — —	— — — — — —	— — — — — —	— — — — — —	— — — — — —	50 52 61 65 67 72	62 67 73 76 79 85	— 3 20 25 27 33	21 27 35 38 42 50	0.070 0.050 0.035 0.025 0.015 Note a	— 0.120 0.070 0.050 0.035 0.025
								RB[b]					
		1/4 Hard	.019/.036 .036/— .011/.028 .028/—	49	59	—	—	40 44 — —	61 65 — —	— — 43 46	— — 57 60	—	—
		1/2 Hard	.019/.036 .036/— .011/.028 .028/—	55	65	—	—	57 60 — —	71 74 — —	— — 54 56	— — 64 66	—	—
		3/4 Hard	.019/.036 .036/— .011/.028 .028/—	62	72	—	—	70 73 — —	77 80 — —	— — 65 67	— — 69 71	—	—

ed. TABLE 2B—MINIMUM MECHANICAL PROPERTIES OF WROUGHT COPPER ALLOYS (CONTINUED)

Customary Units													
Copper or Copper Alloy UNS No.[a,c]	Form	Temper	Size Section, in	Tensile Strength, ksi		Yield Strength, Min ksi	Elongation, Min %[c]	Hardness				Grain Size, mm	
			Over/Thru	Min	Max	0.5% Ext Under Load	In 4 × Dia or Thickness of Specimen	Min	Max	Min	Max	Min	Max
								RB[b]		R30T[b]			
C26800	Plate,[t] Sheet, Strip and Rolled Bar	Hard	.019/.036 .036/— .011/.028 .028/—	68	78	—	—	76 78 — —	82 84 — —	— — 68 69	— — 72 73	— — — —	— — — —
		Extra Hard	.019/.036 .036/—	79	89	—	—	83 85	87 90	— —	— —	— —	— —
		Extra Hard	.011/.028 .028/—	79	89	—	—	— —	— —	73 74	75 76	— —	— —
		Spring	.019/.036 .036/— .011/.028 .028/—	86	95	—	—	87 89 — —	90 92 — —	— — 75 76	— — 77 78	— — — —	— — — —
		Extra Spring	.019/.036 .036/— .011/.028 .028/—	90	99	—	—	88 90 — —	91 93 — —	— — 76 77	— — 78 79	— — — —	— — — —
C27000	Wire	Annealed 0.100 mm 0.070 mm 0.050 mm 0.035 mm 0.025 mm 0.015 mm	 — — — — — —	 — — — — — —	 — — — — — —	 — — — — — —	 — — — — — —	 — — — — — —	 — — — — — —	 — — — — — —	 — — — — — —	 0.070 0.050 0.035 0.025 0.015 Note a	 — 0.100 0.070 0.050 0.035 0.025
		1/8 Hard 1/4 Hard 1/2 Hard 3/4 Hard Hard[h] Extra Hard[i]	— — — — — —	50 67 79 92 102 115	65 77 94 107 117 129	— — — — — —	— — — — — —	— — — — — —	— — — — — —	— — — — — —	— — — — — —	— — — — — —	— — — — — —
		Spring[j]	—	120	—	—	—	—	—	—	—	—	—
			Wall Thickness					RF[d]		R30T[d]			
C33000	Tube	Soft Anneal	—/.030 .030/—	— —	— —	— —	— —	— —	— 80	— —	40 —	0.025 0.025	0.060 0.060
		Light Anneal	—/.030 .030/—	— —	— —	— —	— —	— —	— 90	— —	60 —	Note a Note a	0.035 0.035
		Drawn (General Purpose)	All Sizes	54	—	—	—	—	—	53	—	—	—
			OD; Wall										
		Hard Drawn[g]	—/4.0; .019/.250	66	—	—	—	—	—	70	—	—	—
			Wall Thickness										
C33100	Tube	Soft Anneal	—/.030 .030/—	— —	— —	— —	— —	— —	— 80	— —	40 —	0.025 0.025	0.060 0.060
		Light Anneal	—/.030 .030/—	— —	— —	— —	— —	— —	— 90	— —	60 —	Note a Note a	0.035 0.035
		Drawn (General Purpose)	All Sizes	54	—	—	—	—	—	53	—	—	—
			OD; Wall										
		Hard Drawn	—/4.0; .019/.250	66	—	—	—	—	—	70	—	—	—
								RF[b]		R30T[b]			
C34200 C35000	Plate, Sheet, Strip and Rolled Bar	Annealed 0.070 mm 0.050 mm 0.035 mm 0.025 mm	 All Sizes All Sizes All Sizes All Sizes	 — — — —	 — — — —	 — — — —	 — — — —	 54 61 65 67	 67 73 76 79	 12 20 25 27	 27 35 38 42	 0.050 0.035 0.025 0.015	 0.100 0.070 0.050 0.035

(Table continued on next page)

ed. TABLE 2B—MINIMUM MECHANICAL PROPERTIES OF WROUGHT COPPER ALLOYS (CONTINUED)

Customary Units

Copper or Copper Alloy UNS No.[a,a]	Form	Temper	Size Section, in Over/Thru	Tensile Strength, ksi Min	Tensile Strength, ksi Max	Yield Strength, Min ksi 0.5% Ext Under Load	Elongation, Min %[c] In 4 × Dia or Thickness of Specimen	Hardness RB[b] Min	Hardness RB[b] Max	Hardness R30T[b] Min	Hardness R30T[b] Max	Grain Size, mm Min	Grain Size, mm Max
C34200 C35000	Plate, Sheet, Strip and Rolled Bar	1/4 Hard	All Sizes	49	59	—	—	40	65	43	60	—	—
		1/2 Hard	All Sizes	55	65	—	—	57	74	54	66	—	—
		Hard	All Sizes	68	78	—	—	76	84	68	73	—	—
		Extra Hard	All Sizes	79	89	—	—	83	89	73	76	—	—
C34500 C35000	Rod	Soft	—/.50	46	—	16	20	—	—	—	—	—	—
			.50/1.0	44	—	15	25	—	45	—	—	—	—
			1.0/2.0	40	—	15	30	—	45	—	—	—	—
		1/4 Hard	—/.50	52	—	25	10	50	75	—	—	—	—
			.50/1.0	50	—	20	15	40	70	—	—	—	—
			1.0/2.0	42	—	15	20	35	65	—	—	—	—
		1/2 Hard	—/.50	57	—	25	7	60	80	—	—	—	—
			.50/1.0	55	—	25	10	55	75	—	—	—	—
			1.0/2.0	50	—	20	15	40	70	—	—	—	—
C36000	Rod	Soft	—/1.0	48	—	20	15	—	—	—	—	—	—
			1.0/2.0	44	—	18	20	—	—	—	—	—	—
			2.0/—	40	—	15	25	—	—	—	—	—	—
		1/2 Hard	—/.50	57	—	25	7	—	—	—	—	—	—
			.50/1.0	55	—	25	10	—	—	—	—	—	—
			1.0/2.0	50	—	20	15	—	—	—	—	—	—
			2.0/4.0	45	—	15	20	—	—	—	—	—	—
			4.0/—	42	—	15	20	—	—	—	—	—	—
		Hard	.061/.088	80	—	45	—	—	—	—	—	—	—
			.088/.500	70	—	35	4	—	—	—	—	—	—
			.500/.750	65	—	30	6	—	—	—	—	—	—
	Flat Products		Thickness / Width										
		Soft	—/1.0 / —/6.0	44	—	18	20	—	—	—	—	—	—
			1.0/— / 6.0/—	40	—	15	25	—	—	—	—	—	—
		1/2 Hard	—/.50 / —/1.0	50	—	25	10	—	—	—	—	—	—
			—/.50 / 1.0/6.0	45	—	17	15	—	—	—	—	—	—
			.50/2.0 / —/2.0	45	—	17	20	—	—	—	—	—	—
			.50/2.0 / 2.0/6.0	40	—	15	20	—	—	—	—	—	—
			2.0/— / 2.0/4.0	40	—	15	20	—	—	—	—	—	—
C37700	Die Forgings		Over/Thru										
		As Forged	—/1.50	50	—	18	25	—	—	—	—	—	—
			1.50/—	46	—	15	20	—	—	—	—	—	—
C46400 C46500 C46600 C46700	Rod and Bar	Soft	—/1.0	54	—	20	30	—	—	—	—	—	—
			1.0/2.0	52	—	20	30	—	—	—	—	—	—
			2.0/—	50	—	20	30	—	—	—	—	—	—
		1/2 Hard or Light Annealed	—/.50	60	—	27	22	—	—	—	—	—	—
			.50/1.0	60	—	27	25	—	—	—	—	—	—
			1.0/2.0	58	—	26	25	—	—	—	—	—	—
			2.0/3.0	54	—	25	25	—	—	—	—	—	—
			3.0/4.0	54	—	22	27	—	—	—	—	—	—
			4.0/—	54	—	22	30	—	—	—	—	—	—
		Hard	—/1.0	67	—	45	13	—	—	—	—	—	—
			1.0/2.0	62	—	37	18	—	—	—	—	—	—
	Shapes	As Extruded	All Sizes	52	—	20	30	—	—	—	—	—	—
C51000	Sheet and Strip	Soft	.039/—	43	58	—	—	16	64	—	—	—	—
			.029/—					—	—	32	59	—	—
			.019/.039					12	60	—	—	—	—
			.009/.029					—	—	24	53	—	—
		1/2 Hard	.039/—	58	73	—	—	64	85	—	—	—	—
			.029/—					—	—	59	73	—	—
			.019/.039					60	82	—	—	—	—
			.009/.029					—	—	53	69	—	—
		Hard	.039/—	76	91	—	—	86	93	—	—	—	—
			.029/—					—	—	73	78	—	—
			.019/.039					84	91	—	—	—	—
			.009/.029					—	—	71	75	—	—

TABLE 2B—MINIMUM MECHANICAL PROPERTIES OF WROUGHT COPPER ALLOYS (CONTINUED)

Customary Units

Copper or Copper Alloy UNS No.[aa]	Form	Temper	Size Section, in Over/Thru	Tensile Strength, ksi Min	Tensile Strength, ksi Max	Yield Strength, Min ksi 0.5% Ext Under Load	Elongation, Min %[c] In 4 × Dia or Thickness of Specimen	Hardness RB[b] Min	Hardness RB[b] Max	Hardness R30T[b] Min	Hardness R30T[b] Max	Grain Size, mm Min	Grain Size, mm Max
C51000	Sheet and Strip	Extra Hard	.039/—	88	103	—	—	92	96	—	—	—	—
			.029/—					—	—	77	81	—	—
			.019/.039					89	95	—	—	—	—
			.009/.029					—	—	74	78	—	—
		Spring	.039/—	95	110	—	—	94	98	—	—	—	—
			.029/—					—	—	79	82	—	—
			.019/.039					92	97	—	—	—	—
			.009/.029					—	—	76	80	—	—
		Extra Spring	.039/—	100	114	—	—	95	99	—	—	—	—
			.029/—					—	—	80	83	—	—
			.019/.039					94	98	—	—	—	—
			.009/.029					—	—	77	81	—	—
	Rod	Soft	—/.249[aa]	40	58	—	—	—	—	—	—	—	—
		Hard	—/.249[bb]	80	128	—	—	—	—	—	—	—	—
			.249/.500[bb]	70	—	—	13	—	—	—	—	—	—
			.500/1.00[bb]	60	—	—	15	—	—	—	—	—	—
			1.00/—[bb]	55	—	—	18	—	—	—	—	—	—
			.249/.375[cc]	60	—	—	10	—	—	—	—	—	—
			.375/—[cc]	55	—	—	15	—	—	—	—	—	—
		Spring	—/.025[a]	125	—	—	—	—	—	—	—	—	—
		Spring	.025/.062[aa]	115	—	—	—	—	—	—	—	—	—
			.062/.125[aa]	110	—	—	—	—	—	—	—	—	—
			.125/.250[aa]	105	—	—	3.5	—	—	—	—	—	—
			.250/.375[aa]	100	—	—	5.0	—	—	—	—	—	—
			.375/.500[aa]	90	—	—	9.0	—	—	—	—	—	—
	Wire for General Purposes	Soft	—	43	58	—	—	—	—	—	—	—	—
		1/4 Hard	—	60	76	—	—	—	—	—	—	—	—
		1/2 Hard	—	80	97	—	—	—	—	—	—	—	—
		3/4 Hard	—	96	115	—	—	—	—	—	—	—	—
		Hard	—	108	128	—	—	—	—	—	—	—	—
	Wire for Spring Purposes						In 2 in						
		—	—/.025	145	—	—	—	—	—	—	—	—	—
		—	.025/.062	135	—	—	—	—	—	—	—	—	—
		—	.062/.125	130	—	—	—	—	—	—	—	—	—
		—	.125/.250	125	—	—	—	—	—	—	—	—	—
		—	.250/.375	120	—	—	5.0	—	—	—	—	—	—
		—	.375/.500	105	—	—	9.0	—	—	—	—	—	—
C51100 C54400	Sheet and Strip	Soft	.039/—	40	50	—	—	7	50	—	—	—	—
			.029/—					—	—	24	50	—	—
			.019/.039					0	45	—	—	—	—
			.009/.029					—	—	16	46	—	—
		1/2 Hard	.039/—	55	70	—	—	60	81	—	—	—	—
			.029/—					—	—	57	73	—	—
			.019/.039					53	78	—	—	—	—
			.009/.029					—	—	52	71	—	—
		Hard	.039/—	72	87	—	—	82	90	—	—	—	—
			.029/—					—	—	71	77	—	—
			.019/.039					80	88	—	—	—	—
			.009/.029					—	—	69	75	—	—
		Extra Hard	.039/—	84	99	—	—	88	94	—	—	—	—
			.029/—					—	—	75	80	—	—
			.019/.039					86	92	—	—	—	—
			.009/.029					—	—	73	78	—	—
		Spring	.039/—	91	105	—	—	90	96	—	—	—	—
			.029/—					—	—	77	81	—	—
			.019/.039					88	94	—	—	—	—
			.009/.029					—	—	75	79	—	—
		Extra Spring	.039/—	96	109	—	—	92	97	—	—	—	—
			.029/—					—	—	78	82	—	—
			.019/.039					89	94	—	—	—	—
			.009/.029					—	—	76	80	—	—

ed. TABLE 2B—MINIMUM MECHANICAL PROPERTIES OF WROUGHT COPPER ALLOYS (CONTINUED)

Customary Units													
Copper or Copper Alloy UNS No.[ee]	Form	Temper	Size Section, in	Tensile Strength, ksi		Yield Strength, Min ksi	Elongation, Min %[c]	Hardness				Grain Size, mm	
			Over/Thru	Min	Max	0.5% Ext Under Load	In 2 in	Min	Max	Min	Max	Min	Max
								RB[b]		R30T[b]			
C52100	Sheet and Strip	Soft	.039/—	53	67	—	—	29	70	—	—	—	—
			.029/—					—	—	38	68	—	—
		Soft	.019/.039	53	67	—	—	20	66	—	—	—	—
			.009/.029					—	—	27	62	—	—
		1/2 Hard	.039/—	69	84	—		76	91	—	—	—	—
			.029/—					—	—	67	78	—	—
			.019/.039					69	88	—	—	—	—
			.009/.029					—	—	63	75	—	—
		Hard	.039/—	85	100	—	—	91	97	—	—	—	—
			.029/—					—	—	76	81	—	—
			.019/.039					89	95	—	—	—	—
			.009/.029					—	—	73	80	—	—
		Extra Hard	.039/—	97	112	—	—	95	100	—	—	—	—
			.029/—					—	—	78	83	—	—
			.019/.039					93	98	—	—	—	—
			.009/.029					—	—	77	82	—	—
		Spring	.039/—	105	119	—	—	97	102	—	—	—	—
			.029/—					—	—	79	84	—	—
			.019/.039					95	100	—	—	—	—
			.009/.029					—	—	78	83	—	—
		Extra Spring	.039/—	110	122	—	—	98	103	—	—	—	—
			.029/—					—	—	80	84	—	—
			.019/.039					96	101	—	—	—	—
			.009/.029					—	—	79	83	—	—
C52400	Sheet and Strip	Soft	.039/—	58	73	—	—	35	75	—	—	—	—
			.029/—					—	—	40	78	—	—
			.019/.039					25	71	—	—	—	—
			.009/.029					—	—	29	84	—	—
		1/2 Hard	.039/—	76	91	—	—	78	95	—	—	—	—
			.029/—					—	—	67	80	—	—
			.019/.039					74	93	—	—	—	—
			.009/.029					—	—	63	77	—	—
		Hard	.039/—	94	109	—	—	94	101	—	—	—	—
			.029/—					—	—	78	82	—	—
			.019/.039					92	100	—	—	—	—
			.009/.029					—	—	75	81	—	—
		Extra Hard	.039/—	107	122	—	—	93	103	—	—	—	—
			.029/—					—	—	80	84	—	—
			.019/.039					97	102	—	—	—	—
			.009/.029					—	—	79	83	—	—
		Spring	.039/—	115	129	—	—	99	104	—	—	—	—
			.029/—					—	—	81	85	—	—
			.019/.039					98	103	—	—	—	—
			.009/.029					—	—	80	84	—	—
		Extra Spring	.039/—	120	133	—	—	100	105	—	—	—	—
			.029/—					—	—	82	86	—	—
		Extra Spring	.019/.039	120	133	—	—	99	104	—	—	—	—
			.009/.029					—	—	81	85	—	—
	Sheet and Strip	See C51100											
C54400	Rod						In 4 × Dia or Thickness of Specimen						
		Hard	.061/.250[bb]	65	—	—	8	—	—	—	—	—	—
			.249/.500[bb]	60	—	—	10	—	—	—	—	—	—
			.500/1.0[bb]	55	—	—	12	—	—	—	—	—	—
			1.0/—[bb]	50	—	—	15	—	—	—	—	—	—
	Flat Products	Hard	.249/.375[cc]	55	—	—	10	—	—	—	—	—	—
			.375/—[cc]	50	—	—	15	—	—	—	—	—	—
C60800	Tube	Annealed	All Sizes	50	—	19	—	—	—	—	—	0.010	0.045

ed. TABLE 2B—MINIMUM MECHANICAL PROPERTIES OF WROUGHT COPPER ALLOYS (CONTINUED)

Customary Units													
Copper or Copper Alloy UNS No.[c,e]	Form	Temper	Size Section, in	Tensile Strength, ksi		Yield Strength, Min ksi	Elongation, Min %[c]	Hardness				Grain Size, mm	
			Over/Thru	Min	Max	0.5% Ext Under Load	In 2 in	Min	Max	Min	Max	Min	Max
C61300	Plate,[t] Sheet, Strip and Rolled Bar		Thickness / Width					RB[b]		BHN 1000 kg			
		Soft	—/.500 All Widths	75	—	36	35	—	—	—	—	—	—
			.500/2.0 All Widths	72	—	32	35	—	—	—	—	—	—
			2.0/5.0 All Widths	65	—	28	35	—	—	—	—	—	—
C61400	Plate,[t] Sheet, Strip and Rolled Bar		Thickness / Width					RB[b]		BHN 1000 kg			
		Soft	—/.500 All Widths	72	—	32	35	—	—	—	—	—	—
			.500/2.0 All Widths	70	—	30	35	—	—	—	—	—	—
			2.0/5.0 All Widths	65	—	28	35	—	—	—	—	—	—
		Hard	—/.500 All Widths	80	—	45	25	—	—	—	—	—	—
			.500/1.0 All Widths	70	—	40	30	—	—	—	—	—	—
			Size Section, in				In 4 × Dia						
	Rod and Bar	—	—/.500	80	—	40	30	—	—	—	—	—	—
			.500/1.0	75	—	35	30	—	—	—	—	—	—
			1.0/2.0	70	—	32	30	—	—	—	—	—	—
			2.0/3.0	70	—	30	30	—	—	—	—	—	—
C61800	Rod	1/2 Hard	—/3.0	—	—	—	—	—	—	—	—	—	—
C62300	Rod and Bar	Drawn	—/.500	90	—	45	12	90	—	155	—	—	—
			.500/1.0	88	—	44	15	—	—	—	—	—	—
			1.0/2.0	84	—	40	15	—	—	—	—	—	—
			2.0/3.0	76	—	37	20	—	—	—	—	—	—
			3.0/—	75	—	30	20	—	—	—	—	—	—
	Shapes	—	All Sizes	75	—	30	20	—	—	—	—	—	—
	Forgings	As Forged	—/1.5	75	—	30	20	—	—	—	—	—	—
			1.5/—	72	—	28	25	—	—	—	—	—	—
C62400										3000 kg			
	Rod	As Extruded	All Sizes	80	—	45	7.0	—	—	175	—	—	—
		As Forged	—	80	—	45	7.0	—	—	175	—	—	—
	Forgings	Hardened and H_2O Quenched	—	—	—	—	—	—	—	240	—	—	—
		Hardened, H_2O Quenched and Tempered	—	87	—	—	8.0	—	—	179	—	—	—
C63000										RF[b]			
	Rod and Bar	Annealed	.499/1.0	100	—	50	5	—	—	—	—	—	—
			1.0/2.0	90	—	45	6	—	—	—	—	—	—
			2.0/4.0	85	—	42.5	10	—	—	—	—	—	—
	Shapes	As Extruded	All Sizes	85	—	42.5	10	—	—	—	—	—	—
C64200	Rod and Bar	Drawn	—/.500	90	—	45	9	—	—	—	—	—	—
			.500/1.0	85	—	45	12	—	—	—	—	—	—
			1.0/2.0	80	—	42	12	—	—	—	—	—	—
			2.0/3.0	75	—	35	15	—	—	—	—	—	—
C65500	Plate,[t] Sheet, Strip and Rolled Bar	Annealed											
		0.070 mm	—	52	58	—	—	—	—	70	82	0.050	0.110
		0.040 mm	—	55	64	—	—	—	—	76	93	Note a	0.055
		1/4 Hard	—	62	72	—	—	65	80	—	—	—	—
		1/2 Hard[k]	—	71	81	—	—	79	91	—	—	—	—
		Hard[k]	—	87	97	—	—	88	96	—	—	—	—
		Extra Hard[k]	—	99	108	—	—	93	98	—	—	—	—
		Spring[k]	—	105	113	—	—	94	99	—	—	—	—
		Hot Rolled	—	55	72	—	—	—	—	72	—	—	—
		Hot Rolled and Cold Rolled Finish	—	58	72	—	—	60	80	—	—	—	—

ed. TABLE 2B—MINIMUM MECHANICAL PROPERTIES OF WROUGHT COPPER ALLOYS (CONTINUED)

Customary Units

Copper or Copper Alloy UNS No.[ee]	Form	Temper	Size Section, in Over/Thru	Tensile Strength, ksi Min	Tensile Strength, ksi Max	Yield Strength, Min ksi 0.5% Ext Under Load	Elongation, Min %[c] In 4 × Dia or Thickness of Specimen	Hardness RB[b] Min	Hardness RB[b] Max	Hardness RF[b] Min	Hardness RF[b] Max	Grain Size, mm Min	Grain Size, mm Max
C65500	Rod, Bar and Shapes	Soft	All Forms and Sizes	52	—	15	35	—	—	—	—	—	—
		1/4 Hard	All Forms and Sizes	55	—	24	25	—	—	—	—	—	—
		1/2 Hard	—/2.0[dd]	70	—	38	17	—	—	—	—	—	—
		Hard	—/.250[dd] .250/1.500[dd]	85 85	— —	50 50	8 13	— —	— —	— —	— —	— —	— —
		Extra Hard	—/.500[w]	100	—	55	7	—	—	—	—	—	—
	Bar	Soft	All Sizes	52	—	15	35	—	—	—	—	—	—
		Hard	—/1.0 1.0/1.5 1.5/3.0	65 60 55	— — —	38 30 24	20 25 27	— — —	— — —	— — —	— — —	— — —	— — —
C67000	Rod and Bar	Soft	All Sizes	85	—	45	10[v]	—	—	—	—	—	—
		1/2 Hard Hard	All Sizes All Sizes	105 115	— —	60 68	7[v] 5[v]	— —	— —	— —	— —	— —	— —
	Forgings	Soft	—	85	—	45	10	—	—	—	—	—	—
		1/2 Hard Hard	— —	93 100	— —	50 55	7 5	— —	— —	— —	— —	— —	— —
C67300	Rod and Bar	As Extruded	All Sizes	55	—	25	20	60	—	—	—	—	—
		Soft	All Sizes	55	—	25	20	50	—	—	—	—	—
		1/2 Hard[w]	—/1.0	65	—	40	12	70	—	—	—	—	—
										R30T[b]			
		1/2 Hard[w]	1.0/3.0 3.0/—	58 55	— —	35 30	15 18	70 65	— —	— —	— —	— —	— —
		1/2 Hard[x]	All Sizes	60	—	30	20	70	—	—	—	—	—
		Hard[w]	—/1.0 1.0/2.0	70 62	— —	50 42	10 15	70 70	— —	— —	— —	— —	— —
	Shapes	As Extruded	All Sizes	55	—	25	20	60	—	—	—	—	—
	Forgings	As Forged	—	55	—	25	20	60	—	—	—	—	—
		Forged and Heat Treated	—	69	—	35	12	70	—	—	—	—	—
C67400	Rod and Bar	As Extruded	All Sizes	70	—	34	12	75	—	—	—	—	—
		Extruded and Drawn	—/1.0 1.0/2.0 2.0/3.0	78 75 70	— — —	40 40 36	B 10 12	84 80 78	— — —	— — —	— — —	— — —	— — —
	Shapes	As Extruded	All Sizes	70	—	34	12	75	—	—	—	—	—
	Forgings	As Forged	—	65	—	30	15	75	—	—	—	—	—
C67500	Rod	Soft	All Sizes	55	—	22	20	—	—	—	—	—	—
		1/2 Hard	—/1.0 1.0/2.5 2.5/—	72 70 65	— — —	36 35 32	13 15 17	— — —	— — —	— — —	— — —	— — —	— — —
		Hard	—/1.0 1.0/1.5 1.5/2.5 2.5/—	80 76 73 68	— — — —	56 52 48 45	8 10 12 16	— — — —	— — — —	— — — —	— — — —	— — — —	— — — —

ed. TABLE 2B—MINIMUM MECHANICAL PROPERTIES OF WROUGHT COPPER ALLOYS (CONTINUED)

Customary Units														
Copper or Copper Alloy UNS No.[ee]	Form	Temper	Size Section, in	Tensile Strength, ksi		Yield Strength, Min ksi	Elongation, Min %[c]		Hardness				Grain Size, mm	
			Over/Thru	Min	Max	0.5% Ext Under Load	In 4 × Dia or Thickness of Specimen		Min	Max	Min	Max	Min	Max
									RB[b]		R30T[b]			
C67500	Bar	Soft	All Sizes	55	—	22	20		—	—	—	—	—	—
		1/2 Hard	—/1.0	72	—	36	13		—	—	—	—	—	—
			1.0/2.5	70	—	35	15		—	—	—	—	—	—
			2.5/—	65	—	32	17		—	—	—	—	—	—
		Hard	—/1.0	76	—	52	8		—	—	—	—	—	—
			1.0/2.5	72	—	47	12		—	—	—	—	—	—
			2.5/—	68	—	45	16		—	—	—	—	—	—
	Shapes	Soft	All Sizes	55	—	22	20		—	—	—	—	—	—
							In 2 in							
C70600	Condenser Tube Plate	—	—/2.5	40	—	15	30		—	—	—	—	—	—
	Tube	Annealed	—	40	—	15	—		—	—	—	—	—	—
		Light Drawn	—	45	—	35	—		—	—	—	—	—	—
							Hardness Min	Hardness Max						
							RF[b]							
C71000	Tube	Annealed	—	45	—	16	—		—	—	—	—	—	—
	Plate,[t] Sheet, Strip and Rolled Bar	Annealed 0.035 mm	—	—	—	—	67	76	18	35	28	40	0.025	0.050
		0.015 mm	—	—	—	—	76	90	35	58	40	55	Note a	0.020
		1/4 Hard	—	47	63	—	—	—	45	72	46	65	—	—
		1/2 Hard	—	56	70	—	—	—	64	78	59	69	—	—
		Hard	—	67	79	—	—	—	76	84	67	73	—	—
		Extra Hard	—	72	84	—	—	—	79	87	69	75	—	—
		Spring	—	76	87	—	—	—	82	88	71	75	—	—
							Elongation, Min %[c] In 2 in							
C71500	Condenser Tube Plate	—	—/2.5	50	—	20	35		—	—	—	—	—	—
			2.5/5.0	45	—	18	35		—	—	—	—	—	—
	Tube	Annealed	—	52	—	18	—		—	—	—	—	—	—
		Drawn and Stress Relieved	—/.048 Wall	72	—	50	12		—	—	—	—	—	—
			.048/— Wall	72	—	50	15		—	—	—	—	—	—
							Hardness Min	Hardness Max						
							RF[b]							
	Plate,[t] Sheet, Strip and Rolled Bar	Annealed 0.035 mm	—	—	—	—	70	85	23	45	31	46	0.025	0.050
		0.015 mm	—	—	—	—	74	93	37	63	40	58	Note a	0.025
		1/4 Hard	—	58	72	—	—	—	67	81	61	71	—	—
		1/2 Hard	—	66	80	—	—	—	76	85	67	74	—	—
		Hard	—	75	88	—	—	—	83	89	72	76	—	—
		Extra Hard	—	80	92	—	—	—	85	91	73	77	—	—
		Spring	—	84	94	—	—	—	87	91	74	77	—	—

ϕ *ed.* **TABLE 2B—MINIMUM MECHANICAL PROPERTIES OF WROUGHT COPPER ALLOYS (CONTINUED)**

Copper or Copper Alloy UNS No.[ee]	Form	Temper	Size Section, in Over/Thru	Customary Units Tensile Strength, ksi Min	Tensile Strength, ksi Max	Yield Strength, Min ksi 0.5% Ext Under Load	Hardness Min	Hardness Max	Hardness Min	Hardness Max	Hardness Min	Hardness Max	Grain Size, mm Min	Grain Size, mm Max
							RF[b]		RB[b]		R30T[b]			
C75200	Plate,[t] Sheet Strip and Rolled Bar	Annealed												
		0.070 mm	—	—	—	—	70	80	25	40	32	43	0.050	0.100
		0.035 mm	—	—	—	—	75	88	35	55	40	53	0.025	0.050
		0.015 mm	—	—	—	—	83	93	45	70	46	64	Note a	0.025
		1/4 Hard	—	58	72	—	—	—	50	75	49	67	—	—
		1/2 Hard	—	66	80	—	—	—	68	82	62	72	—	—
		Hard	—	78	91	—	—	—	80	90	70	76	—	—
		Extra Hard	—	86	96	—	—	—	87	94	74	79	—	—
		Spring	—	90	101	—	—	—	89	96	75	80	—	—
	Rod and Bar	Annealed												
		0.070 mm	—	—	—	—	—	—	—	—	—	—	0.050	0.100
		0.035 mm	—	—	—	—	—	—	—	—	—	—	0.025	0.050
		0.015 mm	• —	—	—	—	—	—	—	—	—	—		0.030
		1/4 Hard	.049/.500[y]	60	80	—	—	—	—	—	—	—	—	—
		Hard	.019/.250[w]	80	100	—	—	—	—	—	—	—	—	—
			.250/.500[w]	70	90	—	—	—	—	—	—	—	—	—
			.500/1.0[w]	65	85	—	—	—	—	—	—	—	—	—
			1.0/—[w]	60	80	—	—	—	—	—	—	—	—	—
			All Sizes[x]	68	88	—	—	—	—	—	—	—	—	—
C77000	Plate,[t] Sheet, Strip and Rolled Bar	Annealed												
		0.070 mm	—	—	—	—	72	83	29	45	35	46	0.050	0.100
		0.035 mm	—	—	—	—	76	91	37	60	41	57	0.025	0.050
		0.015 mm	—	—	—	—	84	98	47	73	47	65	Note a	0.025
							RG[b]							
		1/4 Hard	—	69	87	—	23	62	70	88	63	75	—	—
		1/2 Hard	—	78	95	—	51	69	81	92	71	78	—	—
		Hard	—	92	107	—	67	76	90	96	76	80	—	—
		Extra Hard	—	102	115	—	73	80	95	99	79	82	—	—
		Spring	—	108	120	—	77	83	97	100	80	—	—	—
	Rod and Bar	Annealed												
		0.070 mm	—	—	—	—	—	—	—	—	—	—	0.050	0.100
		0.035 mm	—	—	—	—	—	—	—	—	—	—	0.025	0.050
		0.015 mm	—	—	—	—	—	—	—	—	—	—	—	0.030
		1/4 Hard	.019/.500[y]	75	95	—	—	—	—	—	—	—	—	—
		Hard	.019/.050[w]	90	110	—	—	—	—	—	—	—	—	—
			.250/.500[w]	80	100	—	—	—	—	—	—	—	—	—
			.500/1.0[w]	75	95	—	—	—	—	—	—	—	—	—
			1.0/—[w]	70	90	—	—	—	—	—	—	—	—	—
			All Sizes[x]	75	95	—	—	—	—	—	—	—	—	—

[a] Although no minimum grain size is required, this material must be fully recrystallized.

[b] Values are approximate. F and B scales for metal .020 inch and over in thickness. 30T scale for metal .012 inch and over in thickness. (.015 inch for annealed material to ASTM B36 and B122).

[c] In any case, a minimum gage length of 1 inch shall be used.

[d] Hardness values shall apply only to tubes having a wall thickness of .015 inch or over for annealed temper and .020 inch or over for drawn temper (.012 inch for drawn temper to ASTM B135), to round tubes having an inside diameter of .312 inch or over, and to rectangular, including square, tubes having an inside major distance between parallel surfaces of .188 inch or over. For all other tubes, no Rockwell values shall apply. Hardness tests shall be made on the inside surface of the tube. When suitable equipment is not available for determining the specified hardness, other Rockwell scales and values may be specified, subject to agreement between purchaser and supplier.

[e] .125 to .875 inch outside diameter; .030 to .045 inch wall.

[f] Generally available in round, hexagonal, and octagonal.

[g] Normally available in round only.

[h] Not generally available in sizes over .500 inch in diameter.

[i] Not generally available in sizes over .375 inch in diameter. Square and rectangular wire not generally available.

[j] Not generally available in sizes over .250 inch in diameter. Square and rectangular wire not generally available.

[k] Commercially supplied only as strip. Manufacturer should be consulted for sheet or plate.

[l] Capable of being hardened by further heat treatment.

[m] Rods and bars.

[n] Applicable to material .004 inch and over.

[o] Applicable to material .032 inch and over.

[p] Applicable to material .015 inch and over.

[q] When stated on contract or order, tension test shall be waived provided the strip meets the hardness requirement. In case of dispute, tension test shall be the basis for acceptance.

[r] Commonly supplied only as strip.

[s] .250 inch and over.

[t] Plate generally available only in annealed, quarter hard, and half hard.

[u] Type A material to listed hardness limits supplied unless otherwise specified.

[v] Cold finished.

[w] Rods only.

[x] Bars only.

[y] After heat treatment.

[z] After mill heat treatment.

[aa] Rounds only.

[bb] Rounds and hexagons.

[cc] Squares and rectangles.

[dd] Rods and square bars.

[ee] Unified Number System. For cross reference to SAE, former SAE, ASTM and former trade names, see SAE J461.

ϕ *ed.* TABLE 3—INDEX TO STANDARD PRODUCT TOLERANCE TABLES

Copper or Copper Alloy UNS No.[a]	Classification[b]	Copper or Copper Alloy UNS No.[a]	Classification[b]	Copper or Copper Alloy UNS No.[a]	Classification[b]	Copper or Copper Alloy UNS No.[a]	Classification[b]
C10200	Nonrefractory	C17500	Refractory	C34500	Nonrefractory	C61800	Refractory
C11000	Nonrefractory	C17600	Refractory	C35000	Nonrefractory	C62300	Refractory
C11100	Nonrefractory	C18400	Refractory[d]	C36000	Nonrefractory	C62400	Refractory
C11300	Nonrefractory	C18700	Nonrefractory	C37700	Refractory[e]	C63000	Refractory
C11400	Nonrefractory	C19200	Nonrefractory	C46400	Refractory[e,f]	C64200	Refractory
C11500	Nonrefractory	C21000	Nonrefractory	C46500	Refractory[e]	C65500	Refractory[e]
C11600	Nonrefractory	C22000	Nonrefractory	C46600	Refractory[e]	C67000	Refractory[e]
C12000	Nonrefractory	C23000	Nonrefractory	C46700	Refractory[e]	C67300	Refractory[e]
C12200	Nonrefractory	C24000	Nonrefractory	C51000	Refractory[e]	C67400	Refractory[e]
C14500	Nonrefractory	C26000	Nonrefractory	C51100	Refractory[e]	C67500	Refractory[e]
C14700	Nonrefractory	C26800	Nonrefractory	C52100	Refractory[e]	C70600	Refractory
C15000	Nonrefractory[c]	C27000	Nonrefractory	C52400	Refractory[e]	C71000	Refractory
C16200	Nonrefractory[c]	C33000	Nonrefractory	C54400	Refractory[e]	C71500	Refractory
C17000	Refractory	C33100	Nonrefractory	C60800	Refractory	C75200	Refractory[e]
C17200	Refractory	C34200	Nonrefractory	C61400	Refractory	C77000	Refractory

[a] Unified Numbering System. For cross reference to SAE, former SAE, ASTM, and former trade names, see SAE J461.
[b] To determine tolerances, use the applicable portion of the standard product tolerance Tables 4–11. This index does not imply that all wrought forms of each of the listed alloys are readily available.
[c] Refractory for hot rolled or as extruded rod and bar.
[d] Nonrefractory for round wire and round tube.
[e] Nonrefractory for hot rolled or as extruded rod and bar.
[f] Nonrefractory for rectangular bar and wire.

TABLE 4A—THICKNESS TOLERANCES—FLAT PRODUCTS
COLD ROLLED WITH SLIT, SLIT AND EDGE ROLLED, SHEARED, SAWED, OR MACHINED EDGES

Metric (SI) Units

Thickness mm		Thickness Tolerances, Plus and Minus,[a] mm for Specified Width, mm															
		Nonrefractory								Refractory							
Over	Thru	Over-Thru 200	200 300	300 350	350 500	500 700	700 900	900 1200	1200 1500	— 200	200 300	300 350	350 500	500 700	700 900	900 1200	1200 1500
		Strip				Sheet				Strip				Sheet			
—	0.1	0.008	0.015	0.015	—	—	—	—	—	0.010	0.02	0.02	—	—	—	—	—
0.1	0.2	0.015	0.025	0.025	0.040	—	—	—	—	0.020	0.03	0.03	0.05	—	—	—	—
0.2	0.3	0.020	0.030	0.030	0.045	0.06	0.08	0.09	0.10	0.025	0.03	0.03	0.06	—	—	—	—
0.3	0.4	0.025	0.040	0.040	0.050	0.06	0.08	0.09	0.12	0.030	0.05	0.05	0.06	—	—	—	—
0.4	0.5	0.03	0.045	0.045	0.050	0.08	0.09	0.10	0.13	0.035	0.06	0.06	0.08	—	—	—	—
0.5	0.6	0.04	0.05	0.05	0.06	0.08	0.09	0.10	0.13	0.05	0.06	0.06	0.08	0.10	0.13	0.15	0.18
0.6	0.8	0.05	0.05	0.05	0.06	0.09	0.10	0.13	0.15	0.06	0.08	0.08	0.09	0.13	0.15	0.18	0.20
0.8	1.0	0.05	0.06	0.06	0.08	0.10	0.13	0.15	0.18	0.08	0.09	0.09	0.10	0.15	0.18	0.20	0.25
1.0	1.5	0.06	0.08	0.08	0.09	0.13	0.15	0.18	0.20	0.09	0.10	0.10	0.12	0.18	0.20	0.25	0.30
1.5	3.0	0.08	0.09	0.09	0.10	0.15	0.18	0.20	0.25	0.10	0.12	0.12	0.13	0.20	0.25	0.30	0.35
3.0	5.0	0.09	0.10	0.10	0.12	0.18	0.20	0.25	0.30	0.12	0.13	0.13	0.15	0.25	0.30	0.35	0.40
		Bar		Plate						Bar		Plate					
5.0	7.5	0.10	0.12	0.12	0.13	0.23	0.25	0.30	0.35	0.13	0.15	0.15	0.18	0.30	0.35	0.40	0.45
7.5	12.0	0.12	0.13	0.13	0.15	0.30	0.33	0.38	0.45	0.15	0.18	0.18	0.20	0.38	0.43	0.48	0.58
12.0	20.0	0.14	0.18	0.18	0.23	0.38	0.43	0.48	0.58	0.20	0.25	0.25	0.30	0.48	0.53	0.60	0.73
20.0	30.0	0.18	0.23	0.23	0.28	0.45	0.53	0.60	0.73	0.25	0.30	0.30	0.38	0.58	0.65	0.75	0.93
30.0	40.0	0.55	0.55	0.55	0.55	0.63	0.73	0.90	0.70	0.70	0.70	0.70	0.70	0.80	0.93	1.13	
40.0	50.0	0.65	0.65	0.65	0.65	0.65	0.75	0.90	1.10	0.83	0.83	0.83	0.83	0.83	0.95	1.13	1.28

[a] NOTE to users: If tolerances are desired all plus or all minus, it is normal practice to specify double the values given herein.

TABLE 4B—THICKNESS TOLERANCES OF STRIP, SHEET, PLATE, AND ROLLED BAR

Thickness mm		Customary Units															
		Thickness Tolerances, Plus and Minus,[a] in for Specified Width, in															
		Nonrefractory								Refractory							
Over	Thru	Over-Thru 8.00	8.00 12.00	12.00 14.00	14.00 20.00	20.00 28.00	28.00 36.00	36.00 48.00	48.00 60.00	— 8.00	8.00 12.00	12.00 14.00	14.00 20.00	20.00 28.00	28.00 36.00	36.00 48.00	48.00 60.00
		Strip			Sheet					Strip				Sheet			
—	.004	.0003	.0006	.0006	—	—	—	—	—	.0004	.0008	.0008	—	—	—	—	—
.004	.006	.0004	.0008	.0008	.0013	—	—	—	—	.0006	.0010	.0010	.0015	—	—	—	—
.006	.009	.0006	.0010	.0010	.0015	—	—	—	—	.0008	.0013	.0013	.0020	—	—	—	—
.009	.013	.0008	.0013	.0013	.0018	.0025	.0030	.0035	.0040	.0010	.0015	.0015	.0025	—	—	—	—
.013	.017	.0010	.0015	.0015	.0020	.0025	.0030	.0035	.0045	.0013	.0020	.0020	.0025	—	—	—	—
.017	.021	.0013	.0018	.0018	.0020	.0030	.0035	.0040	.0050	.0015	.0025	.0025	.0030	—	—	—	—
.021	.026	.0015	.0020	.0020	.0025	.0030	.0035	.0040	.0050	.0020	.0025	.0025	.0030	.0040	.0050	.0060	.0070
.026	.037	.0020	.0020	.0020	.0025	.0035	.0040	.0050	.0060	.0025	.0030	.0030	.0035	.0050	.0060	.0070	.0080
.037	.050	.0020	.0025	.0025	.0030	.0040	.0050	.0060	.0070	.0030	.0035	.0035	.0040	.0060	.0070	.0080	.0100
.050	.073	.0025	.0030	.0030	.0035	.0050	.0060	.0070	.0080	.0035	.0040	.0040	.0045	.0070	.0080	.0100	.0120
.073	.130	.0030	.0035	.0035	.0040	.0060	.0070	.0080	.0100	.0040	.0045	.0045	.0050	.0080	.0100	.0120	.0140
.130	.188	.0035	.0040	.0040	.0045	.0070	.0080	.0100	.0120	.0045	.0050	.0050	.0060	.0100	.0120	.0140	.0160
		Rolled bar			Plate					Rolled bar		Plate					
.188	.205	.0035	.0040	.0040	.0045	.0070	.0080	.0100	.0120	.0045	.0050	.0050	.0060	.0100	.0120	.0140	.0160
.205	.300	.0040	.0045	.0045	.0050	.0090	.0100	.0120	.0140	.0050	.0060	.0060	.0070	.0120	.0140	.0160	.0180
.300	.500	.0045	.0050	.0050	.0060	.0120	.0130	.0150	.0180	.0060	.0070	.0070	.0080	.0150	.0170	.0190	.0230
.500	.750	.0055	.0070	.0070	.0090	.0150	.0170	.0190	.0230	.0080	.0100	.0100	.0120	.0190	.0210	.0240	.0290
.750	1.000	.0070	.0090	.0090	.0110	.0180	.0210	.0240	.0290	.0100	.0120	.0120	.0150	.0230	.0260	.0300	.0370
1.000	1.500	.0220	.0220	.0220	.0220	.0220	.0250	.0290	.0360	.0280	.0280	.0280	.0280	.0280	.0320	.0370	.0450
1.500	2.000	.0260	.0260	.0260	.0260	.0260	.0300	.0360	.0440	.0330	.0330	.0330	.0330	.0330	.0380	.0450	.0550

[a] NOTE to user: If tolerances are desired all plus or all minus, it is normal practice to specify double the values given herein.

φ

TABLE 5A—WIDTH TOLERANCES SLIT METAL AND SLIT METAL WITH ROLLED EDGES

Width, mm		Metric (SI) Units			
		Width Tolerances,[a] Plus and Minus, mm for Specified Thickness, mm			
Over	Thru	Over 0.1 Thru 1.0	1.0 3.0	3.0 5.0	5.0 13.0
—	50	0.13	0.25	0.30	0.38
50	200	0.20	0.33	0.38	0.38
200	600	0.40	0.40	0.40	0.80

[a] NOTE to users: If tolerances are specified as all plus or all minus, double the values given.

TABLE 5B—WIDTH TOLERANCES STRIP METAL WITH SLIT EDGES AND SLIT METAL WITH ROLLED EDGES

Width in		Customary Units			
		Width Tolerances,[a] Plus and Minus, in for Specified Thickness, in			
Over	Thru	Over .003 Thru. 032	.032 .125	.125 .188	.188 .500
—	2.0	.005	.010	.012	.015
2.0	8.0	.008	.013	.015	.015
8.0	20.0	.016	.016	.016	.031

[a] If tolerances are specified as all plus or all minus, double the values given.

TABLE 6A—THICKNESS TOLERANCES FOR FLAT PRODUCTS—WITH ROLLED OR DRAWN EDGES INCLUDING SQUARES AND BUS BAR STOCK—WITH ANY STANDARD EDGE CONTOUR

Metric (SI) Units

Nonrefractory

Thickness, mm		Thickness Tolerances, Plus and Minus,[a] mm for Specified Width, mm					
Over	Thru	Over–Thru 12	12–30	30–50	50–100	100–200	200–300
		Flat Wire		Strip			
—	0.5	0.2	0.03	—	—	—	—
0.5	1.5	0.03	0.04	0.05	—	—	—
1.5	2.5	0.04	0.05	0.08	0.09	—	—
2.5	3.5	0.05	0.06	0.09	0.10	—	—
3.5	5.0	0.08	0.09	0.10	0.12	0.15	0.20
				Bar			
5.0	15.0	0.09	0.10	0.12	0.12	0.15	0.20
15.0	25.0	—	0.12	0.13	0.13	0.18	0.23
25.0	50.0	—	0.13	0.13	0.15	0.20	—
50.0	100.0	—	—	—	0.60%[b]	—	—

Refractory

Thickness, mm		Thickness Tolerances, Plus and Minus,[a] mm for Specified Width, mm					
Over	Thru	Over–Thru 12	12–30	30–50	50–100	100–200	200–300
		Flat Wire			Strip		
—	1.5	0.04	0.05	—	—	—	—
1.5	2.5	0.05	0.08	0.10	0.13	—	—
2.5	3.5	0.08	0.10	0.12	0.15	—	—
3.5	5.0	0.10	0.12	0.13	0.18	0.23	0.30
				Bar			
5.0	15.0	0.13	0.13	0.15	0.18	0.23	0.30
15.0	25.0	—	0.15	0.18	0.20	0.25	0.33
25.0	50.0	—	0.15	0.18	0.23	0.28	—
50.0	100.0	—	—	—	1.00%[b]	—	—

[a] NOTE to users: If tolerances are desired all plus or all minus, it is normal practice to specify double the values given herein.
[b] Expressed to the nearest 0.03 mm.

ed. **TABLE 6B—THICKNESS TOLERANCES FOR BAR (RECTANGULAR AND SQUARE) AND WIRE**

Customary Units

Thickness, in		Thickness Tolerances, Plus and Minus,[a] in for Specified Width, in							
		Bar						Wire	
Over	Thru	Over–Thru .500	.500–1.250	1.250–2.000	2.000–4.000	4.000–8.000	8.000–12.000	—–.500	.500–1.250
				Nonrefractory					
—	.013	—	—	—	—	—	—	.0010	.0013
.013	.050	—	—	—	—	—	—	.0013	.0015
.050	.090	—	—	—	—	—	—	.0015	.0020
.090	.130	—	—	—	—	—	—	.0020	.0025
.130	.188	—	—	—	—	—	—	.0030	.0035
.188	.500	.0035	.0040	.0045	.0045	.0060	.0080	—	—
.500	1.000	—	.0045	.0050	.0050	.0070	.0090	—	—
1.000	2.000	—	.0050	.0050	.0060	.0080	—	—	—
2.000	4.000	—	—	—	.30%[b]	—	—	—	—
				Refractory					
—	.050	—	—	—	—	—	—	.0015	.0020
.050	.090	—	—	—	—	—	—	.0020	.0030
.090	.130	—	—	—	—	—	—	.0030	.0040
.130	.188	—	—	—	—	—	—	.0040	.0045
.188	.500	.0050	.0050	.0060	.0070	.0090	.0120	—	—
.500	1.000	—	.0060	.0070	.0080	.0100	.0130	—	—
1.000	2.000	—	.0060	.0070	.0090	.0110	—	—	—
2.000	4.000	—	—	—	.50%[b]	—	—	—	—

[a] NOTE to users: If tolerances are desired all plus or all minus, it is normal practice to specify double the values given herein.
[b] Expressed to the nearest 0.001 in.

ϕ *ed.* **TABLE 7—WIDTH TOLERANCES FOR BAR (RECTANGULAR ONLY) AND FLAT WIRE**

TABLE 7A—METRIC (SI) UNITS

Width, mm		Width Tolerance Plus and Minus, mm		Width, mm		Width Tolerance Plus and Minus, mm	
Over	Thru	Nonrefractory	Refractory	Over	Thru	Nonrefractory	Refractory
—	1.5	0.03	0.04				
1.5	2.5	0.04	0.05	15.0	30.0	0.13	0.18
2.5	3.5	0.05	0.08	30.0	50.0	0.20	0.25
3.5	5.0	0.08	0.10	50.0	100.0	0.30	0.38
5.0	15.0	0.09	0.13	100.0	300.0	0.60%[b]	1.00%[b]

TABLE 7B—CUSTOMARY UNITS

Width, in		Width Tolerance[a] Plus and Minus, in		Width in		Width Tolerance Plus and Minus, in	
Over	Thru	Nonrefractory	Refractory	Over	Thru	Nonrefractory	Refractory
—	.050	.0013	.0015				
.050	.090	.0015	.0020	.500	1.250	.0050	.0070
.090	.130	.0020	.0030	1.250	2.000	.0080	.0100
.130	.188	.0030	.0040	2.000	4.000	.0120	.0150
.188	.500	.0035	.0050	4.000	12.00	.30%[c]	.50%[c]

[a] NOTE to users: If tolerances are desired all plus or all minus, it is normal practice to specify double the values given herein.
[b] Expressed to the nearest 0.03 mm.
[c] Expressed to the nearest .001 in.

ϕ **TABLE 8A—CROSS SECTION TOLERANCES**

Metric (SI) Units

TABLE 8A1—WIRE,[a] BARE AND METALLIC COATED, DRAWN TO SIZE

Diameter or Distance Between Parallel Surfaces, mm		Tolerances, Plus and Minus, mm			
		Nonrefractory		Refractory	
Over	Thru	Round	Hexagon Octagon	Round	Hexagon Octagon
—	0.25	0.003	—	0.005	—
0.25	0.50	0.005	—	0.008	—
0.50	0.75	0.008	—	0.013	—
0.75	1.00	0.010	0.020	0.018	0.05
1.00	1.25	0.013	0.025	0.020	0.08
1.25	1.50	0.015	0.03	0.03	0.08
1.50	2.00	0.020	0.04	0.040	0.10
2.00	4.00	0.025	0.05	0.05	0.10
4.00	12.00	0.040	0.08	0.05	0.10
12.00	19.00	0.050	0.10	0.08	0.13

TABLE 8A2—ROD[b] AND WIRE

Diameter or Distance Between Parallel Surfaces, mm		Tolerances, Plus and Minus, mm			
		Nonrefractory		Refractory	
Over	Thru	Round	Hexagon Octagon	Round	Hexagon Octagon
—	5.0	0.033	0.06	0.05	—
5.0	15.0	0.038	0.08	0.05	0.10
15.0	25.0	0.050	0.10	0.08	0.13
25.0	50.0	0.06	0.13	0.10	0.15
50.0	—	0.30%[c]	0.60%[c]	0.40%[c]	0.80%[c]

TABLE 8A3—EXTRUDED ROD, BAR AND WIRE—FINISHED AS EXTRUDED

Diameter or Distance Between Parallel Surfaces mm		Tolerances, Plus and Minus, mm — Round, Square, Rectangular, Hexagon and Octagon	
Over	Thru	Nonrefractory	Refractory
—	25.0	0.25	0.50
25.00	50.0	0.38	0.75
50.0	75.0	0.63	1.25
75.0	90.0	0.88	1.75
90.0	100.0	1.50	3.00

ed. **TABLE 8A4—DIAMETER TOLERANCES HOT ROLLED ROD (ROUND ONLY) AND WIRE**

Diameter, mm		Tolerances Plus and Minus, mm
Over	Thru	
6.3	20.0	0.38
20.0	30.0	0.50
30.0	40.0	0.75
40.0	75.0	1.60
75.0	—	3.15

[a] Wire for redrawing or rerolling, double the following tolerances.
[b] Rod-Cold drawn to size—except piston finish rod.
[c] Expressed to the nearest 0.03 mm.

TABLE 8B—DIAMETER (ACROSS FLATS) TOLERANCES OF WIRE, ROD AND BAR

Customary Units

Dia or Dist Between Parallel Surfaces, in		Tolerances, Plus and Minus,[a] in										
		Wire				Cold Drawn Rod				As Extruded Rod and Bar		Hot Rolled Round Rod
		Nonrefractory		Refractory		Nonrefractory		Refractory		Nonrefractory	Refractory	Nonrefractory and Refractory
										Rounds, Squares, Rectangles, Hexagon, Octagon	Rounds, Squares, Rectangles, Hexagon, Octagon	
Over	Thru	Round	Hexagon, Octagon	Round	Hexagon, Octagon	Round	Hexagon, Octagon	Round	Hexagon, Octagon			Rounds
—	.010	.0001	—	.0002	—	—	—	—	—	—	—	—
.010	.020	.0002	—	.0003	—	—	—	—	—	—	—	—
.020	.030	.0003	—	.0005	—	—	—	—	—	—	—	—
.030	.040	.0004	.0008	.0007	.0020	—	—	—	—	—	—	—
.040	.050	.0005	.0010	.0008	.0030	—	—	—	—	—	—	—
.050	.060	.0006	.0012	.0010	.0030	—	—	—	—	—	—	—
.060	.080	.0008	.0016	.0015	.0040	Note c	Note c	Note c	—	—	—	—
.080	.150	.0010	.0020	.0020	.0040	.0013	.0025	.0020	—	—	—	—
.150	.249	.0015	.0030	.0020		.0015	.0030	.0020	.0040	—	—	—
.250 only		—	—	—	—					—	—	+.020–.010
.250	.500	.0015	.0030	.0020	.0040	.0015	.0030	.0020	.0040	—	—	.015
.500	.750	.0020	.0040	.0030	—	.0020	.0040	.0030	.0050	—	—	.015
.750	1.000	—	—	—	—	.0020	.0040	.0030	.0050	.010[d]	.020[d]	.020
1.000	1.250	—	—	—	—	.0025	.0050	.0040	.0060	.015	.030	.020
1.250	1.500	—	—	—	—	.0025	.0050	.0040	.0060	.015	.030	.030
1.500	2.000	—	—	—	—	.0025	.0050	.0040	.0060	.015	.030	.062
2.000	3.000	—	—	—	—	.15%[b]	.30%[b]	.20%[b]	.40%[b]	.025	.050	.062
3.000	3.500	—	—	—	—	.15%[b]	.30%[b]	.20%[b]	.40%[b]	.035	.070	.125
3.500	4.000	—	—	—	—	.15%[b]	.30%[b]	.20%[b]	.40%[b]	.060	.120	.125
4.000	—	—	—	—	—	.15%[b]	.30%[b]	.20%[b]	.40%[b]	—	—	.125

[a] If tolerances are desired all plus or all minus, double the values given.
[b] Expressed to the nearest .001 in.
[c] Up to and including .150 in.
[d] Up to and including 1.000 in.

φ

TABLE 9A—WALL THICKNESS TOLERANCES[a,b] OF ROUND TUBE

Metric (SI) Units

Wall Thickness mm		Tolerances, Plus and Minus, mm for Specified Outside Diameters,[c] mm													
		Over 0.8 Thru 3.2		3.2 15.9		15.9 25.4		25.4 50.8		50.8 101.6		101.6 177.8		177.8 254.0	
Over	Thru	Nonrefractory	Refractory	Nonrefractory	Refractory	Nonrefractory	Refractory	Nonrefractory	Refractory	Nonrefractory	Refractory	Nonrefractory	Refractory	Nonrefractory	Refractory
—	0.46	0.05	0.06	0.03	0.04	0.04	0.05	0.05	0.06	—	—	—	—	—	—
0.46	0.64	0.08	0.10	0.05	0.06	0.05	0.06	0.06	0.08	—	—	—	—	—	—
0.64	0.89	0.08	0.10	0.06	0.08	0.06	0.08	0.08	0.10	0.10	0.13	—	—	—	—
0.89	1.47	0.08	0.10	0.08	0.10	0.09	0.11	0.09	0.11	0.13	0.17	0.18	0.23	—	—
1.47	2.11	—		0.09	0.11	0.10	0.13	0.10	0.13	0.15	0.19	0.20	0.25	0.25	0.33
2.11	3.05		—	0.10	0.13	0.13	0.17	0.13	0.17	0.18	0.23	0.23	0.28	0.28	0.36
3.05	4.19	—	—	0.13	0.18	0.15	0.18	0.15	0.19	0.20	0.25	0.25	0.33	0.30	0.38
4.19	5.59	—	—	0.18	—	0.19	0.23	0.20	0.25	0.25	0.33	0.30	0.38	0.36	0.46
5.59	7.21	—	—	—	—	0.23	0.30	0.25	0.33	0.30	0.38	0.36	0.46	0.41	0.51
7.21	9.65	—	—	—	—	0.28	—	0.30	0.38	0.36	0.46	0.41	0.51	0.46	0.58
9.65	—	—	—	—	—	—	—	5%	6%	5%	6%	6%	8%	6%	8%

[a] Maximum deviation at any point, if tolerances all plus or all minus are desired, double the values given.
[b] Tolerances of following dimensions may be specified for any two, but not all three: outside diameter, inside diameter, wall thickness.
[c] When round tube is ordered by outside and inside diameters, the maximum plus and minus deviation of the wall thickness from the mean at any point shall not exceed the values given in this table by more than 50%.

TABLE 9B—WALL THICKNESS TOLERANCES OF ROUND TUBE

Customary Units

Wall Thickness, in		Tolerances, Plus and Minus,[a] in for Specified Outside Diameters,[b] in													
		Over .030 Thru .125		.125 .625		.625 1.00		1.00 2.00		2.00 4.00		4.00 7.00		7.00 10.00	
Over	Thru	Nonrefractory	Refractory	Nonrefractory	Refractory	Nonrefractory	Refractory	Nonrefractory	Refractory	Nonrefractory	Refractory	Nonrefractory	Refractory	Nonrefractory	Refractory
—	.017	.0020	.0025	.0010	.0015	.0015	.0020	.0020	.0025	—	—	—	—	—	—
.017	.024	.0030	.0040	.0020	.0025	.0020	.0025	.0025	.0030	—	—	—	—	—	—
.024	.034	.0030	.0040	.0025	.0030	.0025	.0030	.0030	.0040	.0040	.0050	—	—	—	—
.034	.057	.0030	.0040	.0030	.0040	.0035	.0045	.0035	.0045	.0050	.0065	.0070	.0090		
.057	.082	—	—	.0045	.0045	.0040	.0050	.0040	.0050	.0060	.0075	.0080	.0100	.0100	.0130
.082	.119	—	—	.0040	.0050	.0050	.0065	.0050	.0065	.0070	.0090	.0090	.0110	.0110	.0140
.119	.164	—	—	.0050	.0070	.0060	.0070	.0060	.0075	.0080	.0100	.0100	.0130	.0120	.0150
.164	.219	—	—	.0070		.0075	.0090	.0080	.0100	.0100	.0130	.0120	.0150	.0140	.0180
.219	.283	—	—	—	—	.0090	.0120	.0100	.0130	.0120	.0150	.0140	.0180	.0160	.0200
.283	.379					.0110		.0120	.0150	.0140	.0180	.0160	.0200	.0180	.0230
.379	—	—	—	—	—	—	—	5%	6%	5%	6%	6%	8%	6%	8%

[a] Maximum deviation at any point. Note to Users: If tolerances are desired all plus or all minus, it is normal practice to specify double the values given herein.
[b] When round tube is ordered by outside and inside diameters, the maximum plus and minus deviation of the wall thickness from the nominal at any point shall not exceed the values given in this table by more than 50 percent.

TABLE 10—AVERAGE DIAMETER TOLERANCES OF ROUND TUBE[a,b]

TABLE 10A—METRIC (SI) UNITS

Diameter, mm		Application of Tolerance	Diameter Tolerances Plus and Minus, mm	
Over	Thru		Nonrefractory	Refractory
—	3.2	ID	0.05	0.08
—	3.2	OD	0.05	0.06
3.2	15.9	ID or OD	0.05	0.06
15.9	25.4	ID or OD	0.06	0.08
25.4	50.8	ID or OD	0.08	0.10
50.8	76.2	ID or OD	0.10	0.13
76.2	101.6	ID or OD	0.13	0.15
101.6	127.0	ID or OD	0.15	0.20
127.0	152.4	ID or OD	0.18	0.23
152.4	203.2	ID or OD	0.20	0.25
203.2	254.0	ID or OD	0.25	0.33

TABLE 10B—CUSTOMARY UNITS

Diameter, in		Application of Tolerance	Diameter Tolerances Plus and Minus, in	
Over	Thru		Nonrefractory	Refractory
—	.125	ID	.0020	.0030
—	.125	OD	.0020	.0025
.125	.625	ID or OD	.0020	.0025
.625	1.00	ID or OD	.0025	.0030
1.00	2.00	ID or OD	.0030	.0040
2.00	3.00	ID or OD	.0040	.0050
3.00	4.00	ID or OD	.0050	.0060
4.00	5.00	ID or OD	.0060	.0080
5.00	6.00	ID or OD	.0070	.0090
6.00	8.00	ID or OD	.0080	.0100
8.00	10.00	ID or OD	.0100	.0130

[a] The average outside or inside diameter of a tube is the average of the maximum and minimum outside diameters, or of the maximum and minimum inside diameters, whichever is applicable, as determined at any cross-section of the tube.
[b] Tube tolerances—tolerances of the following dimensions may be specified for any two, but not all three: outside diameter, inside diameter, wall thickness.

TABLE 11—ROUNDNESS TOLERANCES OF ROUND TUBE

T/D Ratio of Nominal Wall Thickness to Nominal Outside Diameter		Roundness Tolerances,[a] % Nominal Outside Diameter Expressed to Nearest 0.03 mm (.001 in)
Over	Thru	
0.01	0.03	1.5%
0.03	0.05	1.0%
0.05	0.10	0.8% or 0.05 mm (.002 in)[b]
0.10	—	0.7% or 0.05 mm (.002 in)[b]

[a] The deviation from roundness is measured as the difference between major and minor outside diameters, as determined at any one cross-section of the tube.
[b] Whichever value is greater.

NOTE: For tube in any drawn temper in straight lengths. Not applicable to as extruded tube, redraw tube, annealed tube or any tube furnished in coils, or drawn tube whose wall thickness is under 0.40 mm (.016 in). Compliance with the roundness tolerance shall be determined by taking measurements on the outside diameter only, irrespective of the manner in which the tube dimensions are specified; whether outside diameter and wall thickness; outside diameter and inside diameter; or inside diameter and wall thickness.

MAGNESIUM ALLOYS—SAE J464 JAN1989

SAE Information Report

Report of the SAE Nonferrous Metals Division approved January 1940, revised by the SAE Nonferrous Metals Committee April 1979, and reaffirmed by the SAE Cast Aluminum Committee January 1989.

Foreword—This Document has not changed other than to put it into the new SAE Technical Standards Board Format.

1. Scope—This report on magnesium alloys covers those alloys which have been more commonly used in the United States for automotive, aircraft, and missile applications. Basic information on nomenclature and temper designation is given. Design data and many characteristics covered by a purchase specification are not included.

2. References

2.1 Applicable Publications—The following publications form a part of the specification to the extent specified herein. Unless otherwise indicated the latest revision of SAE publications shall apply.

2.1.1 ASTM PUBLICATIONS—Available from ASTM, 100 Barr Harbor Drive, West Conshohocken, PA 19428-2959.

ASTM B 275— Recommended Practice for Codification of Light Metals and Alloys, Cast and Wrought

ASTM B 296—Recommended Practice for Temper Designation of Magnesium Alloys, Cast and Wrought

3. Sources of Magnesium—Magnesium is the third most abundant structural element in the earth's crust, and considered inexhaustible. Common sources are sea water, natural brines, magnesite, and dolomite. Three methods of extraction are used in the United States. One method involves treating sea water with a source of alkalinity (lime or caustic soda) to precipitate the magnesium as hydroxide, which is then mixed with hydrochloric acid to produce magnesium chloride. The magnesium chloride is reduced electrolytically to produce magnesium metal and a mixture of chlorine and hydrochloric acid. A second method produces coproduct magnesium metal and pure chlorine in the electrolytic cell by the reduction of anhydrous magnesium chloride. The anhydrous cell feed results from the dehydration of natural brines. Another method of extraction which is also used in the United States and in other countries is a thermal reduction method, generally referred to as the ferro-silicon process, employing an alloy of iron and silicon to reduce magnesium oxide. Most of the magnesium ingot sold is of 99.80% purity. Grades of magnesium of 99.90, 99.95, and 99.98% purity are also available. The higher purity grades are used mostly in nuclear applications and for reduction purposes.

4. Properties—Magnesium is extremely light with the common alloys having a specific gravity of about 1.8 compared to 2.7 for aluminum. The heavier structural metals like iron, copper, and zinc are approximately four times as heavy as magnesium. Magnesium melts at 650°C (1202°F). The coefficient of thermal expansion between 20–100°C (68–212°F) is approximately 0.0000261/°C (0.0000145/°F) and is slightly higher than for aluminum, 0.000023/°C (0.000013/°F), and over twice that of steel. The thermal and electrical conductivities of magnesium are relatively high and some alloys approach values comparable to aluminum alloys. The modulus of elasticity is approximately 45 GPa (6 500 000 psi). The pure metal is not used for structural applications. A number of alloys have been developed with good strength-to-weight ratios.

5. Alloying Elements—Common alloying elements used in magnesium alloys are aluminum, manganese, rare earths, silver, thorium, zinc, and zirconium. Alloys are stronger than the pure metal but have lower electrical and thermal conductivities. Certain of the alloys respond to heat treatment with an increase in strength and hardness. Another means used to increase the strength of magnesium is by cold work. Most commercial alloys are stable at room temperature. Certain alloying elements such as the rare earths and thorium give better high temperature strength than can be obtained with the more common alloying elements aluminum and zinc.

6. Alloy Nomenclature—A designation system for magnesium alloys used commercially and described in ASTM B 275, Recommended Practice for Codification of Light Metals and Alloys, Cast and Wrought, was adopted by SAE in 1971. The initial letter(s) represent the major alloying element(s) with the following numeral(s) representing the nominal percent by weight of each element. The final letter is assigned arbitrarily.

7. Temper Designation—The same temper designation system is used for both aluminum base and magnesium base alloys. It is described in detail under the aluminum alloy section of this book and in ASTM B 296, Recommended Practice for Temper Designation of Magnesium Alloys, Cast and Wrought.

8. Working—Magnesium alloys are available in most commercial forms such as die castings, investment, sand and permanent mold castings, extrusion, forgings, sheet, and plate. It can be formed by drawing, spinning, and pressing. The working is done best at elevated temperatures because of improved workability and freedom from springback. Magnesium can be joined by adhesive bonding, bolting, riveting, and welding. Arc welding, using an inert gas shield, is the most commonly used method of fusion welding. Spot welding is used extensively. Magnesium, in all its forms, can be readily machined with exceptional speed and tool life.

9. Finishing and Coating—Bare magnesium is suitable for many applications. Protective finishes may be required to prevent tarnishing or for protection from corrosion in humid industrial or marine atmospheres. It is subject to galvanic attack when coupled to most other metals, and such connections should be adequately protected if moisture will be present. Magnesium can be finished by plating and painting for either protection or decoration.

10. Testing—Magnesium alloys are tested like other metals using standard ASTM methods. The tensile and compressive yield strengths are defined as the stress at which the stress-strain curve deviates 0.2% from the initial modulus line.

MAGNESIUM CASTING ALLOYS—SAE J465 JAN1989 SAE Standard

Report of the SAE Nonferrous Metals Division approved January 1940, completely revised by the SAE Nonferrous Metals Committee June 1983, and reaffirmed by the SAE Wrought Aluminum, Magnesium, and Zinc Committee January 1989.

1. Scope—This document has not changed other than to put it into the new SAE Technical Standards Board Format

This SAE Standard covers the most commonly used magnesium alloys suitable for casting by the various commercial processes. The chemical composition limits and minimum mechanical properties are shown. Over the years, magnesium alloys have been identified by many numbering systems, as shown in Table 1. Presently, SAE is recommending the use of the use of the UNS numbering system to identify those materials. Other equally important characteristics such as surface finish and dimensional tolerances are not covered in this standard.

1.1 Sources of Magnesium—Sources of Magnesium—Magnesium is the third most abundant structural element in the earth's crust, and considered inexhaustible. Common sources are sea water, natural brines, magnesite, and dolomite. Three methods of extraction are used in the United States. One method involves treating sea water with a source of alkalinity to precipitate the magnesium as hydroxide, mixing with hydrochloric acid to produce hydrated magnesium chloride, and then partially drying. The hydrous magnesium chloride is reduced electrolytically to produce magnesium metal and a mixture of chlorine and hydrochloric acid. A second method produces co-products magnesium metal and pure chlorine in the electrolytic cell by the reduction of anhydrous magnesium chloride or by the chlorination of MgO. The anhydrous cell feed results from the complete dehydration of natural brines. Another method of extraction, which is also used in the United States and in other countries, is by thermal reduction of magnesium oxide by ferrosilicon. Most of the magnesium ingot sold is of 99.80% purity. Grades of magnesium of 99.90, 99.95, and 99.98% purity are also available. The higher purity grades are used mostly in nuclear applications and for reduction purposes.

1.2 Castings—Magnesium alloys are cast by all casting methods, the most common being pressure die casting, investment casting, sand casting, and permanent mold casting. Many alloys are available for use as sand, investment, and permanent mold castings to give the desired end use and production characteristics. Most of these are not suitable for use in the pressure die casting process. Most of the alloys used for sand, investment, and permanent mold castings may be heat treated to increase strength or improve stability. Die castings, while in the same composition range as some of the sand castings, are not heat treated because of undesirable effects such as grain growth and blistering. Magnesium alloy sand, investment, and permanent mold castings are generally sold in the solution heat treated (T4) condition for best ductility. Artificial aging after solution heat treatment (T6) increases the yield strength considerably but decreases the ductility. Many times an artificial age (T5) from the as-cast condition (F) is sufficient to give the desired strength and stability.

1.3 Alloying Elements—Common alloying elements used in magnesium alloys are aluminum, manganese, rare earths, silicon, silver, thorium, zinc, and zirconium. Alloys are stronger than the pure metal, but have lower electrical and thermal conductivities. Certain of the alloys respond to heat treatment with an increase in strength and hardness. Most commercial alloys are stable at room temperature. Certain alloying elements such as the rare earths and thorium improve the high temperature strength of magnesium alloys.

1.4 Alloy Nomenclature—A designation system for magnesium alloys used commercially and described in ASTM B 275, Recommended Practice for Codification of Light Metals and Alloys, Cast and Wrought, was adopted by SAE in 1971. The initial letters represent the major alloying elements with the following numerals representing the nominal percent by weight of each element. The final letter is assigned arbitrarily.

TABLE 1—PHYSICAL PROPERTIES AND CHARACTERISTICS OF MAGNESIUM SAND-CASTING ALLOYS

Alloy Designation			Approximate Melting Range, °F (°C)			Foundry Characteristics(1)						Other Characteristics				
UNS	ASTM and SAE	Old SAE	Non-Equilibrium Solidus(2)	Solidus	Liquidus	Pattern Shrinkage Allowance in/ft (mm/m)(3)	Pressure Tightness	Fluidity(4)	Micro-porosity Tendency (5)	Normally Heat Treated	Cast-ability	Machining (6)	Electro-plating(7)	Surface Treatment(8)	Suit-ability to Brazing (9)	Suit-ability to Welding (10)
M10100 (11)	AM100A	502	810 (432)	867 (464)	1100 (593)	5/32 (13.0)	2	1	2	Yes	2	1	2	2	No	1
M11630	AZ63A	50	685 (363)	850 (454)	1130 (610)	5/32 (13.0)	3	1	3	Yes	3	1	1	1	No	3
M11810(11)	AZ81A	505	790 (421)	882 (472)	1115 (602)	5/32 (13.0)	2	1	2	Yes	1	1	2	2	No	1
M11914(11)	AZ91C	504	785 (418)	875 (468)	1105 (596)	5/32 (13.0)	2	1	2	Yes	1	1	2	2	No	2
M11920(11)	AZ92A	500	770 (410)	830 (443)	1100 (593)	5/32 (13.0)	2	1	2	Yes	2	1	2	2	No	2
M12330(12)	EZ33A	506	— —	1010 (543)	1189 (643)	3/16 (15.5)	1	2	1	Yes	1	1	1	1	No	1
M13310(11)	HK31A	507	— —	1092 (589)	1204 (651)	7/32 (18.0)	1	2	1	Yes	1	1	1	1	—(13)	1
M13320(11)	HZ32A	—	— —	1026 (552)	1198 (648)	3/16 (15.5)	1	2	1	Yes	1	1	—	2	—(13)	2
M18010 (14)	K1A	—	— —	— —	1205 (652)	3/16 (15.5)	2	2	2	No	2	1	3	2	—(13)	1
M18210	QH21A	—	— —	1004 (539)	1184 (640)	3/16 (15.5)	2	2	2	Yes	1	1	2	1	No	—
M18220(11)	QE22A	—	— —	1020 (549)	1190 (643)	5/32 (13.0)	2	2	2	Yes	1	1	2	1	—(13)	1
M16410(14)	ZE41A	—	— —	950 (510)	1184 (640)	3/16 (15.5)	—(13)	2	—(13)	Yes	1	1	1	1	No	2
M16630(14)	ZE63A	—	— —	510 (266)	950 (510)	3/16 (15.5)	1	2	1	Yes	1	1	—(13)	1	No	1
M16620	ZH62A	508	— —	— —	1169 (632)	5/32 (13.0)	2	2	2	Yes	2	1	1	1	No	—(13)
M16510	ZK51A	509	— —	1020 (549)	1185 (641)	5/32 (13.0)	3	2	3	Yes	3	1	2	2	No	3
M16610	ZK61A	513	— —	985 (529)	1175 (635)	532 (13.0)	3	2	3	Yes	3	1	2	1	No	3

1. Rating of 1 indicates best of group; 3 indicates poorest of group.
2. As measured on metal solidified under normal casting conditions.
3. Allowance for average castings. Shrinkage requirements will vary with intricacy of design and dimensions. (1 in/ft x 8.333 = % Shrinkage.)
4. Ability of liquid alloy to flow readily in mold and fill thin sections.
5. Based on radiographic evidence.
6. Composite rating based on ease of cutting, chip characteristics, quality of finish, and tool life. Ratings, in the case of heat-treatable alloys, based on —T6 type temper. Other tempers, particularly the annealed temper, may have lower ratings.
7. Ability of casting to take and hold an electroplate applied by present standard methods.
8. Ability of castings to be cleaned in standard pickle solutions and to be conditioned for best paint adhesion.
9. Refers to suitability of alloy to withstand brazing temperature without excessive distortion or melting.
10. Based on ability of material to be fusion welded with filler rod of same alloy.
11. Properties applicable for permanent mold and investment castings.
12. Properties applicable for permanent mold castings also.
13. Inexperience with these alloys under wide production conditions makes it undesirable to supply ratings at this time.
14. Properties applicable for investment castings also.

1.5 Temper Designation—The same temper designation system is used for both aluminum-base and magnesium-base alloys. It is described in detail under the aluminum alloy section of this book and in ASTM B 296, Recommended Practice for Temper Designation of Magnesium Alloys, Cast and Wrought.

1.6 Finishing and Coating—Bare magnesium is suitable for some applications. Protective finishes may be required to prevent tarnishing or for protection from corrosion in humid industrial or marine atmospheres. It is subject to galvanic attack when coupled to most other metals, and such connections should be adequately protected if moisture will be present. Magnesium can be finished by plating and painting for either protection or decoration.

1.7 Testing—Magnesium alloys are tested like other metals using standard ASTM methods. The tensile and compressive yield strengths are defined as the stress at which the stress-strain curve deviates 0.2% from the initial modulus line.

2. References

2.1 Applicable Publications—The following publications form a part of the specification to the extent specified herein. Unless otherwise indicated the latest revision of SAE publications shall apply.

2.1.1 ASTM—Available from ASTM, 100 Barr Harbor Drive, West Conshohocken, PA 19428-2959.

ASTM B 275—Recommended Practice for Codification of Light Metals and Alloys, Cast and Wrought

ASTM B 296—Recommended Practice for Temper Designation of Magnesium Alloys, Cast and Wrought

ASTM B 557—Method of Tension Testing Wrought and Cast Aluminum- and Magnesium-Alloy Products

3. Sand Castings

3.1 General—Sand castings are used when a small number of castings are required or the casting is large or complicated. In many cases, sand cores are used with permanent mold castings. Dimensional tolerances, on the whole, are greater for sand castings than for permanent mold castings and the surface is not as smooth.

In the design of patterns, a shrinkage factor of 5/32 in/ft (13 mm/m) is generally used, but this may be reduced to 1/8 in/ft (10 mm/m) or less if free shrinkage is restrained by bosses, internal cores, or grates and risers. Walls as thin as 0.150 in (3.80 mm) can be readily made in large size castings. Thinner walls are possible for smaller areas. For example, a 0.120 in (3.05 mm) thick wall can be cast covering an area of about 1 ft^2 (0.1 m^2).

In order to obtain the best results from castings, the foundry should be consulted on the design of the casting, choice of alloy, heat treatment, and properties attainable. The selection of the alloy and heat treatment is governed by the characteristics desired in the casting and the limitations of the casting process. Considerations of cost and secondary characteristics such as finishing, welding, and pressure tightness may be the deciding factor on which alloy to use.

3.2 Physical Properties and Characteristics

3.2.1 PURE MAGNESIUM—Magnesium is extremely light with the common alloys having a specific gravity of about 1.8 compared to 2.7 for aluminum. The heavier structural metals like iron, copper, and zinc are approximately four times as heavy as magnesium. Magnesium melts at 1202 °F (650 °C). The coefficient of thermal expansion between 68–212 °F (20–100 °C) is approximately 0.0000145/°F (0.0000261/°C) and is slightly higher than for aluminum, 0.000013/°F (0.000023/°C), and over twice that of steel. The thermal and electrical conductivities of magnesium are relatively high and some alloys approach values comparable to aluminum alloys. The modulus of elasticity is approximately 6 500 000 psi (45 GPa). The pure metal is not used for structural applications, but a number of alloys have been developed with good strength-to-weight ratios.

3.2.2 ALLOYS—The physical properties and characteristics of the most commonly used alloys for sand casting are compared in Table 1, which was compiled by the American Foundrymen's Society.

Approximately the same ratings shown in Table 1 would apply for the same alloys when used for permanent mold and investment castings, although not all sand casting alloys are suitable for use in permanent molds.

3.3 Composition and Its Effects—The compositions of magnesium casting alloys are given in Table 2.

Alloys M10100, M11630, M11810, M11914, and M11920 are used for most commercial applications. With the exception of M10100, which is a binary magnesium-aluminum alloy, they contain aluminum and zinc as alloying elements. This alloy family is used where moderately high strength at room temperature is desired. These alloys generally have good castability and are the lowest in cost of the commercial alloys. Individual differences in strength, ductility, and pressure tightness exist in this family of alloys. M11630 has the best toughness but has a tendency to microporosity in complex designs. M11920 has the highest tensile yield strength of the Mg-Al-Zn alloys. It has been used extensively in aircraft engines. M10100 has good castability and pressure tightness. Alloys M11914 and M11810 have better pressure tightness than M11630 and have good weldability. Both M11914 and M11810 have been used extensively in aircraft and racing car wheels. The upper operating limit for the Mg-Al-Zn casting alloys is generally considered to be about 300 °F (149 °C).

A second series of alloys is based upon the Mg-Zn-Zr alloy system. These alloys are also generally used at service temperatures below 300 °F (149 °C), although the addition of rare earth metals (alloy M16410) and thorium (alloy M16620) somewhat improves their ability to withstand exposure to more elevated temperatures. Alloys M16410 and M16620 have improved foundry characteristics and weldability over M16510 and M16610. Alloy M16610-T6 has a high strength-to-weight ratio compared to most commercial casting alloys, but shows less favorable foundry characteristics. Alloy M16630-T6 has a high strength-to-weight ratio, is readily castable, and shows little or no tendency to microporosity. It is designed to take advantage of a new principle of heat treatment involving the inward diffusion of hydrogen and formation of hydrides. M18010 is a low-strength casting alloy intended for applications requiring exceptionally good damping characteristics.

A third group of alloys is based on the Mg-Re-Zr system. These alloys are used in applications for operation at temperatures up to 550 °F (288 °C) where tensile or creep strength is a requirement. Alloy M12330 also is excellent where pressure tightness is a requirement. It rates second to M18010 in damping capacity.

The fourth group of alloys consists of Mg-Th-Zr alloys with or without zinc, which find applications in parts operating at temperatures up to 650 °F (343 °C). Alloy M18210 has the best short-time strength properties up to 400 °F (205 °C) of all magnesium alloys.

3.4 Mechanical Properties—The mechanical properties given in Table 3 are those obtained from separately cast test specimens. These test specimens are cast and heat treated under conditions that duplicate, as closely as possible, the conditions under which the castings they represent are made. The test bars are not machined except to fit the grips of the testing machine.

The mechanical properties of test specimens machined from castings will depend upon the type and size of casting and the location from which the specimen is taken. Specimens from thin sections or heavily chilled sections may have properties comparable to or superior to those from separately cast test specimens. Specimens from sections near gates and risers generally have lower properties. Separately cast test bars serve as a control on the metal quality and the heat treating process, if such are used. Minimum properties of test specimens cut from castings are generally guaranteed on the basis of an average of not less than three specimens each from the thickest, the thinnest, and an average cross-section. Minimum mechanical properties for designated areas are sometimes specified.

The concept of premium quality castings has been introduced by research workers and the foundry industry. The most important feature of premium quality is higher integrity of the product, and the reliability of properties in designated areas of each and every single casting. Table 4 shows the minimum requirements for mechanical properties in designated and other areas of premium quality castings.

4. Permanent Mold Castings—Any of the alloys listed in Table 3 as sand casting alloys can be used for permanent mold castings. Cracking tendencies limit the usefulness of many of the alloys since they cannot be cast in large sizes or complicated shapes. Permanent mold castings are used for economy of production when the number of pieces required justifies the increased mold cost. Permanent mold casting permits the production of more uniform castings, with closer dimensional tolerances and superior surface finish than with sand casting. The minimum wall thickness that it is possible to obtain is somewhat greater on permanent mold castings than for sand castings because of the chilling effect of the mold. However, thicknesses down to 0.150 in (3.80 mm) covering large areas may sometimes be cast. Thinner walls can be cast covering smaller areas. Complex parts which cannot be made entirely as a permanent mold casting, can often be produced in semi-permanent molds using sand cores. The characteristics of the various magnesium base alloys are typical of the alloy, whether cast in sand, investment, or permanent molds. Some of the characteristics, such as hot shortness, limit the usefulness of some of the alloys to such an extent that they are seldom used for permanent mold castings. In the Mg-Al-Zn alloy group, M11920, M10100, M11914, and M11810 are most commonly used as permanent mold castings. M12330, M13310, and M18220 alloys can be cast in permanent molds quite readily.

The minimum properties of separately cast test bars and test specimens cut from castings are generally the same for a given alloy, whether cast in sand or permanent molds. The same minimum mechanical properties are used for both sand and permanent mold casting of the same alloy. Hence, those shown in Table 3 for sand castings are used for permanent mold castings. Applications for permanent mold castings are the same as for sand castings. Producibility, cost, surface, and tolerances should be considered in deciding the process to be used.

TABLE 2—COMPOSITION OF MAGNESIUM CASTING ALLOYS

Alloy Designation			Elements, wt. %									
UNS	ASTM and SAE	Old SAE	Al	Mn, min	Zn	Th	Rare Earths	Zr	Cu, max	Ni, max	Si, max	Total Other Elements, max
M10600	AM60A		5.5–6.5	0.13	0.22	—	—	—	0.35	0.03	0.50	—
M10100	AM100A	502	9.3–10.7	0.10	0.30 max	—	—	—	0.10	0.01	0.30	0.30
M10410	AS41A		3.7–4.8	0.22–0.48	0.10 max	—	—	—	0.04	0.01	0.60–1.4	0.30
M11630	AZ63A	50	5.3–6.7	0.15	2.5–3.5	—	—	—	0.25	0.01	0.30	0.30
M11810	AZ81A	505	7.0–8.1	0.13	0.40–1.0	—	—	—	0.10	0.01	0.30	0.30
M11910	AZ91A	501	8.3–9.7	0.13	0.35–1.0	—	—	—	0.10	0.03	0.50	0.30
M11912	AZ91B	501A	8.3–9.7	0.13	0.35–1.0	—	—	—	0.35	0.03	0.50	0.30
M11914	AZ91C	504	8.1–9.3	0.13	0.4–1.0	—	—	—	0.10	0.01	0.30	0.30
M11920	AZ92A	500	8.3–9.7	0.10	1.6–2.4	—	—	—	0.25	0.01	0.30	0.30
M12330	EZ33A	506	—	—	2.0–3.1	—	2.5–4.0	0.50–1.0	0.10	0.01	—	0.30
M13310	HK31A	507	—	—	0.30 max	2.5–4.0	—	0.40–1.0	0.10	0.01	—	0.30
M13320	HZ32A	—	—		1.7–2.5	2.5–4.0	0.10 max	0.50–1.0	0.10	0.01	—	0.30
M18010	K1A	—	—		—	—	—	0.40–1.0	—	—	—	0.30
M18210	QH21A (1)	—	—		0.2 max	0.6–1.6 (2)	0.6–1.5 (3)	0.40–1.0	0.10	0.01	—	0.30
M18220	QE22A[1]	—	—		—	—	1.8–2.5 (4)	0.40–1.0	0.10	0.01	—	0.30
M16410	ZE41A	—	—	0.15 max	3.5–5.0	—	0.75–1.75	0.40–1.0	0.10	0.01	—	0.30
M16630	ZE63A	—	—		5.5–6.0	—	2.1–3.0	0.40–1.0	0.10	0.01	—	0.30
M16620	ZH62A	508	—		5.2–6.2	1.4–2.2	—	0.50–1.0	0.10	0.01	—	0.30
M16510	ZK51A	509	—		3.6–5.5	—	—	0.50–1.0	0.10	0.01	—	0.30
M16610	ZK61A	513	—		5.5–6.5	—	—	0.6–1.0	0.10	0.01	—	0.30

1. Silver content in M18220 shall be 2.0–3.0.
2. Th and didymium total is 1.5–2.4%.
3. Rare earth elements are in the form of didymium with not less than 70% neodymium and the remainder substantially praseodymium.
4. Rare earth elements in M18220 are in the form of didymium; in alloys M16410 and M16630, in the form of mischmetal.

TABLE 3—MINIMUM MECHANICAL PROPERTIES OF SEPARATELY CAST TEST BARS MAGNESIUM SAND CASTING ALLOYS(1)

Alloy or Temper Designation				Ultimate Tensile Strength		Yield Strength 0.2% Offset		Elongation in 2 in (50.8 mm),
UNS	ASTM and SAE	Temper		psi	MPa	psi	MPa	%
M10100	AM100A	F	As-cast	20 000	138	— (2)	—(2)	—(2)
		–T4	Solution heat treated	34 000	234	— (2)	— (2)	6
		–T6	Solution heat treated and artificially aged	35 000	241	17 000	117	—(2)
M11630	AZ63A	F	As-cast	26 000	179	11 000	76	4
		–T4	Solution heat treated	34 000	234	11 000	76	7
		–T5	Artificially aged only	26 000	179	12 000	83	2
		–T6	Solution heat treated and artificially aged	34 000	234	16 000	110	3
M11810	AZ81A	–T4	Solution heat treated	34 000	234	11 000	76	7
M11914	AZ91C	F	As-cast	23 000	159	11 000	76	—(2)
		–T4	Solution heat treated	34 000	234	11 000	76	7
		–T5	Artificially aged only	23 000	159	12 000	83	2
		–T6	Solution heat treated and artificially aged	34 000	234	16 000	110	3
M11920	AZ92A	F	As-cast	23 000	159	11 000	76	—(2)
		–T4	Solution heat treated	34 000	234	11 000	76	6
		–T5	Artificially aged only	23 000	159	12 000	83	—(2)
		–T6	Solution heat treated and artificially aged	34 000	234	18 000	124	1
M12330	EZ33A	–T5	Artificially aged only	20 000	138	14 000	97	2
M13310	HK31A	–T6	Solution heat treated and artificially aged	27 000	186	13 000	90	4
M13320	HZ32A	–T5	Artificially aged only	27 000	186	13 000	90	4
M18010	K1A	F	As-cast	24 000	165	6 000	41	14
M18210	QH21A	–T6	Solution heat treated and artificially aged	35 000	241	27 000	186	2
M18220	QE22A	–T6	Solution heat and artificially aged	35 000	241	25 000	172	2
M16410	ZE41A	–T5	Artificially aged only	29 000	200	19 500	134	2.5
M16630	ZE63A	–T6	Solution heat treated and artificially aged	40 000	276	27 000	186	5
M16620	ZH62A	–T5	Artificially aged only	35 000	241	22 000	152	5
M16510	ZK51A	–T5	Artificially aged only	34 000	234	20 000	138	5
M16610	ZK61A	–T6	Solution heat treated and artificially aged	40 000	276	26 000	179	5

1. Alloy suitable for permanent mold and/or investment castings should meet these properties.
2. Not required.

TABLE 4—MINIMUM MECHANICAL PROPERTIES OF TEST SPECIMENS FROM DESIGNATED AREAS OF PREMIUM QUALITY CASTINGS OF MAGNESIUM ALLOYS (ACCORDING TO SPECIFICATIONS IN MIL-M-46062)

Alloy Designation					Guaranteed Minimum Properties in Designated Areas		
UNS	ASTM and SAE	Old SAE	Temper	Class[1]	Ultimate Tensile Strength, psi (MPa)	Yield Strength 0.2% Offset, psi (MPa)	Elongation in 2 in (50.8 mm), %
M11914	AZ91C	504	–T6	1	35 000 (241)	18 000 (124)	4
				2	29 000 (200)	16 000 (110)	3
				3	27 000 (186)	14 000 (97)	2
				X	17 000 (117)	12 000 (83)	0.75
M11920	AZ92A	500	–T6	1	40 000 (276)	25 000 (172)	3
				2	34 000 (234)	20 000 (138)	1
				3	30 000 (207)	18 000 (124)	0.75
				X	17 000 (117)	13 500 (93)	0.25
M13310	HK31A	507	–T6	1	33 000 (228)	16 000 (110)	6
				2	29 000 (200)	14 000 (97)	3
				3	25 000 (172)	12 000 (83)	1
				X	19 000 (131)	10 500 (72)	1
M18220	QE22A	—	–T6	1	40 000 (276)	28 000 (193)	4
				2	37 000 (255)	26 000 (179)	2
				3	33 000 (228)	23 000 (159)	2
				X	28 000 (193)	20 000 (138)	2
M16220	ZH62A	508	–T5	1	38 000 (262)	23 000 (159)	5
				2	34 000 (234)	21 000 (145)	3
				3	31 500 (217)	19 000 (131)	2
				X	28 500 (197)	17 500 (121)	1.25
M16510	ZK51A	509	–T5	1	36 000 (248)	21 000 (145)	6
				2	32 000 (221)	19 000 (131)	4
				3	29 000 (200)	17 000 (117)	3
				X	24 000 (165)	14 000 (97)	1.25
M16610	ZK61A	513	–T6	1	42 000 (290)	29 000 (200)	6
				2	37 000 (255)	26 000 (179)	4
				3	34 000 (234)	23 000 (159)	2
				X	30 000 (207)	21 000 (145)	1.25

1. Stress levels of various sections of the castings should be carefully considered before specifying the class of mechanical properties for any particular casting section. Since a uniform stress level is seldom required in casting design, it would be advantageous from the design and foundry aspect to have higher properties in local designated areas with the remainder of the casting having lower properties. Three classes (1–3) of mechanical properties are therefore incorporated in the specification for various stress levels. In addition, minimum properties are given for test specimens taken from castings in unspecified areas (X) of castings.

5. *Investment Mold Castings*—Any of the alloys listed in Table 3 may be used for investment castings. The complexity and quality requirements of investment castings has limited the application of most alloys except M11914, M10100, and to a lesser extent, M11920. However, alloys such as M18220, M12330, and M18010 are frequently used for investment castings.

Specifications applicable to sand and permanent mold castings (Table 3) are used commonly for investment castings, including composition and minimum properties limitations as called out in Tables 2 and 3.

Magnesium investment castings are used widely in applications requiring moderate to high degrees of configuration complexity, including coring and minimum weight, section thicknesses of 0.060 in (1.52 mm) being normal and 0.040 in (1.02 mm) possible in some cases over smaller areas. Tool costs are usually high relative to sand and permanent mold tools, and must be related to volume.

6. *Die Casting*

6.1 Introduction—The die casting process offers many advantages as a method of fabricating magnesium alloys, including low cost in quantity production, decrease in amount of machining, excellent surface finish, dimensional accuracy, and metal saving by virtue of being able to cast thin sections.

While most magnesium die castings are still produced on conventional cold-chamber die-casting machines, the use of hot-chamber machines for magnesium die castings is growing rapidly. With the exception of the metal melting equipment, both the machines and dies used in the cold-chamber process are practically interchangeable with those used for aluminum die casting.

The melting of magnesium is done in a non-oxidizing atmosphere, sometimes with a protective flux. Casting temperatures range from 1150–1250 °F (621–677 °C). When automatic metering of the magnesium is used, the metal is usually protected with a layer of molten flux. Some installations use protective gas atmospheres. When hand ladling, the metal is protected with either flux, sulfur dioxide, or an atmosphere of air-SF_6. Metal in hot-chamber die-casting machines is generally protected with an air-SF_6 atmosphere. Metal injection pressures lie between 2000 and 15 000 psi (14 and 103 MPa).

In amenability to intricate coring, magnesium die castings rank between zinc, which is the best, and aluminum. Required draft is greater than for zinc and less than for aluminum.

Magnesium castings do not have a tendency to solder or adhere to the die. Consequently, in contrast with aluminum, die coating solutions are not necessary and the need for die lubrication is decreased.

Molten magnesium does not react with iron or steel and can, therefore, be transferred in the molten state through steel pipes. This makes magnesium adaptable to automatic ladling and metal handling devices.Due to the low heat content of magnesium, a part made with equivalent machines and dies may be cast at rates comparable to those obtained with zinc alloys, and at higher rates than for aluminum. The magnesium cools faster, permitting earlier removal from the die.

6.2 General Information—Alloys M11910 and M11912 - Magnesium alloy die castings have been used more extensively on automobiles than magnesium in any other form. Magnesium has been accepted as a competitive material in such applications as steering column parts such as shrouds, brackets, collars, and signal switches; instruments and transmission components; convertible top mechanism; generator end plates; clutch housings; fuel pump body and parts; oil pumps; and crankcases of air-cooled engines.

M11910 and M11912 are equivalent for most applications, with M11910 having greater purity and somewhat better corrosion resistance upon exposure to salt water. M11912 is more readily available and cheaper. Both alloys are dimensionally stable and will withstand relatively high stresses without cold flow. In many die casting applications, magnesium can be substituted for other materials using the same section thickness as the metal replaced.

Alloy M10600 - Magnesium alloy M10600 approaches alloys M11910 and M11912 in castability. Because of its excellent ductility, this alloy is used in applications where impact resistance is important.

Alloy M10410 - Magnesium die casting M10410 has excellent resistance to creep at temperature and is used for castings which operate under a combination of high temperature (up to 350°F (177°C)) and stress.

6.3 Mechanical Properties—The typical properties obtained with magnesium die-casting alloys on separately cast-to-shape test bars similar to Figure 13 in ASTM B 557 are shown in Table 5.

TABLE 5—TYPICAL MECHANICAL PROPERTIES OF SEPARATELY CAST TEST BARS MAGNESIUM DIE CASTING ALLOYS

Alloy Designation					
UNS	ASTM and SAE	Old SAE	Tensile Strength, psi (MPa)	Yield Strength 0.2% Offset, psi (MPa)	Elongation in 2 in (50.8 mm), %
M11910	AZ91A	501	34 000 (234)	23 000 (159)	3
M11912	AZ91B	501A	34 000 (234)	23 000 (159)	3
M10600	AM60A		32 000 (221)	19 000 (131)	8
M10410	AS41A		31 000 (214)	20 000 (138)	6

No minimum properties are required of die castings.

7. *Other Specifications*—Table 6 lists similar ASTM, AMS, Federal, and Military Specifications covering the SAE sand casting alloys given in this standard.

TABLE 6—SIMILAR SPECIFICATIONS OF MAGNESIUM CASTING ALLOYS

Alloy Designation			Form	ASTM	AMS	Federal	Military
UNS	ASTM and SAE	Old SAE					
M10100	AM100A	502	Sand Cast	B80	—	—	—
			Permanent Mold	B199	4483	QQ-M-55	—
			Investment	B403	4455	—	—
M11630	AZ63A	50	Sand Cast	B80	4420	QQ-M-56	—
					4422		
					4424		
M11810	AZ81A	505	Sand Cast	B80	—	QQ-M-56	—
			Permanent Mold	B199	—	QQ-M-55	—
			Investment	B403	—	—	—
M11910	AZ91A	501	Die Cast	B94	4490	QQ-M-38	—
M11912	AZ91B	501A	Die Cast	B94	—	—	—
M11914	AZ91C	504	Sand Cast	B80	4437	QQ-M-56	Mil-M-46062
			Permanent Mold	B199	—	QQ-M-55	—
			Investment	B403	—	—	—
M11920	AZ92A	500	Sand Cast	B80	4434	QQ-M-56	Mil-M-46062
			Permanent Mold	B199	4484	QQ-M-55	Mil-M-46062
			Investment	B403	4453	—	—
M12330	EZ33A	506	Sand Cast	B80	4442	QQ-M-56	—
			Permanent Mold	B199	—	QQ-M-55	—
			Investment	B403	—	—	—
M13310	HK31A	507	Sand Cast	B80	4445	QQ-M-56	Mil-M-46062
			Permanent Mold	B199	—	QQ-M-55	Mil-M-46062
			Investment	B403	—	—	—
M13320	HZ32A	—	Sand Cast	B80	4447	QQ-M-56	—
						QQ-M-55	
M18010	K1A	—	Sand Cast	B80	—	—	Mil-M-45207
			Investment	B403	—	—	
M18220	QE22A	—	Sand Cast	B80	4418	QQ-M-56	Mil-M-46062
			Permanent Mold	B199	—	QQ-M-55	—
			Investment	B403	—	—	—
M16410	ZE41A	—	Sand Cast	B80	4439	QQ-M-56	—
M16510	ZK51A	509	Sand Cast	B80	4443	QQ-M-56	Mil-M-46062
M16610	ZK61A	513	Sand Cast	B80	4444	QQ-M-56	Mil-M-46042
			Investment	B403	—	—	—
M16630	ZE63A	—	Sand Cast	B80	—	—	—
			Investment	—	—	—	—
M16620	ZH62A	508	Sand Cast	B80	4438	QQ-M-56	Mil-M-46062
M10600	AM60A	—	Die Cast	—	—	—	—
M10410	AS41A	—	Die Cast	—	—	—	—

MAGNESIUM WROUGHT ALLOYS—SAE J466 DEC1989 SAE Standard

Report of the SAE Nonferrous Metals Division approved January 1940 and completely revised by the SAE Nonferrous Metals Committee April 1979. Reaffirmed by the SAE Wrought Aluminum, Magnesium, and Zinc Committee January 1989 and December 1989.

Foreword—This Document has not changed other than to put it into the new SAE Technical Standards Board Format.

1. Scope—This SAE Standard covers the most common magnesium alloys used in wrought forms, and lists chemical composition and minimum mechanical properties for the various forms. A general indication of the usage of the various materials is also provided.

1.1 Introduction—Magnesium wrought alloys are produced and fabricated by all the common production methods such as rolling, extrusion, and forging. Forms available are sheet, plate, wire, rod, bar, shapes, tubes, forgings, and impact extrusions. Magnesium alloys can be formed by bending, drawing, spinning, and pressing. The work is generally done hot except for simple operations. When done hot, magnesium alloys have exceptional workability. The temperature used varies from 300–750°F (149–399°C), depending on operation, alloy, and condition. All of the wrought alloys can be joined by adhesive bonding, spot welding, riveting, and bolting. Most of them are readily fusion welded and some do not require stress relief after welding. As with the cast alloys, all wrought alloys machine readily.

The temper designations used for wrought magnesium are similar to those used for aluminum alloys. Temper designations are covered by ASTM B 296-67 (1972), Recommended Practice for Temper Designations of Magnesium Alloys, Cast and Wrought. Mechanical properties are obtained by standard ASTM procedures. The tensile and compressive yield strength is taken at an offset of 0.2% from the initial modulus line.

Table 1 lists similar ASTM, AMS, Military, and Federal specifications covering the SAE wrought alloys in this SAE Standard.

TABLE 1—SIMILAR SPECIFICATIONS OF MAGNESIUM WROUGHT ALLOYS

Alloy Designation						
UNS	ASTM and SAE	Old SAE	Form	ASTM	AMS	Military or Federal
M11311	AZ31B	510	Sheet and plate	B90	4375, 4376, 4377	QQ-M-44
			Bar, rod, shapes	B107	—	QQ-M-31
			Tube	B107	—	WW-T-825
			Forgings	B91	—	QQ-M-40
M11610	AZ61A	520	Bar, rod, shapes	B107	4350	QQ-M-31
			Tube	B107	4350	WW-T-825
			Wire (welding rod)	—	—	Mil-R-6944
			Forgings	B91	4358[1]	QQ-M-40
M11800	AZ80A	523	Bar, rod, shapes	B107	—	QQ-M-31
			Forgings	B91	4360[1]	QQ-M-40
M14141	LA141A		Sheet and plate	B90	—	—
M13310	HK31A	507	Sheet and plate	B90	4384, 4385	Mil-M-26075
M13210	HM21A		Sheet and plate	B90	4383, 4390	Mil-M-8917
			Forgings	—	4363	QQ-M-40
M13312	HM31A		Bar, rod, shapes	—	4388, 4389	Mil-M-8916
M15100	M1A	522	Bar, rod, shapes	B107	—	QQ-M-31
			Forgings	—	—	QQ-M-40
M16100	ZE10A	534	Sheet and plate	B90	—	Mil-M-46037
M16400	ZK40A		Bar, rod, shapes	B107	—	—
M16600	ZK60A	524	Bar, rod, shapes	B107	4352	QQ-M-31
			Tube	B107	4352	WW-T-825
			Forgings	B91	4362	QQ-M-40

1. Noncurrent specifications.

2. References

2.1 Applicable Publications—This Document has not changed other than to put it into the new SAE Technical Standards Board Format.

2.1.1 ASTM PUBLICATIONS—Available from ASTM, 100 Barr Harbor Drive, West Conshohocken, PA 19428-2959

ASTM B 90-70—Specification for Magnesium-Alloy Sheet and Plate

ASTM B 107-70—Specification for Magnesium-Alloy Extruded Bars, Rods, Shapes, Tubes, and Wire

ASTM B 296—Recommended Practice for Temper Designations of Magnesium Alloys, Cast and Wrought

3. Sheet And Plate:

3.1 Introduction—Magnesium alloy sheet is rolled to a thickness of 0.006-0.249 in (0.15-6.32 mm). Plate is 0.250 in (6.35 mm) or over in thickness. Dimensional tolerances used are the same as for aluminum alloys and are given in the current issue of ASTM B 90-70.

Magnesium sheet and plate is flattened thermally and can be obtained commercially, with smaller flatness tolerances than for most other metals. One grade of specially flattened plate is used extensively as tooling plate. The annealed condition (–0) is used for maximum formability and ductility. The cold rolled and partially annealed condition (–H24) has better strength and less ductility than the –0 temper. Tensile properties of the sheet and alloys covered by this standard are given in Table 3 and the chemical composition limits are given in Table 2.

3.2 General Data—Alloy M11311 is the most commonly used of the sheet alloys and is available in either the annealed (–0) or cold rolled and partially annealed (–H24 and –H26) conditions. M11311 alloy can be formed and welded readily. It has found widespread use. Applications most familiar in the automotive field would be its use in truck bodies, ramps, and dockboards and the various places such as patterns, jigs, and fixtures in which tooling plate has been used.

M16100 is not as strong as M11311. It has good formability and excellent weldability and does not require stress relieving after welding. It is used in place of M11311 primarily in tanks and large structures where stress relieving would be a problem. It is available in either the annealed (–0) or cold rolled and partially annealed (–H24) conditions.

M13310 was developed primarily for elevated temperature use in the 300–700 °F (149–371 °C) range. It is more costly than M11311 and M16100. M13310 alloy has excellent weldability and good formability. It is available in either the annealed (–0) or cold rolled and partially annealed (–H24) conditions. It has been used primarily in aircraft and missiles. M13210 was also developed for elevated temperature use in aircraft, missiles, and electronics.

M14141, containing 14% Li, is the only magnesium alloy with a body-centered cubic rather than hexagonal-close-packed crystal structure. It was developed as a very ductile and highly formable alloy.

4. Extrusions

4.1 Introduction—Magnesium alloys in general are extruded to size without subsequent drawing operations. Some sizing or shaving has been used to get better tolerances than can be obtained by extrusion. Wire, rod, bar, tubes, and special shaped sections are produced as extrusions. Dimensional tolerances on the various forms are given in the current issue of ASTM B 107-70.

Magnesium alloys produced as extrusions are available in the as-extruded (–F) condition. In some alloys an increase in strength is obtained by artificial aging to the extruded and aged (–T5) condition. Minimum mechanical properties of the SAE extrusion alloys are shown in Table 4. The chemical composition of the SAE alloys used for extrusions is given in Table 2.

4.2 General Data—M11311, M11610, and M11800 contain aluminum and zinc as the principal alloying elements. M11311-F has moderate strength, good ductility, and good weldability. It is used where maximum strength is not a requirement. M11610-F has slightly better strength than M11311 but less than M11800. It has been supplanted to a large degree by the higher strength alloys, although still widely used as welding wire. M11800 has the highest strength of these three alloys. Low ductility has caused it to be replaced largely by M16600. Alloy M11800 is not as weldable as M11311 and M11610, which have excellent welding characteristics. M11311 has been used in truck bodies, ramps, and docks, and with tooling plate in making jigs and fixtures.

M15100 has excellent weldability and good corrosion resistance. It is a low strength alloy with good ductility. It has been replaced for most applications by M11311.

M16600 combines high strength with good ductility and toughness. However, it has limited weldability. M16600 costs more than M11311, M16610, M11800, and M15100. It has been used primarily in military applications and aircraft. M13312 alloy was developed for use at elevated temperatures in the range of 300–800°F (149–427°C). M16400 possesses high yield strength and has better extrusion characteristics than M16610.

TABLE 2—COMPOSITION OF WROUGHT MAGNESIUM ALLOYS

Alloy Designation			Elements, weight %												
UNS	ASTM and SAE	Old SAE	Al	Mn min	Zn	Zr	Rare Earths	Th	Ca, max	Cu, max	Fe, max	Na, max	Ni, max	Si, max	Total Other Elements, max
M11311	AZ31B	510	2.5–3.5	0.20	0.6–1.4	—	—	—	0.04	0.05	0.005	—	0.005	0.10	0.30
M11610	AZ61A	520	5.8–7.2	0.15	0.40–1.5	—			—	0.05	0.005	—	0.005	0.10	0.30
M11800	AZ80A	523	7.8–9.2	0.12	0.20–0.8	—			—	0.05	0.005	—	0.005	0.10	0.30
M13310	HK31A	507		—	0.30 max	0.40–1.0	—	2.5–4.0	—	0.10	—	—	0.01	—	0.30
M13210	HM21A	—	—	0.45–1.1		—		1.5–2.5	—	—	—	—	—	—	0.30
M13312	HM31A	—	—	1.2	—	—		2.5–3.5	—	—	—	—	—	—	0.30
M14141[1]	LA141A	—	1.0–1.5	0.15	—	—			—	0.04	0.005	0.005	0.005	0.10	0.30
M15100	M1A	522	—	1.2	—	—	—	—	0.30	0.05	—	—	0.01	0.10	0.30
M16100	ZE10A	534	—	—	1.0–1.5	—	0.12–0.22[2]	—	—	—	—	—	—	—	0.30
M16400	ZK40A	—		—	3.5–4.5	0.45 min			—	—	—	—	—	—	0.30
M16600	ZK60A	524		—	4.8–6.2	0.45 min			—	—	—	—	—	—	0.30

1. LA141 contains 13–15% LI.
2. Rare earth elements are in the form of mischmetal.

TABLE 3—MINIMUM MECHANICAL PROPERTIES OF MAGNESIUM ALLOY SHEET AND PLATE

UNS	ASTM and SAE	Old SAE	Temper	Thickness in (mm)	Tensile Strength psi (MPa)	Yield Strength 0.2% Offset, psi (MPa)	Elongation in 2 in (50.8 mm), %
M11311	AZ31B	510	–0	0.016–0.250 (0.41–12.70)	32 000 (221)[1]	—	12
				0.251–2.000 (12.73–50.80)	32 000 (221)[1]	—	10
				2.001–3.000 (50.83–76.20)	32 000 (221)[1]	—	9
			–H24	0.016–0.249 (0.41–6.32)	39 000 (269)	29 000 (200)	6
				–0.374 (6.35–9.50)	38 000 (262)	26 000 (179)	8
				–0.500 (9.52–12.70)	37 000 (255)	24 000 (165)	8
				0.501–1.000 (12.73–25.40)	36 000 (248)	22 900 (152)	8
				1.001–2.000 (25.43–50.80)	34 000 (234)	20 000 (138)	8
				2.001–3.000 (50.83–76.20)	34 000 (234)	18 000 (124)	8
			–H26	0.250–0.374 (6.35–9.50)	39 000 (269)	27 000 (186)	6
				–0.500 (9.52–12.70)	38 000 (262)	26 000 (179)	6
				0.501–0.750 (12.73–19.05)	37 000 (255)	25 000 (172)	6
				0.751–1.000 (19.08–25.40)	37 000 (255)	23 000 (159)	6
				1.001–1.500 (25.43–38.10)	35 000 (241)	22 000 (152)	6
				1.501–2.000 (38.13–50.80)	35 000 (241)	21 000 (145)	6
M13310	HK31A	507	–0	0.016–0.250 (0.41–6.35)	30 000 (207)[2]	18 000 (124)	12
				0.251–0.500 (6.38–12.70)	30 000 (207)	16 000 (110)	12
				0.501–1.000 (12.73–25.40)	30 000 (207)	15 000 (103)	12
				1.001–3.000 (25.43–76.20)	29 000 (200)	14 000 (97)	12
			–H24	0.016–0.125 (0.41–3.18)	34 000 (234)	26 000 (179)	4
				0.126–0.250 (3.20–6.35)	34 000 (234)	24 000 (165)	4
				0.251–1.000 (6.38–25.40)	34 000 (234)	23 000 (159)	4
				1.001–3.000 (25.43–76.20)	33 000 (228)	23 000 (159)	4
M13210	HM21A		–T8	0.016–0.250 (0.41–6.35)	33 000 (228)	18 000 (124)	6
				0.251–0.500 (6.38–12.70)	32 000 (221)	21 000 (145)	6
				0.501–3.000 (12.73–76.20)	30 000 (207)	21 000 (145)	6
M14141	LA141A		–T7	0.010–0.090 (0.25–2.29)	19 000 (131)	15 000 (103)	10
				0.091–0.250 (2.31–6.35)	19 000 (131)	14 000 (97)	10
				0.251–2.000 (6.38–50.80)	18 000 (124)	13 000 (90)	10
M16100	ZE10A	534	-0	0.016–0.060 (0.41–1.52)	30 000 (207)	18 000 (124)	15
				0.061–0.250 (1.55–6.35)	30 000 (207)	15 000 (103)	15
				0.251–0.500 (6.38–12.70)	29 000 (200)	12 000 (83)	12
			–H24	0.016–0.125 (0.41–3.18)	36 000 (248)	25 000 (172)	4
				0.126–0.188 (3.20–4.78)	34 000 (234)	22 000 (152)	4
				0.189–0.250 (4.80–6.35)	31 000 (214)	20 000 (138)	4

1. Maximum tensile strength shall be 40 000 psi (276 MPa).
2. Maximum tensile strength shall be 38 000 psi (262 MPa).

TABLE 4—MINIMUM MECHANICAL PROPERTIES OF MAGNESIUM ALLOY EXTRUSIONS

Alloy Designation							Minimum Properties		
UNS	ASTM and SAE	Old SAE	Temper	Form	Dia or Thickness, in (mm)	Cross Sectional Area, in^2 (cm^2)	Tensile Strength, psi (MPa)	Yield Strength 0.2% Offset, psi (MPa)	Elongation in 2 in (50.8 mm), %
M11311	AZ31B	510	–F	Bars, rods, shapes	0.249 (6.32) and under	All	35 000 (241)	21 000 (145)	7
					0.250–1.499 (6.35–38.07)	All	35 000 (241)	22 000 (152)	7
					1.500–2.499 (38.10–63.47)	All	34 000 (234)	22 000 (152)	7
					2.500–4.999 (63.50–126.97)	All	32 000 (221)	20 000 (138)	7
				Hollow shapes	All	All	32 000 (221)	16 000 (110)	8
				Tubes	0.028–0.250 (0.71–6.35)	6.000 (38.71) and under	32 000 (221)	16 000 (110)	8
					0.251–2.499 (6.38–63.47)	6.000 (38.71) and under	32 000 (221)	16 000 (110)	4
M11610	AZ61A	520	–F	Bars, rods, shapes	0.249 (6.32) and under	All	38 000 (262)	21 000 (145)	8
					0.250–2.499 (6.35–63.47)	All	39 000 (269)	24 000 (165)	9
					2.500–4.999 (63.50–126.97)	All	40 000 (276)	22 000 (152)	7
				Hollow shapes	All	All	36 000 (248)	16 000 (110)	7
				Tubes	0.028–0.750 (0.71–19.05)	6.000 (38.71) and under	36 000 (248)	16 000 (110)	7
M11800	AZ80A	523	–F	Bars, rods, shapes	0.249 (6.32) and under	All	43 000 (296)	28 000 (193)	9
					0.250–1.499 (6.35–38.07)	All	43 000 (296)	28 000 (193)	8
					1.500–2.499 (38.10–63.47)	All	43 000 (296)	28 000 (193)	6
					2.500–4.999 (63.50–126.97)	All	42 000 (290)	27 000 (186)	4
			–T5	Bars, rods, shapes	0.249 (6.32) and under	All	47 000 (324)	30 000 (207)	4
					0.250–2.499 (6.35–63.47)	All	48 000 (331)	33 000 (228)	4
					2.500–4.999 (63.50–126.97)	All	45 000 (310)	30 000 (207)	2
M13312	HM31A		–T5	Bars, rods, shapes	Under 1.000 (25.40)	All	37 000 (255)	26 000 (179)	4
					1.000–3.999 (25.40–101.57)	All	37 000 (255)	26 000 (179)	4
M15100	M1A	522	–F	Bars, rods, shapes	0.249 (6.32) and under	All	30 000 (207)	—[1]	2
					0.250–1.499 (6.35–38.07)	All	32 000 (221)	—[1]	3
					1.500–4.999 (38.10–126.97)	All	29 000 (200)	—[1]	2
				Hollow shapes	All	All	28 000 (193)	—[1]	2
				Tubes	0.028–0.750 (0.71–19.05)	6.000 (38.71) and under	28 000 (193)	—[1]	2
M16400	ZK40A		–T5	Bars, rods, shapes, and wires	All	4.999 (32.25) and under	40 000 (276)	37 000 (255)	4
				Hollow shapes	All	All	40 000 (276)	37 000 (255)	4
				Tubes	0.062–0.500 (1.57–12.70)	3.000 (19.35) and under	40 000 (276)	36 000 (248)	4
M16600	ZK60A	523	–F	Bars, rods, shapes	All	4.999 (32.25) and under	43 000 (296)	31 000 (214)	4
				Hollow shapes	All	All	40 000 (276)	28 000 (193)	5
				Tubes	0.028–0.750 (0.71–19.05)	3.000 (19.35) and under	40 000 (276)	28 000 (193)	5
		524	–T5	Bars, rods, shapes	All	4.999 (32.25) and under	45 000 (310)	36 000 (248)	4
				Hollow shapes	All	All	46 000 (317)	38 000 (262)	4
				Tubes	0.028–0.250 (0.71–6.35)	3.000 (19.35) and under	46 000 (317)	38 000 (262)	4

1. Not required.

5. Forgings

5.1 Introduction—Magnesium alloys are available as both hammer forgings and press forgings. The stronger alloys are too tender at hot working temperature to stand the shock of hammer forging and must be worked slowly under hydraulic presses. They may be forged sometimes to advantage by first pressing to shape and finishing on the hammer.

Die equipment built for aluminum alloy forgings can, in many cases, be used without change for producing magnesium alloy hammer forgings. This also applies to small die forgings made by pressing. Large press forgings comparable in size to an aircraft radial motor crankcase require special equipment and can usually be supplied only as oversize die forgings. Compared with an aluminum forging, magnesium press forgings frequently require an extra blocking die.

Forgings subject to shock, vibration, or repeated stresses must be carefully designed and carefully machined to avoid notches, sharp corners, tool marks, and other stress raisers. Minimum machining radius is 0.040 in (1.02 mm), and all sharp corners and feather edges must be broken. Magnesium alloy forgings may have marked directional properties, especially with regard to yield strength in tension and in compression. For this reason, it is advisable for user to consult with manufacturer on design of forgings.

5.2 General Data—M11311, M11610, M11800, M13210, and M16600 alloys are used principally as press forgings. M11311 and M11610 are used where moderately high strength and good ductility are desired. Alloys M11800 and M16600 are used where greater strength is required. M13210 alloy was developed for use at temperatures of 300–800°F (149–427°C). The chemical composition of the SAE alloys used for forgings is given in Table 2.

5.3 Mechanical Properties—The properties for forgings are those obtained from tensile test specimens taken with the longitudinal axis of the specimen parallel to the direction of maximum flow of the metal or from separately forged coupons. Minimum properties of magnesium alloy forgings are given in Table 5.

TABLE 5—MINIMUM MECHANICAL PROPERTIES OF MAGNESIUM ALLOY FORGINGS

Alloy Designation						
UNS	ASTM and SAE	Old SAE	Temper	Tensile Strength psi (MPa)	Yield Strength 0.2% Offset, psi (MPa)	Elongation in 2 in (50.8 mm), %
M11311	AZ31B	510	–F	34 000 (234)	19 000 (131)	6
M11610	AZ61A	520	–F	38 000 (262)	22 000 (152)	6
M11800	AZ80A	523	–F	42 000 (290)	26 000 (179)	5
			–T5	42 000 (290)	28 000 (193)	2
M13210	HM21A		–F	34 000 (234)	25 000 (172)	3
			–T5[1]	33 000 (228)	25 000 (172)	3
M16600	ZK60A	524	–T5[2]	42 000 (290)	26 000 (179)	7
			–T6[3]	42 000 (290)	32 000 (221)	4

1. For forgings 4 in (102 mm) or less in thickness.
2. For forgings 3 in (76 mm) or less in thickness.
3. For forgings 2 in (51 mm) or less in thickness.

SPECIAL PURPOSE ALLOYS ("SUPERALLOYS") —SAE J467b OCT1968

SAE Information Report

Report of the SAE Nonferrous Metals Committee approved January 1956 and last revised July 1968. Editorial change October 1968. Prepared in cooperation with Aerospace Materials Division of SAE Aerospace Council.

Foreword—This Document has not changed other than to put it into the new SAE Technical Standards Board Format.

1. Scope—The data given in Tables 1–4 are typical values only and are not intended for design parameters. Mechanical properties of the special purpose alloys depend greatly upon processing variables and heat treatment. It is recommended that design data be obtained by actual testing or by consultation with the producers of the alloys.

2. References—There are no referenced publications specified herein.

TABLE 1—SIMILAR MATERIAL SPECIFICATION DESIGNATIONS

Material Commercial Designation	AISI No.	ASTM No.	SAE No.	Military	Aerospace Material Specifications				
					Castings	Bars and Forgings	Sheet and Plate	Tubing	Wire
Martensitic Low Alloy Steels									
"17-22-A"	—	—	—	—	—	6304	—	—	—
"17-22-A" S	—	—	—	—	—	6302	6385	—	6458
"17-22-A" V	—	—	—	—	—	6303	6436	—	—
Chromoloy	—	—	—	—	—	—	—	—	—
D6A	—	—	—	—	—	6431	6438	—	—
300M	—	—	—	—	—	6416	—	—	—
UCX2	—	—	—	—	—	—	—	—	—
Martensitic Secondary Alloy Steels									
H11	—	—	J438	—	—	6485	6437	—	—
H12	—	—	J438	—	—	—	—	—	—
H13	—	—	J438	—	—	—	—	—	—
M2	—	—	J438	—	—	—	—	—	—
M10	—	—	—	—	—	—	—	—	—
M50	—	—	—	—	—	6490	—	—	—
Martensitic Chromium Steels									
410	—	A176	51410	QQ-S-763	5350	5612	5504	—	5776
	—	A276	60410	MIL-S-16993	5351	5613	5505	5591	5821
Greek Ascoloy	—	—	—	—	5354	5616	5508	—	5817
422	—	—	—	—	—	5655	—	—	—
422M	—	—	—	—	—	—	—	—	—
422M (Cast)	—	—	—	—	—	—	—	—	—
440C	—	—	51440C	QQ-S-763	5352	5630	—	—	—
14Cr-4Mo	—	—	—	—	—	—	—	—	—
Lapelloy	—	—	—	—	—	—	—	—	—
Lapelloy C	—	—	—	—	—	—	—	—	—
H-46	—	—	—	—	—	—	—	—	—
Semi Austenitic Precipitation and Transformation Hardening Steels									
AM-350	—	—	—	QQ-S-763	—	—	5546	—	5774
	—	—	—	MIL-S-8840	—	5745	5548	5554	5775
AM-355	—	A461	—	—	5359	—	5547	—	5780
	—	—	—	—	5368	5743	5549	—	5781
Stainless W	—	—	—	—	—	—	—	—	—
14-4PH	—	—	—	—	5340	—	—	—	5727
17-4PH	—	A461	—	—	5355	—	—	—	—
	—	—	—	MIL-S-853	5398	5643	—	—	5825
17-7PH	—	A461	—	—	—	—	5528	—	—
	—	—	—	—	—	5644	5529	5568	5673
PH15-7MO	—	A461	—	—	—	—	—	—	5812
	—	—	—	—	—	5657	5520	—	5813
Austenitic Nickel-Chromium-Iron Steels									
302	302	—	30302			5636	5515	—	—
	—	—	60302	QQ-S-763	5358	5637	5516	—	5688
304	304	—	30304	QQ-S-763	—	—	—	5560	—
	—	—	60304	MIL-T-8506	—	5639	5513	5565	5697
304L	304L	—	30304L	—	5370	—	—	—	—
	—	—	60304L	QQ-S-763	5371	5647	5511	—	—
309S	3095	—	—	QQ-S-763	—	5650	5523	5574	—
310	310	—	30310	—	5365	—	—	5572	5694
	—	—	60310	QQ-S-766	5366	5651	5521	5577	5695
314	314	—	30314	—	—	5652	5522	—	—
316	316	—	30316	—	5360	—	—	—	5690
	—	—	60316	QQ-S-763	5361	5648	5524	5573	5691

TABLE 1—SIMILAR MATERIAL SPECIFICATION DESIGNATIONS (continued)

Material Commercial Designation	AISI No.	ASTM No.	SAE No.	Military	Aerospace Material Specifications				
					Castings	Bars and Forgings	Sheet and Plate	Tubing	Wire
321	321	A269	—	—	—	—	—	5570	—
	—	A271	30321	QQ-S-763	—	5645	5510	5576	5689
347	347	—	30347	—	5362	—	—	5571	5680
	—	—	60347	QQ-S-763	5363	5646	5512	5575	5681
Austenitic Iron Base Alloys									
A286	—	—	—	—	—	5731–32	—	—	—
	—	—	—	—	—	5734–35	—	—	5804
	—	—	—	—	—	5736–37	5525	—	5805
V-57	—	—	—	—	—		—	—	—
Discaloy	—	—	—	—	—	5733	—	—	—
N-155	—	—	—	—	—	5768	5531	—	—
					5376	5769	5532	5585	5794
D-979	—	—	—		—	5746	—	—	—
W-545	—		—			5741	5543	—	—
S590	—	—	—	—	—	5770	5533	—	—
RA330	—	—	—	—	—	5716	5592	—	—
Unitemp 212	—	—	—	—	—	—	—	—	—
CRM-6D	—	—	—	—	—	—	—	—	—
CRM-15D	—	—	—	—	—	—	—	—	—
16-25-6	—	—	—	MIL-S-16538	—	5727	—	—	—
						5728			
						5720	5526	—	—
19-9DL	—	—	—	—	—	5722	5527	—	—
19-9DX	—	—	—	—	—	5723	5538	—	—
						5724	5539	—	—
17-14CuMo	—	—	—	—	—	—	—	—	—
G-192	—	—	—	—	—	—	—	—	—
AF-71	—	—	—			—	—	—	—
Incoloy 800	—	—	—	—	—	—	—	—	—
Incoloy 801	—	—	—	—	—	—	5552	—	—
Incoloy 805	—	—	—	—	—	—	—	—	—
Incoloy 810	—	—	—	—	—	—	—	—	—
Cobalt Base Alloys									
L-605	—	—	—	—	—	5759	5537	—	5797
S-816	—	—	—	—	—	5765	5534	—	—
HS-31 (X-40)	—	—	—	—	5382	—	—	—	—
HS-21	—	—	—	—	5385	—	—	—	—
Stellite 6	—	—	—	—	5373	—	—	—	—
	—	A399	—	MIL-R-17131	5387	—	—	—	5788
Haynes No. 151	—	—	—	—	—	—	—	—	—
WI-52	—	—	—	—	—	—	—	—	—
V-36	—	—	—	—	—	—	—	—	—
MAR-M 302	—	—	—	—	—	—	—	—	—
MAR-M 322	—	—	—	—	—	—	—	—	—
UMCo-50	—	—	—	—	—	—	—	—	—
UMCo-51	—	—	—	—	—	—	—	—	—
Nivco-10	—	—	—	—	—	—	—	—	—
Elgiloy	—	—	—	—	—	—	—	—	—
MAR-M 509	—	—	—	—	—	—	—	—	—
Austenitic Nickel Base Alloys									
Hastelloy X	—	—	—	—	5390	5754	5536	—	5799
Incoloy 901	—	—	—	—	—	5660	—	—	—
Incoloy 901 Mod.	—	—	—	—	—	5661	—	—	
Rene 41	—	—	—	—	—	5712	—	—	—
	—	—	—	—	—	5713	5545	—	5800
Udimet 500	—	—	—	—	—	5751	—	—	—
	—	—	—	—	5384	5753	—	—	

TABLE 1—SIMILAR MATERIAL SPECIFICATION DESIGNATIONS (continued)

Material Commercial Designation	AISI No.	ASTM No.	SAE No.	Military	Aerospace Material Specifications				
					Castings	Bars and Forgings	Sheet and Plate	Tubing	Wire
Waspaloy	—	—	—	—	—	5544	—	5586	5828
	—	—	—	—	—	5704	—	—	—
	—	—	—	—	—	5706	—	—	—
	—	—	—	—	—	5707	—	—	—
	—	—	—	—	—	5708	—	—	—
	—	—	—	—	—	5709	—	—	—
R-235	—	—	—	—	—	—	—	—	—
Udimet 700	—	—	—			—	—	—	—
Inconel X-750	—	—	—	MIL-N-7786	—	5667	—	—	5698
	—	—	—	MIL-N-8550	—	5668	5542	5582	5699
M-252	—	—	—	—	—	5756	—	—	—
	—	—	—	—	—	5757	5551	—	—
Refractaloy 26	—	—	—	—	—	—	—	—	—
Astroloy	—	—	—	—	—	—	—	—	—
GMR-235	—	—	—	—	—	—	—	—	—
GMR-235D	—	—	—	—	—	—	—	—	—
Hastelloy B	—	B333	—	—	—	—	—	—	—
	—	B335	—	MIL-R-5031	5396	—	—	—	—
Hastelloy C	—	B334	—	—	5388	—	—	—	—
	—	B336	—	MIL-N-18088	5389	5750	5530	—	—
Hastelloy F	—	—	—	—	—	—	—	—	—
Hastelloy N	—	—	—	—	—	—	—	—	—
Hastelloy W	—	—	—	—	—	5755	—	—	5786
Inconel 600	—	—	—	MIL-N-6840	—	—	—	—	—
	—	—	—	MIL-N-6710	—	5665	5540	5580	—
Inconel 604	—	—	—	—	—	—	—	—	—
Inconel 610	—	—	—	—	—	—	—	—	—
Inconel 700	—	—	—	—	—	—	—	—	—
Inconel 702	—	—	—	—	—	—	5550	—	—
Inconel 705	—	—	—	—	—	—	—	—	—
Alloy 713C	—	—	—	—	5391	—	—	—	—
Inconel 718	—	—	—	—	—	—	5596	—	—
Inconel 722	—	—	—	—		—	5541	—	—
AF 1753	—	—	—	—	—	—	—	—	—
IN100	—	—	—	—	5397	—	—	—	—
Nimonic 75	—	—	—	—	—	—	—	—	—
Nimonic 80A	—	—	—	—	—	—	—	—	—
Nimonic 90	—	—	—	—	—	—	—	—	—
Nimonic 105	—	—	—	—	—	—	—	—	—
Nimonic 115	—	—	—	—	—	—	—	—	—
MAR-M 200	—	—	—	—	—	—	—	—	—
RA-333	—	—	—	—	—	5717	5593	—	—
Titanium Base Alloys—Commercially Pure									
A40	—	—	—	—	—	—	—	4941	—
	—	—	—	MIL-T-9046	—	—	4902	4942	4951
A55	—	—	—	MIL-T-9046	—	—	4900	—	—
A70	—	—	—	MIL-T-9046	—	—	—	—	—
	—	—	—	MIL-T-9047	—	4921	4901	—	—
Titanium Base Alloys—Alpha Alloy Grades									
5Al-2.5 Sn	—	—	—	MIL-T-9046	—	4926	—	—	—
	—	—	—	MIL-T-9047	—	4966	4910	—	4953
5Al-5 Sn-5 Zr	—	—	—	—	—	—	4968	—	—
7Al-12 Zr	—	—	—	—	—	—	—	—	—
7Al-2 Cb-1 Ta	—	—	—	—	—	—	—	—	—
8Al-1 Mo, 1 V	—	—	—	—	—	4972	4915	—	4955
	—	—	—	—	—	4973	4916	—	—
Ti-679	—	—	—	—	—	—	—	—	—
Titanium Base Alloys—Alpha-Beta Alloy Grades									
Ti-155A	—	—	—	—	—	4929	—	—	—
8Mn	—	—	—	MIL-T-009046		—	4908	—	—
2.5Al-16V	—	—	—	—	—	—	—	—	—
3Al-2.5V	—	—	—	—	—		—	—	—
4Al-4Mn	—	—	—	MIL-T-9047	—	—	—	—	—
	—	—	—	MIL-T-12117	—	4925	—	—	—
4Al-3Mo-1V	—	—	—	—	—	—	4912	—	—
	—	—	—	MIL-T-8884	—	—	4913	—	—

TABLE 1—SIMILAR MATERIAL SPECIFICATION DESIGNATIONS (continued)

Material Commercial Designation	AISI No.	ASTM No.	SAE No.	Military	Aerospace Material Specifications				
					Castings	Bars and Forgings	Sheet and Plate	Tubing	Wire
5Al-1.25 Fe-2.75 Cr	—	—	—	—	—	—	—	—	—
6Al-4V	—	—	—	MIL-T-9046	—	4928	—	—	—
	—	—	—	MIL-T-9047	—	4935	4911	—	4954
6Al-6V-2 Sn	—	—	—	MIL-T-46035	—	—	—	—	—
	—	—	—	MIL-T-46038	—	4971	4918	—	—
7Al-4 Mo	—	—	—	—	—	4970	—	—	—
2Cr-2 Fe-2 Mo	—	—	—	MIL-T-9047	—	4923	—	—	—
Titanium Base Alloys—Beta Alloy Grades									
1Al-8V-5 Fe	—	—	—	—	—	—	—	—	—
3Al-13V-11 Cr	—	—	—	—	—	—	4917	—	—

TABLE 2—NOMINAL CHEMICAL COMPOSITIONS, %

Material Commercial Designation	C	Mn	Si	Cr	Ni	Co	Mo	W	Cb	Ti	Al	B	Fe	V	Zr	Cu	N	Other
Martensitic Low Alloy Steels																		
"17-22-A"	0.45	0.55	0.65	1.25	—	—	0.55	—	—	—	—	—	Bal	0.30	—	—	—	—
"17-22-A" S	0.30	0.55	0.65	1.25	—	—	0.50	—	—	—	—	—	Bal	0.25	—	—	—	—
"17-22-A" V	0.28	0.75	0.65	1.25	—	—	0.50	—	—	—	—	—	Bal	0.85	—	—	—	—
Chromoloy	0.20	0.50	0.75	1.00	—	—	1.00	—	—	—	—	—	Bal	0.10	—	—	—	—
D6A	0.47	0.75	0.22	1.05	0.55	—	1.00	—	—	—	—	—	Bal	0.10	—	—	—	—
300M	0.40	0.75	1.60	0.85	1.85	—	0.40	—	—	—	—	—	Bal	0.08	—	—	—	—
UCX2	0.39	0.70	1.00	1.10	—	1.00	0.25	—	—	—	—	—	Bal	0.15	—	—	—	—
Martensitic Secondary Alloy Steels																		
H11	0.35	0.30	1.00	5.10	—	—	1.50	—	—	—	—	—	Bal	0.40	—	—	—	—
H12	0.35	0.35	1.05	5.10	—	—	1.35	1.25	—	—	—	—	Bal	0.30	—	—	—	—
H13	0.35	0.30	1.00	5.10	—	—	1.50	—	—	—	—	—	Bal	1.00	—	—	—	—
M2	0.84	0.30	0.30	4.20	—	—	5.00	6.15	—	—	—	—	Bal	1.90	—	—	—	—
M10	0.87	0.20	0.30	4.00	—	—	8.25	—	—	—	—	—	Bal	1.90	—	—	—	—
M50	0.81	0.30	0.20	4.08	—	—	4.25	—	—	—	—	—	Bal	1.00	—	—	—	—
Martensitic Chromium Steels																		
410	0.12	0.50	0.35	12.25	0.40	—	0.30	—	—	—	—	—	Bal	—	—	—	—	—
Greek Ascoloy	0.15	0.40	0.30	13.0	2.00	—	0.15	3.00	—	—	—	—	Bal	—	—	0.15	—	—
422	0.22	0.75	0.40	12.5	0.75	—	1.00	1.00	—	—	—	—	Bal	0.22	—	—	—	—
422M	0.85	0.84	0.25	12.0	0.20	—	2.25	1.70	—	—	—	—	Bal	0.50	—	—	—	—
422M (Cast)	0.26	1.00	0.40	13.0	—	—	2.50	1.50	—	—	—	—	Bal	0.50	—	—	—	—
440C	1.10	0.50	0.40	17.5	—	—	0.50	—	—	—	—	—	Bal	—	—	—	—	—
14Cr-4Mo	1.05	0.50	0.30	14.5	—	—	4.00	—	—	—	—	—	Bal	0.12	—	—	—	—
Lapelloy	0.30	1.00	0.25	12.0	0.30	—	2.75	—	—	—	—	—	Bal	0.25	—	—	—	—
Lapelloy C	0.22	0.80	0.25	11.5	0.20	—	2.75	—	—	—	—	—	Bal	—	—	2.00	0.08	—
H-46	0.17	0.65	0.40	12.0	0.45	—	0.65	—	0.40	—	—	—	Bal	0.30	—	—	0.08	—
Semi Austenitic Precipitation and Transformation Hardening Steels																		
AM-350	0.10	1.00	0.40	16.5	4.25	—	2.75	—	—	—	—	—	Bal	—	—	—	0.10	—
AM-355	0.15	1.00	0.40	15.5	4.25	—	2.75	—	—	—	—	—	Bal	—	—	—	0.10	—
Stainless W	0.06	0.55	0.60	17.0	7.00	—	—	—	—	0.80	0.20	—	Bal	—	—	—	0.02	—
14-4PH	0.03	0.35	0.75	14.1	4.25	—	2.38	—	0.25	—	—	—	Bal	—	—	3.25	0.02	—
17-4PH	0.04	0.28	0.60	16.0	4.25	—	—	—	0.27	—	—	—	Bal	—	—	3.30	—	—
17-7PH	0.07	0.50	0.30	17.0	7.10	—	—	—	—	—	1.17	—	Bal	—	—	—	—	—
PH 15-7 Mo	0.07	0.50	0.30	15.0	7.00	—	2.20	—	—	—	1.17	—	Bal	—	—	—	—	—
Austenitic Nickel-Chromium-Iron Steels																		
302	0.08	1.00	0.50	18.0	9.0	—	—	—	—	—	—	—	Bal	—	—	—	—	—
304	0.04	1.00	0.50	19.0	10.0	—	—	—	—	—	—	—	Bal	—	—	—	—	—
304L	0.02	1.00	0.40	19.0	10.0	—	—	—	—	—	—	—	Bal	—	—	—	—	—
309S	0.04	1.00	0.50	23.0	13.5	—	0.25	—	—	—	—	—	Bal	—	—	0.25	—	—
310	0.12	1.00	0.40	25.0	20.5	—	—	—	—	—	—	—	Bal	—	—	—	—	—
314	0.12	1.00	2.25	24.5	20.5	—	—	—	—	—	—	—	Bal	—	—	—	—	—
316	0.05	1.00	0.40	17.0	12.5	—	2.50	—	—	—	—	—	Bal	—	—	—	—	—
321	0.04	1.00	0.40	18.5	11.0	—	—	—	—	0.40	—	—	Bal	—	—	—	—	—
347	0.05	1.00	0.40	18.5	11.0	—	—	—	0.70	—	—	—	Bal	—	—	—	—	—
Austenitic Iron Base Alloys																		
A286	0.05	1.40	0.40	15.0	26.0	—	1.30	—	—	2.15	0.20	0.004	Bal	0.30	—	—	—	—
V-57	0.05	0.20	0.35	14.75	27.25	—	1.30	—	—	3.00	0.20	0.01	Bal	0.30	—	—	—	—
Discaloy	0.08	0.90	0.80	13.5	26.0	—	2.75	—	—	1.75	0.07	0.005	Bal	—	—	—	—	—
N-155	0.15	1.50	0.50	21.0	20.0	20.0	3.00	2.50	1.00	—	—	—	Bal	—	—	—	0.13	—
D-979	0.06	0.25	0.20	14.90	44.30	—	4.05	3.65	—	3.00	1.05	0.01	Bal	—	—	—	—	—
W-545	0.03	1.65	0.80	13.5	26.0	—	1.75	—	—	3.00	0.15	0.02	Bal	—	—	—	—	—

TABLE 2—NOMINAL CHEMICAL COMPOSITIONS, % (continued)

Material Commercial Designation	C	Mn	Si	Cr	Ni	Co	Mo	W	Cb	Ti	Al	B	Fe	V	Zr	Cu	N	Other
S590	0.43	1.25	0.40	21.0	20.0	20.0	4.00	4.00	4.00	—	—	—	Bal	—	—	—	—	—
RA330	0.06	1.00	1.25	19.0	35.0	—	—	—	—	—	—	—	Bal	—	—	—	—	—
Unitemp 212	0.08	0.05	0.15	16.0	25.0	—	—	—	0.50	4.00	0.15	0.06	Bal	—	0.05	—	—	—
CRM-6D	1.00	5.00	0.50	20.0	5.00	—	1.00	1.00	1.00	—	—	—	Bal	—	—	—	—	—
CRM-15D	1.00	5.00	0.50	20.0	5.00	—	2.00	2.00	2.00	—	—	—	Bal	—	—	—	0.20	—
16-25-6	0.50	1.75	—	16.0	25.0	—	6.00				—	—	Bal	—	—	—	0.15	—
19-9DL	0.32	1.15	0.55	18.5	9.00	—	1.40	1.35	0.40	0.25	—		Bal	—	—	—	—	—
19-9DX	0.32	1.15	0.55	18.5	9.00	—	1.60	1.35	—	0.55	—		Bal	—	—	—	—	—
17-14-CuMo	0.12	0.75	0.50	15.9	14.1	—	2.50	—	0.45	0.25	—		Bal	—	—	3.00	—	—
Austenitic Iron Base Alloys (Continued)																		
G-192	0.60	8.50	0.50	22.0	—	—	—	—	—	—	—		Bal	—	—	—	0.35	
AF71	0.30	18.0	0.30	12.5	—	—	3.00	—	—	—	—	0.20	Bal	0.90	—	—	0.20	
Incoloy 800	0.04	0.75	0.35	20.5	32.0	—	—	—	—	—	—		Bal	—	—	0.30	—	
Incoloy 801	0.04	0.75	0.35	20.5	32.0	—	—	—	—	1.10	—		Bal	—	—	0.15	—	
Incoloy 805	0.12	0.60	0.50	7.50	36.0	—	0.50	—	—	—	—		Bal	—	—	0.10	—	
Incoloy 810	0.25	0.90	0.80	21.0	32.0	—	—	—	—	—	—		Bal	—	—	0.50	—	
Cobalt Base Alloys																		
L-605	0.10	1.50	0.60	20.0	10.0	Bal	—	15.0	—	—	—	—	1.60	—	—	—	—	—
S-816	0.37	1.50	0.55	20.0	20.0	Bal	4.0	4.0	4.0	—	—	—	3.40	—	—	—	—	—
HS-31 (X-40)	0.50	0.75	0.75	25.5	10.5	Bal	—	7.5	—	—	—	—	1.50	—	—	—	—	—
HS-21	0.25	—	—	27.0	2.5	Bal	5.5	—	—	—	—	0.007	1.75	—	—	—	—	—
Stellite 6	1.15	0.45	0.55	29.0	1.5	Bal	0.75	4.5	—	—	—	—	1.50	—	—	—	—	—
Haynes No. 151	0.47	0.50	0.50	20.0	—	Bal	—	12.8	—	0.15	—	0.05	—	—	—	—	—	—
WI-52	0.45	0.25	0.25	21.0	0.50	Bal	—	11.0	2.0	—	—	—	2.00	—	—	—	—	—
V-36	0.29	0.60	0.50	25.0	20.0	Bal	4.0	2.0	2.0	—	—	—	2.40	—	—	—	—	—
MAR-M 302	0.85	0.10	0.20	21.5	—	Bal	—	10.0	—	—	—	0.005	0.75	—	0.20	—	—	Ta, 9.0
MAR-M 322	1.00	0.10	0.10	21.5	—	Bal	—	9.0	—	0.75	—	—	0.75	—	2.25	—	—	Ta, 4.5
UMCo-50	0.08	0.65	0.75	28.0	—	50.0					—	—	20.5	—	—	—	—	—
UMCo-51	0.32	0.75	0.75	28.0	—	50.0	—	—	2.1	—	—	—	18.0	—	—	—	—	—
Nivco-10	0.03	0.35	0.20	—	22.5	Bal	—	—	—	1.75	0.22	—	0.50	—	0.62	—	—	—
Elgiloy	0.15	2.00	—	20.0	15.00	Bal	7.00	—	—	—	—	—	16.00	—	—	—	—	Be, 0.04
MAR-M 509	0.60	0.05	0.05	23.0	10.0	Bal	—	7.0	—	0.20	—	0.005	—	—	0.50	—	—	Ta, 3.50
Austenitic Nickel Base Alloys																		
Hastelloy X	0.10	0.65	0.60	22.0	Bal	1.50	9.00	0.60				—	18.5	—	—	—	—	—
Incoloy 901	0.05	0.24	0.12	12.5	Bal	—	6.00	—	—	2.70	0.15	0.015	34.0	—	—	—	—	—
Incoloy 901 Mod.	0.05	0.09	0.08	12.5	Bal	—	5.80	—	—	2.90	—	0.015	34.0	—	—	—	—	—
Rene 41	0.09	0.25	0.25	19.0	Bal	11.0	10.0	—	—	3.10	1.50	0.005	1.80	—	—	—	—	—
Udimet 500	0.10	0.10	0.10	17.50	Bal	18.45	4.25	—	—	3.00	3.00	0.005	0.50	—	0.06	—	—	—
Waspaloy	0.07	0.10	0.10	19.75	Bal	13.50	4.45	—	—	3.00	1.40	0.005	0.75	—	0.04	—	—	—
R-235	0.12	0.10	0.30	15.00	Bal	1.15	5.50	—	—	2.50	2.00	—	10.00	—	—	—	—	—
Udimet 700	0.07	—	—	15.00	Bal	18.50	5.25	—	—	3.50	4.25	0.03	0.50	—	—	—	—	—
Inconel X-750	0.04	0.70	0.30	15.00	Bal	—		—	0.85	2.50	0.80	—	6.75	—	—	—	—	—
M-252	0.15	0.50	0.50	20.00	Bal	10.00	10.00	—	—	2.60	1.00	0.005	—	—	—	—	—	—
Refractaloy 26	0.03	0.80	1.00	18.00	Bal	20.00	3.20	—	—	2.75	0.20	—	16.00	—	—	—	—	—
Astroloy	0.06	—	—	15.0	Bal	15.0	5.25	—	—	3.50	4.40	0.03	—	—	—	—	—	—
GMR-235	0.15	0.13	0.30	15.5	Bal	—	5.25	—	—	2.00	3.00	0.06	10.00	—	—	—	—	—
GMR-235D	0.15	0.05	0.15	15.5	Bal	—	5.00	—	—	2.50	3.50	0.05	4.50	—	—	—	—	—
Hastelloy B	0.10	0.80	0.70	0.60	Bal	1.25	28.0	—	—	—	—	—	5.50	0.30	—	—	—	—
Hastelloy C	0.07	0.80	0.70	16.0	Bal	1.25	17.0	4.0	—	—	—	—	5.75	0.30	—	—	—	—
Hastelloy F	0.02	1.50	0.50	22.0	Bal	1.25	6.5	0.50	2.10	—	—	—	21.0	—	—	—	—	—
Hastelloy N	0.06	0.40	0.25	7.0	Bal	0.25	16.5	0.20	—	—	—	0.01	3.0	—	—	0.10	—	—
Hastelloy W	0.06	0.50	0.50	5.0	Bal	1.25	24.5	—	—	—	—	—	5.5	0.6	—	—	—	—
Inconel 600	0.04	0.20	0.20	15.8	Bal	—	—	—	—	—	—	—	7.20	—	—	0.10	—	—
Inconel 604	0.04	0.20	0.20	15.8	Bal	—	—	—	2.00	—	—	—	7.20	—	—	0.10	—	—
Inconel 610	0.20	0.90	2.00	15.5	Bal	—	—	—	1.00	—	—	—	9.00	—	—	0.50	—	—
Inconel 700	0.12	0.10	0.30	15.0	46.0	28.5	3.75	—	—	2.20	3.00	—	0.70	—	—	0.05	—	—
Inconel 702	0.04	0.05	0.20	15.6	Bal	—	—	—	—	0.70	3.40	—	0.35	—	—	0.10	—	—
Inconel 705	0.30	0.90	5.50	15.5	Bal	—	—	—	—	—	—	—	8.00	—	—	0.50	—	—
Alloy 713C	0.12	0.10	0.30	12.5	Bal	—	4.50	—	2.00	0.60	6.00	0.012	1.00	—	0.10	—	—	—
Alloy 713LC	0.05	0.10	0.30	12.00	Bal	—	4.50	—	2.00	0.60	5.90	0.01	0.30	—	0.10	—	—	—
Inconel 718	0.04	0.20	0.20	18.6	Bal	—	3.10	—	5.00	0.90	0.40	—	18.50	—	—	—	—	—
Inconel 722	0.04	0.55	0.20	15.0	Bal	—	—	—	—	2.40	0.60	—	6.50	—	—	—	—	—
AF 1753	0.24	0.05	0.10	16.25	Bal	7.20	1.60	8.40	—	3.20	1.90	0.008	9.50	—	0.06	—	—	—
IN 100	0.18	—	—	10.0	Bal	15.0	3.0	—	—	4.75	5.50	0.015	—	—	0.06	—	—	—
Nimonic 75	0.10	0.45	0.50	19.5	Bal	—	—	—	—	0.40	0.20	—	2.40	—	—	0.05	—	—
Nimonic 80A	0.06	0.10	0.70	19.5	Bal	1.1	—	—	—	2.50	1.30	—	2.40	—	—	—	—	—
Nimonic 90	0.07	0.50	0.75	19.5	Bal	18.0	—	—	—	2.40	1.40	—	2.50	—	—	0.05	—	—

TABLE 2—NOMINAL CHEMICAL COMPOSITIONS, % (continued)

Material Commercial Designation	C	Mn	Si / O	Cr	Ni / H	Co / Sn	Mo	W / Ta	Cb	Ti	Al	B	Fe	V	Zr	Cu	N	Other
Nimonic 105	0.13	0.10	0.25	15.0	Bal	20.0	5.0	—	—	1.20	4.50	—	0.40	—	—	0.25	—	—
Nimonic 115	0.15	—	—	15.0	Bal	15.0	3.50	—	—	4.00	5.00	—	—	—	—	—	—	—
MAR-M200	0.15	—	—	9.0	Bal	10.0	—	12.5	1.00	2.00	5.00	0.015	—	—	0.05	—	—	—
RA-333	0.04	1.00	1.15	25.5	Bal	3.25	3.25	3.25	—	—	—	—	17.0	—	—	0.10	—	—
Titanium Base Alloys—Commercially Pure																		
			O		H	Sn		Ta										
A40	0.04	—	0.08	—	0.006	—	—	—	—	Bal	—	—	0.25	—	—	—	0.02	—
A55	0.04	—	0.08	—	0.007	—	—	—	—	Bal	—	—	0.25	—	—	—	0.03	—
A70	0.05	—	0.09	—	0.005	—	—	—	—	Bal	—	—	0.35	—	—	—	0.03	—
Titanium Base Alloys—Alpha Alloy Grades																		
5Al-2.5Sn	0.15	—	0.09	—	0.009	2.50	—	—	—	Bal	5.00	—	—	—	—	—	0.03	—
5Al-5Sn-5Zr	0.02	—	0.06	—	0.007	4.80	—	—	—	Bal	5.00	—	0.07	—	5.20	—	0.02	—
7Al-12Zr	0.02	—	0.04	—	0.005	—	—	—	—	Bal	7.00	—	0.07	—	12.0	—	0.015	—
7Al-2Cb-1Ta	0.04	—	0.08	—	0.009	—	—	1.00	2.00	Bal	7.00	—	—	—	—	—	—	—
8Al-1Mo-1V	0.04	—	0.07	—	0.008	—	1.00	—	—	Bal	8.00	—	0.15	1.00	—	—	0.02	—
Ti-679	0.02	—	0.07	—	0.004	11.0	1.00	—	—	Bal	2.25	—	—	—	5.00	—	0.02	—
Titanium Base Alloys—Alpha-Beta Alloy Grades																		
Ti-155A	0.04	—	0.06	1.40	0.005	—	1.20	—	—	Bal	5.50	—	1.40	—	—	—	0.02	—
8Mn	0.10	8.00	0.10	—	0.008	—	—	—	—	Bal	—	—	—	—	—	—	0.04	—
2.5Al-16V	0.04	—	0.07	—	0.007	—	—	—	—	Bal	2.50	—	—	16.0	—	—	0.01	—
3Al-2.5V	0.02	—	0.06	—	0.007	—	—	—	—	Bal	3.00	—	—	2.50	—	—	0.01	—
4Al-4Mn	0.05	4.00	0.11	—	0.012	—	—	—	—	Bal	4.00	—	—	—	—	—	0.02	—
4Al-3Mo-1V	0.04	—	0.10	—	0.005	—	3.00	—	—	Bal	4.25	—	0.15	1.00	—	—	0.03	—
5Al-1.25 Fe-2.75 Cr	0.08	—	0.08	2.75	0.006	—	—	—	—	Bal	5.00	—	1.25	—	—	—	0.02	—
6Al-4V	0.023	—	0.097	—	0.008	—	—	—	—	Bal	6.18	—	0.22	3.81	—	—	0.026	—
6Al-6V-2Sn	0.02	—	0.10	—	0.006	2.00	—	—	—	Bal	5.50	—	0.70	5.50	—	0.70	0.02	—
7Al-4Mo	0.05	—	0.10	—	0.006	—	4.00	—	—	Bal	6.90	—	0.15	—	—	—	0.02	—
2Cr-2 Fe-2Mo	0.05	—	0.10	2.25	0.005	—	2.25	—	—	Bal	—	—	2.25	—	—	—	0.05	—
Titanium Base Alloys—Beta Alloy Grades																		
1Al-8V-5Fe	0.05	—	0.09	—	0.012	—	—	—	—	Bal	1.00	—	5.00	8.00	—	—	0.07	—
3Al-13V-11Cr	0.02	—	0.10	11.0	0.007	—	—	—	—	Bal	3.00	—	—	13.5	—	—	0.03	

TABLE 3—AVERAGE PHYSICAL PROPERTIES

Material Commercial Designation	Density at 70 F lb/in3	Specific Gravity g/cc	Melting Range F	Thermal Conductivity F	Thermal Conductivity Btu/ ft2/hr/ F/in.	Electrical Resistivity F	Electrical Resistivity microhm, in.	Coefficient of Linear Thermal Expansion in./in./F × 10–6 70–200	70–400	70–600	70–800	70–1000	70–1200	70–1400	70–1600	70–1800	70–2000	Modulus of Elasticity in Tension (E) 106 psi F	E	F	E	F	Modulus of Rigidity (G) 106 psi G	F	G	Poison's Ratio at 70 F
Martensitic Low Alloy Steels																										
"17-22-A"	0.283	—	—	1000	227	—	—	—	—	—	7.66	7.80	7.93	—	—	—	—	70	30.8	1000	25.8	70	11.9	1000	9.8	0.296
"17-22-A" S	0.283	7.84	2700-2750	1200	200	—	—	6.80	6.88	7.32	7.57	7.77	7.95	—	—	—	—	70	29.5	1000	20.0	70	11.9	1000	9.5	0.296
"17-22-A" V						—	—	—	6.67	7.04	7.19	7.39	7.50	—	—	—	—	70	31.0	1000	25.2	70	12.1	1000	9.6	0.296
Chromoloy	0.285	—	—	—	—	—	—	7.0	7.15	7.30	7.55	7.90	8.30	—	—	—	—	70	31.7	1000	25.3	70	12.3	1000	9.6	0.280
D6A	0.284	7.87	—	—	—	—	—	7.31	—	—	—	—	—	—	—	—	—	80	29.65	1000	23.2	—		—	—	0.269
300M	0.283	—	—	70	260	—	—	—	—	—	—	—	—	—	—	—	—	80	29.5	—	—	—	—	—	—	
UCX2	0.276	7.68	—	—	—	—	—	—	—	5.68	—	—	—	—	—	—	—	80	29.4	—	—	—	—	—	—	—
Martensitic Secondary Alloy Steels																										
H11	0.282	7.77	2500–2600	890	196	—	—	6.1	6.4	—	6.68	6.90	7.11	—	—	—	—	70	30.5	1000	22.7	70	12.0	1000	9.0	0.27
H12	0.282	—	—	—	—	—	—	6.1	6.5	—	7.0	—	7.1	—	—	—	—	70	30.0	—	—	—	—	—	—	—
H13	0.282	7.76	—	890	196	—	—	5.8	—	—	6.9	7.0	7.4	—	—	—	—	80	30.0	1000	23.0	—	—	—	—	—
M2	0.293	8.16	2500–2600	—	—	—	—	5.69	6.09	6.42	6.67	6.97	—	—	—	—	—	70	29.5	—	—	—	—	—	—	—
M10	0.285	7.88	2500–2600	—	—	—	—	—	—	—	—	6.95	—	—	—	—	—	70	29.5	—	—	—	—	—	—	—
M50	0.286	7.87	2500–2600	—	—	—	—	6.23	6.58	6.83	7.05	7.38	—	—	—	—	—	70	29.5	1000	23.5	—	—	—	—	—
Martensitic Chromium Steels																										
410	0.280	7.78	2700–2790	932	199	750	34.6	5.5	—	5.6	—	6.4	6.5	—	—	—	—	70	29.8	900	23.8	70	12.0	900	10.0	0.24
Greek Ascoloy	0.286	7.87	2600–2700	—	—	77	31.0	5.83	6.12	6.20	6.37	6.52	6.63	—	—	—	—	70	29.0	1000	21.5	—	—	—	—	—
422	0.280	7.78	2600–2700	800	190	—	—	5.90	6.10	6.20	6.30	6.50	6.70	—	—	—	—	70	29.8	1000	21.5	—	—	—	—	0.23
422M	—	—	—	—	—	—	—	—	—	—	—	—	—	—	—	—	—	—	—	—	—	—	—	—	—	—
422M (Cast)	—	—	—	—	—	—	—	—	—	—	—	—	—	—	—	—	—	—	—	—	—	—	—	—	—	—
440C	0.277	7.68	2450–2550	212	168	—	—	—	—	—	—	—	5.60	—	—	—	—	70	29.0	—	—	—	—	—	—	—
14Cr-4Mo	0.280	7.78	2450–2550	—	—	—	—	—	—	—	—	6.67	—	—	—	—	—	70	29.0	—	—	—	—	—	—	—
Lapelloy	0.285	7.85	2700–2750	1000	198	—	—	5.90	6.10	6.20	6.30	6.50	6.70	—	—	—	—	70	30.0	1000	23.1	—	—	—	—	—
Lapelloy C	0.285	7.85	2650–2750	—	—	—	—	5.90	—	—	6.30	—	6.70	—	—	—	—	80	30.0	—	—	—	—	—	—	—
H-46	0.280	7.75	2650–2750	—	—	—	—	—	—	—	—	—	6.72	—	—	—	—	80	31.3	—	—	—	—	—	—	—

TABLE 3—AVERAGE PHYSICAL PROPERTIES (continued)

Material Commercial Designation	Density at 70 F lb/in3	Specific Gravity g/cc	Melting Range F	Thermal Conductivity		Electrical Resistivity		Coefficient of Linear Thermal Expansion in./in./F × 10–6										Modulus of Elasticity in Tension (E) 106 psi				Modulus of Rigidity (G) 106 psi				Poison's Ratio at 70 F
				F	Btu/ft2/hr/F/in.	F	microhm, in.	70–200	70–400	70–600	70–800	70–1000	70–1200	70–1400	70–1600	70–1800	70–2000	F	E	F	E	F	G	F	G	
Semi Austenitic Precipitation and Transformation Hardening Steels																										
							cm																			
AM-350	0.282	—	2500–2550	800	141	80	78.8	6.3	—	6.8	—	7.2	—	6.72	—	—	—	70	29.4	800	24.3	80	11.3	800	9.3	—
AM-355	0.281	—	2500–2550	800	139	80	75.6	6.4	—	6.8	—	7.2	—	6.5	—	—	—	80	29.3	800	24.6		11.4	800	9.4	—
																						80				
Stainless W	0.280	7.65	—	752	170	70	85	—	—	—	—	—	—	—	—	—	—	77	28.2	—	—	70	11.3	—	—	—
14-4PH	—	—	—	—	—	—	—	—	—	—	—	—	—	—	—	—	—	—	—	—	—	—	—	—	—	—
17-4PH	0.282	7.80	2660–2720	900	157	70	77	6.0	6.1	6.3	6.5	—	—	—	—	—	—	70	28.5	600	26.0	70	11.2	600	10.2	0.272
17-7PH	0.276	7.65	—	900	146	70	83	5.7	6.6	6.8	6.9	—	—	—	—	—	—	70	29.0	—	—	70	11.0	—	—	—
PH15-7Mo	0.277	7.68	—	1000	150	70	83	5.0	5.4	5.6	5.9	6.1	—	—	—	—	—	70	29.0	—	—	70	11.0	—	—	—
Austenitic Nickel-Chromium-Iron Steels																										
302	0.29	—	2550–2590	—	—	1200	109	—	—	—	—	—	—	—	—	—	—	70	27.9	1200	21.8	70	12.5	1200	8.2	—
304	0.287	7.94	2550–2650	—	—	1200	114	8.8	9.2	9.5	9.8	10.0	10.4	—	—	—	—	70	27.9	1200	21.1	70	12.5	1200	8.3	—
304L	0.287	7.94	2550–2650	—	—	68	72	—	—	9.9	—	10.2	10.4	—	—	—	—	70	28.0	—	—	70	12.5	—	—	—
309S	0.285	7.88	2550–2650	—	—	1200	116	—	—	9.3	—	9.6	10.0	—	—	11.5	—	70	29.0	1200	21.8	—	—	—	—	—
310	0.288	7.98	2550–2650	—	—	1200	124	8.4	8.8	9.0	9.3	9.5	—	—	—	—	—	70	28.2	1200	21.8	—	—	1200	7.9	—
314	0.279	7.72	—	932	—	68	77	—	—	—	—	—	—	—	—	—	—	70	29.0	—	—	—	—	—	—	—
316	0.286	7.91	2500–2550	—	—	1200	110	8.9	9.3	9.6	9.8	10.0	10.3	—	—	—	—	70	28.1	1200	21.5	—	—	1200	8.1	—
321	0.285	7.89	2550–2600	1000	150	1200	117	—	—	9.5	—	10.3	10.7	—	—	11.2	—	70	28.0	1200	21.2	—	—	1200	7.9	—
347	0.290	8.02	2500–2600	—	—	1200	111	9.0	9.4	9.7	9.9	10.1	—	—	—	11.1	—	70	28.2	1200	21.4	—	—	1200	8.1	—
Austenitic Iron Base Alloys																										
							in																			
A286	0.286	7.94	2500–2600	1200	172	1200	46.8	9.17	9.35	9.47	9.64	9.78	9.88	10.32	—	—	—	70	29.1	1500	18.7	70	11.0	1500	6.8	0.306
V-57	0.287	7.96	—	—	—	—	—	9.0	9.2	—	—	9.9	—	10.8	—	—	—	80	28.5	1200	22.2	—	—	—	—	0.29
Discaloy	0.288	7.97	2515–2665	1200	158	—	—	8.5	8.7	9.1	9.4	9.5	9.6	9.8	—	—	—	75	28.4	1200	21.0	—	—	—	—	—
N-155	0.298	8.20	2350–2475	1200	144	—	—	7.75	8.50	8.52	8.65	9.13	9.46	9.72	9.90	10.10	10.26	70	29.3	1500	20.8	—	—	—	—	0.298
D-979	0.295	8.17	—	1472	151	—	—	—	—	—	—	—	—	—	—	—	—	75	30.0	1500	21.9	75	11.6	1500	8.2	0.29
W-545	0.285	—	2455–2530	1400	141	—	—	—	—	9.67	—	—	10.1	—	11.0	—	—	80	28.4	1400	17.5	80	11.5	1400	6.65	0.23
S590	0.301	8.34	2400–2500	1292	155	—	—	8.0	—	8.3	—	—	—	—	9.2	—	—	80	31.1	—	—	80	11.9	—	—	—
RA330	0.286	7.86	2500–2600	500	130	—	—	—	—	—	—	—	8.9	—	9.3	—	9.8	80	29.0	—	—	—	—	—	—	—
Unitemp 212	0.286	—	2430–2530	1292	170	—	—	—	8.8	9.0	9.2	9.4	9.6	9.8	10.3	—	—	80	29.0	1400	20.5	70	10.4	—	—	—
CRM-6D	0.284	7.86	2400–2500	800	170	—	—	7.5	8.1	8.7	9.3	9.5	9.7	9.85	9.9	10.1	10.2	70	28.7	1200	18.0	70	11.5	—	—	0.26
CRM-15D	0.286	7.92	2400–2500	—	—	—	—	—	—	—	—	—	—	—	—	—	—	—	—	—	—	—	—	—	—	—
16-25-6	0.291	8.06	2550–2650	1100	180	—	—	—	—	9.28	9.29	9.36	9.52	10.8	11.7	—	—	70	29.1	1100	22.8	70	11.0	1100	8.2	0.295
19-9 DL	0.286	7.93	2525–2625	1200	147	—	—	8.50	9.11	9.31	9.59	9.78	9.97	—	—	—	—	70	29.5	1200	22.1	70	11.4	1200	8.2	0.286
19-9 DX	0.287	7.94	2500–2600	—	—	—	—	8.52	9.11	9.31	9.59	9.78	9.97	—	—	—	—	70	29.5	—	—	70	11.4	—	—	—
17-14 CuMo	0.287	8.01	—	600	128	—	—	—	—	—	—	9.69	—	—	—	—	—	70	28.0	900	23.0	—	—	—	—	—
G-192	0.279	—	2400–2600	—	—	—	—	8.6	8.9	9.3	9.7	10.1	10.3	10.5	10.7	—	—	70	29.9	1500	19.6	70	11.6	1500	7.34	0.29
AF71	0.281	—	2400–2500	—	—	—	—	5.6	7.4	—	—	—	—	—	—	—	—	70	28.4	1500	19.0	70	11.1	1500	7.14	0.27
Incoloy 800	0.290	8.02	2475–2525	212	97	—	—	8.0	8.4	8.7	9.0	9.3	9.6	9.8	10.0	10.2	—	70	28.2	—	—	—	—	—	—	—
Incoloy 801	0.288	7.97	—	—	—	—	—	—	—	—	—	—	—	—	—	—	—	70	29.0	1350	17.0	—	—	—	—	—
Incoloy 805	—	—	—	—	—	—	—	—	—	—	—	—	—	—	—	—	—	—	—	—	—	—	—	—	—	—
Incoloy 810	—	—	—	—	—	—	—	—	—	—	—	—	—	—	—	—	—	—	—	—	—	—	—	—	—	—
Cobalt Base Alloys																										
L-605	0.330	9.13	2425–2570	1200	153	75	34.9	6.83	7.19	7.59	7.77	8.02	8.24	8.61	9.06	9.41	9.84	70	34.2	1500	25.6	—	—	—	—	0.294
S-816	0.313	8.66	2350–2450	1200	161	—	—	7.38	7.45	7.65	7.91	8.11	8.40	8.75	9.00	9.25	—	70	35.2	1500	26.2	80	13.6	1500	9.6	0.294
HS-31 (X-40)	0.311	8.60	2445–2545	1200	158	70	38.2	—	—	7.84	8.08	8.39	8.75	9.19	—	—	—	70	32.8	1600	22.8	—	—	—	—	—
HS-21	0.300	8.30	2465	1112	142	70	34.4	—	—	7.83	7.96	8.18	8.38	—	—	—	—	—	—	—	—	—	—	—	—	—
Stellite 6	0.303	8.38	2310–2460	72	102.7	72	35.8	7.44	7.72	8.03	8.18	8.32	8.65	8.93	9.30	9.62	—	70	30.4	—	—	—	—	—	—	—
Haynes No. 151	—	—	—	—	—	—	—	—	—	—	—	—	—	—	—	—	—	—	—	—	—	—	—	—	—	—
WI-52	0.321	8.87	2400–2450	1200	195	—	—	—	7.5	7.6	7.8	8.0	8.3	8.6	9.0	9.2	9.7	—	—	—	—	—	—	—	—	—
V-36	0.303	8.41	2350–2450	—	—	—	—	—	—	—	—	—	—	—	—	9.1	—	70	32.4	1500	23.8	70	12.4	1500	8.84	0.30
MAR-M 302	0.333	9.21	2400–2450	1200	155	—	—	—	6.9	7.2	7.4	7.6	7.8	8.0	8.3	8.7	9.2	70	36.2	1800	24.2	—	—	—	—	—
MAR-M 322	0.322	8.91	2425–2475	—	—	—	—	—	—	—	—	—	—	—	—	—	—	—	—	—	—	—	—	—	—	—
UMCo-50	0.291	8.05	2515–2540	70	63	70	32.5	—	—	—	—	—	—	—	—	9.33	—	70	31.5	—	—	—	—	—	—	—
UMCo-51	0.288	7.79	2420–2450	—	—	70	40.1	—	—	—	—	—	—	—	—	6.68	—	70	27.6	—	—	—	—	—	—	—
Nivco-10	0.312	8.65	—	1472	198	70	—	—	—	—	—	7.36	—	—	—	—	—	70	30.5	1200	25.3	—	—	—	—	0.32
Elgiloy	0.300	8.3		392	112	70	39.27	—	—	—	8.43	—	—	—	—	—	—	70	29.5	—	—	—	—	—	—	—
MAR-M 509	0.320	8.86	2350–2550	—	—	—	—	—	—	—	—	—	—	—	—	—	—	—	—	—	—	—	—	—	—	—
Austenitic Nickel Base Alloys																										
							cm																			
Hastelloy X	0.297	8.23	2300–2400	1500	173	R.T.	—	7.70	7.82	7.90	8.15	8.39	8.56	8.81	9.02	9.20	—	70	28.6	1800	18.5	—	—	—	—	0.320
Incoloy 901	0.297	8.23	2245–2580	1400	142	—	—	7.75	7.85	8.02	8.27	8.50	8.79	9.15	—	—	—	75	29.9	1200	22.1	—	—	—	—	—
Incoloy 901 Mod	—	—	—	—	—	—	—	—	—	—	—	—	—	—	—	—	—	—	—	—	—	—	—	—	—	—
Rene 41	0.298	8.26	2400–2500	1600	160	—	—	6.7	6.8	7.0	7.2	7.5	7.8	8.2	8.70	9.3	9.9	80	31.9	1600	23.6	80	12.1	1550	8.8	0.31
Udimet 500	0.290	8.02	2350–2450	1800	177.1	1800	135.9	6.75	7.15	7.40	7.60	7.80	8.05	8.50	8.95	9.85	—	72	32.1	1800	21.0	—	—	—	—	—
Waspaloy	0.296	8.19	2425–2475	1800	182	—	—	6.8	7.1	7.3	7.6	7.8	8.0	8.5	8.9	9.8	10.4	70	29.0	1600	20.2	—	—	—	—	—
R-235	0.296	8.19	2460–2530	1800	173.1	—	133	6.70	7.17	7.51	7.72	7.98	8.13	8.44	8.92	9.58	10.18	70	30.5	1600	18.8	—	—	—	—	0.330
Udimet 700	0.285	7.91	2230–2450	1800	240	1800	146.1	—	7.50	7.52	7.60	7.74	7.98	8.35	8.95	9.65	10.30	70	32.4	1800	22.1	—	—	—	—	—
Inconel X-750	0.298	8.25	2540–2600	1600	164	—	—	6.96	7.14	7.46	7.76	8.10	8.41	8.84	9.33	9.75	—	80	31.0	1800	20.0	80	11.0	—	—	0.29

TABLE 3—AVERAGE PHYSICAL PROPERTIES (continued)

Material Commercial Designation	Density at 70 F lb/in3	Specific Gravity g/cc	Melting Range F	Thermal Conductivity F	Thermal Conductivity Btu/ft2/hr/F/in.	Electrical Resistivity F	Electrical Resistivity microhm, in.	Coefficient of Linear Thermal Expansion in./in./F × 10–6: 70–200	70–400	70–600	70–800	70–1000	70–1200	70–1400	70–1600	70–1800	70–2000	Modulus of Elasticity in Tension (E) 106 psi: F	E	F	E	Modulus of Rigidity (G) 106 psi: F	G	F	G	Poison's Ratio at 70 F
M-252	0.298	8.26	2400–2500	1500	149	—	—	6.7	6.8	7.0	7.2	7.5	7.8	8.2	8.8	9.3	—	80	29.8	1600	21.0	80	12.0	1600	8.3	0.314
Refractaloy 26	0.296	8.19	2450–2500	1200	177	—	—	7.8	7.9	8.0	8.1	8.2	8.4	—	—	—	—	70	30.6	1600	19.5	—	—	—	—	—
Astroloy	—	—	—	—	—	—	—	—	—	—	—	—	—	—	—	—	—	—	—	—	—	—	—	—	—	—
GMR-235	0.290	—	—	800	106	—	—	—	—	—	—	7.6	—	8.1	8.6	9.1	—	—	—	—	—	—	—	—	—	—
GMR-235D	0.291	8.05	—	—	—	—	—	—	—	—	—	—	—	—	—	—	—	70	28.7	1800	17.0	—	—	—	—	—
Hastelloy B	0.334	9.24	2400–2460	1112	114	—	—	—	—	6.41	6.57	6.66	6.73	—	7.78	—	—	80	28.5	—	—	—	—	—	—	—
Hastelloy C	0.323	8.94	2310–2380	1112	118	—	—	—	—	7.02	7.35	7.44	7.73	—	8.20	—	—	80	28.5	—	—	—	—	—	—	—
Hastelloy F	0.295	8.16	2300–2400	—	—	—	112	8.1	8.3	8.7	8.8	8.9	9.2	9.5	9.8	10.2	—	80	29.0	—	—	—	—	—	—	0.305
Hastelloy N	0.317	8.79	2470–2555	1112	140.1	—	—	—	6.45	6.76	7.09	7.43	7.81	8.16	8.51	8.85	—	80	31.3	1500	25.8	—	—	—	—	—
Hastelloy W	0.298	8.26	2540–2600	—	—	—	—	—	—	—	—	—	—	—	—	—	—	80	31.0	—	—	—	—	—	—	—
Inconel 600	0.301	8.33	2500–2600	1600	200	—	—	7.4	7.7	7.9	8.1	8.4	8.6	8.9	9.1	9.3	—	80	31.4	1600	23.1	80	11.0	—	—	—
Inconel 604	0.305	8.45	—	—	—	—	—	6.75	—	—	7.75	—	8.25	—	—	—	—	80	31.0	1350	24.5	—	—	—	—	—
Inconel 610	—	—	—	—	—	—	—	—	—	—	—	—	—	—	—	—	—	—	—	—	—	—	—	—	—	—
Inconel 700	0.295	8.16	2450–2600	1600	126	—	—	6.84	7.21	7.48	7.79	8.02	8.32	8.68	9.27	—	—	70	32.5	1600	23.6	—	—	—	—	—
Inconel 702	0.304	8.41	—	1200	235	—	—	6.7	7.5	7.8	8.0	8.3	8.7	9.1	9.4	10.0	—	70	31.5	1800	20.8	—	—	—	—	—
Inconel 705	0.292	8.06	2500–2580	—	—	—	—	—	—	—	—	—	—	9.20	—	—	—	80	25.0	—	—	—	—	—	—	—
Alloy 713C	0.286	7.91	2300–2350	1600	218	1600	158	5.92	6.61	7.00	7.26	7.52	7.81	8.17	8.63	9.13	9.48	70	29.9	1600	22.6	—	—	—	—	—
Inconel 718	0.296	8.19	2200–2450	—	—	—	—	7.1	7.5	7.7	7.9	8.0	8.4	8.9	—	—	—	70	29.0	1400	23.3	—	—	—	—	0.293
Inconel 722	0.298	8.26	2540–2600	—	—	—	—	6.5	7.3	7.6	7.7	7.9	8.2	8.6	9.1	9.3	9.5	70	31.0	1600	22.6	—	—	—	—	—
AF 1753	0.305	8.45	2525–2575	—	—	—	132.0	—	—	6.7	7.0	7.3	7.5	7.8	8.2	8.5	—	70	31.0	1800	20.4	—	—	—	—	—
IN 100	0.280	7.75	2305–2435	—	—	—	—	—	7.2	7.3	7.5	7.7	8.0	8.3	8.8	9.3	10.1	70	30.8	1600	23.4	—	—	—	—	—
Nimonic 75	0.301	8.33	2530–2600	1472	180	1472	113	—	—	—	—	—	—	—	—	—	—	70	27.0	—	—	—	—	—	—	—
Nimonic 80A	0.295	8.16	2480–2540	1400	142	—	—	7.0	7.2	7.4	7.6	7.7	7.9	8.2	8.6	—	—	70	31.2	1600	22.7	—	—	—	—	—
Nimonic 90	0.296	8.19	2480–2540	1400	144	1472	124	6.4	7.0	7.2	7.5	7.7	8.1	8.5	9.0	—	—	70	32.1	1600	22.9	—	—	—	—	—
Nimonic 105	0.289	8.00	2440–2520	1400	129	1472	142	6.8	7.2	7.5	7.8	8.0	8.3	8.8	9.5	10.6	—	70	32.9	1600	24.7	—	—	—	—	—
Nimonic 115	0.284	7.85	—	—	—	—	—	—	7.05	7.15	7.40	7.70	8.00	8.45	9.00	9.75	—	70	32.4	1600	23.8	—	—	—	—	—
MAR-M 200	0.308	8.53	2400–2450	2000	198	—	—	—	6.6	6.9	7.1	7.3	7.5	7.8	8.2	8.8	9.8	80	31.6	1800	22.9	—	—	—	—	—
RA-333	0.298	8.26	—	—	—	—	—	—	—	—	—	—	—	—	—	8.85	—	75	31.3	1600	16.6	—	—	—	—	—
Titanium Base Alloys—Commercially Pure																										
A40	0.163	4.54	2950–3100	—	—	70	56	4.8	—	5.2	—	5.5	5.6	—	—	—	—	70	14.9	—	—	70	6.5	—	—	—
A55	0.163	4.54	2950–3100	1000	128.4	1000	132	4.8	—	5.3	—	5.5	5.6	—	—	—	—	70	15.0	—	—	70	6.5	—	—	—
A70	0.163	4.54	2985–3085	1000	126.0	1000	150	4.8	4.9	5.0	5.1	5.3	5.4	5.7	—	—	—	70	15.1	1000	10.0	70	6.5	—	—	0.340
Titanium Base Alloys—Alpha Alloy Grades																										
5Al-2.5Sn	0.162	—	2820–3000	800	86.4	800	183	5.2	5.2	5.3	5.3	5.4	5.5	5.6	5.7	—	—	70	16.0	—	—	70	7.0	—	—	—
5Al-5Sn-5Zr	0.166	—	2950–3050	—	—	—	—	—	—	—	—	—	—	—	—	—	—	70	16.0	—	—	—	—	—	—	—
7Al-12Zr	0.165	—	2950–3050	—	—	—	—	—	—	—	—	—	—	—	—	—	—	70	16.5	—	—	—	—	—	—	—
7Al-2Cb-1Ta	0.160	—	3065–3115	—	—	—	—	—	—	—	—	—	5.0	—	—	—	—	70	17.7	—	—	—	—	—	—	—
8Al-1Mo-1V	0.156	4.37	—	—	—	800	201	4.7	4.9	5.0	—	5.6	5.7	—	—	—	—	70	18.5	—	—	—	—	—	—	—
Ti-679	0.174	—	—	800	81.6	800	185	5.0	—	5.7	—	5.8	—	—	—	—	—	70	—	—	—	—	—	—	—	—
Titanium Base Alloys—Alpha-Beta Alloy Grades																										
Ti-155A	0.163	—	—	800	83.6	800	180	—	—	—	—	5.7	—	—	—	—	—	70	16.5	1000	12.3	80	6.3	1000	4.5	0.327
8Mn	0.171	—	2730–2970	800	108	800	140	4.8	5.1	5.4	5.7	6.0	6.5	—	—	—	—	70	16.4	—	—	70	7.0	—	—	—
2.5Al-16V	0.166	—	3050–3150	—	—	—	—	—	—	—	—	4.9	5.0	—	—	—	—	70	15.0	—	—	—	—	—	—	—
3Al-2.5V	0.162	—	3050–3150	—	—	—	—	5.3	—	5.5	—	5.5	—	—	—	—	—	70	15.5	—	—	—	—	—	—	—
4Al-4Mn	0.163	—	2920–3050	800	88.8	800	172	4.9	4.9	5.1	5.3	5.4	5.6	—	—	—	—	70	16.4	—	—	70	7.3	—	—	—
4Al-3Mo-1V	0.163	—	2950–3050	800	81.6	—	—	5.0	5.1	5.3	5.4	5.5	—	—	—	—	—	70	16.5	—	—	70	7.0	—	—	—
5Al-1.25Fe-2.75Cr	0.162	—	—	—	—	—	—	5.2	—	5.3	—	5.5	—	—	—	—	—	70	16.5	—	—	—	—	—	—	—
6Al-4V	0.160	4.424	2950–3050	800	81.6	800	187	4.8	5.0	5.1	5.2	5.3	6.1	—	—	—	—	70	16.5	—	—	70	6.2	—	—	—
6Al-6V-2Sn	0.164	—	3050–3150	—	—	—	—	5.0	5.05	5.20	5.25	5.30	—	—	—	—	—	70	16.5	—	—	—	—	—	—	—
7Al-4Mo	0.162	—	2950–3050	800	81.6	800	183	4.92	5.09	5.21	5.38	5.55	5.80	6.15	—	—	—	70	16.2	800	13.2	70	6.5	—	—	—
2Cr-2Fe-2Mo	—	—	—	—	—	—	—	—	—	—	—	—	—	—	—	—	—	—	—	—	—	—	—	—	—	—
Titanium Base Alloys—Beta Alloy Grades																										
1Al-8V-5Fe	0.168	—	—	—	—	—	—	5.2	—	5.6	—	5.9	—	—	—	—	—	70	14.2	—	—	—	—	—	—	—
3Al-13V-11Cr	0.175	—	—	800	98.4	—	—	5.2	—	5.6	—	5.9	—	—	—	—	—	70	14.7	1000	11.6	70	6.2	—	—	0.304

TABLE 4—TYPICAL MECHANICAL PROPERTIES

Material Commercial Designation	Material Condition	Ultimate Tensile Strength F	Ksi	F	Ksi	Yield Strength at 0.2% offset F	Ksi	F	Ksi	Elongation in 2 in. or 4D F	%	F	%	Reduction of Area F	%	F	%	Charpy Impact, ft-lb	Hardness No.	Stress Rupture Strength, 1000 psi: 800 F 100	800 F 1000	1000 F 100	1000 F 1000	1200 F 100	1200 F 1000	1400 F 100	1400 F 1000
Martensitic Low Alloy Steels																											
"17-22-A"	Oil quench (1200 F)	80	169	1000	86	80	161	1000	74	80	13	1000	28	80	46	1000	82	58	Bhn 341	84	72	49	36	—	—	—	—
"17-22-A" S	Norm (1200 F)	80	153	1000	108	80	134	1000	92	80	18	1000	21	80	53	1000	70	25	Bhn 320	—	—	75	60	14	6	—	—
"17-22-A" V	Norm (1200 F)	80	160	1000	100	80	145	1000	92	80	17	1000	21	80	52	1000	66	18	Bhn 341	—	—	67	49	25	14	—	—
Chromoloy	Air cooled, (1200 F)	70	138	1000	110	70	117	1000	85	70	7	1000	—	70	45	1000	—	—	Rc 30	—	—	75	51	—	—	—	—
D6A	Oil quench, (600 F)	80	267	—	—	80	247	—	—	80	10	—	—	80	41	—	—	13	Rc 53	—	—	—	—	—	—	—	—
300M	Oil quench, (600 F)	80	289	—	—	80	245	—	—	80	9	—	—	80	34	—	—	22	Bhn 525	—	—	—	—	—	—	—	—
UCX2	Oil quench, (600 F)	80	272	—	—	80	235	—	—	80	6	—	—	80	—	—	—	—	Rc 51	—	—	—	—	—	—	—	—

TABLE 4—TYPICAL MECHANICAL PROPERTIES (continued)

Material Commercial Designation	Material Condition	Ultimate Tensile Strength				Yield Strength at 0.2% offset				Elongation in 2 in. or 4D				Reduction of Area				Charpy Impact, ft-lb	Hardness No.	Stress Rupture Strength, 1000 psi							
		F	Ksi	F	Ksi	F	Ksi	F	Ksi	F	%	F	%	F	%	F	%			100	1000	100	1000	100	1000	100	1000
Martensitic Secondary Alloy Steels																											
H11	Air cooled, (1050 F)	70	262	1000	180	70	215	1000	141	70	10	1000	12	70	35	1000	41	—	Rc 52	205	190	100	47	—	—	—	—
H12	Air cooled, (1050 F)	80	205	1000	137	80	185	1000	120	80	12	1000	25	80	42	1000	64	15	Rc 44	—	—	—	—	—	—	—	—
H13	Air cooled, (1100 F)	70	215	1000	143	70	184	1000	103	70	13	1000	19	70	45	1000	65	18	Rc 45	—	—	—	—	—	—	—	—
M2	—	—	—	—	—	—	—	—	—	—	—	—	—	—	—	—	—	—	—	—	—	—	—	—	—	—	—
M10	—	—	—	—	—	—	—	—	—	—	—	—	—	—	—	—	—	—	—	—	—	—	—	—	—	—	—
M50	Air cooled, (1025 F)	70	411	1000	309	70	338	1000	250	70	2	1000	6	70	2	1000	12	—	Rc 64	—	—	—	—	—	—	—	—
Martensitic Chromium Steels																											
410	Oil quench, (1000 F)	70	157	1000	101	70	145	1000	93	70	13	1000	16	70	69	1000	77	25	Bhn 300	60	55	32	26	8	6	3	—
Greek Ascoloy	Oil quench, (1050 F)	70	160	1000	95	70	135	1000	84	70	16	1000	17	70	45	1000	64	19	Rc 35	—	—	52	41	19	11	—	—
422	Oil quench, (1200 F)	70	149	1000	96	70	125	1000	82	70	18	1000	25	70	52	1000	67	19	Rc 43	—	—	63	57	25	18	—	—
422M	—	—	—	—	—	—	—	—	—	—	—	—	—	—	—	—	—	—	—	—	—	86	72	26	16	—	—
422M (Cast)	—	—	—	—	—	—	—	—	—	—	—	—	—	—	—	—	—	—	—	—	—	—	—	34	20	—	—
440C	Oil quench, (600 F)	70	285	1000	122	70	275	—	—	70	2	—	—	70	10	—	—	—	Bhn 580	—	—	—	—	—	—	—	—
14Cr-4Mo	—	—	—	—	—	—	—	—	—	—	—	—	—	—	—	—	—	—	—	—	—	—	—	—	—	—	—
Lapelloy	Oil quench, (1275 F)	70	155	1000	95	70	140	1000	85	70	17	1000	15	70	35	1000	45	—	Rc 35	—	—	65	55	25	15	—	—
Lapelloy C	Oil quench, (1200 F)	80	155	1000	98	80	120	1000	95	80	17	1000	19	80	44	1000	60	30	Rc 33	—	—	70	55	24	13	—	—
H-46	Air cooled, (1200 F)	80	150	1000	99	80	128	1000	88	80	20	1000	25	80	56	1000	61	—	Bhn 302	—	—	75	65	35	25	—	—
Semi Austenitic Precipitation and Transformation Hardening Steels																											
AM-350	SCT [1], (850 F)	70	203	1000	106	70	170	1000	85	70	13	1000	16	—	—	—	—	14	—	183	181	—	—	—	—	—	—
AM-350	SCT, (850 F)	70	169	800	129	70	147	800	104	70	15	800	8	—	—	—	—	—	—	130	127	—	—	—	—	—	—
AM-355	SCT, (850 F)	70	216	1000	144	70	182	1000	97	70	19	1000	16	70	39	1000	57	17	Rc 48	186	180	70	57	—	—	—	—
AM-355	SCT, (1000 F)	70	186	1000	115	70	171	1000	96	70	19	1000	19	70	57	1000	65	45	Rc 38	134	132	73	61	—	—	—	—
Stainless W	Solution + 1000 F	70	192	1000	94	70	187	1000	54	70	13	1000	22	70	53	1000	75	13	Rc 44	—	—	31	—	12	—	—	—
14-4PH	—	—	—	—	—	—	—	—	—	—	—	—	—	—	—	—	—	—	—	—	—	—	—	—	—	—	—
17-4PH	H900	70	203	900	149	70	186	900	132	70	11	900	10	70	50	900	30	20	Rc 44	140	128	—	—	—	—	—	—
17-7PH	RH 950 Sheet	70	230	900	133	70	217	900	114	70	6	900	15	70	30	—	—	—	Rc 48	113	92	—	—	—	—	—	—
17-7PH	TH 1050 Sheet	70	193	900	124	70	182	900	100	70	10	900	10	—	—	—	—	—	Rc 42	110	90	—	—	—	—	—	—
PH15-7MO	RH 950	70	240	1000	130	70	225	1000	105	70	6	1000	14	—	—	—	—	—	Rc 48	174	171	—	—	—	—	—	—
Austenitic Nickel-Chromium-Iron Steels																											
302	Annealed	70	92	1200	44	70	38	1200	11	70	68	1200	40	70	78	1200	62	—	Rb 85	—	—	—	35	—	14	—	6
304	Annealed	70	85	1200	45	70	30	1200	11	70	60	1200	—	70	70	1200	—	—	Rb 80	—	—	—	35	—	14	—	6
304L	Annealed	70	80	1000	52	70	30	1000	12	70	60	1000	45	70	77	1000	67	—	Rb 80	—	—	—	32	26	14	11	5
309S	Annealed	70	90	1400	36	70	40	1400	26	70	50	1400	40	70	65	1400	42	—	Rb 83	—	—	—	—	—	20	—	7
310	Annealed	70	92	1300	50	70	40	1300	22	70	47	1300	36	70	73	1300	52	80	Rb 89	—	—	—	32	—	17	—	6
314	Annealed	70	100	—	—	70	50	—	—	70	45	—	—	70	60	—	—	—	Rb 89	—	—	—	—	22	14	—	—
316	Annealed	70	85	1300	46	70	38	1300	19	70	60	1300	42	70	77	1300	58	80	Rb 80	—	—	—	—	—	24	—	11
321	Annealed	70	85	1300	37	70	33	1300	16	70	58	1300	56	70	75	1300	78	70	Rb 80	—	—	—	—	—	17	—	5
347	Annealed	70	91	1300	40	70	39	1300	24	70	50	1300	51	70	71	1300	74	48	Bhn 160	—	—	—	32	26	19	—	7
Austenitic Iron Base Alloys																											
A286	1800, 1325 F	70	145	1200	103	70	95	1200	88	70	24	1200	13	70	45	1200	14	64	Rc 26	99	88	61	46	25	—	—	—
A286	1650, 1325 F	70	157	1200	109	70	102	1200	90	70	25	1200	18	70	46	1200	25	—	Bhn 302	—	—	59	47	—	—	—	—
V-57	1800, 1350 F	80	175	1300	120	80	125	1300	—	80	21	1300	—	80	35	1300	—	—	Bhn 331	112	102	77	64	35	—	—	—
Discaloy	1850, 1350, 1200 F	70	145	1200	104	70	106	1200	91	70	19	1200	19	70	23	1200	24	—	Bhn 293	90	72	52	43	18	8	—	—
N-155	2150, 1400 F	70	119	1400	60	70	57	1400	36	70	43	1400	31	70	50	1400	41	43	Bhn 210	—	—	52	38	24	20	12	8
D-979	1900, 1550, 1300 F	70	204	1500	74	70	146	1500	63	70	15	1500	28	70	23	1500	57	8	—	—	—	88	70	43	30	—	—
W-545	1875, 1415, 1350 F	70	181	1400	91	70	132	1400	82	70	19	1400	28	70	30	1400	56	30	—	120	105	82	66	40	23	—	—
S590	2250, 1400 F	70	145	1200	95	70	82	1200	71	70	20	1200	22	70	25	1200	24	14	—	90	74	48	38	—	—	12	9
RA330	Annealed	70	89	1600	28	—	—	—	—	70	43	1600	21	70	68	1600	24	—	Rb 80	—	—	—	—	—	—	—	4
Unitemp 212	1850, 1325 F	80	187	1400	102	80	130	1400	97	80	23	1400	16	80	40	—	—	—	Rc 39	—	—	100	88	46	28	—	—
CRM-6D	Aged	70	110	1500	51	70	78	1500	40	70	2	1500	12	70	3	1500	17	—	Rc 35	90	—	61	52	36	29	20	16
CRM-15D	Aged	70	115	1500	58	70	90	1500	46	70	1	1500	11	70	3	1500	16	—	Rc 37	93	—	67	54	38	28	20	15
16-25-6	Hot cold worked	70	162	1200	106	70	143	1200	93	70	15	1200	13	70	34	1200	28	—	Bhn 326	57	42	50	36	18	11	—	—
19-9 DL	Stress relieved	70	118	1200	75	70	69	1200	37	70	56	1200	34	70	55	1200	34	46	Bhn 215	64	56	44	37	20	10	—	—
19-9 DX	Stress relieved	70	118	1200	75	70	69	1200	37	70	55	1200	33	70	54	1200	33	46	Bhn 216	64	56	48	39	—	—	—	—
17-14CuMo	2250, 1350 F	75	86	1000	72	75	42	1000	28	75	45	1000	32	75	63	1000	45	26	Rb 80	—	—	43	37	—	—	—	—
G-192	2150, 1400 F	70	136	1500	41	70	86	1500	32	70	5	1500	24	70	4	1500	28	—	—	—	—	42	—	—	—	—	—
AF71	2050, 1325 F	70	151	1500	48	70	106	1500	43	70	25	1500	29	70	35	1500	58	—	—	—	—	69	54	—	—	—	—
Incoloy 800	Annealed	80	87	1400	35	80	47	1400	27	80	42	1400	70	80	69	1400	64	207	—	62	49	32	23	12	8	5	3
Incoloy 801	—	80	90	1400	43	80	40	1400	27	80	36	1400	16	—	—	—	—	—	—	—	—	33	26	—	—	—	—
Incoloy 805	—	—	—	—	—	—	—	—	—	—	—	—	—	—	—	—	—	—	—	—	—	—	—	—	—	—	—
Incoloy 810	—	—	—	—	—	—	—	—	—	—	—	—	—	—	—	—	—	—	—	—	—	—	—	—	—	—	—
Cobalt Base Alloys																											
																				1200 F		1400 F		1600 F		1800 F	
L-605	Solution at 2250 F	70	160	1600	40	70	86	1600	37	70	47	1600	25	—	—	—	—	—	Bhn 230	70	54	35	27	15	10	7	3
S-816	Solution, precipitate at 1400 F	70	140	1600	51	70	55	1600	35	70	35	1600	17	70	29	1600	20	—	Rc 31	65	50	36	28	16	9	—	—
HS-31 (X-40)	As cast	70	108	1500	63	70	76	1500	—	70	9	1500	15	70	11	1500	18	6	Bhn 228	56	51	37	33	20	16	11	10
HS-21	As cast	70	101	1600	55	70	82	1600	—	70	8	1600	23	70	9	1600	48	10	Bhn 237	52	42	24	15	16	11	—	—
Stellite 6	As cast	70	115	1500	70	70	96	1500	—	70	3	1500	—	70	3	1500	12	9	Rc 41	—	—	—	—	—	—	—	—
Haynes No. 151	As cast	70	106	1500	64	70	74	1500	43	70	8	1500	11	70	—	1500	—	—	Rc 33	73	68	—	—	27	24	—	—
WI-52	As cast	70	120	1400	94	70	89	1400	49	70	—	1400	10	70	—	1400	12	—	—	—	—	—	—	25	22	13	10
V-36	Water quench (2250 F)																										
	Air cooled (1400 F)	70	146	1500	61	70	83	1500	47	70	2	1500	18	70	—	1500	—	—	—	64	43	32	24	17	12	—	—

TABLE 4—TYPICAL MECHANICAL PROPERTIES (continued)

Material Commercial Designation	Material Condition	Ultimate Tensile Strength				Yield Strength at 0.2% offset				Elongation in 2 in. or 4D				Reduction of Area				Charpy Impact, ft-lb	Hardness No.	Stress Rupture Strength, 1000 psi							
		F	Ksi	F	Ksi	F	Ksi	F	Ksi	F	%	F	%	F	%	F	%			100	1000	100	1000	100	1000	100	1000
MAR-M 302	As cast	70	136	1600	67	70	100	1600	45	70	2	1600	10	70	—	1600	—	—	Rc 37	—	—	—	—	27	—	14	—
MAR-M 322	As cast	70	121	1600	80	70	91	1600	50	70	3	1600	12	70	4	1600	12	—	Rc 35	—	—	—	—	32	—	20	—
UMCo-50	As cast	70	78	1650	18	70	46	1650	15	70	8	1650	8	70	—	1650	9	27	Dpn 250	—	—	—	—	—	—	—	—
UMCo-51	As cast	70	91	900	30	70	72	900	26	70	2	900	14	70	—	—	—	—	Dpn 280	—	—	—	—	—	—	—	—
Nivco-10	Bar	70	165	1200	105	70	110	1200	75	70	25	1200	20	70	28	1200	35	31	—	51	38	—	—	—	—	—	—
Elgiloy	Strip	70	368	—	—	70	280	—	—	70	—	—	—	70	—	—	—	—	Rc 58	—	—	—	—	—	—	—	—
MAR-M 509	As cast	70	112	1600	68	70	83	1600	45	70	3	1600	7	70	6	1600	13	—	Rc 32	—	—	—	—	29	—	17	—
Austenitic Nickel Base Alloys																											
																	50										
Hastelloy X	Solution at 2175 F	70	115	1800	23	70	52	1800	21	70	52	1800	66	70	64	1800	15	88	Rb 90	42	31	21	15	9	6	4	3
Incoloy 901	2000, 1450, 1325 F	70	175	1300	130	70	125	1300	114	70	15	1300	11	70	19	1300	21	—	—	78	61	37		—	—	—	—
Incoloy 901	2000, 1450, 1325 F	70	175	1300	129	70	130	1300	111	70	14	1300	13	70	17	1300		—	—	90	76	44	30	—	—	—	
Rene 41	1950, 1400 F	70	206	1600	90	70	154	1600	80	70	14	1600	19	—	—	—	—	—	Rc 31	110	100	64	40	23	14	10	
Udimet 500	1975, 1550, 1400 F	70	175	1800	40	70	115	1800	35	70	16	1800	22	70	16	1800	40	—	—	135	110	65	47	30	18	12	—
Waspaloy	Solution, stabilize, precipitate	70	185	1600	76	70	115	1600	75	70	25	1600	34	70	20	1600	54	—	Rc 36	110	86	60	42	25	16	6	—
R-235	Solution, precipitate	70	169	1600	76	70	116	1600	58	70	21	1600	14	—	—	—	—	—	—	52	40	39	29	22	15	8	5
Austenitic Nickel Base Alloys (continued)																											
Udimet 700	Solution, stabilize, precipitate	70	204	1800	52	70	140	1800	44	70	17	1800	28	70	20	1800	28	—	—	—	102	79	62	42	28	16	7
Inconel X-750	2100, 1550, 1300 F	80	162	1500	52	80	92	1500	44	80	24	1500	22	80	30	1500	34	37	Rc 33	80	68	40	30	13	7	3	2
M-252	1950, 1400 F	70	176	1500	91	70	110	1500	84	70	25	1500	24	70	—	1500	—	—	Bhn 363	100	79	52	38	23	13	—	—
Refractaloy 26	Solution, precipitate	70	154	1500	71	70	96	1500	68	70	19	1500	29	70	20	1500	35	—	—	77	63	40	3	—	—	—	—
Astroloy	—																			—	—	—	—	37	—	—	
GMR-235	—	80	103	1500	105	80	93	1500	78	80	3	1500	3	—	—	—	—	—	—	—	—	—	—	26	18	11	
GMR-235D	—	80	112	1500	121	80	103	1500	81	80	3	1500	3	—	—	—	—	—	—	110	100	77	60	32	23	17	12
Hastelloy B	As cast	80	85	1500	58	80	53	—	—	80	15	1500	19	80	15	1500	18	13	Rb 93	51	40	—	—	—	—	—	—
Hastelloy C	As cast	80	89	1500	56	80	52	—	—	80	11	1500	18	80	12	1500	15	—	—	49	42	—	—	13	9	—	—
Hastelloy F	Solution at 2125 F	80	102	1400	54	80	45	1400	29	80	46	1400	47	—	—	—	—	—	—	42	36	—	—	9	—	—	
Hastelloy N	Solution at 2150 F	80	115	1500	56	80	45	1500	29	80	50	1500	24	—	—	—	—	85	—	42	29	—		8	3	—	
Hastelloy W	2000, 1300 F	80	158	1500	59	80	82	1500	46	80	26	1500	24	—	—	—	—	—	—	74	54	—	—	7	5	3	
Inconel 600	Annealed	80	90	1400	27	80	37	1400	17	80	47	1400	46	80	64	1400	60	—	—	23	14	12	8	5	3	3	2
Inconel 604	Annealed 2050 F	80	102	—	—	80	33	—	—	80	48	—	—	80	62	—	—	—	—	37	27	16	11	—	—	—	—
Inconel 610	—	—	—	—	—	—	—	—	—	—	—	—	—	—	—	—	—	—	—	—	—	—	—	—	—	—	—
Inconel 700	Solution, aged 1600 F	80	171	1500	107	80	104	1500	75	80	25	1500	6	80	27	1500	8	—	—	100	87	—	—	27	17	6	3
Inconel 702	2000, 1350 F	80	148	1400	72	80	84	1400	62	80	35	1400	4	—	—	—	—	—	—	56	43	24	15	7	4	3	2
Inconel 705	—	—	—	—	—	—	—	—	—	—	—	—	—	—	—	—	—	—	—	—	—	—	—	—	—	—	—
Alloy 713C	As cast	70	123	1600	105	70	106	1600	72	70	8	1600	14	70	11	1600	20	—	Rc 38	—	—	83	65	42	28	21	13
Inconel 718	1800, 1325, 1150 F	80	208	1400	107	80	172	1400	138	80	21	1400	25	—	—	—	—	—	—	105	86	44	25	—	—	—	—
Inconel 722	1975, 1300 F	80	158	1500	59	80	82	1500	46	80	26	1500	24	—	—	—	—	—	—	74	54	37	22	7	5	3	—
AF 1753	2150, 1400 F	70	194	1500	113	70	129	1500	108	70	20	1500	13	70	22	1500	19	—	—	115	98	65	51	32	22	10	6
IN 100	As cast	70	144	1800	80	70	124	1800	66	70	8	1800	6	—	—	1800	8	—	—	—	—	89	72	55	37	25	15
Nimonic 75	Annealed	70	116	1400	33	70	49	1400	22	70	44	1400	47	70	62	1400	35	—	—	—	—	—	—	—	—	—	—
Nimonic 80A	Solution, aged 1290 F	70	145	1400	87	70	90	1400	73	70	39	1400	17	70	38	1400	19	—	—	76	61	37	23	11	—	—	—
Nimonic 90	Solution, aged 1290 F	70	179	1400	95	70	117	1400	78	70	33	1400	12	—	—	—	—	—	—	79	66	45	30	15	9	—	—
Nimonic 105	2100, 1925, 1550 F	70	143	1400	118	70	116	1400	94	70	7	1400	14	70	7	1400	17	—	—	107	89	65	50	28	19	8	4
Nimonic 115	2175, 2010 F	70	180	1800	67	70	125	1800	35	70	27	1800	23	—	—	—	—	—	—	—	—	79	61	38	27	16	9
MAR-M 200	As cast	80	135	1600	123	80	120	1600	110	80	7	1600	4	—	—	—	—	—	—	—	—	94	84	58	43	26	18
RA-333	Annealed	70	108	1600	28	70	51	1600	24	70	43	1600	30	—	—	—	—	—	—	—	—	18	—	7	—	—	—
Titanium Base Alloys—Commercially Pure																											
																				400 F		600 F		800 F		1000 F	
A40	Annealed	75	60	600	28	75	45	600	13	75	28	600	45	75	50	—	—	32	Bhn 200	—	—	—	—	—	—	—	—
A55	Annealed	75	75	600	33	75	60	600	19	75	25	600	33	75	45	600	73	28	Bhn 225	—	42	—	36	20	10	—	4
A70	Annealed	75	96	600	43	75	78	600	27	75	20	600	28	75	49	600	57	13	Bhn 265	—	44	—	32	—	16	—	5
Titanium Base Alloy—Alpha Alloy Grades																											
5Al-2.5Sn	Annealed	75	125	600	82	75	117	600	65	75	18	600	19	75	40	600	45	19	Rc 36	84	78	70	65	64	58	32	20
5Al-5Sn-5Zr	Annealed 1650 F	75	125	600	94	75	120	600	74	75	18	600	20	75	26	600	40	—	—	—	—	—	—	—	—	60	—
7Al-12Zr	Annealed 1650 F	75	135	600	109	75	130	600	86	75	15	600	21	75	24	600	40	—	—	—	—	—	—	—	—	—	—
7Al-2Cb-1Ta	Annealed 1650 F	75	126	600	100	75	120	600	81	75	17	600	25	75	28	600	30	—	Rc 36	—	—	—	—	—	—	—	32
8Al-1Mo-1V	Duplex annealed 1650 F	75	145	600	110	75	138	600	84	75	15	600	20	75	28	600	38	24	—	—	—	—	—	—	—	—	—
Ti-679	Aged	70	154	600	118	70	134	600	96	70	13	600	13	—	—	—	—	—	—	—	—	—	—	—	—	—	—
Titanium Base Alloys—Alpha-Beta Alloy Grades																											
TI-155A	Annealed	75	155	600	80	75	140	600	69	75	15	600	15	75	35	600	48	11	—	—	—	—	—	—	—	—	—
8Mn	Annealed	75	137	600	98	75	125	600	75	75	15	600	13	75	32	—	—	—	—	—	100	—	91	—	26	—	—
2.5Al-16V	Solution + aged	75	180	600	145	75	165	600	127	75	6	600	5	—	—	—	—	—	—	—	—	90	—	—	—	—	—
3Al-2.5V	Annealed	75	100	600	70	75	85	600	50	75	20	600	25	—	—	—	—	—	—	—	—	—	—	—	—	—	—
4Al-4Mn	Annealed	75	148	600	110	75	135	600	90	75	15	600	17	75	25	1000	65	16	Rc 35	—	110	—	95	—	46	—	—
4Al-3Mo-1V	Annealed	75	140	1000	65	75	120	1000	55	75	15	1000	35	—	—	—	—	—	Rc 35	—	—	—	—	—	—	—	—
5Al-1.25Fe-2.75Cr	Annealed	75	155	600	122	75	145	600	102	75	15	600	20	75	25	1000	38	—	Rc 35	—	—	—	100	—	75	—	13
6Al-4V	Annealed	75	138	600	105	75	128	600	95	75	12	600	11	75	37	1000	68	18	Rc 32	—	95	98	78	68	50	—	10
6Al-6V-2Sn	Annealed	75	165	600	132	75	150	600	117	75	15	600	20	75	42	—	—	15	—	—	—	—	—	—	—	—	—
7Al-4Mo	Annealed	75	160	600	127	75	150	600	108	75	16	600	18	75	22	1000	50	18.0	Rc 38	—	—	—	—	—	—	—	—
2Cr-2Fe-2Mo	Annealed	75	137	800	75	75	125	800	55	75	18	800	30	—	—	—	—	13	—	—	—	—	—	—	—	—	—
Titanium Base Alloys—Beta Alloy Grades																											
1Al-8V-5Fe	Annealed	75	177	600	128	75	170	600	115	75	8	600	19	—	—	—	—	—	—	—	—	—	—	—	—	—	—
3Al-13V-11Cr	Solution	75	185	800	160	75	175	800	120	70	8	800	12	—	—	—	—	8	Rc 34	—	—	—	—	—	—	—	—

1. Subcritical Transformation.

ZINC ALLOY INGOT AND DIE CASTING COMPOSITIONS—SAE J468 DEC1988

SAE Standard

Report of the SAE Nonferrous Metals Division approved June 1934, last revised by the SAE Nonferrous Metals Committee June 1983, and reaffirmed by the SAE Cast Aluminum Committee December 1988.

Foreword—This Document has not changed other than to put it into the new SAE Technical Standards Board Format.

1. Scope—SIMILAR SPECIFICATIONS—UNS Z33521, former SAE 903, ingot is similar to ASTM B 240-79, Alloy AG40A; and UNS Z33520, former SAE 903, die casting is similar to ASTM B 86-76, Alloy AG40A. UNS Z35530, former SAE 925, ingot is similar to ASTM B 240-79, Alloy AC41A; and UNS Z35531, former SAE 925, die casting is similar to ASTM B 86-82a, Alloy AC41A.

2. References

2.1 Applicable Publications—The following publications form a part of the specification to the extent specified herein. Unless otherwise indicated the latest revision of SAE publications shall apply.

2.1.1 ASTM PUBLICATION—Available from ASTM, 100 Barr Harbor Drive, West Conshohocken, PA 19428-2959.

ASTM B 86-76—Specification for Zinc-Alloy Die Castings
ASTM B 86-82a—Specification for Zinc-Alloy Die Castings
ASTM B 240-79—Specification for Zinc Alloys in Ingot Form for Die Castings

TABLE 1—ZINC ALLOY INGOT AND DIE CASTING COMPOSITIONS

	Composition(1)(2), %						
	Al	Cu	Mg	Fe	Pb	Cd	Sn
Ingot (UNS Z33521)	3.9–4.3	0.10	0.025–0.05	0.075	0.004	0.003	0.002
Castings (UNS Z33520)	3.5–4.3	0.25 (3)	0.020–0.05 (4)	0.10	0.005	0.004	0.003
SAE 903							
Ingot (UNS Z35530)	3.9–4.3	0.75–1.25	0.03–0.06	0.075	0.004	0.003	0.002
Castings (UNS Z35531)	3.5–4.3	0.75–1.25	0.03–0.08	0.10	0.005	0.004	0.003
SAE 925							

1. Percentages given are maximum except where indicated as a range. Zinc is remainder.
2. Zinc alloy die castings may contain nickel, chromium, silicon, and manganese in amounts up to their solubility (0.02, 0.02, 0.035, and about 0.5%, respectively) at the freezing temperature. No harmful effects have ever been noted due to the presence of these elements in these concentrations and, therefore, analyses are not required for these elements.
3. For the majority of commercial applications, a copper content in the range of 0.25 to 0.75% will not adversely affect the serviceability of die castings and should not serve as a basis for rejection.
4. Magnesium may be as low as 0.005% provided that at least 0.005% nickel is present, and lead, cadmium, and tin do not exceed 0.0030, 0.0020, and 0.0010%, respectively.

ZINC DIE CASTING ALLOYS—SAE J469 JAN1989 SAE Information Report

Report of the SAE Nonferrous Metals Division approved June 1934, last revised by the SAE Nonferrous Metals Committee June 1983, and reaffirmed by the SAE Wrought Aluminum Committee January 1989.

Foreword—This Document has not changed other than to put it into the new SAE Technical Standards Board Format.

1. Scope—Because of the drastic chilling involved in die casting and the fact that the solid solubilities of both aluminum and copper in zinc change with temperature, these alloys are subject to some aging changes, one of which is a dimensional change. Both of the alloys undergo a slight shrinkage after casting, which at room temperature is about two-thirds complete in five weeks. It is possible to accelerate this shrinkage by a stabilizing anneal, after which no further changes occur. The recommended stabilizing anneal is 3 to 6 h at 100 °C (212 °F), or 5 to 10 h at 85 °C (185 °F), or 10 to 20 h at 70 °C (158 °F). The time in each case is measured from the time at which the castings reach the annealing temperature. The parts may be air cooled after annealing. Such a treatment will cause a shrinkage (0.0004 in per in) of about two-thirds of the total, and the remaining shrinkage will occur at room temperature during the subsequent few weeks. Stabilizing results in a decrease in dimensions of about 0.0005 in per in from the original size of the casting. Stabilizing is, of course, unnecessary if the machine or fitting operations can be delayed until the castings have aged five weeks at room temperature.

When exposed to stagnant moisture or condensation with limited access to oxygen, a nonuniform type of corrosion may occur on zinc die castings, which often results in the formation of a bulky film of white corrosion products. This may hinder the operation of such parts as automobile lock cylinders, fuel pumps, and carburetors, and in severe cases result in rather rapid loss of zinc. Various types of chromate films are available to satisfactorily overcome this condition.

The same electroplating or enameling procedure is used with both alloys. Organic finishes are quite variable in their ability to adhere well to zinc surfaces. The phosphate type of chemical pretreatment has received widest commercial utilization, and most zinc die castings which are to be finished with lacquers or enamels are phosphate pretreated. In general, a much wider selection of finishes can be used on pretreated die castings.

The relative merits of the two SAE alloys may be outlined as follows:

2. References—There are no referenced publications specified herein.

3. Z33520—When the shrinkage referred to above has been removed by normal aging or by a stabilizing anneal, the dynamic and dimensional properties of this alloy are permanent at service temperatures up to 100 °C (212 °F). Castings stabilized at elevated or at room temperature prior to final machining, assembling, or other adjusting of dimensions will permanently maintain such dimensions within a tolerance of ±0.00025 in per in the absence of excessive moisture. When exposed to high humidity and temperature (as wet steam at atmospheric pressure or humid tropical climates), any change of either properties or dimensions will be only that resulting from surface corrosion analogous to that occurring in any other materials which are not totally resistant to oxidation.

4. Z35531—This alloy is somewhat stronger and harder than Z33520. At room temperature, it is equal to Z33520 in permanence of dimensions and impact strength. At elevated temperatures it is subject to slight growth in dimensions and some loss of impact strength.

TABLE 1—TYPICAL PHYSICAL AND MECHANICAL PROPERTIES IN THE AS-CAST STATE AT ROOM TEMPERATURE

Physical Properties

	Alloy			Alloy	
SI Units	**Z33520**	**Z35531[1]**	**English Units**	**Z33520**	**Z35531[1]**
Density, g/cm^3 at 21°C	6.6	6.7	Density, lb/cu in at 70 °F	0.24	0.24
Solidification Shrinkage, %	1.17	1.17	Solidification Shrinkage, %	1.17	1.17
Solidification Temperature Range, °C	387-381	386-380	Solidification Temperature Range, °F	728-718	727-717
Thermal Expansion, mm/mm/°C at 20-100 °C (x 10^{-6})	27.4	27.4	Thermal Expansion, μ in/in/°F at 68-212 °F	15.2	15.2
Specific Heat Capacity, J/kg/°C at 20-100 °C	418.7	418.7	Specific Heat Capacity, BTU/lb/°F at 68-212 °F	0.10	0.10
Thermal Conductivity, W/m/°C at 70-140 °C	113.0	108.9	Thermal Conductivity, BTU/ft/h/ft^2/°F	65.3	62.9
Electrical Conductivity, % IACS	27	26	Electrical Conductivity, % IACS	27	26
Electrical Resistivity, μ ohm-cm at 20 °C	6.3694	6.5359			

Mechanical Properties

	Alloy			Alloy	
SI Units	Z33520	Z35531[1]	English Units	Z33520	Z35531[1]
Ultimate Tensile Strength[2],MPa	283	328	Ultimate Tensile Strength[2], ksi	41	47.6
Elongation (in 51 mm), %	10	7	Elongation (in 2 in), %	10	7
Hardness, Brinell 500 kg	82	91	Hardness, Brinell 500 kg	82	91
Shear Strength, MPa	214	262.0	Shear Strength, ksi	31	38
Compressive Strength, Mpa - 0.1% Offset - Failure or Fracture	414	600	Compressive Strength, ksi - 0.1% Offset - Failure or Fracture	60	87
Impact Strength[3], Joules (6.35 mm x 6.35 mm bar) unnotched)	58	65	Impact Strength[3], ft-lb (1/4 in x 1/4 in bar unnotched)	43	48
Fatigue Strength, Mpa (5 x 10^8 cycles)	48	57	Fatigue Strength, ksi (5 x 10^8 cycles) Note: Unit is ksi (4 places)	6.9	8.2

1. Die castings of alloy Z35531 shall not be used in applications where they will be subjected to prolonged temperature, above 93.3 °C (200 °F).
2. Tensile properties are determined from test specimens cast in a die and conforming to chemical composition specified. Test bars machined from castings do not provide a reliable measure of the strength properties of the casting and this method should not be used to determine conformance to data shown in Table 1.
3. Impact strength drops rapidly below 0°C (32°F) to approximately 2.95 J (4 ft-lb) at –20 °C (–4 °F) and 1.48 J (2 ft-lb) at –40 °C (–40 °F).

WROUGHT NICKEL AND NICKEL-RELATED ALLOYS—SAE J470c JUL1976

SAE Information Report

Report of the SAE Nonferrous Metals Committee approved January 1946 and last revised July 1976.

Foreword—This Reaffirmed Document has been changed only to reflect the new SAE Technical Standards Board Format.

1. Scope—This Report presents general information on over 50 alloys in which nickel either predominates or is a significant alloying element. It covers primarily wrought materials, and is not necessarily all inclusive. Values given are in most cases average or nominal, and if more precise values are required the producer(s) should be contacted. This report does not cover the so-called "superalloys," or the iron base stainless steels. Refer to SAE J467, Special Purpose Alloys, and SAE J405, Chemical Compositions of SAE Wrought Stainless Steels, respectively, for data on these alloys.

2. References

2.1 Applicable Publications—The following publications form a part of the specification to the extent specified herein. Unless otherwise indicated the lastest revision of SAE publications shall apply.

2.1.1 SAE PUBLICATIONS—Available from SAE, 400 Commonwealth Drive, Warrendale, PA 15096-0001.

SAE J467—Special Purpose Alloys

SAE J405—Chemical Compositions of SAE Wrought Stainless Steels

TABLE 1

Key No.*	Alloy Groups and Alloys	Commercial Designations**	Characteristics and Applications
1	*NICKEL*		
1A	Nickel UNS N02200	NICKEL 200[1a] HARDER[12a] 200	Commercially pure, malleable nickel, containing about 99.40% nickel and including a few tenths of a percent of cobalt, which is counted as nickel because its effect upon the significant properties of the alloy is not detrimental. Applications—Electron tube cathodes and grilles, hot caustic handling equipment, catalysts, printed circuits.
1B	Age Hardenable Nickel	DURANICKEL[1a] Alloy 301[1]	Age hardenable, high nickel alloy with high strength and hardness as well as the general corrosion characteristics of nickel. Alloy has good spring properties. Applications—Extrusion press parts, molds used in glass industry, clips, diaphragms and springs.
1C	High Purity Nickel UNS N02270	Nickel 270[1]	A high purity product containing about 99.98% nickel and maximum of 0.001% cobalt. Due to the low level of impurities, the alloy exhibits good thermal conductivity. Applications—Cathode shanks, fluorescent lamps, hydrogen-thyratron components, plates (anodes) and passive cathodes, heat exchangers and heat shields.
2	*NICKEL-BERYLLIUM*		
2A	2 Be—97 Ni—0.5 Ti	BERYLCO[9a] Nickel 440	Age hardenable alloy possessing high strength, extreme hardness and good ductility. Used up to 420 °C (800 °F). Good impact and fatigue properties. Applications—Heat resistant springs and switches, diaphragms, bellows, retainer clips, feather valves, contact springs, electrical shunts.
3	*NICKEL-MANGANESE*		
3A	95 Ni—4 Mn—1 Si	Alloy 667[2] R63 alloy[5]	Highly resistant to attack by the corrosive elements of internal combustion engine fuels—particularly sulphur and lead compounds. Applications—General purpose spark plug electrode.
4	*NICKEL-MANGANESE-ALUMINUM-SILICON*		
4A	95 Ni—2 Mn—2 Al—1 Si	NIAL[3a] T-2[5] ALUMEL[2a]	Applications—Negative leg of ANSI Type K thermocouples; used with 90 Ni—20 Cr alloy as positive element.
5	*NICKEL-COPPER*		
5A	70 Ni—30 Cu UNS N04400	MONEL[1a] alloy 400 CUNEL[11a] HARPER[12a] 400 D-H[5a] 400 alloy	These alloys have high strength and hardness, good resistance to corrosion. The age hardenable alloy contains approximately 2.75% aluminum and is non-magnetic at temperatures down to -100 °C (-150 °F). Its mechanical properties, particularly in large sections, are comparable with those of heat treated alloy steels. The free-machining alloy is suitable for use in automatic screw machines, its free machining characteristics being achieved by a sulphur content of approximately 0.035%. Adjustments in carbon and titanium contents of the age hardenable grade result in an alloy with improved machinability. Applications—Heat exchanger tubing, transmission oil cooler, marine engine components. The age hardenable grade is used for fasteners, pump and propeller shafts, and valve stems.
5B	Age Hardenable 70 Ni—30 Cu—2.75 Al UNS N05500	MONEL[1a] alloy K 500	
5C	Free Machining 70 Ni—30 Cu UNS N04405	MONEL[1a] alloy R-405	
5D	Age Hardenable Free Machining 70 Ni—30 Cu—2.75 Al UNS N05502	MONEL[1a] alloy 502	

TABLE 1 (CONTINUED)

Key No.*	Alloy Groups and Alloys	Commercial Designations**	Characteristics and Applications
6	*COPPER-NICKEL*		
6A	55 Cu—45 Ni	ADVANCE[5a] CUPRON[3a]	These alloys are of the "Constantan" type and are used extensively with iron or copper as thermoelectric elements for temperature measurement and control. They are used for electrical resistance purposes at temperatures up to 500 °C (930 °F) and for thermocouple purposes up to 760 °C (1400 °F). Their temperature coefficient of electrical resistivity is very small in the temperature range 20 to 100 °C (68 to 212 °F), or higher. Applications—Type T, J, and E thermocouples, wire wound resistors, rheostats, low temperature heaters.
6B	77 Cu—23 Ni	MIDOHM[5a] 180 alloy[3]	These alloys are widely used in instruments and controls where resistivity and temperature coefficient must be held within very close limits. This is accomplished by careful control in melting and fabricating Applications—Radio and automotive resistors, high current edge-wound resistors, resistor leads, voltage control relays, and rheostats.
6C	89 Cu—11 Ni	90 alloy[3.5]	
6D	93 Cu—6 Ni	L OHM[5a] 60 alloy[3]	
6E	97.5 Cu—2.5 Ni	30 alloy[3.5]	
7	*COPPER-NICKEL-IRON*		
7A	60 Cu—20 Ni—20 Fe	Cunife[1,3,14,15]	A permanent magnet alloy used in speedometers and small synchronous motors. It is ductile and easily formed after heat treatment. Applications—Permanent magnets which require ductility.
8	*COPPER-NICKEL-MANGANESE*		
8A	83 Cu—13 Mn—4 Ni	Manganin 130 manganin[3]	These alloys are extremely stable with respect to electrical resistance change with time, and have very low temperature coefficients of electrical resistance over certain temperature ranges. Consequently they find wide use as windings for precision and standard resistors. Shunt manganin is designed to carry high currents which cause it to heat-up in service. Therefore the composition of shunt manganin is adjusted so that the temperature range, over which it possesses a low temperature coefficient of resistance, is higher than that at which the other manganins exhibit this property. Applications—Precision resistors, standard resistors, and shunts.
8B	86 Cu—10 Mn—4 Ni	Shunt manganin Manganin (shunt)[3]	
9	*NICKEL-IRON*		
9A	70 Ni—30 Fe	BALCO[3a] HYTEMCO[5a]	Alloy has a high temperature coefficient of resistance along with moderate resistivity useful in various electrical instruments. Applications—Ballast resistors, voltage regulators, resistive thermometers, temperature compensators, low temperature heaters and ballistic devices in instruments and controls.
9B	50 to 51.5 Ni—48.5 to 50 Fe	152 alloy[5] NIRON[3a] 52 Glass sealing 52[7] UNISEAL[6a] 52	Alloy has expansion characteristics for certain glass to metal seals, and has high magnetic permeability for high field strengths. Applications—Reed switches, mercury switches, contact rectifiers, amplifier coils. Glass to metal seals for matching to lead sealing glasses.
9C	47 to 50 Ni—50 to 53 Fe	49 PERMALLOY[3a] SIMALLOY[4a] magnetic 50 UNIMAG[6a] 50 Low expansion 49[7]	A medium high initial permeability alloy and medium high magnetic saturation alloy employed in manufacture of laminated magnetic cores and solid magnetic core configurations. Applications—Magnetic applications in communications industry, sensitive control devices and relays.

TABLE 1 (CONTINUED)

Key No.*	Alloy Groups and Alloys	Commercial Designations**	Characteristics and Applications
9D	46 Ni—54 Fe	146 alloy[5] Glass sealing 46 gas free[7] NIROMET 46[3a]	Expansion properties and inflection temperature between 50 Ni—50 Fe alloys and 42 Ni—58 Fe alloys. Applications—Terminals on vitreous enamelled resistors.
9E	42 Ni—58 Fe	NIROMET[3a] 42 SIMALLOY[4a] glass seal 42 UNISEAL[6a] 42 142 alloy[5] Glass sealing 42 gas free[7]	Alloy has low expansion, matching thermal expansion of some common glasses. It is used for sealing in glass and other controls at temperatures above those for which Invar is suitable. Applications—Headlights, lamps, audio transformers, coils, relays.
9F	36 Ni—64 Fe	Free cut Invar 36[7] NIRON[3a] 36 SIMALLOY[4a] glass seal 36 UNISPAN[6a] 36 NILBAR[5a] CARPENTER[7a] invar UNISPAN[6a] LR 35	Generally known as Invar and has the lowest coefficient of thermal expansion of any known alloy (up to 150C). Used extensively for thermostats and precision instrument parts for aeronautical use, struts in aluminum pistons, and other applications for low thermal expansion. Applications—Thermostat and precision instrument components. Base metal on which to solder silicon chips, bimetal component.
9G	32.5 Ni—67.5 Fe	SIMALLOY[4a] compensator #1 Temperature compensator 32[7]	These two alloys are generally known as magnetic compensator alloys. (The magnetism and permeability of these alloys change gradually and predictably with changes in temperature.) They are used extensively in automotive speedometer applications. Both alloys are representative of a family of alloys in this composition range. Applications—Instrumentation components.
9H	30 Ni—70 Fe	SIMALLOY[4a] compensator #4 Temperature compensator 30[7]	
10	*NICKEL-CHROMIUM*		
10A	90 Ni—10 Cr	CHROMEL[2a] T-1[5] TOPHEL[3a]	This alloy is the positive element in standard ANSI Type K thermocouples. The negative element is basically nickel with an approximate total of 5% of manganese, aluminum, and silicon. Applications—Thermocouple Type K.
10B	80 Ni—20 Cr	NICHROME[5a] V CHROMEL[2a] A TOPHET[3a] A PYROMET[7a] 80-20	A commercially iron-free, non-magnetic alloy developed especially to give maximum life as electrical heating elements which are expected to standup under the most adverse conditions up to surface temperatures of 1175 °C (2150 °F) in air. Its exceptional resistance to oxidation at elevated temperatures, high electrical resistivity, low temperature coefficient of electrical resistance, high tensile strength at temperature, and resistance to chemical corrosion has given it a wide variety of applications. Applications—Heating elements, wire wound resistors, high temperature conveyor belts, thermocouple wire, furnace components and thermocouple tubes.
10C	78 Ni—20 Cr—1 Cb—1 Si	242 alloy[5] TOPHET[3a] A + Cb	A special grade of 80 Ni—20 Cr. Inhibits "green rot" attack in high temperature mechanical or structural applications in reducing or marginal atmospheres.
10D	74 Ni—20 Cr—3 Al—2 Cu—1 Si	EVANOHM[3a] K	These alloys have low temperature coefficient of resistance up to 150 °C and high resistivity.

TABLE 1 (CONTINUED)

Key No.*	Alloy Groups and Alloys	Commercial Designations**	Characteristics and Applications
10E	72 Ni—20 Cr—3 Al— 5 Mn	EVANOHM[3a] S	Applications—Precision wound resistors and potentiometers.
10F	70 Ni—30 Cr	TOPHET[3a] 30	Excellent high temperature oxidation resistance. High resistivity and low temperature coefficient of resistance. Applications—Heating elements, wire wound power resistors, high temperature conveyor belts, thermostats.
10G	50 Ni—50 Cr	INCONEL[1a] 671 50 Nickel— 50 Chromium[1]	Excellent elevated temperature liquid phase corrosion resistance; especially suitable in highly sulfidizing, high temperature environments. Applications—High temperature and exhaust components, high temperature baffles, supports in high sulphur atmospheres.
11	*NICKEL-CHROMIUM-IRON*		
11A	76 Ni—15 Cr—9 Fe UNS N06600	SIMALLOY[4a] 600 INCONEL[1a] alloy 600 NIREX[5a] PYROMET[7a] 600 HARPER[12a] 600	Good resistance to a great variety of corrosive media, to high temperature oxidation and scaling, and to intercrystalline attack at elevated temperatures. A restricted chemistry modification of this alloy is used for spark plug electrodes. Applications—Heat treating, nitriding, and carburizing fixtures. High temperature belts, screens, pickling baskets, retorts, radiant tubes, exhaust control afterburners.
11B	Age Hardenable 73 Ni—15.5 Cr—8 Fe— 2.5 Ti—0.95 Cb + Ta UNS N07750	UNITEMP[6a] 750 SIMALLOY[4a] 750 INCONEL[1a] alloy X750[1a]	Maximum strength and resistance to oxidation at temperatures of 650 to 815 °C (1200 to 1500 °F) for gas turbine and heat engine components. Desirable spring characteristics at temperatures up to 540 °C (1000 °F). Applications—Diesel exhaust valves, high temperature springs, gas turbine parts, bolts, nuclear reactors.
11C	61 Ni—21.5 Cr—5 Fe— 9 Mo—3.6 Cb + Ta UNS N06625	INCONEL[1a] alloy 625 SIMALLOY[4a] 625	High strength and toughness from cryogenic temperatures to 1090 °C (2000 °F). High fatigue strength. Good oxidation resistance and resistance to many corrosive media. Virtually immune to chloride stress-corrosion cracking. Good fabrication properties. Applications—Ducting and combustion systems, thrust reversers, fuel nozzles, afterburners, spray bars.
11D	60.5 Ni—14 Cr—24 Fe— 1.4 Al UNS N06601	INCONEL[1a] alloy 601	Excellent resistance to oxidizing, carburizing, and sulphur-containing environments. Resistance to oxidation and scaling up to temperatures as high as 1260 °C (2300 °F). Applications—Heat treating baskets and fixtures, radiant furnace tubes, strand-annealing tubes, thermocouple protection tubes, and furnace muffles and retorts. Thermal reactors for controlling automotive emissions.
11E	60 Ni—16 Cr—23 Fe— 1 Si UNS N06004	NICHROME[5a] TOPHET[3a] C CHROMEL[2a] C	Maximum life as electrical heating elements up to 1065 °C (1950 °F) in air, non-magnetic, resists chemical corrosion, high electrical resistivity and low thermal coefficient of electrical resistance. Applications—Heating elements, rheostats, potentiometers.
11F	42 Ni—21.5 Cr—32 Fe— 3 Mo UNS N08825	INCOLOY[1a] alloy 825	For use in aggressively corrosive environments. Resistant to chloride-ion stress-corrosion cracking. Resistant to reducing acids, as well as to sulphuric acid and phosphoric acid solutions and to sea water. Applications—Phosphoric acid evaporators, pickling tank heaters, hooks and equipment, propeller shafts and tank trucks.
11G thru 11J	32 to 37 Ni—18 to 21 Cr—42 Fe—(Si, Cb)		This family of alloys is one of the most versatile and widely used groups of alloys made. There are numerous modifications around the basic 35-20 analysis to produce alloys for specific, highly demanding applications. Included are chemical corrosion resistance, high temperature strength and oxidation resistance and electrical resistance applications. Some of the specific properties of each alloy are listed next to the names below.

TABLE 1 (CONTINUED)

Key No.*	Alloy Groups and Alloys	Commercial Designations**	Characteristics and Applications
11G		NICHROME[5a] I CHROME[2a] I	Electrical resistance, high temperature strength, oxidation resistance.
11H	UNS N08330	CHROMEL[2a] D CHROMAX[5a] 525 RA 330[8a] SIMALLOY[4a] TOPHET[3a] D	High temperature strength, oxidation resistance, and carburization resistance.
11I	UNS N08800	INCOLOY[1a] alloy 800 HARPER[12a] 800	High temperature, strength, oxidation resistance, carburization resistance and chemical corrosion resistance.
11J		CHROMAX[5a] 520	Higher strength modification of UNS N08330 alloy for mechanical applications.
12	*NICKEL-IRON-COBALT*		
12A	38 Ni—41 Fe—15 Co— 3 Cb—1.6 Ti—0.8 Al— (.008 B)	INCOLOY[1a] alloy 903 PYROMET[7a] CTX-1	Precipitation-hardenable alloy which has a constant, low coefficient of thermal expansion, a constant modulus of elasticity, and high strength. Applications—Rocket engine thrust chambers, steam turbine bolts, springs, gage blocks, and ordnance hardware.
12B	29 Ni—54 Fe—17 Co	THERLO[5a] KOVAR[7a] LOCKINVAR[4a] RODAR[3a]	Sealing alloy for hard (borosilicate) glass-to-metal alloy seals.
13	*NICKEL-MOLYBDENUM-IRON*		
13A	65 Ni—28 Mo—5.5 Fe UNS N10001	HASTELLOY[10a] alloy B	Chromium-free alloy used for handling hydrochloric acid. Gas turbine applications, bolting, shafting, high stresses up to 760 °C (1400 °F) in oxidizing atmosphere, and higher temperatures in reducing atmospheres. Applications—Components for hydrochloric acid service. Gas turbine bolting and shafting.
13B	69 Ni—28 Mo—2 Fe	HASTELLOY[10a] alloy B-2 UNILOY[6a] LR-HB	This alloy is a lower carbon, more ductile version of UNS N10001, above. The lower carbon reduces formation of grain boundry carbide formation during welding. Other properties are very similar.
14	*NICKEL-CHROMIUM-MOLYBDENUM-(COBALT-TUNGSTEN-COPPER)*		
14A	64 Ni—16 Cr—16 Mo— 3 Fe	HASTELLOY[10a] alloy C-4	Excellent high temperature strength and oxidation resistance. Outstanding corrosion resistance in certain environments. Good thermal shock properties up to 980 °C (1800 °F). Applications—Combustion cups for diesel engines, turbine blade jet engine components. Fixtures in nitric acid and organic acid salts service.
14B	58 Ni—16 Cr—6 Mo— 6 Fe—3.5 W UNS N10002	CARPENTER[7a] alloy C UNILOY[6a] C	One of the most universally corrosion resistant alloys available, with excellent high-temperature properties. Resistant to oxidizing and reducing atmospheres up to 1090 °C (2000 °F). Is particularly useful where parts are either highly stressed or subject to repeated thermal shock at temperatures from 870 to 980 °C (1600 to 1800 °F). Exceptional resistance to strong oxidizing agents such as ferric chloride and cupric chloride.

TABLE 1 (CONTINUED)

Key No.*	Alloy Groups and Alloys	Commercial Designations**	Characteristics and Applications
14C	57 Ni—16 Cr—16 Mo— 6 Fe—4 W UNS N10276	HASTELLOY[10a] alloy C 276 UNITEMP[6a] C 276	A modified version of UNS N10002 with improved fabricability. Resists formation of grain boundry precipitates in weld heat-affected zone. Excellent resistance to pitting, stress-corrosion cracking and to oxidizing environments up to 1040 °C (1900 °F).
14D	45 Ni—22 Cr—9 Mo— 1 Co—0.8 W UNS N06002	SIMALLOY[4a] HX UNITEMP[6a] HX HASTELLOY[10a] alloy X PYROMET[7a] 680	Excellent high temperature properties. Suitable for sheet metal and bar components in jet engines, valve parts, furnace parts and heat treat containers and fixtures. Noted for excellent carburization, oxidation resistance and strength properties at temperatures up to 1150 °C (2100 °F). Good resistance to stress corrosion cracking. Applications—Combustion cans, heat treat fixtures, and components.
14E	45 Ni—25 Cr—3 Mo— 3 W—3 Co—1.25 Si UNS N06333	RA 333[8a]	
14F	43 Ni—22 Cr—7 Mo— 1 W—20 Fe—2 Cu	HASTELLOY[10a] G	Excellent resistance to hot sulfuric acid and phosphoric acids. Resists corrosive effects of both oxidizing and reducing agents and both acid and alkaline solutions. Resists stress corrosion cracking and formation of grain boundary precipitates.
14G	35 Ni—20 Cr—2.5 Mo— 3.5 Cu—37 Fe— 1 Cb + Ta	CARPTENTER[7a] 20 Cb 3	Austenitic stainless steel with superior resistance to 10 to 40% sulfuric acid, and many other corrosive media. Weldable. Applications—Mixing tanks, heat exchanges, process piping, pump shafts and rods.
15	*COPPER-NICKEL-ZINC (NICKEL SILVERS)*		
15A	72 Cu—18 Ni—10 Zn UNS C73500	CDA 735	These alloys, known as nickel-silvers, find application as car keys (especially, the leaded versions), electrically conductive springs, and switches. They have excellent spring characteristics, mechanical properties, are corrosion resistant, machinable and formable, along with a relatively high electrical conductivity.
15B	55 Cu—18 Ni—27 Zn UNS C77000	CDA 770	
15C	60 Cu—12 Ni—28 Zn UNS C76200	CDA 762	

* See same Key Number in each table for complete information on each alloy. (Key is used to avoid duplication of data in each table.)
** Superscript numerals (1 to 15) denote producer as shown in Table 6; subscript letter (a) denotes trademark.

TABLE 2—NOMINAL CHEMICAL COMPOSITIONS

Key [1] No.	Percent by Weight							
	Ni [2]	Cu	Cr	Fe	Mn	Si	C	Other
1A	99.4	0.1	—	0.15	0.18	0.18	0.05	0.005 S
1B	93.7	0.13	—	0.35	0.3	0.5	0.17	4.4 Al, 0.005 S, 0.63 Ti
1C	99.98	<0.001	<0.001	0.003	<0.001	<0.001	0.01	<0.001 S, Ti, Co, Mg
2A	97.5			—	—	—	—	1.95 Be, 0.5 Ti
3A	95	—	—	—	4	1	—	—
4A	94	—	—	0.25	2.5	1.0	—	2.0 Al
5A	67	30	—	1.4	1	0.25	0.15	0.012 S
5B	66	29	—	1	0.75	0.25	0.15	0.005 S, 2.75 Al, 0.60 Ti
5C	67	30	—	1.4	1	0.25	0.15	0.035 S
5D	66.5	28	—	1	0.75	0.25	0.05	0.005 S, 3 Al, 0.25 Ti
6A	43	55	—	0.25	0.5–1.0	—	0.05	—
6B	23	77	—	—	—	—	—	—
6C	11	89	—	—	—	—	—	—
6D	6	93	—	—	—	—	—	—
6E	2.5	97.5	—	—	—	—	—	—
7A	20	60	—	20	—	—	—	—
8A	4	83	—	—	1	—	—	—
8B	4	86	—	—	10	—	—	—
9A	70		—	29	1	0.05	0.05	—
9B	50–51.5		—	47.5–50	0.05	0.35	0.02	—
9C	47–50		—	50–53	0.5	0.40	0.05	—
9D	46	—	—	54	0.1	0.05	0.05	—
9E	42	—	—	58	0.1	0.05	0.05	—
9F	36	—	—	64	0.1	0.05	0.05	—
9G	32.5	—	—	67.5	0.7	0.3	0.1	—
9H	30	—	—	70	0.75	0.2	0.1	—
10A	90		10	—	—	—	—	—
10B	77	—	20	0.5	0.2–2	1.25–1.4	0.06–0.1	—
10C	78	—	20	—		1	—	1 Cb
10D	74	2	20	—	—	1	—	3 Al
10E	72	—	20	—	5	1	—	3 Al
10F	70	—	30	—				—
10G	51	—	48	—	—	—	0.5	0.35 Ti
11A	76	0.5	15.5	9	1	0.5	0.15	—
11B	73	0.5	15.5	8	1	0.5	0.08	0.7 Al, 2.5 Ti, 0.9 Ca + Ta
11C	68	—	21.5	5	0.5	0.5	0.1	0.4 Al, 0.4 Ti, 1.0 Co, 9.0 Mo
11D	60.5	1	23	13	1	0.5	0.1	1.3 Al
11E	60	—	16	23	—	1.0	—	—
11F	42	2.25	21.5	—	1		0.05	0.2 Al, 0.9 Ti, 3.0 Mo
11G	36	—	20	42	—	2	—	—
11H	35	—	19	45	—	1.25	—	—
11I	32.5	0.75	21	—	1.5	1	0.1	0.4 Al, 0.45 Ti
11J	35	—	21	42	—	2	—	1.0 Cb
12A	38	0.50 max	0.20 max	41	0.20 max	0.20 max	0.03	0.8 Al, 1.6 Ti, 1.5 Co, 3 Cb, (0.008 B)
12B	29	—	—	54	—	—	—	17 Co
13A	65	—	—	5.5	1 max	1 max	0.05 max	28 Mo
13B	69	—	—	2–5 max	1 max	0.1 max	0.02 max	28 Mo
14A	64	—	16	3 max	1 max	0.08 max	0.015 max	16 Mo, 0.7 Ti
14B	57	—	16	6	1 max	1 max	0.08 max	16 Mo, 4 W
14C	57	—	16	6	1 max	0.05 max	0.02 max	16 Mo, 4 W
14D	45	—	22	18	1 max	1 max	0.10	9 Mo, 1 Co, 0.8 W
14E	45	—	25	20	2 max	1.25	0.08 max	3 Mo, 3 W, 3 Co
14F	43	2	22	20	2 max	1 max	0.05 max	7 Mo, 1 W, 2 Cb + Ta
14G	35	3.5	20	37	2 max	1 max	0.06 max	2.5 Mo, 1 Cb + Ta
15A	18	72	—	—	0.25	—	—	10 Zn
15B	18	55	—	—	0.25	—	—	27 Zn
15C	18	57	—	—	0.25	—	—	28 Zn

1. See Key Number in each table for complete information on each alloy.
2. Includes a small amount of cobalt which is counted as nickel.

TABLE 3—AVERAGE PHYSICAL CONSTANTS(1)

Key No.	Density at 20 °C g/cm^3 (lb/in^3)	Melting Range, Solidus-Liquidus °C (°F)	Thermal Conductivity 0-100 °C (32-212 °F) W/m·K (Btu/hr/ft^2/F/in)	Coefficient of Linear Thermal Expansion °C^{-1} x 10^{-6} (°F^{-1} x 10^{-6})		Specific Heat 0-100 °C (32-212 °F) J/kg K (Btu/lb·°F)	Electrical Resistivity at R.T. Ω·mm^2/m (ohm) circular-mil/ft)	Temperature Coefficient of Electrical Resistance		Magnetic Properties		Max Operating Temp. in Air (Sulfur Free) °C (°F)
				0-100 °C (32-212 °F)	0-1000 °C (32-1832 °F)			20-100 °C Per °C	20-1000 °C Per °C	Condition at R.T.	Curie Temp. °C (°F)	
** →	X27.68	—	X0.1441	X1.8	X1.8	X4186.8	X0.16624	—	—	—	—	—
1A	8.88 (0.321)	1435-1446 (2615-2635)	60.52 (420)	13.0 (7.2)	— —	544 (0.13)	9.5 (57)	0.00432	— —	Ferromagnetic	360 (680)	1038 (1900)
1B	8.75 (0.316)	1435-1446 (2615-2635)	60.52 (420)	13.0 (7.2)	— —	544 (0.13)	15.7 (94.5)	0.0036	— —	Ferromagnetic	290-299 (555-570)	— —
1C	8.88 (0.321)	1455 (2650)	79 (548)	13.3 (7.4)	— —	460 (0.11)	7.5 (45)	— —	— —	Ferromagnetic	353 (667)	— —
2A	8.36 (0.302)	1220-1370 (2240-2500)	32 (220)	14.5 (8.0)[1]	— —	473 (0.113)	23.8 (143)	— —	— —	Ferromagnetic	— —	— —
3A	8.40 (0.3035)	1416-1445 (2550-2600)	28.5 (198)	13.2 (7.33)	16.0 (8.89)	— —	22 (130)	— —	0.00135	Strongly Magnetic	— —	— —
4A	8.60 (0.3107)	1380-1410 (2525-2575)	29.7 (206)	12.0 (6.66)	— —	523 (0.125)	29-32 (177-191)	0.00188	— —	Strongly Magnetic	— —	1260 (2300)
5A	8.83 (0.319)	1300-1350 (2370-2460)	25.94 (180)	14.04 (7.8)	14.22 (8.9)	544.3 (0.13)	48.2 (290)	0.00198	— —	Slightly Ferromagnetic	43-60 (110-140)	540 (1000)
5B	8.47 (0.306)	1315-1350 (2400-2460)	18.73 (130)	14.04 (7.8)	14.22 (8.9)	544.3 (0.13)	58.1 (350)	0.00198	— —	Ferromagnetic	-101 (-150)	— —
5C	8.83 (0.319)	1300-1350 (2370-2460)	24.94 (180)	14.04 (7.8)	— —	544.3 (0.13)	48.2 (290)	0.00198	— —	Slightly Ferromagnetic	43-60 (110-140)	— —
5D	8.44 (0.305)	1315-1350 (2400-2460)	— —	13.68 (7.6)	— —	418.7 (0.10)	61.5 (370)	— —	— —	Paramagnetic	<-101 (<-150)	— —
6A	8.88 (0.321)	— —	22.9 (159)	14.6 (8.1)	18.7 (10.4)	394 (0.094)	49 (294)	0.00002	— —	Paramagnetic	— —	760 (1400)
6B	8.88 (0.321)	1130-1210 (2065-2210)	33.4 (232)	15.8 (8.8)	17.5 (9.7)	385 (0.092)	30 (180)	0.0003	— —	Paramagnetic	— —	540 (1000)
6C	8.88 (0.321)	1105-1150 (2020-2100)	38.4 (267)	16.0 (8.9)	— —	385 (0.092)	15 (90)	0.0004	— —	Paramagnetic	— —	430 (800)
6D	8.88 (0.321)	1030-1110 (1995-2030)	37.6 (261)	16.4 (9.1)	18.0 (10.0)	385 (0.092)	10 (60)	0.0005	— —	Paramagnetic	— —	320 (600)
6E	8.88 (0.321)	1083-1100 (1980-2010)	37.7 (262)	16.6 (9.2)	— —	385 (0.092)	5 (30)	0.0013	— —	Paramagnetic	— —	320 (600)
7A	8.61 (0.311)	1146-1330 (2095-2425)	— —	— —	— —	— —	18 (108)	— —	— —	Ferromagnetic	355 (670)	260 (500)
8A	8.41 (0.304)	1020- (1870-)	20.5 (142)	18.72 (10.4)[2]	— —	— —	48.2 (290)	0.0000144[2]	— —	Nonmagnetic	— —	— —
8B	8.48 (0.31)	1020- (1870-)	20.5 (142)	18.72 (10.4)	— —	— —	38.3 (230)	0.0000144[3]	— —	Nonmagnetic	— —	— —
9A	8.44 (0.305)	1432 (2610)	9.2 (64)	12.42 (6.9)	14.94 (8.3)	523 (0.125)	20 (120)	0.0045	0.0054[4]	Ferromagnetic	610 (1130)	594 (1100)
9B	8.30 (0.300)	1424- (2596-)	13 (90)	9.36 (5.2)	12.96 (7.2)	481 (0.115)	43 (260)	0.00306	0.0018	Ferromagnetic	500 (932)	524 (975)
9C	8.25 (0.298)	1427- (2600-)	13 (90)	9.36 (5.2)	— —	500 (0.12)	48 (290)	— —	0.0036[5]	Ferromagnetic	450-500 (840-930)	— —
9D	8.17 (0.295)	1435-1441 (2615-2625)	14.1 (98)	13.5[6] (7.5)	15.48 (8.6)[6]	490 (0.117)	46 (275)	0.0032	— —	Ferromagnetic	490 (914)	600 (1112)
9E	8.11 (0.293)	1441-1452 (2625-2645)	10.7 (74.5)	4.86 (2.7)	12.96 (7.2)	498 (0.119)	67 (400)	0.00216	— 0.000936	Ferromagnetic	380 (716)	374 (705)

TABLE 3—AVERAGE PHYSICAL CONSTANTS(1) (CONTINUED)

Key No.	Density at 20 °C g/cm³ (lb/in³)	Melting Range, Solidus-Liquidus °C (°F)	Thermal Conductivity 0-100 °C (32-212 °F) W/m·K (Btu/hr/ft²/F/in)	Coefficient of Linear Thermal Expansion °C⁻¹ x 10⁻⁶ (°F⁻¹ x 10⁻⁶) 0-100 °C (32-212 °F)	Coefficient of Linear Thermal Expansion 0-1000 °C (32-1832 °F)	Specific Heat 0-100 °C (32-212 °F) J/kg K (Btu/lb·°F)	Electrical Resistivity at R.T. Ω·mm²/m (ohm) circular-mil/ft)	Temperature Coefficient of Electrical Resistance 20-100 °C Per °C	Temperature Coefficient of Electrical Resistance 20-1000 °C Per °C	Magnetic Properties Condition at R.T.	Magnetic Properties Curie Temp. °C (°F)	Max Operating Temp. in Air (Sulfur Free) °C (°F)
→	X27.68	—	X0.1441	X1.8	X1.8	X4186.8	X0.16624	—	—	—	—	—
9F	8.05 (0.291)	1446-1460 (2635-2660)	10.5 (73)	1.44 (0.8)	14.4 (8)	515 (0.123)	80 (484)	0.00135	— —	Ferromagnetic	280 (536)	200 (390)
9G	8.11 (0.293)	— —	11.5 (80)	10.8 (6.0)	— —	502 (0.12)	80 (480)	0.00126	— —	Ferromagnetic	— —	— —
9H	8.19 (0.296)	— —	11.5 (80)	7.70 (4.28)	— —	502 (0.12)	80 (480)	0.00126	— —	Ferromagnetic	— —	— —
10A	8.72 (0.315)	1430- (2610-)	19.16 (133)	23.4 (13)	— —	452 (0.107)	70.6 (425)	0.00036	0.000324[7]	Paramagnetic	—	1149 (2100)
10B	8.41 (0.304)	1400- (2552-)	15 (104)	11.9-13.7 (6.6-7.6)	17.1-17.6 (9.5-9.8)	435-452 (0.104-0.107)	108 (650)	0.000056	0.0000014- 0.0000067	Paramagnetic	—	1177 (2150)
10C	8.41 (0.304)	1400- (2552-)	15 (104)	— —	17 (9.4)	435-452 (0.104-0.107)	111 (670)	— —	0.00011[8]	Paramagnetic	— —	1150 (2100)
10D	8.41 (0.304)	1400- (2552-)	15 (104)	12.6 (7.0)	— —	— —	133 (800)	— —	±0.000005	Nonmagnetic	— —	315 (600)
10E	7.14 (0.258)	1350-1380 (2460-2510)	14.6 (101)	13 (7.2)	— —	— —	137 (825)	— —	<±0.000005	Nonmagnetic	— —	315 (600)
10F	8.11 (0.293)	1377- (2510-)	15.85 (110)	12.2 (6.8)	— —	452 (0.107)	118 (710)	0.00009	— —	Paramagnetic	— —	1260 (2300)
10G	7.89 (0.285)	1308-1318 (2386-2404)	16.43 (114)	10.0 (5.54)	13.8 (7.66)	456 (0.109)	93 (556)	— —	— —	— —	— —	— —
11A	8.50 (0.307)	1343-1427 (2540-2600)	14.98 (104)	11.5 (6.4)	12.4 (6.9)	460 (0.11)	103 (620)	— —	— —	Paramagnetic	-40 (-40)	1094 (2000)
11B	8.30 (0.3)	1343-1427 (2540-2600)	14.7 (102)	13.7 (7.6)	17.1 (9.5)	460 (0.11)	122 (734)	— —	— —	Paramagnetic	-174 (-280)	815 (1500)
11C	8.44 (0.305)	1288-1349 (2350-2460)	9.80 (68)	12.8 (7.1)	15.7 (8.7)	410 (0.098)	129 (776)	— —	— —	Paramagnetic	<-196 (<-320)	— —
11D	8.05 (0.291)	1301-1368 (2374-2494)	12.54 (87)	13.7 (7.6)	16.7 (9.3)	448 (0.107)	119 (717)	— —	— —	Paramagnetic	<-196 (<-320)	— —
11E	8.41 (0.304)	1350-1375 (2460-2500)	13.3 (92)	— —	17 (9.4)	460 (0.11)	108 (650)	0.000133	0.00009	Paramagnetic	— —	1010 (1850)
11F	8.14 (0.294)	1371-1399 (2500-2550)	— —	14.0 (7.8)	17.3 (9.6)	— —	113 (678)	— —	— —	Paramagnetic	<-196 (<-320)	— —
11G	7.94 (0.287)	1380- (2515-)	13.0 (90)	14.0 (7.8)	18 (10)	502 (0.12)	108 (650)	0.0004	0.00025	Paramagnetic	— —	994 (1800)
11H	8.0 (0.289)	1399-1427 (2550-2600)	13.15 (91.2)	14.9 (8.3)	18.0 (10)	460 (0.11)	102 (612)	0.00035	0.00023	Paramagnetic	— —	954 (1750)
11I	7.94 (0.287)	1368-1380 (2475-2525)	11.53 (80)	14.2 (7.9)	18.2 (10.1)	502 (0.12)	100 (600)	— —	— —	Paramagnetic	-115 (-175)	— —
11J	7.94 (0.287)	1382- (2520-)	13.0 (90)	14.0 (7.8)	18 (10)	502 (0.12)	106 (640)	0.0004	0.00025	Paramagnetic	— —	994 (1800)
12A	8.14 (0.294)	1318-1393 (2405-2539)	17.1 (119)	7.9 (4.4)	— —	435 (0.104)	61.0 (367)	— —	— —	Ferromagnetic	460 (860)	— —
12B	8.36 (0.302)	1450- (2640-)	16.4 (114)	9.2 (5.1-5.5)°	12 (6.7)	461 (0.11)	49 (294)	0.0033	— —	Ferromagnetic	435 (815)	— —
13A	9.25 (0.334)	1302-1368 (2375-2495)	11.3 (78.5)	10.0 (5.6)	14.6 (8.1)	381 (0.091)	135 (812)	— —	— —	Paramagnetic	— —	760 (1400)
13B	9.22 (0.333)	1302-1365 (2375-2490)	11.7 (81)	10.26 (5.7)	— —	381 (0.091)	130 (785)	— —	— —	— —	— —	— —

TABLE 3—AVERAGE PHYSICAL CONSTANTS(1) (CONTINUED)

Key No.	Density at 20 °C g/cm³ (lb/in³)	Melting Range, Solidus-Liquidus °C (°F)	Thermal Conductivity 0-100 °C (32-212 °F) W/m·K (Btu/hr/ft²/F/in)	Coefficient of Linear Thermal Expansion °C⁻¹ x 10⁻⁶ (°F⁻¹ x 10⁻⁶) 0-100 °C (32-212 °F)	Coefficient of Linear Thermal Expansion 0-1000 °C (32-1832 °F)	Specific Heat 0-100 °C (32-212 °F) J/kg K (Btu/lb·°F)	Electrical Resistivity at R.T. Ω·mm²/m (ohm) circular-mil/ft)	Temperature Coefficient of Electrical Resistance 20-100 °C Per °C	Temperature Coefficient of Electrical Resistance 20-1000 °C Per °C	Magnetic Properties Condition at R.T.	Magnetic Properties Curie Temp. °C (°F)	Max Operating Temp. in Air (Sulfur Free) °C (°F)
** →	X27.68	—	X0.1441	X1.8	X1.8	X4186.8	X0.16624	—	—	—	—	—
14A	8.64 (0.312)	— —	10.66 (74.0)	10.8 (6.0)	15.7 (8.7)	419 (0.100)	125 (752)	— —	— —	Paramagnetic	— —	1038 (1900)
14B	8.94 (0.323)	1210-1305 (2318-2381)	11.3 (78)	11.3 (6.3)	15.3 (8.5)	385 (0.092)	130 (779)	— —	— —	Paramagnetic	— —	1038 (1900)
14C	8.88 (0.321)	1324-1371 (2415-2500)	10.23 (71.0)	11.2 (6.2)	15.8 (8.8)	427 (0.102)	130 (782)	— —	— —	Paramagnetic	— —	1038 (1900)
14D	8.23 (0.297)	1260-1355 (2300-2470)	11.6 (80.5)	13.8 (7.7)	14.9 (8.4)	486 (0.116)	118 (712)	— —	— —	Paramagnetic	— —	1204 (2200)
14E	8.25 (0.298)	1327-1352 (2420-2465)	11.0 (76.2)	13.9 (7.7)	17.5 (9.7)	460 (0.11)	114 (687)	0.00027	0.000127	Paramagnetic	— —	1204 (2200)
14F	8.30 (0.300)	1260-1343 (2300-2450)	10.66 (74.0)	13.5 (7.5)	— —	460 (0.110)	— —	— —	— —	— —	— —	— —
14G	8.05 (0.291)	— —	— —	14.96 (8.31)	16.74 (9.43)	502 (0.12)	104 (625)	— —	— —	— —	— —	— —
15A	8.80 (0.318)	— —	38.6 (268)	14.9 (8.3)	16.4 (9.1)[10]	— —	21.6 (130)	— —	— —	Paramagnetic	— —	— —
15B	8.69 (0.314)	— —	29.4 (204)	16.7 (9.3)	16.7 (9.3)	— —	31.4 (189)	0.000093	— —	Paramagnetic	— —	— —
15C	8.69 (0.314)	— —	41.8 (290)	15.8 (8.8)	16.0 (8.9)	— —	19.9 (120)	— —	— —	Paramagnetic	— —	— —

* Consult producer for more specific values.

** Metric values shown were computed by use of these conversion factors.

[1] At 20 to 550 °C

[2] At 59 to 95 °F

[3] At 104 to 140 °F

[4] At 0 to 500 °C

[5] At -20 to 500 °C

[6] At 30 to 350 °C

[7] At 25 to 870 °C

[8] At 20 to 500 °C

[9] At 30 to 450 °C

[10] At 68 to 572 °F

TABLE 4—RANGE OF MECHANICAL PROPERTIES[1]

Key No.	Available Forms[2]	Yield Strength 0.2% Offset 10^6Pa (10^3psi)	Tensile Strength 10^6Pa (10^3psi)	Elongation in 50 mm (2 in) %	Reduction of Area %	Hardness Brinell 3000 kg	Hardness Rockwell	Modulus of Elasticity 10^9Pa (10^6psi)	Endurance Limit 10^8Cycles 10^6Pa (10^3psi)	Impact at R.T. Standard Izod J (ft–lb)	Impact at R.T. Standard Charpy J (ft–lb)
(3) →		X6.9	X6.9	—	—	—	—	X6.9	X6.9	X1.356	X1.356
1A	A,B,C,D,E,F,G	103–1070 (15–155)	415–1140 (60–165)	50-2	75-50	90–230	B40–100	207 (30)	160–250 (23–36)	163 (120)	301–264 (222-195)
1B	A,C,E	207–1030 (30–150)	620–1030 (90–150)	50-2	65-15	140–380	B75–C46	207 (30)	360–407 (52–59)	163-34 (120-25)	325-49 (240-36)
1C	A,C,D,E,F	110–620 (16–90)	345–655 (50–95)	50-4	— —	80–210	B35–95	207 (30)	— —	— —	— —
2A	D,E	310–1588 (45–230)	724–1863 (105–270)	40-2	— —	— —	B70–C51	186–207 (27–30)	655–966 (95–140)	— —	149-81 (110-60)
3A	C,E	— —	— —	— —	— —	— —	— —	— —	— —	— —	— —
4A	A,C,E	193 (28)	587–1173 (85–170)	45	— —	— —	— —	— —	— —	— —	— —

Key No.	Available Forms[2]	Yield Strength 0.2% Offset 10^6Pa (10^3psi)	Tensile Strength 10^6Pa (10^3psi)	Elongation in 50 mm (2 in) %	Reduction of Area %	Hardness Brinell 3000 kg	Rockwell	Modulus of Elasticity 10^9Pa (10^6psi)	Endurance Limit 10^8Cycles 10^6Pa (10^3psi)	Impact at R.T. Standard Izod J (ft–lb)	Standard Charpy J (ft–lb)
(3) →		X6.9	X6.9	—	—	—	—	X6.9	X6.9	X1.356	X1.356
5A	A,B,C,D,E,F,G	172–1104 (25–160)	483–1173 (70–170)	50-2	75-50	110–250	B60–C23	179.4 (26.0)	207–345 (30–50)	163-102 (120-75)	298-203 (220-150)
5B	A,B,C,D,E,F	276–1207 (40–175)	620–1380 (90–200)	45-2	70-25	140–320	B75–C40	179.4 (26.0)	283–407 (41–59)	163-35 (120-26)	230-57 (170-42)
5C	A,C	172–897 (25–130)	483–966 (70–140)	50-4	70-50 —	110–230	B60–100	179.4 (26.0)	193–283 (28–41)	163-130 (120-96)	266-190 (196-140)
5D	A,C,D,E,F	255–648 (37–94)	586–973 (85–141)	47-25	—	135–255	B74-C25	179.4 (26.0)	— —	— —	— —
6A	A,B,C,E	207–828 (30–120)	414–931 (60–135)	45-0.5	70-25	— —	B50–93	— —	— —	— —	— —
6B	A,B,C,E	138–483 (20–70)	276–552 (40–80)	55-2	75-50	— —	B50–85	— —	— —	— —	— —
6C	A,B,C,E	138–483 (20–70)	276–552 (40–80)	55-2	75-50	— —	B50–85	— —	— —	— —	— —
6D	A,B,C,E	138–483 (20–70)	276–552 (40–80)	55-2	75-50	— —	B50–85	— —	— —	— —	— —
6E	A,B,C,E	138–483 (20–70)	276–552 (40–80)	55-2	75-50	— —	B50–85	— —	— —	— —	— —
7A	C,E	— —	— —	— —	— —	— —	— —	— —	— —	— —	— —
8A	C	— (25–40)	276–621 (40–90)	15–30	— —	— —	— —	— —	— —	— —	— —
8B	E	— (25–40)	345–690 (50–100)	15–30	— —	— —	— —	— —	— —	— —	— —
9A	A,B,C,E	241–965 (35–140)	483–1035 (70–150)	35-0.5	60-30	— —	B58–93	— —	— —	— —	— —
9B	A,B,C,D,E	241–965 (35–140)	483–1035 (70–150)	35-0.5	60-30	— —	B58–100	165 (24)	— —	— —	— —
9C	A,B,C,D,E	241–965 (35–140)	483–1035 (70–150)	35-0.5	60-30	— —	B58–100	165 (24)	— —	— —	— —
9D	A,C,E	207–965 (30–140)	552–1035 (80–150)	35-0.5	70-40	— —	B58–93	— —	— —	— —	— —
9E	A,B,C,D,E	241–965 (35–140)	483–1035 (70–150)	35-0.5	65-30	— —	B58–93	145 (21)	— —	— —	— —
9F	A,B,C,D,E	241–965 (35–140)	483–1035 (70–150)	40-0.5	65-30	— —	B58–98	141 (20.5)	— —	— —	— —
9G	E	276 (40)	483 (70)	35	— —	— —	B75 Ann.	152 (22)	— —	— —	— —
9H	E	276 (40)	483 (70)	35	— —	— —	B75 Ann.	152 (22)	— —	— —	— —
10A	C	— —	655–1138 (95–165)	— —	— —	— —	— —	— —	— —	— —	— —
10B	A,B,C,D,E,F,G	345–1311 (50–190)	690–1380 (100–200)	35-0.5	70-40	150–320	B85–C30	214 (31)	— —	— —	— —
10C	A,C,E	345–1311 (50–190)	690–1380 (100–200)	35-0.5	70-40	150–320	B80–85	214 (31)	— —	— —	— —
10D	A,C,E	517–655 (75–95)	966–1104 (140–160)	35-15	— —	— —	— —	— —	— —	— —	— —
10E	A,C,E	517–655 (75–95)	966–1104 (140–160)	35-15	— —	— —	— —	— —	— —	— —	— —

Key No.	Available Forms[2]	Yield Strength 0.2% Offset 10^6Pa (10^3psi)	Tensile Strength 10^6Pa (10^3psi)	Elongation in 50 mm (2 in) %	Reduction of Area %	Hardness Brinell 3000 kg	Hardness Rockwell	Modulus of Elasticity 10^9Pa (10^6psi)	Endurance Limit 10^8Cycles 10^6Pa (10^3psi)	Impact at R.T. Standard Izod J (ft–lb)	Impact at R.T. Standard Charpy J (ft–lb)
[3] →		X6.9	X6.9	—	—	—	—	X6.9	X6.9	X1.356	X1.356
10F	A,C,E	414–586 (60–85)	828–1035 (120–150)	30-10	— —	— —	— —	166 (24)	— —	— —	— —
10G	A,D,G	497 (72)	1035 (150)	19	25	— —	— —	— —	— —	— —	— —
11A	A,B,C,D,E,F,G	172–1207 (25–175)	552–1276 (80–185)	50-2	70-40	120–190	B65–C30	214 (31)	283–414 (41–60)	163-95 (120-70)	312-205 (230-151)
11B	A,B,C,D,E,F,G	345–1656 (50–240)	759–1897 (110–275)	45-2	60-30	200–500	B93–C47	214 (31)	310–448 (45–65)	54 (40)	— —
11C	A,B,C,D,E,F	290–759 (42–110)	724–1104 (105–160)	65-30	— —	110–240	— —	207 (30)	— —	— —	— —
11D	A,B,C,D,E,F	193–345 (28–50)	586–759 (85–110)	58-45	— —	115–160	— —	206 (29.9)	— —	— —	— —
11E	A,C,E	311–1346 (45–195)	656–1380 (95–200)	40-20	50-20	83	B85–C30	214 (31)	— —	— —	— —
11F	A,B,C,D,E,F	241–448 (35–65)	586–724 (85–105)	50-30	— —	120–180	— —	193 (28.0)	— —	— —	— —
11G	A,C,E	207–1000 (30–145)	483–1035 (70–150)	35-0.5	— —	— —	B80	— —	— —	— —	— —
11H	A,C,D,E	290 (42)	586 (85)	45	65	— —	B75-85	197 (28.5)	—	— —	>325 (>240)
11I	A,B,C,D,E,F	241–862 (35–125)	517–1035 (75–150)	60-10	— —	120–130	— —	197 (28.5)	— —	— —	— —
11J	A,C,E	207–1000 (30–145)	483–1035 (70–150)	35-0.5	— —	— —	B80	— —	— —	— —	— —
12A	A,C,D,E,F	362–1242 (52.5–180)	652–1476 (94.5–214)	52-13	— —	— —	— —	152 (22)	— —	— —	— —
12B	A,C,D,E	276–966 (40–140)	517–1035 (75–150)	30-0.5	— —	— —	B82-100	— —	— —	— —	— —
13A	A,B,C,D,E,F	462 (67)	925 (134)	51	— —	— —	B96	215 (31.1)	— —	81 (60)	— —
13B	A,B,C,D,E,F	504 (73)	987 (143)	51	— —	— —	— —	217 (31.4)	— —	— —	240 (177)
14A	A,B,C,D,E,F	414 (60)	766 (111)	52	— —	— —	B90	212 (30.8)	— —	— —	— —
14B	A,B,C,D,E,F	462–828 (67–120)	759–1000 (110–115)	24–60	— —	— —	B90-105	206 (29.8)	— —	— —	28–31 (21–23)
14C	A,B,C,D,E,F	462–828 (67–120)	759–1000 (110–145)	24–60	— —	— —	B90–105	206 (29.8)	— —	— —	28–31 (21–23)
14D	A,B,C,D,E,F	380 (55)	780 (113)	50	65	192	B88	196 (28.5)	— —	121 (89)	119-73 (88–54)
14E	A,B,C,D,E	345 (50)	690 (100)	50	57	160–202	B82-92	193 (28)	— —	— —	150 (110)
14F	A,B,C,D,E,F	317 (46)	704 (102)	61	52	— —	B84	— —	— —	— —	— —
14G	A,B,C,D,E,F	310 (45)	628 (91)	45	67	160	B84-90	193 (28)	— —	— —	— —
15A	A,B,C,D,E,F,G	179–497 (26–72)	373–545 (54–79)	43	— —	— —	B35-90	— —	— —	— —	— —
15B	A,B,C,D,E,F,G	186–586 (27–85)	414–690 (60–100)	40	— —	— —	— —	124 (18)	— —	— —	— —

Key No.	Available Forms(2)	Yield Strength 0.2% Offset 10^6Pa (10^3psi)	Tensile Strength 10^6Pa (10^3psi)	Elongation in 50 mm (2 in) %	Reduction of Area %	Hardness Brinell 3000 kg	Hardness Rockwell	Modulus of Elasticity 10^9Pa (10^6psi)	Endurance Limit 10^8Cycles 10^6Pa (10^3psi)	Impact at R.T. Standard Izod J (ft–lb)	Impact at R.T. Standard Charpy J (ft–lb)
(3) →		X6.9	X6.9	—	—	—	—	X6.9	X6.9	X1.356	X1.356
15C	A,B,C,D,E,F,G	152-566 (22-82)	380-662 (55-96)	40	— —	— —	— —	— —	— —	— —	— —

1Consult producers for more specific values.
2A—Rods and bars over 1/2 in dia.
B—Forgings
C—Wire 1/2 in dia. max.
D—Sheet
E—Strip
F—Tubing
G—Castings
3Metric values shown were computed by use of these conversion factors.

TABLE 5—AVAILABLE SPECIFICATION

Key No.	ASTM	Federal	Military	AMS	ASME	Other
1A	B160, B161, B162, B163, B366	—	—	—	SB160, SB161, SB162, SB163	—
1B	—	—	—	—	—	—
1C	F239	—	—	—	—	—
2A	—	—	—	—	—	—
3A	—	—	—	—	—	—
4A	E230	—	MIL-W-5846	—	—	ANSI C96.1
5A	B127, B163, B164, B165, B366, B564	QQ-N-281 — — — —	MIL-N-894 MIL-N-24106 MIL-T-842 MIL-T-1368 MIL-T-23520	4544, 4575 4674 4675 4730, 4731 7322	SB127 SB163 SB164 SB165 —	—
5B	B164	QQ-N-286 —	MIL-N-894 —	4674, 4676 7234	SB164 —	—
5C	—	QQ-N-286 — —	MIL-F-23999 MIL-N-17506 MIL-W-4471	4676 — —	— — —	—
5D	—	QQ-N-286	—	—	—	—
6A	B267	QQ-R-175 —	MIL-W-5845 MIL-W-5908	— —	— —	—
6B	B267	—	—	—	—	—
6C	B267	—	—	—	—	—
6D	B267	—	—	—	—	—
6E	B267	—	—	—	—	—
7A	—	—	—	—	—	—
8A	B267	—	—	—	—	—
8B	B267	—	—	—	—	—
9A	B267	—	—	—	—	—
9B	F30	—	MIL-I-23011	—	—	—
9C	F30	—	—	—	—	—
9D	F30	—	MIL-I-23011	7717, 7718, 7719	—	—
9E	F30	—	MIL-I-22011	—	—	—
9F	—	—	MIL-S-16598	—	—	—
9G	—	—	—	—	—	—
9H	—	—	—	—	—	—
10A	E120	—	—	—	—	—
10B	B344 B267	QQ-R-175 —	MIL-W-16970 MIL-W-14593	5676, 5677 —	— —	—
10C	—	—	—	—	—	—
10D	B267	—	—	—	—	—
10E	—	—	—	—	—	—
10F	—	—	—	—	—	—
10G	—	—	—	—	—	—
11A	B163, B166, B167, B168	QQ-W-390 — — — —	MIL-N-6710 MIL-T-7840 MIL-N-6840 MIL-N-23228 MIL-N-23229	5665, 5580 5540, 5687 7232	SB163, SB166 SB167, SB168 —	—
11B	—	— — —	MIL-N-24114 MIL-N-8550 MIL-N-7786	5542, 5598 5667, 5668 5669, 5670 5671, 5698 5699	— — — —	Air Research EMS 56 9A GE B50T1232 GE B50YP44 Westinghse 15125
11C	B443, B444 B446 —	— — —	— — —	5599, 5666 SB37 —	SB443, SB444 SB446 CC1409-1 CC1422	
11D	—	—	—	—	—	—
11E	B344	QQ-R-175	—	—	—	—
11F	B163, B423 B424, B425	— —	— —	— —	SB163, SB423 SB424, SB425	—
11G	B344	—	—	—	—	—
11H	—	—	—	—	—	—
11I	B163, B407 B408, B409	— — —	— — —	— — —	SB163, SB407 SB408, SB409 CC1325-5	—
12A	—	—	—	—	—	—
12B	F15	—	MIL-I-23011	7726, 7727 7728	—	—
13A	B333	—	MIL-N-18008	—	Case 1323	—
13B	B333, B335	—	—	5752	Case 1642	—
14A	—	—	—	—	Case 1641	—
14B	A296, A494 A567 B334, B336 B366	— —	— —	5388, 5389 5530 5750	SFA 5.14 SFA 15.11 SB334, SB336	—
14C	B574, B575	— —	— —	5388, 5389 5530 5750	Case 1410	—
14D	B434, A567 B366 B572, B435	— —	— —	5754 5536	SB434, SB435 Case 1321	GE B50T F24-54
14E	—	—	—	5593, 5717	—	—
14F	—	—	—	—	Case 1472	—
14G	B462, B463 B464, B468 B471, B472 B473, B474 B475	—	—	—	SB462, SB463 SB464	—
15A	B122, B121	QQ-C-585	—	—	—	—
15B	B122, B151 B206	QQ-C-585 QQ-C-586 QQ-C-W321	— — —	— — —	— — —	— — —
15C	B122, B151 B206	QQ-C-585	—	—	—	—

TABLE 6—PRODUCER

Super-script Numeral [(1)]	Name and Address
1	Huntington Alloys Inc., Huntington, WV 25720
2	Hoskins Manufacturing Co., 4445 Lawton Ave., Detroit, MI 48208
3	Wilber B. Driver Co., 1875 McCarter Highway, Newark, NJ 07104
4	Simonds Steel, Wallace Murray Corp., Lockport, NY 14094
5	Driver-Harris, Harrison, NJ 07029
6	Cyclops Corp., 650 Washington Rd., Pittsburgh, PA 15228
7	Carpenter Technology, Reading, PA 19603
8	Rolled Alloys, Inc., 5311 Concord Ave., Detroit, MI 48211
9	Kawecki Berylco Industries, Inc., 220 East 42nd St., New York, NY 10017
10	Cabot Corp., Stellite Div., 1020 West Park Ave., Kokoma, IN 46901
11	Wolverine Tube Div., UOP, Box 2202, 2100 Market St., N.E., Decatur, AL 35601
12	H. M. Harper Co., Morton Grove, IL 60053
13	Indiana General, 407 Elm St., Valparaiso, IN 46383
14	Arnold Engineering Co., Railroad Ave. and West, Box G, Marengo, IL 60152
15	Colt Industries, Crucible Magnetic Div., Box 100, Elizabethtown, KY 42701

1. As shown in Table 1.

SELECTION OF ZINC AND ZINC-ALLOY (HOT-DIPPED AND ELECTRODEPOSITED) COATED STEEL SHEET —SAE J1562 DEC1999

SAE Recommended Practice

Report of the SAE Iron and Steel Committee Division 32—Sheet and Strip Steel approved December 1999.

1. Scope—Zinc and zinc-alloy coated steel is used to enhance a structure's protection against corrosion degradation. For the purpose of this SAE Recommended Practice, a galvanized coating is defined as a zinc or zinc-alloy metallic coating. The selection of the optimum galvanized steel sheet product depends on many factors, the most important being: desired corrosion protection, formability, weldability, surface characteristics, and paintability. The trade-offs of these product characteristics are more complex than is the case with uncoated steel sheet products.

1.1 Purpose—This document defines preferred product characteristics. It also explains the various manufacturing processes, presents the advantages and disadvantages of the resulting product characteristics, and discusses the trade-offs between corrosion protection properties and fabricating, assembling, and finish-coating process.

2. References

2.1 Applicable Publications—The following publications form a part of this specification to the extent specified herein. Unless otherwise indicated, the latest version of SAE publications shall apply.

2.1.1 SAE PUBLICATIONS—Available from SAE, 400 Commonwealth Drive, Warrendale, PA 15096-0001.

SAE J1392 JUN84—Steel, High Strength, Hot Rolled Sheet and Strip, Cold Rolled Sheet, and Coated Sheet

SAE J2329 MAY97—Categorization and Properties of Low-Carbon Automotive Sheet Steels

SAE J2340 OCT1999—Categorization and Properties of Dent Resistant, High Strength, and Ultra
High Strength Automotive Sheet Steel

2.1.2 ASTM PUBLICATIONS—Available from ASTM, 100 Barr Harbor Drive, West Conshohocken, PA 19428-2959.

ASTM A90—Test Method for Weight (Mass) of Coating on Iron and Steel Articles with Zinc or Zinc-Alloy Coatings

ASTM A653/A653M—Specification for Steel Sheet, Zinc-Coated (Galvanized) or Zinc-Iron Alloy-Coated (Galvannealed) by the Hot-Dip Process

ASTM A754—Test Method for Coating Thickness by X-Ray Fluorescence

ASTM A879-96—Specification for Steel Sheet, Zinc Coated by the Electrolytic Process for Applications Requiring Designation of the Coating Mass on Each Surface

3. The Galvanizing Process—Two generic processes for metallic coated steels are currently used in the automotive industry: (1) hot-dipped coating and (2) electrolytic coating. Coating line conditions can be adjusted to produce a variety of coating masses and coating compositions.

3.1 The Hot-Dip Process—The uncoated coil product is usually annealed in-line or in a separate furnace. The steel is then passed continuously through a molten metal bath. Upon emergence from the bath, the molten metal coating mass is controlled by air (or other gas) knives or mechanical wipers before the coating solidifies. This produces the commonly used two-side zinc-coated sheet.

3.2 The Electrodeposition Process—Electrolytic coating is done in a continuous coating process using cells in which the metals are electrodeposited on pre-annealed steel. Coating mass is controlled by the electrodeposition rate in the plating cells. This product is available in one or two side coated sheet.

4. The Galvanized Coating—The galvanized coating is applied to the steel sheet prior to delivery to the fabricating plant. The coating remains substantially intact through subsequent forming, and painting operations. The coating provides both barrier and sacrificial protection.

4.1 Composition of Coatings

4.1.1 TYPES OF COATINGS[1]—Types of commercially produced coatings include: (1) zinc, (2) zinc-iron (<20% iron) alloys, (3) aluminum-zinc silicon (55, 43, and 2 weight percent respectively) alloy, (4) zinc-aluminum (5% aluminum) alloy, and (5) zinc-nickel (<20% nickel) alloy. Coatings (1) and (2) can be applied by either electroplating or hot-dip coating. Coatings (3) and (4) are applied by hot-dip coating while coating (5) is applied by electroplating.

4.1.2 ZINC COATINGS—Coatings that are considered essentially pure zinc coatings are typically referred to as hot-dip galvanized or electrogalvanized. Hot-dip galvanized coatings may contain small amounts of aluminum, lead, and antimony which are added to enhance coating properties. Electrogalvanized coatings are typically high-purity zinc and control only trace amounts of other elements.

4.1.3 ALLOY COATINGS—The most common alloy coatings are zinc-iron alloys. They are used to enhance spot welding and certain aspects of paintability. Zinc-iron coatings can be produced by the electroplating process in which zinc and iron are codeposited onto the steel sheet surface. The iron content of the coating is controlled by adjustment of electrolytic solution and plating current.

When processed on a hot-dip coating line, the zinc-iron coating is called Galvannealed and is produced using a thermal process after hot dipping. This process promotes diffusion of iron from the steel base into the coating which typically contains an average of 8 to 12% iron.

Aluminum-zinc-silicon and zinc-aluminum hot-dip alloyed coatings are produced by conventional hot-dip coating processes. The molten coating bath contains approximately the same composition as the coating on the steel.

Zinc-nickel (<20% nickel) alloy electroplated coatings are produced by conventional electroplating techniques. The plating electrolyte contains zinc and nickel ions that are codeposited as an alloy mixture.

4.2 Coating Mass—This document addresses the needs of automotive engineering by identifying the coating masses most commonly used in component design and by expressing the coating mass measurements as a minimum and maximum single-spot test for a given side. For example, 70 g/m^2 is the minimum coating mass on a single-spot test for the designated side of coating Category 70. The maximum coating mass for this Category is 100 g/m^2 for hot-dip galvanized products, or 90 g/m^2 for electroplated products.

This definition of coating mass represents a departure from the practice described in ASTM methods A653 and A653M for hot-dipped galvanized steel sheet, and ASTM method A879-93, except for Table 1, for electrolytic zinc-coated steel sheet. The ASTM Standard Specifications have been the principal public standards prior to the publication of this document.

The thickness of the coating is not an acceptable practice for specifying the quantity of coating to be deposited on the base steel.

4.3 Coating Designation—This document uses a nine-character designation that identifies the coating process, coating mass, and coating composition of each side, and the intended use of the coated steel with regard to the surface appearance quality required, i.e., exposed and unexposed. The terms "exposed" and "unexposed" are not related to corrosion requirements. The coating designation shall be stated using the following procedure:

a. 1st and 2nd Character—represent the coating process where HD = hot dip galvanized, and EG = electrogalvanized
b. 3rd and 4th Character—The numbers shown in the "Coating Mass Category" column of Table 1 indicates the coating mass of the unexposed side
c. 5th Character—Coating composition of the unexposed side where G = zinc coating, A = zinc-iron coating, N = zinc-nickel coating, X = other than G, A, or N
d. 6th and 7th Character—The numbers shown in the "Coating Mass Category" column of Table 1 indicates the coating mass of the other side (exposed side, if applicable)
e. 8th Character—Coating composition of the other side (exposed side, if applicable) where G = zinc coating, A = zinc-iron coating, X = other than G, A, or N
f. 9th Character—Intended use where E = exposed, U = unexposed, and Z = semi-exposed

1. All coating compositions included in t his section are approximate values in mass percent.

TABLE 1—RECOMMENDED COATING MASS FOR GALVANIZED STEEL SHEET

Coating mass Category	Coating Mass Per Side Single Spot Test Hot Dipped and Electroplated min g/m^2	Coating Mass Per Side Single Spot Test Hot Dipped max g/m^2	Coating mass Per Side Single Spot Test Electroplated max g/m^2
00	00	NA	00
20	20	50	30
30	30	60	45
40	40	70	55
45	45	75	60
50	50	80	70
55	55	85	75
60	60	90	80
70	70	100	90
90	90	120	110
98	98	130	130

NOTE: For approximate conversion from mass to thickness, use: microns = g/m^2 x 0.14
mils = g/m^2 x 0.006

Examples of the more commonly used galvanized steels expressed in terms of Table 1 are:

EG70G70GE = 70 g/m^2 minimum of zinc coating on each side for an exposed application.

HD70G20AE = 70 g/m^2 minimum of zinc coating on the unexposed side and 20 g/m^2 minimum of zinc-iron coating on the exposed side for an exposed application.

HD90G90GU = 90 g/m^2 minimum of zinc coating on each side for an unexposed application.

HD45A45AU = 45 g/m^2 minimum of zinc-iron coating on each side for an unexposed application.

EG30N30NE = 30 g/m^2 minimum of zinc-nickel coating on each side for an exposed application.

EG70G00XE = 70 g/m^2 minimum of zinc coating on the unexposed side and no coating on the exposed side ("one-side") for an exposed application.

4.4 Coating Mass Determination—The coating mass requirements in Table 1 refer to any single spot test per side.

There are several methods of determining coating mass. Modern galvanizing lines use X-ray fluorescence techniques described in ASTM method A754 to continuously monitor coating mass throughout the coil during the galvanizing process. The referee method is the "weigh-strip-weigh" method as described in ASTM method A 90 except, coating on each side must be measured separately.

4.4.1 MINIMUM COATING MASS—If the initial testing produces a value less than the minimum shown in Table 1, two additional test specimens shall be taken from the same lift of blanks or cut lengths or coil, except that no portion of the retest specimen may be any closer than 25 mm to the edge of the as-received steel. Both retests must conform to the minimum value of Table 1 for the Coating Mass Category specified; otherwise, the lift of blanks or cut lengths or coil can be considered unacceptable.

4.4.2 MAXIMUM COATING MASS—If the initial testing produces a value more than the maximum shown in Table 1, three additional test specimens shall be taken from the same lift of blanks or cut lengths or coil, except that no portion of the retest specimen may be any closer than 25 mm to the edge of the as-received steel. The average of the three retest specimens must conform to the maximum value of Table 1 for the Coating Mass Category specified, and no retest specimen may exceed the maximum in Table 1 by more than 30%. Otherwise, the lift of blanks or cut lengths or coil can be considered unacceptable.

4.5 Coated Surface Finish and Conditions—The user of galvanized steel should specify either exposed (E), semi-exposed (Z), or unexposed (U), surface quality as required (see 4.3). The steel supplier's responsibility is to supply a galvanized surface finish suitable for the application.

The following coated surfaces and conditions are available. References to spangle conditions do not apply to zinc-iron or electrodeposited coatings since these coatings do not develop spangles. Unexposed (U) hot-dip applications should be supplied with a minimized spangle surface finish.

4.5.1 REGULAR SPANGLE (HOT-DIPPED ONLY)—A commonly seen type of coating in non-automotive markets is regular spangle, typified by the flower-like or snowflake-like design (spangle pattern) that results from an uneven topographical relief, which shows prominently through most primer/paint systems used in the automotive industry. Regular spangle coatings are not considered acceptable for automotive applications.

4.5.2 MINIMIZED SPANGLE (HOT-DIPPED ONLY)—By application of various processing techniques during the transition period when the zinc coating freezes, the size and texture of the developing spangle can be altered (refined) substantially. The intent of these processing techniques is to produce very small spangles, and thereby, decrease the surface roughness associated with relief of the spangles normally formed. The surface finish of minimized spangle may be suitable for some less visible exposed applications. When the spangle is minimized to the extent that it is not visible to the unaided eye, the finish is termed spangle-free. Product intended for "U," Unexposed applications.

4.5.3 EXTRA SMOOTH (HOT-DIPPED ONLY)—Following the galvanizing operation, rolling processes can be used to improve the smoothness of the zinc-coated steel. The most frequently used rolling process is called temper rolling (skin passing). This additional processing step is used to produce a very uniform matte surface that is readily painted. Usually, the extra smooth product is produced by temper rolling minimized spangle product. Product intended for "Z," Semi-exposed applications.

In addition to enhancing the painted surface quality, extra smooth processing minimizes or eliminates the objectionable appearance of fluting or stretcher strains.

4.5.4 EXTRA SMOOTH SPANGLE FREE (HOT-DIPPED ONLY)—This product is produced by temper rolling a spangle free coating. Product intended for "E," Exposed application.

4.5.5 PHOSPHATE-TREATED—Hot-dipped and electrogalvanized sheets for automotive applications can be treated with either a crystaline-phosphate coating, applied by spray or dipping, or an amorphous phosphate coating, applied by roll coating. The phosphate coating is applied between 0.5 to 1.5 g/m^2, followed by oiling. The treatment has been found to enhance the formability of galvanized (chiefly zinc-iron alloy and electrogalvanized) sheet, and eliminates the need for draw die lubrication at the press line.

4.5.6 CHEMICALLY TREATED—Chromium compound chemical treatments can be applied in-line on galvanizing lines to provide protection against wet storage straining. However, these chemical treatments are not used for automotive applications since they adversely affect automotive cleaning, phosphating, and painting processes.

4.5.7 MILL OILS—Special oil is applied by the manufacturing facility after the base metal is coated. The purpose of this oil is to provide protection from oxidation staining during shipment to the buyer's facility and for a reasonable storage period.

4.5.8 PRELUBRICATED—Galvanized steel sheet can be processed with special lubricants that are applied by the steel mills to replace both mill oils (used for rust prevention) and drawing compounds applied at stamping plants.

5. Characteristics of Galvanized Steel Sheet

5.1 Thickness Definition—The thickness of galvanized steel sheet is determined by measuring as a single unit the combination of the base metal and all galvanized coatings.

5.2 Formability—For a given forming process, the steel sheet is only one element in the system. Forming is also influenced by such factors as the nature of the press, die design, blank/part shape, and lubrication. Since manufacturing conditions may vary, it is recommended that the producer and user consult regarding the features involved in specific applications.

The majority of hot-dip galvanized steel is produced on in-line annealing lines. For conventional steel compositions and standard processing, the relatively short annealing cycles plus exposure to a pot temperature in the vicinity of 460 °C, result in formability properties different from batch annealed cold-rolled steel. Recent technical developments can minimize these differences. Through the use of special extra low carbon steels, interstitial-free steels, or with extra processing of conventional grades, it is now possible to obtain in-line annealed and out-of-line annealed hot-dip galvanized steel with mechanical properties equivalent to cold-rolled steel sheet.

In contrast to the hot-dip process, electrolytic zinc coatings are applied in an environment near room temperature and the coating process does not significantly affect the mechanical properties of the incoming steel. These steels can, therefore, be designed for specific properties by various compositional and thermomechanical treatments prior to coating with the assurance that the properties will not be altered by the coating process.

5.3 Coating Adhesion—Coated steels are susceptible to flaking and powdering during forming which can result in die-pickup. Additional die cleaning and maintenance is usually required in stamping plants when forming galvanized steel parts as compared to uncoated steel parts.

Pure zinc coatings are soft and malleable with good coating adhesion. The soft nature of the zinc coating relative to the steel requires that more attention be paid to handling damage and scratches during forming operations. The zinc-alloy coatings are harder and more brittle, making them more susceptible to flaking and powdering.

5.3.1 BEND TESTING—Test specimens of coated sheet shall be capable of being bent through 180 degrees in any direction without flaking of the coating on the outside bend only. The coating bend test inside diameter shall have a relation to the thickness of the specimen as shown in ASTM method A653/A653M.

5.3.2 POWDERING AND FLAKING TESTS—Alloy coated sheet products which tend to powder and/or flake, are evaluated by numerous test methods, therefore customers should be contacted for their specific test method requirements and acceptance criteria. The more common test methods used in the automotive industry are: (1) double reverse olsen cup adhesion test, (2) draw bead test, and (3) 60 and 90 degrees reverse bend test.

5.4 Base Metal Quality—Galvanized steel sheet is available in the chemical compositions and mechanical properties normally produced for uncoated steel sheet. Base metal quality is dependent upon user requirements. This is normally expressed by a grade designation with reference to specific forming properties (see SAEJ2329 MAY97) for low-carbon steels, or (see SAE J1392 JUN84 and J2340 OCT1999) high-strength steels.

5.5 Weldability—The welding of zinc-coated steels is more difficult than uncoated steels. This is true whether the coating is applied electrolytically or by hot-dip processing. The major drawbacks in resistance welding of zinc-coated steels are a reduction in useful electrode life, and an increase in the required welding currents and times. Once these problems are properly addressed, however, zinc-coated steels can be satisfactorily welded. The following general comments apply: Lighter coatings and less variation generally improve welding performance. Zinc-iron coatings are generally more readily welded than zinc coatings. The behavior of differentially coated (including one side coated materials) depends upon the orientation of the coating with regard to the welding electrodes.

Zinc-coated steels can also readily be welded by any of the arc welding processes or by high energy techniques (laser, electron beam, for example). The primary problem is usually associated with zinc fumes and their possible health hazards. These can usually be negated with proper venting.

The cosmetic appearance of spot welds on galvanized steel sheet is different from spot welds used on uncoated steel sheet.

5.6 Adhesive Bonding—Adhesive bond strength is a function of the type of coated steel.

5.7 Paintability—Parts fabricated from galvanized steel sheet are readily primed and top coated. As in all cases, the components to be painted should be thoroughly cleaned prior to the application of pretreatments, primers, and top coats. Of particular note is that pretreatments are different for galvanized steel than those used for uncoated steel.

6. Corrosion—Corrosion is primarily an electrochemical phenomenon that degrades appearance and structural integrity. Physical design, chemical, and mechanical factors are often involved in the corrosion process.

In galvanized steel sheet, zinc protects the base metal through two mechanisms. The first is its action as a simple barrier which prevents contact to the base metal with the corrosive environment. The second is by acting as a sacrificial anode, commonly referred to as "galvanic protection." This mechanism serves to protect the base metal even if the zinc coating is locally damaged. Some corrosion protection is even offered to the uncoated cut edge of galvanized sheet.

Unpainted galvanized sheet generally offers protection from corrosion of the base metal in direct proportion to the coating weight. Painted galvanized sheet enhances protection compared to unpainted galvanized, but in varying degrees that are dependent upon the metal preparation prior to painting, the type of organic coating, and the thickness of the organic coating.

7. Marking and Identification—It is recommended that the seller and buyer agree to marking and identification requirements prior to placing orders for galvanized steel sheet. A review of these requirements will help reduce the potential for misapplication of material due to the variety of coating masses and compositions used in many manufacturing facilities. The marking should be made at the seller's facility directly on the coated steel surface, preferably in a continuous process. This allows blanks and cut lengths to be identified throughout fabrication up to the point of painting or a subsequent application of a coating.

In determining the type and location of markings, the following conditions should be considered:

a. Exposed side versus unexposed side (marking the exposed side should be avoided, if possible)
b. Differential coating masses, e.g., Coating Mass Category 90 on one side and Coating Mass Category 70 on the other side
c. Differential Coating Compositions, e.g, zinc on one side and zinc-iron on the other side

Identification markings should include:

a. Name or commonly recognized mark, e.g., logo, that identifies manufacturer
b. Coating designation (see 4.3), e.g, EG70G70GE, HD45A45AU, EG98G00XE

Other identification markings and special locations of the markings should be discussed with the seller to determine the capability of performing. Such markings could include the manufacturers location (mill), date coated, specification number, heat number, and coil number.

8. Recommended Ordering Information—When galvanized steel sheet is ordered, the following information should be considered so that adequate description of the required material is communicated to the producer.

a. Product name (hot-dip galvanized sheet or electrodeposited galvanized steel sheet or galvanized steel sheet which permits the producer to apply either coating process)
b. Base metal quality (low-carbon automotive grade, high strength, public, and proprietary specification)
c. Coating designation (see 4.3)
d. State whether or not chemical treatment is required
e. State whether oiled or not-oiled is required
f. Coated surface finish and condition (specify only if hot-dip coating, and application requires other than extra smooth or extra smooth-spangle free for exposed application, or other than minimized spangle for unexposed application)
g. phosphate treated (if required)
h. Mill lube treated (if required - state specific name of lubricant)
i. Dimensions (thickness, width, length, if cut length)
j. Coil size requirements (ID, OD, maximum weight) if required
k. Application (part name)
l. Part number
m. Special requirements not identified by any of the preceding

ELECTROPLATING OF NICKEL AND CHROMIUM ON METAL PARTS—AUTOMOTIVE ORNAMENTATION AND HARDWARE—SAE J207 FEB1985

SAE Standard

Report of the SAE Nonferrous Metals Committee approved August 1970, reaffirmed without change, SAE Automotive Bright Trim Committee, February 1985.

Foreword—This Document has not changed other than to put it into the new SAE Technical Standards Board Format.

1. Scope—This standard covers requirements for several types and grades of electrodeposited nickel/chromium coatings on ferrous or copper alloy basis metals and copper/nickel/chromium on zinc or aluminum alloys for the finishing and corrosion protection of decorative ornamentation and hardware of motor vehicles and marine controls and fittings. Four grades of coatings are provided to correlate with the service conditions under which each is expected to provide satisfactory performance, namely: very severe, severe, moderate, and mild. Definitions and typical examples of these service conditions are provided in Appendix A.[1] Information contained in this document generally conforms to the information contained in ASTM B 456, Specification for Electrodeposited Coatings of Nickel plus Chromium.

2. References

2.1 Applicable Publications—The following publications form a part of the specification to the extent specified herein.

2.1.1 ASTM PUBLICATIONS—Available from ASTM, 100 Barr Harbor Drive, West Conshohocken, PA 19428-2959

ASTM A 219—Methods of Test for Local Thickness of Electrodeposited Coatings
ASTM B 183—Preparation of Low Carbon Steel for Electroplating
ASTM B 242—Preparation of High Carbon Steel for Electroplating
ASTM B 252—Preparation of Zinc Die Castings for Electroplating
ASTM B 253-68—Preparation of and Electroplating on Aluminum Alloys by the Zincate Process
ASTM B 281—Preparation of Copper and Copper Alloys for Electroplating
ASTM B 287
ASTM B 320—Preparation of Iron Castings for Electroplating
ASTM B 368—Method for Copper-Accelerated Acetic Acid-Salt Spray (Fog) Testing (CASS Test)
ASTM B 380—Methods for Corrosion Testing of Decorative Chromium Electoplating by the Corrodkote Procedure
ASTM B 456—Specification for Electrodeposited Coatings of Nickel Plus Chromium
ASTM E 105—Practice for Probability Sampling of Materials
ASTM E 122—Practice for Choice of Sample Size to Estimate a Measure of Quality for a Lot or Process

2.2 Other Publications

50th Technical Proceedings of the American Electroplaters' Society (1963)

3. Manufacture

3.1 Only those parts shall be plated that are free from visible surface defects, such as scratches, porosity, nonconducting inclusions, roll and die marks, cold shuts, cracks, etc., which may adversely affect the appearance and the performance of coatings. In order to minimize problems of this sort, the specifications covering the basis material or the item to be plated should be appropriately specified.

3.2 When required, the basis metal shall be subjected to such polishing, buffing, or finishing operations as are necessary to yield deposits with the desired final appearance. (see 5)(See Section 5)

3.3 Proper preparatory procedures and thorough cleaning of the basis metal surface are essential in order to assure satisfactory adhesion and corrosion performance of the coating. Accordingly, it is suggested that the following ASTM documents on the preparation of various basis metals for electroplating be followed where appropriate:

ASTM B 183—Preparation of Low Carbon Steel for Electroplating
ASTM B 242—Preparation of High Carbon Steel for Electroplating
ASTM B 253-68—Preparation of and Electroplating on Aluminum Alloys by the Zincate Process
ASTM B 252—Preparation of Zinc Die Castings for Electroplating
ASTM B 281—Preparation of Copper and Copper Alloys for Electroplating
ASTM B 320—Preparation of Iron Castings for Electroplating

4. Significant Surfaces—Significant surfaces are defined as those normally visible—directly or by reflection—which are essential to the appearance or serviceability of the article when assembled in normal position, or which can be the source of corrosion products that deface visible surfaces on the assembled article. When necessary, the significant surface shall be the subject of agreement between purchaser and manufacturer and shall be indicated on the drawings of the parts, or by the provision of suitably marked samples.[2]

5. Appearance

5.1 The significant surface of the plated article shall be free from clearly visible plating defects, such as blisters, pits, roughness, cracks, or unplated areas, and shall not be stained or discolored. On articles where a visible contact mark is unavoidable, its position shall be the subject of agreement between the manufacturer and the purchaser.

5.2 The plated article shall be clean and free from damage. The purchaser shall specify the appearance required, for example, bright, dull or satin. Alternatively, samples showing the required finish or range of finish shall be supplied or approved by the purchaser.

6. Manner of Specifying Requirements

6.1 Coating Classification Number or Service Condition Number—When ordering articles to be plated in accordance with this standard, the purchaser shall state, in addition to SAE J207, either the classification number of the particular coating required (see 6.4) or the basis metal and the service condition number denoting the severity of the conditions it is required to withstand (see paragraph 6.2). If the service condition number is quoted but not the classification number, the manufacturer is free to supply any of the classes of coating corresponding to the service condition number; but when requested to do so, the manufacturer shall inform the purchaser of the classification number of the coating supplied.

6.2 Service Condition Number—The service condition number indicates the severity of the service conditions in accordance with the following scale:

SC 4—very severe service
SC 3—severe service
SC 2—moderate service
SC 1—mild service

Typical service conditions for which the various service condition numbers are appropriate are given in Appendix A.

6.3 Coating Classification Number—The coating classification number comprises:

a. The chemical designation for the basis metal (or for the principle metal if an alloy). The following chemical symbols are used:
   FE—for steel (or iron)
   ZN—for zinc alloy
   CU—for copper or copper alloy
   AL—for aluminum
b. The chemical designation for nickel (NI).
c. A number indicating the minimum thickness of the nickel coating, in micrometers.[3]
d. A letter designating the type of nickel deposit.
e. The chemical designation for chromium (CR).
f. A letter (or letters) designating the type of chromium deposit.

6.3.1 TYPE OF NICKEL AND DEPOSIT THICKNESS

6.3.1.1 Type of Nickel—The type of nickel[4] is designated by the following symbols:

B—For nickel deposited in the fully bright condition.

P—For dull or semi-bright nickel requiring polishing to give full brightness, containing less than 0.005% sulfur[5], and having an elongation not less than 8% when tested by the method given in Appendix C.

1. It is recognized that uses exist in which either thicker or thinner coatings than those covered by these specifications may be required. In such cases, the particular thickness desired by the purchaser (minimum, maximum, or range of thickness permissible) should be the subject of agreement between the purchaser and the plater.

2. When significant surfaces are involved on which the specified thickness of deposit cannot readily be controlled, such as threads, holes, deep recesses, bases of angles, and similar areas, the purchaser and the manufacturer should recognize the necessity for either thicker deposits on the more accessible surfaces or for special racking. Special racks may involve the use of conforming, auxiliary electrodes, or nonconducting shields.

3. The approximately equivalent coating thickness in mils are given in Tables 1–4. (1 µm = approximately 0.04 mil; 1 mil = 0.001 in = 25 µm.)

4. ASTM A 219, section on microscopic examination of polished and etched.

D—For a double-layer or triple-layer nickel coating, of which the bottom layer contains less than 0.005% sulfur[6], and which has an elongation not less than 8% when tested by the method given in Appendix C, and the top layer contains more than 0.04% sulfur[6]. The thickness of the bottom layer in double-layer coatings shall be not less than 75% of the total nickel thickness, and in triple-layer coatings shall be not less than 50% of the total nickel thickness; the thickness of the top layer in either case being not less than 10% of the total nickel thickness. If there are three layers, the intermediate layer shall contain more sulfur than the top layer and shall not exceed 10% of the total nickel thickness.

6.3.1.2 Thickness of Nickel Deposits—The number following the chemical designation NI indicates, in micrometers[7], the minimum thickness of the nickel deposit, measured in accordance with ASTM A 219, Methods of Test for Local Thickness of Electrodeposited Coatings, at points on the significant surface.

6.3.2 TYPE OF CHROMIUM AND DEPOSIT THICKNESS—The thickness of the chromium deposit shall be measured by the method given in ASTM A 219, at points on the significant surface.

The type of chromium and thickness of deposit is designated by the following symbols placed after the chemical designation CR (numerals are not used in this case to specify thickness as in the case of nickel):

R—For regular (that is, conventional) chromium, having a minimum thickness of 0.25 µm (0.01 mil), except in the case of SC 1 where the minimum thickness is 0.12 µm (0.005 mil).

MC—For microcracked chromium, having more than 300 cracks/cm (750 cracks/in) (method for measurement is given in Appendix D) in any direction over the whole of the significant surface, and having a minimum thickness of 0.8 µm (0.03 mil), unless it can be demonstrated by the plater that equally good performance can be obtained with a lower thickness.

MP—For microporous chromium, having a minimum thickness of 0.25 µm (0.01 mil) and containing a minimum of 10 000 pores per cm^2 (64 500 per in^2).

6.3.3 EXAMPLE OF COMPLETE CLASSIFICATION NUMBER—A coating on steel comprising 40 µm (1.6 mils) minimum bright nickel plus 0.8 µm (0.03 mil) minimum microcracked chromium has the classification number: FE/N140B/CRMC.

6.4 Coatings Appropriate to Each Service Condition Number—Tables 1, 2 and 3 show, for the various basis metals, the coating classification numbers appropriate for each service condition number.

6.5 Adhesion—The coating shall be sufficiently adherent to the basis metal, and the separate layers of multilayer coatings shall be sufficiently adherent to each other, to pass the tests described in Appendix B. The particular test or tests to be used shall be subject to agreement between the purchaser and the manufacturer.

6.6 Corrosion Resistance or Corrosion Protection of Coatings

6.6.1 Coated articles shall be subjected to one of the corrosion tests for the stated time shown in Tables 1, 2, 3, and 4 to be appropriate for the particular service condition number. The particular test to be used in any instance shall be specified by the purchaser or shall be the subject of agreement between the purchaser and the manufacturer. The tests are described in detail in the referenced ASTM documents.[8]

6.6.2 After subjecting the article to the treatment described in the relevant test method, it shall be examined for evidence of corrosion of the basis metal or blistering of the coating. Any evidence of basis metal corrosion or blistering of the coating shall be cause for rejection, unless otherwise agreed between the purchaser and the manufacturer.[9]

6.6.3 Surface deterioration of the coating itself is expected to occur during the testing of some types of coatings. The extent to which such surface deterioration will be tolerated shall be subject to agreement between purchaser and manufacturer.[9]

5. The sulfur contents are specified in order to indicate the type of nickel plating solution that is to be used. Although no simple method exists for determining the sulfur content of a nickel deposit on a coated article, the x-ray fluorescence technique can be used. A chemical determination is possible on a specially prepared test specimen.
6. The sulfur contents are specified in order to indicate the type of nickel plating solution that is to be used. Although no simple method exists for determining the sulfur content of a nickel deposit on a coated article, the x-ray fluorescence technique can be used. A chemical determination is possible on a specially prepared test specimen.
7. The sulfur contents are specified in order to indicate the type of nickel plating solution that is to be used. Although no simple method exists for determining the sulfur content of a nickel deposit on a coated article, the x-ray fluorescence technique can be used. A chemical determination is possible on a specially prepared test specimen.
8. The corrosion tests indicated in Tables 1–4 are a means of controlling the continuity and quality of the coatings and the duration of the tests does not necessarily have a fixed relationship with the service life of the finished article.
9. It is to be understood that occasional, widely scattered, small corrosion defects may be observed after the testing period. In general, "acceptable resistance" shall mean that such defects are not significantly defacing or otherwise deleterious to the function of the plated part.

7. Sampling

7.1 Since test methods may be destructive and since 100% inspection is expensive and usually unnecessary, it is recommended that the purchaser select suitable sampling plans for the acceptance testing of lots of coated items. General information on sampling procedures is given in ASTM E 105 and ASTM E 122. Standard sampling plans have been published by several sources. In order that the manufacturer know the quality expected to be met, the plans selected should be made a part of the purchase contract.

TABLE 1—NICKEL/CHROMIUM COATINGS ON STEEL(1)

Service Condition No.	Classification No.	Equiv. Nickel Thickness, mile (approx)(2)	Corrosion Test Duration, h Case ASTM B 368	Corrosion Test Duration, h Corrodkote ASTM B 380	Corrosion Test Duration, h Acetic-Salt ASTM B 287
SC 4	FE/NI40D/CRR	1.6(3)	22	20	144
	FE/NI30D/CRMC	1.2	22	20	144
	FE/NI30D/CRMP	1.2	22	20	144
SC 3	FE/NI30D/CRR	1.2(3)	16	16	96
	FE/NI25D/CRMC	1.0	16	16	96
	FE/NI25D/CRMP	1.0	16	16	96
	FE/NI40P/CRR	1.6	16	16	96
	FE/NI30P/CRMC	1.2	16	16	96
	FE/NI30P/CRMP	1.2	16	16	96
SC 2 (4)	FE/NI20B/CRR	0.8	—	—	24
	FE/NI15B/CRMC	0.6	—	—	24
	FE/NI15B/CRMP	0.6	—	—	24
SC 1(4)	FE/NI10B/CRR	0.4	—	—	8

1. When agreed by the purchaser and the manufacturer, copper may be used as an undercoat for the nickel but is not substitutable for any part of the nickel thickness specified.
2. 1 mil = 0.001 in = 25.4 µm.
3. Copper can contribute to the protection of the basis metal. This protection is enhanced when the chromium deposit is microcracked or microporous and the final nickel layer is an active sulfur-containing nickel deposit.
In double nickel system, buffing one of the nickel deposits may be beneficial to the corrosion resistance
4. P or D nickel may be substituted for B nickel and MC or MP chromium may be substituted for R chromium in service condition No. 1; P or D nickel may be substituted for B nickel in service condition No. 2.

TABLE 2—COPPER/NICKEL/CHROMIUM COATINGS ON ZINC ALLOY(1)

Service Condition No.	Classification No.	Equiv. Nickel Thickness, mils (approx)(2)	Corrosion Test Duration, h Cass ASTM B 368	Corrosion Test Duration, h Corrodkote ASTM B 380	Corrosion Test Duration, h Acetic-Salt ASTM B 287
SC 4	ZN/NI40D/CRR	1.6	22	20	144
	ZN/NI30D/CRMC	1.2	22	20	144
	ZN/NI30D/CRMP	1.2	22	20	144
SC 3	ZN/NI30D/CRR	1.2	16	16	96
	ZN/NI25D/CRMC	1.0	16	16	96
	ZN/NI25/CRMP	1.0	16	16	96
	ZN/NI40P/CRR	1.6	16	16	96
	ZN/NI30P/CRMC	1.2	16	16	96
	ZN/NI30P/CRMP	1.2	16	16	96
SC 2 (3)	ZN/NI20B/CRR	0.8	4	4	24
	ZN/NI15B/CRMC	0.6	4	4	24
	ZN/NI15B/CRMP	0.6	4	4	24
SC 1(4)	ZN/NI10B/CRR	0.4	—	—	8

1. All these coatings shall be applied over an undercoat of copper or yellow brass having a minimum thickness on significant surfaces of 5 µm (0.2 mil) as measured in accordance with ASTM A 219, Methods of Test for Local Thickness of Electrodeposited Coatings.
2. 1 mil = 0.001 in = 25.4 µm.
3. P or D nickel may be substituted for B nickel and MC or MP chromium may be substituted for R chromium in service condition No. 1; P or D nickel may be substituted for B nickel in service condition No. 2 or 1.

TABLE 3—NICKEL/CHROMIUM COATINGS ON COPPER OR COPPER ALLOYS[1]

Service Condition No.	Classification No.	Equiv. Nickel Thickness, miles (approx)[2]	Corrosion Test Duration, h Cass ASTM B 368	Corrosion Test Duration, h Corrodkote ASTM B 380	Corrosion Test Duration, h Acetic-Ssalt ASTM B 287
SC 4	CU/NI30D/CRR	1.2	22	20	144
	CU/NI25D/CRMC	1.0	22	20	144
	CU/NI25D/CRMP	1.0	22	20	144
SC 3	CU/NI25D/CRR	1.0	16	16	96
	CU/NI20D/CRMC	0.8	16	16	96
	CU/NI20D/CRMP	0.8	16	16	96
	CU/NI30B/CRR	1.2	16	16	96
	CU/NI25B/CRMC	1.0	16	16	96
	CU/NI25B/CRMP	1.0	16	16	96
	CU/NI25P/CRR	1.0	16	16	96
	CU/NI20P/CRMC	0.8	16	16	96
	CU/NI20P/CRMP	0.8	16	16	96
SC 2[3]	CU/NI15B/CRR	0.6	—	—	24
	CU/NI10B/CRMC	0.4	—	—	24
	CU/NI10B/CRMP	0.4	—	—	24
SC 1[3]	CU/NI5B/CRR	0.2	—	—	8

1. All these coatings shall be applied directly to the basis metal or over a copper strike.
2. 1 mil = 0.001 in = 25.4 μm.
3. P or D nickel may be substituted for B nickel in service condition Nos. 2 and 1, and MC or MP chromium may be substituted for R chromium in service condition No. 1.

TABLE 4—COPPER/NICKEL/CHROMIUM COATINGS ON ALUMINUM[1]

Service Condition No.	Classification No.	Equiv. Nickel Thickness, mils (approx)[2]	Corrosion Test Duration, h Cass ASTM B 368	Corrosion Test Duration, h Corrodkote ASTM B 380	Corrosion Test Duration, h Acetic-Salt ASTM B 287
SC 4	AL/NI40D/CRR	1.6	22	20	144
	AL/NI30D/CRMC	1.2	22	20	144
	AL/NI30D/CRMP	1.2	22	20	144
SC 3	AL/NI30D/CRR	1.2	16	16	96
	AL/NI25D/CRMC	1.0	16	16	96
	AL/NI25D/CRMP	1.0	16	16	96
	AL/NI40P/CRR	1.6	16	16	96
	AL/NI30P/CRMC	1.2	16	16	96
	AL/NI30P/CRMP	1.2	16	16	96
SC 2[3]	AL/NI20B/CRR	0.8	—	—	24
	AL/NI15B/CRMC	0.6	—	—	24
	AL/NI15B/CRMP	0.6	—	—	24
SC 1[3]	AL/NI10B/CRR	0.4	—	—	8

1. All these coatings shall be applied over an undercoat of copper having a minimum thickness on significant surfaces of 5 μm (0.2 mil) as measured in accordance with ASTM A 219, Methods of Test for Local Thickness of Electrodeposited Coatings.
2. 1 mil = 0.001 in = 25.4 μm.
3. P or D nickel may be substituted for B nickel and MC or MP chromium may be substituted for R chromium in service condition No., 1; P or D nickel may be substituted for B nickel in service condition Nos. 2 or 1.

APPENDIX A
DEFINITIONS OF SERVICE CONDITIONS FOR WHICH THE VARIOUS SERVICE CONDITION NUMBERS ARE APPROPRIATE

A.1 Service Condition No. SC 4 (Very Severe)—Service conditions which include exposure to very severe, heavy corrosive environments such as those found in an area where there is heavy industry accompanied by snow and below-freezing temperatures, and conditions where parts are subjected to continued exposure in a salt water environment.

A.2 Service Condition No. SC 3 (Severe)—Exposure which is likely to include severe industrial or seacoast environments and areas where frequent wetting by rain or dew is experienced. Severe exposure is defined as that which is likely to include occasional or frequent wetting by rain, dew, or snow in an industrial or seacoast environment.

A.3 Service Condition No. SC 2 (Moderate)—Moderate exposure is defined as that which is likely to include normally dry sheltered locations, but with coating subject to occasional condensation of moisture, wear, or abrasion.

A.4 Service Condition No. SC 1 (Mild)—Exposure to normally warm, dry interior atmospheres.

APPENDIX B
TESTS FOR ADHESION OF COATINGS[10]

B.1 Bend Test for Adhesion—The plated part shall be repeatedly flexed or deformed in some manner until fracture occurs. The ability to peel the coating or to separate the different layers of the coating, at other than the immediate area of the fracture, is evidence of failure to conform to the adhesion requirement.

B.2 File Test for Adhesion—Saw a piece off the plated article, hold it in a vise, and apply a coarse file (12–20 cuts per in) to the cut edge in such a manner as to attempt to raise the deposit. Peeling of the coating away from the cut edge or separation of the different layers of the coating is evidence of failure to conform to the adhesion requirement.

B.3 Quenching Test for Adhesion[11]—Heat the plated article for 1 h in an oven maintained at the following temperatures, within ±10°C:

Basis Metal	Temperature, °C (°F)
Steel	350 (662)
Zinc alloy	150 (302)
Copper or copper alloy	250 (482)
Aluminium	250 (482)

Quench the articles in water at room temperature.

Any lifting or blistering of the coating is evidence of failure to conform to the adhesion requirement.

10. There is no single satisfactory test for evaluating the adhesion of electrodeposited coatings. Those given above are widely used; however, other tests may prove more applicable in specific cases. If so, such tests should be made a part of the purchase order. A review of methods of measuring adhesion is given in the 50th Technical Proceedings of the American Electroplaters' Society (1963).
11. CAUTION: This test may have an adverse effect on the mechanical properties of the article tested.

APPENDIX C
DUCTILITY TEST[12]

C.1 Preparation of Test Piece—Prepare a plated test strip, 150 mm long, 10 mm wide, and 1 mm thick (approximately 6 in x 0.4 in x 0.040 in), by the following method:

Polish a sheet of the appropriate basis metal, similar to that of the articles being plated, except that the sheet may be of soft brass if the basis metal is zinc alloy. (Use a sheet that is sufficiently large to allow the test strip to be cut from it after trimming off a border at least 25 mm (1.0 in) wide all around.) Place the sheet on one side with nickel to a thickness of 25 µm (1.0 mil) under the same conditions and in the same bath as the corresponding articles.

Cut the test strip from the plated sheet with a flat shear. Round or chamfer the longer edges of the test strip, at least on the plated side, by carefully filing or grinding.

C.2 Procedure—Bend the test strip with the plated side in tension, by steadily applied pressure, through 180 deg over a mandrel of diameter 11.5 mm (0.45 in) until the two ends of the test strip are parallel. Ensure that contact between the test strip and the mandrel is maintained during bending.

C.3 Assessment—The plating is deemed to comply with the minimum requirement of an elongation of 8% provided that after testing there are no cracks passing completely across the convex surface. Small cracks at the edges do not signify failure.

APPENDIX D
DETERMINATION OF CHROMIUM DISCONTINUITY

D.1 Equipment

- Metallurgical microscope (B & L 31-20-6637 or equivalent)
  - Eyepiece 10X (B & L 31-15-09 or equivalent)
  - Objective 5X (B & L 42-33-51 or equivalent)
  - Objective 10X (B & L 42-33-53 or equivalent)
  - Howard disc (B & L 31-16-15 or equivalent)
  - Cross-line disc (B & L 31-16-30 or equivalent)
- Stage micrometer (B & L 31-16-89)
- Soft bristle brush
- Hot alkaline cleaner (4 oz/gal trisodium phosphate plus 2 oz/gal sodium hydroxide)
- Stainless steel beaker, 4000 mL capacity
- Copper plating solution (28–32 oz/gal copper sulfate ($CuSO_4{\cdot}5H_2O$) plus 6–8 fluid oz/gal sulfuric acid (H_2SO_4))
- Plastic plating tank—Capacity depending on parts to be tested
- Copper anodes
- Low voltage rectifier (E. H. Sargent Co., Cat. No. S-30968 or equivalent)
- Platers tape (3M Co., Pressure Sensitive Tape No. 470, 3/4 in width)
- Acid dip (5% by volume sulfuric acid in water)
- Hot plate

TABLE D1—

Procedure	Explanation	Precautions
A. Preparation of Solutions		
1. Alkaline Cleaner		
(a) Into the stainless steel beaker place 1 gal of water, 4 oz trisodium phosphate, and 2 oz sodium hydroxide.	(a) This is the alkaline cleaner.	(a) Wear rubber gloves to avoid caustic burns.
(b) Stir the solution until the chemicals are dissolved and then heat to 150–160 °F.	(b) This is the operating temperature.	(b) Wear suitable safety equipment.
2. Copper Plating Solution		
(a) Fill the plastic plating tank about 3/4 full with water.	(a) Measure the amount of water.	
(b) For each gallon of water in the tank, add 28–32 oz of copper sulfate and stir to dissolve.		
(c) For each gallon of water in the tank, add 6–8 oz of sulfuric acid and stir to mix.	(c) This is the copper plating solution. This solution is used at room temperature.	(c) Wear suitable safety equipment.
(d) Insert the copper anodes in the bath and connect them to the positive terminal of the rectifier.		
B. Plating of Parts		
1. Connect a copper wire to the part long enough to immerse in the plating tank.	1. The wire should be masked with platers tape where it does not make electrical contacts.	
2. If the part has been cut, tape the edges with platers tape.	2. Cut edges will interfere with copper plating.	
3. Rinse the parts, if necessary, with an organic solvent.	3. To remove any grease or oil.	
4. Dip the brush in the hot alkaline cleaner and gently wash the part, avoiding scrubbing.	4. If you scratch the test part, the scratches will plate.	4. Do not dip the part in the hot cleaner; this may crack chromium that otherwise would not crack
5. Rinse in running water.	5. To remove alkaline cleaner.	
6. Dip the part for 5 s in the 5% sulfuric acid solution.		
7. Rinse in running water.	7. To remove acid.	

12. This test is used to check that the type of nickel deposit complies with the appropriate definition given in 6.3.1.1, and should not be used to assess the acceptability of a plated article.

TABLE D1—

Procedure	Explanation	Precautions
8. Inspect the part for water breaks. If the part shows no water break, proceed to the next step. If the part shows water breaks, repeat steps 4–7.	8. To insure a clean part.	8. Do not touch the part with hands.
9. Connect a copper wire to the negative terminal of the rectifier and to the racking wire (step B-1).		
10. Immerse the part into the plating solution and turn on the rectifier.		10. Do not let the part touch the anodes as this will cause a short circuit.
11. Adjust the rectifier so that the voltage reading is about 0.3 V and plate for 3–15 min.	11. The time for plating will vary depending on many factors, such as the type of chromium, chromium coverage, etc. The parts should be plated until a copper deposit is barely visible.	
12. Shut off therectifier, remove the part from the plating bath, and rinse in running warm water. Allow it to dry.	12. This the end of the plating cycle.	12. Handle the part by the edges only, as the copper deposit can be wiped off.
C. Calibration of Microscope		
1. Insert the Howard disc into a 10X eyepiece.		
2. Insert the eyepiece and 5X objective into the microscope.	2. This will give a 50X magnification used for measuring microporous chromium.	
3. Place the stage micrometer on the stage of the microscope and focus the microscope on it.		
4. Rotate the eyepiece so that the grid can be measured with the stage micrometer.		
5. Determine the length of the grid to the nearest 0.001 in.	5. This is L.	
6. Rotate the eyepiece 90 deg and determine the width of the grid to the nearest 0.001 in.	6. This is W.	
7. Calculate the area of the grid.	7. L x W = Area	
8. Calculate the factor for the microscope. This will be used when measuring microporous chromium.	8. $\text{Factor} = \frac{1}{\text{Area, in}^2}$	
9. Insert the crossline disc in a 10X eyepiece.		
10. Insert the eyepiece and the 10X objective into the microscope.	10. This will give 100X magnifications used for measuring microcracked chromium.	
11. Place the stage micrometer on the stage of the microscope and focus the microscope on it.		
12. Rotate the eyepiece until one of the lines in the cross is at right angles to the lines of the stage micrometer.		
13. Determine the length of the line within the field of view to the nearest 0.001 in.		
14. Calculate the factor for this microscope setup. This will be used when measuring microcracked chromium.	14. $\text{Factor} = \frac{1}{\text{Length, in}}$	
D. Measuring Chromium Pattern		
1. Determine what type of chromium is on the part.	1. When viewed under the microscope microporous chromium will show numerous black spots, while microcracked chromium will show numerous fine cracks.	
2. Set the microscope up for the particular type of chromium.	2. For microporous chromium use the 5X objective and the 10X eyepiece with the Howard disc. For microcracked chromium, use the 10X objective and the 10X eyepiece with the crossline disc.	2. Be sure to use the correct setup for each type of chromium.
3. Place the treated test part under the microscope and focus the microscope on the part.	3. The test part has been plated with copper as per section B of this procedure.	3. Handle the part carefully as the copper can be wiped off.
4. If the part is microporous chromium, count the number of spots in the grid and multiply this by the factor determined in C-8.	4. This will give the pore count per square inch.	
5. If the part is microcracked chromium, count the number of cracks which cross one of the lines in the crossline eyepiece and multiply this by the factor determined in step C-14.	5. This will give the cracks per inch.	

TABLE D1—

Procedure	Explanation	Precautions
E. Alternate Methods of Measuring Chromium Pattern		
1. Photographic—Using a Platers Microscope		
(a) Insert a 10X eyepiece and a 5X objective into the microscope.	(a) This will give a 50X magnification for use with microporous chromium.	
(b) Attach the camera to the microscope.		
(c) Place the stage micrometer on the stage of the microscope and focus the microscope on it.		
(d) Photograph the slide and develop it.		
(e) Measure with an accurate scale the separation between each 0.01 in marking of the stage micrometer on the photograph and determine the magnification.	$\text{Magnification} = \dfrac{100}{\text{Measurements from photograph, in}}$	
(f) Determine factor for this setup.	(f) Factor = Magnification x magnification	
(g) Place test part prepared as in Section B under the microscope and focus on H.		
(h) Photograph this area and develop the photograph.		
(i) Count the number of spots in an area 1.0 in x 1.0 in. Repeat this three times on different areas of the photograph.	(i) A linen tester will be of great assistance for this measurement.	
(j) Average the number of spots and multiply by the factor determined in step E-1-f.	(j) This will give the pores per square inch.	
(k) If the discontinuities in the chromium are microcracks use a 10X eyepiece and a 10X objective and proceed with the calibration as in steps E-1-b,c,d, and e.	(k) The magnification determined by this method is also the factor for microcracked chromium.	
(l) Place the test part under the microscope and focus on it.		
(m) Photograph this area and develop the photograph.		
(n) Draw a straight line across the photograph and count the number of cracks which intersect the line per linear inch.		
(o) Multiply the number of cracks by the factor determined in k.	(o) This is the cracks per linear inch.	
2. Using a Metallograph		
(a) If a photograph is taken, proceed as in step E-1.		
(b) If the image is projected on a ground glass screen and not photographed, proceed as in step E-1, treating the image on the ground glass screen as the photograph.		

ELECTROPLATE REQUIREMENTS FOR DECORATIVE CHROMIUM DEPOSITS ON ZINC BASE MATERIALS USED FOR EXTERIOR ORNAMENTATION—SAE J1837 JUN1991 SAE Standard

Report of the SAE Bright Trim Executive Committee approved June 1991.

Foreword—This Document has not changed other than to put it into the new SAE Technical standards board Format.

1. Scope—This SAE Standard covers the physical and performance requirements for electrodeposited copper, nickel, and chromium deposits on exterior ornamentation fabricated from die cast zinc alloys (SAE J468 alloys 903 and 925), and wrought zinc strip (ASTM B 69). This type of coating is designed to provide a high degree of corrosion resistance for automotive, truck, marine, and farm usage where a bright, decorative finish is desired.

1.1 Purpose—This document details the physical and chemical properties that are necessary to optimize coating appearance and durability of decoratively plated parts. When properly applied, the electroplate described in this document has a bright, highly reflective, and specular finish with an inherently high degree of corrosion resistance. The coating's resistance to a corrosive environment is highly dependent on the proper maintenance of the processes used to produce the coating. Since the treatment of processing variables is outside the scope of this document, it is important for applicators of this coating to develop an intimate knowledge of their process, and control all parameters that affect the quality of the end product. The use of techniques such as statistical process control (SPC), capability studies, design of experiments, process optimization, etc., are critical to produce a material of consistently high quality.

The subjects included in this document are: substrate preparation, metal finishing, plate thickness, electrochemical potential difference, ductility, chromium microdiscontinuity, accelerated corrosion, adhesion, bend testing, and sampling. The appropriate specification limits and test methods are described in each section. Where possible, the test methods specified are well established and accepted within the plating industry. In a few instances, several test methods are specified. In these cases, it is up to the purchaser and supplier to agree on the test method to be used.

2. References

2.1 Applicable Publications—The following publications form a part of this specification to the extent specified herein. The latest issue of SAE publications shall apply.

2.1.1 SAE PUBLICATION—Available from SAE, 400 Commonwealth Drive, Warrendale, PA 15096-0001.

SAE J468—Zinc Alloy Ingot and Die Casting Compositions

2.1.2 ASTM PUBLICATIONS—Available from ASTM, 100 Barr Harbor Drive, West Conshohocken, PA 19428-2959.

ASTM B 69—Specification for Rolled Zinc
ASTM B 252—Preparation of Zinc Alloy Die Castings for Electroplating and Conversion Coatings
ASTM B 368—Copper-Accelerated Acetic Acid-Salt Spray (Fog) Testing (CASS Test)
ASTM B 374—Standard Definitions of Terms Relating to Electroplating
ASTM B 456—Electrodeposited Coatings of Copper Plus Nickel Plus Chromium and Nickel Plus Chromium
ASTM B 487—Measurement of Metal and Oxide Coating Thickness by Microscopical Examination of a Cross Section
ASTM B 490—Micrometer Bend Test for Ductility of Electrodeposits
ASTM B 504—Measurement of Thickness of Metallic Coatings by the Coulometric Method
ASTM B 507—Design of Articles to be Electroplated on Racks
ASTM B 537—Rating of Electroplated Panels Subjected to Atmospheric Exposure
ASTM B 556—Measurement of Thin Chromium Coatings by the Spot Test
ASTM B 571—Adhesion of Metallic Coatings
ASTM B 602—Attribute Sampling of Electrodeposited Metallic Coatings and Related Finishes
ASTM B 697—Selection of Sampling Plans for Inspection of Electrodeposited Metallic Coatings and Related Finishes on Products
ASTM B 762—Variables Sampling of Metallic and Inorganic Coatings
ASTM B 764—Simultaneous Thickness and Electrochemical Potential Determination of Individual Layers in Multilayer Nickel Deposit (STEP Test)

3. Definitions

3.1 Significant Surfaces—These are defined as surfaces that are visible when the finished component is assembled onto the vehicle and is observed in normal viewing position. Nonsignificant surfaces that may cause corrosion products to run onto significant surfaces are significant. Also, nonvisible surfaces, when designated by the customer, are significant.

3.2 Microdiscontinuous—A chromium deposit in which microscopic voids exist in the chromium, exposing the underlying nickel layer. The production of suitable microscopic voids or sites in the chromium layer causes a dispersion of the corrosion potential over a relatively large surface area. The resulting corrosion potential dispersion reduces the effects of localized high corrosion potentials and the associated large corrosion pits.

3.2.1 ASTM B 374 provides definitions of the more common terms related to plating.

4. Appearance—All parts manufactured to this document shall meet the visual requirements for color, luster, and other specific finish standards agreed on between the customer and supplier, on all significant surfaces.

Standard panels or typical production parts should be used to define the various appearance levels for major surfaces and parting line finishes.

Various classes or types of finish may be specified by the purchaser. The production drawing should indicate, via symbols or notes, the specifics of these requirements. Visual standards, including textured surface standards, may be used to supplement the drawing notes showing minimum acceptable appearance conditions.

5. Substrate Preparation—The substrate surface finish can affect the plated appearance. Suitable precautions in casting, forming, finishing, and cleaning must be taken to assure a satisfactorily finished plated part.

Evidence of surface porosity, stress cracks, blisters, or other surface defects may indicate improper substrate preparation or inferior castings that may not have adequate durability after plating. The proper practices for preparing the zinc die casting for plating are discussed in ASTM B 252.

6. Design Guidelines—An entire document could be written on "design guidelines" and the reader is urged to consult a document such as ASTM B 507.

7. Metal Finishing—Buffing or other mechanical treatments of the substrate, copper or nickel deposits are permitted provided that minimum plating thickness, chromium microdiscontinuity, and other applicable requirements are met following these treatments. Buffing of the final chromium plate is not permitted as it will adversely affect corrosion resistance.

8. Plate Thickness

8.1 The plate thicknesses listed in Table 1 shall be met on all areas of the significant surfaces. These thicknesses also apply to nonsignificant surfaces which, on corroding, may drip onto or otherwise affect a significant surface.

TABLE 1—PLATE THICKNESS

	Thickness, μm (minimum)	in (minimum)
Copper Strike	5 (a)	0.0002
Copper	15 (b)	0.0006
Semibright Nickel	20	0.0008
Bright Nickel	10 (c)	0.0004
Total Semibright and Bright Nickel	30	0.0012
Microdiscontinuous Chromium	0.25 (d)	0.00001

a. Generally consists of a cyanide copper layer. It is up to the customer and supplier to agree on what type of copper or other plating process is utilized as the initial layer on zinc base parts.
b. The copper layer may be plated from either a cyanide copper bath or an acid copper bath and it is up to the customer and supplier to agree on an acceptable plating bath.
c. The use of a "high potential" nickel layer (generally 2.5 μm or 0.0001 in thick) between the bright and semibright nickels can improve corrosion performance of the composite plate. The semibright nickel thickness may, therefore, be reduced by the thickness of the "high potential" nickel layer if approved by the customer.
d. If trivalent chromium is employed, the minimum thickness shall be 0.50 μm (0.00002 in).

8.2 If, due to part geometry, the specified plating thickness on significant surfaces cannot be met, the customer and supplier shall agree on a minimum plate thickness or the use of an alternate coating method, e.g., auxiliary anodes.

8.3 Thickness Measurements—The thickness of the individual copper and nickel layers may be determined using the microscopic method, ASTM B 487, or the coulometric method, ASTM B 504. The nickel layers may also be measured using the "STEP" test, ASTM B 764. Chromium thickness may be measured using ASTM B 504 or the spot test, ASTM B 556. In case of disputes, the microscopic method for measuring thickness shall be the referee method.

9. "Step" Test Requirements

9.1 Procedure—The "STEP" test shall be carried out in accordance with ASTM B 764. To obtain reliable and reproducible results, the following precautions should be adhered to:

a. Prevent the reference electrode from drying out when not in use by keeping it immersed in either water, "STEP" test electrolyte or dilute (5 to 10%) hydrochloric acid solution.
b. Run sufficient verification tests on a primary or secondary standard to insure that the instrument is working properly, before carrying out a test on an unknown sample. If the STEP value of the primary standard or secondary standard cannot be reproduced to within at least ±5% of the reported value of the standard after three attempts, the instrument should be thoroughly checked for possible problems, e.g., plate buildup on inside of cell, faulty reference electrode, miscalibrated chart recorder, etc. Primary standard test panels are available from the National Institute of Standards and Technology,[1] while some instrument suppliers provide secondary standards. Tertiary standards may be actual parts or prepared plated panels that have been calibrated against a primary or secondary standard.
c. Keep plate buildup on the inside surfaces of the metal test cell to a minimum by frequent cleaning.
d. Make sure the pH of the test electrolyte is 3.0 ± 0.1 when preparing new solution or checking old solution.

9.2 Interpretation of Results

a. The "STEP" test may be used to measure the thickness of individual nickel layers when the instrument is properly calibrated. The thickness of the individual nickel layers shall meet the requirements of this document (see 8.1)(See 8.1).
b. Measurements should normally be made in low to medium current density areas on significant surfaces whenever part geometry permits. The customer specified plating thickness check points are usually suitable locations for making "STEP" test measurements. High current density areas of a part can be expected to exhibit values at least 15 to 20 mV greater than the low current density areas of the same part.
c. At least two measurements should be made at any given test site and the average value reported. Test spots must not touch or overlap each other. The individual readings at any one site should not vary from each other by more than 10%. Large variations suggest poor technique, faulty equipment, or defective deposits (e.g., cracks, pits, dirt inclusion, etc.).
d. The millivolt "STEP" potential difference between the various nickel layers shall be measured at the mid or low current density areas (see 9.2) (See 9.2 [b]) and shall exhibit the relative values and activities listed as follows:
   1. 100 mV: Minimum difference between bright and semibright nickel layers with the bright nickel more active than the semibright. A difference of at least 125 mV is recommended as the statistical mean with values of 100 mV as the absolute minimum. Maximum values have yet to be determined, but generally should not exceed 200 mV.
   2. 20 mV: Minimum difference between the bright nickel and the high activity nickel strike (between the semibright and bright nickel) when one is present. The high activity nickel strike shall be more active than the bright nickel layer.
   3. 20 mV: Maximum difference between the bright nickel and any subsequent nickel strike or microdiscontinuous nickel layer when one is present. This layer shall be less active than, or equal to, the activity of the bright nickel layer.
e. It is stressed that successfully meeting the "STEP" requirements of this document without conforming to other deposit requirements, such as thickness, ductility, chromium microdiscontinuity, CASS test, etc., may result in premature failure of the plated part in service. All the requirements of this document must be complied with to achieve maximum corrosion protection.

10. Ductility—Test Method: ASTM B 490

The ductility of the composite electrodeposit on the finished part is considered acceptable when foils plated out of the individual nickel baths meet or exceed the following values:

Semibright Nickel67%
Bright Nickel11%

NOTE—A fully ductile individual nickel layer will have a foil test value 100% when computed using the formula D = 100 T/(2R-T).

11. Specifications for Microdiscontinuity

11.1 Determination of Microdiscontinuity and Active Sites—Determination of microdiscontinuity after chromium plate, and active sites after corrosion testing, shall be conducted as per ASTM B 456, Appendix X4. However, to determine active sites, the chromium layer in the area to be examined shall be stripped using hydrochloric acid (concentrated), so that the corrosion sites in the nickel layer are more easily seen and counted.

11.2 Microdiscontinuity After Chromium Plate—There shall be a minimum of 10 000 pores/cm^2 (64 000/in^2).

A maximum quantity of pores has not been established, but is dictated by visual acceptance, both before and after environmental testing, as agreed on between the customer and supplier. (The minimum number of cracks required when a trivalent chromium deposit is used, has not been established.)

11.3 Active Sites After Corrosion Testing (CASS)—There shall be a minimum of 10 000 pores/cm^2 (64 000/in^2) after 22 h CASS test. The chromium deposit must be stripped off after the CASS test, but prior to counting and measuring the active sites. The active sites shall be limited in depth to the bright nickel layer and the average diameter shall not exceed 31 μm (0.0025 in) in diameter after 44 h CASS test. No individual site shall exceed 63 μm (0.0025 in). Active sites with a diameter less than 10% of the diameter of the largest site present shall not be counted toward meeting the minimum number of active sites.

12. Accelerated Corrosion—The CASS test shall be carried out in strict accordance with ASTM B 368. Nickel weight loss panels[2], collection rates, pH and specific gravity should preferably be run with every CASS test cycle (22 h) or at least once a week. Nickel panel weight loss measurements shall be made whenever a new test solution is used or when the cabinet is restarted after any shutdown.

The copper accelerated acetic acid salt spray or CASS test is presently the most widely used accelerated corrosion test in the automotive industry and is the only test considered in this document. The CASS test is not used to predict the number of years a part may last in service, but rather to evaluate the integrity of the entire casting, metal finishing, and plating operation. The CASS test does not have an exact correlation to years of corrosion protection in service. Failure to pass the test may be regarded as a probable indication of early failure in service. The results of other plating test requirements such as deposit thickness, ductility, STEP values, chromium porosity, etc., must also be considered when attempting to predict the performance of plated parts under actual service conditions.

The number of CASS test cycles and hours per cycle shall be specified by the purchaser. Any basis metal corrosion (white rust) on significant surfaces after 22 h of CASS testing means the part has failed. The corrosion and appearance rating after one 22 h CASS cycle shall be at least 10/9 when evaluated according to ASTM B 537 unless otherwise specified by the purchaser.

Parts shall not be rejected because of the formation of the specified active corrosion sites (10.3) normally observed with microdiscontinuous chromium deposits. The appearance of test parts after CASS testing may not reflect the appearance of identical parts in outdoor service.

13. Adhesion—Adhesion of the electroplate to the base metal and between layers of plating must conform to bend (fracture), file, grind, saw, or heat quench requirements as specified by ASTM Standard B 571. No peeling, flaking, or lift-off of the electroplate from the substrate or itself is permitted. Loss of adhesion of the substrate to itself is not considered a plating failure.

It is expected that parts will be capable of meeting all adhesion requirements. Not all the methods listed may be applicable to every part, and test methods used for routine lot control should be established between the user and the supplier.

14. Sampling—Sampling for quality control purposes shall be agreed on between the supplier and purchaser. Various sampling plans are available, such as ASTM B 602, ASTM B 697, or ASTM B 762.

1. National Institute of Standards and Technology Office of Standard Reference Materials, Room B-311 Chemistry Building, Gaithersburg, MD 20899.

2. Suitable nickel panels are obtainable from Metal Samples, Route 1, Box 152, Munford, AL 36268.

SOLDERS—SAE J473a JUN1962

SAE Standard

Report of the SAE Nonferrous Metals Division approved June 1911 and last revised by the SAE Nonferrous Metals Committee June 1962.

Foreword—This Document has not changed other than to put it into the new SAE Technical Standards Board Format.

1. Scope—The choice of the type and grade of solder for any specific purpose will depend on the materials to be joined and the method of applying. Those with higher amounts of tin usually wet and bond more readily and have a narrower semi-molten range than lower amounts of tin.

For strictly economic reasons, it is recommended that the grade of solder metal be selected that contains least amount of tin required to give suitable flowing and adhesive qualities for application.

All the lead-tin solders, with or without antimony, are usually suitable for joining steel and copper base alloys. For galvanized steel or zinc, only Class A solders should be used. Class B solders, containing antimony usually as a substitute for some of the tin or to increase strength and hardness of the filler metal, form intermetallic antimony-zinc compounds, causing the joint to become embrittled. Lead-tin solders are not recommended for joining aluminum, magnesium, or stainless steel.

Permissible impurity levels are shown:

MAX IMPURITIES, %

Bismuth	0.25	Zinc	0.005
Copper	0.08	Aluminum	0.005
Iron	0.02	Other elements, total	0.08

In dipping solders, 0.5% max copper is permissible because of pickup in bath.

Compositions, temperatures, and similar specifications of these SAE solders are shown in Table 1.

TABLE 1—COMPOSITIONS, TEMPERATURES, AND SIMILAR SPECIFICATIONS

SAE No.	Sn	Pb	Sb	Temperature, F Solidus	Temperature, F Liquidus	Similar ASTM Grades in Specification B 32-58T
1A	45.0, –1.0	Remainder	0.4 max	360	440	Alloy 45B
1B	43.0, +0.5	Remainder	1.5–2.00	365	435	
2A	40.0, –1.0	Remainder	0.4 max	360	455	Alloy 40B
2B	38.0, +0.5	Remainder	1.5–2.00	365	450	
3A	30.0, –1.0	Remainder	0.5 max	360	490	Alloy 30B
3B	30.0, –1.0	Remainder	0.75–1.25	365	485	
4A	25.0, –1.0	Remainder	0.4 max	360	510	Alloy 25B
4B	25.0, –1.0	Remainder	1.25–1.75	365	500	
5A	20.0, –1.0	Remainder	0.4 max	360	535	Alloy 20B
5B	20.0, –1.0	Remainder	1.25–1.75	365	510	
6A	15.0, –1.0	Remainder	0.4 max	435	555	Alloy 15B
6B	15.0, –1.0	Remainder	As specified (1)	435–445	530–555	
7A	51.0, –2.0	Remainder	0.4 max	360	420	Alloy 50B
8A	35.0, –1.0	Remainder	0.4 max	360	475	Alloy 35B
9B	2.75, –0.25	Remainder	4.90–5.40 (2)	465	555	

1. Maximum, 2.75%.
2. Also contains 0.40–0.60 arsenic; this solder should be used only with previously tinned base metal. Pure tin or higher tin-lead alloys may be used.

2. References—There are no referenced publications specified herein.

ELECTROPLATING AND RELATED FINISHES —SAE J474 FEB1985

SAE Information Report

Report of the SAE Nonferrous Metals Division approved January 1930, last revised, SAE Nonferrous Metals Committee, June 1972, reaffirmed without change, February 1985.

Foreword—This Document has not changed other than to put it into the new SAE Technical Standards Board Format.

1. Scope—Electroplating is a process whereby an object is coated with one or more relatively thin, tightly adherent layers of one or more metals. It is accomplished by placing the object to be coated on a plating rack or a fixture, or in a basket or in a rotating container in such a manner that a suitable current may flow through it, and then immersing it in a series of solutions and rinses in planned sequence. The advantage to be gained by electroplating may be considerable; broadly speaking, the process is used when it is desired to endow the basis material (selected for cost, material conservation, and physical property reasons) with surface properties it does not possess.

It should be noted that although electroplating is the most widely used process for applying metals to a substrate, they may also be applied by spraying, vacuum deposition, cladding, hot dipping, chemical reduction, mechanical plating, etc. The purpose for applying an electroplate and the metals used for various applications follow.

2. References

2.1 Applicable Publications—The following publications form a part of the specification to the extent specified herein. Unless otherwise indicated the latest revision of SAE publications shall apply.

2.1.1 SAE PUBLICATION—Available from SAE, 400 Commonwealth Drive, Warrendale, PA 15096-0001.

SAE J207—Electroplating of Nickel and Chromium on Metal Parts—Automotive Ornamentation and Hardware

2.1.2 ASTM PUBLICATIONS—Available from ASTM, 100 Barr Harbor Drive, West Conshohocken, PA 19428-2959.

ASTM Book of Standards—Part 7
ASTM A 164—Electrodeposited Coatings of Zinc on Steel
ASTM A 165—Electrodeposited Coatings of Cadmium on Steel
ASTM B 177—Chromium Plating on Steel for Engineering Use
ASTM B 200 —Electrodeposited Coatings of Lead on Steel
ASTM B 253—Preparation of and Electroplating on Aluminum Alloys by the Zincate Process
ASTM B 254—Preparation of and Electroplating on Stainless Steel
ASTM B 456—Electrodeposited Coatings of Nickel Plus Chromium
ASTM B 503—Use of Copper and Nickel Electroplating Solutions for Electroforming
ASTM B 545—Electrodeposited Coatings of Tin

2.1.3 OTHER PUBLICATIONS

Allen Gray, *Modern Electroplating*. The Electrochemical Society, Inc. Vols. 1 and 2, New York: John Wiley & Sons.

Herbert H. Uhlig, *Corrosion Handbook*. The Electrochemical Society, Inc. New York: John Wiley & Sons.

William Blum and George B. Hogaboom, *Principles of Electroplating and Electroforming*. New York: McGraw-Hill.

A. K. Graham and H. L. Pinkerton, *Electroplating Engineers Handbook* (Second Edition). New York: Reinhold Publishing Co.

Metal Finishing Guide Book and Directory. Westwood, N.J.: Metal and Plastics Publications.

Lester F. Spencer, "Electroplated Coatings—Selection Factors." *Metal Finishing*, Vol. 69, No. 9 (September 1971) and No. 10 (October 1971).

J. B. Mohler, "Primer on Electrodeposited Coatings." *Materials Engineering*, Vol. 75, No. 1 (January 1972).

3. Decorative-Protective Coatings—This type of coating has as its prime purpose the maintenance of an acceptable appearance on a product exposed to various service conditions involving wear and/or corrosion, Typical examples are door handles, bumpers, nameplates, and other bright finished hardware. For this application the copper/nickel/chromium, the nickel/chromium, or other combinations of these metals are most frequently used. However, zinc, brass, tin, cadmium, gold, silver, and rhodium may also be used where a unique appearance and/or a specific protective quality is desired. (See SAE J207.)

4. Protective Coatings—Protective coatings can be classified as either sacrificial or barrier type. Both cadmium and zinc are well known as sacrificial coatings, being more active chemically than the substrate and offering protection by being preferentially attacked. Since it is relatively inexpensive and readily applied in a plating barrel or tank, or mechanically applied, zinc is often preferred for coating ferrous parts. However, due to the lesser amount of corrosion products that may form under similar corrosive conditions, cadmium is preferred over zinc in applications where the buildup of corrosion products would have a detrimental effect, such as restricted movement of closely fitted parts of the prevention of current flow in electrical components. In addition, cadmium is more readily solderable.

Tin and its alloys are examples of barrier-type coatings. These coatings protect by serving as an inactive barrier between the substrate and the environment. Such coatings must be thick enough to be free of discontinuities, otherwise corrosion will take place at any void in the coating. Applications of protective coatings include screws, nuts, bolts, and other fasteners; components of mechanical assemblies, and control mechanisms.

5. Engineering Coatings—Functional enhancement of a component by the use of an electroplated coating is recognized. Among the many applications, the more important usages include:

a. Abrasion and scratch protection as provided by a coating that is harder than the basis metal. Coatings of chromium, nickel (both electrodeposited and electroless), tin-nickel, or iron are examples of hard coatings.
b. Use of soft electrodeposits, such as silver, lead, tin-lead, indium, or lead-indium which adjust to minor imperfections in mating surfaces, are suitable as bearing surfaces.
c. Use of electrodeposits such as chromium, iron, or nickel for rebuilding undersized parts.
d. The use of various electrodeposits in specialized fields such as in coating of conductors and plating of plastics and ceramics, in both the electrical and electronic fields.

6. Electroforming—Electroforming is the production or reproduction of articles by electrodeposition. Typical applications are the production of printing plates, phonograph matrices, patterns, molds, dies, and paint masks made of electrodeposited copper, iron, nickel, and other metals.

NOTE—It should be stressed that this writing is only a very brief introduction to the subject of electroplating and related finishes. Detailed information on the subject may be found in one or more of the publications appearing in the bibliography and in the specifications listing.

7. Bibliography

1. Allen Gray, *Modern Electroplating*. The Electrochemical Society, Inc. Vols. 1 and 2, New York: John Wiley & Sons.
2. Herbert H. Uhlig, *Corrosion Handbook*. The Electrochemical Society, Inc. New York: John Wiley & Sons.
3. William Blum and George B. Hogaboom, *Principles of Electroplating and Electroforming*. New York: McGraw-Hill.
4. A. K. Graham and H. L. Pinkerton, *Electroplating Engineers Handbook* (Second Edition). New York: Reinhold Publishing Co.
5. *Metal Finishing Guide Book and Directory*. Westwood, N.J.: Metal and Plastics Publications.
6. Lester F. Spencer, "Electroplated Coatings—Selection Factors." *Metal Finishing*, Vol. 69, No. 9 (September 1971) and No. 10 (October 1971).
7. J. B. Mohler, "Primer on Electrodeposited Coatings." *Materials Engineering*, Vol. 75, No. 1 (January 1972).

8. ASTM Specifications [1]

9. Decorative-Protective Coatings—B 456 Electrodeposited Coatings of Nickel Plus Chromium

B 253 Preparation of and Electroplating on Aluminum Alloys by the Zincate Process

B 254 Preparation of and Electroplating on Stainless Steel

10. Protective Coatings—A 165 Electrodeposited Coatings of Cadmium on Steel

B 545 Electrodeposited Coatings of Tin

A 164 Electrodeposited Coatings of Zinc on Steel

11. Engineering Coatings—B 488 Electrodeposited Coatings of Gold for Engineering Uses

B 200 Electrodeposited Coatings of Lead on Steel

B 177 Chromium Plating on Steel for Engineering Use

12. Electroforming—B 503 Use of Copper and Nickel Electroplating Solutions for Electroforming

1. These and other specifications related to electroplating may be found in ASTM Book of Standards, Part 7.

NONMETALLIC MATERIALS

11 Nonmetallic Materials

CLASSIFICATION SYSTEM FOR RUBBER MATERIALS—SAE J200 NOV2003

SAE Recommended Practice

Report of the SAE Nonmetallic Materials Committee approved May 1962, revised by the SAE Committee on Automotive Rubber Specifications June 1989. Rationale statement available. Completely revised by the SAE Committee on Automotive Rubber Specifications June 1990, and revised June 1991, June 1992, May 1993, June 1994, July 1996, April 1997, and March 1998. Revised by the SAE Coolant Hose Committee November 2001. Rationale statement available. Revised by the SAE Committee on Automotive Rubber Specifications December 2001 and November 2003. Rationale statement available.

Foreword—The original version of this SAE Recommended Practice was prepared jointly by the Society of Automotive Engineers and the American Society for Testing and Materials and bore the designation SAE J200/ANSI/ASTM D 2000. This document superseded and replaced SAE J14/ASTM D 735 and was intended to be used as a source of material quality "line call-out" specifications on procurement documents and drawings.

This Recommended Practice is now under the sole jurisdiction of the SAE Committee on Automotive Rubber Specifications and bears the designation SAE J200.

This document is based on basic physical properties of rubber materials obtained directly from standard compression molded test specimens. Test specimens may be fashioned from finished products or by alternate methods. However, test specimens so prepared may be affected by forming of the product or sample and/or by shaping them for testing. Therefore, test results prepared from finished products or by alternate methods may not duplicate values obtained from standard test specimens.

1. Scope—This classification system tabulates the properties of vulcanized rubber materials (natural rubber, reclaimed rubber, synthetic rubbers, alone or in combination) that are intended for, but not limited to, use in rubber products for automotive applications.

NOTE 1— The SAE Committe on Automotive Rubber Specifications (CARS) has the sole responsibility for SAE J200. CARS Works closely with and receives input from ASTM Subcommittee D11.30 on Classification of Rubber Compounds with the goal to keep SAE J200 and ASTM D 2000 technically equivalent. Candidate materials presented for development of new tables or for inclusion in Tables A1 or A2 of SAE J200 or Table X1.1 of ASTM D 2000 shall be initiated with the SAE CARS Committee. The procedure to be followed is detailed in Appendix C of SAE J200.

NOTE 2— This document may serve many of the needs of other industries in much the same manner as SAE numbered steels. It must be remembered, however, that this system is subject to revision when required by automotive needs. It is recommended that the latest revision always be used. This document is based on the premise that all rubber materials intended for use in rubber products can be arranged into characteristic designations. These designations are determined by types, based on resistance to heat aging, and classes, based on resistance to swelling by oil. Basic levels are thus established which, together with values describing additional requirements, permit complete description of the quality of all rubber materials. In all cases where provisions of this document would conflict with those of the detailed specifications for a particular product, the latter shall take precedence.

NOTE 3— When the rubber product is to be used for purposes where the requirements are too specific to be completely prescribed by this classification system, it is necessary for the purchaser to consult the supplier in advance to establish the appropriate properties, test methods, and specification test limits.

1.1 Purpose

1.1.1 The purpose of this document is to provide guidance to the engineer in the selection of practical, commercially available rubber materials, and further to provide a method for specifying these materials by the use of a simple line call-out designation.

1.1.2 This document was developed to permit the addition of descriptive values for future rubber materials without complete reorganization of the classification system and to facilitate the incorporation of future new methods of test to keep pace with changing industry requirements.

2. References

2.1 Applicable Publications—The following publications form a part of this specification to the extent specified herein.

2.1.1 ASTM Publications—Available from ASTM, 100 Barr Harbor Drive, West Conshohocken, PA 19428-2959.

ASTM D 395—Test Methods for Rubber Property-Compression Test
ASTM D 412—Test Methods for Rubber Properties in Tension
ASTM D 429—Test Methods for Rubber Property—Adhesion to Rigid Substrates
ASTM D 430—Test Methods for Rubber Deterioration-Dynamic Fatigue
ASTM D 471—Test Methods for Rubber Property-Effect of Liquids
ASTM D 573—Test Methods for Rubber Deterioration in an Air Oven
ASTM D 575—Test Methods for Rubber Properties in Compression
ASTM D 624—Test Methods for Rubber Property-Tear Resistance
ASTM D 865—Test Methods for Rubber Deterioration by Heating in Air (Test Tube Enclosure)
ASTM D 925—Test Methods for Rubber Property-Staining of Surfaces (Contact, Migration, and Diffusion)
ASTM D 945—Test Methods for Rubber Properties in Compression or Shear (Mechanical Oscillograph)
ASTM D 1053—Test Method for Rubber Property—Stiffening at Low Temperature; Flexible Polymers and Coated Fabrics
ASTM D 1171—Test Method for Rubber Deterioration—Surface Ozone Cracking Outdoors or Chamber (Triangular Specimens)
ASTM D 1329—Test Method for Evaluating Rubber Property—Retraction at Low Temperatures (TR Test)
ASTM D 1349—Practice for Rubber—Standard Temperatures for Testing
ASTM D 1418—Practice for Rubber and Rubber Lattices—Nomenclature
ASTM D 2137—Test Methods for Rubber Property—Brittleness Point of Flexible Polymers and Coated Fabrics
ASTM D 2240—Test Method for Rubber Property-Durometer Hardness
ASTM D 3183—Practice for Rubber—Preparation of Pieces for Test Purposes from Products

2.1.2 ISO Publications—Available from ANSI, 11 West 42nd Street, New York, NY 10036-8002.

ISO 1629—Rubber and latices—Nomenclature
ISO Guide 25

3. Type and Class

3.1 The prefix letter M shall be used to indicate that this classification system is based on SI units.

NOTE 4—Call-outs not prefixed by the letter M refer to an earlier classification system based on U.S. customary units. This was published in editions prior to 1979.

3.2 Rubber materials shall be designated on the basis of type (heat aging resistance) and class (oil swelling resistance). Type and class are each indicated by letter designations as shown in Tables 1 and 2 and illustrated in 8.1. Type is the first letter after the grade number and class is the second letter. See Appendix A for the types of polymers most often used to meet the specification.

TABLE 1—BASIC REQUIREMENTS FOR ESTABLISHING TYPE BY TEMPERATURE

Type	Test Temperature, °C
A	70
B	100
C	125
D	150
E	175
F	200
G	225
H	250
J	275
K	300

TABLE 2—BASIC REQUIREMENTS FOR ESTABLISHING CLASS BY VOLUME SWELL

Class	Volume Swell, max, %
A	no requirement
B	140
C	120
D	100
E	80
F	60
G	40
H	30
J	20
K	10

3.3 Type is based on changes in tensile strength of not more than ±30%, elongation of not more than -50%, and hardness of not more than ±15 points after heat aging for 70 h at an appropriate temperature. The temperatures at which these materials shall be tested for determining type are listed in Table 1.

3.4 Class is based on the resistance of the material to swelling in ASTM Oil No. 3 after 70 h immersion at a temperature determined from Table 1, except that a maximum temperature of 150 °C (the upper limit of oil stability) shall be used. Limits of swelling for each class are shown in Table 2.

NOTE 5—The selection of type based on heat aging resistance is understood to be indicative of the inherent heat aging resistance that can be normally expected from commercial compositions. Differences in severity of two approved heat aging test methods (ASTM D 865 and D 573) may invalidate direct comparison between those classes of rubber material not tested by the same method. Likewise, choice of class is based on the range of volume swell normally expected from such commercial compositions as established by type. The fact that a type and class of material is listed under Basic Requirements, indicates that materials that meet these requirements for heat aging and oil swelling resistance are commercially available.

NOTE 6—ASTM Oil No. 3 is no longer available (as of December 1993). It has been replaced by IRM903[1], which does not necessarily produce the same degree of swelling as ASTM Oil No. 3. Comparison of the effect of IRM903 versus ASTM Oil No. 3, on most elastomers tested, produces a close correlation.

NOTE 7—Oil aged data in the SAE J200 tables are to be used as a guideline for material selection. Continued conformance will be based on testing in IRM903 oil. Requirements shall be agreed upon between the customer and the material supplier and be specified by use of a "Z" suffix.

3.5 The letter designations shall always be followed by a three-digit number to specify the hardness and the tensile strength—for example, 505. The first digit indicates durometer hardness, for example, 5 for 50 ± 5, 6 for 60 ± 5. The next two digits indicate the minimum tensile strength - for example, 05 for 5 MPa, 14 for 14 MPa. Correlation of available materials for desired hardness and tensile strength is obtained through the elongation values (see 6.2).

4. Grade Numbers, Suffix Letters, and Numbers

4.1 Grade Numbers—Since the basic requirements do not always sufficiently describe all the necessary qualities, provision is made for deviation or adding requirements through a system of prefix grade numbers, suffix letters, and suffix numbers. Grade No. 1 indicates that only the basic requirements are compulsory and no suffix requirements are permitted. Grades other than No. 1 are used for expressing deviations or additional requirements. A grade number is written as a material prefix number preceding the letters for type and class (see 8.1). Grade No. 1 is always an available suffix grade number, and thus is not referenced in the last column of each basic requirement table.

4.2 Suffix Letters—The suffix letters that may be used together with their meaning, appear in Table 3.

4.3 Suffix Numbers—Each suffix letter should preferably be followed by two suffix numbers (see Note 8 in 7.1). The first suffix number always indicates the method of test; time of test is part of the method and is taken from the listings in Table 4. The second suffix number, if used, always indicates the temperature of test and is taken from Table 5. Where three-digit numbers are required, a dash (–) is used for separation, for example: A1–10; B4–10; F1–11.

TABLE 3—MEANING OF SUFFIX LETTERS

Suffix Letter	Test Required
A	Heat Aging Resistance
B	Compression Set
C	Ozone or Weather Resistance
D	Compression-Deflection Resistance
EA	Fluid Resistance (Aqueous)
EF	Fluid Resistance (Fuels)
EO	Fluid Resistance (Oils and Lubricants)
F	Low-Temperature Resistance
G	Tear Resistance
H	Flex Resistance
J	Abrasion Resistance
K	Adhesion
M	Flammability Resistance
N	Impact Resistance
P	Staining Resistance
R	Resilience
Z	Any special requirement which shall be specified in detail

1. Available from R.E. Carroll, P.O. Box 139, Trenton, NJ 08801.

TABLE 4—ASTM METHODS OF TEST(1)

Requirement or Suffix Letter	Basic	1	2	3	4	5	6	7	8
Durometer Hardness (Type A)	D 2240	—	—	—	—	—	—	—	—
Tensile Strength, Elongation	D 412 die C	—	—	—	—	—	—	—	—
Suffix A, Heat Aging Resistance	—	D 573, 70 h	D 865, 70 h	D 865, 168 h	D 573, 168 h	D 573, 1000 h	D 865, 1000 h	—	—
Suffix B, Compression Set	—	D 395, 22 h, Method B, solid	D 395, 70 h, Method B, solid	D 395, 22 h, Method B, plied	D 395, 70 h, Method B, plied	D 395, 1000 h Method B, solid	D 395, 1000 h Method B, plied	—	—
Suffix C, Ozone or Weather Resistance	—	D 1171,(2) ozone exposure, Method A	D 1171,(3) weather exposure	D 1171,(4) ozone exposure, Method B	—	—	—	—	—
Suffix D, Compression-Deflection Resistance	—	D 575, Method A	D 575, Method B	—	—	—	—	—	—

TABLE 4—ASTM METHODS OF TEST[1] (continued)

Requirement or Suffix Letter	Basic	1	2	3	4	5	6	7	8
Suffix EA, Fluid Resistance (Aqueous)	—	D 471, water 70 h[5]	D 471, water-ethylene glycol, 70 h[6]	—	—	—	—	—	—
Suffix EF, Fluid Resistance (Fuels)	—	D 471, Reference Fuel A, 70 h	D 471, Reference Fuel B, 70 h	D 471, Reference Fuel C, 70 h	D 471, Reference Fuel D, 70 h	D 471, 85 volume percent Reference Fuel D plus 15 volume percent denatured anhydrous ethanol,[7] 70 h	D 471, 85 volume percent Reference Fuel C plus 15 volume percent anhydrous ethanol,[7] 70 h	D 471, 85 volume percent Reference Fuel C plus 15 volume percent anhydrous methanol	—
Suffix EO, Fluid Resistance (Oils and Lubricants)	—	D 471, ASTM Oil No. 1,[8] 70 h	D 471, ASTM Oil No. 2,[8] 70 h	D 471, ASTM Oil No. 3,[8] 70 h	D 471, ASTM Oil No. 1,[8] 168 h	D 471, ASTM Oil No. 2,[8] 168 h	D 471, ASTM Oil No. 3, [8] 168 h	D 471, Service Fluid No. 101, [8] 70 h	D 471, Fluid as designated in Table 6, [8] 70 h
Suffix F, Low-Temperature Resistance	—	D 2137, Method A, paragraph 9.3.2 3 min	D 1053, 5 min T_2 or T_5 or T_{10} or T_{50} or T_{100}	D 2137, Method A, Paragraph 9.3.2, 22 h	D 1329, 38.1 mm die, 50% elongation, 10 min, paragraph 7.5, retraction 10% min	D 1329, 38.1 mm 50% elongation, 10 min, paragraph 7.5, retraction 50% min	—	—	—
Suffix G, Tear Resistance	—	D 624, die B	D 624, die C	—	—	—	—	—	—
Suffix H, Flex Resistance	—	D 430, Method A	D 430, Method B	D 430, Method C	—	—	—	—	—
Suffix J, Abrasion Resistance[9]	—			—	—	—	—	—	—
Suffix K, Adhesion	—	D 429, Method A	D 429, Method B	[10]	—	—	—	—	—
Suffix M, Flammability Resistance[9]	—	—	—	—	—	—	—	—	—
Suffix N, Impact Resistance[9]	—	—	—	—	—	—	—	—	—
Suffix P, Staining Resistance	—	D 925, Method A	D 925, Method B, Control Panel	—	—	—	—	—	—
Suffix R, Resilience	—	D 945	—	—	—	—	—	—	—
Suffix Z, Special Requirement[9]	—	—	—	—	—	—	—	—	—

1. The designations refer to the following methods of the American Society for Testing and Materials.
   ASTM D 395—Test Methods for Rubber Property-Compression Test
   ASTM D 412—Test Methods for Rubber Properties in Tension
   ASTM D 429—Test Methods for Rubber Property-Adhesion to Rigid Substrates
   ASTM D 430—Test Methods for Rubber Deterioration-Dynamic Fatigue
   ASTM D 471—Test Methods for Rubber Property-Effect of Liquids
   ASTM D 573—Test Methods for Rubber Deterioration in an Air Oven
   ASTM D 575—Test Methods for Rubber Properties in Compression
   ASTM D 624—Test Methods for Rubber Property-Tear Resistance
   ASTM D 865—Test Methods for Rubber Deterioration by Heating in Air (Test Tube Enclosure)
   ASTM D 925—Test Methods for Rubber Property-Staining of Surfaces (Contact, Migration, and Diffusion)
   ASTM D 945—Test Methods for Rubber Properties in Compression or Shear (Mechanical Oscillograph)
   ASTM D 1053—Test Method for Rubber Property-Stiffening at Low Temperature; Flexible Polymers and Coated Fabrics
   ASTM D 1171—Test Methods for Rubber Deterioration-Surface Ozone Cracking Outdoors or Chamber (Triangular Specimens)
   ASTM D 1329—Test Method for Evaluating Rubber Property-Retraction at Low Temperatures (TR Test)
   ASTM D 1349—Practice for Rubber-Standard Temperatures for Testing
   ASTM D 1418—Practice for Rubber and Rubber Lattices — Nomenclature
   ASTM D 2137—Test Methods for Rubber Property-Brittleness Point of Flexible Polymers and Coated Fabrics
   ASTM D 2240—Test Method for Rubber Property-Durometer Hardness
   ASTM D 3183—Practice for Rubber-Preparation of Pieces for Test Purposes from Products
2. Use ozone chamber exposure method of ASTM Method D 1171, Method A.
3. ASTM Method D 1171, Weather Test, is 6 weeks duration. Test area and time of year to be agreed upon by the purchaser and the manufacturer.
4. Use ozone chamber exposure method of ASTM Method D 1171, Method B.
5. Distilled water shall be used. Volume increase by water displacement method, except alcohol dip omitted. When determining changes in tensile strength, elongation, and hardness, test tube to be 3/4 full after specimens are immersed. Determination to be made after 30 min. Cool in distilled water; acetone dip to be omitted.
6. Equal parts by volume of distilled water and reagent grade ethylene glycol. Volume increase by displacement method, except alcohol dip omitted. When determining changes in tensile strength, elongation, and hardness, test tube to be 3/4 full after specimens are immersed. Determination to be made after 30 min. Cool in distilled water; acetone dip to be omitted.
7. Anhydrous ethanol denatured with unleaded gasoline according to CDA formula #20. Sources are Archer-Daniels-Midland, P.O. Box 1445, Cedar Rapids, Iowa 52406 and Ralph Shrader Inc., 2450 Lovette Avenue, Detroit, Michigan 48210.
8. ASTM Oil No. 1 is available from: MZF Assoc., 11200 Homedale Street, Los Angeles, CA 90049.
   ASTM Oils No. 2 and 3 are no longer commercially available.
   ASTM Service Fluid 101 is available as Anderol 774 from Hüls AG Division, P.O. Box 2, Turner Place, Piscataway, NJ 08854.
   ASTM Service Fluid 102 consists of 95 mass percent ASTM No. 1 Oil + 5 mass percent Anglamol 99. Anglamol 99 is available from Lubrizol Corp., P.O. Box 17100, Cleveland, OH 44117.
   The above fluids are intended for comparative testing purposes. Commercial fluids may produce different results.
9. Test Method to be specified.
10. Bond made after vulcanization. Method of evaluation and requirement shall be based on agreement between fabricator and end user.

TABLE 5—SUFFIX NUMBERS TO INDICATE TEMPERATURE OF TEST

Applicable Suffix Requirements	Second Suffix No.	Test Temperature °C(1)
	11	275
	10	250
	9	225
	8	200
	7	175
	6	150
A, B, C,	5	125
EA, EF, EO,	4	100
G, K,	3	70
	2	38
	1	23
	0	(2)
	1	23
	2	0
	3	−10
	4	−18
	5	−25
	6	−35
F	7	−40
	8	−50
	9	−55
	10	−65
	11	−75
	12	−80

1. These test temperatures are based on the ASTM Recommended Practice D 1349. Annual Book of ASTM Standards, Parts 37 and 38.
2. Ambient temperature in the case of outdoor testing.

5. Composition and Manufacture

5.1 This classification is predicated upon materials, furnished under a specification based thereon, being manufactured from natural rubber, reclaimed rubber, synthetic rubber, alone or in combination, together with added compounding materials of such nature and quantity as to produce vulcanizates that comply with the specified requirements. All materials and workmanship shall be in accordance with good commercial practice, and the resulting product shall be free of porous areas, weak sections, bubbles, foreign matter, or other defects affecting serviceability.

5.2 Color—With the exception of FC, FE, FK, and GE materials, the values in the material tables are based on black compounds and comparable values may not be available in color.

6. Basic Requirements

6.1 The basic requirements for physical properties of available rubber materials are listed in Tables 6.AA to 6.KK[2] are based on test results obtained on test specimens having the highest and lowest tensile strength specified for each grade and durometer range.

Test results from specimens prepared from finished products may not duplicate values obtained from standard test specimens.

NOTE 8—When standard test specimens can be cut from finished parts in accordance with ASTM D 3183[3] a deviation to the extent of 10% (on tensile strength and elongation values only) is permissible when agreed upon by the purchaser and the supplier. This deviation is permissible only because of the recognized effects of knitting, grain, and buffing on the material when test specimens are prepared from finished parts and tested for tensile strength and elongation. This deviation is intended to apply to goods purchased by the government. For all other uses, when differences due to the method of processing or to the difficulty in obtaining suitable test specimens from the finished part arise, the purchaser and the supplier may agree on acceptable deviations. This can be done by comparing results of standard test specimens with those obtained on actual parts.

6.2 The available materials are listed in the appropriate material section of the table, giving each hardness and tensile strength grade with its appropriate elongation value. Also, there is a repetition of the values for the basic heat and oil aging requirements for the material resulting from the assignment of type and class. Compression set values are basic requirements to ensure proper vulcanization.

6.3 Available suffix numbers for each available rubber material are shown in the last column under Basic Requirements.

7. Suffix Requirements

7.1 Supplementary (suffix) requirements for available grades are listed in Tables 6.AA to 6.HK.

Suffix requirements shall be specified only as needed to define qualities necessary to meet service requirements. These suffix requirements are set forth for the various grade numbers. Suffix letters and suffix numbers describing these suffix requirements may be used singly or in combination, but not all suffix values available for a given material need be specified.

2. Tensile strength values (psi) shown in Tables 6.AA to 6.KK are for information purposes only.
3. Annual Book of ASTM Standards, Section 9, Volume 09.01.

TABLE 6.AA—BASIC AND SUPPLEMENTARY (SUFFIX) REQUIREMENTS FOR CLASSIFICATION OF RUBBER MATERIALS—AA MATERIALS

Durometer Hardness, ±5 points	Tensile Strength, min (MPa)	Tensile Strength, min (psi)	Ultimate Elongation, min, %	Heat Aged, ASTM D 573, 70 h at 70 °C	Oil Immersion, ASTM D 471, No. 3 Oil[1] 70 h at 70 °C	Compression Set, ASTM D 395, Method B, Solid, max, %, 22 h at 70 °C	Available Suffix Grade Numbers
30	7	1015	400				2, 4
30	10	1450	400				2, 4
30	14	2031	400				2, 4
40	7	1015	400				2, 4
40	10	1450	400				2, 4
40	14	2031	400				2, 4
40	17	2466	500				2, 4
40	21	3046	600				2, 4
50	3	435	250				2
50	6	870	250				2
50	7	1015	400				2, 3
50	8	1160	400				2, 3
50	10	1450	400				2, 3, 4, 5
50	14	2031	400				2, 3, 4, 5
50	17	2466	400				2, 3, 4, 5
50	21	3046	500				2, 3, 4, 5
60	3	435	250				2
60	6	870	250	Change in durometer hardness,			2
60	7	1015	300	±15 points			2, 3
60	8	1160	300	Change in tensile strength, ±30%	No requirement	Compression set, 50% max	2, 3
60	10	1450	350	Change in ultimate elongation,			2, 3, 4, 5
60	14	2031	400	-60% max			2, 3, 4, 5
60	17	2466	400				2, 3, 4, 5
60	21	3046	400				2, 3, 4, 5
60	24	3481	500				2, 3, 4, 5
70	3	435	150				2
70	6	870	150				2
70	7	1015	200				2, 3
70	8	1160	200				2, 3
70	10	1450	250				2, 3, 4, 5
70	14	2031	300				2, 3, 4, 5
70	17	2466	300				2, 3, 4, 5
70	21	3046	350				2, 3, 4, 5
80	3	435	100				2
80	7	1015	100				2
80	10	1450	150				2
80	14	2031	200				2
80	17	2466	200				2
90	3	435	75				2
90	7	1015	100				2
90	10	1450	125				2

1. See Note 6 in 3.4.

TABLE 6.AA—SUPPLEMENTARY (SUFFIX) REQUIREMENTS FOR CLASSIFICATION OF RUBBER MATERIALS—AA MATERIALS (Continued)

	Suffix Requirements	Grade 1	Grade 2	Grade 3	Grade 4	Grade 5	Grade 6	Grade 7	Grade 8
A13	Heat aging resistance, ASTM D 573, 70 h at 70° C:								
	Change in hardness, max, points	Basic Requirements Only	±15		+10	+10			
	Change in tensile strength, max, %	Basic Requirements Only	±30		-25	-25			
	Change in ultimate elongation, max, %	Basic Requirements Only	-50		-25	-25			
B13	Compression set, ASTM D 395, Method B, 22 h at 70 °C, max, %	Basic Requirements Only		25	25	25			
B33	Compression set, ASTM D 395, Method B, 22 h at 70 °C, max, %	Basic Requirements Only		35	35	35			
C12	Resistance to ozone, ASTM D 1171, quality retention rating, min, %	Basic Requirements Only	85		85				
C20	Resistance to outdoor aging, ASTM D 1171, quality retention rating, min, %	Basic Requirements Only	85	85	85	85			
EA14	Fluid resistance, ASTM D 471, water, 70 h at 100 °C, volume change, max, %	Basic Requirements Only	10	10	10	10			
F17	Low-temperature resistance, ASTM D 2137, Method A, paragraph 9.3.2, nonbrittle after 3 min at -40 °C	Basic Requirements Only	pass	pass	pass	pass			
G21	Tear resistance, ASTM D 624, Die C:								
	Under 7.0 MPa tensile strength, min, kN/m	Basic Requirements Only		22	22	22			
	Over 7.0 MPa tensile strength, min, kN/m	Basic Requirements Only		26	26	26			
K11	Adhesion, ASTM D 429, Method A, min, MPa	Basic Requirements Only	1.4	2.8	1.4	2.8			
K21	Adhesion, ASTM D 429, Method B, min, kN/m	Basic Requirements Only	7	7	7	7			
P2	Staining resistance, ASTM D 925, Method B, Control Panel, Nonstaining	Basic Requirements Only	pass	pass	pass	pass			
Z	Special requirements, specified in detail (including test methods & aging parameters), or additional requirements per Tables 3, 4, and 5 specified as in Section 8.2								

TABLE 6.AK—BASIC REQUIREMENTS FOR CLASSIFICATION OF RUBBER MATERIALS—AK MATERIALS

Durometer Hardness, ±5 points	Tensile Strength, min (MPa)	Tensile Strength, min (psi)	Ultimate Elongation, min, %	Heat Aged, ASTM D 573, 70 h at 70 °C	Oil Immersion, ASTM D 471, No. 3 Oil(1) 70 h at 70 °C	Compression Set, ASTM D 395, Method B, Solid, max, %, 22 h at 70 °C	Available Suffix Grade Numbers
40	3	435	400				2
50	3	435	400				2
60	5	725	300	Change in durometer hardness, ±15 points Change in tensile strength, ±30% Change in ultimate elongation, -50% max	Volume change, +10% max	Compression set, 50% max	2
70	7	1015	250				2
80	7	1015	150				3
90	7	1015	100				3

1. See Note 6 in 3.4.

TABLE 6.AK—SUPPLEMENTARY (SUFFIX) REQUIREMENTS FOR CLASSIFICATION OF RUBBER MATERIALS—AK MATERIALS (CONTINUED)

	Suffix Requirements	Grade 1	Grade 2	Grade 3	Grade 4	Grade 5	Grade 6	Grade 7	Grade 8
A14	Heat aging resistance, ASTM D 573, 70 h at 100 °C:								
	Change in durometer hardness, max, points	Basic Requirements Only	+15	+15					
	Change in tensile strength, max, %	Basic Requirements Only	-15	-15					
	Change in ultimate elongation, max, %	Basic Requirements Only	-40	-40					
B33	Compression set, ASTM D 395, Method B, 22 h at 70 °C max, %	Basic Requirements Only	50	50					
EO14	Fluid resistance, ASTM D 471, No. 1 Oil, 70 h at 100 °C:								
	Change in volume, %	Basic Requirements Only	-3 to +5	-3 to +5					
EO34	Fluid resistance, ASTM D 471, No. 3 Oil(1), 70 h at 100 °C:								
	Change in durometer hardness, points	Basic Requirements Only	-5 to +10	-5 to +10					
	Change in tensile strength, max, %	Basic Requirements Only	-30	-30					
	Change in ultimate elongation, max, %	Basic Requirements Only	-50	-50					
F17	Low-temperature resistance, ASTM D 2137, Method A, 9.3.2, nonbrittle, 3 min at -40 °C	Basic Requirements Only	pass						
Z	Special requirements, specified in detail (including test method & aging parameters), or additional requirements per Tables 3, 4, and 5 per Section 8.2.								

1. See Note 6 in 3.4.

TABLE 6.BA—BASIC REQUIREMENTS FOR THE CLASSIFICATION OF RUBBER MATERIALS—BA MATERIALS

Durometer Hardness, ±5 points	Tensile Strength, min (MPa)	Tensile Strength, min (psi)	Ultimate Elongation, min, %	Heat Aged, ASTM D 573, 70 h at 100 °C	Oil Immersion, ASTM D 471, No. 3 Oil[1] 70 h at 100 °C	Compression Set, ASTM D 395, Method B, Solid, max, %, 22 h at 70 °C	Available Suffix Grade Numbers
20[2]	6	870	400				3
30	7	1015	400				2
30	10	1450	400				2,3,4,5
30	14	2031	400				2,3,4,5
40	3	435	300				2,8
40	7	1015	300				2,8
40	10	1450	400				2,3,4,5,6
40	14	2031	400				2,3,4,5
50	7	1015	300				2,8
50	10	1450	400				2,3,4,5,6
50	14	2031	400				2,3,4,5
50	17	2466	400				2,3,4,5
60	3	435	250				8
60	6	870	250	Change in durometer hardness,			8
60	7	1015	300	±15 points			2,8
60	10	1450	350	Change in tensile strength, ±30%	No requirement	Compression set, 50% max	2,3,4,5,6
60	14	2031	400	Change in ultimate elongation,			2,3,4,5,6
60	17	2466	400	-50% max			2,3,4,5,6
70	3	435	150				8
70	6	870	150				8
70	7	1015	200				2,8
70	8	1160	200				8
70	10	1450	250				2,3,4,5,6
70	14	2031	300				2,3,4,5
70	17	2466	300				2,3,4,5
80	7	1015	100				2,7
80	10	1450	150				2,4
80	14	2031	200				2,4
90	3	435	75				7
90	7	1015	100				2,7
90	10	1450	125				2,4

1. See Note 6 in 3.4.
2. Materials would typically be 20 to 25 durometer based upon current capability.

TABLE 6.BA—SUPPLEMENTARY (SUFFIX) REQUIREMENTS FOR THE CLASSIFICATION OF RUBBER MATERIALS—BA MATERIALS (CONTINUED)

	Suffix Requirements	Grade 1	Grade 2	Grade 3	Grade 4	Grade 5	Grade 6	Grade 7	Grade 8
A14	Heat aging resistance ASTM D 573, 70 h at 100 °C:								
	Change in hardness, max, points	Basic Requirements Only		+10	+10				
	Change in tensile strength, max, %	Basic Requirements Only		-25	-25				
	Change in ultimate elongation, max, %	Basic Requirements Only		-25	-25				
B13	Compression set, ASTM D 395, Method B, 22 h at 70 °C, max, %	Basic Requirements Only		25			25		25
C12	Resistance to ozone, ASTM D 1171, quality retention rating, min, %	Basic Requirements Only	100	100	100	100	100	100	100
F17	Low-temperature resistance, ASTM D 2137, Method A, 9.3.2, nonbrittle after 3 min at -40 °C	Basic Requirements Only	pass	pass	pass	pass			
F19	Low-temperature resistance, ASTM D 2137, Method A, 9.3.2, nonbrittle after 3 min at -55 °C	Basic Requirements Only		pass		pass			
K11	Adhesion, ASTM D 429, Method A, min, MPa	Basic Requirements Only		1.4	1.4	1.4	1.4		
K21	Adhesion, ASTM D 429, Method B, min, kN/m	Basic Requirements Only		7.0	7.0	7.0			
K31	Adhesion, bond made after vulcanization	Basic Requirements Only		(1)	(1)	(1)			
Z	Special requirements, specified in detail (including test method & aging parameters), or additional requirements per Tables 3, 4, and 5 per Section 8.2								

1. Method of evaluation and requirement shall be based on agreement between fabricator and end user.

TABLE 6.BC—BASIC REQUIREMENTS FOR THE CLASSIFICATION OF RUBBER MATERIALS—BC MATERIALS

Durometer Hardness, ±5 points	Tensile Strength, min (MPa)	Tensile Strength, min (psi)	Ultimate Elongation, min, %	Heat Aged, ASTM D 573, 70 h at 100 °C	Oil immersion, ASTM D 471, No. 3 Oil[1] 70 h at 100 °C	Compression Set, ASTM D 395, Method B, Solid, max, %, 22 h at 100 °C	Available Suffix Grade Numbers
30	3	435	300				2, 5
30	7	1015	400				2, 5
30	10	1450	500				2, 5
30	14	2031	500				2
40	3	435	300				2
40	7	1015	400				2, 5
40	10	1450	500				2, 5
40	14	2031	500				2, 5
40	17	2466	500				2
50	3	435	300				2, 5
50	7	1015	300				2, 5
50	10	1450	350				2, 5, 6
50	14	2031	400				2, 5, 6
50	17	2466	450				2, 6
50	21	3046	500				2, 6
50	24	3481	500				2, 6
60	3	435	300				3, 5
60	7	1015	300	Change in durometer hardness,			3, 5
60	10	1450	350	±15 points	Volume change,	Compression set, 80% max	3, 5, 6
60	14	2031	350	Change in tensile strength, ±30%	+120% max		3, 6
60	17	2466	400	Change in ultimate elongation,			3, 6
60	21	3046	400	-60% max			3, 6
60	24	3481	400				3, 6
70	3	435	200				3, 5
70	7	1015	200				3, 5
70	10	1450	250				3, 5, 6
70	14	2031	300				3, 5, 6
70	17	2466	300				3, 6
70	21	3046	300				3, 6
80	3	435	100				4
80	7	1015	100				4
80	10	1450	100				4
80	14	2031	150				4
90	3	435	50				4
90	7	1015	100				4
90	10	1450	150				4
90	14	2031	150				4

1. See Note 6 in 3.4.

TABLE 6.BC—SUPPLEMENTARY (SUFFIX) REQUIREMENTS FOR THE CLASSIFICATION OF RUBBER MATERIALS—BC MATERIALS (CONTINUED)

	Suffix Requirements	Grade 1	Grade 2	Grade 3	Grade 4	Grade 5	Grade 6	Grade 7	Grade 8
A14	Heat aging resistance, ASTM D 573, 70 h at 100 °C:								
	Change in hardness, max, points	Basic Requirements Only	+15	+15	+15	+15	+15		
	Change in tensile strength, max, %	Basic Requirements Only	-15	-15	-15	-15	-15		
	Change in ultimate elongation, max, %	Basic Requirements Only	-40	-40	-40	-40	-40		
B14	Compression set, ASTM D 395, Method B, 22 h at 100 °C, max, %	Basic Requirements Only	35	35	35	35	35		
C12	Resistance to ozone, ASTM D 1171, quality retention rating, min, %	Basic Requirements Only	100	100	100	100	100		
EO14	Fluid resistance, ASTM D 471, No. 1 Oil, 70 h at 100 °C:								
	Change in hardness, points	Basic Requirements Only	±10	±10	±10	±10	±10		
	Change in tensile strength, max, %	Basic Requirements Only	-30	-30	-30	-30	-30		
	Change in ultimate elongation, max, %	Basic Requirements Only	-30	-30	-30	-30	-30		
	Change in volume, %	Basic Requirements Only	-10 to +15	-10 to +15	-10 to +15	-10 to +15	-10 to +15		
EO34	Fluid resistance, ASTM D 471, No. 3 Oil[1] 70 h at 100 °C:								
	Change in tensile strength, max, %	Basic Requirements Only	-70	-60	-45	-60	-60		
	Change in ultimate elongation, max, %	Basic Requirements Only	-55	-50	-30	-60	-50		
	Change in volume, max, %	Basic Requirements Only	+120	+100	+80	+100	+100		
F17	Low-temperature resistance, ASTM D 2137, Method A, 9.3.2, nonbrittle after 3 min at -40 °C	Basic Requirements Only	pass	pass	pass		pass		
F19	Low-temperature resistance, ASTM D 2137, Method A, 9.3.2, nonbrittle after 3 min at -65 °C					pass			
G21	Tear resistance, ASTM D 624, Die C:								
	Under 7.0 MPa tensile strength, min, kN/m	Basic Requirements Only	22	22	22				
	7.0 to 10 MPa tensile strength, min, kN/m	Basic Requirements Only	26	26	26				
	10 MPa tensile strength and over, min, kN/m	Basic Requirements Only	26	26	26	26	26		
K11	Adhesion, ASTM D 429, Method A, min, MPa	Basic Requirements Only	1.4	1.4	1.4	1.4	2.8		
P2	Staining resistance, ASTM D 925, Method B, Control Panel, Nonstaining	Basic Requirements Only	pass	pass	pass				
Z	Special requirements, specified in detail (including test method & aging parameters), or additional requirements per Tables 3, 4, and 5 per Section 8.2								

1. See Note 6 in 3.4.

TABLE 6.BE—BASIC REQUIREMENTS FOR THE CLASSIFICATION OF RUBBER MATERIALS—BE MATERIALS

Durometer Hardness, ±5 points	Tensile Strength, min (MPa)	Tensile Strength, min (psi)	Ultimate Elongation, min, %	Heat Aged, ASTM D 573, 70 h at 100 °C	Oil Immersion, ASTM D 471, No. 3 Oil[1] 70 h at 100 °C	Compression Set, ASTM D 395, Method B, Solid, max, %, 22 h at 100 °C	Available Suffix Grade Numbers
40	3	435	500			40	2
40	7	1015	500			40	2
50	3	435	350			40	2
50	6	870	350			40	2
50	7	1015	400			40	2
50	10	1450	400			40	2,3
50	14	2031	400			40	2
60	3	435	300			40	2
60	6	870	300			40	2
60	7	1015	350	Change in durometer hardness,		40	2
60	10	1450	350	±15 points	Volume change,	40	2,3
60	14	2031	350	Change in tensile strength, ±30%	+80% max	40	2
				Change in ultimate elongation,			
70	3	435	200	-60% max		50	2
70	6	870	200			50	2
70	7	1015	200			50	2
70	10	1450	250			50	2,3
70	14	2031	250			50	2
70	17	2466	250			50	2
80	7	1015	100			50	2
80	10	1450	100			50	2
80	14	2031	150			50	2
80	17	2466	150			50	2
90	7	1015	100			50	2
90	10	1450	100			50	2
90	14	2031	150			50	2

1. See Note 6 in 3.4.

TABLE 6.BE—SUPPLEMENTARY (SUFFIX) REQUIREMENTS FOR THE CLASSIFICATION OF RUBBER MATERIALS—BE MATERIALS (CONTINUED)

	Suffix Requirements	Grade 1	Grade 2	Grade 3	Grade 4	Grade 5	Grade 6	Grade 7	Grade 8
A14	Heat aging resistance, ASTM D 573, 70 h at 100° C:								
	Change in hardness, max, points	Basic Requirements Only	+15	+15					
	Change in tensile strength, max, %	Basic Requirements Only	-15	-15					
	Change in ultimate elongation, max, %	Basic Requirements Only	-40	-40					
B14	Compression set, ASTM D 395, Method B 22 h at 100 °C, max, %	Basic Requirements Only	25	25					
C12	Resistance to ozone, ASTM D 1171, quality retention rating, min, %	Basic Requirements Only	100	100					
EO14	Fluid resistance, ASTM D 471, No. 1 Oil, 70 h at 100 °C:								
	Change in hardness, points	Basic Requirements Only	±10	±10					
	Change in tensile strength, max, %	Basic Requirements Only	-30	-30					
	Change in ultimate elongation, max, %	Basic Requirements Only	-30	-30					
	Change in volume, %	Basic Requirements Only	-10 to +15	-10 to +15					
EO34	Fluid resistance, ASTM D 471, No. 3 Oil[1], 70 h at 100 °C:								
	Change in tensile strength, max, %	Basic Requirements Only	-50	-50					
	Change in ultimate elongation, max, %	Basic Requirements Only	-40	-40					
F17	Low-temperature resistance, ASTM D 2137, Method A, 9.3.2, nonbrittle after 3 min at -40 °C	Basic Requirements Only	pass						
F19	Low-temperature resistance, ASTM D 2137, Method A, 9.3.2, nonbrittle after 3 min at -55 °C	Basic Requirements Only		pass					
G21	Tear resistance, ASTM D 624, Die C:								
	10 MPa tensile strength and over, min, kN/m	Basic Requirements Only		26					
K11	Adhesion, ASTM D 429, Method A, min, MPa	Basic Requirements Only		1.4					
Z	Special requirements, specified in detail (including test method & aging parameters), or additional requirements per Tables 3, 4, and 5 per Section 8.2								

1. See Note 6 in 3.4.

TABLE 6.BF—BASIC REQUIREMENTS FOR THE CLASSIFICATION OF RUBBER MATERIALS—BF MATERIALS

Durometer Hardness, ±5 points	Tensile Strength, min (MPa)	Tensile Strength, min (psi)	Ultimate Elongation, min, %	Heat Aged, ASTM D 573, 70 h at 100 °C	Oil Immersion, ASTM D 471, No. 3 Oil[(1)] 70 h at 100 °C	Compression Set, ASTM D 395, Method B, Solid, max, %, 22 h at 100 °C	Available Suffix Grade Numbers
60	3	435	200				2
60	6	870	200				2
60	7	1015	250				2
60	8	1160	250				2
60	10	1450	300				2
60	14	2031	350				2
60	17	2466	350				2
70	3	435	150				2
70	6	870	150	Change in durometer hardness, ±15 points			2
70	7	1015	200		Volume change, +60% max	Compression set, 50% max	2
70	8	1160	200	Change in tensile strength, ±30%			2
70	10	1450	250	Change in ultimate elongation, −50% max			2
70	14	2031	250				2
70	17	2466	300				2
80	3	435	100				2
80	7	1015	100				2
80	10	1450	125				2
80	14	2031	125				2

1. See Note 6 in 3.4.

TABLE 6.BF—SUPPLEMENTARY (SUFFIX) REQUIREMENTS FOR THE CLASSIFICATION OF RUBBER MATERIALS—BF MATERIALS (CONTINUED)

	Suffix Requirements	Grade 1	Grade 2	Grade 3	Grade 4	Grade 5	Grade 6	Grade 7	Grade 8
B14	Compression set, ASTM D 395, Method B, 22 h at 100 °C max, %	Basic Requirements Only	25						
B34	Compression set, ASTM D 395, Method B, 22 h at 100 °C max, %	Basic Requirements Only	25						
EO14	Fluid resistance, ASTM D 471, No. 1 Oil, 70 h at 100 °C:								
	Change in hardness, points	Basic Requirements Only	±10						
	Change in tensile strength, max, %	Basic Requirements Only	-25						
	Change in ultimate elongation, max, %	Basic Requirements Only	-45						
	Change in volume, %	Basic Requirements Only	-10 to +10						
EO34	Fluid resistance, ASTM D 471, No. 3 Oil[(1)], 70 h at 100 °C:								
	Change in hardness, max, points	Basic Requirements Only	-20						
	Change in tensile strength, max, %	Basic Requirements Only	-45						
	Change in ultimate elongation, max, %	Basic Requirements Only	-45						
	Change in volume, %	Basic Requirements Only	0 to +60						
F19	Low-temperature resistance, ASTM D 2137, Method A, 9.3.2, nonbrittle after 3 min at -55 °C	Basic Requirements Only	pass						
Z	Special requirements, specified in detail (including test method & aging parameters), or additional requirements per Tables 3, 4, and 5 per Section 8.2								

1. See Note 6 in 3.4.

TABLE 6.BG—BASIC REQUIREMENTS FOR THE CLASSIFICATION OF RUBBER MATERIALS—BG MATERIALS

Durometer Hardness, ±5 points	Tensile Strength, min (MPa)	Tensile Strength, min (psi)	Ultimate Elongation, min, %	Heat Aged, ASTM D 573, 70 h at 100 °C	Oil Immersion, ASTM D 471, No. 3 Oil[1] 70 h at 100 °C	Compression Set, ASTM D 395, Method B, Solid, max, %, 22 h at 100 °C	Available Suffix Grade Numbers
40	7	1015	450				2, 5
40	10	1450	450				2, 5
50	3	435	300				2, 5
50	6	870	300				2
50	7	1015	350				2, 5
50	8	1160	350				2
50	10	1450	300				2, 3, 4, 5
50	14	2031	350				2, 3, 4, 5
50	21	3046	400				3, 4
60	3	435	200				2, 5
60	6	870	200				2
60	7	1015	250				2, 5
60	8	1160	250				2
60	10	1450	300				2, 5
60	14	2031	300				2, 3, 4, 5
60	17	2466	350	Change in durometer hardness,			2
60	21	3046	350	±15 points			3, 4
60	28	4061	400	Change in tensile strength, ±30%	Volume change,	Compression set, 50% max	3, 4
				Change in ultimate elongation,	+40% max		
70	3	435	150	-50% max			2, 5
70	6	870	150				2
70	7	1015	200				2, 5
70	8	1160	200				2
70	10	1450	250				2, 5
70	14	2031	250				2, 3, 4, 5
70	17	2466	300				2, 3
70	21	3046	350				3, 4
70	28	4061	400				3, 4
80	3	435	100				6, 7
80	7	1015	100				6, 7
80	10	1450	125				6, 7
80	14	2031	125				3, 4, 6, 7
80	21	3046	300				3, 4
80	28	4061	350				3, 4
90	3	435	50				6, 7
90	7	1015	100				6, 7
90	10	1450	100				6, 7

1. See Note 6 in 3.4.

TABLE 6.BG—SUPPLEMENTARY (SUFFIX) REQUIREMENTS FOR THE CLASSIFICATION OF RUBBER MATERIALS—BG MATERIALS (CONTINUED)

	Suffix Requirements	Grade 1	Grade 2	Grade 3	Grade 4	Grade 5	Grade 6	Grade 7	Grade 8
A14	Heat aging resistance, ASTM D 573, 70 h at 100 °C:								
	Change in hardness, max, points	Basic Requirements Only			±5	±15	±15		
	Change in tensile strength, max, %	Basic Requirements Only			±15	-20	-20		
	Change in ultimate elongation, max, %	Basic Requirements Only			-15	-40	-40		
B14	Compression set, ASTM D 395, Method B, 22 h at 100 °C max, %	Basic Requirements Only	25	50	50	25	25	25	
B34	Compression set, ASTM D 395, Method B 22 h at 100 °C max, %	Basic Requirements Only	25			25	25		
EA14	Fluid resistance, ASTM D 471, water, 70 h at 100 °C:								
	Change in hardness, points	Basic Requirements Only	±10					±10	
	Change in volume, %	Basic Requirements Only	±15					±15	
EF11	Fluid resistance, ASTM D 471, Reference Fuel A, 70 h at 23 °C:								
	Change in hardness, points	Basic Requirements Only	±10					±10	
	Change in tensile strength, max, %	Basic Requirements Only	-25					-25	
	Change in ultimate elongation, max, %	Basic Requirements Only	-25					-25	
	Change in volume, %	Basic Requirements Only	-5 to +10					-5 to +10	
EF21	Fluid resistance, ASTM D 471, Reference Fuel B, 70 h at 23 °C:								
	Change in hardness, points	Basic Requirements Only	0 to -30					0 to -30	
	Change in tensile strength, max, %	Basic Requirements Only	-60					-60	
	Change in ultimate elongation, max, %	Basic Requirements Only	-60					-60	
	Change in volume, %	Basic Requirements Only	0 to +40					0 to +40	
EO14	Fluid resistance, ASTM D 471, No. 1 Oil, 70 h at 100 °C:								
	Change in hardness, max, points	Basic Requirements Only	-5 to +10	-7 to +5	-7 to +5	-5 to +15	-5 to +15	-5 to +15	
	Change in tensile strength, max, %	Basic Requirements Only	-25	-20	-20	-25	-25	-25	
	Change in ultimate elongation, max, %	Basic Requirements Only	-45	-40	-40	-45	-45	-45	
	Change in volume, %	Basic Requirements Only	-10 to +5	-5 to +10	-5 to +5	-10 to +5	-10 to +5	-10 to +5	
EO34	Fluid resistance, ASTM D 471, No. 3 Oil,[1] 70 h at 100 °C:								
	Change in hardness, points	Basic Requirements Only	-10 to +5	-10 to +5	-10 to +5	0 to -15	0 to -20	-10 to +5	
	Change in tensile strength, max, %	Basic Requirements Only	-45	-35	-35	-45	-45	-45	
	Change in ultimate elongation, max, %	Basic Requirements Only	-45	-40	-40	-45	-45	-45	
	Change in volume, %	Basic Requirements Only	0 to +25	+16 to +35	0 to +6	0 to +35	0 to +35	0 to +25	
F16	Low-temperature resistance, ASTM D 2137, Method A, 9.3.2, nonbrittle after 3 min at -35 °C	Basic Requirements Only						pass	
F17	Low-temperature resistance, ASTM D 2137, Method A, 9.3.2, nonbrittle after 3 min at -40 °C	Basic Requirements Only	pass				pass		
F19	Low-temperature resistance, ASTM D 2137, Method A, 9.3.2, nonbrittle after 3 min at -55 °C	Basic Requirements Only		pass	pass	pass			
P2	Staining resistance, ASTM D 925, Method B, Control Panel, Nonstaining	Basic Requirements Only		pass	pass				
Z	Special requirements, specified in detail (including test method & aging parameters), or additional requirements per Tables 3, 4, and 5 per Section 8.2								

1. See Note 6 in 3.4.

TABLE 6.BK—BASIC REQUIREMENTS FOR THE CLASSIFICATION OF RUBBER MATERIALS—BK MATERIALS

Durometer Hardness, ±5 points	Tensile Strength, min (MPa)	Tensile Strength, min (psi)	Ultimate Elongation, min, %	Heat Aged, ASTM D 573, 70 h at 100 °C	Oil Immersion, ASTM D 471, No. 3 Oil[1] 70 h at 100 °C	Compression Set, ASTM D 395, Method B, Solid, max, %, 22 h at 100 °C	Available Suffix Grade Numbers
60	3	435	200				4
60	6	870	200				4
60	7	1015	250				4
60	8	1160	250				4
60	10	1450	300				4
60	14	2031	350				4
60	17	2466	350				4
70	3	435	150				4
70	6	870	150	Change in durometer hardness,			4
70	7	1015	200	±15 points	Volume change,	Compression set, 50% max	4
70	8	1160	200	Change in tensile strength, ±30%	+10% max		4
70	10	1450	250	Change in ultimate elongation,			4
70	14	2031	250	-50% max			4
70	17	2466	300				4
80	3	435	100				4
80	7	1015	100				4
80	10	1450	125				4
80	14	2031	125				4
90	3	435	50				4
90	7	1015	100				4
90	10	1450	100				4

1. See Note 6 in 3.4.

TABLE 6.BK—SUPPLEMENTARY (SUFFIX) REQUIREMENTS FOR THE CLASSIFICATION OF RUBBER MATERIALS—BK MATERIALS (CONTINUED)

	Suffix Requirements	Grade 1	Grade 2	Grade 3	Grade 4	Grade 5	Grade 6	Grade 7	Grade 8
A24	Heat aging resistance, ASTM D 865, 70 h at 100 °C:								
	Change in hardness, points	Basic Requirements Only			±10				
	Change in tensile strength, max, %	Basic Requirements Only			-20				
	Change in ultimate elongation, max, %	Basic Requirements Only			-30				
B14	Compression set, ASTM D 395, Method B, 22 h at 100 °C, max, %	Basic Requirements Only			25				
B34	Compression set, ASTM D 395, Method B, 22 h at 100 °C, max, %	Basic Requirements Only			25				
EF11	Fluid resistance, ASTM D 471, Reference Fuel A, 70 h at 23 °C:								
	Change in hardness, points	Basic Requirements Only			±5				
	Change in tensile strength, max, %	Basic Requirements Only			-20				
	Change in ultimate elongation, max, %	Basic Requirements Only			-20				
	Change in volume, %	Basic Requirements Only			±5				
EF21	Fluid resistance, ASTM D 471, Reference Fuel B, 70 h at 23 °C:								
	Change in hardness, points	Basic Requirements Only			0 to -20				
	Change in tensile strength, max, %	Basic Requirements Only			-50				
	Change in ultimate elongation, max, %	Basic Requirements Only			-50				
	Change in volume, %	Basic Requirements Only			0 to +25				
EO14	Fluid resistance, ASTM D 471, No. 1 Oil, 70 h at 100 °C:								
	Change in hardness, points	Basic Requirements Only			±5				
	Change in tensile strength, max, %	Basic Requirements Only			-20				
	Change in ultimate elongation, max, %	Basic Requirements Only			-20				
	Change in volume, %	Basic Requirements Only			-10 to 0				
EO34	Fluid resistance, ASTM D 471, No. 3 Oil[1] 70 h at 100 °C:								
	Change in hardness, points	Basic Requirements Only			-10 to +5				
	Change in tensile strength, max, %	Basic Requirements Only			-20				
	Change in ultimate elongation, max, %	Basic Requirements Only			-30				
	Change in volume, %	Basic Requirements Only			0 to +5				
Z	Special requirements, specified in detail (including test method & aging parameters), or additional requirements per Tables 3, 4, and 5 per Section 8.2								

1. See Note 6 in 3.4.

TABLE 6.CA—BASIC REQUIREMENTS FOR THE CLASSIFICATION OF RUBBER MATERIALS—CA MATERIALS

Durometer Hardness, ±5 points	Tensile Strength, min (MPa)	Tensile Strength, min (psi)	Ultimate Elongation, min, %	Heat Aged, ASTM D 573, 70 h at 125 °C	Oil Immersion, ASTM D 471, No. 3 Oil[1] 70 h at 125 °C	Compression Set, ASTM D 395, Method B, Solid, max, %, 22 h at 100 °C	Available Suffix Grade Numbers
30	7	1015	500				2
30	10	1450	500				2
40	7	1015	400				2
40	10	1450	400				2
40	14	2031	400				2
50	7	1015	300				3
50	10	1450	300				4
50	14	2031	350	Change in durometer hardness,			4
50	17	2466	350	±15 points			4
				Change in tensile strength, ±30%	No requirements	Compression set, 60% max	
60	7	1015	250	Change in ultimate elongation,			3
60	10	1450	250	-50% max			4
60	14	2031	250				4
70	7	1015	200				3
70	10	1450	200				4,5
70	14	2031	200				4,5
80	7	1015	150				6
80	10	1450	150				7,8
80	14	2031	150				7,8
90	7	1015	100				6
90	10	1450	100				7,8

1. See Note 6 in 3.4.

TABLE 6.CA—SUPPLEMENTARY (SUFFIX) REQUIREMENTS FOR THE CLASSIFICATION OF RUBBER MATERIALS—CA MATERIALS (CONTINUED)

	Suffix Requirements	Grade 1	Grade 2	Grade 3	Grade 4	Grade 5	Grade 6	Grade 7	Grade 8
A25	Heat aging resistance, ASTM D 865, 70 h at 125 °C:								
	Change in hardness, max, points	Basic Requirements Only	+10	+10	+10	+10	+10	+10	+10
	Change in tensile strength, max, %	Basic Requirements Only	-20	-20	-20	-20	-20	-20	-20
	Change in ultimate elongation, max, %	Basic Requirements Only	-40	-40	-40	-40	-40	-40	-40
B35	Compression set, ASTM D 395, Method B, 22 h at 125 °C, max, %	Basic Requirements Only	70	70	70	50	70	70	50
B44	Compression set, ASTM D 395, Method B, 70 h at 100 °C, max, %	Basic Requirements Only	35	50					
C32	Resistance to ozone, ASTM D 1171, Method B	Basic Requirements Only	pass	pass	pass	pass	pass	pass	pass
EA14	Fluid resistance, ASTM D 471, water, 70 h at 100 °C, volume change, %	Basic Requirements Only	±5	±5	±5	±5	±5	±5	±5
F17	Low-temperature resistance, ASTM D 2137, Method A, 9.3.2, nonbrittle, after 3 min at -40 °C	Basic Requirements Only	pass	pass	pass	pass	pass	pass	pass
F18	Low-temperature resistance, ASTM D 2137, Method A, 9.3.2, nonbrittle after 3 min at -50 °C	Basic Requirements Only	pass	pass	pass	pass		pass	
F19	Low-temperature resistance, ASTM D 2137, Method A, 9.3.2, nonbrittle after 3 min at -55 °C	Basic Requirements Only			pass				
G11	Tear resistance, ASTM D 624, Die B, min, kN/m	Basic Requirements Only	17	26	26	26	26	26	26
G21	Tear resistance, ASTM D 624, Die C, min, kN/m	Basic Requirements Only	17	26	26	26	26	26	26
K11	Adhesion, ASTM D 429, Method A, min, MPa	Basic Requirements Only		1.4	2.8	2.8	1.4	2.8	2.8
P2	Staining resistance, ASTM D 925, Method B, Control Panel, Nonstaining	Basic Requirements Only	pass	pass	pass	pass	pass	pass	pass
R11	Resilience in compression, ASTM D 945, min, %	Basic Requirements Only	70	50	60				
Z	Special requirements, specified in detail (including test method & aging parameters), or additional requirements per Tables 3, 4, and 5 per Section 8.2								

TABLE 6.CE—BASIC REQUIREMENTS FOR THE CLASSIFICATION OF RUBBER MATERIALS—CE MATERIALS

Durometer Hardness, ±5 points	Tensile Strength, min (MPa)	Tensile Strength, min (psi)	Ultimate Elongation, min, %	Heat Aged, ASTM D 573, 70 h at 125 °C	Oil Immersion, ASTM D 471, No. 3 Oil[1] 70 h at 125 °C	Compression Set, ASTM D 395, Method B, Solid, max, %, 22 h at 70 °C	Available Suffix Grade Numbers
50	14	2031	400				2,3
60	10	1450	350				2,3
60	14	2031	400				2,3
60	17	2466	400	Change in durometer hardness,			2,3
				±15 points			
70	7	1015	200	Change in tensile strength, ±30%	Volume change,	Compression set, 80% max	2,3
70	10	1450	250	Change in ultimate elongation,	+80% max		2,3
70	14	2031	300	-60% max			2,3
70	27	2466	300				2,3
80	7	1015	200				2,3
80	10	1450	250				2,3
80	14	2031	250				2,3

1. See Note 6 in 3.4.

TABLE 6.CE—SUPPLEMENTARY (SUFFIX) REQUIREMENTS FOR THE CLASSIFICATION OF RUBBER MATERIALS—CE MATERIALS (CONTINUED)

	Suffix Requirements	Grade 1	Grade 2	Grade 3	Grade 4	Grade 5	Grade 6	Grade 7	Grade 8
A16	Heat aging resistance, ASTM D 573, 70 h at 150 °C:								
	Change in hardness, points	Basic Requirements Only	±20						
	Change in tensile strength, %	Basic Requirements Only	±30						
	Change in ultimate elongation, max, %	Basic Requirements Only	-60						
B15	Compression set, ASTM D 395, Method B, 22 h at 125 °C, max, %	Basic Requirements Only	60	80					
F19	Low-temperature resistance, ASTM D 2137, Method A, 9.3.2, nonbrittle after 3 min at -55 °C	Basic Requirements Only	pass	pass					
P2	Staining resistance, ASTM D 925, Method B, Control Panel, Nonstaining	Basic Requirements Only	pass	pass					
Z	Special requirements, specified in detail (including test method & aging parameters), or additional requirements per Tables 3, 4, and 5 per Section 8.2								

TABLE 6.CH—BASIC REQUIREMENTS FOR THE CLASSIFICATION OF RUBBER MATERIALS—CH MATERIALS

Durometer Hardness, ±5 points	Tensile Strength, min (MPa)	Tensile Strength min (psi)	Ultimate Elongation min, %	Heat Aged, ASTM D 865, 70 h at 125 °C	Oil Immersion, ASTM D 471, No. 3 Oil [1] 70 h at 125 °C	Compression Set, ASTM D 395, Method B, Solid, max, % 22 h at 100 °C	Available Suffix Grade Numbers
60	3	435	200				2,3
60	6	870	200				2,3
60	7	1015	250				2,3
60	8	1160	250				2,3
60	10	1450	300				2,3,5,6
60	14	2031	350				2,3
60	17	2466	350				2,3
70	3	435	150				2,3
70	6	870	150	Change in durometer hardness,			2,3
70	7	1015	200	±15 points			2,3
70	8	1160	200	Change in tensile strength, ±30%	Volume change,	Compression set, 50% max	2,3
70	10	1450	250	Change in ultimate elongation,	+30% max		2,3
70	14	2031	250	-60% max			2,3,5,6
70	17	2466	300				2,3
80	3	435	100				3,4
80	7	1015	100				3,4
80	10	1450	125				3,4
80	14	2031	125				3,4,5,6

TABLE 6.CH—BASIC REQUIREMENTS FOR THE CLASSIFICATION OF RUBBER MATERIALS—CH MATERIALS (continued)

Durometer Hardness, ±5 points	Tensile Strength, min (MPa)	Tensile Strength min (psi)	Ultimate Elongation min, %	Heat Aged, ASTM D 865, 70 h at 125 °C	Oil Immersion, ASTM D 471, No. 3 Oil [1] 70 h at 125 °C	Compression Set, ASTM D 395, Method B, Solid, max, % 22 h at 100 °C	Available Suffix Grade Numbers
90	3	435	50				3,4
90	7	1015	100				3,4
90	10	1450	100				3,4,5,6

1. See Note 6 in 3.4.

TABLE 6.CH—SUPPLEMENTARY (SUFFIX) REQUIREMENTS FOR THE CLASSIFICATION OF RUBBER MATERIALS—CH MATERIALS (CONTINUED)

	Suffix Requirements	Grade 1	Grade 2	Grade 3	Grade 4	Grade 5	Grade 6	Grade 7	Grade 8
A25	Heat aging resistance, ASTM D 865, 70 h at 125 °C:								
	Change in hardness, points	Basic Requirements Only	0 to +15	0 to +15	0 to +15	0 to +10	0 to +10		
	Change in tensile strength, max, %	Basic Requirements Only	-25	-25	-25	-10	-20		
	Change in ultimate elongation, max, %	Basic Requirements Only	-50	-50	-50	-40	-30		
B14	Compression set, ASTM D 395, Method B, 22 h at 100 °C, max, %	Basic Requirements Only	25	25	25	30	25		
B34	Compression set, ASTM D 395, Method B, 22 h at 100 °C, max, %	Basic Requirements Only	25	25		30	25		
C12	Resistance to ozone, ASTM D 1171, quality retention rating, min, %	Basic Requirements Only				100	100		
EF31	Fluid resistance, ASTM D 471, Reference Fuel C, 70 h at 23 °C:								
	Change in hardness, points	Basic Requirements Only	0 to -30		0 to -30	0 to -20	0 to -20		
	Change in tensile strength, max, %	Basic Requirements Only	-60		-60	-50	-50		
	Change in ultimate elongation, max, %	Basic Requirements Only	-60		-60	-60	-50		
	Change in volume, %	Basic Requirements Only	0 to +50		0 to +50	0 to +40	0 to +40		
EO15	Fluid resistance, ASTM D 471, No. 1 Oil, 70 h at 125 °C:								
	Change in hardness, points	Basic Requirements Only	0 to +10		0 to +10				
	Change in tensile strength, max, %	Basic Requirements Only	-20		-20				
	Change in ultimate elongation, max, %	Basic Requirements Only	-35		-35				
	Change in volume, %	Basic Requirements Only	-15 to +5		-15 to +5				
EO16	Fluid resistance, ASTM D 471, No. 1 Oil, 70 h at 150 °C:								
	Change in hardness, points	Basic Requirements Only		0 to +10					
	Change in tensile strength, max, %	Basic Requirements Only		-20					
	Change in ultimate elongation, max, %	Basic Requirements Only		-40					
	Change in volume, %	Basic Requirements Only		-15 to +5					
EO35	Fluid resistance, ASTM D 471, No. 3 Oil[1], 70 h at 125 °C:								
	Change in hardness, points	Basic Requirements Only	±10		±10				
	Change in tensile strength, max, %	Basic Requirements Only	-15		-15				
	Change in ultimate elongation, max, %	Basic Requirements Only	-30		-30				
	Change in volume, %	Basic Requirements Only	0 to +25		0 to +25				
EO36	Fluid resistance, ASTM D 471, No. 3 Oil[1], 70 h at 150 °C:								
	Change in hardness, points	Basic Requirements Only		±10		-5 to +10	-5 to +10		
	Change in tensile strength, max, %	Basic Requirements Only		-35		-10	-15		
	Change in ultimate elongation, max, %	Basic Requirements Only		-35		-50	-40		
	Change in volume, %	Basic Requirements Only		0 to +25		0 to +10	0 to +15		
F14	Low-temperature resistance, ASTM D 2137, Method A, 9.3.2, nonbrittle after 3 min at -18 °C	Basic Requirements Only				pass			
F16	Low-temperature resistance, ASTM D 2137, Method A, 9.3.2, nonbrittle after 3 min at -35 °C	Basic Requirements Only			pass				
F17	Low-temperature resistance, ASTM D 2137, Method A, 9.3.2, nonbrittle after 3 min at -40 °C	Basic Requirements Only	pass				pass		
Z	Special requirements, specified in detail (including test method & aging parameters), or additional requirements per Tables 3, 4, and 5 per Section 8.2								

1. See Note 6 in 3.4.

TABLE 6.DA—BASIC REQUIREMENTS FOR THE CLASSIFICATION OF RUBBER MATERIALS—DA MATERIALS

Durometer Hardness, ±5 points	Tensile Strength, min (MPa)	Tensile Strength, min (psi)	Ultimate Elongation, min, %	Heat Aged, ASTM D 573, 70 h at 150 °C	Oil Immersion, ASTM D 471, No. 3 Oil[(1)], 70 h at 150 °C	Compression Set, ASTM D 395, Method B, Plied, max, %, 22 h at 150 °C	Available Suffix Grade Numbers
50	7	1015	300				2
50	10	1450	300				2
50	14	2031	350				2
60	7	1015	250				2,3
60	10	1450	250	Change in durometer hardness,			2,3
60	14	2031	300	±15 points			2,3
				Change in tensile strength, ±30%	No requirement	Compression set, 50% max	
70	7	1015	200	Change in ultimate elongation,			2,3
70	10	1450	200	-60% max			2,3
70	14	2031	200				2,3
80	7	1015	150				2,3
80	10	1450	150				2,3
80	14	2031	150				2,3

1. See Note 6 in 3.4.

TABLE 6.DA—SUPPLEMENTARY (SUFFIX) REQUIREMENTS FOR THE CLASSIFICATION OF RUBBER MATERIALS—DA MATERIALS (CONTINUED)

	Suffix Requirements	Grade 1	Grade 2	Grade 3	Grade 4	Grade 5	Grade 6	Grade 7	Grade 8
A26	Heat aging resistance, ASTM D 865, 70 h at 150 °C:								
	Change in hardness, max, points	Basic Requirements Only	+10	+10					
	Change in tensile strength, max, %	Basic Requirements Only	-20	-20					
	Change in ultimate elongation, max, %	Basic Requirements Only	-20	-20					
B36	Compression set, ASTM D 395, Method B, 22h at 150 °C, max,%	Basic Requirements Only	40	25					
C32	Resistance to ozone, ASTM D 1171, exposure Method B	Basic Requirements Only	pass	pass					
EA14	Fluid resistance, ASTM D 471, water, 70 h at 100 °C, volume change, max, %	Basic Requirements Only	±5	±5					
F19	Low-temperature resistance, ASTM D 2137, Method A, 9.3.2, nonbrittle after 3 min at -55 °C	Basic Requirements Only	pass	pass					
G11	Tear resistance, ASTM D 624, Die B, min, kN/m	Basic Requirements Only	17	17					
G21	Tear resistance, ASTM D 624, Die C, min, kN/m	Basic Requirements Only	17	17					
K11	Adhesion, ASTM D 429, Method A, min, MPa	Basic Requirements Only		1.4					
P2	Staining resistance, ASTM D 925, Method B, Control Panel, Nonstaining	Basic Requirements Only	pass	pass					
R11	Resilience in compression, D 945, min, %	Basic Requirements Only	60	60					
Z	Special requirements, specified in detail (including test method & aging parameters), or additional requirements per Tables 3, 4, and 5 per Section 8.2								

TABLE 6.DE—BASIC REQUIREMENTS FOR THE CLASSIFICATION OF RUBBER MATERIALS—DE MATERIALS

Durometer Hardness, ±5 points	Tensile Strength, min (MPa)	Tensile Strength, min (psi)	Ultimate Elongation, min, %	Heat Aged, ASTM D 573, 70 h at 150 °C	Oil Immersion, ASTM D 471, No. 3 Oil (1) 70 h at 150 °C	Compression Set, ASTM D 395, Method B, Solid, max, %, 22 h at 125 °C	Available Suffix Grade Numbers
60	10	1450	350				2
60	14	2031	400				2, 3
60	17	2466	400				2, 3, 4
70	7	1015	200				2
70	10	1450	250	Change in durometer hardness,			5
70	14	2031	300	±15 points	Volume change,	Compression set, 80% max	
70	17	2466	300	Change in tensile strength, ±30%	+80% max		6
				Change in ultimate elongation,			
80	7	1015	200	-50% max			
80	10	1450	200				
80	14	2031	250				2
90	10	1450	150				
90	14	2031	150				5

1. See Note 6 in 3.4.

TABLE 6.DE—SUPPLEMENTARY (SUFFIX) REQUIREMENTS FOR THE CLASSIFICATION OF RUBBER MATERIALS—DE MATERIALS (CONTINUED)

	Suffix Requirements	Grade 1	Grade 2	Grade 3	Grade 4	Grade 5	Grade 6	Grade 7	Grade 8
A16	Heat aging resistance, ASTM D 573, 70 h at 150 °C:	Basic Requirements Only							
	Change in hardness, points		15	15	15		15		
	Change in tensile strength, %		30	30	30		30		
	Change in ultimate elongation, max, %		-30	-30	-30		-30		
B15	Compression set, ASTM D 395, Method B, 22 h at 125 °C, max, %	Basic Requirements Only	55	35	25	35	30		
EO36	Fluid resistance, ASTM D 471, No. 3 Oil(1), 70 h at 150 °C:	Basic Requirements Only							
	Volume change, max, %		+70	+70		+60			
F16	Low-temperature resistance, ASTM D 2137, Method A, 9.3.2, nonbrittle after 3 min at -35 °C	Basic Requirements Only	pass			pass			
F17	Low-temperature resistance, ASTM D 2137, Method A, 9.3.2, nonbrittle after 3 min at -40 °C	Basic Requirements Only		pass	pass		pass		
Z	Special requirements, specified in detail (including test method & aging parameters), or additional requirements per Tables 3, 4, and 5 per Section 8.2								

1. See Note 6 in 3.4.

TABLE 6.DF—BASIC REQUIREMENTS FOR THE CLASSIFICATION OF RUBBER MATERIALS—DF MATERIALS

Durometer Hardness, ±5 points	Tensile Strength, min (MPa)	Tensile Strength, min (psi)	Ultimate Elongation, min, %	Heat Aged, ASTM D 865, 70 h at 150 °C	Oil Immersion, ASTM D 471, No. 3 Oil[1] 70 h at 150 °C	Compression Set, ASTM D 395, Method B, Solid, max, %, 22 h at 150 °C	Available Suffix Grade Numbers
40	6	870	225			80	2
50	7	1015	225			80	2
60	8	1160	175	Change in durometer hardness		80	2
				±15 points	Volume change,		
70	6	870	100	Change in tensile strength, ±30%	+60% max	90	5
70	8	1160	150	Change in ultimate elongation,		80	2
				-50% max			
80	6	870	100			90	5
80	8	1160	150			80	3
90	7	1015	125			85	4

1. See Note 6 in 3.4.

TABLE 6.DF—SUPPLEMENTARY (SUFFIX) REQUIREMENTS FOR THE CLASSIFICATION OF RUBBER MATERIALS—DF MATERIALS (CONTINUED)

	Suffix Requirements	Grade 1	Grade 2	Grade 3	Grade 4	Grade 5	Grade 6	Grade 7	Grade 8
A26	Heat aging resistance, ASTM D 865, 70 h at 150 °C:								
	Change in hardness, max, points	Basic Requirements Only	+10	+10	+10	+10			
	Change in tensile strength, max, %	Basic Requirements Only	-25	-25	-25	-25			
	Change in ultimate elongation, max, %	Basic Requirements Only	-30	-30	-30	-30			
B16	Compression set, ASTM D 395, Method B, 22 h at 150 °C, max, %	Basic Requirements Only	50	60	75	80			
B36	Compression set, ASTM D 395, Method B, 22 h at 150 °C, max, %	Basic Requirements Only	75	80	85				
EO16	Fluid resistance, ASTM D 471, No. 1 Oil, 70 h at 150 °C:								
	Change in hardness points	Basic Requirements Only	-8 to +15	-8 to +10	-8 to +10	-8 to +10			
	Change in tensile strength, max, %	Basic Requirements Only	-20	-20	-20	-30			
	Change in ultimate elongation, max, %	Basic Requirements Only	-30	-30	-30	-50			
	Change in volume, %	Basic Requirements Only	-5 to +10	-5 to +10	-5 to +10	-5 to +10			
EO36	Fluid resistance, ASTM D 471, No. 3 Oil[1], 70 h at 150 °C:								
	Change in hardness, max, points	Basic Requirements Only	-30	-30	-30	-30			
	Change in tensile strength, max, %	Basic Requirements Only	-60	-60	-60	-60			
	Change in ultimate elongation, max, %	Basic Requirements Only	-40	-30	-30	-50			
	Change in volume, max, %	Basic Requirements Only	+50	+50	+50	+50			
F14	Low-temperature resistance, ASTM D 2137, Method A, 9.3.2, nonbrittle after 3 min at -18 °C	Basic Requirements Only		pass	pass	pass			
F15	Low-temperature resistance, ASTM D 2137, Method A, 9.3.2, nonbrittle after 3 min at -25 °C	Basic Requirements Only	pass						
K11	Adhesion, ASTM D 429, Method A, min, MPa	Basic Requirements Only	1.4	1.4	1.4	1.4			
Z	Special requirements, specified in detail (including test method & aging parameters), or additional requirements per Tables 3, 4, and 5 per Section 8.2								

1. See Note 6 in 3.4.

TABLE 6.DH—BASIC REQUIREMENTS FOR THE CLASSIFICATION OF RUBBER MATERIALS—DH MATERIALS

Durometer Hardness, ±5 points	Tensile Strength, min (MPa)	Tensile Strength, min (psi)	Ultimate Elongation, min, %	Heat Aged, ASTM D 865, 70 h at 150 °C	Oil Immersion, ASTM D 471, No. 3 Oil [(1)], 70 h at 150 °C	Compression Set, ASTM D 395, Method B, Solid, max, %, 22 h at 150 °C	Available Suffix Grade Numbers
40	7	1015	300			60	2
50	8	1160	250			60	2
60	8	1160	200			60	2
60	10	1450	200			60	2
60	14	2030	250			40	4
70	6	870	100	Change in durometer hardness, ±15 points	Volume change,	75	5
70	8	1160	200	Change in tensile strength, ±30%	+30% max	60	3
70	10	1450	200	Change in ultimate elongation,		60	3
70	16	2320	250	-50%		40	4
80	6	870	100			75	5
80	8	1160	175			60	3
80	10	1450	175			60	3
80	20	2900	150			40	4
90	10	1450	100			60	4
90	20	2900	100			45	

1. See Note 6 in 3.4.

TABLE 6.DH—SUPPLEMENTARY (SUFFIX) REQUIREMENTS FOR THE CLASSIFICATION OF RUBBER MATERIALS—DH MATERIALS (CONTINUED)

	Suffix Requirements	Grade 1	Grade 2	Grade 3	Grade 4	Grade 5	Grade 6	Grade 7	Grade 8
A26	Heat aging resistance ASTM D 865, 70 h at 150 °C:								
	Change in hardness, max, points	Basic Requirements Only	+10	+10	+10	+10			
	Change in tensile strength, max, %	Basic Requirements Only	-25	-25	-15	-25			
	Change in ultimate elongation, max, %	Basic Requirements Only	-30	-30	-25	-30			
B16	Compression set, ASTM D 395, Method B, 22 h at 150 °C, max, %	Basic Requirements Only	30	30		60			
B36	Compression set, ASTM D 395, Method B, 22 h at 150 °C, max, %	Basic Requirements Only	50	50	35				
EO16	Fluid resistance, ASTM D 471, No. 1 Oil, 70 h at 150 °C:								
	Change in hardness, points	Basic Requirements Only	-5 to +10	-5 to +10	-5 to +10	-5 to +10			
	Change in tensile strength, max, %	Basic Requirements Only	-20	-20	-20	-20			
	Change in ultimate elongation, max, %	Basic Requirements Only	-30	-40	-30	-40			
	Change in volume, %	Basic Requirements Only	±5	±5	-10 +5	±5			
EO36	Fluid resistance, ASTM D 471, No. 3 Oil[(1)], 70 h at 150 °C:								
	Change in hardness, max, points	Basic Requirements Only	-15	-15	-15	-15			
	Change in tensile strength, max, %	Basic Requirements Only	-40	-30	-40	-40			
	Change in ultimate elongation, max, %	Basic Requirements Only	-40	-30	-30	-40			
	Change in volume, max, %	Basic Requirements Only	+25	+25	+25	+25			
F13	Low-temperature resistance, ASTM D 2137, Method A, 9.3.2, nonbrittle after 3 min at -10 °C	Basic Requirements Only		pass		pass			
F14	Low-temperature resistance, ASTM D 2137, Method A, 9.3.2, nonbrittle after 3 min at -18 °C	Basic Requirements Only	pass						
F17	Low-temperature resistance, ASTM D 2137, Method A, 9.3.2, nonbrittle after 3 min at -40 °C				pass				
K11	Adhesion, ASTM D 429, Method A, min, MPa	Basic Requirements Only	1.4	1.4		1.4			
Z	Special requirements, specified in detail (including test method & aging parameters), or additional requirements per Tables 3, 4, and 5 per Section 8.2								

1. See Note 6 in 3.4.

TABLE 6.EE—BASIC REQUIREMENTS FOR THE CLASSIFICATION OF RUBBER MATERIALS—EE MATERIALS

Durometer Hardness, ±5 points	Tensile Strength, min (MPa)	Tensile Strength, min (psi)	Ultimate Elongation, min, %	Heat Aged, ASTM D 865, 70 h at 175 °C	Oil Immersion, ASTM D 471, No. 3 Oil[1] 70 h at 150 °C	Compression Set, ASTM D 395, Method B, Solid, max, %, 22 h at 150 °C	Available Suffix Grade Numbers
50	8	1160	400				
50	10	1450	500				3
50	12	1740	500				3
50	14	2031	500				
60	6	870	200				4
60	8	1160	300				3,4,5
60	12	1740	300				3
60	14	2031	400				3
70	8	1160	200	Change in durometer hardness, ±15 points Change in tensile strength, ±30% Change in ultimate elongation, -50% max	Volume change, +80% max	Compression set, 75% max	3,4,5
70	10	1450	200				4
70	12	1740	300				3
80	10	1450	200				4
80	12	1740	200				3,4
80	14	2031	200				3,4,5
80	16	2320	200				3
90	6	870	100				
90	10	1450	100				4
90	14	2031	100				3

1. See Note 6 in 3.4.

TABLE 6.EE—SUPPLEMENTARY (SUFFIX) REQUIREMENTS FOR THE CLASSIFICATION OF RUBBER MATERIALS—EE MATERIALS (CONTINUED)

	Suffix Requirements	Grade 1	Grade 2	Grade 3	Grade 4	Grade 5	Grade 6	Grade 7	Grade 8
A47	Heat resistance, ASTM D 573, 168 h at 175 °C:								
	Change in hardness, max, points	Basic Requirements Only		+10	+20	+10			
	Change in tensile strength, max, %	Basic Requirements Only		-30	-30	-30			
	Change in ultimate elongation, max, %	Basic Requirements Only		-50	-65	-50			
B46	Compression set, ASTM D 395, Method B, 70 h at 150 °C, max, %	Basic Requirements Only		50	75	50			
B37	Compression set, ASTM D 395, Method B, 22 h at 175 °C, max, %	Basic Requirements Only		50	75	50			
EO16	Fluid resistance, ASTM D 471, No. 1 Oil, 70 h at 150 °C:								
	Change in hardness, max, points	Basic Requirements Only		-10 to +5	-10 to +5	-10 to +5			
	Change in tensile strength, max, %	Basic Requirements Only		-25	-25	-25			
	Change in ultimate elongation, max, %	Basic Requirements Only		-35	-35	-35			
	Change in volume, %	Basic Requirements Only		±15	±10	±10			
EO36[1]	Fluid resistance, ASTM D 471, No. 3 Oil[2] 70 h at 150 °C:								
	Change in tensile strength, max, %	Basic Requirements Only		-60	-50	-50			
	Change in ultimate elongation, max, %	Basic Requirements Only		-55	-50	-50			
	Change in volume, max, %	Basic Requirements Only		+70	+60	+50			
EA14	Water resistance, ASTM D 471, 70 h at 100 °C:								
	Change in volume, max, %	Basic Requirements Only		+15	+15	+15			
F17	Low-temperature resistance, ASTM D 2137, Method A, 9.3.2, nonbrittle after 3 min at -40 °C	Basic Requirements Only		pass	pass	pass			
G21	Tear resistance, ASTM D 624, Die C, min, kN/M	Basic Requirements Only		20	20	20			

1. EO36 change in hardness was not included as data contained too much scatter.
2. See Note 6 in 3.4.

TABLE 6.EH—BASIC REQUIREMENTS FOR THE CLASSIFICATION OF RUBBER MATERIALS—EH MATERIALS

Durometer Hardness, ±5 points	Tensile Strength, min (MPa)	Tensile Strength, min (psi)	Ultimate Elongation, min, %	Heat Aged, ASTM D 865, 70 h at 175 °C	Oil Immersion, ASTM D 471, No. 3 Oil[1] 70 h at 150 °C	Compression Set, ASTM D 395, Method B, Solid, max, %, 22 h at 175 °C	Available Suffix Grade Numbers
40	7	1015	250			75	3
50	8	1160	175			75	3
60	6	870	100	Change in durometer hardness,		75	3
60	9	1306	150	±15 points	Volume change,	75	3
				Change in tensile strength, ±30%	+30% max		
70	6	870	100	Change in ultimate elongation,		75	3
70	9	1306	125	-50% max		75	3
80	7	1015	100			75	3

1. See Note 6 in 3.4.

TABLE 6.EH—SUPPLEMENTARY (SUFFIX) REQUIREMENTS FOR THE CLASSIFICATION OF RUBBER MATERIALS—EH MATERIALS (CONTINUED)

	Suffix Requirements	Grade 1	Grade 2	Grade 3	Grade 4	Grade 5	Grade 6	Grade 7	Grade 8
A27	Heat resistance, ASTM D 865, 70 h at 175 °C:								
	Change in hardness, max, points	Basic Requirements Only		+10					
	Change in tensile strength, max, %	Basic Requirements Only		-30					
	Change in ultimate elongation, max, %	Basic Requirements Only		-40					
B17	Compression Set, ASTM D 395, Method B, 22 h at 175 °C, max, %	Basic Requirements Only		60					
B37	Compression Set, ASTM D 395, Method B 22 h at 175 °C, max, %	Basic Requirements Only		60					
EO16	Fluid resistance ASTM D 471, No. 1 Oil, 70 h at 150 °C:								
	Change in hardness, points	Basic Requirements Only		±5					
	Change in tensile strength, max, %	Basic Requirements Only		-20					
	Change in ultimate elongation, max, %	Basic Requirements Only		-30					
	Change in volume, %	Basic Requirements Only		±5					
EO36	Fluid resistance ASTM D 471, No. 3 Oil[1], 70 h at 150 °C:								
	Change in hardness, points	Basic Requirements Only		-20					
	Change in tensile strength, max, %	Basic Requirements Only		-40					
	Change in ultimate elongation, max, %	Basic Requirements Only		-30					
	Change in volume, %	Basic Requirements Only		+25					
F14	Low-temperature resistance, ASTM D 2137, Method A, 9.3.2, nonbrittle after 3 minutes at -18 °C	Basic Requirements Only		pass					
F25	Low-temperature resistance, ASTM D 1053, T100, -25 °C	Basic Requirements Only		pass					
K11	Adhesion, ASTM D 429, Method A, min, MPa	Basic Requirements Only		1.4[2]					
Z	Special requirements, specified in detail (including test method & aging parameters), or additional requirements per Tables 3, 4, and 5 per Section 8.2								

1. See Note 6 in 3.4.
2. From current DH specification.

TABLE 6.EK—BASIC REQUIREMENTS FOR THE CLASSIFICATION OF RUBBER MATERIALS—EK MATERIALS

Durometer Hardness, ±5 points	Tensile Strength, min (MPa)	Tensile Strength, min (psi)	Ultimate Elongation, min, %	Heat Aged, ASTM D 573, 70 h at 175 °C	Oil Immersion, ASTM D 471, No. 3 Oil(1) 70 h at 150 °C	Compression Set, ASTM D 395, Method B, Solid, max, %, 22 h at 175 °C	Available Suffix Grade Numbers
50	9	1305	125	Change in durometer hardness, ±15 points	Volume change,	60	2
70	10	1450	125	Change in tensile strength, ±30% Change in ultimate elongation,	+10% max	60	2
80	10	1450	100	-50% max		60	2

1. See Note 6 in 3.4.

TABLE 6.EK—SUPPLEMENTARY (SUFFIX) REQUIREMENTS FOR THE CLASSIFICATION OF RUBBER MATERIALS—EK MATERIALS (CONTINUED)

	Suffix Requirements	Grade 1	Grade 2	Grade 3	Grade 4	Grade 5	Grade 6	Grade 7	Grade 8
A17	Heat aging resistance, ASTM D 573, 70 h at 175 °C:								
	Change in hardness, points	Basic Requirements Only	±10						
	Change in tensile strength, %	Basic Requirements Only	-25						
	Change in ultimate elongation, max, %	Basic Requirements Only	-20 to +30						
A18	Heat aging resistance, ASTM D 573, 70 h at 200 °C:								
	Change in hardness, points	Basic Requirements Only	-15 to +10						
	Change in tensile strength, max, %	Basic Requirements Only	-60						
	Change in ultimate elongation, %	Basic Requirements Only	-10 to +40						
B17	Compression set, ASTM D 395, Method B, solid, 22 h at 175 °C, max, %	Basic Requirements Only	60						
B26	Compression set, ASTM D 395, Method B, solid, 70 h at 150 °C, max, %	Basic Requirements Only	50						
C32	Resistance to ozone, ASTM D 1171, Method B	Basic Requirements Only	pass						
EA14	Fluid resistance, ASTM D 471, water, 70 h at 100 °C:								
	Change in hardness, points	Basic Requirements Only	-5 to +10						
	Change in volume	Basic Requirements Only	0 to +20						
EF31	Fluid resistance, ASTM D 471, Reference Fuel C, 70 h at 23 °C								
	Change in hardness, points	Basic Requirements Only	-20 to +5						
	Change in tensile strength, max, %	Basic Requirements Only	-50						
	Change in ultimate elongation, max, %	Basic Requirements Only	-50						
	Change in volume, max, %	Basic Requirements Only	+40						
EO16	Fluid resistance, ASTM D 471, No. 1 Oil, 70 h at 150 °C:								
	Change in hardness, points	Basic Requirements Only	-10 to +5						
	Change in tensile strength, max, %	Basic Requirements Only	-10						
	Change in ultimate elongation, max, %	Basic Requirements Only	-20						
	Change in volume, max, %	Basic Requirements Only	+10						
EO36	Fluid resistance, ASTM D 471, No. 3 Oil(1) 70 h at 150 °C:								
	Change in hardness, points	Basic Requirements Only	-15 to 0						
	Change in tensile strength, max, %	Basic Requirements Only	-20						
	Change in ultimate elongation, max, %	Basic Requirements Only	-20						
	Change in volume, max, %	Basic Requirements Only	+10						
F19	Low-temperature resistance, ASTM D 2137, Method A, 9.3.2, nonbrittle after 3 min at -55 °C	Basic Requirements Only	pass						
F49	Low-temperature resistance, ASTM D 1329, after 10 min at -55 °C, 10% retraction, min	Basic Requirements Only	pass						

1. See Note 6 in 3.4.

TABLE 6.FC—BASIC REQUIREMENTS FOR THE CLASSIFICATION OF RUBBER MATERIALS—FC MATERIALS

Durometer Hardness, ±5 points	Tensile Strength, min (MPa)	Tensile Strength, min (psi)	Ultimate Elongation, min, %	Heat Aged, ASTM D 573, 70 h at 200 °C	Oil Immersion, ASTM D 471, No. 3 Oil[1] 70 h at 150 °C	Compression Set, ASTM D 395, Method B, Plied, max, %, 22 h at 175 °C	Available Suffix Grade Numbers
30	3	435	350			60	2
30	5	725	400			60	2
40	7	1015	400			60	3
				Change in durometer hardness,			
50	7	1015	400	±15 points	Volume change,	60	3
50	8	1160	500	Change in tensile strength, ±30%	+120% max	80	4
				Change in ultimate elongation,			
60	7	1015	300	−60% max		60	3
60	8	1160	400			80	4
70	7	1015	200			60	3

1. See Note 6 in 3.4.

TABLE 6.FC—SUPPLEMENTARY (SUFFIX) REQUIREMENTS FOR THE CLASSIFICATION OF RUBBER MATERIALS—FC MATERIALS (CONTINUED)

	Suffix Requirements	Grade 1	Grade 2	Grade 3	Grade 4	Grade 5	Grade 6	Grade 7	Grade 8
A19	Heat aging resistance, ASTM D 573, 70 h at 225 °C:								
	Change in hardness, max, points	Basic Requirements Only	+10	+10	+15				
	Change in tensile strength, max, %	Basic Requirements Only	−40	−40	−50				
	Change in ultimate elongation, max, %	Basic Requirements Only	−40	−40	−50				
B37	Compression set, ASTM D 395, Method B, 22 h at 175 °C, max, %	Basic Requirements Only	40	45	60				
EA14	Fluid resistance, ASTM D 471, water, 70 h at 100 °C:								
	Change in hardness, points	Basic Requirements Only	±5	±5	±5				
	Change in volume, %	Basic Requirements Only	±5	±5	±5				
EO16	Fluid resistance, ASTM D 471, No. 1 Oil, 70 h at 150 °C:								
	Change in hardness, points	Basic Requirements Only	0 to −10	0 to −15	0 to −15				
	Change in tensile strength, max, %	Basic Requirements Only	−50	−50	−50				
	Change in ultimate elongation, max, %	Basic Requirements Only	−30	−50	−50				
	Change in volume, %	Basic Requirements Only	0 to +20	0 to +20	0 to +20				
F1-11	Low-temperature resistance, ASTM D 2137, Method A, 9.3.2, nonbrittle after 3 min at −75 °C	Basic Requirements Only	pass	pass	pass				
G11	Tear resistance, ASTM D 624, Die B:								
	Under 7.0 MPa tensile strength, min, kN/m	Basic Requirements Only	5						
	7.0–10 MPa tensile strength, min, kN/m	Basic Requirements Only		17	26				
Z	Special requirements, specified in detail (including test method & aging parameters), or additional requirements per Tables 3, 4, and 5 per Section 8.2								

TABLE 6.FE—BASIC REQUIREMENTS FOR THE CLASSIFICATION OF RUBBER MATERIALS—FE MATERIALS

Durometer Hardness, ±5 points	Tensile Strength, min (MPa)	Tensile Strength, min (psi)	Ultimate Elongation, min, %	Heat Aged, ASTM D 573, 70 h at 200 °C	Oil Immersion, ASTM D 471, No. 3 Oil[1] 70 h at 150 °C	Compression Set, ASTM D 395, Method B, Solid, max, %, 22 h at 175 °C	Available Suffix Grade Numbers
30	3	435	400	Change in durometer hardness,		60	2
30	7	1015	500	±15 points		60	5
				Change in tensile strength, ±30%	Volume change,		
40	8	1160	500	Change in ultimate elongation,	+80% max	60	3
				-50% max			
50	8	1160	500			80	4

1. See Note 6 in 3.4.

TABLE 6.FE—SUPPLEMENTARY (SUFFIX) REQUIREMENTS FOR THE CLASSIFICATION OF RUBBER MATERIALS—FE MATERIALS (CONTINUED)

	Suffix Requirements	Grade 1	Grade 2	Grade 3	Grade 4	Grade 5	Grade 6	Grade 7	Grade 8
A19	Heat aging resistance, ASTM D 573, 70 h at 225 °C:								
	Change in hardness, max, points	Basic Requirements Only	+10	+10	+15	+10			
	Change in tensile strength, max, %	Basic Requirements Only	-60	-40	-40	-50			
	Change in ultimate elongation, max, %	Basic Requirements Only	-60	-60	-60	-50			
B37	Compression set, ASTM D 395, Method B, 22 h at 175 °C, max, %	Basic Requirements Only	45	50	65	35			
EA14	Fluid resistance, ASTM D 471, water, 70 h at 100 °C:								
	Change in hardness, points	Basic Requirements Only	±5	±5	±5	±5			
	Change in volume, %	Basic Requirements Only	±5	±5	±5	±5			
EO16	Fluid resistance, ASTM D 471, No. 1 Oil, 70 h at 150 °C:								
	Change in hardness, points	Basic Requirements Only	0 to -10	0 to -10	0 to -10	0 to -10			
	Change in tensile strength, max, %	Basic Requirements Only	-50	-50	-50	-40			
	Change in ultimate elongation, max, %	Basic Requirements Only	-50	-50	-50	-40			
	Change in volume, %	Basic Requirements Only	0 to +20	0 to +20	0 to +20	0 to +20			
EO36	Fluid resistance, ASTM D 471, No. 3 Oil, [1] 70 h at 150 °C:								
	Change in hardness, points	Basic Requirements Only			-40				
	Change in volume, max, %	Basic Requirements Only		+80	+80	+65			
F19	Low-temperature resistance, ASTM D 2137, Method A, 9.3.2, nonbrittle after 3 min at -55 °C	Basic Requirements Only	pass	pass	pass				
G11	Tear resistance, ASTM D 624, Die B:								
	Under 7.0 MPa tensile strength, min, kN/m	Basic Requirements Only	9						
	7.0–10 MPa, tensile strength, min, kN/m	Basic Requirements Only		22	26	25			
K31	Adhesion, bond made after vulcanization	Basic Requirements Only	(2)	(2)	(2)	(2)			
P2	Staining resistance, ASTM D 925, Method B, Control Panel, Nonstaining	Basic Requirements Only	pass	pass	pass				
Z	Special requirements, specified in detail (including test method & aging parameters), or additional requirements per Tables 3, 4, and 5 per Section 8.2								

1. See Note 6 in 3.4.
2. Materials must be free from surface conditions and compound constituents that are or may become deleterious to adhesion.

TABLE 6.FK—BASIC REQUIREMENTS FOR THE CLASSIFICATION OF RUBBER MATERIALS—FK MATERIALS

Durometer Hardness, ±5 points	Tensile Strength, min (MPa)	Tensile Strength, min (psi)	Ultimate Elongation, min, %	Heat Aged, ASTM D 573, 70 h at 200 °C	Oil Immersion, ASTM D 471, No. 3 Oil (1) 70 h at 150 °C	Compression Set, ASTM D 395, Method B, Plied, max, %, 22 h at 175 °C	Available Suffix Grade Numbers
60	6	870	150	Change in durometer hardness, ±15 points Change in tensile strength, ±30% Change in ultimate elongation, -50% max	Volume change, +10% max	50	2

1. See Note 6 in 3.4

TABLE 6.FK—SUPPLEMENTARY (SUFFIX) REQUIREMENTS FOR THE CLASSIFICATION OF RUBBER MATERIALS—FK MATERIALS (CONTINUED)

	Suffix Requirements	Grade 1	Grade 2	Grade 3	Grade 4	Grade 5	Grade 6	Grade 7	Grade 8
A19	Heat aging resistance, ASTM D 573, 70 h at 225 °C:								
	Change in hardness, max, points	Basic Requirements Only	+15						
	Change in tensile strength, max, %	Basic Requirements Only	-45						
	Change in ultimate elongation, max, %	Basic Requirements Only	-45						
EF31	Fluid resistance, ASTM D 471, Reference Fuel C, 70 h at 23 °C								
	Change in hardness, points	Basic Requirements Only	0 to -15						
	Change in tensile strength, max, %	Basic Requirements Only	-60						
	Change in ultimate elongation, max, %	Basic Requirements Only	-50						
	Change in volume, %	Basic Requirements Only	0 to +25						
EO36	Fluid resistance, ASTM D 471, No. 3 Oil (1), 70 h at 150 °C:								
	Change in hardness, points	Basic Requirements Only	0 to -10						
	Change in tensile strength, max, %	Basic Requirements Only	-35						
	Change in ultimate elongation, max, %	Basic Requirements Only	-30						
	Change in volume, %	Basic Requirements Only	0 to +10						
F19	Low-temperature resistance, ASTM D 2137, Method A, 9.3.2, nonbrittle after 3 min at -55 °C	Basic Requirements Only	pass						
Z	Special requirements, specified in detail (including test method & aging parameters), or additional requirements per Tables 3, 4, and 5 per Section 8.2								

1. See Note 6 in 3.4.

TABLE 6.GE—BASIC REQUIREMENTS FOR THE CLASSIFICATION OF RUBBER MATERIALS—GE MATERIALS

Durometer Hardness, ±5 points	Tensile Strength, min (MPa)	Tensile Strength, min (psi)	Ultimate Elongation, min, %	Heat Aged, ASTM D 573, 70 h at 225 °C	Oil Immersion, ASTM D 471, No. 3 Oil[1] 70 h at 150 °C	Compression Set, ASTM D 395, Method B, Plied, max, %, 22 h at 175 °C	Available Suffix Grade Numbers
30	3	435	300			50	2
30	5	725	400			50	2
30	6	870	400			50	8
40	3	435	200			50	2
40	5	725	300			50	2
40	6	870	300			50	8
50	3	435	200			50	3
50	5	725	250	Change in durometer hardness, ±15 points Change in tensile strength, ±30% Change in ultimate elongation, -50% max	Volume change, +80% max	70	4, 5
50	6	870	250			50	5
50	8	1160	400			60	9
60	3	435	100			50	3
60	5	725	200			70	4, 5
60	6	870	200			50	5
70	3	435	60			50	6
70	5	725	150			50	7
70	6	870	150			50	5
80	3	435	50			50	6
80	5	725	100			50	7
80	6	870	100			50	5

1. See Note 6 in 3.4.

TABLE 6.GE—SUPPLEMENTARY (SUFFIX) REQUIREMENTS FOR THE CLASSIFICATION OF RUBBER MATERIALS—GE MATERIALS (CONTINUED)

	Suffix Requirements	Grade 1	Grade 2	Grade 3	Grade 4	Grade 5	Grade 6	Grade 7	Grade 8	Grade 9
A19	Heat aging resistance, ASTM D 573, 70 h at 225 °C:									
	Change in hardness, max, points	Basic Requirements Only	+10	+10	+10	+10	+10	+10	+10	+10
	Change in tensile strength, max, %	Basic Requirements Only	-25	-25	-30	-25	-25	-25	-25	-30
	Change in ultimate elongation, max, %	Basic Requirements Only	-30	-30	-30	-30	-30	-30	-25	-30
B37	Compression set, ASTM D 395, Method B, 22 h at 175 °C, max, %	Basic Requirements Only	25	30	50	25	30	30	25	40
EA14	Fluid resistance, ASTM D 471, water, 70 h at 100 °C:									
	Change in hardness, max, points	Basic Requirements Only	±5	±5	±5	±5	±5	±5	±5	±5
	Change in volume, %	Basic Requirements Only	±5	±5	±5	±5	±5	±5	±5	±5
EO16	Fluid resistance, ASTM D 471, No. 1 Oil, 70 h at 150 °C:									
	Change in hardness, points	Basic Requirements Only	0 to -10	0 to -15	0 to -15	0 to -15	0 to -15	0 to -15	0 to -10	0 to -10
	Change in tensile strength, max, %	Basic Requirements Only	-30	-20	-20	-20	-20	-20	-30	-30
	Change in ultimate elongation, max, %	Basic Requirements Only	-30	-20	-20	-20	-20	-20	-20	-30
	Change in volume, %	Basic Requirements Only	0 to +15	0 to +10	0 to +15	0 to +10	0 to +10	0 to +15	0 to +15	0 to +10
EO36	Fluid resistance, ASTM D 471, No. 3 Oil[1], 70 h at 150 °C:									
	Change in hardness, max, points	Basic Requirements Only		-30	-35	-30	-40	-40	(1)	-30
	Change in volume, max, %	Basic Requirements Only	+60	+60	+60	+60	+60	+60	+60	+60
F19	Low-temperature resistance, ASTM D 2137, Method A, 9.3.2, nonbrittle after 3 min at -55 °C	Basic Requirements Only	pass	pass	pass	pass	pass	pass	pass	pass
G11	Tear resistance, ASTM D 624, Die B:									
	Under 7.0 MPa tensile strength, min, kN/m	Basic Requirements Only	5	6	9	9	5	9	9	
	7.0–10 MPa, tensile strength, min, kN/m	Basic Requirements Only								25
K31	Adhesion, bond made after vulcanization	Basic Requirements Only	(2)	(2)	(2)	(2)	(2)	(2)	(2)	(2)
P2	Staining resistance, ASTM D 925, Method B, Control Panel, Nonstaining	Basic Requirements Only	pass	pass	pass	pass	pass	pass	pass	pass
Z	Special requirements, specified in detail (including test method & aging parameters), or additional requirements per Tables 3, 4, and 5 per Section 8.2									

1. See Note 6 in 3.4.
2. Method of evaluation and requirement shall be based on agreement between fabricator and end user.

TABLE 6.HK—BASIC REQUIREMENTS FOR THE CLASSIFICATION OF RUBBER MATERIALS—HK MATERIALS

Durometer Hardness, ±5 points	Tensile Strength, min (MPa)	Tensile Strength, min (psi)	Ultimate Elongation, min, %	Heat Aged, ASTM D 573, 70 h at 250 °C	Oil Immersion, ASTM D 471, No. 3 Oil[1] 70 h at 150 °C	Compression Set, ASTM D 395, Method B, Plied, max, %, 22 h at 175 °C	Available Suffix Grade Numbers
60	7	1015	200				2, 4, 6
60	10	1450	200				2, 4, 6
60	14	2031	200				2, 4, 6
70	7	1015	175				2, 4, 6
70	10	1450	175	Change in durometer hardness, ±15 points Change in tensile strength, ±30% Change in ultimate elongation, -50% max	Volume change, +10% max	Compression set, 35% max	2, 4, 6
70	14	2031	175				2, 4, 6
80	7	1015	150				2, 4, 6
80	10	1450	150				2, 4, 6
80	14	2031	150				2, 4, 6
90	7	1015	100				3, 5, 7
90	10	1450	100				3, 5, 7
90	14	2031	100				3, 5, 7

1. See Note 6 in 3.4.

TABLE 6.HK—SUPPLEMENTARY (SUFFIX) REQUIREMENTS FOR THE CLASSIFICATION OF RUBBER MATERIALS—HK MATERIALS (CONTINUED)

	Suffix Requirements	Grade 1	Grade 2	Grade 3	Grade 4	Grade 5	Grade 6	Grade 7	Grade 8
A1–10	Heat aging resistance, ASTM D 573, 70 h at 250 °C:								
	Change in hardness, max, points	Basic Requirements Only	+10	+10			+10	+10	
	Change in tensile strength, max, %	Basic Requirements Only	-25	-25			-25	-25	
	Change in ultimate elongation, max, %	Basic Requirements Only	-25	-25			-25	-25	
A1–11	Heat aging resistance ASTM D 573, 70 h at 275 °C:								
	Change in hardness, max, points	Basic Requirements Only			+10	+10	-5 to +10	-5 to +10	
	Change in tensile strength, max, %	Basic Requirements Only			-40	-40	-40	-40	
	Change in ultimate elongation, max, %	Basic Requirements Only			-20	-20	-20	-20	
B31	Compression set, ASTM D 395, Method B, 22 h at 23 °C, max, %	Basic Requirements Only					15	20	
B37	Compression set, ASTM D 395, Method B, 22 h at 175 °C, max, %	Basic Requirements Only	50	30					
B38	Compression set, ASTM D 395, Method B, 22 h at 200 °C, max, %	Basic Requirements Only	50	50	50	50	15	20	
C12	Resistance to ozone, ASTM D 1171	Basic Requirements Only	pass	pass	pass	pass	pass	pass	
C20	Resistance to outdoor aging, ASTM D 1171	Basic Requirements Only	pass	pass	pass	pass	pass	pass	
EF31	Fluid resistance, ASTM D 471, Reference Fuel C, 70 h at 23 °C								
	Change in hardness, points	Basic Requirements Only	±5	±5	±5	±5	±5	±5	
	Change in tensile strength, max, %	Basic Requirements Only	-25	-25	-25	-25	-25	-25	
	Change in ultimate elongation, max, %	Basic Requirements Only	-20	-20	-20	-20	-20	-20	
	Change in volume, %	Basic Requirements Only	0 to +10	0 to +10	0 to +10	0 to +10	0 to +10	0 to +10	
EO78	Fluid Resistance, ASTM D 471, Service Liquid No. 101[1], 70 h at 200 °C:								
	Change in hardness, points	Basic Requirements Only	-15 to +5	-15 to +5	-15 to +5	-15 to +5			
	Change in tensile strength, max, %	Basic Requirements Only	-40	-40	-40	-40			
	Change in ultimate elongation, max, %	Basic Requirements Only	-20	-20	-20	-20			
	Change in volume, %	Basic Requirements Only	0 to +15	0 to +15	0 to +15	0 to +15			
EO88	Fluid resistance, ASTM D 471, SAE Fluid 2, Stauffer 7700[2], 70 h at 200 °C:								
	Change in hardness, points	Basic Requirements Only					-15 to +5	-15 to +5	
	Change in tensile strength, max, %	Basic Requirements Only					-40	-40	
	Change in ultimate elongation, max, %	Basic Requirements Only					-20	-20	
	Change in volume, max, %	Basic Requirements Only					+25	+25	
F15	Low-temperature resistance, ASTM D 2137, Method A, 9.3.2, nonbrittle after 3 min at -25 °C	Basic Requirements Only	pass			pass	pass		
F17	Low-temperature resistance, ASTM D 2137, Method A, 9.3.2, nonbrittle after 3 min at -40 °C	Basic Requirements Only			pass				
Z	Special requirements, specified in detail (including test method & aging parameters), or additional requirements per Tables 3, 4, and 5 per Section 8.2								

1. Service Liquid 101- di 2 ethyl hexyl sebacate, 99.5 mass %; phenothiazine, 0.5 mass %.
2. Available from Akzo Nobel Chemicals, Inc., 5 Livingstone Avenue, Debbs Ferry, NY 10522, 1-800-666-1200.

TABLE 6.KK—BASIC REQUIREMENTS FOR THE CLASSIFICATION OF RUBBER MATERIALS—KK MATERIALS

Durometer Hardness, ±5 points	Tensile Strength, min (MPa)	Tensile Strength, min (psi)	Ultimate Elongation, min, %	Heat Aged, ASTM D 573, 70 h at 300 °C	Oil Immersion, ASTM D 471, IRM 903 Oil 70 h at 150 °C	Compression Set, ASTM D 395, Method B, Plied max, % 22 h at 200 °C
80	11	1595	125	Change in durometer hardness ±15 points Change in tensile strength, ±30% Change in ultimate elongation, –50% max	Volume Change, (+10% max)	Compression set, 25% max

NOTE—Examples of the use of suffix letters and numbers would be A14 and EO34. Suffix A (Table 11) stands for heat resistance. Suffix 1 (Table 12) specifies that the test be run according to ASTM Method D 573[4] for 70 h, and Suffix 4 (Table 13) indicates the temperature of test as 100 °C. Similarly, Suffix EO34 indicates resistance in ASTM Oil No. 3 measured in accordance with ASTM Method D 471[4] for 70 h at 100 °C.

7.2 Basic requirements are always in effect, unless superseded by specific suffix requirements in the line call-out.

8. Line Call-outs

8.1 A line call-out, which is a specification, shall contain: The document designations, the prefix letter M, the grade number, the material designation (type and class), and the hardness and tensile strength, followed by the appropriate suffix requirements. Figure 1 is an example of a line call-out.

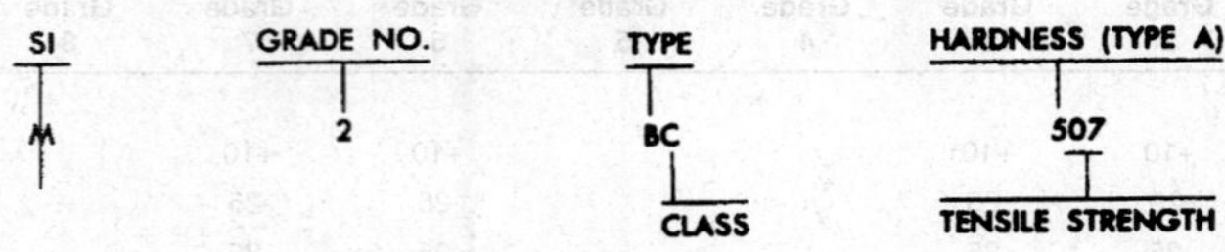

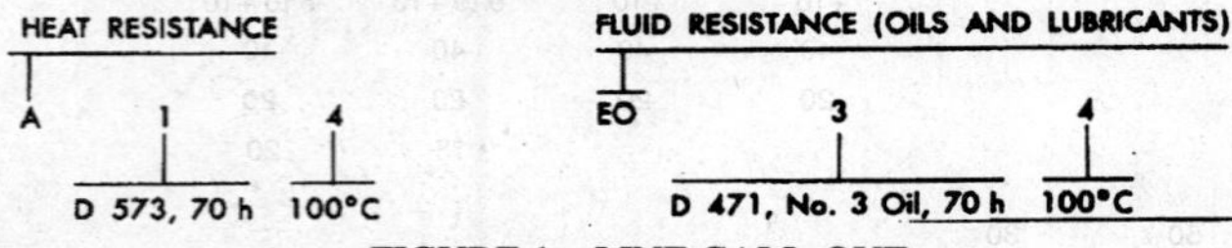

FIGURE 1—LINE CALL-OUT

In this example, the basic requirements for heat aging resistance and oil swelling resistance are superseded for suffix requirements. However, the basic requirements of 80% for compression set, which is not included as a suffix requirement, is not superseded and, therefore, shall be met as specified in Table 6.BC.

NOTE—Following is an example of a valid "line call-out," or specification.

SAEJ200M2BC507A14EO34

The line call-out is valid since Grade No. 2 is available for BC 507 in the list of Available Suffix Grade Numbers Table 6.BC and both A14 and EO34 are available Suffix Requirements for Grade No. 2 materials. The Grade No. 5 would be the only other grade available to a BC 507 material.

8.2 A step-by-step guide to establishing line call-outs is given in Appendix B.

4. Annual Book of ASTM Standards, Section 9, Volume 09.01.

NOTE 9—An invalid "line call-out" is unacceptable. An example of an invalid "line call-out" would be as follows:

SAEJ200M4BG617A14B14EO14F17

The suffix requirements included are all available for a Grade 4; however, 4 is not an Available Suffix Grade Number for a BG 617. The only Available Suffix Grade Number for a BG 617 is 2 and available Suffix Requirements would include B14, B34, EA14, EF11, EF21, EO14, EO34, F17, and Zs. Since no A14 suffix requirement is available, heat resistance would be either (1) that specified under basic BG requirements, or (2) that provided for by a special Z suffix requirement. When Z(s) are used, complete test conditions as well as requirements shall be specified.

Test conditions may be specified by referencing the suffix letter from Table 3 corresponding to the appropriate test, along with the suffix numbers from Tables 4 and 5 corresponding to the desired test method, exposure media, and exposure time. Deviations to durometer hardness, tensile strength, and elongation shall default to the industry method outlined in Table 4, unless otherwise specified. Methods other than those listed in Table 4 must be specified in detail. The requirement shall always follow the test method/condition when using a "Z" suffix. The final form of a callout using this method is:

SAEJ200M2BG617B14EO14F17Z1

Suffix Z1 – A14, hardness change, ±5 points max; tensile strength change, ±15% max; ultimate elongation change, –15% max.

9. Methods of Test

9.1 The applicable methods of test are listed in Table 4.

10. Sampling and Inspection

10.1 A lot, unless otherwise specified, shall consist of all products of the same material submitted for inspection at the same time.

10.2 When proof of conformance with a specification based on this classification system is required, the supplier shall, upon request of the purchaser at the time of ordering, furnish a sufficient number of samples to perform the required tests. Test specimens shall be prepared as prescribed in 6.1. The samples shall be warranted to have equivalent cure and to be from the same run or batch of compound used in the lot.

11. Limitations of Document in Establishing Material Specifications

11.1 The data in Table 6 are based on physical properties of rubber materials obtained directly from standard compression moulded test specimens made from compounds mixed under ideal conditions (for example, in a laboratory). They indicate the combinations of properties that are believed to be obtainable. Table 6 was not necessarily developed on the basis of statistical data. See Appendix C for the development of and additions to this table.

Setting of material specifications, the determination of Cpk values and a quality control plan are the responsibility of the producer and consumer.

11.2 It must be borne in mind that all physical tests are subject to test errors as indicated by precision statements included in many ASTM test procedures.

APPENDIX A
DESIGNATION (TYPE AND CLASS) AND POLYMER

A.1 Appendix A is intended to assist the users of SAE J200 and is not to be considered as part of the system. Tables A1 and A2 list the SAE J200 designation (Type and Class) and the type of polymer most often used in meeting the material requirements. Table A1 is not intended to be limiting; other polymers may be used to meet the same specification.

TABLE A1—SAE J200 DESIGNATION

SAE J200 Material Designation (Type & Class)	Type of Polymer[1] Most Often Used
AA	NR, SBR, IR, IIR, BIIR, CIIR, EPM, EPDM, BR, Reclaim RBR
AK	T
BA	SBR, IIR, BIIR, CIIR, EPM, EPDM
BC	CR, CM
BE	CR, CM
BF	NBR
BG	NBR, AU, EU
BK	NBR
CA	EPM, EPDM
CE	CSM, CM
CH	NBR, CO, ECO
DA	EPM, EPDM
DE	CM, CSM
DF	ACM
DH	ACM
EE	AEM
EH	ACM
EK	FZ
FC	PVMQ
FE	MQ
FK	FVMQ
GE	VMQ
HK	FKM
KK	FFKM

1. Symbols and names are based on ASTM D 1418. Trade Names for the majority of rubber compounds utilizing above polymers may be located in the following and other publications of the rubber industry:
"The Synthetic Rubber Manual," International Institute of Synthetic Rubber Producers, Inc.
"Rubber World Magazine Blue Book," Lippincott & Peto.

TABLE A2—POLYMER MOST OFTEN USED FOR MATERIAL REQUIREMENTS

Polymer Symbol	Common Name (Chemical Name)	Polymer Symbol	Common Name (Chemical Name)[1]
NR	Natural Rubber	NBR	Nitrile Rubber (Acrylonitrile Butadiene Copolymer)
Reclaim RBR	Reclaimed Rubbers		
IR	Isoprene (Synthetic Rubber		
SBR	Styrene Butadiene Rubber	HNBR	Hydrogenated Nitrile Rubber (Hydrogentated Acrylonitrile Butadiene Copolymer)
BR	Butadiene Rubber		
IIR	Butyl Rubber (Isobutene-Isoprene)		
CIIR	Chlorobutyl Rubber (Chloro Isobutene-Isoprene)	CM	Chlorinated Poly-ethylene
BIIR	Bromobutyl Rubber (Bromo Isobutene-Isoprene)	CSM	Chlorosulfonated Polyethylene
T	Polysulfide Rubbers	ACM	Polyacrylate Rubber (Acrylic Esters Copolymer)
EPM	Ethylene Propylene Copolymer		
EPDM	Ethylene Propylene Diene Terpolymer	AU	Polyurethane - Ester Type
CR	Polychloroprene		
CO	Epichlorohydrin Homopolymer (Polychloromethyl Oxirane)	EU	Polyurethane - Ether Type
AEM	Acrylic Ester/Ethylene Copolymer	MQ (MQ, VMQ, PVMQ)	Silicone Rubbers
		FVMQ	Fluorosilicone Rubber
FZ	Fluoroalkoxyphosphazene Rubber	FKM	Fluorocarbon Rubber
ECO	Epichlorohydrin/ Ethylene Oxide (Oxirane) Copolymer	FFKM	Perfluoroelastomer

1. Symbols and names are based on ASTM D 1418. Trade names for the majority of rubber compounds utilizing above polymers may be located in the following and other publications of the rubber industry:
"The Synthetic Rubber Manual," International Institute of Synthetic Rubber Producers, Inc.
"Rubber World Magazine Blue Book," Lippincott & Peto.

APPENDIX B
GUIDELINES FOR ESTABLISHING A LINE CALL-OUT

B.1 Step 1—Using Tables 1 and 2, find the type and class which correspond to the temperature resistance and ASTM No. 3 oil volume swell requirements of the material; for example, AA, BA, BC, etc. Before proceeding, consult Tables 6.AA to 6.KK to make sure you have selected a type-class which corresponds to a material which is listed in the table. For example, it would be improper to select an AB material since Tables 6.AA to 6.KK include no such material.

B.2 Step 2—Under the basic requirements heading in the appropriate type-class section of Tables 3 to 10, select the desired durometer-tensile-elongation combination. For example, in Table 6.BC, a 50 ±5 Type A durometer material having a minimum tensile strength of 7 MPa would be described as a BC 507 material. This material will have a minimum elongation of 300%.

NOTE—Use only those durometer-tensile-elongation combinations specified in the table.

B.3 Step 3—Determine whether the remaining basic requirements (under the headings "Heat Aged," "Oil Immersion," and "Compression Set") are satisfactory for the line call-out which is being established. If the basic requirements accurately and thoroughly describe the desired properties of the material, the line call-out is completed at this step. Steps 4 through 7 do not apply in this case. Prefix the line call-out with SAEJ200, the SI code "M" and the grade number of 1. Write the final form of the line call-out as:

SAEJ200M1BC507

The call-out is written as one continuous string having no spaces between characters.

B.4 Step 4—If the basic requirements are not as stringent or complete as you would like, examine the available suffix grade numbers in the far right column of the table. In this example, for a BC 507 material, suffix grades 2 and 5 are available.

B.5 Step 5—Go to the portion of Tables 6.AA to 6.HK headed "Suffix Requirements." Decide which of the suffix requirements are applicable to the material (such as heat aging resistance, fluid resistance, and so forth). Then choose the grade number which encompasses all or most of the applicable suffix requirements.

NOTE—Only suffix requirements appearing in the chosen grade number column may be specified. Of those suffix requirements which appear, only those which are necessary shall be added to the line call-out. In the example of 8.1, grade 2 was chosen and suffix requirements A14 and EO34 were selected for heat aging and fluid resistance, respectively. Thus, the suffix requirements are added to the line call-out in the following manner:

2BC507A14EO34

B.6 Step 6—Special requirements that are demanded of the material but not shown in Table 6.AA to 6.HK shall be designated by a "Z" suffix. When indicating special requirements, keep in mind that they must be consistent with the type and class of the material. Do not specify, for example, a special requirement of 20% maximum volume swell in ASTM No. 3 oil for a BC material. The basic requirement for a BC material is 120% maximum volume swell.

If several special requirements exist, they are denoted by Z1, Z2, Z3, etc. "Z" requirements shall be specified in detail whenever used, including test method and test conditions. The format for specifying Z requirements is given in the following call-out:

2BC507A14EO34Z1Z2Z3

suffix Z1 (for example)—polymer content of rubber compound shall be 100% polychloroprene

suffix Z2 (for example)—55 ±5 Type A durometer, ASTM D 2240

suffix Z3 (for example)—20% maximum tension set, ASTM D 412 (elongate to 200% for 10 min, measure set after 10 min recovery)

B.7 Step 7—Complete the line call-out by prefixing the line with SAE J200 and the SI code "M." The call-out is written as one continuous string having no spaces between characters. The final form of the example call-out is shown as follows:

SAEJ200M2BC507A14EO34Z1Z2Z3

suffix Z1—polymer content of rubber compound shall be 100% polychloroprene

suffix Z2—55 ±5 Type A durometer, ASTM D 2240

suffix Z3—20% maximum tension set, ASTM D 412 (elongate to 200% for 10 min, measure set after 10 min recovery)

The line call-out is valid since Grade No. 2 is available for BC 507 in the list of Available Suffix Grade Numbers (Table 6.BC) and both A14 and EO34 are available Suffix Requirements for Grade No. 2 materials. Grade Number 5 would be the only other grade available to a BC 507 material.

APPENDIX C
DEVELOPMENT OF AND ADDITIONS TO THE SAE J200 AND J3000 TABLES

C.1 Purpose—The purpose of this section is to set forth the procedure for establishing new tables or additions to existing tables for the SAE J200 document.

C.2 Proposed SAE J200 Table Development Pre-Requisites

C.2.1 Present to the Committee on Automotive Rubber Specifications a proposal for an additional table or a revision to an existing table based upon preliminary laboratory data.

C.2.1.1 The proposed compound(s) must be a vulcanized commercial thermoset rubber prior to program initiation.

C.2.1.2 The proposed compound or family of materials currently under consideration and development is intended for, but not limited to, an automotive application.

C.2.1.3 Subsequent table data must represent commercial compounds convertible to useable goods.

C.2.1.4 The chemical family of materials, from which the compound is produced, must have an ASTM D 1418 or ISO 1629 chemical classification. This aids in table assignment and potential recycling identification. The ASTM D11.8 committee gives chemical classification designations. This may be done concurrent with table development.

C.2.2 Proposed SAE J200 Table Development

C.2.2.1 Identify the number of compositions intended to be tested and the basic requirements for each composition.

C.2.2.2 Identify the proposed suffix requirements, if any, for each of the compositions intended to be tested.

C.3 Approved SAE J200 Development Program

C.3.1 For an approved program, the proposer shall either co-ordinate the program, or shall designate a coordinator. The coordinator shall be responsible for the full implementation of the program and shall report back to Committee on Automotive Rubber Specifications at each subsequent committee meeting.

C.3.2 In conjunction with the committee, secure a minimum of six laboratories which may include the proposer's or coordinator's laboratory. Assign an alphanumeric code to each laboratory to insure anonymity.

C.3.3 The sponsor will obtain from the committee chair, a file copy of the reporting format. The sponsor shall remove any test sections from the file which are not pertinent to their round robin. If the round robin is to include additional test(s) not currently included in SAE J200, the sponsor shall add those tests to the file in the same format. The sponsor shall make sufficient disk copies and supply them to the participating laboratories (alternately the sponsor may Email these files). In the event a participating laboratory does not have the appropriate spreadsheet program, the sponsor shall supply a hard copy of the format.

C.3.4 The sponsor shall request the labs to respond as to which tests they are able to run internally. If any of the original six laboratories are unable to perform specific required tests, secure additional laboratories to perform those specific tests. The additional laboratories need not complete the entire test program.

C.3.5 Sample Preparation

C.3.5.1 Prepare a sufficient quantity of each of the compositions to provide samples for all of the required testing (five test specimens, per test per laboratory). It is preferable to use production compositions but laboratory prepared compositions are acceptable. Compositions shall be molded as designated by ASTM, or other approved procedures. It is imperative that all steps be taken to reduce variation. Prior to molding, and periodically throughout the molding, the mold temperature shall be checked using a pyrometer or similar instrument. All plaques for dumbbell samples shall be produced from a single mold. All samples for testing volume change, hardness, etc., shall be produced from a single mold.

C.3.5.2 Using the appropriate die, cut all test specimens required for a given composition. One operator shall cut all samples, and the die shall be inspected before cutting samples from a different composition. If a die is damaged during the course of cutting a composition it shall be repaired, and a new set of samples from that composition shall be prepared.

C.3.5.3 Test for tensile, elongation, hardness, and compression set to verify the composition meets the anticipated requirements.

C.3.5.4 When all the required test specimens have been prepared from a given composition, all of the test specimens of the same type shall be mixed, and the appropriate number randomly selected for each laboratory.

C.3.5.5 Each testing laboratory shall be provided five test specimens for each test that they are to conduct.

C.3.5.6 Sets of specimens should be placed in a small plastic bag with a label indicating the composition designation, ASTM test identification, the time, temperature, and environment for testing. All sample bags for a given composition should be placed in a large bag with a report form for that composition.

C.3.5.7 The report form should include the composition designation, the tests to be performed and space for recording the test result for each individual specimen.

C.4 Sample Testing

C.4.1 Inform the laboratories by letter of any special procedures to be used or precautions to be taken. A due date for returning data should be included.

C.4.2 Each testing laboratory is to carry out the tests that they have agreed to perform, taking care to ensure that the proper test procedures are followed and that all test temperatures are correct.

C.4.3 The participating laboratories shall include 5 data points (per test) on the spreadsheet. Averages are not allowed. All Data entries, where applicable, shall be in metric. The completed speadsheet file shall be forwarded to the program sponsor. The participating laboratories are to keep a copy of the spreadsheet, until 1 year after publication.

C.4.4 If 50% or more the test labs providing table data are ISO Guide 25 Accredited, that portion of the table shall be identified using the "A" symbol.

C.5 Data Processing

C.5.1 Submit the test data on the report form to SAE "CARS" including the proposed basic and suffix requirements and line call-outs.

C.5.2 A subcommittee of the Committee on Automotive Rubber Specifications will analyze the data and make the final recommendation to Committee on Automotive Rubber Specifications for inclusion into SAE J200 as appropriate.

C.6 Non-SAE CARS J200 Development

C.6.1 Partial or complete table development programs conducted with the approval of Committee on Automotive Rubber Specifications, but not by members of CARS shall be credited with the accomplishment by way of a footnote at the bottom of that table. In the case of partial development for additions to a table, the footnote shall designate the applicable section.

APPENDIX D
SAE J200 AND ASTM D 2000 SPECIFICATION SYSTEMS

D.1 Purpose. The SAE Committee on Automotive Rubber Specifications, (CARS), and the ASTM D11.30 Committee affirm that we will work together to maintain the SAE J200 and ASTM D 2000 specification systems. It is our goal to keep the tables in these two documents equivalent. As such, the SAE Committee on Automotive Rubber Specifications will be the gatekeeper of any changes and additions to the tables in these specification systems. They will consider, as necessary, the expansion of current tables or the addition of new tables based on new rubber materials that will better serve both the rubber industry and their customer. SAE Committee on Automotive Rubber Specifications may ask for assistance from ASTM D 11.30 Committee to provide the necessary laboratories for performing the required inter-laboratory testing. In the unlikely event that the SAE Committee on Automotive Rubber Specifications declines to make any additions or changes to the tables, then the ASTM D11.30 Committee may choose to proceed with making those changes or additions if they deem them as additive for the rubber industry.

MARKING OF RUBBER PARTS —SAE J2332 APR1997

SAE Recommended Practice

Report of the SAE Committee on Automotive Rubber Specifications approved April 1997.

1. Scope—This SAE Recommended Practice provides a system for marking thermoset rubber parts to designate the general type of material from which the part was fabricated.

1.1 Purpose—The purpose of this document is to provide information to facilitate the:

a. Selection of materials and procedures for rubber parts
b. Collection and handling of parts for subsequent recycling

2. References

2.1 Applicable Publications—The following publications form a part of this specification to the extent specified herein.

2.1.1 ASTM PUBLICATION—Available from ASTM, 100 Barr Harbor Drive, West Conshohocken, PA 19428-2959.

ASTM D 1418—Standard Practice for Rubber and Rubber Latices—Nomenclature

2.1.2 ISO PUBLICATION—Available from ANSI, 11 West 42nd Street, New York, NY 10036-8002.

ISO 1629—Rubber and Latices—Nomenclature

2.1.3 IISRP PUBLICATION—Available from the International Institute of Synthetic Rubber Producers, Inc., 2077 South Fessner Road, Suite 133, Houston, TX 77063-1123.

The Synthetic Rubber Manual

2.1.4 VDA PUBLICATION—Available from DIN Deutsches, Institut fur Normung, Burggrafeng Strasse 6, Postfach 1107, D-1000 Berlin 30 Germany.

VDA 260—German Motor Vehicles—Marking of Parts of Polymeric Materials

2.2 Related Publications—The following publications are provided for information purposes only and are not a required part of this document.

2.2.1 ISO PUBLICATIONS—Available from ANSI, 11 West 42nd Street, New York, NY 10036-8002.

ISO 1043-1—Plastics—Symbols—Part 1: Basic polymers and their special characteristics

ISO 1043-2—Plastics—Symbols—Part 2: Fillers and reinforcing materials

ISO 11469—Plastics—Generic identification and marking of plastic products

3. Description

3.1 The system is based on standard symbols for terms relating to rubber (ISO 1629). Most commonly used symbols, including some not covered by ISO are shown in Table 1. In addition, symbols for commerical rubber materials are shown in Table 2, derived from the latest version of the Synthetic Rubber Manual and symbols for commonly used automotive fillers/reinforcements derived from ISO 1043-2 are shown in Table D1.

3.2 If additional symbols are required to cover new materials, the form in Appendix A shall be completed and submitted to SAE. New symbols will be included in the next revision to this document.

TABLE 1—SYMBOLS FOR MARKING RUBBER PARTS

Elastomeric "Family" Name Chemical Composition of Polymer Chain	Common Name(1)	Standard Symbol	(Previous)(2)(3)
Class M			
Copolymers of ethyl or other acrylate and a small amount of monomer which facilitates vulcanization		ACM	
Copolymers of ethyl and other acrylates and ethylene		AEM	
Copolymers of ethyl or other acrylate and acrylonitrile		ANM	
Chloro-polyethylene		CM	
Polychloro-trifluoro-ethylene		CFM	
Chloro-sulfonyl-polyethylene		CSM	
Terpolymer of ethylene, propylene, and a diene with the residual unsaturated portion of the diene in the side chain		EPDM	
Copolymers of ethylene and propylene		EPM	
Copolymers of ethylene and vinyl acetate		EVM	
Copolymer of tetrafluoroethylene and propylene		FEPM	
Perfluoro rubbers of the polymethylene type having all substituent groups on the polymer chain either fluoro, perfluoroalkyl, or perfluoroalkoxy groups		FFKM	
Fluoro rubber of the polymethylene type having substituent fluoro and perfluoroalkyl or perfluoroalkoxy groups on the polymer chain		FKM	
Styrene-ethylene/butylene		SEBM	
Styrene-ethylene/propylene		SEPM	
Class O			
Polychloromethyl oxirane (epichlorohydrin polymer).		CO	
Ethylene oxide (oxirane) and chloromethyl oxirane (epichlorohydrin copolymer)		ECO	
Epichlorohydrin-ethylene oxide-allylglycidylether terpolymer		GECO	
Polypropylene oxide and allyl glycidyl ether		GPO	
Class Q			
Silicone rubber having fluorine, vinyl, and methyl substitute groups on the polymer chain.		FVMQ	
Silicone rubbers having both methyl and phenyl, and vinyl substituent groups on the polymer chain		PMQ	
Silicone rubbers having both methyl and phenyl substituent groups on the polymer chain		PVMQ	
Silicone rubbers having only methyl substituent groups on the polymer chain		MQ	
Silicone rubber having both methyl and vinyl substitute groups on the polymer chain		VMQ	
Class R			
Acrylate-butadiene		ABR	
Bromo-isobutene-isoprene		BIIR	
Butadiene		BR	
Chloro-isobutene-isoprene		CIIR	
Chloroprene		CR	

TABLE 1—SYMBOLS FOR MARKING RUBBER PARTS (continued)

Elastomeric "Family" Name Chemical Composition of Polymer Chain	Common Name[1]	Standard Symbol	(Previous)[2][3]
Hydrogenated acrylonitrile-butadiene		HNBR	
Isobutene-Isoprene		IIR	
Isoprene, synthetic		IR	
Acrylonitrile-butadiene		NBR	
Acrylonitrile-chloroprene		NCR	
Acrylonitrile-isoprene		NIR	
Natural rubber		NR	
Vinylpyridine-butadiene		PBR	
Vinylpyridine-styrene-butadiene		PSBR	
Sytrene-butadiene		SBR	
Sytrene-chloroprene		SCR	
Styrene-isoprene rubbers		SIR	
Carboxylic-styrene-butadiene		XSBR	
Carboxylic-acrylonitrile-butadiene		XNBR	
Carboxylic-hydrogenated-acrylonitrile-butadiene		XHNBR	
Class T			
Rubber having either a $-CH_2-CH_2-O-CH_2-O-CH_2-CH_2-$ group or occasionally a -R-group, where R is an aliphatic hydrocarbon between the polysulfide linkages in the polymer chain		OT	
Rubber having either a $-CH_2-CH_2-O-CH_2-O-CH_2-CH_2-$ group and -R-groups that are usually $-CH_2-CH_2-$ but occasionally other aliphatic groups between the polysulfide linkages in the polymer chain		EOT	
Class U			
Terpolymer of tetrafluoroethylene, trifluoronitrosomethane, and nitrosoperfluorobutyric acid		AFMU	
Polyester urethane		AU	
Polyether urethane		EU	
Class Z			
Rubber having a -P=N-chain and having fluoroalkoxy groups attached to the phosphorus atoms in the chain		FZ	
Rubber having a -P=N-chain and having aryloxy (phenoxy and substituted phenoxy) groups attached to the phosphorus atoms in the chain		PZ	

1. Common names and trademarks for each plastic "family" name are shown in Appendix C, and are intended as a guide to aid the user in selecting the correct standard symbol for the material under consideration.
2. (Previous)—SAE JXXXX or other commonly used marking parts.
3. Symbols listed as ("Previous Symbols") are former designations and should not be used.

TABLE 2—SYMBOLS FOR COMMERCIAL RUBBER MATERIALS

Commercial Materials	Standard Symbol	(Previous)
Class M		
ACRALEN, A, Bayer	ACM	
EUROPRENE AR, C, L & R, EniChem Elastomeri S.r.l.		
JSR, Japan Synthetic Rubber		
CROSLENE, Takeda Chemical Industries		
ACRON, Tohpe Corp.		
HYTEMP, NIPOL AR, Zeon Chemicals Inc.		
VAMAC, DuPont Dow Elastomers	AEM	
	ANM	
TYRIN, DuPont Dow Elastomers	CM	
KEL-F, DYNEON	CFM	
HYPALON, DuPont Dow Elastomers	CSM	
BUNA EP, Bayer Buna GmbH, Bayer Corp.	EPDM	
KELTAN, DSM Elastomers Europe B.V., DSM Copolymer Inc.		
NORDEL, DuPont Dow Elastomers		
DUTRAL TER, EniChem Elastomeri S.r.l.		
VISTALON, Exxon Chemical Co., Butyl Americas		
HERLENE, Herdillia Unimers Ltd.		
MITSUI-EPT, Mitsui Petrochemical Industries, Inc.		
NITRIFLEX EP, Nitriflex S.A.		
ESPRENE, Sumitomo Chemical Co., LTD.		
ElastoFlo, Union Carbide Corporation		
ROYALENE, Uniroyal Chemical Co.		
SUPRENE, Yukong Ltd.		
Keltan, DSM Copolymer Inc., DSM Elastomers Europe B.V.	EPM	

TABLE 2—SYMBOLS FOR COMMERCIAL RUBBER MATERIALS (continued)

Commercial Materials	Standard Symbol	(Previous)
DUTRAL CO., EniChem Elastomeri S.r.l.		
VISTALON, Exxon Chemical Co., Societe du Caoutchouc		
BUNA EP, Bayer Corp.		
TOTAL EP, Societe du Caoutchouc Butyl		
ElastoFlo, Union Carbide Corporation		
ROYALENE, Uniroyal Chemical Co.		
SUPRENE, Yukong Ltd.		
LEVAPREN, Bayer AG	EVM	EAM
AFLAS'TFE, DYNEON	FEPM	
	FFKM	
FLUOREL, DYNEON	FKM	
?, Kazan NPO Zavod SK		
SYLUN, Shin-Etsu Chemical Co., Ltd.		
TECHNOFLON, Montifluos		
VITON, DuPont Dow Elastomers		
	SEBM	
	SEPM	
Class O		
HYDRIN, Zeon Chemicals Inc.	CO	
GECHRON, Nippon Zeon Co. Ltd.		
HYDRIN, Zeon Chemicals Inc.	ECO	
GECHRON, Nippon Zeon Co. Ltd.		
GECHRON, Nippon Zeon Co., Ltd.	GECO	
HYDRIN, Zeon Chemicals Inc.		
PAREL, Zeon Chemicals Inc.	GPO	
Class Q		
SILASTIC, Dow Corning Corporation	FVMQ	
SILPLUS, General Electric Company		
?, Kazan NPO Zarod SK		
POWERSIL, Wacker-Chemie GmbH		
SILASTIC, Dow Corning Corporation	PMQ	
SILASTIC, Dow Corning Corporation	PVMQ	
?, Kazan NPO Zarod SK		
POWERSIL, Wacker-Chemie GmbH		
SILASTIC, Dow Corning Corporation	MQ	
TUFGL, General Electric Company		
SILASTIC, Dow Corning Corporation	VMQ	
SILPLUS, General Electric Company		
?, Kazan NPO Zarod SK		
Elastosil, Wacker Silicones Corp., Wacker-Chemie GmbH		
Elektorguard, Wacker Silicones Corp.		
Powersil, Wacker Silicones Corp.		
SILOPREN, Bayer AG	Q	
Class R		
BUTAKON, Doverstrand Ltd.	ABR	
POLYSAR Bromobutyl, BROMOBUTYL, Bayer Rubber Inc.	BIIR	
EXXON BROMOBUTYL, EXXON SB BROMOBUTYL, Exxon Chemical		
BROMOBUTYL, Japan Butyl Company, Ltd.		
CISDENE, American Synthetic Rubber Corporation	BR	
E-BR, Ameripol Synpol Company		
ADADENE, Asahi Chemical Industry Co., Ltd.		
AUSTRAPOL, Australian Synthetic Rubber Co., Ltd.		
BUNA CB, BUNA VI, Bayer		
COPERFLEX BR, Companhia Pernambucana de Borracha Sintetica (COPERBO)		
?, Efremov Synthetic Rubber Enterprise		
EUROPRENE CIS, Enichem Elastomeri S.r.l.		
EUROPRENE NEOCIS, Enichem Elastomers S.p.A.		
DIENE, Firestone Synthetic Rubber & Latex Company		
BUDENE, Goodyear Tire & Rubber Company		
CISAMER, Indian Petrochemicals Corporation, Ltd.		
ASAPRENE, Japan Elastomer Co., Ltd.		
JSR, Japan Synthetic Rubber Co., Ltd.	BR	
AFDENE, NEODENE, Karbochem Division of Sentrachem Ltd.		

TABLE 2—SYMBOLS FOR COMMERCIAL RUBBER MATERIALS (continued)

Commercial Materials	Standard Symbol	(Previous)
KRASOL, Kaucuk Elastomers Div.		
AUSTRAPOL, Kemcor Australia		
BUNA, Kombinat VEB, Chemische Werke		
KOSYN, Korea Kumho Petrochemical Co., Ltd.		
SOLPRENE, Negromex, S.A., de C.V.		
NIPOL, Nippon Zeon Co., Ltd.		
PETKAUCUK, Petkim Petrokimya A.S.		
FINAPRENE, Petrochim N.V.		
TAKTENE, Bayer Corp.		
CALPRENE, Repsol Quimica S.A.		
BUTAKON, Revertex Ltd.		
CARIFLEX BR, Shell Chemicals Europe		
TAIPOL, Taiwan Synthetic Rubber Corporation		
UBEPOL-BR, UBEPOL-VCR, UBE Industries, Ltd.		
KER, Zaklady Chemiczne Oswiecim		
CHLOROBUTYL, Bayer Rubber Belguim	CIIR	
EXXON CHLOROBUTYL, EXXON SB CHLOROBUTYL, Exxon Chemical International		
POLYSAR Chlorobutyl, Bayer Rubber Inc.		
CHLOROBUTYL, Japan Butyl Company, Ltd.		
BAYPREN, Bayer	CR	
Denka Chloroprene, Denki Kagaku Kogyo, K.K.		
BUTACLOR, DISTUGIL		
NEOPRENE, DuPont Dow Elastomers		
Skyprene, TOSOH Corporation		
THERBAN, Bayer Corporation	HNBR	
ZETPOL, Zeon Chemicals Inc.		
BUTYL, POLYSAR BUTYL, Bayer	IIR	
EXXON BUTYL, EXXON SB BUTYL, Exxon Chemical Americas		
JSR BUTYL, BUTYL, Japan Butyl Co., Ltd.		
JSR, Japan Synthetic Rubber Co., Ltd.		
NATSYN, Goodyear Tire & Rubber Company	IR	
AFPRENE, Karbochem Division of Sentrachem Ltd.		
KURARAY, Kuraray Company Ltd.		
?, Nizhnekamskneftechim		
PERBUNAN N, Bayer	NBR	
KRYNAC, Bayer		
HYCAR EMULSION, B.F. Goodrich		
BREON, Zeon Chemicals Europe, Ltd.		
BUTAKON, Doverstrand Ltd.		
Nysyn, Nysynblak, DSM Elastomers Europe B.V., DSM Copolymer, Inc.		
CHEMIGUM, Goodyear Tire & Rubber Company, Goodyear Chemicals Europer		
EUROPRENE N, EniChem Elastomeri S.r.l.		
HUMEX, Huels Mexicanos, S.A.	NBR	
JSR, Japan Synthetic Rubber Co., Ltd.		
BUNA, Buna GMBH		
KOSYN, Korea Kumho Petrochemical Co., Ltd.		
?, Krasnoyarsk SR Plant Co.		
NITRIFLEX N & NP, Nitriflex S.A. Industria e Comercio		
NIPOL, Nippon Zeon Co., Ltd.		
DAREX, Organic Chem. Div., W.R. Grace & Co.		
ARNIPOL, PASA S.A.		
TYLAC, Reichhold Chemicals, Inc.		
REVINEX, Revertex Ltd.		
CHEMAPRENE, Synthetics & Chemicals Ltd.		
SAVINEX, Synthetic Latex Company (Pty.) Ltd.		
CROSLENE, Takeda Chemical Industries		
PARACRIL, Uniroyal Chemical Company, Inc.		
	NCR	
	NIR	
	NR	
	PBR	

TABLE 2—SYMBOLS FOR COMMERCIAL RUBBER MATERIALS (continued)

Commercial Materials	Standard Symbol	(Previous)
? Omsk Kanchuk Co.	PSBR	
AMERIPOL, SYNPOL, TRAXOL, MICROBLAK, ROVENE, Ameripol Synpol Corp.	SBR	
TUFDENE, Asahi Chemical Industry Co., Ltd.		
AUSTRAPOL, Australian Synthetic Rubber Co., Ltd.		
BUTANOL, BASF Corp.		
BUNA BL, SL, VSL, POLYSAR S, SS, KRYLENE SBR, KRYNOL, Bayer		
BORG-WARNER LATEX, Borg-Warner (Australia) Ltd.		
BUNA, Buna GmbH		
KRALEX, Chemopetrol-Kaucuk		
CAROM, Combinatul Petrochimic Borzesti		
COPERFLEX SBR, COPERBO		
COPO, CARBOMIX, DSM Elastomers Europe B.V., DSM Copolymer, Inc.		
REVINEX, Doverstrand Ltd.		
GENTRO, GENTRO-JET, Dynagen, Inc.		
EUROPRENE, HS, EUROPRENE SOL, SOL S, EniChem Elastomeri S.r.l.		
DURADENE, STEREON, Firestone Synthetic Rubber & Latex Company		
PLIOLITE, PLIOFLEX, Goodyear Tire & Rubber Company		
BUNATEX, LIPOLAN, LITEX, Hüls AG		
HUMEX, Hüls Mexicanos, S.A.		
ARLATEX, Industrias Resistol S.A.		
ASAPRENE, Japan Elastomer Co., Ltd.		
JSR, Japan Synthetic Rubber Co., Ltd.	SBR	
AFPOL, AFSOL, Karbochem Division of Sentrachem Ltd.		
?, Kauchuk Co.		
KRALEX, Kaucuk a.s. Elastomers Division		
AUSTRAPOL, KEMCOR Australia		
KOSYN, Korea Kumho Petrochemical Co., Ltd.		
ROVENE, Mallard Creek Polymers		
DIAPOL, Mitsubishi Chemical Corporation		
BULTEX, Neftochim		
SOLPRENE, Negromex, S.A., de C.V.		
NITRIFLEX, Nitriflex S.A. Industria e Comércio		
NIPOL, Nippon Zeon Co., Ltd.		
?, Omsk Kauchuk Co.		
ARPOL, PASA S.A.		
PETKAUCUK, Petkim Petrokimya A.S.		
FINAPRENE, Petrochim N.V.		
PETROFLEX, PETROLATEX, Petroflex Industria e Comercio S.A.		
TYLAC, Reichhold Chemicals, Inc.		
CALPRENE, Repsol Quimica S.A.		
REVINEX, Revertex Ltd.		
CARIFLEX S, Shell Nederland Chemie		
SUMITOMO SBR, Sumitomo Chemical Company Ltd.		
NAUGATEX, PYRATEX, SN, Sumitomo Naugatuck Co., Ltd.		
SYNAPRENE, Synthetics & Chemicals Ltd.		
AFTEX, Synthetic Latex Company (Pty.) Ltd.		
TAIPOL, Taiwan Synthetic Rubber Corporation		
?, Togliattisyntezkauchuk Co.		
?, Voronezhsyntezkachuk Co.		
KER, LBS, Zaklady Chemiczne Oswiecim		
DAREX, W.R. Grace		
	SCR	
	SIR	
JSR, Japan Synthetic Rubber	XSBR	
KOSYN, Korea Kumho Petrochemical Co., Ltd.		
NIPOL, Nippon Zeon Co., Ltd.		
NITRIFLEX NTL, VP, Nitriflex S.A. Industria e Comércio		
?, Omsk Kauchuk Co.		
SYNTHOMER, Synthomer Chemie GmbH		
?, Voronezhsyntezkachuk Co.		
LBSK, Zaklady Chemiczne Oswiecim		
CHEMIGUM, Goodyear Tire & Rubber Co.	XNBR	

TABLE 2—SYMBOLS FOR COMMERCIAL RUBBER MATERIALS (continued)

Commercial Materials	Standard Symbol	(Previous)
NIPOL, Nippon Zeon Co. Ltd.		
	XHNBR	
	OT	
	EOT	
Class U		
	AFMU	
UREPAN, Bayer AG	AU	
ESTANG TPU, The B.F. Goodrich Co.		
VIBRATHANE, Uniroyal Chemical Company Inc.		
ADIPRENE, Uniroyal Chemical Company Inc.		
ESTANG TPU, The B.F. Goodrich Co.	EU	
VIBRATHANE, Uniroyal Chemical Company Inc.		
ADIPRENE, Uniroyal Chemical Company Inc.		
Class Z		
	FZ	
	PZ	

4. Use of Marking Symbols

4.1 In view of the wide variety of parts used in substantially different assembly situations, this document does not prescribe the location, and/or method of marking; however, the following guidelines should be followed:

4.1.1 Field service people should be informed regarding the material from which the part is made so suitable recycling procedures may be used.

4.1.2 Wherever practicable, the marking should be located where it may be observed while the part is in use. Consideration should be given to the use of multiple markings on large or complex-shaped parts.

4.1.3 From the standpoint of field service people, marking on the outside surface of the part (in an unobtrusive location from the viewpoint of the owner) is preferred.

4.1.4 Markings applied with inks, dyes, or paints, should not bleed, run, smudge, or stain other materials which may come in contact with the marking.

4.1.5 Marking should be designed to remain legible during the entire life of the part.

4.1.6 Markings which are molded into the part are preferred since they are permanent and do not require separate manufacturing operations as do those applied to the surface of the part after molding. Molded in markings should not create a stress concentration site which could result in premature cracking of the part.

4.1.7 The recommended practice for the standard marking symbol (Figure 1) is consistent with ISO 11469 and VDA 260. Dimensions are suggested guidelines. Markings should be proportional to part size.

>NBR< ←(3 mm Letter Height)

FIGURE 1—STANDARD MARKING SYMBOL

4.1.8 EXAMPLES—See Figure 2.

>VMQ<	**silicone w. methyl & vinyl gp.**
>FKM<	**fluoroelastomer**
>NBR<	**acrylonitrile-butadiene**

FIGURE 2—EXAMPLES OF STANDARD MARKING SYMBOLS

4.1.9 For small parts that cannot accommodate the 3.0 mm letter guidelines, the use of smaller letters should be considered in lieu of not marking the part at all.

4.2 For parts using rubber materials containing 10% or more by mass fillers/reinforcements, use the same designation for the "family name" as defined in Table 1 and, in addition, alpha codes from ISO 1043-2, followed by a numeric value representing the nominal percentage of filler/reinforcer. The polymer family codes shall be separated from the filler/reinforcement codes and value by use of a hyphen.

4.2.1 EXAMPLES—See Figure 3.

>VMQ-Rayon15<

>FKM-Aramid10<

>NBR-(Rayon10+Polyester10)<

FIGURE 3—EXAMPLES OF STANDARD MARKING SYMBOLS FOR RUBBER WITH FILLER OR REINFORCEMENT LEVELS ≥10% BY WEIGHT

4.3 Parts fabricated from two or more materials, some of which are not readily visible, may be marked so the primary visible material is identified first by the system specified in 3.1 followed by the identification of the other material(s) where the individual identification(s) is separated by a comma. Identify the main mass component by underlining.

4.3.1 EXAMPLES—For a product made of two components, see Figure 4.

>NR,BR<

FIGURE 4—EXAMPLES OF STANDARD MARKING SYMBOLS FOR MIXED/BLENDED

5. Notes

5.1 Additional Information—Appendices C and D are cross reference listings designed to assist the user in relating SAE marking symbols to common rubber names and supplier trademarks.

APPENDIX A
REQUEST TO ADD NEW MARKING SYMBOLS AND/OR TRADEMARKS

A.1 The following procedure is to be utilized to apply for inclusion of new marking symbols and/or trademarks into SAE JXXXX.

A.1.1 Complete Form A1. See Figure A1.

- Rubber or Rubber Blend "Family" Name:____________________

____

- Proposed Marking Symbol: (Check One) New Symbol________ Existing________
- Supplier's Trade Mark (If any):____________________
- Supplier:____________________
- Name of Submitter:____________________
- Telephone Number: ( )
- Date Submitted:____________________
- Signature____________________

Mail This Form To:

SAE
Land & Sea Technical Division
Materials Staff Engineer
400 Commonwealth Drive
Warrendale, PA 15096-0001

FIGURE A1—REQUEST TO ADD NEW MARKING SYMBOLS AND/OR TRADEMARKS FORM

APPENDIX B
PROCESS FLOW CHART—ADDING NEW SYMBOLS TO JXXXX

Preface—The procedure shown in Appendix B will be used to process requests for addition of new symbols. Requests to add trademarks to cross reference listings will be handled as editorial changes.

B.1 See Figure B1.

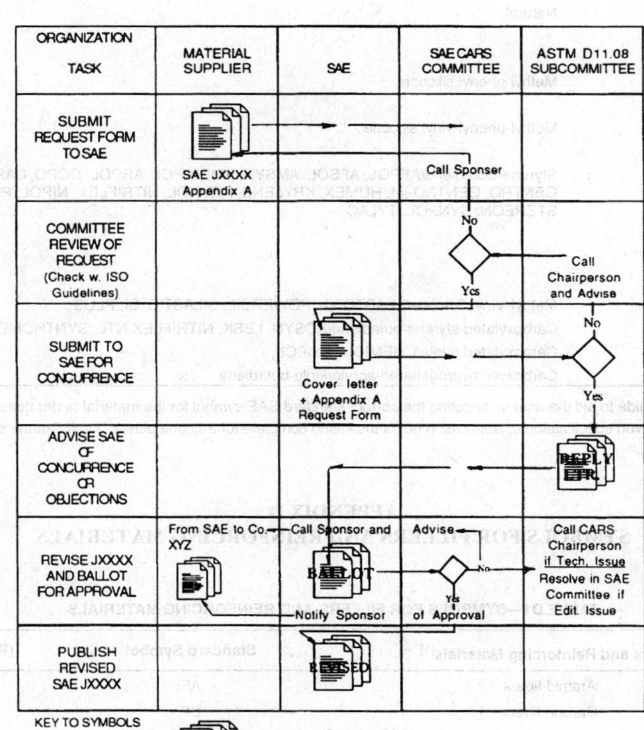

FIGURE B1—PROCESS FLOW CHART—ADDING NEW SYMBOLS TO JXXXX

APPENDIX C
CROSS REFERENCE—SYMBOLS TO COMMON NAMES/TRADEMARKS

C.1 See Table C1.

TABLE C1—CROSS REFERENCE—SYMBOLS TO COMMON NAMES/TRADEMARKS

Standard Symbol	Previous	Example of Common Names and/or Trademarks[1]
ABR		
ACM		Polyacrylic/ACRON ACRALEN A, CROSLENE, EUROPRENE, HYTEMP, NIPOL AR
AEM	EEA	Ethylene/Acrylic/VAMAC
AFMU		
ANM		
AU		Urethane/ADIPRENE, ESTANG TPU, VIBRATHANE, UREPAN
BIIR		Bromobutyl/Exxon and Polysar
BR		Polybutadiene/AUSTRAPOL, ASADENE, ASAPRENE, BUDENE, BUNA, CALPRENE, CARIFLEX, CISAMER, COPERFLEX, DIENE, EUROPRENE CIS, FINAPRENE, INTENE, INTOLENE, JSR, KER, KOSYN, NIPOL, PETKAUCUK, SOLPRENE, TAKTENE, TAIPOL, UBEPOL
CIIR		Chlorobutyl/Exxon and Polysar
CFM		
CM		Chloronated Polyethylene, TYRIN
CR		Neoprene or Chloroprene/BAYPREN, BUTACLOR, CHLOROPRENE, DENKA-USA, NEOPRENE, SKYPRENE
CSM		Chlorosulfonated Polyethylene/HYPALON
ECO		Epichlorohydrin (copolymer)/HYDRIN
EOT		
EPDM		Ethylene Propylene/BUNA AP, DUTRAL TER, EPsyn, ESPRENE, KELTAN, MITSUI-EPT, NITRIFLEX EP, NORDEL, POLYSAR EPDM, ROYALENE, SUPRENE, TOTAL EP, VISTALON
EPM		Ethylene propylene (copolymer)/DUTRAL, KELTAN, POLYSAR EPM, ROYALENE, SUPRENE, TOTAI EP
EVM		/LEVAPREN
EU		Urethane/ADIPRENE, Vibrathane
FEPM		/AFLAS‘ TFE
FFKM		
FKM		Fluorocarbon, Fluoroelastomer/FLUOREL‘ , SYLUN, VITON‘
FVMQ		Fluorosilicone, Fluoro-vinyl-methyl silicone/SILASTIC, SILPLUS
GPO		/PAREL
HNBR		Hydrogenated Nitrile/THERBAN, ZETPOL
IIR		Butyl/Polysar BUTYL/Exxon BUTYL
IR		Synthetic Polyisoprene/KURARAY, NATSYN
MQ		Methyl silicone/TUFGL, SILASTIC
NBR		Nitrile/ARNIPOL, CHEMIGUM, KRYNAC, KOSYN, NIPOL, NYSYN, PARACRIL, PERBUNAN N, TYLAC
NCR		
NIR		
NR		Natural
OT		
PBR		
PMQ		Methyl-phenyl silicone
PSBR		
PVMQ		Methyl-phenyl-vinyl silicone
PZ		
SBR		Styrene-Butadiene/AFPOL, AFSOL, AMSYN, AMERIPOL, ARPOL, COPO, CARBOMIX, DAREX, DIAPOL, DURADENE, GENTRO, GENTRO-jet, HUMEX, KRYLENE, KRYNOL, NITRIFLEX, NIPOL, PLIOFLEX, PLIOLITE, SOLPRENE, STEREON, SYNPOL, TYLAC
SCR		
SEBM		
SEPM		
VMQ		Methyl-Vinyl Silicone/ELASTOSIL, POWERSIL, SILASTIC, SILPLUS
XSBR		Carboxylated styrene-butadiene/KOSYN, LBSK, NITRIFLEX NTL, SYNTHOMER
XNBR		Carboxylated nitrile/CHEMIGUM/NIPOL
XHNBR		Carboxylic-hydrogenated-acrylonitrile-butadiene

1. The trademarks listed are intended as a guide to aid the user in selecting the correct standard SAE symbol for the material under consideration. It is not intended or implied that the listing is a material apoproval for any given specification or application nor is the listing complete for any one plastic "family" name since additional materials may be available which are not marketed under a trademark.

APPENDIX D
SYMBOLS FOR FILLERS AND REINFORCING MATERIALS

D.1 See Table D1.

TABLE D1—SYMBOLS FOR FILLERS AND REINFORCING MATERIALS

Fillers and Reinforcing Materials[1]	Standard Symbol	(Previous)
Aramid fibers	AF	
Carbon fibers	CF	
Glass fibers	GF	
Glass mat	GM	
Metal	M	

1. Mixtures of fillers may be shown in parentheses by combining the relevant symbols with the "+" sign.

THERMOPLASTIC ELASTOMER CLASSIFICATION SYSTEM—SAE J3000 SEP2003

SAE Standard

Report of the SAE Thermoplastic Elastomer Subcommittee of the SAE Committee on Automotive Rubber Specifications approved June 1992, and revised June 1993 and January 1997. Revised by the SAE Thermoplastic Elastomer Subcommittee of the SAE Committee on Automotive Rubber Specifications August 1997 and September 2003. Rationale statement available.

Foreword—SAE J3000 will be canceled in calendar year 2005. Users should discontinue use of J3000 for all current and future applications, and refer to the replacement classification document SAE J2558. SAE J2558 is not a "drop-in" replacement specification, and requires the user to define each property and requirements via an alphanumeric sequence.

1. Scope—This classification system tabulates the properties of thermoplastic elastomers (TPEs) that are intended for, but not limited to, use in automotive applications.

NOTE 1—For the purposes of this document a TPE is defined as a polymeric material that, without further chemical modification, is capable of recovering from deformations quickly and forcibly and is also capable of being repeatedly softened by heating and hardened by cooling within a temperature range characteristic of the material.

NOTE 2—When the TPE product is to be used for purposes where the requirements are too specific to be completely prescribed by this classification system, it is necessary for the purchaser to consult the supplier in advance to establish the appropriate properties, test methods, and specification test limits.

This classification system is based on the premise that the properties of TPEs can be arranged into characteristic material designations. These designations are determined by type, based on resistance to heat aging; and class, based on resistance to volume change resulting from oil immersion. Basic levels are thus established which, together with values describing additional requirements, permit complete description of the properties of all TPEs.

In all cases where provisions of this classification system would conflict with those of the detailed specifications for a particular product, the latter shall take precedence.

This classification is based on SI units.

1.1 Purpose—The purpose of this classification system is to provide guidance to the engineer in the selection of practical, commercially available TPE materials, and further, to provide a method by which these materials may be specified by the use of a simple line call-out designation.

This classification system was developed to permit the addition of descriptive values for future materials without complete reorganization of the classification system and to facilitate the incorporation of future new methods of test to keep pace with changing industry requirements. See Appendix A for the development of additions to this document.

2. References

2.1 Applicable Publications—The following publications form a part of this specification to the extent specified herein.

2.1.1 SAE PUBLICATIONS—Available from SAE, 400 Commonwealth Drive, Warrendale, PA 15096-0001.

SAE J200—Classification System for Rubber Materials

SAE J369—Flammability of Automotive Interior Materials—Horizontal Test Method

SAE J1885—Accelerated Exposure of Automotive Interior Trim Components Using a Controlled Irradiance Water Cooled Xenon-Arc Apparatus

2.1.2 ASTM PUBLICATIONS—Available from ASTM, 100 Barr Harbor Drive, West Conshohocken, PA 19428-2959.

ASTM D 256—Standard Test Methods for Impact Resistance of Plastics and Electrical Insulating Materials

ASTM D 297—Standard Test Methods for Rubber Products—Chemical Analysis

ASTM D 369—Standard Test Method for Specific Gravity of Creosote Fractions and Residues

ASTM D 395—Standard Test Methods for Rubber Property—Compression Set

ASTM D 412—Standard Test Methods for Rubber Properties in Tension

ASTM D 430—Standard Test Methods for Rubber Deterioration—Dynamic Fatigue

ASTM D 471—Standard Test Method for Rubber Property—Effect of Liquids

ASTM D 518—Standard Test Method for Rubber Deterioration—Surface Cracking

ASTM D 573—Standard Test Method for Rubber—Deterioration in an Air Oven

ASTM D 624—Standard Test Method for Rubber Property—Tear Resistance

ASTM D 696—Standard Test Method for Coefficient of Linear Thermal Expansion of Plastics

ASTM D 750—Standard Test Method for Rubber Deterioration in Carbon-Arc or Weathering Apparatus

ASTM D 790—Standard Test Methods for Flexural Properties of Unreinforced and Reinforced Plastics and Electrical Insulating Materials

ASTM D 792—Standard Test Methods for Specific Gravity (Relative Density) and Density of Plastics by Displacement

ASTM D 865—Standard Test Method for Rubber—Deterioration by Heating in Air (Test Tube Enclosure)

ASTM D 925—Standard Test Methods for Rubber Property—Staining of Surfaces (Contact, Migration, and Diffusion)

ASTM D 1052—Standard Test Method for Rubber Deterioration—Cut Growth Using Ross Flexing Apparatus

ASTM D 1053—Standard Test Methods for Rubber Property—Stiffening at Low Temperatures; Flexible Polymers and Coated Fabrics

ASTM D 1171—Standard Test Method for Rubber Deterioration—Surface Ozone Cracking Outdoors or Chamber (Triangular Specimens)

ASTM D 1329—Standard Test Method for Evaluating Rubber Property—Retraction at Low Temperature (TR Test)

ASTM D 1349—Standard Practice for Rubber—Standard Temperatures for Testing

ASTM D 1505—Standard Test Method for Density of Plastics by the Density-Gradient Technique

ASTM D 1525—Standard Test Method for Vicat Softening Temperature of Plastics

ASTM D 2137—Standard Test Methods for Rubber Property—Brittleness Point of Flexible Polymers and Coated Fabrics

ASTM D 2240—Standard Test Method for Rubber Property—Durometer Hardness

ASTM D 2990—Standard Test Methods for Tensile, Compressive, and Flexural Creep and Creep Rupture of Plastics

ASTM D 3029—Standard Test Methods for Impact Resistance of Rigid Plastic Sheeting or Parts by Means of a Tup (Falling Weight)

ASTM D 3418—Standard Test Method for Transition Temperatures of Polymers by Thermal Analysis

ASTM D 3677—Standard Test Methods for Rubber—Identification by Infrared Spectrophotometry

ASTM D 3850—Standard Test Method for Rapid Thermal Degradation of Solid Electrical Insulating Materials by Thermogravimetric Method

ASTM E 691—Practice for Conducting an Interlaboratory Test Program to Determine the Precision of Test Methods

ASTM G 53—Recommended Practice for Operating Light- and Water-Exposure Apparatus (Fluorescent UV-Condensation Type) for Exposure of Nonmetallic Materials

2.1.3 FMVSS PUBLICATION—Available from the Superintendent of Documents, U.S. Government Printing Office, Washington, DC 20402.

FMVSS 302—Flammability of Interior Materials—Passenger Car, Multi-Purpose Passenger Vehicles

2.1.4 ISO PUBLICATIONS—Available from ANSI, 11 West 42nd Street, New York, NY 10036-8002.

ISO 34—Rubber, vulcanized—Determination of tear strength (trouser, angle and crescent test pieces)

ISO 899—Plastics—Determination of tensile creep

ISO 3384—Rubber, vulcanized—Determination of stress relaxation in compression at ambient and at elevated temperatures

ISO 3795—Road vehicles, and tractors and machinery for agriculture and forestry—Determination of burning behaviour of interior materials

2.1.5 UL PUBLICATION—Available from Underwriters Laboratories, 333 Pfingsten Road, Northbrook, IL 60062-2096.

UL-94—Test for Flammability of Plastic Materials for Parts, Devices, and Appliances

3. Type and Class

3.1 TPEs shall be designated on the basis of type (heat aging resistance), and class (resistance to volume change resulting from oil immersion). These are each indicated by the letter designations as shown in Tables 1 and 2.

TABLE 1—BASIC REQUIREMENTS FOR ESTABLISHING TYPE BY TEMPERATURE

Type	Test Temperature °C
A	70
B	100
C	125
D	150
E	175
F	200
G	225
H	250
J	275

3.1.1 Type is based on changes in tensile strength (measured in the stronger direction) of not more than –30%, in elongation (measured in the same direction as tensile strength) of not more than –50%, and in hardness of not more than ±15 points after heat aging for 70 h according to ASTM D 573 at an appropriate temperature. The temperatures at which these materials shall be tested for determining type are listed in Table 1.

3.1.2 Class is based on the resistance of the material to volume change after 70 h immersion according to ASTM D 471 in IRM903 Oil[1] at the same temperature used to determine type, except that a maximum temperature of 150 °C (the upper limit of oil stability) shall be used. Limits of volume changes for each class are shown in Table 2. Note that some TPEs classified as Class A (no requirement for oil resistance) are so classified because they contain components that are extracted during oil immersion. This extraction results in apparent volume changes that are misleading in that they indicate that such materials are suitable for service requiring oil immersion, when in fact they are not.

1. See 3.1.2.

TABLE 2—BASIC REQUIREMENTS FOR ESTABLISHING CLASS BY VOLUME CHANGE RESULTING FROM IMMERSION IN IRM903 OIL

Class	Volume Change, Max, %
A	No requirement[1]
B	–20 to 140
C	–20 to 120
D	–20 to 100
E	–10 to 80
F	–10 to 60
G	–10 to 40
H	–5 to 30
J	–5 to 20
K	–5 to 10

1. See 3.1.2.

3.2 The letter designations shall always be followed by a one-digit number and a letter to specify the hardness (Shore A or D) measured after a 5 s delay, and two two-digit numbers (separated by a solidus) to specify the tensile strength – for example 5A15/08. The first digit and the letter indicate durometer hardness, for example, 5A for 50 ± 5 Shore A. The next two-digit numbers indicate the tensile strengths measured in the parallel (i.e., with the long axis of the test specimen parallel to the direction of flow) and perpendicular directions, respectively; for example, 15/08 for 15 MPa in the parallel direction and 8 MPa in the perpendicular direction.

4. Grade Numbers, Suffix Letters, and Numbers

4.1 Grade Numbers—Since the basic requirements do not always sufficiently describe all the necessary qualities, provision is made for deviation or adding requirements through a system of prefix grade numbers. Grade No. 1 indicates that only the basic requirements are compulsory and no suffix requirements are permitted. Grades other than No. 1 are used to indicate that deviations or additional requirements are necessary. Available Suffix Grade Numbers are listed in the last column of the Basic Requirements Table (Table 3). A grade number is written as a material prefix number preceding the letters for type and class.

TABLE 3—BASIC REQUIREMENTS AND AVAILABLE SUFFIX GRADE NUMBERS FOR CLASSIFICATION OF TPE MATERIALS[1]

Durometer Hardness Shore A ± 5 Points	Tensile Strength min. MPa Par./Perp.	Ultimate Elongation min. % Par./Perp.	Heat Aged ASTM D 573 70 h @ 125 °C	Oil Immersion ASTM D 471 IRM903 Oil 70 h @ 125 °C	Compression Set ASTM D 395 Method B, Plied Max % 22 h @ 70 °C	Available Suffix Grade Numbers
CA Materials—Basic Requirements						
60	3/4	600/700	Hardness ±15 Pts	No Requirement	60	—
60	3/5	250/600	Tensile –30% Max.	No Requirement	55	—
70	4/4	100/350	Elongation –50% Max.	No Requirement	65	—
CC Materials—Basic Requirements						
70	5/5	150/200	Hardness ±15 Pts Tensile –30% Max. Elongation –50% Max.	Volume Change –10% to 120% Max.	45	—
CD Materials—Basic Requirements						
70	4/5	250/300	Hardness ±15 Pts Tensile –30% Max.	Volume Change –10% to 100% Max.	35	—
80	5/6	200/350	Elongation –50% Max.		40	—
CF Materials—Basic Requirements						
70	5/6	200/250	Hardness ±15 Pts Tensile –30% Max. Elongation –50% Max.	Volume Change –10% to 60% Max.	65	—

1. All appropriate ASTM specifications will be adhered to except for test specimen gages. Test specimen gages will be specified in 10.1 of this specification.

4.2 Suffix Letters—The suffix letters which indicate additional tests, together with their meaning, appear in Table 4.

TABLE 4—MEANING OF SUFFIX LETTERS

Suffix Letter	Test Required
A	Heat Resistance
B	Compression Set Resistance
C	Ozone Resistance
D	Flexural Modulus
EA	Fluid Resistance (Aqueous)
EF	Fluid Resistance (Fuels)
EO	Fluid Resistance (Oils and Lubricants)
F	Low-Temperature Resistance
G	Tear Resistance
H	Flex Resistance
J	Abrasion Resistance
K	Adhesion
M	Flammability Resistance
N	Impact Resistance
P	Staining Resistance
Q	Analytical Properties
T	Creep Resistance/Stress Relaxation
U	Thermal Properties—High-Temperature Testing
W	UV Resistance
Y	Specific Gravity
Z	Special Requirements

4.3 Suffix Numbers—Each suffix letter shall be followed by two suffix numbers. The first suffix number indicates the method of test; time of test is part of the method and is taken from the listings in Table 5. The second suffix number indicates the temperature of test and is taken from Table 6.

5. Composition and Manufacture

5.1 Materials specified according to this classification shall be manufactured from polymers, together with added compounding materials of such nature and quantity as to produce materials that comply with the specified requirements. All materials and workmanship shall be in accordance with good commercial practice, and the resulting product shall be free of porous areas, weak sections, bubbles, foreign matter, or other defects affecting performance.

5.2 Color—Materials shall be tested in their typical commercially available colors.

6. Basic Requirements

6.1 The basic requirements for physical properties specified in Table 3 are based on test results obtained on test specimens having the highest and lowest tensile strength specified for each grade and durometer range. Test results from specimens prepared from finished products may not duplicate values obtained from standard test specimens.

6.2 The available materials are listed in the appropriate sections of Table 3, giving each hardness (measured after a 5 s delay) and tensile strength grade with its appropriate elongation value. The values of tensile strength and elongation are given for both the parallel (i.e., with the long axis of the test specimen parallel to the direction of flow) and perpendicular directions. The basic heat and oil aging requirements are also shown in this table.

7. Suffix Requirements

7.1 Suffix requirements shall be specified only as needed to define qualities necessary to meet service requirements. These suffix requirements are set forth for the various grade numbers. Not all available suffix requirements for a given material need be specified.

NOTE—Examples of the use of suffix letters and numbers would be A14 and EO34. Suffix A (Table 4) stands for heat resistance. Suffix 1 (Table 5) specifies that the test be run according to ASTM Method D 573 for 70 h, and Suffix 4 (Table 6) indicates the temperature of test as 100 °C. Similarly, Suffix EO34 indicates resistance to volume change resulting from immersion in IRM903 Oil, measured in accordance with ASTM Method D 471 for 70 h at 100 °C.

Basic requirements are always in effect, unless superseded by specific suffix requirements in the line call-out.

8. Line Call-Outs

8.1 A line call-out, which is used as a specification, shall contain the following: the document designation, the grade number, the material designation (type and class), the hardness and the tensile strengths in both parallel and perpendicular directions, followed by the appropriate suffix requirements. Figure 1 is an example of a line call-out:

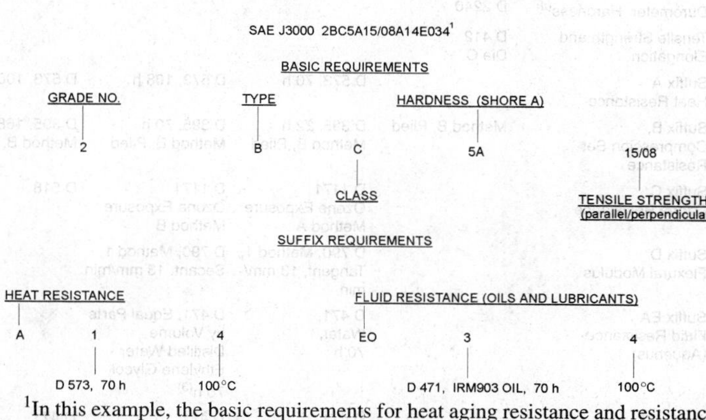

[1]In this example, the basic requirements for heat aging resistance and resistance to volume change resulting from oil immersion are superseded by suffix requirements.

FIGURE 1—LINE CALL-OUTS

9. Methods of Test

9.1 The applicable methods of test are listed in Table 5.

10. Sample Preparation

10.1 Unless otherwise noted, samples are to be die-cut from injection molded rectangular plaques 3.0 mm ± 0.4 mm thick specimens of other thickness will not necessarily give comparable results. Annealing of test specimens and plaques or the use of atypical molding conditions is not permitted. Where appropriate, samples are to be tested in both parallel (i.e., with the long axis of the test specimen parallel to the direction of flow) and perpendicular directions. Plaque dimensions must be sufficient to permit this. Three samples are to be tested in each direction and the mean value in each direction is to be recorded for each property. If the properties of a material are measured on other than injection molded plaques, this shall be so noted.

10.2 Preparation of compression set test specimens shall be accomplished via injection or compression molding as specified in ASTM D 395, paragraph 5.2 or 5.3, or via plying up cylindrical discs cut from slabs as described in paragraph 5.5 of ASTM D 395. Preparation of standard test sheets or plaques for plying up discs shall be specified in 10.1 of this specification. Only Type 1 specimens (ASTM D 395, Section 5) are permitted.

11. Sampling and Inspection

11.1 A lot, unless otherwise specified, shall consist of all products of the same material submitted for inspection at the same time. It is recommended that the manufacturer should examine the current specification (based on statistically significant number of production lots) to verify that the data statistically reflect the maxima and/or minima of the product specification.

11.2 When proof of conformance with a specification based on this classification system is required, the supplier shall, upon request of the purchaser at time of ordering, furnish a sufficient number of samples to perform the required tests. Test specimens shall be prepared as described in 10.1.

12. Limitations of the Document in Establishing Material Specifications

12.1 The data in Table 3 are based on physical properties of thermoplastic elastomers obtained directly from standard samples die-cut from rectangular plaques injection molded under ideal conditions (for example, in a laboratory). They indicate combinations of properties that are believed to be obtainable. Table 3 was not necessarily developed on the basis of statistical data.

12.2 Setting of material specifications, the determination of Cpk values and a quality control plan are the responsibility of the producer and consumer.

12.3 It must be borne in mind that all physical tests are subject to test errors as indicated by precision statements included in many ASTM test procedures.

TABLE 5—TEST METHODS[1]

Basic Requirements and First Suffix No. Requirement or Suffix Letter	Basic	1	2	3	4	5	6	7	8
Durometer Hardness[2]	D 2240								
Tensile Strength and Elongation	D 412 Die C								
Suffix A Heat Resistance		D 573, 70 h	D 573, 168 h	D 573, 1008 h	D 865, 70 h	D 865, 168 h	D 865, 1008 h		
Suffix B, Compression Set Resistance	Method B, Plied	D 395, 22 h Method B, Plied	D 395, 70 h Method B, Plied	D 395, 168 h Method B, Plied	D 395, 1008 h Method B, Solid	D 395, 22 h Method B, Solid	D 395, 70 h Method B, Solid	D 395, 168 h Method B, Solid	D 395, 1008 h
Suffix C, Ozone Resistance		D 1171 Ozone Exposure Method A	D 1171 Ozone Exposure Method B	D 518					
Suffix D Flexural Modulus		D 790, Method 1, Tangent, 13 mm/min	D 790, Method 1, Secant, 13 mm/min						
Suffix EA Fluid Resistance (Aqueous)		D 471, Water, 70 h	D 471, Equal Parts by Volume Distilled Water - Ethylene Glycol 70 h[3]						
Suffix EF, Fluid Resistance (Fuels)		D 471, Reference Fuel A 70 h	D 471, Reference Fuel B, 70 h	D 471, Reference Fuel C, 70 h	D 471, Reference Fuel D, 70 h	D 471, 85 Volume % Reference Fuel D Plus 15 Vol % Denatured Anhydrous Ethanol, 70 h	D 471, 85 Volume % Reference Fuel C Plus 15 Vol % Denatured Anhydrous Methanol, 70 h	D 471, 85 Volume % Reference Fuel C Plus 15 Vol % Denatured Anhydrous Ethanol, 70 h	
Suffix EO, Fluid Resistance (Oils and Lubricants)		D 471, ASTM Oil No. 1 70 h	D 471, IRM902 Oil 70 h	D 471, IRM903 Oil 70 h	D 471, IRM903 Oil 168 h	D 471, IRM902 Oil, 168 h	D 471, IRM903 Oil 168 h	D 471, Service Fluid No. 101, 70 h	D 471, Fluid as Designated in Table 3 of this Spec, 70 h
Suffix F, Low-Temperature Resistance		D 2137, Method A 5 min, Para 9.3.2, 3 min	D 1053, Method A	D 2137, 38.1 mm Die, Para 9.3.2, 22 h	D 1329, 38.1 mm Die, 50% Elongation, 10% min Retraction	D 1329 50% Elongation 50% min Retraction			
Suffix G, Tear Resistance		D 624, Die B	D 624, Die C	ISO 34 Trouser Tear					
Suffix H, Flex Resistance		D 430, Method A	D 430, Method B	D 430, Method C	D 1052				
Suffix J, Abrasion Resistance[4]									
Suffix K, Adhesion[4]									
Suffix M, Flammability Resistance		ISO 3795		SAE J369	UL-94	FMVSS-302			
Suffix N, Impact Resistance		D 3029	D 256						
Suffix P, Staining Resistance		D 925, Method A	D 925, Method B, Control Panel						
Suffix Q, Analytical Properties		D 3677	D 297	D 3850	D 3418				
Suffix T, Creep Resistance/Stress Relaxation			D 2990	ISO 3384	ISO 899				
Suffix U, Thermal Properties		D 412 Die C	D 696		D 1525				
Suffix W, UV Resistance[5]		1 Year Fla Under Glass 5 Degrees	1 Year Fla Direct Exposure 5 degrees	D 750	G 53	SAE J1885			
Suffix Y, Specific Gravity		D 792	D 1505	D 297					
Suffix Z, Special Requirement									

1. All test methods are ASTM unless otherwise noted. All appropriate ASTM specifications will be adhered to except for test specimen gages. Test specimen gages will be specified in 10.1 of this specification.
2. For the purpose of developing Table 3, hardness values shall be obtained using 5 s delay. If the Shore A value is less than or equal to 90, only this value shall be reported. Otherwise, only the Shore D value shall be reported.
3. Volume increase by displacement method, except alcohol dip omitted. When determining changes in tensile strength, elongation, and hardness, test tube shall be 3/4 full after specimens are immersed. Determination to be made after 30 min. Cool in distilled water, acetone dip to be omitted.
4. Test methods to be determined.
5. This tests requires a sample of minimum dimensions 152 mm by 76 mm and a minimum thickness of 1.8 mm.

TABLE 6—SUFFIX NUMBERS TO INDICATE TEST TEMPERATURE

Applicable Suffix Requirements	Second Suffix Number	Test Temperature, °C(1)
	11	275
	10	250
	9	225
	8	200
	7	175
A, B, C, EA,	6	150
EF, EO, G,	5	125
H, K, L, T	4	100
	3	70
	2	38
	1	23
	0	(2)
	22	0
	23	−10
	24	−18
	25	−25
F, H, K	26	−35
	27	−40
	28	−50
	29	−55
	30	−65
	31	−75
	32	−80

1. These test temperatures are based on ASTM D 1349.
2. Ambient temperatures in the case of outdoor weathering.

APPENDIX A
DEVELOPMENT AND ADDITIONS OF THE SAE J3000 TABLES

A.1 Purpose—The purpose of this section is to set forth the procedure for establishing new tables or additions to existing tables for the SAE J3000 document.

A.2 Program Initiation

A.2.1 Present to the Committee on Automotive Rubber Specifications a proposal for an additional table or a revision to an existing table based upon preliminary laboratory data.

A.2.2 Identify the type and class of material to be added or the current material table to be modified.

A.2.3 Identify the number of compositions intended to be tested and the basic requirements for each composition.

A.2.4 Identify the proposed suffix requirements, if any, for each of the compositions intended to be tested.

A.2.5 In conjunction with the committee, secure a minimum of three accredited[2] laboratories which may include the proposer's laboratory. Assign a code number to each laboratory to ensure anonymity.

A.2.6 Provide a list of the required tests and test conditions to the three accredited laboratories requesting that the labs respond as to which tests they are able to run internally.

A.2.7 If any of the original three laboratories are unable to perform specific required tests, secure additional accredited laboratories to perform those specific tests. The additional laboratories need not complete the entire test program.

A.3 Sample Preparation

A.3.1 Prepare sufficient quantity of each of the compositions to provide samples for all of the required testing (five or three test specimens, as required, per test per laboratory). It is preferable to use production compositions but laboratory prepared compositions are acceptable.

A.3.2 Test for tensile, elongation, hardness, and compression set to verify that the composition meets the anticipated requirements.

A.3.3 Prepare the composition for molding and mold the samples as designated by ASTM or other approved procedures. It is imperative that all steps be taken to reduce variation. A single operator shall prepare the material for molding, and a single operator shall mold the samples. Prior to molding and periodically throughout the molding, the mold temperature shall be checked using a pyrometer or similar instrument. All slabs for dumbbell samples shall be produced from a single mold. All samples for testing volume, hardness etc., shall be produced from a single mold if possible.

A.3.4 Using the appropriate die, cut all test specimens required for a given composition. One operator shall cut all samples, and the die shall be inspected before cutting samples from a different composition. If a die is damaged during the course of cutting a composition it shall be repaired, and a new set of samples from that composition shall be prepared.

A.3.5 When all the required test specimens have been prepared from a given composition, all of the test specimens of the same type shall be mixed, and the appropriate number randomly selected for each laboratory.

A.3.6 Each testing laboratory shall be provided five test specimens for each test that they are to conduct.

A.3.7 Sets of specimens should be placed in a small plastic bag with a label indicating the composition designation, ASTM test identification, the time, temperature, and environment for testing. All sample bags for a given composition should be placed in a large bag with a report form for that composition.

A.3.8 The report form should include the composition designation, the tests to be performed and space for recording the test result for each individual specimen.

A.4 Sample Testing

A.4.1 Inform the laboratories by letter of any special procedures to be used or precautions to be taken. A due date for returning data should be included.

A.4.2 Each testing laboratory is to carry out the tests that they have agreed to perform, taking care to ensure that the proper test procedures are followed and that all test temperatures are correct.

A.5 Data Processing

A.5.1 Submit the test data on the report form to SAE "CARS" including the proposed basic and suffix requirements and line call-outs.

2. An accredited laboratory is one accredited (certified) by a generally recognized accrediting organization such as the American Association for Laboratory Accreditation (A2LA) or the International Organization for Standardization (ISO).

NON-CONTACT HOSE MEASUREMENT STUDY 1—SAE J2605 AUG2001

SAE Information Report

Report of the SAE Coolant Hose Committee approved August 2001. Rationale statement available.

1. Scope—The Hose Measurement Task Force conducted a round-robin study to determine the measuring capability of automotive suppliers and users to simultaneously measure the Inside Diameter (ID), Outside Diameter (OD), Wall Thickness (Wall), and Wall thickness Variation (WV) of hose using a laser-based, non-contact LOTIS QC-20 gauging device. Three (3) companies (all end users) participated in this testing with one of the three companies performing the GR&R calculations presented herein. Based upon the round-robin study this report will detail procedures, test measuring devices, results, and conclusions.

2. References

2.1 Applicable Publication—The following publication forms a part of this specification to the extent specified herein.

2.1.1 SAE PUBLICATION

SAE J1759—SAE Hose Measurement Study, Issued 2000-10. Summary of a GR&R study completed using plug gauges, PI tapes and calipers.

2.2 Related Publication—The following publication is provided for information purposes only and is not a required part of this document.

2.2.1 AIAG PUBLICATION—Available from Automotive Industry Action Group, Suite 200, 262 Lahser Road, Southfield, MI 48034

(MSA) Manual-Measurement Systems Analysis Manual

3. Procedure—The following procedures were employed in the round-robin study:

3.1 This study attempted to duplicate the methodology and data presentation used in SAE J1759 as much as practical. Specifically this includes using identical tolerance levels as well as presenting both the detailed and average GR&R results.

3.2 Three (3) sets of hoses were measured; with 10 samples in each set. The three hose sets consisted of two straight sections (parts X & Y) and one curved (part Z). The specific hose parameters are provided in Table A1 of Appendix A within this document. All three sets of hoses were black.

3.3 One end of each hose was uniquely marked for measurement. The measurements were taken at approximately 19 mm (0.75 in) from the end.

NOTE—All measurements were made using metric units.

3.4 Three (3) people repeated each measurement three (3) times at each of the three (3) testing locations (plants). Subsequently designated plants A, B, and C.

3.5 The data were recorded on forms supplied with the samples.

3.6 Hose samples and measuring devices were brought to equilibrium for 24 h in a reasonably controlled environment of 23 degrees and a target relative humidity of 50%.

4. Attributes

4.1 Procedure—All of the samples were forwarded to the three participants in order. Each participant used their own QC-20 to perform the tests. The form for recording the measurements and test instructions (Appendix A) were also included. After taking the measurements, the data were sent to Plant A for analysis. The attributes were measured as follows:

4.1.1 INSIDE DIAMETER (ID)—The ID of the sample hoses were measured using a 12 mm QC-20 non-contact hose measurement system. The device makes 1600 ID radius measurements to compute the ID.

4.1.2 OUTSIDE DIAMETER (OD)—The OD of the sample hoses were measured using a 12 mm QC-20 non-contact hose measurement system. The device makes 1600 OD radius measurements to compute the OD.

4.1.3 WALL THICKNESS (WT)—The wall thickness is computed from the ID and OD results.

4.1.4 WALL THICKNESS VARIATION (WV)—The wall thickness variation is computed using the inside and outside radii results.

5. Results—The gage R&R calculation is based upon the Automotive Industry Action Group Measurement Systems Analysis (MSA) manual. The results are presented in Tables 1 through 6. Two (2) separate GR&R calculations were made.

5.1 GR&R Calculation 1—This is done for each hose set in each plant using the data from the 3 operators at each plant. A summary of the average GR&R for all three plants and for each hose and dimension is shown in Table 1. Detailed results are provided in Tables 2 through 5. This data is presented in manner similar to SAE J1759.

The *average* results for *straight* hoses (X and Y) across all measurements (ID, OD, WT, and WV) and all plants (A, B, C) from Tables 2 through 5 are:

Repeatability (% of tolerance) 8.9%
Reproducibility (% of tolerance) 4.6%
R&R (% of tolerance) 10.6%

The *average* results for *curved* hose (Z) across all measurements (ID, OD, WT, and WV) and all plants (A, B, C) from Tables 2 through 5 are:

Repeatability (% of tolerance) 10.7%
Reproducibility (% of tolerance) 8.0%
R&R (% of tolerance) 14.6%

5.2 GR&R Calculation 2—This second calculation was performed by using the data from operator #1 from each of the 3 plants. Those results are presented in Table 6. It is important to note that when combining the results from 3 different instruments the calibration offset between instruments will result in higher GR&R numbers. The QC-20 factory calibration only ensures absolute calibration of ±0.051 mm. Hence, the maximum deviation between systems is ±0.102 mm. Ten percent (10%) of the OD, wall, and wall variation tolerance and 13% of the ID tolerance is used up as a result of this difference. This effect is demonstrated in comparing the Repeatability and Reproducibility columns in Table 6. *This calculation was not performed in SAE J1759 but provides useful information to quality control personnel using multiple gauges.*

A tolerance of 0.76 mm was used for all ID calculations. All other calculations used 1.02 mm.

6. Conclusions

a. The LOTIS QC-20 non-contact measurement gauge provides a significantly better gauge R&R as compared to the results obtained for plug gauges, pi tapes and calipers as presented in SAE J1759. In addition, the ID, OD, wall thickness and wall variation measurements are collected simultaneously without touching the surface of the hose.
b. The GR&R is sufficient to settle measurement differences between suppliers and end users.
c. The results presented in Tables 2, 3, 4, and 5 use the conventional AIAG methods for GR&R calculations.
d. This committee recommends a standard procedure be developed for gauge evaluation using this study and SAE J1759 as a basis. The new gauge evaluation procedure would be used for evaluation of any future hose gauges.

TABLE 1—SUMMARY RESULTS
3 OPERATORS/1 SYSTEM AVERAGED OVER 3 PLANTS
(METRIC UNITS)[1]

Characteristic[2]	Gage/Method	%R&R Median	Actual Median	%R&R Average	Actual Average
ID X	QC-20 12 mm	10.87	0.08	10.18	0.08
ID Y	QC-20 12 mm	14.28	0.11	13.19	0.10
ID Z	QC-20 12 mm	13.91	0.11	14.49	0.11
OD X	QC-20 12 mm	8.68	0.09	11.07	0.11
OD Y	QC-20 12 mm	9.70	0.10	13.57	0.14
OD Z	QC-20 12 mm	17.57	0.18	19.41	0.20
Wall X	QC-20 12 mm	4.49	0.05	5.00	0.05
Wall Y	QC-20 12 mm	10.82	0.11	10.52	0.11
Wall Z	QC-20 12 mm	11.09	0.11	10.06	0.10
W.V. X	QC-20 12 mm	6.24	0.06	7.68	0.05
W.V. Y	QC-20 12 mm	13.44	0.14	13.61	0.14
W.V. Z	QC-20 12 mm	14.30	0.15	14.33	0.15

1. 25.4 mm = 1 in
2. Hoses X and Y are straight sections and Hose Z is curved.

This table is an average of the GR&R results obtained from plants A, B, and C. Although it is not standard practice to provide GR&R results as averages, it is provided here to allow comparison with the results provided in Figure 1 of SAE J1759.

TABLE 2—ID RESULTS FROM EACH PLANT (A, B, AND C)
3 OPERATORS/1 SYSTEM
METRIC UNITS[1]

Co./Hose	Dim.	Gage Used	Repeat % of Tol.	Actual Tol. Used	Reprod. % of Tol.	Actual Tol. Used	Gage R&R %	Actual Tot. Tol. Used	Spec. Tol.
A/X	ID	QC-20 12 mm	4.68	0.0356	0.99	0.0075	4.79	0.0364	0.76
B/X	ID	QC-20 12 mm	6.01	0.0457	9.05	0.0688	10.87	0.0826	0.76
C/X	ID	QC-20 12 mm	12.58	0.0956	7.96	0.0605	14.88	0.1131	0.76
		Average:	**7.76**		**6.00**		**10.18**		
A/Y	ID	QC-20 12 mm	11.11	0.0844	9.01	0.0685	14.30	0.1087	0.76
B/Y	ID	QC-20 12 mm	9.09	0.0691	6.17	0.0469	11.00	0.0836	0.76
C/Y	ID	QC-20 12 mm	11.91	0.0905	7.88	0.0599	14.28	0.1085	0.76
		Average:	**10.70**		**7.69**		**13.19**		
A/Z	ID	QC-20 12 mm	10.03	0.0762	7.11	0.0540	12.30	0.0935	0.76
B/Z	ID	QC-20 12 mm	13.91	0.1057	0.00	0.0000	13.91	0.1057	0.76
C/Z	ID	QC-20 12 mm	12.04	0.0915	12.36	0.0939	17.25	0.1311	0.76
		Average:	**11.99**		**6.49**		**14.49**		

1. 25.4 mm = 1 in

TABLE 3—OD RESULTS FROM EACH PLANT (A, B, AND C)
3 OPERATORS/1 SYSTEM
METRIC UNITS(1)

Co./Hose	Dim.	Gage Used	Repeat % of Tol.	Actual Tol. Used	Reprod. % of Tol.	Actual Tol. Used	Gage R&R %	Actual Tot. Tol. Used	Spec. Tol.
A/X	OD	QC-20 12 mm	4.70	0.0478	7.30	0.0742	8.68	0.0882	1.02
B/X	OD	QC-20 12 mm	7.71	0.0783	0.00	0.0000	7.71	0.0783	1.02
C/X	OD	QC-20 12 mm	16.81	0.1708	0.44	0.0045	16.82	0.1709	1.02
		Average:	**9.74**		**2.58**		**11.07**		
A/Y	OD	QC-20 12 mm	8.00	0.0813	5.48	0.0557	9.70	0.0986	1.02
B/Y	OD	QC-20 12 mm	8.31	0.0844	2.08	0.0211	8.56	0.0870	1.02
C/Y	OD	QC-20 12 mm	20.01	0.2033	10.17	0.1033	22.45	0.2281	1.02
		Average:	**12.11**		**5.91**		**13.57**		
A/Z	OD	QC-20 12 mm	7.51	0.0763	15.89	0.1614	17.57	0.1785	1.02
B/Z	OD	QC-20 12 mm	15.21	0.1545	23.13	0.2350	27.69	0.2813	1.02
C/Z	OD	QC-20 12 mm	12.51	0.1271	3.48	0.0354	12.98	0.1319	1.02
		Average:	**11.74**		**14.17**		**19.41**		

1. 25.4 mm = 1 in

TABLE 4—WALL RESULTS FROM EACH PLANT (A, B, AND C)
3 OPERATORS/1 SYSTEM
METRIC UNITS(1)

Co./Hose	Dim.	Gage Used	Repeat % of Tol.	Actual Tol. Used	Reprod. % of Tol.	Actual Tol. Used	Gage R&R %	Actual Tot. Tol. Used	Spec. Tol.
A/X	Wall	QC-20 12 mm	1.51	0.0153	4.06	0.0413	4.33	0.0440	1.02
B/X	Wall	QC-20 12 mm	2.10	0.0213	3.97	0.0403	4.49	0.0456	1.02
C/X	Wall	QC-20 12 mm	5.91	0.0600	1.83	0.0186	6.18	0.0628	1.02
		Average:	**3.17**		**3.29**		**5.00**		
A/Y	Wall	QC-20 12 mm	3.60	0.0366	6.16	0.0626	7.15	0.0726	1.02
B/Y	Wall	QC-20 12 mm	8.31	0.0844	2.08	0.0211	10.82	0.1099	1.02
C/Y	Wall	QC-20 12 mm	11.21	0.1139	7.71	0.0783	13.60	0.1382	1.02
		Average:	**7.71**		**5.31**		**10.52**		
A/Z	Wall	QC-20 12 mm	4.80	0.0488	10.24	0.1040	11.31	0.1149	1.02
B/Z	Wall	QC-20 12 mm	6.90	0.0701	8.68	0.0882	11.09	0.1127	1.02
C/Z	Wall	QC-20 12 mm	4.50	0.0457	6.33	0.0643	7.77	0.0789	1.02
		Average:	**5.40**		**8.42**		**10.06**		

1. 25.4 mm = 1 in

TABLE 5—WALL VARIATION RESULTS FROM EACH PLANT (A, B, AND C)
3 OPERATORS/1 SYSTEM
METRIC UNITS(1)

Co./Hose	Dim.	Gage Used	Repeat % of Tol.	Actual Tol. Used	Reprod. % of Tol.	Actual Tol. Used	Gage R&R %	Actual Tot. Tol. Used	Spec. Tol.
A/X	Wall Var.	QC-20 12 mm	6.00	0.0610	1.71	0.0174	6.24	0.0634	1.02
B/X	Wall Var.	QC-20 12 mm	7.01	0.0712	1.70	0.0173	7.20	0.0732	1.02
C/X	Wall Var.	QC-20 12 mm	9.61	0.0976	0.00	0.0000	9.61	0.0976	1.02
		Average:	**7.54**		**1.14**		**7.68**		
A/Y	Wall Var.	QC-20 12 mm	11.11	0.1129	4.13	0.0420	11.85	0.1204	1.02
B/Y	Wall Var.	QC-20 12 mm	11.60	0.1179	6.76	0.0687	13.44	0.1365	1.02
C/Y	Wall Var.	QC-20 12 mm	15.21	0.1545	3.22	0.0327	15.55	0.1580	1.02
		Average:	**12.64**		**4.70**		**13.61**		
A/Z	Wall Var.	QC-20 12 mm	12.61	0.1281	4.50	0.0457	13.39	0.1360	1.02
B/Z	Wall Var.	QC-20 12 mm	13.51	0.1373	4.70	0.0478	14.30	0.1453	1.02
C/Z	Wall Var.	QC-20 12 mm	15.31	0.1556	0.00	0.0000	15.31	0.1556	1.02
		Average:	**13.81**		**3.07**		**14.33**		

1. 25.4 mm = 1 in

TABLE 6—SUMMARY RESULTS BY HOSE X, Y, AND Z
3 OPERATORS/3 SYSTEMS
METRIC UNITS(1)

Hose(2)	Dim.	Gage Used	Repeat % of Tol.	Actual Tol. Used	Reprod. % of Tol.	Actual Tol. Used	Gage R&R %	Actual Tot. Tol. Used	Spec. Tol.
X	ID	QC-20 12mm	4.93	0.0376	19.93	0.1519	20.54	0.1565	0.76
Y	ID	QC-20 12mm	9.07	0.0691	20.49	0.1561	22.40	0.1707	0.76
Z	ID	QC-20 12mm	9.34	0.0712	14.42	0.1099	17.19	0.1310	0.76
X	OD	QC-20 12mm	4.20	0.0427	4.09	0.0416	5.87	0.0596	1.02
Y	OD	QC-20 12mm	9.80	0.0996	7.86	0.0799	12.57	0.1277	1.02
Z	OD	QC-20 12mm	8.60	0.0874	2.03	0.0206	8.84	0.0898	1.02
X	Wall	QC-20 12mm	1.90	0.0193	5.93	0.0602	6.22	0.0632	1.02
Y	Wall	QC-20 12mm	7.51	0.0763	3.45	0.0351	8.27	0.0840	1.02
Z	Wall	QC-20 12mm	3.80	0.0386	5.90	0.0599	7.02	0.0713	1.02
X	W.V.	QC-20 12mm	8.00	0.0813	5.75	0.0584	9.86	0.1002	1.02
Y	W.V.	QC-20 12mm	12.30	0.1250	10.85	0.1102	16.41	0.1667	1.02
Z	W.V.	QC-20 12mm	13.91	0.1413	11.51	0.1169	18.05	0.1834	1.02

1. 25.4 mm = 1 in
2. Hoses X and Y are straight sections and Hose Z is curved.

These results utilize a combination of data from all three plants that participated in the study. Each plant used their own QC-20. This is NOT the traditional method of performing GR&R calculations but is provided here as an additional measure of gauge capability.

APPENDIX A
GR&R NON-CONTACT GAGING STUDY

A.1 QC-20 Inspection Procedure

A.1.1 You will receive a box of 30 test hoses for this study. This Test Package includes shipping labels, labeled floppy disks for data archival, test instructions and data sheets for recording measurement data. Please keep the box that the test hoses arrived in so they can be shipped to the next test location.

A.1.2 Set up the QC-20 system and the 30 test hoses in the inspection area. Bring all items to equilibrium for 24 h in a reasonably controlled environment of 23 degrees and target a relative humidity of 50%. Turn on the power to the QC-20 during the 24-h stability period. The next 5 steps can be completed during the stabilization period.

A.1.3 Look over the test hoses. The three (3) sets of test hoses will have the inspection end marked and all hoses will be labeled with the hose name and hose number as follows: *X1* where **X** is the name and *1* is the first hose in the set of 10. The **X** test hoses are the smallest ID straight set of 10, the **Y** test hoses are the biggest ID straight set of 10 and the **Z** test hoses are the curved set of 10. Each hose set should be placed in a pile next to the QC-20 and pulled out randomly for inspection.

A.1.4 Review the data sheets. The data sheets are set up to identify each set of 10 hoses as **X, Y, Z**. Each group of 10 hoses will be inspected by each operator before changing to the next set of 10. **Only the marked end of each hose is to be inspected as shown in the enclosed printed photos.**

A.1.5 Input the hose specifications for each of the three hose sets as listed in Table A1 using the ALT159 menu on the QC-20 computer.

Name the smallest ID straight hose **X**, name the largest ID straight hose *Y*, and name the curved hose **Z**.

The data saved to the computer will be analyzed once the testing is complete. The computer data is saved in a file under the DATALOG directory (folder). The file is named with a date code and all scans from one 24-h period are saved to the one file. To insure that only the test results are in the datecoded file, please do not inspect any other parts during the tests until the file is archived to a floppy disk as described later.

A.1.6 The data must be collected and saved in metric units. Set up the QC-20 to display and save the data in metric units. With the main menu up, press ALT157 to get to the *Edit System Parameters* menu. Arrow down to *Display Units* and use the enter key to change inches to mm. Arrow back to the top and select Store Parameters to save changes. Press the Ecs key once to clear the screen back to the Main Menu. This process will need to be repeated to switch back to inches after the testing is complete; be sure to save changes.

A.1.7 Once the 24-h equilibrium period is complete, the inspection process can begin. Fill out the top section of the first data sheet. Run the QC-20 the offset calibration sequence, *Calibrate Inspection System*. Record the offset values on the data sheet.

A.1.8 Pick the menu item *Select Product for Inspection* and type in CalRing5. Remove CalRing2 and allow the QC-20 to set up for CalRing5. Once the QC-20 stops moving and is ready to inspect CalRing5, press the Esc key once to clear the screen and abort the inspection. This sequence cycles the probes over their range of motion.

A.1.9 Pick the menu item *Select Product for Inspection* and type in CalRing2. The QC-20 will set up to inspect CalRing2.

A.1.10 Follow the instructions on the computer to inspect CalRing2 and record the measurements on the data sheet.

A.1.11 Press the Esc key once to clear the data screen. Pick the menu item *Select Product for Inspection* and type in **X**. The QC-20 will set up for test hose **X**.

A.1.12 Operator #1 should inspect all 10 hoses in random order by pulling a hose from the pile, inspecting it, recording the data on the sheet and putting the hose back in the inspection pile until each one is inspected 3 times. **Do not inspect the same hose 3 times in a row**. The letters A, B and C following the hose name/number listed on the data sheet designates the first, second and third inspection of the same part (see example as follows). A separate pile should be made for the hoses that have been inspected 3 times. Record all measurements on the data sheet (30 rows of data) by checking the hose number and recording the values on the data sheet in the appropriate row.

EXAMPLE—The inspection results for randomly selected **X5** is entered on the data sheet in the row labeled **X5A**.

The next time **X5** is pulled from the inspection pile, the measurement data is entered in the row labeled **X5B**.

The third time *X5* is pulled from the inspection pile, its data is recorded on the data sheet in the row labeled *X5C*. Place **X5** in the completion pile. Continue with this pattern until the inspection pile is empty.

Insert the hose approximately 19 mm (3/4) in over the probe ends by aligning the front edge of the mark on the hose to the edge of the gold colored finger guards on the QC-20. It is important that the hose does not move during the scan cycle. Use the footswitch for hoses that require both hands to hold the part steady (curved hose).

A.1.13 Operator #2 and #3 should follow this same sequence until each person has recorded 30 rows of measurement data for all 10 of hose set **X**.

A.1.14 Press the Esc key once to clear the data screen. Pick the menu item *Select Product for Inspection* and type in **Y**. The QC-20 will set up for test hose **Y**.

A.1.15 Repeat steps A.1.12 to A.1.14 for each set of 10 of **Y** and *Z* parts. 90 rows of measurement data should be recorded once all parts are inspected.

A.1.16 Inspect CalRing2 one last time to complete the GR&R data sheet as follows: press the Esc key once to clear the data screen. Pick the menu item *Select Product for Inspection* and type in CalRing2. The QC-20 will set up for CalRing2. Inspect CalRing2 and record the measurements on the data sheet. Record the time that the final scan was completed on the last page of the data sheet.

A.2 Data Archival and Shipping

A.2.1 The data from the computer hard drive needs to be saved to two floppy disks for shipment to the analysis team. Included in the package are two floppy disks labeled for the datalog file along with an addressed envelope for mailing.

a. Exit the QC-20 program using ALT+F4 and type *cd\datalog* <enter>
b. Type *dir *.csv* <enter> and look for the datalog file created on the day of the inspections. All datalog files start with DL followed by a date code. Verify the correct file by checking the date it was created (to the right of the file name).
c. Type *copy dl??????.csv a:* <enter> where ? = date code name formatted as YYMMDD. Make sure the file was copied to the floppy disk by typing *dir a:* <enter> to see what is on the disk.
d. Pull out the disk and insert the second one. Repeat the previous step to copy the datalog file to the second disk and check that it was saved.
e. Write the datalog filename and date the data was collected on the outside of each floppy disk in the space provided.

A.2.2 A copy of the floppy disks and data sheets need to be shipped to two different locations. The Test Package includes an addressed manila envelope for each shipment.

a. Place each labeled disk in a floppy disk mailer and put one into each manila envelope.
b. Make sure all data sheets are completely filled out and place a copy of each set of sheets into each of the manila envelopes.

A.2.3 Please ship both packages via UPS Blue, 2-day air to the destination on the label..

A.2.4 The test hoses need to be forwarded to the next test location. The test hoses need to be packed carefully to prevent them from being squished. You will find an address label in the Test Package. Please attach the address label to the original box that the parts arrived in and ship it UPS Blue.

TABLE A1—HOSE SPECIFICATION—METRIC UNITS

	Straight Hose Set X (mm)	Straight Hose Set Y (mm)	Curved Hose Set Z (mm)
ID Minimum	25.10	40.13	33.50
ID Maximum	26.11	50.29	34.52
Target ID	25.60	45.21	34.01
WALL Minimum	3.63	4.39	3.30
WALL Maximum	4.09	5.21	4.83
Target WALL	3.86	4.8	4.06
OD Minimum	34.29	48.92	41.00
OD Maximum	36.83	60.71	43.00
Target OD	35.56	54.81	42.01

CLASSIFICATION SYSTEM FOR THERMOPLASTIC ELASTOMERS—SAE J2558 APR2002

SAE Standard

Report of the SAE Thermoplastic Elastomers Task Force of the SAE Committee on Automotive Rubber Specifications approved April 2002.

1. Scope—This SAE Standard provides a system for specifying significant material properties of thermoplastic elastomers (TPEs) that are intended for, but not limited to, use in automotive applications.

NOTE 1—For the purposes of this document a TPE is defined as a polymeric material that, without further chemical modifications, is capable of recovering from deformations quickly and forcibly and is also capable of being repeatedly softened by heating and hardened by cooling within a temperature range characteristic of the material.

NOTE 2—When the TPE product is to be used for purposes where the requirements are too specific to be completely prescribed by this classification system, it is necessary for the purchaser to consult the supplier in advance to establish the appropriate properties, test methods, and specification test limits.

In all cases where provisions of this classification system would conflict with those of the detailed specifications for a particular product, the latter shall take precedence.

This classification is based on SI units.

1.1 Purpose—The purpose of this classification system is to provide a method by which TPEs may be specified by the use of a simple line call-out designation. To allow line call-outs, the system includes a symbol for the type of TPE to be used and letters and numbers for each level of property or characteristic.

EXAMPLE—A thermoplastic vulcanizate might be specified as follows:

SAE J2558 TPV (A35445, BS2440, DA55, EL290, G15, SGA970, TS4)

2. References

2.1 Applicable Publications—The following publications form a part of this specification to the extent specified herein. Unless otherwise indicated, the latest version of SAE publications shall apply.

2.1.1 SAE PUBLICATIONS—Available from SAE, 400 Commonwealth Drive, Warrendale, PA 15096-0001

SAE J369–Flammability of Automotive Interior Materials—Horizontal Test Method

SAE J1545–Instrumental Color Difference Measurement for Exterior Finishes, Textiles and Colored Trim

SAE J1756—Determination of Fogging Characteristics of Interior Automotive Materials

SAE J1885—Accelerated Exposure of Automotive Interior Trim Components Using a Controlled Irradiance Water Cooled Xenon-Arc Apparatus

SAE J1960—Accelerated Exposure of Automotive Exterior Materials Using a Controlled Irradiance Water Cooled Xenon-Arc Apparatus

2.1.2 FMVSS PUBLICATION—Available from the Superintendent of Documents, U.S. Government Printing Office, Washington, DC 20402.

FMVSS 302—Flammability of Interior Materials—Passenger Car, Multi-Purpose Passenger Vehicles

2.1.3 ISO PUBLICATIONS—Available from ANSI, 25 West 43rd Street, New York, NY 10036-8002.

ISO 34—Rubber, vulcanized—Determination of tear strength (trouser, angle and crescent test pieces)

ISO 37—Rubber, vulcanized or thermoplastic—Determination of tensile stress-strain properties

ISO 188—Rubber, vulcanized—Accelerated aging or heat resistance tests

ISO 812—Rubber, vulcanized—Determination of low-temperature brittleness

ISO 815—Rubber, vulcanized or thermoplastic—Determination of compression set at ambient, elevated or low temperature

ISO 868—Plastics and ebonite—Determination of indentation hardness by means of a durometer (Shore hardness)

ISO 1183—Plastics—Methods for determining the density and relative density of non-cellular plastics

ISO 1431-1—Rubber, vulcanized or thermoplastic—Resistance to ozone cracking—Part 1: Static strain test

ISO 1817—Rubber, vulcanized—Determination of the effect of liquids

ISO 3384—Rubber, vulcanized—Determination of stress relaxation in compression at ambient and at elevated temperatures

ISO 3795—Road vehicles, and tractors and machinery for agriculture and forestry—Determination of burning behaviour of interior materials

ISO 3865—Rubber, vulcanized or thermoplastic—Methods of test for staining in contact with organic material third edition

ISO 8013—Rubber, vulcanized—Determination of creep in compression or shear

2.1.4 AATCC PUBLICATION—Available from American Association of Textile Chemists and Colorists 1 Davis Drive, P.O. Box 12215, Research Triangle Park, NC 27709-2215.

AATCC Evaluation Procedure 1 - Gray Scale Color Change

2.2 Related Publication—The following publication is provided for information purposes only and is not a required part of this document.

2.2.1 UL PUBLICATION—Available from Underwriters Laboratories, 333 Pfingsten Road, Northbrook, IL 60062-2096.

UL-94—Test for Flammability of Plastic Materials for Parts, Devices, and Appliances

3. General Classification

3.1 TPEs shall be identified by a symbol following the SAE J2558 specification number based on family type as found in Table 1.

TABLE 1—Symbols for TPE Families

Symbol	TPE Family Name
TECEA	Thermoplastic Elastomer – Chlorinated Ethylene Alloy
TEEE	Thermoplastic Elastomer, Ether-Ester
TES	Thermoplastic Elastomer Styrenic
TPO	Thermoplastic Polyolefin
TPV	Thermoplastic Vulcanizate
TPU	Thermoplastic Polyurethane

4. Compound Properties

4.1 Suffix Letters—The suffix letters, which indicate additional tests, together with their meaning, appear in Table 2.

TABLE 2—Meaning of Suffix Letters

Suffix Letter	Test Required
A	Heat Resistance
B	Compression Set Resistance
C	Ozone Resistance
D	Hardness
EA	Fluid Resistance (Aqueous)
EF	Fluid Resistance (Fuels)
EO	Fluid Resistance (Oils and Lubricants)
EL	Elongation
F	Low Temperature Resistance
G	Tear Resistance
H	Fogging Characteristics
J	Abrasion Resistance
M	Flammability Resistance
P	Staining Resistance
SR	Stress Relaxation
SG	Specific Gravity
T	Creep Resistance
TM	Tensile Stress at a Given Elongation
TS	Tensile Strength
WE	UV Resistance (Exterior)
WI	UV Resistance (Interior)
Z	Special Requirements

4.2 Heat Resistance (Suffix Letter A)—As determined by ISO 188. The first digit following the suffix letter A, in Table 3, shall designate the test time. The second digit following the suffix letter A, in Table 3, shall designate the test temperature.

The third, fourth and fifth digits are obtained from Suffix Table 4 and indicate changes in hardness, tensile strength, and elongation following heat aging.

TABLE 3—Heat Resistance Suffix Number Designations

1st Digit	Time (h)	2nd Digit	Temperature (°C)
1	22	1	23
2	70	2	70
3	168	3	100
4	1008	4	125
		5	150

TABLE 4—Property Change Table

	Property	0	1	2	3	4	5	6
3rd Digit	Hardness change, Shore pts	Unspecified	±2	±3	±4	±5	±8	±10
4th Digit	Tensile, % change max	Unspecified	±5	±10	±20	±30	±40	±50
5th Digit	Elongation, % change max	Unspecified	±5	±10	±20	±30	±40	±50

EXAMPLE—A44535 = 1008 h at 125 °C, ±8 max hardness change, ±20 max tensile change, ±40 max elongation change.

4.3 Compression Set (Suffix Letter B)—As determined by ISO 815 Type A. Specimen type shall be denoted by means of the letter S (solid) or P (plied) following the B symbol. The test time shall be designated by the first digit following the suffix letters (BS or BP symbol) in Table 5. The second digit following the suffix letters in Table 5 shall designate the test temperature. The percent compression set value shall be no more than the numerical value expressed by the third and fourth digits following the suffix letters (BS or BP symbol).

TABLE 5—Compression Set Suffix Number Designations

1st Digit	Time (h)	2nd Digit	Temperature (°C)
1	22	1	23
2	70	2	70
3	168	3	100
4	1008	4	125
		5	150

EXAMPLE—BS2325 = 25% max compression set after 70 h at 100 °C.

4.4 Ozone Resistance (Suffix letter C)—As determined by ISO 1431-1. The ozone concentration shall be specified by the first digit following the C symbol in Table 6. The percent elongation shall be designated by the second digit following the C symbol in the table below. No cracking shall be allowed following testing according to Procedure A.

TABLE 6—Ozone Resistance Suffix Number Designations

1st Digit	Partial Pressure O_3	2nd Digit	% Elongation	2nd Digit	% Elongation
1	25 MPa ± 5 MPa	1	5 ± 1	6	40 ± 2
2	51 MPa ± 5 MPa	2	10 ± 1	7	50 ± 2
3	101 MPa ± 10 MPa	3	15 ± 2	8	60 ± 2
4	201 MPa ± 20 MPa	4	20 ± 2	9	80 ± 2
		5	30 ± 2		

4.5 Hardness (Suffix letter D)—Shall be determined by ISO 868 using either the Type A or Type D scale as indicated by the amending letter. The hardness shall be shown by the numerical value following the amending letter with a tolerance of ±5 points for Type A values and ±3 for Type D values.

EXAMPLE—DA60 = 60 ± 5 Type A

DD40 = 40 ± 3 Type D

4.6 Fluid Resistance (Suffix letters EA - Aqueous, EF - Fuels, and EO - Oils and Lubricants)—As determined by ISO 1817. The first digit following the suffix letters EA, EF or EO in Table 7 shall designate the test time. The second digit following the suffix letters EA, EF, or EO in Table 7 shall designate the test temperature.

The third, fourth, fifth, and sixth digits are obtained from Suffix Tables 8, 9, and 10, depending on fluid type, and indicate changes in hardness, tensile strength, elongation, and volume swell following fluid aging.

TABLE 7—Fluid Resistance Suffix Number Designations

1st Digit	Time (h)	2nd Digit	Temperature (°C)
1	22	1	23
2	70	2	70
3	168	3	100
4	1008	4	125
		5	150

TABLE 8—Fluid Resistance Property Change Table (Aqueous)

	Property	0	1	2	3	4	5	6
3rd Digit	Hardness change, Shore pts	Unspecified	± 2	±3	±4	±5	±8	±10
4th Digit	Tensile, % change max	Unspecified	±5	±10	±20	±30	±40	±50
5th Digit	Elongation, % change max	Unspecified	±5	±10	±20	±30	±40	±50
6th Digit	Change in Volume, % max	Unspecified	+2	+4	+6	+8	+10	+15

The type of aqueous fluid is designated by the letter symbol following the sixth digit as indicated as follows.

A. Distilled water

B. Distilled Water / Ethylene glycol (reagent grade) 50/50 by volume.

EXAMPLE—EA332336B = Age 168 hours at 100 °C in distilled water/ethylene glycol, max changes hardness ±2 points, tensile ±20%, elongation ±20%, volume +15%.

TABLE 9—Fluid Resistance Property Change Table (Fuels)

	Property	0	1	2	3	4	5	6
3rd Digit	Hardness change, Shore pts	Unspecified	−5	−10	−15	−20	−25	−30
4th Digit	Tensile, % change max	Unspecified	±5	±10	±20	±30	±40	±50
5th Digit	Elongation, % change max	Unspecified	±5	±10	±20	±30	±40	±50
6th Digit	Change in Volume, % max	Unspecified	+10	+20	+40	+60	+80	+100

The type of fuel is designated by the letter symbol following the sixth digit as indicated as follows (from ISO 1817, Annex Table 1).

A. Reference Liquid AE. Reference Liquid E

B. Reference Liquid BF. Reference Liquid F

C. Reference Liquid C

EXAMPLE—EF214565C = Age 70 hours at 23 °C in Reference Liquid C, max changes hardness −20 points, tensile ±40%, elongation ±50%, volume +80%.

TABLE 10—Fluid Resistance Property Change Table (OILS)

	Property	0	1	2	3	4	5	6
3rd Digit	Hardness change, Shore pts	Unspecified	−5	−10	−15	−25	−35	−45
4th Digit	Tensile, % change max	Unspecified	±5	±10	±20	±30	±40	±50
5th Digit	Elongation, % change max		±5	±10	±20	±30	±40	±50
6th Digit	Change in Volume, % max	Unspecified	±15	+30	+60	+90	+120	+140

The type of oil is designated by the letter symbol following the sixth digit as indicated as follows.

A. Oil No. 1

B. IRM 902

C. IRM 903

EXAMPLE—EO245665C = Age 70 hours at 125 °C in IRM 903 oil, max changes hardness −35 points, tensile ±50%, elongation ±50%, volume +120%.

4.7 Elongation (Suffix Letters EL)—As determined by ISO 37 the percent elongation shall be no less than the numerical value following the EL symbol.

EXAMPLE—EL430 = 430% minimum

4.8 Low Temperature Brittleness (Suffix F)—As determined by ISO 812, Procedure A. The value required shall be a maximum temperature express by the numerical value multiplied by −1 following the F symbol designated in degrees Celsius.

EXAMPLE—F40 = −40 °C max brittleness temperature.

4.9 Tear Strength (Suffix Letter G)—As determined by ISO 34-1 the test methods shall be specified by the letter symbol following the G symbol as designated as follows. The value required shall be no less than the numerical value following the second letter after the G symbol in kN/m.

Test Methods (second letter)

A. Method A: trouser test piece
B. Method B, procedure (a): angle test piece without nick
C. Method B, procedure (b): angle test piece with nick
D. Method C: crescent test piece

EXAMPLE—GB30 = 30 kN/m minimum, Method B, procedure (a).

4.10 Fogging Characteristics (Suffix letter H)—As determined by SAE J1756. The second letter P designates the photometric procedure and the second letter G designates the gravimetric procedure. The first digit following the second letter shall designate the test time as indicated in Table 11. The second digit shall designate the test temperature. The required fogging number for the photometric method shall be no less than the value indicated by the third and fourth two digit numerical number following the P symbol. The required fog deposit for the gravimetric procedure shall be no more than the value indicated by the third and fourth digit following the G symbol, multiplied by 0.1 mg,

TABLE 11—Fogging Suffix Number Designations

1st Digit	Time (h)	2nd Digit	Temperature (°C)
1	3	1	85
2	6	2	90
3	10	3	95
4	24	4	100
		5	110

EXAMPLE 1—HP3470 = 3 hours at 100 °C, 70 minimum fogging number
EXAMPLE 2—HG3420 = 3 hours at 100 °C, fog deposit 2.0 mg max

Requirements for special observations, e.g., large droplets, dry or oily films, unusual deposits, and/or build-up of crystals, shall be determined between the contractual parties.

4.11 Abrasion Resistance—Specific classification designations are to be determined. Requirements and conditions shall be set according to agreement between contractual parties.

4.12 Flammability Resistance (Suffix Letter M)—As determined by ISO 3795 / FMVSS 302 / SAE J369 the maximum burn rate shall be 100 mm/ minute. The test method shall be designated by the letter following the M symbol as indicated as follows.

A = ISO 3795
B = FMVSS 302
C = SAE J369

EXAMPLE—MA = Burn rate 100 mm/minute maximum following testing according to ISO 3795.

4.13 Staining Resistance (Suffix P)—As determined by ISO 3865. The letter P shall designate the test method, or letter and number following the P symbol as indicated as follows.

A1 = Contact Stain
A2 = Migratory Stain
B = Extraction Stain
C = Penetration Stain

The symbol P alone indicates that all methods are required. The symbol PA indicates that both contact and migratory staining are required.

Evaluation of staining may be in accordance with one of the following methods.

Qualitative - Make a visual assessment - No Staining allowed. The letter V following the test methods shall be designated.

American Association of Textile Chemists and Colorists (AATCC) Evaluation Procedure 1 Gray Scale for Color Change (ISO 105-A02). After exposure the material shall show no color change in excess of the specified Gray Scale rating. This method is specified by adding the letter G following the test methods. A single digit following the letter G shall specify the Gray Scale rating minimum.

EXAMPLE—PAV = No contact or migration staining, visual evaluation.
PA2G4 = Gray scale rating 4 minimum following migratory staining tests.

4.14 Specific Gravity—As determined by ISO 1183, Method A, shall be within the tolerance indicated by the letter following the SG suffix (Table 12), and the value shall be as indicated by the numerals following the SG suffix times the factor of 0.001.

TABLE 12—Specific Gravity Suffix Letters and Tolerances

Suffix	Tolerance	Suffix	Tolerance
SGA	±0.02	SGF	±0.003
SGB	±0.03	SGG	±0.004
SGC	±0.05	SGH	±0.005
SGD	±0.001	SGJ	Minimum
SGE	±0.002	SGK	Maximum

EXAMPLE—SGA970 = 0.97 ± 0.02

4.15 Stress Relaxation (Suffix SR)—As determined by ISO 3384. Specific classification designations are to be determined. Requirements and conditions shall be set according to agreement between the contractual parties.

4.16 Creep Resistance (Suffix T)—As determined by ISO 8013. Specific classification designations are to be determined. Requirements and conditions shall be set according to agreement between the contractual parties.

4.17 Tensile Stress at a Given Elongation (Suffix Letters TM)—As determined by ISO 37. The letter following the TM symbol as follows shall express the % elongation value.

A = 100%B = 200% C = 300%

The value required shall be no less than the numerical value following the TM symbol in MPa.

EXAMPLE—TMA3 = Tensile stress at 100% elongation = 3 MPa minimum.

4.18 Tensile Strength (Suffix Letter TS)—As determined by ISO 37 the value required shall be no less than the numerical value following the TS symbol in MPa.

EXAMPLE—TS10 = 10 MPa minimum.

Test methods and specimens for Type D hardness materials shall be set according to agreement between the contractual parties.

4.19 UV Resistance—As determined by SAE J1885 (Suffix WI, interior) and SAE J1960 (Suffix WE, exterior). The exposure in xenon arc weatherometer shall be designated using a four-digit numeral to express the actual exposure value in kJ/m^2. Color Changes following exposure may be determined by two methods.

a. Instrumental Color Difference Measurement for Exterior Finishes, Textiles and Colored Trim - SAE J1545. The color of the test specimen shall be measured per SAE J1545, CIELAB color space, 10° observer, illuminant D65, specular included, sphere geometry, before and after exposure. Maximum Delta E = 3.0 this method is specified by adding the letter D following the four digit exposure number.
b. American Association of Textile Chemists and Colorists (AATCC) Evaluation Procedure 1 Gray Scale for Color Change (ISO 105-A02). After exposure the material shall show no color change in excess of the specified Gray Scale rating. Adding the letter G following the four-digit exposure number specifies this method. A single digit following the letter G shall specify the Gray Scale rating minimum.

EXAMPLE—WE2500D = 2500 kJ/m^2 Xenon Arc Weatherometer exterior exposure per SAE J1960, Delta E = 3.0 max

WI0601G4 = 601 kJ/m^2 Xenon Arc Weatherometer interior exposure per SAE J1885, Gray Scale rating 4 minimum.

4.20 Special Requirements (Suffix Z)—Any special requirements, which should be specified in detail, including test methods. These requirements shall be identified in sequence, i.e., Z1, Z2, Z3, etc.

5. *Compositions and Manufacture*

5.1 Materials specified according to this classification shall be manufactured from polymers, together with added compounding materials of such nature and quantity as to produce materials that comply with the specified requirements. All materials and workmanship shall be in accordance with good commercial practice, and the resulting product shall be free of porous areas, weak sections, bubbles, foreign matter, or other defects affecting performance.

5.2 Color—Materials shall be tested in their typical commercially available colors.

6. *Sample Preparation*

6.1 Unless otherwise noted, samples are to be die-cut from injection molded rectangular plaques 2.0 mm ± 0.2 mm thick. Specimens of other thickness will not necessarily give comparable results. Annealing of test specimens and plaques or the use of atypical molding conditions is not permitted. If the properties of a material are measured on other than injection-molded plaques, this shall be so noted.

STANDARD METHOD FOR DETERMINING CONTINUOUS UPPER TEMPERATURE RESISTANCE OF ELASTOMERS —SAE J2236 MAY1999

SAE Standard

Report of the SAE Committee on Automotive Rubber Specifications approved June 1992, and revised May 1999. Rationale statement available.

1. Scope—This method is intended to define the continuous upper temperature resistance (CUTR) of thermoplastic elastomers and thermoset rubber with durometer hardness ≤90 Shore A, to oxidation or other degradation when exposed solely to hot air for an extended period of time.

1.1 This method established the upper thermal aging limits of commercially available compounds as measured at 23 °C by retention of at least 50% original elongation and tensile at break after 1008 h of heat aging. This method does not take into account nor measure the effects of stress, environment, or temperature variations on the thermal aging characteristics of the materials tested.

1.2 This method may involve hazardous materials, operations, and equipment. This SAE Standard does not address the safety problems associated with its use. It is the responsibility of the user of this document to consult and establish appropriate safety and health practices and determine the applicability of regulatory limitations prior to use.

1.3 This test method is based on SI units.

2. References

2.1 Applicable Publications—The following publications form a part of this specification to the extent specified herein. Unless otherwise indicate, the latest issue of SAE publications shall apply.

2.1.1 SAE PUBLICATIONS—Available from SAE, 400 Commonwealth Drive, Warrendale, PA 15096-0001.

SAE J200—Classification System for Rubber Materials
SAE J1344—Marking of Plastic Parts
SAE J3000—Standard Classification System for Thermoplastic Elastomers

2.1.2 ASTM PUBLICATIONS—Available from ASTM, 100 Barr Harbor Drive, West Conshohocken, PA 19428-2959.

ASTM D 412—Standard Test Methods for Rubber Properties in Tension, Method A
ASTM D 573—Standard Test Method for Rubber—Deterioration in an Air Oven
ASTM D 1418—Standard Practice for Rubber and Rubber Lattices—Nomenclature
ASTM D 1972—Practice for Generic Marking of Plastic Products
ASTM D 2240—Standard Test Method for Rubber Property—Durometer Hardness

3. Terms Specific to this Standard

3.1 Continuous Upper Temperature Limit (CUTL)—The temperature at which the material retains a 50% minimum of both the original elongation and tensile at break after 1008 h in an air circulating oven per ASTM D 573, Type IIA or IIB. Note per ASTM D 573: Type IIB ovens are not suitable for test temperatures above 70 °C.

3.2 Test Method—A definitive procedure for identification, measurement, and evaluation of one or more qualities, characteristics, or properties of a material, product system, or service that produces a test result.

3.3 Production Compound—An identifiable, homogeneous quantity of material from a standard production period, with a consistency and properties demonstrated through testing and use.

3.4 Commercial Material—A finished compound developed primarily, but not exclusively for heat resistance, from readily available ingredients and processed on conventional industry equipment.

4. Significance and Use

4.1 Data obtained by this method are applicable to the material under conditions of this test and are not necessarily the same as those obtained in end use applications. The information can be used for comparison, selection, or qualification of commercially available compounds where a level of proficiency is desired beyond short time quality control tests.

4.2 Ultimate elongation was selected over other physical property measurements because of its greater sensitivity to the various effects of air oven aging on elastomers. Tensile Strength is also used since some compounds maintain more than 50% of their original elongation while losing considerable tensile strength after heat aging.

4.3 A material classification CUTL represents the highest temperature value the best compound(s) can achieve per Table A1 guidelines (see Appendix A). The materials are classified according to ASTM D 1418, ASTM D 1972, or SAE J1344. Not all compounds within a material category can reach the listed maximum temperature.

4.4 This document requires aging at elevated temperatures in a hot air circulating oven per ASTM D 573, regardless of what is used in SAE J200. Care must be taken to test only similar generic compounds (i.e., silicone to silicone) in order to avoid cross contamination from volatile products and subsequent variation in test data.

5. General Test Conditions

5.1 Unless otherwise specified, the material shall be tested to ASTM D 412, Method A requirements at 23 °C.

5.2 Aging Temperatures—Variation around a specified temperature shall be within ±2 °C.

5.3 Aging Temperature Increments—Unless otherwise specified, test new materials (per SAE J200 Table 1, plus 135 °C and 165 °C) to establish the upper continuous temperature limit to the definition in 3.1. Material tables shall be established using this criterion to minimize testing burden.

5.4 Aging Time—1008 h ± 2 h

5.5 Uniform Aging Conditions—Tests of samples shall ensure that all surfaces be exposed and the temperature uniform.

6. Sample Requirements

6.1 Thermoplastic elastomer and thermoset rubber elongation and tensile at break data used to establish tables or qualify new materials shall be the median of a minimum of five samples per batch from five batches.

6.2 Sample Dimensions for Thermoset Rubber—Follow ASTM D 412 requirements.

6.3 Thermoplastic Elastomers (from SAE J3000)—Unless otherwise noted, samples are to be die-cut from injection molded rectangular plaques 3.0 mm ± 0.4 mm thick. Specimens of other thickness will not necessarily give comparable results. Plaque dimensions must be sufficient to permit this. Five samples are to be tested in the direction of highest tensile strength and the median value is reported for both elongation and tensile at break.

6.4 Certain elastomers may require post curing or conditions to achieve optimum heat resistance properties.

7. Table Requirements

7.1 The material heat resistance table (Table A1) in the appendix shall be developed using temperatures from SAE J200 Table 1, and additional temperatures (135 °C and 165 °C) appropriate to industry needs. If a material meets a temperature requirements, it is presumed that it will meet all lower temperatures.

7.2 Test commercially available compounds to Section 5 conditions for 1008 h. Determine the percent elongation and tensile at break prior to and immediately after the test period per ASTM D 412 for thermoset and thermoplastic materials with durometer hardness of ≤90 Shore A hardness or less.

7.3 Report the results at 23 °C for the number of samples stated in 6.1 and 6.3 per ASTM D 412.

7.4 A material will qualify for inclusion in the temperature classification table (Table A1) when test data satisfies the requirements of 3.1.

8. Precision and Bias

8.1 No precision statement exists for 1008-h oven aging per ASTM D 573. See ASTM D 573 for the precision of oven aging after 48 and 96 h and ASTM D 412 for precision of tensile testing.

APPENDIX A
(MANDATORY INFORMATION)
TABLE A1 FORMAT REQUIREMENTS

A.1 Table A1 Requirements

a. To qualify for a temperature type, the material must be a commercially available material, developed primarily, but not exclusively for heat resistance. Rubber materials listed in Table A1 are not blends, they contain 100% of the designated polymer. This does not apply to TPEs which are often blends or multi-phase materials.

b. In order to appear on the table, a material must have a ASTM D 1418, ASTM D 1600, ASTM D 1972, or SAE J1344 nomenclature designation. If a TPE material's nomenclature is designated by more than one code, SAE J1344 shall be the preferred usage code and the additional material designation code shall be listed in Table A1 in parenthesis ().
   1. A prospective command must meet or have a current SAE J200 or J3000 type and class designation.

c. To meet the temperature type defined by Table A1, the material's elongation and tensile strength must retain a minimum of 50% of the original values after 1008 h at that temperature. The temperature classification of a material is based on the median of test results obtained from a minimum of 5 samples from each of 5 batches (see 6.1) from one laboratory. Labs submitting data need not be accredited (see A.1.d.(2)).

d. Challenges to test results will be handled as follows:
   1. Labs or companies wanting to verify test results should make a written request to SAE CARS.
   2. SAE CARS will request the compound originator to send samples, or may take custody of the samples for distribution, to two designated independent, third party labs. The labs must be accredited by a recognized firm such as the American Association of Laboratory Accreditation or Standards Council of Canada. Disclosure of the labs is at the discretion of SAE CARS.
   3. Sample testing will be paid for by the challenger. The challenger cannot access the material directly, nor request material left over from the third party testing.
   4. The challenger and SAE CARS will receive the test results and render a decision.
   5. CARS will be the final arbiter of any disputes and decisions.

e. Thermoplastic Elastomer (TPE) temperature selection is based on the median in the direction of highest tensile strength (see 6.3). Please report all data points, along with the median values.

f. Table temperatures are 70 °C, 100 °C, 125 °C, 135 °C, 150 °C, 165 °C, 175 °C, 200 °C, 225 °C, 250 °C, and 275 °C.

TABLE A1—CUTL OF ELASTOMERS

Nomenclature/Classification	Temperature °C
Rubber	
IR, NR, SBR	70
IIR, CR	100
BIIR, CIIR, CO, ECO, NBR	125
ACM, AEM, EPDM, EVM, HNBr[1]	150
VMQ	175
FKM	225
Thermoplastic Elastomers (≤90A)	
TEO, TES	135

1. Degree of saturation must be 96% or more.

COMPRESSION SET OF HOSES OR SOLID DISCS—SAE J1638 MAY1993

SAE Recommended Practice

Report of the SAE Compression Set Task Group of the SAE Coolant Hose Committee approved May 1993.

Foreword—This Document has not changed other than to put it into the new SAE Technical Standards Board Format.

1. Scope—This SAE Recommended Practice is used for establishing the compression set that could be expected to occur with engine coolant hoses under securing clamps. It seeks to reproduce the type of indentation caused by the clamps in the wall of the hose. An excessive compression set measured by this method would indicate a hose that could eventually allow leakage of coolant past the clamps in service. This method has been found to give repeatable results in the range of 25% to 50% initial compression.

2. References

2.1 Applicable Publications—The following publications form a part of this specification to the extent specified herein.

2.1.1 ASTM PUBLICATIONS—Available from ASTM, 100 Barr Harbor Drive, West Conshohocken, PA 19428-2959.

ASTM D 3767—Practice for Rubber—Measurement of Dimensions

ASTM E 145—Specification for Gravity-Convection and Forced-Ventilation Ovens

3. Apparatus Required

3.1 Compression Fixture—Refer to Figures 1 through 4.

3.2 Dial Micrometer—For use in measuring thickness according to ASTM D 3767, Method A1. The measuring foot shall be flat with a diameter of 2.5 mm ± 0.1 mm and a load of 45 g.

3.3 Feeler Gages or Gage Blocks—For setting the specified compression under the indicators.

3.4 Air-Circulating Oven—Conforming to ASTM E 145, Type IIA.

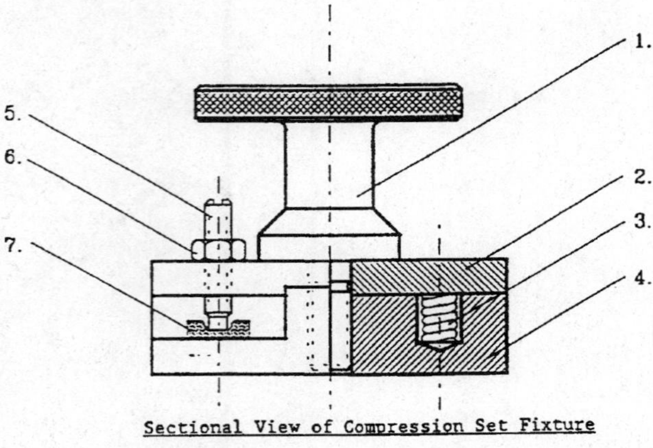

1. Loading Screw
2. Pressure Plate
3. Pressure Spring: O.D. = 8 mm; I.D. = 6 mm; Length = 16.5 mm; Compressed Length = 6.5 mm; Compressed Force = 3.7 kg; Number of Turns = 5.5
4. Base Plate
5. Adjusting Screw and Indenter
6. Lock Nut - M6
7. Test Sample
8. Material: Stainless Steel
9. All dimensions in mm, +/- 0.25

FIGURE 1—SECTIONAL VIEW OF COMPRESSION SET FIXTURES

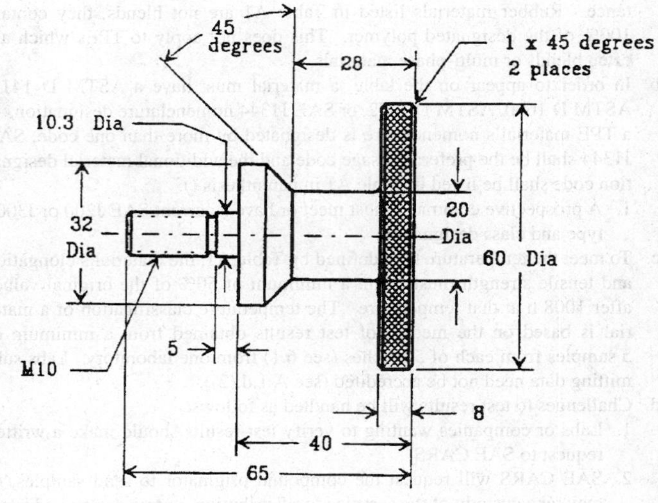

FIGURE 2—LOADING SCREW

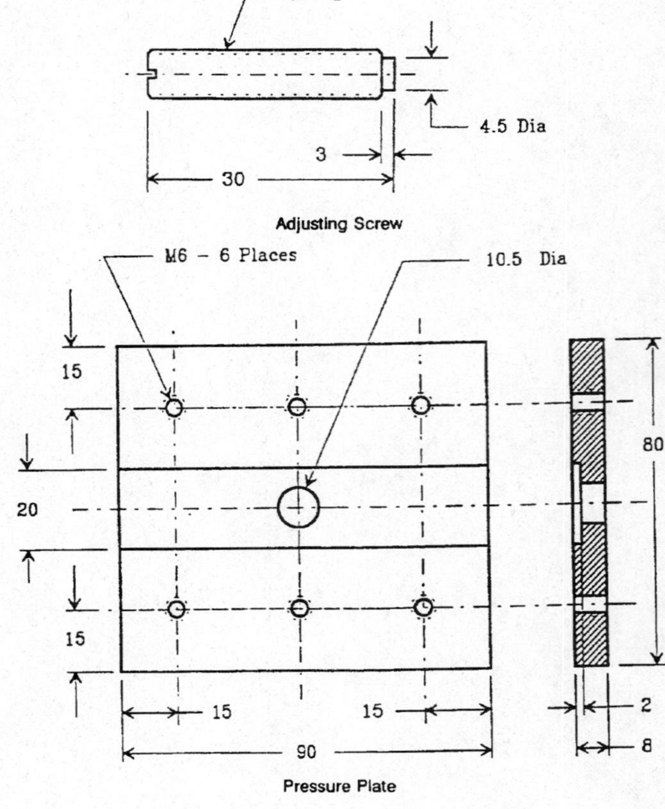

FIGURE 3—ADJUSTING SCREW AND PRESSURE PLATE

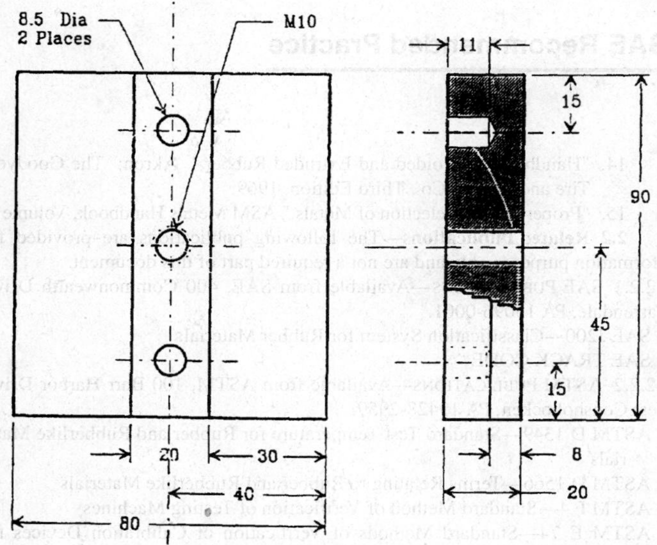

FIGURE 4—BASE PLATE

4. Procedure

a. Using a suitable die, stamp out a 13 mm ± 0.5 mm diameter disc from the wall section of the hose or test material (3 samples for each test). If the surface of the cover is irregular, it shall be lightly buffed around the test area until smooth prior to cutting sample.

b. Measure the thickness of each sample with the cover side down and calculate the required distance between the base plate and the bottom face of the indentor to give the specified compression value.

c. Tighten the compression set fixture plates and, using feeler gages or gage blocks, set each indentor to give the specified compression.

d. Release the top compression plate and insert the test samples under the preset indentors. Replace the top compression plate and tighten fully.

e. Age the compression fixture in the oven for the specified time and temperature.

f. Remove the fixture from the oven and allow to cool for 3 h ± 0.25 h.

g. Remove each sample separately and measure the compressed thickness at the required time of recovery ±0.1 h.

5. Evaluation—Calculate the percent compression set according to the following:

$$\% \text{ Compression Set } = \frac{A - C}{A - B} \times 100 \quad \text{(Eq. 1)}$$

where:

A = initial sample thickness
B = compressed thickness before aging
C = compressed thickness after aging after sample removal and recovery.

Chemicals, materials, parts, and equipment referenced in this document must be used and handled properly. Each party is responsible for determining proper use and handling in its facilities.

RECOMMENDED GUIDELINES FOR FATIGUE TESTING OF ELASTOMERIC MATERIALS AND COMPONENTS —SAE J1183 FEB98

SAE Recommended Practice

Report of the Nonmetallic Materials Committee approved January 1978 and reaffimred without change February 1985. Completely revised by the SAE Vibration Committee May 1997 and revised February 1998.

Foreword—These guidelines describe:

a. A set of definitions and terminology to allow interchange of information on a common basis. (Sectin 3)
b. The manner in which elastomeric materials and components undergo changes due to stresses and/or strains in a fatigue environment that ultimately culminate in failure. (Sections 4 and 5)
c. Factors to be considered in selecting from available test methods or in developing a test method to meet specific requirements. (Sections 6 through 10)
d. Important considerations in the evaluation and reporting of test information. (Section 11)

1. Scope—The purpose of this SAE Recommended Practice is to review factors that influence the behavior of elastomers under conditions of dynamic stress and to provide guidance concerning laboratory procedures for determining the fatigue characteristics of elastomeric materials and fabricated elastomeric components.

2. References

2.1 Applicable Publications—The following publications form a part of this specification to the extent specified herein. Unless otherwise indicated, the latest issue of SAE publications shall apply.

2.1.1 SAE PUBLICATIONS—Available from SAE, 400 Commonwealth Drive, Warrendale, PA 15096-0001.

SAE J1085—Test for Dynamic Properties of Elastomeric Isolators
SAE J1883—Elastomeric Bushing "TRAC" Application Code
SAE Fatigue Design Handbook, Third Edition, 1997

2.1.2 ASTM PUBLICATIONS—Available from ASTM, 100 Barr Harbor Drive, West Conshohocken, PA 19428-2959.

ASTM D 429-81—Test Methods for Rubber Property—Adhesion to Rigid Substrates
ASTM D 430-95—Test Methods for Rubber Deterioration—Dynamic Fatigue
ASTM D 623-93—Test Methods for Rubber Property—Heat Generation and Flexing Fatigue in Compression
ASTM D 813-95—Test Method for Rubber Deterioration—Crack Growth
ASTM D 1052-85—Test Method for Measuring Rubber Deterioration—Cut Growth Using Ross Flexing Apparatus
ASTM D 1149-91—Test Method for Rubber Deterioration—Surface Ozone Cracking in a Chamber

2.1.3 OTHER PUBLICATIONS

1. P. W. Allen, P. B. Lindley, and A. R. Payne, "Use of Rubber in Engineering," London: Maclaren and Sons, Ltd., 1967, pp. 60-71.
2. Anonymous, "Fatigue Failure and Its Reduction in Natural Rubber." Akron: Monsanto Technical Bulletin O/RC-7.
3. Anonymous, "Fatigue to Failure Tester." Akron: Monsanto Literature with attachments.
4. A. B. Davey and A. R. Payne, "Rubber in Engineering Practice." New York: Palmerton Publishers, 1964.
5. McPherson and Klemin, "Engineering Uses of Rubber." New York: Rheinhold, 1956. pp. 132-134, 139, 165-167, 170.
6. A. R. Payne and J. R. Scott, "Engineering Design with Rubber," New York Interscience Publishers, Inc., 1960, pp. 104-106.
7. J. R. Scott, "Physical Testing of Rubber," New York: Palmerton Publishing Co. 1965 pp. 129-113.
8. SAE Fatigue Design Handbook, Vol. 4, 1968.
9. Charles R. Hicks, "Fundamental Concepts in the Design of Experiments," New York: Holt, Rinehart and Winston, 1964.
10. Bernard Ostle, "Statistics in Research," Iowa State University Press, 1964.
11. United States Department of Commerce, "Experimental Statistics," Washington, D.C.: U.S. Government Printing Office (1963).
12. "ASTM Rubber Products, Industrial Specifications and Related Test Methods; Carbon Black; Gaskets; Tires." Annual Book of ASTM Standards, Part 37, 1976.
13. "Webster's New Collegiate Dictionary," Springfield: G & C Merriam Co.
14. "Handbook of Molded and Extruded Rubber," Akron: The Goodyear Tire and Rubber Co., Third Edition, 1969.
15. "Properties and Selection of Metals," ASM Metals Handbook, Volume 1.

2.2 Related Publications—The following publications are provided for information purposes only and are not a required part of this document.

2.2.1 SAE PUBLICATIONS—Available from SAE, 400 Commonwealth Drive, Warrendale, PA 15096-0001.

SAE J200—Classification System for Rubber Materials
SAE TRACK CODE

2.2.2 ASTM PUBLICATIONS—Available from ASTM, 100 Barr Harbor Drive, West Conshohocken, PA 19428-2959.

ASTM D 1349—Standard Test Temperature for Rubber and Rubberlike Materials
ASTM D 1566—Terms Relating to Rubber and Rubberlike Materials
ASTM F 4—Standard Method of Verification of Testing Machines
ASTM E 74—Standard Methods of Verification of Calibration Devices for Verifying Testing Machines
"ASTM General Test Methods," Annual Book of ASTM Standards, Part 41, 1976.

2.2.3 ASME PUBLICATION—Available from ASME, 345 East 47 Street, New York, NY 10017-2330.

Yost, "Fatigue Characteristics of Rubber," ASME Transactions, Vol. 65, pp. 881-888.

2.2.4 OTHER PUBLICATIONS

T. A. Knurek and R. P. Salisbury, "Carbon Black Effect on Engine Mount Compounds." Rubber World (August 1964), pp. 45-57.
G. J. Lake, "Corrosive Aspects of Fatigue," Rubber Age (August 1972). pp. 30-42.

3. Definitions—The following terms and definitions are applicable to this document:

3.1 Aging—The irreversible change of material properties after exposure to an environment for an interval of time. (See 2.1.3 [12].)

3.2 Ambient Temperature—The temperature of the environment surrounding the test specimen. (SAE J1085)

3.3 Bushing—A cylindrical bearing or guide. (See 2.1.3 [15].)

3.4 Compound—An intimate admixture of a polymer with all the materials necessary for the finished article. (See 2.1.3 [12].)

3.5 Compression—Reduction of dimension from an external force.

3.6 Creep—The time-dependent part of a strain resulting from stress. (See 2.1.3 [12].)

3.7 Damping—Decreasing the amplitude of vibrations in the motion of a body subject to influences which cause vibration.

3.8 Elastomer—Macromolecular material that returns rapidly to approximately the initial dimensions and shape after substantial deformation by a weak stress and release of the stress. (See 2.1.3 [12].)

3.9 Elongation—Extension produced by a tensile stress. (See 2.1.3 [12].)

3.10 Equilibrium Temperature—Stable temperature at which heat loss equals heat input.

3.11 Failure—When a material or component ceases to fulfill the design specified responses essential to the successful operation as a sub unit of a system. A rubber part may fail from tearing, cracking, rupture, hardening, softening, heat or chemical degradation, creep, set, or a combination thereof.

3.12 Fatigue—The process of progressive localized permanent structural changes occurring in a material or component subject to conditions which produce fluctuating stresses and strains at some point or points and which may culminate in loss of load bearing ability, cracks or complete fracture after a sufficient number of fluctuations. (See 2.1.1 SAE Fatigue Design Handbook.)

3.13 Fatigue Life—The number of cycles of stress or strain of a specified character that a given specimen sustains before failure of a specified nature occurs. (See 2.1.1 SAE Fatigue Design Handbook.)

3.14 Frequency—The number of complete cycles, whole periods, of forced vibrations per unit of time caused and maintained by a periodic excitation, usually sinusoidal. (SAE J1085)

3.15 Friction—The resistance to relative motion between two bodies in contact. (See 2.1.3 [13].)

3.16 Hysteresis—The percent energy lost per deformation cycle. (See 2.1.3 [14].)

3.17 Maximum Stress - S_{max}—The stress having the highest algebraic value in the stress cycle, tensile stress being considered positive, and compressive stress negative. In this definition, the nominal stress is used most commonly. (See 2.1.1 SAE Fatigue Design Handbook.)

3.18 Mean Stress (or Steady Component of Stress) - S_m—The algebraic average of the maximum and minimum stresses in one cycle, that is, $(S_{max} + S_{min})/2$.

3.19 Minimum Stress - S_{min}—The stress having the lowest algebraic value in the cycle, tensile stress being considered positive and compressive stress negative. (See 2.1.1 SAE Fatigue Design Handbook.)

3.20 Modulus of Elasticity—Ratio of stress to the strain produced by that stress E = Stress/Strain property of material. (See 2.1.3 [14].)

3.21 Nominal Stress - S—The stress at a point calculated on the net cross-section by simple elastic theory, without taking into account the effect on the stress produced by geometric discontinuities such as holes, grooves, fillets, etc. (See 2.1.1 SAE Fatigue Design Handbook.)

3.22 Ozone - O_3—An allotropic form of oxygen. It is a gas with a characteristic odor and is a powerful oxidizing agent.

3.23 Permanent Set—The residual deformation of a specimen or component after removal of the external load.

3.24 Pinching—A phenomena where a fold is formed by deflection of the elastomeric component which causes a high stress concentrated at the surface of the elastomer, causing the elastomer to tear. Reshaping the section to eliminate the pinch condition will typically yield significant gains in fatigue life.

3.25 Polymer—A macromolecular material formed by the chemical combination of monomers having either the same or different chemical composition. (See 2.1.3 [12].)

3.26 Preload—An external static load producing a strain in a test specimen. Preload is imposed prior to forced vibration testing. Preload is usually expressed in force units instead of deflection units. (SAE J1085)

3.27 Resilience—The ratio of energy output to energy input in a rapid (or instantaneous) full recovery of a deformed specimen. (See 2.1.3 [12].)

3.28 Resonant Frequency—The frequency at which maximum amplitude occurs for a given input force in a forced vibration system.

3.29 S-N_f Diagram—A plot of stress against the number of cycles to failure. The stress can be S_{max}, S_{min} or S_a. The diagram indicates the S-N_f relationship and a specified probability of survival. For N_f a log scale is almost always used. For S_a a log scale is used most often but a linear scale is sometimes used. (See 2.1.1 SAE Fatigue Design Handbook.)

3.30 Shear—Force which causes two contiguous parts of the same body to slide relative to each other in a direction parallel to their plane of contact. (See 2.1.3 [13].)

3.31 Silentbloc—A type of bushing consisting of a thin wall, elastomeric cylinder compressed between concentric metal sleeves.

3.32 Specimen Temperature—The temperature obtained by placing or locating a temperature sensing device in or on the specimen. In most cases, temperature gradients that develop within flexing rubber specimens make it necessary to define the precise points and techniques used to measure temperature.

3.33 Spring Rate—Ratio of force to the deflection produced by that force. Spring rate = Force/Deflection property of the particular elastic body under consideration. (See 2.1.3 [14].)

3.34 Strain—Change (in length) per unit length in a linear dimension of a part or specimen. (See 2.1.3 [15].)

3.35 Stress (Uniaxial)—Load on a specimen divided by the area through which it acts.

3.36 Stress Amplitude (or Variable Component of Stress) - S_a—One-half the range of stress, that is $S_a = S/2 = 1/2(S_{max} - S_{min})$.

3.37 Stress Relaxation—The decrease in stress after a given time at a constant strain.

3.38 Tension—Increase in dimension from an external force.

3.39 Torsion—A twisting action resulting in shear stresses and strains.

4. Elastomeric Characteristics—An elastomer is a material that exhibits both viscoelastic and temperature dependent behavior. Viscoelastic materials exhibit both displacement (elastic) and time (viscous) dependencies. The elastic property of the material relates stress versus strain behavior. Because of the viscoelastic characteristics exhibited by elastomers, the dynamic response and mechanical behavior are dependent upon stress or strain history, rate of loading, frequency, and amplitude of strain.

The viscous property of the material causes internal energy loss, or hysteresis (damping). The lost energy is converted into heat and since elastomers are poor heat conductors, this can result in a considerable temperature rise, which affects the previously discussed material properties. In liquid-filled rubber components (e.g., hydraulic engine mounts) heat is generated due to the fluid pumping action as well.

In addition to being viscoelastic and temperature dependent, elastomers have a lower elastic modulus and lower strength than most metals and plastics. Although softer and weaker than structural metals and plastics, elastomers are like these materials from an energy per unit volume standpoint. For elastomers, metals, and plastics, loaded in tension, a power form of a fatigue correlation exists:

$$N_f W^b = C \quad \text{(Eq. 1)}$$

where:

N_f = cycles to failure
W = energy input (~ 1/2 stress x strain)
b and C = constants for specific materials

The application of this fatigue law to elastomers is discussed in Appendix A. Normally, however, conventional design practice avoids loading rubber components in tension. Also, the above relationship is valid only if the frequency of applied loading does not create significant heat in the material, which could generate an elevated temperature condition and result in adversely affecting the fatigue constant of the material. References 2.1.3 [1], [4], [5], [6], and [7] listed in Section 2.1.3 of this document, provide comprehensive information on general elastomeric behavior.

5. Failure Criteria—Since elastomeric components often exhibit more than one failure mode, failure should be defined in such a manner that it can be accurately detected in order to precisely determine the time of its occurrence.

5.1 Commonly Used Failure Criteria:

a. Complete rupture of the specimen, i.e., total separation in tensile specimens, bond failure, or metal-to-metal contact between opposing mounting surfaces in bushings or compression specimens.
b. Time or cycles until appearance of visible cracks of a specified size, or growth of a crack or partial rupture to a specified point. For cracks which initiate from internal stress concentrations, the part is sectioned to reveal crack formation prior to propagation to the surface.
c. A specified level of change in physical properties such as hardness, (Shore Durometer A, International Rubber Hardness degrees (IRHD), etc.), static spring rate (K_s), dynamic spring rate (K_d), or damping (C_d, Loss Angle, etc.)
d. A specified change in static deflection due to creep, set, or abrasive wear.
e. Failure to function as intended.
f. Fluid leakage from a fluid-filled component.
g. Component noise changes.
h. Change of state (embrittlement or reversion).

5.2 Since different failure criteria will rank various elastomers differently, it is important that the definition of failure be relevant to the type of failure that occurs in the intended application.

6. Test Parameters—To achieve accurate and consistent results, test procedures should precisely define the test parameters discussed in this section.

6.1 Specimen History—Mechanical preflexing and temperature history must be the same for all samples for consistency of test results.

6.1.1 MECHANICAL PREFLEXING—Elastomers undergoing load deflection tests will progressively change (as much as 25%) for up to the first 1000 cycles until a steady-state condition is reached. The stiffness on the first cycle will usually recover if a period of approximately 8 h or more elapses between load deflection tests. Consequently, if some specific change in spring rate of the specimen is the failure definition, preflexing influences must be considered to establish the initial stiffness. For shock type applications, the first cycle data might be the basis. For steady-state vibration applications, the third (or more) cycle data might be required. For preflexing to be effective, the load and/or deflection must be at least that at which the stiffness is to be determined.

6.1.2 TEMPERATURE EFFECTS—Because elastomers are viscoelastic materials, it is necessary to know the temperature of the specimen and its temperature history prior to testing.

A specimen stored in a very cold or hot environment influences the amount of preflexing required to achieve a steady state condition.

6.1.3 CONDITIONING OF OIL ASSEMBLED COMPONENTS—Oil assembled components such as silentblocs require approximately one week for the elastomer to absorb the assembly oil to yield more consistent results. Oven conditioning for 3 h at 70 °C is sometimes used as a substitute for natural conditioning.

6.2 Test Specification Selection

6.2.1 MECHANICAL SPECIFICATIONS

6.2.1.1 Direction of Loading—Refer to SAE J1883 for terminology to be used in defining the direction of applied loads.

6.2.1.2 Types of Fatigue Loads—The method of applying and maintaining test loads must be specified. In addition to the dynamic fatigue load, the test specimen may also be subjected to a constant static load, which is applied simultaneously with the dynamic load. Loads may be applied (and specified) through a single axis or through multiple axes. The following load profiles may be specified.

a. Apply a specified dynamic fatigue load.
b. Apply a specified dynamic displacement.
c. Apply and maintain a specified static load and apply a dynamic fatigure load about the static load point.
d. Apply and maintain a specified static load and apply a dynamic displacement about the static load point.
e. Apply and maintain a specified deflection and apply a dynamic displacement about the initial deflection.

6.2.1.3 Magnitude of Load or Displacement—The magnitude of load and displacement specified should reflect the operational environment of the component. This is especially important for fixed displacement testing to assure fatigue results are consistent with in-service performance. Higher load and displacement conditions can be used to accelerate testing, refer to 6.2.4.1.

6.2.1.4 Frequency of Dynamic Excitation—Fluid-filled mounts, for example, tend to be designed to have high damping at specific frequencies. At these peak frequencies, the fluid absorbs a large percentage of the damping energy; while at other frequencies, damping energy is absorbed by the elastomer. Thus the life of the component's elastomeric material can be highly frequency dependent as well as load dependent.

6.2.1.5 Waveform of Dynamic Excitation—The type of waveform excitation, i.e., sinusoidal, random, continuous or intermittent, should be specified. Alternatively, real-time dynamic loads may also be specified if road load data has been measured and test equipment is available to reproduce the measured loads.

6.2.2 PART TEMPERATURE—Elastomers are functional over a rather narrow temperature range compared to other materials such as metals. Further, each component of a given elastomer has its own temperature range where it is functional. Within that functional range will lie a band of temperatures at which maximum fatigue life is obtained. It is not unusual for fatigue life to change by a factor of two or more over a 20 °C change in temperature near the boundaries of that band. Therefore, the temperature specified should be representative of service conditions, and part temperature should be controlled throughout the test.

6.2.2.1 Definition of Part Temperature—Since rubber is a poor heat conductor, thick parts will usually have large temperature gradients. Measurements should, therefore, be made by placing the temperature sensing element as close to the area of heat generation as possible. The location chosen and the type of temperature measurement should be carefully defined and consistently adhered to.

6.2.2.2 Part Temperature Control—Part temperature is a function of ambient temperature, hysteresis of the specimen, energy input, external friction, and heat dissipation off the surface of the part.

Ambient temperature control is necessary. First, it is recommended that the part and associated fixturing be allowed to reach equilibrium with the environment before starting the test. Guidelines for achieving this are given in the Appendix to SAE J1085 for elevated temperature testing. For elevated temperature testing, it is suggested that the part be enclosed in an air circulating heat chamber. At moderate temperatures, circulation of air over the specimen is commonly used to control part temperature. It should be recognized, however, that in some situations this may lower specimen surface temperature but have a relatively small effect on temperature within the specimen. Air cooling magnifies the ability of any fixturing in contact with the specimen to conduct heat out of the specimen (i.e., to behave as a heat sink) so care must be taken to ensure consistency in fixture contact area, shape, and mass. In cases where correlation between test facilities is necessary, air cooling may be undesirable as another source of variability.

Internal heat generation due to the combination of hysteresis and energy input should not cause the part to exceed the desired test temperature. Hysteresis in elastomers will cause an increase in component temperature which will be proportional to frequency and/or amplitude test conditions. This sometimes makes it necessary to adjust test conditions when elastomers of different hysteresis levels are tested. In most cases, it is desirable to design the test in such a way that a significant portion of the testing takes place after the part temperature has stabilized.

Sometimes elastomer hysteresis is falsely blamed for high specimen temperature when the source heat is actually friction due to slip between elastomer and metal components and/or test fixtures. When this is the case, and the elastomer has low hysteresis, reducing the test amplitude and/or load and increasing frequency will sometimes reduce temperature without adding significantly to test time.

6.2.3 OTHER PARAMETERS

6.2.3.1 Ozone Concentration—Some elastomers are inherently ozone resistant so that ozone has little effect on their fatigue life. Other elastomers are not ozone resistant and must be chemically protected to prevent ozone cracking in stressed areas. Ozone cracking results in shortened flex life, particularly so for specimens with a high ratio of exposure surface to mass. Ozone crack rate increases with stress level and temperature.

It is desirable to avoid uncontrolled and excessive ozone concentrations as can be found in close proximity to electrical discharges or some motors. In critical situations, ozone concentration should be measured and reported in test conditions. ASTM D 1149 (see 2.1.3 [12]) describes ozone concentration measurement.

The antiozonants used in many elastomer compositions must migrate to the surface of the specimen before they become fully effective. Testing of recently molded specimens should not be conducted before protective agents have migrated to the surface. Usually, 24 h is the minimum time for migration.

6.2.3.2 Oxidation—The reaction of oxygen (oxidation) with many elastomers can initiate crack formation as well as result in hardening or softening. At temperatures higher than room temperature, the effect of oxygen is accelerated. Test specimens should not be stored for long time periods at elevated temperatures unless this is a necessary and controlled part of the test requirement.

6.2.3.3 Deleterious Fluids and Gases—No elastomer is resistant to all fluids and gases. Oils, oil vapor, and solvents can seriously degrade non-resistant elastomers. Water, steam, coolants, acids, and alkalis in fluid or vapor form can reduce specimen fatigue life. The atmosphere surrounding the test specimen should be free of deleterious fluids and gases unless they are a necessary and controlled part of the test requirement.

6.2.4 ACCELERATION METHODS—Table 1 describes examples of acceleration methods and possible affects they may have on the test and/or specimen.

An elevated temperature presoak may be used to condition the component. This serves to accelerate testing.

A cut may be used to initiate the crack before the start of the test.

6.2.4.1 Effects of Acceleration—Acceleration can introduce obvious or subtle factors that affect the test by changing the point of failure initiation, final location failure, propagation, and major cause of failure. This can be misleading when materials for end use are chosen based on results of such a test.

7. Proper Test Procedures

7.1 Application of Parameters—Methods of applying static and dynamic deformation must be studied carefully to ensure that only the intended parameter is applied to the specimen. Most methods have inherent characteristics resulting from mass, friction, geometry, compliance, misalignment, and nonlinearity which may affect the parameter being applied. Through design, many of these undesirable effects can be reduced to an acceptable level.

7.2 Property Measurement—Since the properties of different elastomeric specimens in a fatigue environment change differently, it is desirable to measure as many of these changes as possible. The instrumentation required will depend on the nature and purpose of the test, i.e., a material evaluation would call for more detailed data than a quality control test. In all cases, however, the instrumentation must be adequate to observe both:

a. Changes corresponding to those that adversely affect performance in the intended application and which, therefore, qualify as criteria for failure.
b. Changes which can affect the severity of the test, obscure the point of failure, or affect the mode of failure, thereby giving misleading results. Stress relaxation, set, and excessive heat buildup due to accelerated test conditions are examples of such changes.

7.2.1 Temperature influences all of the failure definitions previously mentioned. One common situation concerns periodic evaluation of some physical property during fatigue testing. The specimen will heat up during testing due to internal heat generation. Consequently, when the periodic test is run, the specimen must be allowed to cool down or the initial property must be run at this elevated temperature. This is especially important when running low ambient temperature tests.

Tables 2a and 2b show changes that can be anticipated and examples of the types of instrumentation that can be used to detect them.

TABLE 1—ACCELERATION METHODS

Method of Acceleration	Possible Effects on Test and Specimen
Increase static load or displacement	Increase or decrease in cycles to failure (depending upon the load applied and the load-deflection characterisistics of the part). Failure by splitting and tearing (tensile failure) rather than by abrasive wear or fatigue cracking. Failure due to pinching (see definitions). Increased bulge area (compression). Decreased cross-sectional area (tension). Increased creep. Slip between specimen and fixturing. More data scatter (hardness sensitivity).
Increase dynamic load or displacement	Decrease in cycles to failure. Increase in temperature due to hysteresis. Increase in temperature due to slip between specimen and fixturing. Decrease in modulus. Tensile failure rather than abrasive wear or fatigue cracking. Increased bulge area (compression). Decreased cross-sectional area (tension). More data scatter (hardness sensitivity).
Increase frequency of dynamic load or displacement	Increased heat generation per unit time. Change from mechanical to chemical failure. Change in load or displacement waveform. Change in dynamic response of specimen. Increase or decrease in cycles to failure.
Increase ambient temperature (Presoak)	Increased specimen temperature. Decrease in modulus. Change in cycles to failure. Change in dynamic response of specimen. Change in mode of failure.

TABLE 2A—INSTRUMENTATION TO DETECT PHYSICAL CHANGES IN TEST SPECIMEN

Change in Specimen	Method of Observation	Notes
Abrasive wear	Weight change	May be dry or tacky depending on polymer type and formulation.
Amplitude of vibration under fixed force input	LVDT[1], velocity transducer (integrated), accelerometer (integrated twice), leaf spring with strain gauge, optical methods, or micro-switches.	If not fixed or controlled, amplitude usually increases during test due to the combined effect of temperature rise, chemical degradation, tearing, abrasion, etc. In some configurations, amplitude can decrease due to overall movement relative to constraints.
Bond failure (to metal or fabric)	Visual.	Type and percentage of failure may be indicated using terminology of ASTM D 429.
Cracks or tearing—Initiation and rate of growth	Visual or optical. May also be inferred from changes in deflection, damping, or elastic rate.	Possibility of internal failure must be considered with thick specimens, in which case sectioning is required.
Deflection (midpoint) or drift	LVDT[1] leaf spring with strain gauge or micrometer head (if member maintaining fixed load is different than member applying oscillating load) optical methods, micro-switches.	If constant force is maintained by a dead weight or servo system, deflection usually increases due to changes in the material, tearing, abrasion, etc. Temperature rise may result in decreased or increased deflection.
Distortion	Visual	Buckling, banding, etc., can lead to typical failure modes.
Dynamic properties—Elastic rate and viscous damping	Analysis of force and amplitude signals (magnitude and phase angle).	Increases or decreases in either property can occur due to chemical changes or changes in physical dimensions due to set.
Force—Static and dynamic in displacement controlled test equipment	Load cell—Strain gauge or piezoelectric type	Load cell must be placed so as to avoid the effects of the weight of surrounding machine elements and extraneous inertial forces.

1. Linear variable differential transformer.

TABLE 2B—INSTRUMENTATION TO DETECT PROPERTY CHANGES IN TEST SPECIMEN

Property Undergoing Change	Instrumentation	Notes
Permanent set	Direct measurement after a specified period of recovery.	Method of measurement must be carefully defined. Usually not applicable to badly cracked or degraded specimens.
Porosity (internal)	Visual examination of sectioned specimen comparison with standard specimens.	Indicative of chemical degradation due to internal heat build-up.
Temperature	Thermocouple, thermistor in, on, or adjacent to test specimen. Infrared pyrometer for surface temperature.	Sample temperature is normally non-uniform throughout the part due to the internal viscosity and poor heat transfer characteristics of elastomers.

7.3 Instrumentation—Proper instrumentation is a good aid to accuracy in that error can be seen in the parameter measurement and, if recognized as such, and the source of error identified, be corrected. In measuring displacement, direct specimen deflection measurement is recommended rather than that of a test machine component attached to the specimen. In measuring loads, a load measuring device located in series between the specimen and the loading mechanism is recommended.

7.4 Machine Geometry and Test Fixtures

7.4.1 Instrumentation alone is not assurance of equivalent data between machines of different design used to run the same test. Machine geometry can affect specimen restraint, and if significantly different, can dramatically influence test results even though the measured parameters are identical.

7.4.2 In many tests, the specimen will roll, shift, bulge, or otherwise react when the major parameters are applied. These reactions are often of high force magnitude. Improper attempts to completely restrict motions of this type often cause bending and friction in machine components which may adversely affect test repeatability.

7.4.3 It is recommended that the influencing machine geometry that affords the best compromise of the following be chosen:

a. Restrains specimen similar to the intended application
b. Has no inherent adverse effect on test repeatability
c. Has minimum effect on data as a result of wear, changes in friction, minor misadjustment, or other slight loss of precision

7.4.4 Test fixtures, poorly designed or improperly specified, may constitute a test variable. The following should be considered in the specifying of test fixtures:

a. Fixture stiffness
b. Cleanliness and finish of surfaces in contact with specimen
c. Heat sink effects

8. Test Apparatus—This document is intended to apply to all elastomer and elastomeric component fatigue testing apparatus. Typical commercially available testers are:

8.1 Mechanical Testers

a. Chrylser "Diving Board"
b. De Mattia Flexing Machine (ASTM D 430 and D 813 (2.1.3 [12]))
c. E. I. duPont Flexing Machine (ASTM D 430 (2.1.3 [12]))
d. Firestone Flexometer (ASTM D 623 (2.1.3 [12]))
e. Goodrich Flexometer (ASTM D 623 (2.1.3 [12]))
f. Monsanto Flex to Failure Tester (2.1.3 [2]), (2.1.3 [3])
g. Roelig Machine
h. Ross Flexing Machine (ASTM D 1052 (2.1.3 [12]))
i. St. Joe Flexometer
j. Sonntag Low Frequency Fatigue Testing Machine

8.2 Servo-controlled Devices

a. Hydro-dynamic machines (such as marketed by MTS and Schenck)
b. Electrodynamic machines (such as marketed by Unholtz-Dickey and Bruel & Kjaer)

Other applicable test machines may be proprietary or especially constructed to evaluate a specific component.

9. Degree of Test Acceleration—Elastomeric material and component fatigue tests are accelerated to various degrees depending on the type and/or purpose of the test. Most tests fall into one of the following categories:

9.1 Engineering Evaluation Tests—The purpose of evaluation testing is to rank and/or optimize material or component design performance under test conditions simulating the intended application as closely as practical.

9.2 Quality Test—The purpose of quality testing is to measure the fatigue life of a specimen against a standard that is based on tests run on known quality specimens. The test conditions used may or may not simulate the type or direction of deformation found in the intended application, and are usually highly accelerated.

9.3 Comparison Tests—This type of test is performed to compare fatigue performance of materials or components. The initial comparison testing or screening may be performed under accelerated quality test conditions and final evaluation under conditions simulating the intended application.

10. Experimental Design—A designed experiment can obtain more information for less material and process cost than can be obtained by traditional methods. References 2.1.3 [9], 2.1.3 [10], and 2.1.3 [11] listed in Section 2 of this document, cover experiment design in detail.

11. Reporting Data—Reporting test results in a clear, concise manner is every bit as important as assuring that the test conducted was valid and accurate. Also, hardware is often disassembled after a test is completed; the test report is needed to assure that the information of interest is not lost.

Following is a suggested outline of the minimum information that should be presented in a fatigue test report.

11.1 Summary—Present only the important findings with some background information so that the report's contents can be rapidly digested and analyzed.

11.2 Material Specification and Properties—The minimum information presented should include the designation and/or specification, form of product, condition, chemical composition, and note of any special treatment applied.

Also, to be included, is a presentation of the mechanical properties of the material in the test component, designation of the test method used to procure those properties, and identification of the location from which the samples were taken.

11.3 Component Dimensions—Present a drawing(s) or sketch(es) showing test section details, grip section, orientation with respect to force application and geometry of any induced notches.

11.4 Specimen Preparation—Report any observed deterioration of the specimen during storage, such as changes in shape, dimensions, or mechanical properties. Also desirable would be the reporting of any environmental factors in which the specimens were stored and any protection applied to the samples.

11.5 Information on Test Procedures—Included should be information on the test machine, its functional characteristics (electrohydraulic, pneumatic, etc.), frequency of load application, forcing function, method of calibration, and load monitoring procedures. Further information would encompass the direction of loading (Refer to SAE J1883), failure criteria, number of cycles to run out, and the statistical techniques used to design the test program and accommodate expected or unexpected deviations. Also desirable would be the procedure for mounting the specimen in the machine, fixture details, and precautions taken to ensure that unknown stresses induced by vibration, friction, and eccentricity are negligible. Ambient conditions including temperature and humidity average values and ranges together with controls applied should be reported. Special items of interest such as ozone level, deleterious substance presence, and so on, should also appear.

To complete the section, presentation of the reason for test termination for each specimen and a description of the failure and its location is desirable.

11.6 Presentation of Results—Two commonly used methods for presenting fatigue data are tabulation and S-N_f curve. When used, the tabular form should include specimen identification, test sequence, stresses applied, cycles to end of test, cause of termination, results of post test examination, and identification of station and machine used for each test.

On the S-N_f curve, the dependent variable fatigue life (N_f) in cycles is plotted on the abscissa, a logarithmic scale. The independent variable, maximum stress (S), is plotted on the ordinate and may be an arithmetic or logarithmic scale. If the data curve is fitted by regression analysis, the stress-life relation equation and concomitant statistical measures of dispersion should be presented.

As discussed in Appendix A, the straight line obtained by plotting strain versus N_f (number of cycles) on log-log paper may be a more usable form of S-N_f data presentation.

Photographs of failures, together with an explanation, provide a permanent record and valuable supplement to S-N_f curves.

APPENDIX A
FATIGUE CORRELATION FOR ELASTOMERS

A.1 See Equation A1.

$$N_f W^b = C \quad \text{(Eq. A1)}$$

where:

N_f = cycles to failure
W = energy input (1/2 stress x strain)
C = Constant for specific material
b = ~ 2 for natural rubber (NR)
b = ~ 4 for styrene butadiene rubber (SBR)

Assuming linearity for small strains.

A.2 See Equation A2.

$$W = 1/2 \text{ stress x strain} \quad \text{(Eq. A2)}$$

where:

Stress = G x strain
where: G = shear modulus of material

A.3 Therefore: See Equation A3.

$$W = (1/2)(G)(\text{strain})^2 \quad \text{(Eq. A3)}$$

If b = 2 (for natural rubber) and substituting Equation A3 into Equation A1.

A.4 See Equation A4.

$$(N_f)(1/4)G^2(\text{strain})^4 = C \quad \text{(Eq. A4)}$$

A.5 Rearranging, see Equation A5:

$$N_f = (K'/\text{Strain})^4 \quad \text{(Eq. A5)}$$

where:

$$K' = \sqrt[4]{4C/G^2} \quad \text{(Eq. A6)}$$

This shows the fatigue life of natural rubber to be dependent on the fourth power of strain and implies that plotting strain versus N_f (cycles to failure) on log-log paper is a straight line. This applies directly to fatigue tests where the elastomer is stressed in tension only as with the Monsanto Flex to Failure Tester.

The constants b and c could be determined for a component, such as a mount, with two tests at two different strain levels.

Note that the previous relationship is valid only if the frequency of applied loading does not create significant heat in the material, which could generate an elevated temperature condition and result in adversely affecting the fatigue constant of the material.

ELASTOMERIC BUSHING "TRAC" APPLICATION CODE—SAE J1883 OCT1994

SAE Recommended Practice

Report of the SAE Vibration Control Committee approved March 1988. Reaffirmed by the SAE Vibration Committee October 1994.

Foreword—This Reaffirmed Document has been changed only to reflect the new SAE Technical Standards Board Format.

Elastomeric bushing life from different machines has resulted in significant data variations.

The designs of the test machines include differing approaches to creating similar geometric environments.

When examined closely, these differing approaches actually affect the environment of the test specimen.

The "TRAC" code was developed to separate the axes of this environment, so that each may be examined and discussed individually.

The acronym "TRAC" is derived from the labels of the most commonly discussed bushing axes: Torsional Radial Axial Conical.

1. Scope—The bushing "TRAC" code is intended to be a tool that will aid in the definition of the geometric environment for the test, or use, of an elastomeric bushing.

2. Reference—There are no referenced publications specified herein.

3. Test Axes—Since radial load and torsional rotation are the most commonly controlled input quantities to a bushing, they are usually the principal determinants of axis orientation. (See Figure 1).

a. Radial—The translational axis on which the radial load is applied (by definition).
b. Axial—The translational axis coinciding with the bushing inner and outer sleeve axes.
c. Normal—The translational axis perpendicular to both the radial and axial axes.
d. Torsional—The rotational axis coinciding with the axial axis.
e. Conical (1st group)—The rotational axis coinciding with the normal axis.
f. Conical (2nd group)—The rotational axis coinciding with the radial axis.

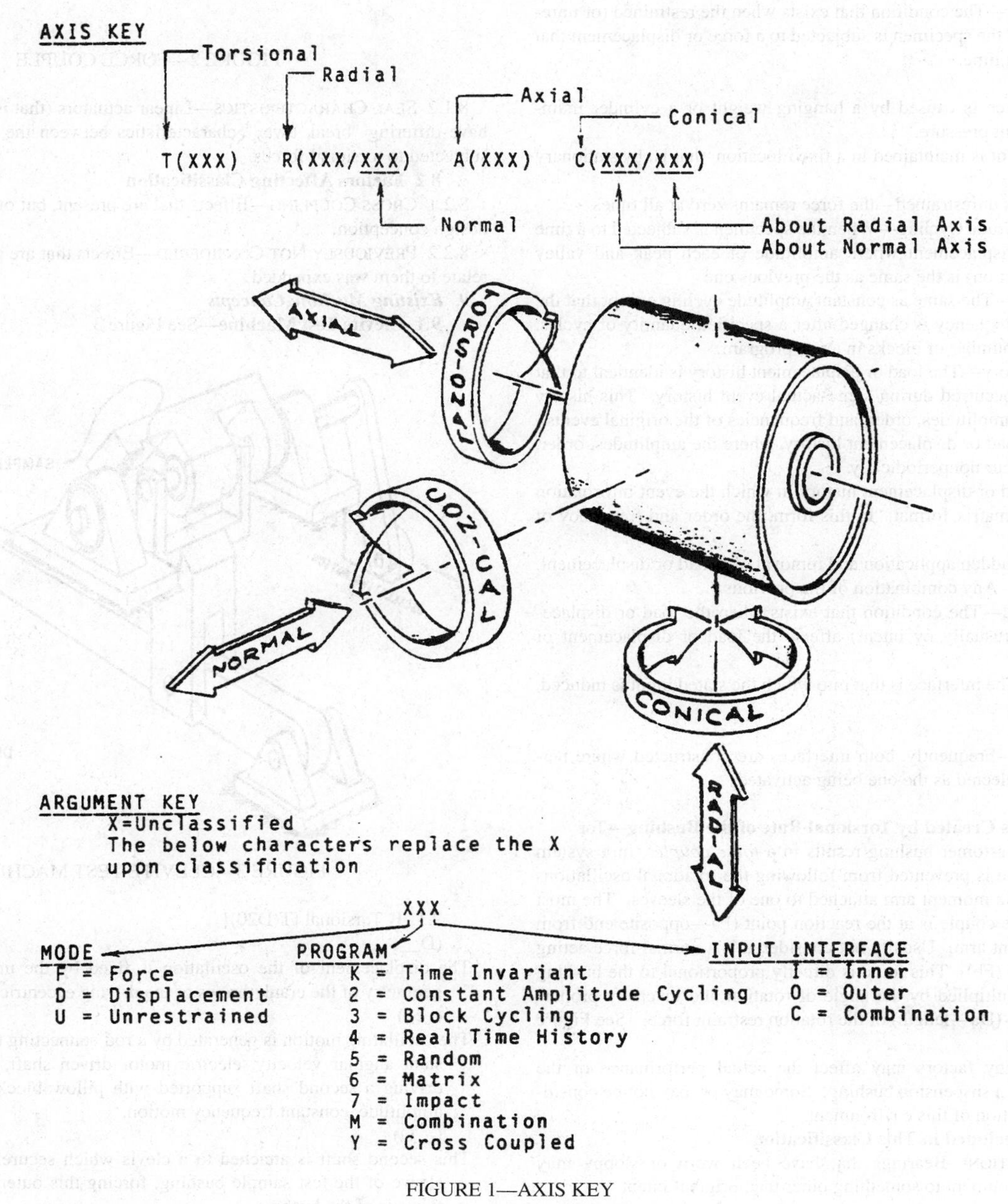

FIGURE 1—AXIS KEY

4. Mode

4.1 F = Force—A force being exerted along an axis.

Typical examples:

a. A force exerted by an air cylinder.
b. The force exerted by a spring supported in a stationary manner at the other end, and with a preload relatively high compared to its rate.
c. The force exerted by a hanging weight.
d. The force exerted by a servo-hydraulic actuator operating in load control.

4.2 Displacement—A controlled deflection of the specimen, whether fixed in a stationary position or time variant.

Typical Examples:

a. The displacement caused by a rotating eccentric or cam.
b. The displacement caused by a servo-hydraulic actuator being operated in displacement control.
c. The displacement (or lack of) caused by securely holding a portion of the specimen in a fixed location.

NOTE—An immobilized (fixed) axis has not been readily perceived as being in displacement mode.

4.3 Unrestrained—The specimen may move freely without restriction.

5. Program

a. K = Time Invariant—The condition that exists when the restrained (or unrestrained) portion of the specimen is subjected to a force or displacement that remains constant in time.

Typical examples:

1. The exerted force is caused by a hanging weight or a cylinder maintained at constant pressure.
2. The displacement is maintained in a fixed location, that is, by stationary fixturing.
3. The specimen is unrestrained—the force remains zero at all times.

b. 2 = Constant Amplitude Cycling—When the specimen is subjected to a time varying force or displacement where amplitude of each peak and valley (usually a sine function) is the same as the previous one.
c. 3 = Block Cycling—The same as constant amplitude cycling except that the amplitude and/or frequency is changed after a specified quantity of cycles. There may be any number of blocks in a test program.
d. 4 = Real Time History—The load or displacement history is identical to that of one which has occurred during some actual event history. This history would include the amplitudes, order, and frequencies of the original events.
e. 5 = Random—A load or displacement history, where the amplitudes, order, and frequencies occur nonperiodically.
f. 6 = Matrix—A load or displacement history in which the event information is tabulated in the matrix format. In this form, the order and frequency of the events are lost.
g. 7 = Impact—The sudden application and removal of a load or displacement.
h. M = Combination—Any combination of the previous.
i. Y = Cross Coupled—The condition that exists when the load or displacement of one axis (usually by intent) affects the load or displacement of another axis.

*6. Input Interface—*The interface is that into which the stated input is induced.

I = Inner
O = Outer
C = Combination—Frequently, both interfaces are constructed where neither may be selected as the one being activated.

7. Discussion

7.1 Normal Forces Created by Torsional Rate of the Bushing—Torsional stressing of the elastomer bushing results in a *force couple*. In a system (test machine), one sleeve is prevented from following the rotational oscillations of the other by means of a moment arm attached to one of the sleeves. The most evident force of the force couple is at the reaction point (Fa—opposite end from the sleeve) of this moment arm. Usually not considered is a normal force acting through the rotation axis (Fb). This force is directly proportional to the bushing torsional (spring) rate multiplied by the angle of rotation and inversely proportional to the moment arm (Da—length) of the rotation restraint force. (See Figure 2).

*8. Design Intent—*Many factors may affect the actual performance of the designed environment of a suspension bushing. Some may or may not be considered during the classification of this environment.

8.1 Factors Not Included in This Classification

8.1.1 BEARING CONDITION—Bearings that have been worn or sloppy may change the bushing environment to something other than original intent.

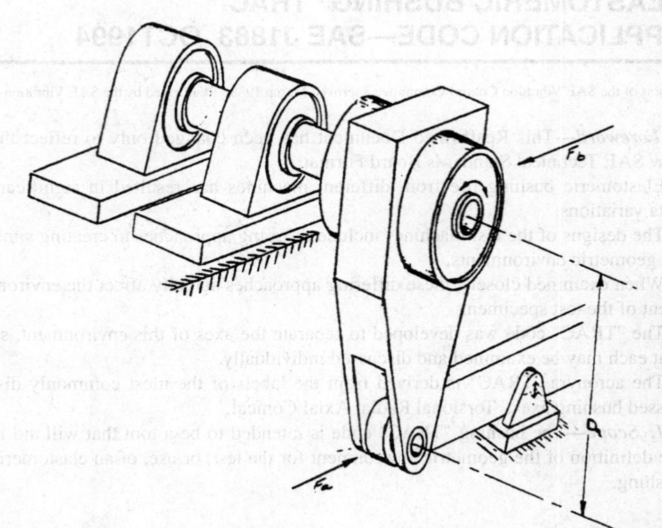

FIGURE 2—FORCE COUPLE

8.1.2 SEAL CHARACTERISTICS—Linear actuators (that is, pneumatic cylinders) have differing "break away" characteristics between the piston and bore when subjected to torsional forces.

8.2 Factors Affecting Classification

8.2.1 CROSS COUPLING—Effects that are present, but often overlooked, during design conception.

8.2.2 PREVIOUSLY NOT CONSIDERED—Effects that are present, but no effort to relate to them was expended.

9. Existing Machine Concepts

9.1 Clevite Test Machine—See Figure 3.

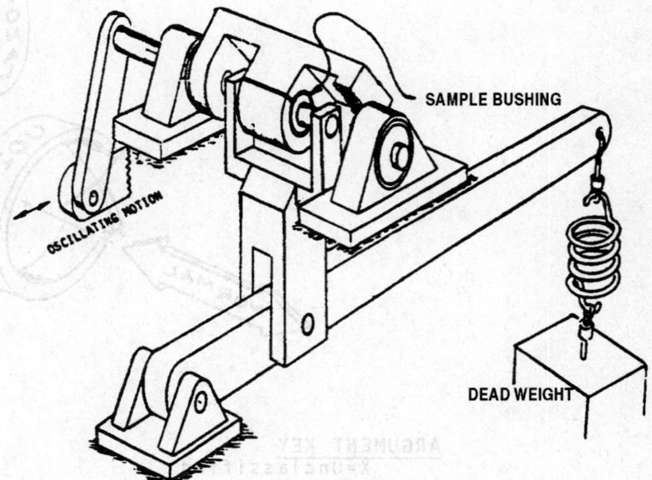

FIGURE 3—CLEVITE TEST MACHINE

9.1.T Torsional [T(D20)]

(D__)

The displacement of the oscillation is fixed by the unchanging lengths and geometry of the crank throws of the driving eccentric and driven crank.

(_2_)

The oscillating motion is generated by a rod connecting the crank arm of a constant angular velocity, electric motor driven shaft, to another crank arm driving a second shaft supported with pillow blocks. This is a constant amplitude, constant frequency motion.

(__O)

This second shaft is attached to a clevis which securely clamps to the outer sleeve of the test sample bushing, forcing this outer sleeve to rotate about the axis of the bushing.

9.1 R Radial [R(FKI/FYI)]
(F_/___)
The force generated by a dead weight is transmitted (and multiplied) along the principal radial axis through a lever and link system.
(_K_/___)
The dead weight generates a constant (time invariant) force. A spring between the end of the lever and the weight minimizes any inertial forces that may be generated by lever motion.
(__I/___)
The principal radial load (defined by this code) is induced into the inner sleeve of the sample bushing.
(___/F___)
A force generated by the bushing torsional rate is induced into the normal (to the principal) to the radial axis by the "other" force of the couple moment (as described in 7.1).
(___/_Y_)
Since this force is generated by the torsional rate of the bushing, as described in 7.1, and not by any directly induced by mechanical design of the system, it is induced by cross coupling.
(___/__I)
This normal force is induced into the inner sleeve of the sample bushing.
9.1 A Axial [A(DKC)]
(D__)
Since a line joint (bolt through a hole) is assumed at the interface of the lever and link, the inner sleeve of the sample bushing is prevented from moving along its axis, and is considered as completely restrained.
(_K_)
The restrained condition is continuous (time invariant).
(__C)
This restraint results from a combination of fixturing that includes both sleeves.
9.1 C Conical [C(DKC/DKC)]
(D__/___)
The principal radial axis (along the input radial force) is along the link. The lower end of the link is restrained from any horizontal motion; by the lever fulcrum in the fore-aft direction and the line joint (bolt through a hole) in the lateral direction. This geometry prevents any motion about the normal axis.
(_K_/___)
This restraint is continuous (time invariant).
(__C/___)
This restraint results from a combination of fixturing that includes both sleeves.
(___/D__)
Rotation about the radial axis is prevented by the line joint (bolt through hole) at the intersection of the lever and the link, resulting in no angular displacement.
(___/_K_)
This restraint is continuous (time invariant).
(___/__C)
This restraint results from a combination of fixturing that includes both sleeves.

9.2 Low Test Machine—See Figure 4.
9.2 T Torsional [T(D2I)]
(D___)
The displacement of the oscillation is fixed by the unchanging lengths and geometry of the crank throws of the driving eccentric and driven crank.
(_2_)
The oscillating motion is generated by a rod connecting the crank arm of a constant angular velocity, electric motor driven shaft, to another crank arm driving a second shaft supported with pillow blocks. This is a constant amplitude, constant frequency motion.
(__I)
This second shaft is attached to the inner sleeve and forces it to rotate about its fixed axis.
9.2 R Radial [R(FKO/FYO)]
(F_/___)
The force generated by a dead weight is transmitted (and multiplied) along the principal radial axis through a lever and link system.
(_K_/___)
The dead weight generates a constant (time invariant) force. A spring between the end of the lever and the weight minimizes any inertial forces that may be generated by lever motion.

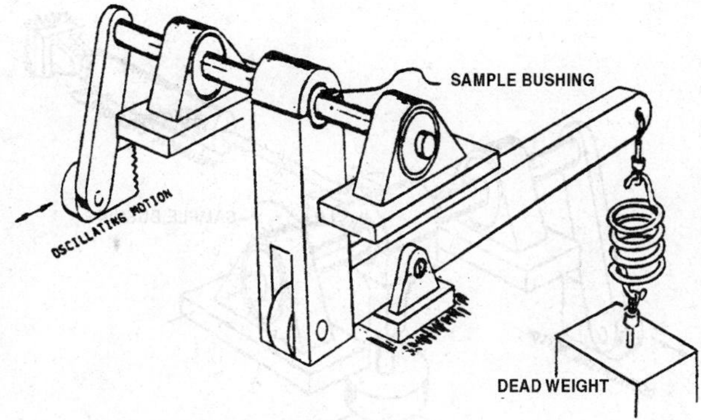

FIGURE 4—LOW TEST MACHINE

(__O/___)
The principal radial load (defined by this code) is induced into the outer sleeve of the sample bushing.
(___/F___)
A force generated by the bushing torsional rate is induced into the normal to the radial axis by the "other" force of the couple moment (as described in 7.1).
(___/_Y_)
Since this force is generated by the torsional rate of the bushing, as described in 7.1, and not directly induced by mechanical design of the system (that is, link length), it is cross coupled.
(___/__O)
This normal force is induced in the outer sleeve of the sample bushing.
9.2 A Axial [A(DKO)]
(D__
Since a line joint (bolt through a hole) is assumed to be at the interface of the lever and link, the inner sleeve of the sample bushing is prevented from moving along its axis and is considered as being completely restrained.
(_K_)
The restrained condition is continuously (time invariant) existent.
(__O)
This restraint is created at the outer sleeve of the sample bushing.
9.2C Conical [C(DKC/DKC)]
(D__/___)
The principal radial axis (along the input radial force) is along the link. The lower end of the link is restrained from any horizontal motion by the lever fulcrum in the fore-aft direction, and the line joint (bolt through hole) in the lateral direction. This geometry prevents any motion about the normal axis.
(_K_/___)
This restraint is continuous (time invariant).
(__C/___)
This restraint results from a combination of fixturing that includes both sleeves.
(___/D__)
Rotation about the radial axis is prevented by the line joint (bolt through hole) at the intersection of the lever and the link, resulting in no angular displacement.
(___/_K_)
This restraint is continuous (time invariant).
(___/__C)
This restraint results from a combination of fixturing that includes both sleeves.

9.3 Wahl Joint Test Machine—See Figure 5.
9.3 T Torsional [T(D2I)]
(D__)
The displacement of the oscillation is fixed by the unchanging lengths and geometry of the crank throws of the driving eccentric and driven crank.
(_2_)
The oscillating motion is generated by a rod connecting the crank arm of a constant angular velocity, electric motor driven shaft, to another crank arm driving a second shaft supported with pillow blocks. This is a constant amplitude, constant frequency motion.
(__I)
This second shaft is attached to the inner sleeve and forces it to rotate about its fixed axis.

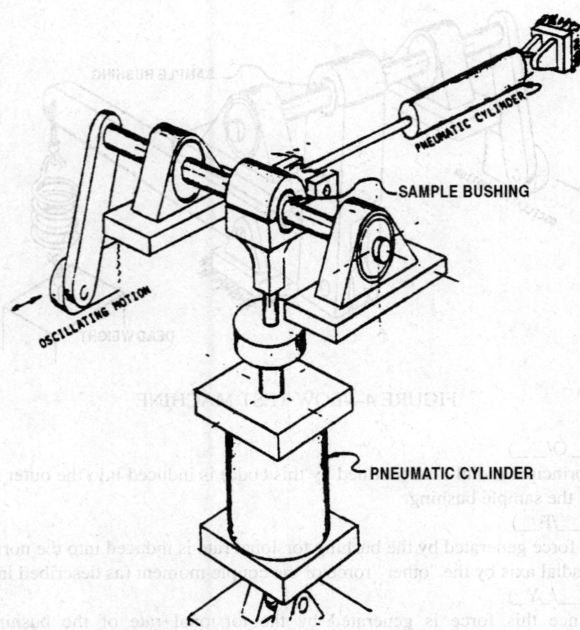

FIGURE 5—WAHL JOINT TEST MACHINE

9.3 R Radial [R(FKO/FMO)]

(F_/__)

A force is imparted to the principal radial axis by a pneumatic cylinder. It is proportional to the air pressure behind the piston. Piston seal friction is either neglected or compensated for by adjusting the air pressure according to the load cell indication of actual imparted force.

(_K_/__)

The constant (time invariant) air pressure maintains a constant force.

An optional mode of machine operation permits this load to be cycled (code entry would then be "_2_/__").

(__O/__)

The principal (defined by this code) radial load is induced into the outer sleeve of the sample bushing.

(___/F__)

A force is imparted to the normal axis by a pneumatic cylinder. It is proportional to the air pressure behind the piston. Piston seal friction is either neglected or compensated for by air pressure adjustment.

(___/_M_)

A combination of two forces is imparted to the sample:

1. The force imparted by the pneumatic cylinder; this force is generally cycled at a level and frequency determined by specific test conditions, and would be classified as [2] constant amplitude cycling if the next phenomenon did not exist.
2. A force is generated by the torsional rate of the bushing (not directly induced by intent of the mechanical system design) cross coupled into a force (as described in 7.1).

(___/__O)

This normal force is induced into the outer sleeve of the sample bushing.

9.3 A Axial [A(DKC)]

(D__)

If a line joint (bolt through a hole) is at the base of the lower pneumatic cylinder, motion of the outer sleeve along the axial axis is prevented, resulting in no axial displacement between the inner and outer sleeves.

If a point joint (swivel or rod end joint) is at the base of the lower pneumatic cylinder, motion of the outer sleeve along its axis is permitted (code entry would then be "U__").

(_K_)

This restrained condition is continuous (time invariant).

(__C)

This restraint results from a combination of fixturing that includes both sleeves.

9.3 C Conical [C(DKC/DKC)]

(D__/___)

Rotational displacement is prevented by the bolt through the hole at the lower end of the lower cylinder, and rotation between the piston and the bore of the pneumatic cylinder is prevented by sufficient seal friction, resulting in no conical displacement.

(_K_/_)

This restraint is continuous (time invariant).

(__C/_____)

This restraint results from a combination of fixturing that includes both sleeves.

(___/D__)

Rotational displacement is prevented by the bolt through the hole at the rear end of the rear cylinder and another bolt at the front end of the piston rod, and rotation between the piston and the bore of the pneumatic cylinder is prevented by sufficient seal friction, resulting in no conical displacement.

(_/_K_)

This restraint is continuous (time invariant).

(___/__C)

This restraint results from a combination of fixturing that includes both sleeves.

RECOMMENDED GUIDELINES FOR LOAD/ DEFORMATION TESTING OF ELASTOMERIC COMPONENTS—SAE J1636 FEB1993

SAE Recommended Practice

Report of the SAE Vibration Committee approved February 1993.

Foreword—These guidelines describe:

a. The basic behavior of elastomeric components subject to changing loads or deformations
b. Definition of a test method to meet specific requirements and a set of definitions and terminology to allow interchange of information on a common basis
c. Important considerations in the evaluation and reporting of test information

1. Scope—The purpose of this SAE Recommended Practice is to review factors that influence the behavior of elastomeric components under conditions of loading or deforming at a constant rate and to provide guidance concerning test procedures used to define or specify the load/deformation characteristics of elastomeric components. This characteristic is referred to as Static Stiffness. This is also referred to as a "Static Deflection Test."

2. References

2.1 Applicable Publication—The following publication forms a part of this specification to the extent specified herein. The latest issue of SAE publications shall apply.

2.1.1 SAE PUBLICATION—Available from SAE, 400 Commonwealth Drive, Warrendale, PA 15096-0001.

SAE J1883 MAR88—Elastomeric Bushing "TRAC" Application Code

3. Elastomeric Behavior—An elastomer is a viscoelastic material. It acts as though it were composed of an elastic component and a viscous component. The elastic component controls stress versus strain behavior. Because of an elastomer's viscoelastic nature, the dynamic response and mechanical behavior are dependent upon stress or strain history, rate of deformation, level of strain, and specimen temperature.

4. Specimen History—Prior to testing it is important to know if the component has experienced any mechanical preflexing or temperature changes and to know the timing of these influences. This is necessary for consistency in comparing test results.

4.1 Mechanical Preflexing—It is well known that elastomers undergoing load/deformation tests will progressively change for up to the first 1000 cycles until a steady-state condition is reached. Depending on the elastomer, this change ranges from about 3 to 25%. It is also known that most of the stiffness on the first cycle can be regained if a period of about 8 h or more elapses between load deflection tests. Consequently, preflexing influences must be considered. For preflexing to be effective, the load and/or deflection must be at least that at which the stiffness is to be determined.

4.2 Temperature Changes—Since elastomers are viscoelastic materials, it is necessary to know the temperature of the specimen and its temperature history prior to testing. Storing a specimen in a very cold or hot atmosphere prior to testing will influence the static data in mechanical testing as well as the time to wait before regaining the first static data after preflexing.

4.3 Aging—Assembled components require sufficient time for the elastomeric material to integrate effects such as assembly oil or precompression. One week is recommended. Oven aging for 3 h at 70 °C is sometimes used as a substitute for natural aging. This serves to yield more uniform results.

5. Test Setup—The type and manner of fixturing a component for evaluation greatly affects the validity of the measured data. The geometry and loading procedure for each fixture should be clearly specified.

5.1 Axial—The test fixture must maintain any predefined relationship between the source of loading or deformation and the component under test during the entire test sequence.

5.2 Rotational—For evaluation of components in rotational modes (i.e., torsional or conical) it will be necessary to specify the mode of loading as rotational with a torque and center of rotation (provides rotation input only) or linear with a force and lever arm (provides rotation and translational inputs). Care should be taken to maintain the predefined geometrical relationships between the fixturing and the component under test during the entire test sequence. Please refer to SAE J1883 for assistance in the definition of the geometric environment for any particular test.

6. Test Sequence—Each test typically consists of a pretest period and a test period.

The pretest period is used to apply a preload level and cyclic loads or displacements to the specimen prior to data acquisition. During the pretest period, ramp to the preload level, perform precycles, ramp back to the preload level, and then maintain the preload level for a hold period. Each precycle consists of a ramp to Precycle Level 1 followed by a ramp to Precycle Level 2.

The test period is used for data acquisition. From the preload level, ramp to Test Level 1 to Test Level 2 and back to Test Level 1. Typically, data is acquired from Test Level 1 to Test Level 2 then back to Test Level 1. (See Figure 1.)

The following must be defined for each Load/Deformation test sequence. Input parameters should relate to specific applications. The test must be fully defined to ensure repeatability and consistency of results.

6.1 Precycle Parameters

a. Number of precycles
b. Preload
c. Rate mode (load or displacement)
d. Precycle ramp rate
e. Precycle level 1 and level 2

6.2 Hold

a. Length of hold

6.3 Test Cycle

a. Rate mode (load or displacement)
b. Test ramp rate
c. Test level 1 and level 2
d. Calculation technique (See Section 8)
e. Direction of loading during measurement (ascending or descending) or average of ascending and descending
f. Analysis point(s)

By definition, level 1 is the first level that is achieved. It may be higher or lower than the preload level. Ascending data is defined to be from test level 1 to test level 2 to avoid confusion concerning the sequence of data collection. For example, it could be confusing to define the end levels as higher or lower (is –500 N higher than –300 N?).

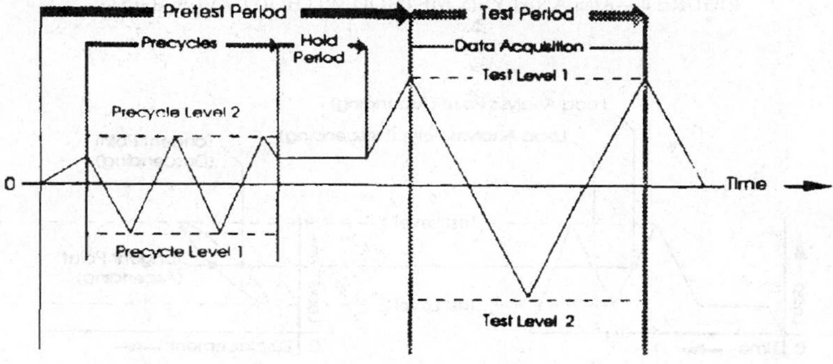

FIGURE 1—SIMPLIFIED TEST LAYOUT

7. Calculation Techniques—Static Stiffness can be calculated in many ways. Static Stiffness can be associated with a segment of time (Kchord analysis method) or with a point in time (Ktan Analysis Method). Static Stiffness can also be measured during the ascending or descending portion of the test or averaged between the two. An alternative to calculating stiffness is to measure the change in load or displacement (Delta(load) or Delta(disp)) resulting from an imposed displacement or load, respectively.

7.1 Kchord Analysis Method—The Kchord analysis method is the stiffness associated with a segment of time. It is calculated by dividing the specimen's change in load by its change in displacement for the selected segment. (See Equation 1.)

$$K_{chord} = \frac{Delta_{(load)}}{Delta_{(disp)}} \quad \text{(Eq. 1)}$$

When the averaging technique is used with the Kchord analysis method, the calculation averages the ascending segment and corresponding descending segment in the calculations. (See Figures 2 and 3.)

7.2 Ktan Analysis Method—The Ktan analysis method determines the instantaneous stiffness of the specimen -- the stiffness at a selected point. One accepted method is to perform a second-order least squares curve fit through the selected point, and through points adjacent to both sides of the selected point. Typically, 10% of the total points acquired are used, i.e., 5% of each side of the selected point.

Calculations are based on equation 2:

$$y = Ax^2 + Bx + C \quad \text{(Eq. 2)}$$

where:

x represents displacement values

y represents load values

A,B,C are coefficients determined in the second-order regression

This calculation yields a second-order line that has the best fit through these points. The stiffness is then calculated as the slope of the second-order line at the selected point, based on equation 3:

$$K_{tan} = \frac{dy}{dx} = 2Ax + B \quad \text{(Eq. 3)}$$

When the averaging technique is used with the Ktan analysis method, the calculation averages the ascending data point and corresponding descending data point in the calculations. (See Figures 4 and 5.)

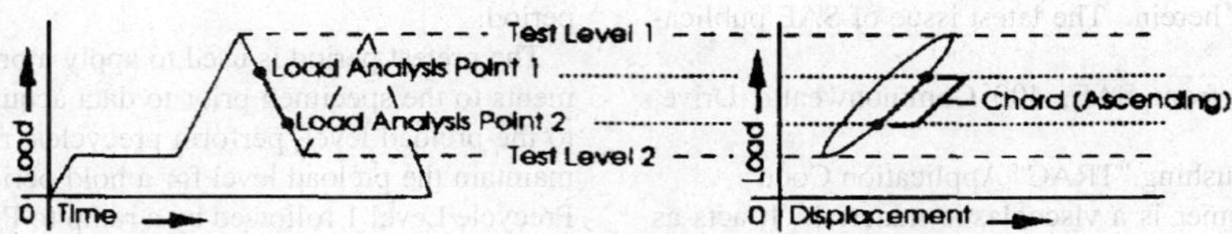

FIGURE 2—Kchord ANALYSIS METHOD WITHOUT AVERAGING

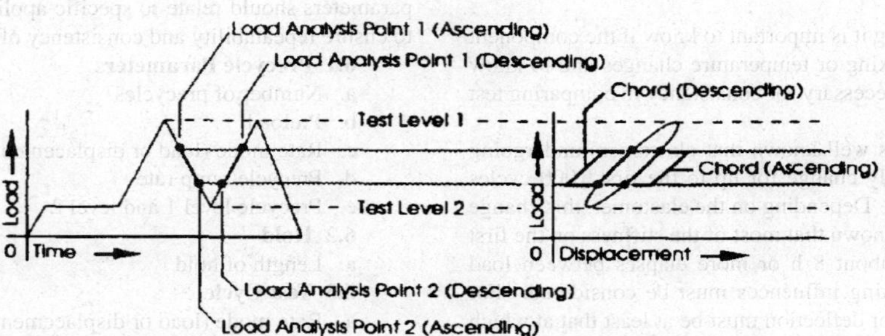

FIGURE 3—Kchord ANALYSIS METHOD WITH AVERAGING

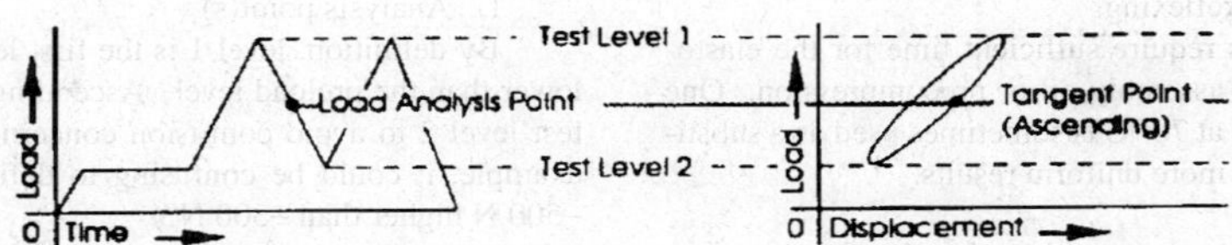

FIGURE 4—Ktan ANALYSIS METHOD WITHOUT AVERAGING

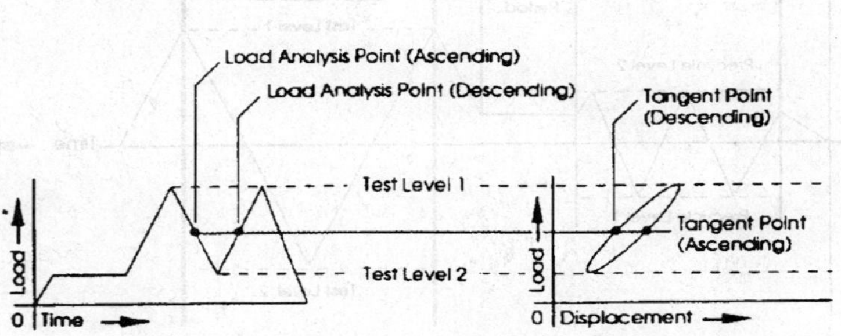

FIGURE 5—Ktan ANALYSIS METHOD WITH AVERAGING

7.3 Delta Analysis Method

7.3.1 Delta(load) analysis method determines the specimen change in load as the result of an applied displacement. (See Figures 6 and 7.)

7.3.2 Delta(disp) analysis method determines the specimen change in displacement as the result of an applied load. (See Figures 8 and 9.)

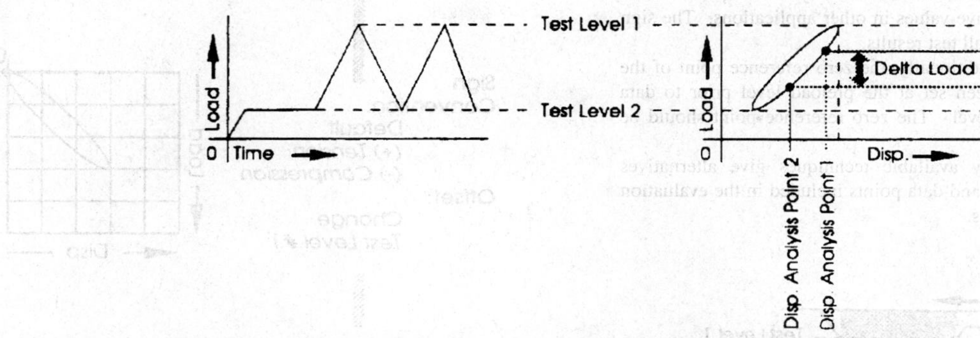

FIGURE 6—DELTA(load) ANALYSIS METHOD WITHOUT AVERAGING

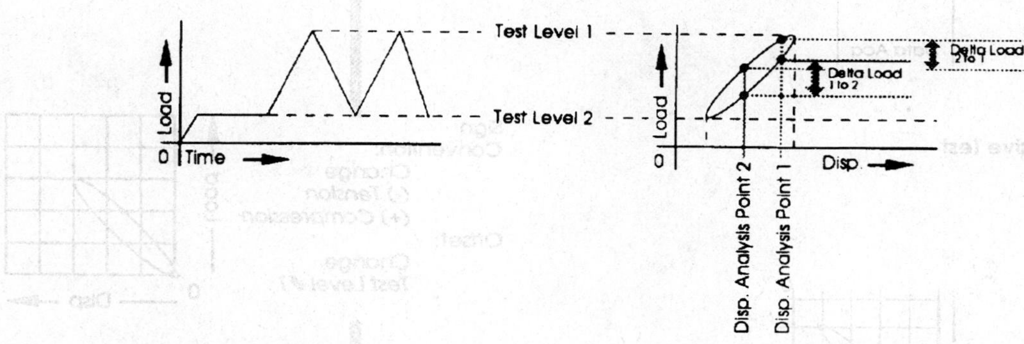

FIGURE 7—DELTA(LOAD) ANALYSIS METHOD WITH AVERAGING

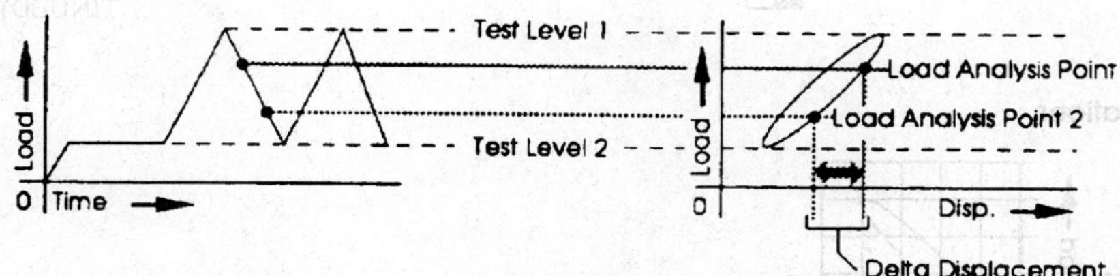

FIGURE 8—DELTA(DISP) ANALYSIS METHOD WITHOUT AVERAGING

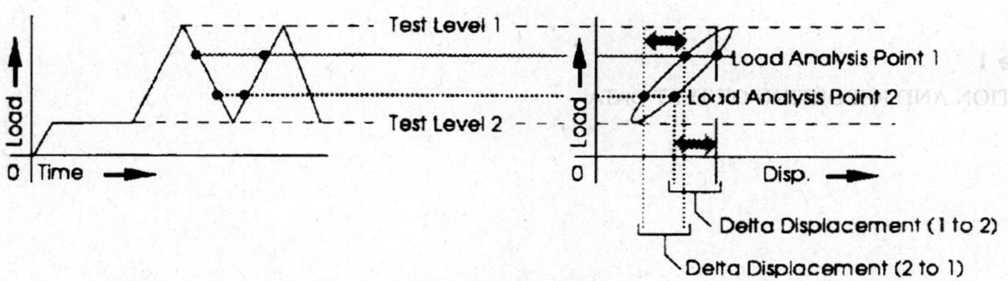

FIGURE 9—DELTA(DISP) ANALYSIS METHOD WITH AVERAGING

8. Evaluation and Reporting of Test Data—As with calculation techniques, there are many commonly used formats for evaluation and reporting of data including tabular and graphical presentation. The key is complete documentation of the test conditions and data presentation. (See Figures 10A and 10B.)

8.1 Sign Convention—Compression has traditionally been represented as positive values in this test but as negative values in other applications. The sign convention should be clearly stated on all test results.

8.2 Zero Reference Offset—Traditionally, the zero reference point of the load and displacement values have been set at the preload level prior to data acquisition as opposed to a no-load level. The zero reference point should be clearly stated on all test results.

8.3 Data Analysis Points—Many available techniques give alternatives for data analysis. The technique used and data points included in the evaluation should be clearly indicated on all results.

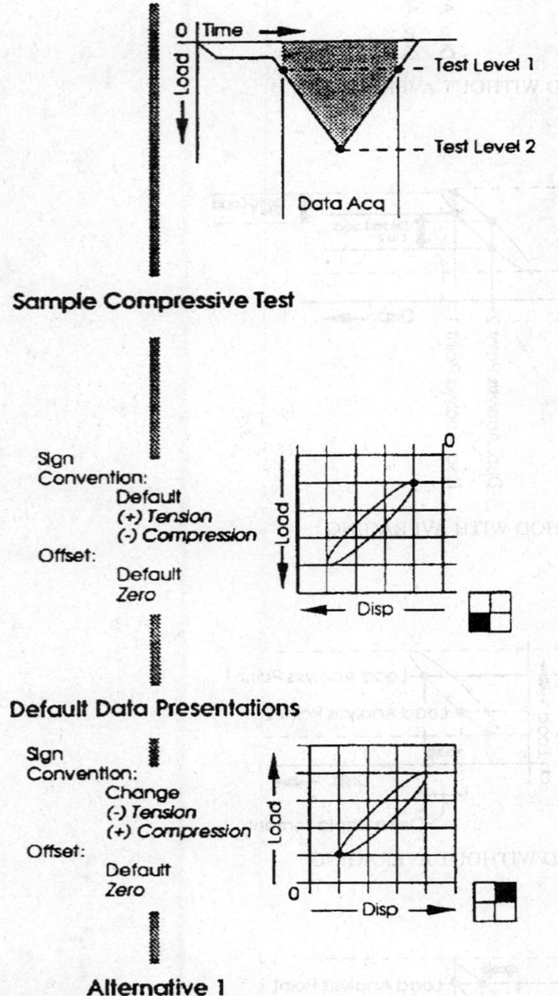

FIGURE 10A—EVALUATION AND REPORTING OF TEST DATA

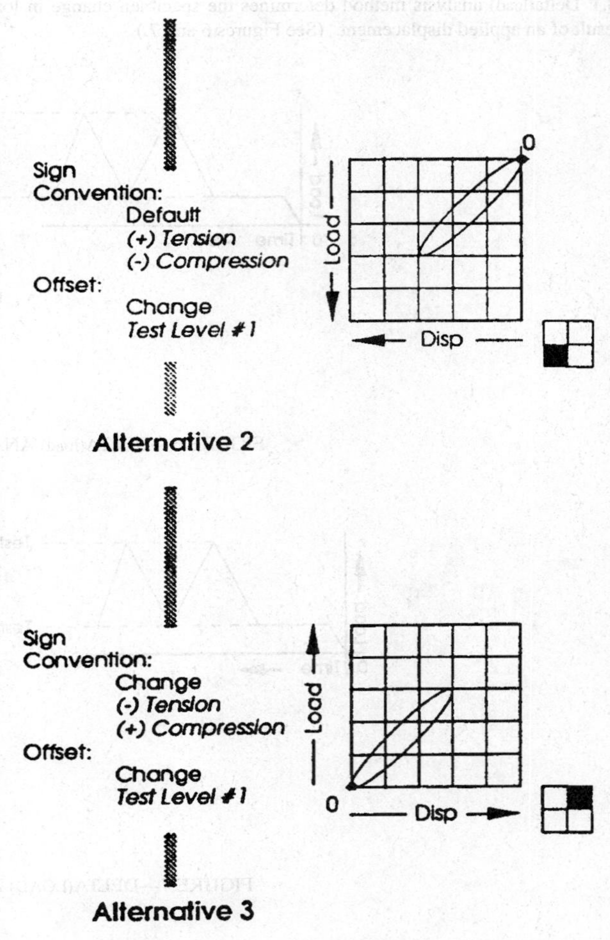

FIGURE 10B—EVALUATION AND REPORTING OF TEST DATA (CONTINUED)

TESTING DYNAMIC PROPERTIES OF ELASTOMERIC ISOLATORS—SAE J1085 MAY1999 SAE Recommended Practice

Report of the Nonmetallic Materials Committee approved September 1974, and revised August 1978. Completely revised by the SAE Vibration Isolation Components Committee November 1995, and revised May 1999. Rationale statement available.

1. Scope—These methods cover testing procedures for defining and specifying the dynamic characteristics of simple elastomers and simple fabricated elastomeric isolators used in vehicle components. Simple, here, is defined as solid (non-hydraulic) components tested at frequencies less than or equal to 25 Hz.

2. References

2.1 Applicable Publications—The following publications form a part of this specification to the extent specified herein.

2.1.1 ASTM PUBLICATIONS—Available from ASTM, 100 Barr Harbor Drive, West Conshohocken, PA 19428-2959.

ASTM D 1349—Recommended Practice for Rubber—Standard Temperatures and Atmospheres for Testing and Conditioning

ASTM D 2231—Recommended Practice for Rubber Properties in Forced Vibration

ASTM D 2234—Method for Collection of a Gross Sample of Coal

ASTM E 177—Practice for Use of the Terms Precision and Bias in ASTM Test Methods

2.1.2 RAPRA PUBLICATIONS—Available from RAPRA Technology Ltd., Shawberry, Shrewsberry, Shrapshire SY44NR, U.K.

D. Hands, "Simple Methods for Heat Flow Calculations," RAPRA Technical Review No. 60, Class No. 96, July 1971

Marion D. Thompson, "Cooling Rubber Slabs," RAPRA Bulletin, May 1972

2.1.3 OTHER PUBLICATIONS

S. D. Gehman, "Heat Transfer in Processing and Use of Rubber," Rubber Chem. & Tech., 1967, pp. 36–99

2.2 Related Publications—The following publications are provided for information purposes only and are not a required part of this document.

2.2.1 SAE PUBLICATION—Available from SAE, 400 Commonwealth Drive, Warrendale, PA 15096-0001.

SAE SP-375, ASTM STP-535—The Measurement of the Dynamic Properties of Elastomers and Elastomeric Mounts, B. M. Hillberry and A. F. Hegerich, Proceedings of Symposium presented at SAE International Automotive Engineering Congress, Detroit, January 1973

2.2.2 ASTM PUBLICATIONS—Available from ASTM, 100 Barr Harbor Drive, West Conshohocken, PA 19428-2959.

ASTM D 832—Recommended Practice for Rubber Conditioning for Low Temperature Testing

ASTM D 1053—Test for Rubber Property—Stiffening at Low Temperature Testing

ASTM D 1229—Test for Rubber Property—Compression Set at low Temperature

ASTM D 1329—Test for Rubber Property—Retraction at Low Temperatures (TR Test)

ASTM D 1566—Definition of Terms Relating to Rubber

ASTM E 4—Verification of Testing Machines

ASTM E 74—Calibration of Force-Measuring Instruments for Verifying the Load Indication of Testing Machines

3. Summary—These methods describe procedures for measuring the dynamic characteristics of automotive elastomeric mountings using forced vibration testing machines. These characteristics are the elastic spring rate, damping coefficient, and loss tangent. Either fabricated mountings or elastomer specimens may be tested. Since measured dynamic properties are highly dependent upon test conditions, emphasis has been placed on the definition of suitable conditions.

4. Description of Terms—These terms are in common use throughout the North American automotive industry. Alternate Terminology has been added to assist in cross-referencing terminology from other areas of the world. Please use SAE terminology to avoid confusion and data inaccuracies.

4.1 Test Temperature

4.1.1 AMBIENT TEMPERATURE—The temperature of the environment surrounding the test specimen. Unless otherwise specified, it is assumed that the sample is at the ambient temperature before being subjected to dynamic flexing.

4.1.2 PART TEMPERATURE—The temperature obtained by locating a temperature-sensing device in or on the specimen. In most cases, temperature gradients that develop within flexing rubber specimens make it necessary to define the precise points and techniques used to measure temperature.

4.2 Frequency (f)—The number of complete cycles, whole periods, of forced vibrations per unit of time caused and maintained by a periodic excitation, usually sinusoidal.

4.3 Preload—An external static load producing a strain in a test specimen. Preload is imposed prior to forced vibration testing. Preload is usually expressed in Newtons (pounds) of force instead of meters (inches) of deflection.

4.4 Double Amplitude (DA)—The peak-to-peak amplitude as applied to the elastomer specimen measured in the direction of the applied vibration. Two times the single peak value in either the plus or minus direction may not be equivalent to the peak-to-peak value.

4.5 Complex Spring Rate (K^*)—The effective spring rate of a part under sinusoidal dynamic stress. It is the peak-to-peak force across the sample divided by the peak-to-peak displacement. The complex spring rate can be visualized as being the vector sum of an elastic component and a viscous damping component.

4.5.1 ALTERNATE TERMINOLOGY

a. Complex Stiffness
b. K-dynamic (K_d, K_{dyn})
c. Dynamic Stiffness (sometimes confused with 4.6)

4.6 Dynamic Spring Rate (K)—The proportionality factor between the component of the applied force vector that is in phase with the displacement and the displacement vector. The dynamic spring rate is equal to the elastic component of the complex spring rate.

4.6.1 ALTERNATE TERMINOLOGY

a. Elastic Spring Rate (K_{el})
b. Dynamic Stiffness (K')
c. Storage Stiffness (K")

4.7 Damping Coefficient (C)—The proportionality factor between the component of the applied force vector which is in phase with velocity and the velocity vector.

4.8 Loss Rate (Cw)—The proportionality factor between the magnitude of the component of the applied force vector that is in phase with the velocity and the magnitude of the displacement vector, where:

$$\omega = 2\pi f \quad \text{(Eq. 1)}$$

NOTE—The magnitudes of the complex spring rate, elastic spring rate, and loss rate are related by Equation 2:

$$K^* = \text{complex spring rate} \quad \text{(Eq. 2)}$$

$$K^* = \sqrt{((K)^2 + (C\omega)^2)} \quad \text{(Eq. 3)}$$

Equation 3 is sometimes written as shown in Equation 4:

$$(K^*)^2 = (K')^2 + (K'')^2 \quad \text{(Eq. 4)}$$

where

$K'' = C\,\omega$

4.8.1 ALTERNATE TERMINOLOGY

a. Loss Stiffness (K")
b. Viscous Stiffness (K")

4.9 Loss Tangent (tan δ)—The tangent of the phase angle between the applied force and the resulting displacement:

$$\tan\delta = \frac{C\omega}{k} \quad \text{(Eq. 5)}$$

4.9.1 ALTERNATE TERMINOLOGY

a. Loss factor

5. General Testing Methods

5.1 Preparation Prior To Testing

5.1.1 Virgin specimens must be allowed to age between manufacturing and testing. Typically, a minimum of 24 h is suggested. Elastomeric specimens that have undergone some permanent deformation (such as that due to an assembly operation) may require additional time to permit relaxation of any internal stresses that may exist.

5.1.2 Parts that have been kept at temperatures other than the test temperature (for example, during shipment, storage, or environmental testing) must be conditioned at the test temperature long enough to achieve uniform temperature stabilization throughout. Minimum conditioning time depends upon many factors, including temperature difference, specimen size and shape, and airflow around the specimen. Guidance for determining the required conditioning time is given in Appendix A.

5.1.3 All test equipment instrumentation should be fully stabilized per manufacturer's instructions. At least 1/2 h is required. Greater stability is obtained by leaving electronic equipment on permanently. It is recommended that at the start and conclusion of every test session or operator change, a quick check of calibration be performed with a control specimen.

5.2 Outline Of Test Procedure

5.2.1 Insert the specimen.

5.2.2 Apply the preload.

5.2.3 Apply and maintain the dynamic conditions of test.

5.2.4 Stabilize specimen properties.

5.2.5 Read data within 1 min.

5.2.6 Remove the specimen if no further measurements are to be made.

5.3 Preferred Test Conditions

5.3.1 Where a single measurement is to be made on a specimen, the following reference test conditions are suggested in the interests of standardization. They take into account: the precision of equipment, stabilization of specimen dynamic properties, minimization of heat buildup, avoidance of regions in which elastomers are most sensitive to changes in test conditions, and relevance to most practical applications.

5.3.1.1 Preload—Selected to correspond to that existing in the intended application. Sufficient preload should be applied to prevent any separation of sample-to-machine interfaces unless all interfaces are securely attached. The preload should be chosen so that any sharp changes in the slope of the load-deflection curve are avoided.

5.3.1.2 Double Amplitude—0.50 mm (0.020 in).

5.3.1.3 Frequency—15 Hz.

5.3.1.4 Ambient Temperature—23 °C ± 2 °C (73.4 °F ± 3.6 °F).

5.3.1.5 Stabilization Period—2 min minimum.

5.3.2 Additional or alternate test conditions should follow the guidelines in ASTM D 2231 and ASTM D 1349. The ambient temperatures in Table 1 are suggested for testing elastomers used in automotive applications:

TABLE 1—AMBIENT TEMPERATURES

°C	°F
–40	–40
–10	+14
+23	+73.4
+100	+212
+150	+302

5.3.3 ALTERNATIVE COLD TEST PROCEDURE

5.3.3.1 Discussion—When a specimen has been temperature stabilized at a test temperature such as –40 °C (–40 °F), any test data obtained in the first few thousand cycles will be transient data. Each unit of energy input will change the specimen's dynamic properties. The following procedure is suggested so data can be obtained in a repeatable manner when specimen response is changing.

5.3.3.2 Pretest Preparation

5.3.3.2.1 Prepare the test machine to record test data continuously during test so that information pertaining to any particular cycle can be determined. Include the following:

a. Test Cycles Count

b. Dynamic Spring Rate

c. Damping Coefficient

d. Test Chamber Ambient Temperature—Temperature sensor will be located to best sense the temperature of the test chamber ambient to which the sample is subjected.

e. Energy Input $\left(\int_0 F(t)V(t)dt \right)$

f. Specimen Temperature—Is assumed the same as chamber ambient when correctly stabilized at start of test.

5.3.3.2.2 Prior to Test—Weigh the specimen (include all specimen elements that are molded together or fastened together).

5.3.3.2.3 Insert the specimen.

5.3.3.2.4 Condition the specimen at test temperature.

5.3.3.2.5 Preload—There are two ways to soak the specimen at ambient temperature with or without preload. Measured dynamic characteristics are influenced by preload history. The desired condition should be specified in test requests.

5.3.3.2.5.1 Soak Period with Preload—The preload will be maintained until the entire soak period and test is complete.

a. Start of Preload:

Load Control—No stabilization required.

Displacement Control—Preload stabilization period will be required.

5.3.3.2.5.2 Soak Period without Preload—The preload is added following the soak period and maintained until the test is complete.

5.3.3.2.6 Precondition to Maximum Load/Deformation—Often precondition cycling to maximum load/deformation conditions is included prior to measurement of dynamic data. Dynamic properties will be influenced by this preconditioning. If this preconditioning is desired, it should be specified in the test procedure.

5.3.3.3 Data Reduction—Should include the following information pertaining to the cycle of interest:

5.3.3.3.1 Number of Cycles

5.3.3.3.2 Spring Rate

5.3.3.3.3 Damping Coefficient

5.3.3.3.4 Total Energy Input

5.3.3.3.5 Total energy input per unit weight of specimen. When reading the dynamic spring rate or damping, use the average for the specified cycle such as: cycle 100 equals the end of 99 to the beginning of 101.

6. Specimens

6.1 Standard Compression Specimens—Specimens used for comparing elastomer properties or standardizing test machines in compression should be chosen based on the following considerations:

6.1.1 The size of the specimens shall be chosen to suit the load capacities of the test machine but should be no less than 12.7 mm (0.50 in) nor more than 50.8 mm (2.0 in) high; the recommended height is 25.4 mm (1.0 in).

6.1.2 The preferred shape factor for comparing elastomer properties is 0.5 where:

$$\text{Shape factor} = \frac{\text{area of one loaded face}}{\text{area free to bulge}} \quad \text{(Eq. 6)}$$

6.1.3 The preferred shape is a right circular cylinder with faces parallel within 0.001 mm/mm or 0.001 in/in.

6.1.4 TEST INTERFACE—For best reproducibility, the sample mentioned in 6.1.2 should have metal plates bonded to both faces during vulcanization.

6.1.5 OPTIONAL-TEST INTERFACE—The test machine will be equipped with loading plates top and bottom of sufficient area to support the loaded specimen. The specimen will be held in place with 300 grit sandpaper, securely bonded to both loading plates. The sandpaper prevents specimen lateral movement and aids in bulge control. The two plates exciting the specimen shall be parallel within 0.001 mm/mm (0.001 in/in) of platen length in neutral position. Plate parallelism will be within tolerances on orthogonal lines.

6.2 Standard Shear Specimens—Shear specimens shall comply with ASTM D 2234 for general configuration. Dimensions may be adjusted to provide required spring rates. Supporting fixtures should be sufficiently rigid to maintain parallelism of all plates.

6.3 Fabricated Mountings or Bushings—The following considerations shall apply when fabricated mountings or bushings are tested:

6.3.1 Supporting fixtures shall be designed to restrain lateral movement of the top or bottom surfaces of the mounting as a result of forces applied in the test direction.

6.3.2 It shall be carefully determined that any lateral forces which may develop as a result of forces applied in the test direction do not influence the test readings.

6.4 Standard specimens to be tested must be clearly marked for identification.

6.5 Standard specimens used for standardizing test machines shall be aged no less than one month and shall be accepted only after repetitive testing indicates that dynamic properties have stabilized.

7. Preferred Test Apparatus—Forced Nonresonant System

7.1 General Description—A forced nonresonant system is comprised of a drive mechanism which forces the specimen through a desired sinusoidal load, displacement, or energy. The desired frequency and amplitude of the test are not affected by the specimen's dynamic response; therefore, test conditions may be quite easily changed.

7.1.1 THEORY—In a forced nonresonant system, the sample is excited with a sinusoidal oscillation which is either force or displacement controlled. The forcing medium causing this sinusoidal oscillation can be an electromechanical, electrohydraulic system, or a pure mechanical system.

This method assumes that the existing force or displacement and the response of the specimen can be considered to be sinusoidal. If this is not the case, special methods of analysis are required.

The transmitted force is measured by a load cell in contact with the sample, preferably on the stationary side to minimize errors due to acceleration of the mass of the fixture. The component of this force which is in phase with velocity and the component that is in phase with the displacement are usually determined electronically. From this information, the values of C and K are usually determined. The vector phase relationships are illustrated in Figure 1.

7.1.2 COMPONENTS—The basic elements of a forced nonresonant system are the drive system, the control system, a loading frame, transducers, and the instrumentation for readout.

7.1.2.1 Drive System—The system should be capable of providing sinusoidal dynamic operation, with minimum harmonic distortion, in the same direction as the applied force.

7.1.2.2 Control—A means of precise control over the input drive unit is required for repeatable test results. Controls for mean input, dynamic input, and frequency should be independently selectable for the desired test condition.

7.1.2.3 Transducers and Instrumentation—Common transducer signals used in forced nonresonant systems for obtaining data are load, displacement, and/or velocity. Each transducer should be calibrated to the following minimum accuracies:

a. Load—± 0.5% of full-scale for each calibrated range
b. Displacement—± 0.5% of full-scale for each calibrated range
c. Velocity—± 0.1% of full-scale for each calibrated range

Readout instrumentation for load, displacement, and velocity transducers should provide a sufficient number of ranges so that it will not be necessary to use less than 20% of range.

Precautions listed in ASTM D 2231, paragraph 4.2 should be observed in selecting transducers, electronics, and techniques of calibration.

7.1.2.4 Preferred Location of Transducers—The load cell shall be mounted on the stationary side of the sample being tested.

The displacement and/or velocity transducer should be located to accurately measure the motion of the dynamic surface of the sample. It should be located parallel to and as close as possible to the centerline of the existing force.

7.1.2.5 Load Path Compliance—A correction factor will be required unless the overall spring rate of the fixtures and the machine elements that are included in the measurement is sufficiently high. The machine and fixture spring rate should be at least 100 times greater than the nominal spring rate of the test specimen. If this degree of rigidity cannot be achieved, the correction factor shall be calculated and applied.

7.1.2.6 Fixture Mass—The mass of the fixture located on the stationary platen shall be minimized to reduce errors due to mass-inertia accelerations. The fixture located on the moving platen shall be rigid to eliminate any possibility of structural resonance near operating frequencies.

8. Report

8.1 Test Conditions—The report shall include the following:

8.1.1 Type of testing machine used.

8.1.2 Test specimen(s) identification.

8.1.3 Type of specimen loading, for example, compression or shear. For specimens of complex configuration, full description of fixtures used, with diagrams if necessary.

8.1.4 Date of test.

8.1.5 Preload[1].

8.1.6 Frequency[1] used at each test point in Hertz.

8.1.7 Double amplitude displacement[1] used at each test point.

8.1.8 Ambient temperature[1].

8.1.9 Specimen internal temperature (optional). If internal temperature is used, the following additional information is required:

8.1.9.1 Internal temperature before flexing.

8.1.9.2 Ambient temperature.

8.1.9.3 Exact location of the temperature measuring transducer.

8.1.9.4 Time from start of flexing until temperature and dynamic property readings are taken.

---

1. Include both actual and specified, if different.

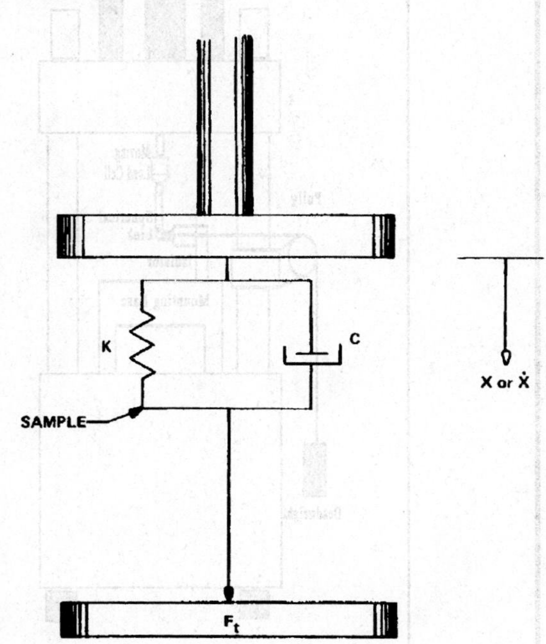

K - DYNAMIC SPRING RATE
C - DAMPING COEFFICIENT
F_t - TRANSMITTED FORCE
δ - PHASE RELATION OF TRANSMITTED FORCE TO DISPLACEMENT
X - DISPLACEMENT, $\frac{\text{DOUBLE AMPLITUDE}}{2}$
Ẋ - VELOCITY

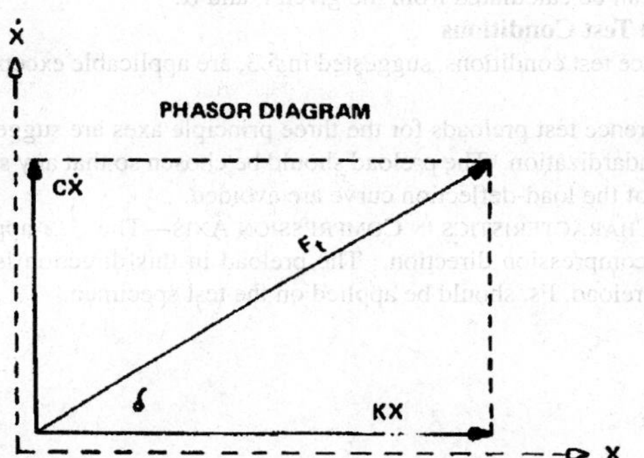

FIGURE 1—VECTOR PHASE RELATIONSHIPS

8.2 Calculated Values—The method for computing C and K from the measured variable shall be described.

8.2.1 Dynamic (elastic) spring rate, K.

8.2.2 Damping coefficient, C.

8.2.3 Loss tangent, Cω/K

8.2.4 For all test machines, as applicable:

8.2.4.1 Range scale settings.

8.2.4.2 Mode of test control, that is, stroke or load.

8.2.4.3 All observed and recorded data on which calculations are based.

9. Precision or Reproducibility—Precision as defined in ASTM E 177-71T is a function of the operator, compound, and maintenance of constant test conditions. The test conditions that can influence "level" are: preload, frequency, double amplitude displacement, temperature, and others not yet well defined.

10. Test for Dynamic Properties of Elastomeric Isolators with Multi-Axis Preloads

10.1 General—The purpose of this section is to review the procedures to determine the dynamic characteristics of automotive elastomeric mounts with multi-axis preloads. To test the dynamic characteristics in its three principle axes of the engine mount is a typical example. The following reference calculation and test setups are suggested in the interests of standardization.

10.2 Multi-Axis Preloads—Figure 2 shows two sandwich mountings in a vee with an included angle of 2 α between the compression axes.

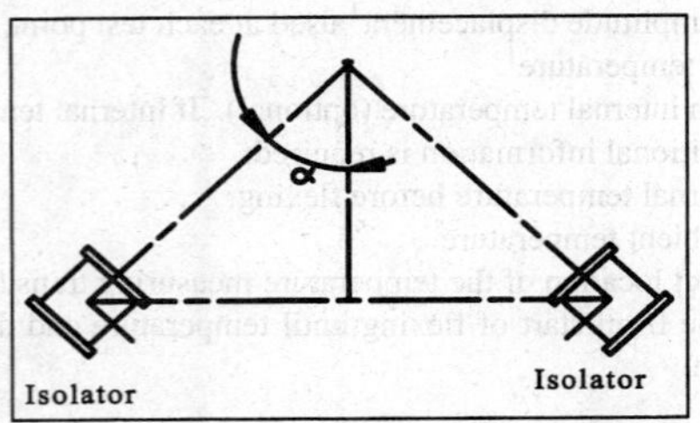

FIGURE 2—MOUNTING ARRANGEMENT

Assume a vertical static force F acts on the system. Figure 3 shows the static force diagram of one isolator.

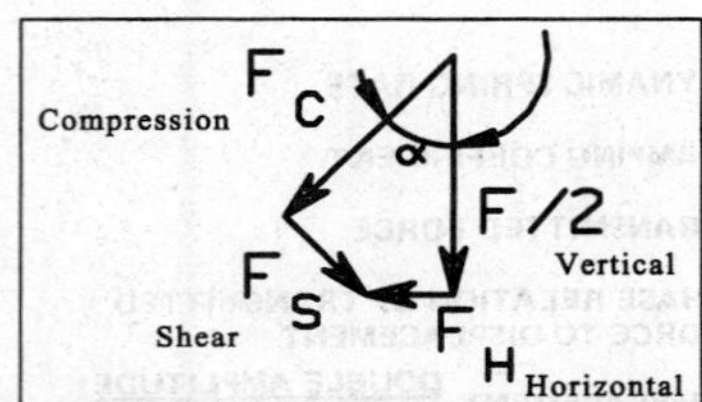

FIGURE 3—STATIC FORCE DIAGRAM

Notation

F - Static vertical force on the system

Fc - Static compression force on one isolator

Fs - Static shear force on one isolator

Fh - Static horizontal force on one isolator

The Fc and Fs can be calculated from the given F and α.

10.3 Preferred Test Conditions

10.3.1 The reference test conditions, suggested in 5.3, are applicable except the preload.

The following reference test preloads for the three principle axes are suggested in the interests of standardization. The preload should be chosen so that any sharp changes in the slope of the load-deflection curve are avoided.

10.3.2 DYNAMIC CHARACTERISTICS IN COMPRESSION AXIS—The applied excitation axis is in compression direction. The preload in this direction is Fc. There is an off-axis preload, Fs, should be applied on the test specimen.

10.3.3 DYNAMIC CHARACTERISTICS IN SHEAR AXIS—The excitation axis is in shear direction. The preload in this direction is Fs. There is an off-axis preload, Fc, should be applied on the test specimen.

10.3.4 DYNAMIC CHARACTERISTICS IN FORE AND AFT AXIS—The excitation axis is in Fore and Aft direction that is perpendicular to compression and shear axis. Sufficient preload in Fore and Aft direction should be applied to prevent any separation of sample-to-machine interfaces unless all interfaces are securely attached. There are two off-axis preloads, Fc and Fs, should be applied on the test specimen.

10.4 Test Setup—There are several methods to apply the off-axis preloads. This section outlines three methods:

10.4.1 MOVING LOAD CELL—Figure 4 shows a test setup for shear and Fore and Aft characterization of isolators. The load cell is mounted on the actuator and the isolator is mounted on the mounting base. The DC conditioner shall compensate the moving load cell. This setup reduces actuator side load, bending moments on the load cell and fixturing mass attached to the load cell, and applies a more easily controlled preload. This method works up to about 15 Hz. The spherical bearings and links lower the amplitude of bending moments and side loads introduced to the actuator and load cell. The attachment to the load cell should be configured so that the dead load can be connected first and then the actuator can be attached to minimize misalignment.

10.4.2 TEST TWO SPECIMENS IN PARALLEL—Use the arrangement shown in Figure 5. Two duplicate isolators are tested at the same time. A constant compression deflection is maintained on the mountings to simulate the results of a compression loading while the mountings are being tested in the shear direction. Special attention should be paid to the fixture design to minimize the fixture mass effect. This setup is not suitable for two off-axis preloads test.

10.4.3 MANUAL TRANSLATION PLATFORM—A manual translation platform is mounted on the load cell and the test isolator is mounted on the platform. Figure 6 shows the setup. By adjusting the translation platform, an off-axis preload is applied on the specimen against a hydrostatic bearing actuator. The test system design should minimize inertia effects.

10.5 Fixture—The resonant frequency of the fixture should be high enough so that these resonances do not affect the dynamic property measurements of the isolators.

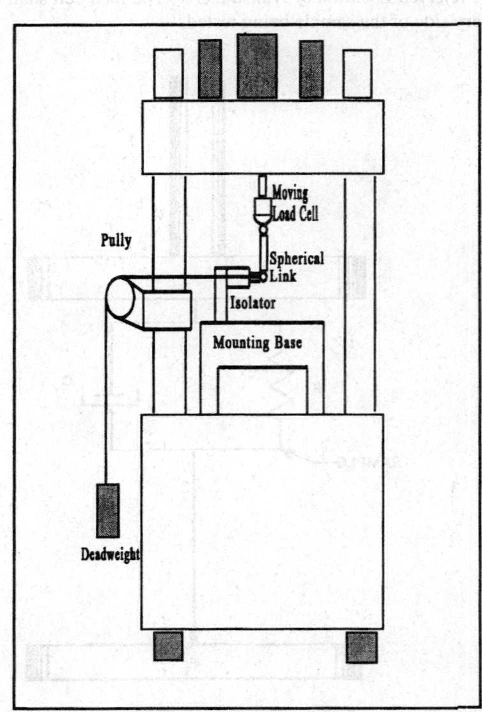

FIGURE 4—MOVING LOAD CELL

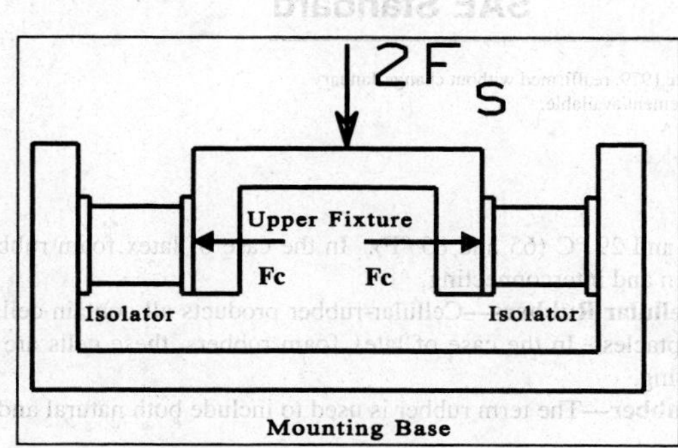

FIGURE 5—TWO ISOLATORS IN PARALLEL

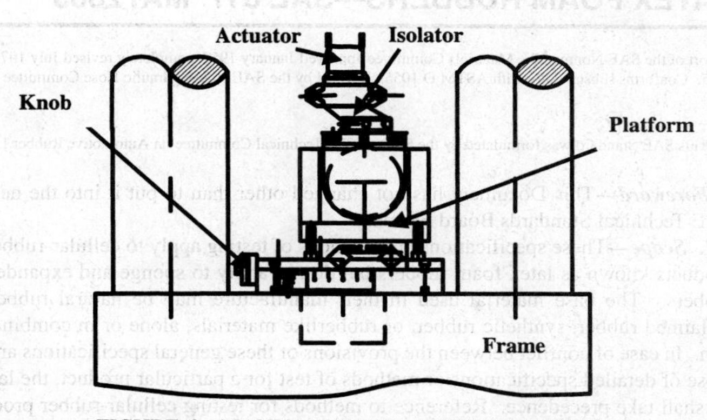

FIGURE 6—MANUAL TRANSLATION PLATFORM

APPENDIX A

A.1 The following information is presented for guidance in determining the amount of time required for rubber parts to substantially reach equilibrium with the desired test temperature.

Figure A1 shows the time required for the center of a rubber part to reach 90% of the desired temperature change under the following conditions:

a. Unrestricted free convection.
b. Thermal conductivity of the elastomer = 0.173 W/m °C (0.1 Btu/h-ft^2 °F/ft).
c. Thermal diffusivity of the elastomer = 0.00024 m^2/H (0.0026 ft^2/H)—a conservative value for most elastomer compositions.
d. Film coefficients = 13.3 W/m^2 °C (2.35 Btu/h-ft^2 °F) and ∞.

The curves apply to shapes approximating spheres, cylinders whose radii are less than 1/4 that of their lengths or slabs whose total thickness is less than 1/4 that of their length and width.

For example, for a 1.27 cm (0.5 in) radius sphere in still air, 35 min are required to reach at least 90% of the desired temperature change throughout; for a 2.54 cm (1 in) thick slab, 2 h are required. Times for actual specimens may be estimated by relating them to these basic shapes or by calculations using the information in References 2.1.2 and 2.1.3. Reference 2.1.3 also discusses the effect of metal plates in, or attached to, elastomeric shapes.

Extra time should be allowed if circulation around each part is restricted or if more precise part temperature control is required, as, for example, at low temperatures where dynamic response is most sensitive to temperature. Conditioning time may be shortened by forced convection, immersion in water baths, or other means suggested in Reference 2.1.2 RAPRA, Cooling Rubber Slabs. The curves for film coefficient equal to ∞ show the minimum times that can be achieved by such methods.

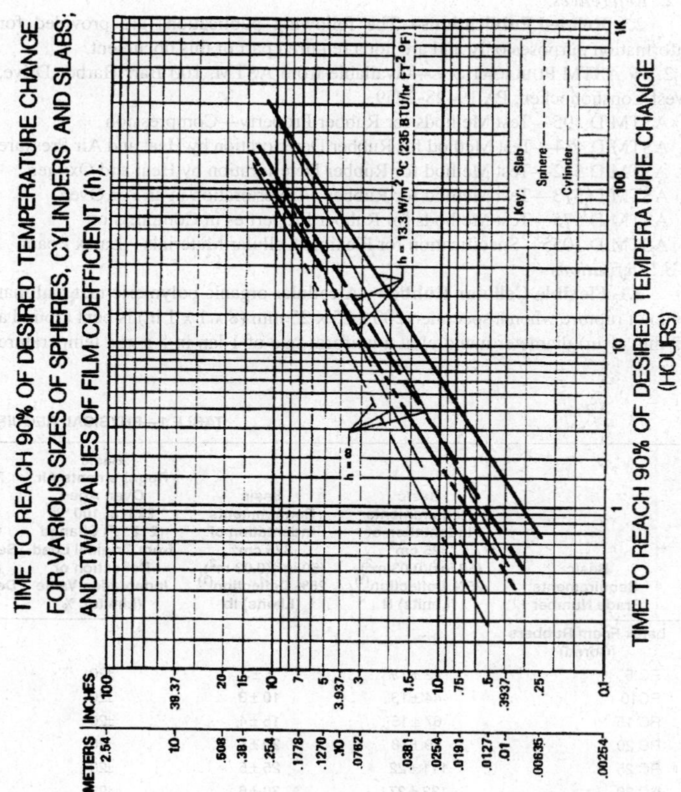

FIGURE A1—TIME TO REACH DESIRED TEMPERATURE CHANGE

LATEX FOAM RUBBERS—SAE J17 MAY2003 SAE Standard

Report of the SAE Nonmetallic Materials Committee approved January 1952, completely revised July 1979, editorial change October 1979, reaffirmed without change January 1985. Conforms substantially with ASTM D 1055. Revised by the SAE Non-Hydraulic Hose Committee May 2003. Rationale statement available.

[This SAE Standard was formulated by the SAE-ASTM Technical Committee on Automotive Rubber.]

Foreword—This Document has not changed other than to put it into the new SAE Technical Standards Board Format.

1. Scope—These specifications and methods of testing apply to cellular-rubber products known as latex foam rubbers but do not apply to sponge and expanded rubbers. The base material used in their manufacture may be natural rubber, reclaimed rubber, synthetic rubber, or rubberlike materials, alone or in combination. In case of conflict between the provisions of these general specifications and those of detailed specifications or methods of test for a particular product, the latter shall take precedence. Reference to methods for testing cellular-rubber products should specifically state the particular test or tests desired. The SAE Committee on Automotive Rubber Specifications has concluded, that in light of the fact that SAE J17 is a mirror image of ASTM D 1055, SAE J17 will be eliminated in the year 2005.

2. References

2.1 Related Publications—The following publications are provided for information purposes only and are not a required part of this document.

2.1.1 ASTM PUBLICATIONS—Available from ASTM, 100 Barr Harbor Drive, West Conshohocken, PA 19428-2959.

ASTM D 395—Test Methods for Rubber Property—Compression
ASTM D 454—Test Method for Rubber Deterioration by Heat and Air Pressure
ASTM D 572—Test Method for Rubber Deterioration by Heat and Oxygen
ASTM D 573—Test Method for Rubber—Deterioration in an Air Oven
ASTM D 575—Test Methods for Rubber Properties in Compression
ASTM D 1055—Specification for Flexible Cellular Materials—Latex Foam

3. Definitions

3.1 Flexible Cellular Rubber—A cellular organic polymeric material that will not rupture when a specimen 200 x 25 x 25 mm (8 x 1 x 1 in) is bent around a 25 mm (1 in) diameter mandrel at a uniform rate of 1 lap in 5 s at a temperature between 18 and 29 °C (65 and 85 °F). In the case of latex foam rubbers, these cells are open and interconnecting.

3.2 Cellular Rubbers—Cellular-rubber products all contain cells or small hollow receptacles. In the case of latex foam rubbers, these cells are open and interconnecting.

3.3 Rubber—The term rubber is used to include both natural and synthetic types.

3.4 Skin—The smooth surface of the latex foam rubber product, formed by contact with mold or cover plates, is defined as a natural skin.

4. Manufacture

4.1 Latex Foam Rubbers—The structure of latex foam rubbers consists of a network of open or interconnecting cells. Latex foam rubbers are made from rubber latices or liquid rubbers. They are manufactured in sheet, strip, molded, or specific shapes. Latex foam rubbers shall have a vulcanized cellular structure with a porous surface. The cells shall be interconnecting and of a uniform character. Latex form rubbers may be either cored or solid. Size, shape, and distribution of coring shall be at the producer's opinion but subject to the approval of the purchaser.

5. Grades of Latex Foam Rubbers—Latex foam rubbers shall have their grade numbers designated by two letters which identify the kind of latex foam rubber as follows:

RC—Latex foam rubbers, cored and
RU—Latex foam rubbers, uncored

Digits following the letters are used to indicate the degree of firmness, the softer grades being identified with the lower numbers and the firmer grades with the higher numbers (see Table 1).

Suffix letters may be added singly or in combination after any grade numbers to indicate additional requirements beyond those specified in Table 1 as basic requirements.

TABLE 1—PHYSICAL REQUIREMENT OF LATEX FOAM RUBBERS

Basic Requirements Grade Number	Basic Requirements Indentation of 325 cm^2 (50 in^2)(0.03 m^2), 25% Deflection(1) (Limits) N	Basic Requirements Indentation of 325 cm^2 (50 in^2)(0.03 m^2), 25% Deflection(1) (Limits) lb	Basic Requirements Air Oven Aged 22 h at 100 °C (212 °F) Change from Original Load Deflection or Indentation Value (Limits), %	Basic Requirements Constant Deflection Compression Set, 22 h at 70 °C (158 °F), 50% Deflections, max, %C_h(2)	Basic Requirements Constant Deflection Compression Set, 22 h at 70 °C (158°F), 50% Deflections, max, %C_d(2)	Requirements Added by Suffix Letters Suffix F Low Temperature Test, Change from Original Deflection, max, %	Requirements Added by Suffix Letters Suffix H Flexing Test Compression Set, max, % C_h(2)	Requirements Added by Suffix Letters Suffix H Flexing Test Compression Set, max, % C_d(2)
Latex Foam Rubbers (Cored)								
RC 5	22 ± 13	5 ± 3	±20	10	20	75	5	10
RC10	44 ± 13	10 ± 3	±20	10	20	75	5	10
RC 15	67 ± 18	15 ± 4	±20	10	20	75	5	10
RC 20	89 ± 18	20 ± 4	±20	10	20	75	5	10
RC 25	111 ± 22	25 ± 5	±20	10	20	75	5	10
RC 30	133 ± 27	30 ± 6	±20	10	20	75	5	10
RC 40	178 ± 31	40 ± 7	±20	10	20	75	5	10
RC 50	222 ± 36	50 ± 8	±20	10	20	75	5	10
RC 60	267 ± 40	60 ± 9	±20	10	20	75	5	10
RC 70	311 ± 53	70 ± 12	±20	10	20	75	5	10
RC 90	400 ± 62	90 ± 14	±20	10	20	75	5	10
Latex Foam Rubbers (Uncored)								
RU 11	49 ± 18	11 ± 4	±20	10	20	75	5	10
RU 20	89 ± 22	20 ± 5	±20	10	20	75	5	10
RU 35	156 ± 44	35 ± 10	±20	10	20	75	5	10
RU 55	245 ± 44	55 ± 10	±20	10	20	75	5	10
RU 80	356 ± 67	80 ± 15	±20	10	20	75	5	10
RU 150	667 ± 245	150 ± 55	±20	10	20	75	5	10

1. Rubber Manufacturers Association buyers' specification designation.
2. As defined in section on compression set.

The significance of the approved suffix letters are shown as follows. The test methods and values must be arranged by agreement between the purchaser and supplier.

C Weather Resistance.
D Load Deflection.
E Oil Resistance. Note that there are no requirements for oil resistance in these specifications.
F1 Low temperature at -40 °C (-40 °F). Required with values as specified in Table 1.
F2 Low Temperature at -55 °C (-67 °F).
G Tear Resistance.
H Flexing Resistance. Test required with values as specified in Table 1.
J Abrasion Resistance.
K1 Adhesion to Metal—Bond made during vulcanization.
K2[1] Adhesion—Cemented bond made after vulcanization.
L Water Resistance.
M Flammability Resistance.
N Impact Resistance.
P Staining Test Required.
R Resilience.
Z Optional Requirements.

Example—Grade RC20 F1H denotes soft, cored latex foam rubber made from natural, reclaimed synthetic, or a blend with a load deflection value of 89 N ± 18 N (20 lb ±4 lb) and requiring, in addition to the basic tests, a low temperature test at -40 °C (-40 °F) and a flexing test.

6. Material and Workmanship—Latex foam rubbers furnished under these specifications shall be manufactured from natural rubber, synthetic rubber, or rubberlike materials together with added compounding ingredients of such nature and quality that the finished product complies with the specification requirements. In permitting choice in use of those materials by the producer it is not intended to imply that the different rubber materials are equivalent in respect to all physical properties. Any special characteristics other than those prescribed in these specifications which may be desired for specific applications shall be specified in the product specifications as they may influence the choice of the type of rubber materials or other ingredients used. All materials and workmanship shall be in accordance with good commercial practice and the resulting cellular rubber shall be free from defects affecting serviceability.

Because of manufacturing conditions, material may have to be altered or repaired. This repaired or altered material will be acceptable under these specifications provided the material used in such repairs or alterations shall be of the same composition and quality as the original product and provided such alterations do not affect the serviceability, size, and shape beyond tolerances as provided herein.

7. Color—Unless otherwise specified, the color of latex foam rubbers shall be optional with the manufacturer.

8. Physical Properties—The various grades of latex foam rubber shall conform to the requirements as to physical properties prescribed in Table 1, together with any additional requirements indicated. When subjected to the static fatigue test, the latex foam specimen shall show no cracking at the folded edge.

9. Methods of Testing—Unless specifically stated otherwise, all tests shall be made in accordance with the methods specified for the following:

9.1 Basic Tests

9.1.1 Accelerated Aging Tests.
9.1.2 Compression Set Under Constant Deflection.
9.1.3 Indentation Test.

9.2 Suffix Tests

9.2.1 H—Flexing Test.
9.2.2 F—Low Temperature Test.

10. Tolerances on Dimensions—Tolerances on dimensions of latex-foam-rubber products are given in the Appendix, Table 2 and Table 3. These tolerances are published as information for guidance only and shall not be considered as a part of these specifications.

1. Suffix K2 denotes that the finished vulcanized part will be adhered to a rigid surface sometime after vulcanization and that all surface imperfections and/or the use of materials which might be on or bloom to the surface and be detrimental to obtaining good bonds must be avoided.

TABLE 2—TOLERANCES ON DIMENSIONS OF LATEX FOAM RUBBER PRODUCTS FOR GENERAL APPLICATIONS

Type	Dimension	Tolerance Plus	Tolerance Minus	Dimension	Tolerance Plus	Tolerance Minus
Thickness, mm						
Cored	0 to 76, incl.	3	2	0 to 3, incl.	1/8	1/16
	76 to 127, incl.	5	3	3 to 5, incl.	3/16	1/8
	127 and over	6	5	5 and over	1/4	3/16
Uncored	Up to and including 12.7	2	2	Up to and including 1/2	1/16	1/16
	From 12.7 to 25.4, incl.	3	2	From 1/2 to 1, incl.	1/8	1/16
	Over 25.4	3	5	Over 1	1/8	3/16
Length and Width, mm						
Cored	0 to 152, incl.	5	2	0 to 6, incl.	3/16	1/16
	152 to 305, incl.	10	3	6 to 12 incl.	3/8	1/8
	305 to 610, incl.	13	6	12 to 24, incl.	1/2	1/4
	610 to 914, incl.	16	10	24 to 36, incl.	5/8	3/8
	914 to 1219, incl.	19	13	36 to 48, incl.	3/4	1/2
	1219 to 1524, incl.	22	16	48 to 60, incl.	7/8	5/8
	1524 to 1829, incl.	25	19	60 to 72, incl.	1	3/4
	1829 and over	29	22	72 and over	1-1/8	7/8
Uncored	0 to 152, incl.	8	2	0 to 6, incl.	5/16	1/16
	152 to 305, incl.	13	3	6 to 12, incl.	1/2	1/8
	305 to 610, incl.	18	6	12 to 24, incl.	11/16	1/4
	610 to 914, incl.	22	10	24 to 36, incl.	7/8	3/8
	914 to 1219, incl.	29	13	36 to 48, incl.	1-1/16	1/2
	1219 to 1524, incl.	35	16	48 to 60, incl.	1-1/4	5/8
	1524 to 1829, incl.	38	19	60 to 72, incl.	1-3/8	3/4
	1829 and over	41	22	72 and over	1-1/2	7/8

TABLE 3—TOLERANCES FOR SPECIAL APPLICATIONS OF LATEX FOAM RUBBERS, SUCH AS AUTOMOTIVE TOPPER PADS, SPRING COVERINGS, ETC.

Type	Dimension	Tolerance Plus	Tolerance Minus	Dimension	Tolerance Plus	Tolerance Minus
Thickness, mm						
Cored	0 to 76, incl.	5	2	0 to 3, incl.	3/16	1/16
	76 to 127, incl.	6	3	3 to 5, incl.	1/4	1/8
	127 and over	8	5	5 and over	5/16	3/16
Uncored	Up to and including 12.7	2	2	Up to and including 1/2	1/16	1/16
	From 12.7 to 25.4, incl.	3	2	From 1/2 to 1, incl.	1/8	1/16
	Over 25.4	3	3	Over 1	1/8	1/8
Length and Width, mm						
Cored	0 to 152, incl.	8	2	0 to 6, incl.	5/16	1/16
and	152 to 305, incl.	13	3	6 to 12 incl.	1/2	1/8
Uncored	305 to 610, incl.	18	6	12 to 24, incl.	11/16	1/4
	610 to 914, incl.	22	10	24 to 36, incl.	7/8	3/8
	914 to 1219, incl.	29	13	36 to 48, incl.	1-1/8	1/2
	1219 to 1524, incl.	35	16	48 to 60, incl.	1-3/8	5/8
	1524 to 1829, incl.	38	19	60 to 72, incl.	1-1/2	3/4
	1829 and over	41	22	72 and over	1-5/8	7/8

11. Packaging and Marketing—The material shall be properly and adequately packaged. Each package or container shall be legibly marked with the name of the material, name or trademark of the manufacturer, and any required purchaser's designations.

12. Inspection and Rejection—All tests and inspection shall be made at the place of manufacture prior to shipment, unless otherwise specified. The manufacturer shall afford the inspector all reasonable facilities for tests and inspection.

The purchaser may make the tests and inspection to govern acceptance or rejection of the material at any chosen laboratory.

All samples for testing, provided as specified in Section 14, Sampling, shall be visually inspected to determine compliance with the material, workmanship, and color requirements.

Any material which fails in one or more of the test requirements may be retested. For this purpose, two additional tests shall be made for the requirement in which failure occurred. Failure of either of the retests shall be cause for final rejection.

Rejected material shall be disposed of as directed by the manufacturer.

13. General Methods—Except as otherwise specified in the methods of testing latex foam rubbers given in ASTM D 1055, the following methods of test of the American Society for Testing and Materials, applicable in general to vulcanized rubber, shall be complied with as required and hereby made a part of these test methods.

13.1 Aging Test—See ASTM D 572, ASTM D 573, and ASTM D 454.

13.2 Compression Set, Suffix B—See ASTM D 395.

13.3 Low Temperature Test, Suffix F1 and F2—See method described in ASTM D 1055.

13.4 Compression—Deflection—See ASTM D 575, ASTM D 1055, and the Indentation Test in this SAE Standard. In case of conflict between provisions of the above methods and the procedures herein specifically described for latex foam rubbers, the latter shall take precedence. In case of conflict between the procedure herein described for latex foam rubbers and the methods of a particular specification or for a particular latex-foam-rubber product, the latter shall take precedence.

14. Sampling—When possible, the completed manufactured product shall be used for the tests specified. Representative samples of the lot being examined shall be selected at random as required.

When it is necessary or advisable to obtain test specimens from the article, as in those cases where the entire sample is not required or adaptable for testing, the method of cutting and the exact position from which specimens are to be taken shall be specified. The apparent density and the state of cure may vary in different parts of the finished product, more especially if the article is of complicated shape or of varying thickness, and these factors affect the physical properties of the specimens. Also, the apparent density is affected by the number of cut surfaces as opposed to the number of skin-covered surfaces on the test specimen.

When the finished product does not lend itself to testing or to the taking of test specimens because of complicated shape or other reasons, manufacturer and purchaser shall agree on the preparation of a suitable test specimen. When differences due to the difficulty in obtaining suitable test specimens from the finished part arise, manufacturer and purchaser may agree on acceptable deviations. This can be done by comparing results of standard test specimens and those obtained on actual parts.

15. Measurement of Test Specimens—Test specimens are to be measured in accordance with ASTM D 1055.

16. Accelerated Aging Tests

16.1 Test Specimens—The test specimen used in any of the aging tests shall be that required by the latex-foam-rubber methods for the particular determination which is to be employed for measuring the effect of the aging exposure.

16.2 Procedure—Either the oxygen-pressure-chamber aging test as described in ASTM D 572, the air-oven aging test as described in ASTM D 573, or the air-pressure heat test as described in ASTM D 454, respectively, may be used for latex foam rubbers as specified, except that in the air-pressure heat test, an air pressure of 415 kPa ± 15 kPa (60 psig ± 2 psig) shall be used in place of the 550 kPa ± 15 kPa (80 psig ± 2 psig) prescribed in ASTM D 454. Deterioration may be expressed as a percent change of compression-deflection values, or the results may be determined by visual observation. No relation between accelerated aging tests and natural aging is given or implied.

17. Compression Set Under Constant Deflection (Calculation Based on Amount of Deflection)

17.1 Test Specimens—The specimens for this test shall have parallel top and bottom surfaces. A cylinder 209 mm (1.129 in) in diameter shall be suitable for slab or uncored stock. Cored stock specimens may be round or rectangular. The minimum dimension on the top and bottom surfaces must be greater than the height of the sample and the surface shall have a minimum area of 0.01 m^2 (16 in^2). The thickness of the test specimen may vary, but shall not be less than 19 mm (0.75 in) for slab or uncored stock. The thickness shall be measured and stated in the report.

17.2 Procedure—The apparatus and procedure shall be the same as prescribed in Method B of ASTM D 395, except as follows: Test specimens shall be compressed 50% of their original thickness. The load shall be released at the end of the test period and the thickness measured after 30 min rest at room temperature. Thickness measurements shall be made as described in Section 5, Measurement of Test Specimens. The temperature of the test shall be 70 °C ± 2 °C (158 °F ± 3.6 °F). The time of the test shall be as specified. Chromium-plated metal plates are not required. Aluminum plates, or any stiff plates that are clean and smooth and that will not deflect measurably under load necessary for deflection of the specimen, may be used.

17.3 Calculations—Calculate the constant deflection compression set, expressed as a percentage of the original height as follows:

$$C_h = \frac{t_0 - t_1}{t_0} \times 100 \qquad \text{(Eq. 1)}$$

where:

C_h = compression set expressed as a percentage of the original height
t_o = original height of test specimen
t_1 = height of test specimen 30 min + 10 or −0 min after removal from the apparatus

Calculate the constant deflection compression set, expressed as a percentage of the original deflection as follows:

$$C_d = \frac{t_0 - t_1}{t_0 - t_s} \times 100 \qquad \text{(Eq. 2)}$$

where:

C_d = compression set expressed as a percentage of the original deflection
t_o = original height of test specimen
t_s = height of spacer bar used
t_l = height of test specimen 30 min + 10 or -0 min after removal from apparatus

18. Indentation Test

18.1 Scope—This test consists of measuring the load necessary to produce a 25% indentation in the latex-foam-rubber product.

18.2 Apparatus—An apparatus having a flat circular indentor foot 0.03 m^2 (50 in^2) in area, connected to a force measuring device by means of a ball-and-socket joint, and mounted in such a manner that the product or specimen can be deflected at a rate of 0.2 to 10 mm/s (0.5 to 25.0 in/min) shall be used for this test. A maximum radius of 2 mm (0.07874 in) is allowable on the edge of the indentor foot. The apparatus shall be arranged to support the specimen on a level horizontal plate which is perforated with 6 mm (0.25 in) holes on 20 mm (0.75 in) centers to allow for rapid escape of air during the test.

NOTE—When testing products with parallel top and bottom surfaces, the ball-and-socket joint is not required.

18.3 Test Specimens—The test specimen shall consist of the entire product sample or a suitable portion of it, except that in no case shall the surface for indentation have dimensions less than 300 x 300 mm (12 x 12 in). The full thickness of the product shall be used.

18.4 Procedure—The procedure for indentation test should be made in accordance with ASTM D 1055. In cases of dispute, the compression readings shall be performed at a temperature of 23 °C ± 1.1 °C (73.4 °F ± 2 °F) and in an atmosphere having a relative humidity of 50 ± 2%. The product shall be conditioned undeflected and undistorted at this temperature and humidity for at least 12 h before being tested. Ordinarily only one test will be made, but in case of dispute the result shall be expressed as the average of a minimum of three tests.

19. Flexing Test (Suffix H)

19.1 Scope—The flexing test consists of subjecting the test specimen to repeated compression and noting the effect on the cellular structure.

19.2 Test Specimens—The test specimen shall consist of the entire product sample or a suitable portion of it as agreed upon by manufacturer and purchaser. The full thickness of the product shall be used.

19.3 Procedure—Flexing test shall be made in accordance with ASTM D 1055.

20. Low-Temperature Test (Suffix F1, 40 °C (-40 °F); Suffix F2, 55 °C (-67 °F))

20.1 Apparatus—The apparatus shall consist of two parallel plates at least 38 mm (1.5 in) in diameter, one of which is movable and the other one stationary, a means of applying a load and a means of accurately measuring the distance between the parallel plates.

20.2 Test Specimens—Cylinders 29 mm (1.129 in) in diameter shall be used for this test. The minimum thickness shall be 19 mm (0.75 in). They shall be dried in a desiccator for not less than 16 h before testing. The thickness shall be measured and recorded.

20.3 Procedure—The compression deflection of the specimen shall first be measured at room temperature and the load in N/m^2 (psi) necessary to obtain a 25% deflection recorded. The specimen shall then be placed in the cold box for 5 h at the specified temperature, at the end of which time the previously determined load shall be applied as rapidly as possible while the specimens are still in the cold box and the deflection recorded 30 s later.

20.4 Calculation—The percent change in deflection shall be calculated as follows:

$$C = \frac{D - E}{D} \times 100 \qquad \text{(Eq. 3)}$$

where:

C = % change in deflection
D = deflection at room temperature
E = deflection at temperature of test

21. Static Fatigue Test

21.1 Procedure

21.1.1 SLAB STOCK—Bend a specimen of latex foam 100 x 230 mm (4 x 9 in) parallel to the 100 mm (4 in) dimension to an angle of 180 degrees between two compression plates and place in a Geer oven at 70 °C ± 2 °C (158 °F ± 3.6 °F) for 22 h. The opening between the two plates should be equal to twice the thickness of the unfolded specimen. The folded edge of the specimen should not extend beyond the edge of the compression plates.

21.1.2 CORED STOCK—Test the specimen of cored stock as above except that the specimen shall be 100 mm (4 in) wide and the length shall be approximately three times the thickness. Fold out the skin side, if present for testing.

APPENDIX A

A.1 Tolerances on Dimensions of Latex-Foam-Rubber Products

The tolerances on dimensions of latex-foam-rubber products shown in Tables 2 and 3 are for guidance only and shall not be considered as part of these specifications.

SPONGE AND EXPANDED CELLULAR RUBBER PRODUCTS[1]—SAE J18 APR2002

SAE Recommended Practice

Report of the SAE Nonmetallic Materials Committee approved January 1992. Completely revised by the SAE Committee on Automotive Rubber Specifications August 1988, and revised July 1992. Completely revised by the SAE Committee on Automotive Rubber Specifications December 2000 and revised April 2002. ISO 6916-1 is similar to this document. Rationale statement available.

1. Scope

1.1 The SAE Committee on Automotive Rubber Specifications has concluded, that in light of the fact that SAE J18 is a mirror image of ASTM D 1056 (Vol. 8.01), SAE J18 will be eliminated in the year 2005.

1.2 This SAE Recommended Practice covers flexible cellular rubber products known as sponge rubber and expanded rubber, but does not apply to latex foam rubber or ebonite cellular rubber. The base material for an open/closed cellular product may be made of synthetic, natural, reclaimed rubber, or a mixture, and may contain other polymers or chemicals, or both, which may be modified by organic or inorganic additives. These elastomeric materials have properties similar to those of vulcanized rubber, namely (a) the ability to be converted from a thermoplastic to a thermosetting state by crosslinking (vulcanization) and or (b) substantial recovery of their original shapes when strained or elongated, or both.

1.3 Extruded or molded shapes of sizes too small for cutting standard test specimens are difficult to classify or test by these methods and will usually require special testing procedures.

1.4 In case of conflict between the provisions of this general specification and those of detailed specifications or test methods for a particular product, the latter shall take precedence. Reference to the test methods in this document should specifically state the particular test or tests desired.

1.5 The values stated in SI units are to be regarded as the standard. English units are included for reference only.

1.6 The following safety hazards caveat pertains only to the test methods portions of this document: *This document does not purport to address all of the safety concerns, if any, associated with its use. It is the responsibility of the user of this document to establish appropriate safety and health practices and determine the applicability of regulatory limitations prior to use.*

NOTE—ASTM D 1056-98 and ISO 6916-1 are similar to this document.

2. References

2.1 Applicable Publications—The following publications form a part of this specification to the extent specified herein.

2.1.1 ASTM PUBLICATIONS—Available from ASTM, 100 Barr Harbor Drive, West Conshohocken, PA 19428-2959.

ASTM D 395—Test Methods for Rubber Property—Compression Set[2]

ASTM D 471—Test Method for Rubber Property—Effect of Liquids[2]

ASTM D 573—Test Method for Rubber—Deterioration in an Air Oven[2]

ASTM D 575—Test Methods for Rubber Properties in Compression[2]

ASTM D 832—Practice for Rubber Conditioning for Low-Temperature Testing[2]

ASTM D 1056—Specification for Flexible Cellular Materials—Sponge or Expanded Rubber[3]

ASTM D 1171—Test Method for Rubber Deterioration—Surface Ozone Cracking Outdoors or Chamber (Triangular Specimens)[2]

ASTM D 3182—Practice for Rubber—Materials, Equipment, and Procedures for Mixing Standard Compounds and Preparing Standard Vulcanized Sheets[2]

ASTM D 3183—Practice for Rubber—Preparation of Pieces for Test Purposes from Products[2]

2.1.2 ISO PUBLICATION—Available from ANSI, 11 West 42nd Street, New York, NY 10036-8002.

ISO 6916-1—Flexible Cellular Polymeric Materials; Sponge and Expanded Cellular Rubber Products—Specification Part 1 Sheet

3. Definitions—Definitions of Terms Specific to this Document.

3.1 Cellular Material—A generic term for materials containing many cells (either open, closed, or both) dispersed throughout the mass.

3.2 Closed Cell—A product whose cells are totally enclosed by its walls and hence not interconnecting with other cells.

3.3 Expanded Rubber—Cellular rubber having closed cells made from a solid rubber compound.

3.4 Flexible Cellular Material—A flexible cellular organic polymeric material will not rupture within 60 s when a specimen 200 x 25 x 25 mm (8 x 1 x 1 in) is bent around a 25 mm (1 in) diameter mandrel at a uniform rate of one lap/5 s in the form of a helix at a temperature between 18 and 29 °C (65 and 85 °F).

3.5 Open Cell—A product whose cells are not totally enclosed by its walls and open to the surface, either directly or by interconnecting with other cells.

3.6 Rubber—A material that is capable of recovering from large deformations quickly and forcibly, and can be, or already is, modified to a state in which it is essentially insoluble (but can swell) in boiling solvent, such as benzene, methyl ethyl ketone, and ethanol-toluene azeotrope.

3.6.1 DISCUSSION—A rubber in its modified state, free of diluents, retracts within 1 min to less than 1.5 times its original length after being stretched at room temperature, 20 to 27 °C (68 °F ± 81 °F) to twice its length and held for 1 min before release.

3.7 Skin—The textured outer surface on the material formed during manufacture by contact with molds, cover plate, air, or other curing medium.

3.7.1 DISCUSSION—Normally, this skin is formed by contact with the mold or cover plates during manufacture. Molded open-cell (sponge) parts usually have a skin on all surfaces, except when cut to length from longer strips. Parts made by cutting from open-cell (sponge) sheets usually have skin on two faces and open cells at the cut edges. Closed-cell (expanded) rubber sheets are frequently split from thicker pieces and consequently do not have the skin faces. On some products, it is desirable to add a solid rubber skin coating. The use to which the cellular rubber product is to be put determines the thickness of added skin required. Products subject to abrasion or open-cell (sponge) rubber that must withstand absorption of water or transmission of gases will ordinarily require an applied skin coating. Closed-cell (expanded) rubber does not usually require an added skin for these reasons.

3.8 Sponge Rubber—Cellular rubber consisting predominantly of open cells made from a solid rubber compound.

4. Classification (Types, Classes, Grades, and Suffix Letters)

4.1 Types—These specifications cover two types of cellular rubber designated by the prefix numbers 1 and 2.

4.1.1 TYPE 1—Open cell rubber.

4.1.2 TYPE 2—Closed cell rubber.

4.2 Classes—Both types are divided into four classes designated by the letters A, B, C, and D added to the number prefix.

4.2.1 CLASS A—Cellular rubber made from synthetic rubber, natural rubber, reclaimed rubber, or rubber-like materials, alone or in combination where specific resistance to the action of petroleum base oils is not required.

4.2.2 CLASS B—Cellular rubber made from synthetic rubber or rubber-like materials alone or in combination, having specific requirements for oil resistance with low mass change.

4.2.3 CLASS C—Cellular rubber made from synthetic rubber or rubber-like materials alone or in combination, having specific requirements for oil resistance with medium mass change.

4.2.4 CLASS D—Cellular rubbers made from synthetic rubber or rubber-like materials alone or in combination having specific requirements for extreme temperature resistance ranging from –75 to 175 °C (–103 to 347 °F); but specific resistance to the action of petroleum-base oils is not required.

NOTE—ASTM Oil No. 3 is no longer available (as of December 1993). It has been replaced by IRM 903[4], which does not necessarily produce the same degree of swelling as ASTM #3 Oil. Comparison of the effect of IRM 903 versus ASTM Oil No. 3, on most elastomers tested, produces a close correlation.

2. Annual book of ASTM Standards, Vol 09.01.

3. Annual Book of ASTM Standards, Vol 08.01.

4. Available from R. E. Carroll, P. O. Box 139, Trenton, NJ 08801

1. This specification is under the jurisdiction of ASTM Committee D-20 on Plastics and is the direct responsibility of Subcommittee D20.22 on Flexible Cellular Materials.

Current edition approved May 10 and June 10, 1997 and April 10, 1998. Published May 1998. Originally published as D 1056-49 T. Last previous edition D 1056-98.

4.3 Grades—Each type and class has been divided into a number of different grades. Each grade is based on a specific range of firmness as expressed by compression-deflection (see Section 17). Grades are designated by digit, the softer grades being identified with the lower numbers and the higher grades being identified with the higher numbers.

4.3.1 GRADE 0—For Types 1 and 2 cellular rubber, a compression-deflection range from 0 to 15 kPa (0 to 2 psi).

4.3.2 GRADE 1—For Types 1 and 2 cellular rubber, a compression-deflection range from 15 to 35 kPa (2 to 5 psi).

4.3.3 GRADE 2—For Types 1 and 2 cellular rubber, a compression-deflection range from 35 to 65 kPa (5 to 9 psi).

4.3.4 GRADE 3—For Types 1 and 2 cellular rubber, a compression-deflection range from 65 to 90 kPa (9 to 13 psi).

4.3.5 GRADE 4—For Types 1 and 2 cellular rubber, a compression-deflection range from 90 to 120 kPa (13 to 17 psi).

4.3.6 GRADE 5—For Types 1 and 2 cellular rubber, a compression-deflection range from 120 to 170 kPa (17 to 25 psi).

5. Materials and Manufacture

5.1 Sponge Rubber—Sponge rubber is made by incorporating into the compound a blowing agent, such as sodium bicarbonate, that gives off a gas which expands the mass during the vulcanization process. Sponge rubber is manufactured in sheet, strip, molded, or special shapes. Unless otherwise specified, sheet and strip sponge rubber shall have a natural skin on both the top and bottom surfaces. Fabric surface impressions are ordinarily not objectionable. The coarseness of the impressions shall be agreed upon by the parties concerned.

5.2 Expanded Rubber—Closed-cell rubbers are made by incorporating gas-forming ingredients in the rubber compound, or by subjecting the compound to high-pressure gas such as nitrogen. Expanded rubber is manufactured in sheet, strip, molded, tube, cord, and profile shapes by molding or extruding. Unless otherwise specified, the presence of skin on the top or bottom surfaces of sheet and strip expanded rubber shall be optional. Extruded shapes have skin on all surfaces except cut ends.

6. Physical Properties

6.1 The various grades of cellular rubber shall conform to the physical property requirements listed in Tables 1 and 2, together with any additional requirements indicated by suffix letters in the grade designations as described in Section 4 and Table 3.

7. Tolerances on Dimensions

7.1 Tolerances on dimensions of cellular rubber products shall be as specified in Table 4.

8. Color

8.1 Unless otherwise specified, the color of cellular rubber shall be black.

TABLE 1A—PHYSICAL REQUIREMENTS OF CELLULAR RUBBERS, TYPE 1, OPEN-CELL SPONGE—BASIC REQUIREMENTS

Grade Number	Compression Deflection, 25% Deflection (Limits), kPa (psi)[1]	Compression Deflection after Oven Aging, % Change from Original 168 h at 70 °C (158 °F)	Compression Deflection after Oven Aging, % Change from Original 22 h at 150 °C (302 °F)	Oil-Aged 22 h at 70 °C (158 °F), Change in Volume in IRM 903 (Limits), %	Compression Set, 50% Deflection, max %, 22 h at 70 °C (158 °F)	Compression Set, 50% Deflection, max %, 22 h at 100 °C (212 °F)	Low-Temperature Flex, 5 h at −55 °C (−67 °F)
Class A, Non-Oil Resistant							
1A0	less than 15 (2)	±20[2]	—	—	15	—	—
1A1	15 to 35 (2 to 5)	±20	—	—	15	—	—
1A2	35 to 65 (5 to 9)	±20	—	—	15	—	—
1A3	65 to 90 (9 to 13)	±20	—	—	15	—	—
1A4	90 to 120 (13 to 17)	±20	—	—	15	—	—
1A5	120 to 170 (17 to 25)	±20	—	—	15	—	—
Class B, Oil-Resistant, Low Mass Change[3]							
1B0	less than 15 (2)	±20[2]	—	-25 to 10	40	—	—
1B1	15 to 35 (2 to 5)	±20	—	-25 to 10	40	—	—
1B2	35 to 65 (5 to 9)	±20	—	-25 to 10	40	—	—
1B3	65 to 90 (9 to 13)	±20	—	-25 to 10	40	—	—
1B4	90 to 120 (13 to 17)	±20	—	-25 to 10	40	—	—
1B5	120 to 170 (17 to 25)	±20	—	-25 to 10	40	—	—
Class C, Oil-Resistant, Medium Swell[3]							
1C0	less than 15 (2)	±20[2]	—	+ 10 to 60	50	—	—
1C1	15 to 35 (2 to 5)	±20	—	+ 10 to 60	50	—	—
1C2	35 to 65 (5 to 9)	±20	—	+ 10 to 60	50	—	—
1C3	65 to 90 (9 to 13)	±20	—	+ 10 to 60	50	—	—
1C4	90 to 120 (13 to 17)	±20	—	+ 10 to 60	50	—	—
1C5	120 to 170 (17 to 25)	±20	—	+ 10 to 60	50	—	—
Class D, High-Temperature-Resistant							
1D0	less than 15 (2)	—	±5	—	—	—	pass
1D1	15 to 35 (2 to 5)	—	±5	—	—	50	pass
1D2	35 to 65 (5 to 9)	—	±5	—	—	30	pass
1D3	65 to 90 (9 to 13)	—	±5	—	—	30	pass
1D4	90 to 120 (13 to 17)	—	±5	—	—	30	pass
1D5	120 to 170 (17 to 25)	—	±5	—	—	30	pass

1. Compression deflection ranges modified to agree with ASTM D 1056-98.
2. If this grade after aging still falls within the compression-deflection requirement of <15 kPa (2 psi), it shall be considered acceptable even though the change from the original is greater than ±20%.
3. Terminology was changed in 1997 from low swell to low mass change to better reflect the data obtained.

TABLE 1B—PHYSICAL REQUIREMENTS OF CELLULAR RUBBERS, TYPE 1, OPEN-CELL SPONGE—Requirements added by Suffix Letters

Grade Number	Compression Deflection, 25% Deflection (Limits), kPa (psi)(1)	A4 Compression Deflection after Oven Aging, % Change From Original, 22 h at 175 °C (347 °F)	B1 Compression Set, 50% Deflection max %, 22 h at 70 °C (158 °F)	F1 Low-Temperature Flex 5 h at −40 °C (−40 °F)	F2 Low-Temperature Flex 5 h at −55 °C (−67 °F)	F3 Low-Temperature Flex 5 h at −75 °C (−103 °F)
Class A, Non-Oil Resistant						
1A0	less than 15 (2)	—	—	pass	pass	—
1A1	15 to 35 (2 to 5)	—	—	pass	pass	—
1A2	35 to 65 (5 to 9)	—	—	pass	pass	—
1A3	65 to 90 (9 to 13)	—	—	pass	pass	—
1A4	90 to 120 (13 to 17)	—	—	pass	pass	—
1A5	120 to 170 (17 to 35)	—	—	pass	pass	—
Class B, Oil-Resistant, Low Mass Change(2)						
1B0	less than 15 (2)	—	—	pass	—	—
1B1	15 to 35 (2 to 5)	—	—	pass	—	—
1B2	35 to 65 (5 to 9)	—	—	pass	—	—
1B3	65 to 90 (9 to 13)	—	—	pass	—	—
1B4	90 to 120 (13 to 17)	—	—	pass	—	—
1B5	120 to 170 (17 to 35)	—	—	pass	—	—
Class C, Oil-Resistant, Medium Mass Change(2)						
1C0	less than 15 (2)	—	25	pass	—	—
1C1	15 to 35 (2 to 5)	—	25	pass	—	—
1C2	35 to 65 (5 to 9)	—	25	pass	—	—
1C3	65 to 90 (9 to 13)	—	25	pass	—	—
1C4	90 to 120 (13 to 17)	—	25	pass	—	—
1C5	120 to 170 (17 to 35)	—	25	pass	—	—
Class D, High-Temperature-Resistant						
1D0	less than 15 (2)	±25	—	pass	—	pass
1D1	15 to 35 (2 to 5)	±25	—	pass	—	pass
1D2	35 to 65 (5 to 9)	±25	—	pass	—	pass
1D3	65 to 90 (9 to 13)	±25	—	pass	—	pass
1D4	90 to 120 (13 to 17)	±25	—	pass	—	pass
1D5	120 to 170 (17 to 35)	±25	—	pass	—	pass

1. Compression deflection ranges modified to agree with ASTM D 1056-98.
2. Terminology was changed in 1997 from low swell to low mass change to better reflect the data obtained.

TABLE 2A—PHYSICAL REQUIREMENTS OF CELLULAR RUBBERS, TYPE 2, CLOSED-CELL EXPANDED—BASIC REQUIREMENTS

Grade Number	Compression Deflection 25% Deflection (Limits) kPa (psi)(1)	Oven-Aged, % Change from Original Compression Deflection Values (Limits), 168 h at 70 °C (158 °F)	Oven-Aged, % Change from Original Compression Deflection Values (Limits), 22 h at 150 °C (302 °F)	Water Absorption, max weight % Density over 160 kg/m^3 (10 lb/ft^3)	Water Absorption, max weight % Density of 160 kg/m^3 (10 lb/ft^3) or less	Fluid Immersion, 7 Days at 23 °C (73.4 °F), max weight %(2) Density over 160 kg/m^3 (10 lb/ft^3)	Fluid Immersion, 7 Days at 23 °C (73.4 °F), max weight %(2) Density 160 kg/m^3 (10 lb/ft^3) or less
Class A, Non-Oil Resistant							
2A0	Less than 15 (2)	±30	—	5	10	—	—
2A1	15 to 35 (2 to 5)	±30	—	5	10	—	—
2A2	35 to 65 (5 to 9)	±30	—	5	10	—	—
2A3	65 to 90 (9 to 13)	±30	—	5	10	—	—
2A4	90 to 120 (13 to 17)	±30	—	5	10	—	—
2A5	120 to 170 (17 to 25)	±30	—	5	10	—	—
Class B, Oil Resistant, Fuel-Resistant, Low Mass Change(3)							
2B0	Less than 15 (2)	±30	—	5	10	50	100
2B1	15 to 35 (2 to 5)	±30	—	5	10	50	100
2B2	35 to 65 (5 to 9)	±30	—	5	10	50	100
2B3	65 to 90 (9 to 13)	±30	—	5	10	50	100
2B4	90 to 120 (13 to 17)	±30	—	5	10	50	100
Class D, High-Temperature-Resistant							
2D0	Less than 15 (2)	—	±5	5	10	—	—
2D1	15 to 35 (2 to 5)	—	±5	5	10	—	—
2D2	35 to 65 (5 to 9)	—	±5	5	10	—	—
2D3	65 to 90 (9 to 13)	—	±5	5	10	—	—
2D4	90 to 120 (13 to 17)	—	±5	5	10	—	—
2D5	120 to 170 (17 to 25)	—	±5	5	10	—	—

TABLE 2A—PHYSICAL REQUIREMENTS OF CELLULAR RUBBERS, TYPE 2, CLOSED-CELL EXPANDED—BASIC REQUIREMENTS (continued)

Grade Number	Compression Deflection 25% Deflection (Limits) kPa (psi)[1]	Oven-Aged, % Change from Original Compression Deflection Values (Limits), 168 h at 70 °C (158 °F)	Oven-Aged, % Change from Original Compression Deflection Values (Limits), 22 h at 150 °C (302 °F)	Water Absorption, max weight % Density over 160 kg/m³ (10 lb/ft³)	Water Absorption, max weight % Density of 160 kg/m³ (10 lb/ft³) or less	Fluid Immersion, 7 Days at 23 °C (73.4 °F), max weight %[2] Density over 160 kg/m³ (10 lb/ft³)	Fluid Immersion, 7 Days at 23 °C (73.4 °F), max weight %[2] Density 160 kg/m³ (10 lb/ft³) or less
2B5	120 to 170 (17 to 25)	±30	—	5	10	50	100
Class C, Fuel-Resistant, Medium Mass Change[3]							
2C0	Less than 15 (2)	±30	—	5	10	150	250
2C1	15 to 35 (2 to 5)	±30	—	5	10	150	250
2C2	35 to 65 (5 to 9)	±30	—	5	10	150	250
2C3	65 to 90 (9 to 13)	±30	—	5	10	150	250
2C4	90 to 120 (13 to 17)	±30	—	5	10	150	250
2C5	120 to 170 (17 to 25)	±30	—	5	10	150	250
Class D, High-Temperature-Resistant							
2D0	Less than 15 (2)	—	±5	5	10	—	—
2D1	15 to 35 (2 to 5)	—	±5	5	10	—	—
2D2	35 to 65 (5 to 9)	—	±5	5	10	—	—
2D3	65 to 90 (9 to 13)	—	±5	5	10	—	—
2D4	90 to 120 (13 to 17)	—	±5	5	10	—	—
2D5	120 to 170 (17 to 25)	—	±5	5	10	—	—

1. Compression deflection ranges modified to agree with ASTM D 1056-98.
2. This test (see Section 19) of weight change in Reference Fuel B is used in place of the usual oil-resistance test of volume change of IRM 903 oil for the following reason: Oil or solvent immersion of flexible closed cellular materials usually causes loss of gas, by diffusion through the softened cell walls, that results in some shrinkage of the test sample. This shrinkage counteracts the swell that would normally occur, therefore invalidating test data based on volume change. Reference Fuel B is used because it produces a wider and more consistent differentiation among the A, B, and C classes than does IRM 903 oil.
3. Standard oil resistance test methods give inconsistent results on closed cellular materials. This test gives a general indication of oil resistance but more reliable information should be obtained by testing in actual or simulated service conditions.
   The values of 150% maximum Class C and 50% maximum Class B apply to cellular materials having densities of more than 160 kg/m³ (10 lb/ft³). For cellular materials with densities of 160 kg/m³ or less, the values of maximum mass change allowed are 250% for Class C and 100% for Class B.
   Terminology was changed in 1997 from low swell to low mass change to better reflect the data obtained.

TABLE 2B—PHYSICAL REQUIREMENTS OF CELLULAR RUBBERS, TYPE 2, CLOSED-CELL EXPANDED—Requirements Added by Suffix Letters

Grade Number	Compression Deflection 25% Deflection (Limits) kPa (psi)	Compression Set, max %, Under Constant Deflection of 50% Suffix B1 22 h at 100 °C (212 °F)	Compression Set, max %, Under Constant Deflection of 50% Suffix B2[1] 22 h at 23 °C (73.4 °F) 24 h recovery	Compression Set, max %, Under Constant Deflection of 50% Suffix B3 22 h at 23 °C (73.4 °F) 24 h recovery	Low-Temperature Flex, Suffix F1 5 h @ –40 °C (–40 °F)	Low-Temperature Flex, Suffix F2 5 h at –55 °C (–67 °F)
Class A, Non-Oil Resistant						
2A0	Less than 15 (2)	—	25	35	pass	—
2A1	15 to 35 (2 to 5)	—	25	35	pass	—
2A2	35 to 65 (5 to 9)	—	25	35	pass	—
2A3	65 to 90 (9 to 13)	—	25	35	pass	—
2A4	90 to 120 (13 to 17)	—	25	35	pass	—
2A5	120 to 170 (17 to 25)	—	25	35	pass	—
Class B, Oil Resistant, Fuel-Resistant, Low Mass Change[2]						
2B0	Less than 15 (2)	—	25	35	pass	—
2B1	15 to 35 (2 to 5)	—	25	35	pass	—
2B2	35 to 65 (5 to 9)	—	25	35	pass	—
2B3	65 to 90 (9 to 13)	—	25	35	pass	—
2B4	90 to 120 (13 to 17)	—	25	35	pass	—
2B5	120 to 170 (17 to 25)	—	25	35	pass	—
Class C, Fuel-Resistant, Medium Mass Change[2]						
2C0	Less than 15 (2)	—	25	35	pass	—
2C1	15 to 35 (2 to 5)	—	25	35	pass	—
2C2	35 to 65 (5 to 9)	—	25	35	pass	—
2C3	65 to 90 (9 to 13)	—	25	35	pass	—
2C4	90 to 120 (13 to 17)	—	25	35	pass	—
2C5	120 to 170 (17 to 25)	—	25	35	pass	—
Class D, High-Temperature-Resistant						
2D0	Less than 15 (2)	80	—	—	—	pass
2D1	15 to 35 (2 to 5)	80	—	—	—	pass
2D2	35 to 65 (5 to 9)	80	—	—	—	pass
2D3	65 to 90 (9 to 13)	80	—	—	—	pass
2D4	90 to 120 (13 to 17)	80	—	—	—	pass
2D5	120 to 170 (17 to 25)	80	—	—	—	pass

1. Previous versions of SAE J18 inadvertently listed the suffix as "B," instead of "B2."
2. Standard oil resistance test methods give inconsistent results on closed cellular materials. This test gives a general indication of oil resistance but more reliable information should be obtained by testing in actual or simulated service conditions.
   The values of 150% maximum Class C and 50% maximum Class B apply to cellular materials having densities of more than 160 kg/m³ (10 lb/ft³). For cellular materials with densities of 160 kg/m³ or less, the values of maximum mass change allowed are 250% for Class C and 100% for Class B.
   Terminology was changed in 1997 from low swell to low mass change to better reflect the data obtained.

TABLE 3—SAE/ASTM TEST METHODS

NOTE—Example: Grade 1A1C1F1 denotes soft sponge rubber containing natural, reclaimed, synthetic, or blends of these rubbers with a compression deflection value of 14 to 35 kPa (2 to 5 psi), having no specific solvent or oil resistance and requiring in addition to the basic tests a weather resistance test run in accordance with Test Method D 1171, Ozone Chamber Exposure, Method A, and a low-temperature test at –40 °C (–40 °F). Examples of specification conversions are given in Figure 1.

Basic Requirements and Suffix Number Requirement or Suffix Letter	Basic Requirements	Suffix Number 1	Suffix Number 2	Suffix Number 3	Suffix Number 4
Compression Deflection	SAE J18, Section 17				
Heat Resistance	SAE J18, Sections 16 and 20, change in compression deflection after aging 7 days at 70 °C (158 °F)				
Oil Resistance (1B and 1C rubber only)	SAE J18, Section 18, 22 h at 70 °C (158 °F)				
Compression Set (1A, 1B, and 1C rubber only)	SAE J18, Section 22, 22 h at 70 °C (158 °F) 50% deflection, 30-min recovery at 23 °C ± 2 °C (73.4 °F ± 3.6 °F)				
Compression Set (1D and 2D rubber only)	SAE J18, Section 22, 22 h at 100 °C (212 °F), 50% deflection, 30-min recovery at 23 °C ± 2 °C (73.4 °F ± 3.6 °F)				
Water Absorption (2A, 2B, 2C, and 2D rubber only)	SAE J18, Sections 21				
Suffix A, Heat Resistance		SAE J18, Sections 17 and 20, change in compression deflection after aging 22 h at 100 °C ± 1 °C (212 °F ± 1.8 °F)	J18, Sections 17 and 20, change in compression deflection after aging 22 h at 125 °C ± 1 °C (257 °F ± 1.8 °F)	J18, Sections 17 and 20, change in compression deflection after aging 22 h at 150 °C ± 1 °C (302 °F ± 1.8 °F, ±5%)	J18, Sections 17 and 20, change in compression deflection after aging 22 h at 175 °C ± 1 °C (347 °F ± 1.8 °F)
Suffix B, Compression Set (1C, 2A, 2B, and 2C)		SAE J18, Section 22, 22 h at 70 °C (158 °F), 50% deflection, 30-min recovery at 23 °C ± 2 °C (73.4 °F ± 3.6 °F), 25% max	J18, Section 22, 22 h at 23 °C ± 2 °C (73.4 °F ± 3.6 °F), 50% deflection, 24-h recovery at 23 °C ± 2 °C (73.4 °F ± 3.6 °F), 25% max	J18, Section 22, 22 h at 23 °C ± 2 °C (73.4 °F ± 3.6 °F), 50% deflection, 24-h recovery at 23 °C ± 2 °C (73.4 °F ± 3.6 °F)	
Suffix C, Ozone or Weather Resistance		ASTM D 1171[1] ozone exposure Method A	ASTM D 1171[1], outdoor exposure	ASTM D 1171[1], ozone exposure, Method B	
Suffix D, Load Deflection[2]					
Suffix E, Fluid Resistance		SAE J18[3] Section 19, 150% max	SAE J18[3], Section 19, 50% max		
Suffix F, Low-Temperature Resistance		SAE J18, Section 23 to 60, 5 h at –40 °C (–40 °F)	SAE J18, Section 23 to 60, 5 h at –55 °C (–67 °F)	SAE J18, Section 23 to 60, 5 h at –75 °C (–103 °F)	
Suffix G, Tear Resistance[2]					
Suffix J, Abrasion Resistance[2]					
Suffix K, Adhesion Capability[2]					
Suffix L, Water Absorption[2]					
Suffix M, Flammability Resistance[2]					
Suffix N, Impact Resistance[2]					
Suffix P, Staining Resistance[2]					
Suffix R, Resilience[2]					
Suffix W, density[2]					
Suffix Z, Special Requirements[2]					

1. Ratings to be arranged between the purchaser and the supplier.
2. Test method and values to be arranged between the purchaser and the supplier.
3. Table 2 for materials having densities of 160 kg/m^3 (10 lb/ft^3) or less.

TABLE 4—TOLERANCES ON DIMENSIONS OF CELLULAR RUBBER PRODUCTS FOR GENERAL APPLICATIONS

Form	Thickness Dimension, mm (in)	Thickness Tolerance, ±, mm (in)	Length and Width Dimension, mm (in)	Length and Width Tolerance, ±, mm (in)
Sponge Rubber				
Sheet and strip	3.2 (0.125) and under	0.4 (0.016)	152 (6) and under	1.6 (0.063)
	Over 3.2 (0.125) to 12.7 (0.50), incl	0.8 (0.032)	Over 152 (6) to 457 (18) incl	3.2 (0.125)
	Over 12.7 (0.50)	1.2 (0.047)	Over 457 (18)	0.5%
Molded or special shapes	6.4 (0.250) and under	0.8 (0.032)	6.4 (0.250) and under	0.8 (0.032)
	Over 6.4 (0.250) to 76.2 (3), incl	1.6 (0.063)	Over 6.4 (0.250) to 76 (3) incl	1.6 (0.063)
			Over 76 (3) to 457 (18) incl	3.2 (0.125)
			Over 457 (18)	0.5%
Expanded Rubber				
Sheet and strip	3.2 (0.125) and under	1.6 (0.063)	152 (6) and under	6.4 (0.250)
	3.2 (0.125) to 12.7 (0.50), incl	1.6 (0.063)	152 (6) and under	6.4 (0.250)
	Over 12.7 (0.50)	2.4 (0.094)	Over 152 (6) to 305 (12) incl	9.6 (0.375)
			Over 305 (12)	3%
Molded or special shapes	3.2 (0.125) to 12.7 (0.50) incl	1.6 (0.063)	152 (6) and under	6.4 (0.250)
	Over 12.7 (0.50) to 38.1 (1.50) incl	2.4 (0.094)	Over 152 (6) to 305 (12) incl	9.6 (0.375)
	Over 38.1 (1.50) to 76.2 (3) incl	3.2 (0.125)	Over 305 (12)	3%

*9. **Workmanship, Finish, and Appearance***—Cellular rubbers furnished under this document shall be manufactured from synthetic rubber, natural rubber, or rubber-like materials together with added compounding ingredients of such nature and quality that the finished product complies with the specification requirements. In permitting choice in use of those materials by the producer, it is not intended to imply that the different rubber materials are equivalent in respect to all physical properties. Any special characteristics other than those prescribed in this document that may be desired for specific applications, shall be specified in the product specifications, as they may influence the choice of the type of rubber material or other ingredients used. All materials and workmanship shall be in accordance with good commercial practice, and the resulting cellular rubber shall be free from defects affecting serviceability.

*10. **Test Methods***

10.1 Unless specifically stated otherwise, all tests shall be made in accordance with the methods specified in Sections 13 through 24 and Table 3.

*11. **Inspection and Rejection***

11.1 All tests and inspection shall be made at the place of manufacture prior to shipment, unless otherwise specified. The manufacturer shall afford the inspector all reasonable facilities for tests and inspection.

11.2 The purchaser may make the tests and inspection to govern acceptance or rejection of the material at his own laboratory or elsewhere. Such tests and inspection shall be made no later than 15 days after receipt of the material.

11.3 All samples for testing, provided as specified in Section 14, shall be visually inspected to determine compliance with the material, workmanship, and color requirements.

11.4 Any material that fails in one or more of the test requirements may be retested. For this purpose, two additional tests shall be made for the requirement in which failure occurred. Failure of either of the retests shall be cause for final rejection.

11.5 Rejected material shall be disposed of as directed by the manufacturer.

*12. **Packaging and Package Marking***—The material shall be properly and adequately packaged. Each package or container shall be legibly marked with the name of the material, name, or trademark of the manufacturer, and any required purchaser's designations.

*13. **General Test Methods***

13.1 Scope—Except as otherwise specified in these methods, the following ASTM test methods and the various test methods in Table 3, applicable in general to vulcanized rubber, shall be complied with as required and are hereby made a part of these methods:

13.1.1 GENERAL PHYSICAL TEST REQUIREMENTS—ASTM D 3182 and D 3183.

13.1.2 AGING TEST—ASTM D 573, with modifications as described in Sections 16 and 20.

13.1.3 COMPRESSION SET, SUFFIX B—Method described in Section 22.

13.1.4 FLUID IMMERSION, SUFFIX E—ASTM D 471 and Sections 18 and 19.

13.1.5 LOW-TEMPERATURE TEST, SUFFIXES F1, F2, AND F3—Method described in Section 23. Suitable low-temperature cabinets and conditioning procedures are described in ASTM D 832.

13.1.6 In case of conflict between provisions of the test methods referenced in 13.1.1 through 13.1.5 and the procedures specifically described herein for cellular rubbers, the latter shall take precedence.

*14. **Sampling***

14.1 When possible, the completed manufactured product shall be used for the tests specified. Representative samples of the lot being examined shall be selected at random as required.

14.2 When it is necessary or advisable to obtain test specimens from the article, as in those cases where the entire sample is not required or adaptable for testing, the method of cutting and the exact position from which specimens are to be taken shall be specified. The apparent density and the state of cure may vary in different parts of the finished product, especially if the article is of complicated shape or of varying thickness, and these factors affect the physical properties of the specimens. Also, the apparent density is affected by the number of cut surfaces as opposed to the number of skin-covered surfaces on the test specimen.

14.3 When the finished product does not lend itself to testing or to the taking of test specimens because of complicated shape, small size, metal or fabric inserts, solid covers, adhesion to metal, or other reasons, standard test slabs shall be prepared. When differences due to the difficulty in obtaining suitable test specimens from the finished part arise, the manufacturer and purchaser may agree on acceptable deviations. This can be done by comparing results of standard test specimens and those obtained on actual parts.

*15. **Test Specimens and Slabs***

15.1 Test Specimens—Standard test specimens shall be disks 28.00 mm ± 0.50 mm (1.10 in ± 0.02 in) in diameter, which yields a 645.70 mm^2 (1 in^2) specimen. The specimens may be cut with a revolving die[5] using a soap solution as a lubricant. If a lubricant is used, the specimens shall be thoroughly dried before proceeding with the testing. In some cases, it may be necessary to freeze the cellular rubber to obtain parallel cut edges. Samples shall not be compression die cut because this process distorts the sample, which will affect the final properties. When cut from standard test slabs, they shall be cut from the center area as shown in Figure 1. The thickness shall be measured as described in 15.3.2. As stated under the test methods, the minimum thickness of test specimens is 6.00 mm (0.24 in). Plied-up samples may be used as indicated in the test methods for compression set and compression deflection (see Note in 17.3.2).

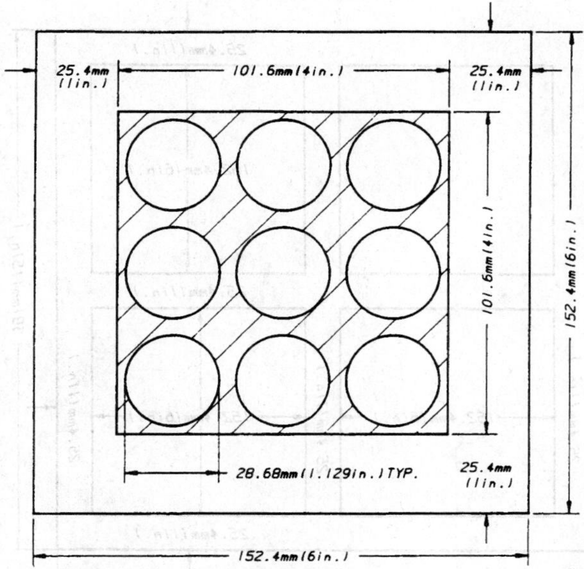

FIGURE 1—LOCATION FROM WHICH STANDARD TEST SPECIMENS ARE TO BE CUT WHEN TESTING STANDARD TEST SLABS OR COMMERCIAL FLAT SHEETS

15.2 Test Slabs—Standard test slabs of all types of cellular rubber shall be pieces 150 mm ±5 mm (nominally 6 in) square and 12.5 mm ±0.5 mm (nominally 0.5 in) in thickness made from the same compound and having the same apparent density and state of cure as the product they represent. In all cases, the surface skin shall be left intact on both top and bottom faces of the test slab. Standard test slabs shall be prepared either by cutting them from flat sheets of the specified thickness or as described in 15.2.1 or 15.2.2.

15.2.1 When specially prepared standard test slabs of sponge rubber are required, they shall be made using the frame shown in Figure 2 together with top and bottom plates each approximately 12.50 mm (0.50 in) in thickness. The frame and plates shall be made of aluminum or steel. The stock shall be in sheet form, cut into squares slightly smaller than the frame cavities. The thickness of the square sheets shall be such as to give the required apparent density when the material is blown during cure to fill the molding cavities. The squares of stock shall be dusted with talc and the excess brushed off to avoid pitting. They shall then be placed in the frame, and fabric sheeting shall be applied on the top and bottom between the frame and the plates to allow venting of gases produced during the cure. This fabric shall be a commercial sheeting with a mass of approximately 135 g/m^2 (4 oz/yd^2), having approximately 2.75 ends/mm (70 ends/in) and 2.36 picks/mm (60 picks/in). The specimens shall be vulcanized in a platen press under conditions of time and temperature chosen to produce the same state of cure in the standard slabs as in the finished products they represent.

15.2.2 Where specially prepared standard test slabs of expanded rubber are required, they shall be made using the same process that was used for the product to be represented by the test slab. The specimens shall be prepared to have approximately the same density, and shall be vulcanized under conditions of time

5. A satisfactory die and its method of application are described in Section 4 of ASTM D 575.

and temperature chosen to produce the same state of cure in the standard slabs, as in the finished products they represent.

15.3 Measurements of Test Specimens

15.3.1 The length and width shall be measured to 0.5 mm (0.02 in). Care shall be taken not to distort the cellular rubber.

15.3.2 Thicknesses up to and including 25.0 mm (1 in) shall be measured using a dial-type gage[6] having a maximum stem and foot mass of 25 g and a foot 30.0 mm (1.25 in) in diameter. Thicknesses over 25 mm (1 in) shall be measured using a sliding caliper gage. When a sliding caliper gage is employed, the gage setting shall be made with the gage out of contact with the cellular rubber. The sample shall be passed through the previously set gage and the proper setting shall be the one in which the measuring faces of the gage contact the surfaces of the article without compressing it.

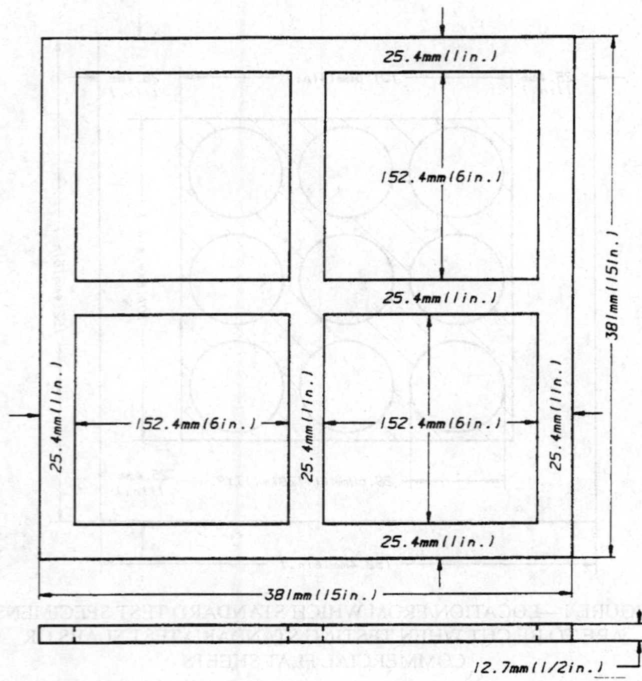

FIGURE 2—FOUR-CAVITY FRAME FOR STANDARD TEST SLABS OF CELLULAR RUBBERS

15.3.3 The steel scale or tape used to measure length or width shall be graduated to 1 mm (0.031 in). The dial gage for measuring thickness shall be graduated to 0.02 mm (0.001 in). The calipers used for measuring thickness shall be graduated to 0.1 mm (0.005 in).

15.3.4 Results reported shall be the average of a minimum of three measurements. If the results vary between the specimens more than 10%, two additional specimens should be taken into the average.

16. Accelerated Aging Tests

16.1 Test Specimen

16.1.1 The test specimen used in any of the aging tests shall be of the size and shape as specified by the appropriate called-out test method.

17. Compression-Deflection Tests

17.1 Scope

17.1.1 This test method consists of measuring the force necessary to produce a 25% deflection on a test specimen.

17.2 Apparatus

17.2.1 Any compression machine that meets the following requirements will be satisfactory. The machine shall be capable of compressing the specimen at a rate of 12.5 to 50 mm/min (0.5 to 2 in/min) gently without impact. The machine may be motor- or hand-driven. It shall be equipped with a gage to measure the deflection caused by the increase in load. The rate of compression of the specimen is specified rather than the rate of the compressing platform of the machine. This is an important consideration when scales are used, since sponges of various compression-deflection characteristics will require different times to compress 25% due to the travel of the scale platform under varying loads.

17.2.2 The deflection shall be read on a dial gage graduated in 0.02 mm (0.001 in). No gage is necessary if the machine automatically compresses the specimen 25%.

17.3 Test Specimens

17.3.1 Standard test specimens can be used for this test.

17.3.2 Test specimen size may vary provided the indenter foot of the apparatus used is larger than the sample. Test specimens may be cylindrical or square. They shall be cut so that opposite edges are parallel, either from the finished product in a manner agreed upon between the parties concerned or, as shown in Figure 2, from standard test slabs or from flat sheets. The thickness of the test specimens may vary, but shall be measured and stated in the report. The minimum thickness shall be 6.0 mm (0.25 in). Thin samples may be plied-up to obtain this thickness, or a standard test slab may be used if agreed upon between the manufacturer and the purchaser.

NOTE—In sponge rubbers, using the same compound, thin sections under 6 mm (0.25 in) do not blow in the same manner as those over 6 mm (0.25 in). The thinner sections are usually higher in compression deflection and density. However, in closed-cell (expanded) rubbers where thin sheets are split from thicker sheets there is usually very little difference between the thin sheet and thicker sheets.

17.4 Procedure—Cellular rubber less than 6 mm (0.250 in) in thickness shall be tested by plying up the proper number of plies to obtain a thickness as near 12.5 mm (0.50 in) as possible. Compress the standard test specimen between the parallel metal plates of the machine until the thickness has been reduced 25%, and take the reading of the load immediately. Repeat the test with the same specimen until the load readings do not change more than 5%. The top and bottom plates shall be at least 38 mm (1.5 in) in diameter.

17.5 Report

17.5.1 The unit load required for the last reading, expressed in kilopascals (or pounds per square inch), shall be reported as the result of the compression-deflection test.

17.6 Precision and Bias

17.6.1 See Section 25.

18. Oil-Immersion Test, Open-Cell Sponge (see Table 1)

18.1 Scope

18.1.1 This test method determines the fluid resistance (oil) of a sample (open cell sponge) by means of measuring volume change after a specified immersion time/temperature.

18.2 Test Specimens

18.2.1 Standard test specimens approximately 12.5 mm (0.50 in) in thickness shall be used for this test. The diameter and thickness shall be measured before and after immersion in the specified petroleum-base oil for 22 h at 70 °C (158 °F) and the percent change in volume calculated. Three specimens shall be run on each test and the average of the three values reported.

18.3 Procedure

18.3.1 Follow the procedure of ASTM D 471, using petroleum base oil IRM 903.

19. Fluid Immersion Test, Closed Cell (Expanded) (See Footnote 2, Table 2)

19.1 Scope

19.1.1 This test method determines the fluid resistance (fuel) of a sample (closed cell foam) by means of measuring weight change after a specified immersion time/temperature.

19.2 Apparatus

19.2.1 Equipment required are an analytical balance, screens, ASTM Reference Fuel B, paper towels, and 250-cm^3 (8-oz) containers (minimum size).

19.3 Test Specimens

19.3.1 The test specimens shall be 25 by 50 by 6 mm (nominally 1 by 2 by 0.250 in). It is preferable that the specimens be cut with clean, square edges.

19.4 Procedure

19.4.1 Weigh the specimens to the nearest 0.01 g. Place a noncorrosive screen having 2-mm openings (10-mesh) on the bottom of the container. Alternatively place specimens of one material and screens into the cans. Use one can per material. Fill the cans with ASTM Reference Fuel B and seal with their lids. Store the cans for 7 days at a temperature of 23 °C ± 2 °C (73.4 °F ± 4 °F). Remove one specimen at a time from the test fluid. Without squeezing the specimen, place it on top of one sheet of paper towel and immediately place a second paper towel on top of it. Blot lightly without squeezing, then remove the top paper towel. Immediately determine the mass of the specimen to the nearest 0.01 g.

6. Supporting data are available from ASTM Headquarters. Request RR: D20-1198.

19.5 Calculation

19.5.1 Calculate the percent change in mass as shown in Equation 1.

$$W = [(A - B)/ B] \times 100 \quad \text{(Eq. 1)}$$

where:

W = change in mass, %
A = final mass of specimen, and
B = initial mass of specimen

19.6 Report

19.6.1 The report should include fluid type, time and temperature of test, data from three specimens, and the average of the three.

19.7 Requirements

19.7.1 See Tables 1 and 2.

19.8 Precision and Bias

19.8.1 See Section 25.

20. Test for Compression-Deflection Change After Oven Aging

20.1 Scope

20.1.1 This test method determines the heat aging properties of a sample by measuring the change in compression deflection after a specified time/temperature.

20.2 Test Specimen

20.2.1 SAMPLE BEFORE OVEN AGING—A representative sample, approximately 12.5 mm (0.5 in) thick and a minimum area of 161 cm^2 (25 in^2).

20.2.2 SPECIMEN SIZE FOR TEST METHOD—Standard specimen size (in accordance with Section 15) shall be a disk 28.00 mm ± 0.50 mm (1.10 in ± 0.02 in) diameter and approximately 12.5 mm (0.5 in) thick. For thin materials, the disks shall be stacked to approximately 12.5 mm (0.5 in) in height.

20.3 Apparatus

20.3.1 The air-oven aging test as described in ASTM D 573 shall be used for cellular rubber, except that the sample and test specimen size shall be as described in Section 19.3. See 17.2 for compression deflection apparatus.

20.4 Procedure

20.4.1 Cut three standard test specimens out of a larger test sample and place the remaining part of the sample in an oven for 168 h ± 1 h oven aging. Allow to cool for at least 2 h but not more than 24 h and then cut three standard test specimens that are at least 1 in from any edge or cut surface. Determine compression deflection (see 17.4). Determine percent change in compression deflection.

20.5 Calculation

20.5.1 Express the results as a percentage of the change in compression deflection, calculated as shown in Equation 2.

$$P = [(A - O)/ O] \times 100 \quad \text{(Eq. 2)}$$

where:

P = Change in compression deflection, %
O = Original compression deflection, and
A = Final compression deflection after oven aging

20.6 Report

20.6.1 Report the following information:

20.6.1.1 Time and temperature of test
20.6.1.2 Original and final compression deflection data
20.6.1.3 Percent change for three specimens
20.6.1.4 Percent change, average of three specimens

20.7 Requirements

20.7.1 See Tables 1 and 2.

20.8 Precision and Bias

20.8.1 See Section 25.

21. Water Absorption Test

21.1 Scope

21.1.1 This test method determines the water absorption properties of a closed cell foam by measuring the change in weight (mass) after a specified immersion period. This test method is indirectly a measure of the sample's cell structure/closed cell content. The water absorption test (see Footnote 1 of Table 2) is applicable to expanded rubber (closed-cell type). It should not be used on sponge rubber (open-cell type) unless they are completely encased in an added skin.

21.2 Test Specimens

21.2.1 Test specimens approximately 12.5 mm (0.050 in) in thickness and 2500 mm^2 (4 in^2) in area shall be used for this test. Round specimens are preferable.

21.3 Procedure

21.3.1 Submerge specimens in distilled water at room temperature, 18 to 35 °C (65 to 95 °F) 50 mm (2 in) below the surface of the water, and reduce the pressure above the water to 17 kPa (2.5 psi absolute) for 3 min. Release the vacuum, and allow the specimen to remain submerged for 3 min at atmospheric pressure. Remove the specimen, blot dry, and calculate the percent change in mass.

21.4 Calculation

21.4.1 Calculate the percent change in mass as shown in Equation 3.

$$W = [(A - B)/ B] \times 100 \quad \text{(Eq. 3)}$$

where:

W = Change in mass, %
A = Final mass of specimen
B = Initial mass of specimen

21.5 Report

21.5.1 Report the following information:

21.5.1.1 Original and final weights of three specimens
21.5.1.2 Percent change in weight for each
21.5.1.3 Average percent change for the three specimens

21.6 Requirements

21.6.1 See Table 2.

21.7 Precision and Bias

21.7.1 See Section 25.

22. Test for Compression Set Under Constant Deflection (Calculations Based on Amount of Deflection) Suffix B (1, 2, 3)

22.1 Scope

22.1.1 This test method determines the recovery properties of a sample when subjected to a constant deflection for a specified time/temperature/deflection by measuring its gage before and after the test period.

22.2 Test Specimens

22.2.1 Standard test specimens shall be used for this test. They shall be cut so that opposite edges are parallel, either from the finished product in a manner agreed upon by the parties concerned, or, as shown in Figure 1, from standard test slabs or from commercial flat sheets. The thickness of the test specimens may vary, but shall be measured and stated in the report. The minimum thickness for open-cell sponge rubber shall be 6 mm (0.250 in). These samples of open-cell sponge rubber may be plied up to obtain this thickness. The minimum thickness for closed-cell expanded rubber shall be 12.5 mm (0.50 in). Thin samples of closed-cell expanded rubber shall not be plied up to obtain this thickness. A standard test specimen may be used for either open-cell sponge or closed expanded material, if agreed upon by the manufacturer and the purchaser.

22.3 Procedure

22.3.1 The apparatus and procedure shall be the same as that prescribed in Method B of ASTM D 395, except as follows: For open-cell (sponge) rubber, compress test specimens to 50% of their original thicknesses. Release the load at the end of 22 h and measure the thickness after a 30 min rest at room temperature. For closed-cell (expanded) rubber, compress the test specimens to 50% of their original thicknesses. Release the load at the end of 22 h and measure the thickness after 24 h at room temperature. In both cases (open-cell sponge and closed-cell expanded rubber), measure the thickness as described in 15.3.2. The temperature of the test for open-cell (sponge) rubber shall be 70 °C ± 2 °C (158 °F ± 4 °F), except for Class 1D rubbers. The temperature of the test for closed-cell (expanded) rubber shall be 23 °C ± 2 °C (73.4 °F ± 4 °F), except for Class 2D rubber. For Class 1D and 2D rubber, the temperature of the test shall be 100 °C ± 1 °C (212 °F ± 2 °F). The time of the test shall be as specified. Chromium-plated metal plates are not required. Aluminum plates or any stiff plates that are clean and smooth, and that will not deflect measurably under the load necessary for deflection of the specimen, may be used.

22.4 Calculation

22.4.1 Calculate the percentage compression set as shown in Equation 4:

$$\text{Compression set, \%} = [(t_0 - t_1)/ (t_0 - t_s)] \times 100 \quad \text{(Eq. 4)}$$

where:

t_0 = Original thickness
t_1 = Thickness of specimen after specified recovery period
t_s = Thickness of space bar used

22.5 Report

22.5.1 Report the following information:

22.5.1.1 Duration and temperature of oven exposure
22.5.1.2 Original and final thickness for three specimens

22.5.1.3 Percent set for each specimen

22.5.1.4 Average percent set for the specimens

22.6 Requirements

22.6.1 See Tables 1 and 2.

22.7 Precision and Bias

22.7.1 See Section 25.

23. Low-Temperature Flex Test

Suffix F1, –40 °C ± 1 °C (–40 °F ± 2 °F)

Suffix F2, –55 °C ± 1 °C (–67 °F ± 2 °F)

Suffix F3, –75 °C ± 1 °C (–103 °F ± 2 °F)

23.1 Scope

23.1.1 This test is to determine the brittleness of cellular rubber at low temperatures.

23.2 Apparatus

23.2.1 A low-temperature chamber capable of –75 °C (–103 °F) that can be accurately controlled for low temperatures. If the box is cooled by dry ice, the specimen should not make direct contact with gaseous CO_2. This chamber must be large enough to permit the bending of the test piece while it is still in the box.

23.2.2 Mandrel diameter shall be approximately 4 times the sample thickness.

23.3 Test Specimens

23.3.1 The test specimens shall be 50 mm ± 10 mm (2 in ± 0.5 in) wide by 140 mm ± 10 mm (6 in ± 0.5 in) long by 3 mm (0.125 in) to 12.5 mm (0.50 in) thick.

23.4 Procedure

23.4.1 Place three test specimens and mandrel in a low-temperature chamber for 5 h ± 0.25 h at –40 °C (–40 °F), –55 °C (–67 °F), or –75 °C (–103 °F) as specified by the suffix letter and number.

23.4.2 At the end of the test period, open the cold box and bend the specimen 180 degrees around the mandrel taking no longer than 2 to 3 s to perform the bend. If there are multiple samples, bend and record results as soon as possible to maintain temperature to within ±5 °C of set temperature.

23.5 Report

23.5.1 Report the following information:

23.5.1.1 Whether the sample showed any indication of cracking or if it was still pliable. All specimens must show no signs of cracking.

24. Test for Density Suffix W

24.1 Scope

24.1.1 DENSITY CALCULATION (SUFFIX W—This test method describes the procedure for determining the density by calculation from the mass and volume of a specimen.

24.2 Test Specimen

24.2.1 Representative specimens of regular shape not less than 16 cm^3 (1 in^3) in volume shall be cut from the sample to be tested.

24.3 Procedure

24.3.1 Weigh the specimen on a balance or scale graduated to permit weighing within ±1% of the mass to be measured.

24.3.2 Determine the volume of the specimen to within ±1% of the sample either by direct measurement or volume displacement.

24.4 Calculation

24.4.1 Calculate the density as shown in Equation 5:

$$\text{density, } kg/m^3 = A/B \quad \text{(Eq. 5)}$$

where:

A = Mass of specimen, kg

B = Volume of specimen, m^3

NOTE—To convert this value to lb/ft^3, multiply by 0.0624.

24.5 Report

24.5.1 Report the following information:

24.5.1.1 Mass, volume, and density of each specimen as well as the average value.

24.6 Requirements

24.6.1 To be determined between the supplier and the purchaser.

24.7 Precision and Bias

24.7.1 See Section 25.

25. Precision and Bias

25.1 Precision and Bias

25.1.1 Precision and bias for SAE J18/ASTM D 1056 are based on a round robin study conducted in 1996/1997 in accordance with ASTM E 691, involving 3 materials tested by 14 laboratories. For each material, all the samples were prepared at one source, but the individual specimens were prepared at the laboratories that tested them. Each test result was the average of three individual determinations. Each laboratory obtained two test results for each material. The number of data points for each test varied because not all laboratories were able to participate in each test. The data obtained and the number of laboratories participating in each test is indicated in Tables 5 through 10.

NOTE—CAUTION—The explanations of r and R (25.1.2 through 25.1.2.2) are only intended to present a meaningful way of considering the approximate precision of this test method. The data should not be applied to acceptance or rejection of materials, as these data apply only to the materials listed in the round robin and are unlikely to be rigorously representative of other lots, formulations, conditions, materials, or laboratories. Users of this test method should apply the principles outlined in ASTM E 691 to generate data specific to their materials and laboratory (or between specific laboratories).

TABLE 5—COMPRESSION-DEFLECTION IN ACCORDANCE WITH SAE J18/ASTM D 1056, SECTION 17

NOTE 1—Values expressed in units of kPa.
NOTE 2—Data based on results from 14 laboratories.

Material	x (average)	S_r(1)	S_R(2)	r(3)	R(4)
C	30.84	0.88	4.48	2.45	12.55
B	43.36	1.19	4.51	3.32	12.62
A	104.11	1.95	12.64	5.47	35.38

1. S_r = within laboratory standard deviation for the indicated material. It is obtained by pooling the within laboratory standard deviations of the test results from all of the participating laboratories, as follows:
$S_r = [[(S_1)^2 + (S_2)^2 \ldots + (S_n)^2]/n]^{1/2}$
2. S_R = between laboratories reproducibility, expressed as a standard deviation, as follows:
$S_R = [(S_r)^2 = (S_L)^2]^{1/2}$
where S_L = standard deviation of laboratory means.
3. r = within laboratory critical interval between the two test results = 2.8 x S_r.
4. R = between laboratories critical interval between two test results = 2.8 x S_R.

TABLE 6—COMPRESSION SET IN ACCORDANCE WITH SAE J18/ASTM D 1056, SECTION 22

NOTE 1—Values expressed in percent.
NOTE 2—Data based on results from 12 laboratories.

Material	x (average)	S_r(1)	S_R(2)	r(3)	R(4)
C	20.02	0.60	3.28	1.87	9.18
B	20.06	0.92	3.69	2.57	10.34
A	38.68	0.67	3.43	1.87	9.60

1. S_r = within laboratory standard deviation for the indicated material. It is obtained by pooling the within laboratory standard deviations of the test results from all of the participating laboratories, as follows:
$S_r = [[(S_1)^2 + (S_2)^2 \ldots + (S_n)^2]/n]^{1/2}$
2. S_R = between laboratories reproducibility, expressed as a standard deviation, as follows:
$S_R = [(S_r)^2 = (S_L)^2]^{1/2}$
where S_L = standard deviation of laboratory means.
3. r = within laboratory critical interval between the two test results = 2.8 x S_r.
4. R = between laboratories critical interval between two test results = 2.8 x S_R.

TABLE 7—WATER ABSORPTION IN ACCORDANCE SAE J18/ASTM D 1056, SECTION 21

NOTE 1—Values expressed in percent.
NOTE 2—Data based on results from 7 laboratories.

Material	x (average)	S_r(1)	S_R(2)	r(3)	R(4)
C	0.96	0.05	0.33	0.13	0.93
B	1.44	0.08	0.74	0.22	2.08
A	5.99	0.21	4.45	0.58	12.47

1. S_r = within laboratory standard deviation for the indicated material. It is obtained by pooling the within laboratory standard deviations of the test results from all of the participating laboratories, as follows:
$S_r = [[(S_1)^2 + (S_2)^2 \ldots + (S_n)^2]/n]^{1/2}$
2. S_R = between laboratories reproducibility, expressed as a standard deviation, as follows:
$S_R = [(S_r)^2 = (S_L)^2]^{1/2}$
where S_L = standard deviation of laboratory means.
3. r = within laboratory critical interval between the two test results = 2.8 x S_r.
4. R = between laboratories critical interval between two test results = 2.8 x S_R.

TABLE 8—DENSITY IN ACCORDANCE WITH SAE J18/ASTM D 1056, SECTION 24
NOTE 1—Values expressed in kg/m^3.
NOTE 2—Data based on results from 9 laboratories.

Material	x (average)	Sr[(1)]	S_R[(2)]	r[(3)]	R[(4)]
C	69.17	1.42	4.12	3.98	11.53
B	144.09	4.63	9.05	12.97	25.33
A	201.01	1.35	6.98	3.77	19.54

1. S_r = within laboratory standard deviation for the indicated material. It is obtained by pooling the within laboratory standard deviations of the test results from all of the participating laboratories, as follows:
$S_r = [[(S_1)^2 + (S_2)^2 \ldots + (S_n)^2]/n]^{1/2}$
2. S_R = between laboratories reproducibility, expressed as a standard deviation, as follows:
$S_R = [(S_r)^2 = (S_L)^2]^{1/2}$
where S_L = standard deviation of laboratory means.
3. r = within laboratory critical interval between the two test results = 2.8 x S_r.
4. R = between laboratories critical interval between two test results = 2.8 x S_R.

TABLE 9—CHANGE IN COMPRESSION DEFLECTION AFTER OVEN AGING IN ACCORDANCE WITH SAE J18/ASTM D 1056, SECTION 20
NOTE 1—Values expressed in units of kPa.
NOTE 2—Data based on results from 14 laboratories.

Material	x (average)	Sr[(1)]	S_R[(2)]	r[(3)]	R[(4)]
C	–5.17	2.12	4.46	5.93	12.47
B	–8.44	3.61	5.60	0.83	15.93
A	21.95	4.28	6.33	11.97	17.71

1. S_r = within laboratory standard deviation for the indicated material. It is obtained by pooling the within laboratory standard deviations of the test results from all of the participating laboratories, as follows:
$S_r = [[(S_1)^2 + (S_2)^2 \ldots + (S_n)^2]/n]^{1/2}$
2. S_R = between laboratories reproducibility, expressed as a standard deviation, as follows:
$S_R = [(S_r)^2 = (S_L)^2]^{1/2}$
where S_L = standard deviation of laboratory means.
3. r = within laboratory critical interval between the two test results = 2.8 x S_r.
4. R = between laboratories critical interval between two test results = 2.8 x S_R.

TABLE 10—FLUID IMMERSION IN ACCORDANCE WITH SAE J18/ASTM D 1056, SECTION 19
NOTE 1—Values expressed in percent.
NOTE 2—Data based on results from 11 laboratories.

Material	x (average)	Sr[(1)]	S_R[(2)]	r[(3)]	R[(4)]
C	113.15	3.60	21.61	10.07	60.52
B	153.46	5.54	28.82	15.51	80.70
A	250.21	11.02	36.36	30.85	101.82

1. S_r = within laboratory standard deviation for the indicated material. It is obtained by pooling the within laboratory standard deviations of the test results from all of the participating laboratories, as follows:
$S_r = [[(S_1)^2 + (S_2)^2 \ldots + (S_n)^2]/n]^{1/2}$
2. S_R = between laboratories reproducibility, expressed as a standard deviation, as follows:
$S_R = [(S_r)^2 = (S_L)^2]^{1/2}$
where S_L = standard deviation of laboratory means.
3. r = within laboratory critical interval between the two test results = 2.8 x S_r.
4. R = between laboratories critical interval between two test results = 2.8 x S_R.

25.1.2 CONCEPT OF R AND R IN TABLES 5 THROUGH 10—If S_r and S_R have been calculated from a large enough body of data, and for test results that were averages from testing three specimens for each test result, then the following applies:

25.1.2.1 Repeatability—Two test results obtained within one laboratory shall be judged not equivalent if they differ by more than the r value for that material (r is the interval representing the critical difference between the two test results for the same material, obtained by the same operator using the same equipment on the same day in the same laboratory).

25.1.2.2 Reproducibility—Two test results obtained by different laboratories shall be judged not equivalent if they differ by more than the R value for that material (R is the interval representing the critical difference between two test results for the same material, obtained by different operators, using different equipment in different laboratories).

25.1.2.3 Any judgment in accordance with Tables 5 through 10 would have an approximate 95% (0.9) probability of being correct.

25.1.3 BIAS—There are no recognized standards by which to estimate bias for these test methods.

26. Notes

26.1 Keywords—Expanded rubber, flexible cellular, sponge.

ACCELERATED ENVIRONMENTAL TESTING FOR BONDED AUTOMOTIVE ASSEMBLIES—SAE J2100 AUG1992

SAE Recommended Practice

Report of the SAE Plastics Bonding Subcommittee of the SAE Materials Joining Committee approved August 1992.

Foreword—This Document has not changed other than to put it into the new SAE Technical Standards Board Format

1. Scope—This SAE Recommended Practice defines conditions to which bonded assemblies can be exposed to simulate environmental aging. These recommendations are generally based on existing Original Equipment Manufacturer requirements at this time. (Environmental specifications used for this proposal were from General Motors, Ford, and Chrysler.) The substrate type, dimension, and number are described by the standard for materials being tested and should include control specimens which receive no environmental aging.

2. References

2.1 Applicable Publications—The following publications form a part of this specification to the extent specified herein.

2.1.1 ASTM PUBLICATIONS—Available from ASTM, 100 Barr Harbor Drive, West Conshohocken, PA 19428-2959.

ASTM B 117—Method of Salt Spray (Fog) Testing

ASTM E 171—Specification for Standard Atmospheres for Conditioning and Testing Materials

3. Equipment—All temperatures are ± 2 °C and relative humidities (RH) are ±5% unless otherwise indicated.

3.1 Air circulating ovens capable of maintaining 88 °C and 204 °C.

3.2 Humidity cabinets (noncondensing preferred) capable of maintaining 38 °C/95 to 100% RH and 60 °C/85% RH.

3.3 Salt spray cabinet per ASTM B 117.

3.4 Low-temperature cabinet capable of maintaining -30 °C.

3.5 Deionized water bath capable of maintaining 60 °C.

4. Testing—Evaluate after exposure to each environment and compare to control.

4.1 Control—Test at 23 °C, 50% RH.

4.2 Low Temperature—Test at -30 °C. Precondition at -30 °C for a minimum of 2 h.

4.3 High Temperature

4.3.1 Test at 88 °C. Precondition at 88 °C a minimum of 15 min.

4.3.2 Test at 204 °C. Precondition at 204 °C a minimum of 15 min.

4.4 Water Immersion—Immerse 14 days in deionized water at 60 °C.

4.4.1 WET—Remove specimens from water bath, place in an air-tight container (such as a plastic bag), cool to 23 °C, 15 to 30 min, and test wet at 23 °C.

4.4.2 RECOVERY—Test dry at 23 °C, 50% RH, after 24 h conditioning at 23 °C, 50% RH.

4.5 Heat Aging—After designated time at 88 °C, test at 23 °C, 50% RH after 30 min conditioning at 23 °C, 50% RH.

4.5.1 4 weeks

4.5.2 6 weeks

4.5.3 8 weeks

4.6 Humidity Aging

4.6.1 After designated time at 38 °C/100% RH, remove specimens from humidity chamber, place in air-tight container (such as a plastic bag), cool to 23 °C, 15 to 30 min, and test wet at 23 °C.

4.6.1.1 4 weeks

4.6.1.2 6 weeks

4.6.1.3 8 weeks

4.6.2 After designated time at 38 °C/100% RH, test dry at 23 °C, 50% RH, after 24 h conditioning at 23 °C, 50% RH.

4.6.2.1 4 weeks

4.6.2.2 6 weeks

4.6.2.3 8 weeks

4.7 Salt Spray—After designated time in ASTM B 117 salt spray cabinet, test at 23 °C, 50% RH.

4.7.1 250 h

4.7.2 500 h

4.7.3 1000 h

4.8 Thermal Cycle

4 h at -30 °C

4 h at 88 °C

16 h at 38 °C/100% RH

a. Run 10 cycles
b. No more than 10 min should elapse between each exposure. To maintain 24 h cycles, reduce humidity exposure time.
c. If delay is incurred during thermal cycle, including Saturday and Sunday, storage of specimens in humidity chamber is acceptable.
d. Test at 23 °C, 50% RH, after 24 h conditioning at 23 °C, 50% RH.

4.9 Corrosion Cycle

2 h at -30 °C

2 h at 23 °C/50% RH

2 h at 70 °C

2 h salt spray, ASTM B 117

16 h at 38 °C/100% RH

a. Run 30 cycles
b. No more than 10 min should elapse between each exposure. To maintain 24 h cycles, reduce humidity exposure time.
c. If delay is incurred during corrosion cycle, including Saturday and Sunday, storage of specimens in humidity chamber is acceptable.
d. Test at 23 °C, 50% RH, after 24 h conditioning at 23 °C, 50% RH.

4.10 Scab Cycle

Monday only:

60 min at 60 °C

30 min at -30 °C

15 min immersion in 5% sodium chloride solution at 23 °C

75 min at 23 °C/50% RH

21 h at 60 °C/85% RH

Tuesday thru Friday:

15 min immersion in 5% sodium chloride solution at 23 °C

75 min at 23 °C/50% RH

22.5 h at 60 °C/85% RH

Saturday and Sunday:

60 °C/85% RH

a. Run 20 cycles (one cycle—one 24 h weekday).
b. At completion of last cycle, rinse assemblies in warm water.
c. No more than 10 min should elapse between each exposure. To maintain 24 h cycles, reduce humidity exposure time.
d. If delay is incurred during scab cycle, storage of specimens in humidity chamber is acceptable.
e. Test at 23 °C, 50% RH after 24 h conditioning at 23 °C, 50% RH.

5. Key Words—Accelerated aging, adhesive, bonded assemblies, corrosive, environment, salt spray, scab.

LATEX-DIPPED GOODS AND COATINGS FOR AUTOMOTIVE APPLICATIONS—SAE J19 AUG1997

SAE Standard

Report of the SAE Nonmetallic Materials Committee approved September 1960, completely revised November 1980, and reaffirmed without change January 1985. Conforms with ASTM D 1764. Completely revised by the SAE Committee on Automotive Rubber Specifications August 1997. Rationale statement available.

1. Scope

1.1 These specifications cover dipped goods and coatings made from compounded latex. Products manufactured from this material include boots, coated clips, coated sponge parts, and coated fabrics for automotive applications.

1.2 The compounds listed in Tables 1 and 2 are grouped into classifications based primarily on physical properties which are prescribed in the tables. These values, together with any additional requirements, indicated by suffix letters in the grade designations as described in Section 3, define the properties of the compounds after vulcanization. These values apply to test specimens obtained from standard laboratory dipped films prepared in accordance with procedures described in the applicable ASTM test methods. Test results from finished products may not duplicate the values obtained from standard test films. When differences due to the difficulty in obtaining suitable test specimens from the finished part arise, the purchaser and the supplier may agree on acceptable deviations. This can be done by comparing results obtained on standard test films with those obtained on actual parts.

TABLE 1—PHYSICAL REQUIREMENTS OF TYPE LR COMPOUNDS, NON-OIL RESISTANT

Characteristic	Requirement
Grade Number	LR 420
Durometer Hardness	45 ±5
Tensile Strength, Min MPa (psi)	14.0 (2000)
Ultimate Elongation, Min %	500
Heat Aged 70 h at 70 °C (158 °F)	
Change in Durometer Hardness, Max points	±5
Tensile Strength, Min MPa (psi)	10.5 (1500)
Ultimate Elongation, Min %	400
Permanent Set at 400% Elongation, Max %	10

TABLE 2—PHYSICAL REQUIREMENTS OF TYPE LS COMPOUNDS, CLASS LSC, OIL RESISTANT

Characteristic	Requirement
Grade Number	LSC 515
Basic Requirements	
Durometer Hardness, Points	55 ±5
Tensile Strength, Min MPa (psi)	10.5 (1500)
Ultimate Elongation, Min %	400
Oil Immersion 22 h at 100 °C (212 °F), ASTM Oil No. 2, Volume Change, Max %	80
Heat Aged 70 h at 100 °C (212 °F)	
Change in Durometer Hardness, Max Points	+10
Tensile Strength, Min MPa (psi)	8.5 (1200)
Ultimate Elongation, Min %	300
Permanent Set at 300% Elongation, Max %	20
Added Requirements	
Suffix E2, 22 h at 100 °C (212 °F) in ASTM Oil No. 2, Volume Change, Max %	50

2. References

2.1 Applicable Publications—The following publications form a part of this specification to the extent specified herein.

2.1.1 ASTM PUBLICATIONS—Available from ASTM, 100 Barr Harbor Drive, West Conshohocken, PA 19428-2959.

ASTM D 412—Tests for Rubber Properties in Tension
ASTM D 471—Test for Rubber Property—Effect of Liquids
ASTM D 573—Test for Rubber Deterioration in an Air Oven
ASTM D 925—Test for Rubber Property—Staining of Surfaces (Contact, Migration, and Diffusion)
ASTM D 2137—Test for Rubber Property—Brittleness Point of Flexible Polymers and Coated Fabrics
ASTM D 2240—Test for Rubber Property—Durometer Hardness

3. Types, Classes, and Grades of Compounds

3.1 Types—These specifications cover two types of compounds designated by the prefix letters LR and LS as follows:

3.1.1 TYPE LR—Compounds made from natural rubber, synthetic rubber, or rubberlike materials, alone or in combination, for services where specific resistance to the action of petroleum-base fluids is not required.

3.1.2 TYPE LS—Compounds made from synthetic rubber or rubberlike materials for services where specific resistance to the action of petroleum-base fluids is required.

3.2 Classes—Type LR compounds are of one class only. Type LS compounds were divided into two classes, LSB and LSC. Class LSB has since been deleted.

3.2.1 CLASS LSC—Compounds made from synthetic rubber or rubberlike materials having medium volume swell in low aniline point oils.

3.3 Grades—Each of the compounds may have a number of different grades, each having different physical properties. The grade shall be designated by a grade number following the prefix letters and, when necessary, by suffix letters after the grade number.

3.4 Suffix Letters—Suffix letters may be added singly or in combination after any grade number to indicate additional requirements beyond those specified in the tables as basic requirements for that particular grade.

If no value for the suffix letter requirements is specified in the table, or when no method of test is provided, agreement as to the required value and method of test must be arranged between the purchaser and the supplier. See Table 3.

TABLE 3—SUFFIX LETTERS AND TEST REQUIRED

Suffix Letters	Test Required
C1	Ozone Resistance
E2	Oil Resistance—ASTM Oil No. 2
F1	Low-Temperature Brittleness at -40 °C (-40 °F)
G	Tear Resistance
H	Flex Resistance
K1	Adhesion to Metal—Bond made during vulcanization
K2	Adhesion—Cemented bond made after vulcanization
P	Nonstaining
Z	Special Requirements

4. Materials and Workmanship—All materials and workmanship shall be in accordance with good commercial practice, and the resulting product shall be free of bubbles, voids, foreign matter, or other defects affecting serviceability.

5. Color—Unless otherwise specified, these compounds shall be black and free from objectionable bloom.

6. Methods of Testing—The properties enumerated in these specifications shall be determined in accordance with the following methods of the American Society for Testing and Materials, except as modified in accordance with certain provisions stated herein. All exposure periods and temperatures prescribed in Tables 1 and 2 shall be given preference over those specified in the ASTM methods (latest issue).

6.1 Standard Test Film Preparation—Standard test films shall be prepared using procedures (coagulation, leach, dry, and cure) identical to the preparation of production parts except thickness which shall be 0.63 to 0.75 mm (0.025 to 0.030 in).

6.2 Durometer Hardness—ASTM D 2240, Test for Rubber Property—Durometer Hardness, (Type A), except plied up thickness of test specimen to be between 4.5 and 6.3 mm (0.175 and 0.250 in).

6.3 Tensile Strength, Elongation, and Tension Set—ASTM D 412, Tests for Rubber Properties in Tension, using Die C. Film thickness to be 0.63 to 0.75 mm (0.025 to 0.030 in).

6.4 Immersion, Including Suffix E2—ASTM D 471, Test for Rubber Property—Effect of Liquids.

6.5 Heat Aging—ASTM D 573, Test for Rubber Deterioration in an Air Oven.

6.6 Low-Temperature Brittleness—Suffix F1—ASTM D 2137, nonbrittle after 3 min at -40 °C except specimen thickness to be 0.63 to 0.75 mm (0.025 to 0.030 in).

6.7 Non-Staining, Suffix P—ASTM D 925, Tests for Rubber Property—Staining of Surfaces (Contact, Migration, and Diffusion).

7. Sampling and Inspection

7.1 A lot, unless otherwise specified, shall consist of all products of the same composition and same grade submitted for inspection at the same time.

7.2 Sampling and inspection of the material shall be agreed upon by the purchaser and the supplier as part of the purchase contract.

SYNTHETIC RESIN PLASTIC SEALERS, NONDRYING TYPE—SAE J250 MAY1959

SAE Recommended Practice

Report of the SAE Nonmetallic Materials Committee approved May 1959.

Foreword—This Document has not changed other than to put it into the new SAE Technical Standards Board Format.

1. Scope—The material desired under this recommended practice is a synthetic resin plastic sealer of the nondrying, nonbleeding, and noncorrosive type that may be extruded to the specified size and used as a medium for producing a water tight seal between 2 pressed steel sections or between rubber and steel.

2. References

2.1 Applicable Publications—The following publications form a part of the specification to the extent specified herein.

2.1.1 ASTM Publications—Available from ASTM, 100 Barr Harbor Drive, West Conshohocken, PA 19428-2959.

ASTM D 217—Test Method for Cone Penetration of Lubricating Grease
ASTM D 553—Discontinued
ASTM D 1321—Test Method of Needle Penetration of Petroleum Waxes

3. Color

3.1 Gray—The color of the sealer must be light and shall not smear in order to facilitate clean up in assembly.

3.2 Black

4. Physical Properties

4.1 Consistency

Requirements No. 1—Cone penetration, 7–10 mm.

Method of Test—ASTM D 217 using 150 g cone plus 150 g additional weight.

Requirement No. 2—Needle penetration, 18–22 mm.

Method Test—ASTM D 1321 using total weight including needle of 100 g.

4.2 Solids—99.0% minimum.

Method of Test—ASTM D 553—Weight 3 g sample and bake for 3 hr at 215 °F.

4.3 Cold Resistance—Requirement No. 1—Pliable at –20 °F.

Method of Test—A sample of the material applied to a thin polyethylene or polyester film is exposed to a temperature of –20 °F for 4 hr and immediately upon removal from this temperature bent across a 2 1/2 in. diameter mandrel. Cracks shall not be evident.

Requirement No. 2—No evidence of cracking, embrittlement, or loss of adhesion shall be present.

Method of Test—Apply 3/16 x 6 in. bead of sealer to a 4 x 12 in. enameled or lacquered panel. A piece of waxed Kraft paper is placed on top of the beads and rolled with 3 single passes of a 3 lb roller. The panels are then exposed to –20 °F for 4 hr and slammed at 90 deg in a cold slam fixture, see Figure 1.

4.4 Bleeding—No discoloration or migratory staining of the enameled or lacquered finish will be tolerated when the material is subjected to the following test:

Method of Test—Apply a 3/16 x 6 in. bead of the material to a steel panel which has been primed, painted, and baked according to the users specification and subject to a baking temperature of 280 °F for 1 hr.

4.5 Stability—Method of Test No. 1—A sample of the material shall be exposed for 24 hr to a temperature of 158 °F and after exposure the surface must remain tacky with no appreciable hardening. Bead must be readily removed from backing without stretching over 15%. As received the sealer shall not stretch over 10%.

Method of Test No. 2—A sample of the material after being exposed for 2 weeks to a temperature of 158 °F shall not leach its oils or show cracks when bent across a 1 in. diameter mandrel.

4.6 Water Resistance—The water resistance of the material shall conform to the following:

Method of Test—A sample of the material is held under water, at room temperature, and kneaded with the fingers for 1 minute. During the kneading the material shall not disintegrate nor become short showing loss of cohesion. The sealer must be unaffected by water or a 5% sodium chloride solution when immersed for a period of 24 hr at room temperature.

4.7 Solvent Resistance (When Specified)—The solvent resistance of the material shall conform to the following:

Method of Test—A 3/16 x 2 in. bead shall be immersed in gasoline for a period of 70 hr at room temperature. There shall be no deterioration, evidence of solubility, or loss of adhesion to the metal.

4.8 Sag Characteristics—The material shall not sag, blister, nor pull away from a horizontal metal surface when tested under the following conditions:

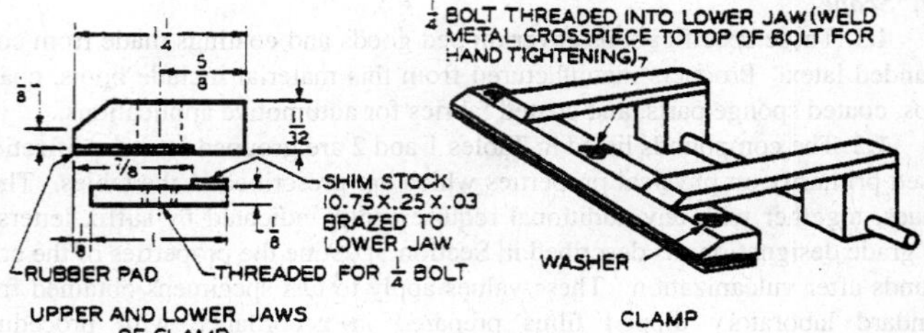

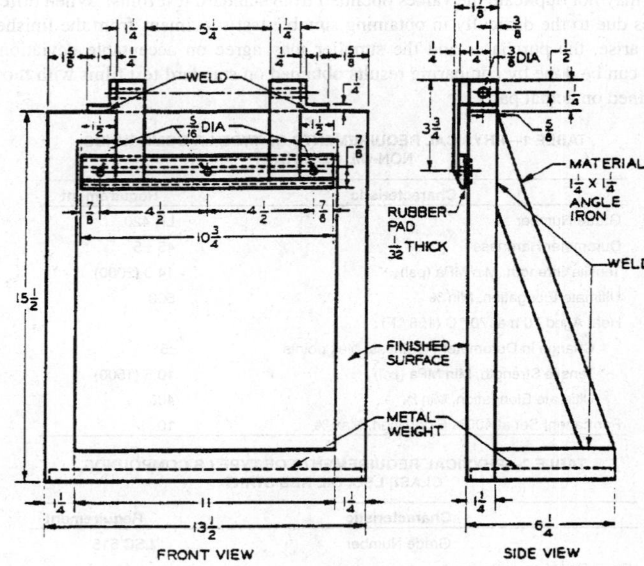

FIGURE 1—DETAILED VIEW OF SLAMMING FIXTURE FOR COLD ADHESION TEST

Method of Test—Apply a 1/2 in. bead of sealer to the angle joint of the fixture shown in Figure 2. (Fixture is to be made from 036–042 gage standard body steel and phosphate coated.) Brush or trowel the bead against the sides of the angle so that the material takes a concave shape. This may be done with the angle pointing up. Immediately invert the panel and block so that one leg is vertical. Place in the inverted position in an oven and heat for 1/2 hr at 400 °F.

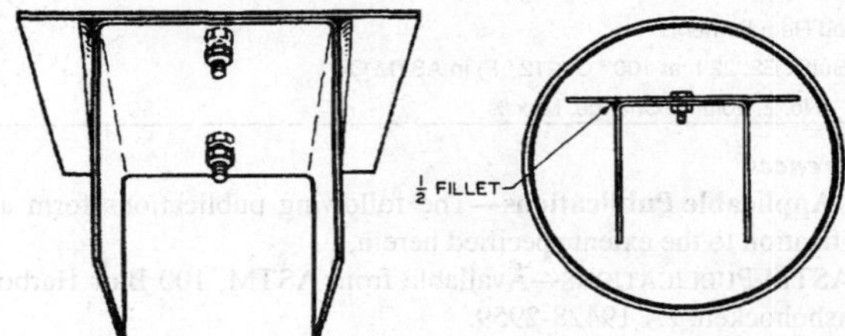

FIGURE 2—FIXTURE FOR SAG CHARACTERISTICS TEST

4.9 Aged Adhesion—The adhesion shall be greater than the cohesive strength of the material when an attempt is made to strip or peel a bead of the sealer from a metal panel after being subjected to the following test:

Method of Test—Apply a 3/16 x 6 in. bead of the material to a 4 x 12 in. steel panel which has been primed, painted, and baked according to the users specifications. A piece of waxed Kraft paper is placed on top of the bead and rolled with 3 single passes of a 3 lb roller. The panel shall then be aged for 1 hr at 280 °F followed by 1 week at 158 °F and a cold cycle of –20 °F for 6 hr.

5. Packaging—Beads shall be supplied as specified by the user and must be packaged in such a manner as to prevent the beads from sticking together.

METHOD FOR EVALUATING THE FLOW PROPERTIES OF PUMPABLE SEALERS—SAE J2025 JUN1989

SAE Recommended Practice

Report of the SAE Adhesives and Body Sealers Committee approved June 1989.

Foreword—This Document has not changed other than to put it into the new SAE Technical Standards Board Format.

1. Scope—This SAE Recommended Practice sets forth a method for evaluating the flow properties of automotive sealers that have been dispensed via a high pressure automatic system.

1.1 Background—For many years, automotive sealers were applied manually by means of an operator-held flow gun. The operator could adjust flow rates by hand speed and/or adjusting the pump pressures up or down as desired. Today, however, some sealers are applied by automated means such as robots, gantry tables, etc. To be effective, an automated system must be capable of applying material at a constant known rate. This demands that the equipment and material handling parameters remain constant, not changing from their initial setup.

2. References—There are no referenced publications specified herein.

3. Principle of Methods—This method involves dispensing a sealer through a standard production system. The material being tested is subjected to three separate dispensing conditions at a temperature of 18 °C (65 °F). The three conditions listed below simulate the typical in-plant pumping variations that can cause variability in sealer delivery rates:

a. Condition #1: The material is pressurized from zero static to 10 350 kPa (1500 psi) dynamic pressure with the resulting flow rate being measured. This simulates a "start-up" condition.

b. Condition #2: The material is pressurized under a static condition of 11 040 kPa (1600 psi) for 1 h followed by 1 h of dynamic pressure of 10 350 kPa (1500 psi) during which the material is pumped continuously followed by a flow rate determination. This simulates an accelerated, constant application of material.

c. Condition #3: The material is held under a static pressure of 11 040 kPa (1600 psi) for 24 h followed by a dynamic pressure of 10 350 kPa (1500 psi) during which the flow rate is determined. This simulates a system being left under pressure, overnight, with a subsequent start up the next day.

4. Equipment

1 - 55 gallon drum of sealant to be tested.

1 - Air operated positive displacement pump (42:1 ratio) with an elevator, follower plate, and air pressure gage(s).

1 - Dispensing system consisting of: (see Figure 1.)

1 - (A) 31.75 mm (1-1/4 in) x 1.83 m (6 ft) hose

3 - (B) Visual test gages - 27 600 kPa (4000 psi), 345 kPa (50 psi) divisions

1 - (C) 50.8 mm (2 in) x 3.05 m (10 ft) header pipe with 31.75 mm (1-1/4 in) I.D.

1 - (D) Limit switch

1 - (E) 31.75 mm (1-1/4 in) to 50.8 mm (2 in) reducing bushing

1 - (F) 50.8 mm (2 in) pipe elbows

2 - (G) Cycle counters

1 - (H) Second timer

2 - (I) Solenoid operated three-way air valve 25.4 mm (1 in)

1 - (J) 50.8 mm (2 in) to 12.7 mm (1/2 in) reducing bushing

1 - (K) 12.7 mm (1/2 in) x 3.05 m (10 ft) hose

1 - (L) 25.4 mm (1 in) x 76.2 mm (3 in) pipe

1 - (M) Reducing bushing with commercial 4.76 mm (3/16 in) nozzle

1 - (N) 25.4 mm (1 in) air actuated ball valve

1 - (O) 25.4 mm (1 in) pipe tee

1 - (P) Cup actuator

1 - (Q) Temperature indicator (digital)

1 - (R) 50.8 mm (2 in) pipe tee

1 - Weight scale (digital)

1 - Air compressor

1 - Control panel for automatic actuators

1 - Climate control room at 18 °C (65 °F)

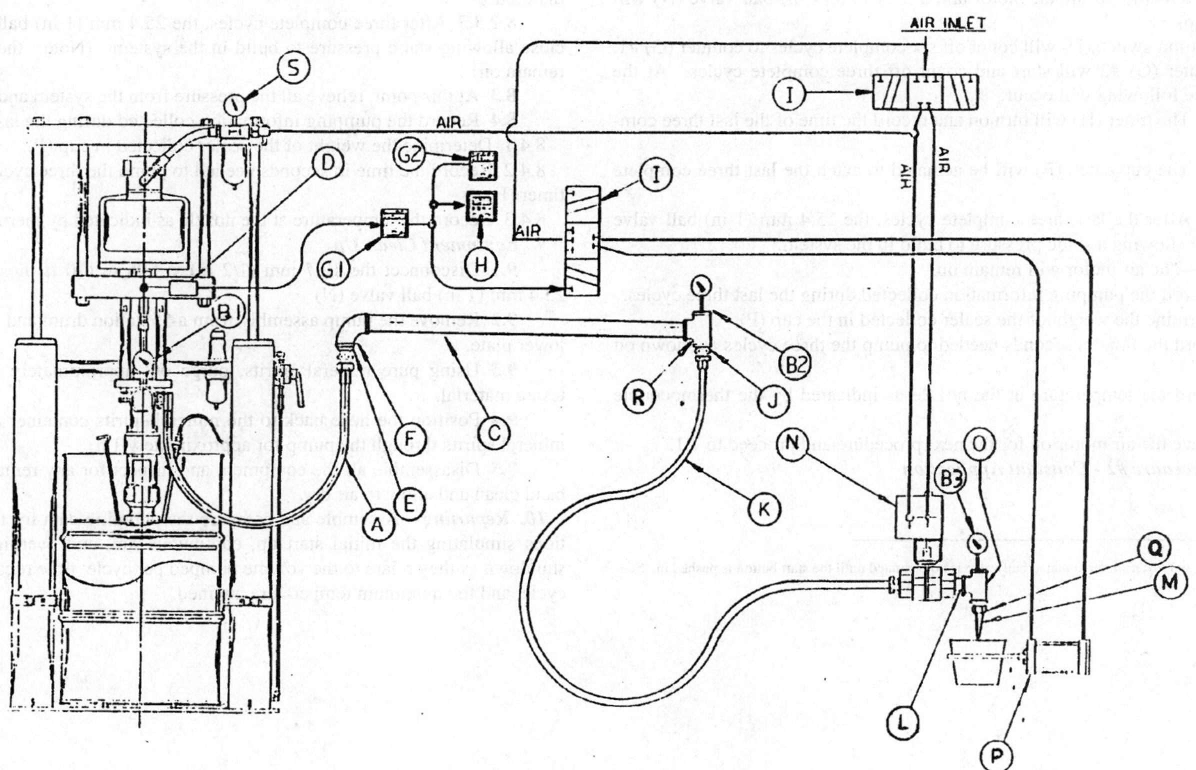

FIGURE 1—

5. Dispensing System Assembly (See Figure 1):

5.1 Mount limit switch (D) to the pump to indicate complete up-to-down cycles.

5.2 Install the gage (B) #1 to the outlet of the pump equipment.

5.3 Attach a 31.75 mm (1-1/4 in) x 1.83 m (6 ft) hose (A) to the outlet of the pump.

5.4 Attach the other end of the hose (A) to the inlet end of 50.8 mm (2 in) header (C).

5.5 Install the gage (B) #2 to 50.8 mm (2 in) pipe tee (R) on the outlet end of 50.8 mm (2 in) header (C).

5.6 Attach a 12.7 mm (1/2 in) x 3.05 m (10 ft) hose (K) to the outlet of 50.8 mm (2 in) pipe tee (R).

5.7 Attach a 12.7 mm (1/2 in) x 3.05 m (10 ft) hose (K) to the inlet of 25.4 mm (1 in) air actuated ball valve (N).

5.8 Attach a 25.4 mm (1 in) x 76.2 mm (3 in) pipe (L) to the outlet of a 25.4 mm (1 in) air actuated ball valve (N).

5.9 Attach a 25.4 mm (1 in) pipe tee (O) to the outlet end of a 25.4 mm (1 in) x 76.2 mm (3 in) pipe (L).

5.10 Install a gage (B) #3 to the outlet end of a 25.4 mm (1 in) pipe tee (O).

5.11 Install a 4.76 mm (3/16 in) nozzle (M) to the outlet end of a 25.4 mm (1 in) tee (O).

5.12 Attach a temperature indicator (Q) to a nozzle (M).

5.13 Install and position a cup catch (P).

6. Test Procedure #1 - Start-Up Condition

6.1 Condition the material, equipment, and room to 18 °C (65 °F), or as specified, for approximately 72 h.

6.2 Purge the entire system with 5 gallons of test material.

6.2.1 While purging the material, adjust the air pressure to achieve a dynamic pressure at gage (B) #3 of 10 350 kPa (1500 psi).

6.2.2 Note what air pressure is required to the air motor on air gage (S).

6.3 At this point, relieve all pressure from the system and allow the material to stabilize for approximately 1 h.

6.4 Set the air pressure from 6.2.2 on gage (S) required for the 10 350 kPa (1500 psi) dynamic material pressure.[1]

6.5 Set the cycle counter (G) #1 to six complete cycles and counter (G) #2 to three complete cycles.

6.6 Press the start button. At this point, the following will occur:

6.6.1 The actuators to the air motor and a 25.4 mm (1 in) ball valve (N) will switch to open.

6.6.2 The limit switch (D) will count off six complete cycles to counter (G) #1.

6.6.3 Counter (G) #2 will start and count off three complete cycles. At the same time, the following will occur:

6.6.3.1 The timer (H) will turn on and record the time of the last three complete cycles.

6.6.3.2 The cup catch (P) will be actuated to catch the last three complete cycles.

6.6.3.3 After the last three complete cycles, the 25.4 mm (1 in) ball valve (N) will close allowing a static pressure to build in the system.

NOTE—The air motor will remain on.

6.7 Record the pumping information collected during the last three cycles.

6.7.1 Determine the weight of the sealer collected in the cup (P).

6.7.2 Record the time in seconds needed to pump the three cycles as shown on the timer (H).

6.7.3 Record the temperature at the nozzle as indicated by the thermocouple (Q).

6.8 Leave the air motor on for the next procedure and proceed to 7.1.

7. Test Procedure #2 - Constant Application

7.1 Allow the system from 6.8 to remain pressurized in a static condition for 1 h at a pressure of 10 350 kPa (1500 psi) to 11 040 kPa (1600 psi).

7.2 Switch off the counters (G) #1 and #2.

7.3 Press the start button. At this point, the following will occur:

7.3.1 The actuator to the 25.4 mm (1 in) ball valve (N) will switch to open.

7.3.2 Dispense the material for 1 h.

7.3.3 Toward the end of the 1 h run, note the time it takes for nine complete cycles to allow sufficient time to activate the counters (G).

7.3.4 Activate the counters (G) at the predetermined point near the end of the 1 h pumping cycle.

7.3.5 The limit switch (D) will count off six complete cycles to counter (G) #1.

7.3.6 The counter (G) #2 will count off three complete cycles. At the same time, the following will occur:

7.3.6.1 Timer (H) will turn on and record the duration of three complete cycles.

7.3.6.2 The cup catch (P) will be actuated to catch three complete cycles of material.

7.3.6.3 After three complete cycles, the 25.4 mm (1 in) ball valve (N) will close allowing static pressure to build in the system.

NOTE—The air motor will remain on.

7.4 Record the pumping information collected during the last three cycles.

7.4.1 Determine the weight of the sealer collected in cup (P).

7.4.2 Record the time in seconds needed to pump the three cycles as shown on timer (H).

7.4.3 Record the temperature at the nozzle as indicated by thermocouple (Q).

7.5 Leave the air motor on for the next procedure and proceed to 8.1.

8. Test Procedure #3 - 24 Hours Static Pressure

8.1 Allow the system from 7.5 to remain pressurized in a static condition for 24 h at a pressure of 10 350 kPa (1500 psi) to 11 040 kPa (1600 psi).

8.2 Press the start button. At this point, the following will occur:

8.2.1 The actuator to the 25.4 mm (1 in) ball valve (N) will switch to open.

8.2.2 The limit switch (D) will count off six complete cycles to counter (G) #1.

8.2.3 The counter (G) #2 will start and count off three complete cycles. At the same time, the following will occur:

8.2.3.1 The timer (H) will turn on and record the duration of three complete cycles.

8.2.3.2 The cup catch (P) will be actuated to catch three complete cycles of material.

8.2.3.3 After three complete cycles, the 25.4 mm (1 in) ball valve (N) will close allowing static pressure to build in the system. (Note: the air motor will remain on)

8.3 At this point, relieve all the pressure from the system and allow to stand.

8.4 Record the pumping information collected during the last three cycles.

8.4.1 Determine the weight of the sealer collected in cup (P).

8.4.2 Record the time in seconds needed to pump the three cycles as shown on timer (H).

8.4.3 Record the temperature at the nozzle as indicated by thermocouple (Q).

9. Equipment Clean Up

9.1 Disconnect the 12.7 mm (1/2 in) x 3.05 m (10 ft) hose (K) from the 25.4 mm (1 in) ball valve (N).

9.2 Remove the pump assembly from a 55 gallon drum and remove the follower plate.

9.3 Using pure mineral spirits, purge out approximately five gallons of tested material.

9.4 Position the hose back to the mineral spirits container and recycle the mineral spirits through the pump for approximately 1 h.

9.5 Disassemble all the equipment and inspect for any remaining material, hand clean and allow to air dry.

10. Reporting—Assemble and compare the pumping data for the three conditions simulating the initial start up, continuous run, and overnight pressurized shutdown as they relate to the volume pumped per cycle, time required to pump a cycle, and the maximum temperature attained.

---

1. The air motor and material; air actuated ball valve is not actuated until the start button is pushed in. See 6.6.

METHODS OF TESTS FOR AUTOMOTIVE-TYPE SEALERS, ADHESIVES, AND DEADENERS —SAE J243 OCT1971

SAE Recommended Practice

Report of the SAE Nonmetallic Materials Committee approved October 1971.

Foreword—This Document has not changed other than to put it into the new SAE Technical Standards Board format.

*1. **Scope***—This SAE Recommended Practice contains a series of test methods for use in measuring characteristics of automotive-type sealers, adhesives, and deadeners. The test methods which are contained in this document are as follows:

ADS-1—Methods of Determining Viscosity
ADS-2—Low Temperature Tests
ADS-3—Weld-Through Tests
ADS-4—Enamel, Lacquer, and Fabric Staining Test
ADS-5—Wash-Off Resistance Test
ADS-7—Solids Test
ADS-8—Flash Point Test
ADS-9—Sag and Bridging Tests
ADS-10—Flow Test

The intent of this document is to provide a series of test methods which can be used in testing the various qualities of sealers, adhesives, and deadener material. In later revisions of this document, attempts will be made to reduce the number of tests now presented. The specific temperatures and times at which some of these tests are to be conducted are not dictated in these test procedures, but they will be found in the material standards which govern each type of material to be tested.

*2. **References***

2.1 Applicable Publications—The following publications form a part of this specification to the extent specified herein.

2.1.1 ASTM PUBLICATIONS—Available from ASTM, 100 Barr Harbor Drive, West Conshohocken, PA 19428-2959.

ASTM D 5—Test for Penetration of Bituminous Materials

ASTM D 93—Standard Method of Test for Flash Point by Pensky-Martin's Closed Tester

ASTM D 217—Test for Cone Penetration of Lubricating Grease

ASTM D 553—Standard Method of Test for Viscosity and Total Solids Content of Rubber Cements

ASTM D 1310—Standard Method of Test for Flash Point of Volatile Flammable Materials by Tag Open Cup Apparatus

ASTM D 1582—Standard Method of Test of Non-Volatile Content of Phenol, Resorcinol and Melamine Adhesives

*3. **ADS-1—Methods of Determining Viscosity***

3.1 Methods of Conditioning Test Materials Prior to Checking Viscosity

3.1.1 FOR VISCOSITY UNAGITATED

3.1.1.1 Conditioning Method A—Check the submitted sample as received. Test in the original container or transfer to the test vessel with minimum handling.

3.1.2 FOR VISCOSITY AGITATED

3.1.2.1 Conditioning Method A—Material shall be subject to the specified number of cycles in a standard mechanical greaseworker as outlined in ASTM D 217, Test for Cone Penetration of Lubricating Grease.

3.1.2.2 Conditioning Method B—Pass the sample once through the sealer cup using specified pressure and orifice.

3.1.2.3 Conditioning Method C—Stir a pint sample to 50 stirs with a 1 x 6 in steel-bladed spatula.

3.1.3 FOR VISCOSITY AGED—Conditioning (agitated or unagitated as specified):

a. Condition the sample in a sealed 1/2 pt can for 72 h in an oven at specified temperature.
b. Remove from the oven, condition the sample to 77 ±2 F, and determine viscosity.

3.2 Viscosity Tests

3.2.1 VISCOSITY, PRESSURE FLOW METHOD

3.2.1.1 Application—This procedure is used to determine the viscosity of adhesives, sealers, and deadeners. The time required for a specified weight of the material to pass through a specified orifice under a given pressure indicates the viscosity of the material.

3.2.1.2 Equipment Required

3.2.1.2.1 Castor-Severs Rheometer or Pressure Flowmeter—The pressure flowmeter required for this test is detailed in Figure 1. The flowmeter is not available commercially but must be fabricated. For example:

	Sealer Cup Orifices							
	A	B	C	D	E	F	G	H
Diameter of Orifice, in	0.052	0.063	0.073	0.104	0.104	0.125	0.200	0.250
Lengths of Orifice, in	0.531	2.00	0.531	0.531	0.750	2.00	0.750	2.00

3.2.1.2.2 Ring stand and clamps for supporting pressure flowmeter.

3.2.1.2.3 Pressure gage, 100 lb maximum air gage, calibrated in 2 lb increments.

3.2.1.2.4 Pressure relief valve—This is an air cock which opens or closes at a single turn.

3.2.1.2.5 Shutoff valve—Same type as pressure relief valve.

3.2.1.2.6 Pressure regulator and extractor—This unit may be of any suitable type which will remove oil and water from the air and which will control the pressure of the air delivered to the pressure flowmeter. The regulator and extractor unit is assembled between the shutoff valve and an adequate air source.

3.2.1.2.7 Pipe cleaners suitable for cleaning orifice of flowmeter.

3.2.1.2.8 Stopwatch or other timing device calibrated in seconds.

3.2.1.2.9 Balance, double beam type or equivalent, sensitivity to 0.01 g.

3.2.1.2.10 Connections 0.25 in pipe and fittings with standard pipe threads as are necessary for assembling equipment, as shown in Figure 1.

3.2.1.2.11 Mechanical convection oven capable of maintaining a temperature of ±2 F.

3.2.1.3 Procedure

3.2.1.3.1 Fill the clean and dry sealer cup equipped with specified orifice with the test material, allowing room for the plunger disc, and assemble the apparatus. Care should be taken to avoid air entrapment.

NOTE—Test material and equipment shall be maintained at a temperature of 77 ±2 F during the test.

3.2.1.3.2 Adjust the air line pressure to the flowmeter as designated by the material standard and bleed until free of air. This should be done while the test material is passing through the pressure flowmeter or Severs Rheometer.

FIGURE 1—CASTOR-SEVERS RHEOMETER OR PRESSURE FLOWMETER (OR KEIL RHEOMETER)

3.2.1.3.3 Close air line valve, place a paper on the balance pan under the flowmeter and bring balance to equilibrium. Add specified weight.

3.2.1.3.4 Open the air line valve and start the timer when the material touches the paper on the weighing pan.

3.2.1.3.5 When the specified weight of the sealer has accumulated on the balance pan, stop the timer, close the air line valve, and open the pressure relief valve.

3.2.1.3.6 Report the viscosity of the material as the number of seconds required for a specified amount of the material to pass through the orifice at the specified pressure. (Note: Take the average of three readings.)

3.2.2 BROOKFIELD METHOD

3.2.2.1 Application—This procedure is to determine the viscosity of adhesives, deadeners, and thin body sealers. The viscosity is indicated by the resistance produced upon a spindle rotating at a definite speed while immersed in the material under test.

3.2.2.2 Equipment—Commercially available Brookfield Viscometer[1] (Figure 2).

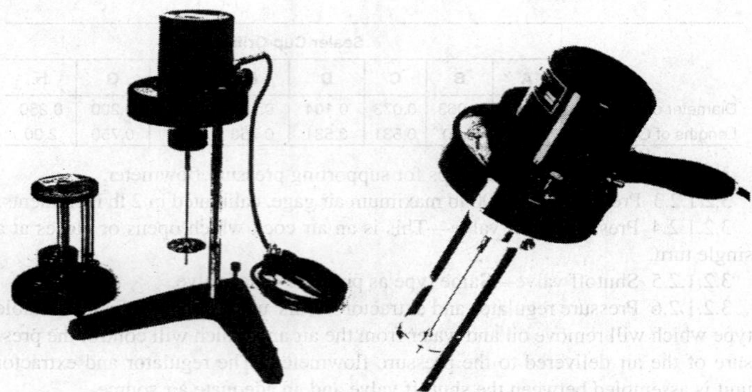

FIGURE 2—BROOKFIELD VISCOMETER

3.2.2.3 Procedure—Test material and equipment shall be maintained at a temperature of 77 ±2 F during the test.

3.2.2.3.1 Insert the specified spindle in a pint of test material, keeping the fluid's level below the immersion groove cut in the spindle shaft.

3.2.2.3.2 Attach spindle to the lower shaft.

3.2.2.3.3 Lower viscometer so that the groove cut in spindle shaft is flush with the fluid's level.

3.2.2.3.4 Level the viscometer and set viscometer speed at specified rpm.

3.2.2.3.5 Depress the clutch and turn on the viscometer motor. Release clutch and allow dial to rotate for 1 min. Take reading at this position. If the pointer has not stabilized at a fixed position after 1 min, the reading shall not be taken until the pointer has stabilized. The time shall then be recorded.

3.2.2.3.6 Using conversion table, convert to centipoise.

3.2.2.3.7 When reporting viscosity, the spindle, rpm, and viscometer and model number shall be indicated. Average of three readings.

3.2.3 MacMichael Method—Used for measuring the viscosity of both Newtonian and non-Newtonian liquids such as sealers, adhesives, and deadeners. The viscosity is given in degrees MacMichael (M).

3.2.3.1 Equipment Required—A commercially available Fisher-MacMichael Viscometer[2] with sample cups, plungers, and different gage wires (Figure 3).

3.2.3.2 Procedure

3.2.3.2.1 Insert specified wire in hollow spindle.

3.2.3.2.2 Attach specified plunger to the spindle.

3.2.3.2.3 Suspend spindle assembly from the pointer assembly support.

3.2.3.2.4 Level apparatus.

3.2.3.2.5 Zero the dial.

3.2.3.2.6 Lift spindle assembly off support.

3.2.3.2.7 Adjust hot plate rotation speed to rotational speed specified.

3.2.3.2.8 Adjust the sample temperature to temperature specified.

3.2.3.2.9 Fill specified clean sample cut (sample depth specified) and place on hot plate.

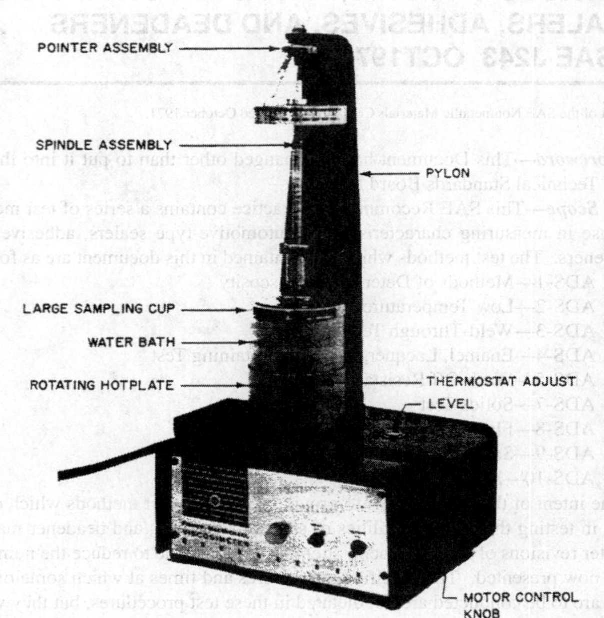

FIGURE 3—FISHER-MACMICHAEL VISCOMETER

3.2.3.2.10 If test temperature is greater than 77 F, adjust thermostat to desired temperature.

3.2.3.2.11 Replace spindle.

3.2.3.2.12 Cover sample cup.

3.2.3.2.13 Check that sample is at desired temperature.

3.2.3.2.14 Take reading by turning on the rotate switch and read degrees M from the dial at point spindle becomes stationary or at specified time.

3.2.3.2.15 When reporting degrees M viscosity, the temperature of material, wire gage, plunger, hot plate rotational speed, sample cup size, and sample depth should be indicated.

3.2.4 Ford Cup Method—Particularly suited for measuring the viscosity of relatively thin adhesives, sealers, and deadeners. The viscosity is given in seconds and is the amount of time it takes for specific amounts of fluid material to pass through a known size orifice.

3.2.4.1 Equipment

3.2.4.1.1 Commercially available Ford Cups[3] (Figure 4).

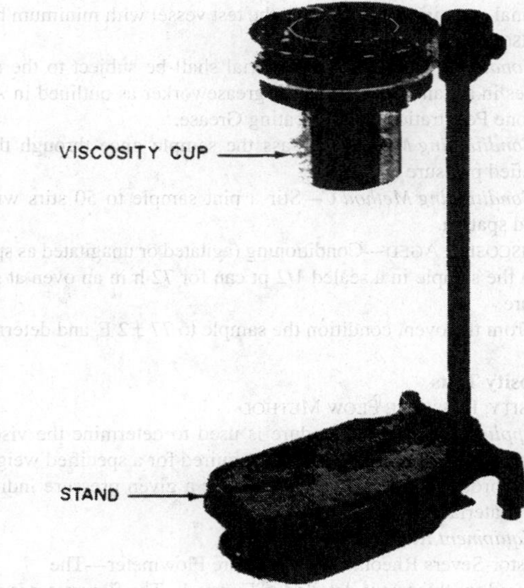

FIGURE 4—FORD CUP

1. Available from Brookfield Engineering Laboratories, 240 Cushing St., Stoughton, Mass.
2. Available from Fischer Scientific Co., 1458 N. Lamon Ave., Chicago, Illinois 60651.
3. Available from Ford Viscosimeter Corp., 7730 W. Fort St., Detroit, Michigan 48209.

3.2.4.1.2 Ring stand and ring for holding Ford Cup.
3.2.4.1.3 Timing device for measuring seconds.

3.2.4.2 Procedure—Test material and equipment shall be at a temperature of 77 ±2 F during the test.

3.2.4.2.1 Holding finger over aperture, fill the specified clean cup and orifice with the material being tested.

3.2.4.2.2 Simultaneously remove finger from aperture and start timing device.

3.2.4.2.3 When a break in the flow of material through the open aperture occurs or a specified amount of material has flowed, stop the timing device.

3.2.4.2.4 When reporting Ford viscosity, indicate the Ford Cup used.

3.2.5 PENETROMETER METHOD—This procedure is used to determine the viscosity of heavy bodied sealers and deadeners. Viscosity is a measure of depth of penetration of a cone or needle into a standard body of material.

3.2.5.1 Equipment Required

3.2.5.1.1 Commercially available universal penetrometer as described in ASTM D 217 or ASTM D 5, Test for Penetration of Bituminous Materials. (Figure 5).

3.2.5.1.2 Weights to place on loading bar.

3.2.5.1.3 Penetrating instrument (cone—ASTM D 217, needle—ASTM D 5).

3.2.5.1.4 Stopwatch.

3.2.5.1.5 Sample cup as specified.

3.2.5.2 Procedure—Test material and equipment shall be at 77 ±2 F during the test.

3.2.5.2.1 Level penetrometer.

3.2.5.2.2 Insert specified penetrating instrument into chuck.

3.2.5.2.3 Set dial reading to zero.

FIGURE 5—PENETROMETER

3.2.5.2.4 Add weights as required to loading bar to achieve specified load. (Load is the total weight of rod and penetrating instrument.)

3.2.5.2.5 Fill clean sample cup level full with test material, smooth surface, and place it in position centered under the penetrating instrument.

3.2.5.2.6 Adjust height so as to bring the point of the penetrating instrument exactly into contact with the smooth surface of the sample.

3.2.5.2.7 Release test rod by pushing the clutch trigger down and holding it down during specified time of the test.

3.2.5.2.8 At the end of the specified time, lock the test rod by releasing the clutch trigger.

3.2.5.2.9 Push down the depth gage rod as far as it will go and read the depth of penetration in tenths of millimeters.

3.2.5.2.10 When reporting penetrometer viscosity, indicate the load, penetration time, and cup size (average of three samples).

3.2.6 GARDNER MOBILOMETER METHOD—This method is used for determining the viscosity of adhesives and "thin" bodied sealers. Viscosity is expressed as the time in seconds for a standard plunger assembly (disc, piston rod, weight pan), loaded or unloaded, to fall through 10 cm of the test product.

3.2.6.1 Equipment

3.2.6.1.1 Commercially available regular Gardner Mobilometer[4] with 51-hole disc, solid disc, and 4-hole disc (Figure 6).

FIGURE 6—REGULAR GARDNER MOBILOMETER

3.2.6.1.2 Weights—Various gram amounts in 50 g increments.

3.2.6.1.3 Timing device for measuring seconds.

3.2.6.2 Procedure—Test material and equipment shall be maintained at a temperature of 77 ±2 F during the test.

3.2.6.2.1 Fill clean cylinder to a depth of 20 cm with material to be tested.

3.2.6.2.2 Level instrument.

3.2.6.2.3 Attach collar bracket cylinder so top of collar bracket is 4 in down from top of cylinder.

3.2.6.2.4 Place piston rod through piston guide and attach specified disc to piston rod.

3.2.6.2.5 Lower disc into material until lowest mark on the piston rod is flush with the top of the piston guide. (If there is only two marks on piston rod, lower the piston rod into the material until the bottom mark is 1/2 in above the piston guide top.)

3.2.6.2.6 If a load is called for, add weights to weight pan to give specified load. By definition, load shall be considered zero if there is no weights added to the weight pan.

3.2.6.2.7 Release piston rod and start timer when second lowest mark reaches top of piston guide. (If there is only two marks on piston rod, start timer when bottom mark reaches top of piston guide.)

3.2.6.2.8 Stop timer when the last mark reaches the top of the piston guide and report viscosity.

3.2.6.2.9 When reporting Gardner viscosity, indicate the disc used and the load applied.

4. ADS-2—Low Temperature Tests

4.1 Method A (Impact Test)—This procedure is used to determine the adhesion properties of sealers when subjected to an impact at a low temperature.

4.1.1 EQUIPMENT REQUIRED

4. Gardner Laboratory, Inc., P.O. Box 5728, Bethesda, Maryland 20014.

4.1.1.1 Slam fixture capable of delivering a uniform impact to the test panel. See Figure 7.

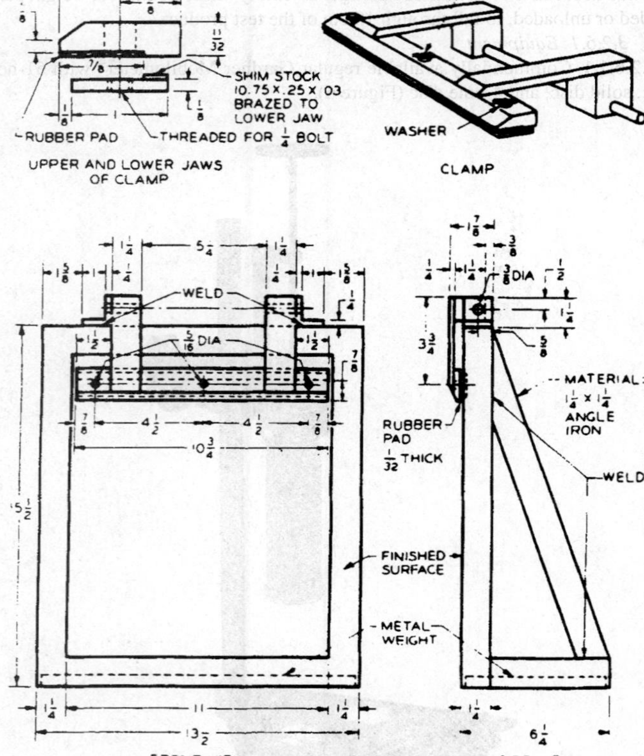

FIGURE 7—DETAILED VIEW OF SLAMMING FIXTURE FOR COLD ADHESION TEST

4.1.1.2 Cold box capable of maintaining a temperature of –40 ±2 F.

4.1.1.3 Circulating air oven capable of maintaining temperatures up to 400 ±2 F.

4.1.1.4 Analytical balance accurate to 1 mg.

4.1.1.5 Metal panels—12 x 12 x 0.036 in cold rolled, low carbon body stock steel, primed or painted as specified.

4.1.1.6 Draw down fixture with opening made to produce the bead size specified.

4.1.2 GENERAL PROCEDURE

4.1.2.1 Samples shall be mixed or otherwise treated as specified before applying.

4.1.2.2 Weigh panel and prepare as specified and record weight.

4.1.2.3 A size bead or ribbon of metal as specified shall be applied to the panel.

4.1.2.4 The applied bead or ribbon of material shall be conditioned, that is, air dried or baked for the time and temperature specified.

4.1.2.5 Weigh test panel and cured material and record weight.

4.1.2.6 Place the panels and specified slam fixture in the cold box for the time and temperature specified.

4.1.2.7 Insert the test panel in the slam fixture with sealer facing out and in the vertical position. Raise panel to a horizontal position. Release panel and allow it to slam against the test fixture. The number of slams to be as specified.

4.1.2.8 Inspect for loss of adhesion and remove loose material; calculate weight of material loss and record results as percent loss of adhesion.

4.2 Method B (Bend Test)—This procedure is used to determine the adhesion properties of seals when bent around a mandrel.

4.2.1 EQUIPMENT REQUIRED

4.2.1.1 Steel mandrel of size diameter as specified.

4.2.1.2 Aluminum foil 0.001–0.003 in thick.

4.2.1.3 Cold box capable of maintaining a temperature of –40 ±2 F.

4.2.1.4 Circulating air oven capable of maintaining temperatures up to 400 ±2 F.

4.2.1.5 Draw down fixture with opening made to produce the bead size specified.

4.2.2 GENERAL PROCEDURE

4.2.2.1 Samples shall be mixed or treated as specified.

4.2.2.2 Aluminum foil shall be prepared as specified.

4.2.2.3 A size bead or ribbon of material as specified shall be applied to the aluminum foil.

4.2.2.4 The applied bead or ribbon of material shall be conditioned, that is, air dried or baked for the time and temperature specified.

4.2.2.5 Place the aluminum foil and the mandrel in the cold box for the time and temperature specified.

4.2.2.6 While at the test temperature, wrap the aluminum foil 180 deg around the mandrel.

4.2.2.7 Inspect for cracking and loss of adhesion. Record number and size of cracks and loss of adhesion.

5. ADS-3—Weld-Through Tests

5.1 Scope—These tests are used to determine acceptability of weld-through sealers.

5.2 Method A

5.2.1 EQUIPMENT AND SUPPLIES

5.2.1.1 Single point spot welder with low inertia head, transformer tap setting of 4–5 V.

5.2.1.2 Two WA 2510 spot welding electrodes with 1/4 in diameter face and a 45 deg truncated cone.

5.2.1.3 A galvanometer-type oscillograph for recording sine wave of the secondary current.

5.2.1.4 A mechanical convection oven capable of maintaining 130 ±2 F.

5.2.1.5 Test coupons 1 x 3 x 0.036 in cold rolled, low carbon, open hearth steel, free from burrs or ragged edges that might provide a shunt path for welding current.

5.2.2 WELDING SCHEDULE

5.2.2.1 Electrode force: 550 lb.

5.2.2.2 Weld time: 9 cycles.

5.2.2.3 Secondary amperes: 11,000 A.

5.2.2.4 Secondary current time: Full sine wave starting at 0 deg point on first half cycle.

5.2.3 PROCEDURE—Weld-through characteristics shall be tested in two groups. Each group shall be tested using 25 sets of test coupons with sealer. Bare test coupons shall be welded at the start and finish of the test.

5.2.3.1 Prepare 50 coupon assemblies with 1 x 0.093 ±0.015 in of sealer, as shown in Figure 8.

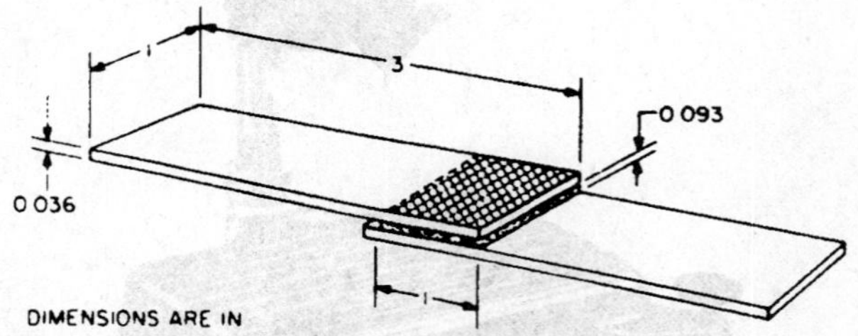

FIGURE 8—COUPON ASSEMBLIES WITH SEALER

5.2.3.2 Age 25 of the assemblies for 30 d at 72 ±5 F (group 1).

5.2.3.3 Condition 25 assemblies for 72 h at 130 ±2 F in a mechanical convection oven (group 2).

5.2.3.4 Verify the above specified weld schedule on a set of bare coupons.

5.2.3.5 Make 25 successive welds on the oven-aged coupons (group 2), one weld for each set of coupons through a bead of sealer. Exercise care to assure that the weld is directly through the sealer material. After each weld, examine the sine wave trace. Acceptable materials must show 90% of full welding current on or before the second half cycle of all welds. The height of the sine wave obtained in welding bare steel of the same thickness shall indicate full welding current.

5.2.3.6 Repeat the welding test on the 25 sets of coupons which were aged for 30 d (group 1), and examine the sine wave trace. Acceptable materials must show 90% of full welding current on or before the second half cycle of all welds.

5.2.3.7 During the above welding tests, the sealer shall show no tendency to ignite. There shall be no fouling of the spot welder points if the sealer is in direct contact.

5.2.3.8 Repeat the verification of the specified weld schedule on a set of bare coupons.

5.2.3.9 All welds must tear the metal when the "sealer-prepared" and "bare" welded panels are pulled in a tensile shear testing machine.

5.2.3.10 Measure the diameter of the weld buttons on the destructed shear strength panels after separating them with a chisel.

5.2.3.11 The material shall flow back around the weld to form a complete seal. Test method: Drill the spot welds from five panels of each of the two groups tested and visually observe for flowback.

5.3 Method B

5.3.1 EQUIPMENT AND SUPPLIES

5.3.1.1 A press type stationary spot welder.

5.3.1.2 Two water-cooled electrodes with 5/8 in diameter shank having a 45 deg truncated cone with a 1/4 in diameter welding face.

5.3.1.3 Test coupons of flat, cold rolled steel free from edge burrs and rust. Size 1 x 4 x 0.035 in and 4 x 24 x 0.035 in

5.3.1.4 Suitable tensile test machine.

5.3.1.5 Locating fixture (Figures 9A and 9B).

5.3.1.6 Notched spreader bar to give 1/32 in effective film thickness.

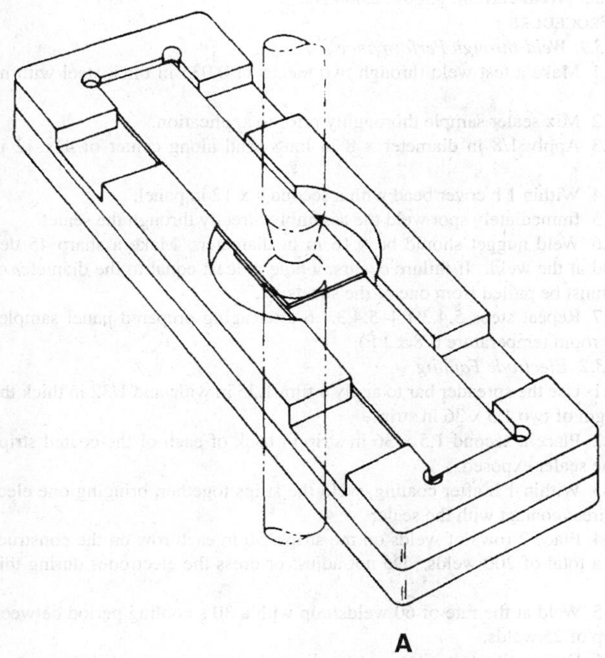

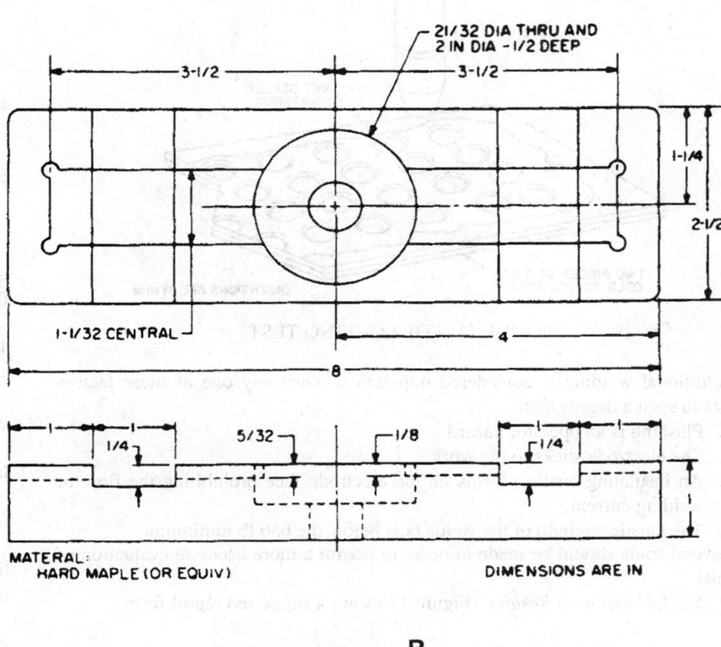

FIGURE 9—LOCATING FIXTURE

5.3.2 WELDING SCHEDULE

5.3.2.1 Electrode force: 500 lb.

5.3.2.2 Weld time: 5 cycles.

5.3.2.3 Weld current: 9500–10,500 A.

5.3.3 PROCEDURE

5.3.3.1 Flat weld 1 x 4 x 0.035 in coupons without sealer to determine if proper weld is being obtained. Pull in tensile tester to check tensile shear.

5.3.3.2 Weldability At Various Drying Times—Condition sealer sample to 77 ±2 F before testing.

Using 1 x 4 in cold rolled steel test panels (Figure 10), apply the spot weld sealer with the notched spreader bar to only one coupon of the weld sample. Material will spread under pressure to form uniform coating of approximately 1/32 in thickness. Weld samples using the following drying times after application:

a. 0 h.
b. 24 h—If not weldable at this drying time, recheck to find limit of drying time relative to weldability.
c. 48 h.
d. 72 h.
e. 96 h.

Weld coupons so that the applied material is in the 1 in lap joint and with a single spot weld in the center of the lap area (Figure 10). Use the locating jig for locating coupons to insure accurate alignment. (See Figures 9A and 9B.) Three welding samples are required for each test.

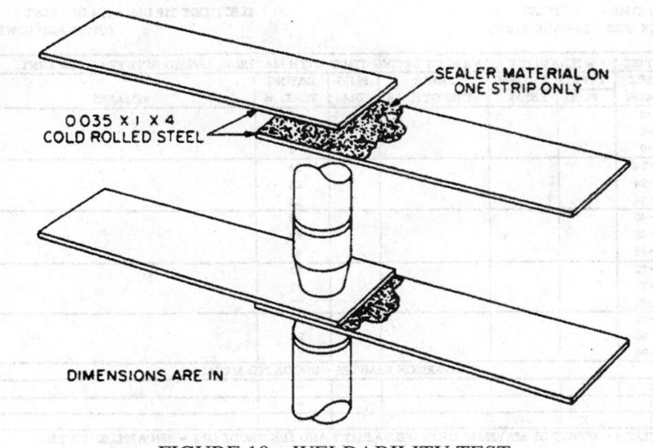

FIGURE 10—WELDABILITY TEST

Weld samples are to be pulled on a tensile test machine. Samples should yield a plug-type failure and a minimum tensile strength of 650 lb.

5.3.3.3 Effect of Material Upon Weldability and Electrode Life—Use same equipment as listed in paragraph 5.3.1.

5.3.3.3.1 Application of Materials—Use same procedure as outlined in paragraph 5.3.3.2.

Weld a strip sample 4 x 24 in immediately after application so that the material, applied to only one strip of the sample, contacts the movable electrode (Figure 11) and note:

a. Flashing.
b. Effect on electrode life.

c. Amount of electrode pickup.

d. Effect of electrode pickup on weldability.

Welds should be at a 1/2 in (approximately) spot spacing. Speed of operation: 100 spots/min, repetitive welds to a minimum of 800 welds.

Chisel test the welded strip and examine the sample for weld quality.

Note burn-out condition of material around weld nugget.

Do not redress the electrodes during this test. This test is to be continued until additional welding is considered impractical because of one of the four factors listed above.

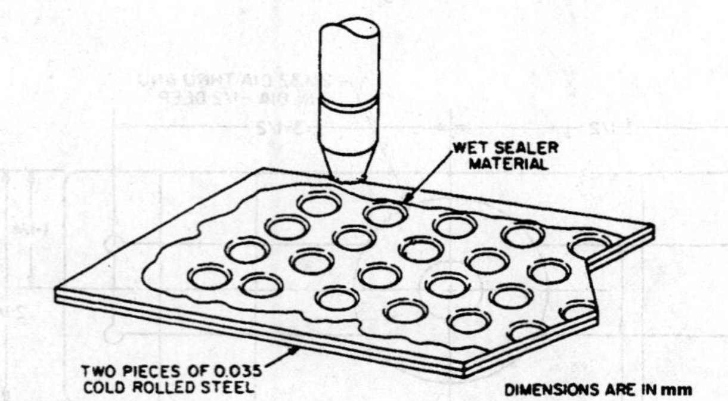

FIGURE 11—TIP FOULING TEST

Additional welding is considered impractical when any one of these factors exists to such a degree that:

a. Flashing is an operator hazard.

b. The electrode sticks to the work.

c. An insulating coating forms on the electrode face prohibiting the flow of welding current.

d. The tensile strength of the welds falls below the 650 lb minimum.

Several trials should be made in order to permit a more accurate evaluation of results.

5.3.3.4 Reported Results—Figure 12 shows a suggested report form.

WELD TEST DATA SHEET FOR PRIMERS, SEALERS, AND COATED STEELS

MANUFACTURER'S NAME ______________ NO. ______
TYPE OF MATERIAL ______________
FISHER SPECIFICATION NO. ______________ DATE ______
DEPARTMENTAL IDENTIFYING NO. ______________

CURRENT: 9500 - 10,500 A — ELECTRODE FORCE - 500 LB
WELD TIME: 5 CYCLES — ELECTRODE TIP DIA - 1/4 IN - FLAT
STOCK SIZE: 20 GAGE (0.035) — (UPPER AND LOWER)

TEST 1 - WELDABILITY AT VARIOUS DRYING TIMES WITH MATERIAL APPLIED BETWEEN WELD JOINT.

SAMPLE NUMBER	TYPE OF FAILURE PLUG	TYPE OF FAILURE SHEAR	SHEAR STRENGTH, LB	PLUG DIA	DRYING TIME, H	REMARKS
1-0					0	
2-0					0	
3-0					0	
1-24					24	
2-24					24	
3-24					24	
1-48					48	
2-48					48	
3-48					48	
1-72					72	
2-72					72	
3-72					72	
1-96					96	
2-96					96	
3-96					96	
COMPARISON SAMPLES - UNCOATED METAL						
1	X				--	
2	X				--	
3	X				--	

TEST 2 - EFFECT OF MATERIAL UPON WELDABILITY AND ELECTRODE LIFE WHEN APPLIED TO THE OUTER SURFACE OF A SAMPLE IN CONTACT WITH MOVABLE ELECTRODE. SPEED OF OPERATION - 100-200 SPOTS/MIN

TRIAL NUMBER	FLASHING	EFFECT ON ELECTRODE	NUMBER OF CONTINUOUS SPOT WELDS	REMARKS
1				
2				
3				
4				
5				

COMMENTS:

FIGURE 12—WELD TEST DATA SHEET FOR PRIMERS, SEALERS, AND COATED STEELS

5.4 Method C

5.4.1 EQUIPMENT AND SUPPLIES

5.4.1.1 150 KVA gun type spot welder.

5.4.1.2 Two water-cooled 5/8 in diameter electrodes with 45 deg truncated cone and 1/4 in diameter welding tip.

5.4.1.3 Panels, 1.5 x 36 x 0.035 in and 4 x 12 x 0.035 in clean, flat, cold rolled steel free from all edge burrs.

5.4.1.4 Spreader bar to coat film 1.25 in wide and 1/32 in thick.

5.4.2 WELDING SCHEDULE

5.4.2.1 Electrode force: 600 lb.

5.4.2.2 Weld time: 8 cycles.

5.4.2.3 Weld current: 9500–12,000 A.

5.4.3 PROCEDURE

5.4.3.1 Weld-through Performance

5.4.3.1.1 Make a test weld through two pieces of 0.035 in thick steel with no sealer.

5.4.3.1.2 Mix sealer sample thoroughly prior to application.

5.4.3.1.3 Apply 1/8 in diameter x 8 in long bead along center of 4 x 12 in panel.

5.4.3.1.4 Within 1 h cover bead with a second 4 x 12 in panel.

5.4.3.1.5 Immediately spot weld the assembly directly through the sealer.

5.4.3.1.6 Weld nugget should be 0.16 in in diameter. Make a sharp 45 deg angle bend at the weld. If failure occurs, a hole at least equal to the diameter of the weld must be pulled from one of the sheets.

5.4.3.1.7 Repeat steps 5.4.3.1.4–5.4.3.1.6 after aging prepared panel samples 1 week at room temperature (78 ±2 F).

5.4.3.2 Electrode Fouling

5.4.3.2.1 Use the spreader bar to apply a film 1.25 in wide and 1/32 in thick the entire length of two 1.5 x 36 in strips.

5.4.3.2.2 Place a second 1.5 x 36 in strip in back of each of the coated strips leaving the sealer exposed.

5.4.3.2.3 Within 1 h after coating, weld the strips together, bringing one electrode in direct contact with the sealer.

5.4.3.2.4 Place 2 rows of welds on the strips, 50 in each row on the constructions, for a total of 200 welds. Do not adjust or dress the electrodes during this test.

5.4.3.2.5 Weld at the rate of 60 welds/min with a 30 s cooling period between each group of 25 welds.

5.4.3.2.6 During this test observe any electrode sticking, corrosion, or excessive degraded sealer building up on the electrode face. This buildup will act as an insulator, resulting in extreme deterioration or complete stoppage of the weld.

5.4.3.2.7 Welds should pass the test outlined in paragraph 5.4.3.1.6.

6. ADS-4—Enamel, Lacquer, And Fabric Staining Test

6.1 Application—The methods A and B outlined in this section are the two general procedures used for determining the staining effects of sealers and adhesives materials on or under painted finishes or fabrics. The equipment suggested in paragraph 6.2.2 are examples of that most generally used by the industry. The procedure and equipment used for this test are predicated on the application and are subject to agreement by the supplier and user.

6.2 Equipment and Materials Required

6.2.1 Phosphatized, primed, enameled, lacquered panels or plastics or specified fabrics.

6.2.2 Groven Fluorescent (F-20) UV Cabinet, S-1 Sunlamp Cabinet, Standard Weather-Ometer, or Fade-Ometer.

6.3 Procedure

6.3.1 METHOD A—ADHESIVE OR SEALANT APPLIED PRIOR TO PAINT BAKE CYCLE

6.3.1.1 Apply a specified amount of the material under test onto the specified test sample or panel.

6.3.1.2 Condition test assembly at specified time and temperature before exposure.

6.3.1.3 Paint and bake the assembly according to the user's regular paint operation using a light-colored, currently released production enamel or lacquer.

6.3.1.4 Expose the test panel assembly or fabric in a Groven Fluorescent UV Cabinet, S-1 Sunlamp Cabinet, Standard Weather-Ometer, or Fade-Ometer at a specified distance from the light source and at a specified temperature and cycle for a length of time, as indicated on the engineering drawing and/or material specification.

6.3.1.5 Examine for contact and/or migration stains.

6.3.2 METHOD B—ADHESIVE OR SEALANT APPLIED AFTER PAINT BAKE CYCLE

6.3.2.1 Paint and bake test assembly according to the user's regular paint operation using a light-colored, currently released production enamel or lacquer.

6.3.2.2 Apply a specified amount of the material under test onto the specified test sample or panel.

6.3.2.3 Condition test assembly at specified time and temperature before exposure.

6.3.2.4 Expose the test panel assembly or fabric in a Groven Fluorescent UV Cabinet, S-1 Sunlamp Cabinet, Standard Weather-Ometer, or Fade-Ometer at a specified distance from the light source and at a specified temperature and cycle for a length of time, as indicated on the engineering drawing and/or material specification.

6.3.2.5 Examine for contact and/or migration stains.

7. ADS-5—Wash-off Resistance Test

7.1 Application—This procedure is used to determine the resistance of automotive sealer, deadeners, and adhesives to wash-off during rinsing and phosphatizing operations.

7.1.1 EQUIPMENT REQUIRED—See Figure 13.

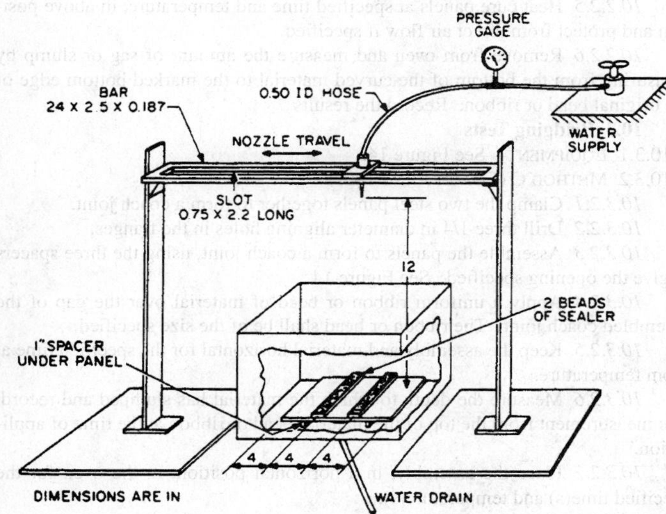

FIGURE 13—WASH-OFF RESISTANCE TEST

7.1.1.1 Cold rolled, low carbon steel body stock panels 12 x 12 in,in 20 gage.

7.1.1.2 Light paraffinic oil having the following properties:

Viscosity SUS at 100 F: 70–100 s

Flash COC: 300 F min.

Pour point: 30 F min.

7.1.1.3 Nozzle—Spraying System No. 1/2 GG-25 full jet or as specified on material standard.

7.1.1.4 Water supply capable of maintaining 160 F and a pressure of 20 psi.

7.1.1.5 Burette graduated in 0.1 cc.

7.1.1.6 Rubber hose 1/2 in ID of adequate lengths to connect water supply outlet with nozzle.

7.1.1.7 Pressure gage with minimum dial diameter of 3.5 in graduated in 1 lb increments and having a 60 psi range.

7.1.1.8 Metal bar 24 x 2.5 x 0.187 in with opening of 0.750 x 22.0 in cut out of center. This is used for a guide for the nozzle during testing.

7.1.2 PROCEDURE: A HORIZONTAL WASH

7.1.2.1 Clean the panels by washing with aliphatic hydrocarbon solvent having a boiling range between 200 and 300 F. (Solvents commonly known as VM&P meet this requirement.) Dry the panels with a lint-free cloth.

7.1.2.2 From a burette apply 0.5 cc of oil to a clean test panel and distribute evenly over the surface by rubbing with two finger tips.

7.1.2.3 Apply two equally spaced beads or ribbons of material to the panel, using the size of bead or ribbon specified in the material standard.

7.1.2.4 Air dry for the period of time specified on the material standards.

7.1.2.5 Refer to Figure 13. Assemble the hose, nozzle, and gage and connect to the water supply. Adjust the water temperature to 135 ± 5 F and the throughput for 1 gal per 20 s or as specified on material standard. Record the pressure required for the desired throughput. Subsequent tests using this equipment can be run at this pressure setting without rechecking volume of flow.

7.1.2.6 Place the panel horizontal with a minimum clearance of 1.0 in between the panel and the bottom of the sink or reservoir to allow the spray water to drain out without accumulating over the panel and giving erroneous test results.

7.1.2.7 Position the nozzle guide directly above the center of the panel so that the nozzle tip is 12.0 in above the test panel and so that the long axis of the guide is at a 90 deg angle with the long axis of the ribbon or bead of material.

7.1.2.8 Place the nozzle on top of the guide so that the spray of water is through the cutout section of the guide and move the nozzle back and forth across the guide in such a manner that the spray of water crosses the panel each 2 s.

7.1.2.9 Visually examine the material for wash-off and displacement. Record the results.

8. ADS-7—Solids Test

8.1 Method A (Fixed Time)—This procedure is used for determining the solid content of adhesives, sealers, and deadeners containing organic solvents.

8.1.1 EQUIPMENT REQUIRED

8.1.1.1 Low form weighing bottle, Fisher Model 3-420 or equivalent.

8.1.1.2 Circulating air oven capable of maintaining temperatures between 70–150 C ±2% (158–302 F ±2%).

8.1.1.3 Desiccator, with drying agent and tray.

8.1.1.4 Analytical balance, accurate to 1 mg.

8.1.1.5 Spatula, square-tipped blade.

8.1.2 PROCEDURE

8.1.2.1 Weigh bottle and cover to nearest milligram. Record weight.

8.1.2.2 Mix sample thoroughly using square-tipped spatula. Care should be taken to avoid entrapment of air and/or loss of solids.

8.1.2.3 Transfer 5–10 g (or other specified weight) of the material into the tared bottle, cover and weigh to nearest milligram. Record weight.

8.1.2.4 Place cover and uncovered bottle containing the sample in the oven at 215 ±5 F for 3 h unless otherwise specified.

8.1.2.5 Remove bottle containing the residue and cover from the oven and immediately place in the desiccator. Allow to cool at room temperature for 3 h minimum.

8.1.2.6 Weigh the covered bottle with the residue to nearest milligram. Record weight.

8.1.2.7 Subtract the weight of bottle and cover as determined in step 8.1.2.1 from the weight recorded in steps 8.1.2.3 and 8.1.2.6.

8.1.2.8 Calculate percent solids, and record the results.

$$\frac{\text{Weight (step 8.1.2.6)} - \text{Weight (step 8.1.2.1)}}{\text{Weight (step 8.1.2.3)} - \text{Weight (step 8.1.2.1)}} \times 100 = \%\ \text{solids} \qquad \text{(Eq. 1)}$$

8.2 Method B (Solids to Constant Weight)—This procedure is used to determine the solid content of adhesives, sealers, and deadeners containing organic solvents. Reference: ASTM D 553, Standard Method of Test for Viscosity and Total Solids Content of Rubber Cements.

8.2.1 EQUIPMENT REQUIRED

8.2.1.1 Low form weighing bottle, Fisher Model 3-402 or equivalent.

8.2.1.2 Circulating air oven capable of maintaining temperatures between 70–150 C ±2% (158–302 F ±2%).

8.2.1.3 Desiccator, with drying agent and tray.

8.2.1.4 Analytical balance, accurate to 1 mg.

8.2.1.5 Spatula, square-tipped blade.

8.2.2 PROCEDURE

8.2.2.1 Weigh bottle and cover to nearest milligram. Record weight.

8.2.2.2 Mix sample thoroughly using square-tipped spatula.

8.2.2.3 Transfer 5–10 g or other specified weights of the material into the tared bottle, cover and weigh to nearest milligram. Record weight.

8.2.2.4 Place cover and uncovered bottle containing the sample in the oven at 215 ±5 F for 3 h unless otherwise specified.

8.2.2.5 Remove bottle containing the residue and cover from the oven and immediately place in the desiccator. Allow to cool to room temperature for 3 h minimum at 73–78 F.

8.2.2.6 Weigh the covered bottle with the residue to nearest milligram. Record weight.

8.2.2.7 Repeat steps 8.2.2.4, 8.2.2.5, and 8.2.2.6 until a constant weight is obtained.

8.2.2.8 Subtract the weight of bottle and cover as determined in step 8.2.2.1 from the weights recorded in steps 8.2.2.3 and 8.2.2.7.

8.2.2.9 Calculate percent solids:

$$\frac{\text{Weight (step 8.2.2.7)} - \text{Weight (step 8.2.2.1)}}{\text{Weight (step 8.2.2.3)} - \text{Weight (step 8.2.2.1)}} \times 100 = \%\ \text{solids} \qquad \text{(Eq. 2)}$$

8.3 Method C (ASTM D 1582)—This method is suitable for determining the nonvolatile content phenol, resorcinol, and melamine adhesives, with or without hardener and containing high boiling and low boiling volatile organic solvents and water, or both.

Procedure reference: ASTM D 1582, Standard Method of Test of Non-Volatile Content of Phenol, Resorcinol and Melamine Adhesives.

9. ADS-8—Flash Point Test

9.1 Method A (Pensky Marten's Closed Cup Method)—This procedure is used to determine the flash point of fuel oils as well as viscous materials and suspensions of solids.

Reference: ASTM D 93, Standard Method of Test for Flash Point by Pensky-Martin's Closed Tester. (See note in paragraph 7 of this test for use with materials having solids in suspension.)

9.2 Method B (Tag Open Cup Method)—This method covers procedures for the determination of flash points of liquids having flash points between O and 235 F. This method, when applied to paints and resin solutions which tend to skin over or which are very viscous, gives less reproducible results than when applied to solvents.

Reference: ASTM D 1310, Standard Method of Test for Flash Point of Volatile Flammable Materials by Tag Open Cup Apparatus.

10. ADS-9—Sag And Bridging Tests

10.1 Application—These tests are used to determine the ability of the material to remain in position and bridge gaps.

10.1.1 EQUIPMENT REQUIRED

10.1.1.1 Circulating air oven capable of maintaining temperatures up to 400 ±5 F.

10.1.1.2 50 ml burette graduated in 1 ml.

10.1.1.3 Light paraffine oil having the following properties:

Viscosity SUS at 100 F: 70–100 s

Flash COC: 300 F minimum

Pour point: 30 F minimum

10.1.1.4 Metal panels 12 x 12 in, 20 gage cold rolled, low carbon steel.

10.1.1.4.1 Phosphatized panels[5] as specified.

10.1.1.4.2 Oiled panels. Clean the panels by first wiping with VM&P naphtha and then dry with a lint-free cloth. Apply 0.5 cc of oil from the burette and distribute it evenly on the surface by rubbing with two finger tips.

10.1.1.4.3 Painted panels to be prepared as specified by customer.

10.1.1.5 Draw down fixture. These are made in a "U" configuration as shown on Figure 14 (flow type), part A with the opening made to give the bead size specified.

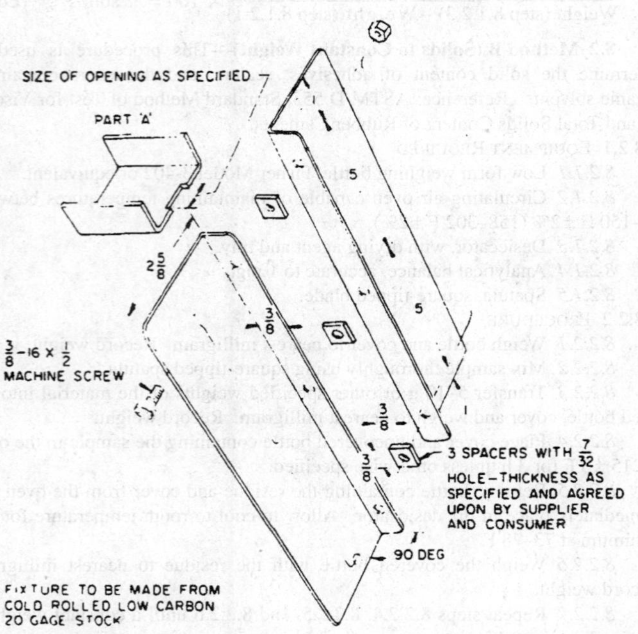

FIGURE 14—DRAW DOWN FIXTURE (FLOW-TYPE MATERIALS)

10.1.2 GENERAL PROCEDURE—Samples shall be mixed or otherwise treated as specified by the customer before applying.

10.2 Sag Tests

10.2.1 METHOD A (INVERTED BRAKE TEST)

10.2.1.1 Apply a prescribed size bead or ribbon of material to a panel treated as specified.

10.2.1.2 Invert panel and air dry at room temperature (material on under side of panel) for 15 min or as specified. Examine at the end of the exposure period and record the results.

10.2.1.3 Bake in the inverted position for specified time and temperature.

10.2.1.4 Cool to room temperature and examine and record the results.

10.2.2 METHOD B (HORIZONTAL AND VERTICAL BAKE TEST)

10.2.2.1 Apply two prescribed size ribbons or beads of material, equally spaced on two panels. The panels are to be of the size and surface treatment as specified.

10.2.2.2 Mark the position of the ribbons or beads.

10.2.2.3 Place one panel in a vertical position, with the ribbon(s) or bead(s) horizontal. Place one panel in a vertical position with the ribbon(s) or bead(s) vertical.

10.2.2.4 Air dry at 73–78 F for 15 min or as specified.

10.2.2.5 Heat cure panels at specified time and temperature, in above position and protect from direct air flow if specified.

10.2.2.6 Remove from oven and measure the amount of sag or slump by measuring from the bottom of the curved material to the marked bottom edge of the original bead or ribbon. Record the results.

10.3 Bridging Tests

10.3.1 EQUIPMENT—See Figure 14.

10.3.2 METHOD C (COACH JOINT TEST)

10.3.2.1 Clamp the two steel panels together to form a coach joint.

10.3.2.2 Drill three 1/4 in diameter aligning holes in the flanges.

10.3.2.3 Assemble the panels to form a coach joint, using the three spacers to give the opening specified. See Figure 14.

10.3.2.4 Apply a uniform ribbon or bead of material over the gap of the assembled coach joint. The ribbon or bead shall be of the size specified.

10.3.2.5 Keep the assembly and material horizontal for the specified time at room temperature.

10.3.2.6 Measure the depth to which the material has slumped and record. The measurement from the top of the material bead or ribbon at the time of application.

10.3.2.7 Place the assembly, in a horizontal position, in the oven for the specified time(s) and temperature(s).

10.3.2.8 Cool to room temperature.

10.3.2.9 Measure the depth the sealer has slumped and record.

10.3.3 METHOD D (METAL PERFORATION)

10.3.3.1 Extrude a 1/2 in diameter bead of material lengthwise over the centerline of the holes of the specified bridging test fixture, as shown in Figures 15 and 16.

10.3.3.2 Air dry assembly at the specified temperature and time.

10.3.3.3 Heat cure the assembly at specified time and temperature.

10.3.3.4 Measure the length of the material that flows through the holes and record as sag, in fixture 1 of Figure 15 (nonflow).

10.3.3.5 Record largest hole size that material bridges in fixture 2 of Figure 16 (controlled flow).

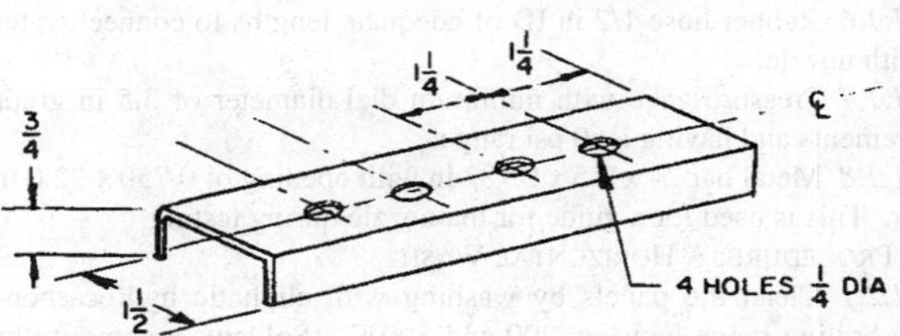

FIGURE 15—BRIDGING TEST FIXTURE 1 (NONFLOW)

5. Phosphatized panels are commercially available from: Q-Panel Co., 15610 Industrial Parkway, Cleveland, Ohio; or Parker Rust Proof Co., Division of Hooker Chemical Corp., 2177 E. Milwaukee Avenue, Detroit, Michigan 48211.

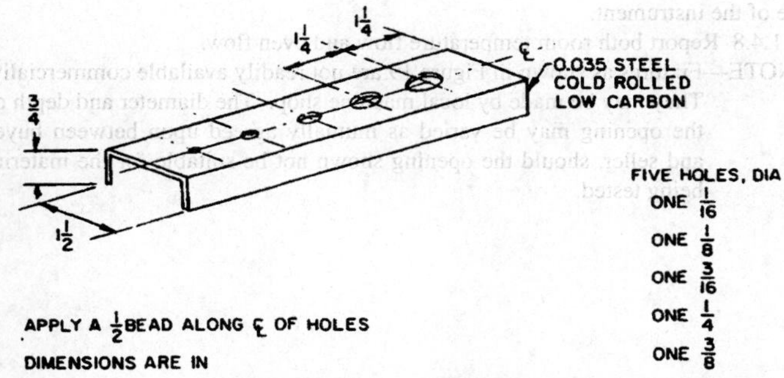

FIGURE 16—BRIDGING TEST FIXTURE 2 (CONTROLLED FLOW)

11. ADS-10—Flow Test

11.1 Application—These tests are used to determine the ability of the material to flow a controlled amount.

11.1.1 EQUIPMENT

11.1.1.1 Circulating air oven capable of maintaining any temperature up to 400 ±5 F.

11.1.1.2 Fixtures as specified in methods A, B, and C.

11.1.2 GENERAL PROCEDURES—Samples shall be mixed or otherwise tested as specified.

11.2 Method A (45 deg Flow Channel)

11.2.1 Block the 1/4 in groove in the flow rate fixture (Figure 17) 6 in from the top edge.

11.2.2 Fill the 6 in upper portion of the groove with material.

11.2.3 Remove the block and air dry the fixture for the specified time at the specified temperature.

11.2.4 Heat cure the fixture at the specified time(s) and at the specified temperature(s).

11.2.5 After heat exposure, measure the amount of flow from the original position and record.

11.3 Method B (45 deg Flow Channel)

11.3.1 Measure 4 in from the top of a flow channel (Figure 18) and apply a strip of masking tape down the sides and across the bottom of the channel at this point. Also apply a strip of masking tape across the end and down the side 1/2 in at the top of the channel.

11.3.2 Place quantity of the material into the 4 in area in the manner specified.

11.3.3 Immediately knife the material flush with the legs of the flow channel, remove the tape that was placed at the 4 in mark, and place the flow channel on the fixture at a 45 deg angle. (See Figure 18.)

11.3.4 Allow the fixture to remain at room temperature for time specified.

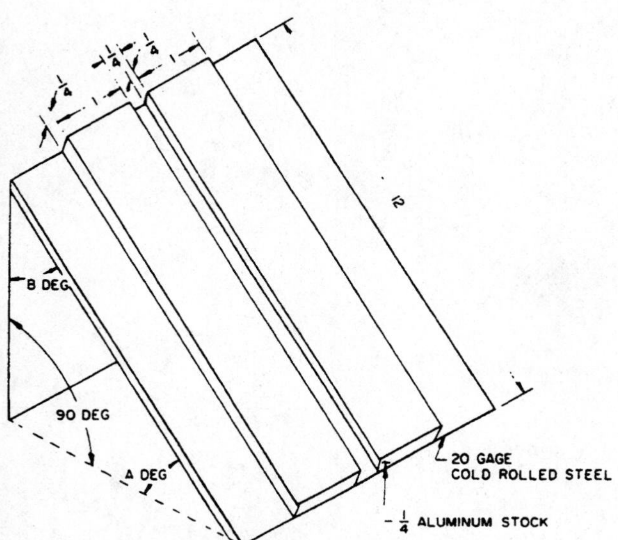

FIGURE 17—FLOW TEST FIXTURE

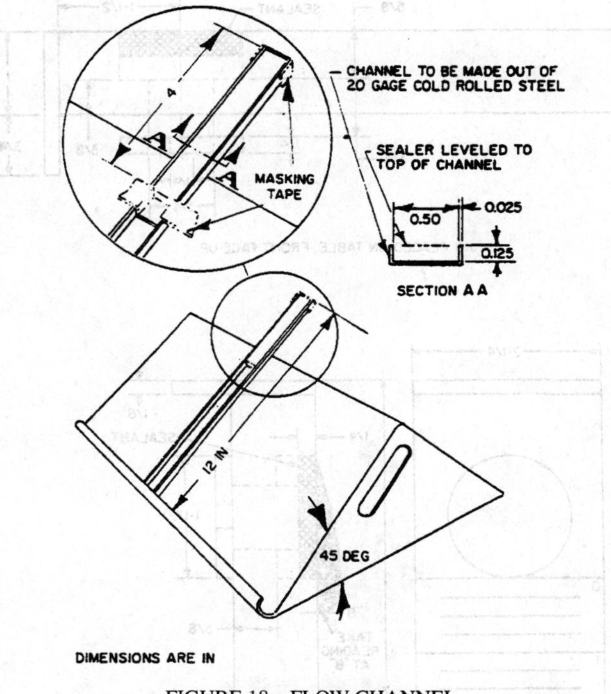

FIGURE 18—FLOW CHANNEL

11.3.5 Place the fixture, without disturbing the flow channel, in a circulating air type oven at the specified temperature(s) and for the specified time(s).

11.3.6 Remove the fixture from the oven, allow it to return to room temperature, and measure the total distance of material flow. Record the results.

11.4 Method C (Boeing Flowmeter Test)

11.4.1 Position the fixture as shown in Figure 19 with the opening on top.

11.4.2 Fill the opening with material and knife off flush, and air dry in a horizontal position at room temperature for time specified.

11.4.3 Place the fixture in an upright position.

11.4.4 Push the plunger forward at the specified time, forcing the material to be discharged from the opening, and air dry at room temperature for the time specified.

11.4.5 Measure the amount of flow on the calibrated face of the instrument and record as room temperature flow.

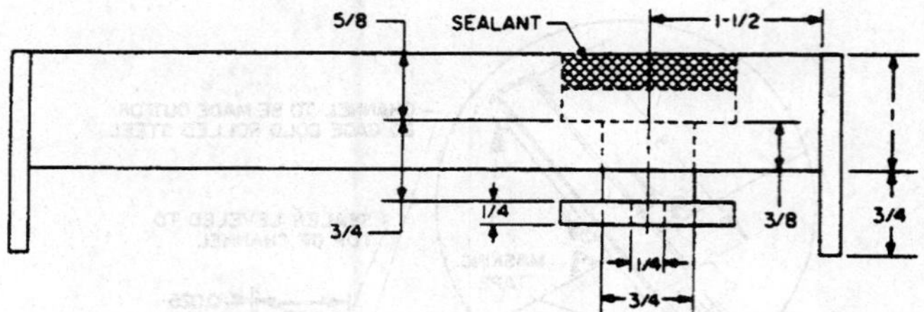

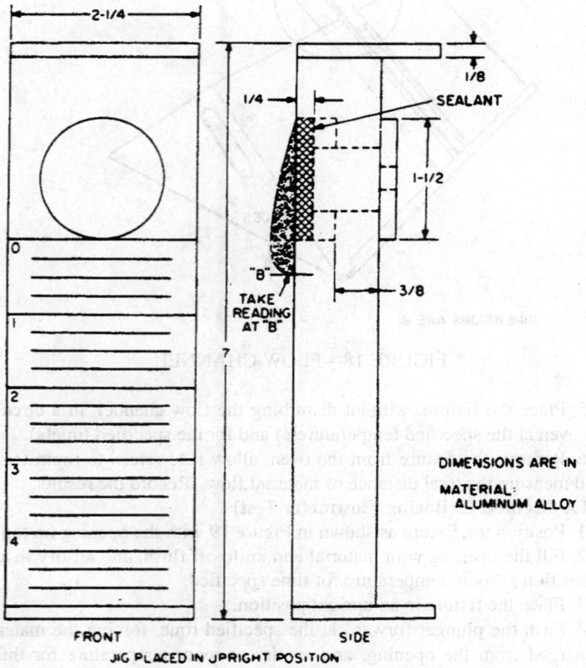

FIGURE 19—BOEING FLOW TEST FIXTURE

11.4.6 Place the fixture and material in an oven in an upright position for the specified heat cure time and temperature.

11.4.7 Measure the amount of flow shown by the material on the calibrated face of the instrument.

11.4.8 Report both room temperature flow and oven flow.

NOTE—Fixtures as shown in Figure 19 are not readily available commercially. They may be made by local machine shop. The diameter and depth of the opening may be varied as mutually agreed upon between buyer and seller, should the opening shown not be suitable for the material being tested.

SOFTENING POINT OF INTERIOR TRIM ADHESIVES—SAE J1700 APR1994

SAE Recommended Practice

Report of the SAE Trim Adhesives Subcommittee of the SAE Materials Joining Executive Committee approved April 1994.

Foreword—This Document has not changed other than to put it into the new SAE Technical Standards Board Format.

1. Scope—This SAE Recommended Practice shall be used to determine the temperature at which an adhesive softens to the point at which it no longer can support a given load.

2. References

2.1 Related Publication—The following publications are provided for information purposes only and are not a required part of this document.

2.1.1 ASTM PUBLICATION—Available from ASTM, 100 Barr Harbor Drive, West Conshohocken, PA 19428-2959.

ASTM D 816-82—Methods of Testing Rubber Cement

2.1.2 OTHER PUBLICATIONS

Adhesives Technology Handbook, Arther H. Landrock, Noyes Publications, 1985

3. Definitions

3.1 Softening Point—The temperature at which an adhesive will soften to the point where it will be unable to sustain a predetermined load.

3.2 Interior Trim Adhesives—Typically solvent or water based, or hot melts, these adhesives typically develop their strength with the application of heat, pressure, and/or time. They are applied to interior components such as door trim panels, arm rests, headlinings, etc.

3.3 Separation—The point at which the bonded substrates disconnect from one another at the adhesive.

3.4 Open Time—The interval of time between application of the adhesive on the adherent and completion of assembly of parts for bonding. During this period, the adhesive-coated surfaces are exposed to air before being assembled together.

3.5 Conditioning Time—The time interval between removal of the joint from conditions of heat and/or pressure used to accomplish the bonding and the attainment of approximately maximum-bond strength.

3.6 Creep—The dimensional change with time of a material under load. Creep at room temperature is sometimes called cold flow.

4. Equipment Required

4.1 Oven—Capable of holding a temperature to within ±1 °C (1.8 °F) in the 37.8 °C (100 °F) to 205 °C (400 °F) range.

4.2 Thermocouple and Recorder

4.3 Timer—60 min

4.4 1.85 Cotton-Drill Cloth Coupons—Cut into 25.4 x 114.3 mm (1 x 4.5 in) pieces with a centered hole at one end—minimum 9—one possible source is Industrial Coatings Group Inc., 220 Broad Street, Kingsport, TN 37660.

NOTE—1.85 cotton-drill cloth is used for the coupon application because of its consistent surface and negligible weight.

4.5 Roller—Able to apply a load of 0.357 kg/cm (2 lb/in) width.

4.6 Weights—50 g—minimum 6.

4.7 Steel Panels—Clean uncoated, cold rolled—101.6 x 152.4 mm (4 x 6 in)—minimum 3.

4.8 Clamps, Stand—Capable of securing coupon/steel panel test assembly vertically while in oven environment.

5. Sample Preparation—Softening Point Coupons

5.1 Make a 0.2 mm (0.008 in) wet-film thickness (or manufacturer's recommendations) by 12.7 x 101.7 mm (0.5 x 4.0 in) adhesive strip parallel with the 152.4 mm (6 in) edge at the center of the steel panel.

5.2 After 1 min open time (or manufacturer's recommended open time) locate three coupons evenly spaced at their ends along the 101.6 mm (4 in) steel panel edge opposite the centered hole and with the centered holes on the 25.4 x 114.3 mm (1 x 4.5 in) coupons opposite the 25.4 mm (1 in) overlap bonded area. Roll the coupons against the steel using 0.357 kg/cm (2 lb/in) roller making three passes.

NOTE—Three cotton cloth coupon/steel panel-test assemblies are required per condition.

5.3 Condition the cotton cloth coupon/steel panel-test assemblies for a minimum of 24 h at room temperature (or manufacturer's recommendations).

6. Test Procedure—Softening Point

6.1 Preheat the oven to 37.8 °C (100 °F).

6.2 Secure the control (first) test assembly at room temperature in a vertical position in a stand with the coupon-centered holes down. Hang one 50 g weight from each of the three cotton-drill coupons in this first test assembly. Set the first test assembly aside as the control panel.

6.3 Secure a second test assembly in a vertical position in a stand with the coupon centered holes down and hang one 50 g weight from each of the three cotton drill coupons. Attach a thermocouple to the center backside of the test assembly steel panel and carefully place the entire assembly in the 37.8 °C (100 °F) preheated oven. Gently close the door and set the timer for 15 min.

6.4 After 15 min, carefully observe both test assemblies to determine if any coupons have separated from the steel panel. If no separation is observed, gently close the oven door, increase the open temperature 5.6 °C (10 °F), and set the timer for another 15 min. Repeat this procedure until separation occurs.

6.5 When separation occurs record the oven temperature. Observe the control panel; signs of creep or separation existing on the control panel make the test invalid.

6.6 Remove the test assembly components, thermocouple, coupons, and weights from the oven. Decrease the oven temperature 5.6 °C (10 °F). Secure the last test assembly vertically in a stand with the coupon centered holes down. Hang one 50 g weight from each of the three coupons and attach the thermocouple to the center backside of the test assembly steel panel. After the oven temperature has stabilized, carefully place the assembly in the oven and gently close the door. Set the timer for 15 min.

6.7 After 15 min, open the oven and carefully observe the test assembly to determine if any of the three test coupons have separated from the steel panel. If no separation has occurred gently close the oven and increase the temperature 1.1 °C (2 °F). Set the timer for another 15 min. Repeat until separation occurs.

6.8 When separation occurs record the temperature, this is the adhesive's softening point ±1.1 °C (2 °F). Observe the control panel; signs of creep or separation existing on the control panel will make the test invalid.

7. Report Requirements

7.1 Report the test method and any deviations from the recommended test method.

7.2 Report complete identification of samples (coupon and steel type, adhesive type, and wet film thickness), sample preparation (open time, conditioning time, temperature, and humidity during preparation, etc.), and humidity during testing.

7.3 Report any inconsistencies or irregularities (substrate elongation, deformation, etc.) noted during the test.

PEEL STRENGTH OF SOFT TRIM ADHESIVES—SAE J1679 APR1994

SAE Recommended Practice

Report of the SAE Trim Adhesives Subcommittee of the SAE Materials Joining Executive Committee approved April 1994.

Foreword—This Document has not changed other than to put it into the new SAE Technical Standards Board Format.

1. Scope—This SAE Recommended Practice shall be used to determine the peel strength achieved by an adhesive when used to bond various decorative, flexible substrates such as cloth supported vinyl or carpet, to rigid (steel), semi-rigid (SMC plastic), or other similar substrates.

2. References

2.1 Applicable Publication—The following publication forms a part of this specification to the extent specified herein.

2.1.1 ASTM PUBLICATION—Available from ASTM, 100 Barr Harbor Drive, West Conshohocken, PA 19428-2959.

ASTM D 1002—Test Method for Strength Properties of Adhesives in Shear by Tension Loading (Metal-to-Metal)

3. Definitions

3.1 Soft Trim Adhesives—These adhesives, typically solvent or water based, or hot melts, are applied to one or both of the substrates. They develop their strength with the application of heat, pressure, and/or time.

3.2 Peel Strength—Peel strength is the force required to separate bonded substrates of a predetermined width from one another at a predetermined rate of speed. The force may be applied at an angle of 90 degrees (perpendicular) or 180 degrees (parallel) to the substrates.

3.2.1 BREAKAWAY—Load required to initiate disbond.

3.2.2 AVERAGE PEEL—The peel-strength average recorded from 25 mm (1 in) into peel to termination.

3.3 Flexible Substrates—Decorative cloth, supported vinyl, and carpet materials conforming readily to rigid or semi-rigid substrate are typically used.

3.4 Semi-Rigid/Rigid Substrates—A variety of semi-rigid plastics, hardboards, and sheet metal (painted or unpainted).

3.5 Open Time—The time between adhesive application and assembly (closing) of the bond.

3.6 Peel-Strength Average—The peel-strength average is considered to be the midline of the peel-load variations as displayed on the universal testing machine.

4. Equipment Required

4.1 Universal Testing Machine—Must meet the requirements of ASTM D 1002 (cross head speed of 50 to 500 mm/min (2 to 20 in/min), range 0 to 9.07 kg (0 to 20 lb)).

4.2 Fixture—Constant 90 degree angle frictionless peel fixture.

4.3 Roller—Able to apply a load of 0.357 kg/cm (2 lb/in) width.

4.4 Specimen Cutter—Two single-edged razor blades held in parallel planes, 25.4 mm (1.0 in) apart.

4.5 Timer—0 to 60 min.

4.6 Spray Guns

4.6.1 ATOMIZING—Manufacturer's recommendations—with assorted nozzles, air caps, needles, and pressurizing pots.

4.6.2 AIRLESS—Manufacturer's recommendations—with assorted nozzles, air caps, needles, and pressurizing pots.

5. Method A—90 degree Peel

5.1 Sample Preparation—90 degree Peel

5.1.1 Select one 100 x 300 mm (4 x 12 in) semi-rigid/rigid substrate panel for each test condition masking a 25 x 100 mm (1 x 4 in) strip along a 100 mm (4 in) panel edge.

NOTE—25 panel/strip 90 degree peel-test assemblies are required for each adhesive open time, warp, fill, and adhesive wet-film thickness condition being evaluated. In instances where only one substrate is coated with the adhesive, mask only that substrate.

5.1.2 Cut the flexible material into one 25 x 300 mm (1 x 12 in) test strip for each semi-rigid/rigid substrate panel.

NOTE—When cutting fabrics with a defined weave, cut one set parallel to the warp and one set parallel to the fill. Both sets shall be tested.

5.1.3 Apply the test adhesive for approximately 200 mm (8 in) from one end of the flexible test material strips.

NOTE—For spray-applied adhesives, mask 100 mm (4 in) from one end of the substrate aligning the test strips side by side with their intended bonded surfaces facing up. Adhesive wet-film thickness shall be per manufacturer's recommendations.

5.1.4 Immediately start the open-time timer after applying the adhesive. Carefully remove the masking material from the flexible test strip(s) before applying each strip to the center of a panel.

5.1.5 At the appropriate open time(s), apply a flexible test material strip to the center of a semi-rigid/rigid panel aligning the strip with the panels 300 mm (12 in) edges and assuring that the unbonded portion of the flexible strip is on the 100 mm (4 in) masked edge with the bonded portion of the flexible strip starting 25 mm (1 in) from the panel's edge. Immediately pressurize the full-bond area rolling it four times (two times forward and two back) using the 0.91 kg (2 lb) roller.

NOTE—Every effort to eliminate the effects of adhesive squeeze-out on the peel sample should be made.

5.1.6 Repeat the same procedure for the balance of conditions or until all samples are assembled. Remove any masking from the semi-rigid/rigid panels.

5.1.7 On the back of each panel describe the adhesive open time, warp and fill direction, adhesive film thickness, and number the test assembly.

5.1.8 Condition the panel/strip test assemblies for 24 h at 24 °C ±2 °C (75 °F ±3 °F) (or manufacturer's recommendations).

5.2 Peel Procedure—90 degrees

5.2.1 Mount the 90-degree peel fixture in the universal tester.

5.2.2 Install a test assembly in the 90-degree peel fixture aligning the flexible test strip with the universal testers jaw to assure a 90-degree orientation before securing the assembly in the peel fixture and the flexible strip in the jaw.

NOTE—After securing the test assembly, assure the peel fixture continues to move freely.

5.2.3 Activate the universal-testing machine to peel the strip from the panel at arate of 304.8 mm/min (12 in/min) for a minimum of 152 mm (6 in).

NOTE—Pay particular attention that the 90-degree peel fixture continues to move easily maintaining a perpendicular alignment during the peel process. If alignment along this axis exceeds ±10 degrees, that portion of the test-strip sample should be disregarded.

5.2.4 Record the breakaway and average peel value for each test assembly.

5.3 Report Requirements—90-degree Peel

5.3.1 Report the test method number and any deviations from the recommended test method.

5.3.2 Report complete identification of samples (open time, warp or fill, adhesive wet-film thickness), adhesive type, as well as conditioning time, temperature, and humidity prior to aging and testing.

5.3.3 Report the average of the breakaway and average peel values for the samples (in kilograms per centimeter [kg/cm] width or ounces per inch [oz/in] width).

5.3.4 Report any inconsistencies or irregularities (substrate elongation, deformation, etc.) noted during the test.

6. Method B—180-degree Peel

6.1 Sample Preparation—180-degree Peel

6.1.1 Select one 100 x 300 mm (4 x 12 in) semi-rigid/rigid substrate panel for each test assembly masking a 25 x 100 mm (1 x 4 in) strip along a 100 mm (4 in) panel edge.

NOTE—25 panel/strip 180-degree peel test assemblies are required for each adhesive open time, warp, fill, and adhesive wet-film thickness condition being evaluated. In instances where only one substrate is coated with the adhesive, mask only that substrate.

6.1.2 Cut the flexible test material into one 25 x 500 mm (1 x 20 in) test strip for each semi-rigid/rigid substrate panel.

NOTE—When cutting fabrics with a defined weave, cut one set parallel to the warp and one set parallel to the fill. Both sets shall be tested.

6.1.3 Apply the test adhesive for approximately 200 mm (8 in) from one end of the flexible test material strips.

NOTE—For spray-applied adhesives, mask 300 mm (12 in) from one end of the flexible substrate aligning the test strips side by side with their intended bonded surfaces facing up. Adhesive wet-film thickness shall be per manufacturer's recommendations.

6.1.4 Immediately start the open-time timer after applying the adhesive. Carefully remove the masking material from the flexible test strip(s) before applying each strip to the center of a panel.

6.1.5 At the appropriate open time(s), apply a flexible test material strip to the center of a semi-rigid/rigid panel aligning the strip with the panel's 300 mm

(12 in) edges and assuring that the unbonded portion of the flexible strip is on the 10 cm (4 in) masked edge with the bonded portion of the flexible strip starting 2.5 cm (1 in) from the panel's edge.

6.1.6 Immediately upon application, roll the entire bonded area of the flexible strip four times (two times forward and two back) using the two-pound roller.

NOTE—Every effort to eliminate the effects of adhesive squeeze-out on the peel sample should be made.

6.1.7 Repeat the same procedure for the balance of conditions or until all samples are assembled.

6.1.8 Condition the panel/strip test assemblies for 24 h at 24 °C ±2 °C (75 °F ±3 °F) (or manufacturer's recommendations).

6.2 Peel Procedure—180 degrees

6.2.1 Insert the 100 mm (4 in) adhesive free edge of the semi-rigid/rigid panel into one of the universal tester jaws. Double back the loose 300 mm (12 in) of unbonded flexible strip aligning it between the universal testing machine jaws. Secure both the panel and the aligned flexible strip in the jaws.

6.2.2 Activate the universal tester to peel the flexible strip completely from the panel at a rate of 304 mm/min (12 in/min)

6.2.3 Peel for a minimum of 152 mm (6 in) recording the breakaway value and average peel value for each test assembly.

6.3 Report Requirements—180 degrees

6.3.1 Report the test method number and any deviations from the recommended test method.

6.3.2 Report complete identification of samples (open time, warp or fill, adhesive wet-film thickness), adhesive, as well as conditioning time, temperature, and humidity prior to aging and testing.

6.3.3 Report average breakaway, and average remaining peel run values of the samples (in kilograms per centimeter [kg/cm] width or ounces per inch [oz/in] width).

6.3.4 Report any inconsistencies or irregularities (substrate elongation, deformation, etc.) noted during the test.

METAL TO METAL OVERLAP SHEAR STRENGTH TEST FOR AUTOMOTIVE TYPE ADHESIVES —SAE J1523 NOV1993

SAE Recommended Practice

Report of the SAE Nonmetallic Materials Committee, Adhesives and Body Sealer Subcommittee approved June 1985. Reaffirmed by the SAE Materials Joining Committee November 1993.

Foreword—This Reaffirmed Document has been changed only to reflect the new SAE Technical Standards Board format.

1. Scope—This SAE Recommended Practice defines a procedure for determining shear strengths of adhesives used for bonding automotive oil metal substrates.

2. References

2.1 Applicable Publications—The following publication forms a part of this specification to the extent specified herein.

2.1.1 ASTM PUBLICATION—Available from ASTM, 100 Barr Harbor Drive, West Conshohocken, PA 19428-2959.

ASTM D 1002—Test Method for Strength Properties of Adhesives in Shear by Tension Loading (Metal-to-Metal)

3. Test Substrates

3.1 Substrates—Metal composition and roughness as specified.

3.2 Dimensions—Metal substrates shall be cut into flat coupons 25.4 mm (1.000 in) x 100 mm (4.000 in) at 0.8 mm (0.030 in) nominal thickness unless otherwise specified. Coupons shall be free from burrs or other surface imperfections.

3.3 Surface Preparation—Remove contaminant from test coupon surface using a neutral solvent such as acetone or methyl ethyl ketone. Apply a uniform 0.025 mm (0.001 in) wet thickness coating of light mineral oil over test coupons unless otherwise specified. Condition coupons at 23 °C ± 2 °C and 50% ± 5% humidity for 1 h minimum before bonding.

4. Preparation of Test Joints

4.1 Joint Geometry—Joint geometry will be as shown in Figure 1. A 3.2 cm^2 (0.5 in^2) overlap is recommended.

4.2 Adhesive Bondline Thickness—Evaluate adhesive bondline thickness at 0.13 mm (0.005 in) and 0.8 mm (0.030 in). Bondline thickness can be controlled by inserting wire or glass bead spacers into the adhesive. The spacer volume shall not exceed 1% of the total adhesive volume.

4.3 Adhesive Application—The quantity of adhesive used to prepare the bond should be regulated to avoid excess squeeze-out. Squeeze-out at the edges of the bond shall be removed prior to curing.

4.4 Clamping and Fixturing—Bonding surfaces shall be firmly fixed and retained through cure cycle.

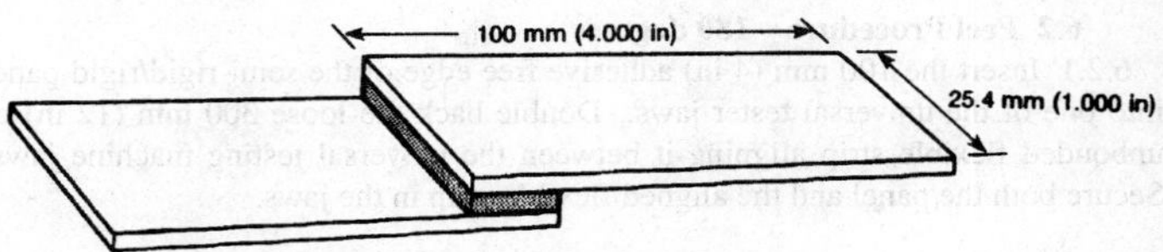

FIGURE 1—JOINT GEOMETRY

4.5 Adhesive Cure—Adhesive shall be cured in accordance with the adhesive suppliers or automotive engineer's recommendation.

4.6 Conditioning—Bonded specimens shall be allowed to return to ambient temperatures for 1 h minimum prior to testing.

5. Testing

5.1 Apparatus—Test apparatus as described in ASTM D 1002.

5.2 Sample Clamping—The distance between clamping jaws shall be 100 mm (4.000 in) with each jaw grasping 25 mm (1.000 in) minimum of test specimens.

5.3 Test Rate—Specimens shall be tested at a pull rate of 13 mm (0.500 in)/min.

5.4 Test Quantity—A minimum of five sample lap shears shall be prepared for each test condition.

6. Report Results

6.1 Report individual peak load values, sample average, and standard deviation. Bond values shall be reported as the value obtained for 3.2 cm^2 (0.500 in^2) bond. Do not interpolate to 6.5 cm^2 (1.000 in^2).

6.2 Report composition, roughness, and thickness of substrate.

6.3 Report value for 0.13 mm (0.005 in) and 0.8 mm (0.003 in) bonds.

6.4 Report metal preparation materials and thickness applied.

6.5 Report mode of failure (adhesive, cohesive, or substrate failure).

6.6 Report adhesive cure schedule, time, and temperature.

METHOD OF VISCOSITY TEST FOR AUTOMOTIVE TYPE ADHESIVES, SEALERS, AND DEADENERS —SAE J1524 AUG1995

SAE Recommended Practice

Report of the SAE Nonmetallic Materials Committee approved June 1985, and revised November 1988. Completely revised by the SAE Materials Joining Executive Committee August 1995.

1. Scope—This SAE Recommended Practice contains a series of test methods for use in measuring the viscosity of automotive-type adhesives, sealers, and deadeners.

The test methods which are contained in this document are as follows:

1.1 Brookfield® Method
1.2 Castor-Severs Rheometer or Pressure Flowmeter
1.3 Penetrometer
1.4 Capillary Rheometer
1.5 Plate Rheometers

2. References

2.1 Applicable Publications—The following publications form a part of this specification to the extent specified herein.

2.1.1 ANSI/ASME Publication—Available from ANSI, 11 West 42nd Street, New York, NY 10036-8002.

ANSI/ASME B40.1—Pressure Gauge

2.1.2 ASTM Publications—Available from ASTM, 100 Barr Harbor Drive, West Conshohocken, PA 19428-2959.

ASTM D 5—Needle Penetrometer
ASTM D 217—Cone Penetrometer
ASTM D 1823—Standard Test Method for Apparent Viscosity of Plastisols and Organosols at High Shear Rates by Extrusion Viscometer
ASTM D 1824—Standard Test Method for Apparent Viscosity of Plastisols and Organosols at Low Shear Rates
ASTM D 2196—Standard Test Methods for Rheological Properties of Non-Newtonian Materials by Rotational (Brookfield®) Viscometer
ASTM D 2240—Durometer
ASTM D 3364—Standard Test Method for Flow Rates for Poly(Vinyl Chloride) and Rheologically Unstable Thermoplastics
ASTM D 3835—Standard Test Method for Determination of Properties of Polymeric Materials by Means of a Capillary Rheometer
ASTM D 4440—Standard Practice for Rheological Measurement of Polymer Melts Using Dynamic Mechanical Procedures

3. Principle of Methods—The viscosity of a material is a measurement of the shear stress that must be applied before a change of form (shear rate) can be accomplished. For the purpose of this test method, however, viscosity refers to a finished product parameter that is quantified in various ways and used by the automotive industry as a means of identifying and assigning a minimum and maximum value for the application characteristics of a material.

The use of these values should be tempered by the knowledge that the numbers generated are quality control aids and may not fully address the plant-to-plant variations encountered in application systems.

Each piece of equipment is best suited to a particular viscosity and shear rate range, although there are no sharp viscosity demarcations between the various viscometers. Each method has its own idiosyncrasies and limitations and therefore must be evaluated with the particular material being tested. The rheometers (1.4 and 1.5) have the ability to compare results under a range of conditions, and thus determine the sensitivity of the material to shear rate, shear history, and temperature. The following suggestions are intended as general guidelines for use of these viscosity measuring devices. They may be used outside the suggested ranges if desired.

Generally, a Brookfield® viscometer is used for low viscosity materials in the 0.025 to 200 Pa·s (Pa·s = 1000 cP) range with limited shear thinning. The pressure flowmeter is usually used for materials with viscosities up to 80 Pa·s at 50 s^{-1}. Since these materials are highly shear thinning they may exceed 1000 Pa·s at 1 s^{-1}. The penetrometer is used for very high viscosity materials such as putties and highly gelled compounds.

The capillary rheometer is used for materials from 1 to 10 000 Pa·s at shear rates from 10 to 50 000 s^{-1}. The plate rheometers are used for materials from 0.025 to 1000 Pa·s at shear rates from 10^{-7} to 200 s^{-1}.

4. Sample Temperature Conditioning—Prior to the actual viscosity measurement, the sample to be tested must be conditioned thermally.

4.1 As Received Viscosity—Unless specified otherwise, as received viscosity shall refer to material stored at "room temperature" and tested at 23 °C ± 1 °C (75 °F ± 2 °F) and 50% ± 5% R.H.

4.2 Aged Viscosity—Aged viscosity refers to a value obtained by subjecting a sample prior to testing to a specified temperature for 72 h. The sample is then conditioned to 23 °C ± 1 °C and the viscosity is measured. The size of the sample to be tested should be 500 mL (1 pt). Samples smaller than this conditioned at elevated temperatures may give different results.

5. Sample Mechanical Conditioning—Prior to the actual viscosity measurement, the sample to be tested must be conditioned mechanically.

5.1 Conditioning Method A—Unagitated—Unagitated testing refers to the transfer of materials from the shipping container to the testing apparatus with the minimum amount of agitation. This viscosity is supposed to be indicative of a compound in its shipping container prior to use. The tester should be aware that the very act of removing a sample for test can affect the rheology of thixotropic materials and, in so doing, may substantially alter the value measured.

5.2 Conditioning Method B—Moderate Agitation—Moderate agitation of a sample is achieved by stirring a 500 mL sample 50 stirs in 60 s with a 25 x 150 mm (1 x 6 in) steel bladed spatula. This agitation can also be used to assure the uniform 23 °C necessary for testing.

5.3 Conditioning Method C—Grease Working—Grease working refers to subjecting a sample to 150 cycles, unless otherwise specified, in a standard mechanical grease-worker, as outlined in ASTM D 217.

5.4 Conditioning Method D—Pre-shear—Steady shear rheometers including Brookfield® and Plate devices allow the sample to be pre-sheared at a fixed shear rate for a known time before testing. Ten s^{-1} for 10 min is a suggested condition.

6. Brookfield® Method

6.1 Application—This procedure is used to determine the viscosity of adhesives, sprayable sound deadeners, and thin body sealers. The values obtained are expressed in Pa•s (Pa•s = 1000 cP) and are a measure of the resistance a rotating spindle encounters when immersed in the compound to be tested. Due to secondary flows, this method provides only relative values for shear thinning materials. Refer to ASTM D 1824 and ASTM D 2196 for additional details and reproducibility data.

6.2 Equipment—Commercially available Brookfield® Viscometer (see Figure 1), or equivalent.

6.3 Procedure—Test equipment and sample shall be maintained at 23 °C ± 1 °C.

6.3.1 Set viscometer at specified rpm.

6.3.2 Attach specified spindle.

6.3.3 Lower viscometer into 500 mL of test material so that the groove cut in the spindle is flush with the fluid's level.

6.3.4 Level the viscometer.

6.3.5 Depress the clutch, turn on the viscometer, and release the clutch. Take the reading and record the time after the indicator has stabilized or after a specified time, typically 60 s. (When measuring thixotropic materials at specific times, other than stable readings, it will be necessary to test separate samples in order to obtain reproducible values.)

6.3.6 Use conversion table to convert to centipoise.

6.3.7 Take the average of three readings and report the viscosity, spindle, rpm, time of recording, and the model of the viscometer used.

6.3.8 Repeat the procedure at a second rpm, and note extent of shear thinning. (Note that Brookfield® results are a relative measure for thixotropic or shear thinning materials.)

7. Castor-Severs Method/Pressure Flowmeter Method

7.1 Application—This procedure is used to determine the viscosity of adhesives, sealers, and sprayable sound deadeners. The values obtained are expressed in seconds and are a measurement of the time needed to extrude a specified mass (20 g) through a specified orifice at a specified pressure. These values can be converted to apparent viscosity in centipoise at a specified shear rate using the capillary rheometer procedure as in ASTM D 3835 or ASTM D 1823. If this step is taken, it is recommended to repeat the procedure at three pressures with at least two orifices to obtain a measure of shear thinning and thixotropy.

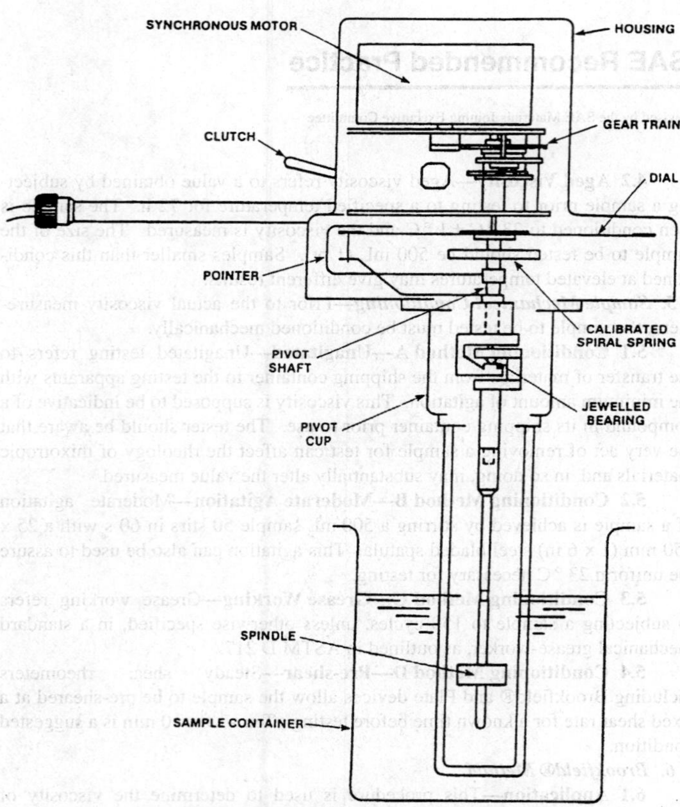

FIGURE 1—BROOKFIELD® VISCOMETER

7.2 Equipment

7.2.1 Rheometer as shown in Figure 2.

7.2.2 Orifices are as follows in Table 1:

TABLE 1—RHEOMETER ORIFICES

No. mm (in)	Diameter mm (in)	Length mm (in)	Typical Use	Limits
1	1.32 (0.052)	13.5 (0.531)	Sprayable	Readings less than 10 s, use Brookfield® Method
2	2.64 (0.104)	13.5 (0.531)	Pumpable	Readings less than 10 s, use orifice 1
3	3.18 (0.125)	51.0 (2.008)	Deadeners	Readings less than 10 s, use orifice 2

Other orifices should be used if the data is to be analyzed by plotting viscosity versus shear rate. A minimum of two orifices is recommended to observe thixotropic behavior. The length should be a minimum of 10 times the diameter. The dimensions should meet the accuracy requirements specified in ASTM D 3835 6.1.3.

7.2.3 Air supply, 700 kPa (100 psi).

7.2.4 Pressure gauge, 700 kPa (100 psi) 1% (ANSI/ASME B40.1-1985 Grade 1A or better).

7.2.5 Pressure regulator and water/oil extractor for air line.

7.2.6 Pipe cleaners for cleaning the orifice.

7.2.7 Stop watch or other timing device calibrated in tenths of seconds.

7.2.8 Balance, double beam type or equivalent, sensitivity to 0.01 g.

7.2.9 Mechanical convection oven capable of maintaining a temperature of ±1 °C (±2 °F), or alternate means where temperature conditioning is specified.

7.2.10 Weight per gallon cup, or other means to determine density within 1%.

7.3 Procedure

7.3.1 Fill the clean, dry, sealer cup equipped with the specified orifice with the material to be tested. The material should be at 23 °C ± 1 °C unless otherwise specified. Care should be taken to avoid air entrapment and to allow enough room for the plunger.

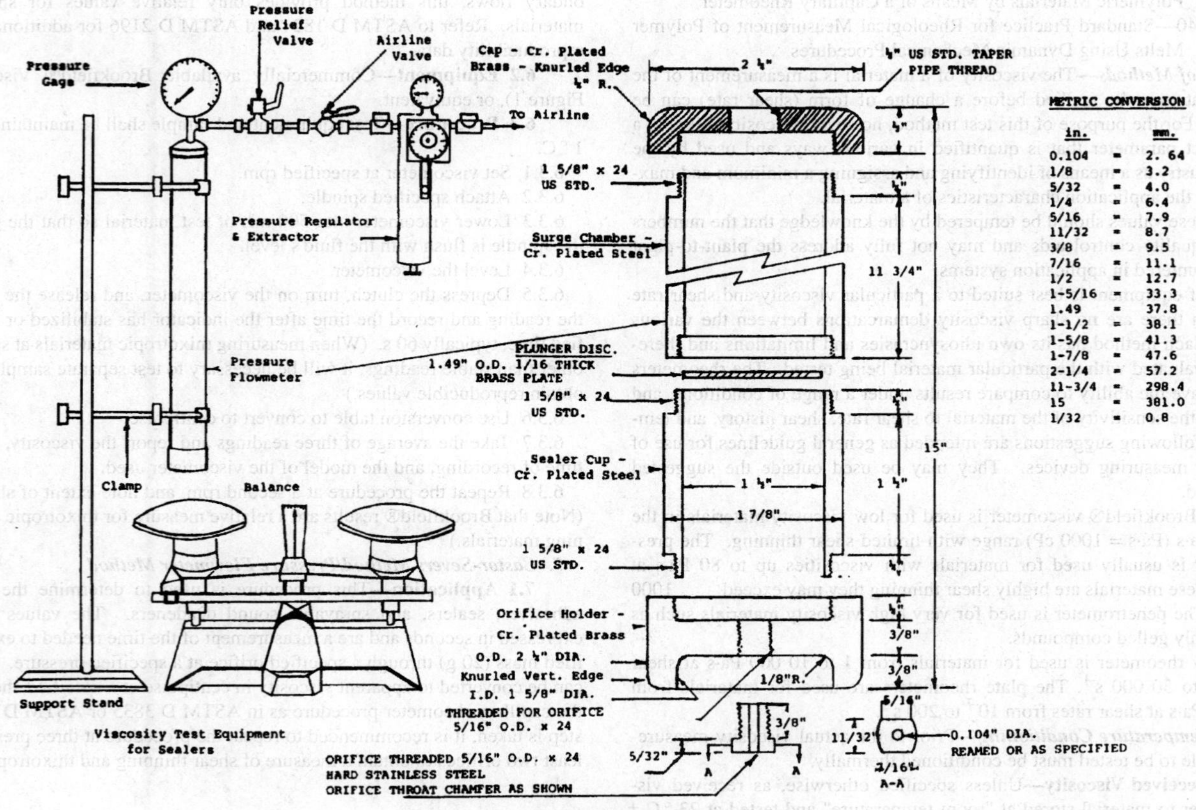

FIGURE 2—RHEOMETER

7.3.2 Adjust line pressure to 276 kPa (40 psi), unless otherwise specified. Open air valve and extrude material through orifice until entrapped air is eliminated. Shut air valve. When plotting viscosity versus shear rate using the equations from ASTM D 1823, it is desirable to repeat this procedure at four pressures. The recommended pressures are 69, 276, 483, and 690 kPa (10, 40, 70, and 100 psi).

7.3.3 Place a paper on the balance, tare and add specified weight (20 g).

7.3.4 Open air valve and start timer when the material touches the paper on the weighing pan.

7.3.5 When 20 g of sealer has accumulated on the balance pan, stop the timer, close the air valve, and open the pressure relief valve.

7.3.6 Take the average of three readings and report the number of seconds, pressure, and orifice length and diameter.

8. Penetration Method

8.1 Application—This procedure is used to determine the viscosity of heavy-bodied sealers, extrudable and die cut deadeners. In this method, viscosity is a measurement of the depth of penetration by a cone or needle into the material tested and is expressed in 0.1 mm of penetration.

8.2 Equipment

8.2.1 Commercially available penetrometer (Figure 3), as described in Table 2.

TABLE 2—PENETRATION INSTRUMENTS

No.	Penetrometer	Typical Use	Limits
1	Cone ASTM D 217	Deadeners	Readings less than 5 mm use Penetrometer No. 2
2	Needle ASTM D 5	Thumbable Materials	Readings less than 5 mm use Durometer hardness ASTM D 2240

8.2.2 Stop watch

8.2.3 Weights to place on loading bar

8.2.4 Penetration instruments (cone ASTM D 217 and needle ASTM D 5).

8.2.5 Sample Cup—75 mm diameter by 60 mm depth, or as specified.

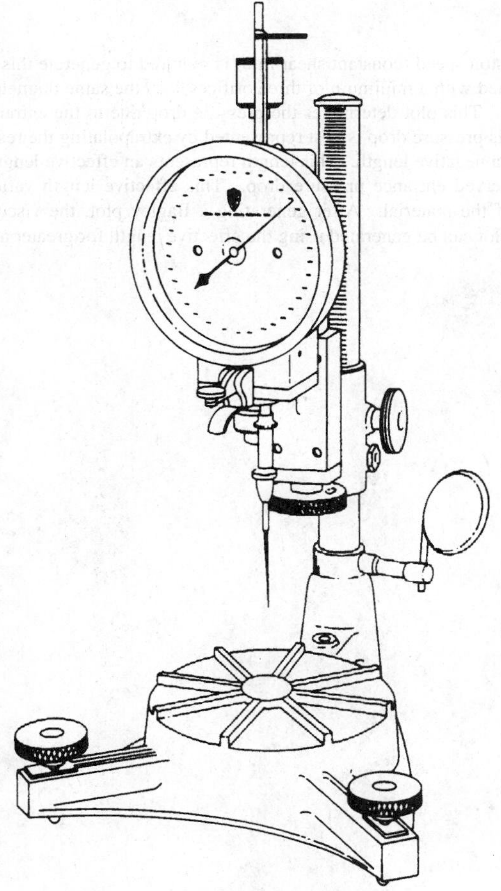

FIGURE 3—PENETROMETER

8.3 Procedure—Test material at 23 °C ± 1 °C.

8.3.1 Level penetrometer.

8.3.2 Insert specified penetrating instrument into chuck.

8.3.3 Set dial reading to zero.

8.3.4 Add weight to loading bar, as needed, to achieve the specified moving load. Use a 150 g total weight, including rod and added weights, unless otherwise specified.

8.3.5 Place the sample to be tested on the center of base plate.

8.3.6 Adjust the zeroed height of the penetrometer so that the point of the penetrating instrument is exactly in contact with the surface of the material to be tested.

8.3.7 Release test rod by depressing the trigger and keep in this position for 5 s unless otherwise specified.

8.3.8 At the end of the specified "drop" period, release the trigger.

8.3.9 Gently push the depth gage rod down as far as it will go and record the depth of penetration, units are in 0.1 mm.

8.3.10 Take the average of three readings and report the depth of penetration, moving load, and penetration time.

9. Capillary Rheometer Method

9.1 Application—This method is used to determine the viscosity versus shear rate characteristics of adhesives, sealers, and deadeners per ASTM D 3835 (ISO DIS11443). The basic test determines apparent viscosity versus apparent shear rate over a typical shear rate range of 100 to 50 000 s^{-1}. Various corrections are outlined in ASTM D 3835. The piston in barrel arrangement outlined in ASTM D 3835 is preferred for reaching high-shear rate, but the apparatus in Figure 2 and ASTM D 1823 is acceptable as a moderate shear rate screening tool (10 to 100 s^{-1}). Round Robin results are reported in ASTM D 1823.

9.2 Equipment

9.2.1 Capillary Rheometer per ASTM D 3835 (ISO DIS11443) and associated orifices (preferred).

9.2.2 Castor Severs rheometer as in Figure 2 is an alternate with limited shear rate range. This rheometer will require a balance, a timer, and a means to determine density within 1%, and thus volumetric flow rate. This will follow ASTM D 1823.

9.2.3 A set of orifices chosen for the material as outlined in the ASTM specification. If a Bagley plot is not generated, then a length to diameter ratio of at least 10 is desired to minimize the effect of entrance pressure losses. Diameters from 1 to 4 mm (0.050 to 0.150 in) and lengths from 13.5 to 100 mm (0.5 to 4 in) are well suited to the pressures available in the Castor Severs rheometer.

9.3 Procedure—Follow ASTM D 3835 (ISO DIS11443), this is a summary.

9.3.1 Clean and inspect barrel and capillary.

9.3.2 Charge the barrel with material with minimum air pockets.

9.3.3 Place the piston in the barrel, extrude a small quantity, and preheat for at least 6 min.

9.3.4 Start extrusion. Verify that steady state is reached. Record force (or pressure) and data necessary to calculate volumetric flowrate Q.

9.3.5 Repeat to check for flow stability. Report degree of repeatability observed. Repeat at desired shear rates. Refill barrel and re-equilibrate as necessary.

9.3.6 Repeat with at least one other orifice. Differences between curves from different orifices are due to change in shear history or slip at the wall.

9.3.7 Discharge any remaining material and clean the apparatus.

9.4 Reporting—Capillary results are typically reported on a viscosity versus shear rate plot or a shear stress versus shear rate plot as in Appendix A. The equations to derive this are in ASTM D 3835 and D 1823 and are summarized as follows in Equations 1 to 3. Plot individual data points so that repeatability is apparent on the graph, rather than averaging results. If the Castor-Severs type rheometer (8.2.2) is substituted, this should be noted.

$$\text{Shear Stress, Pa} = Pr/\ 2L \text{ (at the wall)} \qquad \text{(Eq. 1)}$$

$$\text{Shear Rate, } s^{-1} = 4Q/\ \pi r^3 \text{(Apparent shear rate, uncorrected)} \qquad \text{(Eq. 2)}$$

$$\text{Viscosity, Pa} \cdot s = P\pi r^4/\ 8LQ \text{(Apparent viscosity, uncorrected)} \qquad \text{(Eq. 3)}$$

where:

P = Barrel pressure, Pa
r = Capillary radius, m
L = Capillary length, m
Q = Volumetric flow rate, m^3/s= Mass flow rate (kg/s)/density (kg/m^3)

It is also important to record observations made during the test as to repeatability and stability of the extrusion. If stability is a concern, ASTM D 3364 can provide guidance in detecting and controlling the level of instability. When requested, it is desirable to perform the Rabinowitsch Shear Rate correction outline in ASTM D 3835 section 11.8 and the Bagley entrance correction outlined in ASTM section 11.7 and Appendix A. Various curve fits to the data may be requested, and a goodness of fit, which often relates to the flow instability of the material, should be reported.

10. Plate Rheometer Method

10.1 Application—This procedure is used to determine the viscosity versus shear rate characteristics of adhesives, sealers, and deadeners. This test uses instrumentation available for dynamic mechanical measurements on polymer melts as outlined in ASTM D 4440. However, these materials are generally not linear viscoelastic, so processing viscosity is not generally the same as complex viscosity. Therefore, it is typically desirable to use these instruments in steady shear mode and report apparent viscosity.

10.2 Equipment—A variety of equipment is commercially available for this type of testing. Both controlled stress and controlled rate units are available, and each have advantages in some measurements. The majority of units are rotational, but sliding plate rheometers are also available. The rotational units utilize both cone and plate and parallel plate geometries. While the cone and plate subjects all the material to a constant shear rate, the parallel plate geometry is typically preferred due to the interference of particles present in the formulation. The parallel plate geometry is required for temperature sweeps to allow compensation for tool expansion.

10.3 Procedure—Follow ASTM D 4440 where applicable. This is a summary.

10.3.1 Equilibrate the test fixture at the desired test temperature.

10.3.2 Touch the plates together and zero the gap indicator.

10.3.3 Open the tool and apply an adequate amount of material to the test fixture. Minimize bubbles as much as possible.

10.3.4 Close the test fixture to an appropriate gap, 1 to 3 mm is recommended. Remove excess material. Allow the sample to equilibrate to the desired initial temperature.

10.3.5 Program the desired test.

a. A thixotropic loop is recommended as a qualitative measure of the effect of time and shear history. Note that this test can be dependent on sample preparation.

b. A steady shear (or stress) sweep where the sample is allowed to equilibrate at each shear condition is also recommended.

c. A temperature sweep may be desired. Before performing a temperature sweep, monitor viscosity versus time at the shear conditions that the sweep will be performed to insure that shear history does not affect results. If viscosity changes with time, separate tests will have to be conducted at each temperature. Note that only the controlled rate instruments will allow viscosity versus temperature to be plotted at constant shear rate. A constant shear stress temperature sweep will combine the change in viscosity due to temperature and shear thinning as the shear rate increases.

10.3.6 Conduct the desired test. Watch the sample and stop the test if the sample slips away from one plate or separates at the edges. Edge separation limits the maximum valid shear rate. Edge separation is indicated if torque drops at higher shear rates. For an equilibrium sweep (10.3.5b), results obtained prior to separation may be reported. For a thixotropic loop, the test must be repeated with a lower maximum shear rate value. In this test even a small edge separation will appear as hysteresis in the material.

10.3.7 A new sample should be loaded for each test as these materials are sensitive to shear history.

10.3.8 Remove the sample and clean the test fixture.

10.4 Reporting—Rheometer tests are typically reported as a plot of viscosity versus shear rate or shear stress versus shear rate as in Appendix A. Include the type of instrument, test geometry, gap setting, and temperature. An overlay of the thixotropic loop and equilibrium sweep data is desired to demonstrate the degree of sensitivity to shear history. Various curve fits may be applied as requested.

11. Notes

11.1 Key Words—Viscosity, sealer, adhesive, rheology

APPENDIX A

A.1 Sample plots for the reporting of viscosity versus shear rate data are attached. Shear rate is plotted as the abscissa (x axis) (Figure A1), and either viscosity or shear stress is plotted as the ordinate (y axis) (Figure A2). The viscosity plot is more common, but the shear stress plot allows extrapolation to determine the yield stress. Log/Log plots are preferred because the values typically vary by more than one order of magnitude and changes in the lower values will not be obvious on a linear plot.

A sample Bagley plot (Figure A3) is also attached to help explain the correction procedure outlined in ASTM D 3835 paragraph 11.7. A capillary rheometer with constant piston speed (constant shear rate) is required to generate this plot. Tests are performed with a minimum of three orifices with the same diameter and various lengths. This plot determines the pressure drop due to the entrance into the orifice. This pressure drop is best represented by extrapolating the results to zero pressure at a negative length. This length represents an effective length of tubing for the observed entrance pressure drop. This effective length varies with the elasticity of the material. After generating a Bagley plot, the viscosity versus shear rate plot can be generated using the effective length for greater accuracy.

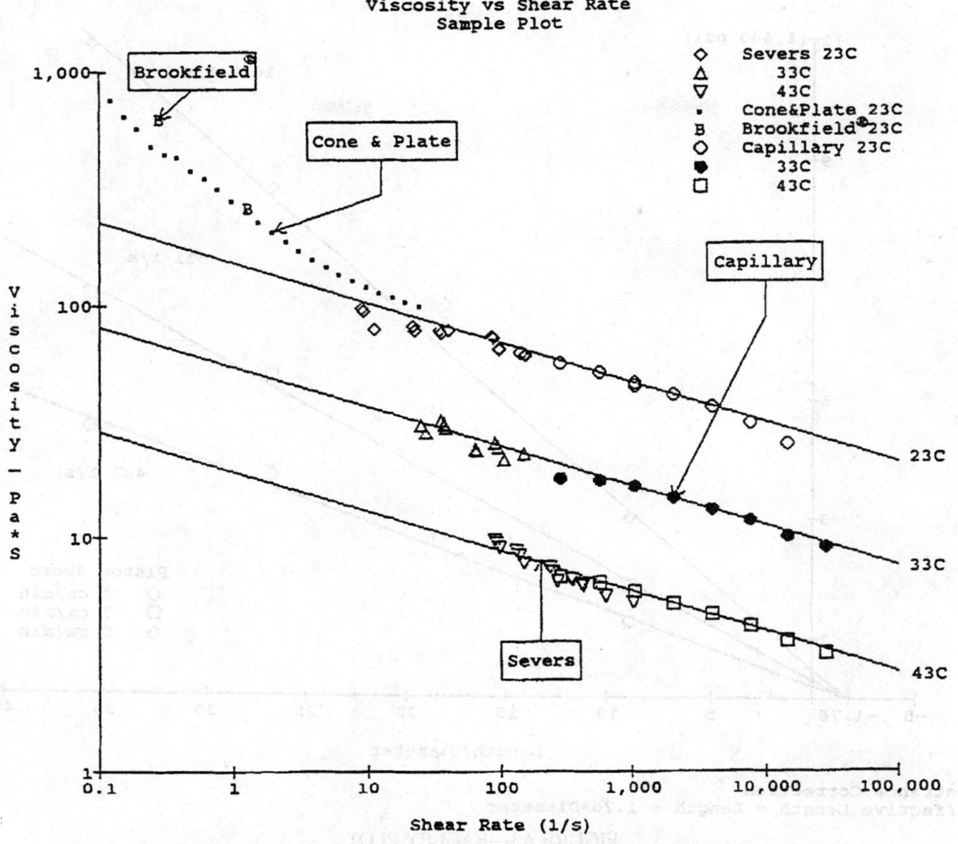

FIGURE A1—VISCOSITY VERSUS SHEAR RATE SAMPLE PLOT

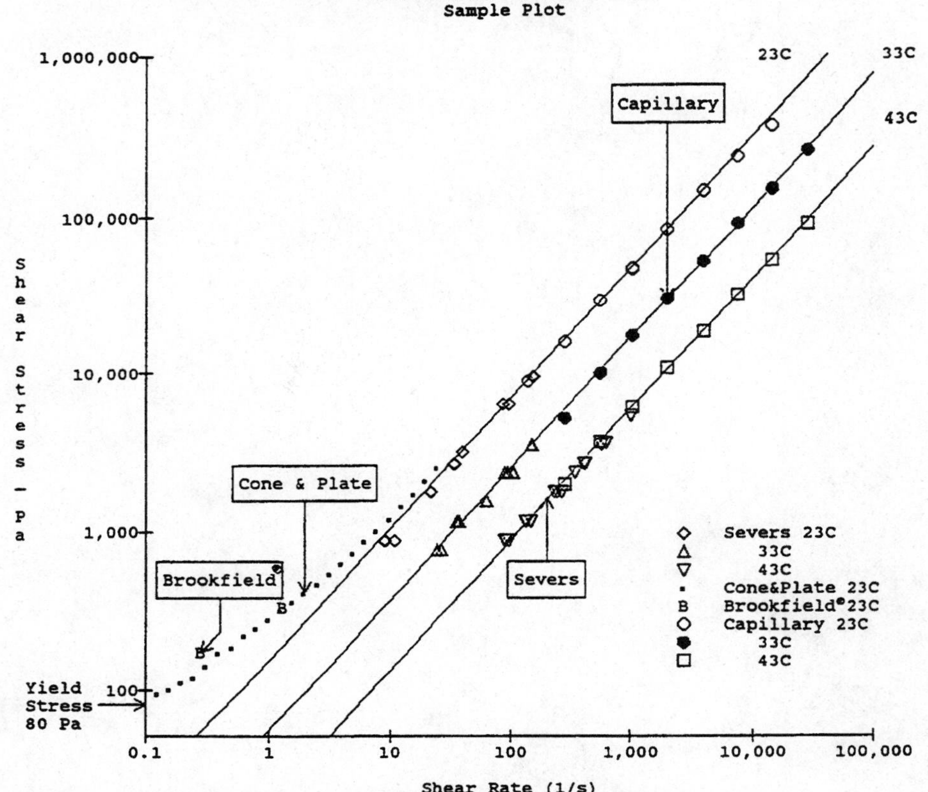

FIGURE A2—SHEAR STRESS VERSUS SHEAR RATE SAMPLE PLOT

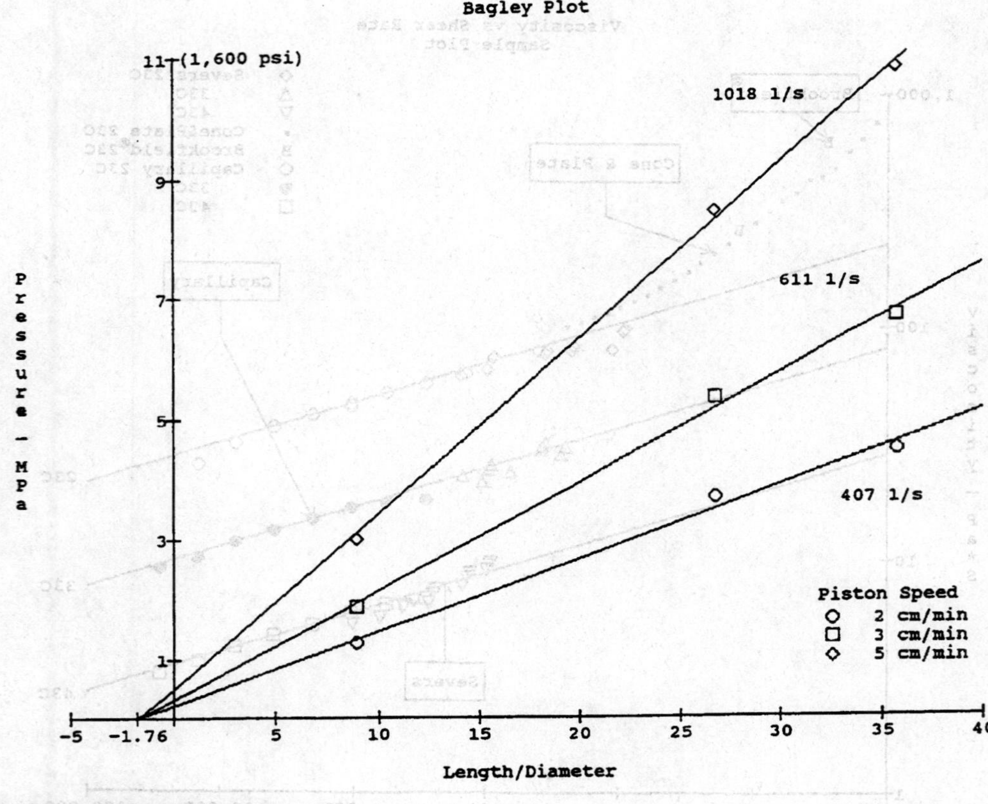

FIGURE A3—BAGLEY PLOT

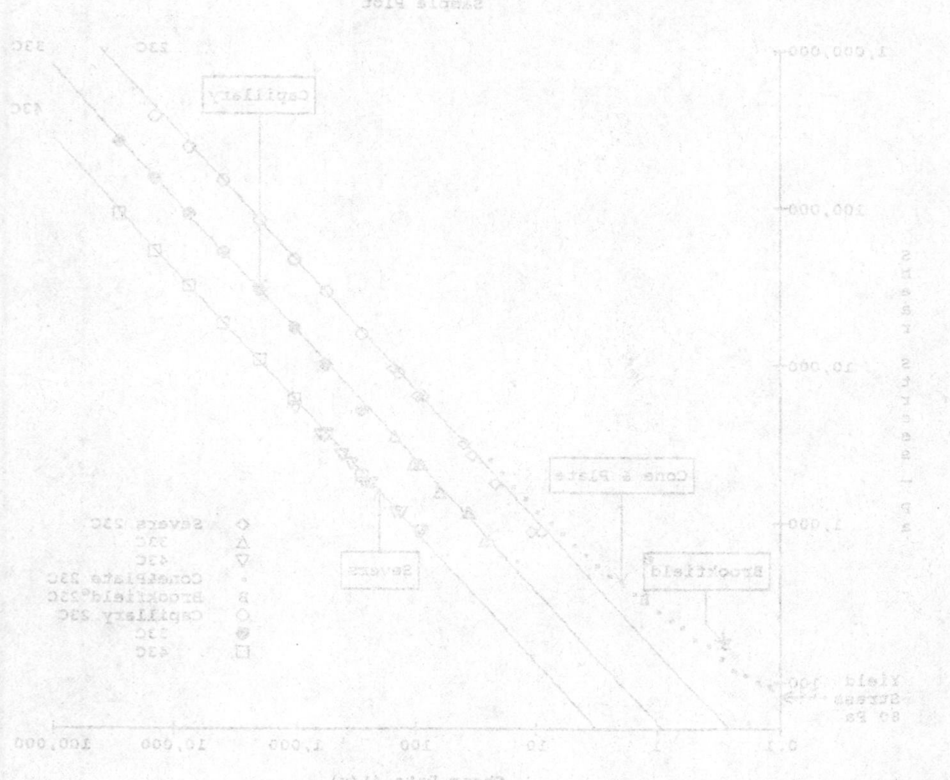

LAP SHEAR TEST FOR AUTOMOTIVE-TYPE ADHESIVES FOR FIBER REINFORCED PLASTIC (FRP) BONDING—SAE J1525 JUN1985

SAE Recommended Practice

Report of the SAE Nonmetallic Materials Committee approved June 1985. Originated in the SAE Adhesives and Body Sealers Subcommittee.

Foreword—This Document has not changed other than to put it into the new SAE Technical Standards Board Format.

1. Scope—This SAE Recommended Practice describes a lap shear test method for use in measuring the bonding characteristics of automotive-type adhesives for joining fiber reinforced plastics to themselves and to metals.

2. References

2.1 Applicable Publication—The following publication forms a part of this specification to the extent specified herein.

2.1.1 ASTM PUBLICATION—Available from ASTM, 100 Barr Harbor Drive, West Conshohocken, PA 19428-2959.

ASTM D 1002—Test Method for Strength Properties of Adhesives in Shear by Tension Loading (Metal-to-Metal)

3. Test Substrate

3.1 Substrates—Fiber reinforced plastic as specified. Metal composition and roughness as specified.

3.2 Dimensions—Fiber reinforced plastic parts shall be cut into flat coupons 25.4 x 100 mm (1.000 x 4.000 in) at a nominal thickness of 2.5 mm (0.100 in). In the case of FRP to metal bonding, metal thickness will be nominally 1.5 mm (0.060 in).

3.3 Surface Preparation—Surface preparation of FRP will be in accordance with adhesive suppliers' recommendations. Surface roughening solvent cleaning and surface primers are acceptable provided they do not reduce FRP bulk properties. Any surface preparation must be adaptable to actual production situations. Metals will be machined to eliminate burrs or bevels. They will be clean and dry, or surface treated prior to bonding according to procedures prescribed by the adhesive manufacturer.

4. Preparation of Test Joints

4.1 Application of Adhesive—Adhesive will be applied in accordance with adhesive suppliers' recommendations. In the case of two-part adhesives, mixing will be in accordance with suppliers' suggested procedures.

4.2 Adhesive Cure—Adhesive will be cured at room temperature or elevated temperature using prescribed conditions determined by adhesive supplier, provided they can be reasonably adapted to production situations.

4.3 Joint Geometry—Joint geometry will be as shown in Figure 1. Joint geometry will be controlled by appropriate fixturing using glass beads or other suitable means to control a 0.76 mm (0.030 in) adhesive glueline thickness. The amount of glass beads in the glueline will be the minimum number needed to hold glueline thickness. Fixturing pressure will be allowed.

4.4 Excess Adhesive—Excess adhesive (squeeze out) will be removed from bonded lap shear prior to testing.

4.5 Conditioning—Bonded parts will be allowed to return to ambient temperature for at least 1 h if elevated temperature cures are employed. If adhesive is room temperature cured, full cure time plus 10% will be allowed prior to testing.

5. Testing

5.1 Apparatus—The testing machine shall conform to the requirements of and have the capabilities of the machine prescribed in ASTM D1002.

It shall have a suitable pair of grips to hold test samples without allowing slip. Initial grip separation shall be 100 mm (4.000 in) with 25 mm (1.000 in) minimum of each sample and firmly held.

5.2 Test Rate—Fixture loading shall be in a consistent manner with a rate of 13 mm (0.5000)/min preferred.

5.3 Test Samples—Five lap shear samples will be prepared in each case and tested.

6. Report

6.1 Complete identification of the adhesive tested, including type and manufacturer's code number.

6.2 Complete identification of the substrates used and method of surface preparation prior to bonding.

6.3 Cure schedule, time, and temperature for bonding sample.

6.4 Individual peak load values (psi or kPa), averages, and failure modes with estimated percentages.

Failure mode will be reported as shown in Figure 2. Close visual observation will be used to determine failure mode.

If primers are employed, the failure modes shown in Figure 3 will be included.

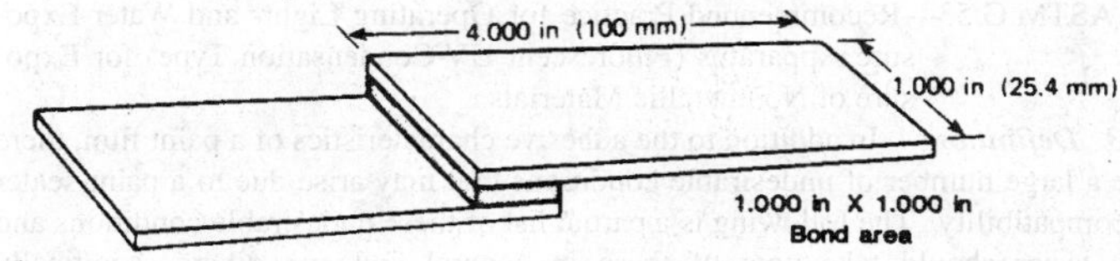

FIGURE 1—

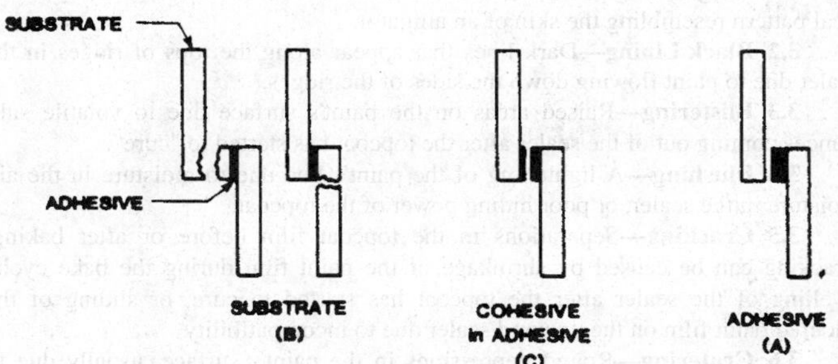

FIGURE 2—

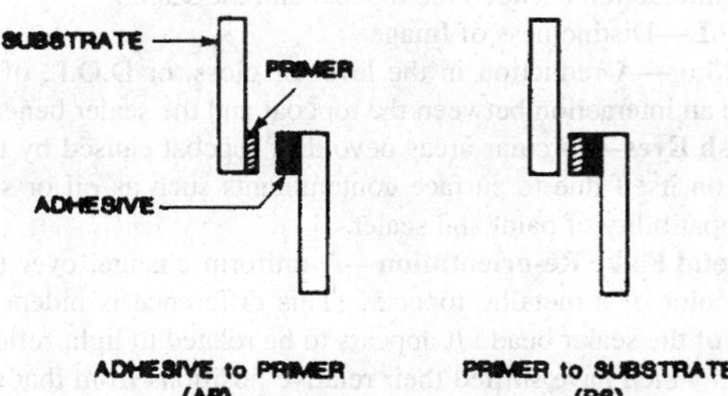

FIGURE 3—

METHOD FOR EVALUATING THE PAINTABLE CHARACTERISTICS OF AUTOMOTIVE SEALERS —SAE J1800 APR1987

SAE Recommended Practice

Report of the SAE Adhesives and Body Sealers Committee approved April 1987.

Foreword—This Document has not changed other than to put it into the new SAE Technical Standards Board Format.

1. Scope—This SAE Recommended Practice sets forth a method for testing and evaluating the paintable characteristics of automotive sealers. This document contains three samples preparation procedures:

Method #1: Topcoat over cured primer and cured sealer
Method #2: Topcoat over cured sealer
Method #3: Topcoat over uncured sealer

2. References

2.1 Applicable Publications—The following publications form a part of the specification to the extent specified herein. Unless otherwise indicated the lastest revision of SAE publications shall apply.

2.1.1 ASTM PUBLICATIONS—Available from ASTM, 100 Barr Harbor Drive, West Conshohocken, PA 19428-2959.

ASTM D 3359-78—Method for Measuring Adhesion by Tape Test
ASTM G 53—Recommended Practice for Operating Light- and Water-Exposure Apparatus (Fluorescent UV-Condensation Type) for Exposure of Nonmetallic Materials

3. Definitions—In addition to the adhesive characteristics of a paint film, there are a large number of undesirable conditions that may arise due to a paint-sealer incompatibility. The following is a partial list of these undesirable conditions and the tester should take note of these in general and any others specifically requested.

3.1 Alligatoring—A uniform distribution of surface cracking in a symmetrical pattern resembling the skin of an alligator.

3.2 Black Lining—Dark lines that appear along the tops of ridges in the sealer due to paint flowing down the sides of the ridges.

3.3 Blistering—Raised areas on the paint's surface due to volatile substances coming out of the sealer after the topcoat has started to "cure".

3.4 Blushing—A lightening of the paint's hue due to moisture in the air, moisture in the sealer, or poor hiding power of the topcoat.

3.5 Cracking—Separations in the topcoat film before or after baking. Cracking can be caused by shrinkage of the paint film during the bake cycle, swelling of the sealer after the topcoat has started to cure, or sliding of the uncured paint film on the uncured sealer due to incompatibility.

3.6 Cratering—Round depressions in the paint's surface, usually due to contaminants in the paint or on the surface being painted.

3.7 Discoloring—A change in the absolute color of the topcoat usually due to a chemical interaction between the topcoat and the sealer.

3.8 D.O.I.—Distinctness of Image

3.9 Dulling—A reduction in the level of gloss, or D.O.I., of the topcoat, usually due to an interaction between the topcoat and the sealer beneath.

3.10 Fish Eyes—Circular areas devoid of topcoat caused by the wet paint "drawing" in on itself due to surface contaminants such as oil or silicones or a general incompatibility of paint and sealer.

3.11 Metal Flake Re-orientation—A uniform change, over the sealer, in the apparent color of a metallic topcoat. This difference is independent of the configuration of the sealer bead. It appears to be related to light reflecting off the metallic flakes which have shifted their relative positions from that of the rest of the panel, probably the result of floating, or vertical pigment separation, due to currents set up in a Benard cell.

3.12 Metal Flake Mottling—A puddling of the metallic and non-metallic pigments in a topcoat giving it a blotchy appearance.

3.13 Pinholing—Small holes, the size of a pinpoint, in the surface of the topcoat that result when small bubbles burst as the paint cures.

3.14 Popping—Usually refers to a fairly uniform distribution of small blisters caused the volatilization of entrapped solvent beneath a topcoat that has started to cure. The volatile material can be from the sealer coated or from a layer of paint that is excessively thick.

3.15 Running—A movement or flowing of wet topcoat over the sealer caused by a paint-sealer incompatibility or an excessive application of topcoat.

3.16 Seedy Appearance—A paint-sealer incompatibility causing pigment flocculation leading to a surface that is spotted with raised "grainy" looking particles.

3.17 Soft Paint—A paint film that has not achieved its specified hardness. This can be caused by the migration of plasticizers, into the topcoat, from the sealer, or by the sealer chemically retarding the topcoat's curing system.

3.18 Staining—A discoloring of the topcoat due to a sealer-topcoat interaction.

3.19 Tacky Topcoat—A more severe form of "soft paint" in which the sealer has interferred with the topcoat curing mechanism to the degree that fingerprints can be left on the paint's surface.

3.20 Yellowing—A particular form of staining in which a yellowish stain appears, usually associated with light color topcoats.

3.21 Wrinkling—A paint-sealer incompatibility which causes the topcoat's surface to cure at a different rate resulting in the formation of ridges. These ridges can vary in absolute size but generally are uniform in size on any one particular panel.

4. Principal of Methods—This SAE test specification is to be used as a method for evaluating the performance of automotive primers and/or topcoats when applied over "cured" or "uncured" sealers. This specification includes a list of the needed test equipment, application and baking parameters, and a glossary of terms describing undesirable characteristics that should be noted by the tester.

This specification covers the performance and quality of an automotive topcoat when applied over a sealer, along with the integrity of bond between the paint and the sealer. It does not cover sealer performance characteristics, such as sealer to substrate bonding, nor does it include a procedure governing the actual spraying of the topcoat.

It is assumed that the tester is well versed in the techniques of spraying automotive topcoat, but if this information is needed, it is available from paint suppliers.

5. Equipment and Supplies

a. Mechanical convection oven (gas fired recommended for curing paint)
b. Spray equipment, including compressor
c. Paint as specified
d. Ample supply of test panels as specified
e. Sealer to be coated
f. Q.U.V. Cabinet (per ASTM G 53)
g. Sealer template - 150 mm x 25 mm x 1 mm (6 in x 1 in x 0.040 in)
h. Hacksaw blade (24 teeth/25 mm)
i. Adhesive tape as specified in ASTM D 3359-78

6. Paint Sample Conditioning—Prior to spraying primer or paint, certain thermal, mechanical, and dilution parameters must be met.

6.1 Mechanical Conditioning—Before spraying primer or paint, it must be thoroughly agitated per manufacturer's instructions to insure a homogenous distribution of the various pigments.

6.2 Thermal Conditioning—The paint should be sprayed at the proper temperature and humidity (per manufacturer's instructions) to prevent various undesirable conditions, such as blushing, running, popping, etc.

6.3 Viscosity Conditioning—To ensure atomization, the viscosity of the paint must be in the range as stated by the manufacturer.

7. Sealant Sample Conditioning—Mechanical conditioning of the sealer may be required of the tester to evaluate the leveling characteristics in conjunction with its paintability. This should be done as required.

8. Test Sample Preparation—In the following procedures, primers should have a wet film applied equivalent to 0.6 to 1.2 dry mils unless otherwise specified. Topcoat systems shuld be applied at a thickness equivalent to 1.5 to 2.0 dry mills with metallics being applied at the lower end of the spectrum and solid colors at the higher end unless otherwise specified.

The application of base coat/clear coat requires a color coat equivalent to 0.6 mils to 1.2 mils dry, or as specified. Again, metallic colors should be applied at the lower end of the spectrum, and solid colors toward the higher end. Clear coat should be applied within 5 min of the color coat at a thickness equivalent to 0.8 mils to 1.0 mils dry, or as specified.

8.1 Method #1—This method involves spraying primer over uncured sealer, baking the panel at the prime bake, spraying topcoat over the baked panel, and baking the panel at the topcoat bake.

8.1.1 Take the required number of panels (type as requested) and apply by means of a template, the sealer to be tested. Scrape one end, 50 mm, with hacksaw blade to evaluate leveling properties.

8.1.2 Store sealer panels in a vertical position prior to painting, unless requested otherwise.

8.1.3 Apply primer to a wet film thickness resulting in 0.7 to 1.0 dry mils of primer, or as specified.

8.1.4 Air dry wet panels in the vertical position at the temperature and humidity recommended by the primer manufacturer.

8.1.5 After recommended air dry time, evaluate the panels for undesirable characteristics, such as fish eyes, primer flowing off sealer, etc.

8.1.6 Bake primer panels in an air circulating oven for 30 min at 150 °C (300 °F), or as specified.

8.1.7 Evaluate baked panels for undesirable characteristics such as tacky film, popping, etc.

8.1.8 Condition panels to room temperature and apply topcoat to a wet film thickness equivalent to 1.5 to 2.0 dry mils, or as specified. There should be two sets of topcoat panels prepared. One set with white and one with light blue or silver metallic.

8.1.9 Air dry panels for recommended period at recommended temperature and humidity in the vertical position, and record any adverse developments.

8.1.10 Bake topcoated panels in air circulating oven for 17 min at 130 °C (265 °F) for lacquers, 30 min at 150 °C (300 °F), or as specified.

8.1.11 Evaluate baked panels for undesirable characteristics and record the results.

8.2 Method #2—This method involves applying sealer to a primed panel, baking the panel at the prime bake, spraying topcoat over the baked panel, and baking the panel at the topcoat bake.

8.2.1 Take the required number of panels (type as requested) and apply, by means of a template, the sealer to be tested. Scrape one end, 50 mm, with hacksaw blade to evaluate leveling properties.

8.2.2 Bake panels in an air circulating oven in the vertical position for 30 min at 150 °C (300 °F), or as specified.

8.2.3 Condition panels to room temperature and apply topcoat to a wet film thickness equivalent to 1.5 to 2.0 mils dry, or as specified. There should be two sets of topcoat panels prepared. One set with non-metallic white and one with light blue or silver metallic.

8.2.4 Air dry panels for recommended period at recommended temperature and humidity in the vertical position and record any adverse developments.

8.2.5 Bake topcoated panels in an air circulating oven for 17 min at 130 °C (265 °F), for lacquers, 30 min at 150 °C (300 °F), or as specified.

8.2.6 Evaluate baked panels for undesirable characteristics and record the results.

8.3 Method #3—This method involves spraying topcoat over uncured sealer and baking the panel at the topcoat bake.

8.3.1 Take the required number of panels (type as requested) and apply, by means of a template, the sealer to be tested. Scrape one end, 50 mm, with a hacksaw blade to evaluate leveling properties.

8.3.2 Apply topcoat to a wet film thickness equivalent to 1.5 to 2.0 dry mils. There should be two sets of topcoat panels prepared. One set with non-metallic white and one with light blue or silver metallic.

8.3.3 Air dry panels for the recommended period at the recommended temperature and humidity in the vertical position and record any adverse developments.

8.3.4 Bake topcoated panels in an air circulating oven for 17 min at 130 °C (265 °F), for lacquers, 30 min at 150 °C (300 °F), or as specified.

8.3.5 Evaluate baked panels for undesirable characteristics and record the results.

9. Accelerated Aging—There are numerous methods of evaluating the weathering characteristics of a painted sealer system, but this test will be limited to Q.U.V. and heat aging.

9.1 Q.U.V. Method

9.1.1 Take the required number of painted panels to be tested, and evaluate them for any imperfections.

9.1.2 Record your observations, along with the time and date that the panels are exposed.

9.1.3 Set the Q.U.V. cabinet cycle as follows:

1. Eight (8) h light at 70 °C (160 °F)
2. QFS-40 bulbs
3. Four (4) h dark, condensing humidity at 50 °C (120 °F)

9.1.4 Expose panels for 500 h with QFS-40 bulbs, in the Q.U.V. method. Evaluate the panels per ASTM G 53 or as specified.

9.1.5 Remove panels after 500 h and repeat observations comparing the results to their original condition.

9.2 Heat Age

9.2.1 Take the required number of painted panels to be tested and evaluate them for any imperfections.

9.2.2 Record your observations, along with the time and date that the panels are exposed.

9.2.3 Expose panels for 336 h (14 days at 70 ± 1 °C (158 ± 2 °F) in an air circulating oven. Evaluate the panels at specified intervals.

9.2.4 Remove panels after 336 h and repeat observations comparing results with the original set of values.

10. Evaluation

10.1 Appearance—At the end of the specified exposure period, compare the exposed test sample with an unexposed test sample and report any staining, discoloration, or other deleterious effects on paint.

10.2 Cross Cut Tape Adhesion Test—The Cross Cut method is a useful procedure for comparing the degree of topcoat adhesion before and after environmental exposures. This method is somewhat empirical and does not quantify the interfacial forces that bond a topcoat to the sealer beneath.

10.2.1 Follow the procedure as set forth in ASTM D 3359-78 Method B Cross Cut Tape Test.

10.2.2 Record the number of squares removed, this number will be a quantitative value.

10.2.3 Compare the values of panels before and after the environmental exposure.

COACH JOINT FRACTURE TEST —SAE J1863 NOV1993

SAE Recommended Practice

Report of the SAE Adhesives and Body Sealers Committee approved April 1987. Reaffirmed by the SAE Materials Joining Committee November 1993.

Foreword—This Reaffirmed Document has not changed other than to put it into the new SAE Technical Standards Board Format.

1. Scope—This SAE Recommended Practice defines a procedure for determining the cleavage strength of an adhesive used for bonding automotive oily metal substrates.

2. References

2.1 Applicable Publication—The following publication forms a part of this specification to the extent specified herein.

2.1.1 ASTM PUBLICATION—Available from ASTM, 100 Barr Harbor Drive, West Conshohocken, PA 19428-2959.

ASTM D 1002—Test Method for Strength Properties of Adhesives in Shear by Tension Loading (Metal-to-Metal)

3. Test Substrates

3.1 Substrates—Metal composition and roughness as specified.

3.2 Dimensions—Metal substrates shall be cut into flat coupons 25.4 mm x 100 mm at 0.8 mm nominal thickness, unless otherwise specified. Coupons shall be free from burrs or other surface imperfections. Form coupon to geometry shown in Figure 1.

3.3 Surface Preparation—Remove contaminant from test coupon surface using a neutral solvent such as acetone or methyl ethyl ketone. Apply a uniform 0.025 mm wet thickness coating of light mineral oil over test coupons, unless otherwise specified. Condition coupons at 23 °C ±2 °C and 50% ±5% humidity for 1 h minimum before bonding.

4. Preparation of Test Joints

4.1 Joint Geometry—Joint geometry will be as shown in Figure 1.

4.2 Adhesive Bondline Thickness—Evaluate adhesive bondline thickness at 0.25 mm and 0.8 mm. Bondline thickness can be controlled by inserting wire or glass bead spacers into the adhesive. The spacer volume shall not exceed 1% of the total adhesive volume.

4.3 Adhesive Application—The quantity of adhesive used to prepare the bond should be regulated to avoid excess squeeze-out. Squeeze-out at the edges of the bond shall be removed prior to curing.

4.4 Clamping and Fixturing—Bonding surfaces shall be firmly fixed and retained through cure cycle.

4.5 Adhesive Cure—Adhesive shall be cured in accordance with the adhesive supplier's or automotive engineer's recommendation.

4.6 Conditioning—Bonded specimens shall be allowed to return to ambient temperatures for 1 h minimum prior to testing.

5. Testing

5.1 Apparatus—Test apparatus as described in ASTM D 1002.

5.2 Sample Clamping—The distance between clamping jaws shall be 100 mm with each jaw grasping 25 mm minimum of test specimens.

5.3 Test Rate—Specimens shall be tested at a pull rate of 13 mm/min.

5.4 Test Quantity—A minimum of five sample lap shears shall be prepared for each test condition.

6. Report Results

6.1 Report each individual peak load values, sample average, and standard deviation. Bond values shall be reported as the peak load (N) per 25.4 mm sample width.

6.2 Report composition, roughness, and thickness of substrate.

6.3 Report adhesive bondline thickness.

6.4 Report metal preparation materials and thickness applied.

6.5 Report mode of failure (adhesive, cohesive, or substrate failure).

6.6 Report adhesive cure schedule (time and temperature).

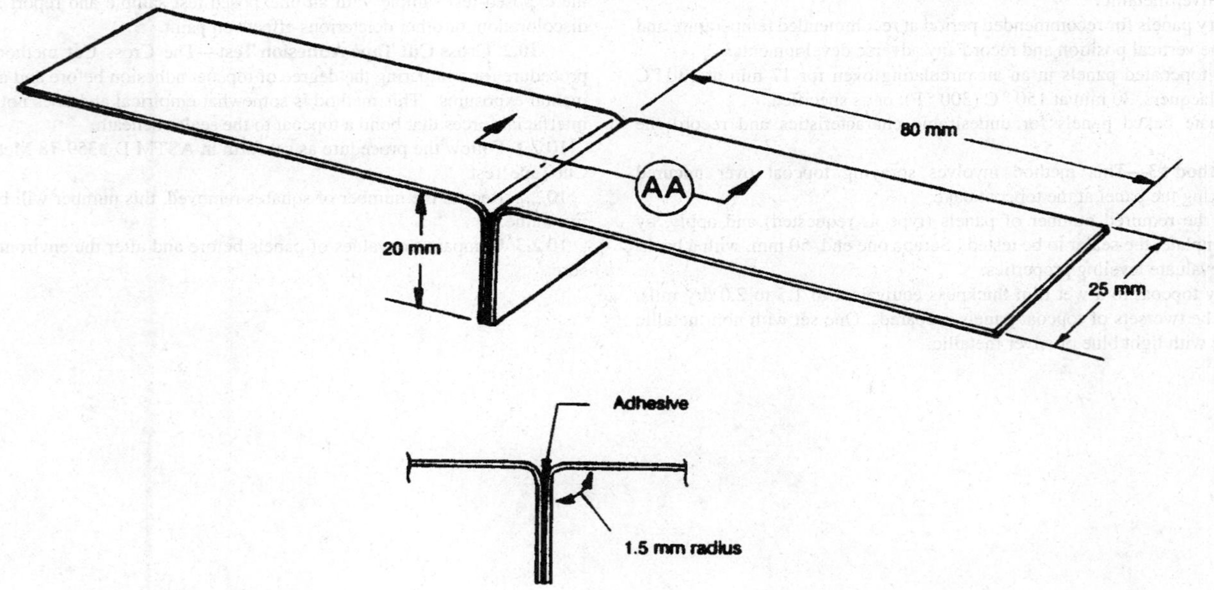

SECTION - AA

FIGURE 1—COACH JOINT FRACTURE SPECIMEN

) METHOD FOR THE DETERMINATION OF EXPANSION AND WATER ABSORPTION IN AUTOMOTIVE SEALERS—SAE J1918 JAN2002

SAE Recommended Practice

Report of the SAE Adhesives and Body Sealers Committee approved May 1988. Completely revised by the SAE Automotive Adhesives and Sealers Committee January 2002. Rationale statement available.

Foreword—This document describes three different methods for measuring the expansion of an automotive sealer

Method #1—Gravimetric Method
Method #2—Volumetric Method
Method #3—Vertical Method

and two methods for measuring water absorption

Method #1—Uncut Method
Method #2—Cut Method

The gravimetric and volumetric methods would be used to determine the amount of compound needed to completely fill an enclosed or "boxed in" area to effect a moisture and/or sound resistant barrier. The gravimetric method, Method #1, is analytical in nature and thus is more precise in its calculated values, and is especially useful when measuring expansions of less than 100%. The volumetric method, Method #2, is a quick way to check expansion where errors of ±5% points are not crucial.

The vertical expansion method, Method #3, measures the vertical rise that a sealer achieves and is useful in determining bead size and expansion requirements in sealing applications, such as roof bows, where the critical function of the compound involves "jumping" an air gap, thereby joining two irregularly spaced surfaces.

The water absorption methods measure a sealer's resistance to moisture transmission when the sealer's outer surface is intact and/or damaged. Generally water absorption values, after 24 h immersion, of 2% or less for intact films and 3% or less for cut films are acceptable.

1. Scope—This SAE Recommended Practice sets forth methods for determining total expansion gravimetrically and volumetrically, calculating vertical expansion and measuring the water absorption of cut and uncut sealer beads.

2. References

2.1 Related Publications—The following publications are provided for information purposes only and are not a required part of this document.

2.1.1 DAIMLERCHRYSLER PUBLICATIONS—Available from DaimlerChrysler Corporation, ????

LP-463NB-5-01 Change C—Volume Change of Heat Expandable Sealers—Determination of, DaimlerChrylser Corporation, Laboratory Procedure (Gravimetric Test Method)

LP-463NB-33-01 Change A—Sealers—Vertical Rise Method of Determining Volume Change, DaimlerChrysler Corporation, Laboratory Procedure (Vertical Expansion Test Method)

LP-463NB-07-01 Change C—Sealers—Water Absorption—Determination of, DaimlerChrysler Corporation, Laboratory Procedure (Water Absorption Test Method)

2.1.2 FORD PUBLICATIONS—Available from Ford Motor Company, ????

FLTM BV 108-02 1992 01 21—Volume Change Test for Adhesives and Sealants, Ford Motor Company, Automotive Safety and Engineering Standards (Gravimetric Test Methods)

ESB-M18P11-A 1988 12 09—3.8 Expansion, Ford Motor Company, Engineering Material Specification (Vertical Expansion Test Method)

FLTM BV 117-01 1992 02 03—Water Absorption Test for Adhesives and Sealants, Ford Motor Company, Engineering Material Specification (Water Absorption Test Method)

2.1.3 GENERAL MOTORS CORPORATION—Available from General Motors Corporation, ????

GM9037P September 1988—Test for Measuring Expansion of Sealers, General Motors Engineering Standards, Materials and Processes—Procedures (Gravimetric Test Method)

GM9640P January 1992—Water Absorption Test for Adhesives and Sealants, General Motors Engineering Standards, Materials and Processes—Procedures (Water Absorption Test Method)

GM9764P October 1989—Test for Measuring the Ramp Expansion of Sealers, General Motors Engineering Standards, Materials and Processes—Procedures (Vertical Expansion Test Method)

3. Equipment—The following materials are required:

3.1 Expansion

3.1.1 GRAVIMETRIC TEST METHODS (METHOD #1)

a. Sealer to be tested
b. Mechanical Convection Oven
c. Analytical Balance (0.0001 g accuracy)
d. 150 mL beaker
e. Three count 0.9 x 25 x 62 mm (0.035 x 1 x 2.5 in) Aluminum Coupons with 0.25 mm diameter wire
f. 0.9 x 300 x 300 mm (0.035 x 12 x 12 in) Cold Rolled Steel Panel
g. 0.9 x 75 x 150 mm (0.035 x 3 x 6 in) Cold Rolled Steel Panel

3.1.2 VOLUMETRIC TEST METHODS (METHOD #2)

a. Sealer to be tested
b. Mechanical Convection Oven
c. 500 mL graduated cylinder (50 mm (2.0 in) diameter)
d. Three count 15 mL (0.5 oz) seamless containers with 0.25 mm (0.010 in) diameter wire
e. 0.9 x 300 x 300 mm (0.035 x 12 x 12 in) Cold Rolled Steel Panel

3.1.3 VERTICAL EXPANSION TEST METHODS (METHOD #3)

a. Sealer to be tested
b. Mechanical Convection Oven
c. Six count 0.9 x 100 x 300 mm (0.035 x 4 x 12 in) Cold Rolled Steel Panels
d. Six count 32 mm Wide Spring Clips

3.2 Water Absorption

a. Sealer to be tested
b. Mechanical Convection Oven
c. Analytical Balance (0.001 g accuracy)
d. 0.9 x 25 x 62 mm (0.035 x 1 x 2.5 in) Aluminum Coupons without wire
e. 0.9 x 300 x 300 mm (0.035 x 12 x 12 in) Cold Rolled Steel Panel

4. Gravimetric Expansion Procedure (Method #1)

4.1 Fabricate a small platform, from a 75 x 150 x 0.9 mm (3 x 6 x 0.035 in) steel panel, that will support a 150 mL beaker full of water as shown in Figure 1 (exact dimensions will vary depending on the model of balance used). The positioning of the platform and beaker should be arranged to allow complete freedom of movement of the pan.

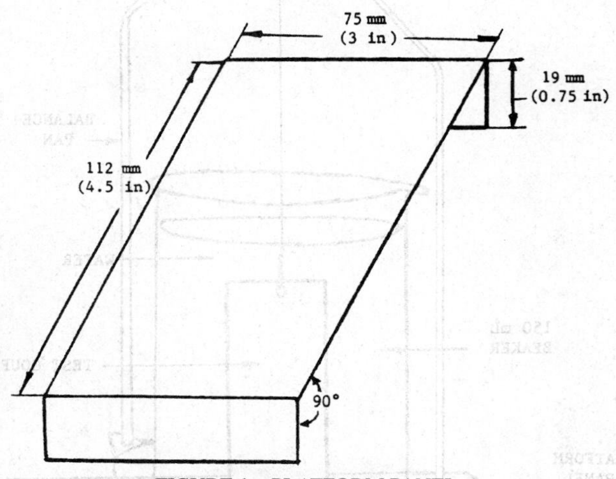

FIGURE 1—PLATFORM PANEL

4.2 Individually identify each of three 0.9 x 25 x 62 mm (0.035 x 1 x 2.5 in) aluminum coupon assemblies, as shown in Figure 2, and determine the dry weight of each panel (W1) to the nearest milligram (0.0001).

4.3 Determine the wet weight of each coupon assembly (W2) to the nearest milligram (0.0001) after suspending each coupon in water as in Figure 3, making sure the entire coupon is submerged.

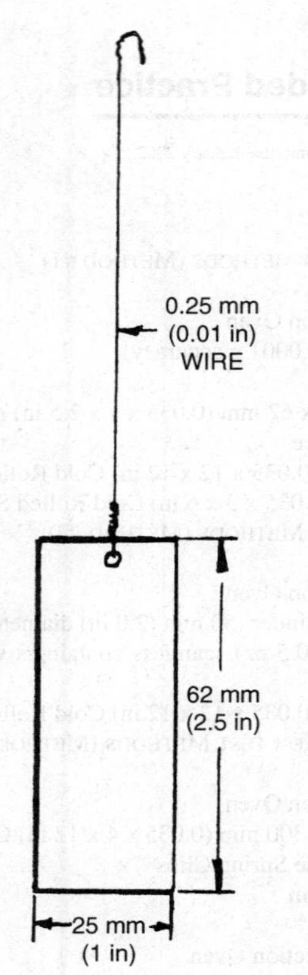

FIGURE 2—COUPON ASSEMBLY

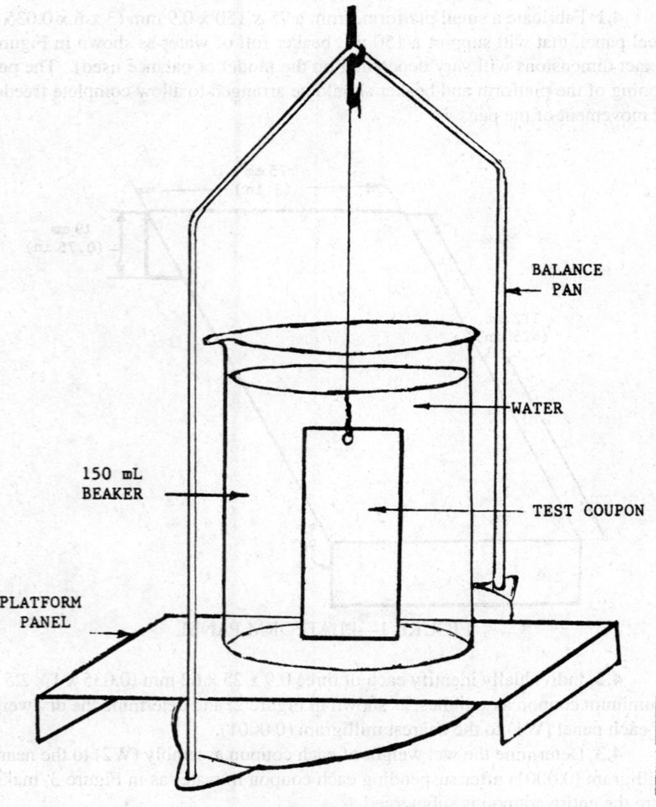

FIGURE 3—ANALYTICAL SCALE SET-UP

4.4 The volume of each coupon (V1) in milliliters is equal to the difference between the dry and wet weights divided by the specific gravity of water, 1 g/mL

$$V1 = \frac{W1(mg) - W2(mg)}{1\ g/\ mL} \quad \text{(Eq. 1)}$$

4.5 Apply a semi-circular bead of sealer, approximately 10 mm (0.39 in) in diameter, down the center of each panel.

4.6 Trim the ends of each bead leaving a 38 mm (1.5 in) length of sealer centered on each coupon as shown in Figure 4.

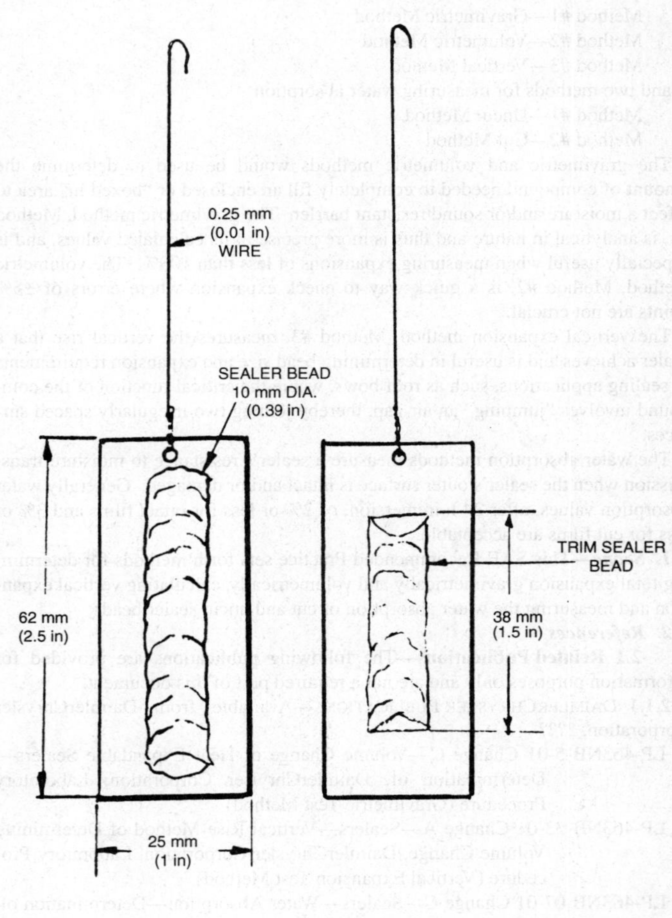

FIGURE 4—GRAVIMETRIC EXPANSION SAMPLE AND COUPON GEOMETRY

4.7 Determine the unexpanded sealer volume (V2) for the three marked and sealer coated coupons by weighing the assemblies dry (W3) and wet (W4) with weights reported in milligrams using the procedure described in 4.2 through 4.3 where,

$$V2(mL) = \left(\frac{[W3(mg) - W4(mg)]}{1\ g/\ mL}\right) - V1(mL) \quad \text{(Eq. 2)}$$

4.8 Place the sealer coupons horizontally in the center of a 300 x 300 x 0.9 mm (12 x 12 x 0.035 in) panel.

4.9 Place the panel, with sealer coupons, in the center of a mechanical convection oven and bake in the horizontal position for the specified time at the specified temperature.

4.10 Allow the coupons to cool to room temperature 23 °C ± 2 °C (73 °F ± 4 °F).

4.11 Determine the expanded sealer volume (V3) for the three marked, coated, and baked coupons by weighing the expanded sealer panels dry (W5) and wet (W6) with the weights reported in milligrams using the procedure described in 4.2 through 4.3 where,

$$V3(mL) = \left(\frac{[W5(mg) - W6(mg)]}{1\ g/\ mL}\right) - V1(mL) \quad \text{(Eq. 3)}$$

4.11.1 If the sealer expansion is great enough to float the coupon assembly, a weight large enough to overcome the buoyancy of expansion, is added to each of a second set of uncoated coupons and the steps 4.1 through 4.11 are repeated.

4.12 Calculate the volume change in the cured sealer as a percentage of the original uncured volume as follows,

$$\text{Percentage Volume Change} = \left(\frac{V3(mL)}{V2(mL)}\right) - 1 \times 100 \quad \text{(Eq. 4)}$$

4.13 Calculate the average expansion of the three coupons and report the results.

5. Volumetric Expansion Procedure (Method #2)

5.1 Fill a 500 mL graduated cylinder to the 400 mL mark (V1) with water and record the volume.

5.2 Mark and individually submerge the 15 mL containers and record the graduated cylinder volume levels (V2) in mL.

5.3 Determine the volume of the empty container (V3) by the following formula:

$$V3(mL) = V2(mL) - V1(mL) \quad \text{(Eq. 5)}$$

5.4 Fill each container with the sealer to be tested, being careful not to create any air pockets.

5.5 Fill the graduated cylinder to the 400 mL mark with water and record the volume (V1) in mL.

5.6 Submerge the individually marked sealer filled containers and record the graduated cylinder volume levels (V4) in mL.

5.7 Determine the volumes of the containers and uncured sealer (V5) by the following formula:

$$V5mL = V4(mL) - V1(mL) \quad \text{(Eq. 6)}$$

5.8 Place the sealer containers in the center of a 300 x 300 x 0.9 mm (12 x 12 x 0.035 in) panel.

5.9 Place the panel, with the sealer containers, in the center of a mechanical convection oven and bake in the horizontal position for the specified time at the specified temperature.

5.10 Allow the containers to cool to room temperature 23 °C ± 2 °C (73 °F ± 4 °F).

5.11 Fill the graduated cylinder to the 400 mL mark with water and record the volume (V1) in mL.

5.12 Submerge the individually marked, expanded sealer filled containers and record the graduated cylinder volume levels (V6) in mL. If the expanded sealer and container float, use a straightened paper clip to force the can beneath the water and record the level. (See Figure 5.)

5.13 Determine the volume of the container and expanded sealer (V7) by the following formula:

$$V7(mL) = V6(mL) - V1(mL) \quad \text{(Eq. 7)}$$

NOTE—After the V6 measurement, remove the expanded material and inspect for voids.

5.14 Calculate the volume change in the sealer as a percentage by the following formula:

$$\% \text{ Volume Change} = \left(\frac{V7(mL) - V5(mL)}{V5(mL) - V3(mL)}\right) \times 100 \quad \text{(Eq. 8)}$$

5.15 Calculate the average expansion of the three containers and report the results.

6. Vertical Expansion Procedure (Method #3)

6.1 Take three 0.9 x 100 x 300 mm (0.035 x 4 x 12 in) panels and fabricate a 90 degree bend, 25 mm long, at one end of each panel as in Figure 6.

6.2 To each fabricated panel apply a 6 x 200 mm semi-circular or, as specified, bead of sealer lengthwise down the center of each panel as shown in Figure 7.

6.3 Attach a straight 0.9 x 100 x 300 mm (0.035 x 4 x 12 in) panel to the top of the first panel securing the two at the narrow end by means of a spring clip as in Figure 8.

6.4 Record the thickness of the unexpanded sealer (T1) in millimeters.

6.5 Place the three assemblies horizontally in the center of a mechanical convection oven and bake the assemblies at the specified temperature for the specified time.

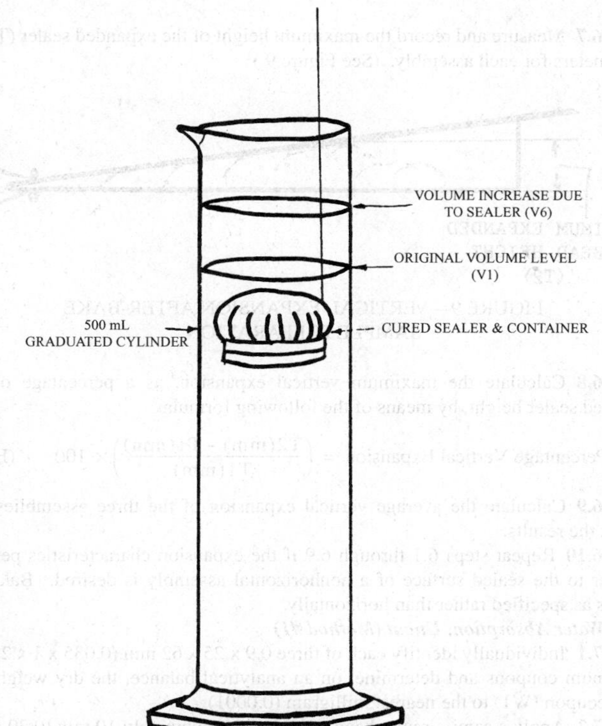

FIGURE 5—VOLUMETRIC EXPANSION SAMPLE EVALUATION

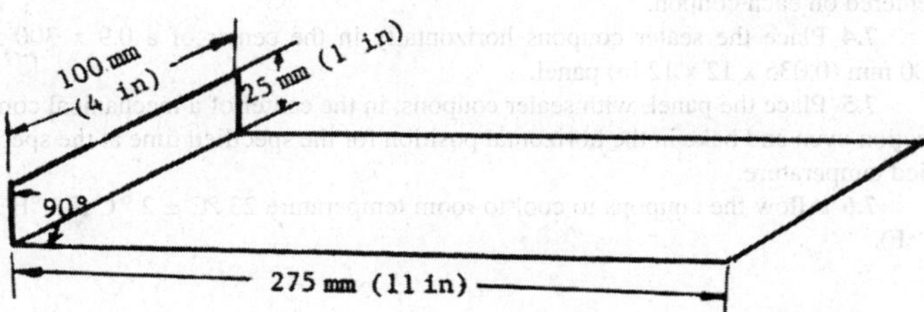

FIGURE 6—VERTICAL EXPANSION SUBSTRATE GEOMETRY

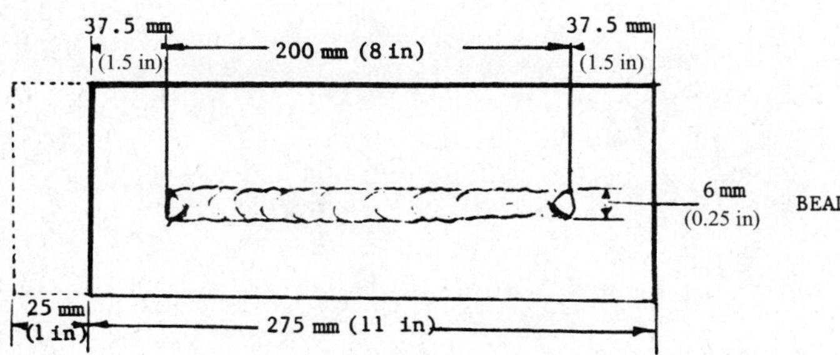

FIGURE 7—VERTICAL EXPANSION SAMPLE/SUBSTRATE GEOMETRY

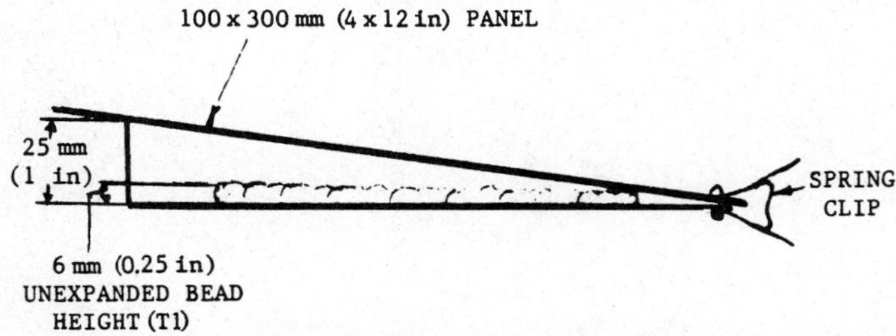

FIGURE 8—VERTICAL EXPANSION PRE-BAKE SAMPLE PREPARATION

6.6 Allow the panels to cool to room temperature 23 °C ± 2 °C (73 °F ± 4 °F).

6.7 Measure and record the maximum height of the expanded sealer (T2) in millimeters for each assembly. (See Figure 9.)

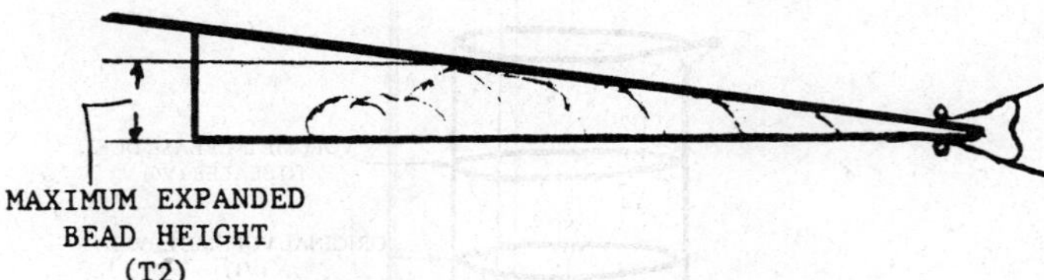

FIGURE 9—VERTICAL EXPANSION AFTER-BAKE SAMPLE PREPARATION

6.8 Calculate the maximum vertical expansion, as a percentage of the uncured sealer height, by means of the following formula:

$$\text{Percentage Vertical Expansion} = \left(\frac{T2(mm) - T1(mm)}{T1(mm)}\right) \times 100 \qquad \text{(Eq. 9)}$$

6.9 Calculate the average vertical expansion of the three assemblies and report the results.

6.10 Repeat steps 6.1 through 6.9 if the expansion characteristics perpendicular to the sealed surface of a nonhorizontal assembly is desired. Bake the panels as specified rather than horizontally.

7. Water Absorption, Uncut (Method #1)

7.1 Individually identify each of three 0.9 x 25 x 62 mm (0.035 x 1 x 2.5 in) aluminum coupons and determine, on an analytical balance, the dry weights of each coupon (W1) to the nearest milligram (0.0001).

7.2 Apply a semi-circular bead of sealer, approximately 10 mm (0.39 in) in diameter, down the center of each panel.

7.3 Trim the ends of each bead leaving a 38 mm (1.5 in) length of sealer centered on each coupon.

7.4 Place the sealer coupons horizontally in the center of a 0.9 x 300 x 300 mm (0.035 x 12 x 12 in) panel.

7.5 Place the panel, with sealer coupons, in the center of a mechanical convection oven and bake in the horizontal position for the specified time at the specified temperature.

7.6 Allow the coupons to cool to room temperature 23 °C ± 2 °C (73 °F ± 4 °F).

7.7 Determine the weight of each expanded sealer bead and coupon (W2) to the nearest milligram (0.0001).

7.8 Totally immerse each expanded seal bead and coupon in water at 23 °C ± 2 °C (73 °F ± 4 °F) for 24 h, or as specified.

7.9 Remove the specimens from the water and lightly blot with an absorbent paper towel.

7.10 Determine the weight of each water soaked specimen (W3) to the nearest milligram (0.0001).

7.11 Calculate the percentage of water absorbed by the following formula:

$$\text{Percentage Water Absorbed} = \left(\frac{W3(mg) - W2(mg)}{W2(mg) - W1(mg)}\right) \times 100 \qquad \text{(Eq. 10)}$$

7.12 Calculate the average water absorption of the three coupons and report the results.

8. Water Absorption, Cut (Method #2)—Repeat procedure in Water Absorption Method #1, except add the following action to 7.6: after the sealer has cooled to room temperature, cut a 12 mm (0.5 in) "X" in the cured sealer bead, as shown in Figure 10, with a razor so as to just break the surface.

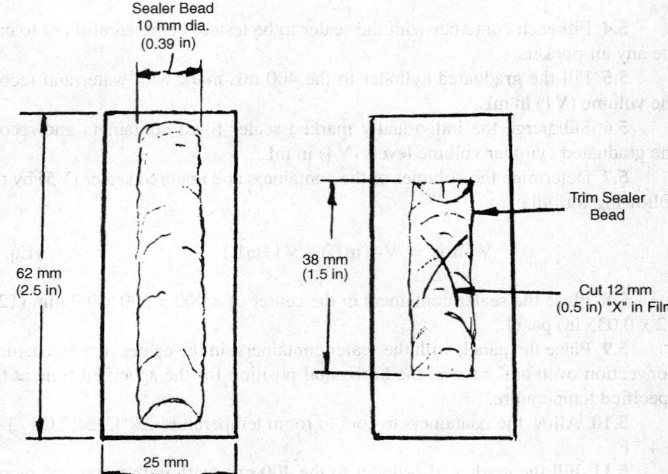

FIGURE 10—CUT WATER ABSORPTION SAMPLE PREPARATION

ELECTROCOAT COMPATIBILITIES OF AUTOMOTIVE SEALERS—SAE J1969 OCT1988

SAE Recommended Practice

Report of the SAE Adhesives and Body Sealers Committee approved October 1988.

Foreword—This Document has not changed other than to put it into the new SAE Technical Standards Board Format.

1. Scope—This SAE Recommended Practice sets forth a method for determining the compatibility of automotive sealers with cathodic electrocoat primer.

2. References—There are no referenced publications specified herein.

3. Principal of Methods—This practice sets forth two methods for evaluating what effect, if any, an automotive sealer has on an electrocoat primer bath or the resulting baked primer coating, or both.

Method #1 determines if a sealer's passage through the bath will "leach out" any material, from the sealer, that will then produce coating irregularities.

Method #2 determines if a bath contaminated with sealer debris, 0.1% by weight, will have any effect on parts processed subsequent to the contamination.

4. Equipment

a. DC Power Source: 0–600 V minimum and 0–10 A
b. One gallon plastic pails 155 mm (6 in) ID and 190 mm (7.5 in) high
c. 7700 mm^2 (12 in^2) stainless steel Anode
d. Laboratory Stirrer: 256 – 1200 rpm
e. Stirring Shaft: 460 x 13 mm (18 x 0.5 in) long
f. Mixing Blades
    1. Dispersion: 75 mm (3 in) standard stainless steel, high dispersion
    2. Agitation: standard stainless steel mixing propeller
g. Sealant Applicator: opening in template is 25 x 1.5 mm (1 x 0.06 in)
h. Oven: Gas fired or electric mechanical convection oven capable of obtaining 190 °C (375 °F) metal temperature on CRS 0.81 mm (0.032 in) in 8 – 10 min
i. Cathodic Electrocoat Primer: 2 gal, at least 24 h old
j. Steel Panels: 100 x 300 x 0.81 mm (4 x 12 x 0.032 in) zinc phosphated
k. Sealant to be tested

5. Sealant Panel Preparation

5.1 Sealant should be conditioned for 24 h at 23 ±2 °C (73 ±4 °F) before use.

5.2 Unless freshly zinc phosphated, test panels should be dried at 120 °C (250 °F) for 6 min prior to sealant application to remove absorbed moisture.

5.3 Using the sealant applicator template, apply a 100 x 25 x 1.5 mm (4 x 1 x 0.060 in) strip of the sealant to be tested to the bottom half of one of the zinc phosphated panels. Start the bead 25 mm (1 in) from the bottom of the panel, see Figure 1.

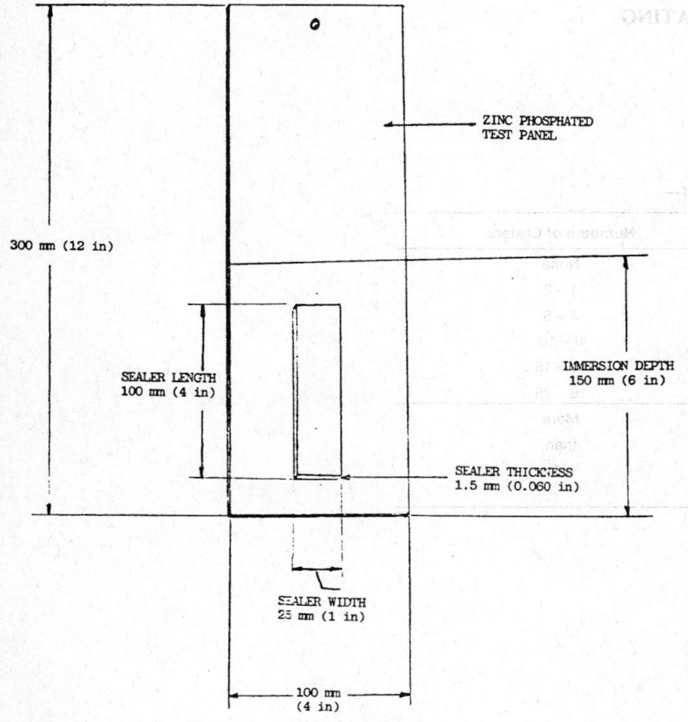

FIGURE 1—

5.4 The sealant coated panel must be conditioned at 23 ±2 °C (73 ±4 °F) for no less than 4 h nor more than 24 h prior to being placed in the primer bath.

5.5 Proceed to Section 6 while sealer panel is setting.

6. Electrocoated Control Panel Preparation

6.1 Fill a 1 gal plastic container, see Figure 2, within 2 in of the top with a sample of cathodic electrocoat primer.[1]

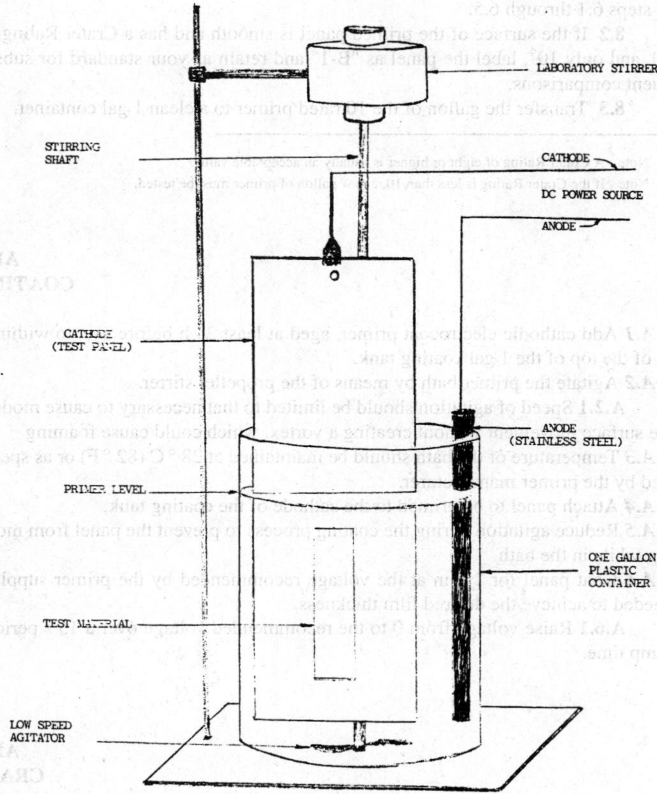

FIGURE 2—

6.2 Condition a 100 x 300 x 0.81 mm (4 x 12 x 0.032 in) zinc phosphated panel as in 5.2.

6.3 Electrocoat the panel at a primer thickness of 0.030 mm (0.0012 in) per the E-coat suppliers recommendations or as defined in Appendix A.

6.4 Bake the primed panel for 30 min at 182 °C (360 °F) or as specified.

6.5 Examine the baked surface, on both sides, for surface irregularities and craters. Use the Crater Rating System listed in Appendix B to grade the surface.

6.6 If the surface of the primed panel is smooth and has a Crater Rating of 10, and only 10[2], label the panel as "A-1" and retain as your standard for subsequent comparisons.

7. Method I - Fresh Bath

7.1 Place the sealer panel prepared in 5.3, after the designated conditioning period, into the 10 rated primer from 6.6. If the sealant is a die cut part, submerge the part in the bath, see Figure 2.

7.2 Agitate the primer bath, with sealant submerged, for 16 – 20 hours.

7.2.1 Agitate the primer bath with the propeller blade 25 mm (1 in) from the bottom with the mixer rpm controlled to avoid foaming or spillage.

7.3 Electrocoat the sealer panel at a minimum primer thickness of 0.030 mm (0.0012 in) per the E-coat supplier's recommendations, or as defined in Appendix A.

7.4 Bake the primed sealer panel for 30 min at 182 °C (360 °F) or as specified.

7.4.1 Label the baked sealer panel as "A-2".

1. Note - The primer should be at least 24 h old.
2. Note - If the Crater Rating is less than 10, a new gallon of primer must be tested.

7.5 Electrocoat another zinc phosphated panel, as described and conditioned in 4.2, at a primer thickness of 0.030 mm (0.0012 in) as in 7.3.

7.6 Bake the primed panel as in 7.4.

7.6.1 Label the baked primed panel as "A-3".

7.7 Examine both sides of panels "A-2" and "A-3" using panel "A-1" as a standard.

7.7.1 Note any film irregularities

7.7.2 Count the total number of craters on both sides of each panel and record the values.

7.7.3 Assign the Crater Rating[3] per Appendix B.

8. Method II - Contaminated Bath

8.1 Evaluate the quality of a second gallon of cathodic electrocoat primer as in steps 6.1 through 6.5.

8.2 If the surface of the primed panel is smooth and has a Crater Rating of 10, and only 10[4], label the panel as "B-1" and retain as your standard for subsequent comparisons.

8.3 Transfer the gallon of the 10 rated primer to a clean 1 gal container.

3. Note - A Crater Rating of eight or higher is usually an acceptable value.
4. Note - If the Crater Rating is less than 10, a new gallon of primer must be tested.

8.4 Add three grams of the sealant to be tested to the primer bath. If the sealant is a die cut part, submerge the part in the bath.

8.5 Agitate the contaminated bath at high rpm with the dispersion blade for 1 h making sure the blade is 25 mm (1 in) from the bottom of the container.

8.6 Return the contaminated primer bath to the test container.

8.7 Agitate the contaminated primer bath for 16 – 20 hours.

8.7.1 Agitate the contaminated primer bath with the propeller blade 25 mm (1 in) from the bottom with the mixer rpm controlled to avoid foaming or spillage.

8.8 Electrocoat a 100 x 300 mm (4 x 12 in) zinc phosphated panel in the contaminated bath as described in Appendix A.

8.9 Bake the primed panel for 30 min at 182 °C (360 °F) or as specified.

8.9.1 Label this panel as "B-2".

8.10 Examine both sides of panel "B-2" using panel "B-1" as a standard.

8.10.1 Note any film irregularities.

8.10.2 Count the total number of craters on both sides of panel "B-2" and record the value.

8.10.3 Assign the Crater Rating[5] per Appendix B.

5. Note - A Crater Rating of eight or higher is usually an acceptable value.

APPENDIX A
COATING PROCEDURE

A.1 Add cathodic electrocoat primer, aged at least 24 h before use, to within 2 in of the top of the 1 gal coating tank.

A.2 Agitate the primer bath by means of the propeller stirrer.

A.2.1 Speed of agitation should be limited to that necessary to cause moderate surface movement without creating a vortex, which could cause foaming.

A.3 Temperature of the bath should be maintained at 28 °C (82 °F) or as specified by the primer manufacturer.

A.4 Attach panel to be primed to the cathode of the coating tank.

A.5 Reduce agitation during the coating process to prevent the panel from moving while in the bath.

A.6 Coat panel for 2 min at the voltage recommended by the primer supplier needed to achieve the desired film thickness.

A.6.1 Raise voltage from 0 to the recommended voltage over a 15 s period, ramp time.

A.6.2 Maintain voltage, at the recommended voltage for 120 s and return to 0 V instantaneously.

A.6.2.1 Decrease voltage if film builds are excessive.

A.6.2.2 Increase bath temperature if film builds are insufficient.

A.6.3 Wash coated panels with deionized water to remove undeposited paint.

A.6.4 Air dry panels at ambient temperature or blow dry with oil free air.

A.6.5 Bake panels in an oven for 30 min at 182 °C (360 °F), or as recommended by the primer supplier.

A.6.6 Evaluate the cured primer for surface imperfections.[6]

6. Note - While the bath is not in use, it should be kept covered to prevent evaporation and introduction of contaminants. A dirty oven may also affect finished film appearance.

APPENDIX B
CRATER RATING

B.1 The following table sets forth a grading scale involving the total number of craters on both sides of a coated panel whose coating dimensions are 100 x 150 mm (4 x 6 in):

TABLE B1—

Rating	Numbers of Craters
10	None
9	1 – 2
8	3 – 5
7	6 – 10
6	11 – 15
5	16 – 25
4	More
3	than
2	25
1	

METHOD FOR EVALUATING MATERIAL SEPARATION IN AUTOMOTIVE SEALERS UNDER PRESSURE IN STATIC CONDITIONS—SAE J1864 MAR1996

SAE Recommended Practice

Report of the SAE Adhesives and Body Sealers Committee approved April 1987. Reaffirmed by the SAE Materials Joining Executive Committee November 1993. Reaffirmed by the SAE Body Sealers Subcommittee of the SAE Materials Joining Executive Committee March 1996.

Foreword—This Document has not changed other than to put it into the new SAE Technical Standards Board Format.

1. Scope—This SAE Recommended Practice sets forth a method for measuring pressure-induced separation in automotive sealers and determining the likelihood of equipment failure due to this separation, also known as "caking."

1.1 Background—Sealers in automotive plants are generally transported and applied via airless pumping equipment whose internal pressures may exceed 20.7 MPa (3000 psi). Some sealers have a tendency to separate when exposed to pressures of this magnitude which results in varying degrees of system blockage.

This pressure-induced "caking," or blockage of the pump and transport lines, reduces sealer delivery rates and can completely shut down the system.

Separation tests run on sealers at 20.7 MPa (3000 psi), 25 °C (77 °F) for 72 h with measured separation volumes of over 6 mL have been known to cause "caking" problems in production pumping equipment whereas sealers with measured separation volumes of 3 mL or less have not caused this type of problem.

2. References—There are no referenced publications specified herein.

3. Principle of Methods—This document involves injecting automotive sealant into a pressure cup assembly equipped with a moveable piston cap (see Figure 1). The sealant is then subjected to a static pressure by applying a force to the pressure cup assembly via the piston cap. This force is supplied by means of a multipower air cylinder for a specified time, after which the pressure is removed, the cylinder is disassembled, and any separated material present is then measured.

4. Equipment

a. Johnstone Sep-Check part no. 110-085-1 or equivalent (see Figure 2)
b. Sealer to be tested; two 350 mL (12 oz) tubes, air free
c. 50 mL graduated cylinder
d. 25 mL graduated cylinder
e. Spatula
f. Cleaner (recommended by sealant manufacturer)
g. Air compressor

5. Pressure Cup Assembly[1]—See Figure 3.

5.1 To assemble pressure cup (see Figure 4), attach three socket screws to piston retainer (see Figure 5) cap and tighten.

5.2 Carefully insert piston through bottom of pressure cup so no damage is done to "O" ring.

5.3 Attach three socket screws to pressure cup bottom cap (see Figure 6) and tighten carefully so no damage is done to "O" ring; make sure bottom cap is flush with bottom of pressure cup.

5.4 Attach gauge and bleeder valve to pressure cup.

5.5 Ready to load with material.

6. Pressure Cup Material Loading

6.1 Acquire two 350 mL (12 oz) tubes of air-free sealant.

6.2 Open bleeder valve on pressure cup container.

6.3 Push the piston cap to the bottom of the pressure cup.

6.4 Remove 6.35 mm (1/4 in) pipe plug. Insert sample tube to the inlet at the bottom cap of the pressure cup.

6.5 Fill the pressure chamber until the material bleeds out of the bleeder valve; then close.

6.6 Continue to fill until the piston cap reaches the top of the pressure cup.

6.7 Remove the sample tube and plug the 6.35 mm (1/4 in) inlet.

6.8 Reopen the bleeder valve to allow the excess pressure to escape; then close.

7. Testing Parameters[2]—See Figure 2.

7.1 Set the multipower cylinder predetermined air pressure to equal a 20.7 MPa (3000 psi) load to the pressure cup, or as specified.

7.2 Insert the pressure cup into the slot of the base stand.

7.3 Position the four-way hand valve in down mode. (At this point, air cylinder must remain on.)

7.4 72 h under these conditions are required, or as specified.

1. Test cylinder shall be 44.45 mm (1.75 in) ID x 76.2 mm (3.0 in) in length with equidistant 0.0254 mm (0.001 in) gap between the cylinder wall and piston edge.
2. Any equipment capable of maintaining a constant load of at least 20.7 MPa (3000 psi) on the pressure cup may be used.

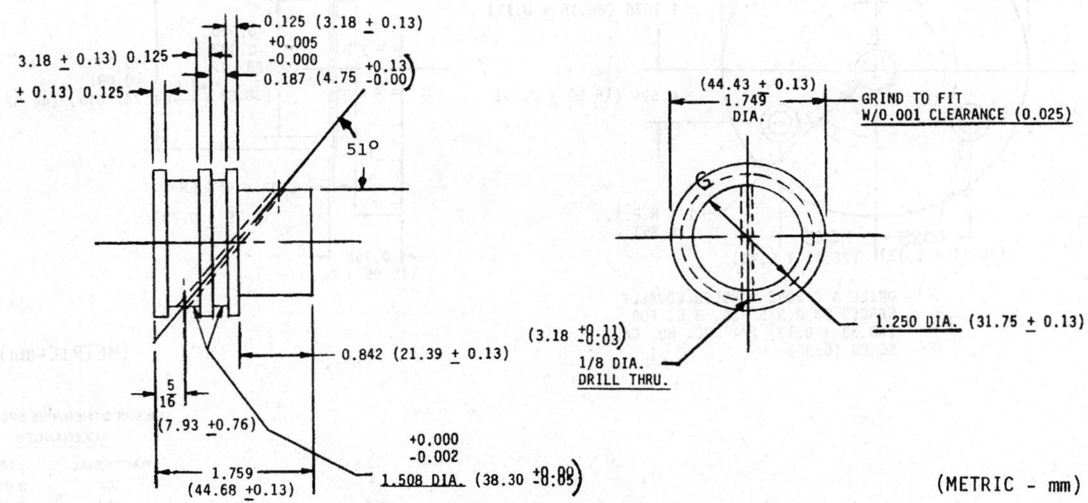

FIGURE 1—PISTON CAP

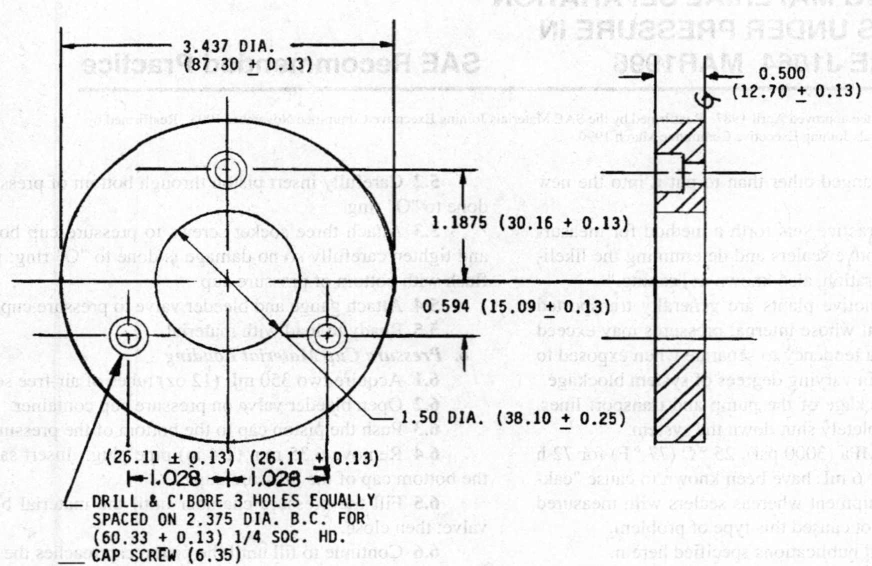

(METRIC-mm)

UNLESS OTHERWISE SPECIF
TOLERANCES

FRACTIONAL	± 1/32
.0X	±.010
.00X	±.005
.000X	±.0005

BREAK ALL UNNECESSARY
SHARP CORNERS.

MATERIAL: 1117 CRS

FIGURE 2—TEST SET-UP

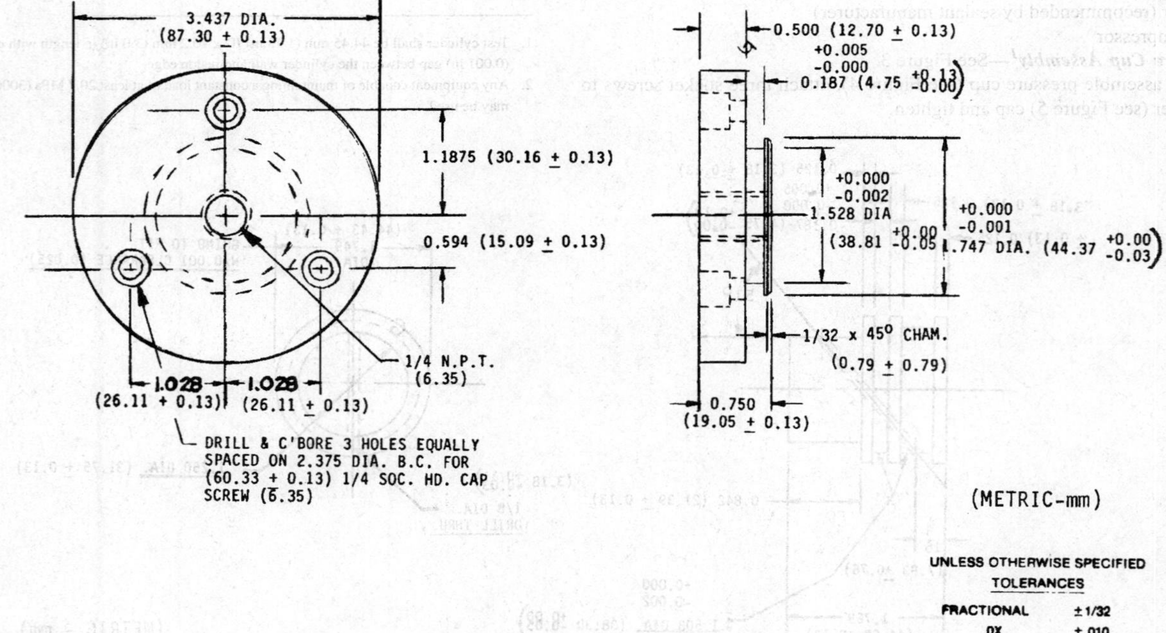

UNLESS OTHERWISE SPECIFIED
TOLERANCES

FRACTIONAL	± 1/32
.0X	±.010
.00X	±.005
.000X	±.0005

BREAK ALL UNNECESSARY,
SHARP CORNERS.

MATERIAL: 1117 CRS

FIGURE 3—PRESSURE CUP ASSEMBLY

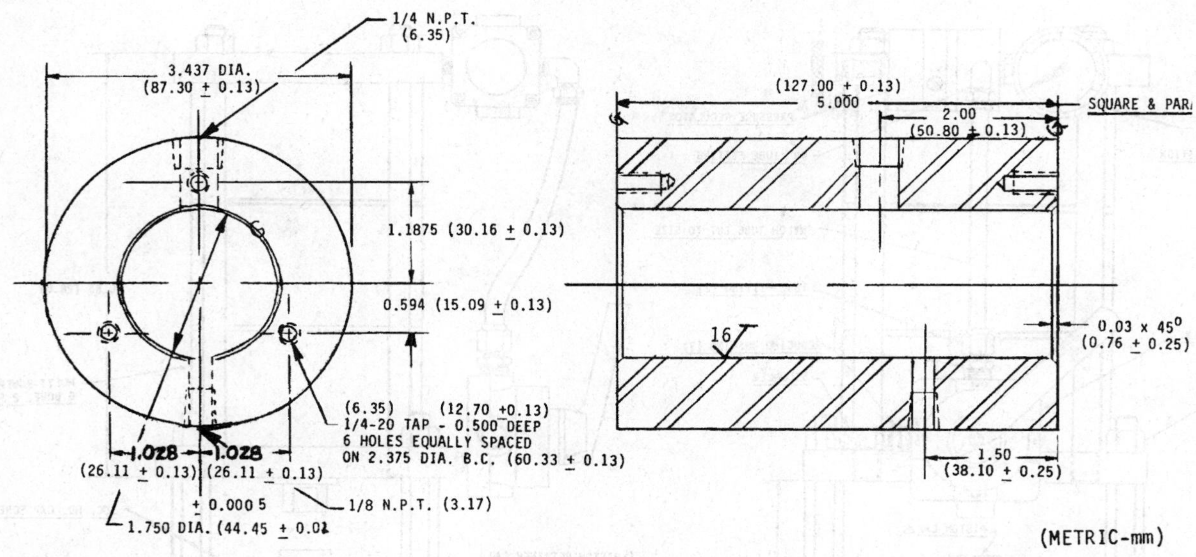
1/4 N.P.T.
(6.35)
3.437 DIA.
(87.30 ± 0.13)
1.1875 (30.16 ± 0.13)
0.594 (15.09 ± 0.13)
(6.35) (12.70 ±0.13)
1/4-20 TAP - 0.500 DEEP
6 HOLES EQUALLY SPACED
ON 2.375 DIA. B.C. (60.33 ± 0.13)
1.028 1.028
(26.11 ± 0.13) (26.11 ± 0.13)
± 0.0005
1.750 DIA. (44.45 ± 0.01
1/8 N.P.T. (3.17)
(127.00 ± 0.13)
5.000
2.00
(50.80 ± 0.13)
SQUARE & PAR
16
0.03 x 45°
(0.76 ± 0.25)
1.50
(38.10 ± 0.25)
(METRIC-mm)
UNLESS OTHERWISE SPECIFI
TOLERANCES
FRACTIONAL ±1/32
.0X ±.010
.00X ±.005
.000X ±.0005
BREAK ALL UNNECESSARY, SHARP CORNERS.
MATERIAL: 1117 C.R.S.

FIGURE 4—PRESSURE CUP

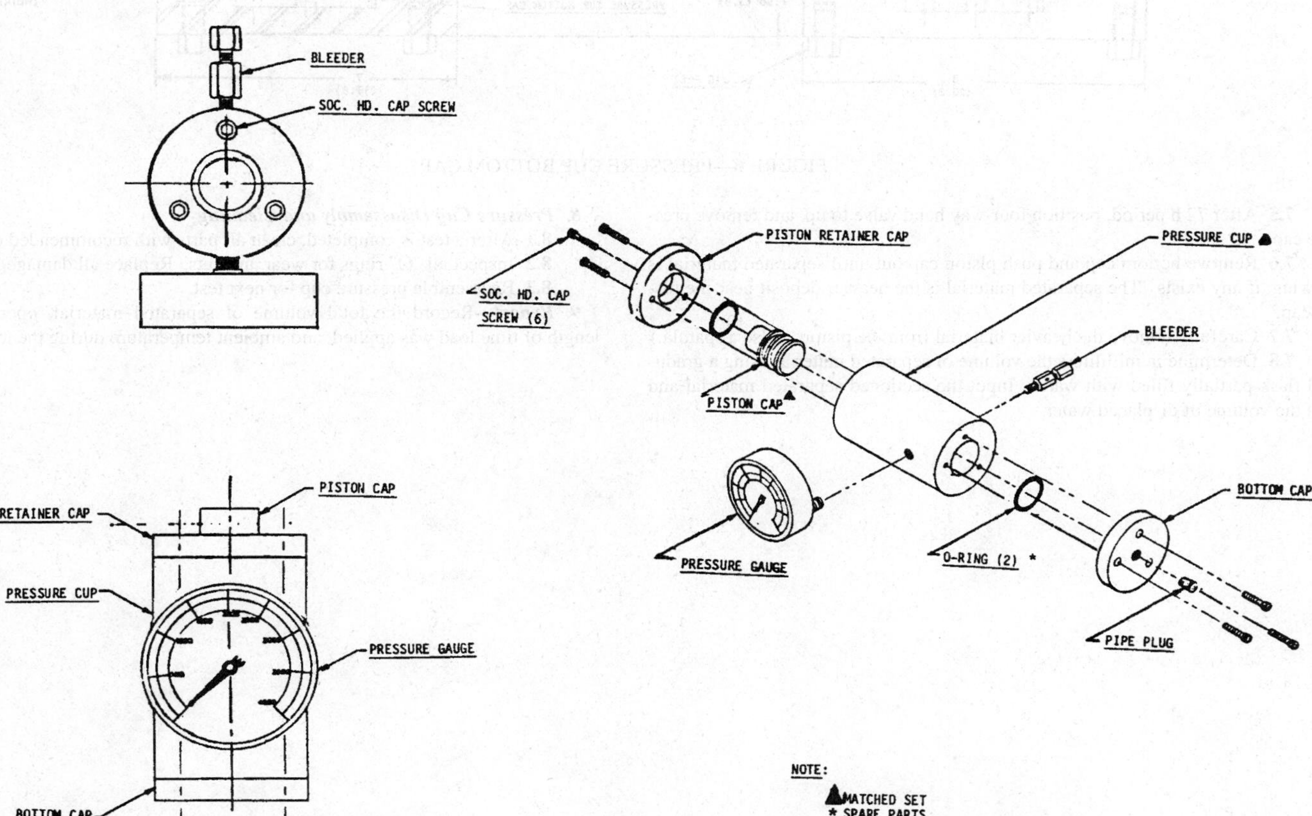
BLEEDER
SOC. HD. CAP SCREW
PISTON RETAINER CAP
PRESSURE CUP
SOC. HD. CAP SCREW (6)
BLEEDER
PISTON CAP
PISTON CAP
RETAINER CAP
PRESSURE CUP
PRESSURE GAUGE
BOTTOM CAP
PRESSURE GAUGE
O-RING (2) *
BOTTOM CAP
PIPE PLUG
NOTE:
MATCHED SET
* SPARE PARTS

FIGURE 5—PISTON RETAINER CAP

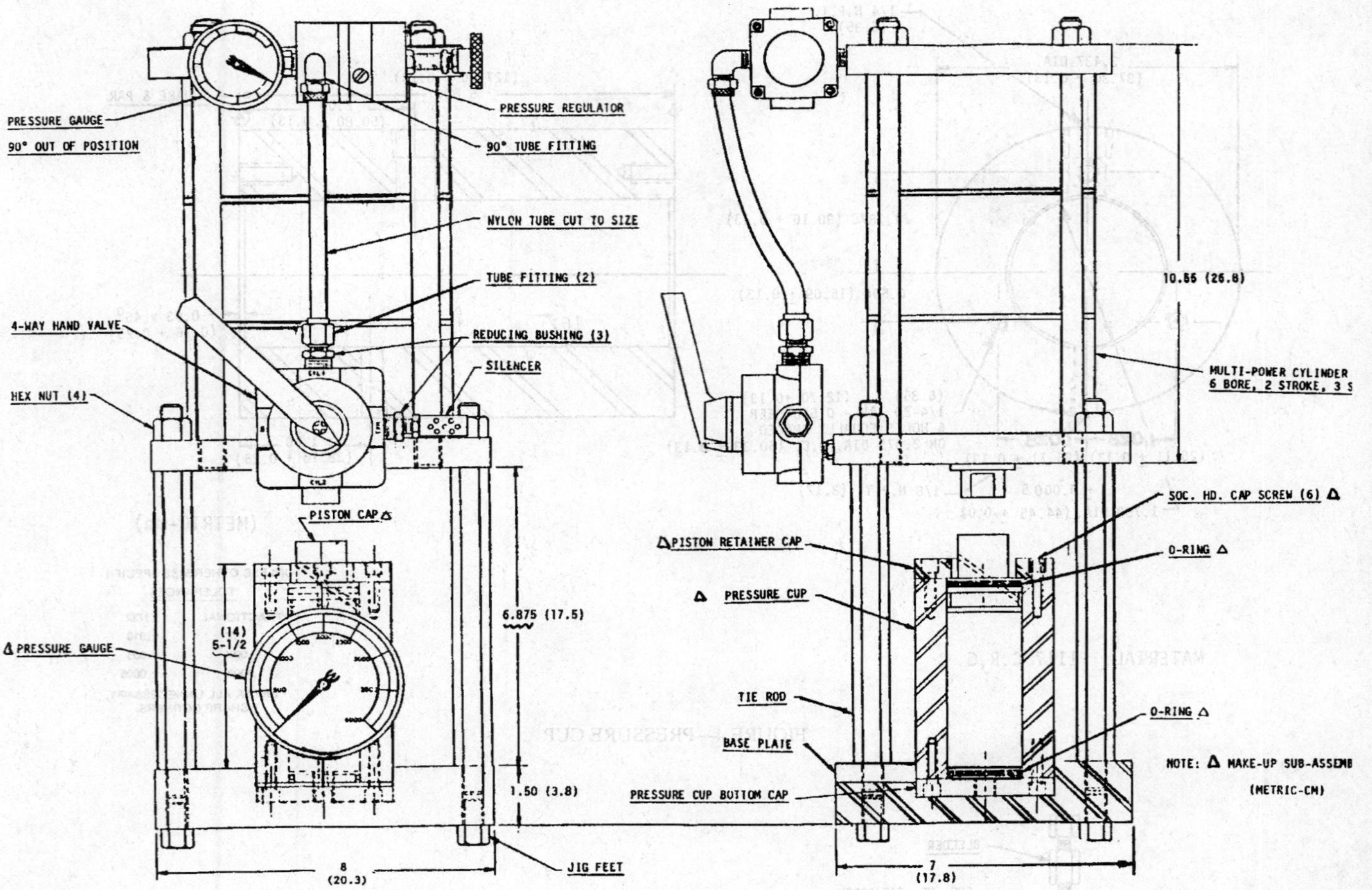

FIGURE 6—PRESSURE CUP BOTTOM CAP

7.5 After 72 h period, position four-way hand valve to up, and remove pressure cap.

7.6 Remove bottom cap and push piston cap out until separated material is showing, if any exists. The separated material is the heavier deposit near the piston cap.

7.7 Carefully remove the heavier material from the piston. (Use a spatula.)

7.8 Determine in milliliters the volume of separated material using a graduated flask partially filled with water. Input the sectioned separated material and note the volume of displaced water.

*8. **Pressure Cup Disassembly and Cleaning***

8.1 After a test is completed, clean all parts with recommended cleaner.

8.2 Inspect all "O" rings for wear and cuts. Replace all damaged "O" rings.

8.3 Reassemble pressure cup for next test.

*9. **Report***—Record the total volume of separated material, operating load, length of time load was applied, and ambient temperature during the test.

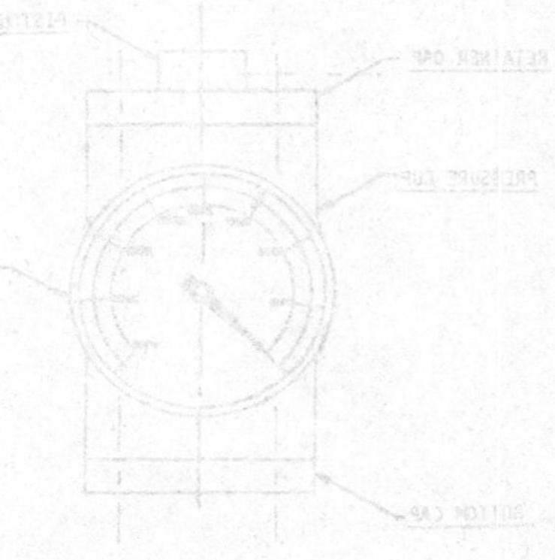

OVERLAP SHEAR TEST FOR AUTOMOTIVE TYPE SEALANT FOR STATIONARY GLASS BONDING —SAE J1529 MAY1986

SAE Recommended Practice

Report of the SAE Nonmetallic Materials Committee approved May 1986.

Foreword—This Document has not changed other than to put it into the new SAE Technical Standards Board Format.

1. Scope—This SAE Recommended Practice defines a procedure for the construction and testing of glass to metal lap shears for determining shear strength of sealant adhesives for automotive stationary glass bonding. This procedure can also be used for fiber reinforced plastic (FRP) when used in place of metal.

2. References—There are no referenced publications specified herein.

3. Test Substrates

3.1 Substrates and Dimensions—The metal coupons shall be cut from automotive sheet metal into flat strips 25.4 x 102 mm (1.000 x 4.000 in) coupons at a nominal thickness of 0.8 mm (0.032 in). The glass coupons shall be cut from float glass or ceramic coated fleet glass into 25.4 x 102 mm (1.000 x 4.000 in) at a nominal thickness of 5.5 mm (0.220 in). Fiber reinforced plastic coupons shall be cut into flat strips 25.4 x 102 mm (1.000 x 4.000 in) at a nominal thickness of 2.54 mm (0.100 in). All test coupons shall be free of flaws such as nicks and splinters that would give erroneous test results.

3.2 Surface Coatings—The metal and FRP shall be coated with paints recommended by the automotive engineer. Also, the ceramic on the glass shall be the type recommended by the automotive engineer.

3.3 Surface Preparation—Surface preparation with respect to cleaning and primer application shall be in accordance with adhesive supplier or automotive engineer recommendation.

4. Preparation Of Test Joints

4.1 Joint Geometry—The final joint geometry shall be shown in Figure 1 with tolerances specified under 4.3.

The joint geometry can be controlled by the use of a lap shear board as illustrated in Figure 2.

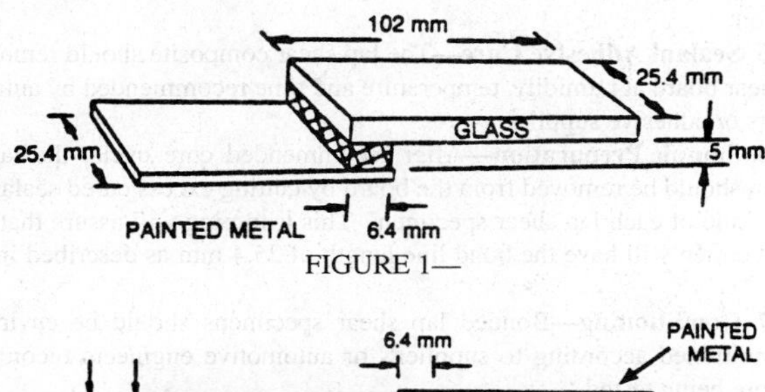

FIGURE 1—

FIGURE 2—

The lap shear board should be constructed as in Figure 2 to give the proper dimensions for the lap shear as described in Figure 1. The glass coupons shall be taped onto the board so that the one inch side is 6.4 mm away from the board. Glass coupons can be laid down side-by-side to make multiple lap shears.

4.2 Replacement of Metal with FRP—Fiber reinforced plastic coupons can replace metal coupons on the top section of the board in Figure 2.

4.3 Adhesive Bond Line Tolerance—Final bond tolerance width shall be 6.4 ±0.5 mm (0.25 ±0.02 in) and height of 5 ±0.5 mm (0.2 ±0.02 in).

4.4 Sealant Application—The sealants wet bead dimensions can be controlled to give the cured bond dimensions specified in Figure 1. The sealant shall be extruded using a 6.4 mm (0.250 in) high bead along the one inch side of the glass coupon. The bead shall also be high enough so that when the metal coupon is placed down on wet sealant to the required 5 mm (0.200 in) height, the resulting bond width on the metal will be comparable to bead width on the glass side of 6.4 mm (0.250 in). Adhesive open time shall be prescribed by adhesive supplier or automotive engineer.

4.5 Adhesive Cure—The bonded lap shear shall be cured at the temperature and time prescribed by adhesive supplier or automotive engineer.

4.6 Sample Preparation—After the recommended cure cycle, the lap shear shall be removed from the board by cutting excess cured sealant away from the edge of the lap shear. This trimming will assure that the lap shear will have the final bond line length of 25.4 mm (1.000 in) as described in Figure 1.

4.7 Conditioning—Bonded lap shears shall be conditioned according to adhesive supplier or automotive engineer recommendation before being tested.

5. Testing

5.1 Apparatus—Test apparatus as described in ASTM D 1002.

5.2 Sample Fixture—The sample fixture described in Figure 3 shall be used when testing lap shears on the tensile tester. The glass coupon shall fit into the space provided with the bottom end of the lap shear resting on the shoulder of the fixture. This will allow the metal part to hang down to allow clamping to the lower jaw of tensile tester.

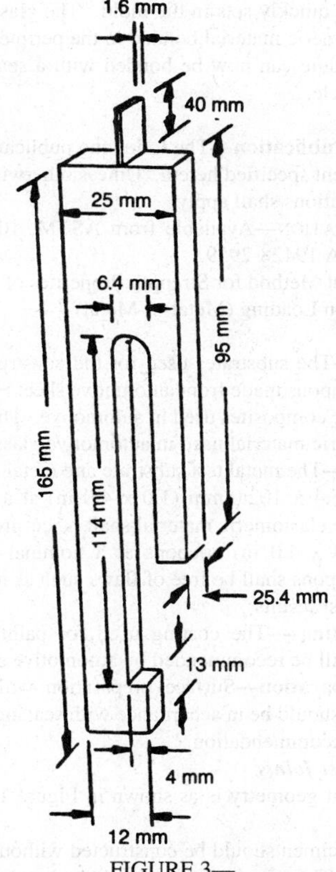

FIGURE 3—

5.3 Sample Clamping—The sample clamping distance between the bottom edge of the glass in the fixture and clamping jaw on the metal shall be 38 mm (1.500 in).

5.4 Test Rate—Lap shears shall be tested at a pull rate of 50.8 mm (2 in)/min.

5.5 Test Quantity—A minimum of 5 sample lap shears shall be prepared for each test condition.

6. Report

6.1 Complete identification and application of sealant and primer(s) used, including type and manufacturer's code number.

6.2 Complete identification of the substrate. The paint system on the metal and FRP and the ceramic on the glass shall be described by type and supplier.

6.3 Bonding conditions used in preparing samples and environmental conditions used in test procedure.

6.4 Shear strength as pounds per square inch (PSI) and kilopascals (kPa) by measuring the failed bond area.

6.5 Averages of lap shear values with individual values. Mode of failure on individual lap shears and percentage of all these failures.

SCF	Substrate failure (FRP, glass)
CF	Cohesive failure of sealant
P	Primer failure specifying the substrate
AF	Adhesive failure of the sealant specifying the substrate
PTF	Paint failure specifying the substrate

OVERLAP SHEAR TEST FOR SEALANT ADHESIVE BONDING OF AUTOMOTIVE GLASS ENCAPSULATING MATERIAL TO BODY OPENING—SAE J1836 OCT1988

SAE Recommended Practice

Report of the SAE Adhesives and Body Sealers Committee approved October 1988.

Foreword—This Document has not changed other than to put it into the new SAE Technical Standards Board Format.

1. Scope—This recommended practice defines a procedure for the construction of a lap shear specimen for the purpose of testing the bondability of an automotive sealant adhesive to the elastomeric material used in automotive encapsulating.

The present practice of encapsulating automotive glass is described as molding elastomeric material onto the outer edge of the glass using thermoplastic or thermosetting material that quickly sets in the mold. The glass is removed from the mold with cured elastomeric material bonded to the perimeter of thee glass. This encapsulated glass module can now be bonded with a sealant adhesive into the body opening of a vehicle.

2. References

2.1 Applicable Publication—The following publication forms a part of the specification to the extent specified herein. Unless otherwise indicated the lastest revision of SAE publications shall apply.

2.1.1 ASTM PUBLICATION—Available from ASTM, 100 Barr Harbor Drive, West Conshohocken, PA 19428-2959.

ASTM D 1002—Test Method for Strength Properties of Adhesives in Shear by Tension Loading (Metal-to-Metal)

3. Test Substrates

3.1 Substrates—The substrates used for the construction of the lap shear specimen should be coupons made from automotive sheet metal or any other rigid substrate such as plastic composites used in automotive. The other coupon should be made from elastomeric material used in automotive glass encapsulation.

3.2 Dimensions—The metal test substrate and metal support substrate shall be cut into coupons 25.4 x 102.0 mm (1.0 x 4.0 in) at a nominal thickness of 0.8 mm (0.032 in). The elastomeric material shall be cut from molded sheets into 25.4 x 102.0 mm (1.0 x 4.0 in) coupons at a nominal thickness of 3.2 mm (0.125 in). All test coupons shall be free of flaws such as nicks and splinters that could give erroneous test results.

3.3 Surface Coatings—The coating used for painting the metal or any other rigid substrate shall be recommended by automotive engineers.

3.4 Surface Preparation—Surface preparation with respect to cleaning and primer application should be in accordance with sealant adhesive suppliers, or automotive engineers recommendation.

4. Preparation of Test Joints

4.1 The final joint geometry is as shown in Figure 1 with tolerance specified under 4.3.

The lap shear specimen should be constructed without the metal backing as illustrated in Figure 2. The metal support should be bonded onto the back of the elastomeric coupon just prior to testing. The adhesive should be of suitable type to have good bondability to the metal and elastomeric coupon in order to minimize stretching or premature ripping of the elastomeric coupon while testing.

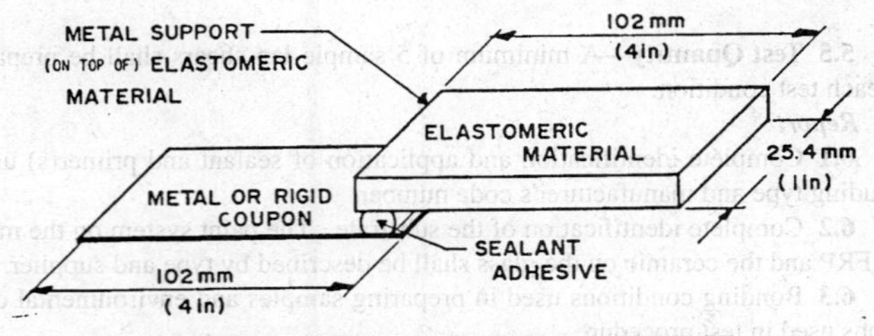

FIGURE 1—THREE DIMENSIONAL VIEW OF OVERLAPSHEAR TEST SPECIMEN

The lap shear board should be constructed as in Figure 2, to give the proper dimensions for the lap shear as described in Figure 1. The elastomeric coupons should be taped onto the board so that the one in side is approximately 3.0 to 6.0 mm (0.12 to 0.24 in) from the edge of the board. Coupons can be laid side-by-side on the board to make multiple lap shear specimens.

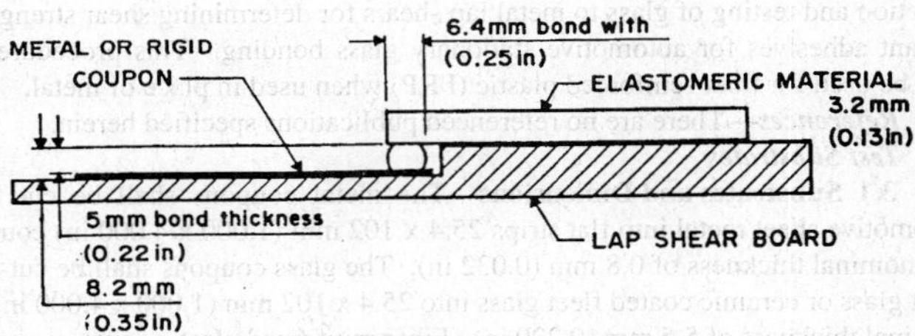

FIGURE 2—SIDE VIEW OF OVERLAPSHEAR SPECIMEN

4.2 Replacement of Metal with Other Substrates—The rigid substrates that are used to replace the metal coupons on the top section of the board in Figure 2 should be of a thickness designated by automotive engineers.

4.3 Sealant Adhesive Bond Tolerance—Final bond tolerance should be 25.4 ± 1.0 mm (1.0 ± 0.04 in) long, 6.4 ± 1.0 mm (0.25 ± 0.04 in) wide, and a height of 5.0 ± 1.0 mm (0.2 ±0.04 in).

4.4 Sealant Adhesive Application—The sealant adhesive wet bead dimensions can be controlled to give the cured bond dimensions specified in Figure 1. The sealant adhesive shall be extruded using a 6.4 mm (0.250 in) wide bead along the one in side of the elastomeric coupon. The bead should also be high enough so that when the metal coupon is placed down on the wet sealant adhesive, the required 5 mm (0.200 in) height shall be achieved. The sealant adhesive open time should be prescribed by adhesive supplier or automotive engineer's recommendation.

4.5 Sealant Adhesive Cure—The lap shear composite should remain fixed to lap shear board at humidity, temperature and time recommended by automotive engineers or adhesive supplier.

4.6 Sample Preparation—After recommended cure cycle, the lap shear specimen should be removed from the board by cutting excess cured sealant away from the side of each lap shear specimen. This trimming will assure that the lap shear specimen will have the bond line length of 25.4 mm as described in Figure 1.

4.7 Conditioning—Bonded lap shear specimens should be environmentally conditioned according to supplier's or automotive engineers recommendation before being tested.

5. Testing

5.1 Apparatus—Tensile tester as described in ASTM D 1002.

5.2 Sample Fixture—The sample fixture described in Figure 3 should be used when testing lap shear specimens on the tensile tester. The elastomeric coupon with the metal support should fit into the space provided with the lap shear specimen resting on the shoulder of the fixture. This will permit the metal or rigid coupon part to hang down to allow clamping to the lower jaw of the tensile tester.

5.3 Sample Clamping—The elastomeric coupon should be clamped onto the front end of the fixture to prevent bending and ripping of the elastomer away from the metal support. The sample clamping distance between bottom edge of the elastomeric supported coupon composite in fixture and clamping jaw on metal should be 38 mm (1.5 in) as illustrated in Figure 4.

5.4 Test Rate—Lap shear specimens should be tested at a pull rate of 50.8 mm (2 in)/minute.

5.5 Test Quantity—A minimum of five lap shear specimens should be prepared for each test condition.

6. Report

6.1 Complete identification and application of adhesive sealant and primer(s) used, including type and manufacturer's description.

6.2 Complete Identification of the Elastomeric Material

6.2.1 Type of elastomeric material should be described with its generic name (such as Urethane, VINYL, etc.) and manufacturer's product identification.

6.2.2 The physical properties of the material such as the elongation, tensile strength, flexural modulus, etc.

6.2.3 Description of surface treatment such as paint, mold release, cleaning conditions, etc.

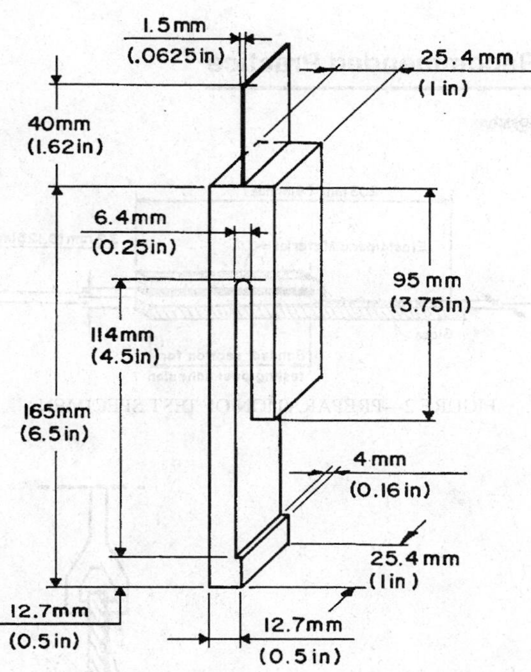

FIGURE 3—FIXTURE USED FOR TESTING OVERLAPSHEAR TEST SPECIMEN

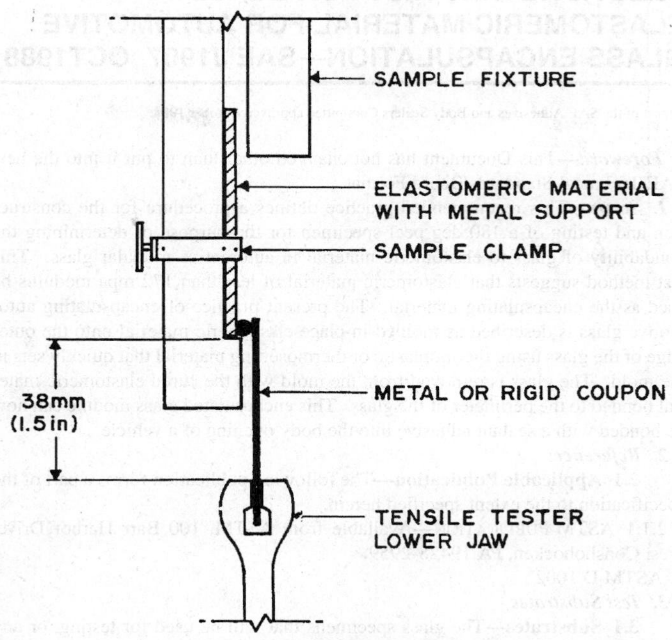

FIGURE 4—PLACEMENT OF OVERLAP SHEAR TEST SPECIMEN INTO TEST FIXTURE

6.3 Complete identification of test metal coupon or rigid substrate including thicknesses, description of rigid substrate and paint system.

6.4 Sample History

6.4.1 Description of primers and sealant adhesives conditions before application.

6.4.2 Description of open time of primers and sealant adhesives in construction of lap shear specimens.

6.4.3 Description of curing history of constructed lap shear specimens.

6.4.4 Environmental conditions used prior to testing such as humidity, heat age, artificial weathering, etc.

6.5 Report shear strength as pounds per square inch (psi) and Newtons per square meter (Pa) by measuring bond area.

6.6 Report average of lap shear specimen values with individual lap shear values. Indicate mode of failure on individual lap shears with estimated percentages of failure.

SF .... Substrate failure of elastomeric material with description
CF .... Cohesive failure of sealant
PF .... Primer failure specifying which substrate
AF .... Adhesive failure of sealant specifying which substrate
PTF .... Paint failure specifying which substrate

PEEL ADHESION TEST FOR GLASS TO ELASTOMERIC MATERIAL FOR AUTOMOTIVE GLASS ENCAPSULATION—SAE J1907 OCT1988

SAE Recommended Practice

Report of the SAE Adhesives and Body Sealers Committee approved October 1988.

Foreword—This Document has not changed other than to put it into the new SAE Technical Standards Board Format.

1. Scope—This recommended practice defines a procedure for the construction and testing of a 180 deg peel specimen for the purpose of determining the bondability of glass to elastomeric material in automotive modular glass. This test method suggests that elastomeric material of less than 172 mpa modulus be used as the encapsulating material. The present practice of encapsulating automotive glass is described as molded-in-place elastomeric material onto the outer edge of the glass using thermoplastic or thermosetting material that quickly sets in the mold. The glass is removed from the mold with the cured elastomeric material bonded to the perimeter of the glass. This encapsulated glass module can now be bonded with a sealant adhesive into the body opening of a vehicle.

2. References

2.1 Applicable Publication—The following publication forms a part of the specification to the extent specified herein.

2.1.1 ASTM PUBLICATION—Available from ASTM, 100 Barr Harbor Drive, West Conshohocken, PA 19428-2959.

ASTM D 1002

3. Test Substrates

3.1 Substrates—The glass specimens that will be used for testing, or any surface conditioner such as ceramic coating, should be of the type recommended by automotive engineers.

The thermoplastic or thermosetting material should have a modulus of less than 172 MPa and be of the type used in automotive glass encapsulation.

3.2 Dimensions—The recommended glass sample size should be at least 203 mm (8 in) long and at least 3.2 mm (0.125 in) thick and at least 25.4 mm (1 in) wide.

3.3 Glass Surface Preparation—Glass surface preparation, such as cleaning and priming application, should be in accordance with supplier's or automotive engineer's recommendation.

4. Test Specimen

4.1 Glass Encapsulation—The samples for testing should be from glass encapsulated using injection molding equipment and procedures recommended by automotive engineers.

4.2 Preparation for Specimen—For ease of test specimen preparation in 3.5, it is recommended that the glass not be primed where the elastomeric material is to be cut out.

4.3 Encapsulation Dimensions and Tolerances—The elastomeric material should be molded onto the glass such that the width dimensions shall be at 6.4 mm (0.25 in) with a tolerance of ±0.25 mm (0.01 in). The thickness dimensions shall be at 3.2 mm (0.125 in) with a tolerance of ±0.128 mm (0.005 in). The overall length of the encapsulation shall be at least 203 mm (8 in) and should not have any flaws or nicks that could result in erroneous test results.

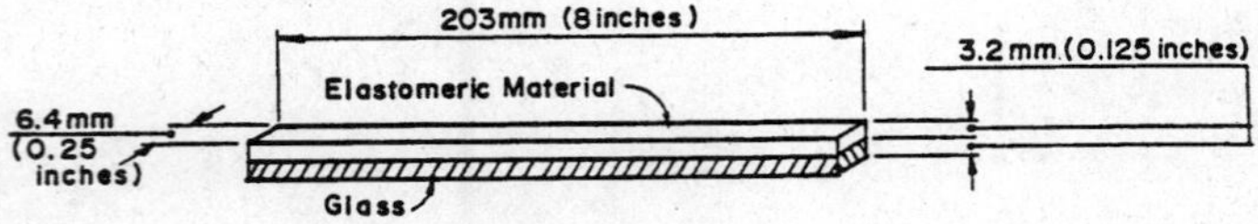

FIGURE 1—ENCAPSULATED TEST SPECIMEN

4.4 Test Specimen Conditioning and Aging—The molded glass should be conditioned according to suppliers or automotive engineers recommendation.

4.5 Test Specimen Preparation—At least 102 mm (4 in) should be cut away from the glass as illustrated in Figure 2 below in order to be used for clamping to the tensile tester.

5. Testing

5.1 Apparatus—Test apparatus should be a tensile tester described in ASTM D 1002.

5.2 Sample Clamping—The top jaw should be clamped to the glass portion and the bottom jaw should be clamped to elastomeric material as described in Figure 3. If necessary, an extender can be attached to the elastomeric material to facilitate clamping.

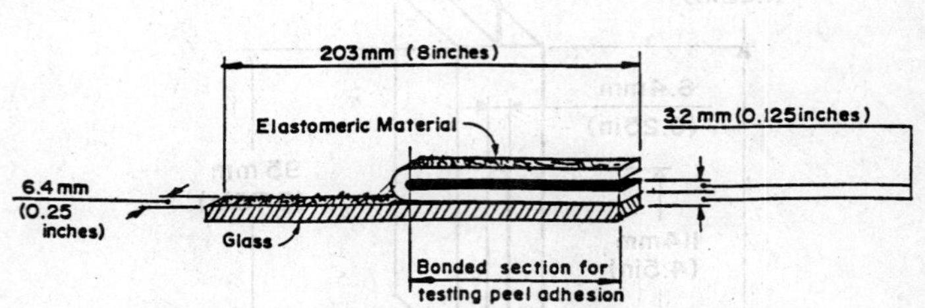

FIGURE 2—PREPARATION OF TEST SPECIMEN

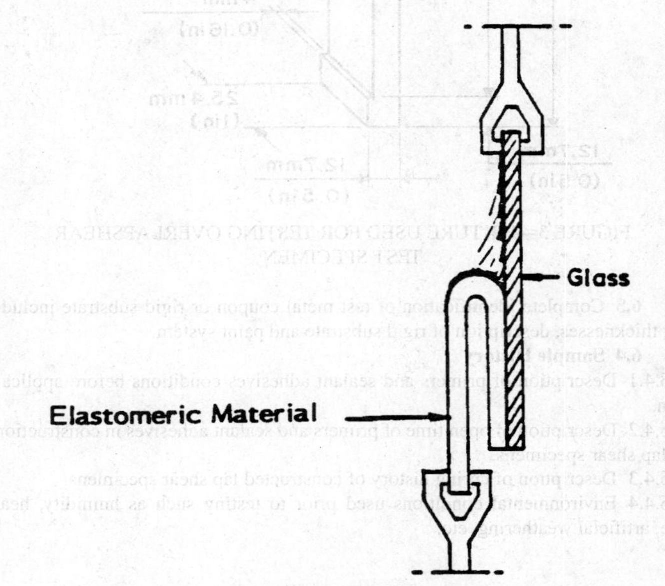

FIGURE 3—TESTING SPECIMEN ON TENSILE TESTER

5.3 Test Conditions—Pull specimens at ±23 °C and 50% relative humidity or as otherwise specified.

5.4 Test Rate—Test specimens shall be tested at pull rate of 50.8 mm (2 in) per minute.

5.5 Test Observations—Record bond values and type of failure every 12.7 mm (0.5 in) for at least 63.5 mm (2.5in).

6. Report

6.1 Complete identification of glass and elastomeric material used for encapsulation.

6.2 Complete identification of material and procedures used for priming and cleaning glass.

6.3 Encapsulation conditions used for molding.

6.4 Environmental conditions prior to testing.

6.5 Peel strength as pounds per linear inch and Newtons per linear centimeter.

6.6 Bond values every 12.7 mm (0.5 in) for at least 63.5 mm (2.5 in) with an average of these values.

6.7 Type of failure every 12.7 mm (0.5 in) for at least 63.5 mm (2.5 in) with an average of these values. Abbreviations for type of failure are:

CF—Cohesive failure of elastomeric material.

AF—Adhesive failure of elastomeric material off primed glass.

PF—Primer failure off glass, if it is detectable.

(R) CROSS PEEL TEST FOR AUTOMOTIVE-TYPE ADHESIVES FOR FIBER-REINFORCED PLASTIC (FRP) BONDING—SAE J1553 APR1995

SAE Standard

Report of the SAE Nonmetallic Materials Committee approved May 1986. Completely revised by the SAE Plastic Bonding Task Force of the SAE Materials Joining Executive Committee April 1995.

1. Scope—This SAE Recommended Practice describes a cross peel test method for use in measuring the bonding characteristics of automotive-type adhesives for joining fiber-reinforced plastics to themselves and to metals.

2. References

2.1 Applicable Publications—The following publications form a part of the specification to the extent specified herein. Unless otherwise indicated the latest revision of SAE publications shall apply.

2.1.1 ASTM PUBLICATIONS—Available from ASTM, 100 Barr Harbor Drive, West Conshohocken, PA 19428-2959.

ASTM D 1002—Test Method for Strength Properties of Adhesives in Shear by Tension Loading (Metal-to-Metal)

ASTM D 5573

3. Test Substrate

3.1 Substrates—Fiber-reinforced plastic as specified. Metal composition and roughness as specified.

3.2 Dimensions—Fiber-reinforced plastic parts shall be cut into flat coupons 25.4 mm x 75 mm (1.0 in x 3.0 in) at a nominal thickness of 2.5 mm (0.1 in). In the case of FRP to metal bonding, metal thickness will be nominally 1.5 mm (0.060 in) or as agreed upon by the automotive engineer. Shearing the FRP coupons is not recommended.

NOTE—If samples are cut with a diamond saw which is water cooled, the samples must be dry prior to bonding.

3.3 Surface Preparation—Surface preparation of FRP will be in accordance with the adhesives suppliers' recommendations. Surface roughening, solvent cleaning, and surface primers are acceptable provided they do not reduce FRP bulk properties. Any surface preparation must be adaptable to actual production situations. Metals will be machined to eliminate burrs or bevels. They will be clean and dry, or surface treated prior to bonding according to procedures prescribed by the adhesive manufacturer.

4. Preparation of Test Joints

4.1 Application of Adhesive—Adhesive will be applied in accordance with the adhesive suppliers' recommendations. In the case of two-part adhesives, mixing will be in accordance with suppliers' suggested procedures.

4.2 Adhesive Cure—Adhesive will be cured at room temperature or elevated temperature using prescribed conditions determined by the adhesive supplier, provided they can be reasonably adapted to production situations.

4.3 Joint Geometry—Joint geometry will be as shown in Figure 1. Joint geometry will be controlled by appropriate fixturing using glass beads or other suitable means to control a 0.76 mm (0.030 in) adhesive bondline thickness. The amount of glass beads in the bondline will be the minimum number needed to hold bondline thickness. Fixturing pressure will be allowed.

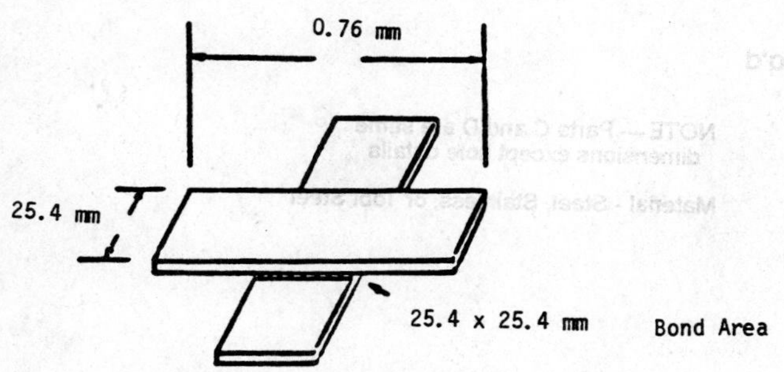

FIGURE 1—FIGURE JOINT GEOMETRY

4.4 Excess Adhesive—Excess adhesive (squeeze-out) will be removed from the bonded lap shear prior to testing without disturbing the bond area. If wire spacers are used, care should be taken not to disturb them when removing excess adhesive. Care should also be taken not to score the substrate, which will create a weak point.

4.5 Conditioning—Bonded parts will be allowed to return to ambient temperature for at least 1 h if elevated temperature cures are employed. If adhesive is room temperature cured, full cure time plus 10% will be allowed prior to testing.

5. Testing

5.1 Apparatus—The testing machine shall conform to the requirements of and have the capabilities of the machine prescribed in ASTM D 1002. It shall have a suitable pair of grips to hold the test fixture without allowing slip.

5.2 Test Rate—Fixture loading shall be in a consistent manner with a rate 13 mm (0.50 in)/min unless otherwise specified.

5.3 Test Samples—Five lap shear samples will be prepared in each case and tested.

5.4 Specimen Holding Grips—Grips as shown in Figures 2 and 3 shall be used to hold the test specimen. Parts C and D are designed to rotate out of the way and allow for easy insertion of the test specimen into the grips. Once the specimen is loaded, parts C and D are rotated back into position and the thumb screws are tightened to clamp the specimen in the grips.

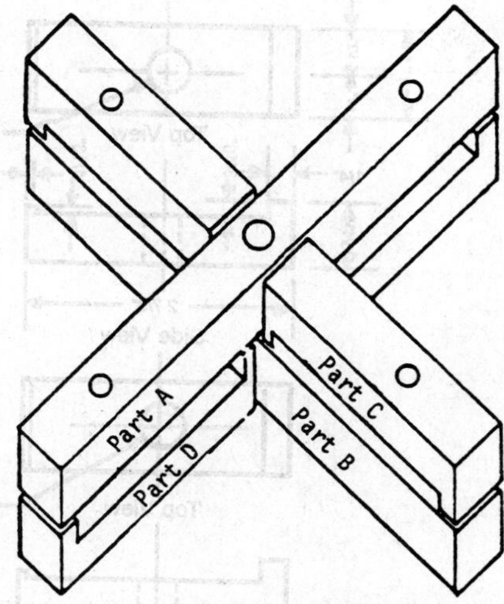

FIGURE 2—SPECIMEN HOLDING GRIP

6. Report

6.1 Complete identification of the adhesive tested, including type, manufacturer's code number, and expiration date.

6.2 Complete identification of the substrates used and method of sample and surface preparation prior to bonding.

6.3 Cure schedule, time, and temperature for bonding sample.

6.4 Individual peak load values (kPa and/or psi), averages, and failure modes with estimated percentages. Failure mode will be reported as shown in ASTM D 5573. Close visual observation will be used to determine failure mode.

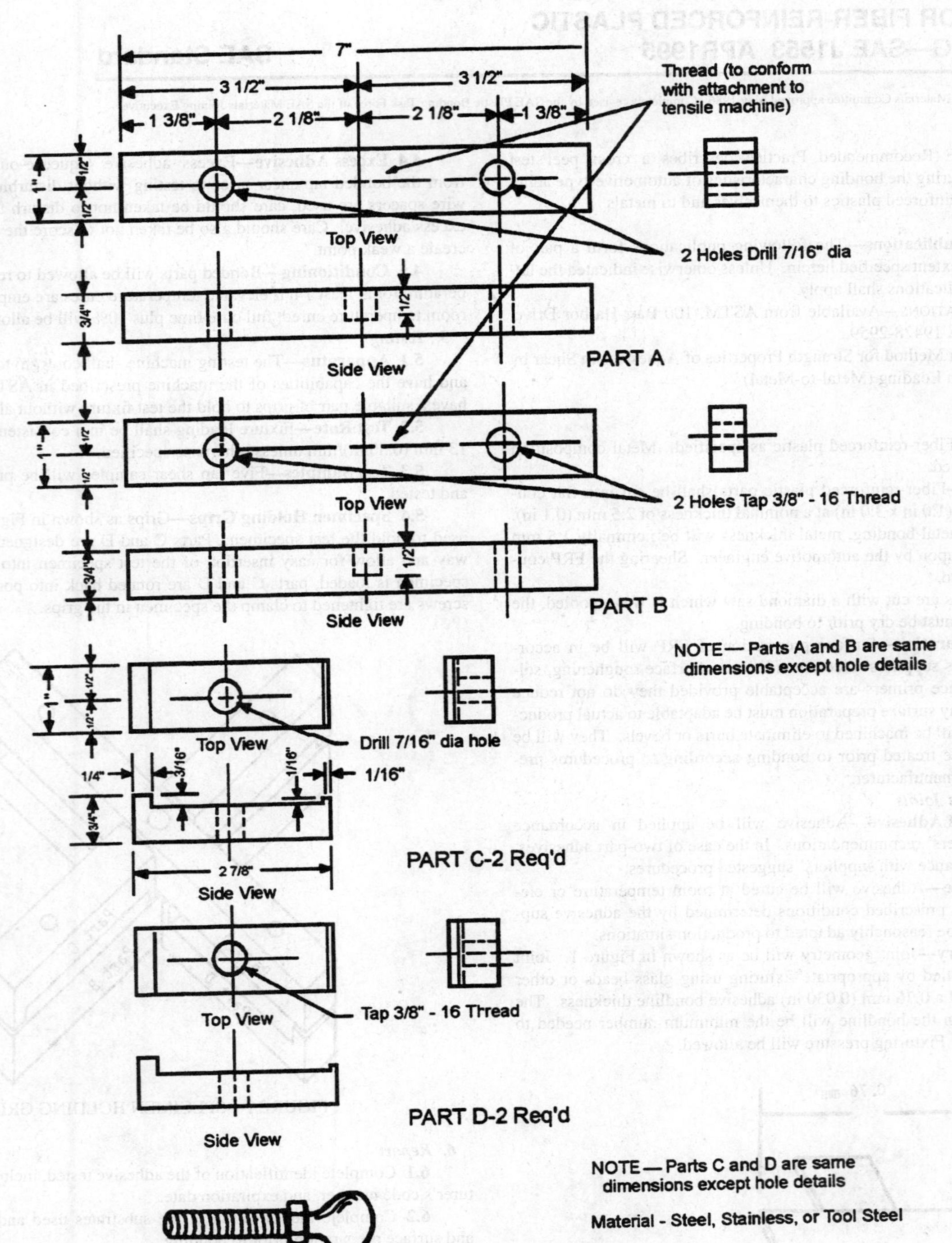

FIGURE 3—ADHESION TEST FOR ADHESIVES AND SEALANTS

) TEST METHOD FOR DETERMINING RESISTANCE TO FIBER LOSS, RESISTANCE TO ABRASION AND BEARDING OF AUTOMOTIVE CARPET MATERIALS—SAE J1530 NOV2003

SAE Recommended Practice

Report of the SAE Nonmetallic Materials Committee approved June 1985. Completely revised by the SAE Textiles and Flexible Plastics Committee August 1994 and November 2003. Rationale statement available.

1. Scope—This test method covers determination of abrasion resistance, fiber loss and bearding resistance of automotive carpet materials.

2. References—There are no referenced publications specified herein.

3. Resistance to Fiber Loss by Weight of Specimen

3.1 Materials and Equipment Required

3.1.1 Taber Abraser Model No. 5150 with vacuum accessory or equivalent.

3.1.2 H-18 wheels or equivalent.

3.1.3 Weights that yield a combined load of 1000 g on each of the abrasive wheels.

3.1.4 S-11 abrasive paper or equivalent.

3.1.5 Mounting Card S37, or equivalent.

3.1.6 Calibrated balance.

3.1.7 Clear plastic bags suitable for collecting the fiber.

3.1.8 Crockmeter cloth (80 x 84 thread count, combed cotton, de-sized and bleached).

3.2 Test Specimens

3.2.1 Unless otherwise specified, specimens shall be taken at least 100 mm away from the edges of the material.

3.2.2 Prepare specimen using 101 mm circular die or cut along the circular line on the mounting card. Use a punch to cut a 6 mm diameter hole in the center of the specimen.

3.2.3 Specimens must be conditioned at 22 °C ± 3 °C and 50% ± 5% relative humidity for a minimum of 24 hours.

3.3 Procedure

3.3.1 Adjust test instrument for a 1000 g load or specified. Reface abrasive wheels before testing each specimen by running them against the S-11 type abrasive paper disc mounted on the turntable for a minimum of 25 cycles.

3.3.2 If the wheels are out-of-round, crowned or excessively clogged with abraded material, the wheels should be dressed using a diamond wheel reface machine until the condition is corrected. If there is any doubt about the condition of the wheels, new wheels should be used.

3.3.3 Vacuum or brush the refaced abrasive wheels to remove any loose particles.

3.3.4 Weigh the specimen to the nearest 0.1 g. Record weight as W_1.

3.3.5 When loss fibers need to be collected, cover the vacuum hose with a piece of crockmeter cloth to collect the abraded fiber and insert the hose into the vacuum port of the taber abraser.

3.3.6 Place the specimen on the turntable. Place the washer over the turntable screw and tighten the nut. Adjust the clamping ring to a tight fit over the specimen and turntable. Press down and hold the clamping ring over the circumference of the turntable. Remove any wrinkles in the specimen by adjusting the specimen edges under the clamping ring. Then tighten the adjusting screw of the ring. Lower the abrasive wheels to the surface of the specimen. Position the vacuum nozzle 3 mm above the surface of the specimen and set vacuum in the range of 60 to 70.

3.3.7 A mounting card may be used to stabilize the specimens if necessary.

3.3.8 Turn on the vacuum and run the test to the specified number of cycles.

3.3.9 Remove the vacuum hose from the vacuum port if fiber has been collected. Carefully hold the crockmeter cloth and place the collected fiber into the clear plastic bag. Discard the crockmeter cloth.

3.3.10 Remove the specimen from the turntable. Vacuum the specimen with the vacuum hose to remove any loose fiber. Replace the vacuum hose in the taber abraser.

3.3.11 Weigh the specimen to the nearest 0.1 g. Record the weight as W_2 in grams.

3.3.12 Calculate the fiber loss in grams (W_3) as shown in Equation 1:

$$W_3 = W_1 - W_2 \qquad \text{(Eq. 1)}$$

4. Abrasion Resistance

NOTE—Abrasion resistance is a continuation of the fiber loss testing unless otherwise specified.

4.1 Remount the specimen on the abraser and continue to run the test to the specified number of cycles for the abrasion requirements.

4.2 Report results as agreed to by the contractual parties.

5. Resistance to Bearding (Fuzzing)

5.1 Apparatus and Material Required

5.1.1 WYZENBEEK WEAR TESTER OR EQUIVALENT—The hardness of the rubber pads should remain between 55 and 75 when tested with a type "00" durometer on the flat surfaces. Rubber pads which do not fit snugly in their respective holders should be replaced.

Due to misalignment or wear during use, the following procedure should be performed when necessary. Clean the drum surface with a solvent, insert a piece of 36 grit sandpaper and clamp into position. Lower the arms removing all applied pressure and abrade the rubber pad for 400 cycles or until they conform to the shape of the drum. Clean the resurfaced rubber pad with a stiff brush and reinsert in the same holder and in the same position. Once a rubber pad has been put through this procedure *do not* use in any other holder without resurfacing.

5.1.2 3-INCH WIDE CAGING, NO. 600-0 A ABRADANT OR EQUIVALENT

NOTE—Variation of the surface roughness of this material has been experienced. This affects the test results. However, a replacement material cannot be determined at the time of this revision of this test method.

5.2 Test Specimens

5.2.1 Unless otherwise specified, specimens shall be taken at least 100 mm away from the edges of the material.

5.2.2 Test specimens are prepared to the template (Figure 1) dimension in both the machine and cross machine directions.

5.2.3 Specimens must be conditioned at 22 °C ± 3 °C and 50% ± 5% relative humidity for a minimum of 24 h.

5.3 Procedure

5.3.1 A new abradant should be used for each set of specimens.

5.3.2 Place the specimen in the clamps with the long dimension parallel to the direction of abrasion. Specimen may be backed with tape if necessary.

5.3.3 Draw the specimen tight enough to bring the weighted tension scale bar into a horizontal position using a 1.35 kg dead weight load.

NOTE—If the specimen stretches during the test bring the scale bar back into a horizontal position by adjusting the screw behind the rear clamp.

5.3.4 Set the weight on the pressure bar at 0.9 kg.

5.3.5 Set the counter to "zero".

5.3.6 Abrade the specimen for the specified number of cycles.

5.3.7 Remove the specimen from the wear tester for evaluation.

5.3.8 Report the results as agreed to by the contractual parties.

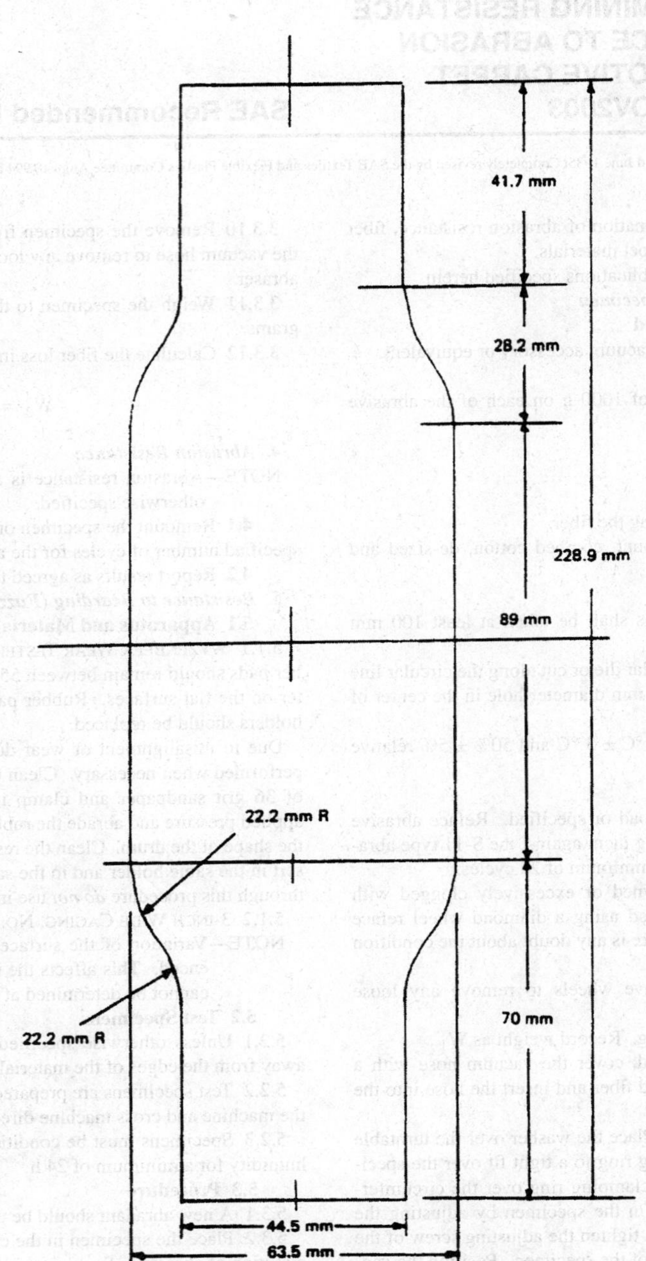

FIGURE 1—TEST SPECIMEN TEMPLATE

INDUCTION CURE TEST FOR METAL BONDING ADHESIVES—SAE J1851 MAY1987

SAE Recommended Practice

Report of the SAE Adhesives and Body Sealers Committee approved May 1987.

Foreword—This Document has not changed other than to put it into the new SAE Technical Standards Board Format.

1. Scope—This SAE Recommended Practice defines a procedure for determining the adhesion strength characteristics of heat-cured metal bonding adhesives subjected to induction heating.

2. References

2.1 Applicable Publication—The following publication forms a part of the specification to the extent specified herein. Unless otherwise indicated the lastest revision of SAE publications shall apply.

2.1.1 ASTM PUBLICATION—Available from ASTM, 100 Barr Harbor Drive, West Conshohocken, PA 19428-2959.

ASTM D 1102—Test Method for Ash in Wood

3. Apparatus Required—Induction equipment schematic diagram - See Figure 1.

3.1 Power Supply—A 20 kW, 10 kHz, frequency generator.

3.2 Heat Station—Robotron 20 kW - 10 kHz heat station to match impedance load to coil to power supply.

3.3 Inductor—Fabricated as shown in Figure 2.

3.4 Clamping Fixture—Fabricated as shown in Figure 3.

3.5 Temperature Pyrometer—Temperature measurement instrument with capability of 23 – 300 °C temperature range and ±3 °C accuracy.

3.6 Test Coupons—Test coupons shall be 25 x 100 x 0.8 mm CRLC steel body stock or otherwise specified by the applicable Engineering Material Specification.

3.7 Tensile Test Machine—Instron or equivalent with an accuracy of 0.5% of the range used.

Test apparatus as described in ASTM D 1102.

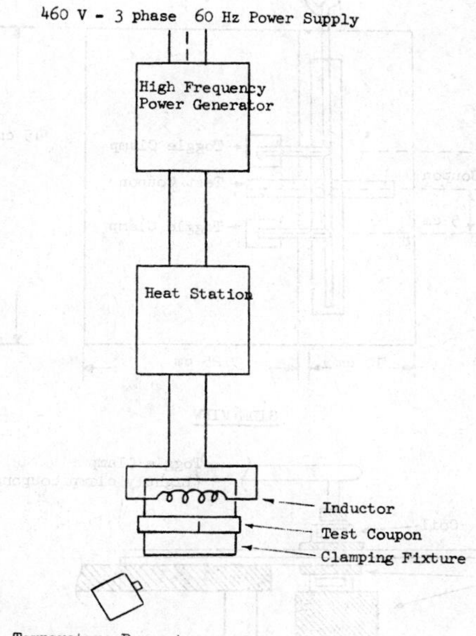

FIGURE 1—EQUIPMENT SCHEMATIC

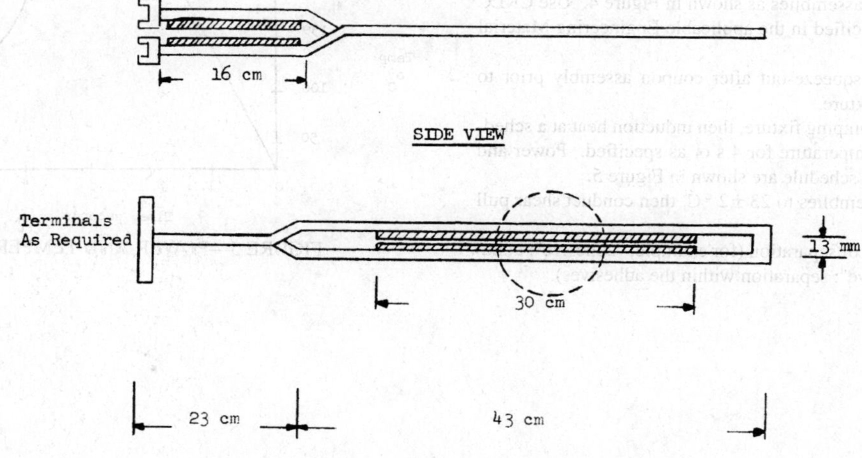

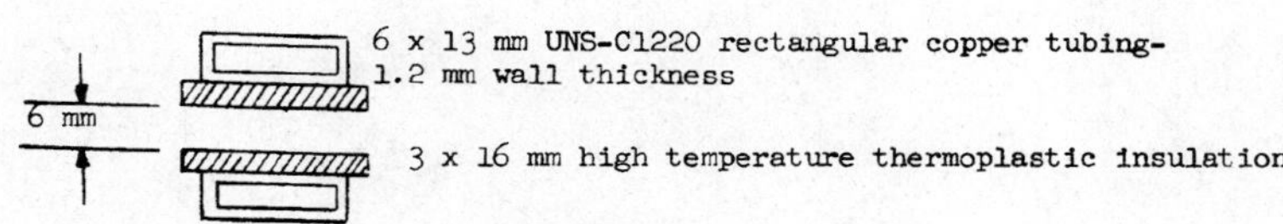

FIGURE 2—INDUCTOR

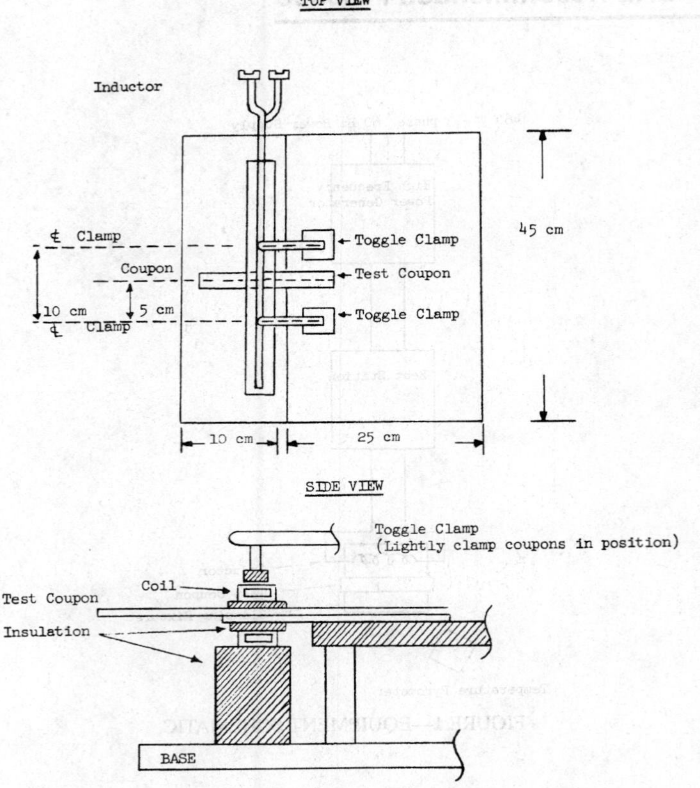

FIGURE 3—CLAMPING FIXTURE

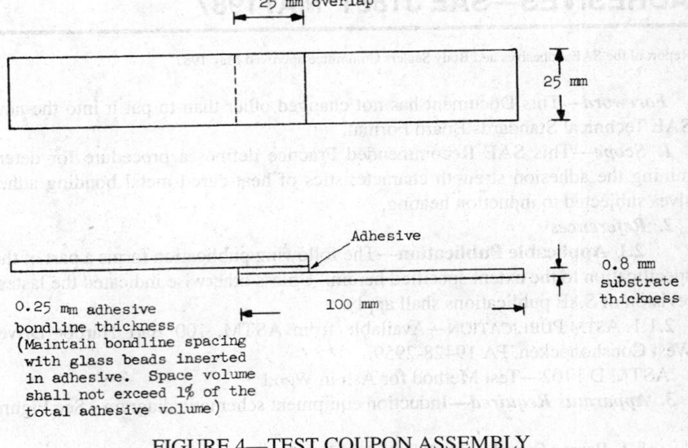

FIGURE 4—TEST COUPON ASSEMBLY

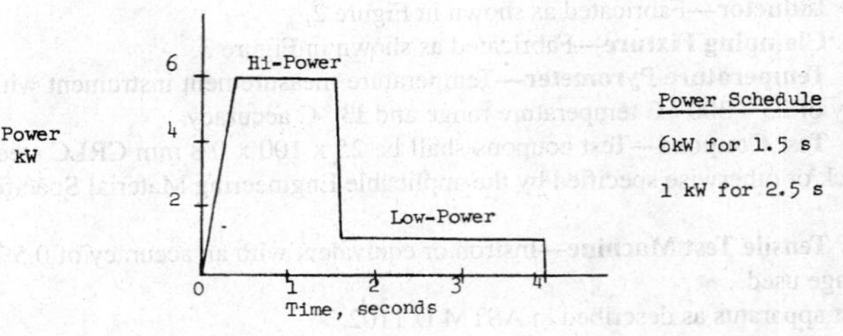

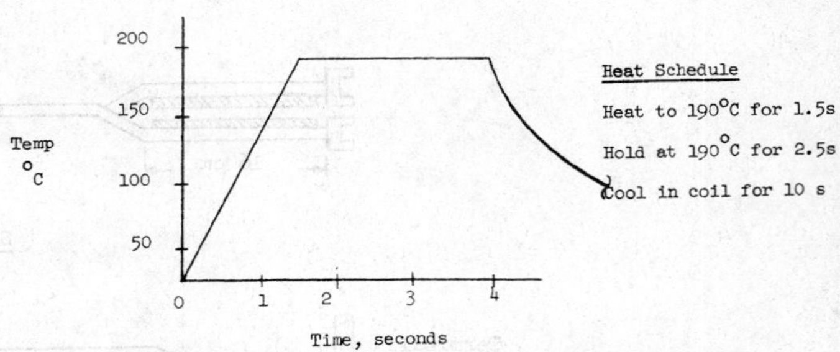

FIGURE 5—POWER AND TEMPERATURE CURVES

4. Procedure

4.1 Condition test materials for 24 h at 23 ± 2 °C and 50 ± 5% relative humidity before preparing assemblies.

4.2 Prepare overlap shear test assemblies as shown in Figure 4. Use CRLC steel substrates unless otherwise specified in the applicable Engineering Material Specification.

4.3 Remove excess adhesive squeeze-out after coupon assembly prior to positioning in induction clamping fixture.

4.4 Mount test assembly in clamping fixture, then induction heat at a schedule of 190 ± 10 °C metal surface temperature for 4 s or as specified. Power and temperature curves representing this schedule are shown in Figure 5.

4.5 Condition bonded test assemblies to 23 ± 2 °C, then conduct shear pull test at a rate of 13 mm per minute.

4.6 Report peak load and type of separation (for example, "adhesive": adhesive to substrate separation; "cohesive": separation within the adhesives).

ACOUSTICAL AND THERMAL MATERIALS TEST PROCEDURE—SAE J1324 OCT1989

SAE Recommended Practice

Report of the SAE Nonmetallic Materials Committee approved December 1981, completely revised, SAE Sound and Heat Insulation Materials Subcommittee, November 1984. Revised by the SAE Sound and Heat Insulation Materials Committee October 1989.

Foreword—This document has also changed to comply with SAE Technical Standards Board format. References were added as Section 2.

1. Scope—This SAE Recommended Practice provides test methods for determining the characteristics of acoustical and thermal materials. Where applicable, methods of test developed by SAE and ASTM have been referenced.

2. References

2.1 Applicable Publications—The following publications form a part of this specification to the extent specified herein. Unless otherwise indicated, the latest version of SAE publications shall apply.

2.1.1 SAE PUBLICATIONS—Available from SAE, 400 Commonwealth Drive, Warrendale, PA 15096-001.

SAE J315—Fiberboard Test Procedures
SAE J1325—Test Method for Measuring the Relative Drapeability of Flexible Insulation Materials
SAE J1326—Test Method for Measuring Wet Color Transfer Characteristics
SAE J1351—Hot Odor Test for Insulation Materials
SAE J1352—Compression and Recovery of Insulation Paddings
SAE J1355—Test Method for Measuring Thickness of Resilient Insulating Paddings
SAE J1361—Hot Plate Methods for Evaluating Heat Resistance and Thermal Insulation Properties of Materials
SAE J1389—Corrosion Test for Insulation Materials
SAE J1400—Laboratory Measurement of the Airborne Noise Reduction of Acoustical Materials

2.1.2 ANSI PUBLICATION—Available from ANSI, 11 West 42nd Street, New York, NY 10036-8002.

ANSI 1.1-1960 (R 1971)

2.1.3 ASTM PUBLICATIONS—Available from ASTM, 100 Barr Harbor Drive, West Conshohocken, PA 19428-2959.

ASTM C 177—Test Method for Steady-State Heat Flux Measurements and Thermal Transmission Properties by Means of the Guarded-Hot-Plate Apparatus
ASTM C 384—Test Method for Impedance and Absorption of Acoustical Materials by the Impedance Tube Method
ASTM C 423—Test Method for Sound Absorption and Sound Absorption Coefficients by the Reverberation Room Method
ASTM C 518—Test Method for Steady-State Heat Flux Measurements and Thermal Transmission Properties by Means of the Heat Flow Meter Apparatus
ASTM C 870—Practice for Conditioning of Thermal Insulating Materials
ASTM E 756—Method for Measuring Vibration-Damping Properties of Materials
ASTM E 1050—Test Method for Impedance and Absorption of Acoustical Materials Using a Tube, Two Microphones, and a Digital Frequency Analysis System

3. Terminology

3.1 Acoustical Terminology

3.1.1 SOUND ABSORPTION—Sound absorption is the change of sound energy into some other form, usually heat, in passing through a medium or on striking a surface.

3.1.2 TRANSMISSION LOSS—Transmission loss is the reduction in the magnitude of some characteristic of a signal, between two stated points in a transmission system.

3.1.3 DAMPING—Damping is the dissipation of energy with time or distance.

NOTE—Acoustical terminology adopted from ANSI 1.1-1960 (R 1971).

3.2 Thermal Terminology

3.2.1 CONDUCTION—The transfer of heat from one part of a body to another part of the same body or between bodies in physical contact.

3.2.2 CONVECTION—The transfer of heat by movement of the heated and/or cooled particles of a fluid medium.

3.2.3 RADIATION—A process of emitting energy electromagnetically. (Thermal radiation differs from other forms of heat transfer in that its speed of propagation equals that of light and no intervening medium is required for its transmission.)

3.2.4 EMITTANCE—The ability of a surface to emit radiant energy. It is expressed as the ratio of the radiant energy emitted per unit time, per unit area, by an opaque material to that by a blackbody at the same temperature.

3.2.5 THERMAL CONDUCTIVITY (K-FACTOR)—The rate of heat flow through a homogeneous material under steady-state conditions, through unit area, per unit temperature gradient in the direction perpendicular to an isothermal surface.

$$k = \frac{\text{Btu} \cdot \text{in}}{\text{h} \cdot \text{ft}^2 \cdot {}^\circ\text{F}} \qquad \lambda = \frac{\text{W}}{\text{m}^2 \cdot \text{K}} \qquad \text{(Eq. 1)}$$

3.2.6 THERMAL CONDUCTANCE (C-FACTOR)—The rate of heat flow under steady-state conditions between two definite surfaces at uniform separation, divided by the difference of their average temperatures and by the area of one surface. The average temperature is one which adequately approximates that obtained by integrating the temperatures of the entire surface.

$$C = \frac{\text{Btu}}{\text{h} \cdot \text{ft}^2 \cdot {}^\circ\text{F}} \qquad C = \frac{\text{W}}{\text{m}^2 \cdot \text{K}} \qquad \text{(Eq. 2)}$$

3.2.7 THERMAL TRANSMITTANCE (U-FACTOR) (OVERALL COEFFICIENT OF HEAT TRANSFER)—The rate of heat flow under steady-state conditions from surroundings on one side of a body, through a unit area of the body, to the surroundings on its opposite side, divided by the temperature difference between the two surroundings.

$$U = \frac{\text{Btu}}{\text{h} \cdot \text{ft}^2 \cdot {}^\circ\text{F}} \qquad U = \frac{\text{W}}{\text{m}^2 \cdot \text{K}} \qquad \text{(Eq. 3)}$$

3.2.8 TABLE OF ABBREVIATIONS

Btu = British thermal units
ft = foot
h = hour
°F = degree Fahrenheit
in = inch
λ = metric symbol for thermal conductivity
W = watt
m = meter
K = degree Kelvin
°C = degree Celsius (centrigrade)

4. Test Procedures

4.1 Thickness—See SAE J1355.

4.2 Mass (Weight) per Unit Area—The mass (weight) per unit area determination shall be made according to the method described in SAE J315 Section 6, and shall be reported as kg/m^2 (lb/ft^2).

4.3 Density—The density shall be calculated, using the thickness and mass (weight) per unit area figures from 4.1 and 4.2 and using the formula

$$d = \frac{M}{t} \qquad \text{(Eq. 4)}$$

where:

d = density in kg/m^3 (lb/ft^3)
M = mass (weight per unit area in kg/m^2 (lb/ft^2)
t = thickness in m (ft)

4.4 Thermal Conductivity (k-Factor)—For routine evaluation, quality control, and classification of materials, testing shall be conducted according to the method specified in ASTM C 518. For arbitration purposes, the test method specified in ASTM C 177, shall be used. Test results shall be reported in units of: λ or k.

The mean temperature, at which the k-Factor was determined, shall be reported. The temperature of the top and bottom platens contacting the surfaces of the test specimen shall also be reported.

4.5 Resistance to Heat Flow (R-Factor)—The R-Factor for a homogeneous material can be calculated from its k-Factor and the thickness (t) of the material by the following formula:

$$R = \frac{t}{k} \qquad \text{(Eq. 5)}$$

4.6 Heat Resistance—See SAE J1361.

4.7 Resistance of Staining—See SAE J1326.

4.8 Stiffness - Drapeability Test—See SAE J1325.

4.9 Compression-Recovery—See SAE J1352.

4.10 Dimensional Stability—The linear expansion and contraction shall be determined by the test methods described in SAE J315.

4.10.1 EXPANSION—Use Method A.

4.10.2 CONTRACTION—Use Method A, followed by Method C.

4.11 Odor—See SAE J1351.

4.12 Corrosion—See SAE J1389.

4.13 Sound Absorption

4.13.1 NORMAL INCIDENCE—Two standardized methods exist. The differences between the two are in the equipment needed and the time required to perform the test. The results from one should match the other. See ASTM C 384 and ASTM E 1050.

4.13.2 RANDOM INCIDENCE—See ASTM C 423.

4.14 Vibration Damping—See ASTM E 756.

4.15 Airborne Noise Reduction—See SAE J1400.

5. General Comments

5.1 Conditioning—Some materials require specific conditioning prior to testing; when applicable, see ASTM C 870.

THERMAL EFFECTIVENESS OF SLEEVE INSULATION —SAE J2302 NOV1996

SAE Standard

Report of the SAE Thermal Materials Committee approved November 1996.

1. Scope—This procedure measures the resistance to radiant heat flow of insulating materials in sleeve form. The sleeve's effectiveness (S_E) is determined by measuring the difference in surface temperature of a flat black, single-diameter ceramic cylinder with and without the standard diameter sleeve at the specified temperature, position, and distance from the radiant heat source.

1.1 Safety—This method may involve hazardous materials, operations, and equipment. This SAE Standard does not address the safety problems associated with its use. It is the responsibility of the user of this document to consult and establish appropriate safety and health practices and determine the applicability of regulatory limitations prior to use.

1.2 Limitations—The temperature measurement range of this procedure is 121 °C to 482 °C. Sleeve size is limited to 19 mm nominal ID and 30 cm ± 2 cm long. The test distance is the shortest measured span from the surface of the radiant heat source to the surface of the ceramic cylinder. Unless otherwise specified, the standard distance is 25 mm ± 2 mm with the cylinder position parallel to and directly above the heat source. This procedure is performed under static (passive) air flow with no vibration. Do not adapt the temperature sequencing as a thermal cycle.

1.3 This test method is based on SI units.

1.4 Note to Users—Use the appropriate alphanumeric codes to specify temperature condition (Table 1), sequence (Table 2), smoke generation option (see 6.3.2) and sample position (see 6.3.3) when referencing this document. For example, a line code of B(2)S(25)P(3)D(20) after the SAE document number means: Heating to a two-step sequence (B2), first at 121 °C, then 260 °C measuring smoke generation (S) at a level not exceeding 25 s. The sample position (P) is at 3 o'clock, 20 mm (D) from the heat source. Bracket numbers in parentheses.

2. References

2.1 Applicable Publication—The following publication forms a part of this specification to the extent specified herein.

2.1.1 NIST PUBLICATION—Available from the National Institute of Standards and Technology, U.S. Department of Commerce, Gaithersburg, MD 20899. (Formerly NBS)

NIST (NBS) Circular 590—Methods of Testing Thermocouples and Thermocouple Materials

3. Summary—This method describes the procedure and equipment for measuring the thermal effectiveness of sleeves. The test also contains the option of monitoring smoke generation time at the conditions specified. A base line is established first by exposing a 16 mm OD, flat black ceramic cylinder to the specified radiant heat source. Normally, the ceramic cylinder is parallel to and directly above the heat source at the specified distance. Other ceramic cylinder positions are possible. During the test, both facing surface temperatures of the radiant heat source and cylinder are recorded. After establishing the base line surface temperature, the ceramic cylinder is sleeved with the protective material and tested again. The surface temperatures of the heat source, sleeve, and cylinder are recorded. In both test sequences, measuring the radiant source temperature and sleeve surface temperatures ensures consistent and fair measure of the sleeve's effectiveness. A significant variation in these values requires a repetition of the test sequence.

4. Significance and Use

4.1 Data obtained by this method are applicable to the material under conditions of this test and are not necessarily the same as those obtained in end use applications. The information permits comparison, selection, or qualification of commercially available sleeves where a level of proficiency is desired beyond short time quality control tests.

4.2 The test set-up (see Figure 1) can be modified to reduce the effects of convective heat transfer by aligning the sleeve horizontal (3 o'clock position) to the heat source. Indicate other positions and distances from the heat source using item 6.3.3 protocol.

4.3 Test conditions and requirements using a line code must follow the order of temperature, sequence, smoke generation (optional), position by the clock, and distance from the heat source. See 1.4. Bracket all numbers in parentheses.

4.3.1 TEMPERATURE AND SEQUENCE PROTOCOL—List single or multiple test temperatures using the appropriate Table 1 condition letter. Condition A cannot use the sequence number 2 or 3 because it is the lowest specified temperature. If a step sequence is desired with Condition A as the upper temperature, use the Z suffix. Using a 2 or 3 test sequence after a B or C condition means the sequence follows the lower temperatures in Table 1. Always use the Z suffix to indicate a departure from the Table 1 temperature sequence. When using the Z suffix, indicate the preferred temperatures in degrees celsius in parentheses, separating the temperatures with a slash mark (/) - for example, Z2 (100 °C/121 °C).

4.3.2 POSITION AND DISTANCE PROTOCOL—The letter P followed by the appropriate number in parentheses indicates the circumferential clock position of the ceramic cylinder to the heat source. The radial distance D from the surface of the heat source to the surface of the ceramic cylinder is specified in mm bracketed by parentheses. If no position or distance is specified, the standard conditions apply.

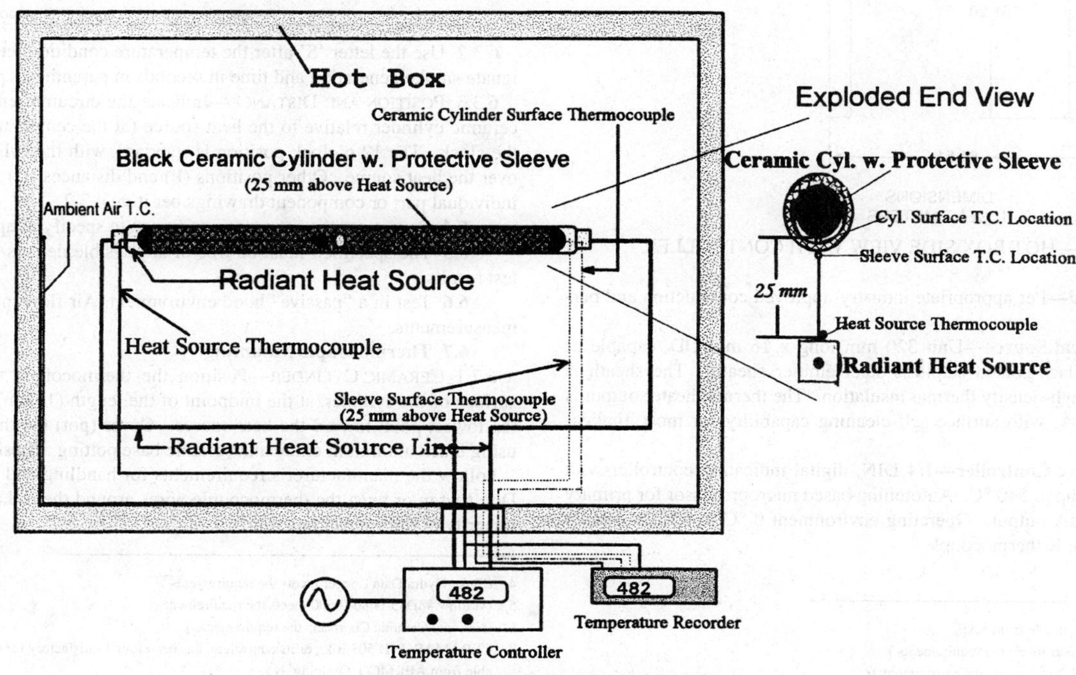

FIGURE 1—TEST SET-UP TOP VIEW

5. Equipment[1]

5.1 Hot Box—Fabricated from non-conductive, fire-resistant, thermal-insulation board material (see detail drawing Figures 2A and 2B), open at the top with nominal internal dimensions of 50 cm x 50 cm x 50 cm. Angle iron 50 mm x 50 mm x 4 mm supports the box panels.

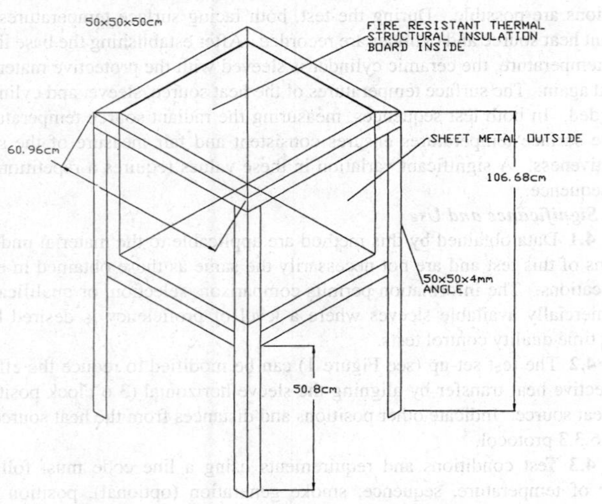

FIGURE 2A—HOT BOX

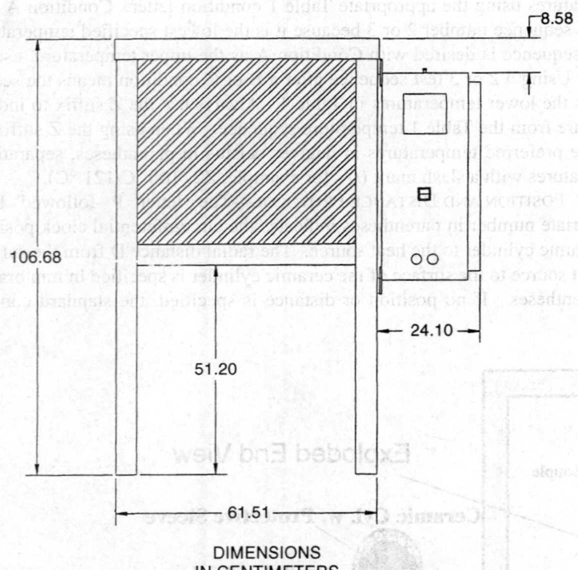

FIGURE 2B—HOT BOX SIDE VIEW WITH CONTROLLER

5.2 Fume Hood—Per appropriate industry-approved construction and performance.

5.3 Radiant Heat Source—Unit 320 mm long x 16 mm OD, capable of reaching 540 °C. Black-coated stainless steel emitter sheath. The sheath is backed with 2.5 cm high-density thermal insulation. The thermal heater output is 1100 W, 240 V, 4.6 A, with surface self-cleaning capability for most applications.[2]

5.4 Temperature Controller—1/4 DIN, digital indicating controller with an accuracy of ±3 °C up to 540 °C. Autotuning based microprocessor for primary output. Four to 20 mA output. Operating environment 0 °C to 65 °C. Sensor input must accept type K thermocouple.[3]

5.5 Temperature Recorder—Computer-controlled data analyzer.[4] Optional manual data recorder with a digital indicator. Ten-channel sensor input selector. Will accept type K thermocouple. Operating environment 0 °C to 55 °C. Accuracy of ±3 °C up to 540 °C.[5]

5.6 Type K Thermocouple—American National Standards Institute (ANSI) code K (yellow) with chromel/alumel base metals. Choose solid bare wire diameter (gauge) at 0.5 mm (AWG 24). Insulation, glass braided over glass wrap or other that meets or exceeds 500 °C capability.

5.7 Ceramic Cylinder—A flat black (not painted) solid black ceramic mandrel rod, 16 mm OD x 320 mm long, composition: 92% Al_2O_3, 8-10% SiO_2 and 0.5-1% Fe_2O_3.[6]

5.8 Enclosure Panel Box—A unit, 51 cm x 41 cm x 20 cm, with a sub-panel 43 cm x 33 cm for mounting the temperature controller, temperature indicator, circuit breaker, transformer, lights, and switches. See Figure 2B.

6. Test Requirements

6.1 Specimen—The test sleeve length must be 28 cm to 32 cm long with a 19 mm nominal ID. Measure the sleeve ID using a plug gauge. The sleeve may or may not incorporate a seam. Seamed sleeves are tested with the seam at the top of the ceramic cylinder. The air space between the test sleeve around the ceramic cylinder (drape gap) will not be uniform. Try to be consistent in placement of repetitive test samples.

6.2 Unless otherwise specified, testing shall be conducted following a specimen conditioning period of 24 h minimum at 23 °C ± 2 °C and 50% R.H. ± 5% R.H.

6.3 Temperatures—For standardization purposes, select one or more of the following test temperature conditions in Table 1:

TABLE 1—TEMPERATURE CONDITIONS

Condition	Temperature °C	Available Sequence Numbers
A	121	1
B	260	1,2
C	482	1,2,3
Z	As specified within the limits of this document.	As specified within the limits of this document.

6.3.1 SEQUENCE—For standardization purposes, select one of the following test sequences in Table 2.

TABLE 2—SEQUENCE

Sequence	Condition
1	Dedicated test at specified isothermal temperature.
2	Two-step sequence using specified temperatures.
3	Three-step sequence using specified temperatures.
9	As specified within the limits of this document.

6.3.2 Use the letter 'S' after the temperature condition letter in Table 1 to designate smoke generation and time in seconds in parentheses. See item 4.3.1.

6.3.3 POSITION AND DISTANCE—Indicate the circumferential position of your ceramic cylinder relative to the heat source (at the center) using the positions of the clock. The 12 o'clock position is standard, with the cylinder 25 mm directly over the heat source. Other positions (P) and distances (D) must be indicated on individual part or component drawings per item 4.3.2.

6.4 Do not use the sequence conditions to specify a repetitive cycle test.

6.5 The specimen must be free of any visible defects that would affect the test results.

6.6 Test in a "passive" hood environment. Air flow must not influence test measurements.

6.7 Thermocouple Mounting

6.7.1 CERAMIC CYLINDER—Position the thermocouple touching the outside surface of the cylinder, at the midpoint of the length (15 cm), and facing down at the lowest point toward the heat source. Cover (pot) the thermocouple junction using black aluminum oxide and ceramic base potting adhesive.[7]

Follow the manufacturer's requirements for handling and cure of the adhesive. Don't wrap or twist the thermocouple wires around the rod and risk breaking the integrity of the contact junction.

1. A complete parts list is available from SAE.
2. (Raymax 1330 radiant heater meets the requirements.)
3. (Watlow Series 945-1FA1-A000 meets the requirements.)
4. (Fluke Hydra Data Logger meets the requirements.)
5. (Watlow #8D45-0080-0-600 meets the requirements.)
6. (National Ceramic Co. meets the requirements.)
7. CERAMABOND 503 Blk., or its equivalent, has been found satisfactory for this purpose. This is obtainable from AERMCO, Ossining, NY.

6.7.2 Test Sleeve—Position the thermocouple at the mid-point (15 cm) and lowest point of the test sleeve facing the radiant heat source. Sewn sleeves should be positioned on the ceramic rod with the seam 180 degrees away from the heat source. The junction point must be in direct contact with the surface of the material. Secure the thermocouple to the sleeve using a fine copper magnet wire wrap or fiberglass thermal tape capable of surviving the test temperatures. Make sure the wire or tape doesn't touch the end of the thermocouple.

6.7.3 Heat Source—As purchased the heat source thermocouple may not be in the proper position. Re-position the thermocouple at the mid-point (15 cm) of the heat source shown in Figure 1. Secure the thermocouple by brazing or using black aluminum oxide and ceramic base potting adhesive.[8]

*7. **Calibration***

7.1 The instrument manufacturer or certified agent should calibrate all recorders to the appropriate National Institute of Standards and Technology (NIST) document for accuracy claimed and the appropriate label displayed on the instrument. Calibration by the test facility is appropriate if substantiated by data measured by calibrated instruments traceable to NIST (formerly NBS).

7.2 Calibrate thermocouples by the comparison method utilizing procedures based upon those described in NBS Circular 590, *Methods of Testing Thermocouples and Thermocouple Materials*. Pre-calibrated thermocouples are available from the manufacturers.

*8. **Procedure***

8.1 Establish the base line (no sleeve) measurements by placing the ceramic cylinder in the Hot Box. Position and secure the thermocouples using the techniques described in 6.7. The ceramic rod is supported on clamps attached to a self-supporting lattice frame work using metal rods found in most lab equipment catalogs. Position the parts in the hot box according to Figures 3A and 3B. Unless otherwise specified, the cylinder must be 25 mm above the heat source (see 6.3.3). Connect the thermocouple to the temperature recorder.

8.2 Check for ground loops, reversed connections and the integrity of all connections. Recalibrate if required. Begin a test sequence at 23 °C ± 2 °C air temperature as indicated by the thermocouple recording the temperature inside the hot box. Cracking of the ceramic bonding agent occurs after five or more heats, resulting in potential loss of surface contact of the thermocouple to the rod. If cracks occur, remove the excess bonding agent, rotate the rod, and remount the thermocouple contact to the new site with fresh bonding agent.

8.3 Turn on the power to the controller and recorder. Set the controller to the required temperature (see Table 1, 6.3). Allow the apparatus sufficient time to stabilize at the selected isothermal temperature. Steady-state is defined as three consecutive readings within ±2 °C of the set temperature. The starting point for determining the initial reaching of steady-state is when the continuous readout (temperature recorder) shows the first indication of the temperature to be measured. As the temperature increases to each set point, there may be a slight overshoot of the setting. Record the first steady-state set value as it is reached and ignore the slight rise (Figure 4). From early lab experience, initial runs of sleeves at all three temperatures took from 18 to 24 min to reach steady-state. Continue to record the air temperature inside the hot box. Do not use steady-state measurements as part of the ten data points.

8.4 After stabilizing the temperature set by the controller, start recording the heat source and cylinder surface temperatures. Record at 3-min intervals for 30 min *after* reaching steady-state. Continue to record the air temperature inside the hot box.

8.4.1 At the end of this period, if additional steps are required (see Table 2, 6.3.1), adjust the controller to the specified sequence condition in Table 2 and repeat the data acquisition steps. After establishing the baseline performance, end the test. Continue to record the air temperature inside the hot box.

8.5 After the test set-up has cooled, remove the set-up from the Hot Box and slide the protective sleeve on the cylinder. Don't move the thermocouple on the cylinder or the cylinder's position to the heat source. Place a second thermocouple on the outer surface of the sleeve, directly above the cylinder thermocouple. To prevent dislodging of the thermocouples, mount them on the test sleeve positioned on a second rod whose height is the same as the test. Carefully slide the sample onto the bare rod after butting the rod ends together to ease the transfer to the test rod. Place the sleeved cylinder back in the Hot Box and locate it 25 mm above the heat source. If applicable, position the sleeve seam away from the heat source.

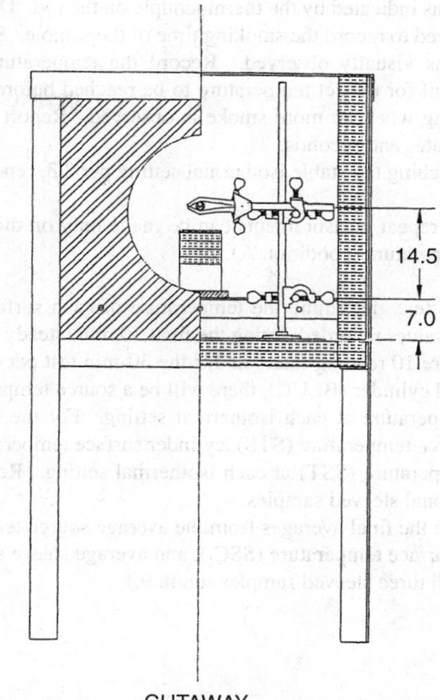

FIGURE 3A—CUTAWAY VIEW SHOWING SAMPLE MOUNTING

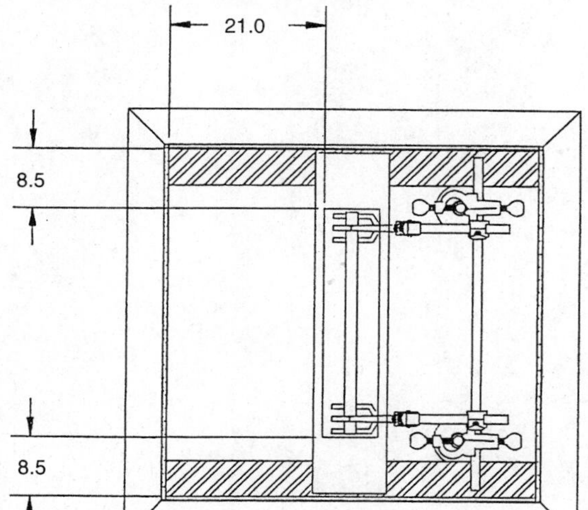

FIGURE 3B—TOP VIEW SHOWING SAMPLE POSITION

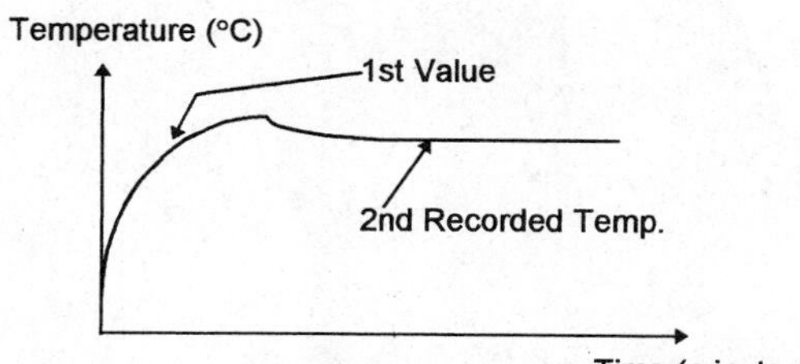

FIGURE 4—INITIAL TEMPERATURE MEASUREMENT POINTS FOR ESTABLISHING STEADY-STATE

8. Same as 7.

8.6 Repeat the sequence described in 8.3. Begin the test sequence at £26 °C of the ceramic rod as indicated by the thermocouple on the rod. During the warm-up phase, be prepared to record the smoking time of the sample. Start the timer as soon as smoking is visually observed. Record the temperature that smoking started. Do not wait for the set temperature to be reached before starting smoke timing. Stop timing when no more smoke is observed. Report the time with a stop watch, in minutes and seconds.

8.7 After reaching the stable isothermal setting per 8.3, repeat steps 8.4 and if applicable, 8.4.1.

8.8 Reliable repeat measurements can be made only on the same sleeve at the lowest test temperature (condition A).

9. Calculation

9.1 For each test, determine the temperature of each surface measured as the average of the values recorded during the final 30 min (steady-state) of the test sequence. There are 10 reading intervals for the 30-min test per sample. For the base line unsleeved cylinder (BLUC), there will be a source temperature (ST) and corresponding temperature at each isothermal setting. For the sleeved samples there will be a source temperature (STS), cylinder surface temperature (SSC), and sleeve surface temperature (SST) at each isothermal setting. Repeat this procedure on two additional sleeved samples.

9.2 Calculate the final averages from the average source temperature (ST_f), average cylinder surface temperature (SSC_f), and average sleeve surface temperature (SST_f) from all three sleeved samples run in 9.1.

9.3 Calculate the effectiveness of the sleeve material (S_E) as the temperature difference between the final averaged sleeved cylinder surface temperature (SSC_f) and the unsleeved cylinder surface temperature (BLUC) at each source isothermal temperature setting. See Equation 1.

$$S_E = BLUC - SSC_f \qquad \text{(Eq. 1)}$$

10. Report

10.1 The report shall include the following:

10.1.1 Description of the specimen, giving the identification number of the material and date of test.

10.1.2 The average unsleeved cylinder surface temperature (BLUC) per 9.1.

10.1.3 The final average sleeved cylinder surface temperature (SSC_f) per 9.2.

10.1.4 The final average sleeved surface temperature (SST_f) per 9.2.

10.1.5 The effectiveness of the sleeve material (S_E) per 9.3.

10.1.6 The air temperature inside the hot box at each stage of the test sequence.

10.1.7 The position of the ceramic cylinder per 6.3.3.

10.1.8 If applicable, the smoking time and smoking initiation temperature of each sample.

10.1.9 The raw data and all calculations for each sample.

THERMAL CONTAINMENT EFFICIENCY OF SLEEVE MATERIALS—SAE J2495 APR1999

SAE Standard

Report of the SAE Thermal Material and Parts Committee approved April 1999. Rationale statement available.

1. Scope—This SAE Standard measures the percent thermal efficiency of materials in sleeve form used to contain heat or insulate around a hot component. The percent thermal efficiency (%TE) is determined by measuring the power difference expended by the heat source (cartridge heater) with and without the test sleeve at the specified temperature. See SAE J2302 to measure radiant heat flow of sleeves.

1.1 Safety—This method may involve hazardous materials, operations and equipment. This document does not address the safety concerns associated with its use. It is the responsibility of the user of this document to consult and establish appropriate safety and health practices and determine the applicability of regulatory limitations prior to use.

1.2 Limitations—The temperature measurement range of this procedure is 260 °C to 700 °C. Sleeve size is limited to 19 mm ± 2 mm ID and 280 to 300 mm long. This procedure is performed under static (passive) air flow with no vibration. Do not adapt the temperature sequencing as a thermal cycle.

1.3 This test method is based on SI units per IEEE/ASTM SI 10.

1.4 Note to Users—Use the appropriate alpha-numeric codes to specify temperature condition (Table 1), sequence (Table 2), smoke generation option (see 6.3.2) and auxiliary thermocouple location(s) (position and distance) when referencing this document. For example, a line code of B(2)P(12)D(10,23) after the SAE document number means: Heating to a step sequence (B2), first at 260 °C, then 427 °C measuring power. The auxiliary thermocouple position (P) is at 12 o'clock, on the sleeve surface in two locations, 100 mm and 230 mm from the cartridge heater flange to the end. Bracket all numbers in parenthesis.

2. References

2.1 Applicable Publications—The following publications form a part of this specification to the extent specified herein. Unless otherwise indicated, the latest version of SAE publications shall apply.

2.1.1 SAE PUBLICATION—Available from SAE, 400 Commonwealth Drive, Warrendale, PA 15096-0001.

SAE J2302—Thermal Effectiveness of Sleeve Insulation

2.1.2 IEEE/ASTM—Available from American Society for Testing and Materials (ASTM), 100 Barr Harbor Drive, West Conshohocken, PA 19428-2959.

IEEE/ASTM SI 10-1997—Standard for Use of the International System of Units (SI): The Modern Metric System

2.1.3 NBS PUBLICATION—National Institute of Standards and Technology, U. S. Department of Commerce, Gaithersburg, MD 20899.

NBS Circular 590—Methods of Testing Thermocouples and Thermocouple Materials

3. Summary—This document describes the method and equipment for measuring the effectiveness of sleeves required to contain heat. The test also contains the option of monitoring smoke generation time at the conditions specified (see item 6.3.2). A base line is established first by exposing a 338 mm long x 16 mm OD, cartridge heater assembly (w. thermocouple) to the specified temperature. The controlling thermocouple is mounted at the midpoint and top surface of the cartridge heater. During the test, four power readings of the cartridge heater are recorded, one every 15 min after the tube reaches thermal equilibrium. After establishing the base line power readings, the cartridge heater is sleeved with the thermocoupled protective material and tested again. The surface temperature of the sleeve is recorded. There is no need to measure the cartridge surface temperature, since the heater surface temperature is controlled by the source temperature setting. At the operator's discretion, auxiliary thermocouples mounted at points along the sleeve surface monitor additional sleeve temperatures. In both test sequences, measuring the power expended by the heater, along with the heat source temperature and sleeve surface temperatures assures consistent and fair measure of the sleeve's effectiveness. Only the ratio of power unsleeved less the power sleeved, divided by the unsleeved power expressed as a percent, determines a sleeve's thermal efficiency. A significant variation in these values requires repetition of the test sequence.

4. Significance and Use

4.1 Data obtained by this method are applicable to the material under conditions of this test and are not necessarily the same as those obtained in end use applications. The information permits comparison, selection, or qualification of commercially available sleeves where a level of proficiency is desired beyond short time quality control tests.

4.2 The test set-up (see Figure 1) accommodates one test sleeve and relevant thermocouples. Indicate other thermocouple positions and distances from the cartridge heater using item 6.3.3 protocol.

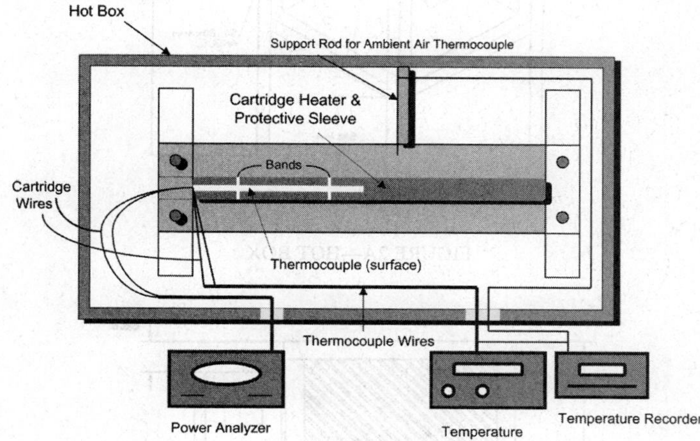

FIGURE 1—TEST SET-UP, TOP VIEW

4.3 Test conditions and requirements using a line code must follow the order of temperature, sequence, and thermocouple position designated by the numbers on a clock. See item 1.4. Bracket all numbers in parenthesis.

4.3.1 TEMPERATURE AND SEQUENCE PROTOCOL—List single or multiple test temperatures using the appropriate Table 1 condition letter. Condition A cannot use the sequence number 2 or 3 because it is the lowest specified temperature. If a step sequence is desired with Condition A as the upper temperature, use the Z suffix. Using a 2 or 3 test sequence after a B or C condition means the sequence follows the lower temperatures in Table 1. Always use the Z suffix to indicate a departure from the Table 1 temperature sequence. When using the Z suffix, indicate the preferred temperature's in degrees centigrade in parenthesis, separating the temperature's with a slash mark (/) - for example Z2 (100 °C/121 °C).

4.3.2 POSITION PROTOCOL—The letter P, followed by the appropriate number in parenthesis, indicates the circumferential clock position of the auxiliary thermocouple(s) on the surface of the cartridge heater and/or sleeve. If no specified position is stated, no measurement is made. Twelve is at the top surface with numbers proceeding clockwise as observed from the tip end (opposite the wires) of the cartridge heater.

5. Equipment[1]

5.1 Hot Box—Fabricated from non-conductive, fire resistant, thermal insulation board material[2], 50 mm x 610 mm x 1220 mm, open at the top with nominal internal dimensions of 500 mm x 500 mm x 500 mm. Angle iron 50 mm x 50 mm x 4 mm supports the box panels (6000 mm total). See detail drawing Figures 2A and 2B.

5.2 Fume Hood—Per appropriate industry approved construction and performance.

5.3 Cartridge Heater—Unit 338 mm long x 16 mm OD, capable of reaching 760 °C. The cartridge length from 292 to 305 mm is heated. No heat zones are located from the sealed tip end to 13 mm toward the flanged base and 38 mm from the lead wire entry point end toward the flange. The cartridge construction consists of a incoloy™ tube (sheath), inside is a wound nickel-chromium wire on a support core of magnesium oxide thermal insulation. The thermal heater output is 1000 to 1100 W, 240 VAC/4.1 A, with surface self-cleaning capability for most applications.[3]

1. All are single items, except as indicated.
2. (McMaster Carr 93371K67 or equivalent meets the requirements.)
3. Power Modules Inc., cartridge heater 4960921-E or 4960811 or equivalent, meets the requirements.

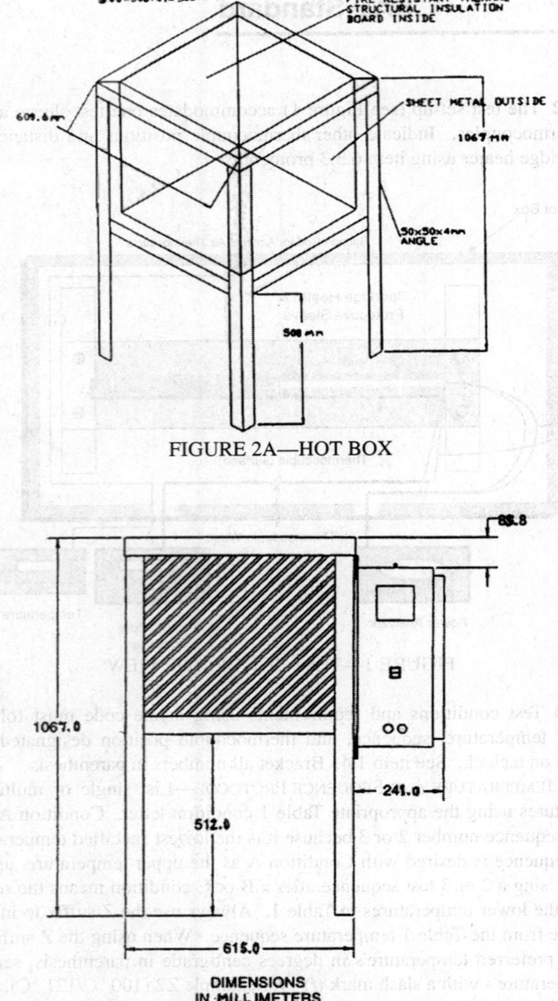

FIGURE 2A—HOT BOX

FIGURE 2B—HOT BOX SIDE VIEW WITH CONTROLLER

5.4 Temperature Controller—1/4 DIN, digital indicating controller with an accuracy of ±3 °C up to 700 °C. Auto tuning based microprocessor for primary output. Four to Twenty mA output. Operating environment 0 °C to 65 °C. Sensor input must accept type K thermocouple.[4] Supplies electrical current to heat cartridge.

5.5 Electric Power Demand Analyzer[5] and Current Probe[6]—Digital indicating analyzer with an accuracy of ±3 °C up to 700 °C. Auto tuning based microprocessor for primary output. Four to Twenty mA output. Operating environment 0 °C to 65 °C. Sensor input must accept type K thermocouple. Monitor's voltage and current, display's power used.

5.6 Temperature Recorder—Computer controlled data analyzer.[7] Optional manual data recorder with a digital indicator.[8] Ten channel sensor input selector. Will accept type K thermocouple. Operating environment 0 °C to 55 °C. Accuracy of ± 3 °C up to 700 °C.

5.7 Type K Thermocouple (Wire)—American National Standards Institute (ANSI) code K (yellow) with chromel/alumel base metals. Choose approximately 50 m of solid bare wire, diameter (gauge) at 0.81 mm (AWG 20). Insulation, glass braided over glass wrap or other that meets or exceeds 700 °C capability.[9]

4. Watlow Series 945-1FA1-A000, 965 and 93 or equivalent, meets the requirements. INCOLOGY™ is a trademark of International Nickel
5. Dranetz Model 808 Power Analyzeror equivalent, meets the requirements.
6. Dranetz Current Probe, Model TR2012A or equivalent, meets the requirements.
7. Fluke Hydra Data Logger 2625A or equivalent, meets the requirements.
8. Watlow #8D45-0080-0-600 or equivalent, meets the requirements.
9. Omega GG-K-20 (solid) or equivalent, meets the requirements.

5.7.1 THERMOCOUPLE CONNECTOR—"K" Type, plug, (3). Attaches to thermocouple leads for connection into module for cartridge heater.[10]

5.7.2 THERMOCOUPLE CONNECTOR—"K" Type, socket. Permits insertion of plug with thermocouple leads into module for cartridge heater.[11]

5.8 Surface Probe—Ceramic tip (spring loaded), (3). Permits surface contact of thermocouple to sleeve.[12]

5.9 Enclosure Panel Box—A unit, 510 mm x 410 mm x 200 mm[13], with a sub panel 430 mm x 330 mm[14] for mounting the temperature controller, temperature indicator, circuit breaker, transformer, lights and switches. See Figure 2B.

5.9.1 TRANSFORMER—500VA, 240/120 VAC to control any in rush currents.[15]

5.9.2 FUSE HOLDER AND FUSES—Panel mount, 2 pole and 1 pole - 250 VAC holder, with two six amp and one three amp fuses.

5.9.3 SWITCH, SELECTOR—2 position maintained 10 A rating (oil tight) for on/off control.

5.9.4 PILOT LIGHT—120 VAC, red, to indicate on and off condition.

5.10 Circuit Breaker—2 pole, 240 V, 15 A through door mount to panel box.[16]

5.11 SCR Power Control—240 V, 15 A, zero voltage firing (signal control = 4-20 mA).[17]

6. Test Requirements

6.1 Specimen—The test sleeve length must be 280 mm to 300 mm long with a 19 mm nominal ID. Measure the sleeve i.d. using a plug gauge. The sleeve may or may not incorporate a seam. Seamed sleeves are tested with the seam at the bottom (6 o'clock) of the cartridge heater.

6.2 Unless otherwise specified, testing shall be conducted following a specimen conditioning period of 24 h minimum at 23 °C ± 2 °C and 50% R.H. ± 5% R.H.

6.3 Temperatures—For standardization purposes, select one or more of the following test temperature conditions:

TABLE 1—TEMPERATURE CONDITIONS

Condition	Temperature °C	Available Sequence Numbers
A	260	1
B	427	1,2
C	537	1,2,3
D	700	1,2,3,4
Z	As specified within the limits of this standard.	

6.3.1 SEQUENCE—For standardization purposes, select one of the following test sequences:

TABLE 2—SEQUENCE

Sequence	Condition
1	Dedicated test at specified isothermal temperature.
2	Two step sequence using specified temperatures.
3	Three step sequence using specified temperatures.
4	Four step sequence using specified temperatures.
9	As specified within the limits of this standard.

6.3.2 Use the letter 'S,' after the temperature condition letter in Table 1, to designate smoke generation and time in seconds in parenthesis. See item 4.3.2.

6.3.3 POSITION AND DISTANCE—indicate the circumferential position of your auxiliary thermocouple(s) relative to the cartridge heater using the positions of the clock. The twelve o'clock thermocouple position (top) is standard, on the surface of the test sleeve. Indicate other positions (P) on individual part or component drawings per item 4.3.2. Distance (D) is measured in centimeters from the wire/flange end of the cartridge heater to the opposite end. Indicate the number in parenthesis for each auxiliary thermocouple.

6.4 Do not use or interpret the sequence conditions as a repetitive cycle test.

6.5 The specimen must be free of any visible defects that would effect the test results.

10. Cole-Parmer E-83840-52 or equivalent, meets the requirements.
11. Cole-Parmer E-93840-53 or equivalent, meets the requirements.
12. Cole-Parmer L-08439-12 or equivalent, meets the requirements.
13. Hoffman D-3L20H1608LPB or equivalent, meets the requirements.
14. McMaster Car 75545K92 or Hoffman (OR) AZOP16 or equivalent, meets the requirements.
15. Jefferson 636-1191 or equivalent, meets the requirements.
16. Square "D" Co. FAL-22015 or equivalent, meets the requirements.
17. Halmar/Robicon 115Z-C or equivalent, meets the requirements.

6.6 Test in a "passive" hood environment. Air flow must not influence test measurements.

6.7 Thermocouple Mounting

6.7.1 CARTRIDGE HEATER—Position the thermocouple touching the outside surface of the cartridge heater, at the midpoint of the heat zone (144 mm)/ of entire length (287 mm), and at the 12 o'clock position. See Section A.1 for repair attachment procedure the thermocouple junction. As a purchased option, with the thermocouple attached, the heat source thermocouple must be at the midpoint of the cartridge heater shown in Figure 3A. Don't wrap or twist the thermocouple wires around the rod and risk breaking the integrity of the contact junction.

6.7.2 TEST SLEEVE—Position the thermocouple ±10 mm to the left or right (offset) of the cartridge heater thermocouple position at the top of the test sleeve mounted to the cartridge heater (Figure 3A). Position sewn sleeves on the cartridge heater with the seam 180 degrees away from the top. The junction point must be in direct contact with the surface of the material. The spring loaded surface probe with ceramic tip (item 5.7) with adjustable mounting bracket, permits surface contact of thermocouple from a variety of angles. If this is not available, secure the thermocouple to the sleeve using a fine copper magnet wire wrap or fiberglass thermal tape capable of surviving the test temperatures. Make sure the wire or tape doesn't touch the end of the thermocouple.

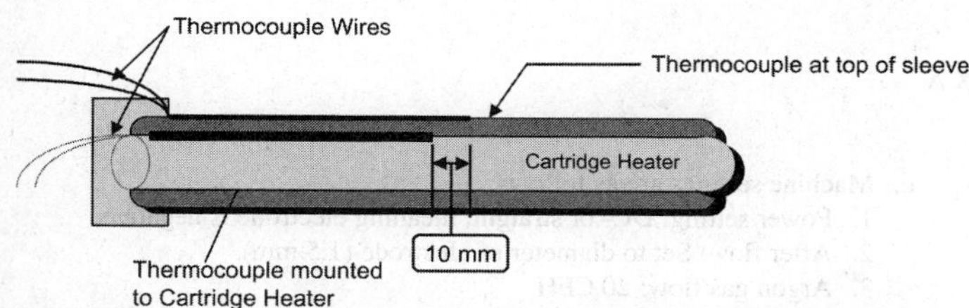

FIGURE 3A—CROSS SECTION SHOWING THERMOCOUPLE OFFSET

6.7.3 THERMOCOUPLE LOCATION—The midpoint location is required for measurement since thermal data of the recommended cartridge heater has shown that only in the center do you get temperature output equivalent to the controller set temperature.

7. Calibration

7.1 The instrument manufacturer or certified agent should calibrate all recorders to the appropriate National Institute of Standards and Technology (NIST) document for accuracy claimed and the appropriate label displayed on the instrument. Calibration by the test facility is appropriate if substantiated by data measured by calibrated instruments traceable to NIST (formerly NBS).

7.2 Calibrate thermocouples by the comparison method utilizing procedures based upon those described in NBS Circular 590, Methods of Testing Thermocouples and Thermocouple Materials. Pre-calibrated thermocouples are available from the manufacturers.

8. Procedure

8.1 Establish the base line (no sleeve) measurements by placing the cartridge heater in the Hot Box. Position and secure the thermocouples using the techniques described in item 6.7. The cartridge heater has a flange with holes for easy attachment to an "L" shaped self-supporting base for positioning on the "H" platform inside the bottom of the box. A thermocouple for ambient temperature measurement is supported by a lattice frame work in the box, using metal rods and joint fittings found in most lab equipment catalogs. Position the parts in the hot box according to Figures 4A and 4B. Unless otherwise specified, the thermocouple test position is at the top (see item 6.3.3). Connect the thermocouple to the temperature recorder.

8.2 Check for ground loops, reversed connections and the integrity of all connections. Re-calibrate if required. Begin a test sequence at 23 °C ± 2 °C air temperature as indicated by the thermocouple recording the temperature inside the hot box. Inspect the thermocouple connection to the cartridge heater every five to ten heats. If contact is lost, repair the connection by rotating the cartridge heater and remount the thermocouple contact to the new center site with new weld (Section A.1).

8.3 Turn on the power to the controller, power analyzer, bare cartridge heater, and recorder. Set the controller to the required temperature (see Table 1, item 6.3). Allow the apparatus sufficient time to stabilize at the selected isothermal temperature. Steady state is defined as three consecutive readings within ±3 °C of the set temperature. The starting point for determining the initial reaching of steady state is when the continuous readout (temperature recorder) shows the first indication of the temperature to be measured. As the temperature increases to each set point, there may be a slight over-shoot of the setting. Record the first steady state set value as it is reached and ignore the slight rise.

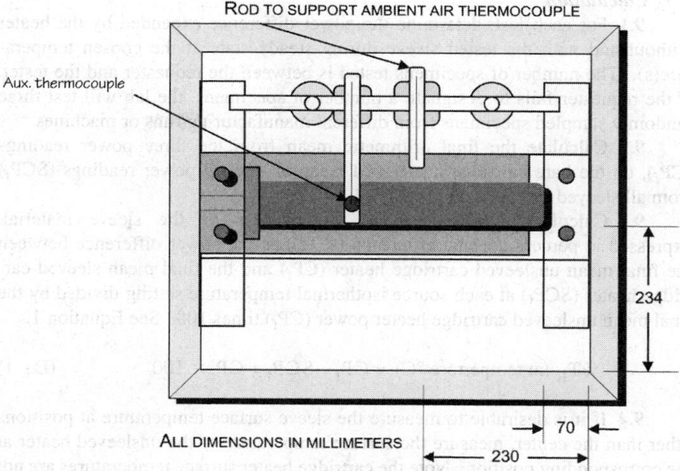

FIGURE 4A—TOP VIEW SHOWING SAMPLE POSITION

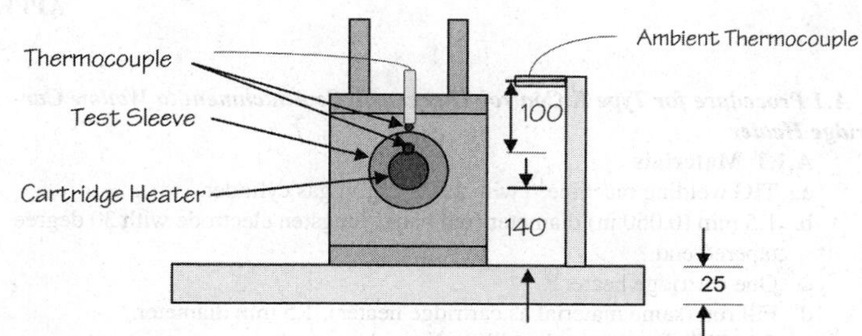

FIGURE 4B—END VIEW SHOWING SPECIMEN MOUNTING

8.4 After stabilizing the temperature set by the controller, start recording the cartridge heater surface temperatures. Record at 3 min intervals for 30 min after reaching steady state. Continue to record the air temperature inside the hot box.

8.4.1 At the end of this period, if additional steps are required (see Table 2, item 6.3.1), adjust the controller to the specified sequence condition in Table 2 and repeat the data acquisition steps. After establishing the base line performance, end the test. Continue to record the air temperature inside the hot box.

8.5 After the test set-up has cooled, remove the set-up from the Hot Box and slide the protective sleeve on the cartridge heater. Don't dislodge the thermocouple on the cartridge. Place a second thermocouple on the outer surface of the sleeve, offset by ±10 mm and above the bare cartridge heater thermocouple (12 o'clock high). Place the sleeved cartridge heater back in the Hot Box in the proper orientation. To help prevent dislodging of the thermocouples, mount them on the test sleeve positioned on a second rod whose height is the same as the test. Carefully slide the sample onto the bare rod after butting the rod ends together to ease the transfer to the test rod. If you use the spring contact to surface method, slide the non-thermocoupled test sleeve onto the cartridge heater then position the contact locator and disengage the spring to permit contact. If applicable, position the sleeve seam pointing to the bottom.

8.6 Repeat the sequence described in item 8.3. Begin the test sequence when the cartridge heater surface temperature is less than or equal to 26 °C, as indicated by the center thermocouple. During the warm-up phase, be prepared to record the smoking time of the sample. Start the timer when smoking is visually observed. Record the temperature that smoking started. Do not wait for the set temperature to be reached before starting smoke timing. Stop timing when no more smoke is observed. Report the time with a stop watch, in minutes and seconds. From early lab experience, initial runs on the cartridge heater at all three temperatures took from eighteen to twenty-four minutes to reach steady state. Continue to record the air temperature inside the hot box. Do not use steady state measurements as part of the ten data points.

8.7 After reaching the stable isothermal setting per 8.3, repeat steps 8.4 and if applicable, 8.4.1.

8.8 Reliable repeat measurements can only be made on the same sleeve at the lowest test temperature (condition A).

9. Calculation

9.1 For each test, determine the power difference expended by the heater without and with the tested sleeve during steady state at the chosen temperature(s). The number of specimens tested is between the requester and the tester. If the requester fails to designate a number of specimens, the lab will test three randomly sampled specimens from different manufacturing runs or machines.

9.2 Calculate the final arithmetic mean from the three power readings (CP_f), on the bare cartridge heater and mean of sleeved power readings (SCP_f) from all sleeved samples run in item 9.1.

9.3 Calculate the containment effectiveness of the sleeve material, expressed in percent thermal efficiency (%TE) as the power difference between the final mean unsleeved cartridge heater (CP_f) and the final mean sleeved cartridge heater (SCP_f) at each source isothermal temperature setting divided by the final mean unsleeved cartridge heater power (CP_f) times 100. See Equation 1.

$$\%T_E \text{ (at temperture °C)} = CP_f - SCP_f \div CP_f \times 100 \qquad \text{(Eq. 1)}$$

9.4 If it is desirable to measure the sleeve surface temperature at positions other than the center, measure the surface temperature of the unsleeved heater at the corresponding position. Note the cartridge heater surface temperatures are not uniform and differ considerably from the set temperature. Do not place thermocouples in the cartridge heater no heat zones.

10. report

10.1 The report shall include the following:

10.1.1 Description of the specimen, giving the identification number of the material and date of test.

10.1.2 The final unsleeved and sleeved cartridge heater power (CP_f) readings per item 9.1.

10.1.3 The final mean unsleeved cartridge heater power (CP_f) per item 9.2.

10.1.4 The final mean sleeved cartridge heater power (SCP_f) per item 9.2.

10.1.5 The percent thermal efficiency of the sleeve material (%T_E) per item 9.3.

10.1.6 The air temperature inside the hot box at each stage of the test sequence (start and measurement phase).

10.1.7 If applicable, the position of the cartridge heater thermocouple(s) per item 6.3.3.

10.1.8 If applicable, the smoking time and smoking initiation temperature of each sample.

10.1.9 The raw data and all calculations for each sample. Retain data for a minimum of three years.

APPENDIX A

A.1 Procedure for Type K Control Thermocouple Attachment to Watlow Cartridge Heater

A.1.1 Materials

a. TIG welding machine[18] with 100% argon gas cylinder.
b. 1.5 mm (0.060 in) diameter (red band) tungsten electrode with 30 degree tapered end.
c. One cartridge heater[19].
d. Fill rod (same material as cartridge heater), 1.5 mm diameter.
e. One "K" thermocouple with wolven glass insulation.
f. Proper anchoring and stand for gas cylinder.
g. Standard personal protection required for tungsten inert gas (TIG) welding procedures.

A.1.2 Procedure—This is a two person operation.

a. Put on protective gear.
b. Place the 1.5 mm diameter electrode into the torch allowing approximately 6 mm of the electrode to protrude past the torch tip.
c. Machine settings are as follows:
   1. Power setting: DC- or straight, meaning electrode is negative.
   2. After flow: Set to diameter of electrode (1.5 mm).
   3. Argon gas flow: 20 CFH
   4. Spark switch: Start only
   5. Current control: Remote
   6. Current range: Low DC (8 - 40 A), fine tuner set at approximately 6.
d. Place cartridge heater into a vice in a horizontal position.
e. Attach grounding cable from welding machine to the vice.
f. Locate placement of the thermocouple at the midpoint (14.4 cm) on the cartridge heater.
g. Holding the TIG torch electrode tip approximately 3 mm above the surface of the cartridge heater, activate the remote power control to create a puddle on the welding substrate of approximately 3 mm in diameter. Use approximately one drop of stainless steel fill from the fill rod to achieve the puddle.
h. Once the puddle is formed, a second person will place the thermocouple with a 6 mm twist into the puddle, while the person operating the TIG welder simultaneously pulls away the TIG electrode to avoid melting the thermocouple end.

18. Lincoln Ideal Arc TIG 250 welding machine with attached 100% argon gas cylinder or equivalent, meets the requirements.
19. Watlow 240 V, 3700 W cartridge heater number 9651 L14A21 D12 or equivalent, meets the requirements.

(R) VIBRATION DAMPING MATERIALS AND UNDERBODY COATINGS—SAE J671 MAY1997

SAE Standard

Report of the SAE Passenger Car Body Engineering and the SAE Nonmetallic Materials Committees approved November 1951. Completely revised by the SAE Nonmetallic Materials Committee April 1982 and May 1997.

1. Scope

1.1 Description of Material—The materials classified under this specification are:

a. Mastic vibration damping materials used to reduce the sound emanating from metal panels.
b. Mastic underbody coatings used to give protection and some vibration damping to motor vehicle underbodies, fenders, and other parts.

1.2 Numbering System

1.2.1 PREFIXES—The prefix "D" is used to indicate a cut back vibration damping material and the prefix "U" is used to indicate a cut back underbody coating material. Should a water emulsion be desired, the prefix should be followed by the letter "E." Should a solvent-water emulsion be desired, the prefix should be followed by the letter "F."

1.2.2 TYPES—The materials are further divided into types, based on the decay rate in decibels per second (dB/s) at 21 °C, and classes, based on the percentage of solids contained in the material.

Types and classes are as follows in Tables 1A and 1B:

TABLE 1A—NOMINAL DECAY RATE, dB/s

Type	Nominal Decay Rate, dB/s
5	5
10	10
15	15
20	20
25	25
30	30

TABLE 1B—NOMINAL SOLIDS CONTENT, %(1)

Class	Nominal Solids Content, %
60	60
65	65
70	70
75	75
85	85
90	90

1. This table will be expanded as additional data is submitted and confirmed.

1.3 Example of the Use of Numbers—A cut back underbody coating having a decay rate of 5 dB/s and a solids content of 65% would be designated by the number U-565. An emulsion body damping material of medium decay rate and maximum solids content would be numbered DE-1090. Any combination of type and class could be used to suit the needs of the application.

2. References

2.1 Applicable Publications—The following publications form a part of this specification to the extent specified herein.

2.1.1 ASTM PUBLICATIONS—Available from ASTM, 100 Barr Harbor Drive, West Conshohocken, PA 19428-2959.

ASTM D 93—Test Methods for Flash Point by Pensky-Martens Closed Tester
ASTM D 217—Test Method for Cone Penetration of Lubricating Grease

3. Physical Properties

3.1 Test Specifications—For testing procedures, see 4.1.

3.1.1 VIBRATION DAMPING MATERIAL—The material shall have a decay rate as shown in Table 2.

TABLE 2—MINIMUM DECAY RATE(1)

Type	Min Decay Rate, dB/s 21 °C	Min Decay Rate, dB/s −18 °C	Min Decay Rate, dB/s 38 °C
5	5	2	2
10	10	4	4
15	15	4	4
20	20	5	5
25	25	—	—
30	30	—	—

1. This table will be expanded as additional data is submitted and confirmed.

3.1.2 SOLIDS—The solids content of the material shall be as specified in Table 3.

TABLE 3—MINIMUM SOLIDS CONTENT BY WEIGHT (1)

Class	Min Solids Content, % by Weight
60	60
65	65
70	70
75	75
85	83
90	88

1. This table will be expanded as additional data is submitted and confirmed.

3.1.3 COLD ADHESION—The average retention of material on three cold test panels shall be as shown in Table 4.

TABLE 4—MINIMUM MATERIAL ON COLD-TEST PANEL

Angle of Slam, degree	Min Material on Panel, %
70	50
60	80
50	100

3.1.4 FLASH POINT—The flash point of an underbody coating shall be at least 38 °C; that of a vibration damping material shall be as agreed upon by the purchaser and the manufacturer.

3.1.5 ABRASION RESISTANCE (WHEN SPECIFIED)—The average retention on three abrasion test panels shall be not less than 95% of the material by weight. Each panel must retain at least 90% of the material, and there shall be no exposed metal surfaces.

3.1.6 SAGGING—The material shall not sag more than 6 mm when tested on an inverted 45-degree panel.

3.1.7 SPRAYABILITY—FLOW RATE—The material shall have a flow rate as follows:

a. Underbody Coatings—45 s/l., max
b. Vibration Damping Material—57 s/l., max

3.1.8 SPRAYABILITY—STABILITY—Emulsion materials shall not break under usual working pressures or conditions.

3.1.9 SPRAYABILITY—SPRAYBACK AND FOGGING—The average of three sprayback and three fogging tapes shall contain no more sprayback and fogging than the standard tapes held by the consumer.

3.1.10 CONSISTENCY (PENETROMETER VISCOSITY)—This shall be agreed between consumer and supplier.

3.1.11 SETTING—The material shall not settle nor separate within a reasonable period of transit and storage to such an extent as to cause difficulty in its use. For the purpose of this specification, the minimum time period shall be 30 days at room temperature.

3.1.12 TOXIC PROPERTIES—The material shall not contain dangerous amounts of toxic ingredients.

NOTE—Although this specification defines special properties necessary in a satisfactory product, it is not to be construed that compliance with this specification relieves the vendor of the responsibility of supplying material commercially suitable for the use specified.

4. Physical Properties—Methods of Test

4.1 Decay Rate (Vibration Damping Materials)—A 500 x 500 x 6 mm steel panel with a decay rate at room temperature of not more than 3 dB/s and a natural frequency of 145 to 165 Hz shall be sprayed with a uniform coating of the material to the test weight of 2.34 to 2.54 kg/m^2 dry weight. After air drying at room temperature for a minimum of 12 h, the panels containing vibration damping materials shall be baked 3 h at 135 °C ± 3 °C. Those containing underbody coatings shall be baked 24 h at 71 °C ±3 °C.

The decay rate shall be determined as follows:

Support the panel at one or more nodal points for the fundamental natural frequency (the nodal pattern is a square connecting the midpoints of the edges of the panel). Excite vibration of the panel at its fundamental frequency and measure the rate of decay for free vibration. This rate of decay expressed in decibels per second is the decay rate.

NOTE—The number of decibels corresponding to the ratio between any two vibration amplitudes is equal to 20 times the logarithm to the base ten of that ratio.

4.2 Solids—The solid content shall be determined by placing 3 to 5 g of the material in a weighted container (anointment can, approximately 50 mm in diameter) and drying 3 h at 105 °C ±3 °C, and reweighed after heating.

4.3 Cold Adhesion—Thoroughly clean three 305 x 305 x 1 mm cold-rolled steel test panels by immersing them in a solution of:

a. 30% by volume concentrated phosphoric acid
b. 30% by volume cellosolve
c. 40% by volume water

and washing thoroughly with a clean rag. Remove the panel from the solution and wipe dry with another clean rag. These panels must have a surface finish of not less than 0.89 nor more than 1.52 µm and each panel may be used only once for cold adhesion testing. Proceed according to the following schedule:

a. Coat a 230 x 230 mm area on each of three panels with a uniform coating to a test weight of 2.34 to 2.54 kg/m^2 dry weight of material.
b. Air dry at room temperature for a minimum of 12 h. A shorter drying time may be considered if the actual application time interval is shorter.
c. Bake
   1. Vibration damping material—3 h at 135 °C ±3 °C.
   2. Underbody coating—24 h at 71 °C ±3 °C.
d. Cool to room temperature.
e. Cool for 3 h at –23 °C ±1 °C.
f. Slam each panel in the cold adhesion test fixture, Figure 1, beginning at an angle of 10 degrees and increasing the angle of slam 10 degrees each successive slam until the 90 degree position is reached. The amount of material remaining on the panel is estimated between each slam.

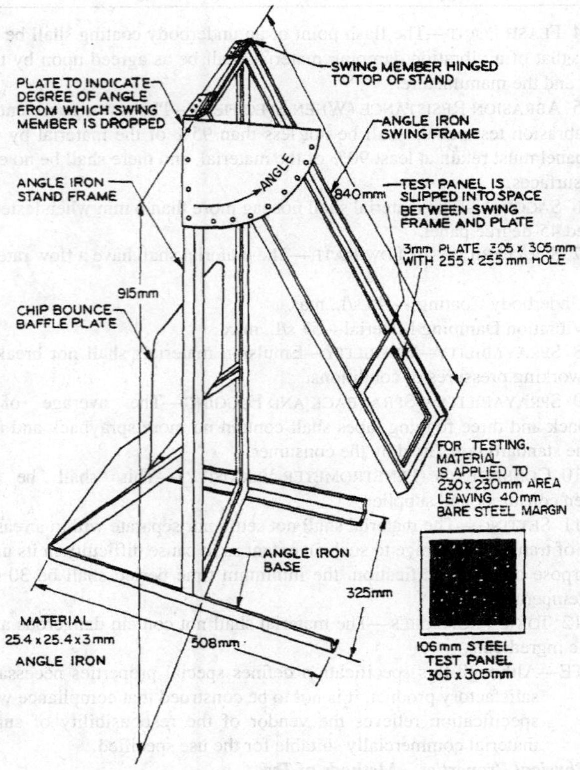

FIGURE 1—SLAMMING FIXTURE

4.4 Flash Point—The flash point shall be determined by the ASTM Pensky-Martens closed tester, ASTM D 93.

4.5 Abrasion Resistance—Clean three 305 x 125 x 1 mm cold-rolled steel panels as specified for the Cold Adhesion Test. Mask each panel to give an exposed area 100 x 305 mm and spray to the test weight of 2.34 to 2.54 kg/m^2 dry weight of material. Air dry at room temperature 12 h minimum and bake 24 h ± 15 min at 71 °C ±3 °C.

Insert each panel in the abrasion tester, Figure 2, and subject to ten cycles of abrasion with 45.3 kg (a total of 453 kg) of No. 780 iron shot at 550 kPa air pressure. Allow the panel to cool to room temperature between cycles. The amount of material retained on each panel shall be determined by weighing.

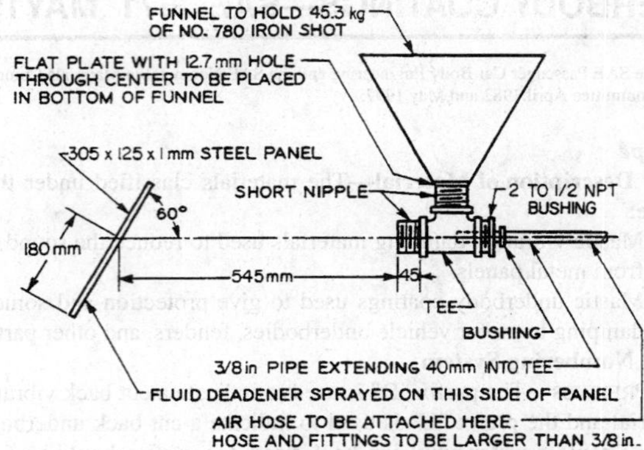

FIGURE 2—ABRASION TEST FIXTURE

4.6 Sagging—Thoroughly clean two 305 x 305 x 1 mm cold-rolled steel test panels as specified for the Cold Adhesion Test. Spray a 230 x 230 mm area on each panel with a uniform coating of the material to the test weight of 3.17 to 3.69 kg/m^2 dry weight. The panels shall then be supported at an inverted 45-degree angle, air dried for 15 min, and baked for 30 min at 135 °C ±3 °C. For undercoating materials, the test weight is to be 2.34 to 2.54 kg/m^2 dry weight, and the baking requirements are not necessary.

4.7 Sprayability—Flow Rate—The flow rate of a body damping material shall be determined by placing the material in a 7.6 L bottom outlet pressure tank with 4.6 m of 19 mm ID fluid hose with a suitable deadener spray gun and 72.7 mm round nozzle. The flow rate shall be measured with 415 kPa pressure on the tank and no atomizing pressure at a temperature of 24 °C ± 3 °C. The flow rate of an underbody coating shall be determined in a like manner except that a 6 mm round nozzle shall be used.

4.8 Sprayability—Sprayback and Fogging—This is a comparative method for determining the sprayback and fogging characteristics of a material. The particles which are blown back during the spraying are caught on the adhesive side of transparent cellulose tapes. The tapes can be mounted on a sheet of white paper for observation. The tapes with the adhesive side facing the panel are designated as sprayback tapes, and those facing away from the panel are fogging tapes.

A 305 x 305 mm test panel shall be mounted in the sprayback and fogging test booth as shown in Figure 3. With the spraygun and test tapes located as shown, the panel shall be sprayed with approximately 0.23 kg of material. The tapes should then be removed and attached to white cards.

4.9 Consistency—For inspection purposes, the consistency may be determined by ASTM D 217 penetration cone.

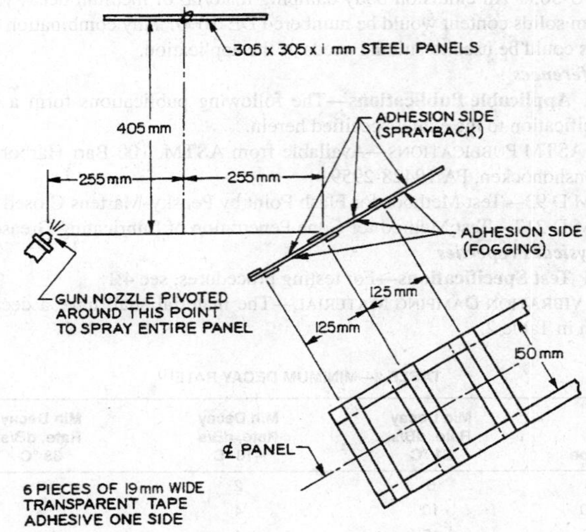

FIGURE 3—RELATIVE POSITIONS OF PANEL, SPRAYGUN, AND TAPES FOR SPRAYBACK AND FOGGING TESTS—PLAIN VIEW

TEST METHOD FOR MEASURING MASS (WEIGHT) OF ORGANIC TRIM MATERIALS—SAE J860 MAY2003

SAE Standard

Report of the SAE Nonmetallic Materials Committee approved June 1963. Completely revised by the SAE Textiles and Flexible Plastics Committee January 1985, January 1996 and revised May 2003. Rationale statement available.

1. Scope—This SAE Standard is used to determine the mass per unit area, in grams per square meter, of materials used for trimming automobile interiors.

2. References—There are no referenced publications specified herein.

3. Procedure

3.1 Condition all test specimens in a standard atmosphere of 23 °C ±2 °C and 50% ±5% relative humidity for 24 h.

3.2 Cut three specimens 100 x 100 mm (or as specified by the contractual parties) not closer than one tenth the width of the material from each selvage and from the center. For materials other than roll goods, cut three specimens from representative areas.

3.3 Measure the length and width of each specimen to the nearest 0.5 mm with a ruler or tape and calculate the area of each in square millimeters.

3.4 Weigh each of the three test specimens to the nearest milligram.

3.5 Calculate the mass per unit area in grams per square meter as shown in Equation 1:

$$\frac{A \times 10^6}{B} = g/\ m^2 \qquad \text{(Eq. 1)}$$

where:

A = Average mass in grams of the three test specimens

B = Average area in square millimeters of the three test specimens

TEST METHOD FOR DETERMINING DIMENSIONAL STABILITY OF AUTOMOTIVE TEXTILE MATERIALS —SAE J883 DEC2002

SAE Recommended Practice

Report of the SAE Nonmetallic Materials Committee approved April 1965 and revised February 1986. Reaffirmed by the SAE Textile/Flexible Plastics Committee January 1994. Revised by the SAE Textile and Flexible Plastics Committee December 2002. Rationale statement available.

1. Scope—This test method can be used to determine the dimensional stability of textile materials and vinyl-coated fabrics when subjected to conditions which cause changes in the moisture content of the materials.

2. References—There are no referenced publications specified herein.

3. Test Specimens—A test specimen 300 mm x 300 mm shall be cut from the material to be tested with one direction parallel to the machine direction (MD) and the other direction parallel to the across machine direction (AMD).

4. Conditioning—The test specimen shall be conditioned for a minimum of 24 h at 21 °C ± 2 °C and 50% ± 5% relative humidity.

5. Procedure

5.1 Mark off accurately a 250 mm x 250 mm square concentric with the square outline of the specimen. This can be done with indelible ink, indelible pencil, or other suitable method, on whichever side of the material is more markable. Also, mark an arrow to indicate the MD of the specimen.

5.2 Place the specimen face side up flat without wrinkles on a 4 mesh screen surface measuring a minimum of 330 mm x 330 mm. Position a similar screen over the specimen using spacers at the corners of the two screens, so that the top screen is not in contact with the top surface of the test specimen. To test more than one specimen at one time, use additional spacers and screens as required.

5.3 Immerse the specimen(s) and screens in a pan or tank of clean tap water containing 1 mL of alkylarylsulfonate synthetic detergent[1] per 21 mL of water at 21 °C for 1 h or as otherwise specified.

5.4 Remove the specimen(s) and screens from the water and allow to drip dry in an atmosphere having a temperature of 21 °C ± 2 °C and a relative humidity of 50% ± 5% for 30 min. If more than one specimen is being tested, separate the screens so that no specimen will drip on any other specimen.

5.5 Lay the specimen(s) flat on a table top. Measure the original 250 mm square with a scale calibrated in 1.0 mm. Make three measurements in both the MD and AMD directions. The measurements shall be made along the centerlines of the square and along lines parallel to and 50 mm in from each side.

5.6 Average the three measurements in each direction and substitute in Equations 1 and 2:

$$D_{MD_1} = \frac{MD_1 - 250}{250} \times 100 \quad \text{(Eq. 1)}$$

where:

D_{MD_1} = Machine Direction

MD_1 = Machine Direction measurement wet

$$D_{AMD_1} = \frac{AMD_1 - 250}{250} \times 100 \quad \text{(Eq. 2)}$$

where:

D_{AMD_1} = Across Machine Direction stability

AMD_1 = Across Machine Direction measurement wet

A plus result indicates expansion and a minus result indicates shrinkage.

5.7 Replace the test specimen(s) on the screens and place the specimen(s) and screens in an air-circulating oven maintained at 80 °C ± 2 °C for 24 h.

5.8 Remove the specimen and screen from the oven and allow to cool in the standard atmosphere described in 5.4 for 10 min. After cooling, place the specimen on a flat table top and remeasure as described in 5.5.

5.9 Average the three measurements in each direction and substitute in Equations 3 and 4:

$$D_{MD_2} = \frac{MD_2 - 250}{250} \times 100 \quad \text{(Eq. 3)}$$

where:

D_{MD_2} = Machine Direction stability

MD_2 = Machine Direction measurement after drying

$$D_{AMD_2} = \frac{AMD_2 - 250}{250} \times 100 \quad \text{(Eq. 4)}$$

where:

D_{AMD_2} = Across Machine Direction stability

AMD_2 = Across Machine Direction measurement after drying

A plus result indicates expansion and a minus result indicates shrinkage.

1. Alkylarylsulfonate type of synthetic detergent is available under various trade names from manufacturers of detergents.

(R) METHOD OF TESTING RESISTANCE TO CROCKING OF ORGANIC TRIM MATERIALS—SAE J861 DEC2003 SAE Standard

Report of the SAE Nonmetallic Materials Committee approved June 1963. Reaffirmed with editorial change January 1971. Editorial change May 1978. Reaffirmed by the SAE Textile/Flexible Plastics Committee January 1994 and completely revised December 2003. Rationale statement available.

1. Scope

This test can be used to determine the resistance to crocking (color rub-off) of organic trim materials such as fabrics, vinyl coated fabrics, leather, coated fiberboard and carpet.

This method is similar to AATCC Method 8 –Colorfastness to Crocking.

2. References

2.1 Applicable Publications

The following publications form a part of this specification to the extent specified herein. Unless otherwise indicated, the latest issue of SAE publications shall apply.

2.1.1 SAE PUBLICATIONS

Available from SAE, 400 Commonwealth Drive, Warrendale, PA 15096-0001.

SAE J361—Visual Color Match to Master Specimen for Fabrics

SAE J1767—Instrumental Color Difference Measurement for Colorfastness of Automotive Interior Trim Materials

2.1.2 AATCC PUBLICATIONS

Available from American Associations of Textile Chemist and Colorists, 1 Davis Drive, PO Box 12215, Research Triangle Park, NC 27709-2215, 919-549-8141, Fax 919-549-8933.

AATCC Method 8—Colorfastness to Crocking

AATCC Method 110—Whiteness of Textiles

AATCC Chromatic Transfer Scale, AATCC Gray Scale to Staining, and Blotting Paper

2.2 Related Publications

The following publications are provided for information purposes only and are not a required part of this document.

2.2.1 ASTM PUBLICATIONS

Available from ASTM, 100 Barr Harbor Drive, West Conshohocken, PA 19428-2959.

ASTM D 2645—Standard Tolerances of Yarns Spun on the Cotton or Worsted System

2.2.2 TESTFABRICS INC.

Available from Testfabric, Inc., 415 Delaware Avenue, P.O. Box 26, West Pittston, PA 18643, 570-603-0432, Fax: 570-603-0433.

2.2.3 SDL ATLAS, (TEXTILE INNOVATORS CORPORATION)

Available from SDL Atlas, 1813A Associates Lane, Charlotte, NC, 28217, 704-329-0911

3. Materials and Equipment

3.1 AATCC Crockmeter

A device which has a 16 mm ± 1 mm diameter rubbing peg, reciprocating in a straight line rubbing motion, to and fro along a 104 mm ± 3 mm track, with a downward force of 9 N ± 0.9 N.

3.2 Crockmeter Test Cloth

Plain weave 80x84 greige (32 ends/cm ± 3 ends/cm and 33 picks/cm ± 3 picks/cm.) 15 Tex ± 4% yarn size, 5.9 turns/cm, Z ± 10% twist, combed cotton, desized, bleached, without finish, and cut into nominal 50 X 50 mm squares. Cloth should have a whiteness rating of 80 or above per AATCC Method 110.

3.3 AATCC Textile Blotting Paper

3.4 AATCC Chromatic Transfer Scale

3.5 AATCC Gray Scale to Staining

3.6 Distilled Water

pH of 6.5 to 7.5

3.7 Transparent Adhesive Tape

(optional)

4. Test Specimen

4.1 A minimum of two specimens are required, one for a dry crock test and one for a wet crock test. Specimen shall be cut 51 X 127 mm with the long dimension 45° nominal, to the machine or cross machine (warp and fill) direction. Additional specimens may be used when higher precision is needed.

4.2 In addition, materials with directional patterns (color, texture, nap) should be cut in machine, cross-machine and 45°, two specimens (one dry and one wet) in each direction.

4.3 Specimen should be as flat as possible.

5. Conditioning

5.1 Prior to testing, condition the test specimens and the crock squares for at least 4 h in an atmosphere of 21 °C ± 2 °C and 50%R.H. ± 5% R.H. by laying each test specimen or crock square separately on a screen or perforated shelf of a conditioning rack.

5.2 Alternate parameters for conditioning may be specified such as 21 °C ± 2 °C and 65% R.H. ± 5% R.H. or as agreed upon by contractual parties. Results may differ from items conditioned in parameters of 5.1 above.

6. Procedures

6.1 Dry Crock Test

6.1.1 Place the test specimen with the long dimension in the direction of the rubbing on the base of the Crockmeter and so that it is flat and uniformly in contact with the abrasive cloth mount.

6.1.2 Fasten a dry crock cloth over the end of the peg with the weave parallel to the direction of the rubbing. Use the spiral wire clip to hold the test square in place.

6.1.3 Lower the peg into contact with the test specimen and turn the crank at a rate of one turn per second so that the peg moves 10 cycles, (10 times to and 10 times fro) on the test specimen. If the crockmeter is motorized, set the counter for 10 cycles and turn on the machine making sure that the peg is positioned to give a complete 10 cycles. Contracting parties may specify other test duration's.

6.1.4 Remove the crock square from the peg and condition per Section 5. In the case of napped, brushed, sanded or flocked material with loose fibers that might interfere with the rating, remove extraneous material by pressing lightly on the crock square with the sticky side of transparent adhesive tape before evaluating.

6.2 Wet Crock Test

6.2.1 Establish a technique for preparing wet crock cloth squares by weighing a preconditioned square, then thoroughly wet out in distilled water. Prepare one square at a time.

6.2.2 Bring wet pickup to 65% ± 5% (or as agreed upon by contractual agreement) by squeezing wet testing square between blotting paper.

6.2.3 Using the prepared wet testing square, continue as directed in 6.1.1 through 6.1.3.

6.2.4 Air dry the crock cloth square, then condition per Section 5 before evaluating. In the case of napped, brushed, sanded or flocked material with loose fibers that might interfere with rating, remove the extraneous material by pressing lightly on the crock square with the sticky side of transparent adhesive tape before evaluating.

7. Evaluation

7.1 Back each test square with three layers of white crocking cloth during the evaluating process.

7.2 Assess visually or instrumentally the color transfer from the specimen to the crock square.

7.2.1 For visually assessing the color transfer, use suitable illumination (SAE J361, Section 4) and either AATCC Gray Scale to Staining or AATCC Chromatic Transfer Scale.

7.2.2 For instrumentally assessing the color transfer, SAE J1767 should be used as a guide. The instrument port size must be less than 15 mm.

7.2.3 Halo effect color change shall not be measured or reported.

8. Report

Should include the following:

8.1 Test description, whether dry and/or wet crocking test.

8.2 Evaluation results per Section 7.

8.3 Number of cycles.

8.4 Conditioning of specimen and crock cloth.

8.5 Material description.

8.6 Equipment used - Instrument, make and model, port size, and viewing geometry if instrumental color difference is used for rating.

9. Notes

Verification of the operation of the test and the apparatus should be made routinely and the results kept in a log. Use an in-house or established crocking calibration specimen and conduct three dry tests.

(R) TEST METHOD FOR MEASURING THICKNESS OF AUTOMOTIVE TEXTILES AND PLASTICS —SAE J882 MAY2002

SAE Recommended Practice

Report of the SAE Nonmetallic Materials Committee approved April 1965, completely revised February 1985. Revised by the SAE Textiles and Flexible Plastics Committee August 1994 and May 2002. Rationale statement available.

1. Scope—This test is designed to measure the thickness of textiles, plastics, and similar materials.

2. References—There are no referenced publications specified herein.

3. Apparatus Required

3.1 A dead weight type of dial micrometer capable of accurately measuring to 0.025 mm. The pressure foot shall have a diameter and mass, including connecting parts, of:

a. 76.2 mm ± 0.8 mm and 340 g ± 3 g for testing tufted floor coverings
b. 28.7 mm ± 0.3 mm and 283 g ± 3 g for testing felts and other nonwovens
c. 6.35 mm ± 0.06 mm and 85 g ± 0.8 g for testing bodycloths, seatbelt webbing, unsupported vinyl films, and coated fabrics
d. Or as agreed between contractual parties.

4. Test Specimens—Cut three test specimens approximately 100 x 100 mm from the center and the two opposite sides of the roll. Unless otherwise specified, specimens shall be taken no nearer the selvage edge than one-tenth of the width of the material, nor nearer than 300 mm from either end of the roll. If the material is not supplied on rolls, the specimen shall be taken from the most representative areas.

5. Procedure

a. Condition the specimens at 21 °C ± 2 °C and 50% ± 5% relative humidity for 24 h.
b. Raise the pressure foot of the thickness gauge.
c. Place the specimen on the base.
d. Gently lower the pressure foot.
e. After 10 s read the thickness of the specimen.
f. Repeat for two additional specimens.
g. Report the average thickness of three specimens.
h. When measuring the thickness of three dimensional material the thickness shall be determined by calculating the average of the three readings taken on the high points of the material

TEST METHOD FOR DETERMINING COLD CRACKING OF FLEXIBLE PLASTIC MATERIALS—SAE J323 JUL1998

SAE Recommended Practice

Report of the SAE Nonmetallic Materials Committee approved August 1968. Editorial change May 1978. Completely revised by the SAE Textiles and Flexible Plastics Committee January 1996 and revised July 1998. Rationale statement available.

*1. **Scope***—This SAE Recommended Practice is applicable for determining the cold characteristics of vinyl-coated fabrics and other automotive plastic materials, as applicable. It consists of three different methods for determining low-temperature properties of materials depending on type of material and end use.

*2. **References***—There are no referenced publications specified herein.

*3. **Method A, Mandrel Test***

3.1 Apparatus and Materials

3.1.1 MANDREL—Steel mandrel 6.35 mm in diameter and 152 mm long attached to a suitable stand. Other diameters may be specified depending on the thickness and rigidity of the material to be tested.

3.1.2 OVEN—Air-circulating oven capable of maintaining a temperature of 82 °C ±2 °C.

3.1.3 COLD BOX—A cold box capable of maintaining a temperature of −34 °C and large enough to permit bending the test specimen while it remains in the box.

3.1.4 GLOVES—Heavy cloth gloves to prevent heat transfer when handling specimens.

3.2 Procedure—Cut 50 x 200 mm specimens in the machine and across machine direction and condition in the oven at 82 °C for 24 h or as specified. (The dimensions of the specimen may vary for extruded or molded parts.) Remove specimens from the oven and condition at room temperature to maintain equilibrium. Place specimens, gloves, and mandrel with stand in the cold box at −34 °C for 4 h or as specified. Put on gloves and grasp each end of the sample and bend, finish side out, 3.1 radians around the mandrel in approximately 0.5 s with a uniform motion. Remove specimens from cold box and examine visually for evidence of cracks.

*4. **Method B, Impact Test***

4.1 Apparatus and Materials

4.1.1 IMPACT TESTER—Impact tester capable of applying a 10.8 J impact with a spherical ball head having a radius of 23.81 mm. (See Figure 1.)

4.1.2 BASE—A 102 x 102 x 19 mm thick wood base with an 89 x 89 mm square marked off in the center for stapling specimen and a 76 x 76 mm square marked off for positioning urethane foam pad.[1]

4.1.3 OVEN—Air-circulating oven capable of maintaining a temperature of 82 °C ±2 °C.

4.2 Procedure—Cut a 100 x 100 mm specimen and age in the oven at 82 °C for 7 days (or as specified). Place a 75 x 75 x 19 mm thick urethane pad in the center of the wood base and attach the aged specimen to the base by stapling 6 mm from the edge of the specimen as indicated in Figure 2 (staples should be 7.9 mm minimum length). Place the specimen in the cold chamber at −29 °C for a minimum of 12 h (or as specified by the contractual parties). While still at −29 °C, the center of the test material shall be impacted with a force of 10.8 J. The height of the impactor shall be as specified between the user and supplier. Remove the specimen from the cold box and examine for cracks.

*5. **Method C, Dynamic Flex Test***

5.1 Apparatus

5.1.1 COLD BOX—A cold box capable of maintaining a temperature of −29 °C and large enough to hold flexing equipment.

5.1.2 OVEN—Air-circulating oven capable of maintaining a temperature of 82 °C ±2 °C.

5.1.3 FLEXING EQUIPMENT—Dynamic flex equipment with reciprocating motion (see Figure 3).

5.2 Procedure—Cut four specimens 75 x 50 mm, two specimens having the long dimension in the warp direction and the remaining two having the long dimension in the filling direction. Condition two specimens (warp and filling directions) for 7 days at 82 °C ±2 °C in an air-circulating oven followed by 4 h at −29 °C. Condition the remaining two specimens at −29 °C for 4 h. Clamp the two ends of the unaged specimens in the cold flex apparatus with the vinyl side facing out. Flex at −29 °C for 700 cycles at 90 cycles/min. Remove and examine for cracks. Flex the two aged specimens for 600 cycles. Remove and examine for cracks.

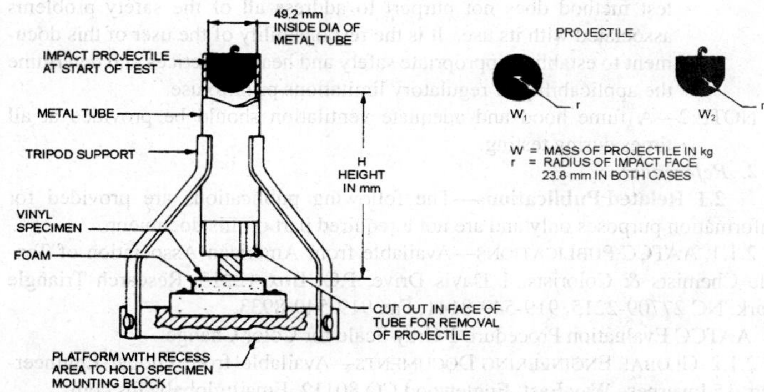

NOTE— Both H and W may be varied as long as HW = 10.8 J and H is not less than 3.048 mm. Dimension r of Projectile must be 23.8 mm and is not variable.

FIGURE 1—IMPACT APPARATUS

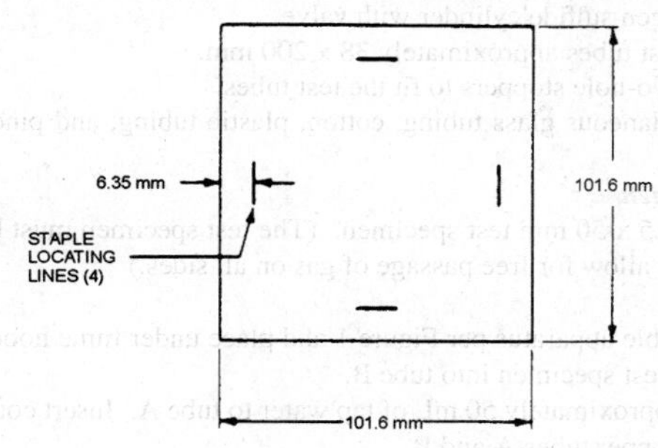

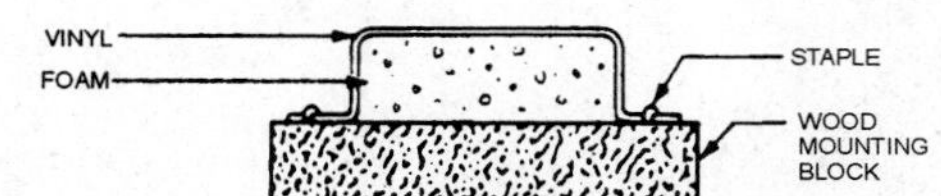

FIGURE 2—SPECIMEN AND SPECIMEN ON BASE

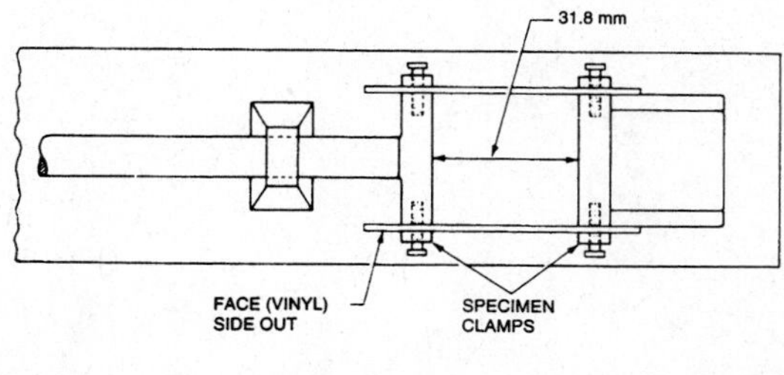

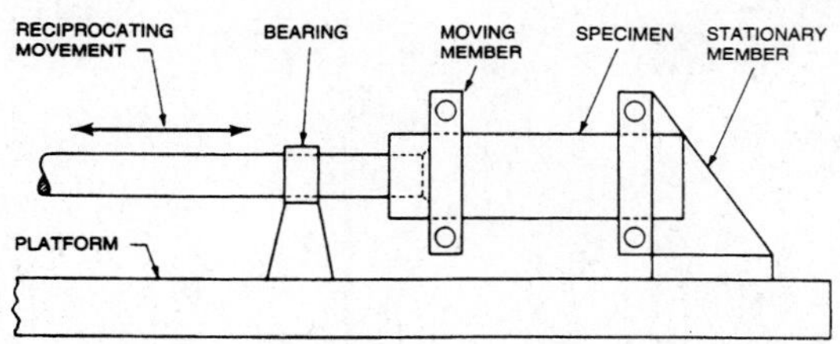

FIGURE 3—BASIC DETAILS OF COLD FOLD TEST APPARATUS

1. Unless otherwise specified, the foam base shall be either a urethane foam or a latex foam material.
The urethane material shall have the following load deflection characteristics: a load deflection at 25% of RT shall be 3.0 to 4.1 kPa and a load deflection of 8 to 18% at −29 °C when tested with a load of 2.59 kPa ±0.07 kPa.
The latex material shall have the following load deflection characteristics: a load of 25% at RT shall be 2.482 to 3.103 kPa and a deflection of 37 to 47% at −29 °C when tested with a load of 2.59 kPa ±0.07 kPa.
The specimen used for checking the −29 °C cold deflection property shall be 100 x 100 mm and preconditioned for a minimum of 12 h at −29 °C prior to testing.

NOTE— The wood and urethane foam base described previously was established primarily for vinyl-coated fabrics. Other plastic materials may require modifications in the base depending on the flexibility of the material to be tested.

NONMETALLIC TRIM MATERIALS—TEST METHOD FOR DETERMINING THE STAINING RESISTANCE TO HYDROGEN SULFIDE GAS—SAE J322 DEC2003 SAE Recommended Practice

Report of the SAE Nonmetallic Materials Committee approved December 1967 and reaffirmed December 1985. Completely revised by the SAE Textiles and Flexible Plastics Committee January 1996 and revised December 2003. Rationale statement available.

1. Scope—This SAE Recommended Practice is designed to reveal discoloration which may occur when nonmetallic materials used for trimming automobiles are exposed for a limited time to an atmosphere containing hydrogen sulfide.

NOTE 1—CAUTION-Hydrogen sulfide gas is extremely hazardous. Use of this substance may be fatal if proper precautions are not taken. This test method does not purport to address all of the safety problems associated with its use. It is the responsibility of the user of this document to establish appropriate safety and health practices and determine the applicability of regulatory limitations prior to use.

NOTE 2—A fume hood and adequate ventilation should be provided at all times during testing.

2. References

2.1 Related Publications—The following publications are provided for information purposes only and are not a required part of this document.

2.1.1 AATCC PUBLICATIONS—Available from American Association of Textile Chemists & Colorists, 1 Davis Drive, P.O. Box 12215, Research Triangle Park, NC 27709-2215, 919-549-8141, Fax 919-549-8933.

AATCC Evaluation Procedure 1 Gray Scale for Color Change

2.1.2 GLOBAL ENGINEERING DOCUMENTS—Available from Global Engineering, 15 Inverness Way East, Englewood CO 80112, Email:global@ihs.com.

SO 105-A02—Textiles–Tests for Colour Fastness–Part A02: Grey Scale for Assessing Change in Colour

3. Materials and Equipment Required

3.1 Hydrogen sulfide cylinder with valve.

3.2 Two test tubes approximately 38 x 200 mm.

3.3 Two two-hole stoppers to fit the test tubes.

3.4 Miscellaneous glass tubing, cotton, plastic tubing, and pinch clamp as in Figure 1.

4. Test Specimen

4.1 Cut a 25 x 50 mm test specimen. (The test specimen must be of such a size and shape to allow for free passage of gas on all sides.)

5. Procedure

5.1 Assemble apparatus per Figure 1 and place under fume hood.

5.2 Insert test specimen into tube B.

5.3 Add approximately 50 mL of tap water to tube A. Insert cotton packing per Figure 1. Stopper tubes A and B.

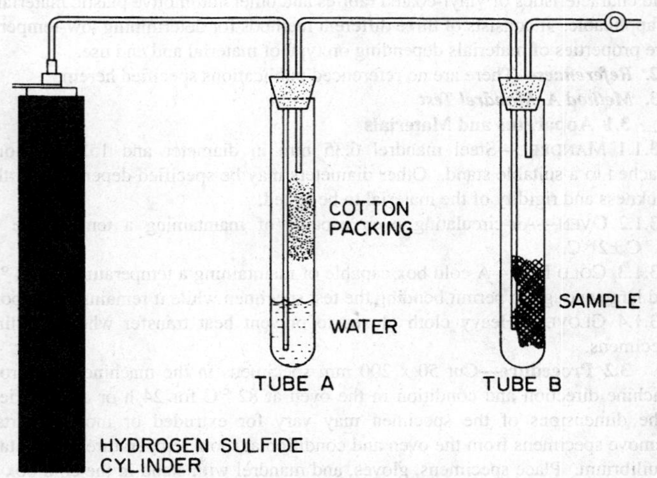

FIGURE 1—STAINING TEST DIAGRAM

5.4 Remove pinch clamp from exhaust hose of tube B and cautiously open the valve on the hydrogen sulfide cylinder. Adjust the valve so hydrogen sulfide gas bubbles through the system at a uniform and controlled rate, with a steady flow of bubbles at 5 bubbles/second.

5.5 Allow the system to purge for 1.5 min, then close the valve and immediately replace the pinch clamp on the exhaust hose of tube B.

5.6 Allow the system to remain in the closed position for an additional 2 min.

5.7 Remove the stopper of tube B and take out the test specimen.

5.8 Compare the test specimen with an unexposed specimen of the same material and report any discoloration which has occurred using as a reference staining grey scale. (Grey Scale for Color Change, AATTC Evaluation Procedure 1, similar to ISO 105-A02.)

ACCELERATED EXPOSURE OF AUTOMOTIVE INTERIOR TRIM MATERIALS USING AN OUTDOOR UNDER GLASS VARIABLE ANGLE CONTROLLED TEMPERATURE APPARATUS—SAE J2229 FEB1993

SAE Standard

Report of the SAE Textiles and Flexible Plastics Committee approved February 1993.

Foreword—This Document has not changed other than to put it into the new SAE Technical Standards Board Format.

1. Scope

1.1 This SAE Standard specifies the operating procedures for the exposure of automotive interior trim materials in an outdoor behind glass apparatus in which the temperature is controlled for part of the day.

1.2 Specimen preparation, test durations, and performance evaluation procedures are covered in material specifications of the different automotive manufacturers.

2. References

2.1 Applicable Publications—The following publications form a part of this specification to the extent specified herein. The latest issue of SAE publications shall apply.

2.1.1 SAE PUBLICATION—Available from SAE, 400 Commonwealth Drive, Warrendale, PA 15096-0001.

SAE J1545—Instrumental Color Difference Measurement for Exterior Finishes, Textiles, and Colored Trim

2.1.2 AATCC PUBLICATION—Available from AATCC, P.O. Box 12215, Research Triangle Park, NC 27709.

AATCC Evaluation Procedure 1 (1987)—Gray Scale for Color Change

2.1.3 ASTM PUBLICATION—Available from ASTM, 100 Barr Harbor Drive, West Conshohocken, PA 19428-2959.

ASTM E 824—Standard Method for Transfer of Calibration from Reference to Field Pyranometers

3. Terminology

3.1 Black Panel Thermometer, n—A temperature measuring device, the sensing unit of which is a stainless steel panel coated with black material designed to absorb most of the radiant energy encountered in fade/weathering testing.

NOTE—This device provides an estimation of the maximum temperature a specimen may attain during exposure to natural or artificial light.

3.2 Blue Wool Lightfastness Standard, n—One of a group of dyed fabrics which are sensitive to the amount of light, heat, and moisture to which the blue wool material is exposed. Because of their unstable nature, these materials are also sensitive to the heat and moisture conditions which exist before exposure testing, after exposure testing, and prior to measurement.

3.3 Center Wavelength, n—The specified wavelength for bandpass filters; the wavelength midway between the half power points, e.g., 340 nm ±2 nm.

3.4 Color Change, n—As used in fade/weathering testing, a change in color of any kind (whether a change in hue, saturation, or lightness).

3.5 Half Power Bandpass, n—The interval between wavelengths at which transmittance is 50% of peak. (It should not exceed 20 nm for a narrow bandpass filter.)

3.6 Irradiance Total, n—The rate at which energy is incident on a surface per unit area (W/m^2).

3.7 Irradiance, Ultraviolet, n—Irradiance integrated over wavelengths 295 to 385 nm ($W/m^2/nm$).

3.8 Irradiance, Center Wavelength, n—Irradiance integrated at wavelength 340 nm ±2 nm ($W/m^2/nm$).

3.9 Irradiation, n—See radiant exposure.

3.10 Radiant Exposure, n—The accumulated amount of irradiance received during a specified time period per unit area (J/m^2). Since irradiance can be measured using a variety of different optical sensors, it is generally recommended that the type of radiant exposure be specified (e.g., radiant exposure from 295 to 385 nm, or radiant exposure at 340 nm ±2 nm).

3.11 Reference Fabric, n—One or more blue wool lightfastness standards selected for exposure as a check on the test apparatus and operating conditions.

3.12 Reference Plastic, n—A clear polystyrene plastic standard selected for exposure as a check on a test apparatus and operating conditions.

NOTE—It has not been verified that these reference materials can be used as a check on a test cabinet or operating conditions for outdoor exposure tests due to seasonal variations in ultraviolet spectral distribution, temperature, relative humidity, and time of wetness during the uncontrolled portion of the test.

3.13 Sample, Laboratory, n—A portion of material taken to represent the lot sample, the original material, or production lot, and is used in the laboratory as a source of test specimens.

3.14 Specimen, n—A specific portion of a material, laboratory sample, or production lot, upon which a test is performed or which is selected for that purpose.

4. Significance and Use

4.1 This method is designed to simulate extreme environmental conditions encountered inside a vehicle due to sunlight, heat, and humidity for the purpose of predicting the performance of automotive interior trim materials.

4.2 Variations in results may be expected when operating conditions are varied within the accepted limits of this method, or tests are conducted in different geographical locations. Therefore, no reference shall be made to results from the use of this method unless accompanied by a report detailing the specific operating conditions and location in compliance with Section 9, Exposure Report.

5. Apparatus

5.1 The mounting stand (Figure 1) shall have a means for variable orientation of the cabinet. Orientation shall be facing the Equator at a seasonally-adjusted tilt angle as follows in Table 1:

TABLE 1—ORIENTATION OF SEASONALLY ADJUSTED CABINET (ASTM E 782)

Period	Tilt Angle
Mar. 1 - 31	station latitude
Apr. 1 - Aug. 31	latitude - 20 degrees
Sep. 1 - 30	station latitude
Oct. 1 - Feb. 28	latitude + 20 degrees

5.2 The test cabinet (Figure 1)[1] shall be constructed of corrosion-resistant metal and contain a specimen rack, air circulation fan(s), and a hinged glass cover.

5.3 The glass cover (Figure 1) shall be a single piece of 3 mm (1/8 in) thick clear tempered safety glass, such as Herculite® [2], or equivalent.

5.4 The specimen rack shall be designed and positioned so that the test specimens may be mounted unbacked with the plane of the test surface parallel to, and not less than 75 mm (3 in) below the glass.

5.5 The cabinet shall be equipped with a sensor, heater(s), fan(s), and a control system capable of maintaining a specified black panel temperature to within ± 5 °C at any location within the specimen exposure area during the hours that the control system is in operation. An example of such a system is given in Figure 1.

5.6 An ultraviolet radiometer shall be used to measure irradiance, and connected to an integrator for computing ultraviolet radiant exposure. The ultraviolet radiometer shall be mounted behind glass, such as Herculite®[2], or equivalent, in a ventilated enclosure to avoid overheating the instrument. The enclosure containing the radiometer shall maintain the same orientation as the test cabinet. Two different types of radiometers may be used.

5.6.1 A wide-band ultraviolet radiometer[3], an instrument which measures irradiance at wavelengths 295 to 385 nm.

5.6.2 A narrow-band ultraviolet radiometer[4], an instrument which measures irradiance at 340 nm ±2 nm.

6. Apparatus Set-Up

6.1 To enhance the possibility of repeatability of tests, maintain and calibrate the apparatus as described in Appendices A and B. Appendix A contains maintenance and calibration instructions. Appendix B describes the use of reference materials which may assist in determining the performance of the apparatus, and interpreting exposure results when compared to previous tests.

1. Available from William Harrison Company, 4595 E. 10th Court, Hialeah, FL 33013, or equivalent.
2. Available from PPG Industries.
3. Available as model TUVR from Eppley Laboratories, 12 Sheffield Avenue, Newport, RI 02840, or equivalent.
4. Available as model LM3A from Atlas Electric Devices Company, 4114 North Ravenswood Avenue, Chicago, IL 60613, or model NBUVR-340 available from DSET Laboratories, Inc., 45601 N. 47th Avenue, Phoenix, AZ 85027, or equivalent.

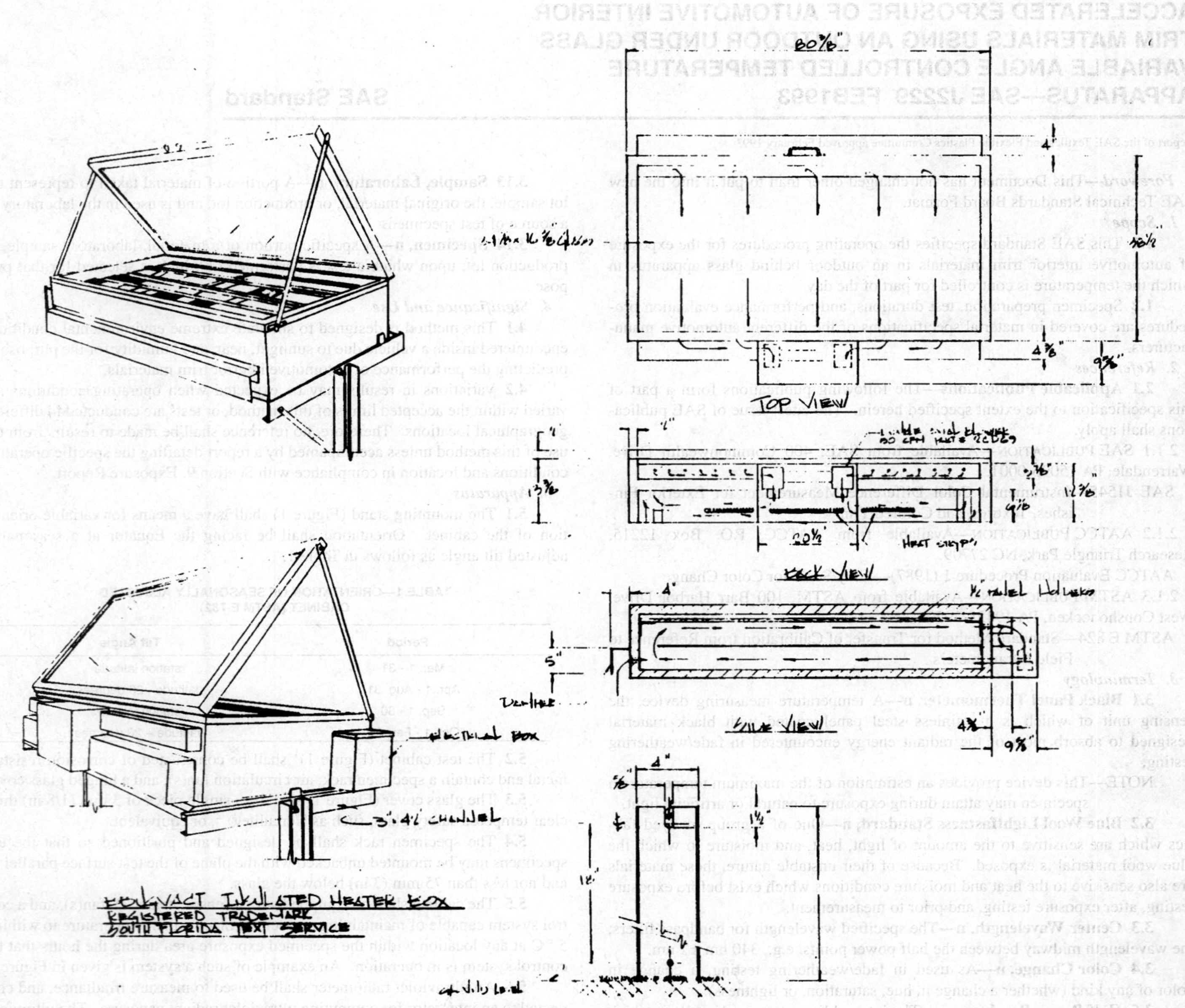

FIGURE 1—EXPOSURE APPARATUS

7. Test Specimens

7.1 Unless otherwise specified, test specimens shall be 75 x 150 mm (3 x 6 in), with a maximum thickness of 25 mm (1 in). For specimens over 25 mm (1 in) thick, formed or configured specimens, and large components, specific instructions must be obtained from the responsible material engineer of the different automotive manufacturers or automotive suppliers.

7.2 Replicate specimens are desirable to provide a record of the changes when they are exposed for different radiant exposure levels. An unexposed specimen should be saved for visual comparison with the exposed specimen.

8. Test Procedure

8.1 Mount test specimens to the specimen rack. Mask the top and bottom area of the specimen in contact with the mounting strips with white cardboard[5]. To minimize variations in results caused by nonuniform exposure conditions, the specimen exposure area is restricted to the dimensions provided in Figure 2 or 3.

8.2 Ensure the timer and temperature set points are correct for the method specified:

a. Timer—0900 to 1500 control system on 1500 to 0900 control system off
b. Temperature—89 °C ±5 °C black panel

Operate continuously, except for performing maintenance and calibration as specified in Appendix A, inspecting specimens, removing specimens, or starting new tests.

8.3 Use one of the following methods for timing the exposure:

8.3.1 Expose specimens for the specified radiant exposure measured in MJ/m^2 total ultraviolet, 295 to 385 nm.

8.3.2 Expose specimens for the specified radiant exposure measured in $kJ/m^2/nm$ at 340 nm ±2 nm.

9. Evaluating and Reporting Degree of Fade

9.1 The degree of fade shall be evaluated and reported as specified between the contractual parties. Instrumental values are recommended:

9.1.1 INSTRUMENTAL MEASUREMENT

9.1.1.1 Color difference values in CIELAB units are obtained by instrumentally measuring the specimen before and after a specified amount of radiant exposure. The instrument used for specimen measurement shall conform to that specified in Appendix B.

5. Franklin, Grain long-felt side up, 110/500 white index made by Union Camp or 9016 White Bristol Card Stock are suitable for this purpose. Franklin white index is usually available from local office supply or art stores, and is also available from Dilliard Paper Company. Any equivalent may be used.

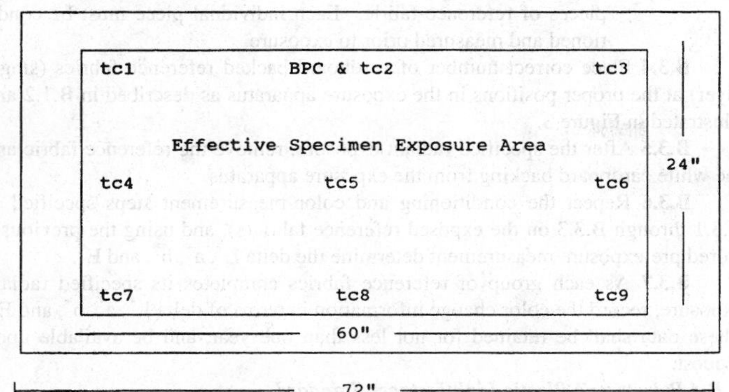

FIGURE 2—EFFECTIVE SPECIMEN EXPOSURE AREA THERMOCOUPLE LOCATIONS FOR TEMPERATURE UNIFORMITY CHECK

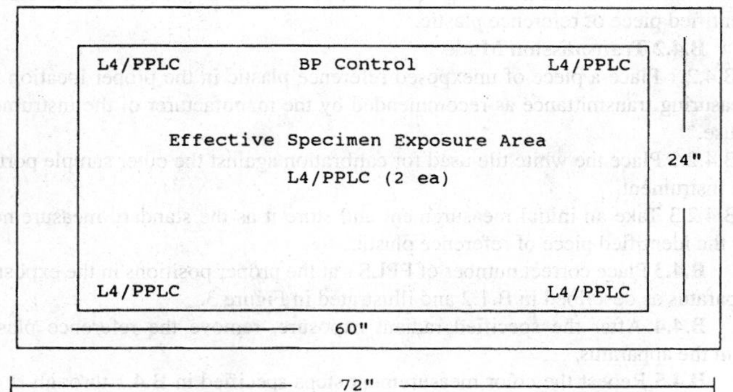

FIGURE 3—EFFECTIVE SPECIMEN EXPOSURE AREA REFERENCE MATERIALS LOCATIONS

9.1.2 VISUAL ASSESSMENT

9.1.2.1 Rating Method A—Assign colorfastness ratings using the AATCC Gray Scale for Color Change in accordance with AATCC Evaluation Procedure 1 (1987).

9.1.2.2 Rating Method B—Using the viewing conditions specified in AATCC Evaluation Procedure 1 (1987), quantify the color change using the following terminology:

a. NONE—No change in hue, lightness, or saturation (chroma).
b. SLIGHT—A change in lightness and/or saturation (chroma) which can be determined only upon close examination but no change in hue.
c. NOTICEABLE—A change in lightness and/or saturation (chroma) which can easily be seen and/or a change in hue.
d. SEVERE—An extreme change in lightness, saturation (chroma), and/or hue.

10. Exposure Report

10.1 The final report shall contain the following:

10.1.1 Laboratory and location

10.1.2 Type and serial number of exposure apparatus

10.1.3 Test method

10.1.4 Specimen identification

10.1.5 Total radiant exposure (MJ/m^2/295 to 385 nm) or (kJ/m^2·nm at 340 nm).

10.1.6 Date specimen exposure was initiated

10.1.7 Date specimen exposure was completed

10.1.8 Special conditions which may have existed during a specific test period, such as control failure, unusual atmospheric conditions, etc.

11. Precision and Bias

11.1 Neither repeatability (precision of multiple determinations at one site) nor reproducibility (precision of multiple determinations at different sites) have been established. Therefore, it is inappropriate to compare results from different sites or results obtained at different times at the same site. It is strongly recommended that a control material having a known history be exposed simultaneously with test specimens if it is desirable to compare results obtained at different times and/or sites.

APPENDIX A

A.1 Maintenance

A.1.1 Specimen Mounting—Check specimens daily to ensure they are properly mounted.

A.1.2 Glass Cover—The glass cover shall be inspected weekly, and both surfaces shall be cleaned whenever there is visual evidence of dirt accumulation or other undesirable deposits.

A.1.3 Ultraviolet Radiometer—The glass cover and the diffusing lens shall be cleaned daily with deionized water. The desiccant visible through the sight glass shall be replaced whenever the color changes from dark blue to light pink.

A.1.4 LM3A Light Monitors—The diffusing lens shall be cleaned daily with deionized water.

A.1.5 Thermocouples—Check readouts monthly during temperature uniformity check to ensure thermocouples are operating properly.

A.1.6 Black Panel Thermometer—Check readouts daily to ensure black panel thermometers are operating properly. Polish monthly using a good quality automotive polish. Replace the black panel when surface luster can no longer be maintained, or when bare metal can be seen.

A.1.7 Heating System—Check temperature readouts daily to ensure proper heating. Check monthly for integrity of electric wiring, loose connections, and all other safety features.

A.1.8 Air Circulation System—Check temperature readouts daily to ensure proper air circulation. Check monthly for integrity of electric wiring, loose connections, and all other safety features.

A.1.9 Temperature Uniformity—Check one 24-h day, at 5 min intervals, monthly for distribution around set point temperature using a minimum of nine thermocouple locations. Thermocouples are attached to the specimen rack (see Figure 2).

A.2 Calibration

A.2.1 Ultraviolet Radiometer—Perform a field transfer calibration every 3 months in accordance with ASTM E 824. Return to the manufacturer no less than annually for absolute calibration.

A.2.2 LM3A Light Monitors—Check every 3 months with a reference unit to verify data. Return to the manufacturer no less than annually for absolute calibration.

A.2.3 Black Panel—Check every 6 months using a hot/cold bath with a NIST traceable thermometer.

A.2.4 Thermocouples—Check every 6 months using a hot/cold bath with a NIST traceable thermometer.

A.2.5 Tilt Angle Verification—Verification of the tilt angle of the exposure cabinet shall be performed at each variable angle change.

APPENDIX B

It has not been verified that these reference materials can be used as a check on a test cabinet or operating conditions for outdoor exposure tests due to seasonal variations in ultraviolet, temperature, relative humidity, and time of wetness during the uncontrolled portion of the test.

B.1 Scope

B.1.1 This appendix describes the procedure for using an AATCC Blue Wool Lightfastness Standard (L-4)[6] and a Polystyrene Plastic Lightfastness Standard (PPLS)[7] as reference materials for the purpose of determining whether the exposure cabinet is operating within a desired range.

B.1.2 Color difference values in CIELAB ΔE units for the L-4 and CIELAB Δb units for the PPLS are obtained by measuring the reference materials before and after a specified radiant exposure.

6. AATCC L-4 Blue Wool Lightfastness Standards may be obtained from AATCC, P.O. Box 12215, Research Triangle Park, NC 27709.
7. PPLS's may be obtained from Testfabrics, Inc., 200 Blackford Avenue, Middlesex, NJ 08846.

B.1.3 The L-4 and PPLS shall be exposed for 20.0 MJ/m^2/295 to 385 nm, or 112.8 kJ/m^2·nm at 340 nm. There shall be no less than six of each reference material in each cabinet at any given time. One of each material shall be placed in the upper right corner (UR), upper left corner (UL), center (C = 2 of each), lower right corner (LR), and lower left corner (LL) of the designated specimen exposure area. Starting dates shall be staggered so that three sets of reference materials complete the stated radiant exposure period at the same time, e.g., UR, C, LL, followed by UL, C, LR. For each set of reference material completing the stated radiant exposure, a new set is started. Reference material sets shall be identified by material, position, and date (day, month, and year), e.g., L-4-UL-070691 or PPLS-C-122591.

B.2 Instrumentation

B.2.1 Instruments used to determine color difference for this procedure require capability for providing CIELAB color values using illuminant D65, 10 degree standard observer data. If an instrument with diffuse geometry is used, the specular component of reflectance shall be included in the measurement. (Refer to SAE J1545, 3.6 for details.)

NOTE—An aperture diameter smaller than 20 mm cannot be used for these measurements.

B.2.2 Calibrate the instrument to be used for the color measurements to the manufacturers' recommendations.

B.3 Blue Wool Lightfastness Standards

B.3.1 Back the reference fabric to be measured with white cardboard[8]. Condition the backed reference fabric in a standard atmosphere (50% RH $\pm$5% RH and 21 °C $\pm$1 °C) for a minimum of 2 h. Insert one layer of unexposed material of the same lightfastness standard between the reference fabric and the backing prior to measurement.

NOTE—The reference fabrics are light sensitive. Therefore, the piece used as the backing layer during measurement will need to be replaced when noticeable color change has occurred (after approximately 50 uses).

B.3.2 Place the reference fabric against the sample port of the instrument in such a way that a smooth surface of the face of the fabric is presented for measurement.

B.3.3 After taking an initial reading in CIELAB units, rotate the reference fabric 90 degrees and take a second reading. Average the readings and store as the standard measurement for the identified piece of reference fabric. REMOVE THE BACKING FABRIC AND PLACE IN A LIGHT TIGHT CONTAINER FOR LATER USE.

NOTE—The measurement obtained in B.3.3 cannot be used for different pieces of reference fabric. Each individual piece must be conditioned and measured prior to exposure.

B.3.4 Place correct number of cardboard backed reference fabrics (single layer) at the proper positions in the exposure apparatus as described in B.1.2 and illustrated in Figure 3.

B.3.5 After the specified radiant exposure, remove the reference fabric and the white cardboard backing from the exposure apparatus.

B.3.6 Repeat the conditioning and color measurement steps specified in B.3.1 through B.3.3 on the exposed reference fabric(s), and using the previously stored pre-exposure measurement determine the delta L^*, a^*, b^*, and E^*.

B.3.7 As each group of reference fabrics completes its specified radiant exposure, record the color change information in terms of delta L^*, a^*, b^*, and E^*. These data shall be retained for not less than one year, and be available upon request.

B.4 Polystyrene Plastic Lightfastness Standard

B.4.1 Reflectance Mode

B.4.1.1 Place a piece of unexposed reference plastic, backed with a white calibration tile, against the sample port of the instrument.

B.4.1.2 Take an initial reading and store it as the standard measurement for the identified piece of reference plastic.

B.4.2 Transmission Mode

B.4.2.1 Place a piece of unexposed reference plastic in the proper location for measuring transmittance as recommended by the manufacturer of the instrument in use.

B.4.2.2 Place the white tile used for calibration against the outer sample port of the instrument.

B.4.2.3 Take an initial measurement and store it as the standard measurement for the identified piece of reference plastic.

B.4.3 Place correct number of PPLS's at the proper positions in the exposure apparatus as described in B.1.2 and illustrated in Figure 3.

B.4.4 After the specified radiant exposure, remove the reference plastic from the apparatus.

B.4.5 Repeat the color measurement steps specified in B.4.1 through B.4.2 on the exposed reference plastic(s), and using the previously stored pre-exposure measurement determine the delta b^*.

B.4.6 As each group of reference plastics completes its specified radiant exposure, record the color change information in terms of delta b^*. These data shall be retained for not less than one year, and be available upon request.

8. Franklin, Grain long-felt side up, 110/500 white index made by Union Camp or 9016 White Bristol Card Stock are suitable for this purpose. Franklin white index is usually available for local office supply or art stores, and is also available from Dilliard Paper Company. Any equivalent may be used.

ACCELERATED EXPOSURE OF AUTOMOTIVE INTERIOR TRIM MATERIALS USING OUTDOOR UNDER-GLASS CONTROLLED SUN-TRACKING TEMPERATURE AND HUMIDITY APPARATUS—SAE J2230 FEB1993

SAE Standard

Report of the SAE Textiles and Flexible Plastics Committee approved February 1993.

Foreword—This Document has not changed other than to put it into the new SAE Technical Standards Board Format.

1. Scope

1.1 This SAE Standard specifies operating procedure for the exposure of automotive interior trim materials in an outdoor behind-glass apparatus in which the temperature is controlled in a 24 h cycle. The humidity is controlled during the dark (night) portion of the cycle.

1.2 Specimen preparation, test durations, and performance evaluation procedures are covered in material specifications of the different automotive manufacturers.

2. References

2.1 Applicable Publications—The following publications form a part of the specification to the extent specified herein. Unless otherwise indicated the lastest revision of SAE publications shall apply.

2.1.1 SAE PUBLICATIONS—Available from SAE, 400 Commonwealth Drive, Warrendale, PA 15096-0001.

SAE J1545—Instrumental Color Difference Measurement for Exterior Finishes, Textiles, and Colored Trim

2.1.2 AATCC PUBLICATIONS—Available from AATCC, P.O. Box 12215, Research Triangle Park, NC 27709.

AATCC Evaluation Procedure 1 (1987), Gray Scale for Color Change

2.1.3 ASTM PUBLICATIONS—Available from ASTM, 100 Barr Harbor Drive, West Conshohocken, PA 19428-2959.

ASTM E824—Standard Method for Transfer of Calibration from Reference to Field Pyranometers

3. Definitions

3.1 Black Panel Thermometer, n.—A temperature-measuring device, the sensing unit of which is a stainless steel panel coated with black material designed to absorb most of the radiant energy encountered in fade/weathering testing.

NOTE—This device provides an estimation of the maximum temperature a specimen may attain during exposure to natural or artificial light.

3.2 Blue Wool Lightfastness Standard, n.—One of a group of dyed fabrics which are sensitive to the amount of light, heat, and moisture to which the blue wool material is exposed. Because of their unstable nature, these materials are also sensitive to the heat and moisture conditions which exist before exposure testing, after exposure testing, and prior to sample measurement.

3.3 Center Wavelength, n.—The specified wavelength for bandpass filters; the wavelength midway between the half power points, e.g., 340 nm ±2 nm.

3.4 Color Change, n.—As used in fade/weathering testing, a change in color of any kind (whether a change in hue, saturation, or lightness).

3.5 Half Power Bandpass, n.—The interval between wavelengths at which transmittance is 50% of peak. (It should not exceed 20 nm for a narrow bandpass filter.)

3.6 Irradiance Total, n.—The rate at which energy is incident on a surface, per unit area (W/m^2).

3.7 Irradiance, Ultraviolet, n.—Irradiance integrated over wavelengths 295 to 385 nm ($W/m^2/nm$).

3.8 Irradiance, Center Wavelength, n.—Irradiance integrated at wavelength 340 nm ±2 nm ($W/m^2/nm$).

3.9 Irradiation, n.—See radiant exposure.

3.10 Radiant Exposure, n.—The accumulated amount of irradiance received during a specified time period per unit area (J/m^2). Since irradiance can be measured using a variety of different optical sensors, it is generally recommended that the type of radiant exposure be specified (e.g., radiant exposure from 295 to 385 nm or radiant exposure at 340 nm ±2 nm).

3.11 Reference Fabric, n.—One or more blue wool lightfastness standards selected for exposure as a check on test apparatus and operating conditions.

3.12 Reference Plastic, n.—A clear polystyrene plastic standard selected for exposure as a check on a test apparatus and operating conditions.

NOTE—It has not been verified that these reference materials can be used as a check on a test cabinet or operating conditions for outdoor exposure tests due to seasonal variations in ultraviolet spectral distribution, temperature, relative humidity, and time of wetness during the uncontrolled portion of the test.

3.13 Sample, Laboratory, n.—A portion of material taken to represent the lot sample, the original material, or production lot, and used in the laboratory as a source of test specimens.

3.14 Specimen, n.—A specific portion of a material, laboratory sample, or production lot, upon which a test is performed or which is selected for that purpose.

4. Significance and Use

4.1 This method is designed to simulate extreme environmental conditions encountered inside a vehicle due to sunlight, heat, and humidity for the purpose of predicting the performance of automotive interior trim materials.

4.2 Variation in results may be expected when operating conditions are varied within the accepted limits of this method, or tests are conducted in different geographical locations. Therefore, no reference shall be made to results from the use of this method unless accompanied by a report detailing the specific operating conditions and location in compliance with Section 10, Exposure Report.

5. Apparatus[1]

5.1 The mounting stand shall be capable of tracking the sun in elevation and rotation with an accuracy of ± 1 degree in order to maintain the front surface of the cabinet normal to the direct beam of the sun (see Figure 1).

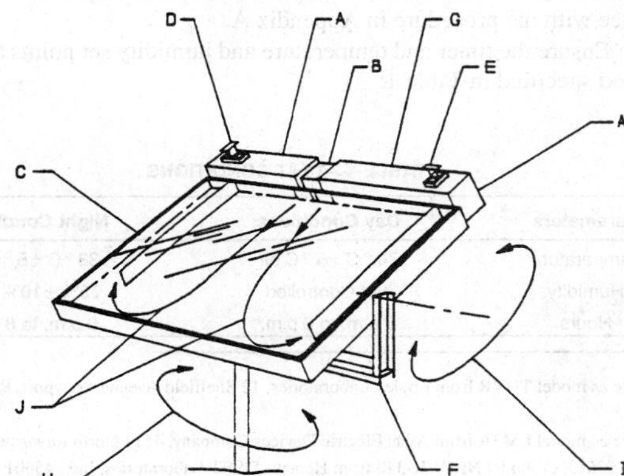

FIGURE 1—EXPOSURE APPARATUS

5.2 The test cabinet (Figure 1) shall be constructed of corrosion-resistant metal and contain a specimen rack, air circulation fan(s), and a hinged glass cover.

5.3 The glass cover (Figure 1) shall be a single piece of 3 mm (1/8 in) thick clear tempered safety glass, such as Herculite®[2], or equivalent.

5.4 The specimen rack shall be designed and positioned so that the test specimens may be mounted with the plane of the test surface parallel to, and not less than 75 mm (3 in) below the glass.

5.5 The cabinet shall be equipped with a sensor, heater(s), fan(s), and a control system capable of maintaining a specified air temperature to within ±5 °C at any location with the specimen exposure area. An example of such a system is given in Figure 1.

---

1. Apparatus from Heraeus DSET Laboratories, Inc., 45601 N. 47th Avenue, Phoenix, AZ 85027-7042, or equivalent.
2. Available from PPG Industries.

5.6 The cabinet shall be equipped with a sensor, controller, and solenoids, evaporators, or ultrasonic humidifiers capable of controlling the relative humidity to within ±10% of the set humidity during the night portion of the cycle. Optionally, the wet-bulb temperature or dew point may be controlled in order to maintain the desired humidity level.

5.7 An ultraviolet radiometer shall be used to measure irradiance, and connected to an integrator for computing ultraviolet radiant exposure. The ultraviolet radiometer shall be mounted behind glass, such as Herculite®, or equivalent, in a ventilated enclosure to avoid overheating the instrument. The enclosure containing the radiometer shall maintain the same orientation as the test cabinet. Two different types of radiometers may be used:

5.7.1 A wide-band ultraviolet radiometer[3], an instrument which measures irradiance at wavelengths 295 to 385 nm.

5.7.2 A narrow-band ultraviolet radiometer [4], an instrument which measures irradiance at 340 nm ±2 nm.

6. Apparatus Set-Up

6.1 To enhance the possibility of repeatability of tests, maintain and calibrate the apparatus as described in Appendices A and B. Appendix A contains maintenance and calibration instructions. Appendix B describes the use of reference materials which may assist in determining the performance of the apparatus, and interpreting exposure results when compared to previous tests.

6.2 Water for humidification must be purified so that it is free of silica and has no more than 20 ppm total dissolved solids.

7. Test Specimens

7.1 Unless otherwise specified, test specimens shall be 75 x 150 mm (3 x 6 in), with a maximum thickness of 25 mm (1 in). For specimens over 25 mm (1 in) thick, formed or configured specimens, and large components, specific instructions must be obtained from the responsible material engineer of the different automotive manufacturers or automotive suppliers.

7.2 Replicate specimens are desirable to provide a record of the changes when they are exposed for different radiant exposure levels. An unexposed specimen should be saved for visual comparison with the exposed specimen.

8. Test Procedure

8.1 Mount test specimens to the specimen rack. To minimize variations in results caused by nonuniform exposure conditions, the sample area is restricted in accordance with the procedure in Appendix A.

8.2 Ensure the timer and temperature and humidity set points are correct for the method specified in Table 1:

TABLE 1—TEST CONDITIONS

Parameters	Day Conditions	Night Conditions
Temperature	70 °C ±5 °C air	38 °C ±5 °C air
Humidity	Not Controlled	75% ± 10% R.H.
Hours	8 a.m. to 6 p.m.	6 p.m. to 8 a.m.

3. Available as model TUVR from Eppley Laboratories, 12 Sheffield Avenue, Newport, RI 02840, or equivalent.
4. Available as model LM3A from Atlas Electric Devices Company, 4114 North Ravenswood Avenue, Chicago, IL 60613, or model NBUVR-340 from Heraeus DSET Laboratories, Inc., 45601 N. 47th Avenue, Phoenix, AZ 85027-7042, or equivalent.

Operate continuously, except for performing maintenance and calibration as specified in Appendix A, inspecting specimens, removing specimens, or starting new tests.

8.3 Use one of the following methods for timing the exposure:

8.3.1 Expose specimens for the specified radiant exposure measured in MJ/m^2 total ultraviolet, 295 to 385 nm.

8.3.2 Expose specimens for the specified radiant exposure measured in kJ/m^2/nm at 340 nm ±2 nm.

9. Evaluating and Reporting the Degree of Fade

9.1 The degree of fade shall be evaluated and reported as specified between the contractual parties. Instrumental values are recommended:

9.1.1 INSTRUMENTAL MEASUREMENT

9.1.1.1 Color difference values in CIELAB units are obtained by instrumentally measuring the specimen before and after a specified amount of radiant exposure. The instrument used for specimen measurement shall conform to that specified in Appendix B.

9.1.2 VISUAL ASSESSMENT

9.1.2.1 Rating Method A—Assign colorfastness ratings using the AATCC Gray Scale for Color Change in accordance with AATCC Evaluation Procedure 1 (1987).

9.1.2.2 Rating Method B—Using the viewing conditions specified in AATCC Evaluation Procedure 1 (1987), quantify the color change using the following terminology:

a. NONE—No change in hue, lightness, or saturation (chroma).
b. SLIGHT—A change in lightness and/or saturation (chroma) which can be determined only upon close examination but no change in hue.
c. NOTICEABLE—A change in lightness and/or saturation (chroma) which can easily be seen and/or a change in hue.
d. SEVERE—An extreme change in lightness, saturation (chroma), and/or hue.

10. Exposure Report

10.1 The final report shall contain the following:

10.1.1 Laboratory and location
10.1.2 Type and serial number of exposure apparatus
10.1.3 Test method
10.1.4 Specimen identification
10.1.5 Total radiant exposure (MJ/m^2/295 to 385 nm) or (kJ/m^2/nm @ 340 nm)
10.1.6 Date specimen exposure was initiated
10.1.7 Date specimen exposure was completed
10.1.8 Special conditions which may have existed during a specific test period, such as control failure, unusual atmospheric conditions, etc.

11. Precision and Bias—Neither repeatability (precision of multiple determinations at one site) nor reproducibility (precision of multiple determinations at different sites) have been established. Therefore, it is inappropriate to compare results from different sites or results obtained at different times at the same site. It is strongly recommended that a control material having a known history be exposed simultaneously with test specimens if it is desirable to compare results obtained at different times and/or sites.

APPENDIX A

A.1 Maintenance

A.1.1 Specimen Mounting—Check specimens daily to ensure they are properly mounted.

A.1.2 Glass Cover—The glass cover shall be inspected weekly, and both surfaces shall be cleaned whenever there is visual evidence of dirt accumulation, outgassing, or other undesirable deposits.

A.1.3 Ultraviolet Radiometer—The glass cover and the diffusing lens shall be cleaned daily with deionized water. The desiccant visible through the sight glass shall be replaced whenever the color changes from dark blue to light pink.

A.1.4 Temperature/Humidity Control System—Check temperature/humidity readouts once during the day cycle and once during the night cycle daily to ensure proper operation of thermocouples, humidity sensors, heaters, air circulation fans, etc.

A.2 Calibration Checks

A.2.1 Temperature—The temperature sensor used to control chamber temperature shall be checked using a NIST traceable temperature sensor at the chamber set points no less often than every 6 months. The sensor shall be adjusted or replaced whenever the measured temperature fails to agree with the reference by an average of more than ±1.5 °C.

A.2.2 Temperature Uniformity—Within the planned exposure area, temperature uniformity shall be measured no less often than every 6 months using Type T thermocouples (attached to the specimen rack) placed as follows in Figure A1:

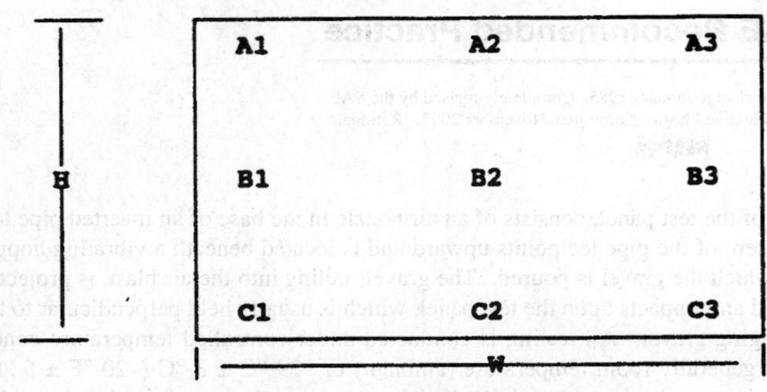

FIGURE A1—THERMOCOUPLE PLACEMENT

Thermocouples shall be monitored no less often than every 15 min for a 24-h period. The exposure area shall be limited to the area over which temperature can be maintained to within ±5 °C of the setpoint temperature.

A.2.3 Irradiance—Perform an absolute calibration no less often than every 6 months either by using a spectroradiometer, by returning the unit to the manufacturer, or by comparing the instrument to a reference instrument in accordance with ASTM E 824.

APPENDIX B

It has not been verified that these reference materials can be used as a check on a test cabinet or operating conditions for outdoor exposure tests due to seasonable variations in ultraviolet, temperature, relative humidity, and time of wetness during the uncontrolled portion of the test.

B.1 Scope

B.1.1 This appendix describes the procedure for using an AATCC Blue Wool Lightfastness Standard (L-4)[5] and a Polystyrene Plastic Lightfastness Standard (PPLS)[6] as reference materials for the purpose of determining whether the exposure cabinet is operating within the desired range.

B.1.2 Color difference values in CIELAB ΔE units for the L-4 and CIELAB Δb units for the PPLS are obtained by measuring the reference materials before and after a specified radiant exposure.

B.1.3 The L-4 and PPLS shall be exposed for 20.0 MJ/m^2/295 to 385 nm.

B.2 Instrumentation

B.2.1 Instruments used to determine color difference for this procedure require capability for providing CIELAB color values using illuminant D65, 10 degree standard observer data. If an instrument with diffuse geometry is used, the specular component of reflectance shall be included in the measurement. (Refer to SAE J1545, 3.6 for details.)

NOTE—An aperture diameter smaller than 20 mm cannot be used for these measurements.

B.2.2 Calibrate the instrument to be used for the color measurements to the manufacturers' recommendations.

B.3 Blue Wool Lightfastness Standards

B.3.1 Back the reference fabric to be measured with white cardboard [7] Condition the backed reference fabric in a standard atmosphere (50% RH ±5% RH and 21 °C ±1 °C) for a minimum of 2 h. Insert one layer of unexposed material of the same lightfastness standard between the reference fabric and the backing prior to measurement.

NOTE—The reference fabrics are light-sensitive. Therefore, the piece used as the backing layer during measurement will need to be replaced when noticeable color change has occurred (after approximately 50 uses).

B.3.2 Place the reference fabric against the sample port of the instrument in such a way that a smooth surface of the face of the fabric is presented for measurement.

B.3.3 After taking an initial reading in CIELAB units, rotate the reference fabric 90 degrees and take a second reading. Average the readings and store as the standard measurement for the identified piece of reference fabric. REMOVE THE BACKING FABRIC AND PLACE IN A LIGHT-TIGHT CONTAINER FOR LATER USE.

NOTE—The measurement obtained in B.3.3 cannot be used for different pieces of reference fabric. Each individual piece must be conditioned and measured prior to exposure.

B.3.4 Place cardboard-backed reference fabric (single layer) at the center of the sample exposure area.

B.3.5 After the specified radiant exposure, remove the reference fabric and the white cardboard backing from the exposure apparatus.

B.3.6 Repeat the conditioning and color measurement steps specified in B.3.1 through B.3.3 on the exposed reference fabric(s), and using the previously stored pre-exposure measurement determine the delta L*, a*, b*, and E*.

B.3.7 As each group of reference fabrics completes its specified radiant exposure, record the color change information in terms of delta L*, a*, b*, and E*. These data shall be retained for not less than one year, and be available upon request.

B.4 Polystyrene Plastic Lightfastness Standard

B.4.1 Reflectance Mode

B.4.1.1 Place a piece of unexposed reference plastic, backed with a white calibration tile, against the sample port of the instrument.

B.4.1.2 Take an initial reading and store it as the standard measurement for the identified piece of reference plastic.

B.4.2 Transmission Mode

B.4.2.1 Place a piece of unexposed reference plastic in the proper location for measuring transmittance as recommended by the manufacturer of the instrument in use.

B.4.2.2 Place the white tile used for calibration against the outer sample port of the instrument.

B.4.2.3 Take an initial measurement and store it as the standard measurement for the identified piece of reference plastic.

B.4.3 Place the PPLS at the center of the sample exposure area.

B.4.4 After the specified radiant exposure, remove the reference plastic from the apparatus.

B.4.5 Repeat the color measurement steps specified in B.4.1 through B.4.2 on the exposed reference plastic(s), and using the previously stored pre-exposure measurement determine the delta b*.

B.4.6 As each group of reference plastics completes its specified radiant exposure, record the color change information in terms of delta b*. These data shall be retained for not less than one year, and be available upon request.

5. AATCC L-4 Blue Wool Lightfastness Standards may be obtained from AATCC, P.O. Box 12215, Research Triangle Park, NC 27709.
6. PPLS's may be obtained from Testfabrics, Inc., 200 Blackford Avenue, Middlesex, NJ 08846.
7. Franklin, Grain long-felt side up, 110/500 white index made by Union Camp or 9016 White Bristol Card Stock are suitable for this purpose. Franklin white index is usually available from local office supply or art stores, and is also available from Dilliard Paper Company. Any equivalent may be used.

TEST FOR CHIP RESISTANCE OF SURFACE COATINGS—SAE J400 NOV2002

SAE Recommended Practice

Report of the SAE Nonmetallic Materials Committee approved July 1968, completely revised June 1980, reaffirmed without change January 1985. Completely revised by the SAE Textiles and Flexible Plastics Committee December 2001. Rationale statement available. Revised by the SAE Textiles and Flexible Plastics Committee November 2002. Rationale statement available.

1. Scope—This SAE Recommended Practice covers a laboratory procedure for testing and evaluating the resistance of surface coating to chipping by gravel impact. The test is designed to reproduce the effect of gravel or other media striking exposed paint or coated surfaces of an automobile and has been correlated with actual field results. The specific intent of the test is to evaluate organic surface coatings or systems on flat test panels; however, It may be possible to extend this type of testing to finished parts or other types of materials such as anodized aluminum or plated plastics if the results are interpreted with respect to the limitations and intent implied by the original testing procedures and rating system.

This document may involve hazardous materials, operations, and equipment. This document does not purport to address all of the safety problems associated with its use. It is the responsibility of whoever uses this document to consult and establish safety and health practices and determine the applicability of regulatory limitations prior to use.

All dimensions are nominal unless otherwise noted.

2. Reference

2.1 Related Publication—The following publication is provided for information purposes only and is not a required part of this document.

2.1.1 GENERAL MOTORS PUBLICATION—Available from GM AC Rochester/GMC, P.O. 1360, Flint, MI 48501-8054.

GMR-767—The Measurements of Chipping of Automotive Finishes, Hays, Donald R., Detroit, MI, General Motors Laboratories, 1968

3. Summary of Method—The test consists of projecting standardized road gravel by means of a controlled air blast onto a suitable test panel. The testing apparatus is called a gravelometer, designed to contain road gravel, a test panel holder, and a gravel projecting mechanism. The projecting mechanism, located in front of the test panel, consists of an air nozzle in the base of an inverted pipe tee. The stem of the pipe tee points upward and is located beneath a vibrating hopper into which the gravel is poured. The gravel, falling into the air blast, is projected toward and impacts upon the test panel, which is usually held perpendicular to the impinging gravel. All testing is conducted under controlled temperature conditions, generally room temperature (ambient) or –29 °C ± 3 °C (–20 °F ± 5 °F). After the gravel impact, tape is applied to remove any loose paint chips remaining on the panel, and the degree of chipping is determined by visual comparison with the SAE Chipping Rating Standards[1], by counting the number and sizes of all chips, or by other methods deemed suitable between the contractual parties involved.

4. Equipment and Materials

4.1 Gravelometer—A gravel projecting test apparatus which is constructed according to the design specifications shown in Figure 1.

4.1.1 OPERATION/MAINTENANCE CHECKLIST—The operation/maintenance checklist shown in Figure 2 shall be completed at least once a month for testers that are operated on a weekly basis and once every 6 months for testers that are operated less frequently.

NOTE—Values in chart are specific to the standard gravel testing protocol. Different specifications may be necessary for other media types.

If the answer to any of the following questions is NO, discontinue testing until the problem has been corrected.

1. Available from Society of Automotive Engineers, Inc., 400 Commonwealth Drive, Warrendale, PA 15096-0001—Identified as EA-400.

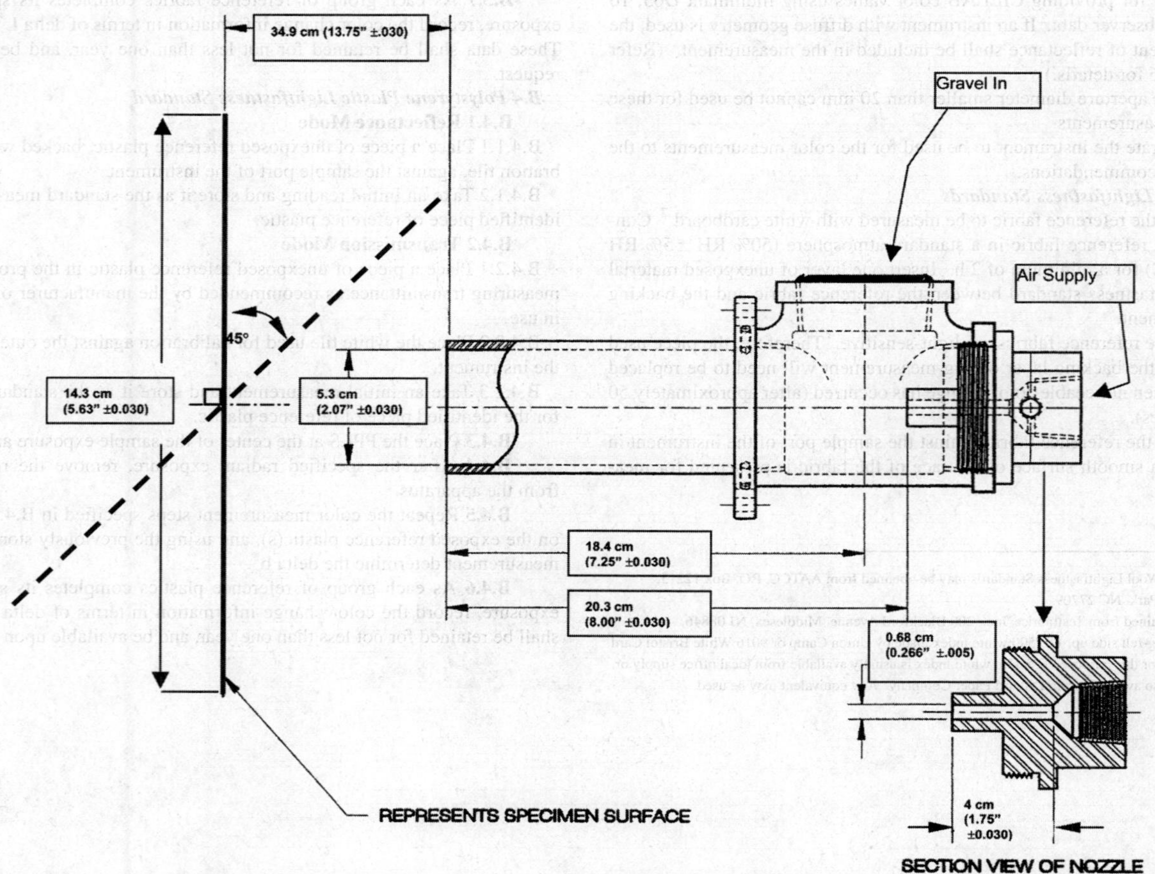

FIGURE 1—TEST APPARATUS

Gravelometer Checklist

Question	Yes	No	Data
Is a pipe size ID of 2.54 cm (1 in) airline connected from the supply pipe to the gravelometer?			
Are the pipe joints free of leaks?			
Does the air pressure hold 483 kPa (70 ± 3 psi) for 10 secs?			
Is the air pressure gauge calibrated?			
Date Last Calibrated:			
Date Last Replaced:			
Is nozzle orifice clear?			
Insert a 6.75 mm (17/64 in.) drill bit or 6.75 ± 0.01mm (0.266 ± .005 in.) plug gauge into nozzle to verify that the nozzle orifice is clear.			
Is the distance of nozzle to sample surface 55.25 cm (21.75 ± .030 in.)?			
Is the distance of gun barrel to sample 34.93 cm (13.75 ± .030 in.)?			
Is sample mounting bracket level top-to-bottom/front-back?			
Is the backer panel edge supported (not solid)?			
Is backer panel tight?			
Are the backer panel angles correct?			
Are stones hitting target in an even/centered pattern?			
Is the gravel screened?			
For older cabinet type gravelometers, is the amount of gravel collected on screen less than 10 pt.?			
Is the correct type and size of gravel being used?			
Does 1pt of gravel empty from the hopper in 7 to 10 seconds?			
Is the filter clear of obstructions?			
Date of last filter cleaning or replacement.			
For older type gravelometers, replace vibrator and bushings if gravel takes longer than 10 s to empty.			
For gravelometers with electronic feed mechanisms, adjust vibrator speed and hopper height so that hopper empties in 7 to 10 seconds.			
Compressor Capacity and Type:			

Below Ambient Testing Information (if required)

Question	Yes	No	Data
Are panels frozen prior to testing?			
How long are panels conditioned in freezer?			
What is the conditioning temperature?			
What is the ambient temperature?			
Time panels exposed to ambient prior to test.			
How far is the QGR from freezer?			

FIGURE 2—CHECKLIST

4.2 Gravel—The gravel for this test shall be water-worn road gravel, not crushed limestone or rock. The gravel will pass through 15.86 mm (5/8 in) space screen when graded, but be retained on 9.53 mm (3/8 in) space screen. It is important to note that mesh screen is not a substitute for space screen. The gravelometer has 9.53 mm (3/8 in) space screen in the bottom to separate fractured pieces of rock and dust smaller than 9.53 mm (3/8 in) so that the retained gravel on this screen may be reused. Because the gravel tends to blunt or fragment after repeated impacts, it should be changed at a regular frequency. For testers that are operated on a weekly basis, 2 pints of gravel shall be replaced with fresh gravel each month. For testers that are operated on less frequent basis, 2 pints of gravel shall be replaced with fresh gravel at least every 6 months.

Gravel must be washed prior to initial use.

Other media may be used as agreed upon by contractual parties.

NOTE—Pint measurements refer to a 1 pint container full to the top.

4.3 Paint Removal Tape—10 cm (4 in) wide or 5 cm (2 in) wide, 3M product #898 filament strapping tape or equivalent. Other tape may be used as agreed upon by contractual parties.

NOTE—The adhesion strength of the tape use makes a significant impact on how much separated paint is removed.

4.4 Temperature Conditioning Equipment—Gravelometer tests are usually run at ambient or a lower temperature, generally –29 °C (–20 °F), which shall be mutually agreed upon by contractual parties. Tests conducted at different temperatures will employ the following:

4.4.1 METHOD A—A cold room or chamber in which the gravelometer and test panels are maintained at the specified temperature of testing.

For freezers that employ a defrosting mechanism, document the method of defrosting and any temperature changes.

4.4.2 METHOD B—A freezer in which the test panels are cooled to 5.6 °C (10 °F) below the test temperature before they are individually transferred and tested immediately in a gravelometer at room temperature located nearby.

4.4.3 METHOD C—Ambient: room maintained at a temperature between 20 °C (68 °F) and 30 °C (86 °F).

4.5 Transparent Grid—A chip counting aid constructed of transparent plastic approximately 3.2 mm x 12.7 cm (1/8 x 5 x 5 in), on which a 10.16 x 10.16 cm (4 x 4 in) grid of 2.54 cm (1 in) squares has been etched or scribed.

4.6 Chipping Rating Standards—A photographic transparency, depicting the size and shape of each chip. See Figure 3 for representation of this transparency. Figure 3 IS A REPRESENTATION ONLY.

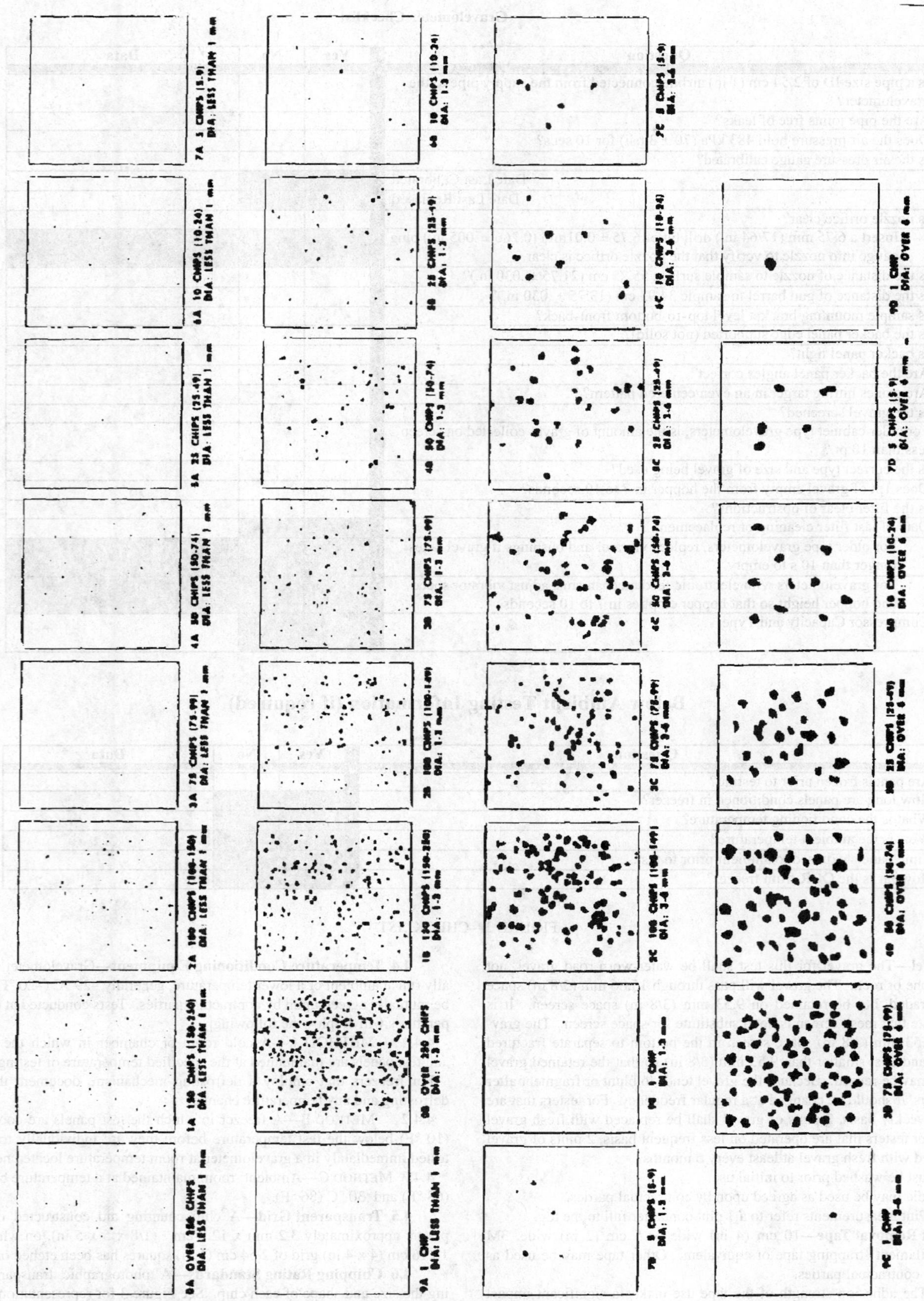

FIGURE 3—CHIPPING RATING STANDARDS (REPRESENTATION ONLY)

4.7 Test Specimens—It is recommended that three replicates of each test specimen be exposed in the gravelometer. The number of replicates will be agreed upon between contractual parties. The test specimens are typically flat and 10.16 x 30.48 cm (4 x 12 in) in size in order to fit into the panel holder of the gravelometer. The test panel material, the panel's thickness or gauge, and preliminary surface treatments (such as phosphating or anodizing) should be the same for all tests in any series and as representative as possible of the actual part. Any deviations in these parameters may produce misleading test results.

For profiled test specimens, or nonstandard test specimens, limits for uniform thickness, uniform backing, and uniform specimen holders must be determined and agreed upon by contractual parties.

5. Setup and Procedures

5.1 Setup

5.1.1 Paint or process the test panels as specified for the systems under test.

It should be noted that the chipping test results will be dependent upon the nature of the coating's formulation, the method and degree of drying or curing of the various coats, and the film thickness involved. Uniformity of film thickness is extremely important, and each component of the system should be controlled as uniformly as possible.

5.1.2 The test specimens must reach the test temperature for a minimum of 15 minutes prior to testing in accordance with the appropriate method specified in 4.5.

In the conditioning environment, proper heat transfer can be facilitated by separating the test specimens so that the conditioned air can circulate freely about the specimen.

5.1.3 Fill a 0.473 L (1 pt) container to the top with grated/screened gravel.

During exposure of multiple specimens, no more than 10 pt of gravel shall be allowed to collect on the sizing screen. Once 10 pt have collected on the screen, scrape the gravel across the screen so that the small rocks will fall beneath the screen. Remove the gravel that remains on top of the screen from the gravelometer for re-use. Remove and discard any stones that have lodged in the screen.

5.1.4 Other media can be used as agreed upon by contractual parties.

5.1.5 Adjust air pressure on the gravelometer to 483 kPa ± 21 kPa (70 psi ± 3 psi) with the air valve open.

For older cabinet type gravelometers, keep lid to gravel chamber on the gravelometer closed during this operation as safety precaution.

5.1.6 Set feed rate so that the hopper empties in 7 to 10 s/pt.

5.1.7 Other air pressures can be used as agreed upon by contractual parties.

5.2 Procedure

5.2.1 OLD CABINET TYPE GRAVELOMETER

a. After the air pressure is adjusted, shut off air valve, and open the lid to the specimen chamber. Place one test specimen conditioned at the desired test temperature in the panel holder with the coated side facing the gravel projecting mechanism. Mount the specimen as tightly as possible so as not to affect the angle of the panel orientation or allow movement during the test.
b. The specimen holder shall have an edge-supported backer plate. Other specimen mounting fixtures may be used as agreed upon by contractual parties.
c. Close lid to panel chamber.
d. Open the gravel feed door and pour gravel from the one pint container obtained from step 5.1.3 into the top of the gravel hopper. Do not allow gravel to fall into the nozzle entrance. Open the air valve to allow the air to project the gravel at the sample.

NOTE 1—The gravel hopper must empty within 7 to 10 s. If gravel remains in the hopper after 10 s, stop the test and investigate the cause. The operator may not touch the gravel during the test or otherwise physically help the gravel into the funnel.

NOTE 2—It is important to note that the vibrator may become frozen when the chamber is installed in a cold room or freezer. If the vibrator is frozen, discontinue the test until the vibrator has thawed and is operating correctly.

NOTE 3—Shut off air valve, open lid to specimen chamber, and remove the test specimen.

5.2.2 MODULAR GRAVELOMETER WITH ELECTRONIC FEED MECHANISM

a. Pull back on the specimen mounting clamp to open the specimen holder on the specimen holder assembly.
b. Clamp to close the specimen holder.
c. Pour gravel from the one pint container obtained from step 5.1.3 into hopper.
d. Set the Test Timer.

5.2.3 There are two ways to operate a test on these units. A Timed Test is a test that shuts off the machine after the preset amount of time has passed. A Manual Test requires the operator to shut off the machine after the desired amount of time has passed.

5.2.3.1 Timed Test

a. Make sure the control switch is set to STOP.
b. Set the Test Timer to the desired test time. This is typically < 10 s.
c. Turn the main power switch to ON.
d. Flip the control switch to TIMED START.

5.2.3.2 Manual Test

a. The manual test requires the operator to manually stop the test. Once started, it will not stop by itself.
b. Make sure the control switch is on OFF.
c. Switch the main power control switch
d. Switch the control switch to MANUAL.
e. After the desired amount of time has passed, flip the control switch to OFF.
f. Once the test is complete, remove the test panel from the specimen holder by pulling back on the specimen clamp and pulling out the test specimen.
g. Remove the rocks from the return receptacle and screen before reuse.
h. If necessary, allow panels to return to room temperature and dry with a soft cloth to remove any condensed moisture.
i. Using the tape referenced in 4.4, remove all loose or damaged paint.
j. Cover the tested area of the specimen with a strip of tape or multiple strips of tape side by side. Firmly adhere the tape to the test specimen by applying uniform pressure. (Uniform pressure can be applied by using items like a tongue depressor or a pencil eraser.) There can be no air bubbles trapped beneath the tape.
k. Remove the tape by pulling straight up.
l. Apply new strip(s) of tape to the specimen and repeat the paint removal process in the opposite direction.
m. Continue this procedure using new strips of tape until all loose or damaged paint is removed.
n. Other tapes or loose paint removal methods may be used as agreed upon by contractual parties.
o. Determine the degree of chipping by one of the following methods of the Gravelometer Rating System.

6. Gravelometer Rating System

6.1 Methods Available

NOTE—other methods may be employed as agreed upon between contractual parties.

6.1.1 There are two methods available for determining the degree of chipping from gravel on the tested panel (other media will require other evaluation methods.) In Method I, the exact number of chips in each size range is tabulated for the specified test area, while Method II utilizes a visual comparison of the tested panel with the SAE Chipping Rating Standards shown in Figure 3 which depict various degrees of chipping severity and are arranged sequentially from best to worst according to chipping size and frequency.

Method I is the most precise and should be used where definitive accuracy is required or as the referee method in case differences arise between laboratories; however, it is more time-consuming than the visual comparison method.

Method II is much faster and, while more of an approximation than the first method, can be used for many routine laboratory evaluations where the accuracy of Method I is not required. Method II also lends itself to field survey work where the chipped areas can be rated by direct comparison with the chipping Rating Standards.

6.1.2 With both methods, the chipped area to be evaluated on the tested panel should be the 10.16 x 10.16 cm (4 x 4 in) square that exhibits the center of the chipped pattern.

6.2 Basic Structure of Rating System—Generally, the basic structure of the chip rating system consists of one or more number-letter combinations in which rating numbers 10-0 indicate the number of chips of each size and rating letter A-D designate the sizes of the corresponding chips. A point of failure notation may also be included in the rating if more descriptive refinement is desired.

6.2.1 NUMBER OF CHIPS—A whole rating number selected from the range of 10-0 in Table 1 is used to indicate the number of chips of each size in the 10.16 x 10.16 cm (4 x 4 in) test area.

TABLE 1—NUMBER CATEGORIES FOR CHIP RATING

Rating Number	Number of Chips	Rating Number	Number of Chips
10	0	4	50–74
9	1	3	75–99
8	2–4	2	100–149
7	5–9	1	150–250
6	10–24	0	>250
5	25–49		

6.2.2 SIZE OF CHIPS—The size of the chip is specified by a rating letter selected from A-D in Table 2. Due to the irregular nature of chipping, the size cannot always be measured exactly so it has to be approximated.

TABLE 2—SIZE CATEGORIES FOR CHIP RATING

Rating Letter	Size of Chips
A	>1 mm (>approximately 0.03 in)
B	1–3 mm (approximately 0.03–0.12 in)
C	3–6 mm (approximately 0.12–0.25 in)
D	>6 mm (>approximately 0.25 in)

6.2.3 POINT OF FAILURE—The coating layer at which the most predominant chipping failure occurs is designated as the point of failure. The notations in Table 3 can be used to designate this information if desired. Other notations may be used with agreement between contractual parties.

TABLE 3—POINT OF FAILURE NOTATION

Notation	Level of Failure	Failure Type
(S/P)	Substrate to Primer	Adhesional
(S/T)	Substrate to Topcoat	Adhesional
(P)	Prime	Cohesional
(P/T)	Primer to Topcoat	Adhesional
(T)	Topcoat	Cohesional

6.3 Details of Method I and Method II

6.3.1 METHOD I—EXACT COUNTING PROCEDURE

6.3.1.1 Counting can be facilitated by the use of a transparent overlay onto which has been etched a grid of 2.54 cm (1 in) squares. The grid is placed over the area to be treated as a guide to remembering the areas that have been counted.

6.3.1.2 The operator examines the area within a 2.54 x 2.54 cm (1 x 1 in) square, decides on the size of each chip as encountered, and records it. Rate all 16 squares and record the results.

6.3.1.3 The actual number of chips counted for each size is then converted into the number-letter combinations utilizing Tables 1 and 2. The number-letter rating is then arranged with the most numerous size first, followed by the next more numerous, etc. This may then be followed by the Point of Failure notation.

For example, for a panel on which there are 20 chips less than 1 mm (A size), 40 chips of 1 to 3 mm (B size), and 3 chips of 3 to 6 mm (C size) with primer-topcoat failure, the number of chips on the rating would be 5B-6A-8C (P/T). This rating can be condensed by converting the total number of chips on the panel to the corresponding number category, which is then followed by the size designations in the same order. In this example, with a total of 63 chips, the rating would be summarized as 4 BAC (P/T).

6.3.2 METHOD II—VISUAL COMPARISON PROCEDURE—The Chipping Rating Standards shown in Figure 3 are utilized.

These have been prepared so the chips of only 1 size are shown in each illustration. The number of chips illustrated in each standard is the fewest number of chips in each rating number category; for example, the No. 5 standards all show 25 chips, the No. 3 standards show 75 chips. All of the No. 8 and No. 10 categories and the lower number D size categories have not been included in order to keep the photographs to a manageable number.

6.3.2.1 Visually compare the area to be rated with the standards.

Since each standard exhibits only one chip and actual chipping seldom occurs in only one size, one or more standards should be superimposed until that combination of standards which more nearly resembles the panel is obtained. Record the standards that were used to achieve the match with the panel under examination.

6.3.2.2 As with Method I, the most numerous chips should be listed first, the next most numerous second, etc. Again, the number-letter ratings may be summarized to give a condensed single number rating based on the total number of chips of all sizes followed by the letter ratings to indicate the relative number of chips of each size.

For example, a panel requiring the superimposition of a 6A standard, a 5B standard, and an 8C standard would be described as 5B-6A-8C (P/T) and summarized as 4 BAC (P/T).

*7. **Precision***—Because of the possibility of slight variations in the number, size, type, and distribution of gravel in each test sequence, some variation in the raw counts of chips in the various size categories will be reflected in the data. However, when these counts are converted into the condensed rating of Method I or the rating that can be obtained by Method II, if the results differ by greater than one number-letter rating, they should by considered suspect.

*8. **Reporting of Results***—Reports of the gravelometer tests shall include the number-letter rating and all applicable test conditions that deviated from the standard as outlined. In addition, reports should include the material type, thickness, and any preliminary surface treatment of the test panel together with the type of surface coating(s), baking, or pertinent processing schedules, and the film thicknesses of finishing system being evaluated.

FLORIDA EXPOSURE OF AUTOMOTIVE FINISHES—SAE J951 JAN1985

SAE Information Report

Report of the SAE Nonmetallic Materials Committee approved June 1966, reaffirmed without change January 1985.

Foreword—This Reaffirmed Document has been changed only to reflect the new SAE Technical Standards Board Format.

*1. **Scope***—The purpose of this SAE Information Report is to compare the results of Florida exposure at 45 deg from the horizontal, facing south, with those at 5 deg from the horizontal, facing south, using various types and colors of automotive finishes.

*2. **References***—There are no referenced publications specified herein.

*3. **Summary***—Fifteen different automotive finishes were used: five nonoxidizing type alkyd enamels, five thermoplastic acrylics, and five thermosetting acrylics. Each group of five included the following colors: white, black, red, blue metallic, and silver metallic.

Several of the finishes selected were not of the maximum durability type currently in use, to insure that differences in gloss retention on exposure would show up.

Sixteen panels of each finish were prepared under constant conditions and the eight sets of 30 panels were exposed (15 at 45 deg and 15 at 5 deg) at six southern Florida exposure sites within a radius of approximately 40 miles of Miami. The total number of panels exposed was 240.

Part of each panel was washed each month using the same washing procedure at each exposure site.

After 12 months exposure all the panels were returned to one location and 60 and 20 deg glossmeter readings were made on both unwashed and washed areas. Readings on all panels were made by one operator using the same glossmeter; the total number of readings was 960.

The panels were then reexposed for an additional 6 months, for a total of 18 months exposure. Gloss readings were again made in the same manner.

One set of panels was returned for additional exposure and was exposed for 32 months.

*4. **Conclusions***

1. Exposure at 5 deg south resulted in greater loss of gloss, on the average, than at 45 deg.
2. Exposure at 5 deg caused faster failure of weaker finishes than did exposure at 45 deg.
3. Finishes with very good gloss retention showed little difference in loss of gloss when exposed at 5 and 45 deg within the duration of this study.
4. While some differences in severity of exposure were noted between the six exposure sites employed, differences were not large and the preceding conclusions hold true regardless of site.
5. The preceding conclusions are supported by gloss retention data from both washed and unwashed areas of the panels.

*5. **Recommendation***—To most quickly evaluate automotive finishes under southern Florida exposure conditions, it is recommended that panels be exposed at 5 deg from the horizontal, facing south.

*6. **Discussion***—Table 1 shows typical examples selected from the data to illustrate the conclusions.

*7. **Exposure Sites***—Six different exposure sites were used. At site 1, three sets of 30 panels were exposed; at each of sites 2–6, one set of panels was exposed.

*8. **Glossmeter Readings***—Although only 60 deg glossmeter readings are shown in the preceding examples, the conclusions reached are supported by both 60 and 20 deg glossmeter readings. The 60 deg glossmeter is generally felt to be more suitable for exposure work as the 20 deg glossmeter is more sensitive and 20 deg readings can be affected by panel surface conditions other than gloss.

TABLE 1—TYPICAL RESULTS OF STUDY

		60 deg Gloss Washed 45 deg	60 deg Gloss Unwashed 5 deg	60 deg Gloss Washed 45 deg	60 deg Gloss Unwashed 5 deg
Finish with Poorer Gloss Retention					
Silver	Original	94	92	94	92
metallic	6 months	89	78	78	67
alkyd	12 months	37	18	34	13
enamel	18 months	12	7	9	5
	24 months	10	8	7	6
	30 months	8	6	7	5
	32 months	8	7	6	5
Finish with Good Gloss Retention					
Blue	Original	91	91	91	91
metallic	6 months	87	84	76	75
alkyd	12 months	76	73	65	57
enamel	18 months	48	38	32	19
	24 months	21	10	12	6
	30 months	14	11	6	5
	32 months	13	15	6	5
Finish with Very Good Gloss Retention					
Blue	Original	90	89	90	89
metallic	6 months	87	84	77	69
thermo-settingc	12 months	85	83	73	66
acrylic	18 months	84	80	66	54
	24 months	80	75	56	46
	30 months	75	69	52	39
	32 months	75	71	46	37
Black	Original	99	98	99	98
thermo-setting	6 months	99	99	95	89
acrylic	12 months	99	99	86	72
	18 months	100	100	68	52
	24 months	100	100	60	44
	30 months	100	100	53	36
	32 months	100	100	50	32

MARKING OF PLASTIC PARTS —SAE J1344 JUL1997

SAE Recommended Practice

Report of the SAE Nonmetallic Materials Committee approved October 1980. Completely revised by the SAE Plastics Committee March 1988 and May 1991, and revised April 1993, June 1995, and July 1997.

1. Scope—This SAE Recommended Practice provides a system for marking plastic parts to designate the type of material from which the part was fabricated.

1.1 Purpose—The purpose of this document is to provide information to facilitate the:

a. Selection of materials and procedures for repairing and repainting plastic parts
b. Collection and handling of parts for subsequent recycling

2. References

2.1 Applicable Publications—The following publications form a part of this specification to the extent specified herein.

2.1.1 ISO PUBLICATIONS—Available from ANSI, 11 West 42nd Street, New York, NY 10036-8002.

ISO 1043-1—Plastics-Symbols—Part 1: Basic polymers and their special characteristics
ISO 1043-2—Plastics-Symbols—Part 2: Fillers and reinforcing materials
ISO 1629—Rubber and latices—Nomenclature
ISO 11469—Plastics—Generic identification and marking of plastic products

2.1.2 VDA STANDARDS—Available from DIN, Deutsches Institut fur Normung, Burggrafeng Strasse 6, Postfach 1107, D-1000 Berlin 30 Germany.

VDA 260—German Motor Vehicles—Marking of Parts of Polymeric Materials

2.2 Related Publications—The following publications are provided for information purposes only and are not a required part of this document.

2.2.1 ASTM PUBLICATIONS—Available from ASTM, 100 Barr Harbor Drive, West Conshohocken, PA 19428-2959.

ASTM D 1600—Standard Terminology Relating to Abbreviations, Acronyms, and Codes for Terms Relating to Plastics

3. Description

3.1 The system is based on standard symbols for terms relating to plastics published by the International Organization for Standardization (ISO 1043). Most commonly used symbols, including some not covered by ISO, are shown in Table 1. In addition, symbols for commercial plastic blends are shown in Table 2, and symbols for commonly used automotive fillers/reinforcements derived from ISO 1043-2 are shown in Table 3.

3.2 If additional symbols are required to cover new materials, the form in Appendix A shall be completed and submitted to SAE. New symbols will be included in the next revision to this document.

4. Use of Marking Symbols

4.1 In view of the wide variety of parts used in substantially different assembly situations, this document does not prescribe the location, and/or method of marking; however, the following guidelines should be followed:

4.1.1 Field service people should be informed regarding the material from which the part is made so suitable repair and paint procedures may be used.

4.1.2 Wherever practicable, the marking should be located where it may be observed while the part is in use. Consideration should be given to the use of multiple markings on large or complex shaped parts.

4.1.3 From the standpoint of field service people, marking on the outside surface of the part (in an unobtrusive location from the viewpoint of the owner) is preferred.

4.1.4 Markings applied with inks, dyes, or paints should not bleed, run, smudge, or stain other materials which may come in contact with the marking.

4.1.5 Marking should be designed to remain legible during the entire life of the part.

4.1.6 Markings which are molded into the part are preferred since they are permanent and do not require separate manufacturing operations as do those applied to the surface of the part after molding. Molded in markings should not create a stress concentration site which could result in premature cracking of the part.

4.1.7 The recommended practice for the standard marking symbol is as shown in Figure 1. Dimensions are suggested guidelines. Markings should be proportional to part size.

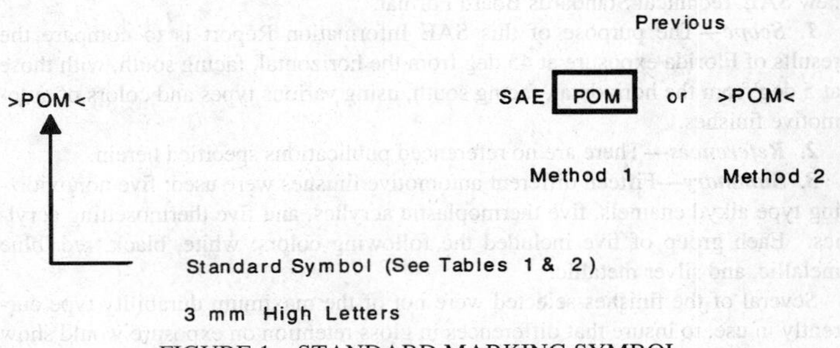

FIGURE 1—STANDARD MARKING SYMBOL

4.1.8 EXAMPLES—(See Figure 2.)

>PP<	Polypropylene
>PA66<	Polyamide 66
>ABS + PC<	Acrylonitrile/butadiene/styrene + Polycarbonate Blend

FIGURE 2—EXAMPLES OF STANDARD MARKING SYMBOL

4.2 For parts using plastic materials containing fillers/reinforcements in the amount of 10% and greater, the same designation shall be used for the "family name" as defined in Table 1 and, in addition, alpha codes from ISO 1043-2, followed by a numeric value representing the nominal percentage of filler/reinforcer. The polymer family codes shall be separated from the filler/reinforcement codes and value by use of a hyphen.

4.2.1 EXAMPLES—(See Figure 3.)

>PBT-GF30<	Polybutylene Terephthalate, 30% Glass Fiber Reinforced
>PBT-(GF + M)40<	
or	
>PBT-(GF15 + M25)<	Polybutylene Terephthalate, 15% Glass Fiber + 25% Mineral Reinforced

FIGURE 3—EXAMPLES OF STANDARD MARKING SYMBOLS FOR REINFORCED PLASTICS

4.3 Parts fabricated from two or more materials, some of which are not readily visible, may be marked so the primary visible material is identified first by the system specified in 3.1 followed by identification of the other material(s) where the individual identification(s) is separated by a comma. The main component by mass is identified by underlining.

4.3.1 EXAMPLES—For a product made of three components, the visible one is a thin coating of poly (vinyl chloride) over a polyurethane containing an insert of acrylonitrile/butadiene/styrene that is the major component by mass, see Figure 4.

>PVC,PUR,ABS<

FIGURE 4—EXAMPLES OF STANDARD MARKING SYMBOLS FOR COMPOSITE PARTS

5. Notes

5.1 Additional Information—Appendicies C, D, and E are cross reference listings designed to assist the user in relating SAE marking symbols to SPI/PBI container codes as well as common plastic names and supplier trademarks. Appendix F references symbols for elastomers, based on ISO 1629, with potential use in plastic blends.

TABLE 1—SYMBOLS FOR MARKING PLASTIC PARTS

Plastic "Family" Name[(1)]	Common Name	Standard Symbol	(Previous)[(2)(3)]
Acrylonitrile/butadiene		AB	
Acrylonitrile/butadiene/acrylate		AB/A	
Acrylonitrile/butadiene/styrene		ABS	
Acrylonitrile/ethylene/styrene		AES	
Acrylonitrile/methyl/methacrylate		A/MMA	
Acrylonitrile/styrene/acrylate		ASA	
Carboxymethyl cellulose		CMC	
Casein		CS	
Cellulose acetate		CA	
Cellulose acetate butyrate		CAB	
Cellulose acetate propionate		CAP	
Cellulose formaldehyde		CF	
Cellulose nitrate		CN	
Cellulose priopionate		CP	
Cellulose triacetate		CTA	
Chlorinated polyethylene		CPE	
Chlorinated poly(vinyl chloride)		CPVC	
Epoxide; Epoxy		EP	
Ethyl cellulose		EC	
Ethylene/ethyl/acrylate		E/EA	
Ethylene/methacrylic acid		E/MA	
Ethylene/propylene/diene		EPDM	
Ethylene/tetrafluorethylene		E/TFE	
Ethylene/vinyl acetate		E/VAC	(EVA)(EVAC)
Ethylene vinyl alcohol		EVAL	(EVOH)
Furan formaldehyde		FF	
Melamine formaldehyde		MF	
Perfluoro(ethylene/propylene): Tetrafluorethylene/hexafluoropropylene		FEP	
Phenol formaldehyde		PF	
Phenol furfural		PFF	
Polyamide	Nylon	PA	
6 Polyamide		PA6	
66 Polyamide		PA66	
66/6 Polyamide		PA66/6	
46 Polyamide		PA46	
69 Polyamide		PA69	
11 Polyamide		PA11	
12 Polyamide		PA12	
610 Polyamide		PA610	
612 Polyamide		PA612	
Polyamide copolymers based on terephthalic acid, hexamethylenediamine, and 2-methylpentamethylenediamine		PA6T/MPMDT	
Polyamide/-imide		PAI	
Polyacrylonitrile		PAN	
Polyarylamid (polyaramide)		PARA	
Polyarylether		PAE	
Polyaryletherketone		PAEK	
Polyarylsulfone		PAS	(PASU)
Polybutene-1		PB	
Polycarbonate plastics		PC	
Polychlorotrifluoroethylene		PCTFE	
Poly(diallyl phthalate)		PDAP	(DAP)
Polydicyclopentadiene		PDCPD	
Polyarylate (polyarylterephthalate)		PAT	
Liquid Crystal Polymer: Copolyester (polyarylterephthalate)		LCP	(ARP)
Poly(butylene terephthalate)		PBT	
Polycyclohexylene terephthalate (poly[1,4 cyclohexylene dimethylene terphthalate])		PCT	
Polyether block amide		PEBA	
Poly(ethylene terephthalate)		PET	
Polyester, thermoset (unsaturated)	SMC, BMC, TMC	UP	
Poly(ether imide)		PEI	
Polyetherketone		PEK	
Poly(ether sulfone)		PES	(PESU)

TABLE 1—SYMBOLS FOR MARKING PLASTIC PARTS (continued)

Plastic "Family" Name[1]	Common Name	Standard Symbol	(Previous)[2][3]
Polyethylene		PE	
Linear Low Density		PE-LLD	(LLDPE)
Low Density		PE-LD	(LDPE)
Linear Medium Density		PE-LMD	(LMDPE)
Medium Density		PD-MD	(MDPE)
High Density		PE-HD	(HDPE)
Ultra-high molecular weight		PE-UHMW	
Poly(ethylene oxide)		PEOX	(PEO)
Perfluoro alkyxyl alkane		PFA	
Polyketone		PK	
Polyimide		PI	
Polyimidesulfone		PIS	(PISU)
Polyisobutylene		PIB	
Poly(methyl methacrylate)	Acrylic	PMMA	
Poly(methyl methacrylate imide)		PMMI	
Poly(4-methylpentene-1)		PMP	
Poly(p-oxybenzoate)		POB	
Polyoxymethylene; polyformaldehyde	Acetal	POM	
Polyphenylene ether		PPE	(PPO)
Polypropylene		PP	
Polystyrene		PS	
Polysulfone		PSU	
Poly(phthalamide)		PPA	
Poly(propylene oxide)		PPOX	
Poly(phenylene sulfide)		PPS	
Poly(phenylene sulfone)		PPSU	
Polytetrafluoroethylene		PTFE	
Polyurethane, thermoset (unsaturated)		PUR	
Poly(vinyl acetate)		PVAC	
Poly(vinyl alcohol)		PVAL	
Poly(vinyl butyral)		PVB	
Poly(vinyl butyrate)		PVB	
Polyvinylcarbazole		PVK	
Poly(vinyl chloride)		PVC	
Poly(vinyl chloride acetate)		PVCA	
Poly(vinyl fluoride)		PVF	
Poly(vinyl formal)		PVFM	
Poly(vinylidene chloride)		PVDC	
Poly(vinylidene fluoride)		PVDF	
Polyvinylpyrrolidone		PVP	
Silicone		SI	
Styrene/acrylonitrile		SAN	
Styrene/butadiene		S/B	
Styrene/maleic anhydride plastics		SMA	(S/MA)
Styrene/a-methylstyrene		S/MS	
Thermoplastic Elastomers:			
Chlorinated ethylene alloy		TECEA	
Polyether block amide		PEBA	
Polyolefinic		TEO	(TPO)(E/P)
Ether ester block copolymer		TEEE	(EEBC)
Polyurethane		TPU (PUR-T)	(TPUR)(RTPU)
Urea-formaldehyde		UF	
Vinyl chloride/ethylene		VC/E	
Vinyle chloride/ethylene/methyl acrylate		VC/E/MA	
Vinyl chloride/methyl acrylate		VC/MA	
Vinyl choride/vinyl acetate		VC/VAC	
Vinyl chloride/vinylidene chloride		VC/VDC	

1. Common names and trademarks for each plastic "family" name are shown in Appendix C.1, and are intended as a guide to aid the user in selecting the correct standard symbol for the material under consideration.
2. Previous—SAE J1344 or other commonly used marking symbols
3. Symbols listed as ("PREVIOUS SYMBOLS") are former designations and should not be used on new parts. Intent of this is that changes are to be implemented on new or redesigned parts.

TABLE 2—SYMBOLS FOR COMMERCIAL BLENDS

Commercial Blends[1]	Standard Symbol	(Previous)
Acrylonitrile/butadiene/styrene + polyamide	ABS+PA	
Acrylonitrile/butadiene/styrene + polycarbonate	ABS+PC	
Acrylonitrile/butadiene/styrene + polyphenylene sulfone	ABS+PPSU	
Acrylonitrile/butadiene/styrene + polytetrafluoroethylene	ABS+PTFE	
Acrylonitrile/butadiene/styrene + polyvinyl chloride	ABS+PVC	
Acrylonitrile/butadiene/styrene + styrene maleic anhydride	ABS+SMA	(ABS+S/MA)
Acrylonitrile/butadiene/styrene + thermoplastic polyurethane	ABS+TPU	(ABS+TPUR)
Acrylonitrile/styrene/acrylate + polycarbonate	ASA+PC	
Acrylonitrile/styrene/acrylate + poly(methyl methacrylate)	ASA+PMMA	
Acrylonitrile/styrene + polyvinyl chloride	ASA+PVC	
Poly(methylmethacrylate, co-styrene, co-acrylonitrile) + poly(butadiene, co-methylmethacrylate, co-styrene)	MMA/S/AN + B/MMA/S	
Poly(methylmethacrylate, co-styrene, co-ethylacrylate + poly(butadiene, co-methylmethacrylate, co-styrene	(MMA/S/EA+B/MMA/S)	
Polyamide + ethylene methacrylic acid (ionomer)	PA+E/MA	
Polyamide (amorphous) blend	PA+	
Polyamide + polyethylene	PA+PE	
Polyamide + styrene/acrylonitrile	PA+SAN	
Polycarbonate + poly (butylene terephthalate)	PC+PBT	
Polycarbonate + poly (ethylene terephthalate)	PC+PET	
Polycarbonate + polycyclohexylene terephthalate	PC+PCT	
Polycarbonate + styrene maleic anhydride	PC+SMA	(PC+S/MA)
Polycarbonate + thermoplastic polyurethane	PC+TPU	(PC+TPUR)(PC+PUR-T)
Poly(butylene terephthalate) + acrylonitrile/styrene/acrylate	PBT+ASA	
Poly(butylene terphthalate) + poly(ethylene terphthalate)	PBT+PET	
Poly(butylene terphthalate) + poly(phenylene ether)	PBT+PPE	
Ether ester block copolymer + polybutylene terphthalate	TEE+PBT	
Poly(ethylene terphthalate) + polymethyl methacrylate	PET+PMMA	
Poly(ethylene terephthalate) + polyphenylene sulfone	PET+PPSU	
Polyoxymethylene + polytetrafluoroethylene	POM+PTFE	
Poly(phenylene ether) + polyamide	PPE+PA	(PA+PPE)
Poly(phenylene ether) + high impact polystyrene	PPE+PS-HI	
Poly(phenylene sulfide) + polytetrafluoroethylene	PPS+PTFE	
Polypropylene + ethylene/propylene/diene	PP+EPDM	
Polysulfone + acrylonitrile/butadiene/styrene	PSU + ABS	
Polysulfone + polycarbonate	PSU + PC	
Polysulfone + poly(ethylene terephthalate)	PSU+ PET	
Poly(vinyl chloride) + chlorinated polyethylene	PVC + CPE	
Polyvinyl chloride + nitrile butadiene rubber	PVC + NBR	
Polyvinyl chloride + poly(methyl methacrylate)	PVC + PMMA	
Polyvinyl chloride + polyurethane	PVC + PUR	(PVC + PU)
Styrene/maleic anhydride + high impact polystyrene	SMA + PS-HI	(S/MA + PS)

1. Commercial mixtures/blends (alloys) of plastic resins.

TABLE 3—SYMBOLS FOR FILLERS AND REINFORCING MATERIALS

Fillers and Reinforcing Materials	Standard Symbol	Previous Symbol
Barium Sulfate®	U	BS
Glass spheres	GB	
Glass fiber	GF	
Glass fiber/mineral[1]	(GF+M)[2]	
Glass fiber/mica[3]	(GF+P)[3]	
Glass mat	GM	
Carbon, graphite	C	
Carbon fiber	CF	
Aramid fibers	RF	
Mineral[1]	M	
Clay[2]	E	
Calcium carbonate[2] powder	KD	
Mica[2]	P	
Talc powder	TD	
Wiood powder	WD	

1. The "mineral designation indicated here is generic, i.e., the type of mineral used as a filler is unknown.
2. Mixtures of fillers may be shown in parentheses by combining the relevant symbols with the sign "+".
3. When specific minerals are used as fillers, such as clay, calcium carbonate, mica, talc, etc., the precise symbol should be used. The form of the "mineral" should also be identified when available , e.g., beads (B); powder (D); fiber (F); whiskers (H); flake (S), yarn (Y).

APPENDIX A
REQUEST TO ADD NEW MARKING SYMBOLS AND/OR TRADEMARKS

A.1 Complete Figure A1 to apply for inclusion of new marking symbols and/or trademarks into SAE J1344.

Plastic or Plastic Blend "Family" Name:____________________________________

____

(Check One)

Proposed Marking Symbol: _________________________ New Symbol _________

Existing _________

Supplier's Trademark (If any): ____________________________________

Supplier:____

Name of Submitter: ____

Telephone Number: (   )

Date Submitted:____

Signature: ____

Mail This Form To:

SAE

Standards Development and Research

Materials Staff Engineer

400 Commonwealth Drive

Warrendale, PA 15096-0001

NOTE—The procedure shown in Appendix B will be used to process requests for the addition of new symbols only.

Requests to add trademarks to cross reference listings will be handled as editorial changes.

FIGURE A1—REQUEST FORM TO ADD NEW MARKING SYMBOLS AND/OR TRADEMARKS

APPENDIX B
PROCESS FLOW CHART—ADDING NEW SYMBOLS TO J1344

B.1 See Figure B1.

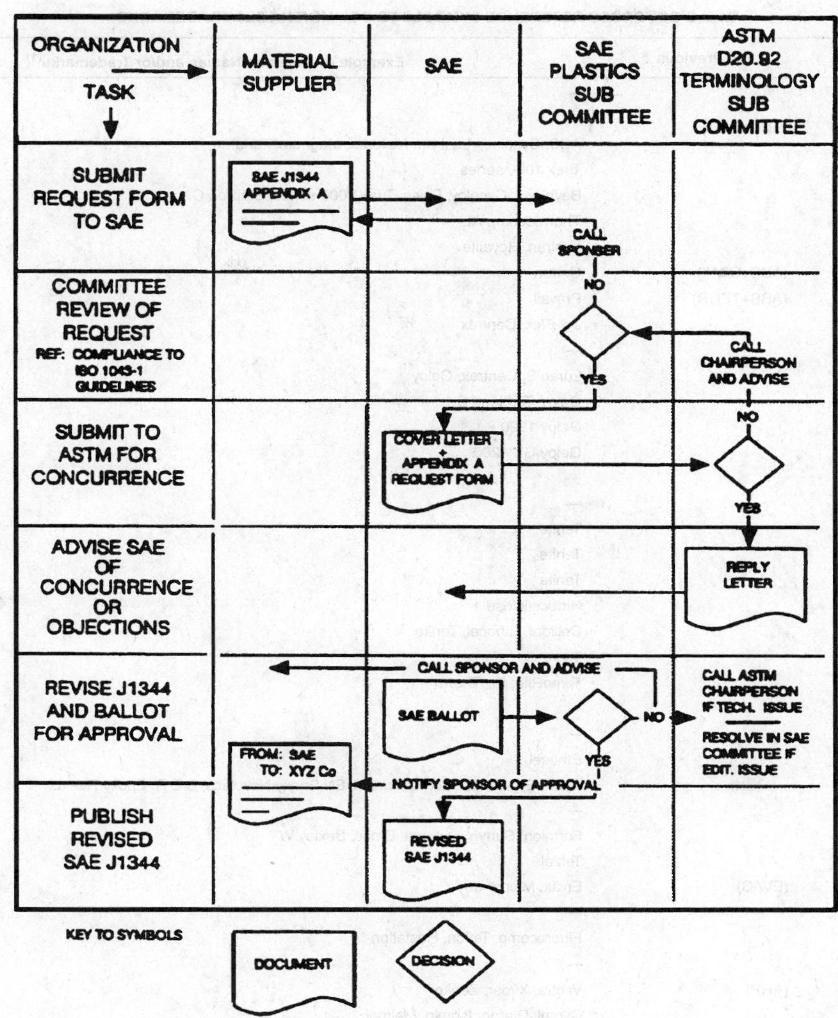

FIGURE B1—PROCESS FLOW CHART—ADDING NEW SYMBOLS TO SAE J1344

APPENDIX C
CROSS REFERENCE SYMBOLS TO COMMON NAMES/TRADEMARKS

C.1 See Table C1.

TABLE C1—CROSS REFERENCE SYMBOLS TO COMMON NAMES/TRADEMARKS

Standard Symbol	Previous	Example of Common Names and/or Trademarks[1]
AB		—
A/B/A		—
ABS		ABS, Cycolac, Lustran, Novodur, Magnum, Terluran,
ABS+PA		Triax 1000 series
ABS+PC		Bayblend, Cycoloy, Pulse, Triax 2000 series, Stapron C
ABS+PTFE		Thermocomp AL
ABS+PVC		Lustran, Royalite
ABS+SMA	(ABS+S/MA)	Cadon
ABS+TPU	(ABS+TPUR)	Prevail
AES		Jet-Flex, Centrex
AMMA		—
ASA		Luran S, Centrex, Geloy
ASA+PC		Geloy, Terblend S
ASA+PMMA		Geloy 1320
ASA+PVC		Geloy GY 1200
CMC		—
CS		—
CA		Tenite
CAB		Tenite
CAP		Tenite
CN		Nitrocellulose
CP		Cellidor, Ethocel, Tenite
CPE		Tyrin
CPVC		TempRite, ProTherm
CP		—
CTA		—
EC		Ethocel
EP		Epon, Epotuf, Epolite, Epocast, DEN Epoxy Novolacs, D.E.R. Epoxy Resins
E/EA		—
E/MA		Formion, Surlyn, Optema, Emac, Bexloy W
E/TFE		Tefzel
E/VAC	(EVAC)	Elvax, Microthane
FCEA		—
FEP		Fluorocomp, Teflon, Hostaflon
FF		—
LCP	(ARP)	Vectra, Xydar, Zenite
MF		Cymel, Diaron, Isomin, Melmac
PA+PE		Selar RB
PA+SAN		N5
PA6		Nylon 6, Akulon, Ashlene, Capron, Nydur, Nylatron, Nypel, Texalon, Thermocomp, Ultramid, Wellamid, Durethan, Grilon, Celanese Nylon, Zytel
PA66		Nylon 66, Akulon, Ashlene, Maranyl, Minlon, Nylafil, Nylatron, Texalon, Technyl, Ultramid, Vydyne, Wellamid, Zytel, Grilon, Celanese Nylon
PA46		Nylon 46, Stanyl
PA66/6		Nylon 66/6, Zytel, Wellamid, Capron, Ultramid C, Vydyne
PA69		Nylon 69, Vydyne
PA11		Nylon 11, Rilsan, RTP, Thermocomp, Lubricomp, CTI Nylon
PA12		Nylon 12, Grilamid, Rilsan,Thermocomp, Ashlene
PA610		Nylon 610, Hiloy, Maranyl, Nylafil, RTP, Ultramid S
PA612		Nylon 612, Grilon, Zytel, CTI Nylon, Lubricomp
PA6T/MPMDT		Polyamide copolymer based on terephthalic acid, hexamethylenediamine, and 2-methylpantemethylenediamine, Zytel HTN
PAE		—
PAEK		Kadel, Ultrapec, Victrex
PAI		Torlon
PARA		Aramid, Mindel, Vespel, Ixef
PAS	(PASU)	Radel
PAT		Apec, Ardel, Arylon, Durel, Econol
PB		Duraflex
PBT		Celanex, Petra, Pocan, Ultradur, Valox, Vandar, Wellite, Crastin
PBT+ASA		Ultradur S
PBT+PET		Celanex, Valox

TABLE C1—CROSS REFERENCE SYMBOLS TO COMMON NAMES/TRADEMARKS (continued)

Standard Symbol	Previous	Example of Common Names and/or Trademarks[1]
PBT+PPE		Gemax
PC		Calibre, Lexan, Makrolon
PC+PBT		Makroblend, Valox, Xenoy
PC+PCT		Eastar, Eastalloy
PC+PE		Lexan
PC+PET		Maekroblend, Valox
PC+SMA	(PC+S/MA)	Arloy
PC+TPU	(PC+TPUR)	Texin
PCT		Thermx
PCTFE		Aclar, Halon, Kel-F
PDAP	(DAP)	Dapon, Durex, Poly-Dap
PDCPD		Metton LMR, Telene
PE-HD	(HDPE)	Alathon, Bakelite, Chevron HiD, Empee, Fortiflex, Hi-Fax, Hostalen, Lupolen, Marlex, Paxon, Petrothene, Polyfort, Vestolen
PE-LD	(LDPE)	Alathon, Bakelite,Empee, Esocrene Fortiflex, Petrothene
PE-LLD	(LLDPE)	Alathon, Bakelite, Esocrene, Fortiflex, Petrothene, Dowlex
PE-LMD	(LMDPE)	—
PE-ULD	(ULDPE)	Attane
PE-MD	(MDPE)	Bakelite, Esocrene, Fortiflex, Marlex, Petrothene
PEBA		Dynyl, Estamid(ester), Pebax, Vestamid
PEI		Ultem
PEK		Victrex PEK
PEOX	(PEO)	Hostalen
PES	(PESU)	Ultrason E, Radel A, Victrex PES
PET		Impet, Petlon, Petra, Rynite, Ultradur, Valox, Wellpet, Bexloy K
PET+PMMA		Ropet
PF		Phenolic, Durez, Plenco
PFF		—
PK		Carilon
PI		Envex, Gemon, Kinel, Pyralin, Skybond, Vespel
PIB		Oppanol B
PMMA		Acrylic, Acrylite, Diakon, Oroglas, Plexiglas, XT Polymer, Vedril
PMMI		Kamax
PMP		TPX
POB		Ekkcel
POM		Acetal, Celcon, Delrin, Hostaform, Ultraform
POM+PTFE		Delrin AF, Thermocomp KL
PP		Adpro, Astryn, Azdel, Daplen, FB, Escorene, Hifax, Hostacom, Hostalen, Marlex, Moplen, Mytex, Novolen, Oleflo, Polyfort, Pro-fax, Tenite
PPA		Amodel
PPE	(PPO)	Noryl, Prevex (see BLENDS, Table 2)
PPE+PA	(PA+PPE)	Noryl GTX
PPE+PS		Noryl, Prevex
PPOX		—
PPS		Fortron, Ryton, Supec, Tedur
PPS+PTFE		Polycomp, Alfon SM
PPSU		Udel, Radel R, Ultrason
PS		Dylene, Durathon, Lustrex, Polystyrol, Tuf-Flex, Styron
PSU		Udel, Ultrason S
PSU+ABS		Mindel A
PSU+PC		Mindel S
PSU+PET		Mindel B
PTFE		Fluon, Hostaflon, Teflon
PUR		Adiprane, Bayflex, Casthetane, Cyanaprene, Desmopan, Spectrim, Estane, Elastoflex, Elastolit
PUR-RT		Isoplast
PVAC		Gelva, Vinylite
PVAL		Evanol, Gelvatol
PVB		Butvar, Vinylite, Butacite
PVC		Apex, Geon, Gracon, Pliovic, Polyvin, Unichem, Trosiplast, Vinoflex
PVC+CPE		Hostalite Z
PVC+NBR		Hycar, Paracil, Ozo, Vynite
PVC+PUR		DKE+450, Kydex
PVCA	(PVC+PU)	Vythene
PVF		Tedlar
PVFM		Formvar
PVDC		Saran
PVDF		Kynar

TABLE C1—CROSS REFERENCE SYMBOLS TO COMMON NAMES/TRADEMARKS (continued)

Standard Symbol	Previous	Example of Common Names and/or Trademarks[1]
PVK		—
PVP		Luvican
SI		Silastic, NuSil, RTV-2, GE RTV Silicone
SAN		Lustran, Luran, Tyril
SB		Forsacryl, K-Resin
SMA	(S/MA)	Cadon, Dylark, Stapron S, Styrolux
SMA+PS	(S/MA+PS)	Cadon (see BLENDS, Table 2)
TPES		Thermoplastic Polyester
TECEA		Alcryn
TEO	(TPO)(E/P)	Ektar, Ferroflex, Moplen, Polytrope, Prolastomer, Dexflex, Salflex, Sarlink, Santoprene, Sarlink 2000, Sarlink 3000, Telcar, Trefsin, Vistaflex, Vyram
TEEE	(EEBC)	Hytrel, Lomod, Riteflex BP, TEP
TEEE + PBT		Vandar, Bexloy V
TPU	(TPUR)(RTPU)	Bayflex, Cytor, Estane, Orthane, Pellathane, Polypur, Texin, Desmopan, Elastollan
TES	(SEBS)	Elexar, Kraton
UF		Plaskon, Skanopal
UP		BMC, SMC, XMC, Derakene, Premi-Glas, Selectron, Vibrin-Mat
VC/E		—
VC/E/MA		—
VC/MA		—

1. The trademarks listed are intended as a guide to aid the user in selecting the correct standard SAE symbol for the material under consideration. It is no intended or implied that the listing is a material approved for any given specification or application nor is the listing complete for any one plastic "family" name since additional materials may be available which are not marketed under a trademark.

APPENDIX D
CROSS REFERENCE LIST
SPI/PBI PLASTIC CONTAINER MARKING CODES
TO
SAE PART MARKING SYMBOLS

D.1 See Figure D1.

MATERIAL	SPI/PBI CODE	SAE CODE
POLYETHYLENE TEREPHTHALATE	1 PETE	> PET <
HIGH DENSITY POLYETHYLENE	2 HDPE	> PE-HD <
POLYVINYL CHLORIDE	3 V	> PVC <
LOW DENSITY POLYETHYLENE	4 LDPE	> PE-LD <
POLYPROPYLENE	5 PP	> PP <
POLYSTYRENE	6 PS	> PS <
ALL OTHER RESINS	7 OTHER	SEE TABLES 1 & 2

NOTE: SPI - THE SOCIETY OF THE PLASTICS INDUSTRY, INC
PBI - PLASTIC BOTTLE INSTITUTE

FIGURE D1—CROSS REFERENCE LIST SPI/PBI PLASTIC CONTAINER MARKING CODES TO SAE PART MARKING SYMBOLS

APPENDIX E
CROSS REFERENCE LISTING—TRADEMARKS/SUPPLIERS

E.1 Table E1 is intended to assist in the cross referencing of tradmarks as listed in Table C1 to their suppliers.

TABLE E1—CROSS REFERENCE LISTING—TRADEMARKS/SUPPLIERS

TRADEMARKS[(1)]	SUPPLIER	SYMBOL	PLASTIC "FAMILY" NAME
ACLAR	AUSIMONT	PCTFE	POLYCHLOROTRIFLUOROETHYLENE
ACRYLITE	CYRO INDUSTRIES	PMMA	POLY(METHYLMETHACRYLATE)("ACRYLIC"
ADIPRANE	UNIROYAL INC.	PUR	POLYURETHANE, THERMOSET (UNSATURATED)
ADPRO	GENESIS POLYMERS	PP	POLYPROPYLENE
AKULON	DSM ENGINEERING PLASTICS	P6, PA66	POLYAMIDE 6 & 66—"NYLON 6 & 66"
ALATHON	DUPONT DE NEMOURS & CO.	PE-LD, PE-HD, PE-LLD	POLYETHYLENE, LOW, HIGH, LINEAR LOW DENSITY
ALCRYN	DUPONT DE NEMOURS & CO.	TECEA	THERMOPLASTIC ELASTOMER: CHLORINATED ETHYLENE ALLOY
ALTON	INTERNATIONAL POLYMERS	PPS+PTFE	POLYPHENYLENE SULFIDE + POLYTETRA FLUORETHYLENE
AMODEL	AMOCO CHEMICAL CORP	PPA	POLY PHTHALAMIDE
AMPOL	AMERICAN POLYMERS INC	CA	CELLULOSE ACETATE
APEC	BAYER CORP.	PAT	POLYARYLATE -POLYESTER, THERMOPLASTIC
APEX	TEKNOR APEX CO.	PVC	POLY(VINYL CHLORIDE)
ARALDRITE	CIBA-GEIGY CORP.	EP	EPOXIDE: EPOXY
ARDEL	AMOCO CHEMICAL CORP	PAT	POLYARYLATE -POLYESTER, THERMOPLASTIC
ARLOY	ARCO CHEMICAL CO	PC+SMA	POLYCARBONTE + STYRENE MALEIC ANHYDRIDE
ARNITE	DSM ENGINEERING PLASTICS	PBT, PET	POLYBUTYLENE TEREPHTHALATE, POLYETHYLENE TEREPHTHALATE
ARYLON	DUPONT DE NEMOURS & CO.	PAT	POLYARYLATE -POLYESTER, THERMOPLASTIC
ASHLENE	ASHLEY POLYMERS	PA6, PA66, PA12	POLYAMIDE 6, 66, & 12—"NYLON 6, 66 & 12"
ASTREL	AMOCO CHEMICAL CORP.	PAS	POLYARYLSULFONE
ASTRYN	MONTELL	PP	POLYPROPYLENE
AZDEL	AZDEL INC.	PP	POLYPROPYLENE
BAKELITE	UNION CARBIDE CORP.	PE-LD, PE-MD, PE-HD	POLYETHYLENE, LOW, MEDIUM, HIGH DENSITY
BAKELITE	UNION CARBIDE CORP.	PF	PHENOL FORMALDEHYDE
BAKELITE	UNION CARBIDE CORP.	PE-LLD	POLYETHYLENE, LINEAR LOW DENSITY
BAYBLEND	BAYER CORP.	ABS+PC	ACRYLONITRILE/BUTADIENE/STYRENE + POLYCARBONATE
BAYFLEX	BAYER CORP.	PUR	POLYURETHANE, THERMOSET
BAYFLEX	BAYER CORP.	TPU	POLYURETHANE THERMOPLASTIC ELASTOMER
BEXLOY	DUPONT DE NEMOURS & CO	PET	POLYETHYLENE TEREPHTHALATE
BEXLOY V	DUPONT DE NEMOURS & CO	TEEE + PBT	ETHER ESTER BLOCK COPOLYMER + POLYBUTYLENE TEREPHTHLATE
BEXLOY W	DUPONT DE NEMOURS & CO.	EMA	ETHYLENE/METHACRYLIC ACID
BUTACITE	DUPONT DE NEMOURS & CO.	PVB	POLY(VINYL BUTYRAL)
BUTVAR	BAYER CORP.	PVB	POLY(VINYL BUTYRAL)
CADON	BAYER CORP.	ABS	ACRYLONITRILE/BUTADIENE/STYRENE
CADON	MONSANTO CO.	ABS+SMA	ACRYLONITRILE/BUTADIENE/STYRENE + STYRENE MALEIC ANHYDRIDE
CADON	MONSANTO CO.	SMA	STYRENE MALEIC ANHYDRIDE
CALIBRE	DOW CHEMICAL CO.	PC	POLYCARBONATE
CAPRON	ALLIED SIGNAL	PA6, PA6/66	POLYAMIDE 6, 6/66—"NYLON 6, 6/66"
CARILON	SHELL	PK	POLYKETONE
CELANESE	HOECHST CELANESE	PA66	POLYAMIDE 66("NYLON 66"
CELANEX	HOECHST CELANESE	PBT	POLYBUTYLENE TEREPHTHALATE
CELANEX	HOECHST CELANESE	PBT+PET	POLYBUTHYLENE TEREPHTHALATE + POLYETHYLENE TEREPHTHALATE
CELCON	HOECHST CELANESE	POM	POLYOXYMETHYLENE: POLYFORMALDEHYDE — "ACETAL"
CENTREX	BAYER CORP.	ASA	ACRYLONITRILE/STYRENE/ACRYLATE
CENTREX	BAYER CORP.	ASA + AEC	ACRYLONITRILE/STYRENE/ACRYLATE + ACRYLONITRILE/ETHYHLENE/STYRENE
CHEVRON H.D	CHEVRON CHEMICAL CO.	PE-HD	POLYETHYLENE, HIGH DENSITY
CORVEL	POLYMER CORP.	EP	EPOXIDE
CTI NYLON	CTI	PA11, PA6/12	POLYAMIDE 11, 6/12, "NYLON 11, 6/12"
CYANAPRENE	AMERICAN CYANAMID CO.	PUR	POLYURETHANE, THERMOSET (UNSATURATED)
CYCOLAC	GENERAL ELECTRIC CO.	ABS	ACRYLONITRILE/BUTADIENE/STYRENE
CYCOLOY	GENERAL ELECTRIC CO.	ABS+PC	ACRYLONITRILE/BUTADIENE/STYRENE + POLYCARBONATE
CYCOLIN	GENERAL ELECTRIC CO.	ABS + PBT	ACRYLONITRILE/BUTADIENE/STYRENE + POLYBUTYLENE TEREPHTHALATE
CYCOVIN K	GENERAL ELECTRIC CO.	ABS+PVC	ACRYLONITRILE/BUTADIENE/STYRENE + POLYVINYL CHLORIDE
CYMEL	AMERICAN CYANAMID CO.	MD	MELAMINE-FORMALDEHYDE
CRASTIN	DUPONT DE NEMOURS & CO	PBT	POLYBUTYLENE TERPHTHALATE
CYROLITE	CYRO INDUSTRIES	MMA/S/EA + B/MMA/S	POLY(METHYL METHACRYLATE)/STYRENE, ETHYL ACRYLATE + POLY(BUTADIENE)/ METHYL METHACRYLATE/STYRENE
CYTOR	UNKNOWN	TPU	POLYURETHANE, THERMOPLASTIC
DAPLEN	POLYDAN INTERNATIONAL	PP	POLYPROPYLENE
DAPON	POLYDAN INTERNATIONAL	PDAP	POLY(DIALLYL PHTHALATE)

TABLE E1—CROSS REFERENCE LISTING—TRADEMARKS/SUPPLIERS (continued)

TRADEMARKS[1]	SUPPLIER	SYMBOL	PLASTIC "FAMILY" NAME
DELRIN	DUPONT DE NEMOURS & CO.	POM	POLYOXYMETHYLENE: POLYFORMALDEHYDE — "ACETAL"
DELRIN AF	DUPONT DE NEMOURS & CO.	POM+PTFE	POLYOXYMETHYLENE + POLYTETRA FLUORETHYLENE
DERAKANE	DOW CHEMICAL CO.	EP	EPOXY VINYL ESTER RESINS
DESMOPAN	BAYER CORP.	PUR	POLYURETHANE, THERMOSET (UNSATURATED)
DEXFLEX	D&S PLASTICS	TEO	THERMOPLASTIC POLYOLEFIN ELASTOMER
DIAKON	ICI HYDE GROUP	PMMA	POLY(METHYL METHACRYLATE)—"ACRYLIC"
DIARON	REICHOLD CHEMICALS INC.	MF	MELAMINE-FORMALDEHYDE
DIAMOND ABS	DIAMOND	ABS	ACRYLONITRILE BUTADIENE STYRENE
DKE+450	SUMITOMO CORP. OF AMERICA	PVC+PMMA	POLYVINYL CHLORIDE + POLYMETHYL METHACRYLATE
DOWLEX	DOW CHEMICAL CO.	PE-LLD	POLYETHYLENE: LINEAR, LOW
DURAFLEX	SHELL CHEMICAL CO.	PB	POLYBUTENE-1
DURATHAN	BAYER CORP.	PA6	POLYAMIDE 6—"NYLON 6"
DURATHON	BAYER CORP.	PS	POLYSTYRENE
DURETHAN	BAYER CORP.	PA6, PA66	POLYAMIDE 6 & 66—"NYLON 6 & 66"
DUREZ	OCCIDENTAL CHEMICAL	PDAP	POLYDIALLYL PHTHALATE)
DUREZ	OCCIDENTAL CHEMICAL	PF	PHENOL FORMALDEHYDE
DURILITE	UNKNOWN	EC	ETHYL CELLULOSE
DYLARK	ARCO CHEMICAL CO.	SMA	STYRENE MALEIC ANHYDRIDE
DYLENE	ARCO CHEMICAL CO.	PS	POLYSTYRENE
DYNYL	RHONE POULENC INC.	PEBA	POLYETHER BLOCK AMIDE, THERMOPLASTIC ELASTOMER
ECONOL	SOHIO CHEMICAL CO.	PAT	POLYARYLATE -THERMOPLASTIC POLYESTER
EKKCEL	CARBORUNDUM CO.	POB	POLY-P-OXYBENZOATE
EASTAPAC	EASTMAN CHEMICAL	PET	POLY(ETHYLENE TEREPHTHALALTE)
EASTAR	EASTMAN CHEMICAL, INC	PCT	POLYCYCLOHEXYLENE TEREPHTHALATE
EASTAR FB	EASTMAN CHEMICAL, INC	PET	POLY(ETHYLENE TEREPTHALATE)
EASTAR MB	EASTMAN CHEMICAL, INC	PC+PCT	POLYCARBONATE + POLYCYCLOHEXYLENE TEREPHTHALATE
EASTAR MB	EASTMAN CHEMICAL, INC	PC+PET	POLYCARBONATE + POLYETHYLENE TEREPHTHALATE
ELASTOFLEX	BASF CORP.	PUR	POLYURETHANE, THERMOSET
ELASTOFOAM	BASF CORP.	PUR	POLYURETHANE, THERMOSET
ELASTOLIT	BASF CORP.	PUR	POLYURETHANE, THERMOSET
ELASTOLLAN	BASF CORP.	TPU	THERMOPLASTIC POLYURETHANE
ELEXAR	SHELL CHEMICAL CO.		STYRENE-BUTADIENE
ELEXAR	SHELL CHEMICAL CO.	TES	THERMOPLASTIC ELASTOMER—STYRENE BLOCK COPOLYMER
ELVAX	DUPONT DE NEMOURS & CO.	E/VAC	ETHYLENE/VINYL ACETATE
EMAC	CHEVRON	E/MA	ETHYLENE/METHACRYLIC ACRYLATE
EMPEE	MONMOUTH PLASTICS INC.	PE-LD, PE-MD	POLYETHYLENE, LOW, MEDIUM DENSITY
ENVEX	ROGERS CORP.	PI	POLYIMIDE
EPOCAST	CIBA-GEIGY	EP	EPOXIDE: EPOXY
EPOLITE	HEXCEL	EP	EPOXIDE: EPOXY
EPON	SHELL CHEMICAL CO.	EP	EPOXIDE: EPOXY
EPOTUF	REICHOLD CHEMICALS INC.	EP	EPOXIDE: EPOXY
ESCORENE	EXXON CHEMICAL AMERICAS	PE-LD, PE-LLD, PE-MD	POLYETHYLENE: LOW, LINEAR LOW, MEDIUM DENSITY
ESCORENE	EXXON CHEMICAL AMERICAS	PP	POLYPROPYLENE
ESTANE	B.F. GOODRICH CHEMICAL	ABS+TPU	ACRYLONITRILE/BUTADIENE/ STYRENE + THERMOPLASTIC POLYURETHANE ELASTOMER
ESTANE	B.F. GOODRICH CHEMICAL	TPU	THERMOPLASTIC POLYURETHANE ELASTOMER
ETHOCEL	DOW CHEMICAL CO.	EC	ETHYL CELLULOSE
EVANOL	UNKNOWN	PVAL	POLY(VINYL ALCOHOL)
FERROFLEX	FERRO CORP.	TEO	THERMOPLASTIC POLYOLEFIN ELASTOMER
FIBERFIL	DSM ENGINEERING PLASTICS	ABS, PP	ACRYLONITRILE BUTADIENE STYRENE, POLYPROPYLENE
FIBERCO	POLYMER COMPOSITES INC.	PA6, PA66	POLYAMIDE 6 & 66—"NYLON 6 & 66"
FLUON	ICI AMERICAS INC.	PTFE	POLYTETRAFLUOROETHYLENE
FLUOROCOMP	LNP CORPORATION	FEP	PERFLUORO (ETHYLENE/PROPYLENE)
FORMION	A. SCHULMAN INC.	E/MA	ETHYLENE METHACRYLATE ACID
FORMVAR	MONSANTO CO.	PVFM	POLY(VINYL FORMAL)
FORSACRYL	UNKNOWN	SAN	STYRENE-ACRYLONITRILE
FORTIFLEX	SOLVAY POLYMERS INC.	PE-LD, PE-MD, PE-HD, PE-LLD	POLYETHYLENE, LOW, MEDIUM, HIGH, LINEAR LOW DENSITY LINEAR LOW DENSITY
FORTRON	HOECHST CELANESE	PPS	POLY(PHENYLENE SULFIDE)
GE RTV	GENERAL ELECTRIC CO.	SI	SILICONE
GELOY 1200	GENERAL ELECTRIC CO.	ASA+PVC	ACRYLONITRILE/STYRENE/ ACRYLATE + POLYVINYL CHLORIDE
GELOY 1320	GENERAL ELECTRIC CO.	ASA+PMMA	ACRYLONITRILE/STYRENE/ ACRYLATE + POLYMETHYL METHACRYLATE BLEND
GELVA	MONSANTO CO.	PVAC	POLY(VINYL ACETATE)

TABLE E1—CROSS REFERENCE LISTING—TRADEMARKS/SUPPLIERS (continued)

TRADEMARKS[1]	SUPPLIER	SYMBOL	PLASTIC "FAMILY" NAME
GELVATOL	MONSANTO CO.	PVAL	POLY(VINYL ALCOHOL)
GEMAX	GENERAL ELECTRIC CO.	PBT+PPE	POLYBUTYLENE TEREPHTHALATE + POLYPHENYLENE ETHER BLEND
GEMON	GENERAL ELECTRIC CO.	PI	POLYIMIDE
GEON	B.F. GOODRICH CHEMICAL	PVC	POLY(VINYL CHLORIDE)
GEON	B.F. GOODRICH CHEMICAL	VC/VDC	VINYL CHLORIDE/VINYLIDENE CHLORIDE
GRACON	W.R. GRACE CO.	PVC	POLY(VINYL CHLORIDE)
GRILON	EMS AMERICAN GRILON	PA 6, PA66, PA11, PA12	POLYAMIDE 6, 66, 11, AND 12—"NYLON 6, 66, 11, AND 12"
HALAR	ALLIED SIGNAL	PCTFE	POLYCHLOROTRIFLUOROETHYLENE
HALAR	ALLIED SIGNAL	PTFE	POLYTERAFLUOROETHYLENE
HIFAX	MONTELL	TEO	THERMOPLASTIC POLYOLEFIN ELASTOMER
HOSTACOM	HOECHST AG	PP	POLYPROPYLENE
HOSTADUR	HOECHST AG	PET	POLYETHYLENE TEREPHTHALATE
HOSTAFLON	HOECHST AG	PTFE	POLYTETRAFLUOROETHYLENE
HOSTAFORM	HOECHST AG	POM	POLYOXYMETHYLENE: POLYFORMALDEHYDE—"ACETAL"
HOSTALEN	HOECHST AG	PE-HD	POLYETHYLENE, HIGH DENSITY
HOSTALEN GUR	HOECHST AG	PE-UHMW	POLYETHYLENE, ULTRA-HIGH MOLECULAR WEIGHT
HOSTALEN PP	HOECHST AG	PP	POLYPROPYLENE
HOSTALITE Z	HOECHST AG	PVC+CPE	POLYVINYL CHLORIDE + CHLORINATED POLYETHYLENE
HYCAR	B.F. GOODRICH CHEMICAL	PVC+NBR	POLYVINYL CHLORIDE + NITRILE BUTADIENE RUBBER
HYTREL	DUPONT DE NEMOURS & CO.	TEEE	THERMOPLASTIC ELASTOMER - ETHER ESTER BLOCK COPOLYMER
IMPET	HOECHST CELANESE	PET	POLYETHYLENE TEREPHTHALATE
ISOMIN	UNKNOWN	MF	MELAMINE-FORMALDEHYDE
ISOPLAST	DOW CHEMICAL CO.	PUR	RIGIG THERMOPLASTIC POLYURETHANE
IXEF	SOLVAY	PARA	POLYARYLAMID (POLYARAMIDE)
JETFLEX	MULTIBASE	AES	ACRYLONITRILE/ETHYLENE/STYRENE
KADEL		PAEK	POLYARYLETHERKETONE
KAMAX	ROHM & HAAS CO.	PMMI	POLY(METHYLMETHACRYLATE IMIDE)
KEL-F	3M COMPANY	PCTFE	POLYCHLOROTRIFLUOROETHYLENE
KINEL	RHONE POULENC INC.	PI	POLYIMIDE
KOBLEND	ENICHEM	ABS + PC	ACRYLONITRILE/BUTADIENE/STYRENE
KRALASTIC FVM	UNIROYAL INC.	ABS + PVC	ACRYLONITRILE/BUTADIENE/STYRENE + POLYVINYL CHLORIDE
KRATON	SHELL CHEMICAL CO.	TES	THERMOPLASTIC ELASTOMER STYRENE BLOCK COPOLYMER
KYDEX	ROHM & HAAS CO.	PVC+PMMA	POLYVINYL CHLORIDE + POLYMETHYL METHACRYLATE
KYNAR	ATOHAAS	PVDF	POLY(VINYLIDENE FLUORIDE)
K-RESINS	PHILLIPS CHEMICAL CO.	S/B	STYRENE-BUTADIENE
LEXAN	GENERAL ELECTRIC CO.	PC	POLYCARBONATE PLASTICS
LEXAN	GENERAL ELECTRIC CO.	PC+PE	POLYCARBONATE + POLYETHYLENE
LOMOD	GENERAL ELECTRIC CO.	TEEE	THERMOPLASTIC ELASTOMER (ETHER ESTER BLOCK COPOLYMER
LUPOLEN	BASF CORP.	PE-HD	POLYETHYLENE, HIGH DENSITY
LURAN	BASF CORP.	ASA	ACRYLONITRILE/STYRENE/ACRYLATE
LURAN	BASF CORP.	SAN	STYRENE/ACRYLONITRILE
LUSTRAN	BAYER CORP.	ABS	ACRYLONITRILE/BUTADIENE/STYRENE
LUSTRAN	BAYER CORP.	ABS+PVC	ACRYLONITRILE/BUTADIENE/STYRENE + POLYVINYL CHLORIDE
LUSTRAN	BAYER CORP.	SAN	STYRENE/ACRYLONITRILE
LUSTREX	POLYSAR INC.	PS	POLYSTYRENE
LUVICAN	BASF CORP.	PVK	POLYVINYLCARBAZOLE
MAKROBLEND	BAYER CORP.	PC+PBT	POLYCARBONATE + POLYBUTYLENE TEREPHTHALATE
MAKROBLEND	BAYER CORP.	PC+PET	POLYCARBONATE + POLYETHYLENE TEREPHTHALATE
MAKROLON	BAYER CORP.	PC	POLYCARBONATE PLASTICS
MAGNUM	DOW CHEMICAL CO.	ABS	ACRYLONITRILE/BUTADIENE/STYRENE
MARLEX	PHILLIPS CHEMICAL CO.	PE-MD, PE-HD	POLYETHYLENE, MEDIUM, HIGH DENSITY
MARLEX	PHILLIPS CHEMICAL CO.	PP	POLYPROPYLENE
MELMAC	PHILLIPS CHEMICAL CO.	MF	MELAMINE-FORMALDEHYDE
METTON LMR	METTON AMERICA INC.	PDCPD	POLYDICYCLOPENTADIENE
MICROTHANE	UNKNOWN	EVAC	ETHYLENE/VINYL ACETATE
MINDEL A	AMOCO CHEMICAL CORP.	PSU+ABS	POLYSULFONE + ABS
MINDEL B	AMOCO CHEMICAL CORP.	PSU+PET	POLY(PHENYLENE SULFONE)(POLYSULFONE + POLYETHYLENE TEREPHTHALATE
MINDEL S	AMOCO CHEMICAL CORP.	PSU+PC	POLYSULFONE + POLYCARBONATE
MINLON	DUPONT DE NEMOURS & CO.	PA66	POLYAMIDE 66—"NYLON 66"
MOPLEN	MONTELL	PP	POLYPROPYLENE
MULTI-ABS	MULTIBASE	ABS	ACRYLONITRILE BUTADIENE STYRENE
MULTIFLEX	MULTIBASE	SEBS	
N5	THERMOFIL INC.	PA+SAN	POLYAMIDE + STYRENE/ACRYLONITRILE
MYTEX	EXXON CHEMICAL CO	PP	POLYPROPYLENE
NORYL	GENERAL ELECTRIC CO.	PPE	POLYPHENYLENE ETHER PLASTICS
NORYL	GENERAL ELECTRIC CO.	PPE+PS	POLYPHENYLENE ETHER + HIGH IMPACT POLYSTYRENE

TABLE E1—CROSS REFERENCE LISTING—TRADEMARKS/SUPPLIERS (continued)

TRADEMARKS[1]	SUPPLIER	SYMBOL	PLASTIC "FAMILY" NAME
NORYL GTX	GENERAL ELECTRIC CO.	PPE+PA	POLYAMIDE + POLYPHENYLENE ETHER
NOVODUR	BAYER CORP.	ABS	ACRYLONITRILE/BUTADIENE/STYRENE
NOVOLEN	BASF CORP.	PP	POLYPROPYLENE
NUSIL	NUSIL	SI	SILICONE
NYDUR	BAYER CORP.	PA6	POLYAMIDE 6—"NYLON 6"
NYLATRON	DSM ENGINEERING PLASTICS	PA6, PA66	POLYAMIDE 6 & 66—"NYLON 6 & 66"
NYPEL	ALLIED SIGNAL	PA6	POLYAMIDE 6—"NYLON 6"
OLEFLO	AVISUN	PP	POLYPROPYLENE
OPPANOL B	BASF CORP.	PIB	POLYISOBUTYLENE
OPTEMA	EXXON	E/MA	ETHYLENE/METHACRYLIC ACID
OROGLAS	ROHM & HAAS CO.	PMMA	POLY(METHYL METHACRYLATE)—"ACRYLIC"
ORTHANE	EAGLE PICHER PLASTICS DIV.	TPU	POLYURETHANE, THERMOPLASTIC
OZO	UNKNOWN	PVC+NBR	POLYVINYL CHLORIDE + NITRILE BUTADIENE RUBBER
PARACRIL	UNIROYAL INC.	PVC+NBR	POLYVINYL CHLORIDE + NITRILE BUTADIENE RUBBER
PAXON	ALLIED SIGNAL	PE-HD	POLYETHYLENE, HIGH DENSITY
PEBAX	ELF ATO	PEBA	POLYETHER BLOCK AMIDE-THERMOPLASTIC ELASTOMER
PEEK	VICTREX, U.S.A., INC.	PAEK	POLYARYL ETHER KETONE
PELLETHANE	DOW CHEMICAL CO.	TPU	THERMOPLASTIC POLYURETHANE ELASTOMER
PENTON	HERCULES INC.	CPE	CHLORINATED POLYETHYLENE
POCAN	BAYER CORP.	PBT	POLYBUTYLENE TEREPHTHALATE
PETLON	BAYER CORP.	PET	POLYETHYLENE TEREPHTHALATE
PETRA	ALLIED SIGNAL	PBT	POLYBUTYLENE TEREPHTHALATE
PETRA	ALLIED SIGNAL	PET	POLYETHYLENE TEREPHTHALATE
PETROTHENE	QUANTUM CHEM., USI DIV.	PE-LD, PE-MD, PE-HD, PE-LLD	POLYETHYLENE, LOW, MEDIUM, HIGH, LINEAR LOW DENSITY
PLASKON	PLASKON ELECTRONIC MTLS.	UF	UREA-FORMALDEHYDE
PLENCO	PLASTICS ENGINEERING CO.	PF	PHENOL-FORMALDEHYDE
PLEXIGLAS	ROHM & HAAS CO.	PMMA	POLY(METHYL METHACRYLATE)—"ACRYLIC"
PLIOLITE	GOODYEAR TIRE & RUBBER	S/B	STYRENE-BUTADIENE
PLIOVIC	GOODYEAR TIRE & RUBBER	PVC	POLY(VINYL CHLORIDE)
POLYCOMP	LNP CORPORATION	PPS+PTFE	POLYPHENYLENE SULFIDE + FLUOROETHYLENE
POLYFABS	A. SCHULMAN INC.	ABS	ACRYLONITRILE BUTADIENE STYRENE
POLYFORT	A. SCHULMAN INC.	PE-HD	POLYETHYLENE, HIGH DENSITY
POLYFORT	A. SCHULMAN INC.	PP	POLYPROPYLENE
POLYLAC	CHI MEI	ABS	ACRYLONITRILE BUTADIENE STYRENE
POLYPUR	A. SCHULMAN INC.	TPU	THERMOPLASTIC POLYURETHANE ELASTOMER
POLYSTYROL	BASF CORP.	PS	POLYSTYRENE
POLYSTYROL	BASF CORP.	SB	STYRENE/BUTADIENE
POLYSTYROL SB	BASF CORP.	PS	POLYSTYRENE, HIGH IMPACT
POLYTROPE	A. SCHULMAN INC.	TEO	THERMOPLASTIC POLYOLEFIN ELASTOMER
POLYVIN	A. SCHULMAN INC.	PVC	POLY(VINYL CHLORIDE)
POLY-DAP	DAP	PDAP	POLY(DIALLYL PHTHALATE)
PREMI-GLAS	PREMIX INC.	UP	POLYESTER, UNSATURATED THERMOSET
PREVAIL	DOW CHEMICAL CO.	ABS+TPU	ACRYLONITRILE/BUTADIENE/STYRENE + THERMOPLASTIC URETHANE
PREVEX	GENERAL ELECTRIC CO.	PPE	POLYPHENYLENE ETHER PLASTICS
PREVEX	GENERAL ELECTRIC CO.	PPE+PS	POLYPHENYLENE ETHER + HIGH IMPACT POLYSTYRENE
PRO-FAX	MONTELL	PP	POLYPROPYLENE
PROLASTOMER	SYNTENE COMPANY	TEO	THERMOPLASTIC POLYOLEFIN ELASTOMER
PYRALIN	DUPONT DE NEMOURS & CO.	PI	POLYIMIDE
RADEL A	AMOCO CHEMICAL CORP.	PES	POLYETHERSULFONE
RADEL R	AMOCO CHEMICAL CORP.	PPSU	POLYPHENYLENE SULFONE
REXENE	REXENE	PE-LD	POLYETHYLENE, LOW DENSITY
RILSAN	ELF ATOCHEM	PA11, PA12	POLYAMIDE 11 & 12—"NYLON 11 & 12"
RITEFLEX BP	HOECHST CELANESE	TEEE	THERMOPLASTIC ELASTOMER—ETHER ESTER BLOCK COPOLYMER
ROPET	ROHM & HAAS CO.	PET+PMMA	POLYETHYLENE TEREPHTHALATE + POLYMETHYL METHACRYLATE
ROYALITE	ROYALITE TP	ABS + PVC	ACRYLONITRILE/BUTADIENE/STYRENE + POLYVINYL CHLORIDE
RYNITE	DUPONT DE NEMOURS & CO.	PET	POLYETHYLENE TEREPHTHALATE
RYTON	PHILLIPS CHEMICAL CO.	PPS	POLY(PHENYLENE SULFIDE)
SALFLEX	SALFLEX POLYMERS LTD	TEO	THERMOPLASTIC POLYOLEFIN ELASTOMER
SANTOPRENE	ADVANCED ELASTOMER SYS.	TEO	THERMOPLASTIC POLYOLEFIN ELASTOMER, FULLY CROSSLINKED
SARAN	DOW CHEMICAL CO.	PVDC	POLY(VINYLIDENE CHLORIDE)
SARLINK 2000	DSM THERMOPL.ELASTOM.	TEO	THERMOPLASTIC POLYOLEFIN ELASTOMER
SARLINK 3000	DSM THERMOPL.ELASTOM.	TEO	THERMOPLASTIC POLYOLEFIN ELASTOMER
SELAR RB	DUPONT DE NEMOURS & CO.	PA+PE-HD	POLYAMIDE + POLYETHYLENE
SELECTRON	PPG INDUSTRIES INC.	UP	POLYESTER, THERMOSET (UNSATURATED)
RTV-2	SILICONES INC.	SI	SILICONE

TABLE E1—CROSS REFERENCE LISTING—TRADEMARKS/SUPPLIERS (continued)

TRADEMARKS[1]	SUPPLIER	SYMBOL	PLASTIC "FAMILY" NAME
SILASTIC	DOW CORNING	SI	SILICONE
SINKRAL	ENICHEM	ABS	ACRYLONITRILE BUTADIENE STYRENE
SKANOPAL	PERSTORP INC.	UF	UREA-FORMALDEHYDE
SKYBOND	MONSANTO CO.	PI	POLYIMIDE
SNIAMID	NYLTECH	PA6	POLYAMIDE 6—"NYLON 6"
SPECTRIM	DOW CHEMICAL CO.	PUR	POLYURETHANE, THERMOSET
STANYL	DSM ENGINEERING PLASTICS	PA46	POLYAMIDE 46—"NYLON 46"
STAPRON C	DSM ENGINEERING PLASTICS	PC + ABS	POLYCARBONATE + ACRYLONITRILE BUTADIENE STYRENE
STAPRON E	DSM ENGINEERING PLASTICS	PC + PET	POLYCARBONATE + POLYETHYLENE TEREPHTHALATE
STAPRON N	DSM ENGINEERING PLASTICS	ABS + PA	ACRYLONITRILE BUTADIENE STYRENE + POLYAMIDE
STAPRON S	DSM ENGINEERING PLASTICS	SMA	STYRENE/MALEIC ANHYDRIDE
STYROLUX	WESTLAKE PLASTICS CO.	SB	STYRENE-BUTADIENE
STYRON	DOW CHEMICAL CO.	PS	POLYSTYRENE
SURLYN	DUPONT DE NEMOURS & CO.	EMA	ETHYLENE/METHACRYLIC ACID—"IONOMER"
TECHNYL	NYLTECH	PA66, PA66/6	POLYAMIDE 66, PA66/6—"NYLON 66"
TEDLAR	DUPONT DE NEMOURS & CO.	PVF	POLY(VINYL FLUORIDE)
TEFLON	DUPONT DE NEMOURS & CO.	FEP	PERFLUORO (ETHYLENE/PROPYLENE)
TEFLON	DUPONT DE NEMOURS & CO.	PTFE	POLYTETRAFLUOROETHYLENE
TEFLON Z	DUPONT DE NEMOURS & CO.	FEP	TETRAFLUOROETHYLENE/HEXA-FLUORO PROPYLENE
TEFZEL	DUPONT DE NEMOURS & CO.	ETFE	ETHYLENE/TETRAFLUOROETHYLENE
TELCAR	TEKNOR APEX CO.	TEO	THERMOPLASTIC POLYOLEFIN ELASTOMER
TELENE	BF GOODRICH CO.	PDCPD	POLYDICYCLOPENTADIENE
TEMPRITE	BF GOODRICH CO.	CPVC	CHLORINATED POLY(VINYL CHLORIDE)
TENITE	EASTMAN CHEM. PRODUCTS	CA	CELLULOSE ACETATE
TENITE	EASTMAN CHEM. PRODUCTS	CAB	CELLULOSE ACETATE BUTYRATE
TENITE	EASTMAN CHEM. PRODUCTS	CAP	CELLULOSE ACETATE PROPIONATE
TENITE	EASTMAN CHEM. PRODUCTS	CP	CELLULOSE PROPIONATE
TENITE	EASTMAN CHEM. PRODUCTS	PE-LD	POLYETHYLENE
TENITE	EASTMAN CHEM. PRODUCTS	PP	POLYPROPYLENE
TERBLEND S	BASF CORP.	ASA+PC	ACRYLONITRILE/STYRENE/ACRYLATE + POLYCARBONATE
TERLURAN	BAYER CORP.	ABS	ACRYLONITRILE/BUTADIENE/STYRENE
TETRAN	PENNWALT CORP.	PTFE	POLYTETRAFLUOROETHYLENE
TEXALON	TEXAPOL CORP.	PA6, PA66	POLYAMIDE 6 & 66—"NYLON 6 & 66"
TEXIN	BAYER CORP.	PC+TPU	POLYCARBONATE + THERMOPLASTIC POLYURETHANE
TEXIN	BAYER CORP.	TPU	POLYURETHANE, THERMOPLASTIC
THERMX	EASTMAN	PCT	POLYCYCLOHEXYLENE TERPHTHALATE
THERMO	UNKNOWN	CPE	CHLORINATED POLYETHYLENE
THERMOCOMP AL	LNP CORPORATION	ABS+PTFE	ACRYLONITRILE/BUTADIENE/STYRENE + POLYTETRA FLUOROETHYLENE
THERMOCOMP KL	LNP CORPORATION	POM+PTFE	POLYOXYMETHYLENE + POLYTETRA FLUOROETHYLENE
THERMOCOMP PF	LNP CORPORATION	PA6, PA66	POLYAMIDE 6 & 66—"NYLON 6 & 66"
TORLON	AMOCO CHEMICAL CORP.	PAI	POLYAMIDE-IMIDE
TPX	MITSUI & CO.	PMP	POLY(4-METHYLPENTENE-1)
TREFSIN	ADVANCED ELASTOMER SYS.	TEO	THERMOPLASTIC POLYOLEFIN ELASTOMER, FULLY CROSSLINKED
TRIAX 1000	BAYER CORP.	ABS+PA	ACRYLONITRILE/BUTADIENE/STYRENE + POLYAMIDE
TRIAX	BAYER CORP.	ABS+PC	ACRYLONITRILE/BUTADIENE/STYRENE + POLYCARBONATE
TROSIPLAST	KAY-FRIES INC.	PVC	POLY(VINYL CHLORIDE)
TYRIL	DOW CHEMICAL CO.	SAN	STYRENE/ACRYLONITRILE
TYRIN	DOW CHEMICAL CO.	CPE	CHLORINATED POLYETHYLENE
UDEL	AMOCO CHEMICAL CORP.	PSU	POLYSULFONE
ULTEM	GENERAL ELECTRIC CO.	PEI	POLYETHERIMIDE
ULTRABLEND	BASF CORP.	PBT+ASA	POLYBUTHYLENE TEREPHTHALATE + ACRYLONITRILE/STYRENE/ACRYLATE BLEND
ULTRAMID C	BASF CORP.	PA66/6	POLYAMIDE 66/6—"NYLON 66/6"
ULTRAMID S	BASF CORP.	PA610	POLYAMIDE 610—"NYLON 610"
ULTRADUR	BASF CORP.	PBT	POLYBUTYLENE TEREPHTHALATE
UTRAFORM	BASF CORP.	POM	POLYOXYMETHYLENE: POLYFORMALDEHYDE("ACETAL"
ULTRAMID	BASF CORP.	PA6, PA66	POLYAMIDE 6 & 66—"NYLON 6 & 66"
ULTRAMID T	BASF CORP.	PA6/PA6T	POLYAMIDE COPOLYMER
ULTRASON	BASF CORP.	PES	POLYETHER SULFONE
ULTRASON	BASF CORP.	PSU	POLYSULFONE
ULTRASON	BASF CORP.	PPSU	POLY(PHENYLENE SULFONE)
UNICHEM	COLORITE PLASTICS CO.	PVC	POLY(VINYL CHLORIDE)
UVEX	EASTMAN CHEM. PRODUCTS	CAB	CELLULOSE ACETATE BUTYRATE
VALOX	GENERAL ELECTRIC CO.		POLYBUTYLENE TEREPHTHALATE
VALOX	GENERAL ELECTRIC CO.	PBT+PET	POLYBUTYLENE TEREPHTHALATE + POLYETHYLENE TEREPHTHALATE
VANDAR	HOECHST CELANESE	TEEE + PBT	THERMOPLASTIC ELASTOMERS: ETHER ESTER BLOCK COPOLYMER + POLYBUTYLENE TEREPHTHALATE

TABLE E1—CROSS REFERENCE LISTING—TRADEMARKS/SUPPLIERS (continued)

TRADEMARKS[1]	SUPPLIER	SYMBOL	PLASTIC "FAMILY" NAME
VECTRA	HOECHST CELANESE	LCP	LIQUID CRYSTAL POLYMER- POLYESTER, THERMOPLASTIC
VEDRIL	VEDRIL SPA (SPAIN)	PMMA	POLY(METHYL METHACRYLATE)—"ACRYLIC"
VESPEL	DUPONT DE NEMOURS & CO.	PARA	POLYARYLAMID (POLYARAMIDE)—"ARAMID"
VESPEL	DUPONT DE NEMOURS & CO.	PI	POLYIMIDE
VESTAMID	HUELS AG/HUELS AMERICA	PA12	POLYAMIDE 12—"NYLON 12"
VIBRIN-MAT	U.S. RUBBER CO.	UP	POLYESTER, THERMOSET (UNSATURATED)
VINOFLEX	BASF CORP.	PVC	POLY(VINYL CHLORIDE)
VINYLITE	CANADIAN RESINS & CHEM	PVAC	POLY(VINYL ACETATE)
VINYLITE	CANADIAN RESINS & CHEM	PVB	POLY(VINYL BUTYRAL)
VINYLITE	CANADIAN RESINS & CHEM	PVC	POLY(VINYL CHLORIDE)
VINYLITE	CANADIAN RESINS & CHEM	VCVAC	VINYL CHLORIDE/VINYL ACETATE
VISTAFLEX	ESSO CHEMICALS (EUROPE)	TEO	THERMOPLASTIC POLYOLEFIN ELASTOMER
VYDYNE	MONSANTO CO.	PA66, PA66/6	POLYAMIDE 66—"NYLON 66", NYLON 66/6
VYNITE	ALLIED SIGNAL	PVC+NBR	POLYVINYL CHLORIDE + NITRILE BUTADIENE RUBBER
VYRAM	ADVANCED ELASTOMER SYST.	TEO	THERMOPLASTIC POLYOLEFIN ELASTOMER
VYTHENE	ALPHA CHEM. & PLASTICS CO.	PVC+PUR	POLYVINYL CHLORIDE + POLYURETHANE
WELLAMID	WELLMAN INC.	PA6, PA66, PA66/6	POLYAMIDE 6, 66, & 66/6—"NYLON 6, 66, & 66/6"
WELLITE	WELLMAN INC.	PBT	POLYBUTYLENE TEREPHTHALATE
WELLPET	WELLMAN INC.	PET	POLYETHYLENE TEREPHTHALATE
XENOY	GENERAL ELECTRIC CO.	PC+PBT	POLYCARBONATE + POLYBUTYLENE TEREPHTHALATE
XT POLYMER	CYRO INDUSTRIES	(MMA/S/AN + B/MMA/S)	POLY(METHYL METHACRYLATE), CO-STYRENE, CO-ACRYLONITRILE) + POLY(BUTADIENE, CO-METHYLMETHACRYLATE, CO-STYRENE)
XYDAR	AMOCO CHEMICAL CORP.	LCP	LIQUID CRYSTAL POLYMER-POLYESTER, THERMOPLASTIC
ZENITE	DUPONT DE NEMOURS & CO.	LCP	LIQUID CRYSTAL POLYMER-POLYESTER, THERMOPLASTIC
ZYTEL	DUPONT DE NEMOURS & CO.	PA 66, 66/6, 6	POLYAMIDE 66, 66/6, 6— "NYLON 66, 66/6, 6"
ZYTEL	DUPONT DE NEMOURS & CO.	PA612	POLYAMIDE 612—"NYLON 612"
ZYTEL HTN	DUPONT DE NEMOURS & CO.	PA6T/MPMDT	POLYAMIDE COPOLYMER...

1. The trademarks listed are intended as a guide to aid the user in selecting the correct standard SAE symbol for the material under consideration. It is not intended or implied that the listing is a material approval for any given specification or application nor is the listing complete for any one plastic "family" name since additional materials may be available which are not marketed under a trademark.

APPENDIX F
SYMBOLS FOR COMMONLY USED AUTOMOTIVE ELASTOMERS (BASED ON ISO 1629)

TABLE F1—ELASTOMERS, SYMBOLS

Elastomer	Standard Symbol
Acrylic rubber	ACM
Copolymer of ethylacrylate and acrylonitrile	ANM
Polyester urethane	AU
Polyether urethane	EU
Butadiene rubber	BR
Chloroprene rubber	CR
Chlorosulfonylpolyethylene	CSM
Epichlorohydrin copolymer	ECO
Terpolymer of ethylene, propylene, and a diene	EPDM
Fluoroelastomers	FPM
Fluorosilicone elastomer (with methyl groups)	FMQ
Fluorosilicone elastomer (with vinyl groups)	FVMQ
Silicone elastomer (with methyl groups only)	MQ
Silicone elastomer (with methyl and vinyl groups)	VMQ
Acrylonitrile/butadiene (nitrile) rubber	NBR
Carboxylated acrylonitrile/butadiene (nitrile) rubber	XNBR
Natural, isoprene rubber	NR
Styrene/butadiene rubber	SBR

CLASSIFICATION SYSTEM FOR AUTOMOTIVE POLYAMIDE (PA) PLASTICS—SAE J1639 MAY1995 SAE Recommended Practice

Report of the SAE Plastics Committee approved March 1993 and completely revised May 1995.

Foreword—This Document has not changed other than to put it into the new SAE Technical Standards Board Format.

1. Scope—This SAE Recommended Practice provides a system for classification and specification for limited number of polyamides (nylons) used in the Automotive Industry. Based upon ASTM D 4066, Classification System for Nylon Injection and Extrusion Materials (PA), it calls for additional descriptive characteristics and properties commonly used in the Automotive Industry.

This document applies to natural and non-color matched black, heat-stabilized polyamide compounds only. Color matched compounds shall be defined by the proprietary OEM standards.

This document allows for the use of recycled, reconstituted, and regrind materials provided that the requirements as stated in this document are met, the material has not been altered or modified to change its suitability for safe processing and use, and the material shall be identified as such.

1.1 Purpose—The purpose of this document is to:

a. Standardize the grades of unreinforced and reinforced polyamides (nylons) 66, 6, and 66/6 used for the Automotive Industry
b. Standardize the test methods used to characterize the properties of these materials
c. Provide a method for specifying these materials by the use of a simple line call-out designation

2. References

2.1 Applicable Publications—The following publications form a part of this specification to the extent specified herein. The latest issues of ISO, SAE, and ASTM publications shall apply.

2.1.1 SAE PUBLICATIONS—Available from SAE, 400 Commonwealth Drive, Warrendale, PA 15096-0001.

SAE J369—Flammability of Automotive Interior Materials-Horizontal Test Method
SAE J1756—Test Procedure to Determine the Fogging Characteristics of Interior Automotive Materials
SAE J1885—Exposure to Interior Xenon-Arc Weatherometer
SAE J1960—Exposure to Exterior Xenon-Arc Weatherometer
SAE J1976—Outdoor Weathering of Exterior Materials

2.1.2 ASTM PUBLICATIONS—Available from ASTM, 100 Barr Harbor Drive, West Conshohocken, PA 19428-2959.

ASTM D 789-92—Determination of Relative Viscosity, Melting Point, and Moisture Content of Polyamide (PA)
ASTM D 3763-93—High Speed Puncture Properties Plastics Using Load Displacement Sensors
ASTM D 4066-92a—Nylon Injection and Extrusion Materials (PA)
ASTM D 5279-92—Measuring Dynamic Mechanical Properties of Plastics in Torsion
ASTM E 831-86—Linear Thermal Expansion of Solid Materials by Thermomechanical Analysis

2.1.3 ISO PUBLICATIONS—Available from ANSI, 11 West 42nd Street, New York, NY 10036-8002.

ISO 75-1:1993—Plastics—Determination of temperature of deflection under load—Part 1: General test methods
ISO 75-2:1993—Plastics—Determination of temperature of deflection under load—Part 2: Plastic and Ebonite
ISO 105/A02:1993—Textiles—Grey scale for assessing change in color
ISO 178:1993—Plastics—Determination of flexural properties
ISO 180:1993—Plastics—Determination of Izod impact strength
ISO 188:1982—Rubber—Accelerated aging
ISO/DIS 294-1:1995—Plastics—Injection molding of test specimens of thermoplastic materials
ISO/DIS 294-3:1995—Plastics—Injection molding of test specimens of thermoplastic materials—Part 3: Plates (ISO mold type D)
ISO/DIS 294-4:1995—Plastics—Injection molding of test specimens of thermoplastic materials—Part 4: Determination of molding shrinkage
ISO 295:1991—Plastics—Compression molding of test specimens of thermosetting materials
ISO 527-1:1993—Plastics—Determination of tensile properties—Part 1: General principles
ISO 527-2:1993—Plastics—Determination of tensile properties—Part 2: Testing conditions
ISO 960:1988—Plastics—Polyamides (PA)—Determination of water content
ISO 1183:1987—Plastics—Methods for determining the density of non-cellular plastics
ISO 1874-2:1995—Plastics—Polyamide (PA) molding and extrusion materials—Part 2: Preparation of test specimens and determination of properties
ISO 3146:1985—Plastics—Determination of melting behavior of semi-crystalline polymers
ISO 3167:1993—Plastics—Preparation and use of multipurpose test specimen
ISO 3451/4:1986—Plastics—Determination of ash—Part 4: Polyamides
ISO 3795:1989—Road vehicles—Determination of burning behavior of interior materials for motor vehicles

2.1.4 AATCC GRAY SCALE PUBLICATION—Available from AATCC, P.O. Box 12215, Research Triangle Park, North Carolina 27709 and British Standard Institution, 10 Blackfriars Str., Manchester, M3 5TD, England.

AATCC Evaluation Procedure 1

2.1.5 FMVSS PUBLICATION—Available from The Superintendent of Documents, U.S. Government Printing Office, Washington, DC 20402.

FMVSS 302

2.2 Related Publications—The following publications are provided for information purposes only and are not a required part of this document.

2.2.1 SAE PUBLICATION—Available from SAE, 400 Commonwealth Drive, Warrendale, PA 15096-0001.

SAE J1344—Marking of Plastic Parts

2.2.2 ISO PUBLICATION—Available from ANSI, 11 West 42nd Street, New York, NY 10036-8002.

ISO 62:1980—Plastics—Determination of water absorption

3. Description

3.1 This classification system was developed to permit the addition of descriptive characteristics and values commonly used in Automotive Material Specifications for polyamides. All the requirements listed in Section 7 shall apply for initial qualification of the material. The requirements listed in Section 8 shall be required for initial qualification when the particular suffix is included in the line call-out for the material. The requirements listed in Appendix A, Table A1 for initial product certification shall be met with data representing 3 sigma values per 6.2. Production lots shall meet property control plan as agreed to between material supplier and user of this document.

4. Classification

4.1 Polyamide 6, 66, and 66/6 plastics are classified into "groups" based on the chemical composition. These groups are subdivided into "classes" and "grades" as shown in the Appendix A, Table A1.

4.2 An example of this classification system is as follows:

The designation PA1122 would indicate:

PA = polyamide (nylon)
11 = reinforced PA66
2 = glass reinforced, impact modified, heat stabilized
2 = 15% glass

5. Line Call-outs

5.1 A line call-out, which is a specification, shall contain this document's identification number and a material designation from Table 1 as illustrated in 4.2.

5.2 The line call-out specifies material meeting all requirements of this document. Note additional characterizations in Section 7 and Section 8—Suffixes.

The following is an example of a line call-out:

SAEJ1639PA1122

The previous specification would indicate:

SAE J1639 Classification System for Automotive PA Plastics
PA = polyamide (nylon)
11 = reinforced PA66
2 = glass reinforced, impact modified, heat stabilized
2 = 15% glass

TABLE 1—STANDARDIZED AUTOMOTIVE GRADES OF HEAT STABILIZED POLYAMIDES (PA)[1]

PA Group	Description[2]	Filler Content	Designation	Previous
66	General, Injection Molding	Unreinforced	0121	
	General, Extrusion Molding	Unreinforced	0122	none
	Impact modified	Unreinforced	0171	
	Impact modified	Unreinforced	0172	
	Glass fiber reinforced	15%	1112	
	Glass fiber reinforced	35%	1116	
	Glass fiber reinforced, impact modified	15%	1122	
	Mineral filled	40%	1137	
	Mineral/glass fiber reinforced	20%	1143	none
	Mineral/glass fiber reinforced	40%	1147	
	Mineral filled, impact modified	40%	1157	1156 (35%)
	Glass fiber reinforced, hydrolysis resistant	25%	1164	none
	Glass fiber reinforced, hydrolysis resistant	35%	1166	1165 (30%)
6	General, Injection Molding	Unreinforced	0222	
	General, Extrusion Molding	Unreinforced	0223	none
	Impact modified	Unreinforced	0282	
	Glass fiber reinforced	15%	1212	
	Glass fiber reinforced	25%	1214	
	Glass fiber reinforced	35%	1216	
	Glass fiber reinforced, impact modified	30%	1225	
	Mineral filled	30%	1235	
	Mineral filled	40%	1237	
	Mineral/glass fiber reinforced	40%	1247	
66/6	Glass fiber reinforced	35%	1816	1815 (30%)

1. Grades commonly used in Automotive Industry. Additional grades may be included in the future as agreed to by the SAE Plastic Committee.
2. All materials are heat stabilized.

5.3 The following definitions for tables in Appendix A of this document apply to unfilled and filled polyamides.

a. Group 01 Unreinforced polyamide 66 (PA66) (all classes heat stabilized)
   Class 2 Injection and extrusion molding
   Class 7 Impact modified
b. Group 02 Unreinforced polyamide 6 (PA6) (all classes heat stabilized)
   Class 2 Injection and extrusion molding
   Class 8 Impact modified
c. Group 11 Reinforced/filled polyamide 66 (PA66) (all classes heat stabilized)
   Class 1 Glass fiber reinforced
   Class 2 Glass fiber reinforced, impact modified
   Class 3 Mineral filled
   Class 4 Mineral/glass fiber filled
   Class 5 Mineral filled, impact modified
   Class 6 Glass fiber reinforced, hydrolysis resistant
d. Group 12 Reinforced/filled polyamide 6 (PA6) (all classes heat stabilized)
   Class 1 Glass fiber reinforced
   Class 2 Glass fiber reinforced, impact modified
   Class 3 Mineral filled
   Class 4 Mineral/glass fiber filled
e. Group 18 Reinforced/filled polyamide 66/6 (PA66/6) (all classes heat stabilized)
   Class 1 Glass fiber reinforced

The fourth digit in groups 11, 12, and 18 will define the nominal amount of reinforcement. Numerals 1 to 9 will designate the following:

1 = 10% (Not specified)	6 = 35%
2 = 15%	7 = 40%
3 = 20%	8 = 45% (Not specified)
4 = 25%	9 = 50% (Not specified)
5 = 30%	0 = Other

6. Testing and Conditioning

6.1 Test Specimens—Test specimens shall be prepared as specified in Table 2. Unless otherwise specified, all tests shall be carried out on injection molded one-end gated test specimens.

The specimens in Table 2 are required:

Test specimen A shall be molded using molding conditions defined in ISO 1874-2. Specimens with shorter dimensions shall be cut from the center portion of the test specimen A. No annealing allowed.

TABLE 2—TEST SPECIMENS

	Defined by:	Molded According to:
A. 150 minimum x 10 x 4.0 mm ±0.2 mm	ISO 3167, Type A	ISO/DIS 294-1
B. 60 x 60 x 2.0 mm ±0.1 mm	ISO 294-3:1995	ISO/DIS 294-3
C. 100 mm diameter x 3.2 mm ±0.2 mm		Not Available
D. 355 x 100 x 2.0 mm ±0.1 mm	FMVSS 302	ISO/DIS 294-1 (injection) ISO 295 (compression)

6.2 Statistical Data—Statistical data shall be derived from testing a minimum of 30 lots. The statistical data shall be submitted with initial characterization data (Section 7) of the material. The following properties are affected: tensile strength, flexural modulus, Izod impact at 23 °C ±2 °C, and heat deflection temperature.

The user of this document shall define requirements for provisional approval prior to completion of 30 lot testing.

6.3 Conditioning and Test Conditions—All test values indicated herein are based on material with moisture content of 0.2% maximum (ISO 960, Method A/ASTM D 789). Immediately after molding, specimens shall be sealed in moisture-proof containers and stored at 23 °C ±2 °C for at least 24 h. All tests shall be performed immediately after removal from the containers in a controlled atmosphere of 23 °C ±C °C and 50% ±5% relative humidity unless otherwise specified.

7. Initial Characterization of Automotive Materials—The following test results shall be submitted as initial characterization of the material.

7.1 Infrared Spectrophotometry and/or Thermal Analysis—Infrared and/or thermal analysis spectra shall constitute the reference standard for the material supplied to a specification based on this classification system and shall be available on request.

7.2 Shear Modulus—A plotted curve, as described as follows, shall constitute the reference standard for the material supplied to a specification based on this classification system and shall be available on request.

Shear modulus versus temperature curve shall be plotted for -50 to +210 °C (PA6), 240 °C (PA66) temperature range, at 5 °C intervals.

7.2.1 TEST METHOD—ASTM D 5279, forced constant amplitude, fixed frequency of 1 Hz ± 15%, strain level below 1% 60 x 10 x 4.0 mm specimen, cut from the center of tensile specimen (specimen A). Specimen length between clamps 35 to 40 mm. Soak time at each temperature interval 3 min minimum.

7.3 Density

7.3.1 TEST METHOD—ISO 1183, Method A—Report density in g/cm^3

7.4 Heat Aging Performance—After aging for 1000 h at the appropriate temperature listed as follows, the tensile strength, Izod impact strength, or both must retain at least 75% of their original values. For unreinforced materials, tensile strength, 75% retention data, and impact strength value (or percent loss) are required. 75% Izod impact strength retention data is required for reinforced materials. For impact modified grades properties shall be retained at 75% of original minimums.

7.4.1 TEST METHOD—ISO 188, 150 air changes/h ± 50 air changes/h. After heat aging, test specimens are to be conditioned in a desiccator for 3 to 5 h at 23 °C ± 2 °C. Impact strength test specimens shall be notched before heat aging. Unaged property values shall be determined at the time of the aged properties determination. Oven aging temperatures: 110 °C for unreinforced grades, 140 °C for reinforced grades.

7.5 Engine Coolant Resistance—Use only for hydrolysis resistant PA66—After immersion for 1000 h at 125 °C and 103 kPa pressure in 50/50 solution of water and approved automotive coolant concentrate, the tensile strength must retain a minimum of 20% of the original value listed in Appendix A, Table A1.

7.5.1 TEST METHOD—ISO 527-1 and ISO 527-2, 150 minimum x 10 x 4.0 mm specimen (specimen A), test speed 5 mm/min. Report type of stress (yield and/or break). Unaged property values shall be determined at the time of the aged properties determination. A minimum of 10 specimens shall be tested.

7.6 Impact Strength, Multiaxial—Applicable to impact modified materials only.

7.6.1 TEST METHOD—ASTM D 3763, 100 mm diameter x 3.2 mm thick smooth surface injection-molded specimen (specimen C).

Impact velocity—2.2 m/s for exterior, 6.6 m/s for interior applications.

Test at -40 °C ± 2 °C, or -30 °C ± 2 °C, or -15 °C ± 2 °C, or 0 °C ± 2 °C, and 23 °C ± 2 °C. Present all data and define the temperature at which ductile failure was observed.

Test specimens must be conditioned for a minimum of 6 h at test temperature prior to impact testing. Low temperature testing shall be conducted within the same environmental chamber as the clamp mechanism of the impact device. No transfer through ambient conditions is permitted.

Test a minimum of 10 specimens from 3 individual lots at a single condition.

Report should include:

a. Detailed description of specimen preparation
b. Molding conditions; melt and mold surface temperatures, and average injection velocity
c. Number of samples tested per lot per temperature
d. Numbers of lots tested
e. Number of samples with ductile failure per each test condition
f. Representative force versus deflection curve for each impact event
g. Number of cracks and maximum length

Summarize testing at each condition by providing the energy in Joules (mean value) at maximum load (all the high and low values should be reported).

Report energy in Joules (mean value) at maximum load at 23 °C ± 2 °C and at the lowest temperature that yields ductile failure, the standard deviation attained for that test run, and the impact velocity of the test.

A ductile failure is defined as a crack that does not radiate more than 10 mm from the point of impact.

7.7 Impact Strength, Izod At -40 °C ± 1 °C

7.7.1 TEST METHOD—ISO 180/1A, 80 x 10 x 4.0 mm specimen (use center section of specimen A), test at -40 °C ± 2 °C. The test specimen must be conditioned for a minimum of 6 h at the previously specified temperature prior to impact test. Low temperature testing shall be done within the cold chamber, if not possible, test may be conducted outside, but within 5 s.

7.8 Flammability

7.8.1 TEST METHOD—ISO 3795/SAE J369, 100 mm/min maximum burn rate, 355 x 100 x 1.0 mm smooth surface injection- or compression-molded specimen (specimen D).

7.9 Coefficient of Linear Thermal Expansion

7.9.1 TEST METHOD—ASTM E 831 (TMA), -30 to ±30 °C

Report average value x E-5/° C, for both the flow and cross-flow directions.

7.10 Mold Shrinkage

7.10.1 TEST METHOD—ISO/DIS 294-4, 60 x 60 x 2.0 mm smooth surface injection-molded specimen (specimen B).

Report values in percent (%) for both the flow and cross-flow directions, under the following conditions:

a. Mold Shrinkage after 48 h storage at 23 °C ± 2 °C at 50% ± 5% relative humidity
b. Post Shrinkage after 48 h at 80 °C
c. Post Shrinkage after 30 min at 120 °C

8. Initial Characterization of Automotive Materials—Suffixes—The following requirements are available in addition to the basic call-out by use of suffixes Z1, Z2, Z3, Z4, Z5, and Z6.

All test results shall be submitted with initial characterization, when specified.

8.1 Suffix Z1—UV Light Resistant, Interior Xenon-Arc Exposure—Applicable to color matched unpainted compounds only.

8.1.1 TEST METHOD—SAE J1885, 601 kJ/m^2 minimum exposure. 60 x 60 mm minimum x 2.0 mm, smooth surface, low-gloss injection-molded specimen (specimen B). Rating 4, minimum (AATCC Evaluation Procedure 1/ISO 105/A02)

No objectional color change or surface defects allowed.

8.2 Suffix Z2—UV Light Resistant, Under Glass, Interior Florida Exposure—Applicable to color matched unpainted compounds only.

8.2.1 TEST METHOD—1 year, 5 degrees south, under PPG Herculite K, tempered safety glass, 3 mm thick. Applicable method shall be specified by the user of this document. 60 x 60 mm minimum x 2.0 mm, smooth surface, low-gloss injection-molded specimen (specimen B). Rating 4, minimum (AATCC Evaluation Procedure 1/ISO 105/A02)

No objectional color change or surface defects allowed.

8.3 Suffix Z3—UV Light Resistant, Exterior—Applicable to color matched unpainted compounds only.

8.3.1 XENON-ARC EXPOSURE—SAE J1960, 2500 kJ/m^2 minimum exposure. 60 x 60 mm minimum x 2.0 mm, smooth surface, low-gloss injection-molded specimen (specimen B). Rating 4, minimum (AATCC Evaluation Procedure 1/ISO 105/A02)

8.3.2 FLORIDA AND ARIZONA EXPOSURE—SAE J1976, 2 years, 5 degrees south, direct exposure. 60 x 60 mm minimum x 2.0 mm, smooth surface, low-gloss injection-molded specimen (specimen B). Rating 4, minimum (AATCC Evaluation Procedure 1/ISO 105/A02)

No objectional color change or surface defects allowed.

8.4 Suffix Z4—Fogging—Use only for interior application materials.

8.4.1 TEST METHOD—SAE J1756, 3 h at 100 °C ± 0.5 °C bath temperature, 21 °C ± 0.5 °C cooling temperature. Report minimum Fog Number.

8.5 Suffix Z5—Gloss—NOT APPLICABLE

8.6 Suffix Z6—Material is not Heat Stabilized—For color matched applications only.

8.6.1 The heat stabilizer package is deleted from the polyamide formulation for color matched and/or natural applications if the user of this document specifies Suffix Z6 as a part of the call-out.

8.7 The following is an example of a line call-out for a UV light resistant, color matched interior application polyamide 66 requiring use of suffixes Z1, Z2, and Z6:

SAEJ16390121Z1Z2Z4Z6

Z1 = UV Resistant, Interior, Xenon-Arc Exposure
Z2 = UV Resistant, Under Glass, Interior, Florida Exposure
Z4 = Fog Number 90 minimum
Z6 = Material is not heat stabilized

9. Test Methods—All requirements are listed in Appendix A, Table A1.

9.1 Tensile Strength

9.1.1 TEST METHOD—ISO 527-1 and ISO 527-2, 150 minimum x 10 x 4.0 mm specimen (specimen A), test speed: 50 mm/min (unreinforced and/or materials without yield point with elongation equal or greater than 10%), and 5 mm/min (reinforced and/or materials without yield point with elongation below 10%). Report type of stress (yield and/or break).

9.2 Flexural Modulus

9.2.1 TEST METHOD—ISO 178, 80 x 10 x 4.0 mm specimen (use center section of specimen A), 2 mm/min test speed, 64 mm support span.

9.3 Impact Strength, Izod

9.3.1 TEST METHOD—ISO 180/1A, 80 x 10 x 4.0 mm specimen (use center section of specimen A), test at 23 °C ± 2 °C. Minimum of 10 specimens for each test.

9.4 Heat Deflection Temperature at 1.80 MPa

9.4.1 TEST METHOD—ISO 75-1 and ISO 75-2, 80 x 10 x 4.0 mm specimen (use center section of specimen A), test flatwise at standard deflection of 0.34 mm ±0.01 mm. Report minimum temperature in °C.

9.5 Filler Content (Reinforced Materials Only)

9.5.1 TEST METHOD—ISO 3451/4—Report the temperature of calcination if different from ISO 3451/4.

APPENDIX A

TABLE A1—REQUIREMENTS FOR POLYAMIDES 6, 66, AND 66/6 DRY-AS-MOLDED(1), HEAT STABILIZED STANDARDIZED AUTOMOTIVE GRADES

GROUP	CLASS Description	GRADE Description	Statistical Data Tensile Strength MPa min	Statistical Data Flexural Modulus MPa min	Statistical Data Izod Impact Resistance at 23 °C kJ/m	Statistical Data Heat Deflection Temperature at 1.80 MPa °C min	Initial Characterization Izod Impact Resistance at -40 °C(2) kJ/m² min	Initial Characterization Density(2) g/cm(3)
01 Polyamide 66(3)	2 General, HS	1 Injection molding	70	2300	3.0	60	2.0	1.13–1.15
		2 Extrusion molding	70	2300	3.0	60	2.0	1.13–1.15
	7 Impact modified, HS	1 Injection molding	52	1700	9.0	50	4.0	1.06–1.10
		2 Injection molding	42	1500	40	45	8.0	1.06–1.10
02 Polyamide 6(4)	2 General, HS	2 Injection molding	70	2400	4.5	54	4.5	1.12–1.14
		3 Extrusion molding	70	2400	4.5	50	4.5	1.12–1.14
	8 Impact modified, HS	2 Injection molding	60	2000	6.0	50	4.0	1.05–1.16
11 Polyamide 66 Reinforced/filled(5)	1 Glass reinforced, HS	2 15%	100	4000	3.0	220	3.0	1.20–1.26
		6 35%	170	8000	7.0	235	5.0	1.35–1.45
	2 Glass reinforced, Impact modified, HS	2 15%	85	3000	6.0	210	3.0	1.15–1.21
	3 Mineral filled, HS	7 40%	80	5000	2.0	150	1.0	1.45–1.55
	4 Mineral/glass filled, HS	3 20%	70	3200	1.5	50	0.8	1.23–1.31
		7 40%	100	5500	2.5	200	1.8	1.43–1.53
	5 Mineral filled, Impact modified, HS	7 40% Mineral	75	4500	4.0	NA	3.0	1.45–1.55
	6 Glass reinforced, hydrolysis resistant(6), HS	4 25%	140	6000	5.0	225	3.0	1.29–1.37
		6 35%	170	8000	7.0	235	5.0	1.35–1.45
12 Polyamide 6 Reinforced/filled(5)	1 Glass reinforced, HS	2 15%	110	4500	4.5	180	4.0	1.20–1.28
		4 25%	140	6500	6.5	190	6.0	1.28–1.36
		6 35%	155	7500	9.0	190	7.0	1.34–1.40
	2 Glass reinforced impact modified, HS	5 30%	135	6500	15.0	190	10.5	1.32–1.40
	3 Mineral filled, HS	5 30%	70	3200	2.4	60	2.2	1.30–1.40
		7 40%	80	5000	4.5	75	3.5	1.42–1.47
	4 Mineral/glass filled, HS	7 40%	100	6000	3.0	190	2.5	1.42–1.50
18 Polyamide 66 and 6 Copolymers(7), HS Reinforced/filled(6)	1 Glass reinforced PA66/6	6 35%	160	7500	8.0	190	5.0	1.35–1.45

1. Moisture content 0.2% maximum. Test method: ISO 960, Method A/ASTM D 789
2. Values reported are for initial characterization of materials.
3. Melting Point 250 to 265 °C. Test method: ISO 3146, Method C
4. Melting Point 210 to 225 °C. Test method: ISO 3146, Method C
5. Filler content determination based on ISO 3451/4 Section 9.5
6. Hydrolysis resistance 1000 h test at 125 °C required Section 7.5
7. Melting Point for the copolymer products shall be reported at the time of initial characterization of the material. ISO 3146, Method C

NA Not Available

All values in the table are based on a limited ISO statistical data base (see 6.2) and will be revised as more data becomes available. Presently, certification of individual materials will be carried out through the Control Plan process.

APPENDIX B
INFORMATIVE

B.1 The following information is provided for clarification and assistance in meeting this standard.

The technical aspects of ISO documents referenced on Section 2 of this document are handled by U.S. Technical Advisory Group for ISO TC-61/ASTM D20.61. Mr. Steve Watson is the chairman of the Group.

ISO/DIS—Draft International Standard is the last draft version, allowing no additional technical changes before final release as an International Standard (ISO).

ISO/CD—Committee Draft allows for technical changes until the document becomes ISO/DIS.

SAE J1639 will be updated as ISO/DIS documents are advanced. Mr. Steve Watson (Chairman of U.S. Technical Advisory Group for ISO TC-61) has agreed to provide necessary updates, and in the interim, will answer questions pertaining to these documents.

Mr. Watson may be reached by telephone on 302-999-2536, or by fax on 302-999-5659.

CLASSIFICATION SYSTEM FOR AUTOMOTIVE ACRYLONITRILE/BUTADIENE/STYRENE (ABS) AND ABS + POLYCARBONATE BLENDS (ABS+PC) BASED PLASTICS—SAE J1685 MAY1995

SAE Recommended Practice

Report of the SAE Plastics Committee approved May 1995.

Foreword—This Document has not changed other than to put it into the new SAE Technical Standards Board Format.

1. Scope—This SAE Recommended Practice provides a system for classification and specification for limited number of acrylonitrile/butadiene/styrene (ABS) and blends with polycarbonate (ABS+PC) plastics used in the Automotive Industry. Based upon ASTM D 4673, Classification System for (ABS) Molding Materials, it calls for additional descriptive characteristics and properties commonly used in the Automotive Industry.

This practice applies to natural, non-color matched black, and plating gray compounds only. Color matched compounds shall be defined by the proprietary OEM standards.

This practice allows for the use of recycled, reconstituted, and regrind materials provided that the requirements as stated in this document are met, the material has not been altered or modified to change its suitability for safe processing and use, and the material shall be identified as such.

1.1 Purpose—The purpose of this document is to:

a. Standardize the grades of unreinforced and reinforced ABS and ABS+PC used for the Automotive Industry
b. Standardize the test methods used to characterize the properties of these materials
c. Provide a method for specifying these materials by the use of a simple line call-out designation

2. References

2.1 Applicable Publications—The following publications form a part of the specification to the extent specified herein. Unless otherwise indicated the latest revision of SAE publications shall apply.

2.1.1 SAE PUBLICATIONS—Available from SAE, 400 Commonwealth Drive, Warrendale, PA 15096-0001.

SAE J369—Flammability of Automotive Interior Materials-Horizontal Test Method
SAE J1344—Marking of Plastic Parts
SAE J1756—Test Procedure to determine the Fogging Characteristics of Interior Automotive Materials
SAE J1885—Exposure to Interior Xenon-Arc Weatherometer
SAE J1960—Exposure to Exterior Xenon-Arc Weatherometer
SAE J1976—Outdoor Weathering of Exterior Materials

2.1.2 ASTM PUBLICATIONS—Available from ASTM, 1916 Race Street, Philadelphia, PA 19103-1187.

ASTM D 2457-90—Specular Gloss of Plastic Film and Solid Plastics
ASTM D 3763-92—High Speed Puncture Properties Plastics Using Load Displacement Sensors
ASTM D 4673-87—Acrylonitrile-Butadiene-Styrene (ABS) Molding and Extrusion Materials
ASTM D 5279-92—Measuring Dynamic Mechanical Properties of Plastics in Torsion
ASTM E 831-86—Linear Thermal Expansion of Solid Materials by Thermomechanical Analysis

2.1.3 ISO PUBLICATIONS—Available from ANSI, 11 West 42nd Street, New York, NY 10036-8002.

ISO 75-1:1993—Plastics—Determination of temperature of deflection under load—Part 1: General test methods
ISO 75-2:1993—Plastics—Determination of temperature of deflection under load—Part 2: Plastic and Ebonite
ISO 105/A02:1993—Textiles—Grey scale for assessing change in color
ISO 178:1993—Plastics—Determination of flexural properties
ISO 180:1993—Plastics—Determination of Izod impact strength
ISO 188:1982—Rubber—Accelerated aging
ISO/DIS 294-1:1995—Plastics—Injection molding of test specimens of thermoplastic materials
ISO/DIS 294-3:1995—Plastics—Injection molding of test specimens of thermoplastic materials—Part 3: Plates (ISO mold type D)
ISO/DIS 294-4:1995—Plastics—Injection molding of test specimens of thermoplastic materials—Part 4: Determination of molding shrinkage
ISO 295:1991—Plastics—Compression moulding of test specimens of thermosetting materials
ISO 306:1994—Plastics—Thermoplastic materials—determination of Vicat softening temperature
ISO 527-1:1993—Plastics—Determination of tensile properties—Part 1: General principles
ISO 527-2:1993—Plastics—Determination of tensile properties—Part 2: Testing conditions
ISO 1133:1991—Plastics—Determination of melt mass-flow rate (MFR) and the melt-volume rate (MVR) of thermoplastics
ISO 1183:1987—Plastics—Methods for determining the density of non-cellular plastics
ISO 2580-2:1995—Plastics—Acrylonitrile/butadiene/styrene (ABS) molding and extrusion materials—Part 2: Preparation of test specimens and determination of properties
ISO 3167:1993—Plastics—Preparation and use of multipurpose test specimen
ISO 3451/1:1981—Plastics—Determination of ash—Part 1: General Methods
ISO 3795:1989—Road vehicles—Determination of burning behavior of interior materials for motor vehicles

2.1.4 AATCC PUBLICATION—Available from AATCC, P.O. Box 12215, Research Triangle Park, North Carolina 27709 and British Standard Institution, 10 Blackfriars Str. Manchester, M3 5TD, England.

AATCC Gray Scale

2.1.5 FMVSS PUBLICATION—Available from The Superintendent of Documents, U.S. Government Printing Office, Washington, DC 20402.

FMVSS 302

3. Description

3.1 This classification system was developed to permit the addition of descriptive characteristics and values commonly used in Automotive Material Specifications for ABS and ABS+PC based materials. All the requirements listed in Section 7 shall apply for initial qualification of the material. The requirements listed in Section 8 shall be required for initial qualification when the particular suffix is included in the line call-out for the material. The requirements listed in Appendix A, Table A1 for initial product certification shall be met with data representing 3 sigma values per 6.2. Production lots shall meet property control plan as agreed to between material supplier and user of this document.

4. Classification

4.1 Acrylonitrile/butadiene/styrene (ABS) and ABS+PC based plastics are classified into "groups" based on the chemical type and processing method. These groups are subdivided into "classes" and "grades" as shown in Appendix A, Table A1.

4.2 An example of this classification system is as follows:

The designation ABS0121 would indicate:

ABS = acrylonitrile/butadiene/styrene, generic symbol according to SAE J1344
01 = unreinforced, injection molding ABS
2 = high impact
1 = requirements as given in Appendix A, Table A1

5. Line Call-outs

5.1 A line call-out, which is a specification, shall contain this document's identification number and a material designation from Table 1 as illustrated in 4.2.

5.2 The line call-out specifies material meeting all requirements of this document. Note additional characterization in Section 7 and Section 8 - suffixes.

The following is an example of a line call-out:

SAEJ1685ABS0121

The above specification would indicate:

SAE J1685 Classification System for automotive ABS and ABS+PC Blends Plastics

ABS = acrylonitrile/butadiene/styrene, generic symbol according to SAE J1344
01 = unreinforced, injection molding ABS
2 = high impact
1 = requirements as given in Appendix A, Table A1

TABLE 1—STANDARDIZED AUTOMOTIVE GRADES OF ABS AND ABS+PC BLENDS BASED PLASTICS(1),(2)

Group	Description	Designation
01	ABS, Injection Molding, Unreinforced	
	Medium Impact (3)	0111
	High Impact	0121
	High Heat	0131
	High Heat	0132
	Plating	0141
04	ABS+PC Blends, Injection Molding, Unreinforced	
	Medium Impact3	0411
	High Impact	0412
	High Impact	0421
	High Heat, High Impact	0431
	High Heat, High Impact	0432
14	Plating	0441
	ABS+PC, Injection Molding, Reinforced	
	10% Glass Fiber	1411
	10% Mineral	1421

1. Grades commonly used in Automotive Industry. Additional grades may be included in the future as agreed to by the SAE Plastics Committee.
2. Low gloss grades will be defined by use of Suffix Z5 (8.4)
3. Grades commonly described as "general purpose"

5.3 The following definitions for tables in Appendix A, Table A1 of this document apply to ABS and ABS+PC blends.

a. Group 01 Unreinforced, injection molding acrylonitrile/butadiene/styrene (ABS)
   - Class 1 Medium Impact
   - Class 2 High Impact
   - Class 3 High Heat
   - Class 4 Plating

b. Group 04 Unreinforced, injection molding acrylonitrile/butadiene/styrene + polycarbonate blends (ABS+PC)
   - Class 1 Medium Impact
   - Class 2 High Impact
   - Class 3 High Heat, High Impact
   - Class 4 Plating

The fourth digit in groups 01 and 04, when listed, will define specific grade requirements in the designated class.

c. Group 14 Reinforced/filled, injection molding ABS+PC Blends
   - Class 1 Glass fiber reinforced
   - Class 2 Mineral filled

The fourth digit in group 14 will define the amount of reinforcement/filler. The following numeral will designate:

1 = 8 to 12%

6. Testing and Conditioning

6.1 Test Specimens—Test specimens shall be prepared as specified in Table 2. Unless otherwise specified all tests shall be carried out on injection molded one-end gated test specimens.

The following specimens are required:

TABLE 2—TEST SPECIMENS

	Defined by:	Molded According to:
A. 150 minimum x 10 x 4.0 ±0.2 mm	ISO 3167, Type A	ISO/DIS 294-1
B. 60 x 60 x 2.0 ±0.1 mm	ISO/DIS 294-3	ISO/DIS 294-3
C. 100 mm diameter x 3.2 ±0.2 mm		Not Available
D. 355 x 100 x 2.0 ±0.1 mm	FMVSS 302	ISO/DIS 294-1 (injection) ISO 295 (compression)

Test specimen A shall be molded using molding conditions defined in ISO 2580-2. Specimens with shorter dimensions shall be cut from the center portion of the test specimen A. No annealing allowed.

6.2 Statistical Data—Statistical data shall be derived from testing a minimum of 30 lots. The statistical data shall be submitted with initial characterization data (Section 7) of the material. The following properties are affected: melt flow rate, tensile strength, flexural modulus, Izod impact, Vicat softening temperature, and heat deflection temperature.

The user of this document shall define requirements for provisional approval prior to completion of 30 lot testing.

6.3 Conditioning and Test Conditions—All test values indicated herein are based on material conditioned in a controlled atmosphere of 23 °C ±2 °C and 50% ±5% relative humidity for not less than 24 h prior to testing and tested under the same conditions unless otherwise specified.

7. Initial Characterization of Automotive Materials—The following test results shall be submitted as initial characterization of the material.

7.1 Infrared Spectrophotometry and/or Thermal Analysis—Infrared and/or thermal analysis spectra shall constitute the reference standard for the material supplied to a specification based on this classification system and shall be available on request.

7.2 Shear Modulus—A plotted curve, as described as follows, shall constitute the reference standard for the material supplied to a specification based on this classification system and shall be available on request.

Shear modulus versus temperature curve shall be plotted for -50 to +50 °C temperature range, at 5 °C intervals.

7.2.1 TEST METHOD—ASTM D 5279, forced constant amplitude, fixed frequency of 1 Hz ± 15%, strain level below 1%. 60 x 10 x 4.0 mm specimen, cut from the center of tensile specimen (specimen A). Specimen length between clamps 35 to 40 mm. Soak time at each temperature interval 3 min minimum.

7.3 Density

7.3.1 TEST METHOD—ISO 1183, Method A. Report density in g/cm^3.

7.4 Heat Aging Performance—After aging for 1000 h at the appropriate temperature, listed as follows, the tensile strength and Izod impact strength must retain at least 75% of their original values.

7.4.1 TEST METHOD—ISO 188, 150 air changes/h ±50 air changes/h. Unaged property values shall be determined at the time of the aged properties determination. Impact strength test specimens shall be notched before heat aging. Oven aging temperatures: 80 °C for ABS and 90 °C for ABS+PC.

7.5 Heat Deflection Temperature at 1.80 MPa

7.5.1 TEST METHOD—ISO 75-1 and ISO 75-2, 80 x 10 x 4.0 mm specimen (use center section of specimen A), test flatwise at standard deflection of 0.34 mm ±0.01 mm. Report minimum temperature in °C.

7.6 Impact Strength, Multiaxial—Applicable to grades 0121, 0421, 0431, and 0432 only.

7.6.1 TEST METHOD—ASTM D 3763, 100 mm diameter x 3.2 mm thick smooth surface injection-molded specimen (specimen C).

Impact velocity—2.2 m/s for exterior, 6.6 m/s for interior applications.

Test at -40 °C ±2 °C, or -30 °C ±2 °C, or -15 °C ±2 °C, or 0 °C ±2 °C, and 23 °C ±2 °C. Present all data at the temperature at which ductile failure was observed.

Test specimens must be conditioned for a minimum of 6 h at test temperature prior to impact testing. Low temperature testing shall be conducted within the same environmental chamber as the clamp mechanism of the impact device. No transfer through ambient conditions is permitted.

Test a minimum of 10 specimens from 3 individual lots at a single condition. Report should include the:

a. Detailed description of specimen preparation
b. Molding conditions; melt and mold surface temperatures, and average injection velocity
c. Number of samples tested per lot per temperature
d. Numbers of lots tested
e. Number of samples with ductile failure per each test condition
f. Representative force versus deflection curve for each impact event
g. Number of cracks and maximum length

Summarize testing at each condition by providing the energy in Joules (mean value) at maximum load (all the high and low values should be reported).

Report energy in Joules (mean value) at maximum load at 23 °C ±2 °C and at the lowest temperature that yields ductile failure, the standard deviation attained for that test run, and the impact velocity of the test.

A ductile failure is defined by describing the size, length, and type of cracks produced while testing a specimen to failure. Ductile failure will be defined and qualified by the individual users of this document.

7.7 Impact Strength, Izod At -40 °C

7.7.1 TEST METHOD—ISO 180/1A, 80 x 10 x 4.0 mm specimen (use center section of specimen A), test at -40 °C ±2 °C. The test specimen must be conditioned for a minimum of 6 h at the previously specified temperature prior to impact test. Low temperature testing shall be done within the cold chamber, if not possible, test may be conducted outside, but within 5 s.

7.8 Flammability

7.8.1 TEST METHOD—ISO 3795/SAE J369, 100 mm/minute maximum burn rate, 355 x 100 x 2.0 mm smooth surface injection, extrusion, or compression-molded specimen (specimen D).

7.9 Coefficient of Linear Thermal Expansion

7.9.1 TEST METHOD—ASTM E 831 (TMA), -30 to +30 °C.

Report average value x E-5/ °C, for both the flow and cross-flow directions.

7.10 Mold Shrinkage

7.10.1 TEST METHOD—ISO/CD 294-4, 60 x 60 mm x 2.0 mm smooth surface injection-molded specimen (specimen B).

Report values in percent (%) for both the flow and cross-flow directions, under the following conditions:

a. Mold Shrinkage after storage at 23 °C ±2 °C at 50% ±5% relative humidity

b. Post Shrinkage after 48 h at 80 °C

8. ***Initial Characterization of Automotive Materials—Suffixes***—The following requirements are available in addition to the basic call-out by use of suffixes Z1, Z2, Z3, Z4, and Z5.

All test results shall be submitted with initial characterization, when specified.

8.1 Suffix Z1—UV Light Resistant, Interior Xenon-Arc Exposure— Applicable to color matched unpainted compounds only.

8.1.1 TEST METHOD—SAE J1885, 263.2, or 300.8, or 601 kJ/m^2 minimum exposure (as specified by the standard user). 60 x 60 mm minimum x 2.0 mm, smooth surface, low-gloss injection-molded specimen (specimen B). SPI #1 mold finish. Rating 4, minimum (AATCC Evaluation Procedure 1/ISO 105/A02).

8.2 Suffix Z2—UV Light Resistant, Under Glass, Interior Florida Exposure—Applicable to color matched unpainted compounds only

8.2.1 TEST METHOD—1 year, 5 degrees south, under PPG Herculite K, tempered safety glass, 3 mm thick. Applicable method shall be specified by the user of this document. 60 x 60 mm minimum x 2.0 mm, smooth surface, low-gloss injection-molded specimen (specimen B). SPI #1 mold finish. Rating 4, minimum (AATCC Evaluation Procedure 1/ISO 105/A02).

No objectional color change or surface defects allowed.

8.3 Suffix Z3—UV Light Resistant, Exterior—Applicable to color matched unpainted compounds only.

8.3.1 XENON-ARC EXPOSURE—SAE J1960, 2500 kJ/m^2 minimum exposure. 60 x 60 mm minimum x 2.0 mm, smooth surface, low-gloss injection-molded specimen (specimen B). Rating 4, minimum (AATCC Evaluation Procedure 1/ ISO 105/A02).

8.3.2 FLORIDA AND ARIZONA EXPOSURE—SAE J1976, 2 years, 5 degrees south, direct exposure. 60 x 60 mm minimum x 2.0 mm, smooth surface, low-gloss injection-molded specimen (specimen B). Rating 4, minimum (AATCC Evaluation Procedure 1/ISO 105/A02).

No objectional color change or surface defects allowed.

8.4 Suffix Z4—Fogging—Use only for interior application materials.

8.4.1 TEST METHOD—SAE J1756, Temperatures used for testing shall be specified by the user of this document. Report minimum Fog Number.

8.5 Suffix Z5—Gloss—Use only for interior application materials.

8.5.1 TEST METHOD—ASTM D 2457, 60 degree glossmeter, 5 measurements minimum on grained surface. Grain surface and maximum Gloss Level shall be specified by the user of this document.

8.6 The following is an example of a line call-out for a low gloss, UV light resistant, color matched interior application material requiring use of suffixes Z1, Z2, Z4, and Z5:

SAEJ1685ABS0123Z1Z2Z4Z5
Z1 = UV Resistant, Interior, Xenon-Arc Exposure
Z2 = UV Resistant, Under Glass, Interior, Florida Exposure
Z4 = Fog Number 80 minimum
Z5 = Gloss 2 to 3%

9. ***Test Methods***—All requirements, with exception of Melt Flow Rate requirement, are listed in Appendix A, Table A1.

9.1 Melt Flow Rate

9.1.1 TEST METHOD—ISO 1133, 220 °C, 10 kg load for ABS and 265 °C, 5 kg load for ABS+PC blends.

Report Melt Flow Rate range in g/10 min.

9.2 Tensile Strength

9.2.1 TEST METHOD—ISO 527-1 and ISO 527-2, 150 minimum x 10 x 4.0 mm specimen (specimen A), test speed: 50 mm/min (unreinforced and/or materials without yield point with elongation equal or greater than 10%), and 5 mm/min (reinforced and/or materials without yield point with elongation below 10%). Report type of stress (yield and/or break).

9.3 Flexural Modulus

9.3.1 TEST METHOD—ISO 178, 80 x 10 x 4.0 mm specimen (use center section of specimen A), 2 mm/min test speed, 64 mm support span.

9.4 Impact Strength, Izod

9.4.1 TEST METHOD—ISO 180/1A, 80 x 10 x 4.0 mm specimen (use center section of specimen A), test at 23 °C ±2 °C. Minimum of 10 specimens for each test.

9.5 Vicat Softening Temperature

9.5.1 TEST METHOD—ISO 306, Method B, 50 N load, silicone oil bath, 10 x 10 x 4.0 mm specimen (use center section of specimen A).

9.6 Filler Content (Reinforced Materials Only)

9.6.1 TEST METHOD—ISO 3451/1, Method A.

Report the temperature of calcination if different from from ISO 3451/1.

APPENDIX A

TABLE A1—REQUIREMENTS FOR STANDARDIZED AUTOMOTIVE GRADES OF ABS AND ABS+PC BLENDS BASED PLASTICS

GROUP	CLASS Description	GRADE Description	Statistical Data Tensile Strength(1) MPa, min	Statistical Data Flexural Modulus(1) MPa, min	Statistical Data Izod Impact Resistance at 23 °C(1) kJ/m^2, min	Statistical Data Vicat Softening Temperature(1) at 50.0 N °C, min	Initial Characterization Izod Impact Resistance at -40 °C(1),(2) kJ/m^2, min
01							
ABS, Unreinforced	1 Medium Impact	1	32	1600	9	85	3
	2 High Impact	1	30	1600	23	85	8
	3 High Heat	1	34	1700	8	93	2
		2	32	1800	6	100	2
	4 Plating	1	34	2200	10	88	3
04							
ABS+PC Blends, Unreinforced	1 Medium Impact	1	40	1900	9	100	2
	2 High Impact	1	45	2000	32	114	10
		2	48	2100	35	105	8
	3 High Heat,	1	45	2000	40	123	10
	High Impact	2	45	2000	40	115	20
	4 Plating	1	37	1900	41	103	20
14							
ABS+PC Blend, Reinforced (3)	1 Glass fiber reinforced	1 8 to 12%	45	3500	8	125	3
	2 Mineral filled	1 6 to 10%	55	3000	20	125	5

All values in the table are based on a limited ISO statistical data base (see 6.2) and will be revised as more data becomes available. Presently, certification of individual materials will be carried out through the Control Plan process.

1. All test methods are defined in Section 9
2. Values reported are for initial characterization of materials
3. Filler content determination based on ISO 3451/1, Method A (see 9.5)

APPENDIX B
INFORMATIVE

B.1 The following information is provided for clarification and assistance in meeting this document.

The technical aspects of ISO documents referenced on Section 2 of this document are handled by U.S. Technical Advisory Group for ISO TC-61/ASTM D20.61. Mr. Steve Watson is the chairman of the Group.

ISO/DIS—Draft International Standard is the last draft version, allowing no additional technical changes before final release as an International Standard (ISO).

ISO/CD—Committee Draft allows for technical changes until the document becomes ISO/DIS.

SAE J1685 will be updated as ISO/DIS documents are advanced. Mr. Steve Watson has agreed to provide necessary updates, and in the interim, will answer questions pertaining to these documents.

Mr. Watson may be reached by telephone on 302-999-2536, or by fax on 302-999-5659.

INTERIOR AUTOMOTIVE PLASTIC PART TESTING—SAE J1717 JUN1994

SAE Recommended Practice

Report of the SAE Plastics Committee approved June 1994.

Foreword—This Document has not changed other than to put it into the new SAE Technical Standards Board format.

This document is intended to be used for interior automotive plastic parts in lieu of SAE J1345, Automotive Plastic Parts Specification.

The basis for creation of this SAE Recommended Practice was the existence of variation in testing requirements of finished plastic interior parts within the automotive industry. Considerable benefit to the industry could be obtained if guidelines were developed and adhered to with regards to standardizing:

a.Minimum testing required to predict in-vehicle performance of plastic parts
b.Test methods to evaluate plastic part performance

TABLE OF CONTENTS

1. Scope—SAE J1717 is an advisory document suggesting minimum recommended testing, appearance evaluation, and protocol for specifying the recommendations with regard to Singular Unassembled Automotive Interior Trim Parts.

1.1 Purpose—The purpose of this SAE Recommended Practice is to:

a. Standardize the testing and appearance evaluation requirements for interior unassembled plastic parts for the automotive industry
b. Standardize the associated test and appearance evaluation methods
c. Provide a method for specifying these requirements by the use of a simple line call-out designation

2. References

2.1 Applicable Publications—Testing shall be performed in accordance with current ISO, SAE, ASTM, or test methods detailed in this procedure. The following documents are required to perform the testing specified in SAE J1717.

The following publications form a part of this specification to the extent specified herein. The latest issue of SAE publications shall apply.

2.1.1 SAE PUBLICATIONS—Available from SAE, 400 Commonwealth Drive, Warrendale, PA 15096-0001.

SAE J1545—Instrumented Color Difference Measurement for Exterior Finishes, Textile, and Colored Trim

SAE J1885—Accelerated Exposure of Automotive Interior Trim Components Using a Controlled Radiance Water Cooled Xenon-Arc Apparatus

2.1.2 ASTM PUBLICATIONS—Available from ASTM, 100 Barr Harbor Drive, West Conshohocken, PA 19428-2959.

ASTM D 523—Standard Test Method for Specular Gloss

ASTM D 3029—Impact Resistance of Rigid Plastic Parts by means of a Tup (Falling Weight)

3. Definitions

3.1 Automotive Industry—Includes passenger cars, vans, and trucks.

3.2 User—The individual utilizing this document to specify component performance requirements.

3.3 Singular Unassembled Automotive Interior Plastic Trim Parts—Intended to describe plastic parts, as molded, and/or after painting, used for interior components.

3.4 In-Vehicle Performance—The performance of plastic parts after final assembly into a vehicle and exposure to in-service or other specified environment.

3.5 CHMSL—Central High-Mounted Stop Light

3.6 PRNDL—Transmission Detent Indicator (Park, Reverse, Neutral, Drive, Low)

3.7 IP—Instrument Panel

3.8 HVAC—Heating Ventilation and Air Conditioning

3.9 Escutcheons—Enclosure trim

4. Recommended Appearance Evaluation and Testing of Singular Unassembled Interior Plastic Molded Parts

4.1 The recommended appearance evaluation and testing for specific components as reference should be selected from the following:

Appendix A—Appearance as Molded
  A1—Color
  A2—Gloss
  A3—Surface/Grain
Appendix B—Dimensional Stability at Service Temperature
Appendix C—Dimensional Stability After Hot/Cold Cycling
Appendix D—Cold Impact
  D1—Pendulum Method
  D2—Gardner Method (alternate method)
Appendix E—Color and Gloss Retention

5. Evaluation and Test Equipment

5.1 The following test equipment and documentation is required to perform the testing specified in this document.

A—Appearance as Molded or After Painting
  A1—Color Match to Master
    Color Standard
    MacBeth Spectralight* (or equivalent)
    Color Analyzer (adjustable to SAE J1545)
    Procedure—SAE J1545-Appendix A1
  A2—Gloss Match to Master
    Gloss Master
    Glossmeter (60 degree)
    MacBeth Spectralight* (or equivalent)
    Procedure—ASTM D 523—Appendix A2
  A3—Surface/Grain to Master
    Grain Standard
    MacBeth Spectralight* (or equivalent)
    Procedure—Appendix A3
B—Dimensional Stability at Service Temperature
    Forced-air oven
    Measurement and scribe tools
    Dimensional Coordinate Machine (CCM) or equivalent measuring devices
    Procedure—Appendix B
C—Dimensional Stability After Hot/Cold Cycling
    Forced-air oven
    Cold environmental chamber
    Measurement and scribe tool
    Dimensional Coordinate Machine (CCM) or equivalent measuring devices
    Procedure—Appendix C
D—Cold Impact
    Pendulum impact tester
    Gardner impact tester (modified)
    Cold environmental chamber
    Procedure—ASTM D 3029-Appendix D
E—Color and Gloss Retention
    Atlas CI35, CI65, CI65A Weatherometers
    Glossmeter (60 degree)
    MacBeth Analyzer (adjustable to SAE J1545)
    MacBeth Spectralight* (or equivalent)
    Procedure—SAE J1885—Appendix E

6. Line Call-outs

6.1 A line call-out, which is a part performance specification, shall contain:

a. This document identification number (SAE J1717)
b. The requirement code options as shown in Figure 1, paragraph 5.2, used in conjunction with this component call-out in Section 6.

6.2 Table 1 is intended to provide guidance for creating consistent SAE J1717 line call-out codes.

6.3 Maximum service temperatures are selected to represent the interior temperature profile in the area of the vehicle in which the component is located.

6.4 Figure 1 is an example of a line call-out for SAE J1717 (A123, B85, C85, D20, E600).

This Line Call-out would, for example, indicate:

SAE J1717	Appearance evaluation and testing of unassembled interior molded parts.
A123	Evaluate the appearance as molded or after painting for: 1 = color 2 = gloss 3 = surface/grain
B85	Dimensional stability as molded, at +85 °C
C85	Dimensional stability after Hot/Cold Cycling: Hot temperature: +85 °C Cold temperature: -29 °C
D20	Cold Impact, 2.0 Joules at -29 °C
E600	Color and gloss retention after 600 kJ/m of xenon arc exposure.

FIGURE 1—LINE CALL-OUT EXAMPLE

TABLE 1—LINE CALL-OUT CODES

Parameter	Procedure	Options	Comments
APPEARANCE, as molded or after painting	Appendix A	A1	Color
		A2	Gloss
		A3	Grain
		A12	Color-Gloss
		A13	Color-Grain
		A23	Gloss-Grain
		A123	Color-Gloss-Grain
DIMENSIONAL STABILITY, at service temperature	Appendix B	B75 B85 B95 B100 B110	Select numerical suffix that is closest to the maximum (heat) inservice temperature (C)
DIMENSIONAL STABILITY, following hot/cold cycling	Appendix C	C75 C85 C100 C110	Select numerical suffix that represents the maximum (heat) inservice temperature (C)
			Cold temperature standardized at -29 °C
COLD IMPACT (as molded)	Appendix D	D XXX	Cold impact temperature standardized at -29 °C
COLD IMPACT (following heat aging)		DH XXX	Heat aging temperature to be same temperature as selected for call-out B and C previously
Color impact temperature standardized at -29 °C			XXX times 0.1 = Joules of impact energy
COLOR AND GLOSS RETENTION	Appendix E	E XXX	XXX = kJ/m of exposure energy

6.4.1 NOTE—With reference to A123 in Figure 1, SAE J1717 is not intended to provide a means of detailing specific appearance requirements (color, gloss, grain values). The user must specify these requirements by other means.

6.4.2 SAE J1717 is primarily intended to provide direction for evaluation of color, gloss, and grain before and after environmental testing.

6.5 Color and gloss retention may, at user discretion, be demonstrated in plaque form in lieu of part evaluation.

7. *Recommended Line Call-outs for Interior Components*—Table 2.

TABLE 2—COMPONENT LINE CALL-OUTS

Systems	Components	Recommended Call-outs
Instrument Panels	Grilles/Outlets	SAE J1717 (A123, C___)
	IP Retainers	SAE J1717 (C___, DH___)
	HVAC Ductwork	SAE J1717 (C___)
	Glove Box Door	SAE J1717 (A123, B___, D___)
	Glove Trim Box	SAE J1717 (B___)
	Trim Plates	SAE J1717 (A123, B___, E___)
	Speaker Grilles	SAE J1717 (A123, B___, C___, E___)
Center Console	Housing	SAE J1717 (A123, C___)
	Bin	SAE J1717 (B___)
	Lid	SAE J1717 (A123, B___, D___, E___)
	PRNDL-Trim Plate	SAE J1717 (A12)
	PRNDL-Trim Lens	SAE J1717 (A1)
	PRNDL-Indicator	SAE J1717 (A1)
Overhead Console	Housing	SAE J1717 (C___)
	Lamp Lenses	SAE J1717 (A1)
	Switch Buttons	SAE J1717 (A1)
Rear Seat Mirror	Mirror Housing	SAE J1717 (C___)
Seat	Seat Back	SAE J1717 (B___, C___)
	Tilt Handle	SAE J1717 (A123)
	Seat Trim	SAE J1717 (A123, E___)
Interior Door	Door Panel	SAE J1717 (A123, B___, C___, D___, E___)
	Escutcheons	SAE J1717 (A123, E___)
	Arm Rest Retainer	SAE J1717 (B___, C___)
	Handles	SAE J1717 (A123)
	Map Pockets	SAE J1717 (A123, B___, C___, D___, E___)
Sidewall Trim	Pillar Moldings	SAE J1717 (A123, B___, E___)
	Garnish Moldings	SAE J1717 (A123, B___, E___)
	Sill Plates	SAE J1717 (A123, C___, D___, E___)
	Rear Qtr Panels	SAE J1717 (A123, B___, D___)
	Lamp Housings	SAE J1717 (B___)
	Lenses	SAE J1717 (A1)
Rear Shelf	Speaker Grilles	SAE J1717 (A123, C___, E___)
	CHMSL	SAE J1717 (A123, B___, E___)
	Storage Bin	SAE J1717 (A123, B___)

Note—The spaces in the line call-outs above indicated by ____ require values to be specified by user in accordance with Table 1.

APPENDIX A
APPEARANCE AS MOLDED OR AFTER PAINTING

A.1 Color (Match to Master)

A.1.1 A color standard, color master, or a numerical number reference value, must be available to perform color matching.

A.1.2 A visual color match shall take place under a MacBeth Spectralight*, or equivalent viewing equipment. The visual match shall be conducted under the following light conditions:

a. Lab conditions shall be 23 °C ±2 °C and 50% ±5% relative humidity.
b. North Sky Daylight (7500 K ± 200 K) with intensity of 100 to 120 ft-c (light meter). Also, the ultraviolet source shall be used to exaggerate the optical effects of the color pigmentation and resins.
c. Horizon Sunlight (2300 K) and Minus Red (4400 K).

A.1.3 Visual assessment shall be performed as molded, after painting or after environmental testing. Describe any change in color or lightness. Visual color discrepancies may include both gloss and surface defects. Report any visual variation when comparing part to color master.

A.1.4 A Color Analyzer may be used to display color measurements and trends. It is required that the color equipment meet the requirements of SAE J1545. SAE J1545 specifies the uniform color space CIELAB 1976 (L*a*b*scale), 10 degree standard observer, illuminant D65, specular included. The following uniform color space tolerances are suggested, when comparing an unexposed part to the color master.

a. DL* (lightness) = ±1.0
b. Da* (green-red) = ±0.5
c. Db* (blue-yellow) = ±0.5
d. DE* (difference) = <1.0

A.1.5 The customer may specify the area of the part that will be measured for color. If not specified, perform five color measurements using the color analyzer across the entire surface of the part. Average these five measurements to determine the actual color values.

A.1.6 While the Color Analyzer will present useful data trends and displays, the visual assessment of the part to the color master shall be used as the preferred method to qualify color.

A.2 Gloss (Match to Master)

A.2.1 A 60 degree glossmeter shall be used to perform the gloss measurement. The user will supply a gloss master or a numerical gloss value to evaluate the appearance of the part surface.

A.2.2 The gloss measurements shall be performed as described in ASTM D 523.

A.2.3 The gloss measurement shall be performed under the following lab conditions:

a. Lab conditions shall be: 23 °C ±2 °C and 50% ±5% relative humidity

A.2.4 In order to achieve accurate and repeatable results, the following should be observed:

a. Flat surfaces are required for gloss measurements.
b. Master and part should be similar in color and lightness.
c. Measurements shall be taken free from ribs, knit lines, and other obstructions on parts.

A.2.5 There shall be a visual match between the master and the part under test. It is suggested that gloss evaluation be performed using a MacBeth Spectralight* or equivalent viewing equipment. The visual match shall be conducted under the following light conditions:

a. North Sky Daylight (7500 K ± 200 K) with intensity of 100 to 120 ft-c (light meter). Also, the ultraviolet source shall be used to exaggerate the optical effects of the color pigmentation and resins.
b. Horizon Sunlight (2300 K) and Minus Red (4400 K).

A.2.6 The preferred method of performing gloss measurements will be to take five readings representative of the entire part surface. Average these five glossmeter readings.

A.2.7 The tolerance and angle of measurement shall be as follows:

a. Angle of measurement—60 degrees
b. Gloss tolerance—±1.0 gloss unit

A.3 Surface/Grain (Match to Master)

A.3.1 A grain master is required to perform the grain/surface evaluation. The grain master will be supplied by the user.

A.3.2 It is suggested that the grain/surface match be evaluated under a MacBeth Spectralight*, or equivalent viewing equipment. The grain/surface match shall be conducted under the following light conditions:

a. North Sky Daylight (7500 K ± 200 K) with intensity of 100 to 120 ft-c (light meter). Also, the ultraviolet source shall be used to exaggerate the optical effects of the color pigmentation and resins.
b. Horizon Sunlight (2300 K) and Minus (4400 K).

A.3.3 If parts are of right/left configuration, both sides must be evaluated. Consideration shall also be given to the direction of the grain when comparing parts to the grain/surface master.

A.3.4 It is recommended that acceptable sample parts be retained for future grain/surface referencing.

APPENDIX B
DIMENSIONAL STABILITY AT SERVICE TEMPERATURE

B.1 Testing shall be performed using a forced-air oven, large enough to permit the part to be fixtured and tested in the proper in-vehicle orientation.

B.1.1 Simple part fixturing is acceptable provided the key attachment points are consistent with the assembly and intent of the part. Report the position of exposure. Care must be used to prevent warp or sag in the as-fixtured position.

B.1.2 The parts shall be dimensionally checked before and after the oven exposure. The test conditions are:

a. Oven temperature—As specified in line call-out
b. Tolerance—±2 °C from line call-out
c. Test duration—4 h
d. Room conditions—23 °C ±2 °C and 50% ±5% RH

B.1.3 Following oven exposure, the parts should be allowed to cool at room temperature for 30 min before measuring.

B.1.4 The preferred method of measurement is to use a Coordinate Measuring Machine (CMM). Average the dimensional change of five critical measurement points.

B.1.5 The alternate method of measurement can be performed using calibrated verniers, rule, and sharp scribe.

a. Etch three scribe lines in the direction of flow. If possible (on flat areas), position the scribe lines in center and at both ends of the part.
b. Etch three scribe lines 90 degrees across the direction of the flow. If possible (on flat areas), place a scribe line in center and at both ends of part.

B.1.6 Measure and average the dimensional change of the six measurement points prior to exposure and compare results from same measurement points following the oven exposure.

B.1.7 A check fixture is also an acceptable method for checking dimensional stability. Following the dimensional stability testing, the part shall comply to the fixture dimensions.

B.1.8 Acceptable dimensional stability test results shall be less than 0.5% change (averaged) from before the oven exposure and following the oven exposure.

APPENDIX C
DIMENSIONAL STABILITY AFTER HOT/COLD CYCLING

C.1 The Dimensional Stability testing shall consist of three cycles. The hot and cold chambers shall be large enough to permit a complete part or assembly to be tested in the in-vehicle position. Observe the position of exposure. Care must be used to prevent warp or sag in the as-fixtured position.

C.1.1 Observe the following test conditions:

a. Hot temperature—As specified in line call-out
b. Cold temperature— –29 °C
c. Tolerance—±2 °C from line call-out
d. Test duration—Three cycles
e. Room conditions—23 °C ±2 °C and 50% RH ±5% RH

C.1.2 Each one cycle shall consist of the following:

a. 4.0 h at hot temperature (line call-out)
b. 0.5 h at room temperature
c. 4.0 h at cold temperature (–29 °C)
d. 0.5 h at room temperature

C.1.3 When the test continuity is interrupted due to end of shift, weekends, or holidays, samples shall be left at the ambient lab temperature.

C.1.4 Simple part fixturing is acceptable provided the key attachment points are consistent with the assembly and intent of the part. The part shall be tested in the in-vehicle position or assembly position. Additional mounting information may be included in the part drawing.

C.1.5 The preferred method of measurement is to use a Coordinate Measuring Machine (CMM). Average the dimensional change of five critical measurement points.

C.1.6 The alternate method of measurement can be performed using calibrate verniers, rule, and sharp scribe:

a. Etch three scribe lines in the direction of flow. If possible (on flat areas), position the scribe lines in center and at both ends of the part.
b. Etch three scribe lines 90 degrees across the direction of the flow. If possible (on flat areas), position a scribe line in center and both ends of part.
c. Measure and average the dimensional change of these six measurement points.

C.1.7 A check fixture is also an acceptable method for checking dimensional stability. Following the temperature cycling, the part shall comply to the fixture dimensions.

C.1.8 Acceptable dimensional stability test results shall be less than 0.5% change (averaged) from before the cycling exposure and following the cycle exposure.

APPENDIX D
COLD-IMPACT TESTING, AS MOLDED OR FOLLOWING ENVIRONMENTAL CONDITIONING

D.1 Pendulum impact is the recommended method for performing the cold impact testing referenced in this SAE J1717 document. This method was selected to promote industry-wide consistency in determining the amount of energy to evaluate fracture resistance of the molded interior part.

D.1.1 It is suggested that the pendulum testing be performed inside a cold environmental chamber. Figure D1 for the suggested configuration of the pendulum impact tester.

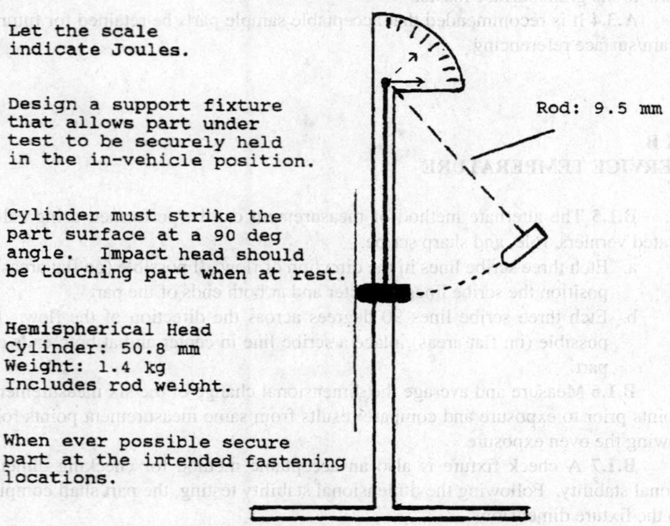

Let the scale indicate Joules.

Rod: 9.5 mm

Design a support fixture that allows part under test to be securely held in the in-vehicle position.

Cylinder must strike the part surface at a 90 deg angle. Impact head should be touching part when at rest.

Hemispherical Head
Cylinder: 50.8 mm
Weight: 1.4 kg
Includes rod weight.

When ever possible secure part at the intended fastening locations.

FIGURE D1—PENDULUM TEST FIXTURE

D.1.2 The Pendulum test is performed with the spherical impact head being swung in an arc into the molded part. The molded part must be secured at the intended fastening location during this test.

D.1.3 Caution must be used to prevent corrosion or rust buildup following extended cold environmental testing from interfering with the pendulum (pivot) operations.

D.1.4 Design a support fixture that allows the part, or that portion of the part under test, to be securely held in the in-vehicle position for testing. The actual mating part or mating assembly may be used for mounting purposes. Secure part at intended fastening location.

D.1.5 The acceptable method is to perform a minimum of three strikes at the location specified by the user. This may be verbal or the information may be included in the part drawing. If no location is identified, the three strikes will be performed at different areas across the part surface, being careful that one impact area does not interfere with another.

D.1.6 Always perform the impact testing on the outside or exposed side of the part.

D.1.7 Standard Operating Procedure

a. Adjust base (clamping fixture) so that the cylinder is touching the part surface when at rest. Cylinder must be 90 degrees to part surface.
b. Note position of scale (pointer).
c. Return striker (back swing) to the distance which will equal the desired impact energy when it strikes the part.
d. Release striker. Prevent multiple impacting, do not allow striker to bounce on part.
e. Conversion(s):
   1. in-lb x 0.113 = Joules
   2. Joules x 8.85 = in-lb

D.1.8 Following impact, visually examine the impacted and reverse sides of part. It is expected that no cracks or breakage should occur. Report any evidence of part of grain damage to the user.

D.2 Gardner Impact, ASTM D 3029, Method G (Falling Weight) (Alternate Method)

D.2.1 The Gardner impact is an alternate test method. When the part size or part configuration will not permit the pendulum impact test to be used, a Gardner impact tester (modified) as described in this section and ASTM D 3029 will be used.

D.2.2 The Gardner impact tester shall be modified to the following test configuration Figure D2:

a. Head/striker diameter—05.8 mm
b. Nose radius—25.4mm
c. Head/striker weight—0.45 kg
d. Support ring/well—75 mm
e. Test temperature— –29 °C ±2 °C
f. Impact energy—As specified in line call-out

D.2.3 When the part cannot be tested, a portion of the part or a test plaque 125 mm square or 125 mm diameter may be used. The 0.45 kg/50.8 mm diameter head/striker will be vertically dropped, with the head striking the part at a 90 degree angle.

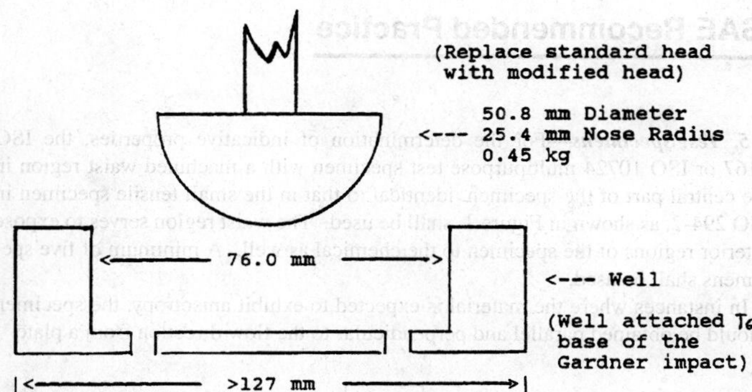

FIGURE D2—MODIFIED TEST CONFIGURATION FOR GARDNER IMPACT TEST

D.2.4 Standard Operating Procedure

a. Adjust the Gardner impact so that the impact head will be resting on the part/testing plaque. The location of these strikes may be verbal or specified in the part drawing.
b. The transference of the part/test plaque shall be as rapid as safety will permit. The operator may need to develop a system for this rapid transference from freezer to Gardner. The part/test plaque must be firmly held or clamped to well/base of the Gardner.
c. Raise Gardner weight to desired height corresponding to the desired impact energy specified in the line callout.
d. Release weight.
e. Repeat this test on a minimum of five parts.

D.2.5 Following the impact test, visually examine the impacted and reverse sides of the part. It is expected that no cracks or breakage should occur. Report any evidence of part or grain damage to user.

APPENDIX E
COLOR AND GLOSS RETENTION

E.1 Xenon-Arc Weatherometer per SAE J1885 (method BH) and this SAE J1717 document will provide operating procedures for the accelerated exposure of interior trim components (see SAE J1717, 5.5).

E.1.1 The Atlas Xenon-Arc Weather-Ometer*, models CI35, CI65 and CI65A are recommended to perform this testing. Apparatus set-up shall be as described in SAE J1885 (see SAE J1885, Section 5).

E.1.2 Evaluate the test specimens before and following the accelerated exposure specified in the line call-out. Measure the color and gloss retention using the following procedures:

a. SAE J1545, CIELAB color space, 10 degrees observer, standard illuminant D65, and specular included.
b. ASTM D 523, 60 degree glossmeter.

E.1.3 It is suggested that test panels be exposed in multiples of 37.6 kJ/m/340 cm to promote industry-wide consistency and the elimination of multiple testing. It is suggested that exposure requirements be selected in increments consistent with those shown in Table E1.

E.1.4 Testing shall be performed on the exposed surface of part.

E.1.5 A molded test specimen may be used if part size prohibits.

E.1.6 The degree of fading per CIELAB, SAE J1545, must be reported. The user may specify upper and lower tolerance limits to the DL*, DC*, and DH* measurements. The suggested tolerances are:

a. DE* (difference) = <3.0
b. D Gloss (difference) = <3.0 gloss units

TABLE E1—EXPOSURE REQUIREMENT INCREMENTS

Day	kJ/m	Day	kJ/m	Day	kJ/m
1	37.6	11	413.6	21	789.6
2	75.2	12	451.2	22	827.2
3	112.8	13	488.8	23	864.8
4	150.8	14	526.4	24	902.4
5	188.0	15	564.0	25	940.0
6	225.6	16	601.6	50	1880.0
7	263.4	17	639.2	75	2820.0
8	300.8	18	676.8	100	3760.0
9	338.4	19	714.4	500	18 800.0
10	376.0	20	752.0	1000	37 600.0

E.1.7 Visual Color Assessments—Describe any change in the color hue, lightness, saturation, or gloss change. Report any appearance variation from the color master to the user.

(R) CHEMICAL STRESS RESISTANCE OF POLYMERS —SAE J2016 NOV1999

SAE Recommended Practice

Report of the SAE Plastics Committee approved June 1989 and completely revised November 1999.

1. Scope

1.1 This SAE Recommended Practice provides a screening procedure for evaluating the susceptibility of plastics to environmental stress cracking by testing their resistance to pure solvents or their mixtures. This method can be used to evaluate effect of complex chemical mixtures with unknown or suspect components, which may be encountered in the polymer's environment.

1.2 The list of chemicals in Appendix A is intended only to serve as a guide and does not exclude any chemical that may represent the environment the polymer is subjected to in a specific application. As specific environment and exposure conditions are application dependent and could vary significantly from one application to another, the user of the document is recommended to choose the appropriate solvents relevant to the actual application enviroment and is not under any obligation to test the effect of all the chemicals listed in Appendix A.

2. References

2.1 Applicable Publications—The following publications form a part of the specification to the extent specified herein.

2.1.1 ISO PUBLICATIONS—Available from ANSI, 11 West 42nd Street, New York, NY 10036-8002.

ISO/DIS 175:1998—Plastics—Determination of the effects of liquid chemicals, including water

ISO 291:1997—Plastics—Standard atmospheres for conditioning and testing

ISO 294-1:1996—Plastics—Injection moulding of test specimens of thermoplastic materials—Part 1: General principles and multipurpose test specimens (ISO type A mould) and bars (ISO type B mould)

ISO 294-2:1996—Plastics—Injection moulding of test specimens of thermoplastic materials—Part 2: Small tensile bars

ISO 2818:1994—Plastics—Preparation of test specimens by machining

ISO 3167:1993—Plastics—Multipurpose test specimens

ISO 6252:1992—Plastics—Determination of environmental stress cracking—Constant tensile stress method

ISO 10724:1994—Plastics—Thermosetting moulding materials—Injection moulding of multipurpose test specimens

ISO 11404-3:1998—Plastics—Acquisition and presentation of comparable multipoint data—Part 3: Environmental influences on properties

2.2 Related Publications—The following publications are provided for information purposes only and are not a required part of this document.

2.2.1 ISO PUBLICATIONS—Available from ANSI, 11 West 42nd Street, New York, NY 10036-8002.

ISO 527-1:1993—Plastics—Determination of tensile properties—Part 1: General principles

ISO 527-2:1993—Plastics—Determination of tensile properties—Part 2: Testing conditions for moulding and extrusion materials

3. Definitions

3.1 Environmental Stress Cracking—Susceptibility of the plastic to cracking or crazing under applied tensile stress or strain in presence of an environment that accelerates development of such cracks.

3.2 Indicative Property—A property that has been selected to reveal the influence of the environment on a material through a comparison of measurements of the property before and after exposure.

3.3 Tensile Work to Break—The area under the tensile stress-strain plot, where applied stress is determined from the ratio of the tensile force to the minimum initial cross-sectional area of the specimen. It is expressed in kJ/m^2.

4. Symbols

- σ_y tensile strength at yield
- σ_B tensile strength at break
- w_{tB} tensile work to break
- σ_{uo} Reference value of tensile stength, prior to the exposure to the chemical
- σ_{sc}^{100} stress corresponding to a 25% reduction in the tensile strength after 100 h loading time with exposure to the chemical
- σ_{wc}^{100} stress corresponding to a 50% reduction in the work to break after 100 h loading time with exposure to the chemical
- σ_{sc}^{1000} stress corresponding to a 25% reduction in the tensile strength after 1000 h loading time with exposure to the chemical
- σ_{wc}^{1000} stress corresponding to a 50% reduction in the work to break after 1000 h loading time with exposure to the chemical

5. Test Specimens—For the determination of indicative properties, the ISO 3167 or ISO 10724 multipurpose test specimen with a machined waist region in the central part of the specimen, identical to that in the small tensile specimen in ISO 294-2, as shown in Figure 1, shall be used. The waist region serves to expose interior regions of the specimen to the chemical as well. A minimum of five specimens shall be used.

In instances where the material is expected to exhibit anisotropy, the specimen should be obtained parallel and perpendicular to the flow direction from a plate.

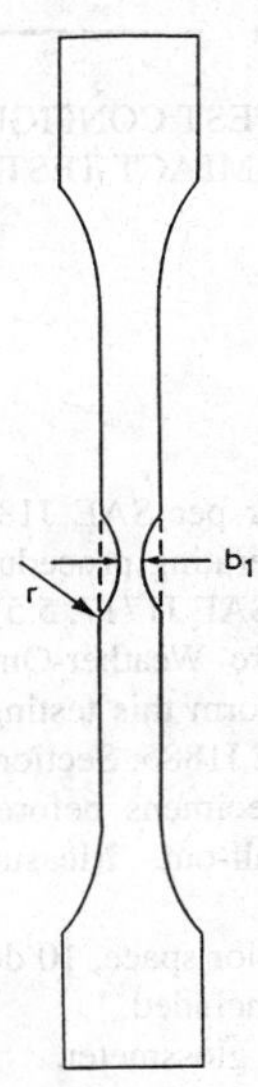

FIGURE 1—TEST SPECIMEN FOR THE MEASUREMENT OF CHEMICAL STRESS RESISTANCE PREPARED BY MACHINING THE MULTIPURPOSE TEST SPECIMEN (ISO 3167 OR ISO 10724) TO OBTAIN A CENTRAL WAIST REGION (radius, r = 15 mm ± 1 mm and minimum width, b_1 = 3 mm ± 0.2 mm)

6. Specimen Preparation—The test specimens for the evaluation of chemical stress resistance of polymers shall be prepared by injection molding, according to the procedures described in ISO 294-1 or ISO 10724, where possible unless otherwise specified in the Part 2 of the ISO material standards relevant to the material. The central region of the specimen shall be reduced to a width of 3 mm by machining circular notches of radius 15 mm (see Figure 1, ISO 2818). It is recommended that precautions should be taken during machining to avoid introducing stress concentrations in the direction perpendicular to the long axis of the specimen by ensuring that the cutting direction is parallel to the length of the specimen.

The molding conditions will depend on the material being molded and where possible, on molding conditions specified in the Part 2 of the ISO materials standards relevant to the material. For those plastics for which molding conditions have not yet been standardized, the conditions employed shall be within the range recommended by the plastics manufacturer, and shall be the same for each specimen. Where molding conditions are not stipulated in any International Standard, the melt temperature, mold temperature, average injection velocity shall be recorded.

7. Conditioning—Specimen conditioning shall be carried out at 23 °C ± 1 °C and 50% ± 5% RH for a minimum of 88 h (consistent with ISO 291) except where special conditioning or a maximum conditioning time is required by the appropriate Part 2 of the ISO material standard. Unless otherwise stated, specimens of materials that absorb moisture shall be in equilibrium with an atmosphere of 50% ± 5% RH at 23 °C ± 1 °C before exposure to the chemical and for measurement of indicative properties. Reference to the use of any special conditioning shall be recorded.

NOTE—The change from 2 °C to 1 °C tolerance is made to be consistent with ±5% tolerance for the RH in the revised ISO 291 standard.

8. Chemicals—A list of representative chemicals is included in Appendix A.

9. Indicative Properties—The following tensile properties are selected as indicative properties:

a. Tensile strength at yield (σ_y) or tensile strength at break (σ_B) for brittle materials

b. Tensile work to break (w_{tB})

10. Procedure

10.1 Measure the reference values, σ_{uo} (prior to the exposure to the chemical) at 23 °C ± 1 °C using a minimum of 5 test specimens in accordance with ISO 527-1 and ISO 527-2. For polymers that exhibit a strain at break less than 10% at a test speed of 50 mm/min, a test speed of 5 mm/min shall be used. For polymers that exhibit yield or a strain at break ≥10%, the test speed shall be 50 mm/min.

10.2 Condition the test specimens for 24 h at 23 °C ± 1 °C and 50% ± 5% relative humidity.

10.3 Expose the test specimens to the chemical for periods of 100 h and 1000 h at a series of stress levels chosen to give reductions in the tensile strength that are above and below 25% and in the work to break that are above and below 50%. A minimum of 4 stress levels and a minimum of 5 specimens at each stress shall be used.

10.4 Immediately following the exposure time, measure the indicative properties at the same test speeds employed prior to the exposure to chemical.

10.5 Plot the indicative property values against the applied stress and determine the creep stresses (Figure 2).

a. $\sigma_{sc}{}^{100}$ and $\sigma_{wc}{}^{100}$ that gives a 25% reduction in the tensile strength and a 50% reduction in the work to break respectively.

b. $\sigma_{sc}{}^{1000}$ and $\sigma_{wc}{}^{1000}$ that gives a 25% reduction in the tensile strength and a 50% reduction in the work to break respectively.

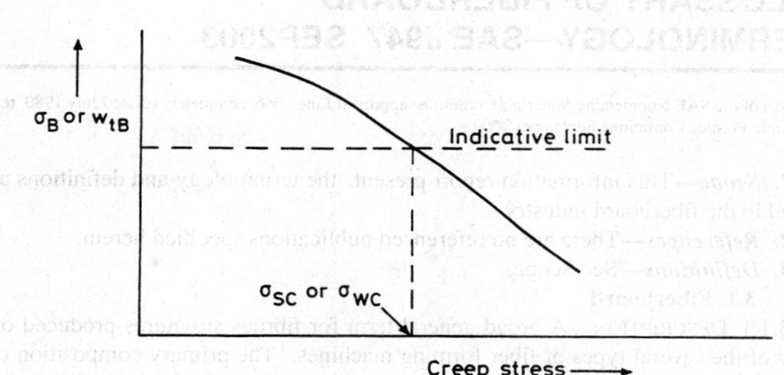

FIGURE 2—PLOT OF INDICATIVE PROPERTY VALUES, MEASURED AFTER THE TENSILE STRESS LOADING, AGAINST APPLIED STRESS SHOWING HOW THE QUANTITIES σsc AND Σ_{WC} ARE DETERMINED

10.6 Record the ratios, $\sigma_{sc}{}^{100}/\sigma_{uo}$ and $\sigma_{sc}{}^{1000}/\sigma_{uo}$ as well as $\sigma_{wc}{}^{100}/\sigma_{uo}$ and $\sigma_{wc}{}^{1000}/\sigma_{uo}$.

NOTE—The final testing should be conducted on prototype parts which includes the evaluation of parts exposed to chemicals and unexposed parts. Since the reactivity of a chemical depends on the total strain imposed on the polymer as well as any other influences that may degrade the polymer, care should be given to closely represent all fabrication and end use conditions.

APPENDIX A
LIST OF CHEMICALS

A.1 To aid the comparability of the data generated for different plastics and from different sources, this practice requires that the materials shall be exposed to the listed solvents, which represent typical "chemical types" encountered in automotive environment. If a particular plastic is known to be not suitable for use in presence of any of these chemicals, then it shall be indicated by the letters NS (not suitable) in place of experimental data. See Table A1.

Results of exposure to other chemicals may be presented in addition. It is recommended that the chemicals be chosen from the list included in ISO 11403-3 and ISO 175.

TABLE A1—LIST OF CHEMICALS

Volatile	Nonvolatile
Polar	*Polar*
1. Acetone	1. n-Butanol
2. Methanol	2. Monoethanolamine
	3. Ethylene Glycol (50% by mass in water)
	4. Deionized Water
	5. IGEPAL CO-630 (0.025% solution)
	6. Tergitol 25-L-7 (0.025% solution)
	7. $ZnCl_2$ solution (50% by mass in water)
	8. Sulfuric acid (38% by mass)
	8. Sodium Hydroxide (35% by mass)
Non-Polar	*Non-Polar*
1. N-hexane	1. Multigrade motor oil SAE 10W40
2. Toluene	2. Hypoid gear oil SAE 80/90
	Semi-Polar
	1. Dibutylphthalate
	2. Butyl Cellosolve Acetate
	3. Brake fluid DOT 4

GLOSSARY OF FIBERBOARD TERMINOLOGY—SAE J947 SEP2003

SAE Information Report

Report of the SAE Nonmetallic Materials Committee approved June 1966, completely revised July 1980, reaffirmed without change January 1985. Revised by the SAE Textiles and Flexible Plastics Committee September 2003.

1. Scope—This information report presents the terminology and definitions as used in the fiberboard industry.

2. References—There are no referenced publications specified herein.

3. Definitions—See Scope.

3.1 Fiberboard

3.1.1 DESCRIPTION—A broad general term for fibrous structures produced on any of the several types of fiber forming machines. The primary composition of these boards is normally refined cellulosic or matted wood fibers which may or may not be supplemented by the use of synthetic materials or chemical additives. The manufacture of fiberboards normally involves the formation of a wet web of suspended fibers, which is subsequently pressed, dried, and often calendared or laminated to develop desired end use properties.

3.1.2 PHYSICAL/MECHANICAL PROPERTIES—Except for the characteristic fibrous structure, the physical properties may vary over a wide range. The term fiberboard is normally limited to thicknesses of 0.009 in (0.23 mm) or above.

3.1.3 APPLICATIONS—The normal uses for this material include nearly all automotive applications where fibrous board structures are specified.

3.2 Fiberboards Classified by Manufacture

3.2.1 HARDBOARD

3.2.1.1 Description—A generic term for a sheet manufactured primarily from interfelted lignocellulosic fibers (usually wood) consolidated under heat and pressure in a hot press to a density of 55–65 lb/ft^3 (880–1041 kg/m^3) (specific gravity 0.9–1.0) or greater, and to which other materials may have been added during manufacture to improve certain properties.

3.2.1.2 Physical/Mechanical Properties—This material is generally a stiff grade of fiberboard with isotropic physical properties.

3.2.1.3 Applications—The normal uses for this material include nearly all automotive applications where fibrous board structures are specified.

3.2.2 PAPERBOARD

3.2.2.1 Description—A generic term for a sheet manufactured primarily from cellulosic fibers produced by conventional pulping and paper making process and equipment.

3.2.2.2 Physical/Mechanical Properties—Except for the characteristic fibrous structure, the physical properties may vary over a wide range. The paperboards are anisotropic with the board machine direction having greater strength and dimensional stability.

3.2.2.3 Applications—The normal uses for this material include nearly all automotive applications where fibrous board structures are specified.

3.2.3 CHIPBOARD

3.2.3.1 Description—A general term describing a type of fiberboard produced primarily from mixed grades of waste paper and most often produced on a cylinder machine. The final product may be sold as either a single ply or laminated board.

3.2.3.2 Physical/Mechanical Properties—The material is usually characterized by low density and gray color and is used where strength and quality are not required. The final product may be modified by the addition of nonfibrous components to impart water resistance or other special properties. The normal range of thickness is from about 0.009–0.045 in (0.23–1.14 mm) for single ply and 0.050 to over 0.200 in (1.27–5.08 mm) for laminated constructions.

3.2.3.3 Applications—Used in applications where appearance and ultimate strength are not important. Typical uses include visor cores, trim panel subfoundations, and some gasket applications.

3.2.4 LAMINATED BOARD

3.2.4.1 Description—A general term describing a board comprised of two or more single plies of board, paper, or other sheet materials in any combination, firmly adhered to each other by means of an adhesive between the plies. The adhesion and cohesion of the entire finished structure are such that it will function as a single unit.

3.2.4.2 Physical/Mechanical Properties—Except for the multiple structure, the physical characteristics of laminated boards vary over a wide range of properties. Because of the general nature of the term, there are few typical physical characteristics.

3.2.4.3 Applications—Typical uses include head liners, trunk liners, glove boxes, and door panels.

3.2.5 WET MACHINE BOARD (HOMOGENEOUS)

3.2.5.1 Description—This material is produced on a one cylinder wet machine. It is manufactured by the building up on a roll of a number of wet plies of paper stock (refined cellulose fibers) from a continuous web. The wet plies adhere mechanically to one another in the wet state and, when the desired thickness of board has been reached, the wet stock (approximately 40% solids) is removed from the make roll as a sheet. It is then pressed, dried, and calendared to the desired finished thickness. The pressing and drying operations develop strong fiber-to-fiber chemical and mechanical bonds within the plies and between the ply interfaces.

3.2.5.2 Physical/Mechanical Properties—This board is characterized by high density stiffness and strength. This material is commonly produced in galipers ranging from a minimum of 0.050 or 0.060 In (1.27 Or 1.52 mm) up to a thickness of 0.500–1.0 in (12.7–25.4 mm) for various applications. This material frequently contains nonfibrous components such as resins or asphalt to develop water resistance, formability, or other special properties.

3.2.5.3 Applications—Typical uses include tacking strips and dash insulators.

3.2.6 KRAFT PAPER

3.2.6.1 Description—Kraft is the generic name for paper of high strength which identifies the sulfate chemical pulping process from which the paper is made. The sulfate pulping process involves cooking wood fibers in an alkaline medium to produce strong, cellulosic fiber which is normally converted to paper on a Fourdrinier paper machine.

3.2.6.2 Physical/Mechanical Properties—The term paper is normally restricted to materials 0.009 in (0.23 mm) or under in caliper and usually less than 26 lb/1000 ft^2 (127 g/m^2). The kraft paper is characterized by a reddish-brown color in the unbleached state, but may be bleached to a very high brightness white for some applications. This material normally has high strength and is relatively dense.

3.2.6.3 Applications—Uses include wire wrapping, braided insulators, liner for laminated fiberboards, and water shields.

3.3 Fiberboards Classified by Manufacture

3.3.1 FOUNDATION BOARD

3.3.1.1 Description—A fiberboard, usually a hardboard or a laminated kraft paper board, that is used as a structural foundation or a supporting member in a trim panel assembly.

3.3.1.2 Physical/Mechanical Properties—Boards selected for foundation applications generally require a high degree of strength, rigidity, and dimensional stability; hence, most foundation boards are specified in thicknesses of 0.08 in (2.03 mm) or greater. Various applications may require this board to be coated to facilitate dielectric bonding or to be painted, embossed, or perforated for decorative purposes.

3.3.1.3 Applications—Typical applications include door and rear quarter panels, package tray panels, and headlining applications.

3.3.2 SUBFOUNDATION BOARD

3.3.2.1 Description—A fiberboard or liner used as a subfoundation in combination with a foundation board. It is used as a carrier for subsequent trim or product applications.

3.3.2.2 Physical/Mechanical Properties—These boards are often chosen for their flexibility and as a result caliper usually ranges from 0.010–0.030 in (0.25–0.76 mm). In some cases, the boards may be coated to facilitate dielectric bonding. They are usually characterized by medium strength, good plybond, good dimensional stability, and are usually treated for water resistance.

3.3.2.3 Applications—Typical automotive uses are in conjunction with door panels and real quarter panels.

3.3.3 FORMING BOARD

3.3.3.1 Description—A board suitable for shallow forming or forming into random three-dimensional shapes through the use of heat and pressure applied in a matched set of dies. This board may be one ply or a laminated combination of basic boards or a molded fiber pulp product.

3.3.3.2 Physical/Mechanical Properties—The primary composition of these boards is normally refined cellulosic fibers which may or may not be supplemented by the addition of some synthetic fibers. Usually these boards contain various amounts of thermoplastic or thermosetting resins to facilitate formability and to enhance the stability and rigidity of the formed part. Normal thicknesses range from about 0.070–0.120 in (1.78–3.05 mm).

3.3.3.3 Applications—Used in parts requiring three-dimensional shapes with rounded corners, such as formed arm rests, heater ducts, firewall components, and package trays.

3.3.4 Bending Board

3.3.4.1 Description—A paperboard, either single ply or laminated, the components of which are comprised primarily of refined cellulosic fibers.

3.3.4.2 Physical/Mechanical Properties—This material is constructed in such a way that the liner or liners are capable of accepting a suitable score and can later be bent on this score to varying degrees with little or no fracture of the surface fibers. This requirement is usually satisfied by using relatively long, strong fibers on the bending surfaces. In some cases, the visual requirements of the bent scores are obtained by covering the surface with an extensible coating or by laminating a pliable film to the surface, prior to scoring and bending. Thickness is usually confined to the 0.016–0.100 in (0.41–2.54 mm) range.

3.3.4.3 Applications—Typical applications include scored glove boxes, package trays, visors, and trunk liners.

3.3.5 Properties

3.3.5.1 Creasing—Method of scoring without cutting. See definition of scoring, paragraph 3.3.5.3.

3.3.5.2 Bending—The folding movement applied to fiberboard, usually along impressed or cut scored lines. See definition for scoring, paragraph 3.3.5.3.

3.3.5.3 Scoring—The method by which fiberboard may be depressed, or partially cut in basically linear configurations in any direction, which will later facilitate bending along the depressed or cut scores into various three-dimensional shapes.

3.3.5.4 Sizing—Sizing is a broad term referring to the resistance of fiberboard to the penetration of liquids and to the process and chemicals for developing this resistance. Surface sizing (surface application) and beater sizing (internal application) are the methods of applying the sizing materials.

3.3.5.5 Cohesive Strength—The tensile strength required to fracture internal bonds with the force applied perpendicularly to the plane of the board. Also referred to as Z direction tensile or plybond.

FIBERBOARD TEST PROCEDURE—SAE J315 JAN1985 SAE Standard

Report of the SAE Passenger Car Body Engineering Committee and SAE Nonmetallic Materials Committee approved August 1951, last revised, SAE Nonmetallic Materials Committee, Fiberboard Materials Subcommittee, January 1985.

Foreword—This Document has not changed other than to put it into the new SAE Technical Standards Board Format.

1. Scope—This SAE Standard provides test methods for determining the critical characteristics of basic or finished fiberboard products. Where applicable, methods of test developed by SAE and ASTM have been referenced.

2. References

2.1 Applicable Publications—The following publications form a part of this specification to the extent specified herein. Unless otherwise indicated, the latest issue of SAE publications shall apply.

2.1.1 SAE PUBLICATIONS—Available from SAE, 400 Commonwealth Drive, Warrendale, PA 15096-0001.

SAE J361—Procedure for Visual Evaluation of Interior and Exterior Automotive Trim
SAE J365—Method of Testing Resistance to Scuffing of Trim Materials
SAE J369—Flammability of Polymeric Interior Materials—Horizontal Test Method
SAE J912—Test Method for Determining Blocking Resistance and Associated Characteristics of Automotive Trim Materials
SAE J913—Test Method for Wicking of Automotive Fabrics and Fibrous Materials
SAE J947—Glossary of Fiberboard Terminology
SAE J948—Test Method for Determining Resistance to Abrasion of Automotive Boadycloth, Vinyl, and Leather, and the Snagging of Automotive Bodycloth
SAE J949—Test Method for Determining Stiffness (Modulus of Bending) of Fiberboards

2.1.2 ASTM PUBLICATIONS—Available from ASTM, 100 Barr Harbor Drive, West Conshohocken, PA 19428-2959.

ASTM D 95—Method of Test for Water in Petroleum Products and Other Bituminous Materials
ASTM D 644—Method of Test for Moisture in Paper
ASTM D 645—
ASTM D 747—Test Method for Apparent Bending Modulus of Plastics by Means of a Cantilever Beam
ASTM D 774—Method of Test for Bursting Strength of Paper
ASTM D 2045—Test Methods for Water Absorption on Non-bibulous Paper and Paper Boards (Cobb Test)
ASTM D 2529—Methods of Test for Bursing Strength of Paperboard or Linerboard
ASTM D 3029—Test Method for Impact Resistance of Rigid Plastic Sheeting or Parts by Means of a Tup (Falling Weight)

2.1.3 TAPPI PUBLICATION

TAPPI T451

3. Fiberboard Terminology—See SAE J947.

4. Recommendations—Fiberboard fabrication and finishing techniques, such as crease bending, scoring, forming, perforating, and the application of barrier coatings or paints, will modify the characteristics of the producer's basic material. Consequently, it is recommended that separate but related specifications be established for (1) the properties of the basic product and (2) the finished processed material.

5. Conditioning—Tests for material classification and for arbitration purposes shall be made on material conditioned to a constant weight in a controlled atmosphere of 21 °C ± 1 °C (70 °F ± 2 °F) and 50 or 65% relative humidity. Quality control tests can be conducted on unconditioned specimens unless otherwise specified by the user.

6. Thickness—Thickness shall be measured by a micrometer having two plane, parallel faces, the smaller of which should be circular and 161—212 mm^2 (0.25—0.33 in^2) in area. When the specimen is clamped between the faces, it should be under a steady pressure of 48.23—62.0 kPa (7.0—9.0 psi). The graduations of the dial face should be such as to permit estimating the thickness to at least 0.013 mm (0.0005 in).

The sample should be comprised of at least three representative specimens, each of which should be tested in four separate places. The test should be made by placing the specimen between the jaws of the micrometer and lowering the pressure foot gently upon the surface of the specimen, taking care that the edge of the foot is at least 0.25 in (6.3 mm) from the edge of the specimen. The average thickness should be reported in decimals of an inch (millimeter) to the nearest 0.013 mm (0.0005 in) and may be supplemented by maximum and minimum readings.

Fundamental technique and apparatus used shall be similar to those of ASTM D 645.

NOTE—Specimens cut for dimensional stability tests are satisfactory for these measurements.

7. Weight—The weight shall be determined by weighing 305 x 205 mm (1 x 1 ft) of material to the nearest 0.10 g. Dimensions shall be measured accurately to the nearest 0.25 mm (0.01 in). Three representative specimens shall be weighed and the average computed and reported in pounds per 1000 ft^2 or grams per square meter.

8. Density—Density in pounds per cubic foot (kilograms per cubic meter) shall be computed using data obtained from the average thickness and weight report.

9. Bursting Strength—The bursting strength shall be determined using the conventional power-driven hydraulic type machine. The average value to the nearest 34.5 kPa (5 psi) obtained by making five bursts on each side of three specimens is to be reported. Fundamental technique and apparatus used shall conform to ASTM D 774, Method of Test for Bursting Strength of Paper, or ASTM D 2529, Methods of Test for Bursting Strength of Paperboard or Linerboard.

10. Cohesive Strength—This test is designed to measure the force required to rupture a sample of paperboard at the weakest layer.

10.1 Apparatus—JUMBO MULLEN TESTER (Figure 1):

a. Brass disks, 1.6 mm (0.063 in) thick and 60.71 mm (2.390 in) diameter
b. Annular brass disks, 1.6 mm (0.063 in) thick, 76 mm (3 in) outer diameter, and 34.93 mm (1.375 in) inner diameter
c. Steel sleeve, approximately 69.9 mm (2.75 in) inside diameter, 13 mm (0.5 in) high, and 3.18 mm (0.125 in) thick
d. Means of cleanly cutting an annular sample of 60.71 mm (2.390 in) outer diameter and 34.93 mm (1.375 in) inner diameter

10.2 Procedure—Cut a 356 x 76 mm (14 x 3 in) sample of the board to be tested. Cover each side with a strip of 76 mm (3 in) double-face, pressure-sensitive tape or equivalent without peeling the protective liner, and die cut four annular specimens for testing. Peel one of the protective liners from each sample and press lightly to one of the solid disks; then peel the other liner and place an annular disk on the other side, using the hole in each for alignment.

Press the sample between the disks under about 690 kPa (100 psi). This can be done using the sample clamp of the Mullen tester itself. A pile of a dozen samples may be pressed at one time.

Place one sample on the lower platen of the Mullen tester with the annular disk down and centrally located so that the hole in the disk is aligned with the hole in the platen. Place the steel sleeve upon the annular disk and clamp in place with the upper platen. Operate the tester until the expansion of the diaphragm against the solid disk ruptures the sample. Use the 0—1380 kPa (0—200 psi) scale.

Record the maximum pressure and note the location of the rupture. Failure of the tape bond invalidates a test.

Since the area of contact between diaphragm and solid disk varies according to the pressure, do not calculate the pressure per square inch of sample, but report the results as gage readings, in kPa (psi). However, the area of the sample is exactly 19.4 cm^2 (3 in^2) if the user desires to calculate kPa (psi).

11. Moisture Content—The moisture content shall be determined by observing the loss in weight of a 100 x 100 mm (4 x 4 in) specimen (the test specimen may be delaminated to facilitate moisture removal), upon drying in an air circulating oven maintained at 102 °C ± 3 °C) 215 °F ± 5 °F until a constant weight is obtained. The weight loss shall be expressed as percent moisture on the basis of the initial weight of the specimen. For reference purposes, see ASTM D 644, Method of Test for Moisture in Paper. In cases where appreciable volatile material other than water is known to exist, the Dean and Stark apparatus may be used. See ASTM D 95, Method of Test for Water in Petroleum Products and Other Bituminous Materials.

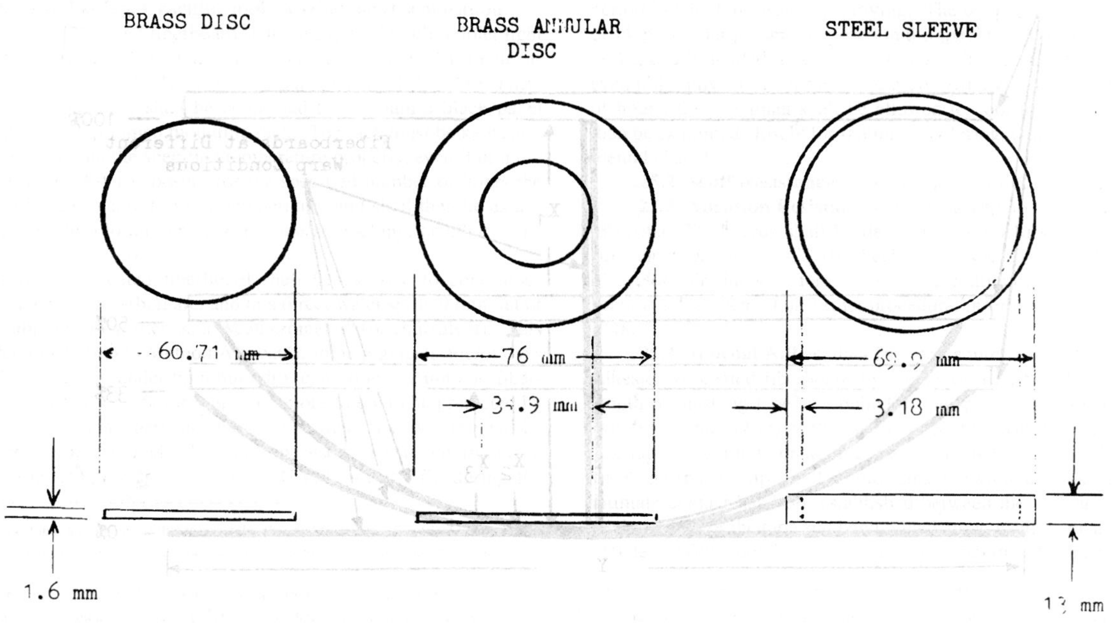

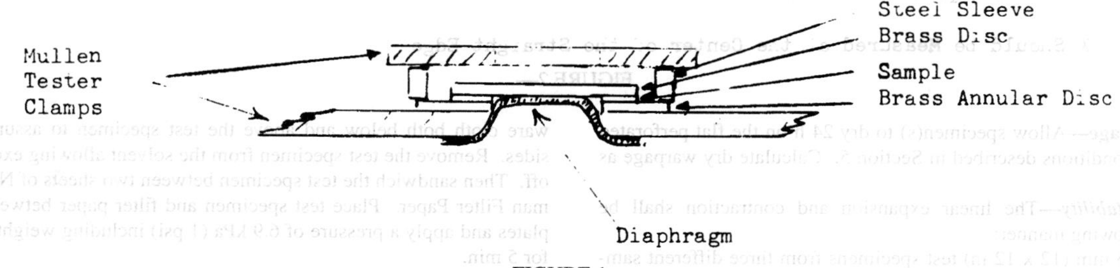

FIGURE 1—

12. Water Absorption—The percent of water absorption shall be determined by observing the gain in weight of each of three 100 x 100 mm (4 x 4 in) specimens upon immersion in distilled or deionized water. The test specimens shall be cut with a paper cutter or band saw to prevent delamination of the edges. The specimens shall be weighed to the nearest 0.01 g and then submerged horizontally under 25 mm (1 in) of water maintained at 21 °C ± 1 °C (70 °F ± 2 °F) and at a pH of 7.0 ± 0.5. The samples were removed after periods of 2.5 and 24 h, ± 5% and visible surface water is removed by wiping or blotting. The specimens shall be immediately reweighed to the nearest 0.01 g. The weight of absorbed water shall be calculated and the water absorption expressed as percent by weight based on the initial weight. The average value for each time period is reported.

13. Thickness Swell—The thickness shall be determined to the nearest 0.025 mm (0.001 in) by averaging four readings taken at the center of each side of the water absorption specimen and 25 mm (1 in) from the edge. The caliper reading shall be taken using the same apparatus as described in Section 5. The specimen shall be soaked and treated in the same manner as established in Section 11. Immediately following the tests, the specimen shall be recalipered in the same location and manner, and the average reading established for each soaked specimen. The following formula shall be used when calculating the percent of swelling:

$$S = \left[\frac{T_2 - T_1}{T_1}\right]100 \qquad \text{(Eq. 1)}$$

where:

S = swelling, %

T_1 = average thickness before soaking, mm (in)

T_2 = average thickness after soaking, mm (in)

14. Surface Water Absorption—Refer to ASTM D 2045, Test Methods for Water Absorption on Non-bibulous Paper and Paper Boards (Cobb Test).

15. Warpage—The original, wet, and dry warpage shall be determined by the following test methods:

15.1 Original Warpage—Prepare three test specimens 305 x 305 mm (12 x 12 in) from three different samples of fiberboard which are representative of a shipment.

Lay a specimen on a flat horizontal surface, and hold a straight edge so that it bridges the specimen in the area of maximum bow. Do not allow the weight of the straight edge to bear on the specimen.

Using a steel scale, graduated in 0.25 mm (0.01 in), measure the distance x at the midpoint of the straight edge bridging the bow. This distance must be measured on a perpendicular line to the straight edge. (See Figure 2.)

Calculate the original warpage by substituting in the following equation:

$$\frac{2X}{Y} \times 100 = \%\text{warpage} \qquad \text{(Eq. 2)}$$

where:

X = the dimensions in inches (millimeters) as measured previously

Y = the dimensions in inches (millimeters) of the specimen before warpage (The measurement for Y must be in the exact same line in which the straight edge was laid to measure X.)

15.2 Wet Warpage—Expose specimen(s) horizontally on a sheet of perforated metal[1] so that air can contact specimen(s) on both sides for 24 h at 38 °C ± 1 °C (100 °F ± 2 °F) and 98% ± 2% RH.

Remove conditioned specimen(s) and perforated metal sheet and allow specimen(s) to remain on perforated metal surface to dry for 30 min at room temperature. Calculate wet warpage as in 15.1.

1. "Perfex" perforated metal—40% open area or equivalent. Source of "perfex" is Joseph J. Ryerson & Sons, Inc., 1600 E. Euclid, Detroit, MI.

STANDARD CLASSIFICATION SYSTEM FOR FIBERBOARDS—SAE J1323 DEC2003

SAE Standard

Report of the SAE Nonmetallic Materials Committee approved August 1980 and revised June 1983. Reaffirmed by the SAE Fiberboard Materials Committee September 1990. Revised by the SAE Textiles and Flexible Plastics Committee December 2003. Rationale statement available.

1. Scope—This SAE Standard provides a means for specifying or describing the pertinent properties of fiberboards for automotive applications. The materials normally specified by this standard are defined in SAE J947. The test methods commonly used for fiberboards are defined in SAE J315.

1.1 Purpose—The purpose of this classification system is to provide guidance to the engineer in the selection of commercially available fiberboards and further provide a method for specifying the fiberboard and its critical properties by use of a standard line call-out.

2. References

2.1 Applicable Publications—The following publications form a part of the specification to the extent specified herein. Unless otherwise indicated the lastest revision of SAE publications shall apply.

2.1.1 SAE PUBLICATIONS—Available from SAE, 400 Commonwealth Drive, Warrendale, Pa 15096-0001.

SAE J315—Fiberboard Test Procedure

SAE J947—Glossary of Fiberboard Terminology

2.1.2 AATCC PUBLICATION

AATCC Evaluation Form 2 (Gray Scale for Staining)

3. Numbering System

3.1 The Basic Five Characters—This classification establishes alpha-numeric characters for various performance levels of each fiberboard property or characteristic. In specifying or describing fiberboard materials, each line call-out shall include the number SAE J1323, followed by a sequence of alpha-numerics to describe the fiberboard and its properties. The first five alpha-numeric characters of the call-out after SAE J1323 are mandatory, since they identify the material and specify the critical fiberboard properties, thickness, fiberboard type, and dimensional stability.

3.2 Suffix Letters—To further specify or describe the fiberboard, each line call-out may include one or more suffix - alpha-numeric symbols as listed in Section 5. These suffix letters, when appended to the basic number, specify additional physical or mechanical property requirements. Suffix symbols may be used singly or in combination to describe the properties desired in the fiberboard.

3.3 Special Numbers—The numeral 0 is used when the description of any characteristic is not desired. The numeral 9 is used when the description of any characteristic (or test related thereto) is specified by some supplement to this classification system, such as notes on engineering drawings.

3.4 Special Letter—To identify other characteristics not covered by the existing suffix symbols, the letter Z shall be used. The Z characteristics shall be specified in detail on the engineering drawing or other supplement to this classification. If more than one Z characteristic is specified, they should be identified by subnumeral, for example, Z_1, Z_2, Z_3, etc.

3.5 Example—The line call-out SAE J1323 B2A23A1B7C3D9Z would be broken down to indicate the type of fiberboard and properties as in Figure 1:

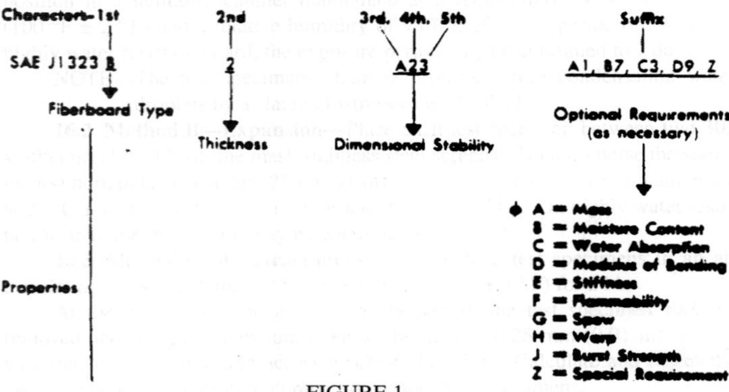

FIGURE 1—

By using the breakdown in Figure 1 and Tables 1 to 4, the example line call-out specifies a hardboard, 2.03 mm thick, with a 0.5% maximum expansion and a 0.75% maximum contraction after humidity exposure. The optional requirements include a weight of 1 kg/m^2 ±0.05, a moisture content of 5 to 9%, water absorption of 30% maximum, and a special modulus bending requirement.

4. Basic Fiberboard Characteristics—Fiberboards identified by this classification system shall have the following three basic characteristics indicated by the first five alpha-numeric symbols.

4.1 Fiberboard Type—The first character of the line call-out specifies the type of fiberboard as defined in SAE J947, and listed in Table 1:

TABLE 1—

First Character	Fiberboard Type
A	None Specified
B	Hardboard
C	Paperboard - Laminated
D	Paperboard - Single Ply
E	Paperboard - Wet Machine Board
F	Molded Cellulosic Fiber Pulp Product
G	Kraft Paper
H	Paperboard - Corrugated
Z	Special Requirements, as Necessary

4.2 Thickness—The second character of the line call-out specifies the fiberboard thickness in millimeters as determined in SAE J315, and listed in Table 2. The thickness tolerance for paperboard is ±5% from the average panel thickness; however, the thickness variation within a hardboard panel (in the range of 1.65 to 3.18 mm thick) is ±0.25 mm from the average panel thickness.

TABLE 2—

Second Character	G (Paper) mm	D and E (Single Ply Paperboard) mm	C (Laminated Paperboard) mm	B and F (Hardboard or Molded Fiberboard) mm	H (Corrugated Fiberboard(1)) mm
1	0.025	0.25	1.02	1.65	2.26 (E flute)
2	0.051	0.64	1.65	2.03	3.00 (B flute)
3	0.076	0.76	1.78	2.54	4.19 (C flute)
4	0.102	1.02	2.03	3.18	5.13 (A flute)
5	0.127		2.54		
6	0.152		3.05		
7	0.178		3.18		
8	0.203				
9	Special Requirements, as Necessary				

1. The corrugated fiberboard thickness values are based upon the use of 42/1000 ft^2 (195 g/m^2) kraft paper. The flute designations indicate the following construction:
A flute = 118 ± 10 flutes/m
B flute = 164 ± 10 flutes/m
C flute - 138 ± 10 flutes/m
E flute = 308 ± 13 flutes/m

4.3 Dimensional Stability—The third, fourth, and fifth characters of the line call-out specify the maximum[1] percent expansion and contraction of the fiberboard for both the machine and across-machine direction, as determined in SAE J315, and listed in Tables 3 and 4. The third character denotes the method of test in SAE J315, the fourth character specifies the maximum expansion, and, the fifth character specifies the maximum contraction.

5. Supplementary Characteristics—Additional fiberboard requirements can be included by adding one or more of the following suffixes:

5.1 Suffix Letter A—Mass determined in accordance with SAE J315. Specify the mass in kg/m^2. (See Table 5.) The tolerance unless otherwise specified shall be ±5%.

TABLE 3—

Third Character	Test Method
A	Method A (humidity)
B	Method B (water immersion)

1. The maximum dimensional movement on fiberboards will occur in the across-machine direction. Paper and paperboards will usually have only half the dimensional movement in the machine direction, due to linear fiber orientation during manufacture.

TABLE 4—

Fourth and Fifth Characters	Expansion or Contraction % max
0	None specified
1	0.25
2	0.50
3	0.75
4	1.0
5	1.5
6	2.0
7	3.0
8	4.0
9	Special Requirement, as Necessary

TABLE 5—

Suffix Number	kg/m^2
A1	1 ±0.05 kg/m^2
A1.5	1.5 ±0.075 kg/m^2
A9	Special Requirement

5.2 Suffix Letter B—Moisture Content determined in accordance with SAE J315. Specify the moisture content in percent with a range of ±2%. (See Table 6.)

TABLE 6—

Suffix Number	% Moisture Content
B1	0–3
B2	0–4
B3	1–5
B4	2–6
B5	3–7
B6	4–8
B7	5–9
B8	6–10
B9	Special Requirement

5.3 Suffix Letter C—Water Absorption determined in accordance with SAE J315. (See Table 7.)

TABLE 7—

Suffix Number	Water Absorption % max
C1	10 for 2.5 h immersion
C2	20 for 2.5 h immersion
C3	30 for 2.5 h immersion
C4	60 for 2.5 h immersion
C5	10 for 24 h immersion
C6	20 for 24 h immersion
C7	30 for 24 h immersion
C8	60 for 24 h immersion
C9	Special Requirement

5.4 Suffix Letter D—Stiffness (modulus of bending) determined in accordance with SAE J949a. (See Table 8.)

a. First Suffix Number - machine direction stiffness min
b. Second Suffix Number - across-machine direction stiffness min

TABLE 8—

Suffix Number	Stiffness
D1	350 kPa
D2	700 kPa
D3	2000 kPa
D4	3500 kPa
D5	6000 kPa
D9	Special Requirement

Example: D21 = 700 kPa M.D. min and 350 kPa A.M.D. min

5.5 Suffix Letter E—Stiffness (cantilever beam) determined in accordance with ASTM D 747. (See Table 9.)

a. First Suffix Number - M.D. stiffness min
b. Second Suffix Number - A.M.D. stiffness min

TABLE 9—

Suffix Number	Stiffness
E1	500 kPa
E2	1000 kPa
E3	1500 kPa
E4	2000 kPa
E9	Special Requirement

5.6 Suffix Letter F—Flammability determined in accordance with SAE J369. (See Table 10.)

TABLE 10—

Suffix Number	Burn Rate max
F1	Does Not Ignite
F2	Self-Extinguishing
F3	Burn Rate - 25 mm/min
F4	Burn Rate - 51 mm/min
F5	Burn Rate - 76 mm/min
F6	Burn Rate - 101 mm/min
F9	Special Requirement

5.7 Suffix Letter G—Spew determined in accordance with SAE J315 and AATCC Evaluation Procedure 2 (Gray Scale for Staining). (See Table 11.)

TABLE 11—

Suffix Number	Gray Scale Rating
G1	No. 1 Very Heavy Stain
G2	No. 2 Heavy Stain
G3	No. 3 Moderate Stain
G4	No. 4 Slight Stain
G5	No. 5 Unstained
G9	Special Requirement

5.8 Suffix Letter H—Warp determined in accordance with SAE J315. The maximum allowable warp should be directly expressed as a percent. (See Table 12.)

TABLE 12—

Suffix Number	Warp % max
H1	1
H2	2
H3	3
H4	4
H5	5
H6	6
H7	7
H8	8
H9	Special Requirement

5.9 Suffix Letter J—The Minimum Bursting Strength as determined in accordance with SAE J315. (See Table 13.)

TABLE 13—

Suffix Number	Minimum kPa/mm Thickness
J1	250
J2	500
J3	750
J4	1000
J5	1250
J6	1500
J7	1750
J8	2000
J9	Special Requirement, as Necessary

6. Conclusion—A word of caution is extended in utilizing this classification system. It could be possible for a consumer to call out a product that cannot be manufactured. Close cooperation will be necessary between the consumers and suppliers to assure feasibility of the line call-out.

(R) TEST METHOD FOR WICKING OF AUTOMOTIVE FABRICS AND FIBROUS MATERIALS—SAE J913 JAN1996

SAE Standard

Report of the SAE Nonmetallic Materials Committee approved July 1965 and completely revised February 1985. Reaffirmed by the SAE Textiles and Flexible Plastics Committee January 1994 and completely revised January 1996.

Foreword—This Document has not changed other than to put it into the new SAE Technical Standards Board Format.

1. Scope—This SAE Standard is applicable for determining the wicking characteristics of seat fabrics, convertible tops, headlining, fiber padding, and other automotive textile materials.

2. References—There are no referenced publications specified herein.

3. Apparatus and Materials Required

3.1 Indelible pencil

3.2 Solutions

a. 100 mg fluorescein dye (fluorescein sodium salt, "Uramine" or equivalent) dissolved in 1000 mL of distilled water (pH 7 max).
b. 50% fluorescein dye as in solution (a); 50% alkyl aryl sulfonate solution (10 g of "Nacconal 40F" or equivalent—40% alkyl aryl sulfonate dissolved in 1000 mL of distilled water—3.0 to 7.0 pH range).
c. Distilled water.

3.3 Apparatus for Suspending Specimens in Beakers

3.4 UV Lamp

4. Test Specimens—Cut strips of material to be tested 200 mm long and 51 mm wide, one set in the machine direction and another set in the cross-machine direction, then condition at 21 °C ±2 °C and 50% ±5% relative humidity for 24 h. Use a separate beaker for each sample.

5. Procedure—Draw a line with an indelible pencil 50 mm from end of specimens to be immersed. Prepare a suitable container with a 75 mm minimum depth of solutions (a), (b), or (c) as specified and immerse specimens to a point where upper meniscus just touches line marked with indelible pencil. Allow specimens to remain for a specified period in solution while maintaining solution to within 2 mm. Tests shall be run in a controlled atmosphere of 21 °C ±2 °C and 50% ± 5% relative humidity.

At the end of the specified period, remove specimens from test solution (a) or (b) and examine under "UV lamp[1]". Travel of fluorescein dye above marked line indicates degree of wicking. Specimens tested in solution (c) shall be examined for wicking, migration, and discoloration under normal light.

For test in solution (c) use 4 mm notches instead of an indelible pencil line.

1. Available from Hanovia Company.

METHOD OF TESTING RESISTANCE TO SCUFFING OF TRIM MATERIALS—SAE J365 AUG1994

SAE Standard

Report of the SAE Nonmetallic Materials Committee approved October 1968, and revised February 1985. Revised by the SAE Textiles and Flexible Plastics Committee August 1994.

1. Scope—This test can be used to determine the resistance to scuffing of test specimens such as fiberboards, fabrics, vinyl-coated fabrics, leathers, and similar trim materials.

2. References—There are no referenced publications specified herein.

3. Materials and Equipment Required

3.1 Abraser—Taber Model 5150 or equivalent. Equipment which meets the requirements of this test can be obtained from the Taber Instrument Corp., North Tonawanda, NY.

3.2 Specimen Holder—Catalog No. E-100-125[1]. 108 mm OD.

3.3 Hold-Down Ring—Catalog No. E-100-101[1]. 108 mm OD.

3.4 Rubber Pad—Catalog No. S-19[1].

3.5 Clamp Plate—54 mm OD for fabrics, leather, coated fabrics, and similar flexible materials. 32 mm OD for carpets and other floor covering materials.

3.6 Scuff Fixture—The special scuff fixture head, weight, and other components are shown in Figure 1 and are assembled as shown in Figure 2. The scuff fixture is attached to the abrader as shown in Figure 3. The scuff head is held at a 110 degree angle. The vertical centerline of the scuff head is 32 mm from the specimen holder center pin. The tip is centered under the 0.9 kg weight and in a horizontal alignment with the center pin as shown in Figure 3.

NOTE—The attachment bracket shown in Figure 1, detail 8 may be modified for other abrader models, provided the scuff head position is maintained and test results correlate.

The scuff head tip shown in Figure 1, detail 11 must be frequently checked for dimensions and reground or replaced if found to deviate from the specified tolerances.

4. Procedure

4.1 Conditioning—The test specimens shall be conditioned for a minimum of 24 h at 21 °C ±2 °C and 50% ±5% relative humidity for this test. Unless otherwise specified, the test shall be conducted under the same controlled conditions since a change in relative humidity and temperature can affect test results.

1. Taber catalog numbers.

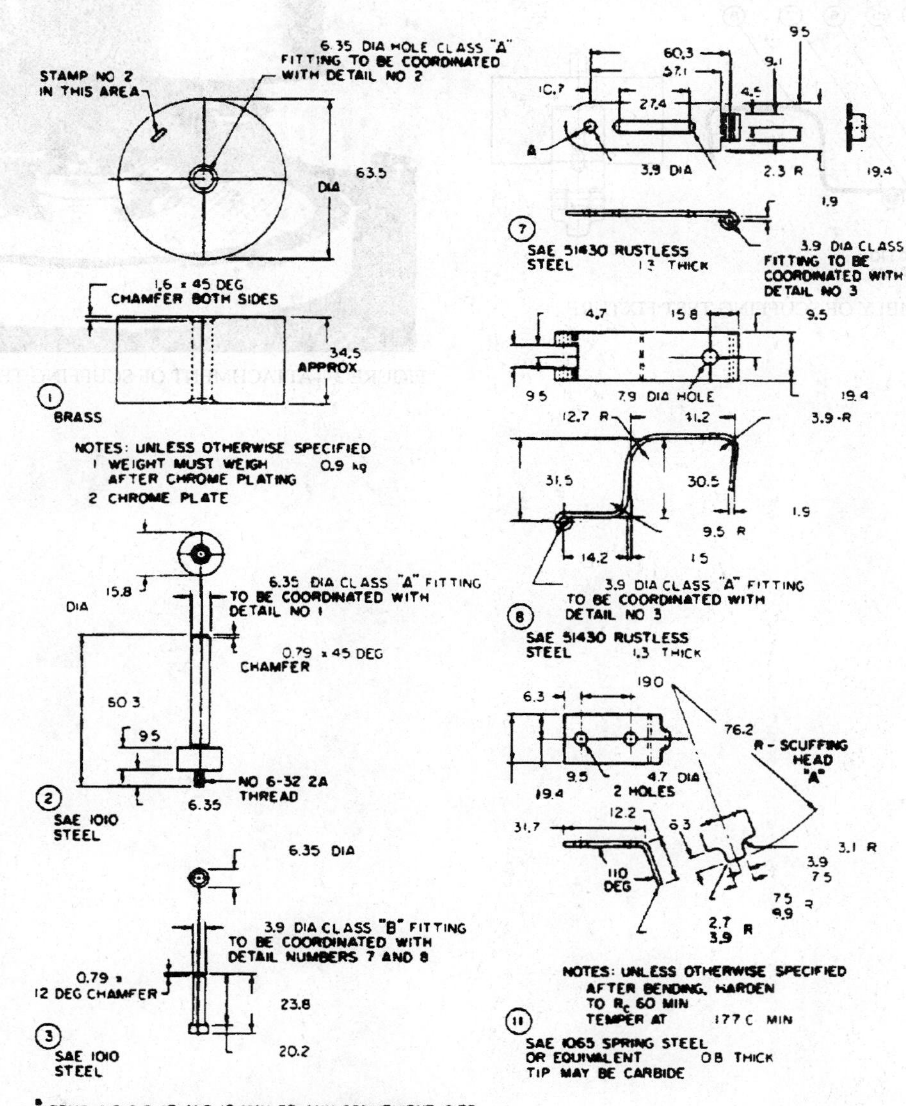

FIGURE 1—COMPONENTS OF SCUFFING ASSEMBLY

4.2 Test Samples for Textiles, Coated Fabrics, Leather, or Similar Flexible Materials

a. Cut a 6.4 mm hole in the center of a 131 mm diameter specimen.
b. Place the specimen on the rubber pad of the specimen holder.
c. Place a 54 mm OD clamp plate over the material and tighten down securely with the clamping nut.
d. Press the hold-down ring over the test specimen so that the material is drawn taut over the specimen holder with no wrinkles or bulges.
e. Tighten the adjusting screw of the hold-down ring just enough to hold the test specimen but not so tight as to cause wrinkling or bulging.
f. Place the assembled test specimen on the abrading machine and lower the scuff fixture onto the test specimen as shown in Figure 3.
g. Scuff for the number of cycles indicated by the engineering specification.

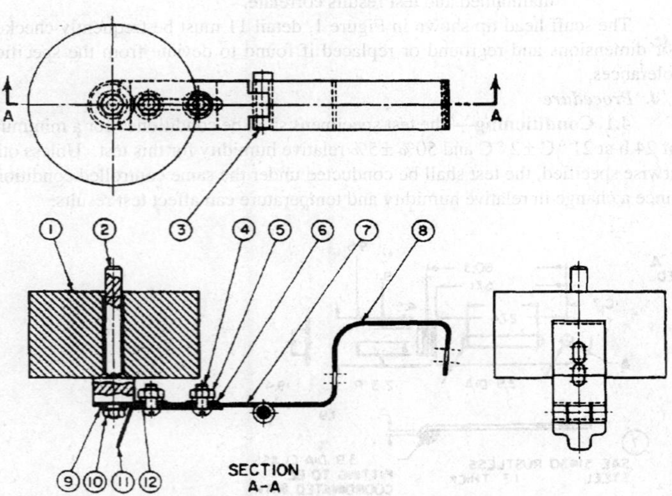

FIGURE 2—ASSEMBLY OF SCUFFING TEST FIXTURE

4.3 Test Samples for Fiberboard, Rubber Floor Mats, Carpets, and Other Semirigid Materials

a. Cut a 6.4 mm hole in the center of a 106 mm diameter test specimen.
b. Place the test specimen on the rubber pad on the specimen holder and tighten down securely with a 32 mm clamp plate and nut.
c. Place the hold-down ring over the test specimen, press the ring with the fingers, and tighten it. The specimen, when properly secured, shall be free of wrinkles and bulges.
d. Place the assembled test specimen on the brading machine and lower the scuff fixture onto the test specimen as shown in Figure 3.
e. Scuff the test specimen for the number of cycles indicated by the engineering specification.

5. Reporting—Observe and report scuff resistance by comparing the test specimen to an approved master scuff specimen established by the consumer.

FIGURE 3—ATTACHMENT OF SCUFFING TEST FIXTURE TO ABRADER

TEST METHOD FOR DETERMINING BLOCKING RESISTANCE AND ASSOCIATED CHARACTERISTICS OF AUTOMOTIVE TRIM MATERIALS—SAE J912 JUL2002

SAE Standard

Report of the SAE Nonmetallic Materials Committee approved June 1965 and revised August 1972. Reaffirmed without change May 1978. Revised by the SAE Textiles and Flexible Plastics Committee August 1995 and July 2002. Rationale statement available.

1. Scope—This test method is designed to indicate the degree of surface tackiness, color transfer, loss of embossment, and surface marring when two trim materials are placed face to face under specific conditions of time, temperature, and pressure. These specific conditions are not dictated in this test procedure but will be found in the material standards which govern each type of trim material to be tested.

2. References—There are no referenced publications specified herein.

3. Materials and Equipment Required

3.1 Weights or compression fixture capable of exerting uniform pressure over a 50 x 50 mm area.

3.2 Air circulating oven.

3.3 Small capacity tensile machine capable of determining increments of 0.5 N or less over a 0 to 90 N range. Front and back jaws shall have a minimum width of 50 mm.

4. Test Specimens—Cut one 50 x 75 mm test specimen from each trim material to be tested. If only one material is to be tested, cut two test specimens.

5. Procedure

5.1 Preheat Oven and weight (or compression fixture) to specified temperature for at least 1 h.

5.2 Place two test specimens face to face and align all edges.

5.3 Place assembly into the preheated oven.

5.4 Apply specified pressure to only upper 2/3 area of sandwich. This will allow an end flap of 25 x 50 mm on each specimen which will not be under pressure. See Figure 1.

5.5 After specified time has elapsed, remove assembly from oven, release pressure, and allow a cooling period at room temperature for at least 0.5 h.

5.6 Position specimens in tensile machine so that one flap is in upper jaw and other flap is in lower jaw. Disengage pawls. Separate specimens at a rate of 50 mm/min and record average reading.

5.7 Record also, observations concerning surface appearance of specimens as listed under Section 1.

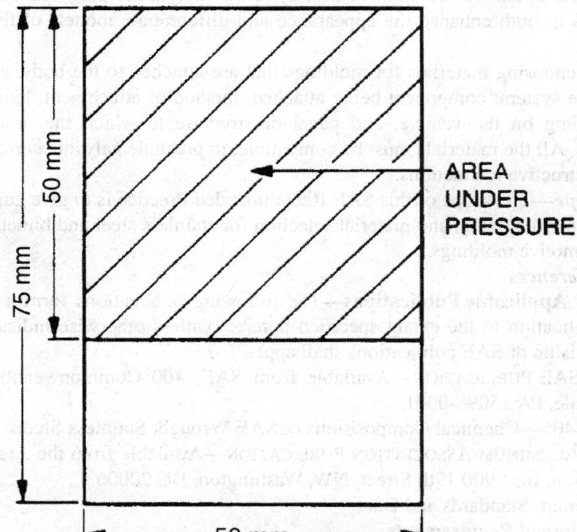

FIGURE 1—PROCEDURE FOR BLOCKING

GUIDELINES FOR USAGE OF STAINLESS STEEL AND BIMETAL FOR EXTERIOR AUTOMOTIVE BRIGHT TRIM—SAE J1755 JAN1995

SAE Recommended Practice

Report of the SAE Stainless Steel and Bimetal Subcommittee of the SAE Bright Trim Committee approved January 1995.

Foreword—This Document has not changed other than to put it into the new SAE Technical Standards Board Format.

Stainless steel and bimetal have been used extensively for many years on automotive molding systems, as well as functional systems. These alloys provide an economical option for automotive trim systems. Bright moldings have allowed designers to both enhance the appearance and differentiate models of the same platform.

When choosing materials for moldings that are attached to the body, consider the whole system: component being attached, method of attachment, location of the molding on the vehicle, and panel or structure to which the molding is attached. All the materials must be compatible, to preclude galvanic corrosion or other destructive interactions.

1. Scope—The scope of this SAE Recommended Practice is to give guidelines for design, processing, and material selection for stainless steel and bimetal exterior automotive moldings.

2. References

2.1 Applicable Publications—The following publications form a part of the specification to the extent specified herein. Unless otherwise indicated the latest revision of SAE publications shall apply.

2.1.1 SAE PUBLICATION—Available from SAE, 400 Commonwealth Drive, Warrendale, PA 15096-0001.

SAE J405—Chemical Compositions of SAE Wrought Stainless Steels

2.1.2 ALUMINUM ASSOCIATION PUBLICATION—Available from the Aluminum Association, Inc., 900 19th Street, NW, Washington, DC 20006.

Aluminum Standards and Data

3. Technical Requirements

3.1 General Design Considerations

3.1.1 CREVICE CORROSION—Avoid system designs that promote crevice corrosion, such as pockets or flat horizontal shelves that could collect corrosion promoting media. Crevice corrosion is intense localized corrosion that occurs in crevices or other shielded areas that are exposed to corrosive media. Stainless steel is susceptible to crevice corrosion. If possible, leave an open gap between the molding and the sheet metal to allow good air circulation. Eliminate rough edges and minimize the effects of cold work on the edges to help make the molding less susceptible to crevice corrosion.

3.1.2 CHROMIUM PLATING—Chromium plated moldings have special shape requirements. Sharp corners and projections are prone to excessive plating build-up and/or burning, and therefore should be avoided. Deep recesses, sharp radius concavities, and long return flanges tend to receive little or no plating, so those kinds of features should be avoided. To achieve uniform plating thickness, keep all appearance surfaces as close as possible to the major plane of the part. Parts to be plated may need a hole in them for mounting on racks.

3.1.3 GALVANIC CORROSION—Stainless steel will cause galvanic corrosion of mild steel (galvanized or bare) or aluminum panels which it touches in the presence of an electrolyte, such as salt water. Therefore, stainless steel should never be allowed to be grounded to the body. Do not count on the body paint to provide sufficient isolation. When stainless steel in the vicinity of a paint chip or scratch is connected to the exposed metal substrate via an electrolyte such as salt water, it will cause severe localized corrosion of the exposed metal.

The stainless steel can be isolated from the body by encapsulating the molding in plastic or using a foam or other nonconductive tape on the back. If the molding must be grounded to the body panel, then bimetal should be used. Bimetal consists of stainless steel on the front side, with aluminum clad on the back. The molding is formed of this sandwich material. The aluminum on the back provides sacrificial protection for the body. Note that when the aluminum corrodes, a white corrosion product forms which may bleed around onto the front of the molding. This is most prevalent when the molding edges are not curled around to the back.

3.2 Fastening Considerations

3.2.1 DESIGN—Do not put holes in any body panel after paint! Even when holes are put in body panels before paint, they should only be put in "wet" panels. Weld studs are preferred instead of fasteners that are inserted through holes.

3.2.2 FASTENER MATERIAL—The fastener material must be chosen carefully. Do not use stainless steel fasteners unless they touch only stainless steel, brass, and/or plastic. If the part is not too heavy, adhesives may be used. Plastic or coated aluminum fasteners may be used, depending on the molding material to which they are attached. Steel fasteners must have corrosion protective coatings that are designed to resist the exterior environment.

If the moldings are solid stainless, they should not have any metal fasteners touching them (except stainless steel[1]). Plastic clips can be used to hold moldings to metal studs on the panel. Or adhesive foam tape may be possible. If the stainless steel is partly encapsulated in plastic, metal fasteners may be used only in the plastic, and only if they do not go through a stainless steel core.

3.3 Processing Considerations

3.3.1 SURFACE CONTAMINATION—Iron abrasion can lead to red rust and potentially pit corrosion. During forming or other manufacture, it is important to avoid tool wear or other abrasion that can contaminate the stainless surface. This is especially true if such tools have previously been used to process carbon steels or other material.

If such contamination is unavoidable, the stainless surface should be treated with diluted nitric acid or other suitable cleanser with subsequent careful rinsing with water in order to reestablish the noncorrosive character of the surface.

3.3.2 SURFACE SMOOTHNESS—The smoother a stainless surface is, the easier it is to keep it clean. Bright annealing or buffing achieve such smoothness. Note that dust or other particles may adhere more easily to a material's *horizontal* (buffing) lines and can be drained off more easily from *vertical* (buffing) lines.

3.3.3 SURFACE CLEANLINESS—A mild detergent should be used regularly to clean the stainless surface. Frequent cleaning enhances appearance and long-term corrosion resistance of the stainless.

3.4 Material Selection—Remember, only use stainless steel if it is insulated from the rest of the car! Bimetal (aluminum-backed stainless steel) is available for designs that cannot be isolated.

3.4.1 STAINLESS STEEL (SAE J405)—SAE 51434 is a chromium-molybdenum bearing alloy used where resistance to pitting and rusting is required. It is used when roping control is not required for the product application. Roping becomes a concern on parts stretched more than 3 to 5%. SAE 51436 is similar to SAE 51434 in corrosion resistance. The addition of columbium allows its use when roping control is required for the product application. SAE 51434 and SAE 51436 do not need chromium plating to attain an acceptable, attractive appearance. However, chromium flashing will increase the corrosion resistance of SAE 51434 and 51436. Note that those two alloys have had occurrences of pitting and red rust when used below the beltline. Generally, 0.10 to 0.12 μm of chromium is recommended for achieving the additional corrosion protection without causing a milky appearance. Buffing before chromium flashing may be needed to achieve the best appearance.

SAE 30201 is a chromium-manganese-nickel bearing alloy that is stronger, more ductile, and has better corrosion resistance than SAE 51434 and 51436, unless parts are chromium flashed. It is sometimes used for automotive trim fabrication where increased ductility is required for deep drawing or where increased atmospheric corrosion resistance is required. SAE 30301 is a chromium-nickel bearing alloy which has greater formability than the above alloys. It is used for trim parts requiring deep drawing or stretching operations or where increased atmospheric corrosion resistance is required. SAE 30201 and SAE 30301 will appear yellowish unless they are chromium flashed or chromium plated. The minimum thickness requirement for chromium flash is 0.12 μm for color match.

3.4.2 BIMETAL (SAE J405 FOR THE STAINLESS STEEL PORTION AND ALUMINUM STANDARDS AND DATA FOR THE ALUMINUM PORTION)—Bimetal as used for exterior automotive trim consists of cold rolled SAE 51434 or SAE 30201 stainless steel metallurgically bonded to either an AA1100 or AA3003 aluminum alloy or an AA5052 alclad with AA1100 series equivalent alloy. The stainless steel surface is intended to form the significant or visible side of fabricated parts. The bimetal is to be comparable in appearance to solid stainless steel and offer some corrosion protection to the vehicle due to the galvanic protection provided by the aluminum.

1. If the screw goes into a brass or stainless steel nut that is isolated from the body, then it should be stainless or brass.

The selection of which bimetal to use will be based more on formability than appearance. The formability is affected by temper, aluminum alloy backing, and ratio of stainless steel thickness to aluminum thickness. The supplier who will be forming the part should be consulted to help determine which choice of bimetal would be most appropriate for a particular part.

As noted previously, the SAE 51434 alloy is susceptible to pitting and red rust when used below the beltline. Therefore, chromium flash on the stainless steel side of the part may be needed for additional corrosion protection. Follow the same guidelines as previously mentioned for SAE 51434 with chromium flash. When chromium flashing bimetal, one should run high current densities, and very short times in order to not dissolve too much aluminum in the chrome tank.

3.4.3 NICKEL/CHROMIUM PLATING—For a deeper chromium plating appearance, nickel/chromium plating can be used on any of the previously mentioned alloys. Different processing is used for SAE 51434 and SAE 51436 than for SAE 30201 and SAE 30301.

INSTRUMENTAL COLOR DIFFERENCE MEASUREMENTS FOR COLORFASTNESS OF AUTOMOTIVE INTERIOR TRIM MATERIALS—SAE J1767 JAN1995

SAE Recommended Practice

Report of the SAE Textiles and Flexible Plastics Committee approved January 1995.

Foreword—This Document has not changed other than to put it into the new SAE Technical Standards Board Format.

1. Scope—The practice described applies to textile and flexible plastic parts and materials used in automotive vehicles. Special care should be taken when high pile carpet samples are being evaluated.

1.1 Purpose—The intent of this SAE Recommended Practice is to specify procedures for the instrumental measurement of color differences brought about by the exposure of textile and flexible plastic automotive parts to various colorfastness tests. It may be used for the specification of limits of color differences which may be tolerated in a specific test.

2. References

2.1 Applicable Publications—The following publications form a part of this specification to the extent specified herein.

2.1.1 CIE PUBLICATION—Available from U.S. National Committee, CIE (Commission Internationale de l'Eclairage), c/o Mr. Tom Lemons, TLA, Lighting Consultants, 7 Pond Street, Salem, MA 01970, 508-745-6870, Fax 508-741-4420.

CIE Publication No. 15.2—Colorimetry, 2nd edition, 1986

2.1.2 AATCC PUBLICATION—Available from American Association of Textile Chemists & Colorists, 1 Davis Drive, P.O. Box 12215, Research Triangle Park, NC 27709-2215, 919-549-8141, Fax 919-549-8933.

AATCC Method 173-1992—Calculation of Small Color Differences for Acceptability

3. Definitions

3.1 Colorfastness—The resistance of a material to change in any of its color characteristics, to transfer its colorant(s) to adjacent materials, or both, as a result of the exposure of the material to any environment that might be encountered during testing.

3.2 Color Difference—A color change in a sample or in a fabric, in which color has been altered or transferred from the sample as a result of testing.

3.2.1 COLOR CHANGE—A change in color of any kind, whether in lightness, hue, or chroma that may be measured instrumentally by comparing materials before and after testing.

4. Basic Color Measurement Specifications

4.1 Uniform Color Space—All measurements and calculations will be made using CIE 1976 $L^*a^*b^*$ Uniform Color Space, which may be abbreviated CIELAB (see 2.1.1).

4.2 Standard Illuminant—The Standard Illuminant for colorimetric determinations will be the CIE illuminant D65 (see 2.1.1). No other illuminant may be used except by agreement between contractual parties.

4.3 Standard Observer—The Standard Observer for colorimetric determinations will be the CIE 10 degrees observer. No other observer may be used except by agreement between contractual parties.

5. Color Difference Calculations—Three sets of color difference calculations may be used:

5.1 Delta L^*, a^*, b^*

$$DL^* = (L^*_t - L^*_o) \quad \text{(Eq. 1)}$$

$$Da^* = (a^*_t - a^*_o) \quad \text{(Eq. 2)}$$

$$Db^* = (b^*_t - b^*_o) \quad \text{(Eq. 3)}$$

$$DE^* = \{(DL^*)^2 - (Da^*)^2 + (Db^*)^2\}^{1/2} \quad \text{(Eq. 4)}$$

where subscripts 'o' and 't' refer to measurements in the original and final material.

5.2 Delta L^*, C^*, H^*

$$DL^* = (L^*_t - L^*_o) \quad \text{(Eq. 5)}$$

$$DC^* = \left\{(a^{*2}_t + b^{*2}_t)^{1/2} - (a^{*2}_o + b^{*2}_o)^{1/2}\right\} \quad \text{(Eq. 6)}$$

$$DH^* = (DE^*)^2 - (DL^*)^2 - (DC^*)^2 \quad \text{(Eq. 7)}$$

5.3 Delta CMC—The CMC method of color difference measurement is one which is being used with increasing frequency and the necessary calculations are given in 2.2.1 (reference only).

6. Color Difference Specifications—Color difference specifications shall be determined by the contractual parties. The specifications should be in the form described in Section 4.

7. Color Measuring Instruments—The instruments used to determine color must have capabilities to meet the requirements set forth in Section 3. If a sphere instrument is used, the specular component must be included in the measurement. The angle between the specimen normal and the illuminating beam or vice-versa in the sphere instruments must not exceed 10 degrees.

8. Color Measurement Method

8.1 Color Difference Sample—A single sample is used. The color properties of the sample are measured first and the data stored, the sample is exposed to the test conditions, and the color is again measured.

It is imperative that the measured location be identified exactly in order that the same spot and orientation on the fabric surface can be measured each time.

8.2 Sample Preparation—Particular attention shall be given to the appearance of the sample. The sample shall be cut so that the direction or lay of the pile or fabric is easily identified and oriented in a constant direction during the exposure and measurement of its color. It shall be freed from lint, etc., using a lint brush and if it has a pile, it shall be brushed in the direction of the pile lay before reading and exposure.

8.3 Sample Mounting—The sample shall be mounted on a flat surface so that it is presented to the measuring port of the color measuring instrument in a uniform reproducible manner. If the sample is transparent it shall be backed with a sufficient thickness of the test fabric to eliminate a contribution of the backing material to the measurement. The direction of the natural lay of the sample shall be identified on the back of the mounting surface to facilitate correct sample orientation in the measurement instrument.

8.3.1 INSTRUMENT SET UP—The instrument used for the color measurement shall be standardized according to the procedures specified by its manufacturer.

8.3.2 SAMPLE EQUILIBRATION—The sample shall be in equilibrium with the standard laboratory environment before reading on the measurement instrument. The time to reach equilibrium will be different for different fabric types and should be agreed upon by the contractual parties. The standard laboratory environment is 21 °C ± 2 °C and 50% ± 5% R.H. or as agreed to by the contractual parties.

8.3.3 PRESENTATION OF THE SAMPLE TO THE INSTRUMENT—The instrument port shall be matched to the size of the sample being measured (it will be close to 25 mm in diameter). The sample shall be loaded in the instrument port without glass and using a sufficient pressure to hold the sample in place without forcing the pile into the measurement chamber. Having been established, this pressure shall remain constant for the sample being tested. Typically 500 g ± 10 g per 5 cm x 10 cm sample area is satisfactory. Special situations may require that the contractual parties agree on a different value.

The sample shall be oriented in a standard direction. Identifying markings on the sample or its mounting shall be used to ensure that the orientation and position of the sample in the port is the same before and after testing.

8.3.4 SAMPLE HANDLING AND STORAGE—Color measurement, especially in high pile carpets, can be greatly influenced by the physical condition of the material surface. It is therefore important to keep the surface constant after the surface has been prepared. Handling of the sample surface to be measured must be avoided.

8.3.5 COLOR MEASUREMENT—Two readings, initial and 90 degrees rotation, are to be averaged, unless the instrument has been proven insensitive to specimen orientation, in which case a single color reading will be taken.

9. Reporting—The color difference measurement should be calculated as agreed in Section 5, with reporting as agreed between contractual parties.

) TEST METHOD FOR MEASURING WET COLOR TRANSFER CHARACTERISTICS —SAE J1326 FEB1985

SAE Recommended Practice

Report of the SAE Nonmetallic Materials Committee approved August 1980, completely revised February 1985.

Foreword—This Document has not changed other than to put it into the new SAE Technical Standards Board Format.

1. Scope—This procedure describes a method of measuring the resistance to wet color transfer of dyed, printed, or otherwise colored textile yarns and composites thereof.

1.1 Purpose—The purpose of this testing method is to establish a means of ranking the relative resistance to wet staining of composites which contain dyed or colored textile fibers.

2. References—There are no referenced publications specified herein.

3. Apparatus and Materials

3.1 AATCC Perspiration Tester, Perspirometer, or equivalent device.[1]

3.2 Plates—Glass or plastic, at least 6 mm (0.2 in) larger than the dimensions of the test specimen on all sides.

3.3 Drying Oven

3.4 Multi-fiber Standard Test Fabric, non-fused edges (AATCC) Type I, 6 fiber, pH between 6.5 and 7.5.[2]

3.5 AATCC Chromatic Transference Scale[1]

3.6 Wringer

1. Atlas Electric Devices Co., 4114 No. Ravenwood Ave., Chicago, IL 60613.
2. Testfabrics, Inc., P.O. Box 53, Middlesex, NJ 08846.

4. Test Specimen—From the multi-fiber test fabric, cut a sample whose width includes all of the 6 fibers, and whose length is equal to or greater than the width. Cut a specimen, which has the same dimensions as the test fabric, from the material to be treated, and place the surface to be tested against the multi-fiber test fabric.

5. Procedure

5.1 Immerse the test specimen in either freshly boiled distilled water or deionized water from an ion-exchange device at room temperature with occasional agitation to insure thorough wetting out (approximately 15 min generally required).

5.2 Remove the specimen and pass through the wringer to remove excess liquid when the wet mass is more than three times the dry mass. Whenever possible, the wet mass of the specimen will be 2.5 - 3 times its dry mass.

5.3 Place the specimen between glass or plastic plates and insert in the specimen unit of the perspiration tester. Adjust the perspiration tester to produce a pressure of 14 kPa on the specimen.

5.4 Place the loaded specimen unit in an oven at 38 ± 1 °C so that the plates are in a vertical position and heat for 18 h. Remove the specimen from the unit and complete drying by hanging in air at room temperature. Do not press dry.

6. Report—Classify the staining:

CLASS 5 - neglible or no staining
CLASS 4 - staining equivalent to Row 4 on the AATCC scale
CLASS 3 - staining equivalent to Row 3 on the AATCC scale
CLASS 2 - staining equivalent to Row 2 on the AATCC scale
CLASS 1 - staining equivalent to Row 1 on the AATCC scale

TEST METHOD FOR MEASURING THE RELATIVE DRAPEABILITY OF FLEXIBLE INSULATION MATERIALS—SAE J1325 FEB1994

SAE Recommended Practice

Report of the SAE Nonmetallic Materials Committee approved September 1980, reaffirmed without change February 1985. Reaffirmed by the SAE Sound and Heat Insulation Committee February 1994.

Foreword—This Reaffirmed Document has been changed only to reflect the new SAE Technical Standards Board Format.

1. Scope—This SAE Recommended Practice describes a method of determining the relative flexibility of padding and/or acoustical composites.

1.1 Purpose—The purpose of this testing method is to establish a means for measuring the three-dimensional drapeability of flexible insulation materials, such as automotive floor pan insulation composites.

2. References—There are no references specified herein.

3. Apparatus

3.1 Cylinder—Inside diameter 305 mm (12 in), length 305 mm (12 in).

3.2 Clamps—Hoffman, screw compressor, open side—maximum opening 19 mm (0.75 in).

3.3 Scale—610 mm (24 in) minimum—graduated in millimeters or 0.01 in.

3.4 Chocks—Any type capable of preventing the cylinder from rolling.

4. Test Specimen—From the material to be tested, cut a 610 mm x 610 mm (24 in x 24 in) specimen.

5. Conditioning

5.1 Test for material classification and for arbitration purposes shall be made on material conditioned to a constant weight in a controlled atmosphere of 21 °C ± 1 °C (70 °F ± 2 °F) and 50% ± 5% relative humidity. Quality control tests can be conducted on unconditioned specimens unless otherwise specified by the user.

5.2 Lay the specimen on a flat surface for a minimum of 24 h before conducting the test.

6. Procedure

6.1 Lay the cylinder horizontally on top of a table, using the chocks to prevent rolling of the cylinder. See Figure 1.

6.2 Place the specimen in the interior of the cylinder, matching one end of the specimen with the end of the cylinder.

6.3 Orient the specimen so that the surface which would face toward the supporting structure in the proposed application faces downward in the cylinder.

6.4 Smooth the specimen against the inner circumference of the cylinder, making sure the sides of the specimen are equidistant from the base of the cylinder.

6.5 Securely clamp the corners of the specimen, at the flush end, to the cylinder. See Figure 1.

6.6 The specimen should protrude 305 mm (12 in) out of the other end of the cylinder.

6.7 Measure the distance (outside dimension) between the corners of the protruding portion of the specimen. Record this distance as L_1. See Figure 1.

6.8 Measure the distance (outside dimension) from edge to edge of the specimen at the end of the cylinder. Record this distance as L_2. See Figure 1.

6.9 Rotate the specimen 90 degrees in the same plane and repeat 6.1 to 6.8.

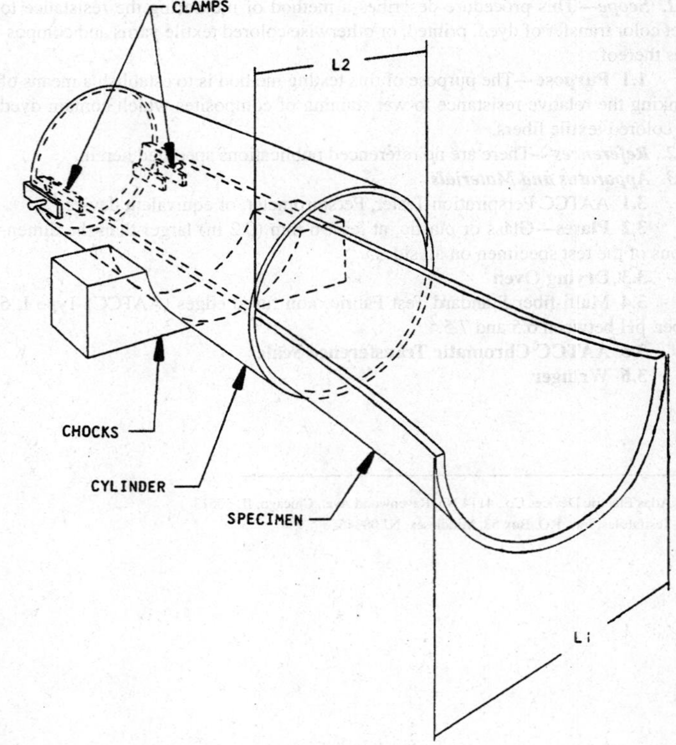

FIGURE 1—DRAPEABILITY APPARATUS

7. Report—Calculate the percent drape and record the results. Use Equation 1 for calculation:

$$D = \frac{L_1 - L_2}{L_2} \times 100 \quad \text{(Eq. 1)}$$

where:

D = % drape
L_1 = measurement taken in 6.7
L_2 = measurement taken in 6.8

TEST METHOD FOR MEASURING THICKNESS OF RESILIENT INSULATING PADDINGS —SAE J1355 MAY1993

SAE Recommended Practice

Report of the SAE Nonmetallic Materials Committee approved March 1981 and reaffirmed by the SAE Sound and Heat Insulating Materials Committee April 1987. Reaffirmed by the SAE Sound and Heat Committee May 1993.

Foreword—This Reaffirmed Document has been changed only to reflect the new SAE Technical Standards Board Format.

1. Scope—This SAE Recommended Practice is applicable for determining the thickness of various resilient materials, such as insulating padding used in the automotive industry.

1.1 Purpose—This test method is intended to establish a uniform procedure for determining the thickness of various resilient thermal and acoustical insulating pad materials.

2. References—There are no referenced publications specified herein.

3. Apparatus

3.1 Thickness Gauge—Dial type, with a single point-contact loading foot.

3.2 Ring stand or equivalent device for mounting the thickness gauge.

3.3 Pressure Plate—Circular having a diameter of 200 mm (8 in) and a mass of 160 g (5.6 oz). When the size of the specimen is limited to something less than the size recommended in 4.1, the size of the pressure plate shall be reduced so as to maintain the overlap specified in 4.2, and the mass shall be proportionately reduced to maintain a loading force of 50 N/m^2 (1 lbf/ft^2).

NOTE—Thickness readings obtained are affected by plate and sample size. Data obtained from samples and foot sizes other than standard can be used only for comparison with data from other samples of the same size.

4. Test Specimen

4.1 The minimum recommended specimen dimensions should be 250 mm x 250 mm (10 in x 10 in). However, in some instances, sample dimensions may preclude the usage of specimens this large. In these cases, the specimen may be downsized and the size and mass of the pressure plate adjusted accordingly, per 3.3.

4.2 The specimen shall overlap at least 25 mm (1 in) on all sides of the pressure plate to minimize the contributions of edge effects.

4.3 Three or more specimens shall be taken from the same lot (roll or articles) and shall be free from folds or distortions.

5. Conditioning

5.1 Tests for material classification and for arbitration purposes shall be made on material conditioned to a constant weight in a controlled atmosphere of 21 °C ± 1 °C (70 °F ± 2 °F) and 50% ± 5% relative humidity. Quality control tests can be conducted on unconditioned specimens unless otherwise specified by the user.

5.2 Lay the specimen on a flat surface for a minimum of 24 h before conducting the test. If the sample is in a compressed state and circumstances will not permit lengthy sample conditioning, the specimen shall be released from compression and allowed to recover for at least 30 min before testing.

6. Procedure

6.1 Mount the thickness gauge on the ring stand and place the assembly on a flat surface large enough to accommodate the specimen.

6.2 Adjust the thickness gauge to read zero on the test surface.

6.3 Place the pressure plate on the test surface and measure its thickness. All measurements shall be accurate to within 0.25 mm (0.01 in). Record this thickness as T_0.

6.4 Remove the pressure plate.

6.5 Place the specimen on the test surface. Gently lay the pressure plate on the specimen so that there is uniform overlap on all sides. Allow the sample to compress for 15 s, then measure the combined thickness of the plate and the specimen. Record this thickness as T_1. (The loading foot of the thickness gauge should rest approximately on the center of the plate.)

7. Report—Calculate the thickness of the specimen using the following formula, and record the dimensions of the specimen tested, and the diameter and mass of the pressure plate:

$$T_2 = T_1 - T_0 \quad \text{(Eq. 1)}$$

where:

T_0 = Thickness of pressure plate
T_1 = Thickness of specimen and pressure plate
T_2 = Thickness of specimen

The thickness measurement reported will be the average of three or more readings taken on three or more representative samples prepared in accordance with 4.1 and conditioned in accordance with 5.1.

Test results obtained on specimens having only the 30 min recovery period shall be so indicated in the report.

HOT PLATE METHOD FOR EVALUATING HEAT RESISTANCE AND THERMAL INSULATION PROPERTIES OF MATERIALS—SAE J1361 OCT2001

SAE Recommended Practice

Report of the SAE Nonmetallic Materials Committee approved April 1981. Reaffirmed by the SAE Sound and Heat Insulating Materials Committee April 1987. Reaffirmed by the SAE Acoustical Materials Committee August 1994 and revised October 2001. Rationale statement available.

Foreword—This Reaffirmed Document has been changed only to reflect the new SAE Technical Standards Board Format.

1. Scope—This test method is applicable for rating various materials, such as automotive trim materials and insulation composites, for their ability to resist heat transfer, heat degradation, odor, smoking, and exothermic reaction.

1.1 Purpose—The purpose of this testing method is to obtain comparative data which can be used to evaluate heat resistance and thermal insulation properties of various materials or composites when subjected to time and temperature conditions which reflect "in-car" situations.

2. References—There are no referenced publications specified herein.

3. Apparatus and Materials

3.1 Hot Plate—Thermostatically controlled, with a minimum surface area of 525 cm^2 (81 in^2), and capable of maintaining the specified temperature within ±1.5 °C (3 °F).

3.2 Temperature Probe—A temperature sensor, which will operate within the desired temperature range, having a maximum diameter of 0.65 mm (0.026 in), a minimum length of 150 mm (6 in), and a maximum error limit of ±2 °C (4 °F).

3.3 Temperature Indicating Device—With capacity for multiple channel readings, a maximum error of 0.1 °C (0.2 °F) full scale.

3.4 Timing Device—Calibrated in seconds and able to operate for the duration of the test.

3.5 Shield—Placed around the hot plate to minimize the effects of drafts.

3.6 Grid—An expanded metal grating with diamond-shaped openings. The openings shall have dimensions of approximately 50 x 25 mm (2 x 1 in), and the grating shall have sufficient mass to maintain a loading force of 48 Pa (1 lb/ft^2). (If the mass is insufficient to attain this loading force, weights may be added to each corner of the grid to compensate.) The grid shall be at least as large as the hot plate surface.

3.7 Test Materials—Any necessary materials (such as carpet, burlap, padding, mastic, etc.) that are needed to establish the specific composite.

4. Test Specimens and Conditioning—Cut the materials to be tested to match the dimensions of the hot plate surface. Condition the samples for 24 h at 21 °C ± 1 °C (70 °F ± 2 °F) and 50% ± 5% relative humidity prior to testing (unless otherwise specified).

It is recommended that this test be conducted in the standard laboratory atmosphere as stated previously.

5. Procedure

5.1 Prior to starting the test, the following items must be defined by the individual requesting the test for the individual performing the test:

a. The time versus temperature program for the test. (It should usually simulate actual in-car use and conditions.) This program must detail the following: hot plate temperature at the start of testing, the rate of heating, and the time at maximum temperature conditions.

b. The specific type of material or composite build-up to be used.

c. At what layers the temperature probes will be placed.

d. How often the temperatures will be recorded.

When all items as stated in Section 4 and 5.1 have been satisfactorily met, the actual test can be started by following the procedure listed in 5.2 through 5.6.

5.2 Position at least one temperature probe at the center of the hot plate. If more than one probe is being used, they should be spaced evenly around the surface of the hot plate. If needed, tape can be used to fix the probe to the surface of the hot plate, but should be at least 25 mm (1 in) from the tip of the probe.

5.3 Insert the probes between the layers of the various materials to achieve the required build. Care should be taken to ensure that the probes are approximately above each other.

5.4 When the test setup has been completed, initiate the time versus temperature program desired. (Several of these sequences can be run consecutively, when it is necessary, in order to accurately duplicate in-car conditions.)

5.5 During the test, all temperatures are to be monitored. It is suggested that each temperature be checked at least every 3 min and recorded during the course of the test.

5.6 Run the test until the scheduled time versus temperature program is completed.

6. Report—The following items are to be incorporated into the laboratory report:

6.1 Complete description of the sample build-up.

6.2 Time versus temperature program describing how the test was run.

6.3 Time and temperature data (could be in the form of a graph, or a chart from a temperature recorder.)

6.4 Any observations about the material, odor, smoke, specimen degradation, etc., and also the temperatures at which the observations were made.

6.5 Laboratory conditions, temperature, and relative humidity.

6.6 Data, specimen's number of identification, and any further information.

6.7 Conclusion.

COMPRESSION AND RECOVERY OF INSULATION PADDINGS—SAE J1352 JUN1994

SAE Recommended Practice

Report of the SAE Nonmetallic Materials Committee approved May 1981. Reaffirmed by the SAE Sound and Heat Insulating Materials Committee April 1987. Revised by the SAE Acoustical Materials Committee June 1994.

Foreword—This Document has also changed to comply with the new SAE Technical Standards Board format.

*1. **Scope***—This test method is applicable for determining the relative compression and recovery of fibrous insulation padding materials.

1.1 Purpose—The purpose of this test method is to establish a means of measuring the ability of fibrous insulation materials to resist compression and recover after being compressed, dry or wet. It should be noted that there are two test methods for each dry and wet test. Two methods have been found necessary for different loading applications, and also due to large variation in surface density of the padding materials. The results of these two test methods cannot be correlated to each other. The material specification should indicate which test is necessary for each application.

*2. **References***—There are no referenced publications specified herein.

3. Apparatus

3.1 Platen

3.1.1 Method A, 100 x 100 mm with a mass of 300 g.

3.1.2 Method B, 100 x 100 mm with a mass of 100 g.

3.2 Compression Machine (Optional)—Capable of compressing the specimen at a rate of 50 mm/min without impact.

*4. **Test Specimen***—From the material to be tested, cut enough specimens 100 x 100 mm to achieve a minimum thickness of 25 mm when plied together.

*5. **Conditioning***—Test for material classification and for arbitration purposes shall be made on material conditioned to a constant weight in a controlled atmosphere of 21 °C ± 1 °C and 50% ±5% relative humidity. Quality control tests can be conducted on unconditioned specimens unless otherwise specified by the user.

6. Procedure—Method A, Normal

6.1 Ply sufficient layers of the specimen together to achieve a minimum thickness of 25 mm.

6.2 Add the 300 g platen and place in the compression apparatus.

6.3 Apply a load of 2.25 kg for 1 min. Remove the load and measure the thickness of the specimen at the center of the four sides and record the average as T_1.

6.4 Apply a load of 35 kg. If a dead weight is used, add it slowly without impact. If a compression machine is used, apply the load at a rate of 50 mm/min. Measure the average thickness as soon as the full load is attained and record as T_2.

6.5 Hold this load for 5 min, then remove the load and allow specimen to recover for 5 min with the platen on the specimen.

6.6 Measure the average thickness and record as T_3.

7. Procedure—Method B, Normal

7.1 Ply sufficient layers of the specimen together to achieve a minimum thickness of 25 mm.

7.2 Add 100 g platen and measure the thickness of the specimen at the center of the four sides of the platen. Record the average as T_1.

7.3 Apply a load of 3 kg for 1 min. Measure the average thickness as soon as full load is attained and record as T_2.

7.4 Remove the load and allow the specimen to recover for 3 min.

7.5 Measure the average thickness and record as T_3.

8. Procedure—Method C, Compression and Recovery—Wet

8.1 Determine and record T_1 as described in 7.1 and 7.2, Method B.

8.2 Immerse specimen in distilled water at 21 °C ± 1 °C for 30 min.

8.3 Shake out excess water and follow Method B for determining T_2 and T_3.

9. Procedure—Method D, Recovery—Wet

9.1 Determine and record T_1 as described in 7.1 and 7.2, Method B.

9.2 Immerse specimen in distilled water at 21 °C ± 1 °C for 30 min.

9.3 Determine T_2 as in Method C.

9.4 After T_2 is measured, remove load and platen and dry separated samples in a 102 °C oven for 1 h. Remove from oven and bring back to standard conditions.

9.5 Stack the samples, apply to 100 g platen and after 3 min measure and record T_3.

*10. **Report***—Calculate the percent compression and recovery dry or wet, as in Equations 1 and 2:

$$\%\ \text{Compression} = \frac{T_2 - T_2}{T_1} \times 100 \quad \text{(Eq. 1)}$$

$$\%\ \text{Recovery} = \frac{T_3 - T_2}{T_1 - T_2} \times 100 \quad \text{(Eq. 2)}$$

Report which method was used for each test result.

HOT ODOR TEST FOR INSULATION MATERIALS—SAE J1351 JUN1993

SAE Recommended Practice

Report of the SAE Nonmetallic Materials Committee approved July 1981. Reaffirmed by the SAE Sound and Heat Insulation Materials Committee April 1987 and June 1993.

Foreword—This Reaffirmed Document has been changed only to reflect the new SAE Technical Standards Board Format.

1. Scope—This test applies to various materials used for insulation and other applications.

1.1 Purpose—The purpose of this test is to evaluate and compare the odor characteristics of various trim and insulation materials and composites. Odor is a difficult property to quantify. Therefore, the data from this test are probably most useful when compared to data obtained from samples with known odor characteristics.

2. References—There are no referenced publications specified herein.

3. Apparatus

3.1 Metallic Cans—The volume of the cans should be about 1 L (1.06 qt). The cans must be odorless, both at room temperature and at 65 °C (149 °F). The cans should have loose-fitting lids which can be easily removed and replaced.

3.2 Oven—The oven should be an air-circulating type able to maintain a temperature of 65 °C ±3 °C (149 °F ±5 °F).

3.3 Odor Panel—To obtain consistent data, an odor panel should be carefully selected. Strong smokers, heavy users of aromatic cosmetics, habitual gum or tobacco users, or people with sinus problems may not be suitable. Once selected, the panel should remain as stable as possible.

3.4 Test Room—Tests should be conducted in an odor-free environment. Conditioned space is desirable, but not required.

4. Test Specimens and Conditioning—Test specimens should be representative of the material or composite being evaluated. Test specimens should have surface area (including all surfaces) of 250 cm^2 ± 25 cm^2 (0.28 ft^2 ± 0.028 ft^2). Test specimens can be cut to any dimension compatible to the dimensions of the can, provided the specimen surface area is maintained at 250 cm^2.

Prior to the test, the specimens should be conditioned for 24 h at 21 °C ± 1 °C (70 °F ± 2 °F) and 50% RH ± 5% RH.

5. Procedure

5.1 To avoid contamination, thoroughly clean the cans (including lids). Rinse the cans with hot water. Scrub the cans with a laboratory glassware detergent. Rinse thoroughly with cold water.

5.2 Samples are to be tested dry and in presence of moisture. For the dry test, place a test specimen in a can and cover with the lid. For the wet test, put 2 cc of distilled water and the test specimen in a can and cover with the lid. Include one empty can for control.

5.3 Place cans in an oven preheated to 65 °C ±3 °C (149 °F ±5 °F) for 1 h. This temperature was selected to be representative of automotive applications. However, at the discretion of the test engineer, the temperature can be modified to any temperature or set of temperatures.

CAUTION—This test should not be used to test materials that will release toxic fumes. The test engineer should be aware of the chemical composition of the materials being tested. In all cases, observers should be instructed to slowly inhale the air from the cans to minimize the risk of inhaling noxious fumes.

5.4 Remove the cans. The first panelist should position his head near the control can (about 15 cm away) and remove the lid. Then, with a cupped hand, he should draw the air from the can to his nose and slowly inhale. He should then immediately repeat the procedure for the first test specimen (dry) and record the appropriate rating listed in Section 6. Lids should not be off the cans longer than 5 s. Tests must be conducted in an environment free from drafts and contaminant odors.

5.5 Wait 2 min and repeat step 5.4 for the wet test specimens.

5.6 Repeat steps 5.4 and 5.5 for each sample.

5.7 Replace the cans in the oven for 15 min between observers and repeat steps 5.4, 5.5, and 5.6 for at least three panelists.

5.8 Report description of test samples, median and range of ratings, and any deviations from the test procedure.

6. Odor Scale—See Table 1.

TABLE 1—ODOR SCALE

Rating	Description
1	No noticeable odor
2	Slight, but noticeable odor
3	Definite odor, but not strong enough to be offensive
4	Strong offensive odor
5	Very strong offensive odor

Note that the scale is arbitrary. Since the test applies to a variety of materials and applications, it is not practical to assign a standard for each rating. The tester has the responsibility to establish the level of odor that applies to each scale rating depending on the particular application and materials being used.

CORROSION TEST FOR INSULATION MATERIALS—SAE J1389 OCT2001

SAE Recommended Practice

Report of the SAE Nonmetallic Materials Committee approved May 1982 and reaffirmed by the SAE Sound and Heat Insulation Materials Committee December 1988. Reaffirmed by the SAE Sound and Heat Committee May 1993 and October 2001. Rationale statement available.

Foreword—This Document has not changed other than to put it into the new SAE Technical Standards Board Format.

1. Scope—This SAE Recommended Practice applies to various insulation materials used in vehicles for control of heat and noise and other applications.

1.1 Purpose—The purpose of this test is to provide a means to evaluate and compare the corrosiveness of insulation materials. Three panelists compare a sample insulation material to a standard (inert fibrous material). The rationale for the test is that the corrosion of steel should not be greater for the insulation material than for an inert fibrous material.

2. References—There are no referenced publications specified herein.

3. Apparatus

3.1 Steel Test Plates—The plates shall be 2.5 cm (1.0 in) wide, 10 cm (4.0 in) long, and 0.05 cm (0.020 in) thick. The steel shall be SAE grade number 1010, cold-rolled, strip steel. The steel shall have bright No. 2 finish and No. 3 temper—quarter hard.

3.2 Wire Mesh—The wire mesh shall be type 304 stainless steel wire cloth with 1.25 cm (0.5 in) mesh. The mesh should be cut to 3.8 cm (1.5 in) wide by 11.5 cm (4.5 in) long.

3.3 Humidity Chamber—The humidity chamber shall be clean and maintain a temperature of 49 °C ± 2 °C (120 °F ± 3 °F) and 95% ± 3% relative humidity.

3.4 Inert Fibrous Standard Material—Any fibrous material free from chemical contaminants is satisfactory as a standard material. Two materials that have been shown to be satisfactory are:

a. Unbonded, unlubricated fibrous glass.
b. Sterile cotton, extracted in acetone for 48 h and vacuum dried at low heat. Because cotton has variable amounts of oil on it, it must be extracted in solvent to obtain reproducible results.

3.5 Rubber Bands—Rubber bands shall be No. 12.

4. Test Specimens and Conditioning

4.1 Test specimens should be representative of the material being evaluated. Test specimens should be 3.8 cm (1.5 in) wide by 11.5 cm (4.5 in) long by 1.3 cm (0.5 in) thick. Two specimens are required for each sample.

4.2 Prior to the test, the specimens must be brought to room temperature.

5. Procedure

5.1 Clean the steel plates until they are free of water breaks. Breaks are characterized by uneven cling or coating on the surface of the metal. First, wash the plates with a laboratory-grade detergent and rinse with distilled water. Then place the plates in a hot caustic (not boiling) of 15% potassium hydroxide.

CAUTION—Potassium hydroxide can cause severe burns and damage eyes. The caustic bath should be done under a laboratory hood.

Rinse in distilled water and check for water breaks. If there are none, dry immediately with laboratory-type paper wipe. Repeat procedure if necessary.

5.2 Boil the No. 12 rubber bands in distilled water for 30 min to remove contamination.

5.3 Place one steel panel between two specimens, per Figure 1. Both specimens must be cut from the same sample. Place wire mesh on both sides of assembly and secure with two No. 12 rubber bands.

5.4 Prepare standard panel in same manner as in 5.2, except use inert fibrous standard material.

5.5 Suspend test assemblies vertically in the humidity chamber that has been preset to 49 °C ± 2 °C (120 °F ± 3 °F) and 95% ± 3% RH. The samples must be left in the humidity chamber for 96 h. (Since the test compares sample material to a standard, other test conditions may be chosen provided they produce acceptable rates of corrosion.)

5.6 Remove the samples and grade the test panels according to the scale in Figure 2 using the control panel for comparison:

Surface blush or stain rust should be ignored. Heavy rust, flaking, and pitting should be weighed heavily in the ratings.

5.7 Repeat 5.6 for at least two other knowledgeable panelists.

5.8 Report for each sample:

a. Median and all numerical ratings.
b. Type of rust and description of pattern observed per 5.5.
c. Complete description of sample insulation material including generic composition, manufacturing, material identification, thickness, and weight.

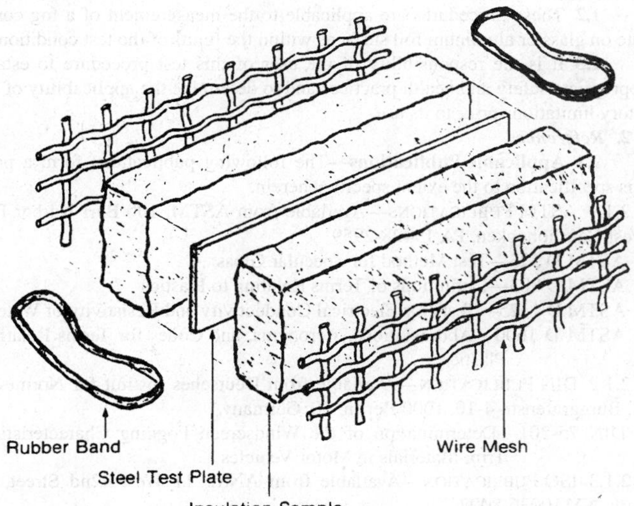

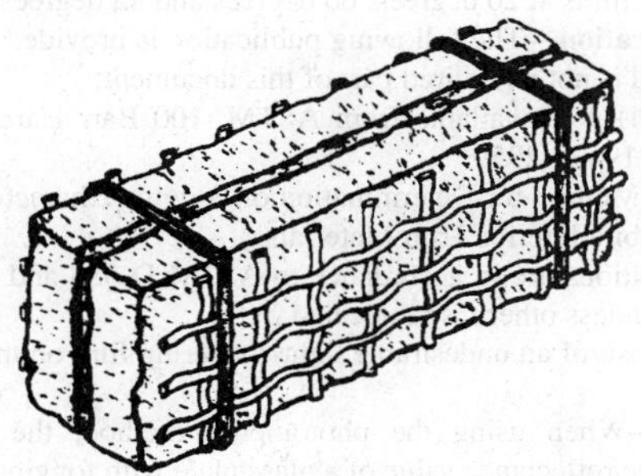

FIGURE 1—TEST ASSEMBLY

Worse
Standard
Better

1—Substantially worse than standard
2—Moderately worse than standard
3—Slightly worse than standard
4—No significant difference
5—Slightly better than standard
6—Moderately better than standard
7—Substantially better than standard

FIGURE 2—SCALE

TEST PROCEDURE TO DETERMINE THE FOGGING CHARACTERISTICS OF INTERIOR AUTOMOTIVE MATERIALS—SAE J1756 DEC1994

SAE Recommended Practice

Report of the SAE Textiles and Flexible Plastics Committee approved December 1994.

Foreword—This Document has not changed other than to put it into the new SAE Technical Standards Board Format.

1. Scope

1.1 This procedure describes two methods for determining the tendency of interior materials used in automobiles and other vehicles to (a) produce a light scattering film (fog) on a glass surface, or (b) produce a measurable deposit (mass) on aluminum foil.

1.2 These procedures are applicable to the measurement of a fog condensate on glass or aluminum foil surfaces within the limits of the test conditions.

1.3 It is the responsibility of the user of this test procedure to establish appropriate safety and health practices and to determine the applicability of regulatory limitations prior to its use.

2. References

2.1 Applicable Publications—The following publications form a part of this specification to the extent specified herein.

2.1.1 ASTM PUBLICATIONS—Available from ASTM, 100 Barr Harbor Drive, West Conshohocken, PA 19428-2959.

ASTM D 523—Test Method for Specular Gloss

ASTM D 883—Definitions of Terms Relating to Plastics

ASTM D 1125—Tests for Electrical Conductivity and Resistivity of Water

ASTM D 1600—Abbreviations, Acronyms, and Codes for Terms Relating to Plastics

2.1.2 DIN PUBLICATION—Available from Deutsches Institut fur Normung, e. V., Burggrafenstr. 4-10, 1000 Berlin, 30, Germany.

DIN 75-201—Determination of the Windscreen Fogging Characteristics of Trim Materials in Motor Vehicles

2.1.3 ISO PUBLICATION—Available from ANSI, 11 West 42nd Street, New York, NY 10036-8002.

ISO 2813—Paints and varnishes-Measurement of specular gloss of non-metallic paint films at 20 degrees, 60 degrees and 85 degrees

2.2 Related Publication—The following publication is provided for information purposes only and is not a required part of this document.

2.2.1 ASTM PUBLICATION—Available from ASTM, 100 Barr Harbor Drive, West Conshohocken, PA 19428-2959.

ASTM D 5393—Test Method for Determination of Fogging Characteristics of Automobile Interior Trim Materials

3. Definitions—Definitions are in accordance to ASTM D 883 and abbreviations to ASTM D 1600, unless otherwise indicated.

3.1 Fog—The deposit of an undesirable light-scattering film on the interior glass surface of vehicles.

3.2 Fog Number—When using the photometric method, the quotient, expressed as the 60 degree reflectance value of a glass plate with fogging deposits and the 60 degree reflectance value of the same glass plate without fogging deposits, multiplied by 100.

3.3 Fog Mass—When using the gravimetric method, the difference between the weight in grams of the aluminum foil and condensate after testing, and the original weight of the clean foil.

4. Apparatus and Materials Required

4.1 Fog Test Units—A controlled heating unit with multiple chambers with a typical temperature range from 60 to 120 °C. Cooling of the glass plate for each test chamber in the unit is required with a typical temperature range from 20 to 40 °C. Equipment from the sources listed as follows has produced acceptable data under laboratory conditions. Correlation between the two brands of equipment has been good based on a limited number of trials. Some equipment modifications may be necessary. Contact the appropriate manufacturer for information.

The heating unit and the cooling system must be able to maintain the temperature to within ±0.5 °C. A temperature override cut-out to prevent overheating in the event of thermostat failure should be an integral part of the unit. Temperatures of the heating unit and the cooling system may be monitored and recorded for the duration of each test. This is most easily achieved using a calibrated chart recorder. Specific requirements shall be at the option of the contractual automotive company.

The cooling plates, which are laid upon the glass plates, should apply a weight of approximately 1 kg. This is to assure a good seal for the test chamber.

Numbering of the fog test chambers is given in Appendix A and Appendix B. Test operators are requested to adhere to this numbering scheme.

4.1.1 Haake Buchler Instruments Incorporated, 53 West Century Road, Paramus, NJ 07652, (201) 265-7865

NOTE—Older models may require modifications, contact the source at the above number.

4.1.1.1 A water soluble Modified Polyvalent Aliphatic Alcohol or equivalent shall be used as the heating liquid. Alcohol that meets the requirements is identified as Part No. 999-0063 and may be purchased from Haake Buchler. It is recommended that this heating liquid be changed at least once a year. It is normal for the alcohol to change in color to a clear light brown.

4.1.2 Hart Scientific, 220 North 1300 West, P.O. Box 435, Pleasant Grove, UT 84062-0435, (800) 438-4278 - (801) 785-1600 - Fax (801) 785-7118

4.2 Training Video—A VHS tape dated 1994 showing proper techniques of performing the fog test. Available from: The Industrial Fabrics Association International, Suite 800, 345 Cedar Street, St. Paul, MN 55101, (612) 222-2508; Attention: Transportation Division Staff Director.

4.3 Glass Plates—Float glass plates 3.0 mm ±0.2 mm in thickness must be used. The glass plates must be purchased from either the Hart Scientific Company or the Haake Buchler Industries.

4.3.1 The glass must have the tin and non-tin surfaces identified.

4.3.1.1 The tin and non-tin surfaces of the glass plates can be identified by viewing the surfaces in a darkened room under a UV light at 254 nm wavelength. The tin surface will fluoresce (have a white/yellow hue) when it is exposed to the UV light. The non-tin surface will have a blue/purple hue when it is exposed to UV light. The tin surface shall be engraved for identification purposes. The non-tin surface is the test surface and faces the sample during the test.

4.3.2 A new glass plate must be used for each test.

4.4 Beakers—Heat resistant glass, as recommended for use in the Haake unit, is used as the sample chambers.

4.4.1 Corning beakers, as recommended for use in the Hart unit, require the top edge and the bottom surface to be "leveled" using 250 grit Tri-M-Ite Wet or Dry Sandpaper or equivalent procedure, to ensure adequate contact of the gasket to the upper rim and to allow uniform contact in the heating chamber.

4.5 Metal Rings—Rings having a uniform weight and made of a stainless steel or other inert material with a diameter to fit inside the beaker. The metal ring prevents the test specimen from curling and producing non-uniform heating. The approximate dimensions and weights are:

4.5.1 HAAKE UNITS—73 mm ±1 mm ID; 79 mm OD - 55 g ±2 g.

4.5.2 HART UNITS—51 mm ±0.7 mm ID; 57 mm OD - 38 g ±1 g.

4.6 Annular Seals—Silicone rubber seals, as recommended by the manufacturer, with a diameter to match the beaker rim.

4.6.1 Annular seals must be inspected before each usage. They must be soft and pliable with no cracks or voids. Seals that do not meet this requirement will give unreliable high test results and must be discarded.

4.7 Dioctyl Phthalate (DOP) or Diisodecyl Phthalate (DIDP)—Used as an internal laboratory performance guide. These materials have been used as calibration standards in the past. They are now used only for laboratory quality control purposes. Standard practice, as agreed between contractual companies, should be employed.

4.8 Glossmeter—A suitable 60 degree glossmeter (gloss reflectometer) meeting the requirements of ASTM D 523 (Section 6.2), or ISO 2813. (Photometric method)

4.8.1 BYK-Gardner Incorporated or equivalent, 2435 Linden Lane, Silver Spring, MD 20910, (301) 495-7150

4.9 Black Matte Surface—The matte surface shall have specular reflectance reading of less than 0.5 gloss units when measured with the 60 degree glossmeter. (Photometric method)

4.10 Measuring Template (Optional)—The template is to be constructed from acrylic (or equivalent). The template is used to precisely position a glossmeter on the glass plate. Refer to DIN 75-201 for detailed information. (Photometric method)

4.10.1 If a measuring template is used, a notation must be made on the Data Report (Figure A1).

4.11 Microscope (Optional)—A suitable microscope with a 100 to 400 X magnification. This instrument is used to view the condensed material on the glass plate. (Photometric method)

4.12 Analytical Balance—A suitable analytical balance capable of weighing accurately to five places beyond the decimal point or a minimum accuracy of 0.00001 g. (Gravimetric method)

4.12.1 Previous Gravimetric Method testing has demonstrated the inadequacy of using balances capable of 0.0001 g accuracy.

4.13 Aluminum Foil—The size of the foil shall be cut to fit the Fog Test Unit being used. The foil is identified as Part No. 01-213-11 (0.025mm) from Fisher Scientific (1-800-766-7000), or equivalent.

4.14 Labconco Steam Scrubber Washer/Dryer or equivalent.

4.14.1 Model No. 44004 available from Fisher Scientific, 2775 Pacific Drive, P.O. Box 4829, Norcross, GA 30091, 1-800-766-7000.

4.14.2 2 model 44017 inserts for holding the beakers, 2 model 44019 retainer tops, and 1 model 44022 basket are recommended accessories.

4.15 Detergent—Alcojet, Sparkleen 2 or equivalent non-foaming laboratory detergent for dishwasher cleaning.

4.15.1 DETERGENT—Alconox or equivalent laboratory detergent, non-ionic for all manual precleaning requirements.

4.16 Cotton Cloth—Laboratory quality, lint free.

4.17 Deionized Water—Shall have a quality of 20 µs/cm at 25 °C maximum conductivity as outlined in ASTM D 1125.

4.18 Forceps and/or Tweezers—Used to "handle" the various pieces of material.

4.19 Hydraulic cutting press and circular dies or other suitable cutting method.

4.20 Calibrated Timer—Used where timing is a factor.

4.21 Denatured Ethyl Alcohol (90% Ethyl Alcohol - 5% Methyl Alcohol - 5% Isopropyl Alcohol or Equivalent)—Used to clean the cooling plates.

4.22 Data Reports—Located in Appendix A (Photometric Method) and B (Gravimetric Method)—The report form for recording all pertinent data.

5. Cleaning Procedure

5.1 Preclean Haake beakers using Alconox (or equivalent) or alone in the dishwasher, prior to washing in the dishwasher with other implements.

5.1.1 If a solvent test was previously performed, place the seals in an air circulating oven set at 75 °C ±2 °C for a minimum of 2 h to allow the solvent to dissipate.

5.2 A laboratory dishwasher having a deionized water rinse and steaming cycle is required (refer to 4.14).

5.2.1 The following cycle is recommended for the dishwasher for final cleaning of the silicone rubber seals, metal rings, glass beakers, forceps, and engraved glass plates:

5.2.1.1 Pre-wash (5 min), Wash (8), Steam (10), Main wash (35), 1st rinse (5), 2nd rinse (5), 3rd rinse (12), Deionized water rinse (10) and Dry (30) for a total of 120 min.

NOTE—No additional cleaning, i.e., acetone rinse, is required.

5.2.2 Set the control panel switches and push buttons as follows:

5.2.2.1 Steam Action—on, Final Rinse—Purified Water, Cycle—Heavy Wash, and Dry—Heated.

5.2.3 The temperature of the water must be a minimum of 49 °C.

5.2.4 Deionized water is required for the final rinse.

5.3 The silicone rubber seals (O-rings) used in the Haake unit are to be placed flat during the washing cycle. The metal rings are to be hung on a stainless steel rod and suspended from a rack in the dishwasher.

5.3.1 The silicone rubber seals (flat) and the metal rings used in the Hart unit are to be hung on a stainless steel rod and suspended from a rack in the dishwasher.

5.4 Place the glass beakers in the dishwasher, usually on the lower rack. The glass beakers shall be handled on the outside only and as little as possible.

5.5 Place the glass plates on a rack and then place in the dishwasher. The glass plates may be handled by grasping two opposite edges. Hold toward the corners where possible.

5.6 Load all other implements into the dishwasher.

5.7 Close the dishwasher door and start the machine.

5.8 At the conclusion of the dishwashing cycle, unload the glassware.

5.8.1 Unload the small implements using clean forceps.

5.8.2 If the glassware is not completely dry following the suggested cycle, within 15 min ±5 min of the completion of the 30 min dry cycle, unlatch the door of the dishwasher just enough to allow any retained moisture to escape.

5.9 After removing the beakers from the dishwasher, they are to be placed open side up on clean filter paper and allowed to equilibrate in the standard atmosphere for 1 h prior to use. Beakers should be placed open side down if storage is required.

6. Test Conditions

6.1 Prior to testing, all test specimens are to be conditioned in a controlled atmosphere of 21 °C ±2 °C and 50% ±5% relative humidity for a minimum of 24 h or until moisture equilibrium is obtained. Testing shall be performed under the same controlled conditions.

NOTE—The influence of altitude on test results has not yet been established.

7. Photometric Procedure

7.1 Using a hydraulic cutting press and circular die, or another suitable cutting method, cut three test specimens from each sample of material or component (or as specified by the contractual automotive company) that are the appropriate diameter to fit inside the beakers of the Temperature Controlled Unit. The thickness shall not be greater than 50 mm. For components with irregular surfaces, cut several pieces to make up the required test size.

7.1.1 The diameter of the test specimens shall be 80 mm ±2 mm for the Haake and 58 mm ±1 mm for the Hart unit.

7.1.2 Do not handle the test specimens with your hands or gloves. Use clean forceps to handle the specimens. This will avoid the possibility of contamination and introduction of additional variability to the test.

7.2 Condition the test specimens in the controlled atmosphere of 21 °C ± 2 °C and 50% ±5% RH for a minimum of 24 h or until moisture equilibrium is obtained.

7.3 Clean and dry the glass plates, glass beakers, silicone rubber seals, metal rings, and forceps as in Section 5.

7.4 If using the Haake unit, fill the bath with the heating liquid until the indicator reaches approximately "3". When all glass beakers are in place and the heating liquid is at the testing temperature, the indicator should be at "7" or 60 mm ± 2 mm from the top of the heating liquid to the top of the seals (the underside of the glass plates).

7.5 Turn the Temperature Controlled Units and the Circulator (Haake) on.

7.5.1 The temperature conditions to be used will be prescribed by the contractual automotive company. Examples of temperatures that may be used are:

7.5.1.1 Bath temperature 100 °C ±0.5 °C - Cooling temperature 21 °C ± 0.5 °C.

7.5.1.2 Bath temperature 85 °C ±0.5 °C - Cooling temperature 38 °C ± 0.5 °C.

7.5.1.3 Bath temperature 95 °C ±0.5 °C - Cooling temperature 38 °C ± 0.5 °C.

7.5.1.4 Bath temperature 110 °C ±0.5 °C - Cooling temperature 38 °C ± 0.5 °C.

NOTE—Confirm temperature settings to be used for testing with the contractual automotive company.

7.6 Check the temperature of the Temperature Controlled Unit. If the actual temperature has reached the required test temperature, set a timer for approximately 30 min to signal the end of the equilibration time.

7.6.1 When using a Hart unit, 12 h at temperature may be required to establish thermal equilibrium. Shorter periods may be used when temperature equilibrium can be verified.

7.7 Calibrate the glossmeter according to the manufacturer's instructions.

7.8 Grasp two opposite sides of the glass plate and place the glass surface horizontally, tin side down, on the black matte surface.

7.9 Place the 60 degree glossmeter on top of the glass plate near the center of the exposed area. Record four readings rotating the glossmeter 90 degrees between each reading. Average the four readings and record as R_o on the data report.

7.9.1 The glossmeter readings are to be taken under artificial light. No natural outside light is to be present when taking the gloss readings.

7.9.2 Align the template, if used, with the glass plate and place the glossmeter on top of the template. Record the four readings and the average as R_o on the data report.

NOTE—Make sure the face of the glossmeter that will be near the glass plate is clean.

7.10 Using forceps, place a conditioned test specimen into the bottom of a prepared beaker. The finished side of the test specimen (the side that faces the vehicle interior) should be placed up.

7.10.1 If an internal performance validation material is used, place it 10 g ± 0.2 g into the appropriate beaker. This control test is carried out in parallel with the test on the trim material. **If the values obtained are outside the accepted range, take corrective action but do not adjust the specified set temperature.**

7.10.1.1 If the values of the validation material do not fall within the historical norm for your laboratory, verify the heating and the cooling temperatures, verify the cleanliness of the glassware, and repeat the validation test.

7.10.2 If powder, pastes, or liquids are to be tested, place a quantity of 10 g ± 0.2 g into the bottom of the beaker, ensuring the wall of the beaker is not moistened and the test specimen is evenly distributed over the bottom of the beaker.

7.10.2.1 Materials that may stick to the bottom of the beaker may be placed on aluminum foil and set into the beaker. Note the usage of foil on the data report.

7.11 Using forceps, place the specified metal ring on top of the test specimen. Two rings, one on top of the other, may be used where sample curl during testing is unacceptable.

7.11.1 No metal ring is put into the beaker if powder, pastes, or liquids are being tested.

7.12 Using forceps, place a silicone rubber seal on the rim of the beaker containing the test specimen.

7.13 Cover the test beakers containing the test specimen and the silicone rubber seal with a cleaned glass plate. The non-tin surface of the glass plate is to be facing down toward the specimen and the seal.

7.14 Place an unweighed piece of aluminum foil on top of the glass plate. This piece of foil may be reused as long as it remains flat.

7.14.1 This additional piece of aluminum foil will make the removal of the cooling plate less likely to disturb the deposit on the glass plate.

7.14.2 The diameter of the foil shall be 103 mm ±1 mm for the Haake and 80 mm ±2 mm for the Hart units. They shall be flat with no wrinkles.

7.15 After the 30 min timer has gone off (refer to 7.6) do one of the following:

7.15.1 When using the Haake Unit:

7.15.1.1 Turn the heating unit off, but no longer than 5 min, while inserting the beakers into the oil bath to avoid splash contact with the hot oil.

7.15.1.2 Place the covered beaker assemblies into the Temperature Controlled Unit.

7.15.1.2.1 All cells must contain a beaker and cooling plate that is in position during testing.

7.15.1.3 Wipe the cooling plates with a cotton cloth moistened with ethyl alcohol, then wipe with a dry cotton cloth to remove any contamination/condensation that may be present.

7.15.1.4 Place the cooling plate assemblies on top of the glass plates/foil.

7.15.1.5 Turn the heating unit on.

7.15.2 When using the Hart Unit:

7.15.2.1 Place the covered beaker assemblies into the Temperature Controlled Unit.

7.15.2.2 Wipe the cooling plates with a cotton cloth moistened with ethyl alcohol, then wipe with a dry cotton cloth to remove any contamination/condensation that may be present.

7.15.2.3 Place the cooling plate assemblies on top of the glass plates/foil.

7.16 At this point (the start of the test), the heating temperature will drop; the original heating temperature should be re-attained within 10 min of the start of the test.

7.17 The duration of the testing period will be prescribed by the contractual automotive company. Examples of temperatures that may be used are (refer to 7.5.1):

7.17.1 If the bath temperature is 100 °C, the testing period is 3 h.

7.17.2 If the bath temperature is 85, 95, or 110 °C, the testing period is 6 h.

NOTE—Confirm the testing period to be used with the contractual automotive company.

7.18 Following the testing period, remove the cooling plates from the glass plates/foil on top of the beakers.

7.19 Remove the unweighed piece of aluminum foil.

7.20 Carefully remove the glass plates from the beakers and store them in a horizontal position, fog side up, in a dust-free atmosphere at standard conditions of 21 °C ±2 °C and 50% ±5% relative humidity.

7.21 The post test conditioning period to be used will be prescribed by the contractual automotive company. Examples of post test conditioning periods are 1 h ±0.1 h and 16 h ±0.1 h.

NOTE—Confirm the post test conditioning period to be used for testing with the contractual automotive company.

7.21.1 Be careful to ensure that the fog deposits on the glass plates are not disturbed and are exposed only to artificial light and a lint-free atmosphere. The actual time is to be recorded on the Data Report (Figure A1 and Figure B1).

7.22 Examine the glass plates for signs of large liquid oily droplets, crystalline deposits, or a transparent film covering the exposed area of the glass plate. (The subjective nature of this evaluation may require agreement between contractual parties.) Report all observations and comments on the Data Report (Figure A1 and Figure B1).

7.22.1 The above conditions are likely to introduce errors in the gloss measurement. Gloss measurements may be taken in these cases, but the data must be clearly marked as inconclusive.

7.23 When large liquid oily droplets, etc., are observed, consideration should be given to the use of the Gravimetric Method. The concurrence of the contractual automotive company is required.

7.24 Measure the gloss of the fogged surface and enter the results on the Data Report (Figure A1 and Figure B1).

7.24.1 Grasp two opposite sides of the glass plate and place the fogged surface horizontally, fog side up, on the black matte surface.

7.24.2 Place the 60 degree glossmeter on top of the glass plate near the center of the exposed area. Record four readings rotating the gloss meter 90 degrees between each reading. Average the four readings and record as R on the Data Report (Figure A1 and Figure B1).

7.24.2.1 The glossmeter readings are to be taken under artificial light. No natural outside light is to be present when taking the gloss readings.

7.24.2.2 Optional—Align the template if used, with the glass plate and place the glossmeter on top of the template. Record the readings as specified in 7.24.2.

7.24.2.3 Care must be taken to insure the underside of the glossmeter does not smear the fog residue on the surface of the glass plate.

7.25 If a permanent record of the test result is desired, a clean glass plate may be placed on the fogged plate to "sandwich" the fogged area between the two plates. Seal all edges of the glass plate with a non-porous tape.

7.25.1 Transparent mending tape is recommended.

7.25.2 Used glass plates may be carefully washed and used as the top plate of the "sandwich."

7.26 Discard fog plates that are not being retained.

8. Calculations

8.1 Calculate the ratio of R to R_0 (the fog number) X 100 for each sample and report this value as a whole number for the 1 and/or 16 h data.

8.2 Average the fog number for three equivalent test specimens. If the difference between the individual numbers is greater than 5, or as agreed upon by the contractual parties, the test must be repeated using equivalent specimens. Report the results in the comments section of the Data Report (Figure A1 and Figure B1).

9. Data Report—The Data Report for the Photometric Method (Figure A1) is shown in Appendix A. All results, comments, etc., are to be entered on this form. A copy of this report is to be included with each sample being submitted for approval or as agreed upon by the contractual parties.

10. Gravimetric Procedure

10.1 Using a hydraulic cutting press and circular die, or another suitable cutting method, cut three test specimens from each sample of material or component (or as specified by the contractual automotive company) that are the appropriate diameter to fit inside the beakers of the Temperature Controlled Unit. The thickness shall not be greater than 50 mm. For components with irregular surfaces, cut several pieces to make up the required test size.

10.1.1 The diameters of the test specimens shall be 80 mm for the Haake and 58 mm for the Hart unit.

10.1.2 Do not handle the test specimens with your hands or gloves. Use clean forceps to handle the specimens. This will avoid the possibility of contamination and introduction of additional variability to the test.

10.2 Condition the test specimens in the controlled atmosphere of 21 °C ± 2 °C and 50% ±5% relative humidity for a minimum of 24 h or until moisture equilibrium is obtained.

10.3 Clean and dry the glass plates, glass beakers, silicone rubber seals, metal rings, and forceps as specified in Section 5.

10.4 If using the Haake unit, fill the bath with the heating liquid until the indicator reaches approximately "3". When all glass beakers are in place and the heating liquid is at the testing temperature, the indicator should be at "7" or 60 mm ±2 mm from the top of the heating liquid to the top of the seals (the underside of the glass plates).

10.5 Turn the Temperature Controlled Units and Circulator (Haake) on.

10.5.1 The temperatures to be used will be specified by the contractual automotive company: Examples of temperatures that may be used are:

10.5.1.1 Heating temperature at 100 °C ±0.5 °C.

10.5.1.2 Cooling temperature at 21 °C ±0.5 °C.

NOTE—Confirm temperature settings to be used for testing with the contractual automotive company.

10.6 Check the temperature of the Temperature Controlled Unit. If the actual temperature has reached the test temperature, set a timer for a minimum of 30 min to signal the end of the heating equilibration time.

10.6.1 When using a Hart unit, 12 h at temperature may be required to establish thermal equilibrium. Shorter periods may be used when temperature equilibrium can be verified.

10.7 Using a hydraulic cutting press and a circular die, or another suitable cutting method, cut pieces of the specified aluminum foil to a diameter which is 2 mm larger than the outer diameter of the silicone rubber seals which are provided with your Temperature Controlled Chamber.

10.7.1 The diameter of the foil shall be 103 mm ±1 mm for the Haake and 80 mm ±2 mm for the Hart units.

10.7.2 The pieces of foil shall be cut at the same time and must be cut with the shiny side down.

10.7.2.1 Each piece of foil shall be sandwiched between pieces of paper or card stock, and cut to the appropriate size.

10.7.2.2 Examine the aluminum foil to make sure it is flat. Concave, convex, or wrinkled aluminum foil pieces will cause problems in the accuracy and reproducibility of the results. If needed, before separating the layers, apply sufficient pressure to the cut "sandwich" to flatten the aluminum foil disks. Nonflat aluminum pieces must be discarded.

10.7.2.2.1 Forceps shall be used when examining the aluminum foil.

10.8 Weigh the aluminum foil using an analytical balance that has a minimum accuracy of 0.00001 g. Record the weight as F (initial) on the data report. Zero the balance before, and check the zero after each reading.

10.8.1 Forceps shall be used when handling the aluminum foil.

10.9 Weigh the conditioned test specimens on the same analytical balance used in the previous step. Record the weight as S (initial) on the Data Report (Figure A1 and Figure B1).

10.10 Using forceps, place the weighed test specimen into the bottom of a prepared beaker. The finished side of the test specimen (the side that faces the vehicle interior) should be placed up.

10.10.1 If an internal performance validation material is used, place it 10 g ± 0.2 g into the appropriate beaker. This control test is carried out in parallel with the test on the trim material. **If the values obtained are outside the accepted range, take corrective action but do not adjust the specified set temperature.**

10.10.1.1 If the values of the validation material do not fall within the historical norm for your laboratory, verify the heating and cooling temperatures, verify the cleanliness of the glassware, and repeat the validation test.

10.10.2 If powder, pastes, or liquids are to be tested, place a quantity of 10 g ± 0.2 g into the bottom of the beaker, ensuring the wall of the beaker is not moistened and the test specimen is evenly distributed over the bottom of the beaker.

10.10.2.1 Materials that may stick to the bottom of the beaker may be placed on aluminum foil and set into the beaker. Note the usage of foil on the Data Report (Figure A1 and Figure B1).

10.11 Using forceps, place the specified metal ring on top of the test specimen.

10.11.1 No metal ring is put into the beaker if powder, pastes, or liquids are being tested for fog characteristics.

10.12 Using forceps, place a silicone rubber seal on the rim of the beaker containing the test specimen.

10.13 Using forceps, carefully center the weighed aluminum foil over the seal. The shiny surface of the aluminum foil should be facing the test specimen.

10.13.1 The diameter of the foil shall be 103 mm ±mm for the Haake and 80 mm ±2 mm for the Hart units. They shall be flat with no wrinkles.

10.14 Cover the weighed aluminum foil with a clean glass plate. This plate may be reused only in this same application.

10.15 Place an unweighed piece of aluminum foil on top of the glass plate. This foil may be reused only in this same application.

10.15.1 This additional piece of aluminum foil will make the removal of the cooling unit less likely to disturb the deposit on the weighted foil.

10.15.2 The diameter of the foil shall be 103 mm ± 1 mm for the Haake and 80 mm ±2 mm for the Hart units. They shall be flat with no wrinkles.

10.16 After the 30 min timer has gone off (refer to 7.6) do one of the following:

10.16.1 When using the Haake Unit:

10.16.1.1 Turn the heating unit off, but no longer than 5 min, while inserting the beakers into the oil bath to avoid splash contact with the hot oil.

10.16.1.2 Place the covered beaker assemblies into the Temperature Controlled Unit.

10.16.1.2.1 All cells must contain a beaker and cooling plate that is in position during testing.

10.16.1.3 Wipe the cooling plates with a cotton cloth moistened with ethyl alcohol, then wipe with a dry cotton cloth to remove any contamination/condensation that may be present.

10.16.1.4 Place the cooling plate assemblies on top of the glass plates/foil.

10.16.1.5 Turn the heating unit on.

10.16.2 When using the Hart Unit:

10.16.2.1 Place the covered beaker assemblies into the Temperature Controlled Unit.

10.16.2.2 Wipe the cooling plates with a cotton cloth moistened with ethyl alcohol, then wipe with a dry cotton cloth to remove any contamination/condensation that may be present.

10.16.2.3 Place the cooling plate assemblies on top of the glass plates/foil.

10.17 Wipe the cooling plates with a cotton cloth moistened with the special denatured ethyl alcohol, then wipe with a dry cotton cloth to remove any contamination/condensation that may be present.

10.18 After the 30 min timer has gone off (refer to 10.6), place the covered beaker assembly in the Temperature Controlled Chamber. Cover the unweighed aluminum foil with the cleaned cooling plate.

10.19 At this point (the start of the test), the heating temperature will drop; the original heating temperature of 100 °C should be re-attained within 10 min of the start of the test.

10.20 The duration of the testing period will be specified by the contractual automotive company. An example of a testing period is 16 h ±0.25 h.

NOTE—**Confirm the testing period with the contractual automotive company.**

10.21 After completion of the testing period, carefully remove the cooling plates, unweighed foil, and glass plates from the top of each beaker.

10.21.1 Dispose of the unweighed piece of aluminum foil and the glass plates if not being reused.

10.22 Pry the weighed aluminum foil from the gasket using either clean forceps and a stainless steel pick or two clean forceps.

10.22.1 Use clean forceps for each weighed foil sample to avoid contamination.

10.23 Using forceps, remove the test specimens from the beakers.

10.24 Weigh the test specimens within 5 min after removal from the beakers, using the same analytical balance used in 10.8. Record the weight as S (final) on the Data Report (Figure A1 and Figure B1).

10.25 Carefully store the fogged aluminum foil samples in a horizontal position, fog side up, in a dust-free atmosphere at 21 °C ±2 °C and 50% ±5% relative humidity. Make sure the fog deposits are not disturbed and are exposed to only artificial light.

10.26 After the 4 h ±15 min, or as prescribed by the contractual automotive company, remove the fogged aluminum foil samples from the dust-free atmosphere using forceps. Weigh the fogged aluminum foil samples on the same zeroed balance as used in 10.8. Record the weights on the Data Report (Figure A1 and Figure B1) as F (final).

11. Calculations

11.1 F = F (final) – F (initial)

Report the results, F, as _._ _ _ _ _g.

11.2 S = S (initial) – S (final)

Report the results, S, as _._ _ _ _ _g.

11.3 R = $(F/S_{initial})$ x 100

Report the ratio, R, as _._ _ _%.

12. Data Report—The Data Report for the Gravimetric Method is shown in Appendix B (Figure B1). All results, comments, etc., are to be entered on this form. A copy of this report is to be included with each sample being submitted for approval, or as agreed upon by the contractual parties.

APPENDIX A
PHOTOMETRIC DATA REPORT

APPENDIX A
PHOTOMETRIC DATA REPORT

Company Name ____________ Date of Test ____________
Operator's Name ____________

1. **Instrument Type (Circle):** Haake Hart

Looking Down

Haake: 4 3 / 5 . 2 / 6 1 — Front

Hart: 1 2 3 4 — Front

Haake	Hart
1=	1=
2=	2=
3=	3=
4=	4=
5=	
6=	

2. **Sample Conditioning:** Temp: ____ Humidity: ____ Duration: ____ (hours)
3. **Heating Temperature:** Set: ____ Actual: ____
4. **Cooling Temperature:** Set: ____ Actual: ____
5. **Initial Glossmeter Readings (before testing):**

Sample Identification	1	2	3	4	5	6
R_o^1						
R_o^2						
R_o^3						
R_o^4						
$R_{o(avg)}$						

6. **Final Glossmeter Readings (after 1 h):**

Sample Identification	1	2	3	4	5	6
R_1						
R_2						
R_3						
R_4						
$R_{(avg)}$						

7. **Final Glossmeter Readings (after 16 h):**

Sample Identification	1	2	3	4	5	6
R_1						
R_2						
R_3						
R_4						
$R_{(avg)}$						

8. **Ratio of R to R_o Values (reported as a whole number). EXAMPLE: For Sample No. 1 (R[avg.]/R_o[avg.]) X 100:**

Sample Identification	1	2	3	4	5	6
$(R/R_o)_{avg}$ X 100 [1 h]						
$(R/R_o)_{avg}$ X 100 [16 h]						

9. **Waiting time before taking final gloss readings:** 1 h readings: ____ Hours ____ Minutes
   16 h readings: ____ Hours ____ Minutes
10. **Special Observations (e.g., large droplets dry or oily films, unusual deposits, and/or build-up of crystals):**
11. **A measuring template was / was not used. (circle one)**
12. **Type and value of any internal reference material used:**

FIGURE A1—PHOTOMERIC DATA REPORT

APPENDIX B
GRAVIMETRIC DATA REPORT

GRAVIMETRIC DATA REPORT

Company Name ____________________ Date of Test ____________________
Operator's Name ____________________

1. Instrument Type (Circle): Haake Hart

Looking Down

	Haake		Hart
4	3		
5	2		1 2 3 4
6	1		
Front			Front

1= ______________ 1= ______________
2= ______________ 2= ______________
3= ______________ 3= ______________
4= ______________ 4= ______________
5= ______________
6= ______________

2. Type of Balance: ______________ **Maximum Capacity:** ______________
Balance Readability: ______________
3. Sample Conditioning: Temp: ______ Humidity: ______ Duration: ______ (hours)
4. Heating Temperature: Set: ______ Actual: ______
5. Cooling Temperature: Set: ______ Actual: ______
6. Test Samples Weight: ______ Record test samples initial and final weight in table below:

Weight Loss of Test Samples (S = S(initial) - S(final)): Record results below as _ . _ _ _ _ _ g.

Sample Identification	1	2	3	4	5	6
$S_{initial}$ (g)						
S_{final} (g)						
S (g)						

7. Fog Deposit of Test Samples (F = F(final) - F(initial)): Record as _ . _ _ _ _ _ g.

Sample Identification	1	2	3	4	5	6
$F_{initial}$ (g)						
F_{final} (g)						
F (g)						

8. Percentage of Fog Mass R = (F/$S_{initial}$) X 100: Record results below as _ _ . _ _ _ _ %

Sample Identification	1	2	3	4	5	6
R (%)						

9. Waiting time before weighing specimens : Hours __________ Minutes __________

10. Special Observations (e.g., large droplets dry or oily films, unusual deposits, and/or build-up of crystals): ______________________________

11. Type and value of any internal reference material used: ______________________________

FIGURE B1—GRAVIMETRIC DATA REPORT

(R) LABORATORY MEASUREMENT OF THE AIRBORNE SOUND BARRIER PERFORMANCE OF AUTOMOTIVE MATERIALS AND ASSEMBLIES —SAE J1400 MAY1990

SAE Recommended Practice

Report of the SAE Nonmetallic Materials Committee approved May 1982, and reaffirmed by the SAE Sound and Heat Insulation Materials Committee May 1989. Currently under revision. Rationale statement available. Completely revised by the SAE Sound and Heat Insulation Materials Committee May 1990.

Foreword—This Document has not changed other than to put it into the new SAE Technical Standards Board Format.

1. Scope—This SAE Recommended Practice presents a test procedure for determining the airborne sound barrier performance of materials and composite assemblies commonly installed in surface vehicles and marine products.

This document is intended to provide a means of rank ordering barrier materials according to their sound transmission loss. At each test frequency the transmission loss (TL) is projected from the measured noise reduction of the test specimen using a correlation factor (CF). The respective CF for the test condition is determined as the differences between the measured noise reduction (MNR) of a homogeneous limp panel, such as lead, and its calculated field-incidence transmission loss.

Latitude is permitted in certain test conditions that do not necessarily conform to all of the acoustical requirements of ASTM E 90. This method facilitates the evaluation of automotive materials and assemblies under conditions of representative size, edge constraint, and sound incidence so as to allow better correlation with in-use barrier performance.

2. References

2.1 Applicable Publications—The following publications form a part of the specification to the extent specified herein. Unless otherwise indicated the latest revision of SAE publications shall apply.

2.1.1 SAE PUBLICATIONS—Available from SAE, 400 Commonwealth Drive, Warrendale, PA 15096-0001.

SAE J184—Qualifying a Sound Data Acquisition System

2.1.2 ANSI PUBLICATIONS—Available from ANSI, 11 West 42nd Street, New York, NY 10036-8002.

ANSI S 1.1—Acoustical Terminology

ANSI S 1.4—Specification for Sound Level Meters

ANSI S 1.11—Specification for Octave Band and Fractional Octave Band Filter Sets

2.1.3 INCE PUBLICATIONS—Available from INCE, P.O. Box 3206--Arlington Branch, Poughkeepsie, NY 12603.

Beranek, Leo L., Noise and Vibration Control, Revised Edition, Institute of Noise Control Engineering, New York, 1989.

2.1.4 ASTM PUBLICATIONS—Available from ASTM, 100 Barr Harbor Drive, West Conshohocken, PA 19428-2959.

ASTM E 90, Laboratory Measurement of Airborne Sound Transmission Loss of Building Partitions.

3. Instrumentation—The instrumentation to be used is as follows:

3.1 A sound level meter that meets the Type I requirements of ANSI S 1.4.

3.1.1 As an alternative to making direct measurements using a sound level meter, a microphone and measuring amplifier and/or sound level meter may be used with a graphic level recorder or other indicating instrument providing the system meets the requirements of SAE J184.

3.2 A third-octave filter set covering the range of center frequencies from 100 to 10 000 Hz; the filters shall meet the Class III requirements of ANSI S 1.11.

3.3 A sound level calibrator accurate to ±0.5 dB. (See 6.2)

3.4 An acoustical sound generating system shall be selected to generate a series of bands of random noise containing a continuous distribution of frequencies over each test band.

3.5 A schematic diagram of the instrumentation is shown in Figure 1.

3.6 Temperature and humidity indicators should be used to monitor dry and wet bulb temperatures and humidity.

4. Facilities—The following facilities are recommended for the measurement of noise reduction:

4.1 The source room should have an exterior wall construction of a sufficient sound transmission loss to eliminate flanking paths into the receiving room.

4.2 When the area of the wall separating the receiving room from the source room is large relative to the area of the sample under test, the measurements may be compromised by sound transmitted from source to receiving room via paths other than through the specimen under test. Refer to ASTM E 90 for the procedures to correct filler wall transmission.

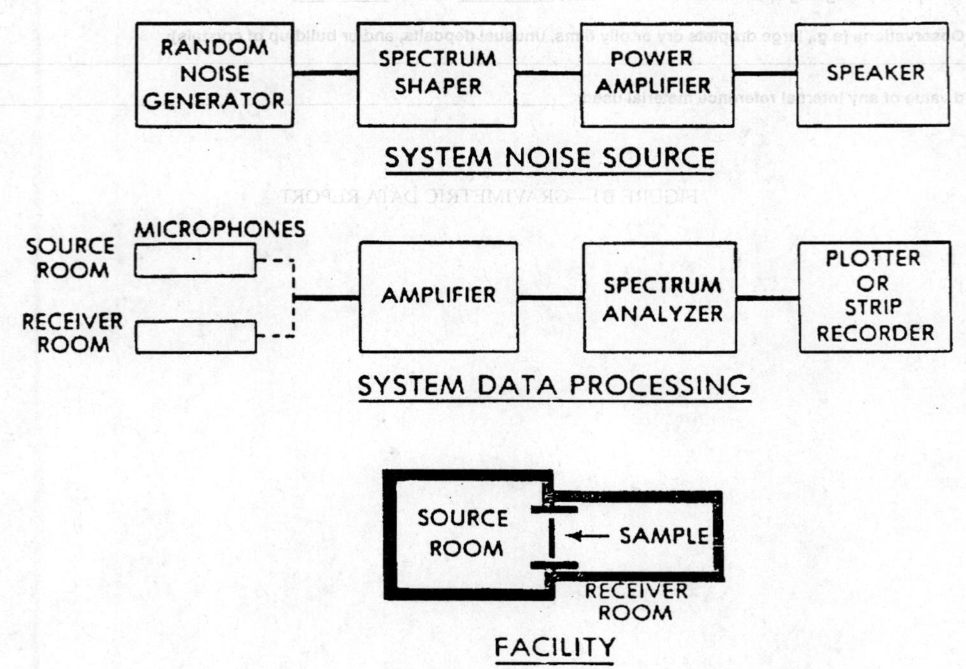

FIGURE 1—TYPICAL MEASUREMENT SYSTEM

4.3 The receiver room should be constructed to achieve a minimum difference of 10 dB between the test signal band level and the band level of the background noise in all frequency bands of interest.

4.4 A test sample fixture should hold the test sample securely between the source and receiver rooms. The fixture should be well sealed to prevent leakage between the source and receiver rooms through the fixture. The fixture should provide means to maintain typical in-use contact between applied barrier treatments and the base panel assembly.

4.5 One or more microphones shall be positioned within the source and receiver rooms. The number and spacing of microphone positions required in each room depends on the statistical precision desired in the time and space average band pressure levels.

4.6 When using a reverberant room, the diffusion in the reverberation room can be enhanced by the use of rotating or stationary diffusers.

4.7 The size of the opening between the source room and the receiver room limits the lowest frequency at which measurements can be reliably made.

NOTE—This lowest frequency is roughly determined by the length of the diagonal of the test specimen panel (see Table 1).

TABLE 1—TABLE FOR DETERMINING LOWEST FREQUENCY[1] OF MEASUREMENT FOR A GIVEN SAMPLE DIAGONAL (DIAMETER)

Diagonal of Opening, m (ft)	Lowest Measurement Frequency, Hz
0.5 (1.64)	172
0.75 (2.46)	114
1.00 (3.28)	86
1.25 (4.10)	69
1.50 (4.92)	57
1.75 (5.74)	49
2.00 (6.56)	43

1. Calculations use second speed of 343 m/s. This sound speed corresponds to an air temperature of 20 °C.

5. Procedure

5.1 Sample Mounting—The test sample should be mounted in the test fixture simulating the edge constraint conditions of the in-use condition. Ancillary shielding or seals may be used to help ensure a minimum of sound transmission flanking the test sample.

5.2 Measurements—The background noise levels within both the source and receiver rooms shall be measured and noted in all measurement bands.

5.2.1 Install the reference sample, a homogeneous limp material such as lead, sealed into the test opening so that its field-incidence sound TL can be calculated from the relation:

$$\mathrm{TL(reference)} = 20\log_{10} W + 20\log_{10} f - 47.2 \quad \text{(Eq. 1)}$$

where:

W = the surface density in kg/m^2

f = the center frequency of the one-third octave measurement band

Round off the calculated TL of the reference sample to the nearest 0.1 dB.

5.2.2 The source signal shall be filtered or shaped so that with the test sample sealed in place, the source room and receiver room signal levels are each 10 dB higher than the background noise levels in the respective facilities.

5.2.3 The time and space averaged third-octave band levels in both the source and receiver rooms shall be measured and recorded over the desired measurement bands with the reference sample sealed into the fixture in the test opening.

5.2.4 After removing the reference sample, the unknown test sample is installed and sealed into the same opening and the measurements of 5.2.3 are repeated.

5.3 Data Analysis—The following procedures are used to project the field incidence TL of the test sample:

5.3.1 BACKGROUND NOISE CORRECTION—If necessary, correct for background noise levels using the equation:

$$L_S = 10\log_{10}(10^{L_C/10} - 10^{L_B/10}) \quad \text{(Eq. 2)}$$

where:

L_S = level of the signal, dB

L_C = level of the signal and background noise combined, dB

L_B = level of the background noise alone, dB

NOTE—This correction is not necessary if the recommendations of 4.3 and 5.2.2 are met.

5.3.2 Compute the measured noise reduction for both the reference sample and the unknown test sample. Using the corrected band pressure levels for each measurement band subtract the receiver room band pressure level from the source room band pressure level to obtain the MNR for both samples.

5.3.3 Determine the CF applicable to the test opening and source and receiver room pair at each test frequency as the difference between the measured noise reduction of the reference sample, MNR(reference) and its calculated TL and TL(reference).

$$\mathrm{CF} = \mathrm{MNR(reference)} - \mathrm{TL(reference)} \quad \text{(Eq. 3)}$$

Round the correlation factor to the nearest 0.1 dB.

5.3.4 Compute the TL of the unknown test sample at each test frequency by subtracting the CF from the MNR of the unknown test sample, MNR(unknown):

$$\mathrm{TL(unknown)} = \mathrm{MNR(unknown)} - \mathrm{CF} \quad \text{(Eq. 4)}$$

The TL of the unknown should be rounded to the nearest whole number of dB.

6. General Comments

6.1 It is essential that technically qualified personnel, trained in the current techniques of sound measurements, select equipment and perform the tests.

6.2 Instrument manufacturers' recommended calibration practices should be made before and after each test. An acoustical coupler type of calibrator is recommended.

6.3 The relative humidity and temperature of the test environment shall be reported with the test results.

6.4 All round-robin data acquired for the correlation of the results of this test method with those of ASTM E 90 were obtained using reverberant source rooms.

6.5 The use of the CF based on the measured noise reduction of the homogeneous limp mass reference sample and its calculated field incidence TL (no significant sound energy incident on the test sample at angles greater than 78 degrees) tends to reduce the dependence of the projected TL on the details of the sound fields in the source and receiver rooms. Because the mechanisms controlling sound transmission in certain frequency ranges may be strongly dependent on the angle of incidence, these mechanisms may be best investigated in a facility with an anechoic source room.

(R) FLAMMABILITY OF POLYMERIC INTERIOR MATERIALS—HORIZONTAL TEST METHOD—SAE J369 MAY2003

SAE Standard

Report of the SAE Nonmetallic Materials Committee approved March 1969, revised June 1972, reaffirmed without change May 1978, and completely revised June 1989. Reaffirmed by the SAE Textiles and Flexible Plastics Committee January 1994 and completely revised May 2003. Rationale statement available.

1. Scope—This SAE Standard pertains to automotive vehicles and off-road, self-propelled work machines used in construction, general purpose industrial, agriculture, forestry, and specialized mining machinery. This standard does not address all of the safety concerns, if any, associated with its use. It is the responsibility of the user of this document to establish safety and health practices and determine the applicability of regulatory limitations prior to use.

1.1 Purpose—This test method is intended for burning rate measurement of polymeric materials used in the operator and passenger compartments as specified by the applicable standard. SAE J369 is technically equivalent to ISO 3795, ASTM D 5132 and FMVSS 302.

2. References

2.1 Applicable Publications—The following publication forms a part of this specification to the extent specified herein.

2.1.1 ISO PUBLICATION—Available from ANSI, 25 West 43rd Street, New York, NY 10036-8002.

ISO 3795—Road vehicles, and tractors and machinery for agriculture and forestry—Determination of burning behaviour of interior materials

2.1.2 ASTM PUBLICATION—Available from ASTM, 100 Barr Harbor Drive, West Conshohocken, PA 19428-2959.

ASTM D 5025—Standard Specification for Laboratory Burner Used in Small-Scale Burning Tests on Plastic Materials

ASTM D 5132—Standard Test Method for Horizontal Burning Rate of Flexible Cellular and Rubber Materials Used in Occupant Compartments of Motor Vehicles

2.1.3 FEDERAL SAFETY STANDARD—Available from Superintendent of Documents, U.S. Government Printing Office, Washington DC, 20402

FMVSS 302 (49 CFR 571.302)—Flammability of Interior Materials—Passenger Cars, Multipurpose Passenger Vehicles, Trucks, and Buses

3. Classifications

3.1 (DNI)—The material does not support the combustion during or following the 15 s ignition period and does not transmit a flame front across either surface to the first scribed line. (No calculation is required.)

Report the results as: DNI.

3.2 (SE/0)—The material ignites on either surface, but the flame extinguishes itself before reaching the first scribed line. (No calculation is required.)

Report the results as: SE/0.

3.3 (SE/NBR)—The material stops burning before it has burned for 60 s from the start of timing, and has not burned more than 51 mm from the point where the timing was started. (No calculation is required.)

Report the results as: SE/NBR.

3.4 (SE/B)—When the leading flame front on either surface progresses beyond the first scribed line, but extinguishes itself before reaching the second scribed line, time and measure its progress to the furthest point where the burning stops and calculate and report the burn rate only if the burned distance exceeds 51 mm or the burn time is 60 s or greater. Report the results as: SE/B. Calculate burn rate.

3.5 (B)—The material burns the full 254 mm.

Report the results as: B. Calculate burn rate.

3.6 (RB)—The material transmits a flame across either surface more than 51 mm beyond the first scribed line at a rate too fast to measure accurately; therefore, no calculation is required. Examples of the materials in this category are extremely thin films that burn rapidly, or napped surfaces that "flash."

Report the results as: RB.

4. Apparatus Required

4.1 Burner—A Tirrill, Bunsen, or equivalent burner with a gas flow regulating valve and a 9.5 mm ± 0.3 mm inside diameter tube, so positioned in the cabinet that the center of the end of the specimen shall be directly above the tip of the flame when the specimen is in place. The burner tube may be mounted on the chamber door provided the alignment on the specimen meets the previous requirements. For more definitive information on the burner see ASTM D 5025.

4.2 Burner Fuel—The gas supplied to the burner shall have a heating value of 37 MJ/m^3 ± 1 MJ/m^3 regulated approximately to 20 kPa.

4.3 Specimen Holder—Consisting of two identical U-shaped metal frames made from chrome or nickel-plated steel, or other metal that will not corrode. The dimensions for these frames are shown in Figure 1. Lines shall be engraved or scribed on both surfaces of each frame located as shown in Figure 1.

4.4 Specimen Holder Support—The specimen holder shall be supported horizontally so that the top of the burner is 19 mm below the top surface of the lower specimen frame.

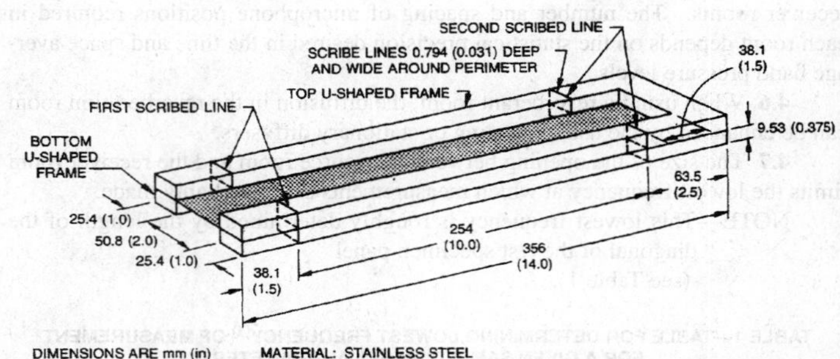

FIGURE 1—SPECIMEN HOLDER, CONSISTING OF TWO IDENTICAL U-SHAPED FRAMES

4.5 Metal Cabinet—The cabinet (Figure 2) for protecting the specimen from drafts shall be fabricated from noncorroding metal and shall be 381 mm long, 203 mm wide, and 356 mm high. It shall have a removable top and a glass observation window in front. For ventilation, the base shall have five 19 mm diameter holes equally spaced along each side of the cabinet. In addition, there shall be a 13 mm ventilating clearance running around the perimeter of the cabinet just below the top. At one end of the cabinet there shall be a door to permit insertion of the specimen holder and the specimen. A small hole may be drilled in the cabinet to accommodate the tubing that connects the gas line to the burner. The cabinet shall have 10 mm risers to permit the circulation of air.

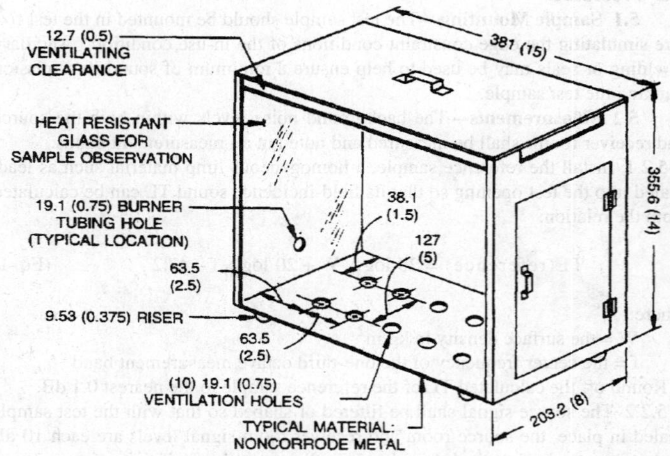

FIGURE 2—HORIZONTAL FLAMMABILITY CABINET

4.6 Combing Device—A comb at least 110 mm in length with 7 to 8 smooth round teeth per 25 mm.

4.7 Timing Device—A stop watch that will indicate time to 0.1 of a second.

5. Test Specimens—Test a minimum of 5 specimens, unless otherwise agreed upon by both parties. In all instances, the largest possible specimen size is to be cut from the material up to the standard specimen size of 102 mm x 356 mm x thickness. The minimum width and length shall be 95 mm x 300 mm. Cut specimens from uniform density samples. The maximum thickness of any specimen shall be 13 mm. If any material to be tested exceeds this, it shall be cut to the previous thickness by a mechanical process applied to the side, which does not face the occupant compartment, so that specimen shall include the primary surface of the part. In case of materials made of different composition which are not composite materials, all the layers within a depth of 13 mm from the surface facing towards the occupant compartment shall be tested individually, as shown in Figure 3. Any material that does not adhere to other material at every point of contact shall be tested separately. Any material that adheres to other material(s) at every point of contact shall be tested as a composite with other material(s). Record the information on specimen preparation in the test report. For composites, laminates, or surface-treated samples, the side nearest to the compartment occupant should be placed facing down during testing. If the material's grain pattern or construction is such that it has a directional effect on the burning rate, testing should be conducted in both the transverse and longitudinal directions. Where the maximum available width of the specimen is 51 mm or less so that the sides of the specimen cannot be held in the two matching U-shaped frames, it is to be supported by the use of.25 mm wires of heat-resistant composition spanning the top surface of the bottom U-shaped frame at 25 mm intervals, as shown in Figure 4. The U-shaped wire frame shall also be used for a specimen that softens and bends at the flaming end.

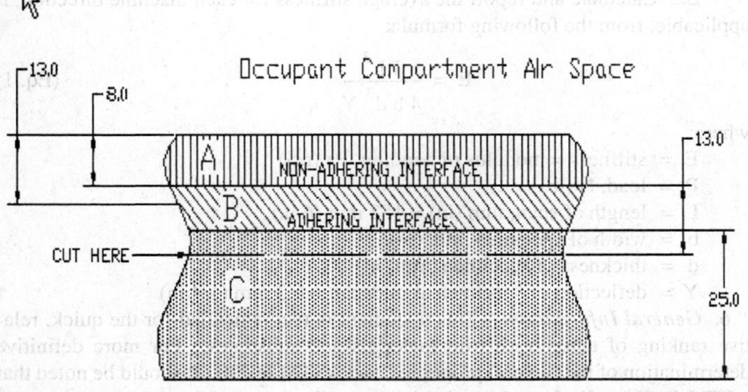

FIGURE 3—SPECIMEN PREPARATION (ILLUSTRATIVE EXAMPLE)

Material A has a non-adhering interface with material B and is tested separately. Part of material B is within 13 mm of the occupant compartment air space, and materials B and C adhere at every point of contact; therefore B and C are tested as a composite. The cut is in material C as shown, to make a specimen 13 mm thick.

5.1 Selection and Direction—Shall be as specified in the applicable standard.

5.2 Surface Preparation—When materials to be tested contain either a napped or a tufted-type surface, this test specimen shall be placed on a hard, flat surface and combed twice against the nap prior to testing.

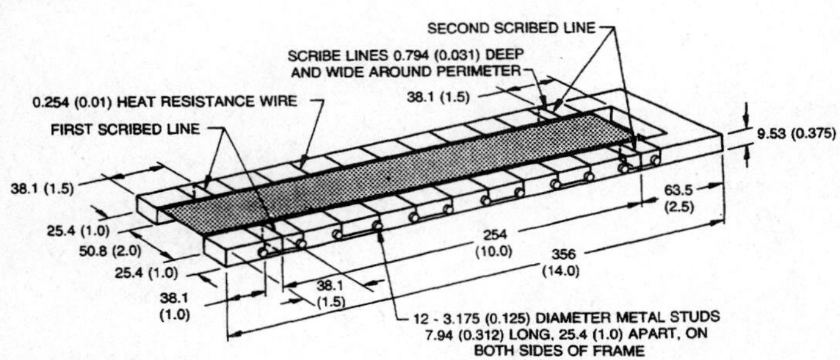

FIGURE 4—BOTTOM U-SHAPED WIRE FRAME USED FOR SPECIMENS THAT ARE 51 MM OR LESS IN WIDTH OR THAT BURN NONUNIFORMLY USED IN CONJUNCTION WITH EITHER FRAME SHOWN IN FIGURE 1

6. Test Procedure

6.1 Prior to testing, each specimen is conditioned for 24 h at a temperature of 23 °C ± 2 °C and 50% ± 5% relative humidity or as otherwise specified.

6.2 For convenience, the samples may be stored up to 1 h in closed polyethylene bags after conditioning and prior to testing.

6.3 The tests should be conducted with the metal cabinet in a draft-free fume hood to prevent fumes from spreading throughout the room. The face velocity of the fume hood shall not exceed 0.4 m/s. The burn room shall have a temperature between 15 °C and 35 °C and a relative humidity between 45% and 75%.

6.4 Close the air intake ports on the burner and adjust the gas flow to produce a flame 38 mm ± 1 mm in height.

6.5 Place the mounted specimen in a horizontal position in the center of the cabinet.

6.6 Position the burner so that the center of the barrel will be directly below the center of the open end of the mounted test specimen.

6.7 Expose the specimen to the flame for 15 s, then extinguish the burner flame or remove the burner from the specimen.

6.8 From the time of the initial burner flame contact with the specimen, observe for any rapid burning or flame front progression across the top or bottom surface of the material. Begin timing (without reference to the 15 s burner flame application), when the leading flame front reaches the first scribed line 38 mm from the open end of the U-shaped frame. If the leading flame front progresses more than 51 mm beyond the first scribed line at such a rapid rate that it cannot be measured with any degree of accuracy, the material shall be classified as RB.

6.9 Stop the timing when the flame is either extinguished or has burned the additional 254 mm to the second engraved line on the specimen holder.

6.10 Record, in seconds, the time required for the flame to travel the 254 mm between the scribed lines of the specimen holder. Or, record the time in seconds and the burned length beyond the 38 mm scribed line if the flame is extinguished before traveling the full 254 mm

6.11 Use the following classifications to report the complete flammability results as illustrated in Figure 5.

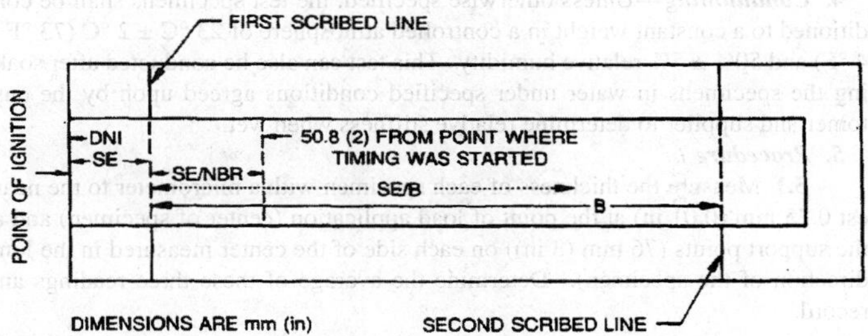

FIGURE 5—ILLUSTRATION OF DEFINITIONS FOR REPORTING TEST RESULTS

7. Calculating and Recording—Calculate and record the burn rate for the conditions SE/B (3.4) and B (3.5) from Equation 1:

$$B = 60 \times \frac{D}{T} \qquad \text{(Eq. 1)}$$

where:

B = Burn rate, mm/min (rounded to one decimal)
D = Length the flame travels starting from the first scribed line, mm (rounded to one decimal)
T = Time (starting from the first scribed line) for the flame to travel D, s

8. Report—The following information shall be on the report.

8.1 Complete identification of the material tested, including generic description, manufacturer, commercial designation, and lot number, color and other information as requested.

8.2 Directionality of the specimens, if pertinent.

8.3 The thickness and type of specimens tested, that is, composite, laminate, finished section, cellular foam, etc.

8.4 Conditioning treatment.

8.5 Any prior treatment before testing, other than cutting, trimming and conditioning.

8.6 Number of specimens tested.

8.7 Burnt distance in mm, and burning time, in seconds.

8.8 All calculated single values of burning rate, in mm/min.

8.9 Average burning rate in millimeters per minute when the flame reaches the specific end point. Report D and T separately for each specimen when the flame propagation stops before reaching the end point.

8.10 The report shall contain the following statement: "This report is not intended to reflect hazards presented by this or any other material under actual fire conditions and shall not be used for fire risk assessment under actual fire conditions."

(R) TEST METHOD FOR DETERMINING STIFFNESS (MODULUS OF BENDING) OF INTERIOR TRIM MATERIALS AND SUBSTRATES—SAE J949 APR2003 SAE Standard

Report of the SAE Nonmetallic Materials Committee approved March 1966, last revised August 1981. Completely revised by the SAE Textiles and Flexible Plastics Committee April 2003.

1. Scope—This SAE Standard presents a method of determining the stiffness of interior trim materials, substrates, and composites by a three-point bending test.

2. References

2.1 Applicable Publications—The following publications form a part of the specification to the extent specified herein.

2.1.1 ASTM PUBLICATIONS—Available from ASTM, 100 Barr Harbor Drive, West Conshohocken, PA 19428-2959.

ASTM D 747—Test Method for Apparent Bending Modulus of Plastics by Means of a Cantilever Beam

ASTM D 790—Test Methods for Flexural Properties of Unreinforced and Reinforced Plastics and Electrical Insulating Materials

3. Test Specimens—Cut three specimens each 76 x 305 mm (3 x 12 in) with the long dimension in the machine direction, if applicable. Cut three additional specimens each 76 x 305 mm (3 x 12 in), with the long dimension in the across-machine direction, if applicable.

4. Conditioning—Unless otherwise specified, the test specimens shall be conditioned to a constant weight in a controlled atmosphere of 23 °C ± 2 °C (73 °F ± 4 °F) and 50% ± 5% relative humidity. This test can also be conducted after soaking the specimens in water under specified conditions agreed upon by the customer and supplier to determine relative stiffness when wet.

5. Procedure

5.1 Measure the thickness of each specimen with a micrometer to the nearest 0.25 mm (0.01 in) at the point of load application (center of specimen) and at the support points (76 mm (3 in)) on each side of the center measured in the long direction of the specimen). Determine the average of these three readings and record.

5.2 Measure the width of the specimen to the nearest 0.25 mm (0.01 in) in the same locations as given in 5.1 and determine the average of the three readings and record.

5.3 Support the flat surface of the specimen on parallel supports 152 mm (6 in) apart and apply the load on a bearing parallel to the end supports. The bearing and supports shall be rounded to a radius of 10 mm (3/8 in) and shall have a minimum length of 76 mm (3 in).

5.4 Apply the load at the rate of 13 mm /min (0.5 in/min) until the specimen is deflected 6.3 mm (1/4 in) at the midspan.

5.5 Calculate and report the average stiffness for each machine direction, if applicable, from the following formula:

$$E = \frac{PL^3}{4\,b\,d^3\,Y} \qquad \text{(Eq. 1)}$$

where:

E = stiffness = modulus of bending, Pa (psi)
P = load, N (lb)
L = length of span, mm (in) = 152 mm (6 in)
b = width of specimen, mm (in)
d = thickness of specimen, mm (in)
Y = deflection of specimen at midspan = 6.3 mm (1/4 in)

6. General Information—This document is recommended for the quick, relative ranking of automotive trim materials and substrates. For more definitive determination of the flexural properties, use ASTM D 790. It should be noted that ASTM D 790 calls for a 16 to 1 thickness to span ratio. Direct comparisons of stiffness between this method and D 790 may only be valid at 10 mm (3/8 in) specimen thicknesses. There are also other technical differences. For determination of stiffness by the cantilever beam method, use ASTM D 747.

TEST METHOD FOR DETERMINING RESISTANCE TO ABRASION OF AUTOMOTIVE BODYCLOTH, VINYL, AND LEATHER, AND THE SNAGGING OF AUTOMOTIVE BODYCLOTH—SAE J948 DEC2003

SAE Standard

Report of the SAE Nonmetallic Materials Committee approved June 1966 and revised February 1986. Revised by the SAE Textiles and Flexible Plastics Committee August 1994 and December 2003. Rationale statement available.

Foreword

NOTE—There are two different tests for wear in this procedure and they are not equivalent. The results from the two test methods (3. Taber and 4. Wyzenbeek) cannot be compared.

1. Scope—These methods of test are applicable for determining the resistance to snagging and abrasion of automotive bodycloth, vinyl and leather.

2. References—There are no referenced publications specified herein.

3. Taber Method

3.1 Materials and Equipment Required

3.1.1 TABER ABRASER MODEL NO. 5150 COMPLETE WITH VACUUM ACCESSORY OR EQUIVALENT

3.1.2 H-18 WHEELS OR EQUIVALENT (FOR SNAGGING TEST)

3.1.3 CS-10 WHEELS OR EQUIVALENT (FOR ABRASION TEST)

3.1.4 DIAMOND WHEEL DRESSER

3.1.5 S-11 ABRASIVE PAPER OR EQUIVALENT

3.1.6 CAMEL'S HAIR BRUSH

3.2 Test Specimens—Test specimens are prepared by folding a 108 x 108 mm specimen (or equivalent circular specimen) once in each direction and then clipping the folded point to produce a small central hole to fit over the turntable clamping screw. Specimens are then conditioned at 21 °C ± 2 °C and 50% ± 5% relative humidity for 24 h.

Unless otherwise specified specimens shall be taken no nearer the selvage edge than 1/10 the width of the material.

3.3 Procedure

a. Mount the refacing disc holder on the Taber Abraser and fasten to the disc holder a piece of S-11 type abrasive paper.

b. Adjust test instrument for a 1000 g load. Loosen the knurled cap nuts and install the new set of wheels on their respective flanged holders as indicated by the printing on the side of the wheel. The one marked right side fits on the right-hand mounting with printed side out; the same with the left. The nut is then replaced and moderately tightened. Check the wheels for alignment. H-18 type wheels shall be used when testing snagging resistance and CS-10 type wheels shall be used when testing abrasion resistance.

c. Reface abrasive wheels 25 cycles by running them against the S-11 type abrasive paper disc mounted on the refacing disc holder. Remove any rough edges on the wheels by manually sanding lightly with the abrasive paper.

d. The wheels must be refaced before each test run to remove abraded materials from the wheels that collected in the prior test.

e. If the wheels are worn out of round, crowned, or excessively clogged with abraded material, they should be dressed using the diamond refacer until the condition is corrected. In cases of doubt about the condition of the abrasive wheels, new wheels shall be used.

f. Dust the refaced abrasive wheels with a small camel's hair brush and remove the refacing disc holder.

g. With specimen turntable removed from the abraser, place test specimen on the turntable. Adjust the clamping ring to a tight fit over the specimen and holder and press the hold-down ring over the circumference of the holder to pull the test material taut.

h. Remove any wrinkles in the test specimen by adjusting the fabric edges which extend below the clamping ring. Then, tighten the adjusting screw of the ring. Place the washer over the turntable screw and tighten the nut. Trim off the excess test specimen which extends beyond the lower edge of the clamping ring.

i. Lower the abrasive wheels carefully from their upright position to the surface of the test specimen. Set the counter mechanism at zero.

j. Position the vacuum nozzle along the diameter of the turntable 3 mm above the surface of the test specimen and set the vacuum dial in the range of 60 to 70.

k. Turn on the vacuum and start the Taber Abraser.

l. Run the specimen the number of cycles specified and remove for evaluation.

m. 400 cycles shall be run for snagging unless otherwise specified.

n. 1000 cycles shall be run for abrasion of bodycloth unless otherwise specified.

4. Wyzenbeek Method—The Wyzenbeek method can be used to determine the resistance to abrasion of automotive vinyl and leather.

4.1 Apparatus and Material Required

4.1.1 WYZENBEEK WEAR TESTER OR EQUIVALENT—The hardness of the rubber pads should remain between 55 to 75 when tested with a type "00" durometer on the flat surfaces. Rubber pads which do not fit snugly in their respective holders should be replaced.

Due to misalignment or wear during use, the following procedure should be performed when necessary; after cleaning the drum surface with a solvent, insert a piece of 36 grit sandpaper and clamp into position. Lower the arms removing all applied pressure and abrade the rubber pad for 400 cycles or until they conform to the shape of the drum. Clean the resurfaced rubber pad with a stiff brush and re-insert in the same holder and in the same position. Once a rubber pad has been put through this procedure *do not* use in any other holder without resurfacing.

4.1.2 100% Cotton Warp Sateen Fabric; Count 104 X 55, 214 g/m^2 or Equivalent

4.1.3 DOUBLE-FACED TAPE—3M—No. 400 or equivalent.

4.1.4 MASKING TAPE, 76 MM WIDE.

4.2 Test Specimens—Test specimens 63.5 x 230 mm are prepared to template (see Figure 1) size in both warp and fill directions. Condition the test specimens for a minimum of 16 h at 21 °C ± 2 °C and 50% ± 5% relative humidity. Unless otherwise specified, samples shall be taken no nearer the selvage edge than one tenth (1/10) the width of the material. All materials other than rigid, nonstretch materials, shall have the back of the test specimen completely covered with 76 mm masking tape.

4.3 Procedure

4.3.1 Cut the abradent 241 (warp) x 305 (fill) mm and apply one length of double-backed tape in the middle, on the back side of the abradent, parallel to the fill direction. The long floats are on the face side of the abradent.

4.3.1.1 Strip the covered side of the double-backed tape and clamp the fabric on the drum in such a manner that the warp direction is parallel to motion of the drum. When pressing down on the taped portion of the fabric, make sure there is good and uniform adhesion between the drum, the tape, and the fabric. Also, this taped area must be completely free from wrinkles.

4.3.2 Place the specimen in the clamps with the long dimension parallel to the direction of abrasion.

4.3.3 Draw the specimen tight enough to bring the weighted tension scale bar into a horizontal position using a 1.8 kg dead weight load.

NOTE—If the specimen stretches during the test, bring the scale bar back into a horizontal position by adjusting the screw behind the rear clamp.

4.3.4 Set the weight on the pressure bar at 1.35 kg.

4.3.5 Set the counter to zero.

4.3.6 Abrade the specimen for the required number of cycles.

4.3.7 Remove the specimen from the wear tester for evaluation.

4.3.8 Change the abradent for each set of specimens.

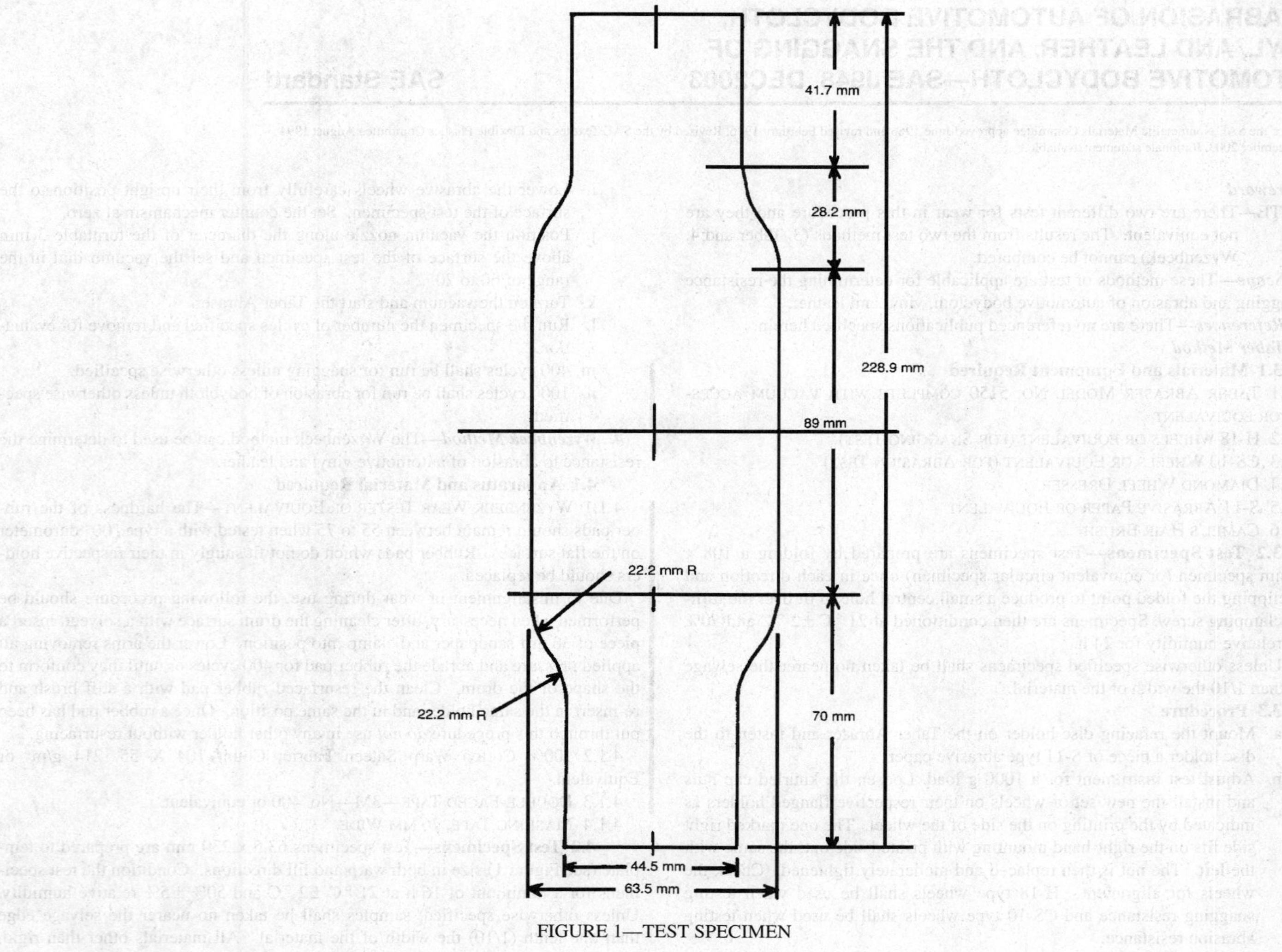

FIGURE 1—TEST SPECIMEN

PROCEDURE FOR VISUAL EVALUATION OF INTERIOR AND EXTERIOR AUTOMOTIVE TRIM—SAE J361 JAN2003

SAE Recommended Practice

Report of the SAE Nonmetallic Materials Committee approved September 1968, and completely revised March 1985. Completely revised by the SAE Textiles and Flexible Plastics Committee April 1996 and January 2003. Rationale statement available.

1. Scope—This SAE Recommended Practice applies to parts and materials used in vehicle manufacture which are intended to be acceptable color matches to a specified standard. This document is intended for use with parts or materials which are opaque or nearly so. Materials covered by this document include top-coat paint finishes, interior soft trim, interior and exterior hard trim, and exterior film and flexible trim.

1.1 Purpose—The intent of this document is to precisely specify procedures for the visual evaluation of appearance of colored materials or parts incorporated in the manufacture of vehicles. The document provides a consistent engineering practice for the determination of visual color difference between materials or parts of the same or like materials. A suitable fixture providing daylight, fluorescent, and horizon lighting conditions is necessary for this evaluation.

2. References

2.1 Applicable Publications—The following publications form a part of the specification to the extent specified herein. Unless otherwise indicated, the latest issue of SAE publications shall apply.

2.1.1 ASTM PUBLICATIONS—Available from ASTM, 100 Barr Harbor Drive, West Conshohocken, PA 19428-2959.

ASTM E 284—Terminology of Appearance

ASTM E 308—Practice for Computing the Colors of Objects by using the CIE System

ASTM E 1499-97—Standard Guide to the Selection, Evaluation and Training of Observers

2.1.2 CIE PUBLICATIONS—Available from USNC-CIE Publications Office, TLA Lighting Consultants, 7 Pond St., Salem, Massachusetts, 01970. www.cie-usnc.org.

CIE Publication 51—Method for Assessing the Quality of Daylight Simulators for Colorimetry

2.2 Related Publications—The following publications are provided for information purposes only and are not a required part of this document.

2.2.1 ASTM PUBLICATIONS—Available from ASTM, 100 Barr Harbor Drive, West Conshohocken, PA 19428-2959.

ASTM D 1729—Standard Practice for Visual Evaluation of Color and Color Differences of Diffusely Illuminated Opaque Materials

2.2.2 WILEY PUBLICATION—Available from Wiley Publishers, 111 River Street, Hoboken, NJ 07030. www.wiley.com.

Billmeyer & Saltzman's Principles of Color Technology, by Roy S. Berns, March 2000

3. Definitions

3.1 Master Standard, Sample

3.1.1 MASTER STANDARD—The appropriately identified engineering approved standard sample against which specified similar materials are evaluated.

3.1.2 SAMPLE—The material or part that is evaluated for color and appearance match to the master standard.

3.2 Color Attributes—The color of a material can be described by four basic attributes. Figure 1 shows a diagram of Munsell hue, value, and chroma and their relationship to one another.

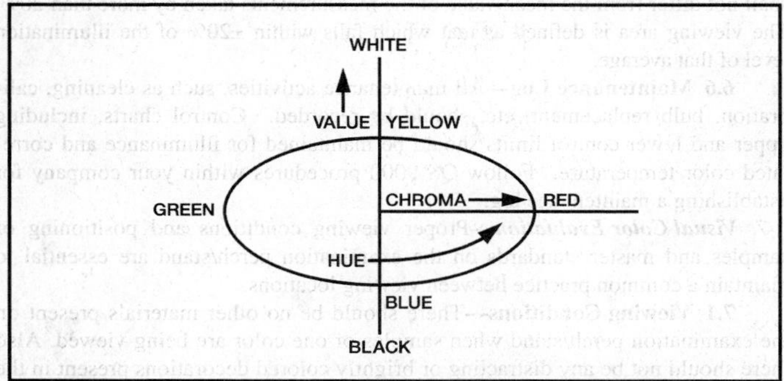

FIGURE 1—MUNSELL HUE, VALUE, AND CHROMA DIAGRAM

3.2.1 HUE—The attribute of color perception by means of which an object is judged to be red, yellow, green, blue, or intermediate between some adjacent pair of these.

3.2.2 VALUE—The attribute of color perception by means of which an object is judged to appear light or dark relative to an object of the same hue and chroma.

3.2.3 CHROMA—The attribute of color perception that expresses the degree of departure from gray, toward the pure hue, at the same value and hue.

3.2.4 METALLIC BRILLIANCE—Departure from solid color (straight shade) appearance to a highly metallized or opalescent appearance, often accompanied by a change in the angle of viewing (goniochromatic effect).

3.2.5 GONIOCHROMATISM—Change in value/lightness, hue or chroma of a specimen upon change in angular illuminating or viewing conditions but without change in light source or observer. When two specimens are compared to each other, they may or may not exhibit metamerism in addition to differences in goniochromatism. They should also be viewed under different lights to check for metamerism. (Reference ASTM E 284)

3.3 Metamerism—Property of two specimens that match under a specified illuminator and to a specified observer and whose spectral reflectances or transmittances differ in the visible wavelengths. (Reference ASTM E 284)

3.3.1 ILLUMINANT METAMERISM—Occurs when two objects match under one light source, but do not match under a different light source. This results when the objects have different spectral reflectance curves but the same color coordinates for one set of viewing conditions.

3.3.2 OBSERVER METAMERISM—Occurs when a metameric pair matches for one person but fails to match when seen by another person under the same viewing conditions.

3.3.3 FIELD SIZE METAMERISM—Occurs when the field size changes, for example from 2 degrees to 10 degrees. A metameric pair which matches when seen at a distance (small field of view) may no longer match when seen closer to the eyes (large field of view).

4. Equipment—The proper lighting unit(s) and measuring equipment are essential for consistent appearance evaluation. Figure 2 shows the critical dimensions and relative positions of an examination perch/stand and lighting sources.

4.1 Lighting Unit(s)—Each color evaluation area shall be provided with an overhead lighting unit (along with an accompanying material examination perch/stand) capable of broadcasting the following lighting conditions:

4.1.1 Daylight capable of providing a color temperature of 6500 K ± 200 K at an illuminance of 1080 to 1730 lux (100 to 160 ft-candles). This source is typically provided by filtered Tungsten Halogen Lamps. The resulting spectral power distribution of the incident light must be maintained to conform to ASTM E 308 and CIE Publication 51, Category A.

4.1.2 Cool White Fluorescent (CWF) capable of providing a color temperature of 4150 K ± 200 K at a minimum illuminance of 860 lux (80 ft-candles). This source is typically provided by Cool White Fluorescent tubes.

4.1.3 Simulated horizon sunlight source providing a color temperature of 2300 K ± 200 K at a minimum illuminance of 860 lux (80 ft-candles). This source is typically provided by Tungsten Halogen Lamps to simulate early morning sunrise or late afternoon sunset conditions.

4.1.4 As an option, an ultraviolet lighting source (no Kelvin value associated) can be used alone or in combination with any of the previous light sources to exaggerate the effects of optical brighteners, whitening agents, fluorescent pigments, dyes, or resins. DO NOT USE ULTRAVIOLET LIGHT FOR A COLOR MATCH DECISION. DO NOT LOOK DIRECTLY INTO A ULTRAVIOLET LIGHT SOURCE BECAUSE EYE DAMAGE CAN OCCUR FROM PROLONGED EXPOSURE TO UV LIGHT.

4.1.5 INPUT VOLTAGE—Follow manufacturer's installation instructions for proper input voltage requirements.

4.2 Lighting Booths—As a minimal condition, a light booth can be utilized for color evaluation purposes only if agreed upon by the customer and supplier. The booth should be placed so that it is at least 1070 mm (42 in) above floor level and should be set-up so that direct viewing into the booth is possible.

4.3 Light Meter—A calibrated light meter is required for checking the intensity levels of the lighting sources.

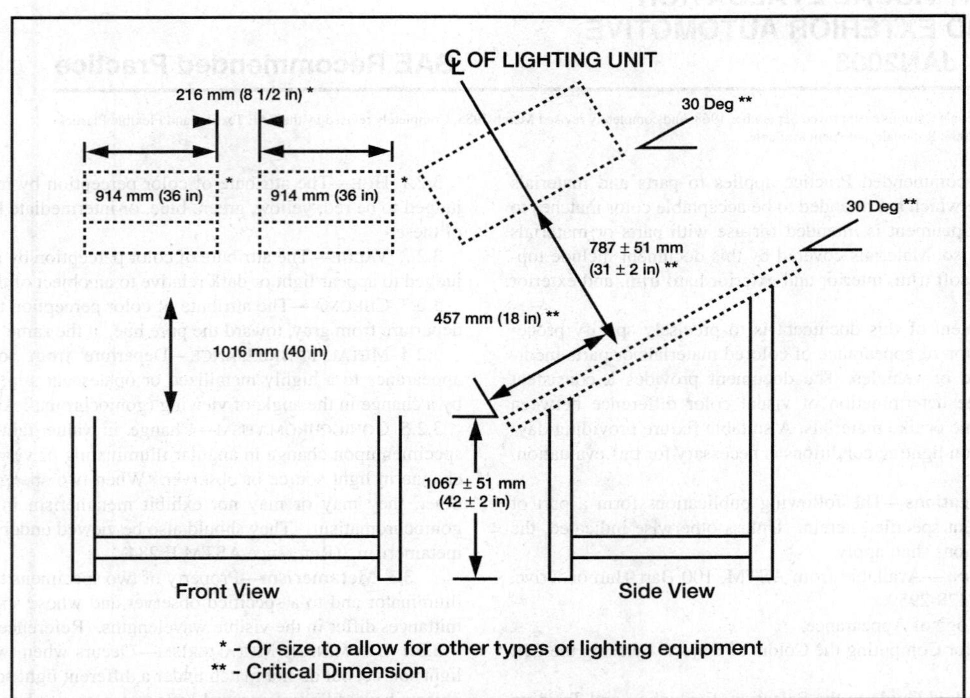

FIGURE 2—RECOMMENDED INSTALLATION FOR LIGHTING UNIT(S)

4.4 Color Temperature Measuring Instrument—A spectro-radiometer or colorimeter must be used to check color temperature of the light sources. These units must be calibrated using a NIST traceable 6500 K source

5. Viewing Environment—To perform accurate visual color matching, the viewing environment must be set up and maintained to be consistent with other locations in the industry. (Refer to Appendix B, Environmental Evaluation Checklist.

5.1 Perch and Surround—Color of Perch and surround shall be neutral gray, defined as Munsell N6-N7 (L*61-71) with a maximum Chroma C*= 1.0, visually appearing neutral.

5.2 Ambient Light—The light units and examination perch shall be placed in an area that WILL NOT ADMIT ambient light into the viewing environment.

5.2.1 ENCLOSED ROOM—An enclosed room is the preferred location for the installation of the light units. The walls shall be painted with Munsell N6-N7 (L*61-71) flat paint. (This paint is available from any major supplier.) Adequate ventilation of the room must be provided to prevent overheating of the lamps.

5.2.2 ENCLOSING CURTAIN—If a room is not available, an enclosing curtain will be suitable. The curtain must be dull in finish and the color must be as close as possible to Munsell N6-N7 (L*61-71). Curtain must also be dense enough to prevent ambient light penetration and must surround the viewing area. A minimum distance of 914 mm (3 ft) must be maintained between the enclosure or curtain and the front of the perch to allow proper viewing from all directions.

5.3 Examination Perch—Gray foam matting, Munsell N6-N7 (L*61-71), napped knit fabric or carpet shall be used on the perch surface. The material shall be suitably textured so that materials and parts will not slide off the perch. As an option, a napped knit fabric, black in Color, Munsell N 0.5-N1.5 (L*5.1-15.4) with a maximum Chroma C* of 1.0, visually appearing neutral, can be used provided that it is located on a separate examination perch/stand or is able to be easily removed from the primary perch/stand.

The optional black perch material helps in eliminating random specular reflections, and is helpful when viewing dark colors or parts at the deep flop angle. Use of this alternate black perch material should be noted with the color comments. Comply with Figure 2 for perch dimensions.

6. Maintenance—Consistency of correlated color temperature, light levels (illuminance) and spectral power distribution among all locations within the lighting unit must be certified by the manufacturer. Proper maintenance of the lighting unit, in accordance with the manufacturer's recommendation, is essential to ensure consistent lighting conditions over time and with respect to other units. A checklist for environmental evaluation is provided in Appendix A.

6.1 Diffuser—The diffuser should be cleaned every 3 months with a glass cleaner.

6.2 Daylight Filters—The Daylight filters should be cleaned and checked for cracks every six months. These filters should be cleaned with a non-streaking glass cleaner and allowed to air dry. (CAUTION: Allow adequate cooling of the daylight filters and lamps before attempting to remove.) If filter replacement is required, replacement filters must be evaluated for spectral power distribution of the transmitted light per 4.1.1.

6.3 Perch—The perch should be cleaned once a month. If any discoloration has occurred, the perch material must be replaced. NOTE: Some materials, such as gray foam material turn yellow over time. When this has occurred, it must be replaced to conform to 5.1.

6.4 Calibration and Certification—Lighting units must be calibrated with NIST traceable certification at least once a year. Prior to and following calibration, the illuminance, correlated color temperature, and CIE Publication 51 ΔE_m* should be recorded for each position. Calibration sticker must be affixed to the front of the unit.

Lamps should be replaced when the unit is out, of specification for color temperature and/or intensity, provided all other factors affecting color temperature or intensity are within tolerance (i.e., units properly calibrated. unit cleanliness, etc.). It is good practice to replace the lamp series (i.e., all daylight bulbs) when one lamp becomes defective.

6.5 Light Level Balance—The light level (illuminance) should be checked monthly. Measurements should be taken directly under each daylight lamp, 635 mm (25 in) below the diffuser. This distance is necessary in order to give a common measurement reference point. Any measurements taken within the viewing area shall not differ from the mean value of the measurements taken by more than 20%. The viewing area is defined as that which falls within ±20% of the illumination level of that average.

6.6 Maintenance Log—All maintenance activities, such as cleaning, calibration, bulb replacement, etc. should be recorded. Control charts, including upper and lower control limits should be maintained for illuminance and correlated color temperature. Follow QS 9000 procedures within your company for establishing a maintenance log.

7. Visual Color Evaluation—Proper viewing conditions and positioning of samples and master standards on the examination perch/stand are essential to maintain a common practice between viewing locations.

7.1 Viewing Conditions—There should be no other materials present on the examination perch/stand when samples of one color are being viewed. Also there should not be any distracting or brightly colored decorations present in the evaluation area. Persons wearing bright or very chromatic clothing should wear a covering such as a smock of neutral gray color to eliminate the influence of extraneous color. Persons viewing color shall not wear tinted contacts or glasses as these affect perceived color. Smoking shall not be allowed in the evaluation area.

In some instances, it is good practice to evaluate materials under natural daylight. There is, however, little control over standard practices due to the natural variability in day-to-day weather conditions, global latitude of the viewing location, time of day during valuation, and the time of the year of the evaluation. As a general rule of thumb, limit outside evaluations to midday hours and view the specimens at waist level.

7.2 Viewing and Positioning—Samples should be placed on the examination perch/stand, centered relative to the light bank. It is important that the samples be parallel in direction and touching one another. When viewed on the perch surface, it is often necessary for the observer to change position and distance relative to the sample so that hue, lightness and chroma may be assessed accurately. All samples should be viewed under daylight, fluorescent and horizon light. Daylight is the most important lighting source to make a color determination with fluorescent and horizon lighting used to evaluate metamerism. Color judgements should be made quickly because sensitivity of the eye to color differences decreases with time of exposure (adaptation). Refer to ASTM E 1499-97 section 8.3.

7.2.1 TEXTILE MATERIALS—The sample and master standard should be viewed looking into the nap (the surface fibers of a fabric) with the samples touching one another. They should be placed so that when rubbing the materials, the nap feels roughest as the hand moves along the fabric to the top of the examination perch/stand. Flat fabrics should be viewed with the machine direction yarns running up and down the examination perch/stand.

7.2.1.1 Flop Matching—The sample and the master standard shall match (with the nap running the same direction for both materials) when rotated in the plane of the examining table, 180 degrees and at 90 degree intermediate points in between.

7.2.2 PAINTED OR GLOSSY SURFACES, PLASTIC, LEATHER OR VINYL MATERIALS—These materials should be considered in two categories: (a) solid or straight shade and (b) metallic and/or opalescent colors. Solid colors should be viewed from two positions commonly referred to as the FACE and FLOP positions as illustrated by Figure 3. For plastic materials, view the samples/parts to the master with the gates facing in the same direction where the flow of the resin is the same or similar. The face position is attained when the observed surface is nearly parallel to the observer, making the surface nearly perpendicular to the line of sight. The flop position is attained by rotating the sample away from the observer and down 90 degrees from the face position. These two viewing positions should be considered critical to all color matching. Metallic and/or opalescent colors should be observed in the same manner. Additional attention should be given to the evaluation of the intermediate angles viewed in a continuous motion. This evaluation is commonly referred to as travel. Figure 3 also illustrates this viewing condition. Color differences between two samples (or a sample and a master standard) may occur at the intermediate angle as a result of varied paint technologies or spray conditions.

7.2.3 When visually comparing a sample to a master, always reverse them left to right and top to bottom to observe any effects on color due to placement of materials relative to one another.

8. Care of Master Standards—All master standards should be protected to ensure their original appearance and should be stored in a cool, dry, dark location. Care should be taken not to crush textile master standards or distort the surface in any way. The packaging material should not chemically attack or scratch the material inside. Specimens containing rubber, asphalt, or other materials that have the potential to stain shall be isolated to themselves, apart from other standards.

9. Color Discrimination—Several tests exist to measure color perception and discrimination. It is recommended that all personnel involved in viewing color pass both a color discrimination/perception test and a color blindness test. Refer to ASTM E 1499-97 for recommended color testing methodology.

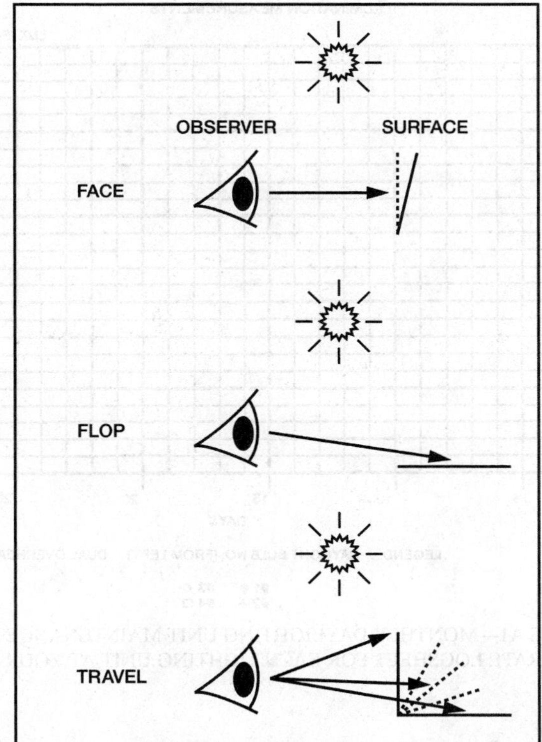

FIGURE 3—FLOP AND TRAVEL EVALUATION

APPENDIX A
MONTHLY DAYLIGHTING UNIT MAINTENANCE LOG

MONTH ______ YEAR ______
COMPANY ______ LOCATION ______
LIGHT MFG. ______ MODEL/TYPE ______ SERIAL NO. ______

MAINTENANCE EVENT RECORD:

DATE ______ ☐ CLEAN ☐ CHECK FILTER ☐ CALIBRATION VOLTS ______
COMMENTS: ☐ REPLACE BULBS ☐ OTHER (EXPLAIN BELOW)

DATE ______ ☐ CLEAN ☐ CHECK FILTER ☐ CALIBRATION VOLTS ______
COMMENTS: ☐ REPLACE BULBS ☐ OTHER (EXPLAIN BELOW)

DATE ______ ☐ CLEAN ☐ CHECK FILTER ☐ CALIBRATION VOLTS ______
COMMENTS: ☐ REPLACE BULBS ☐ OTHER (EXPLAIN BELOW)

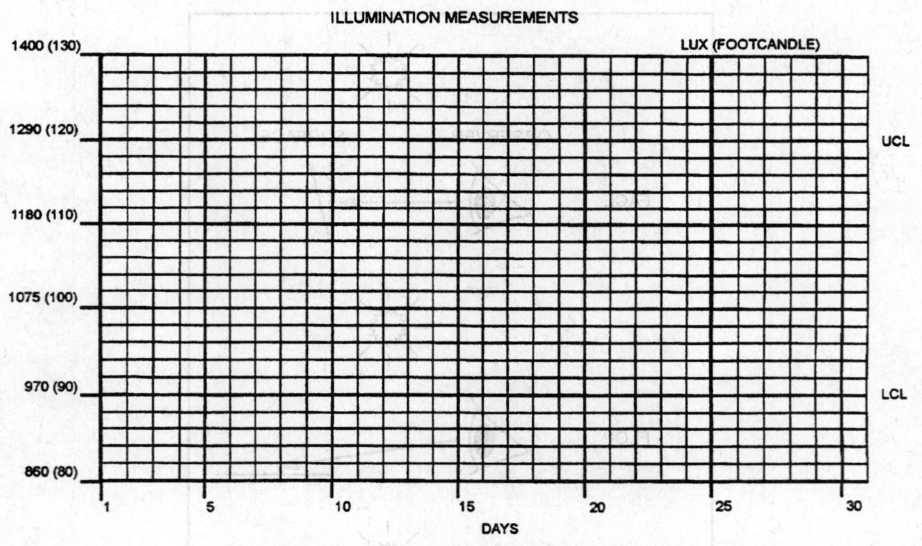

LEGEND: DAYLIGHT BULB NO. (FROM LEFT) DUAL OVERHEAD UNIT

#1 ● #3 ○
#2 + #4 □

FIGURE A1—MONTHLY DAYLIGHTING UNIT MAINTENANCE LOG
(KEEP A SEPARATE LOGSHEET FOR EACH LIGHTING UNIT AT YOUR LOCATION)

MONTH ______________________ YEAR ______________________
COMPANY ______________________ LOCATION ______________________
LIGHT MFG. ______________________ MODEL/TYPE ______________________ SERIAL NO. ______________________

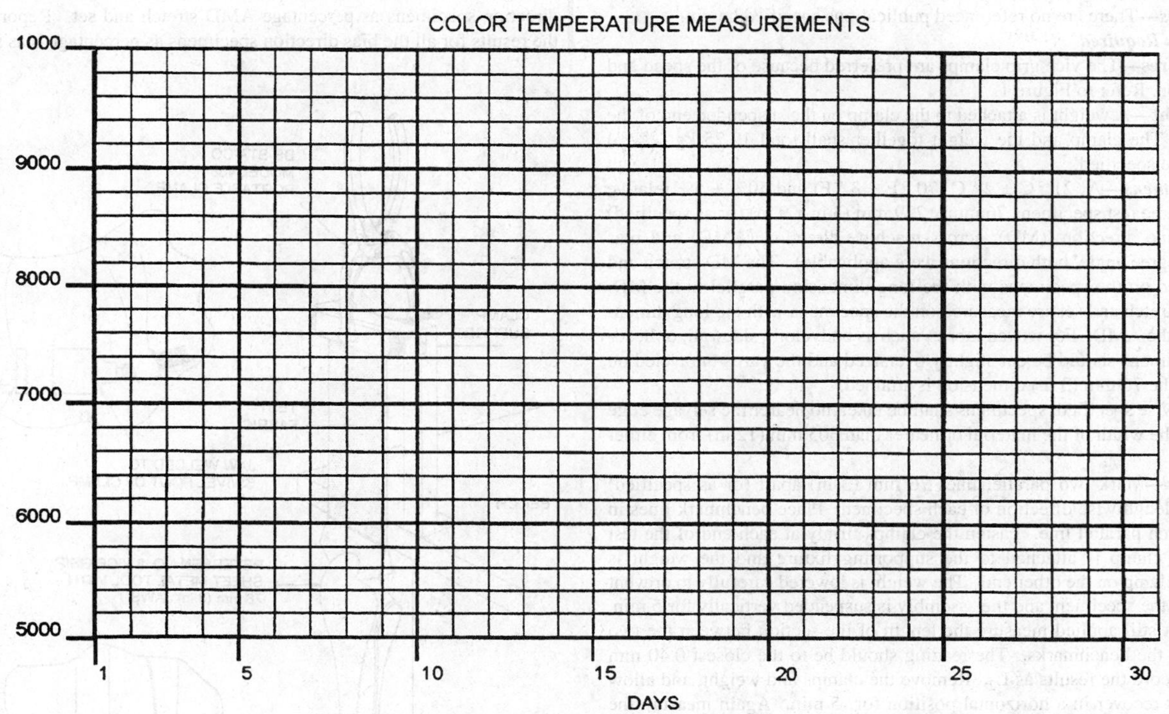

FIGURE A2—MONTHLY DAYLIGHTING UNIT MAINTENANCE LOG (CONTINUED)
(KEEP A SEPARATE LOGSHEET FOR EACH LIGHTING UNIT AT YOUR LOCATION)

APPENDIX B
CHECKLIST FOR ENVIRONMENTAL EVALUATION

1. System Set-up (dimensions)
   a. perch height
   b. perch angle*
   c. perch position under lights
   d. light distance from perch*
   e. distance between light units
   f. perch distance from walls (back, left, right)
   g. light system angle*
2. Perch and walls
   a. surface color*
   b. surface material
   c. perch size
   d. surface cleanliness*
   e. wall color
3. Ambient Light
   a. ability to eliminate ambient light*
   b. curtain in place
4. Inspector
   a. properly trained*
   b. non smoking area
   c. lab coats available
5. Maintenance Program
   a. calibration and certification once per year (minimum)*
   b. maintenance chart (track lamp replacement, cleaning, calibrations, etc.)

* Indicates items considered of primary importance; should carry a higher priority weight.

TEST METHOD OF STRETCH AND SET OF TEXTILES AND PLASTICS—SAE J855 SEP2002

SAE Standard

Report of the SAE Nonmetallic Materials Committee approved June 1963 and revised March 1987. Reaffirmed by the SAE Textile/Flexible Plastics Committee January 1994 and revised September 2002. Rationale statement available.

1. Scope—This method of test applies to the measurement of elastic and recovery properties of materials after being subjected to a low-static load.

2. References—There are no referenced publications specified herein.

3. Apparatus Required

3.1 Fixtures—The vice grip clamps are preferred because of the speed and ease of operation. Refer to Figure 1.

3.2 Weight—A weight is attached to the clamp on the suspended end of the test specimen. The clamp and the weight together shall total 12.25 kg (27 lb) unless otherwise specified.

4. Test Specimens—At 21 °C ± 2 °C (70 °F ± 3 °F) and 50% ± 5% relative humidity, cut three test specimens 76 mm x 229 mm (3 in x 9 in) (or as specified) each the machine direction, (MD), across machine direction (AMD) and bias direction (45 degree angle, both directions were applicable). The MD stretch and set are measured on the specimens with the long dimension parallel to the MD, and the AMD stretch and set are measured on the specimens with the long dimension parallel to the AMD. For woven fabrics such as bodycloth, sidewall, or headlining, the specimens should be cut slightly oversized and the yarns unraveled on each side until the 76 mm (3 in) dimension is attained.

Unless otherwise specified, specimens shall be taken no nearer the selvage edge than one-tenth the width of the material or nearer than 305 mm (12 in) from either end of the roll.

5. Procedure—Mark two parallel lines 76 mm (3 in) apart (or as specified) centered in the lengthwise direction of each specimen. Place benchmark lines in the center of each parallel line. Fasten the clamps firmly at each end of the test specimen. One clamp is attached to the supporting fixture and the weight is attached to the clamp on the other end. The weight is lowered carefully to prevent undue stress on the specimen, and the assembly is suspended vertically for 5 min. With the weight still applied measure the length of the section between the two parallel lines at the benchmarks. The reading should be to the closest 0.40 mm (1/64 in) and record the results as L_2. Remove the clamps and weight, and allow the specimen to recover in a horizontal position for 5 min. Again measure the length of the section between benchmarks and record as L_3.

6. Calculations and Report—Report the data as percent stretch and percent set calculated as follows in Equation 1:

$$\%\ \text{Stretch} = \frac{L_2 - L_1}{L_1} \times 100 \quad \text{(Eq. 1)}$$

$$\%\ \text{Set} = \frac{L_3 - L_1}{L_1} \times 100$$

where measured lengths are taken between parallel lines at benchmarks:

L_1 = Original length between parallel lines at bench marks
L_2 = Measured length after the weight is applied for 5 min
L_3 = Measured length after the 5 min recovery period

Report the average of the results for the three MD direction specimens as percentage MD stretch and set. Report the average of the results for the AMD three direction specimens as percentage AMD stretch and set. Report the average of the results for all the bias direction specimens as percentage bias stretch and set.

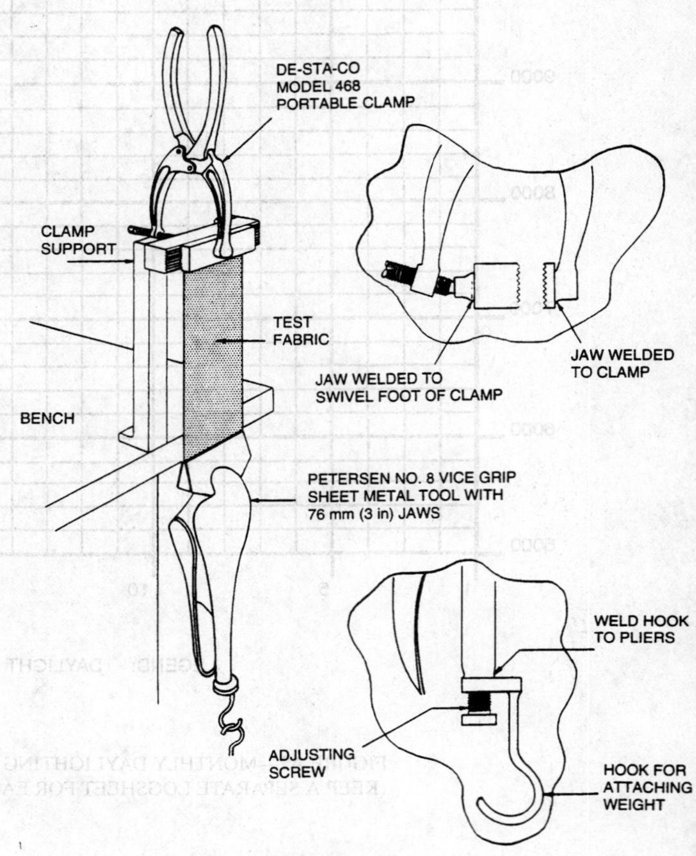

FIGURE 1—CLAMP AND FIXTURE ASSEMBLY FOR STRETCH AND SET OF TEXTILES

FELTS—WOOL AND PART WOOL—SAE J314 JUL2002 SAE Standard

Report of the SAE Parts and Fittings Division approved July 1923. Revised by the SAE Nonmetallic Materials Committee January 1976 and reaffirmed without change May 1981. Reaffirmed by the SAE Textiles and Flexible Plastics Committee May 1994 and revised July 2002. Rationale statement available.

1. Scope—This SAE Standard identifies chemical/mechanical properties, thickness, width, mass, and other requirements recommended for felts (refer to Tables 1 and 2). It was developed with the cooperation of the Standardization Committee of the Felt Association, Inc., and in accordance with the ASTM tests indicated in the document.

The commercial trade designations of the more commonly used grades of automotive felts are given along with complete specifications and tolerances for thickness, mass, wool content, chemical and physical requirements, color, and width.

General information, recommended uses, etc., are published in Appendix A as a guide in the selection of felts for particular uses, but the requirements for each application should be taken into consideration in making final selections.

2. References

2.1 Applicable Publications—The following publications form a part of this specification to the extent specified herein.

2.1.1 ASTM PUBLICATIONS—Available from ASTM, 100 Barr Harbor Drive, West Conshohocken, PA 19428-2959.

ASTM D 276—Identification of Fibers in Textiles

ASTM D 461—Standard Methods of Testing Wool Felt

2.1.2 OTHER PUBLICATIONS

Wool Products Labeling Act, 1939

3. Chemical and Mechanical Properties

3.1 The chemical and mechanical requirements for the several grades of automotive felts given in Table 1 include actual wool content (chemical basis), methyl chloroform soluble (percentage of residual oil and grease), water soluble (sizing and nonfibrous impurities), ash (the amount of residual inorganic matter), tensile strength, and splitting resistance.

3.2 All tests shall be made in accordance with ASTM D 461. If it is desired to detect the presence of, and identify, fibers other than wool, such as other animal fibers, vegetable, and synthetic fibers, the felt shall be tested as described in ASTM D 276.

4. Thickness, Width, and Mass

4.1 Thickness and mass requirements are given in Table 2.

4.2 Felt shall be furnished in standard width as shown in Table 1, unless otherwise specified.

4.3 The thickness tolerances given in Table 2 vary, depending on the density, thickness, and grade or quality of the felt, and are expressed as the permissible minimum and maximum thickness for each grade and thickness rather than as a percentage variation from the nominal thickness.

4.4 Any density or mass determinations shall be based on the thickness of the felt as ordered and no correction shall be made for variations in the thickness of the felt as received. For example, SAE F-1, back-check felt, in 12.7 mm (1/2 in) thickness may, according to Table 2, vary in mass from 4.12 to 4.55 kg/m^2 (7.60 to 8.40 lb/yd^2), while the thickness may, according to Table 1, vary from 12.22 to 13.18 mm (0.481 to 0.519 in). The combination of mass and thickness tolerances control the degree of felting or matting of the fibers, in other words, the hardness or the density, and conversely, the resiliency of the finished felt. Therefore, to maintain the normal density for each grade or type of felt, no correction in mass is permitted to compensate for a variation from the nominal thickness as specified.

NOTE—The mass or density requirements for the several grades of automotive felts given in Table 2 are expressed as the mass in kilograms per square meter (pounds per square yard) for each commercial thickness. This is the established standard unit of mass employed in the felt industry. Density may also be expressed as the mass in grams per cubic centimeter (ounces per cubic inch), specific gravity as compared with water, percentage specific gravity (specific gravity x 100), or as surface density in kilograms per square meter (pounds per square yard) of nominal 25.4 mm (1 in) thickness. The mass or density of cut parts may be expressed as the mass per one hundred (100) parts based on the nominal mass of the felt in the thickness specified.

5. Other Requirements

5.1 Color requirements are given in Table 1.

5.2 Special sizing, adhesives, and impregnating materials used to impart specific properties may alter the chemical and physical requirements specified in Table 1. The specific properties and methods of test for special products shall be agreed upon by supplier and purchaser.

5.3 When specified by the purchaser for ball and roller bearing oil retaining washers, felt shall be sheared on both sides to give a smooth surface free from "surface fuzz" or "flock."

5.4 The quality, appearance, and oil absorption characteristics may be specified by the purchaser to be in accord with approved samples.

TABLE 1—STANDARD MECHANICAL ROLL FELT SPECIFICATIONS

SAE No.	Min Actual Wool Content,(1) %	Max Methyl Chloroform Soluble, %	Max Water Soluble, %	Max Combined Methyl Chloroform and Water, %	Max Ash, %	Min Tensile Strength kPa	Min Tensile Strength psi	Min Splitting Resistance(2) N 5 cm width	Min Splitting Resistance(2) lb 2 in width	Trade Designation	Color	Standard Width cm	Standard Width in
F-1	95	2.5	2.5	3.0	1.5	3450	500	142	32	Back check	White	152	60
F-2	90	2.5	2.5	4.0	2.0	3450	500	125	28	Back check	Any color except gray or black	152	60
F-3	85	2.5	3.0	4.5	2.5	2760	400	98	22	Back check	Gray	152	60
F-5	95	2.5	2.5	3.0	2.0	2760	400	80	18	Extra firm pad	White	152	60
F-6	87	2.5	2.5	4.5	2.5	1900	275	71	16	Extra firm pad	Gray	152 or 183	60 or 72
F-7	80	3.0	4.0	7.0	3.0	1730	250	53	12	Extra firm pad	Gray	183	72
F-10	95	2.5	2.5	3.0	2.5	1550	225	36	8	Firm pad	White	183	72
F-11	87	3.0	2.5	4.5	3.0	1380	200	27	6	Firm pad	Gray	183	72
F-12	85	4.0	2.5	6.5	3.5	690	100	13	3	Firm pad	Gray	183	72
F-13	75	4.0	4.0	8.0	3.5	518	75	9	2	Firm pad	Gray	183	72
F-15	55	4.0	5.0	9.0	4.0	518	75	9	2	Firm pad	Gray	183	72
F-26	45	8.0	6.0	14.0	5.0	—	—	—	—	Soft pad	Gray	183	72
F-50	95	2.5	2.5	3.0	1.5	3450	500	—	—	Ball bearing felt	White	152 or 183	60 or 72
F-51	92	2.5	2.5	4.5	2.5	2070	300	—	—	Ball bearing felt	Gray	152 or 183	60 or 72
F-55	75	4.0	4.0	8.0	3.0	1380	200	—	—	Lining	Gray or black	152 or 183	60 or 72

1. The actual wool content indicates the percent of wool by chemical analysis and is exclusive of traces of other fibers and impurities present in the wool used in fabricating the several grades of felt. For example, SAE F-1, fabricated from 100% wool, may contain incidental traces of cotton and other fibers, residual wool fats, and oils or soaps used in processing which may reduce the actual wool fiber content on analysis to a minimum of 95%.
2. Splitting resistance is not applicable to felts where the thickness is less than 4.75 mm (3/16 in). For materials less than 4.75 mm (3/16 in) in thickness, breaking strength only is recommended as an indicative test.

TABLE 2—STANDARD MECHANICAL ROLL FELT SPECIFICATIONS

SAE No.	Thickness, mm Nominal	Thickness, mm Limits	Thickness, in Nominal	Thickness, in Limits	Mass, kg/m^2 Nominal	Mass, kg/m^2 Limits	Mass (Weight) lb/yd^2 Nominal	Mass (Weight) lb/yd^2 Limits
F-1[(1)]	3.2	2.87–3.48	1/8	0.113–0.137	1.08	1.03–1.14	2.0	1.90–2.10
	4.8	4.45–5.11	3/16	0.175–0.201	1.63	1.54–1.71	3.0	2.85–3.15
	6.4	5.99–6.71	1/4	0.236–0.264	2.17	2.06–2.28	4.0	3.80–4.20
	8.0	7.57–8.33	5/16	0.298–0.328	2.71	2.57–2.85	5.0	4.75–5.25
	9.5	9.12–9.93	3/8	0.359–0.391	3.25	3.09–3.41	6.0	5.70–6.30
	12.7	12.22–13.18	1/2	0.481–0.519	4.34	4.12–4.55	8.0	7.60–8.40
	15.9	15.32–16.43	5/8	0.603–0.647	5.42	5.15–5.69	10.0	9.50–10.50
	19.1	18.42–19.69	3/4	0.725–0.775	6.50	6.18–6.83	12.0	11.40–12.60
	22.2	21.51–22.94	7/8	0.847–0.903	7.59	7.21–7.97	14.0	13.30–14.70
	25.4	24.61–26.19	1	0.969–1.031	8.67	8.24–9.11	16.0	15.20–16.80
F-2	3.2	2.87–3.48	1/8	0.113–0.137	1.08	1.03–1.14	2.0	1.90–2.10
	4.8	4.45–5.11	3/16	0.175–0.201	1.63	1.54–1.71	3.0	2.85–3.15
	6.4	5.99–6.71	1/4	0.236–0.264	2.17	2.06–2.28	4.0	3.80–4.20
	8.0	7.57–8.33	5/16	0.298–0.328	2.71	2.57–2.85	5.0	4.75–5.25
	9.5	9.12–9.93	3/8	0.359–0.391	3.25	3.09–3.41	6.0	5.70–6.30
	12.7	12.22–13.18	1/2	0.481–0.519	4.34	4.12–4.55	8.0	7.60–8.40
	15.9	15.32–16.43	5/8	0.603–0.647	5.42	5.15–5.69	10.0	9.50–10.50
	19.1	18.42–19.69	3/4	0.725–0.775	6.50	6.18–6.83	12.0	11.40–12.60
	22.2	21.51–22.94	7/8	0.847–0.903	7.59	7.21–7.97	14.0	13.30–14.70
	25.4	24.61–26.19	1	0.969–1.031	8.67	8.24–9.11	16.0	15.20–16.80
F-3[(1)]	3.2	2.87–3.48	1/8	0.113–0.137	1.07	0.98–1.14	1.97	1.80–2.10
	4.8	4.45–5.11	3/16	0.175–0.201	1.59	1.47–1.71	2.93	2.71–3.15
	6.4	5.99–6.71	1/4	0.236–0.264	2.11	1.96–2.27	3.90	3.61–4.19
	8.0	7.57–8.33	5/16	0.298–0.328	2.64	2.44–2.84	4.87	4.50–5.24
	9.5	9.12–9.93	3/8	0.359–0.391	3.17	2.93–3.41	5.85	5.41–6.29
	12.7	12.22–13.18	1/2	0.481–0.519	4.23	3.91–4.55	7.80	7.21–8.39
	15.9	15.32–16.43	5/8	0.603–0.647	5.28	4.88–5.69	9.75	9.01–10.49
	19.1	18.42–19.69	3/4	0.725–0.775	6.34	5.86–6.82	11.70	10.81–12.59
	22.2	21.51–22.94	7/8	0.847–0.903	7.40	6.83–7.96	13.65	12.61–14.69
	25.4	24.61–26.19	1	0.969–1.031	8.46	7.81–9.10	15.60	14.41–16.79
F-5	3.2	2.82–3.53	1/8	0.111–0.139	0.83	0.79–0.87	1.53	1.45–1.61
	4.8	4.37–5.18	3/16	0.172–0.204	1.24	1.18–1.31	2.29	2.17–2.41
	6.4	5.89–6.81	1/4	0.232–0.268	1.66	1.57–1.75	3.06	2.90–3.22
	8.0	7.44–8.46	5/16	0.293–0.333	2.07	1.96–2.18	3.82	3.62–4.02
	9.5	8.97–10.08	3/8	0.353–0.397	2.49	2.36–2.62	4.59	4.35–4.83
	12.7	12.04–13.36	1/2	0.474–0.526	3.32	3.14–3.49	6.12	5.80–6.44
	15.9	15.11–16.64	5/8	0.595–0.655	4.15	3.93–4.36	7.65	7.25–8.05
	19.1	18.19–19.91	3/4	0.716–0.784	4.98	4.72–5.24	9.18	8.70–9.66
	22.2	21.26–23.19	7/8	0.837–0.913	5.80	5.50–6.11	10.71	10.15–11.27
	25.4	24.33–26.47	1	0.958–1.042	6.63	6.29–6.98	12.24	11.60–12.88
F-6	3.2	2.82–3.53	1/8	0.111–0.139	0.83	0.79–0.87	1.53	1.45–1.61
	4.8	4.37–5.18	3/16	0.172–0.204	1.24	1.18–1.31	2.29	2.17–2.41
	6.4	5.89–6.81	1.4	0.232–0.268	1.66	1.57–1.75	3.06	2.90–3.22
	8.0	7.44–8.46	5/16	0.293–0.333	2.07	1.96–2.18	3.82	3.62–4.02
	9.5	8.97–10.08	3/8	0.353–0.397	2.49	2.36–2.62	4.59	4.35–4.83
	12.7	12.04–13.36	1/2	0.474–0.526	3.32	3.14–3.49	6.12	5.80–644
	15.9	15.11–16.64	5/8	0.595–0.655	4.15	3.93–4.36	7.65	7.25–8.05
	19.1	18.19–19.91	3/4	0.716–0.784	4.98	4.72–5.24	9.18	8.70–9.66
	22.2	21.26–23.19	7/8	0.837–0.913	5.80	5.50–6.11	10.71	10.15–11.27
	25.4	24.33–26.47	1	0.958–1.042	6.63	6.29–6.98	12.24	11.60–12.88
F-7[(1)]	3.2	2.82–3.53	1/8	0.111–0.139	0.83	0.79–0.87	1.53	1.45–1.61
	4.8	4.37–5.18	3/16	0.172–0.204	1.24	1.18–1.31	2.29	2.17–2.41
	6.4	5.89–6.81	1/4	0.232–0.268	1.66	1.57–1.75	3.06	2.90–3.22
	8.0	7.44–8.46	5/16	0.293–0.333	2.07	1.96–2.18	3.82	3.62–4.02
	9.5	8.97–10.08	3/8	0.353–0.397	2.49	2.36–2.62	4.59	4.35–4.83
	12.7	12.04–13.36	1/2	0.474–0.526	3.32	3.14–3.49	6.12	5.80–6.44
	15.9	15.11–16.64	5/8	0.595–0.655	4.15	3.93–4.36	7.65	7.25–8.05
	19.1	18.19–19.91	3/4	0.716–0.784	4.98	4.72–5.24	9.18	8.70–9.66
	22.2	21.26–23.19	7/8	0.837–0.913	5.80	5.50–6.11	10.71	10.15–11.27
	25.4	24.33–26.47	1	0.958–1.042	6.63	6.29–6.98	12.24	11.60–12.88

TABLE 2—STANDARD MECHANICAL ROLL FELT SPECIFICATIONS (continued)

SAE No.	Thickness, mm Nominal	Thickness, mm Limits	Thickness, in Nominal	Thickness, in Limits	Mass, kg/m^2 Nominal	Mass, kg/m^2 Limits	Mass (Weight) lb/yd^2 Nominal	Mass (Weight) lb/yd^2 Limits
F-10	3.2	2.67–3.68	1/8	0.105–0.145	0.57	0.53–0.62	1.06	0.96–1.14
	4.8	4.19–5.36	3/16	0.165–0.211	0.86	0.80–0.93	1.59	1.47–1.71
	6.4	5.69–7.01	1/4	0.224–0.276	1.15	1.06–1.24	2.12	1.96–2.28
	8.0	7.21–8.69	5/16	0.284–0.342	1.44	1.33–1.54	2.65	2.45–2.85
	9.5	8.71–10.34	3/8	0.343–0.407	1.72	1.59–1.85	3.18	2.94–3.42
	12.7	11.73–13.67	1/2	0.462–0.538	2.30	2.12–2.47	4.24	3.92–4.56
	15.9	14.76–16.99	5/8	0.581–0.669	2.87	2.66–3.09	5.30	4.90–5.70
	19.1	17.78–20.32	3/4	0.700–0.800	3.45	3.19–3.71	6.36	5.88–6.84
	22.2	20.80–23.65	7/8	0.819–0.931	4.02	3.72–4.33	7.42	6.86–7.98
	25.4	23.83–26.97	1	0.938–1.062	4.60	4.25–4.94	8.48	7.84–9.12
F-11	3.2	2.67–3.68	1/8	0.105–0.145	0.57	0.53–0.62	1.06	0.98–1.14
	4.8	4.19–5.36	3/16	0.165–0.211	0.86	0.80–0.93	1.59	1.47–1.71
	6.4	5.69–7.01	1/4	0.224–0.276	1.15	1.06–1.24	2.12	1.96–2.28
	8.0	7.21–8.69	5/16	0.284–0.342	1.44	1.33–1.54	2.65	2.45–2.85
	9.5	8.71–10.34	3/8	0.343–0.407	1.72	1.59–1.85	3.18	2.94–3.42
	12.7	11.73–13.67	1/2	0.462–0.538	2.30	2.12–2.47	4.24	3.92–4.56
	15.9	14.76–16.99	5/8	0.581–0.669	2.87	2.66–3.09	5.30	4.90–5.70
	19.1	17.78–20.32	3/4	0.700–0.800	3.45	3.19–3.71	6.36	5.88–6.84
	22.2	20.80–23.65	7/8	0.819–0.931	4.02	3.72–4.33	7.42	6.86–7.98
	25.4	23.83–26.97	1	0.938–1.062	4.60	4.25–4.94	8.48	7.84–9.12
F-12	3.2	2.67–3.68	1/8	0.105–0.145	0.57	0.53–0.62	1.06	0.98–1.14
	4.8	4.19–5.36	3/16	0.165–0.211	0.86	0.80–0.93	1.59	1.47–1.71
	6.4	5.69–7.01	1/4	0.224–0.276	1.15	1.06–1.24	2.12	1.96–2.28
	8.0	7.21–8.69	5/16	0.284–0.342	1.44	1.33–1.54	2.65	2.45–2.85
	9.5	8.71–10.34	3/8	0.343–0.407	1.72	1.59–1.85	3.18	2.94–3.42
	12.7	11.73–13.67	1/2	0.462–0.538	2.30	2.12–2.47	4.24	3.92–4.56
	15.9	14.76–16.99	5/8	0.581–0.669	2.87	2.66–3.09	5.30	4.90–5.70
	19.1	17.78–20.32	3/4	0.700–0.800	3.45	3.19–3.71	6.36	5.88–6.84
	22.2	20.80–23.65	7/8	0.819–0.931	4.02	3.72–4.33	7.42	6.86–7.98
	25.4	23.83–26.97	1	0.938–1.062	4.60	4.25–4.94	8.48	7.84–9.12
F-13	3.2	2.67–3.68	1/8	0.105–0.145	0.57	0.53–0.62	1.06	0.98–1.14
	4.8	4.19–5.36	3/16	0.165–0.211	0.86	0.80–0.93	1.59	1.47–1.71
	6.4	5.69–7.01	1/4	0.224–0.276	1.15	1.06–1.24	2.12	1.96–2.28
	8.0	7.21–8.69	5/16	0.284–0.342	1.44	1.33–1.54	2.65	2.45–2.85
	9.5	8.71–10.34	3/8	0.343–0.407	1.72	1.59–1.85	3.18	2.94–3.42
	12.7	11.73–13.67	1/2	0.462–0.538	2.30	2.12–2.47	4.24	3.92–4.56
	15.9	14.76–16.99	5/8	0.581–0.669	2.87	2.66–3.09	5.30	4.90–5.70
	19.1	17.78–20.32	3/4	0.700–0.800	3.45	3.19–3.71	6.36	5.88–6.84
	22.2	20.80–23.65	7/8	0.819–0.931	4.02	3.72–4.33	7.42	6.86–7.98
	25.4	23.83–26.97	1	0.938–1.062	4.06	4.25–4.94	8.48	7.84–9.12
F-15	3.2	2.67–3.68	1/8	0.105–0.145	0.57	0.53–0.62	1.06	0.98–1.14
	4.8	4.19–5.36	3/16	0.165–0.211	0.86	0.80–0.93	1.59	1.47–1.71
	6.4	5.69–7.01	1/4	0.224–0.276	1.15	1.06–1.24	2.12	1.96–2.28
	8.0	7.21–8.69	5/16	0.284–0.342	1.44	1.33–1.54	2.65	2.45–2.85
	9.5	8.71–10.34	3/8	0.343–0.407	1.72	1.59–1.85	3.18	2.94–3.42
	12.7	11.73–13.67	1/2	0.462–0.538	2.30	2.12–2.47	4.24	3.92–4.56
	15.9	14.76–16.99	5/8	0.581–0.669	2.87	2.66–3.09	5.30	4.90–5.70
	19.1	17.78–20.32	3/4	0.700–0.800	3.45	3.19–3.71	6.36	5.88–6.84
	22.2	20.80–23.65	7/8	0.819–0.931	4.02	3.72–4.33	7.42	6.86–7.98
	25.4	23.83–26.97	1	0.938–1.062	4.60	4.25–4.94	8.48	7.84–9.12
F-26	3.2	2.16–4.19	1/8	0.085–0.165	0.49	0.44–0.54	0.90	0.81–0.99
	6.4	4.93–7.77	1/4	0.194–0.306	0.98	0.88–1.07	1.80	1.62–1.98
	9.5	7.70–11.35	3/8	0.303–0.447	1.46	1.32–1.61	2.70	2.43–2.97
	12.7	10.46–14.94	1/2	0.412–0.588	1.95	1.76–2.15	3.60	3.24–3.96
	19.1	16.00–22.10	3/4	0.630–0.870	2.93	2.63–3.22	5.40	4.86–5.94
	25.4	21.54–29.26	1	0.848–1.152	3.90	3.71–4.29	7.20	6.84–7.92
F-50	1.2	1.02–1.37	3/64	0.040–0.054	0.41	0.39–0.43	0.750	0.712–0.788
	1.6	1.42–1.78	1/16	0.056–0.070	0.53	0.51–0.55	0.975	0.937–1.013
	2.0	1.80–2.16	5/64	0.071–0.085	0.65	0.63–0.67	1.200	1.162–1.238
	2.4	2.21–2.57	3/32	0.087–0.101	0.77	0.75–0.79	1.425	1.387–1.463

TABLE 2—STANDARD MECHANICAL ROLL FELT SPECIFICATIONS (continued)

SAE No.	Thickness, mm Nominal	Thickness, mm Limits	Thickness, in Nominal	Thickness, in Limits	Mass, kg/m² Nominal	Mass, kg/m² Limits	Mass (Weight) lb/yd² Nominal	Mass (Weight) lb/yd² Limits
F-51	1.2	1.02–1.37	3/64	0.040–0.054	0.41	0.39–0.43	0.750	0.712–0.788
	1.6	1.42–1.78	1/16	0.056–0.070	0.53	0.51–0.55	0.975	0.937–1.013
	2.0	1.80–2.16	5/64	0.071–0.085	0.65	0.63–0.67	1.200	1.162–1.238
	2.4	2.21–2.57	3/32	0.087–0.101	0.77	0.75–0.79	1.425	1.387–1.463
F-55	1.6	1.42–1.78	1/16	0.056–0.070	0.41	0.39–0.43	0.750	0.712–0.788
	2.4	2.21–2.57	3/32	0.087–0.101	0.61	0.59–0.63	1.125	1.087–1.163

1. For thicknesses less than 3.2 mm (1/8 in) for SAE F-1, see SAE F-50; F-3, see SAE F-51; and F-7, see SAE F-55.

APPENDIX A
(FOR GUIDANCE ONLY; NOT A PART OF THE SPECIFICATION)

A.1 General

A.1.1 Felt is a fabric built up by the interlocking of fibers by a suitable combination of mechanical work, chemical action, moisture, and heat, without stitching, weaving, or knitting. Felt may consist of one or more classes of fibers, wool, reprocessed wool, and reused wool, with or without admixture with animal, vegetable, and synthetic fibers.

A.1.2 Felt, as defined here, is commonly referred to as wool felt and does not include needle loomed, woven, synthetically bonded, stitched, quilted, paper, or other materials of felt-like appearance which are products of entirely different constructions and properties.

A.1.3 Clip wools or noils, which are the short fiber combings resulting from the preparation of wool for spinning, as well as reprocessed and reused wools are used in the manufacture of automotive felts. The best grades of wool are white and are used without admixture with other fibers in the highest grade felts.

A.1.4 Varying amounts of cotton, rayon, and other fibers may be used as a filler to reduce the cost of the felt or to impart certain desired characteristics to the finished material. Traces of cotton are found in most commercial "all-wool" felts.

A.1.5 Raw wool contains "wool fat" and "wool perspiration" in addition to mechanically adhering impurities and foreign matter. The foreign matter and some of the wool fat is removed in the scouring operation. Oils and soaps are added in the fabricating process to obtain the necessary degree of felting. Sizing or filler may be used in some of the lower grade felts and in special applications to stiffen or strengthen the finished material. Adhesives and impregnating materials may be used in special-purpose felts to impart specific properties.

A.1.6 Methyl chloroform soluble, water soluble, and ash determinations indicate the cleanliness of the fiber and the amount of fats, oils, and sizing materials present in the finished product.

***A.2 Terminology*—**The terms wool, reprocessed wool, and reused wool are defined essentially in accordance with the Wool Products Labeling Act, 1939, as follows:

A.2.1 Wool—The term "wool" means the fiber from the fleece of the sheep or lamb, or hair of the angora or cashmere goat (and may include the so-called specialty fibers from the hair of the camel, alpaca, llama, and vicuna) which has never been reclaimed from any woven or felted wool product.

A.2.2 Reprocessed Wool—The term "reprocessed wool" means the resulting fiber when wool has been woven or felted into a wool product which, without ever having been utilized in any way by the ultimate consumer, subsequently has been made into a fibrous state.

A.2.3 Reused Wool—The term "reused wool" means the resulting fiber when wool or reprocessed wool has been spun, woven, knitted, or felted into a wool product which, after having been used in any way by the ultimate consumer, subsequently has been made into a fibrous state.

A.3 Recommended Uses

A.3.1 SAE F-1 is suitable for oil retention in installations where the felt is not compressed, for feeding low viscosity or light oil, and where unusual strength and hardness are required. Washers, bushings, wicks, door bumpers, polishing blocks, and parts where wear and resistance to abrasion are required, are typical uses.

A.3.2 SAE F-2 and F-3 are recommended for vibration mountings and the same general purposes as SAE F-1 and where a felt of slightly lower quality is satisfactory. SAE F-5, F-6, and F-7 are recommended for dust shields, wipers, grease retainer washers, wicks, vibration mountings, and in uses where a resilient felt is required.

A.3.3 SAE F-10, F-11, and F-12 are recommended for grease and oil retention where the felt is confined and compressed in assembly. Also recommended for dust shields under less severe operating conditions where F-5, F-6, and F-7 are not required.

A.3.4 SAE F-13 and F-15 are recommended for sound deadening, chassis strips, spacers, dust shields, pedal pads, dash liners, and for mechanical purposes where abrasion and wear are not important factors.

A.3.5 SAE F-26 is suitable for packing or padding when held in place between other materials as in shipping and packaging. This grade should not be used for mechanical purposes.

A.3.6 SAE F-1 to F-26 inclusive can be obtained in thicknesses up to 1 in. The weight and thickness tolerance shall be agreed upon by supplier and purchaser.

A.3.7 SAE F-50 is recommended for ball and roller bearing oil retainer washers and small dust excluding washers; also for mechanical purposes where an accurate, thin, smooth, high grade felt is required.

A.3.8 SAE F-51 is recommended for the same general uses as F-50 but in installations where tolerances and length of life are not as important; also for thin cut parts such as gaskets and liners.

A.3.9 SAE F-55 is recommended for anti-squeak strips and for lining when cemented to fiberboard or metal panels.

AUTOMOTIVE RUBBER MATS—SAE J80 MAY1997 SAE Recommended Practice

Report of the SAE Nonmetallic Materials Committee approved May 1982. Revised by the SAE Committee on Automotive Rubber Specifications January 1988, and completely revised May 1997. Rationale statement available.

Foreword—This document has been changed to comply with the new SAE Technical Standards Board format. This includes, adding the Reference Section as Section 2. All other section numbers have changed. Also 4.3 and 4.7 (previously 3.3 and 3.7) changed.

1. Scope—This SAE Recommended Practice covers the requirements for rubber floor mats made from five types of rubber compounds as required by the physical property requirements of the application.

2. References

2.1 Applicable Publications—The following publications form a part of the specification to the extent specified herein. Unless otherwise indicated the latest revision of SAE publications shall apply.

2.1.1 SAE PUBLICATION—Available from SAE, 400 Commonwealth Drive, Warrendale, PA 15096-0001.

SAE J369—Flammability of Automotive Interior Materials—Horizontal Test

2.1.2 A.A.T.C.C. PUBLICATION—Available from the American Association of Textile Chemist and Colorists

American Association of Textile Chemist and Colorist Test Method 16A

2.1.3 ASTM PUBLICATIONS—Available from ASTM, 100 Barr Harbor Drive, West Conshohocken, PA 19428-2959

ASTM D 412—Test Methods for Rubber Properties in Tension

ASTM D 573—Test Method for Rubber—Deterioration in an Air Oven

ASTM D 624—Test Method for Rubber Property—Tear Resistance

ASTM D1148—Test Method for Rubber Deterioration—Heat and Ultraviolet Light Discoloration of Light-Colored Surfaces

ASTM D2240—Test Method for Rubber Property—Durometer Hardness

3. General Requirements—The following requirements are minimal product standards:

3.1 Sampling—A representative mat shall be selected from each lot to be tested.

3.2 Workmanship and Finish—The workmanship and finish shall be such as to provide a mat with a clean surface, clearly trimmed edges, holes free from slugs, and otherwise neat appearance.

3.3 Color—The color shall be black unless otherwise specified by purchaser.

3.4 Packing, Marking, and Shipping—Details regarding packing, marking, and shipping are subject to individual arrangements between purchaser and supplier.

3.5 Retests and Rejections—Any lot of mats which fails in one or more tests shall be resampled and retested for which purpose two additional mats shall be selected from the lot that failed to meet the requirements. Failure of either of the retested samples to meet any of the specification requirements shall be cause for final rejection.

4. Physical Test Requirements

4.1 Preaging—Sections of automotive mats or mat samples which have been allowed to rest at least 16 h after cure, are to be conditioned 6 h at 70 °C in an air oven by suspending specimens vertically without touching each other or the sides of the aging chamber. Heated air shall be thoroughly circulated in the oven by means of mechanical agitation. (Conditioning to be in accordance with ASTM D 573.) At the termination of the conditioning interval, the sections shall be removed from the oven, placed on a flat surface and allowed to rest 16 h minimum at room temperature before determining physical properties.

4.2 Durometer Hardness—Hardness is to be measured with an instrument according to ASTM D 2240.

4.3 Tensile Strength and Elongation—Tensile strength and elongation shall be determined in accordance with ASTM D 412, Die A, except that the average calculation shall be made on not less than three dumbell specimens with the grain and three across the grain, rather than the method specified in ASTM D 412.

4.4 Tear Resistance—Test shall be made in accordance with ASTM D 624, Die C, except that the tear samples shall be based on the minimum thickness rather than the average of the section involved.

4.5 Bend Test—The bend test shall be performed on conditioned test specimens. The test specimen shall not crack when bent around a 1.60 mm (1/16 in) rod at 24 °C ± 3 °C (70 °F ± 5 °F).

4.6 Low Temperature Flexibility Test—A 25 x 300 mm sample strip cut from a mat shall be conditioned for 16 h in a cold box at –29 °C. Immediately following the conditioning period, the sample shall be flexed, while still in the –29 °C cold box around a 125 mm diameter mandrel, and shall not show any cracks or checks in the mat or coating material.

4.7 Tensile Set Test—The tensile set test shall be determined in accordance with ASTM D 412. Elongate the test specimen 100%, hold under strain for 10 min, release quickly without snap back, and allow to rest for 10 minutes. At the end of the 10 min rest period, measure the length and calculate the percent permanent tensile set.

5. Test Requirements—Test requirements are shown in Table 1.

6. Additional Requirements and Recommended Practices

6.1 Water Spotting—Apply five drops of distilled water to the mat surface and allow to stand at room temperature for 24 h before being examined. There shall be no effect on the surface of the mat.

6.2 Staining (ASTM D 1148)—Samples shall not show objectionable staining or bleaching after 4 h exposure under S-1 or R-S sunlamp.

6.3 Cleanability—Mats must withstand cleaning with detergent and water without showing color transfer to the cloth. A 1% solution of detergent (Tide or equivalent) is used at room temperature with mild rubbing.

6.4 Odor—A mild, non-offensive odor is permitted.

6.5 Flammability (SAE J369)—The material shall not burn or transmit a flame front across its surface at a rate of more than 101.6 mm (4 in) per min when tested in accordance with SAE J369.

6.6 Surface—The mat surface shall be clean and free of constituents which may cause slippery surfaces.

6.7 Coating Adhesion—Coatings, where required, must be 0.05 mm minimum thick, adherent, and flexible. Flexing or twisting, either as received or after aging, must not cause any loss of adhesion or cracking of film.

6.8 Taber Wear Test—Under a 500 g load, solid color coated samples shall receive 200 cycles on the Taber Wear Tester using a CS17 abrasive wheel. There shall be no more than 20 points of failure within the Taber wear pattern. A failure is considered any point of distinct loss of top coat, clearly exposing the substrate material, having a diameter greater than 2 mm. These 20 points of failure can be individual points, each one being greater than 2 mm in diameter, or multiples of smaller points, each one being less than 2 mm in diameter. However, the total area of failure within any 6.4 mm square area shall not exceed 2 mm diameter or it is considered one point of failure.

6.9 Fadeometer Exposure—Mats or mat sections shall not show any loss of topcoat adhesion or noticeable color or gloss change after 60 h of exposure in a Type FDA-R Fadeometer exposed per American Association of Textile Chemist and Colorist (A.A.T.C.C.) Test Method 16A except the black panel temperature is to be 72 °C ± 2 °C.

6.10 Identification—Mats must carry identification to indicate the manufacturer and date of manufacture.

TABLE 1—TEST REQUIREMENTS

Type of Rubber	1	2	3	4	5
Properties After Preaging 6 h at 70° C and Resting 16 h min at 23 °C					
Durometer	70 ±5	70 ±5	70 ±5	70 ±5	65 ±5
Tensile strength, mPa, min	2.8	3.5	5.2	6.9	10.4
Elongation, %, min	150	150	150	200	250
Tear resistance, kN/m, min	13.1	14	21	26.3	52.5
Bend test	No cracking	No cracking	No cracking	No cracking	No cracking
Low temperature flexibility test	No cracking	No cracking	No cracking	No cracking	No cracking
Tensile set test, %, max	15	15	15	15	15
Oven Aging 70 h at 70 °C (After Preaging 6 h at 70 °C) and Resting 16 h Min at 23 °C					
Durometer, points increase, max	10	10	10	10	5
Tensile strength, mPa, min	2.1	2.6	4.2	5.6	8.3
Elongation, %, min	115	115	115	150	200
Tear resistance, % loss, max	25	25	25	25	25
Bend test	No cracking	No cracking	No cracking	No cracking	No cracking

DESIGN GUIDE FOR FORMED-IN-PLACE GASKETS—SAE J1497 APR1994

SAE Recommended Practice

Report of the SAE Seal Committee approved May 1988 and revised December 1988. Reaffirmed by the SAE Gasketing Standards Committee April 994.

Foreword—This Reaffirmed Document has been changed only to reflect the new SAE Technical Standards Board Format.

1. Scope—This SAE Recommended Practice presents information which is intended as a guide for proper designing, selection, application, and servicing of liquid, formed-in-place gasket (FIPG) materials.

1.1 Definition and Description—Formed-in-place gasket materials are liquids of varying consistencies which can be applied to one of the mating joint surfaces before assembly. When parts are mated, the FIPG material is capable of flowing into voids, gaps, scratch marks, and so forth, and cures to form a durable seal. The concept offers a convenient way of manually or automatically dispensing a seal of varying patterns for assembly. Generally, two types of FIPG materials are used, RTV (Room Temperature Vulcanizing) silicones and anaerobic methacrylate esters. Other types of materials are available but restricted to limited applications and, therefore, are not covered in this manual. The following description and properties for each type of material will help determine the recommended choice of material for a given application. One should thoroughly test any application, and independently conclude satisfactory performance before making final selection.

2. References

2.1 Applicable Publications—The following publications form a part of this specification to the extent specified herein.

2.1.1 ASTM PUBLICATIONS—Available from ASTM, 100 Barr Harbor Drive, West Conshohocken, PA 19428-2959.

ASTM D 1002—Test Method for Strength Properties of Adhesives in Shear by Tension Loading (Metal-to-Metal)

ASTM D 1084—Test Methods for Viscosity of Adhesives

3. Types of Sealants

3.1 One Component RTV Silicone Sealant—The silicone formed-in-place gasket (FIPG) comprises the application of a paste-like silicone sealant bead to the area of a component which is then assembled, usually within 10 min. The silicone compound flows to form a gasket which then cures to a rubbery solid by absorbing the moisture vapor in the environment (see Figure 1). The application can be done by hand from a collapsible tube, caulking cartridge, or on an automated dispensing system.

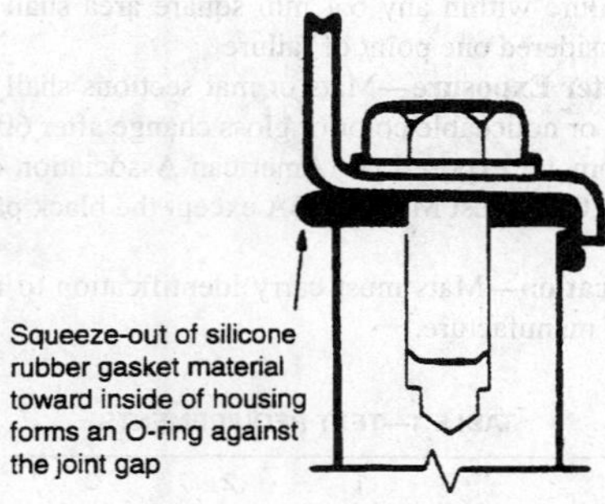

FIGURE 1—JOINT GAP SEAL

3.1.1 THE BASIC CHEMISTRY

3.1.1.1 The FIRST of a three-ingredient silicone sealant is a hydroxy-terminated polysiloxane polymer. See Figure 2.

For most applications, a polydimethyl siloxane polymer is used ($R = CH_3$). However, for applications where fuel or solvent resistance is necessary, a polymethyl-trifluoropropyl siloxane polymer is used ($R = CH_2\ CH_2\ CF_3$). The average molecular weight of the polymers usually ranges from 2.0×10^4 to 1.2×10^5 grams/mole.

The SECOND is the presence of a filler or combination of different fillers like: high surface area silicas, ground quartz, zinc oxide, iron oxide, carbon black, various types of clays and diatomaceous earth.

The THIRD is the moisture vapor affected crosslinking system. It is generally a reactive polyfunctional silane, which is readily hydrolyzable and released during the curing reaction. Examples of the most common crosslinkers and the by-products are shown in Figure 3:

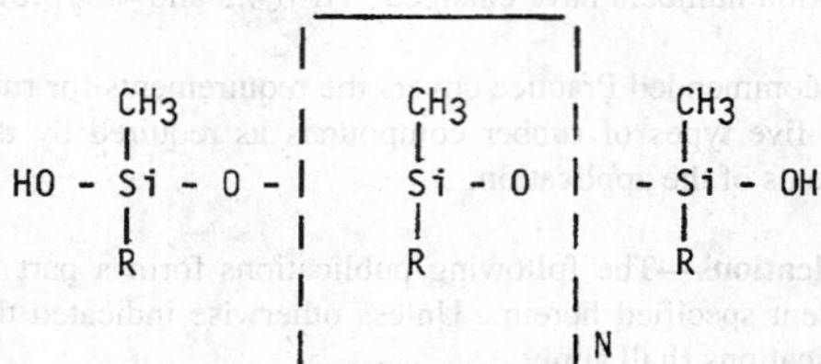

FIGURE 2—HYDROXY-TERMINATED POLYSILOXANE POLYMER

ACETOXY

(1) Methyltriacetoxy Silane — Acetic Acid

$CH_3Si\ (-O-C(=O)-CH_3)_3$ — $CH_3-C(=O)-OH$

ALKOXY

(2) Methyltrimethoxy Silane - Methyl Alcohol

$CH_3Si\ (-O-CH_3)_3$ — CH_3OH

AMINE

(3) Methyltris (cyclohexylamino) Silane - Cyclohexyl Amine

CH_3Si (-N(H)-C6H11)3 — C6H11-N(H)-H

OCTOATE

(4) Methyltrihexanoxy Silane - Hexanoic Acid

$CH_3Si\ (-O-C(=O)-(CH_2)_4CH_3)_3$ — $CH_3(CH_2)_4-C(=O)-OH$

OXIME

(5) Methyltris (methylethylketoxime) Silane - Methyl-ethylketoxime

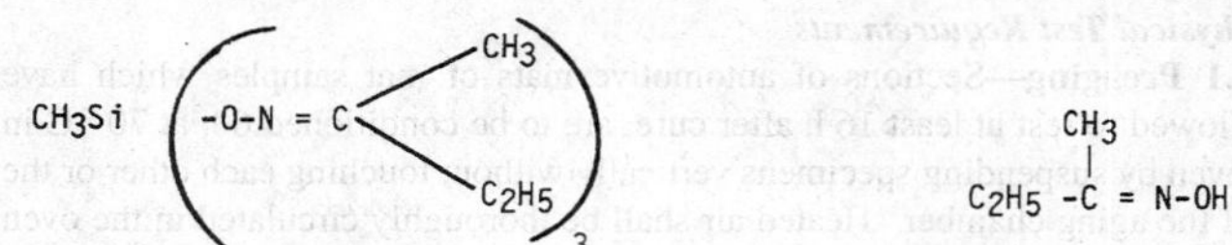

FIGURE 3—EXAMPLES OF THE MOST COMMON CROSSLINKERS AND THE BY-PRODUCTS

3.1.2 SPECIFIC DIFFERENCE IN CURE SYSTEMS—See Table 1:

TABLE 1—CURE SYSTEM 25 °C (77 °F), 50% RH

	(1)	(2)	(3)	(4)	(5)
Tack Free Time (Hours)	0.25–0.5	0.5–4	0.25–0.5	0.25–0.75	0.25–0.5
Cure Time, Hours	12–16	18–24	12–24	16–24	12–24
Adhesion to Iron/ Aluminum [(1)]	Good/Exc.	Good	Fair/Good	Fair/Good	Good/Exc.
Corrosion to Steel [(2)]	Heavy	None	None	Slight	None
Corrosion to Aluminum[(2)]	None	None	Slight	None	None

Exc.—Excellent

1. Adhesion to plastics is variable and must be individually tested.
2. As tested in a nonvented environment with high humidity per MIL-A-46146A.

3.1.3 Typical Uncured (As Received) Physical Property Ranges

3.1.3.1 Viscosity/Application Rate—The rheological properties of the sealant can be measured in terms of blow-out resistance and extrusion rate as well as a traditional viscosity measurement. The viscosity of the sealing compound can be determined in accordance with ASTM D 1084, Method B. The viscosimeter model, spindle number, and speed shall be reported as part of the viscosity determination.

3.1.3.2 Application Rate Method (Grams/Minute)

3.1.3.2.1 Apparatus

a. [1]Semco model 250-6 sealant gun
b. [1]Semco plastic nozzle #440 (101.6 mm long × 3.18 mm orifice diameter)
c. [1]Semco plastic cartridge #250-C6, #250-WP wiper, #250-TS Tri-Seal (standard drum sample)
d. Stop Watch

3.1.3.2.2 Procedure

a. Load the cartridge containing the silicone compound into the sealant gun.
b. Remove the seal and clear out any cured RTV. Attach the nozzle to the cartridge.
c. Connect the sealant gun to 620.6 kPa ± 13.8 kPa air supply and extrude 5 to 10 g of compound to prep the nozzle.
d. Extrude the RTV compound in a tared aluminum weighing dish for a period of 10 s, so the test specimen weighs at least 10 g or more.
e. The number of test specimens depends on the quantity of compound. Recommendation is to use at least three and average.
f.

$$\text{Grams/minute} = \frac{\text{Weight in Grams}}{10\text{s}} \times \frac{60\text{s}}{\text{Minute}} \qquad \text{(Eq. 1)}$$

g. Typical application rates 200 to 450 g/min.

3.1.3.3 Application Rate Method (Seconds/50 g)

3.1.3.3.1 Apparatus

a. [1] Semco model 250-6 sealant gun
b. Special nozzle (50.8 mm long × 3.18 mm orifice diameter) CR-1010 Steel 1 (Figure 4)
c. [1] Semco plastic cartridge #250-6, #250-WP wiper, #250-TS Tri-Seal (standard drum sample)
d. Stop Watch
e. Laboratory balance (0.01 g)
f. Weighing Dish
g. Pipe Cleaners (for cleaning nozzles)

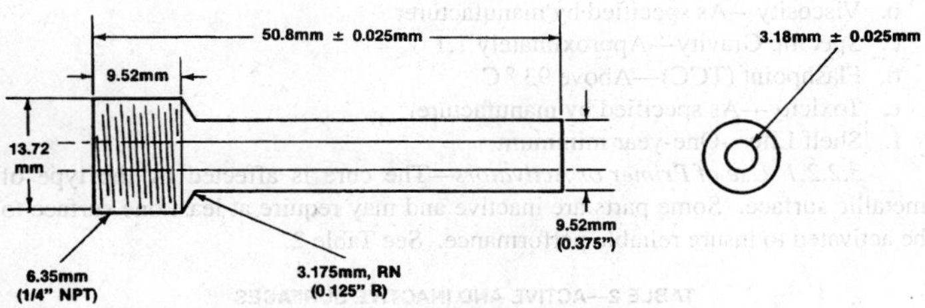

FIGURE 4—SPECIAL NOZZLE

3.1.3.3.2 Procedure

a. Load the cartridge containing the silicone compound into the sealant gun.
b. Remove the seal cap and clear out any cured RTV. Attach the nozzle to the cartridge.
c. Connect the sealant gun to 448.2 kPA ± 13.8 kPa air supply and extrude a few grams of compound to prep the nozzle.
d. Extrude the RTV compound in a tared weighing dish for a period of 10 s, so the test specimen weighs at least 10 g or more.
e. The number of test specimens depends on the quantity of compound; recommendation is at least three and average.
f.

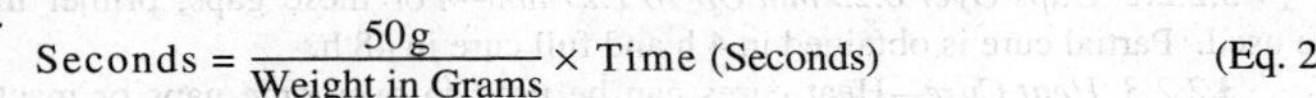

$$\text{Seconds} = \frac{50\text{g}}{\text{Weight in Grams}} \times \text{Time (Seconds)} \qquad \text{(Eq. 2)}$$

1. Semco, a Division of: Products Research & Chemical Corp.
5454 San Fernando Road
Glendale, CA 91203

Also available from other sources.

3.1.3.4 Flow Resistance—The flow test shall be conducted with a flow test jig as shown in Figure 5. Depth of plunger tolerance is critical and shall be controlled within the tolerance during all tests. The flow test jig shall be placed on a table with the front face upward and with the plunger depressed to the limit of its travel. Enough of the silicone compound to fill the recessed cavity of the jig shall be rapidly transferred from a representative sample container. The compound should not be worked with a spatula but shall be leveled off even with the block by scraping with a spatula in two passes, each starting in the center and moving toward the sides of the jig. Within 10 s after the leveling operation, the jig shall be placed on its base and the plunger immediately advanced to the limit of its forward travel. The cylindrical section formed in the flow test jig shall be allowed to flow under its own weight on a vertical surface.

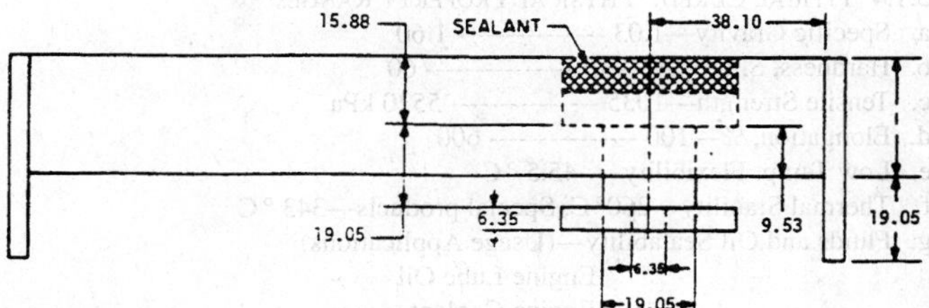

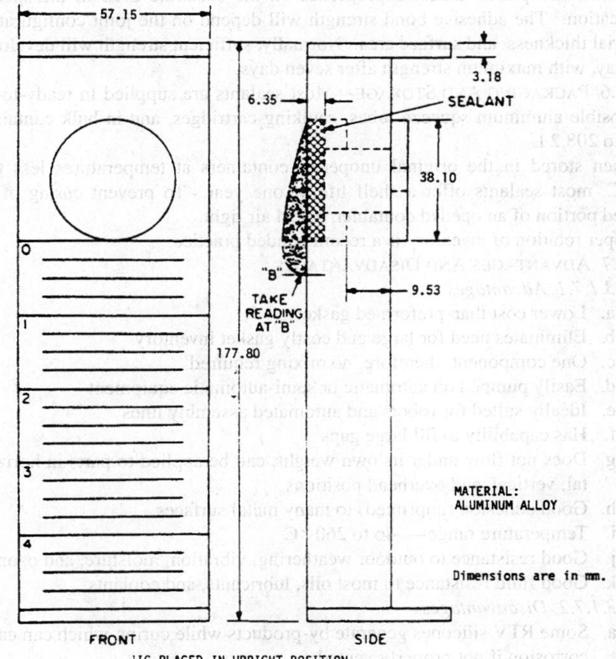

FIGURE 5—FLOW TEST FIXTURE

The flow test shall be when the plunger is advanced to the limit of its forward travel, and the flow measurement shall be taken immediately after the expiration of 3 to 30 min. The flow shall be measured from tangent to the lower edge of the plunger to the farthest point to which flow has occurred. The measurement after the indicated interval shall be considered the initial flow of the silicone compound.

3.1.3.5 Tack Free Time/Cure Rate

3.1.3.5.1 Apparatus

a. Strip of polyethylene film 50.8 × 152.4 × 0.076 mm
b. Spatula or doctor blade
c. Stop Watch

3.1.3.5.2 Procedure

a. Apply the RTV compound from the container.
b. The quantity of compound varies. However, a typical 25.4 mm "Hershey Dot" is the recommendation.
c. With a spatula or doctor blade, spread the compound down the polyethylene film as soon as possible (within 1 min). The shape of an elongated triangle with the initial start area about 3.18 mm thick to a feather ending about 0.127 mm.
d. Beginning at the time the compound is first applied, determine the tack free time by slightly touching the compound with a fingertip at 5 min intervals.
e. The test is completed when the surface is dry to the touch and no compound is transferred to the finger.
f. Typical values are 10 to 30 min at 21.1 °C and 50% RH.

3.1.4 TYPICAL CURED[2] PHYSICAL PROPERTY RANGES

a. Specific Gravity—1.03 -------------- 1.60
b. Hardness, Shore "A"—15 -------------- 60
c. Tensile Strength—1035 -------------- 5520 kPa
d. Elongation, %—100 -------------- 600
e. Low Temp. Flexibility— -45.5 °C
f. Thermal Stability—260° C, Special products—343 °C
g. Fluids and Oil Sealability—(Usage Applications)
   Engine Lube Oil
   Engine Coolant
   Automatic Transmission Fluid
   Rear Axle Lubricant

3.1.5 BOND STRENGTH DEVELOPMENT—Most silicone sealants bond to clean surfaces without the aid of primers. A preliminary evaluation should be made to determine acceptable adhesive properties on the substrate used in the specific application. The adhesive bond strength will depend on the joint configuration, material thickness, and surface area. Normally, sufficient strength will develop in one day, with maximum strength after seven days.

3.1.6 PACKAGING AND STORAGE—Most sealants are supplied in ready-to-use collapsible aluminum squeeze tubes, caulking cartridges, and in bulk containers 18.9 to 208.2 L.

When stored in the original unopened containers at temperatures less than 27 °C, most sealants offer a shelf life of one year. To prevent curing of the unused portion of an opened container, reseal air tight.

Proper rotation of inventory is a recommended practice.

3.1.7 ADVANTAGES AND DISADVANTAGES

3.1.7.1 Advantages

a. Lower cost than preformed gaskets
b. Eliminates need for large and costly gasket inventory
c. One component, therefore, no mixing required
d. Easily pumped on automatic or semi-automatic equipment
e. Ideally suited for robots and automated assembly lines
f. Has capability to fill large gaps
g. Does not flow under its own weight; can be applied to parts in horizontal, vertical, and overhead positions
h. Good adhesion (unprimed) to many metal surfaces
i. Temperature range— -46 to 260 °C
j. Good resistance to outdoor weathering, vibration, moisture, and ozone
k. Good fluid resistance to most oils, lubricants, and coolants.

3.1.7.2 Disadvantages

a. Some RTV silicones generate by-products while curing which can cause corrosion if not properly vented
b. Prolonged contact with uncured sealant can cause irritation to skin and eyes
c. Working time is dependent on temperature and humidity
d. Requires clean mating surfaces
e. Slower cure in low humidity environment
f. Removal of cured sealant difficult when applied to clean surfaces
g. Most sealants cannot be painted
h. Due to the low thickness as clamped, limited ability to follow movement between flanges

3.2 Anaerobic Methacrylate Ester Sealant—The word "anaerobic" is derived from the Greek, meaning life in the absence of air. Hence, anaerobic compounds cure in the absence of air and in the presence of metal or other active surfaces.

Cure rates at room temperatures range anywhere from a few minutes to several hours. Since there are no solvents, the conversion from liquid to solid is virtually 100%, completely filling the voids, surface imperfections, tool marks, and so forth, eliminating all potential leak paths.

There are a variety of sealant types, selection of which depends on the following:

a. Fluid/gas to be sealed
b. System pressure/temperature
c. Surface configuration and finish
d. Flange makeup (rigid/flexible)
e. Number, grade, and size of bolts
f. Disassembly requirements

3.2.1 THE BASIC CHEMISTRY—Anaerobic formed-in-place gaskets cure through a process called "polymerization." These long cross-linked polymer chains are typical of the cured anaerobic products and are indicated chemically in Figure 6.

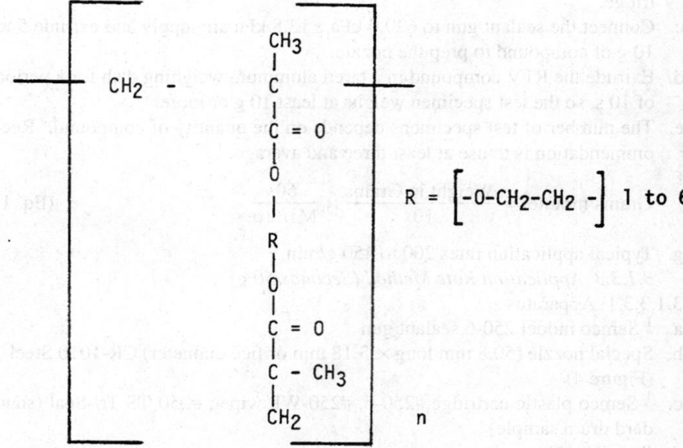

FIGURE 6—CHEMICAL STRUCTURE

3.2.2 UNCURED PROPERTIES

a. Resin (Anaerobic)—Methacrylate Ester
b. Viscosity—As specified by manufacturer
c. Specific Gravity—Approximately 1.1
d. Flashpoint (TCC)—Above 93 °C
e. Toxicity—As specified by manufacturer
f. Shelf Life—One-year minimum

3.2.2.1 Use of Primer or Activators—The cure is affected by the type of metallic surface. Some parts are inactive and may require at least one surface to be activated to insure reliable performance. See Table 2.

TABLE 2—ACTIVE AND INACTIVE SURFACES

Active Surfaces	Inactive Surfaces
Steel	Zinc
Iron	Pure Aluminum
Copper	Stainless Steel
Brass	Cadmium
Manganese	Magnesium
Bronze	Bright Platings
Nickel	Anodized Surfaces
Commercial Aluminum	Passivated Surfaces
	Titanium

3.2.2.2 Gaps Over 0.25 mm Up To 1.27 mm—For these gaps, primer must be used. Partial cure is obtained in 4 h and full cure in 48 h.

3.2.2.3 Heat Cure—Heat cures can be used to overcome gaps or inactive surfaces as follows in Table 3:

TABLE 3—CURE TIME VERSUS GAP SIZE USING HEAT AT 120 °C

Gap	Cure Time Required 120 °C
0.51 to 0.76 mm	2 h
1.27 mm	3 h

2. Cured 7 days at 25 °C and 50% RH.

3.2.3 TYPICAL CURED PROPERTIES

a. Resin—Flexible Methacrylate Polymer
b. Temperature Range—Continuous -53 to 149 °C operation for sealability
c. Percent Elongation—Approximately 30%
d. Tensile Shear Strength—3.4 to 6.9 MPa at 0.50 mm film thickness

3.2.3.1 Method for Preparation of Bubble Free Films of Gasketing Products

3.2.3.1.1 Test Apparatus

a. 152.4 x 152.4 mm plate glass panes
b. 0.76 mm thick sheet polyethylene
c. 2% solution of lecithin in 1,1,1,-trichloroethane
d. Lab centrifuge
e. 10 mL disposable syringes or equivalent
f. Cotton swabs
g. 8 x #1 Hargrave clamps or equivalent

3.2.3.1.2 Preparation

a. Using cotton swabs, coat one side of two glass panes with an even coating of lecithin solution. Allow all solvent to flash off.
b. Cut 0.76 mm thick polyethylene to produce a 152.4 x 152.4 x 12.7 mm square edging. This provides a 0.76 mm gap while also preventing excessive material run out.
c. Heat seal the bottom of a Luer lock tip so that the syringe becomes leakproof. This may be accomplished by heating the tip with a lighter or other convenient flame source and crimping with a pair of needle nose pliers.
d. Fill sealed syringe with gasketing material and place in lab centrifuge. Centrifuge at high speed for at least 10 min and check material for air content. Continue to centrifuge until all air is dissipated.

3.2.3.1.3 Assembly

a. If primer curing, apply recommended primer to both lecithin-coated surfaces of the glass panes. Allow all solvent to flash off.
b. Place 152.4 x 152.4 x 12.7 mm polyethylene square edging along edges of one glass pane.
c. Cut off the centrifuged syringe with a razor blade as close to the bottom of the syringe as possible so that the largest diameter opening is obtained.
d. Using the syringe plunger, slowly push the gasketing material out onto the center of the polyethylene-edged glass pane to form a contour-free mound. The amount of material needed to produce the desired film can vary depending on the gasketing product used. In general, four centrifuged syringes of material is a good starting point.
e. Place the remaining glass pane, coated side down, gently onto the mound of gasketing material taking care to ensure that air entrapment is avoided.
f. Press down slowly until the top glass pane contacts the polyethylene edging on the bottom pane while ensuring that the gasketing material has wetted the surface.
g. Clamp the glass panes with even spacing all around the material and allow to cure. If primer-cured, a minimum of 24 h at room temperature is required. If a heat cure is desired, a minimum cure of 2 to 4 h at 93.3 °C is recommended.

3.2.3.1.4 Disassembly

a. Place the edge of a razor blade or putty knife between the polyethylene edging and glass pane.
b. Slowly, run the edge of the sharp tool around the perimeter of the film and separate the glass from the cured film.

3.2.3.2 Typical Environmental Resistance—Hot Strength and Heat Aging tests were started after 24 h cure at room temperature. Figures 7 and 8 depict the test results.

NOTE—Test method ASTM D 1002 with sandblasted steel lap shears.

3.2.3.3 Solvent Resistance—Cured sections of material were weighed, measured for hardness, and then submerged in various solvents for 15 days at 86.7 °C. Changes in weight and hardness are given in Table 4:

TABLE 4—WEIGHT CHANGE AND HARDNESS CHANGE AFTER SUBMERSION IN VARIOUS SOLVENTS

Solvent	% Weight Change	Shore "A" Hardness Before	Shore "A" Hardness After
Water	+60%	90	90
10W30 Motor Oil	0%	90	90
Isopropyl Alcohol	+25%	90	82
Unleaded Gasoline (1)	+31%	92	86
Toluene	+38%	90	86
1,1,1 Trichloroethane	+50%	91	72
Phosphate Ester Oil	+46%	90	87

1. Test at room temperature.

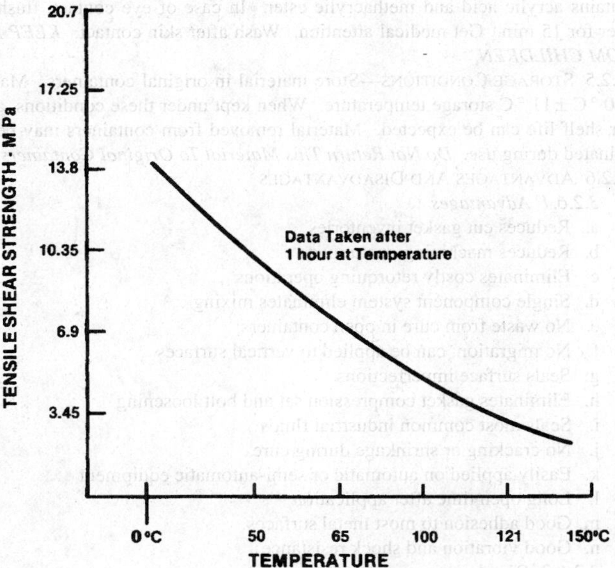

FIGURE 7—HOT STRENGTH

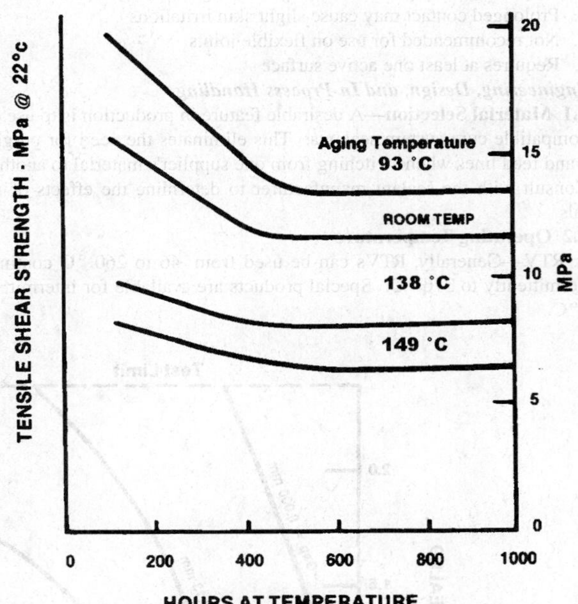

FIGURE 8—HEAT AGING

3.2.4 USE AND APPLICATION—Material can be used to seal rough or nonmachined surfaces and precut gaskets. To obtain best results, contaminants such as grease, heavy oils, and dirt *must* be removed with adequate solvent. Material can eliminate some gaskets 0.76 mm or less thick and can be used to coat hard or soft cut gaskets to obtain good reliability. It remains flexible when not used over 121 °C and will maintain static seals up to 149 °C.

3.2.4.1 Application Techniques—Manual—Material is an easily workable tacky gel which can be extruded onto one side of a flange surface from a tube or caulking cartridge. Breaks in the bead are easily repaired by manipulation. Small parts can be covered adequately by pressing them into a saturated polyester urethane sponge or by roll coating them with a short nap roller.

3.2.4.1.1 Screen Printing—The material responds well to screen printing techniques. Complex shapes can be coated in seconds with precise control of material quantity and placement.

Excess material can be cleaned by wiping with recommended solvent. Material on hands can be cleaned with waterless mechanics' hand soap followed by soap and water.

3.2.4.2 Warning—EYE IRRITANT. MAY IRRITATE SENSITIVE SKIN—Contains acrylic acid and methacrylic ester. In case of eye contact, flush with water for 15 min. Get medical attention. Wash after skin contact. *KEEP AWAY FROM CHILDREN.*

3.2.5 STORAGE CONDITIONS—Store material in original containers. Maintain at 20 °C ± 11 °C storage temperature. When kept under these conditions, a one-year shelf life can be expected. Material removed from containers may be contaminated during use. *Do Not Return This Material To Original Containers.*

3.2.6 ADVANTAGES AND DISADVANTAGES

3.2.6.1 Advantages

a. Reduces cut gasket inventories
b. Reduces machining operations
c. Eliminates costly retorquing operations
d. Single component system eliminates mixing
e. No waste from cure in open containers
f. No migration; can be applied to vertical surfaces
g. Seals surface imperfections
h. Eliminates gasket compression set and bolt loosening
i. Seals most common industrial fluids
j. No cracking or shrinkage during cure
k. Easily applied on automatic or semi-automatic equipment
l. Long open time after application
m. Good adhesion to most metal surfaces
n. Good vibration and shock resistance

3.2.6.2 Disadvantages

a. Requires use between closely-fitted surfaces; does not have large gap filling ability
b. Requires handling care to insure full flange coverage upon assembly
c. Prolonged contact may cause slight skin irritations
d. Not recommended for use on flexible joints
e. Requires at least one active surface

4. Engineering, Design, and In-Process Handling

4.1 Material Selection—A desirable feature in production is to use chemically compatible cure system sealants. This eliminates the need for purging the pumps and feed lines when switching from one supplier's material to another.

Consult with the sealant manufacturer to determine the effects of mixing materials.

4.2 Operating Temperature

4.2.1 RTV—Generally, RTVs can be used from -46 to 260 °C continuously and intermittently to 316 °C. Special products are available for intermittent use to 343 °C.

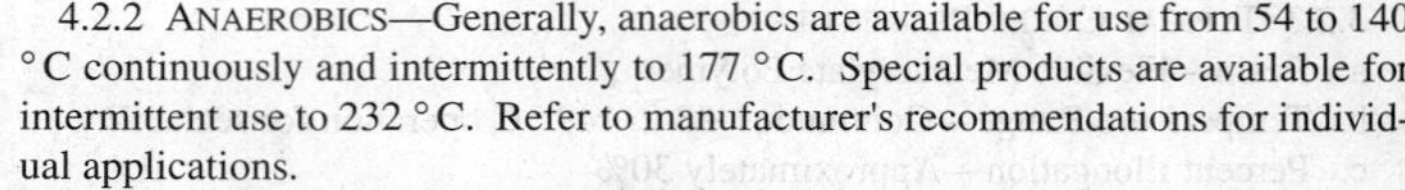

4.2.2 ANAEROBICS—Generally, anaerobics are available for use from 54 to 140 °C continuously and intermittently to 177 °C. Special products are available for intermittent use to 232 °C. Refer to manufacturer's recommendations for individual applications.

4.3 Operating Pressures—Pressure tolerance is dependent upon several conditions: time, joint width, gap clamp load, and other factors.

Figures 9 and 10 show typical gap and pressure data.

Confirming tests should be conducted using actual parts for each particular application.

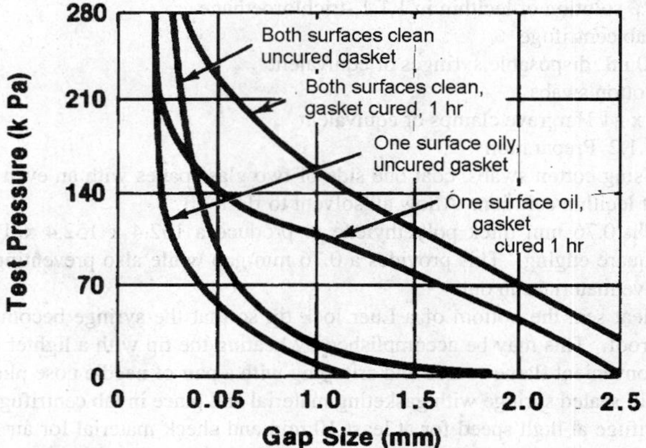

FIGURE 9—TYPICAL RTV GAP VERSUS PRESSURE

4.4 Fluids to be Sealed—The sealant must be resistant to the fluids to be sealed. Refer to manufacturer for recommendations.

4.5 Design

4.5.1 THERMAL EXPANSION—Differential expansion of mating flanges is very critical. The sealant must be capable of tolerating the relative movement while maintaining seal integrity. This can be accommodated through proper selection of sealant, gap thickness, and flange material.

4.5.2 GAP THICKNESS—RTV can generally accommodate gaps up to 2.5 mm. Anaerobic sealants can accommodate gaps to 0.25 mm. The use of primer allows larger gaps. Gap thickness is affected by cure time and pressures encountered during assembly and operation.

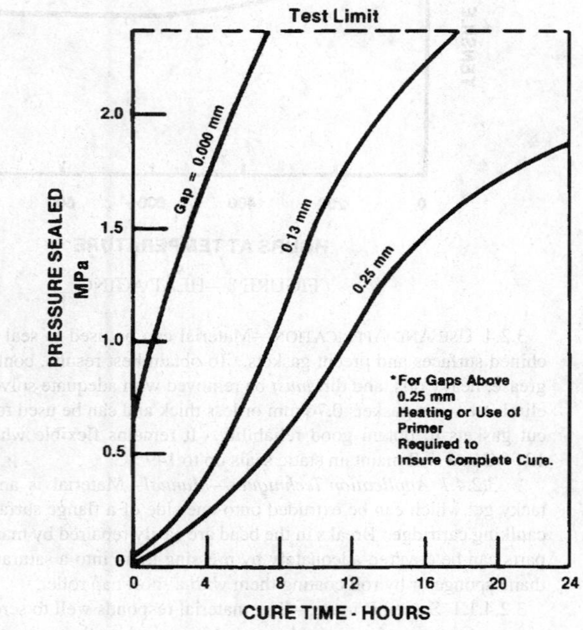

Data was obtained on 9.5 mm wide steel flanges with gaps between mating parts held at 0.00 mm, 0.13 mm and 0.25 mm. Test pressurization was limited to 2.07 MPa. See sketch.

The high pressure test fixtures could be sealed at 6.9 MPa with a 1.33 mm gap. Cure was assured by using Accelerator-Primer and waiting 48 hours.

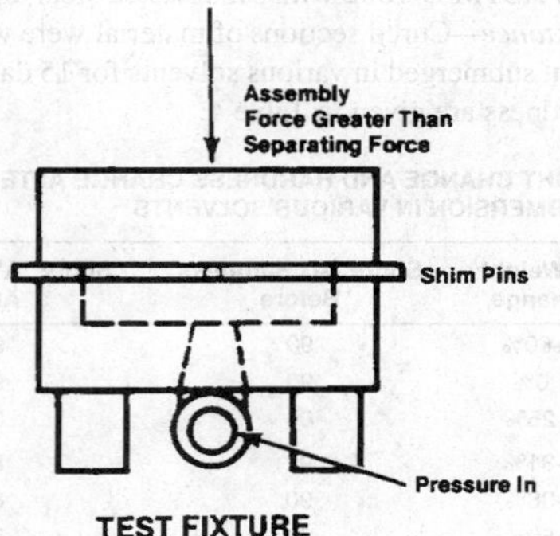

FIGURE 10—TYPICAL ANAEROBIC GAP VERSUS PRESSURE

4.5.3 FLANGE SURFACE—To assure efficient sealing, design parameters such as flatness and surface finish must be defined and specified to keep mating parts under control.

4.5.4 FASTENERS—In joints where there is excessive relative movement due to pressure or expansion, bolt spacing and clamp load are important in maintaining proper gap.

The joint integrity should not allow gap increase during "in process" testing or during operation.

Do not allow sealant into blind holes as hydrostatic lock may occur, resulting in false torque readings (low clamp load).

4.5.5 MINIMUM SEALING WIDTH—Generally, the minimum sealing width for (A) is 5 mm and for (B), 3 mm (see Figure 11). Wider flanges are strongly recommended.

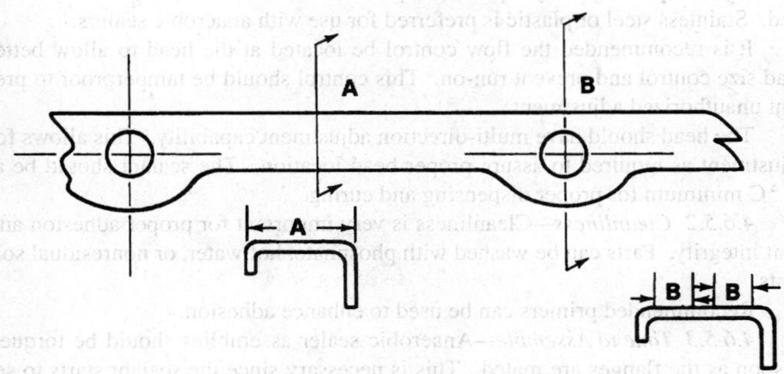

FIGURE 11—MINIMUM SEALING WIDTH

4.5.6 FLANGE DESIGN—Since liquid gaskets depend on flange adhesion to seal, the joint must be designed so the sealant does not fail in shear or adhesion. The thickness of sealant must be sufficient to accommodate movement induced by vibration, impact, and differential thermal expansion (see Figures 12, 13, and 14 for examples).

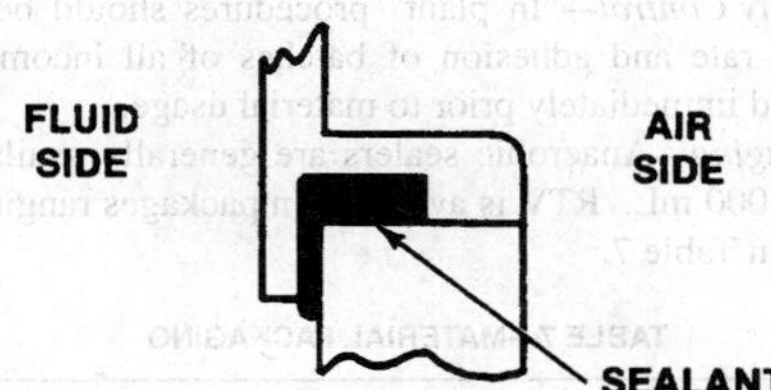

FIGURE 12—SHIELDED STEP FLANGE

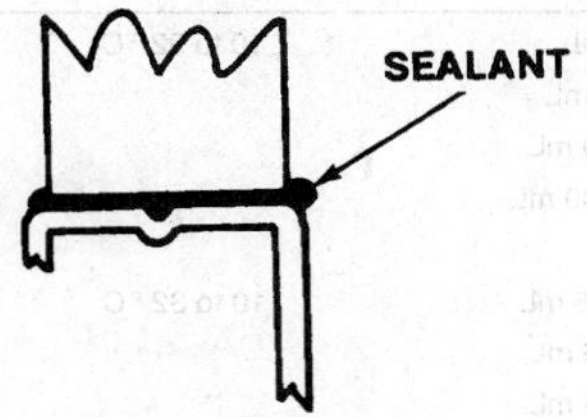

FIGURE 13—GROOVED FLANGE

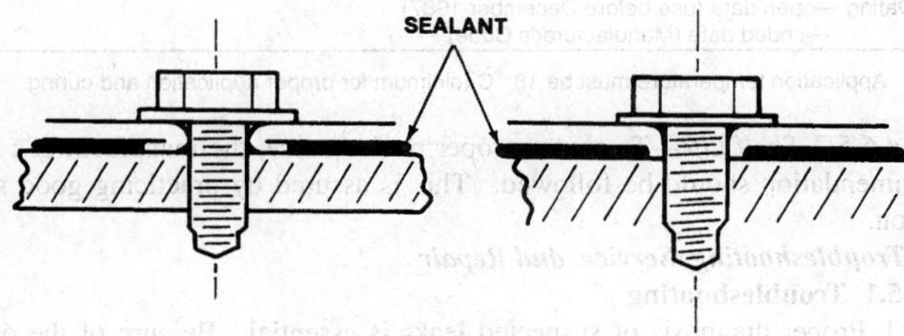

FIGURE 14—GAPPED FLANGE

4.5.7 BEAD SIZE—Increasing the bead size may increase the pressure capability of a joint, but too large a bead may decrease pressure capability. This is due to the effect of cure time when using RTV.

Establishing minimum bead size requires experimentation during the initial development and during an assembly plant trial. Table 5 shows the length of bead versus the bead size diameter that will result when using 28 cc of silicone sealant material.

Figure 15 can be used as a guide for selecting the proper bead diameter for various joint widths and gap sizes for RTV. Figure 16 shows anaerobic recommendations. The gap in this instance is due to inherent out-of-flat of the mating flanges.

TABLE 5—LINEAR MM OF GASKET PER 28 CC OF SILICONE SEALANT

Bead Size Diameter	Length
0.79 mm	(57.58×10^3 mm)
1.57 mm	(14.48×10^3 mm)
2.36 mm	(6.38×10^3 mm)
3.18 mm	(3.58×10^3 mm)
4.76 mm	(1.60×10^3 mm)

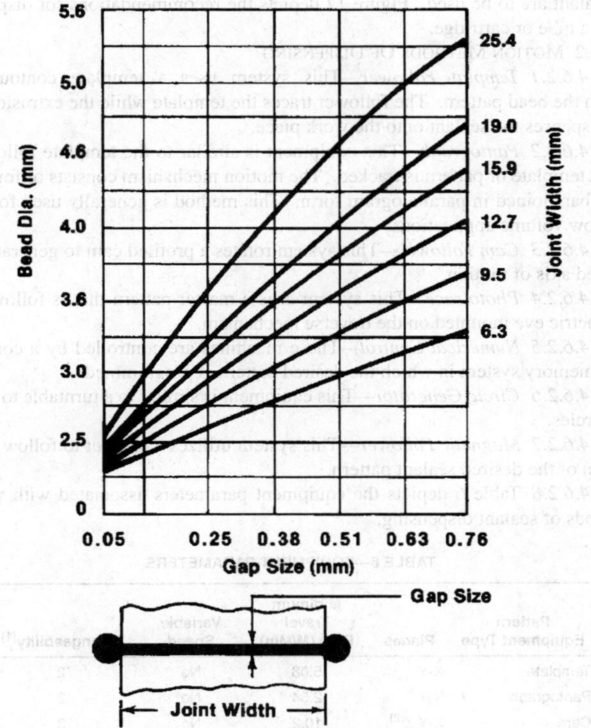

FIGURE 15—RTV BEAD SIZE

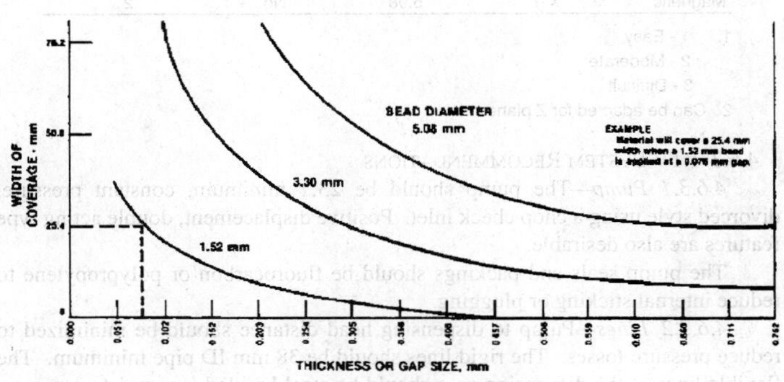

FIGURE 16—ANAEROBIC SEALER BEAD SIZE

4.5.8 FUNCTIONAL OPERATION—The type of functional operation is an influencing factor in the design of the flange.

4.5.8.1 Types of Operation Include

a. Vibration—such as 4-cylinder engines where high vibration forces are encountered.
b. Impact—such as an oil pan that may encounter a curb or parking lot bumper.
c. Structural—where the entire housing acts as a structural member. In this case, forces are transmitted through the inspection covers or oil pan.

4.6 Manufacturing Process Requirements

4.6.1 APPLICATION EQUIPMENT SYSTEMS

4.6.1.1 Screen Printing—This method uses a mesh screen containing the sealant pattern. The screen is placed on top of the work piece and the sealant is extruded through the mesh onto the work piece. This system is best for anaerobics.

4.6.1.2 Roller Coating—The sealant (usually anaerobic) is applied to a roller. The work piece is then rolled, leaving a thin film of sealant across the work piece.

4.6.1.3 Caulking Gun/Cartridges—This method is commonly used in the field and where the work piece is too large to be removed.

4.6.1.4 Tubes/Cartridges—This method is used where very small amounts of sealant are to be used. Figure 17 depicts the recommendations for dispensing from a tube or cartridge.

4.6.2 MOTION METHODS OF DISPENSING

4.6.2.1 Template Follower—This system uses a template contoured to match the bead pattern. The follower traces the template while the extrusion nozzle dispenses the sealant onto the work piece.

4.6.2.2 Pantograph—This equipment is similar to the template follower in that a template or pattern is tracked. The motion mechanism consists of four light rigid bars joined in parallelogram form. This method is generally used for manual, low volume applications.

4.6.2.3 Cam Follower—This system rotates a profiled cam to generate each desired axis of motion.

4.6.2.4 Phototrace—This system uses a master pattern that is followed by an electric eye mounted on the traverse mechanism.

4.6.2.5 Numerical Control—These machines are controlled by a computer type memory system in which the desired pattern is programmed.

4.6.2.6 Circle Generator—This equipment is similar to a turntable to generate circles.

4.6.2.7 Magnetic Follower—This system utilizes a magnet to follow a steel ribbon of the desired sealant pattern.

4.6.2.8 Table 6 depicts the equipment parameters associated with various methods of sealant dispensing.

TABLE 6—EQUIPMENT PARAMETERS

Pattern Equipment Type	Planes	Minimum Travel Rate (M/Min)	Variable Speed	Changeability[1]
Template	X-Y	5.08	No	2
Pantograph	X-Y	2.54	No	2
Cam	X-Y-Z[2]	10.2	No	3
Photo	X-Y-Z[1]	5.08	No	2
NC	X-Y-Z	10.2	Yes	1
Circle	X-Y	15.2	No	1
Magnetic	X-Y	5.08	No	2

1. 1 - Easy
   2 - Moderate
   3 - Difficult
2. Can be adapted for Z plane

4.6.3 RTV SYSTEM RECOMMENDATIONS

4.6.3.1 Pump—The pump should be 23:1 minimum, constant pressure, divorced style using a chop check inlet. Positive displacement, double acting type features are also desirable.

The pump seals and packings should be fluorocarbon or polypropylene to reduce internal sticking or plugging.

4.6.3.2 Lines—Pump to dispensing head distance should be minimized to reduce pressure losses. The rigid lines should be 38 mm ID pipe minimum. The flexible lines at the dispensing area should be steel braided, nonmoisture permeable lines, flexible hose. The hose ID should be 9.5 mm minimum.

4.6.3.3 Regulators—Mastic type regulators are recommended and should be located as close to the dispensing head as possible.

4.6.4 ANAEROBICS SYSTEM RECOMMENDATIONS

4.6.4.1 Pump—The pump should be a 1:1 constant pressure, positive displacement, double-acting pump. The pump should be capable of 414 kPa minimum.

4.6.4.2 Lines—The pump to dispensing head distance should be minimized to reduce pressure losses. The delivery line should be wire wrapped, low-density polypropylene tubing. The tubing should be 4.7 mm ID minimum. Metal tubing or pipes and fittings, especially copper, must be avoided.

4.6.5 GENERAL SYSTEMS RECOMMENDATIONS (RTV AND ANAEROBICS)

4.6.5.1 Dispensing Head Requirements—A dispensing head incorporating a "snuff back" (no drip) feature is desirable. This prevents "stringing" of sealant onto the work piece. Easily replaceable plastic or metal nozzles should be considered. Stainless steel or plastic is preferred for use with anaerobic sealers.

It is recommended the flow control be located at the head to allow better bead size control and prevent run-on. This control should be tamperproof to prevent unauthorized adjustment.

The head should have multi-direction adjustment capability. This allows for adjustment as required to assure proper bead location. The sealant should be at 18 °C minimum for proper dispensing and curing.

4.6.5.2 Cleanliness—Cleanliness is very important for proper adhesion and joint integrity. Parts can be washed with phosphate, hot water, or nonresidual solvents.

Recommended primers can be used to enhance adhesion.

4.6.5.3 Time to Assemble—Anaerobic sealer assemblies should be torqued as soon as the flanges are mated. This is necessary since the sealant starts to set up as soon as oxygen is excluded.

RTV joints should be assembled and torqued immediately after dispensing the bead. This is necessary since the material begins to cure upon exposure to moisture (humidity).

4.6.5.4 Production Leak Test—Position the application equipment and test equipment to allow sufficient cure time to pass in-process testing. Factors affecting this are maximum fill pressure, test pressure, time at pressure, temperature, and humidity.

4.6.5.5 Quality Control—"In plant" procedures should be incorporated to assure proper cure rate and adhesion of batches of all incoming stock. This should be performed immediately prior to material usage.

4.6.5.6 Packaging—Anaerobic sealers are generally available in packages ranging from 6 to 1000 mL. RTV is available in packages ranging from 88.5 mL to 209 L as shown in Table 7.

TABLE 7—MATERIAL PACKAGING

	Container Size	Recommended Storage Temp.[1] Range	Shelf Life (minimum)
Anaerobic	6 mL	10 to 32 °C	12 months
	50 mL		
	300 mL		
	1000 mL		
RTV	88.5 mL	10 to 32 °C	12 months
	236 mL		
	295 mL		
	19 L		
	209 L		

Dating —open date (use before December 1987)
—coded date (Manufacturer's Code)

1. Application temperature must be 18 °C minimum for proper application and curing.

4.6.5.7 Shelf Life—To assure proper performance, the manufacturer's shelf recommendation should be followed. This is assured by practicing good stock rotation.

5. Troubleshooting, Service, and Repair

5.1 Troubleshooting

5.1.1 Proper diagnosis of suspected leaks is essential. Be sure of the origin point of a leak. Check with the owner of maintenance records. They may provide a clue as to the origin of the leak. Engine fluids tend to migrate to other areas giving the false impression of the leak location. A clear view of the suspected leak area is important. This may necessitate removal of adjacent parts.

Recommendations for Hand Dispensing One-Component RTV Silicone Sealants

Applications in which RTV silicone sealants are dispensed by hand frequently require that the material be dispensed into a crack as a seal, into a corner as a fillet, or onto one of the mating surfaces of two parts to be joined, either as a bond or as a formed-in-place gasket.

When RTV silicone sealant is dispensed by hand into a crack or into a corner as a fillet, the preferred technique is to cut the nozzle at an angle and push the material ahead of the nozzle. Tooling the material, if desired, must be performed immediately.

If the RTV silicone sealant is dispensed as a formed-in-place gasket, or in any application where a uniform bead is required, the following technique is recommended:

1 Cut the nozzle tip off so that the nozzle diameter is equal to the desired bead diameter.

2 Adjust the dispensing rate to a very slow speed of the bead to approximately ½ in. per second if you are using an air-operated gun.

3 Place the nozzle tip against the work surface and begin dispensing the bead. (Step A.)

4 As the bead begins to extrude, raise the nozzle approximately 1 in. to 1½ in. above the work piece so that the bead hangs from the tip of the nozzle like a rubber hose. The thixotropic characteristic of the material prevents the bead from breaking providing a certain amount of slack or drape is maintained. This slack will allow small erratic movements of the nozzle due to normal shakiness of the hand without affecting the location of the bead. (Step B.)

5 Continue to extrude the bead from the nozzle with nozzle tip raised above the part, but concentrate on the exact point where the draped bead contacts the surface. (Step C.)

6 When the bead pattern is near completion, judge the distance to complete the bead as slightly less than the distance at which you are holding the nozzle above the part, and stop extruding the beac. Complete the pattern with the remainder of the bead draped from the top of the nozzle. (Step D.)

7 A slight wipe of the nozzle tip against the surface breaks the bead neatly from the nozzle tip.

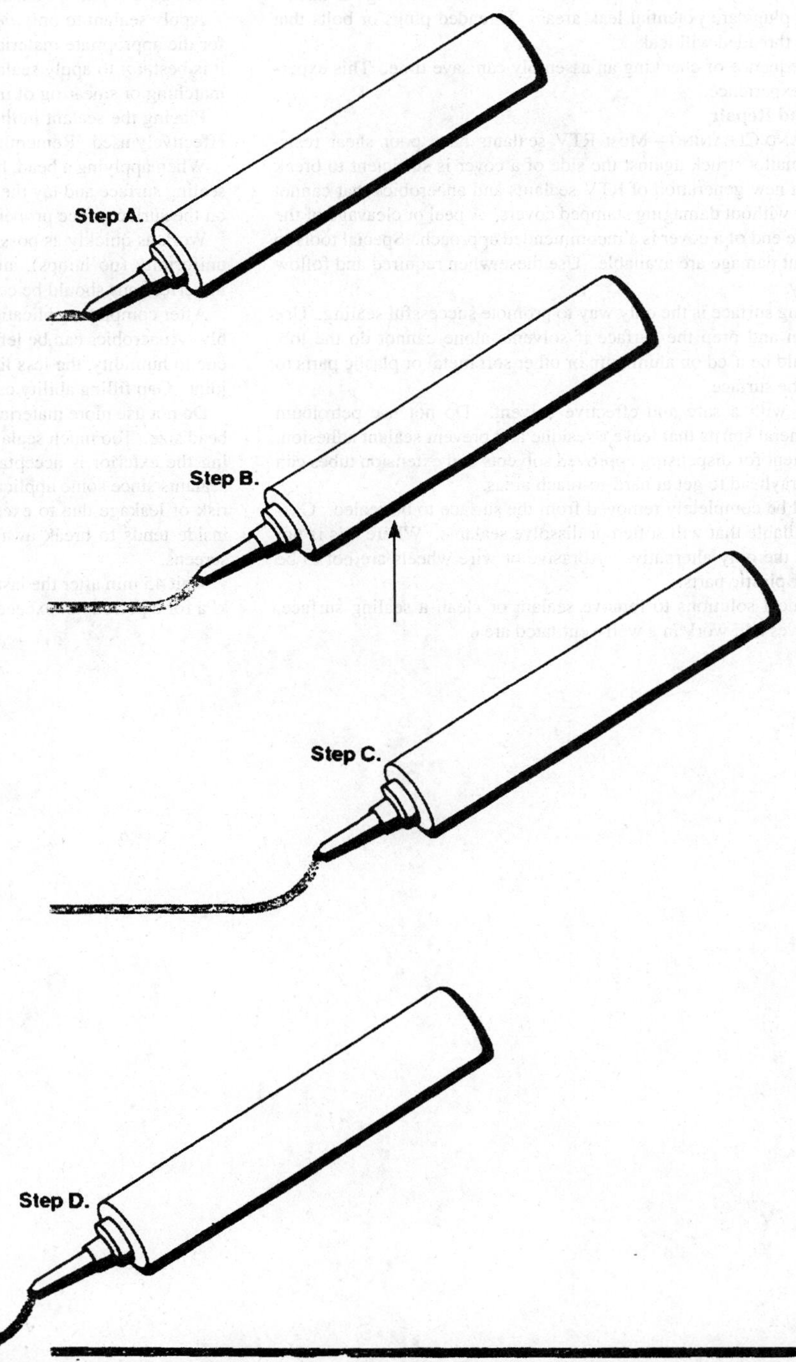

FIGURE 17—RECOMMENDATIONS FOR HAND DISPENSING ONE-COMPONENT RTV SILICON SEALANTS

5.1.2 UV sensitive fluorescent dyes used with a black light are an effective method for leak detection. Remember that anaerobics fluoresce under UV light. Use a high quality dye that has a good shelf life and give an intense color response to black light with minimal use. Other detection methods commonly used are air pressure with soap solution and aerosol powders (foot powder).

5.1.3 Allow sufficient time for the dye to circulate in the system. The smaller the potential leaks, the longer it takes the dye to penetrate. Check (for leaks) incrementally after sufficient running time.

5.1.4 Cleaning the assembly is strongly recommended to make detection easier.

5.1.5 Pressurizing the system with air up to 13.8 kPa maximum is recommended to promote leak detection. Use sensitive, accurate gages intended for this pressure range.

5.1.6 Leaks do not always occur at joint areas. Pin holes in castings or undertorqued, misaligned plugs are potential leak areas. Threaded plugs or bolts that are stripped or cross threaded will leak.

5.1.7 A plan or sequence of checking an assembly can save time. This expertise will come with experience.

5.2 Service and Repair

5.2.1 Removal And Cleaning—Most RTV sealants have poor shear resistance and a rubber mallet struck against the side of a cover is sufficient to break the bond. There is a new generation of RTV sealants and anaerobics that cannot be removed this way without damaging stamped covers. A peel or cleavage of the material by lifting the end of a cover is a recommended approach. Special tools to separate parts without damage are available. Use these when required and follow instructions carefully.

Cleaning the sealing surface is the only way to promote successful sealing. Use proper tools to clean and prep the surface if solvents alone cannot do the job. Plastic scrapers should be used on aluminum or other soft metal or plastic parts to prevent gouging of the surface.

Clean the surface with a safe and effective solvent. Do not use petroleum cleaners, such as mineral spirits that leave a residue and prevent sealant adhesion. Aerosols are convenient for dispensing approved solvents and extension tubes can be attached to the sprayhead to get at hard-to-reach areas.

Old sealant should be completely removed from the surface to be sealed. Gasket removers are available that will soften or dissolve sealants. Where this is not possible, scraping is the only alternative. Abrasive or wire wheels are not to be used on aluminum or plastic parts.

When using chemical solutions to remove sealant or clean a sealing surface, remember to use gloves and work in a well-ventilated area.

When possible, suggest and identify approved equivalent cleaning and sealing material. This enables the mechanic to use the correct material for the job and eliminate guesswork.

5.2.2 Resealing—Primers are available to promote adhesion for RTV sealants or anaerobics. Follow recommended practices for the product or application.

Follow the proper sequence of assembly during service for your particular equipment. Joining of parts in a timely sequence is dictated by the material. RTV sealant applied to a joint must be assembled immediately. Anaerobics can be left open, but never rest a cover on it without torquing it down. Partial cure can result where the cover contacts the anaerobic.

Use the correct material to seal job. To correctly seal an application, you must know the limits of your material. For example, FIPG materials have different temperature limits, seal a range of gaps, have various cure times, and possess different cure depths. Consult raw material source for literature and guidelines.

Apply sealant to only *one* of the sealing surfaces. Follow outlined instructions for the appropriate material, bead shape, and dimension. In service applications, it is best *not* to apply sealant to the cover unless instructed to do so to avoid mismatching or smearing of material.

Placing the sealant in the correct location is necessary if all the sealant is to be effectively used. Remember to circle the bolt holes when hand applying sealant.

When applying a bead, hold the cartridge/tube tip up and slightly away from the sealing surface and lay the bead onto the joint. Do not hold the nozzle tip directly on the surface since proper bead shape will be harder to control.

Work as quickly as possible when applying RTV sealants. Inspect the bead for uniformity (no lumps), air pocket voids, thin areas, or skips. Repairs to these imperfections should be completed as soon as possible.

After complete application of the sealant, RTV joints require immediate assembly. Anaerobics can be left open for a short time. The heavier the skin formation due to humidity, the less likely the material will flow uniformly in the assembled joint. Gap filling ability can be greatly sacrificed.

Do not use more material than necessary to seal a joint; apply the recommended bead size. Too much sealant tends to squeeze out on either side of the joint. Wiping the exterior is acceptable for anaerobics, but is not recommended for RTV sealants since some applications are of the positive gap type and there is a greater risk of leakage due to excessive removal of material. Excessive material on the inside tends to break away in the assembly plugging coolant passageways and screens.

Wait 45 min after the last repair before pressure testing at no more than 13.8 kPa for a period not exceeding 2 min.

STANDARD CLASSIFICATION SYSTEM FOR NONMETALLIC AUTOMOTIVE GASKET MATERIALS—SAE J90 MAR1995

SAE Recommended Practice

Report of the SAE Nonmetallic Materials Committee approved January 1952 and revised August 1970. Editorial change July 1971. Completely revised by the SAE Gasketing Standards Committee June 1990, and reaffirmed March 1995.

Foreword—This reaffirmed document has not changed other than to put it into the new SAE Technical Standards Board Format.

1. Scope

1.1 The classification system provides a means for specifying or describing pertinent properties of commercial nonmetallic gasket materials. Materials composed of asbestos, cork, cellulose, and other organic or inorganic materials in combination with various binders or impregnants are included. Materials normally classified as rubber compounds are not included, since they are covered in SAE J200—ASTM D 2000. Gasket coatings are not covered, since details thereof are intended to be given on engineering drawings or in separate specifications.

1.2 Since all of the properties that contribute to gasket performance are not included, use of the classification system as a basis for selecting materials is limited.

1.3 The values stated in SI units are to be regarded as the standard. The values given in parentheses are for information only.

1.4 This SAE Recommended Practice may involve hazardous materials, operations, and equipment. This document does not purport to address all of the safety problems associated with its use. It is the responsibility of the user of this document to establish appropriate safety and health practices and determine the applicability of regulatory limitations prior to use.

2. References

2.1 Applicable Publications—The following publications form a part of this specification to the extent specified herein. The latest issue of SAE publications shall apply.

2.1.1 SAE PUBLICATIONS—Available from SAE, 400 Commonwealth Drive, Warrendale, PA 15096-0001.

SAE J90—Standard Classification System for Nonmetallic Automotive Gasket Materials

SAE J200—Classification System for Rubber Products in Automotive Applications

2.1.2 ASTM PUBLICATIONS—Available from ASTM, 100 Barr Harbor Drive, West Conshohocken, PA 19428-2959.

ASTM D 2000—Classification System for Rubber Products in Automotive Applications

ASTM E 11—Specification for Wire-Cloth Sieves for Testing Purposes

ASTM F 36—Test Method for Compressibility and Recovery of Gasket Materials

ASTM F 37—Test Methods for Sealability of Gasket Materials

ASTM F 38—Test Methods for Creep Relaxation of a Gasket Material

ASTM F 146—Test Methods for Fluid Resistance of Gasket Materials

ASTM F 147—Test Method for Flexibility of Non-Metallic Gasket Materials

ASTM F 148—Test Method for Binder Durability of Cork Composition Gasket Materials

ASTM F 152—Test Methods for Tension Testing of Nonmetallic Gasket Materials

ASTM F 433—Practice for Evaluating Thermal Conductivity of Gasket Materials

ASTM F 607—Test Method for Adhesion of Gasket Materials to Metal Surfaces

3. Significance and Use

3.1 This classification is intended to encourage uniformity in reporting properties; to provide a common language for communications between suppliers and consumers; to guide engineers and designers in the test methods commonly used for commercially available materials; and to be versatile enough to cover new materials and test methods as they are introduced.

3.2 It is based on the principle that nonmetallic gasket materials should be described, insofar as is possible, in terms of specific physical and mechanical characteristics, and that an infinite number of such descriptions can be formulated by use of one or more standard statements based on standard tests. Therefore, users of gasket materials can, by selecting different combinations of statements, specify different combinations of properties desired in various parts. Suppliers, likewise, can report properties available in their respective products.

4. Basis of Classification

4.1 To permit "line call-out" of the descriptions mentioned in 3.2, this classification system establishes letter or number symbols or both for various performance levels of each property or characteristic (see Table 1).

4.2 In specifying or describing gasket materials, each "line call-out" shall include the number of this system (minus date symbol) followed by the letter "F" and six numerals, for example: SAE J90 (F125400). Since each numeral of the call-out represents a characteristic (as shown in Table 1), six numerals are always required. The numeral "0" is used when the description of any characteristic is not desired. The numeral "9" is used when the description of any characteristic (or test related thereto) is specified by some supplement to this classification system, such as notes on engineering drawings.

4.3 To further specify or describe gasket materials, each "line call-out" may include one or more suffix letter-numeral symbols, as listed in Table 2, for example: SAE J90 (F125400-B2M4). Various levels of definition may be established by increasing or decreasing the number of letter-numeral symbols used in the "line call-out."

4.4 For convenience, gasket materials are referred to by Type according to the principal fibrous or particulate reinforcement or other material from which the gasket is made and by Class according to the manufacturing method, or the common trade designation. Type numbers correspond with the first numeral, and class numbers correspond with the second numeral of the basic six-digit line call-out, as shown in Table 1.

NOTE—While this "cell-type" format provides the means for close characterization and specification of each property and combinations of properties for a broad range of materials, it is subject to possible misapplications, since impossible property combinations can be coded if the user is not familiar with available commercial materials. Table A1 of this classification indicates properties, characteristics, and test methods that are normally considered applicable to each type of material.

5. Physical and Mechanical Requirements

5.1 Gasket materials identified by this classification shall have the characteristics or properties indicated by the first six numerals of the line call-out, within the limits shown in Table 1, and by additional letter-numeral symbols shown in Table 2.

6. Thickness Requirements

6.1 Gasket materials identified by this classification system shall conform to the thickness tolerances specified in Table 3.

7. Sampling

7.1 Specimens shall be selected from finished gaskets or sheets of suitable size, whichever is the more practicable. If sheets are used, they shall, where applicable, be cut squarely with the grain of the stock, and the grain direction shall be noted by an arrow. If finished gaskets are used, the dimensions of sample and any variations from method must be reported.

7.2 For qualification purposes, thickness shall be 0.8 mm (0.03 in), except for Type 2, where the qualification thickness is to be 1.5 to 6.4 mm (0.06 to 0.25 in), and Type 5 Class 1, where the qualification thickness is to be 0.4 mm (0.015 in). When thicknesses other than those shown previously are to be tested, the specification limits shall be agreed to in writing between the purchaser and the supplier.

7.3 Sufficient specimens shall be selected to provide a minimum of three determinations for each test specified. The average of the determinations shall be considered as the result.

8. Conditioning

8.1 Prior to all applicable tests, specimens shall be conditioned as follows:

8.1.1 When the first numeral of line call-out is "1" (Type 1 materials), specimens shall be conditioned in an oven at 100 °C ± 2 °C (212 °F ± 3.6 °F) for 1 h and allowed to cool to 21 to 30 °C (70 to 85 °F) in a desiccator containing anhydrous calcium chloride; except when second numeral of line call-out is "3" (Class 3 materials), the specimens shall be conditioned in an oven for 4 h at 100 °C ± 2 °C (212 °F ± 3.6 °F).

TABLE 1—BASIC PHYSICAL AND MECHANICAL CHARACTERISTICS

Basic Six-Digit Number	Basic Characteristic	
First Numeral	"Type" of material (the principal fibrous or particulate reinforcement material from which the gasket is made) shall conform to the first numeral of the basic six-digit number, as follows:	
	0 = not specified	
	1 = asbestos	
	2 = cork	
	3 = cellulose	
	4 = fluorocarbon polymer	
	5 = flexible graphite	
	7 = nonasbestos, tested as Type 1	
	9 = as specified[1]	
Second Numeral	Class of material (method of manufacture or common trade designation) shall conform to the second numeral of the basic six-digit number, as follows:	
	When first numeral is "0" or "9," second numeral:	
	0 = not specified	
	9 = as specified[1]	
	When first numeral is "1" or "7," second numeral:	
	0 = not specified	
	1 = compressed sheeter process	
	2 = beater process	
	3 = paper and millboard	
	9 = as specified[1]	
	When first numeral is "2," second numeral:	
	0 = not specified	
	1 = cork composition (Class 1)	
	2 = cork and elastomeric (Class 2)	
	3 = cork and cellular rubber (Class 3)	
	9 = as specified[1]	
	When first numeral is "3," second numeral:	
	0 = not specified	
	1 = untreated fiber—tag, chipboard, vulcanized fiber, etc. (Class 1)	
	2 = protein treated (Class 2)	
	3 = elastomeric treated (Class 3)	
	4 = thermosetting resin treated (Class 4)	
	9 = as specified[1]	
	When first numeral is "4," second numeral:	
	0 = not specified	
	1 = sheet PTFE	
	2 = PTFE of expanded structure	
	3 = PTFE filaments, braided, or woven	
	4 = PTFE felts	
	5 = filled PTFE	
	9 = as specified	
	When first numeral is "5," second numeral:	
	0 = not specified	
	1 = homogeneous sheet	
	2 = laminated sheet	
	9 = as specified[1]	
Third Numeral	Compressibility characteristics, determined in accordance with 9.2, shall conform to the percent indicated by the third numeral of the basic six-digit number. (Example: 4 = 15 to 25%)	
	0 = not specified	5 = 20 to 30%
	1 = 0 to 10%	6 = 25 to 40%
	2 = 5 to 15%*	7 = 30 to 50%
	3 = 10 to 20%	8 = 40 to 60%
	4 = 15 to 25%	9 = as specified[1]
	*7 to 17% for compressed sheeter process	
Fourth Numeral	Thickness increase when immersed in ASTM No. 3 Oil: determined in accordance with 9.3, shall conform to the percent indicated by the fourth numeral of the basic six-digit number. (Example: 4 = 15 to 30%)	
	0 = not specified	5 = 20 to 40%
	1 = 0 to 15%	6 = 30 to 50%
	2 = 5 to 20%	7 = 40 to 60%
	3 = 10 to 25%	8 = 50 to 70%
	4 = 15 to 30%	9 = as specified[1]
Fifth Numeral	Weight increase when immersed in ASTM No. 3 Oil: determined in accordance with 9.3, shall conform to the percent indicated by the fifth numeral of the basic six-digit number. (Example: 4 = 30% max)	
	0 = not specified	5 = 40%, max
	1 = 10%, max	6 = 60%, max
	2 = 15%, max	7 = 80%, max
	3 = 20%, max	8 = 100%, max
	4 = 30%, max	9 = as specified[1]
Sixth Numeral	Weight increase when immersed in water: determined in accordance with 9.3, shall conform to the percent indicated by the sixth numeral of the basic six-digit number. (Example: 4 = 30%, max)	
	0 = not specified	5 = 40%, max
	1 = 10%, max	6 = 60%, max
	2 = 15%, max	7 = 80%, max
	3 = 20%, max	8 = 100%, max
	4 = 30%, max	9 = as specified[1]

1. On engineering drawings or other supplement to this classification system.

TABLE 2—SUPPLEMENTARY PHYSICAL AND MECHANICAL CHARACTERISTICS

Suffix Symbol	Supplementary Characteristics	
A9	Sealability characteristics shall be determined in accordance with 9.4. External load, internal pressure, other details of test, and results shall be as specified on engineering drawing or other supplement to this classification.	
B1 through B9	Creep relaxation characteristics shall be determined in accordance with 9.5. Loss of stress at end of 24 h shall not exceed the amount indicated by the numeral of the B-symbol.	
	B1 = 10%	B5 = 30%
	B2 = 15%	B6 = 40%
	B3 = 20%	B7 = 50%
	B4 = 25%	B8 = 60%
		B9 = as specified[(1)]
D00 through D99	The former ASTM standard F 64, Test Method for Corrosive and Adhesive Effects of Gasket Materials on Metal Surfaces, was discontinued in 1980. The recently established test for adhesion has become Test Method ASTM F 607.	
E00 through E99	Weight and thickness change after immersion in ASTM Fuel B shall be determined in accordance with 9.3. Weight increase shall not exceed the standard rating number indicated by the first numeral of the two-digit number of the E-symbol. Thickness increase shall not exceed the standard rating number indicated by the second numeral of the E-symbol.	
	Weight Increase, % (first numeral)	Thickness Increase, % (second numeral)
	E0_ = not specified	E_0 = not specified
	E1_ = 10	E_1 = 0 to 5
	E2_ = 15	E_2 = 0 to 10
	E3_ = 20	E_3 = 0 to 15
	E4_ = 30	E_4 = 5 to 20
	E5_ = 40	E_5 = 10 to 25
	E6_ = 60	E_6 = 15 to 35
	E7_ = 80	E_7 = 25 to 45
	E8_ = 100	E_8 = 30 to 60
	E9_ = as specified[(1)]	E_9 = as specified[(1)]
H	Adhesion characteristics shall be determined in accordance with 9.6. Results shall be as specified on engineering drawing or other supplement to this classification.	
K1 through K9	Thermal conductivity characteristics shall be determined in accordance with 9.10. The K-factor obtained in W/(m·K)(Btu·in/h·ft^2·°F) shall fall within the ranges indicated by the numeral of a K symbol.	
	K1 = 0.00 to 0.09 (0.00 to 0.65)	K5 = 0.29 to 0.38 (2.00 to 2.65)
	K2 = 0.07 to 0.17 (0.50 to 1.15)	K6 = 0.36 to 0.45 (2.50 to 3.15)
	K3 = 0.14 to 0.24 (1.00 to 1.65)	K7 = 0.43 to 0.53 (3.00 to 3.65)
	K4 = 0.22 to 0.31 (1.50 to 2.15)	K8 = 0.50 to 0.60 (3.50 to 4.15)
		K9 = as specified[(1)]
M1 through M9	Tensile strength characteristics shall be determined in accordance with 9.7. Results in MPa (psi) shall be no less than the value indicated by the numeral of the M-symbol.	
	M1 = 0.689 (100)	M5 = 10.342 (1500)
	M2 = 1.724 (250)	M6 = 13.790 (2000)
	M3 = 3.447 (500)	M7 = 20.684 (3000)
	M4 = 6.895 (1000)	M8 = 27.579 (4000)
		M9 = as specified[(1)]
R	Binder Durability characteristics shall be determined in accordance with 9.8. There shall be no evidence of disintegration at conclusion of test.	
S9	Volume change characteristics, when immersed in ASTM No. 1 Oil, ASTM No. 3 Oil, and ASTM Reference Fuel A, shall be determined in accordance with 9.3. Results shall be as specified on engineering drawing or other supplement to this classification.	
T	Flexibility characteristics shall be determined in accordance with 9.9. There shall be no evidence of cracks, breaks, or separation at conclusion of test.	
Z	Other characteristics shall be as specified on engineering drawing or other supplement to this classification.	

1. On engineering drawing or other supplement to this classification system.

TABLE 3—THICKNESS TOLERANCES

Type and Class of Material (First Two Numerals of Basic Six-Digit Number)	Thickness Specified, mm (in)	Applicable Tolerance,[1] mm (in)
11 and 12	0.41 (0.016) and under	+0.13 (+0.005) -0.05 (-0.002)
	over 0.41 (0.016) and under 1.57 (0.062)	±0.13 (±0.005)
	1.57 (0.062) and over	±0.20 (±0.008)
13	up to 3.18 (0.125)	±0.13 (±0.005)
	3.18 (0.125) to 12.70 (0.500)	±0.25 (±0.010)
21	all thicknesses	±10%, or ±0.25 (±0.010) whichever is the greater
22	under 1.57 (0.062)	±0.25 (±0.010)
	1.57 (0.062) and over	±0.38 (±0.015)
23	1.57 (0.062) and over	±0.38 (±0.015)
31, 32, and 33 (also 00 and 99) [2]	0.41 (0.016) and under	±0.089 (±0.0035)
	over 0.41 (0.016) to 1.57 (0.062)	±0.13 (±0.005)
	over 1.57 (0.062) to 2.39 (0.094)	±0.20 (±0.008)
	over 2.39 (0.094)	±0.41 (±0.016)
51	1.6 (0.062) and under	±0.051 (±0.002)
52	12.7 (0.5) and under	±10%

1. Tolerances listed are permissible variations applicable to a given lot of sheets or gaskets. Where other thickness tolerances are necessary due to the gasket application, tolerances applicable to individual sheet or gasket may be agreed to in writing between the purchaser and the supplier.
2. Unless otherwise specified on engineering drawing or other supplement to this classification system.

8.1.2 When the first numeral of line call-out is "2" (Type 2 materials), specimens shall be conditioned at least 46 h in a controlled-humidity room or in a closed chamber with gentle mechanical circulation of the air at 21 to 30 °C (70 to 85 °F) and 50 to 55% relative humidity.

NOTE—If a mechanical means of maintaining 50 to 55% relative humidity is not available, a tray containing a saturated solution of reagent grade magnesium nitrate, $Mg(NO_3)_2 \cdot 6H_2O$, shall be placed in the chamber to provide the required relative humidity.

8.1.3 When the first numeral of line call-out is "3" (Type 3 materials), specimens shall be preconditioned for 4 h at 21 to 30 °C (70 to 85 °F) in a closed chamber containing anhydrous calcium chloride as a desiccant. The air in the chamber shall be circulated by gentle mechanical agitation. Specimens shall then be transferred immediately to a controlled-humidity room or closed chamber with gentle mechanical circulation of the air and conditioned for at least 20 h at 21 to 30 °C (70 to 85 °F) and 50 to 55% relative humidity.

8.1.4 When the first numeral of a line call-out is "4", no conditioning of specimens is necessary.

8.1.5 When the first numeral of a line call-out is "5", test specimens shall be conditioned in accordance with 8.1.1 (Type 1 materials).

8.1.6 When the first numeral of a line call-out is "0" or "9", specimens shall be conditioned as in 8.1.3, unless otherwise specified in supplements to this classification.

8.2 In all cases where testing is conducted outside the area of specified humidity, specimens shall be removed from the chamber one at a time just prior to testing.

9. Test Methods

9.1 Thickness

9.1.1 The specimens shall be measured with a device actuated by a deadweight load. The device shall be capable of reading in 0.02 mm (0.001 in) or smaller units, and readings shall be estimated to the nearest 0.002 mm (0.0001 in). The presser foot shall be 6.40 mm ±0.13 mm (0.252 in ±0.005 in) in diameter. The anvil shall have a diameter not less than that of the presser foot. The pressure on the sample shall be as specified in Table 4.

TABLE 4—THICKNESS MEASUREMENT STRESSES AND FORCES

Type of Material of First Numeral of Six-Digit Number	Pressure on Sample, kPa (psi)	Total Force on Presser Foot, N (oz) (reference)
1	80.3 ±6.9 (11.5 ±1.0)	2.50 (9.0)
2	35 ±6.9 (5.1 ±1.0)	1.11 (4.0)
3	55 ±6.9 (8.0 ±1.0)	1.75 (6.3)
0 and 9 [1]	55 ±6.9 (8.0 ±1.0)	1.75 (6.3)
5	80.3 ±6.9 (11.5 ±1.0)	2.50 (9.0)

1. Unless otherwise specified on engineering drawing or other supplement to this classification system.

9.1.2 The reading shall be taken by lowering the presser foot gently until it is in contact with the specimen. A sufficient number of readings shall be taken, depending on the size of the specimen, to provide a reliable average value.

9.2 Compressibility and Recovery—Specimens shall be tested in accordance with Test Method ASTM F 36 using the procedure which is applicable to the material described by the first two numerals of the basic six-digit number, as given in Table 5.

TABLE 5—COMPRESSIBILITY TEST METHODS

First Two Numerals of Six-Digit Number	Procedure, Test Method ASTM F 36	Pressure, MPa (psi)
11 and 12	A	34.474 (5000)
13	H	6.895 (1000)
21 and 23	F	0.689 (100)
22	B	2.758 (400)
31, 32, 33, and 34	G	6.895 (1000)
00 and 99	G [1]	6.895 (1000)
51 and 52	A	34.474 (5000)
71 and 72	J	34.474 (5000)
73	K	6.895 (1000)

1. Unless otherwise specified on engineering drawing or other supplement to this classification system.

9.3 Fluid Resistance—Specimens shall be tested in accordance with Test Method ASTM F 146.

9.3.1 OTHER TYPES OF MATERIALS (AS INDICATED BY 0 OR 9 FIRST NUMERAL OF BASIC SIX-DIGIT NUMBER)—Use the same apparatus and general procedure outlined for Type 3 materials, unless otherwise specified in the engineering drawing or other supplement to this classification.

9.4 Sealability—Specimens shall be tested in accordance with Test Method ASTM F 37.

9.5 Creep Relaxation—Specimens shall be tested in accordance with Test Method ASTM F 38.

9.6 Adhesion—Specimens shall be tested in accordance with Test Method ASTM F 607.

9.7 Tensile Strength—Specimens shall be tested in accordance with Test Method ASTM F 152.

9.7.1 OTHER TYPES OF MATERIAL (AS INDICATED BY 0 OR 9 FIRST NUMERAL OF BASIC SIX-DIGIT NUMBER)—Use the same apparatus and general procedure outlined for Type 3 materials, unless otherwise specified on engineering drawing or other supplement to this classification.

9.8 Binder Durability—Specimens shall be tested in accordance with appropriate procedures in Test Method ASTM F 148.

9.9 Flexibility—Specimens shall be tested in accordance with appropriate procedures in Test Method ASTM F 147.

9.10 Thermal Conductivity—Specimens shall be tested in accordance with Practice ASTM F 433, using a temperature of 100 °C ± 2 °C (212 °F ± 3.6 °F).

APPENDIX A
(NONMANDATORY INFORMATION)

A.1 Applicable Test Methods

A.1.1 Table A1 indicates properties, characteristics, and test methods that are normally considered applicable to each type of material. It is not intended to limit the use of numeral-symbols as provided in Classification System SAE J90 where experience indicates that the related properties, characteristics, or test methods, or both, are applicable.

A.1.2 Table A2 is being provided to offer an explanation of the system of identification of gasket materials previously used in SAE J90a which has been superseded by Classification System SAE J90.

A.1.3 Tables A3, A4, and A5 are also retained in this appendix to provide a reference for transforming formerly used P-number identification into the present SAE J90.

TABLE A1—TYPICAL TYPES OF MATERIALS

NOTE: "X" indicates that the test conditions shown in first column have been used to characterize the type of material named in column heading.

"Dash" (-) indicates that the test method is either "not applicable" to the material named or has not been commonly used in characterizing the material.

Properties, Characteristics, and Test methods	Type 1, Asbestos or Other Inorganic Fibers	Type 1, Asbestos or Other Inorganic Fibers	Type 1, Asbestos or Other Inorganic Fibers	Type 2, Cork	Type 2, Cork	Type 2, Cork	Type 3, Cellulose or Other Organic Fibers	Type 3, Cellulose or Other Organic Fibers	Type 3, Cellulose or Other Organic Fibers	Type 5, Flexible Graphite	Type 5, Flexible Graphite
	Compressed Asbestos	Beater Addition Asbestos	Asbestos Paper and Asbestos	Cork Composition	Cork and Elastomeric	Cork and Cellular Rubber	Untreated Fiber	Treated Protein	Treated Elastomeric	Homogen-eous Sheet	Laminated Sheet
Compressibility:											
5000-psi load (Test Method F 36, Procedure A)	X	X	—	—	—	—	—	—	—	X	X
5000-psi load (Test Method F 36, Procedure J) (1)	X	X	—	—	—	—	—	—	—	X	X
1000-psi load (Test Method F 36, Procedure H)	—	—	X	—	—	—	—	—	—	—	—
1000-psi load (Test Method F 36, Procedure K)[1]	—	—	X	—	—	—	—	—	—	—	—
1000-psi load (Test Method F 36, Procedure G)	—	—	—	—	—	—	X	X	X	—	—
100-psi load (Test Method F 36, Procedure F)	—	—	—	X	—	X	—	—	—	—	—
400-psi load (Test Method F 36, Procedure B)	—	—	—	—	X	—	—	—	—	—	—
Tensile strength	X	X	X	X	X	X	X	X	X	X	X
Resistance to exposure in ASTM No. 3 Oil:											
Volume change, 70 h at 212° F	—	—	—	—	X	X	—	—	—	—	—
Weight increase, 22 h at 70 85° F	—	—	—	—	—	—	X	X	X	—	—
Thickness increase: 22 h at 70 to 85° F	—	—	—	—	—	—	X	X	X	—	—
5 h at 300° F	X	X	—	—	—	—	—	—	—	—	—
Resistance to exposure in ASTM Fuel B:											
Weight increase: 22 h at 70 to 85° F	—	—	—	—	—	—	X	X	X	—	—
5 h at 70 to 85° F	X	X	—	—	—	—	—	—	—	—	—
Thickness change: 22 h at 70 to 85 ° F	—	—	—	—	—	—	X	X	X	—	—
5 h at 70 to 85 ° F	X	X	—	—	—	—	—	—	—	—	—
Resistance to exposure in ASTM No. 1 Oil:											
Volume change, 70 h at 212 ° F	—	—	—	—	X	X	X	—	—	—	—
Resistance to exposure in ASTM Fuel A:											
Volume change, 22 h at 70 to 85 ° F	—	—	—	—	X	X	X	—	—	—	—
Resistance to exposure in distilled water:											
Weight increase, 22 h at 70 to 85 ° F	—	—	—	—	—	—	X	X	X		
Thickness change, 22 h at 70 to 85 ° F	—	—	—	—	—	—	X	X	X	—	—
Sealability	X	X	X	X	X	X	X	X	X	X	X
Creep relaxation	X	X	—	—	—	—	—	—	—	X	X
Binder durability	—	—	—	X	—	—	—	—	—	—	—
Flexibility	—	—	—	X	X	X	—	—	—	X	X
Thermal conductivity	X	X	X	X	X	X	X	X	X	X	X

1. Type 7, Nonasbestos

TABLE A2—SYSTEM OF IDENTIFICATION

Digit	Type 1	Type 2	Type 3
First Digit (principal fibrous or particulate material)	1. Asbestos or other inorganic fibers	2. Cork	3. Cellulose or other organic fibers
Second Digit (trade designation)	1. Compressed asbestos sheet 2. Asbestos beater sheet 3. Asbestos paper and millboard	1. Cork composition 2. Cork and rubber 3. Cork and cellular rubber	0. Tag 1. Chipboard 2. Vulcanized fiber 3. Cellulose fiber 4. Fiber and filler compositions
Third Digit (binder or treatment other than sizing)	0. None 1. Protein (glue-glycerin or equivalent) 2. Resin 3. Rubber, Type S, Class A (polysulfide or equivalent) 4. Rubber, Type S, Class SB (acrylonitrile or equivalent) 5. Rubber, Type S, Class SC (chloroprene or equivalent) 6. Rubber, Type R (natural, reclaim, styrene, or equivalent)	(Same for all three types)	
Fourth Digit (compressibility index, Test Method ASTM F 36, Procedure G, total load—1000 psi). For identification purposes only. May not agree with compressibility in tables where other loads are employed.	0. 0 to 5% 1. 6 to 15% 2. 16 to 25% 3. 26 to 35% 4. 36 to 45% 5. 46 to 55% 6. 56 to 65% 7. 66 to 75% 8. 76 to 85% 9. 86 to 95%	(Same for all three types)	
Suffix Letter	Used to distinguish grades of material within one 4-digit category which differ sufficiently to justify separate tabular values. If only one grade of material is listed in the table, the letter "A" is used.		

Example: Letter indicating a gasket material included in ASTM D 1170

Cellulose or other organic fibers

Rope or chemical wood, or both

Binder or treatment, rubber, Type S, Class SC

Compressibility index is 26 to 35%

Grade

P 3 3 5 3 A

TABLE A3—TYPE 1—ASBESTOS OR OTHER INORGANIC FIBERS

		Original Properties	Original Properties	Original Properties	Original Properties	Original Properties	Properties after Immersion in Liquids	Properties after Immersion in Liquids	Properties after Immersion in Liquids	Properties after Immersion in Liquids	Properties after Immersion in Liquids
Identification No.(1)	Former "G" No. (for reference only)	Compressibility	Compressibility	Compressibility	Tensile Strength, min, psi	Ignition Loss, max, %	After Aging 5 h at 150 °C ±2 °C (300 °F ±3.6 °F) in ASTM Oil No. 3	After Aging 5 h at 150 °C ±2 °C (300 °F ±3.6 °F) in ASTM Oil No. 3	After Aging 5 h at 150 °C ±2 °C (300 °F ±3.6 °F) in ASTM Oil No. 3	After Aging 5 h at 21 to 30 °C (70 to 85 °F) in ASTM Reference Fuel B	After Aging 5 h at 21 to 30 °C (70 to 85 °F) in ASTM Reference Fuel B
		Total Load, psi	Compressibility, %	Recovery, min, %			Compressibility max, %	Loss in Tensile Strength, max, %	Thickness Increase, %	Weight Increase max, %	Thickness Increase, %
P1141A	1122-1	5000	7 to 17	40	2000	—	20	30	0 to 13	20	0 to 15
P1151A	1123-1	5000	7 to 17	40	2000	—	30	50	15 to 30	30	10 to 25
P1161A	1111-1	5000	7 to 17	40	2000	—	—	70	20 to 50	40	15 to 35
P1161B	—	5000	7 to 17	40	2000	—	—	80	40 to 70	50	25 to 45
P1162A	1111-2	5000	15 to 25	30	1600	—	—	70	20 to 50	40	15 to 35
P1241C	—	5000	13 to 23	35	1000	—	30	35	5 to 20	30	0 to 15
P1242C	—	5000	30 to 40	30	1700	—	45	15	0 to 20	50	0 to 15
P1242D	—	5000	20 to 30	35	200	—	35	20	0 to 20	40	0 to 15
P1243C	1422-2	5000	35 to 50	15	500	—	55	25	0 to 5	50	0 to 5
P1251A	1423-1	5000	10 to 20	40	2000	—	35	40	10 to 20	35	0 to 15
P1252A	1423-2	5000	20 to 30	35	1000	—	—	60	20 to 35	50	05 to 20
P1252D	—	5000	30 to 40	35	1200	—	45	30	10 to 25	50	5 to 20
P1252E	—	5000	20 to 30	35	1200	—	40	40	10 to 25	45	5 to 20
P1253A	1423-3	5000	35 to 50	20	1000	—	—	50	0 to 15	55	0 to 10
P1261A	—	5000	15 to 30	30	1200	—	—	60	10 to 25	60	05 to 20
P1262B	—	5000	25 to 40	35	1000	—	—	80	10 to 40	70	0 to 30
P1301A	4131	1000	6 to 15	40	200	20	—	—	—	—	—
P1302A	4111	1000	16 to 25	30	175	20	—	—	—	—	—

1.Thickness tolerances:

	Thickness	Tolerance
P1100 and P1200 Series	1/64 in and under	+0.005 in -0.002 in
	Over 1/64 in and under 1/16 in	±0.005 in
	1/16 in and over	±0.008 in ±10%
P1301 P1302A	Up to 1/8 in	±0.005 in
	1/8 to 1/2 in	±0.010 in

The above thickness tolerances are permissible variations applicable to a given lot of sheets or gaskets. Where special thickness tolerances are necessary due to application, the tolerance on the individual sheet or gasket shall be agreed to in writing between the purchaser and the supplier.

TABLE A4—TYPE 2—CORK [1]

Identification No. [2]	Former "G" No. (for reference only)	Compressibility	Compressibility	Compressibility	Tensile Strength, min, psi	Density min, lb/ft [3]	Flotation Tests[3]	Flotation Tests[3]	Flotation Tests[3]	Flexibility Factor, F	After Oven Aging, 70 h at 100 °C ±2 °C (212 °F ±3.6 °F)	After Aging 70 h at 100 °C ±2 °C (212 °F ±3.6 °F) In ASTM Oil No. 1	After Aging 70 h at 100 °C ±2 °C (212 °F ±3.6 °F) In ASTM Oil No. 1	After Aging 70 h at 100 °C ±2 °C (212 °F ±3.6 °F) In ASTM Oil No. 3	After Aging 22 h at 21 to 30 °C (70 to 85 °F) In ASTM Reference Fuel A
		Original Properties	Original Properties	Original Properties	Original Properties	Original Properties	Original Properties	Original Properties	Original Properties	Original Properties	Properties after Immersion or Aging	Properties after Immersion or Aging	Properties after Immersion or Aging	Properties after Immersion or Aging	Properties after Immersion or Aging
		Total Load, psi	Compressibility, %	Recovery, min, %			3 h in Boiling Water	1/2 h in Boiling 35% HCl	2 h at 100 °C ± 2 °C (212 °F ±3.6 °F) In ASTM Oil No. 1		Flexibility Factor, F	Flexibility Factor, F	Volume Change, %	Volume Change, %	Volume Change, %
								Cork Composition							
P2116A	2114	100	10 to 25	60	175	24	N	—	N	5	—		—	—	—
P2117A	2113	100	15 to 30	65	150	20	N	—	N	5	—		—	—	—
P2117B	2112	100	20 to 40	75	100	17	N	—	N	5	—		—	—	—
P2118A	2111	100	30 to 50	80	75	14	N	—	N	5	—		—	—	—
P2126A	2214	100	10 to 25	60	175	24	N	N	N	5	—		—	—	—
P2127A	2213	100	15 to 30	65	150	20	N	N	N	5	—		—	—	—
P2127B	2212	10	20 to 40	75	100	17	N	N	N	5	—		—	—	—
P2128A	2211	100	30 to 50	80	75	14	N	N	N	5	—		—	—	—
								Cork and Rubber							
P2236A	1221-3	400	25 to 45	75	200	—	—	—	—	5	16	16	-5 to +5	0 to +10	-5 to +5
P2243A	1222-2	400	15 to 25	75	250	—	—	—	—	5	16	16	-5 to +10	-2 to +15	-2 to +10
P2245A	1222-3	400	25 to 35	75	250	—	—	—	—	5	16	16	-5 to +10	-2 to +15	-2 to +10
P2245B	—	400	40 to 55	70	150	—	—	—	—	5	16	16	-15 to +15	0 to +25	-5 to +15
P2246A	1222-4	400	35 to 45	75	200	—	—	—	—	5	16	16	-5 to +10	-2 to +15	-2 to +10
P2254A	1223-2	400	15 to 25	75	250	—	—	—	—	5	16	16	-2 to +20	+15 to +50	0 to +15
P2255A	1223-3	400	25 to 35	75	250	—	—	—	—	5	16	16	-2 to +20	+15 to +50	0 to +15
P2255B	—	400	40 to 55	75	125	—	—	—	—	5	16	16	-10 to +5	+15 to +50	0 to +35
P2256A	1223-4	400	35 to 45	75	220	—	—	—	—	5	16	16	-2 to +20	+15 to +50	0 to +15
P2265A	1211-3	400	25 to 45	75	150	—	—	—	—	5	16	—			
P2268A	1211-5	400	40 to 60	75	75	—	—	—	—	5	16	—	—	—	
								Cork and Cellular Rubber							
P2347A	—	100	35 to 50	75	100	—	—	—	—	5	16	—	-20 to +5	-10 to -5	-10 to +5
P2357A	—	100	35 to 50	75	75	—	—	—	—	5	16	—	-10 to +10	+15 to +50	0 to +25
P2367A	—	100	35 to 50	75	100	—	—	—	—	5	16	—		—	

1. Grain size may be specified for certain applications. If so, the following will usually apply: Fine—will pass a No. 20 sieve and will be retained on a No. 40 sieve; Medium—will pass a No. 10 sieve and will be retained on a No. 20 sieve; Coarse—will pass a No. 5 sieve and will be retained on a No. 10 sieve. Sieve sizes are as specified in Table 1 of ASTM Specification E 11.
2. Thickness tolerances: P2100 series—±10% or ±0.010 in, whichever is the greater; P2200 series—under 1/16 in, ±0.010 in, 1/16 in and over, ±0.015 in; P2300 series—1/16 in (minimum thickness) and over ±0.015 in
3. N = No disintegration.

TABLE A5—TYPE 3—CELLULOSE OR OTHER ORGANIC FIBERS

		Original Properties	Original Properties	Original Properties	Original Properties	Properties after Immersion in Liquids for 22 h at 21 to 30 °C (70 to 85 °F)	Properties after Immersion in Liquids for 22 h at 21 to 30 °C (70 to 85 °F)	Properties after Immersion in Liquids for 22 h at 21 to 30 °C (70 to 85 °F)	Properties after Immersion in Liquids for 22 h at 21 to 30 °C (70 to 85 °F)	Properties after Immersion in Liquids for 22 h at 21 to 30 °C (70 to 85 °F)	Properties after Immersion in Liquids for 22 h at 21 to 30 °C (70 to 85 °F)
Identification No. (1)	Former "G" No. (for reference only)	Compressi bility	Compressi bility	Compress ibility	Compress ibility	ASTM Reference Fuel B	ASTM Reference Fuel B	ASTM Oil No. 3	ASTM Oil No. 3	Distilled Water	Distilled Water
		Total Load, psi	Compressi bility	Recovery, min, %	Tensile Strength min, psi	Thickness Increase, max, %	Weight Increase, max, %	Thickness Increase, max, %	Weight Increase, max, %	Thickness Increase, max, %	Weight Increase, max, %
P3002A	3111	1000	10 to 25	50	1500	—	—	—	—	—	—
P3102A	3141	1000	20 to 30	45	750	—	—	—	—	—	—
P3200A	3261 to 3262	1000	0 to 10	70	6000	—	—	—	—	—	—
P3301A	3151	1000	5 to 15	60	3000	—	—	—	—	—	—
P3302C	—	1000	15 to 30	40	1500	—	—	—	—	—	—
P3313B	3212	1000	25 to 40	40	2000	5	15	5	15	30	90
P3341A	—	1000	5 to 15	50	4000	5	10	5	15	90	80
P3341D	—	1000	6 to 16	55	3000	12	35	5	35	40	40
P3342C	—	1000	16 to 26	45	3500	20	35	5	20	20	30
P3342F	—	1000	17 to 27	40	1800	30	80	30	80	50	80
P3342G	—	1000	20 to 30	35	1500	10	50	10	50	35	70
P3345A	3232-6	1000	40 to 60	20	500	5	80	10	80	25	65
P3353A	—	1000	25 to 40	25	1500	12	80	12	90	30	75
P3353B	—	1000	20 to 35	40	2000	15	50	15	55	40	50
P3354A	3233-5A	1000	30 to 50	30	800	15	80	15	90	25	65
P3361A	3234-2	1000	5 to 15	40	2000	10	25	10	20	30	25
P3362A	3234-3	1000	15 to 30	40	2000	15	45	15	60	40	50
P3365A	3234-6B	1000	40 to 60	20	500	5	95	5	120	20	70
P3413A	3221	1000	25 to 45	40	1500	5	15	5	15	15	85
P3415A	3222	1000	40 to 55	40	1000	5	30	5	30	30	100
P3421A	3223	1000	10 to 20	50	1500	20	35	5	25	15	30
P3423A	—	1000	25 to 35	50	1000	20	50	5	30	5	20
P3441A	—	1000	5 to 15	45	2200	20	30	20	30	30	30
P3442A	—	1000	10 to 20	35	2500	15	30	0	30	40	60
P3443B	—	1000	25 to 35	55	1100	25	65	0	50	15	25
P3443C	—	1000	25 to 35	40	1200	10	65	0	70	35	50
P3444A	3242-3	1000	30 to 45	25	800	10	75	0	70	20	55
P3464A	3243-3	1000	30 to 45	30	700	30	100	30	105	20	70

1. Thickness tolerances:

ThicknessTolerance
1/64 in and under±0.0035 in
Over 1/64 in to 1/16 in±0.005 in
Over 1/16 in to 3/32 in±0.008 in
Over 3/32 in±0.016 in

The above thickness tolerances are permissible variations applicable to a given lot of sheets or gaskets. Where special thickness tolerances are necessary due to application, the tolerance on the individual sheet or gasket shall be agreed to in writing between the purchaser and the supplier.

ENGINE COOLANTS—SAE J814 NOV1999

SAE Information Report

Report of the SAE Nonmetallic Materials Committee approved March 1962. Revised by the SAE ACAP Division 2—Engine Coolant Subcommittee July 1988. Completely revised by the SAE Cooling Systems Committee August 1996. Revised by the SAE Cooling Systems Standards Committee November 1999.

Foreword—SAE J1034, Automotive and Light Truck Engine Coolant Concentrate—Ethylene Glycol Type, SAE J1941, Coolant Concentrate (Low Silicate, Ethylene Glycol Type Requiring an Initial Charge of Supplemental Coolant Additive) for Heavy-Duty Engines, and SAE J2306 Automobile and Light Truck Engine Coolant Concentrate, Propylene Glycol Type have been voided as a result of the SAE/ASTM Memorandum of Understanding to reduce duplication of effort. These documents are replaced by ASTM D 3306, ASTM D 4985, and ASTM D 5216 respectively.

1. Scope

1.1 This SAE Information Report is a source of information concerning the basic properties of engine coolants which are satisfactory for use in internal combustion engines. Engine coolant concentrate (antifreeze) must provide adequate corrosion protection, lower the freezing point, and raise the boiling point of the engine coolant. For additional information on engine coolants see ASTM D 3306, ASTM D 5216, ASTM D 4985, and ASTM D 6211.

1.2 The values presented describe desirable basic properties. The results from laboratory tests are not conclusive, and it should be recognized that the final selection of satisfactory coolants can be proven only after a series of performance tests in vehicles.

1.3 The main body of this document also describes in general the necessary maintenance procedures for all engine coolants to insure proper performance. In addition, special requirements for coolants for heavy-duty engines are covered in Appendix A.

1.4 This document does not cover maintenance of engine cooling system component parts. That topic is discussed in detail in SAE HS 40.

2. References

2.1 Applicable Publications—The following publications form a part of the specification to the extent specified herein. Unless otherwise indicated, the latest revision of SAE publications shall apply.

2.1.1 SAE PUBLICATIONS—Available from SAE, 400 Commonwealth Drive, Warrendale, PA 15096-0001.

SAE HS 40—Maintenance of Automotive Engine Cooling Systems

2.1.2 ASTM PUBLICATIONS—Available from ASTM, 100 Barr Harbor Drive, West Conshohocken, PA 19428-2959.

ASTM D 1119—Standard Test Method for Ash Content of Engine Coolants and Antirusts
ASTM D 1120—Standard Test Method for Boiling Point of Engine Coolants
ASTM D 1121—Standard Test Method for Reserve Alkalinity of Engine Antifreeze, Antirusts, and Coolants
ASTM D 1122—Standard Test Method for Specific Gravity of Engine Coolants by the Hydrometer
ASTM D 1124—Specification for Hydrometer-Thermometer Field Tester for Engine Coolants
ASTM D 1177—Standard Test Method for Freezing Point of Aqueous Engine Coolant Solution
ASTM D 1287—Standard Test Method for pH of Engine Antifreezes, Antirusts, and Coolants
ASTM D 1384—Standard Method for Corrosion Test for Engine Coolants in Glassware
ASTM D 1881—Standard Test Method for Foaming Tendencies of Engine Coolants in Glassware
ASTM D 1882—Standard Test Method for Effect of Cooling System Chemical Solutions on Organic Finishes for Automotive Vehicles
ASTM D 2570—Test Method for Resistance of Emulsion Paints in the Container to Attack by Microorganisms
ASTM D 2758—Test Method for Wetting Tension of Polyethylene and Polypropylene Films
ASTM D 2809—Test Method for Cavitation Erosion-Corrosion Characteristics of Aluminum Pumps with Engine Coolants
ASTM D 2847—Practice for Testing Engine Coolants in Car and Light Truck Service
ASTM D 3306—Specification for Ethylene Glycol Base Engine Coolant
ASTM D 3321—Standard Practice for Use of the Refractometer for Determining the Freezing Point of Aqueous Engine Coolants
ASTM D 4340—Test Method for Corrosion of Cast Aluminum Alloys in Engine Coolants Under Heat-Transfer Conditions
ASTM D 4985—Standard Specification for Low Silicate, Ethylene Glycol Base Engine Coolant Concentrate for Heavy Duty Engines, Requiring an Initial Charge of Supplemental Coolant Additive (SCA)
ASTM D 5216—Standard Specification for Propylene Glycol Base Engine Coolant for Automobile and Light Duty Service
ASTM D 6211—Fully Formulated Propylene Glycol Base Engine Coolant for Heavy Duty Engines

3. Types of Coolants

3.1 Water—Water has been the most commonly used constituent of engine coolants for internal combustion engines because it has the ability to transfer heat and can be readily obtained. Some properties of water, such as its boiling point and freezing point, limit its usefulness when used alone as a coolant. The natural corrosive action of water on metals is definitely undesirable. Some natural water impurities, such as sulfates, chlorides, and bicarbonates, can increase corrosion. Others, such as calcium and magnesium carbonate, reduce heat transfer by the formation of scale, particularly at hot spots. They can also contribute to radiator clogging if excessive additions of hard water are made to replenish coolant losses.

Clean potable water, low in chloride, sulfate, and hardness is generally acceptable. Brackish or undrinkable water should not be used. Softened, deionized, or distilled water is ideal to dilute engine coolant concentrate. With properly inhibited coolant concentrate, water meeting the requirements outlined in Table 1 is acceptable. Water impurities exceeding these levels can cause excessive scale, sludge deposits, and increased corrosion.

TABLE 1—WATER QUALITY

Property	Requirement
Total Solids, max.	340 ppm (20 grains/gal)
Total Hardness, max.	170 ppm (10 grains/gal)
Chloride (as NaCl), max.	40 ppm (2.5 grains/gal)
Sulfate (as Na_2SO_4), max.	100 ppm (5.8 grains/gal)
pH	5.5 to 9.0

When water freezes to form ice, it expands approximately 9% in volume. If water is allowed to freeze inside the cooling system, the resultant pressure can cause serious damage. In order to prevent coolant freeze damage, coolant concentrate (antifreeze) must be added to the water.

Water alone or water with inhibitors is not normally recommended as an engine coolant. The boiling point increase, provided by a 50% glycol solution, is required to maintain the design cooling index of the cooling system.

3.2 Coolant Concentrate (Antifreeze)

3.2.1 Water containing the proper amount of coolant concentrate (antifreeze) will prevent freeze-cracking damage and can be circulated freely in the cooling system at temperatures well below the freezing point of water alone. There are many requirements for an acceptable coolant concentrate (antifreeze). The most essential of these are:

1. The ability to protect cooling system metals from corrosion or deposits.
2. Minimum loss of heat transfer capability.
3. No deleterious effect on nonmetallic cooling system components.
4. Thermal stability.
5. The ability to lower the freezing point of the engine coolant to the lowest winter operating temperatures likely to be encountered.
6. The ability to raise the boiling point.
7. Little or no odor.
8. Minimum effect on vehicle finishes.
9. An acceptable viscosity at low temperatures.
10. Low coefficient of expansion.
11. Effective for at least one year of service.
12. Easily checked concentration.

In addition, low toxicity, suitable boiling point characteristics, low foaming and evaporative losses, and nonflammability are desirable. No one chemical meets each of these requirements to the fullest. However, there are materials which represent satisfactory compromises.

3.2.2 GLYCOL-BASE COOLANTS—The most commonly used antifreeze material is ethylene glycol. A typical ethylene glycol-base antifreeze (coolant concentrate) will contain 95% minimum antifreeze grade ethylene glycol, corrosion inhibitors, up to 5% total water to dissolve additives, a dye, and an antifoam agent. Occasionally up to 10% of other glycols such as diethylene glycol and propylene glycol are included.

Propylene gylcol-base coolants are also used. Propylene glycol-base coolants have been approved by some automobile manufacturers and by most heavy-duty truck manufacturers in the United States. Propylene glycol-base coolants provide equivalent cooling system performance compared to ethylene glycol-base coolants, and have the advantage of having considerably reduced toxicity compared to ethylene glycol-base coolants. A typical propylene glycol-base antifreeze (coolant concentrate) will contain 94% minimum propylene glycol, corrosion inhibitors, up to 5% total water, a dye, and an antifoam agent. Occasionally up to 1% of dipropylene glycol is included. No other glycols are permitted.

Propylene glycol is nearly as effective a freeze depressant as ethylene glycol and is essentially nontoxic. However, because its specific gravity is very close to that of water, it is not possible to obtain a satisfactory field check for concentration by hydrometer. A simple hand-held refractometer, calibrated to read the freezing point of propylene glycol, is appropriate for this purpose. A dip-and-read test strip is also appropriate.

When compared to water alone, coolant solutions of glycol in water have higher boiling points, lower freezing points, and slightly lower heat transfer characteristics. See Tables 2 and 3.

Note that the boiling point of these coolant mixtures is increased further by causing the cooling system to become pressurized. This is accomplished by using a radiator pressure cap. See Table A2 in the Appendix.

Manufacturers fill the cooling systems of vehicles at the factory year-round and across the country with approximately a 50% concentration of glycol-base antifreeze coolant. The higher boiling points of glycol/water coolant solutions have been found to be beneficial for hot weather operation and in high altitude areas. Glycol-base coolant solutions should be used with thermostats having opening temperatures of 82 °C (180 °F) or higher. When a glycol-base coolant is used, it is recommended that a 50 to 70% concentration be maintained year-round to provide adequate corrosion protection and a sufficiently high boiling point for automobiles and light trucks. 40 to 60% is recommended for heavy-duty engines. Concentrations over 70% result in a loss in freezing protection and heat transfer and an increase in viscosity at low temperature. In heavy-duty engines using SCA's (Supplemental Coolant Additives), glycol concentrations over 60% will contribute to inhibitor precipitation.

3.2.3 PREDILUTED GLYCOL COOLANTS—Glycol-based coolants, already prediluted with deionized water, have been made commercially available for user convenience and for users in areas with poor quality tap water. These products should be used, as supplied, without further dilution with water.

3.2.4 ALCOHOL BASE COOLANTS—Are now obsolete.

3.2.5 OTHER ANTIFREEZE COOLANTS—Various other chemicals are used as antifreeze coolants in special applications.

3.2.5.1 An ethylene glycol, water and glycol ether premixed combination is sometimes used for arctic service. This type of coolant is suitable for service down to –68 °C (–90 °F).

3.2.5.2 Inhibited glycol ether, specifically methoxy propanol, is available for use as a coolant for heavy-duty equipment. Most heavy-duty equipment manufacturers do not recommend its use because it degrades fluorocarbon-based rubber. It is not as effective a freeze depressant as ethylene glycol.

3.2.5.3 All specialty coolant products should be used with strict adherence to the engine manufacturer's and coolant manufacturer's recommendations.

3.2.6 Different types of coolants should not be mixed.

4. Properties—Properties which are considered in testing and evaluating the antifreeze coolant concentrate and its solutions are described in the following paragraphs. The ASTM test methods for measuring these properties are listed as follows:

ASTM D 1119—Standard Test Method for Ash Content of Engine Coolants and Antirusts

ASTM D 1120—Standard Test Method for Boiling Point of Engine Coolants

ASTM D 1121—Standard Test Method for Reserve Alkalinity of Engine Antifreeze, Antirusts, and Coolants

ASTM D 1122—Standard Test Method for Specific Gravity of Engine Coolants by Hydrometer

ASTM D 1177—Standard Test Method for Freezing Point of Aqueous Engine Coolant Solution

ASTM D 1287—Standard Test Method for pH of Engine Antifreezes, Antirusts, and Coolants

ASTM D 1881—Standard Test Method for Foaming Tendencies of Engine Coolants in Glassware

ASTM D 1882—Standard Test Method for Effect of Cooling System Chemical Solutions on Organic Finishes for Automotive Vehicles

ASTM D 3321—Standard Practice for Use of the Refractometer for Determining the Freezing Point of Aqueous Engine Coolants

4.1 Ash Content—Ash content of a coolant concentrate is the residue which remains after ignition. For most formulations, the ash content will be less than 5.0% by weight. While the ash results from the inhibitors used, it is not a measure of inhibitor concentration.

4.2 Equilibrium Boiling Point—Equilibrium boiling point indicates the temperatures at which the coolant begins to boil in a cooling system under equilibrium conditions at atmospheric pressure. The boiling point of a coolant is an important property, especially when high opening temperature thermostats are used or when the cooling system is operated at high ambient temperatures or under high heat load conditions. See Table 2.

4.3 Reserve Alkalinity—Reserve alkalinity is a term applied to engine coolant concentrates and antirusts to indicate the amount of alkaline inhibitors present in the product.

Reserve alkalinity is defined as the number of milliliters, to the nearest 0.1 mL of 0.100 N hydrochloric acid required for the titration to a pH of 5.5 of a 10 mL sample of undiluted antifreeze, antirust, or coolant additive.

Mildly alkaline solutions are generally less corrosive than strongly acid or strongly alkaline solutions. Neither pH nor reserve alkalinity is a sufficient criterion to indicate the quality or level of corrosion inhibitors. Different inhibitor systems have individual optimum pH ranges. Many of the very efficient corrosion inhibitors have very little effect on the reserve alkalinity.

The reserve alkalinity is most useful as part of a qualification test to indicate that a submitted lot is similar to a previously qualified sample.

The reserve alkalinity of a used coolant is not a dependable indication of either existing effectiveness or remaining life of the solution. The measurement gives an indication of the capacity of the coolant to neutralize acids which may be present or form in the cooling system.

TABLE 2—BOILING AND FREEZING POINTS

Volume % Antifreeze	Ethylene Glycol Base Freezing Point °C	Ethylene Glycol Base Freezing Point °F	Ethylene Glycol Base Boiling Point °C	Ethylene Glycol Base Boiling Point °F	Propylene Glycol Base Freezing Point °C	Propylene Glycol Base Freezing Point °F	Propylene Glycol Base Boiling Point °C	Propylene Glycol Base Boiling Point °F
40	–24	–12	106	222	–21	–6	104	219
50	–37	–34	108	226	–33	–27	106	222
60	–52	–62	111	232	–49	–56	109	228
70	–64	–84	114	238	–61	–78	112	234

TABLE 3—HEAT TRANSFER CHARACTERISTICS AT 99 °C (210 °F)

Volume % Antifreeze	Ethylene Glycol Base Viscosity	Ethylene Glycol Base Specific Heat	Ethylene Glycol Base Thermal Cond.	Propylene Glycol Base Viscosity	Propylene Glycol Base Specific Heat	Propylene Glycol Base Thermal Cond.
0	0.29 cP	1.01 Btu/lb/°F	0.39 Btu/h/ft^2/°F/ft	0.29 cP	1.10 Btu/lb/°F	0.39 Btu/h/ft^2/°F/ft
40	0.59 cP	0.90 Btu/lb/°F	0.26 Btu/h/ft^2/°F/ft	0.62 cP	0.95 Btu/lb/°F	0.26 Btu/h/ft^2/°F/ft
60	0.81 cP	0.83 Btu/lb/°F	0.21 Btu/h/ft^2/°F/ft	0.95 cP	0.88 Btu/lb/°F	0.19 Btu/h/ft^2/°F/ft

4.4 Specific Gravity—Specific gravity is the ratio of the mass of a given volume of liquid to the mass of an equal volume of gas-free distilled water at a specific temperature. Its measurement offers a convenient means of identifying the degree of dilution and hence the freezing point of ethylene glycol coolants. While the specific gravity for pure ethylene glycol is 1.115 at 20 °C (68 °F), the specific gravity of the coolant concentrate will be somewhat different depending upon the type and the amount of inhibitors used, on the amount of water present, and on the amount of other glycols present. Because the specific gravity of propylene glycol is similar to that of water, use of specific gravity to measure the freezing point of propylene glycol coolants is not recommended.

4.5 Freezing Point—Freezing point is defined as the temperature at which ice crystallization begins in the absence of supercooling, or the maximum temperature reached immediately after initial ice crystal formation in the case of supercooling. The ASTM method of freezing point determination should be used when freezing point accuracy is desired, as in determining the limiting values for specifications. Hydrometers, refractometers, or test strips are used in the field to determine the expected freezing point of coolants. (The hydrometers will give erroneous results for ethylene glycol-base coolants if the content of other glycols, such as diethylene glycol or propylene glycol is too high.) However, many commercial refractometers also include a scale for propylene glycol.) Because of the limited accuracy of hydrometer-thermometer testers, the results should be viewed as an approximate freezing point rather than a precise measurement. (ASTM D 1124 describes the hydrometer-thermometer field tester for engine coolants.) Freezing points can be determined more accurately by the refractometer type field tester. (ASTM D 3321 describes the use of a refractometer for determining freezing points.) See Appendix A, Table A2A for freezing points of glycol antifreeze/water mixtures.

4.6 pH—pH is a measurement of the hydrogen ion concentration and indicates whether a coolant is acidic neutral, or alkaline. pH measurements are sometimes used for production quality control, but are not reliable indicators to predict service life. However, as the pH approaches neutral, and certainly before it drops below 7, the coolant should be replaced.'

4.7 Foaming Tendency—Foaming tendency of a coolant is measured by the amount of foam generated during aeration under controlled conditions and the time required for this foam to subside. If the coolant foams excessively and the system is open, coolant losses will take place through the overflow tube of the radiator. Heat transfer properties of the coolant are also reduced due to foaming.

4.8 Organic Finishes—Organic finishes shall not be adversely affected by the coolant. This is of particular importance to the vehicle manufacturer during assembly operations and to the vehicle owner during coolant installation in the event of accidental spillage.

4.9 Color—All coolant concentrates must contain a dye as a positive visual identification that an antifreeze coolant is being used. Many colors are used for glycol-base antifreeze coolants. Green through blue green is recommended in ASTM D 3306 and ASTM D 4985.

4.10 Effect on Nonmetallics—The coolant solution should not accelerate failure of the radiator hose, gaskets, and nonmetallic coatings on metallic gaskets. Many immersion tests, as well as other tests, have been proposed for this evaluation. Each supplier and consumer has his favorite procedure. The final evaluation, of course, is service experience. Preliminary indications are obtained when the coolant is tested for corrosion inhibition in simulated service and engine dynamometer tests.

4.11 Storage Stability—Storage stability of the concentrate cannot be determined conclusively by accelerated tests. However, it is evident that the packaged concentrate must be stable for at least 2 years under many different climatic conditions.

5. Corrosion Inhibition

5.1 Corrosion—If corrosion of the cooling system of an internal combustion engine is allowed to proceed without interruption, it not only shortens the life of metallic components but it also reduces the heat transfer efficiency of the cooling system. For these reasons, effective corrosion inhibition must be provided and maintained in the cooling system.

5.2 Corrosion Testing—Because of the elapsed time involved in the field testing of inhibitors and inhibited coolants, accelerated tests are used in an attempt to evaluate the effectiveness of these products. The results from accelerated tests can be indicative of quality only if the tests incorporate many of the factors which affect corrosion in the cooling system. Some of the more important factors to be included are:

1. Coolant concentration
2. Flow rate
3. Aeration
4. Temperature
5. Water quality
6. Galvanic couples and crevices
7. Corrosion products
8. Heat rejecting metal surfaces

As a test incorporates more of these factors, it more nearly simulates service performance, but it usually requires more labor and it becomes more costly. The generally accepted order of evaluation tests is:

1. Screening test (glassware corrosion test)
2. Heat rejecting aluminum test
3. Simulated service test
4. Dynamometer test
5. Field service test

Special tests are required to evaluate the performance of coolants with regard to specific forms of corrosive attack. These stepwise procedures are used to avoid the unnecessary expenditure of time and money performing long expensive tests on obviously poor coolants, and to ensure that better coolants will meet service requirements by the use of more rigorous test conditions. Vehicle service tests are desirable as the final evaluation method because they most closely approximate actual use and conditions.

5.2.1 Glassware Tests—A glassware test procedure can be used to evaluate all types of coolants and inhibitors. The advantages of this type of test are its simplicity, reproducibility, and brevity. For these reasons, it is used to screen a large number of samples with minimal of effort.

Weighed metal specimens common to the engine cooling system are immersed in a heated, aerated test solution for the entire period of the test. Corrosion products are removed from each metal at the end of the test, and the metal weight losses determined. Corrosion inhibition is evaluated on the basis of these metal mass loss values. A material is presumed to fail the test if the mass loss of any metal is above the limit.

A typical glassware corrosion test for the evaluation of coolants is that found in ASTM D 1384.

5.2.2 Simulated Service Tests—This test concept involves the circulation of coolant, at a preselected operating temperature, in a test rig simulating an engine cooling system. Several automobile parts are used in the construction of the test rigs including a coolant pump, coolant outlet, radiator, and radiator hoses. By the use of a large reservoir, or an engine block, a volume of coolant equivalent to that in a cooling system can be used. Coolant flow rates within the normal operating range are achieved by driving the coolant pump with an electric motor. This test simulates the engine cooling system more closely than the glassware test and is more discriminating in coolant performance evaluation. Corrosion inhibition is measured from mass losses of metal specimens placed in the system and by visual examination of the components. If standard radiator hoses are used, coolant effects on the hoses can be observed. By sampling the coolant at intervals during the test, coolant concentration can be controlled and solution properties monitored. Experience has shown that they are useful development tools, but for some specimen metals, repeatability between tests may not be consistent and reproducibility among different laboratories may vary widely. The use of components of different materials, such as an aluminum reservoir versus cast iron or an aluminum radiator versus brass, can significantly affect certain metal specimen weight losses. In view of these circumstances, it is desirable to evaluate test rigs and data by running multiple tests with coolants of known service performance.

Although there are many variations in procedure, a recommended test procedure has been developed under the sponsorship of ASTM Committee D-15. This method is listed as ASTM D 2570.

5.2.3 Dynamometer Tests—Engine coolants can also be evaluated by an engine dynamometer test procedure. The advantage of this method over either the glassware test or the simulated service test is that test conditions such as load, speed, coolant temperature, and heat transfer are observed, controlled, and varied through the operation of a standard engine. The performance of the engine is monitored throughout the test to ensure the reproduction of the proper service conditions. This type of test is more significant if the radiator, pump, and engine combination is the same as that normally used in an actual vehicle.

Corrosion protection is evaluated by the determination of mass losses of metal specimens in contact with the coolant, and by the inspection of parts at the conclusion of the test. Inhibitor stability is determined from changes in pH, reserve alkalinity, and solution appearance. Various qualitative and quantitative analyses may be obtained for the inhibitors known to be present. Although this test is expensive to run, it provides more meaningful results than other laboratory results.

ASTM D 2758 prescribes a 700 h test in a standard passenger car engine.

5.2.4 FIELD TESTS—The final test of any coolant is its performance in vehicles in the field. Closely controlled tests can be made under the supervision of technical personnel. General field tests can be conducted in a large number of vehicles to provide a broad service pattern. Metal specimens may be installed in the coolant stream to determine corrosion rates. The coolant can be sampled periodically to determine its chemical and physical properties. The condition of the cooling system and components should be carefully examined at the end of the test. Information should be obtained from the participants concerning their observations regarding cooling system performance. If at all possible, vehicles from different areas of the country should be utilized for the tests, which will involve a range of antifreeze coolant concentrations with a variety of local waters.

ASTM D 2847 is a standard practice for testing engine coolants in vehicle service. Metal corrosion specimens, mounted in special capsules, are installed in the coolant flow of the test vehicles. The test duration in terms of time or mileage is consistent with the recommended service life of the coolant under test.

5.2.5 ALUMINUM WATER PUMP CAVITATION TESTS—Cavitation erosion corrosion of water pumps constructed of aluminum can be a serious problem because of the rate at which damage may occur. This type of corrosion is usually the result of pump design and cooling system characteristics. At certain coolant velocities, low and high pressure areas develop that cause the formation of vapor bubbles which implode on the surface of the metal and cause segments of metal to be removed. The composition of the coolant has been found to have a contributing effect on cavitation erosion, and it is often necessary to evaluate coolant formulations under cavitating conditions. Many different methods have been used to induce cavitation for laboratory studies, but it is preferable to use an operating pump under controlled conditions.

Final evidence of satisfactory cavitation-erosion prevention may be confirmed by ASTM D 2809. In this procedure, test coolant is pumped through a pressurized, simulated automotive cooling system at a temperature of 112 °C (235 °F) for 100 h. The pump is driven by an electric motor at a high speed and cavitation occurs. After the test, the complete pump is examined and rated by a numerical system.

5.2.6 ALUMINUM HEAT REJECTING CORROSION AND TRANSPORT TESTS—Aluminum corrosion transport deposition may occur with engines containing aluminum cylinder heads or other aluminum heat rejecting (from metal to coolant) surfaces. While the metal loss from aluminum surfaces may be relatively small and have no effect on the strength or durability of the aluminum components, the volume of corrosion products deposited in coolant passages of radiator or heater cores will reduce heat transfer and may result in plugged passages. The composition of the corrosion inhibitors in the antifreeze formulation can affect this type of corrosion.

Several test methods have been used to evaluate engine coolants for aluminum corrosion transport deposition including car tests. The accelerated laboratory tests involve circulating the test coolant in an apparatus so that the coolant is heated by an aluminum part and cooled with a copper, brass, or aluminum part. Performance is evaluated by the amount of corrosion (mass loss) from the heating aluminum part and/or the increase in mass of the cooling part. If the cooling part is a radiator or heater core, evaluation is based on loss in heat transfer or visually observing the quantity of deposits in the water passages.

Screening evaluation of coolants for corrosion of aluminum heat rejecting surfaces can be done using ASTM D 4340. This method does not evaluate the resultant transport deposition which may occur.

5.2.7 ALUMINUM CREVICE AND PITTING CORROSION—Aluminum radiators and heater cores may fail from perforation due to pitting and crevice corrosion. The design of the unit may involve gasketed tank to header joints which create adjacent crevice areas at the gasket to header interface. These locations require specific inhibition from pitting corrosion. Several test methods may be used to evaluate coolant inhibitor performance. Accelerated laboratory electrochemical tests can indicate the tendency for pitting corrosion which should correlate with actual service performance or simulated service tests. An aluminum radiator can be used in a simulated service test such as ASTM D 2570. At test termination, the subject radiator must be disassembled and sectioned for a comprehensive inspection for corrosion sites. Variations of this method involving extended test period, increased coolant temperature, diluted coolant, and more corrosive water may be employed to increase test severity. Extended vehicle tests provide the most conclusive method results but require a longer test period with increased variables, reduced control and increased cost.

6. Maintenance of Engine Coolants—Satisfactory performance of the engine coolant depends upon the use of the proper coolant, changing the coolant at prescribed intervals and maintenance of coolant volume, coolant concentration, cleanliness, and tightness of the engine cooling system.

6.1 Coolant Volume—It is important that the engine coolant be maintained at the level specified by the vehicle manufacturer. The proper level for most modern cars is shown in the coolant recovery tank or container. This container collects the overflow coolant when the coolant expands and from which the coolant is drawn back into the radiator when the coolant cools. The level marks are usually labeled cold and hot or full cold and full hot because the volume present is related to the temperature of the coolant. In cars that do not have a coolant recovery system, the level may be shown by a mark on the tank of the radiator. Periodic inspection of the coolant level in the recovery tank should be made to ensure that the coolant is at the proper level. For heavy-duty engines, the coolant level should be checked as directed by the vehicle manufacturer. Many heavy-duty vehicles do not use coolant recovery tanks.

If overheating should occur even though the coolant level is sufficient, the cooling system should be allowed to cool before opening any closures to check the system contents. A check should be made to see if air is trapped in the radiator, particularly after the system has been drained and filled and the air may not have been released. When it is necessary to add coolant, a a 50/50 mixture of a glycol coolant concentrate and water should be added. Caution see 6.3.

Loss of coolant may usually be attributed to one or more of the following:

6.1.1 OVERFLOWING, AFTER-BOILING, AND OVERHEATING—Overflowing is the loss of coolant during normal driving. The loss occurs because the system has been filled above the manufacturer's recommended level when the system was cold. As the coolant temperature increases, the coolant expands and is forced out of the coolant recovery tank, or radiator in the case of older model cars, and heavy-duty vehicles without recovery tanks. Proper coolant level minimizes the possibility for loss of coolant through overflow.

After-boiling is the boiling of the coolant in the engine block after the engine is stopped when the vehicle has been driven at high speeds or has been under a heavy load. The residual heat in the engine causes the coolant temperature to rise above its boiling point, because the coolant is no longer being circulated and cooled.

Overheating may be defined as a condition where the coolant temperature exceeds the normal operating range as indicated by the coolant warning light or temperature gauge. When this occurs, it is best to reduce the load on the cooling system by shifting the transmission to neutral and turning off the air conditioner. It also helps to reduce coolant temperature by increasing the engine idle speed for 2 or 3 min (to increase fan cooling and coolant pump output) and to turn on or increase the heater to maximum temperature and fan speed. The heater core will function as a small radiator. Several factors can contribute such as a faulty thermostat or radiator cap, fan belt malfunction, radiator tube plugging, or the accumulation of corrosion deposits or scale in the radiator that reduce heat transfer. In addition, the use of coolant solutions with lower boiling points than those provided by the recommended glycol water mixture can also be a factor in after-boiling or overheating. After-boiling or overheating can be minimized by ensuring that components are operating properly and that a satisfactory cooling is used and maintained.

6.1.2 COOLANT LEAKAGE—Leaks usually occur because of loose fitting parts or through cracks or pin holes caused by corrosion or deterioration of materials. Susceptible locations are hose connections, gasketed parts such as the cylinder head to thermostat, core hole plugs, pump seals, and radiator or heater core assemblies. When a leak occurs, the source should be identified and the leakage rate determined before attempting to stop the leak. The leak often can be corrected by tightening a clamp or bolt, but in many cases it may be necessary to replace the component part. Minor leaks may be sealed through the use of commercial stop-leak materials, but one is cautioned that this is never a substitute for mechanical repairs. Furthermore, overuse of stop-leak products contributes to the solids in the cooling system, which can affect heat transfer and tube plugging. Most heavy-duty engine builders recommend that stop-leak not be used.

6.1.3 EXHAUST GAS LEAKAGE, AIR LEAKAGE, AND FOAMING—Air can be drawn into the coolant at loose hose connections or through the water pump seal. Exhaust gas leakage into the coolant occurs between the combustion chamber and the water jacket, usually because of a loose gasket or a cracked casting. Gases that enter the system become entrained in the coolant, occupying space and increasing the volume of the coolant. Gases can also rise to high points in the system as foam. Antifoam agents are usually added to the coolant concentrate to reduce the formation of foam, but these agents may be dissipated rather rapidly.

The increased volume occupied by the gas-liquid mixture can cause coolant losses during thermal expansion. In addition, the entrained gases can reduce the transfer of heat from the engine to the coolant and subsequently to the outside air through the radiator. Any of these effects can contribute to overheating.

Continued aeration of the system accelerates depletion of coolant inhibitors and can contribute to increased corrosion and/or erosion in the system. Air leakage to the coolant can be minimized by maintaining a proper coolant level and by good maintenance to ensure satisfactory operation of parts and tight joints.

Exhaust gases are normally acidic and leakage into the cooling system contributes not only to foaming and overheating but also to inhibitor depletion, accelerated corrosion, and a more rapid breakdown of glycol solutions. Any evidence of leakage requires immediate mechanical repair.

6.2 Antifreeze Coolant Concentration—Essentially all liquid cooled engines are designed for aqueous glycol coolant systems. Since water alone is inadequate (see 3.1 and 3.2), a coolant concentrate (antifreeze) is usually added. Most automobile manufacturers and heavy-duty manufacturers fill the cooling system with approximately a 50% ethylene glycol-base coolant. This concentration will supply more freeze protection than is required for most climates, but is recommended to ensure adequate concentration of corrosion inhibitors. Freeze point depression with ethylene glycol is obtained with 68% concentrate. To achieve higher boiling points for use at higher ambient temperatures, under heavy loads, or at higher altitudes, a maximum of 70% ethylene glycol-base coolant can be used, except for heavy-duty engines using SCA's, where glycol concentrations over 60% will contribute to undesirable inhibitor precipitation. When replenishing the cooling system, the proper proportions of water and glycol should be added to maintain the desired ratio.

Should the coolant freeze, the automobile should not be operated until normal circulation is restored by a suitable thawing operation. The coolant can form a slush which will clog the radiator, resulting in overheating, loss of coolant, and consequent damage to the engine such as cylinder head cracking at the combustion chamber.

6.3 Caution—If the coolant becomes overheated, the entire coolant solution must be cooled down before opening the radiator cap. If the cooling system is opened, the pressure will be reduced to atmospheric and coolant above its boiling point at this lower pressure will flash to a vapor and force out hot coolant. The risk of personal injury is very great.

6.4 Coolant Replacement—The vehicle manufacturer's and/or coolant manufacturer's directions for periodic changes should be followed. Periodic replacement of coolant solutions is required because the solutions may become corrosive due to chemical reaction, contamination, or inhibitor depletion. In heavy-duty systems using SCA's, the total dissolved solids can become too high.

6.5 Coolant Selection—An engine coolant should be selected with care to ensure adequate corrosion protection. Only those products conforming to recognized SAE and/or ASTM standards for the engine system involved should be used.

Automobile and light truck applications will require ASTM D 3306 ethylene glycol type or ASTM D 5216 propylene glycol type coolant offering protection of aluminum heat rejecting surfaces. This is critical in engine systems which contain heat rejecting aluminum surfaces such as heads or blocks.

Heavy-duty engine applications will require ASTM D 4895 ethylene glycol coolant concentrates and periodic additions of supplemental coolant additives (SCA's), or ASTM D 6211 fully formulated propylene glycol base engine coolant.

6.6 Extension of Coolant Use and Coolant Recycling—Due to the high cost and shortages of ethylene glycol in 1988 and increasing environmental awareness, extending the useful life of coolants in light-duty applications and also recycling of spent coolant from both light- and heavy-duty engines has become attractive. (The life of coolants used in heavy-duty engines has historically been extended by use of periodic SCA additions and on-board coolant filtration. See Appendix A.)

The only processes currently approved by light- and heavy-duty OEM's are those that recover pure glycol (of antifreeze grade) from the spent coolant. This glycol is then used to blend essentially new antifreeze.

Other processes (such as off-board filters coupled with SCA additions) for extending coolant life for coolants used in light-duty applications have been commercialized.

6.7 Cleaning—A properly inhibited, normally functioning cooling system should not require chemical cleaning. Cooling systems should be cleaned only when indicated by the appearance of rust or sediment or persistent overheating. The type of cleaner to be used is indicated by the condition of the system and the types of metal components in the system.

Conventional cooling systems, with brass, copper, and cast iron used in major components, can be treated with available flush-type cleaners for oily deposits and acid-type cleaners or chelators for rust deposits. Cooling systems utilizing aluminum components should use only those cleaners specified as safe for aluminum. In general, these cleaners are neither strong acids nor strong alkalies.

Residual cleaning components (including neutralizers) should be flushed from the system because some cleaners, if left in the cooling system, may attack components and shorten the service life of newly installed antifreeze coolants or supplemental additives.

Clogged radiators will not respond to chemical treatment and will require repair or replacement.

APPENDIX A
SPECIAL COOLANT CONSIDERATIONS FOR HEAVY-DUTY ENGINES

A.1 Automobile Versus Heavy-Duty Engine Service—The unique needs of the heavy-duty system are both a function of the system design and the demands made upon the system. These differences can be summed up as:

a. Life
b. Load
c. Usage
d. Wet sleeves

Table A1 contrasts in more detail the differences between automobile and heavy-duty engine service.

TABLE A1—DIFFERENCES BETWEEN AUTOMOBILE AND HEAVY-DUTY ENGINE SERVICE

	Automobile	Heavy-Duty Engines
Expected life to first overhaul	160 000 km (100 000 miles)	800 000 km (500 000 miles) or 15 000 h
Total expected life	240 000 km (150 000 miles)	1 160 000 km (1 000 000 miles) or >30 000 h
Usage rate	24 000 km/year (15 000 miles/year)	24 000 km/month (15 000 miles/month) or 500 h/month
Load factor	less than 30%	about 70%
GWV per HP (watt)	40.0 x 10^2 kg (30 lb)	2.7 x 10^1 kg (200 lb)
Uses wet sleeve cylinders	very few	most

A.2 Supplemental Coolant Additives and Their Economics—Heavy-duty engine builders began using supplemental coolant additives (SCA's) in the 1950's to control the pitting of cast iron cylinder liners. Since that time, SCA's have proven effective for long-term protection of the heavy-duty engine cooling system. At this time, all heavy-duty engine manufacturers in the United States recommend the use of some type of SCA.

The SCA may be initially added to the cooling system to make up for some deficiencies of the coolant concentrate (antifreeze) additive package in protecting heavy-duty engine cooling systems, such as cast iron cylinder liner cavitation corrosion protection and hot surface scaling protection. However, heavy-duty engine manufacturers are now recommending the use of fully formulated coolants which do not require an initial charge of SCA's. The SCA is also added to the cooling system at the time of each oil change to replace additives lost because of dilution and depletion. Historically, coolant concentrate (antifreeze) additive packages have been formulated to meet the needs of the automobile cooling system; consequently, most coolant concentrates are not optimized to meet the needs of a heavy-duty engine cooling system. Experience has shown that without the use of an SCA, liner pitting can become a problem in as little as 48 000 km (30 000 miles).

Coolant concentrate (antifreeze) for heavy-duty engines can be formulated to overcome the previous deficiencies, but it will still deteriorate over the long term under the conditions of use. Automobile coolant concentrate (antifreeze) has a recommended service life of 24 000 km (15 000 miles). For automobile service, this mileage may take about 1 year to accumulate, but, in many line haul truck fleet operations, 24 000 km (15 000 miles) are accumulated in 1 month. To maintain an adequate level of additive in the system, the coolant could be changed on a monthly bases, but it is far less expansive to add an SCA to keep the protection at adequate levels and extend coolant life.

Assume that an antifreeze coolant actually protects an automobile cooling system for approximately 48 000 km (30 000 miles). Making the same assumption for heavy-duty service, one can calculate the relative cost of changing coolant frequently or using SCA's and extending the use of the initial coolant. For a typical line haul operation using SCA's, the savings amount to $130.00 per unit per year or more. The assumptions on which this cost comparison is made are given as follows:

A.2.1 Assumptions Made in Comparing the Cost of Using SCA's Versus Frequent Coolant Replacement

a. Change coolant service filter each month or change antifreeze coolant every other month
b. Vehicle usage of 24 000 km (15 000 miles) per month
c. Cooling system size of 57 L (15 gal)
d. Coolant concentrate (antifreeze) used at 50% by volume
e. Time to change filter 5 min. or to change coolant 30 min
f. Costs
   1. Labor $30.00/h
   2. Coolant concentrate (antifreeze) $0.80/L ($3.00/gal)
   3. Initial charge coolant filter $7.40
   4. Service coolant filter $4.30

A.2.1.1 COOLANT FOR A HEAVY-DUTY ENGINE CONSISTS OF:

a. Water
b. Coolant Concentrate (antifreeze)
c. Supplemental Coolant Additive (SCA)
d. If freeze and boil over protection are not required, the coolant may consist of simply water and SCA

A.2.1.2 WATER—Water quality affects the efficiency of coolant additives and components. When untreated, all water is corrosive. Water with an extremely high mineral content or corrosive chemicals is unfit for cooling system use. The local water department or the Department of Agriculture should be contacted, or a water sample should be submitted for analysis if there is any question about water quality. S ee 3.1, Table 1, for specific water quality guidelines.

A.2.1.3 COOLANT CONCENTRATE (ANTIFREEZE)—Ethylene or propylene glycol-base coolant concentrate (antifreeze) is used for freeze and boil over protection. Concentration should be maintained between 40 and 60%, depending on operating environment. A low silicate product meeting ASTM D 4985 or ASTM D 6211 should be used.

A.2.1.4 SUPPLEMENTAL COOLANT ADDITIVES—Supplemental coolant additives are used for protection (against deposits, corrosion, and pitting) not provided by the chemicals in the coolant concentrate (antifreeze). SCA's also extend the life of coolant by adding to and replenishing additives that deplete during normal operation. SCA's, however, do not affect the freeze or boil over protection of the coolant.

While the coolant life for heavy-duty engines can be extended with the use of SCA's, a coolant cannot be used indefinitely. It is recommended that coolant not be used for more than 2 years. The reason is that coolant gradually becomes saturated with spent additives. Additive dropout can take place, which, especially without a coolant filter, can foul the cooling system. In addition, the additive package can become imbalanced over long periods of time thus degrading cooling system protection. Other factors that limit coolant life are oil, dirt, combustion gas contamination, and thermal breakdown of the coolant itself.

A.2.1.5 COOLANT MAINTENANCE RECOMMENDATIONS FOR HEAVY-DUTY ENGINES

a. If any of the following recommendations differ from the engine or vehicle manufacturer's recommendations, follow the engine or vehicle manufacturer's recommendations.
b. Use coolant concentrate meeting ASTM D 4985 or ASTM D 6211.
c. Drain and flush the cooling system annually.
d. Follow the engine or vehicle manufacturer's recommendations for SCA precharging of the cooling system after draining and flushing.
e. Use water that does not contain excessive solids, hardness, chloride, or sulfate.
f. Use accurate, reliable equipment such as a refractometer to measure coolant concentrate levels for freeze protection.
g. Use the SCA manufacturer's recommended test kit when testing the coolant for proper SCA concentration. Test kits shall indicate the degree of liner pitting protection present in the coolant.
h. Check freezing point at two different levels when coolant concentrate and water is premixed and stored in bulk or drums to be sure mixing is complete before use.
i. Use coolant mixed at the desired proportions for make-up.
j. Use SCA's at recommended dosage to control deposits, corrosion, and pitting.
k. Periodically check bulk premixed coolant storage tanks for separation of chemicals and contamination.
l. DO NOT add undiluted coolant concentrate as make-up coolant.
m. DO NOT add plain water as make-up coolant.
n. DO NOT substitute precharge coolant filters for service filters. This will result in over treatment (precharge filters contain more SCA than maintenance filters).
o. DO NOT exceed 60% coolant concentrate. More than 68% ethylene glycol-base coolant concentrate actually reduces freeze protection. The maximum recommended coolant concentrate level is 60% which provides freeze protection of –52 °C (–62 °F) for ethylene glycol-base and –49 °C (–56 °F) for propylene glycol-base. Coolant containing 50% coolant concentrate provides freeze protection to –37 °C (–34 °F) for ethylene glycol-base and –33 °C (–27 °F) for propylene glycol-base.
p. DO NOT exceed the recommended dosage of SCA or the recommended concentration of coolant concentrate. Over concentration can result in plugged radiators, heater cores, and charge air coolers. Over concentration can also cause water pump seal leaks.
q. DO NOT reuse coolant which has been drained from a vehicle where over concentration of coolant concentrate or over concentration of supplemental coolant additives have occurred, where the coolant is over 1 year old, or where the container is dirty.
r. DO NOT precharge the cooling system with SCA if the coolant is drained and reused.
s. DO NOT use soluble oil additives.
t. DO NOT use methyl alcohol or methoxy propanol base coolant concentrates.
u. DO NOT use antileak additives if engine cooling system is equipped with a coolant filter, as this may plug the filter element. For all other cooling systems, follow the recommendations of the engine or vehicle manufacturer.

Additional performance considerations for coolants for heavy-duty engines are:

a. The SCA and coolant concentrate (antifreeze) must be compatible.
b. The SCA must provide liner cavitation corrosion protection.
c. The SCA must provide hot surface scaling protection.
d. The SCA and coolant concentrate (antifreeze) must be compatible with elastomers.
e. If the antifreeze is the type that does not require a precharge of SCA, it must provide adequate performance under items the second and third above in addition to the general antifreeze performance requirements.

**TABLE A2A—FREEZING POINTS OF SOLUTIONS OF COOLANT CONCENTRATE[1]
ETHYLENE GLYCOL (CONCENTRATE REQUIRED, qt (gal))**

Cooling System Capacity, qt (gal)	3	4	5	6	7	8	9	10	11	12	13	14	15	16	17
6	-34[2]	-85													
7	-17	-54													
8		-34[2]	-69												
9		-21	-50	-85											
10		-12	-34[2]	-62	-84										
11			-23	-47	-75										
12			-15	-34[2]	-57	-85									
13				-25	-45	-66	-86								
14				-17	-34[2]	-54	-78								
15				-12	-26	-43	-62	-85							
16					-19	-34[2]	-52	-69							
17					-14	-27	-42	-58	-79						
18						-21	-34[2]	-50	-65	-85					
19						-16	-28	-42	-56	-74	-89				
20						-12	-22	-34[2]	-48	-62	-80	-84			
21							-17	-28	-41	-54	-68	-85			
22							-14	-23	-34[2]	-47	-59	-75	-92		
23								-19	-29	-40	-52	-64	-80	-84	
24								-15	-24	-34[2]	-46	-57	-69	-85	
25								-12	-20	-29	-40	-50	-62	-75	-92

1. Temperatures are shown in degrees Fahrenheit. To convert to degrees Celsius, $t^C = 5/9\ (t^F - 32)$.
2. 50% solution of concentrate and water.

**TABLE A2B—FREEZING POINTS OF SOLUTIONS OF COOLANT CONCENTRATE[1]
PROPYLENE GLYCOL (CONCENTRATE REQUIRED, qt (gal))**

Cooling System Capacity, qt (gal)	2	3	4	5	6	7	8	9	10	11	12	13
4	−26[2]											
6	+5	−26[2]	−76									
8	+14	0	−26[2]	−60								
10	+19	+10	−4	−26[2]	−54							
12		+14	+5	−8	−26[2]	−51						
14		+18	+10	+3	−8	−26[2]	−44					
16		+19	+14	+9	+1	−9	−26[2]	−44				
18		+21	+18	+12	+5	0	−13	−26[2]	−38	−53		
20			+19	+14	+9	+3	−6	−15	−26[2]	−38	−53	
25				+19	+16	+10	+9	+3	−13	−13	−22	−44

1. Temperatures are shown in degrees Fahrenheit. To convert to degrees Celsius, $t^C = 5/9\ (T^F - 32)$.
2. 50% solution of concentrate and water.

TABLE A3—BOILING POINTS OF SOLUTIONS OF COOLANT CONCENTRATE

Volume % Concentrate	Boiling Point At Atmospheric Pressure (760 mm) °C	Boiling Point At Atmospheric Pressure (760 mm) °F	Boiling Point Using 62 N (14 lb) Pressure Cap in Good Condition °C	Boiling Point Using 62 N (14 lb) Pressure Cap in Good Condition °F
Ethylene Glycol				
40	105.5	222	126.1	259
50	107.8	226	128.3	263
60	111.1	232	131.1	268
70	114.4	238	134.4	274
Propylene Glycol				
40	103.9	219	123.3	254
50	105.5	222	125.0	257
60	107.2	225	127.2	261
70	110.0	230	130.0	266

COOLANT CONCENTRATE (LOW SILICATE, ETHYLENE GLYCOL TYPE REQUIRING AN INITIAL CHARGE OF SUPPLEMENTAL COOLANT ADDITIVE FOR HEAVY-DUTY ENGINES—SAE J1941 APR1990 SAE Recommended Practice

Report of the SAE ACAP Executive Committee approved April 1990.

Foreword—This Document has not changed other than to put it into the new SAE Technical Standards Board Format.

1. Scope—This SAE Recommended Practice applies to engine coolant concentrate, low silicate ethylene glycol base, for use in cooling systems of heavy-duty engines. An initial charge of supplemental coolant additive (SCA) is required when using this type of coolant concentrate.

This document applies to engine coolant concentrates for heavy-duty engine requirements. SAE J1034 applies to coolant concentrates for automobile and light truck applications.

For further information on engine coolants, see SAE J814.

2. References—The following related documents may be referred to when carrying out the requirements of this document. Where there is any variance with this document, the requirements of this document shall prevail.

Reference to the following publications is to the latest issues unless otherwise specified by the authority applying this document:

2.1 Applicable Publications—The following publications form a part of the specification to the extent specified herein. Unless otherwise indicated the latest revision of SAE publications shall apply.

2.1.1 SAE PUBLICATIONS—Available from SAE, 400 Commonwealth Drive, Warrendale, PA 15096.

SAE Handbook
SAE J20—Coolant System Hoses
SAE J814—Engine Coolants
SAE J1034—Automotive and Light Truck Engine Coolant Concentrate—Ethylene-Glycol Type
SAE HS 40—Maintenance of Automotive Engine Cooling Systems

2.1.2 ASTM PUBLICATIONS—Available from ASTM, 100 Barr Harbor Drive, Warrendale, PA 15096-0001.

ASTM Annual Book of ASTM Standards
ASTM D 1119—Standard Test Method for Ash Content of Engine Coolants and Antirusts
ASTM D 1120—Standard Test Method for Boiling Point of Engine Coolants
ASTM D 1121—Standard Test Method for Reserve Alkalinity of Engine Antifreeze, Antirusts, and Coolants
ASTM D 1122—Standard Test Method for Specific Gravity of Engine Coolants by the Hydrometer
ASTM D 1123—Standard Test Methods for Water in Engine Coolant Concentrate by Karl Fischer Reagent Method
ASTM D 1176—Standard Method for Sampling and Preparing Aqueous Solutions of Engine Coolants or Antirusts for Testing Purposes
ASTM D 1177—Standard Test Method for Freezing Point of Aqueous Engine Coolant Solution
ASTM D 1287—Standard Test Method for pH of Engine Antifreeze, Antirusts, and Coolants
ASTM D 1384—Standard Test Method for Corrosion Test for Engine Coolants in Glassware
ASTM D 1881—Standard Test Method for Foaming Tendencies of Engine Coolants in Glassware
ASTM D 1882—Standard Test Method for Effect of Cooling System Chemical Solutions on Organic Finishes for Automotive Vehicles
ASTM D 2570—Standard Test Method for Simulated Service Corrosion Testing of Engine Coolants
ASTM D 2809—Standard Test Method for Cavitation Erosion-Corrosion Characteristics of Aluminum Pumps With Engine Coolants
ASTM D 3634—Standard Test Method for Trace Chloride Ion in Engine Coolant
ASTM D 4985—Standard Specification for Low Silicate, Ethylene Glycol Base Engine Coolant Concentrate for Heavy Duty Engines, Requiring an Initial Charge of Supplemental Coolant Additive (SCA)
ASTM D 4725—Standard Terminology for Engine Coolants
ASTM E 29—Recommended Practice for Indicating Which Places of Figures are to be Considered Significant in Specified Limiting Values
ASTM E 202—Standard Test Method for Analysis of Ethylene Glycols and Propylene Glycols
STP120—Selection and Use of Engine Coolants and Cooling System Chemicals

3. Terminology

3.1 Life Expectancy—The period of protection for which the engine coolant is suitable for use in internal combustion engine cooling systems without adversely affecting coolant flow and heat transfer.

3.2 Engine Coolant—A solution used in an engine cooling system to transfer heat from the engine to the radiator, which provides adequate protection against freezing, boiling, and corrosion. In this document, engine coolant is comprised of 40 to 60% (see NOTE) coolant concentrate, water, and supplemental coolant additive.

NOTE—Forty percent provides freeze protection to −12 °F (−24 °C) while 60% provides freeze protection to −62 °F (−52 °C). Higher concentrations are not recommended because they can cause seal seepage, silicate gelation, and other problems. Lower concentrations are not recommended because they can result in inadequate freeze and corrosion protection.

3.3 Coolant Concentrate—A concentrated solution of ethylene glycol containing additives, such as corrosion inhibitors and a foam suppressor, which is used to prepare an engine coolant for use in internal combustion engine cooling systems.

3.4 Heavy-Duty Engine—A diesel, gasoline, or similarly fueled internal combustion engine, having operating characteristic of long duty cycle at or near maximum rated conditions. Such engines are typically used in Class 5 to 8 over-the-road vehicles; off highway machinery for agriculture, mining, earthmoving, and construction; high output stationary engine installations; and locomotive and marine installations.

3.5 Supplemental Coolant Additive (SCA)—A material added to the cooling systems of heavy duty engines to provide cavitation corrosion protection and minimize deposits on heat transfer surfaces not normally provided by the additives in the coolant concentrate (antifreeze). The SCA is also used to extend the useful life of the coolant by replenishing the additive at the appropriate maintenance interval.

4. General Requirements

4.1 The coolant concentrate shall consist of ethylene glycol containing additives (such as corrosion inhibitors and a foam suppressor) required to provide freeze and general corrosion protection to cooling system components of heavy duty engines. An initial charge of SCA is required for complete protection. Other glycols such as propylene and diethylene may be included providing the physical and performance properties are met.

4.1.1 The coolant concentrate shall contain sufficient water to ensure continued solution of the dissolved additives under recommended storage conditions.

4.1.2 The coolant concentrate is intended to be diluted with water and charged with an initial dose of SCA at the point of use to produce the desired engine coolant.

4.2 The coolant concentrate shall be clear and free from solids.

4.3 The coolant concentrate shall have an identifying color (preferably green or blue-green).

4.4 The coolant concentrate shall not affect nor be affected by its container after storage for one year when exposed to temperatures ranging from 0 °F (−18 °C) to 122 °F (50 °C).

4.5 The engine coolant life expectancy when using an engine coolant concentrate meeting the requirements of this document shall be a minimum of one year, when installed and maintained in accordance with the recommendations of the engine and coolant concentrate manufacturers and treated with appropriate maintenance doses of SCA.

4.6 The water used for preparing engine coolants for service shall be of such quality that it does not contain excessive solids, hardness salts, sulfates, or chlorides. Water containing excessive hardness salts may be softened to minimize formation of hard water scale. Excessive amounts of chloride and sulfate may increase the corrosion rate of the engine cooling system metals. The chloride and sulfate may be removed by deionization or distillation.

Water meeting the requirements in Appendix A is considered acceptable for service.

5. Detail Requirements

5.1 The engine coolant shall comply with the following detail requirements Table 1, the limits of which are absolute and not subject to correction for tolerances of test methods. The document for indicating which places of figures are to be considered significant shall be ASTM E 29. U.S. traditional units are standard. SI units may be approximate.

5.1.1 Effects on Painted Finishes—There shall be no discoloration, loss of gloss, softening, swelling, or other visible effects when tested in accordance with ASTM D 1882 as modified to use paints typical of heavy duty engines and vehicles.

5.1.2 Compatibility with Cooling System Nonmetals—Solutions of the coolant concentrate as normally used in cooling systems shall not have deleterious effects on the nonmetallic components, as determined from examination of the nonmetallic components used in conjunction with ASTM D 2570 corrosion test. The hoses used in the test shall conform to SAE J20. After test, the coolant hose must meet the physical requirements of the coolant immersion test of SAE J20 (J20R4, Class D-1).

6. Inspection and Labeling

6.1 Sampling—When testing to the requirements of this document a sample size of not less than 5 gal (20 L) shall be obtained for testing in accordance with ASTM D 1176 unless otherwise specified.

6.2 Labeling—Products claimed to meet this document shall be labeled on the containers:

"Meets SAE J1941".

TABLE 1—

	MIN	MAX	TEST METHOD ASTM
Other glycols	—	15.0	E 202
Specific Gravity at 60 °F	1.110	1.145	D 1122
Freezing Point, 50% by volume in distilled H_2O, °F (°C)	—	-34 (-37)	D 1177
Boiling Point, °F (°C)			D 1120
Concentrate	325 (163)	—	
Dilute (50% by volume in distilled water)	226 (108)		
pH, dilute (50% by volume in distilled water)	7.5	11.0	D 1287
Chloride, ppm	—	25	D 3634
Total Apparent Water, % mass	—	5	D 1123
Corrosion (Glassware) loss in mass, mg			D 1384
Copper	—	10	
Solder	—	30	
Brass	—	10	
Steel	—	10	
Cast Iron	—	10	
Aluminum	—	30	
Corrosion (Simulated Service) loss in mass, mg			D 2570
Copper	—	20	
Solder	—	60	
Brass	—	20	
Steel	—	20	
Cast Iron	—	20	
Aluminum	—	60	
Ash content, % mass	—	5	D 1119
Foaming Tendency			D 1881
Foam Volume, mL	—	150	
Break Time, s	—	5	
Silicon, ppm	—	250	Under Consideration
Reserve alkalinity	10	—	D 1121
Cavitation Erosion Corrosion rating for pitting, cavitation, or erosion of the water pump.	8	—	D 2809

APPENDIX A
WATER QUALITY

TABLE A1—

Property	Requirement	ASTM Test Method
Total Solids (maximum)	340 ppm (19.9 grain/gallon)	D 1888
Total Hardness (as $CaCO_3$, maximum)	170 ppm (9.9 grain/gallon)	D 1126
Chloride (as Cl, maximum)	40 ppm (2.3 grain/gallon)	D 512
Sulfate (as SO_4, maximum)	100 ppm (5.8 grain/gallon)	D 516

R134a REFRIGERANT AUTOMOTIVE AIR-CONDITIONING HOSE—SAE J2064 JUN1999

SAE Standard

Report of the SAE R134a Subcommittee of the SAE Coolant Hose Committee approved June 1993, completely revised August 1998, and revised June 1999. Rationale statement available.

1. Scope—This SAE Standard covers hose and hose assemblies intended for conducting liquid and gaseous R134a refrigerant in automotive air-conditioning systems. The hose shall be designed to minimize permeation of R134a refrigerant, contamination of the system, and to be functional over a temperature range of –30 to 125 °C. Specific construction details are to be agreed upon between user and supplier. A hose marked "J2064" signifies that it has been coupled, tested, and has met the requirements of SAE J2064. It is the hose assembly manufacturer's responsibility to see that the assemblies meet the specified acceptance criteria for this specification.

2. References

2.1 Applicable Publication—The following publication forms a part of this specification to the extent specified herein.

2.1.1 ASTM Publication—Available from ASTM, 100 Barr Harbor Drive, West Conshohocken, PA 19428-2959.

ASTM D 380—Methods of Testing Rubber Hose

3. Manufacture

3.1 Size—Standard dimensions are given in the first column of Table 1.

3.2 Types—Including, but not limited to the following:

3.2.1 Type A—Elastomeric, Textile Reinforced—The hose shall be built having a suitable seamless synthetic elastomeric tube. The reinforcement shall consist of textile yarn, cord, or fabric adhered to the tube and cover. The outer cover shall be heat- and ozone-resistant synthetic elastomer.

3.2.2 Type B—Elastomeric, Wire Reinforced—The hose shall be built having a suitable seamless synthetic elastomeric tube. The reinforcement shall consist of steel wire adhered to the elastomeric tube. The cover shall consist of a heat-resistant textile yarn impregnated with a synthetic elastomeric cement.

3.2.3 Type C—Barrier, Textile Reinforced—The hose shall have a suitable thermoplastic barrier between elastomeric layers. The reinforcement shall consist of suitable textile yarn, cord, or fabric adhered to the tube and cover. The outer cover shall be heat- and ozone-resistant synthetic elastomer.

3.2.4 Type D—Thermoplastic, Textile Reinforced, Elastomeric Cover—The hose shall have a suitable thermoplastic tube. The reinforcement shall consist of a suitable textile yarn, cord, or fabric adhered to the tube and cover. The outer cover shall be heat- and ozone-resistant synthetic elastomer.

TABLE 1—CONVERSION FACTORS

Fractional Hose Size mm (in)	Mean Hose ID mm (in)	Multiply g/day by Factor Shown to Obtain kg/m²/year	Multiply g/day to Obtain lb/ft²/year
8 (5/16)	8.1 (0.320)	13.452	2.746
10 (13/32)	10.6 (0.418)	10.280	2.102
13 (1/2)	13.0 (0.510)	8.382	1.723
16 (5/8)	16.1 (0.635)	6.768	1.384
19 (3/4)	19.4 (0.765)	5.617	1.149

3.2.5 Type E—Veneer, Textile Reinforced—The hose shall have a suitable thermoplastic veneer lining the inside diameter with an elastomeric tube outer layer. The reinforcement shall consist of a textile yarn, cord, or fabric adhered to the tube and cover. The cover shall be heat- and ozone-resistant synthetic elastomer.

3.2.6 Type F—Veneer, Barrier, Thermoplastic Liner—The hose shall have a suitable thermoplastic veneer liner with a thermoplastic barrier between elastomeric layers. The reinforcement shall consist of a suitable textile yarn, cord, or fabric adhered to the tube and cover. The cover shall be heat- and ozone-resistant elastomer.

3.3 Moisture Vapor Ingression Hose Classes

Class I—Not greater than 0.039 g/cm²/year

Class II— Not greater than 0.111 g/cm²/year

4. Hose Identification—The hose shall be identified with the SAE number, type, class, and size of inside diameter in fraction of inches or metric millimeter equivalents, or both, and hose manufacturer's code marking. This marking shall appear on the outer cover of the hose at intervals not greater than 380 mm.

4.1 Hose Assemblies—Hose Assemblies may be fabricated by the manufacturer, an agent for or customer of the manufacturer, or by the user. Fabrication of permanently attached fittings to refrigerant hose requires specialized assembly equipment. Refrigerant hose from one manufacturer may not be compatible with fittings supplied by another manufacturer. Similarly, assembly equipment from one manufacturer may not be interchangeable with that of another manufacturer.

5. Testing—The test procedures described in the current issue of ASTM D 380, shall be followed whenever applicable.

5.1 Test Conditions—The temperature of the testing room shall be maintained at 23 °C ± 2 °C. The temperature of the test hose or hose assemblies shall be stabilized for 24 h at the testing room temperature prior to testing.

5.2 Permeation Test

5.2.1 Test Specimens—107 cm Samples—The test specimens are to consist of four coupled hose assemblies that have 107 cm ± 1.2 cm of exposed hose between couplings. Three of the coupled hose assemblies are to be used for determining the permeation rate through the hose at a specific temperature. The fourth coupled and plugged hose assembly is to be used for a control hose.

One end of each hose assembly is to be fitted with a capped charge fitting. The other end is to be attached to a canister (optional) or plugged with a fitting. If a canister is used, the coupled hose assemblies are to be connected to canisters each having an internal volume of 510 cm³ ± 25 cm³ and having a minimum burst strength of 8.6 MPa.

5.2.2 Charging Procedure and Initial Weights—The coupled hose assemblies are to be weighed and recorded to 0.01 g to establish an initial weight prior to charging. The test samples (control sample not charged) are to be charged with refrigerant to 70% ± 3% of the internal volume of the assembly and then reweighed. Evacuation and cooling of samples is recommended for ease of charging.

5.2.3 Temperature Exposure—The test temperature is 80 °C ± 2 °C.

5.2.4 Establish Constant Loss Rate—Weigh the samples at the end of the first 24 h temperature exposures and weighing at periodic intervals (minimum period must be 24 h). The weighings should be taken in net loss of grams, charged sample weight loss minus control sample weight loss. The net weight loss versus time should continue to be recorded until steady-state is reached. Steady-state is reached when the last four readings are within 10% of the lowest reading or after 25 days, whichever comes first.

This is not to be a lot release test. The lot release test is to be agreed upon between the vendor and consumer.

5.2.5 Loss Rate Determination—No charged specimen may lose more than 40 g during the first 24 h period. The permeation rate for each specimen may be determined as follows:

a. For Samples that Meet the 10% Rule—Establish the slope of steady-state net loss in grams per day for the 107 cm length specimen and multiply by factors in Table 1 to obtain permeation rate.
b. For Samples that Run for 25 Days—The final weighing period, in which the data recorded will be used to determine the permeation rate, shall be the last 5 days or 7 days of the test period. The samples during the final period shall be weighed 5 times at least 24 h apart. The total net weight loss for the final period, divided by the number of days in the period are multiplied by the factors in Table 1 to obtain the permeation rate.

At the end of the temperature exposure period, the refrigerant charge remaining should be 50% of the original charge minimum. At the conclusion of the test, the refrigerant charge in each specimen should be exhausted to a suitable reclamation container.

5.2.6 Acceptance Determination—The coupled hose assembly shall not be permeable to a refrigerant loss at a rate greater than 29 kg/m²/year for type A and B or a rate greater than 9.7 kg/m²/year for types C, D, E, and F.

5.3 Coupling Integrity—It is the assembly manufacturer's responsibility to verify that the combination of coupling type and specific Hose Manufacturer's Hose Material will meet the following acceptance criteria at all possible combinations of the dimensional tolerances. Either Test Option 1 or Test Option 2 may be used.

5.3.1 Test Specimens—Six production coupled assemblies shall have 76 mm ± 3 mm of exposed hose and 56 mm ± 8 mm of straight tubing between the couplings with suitable connector and sealed at the other (pinch-welding permitted). Each assembly is attached to a canister having an internal volume of 1260 cm³ ± 25 cm³ and equipped with a charging fitting.

5.3.2 Test Procedure

5.3.2.1 Charging—Charge the canister assembly with an amount of R134a compatible lubricant equivalent to half of the internal volume of the hose assembly. Evaluate and add 103 g ± 1 g of R134a and record original weight. Check all fittings to insure against extraneous R134a leakage. This weighing and all subsequent weighings are to be made at 18 to 29 °C to the nearest 0.01 g. For a canister size other than previously mentioned, the internal volume of the assembly must be determined and the R134a charge in grams shall equal system volume (cubic centimeters) x 0.0783 g/cm^3 (the density) constant for R134a gas at 125 °C and 2.07 MPa. After charging, agitate the assembly to insure mixing with the lubricant and wetting of all internal surfaces.

5.3.2.2 Test Exposure—The assembly shall be oriented so that the canister axis is 4 degrees ± 2 degress above the horizontal, insuring that the liquid phase will always drain into the test coupling assembly. The test shall include four exposure intervals with Test Option 1 or six exposure intervals with Test Option 2, each followed by a leakage evaluation and possible recharging before the next exposure.

Test Option 1—The four exposure intervals in sequential order are as follows:

a. Exposure 1—96 h at 125 °C ± 2 °C with canister pressure at 2.07 MPa.
b. Exposure 2—48 h thermal cycling from –30 to 125 °C in a timer-controlled chamber. The chamber temperature shall change every 4 h and canisters shall reach the desired temperature within 3 h after a temperature change.
c. Exposure 3—96 h at 125 °C ± 2 °C with canister pressure at 2.07 MPa.
d. Exposure 4—48 h thermal cycling from –30 to 125 °C in a timer-controlled chamber. The chamber temperature shall change every 4 h and canisters shall reach the desired temperature within 3 h after a temperature change.

Test Option 2—The six exposure intervals in sequential order are as follows:

a. Exposure 1—96 h at 121 °C ± 2 °C with canister pressure at 2.0 MPa.
b. Exposure 2—48 h at –29 to 121 °C in a timer-controlled chamber. The chamber temperature shall change every 4 h and canisters shall reach the desired temperature within 3 h after a temperature change.
c. Exposure 3—96 h at 121 °C ± 2 °C with canister pressure at 2.0 MPa.
d. Exposure 4—48 h at –29 to 121 °C in a timer-controlled chamber. The chamber temperature shall change every 4 h and canisters shall reach the desired temperature within 3 h after a temperature change.
e. Exposure 5—96 h at 121°C ± 2°C with canister pressure at 2.0 MPa.
f. Exposure 6—48 h at –29 to 121 °C in a timer-controlled chamber. The chamber temperature shall change every 4 h and canisters shall reach the desired temperature within 3 h after a temperature change.

5.3.2.3 Leakage Evaluation—At the end of each exposure interval, as soon as a canister assembly reaches room temperature of 18 to 29 °C, it shall be evaluated as follows:

a. Weigh and record the loss in grams for the interval.
b. If the loss is greater than 7 g, terminate the test.
c. Flex test the coupled assembly on the canister to ±15 degrees. Make 10 flex cycles in approximately 10 s in each of two perpendicular planes on a coupling assembly. Immediately evaluate the leakage at each coupling as follows:
   1. Listen for hissing (charge loss).
   2. Look for fluid leakage.
d. Reweigh after flex testing and continue with the next exposure interval if the weight is within 4 g of original weight. If not, recharge to original weight before continuing. Maintaining the weight within 4 g of original weight insures that the canister assembly R134a restarting pressure is no less than 2.0 MPa at 125°C.

5.3.3 Acceptance Determination

a. Applies to six canister assemblies (12 couplings).
b. Maximum weight loss per canister (2 couplings) per Test Option 1 or Test Option 2 shall not exceed 10 g.
c. All post-interval flexing evaluations shall not produce hissing or visible oil loss at any location in the coupling assembly.

5.4 Aging Test—The hose shall show no cracks or other disintegration when tested as specified after aging at 125 °C ± 2 °C for 168 h. The mandrel used shall have a diameter eight times the nominal OD of the hose. The test unit shall have a free hose length not less than 300 mm or more than 1000 mm.

5.4.1 Procedure—Capped hose assembly shall be evacuated and charged with one atmosphere of refrigerant or nitrogen before coiling around the mandrel of the designated size. Place in a circulating air oven for the time and at the temperature specified. Allow the hose assembly to cool to room temperature, after removal from the oven. Open the hose assembly to a straight length and examine the hose for internal and external cracks visible to the naked eye for exposed hose only.

5.5 Cold Test—The hose shall show no evidence of cracking or breaking when tested as specified. The mandrel used for the hose shall have a diameter eight times the nominal OD of the hose. The test hose assembly shall have a free hose length not less than 600 mm or more than 1000 mm.

5.5.1 Procedure—Load the test hose assembly to 70% of capacity with R134a refrigerant at room temperature. For convenience, the hose assembly and R134a refrigerant may be chilled below the boiling point of the R134a refrigerant in order that the R134a refrigerant may be handled in the liquid state. Place the loaded hose assembly in an air oven at 70 °C ± 2 °C for 48 h. Remove hose assembly from the air oven and allow to cool to room temperature.

Place the hose assembly in a straight position along with designated size mandrel in a cold chamber at –30 °C for 24 h. The cold chamber shall be capable of maintaining a uniform atmosphere of cold dry or a mixture of air and carbon dioxide at the specified temperature with a tolerance of ±2 °C. Without removing the hose assembly from the cold chamber, bend it through 180 degrees over the mandrel of the designated size at a uniform rate within a time period of 4 to 8 s. The refrigerant charge in each specimen shall be exhausted into a suitable reclamation container. Examine the hose for internal or external cracks or disintegration.

5.6 Vacuum Flattening

5.6.1 Scope—Flattening of a hose restricts internal fluid flow. This test evaluates the hose construction at room temperature condition for its ability to resist internal area reduction under vacuum conditions.

5.6.2 The coupled hose assembly shall be bent (with the natural curvature of the hose) at room temperature into a "U" shape, with the inside radius of the "U" equal to five times (six times for 0.765 nominal ID) the normal outside diameter of the hose. Measure the minimum outside diameter of the hose in any plane at the base of the "U" (hose OD shall not be less than 80% of original OD). Evacuate the hose to an absolute pressure of 10 mm Hg ± 5 mm Hg. Maintain this pressure in the bent hose specimen for 2 min. At the end of this period, while the hose is still under vacuum, measure the minimum outside diameter in any place at the base of the "U".

5.6.3 Acceptance Criteria

a. The minimum diameter dimension shall not be less than 80% of the minimum hose outside diameter as measured in 5.6.2 in the "U" shape prior to the application of the vacuum.
b. Examine the hose externally for cracks or loose cover. If these imperfections exist, the hose fails.
c. If the hose passes (5.6.3.a and b) cut the hose off at the coupling and section longitudinally. Check the hose internally for blisters, delamination, cracks, or other surface imperfections. Any such imperfections result in hose failure.

5.7 Length Change—All hose types shall not contract in length more than 4% or elongate more than 2% when subjected to a pressure of 2.4 MPa for suction hose and 2.7 MPa for liquid and discharge hose. Test in accordance with ASTM D 380.

5.8 Bursting Strength—The minimum bursting strength for hose and hose assemblies shall be 13.7 MPa for discharge and liquid line, 12 MPa for suction hose. Test in accordance with ASTM D 380.

5.9 Proof Test—All hose shall satisfactorily withstand a hydrostatic proof test with a minimum hydrostatic pressure equal to 50% of the minimum required burst strength for a period not less than 30 s or more than 5 min.

5.10 Extraction Test—The extractables of the inside surface of the hose tube shall not exceed 118 g/m^2 and any extractables shall be oily or soft/greasy in nature. The test hose assembly shall have a free hose length not less than 450 mm or more than 1000 mm.

5.10.1 Procedure—Fill the hose assembly to capacity with suitable solvent and then empty it immediately to remove any surface material. Load the hose assembly to approximately 70% capacity with R134a refrigerant at room temperature. For convenience, the hose assembly and R134a refrigerant may be chilled below the boiling point of R134a refrigerant in order that the R134a refrigerant may be handled in the liquid state. Place the loaded hose assembly in the air oven at 70 °C ± 2 °C for 24 h. At the end of the aging period, chill the hose assembly to –30 °C or colder and pour the liquid R134a refrigerant into a weighed vacuum flask, chilled to –30 °C or colder, then attach the flask to an R134a recovery unit and recover all R134a. After the R134a refrigerant has evaporated, condition the beaker at approximately 70 °C for 1 h to remove condensed moisture, then weigh the beaker again. Report the extract in terms of grams per square meter (milligrams per square inch) of the hose inner surface based on the nominal inside diameter of the hose.

5.11 Ozone Test—When the hose is bent around a mandrel with a diameter 8 times the nominal diameter of the hose and exposed for 70 h to ozone air atmosphere in which the ozone partial pressure is 50 MPa ± 5 MPa at 40 °C ± 2 °C, the outer cover of the hose shall show no cracks when examined under 7X magnification. The test hose shall be about 250 mm longer than the mandrel circumference. Test in accordance with ASTM D 380.

5.12 Cleanliness Test—The bore of all hose and hose assemblies shall be clean and dry. When subjected to this test, there shall not be more than 270 mg/m^2 of foreign material. The test hose shall not be less than 300 mm.

5.12.1 PROCEDURE—Bend the hose or hose assembly to a "U" shape, the legs of the "U" being of equal length. Position the hose in a vertical plane and fill the hose to capacity with suitable solvent. Then filter the suitable solvent through a prepared Gooch crucible, sintered glass crucible, or 0.8 μm filter of known weight. After dying at approximately 70 °C for 20 min, determine by weight difference the insoluble contamination.

5.13 Moisture Ingression—The purpose of the moisture ingression test is to measure the amount of moisture that permeates the hose samples when the hose samples are subjected to humid environment with vacuum being drawn on the ID of the hose samples.

5.13.1 TEST APPARATUS—See Figure 1.

a. Humidity chamber
b. Methanol cold bath maintained at –70 °C or lower (see Figure 1)
c. Vacuum/cold trap system
d. Vacuum pump
e. Nitrogen gas or dry air supply
f. Distilled water
g. Oven capable of 80 °C
h. Drying desiccator
i. Balance capable of 0.1 mg accuracy

5.13.2 TEST SAMPLES

a. Install test assemblies in the humidity cabinet by plugging one end fitting and attaching the other end to the vacuum lines located in the cabinet. Arrange the test assemblies to maximize surface exposure to environmental conditions (see Figure 1).
b. Seal the humidity cabinet and set the dry bulb temperature at 50 °C and wet at 47.2 °C. Allow cabinet to stabilize for at least 4 h at the specified temperatures and 85% ± 5% relative humidity.
c. Thoroughly clean all vacuum traps, inside and out, by using compressed air and suitable solvent.
d. Wipe off traps and then place in an oven set at 80 °C minimum for 1 h.
e. Upon removing the traps from the oven, immediately transfer to a drying desiccator for stabilization to room temperature.
f. After the traps reach room temperature, remove one at a time, wipe trap exterior with lint-free towels, and immediately weigh to the nearest 0.1 mg. Plug the end of the trap immediately. Record these weighs.
g. Immediately after weighing, install the traps (Item 3 in Figure 1) in a bath maintained at –70°C and attach traps to connecting lines using vacuum grease on all O-ring connections.
h. After all connections are made, turn on the vacuum pump and open valve no. 12 and then valve no. 2 and no. 11.
   1. A quick vacuum check can be done by closing valve no. 12
   2. Shut off the pump for approximately 5 min noting any vacuum drop. If there is any loss, the leak should be sealed and then rechecked.
   3. Restart the vacuum pump and open valve no. 12.
   4. After running system for 1 h, close valve no. 12 and turn off the vacuum pump for 30 min. If there is any loss of vacuum, the test is to be discontinued. Leak is to be sealed and the technician is to return to step c.
i. Once the system is evacuated and integrity is ensured, maintain vacuum pump with a maximum pressure of 50 mm of Hg (95 kPa). Record time and temperatures.
j. After a 24 h time duration has taken place, proceed to the sequence of operation in step k. Longer periods may be used as long as the data is adjusted for the specified time period (96 h and 72 h periods recommended).
k. Sequence of operation (for installation of new moisture traps).
   1. Record time and temperatures.
   2. Close valve no. 2.
   3. Close valve no. 12.
   4. Turn off vacuum pump.
   5. Slowly open valve no. 9 and then valve no. 11. This sequence is necessary to ensure the traps are charged with dry nitrogen or dry air atmospheric pressure. (Nitrogen source should have regulator set at 1 psi.)
   6. Remove traps one at a time and immediately plug all tubing connections.
   7. Install another set of traps that were already prepared from steps d through g.
   8. Allow traps to return to room temperature in a desiccator.
   9. Wipe the trap exterior with lint-free towels, remove plugs, and immediately weigh each.
   10. Calculate the change in weight and record.
l. Repeat steps h, i, and k at 96 h and 72 h intervals until steady-state conditions are achieved. Steady-state is reached when the last four readings are within 10% of the lowest reading of the last four.
m. Calculate the rate of moisture ingression to the test specification that have been assigned (see examples 1 and 2).

Example 1:

$$\text{Average Condensate Weight} = \frac{\text{Reading 1} + \text{Reading 2} + \text{Reading 3} + \text{R}}{4} \quad \text{(Eq. 1)}$$

NOTE—Last four readings after steady-state is achieved are used for calculation of rate. Reading is for a 2-h reading or adjusted reading time, and for a 152 cm exposed hose lengths as taken from the moisture ingression test data sheet.

Example 2:

To convert the average condensate weight from g/24 h/152 cm length, multiply the average condenste weight by the following number, depending on hose ID to arrive at g/cm^2/year (see Table 2).

n. Acceptance Determination

Class I—Moisture Resistant = 0.039 g/cm^2/year
Class II—Medium Moisture Resistant = 0.111 g/cm^2/year

TABLE 2—MOISTURE INGRESSION RATE CONVERSION TABLE

Fractional Hose Size mm (in)	Multiply g/day by Factor Shown to Obtain g/in^2/year	Multiply g/day by Factor Shown to Obtain g/cm^2/year
8 (5/16)	0.9404	6.067
10 (13/32)	0.7199	4.644
13 (1/2)	0.5900	3.806
16 (5/8)	0.4739	3.057
19 (3/4)	0.3939	2.541

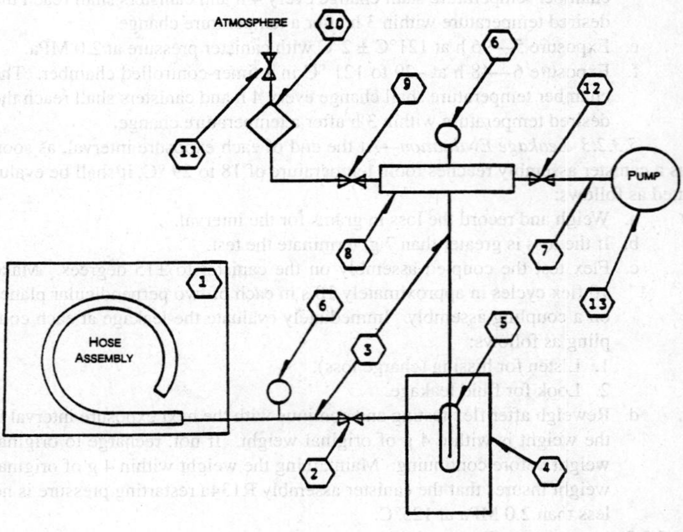

FIGURE 1—MOISTURE INGRESSION TEST SCHEMATIC

COOLANT SYSTEM HOSES—SAE J20 JAN2003 SAE Standard

Report of the SAE Nonmetallic Materials Division approved January 1944. Revised by the SAE Coolant Hose Committee March 1988, completely revised May 1994, revised October 1997, November 2001, and January 2002. Rationale statement available. Revised by the SAE Non-Hydraulic Hose Committee January 2003. Rationale statement available.

1. Scope—This SAE Standard covers reinforced and flexible hoses intended for use in water and ethylene glycol-based engine-coolant system applications.

2. References

2.1 Applicable Publications—The following publications form a part of the specification to the extent specified herein. Unless otherwise indicated, the latest revision of SAE publications shall apply.

2.1.1 SAE PUBLICATIONS—Available from SAE, 400 Commonwealth Drive, Warrendale, PA 15096–0001.

SAE J1231—Formed Tube Ends for Hose Connections and Hose Fittings
SAE J1508—Hose Clamp Specification
SAE J1610—Test Method for Evaluating the Sealing Capability of Hose Connections with a PVT Test Facility
SAE J1638—Compression Set of Hoses or Solid Discs
SAE J1684—Test Method for Evaluating the Electrochemical Resistance of Coolant System Hoses and Materials
SAE J2370—Geometric Dimensions and Tolerancing for Curved Hose
SAE J2387—Dimensions and Tolerances for Coolant System Hoses
SAE J2605—Non-Contact Hose Measurement Study 1

2.1.2 ASTM PUBLICATIONS—Available from ASTM, 100 Barr Harbor Drive, West Conshohocken, PA 19428–2959.

ASTM D 380—Methods of Testing Rubber Hose
ASTM D 395—Test Methods for Rubber Property Compression Set
ASTM D 412—Test Method for Rubber Properties in Tension
ASTM D 413—Test Methods for Rubber Property Adhesion to Flexible Substrate
ASTM D 471—Test Method for Rubber Property Effect of Liquids
ASTM D 573—Test Method for Rubber Deterioration in an Air Oven
ASTM D 1149—Test Method for Rubber Deterioration Surface Ozone Cracking in a Chamber (Flat Specimens)
ASTM D 2240—Test Method for Rubber Property Durometer Hardness

2.1.3 ISO PUBLICATION—Available from ANSI, 25 West 43rd Street, New York, NY 10036-8002.

ISO 9001—Quality systems—Model for quality assurance in design, development, production, installation and servicing

2.1.4 AUTOMOTIVE INDUSTRY PUBLICATION—Available from AIAG, 26200 Lasher Road, Suite 200, Southfield, MI 48034-7100.

QS 9000—Quality System Requirements

2.2 Related Publications—The following publications are provided for information purposes only and are not a required part of this document.

2.2.1 SAE PUBLICATIONS—Available from SAE, 400 Commonwealth Drive, Warrendale, PA 15096-0001.

SAE J20-1—Coolant Hose (Supplement to SAE J20 for Government Use Replacing Part of MS51230)
SAE J20-2—Coolant Hose—Normal Service Type Convoluted, Wire Support Hose (Supplement to SAE J20 for Government Use Replacing Part of MS51008)

3. Definitions of Hose Types

3.1 SAE 20R1—Heavy-duty type for service in heavy-duty application. This type is available in two wall thicknesses as indicated in 6.3.

3.2 SAE 20R2—Flexible heavy-duty wire embedded type for the same service as SAE 20R1.

3.3 SAE 20R3—Heater hose for normal service.

3.4 SAE 20R4—Radiator hose for normal service.

3.5 SAE 20R5—Convoluted wire supported type for normal service.

3.6 Hose Special Designators for SAE 20RXY—X Refers to the hose type. Y designators may be used for hoses with special features. Multiple Y designators may be used if needed.

3.6.1 HT—This High Temperature designation is for any hose type, SAE 20R1 to SAE 20R5, which is required to operate in an environment above 125 °C. (See Section 11.)

3.6.2 EC—This Electrochemical designation is for any hose type SAE 20R1 to SAE 20R5 which is required to have electrochemical resistance as defined by SAE J1684. (See Section 12.)

3.6.3 LT—This Low Temperature designation is for any hose type SAE 20R1 to SAE 20R5 which is required to operate in an environment down to –55 °C. (See Section 13.)

3.7 Hose Classes—Compounds based on different synthetic rubber grades are specified and designated (see 5.2 for test methods):

Class A—high-temperature resistant
Class B—high oil resistant
Class C—medium oil resistant
Class D-1—low oil resistant, improved service
Class D-2—low oil resistant, standard service
Class D-3—low oil resistant, high-temperature resistant, premium service
Class E—low oil resistant, fiber elastomer composite

Physical characteristics for each hose class are shown in Table 1.

TABLE 1—COOLANT SYSTEM HOSE ELASTOMERIC MATERIAL, PHYSICAL PROPERTIES

SAE Designation Typical Elastomer	Class A Silicone	Class B NBR	Class C CR	Class D–1 EPDM	Class D–2 EPDM	Class D–3 EPDM	Class E EPDM/Fiber
Typical Temperature Range, °C	–55 to 175	–40 to 100	–40 to 100	–40 to 125	–40 to 125	–40 to 150	–40 to 125
Original Properties							
Durometer, points Shore A	55 to 75	55 to 75	55 to 75	55 to 75	55 to 75	55 to 75	65 to 85
Tensile, min, MPa	5.5	8.5	7.0	7.0	5.0	7.0	5.0
Elongation, min, %	200	250	200	250	150	250	100
Oven Aging Conditions and Change Limits, Hours/°C	70/175	70/100	70/100	70/125	70/125	168/150	70/125
Durometer, points Shore A	+10	+15	+20	+15	+15	+15	+15
Tensile, max %	–15	–15	–20	–20	–20	–35	–20
Elongation, max, %	–40	–50	–50	–50	–50	–65	–50
Oil Immersion Change Limits							
ASTM No. 3 Oil or IRM 903 (IRM 903 is being phased in to replace ASTM No. 3)							
Hours/°C	70/100	70/100	70/100	—	—	—	—
Volume, max, %	0 to +45	–5 to +25	+80	—	—	—	—
Tensile, max, %	–40	–20	–50	—	—	—	—
Coolant Immersion (Tube only)							
Change Limits							
Hours/at Boiling Point	70	70	70	70	70	168	70
Volume, %	0 to +40	0 to +20	0 to +20	–5 to +20	–5 to +20	–5 to +20	–5 to +20
Durometer, points Shore A	–10 to +10	–10 to +10	–10 to +10	–10 to +10	–10 to +10	–10 to +10	–10 to +10
Tensile, max, %	–30	–20	–20	–20	–20	–20	–20
Elongation, max, %	–25	–40	–40	–50	–25	–25	–25
Compression Set °C	125	100	100	125	125	125	125
70 h, max, %	40	50	75	75	85	75	85
Cold Flexibility (°C)(1)	–40	–40	–40	–40	–40	–40	–40

1. LT designator extends the low temperature flexibility to –55 °C.

3.8 Marking—The outer cover will be printed with the designation SAE 20RXY (the X being the hose type and Y any special designator(s) such as "LT"), class, size of the inside diameter in millimeters, hose manufacturer's code marking, and any other identification as agreed upon between user and manufacturer/supplier. It is recommended that this marking shall appear on the outer cover of the hose at intervals not greater than 380 mm.

3.8.1 SMALL ID OR SHORT HOSE—If there is insufficient space on the hose for the required marking due to size or configuration, the marking shall be agreed upon by the customer and the manufacturer/supplier.

4. Dimensional Requirements—Geometric Dimensioning and Tolerancing requirements are outlined in SAE J2370. The following requirements are minimal standards:

4.1 Tube and Cover Thickness—Minimum thickness shall be 1.6 mm for the tube and 0.8 mm for the cover.

NOTE—This requirement does not apply for hoses without distinctive tube and cover construction.

4.2 Length Tolerance

a. Straight Hose—Unless otherwise specified by the customer or manufacturer, Commercial Tolerances will be used. See Table 2.

TABLE 2—LENGTH TOLERANCE

Length mm	Precision Tolerance mm	Commercial Tolerance mm
0–300	±3.2	+9.7–3.2
>300	±1%	+3%–1%

b. Curved Hose—The tolerances on arm lengths, measured from end to intersection of nearest centerline, shall be as shown in Table 3.

TABLE 3—TOLERANCE ON ARM LENGTH

Arm Length mm	Precision Tolerance mm	Commercial Tolerance mm
0–300.0	±4.0	±6.4
300.1–610.0	±4.8	±7.2
610.1–910.0	±6.4	±9.7
910.1–1220.0	±9.7	±11.2
1220.1–1830.0	±12.7	±15.9
over 1830	±1%	±2%

4.3 General Layout Tolerances, Curved Hose—Dimensions locating bend intersections and centerline radii are to establish the theoretical design centerline of the hose. Actual outside contour of hose must be held within a total range of 9.6 mm of all planes with respect to theoretical outside contour of hose. For hose check, hose ends should first be placed in theoretical design position before checking (hose may have to be flexed to correct for any distortion caused by handling or during shipment). SAE arm length tolerances shall apply.

Tolerances apply to all arm and body lengths in addition to contour tolerances. Dimensions covering more than one arm or body length are reference only and have no tolerances. The wall thickness within bends of a curved hose may differ from the wall thickness of the straight by no more than 33%.

When an alignment mark is required for assembly operations, the basic identifier in Figure 1 is recommended:

FIGURE 1—ALIGNMENT MARK

Location of the alignment mark and/or additional information shall be determined by the customer and the manufacturer.

4.4 Enlarged Ends—When the ID of one end of the hose is enlarged, normally the ID of the enlarged end should not exceed the ID of the rest of the hose by more than 33%. Enlarged ends should be considered arm lengths for tolerance purposes. The wall thickness normally changes with enlarged ends.

4.5 End Squareness—All points on the hose end surface must lie within a tolerance zone consisting of two parallel planes perpendicular to the hose axis. The tolerance zone is determined by Table 4.

TABLE 4—END SQUARENESS

Hose ID	Precision Tolerance	Commercial Tolerance
25.4 mm and larger	10% of ID	15% of ID
smaller than 25.4 mm	2.54 mm	3.75 mm

4.6 Finish and Roundness on Connections—Users of coolant hose should take every precaution to obtain connections as smooth and round as practical. (Reference SAE J1231)

4.7 Clamps—Refer to SAE J1508 for available clamp types.

5. Physical Test Requirements and Procedures

5.1 Finished Product

5.1.1 ADHESION—When applicable, use test procedure ASTM D 413. The minimum requirement is 1400 N/m between all elastomer or elastomer-coated plies.

5.1.2 COLD FLEXIBILITY—The following procedure shall be used:

For hose 25.4 mm ID and smaller, specimen shall consist of a complete hose of length sufficient to perform bend test described as follows: the hose shall be placed in a cold box for 5 h at the temperature specified in Table 1. The hose shall then be flexed in the cold chamber through 180 degrees from the centerline to a diameter of ten times the maximum outside diameter of the hose within 4 s. The hose shall not fracture and shall not show any cracks or breaks in the tube or cover.

For hose larger than 25.4 mm ID, specimens are to be 25.4 mm long sections of the complete hose. The specimen and test fixture shall be placed in a cold box for 5 h at the temperature specified in Table 1. The specimen is then compressed to 50% of its original inside diameter between parallel plates within 4 s. The specimen shall not crack or break. The testing fixture shall be in the cold box during the entire test.

NOTE—For LT hose, refer to Section 13 for specific cold flexibility requirements.

5.1.3 OZONE TEST AND REQUIREMENTS—The following test and requirements apply:

When applicable, use test procedure ASTM D 1149.

For hose 25.4 mm ID and smaller, a specimen of hose of sufficient length shall be bent around a mandrel with an outside diameter equal to eight times the specified OD of the sample. The two ends shall be tied at their crossing with enameled copper or aluminum wire. After mounting, the specimen shall be allowed to rest in an ozone-free atmosphere for 24 h at standard laboratory test temperature. The mounted specimen shall be placed in a test chamber containing ozone at a partial pressure of 50 mPa ± 5 mPa at a temperature of 40 °C ± 1 °C.

After 100 h of exposure, the specimen shall be removed and allowed to cool to standard laboratory test temperature and then be inspected visually under 7X magnification. The sample must not show any cracks except for the area immediately adjacent to the wire, which shall be ignored.

For hose larger than 25.4 mm ID, prepare a specimen by cutting a strip of the whole hose 12.7 mm x 100 mm and tie specimen (cover out) around a 12.7 mm diameter mandrel. Condition in the same manner as specified previously for the whole hose and apply the same conditions and requirements. This test applies to the cover only and cracks in the exposed tube or cut edges of the cover shall be ignored.

5.1.4 KINK TEST—This test applies to SAE 20R3 hose only. (Not recommended for formed hoses.)

5.1.4.1 Test Procedure—Condition specimen length of hose at standard laboratory test temperature for at least 2 h. Measure the minimum OD at the approximate center of the specimen length. When a sufficient length of hose is available, it is permissible and suggested that a length in excess of the specimen length be used in an effort to minimize the handling variable and overbending. Insert one end of the hose into one hole of the specified test fixture, carefully bend the hose (in direction of natural curvature) and insert the other hose end into the second test fixture hole. Do not overbend or bend hose with sharp motion to prevent excessive kinking or collapse. Within 30 s, measure the minimum diameter at the point of greatest collapse.

5.1.4.2 Test Fixture—Shall consist of 25.4 mm thick flat plate drilled with holes not to exceed the hose OD by more than 1.6 mm and separated by the specified center distances.

5.1.4.3 Test Requirements—See Table 5.

TABLE 5—KINK TEST REQUIREMENTS FOR SAE 20R3 HOSE

Nominal Hose ID mm	Specimen Length mm	Center Distance mm	Collapse of Hose Allowed, %
15 and larger	24 x ID	10 x ID	25
smaller than 15	24 x ID	8 x ID	25

5.1.5 VACUUM COLLAPSE TEST—When practical, the entire hose shall be tested as specified in Tables 6A and 6B. The minimum outside diameter shall decrease by no more than 20% during application of vacuum for 15 s and not to exceed 30 s.

5.1.6 BURST—This test shall be performed on a straight length of hose in accordance with ASTM D 380 to meet the requirement in Tables 6A and 6B.

For curved 20R3 and 20R4 hose, the same reference applies, except that the test shall be performed on the individual curved hose with one end free and unrestrained and the rate of application of pressure shall be not less than 2.0 MPa nor more than 7.0 MPa/min. The aged burst requirement (11.2.2) will apply to all HT hoses.

5.1.7 PRESSURE VIBRATION AND TEMPERATURE OR PRESSURE AND TEMPERATURE TEST—This test shall be used when agreed upon between customer and manufacturer/supplier, using SAE J1610 as the referenced test method. If required, test limits can be modified if agreed upon by the customer and manufacturer/supplier.

TABLE 6A—BURST AND VACUUM VALUES (20R1 AND 20R2)

Nominal Size mm	20R1 Heavy-Duty Standard Wall Min Burst MPa	20R1 Heavy-Duty Standard Wall Min Vacuum kPa	20R1 Heavy-Duty Heavy Wall Min Burst MPa	20R1 Heavy-Duty Heavy Wall Min Vacuum, kPa	20R2 Wire Inserted Min Burst MPa	20R2 Wire Inserted Min Vacuum kPa
10	3.29	33.8				
13	2.93	33.8				
16	2.59	27.0				
19	2.24	27.0				
22	2.24	23.6				
25	2.06	23.6			2.06	84.4
29	2.06	20.3				
32	1.90	16.9	3.45	33.8	1.90	84.4
35	1.90	13.5				
38	1.72	10.1	3.10	33.8	1.72	84.4
41	1.72	6.8				
44	1.55	3.4	2.76	16.9	1.55	84.4
51	1.38		2.41	10.1	1.38	84.4
57	1.21		2.41	3.4	1.21	84.4
60	1.21					
64	1.03		2.06		1.03	84.4
70	0.86		1.72		0.86	84.4
76	0.60		1.72		0.69	84.4
83						
89	0.52		1.38		0.52	84.4
102	0.34		1.03		0.34	84.4

NOTE—For hose sizes between sizes listed, use the values for the next larger size.

TABLE 6B—BURST AND VACUUM VALUES (20R3, 20R4, and 20R5)

Nominal Size mm	20R3 Heater Min Burst MPa	20R3 Heater Min Vacuum kPa	20R4 Radiator Min Burst MPa	20R4 Radiator Min Vacuum kPa	20R5 Wire Supported Min Burst MPa	20R5 Wire Supported Min Vacuum kPa
5	1.72	33.8				
6	1.72	33.8				
7	1.72	33.8				
8	1.72	33.8				
9	1.72	33.8				
10	1.72	33.8	1.24			
13	1.72	33.8	1.17			
16	1.72	27.0	1.10			
19	1.38	23.6	1.03			
22						
25	1.21	20.3	0.97		0.97	
29						
32	1.21	16.9	0.90		0.90	
35						
38			0.83		0.83	
41						
44			0.76		0.76	
51			0.69		0.69	
57			0.62		0.62	
60						
64			0.55		0.55	
70			0.48			
76			0.41			
83			0.34			
89			0.27			
102						

NOTE—For hose sizes between sizes listed, use the values for the next larger size.

5.2 Physical Properties are to be Obtained from Specimens Removed from Hose—See ASTM D 380 for procedure. For thin specimens (less than 1.5 mm) use ASTM slab testing per ASTM D 380.

NOTE—For 20R5 hoses, test specimens are to be taken from the cuffs.

5.2.1 DUROMETER HARDNESS—Hardness shall be measured with a Shore A Durometer according to ASTM D 2240.

5.2.2 TENSILE STRENGTH AND ELONGATION—Test according to ASTM D 412.

5.2.3 OVEN AGING—Shall conform to ASTM D 573.

5.2.4 COOLANT IMMERSION—Volume change, tensile, elongation, and durometer changes shall be observed after immersion in the following mixture maintained at the boiling point under a water-cooled reflux condenser. Maintain the fluid level during the test by adding distilled water as needed.

a. 1/2 by volume, distilled water
b. 1/2 by volume, ethylene glycol-based coolant agreed to between supplier and customer

Measurements of tensile, elongation, durometer, and volume change shall be made in accordance with appropriate ASTM methods.

5.2.5 OIL IMMERSION—Shall conform to ASTM D 471.

5.2.6 COMPRESSION SET—Test to be performed per ASTM D 395, Method B. For cover specimens, ply to 8.9 mm ± 1 mm, not to exceed 7 plies where applicable. For tube specimens, ply to 12.7 mm ± 1 mm, not to exceed 7 plies. When unable to meet the required thickness, use standard ASTM slabs cured at similar cure conditions as the hose.

NOTE—SAE J1638 may be considered as an alternate test method with criteria to be agreed upon between customer and manufacturer.

6. SAE 20R1 Heavy-Duty Type

6.1 Scope—This type of hose is primarily for heavy-duty service of which the diesel-locomotive application is a typical example. The hose is intended to withstand the effects of higher pressure systems. When desired, hose with one class of material in the tube and another in the cover may be obtained. In such cases, the physical properties specified for respective parts shall apply.

6.2 Reinforcement—The reinforcement may consist of multiple plies of woven or cord fabric, or ply or plies of braided, knit, or spiraled yarn and shall be such that the hose meets the minimum burst and vacuum requirements as given in Table 6A.

6.3 Dimensions—The ID Tolerance is ±0.8 mm for sizes smaller than 51 mm and ±1.6 mm for sizes 51 mm and larger. The Wall Thickness Range for Standard Wall Thickness hose is 4.3 to 5.6 mm. The Wall Thickness Range for Heavy Wall Thickness Hose is 5.8 to 7.1 mm. These dimensions shall be measured at a section not including a lap.

7. SAE 20R2 Heavy-Duty Wire Embedded Type

7.1 Scope—This is similar to SAE 20R1 hose except that it utilizes wire helix or helices built into the wall of the hose. The hose is intended to withstand high vacuum and/or some forced curvature.

7.2 Reinforcement—The reinforcement is typically multiple plies of woven or cord fabric or ply or plies of braided or knot yarn and wire helix or helices such that the hose will meet the minimum vacuum and burst requirements as given in Table 6A.

7.3 Dimensions—The ID Tolerance is ±0.8 mm for sizes smaller than 51 mm and ±1.6 mm for sizes 51 mm and larger. The Wall Thickness Range at hose ends exclusive of wire gauge is 4.3 to 6.4 mm.

8. SAE 20R3 Heater Hose

8.1 Scope—This type of hose is used in connecting heater systems and other components in the coolant circulating systems of ground vehicles.

8.2 Reinforcement—The reinforcement typically consists of one or more plies of woven, braided, knit, or spiraled yarn, or class E material, and shall be such that the hose will meet the minimum burst and vacuum requirements in Table 6B.

8.3 Dimensions and Tolerances—Target dimensions and tolerances are shown in Tables 7A and 7B. Contact or non-contact measurement method must be agreed upon by manufacturer and customer. Since expanded ends may cause wall thickness to change, ODs and tolerances for the expanded ends must also be agreed upon by the manufacturer and customer. Tolerances and dimensions other than those listed as follows must be agreed upon by manufacturer and customer. The values in Tables 7A and 7B are standard wall dimensions and commercial tolerances. If thin-wall dimensions or precision tolerances are required, refer to SAE J2387.

TABLE 7A—STANDARD DIMENSIONS AND COMMERCIAL TOLERANCES FOR SAE 20R3 Tolerances and Method for Contact Measurement

ID mm	ID Tolerance, mm	Target OD(1) mm	OD Tolerance mm	Reference Wall mm	Maximum Wall Thickness Variation mm
5.0 to <9.0	±0.8	Maximum ID Plus 7 mm	±0.8	3.5	1.0
9.0 to <25.4	±0.8	Maximum ID Plus 8 mm	±0.8	4.0	1.0
25.4	±0.8	34	±1.2	4.3	1.0
>25.4	±0.8	Maximum ID Plus 9.9 mm	±1.6	4.95	1.0

1. The target OD should be measured over a plug gauge equal to the specified maximum ID.

TABLE 7B—STANDARD DIMENSIONS AND COMMERCIAL TOLERANCES FOR SAE 20R3 Tolerances for Non-Contact Measurement (see SAE J2605)

ID mm	ID Tolerance mm	Target Wall Thickness mm	Wall Thickness Tolerance mm	Maximum Wall Thickness Variation mm
5.0 to <9.0	±0.8	3.5	±0.4	1.0
9.0 to <25.4	±0.8	4.0	±0.4	1.0
25.4	±0.8	4.3	±0.6	1.0
>25.4	±0.8	4.95	±0.8	1.0

9. SAE 20R4 Radiator Hose Normal Service Type

9.1 Scope—This is a hose for coolant circulating systems of automotive type engines, commonly known as radiator hose. When resistance to vacuum collapse is a requirement, an inserted wire helix may be specified if desired.

9.2 Reinforcement—The reinforcement typically consists of one or more plies of woven, braided, knit, or spiraled yarn, or Class E material, and shall be such that the hose will meet the minimum burst and vacuum requirements in Table 6B.

9.3 Dimensions—Target dimensions and tolerances are shown in 9.3.1. Measurement method must be agreed upon by manufacturer and customer. Since expanded ends may cause wall thickness to change, ODs and tolerances for the expanded ends must also be agreed upon by the manufacturer and customer. Tolerances and dimensions other than those listed as follows must be agreed upon by the manufacturer and customer. Since the wall thickness may change due to bends near the end of hoses, the wall thickness reported will be the average of 4 readings taken 90 degrees apart. The values in 9.3.1 are standard wall dimensions and commercial tolerances. If thin-wall dimensions or precision tolerances are required, refer to SAE J2387.

9.3.1 DIMENSIONS AND TOLERANCES—The ID tolerance is ±0.8 mm for hose sizes smaller than 70 mm and ±1.6 mm for hose sizes 70 mm and larger. The wall thickness and tolerance is 4.95 mm ± 0.65 mm (4.3 to 5.6 mm) for hose sizes smaller than 50.8 mm and 5.35 mm ± 1.05 mm (4.3 to 6.4 mm) for hose sizes 50.8 mm and larger.

10. SAE 20R5 Normal Service Type Convoluted, Wire Supported Hose

10.1 Scope—This is a wire reinforced hose for coolant circulating systems of automotive type engines, commonly known as universal type hose. This hose consists of a convoluted section with plain ends. The hose shall contain a wire helix or helices in the convoluted section.

10.2 Reinforcement—The reinforcement is typically a ply or plies of woven or cord fabric, braided, knot, or spiraled yarn. The hose must meet the minimum burst requirements listed in Table 6B.

10.3 Dimensions—The ID Tolerance is +0.8 to –1.6 mm. The Wall Thickness Range is 3.6 to 4.8 mm.

11. High-Temperature Service Hose HT

11.1 Scope—Any hose type SAE 20R1 to SAE 20R5 which is required to be operated in an environment above 125 °C. The letters HT will be used to designate this new requirement, for example, SAE 20R1 HT Class A standard wall.

11.2 Requirements

11.2.1 TUBE AND COVER—The tube and cover compounds must be Class A or Class D-3.

11.2.2 AGED BURST—The reinforcement yarn or fabric must be such that the hose passes the minimum burst requirements given on the appropriate table after aging 168 h at 150 °C in a hot air oven.

12. Electrochemical Resistant Hose EC

12.1 Scope—Any hose type SAE 20R1 to SAE 20R5 which is required to have electrochemical resistance. The letters EC will be used to designate this requirement, for example SAE 20R1 EC.

12.2 Requirement—Hoses shall be tested in accordance with SAE J1684. Test method 1 shall be utilized to determine the electrochemical resistance of the hose assembly.

13. Low-Temperature Service Hose LT

13.1 Scope—Any hose type SAE 20R1 to SAE 20R5 and any hose class which is required to be operated in an environment down to –55 °C. The letters LT will be used to designate this requirement, for example, SAE 20R1LT Class A standard wall.

13.2 Requirements—Test frequency is a minimum of annually, per QS 9000.

13.2.1 RESISTANCE TO VIBRATION—This applies to SAE 20R2 wire embedded hoses only. The requirements of 5.1.7 shall apply, using SAE J1610, Test Procedure #1, as the recommended practice.

13.2.2 PROOF PRESSURE—This test shall be performed on a straight length of hose in accordance with ASTM D 380 with the pressure being equal to 50% of the Burst Pressure requirement in Tables 6A and 6B. For curved 20R3 and 20R4 hose, the same reference applies, except that the test shall be performed on the individual curved hose with one end free and unrestrained and the rate of application of pressure shall be not less than 2.0 MPa/min nor more than 7.0 MPa/min.

13.2.3 COLD FLEXIBILITY—The test temperature shall be –55 °C. Test per 5.1.2.

COOLANT HOSE (SUPPLEMENT TO SAE J20 FOR GOVERNMENT USE REPLACING PART OF MS52130)—SAE J20-1 JUN2002

SAE Standard

Report of the SAE Coolant Hose Committee approved November 2001. Rationale statement available. Revised by the SAE Non-Hydraulic Hose Committee May 2002. Rationale statement available. Revised by the SAE Non-Hydraulic Hose Committee June 2002. Rationale statement available.

1. Scope—This SAE Standard provides ordering information for any SAE 20R1 through SAE 20R4 hose type (such as EC, HT, LT, or combination thereof.) It is a supplement for Government use but may be used by others.

2. References

2.1 Applicable Publications—The following publications form a part of this specification to the extent specified herein. Unless otherwise indicated, the latest version of SAE publications shall apply.

2.1.1 SAE Publication—Available from SAE, 400 Commonwealth Drive, Warrendale, PA 15096-0001.

SAE J20—Coolant System Hoses

2.1.2 ISO Publication—Available from ANSI, 11 West 42nd Street, New York, NY 10036-8002.

ISO 9001—Quality systems—Model for quality assurance in design, development, production, installation and servicing

2.1.3 Government Publications—Available from U. S. Government, DOD SSP, Subscription Service Division, Building 4D, 700 Robbins Avenue, Philadelphia, PA 19111-5094

Federal Specification ZZ-H-428—Hose; Non-Metallic and Hose; Preformed: (for Coolant Systems of Automotive and Other Liquid-Cooled Engines)

Military Drawing MS52130—Hose, Nonmetallic: Straight, Engine Coolant

2.1.4 Automotive Industry Publication—Available from AIAG, 26200 Lasher Road, Suite 200, Southfield, MI 48034-7100.

QS 9000—Quality System Requirements

3. Technical Requirements—The following requirements are in addition to the requirements of SAE J20.

3.1 Certification—Manufacturers/suppliers of hose to the Government must be ISO-9001 or QS-9000 certified and provide their certification to the Government before providing SAE 20R1, 20R2, 20R3 or 20R4 hose.

3.2 Lengths—The lengths shall comply with SAE J20 tolerances.

3.3 Inside Diameters—The inside diameters specified in Table 1 shall comply with SAE J20 tolerances.

3.4 Wall Thickness Range—Wall gauge range shall comply with SAE J20.

3.4.1 Wall Thickness for SAE 20R1 Heavy-Duty Type Hose—There are two wall thicknesses available for R1 Hose per SAE J20 paragraph 6.3. Standard wall thickness hose is 4.3 mm to 5.6 mm wall. Heavy Wall Thickness hose is 5.8 to 7.1 mm wall. The part number code for standard wall is "S" and for heavy wall is "H". See part numbering example in 4.1.

3.5 Bulk Hose—Bulk hose shall be furnished in lengths of 3.66, 7.62, or 12.19 m (12, 25, or 40 ft, respectively) or in multiples thereof, except that on such orders up to 10% may be furnished in random lengths over 4.57 m (15 ft). An additional 10% may be furnished in random lengths over 915 mm (36 in).

3.6 Markings for U.S. Government use only—For U.S. Government use only, marking shall consist of the following:

a. Part Identification Number (see 4.2)
b. Manufacturer's Identification code (CAGE) or trademark symbol
c. Month and year of manufacture

TABLE 1—CROSS REFERENCE OF NOMINAL INSIDE DIAMETERS AND APPLICABILITY

J20 Nominal Size (mm)	MS52130 Size No.	MS52130 Nominal ID (inch)	R1 Hose	R2 Hose	R3 Hose	R4 Hose
10	01	3/8	X		X	X
13	02	1/2	X		X	X
16	03	5/8	X		X	X
19	04	3/4	X		X	X
22	05	7/8	X		X	X
25	06	1	X	X	X	X
29	07	1-1/8	X	X	X	X
32	08	1-1/4	X	X	X	X
33	09	1-5/16	X	X		X
35	10	1-3/8	X	X		X
37	11	1-7/16	X	X		X
38	12	1-1/2	X	X		X
40	13	1-9/16	X	X		X
41	14	1-5/8	X	X		X
44	15	1-3/4	X	X		X
48	16	1-7/8	X	X		X
51	17	2	X	X		X
54	18	2-1/8	X	X		X
57	19	2-1/4	X	X		X
60	20	2-3/8	X	X		X
64	21	2-1/2	X	X		X
67	22	2-5/8	X	X		X
70	23	2-3/4	X	X		X
73	24	2-7/8	X	X		X
76	25	3	X	X		X
79	26	3-1/8	X	X		X
83	27	3-1/4	X	X		X
86	28	3-3/8	X	X		X
89	29	3-1/2	X	X		X
95	30	3-3/4	X	X		
102	31	4	X	X		
114	32	4-1/2	X			

3.6.1 If there is insufficient space on the hose for the required marking due to small ID hose or too short a straight length, a label carrying the required information shall be taped around the individual pieces of hose in lieu of the standard method of marking.

3.6.2 Marking for non-Government users shall be agreed upon by the customer and manufacturer.

4. Notes

4.1 Part Identification Number—Part numbers shall be constructed as indicated in Figure 1.

SAE-20	*R*	****	- ** *X*	- *** *X*	***
Basic type	Hose type	Special Characteristics 1/ 2/	Class 1/ 3/	Inside diameter (See Table 1)	Nominal Length 4/

Notes: 1/ See SAE J20.
2/ Examples are EC, LT, HT, and for R1 hose wall; S, H
3/ For Class D-1, use "D1". For Class D-3, use "D3".
4/ When random lengths of hose are permissible, use an "R".

FIGURE 1—PART IDENTIFICATION NUMBER

EXAMPLE—SAE-20R1LTH-A-51X280 indicates a hose with low temperature characteristics, heavy wall, in a Class A compound that is nominally 51 by 280 mm (50.8 mm (2.00 in) ID by 279.4 mm (11.00 in) length.)

4.2 Government Specification Replacement—This document is a replacement for Military Drawing MS52130, "Hose, Nonmetallic: Straight, Engine Coolant" and portions of Federal Specification ZZ-H-428, "Hose; Non-Metallic and Hose; Preformed: (for Coolant Systems of Automotive and Other Liquid-Cooled Engines.)"

4.3 Cross Reference Information—Table 2 shows the relationship between designations in this document and ZZ-H-428. MS52130 provided part numbers for ZZ-H-428, Types I through IV hose.

TABLE 2—CROSS REFERENCE DESIGNATIONS

J20 Designation	J20 Class	ZZ-H-428 Type	ZZ-H-428 Grade	ZZ-H-428 Class
SAE-20R1ECLTH	A	II	A	2
SAE-20R1ECLTH	A	II	A	4
SAE-20R1ECH	B	II	B	1
SAE-20R1ECH	C	II	B	2
SAE-20R1ECH	D-1	II	B	3
SAE-20R1ECH	D-3	II	B	4
SAE-20R1ECLTS	A	I	A	2
SAE-20R1ECLTS	A	I	A	4
SAE-20R1ECS	B	I	B	1
SAE-20R1ECS	C	I	B	2
SAE-20R1ECS	D-1	I	B	3
SAE-20R1ECS	D-3	I	B	4
SAE-20R3ECLT	A	IV	A	2
SAE-20R3ECLT	A	IV	A	4
SAE-20R3EC	B	IV	B	1
SAE-20R3EC	C	IV	B	2
SAE-20R3EC	D-1	IV	B	3
SAE-20R3EC	D-3	IV	B	4
SAE-20R4ECLT	A	III	A	2
SAE-20R4ECLT	A	III	A	4
SAE-20R4EC	C	III	B	2
SAE-20R4EC	D-1	III	B	3
SAE-20R4EC	D-3	III	B	4

4.4 Key Words—Automotive, coolant hose, flexible hose, heater hose, preformed hose, wire reinforced hose.

COOLANT HOSE—NORMAL SERVICE TYPE CONVOLUTED, WIRE SUPPORT HOSE (SUPPLEMENT TO SAE J20 FOR GOVERNMENT USE REPLACING PART OF MS51008)—SAE J20-2 NOV2001

SAE Standard

Report of the SAE Coolant Hose Committee approved November 2001. Rationale statement available.

1. Scope—This SAE Standard provides ordering information for any SAE 20R5 hose type (such as "EC, HT, LT" or combination thereof.) This is a wire-reinforced hose for coolant circulating systems of automotive type engines. This hose consists of a convoluted section with plain ends. The hose shall contain a wire helix or helices in the convoluted section. It is a supplement for Government use but may be used by others.

2. References

2.1 Applicable Publications—The following publications form a part of this specification to the extent specified herein. Unless otherwise indicated, the latest version of SAE publications shall apply.

2.1.1 SAE PUBLICATION—Available from SAE, 400 Commonwealth Drive, Warrendale, PA 15096-0001.

SAE J20—Coolant System Hoses

2.1.2 ISO PUBLICATIONS—Available from ANSI, 11 West 42nd Street, New York, NY 10036-8002.

ISO 9001—Quality systems—Model for quality assurance in design, development, production, installation and servicing

2.1.3 GOVERNMENT PUBLICATIONS—Available from U. S. Government, DOD SSP, Subscription Service Division, Building 4D, 700 Robbins Avenue, Philadelphia, PA 19111-5094.

Federal Specification ZZ-H-428—Hose; Non-Metallic and Hose; Preformed: (for Coolant Systems of Automotive and Other Liquid-Cooled Engines)

Military Drawing MS51008—Hose, Preformed: Flexible, Engine Coolant, 1-1/4, 1-1/2, 1-3/4, 2, 2-1/4, 2-1/2, 3 ID

2.1.4 AUTOMOTIVE INDUSTRY PUBLICATION—Available from AIAG, 26200 Lasher Road, Suite 200, Southfield, MI 48034-7100.

QS 9000—Quality System Requirements

3. Technical Requirements—The following requirements are in addition to the requirements of SAE J20.

3.1 Certification—Manufacturers/suppliers of hose to the Government must be ISO 9001 or QS-9000 certified and provide their certification to provide this SAE J20/2 hose.

3.2 Lengths—The lengths specified in Table 1 shall comply with SAE J20 Table 2 tolerances.

3.3 Inside Diameters—The inside diameters specified in Table 2 shall comply with SAE J20 tolerances.

3.4 Wall Gauge Range—Wall gauge range shall comply with SAE J20.

3.5 Marking—For U.S. Government use only, marking shall consist of the following on one or both cuffs:

a. Part Identification Number (see 4.2)
b. Manufacturer's identification code (CAGE) or trademark symbol
c. Month and year of manufacture

3.5.1 If there is insufficient space on the hose for the required marking due to small ID hose or too short a straight length, a label carrying the required information taped around the individual pieces of hose in lieu of the previous method of marking.

3.5.2 Marking for non-Government users shall be agreed upon by the customer and manufacturer.

4. Notes

4.1 Intended Use—The flexible, wire-reinforced coolant hose is intended for use in automotive cooling systems. It is commonly known as universal type hose.

4.2 Part Identification Number—Part numbers shall be constructed as indicated in Figure 1.

4.3 Government Specification Replacement—This document is a replacement for portions of Federal Specification ZZ-H-428, "Hose; Non-Metallic and Hose; Preformed: (for Coolant Systems of Automotive and Other Liquid-Cooled Engines.)" This document is also a replacement for part of Military Drawing MS51008, "Hose, Preformed: Flexible, Engine Coolant, 1-1/4, 1-1/2, 1-3/4, 2, 2-1/4, 2-1/2, 3 ID."

4.4 Cross Reference Information—Table 3 shows the relationship between designations in ZZ-H-428 and this document. MS51008 only provided part numbers for ZZ-H-428, Type V, Grade A, Class 2 hose. Those part numbers are now replaced by SAE J20/2ECLT Class A part numbers.

TABLE 1—NOMINAL LENGTHS

Nominal Length mm	Actual Length mm (in)
127	127.0 (5.00)
152	152.4 (6.00)
178	177.8 (7.00)
203	203.2 (8.00)
229	228.6 (9.00)
254	254.0 (10.00)
280	279.4 (11.00)
305	304.8 (12.00)
356	355.6 (14.00)
406	406.4 (16.00)
457	457.2 (18.00)
508	508.0 (20.00)
550	550.0 (22.00)
610	609.6 (24.00)
660	660.4 (26.00)
711	711.2 (28.00)
762	762.0 (30.00)
813	812.8 (32.00)
864	863.6 (34.00)
914	914.4 (36.00)
965	965.2 (38.00)

TABLE 2—NOMINAL INSIDE DIAMETERS (ID)

Nominal ID mm	Actual ID mm (in)
25	25.40 (1.00)
32	31.75 (1.25)
38	37.50 (1.50)
44	44.45 (1.75)
51	50.80 (2.00)
57	57.15 (2.25)
64	63.50 (2.50)
76	76.20 (3.00)

SAE-20	*R**	****	- **	- *** *X*	***
Basic type	Hose type 1/	Special Characteristics 1/ 2/	Class 1/ 3/	Inside diameter (See Table 1)	Nominal Length 4/

Notes: 1/ See SAE J20.
2/ Examples are EC, LT, HT, etc.
3/ For Class D-1, use "D1". For Class D-3, use "D3".
4/ When random lengths of hose are permissible, use an "R".

FIGURE 1—PART IDENTIFICATION NUMBER

TABLE 3—CROSS REFERENCE DESIGNATION

J20 Designation	J20 Class	ZZ-H-428 Type	ZZ-H-428 Grade	ZZ-H-428 Class
SAE-J20/2ECLT	A	V	A	2
SAE-J20/2ECLT	A	V	A	3
SAE-J20/2EC	B	V	B	1
SAE-J20/2EC	C	V	B	2
SAE-J20/2EC	D-1	V	B	3
SAE-J20/2EC	D-3	V	B	4

4.5 Other Sizes—Sizes and tolerances other than those listed in this document shall be agreed upon by the supplier and purchaser. The requirements of SAE J20 shall be the met.

4.6 Key Words—Automotive, flexible hose, universal hose.

GEOMETRIC DIMENSIONS AND TOLERANCING FOR CURVED HOSE—SAE J2370 MAY2001

SAE Recommended Practice

Report of the SAE Coolant Hose Committee approved May 2001.

Foreword—The design engineer assigning tolerances for size, length and geometry must consider function, mating relationships, virtual condition, datums, and economy. Owing to the construction of rubber hoses (synthetic elastomeric material) and being a "non-rigid" product that can be deformed by shipping conditions, measurement forces, and in many cases it's own weight, care must be taken in applying GD&T procedures.

American Society of Mechanical Engineers, ASME, Dimensioning and Tolerancing Standard Y14.5M is in wide use today in a variety of industries to prevent ambiguous interpretation of design intent between designers, customers, suppliers,, manufacturers, and quality engineers. ASME Y14.5M Dimensioning and Tolerancing, standardizes definitions and methods for expressing a designer's intent for a work piece in the form of an engineering drawing. It may be most cost effective for customer and supplier, to agree upon a frequency of gaging using this document, along with high volume cost effective gaging methods currently used in industry

Due to variation in hose wall thickness, material, shape, length, diameter, etc.; no tolerances for true position outer boundary (see Section 3) will be included with this document. The true position tolerance for the outer boundary shall be determined by customer and supplier and should be based on feasibility analysis conducted prior to final release of design record.

1. Scope—To provide the curved hose industry and their customers with a recommended practice for applying GD&T procedures to curved hoses and to provide generic curved hose drawings that represent the application of GD&T to typical curved hose parts. Dimensioning and Tolerancing will be in accordance with ASME Y14.5M.

2. References

2.1 Applicable Publications—The following publications form a part of this specification to the extent specified herein. Unless otherwise indicated, the latest issue of the publications shall apply.

2.1.1 SAE PUBLICATION—Available from SAE, 400 Commonwealth Drive, Warrendale, PA 15096-0001.

SAE J20—Coolant System Hoses

2.1.2 ASME PUBLICATION—Available from ASME, 345 East 47 Street, New York, NY 10017-2330.

ASME Y14.5M 1994—Dimensioning and Tolerancing

3. Definitions

3.1 Geometric Dimensioning and Tolerancing (GD&T) is:

a. The engineering product definition methods that geometrically describe design intent and provide the documentation base for the design of the quality control and production systems.
b. A technique of communication between customer engineers and supplier engineers that promotes a uniform interpretation of the acceptance requirements for a component in terms of its dimensions and tolerances.

GD&T provides the method for dimensioning and tolerancing in a language that helps to eliminate confusing and inconsistent notes. It replaces them with symbols that refer to a common code, ASME Y14.5M: which is the American National Standard. This code describes the dimensions and tolerances of the component with reference to the relationship of its features to each other and their functional interfaces with mating parts, assemblies, etc.

3.2 Reference to Standards Documents—When this document applies, there shall be a note on the drawing or in a document referenced on the drawing, which refers to ASME Y14.5M, SAE J20, and SAE J2370.

3.3 Reference to Gauging—This document and the ASME Y14.5M are not intended as gauging standards. Any reference to gauging is included for explanatory purposes only.

3.4 Figures—The figures in this document are illustrations intended only as an aid to the user in understanding the application of GD&T to curved hose. Any numerical values shown are for illustrative purposes only.

3.5 Theoretical Design Attitude—The theoretical design attitude is: The position of the hose when in the final installed attitude unless otherwise agreed upon by customer and supplier.

3.6 Boundary—The outside contour of the hose is controlled by a true position outer boundary tolerance zone. The tolerance zone follows the basic centerline of the hose, and its zone is equal to the hose outside diameters' MMC size plus the positional tolerance. The outside surface of the hose must reside within this boundary. To invoke this concept, the term BOUNDARY is placed beneath the feature control frame (see Figures 1 to 4).

4. Drawing Views

4.1 Projection—The drawing must specify either third (3rd) or first (1st) angle projection including the appropriate projection symbol.

4.2 Minimum Views—A minimum of two orthographic views is recommended on three dimensional hose shapes.

4.3 End View—A true end view of the hose, dimensioning any radially located features (orientation marks, stripes, etc.) to the next adjacent body length. This view is required for any radially located feature that is used as a tertiary datum.

4.4 Identification—Views are to be identified such as: Top or Plan, and Bottom or Front.

5. Dimensions

5.1 Dimensions, Angles—All dimensions are to be in metric. Angles are to be in decimal degrees.

5.2 Origin—Dimensions may originate from any hose end.

5.3 Basic Dimensions—The contour of the hose must be defined with basic dimensions.

5.3.1 COORDINATE BOX—Dimensions may be shown in a Coordinate Table or Chart based on the "right hand rule" (see Figure 5). All coordinate dimensions in a Table or Chart must be noted that: "All chart dimensions are basic".

5.3.2 XYZ DIMENSIONS

a. If charted, the XYZ location dimensions as installed are required.
b. Dimensions may be shown as ordinate dimensions on the hose, and should be indicated as basic.

6. Datums General—Features of the hose must be identified as datum features for the purpose of establishing geometric relationships imposed by a feature control frame. Datums are theoretically exact points, axes, and planes. These elements exist within a framework of three mutually perpendicular intersecting planes known as the datum reference frame. In the datum reference frame, from left to right, the first datum is the primary, the second datum is the secondary and the third datum is the tertiary. Sufficient datum features, those most important to the design of a part are chosen to position the part in the datum reference frame. This reference frame exists in theory only and not on the part. Therefore, it is necessary to establish a method of simulating the theoretical reference frame from the actual features of the part. Due to the nature of a rubber hose (synthetic elastomeric materials) and being a non-rigid material subject to free state variation, and because its surface is curved or free-form, the datum planes may be described in one of two methods (referred to as methods 1 or 2) described as follows.

6.1 Method 1—Because of the requirement to inspect the contour of the hose in its theoretical design attitude, and because it's surface is curved or free-form, the datum planes will generally be located completely offset from the actual datum features (see Figures 3 and 4). The three mutually perpendicular planes will remain parallel and normal to the horizon, and will reside in the checking fixture (see Figure 6). When multiple datum features of equal importance are used to establish a single datum, the appropriate datum reference letters and associated modifiers, separated by a dash, are entered into one compartment of the feature control frame.

6.1.1 PRIMARY DATUM—The primary datum feature is the Internal Diameter(s) (I.D.) of the hose. Because both ends must be used, and due to their equal importance, a multiple datum is created by using multiple datum features located on the I.D. of the ends. Datum targets are used to identify only the functional portion to be used, since controlling the entire surface is not required.

6.1.2 SECONDARY DATUM—The secondary datum is a multiple datum feature using the end(s) of the hose and is always RFS (regardless of feature size).

6.1.3 TERTIARY DATUM—A tertiary datum is required and will be a specified physical feature on the hose. This datum may be multiple datum feature(s) located on the ends (see datums C and F in Figures 1 and 3) or a datum target(s) (see datum E in Figure 2, or datum C in Figure 4). It should be kept in mind that when an alignment mark is used as a datum, there may not be a "surface of the part to physically contact the processing equipment or mating assembly surface." Therefore, the act of aligning the mark may affect the value of measurements (on a fixture) or assembly. Never the less, the use of an alignment mark may be desirable because of other considerations. This feature must be dimensioned and toleranced for width and length plus any other dimensions and tolerances necessary to define its shape or location.

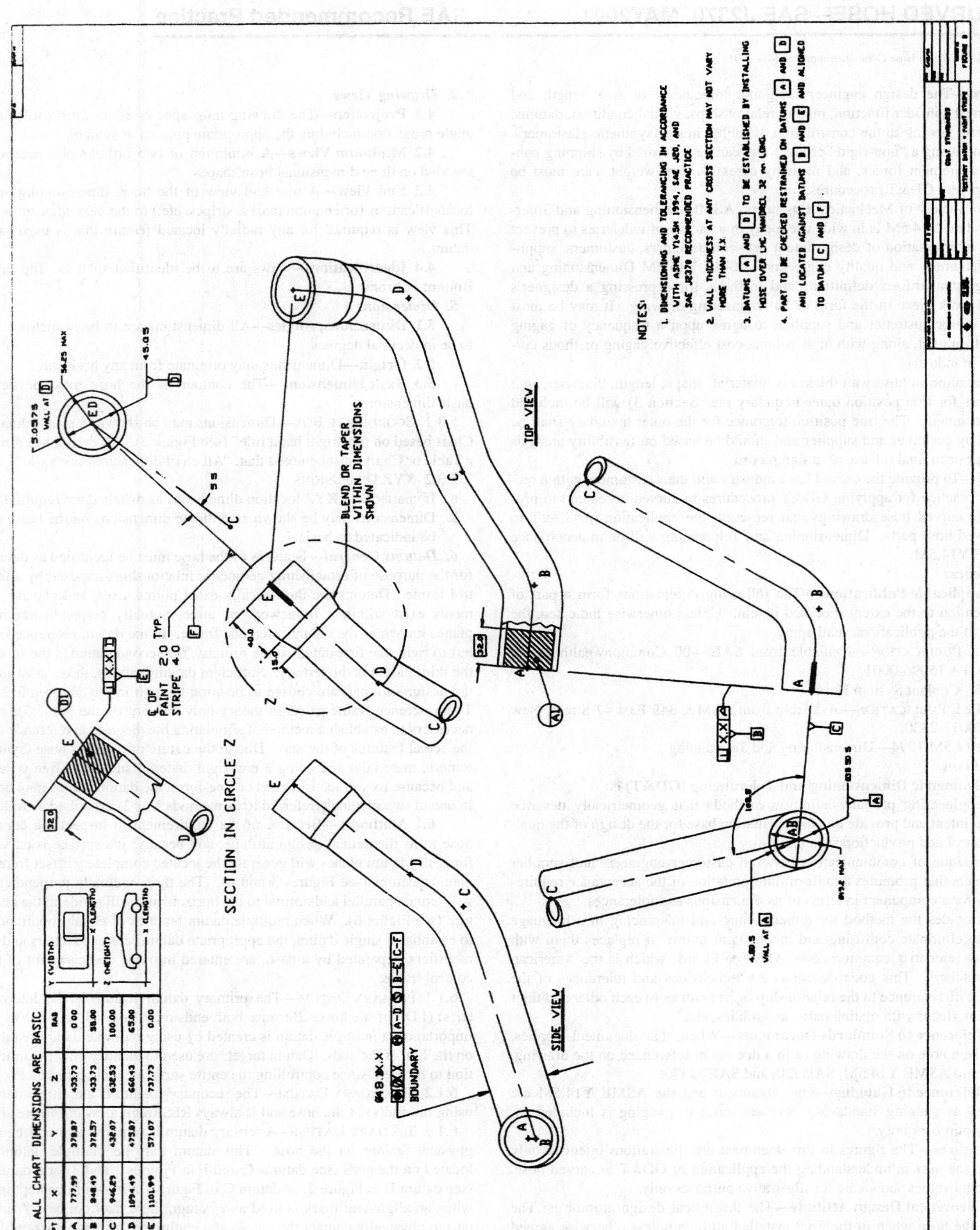

FIGURE 1—DRAWING WITH MULTIPLE DATUM FEATURES

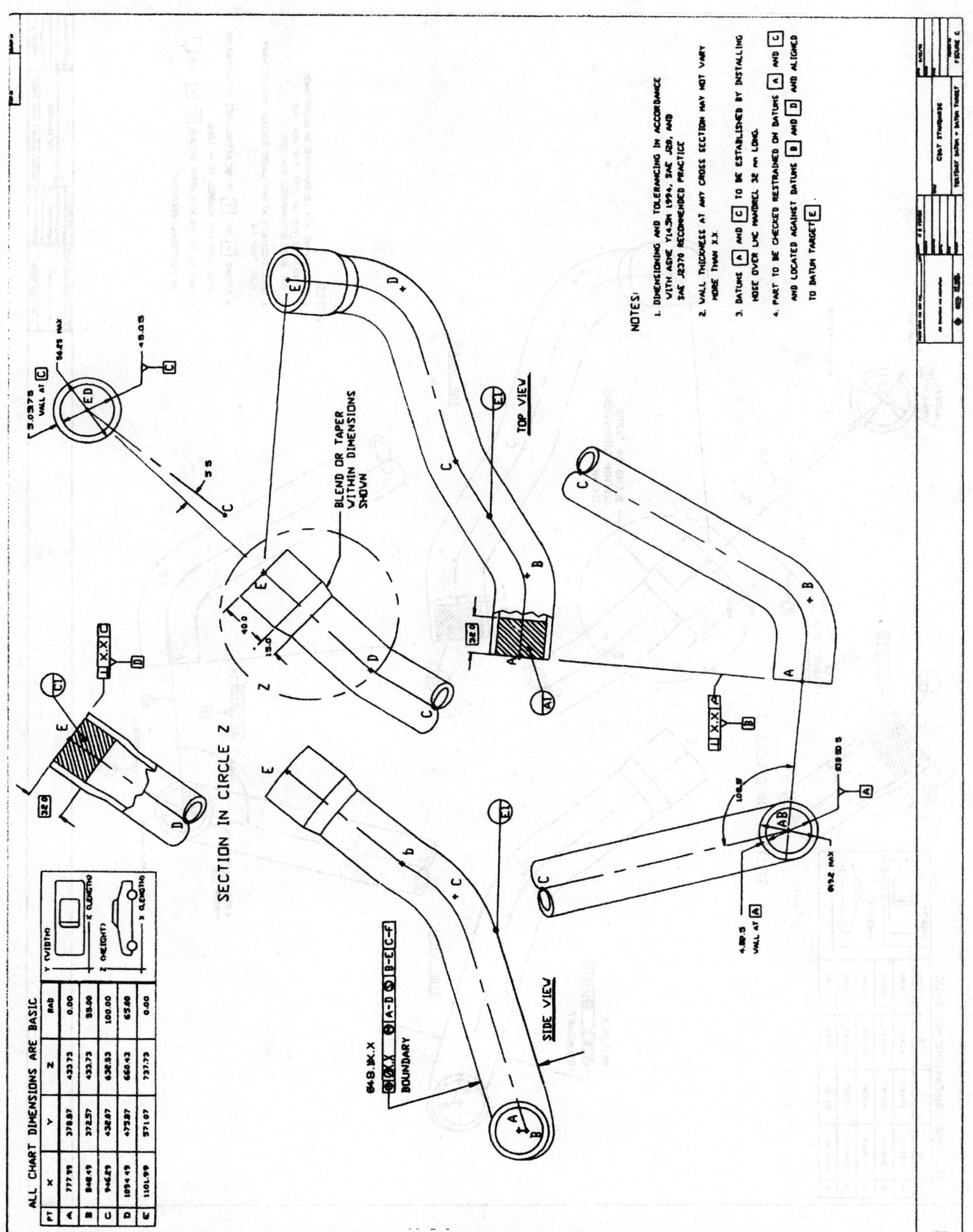

FIGURE 2—DRAWING WITH DATUM TARGETS

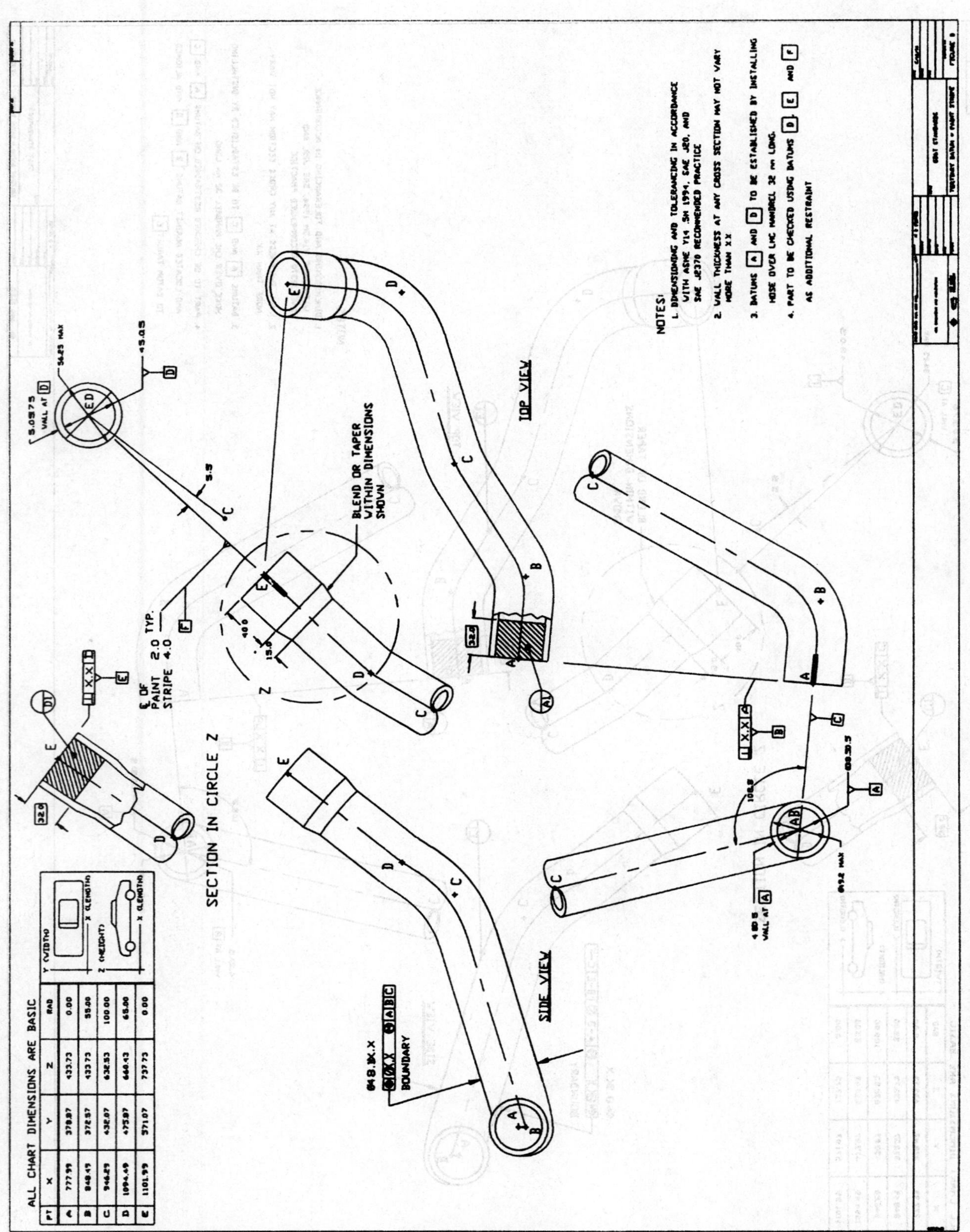

FIGURE 3—DRAWING WITH MULTIPLE DATUM FEATURES AND DATUM PLANES OFFSET FROM FEATURES

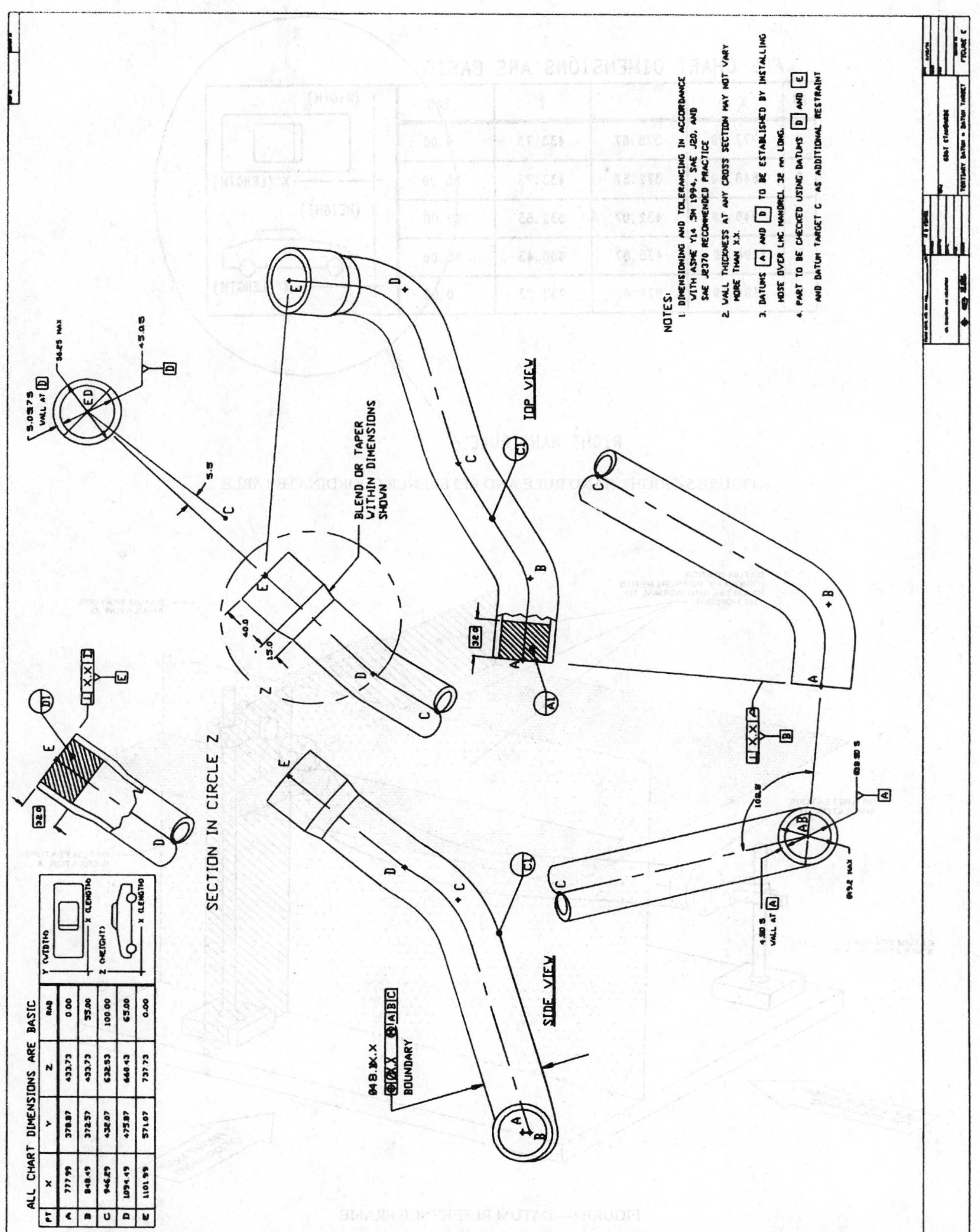

FIGURE 4—DRAWING WITH DATUM TARGETS AND DATUM PLANES OFFSET FROM FEATURES

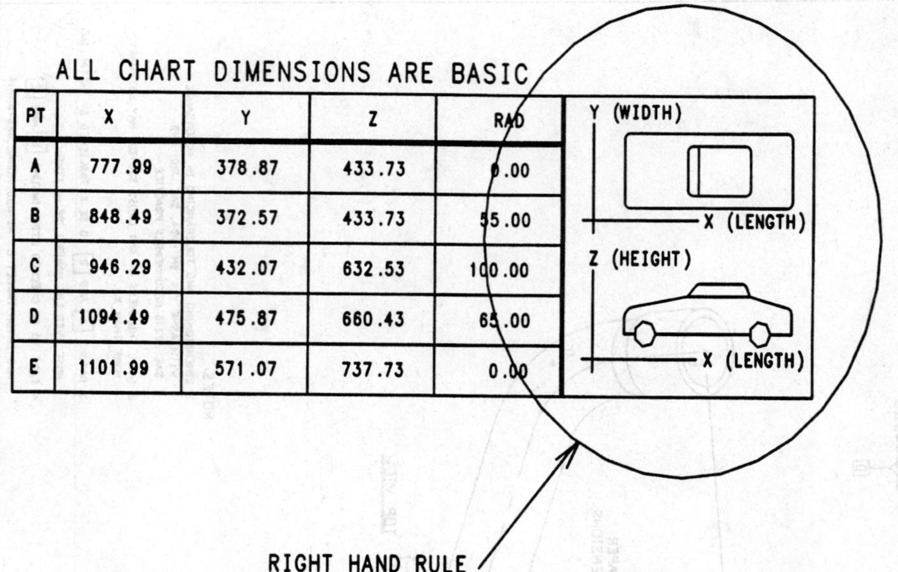

ALL CHART DIMENSIONS ARE BASIC

PT	X	Y	Z	RAD
A	777.99	378.87	433.73	0.00
B	848.49	372.57	433.73	55.00
C	946.29	432.07	632.53	100.00
D	1094.49	475.87	660.43	65.00
E	1101.99	571.07	737.73	0.00

Y (WIDTH)
X (LENGTH)
Z (HEIGHT)
X (LENGTH)
RIGHT HAND RULE

FIGURE 5—RIGHT HAND RULE AND REFERENCE COORDINATE TABLE

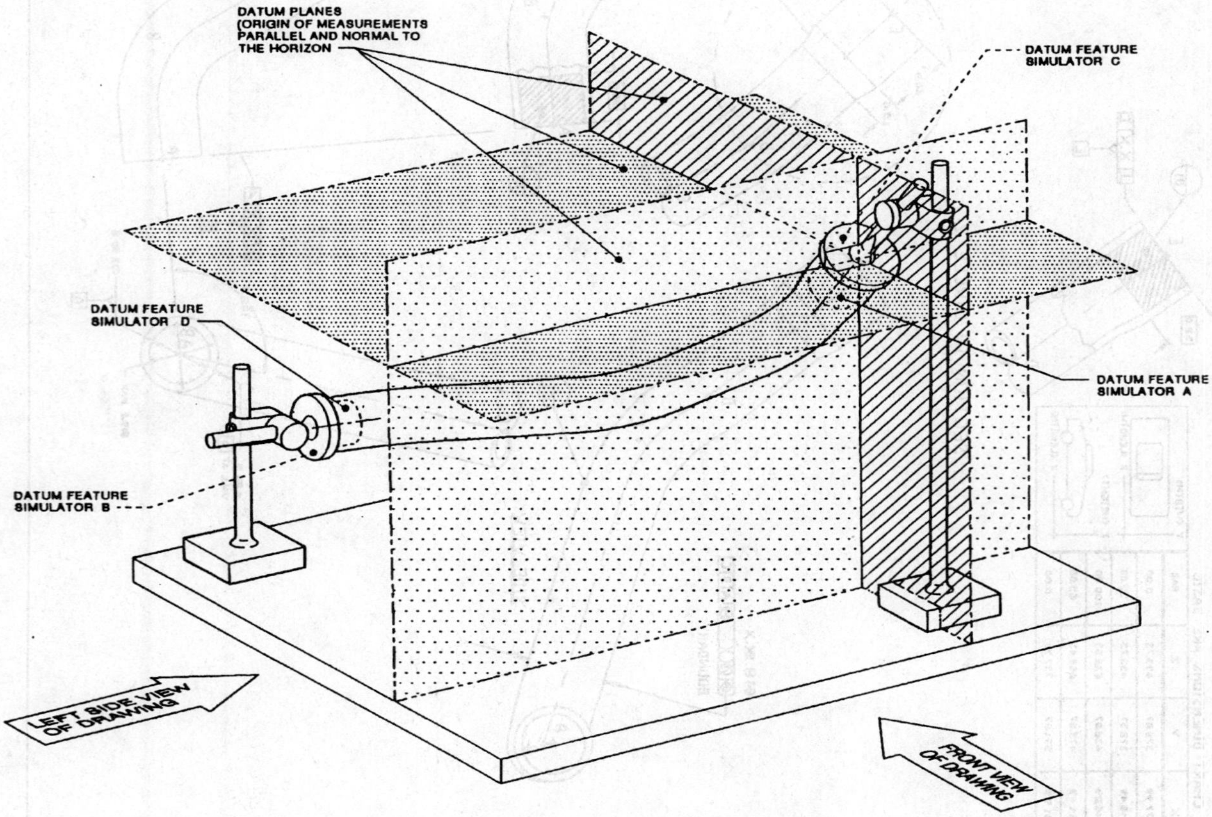

DATUM PLANES (ORIGIN OF MEASUREMENTS PARALLEL AND NORMAL TO THE HORIZON
DATUM FEATURE SIMULATOR C
DATUM FEATURE SIMULATOR D
DATUM FEATURE SIMULATOR A
DATUM FEATURE SIMULATOR B
LEFT SIDE VIEW OF DRAWING
FRONT VIEW OF DRAWING

FIGURE 6—DATUM REFERENCE FRAME

6.1.4 DATUMS SIMULATED, (FOR INSPECTION PURPOSES)—Datum feature simulators will be used to fixture the hose in its basic theoretical design attitude, using the specified datum features identified in the feature control frame. The primary datum feature(s) will be affixed to gage plugs with diameters equal to the maximum inside diameter to obtain a least material condition (LMC). The secondary datum feature(s), the hose end(s) will be positioned against datum feature simulators (surfaces) using a minimum of one point contact. The tertiary datum feature(s) will be aligned to an index mark(s) on the fixture; or if datum targets are designated, positioned against datum target features simulators. Other than locating on the specified datum features and other datum target features (support points) as designated on the drawing, the hose will be considered to be in it's "free-state."

6.2 Method 2

6.2.1 The part may also be described by establishing a datum reference frame at one end of the hose and providing additional support or restraint as necessary (see Figures 3 and 4).

6.2.2 PRIMARY DATUM—The primary datum feature is the internal diameter (I.D.) of one of the hose ends. The datum is the axis of the internal diameter over a prescribed length. The axis is theoretically the intersection of two mutually perpendicular planes, which are the origin of measurement in two (of three) directions.

6.2.3 SECONDARY DATUM—The secondary datum feature is the end surface of the hose. The datum is a plane which is perpendicular to the primary datum axis (and planes) and is the origin of measurement in the third direction.

6.2.4 TERTIARY DATUM—The tertiary datum feature may be an alignment mark or datum target which can be used when orientation is essential. Since the three datum planes and directions of measurement have already been established, the tertiary datum merely orients the part in space relative to them.

6.2.5 Since a hose is flexible, supplemental support or restraint may be required beyond those identified in the datum reference frame. These features may be covered in a note on the drawing and must be used for inspection as indicated. By placing the datum and additional support features in a holding fixture in relative location and orientation, according to the car coordinate information, the hose can be inspected as installed (see Figures 3 and 4).

7. Drawing Notes and Symbols

7.1 True Position Symbol—The hose contour is specified by using a True Position Symbol with a cylindrical tolerance zone at Maximum Material Condition (MMC) for the feature tolerance. Datums, if applicable are specified as Regardless of Feature Size (RFS).

7.2 Support Points—All vehicle hose support points, or restrictions (brackets etc.) are to be identified and located with appropriate geometric tolerancing dimensions and symbols.

7.3 Boundary—The outside contour of the hose is controlled by a true position outer boundary tolerance zone. The tolerance zone follows the basic centerline of the hose, and its zone is equal to the hose outside diameters' MMC size plus the positional tolerance. The outside surface of the hose must reside within this boundary. To invoke this concept, the term BOUNDARY is placed beneath the feature control frame (see Figures 1 to 4).

TEST PROCEDURE TO DETERMINE THE HYDROCARBON LOSSES FROM FUEL TUBES, HOSES, FITTINGS, AND FUEL LINE ASSEMBLIES BY RECIRCULATION —SAE J1737 AUG1997

SAE Recommended Practice

Report of the SAE Fuel Permeation Task Force of the SAE Fuel Supply Systems Forum Commitee approved August 1997.

TABLE OF CONTENTS

1. Scope—This SAE Recommended Practice is intended for the determination of the losses of hydrocarbon fluids, by permeation through component walls as well as through "microleaks" at interfaces of assembled components while controlling temperature and pressure independently of each other. This is achieved in a recirculating system in which liquids which are transported through walls and joints are collected by a controlled flow of nitrogen (dry) and adsorbed by activated charcoal.

2. References

2.1 Applicable Publication—The following publication forms a part of the specification to the extent specified herein. Unless otherwise indicated, the latest revision of SAE publications shall apply.

2.1.1 SAE PUBLICATION—Available from SAE, 400 Commonwealth Drive, Warrendale, PA 15096-0001.

SAE J1681—Gasoline/Methanol Mixtures for Material Testing

3. Background Information—New State and Federal Government regulations are establishing more stringent standards for the total quantity of evaporative hydrocarbon emissions that are permitted to come from a vehicle. Besides indicating much lower levels of emissions to be achieved, they are also establishing schedules and deadlines for achieving those levels.

Hydrocarbon evaporative emissions can arise from many sources on a vehicle. A major part of those are associated with the fuel and fuel vapor systems. These hydrocarbon emissions can come from the many different parts of the fuel system and from its general usage:

a. Refueling the vehicle
b. Normal operation of the vehicle (running losses)
c. Permeation of the fuel constituents through the walls of the components that contain the fuel
d. Migration of the fuel or vapor through connections, interfaces, and any other potential leak paths of the fuel system (microleaks)

3.1 Sealed Housing Evaporative Determination (S.H.E.D.) Units—One of the primary techniques for measurement of vehicle hydrocarbon emissions is the Sealed Housing Evaporative Determination (S.H.E.D.) test. This test uses enclosed cells or structures that contain the item being tested (vehicle, system, or component). The environment of the unit is controlled and periodically analyzed to determine the quantities of hydrocarbons that are present. This technique is specified in the overall governing regulations from the Environmental Protection Agency (EPA) and the California Air Resources Board (CARB). They are used primarily for three of the aspects of the hydrocarbon emissions: static testing, normal operation, and refueling; large components (e.g., tanks) and fuel systems typically utilize this technique as well. Other procedures, such as mini-shed, and some weight change methods are normally used to measure permeability of materials or smaller components and the performance of specific interfaces.

3.2 Other Measurement Techniques—With the development of the lower emissions standards, the ability of parts and materials to contain hydrocarbons must improve significantly. There are two different aspects of the emissions of the hydrocarbons in a system:

a. Rate of permeation of constituents of fuel or fuel vapor through the walls of a component into the external environment
b. Performance of connections, seals, interfaces, and any other areas where different parts of a fuel or vapor system are assembled or joined together (sometimes referred to as microleaks)

In the past, permeability of materials or components has been measured by a fairly simple weight-loss technique. In general, these have involved filling a component (or a test assembly consisting of a component and a reservoir) with fuel and then measuring any weight changes that occur over a prescribed period of time and under a specific set of conditions. The most common of these long-used techniques are those described by SAE J30 and J1527; generally these do not have the level of sensitivity that is required to measure the very low rates of permeation necessary to meet the new government regulations.

When parts or materials have significantly reduced rates of permeation, the measurement techniques that are used must be able to detect much smaller quantities and changes in hydrocarbon levels. This document describes a technique that has the level of sensitivity for measurement of very low rates of permeation that is required.

3.3 Measuring Steady-State Conditions—When rates of permeation are measured, the initial performance of a component or material is not the same as the eventual equilibrium value. It takes a certain amount of time for the migration of the fuel through the wall or at the interfaces to achieve its steady-state rate after first exposure to the fuel. Also, with some materials, there can be other components present (e.g., plasticizer) that are driven off by the fuel, temperature, or other test conditions. Time must be allowed for these other emanations to stop contributing to any weight-loss measurements. There may also be a change in crystallinity when measuring at elevated temperatures.

It is important to note that the better a material or component's resistance to permeation, the longer it takes to achieve the steady-state conditions. For this reason, these new measurement techniques are operated at conditions that cause permeation to be accelerated. The more permeation is accelerated, the sooner equilibrium is achieved. The amount of time it takes to reach equilibrium in the permeation measurement unit can be shortened by preconditioning the specimen. Refer to 7.2 for details concerning this.

3.3.1 TIME TO REACH STEADY-STATE—For an indication of the amount of time involved in achieving steady-state conditions, experience has shown that it can take several hundreds of hours. Table 1 was developed from experience with (10% to 25%) range of alcohol-blend test fuels and 60 °C permeation test temperatures.

TABLE 1—STEADY-STATE PERMEATION RESISTANCE MEASUREMENT ($GRAMS/METER^2/DAY$)

Methanol Blend Test Fuels	Ethanol Blend Test Fuels	Approximate Time Necessary to Achieve Steady-State Permeation Measurement (Hours)
0 to 25	0 to 10	over 1000
25 to 50	10 to 20	1000
50 to 100	20 to 40	800
100 to 200	40 to 80	600
200 to 400	80 to 160	500
over 400	160 and over	400

This time is the continuous exposure time to the identified test conditions. It is a summation of the preconditioning step and time in the permeation test unit (see 7.2). If temperatures are lower than 60 °C or test fuels are "less active" than those containing alcohol, the overall time will be longer than shown in Table 1.

3.3.2 DETERMINING STEADY-STATE—Equilibrium can be determined by three different techniques. Each of them are described as follows in general terms. In all such procedures, however, there are small measurement errors that can arise because of rounding-off of units, seemingly insignificant changes in test conditions, minuscule differences in procedures followed, etc. The second section describes a procedure for determining if steady-state is achieved that includes the effects of these variations.

3.3.2.1 General Means to Determine Steady State

3.3.2.1.1 Length Change Measurement—Many materials being tested for permeation will simultaneously experience changes in length when exposed to the test fuel. The point at which all length changes have ceased, can give an estimate that the effects of the fuel on the specimen have reached steady state. This means that the permeation of the fuel through the walls of the specimens are at steady state also. This is not always practical to follow as a procedure because permeation rate can be at a steady-state level (for all practical purposes) well before dimensional changes of the component being tested have truly stopped altogether.

3.3.2.1.2 Rate of Weight Change—Plot canister weight as a function of time. Before steady state is reached, the line that is plotted will show a changing slope. When such a plot shows that at least 5 successive points establish a straight line, steady-state has been achieved. The slope of that line (gm/day) is the equilibrium rate of permeation for the specific specimen being tested.

3.3.2.1.3 Weight Gain—Plot canister weight change that occurs at each measurement time. Before steady state is achieved, the weight change will fluctuate or will show some sort of a trend. When the plot shows that at least 5 successive measurements yield the same weight change, then the steady-state weight change per unit time is the equilibrium rate.

3.3.2.2 Caution Concerning Steady-State Conditions—Care must be taken to be sure that the conditions described in the "Rate of Weight Change" and "Weight Gain" sections are not due to the inability of the charcoal to adsorb any more fuel. Complete saturation of the charcoal is not steady-state permeation (refer to 4.1.17, 5.3, 7.4, and Appendix A).

3.3.2.3 Practical Means to Determine Steady State—As the canisters are weighed, the permeation rate that the specific weight measurement represents should be calculated. That rate would be expressed in terms of grams/day, grams/meter^2/day, etc. (refer to 3.5 and 8.3). The calculated rate on 2 successive days should be used to determine a 2-day moving average (average of Day 1 and Day 2 measurements is first data point; average of Day 2 and Day 3 measurements is second data point, and the average of next to last and last days measurements is last data point). Once the moving 2-day averages the rate of permeation have been calculated for at least 3 to 4 weeks of test results, the following steps should be followed:

a. Plot 2-day moving average as a function of time (days).
b. As the rate of permeation nears steady state, that plot will approach horizontal.
c. Calculate a least - squares line for the 5 most recent points used to make the plot.
d. Steady state can be defined as the time when that least squares line is horizontal within ±5% of the absolute value of the rate of permeation indicated as the steady-state value.

EXAMPLE—An example of this are an absolute rate of 20 grams/meter^2/day would have to show a 5-day least squares plot of the five 2-day moving average points within ±1 g/m^2/day of being horizontal over the whole 5-day period.

3.4 Test Conditions—For permeation rate to be measured accurately, many different aspects of the test procedure must be controlled carefully. They are all factors to consider, but can have a wide variation in importance. The following paragraphs form the list of common test conditions which control permeation and give an indication of their importance in obtaining accurate permeation test results. Whenever the permeation performance of one material, construction, or part is compared to another, test conditions must be as consistent as possible. No comparison is possible when these aspects of the test differ.

3.4.1 TEMPERATURE—This is a significant factor that must be controlled very carefully because the rate of permeation will change significantly with relatively small temperature changes. For example, the permeation rate of most hydrocarbons through Nylon 12 will double with a temperature increase of only 10 or 15 °C. The rate can increase even more when multilayer wall constructions are involved. For such multilayer walls, the rate of permeation can increase 10 or even 20 times as temperature rises from ambient to 60 °C. Another example are materials that change dramatically when you go from 40 °C to 60 °C (such as EVOH). Because EVOH's glass transition temperature is ≈ 55 °C, the material changes structure during the transition to 60 °C; the result is a greater change in rate of permeation. For precise permeation measurement, the temperature of the fuel must be controlled very closely in the test.

3.4.2 TYPE OF FUEL—Alcohol-blend fuels have been used to evaluate materials for potential use in fuel and emissions applications. The effect of such blends on specific materials and composites of more than one material can be significant. For this reason, the test fuel used should be representative of what is likely to be actually encountered in the field. Also, if any comparisons among materials in the area of permeation resistance are ever made, the test fuel used must be as much the same as possible. Typical fuels used in this test are alcohol blends between 5% and 25%. The basic test fuel for use with this procedure should be CM15; with CE10, (ASTM Ref. Fuel C and 10% Ethanol by volume) used a second test fuel; refer also to 5.1, 7.5, and SAE J1681).

Permeation is a result of the solubility and diffusivity of a fluid in a material. Therefore, fuel permeability is affected by the solubility of a given fuel constituent in a given fuel containment material. This solubility effect can be readily observed by measuring the volume swell of a given material when exposed to a specific type of fuel. In many cases, when comparing two different materials that do not have a plasticizer, the greater the swell, the more easily the fuel is dissolved into the material; the resulting permeation rate will then be higher. In other cases, differences in diffusion will cause permeation to be different from predictions based on solubility alone.

Fuel constituents can be broadly classified in two ways: as polar/non-polar and as solvents/co-solvents. Polar or non-polar types will mix readily with their own kind but not with their opposites. Co-solvents permit polar and non-polar solvents to mix. The majority of hydrocarbon compounds in fuel are non-polar. Methanol is one of the most strongly polar fuel constituents. Aromatic hydrocarbons are co-solvents. Their presence is essential for methanol to mix in gasoline.

Plastic and elastomeric materials can also be broadly classified as polar and non-polar. For example, Polyethylene is non-polar, Nylon is polar. Therefore, gasoline (a primarily non-polar solvent) tends to permeate Polyethylene readily. However, Polyethylene is quite resistant to permeation of pure methanol. The opposite is true for Nylon which is permeated by methanol much more readily than gasoline.

The behavior of mixtures of gasoline is non-ideal in that the resulting properties or effects are not a linear relationship between the effects measured in a pure sample of either liquid. Gasoline/Methanol mixtures tend to produce much greater effects on materials at a methanol concentration of at between 5% and 60%. If one is designing a fuel system for minimum permeation, it is essential to know what fuel mixtures will be encountered.

3.4.3 PRESSURE—The pressure of the fuel/fuel vapor in the component must also be controlled even though its effect is far less than that of temperature. The pressure can have a small influence on the rate of permeation through the wall, when fuel vapor is present, to the extent that the pressure can affect the concentration of the vapor. For a liquid, the concentration is already 100% and cannot be changed by a pressure change.

Another consideration for changes in pressure and the effect on apparent permeation rate is in the sealing of the joints where the tubing or component being tested is attached to another component or the test cell. When the described test procedure is used to determine the leakage of quick connectors (or other attachment devices), changes in pressure may lead to different results because of the effect of pressure on microleakage at the joints. Problems that may arise can be solved by connecting the tubing being tested to the fuel supply at a location outside of the measurement test cell.

3.4.4 WALL THICKNESS—According to the basic equations for permeation, permeation rate is directly related to wall thickness, therefore (theoretically), doubling wall thickness would cause permeation rate to be decreased by a factor of two. For materials that are crystalline in nature, permeation resistance tends to be better when the amount of crystallinity in the molecular structure is greater. For parts with thicker walls, the amount of crystallinity is usually higher because of the heat retained by the greater thickness during processing. As a result, if wall thickness is doubled, the permeation rate can decrease by more than a factor of two.

3.4.5 CONSTRUCTION OF THE PART—A given part can be made of a single material or be composed of different layers of unlike materials. This again should be noted so the most accurate comparisons and conclusions can be made when comparing different products.

3.4.6 MOISTURE CONTENT—The permeation rate being measured can be affected by the moisture content of the fuel. The barrier properties of some materials used to reduce permeation can deteriorate as moisture is absorbed. To make consistent comparisons of one material to another, the moisture content of the fuel used should be kept to a minimum by using reagent grade materials, and stored in sealed containers.

3.5 Units of Measurement

3.5.1 TYPES OF UNITS OF MEASUREMENT—For permeation resistance, the units of measurement are expressed in one of three ways:

3.5.1.1 Grams/Day—For a given vehicle, system, or complex component, it is most practical to measure permeation in terms of amount of emissions per unit of time. This is usually expressed in grams/day. When directly comparing the performance of two different components or systems, it is important that they be the same size or are designed to perform exactly the same task. If the overall surface area of a given part being tested is significantly different than another, similar part, conclusions on permeation performance could be misleading. Care must be taken to compare systems or parts on as much of an equal basis as possible.

3.5.1.2 Grams/Meter/Day—When the specimen being tested is some sort of tube or hose configuration, the amount of permeation is expressed in terms of amount of emissions per unit of length and per unit of time.

3.5.1.3 Grams/Meter^2/Day—When parts tested have a very simple geometry (such as a tube), the permeation rate can be expressed measured in terms of grams per unit of area per day. By including the "unit area" aspect, the actual size of the part is eliminated from the measurement. It's important to note that the area referred to is that part of the material or component actually "wetted" by the fuel.

3.5.2 CAUTIONS ABOUT UNITS OF MEASUREMENT—When using these units of measurement to compare the performance of one part to another, one material to another, one fuel to another, etc., there are a number of aspects that must be kept in mind:

Basis of comparison must be well-defined and carefully documented (see Section 9). The two components, configurations, etc., that are being examined must be compared as much the same basis as possible.

For a specific tube, care must be taken to ensure that grams/meter^2/day is not confused with grams/day per meter of tubing length. For example, a tube with an O.D. of 8 mm and a wall thickness of 1 mm would require more than 53 m of length to equal a square meter of surface area.

When comparing different materials from which a part is made, the most direct comparison in performance is for a tube or other part to have the same wall thickness. If thickness differs significantly between two parts when the measurements for permeation are taken, the thickness of the wall of the part should be recorded to make a more complete set of information for comparison of the two sets of materials that comprise the part. In some cases, the performance of a material can even be expressed in terms of permeation per unit of thickness.

If a particular dimension of a part is significantly different when compared with another part, the results could be misleading unless the difference is carefully noted (an example of this, is reporting permeation in grams per meter^2/day for two hoses that differ significantly in wall thickness). When comparing two parts that may be used in a particular application, it is probably least confusing to test the parts in as close to the actual configuration and size to be used in that application. The permeation would then be best expressed in grams/day or grams/meter^2 day.

4. Apparatus and Equipment—Figure 1 shows a typical schematic of components of the apparatus used to measure permeation by the recirculation technique. Details in the figure are meant to give a general indication of how the apparatus is set up. Modifications are acceptable (such as for equipment availability reasons or for meeting specific end user needs) as long as the general testing procedures, parameters, and other important criteria described in this document are adhered to.

4.1 Elements of Apparatus

NOTE—The last digit of the paragraph numbers that follow correspond to the labeling in Figure 1.

4.1.1 INERT GAS FOR PRESSURIZING FUEL—Supply of gas used to pressurize the test fuel (usually Nitrogen). Must be dry to prevent moisture being introduced into the fuel.

4.1.2 PRESSURE REGULATOR AND GAUGE—Used to set the specific pressure level needed for the test fuel (range typically used is 0 to 4 bar). For safety considerations, it is recommended that pressures should not be allowed to exceed 5 bar (unless the entire unit has been specifically. designed for a higher pressure level).

4.1.3 FUEL CONTAINER—The size of the reservoir for holding the fuel used in the test will depend on the specimen being tested. Minimum size of the reservoir shall be 800 times the internal volume of the part being tested. For a typical test procedure with an 8 x 1 mm tube that is 0.5 m long, the volume of the reservoir should be about 3 L (for each specimen that is in the test).

4.1.3.1 When fuel is first introduced in the system, there must be a means to allow the air that had been in the system to be vented. This can be accomplished with a purge valve which is located at or near the highest point of the fuel circulation system.

4.1.3.2 The operator should closely monitor the volume of the reservoir. The maximum allowable weight loss of the total fuel volume during the full duration of test should not exceed 2%. If the 2% loss level is exceeded, the fuel in the reservoir should be renewed totally, because the measured permeation rate will be significantly affected if a loss of such magnitude is experienced. If the 2% level of fuel loss is ever achieved during a test, the length of time during which that loss occurred shall be noted. From that point on, until the permeation test is complete, the fuel shall be fully renewed at that same time interval.

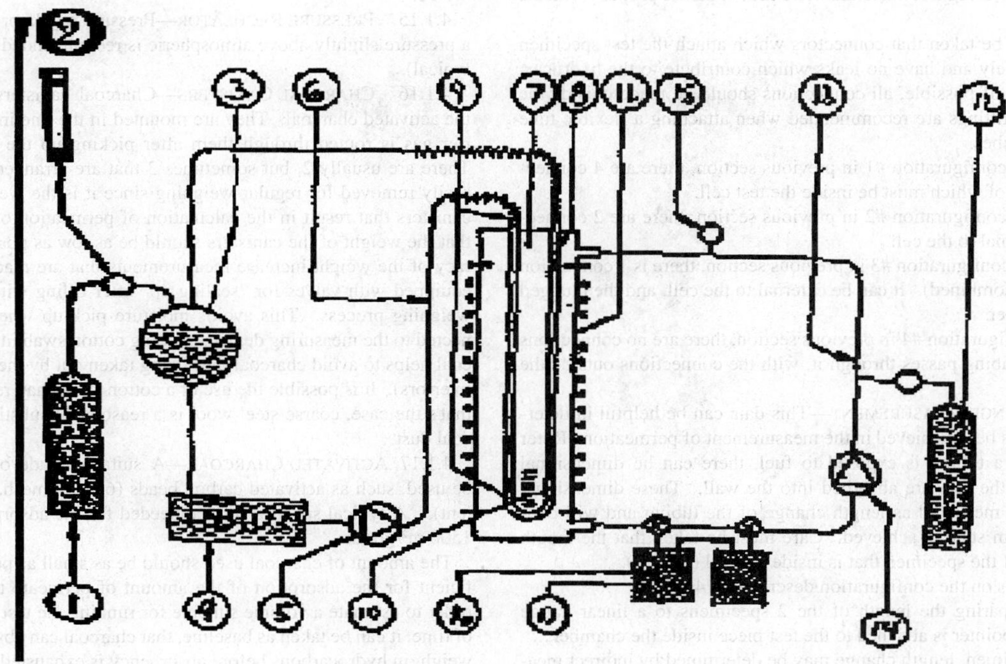

NOTE—The seventeen numbered elements illustrated in this schematic are described in 4.1.1 through 4.1.17.

FIGURE 1—SCHEMATIC—RECIRCULATION TECHNIQUE OF PERMEATION MEASUREMENT

4.1.3.3 For specimens with high permeation rates, the test fuel may need to be renewed to keep it within acceptable limits.

NOTE—Replenishing only a part of the fuel or adjusting composition may lead to errors.

The reservoir should be constructed to allow access to the test fuel while conducting the test when the fuel must be replenished. The permeation test can be stopped briefly (maximum of 2 hours) by following these general steps:

a. Turn off fuel heat sources
b. Turn off fuel pump
c. Carefully reduce pressure on fuel down to ambient level
d. Carefully open purge valve to release any residual pressure
e. Open reservoir and carefully insert additional fuel
f. Reseal reservoir
g. Turn pump on again
h. Bring pressure slowly back up to test levels
i. Open purge valve carefully to vent any excess air or vapor
j. Turn heat sources back on
k. Continue with test

4.1.4 HEATER FOR THE TEST FUEL—This is usually a bath heater. It must have a range up to 80 °C. Included with this component are the necessary controls to keep fuel at the desired temperature ±1 °C. The fuel may be heated at roughly the point shown in Figure 1, but the temperature measurement should be close to the test specimen to ensure the fuel in the test specimen is at the proper temperature.

4.1.5 RECIRCULATION PUMP AND REGULATOR FOR FUEL FLOW RATE—The fuel recirculation system must be able to keep flow of fuel at reasonably constant rate, depending on fuel pressure, temperature, and size of specimen being tested. For 8 x 1 mm test specimen, a typical flow rate is between 10 L/h and 20 L/h. (Higher flow rates are possible, but this may lead to a problem in controlling fuel temperature because fuel will heat up by the flow resistance in the various components).

4.1.6 TUBING TO ROUTE TEST FUEL—Must be able to contain the fuel being tested while allowing minimal loss through permeation or leaks. Typical materials used are metal and fluorocarbon hose constructions. If metal is used, it must be a type that is not corroded by the test fuel. Minimum inner diameter of this line is 4 mm.

4.1.7 TEST CELL—This is a cylinder (usually glass) that contains the specimen being tested and allows the flow of Nitrogen around the test specimen to carry the permeate to the adsorption canisters. Volume of the test cell will depend on the size of the specimens being tested or their configuration in the test cell (see 4.1.9). In general, the cell should be kept as small as possible so the hydrocarbons that do escape from the test specimen will be as high a concentration as is practical in the carrier gas that flows through the cell.

4.1.8 TEST SPECIMEN-GENERAL—This usually involves a tubular-shaped component that is completely inside the cell and through which the test fuel flows at the required temperature and pressure. Individual components or even small assemblies (such as a tube/connector combination) can be tested. The only limitation is its ability to fit within the cell. Even when components or small assemblies are tested, there is usually an amount of tubing involved. The configuration of the specimen will determine the units of permeation that are most likely to be used (see 3.5).

4.1.9 MOUNTING TEST SPECIMEN—This recirculation procedure is ideally suited for testing tubular shaped parts or small assemblies involving mostly tubing. The configuration of the test specimen and the connections that are used are important considerations. It is also important that the specimen mounting technique allows for length changes which the specimen may undergo due to thermal expansion and chemical volume swell.

4.1.9.1 Four test specimen configurations are commonly used. Others may be possible, but must meet the criteria described in this document.

4.1.9.1.1 Two test specimens can be used in the cell. They would be straight, attached to the inlet and outlet that direct the test fuel into and out of the cell, and are joined at the other end by a U-shaped metal tube that completes the fuel circuit (this is the general nature of the drawing that is Figure 1).

4.1.9.1.2 A single test specimen can be used that is bent into a "U" shape and attached to the test fuel inlet and outlet. Care must be taken that the bend is not so severe that the fuel flow is restricted in any way. For thermoplastic tubing, it is recommended that the bend be done by thermo forming.

4.1.9.1.3 A single test specimen can be suspended inside the test cell; it would be straight and would be completely blocked at the end opposite the fuel inlet. The fuel would be inserted into the tube through a hollow needle probe that extends nearly to the very end (blocked) of the test specimen. The fuel flows from the needle probe out the other end of the test specimen, resulting in a fuel recirculation with a single tube. With this technique, there is a need for only one "fuel port" attachment associated with the cell.

4.1.9.1.4 A single test specimen that extends through the length of the test cell, with fittings outside of the housing. These types of chambers can be fabricated from chromatography columns. Because the component is fixed at both ends, length change might lead to bending and thus it might touch the wall of the cell. This has to be avoided by using a suitable diameter cell, to assure proper permeate transport.

4.1.9.2 Care must be taken that connectors which attach the test specimen to the test cell do so safely and have no leaks which contribute to the hydrocarbons that are measured. If possible, all connections should be made outside the test cell. Compression fittings are recommended when attaching a flexible tube test specimen to metal tubes.

4.1.9.2.1 For the test configuration #1 in previous section, there are 4 connections required, at least 2 of which must be inside the test cell.

4.1.9.2.2 For the test configuration #2 in previous section, there are 2 connections. They can be external to the cell.

4.1.9.2.3 For the test configuration #3 in previous section, there is 1 connection (needle probe and tube combined). It can be external to the cell, and the plugged end will be in the chamber.

4.1.9.2.4 For test configuration #4 in previous section, there are no connections in the chamber, as the tubing passes through it, with the connections outside the chamber.

4.1.10 LENGTH CHANGE MEASUREMENT—This data can be helpful in determining if steady state has been achieved in the measurement of permeation. Refer to 3.3 and 7.2. When a tubing is exposed to fuel, there can be dimensional changes as elements of the fuel are absorbed into the wall. These dimensional changes are most easily measured as length change of the tubing and will continue until an equilibrium state is achieved. Care must be taken that the length measure is for the part of the specimen that is inside the cell (see 7.1).

How it is done depends on the configuration described in 4.1.9.1:

1. Measured by comparing the length of the 2 specimens to a linear gauge inside the cell. A pointer is attached to the test piece inside the chamber.
2. For U-shaped specimen, length change may be determined by indirect measurement, then additional calculations.
3. For the single - straight - tube configuration, length change can be measured by use of a linear scale or by a magnet attached to the end of the tube connected to a gauge or other measuring device.
4. Accurate length change measurement for this technique of mounting can only be done by removal from the cell (after the test).

4.1.11 HEATING MANTLE FOR TEST CELL—A heating element for the test cell is a separate means to maintain the heat of the test cell environment at the given test temperature. This is typically done by a jacket that surrounds the cell. Keeping all elements of the test cell at the required temperature will yield more consistent results.

4.1.12 CARRIER GAS FOR FUEL VAPORS—This is typically Nitrogen. Activated charcoal will adsorb water vapor as well as fuel hydrocarbon vapors. Therefore, it is absolutely necessary that gas be dry so moisture is not introduced into the permeate or into the charcoal canisters. This carrier gas could also be heated to the test temperature to produce the most consistent results.

4.1.13 TUBING FOR CARRIER GAS—Fuel hydrocarbon vapors are heavier than air. Thus the carrier gas must be routed so that its outlet is at the lowest part of the test chamber. This location of the outlet along with the temperature and pressure of the carrier gas will help keep the fuel vapor from condensing before it is picked up by the carrier gas and transported to the canisters.

4.1.14 PUMP AND FLOW REGULATOR FOR CARRIER GAS—The flow rate of the carrier gas should be checked routinely. The actual rate of flow is a compromise between two factors:

a. High flow rate carries all vapors that have permeated.
b. Low flow rate is needed to ensure optimum adsorption of all vapors by the activated charcoal.

The volume of gas flowing through the cell within 1 h should be 10 to 15 times the volume of the cell so that a sufficient rate of gas exchange can occur.

A flow rate for the rates of permeation typically encountered for smaller cells is 100 mL/min.

There are two types of systems for handling the Nitrogen carrier gas. One is a closed-loop system (shown in Figure 1). In this system, the Nitrogen is used repeatedly, circulating in the loop between the test cell, the canisters, and the pump. The second system is an "open" design. This means the Nitrogen flows through the system only once and is then exhausted to the atmosphere.

The lower the permeation rate, the lower the optimum gas flow rate. However, care has to be taken that no condensation of the permeate happens on the wall of the cell. This can be avoided by keeping all elements of the cell at the required temperature by heating the Nitrogen to the test temperature to decrease any cooling effect that the circulation of the Nitrogen might cause as described under 4.1.11.

4.1.15 PRESSURE REGULATOR—Pressure regulator for Nitrogen flow keeping a pressure slightly above atmospheric is recommended (0.25 bar above normal is typical).

4.1.16 CHARCOAL CANISTERS—Charcoal canisters are containers that hold the activated charcoal. They are mounted in the line in such manner that the carrier gas is routed through them after picking up the permeate in the test cell. There are usually 2, but sometimes 3 that are arranged in series. They must be easily removed for regular weighing since it is the weight gain of each of these canisters that result in the calculation of permeation of the test specimen. Note that the weight of the canisters should be as low as possible to increase the accuracy of the weight increase measurements that are made. The canisters must be equipped with valves for "sealing up" after filling with charcoal and during the weighing process. This avoids moisture pick-up when the canister is not connected to the measuring device. Adding cotton swab in front and behind the charcoal helps to avoid charcoal dust being taken out by the nitrogen flow (could lead to errors). It is possible the use of a cotton swab may restrict flow excessively. If that's the case, coarse steel wool is a reasonable substitute for blockage of charcoal dust.

4.1.17 ACTIVATED CHARCOAL—A suitable grade of activated charcoal must be used, such as activated carbon beads (6 to 14 mesh, Fisher catalog or equivalent). A typical specific surface needed for the adsorptive capability is 1000 to 1500 m^2/gram.

The amount of charcoal used should be as small as possible as long as it is sufficient for the adsorption of the amount of permeate that will be measured. In order to estimate a volume suitable for running the test over an acceptable period of time, it can be taken as baseline, that charcoal can absorb about 40% of it's own weight in hydrocarbons before absorbency is exhausted.

For efficiency of adsorption, the length to width (or diameter) ratio of the charcoal bed should be 6 to 1 or greater. Refer also to 5.3 and 7.4.3. See the attachment for suggested procedure for measurement of the adsorptive capacity of the charcoal.

4.2 Other Equipment—Besides the apparatus used in the specific test procedure, there are other items needed as this test procedure is carried out.

4.2.1 BALANCE—A suitable device is used to measure the weight increase of the canisters as the permeate is adsorbed into the charcoal. An analytical balance can be used manually to periodically weight each canister or it can be used for automatic weighing. In the "automatic" technique, each canister rests on a balance and is not moved. The readings of the balance are noted periodically or they can be fed directly into a recording device. Devices that are used for automatic weighing must be monitored for drift. Accuracy of balance must be such that weight can be made within ±0.01 grams or ±0.1%, whichever is "better".

4.2.2 FUEL HANDLING ITEMS—Fuel of a specific composition must be mixed for a test. All the necessary fuel and additive storage containers, mixing tanks, and means to transfer it into the reservoir before the permeation test begins are part of the equipment needed for this test.

Care must also be taken for proper disposal of the fuel when the test is completed. The steps and equipment needed must comply with local health and safety laws.

4.2.3 TOOLS—This is the variety of wrenches, screwdrivers, pliers, and other items needed to manipulate the various connectors, clamps, seals, etc.

4.2.4 SAFETY ITEMS—Safety items are necessary for use with the apparatus (see Section 6).

***5. Chemicals*—**For conducting this test procedure, a number of chemicals are needed. Their use is referred to in the detailed discussion of the apparatus (Section 4) and the procedure itself (Section 7). When using these various chemicals, refer to the Material Safety Data Sheets available from the supplier of the materials for guidelines on how to properly handle each one and the safety precautions that must be taken.

5.1 Fuel Mixtures—This will be determined by the specific needs of the test to be performed; the end user should provide guidance on how to proceed and the specific test fuel to use (refer to 3.4.2 and 7.5). The basic test fuel that should be used for comparison of performance of recirculation units or test specimens is CM15 (refer to SAE J1681).

5.2 Nitrogen (Dry)—This is recommended for use as the carrier gas for removal of the permeate and can also be used to pressurize the fuel flow. If Nitrogen is not used, the carrier gas must be inert to the chemicals and components that are part of this test. The gas must be dry to eliminate the effects of the moisture on the accuracy of the test (refer to 4.1.1 and 4.1.12).

5.3 Activated Charcoal—Use activated charcoal beads (6 to 14 mesh, Fisher catalog or equivalent). The charcoal must not be reused in the canisters after it has been exposed to fuel in this permeation test or similar procedures unless it is properly reconditioned.

Charcoal also can be reconditioned and thus be used several times. First tests showed that by heating the charcoal for 45 h at 200 °C in a hot air oven with air exhaust tube, the adsorbed hydrocarbons are sufficiently driven off. Reconditioning at 175 °C takes approximately 100 h. The reconditioning that is done should be in a dry nitrogen atmosphere. Ambient air should not be used inside the oven; it can be a source of unwanted moisture because of the humidity.

The means for determining if the charcoal has been regenerated is by comparison of weights.

a. Weight at beginning before test begins (see 7.4.4)
b. Weight at end of test (see 7.10.2 and 8.1)
c. Weight after the heating step described previously and compare to the weight measured in 7.4.4

Charcoal that will no longer be used in this test should be disposed of properly. Refer also to 4.1.17, 7.4.1, 7.4.2, and 7.4.3.

6. Safety Equipment and Facilities—With fuel being used at elevated temperatures and pressures, special safety precautions must be taken when conducting this permeation test. The operator must follow local laws, regulations, and recommended industry guidelines when setting up the apparatus and conducting all parts of the procedure. Certain equipment is suggested here, but it is meant as an initial guideline. The operator must take responsibility to meet all safety requirements that pertain. Equipment other than what's listed here may be necessary.

6.1 Vapor Control Device—Fumehood or other means of removal of fuel vapors that may emanate from the test apparatus.

6.2 Gloves

6.3 Safety Glasses

6.4 Temperature Controls—Care must be taken to not exceed the recommended maximum temperatures. Measurement, feedback, and control devices must be part of the means by which temperature is kept safely at the desired level.

6.5 Pressure Controls—Care must also be taken to not exceed the recommended maximum pressure levels. Measurement, feedback, and control devices must be part of the means by which pressure is kept safety at the desired levels.

7. Test Procedure—The following are the steps to conduct the permeation measurement of the test specimen. Since there are a variety of acceptable configurations of the apparatus, the steps described here are of a more general nature. Slight modifications will be acceptable if the intent of this document is met and the modifications are necessary to properly utilize the specific test apparatus.

The steps described here are written as if the specimen being tested is a fuel tube. Similar steps would be taken if other elements were being tested (fuel filter, tube/connector assembly, individual connector, etc.

As different steps are described, various parts of the apparatus are occasionally referenced. Refer to Figure 1 for any specific components indicated by item number.

7.1 Test Specimen Preparation—For testing a tube, cut it to the appropriate length. Measure and record the length, width, wall thickness, inside diameter, and any other dimensions that may be useful. The length is the "free length" of the tube that is inside the cell and not covered in any way by elements that are inserted in the ends. Dimensions should be taken as accurately as possible (±0.1% is recommended). Weigh the sample within ± 0.1%. Refer to 8.3 and 9.3. For testing a part with a complex geometry or a small system of more than one part, the dimensions of the components are not as important.

For all specimen tests, the general construction of the parts should also be noted. Such aspects as materials used, layer configuration, layer thickness, types of connections, etc., can all be important (see 9.3).

7.2 Preconditioning Test Specimen—It can take a very long time to achieve the required steady-state permeation level. Even at 60 °C and utilizing methanol content fuels, the time to reach equilibrium can approach 1000 h for tubes with very low permeability (refer also to 3.3).

If it is not necessary to study the phenomena that occur as the material or part reaches equilibrium, the part to be tested can be preconditioned in a recirculation system separate from the permeation tester. The following criteria must be followed during the preconditioning step.

a. Fuel used should be same type of fuel used to measure permeation.
b. Preconditioning should take place with the fuel inside the component only, total immersion of the part is not recommended because it could cause erroneous results and may actually take longer to reach equilibrium.
c. Preconditioning temperature should be the same as the temperature that will be used in the permeation measurement.

Test specimens can be kept in preconditioning until it is estimated that equilibrium has been reached. Some research suggests that length change can be useful for the purpose (refer to 4.1.10). Record the test specimen length during preconditioning. When length changes cease, permeation equilibrium is established and preconditioning can be terminated; leave the specimen in the preconditioning set up until the specimen can be connected to the permeation tester.

For an indication of time involved in preconditioning and permeation testing, refer to 3.3.

7.3 Mounting Test Specimen—Attach test specimen to the inlet and outlet ports and to other connection points that cause the routing of the fuel circulation system to be complete (refer to 4.1.9).

With all connections secure and any appropriate other routing tubes attached, insert the test specimen into the test chamber. Cover of chamber should then be secured so a complete and uniform seal is obtained.

7.4 Preparing Charcoal Canisters—(Refer to 4.1.16 and 4.1.17.)

7.4.1 CHARCOAL ADSORPTIVE CAPACITY—It can be important to determine the adsorptive capacity of the charcoal used in the canisters and the performance of the specific canisters that are used. The adsorptive capacity is a measure of how efficiently the charcoal can adsorb the emissions that come from the test specimens. If less than 90% of the emissions are adsorbed by the charcoal, then there will be inaccuracies in test results. Either the charcoal will need to be replaced by "better" charcoal and the test re-done or the inaccuracy caused by inadequate adsorption of emissions components will have to be accounted for mathematically. Refer to Appendix A for details on this procedure.

7.4.2 DRY THE CHARCOAL—The charcoal should be dried to drive off unwanted moisture that may be present. Typically this takes 36 h at 150 °C, followed by cooling the charcoal in a desiccant box.

7.4.3 CHARCOAL INTO THE CANISTERS—When drying is complete and the charcoal has cooled, place the charcoal into the canisters and close them. A typical amount used is 125 g into a canister with a capacity of 250 mL.

NOTE—Charcoal must not be reused in the canister unless it has been properly regenerated (see 5.3). If it has been previously utilized and not regenerated, it should be disposed of properly (refer also to 4.1.17).

7.4.4 WEIGH THE CANISTERS—Measure and record the weight of each canister. Each canister must be weighed as accurately as the balance will permit. This is a critical starting point for the weight gain measurements that will be made later and that will be used to calculate permeation. Canister must be weighed in the exact configuration in which it will be weighed in subsequent steps.

7.4.5 ATTACH CANISTERS TO APPARATUS—Ensure that all joints are secure, seals are uniform and complete, and appropriate routing of carrier gas is achieved. Canisters should not be exposed to any of the carrier gas or permeate until Steps 7.4 through 7.8 are completed (Refer to 7.9).

7.5 Preparing Fuel Mixture—Add necessary ingredients to the base fuel to make the test fuel to be used that has the required composition. Basic test fuel should be CM15 (refer to SAE J1681). Any other test fuel shall be agreed upon between all parties involved. Use the test fuel to fill the fuel reservoir (refer to 3.4.2 and 5.1).

7.6 Fuel Flow—Begin flow of fuel by activating the pump that is part of the system. As the various components of the fuel circuit fill with fuel, some purging of air from the system may be necessary. This is done at the reservoir. Flow of fuel should be adjusted to be at required rate (10 to 20 L/h is suggested).

7.7 Set Test Temperature—The temperature of the test is defined by the temperature of the fuel that flows through the apparatus. That fuel temperature should be controlled at the inlet and outlet ports of the test cell. If possible, other parts of the apparatus such as the wall of the test cell and even the carrier gas can be at the desired temperature level as well.

NOTE—The carrier gas temperature may be at a higher temperature.

7.7.1 TYPICAL TEST TEMPERATURES—Typical temperatures to be used in this procedure are 60 °C for liquid applications and 40 °C for vapor/emissions system components. For safety considerations, the temperature of the fuel should not exceed 60 °C. For comparison among recirculation units or between specific parts, the "baseline" test temperature should be 60 °C. If other temperatures are used, they should be agreed upon by the producer and end user involved.

7.7.2 RECORD THE TEST TEMPERATURE—Actual temperature used must be recorded. Measure and record the temperature throughout the test to confirm that it is being maintained appropriately.

7.7.3 SUGGESTED PROCEDURE FOR USING TEMPERATURE LESS THAN 60 °C—Permeation rate is influenced significantly by the temperatures involved. Running the test at less than 60 °C can have a dramatic effect on the length of time to reach the final steady-state value (see Table 1, 3.3.1). For conducting tests at temperatures less than 60 °C, the following procedure should be followed to keep the time of the test in the same realm as the times shown on Table 1:

a. Run the test at 60 °C until steady-state permeation levels are achieved (refer to 3.3.2).
b. After steady state has been achieved at a temperature of 60 °C, then drop the test temperature to the lower level (40 °C), for example).
c. Continue the test at the new temperature until a new steady-state level of permeation is achieved. Experience has shown this additional step to typically take about 1 week after temperature was lowered.

7.8 Pressurize the Test Fuel—Using the pressurizing gas (Figure 1, #1) turn on the flow and carefully pressurize the fuel to the desired level (Figure 1, #2). Examine all parts and connections carefully to ensure there are no fuel leaks. A typical pressure used for the fuel in this test is 2 bar. Care should be taken that pressure does not become too high; a typical upper limit used is 5 bar.

It is recommended that the pressure used in this test procedure matches the maximum pressure of the system in which the part being tested will be used. This should be agreed upon by the end user and all other parties involved.

For purposes of comparison among recirculation units or between test specimens, pressure of the used in the test shall be 2 bar for liquid system application and 0.1 bar above the vapor pressure of the test fuel.

7.9 Starting Test—Carrier gas should be introduced into the test cell to purge it. After this is done, the adsorption canisters is attached to the system or the necessary valve should be opened so the Nitrogen flow circuit is complete (a typical flow rate for the Nitrogen carrier gas is 100 mL/min). Once the carrier gas can enter the canisters and routine flow has started, the test has begun.

7.10 Conducting the Test—All fuel and gas flows and the temperature required must be maintained at constant levels throughout the entire duration of the test. All temperature pressures and flow must be monitored continuously to assure they remain within specified limits. They must be recorded whenever weight measurements are made or daily whichever is more frequent.

7.10.1 FIRST 8 HOURS—Determine fuel loss, pressure levels, and any other pertinent items to make sure there are no leaks. If leaks of any kind are detected, follow the shut down procedure of 7.11, correct the leak, and then repeat all of Section 7.

7.10.2 WEIGH THE CHARCOAL CANISTERS—This should be done at regular intervals. Initially, the canisters should be weighed every 24 h. When using smaller canisters, this period may be shorter. For longer duration tests, the weigh interval can be less frequent. As steady state is approached, the interval between weighing of canisters should again be every 24 h (refer to 7.4.1 and Appendix A). This process should continue until it can be confirmed that equilibrium state has been achieved (see 3.3).

To ensure that the permeate is adsorbed in the canisters in a proper way, it has to be guaranteed that no interval is longer than the time to reach the maximum capacity of the canisters.

Having two canisters in line, the weight gain of the second one must not be more than 20% of the total weight gain of both canisters. If weight gain of the second one is higher than 20%, this indicates that the maximum adsorbance capacity of the first one has been exceeded.

7.11 Shutting Down the Test Apparatus

a. Turn off the sources of heat (allow system to cool down before other steps are followed).
b. Turn off source of pressure for test fuel.
c. Turn off fuel pump.
d. Stop flow of carrier gas.
e. Disconnect tube to inlet of test chamber (Figure 1, #6). Use that tube to drain fuel from the tubing in the circulation system. Use 1 to 2 bar Nitrogen to empty the test specimen of fuel. The fuel can be directed into the reservoir or into a separate container.
f. Disconnect the canisters.
g. If test is complete, then dispose of all exposed charcoal according to environmental and safety guidelines or regenerate it as described in Section 5.3. The test fuel must also be disposed of according to environmental and safety guidelines.

8. Calculations

8.1 Weight Gain—Determine weight gain (daily or at other periodic intervals). To calculate the weight gain, subtract the weight value from the previous measurement from newly recorded value for each collection bottle. Add the values together for the summation (of the 2 or 3 weights) of that time period. Refer to 7.1.

8.2 Confirm Dimensions at End of Test—Measure the effective length at the end of the test. If two test specimens are used, add the length of the two together. Refer to 7.1 for the initial dimensions that were measured.

8.3 Calculate Permeation Rate at End of Test—Use Equation 1 for measurement of permeation of tubing once the rate has achieved a steady-state value.

$$P = \frac{A}{ID \cdot \Pi \cdot L \cdot \frac{B}{24}} \cdot \frac{1}{E} \quad \text{(Eq. 1)}$$

where:

P = Permeability in $g/m^2/24$ h
A = Weight gain in grams between two points in time
ID = Inside diameter of tubing in m (measure prior to testing)
P = 3.1416
L = Total length of tubing tested in m (measure prior to testing) (subtract lengths of any metal inserts that are used)
B = Time (hours) weight gain accrued (difference between the two points)
E = Adsorptive factor (efficiency of adsorption as described in 7.4.1 and in Appendix A.

For parts or small systems that have complex geometrics, the permeation rate is calculated by Equation 2.

$$A/(B/24) \quad \text{(Eq. 2)}$$

When the steady-state value of permeation rate measured by this procedure is reported, the result should be rounded off in the manner shown in Table 2:

TABLE 2—ROUNDING OF RESULTS

RANGE OF PERMEATION RATE	RESULT SHOULD BE ROUNDED OFF
0 to 50	to nearest full unit
50 to 100	to nearest even number of units
100 to 200	to nearest 5 units
over 200	to nearest 10 units

9. Reporting Results

9.1 Units of Measurement—Results of conducting this test are reported in one of three ways; the difference being based on the geometry of the components being tested. For irregularly shaped parts, for systems, or any specimen whose surface area wetted by the fuel cannot be easily calculated, the results of the test are to be reported in grams/day. For tubing, the units reported can be reported in grams/meter²/day (for this result, the dimensions of the tube must also be noted). For tubing, the results can also be reported in grams/meter/day (refer also to 3.5).

9.2 Identifying Results—If a specimen is a tube, hose, or other component in where the total emissions measured by this procedure are nearly all due to permeation through the walls, then the results are to be labeled.

9.2.1 PERMEATION LOSSES

NOTE—There may be small additional losses due to microleaks at the interfaces that are part of the apparatus, but they will be included in the previous term.

For situations where connections are part of the test specimen (either as part of a small set of components or as the specific part being tested), then the total losses measured will be a sum of the permeation losses and the losses due to small microleaks at the interfaces. In these cases, the results of this test shall then be labeled.

9.2.2 TOTAL EMISSIONS LOSSES—It is important to note that when the specimen being tested is a "system" of more than 1 component, the measured losses of the system will not be the same as adding together the results of measuring each individual component separately. The reason for this is the effect of the interface between the various components. There can be microleaks at each interface that contribute to total hydrocarbon losses.

9.3 Additional Information—Along with the results described in 9.2., there are additional items of information that should also be reported:

a. Number of samples tested (see 4.1.8 and 4.1.9)
b. Type of fuel used (see 3.4.2, 5.1, and 7.5)
c. Location of fittings (see 4.1.9)
d. Test temperature and pressure used (see 7.7 and 7.8)
e. Time to reach equilibrium (see 3.3)
f. Total length of time of test (see 3.3)
g. Dimensions of specimen tested (if easily measurable - diameter, length, wall thickness, etc.) (see 7.1 and 8.2)
h. Thickness of layers, materials used in the layers, and their specific arrangement in the wall (see 7.1 and 8.2)

APPENDIX A

A.1 Calculation of Adsorptive Capacity of the Charcoal—This is a test procedure that measures the ability of the charcoal used in the canisters to adsorb all the emissions that enter in the carrier gas that comes out of the main test cell. It is done with the same quantity of canisters and in the exact configuration in which they will be used in the recirculation test. The same test conditions are used as will be used in the recirculation test (temperatures, pressure, carrier gas, flow rate, etc.).

A.1.1 Test Preparation—A suitable number of pieces of tubing (typically 5 to 8) are plugged at one end, filled with test fuel and plugged at the other end. Place those tubing pieces in a glass test cell (or one of a similar performing construction) that can be sealed and can allow the flow of the carrier gas through it. Weigh the sealed cell containing the tubing pieces within ±0.1%. Each canister is weighed in a similar manner.

A.1.2 Test Procedure—The carrier gas flows through the glass cell with the specimens (at the same rate as will be used in the recirculation test). The carrier gas picks up permeate from the specimens and enters the canisters where the emissions are adsorbed. The test is run in this manner for a total of 24 h; then all is stopped.

A.1.2.1 WEIGHING PROCEDURE—At the end of the 24-h procedure, the test specimens are removed and weighed again within ±0.1%. The total loss in weight is noted.

Each canister is weighed after the 24-h period with an accuracy of ±0.1%. The weight gain of each canister is noted.

A.1.3 Adsorptive Capacity—This characteristic of the charcoal that is used in the canisters is determined by the ratio shown in Equation A1:

$$\frac{\text{Total of Weight Gain in all Canisters} \times 100}{\text{Total Weight Loss of all Test Specimens}} = \%\ \text{Absorbance} \qquad \text{(Eq. A1)}$$

For charcoal to be acceptable, the adsorptive capacity calculated in this manner should be 90% or better.

When this ratio (% absorbance) is known, it can be used to help improve the accuracy of the results reported:

$$\text{Reported Results} = \frac{\text{Measured}}{\text{Results}} \times \frac{100\%}{\%\ \text{Absorbance}} \qquad \text{(Eq. A2)}$$

NOTE—This 24-h test should be done 3 to 5 times to improve the confidence in the accuracy of the adsorbance ratio.

A.2 Determination of Adsorptive Efficiency of Canisters—The weight gains that were measured in A.1.2 can be used to determine efficiency of the canisters that are used. These weight gains can be used to determine various important ratios.

$$\frac{\text{Weight Gain of 1st Canister} \times 100}{\text{Weight Gain of all Canisters}} = \frac{\text{Canister Efficiency}}{\text{of the 1st Canister}} \qquad \text{(Eq. A3)}$$

If the efficiency is 85% or better, then the canisters have acceptable efficiency. A efficiency of 80% to 85% is still marginally acceptable. If efficiency is less than 80%, then it's recommended that either the canister, the charcoal, or both be changed.

There can be another reason for an efficiency ratio of the first canister that is too low. Excessive flow rate of the carrier gas can lead to inadequate adsorbance of the permeate because residence time in the canisters is too short. If the gas carrying the permeate "blows through" the first canister too quickly, the second or even third canister will adsorb a much larger portion of that permeate. The maximum suitable flow rate can be determined by following the procedure described in A.1.3. Also refer to 4.1.12, 4.1.14, and 7.9.

FUEL AND OIL HOSES—SAE J30 JUN1998 SAE Standard

Report of the SAE Nonmetallic Materials Committee approved January 1946. Revised by the SAE Fuel, Oil, and Emission Hose Committee October 1987, completely revised June 1991, revised May 1993, December 1993, and June 1998. Rationale statement available.

This SAE Standard was formulated by SAE-ASTM Technical Committee on Automotive Rubber.

1. Scope—This SAE Standard covers fuel and oil hose, coupled and uncoupled, for use with gasoline, oil, diesel fuel, lubrication oil, or the vapor present in either the fuel system or in the crankcase of internal combustion engines in mobile, stationary, and marine applications. Sections 7 and 11 cover hose intended to meet the demands of fuel injection systems. Sections 10 and 11 cover hose intended to meet low fuel permeation requirements.

Section 3 covers Coupled and Uncoupled Synthetic Rubber Tube and Cover (SAE 30R2).

Section 4 covers Lightweight Braided Reinforced Lacquer, Cement, or Rubber Covered Hose (SAE 30R3).

Section 5 covers Wire Inserted Synthetic Rubber Tube and Cover (SAE 30R5).

Section 6 covers Low-Pressure Coupled and Uncoupled Synthetic Rubber Tube and Cover (SAE 30R6), (SAE 30R7), (SAE 30R8).

Section 7 covers Fuel Injection Hose Medium-Pressure Coupled and Uncoupled Synthetic Rubber Tube and Cover (SAE 30R9).

Section 8 covers In-Tank, Low-Pressure, Uncoupled Fuel Hoses (SAE 30R10).

Section 9 covers Unified Method for Fuel Hose Permeation.

Section 10 covers Low Permeation Fuel Fill and Vent Hose (SAE 30R11).

Section 11 covers Low Permeation Fuel Feed and Return Hose (SAE 30R12).

2. References

2.1 Applicable Publications—The following publications form a part of this specification to the extent specified herein. Unless otherwise indicated, the latest issue of SAE and ASTM Publications shall apply.

2.1.1 SAE PUBLICATIONS—Available from SAE, 400 Commonwealth Drive, Warrendale, PA 15096-0001.

SAE J1645—Information Report Covering Electrostatic Charge in Fuel Systems

SAE J1681—Gasoline/Methanol Mixtures for Material Testing

SAE J1737—Recommended Practice for Measurement of Permeation Resistance by the Recirculation Technique

SAE J1960—Accelerated Exposure of Automotive Exterior Materials Using a Controlled Irradiance Water Cooled Xenon Arc Apparatus

SAE J2260—Non-Metallic, Low-Permeation Fuel System Tubing with One or More Layers

2.1.2 ASTM PUBLICATIONS—Available from ASTM, 100 Barr Harbor Drive, West Conshohocken, PA 19428-2959.

ASTM B 117—Method of Salt Spray (Fog) Testing

ASTM D 257—DC Resistance or Conductance of Insulating Materials

ASTM D 380—Methods of Testing Rubber Hose

ASTM D 412—Test for Rubber Properties in Tension

ASTM D 413—Test Methods for Rubber Property: Adhesion to Flexible Substrate

ASTM D 471—Test for Rubber Property: Effect on Liquids

ASTM D 573—Test for Rubber: Deterioration in an Air Oven

ASTM D 1149—Test Method for Rubber Deterioration: Surface Ozone Cracking in a Chamber (Flat Specimens)

2.1.3 RMA PUBLICATION—Available from Rubber Manufacturers Association, 1400 K Street, NW, Suite 900, Washington D.C. 20005.

RMA IP-2—Method for Measuring Electrical Resistance of Hose

3. Coupled and Uncoupled Synthetic Rubber Tube and Cover (SAE 30R2)

3.1 Hose Construction

3.1.1 TYPE 1—The construction of this hose embodies a smooth bore tube of suitable synthetic rubber material, reinforced with one ply of braided, knit, spiral, or woven fabric, and finished with a suitable oil- and ozone-resisting synthetic rubber cover.

3.1.2 TYPE 2—The construction of this hose embodies a smooth bore tube of suitable synthetic rubber material, reinforced with two braided plies or multiples of woven fabric, and finished with a suitable oil- and ozone-resisting synthetic rubber cover.

3.1.3 TYPE 3—The construction of this hose embodies a smooth bore tube of suitable synthetic rubber material, a single braided ply of textile reinforcement, and finished with a suitable oil- and ozone-resisting synthetic rubber cover.

3.2 Dimensions—Dimensions and tolerances are shown in Table 1.

3.3 Retests and Rejection—Any hose or assembly that fails in one or more tests shall be resampled and retested. Twice the number of specimens shall be selected from the lot in question for any retests, and failure of any of the retested samples shall be cause for rejection.

3.4 Tests

3.4.1 QUALIFICATION TESTS—For qualification tests, one 7.6 m (25 ft) length of bulk hose or 10 assemblies of each size to be qualified shall be furnished. In order to qualify under this standard, hose and hose assemblies must meet the requirements of the following tests: (a) change-in-length followed by (b) burst, (c) vacuum collapse, (d) cold flexibility, (e) tensile strength and elongation, tube and cover, (f) dry heat resistance, (g) fuel resistance, (h) oil resistance, (i) ozone resistance, and (j) adhesion.

TABLE 1—DIMENSIONS AND TOLERANCES FOR SAE 30R2

Nominal Size mm	Nominal Size in	Inside Diameter in	Inside Diameter mm	Outside Diameter(1) Types 1 and 3 mm Min	Outside Diameter(1) Types 1 and 3 mm Max	Outside Diameter(1) Types 1 and 3 in Min	Outside Diameter(1) Types 1 and 3 in Max	Outside Diameter(1) Type 2 Min	Outside Diameter(1) Type 2 mm Max	Outside Diameter(1) Type 2 in Min	Outside Diameter(1) Type 2 in Max
3.18	1/8	3.18 ±0.25	0.125 ±0.010	8.33	9.53	0.328	0.375	11.13	12.70	0.438	0.500
4.78	3/16	4.78 ±0.40	0.188 ±0.016	9.93	11.13	0.391	0.438	12.70	14.27	0.500	0.562
6.35	1/4	6.35 ±0.40	0.250 ±0.016	11.51	12.70	0.453	0.500	14.27	15.88	0.562	0.625
7.92	5/16	7.92 ±0.40	0.312 ±0.016	13.11	14.27	0.516	0.562	15.88	17.48	0.625	0.688
9.53	3/8	9.53 ±0.40	0.375 ±0.016	14.68	15.88	0.578	0.625	17.48	19.05	0.688	0.750
11.13	7/16	11.13 ±0.58	0.438 ±0.023	—	—	—	—	19.05	20.62	0.750	0.812
12.70	1/2	12.70 ±0.58	0.500 ±0.023	18.26	19.84	0.719	0.781	20.62	22.23	0.812	0.875
15.88	5/8	15.88 ±0.58	0.625 ±0.023	21.44	23.01	0.844	0.906	23.83	25.40	0.938	1.000
19.05	3/4	19.05 ±0.58	0.750 ±0.023	26.97	28.58	1.062	1.125	26.97	28.58	1.062	1.125
22.23	7/8	22.23 ±0.79	0.875 ±0.031	—	—	—	—	30.18	31.75	1.188	1.250
25.40	1	25.40 ±0.79	1.000 ±0.031	32.54	34.93	1.281	1.375	32.54	34.93	1.281	1.375
28.58	1-1/8	28.58 ±0.79	1.125 ±0.031	—	—	—	—	38.10	41.28	1.500	1.625
31.75	1-1/4	31.75 ±0.99	1.250 ±0.039	—	—	—	—	41.28	44.45	1.625	1.750
34.93	1-3/8	34.93 ±0.99	1.375 ±0.039	—	—	—	—	44.45	47.63	1.750	1.875
38.10	1-1/2	38.10 ±0.99	1.500 ±0.039	—	—	—	—	47.63	50.80	1.875	2.000
41.28	1-5/8	41.28 ±0.99	1.625 ±0.039	—	—	—	—	50.80	53.98	2.000	2.125
44.45	1-3/4	44.45 ±0.99	1.750 ±0.039	—	—	—	—	53.98	57.15	2.125	2.250
50.80	2	50.80 ±0.99	2.000 ±0.039	—	—	—	—	60.33	63.50	2.375	2.500

1. Concentricity based on total indicator reading between the inside bore of the hose and the outer surface of the hose shall not exceed the values given below:
Sizes 1/4 in and under: 0/76 mm (0.030 in)
Sizes over 1/4 up to 7/8 in: 1.02 mm (0.040 in)
Sizes over 7/8 in: 1.27 mm (0.050 in)

In addition to the above, hose assemblies shall be subjected to qualification tests as follows: (k) proof, (l) tensile test of assembly, (m) leakage, (n) corrosion, and (o) visual inspection.

3.4.2 FREQUENCY OF TESTING FOR INSPECTION—On uncoupled hose, tests shall be conducted on samples representing each lot of 152 to 3048 m (500 to 10 000 ft). Where a lot is 152 m (500 ft) or less, no tests shall be conducted, but materials and workmanship shall be the same on such lots as on hose previously qualified under this specification.

On coupled hose lots from 100 to 10 000 pieces, not less than two assemblies shall be subjected to all inspection tests except the visual test, which shall apply to 100% of the assemblies.

3.4.3 INSPECTION TESTS—On coupled hose, these inspection tests shall apply: (a) change-in-length, (b) burst, (c) vacuum collapse, (d) cold flexibility, and (e) adhesion.

On coupled hose assemblies, these tests shall apply: (f) burst, (g) proof, (h) tension test of assembly (unaged), and (i) visual inspection (100%).

3.5 Test Requirements

3.5.1 CHANGE-IN-LENGTH TESTS—Tests for change in length shall be conducted in accordance with ASTM D 380, except that the original measurement shall be at 0 MPa (0 psi) pressure. The change in length shall be determined at the pressures specified in Table 2. Requirements are as follows:

3.5.1.1 Type 1—All sizes ±5% maximum.

3.5.1.2 Type 2—Up to 12.70 mm (1/2 in) ID hose, 0 to -8% change in length: 12.70 mm (1/2 in) ID hose and larger, 0 to -6% change in length.

3.5.1.3 Type 3—All sizes, ±5% maximum.

3.5.2 BURST TEST—The minimum bursting strength shall be as specified in Table 2.

3.5.3 VACUUM COLLAPSE TEST—Types 1 and 3: Sizes less than 12.70 mm (1/2 in) ID shall be subjected to 67.5 kPa (20 in Hg) vacuum; 12.70 mm (1/2 in) ID hose shall be subjected to 34 kPa (10 in Hg) vacuum. Sizes greater than 12.70 mm (1/2 in) ID shall be excluded from the vacuum test.

3.5.3.1 Type 2—Sizes less than 15.88 mm (5/8 in) ID shall be subjected to 67.5 kPa (20 in Hg) vacuum. Hose 15.88 mm (5/8 in) through 25.40 mm (1 in) ID shall be subjected to 34 kPa (10 in Hg) vacuum; sizes greater than 25.40 mm (1 in) ID shall be excluded from the vacuum test.

During the vacuum test described, a 915 mm (3 ft) length of hose or a hose assembly shall be held in a straight line, and no diameter shall decrease by more than 20% during application of vacuum for 15 s and not over 30 s.

3.5.4 COLD FLEXIBILITY—Hose 19.05 mm (3/4 in) ID and under, with or without couplings, shall be used for this test. Two samples shall be used for this test. One sample shall be unaged and the other sample shall be immersed in ASTM Oil No. 3 for 70 h at 100 °C ± 1 °C (212 °F ± 2 °F). The aged and unaged samples shall then be subjected to a temperature of -40 °C ± 1 °C (-40 °F ± 2 °F) for a period of 5 h, after which the hose shall be flexed in the cold chamber through 180 degrees from the centerline to a diameter of 10 times the maximum OD of the hose. This flexing shall be within 4 s. The hose shall not fracture and shall not show any cracks, checks, or breaks in the tube or cover. Cracking of the tube may be determined by application of the proof pressure specified in Table 2.

Hose over 19.05 mm (3/4 in) ID shall have specimens 100 x 6.4 mm (4 x 0.25 in) tube and cover thickness. The thickness shall be 2.54 mm (0.10 in) maximum. Cut from the tube and cover if necessary. One set of samples shall be unaged. The other set of samples shall be completely immersed in ASTM Oil No. 3 for 70h at 100 °C ± 1 °C (212 °F ± 2 °F). The unaged and aged specimens shall then be subjected to a temperature of -40 °C ± 1 °C (-40 °F ± 2 °F) for a period of 5 h in an unrestrained loop position between two jaws 50 mm (2 in) wide and 63 mm (2-1/2 in) apart. At the end of 5 h and while still in the cold chamber, the jaws shall be rapidly brought together until they are 25.40 mm (1 in) apart. The specimen shall not fracture and shall not show any cracks, checks, or breaks.

3.5.5 TENSILE STRENGTH AND ELONGATION

a. Original tensile strength of cover: 6.89 MPa (1000 psi) min
b. Original tensile strength of tube: 8.27 MPa (1200 psi) min
c. Original elongation of tube and cover: 200% min

3.5.6 DRY HEAT RESISTANCE—After oven aging for 70 h at a temperature of 100 °C ± 1 °C (212 °F ± 2 °F), the reductions in tensile strength and elongation of specimens taken from the tube and cover shall not exceed the following values:

a. Original tensile strength: -20%
b. Original elongation: -50%

3.5.7 FUEL RESISTANCE

3.5.7.1 After 48 h immersion at room temperature in ASTM Reference Fuel B, the reductions in tensile strength and elongation of specimens taken from the tube shall not exceed the following values:

a. Original tensile strength: -30%
b. Original elongation: -30%

3.5.7.2 In addition, the volume change of specimens taken from the tube shall not exceed the following values:

a. Tube, volume change: -5 to +25%

3.5.8 OIL RESISTANCE

3.5.8.1 After 70 h immersion at a temperature of 100 °C ± 1 °C (212 °F ± 2 °F) in ASTM Oil No. 3, the reduction in tensile strength and elongation of specimens taken from the tube shall not exceed the following values:

a. Original tensile strength: -40%
b. Original elongation: -40%

3.5.8.2 In addition, the volume change of specimens taken from the tube and cover shall not exceed the following values:

a. Tube, volume change: -5 to +25%
b. Cover, volume change: 0 to +100%

TABLE 2—BURST AND CHANGE-IN-LENGTH TESTS FOR SAE 30R2

Nominal Size mm	Nominal Size in	Burst Test, min Type 1 MPa	Burst Test, min Type 1 psi	Burst Test, min Type 2 MPa	Burst Test, min Type 2 psi	Burst Test, min Type 3 MPa	Burst Test, min Type 3 psi	Change-in-Length Test Types 1 and 2 MPa	Change-in-Length Test Types 1 and 2 psi	Change-in-Length Test Type 3 MPa	Change-in-Length Test Type 3 psi
3.18	1/8	4.82	700	4.82	700	—	—	0.79	115	—	—
4.78	3/16	4.82	700	4.82	700	13.80	2000	0.79	115	3.45	500
6.35	1/4	4.82	700	4.82	700	11.04	1600	0.79	115	2.76	400
7.92	5/16	4.82	700	4.82	700	11.04	1600	0.79	115	2.76	400
9.53	3/8	4.82	700	4.82	700	11.04	1600	0.79	115	2.76	400
11.13	7/16	4.82	700	4.82	700	—	—	0.79	115	—	—
12.70	1/2	4.82	700	4.82	700	11.04	1600	0.79	115	2.76	400
15.88	5/8	3.45	500	3.45	500	9.66	1400	0.59	85	2.42	350
19.05	3/4	3.45	500	3.45	500	8.27	1200	0.59	85	2.07	300
22.23	7/8	—	—	3.45	500	—	—	0.59	85	—	—
25.40	1	3.45	500	3.45	500	—	—	0.59	85	—	—
28.58	1-1/8	—	—	2.76	400	—	—	0.45	65	—	—
31.75	1-1/4	—	—	2.76	400	—	—	0.45	65	—	—
34.93	1-3/8	—	—	2.76	400	—	—	0.45	65	—	—
38.10	1-1/2	—	—	2.76	400	—	—	0.45	65	—	—
41.28	1-5/8	—	—	1.73	250	—	—	0.28	40	—	—
44.45	1-3/4	—	—	1.73	250	—	—	0.28	40	—	—
50.80	2	—	—	1.73	250	—	—	0.28	40	—	—

3.5.9 OZONE RESISTANCE—Test procedure shall be in accordance with ASTM D 1149 where applicable.

For hose 25.40 mm (1 in) ID and under, a specimen of hose of sufficient length shall be bent around a mandrel with an outside diameter equal to eight times the nominal OD of the sample. The two ends shall be tied at their crossing with enameled copper or aluminum wire. After mounting, the specimen shall be allowed to rest in an ozone-free atmosphere for 24 h at room temperature. The mounted specimens shall be placed in a test chamber with ozone concentration of 50 mPa at a temperature of 40 °C ± 1 °C (104 °F ± 2 °F).

After 70 h of exposure, the specimen shall be removed and allowed to cool to room temperature and then be inspected visually under 7X magnification. It must meet a rating of "0" except for the area immediately adjacent to the wire, which shall be ignored.

For hose over 25.40 mm (1 in) ID, prepare a specimen by cutting a strip of the whole hose 12.70 x 100 mm (1/2 wide by 4 in long) and tie to a specimen (cover out) around a 12.70 mm (1/2 in) diameter mandrel. Condition in the same manner as specified in the previous paragraphs for the whole hose and apply the same conditions and requirements. This test applies to the cover only and cracks in the exposed tube or cut edges of the cover shall be ignored.

3.5.10 ADHESION TEST

3.5.10.1 Types 1 and 3—The minimum load required to separate tube from reinforcing ply and cover from reinforcing ply shall be 27 N (6 lb).

3.5.10.2 Type 2—The minimum load required to separate tube from ply, cover from ply, and ply from ply shall be 53.4 N (12 lb).

3.5.11 PROOF TEST—Before shipment by the vendor, a suitable number of assemblies from each lot shall be proof tested at 50% of the minimum burst pressure specified in Table 2 for a period of not less than 30 s or more than 60 s, to ensure an acceptable quality level.

3.5.12 TENSILE TEST OF ASSEMBLY—The hose complete with fittings shall be dry-air aged at 100 °C ± 1 °C (212 °F ± 2 °F) for 70 h and then permitted to rest at room temperature for 2 h. The end fittings of the assembly shall be clamped in the jaws of a tension testing machine so that a straight pull may be applied. The jaws of the test machine shall separate at a rate not greater than 25.40 mm (1 in) min. The hose assembly shall withstand, after the aging test, a minimum pull of 444 N (100 lb) on sizes up to, and including, the 6.35 mm (1/4 in). All sizes over 6.35 mm (1/4 in) ID shall withstand a minimum pull of 667 N (150 lb). For inspection tests, unaged samples may be used.

3.5.13 LEAKAGE TEST

3.5.13.1 Types 1 and 2—Coupled hose shall show no leakage under a hydrostatic pressure of 70% of the minimum burst specified in Table 2, following an aging period of 70 h at 100 °C ± 1 °C (212 °F ± 2 °F) oven temperature. The pressure shall be held for a period of not less than 5 min or more than 7 min.

3.5.13.2 Type 3—Coupled hose shall show no leakage under a hydrostatic pressure of 50% of the minimum burst specified in Table 2, following an aging period of 70 h at 100 °C ± 1 °C (212 °F ± 2 °F) oven temperature. The pressure shall be held for a period of not less than 5 min or more than 7 min.

3.5.14 CORROSION TEST—The assembly shall be tested in accordance with ASTM B 117. The period shall be 48 h. There shall be no evidence of corrosion or other deterioration at the expiration of this test.

3.5.15 VISUAL INSPECTION—All assemblies shall be inspected to see that the correct fittings are properly applied.

4. Lightweight Braided Reinforced Lacquer, Cement, or Rubber Covered Hose (SAE 30R3)

4.1 Hose Construction—The construction of this hose embodies a smooth bore tube of suitable synthetic rubber material, reinforced with one braided ply of cotton or other suitable material and finished with a gasoline-, oil-, and water-resistant flexible coating of lacquer, cement, or synthetic rubber.

4.2 Dimensions—Dimensions and tolerances are shown in Table 3.

4.3 Retests and Rejection—Any hose or assembly that fails in one or more tests shall be resampled and retested. Twice the number of specimens shall be selected from the lot in question for any retests, and failure of any of the retested samples shall be cause for rejection.

4.4 Tests—Procedures described in ASTM D 380 shall be followed wherever applicable.

4.4.1 QUALIFICATION TESTS—For qualification tests, one 7.6 m (25 ft) length of bulk hose or 10 assemblies of each size to be qualified shall be furnished. In order to qualify under this specification, hose and hose assemblies must meet the requirements of the following tests: (a) change-in-length followed by (b) burst, (c) vacuum collapse, (d) cold flexibility, (e) tensile strength and elongation of tube, (f) dry heat resistance, (g) fuel resistance, (h) oil resistance, and (i) ozone resistance.

In addition to the previous tests, hose assemblies shall be subjected to qualification tests as follows: (j) proof, (k) tensile test of assembly, (l) leakage, (m) corrosion, and (n) visual inspection.

4.4.2 FREQUENCY OF TESTING FOR INSPECTION—On uncoupled hose, tests shall be conducted on samples representing each lot of 152 to 3048 m (500 to 10 000 ft). Where a lot is 152 m (500 ft) or less, no tests shall be conducted, but materials and workmanship shall be the same on such lots as on hose previously qualified under this specification.

On coupled hose lots of 100 to 10 000 pieces, not less than two assemblies shall be subjected to all inspection tests except the visual test, which shall apply to 100% of the assemblies.

4.4.3 INSPECTION TESTS—On uncoupled hose, these inspection tests shall apply: (a) change-in-length, (b) vacuum collapse, and (c) cold flexibility.

On coupled hose assemblies, these tests shall apply: (d) burst, (e) proof, (f) tension test of assembly (unaged), and (g) visual inspection (100%).

4.5 Test Requirements

4.5.1 CHANGE-IN-LENGTH TESTS—Tests for change in length shall be conducted in accordance with ASTM D 380, except that the original measurement shall be made at 0 MPa (0 psi) pressure. The change in length shall not exceed ±5% at the change-in-length pressures specified in Table 4.

4.5.2 BURST TEST—The minimum bursting strength shall be as specified in Table 4.

4.5.3 VACUUM COLLAPSE TEST—Two assemblies shall be subjected to a vacuum of 67.5 kPa (20 in Hg), and the reduction in OD shall not exceed 20% of the original diameter during application of vacuum for 15 s and not over 30 s. Tests shall be conducted with hose in a straight position.

4.5.4 COLD FLEXIBILITY—Two samples shall be used for this test. One sample shall be unaged and the other sample shall be immersed in ASTM Oil No. 3 for 70 h at 100 °C ± 1 °C (212 °F ± 2 °F). The aged and unaged samples shall then be subjected to a temperature of -40 °C ± 1 °C (-40 °F ± 2 °F) for a period of 5 h, after which the hose shall be flexed in the cold chamber through 180 degrees from the centerline to a diameter of 10 times the maximum OD of the hose. This flexing shall be within 4 s. The hose shall not fracture and shall not show any cracks, checks, or breaks in the tube or cover. Cracking of the tube may be determined by application of the proof pressure specified in Table 4.

4.5.5 TENSILE STRENGTH AND ELONGATION

a. Original tensile strength of tube: 8.27 MPa (1200 psi) min
b. Original elongation of tube: 200% min

4.5.6 DRY HEAT RESISTANCE—After oven aging for 70 h at a temperature of 100 °C ± 1 °C (212 °F ± 2 °F), the reductions in tensile strength and elongation of specimens taken from the tube shall not exceed the following values:

a. Original tensile strength: -20%
b. Original elongation: -50%

TABLE 3—DIMENSIONS AND TOLERANCES FOR SAE 30R3

Nominal Size mm	Nominal Size in	Inside Diameter mm	Inside Diameter in	Outside Diameter (1) Min mm	Outside Diameter(1) Min in	Outside Diameter(1) Max mm	Outside Diameter(1) Max in
4.76	3/16	4.76 ± 0.40	0.188 ± 0.016	8.73	0.344	9.53	0.375
6.35	1/4	6.35 ± 0.40	0.250 ± 0.016	10.32	0.406	11.13	0.438
7.94	5/16	7.94 ± 0.40	0.312 ± 0.016	12.70	0.500	13.49	0.531
9.53	3/8	9.53 ± 0.40	0.375 ± 0.016	14.68	0.578	15.88	0.625

1. Concentricity based on total indicator reading between the inside bore of the hose and the outer surface of the hose shall not exceed the following values:
   Size 1/4 in and under: 0.762 mm (0.030 in)
   Size over 1.016 mm: 1/4 in (0.040 in)

TABLE 4—BURST, HYDROSTATIC, AND CHANGE-IN-LENGTH TESTS FOR SAE 30R3

Nominal Size mm	Nominal Size in	Burst Test, min MPa	Burst Test, min psi	Hydrostatic Proof MPa	Hydrostatic Proof psi	Change-in-Length MPa	Change-in-Length psi
4.76	3/16	13.80	2000	6.89	1000	3.45	500
6.35	1/4	11.04	1600	5.51	800	2.76	400
7.94	5/16	8.27	1200	4.14	600	2.07	300
9.53	3/8	6.20	900	3.10	450	1.53	225

4.5.7 FUEL RESISTANCE

4.5.7.1 After 48 h immersion at room temperature in ASTM Reference Fuel B, the reductions in tensile strength and elongation of specimens taken from the tube shall not exceed the following values:

a. Original tensile strength: -30%
b. Original elongation: -30%

4.5.7.2 In addition, the volume change of specimens taken from the tube shall not exceed the following values:

a. Tube, volume change: -5 to +25%

4.5.8 OIL RESISTANCE

4.5.8.1 After 70 h immersion at a temperature of 100 °C ± 1 °C (212 °F ± 2 °F) in ASTM Oil No. 3, the reductions in tensile strength and elongation of specimens taken from the tube shall not exceed the following values:

a. Original tensile strength: -40%
b. Original elongation: -40%

4.5.8.2 In addition, the volume change of specimens taken from the tube shall not exceed the following values:

a. Tube, volume change: -5 to +25%

4.5.9 OZONE RESISTANCE—Test procedure shall be in accordance with ASTM D 1149, where applicable.

A specimen of hose of sufficient length shall be bent around a mandrel with an OD equal to eight times the nominal OD of the sample. The two ends shall be tied at their crossing with enameled copper or aluminum wire. After mounting, the specimen shall be allowed to rest in an ozone-free atmosphere for 24 h at room temperature. The mounted specimen shall be placed in a test chamber with ozone concentration of 50 mPa at a temperature of 40 °C ± 1 °C (104 °F ± 2 °F).

After 70 h of exposure, the specimen shall be removed and allowed to cool to room temperature and then be inspected visually under 7X magnification. It must meet a rating of "0" except for the area immediately adjacent to the wire, which shall be ignored.

4.5.10 PROOF TEST—Before shipment by the vendor, a suitable number of assemblies from each lot shall be tested at the hydrostatic proof pressure listed in Table 4 for a period of not less than 30 s or more than 60 s, to ensure an acceptable quality level.

4.5.11 TENSILE TEST OF ASSEMBLY—The hose complete with fittings shall be dry aged at 100 °C ± 1 °C (212 °F ± 2 °F) for 70 h and then permitted to rest at room temperature for 2 h. The end fittings of the assembly shall be clamped in the jaws of a tension testing machine so that a straight pull may be applied. The jaws of the test machine shall separate at a rate not greater than 25.40 mm (1 in)/min. The hose assembly shall withstand, after the aging test, a minimum pull of 444 N (100 lb) on the 4.76 mm (3/16 in) size, 556 N (125 lb) on the 6.35 and 7.94 mm (1/4 and 5/16 in) sizes, and 667 N (150 lb) on the 9.53 mm (3/8 in) size. For inspection tests, unaged samples may be used.

4.5.12 LEAKAGE TEST—Coupled hose filled with ASTM Oil No. 3 shall show no leakage under the hydrostatic proof test pressure specified in Table 4 following an aging period of 70 h at 100 °C ± 1 °C (212 °F ± 2 °F). The pressure shall be held for a period of not less than 5 min or more than 7 min.

4.5.13 CORROSION TEST—The assembly shall be tested in accordance with ASTM B 117. The period shall be 48 h. There shall be no evidence of corrosion or other deterioration at the expiration of this test.

4.5.14 VISUAL INSPECTION—All assemblies shall be inspected to see that the correct fittings are properly applied.

5. Wire Inserted Synthetic Rubber Tube and Cover (SAE 30R5)—This section covers a wire inserted hose for fuel and oil filler and vent use in mobile, stationary, or marine applications. The hose is furnished uncoupled in specific lengths and is secured in application by the use of suitable clamps. The hose is particularly useful in applications where it must be installed in a curved configuration and where resistance to collapse is desirable.

5.1 Hose Construction—The hose will consist of a fuel- and oil-resistant tube, a helical high-carbon steel wire embedded in the convoluted section of this hose and running out into the plain[1] ends and an ozone- and oil-resistant cover. A ply of fabric or cord may be applied between the tube or cover and the helical wire. A ply of fabric must be used to reinforce the ends.

5.2 Dimensions and Tolerances—The applicable dimensions and tolerances are shown in Table 5.

5.3 Physical Tests

5.3.1 The minimum burst shall be 0.621 MPa (90 psi) for all sizes.

5.3.2 Test samples for other physical properties shall be taken from the plain[2] ends and shall be conducted per ASTM D 380 unless otherwise agreed upon between vendor and purchaser.

The physical properties of the tube and cover shall be as shown in Table 6.

5.4 Low-Temperature Flexibility—Specimens of the plain end shall be cut 25.40 mm (1 in) wide. They shall be exposed in a cold box for 5 h at -40 °C ± 1 °C (-40 °F ± 2 °F). Without removing it from the cold box, the specimen shall be compressed to 50% of its original ID between parallel plates in 8 to 12 s. After removal and allowing it to come to room temperature, it shall be carefully examined visually. Any evidence of crack or breaking shall be cause for rejection.

5.5 Vacuum Collapse—The hose shall be subjected to 67.5 kPa (20 in Hg) vacuum. During the test, the entire hose shall be mounted on suitable nipples. The OD shall not collapse more than 20% in the body section and there shall be no evidence of separation of the tube from the body wire when examined after application of the vacuum for 30 to 60 s.

5.6 Ozone Test—Due to the construction and application of this type of hose, ozone deterioration of the cover is particularly significant. The test procedure shall be in accordance with ASTM D 1149 where applicable. The entire hose or a section removed therefrom shall be used as agreed between supplier and user and the specimen shall be mounted as agreed. After mounting, the specimen shall be allowed to rest in an ozone-free atmosphere for 24 h at room temperature. This shall then be placed in a test chamber with ozone concentration of 50 mPa at a temperature of 40 °C ± 1 °C (104 °F ± 2 °F).

1. Synonyms may be "straight ends" or "soft ends."
2. Synonyms may be "straight ends" or "soft ends."

TABLE 5—DIMENSIONS AND TOLERANCES FOR SAE 30R5

Nominal ID mm	Nominal ID in	Tolerance mm	Tolerance in	Wall mm	Wall in	Length mm	Length in	Tolerance mm	Tolerance in
19.05	3/4	+0.76-1.52	+0.03-0.06	3.05/5.89	0.12/0.22	0–305	0 thru 12	±6.35	±0.25
25.40	1	+0.76-1.52	+0.03-0.06	3.05/5.89	0.12/0.22	305–610	Over 12 thru 24	±12.70	±0.50
31.75	1-1/4	+0.76 -2.28	+0.03 -0.09	3.05/5.89	0.12/0.22	610–915	Over 24 thru 36	±19.05	±0.75
38.10	1-1/2	+0.76 -2.28	+0.03 -0.09	3.05/5.89	0.12/0.22	915	Over 36	±2%	±2%
44.45	1-3/4	+0.76 -2.28	+0.03 -0.09	3.05/5.89	0.12/0.22	—	—	—	—
50.80	2	+0.76 -2.28	+0.03 -0.09	3.05/5.89	0.12/0.22	—	—	—	—
57.35	2-1/4	+0.76 -2.28	+0.03 -0.09	3.05/5.89	0.12/0.22	—	—	—	—
63.50	2-1/2	+0.76 -2.28	+0.03 -0.09	3.05/5.89	0.12/0.22	—	—	—	—

The minimum tube gage for all sizes shall be 1.57 mm (0.062 in).

TABLE 6—PHYSICAL PROPERTIES OF 30R5 TUBE AND COVER

Property	Tube	Cover
Original tensile, min	8.27 MPa (1200 psi)	6.89 MPa (1000 psi)
Original elongation, min, %	200	200
Tensile after oven aging 100 h at 100 °C ± 1 °C (212 °F ± 2 °F) (ASTM D 573), min, % of original	80	80
Elongation after oven aging 100 h at 100 °C ± 1 °C (212 °F ± 2 °F) (ASTM D 573), min, % of original	70	80
Tensile after immersion in Fuel B, 48 h (ASTM D 471), min, % of original	70	Not required
Elongation after immersion in Fuel B, 48 h (ASTM D 471), min, % of original	70	Not required
Volume change after immersion in Fuel B, 48 h (ASTM D 471), %	-5 to +25	Not required
Tensile after immersion in ASTM No. 3 Oil, 70 h at 100 °C ± 1 °C (212 °F ± 2), min, % of original	60	Not required
Elongation after immersion in ASTM No. 3 Oil, 70 h at 100 °C ± 1 °C (212 °F ± 2), min, % of original	60	Not required
Volume change after immersion in ASTM No. 3 Oil, 70 h at 100 °C ± 1 °C (212 °F ± 2), %	-5 to +25	0 to +100

After 70 h exposure, the specimen shall be removed and allowed to cool to room temperature and then shall be inspected visually under 7X magnification. It must meet a rating of "0" except for areas which have been agreed can be ignored.

5.7 Qualification and Inspection Testing—For qualifications, 10 lengths of each size to be qualified shall be furnished and shall be subjected to all tests as described in 5.3 to 5.6. For inspection testing, not less than two samples shall be selected from each lot which shall not exceed 10 000 pieces and shall be subjected to the burst, vacuum collapse, and low-temperature flexibility tests described above. Any hose that fails in one or more tests shall be resampled and retested. Twice the number of specimens shall be selected from the lot in question for any retest. Failure of any of the retest samples shall be cause for rejection.

6. Low-Pressure Coupled and Uncoupled Synthetic Rubber Tube and Cover (SAE 30R6)[3], (SAE 30R7), (SAE 30R8)—This section covers hose which may be supplied either coupled or uncoupled for use with gasoline, diesel fuel, lubrication oil, or the vapor present in either the fuel system or in the crankcase of internal combustion engines in mobile, stationary, and marine applications. Exposure of these hoses to gasoline or diesel fuel which contain high levels, greater than 5% by volume, of oxygenates, i.e., ethanol, methanol, or MTBE (methyl tertiary butyl ether), may result in significantly higher permeation rates than those listed for 30R6, 7, or 8. This hose is for maximum working pressures of 0.34 MPa (50 psi) up to and including 9.53 mm (3/8 in) ID and 0.24 MPa (35 psi) for over 9.53 mm (3/8 in). For 30R6 hose in excess of 25.40 mm (1 in), the working pressure is 0.11 MPa (16 psi). The hose may be furnished in long lengths, specific cut lengths, or as a part preformed to a specific configuration. This hose is suitable for use in temperatures up to 100 °C (212 °F) for 30R6, 125 °C (257 °F) for 30R7, 150 °C (302 °F) intermittently and 135 °C (275 °F) continuously for 30R8.

6.1 Hose Construction—The construction of this hose embodies a smooth bore tube of fuel- and oil-resistant synthetic rubber compound, suitably reinforced with textile fiber yarn, cord, or fabric, and a cover of suitable oil-, ozone-, and heat-resistant synthetic rubber compound.

6.2 Dimensions

6.2.1 Dimensions and tolerances for inside diameter and outside diameter are shown in Table 7. The ends of hose shall be square within 3.00 mm (0.12 in) for sizes up to and including 19.05 mm (3/4 in) ID, 6.35 mm (0.25 in) for sizes 25.40 mm (1 in) through 50.80 mm (2 in) ID, and 9.5 mm (0.38 in) for sizes over 50.80 mm (2 in) ID. Other tolerances applicable are as in Table 8.

6.2.2 When hose is supplied in specific cut or long lengths, the length tolerances shall be as in Table 8.

6.2.2.1 End squareness shall be measured from a point projected from the short side to the inside of the long side by a line perpendicular to the wall of the hose, to the end of the hose at its longest point. End squareness measurement will be considered equally applicable with length tolerance. The midpoint of the measurement of the deviation from squareness taken on the long side shall fall within the length tolerance.

6.2.3 When hose is supplied as a preformed item, the tolerance shall be as follows:

6.2.3.1 Squareness of Ends—The tolerance on squareness of ends of preformed parts shall be a minimum 15% of nominal hose OD on all sizes through 25.40 mm (1 in) ID, 6.3 mm (0.25 in) for sizes over 25.40 mm (1 in) ID through 50.80 mm (2 in) ID and 9.5 mm (0.38 in) for sizes over 50.80 mm (2 in) ID. End squareness shall be measured as described in 6.2.2.1.

6.2.3.2 Arm Lengths—Measured from end to intersection of nearest centerline. Each end shall be as described in 6.2.2. These tolerances apply also to the length of an expanded end.

6.2.3.3 General Layout—Dimensions locating bend intersections are to establish the theoretical centerline of the hose. Actual outside contour on the hose must be held within 4.8 mm (0.19 in) in all planes with respect to the theoretical outside contour. To check contour, hose ends should first be placed in nominal position (hose may have to be flexed to correct any distortion caused by handling after vulcanization in the producing plant or in shipment) in a checking fixture made in accordance with user requirement from which contour deviation can be measured. Allowance shall be provided in the end mounting area of the fixture for the arm length tolerances which are applicable.

When the ID of an end of the hose is enlarged, the wall gauge of the enlarged end normally changes. Allowable change should be +0.8, -0.5 mm (+0.03, -0.02 in). The wall gauge within bends of a preformed hose may differ from the gauge in straight portions. This difference shall not exceed 33%.

6.3 Retests and Rejection—Any hose or assembly that fails in one or more tests shall be resampled and retested. Twice the number of specimens shall be selected from the lot in question for any retests, and failure of any of the retested specimens shall be cause for rejection.

6.4 Tests—Procedures described by ASTM D 380 are to be followed wherever applicable.

6.4.1 QUALIFICATION TESTS—For the qualification tests, one 7.5 m (24.6 ft) length of bulk hose, 10 preformed parts, or 10 assemblies of each size to be qualified shall be furnished. In order to qualify under this specification, hose and hose assemblies must meet all the test requirements of 6.5.

6.4.2 FREQUENCY OF TESTING FOR INSPECTION—As agreed upon between supplier and user.

6.4.3 INSPECTION TEST—On hose and/or hose assemblies the following inspection tests shall apply: (6.5.1) burst, (6.5.2) vacuum collapse, (6.5.3) cold flexibility, (6.5.10) adhesion, (6.5.11) kink resistance if specified. The kink resistance test shall not normally be required on preformed hose, but may be specified for straight sections of at least 300 mm (11.8 in) length.

3. SAE 30R1 — This specification is presently obsolete and has been superseded by SAE 30R6. (Information on SAE 30R1 was last printed in the 1982 Handbook. This information can be found in SAE J30d.)

TABLE 7—DIMENSIONS AND TOLERANCES FOR SAE 30R6, SAE 30R7, AND SAE 30R8

Nominal Size mm	Nominal Size in	Inside Diameter mm	Inside Diameter in	Outside Diameter(1) mm	Outside Diameter(1) in	Maximum End Out-of-Squareness Angle, Deg(2)
3.97	5/32	3.97 ±0.40	0.156 ±0.016	9.13 ±0.58	0.360 ±0.023	14.5
4.76	3/16	4.76 ±0.40	0.188 ±0.016	10.32 ±0.58	0.406 ±0.023	14.4
5.56	7/32	5.56 ±0.40	0.219 ±0.016	11.11 ±0.58	0.438 ±0.023	14.3
6.35	1/4	6.35 ±0.40	0.250 ±0.016	12.70 ±0.58	0.500 ±0.023	14.2
7.14	9/32	7.14 ±0.40	0.281 ±0.016	13.49 ±0.58	0.531 ±0.023	14.1
7.94	5/16	7.94 ±0.40	0.312 ±0.016	14.29 ±0.58	0.562 ±0.023	14.0
8.73	11/32	8.73 ±0.40	0.344 ±0.016	15.08 ±0.58	0.594 ±0.023	14.0
9.53	3/8	9.53 ±0.40	0.375 ±0.016	15.88 ±0.58	0.625 ±0.023	13.9
11.11	7/16	11.11 ±0.58	0.438 ±0.023	18.26 ±0.79	0.729 ±0.031	13.7
12.7	1/2	12.70 ±0.58	0.500 ±0.023	19.84 ±0.79	0.781 ±0.031	13.5
15.88	5/8	15.88 ±0.79	0.625 ±0.031	23.81 ±0.79	0.938 ±0.031	13.1
19.05	3/4	19.05 ±0.79	0.750 ±0.031	28.58 ±0.79	1.125 ±0.031	12.7
25.40	1	25.40 ±0.79	1.000 ±0.031	34.93 ±1.59	1.375 ±0.062	12.0
31.75	1-1/4	31.75 ±0.99	1.250 ±0.039	Not Specified(3)	Not Specified(3)	11.2
38.10	1-1/2	38.10 ±0.99	1.500 ±0.039	Not Specified(3)	Not Specified(3)	10.4
44.45	1-3/4	44.45 ±0.99	1.750 ±0.039	Not Specified(3)	Not Specified(3)	9.7
50.80	2	50.80 ±0.99	2.000 ±0.039	Not Specified(3)	Not Specified(3)	8.9
57.15	2-1/4	57.15 ±0.99	2.250 ±0.039	Not Specified(3)	Not Specified(3)	8.1
63.50	2-1/2	63.50 ±0.99	2.500 ±0.039	Not Specified(3)	Not Specified(3)	7.4

1. Concentricity based on total indicator reading between the inside bore of the hose and the outer surface of the hose shall not exceed the values given below:
   Sizes 1/4 in and under: 0.762 mm (0.030 in)
   Sizes over 1/4 in up to 1/2 in: 1.016 mm (0.040 in)
   Sizes over 1/2 in: 1.270 mm (0.050 in)
2. These values were determined by the equation:
   A = 15 degrees - K X D
   where:
   A = Maximum out-of-squareness angle
   K = 0.12 degree per mm of diameter (a slope factor derived from linear best-fit previous squareness requirement)
   D = Nominal inside diameter in millimeters
3. The wall gauge for sizes 1-1/4 to 2 in shall be between 4.32 to 5.89 mm (0.17 to 0.22), and for sizes 2-1/4 and 2-1/2 in, between 4.32 to 6.35 mm (0.17 to 0.25 in).

TABLE 8—CUT OR LONG LENGTH TOLERANCES FOR SAE 30R6, SAE 30R7, AND SAE 30R8

Length m	Length in	Precision mm	Precision in	Commercial mm	Commercial in
0-0.3	0–12	±3.0	±0.12	+9.5 - 3.0	+0.38 -0.12
Over 0.31-0.6	Over 12–24	±4.8	±0.19	+ 9.5 - 4.8	+ 0.38 -0.19
Over 0.61-0.9	Over 25–36	±6.3	±0.25	+ 12.7 - 6.3	+ 0.50 -0.25
Over 0.91–1.2	Over 36–48	±9.5	±0.38	+ 12.7 - 9.5	+ 0.50 -0.38
Over 1.21–1.8	Over 48–72	±12.7	±0.50	+ 19.0 - 12.7	+ 0.75 -0.50
Over 1.81	Over 72		±1%		+ 2%

TABLE 9—COLD FLEXIBILITY, PHYSICAL, EXTRACTABLES, AND FUEL PERMEATION PROPERTIES

Specification	Cold Flex IRM 903	Dry Heat Resistance	Oil Resistance IRM 903	Fuel Resistance	Ethanol MOD Fuel Resistance	Extractables	Permeation Maximum Rate/24h(1)(2)	Oxidized Fuel Test
SAE 30R6								
Aging Temperature	100 °C (212 °F)	100 °C (212 °F)	100 °C (212 °F)	23 °C (73 °F)	23 °C (73 °F)			
Cold Temperature	–34 °C (–29 °F)							
Tube								
Tensile Change		–20%	–40%	–45%	–45%	—	—	
Elongation Change		–50%	–40%	–45%	–45%	—	—	
Volume Change		—	–5 to +25%	0 to +50%	0 to +50%	—	—	
Cover								
Tensile Change		–20%	—	—	—	—	—	
Elongation Change		–50%	—	—	—	—	—	
Volume Change		—	0 to +100%	—	—	—	—	
Extractables		—	—	—	—	7.75 gm/m^2	—	
Permeation - Fuel C, 8		—	—	—	—	—	600 gm/m^2	

TABLE 9—COLD FLEXIBILITY, PHYSICAL, EXTRACTABLES, AND FUEL PERMEATION PROPERTIES (continued)

Specification	Cold Flex IRM 903	Dry Heat Resistance	Oil Resistance IRM 903	Fuel Resistance	Ethanol MOD Fuel Resistance	Extractables	Permeation Maximum Rate/24h(1)(2)	Oxidized Fuel Test
Days total								
SAE 30R7								
Aging Temperature	125 °C (257°F)	125 °C (257 °F)	125 °C (257 °F)	23 °C (73 °F)	23 °C (73 °F)			40 °C (104°F)
Cold Temperature	–34 °C (–29 °F)							
Tube								
Tensile Change		–20%	–50%	–45%	–45%	—	—	–35%
Elongation Change		–60%	–50%	–45%	–45%	—	—	–40%
Volume Change		—	–5 to +30%	0 to +50%	0 to +50%	—	—	—
Cover								
Tensile Change		–20%	—	—	—	—	—	—
Elongation Change		–60%	—	—	—	—	—	—
Volume Change		—	0 to +75%	—	—	—	—	—
Extractables		—	—	—	—	5.00 gm/m^2	—	—
Permeation - Fuel C, 8		—	—	—	—	—	550 gm/m^2	—
Days total								
SAE 30R8								
Aging Temperature	150 °C (302 °F)	150 °C (302 °F)	150 °C (302 °F)	23 °C (73 °F)	23 °C (73 °F)			
Cold Temperature	–40 °C (–40 °F)							
Tube								
Tensile Change		–25%	–20%	–35%	35%	—	—	
Elongation Change		–50%	–50%	–35%	–45%	—	—	
Volume Change		—	–5 to +15%	0 to +35%	0 to +40%	—	—	
Cover								
Tensile Change		–25%	—	—	—	—	—	
Elongation Change		–50%	—	—	—	—	—	
Volume Change		—	0 to +15%	—	—	—	—	
Extractables		—	—	—	—	2.50 gm/m^2	—	
Permeation - Fuel C, 8		—	—	—	—	—	200 gm/m^2	
Days total								
SAE 30R9								
Aging Temperature	135 °C (275 °F)	150 °C (302 °F)	150 °C (302 °F)	23 °C (73 °F)	23 °C (73 °F)			40 °C (104 °F)
Cold Temperature	-34 °C (-29 °F)							
Tube								
Tensile Change		—	—	—	-40%	—	—	-30% Max
Elongation Change		—	—	—	-40%	—	—	-20% Max
Volume Change		—	—	+10% Max	0 to +15%	—	—	—
Cover								
Tensile Change		—	+100% Max	—	—	—	—	—
Elongation Change		—	—	—	—	—	—	—
Volume Change		—	—	—	—	—	—	—
Extractables		—	—	—	—	2.5 g/m^2	—	—
Permeation - Fuel C, 8		—	—	—	—	—	15 g/m^2	—
Days total								
SAE 30R10								
Aging Temperature	125 °C (257 °F)	125 °C (257 °F)	150 ^{3}C (302 °F)	23 °C (73 °F)	23 °C (73 ^{3}F)			40 °C (104 °F)
Cold Temperature	–34 °C (–20 °F)	-34 °C (-29 °F)		-34 °C (-29 °F)				
Tube								
Tensile Change		—	—	—	-40%	—	—	–30% Max
Elongation Change		—	—	—	-40%	—	—	–20% Max
Volume Change		—	—	+10% Max	0 to +15%	—	—	—
Cover								
Tensile Change		—	—	—	-40%	—	—	–30% Max
Elongation Change		—	—	—	-40%	—	—	–20% Max
Volume Change		—	—	+10% Max	0 to +15%	—	—	—
Extractables		—	—	—	—	2.5 g/m^2		
Permeation - Fuel C, 8		—	—	—	—	—	Not Required	—
Days total								

1. Total effective length of hose with end plugs inserted shall be 275 mm (10.8 in).
2. A round metal (aluminum or steel) control rod conforming to the dimensions shown in Table 10 for hose sizes 19.05 mm (3/4 in) ID and larger shall be inserted into hose ID as shown in Figure 1. The rod shall be positioned in the end plugs such that it will not contact the hose ID.

6.5 Test Requirements

6.5.1 BURST TEST

6.5.1.1 (30R6). The minimum burst for hose sizes through 9.53 mm (3/8 in) ID shall be 1.72 MPa (250 psi), for hoses over 9.53 mm (3/8 in) ID through 2.54 mm (1 in) ID shall be 1.20 MPa (175 psi), and for hose sizes over 25.40 (1 in) shall be 0.55 MPa (80 psi). These hoses would have maximum working pressures of 0.34 MPa (50 psi), 0.24 MPa (35 psi), and 0.11 MPa (16 psi), respectively.

6.5.1.2 (30R7 and 30R8). The minimum burst for hose sizes through 9.53 mm (3/8 in) ID shall be 1.72 MPa (250 psi) and for sizes over 9.53 (3/8 in) shall be 1.20 MPa (175 psi). These hoses would have maximum working pressures of 0.34 MPa (50 psi) and 0.24 MPa (35 psi), respectively.

6.5.2 VACUUM COLLAPSE TEST. Sizes less than 12.70 mm (1/2 in) ID shall be subjected to 81 kPa (24 in Hg) vacuum. Sizes 12.70 mm (1/2 in) through 25.40 mm (1 in) ID shall be subjected to 34 kPa (10 in Hg) vacuum. This requirement shall not apply to sizes larger than 25.40 mm (1 in) ID. During the vacuum test described, a 1 m (3.28 ft) length of hose or a hose assembly shall be held in a straight line, and no diameter shall decrease by more than 20% during application of vacuum for a minimum of 15 s and not more than 60 s. The vacuum collapse test on preformed parts should be performed on the finished part.

6.5.3 COLD FLEXIBILITY—For straight hose 19.05 mm (3/4 in) ID and under, the whole hose shall be used for this test. Two samples shall be used, one to be unaged and the other immersed in ASTM Oil No. 3 for 70 h at the required temperature (See Table 9). The unaged samples are conditioned at -40 °C ±2 °C (–40 °F ±3.6 °F) for 5 h and then flexed in the cold chamber through 180 degrees from the centerline to a diameter of 10 times the maximum OD of the hose. The aged samples for 30R6 and 30R7 are conditioned at -34 °C ±2 °C (-29.2 °F ±3.6 °F) for 5 h and the aged samples for 30R8 are conditioned at -40 °C ±2 °C (-40 °F ±3.6 °F) for 5 h and then flexed in the cold chamber through 180 degrees from centerline to a diameter of 10 times the maximum OD of the hose. The flexing shall take place within 4 s and the hose must not fracture or show any cracks, checks, or breaks in the tube or cover. Proof pressure of 0.68 MPa (99 psi) may be applied to determine tube damage.

For straight hose over 19.05 mm (3/4 in) ID and all preformed hose, prepare six specimens 100 x 6 mm (4 x 0.25 in) from whole hose wall. One set of three shall be unaged and the other aged in ASTM Oil No. 3 for 70 h at the required temperature (See Table 9). The unaged set shall be conditioned for 5 h at -40 °C ±2 °C (-40 °F ±3.6 °F) in an unrestrained loop positioned between two jaws 50.8 mm (2 in) wide and 63.5 mm (2-1/2 in) apart. The aged samples for 30R6 and 30R7 shall be conditioned for 5 h at -34 °C ±2 °C (-29.2 °F ±3.6 °F) and the aged samples for 30R8 are conditioned for 5 h at -40 °C ±2 °C (-40° F ±3.6 °F) in an unrestrained loop position between two jaws 50.8 mm (2 in) wide and 63.5 mm (2-1/2 in) apart.

After conditioning per ASTM D 380 and while still in the cold chamber, the jaws shall be brought together as rapidly as possible until they are 25.40 mm (1 in) apart. The specimens shall not fracture nor show any cracks, checks, or breaks.

6.5.4 TENSILE STRENGTH AND ELONGATION

a. Original tensile strength of cover: 7.0 MPa (1020 psi) min
b. Original tensile strength of tube: 8.0 MPa (1160 psi) min
c. Original elongation of tube and cover: 200% min

6.5.5 DRY HEAT RESISTANCE—After heat aging per ASTM D 573 for 70 h at the required temperature (See Table 9), the reductions in tensile strength and elongation of specimens taken from the tube and cover shall not exceed the change in values as shown in Table 9.

6.5.6 FUEL RESISTANCE. After 48 h immersion at room temperature, 23 °C ± 2 °C (73 °F ±3.6 °F) per ASTM D 471 in ASTM Reference Fuel C, physical values of specimens taken from the tube shall not exceed the change in values as listed in Table 9.

6.5.7 OIL RESISTANCE—After 70 h immersion at the required temperature (See Table 9) in ASTM Oil No. 3, per ASTM D 471, physical values of specimens taken from the tube and cover shall not exceed the change in values listed in Table 9.

6.5.8 TEST FOR EXTRACTABLES IN HOSE

6.5.8.1 Apparatus and Reagents

6.5.8.1.1 ASTM Fuel C (50 Toluene - 50 isooctane percent by volume).

6.5.8.1.2 Methanol, 99% minimum purity.

6.5.8.1.3 Gooch crucible.

6.5.8.1.4 Glass fiber filter, Grade 934AH.

6.5.8.1.5 Beaker

6.5.8.1.6 Heating unit

6.5.8.1.7 Metal control rod and end plugs (See Figure 1 and Table 10.)

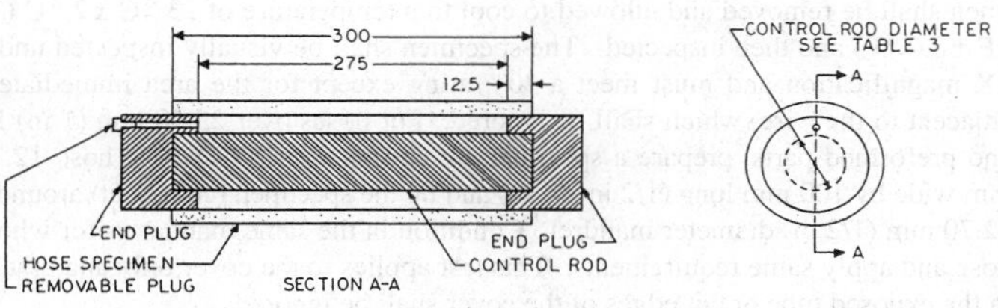

FIGURE 1—TEST FIXTURE FOR EXTRACTABLES

6.5.8.2 Specimens—Hose under test shall be 300 mm (11.8 in) long, plugged at both ends with metal (aluminum or steel) plugs to retain the fluid. Calculate inside surface area based on the actual inside diameter of the hose for its total effective length.

NOTE—Total effective length of hose with end plugs inserted shall be 275 mm (10.8 in).

NOTE—A round metal (aluminum or steel) control rod conforming to the dimensions shown in Table 10 for hose sizes 19.05 mm (3/4 in) ID and larger shall be inserted into hose ID as shown in Figure 1. The rod shall be positioned in the end plugs such that it will not contact the hose ID.

6.5.8.3 Procedure

6.5.8.3.1 Record hose actual inside diameter, length, and inside surface area. Preferred method is with plug ID gauges to nearest 0.025 mm (0.001 in).

6.5.8.3.2 Fill hose with ASTM Fuel C.

6.5.8.3.3 Allow to stand for 24 h at temperature of 23 °C ±2 °C (73 °F ±3.6 °F) with both ends sealed.

NOTE—Solubility of waxy hydrocarbons is affected by temperature.

6.5.8.3.4 Drain fluid from hose into a tared beaker.

6.5.8.3.5 Rinse inside of the specimen with an amount of fresh ASTM Fuel C approximately equal to the volume of the original filling and add to the original extraction.

6.5.8.3.6 Remove solvent by evaporation by heating at 80 to 95 °C (176 to 203 °F) until no fuel odor is detectable and then store sample at room temperature of 23 °C ±2 °C (73 °F ±3.6 °F) under a fume hood for a minimum of 16 h.

6.5.8.3.7 Take up residue with 30 mL of room temperature, 23 °C ±2 °C (73 °F ±3.6 °F), methanol.

6.5.8.3.8 Filter this solution on the tared crucible, rinsing beaker twice with 10 mL of room temperature, 23 °C ±2 °C (73 °F ±3.6 °F), methanol.

6.5.8.3.9 Place crucible in beaker and dry in a 65 to 90 °C (149 to 194 °F) oven to insure complete evaporation of methanol.

TABLE 10—CONTROL ROD DIMENSIONS

Hose Size (Nominal Inside Diameter) mm	Hose Size (Nominal Inside Diameter) in	Control Rod Diameter mm
Below 19.05	N/A	N/A
19.05	3/4	7.8
25.40	1	15.5
31.75	1 1/4	22.4
34.92	1 3/8	25.9
38.10	1 1/2	29.1
44.45	1 3/4	35.6
50.80	2	42.1
57.35	2 1/4	48.6
63.50	2 1/2	55.0

6.5.8.3.10 Weigh the gooch crucible and tared beaker and determine mass of extractables expressed as g/m^2 using surface area of hose in contact with ASTM Fuel C.

6.5.8.4 Value for total g/m^2 shall be values shown in Table 9.

6.5.9 OZONE RESISTANCE—Test procedure and apparatus shall be in accordance with ASTM D 1149, where applicable. For straight hose, 25.40 mm (1 in) ID and under, a specimen of hose of sufficient length shall be bent around a mandrel with OD eight times the nominal OD of the specimen. The two ends shall be tied at their crossing with enameled copper or aluminum wire. After mounting, the specimen shall be allowed to rest in an ozone-free atmosphere for 24 h at room temperature of 23 °C ±2 °C (73 °F ±3.6 °F). The mounted specimen shall be placed in a test chamber with ozone concentration of 100 mPa ± 5 mPa at a temperature of 40 °C ±2 °C (104 °F ±3.6 °F). After 70 h of exposure, the specimen shall be removed and allowed to cool to a temperature of 23 °C ±2 °C (73 °F ±3.6 °F) and then inspected. The specimen shall be visually inspected under 7X magnification and must meet a "0" rating except for the area immediately adjacent to the wire, which shall be ignored. For hoses over 25.40 mm (1 in) ID and preformed parts, prepare a specimen by cutting a strip of whole hose 12.70 mm wide by 100 mm long (1/2 in x 4 in) and tie the specimen (cover out) around a 12.70 mm (1/2 in) diameter mandrel. Condition in the same manner as for whole hose and apply same requirements. This test applies to the cover only and cracks in the exposed tube or cut edges of the cover shall be ignored.

6.5.10 ADHESION TEST—The minimum load required to separate a 25.40 mm (1 in) width of tube and cover shall be 27 N (6 lb).

6.5.11 KINK RESISTANCE—When tested to the following procedure, a ball having a diameter equal to half the nominal inside diameter of the hose shall pass freely through the hose. Use fixture consisting of a 19 mm (0.75 in) thick board or plate with holes and center distances shown in Table 11.

Condition a 300 mm (11.8 in) long specimen of hose for 2 h at room temperature, 23 °C ±2 °C (73 °F ±3.6 °F). Insert one end of hose into board with end flush with opposite side of the board. Carefully bend hose along its natural curvature and insert the other end carefully into the second hole until it projects 63 mm (2.5 in) out the other side. After hose has been in this position for 5 min, insert a steel ball having a diameter equal to half the hose nominal ID. The ball must pass freely from one end to the other.

6.5.12 RATE OF FUEL PERMEATION—Hoses tested by the reservoir method listed as follows shall meet those limits listed in Table 8 when tested with ASTM Fuel C. Exposure to other fuel blends or various fuels (as in sequential fuel testing) could result in significantly different values. Method is shown in Section 9.

6.5.13 ETHANOL MODIFIED FUEL RESISTANCE—After 70 h immersion at room temperature of 23 °C ±2 °C (73 °F ±3.6 °F) per ASTM D 471 using the following test fuel: 85% ASTM Fuel D, 15% anhydrous Denatured Ethanol[4] (denatured with unleaded gasoline per CDA #20), physical values of specimens taken from the tube shall not exceed the changes in values listed in Table 9.

6.5.14 OXIDIZED FUEL TESTING PROCEDURE—Cut three tensile (Die C) specimens for immersion testing per ASTM D 471. No more than three tensile specimens may be immersed per test tube. Each test tube (38 mm diameter by 300 mm long) contains 200 mL of ASTM Fuel "B" to which sufficient tertiarybutyl hydroperoxide has been added to provide a peroxide number, as determined by the method below, of 50. (A well-mixed mixture consisting of 3600 mL of ASTM Fuel "B" and 10 mL of 90% t-butyl hydroperoxide in water will produce a fuel mixture with 50 PN.) All specimen surfaces must be directly exposed to the test liquid. Water-cooled condensers should be attached to the test tubes by non-contaminating means. (Corks, ground glass joints, and foil wrapped rubber stoppers are acceptable.) Place the test tubes in a thermostated environment such that the temperature is maintained at 40 °C ±2 °C. At 1-, 2-, 3-, and 7-day intervals, replace the test fluid with fresh fuel-hydroperoxide (50 PN) mixture. After 14 days of immersion, cool the samples in ASTM Fuel "B". Determine the reduction in tensile strength and elongation per ASTM D 412. The physical values of specimens from the tube shall not exceed the change in values listed in Table 9.

6.5.14.1 Peroxide Number Analytical Method—The peroxide number here is defined as the number of milliequivalents of peroxide per liter of sample solution.

A sample is refluxed 5 min with sodium iodide and acetic acid in dry isopropanol. The liberated iodine is titrated with standardized thiosulfate to the disappearance of the yellow color. The titrant volume is corrected for any titratable substances in the reagents.

6.5.14.2 Apparatus

a. Flasks, Erlenmeyer, with ground joints, 250 mL capacity
b. Condensers, Allihn or Leibig water-cooled type, 300 mm jacket, with joints to fit above flasks
c. Optional—hot plate or equivalent. Equip with rod and clamps to hold condenser
d. Optional—reagent disperser, 25 mL - Convenient for dispensing the acetic acid in isopropanol reagent
e. 10 mL burette with 0.02 mL graduations
f. Optional—electrometric end point apparatus

6.5.14.3 Reagents

a. Acetic acid, glacial, ACS reagent grade, not over 0.5% water by the Karl Fischer method
b. Sodium iodide, ACS reagent grade, granular
c. Isopropyl alcohol, 99%
d. Sodium thiosulfate solution, 0.1 N accurately standardized
e. Sodium iodide, saturated solution in isopropanol. Reflux 22 g NaI in 100 mL isopropanol for a few minutes, cool to room temperature and filter through rapid filter paper. Store in the dark or in a brown reagent bottle. Replace if the solution gives an appreciable blank when titrated with thiosulfate.
f. Acetic acid in isopropanol. Mix 100 mL of glacial acetic acid and 1150 mL of isopropanol.

6.5.14.4 Procedure

a. Add, from an automatic disperser, 25 mL of the acetic acid in isopropanol solution (Reagent 6) to a 250 mL Erlenmeyer flask.
b. Add 10 mL of the saturated NaI in isopropanol solution (Reagent 5) to the flask.
c. With a pipet, quantitatively transfer a 2 mL portion of sample to the Erlenmeyer flask.
d. Connect the flask to the condenser and heat to a gentle boil, reflux for 5 min. The solution should be dark yellow to brown in color.
e. Raise the flask from the hot plate and support it on an asbestos board to cool, or cool in a water bath.
f. Wash down the condenser with 5 mL of water.
g. Disconnect the flask, and titrate with standardized 0.1 N sodium thiosulfate solution to the disappearance of the yellow color, i.e., from a pale yellow to just colorless. (An electrometric end point apparatus may be used.)
h. Simultaneously run a reagent blank by following the above procedure omitting the sample addition in Step c. The titrant volume of the blank should be in the 0.02 to 0.06 mL range.
i. Calculate the peroxide number according to Equation 1.

6.5.14.5 Calculation

$$V_s - V_b)N \times 1000/\ (\text{mL sample}) - \text{Peroxide Number} \quad \text{(Eq. 1)}$$

where:

V_s = volume of titrant consumed by sample, mL
V_b = volume of titrant consumed by blank, mL
N = normality of standardized sodium thiosulfate solution
1000 = conversion mL to liter

4. Available from: Ralph Schrader Company, 3450 Lovett Avenue, Detroit, MI 48210 (or other commercial sources).

TABLE 11—KINK RESISTANCE

Nominal Hose Inside Diameter mm	Nominal Hose Inside Diameter in	Hose Inside Diameter in	Hole Center Distance mm	Hole Center Distance in	Hole Diameter mm	Hole Diameter in
4.76	3/16	0.188	12.7	0.50	12.7	0.500
6.35	1/4	0.250	19	0.75	14.3	0.562
7.94	5/16	0.312	25.4	1.00	15.9	0.625
9.53	3/8	0.375	76.2	3.00	19	0.750
12.70	1/2	0.500	127.0	5.00	23	0.906

6.5.15 Standard Sodium Thiosulfate Solution, 0.1N—Sodium thiosulfate solutions decompose slowly with deposition of sulfur due to bacterial action unless precautions are taken to inhibit bacterial growth. Use of freshly boiled and cooled water in preparation of $Na_2S_2O_3$ solutions and maintaining the pH on the slightly alkaline side usually gives solutions whose factors will remain constant for two to four weeks. Other precautions that can be taken if bacterial growth persists include sterilization of the containers. Glass can be cleaned thoroughly with dichromate-sulfuric acid cleaning solution and rinsed with sterile water. Polyethylene can be washed thoroughly with chloroform and rinsed with sterile water. A few drops of chloroform added to the prepared solution will also aid in preventing bacteria growth.

6.5.15.1 Reagents

a. Sodium thiosulfate, $Na_2S_2O_3 \cdot 5H_2O$, ACS reagent grade
b. Potassium iodide solution, 10%—dissolve 10 g of ACS reagent grade KI in 100 mL of distilled water
c. Sulfuric acid solution, 40%—add 300 mL of concentrated H_2SO_4 slowly with stirring to 750 mL of distilled water
d. Potassium bromate $KBrO_3$, ACS reagent grade

6.5.15.2 Preparation of 0.1N Solution—Dissolve 25 g of $Na_2S_2O_3 \cdot 5H_2O$ in freshly boiled and cooled distilled water and make up to 1 L.

Titrate a 100 mL portion of the solution with 0.1N NaOH solution using phenolphthalein indicator.

Calculate the volume of alkali required to neutralize the remaining solution as follows:

$$\text{mL NaOH} \times \text{N} \times 9 = \text{mL 0.1 N NaOH required} \quad \text{(Eq. 2)}$$

Add the calculated volume of alkali to the remaining solution, mix thoroughly and withdraw 100 mL. Add two or three drops of phenolphthalein indicator solution. The solution should give a slight pink color.

Store the solution in a brown bottle securely capped. Any precautions to protect the solution from air, e.g., sweeping with nitrogen or other inert gas, should be applied. The solution should be standardized at least monthly.

6.5.15.3 Standardization

6.5.15.3.1 Titration of Potassium Bromate—The reaction is as follows:

$$KBrO_3 + 6KI + 3H_2SO_4 \text{--->} 3I_2 + KBr + 3H_2O + 3K_2SO_4$$
$$2Na_2S_2O_3 + I_2 \text{--->} Na_2S_4O_6 + 2NaI$$

Grind a small amount of $KBrO_3$ to a fine powder and dry for 1 h at 180 °C. Weigh to the nearest 0.1 mg 0.015 to 0.25 g of the dried $KBrO_3$ into a 250 mL Erlenmeyer flask. Add 25 mL of distilled water and swirl to dissolve.

Add 2 mL of 10% KI solution and 1 mL of 40% H_2SO_4 solution. Swirl to mix and allow to stand for 2 or 3 min.

Titrate with the $Na_2S_2O_3$ solution, swirling continuously, until the brown color has changed to a pale yellow. Add titrant slowly, dropwise until the yellow color has disappeared and the solution is colorless.

6.5.15.4 Calculation

$$\text{Grams of } KBrO_3 \times 17.9/\ (\text{mL of } Na_2S_2O_3) = \text{N of } Na_2S_2O_3 \text{ solution} \quad \text{(Eq. 3)}$$

Duplicate determination should agree within 0.0003. Report the average of the values found, to the nearest 0.0002, as the normality of the solution.

A number of replicates is advised until the end point change is identified and suitable precision is established.

6.6 Marking—The outer cover will be printed with the designation SAE 30R6, or SAE 30R7, or SAE 30R8 and any other identification as agreed upon between user and manufacturer, repeated every 300 mm (11.8 in).

7. Fuel Injection Hose Medium-Pressure Coupled and Uncoupled Synthetic Rubber Tube and Cover (SAE 30R9)—This section covers hose primarily intended to meet the demands of fuel injection systems. These would include, for example, electronic fuel metering (EFM), electronic fuel injection (EFI), throttle body injection (TBI), and the like. Other areas of utility are those applications requiring fuel permeation resistance exceeding 30R8 and ones which require fuel resistance greater than that obtainable with 30R6, 7, and 8. Exposure of this hose to gasoline or diesel fuel that contains high levels, greater than 5% by volume, of oxygenates, i.e., ethanol, methanol, or MTBE may result in significantly higher permeation rates than realized with ASTM Fuel C. This hose may be supplied in either a coupled or uncoupled form, and is useful in the transportation of gasoline, ethanol extended gasoline, diesel fuel, lubrication oil, or the vapor present in either the fuel system or the crankcase of internal combustion engines in mobile, stationary, and marine applications. This hose has a maximum working pressure of 0.69 MPa (100 psi) up to and including 12.70 mm (1/2 in) ID. This hose may be furnished in long lengths, specific cut lengths, or as a part preformed to a specific configuration. This hose is suitable for use in normal operating temperatures of -34 to 135 °C (-29 to 275 °F) and intermittent use at 150 °C (302 °F).

7.1 Hose Construction—The construction of this hose typically consists of a smooth bore tube or laminated tube[5] of a synthetic rubber compound(s) resistant to chemical attack, swelling, and permeation by gasoline, oxidized ("sour") gasoline, ethanol extended gasoline, diesel fuel, and oil or lubricants. It shall be suitably reinforced with a textile fiber, yarn, cord, or fabric, and a cover of a suitable oil-, ozone-, and heat-resistant elastomer.

7.2 Dimensions and tolerances are shown in Table 12.

7.2.1 When hose is supplied in specific cut or long lengths, the length tolerances shall be as in Table 13.

7.2.1.1 End squareness shall be measured as the angle between a plane intersecting the long and short extremes of the hose end and a plane perpendicular to the hose axis. The allowable maximum out-of-square is specified in Table 14.

5. Laminated tube consists of a thin wall inner tube bonded to an outer tube of a dissimilar material.

TABLE 12—DIMENSIONS AND TOLERANCES FOR SAE 30R9

Nominal Size mm	Nominal Size in	Inside Diameter mm	Inside Diameter in	Outside Diameter(1) mm	Outside Diameter(1) in
6.35	1/4	6.35 ±0.40	0.250 ±0.016	12.70 ±0.58	0.500 ±0.023
7.14	9/32	7.14 ±0.40	0.281 ±0.016	13.49 ±0.58	0.531 ±0.023
7.94	5/16	7.94 ±0.40	0.312 ±0.016	14.29 ±0.58	0.562 ±0.023
8.73	11/32	8.73 ±0.40	0.344 ±0.016	15.08 ±0.58	0.594 ±0.023
9.53	3/8	9.53 ±0.40	0.375 ±0.016	15.88 ±0.58	0.625 ±0.023
11.11	7/16	11.11 ±0.58	0.438 ±0.023	18.26 ±0.79	0.719 ±0.031
12.70	1/2	12.70	0.500 ±0.023	19.84 ±0.79	0.781 ±0.031

1. Concentricity, based on total range of indicator readings between the inside bore of the hose and the outer surface of the hose shall not exceed the following values: Sizes 1/4 in up to 1/2 in: 1.016 mm (0.040 in).

TABLE 13—CUT OR LONG LENGTH TOLERANCES FOR SAE 30R9

Length m	Length in	Precision mm	Precision in	Commercial mm	Commercial in
0–0.3	0–12	±3.0	±0.12	+9.5 –3.0	+0.38 –0.12
Over 0.31-0.6	Over 12–24	±4.8	±0.19	+9.5 –4.8	+0.38 –0.19
Over 0.61–0.9	Over 25–36	±6.3	±0.25	+12.7 –6.3	+0.50 –0.25
Over 0.91–1.2	Over 36–48	±9.5	±0.38	+12.7 –9.5	+0.50 –0.38
Over 1.21–1.8	Over 48–72	±12.7	±0.50	+19.0 –12.7	+0.75 –0.50

TABLE 13—CUT OR LONG LENGTH TOLERANCES FOR SAE 30R9

Length m	Length in	Precision mm	Precision in	Commercial mm	Commercial in
Over 1.81	Over 72		±1%		+2%

TABLE 14—END SQUARENESS

mm	in	Maximum End Out-of-Squareness Angle, Degrees[1]
6.35	1/4	14.2
7.14	9/32	14.1
7.94	5/16	14.0
8.73	11/32	14.0
9.53	3/8	13.9
11.11	7/16	13.7
12.70	1/2	13.5

1. These values were determined by the equation: A = 15 degrees – K x D where:
A = Maximum Out-of-Squareness Angle
K = 0.12 degree per mm of Diameter (A slope factor derived from a linear best-fit line using previous squareness requirements.)
D = Nominal Inside Diameter in mm

7.2.2 When hose is supplied as a preformed item, the tolerances shall be as follows:

7.2.2.1 Arm Lengths—Measured from end to intersection of nearest centerline. Each end shall be as described in 7.2.1. These tolerances apply also to the length of an expanded end.

7.2.2.2 General Layout—Dimensions locating bend intersections are to establish the theoretical centerline of the hose. Actual outside contour of the hose must be held within 4.8 mm (+0.19 in) in all planes with respect to the theoretical outside contour. To check contour, hose ends should first be placed in nominal position (hose may have to be flexed to correct any distortion caused by handling after vulcanization in the producing plant or in shipment) in a checking fixture made in accordance with user requirements from which contour deviation can be measured. Allowance shall be provided in the end mounting area of the fixture for the arm length tolerances which are applicable.

When the ID of an end of the hose is enlarged, the wall gauge of the enlarged end normally changes. Allowable change should be +0.8, -0.5 mm (+0.03, -0.02 in).

7.3 Tests—Procedures described by ASTM D 380 are to be followed wherever applicable.

7.3.1 QUALIFICATION TESTS—For the qualification tests, one 7.5 m (24.6 ft) length of bulk hose, 10 preformed parts, or 10 assemblies of each size to be qualified shall be furnished. In order to qualify under this specification, hose and hose assemblies must meet all the test requirements of 7.4. ASTM test slabs are permissible for testing tube or cover when thickness does not meet ASTM D 412 minimum 1.5 mm (0.060 in).

7.3.2 FREQUENCY OF TESTING FOR INSPECTION—As agreed upon between supplier and user.

7.3.3 INSPECTION TEST—On hose and/or hose assemblies, the following inspection tests shall apply: (7.4.1) burst, (7.4.2) vacuum collapse, (7.4.3) cold flexibility, (7.4.10) adhesion, and (7.4.11) kink resistance, if specified. The kink resistance test shall not normally be required on preformed hose, but may be specified for straight sections of at least 300 mm (11.8 in) length.

7.4 Test Requirements

7.4.1 BURST TEST—The minimum burst for hose sizes through 9.53 mm (3/8 in) ID shall be 6.2 MPa (900 psi). The minimum burst for hose sizes greater than 9.53 mm (3/8 in) ID shall be 3.4 MPa (500 psi). These hoses would have a maximum working pressure of 0.69 MPa (100 psi).

7.4.2 VACUUM COLLAPSE TEST—Test samples shall be subjected to 81 kPa (24 in Hg) vacuum. During the vacuum test described, a 1 m (3.28 ft) length of hose or a hose assembly shall be held in a straight line, and no diameter shall decrease by more than 20% during application of vacuum for a minimum of 15 s and not more than 60 s. The vacuum collapse test on preformed parts should be performed on the finished part.

7.4.3 COLD FLEXIBILITY—For straight hose, the whole hose shall be used for this test. Two samples shall be used. One sample to be dry heat aged for 70 h at the temperature shown in Table 9 and the other completely immersed in ASTM Oil No. 3 for 70 h at the temperature shown in Table 9. After aging, the samples should be conditioned at -34 °C ± 2 °C (-29.2 °F ± 3.6 °F) for 5 h and then flexed in the cold chamber through 180 degrees from the centerline to a diameter of 10 times the maximum OD of the hose. The flexing shall take place within 4 s and the hose must not fracture or show any cracks, checks, or breaks in the tube or cover. Proof pressure of 0.69 MPa (100 psi) may be applied to determine tube damage.

7.4.4 TENSILE STRENGTH AND ELONGATION

a. Original tensile strength of cover: 8 MPa (1160 psi) min
b. Original tensile strength of tube or laminated tube: 5 MPa (725 psi) min
c. Original elongation of cover: 150% min
d. Original elongation of tube or laminated tube: 125% min

NOTE—Laminated tube shall be prepared by buffing the "reinforcement side" of slit specimen to the proper test thickness.

7.4.5 DRY HEAT RESISTANCE—The hose shall show no cracks, charring, or disintegration externally or internally when slowly straightened (taking 4 to 8 s) after being exposed as shown in Figure 2 for a period of 7 days at the required temperature shown in Table 9.

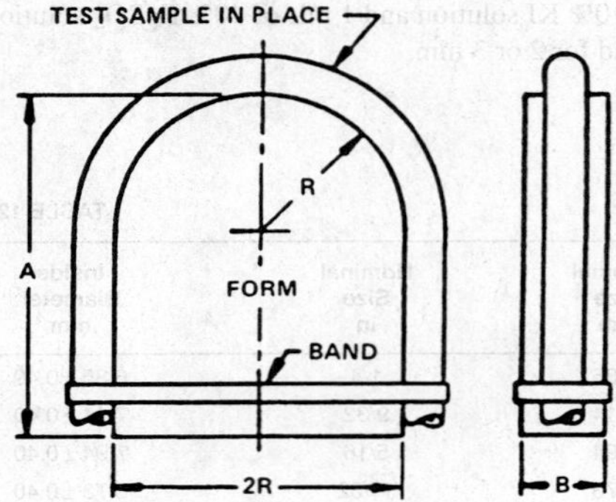

FIGURE 2—TEST SAMPLE ON FORM FOR HEAT AGING TEST (SEE TABLE 15)

7.4.6 FUEL RESISTANCE—After 48 h immersion at room temperature, 23 °C ± 2 °C (73 °F ± 3.6 °F) per ASTM D 471 in ASTM Reference Fuel C, physical values of specimens taken from the tube or from the inner tube when taken from a laminated tube shall not exceed the change in value as listed in Table 9.

NOTE—If a laminated tube is used, the inner tube must be separated and tested alone. If a satisfactory test specimen cannot be provided from inner tube, than a lab prepared test slab is acceptable.

7.4.7 OIL RESISTANCE—After 70 h immersion at 150 °C ± 2 °C (302 °F ± 3.6 °F) in ASTM Oil No. 3 per ASTM D 471, physical values of specimens taken from the cover shall not exceed the change in value as listed in Table 9.

7.4.8 TEST FOR EXTRACTABLES IN HOSE

7.4.8.1 Apparatus and Reagents

7.4.8.1.1 ASTM Reference Fuel C (50 Toluene - 50 isooctane percent by volume)

7.4.8.1.2 Methanol, 99% minimum purity

7.4.8.1.3 Gooch crucible

7.4.8.1.4 Glass fiber filter, Grade 934AH

7.4.8.1.5 Beaker - 100 mL

7.4.8.1.6 Heating unit

7.4.8.2 Specimens—Hose under test shall be 300 mm (11.8 in) long; plugged at both ends with metal (aluminum or steel) plugs to retain the fluid. Calculate inside surface area based on the actual inside diameter of the hose for its total effective length.

NOTE—Total effective length of hose with end plugs inserted shall be 274 mm (10.8 in).

7.4.8.3 Procedure

7.4.8.3.1 Record hose actual inside diameter, length, and inside surface area. Preferred method is with plug gauges to nearest 0.025 mm (0.001 in).

7.4.8.3.2 Fill hose with ASTM Reference Fuel C.

7.4.8.3.3 Allow to stand for 24 h at temperature of 23 °C ±2 °C (73 °F ±3.6 °F) with both ends sealed.

NOTE—Solubility of waxy hydrocarbons is affected by temperature.

7.4.8.3.4 Drain fluid from hose into a tared beaker.

7.4.8.3.5 Rinse inside of the specimen with an amount of fresh ASTM Reference Fuel C approximately equal to the volume of the original filling, and add to the original extraction.

7.4.8.3.6 Remove solvent by evaporation by heating at 80 °C (176 °F) to 95 °C (203 °F) until no fuel odor is detectable and then store sample at room temperature of 23 °C ±2 °C (73 °F ±3.6 °F) under a fume hood for a minimum of 16 h.

7.4.8.3.7 Take up residue with 30 mL of room temperature, 23 °C ±2 °C (73 °F ±3.6 °F), methanol.

7.4.8.3.8 Filter this solution on the tared crucible, rinsing beaker twice with 10 mL of room temperature, 23 °C ±2 °C (73 °F ±3.6 °F), methanol.

7.4.8.3.9 Place crucible in beaker and dry in a 65 to 90 °C (149 to 194 °F) oven for 1 h to insure complete evaporation of methanol.

7.4.8.3.10 Weigh the gooch crucible and tared beaker and determine mass of extractables expressed as g/m^2 using inside surface of hose in contact with ASTM Reference Fuel C.

7.4.8.4 Value for total waxy extractables shall be less than the value in Table 9.

7.4.9 OZONE RESISTANCE—Test procedure and apparatus shall be in accordance with ASTM D 1149, where applicable. For straight hose, sufficient length shall be bent around a mandrel with OD eight times the nominal OD of the specimen. The two ends shall be tied at their crossing with enameled copper or aluminum wire. After mounting, the specimen shall be allowed to rest in an ozone-free atmosphere for 24 h at room temperature of 23 °C ±2 °C (73 °F ±3.6 °F). The mounted specimen shall be placed in a test chamber containing ozone at 100 mPa ±5 mPa at a temperature of 40 °C ±2 °C (104 °F ±3.6 °F). After 70 h of exposure, the specimen shall be removed and allowed to cool to a temperature of 23 °C ±2 °C (73 °F ±3.6 °F) and then inspected. The specimen cover shall be visually inspected under 7X magnification and must meet a "0" rating except for the area immediately adjacent to the wire, which shall be ignored. For preformed parts, prepare a specimen by cutting a strip of hose 12 x 100 mm long (1/2 x 4 in) and tie specimen (cover out) around a 12.0 mm (1/2 in) diameter mandrel. Condition in the same manner as for whole hose and apply same requirements. This test applies to the cover only and cracks in the exposed tube or cut edges of the cover shall be ignored.

7.4.10 ADHESION TEST—The minimum load (force) required to separate a 25.4 mm (1 in) width of tube and cover per ASTM D 413 (strip method) shall be 35.6 N (8 lb). If a laminated tube is used, the adhesion of the inner tube to outer tube shall be a minimum of 35.6 N (8 lb) or be inseparable to the extent that tearing occurs.

7.4.11 KINK RESISTANCE—When tested to the following procedure, a ball having a diameter equal to one-half the nominal inside diameter of the hose shall pass freely through the hose. Use fixture consisting of a 19 mm (0.75 in) thick board or plate with holes and center distances shown in Table 16.

Condition 300 mm (11.8 in) long specimens of hose for 2 h at room temperature 23 °C ±2 °C (73 °F ±3.6 °F). Insert one end of hose into board with end flush with opposite side of the board. Carefully bend hose along its natural curvature and insert the other end carefully into the second hole until it projects 63 mm (2.5 in) out the other side. After hose has been in this position for 5 min, insert a steel ball having a diameter equal to one-half the hose nominal ID. The ball must pass freely from one end to the other.

7.4.12 RATE OF FUEL PERMEATION—Maximum value for fuel permeation shall not exceed limits listed in Table 9 when tested with ASTM Fuel C. If tested with other fuel blends or if exposed to various fuel blends, sequentially, significantly different test results may result. Test method shown in Section 9.

7.4.13 ETHANOL MODIFIED FUEL RESISTANCE—After 70 h immersion at room temperature of 23 °C ±2 °C (73 °F ±3.6 °F) per ASTM D 471 using the following test fuel: 85% ASTM Fuel D, 15% anhydrous Denatured Ethanol[6] (denatured with unleaded gasoline per CDA #20), physical values of specimens taken from lab prepared ASTM test slabs of the tube compound, or inner tube if a laminated tube is used, shall not exceed the change in values listed in Table 9.

7.4.14 OXIDIZED FUEL TEST PROCEDURE—See 6.5.14.

7.4.14.1 Tensile Strength and Elongation—The change in physical values should not exceed the values shown in Table 9.

7.5 Marking—The outer cover will be printed with the designation SAE 30R9 and any other identification as agreed upon between user and manufacturer, repeated every 300 mm (11.8 in).

8. In-Tank, Low-Pressure, Uncoupled Fuel Hoses (SAE 30R10)—This section covers hose intended primarily for use in fuel injection systems where the hose may be submerged in the fuel tank. The hose is capable of handling gasoline, alcohol-extended gasoline or diesel fuel used in mobile, stationary, and marine applications. This hose has a maximum working pressure of 0.69 MPa (100 psi) up to and including 12.7 mm (1/2 in) ID. This hose may be furnished in long lengths, specific cut lengths, or as a part preformed to a specific configuration. This hose is suitable for use in normal operating temperatures of -34 to 100 °C (-29 to 212 °F) and intermittent use at 125 °C (257 °F).

6. Available from: Ralph Schrader Company, 3450 Lovett Avenue, Detroit, MI 48210 (or other commercial sources).

TABLE 15—DIMENSIONS FOR HEATING TEST FORM

Nominal Inside Diameter mm	Nominal Inside Diameter in	Dimensions of Heat Aging Test Form A mm	Dimensions of Heat Aging Test Form R mm	Dimensions of Heat Aging Test Form B min mm
6.35	1/4	115	40	15
7.14	9/32	120	45	20
7.94	5/16	120	45	20
8.73	11/32	120	45	20
9.53	3/8	130	50	20
11.11	7/16	130	50	20
12.70	1/2	130	50	20

TABLE 16—KINK RESISTANCE

Nominal Hose Inside Diameter mm	Nominal Hose Inside Diameter in	Hose Inside Diameter in	Hole Center Distance mm	Hole Center Distance in	Hole Diameter mm	Hole Diameter in
6.3	1/4	0.250	19.0	0.75	14.3	0.562
7.9	5/16	0.312	25.4	1.00	15.9	0.625
9.5	3/8	0.375	76.2	3.00	19.0	0.750
12.7	1/2	0.500	127.0	5.00	23.0	0.906

TABLE 17—LENGTH TOLERANCES FOR IN-TANK, LOW PRESSURE, UNCOUPLED SYNTHETIC RUBBER

Length m	Length in	Precision mm	Precision in	Commercial mm	Commerical in
0–0.3	0–12	±3.0	±0.12	+9.5 –3.0	+0.38 –0.12
Over 0.31–0.6	Over 12–24	±4.8	±0.19	+9.5 –4.8	+0.38 –0.19

8.1 Hose Construction—The construction of this hose consists of a smooth bore tube and cover based on synthetic rubber compound(s) which are resistant to chemical attack or swelling by gasoline, oxidized ("sour") gasoline, alcohol extended gasoline, and diesel fuel. The hose shall be suitably reinforced with a textile fiber, yarn, cord, or fabric which is resistant to the same fuels as the tube and cover.

8.2 Dimensions—Dimensions and tolerances for inside and outside diameters are shown in Table 12.

8.2.1 When hose is supplied in specific cut lengths, the length tolerances shall be as in Table 18.

8.2.1.1 End squareness shall be measured as the angle between a plane intersecting the long and short extremes of the hose end and a plane perpendicular to the hose axis. The allowable maximum out-of-square is specified in Table 14.

8.3 When hose is supplied as a preformed item, the tolerances shall be as follows:

8.3.1 ARM LENGTHS—Measured from end to intersection of nearest centerline. Each end shall be as described in 8.2.1. These tolerances apply also to the length of an expanded end.

8.3.2 GENERAL LAYOUT—Dimensions locating bend intersections are to establish the theoretical centerline of the hose. Actual outside contour of the hose must be held within 4.8 mm (+0.19 in) in all planes with respect to the theoretical outside contour. To check contour, hose ends should first be placed in nominal position (hose may have to be flexed to correct any distortion caused by handling after vulcanization in the producing plant or in shipment) in a checking fixture made in accordance with user requirements from which contour deviation can be measured. Allowance shall be provided in the end mounting area of the fixture for the arm length tolerances which are applicable.

When the ID of an end of the hose is enlarged, the wall gauge of the enlarged end normally changes. Allowable change should be +0.8, -0.5 mm (+0.03, -0.02 in).

8.4 Tests—Procedures described by ASTM D 380, Methods of Testing Rubber Hose, are to be followed wherever applicable.

8.4.1 QUALIFICATION TESTS—For the qualification tests, one 7.5 m (24.6 ft) length of bulk hose, 10 preformed parts, or 10 assemblies of each size to be qualified shall be furnished. To qualify under this specification, hose and hose assemblies must meet all the test requirements of 8.5. ASTM test slabs are permissible for testing tube or cover when thickness does not meet ASTM D 412 minimum 1.5 mm (0.060 in).

8.4.2 FREQUENCY OF TESTING FOR INSPECTION—As agreed upon between supplier and user.

8.4.3 INSPECTION TEST—On hose and/or hose assemblies, the following inspection tests shall apply: (8.5.1) burst, (8.5.2) cold flexibility, (8.5.8) adhesion, (8.5.9) kink resistance, if specified. The kink resistance test shall not normally be required on preformed hose, but may be specified for straight sections of at least 300 mm (11.8 in) length.

8.5 Test Requirements

8.5.1 BURST TEST—The minimum burst for hose sizes through 9.53 mm (3/8 in) ID shall be 3.4 MPa (500 psi). The minimum burst for hose sizes greater than 9.53 mm (3/8 in) ID shall be 2.8 MPa (400 psi). These hoses would have a maximum working pressure of 0.69 MPa (100 psi).

8.5.2 COLD FLEXIBILITY—For straight hose, the whole hose shall be used for this test. Two samples shall be used. One sample to be dry heat aged for 70 h at the temperature shown in Table 9 and the other completely immersed in Fuel C for 70 h at 23 °C ± 2 °C (73 °F ± 3.6 °F). Following immersion in Fuel C, dry out samples for 24 h at 23 °C (73 °F). After aging, the samples should be conditioned at -34 °C ± 2 °C (-29.2 °F ± 3.6 °F) for 5 h and then flexed in the cold chamber through 180 degrees from the centerline to a diameter of 10 times the maximum OD of the hose. The flexing shall take place within 4 s and the hose must not fracture or show any cracks, checks, or breaks in the tube or cover. Proof pressure of 0.69 MPa (100 psi) may be applied to determine tube damage.

8.5.3 TENSILE STRENGTH AND ELONGATION

8.5.3.1 Original Tensile Strength of Tube and Cover—7 MPa (1015 psi) min.

8.5.3.2 Original Elongation of Tube and Cover—200% min.

8.5.4 DRY HEAT RESISTANCE

8.5.4.1 The hose shall show no cracks, charring or disintegration externally or internally when slowly straightened (taking 4 to 8 s) after being exposed, as shown in Figure 5, for a period of 7 days at the temperature shown in Table 9.

8.5.4.2 Age samples of hose for 48 h at room temperature, 23 °C ± 2 °C (73 °F ± 3.6 °F) per ASTM D 471 in ASTM Reference Fuel C, remove from fluid, dry, then age in dry heat per 8.5.4.1 for 70 h at the temperature shown in Table 9. After aging, hose shall show no cracks, charring, or disintegration externally or internally when slowly straightened (taking 4 to 8 s).

8.5.5 FUEL RESISTANCE

8.5.5.1 After 48 h immersion at room temperature, 23 °C ± 2 °C (73 °F ± 3.6 °F) per ASTM D 471 in ASTM Reference Fuel C, physical values of specimens taken from the tube and cover shall not exceed the change in value as listed in Table 9.

8.5.5.2 Samples of finished hose shall be immersed in ASTM Reference Fuel C for 48 h at 23 °C ± 2 °C (73 °F ± 3.6 °F) per ASTM D 471. After aging, the hose shall pass the burst test per 8.5.1.

8.5.6 TEST FOR EXTRACTABLES IN HOSE

8.5.6.1 Apparatus and Reagents

8.5.6.1.1 ASTM Reference Fuel C (50 Toluene - 50 isooctane percent by volume)

8.5.6.1.2 Methanol, 99% minimum purity

8.5.6.1.3 Gooch crucible

8.5.6.1.4 Glass fiber filter, Grade 934AH

8.5.6.1.5 Beaker - 100 mL

8.5.6.1.6 Heating unit

8.5.6.2 Specimens—Hose under test shall be 300 mm (11.8 in) long; plugged at both ends with metal (aluminum or steel) plugs to retain the fluid. Calculate inside surface area based on the actual inside diameter of the hose for its total effective length.

NOTE—Total effective length of hose with end plugs inserted shall be 274 mm (10.8 in).

8.5.6.3 Procedure

8.5.6.3.1 Record hose actual inside diameter, length, and inside surface area. Preferred method is with plug gauges to nearest 0.025 mm (0.001 in).

8.5.6.3.2 Fill hose with ASTM Reference Fuel C.

8.5.6.3.3 Allow to stand for 24 h at temperature of 23 °C ± 2 °C (73 °F ± 3.6 °F) with both ends sealed.

NOTE—Solubility of waxy hydrocarbons is affected by temperature.

8.5.6.3.4 Drain fluid from hose into a tared beaker.

8.5.6.3.5 Rinse inside of the specimen with an amount of fresh Reference Fuel C approximately equal to the volume of the original filling, and add to the original extraction.

8.5.6.3.6 Remove solvent by evaporation by heating at 80 °C (176 °F) to 95 °C (203 °F) until no fuel odor is detectable and then store sample at room temperature of 23 °C ±2 °C (73 °F ±3.6 °F) under a fume hood for a minimum of 16 h.

8.5.6.3.7 Take up residue with 30 mL of room temperature 23 °C ± 2 °C (73 °F ±3.6 °F) methanol.

8.5.6.3.8 Filter this solution on the tared crucible, rinsing beaker twice with 10 mL of room temperature 23 °C ±2 °C (73 °F ±3.6 °F) methanol.

8.5.6.3.9 Place crucible in beaker and dry in a 65 to 90 °C (149 to 194 °F) oven for 1 h to insure complete evaporation of methanol.

8.5.6.3.10 Weigh the gooch crucible and tared beaker and determine mass of extractables expressed as g/m^2 using inside surface area of hose in contact with Reference Fuel C.

8.5.6.4 Value for total waxy extractables shall be less than the value shown in Table 9.

8.5.7 OZONE RESISTANCE—Not required.

8.5.8 ADHESION TEST—The minimum load (force) required to separate a 25.4 mm (1 in) width of tube and cover per ASTM D 413 (strip method) shall be 35.6 N (8 lb).

8.5.9 KINK RESISTANCE—When tested to the following procedure, a ball having a diameter equal to 1/2 the nominal inside diameter of the hose shall pass freely through the hose. Use fixture consisting of a 19 mm (0.75 in) thick board or plate with holes and center distances shown in Table 16.

Condition 300 mm (11.8 in) long specimens of hose for 2 h at room temperature 23 °C ±2 °C (73 °F ±3.6 °F). Insert one end of hose into board with end flush with opposite side of the board. Carefully bend hose along its natural curvature and insert the other end carefully into the second hole until it projects 63 mm (2.5 in) out the other side. After hose has been in this position for 5 min, insert a steel ball having a diameter equal to 1/2 the hose nominal ID. The ball must pass freely from one end to the other.

8.5.10 ALCOHOL MODIFIED FUEL RESISTANCE

8.5.10.1 After 70 h immersion at room temperature of 23 °C ±2 °C (73 °F ± 3.6 °F) per ASTM D 471 using the following test fuel: 85% ASTM Fuel D, 15% anhydrous methanol[7], physical values of specimens taken from the tube and cover shall not exceed the change in values listed as shown in Table 9.

8.5.10.2 Samples of finished hose shall be immersed in the methanol fuel described in 8.5.10.1 for 70 h at 23 °C ±2 °C (73 °F ±3.6 °F) per ASTM D 471. After aging, the hose shall pass the burst test per 8.5.1.

8.5.11 OXIDIZED GASOLINE (GASOLINE CONTAINING HYDROPEROXIDE)—Samples shall be tested according to the procedure described in 6.5.14. After aging, the physical values of the tube and cover shall not exceed the values as shown in Table 9.

8.6 Marking—The outer cover will be printed with the designation SAE 30R10 and any other identification as agreed upon between user and manufacturer, repeated every 300 mm (11.8 in).

9. Unified Method for Fuel Hose Permeation

9.1 Rate of Fuel Permeation—Hoses tested by the reservoir method meet those limits listed in Table 9 when tested with Fuel C. Exposure of these hoses to gasoline or diesel fuel which contain high levels, greater than 5% by volume, of oxygenates, i.e., ethanol, methanol, or MTBE (methyl tertiary butyl ether), may result in significantly higher permeation rates than those listed in Table 9.

9.1.1 RESERVOIR UNITS—See Table 18 for size of reservoir. A screw-top can may be modified by the addition of a standard hose nipple, or fitting, cold soldered into the base at the corner opposite its opening. See Figure 3 for typical equipment. Other types of reservoir units may be used. Examples are cylindrical aluminum and steel containers with appropriate standard hose nipples at one end, and a fill opening if required at the other end. The materials used for construction of the reservoirs should be compatible with the test fuel.

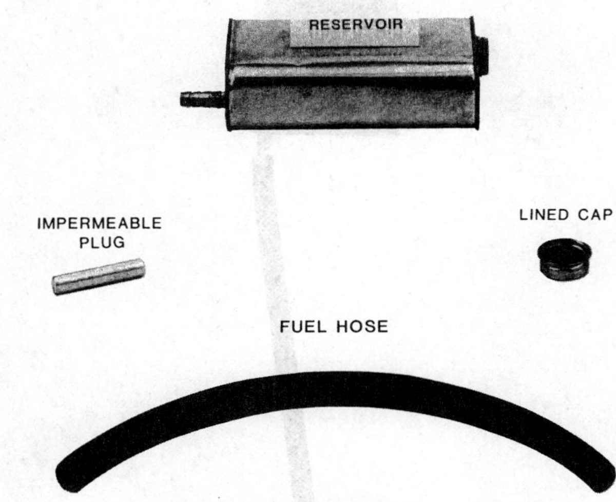

FIGURE 3—FUEL PERMEATION TEST APPARATUS

9.1.2 SCREW CAP—A metal foil or fluoroelastomer-lined cap to seal the reservoir unit. Where the threaded fill opening is designed to seal with an O-ring, a fluoroelastomer O-ring shall be used. The threaded fill opening may be either a female or male thread and sealed with a threaded male plug or female cap.

9.1.3 SCALE OR BALANCE—A weighing unit with sufficient capacity to weigh the filled assemblies, and with a resolution of ±0.01 g.

9.1.4 IMPERMEABLE PLUG—An impermeable plug of sufficient size to seal one end of the hose to a depth of 25 mm.

9.1.5 HOSE CLAMPS—Standard hose clamps of the correct size for the hose being tested.

9.2 Procedure

a. Cut hose to the required length (active length plus the fitting lengths). See Table 18.
b. Measure the inside diameter of the hose and record in mm.
c. Plug one end of hose to the required depth using an impermeable plug and hose clamp.
d. Attach the other end of hose to the fitting on the reservoir and clamp.
e. Measure the active or exposed length of the installed hose in mm and record.
f. Fill the reservoir with the specified amount (see Table 18) of desired fuel blend.
g. Seal reservoir with cap or plug.
h. Weigh reservoir assembly to the nearest 0.01 g and record.
i. To insure complete filling of the hose, orient assembly vertically and gently tap hose to eliminate the possibility of trapped air in the hose. See Figure 4.

7. Reagent grade.

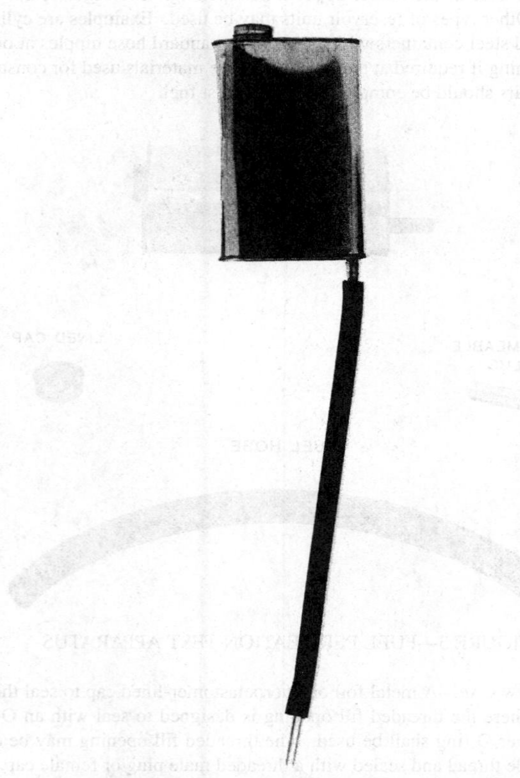

FIGURE 4—FUEL PERMEATION TEST—AIR BUBBLE REMOVAL POSITION

j. Place assembly with the hose horizontal in its storage position for liquid permeation (Figure 5).
k. Weigh the assembly each 24 h ±0.5 h for the required time interval and record each value.
l. After each weighing, invert assembly to drain hose, gently mix fuel, and refill hose as in step i and replace in storage position.
m. Calculate the exposed tube area (A) in m^2: A = L(mm) x ID(mm) x 3.14 x 10^{-6}.
n. Calculate the rate of fuel permeation in terms of $g/m^2/24$ h of exposed tube area on a daily basis.

10. Low Permeation Fuel Fill, Vent, and Vapor Hose (SAE 30R11)—This section covers the minimum requirements for a low permeation hose (100 g/m^2/ day or less) for use as a low pressure (14.5 kPa) liquid or vapor carrying component for use in gasoline or diesel fuel filler, vent, and vapor systems. The construction shall be designed to be functional over a temperature range of –40 °C to 100 °C for T1 designation, or –40 °C to 125 °C for the T2 designation.

FIGURE 5—FUEL PERMEATION RESERVOIR TEST—ASSEMBLY STORAGE POSITION

10.1 Hose Construction—The construction typically consists of a smooth bore or laminated tube of one or more synthetic rubber compound(s) and/or thermoplastic material(s) resistant to chemical attack, swelling, and permeation by gasoline, alcohol extended gasoline, or diesel fuel. It will be suitably reinforced with a textile fiber, yarn, cord, or fabric. It will also be covered with a suitable oil, ozone, and heat-resistant synthetic rubber compound and/or thermoplastic. The specific construction details are to be agreed between the supplier and the original purchaser.

10.2 Dimensions

10.2.1 The ends of the hose shall be square within 3.0 mm for sizes up to but excluding 25.4 mm ID, 6.4 mm for sizes 25.4 mm through 50.8 mm ID, and 9.5 mm for sizes over 50.8 mm ID. Reference Table 19.

10.2.2 When hose is supplied in specific cut or long lengths, the length tolerances shall be as in Table 20.

TABLE 18—TEST PIECE SIZE PARAMETERS

Inside Diameter of Test Hose mm	Active Length of Test Hose mm	Reservoir Size in mL	Fuel Fill Amount mL
≤16.0	300	460 – 490	300
>16.0 to 25.0	300	940 – 1000	750
>25.0 to 32.0	300	3750 – 4000	2500
>32.0	150	3750 – 4000	2500

NOTE 1—Storage location should be temperature controlled to 23 °C ±2 °C (73 °F ±3.6 °F) with free-flowing air to prevent fume buildup.

NOTE 2—If weekend weighings are to be eliminated and the results averaged for the weekends, then the test must be started on a Monday.

10.2.3 End squareness shall be measured as the angle between a plane intersecting the long and short extremes of the hose end and a plane perpendicular to the hose axis. The allowable maximum out-of-squareness is specified in Table 19.

10.3 When a hose is supplied as a preformed item, the tolerance shall be as follows:

10.3.1 SQUARENESS OF ENDS—The tolerance on squareness of ends of preformed parts shall be a minimum 15% of the nominal hose OD on all sizes though 25.4 mm ID, 6.3 mm for sizes over 25.4 mm ID through 50.8 mm ID and 9.5 mm for sizes over 50.8 mm ID. End squareness shall be measured as described in 10.2.1.

10.3.2 ARMS LENGTHS—Measured from end to intersection of nearest centerline. Each end shall be as described in 10.2. These tolerances apply also to the length of an expanded end.

10.3.3 GENERAL LAYOUT—Dimensions locating bend intersections are to establish the theoretical centerline of the hose. Actual outside contour of the hose must be held within 4.8 mm in all planes with respect to the theoretical outside contour. To check contour, hose ends should first be placed in nominal position (it may have to be flexed to correct any distortion caused by handling after vulcanization in the producing plant or in shipment) in a checking fixture made in accordance with user requirements from which contour deviation can be measured. Allowance shall be provided in the end mounting area of the fixture for the arm length tolerances which are applicable.

When the ID of an end of the hose is enlarged, the wall gauge of the enlarged end normally changes. Allowable change should be +0.8/–0.5 mm. The wall gauge within bends of a preformed hose may differ from the gauge in straight portions. The difference shall not exceed 33%.

10.4 Tests—Procedures described by ASTM D 380 are to be followed. All temperature tolerances are ±2 °C unless otherwise specified.

10.4.1 QUALIFICATION TESTING—In order to qualify under this specification, hose or the assembly must meet all the applicable test requirements of 10.5. Hose for testing will be 12.7 mm ID or as agreed upon between supplier and user. The construction must be representative of construction of all other sizes. The impermeable layer thickness cannot be reduced with other data.

TABLE 19—DIMENSIONS AND TOLERANCES FOR SAE 30R11

Nominal Size mm	Inside Diameter mm	Outside Diameter(1) mm	End Out-of Squareness Angles, Deg(2)
4.0	4.0 ± 0.4	9.1 ± 0.6	14.5
4.8	4.8 ± 0.4	10.3 ± 0.6	14.4
5.6	5.6 ± 0.4	11.1 ± 0.6	14.3
6.4	6.4 ± 0.4	12.7 ± 0.6	14.2
7.0	7.0 ± 0.4	13.5 ± 0.6	14.1
7.9	7.9 ± 0.4	14.3 ± 0.6	14.0
8.7	8.7 ± 0.4	15.1 ± 0.6	14.0
9.5	9.5 ± 0.4	15.9 ± 0.6	13.9
11.1	11.1 ± 0.6	18.3 ± 0.8	13.7
12.7	12.7 ± 0.6	19.8 ± 0.8	13.5
15.9	15.9 ± 0.8	23.8 ± 0.8	13.1
19.1	19.1 ± 0.8	28.6 ± 0.8	12.7

TABLE 19—DIMENSIONS AND TOLERANCES FOR SAE 30R11

Nominal Size mm	Inside Diameter mm	Outside Diameter(1) mm	End Out-of Squareness Angles, Deg(2)
25.4	25.4 ± 0.8	34.9 ± 1.6	12.0
31.8	31.8 ± 1.0	not specified(3)	11.2
38.1	38.1 ± 1.0	not specified(3)	10.4
44.5	44.5 ± 1.0	not specified(3)	9.7
50.8	50.8 ± 1.0	not specified(3)	8.9
57.2	57.2 ± 1.0	not specified(3)	8.1
63.5	63.5 ± 1.0	not specified(3)	7.4

1. Concentricity based on total indicator reading between the inside bore and the outer surface of the hose or tube shall not exceed the values given as follows:
   Sizes 6.4 mm and under: 0.762 mm
   Sizes over 6.4 mm up to 12.7 mm: 1.016 mm
   Sizes over 12.7 mm: 1.270 mm
2. These values were determined by the equation:
   A = 15 degrees – K X D
   where:
   A = Maximum out-of-squareness angle
   K = 0.12 degree per mm of diameter (a slope factor derived from linear best-fit previous squareness requirement)
   D = Nominal inside diameter in millimeters
3. The wall gauge for sizes 31.8 mm to 50.8 mm shall be between 4.3 to 5.9 mm, and for sizes 57.2 mm to 63.5 mm, between 4.3 to 6.4 mm

TABLE 20—CUT OR LONG LENGTH TOLERANCES FOR SAE 30R11

Length m	Precision mm	Commercial mm
0–0.3	±3.0	+9.5/–3.0
over 0.3–0.6	±4.8	+9.5/–4.8
over 0.6–0.9	±6.3	+12.7/–6.3
over 0.9–1.2	±9.5	+12.7/–9.5
over 1.2–1.8	±12.7	+19.0/–12.7
over 1.8	±1%	+2%/0%

10.4.2 FREQUENCY OF TESTING FOR QUALIFICATION—Qualification testing to be performed once annually except for permeation testing which only needs to be tested intially.

10.4.3 INSPECTION TESTING—On hose or the assembly, the following inspection shall apply: (10.5.1) burst, (10.5.2), vacuum collapse, (10.5.11.1), original adhesion, (10.5.12), kink resistance, and (10.5.6), electrical conductivity (if required).

10.4.4 FREQUENCY OF TESTING FOR INSPECTION AND QUALITY ACCEPTANCE STANDARDS—Quality acceptance standards to be agreed upon between supplier and the original purchaser.

10.5 Test Requirements

10.5.1 BURST TEST (INSPECTION TEST ON ALL SIZES)—The minimum burst shall be 1.20 MPa per ASTM D 380.

10.5.2 VACUUM COLLAPSE TEST (INSPECTION TEST ON ALL SIZES)—For straight hose, a 1 m length of hose or the assembly shall be held in a straight line. On preformed parts, the vacuum collapse test shall be performed on the finished part. No diameter shall decrease by more than 20% during application of vacuum for a minimum of 15 s and not more than 60 s. Hose sizes as listed in Table 20 shall be subjected to the corresponding vacuum pressure.

10.5.3 LOW TEMPERATURE FLEXIBILITY (QUALIFICATION TEST)—Fill hose with Reference Fuel C and seal both ends. Allow it to condition at 23 °C for 168 h. Drain the fuel. Immediately expose the hose along with a mandrel that is 10 times the nominal ID to a temperature of –40 °C for 24 h. Bend the hose or sample around the mandrel while keeping both at the prescribed temperature. It shall not fracture and shall not show cracks, checks, or breaks in any of the layers of construction.

10.5.4 ORIGINAL MATERIAL PROPERTIES (QUALIFICATION TEST)—The test procedure and apparatus shall be accordance with ASTM D 412, where applicable.

a. Original tensile strength of cover: 7 MPa min
b. Original tensile strength of tube or laminated tube: 7 MPa min
c. Original elongation of cover: 150% min
d. Original elongation of tube or laminated tube: 150% min

NOTE—Test sample shall be prepared by buffing or skiving the "reinforcement side" of the specimen to the proper test thickness.

10.5.5 HEAT RESISTANCE (QUALIFICATION TEST)—Expose a 300 mm length hose for 1000 h at the prescribed test temperature. The test temperature for a T1 construction is 100 °C and 125 °C for the T2 construction. Remove the hose from the oven and allow it to cool to room temperature for a minimum of 2 h. Bend it over a mandrel having a diameter of 10 times the nominal OD within 4 s. Examine it, both inside and outside. The hose shall show no cracks or breaks.

10.5.6 ELECTRICAL CONDUCTIVITY (INSPECITON TEST ON ALL SIZES)—The purpose is to provide a conductive pathway to dissipate any static electrical buildup. **<u>This test is required only for hose that will be designated as electrically conductive.</u>**

An entire hose (maximum length 610 mm) will be used for this test, unless its length exceeds 610 mm, at which time the length for test shall be 610 mm. Insert a brass, steel, or copper plug or fitting into each end. Place clamps on each end of the hose and firmly tighten. Attach the ohmmeter electrodes to the plugs at each end. Measure the resistance between the plugs while applying 550 V DC (±50 V). The maximum resistance allowable is 10 MΩ.

NOTE 1—The diameter of the plug or fitting should be close to the ID of the hose.

NOTE 2—The hose while under test should be placed on a nonconductive surface.

NOTE 3—Ohmmeter must have the capability of measuring resistance from 10^{-1} to 10^3 MΩ at 550 V DC.

10.5.7 OIL RESISTANCE (QUALIFICATION TEST)—After immersion in IRM 903 oil for 70 h at 125 °C per ASTM D 471, the volume change of a sample taken from the hose cover shall not exceed +60%.

10.5.8 FUEL RESISTANCE (QUALIFICATION TEST)—After immersion in ASTM Reference Fuel C for 48 h at 23 °C per ASTM D 471, the physical values of the specimens taken from the tube or inner tube, when taken from a laminated tube, shall not exceed the change in value as follows:

a. Tensile Change:–45% max
b. Elongation Change:–45% max
c. Volume Change:0 to 50%

NOTE—If a laminated tube is used, the inner tube must be separated and tested alone. If a satisfactory test specimen cannot be provided from the inner tube, then a lab prepared test slab is acceptable.

10.5.9 TEST FOR EXTRACTABLES IN HOSE (QUALIFICATION TEST)—Use the procedure described in 6.5.8. Value for total waxy extractables shall be less than 2.50 g/m^2.

10.5.10 OZONE RESISTANCE (QUALIFICATION TEST)—Use the procedure described in 6.5.9. The specimen cover shall be visually inspected under 7X magnificaiton and must meet a "0" rating except for the area immediately adjacent to the wire, which shall be ignored.

NOTE—This test applies to the cover only and cracks in the exposed tube or cut edges of the cover shall be ignored.

10.5.11 ADHESION

10.5.11.1 Original Adhesion (Inspection Test on All Sizes)—Cut out 25 mm samples out of the hose in the transverse direction. The number of samples to be tested is dependant on the construction of the hose but should be enough to test the adhesion between all adjacent layers. When tested in accordance with ASTM D413, Machine Method, Strip Specimen - Type A, 180° Peel, the minimum force required to separate the two layers shall be 1 N/mm or stock tear.

10.5.11.2 Aged Adhesion (Qualification Test)

a. Sample conditioning
   1. Use hose or tube from the permeation test (10.5.13)
   2. Alternate method
      Plug one end of the hose or tube to be tested. Fill with test fuel CM15.
      Plug the other end of the hose or tube in such a manner that it can be periodically removed.
      Expose the filled hose to a temperature of 40 °C for 1000 h continuously. Change the fuel every 168 h.

TABLE 21—VACUUM COLLAPSE PRESSURE FOR SAE 30R11

Hose ID Size	Vacuum Pressure
<12.7 mm	81 kPa
12.7 to 25.4 mm	34 kPa
>25.4 to 44.5 mm	14.3 kPa
>44.5 mm	Limit to be agreed upon between supplier and manufacturer

TABLE 22—MARKING FOR SAE 30R11

"X" Designation	Permeation Range	"Y" Designation	Electrical Conductivity	"Z" Designation	Temperature
A	0 to 25	E	Conductive	T1	100 °C
B	25 to 50	N	Non-conductive	T2	125 °C
C	50 to 100				

b. Cut 25 mm samples out of the hose in the transverse direction. The number of samples to be tested is dependant on the construction but should be enough to test the adhesion between all adjacent layers.
c. Condition the test samples in a 70 °C oven for 24 h followed by 2 h at 23 °C.
d. Test for adhesion in accordance with ASTM D 413, Machine Method, Strip Specimen-Type A, 180° Peel, the minimum force required to separate the two layers shall be 1.0 N/mm or stock tear.

10.5.12 KINK RESISTANCE (INSPECTION TEST ON ALL APPLICABLE SIZES)

NOTE—<u>This test is not applicable for hose over 12.7 mm ID nor for formed hose</u>. Use test procedure described in 6.5.11. The ball must pass freely from one end to the other.

10.5.13 PERMEATION RESISTANCE—(Initial Qualification Test only)

NOTE—<u>After completion of this test, save hose or tube if performing adhesion testing</u>.

a. Test Method—The test procedure and apparatus shall be in accordance with SAE J1737.
b. Test Conditions—CM15 will be used as the fuel source at a temperature of 40 °C and a pressure of 14.5 kPa. The suggested ID is 12.7 mm and the construction shall be representative of planned production hose or tube.
c. Precondition the hose or tube for 664 h at 40 °C, changing the fuel every 168 h followed immediately by permeation testing for a minimum of 336 h at 40 °C.
d. A minimum of 3 specimens must be tested by this procedure. The median of the three measurements shall be used to describe the permeation rate.
e. Units reported from the measurement shall be grams/meter^2/day and shall be reported as a whole number by following all the guidelines of 8.3 of SAE J1737.

10.6 Marking—The outer cover will be printed with the designation SAE 30R11XYTZ along with any other identification agreed upon between user and manufacturer, repeated every 300 mm. The "X" designation (Table 22) shall indicate the range that the permeation rate falls within. The "Y" designation will be either "E" for electrically conductive hose or "N" for non-conductive hose or tube. The "Z" designation will be either 1 for 100 °C heat resistance or 2 for 125 °C heat resistance.

NOTE—Some examples of the markings follow:

SAE 30R11ANT1 This hose is designed to meet the 0 to 25 g/m^2/day permeation range. It will meet the 100 °C heat requirement and is not electrically conductive.

SAE 30R11ANT2 This hose is designed to meet the 0 to 25 g/m^2/day permeation range. It will meet the 125 °C heat requirement and is not electrically conductive.

SAE 30R11AET2 This hose is designed to meet the 0 to 25 g/m^2/day permeation range. It will meet the 125 °C heat requirement and is electrically conductive.

11. Low Permeation Fuel Feed and Return Hose (SAE 30R12)—This section covers the minimum requirements for low permeation reinforced hose suitable for use in fuel supply systems including fuel injection systems. This section applies to hose with an elastomeric inner layer. Hose with a thermoplastic inner layer is specifically excluded.

Low permeation hose, for the purpose of SAE 30R12, is defined as hose having a permeation rate less than 100 g/m^2/day by method SAE J1737 when tested with CM15 fuel at 60 °C.

This hose is intended for use as fuel feed and return hose in applications where low levels of evaporative emissions are required. This hose is useful in this and other applications for the transportation of gasoline, ethanol or methanol extended gasoline, reformulated gasoline (RFG), alcohol fuel, diesel fuel, lubrication oil, or the vapor present in either the fuel system or the crankcase of internal combustion engines in mobile, stationary, and marine applications. This hose has a maximum working pressure of 1.0 MPa (145 psi).

This section covers hose suitable for use in four categories of operating temperature ranges. Category T1 hose is suitable for use in a normal operating temperature range from –40 °C to 100 °C; Category T2 hose is suitable for use in a normal operating temperature range from –40 °C to 125 °C; Category T3 hose is suitable for use in a normal operating temperature range from –40 °C to 135 °C; and Category T4 hose is suitable for use in a normal operating temperature range from –40 °C to 150 °C.

This hose may be furnished in long lengths, specific cut lengths, or as a part preformed to a specific configuration.

11.1 Hose Construction—The construction of this hose typically consists of a smooth bore tube with an internal diameter below 13 mm (0.5 inch) which is resistant to chemical attack, swelling and permeation by gasoline, oxidized ("sour") gasoline, alcohol extended gasoline, reformulated gasoline (RFG), alcohol fuels, diesel fuel and oil or lubricants. The tube may be composed of a single elastomeric material or be a laminated construction of two or more synthetic rubber compounds and/or thermoplastic materials provided the innermost layer is an elastomeric layer. The tube shall be suitably reinforced with a textile fiber, yarn, cord or fabric and covered with an oil, ozone, and heat-resistant elastomer.

11.2 Dimensions and Tolerances

11.2.1 Recommended dimensions and tolerances are the same as those for SAE J30R9 hose shown in Table 12, 7.2. Maximum recommended size for 30R12 hose is 13 mm (0.5 in) ID. However, it is not the intent of this section to exclude hose with different dimensions that comply with all other requirements of this document. Other dimensions and sizes are acceptable if agreed upon between buyer and seller.

11.2.1.1 When hose is supplied in specific cut or long lengths, the length tolerances shall be as in Table 13, 7.2.1.

11.2.1.2 End squareness shall be measured as the angle between a plane intersecting the long and short extremes of the hose end and a plane perpendicular to the hose axis. The allowable maximum out-of-square is specified in Table 14, 7.2.1.1.

11.2.2 When hose is supplied as a preformed item, the tolerances shall be as follows:

11.2.2.1 Arm Lengths Measured from end to intersection of nearest centerline. Each end shall be as described in 7.2.1. These tolerances apply also to the length of an expanded end.

11.2.2.2 General Layout—Dimensions locating bend intersections are to establish the theoretical centerline of the hose. Actual outside contour of the hose must be held within 4.8 mm (+0.9 in) in all planes with respect to the theoretical outside contour. To check contour, hose ends should first be placed in nominal position (hose may have to be flexed to correct any distortion caused by handling after vulcanization in the producing plant or in shipment) in a checking fixture made in accordance with user requirements from which contour deviation can be measured. Allowance shall be provided in the end mounting area of the fixture for the arm length tolerances which are applicable.

When the ID of an end of the hose is enlarged, the wall gauge of the enlarged end normally changes. Allowable change should be +0.8, –0.5 mm (+0.03, –0.02 in).

11.3 Tests—Procedures described by ASTM D 380 are to be followed wherever applicable. ASTM test slabs are permissible for testing tube or cover when thickness does not meet ASTM D 412 minimum 1.5 mm (0.06 in).

11.3.1 QUALIFICATION TESTS—In order to qualify under this specification, hose and/or hose assemblies must meet all the applicable test requirements of 11.4. Qualification testing is to be performed on samples of the largest ID size to be supplied, or on 13 mm (0.5 in) ID hose, whichever is smaller. The hose used for qualification tests must be representative of the construction of all other sizes. The impermeable layer thickness of the qualification sample cannot be greater than that of the other sizes.

11.3.1.1 Frequency of Testing for Qualification—Qualification testing is to be performed once per year, with the exception of permeation testing (11.4.12) which is to be performed on original qualification only.

11.3.2 INSPECTION TESTING—On hose and/or hose assemblies, the following inspection tests shall apply: (11.4.1) burst, (11.4.2) vacuum collapse, (11.4.10.1) original adhesion, (11.4.11) kink resistance and (11.5.2) electrical conductivity (if specified). The kink resistance test shall not normally be required on preformed hose, but may be specified for straight sections of at least 300 mm (11.8 in) length.

11.3.2.1 Frequency of Testing for Inspection and Quality Acceptance Standards—As agreed upon between supplier and user.

11.3.3 TEST TOLERANCES—Temperatures specified in the test procedures shall be held to ±2 °C and pressures shall be held to –0, +0.35 kPa (5 psi) unless otherwise specified. Room temperature is to be taken as 23 °C ± 2 °C.

11.4 Test Requirements

11.4.1 BURST PRESSURE (INSPECTION TEST—ALL SIZES)—The minimum burst pressure shall be 8.0 MPa (1160 psi). These hoses have a maximum working pressure of 1.0 MPa (145 psi).

11.4.2 VACUUM COLLAPSE (INSPECTION TEST—ALL SIZES)—Test samples shall be subjected to 80 kPa (600 mm of Hg) vacuum. During the vacuum test described, a 1 m (3.3 ft) length of hose or a hose assembly shall be held in a straight line, and no diameter shall decrease by more than 20% during application of vacuum for a minimum of 15 s and not more than 60 s. The vacuum collapse test on preformed parts should be performed on the finished part.

11.4.3 LOW TEMPERATURE FLEXIBILITY (QUALIFICATION TEST—ANNUALLY ON NOMINAL 13 mm HOSE)—Fill the hose with Reference Fuel C and seal both ends. Allow the filled hose to condition at 23 °C for 168 h. Drain the fuel from the hose and immediately place the hose in a cold box maintained at –40 °C. Condition the hose for 24 h at –40 °C. After conditioning, flex the hose in the cold chamber through 180 degrees from the centerline to a diameter of 10 times the maximum OD of the hose. The flexing shall take place within 4 s and the hose must not fracture or show any cracks, checks, or breaks in the tube or cover. Proof pressure of 1.0 MPa (145 psi) may be applied to determine tube damage.

11.4.4 ORIGINAL MATERIAL PROPERTIES (QUALIFICATION TEST—ANNUALLY NOMINAL 13 mm HOSE OR TEST SLABS):

a. Original tensile strength of cover:	7 MPa (1015 psi) min
b. Original tensile strength of tube or laminated tube:	7 MPa (1015 psi) min
c. Original elongation of cover:	150% min
d. Original elongation of tube or laminated tube:	150% min

NOTE—Laminated tube shall be prepared by buffing or slitting the "reinforcement side" of slit specimen to obtain the proper test thickness.

11.4.5 DRY HEAT RESISTANCE (QUALIFICATION TEST—ANNUALLY ON NOMINAL 13 mm HOSE)—The hose shall show no cracks, charring, or disintegration externally or internally when slowly straightened (taking 4 to 8 s) after being exposed as shown in Figure 2, 7.4.5 for a period of 1000 h at the upper use temperature for the appropriate temperature category (100 °C for Category T1, 125 °C for Category T2, 135 °C for Category T3, or 150 °C for Category T4).

11.4.6 FUEL RESISTANCE (QUALIFICATION TEST—ANNUALLY ON NOMINAL 13 mm HOSE OR TEST SLABS)—After 168 h immersion at 23 °C per ASTM D 471 in the test fuel, samples of the fuel contact layer cut from the tube or lab prepared samples of fuel contact layer material shall meet the requirements shown as follows:

a. Test Fuel:	CM15	CM85
b. Max volume change:	+25%	+25%
c. Max change in Tensile Strength:	–40%	–40%

11.4.6.1 Oxidized Fuel Resistance (Qualification Test—annually on nominal 13mm hose or test slabs)—Repeat the testing of 11.4.6 using auto-oxidized test fuel prepared according to SAE J1681, 3.2.2.3. After 168 h immersion at 23 °C per ASTM D 471 in the auto-oxidized test fuel, samples of the fuel contact layer cut from the tube or lab prepared samples of fuel contact layer material shall meet the requirements shown as follows:

a. Auto-Oxidized Test Fuel:	CM15[8]	CM85[8]
b. Max volume change	+25%	+25%
c. Max change in Tensile Strength	–40%	–40%

8. Test fuel with 50 milli-mole of t-Butyl Hydroperoxide and 0.01 mg Cu per liter of fuel prepared according to SAE J681, 3.2.2.3.

11.4.7 Oil Resistance (Qualification Test—Annually on Nominal 13 mm Hose)—After immersion in IRM 903 oil for 70 h at the upper use temperature for the appropriate temperature category (100 °C for Category T1, 125 °C for Category T2, 135 °C for Category T3, or 150 °C for Category T4) per ASTM D 471, the volume change of a sample taken from the hose cover shall not exceed +60%.

11.4.8 Extractables (Qualification Test—Annually on Nominal 13 mm Hose)—The value for total waxy extractables shall not exceed 2.50 g/m^2 when the hose is tested by the method in 7.4.8.

11.4.9 Ozone Resistance (Qualification Test—Annually on Nominal 13 mm Hose)—The hose cover shall meet a "0" rating after the hose has been exposed to ozone at 100 mPa at 40 °C per the procedure in 6.5.9.

11.4.10 Adhesion

11.4.10.1 Original Adhesion (Inspection Test—All Sizes)—Cut 25 mm samples out of the hose in the transverse direction. The number of samples to be tested is dependent on the construction of the hose but should be enough to test the adhesion between all adjacent layers. When tested in accordance with ASTM D413, Machine Method, Strip Specimen - Type A, 180° Peel, the minimum force required to separate the cover from the tube, and to separate adjacent layers of a multilayer tube shall be 1.4 N/mm of width or the bond shall be inseparable to the extent that tearing of the materials occurs.

11.4.10.2 Fuel Aged Adhesion (Qualification Test—Annually on Nominal 13 mm Hose)—Condition the hose by filling with CM15 Fuel and sealing both ends. Allow the filled hose to condition at 40 °C for a total of 1000 h. Drain and fill with fresh CM15 fuel every week. (As an option, hose that has undergone permeation testing per 11.4.12 may be used for this test.) Cut 25 mm samples out of the hose in the transverse direction. The number of samples to be tested is dependent on the construction of the hose but should be enough to test the adhesion between all adjacent layers. Condition the cut test specimens in a 70 °C oven for 24 h followed by 2 h at room temperature. When tested in accordance with ASTM D 413, Machine Method, Strip Specimen - Type A, 180° Peel, the minimum force required to separate the cover from the tube, and to separate adjacent layers of a multilayer tube shall be 1.0 N/mm of width or the bond shall be inseparable to the extent that tearing of the materials occurs.

11.4.11 Kink Resistance (Inspection Test—All Sizes)—When tested to the procedure in 7.4.11, a ball having a diameter equal to one-half the nominal inside diameter of the hose shall pass freely through the hose.

11.4.12 Permeation (Qualification Test—Initial Qualification on Nominal 13 mm Hose)—Precondition the hose by filling with CM15 fuel and sealing both ends. Allow the filled hose to condition at 60 °C for a minimum of 664 h or at 40 °C for a minimum of 1000 h. Drain and refill with fresh CM15 fuel every week during the conditioning period.

Permeation test procedure and apparatus shall be in accordance with SAE J1737. Permeation testing shall be performed for 336 h on a minimum of three preconditioned hoses using CM15 fuel at a temperature of 60 °C and a pressure of 0.2 MPa .

Calculate daily permeation rates (exclusive of weekends) for the test period (weight gain of carbon canister from one weighing to the next divided by the time in hours between weighings). At the end of the testing period, calculate the time average permeation for the last 10 days (total weight gain of the carbon canister for the last 10-day period divided by the corresponding time in hours). Calculate permeation in units of $g/m^2/day$ using the permeation rate above and the inside surface area of the hose sample in square meters. Report the median value of the permeation rate of the test samples as a whole number and use this number to determine which of the following low permeation categories the hose complies with:

a. Category A 0 to 25 $g/m^2/day$
b. Category B 26 to 50 $g/m^2/day$
c. Category C 51 to 100 $g/m^2/day$

11.4.13 Electrical Conductivity (Inspection Test—All Sizes, if Applicable)—An entire hose (maximum length 610 mm) shall be tested to the following requirements:

Insert a conductive plug or fitting (brass, steel, or copper) into each end of hose. Clamp with a (12.7 mm) band clamp on each end tightening clamps firmly. After clamping allow the hose to rest for 10 min before testing. Attach the ohmmeter electrodes to the plugs (or fittings) at each end and measure the resistance between the plugs or fittings over the entire length or the part, with the part laid on a non-conductive surface. Voltage applied for the measurement shall be 550 V DC ± 50 V DC. Resistance is to be recorded in megaohms.

The resistivity measured for the hose test sample must be less than or equal to 10 MΩ in order for the hose to be marked "E" (see 11.5)

11.5 Marking—The outer cover will be printed with the designation SAE30R12xyTz along with any other identification agreed upon between user and manufacturer, repeated every 300 mm.

a. The "x" designation shall indicate the range that the permeation rate falls within.

"x" Designation

A 0 to 25 $g/m^2/day$
B 26 to 50 $g/m^2/day$
C 51 to 100 $g/m^2/day$

b. The "y" designation is to be used to show if the hose meets the conductivity requirements of 11.4.13.

"y" Designation

N Non-conductive (no conductivity Requirement)
E Conductivity less than 10 MΩ

c. The "T" designation indicates that the hose meets the upper use temperature category given by "z" and meets the requirements of 11.4.3.2, 11.4.5, and 11.4.7 when tested at the corresponding "z" temperature.

"Tz" Designation

	Upper Use Temperature
T1	100 °C
T2	125 °C
T3	135 °C
T4	150 °C

For example; a non-conductive hose with a permeation rate of 15 $g/m^2/day$ and an upper use temperature of 135 °C would be marked:

SAE 30R12ANT3

and a conductive hose with a permeation rate of 40 $g/m^2/day$ and an upper use temperature of 125 °C would be marked:

SAE 30R12BET2

CLAMPING FORCE TEST PROCEDURE —SAE J2371 AUG1997

SAE Recommended Practice

Report of the SAE Hose Clamp Committee approved August 1997.

1. Scope—This SAE Recommended Practice is a test procedure to obtain force data for self-compensating type clamps (SAE Type E, CTB, and CTW).

2. References—There are no referenced publications specified herein.

3. Equipment

3.1 Three segments with centers spaced 120 degrees apart, attached to load cells (see Figure 1).

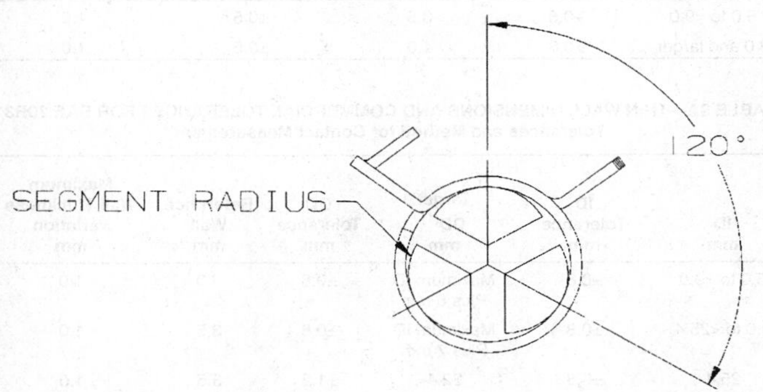

FIGURE 1—CLAMP ORIENTATION OVER THREE SEGMENTS

3.2 The contact area of each segment has a radius that is less than the radius of the smallest test diameter.

3.3 The device is capable of determining individual force of the three load cells.

3.4 Calibration of the device will be performed at the point or points the segment contacts the clamp, taking into account any error due to bending moments.

4. Conditions

4.1 Test is to be performed at ambient 20 °C (68 °F) conditions.

4.2 Friction between the segment fingers and the clamp should be kept to a minimum (see 5.2.2).

5. Test

5.1 Equipment Set-up

5.1.1 The three segments should be arranged to form the test diameter. This test diameter will be defined as a circle tangent to the apex of each radius.

5.1.2 The test diameter will be the nominal clamping diameter.

5.2 Clamp Preparation

5.2.1 All SAE Type E, CTB, and CTW clamps shall be opened to the maximum clamping diameter, using an approved tool, one time prior to installation on tester.

5.2.2 Friction between the clamp and the contact area of the segment must be kept to a minimum.

5.3 Installation and Test

5.3.1 Clamp is to be installed and oriented as shown in Figure 1. SAE Type E and CTW clamps should be installed in a similar fashion to the CTB clamp depicted.

5.3.2 The clamping force shall be defined as the average of the forces detected by each load cell.

DIMENSIONS AND TOLERANCES FOR COOLANT SYSTEM HOSES—SAE J2387 JAN2003

SAE Recommended Practice

Report of the SAE Coolant Hose Committee approved October 1997. Revised by the SAE Non-Hydraulic Hose Committee January 2003. Rationale statement available.

1. Scope—The purpose of this SAE Recommended Practice is to provide dimensions for both standard and thin-wall hoses and to provide commercial and precision tolerances for SAE 20R3 and SAE 20R4 coolant system hoses.

2. References

2.1 Applicable Publications—The following publications form a part of the specification to the extent specified herein. Unless otherwise indicated, the latest revision of SAE publications shall apply.

2.1.1 SAE PUBLICATIONS—Available from SAE, 400 Commonwealth Drive, Warrendale, PA 15096-0001.

SAE J20—Coolant System Hoses

SAE J2605—Non-Contact Hose Measurement Study 1

3. Dimensions and Tolerances for SAE 20R3—Target dimensions and tolerances are shown in Tables 1A through 4B. Contact or non-contact measurement method must be agreed upon by manufacturer and customer. Since expanded ends may cause wall gages to change, O.D.'s and tolerances for the expanded ends must also be agreed upon by the manufacturer and customer. Dimensions and tolerances other than those listed in Tables 1A to 4B must be agreed upon by manufacturer and customer.

TABLE 1A—STANDARD WALL DIMENSIONS AND COMMERCIAL TOLERANCES FOR SAE 20R3
Tolerances and method for Contact Measurement

ID mm	ID Tolerance mm	Target OD(1) mm	OD Tolerance mm	Reference Wall mm	Maximum Wall Thickness Variation mm
5.0 to <9.0	±0.8	Maximum ID Plus 7 mm	±0.8	3.5	1.0
9.0 to <25.4	±0.8	Maximum ID Plus 8 mm	±0.8	4.0	1.0
25.4	±0.8	34	±1.2	4.3	1.0
>25.4	±0.8	Maximum ID Plus 9.9 mm	±1.6	4.95	1.0

1. The target OD should be measured over a plug gauge equal to the specified maximum ID.

TABLE 1B—STANDARD DIMENSIONS AND COMMERCIAL TOLERANCES FOR SAE 20R3
Tolerances for Non-Contact Measurement (see SAE J2605)

ID mm	ID Tolerance mm	Target Wall Thickness mm	Wall Thickness Tolerance mm	Maximum Wall Thickness Variation mm
5.0 to <9.0	±0.8	3.5	±0.4	1.0
9.0 to <25.4	±0.8	4.0	±0.4	1.0
25.4	±0.8	4.3	±0.6	1.0
>25.4	±0.8	4.95	±0.8	1.0

TABLE 2A—STANDARD WALL DIMENSIONS AND PRECISION TOLERANCES FOR SAE 20R3 (GENERALLY APPLIED TO WRAPPED MANDREL-BUILT HOSES ONLY)

ID mm	ID Tolerance mm	Target OD(1) mm	OD Tolerance mm	Reference Wall mm	Maximum Wall Thickness Variation mm
5.0 to <9.0	±0.5	Maximum ID Plus 7 mm	±0.5	3.5	1.0
9.0 and larger	±0.5	Maximum ID Plus 8 mm	±0.5	4.0	1.0

1. The target OD should be measured over a plug gauge equal to the specified maximum ID.

TABLE 2B—STANDARD WALL DIMENSIONS AND PRECISION TOLERANCES FOR SAE 20R3 (GENERALLY APPLIED TO WRAPPED MANDREL-BUILT HOSES ONLY)
Tolerances for Non-Contact Measurement (see SAE J2605)

ID mm	ID Tolerance mm	Target Wall Thickness mm	OD Tolerance mm	Maximum Wall Thickness Variation mm
5.0 to <9.0	±0.8	3.5	±0.5	1.0
9.0 and larger	±0.8	4.0	±0.5	1.0

TABLE 3A—THIN WALL DIMENSIONS AND COMMERCIAL TOLERANCES FOR SAE 20R3
Tolerances and Method for Contact Measurement

ID mm	ID Tolerance mm	Target OD(1) mm	OD Tolerance mm	Reference Wall mm	Maximum Wall Thickness Variation mm
5.0 to <9.0	±0.8	Maximum ID Plus 6 mm	±0.8	3.0	1.0
9.0 to <25.4	±0.8	Maximum ID Plus 7 mm	±0.8	3.5	1.0
25.4	±0.8	32.4	±1.2	3.5	1.0
>25.4	±0.8	Maximum ID Plus 7 mm	±1.2	3.5	1.0

1. The target OD should be measured over a plug gauge equal to the specified maximum ID.

TABLE 3B—THIN WALL DIMENSIONS AND COMMERCIAL TOLERANCES FOR SAE 20R3
Tolerances for Non-Contact Measurement (see SAE J2605)

ID mm	ID Tolerance mm	Target Wall Thickness mm	Wall Thickness Tolerance mm	Maximum Wall Thickness Variation mm
5.0 to <9.0	±0.8	3.0	±0.4	1.0
9.0 to <25.4	±0.8	3.5	±0.4	1.0
25.4	±0.8	3.5	±0.6	1.0
>25.4	±0.8	3.5	±0.6	1.0

TABLE 4A—THIN WALL DIMENSIONS AND PRECISION TOLERANCES FOR SAE 20R3 (GENERALLY APPLIED TO Wrapped MANDREL-BUILT HOSES ONLY)

ID mm	ID Tolerance mm	Target OD(1) mm	OD Tolerance mm	Reference Wall mm	Maximum Wall Thickness Variation mm
5.0 to <9.0	±0.5	Maximum ID Plus 6 mm	±0.5	3.0	1.0
9.0 and larger	±0.5	Maximum ID Plus 7 mm	±0.5	3.5	1.0

1. The target OD should be measured over a plug gauge equal to the specified maximum ID.

TABLE 4B—THIN WALL DIMENSIONS AND PRECISION TOLERANCES FOR SAE 20R3 (GENERALLY APPLIED TO WRAPPED MANDREL-BUILT HOSES ONLY)
Tolerances for non-Contact Measurement (see SAE J2605)

ID mm	ID Tolerance mm	Target Wall Thickness mm	OD Tolerance mm	Maximum Wall Thickness Variation mm
5.0 to <9.0	±0.8	3.0	±0.5	1.0
9.0 and larger	±0.8	3.5	±0.5	1.0

4. Dimensions and Tolerances for SAE 20R4—Target dimensions and tolerances are shown in 4.1 through 4.4. Measurement method must be agreed upon by manufacturer and customer. Since expanded ends may cause wall gages to change, O.D.'s and tolerances for the expanded ends must also be agreed upon by the manufacturer and customer. Dimensions and tolerances other than those listed in the following paragraph must be agreed upon by manufacturer and customer. Since the wall gage may change due to bends near the end of hoses, the wall gage reported will be the average of 4 readings taken 90 degrees apart.

4.1 Standard Wall Dimensions and Commercial Tolerances for SAE 20R4—The I.D. tolerance is ±0.8 mm for hose sizes smaller than 70 mm and ±1.6 mm for hose sizes 70 mm and larger. The wall gage and tolerance is 4.95 mm ± 0.65 mm (4.3 mm to 5.6 mm) for hose sizes smaller than 50.8 mm and 5.35 mm ± 1.05 mm (4.3 mm to 6.4 mm) for hose sizes 50.8 mm and larger.

4.2 Standard Wall Dimensions and Precision Tolerances for SAE 20R4—The I.D. tolerance is ±0.5 mm for hose sizes smaller than 70 mm and ±1.0 mm for hose sizes 70 mm and larger. The wall gage and tolerance is 4.95 mm ± 0.65 mm (4.45 mm to 5.45 mm) for hose sizes smaller than 50.8 mm and 5.35 mm ± 0.8 mm (4.55 mm to 6.15 mm) for hose sizes 50.8 mm and larger.

4.3 Thin-Wall Dimensions and Commercial Tolerances for SAE 20R4—The I.D. tolerance is ±0.8 mm for hose sizes smaller than 38 mm. The wall gage and tolerance is 4.0 mm ± 0.6 mm (3.4 mm to 4.6 mm) for hose sizes smaller than 38 mm. For hose larger than 38 mm, the dimensions and tolerances should be agreed upon between the customer and hose manufacturer.

4.4 Thin-Wall Dimensions and Precision Tolerances for SAE 20R4—The I.D. tolerance is ±0.5 mm for hose sizes smaller than 38 mm. The wall gage and tolerance is 4.0 mm ± 0.5 mm (3.5 mm to 4.5 mm) for hose sizes smaller than 38 mm. For hose larger than 38 mm, the dimensions and tolerances should be agreed upon between the customer and hose manufacturer.

TEST METHOD FOR EVALUATING THE ELECTROCHEMICAL RESISTANCE OF COOLANT SYSTEM HOSES AND MATERIALS—SAE J1684 JUN2000

SAE Recommended Practice

Report of the SAE Electrochemical Resistance Task Group of the SAE Coolant Hose Committee approved January 1994 and revised June 2000.

1. Scope—This test method provides a standardized procedure for evaluating the electrochemical resistance of automotive coolant hose and materials. Electrochemical degradation has been determined to be a major cause of EPDM coolant system hose failures. The test method consists of a procedure which induces voltage to a test specimen while it is exposed to a water/coolant solution. Method #1, referred to as a "Brabolyzer" test, is a whole hose test. Method #2, referred to as a "U" tube test, uses cured plate samples or plates prepared from tube material removed from hose (Method No. 2 is intended as a screening test only). Any test parameters other than those specified in this SAE Recommended Practice, are to be agreed to by the tester and the requester.

2. References

2.1 Related Publications—The following publications are provided for information purposes only and are not a required part of this document.

R. C. Keller, SAE Technical Paper 900576, February 28, 1990

Harold Schneider, Hal Tucker, Dr. Eddie T. Seo, Rubber Division, ACS Technical Paper 73, May 22, 1992

3. Method #1 "Brabolyzer," Whole Hose Test—Materials and Equipment Required

3.1 12 V DC power supply.

3.2 Multivolt ohmmeter.

3.3 Commercial automotive coolant, ethylene glycol based containing an inorganic anticorrosion protection system, shall be used These coolants are typically green in appearance.

3.4 End plugs chemically resistant, electrically nonconductive thermoplastic as polyamide, PTFE, or polypropylene suitable for isolating voltage applied to end of hose from the liquid test media inside the hose. Electrical contact surface for applied voltage should be the inside circumference of test hose. See Figures 1A and 1B for end plug assembly components. The end plugs shown are for 31.8 mm ID hose, which is preferred, but other sizes can also be made.

3.5 Glass insulator to isolate electrically the hose samples attached to the negative and positive terminals. See Figure 2.

3.6 Suitable hose clamps for size of hose used.

3.7 Air-circulating oven configured with wooden or other nonconducting surface for complete electrical isolation of test assembly.

3.8 Suitable electrical leads and clips for connecting power source to end plug.

3.9 Microscope (10X to 20X) for examination of specimens after test. A stereo microscope is best, using a fiber-optic light source that can be adjusted for angle.

3.10 Two 100 mm straight samples for each cell. Curved hose may be used if straight hose is not available.

4. Set-Up Procedure

4.1 Attach one end-plug flush to one end of test hose with appropriate clamp.

4.2 Attach glass insert between the two test hoses with appropriate clamps.

4.3 Fill hose assembly 80% ±5% by volume with a solution of 50:50 distilled water/coolant.

4.4 Attach second end plug to test specimen with appropriate clamp.

4.5 Mark specimen with pertinent identification and positive or negative polarity. Marking should be on the top side of the hose as it lays in the oven for use as a reference point.

4.6 Make three of the previous completed assemblies per test. See Figure 3.

5. Test Procedure

5.1 Place test hose assemblies in air-circulating oven which has been configured to electrically isolate the assemblies. Attach leads to assemblies at the end plugs, ensuring that polarity is consistent with markings. Use volt/ohmmeter to ensure continuity through all components measured with voltage off. Voltage measurements may vary through each hose assembly.

5.2 Apply 12 V, and measure voltage from plug to plug and record. Also measure voltage at source (before hose circuit) and record. If a significant difference exists, check all leads and connections. Voltage may or may not be the same. However, it is critical to ensure that all connections are properly made.

5.3 Heat oven to 100 °C ± 2 °C. Visually check liquid level through glass insulator each day, replenishing liquid, if it drops below 50%.

5.4 After 168 h ±0.5 h, detach leads and remove assemblies from oven and allow to cool to room temperature.

5.5 Remove end plugs and drain fluid from hose. Rinse hose interior thoroughly.

5.6 Cut the negative end of the hose approximately 45 mm from hose end. A smooth, straight cut through the hose with a sharp blade instrument is desirable for examination purposes.

5.7 Examine the cross section of the cut end under magnification (10X to 20X) with a bright, low angle light. Make note of striations. The striations may be long and thin, short and thick, branched or unbranched, liquid filled or dry, or any combination of the previous. Do not confuse knife cut marks with striations.

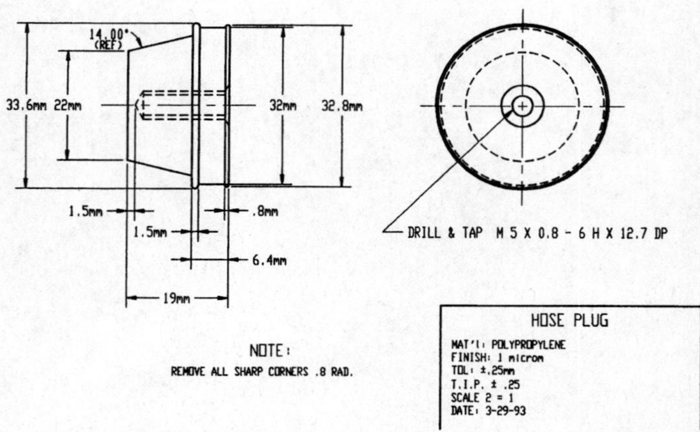

FIGURE 1A—POLYPROPYLENE HOSE PLUG

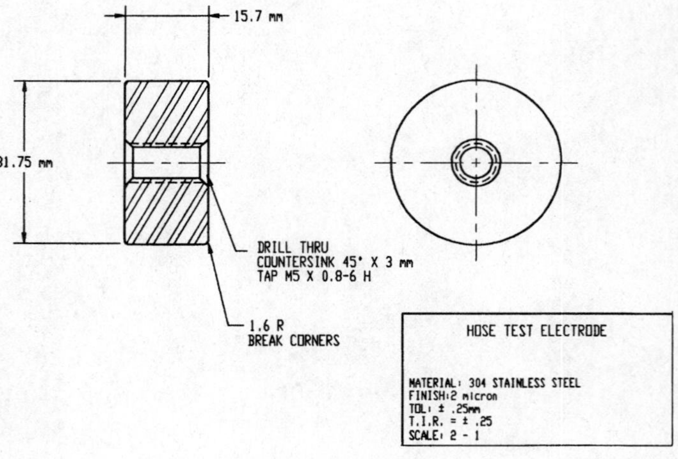

FIGURE 1B—ELECTRODE

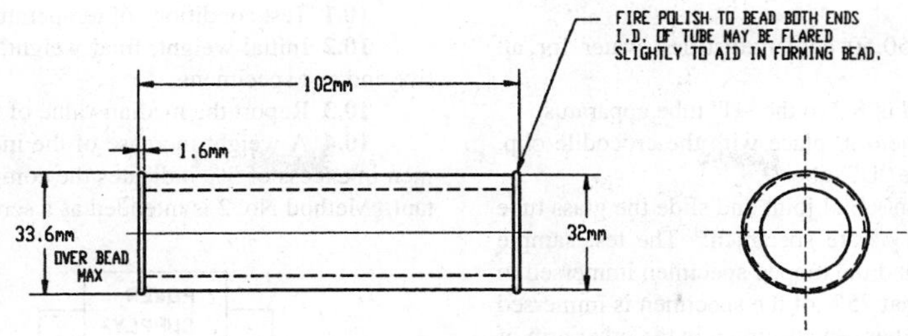

FIGURE 2—GLASS TUBE WITH BEADS ON ENDS

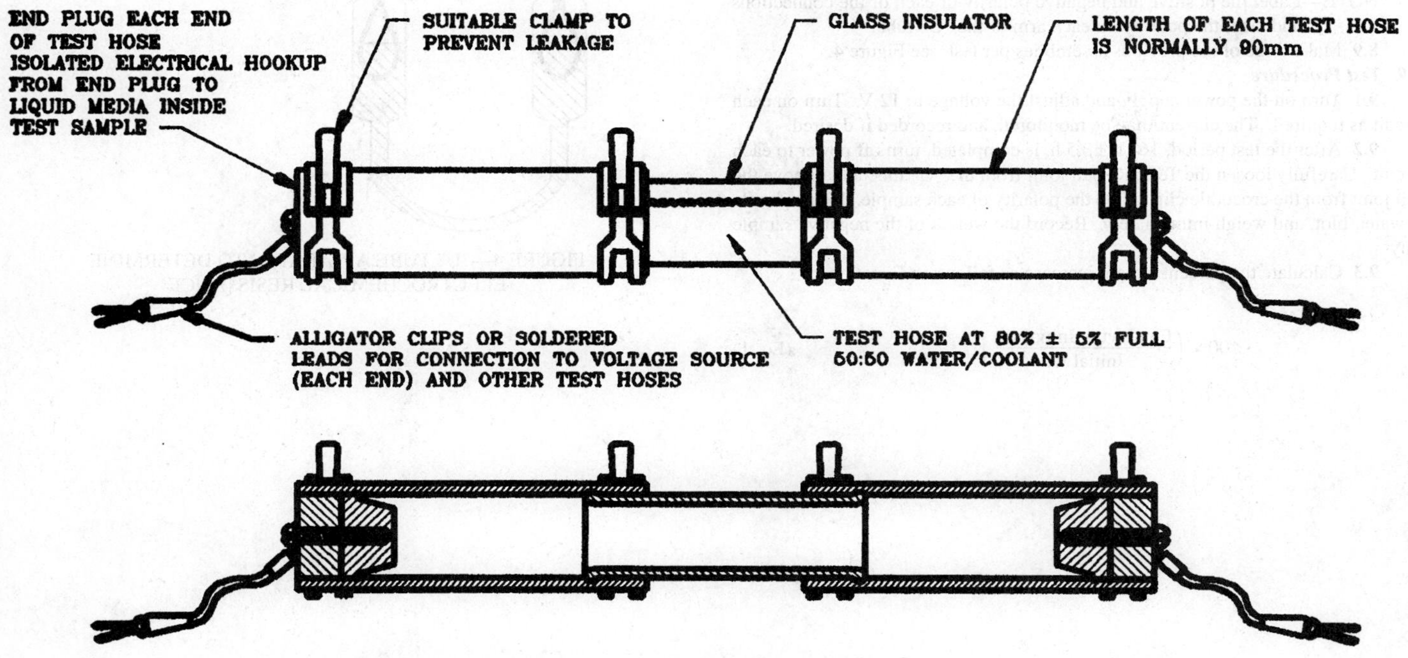

NOTE: 1. HOSES NORMALLY TESTED AT 3 EACH IN PARALLEL (ALL CONNECTED AT BOTH POSITIVE AND NEGATIVE ENDS RESPECTIVELY).
2. HOSES MAY BUILD INTERNAL PRESSURE DUE TO TEMPERATURE AND ELECTROCHEMICAL ACTIVITY. CAUTION SHOULD BE USED WHEN HANDLING.
3. HOSE ASSEMBLIES SHOULD ALWAYS BE PLACED ON A NON-CONDUCTING SURFACE, SUCH AS WOOD, TO PREVENT SHORTING OF POWER SUPPLY AND POSSIBLE GROUNDING TO UNDESIRABLE OBJECTS.
4. LIQUID LEVEL SHOULD BE OBSERVED DAILY THRU GLASS INSULATOR. REFILL AS REQUIRED.
5. OBSERVE DAILY FOR ANY LEAKAGE AT END PLUGS OR ON HOSE SURFACE.

FIGURE 3—BRABOLYZER TEST CONFIGURATION

6. Report

6.1 Report any striations noted during the microscopic examination. Any striations constitute a failure. Additional descriptions such as length, percent of circumference affected, location, branching, moisture present, as well as pictures are helpful in determining degree and type of damage.

7. Method #2 "U" Tube—Materials and Equipment Required

7.1 12 V DC power supply.

7.2 Multivolt ohmmeter.

7.3 Commercial automotive coolant, ethylene glycol based containing an inorganic anticorrosion protection system, shall be used. These coolants are typically green in appearance.

7.4 Test specimen, die-cut from standard laboratory press cure stock. A die-cut sample from the tube removed from a hose may also be used. Dimensions are 10 mm wide x 100 mm long.

7.5 Glass "U" tube assembly.

7.6 Thermostatically controlled heating bath, using water soluble oil as a heating medium. The temperature of the bath oil shall be set at 80 °C.

7.7 Hook-up wire and crocodile clips.

7.8 Balance capable of weighing to 0.01 g.

8. Set-Up Procedure

8.1 Connect the hook-up wire to the crocodile clip and insert through the glass insulation tube as shown in Figure 4.

8.2 Weigh negative test specimen, bend the strip into a loop and clamp the ends with the crocodile clip.

8.3 Prepare a sufficient quantity of 50:50 coolant:distilled water for all tests.

8.4 Add 100 mL of the liquid prepared in 8.3 to the "U" tube apparatus.

8.5 Place a bent loop test specimen, held in place with the crocodile clip, and glass insulation tube into each arm of the "U" tube.

8.6 Loosen the screw cap on the Teflon® ball joint and slide the glass tube up or down to adjust the immersion depth of the specimen. The test sample should be marked 12.5 mm from each end, and the looped specimen immersed in the test fluid to those marks. This ensures that 75% of the specimen is immersed in the fluid. Repeat the process, placing another test specimen in the other arm of the "U" tube.

8.7 Place each "U" tube into the heating bath and clamp so that the coolant solution in the apparatus is just below the level of the heating oil liquid in the bath.

NOTE—The bath should be at the desired temperature before placing the "U" tube in it.

8.8 Connect each "U" tube to the power supply.

NOTE—Label the positive and negative polarity of each of the connections and label the polarity on each arm of the "U" tube.

8.9 Make three of the previous assemblies per test, see Figure 4.

9. Test Procedure

9.1 Turn on the power supply and adjust the voltage to 12 V. Turn on each circuit as required. The current may be monitored, and recorded if desired.

9.2 After the test period, 168 h ±0.5 h, is completed, turn off power to each circuit. Carefully loosen the Teflon® ball joint from the "U" tube and remove the ball joint from the crocodile clip. Note the polarity of each sample. Rinse sample in water, blot, and weigh immediately. Record the weight of the negative sample only.

9.3 Calculate the percent weight increase as follows in Equation 1:

$$100 \times \left(\frac{\text{Final wt.} - \text{Initial wt.}}{\text{Initial wt.}}\right) \quad \text{(Eq. 1)}$$

10. Report

10.1 Test conditions of temperature, voltage, and duration.

10.2 Initial weight, final weight, and percent weight increase of the negative end test specimens.

10.3 Report the median value of the three negative test specimens.

10.4 A weight increase of the median value of the negative end test specimen in excess of 5% indicates the compound may not be electrochemically resistant. Method No. 2 is intended as a screening test only.

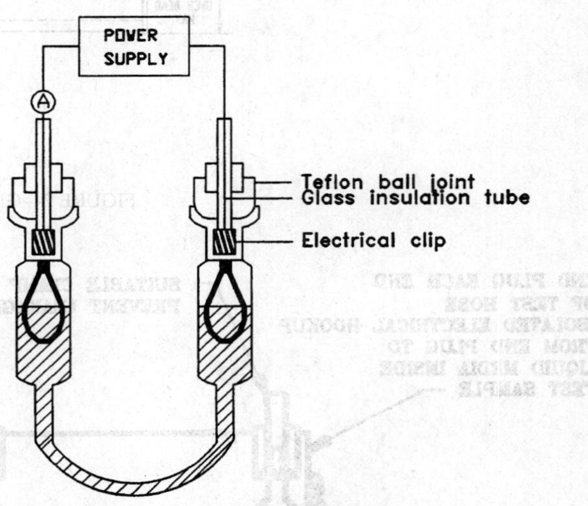

FIGURE 4—"U" TUBE APPARATUS TO DETERMINE ELECTROCHEMICAL RESISTANCE

POWER STEERING PRESSURE HOSE—HIGH VOLUMETRIC EXPANSION TYPE—SAE J188 JUN2003 SAE Standard

Report of the SAE Nonmetallic Materials Committee approved August 1970. Completely revised by the SAE Power Steering Hose Standards Committee October 1989. Revised by the SAE Power Steering Hose Standards Committee January 1998. Rationale statement available. Revised by the SAE Automotive Brake and Steering Hose Standards Committee June 2003. Rationale statement available.

Foreword—This document represents the minimum quality recognized by original equipment manufacturers and hose suppliers as essential for satisfactory and safe operation by the hose itself and other coacting parts of the power steering system. The original equipment manufacturer may, at his option, add or alter tests through OEM specifications.

1. Scope—This document covers two types of hose fabricated from fabric braid and synthetic rubber, assembled with end fittings for use in automotive power steering applications as flexible connections within the temperature range of -40 °C to +120 °C (-40 °F to +250 °F) average, and 135 °C (275 °F) maximum peaks.

These hoses are intended for use in applications where reduction in amplitude of pump pressure pulsations is required.

Type 1 hose shall be suitable for 10.3 MPa (1500 psi) maximum working pressure.

Type 2 hose shall be suitable for 10.3 MPa (1500 psi) maximum working pressure.

2. References

2.1 Applicable Publications—The following publications form a part of the specification to the extent specified herein.

2.1.1 ASTM PUBLICATIONS—Available from ASTM, 100 Barr Harbor Drive, West Conshohocken, PA 19428-2959

ASTM D 380—Methods of Testing Rubber Hose
ASTM D 413—Tests for Adhesion of Vulcanized Rubber (Friction Test)

3. Hose Construction—The construction of this hose embodies a smooth bore inner tube of suitable synthetic rubber material, reinforced with two plies of braided fabric and covered with a synthetic rubber outer cover.

4. Dimensions—Concentricity based on full indicator reading between the inside bore and the outer surface of the hose shall not exceed 0.076 cm (0.030 in). See Table 1.

TABLE 1—HOSE DIMENSIONS

	Type 1	Type 2
ID	0.972/1.03 cm (0.365/0.405 in)	0.912/1.01 cm (0.359/0.398 in)
OD	1.91/2.07 cm (0.750/0.813 in)	1.91/2.07 cm (0.750/0.813 in)

5. Test Procedures—Procedures described in ASTM D 380, shall be followed wherever applicable.

6. Qualification Tests—To qualify hose under this document, all of the requirements shown in Section 8 must be met.

7. Inspection Tests—Production shipments or lots of qualified hose shall be tested in accordance with Table 2 and shall conform to the applicable test requirements, but the user may test hose or hose assemblies from any or all such production shipments or lots to all the test requirements. Fourteen sample hose assemblies, selected at random, as listed in Table 2, are required to conduct a complete test. In the event of a failure, the test or tests that have failed shall be retested using twice the number of samples indicated in Table 2. Failure of any of the retested samples shall be cause for rejection of the entire lot.

TABLE 2—INSPECTION TESTS

Test	Samples Required
1. Volumetric Expansion (9.7) followed by Length Change (9.11) followed by Bursting Strength (9.5)	3
2. Tensile (9.2)	3
3. Adhesion (9.4)	1
4. Low Temperature Flexibility (9.3)	1
5. Impulse (9.1)	6

8. Frequency Of Testing For Inspection—All inspection tests shall be performed on either a bulk hose lot or a coupled hose lot basis or tests may be split between a bulk hose lot and a coupled hose lot.

A coupled hose lot shall not exceed 10 000 hose assemblies and a bulk hose lot shall not exceed 6096 m (20 000 ft) of bulk hose.

9. Test Requirements

9.1 Impulse Test

9.1.1 TEST CONDITIONS

a. Oil Temperature: 135 °C (275 °F)
b. Ambient Temperature: 135 °C ± 6 °C (275 °F ± 10 °F)
c. Cycle Rate: 30 to 40 per minute
d. Cycle Date: Pressure rise time, 0.20 s ± 0.10 s. High pressure hold time, 0.65 s ± 0.20 s. Pressure drop time, 0.20 s ± 0.10 s.
e. Pressure Variation: Type 1 0–0.69 to 10.3 MPa (0–100 to 1500 psi)
Type 2 0–0.69 to 10.3 MPa (0–100 to 1500 psi)

9.1.2 HYDRAULIC FLUID AND TEST FIXTURE—As specified by the original equipment manufacturer.

9.1.3 CYCLE LIFE—Samples submitted to this test shall exceed 100 000 cycles for inspection acceptance and 225 000 cycles for qualification testing, without failure.

9.2 Tensile Test—When tested in accordance with ASTM D 380, hose assemblies shall withstand a minimum tensile load of 5337.9 N (1200 lb) without the fittings pulling off or rupture of the hose.

9.3 Low Temperature Flexibility—Samples shall be subjected to a temperature of -40 °C ± 1 °C (-40 °F ± 2 °F) for a period of 24 h, after which the hose shall be flexed in the cold chamber through 180 degrees from the centerline around a mandrel whose diameter is eight times the nominal hose OD. Flexing shall be accomplished within 3 to 5 s. Hose shall not fracture or show any cracks, checks, or breaks in the tube or cover.

9.4 Adhesion Test—When tested in accordance with ASTM D 413, a pull of not less than 44.48 N (10 lb) shall be required to separate a 2.54 cm (1 in) wide ring section of the bond between any adjacent layers of the hose.

9.5 Bursting Strength—Samples shall meet the following minimum bursting strength requirements:

Type 1 – 41.4 MPa (6000 psi)
Type 2 – 41.4 MPa (6000 psi)

9.6 Ozone Resistance—The outer cover of the hose shall show no cracking when examining the cover of the hose under 7X magnification, ignoring the areas immediately adjacent to or within the area covered by the binding.

Bend the hose around a cylinder, the diameter of which shall be seven times the nominal outside diameter of the hose, and bind the ends. The cylinder and binding shall be made of metal or materials that prevent the consumption of ozone. If the hose collapses when bent around the cylinder, provide for internal support of the hose.

Condition the hose, on the cylinder, for 24.0 h ± 0.5 h at room temperature, and then place it in an exposure chamber containing air mixed with ozone in the proportion of 50 pphm ± 5 ozone in air by volume, for 70 to 72 h. Ambient air temperature in chamber during test shall be 40 °C ± 3 °C (104 °F ± 5 °F).

Examine the cover of the hose for cracks under 7X magnification, ignoring the areas immediately adjacent to or within the area covered by the binding.

9.7 Volumetric Expansion—Samples shall be installed on the test fixture in a manner that allows the hose to lie straight but not under tension when test pressure is applied. Samples shall be preconditioned at 8.97 MPa ± 0.14 MPa (1300 psi ± 20 psi) for 30 s ± 5 s and allowed to recover at 0 pressure for 2 min ± 5 s prior to the test. Test pressure shall then be applied and held for 2 min ± 5 s. At the end of this period, the inlet valve shall be closed and the test fluid allowed to rise in the burrette for a period of 1 min ± 5 s. The outlet valve shall then be closed and the reading taken. The average of three volumetric expansion readings per sample shall not exceed the values listed in Table 3:

TABLE 3—VOLUMETRIC EXPANSION, CC/FT AT 0 TO 8.97 MPa (0 TO 1300 psi)

	max	min
Type 1	8	3
Type 2	17	8

9.8 Tensile Strength and Elongation

a. Original tensile strength of cover: 6.9 MPa (1000 psi) min
b. Original tensile strength of tube: 6.9 MPa (1000 psi) min
c. Original elongation of cover: 175% min
d. Original elongation of tube: 150% min

9.9 Dry Heat Resistance—After oven aging for 70 h at a temperature of 100 °C (212 °F), the reduction in tensile strength and elongation of specimens taken from tube and cover material shall not exceed the following values:

a. Original tensile strength: 20%
b. Original elongation: 50%

9.10 Oil Resistance—After 70 h immersion in ASTM No. 3 oil at a temperature of 121 °C (250 °F), the reduction in tensile strength and elongation of specimens taken from the tube material shall not exceed the following values:

a. Original tensile strength: 65%
b. Original elongation: 50%

In addition, the volume change of specimens taken from the tube and cover material shall not exceed 0 to +100%.

9.11 Length Change—Type 1 hose shall not change in length more than +2%, -5% when pressure is increased from 0 to 10.3 MPa (0 to 1500 psig).

Type 2 hose shall not change in length more than +0%, -8% when pressure is increased from 0 to 10.3 MPa (0 to 1500 psig).

9.12 Identification Marking—Hose shall be identified with the SAE number, type, size of inside diameter in fractions, date code in days of the year, and last digit of the year (for example, 1707 represents the 170th day of 1987), and hose manufacturer's and/or coupling manufacturer's code marking. This marking shall appear on the outer cover of the hose at intervals of not greater than 10 in. Additional identification may be added as agreed on by user and supplier.

9.13 100% Proof Pressure Test—Each hose assembly shall be proof pressure tested using air, oil, or water as the pressure medium. Test pressure shall be 10.3 MPa (1500 psi) when tested with air and 13.8 MPa (2000 psi) when tested with oil or water. Test pressure shall be held for not less than 30 nor more than 60 s. Care should be taken when testing with air due to its explosive nature at high pressure.

POWER STEERING RETURN HOSE—LOW PRESSURE—SAE J189 JUN2003

SAE Standard

Report of the SAE Nonmetallic Materials approved August 1970. Completely revised by the SAE Power Steering Hose Standards Committee December 1989. Revised by the SAE Power Steering Hose Standards Committee January 1998. Rationale statement available. Revised by the SAE Automotive Brake and Steering Hose Standards Committee June 2003. Rationale statement available.

Foreword—This document represents the minimum quality recognized by original equipment manufacturers and hose suppliers as essential for satisfactory and safe operation by the hose itself and other coacting parts of the power steering system. The original equipment manufacturer may, at his option, add or alter tests through OEM specifications.

1. Scope—This SAE Standard covers hose fabricated from fabric braid and synthetic rubber, assembled with end fittings or user applied clamps for use in automotive power steering applications as flexible connections within the temperature range of –40 °C to +120 °C (–40 °F to 250 °F) average and 135 °C (275 °F) maximum peaks. Hose assemblies shall be suitable for 1.72 MPa (250 psi) maximum working pressure with end fittings and 0.69 MPa (100 psi) maximum working pressure with user applied clamps.

2. References

2.1 Applicable Publications—The following publications form a part of this specification to the extent specified herein.

2.1.1 ASTM PUBLICATIONS—Available from ASTM, 100 Barr Harbor Drive, West Conshohocken, PA 19428-2959.

ASTM D 380—Methods of Testing Rubber Hose

ASTM D 413—Tests for Adhesion of Vulcanized Rubber (Friction Test)

3. Hose Construction—The construction of this hose embodies a smooth bore inner tube of suitable synthetic rubber material, reinforced with one ply of braided fabric and covered with a synthetic rubber outer cover.

4. Dimensions—Suggested hose dimensions are given in Table 1B, but it is not the intent of this document to exclude hose with different dimensions that comply with all other requirements of this document.

In addition, concentricity based on full indicator reading between the inside bore and the outer surface of the hose shall not exceed 0.076 cm (0.030 in).

5. Test Procedures—Procedures described in ASTM D 380, shall be followed wherever applicable.

6. Qualification Tests—To qualify hose under this document, all of the requirements shown in Section 9 must be met.

7. Inspection Tests—Production shipments or lots of qualified hose shall be tested in accordance with Table 2 and shall conform to the applicable test requirements, but the user may test hose or hose assemblies from any or all such production shipments or lots to all the test requirements. Fourteen sample hose assemblies, selected at random, as listed in Table 2, are required to conduct a complete test. In the event of a failure, the test or tests that have failed shall be retested using twice the number of samples indicated in Table 2. Failure of any of the retested samples shall be cause for rejection of the entire lot.

TABLE 1A—HOSE DIMENSIONS (METRIC)

Nominal ID cm	Nominal OD, cm	ID Tolerance, cm	OD Tolerance, cm	Recommended Working Pressure, max, MPa With End Fittings	Recommended Working Pressure, max, MPa With User Applied Clamps	Tensile Load, min, lb With End Fittings	Tensile Load, min, N With User Applied Clamps	Burst Strength min, MPa
0.953	1.67	0.991/0.874	1.748/1.588	1.72	0.69	1112	Not Applicable	6.9

TABLE 1B—HOSE DIMENSIONS (ENGLISH)

Nominal ID in	Nominal OD, in	ID Tolerance, in	OD Tolerance, in	Recommended Working Pressure, max, psi With End Fittings	Recommended Working Pressure, max, psi With User Applied Clamps	Tensile Load, min, lb With End Fittings	Tensile Load, min, lb With User Applied Clamps	Burst Strength min, psi
3/8	21/32	0.390/0.344	0.688/0.625	250	100	250	Not Applicable	1000

TABLE 2—INSPECTION TESTS

Test	Samples Required
1. Length Change (9.10) followed by Bursting Strength (9.5)	3
2. Tensile (9.2)	3
3. Low Temperature Flexibility (9.3)	1
4. Adhesion (9.4)	1
5. Impulse (9.1)	6

8. Frequency of Testing for Inspection—All inspection tests except impulse shall be performed on either a bulk hose lot or a coupled hose lot basis or tests may be split between a bulk hose lot and a coupled hose lot.

A coupled hose lot shall not exceed 10 000 hose assemblies and a bulk hose lot shall not exceed 6096 m (20 000 ft) of bulk hose.

9. Test Requirements

9.1 Impulse Test—(Not applicable to hose assembled with user applied clamps.)

9.1.1 TEST CONDITIONS

a. Oil Temperature: 135 °C (275 °F)

b. Ambient Temperature: 135 °C ± 6 °C (275 °F ± 10 °F)

c. Cycle Rate: 30 to 40 per minute

d. Cycle Data: Pressure rise time, 0.20 s ± 0.10 s. High pressure hold time, 0.65 s ± 0.20 s. Pressure drop time, 0.20 s ± 0.10 s.

e. Pressure Variation: 0 to 172.4 kPa (0 to 25 psi) to the maximum recommended working pressure as specified in Table 1B.

9.1.2 HYDRAULIC FLUID AND TEST FIXTURE—As specified by the original equipment manufacturer.

9.1.3 CYCLE LIFE—Samples submitted to this test shall exceed 100 000 cycles for inspection acceptance and 225 000 cycles for qualification testing, without failure.

9.2 Tensile Test—When tested in accordance with ASTM D 380, end fittings shall withstand a minimum tensile load as shown in Table 1B without the fittings pulling off or rupture of the hose.

9.3 Low Temperature Flexibility—Samples shall be subjected to a temperature of –40 °C ± 1 °C (–40 °F ± 2 °F) for a period of 24 h, after which the hose shall be flexed in the cold chamber through 180 degrees from the centerline around a mandrel whose diameter is eight times the nominal hose OD. Flexing shall be accomplished within 3 to 5 s. Hose shall not fracture or show any cracks, checks, or breaks in the tube or cover.

9.4 Adhesion Test—When tested in accordance with ASTM D 413, a pull of not less than 35.586 N (8 lb) shall be required to separate a 1 in wide ring section of the bond between any adjacent layers of the hose.

9.5 Bursting Strength—Samples shall meet the minimum bursting strength requirements shown in Table 1B.

9.6 Ozone Resistance—The outer cover of the hose shall show no cracking when examining the cover of the hose under 7X magnification, ignoring the areas immediately adjacent to or within the area covered by the binding.

Bend the hose around a cylinder, the diameter of which shall be seven times the nominal outside diameter of the hose, and bind the ends. The cylinder and binding shall be made of metal or materials that prevent the consumption of ozone. If the hose collapses when bent around the cylinder, provide for internal support of the hose.

Condition the hose, on the cylinder, for 24.0 h ± 0.5 h at room temperature, and then place it in an exposure chamber containing air mixed with ozone in the proportion of 50 pphm ± 5 ozone in air by volume, for 70 to 72 h. Ambient air temperature in chamber during test shall be 40 °C ± 3 °C (104 °F ± 5 °F).

Examine the cover of the hose for cracks under 7X magnification, ignoring the areas immediately adjacent to or within the area covered by the binding.

9.7 Tensile Strength and Elongation

a. Original tensile strength of cover: 6.9 MPa (1000 psi) min
b. Original tensile strength of tube: 6.9 MPa (1000 psi) min
c. Original elongation of cover: 175% min
d. Original elongation of tube: 150% min

9.8 Dry Heat Resistance—After oven aging for 70 h at a temperature of 100 °C (212 °F), the reduction in tensile strength and elongation of specimens taken from tube and cover material shall not exceed the following values:

a. Original tensile strength: 20%
b. Original elongation: 50%

9.9 Oil Resistance—After 70 h immersion in ASTM No. 3 oil at a temperature of 121 °C (250 °F), the reduction in tensile strength and elongation of specimens taken from the tube material shall not exceed the following values:

a. Original tensile strength: 65%
b. Original elongation: 50%

In addition, the volume change of specimens taken from the tube and cover material shall not exceed 0 to +100%.

9.10 Length Change—Hose shall not change more than +0%, –10% when the pressure is increased from 0 psi to the maximum recommended working pressure shown in Table 1B.

9.11 Identification Marking—Hose shall be identified with the SAE number, size of inside diameter in fractions, date code in days of the year, and last digit of the year (for example, 1707 represents the 170th day of 1987), and hose manufacturer's and/or coupling manufacturer's code marking. This marking shall appear on the outer cover of the hose at intervals of not greater than 25.4 cm (10 in). Additional identification may be added as agreed on by user and supplier.

9.12 100% Proof Pressure Test—Hose shall be proof-pressure tested at the recommended working pressure using air, oil, or water as the pressure medium. Pressure shall be held for not less than 30 nor more than 60 s. Care should be taken when testing with air due to its explosive nature at high pressures.

POWER STEERING PRESSURE HOSE—LOW VOLUMETRIC EXPANSION TYPE—SAE J191 JUN2003

SAE Standard

Report of the SAE Nonmetallic Materials Committee approved August 1970. Completely revised by the SAE Power Steering Hose Standards Committee October 1989. Revised by the SAE Auto Brake and Steering Hose Standards Committee May 1998 and June 2003. Rationale statement available.

Foreword—This document represents the minimum quality recognized by original equipment manufacturers and hose suppliers as essential for satisfactory and safe operation by the hose itself and other coacting parts of the power steering system. The original equipment manufacturer may, at his option, add or alter tests through OEM specifications.

*1. **Scope***—This SAE Standard covers hose fabricated from fabric braid and synthetic rubber, assembled with end fittings for use in automotive power steering applications at pressures as indicated in Table 1B, as flexible connections within the temperature range of -40 °C (-40 °F) to 121°C (250 °F) average, 135 °C (275 °F) maximum peaks.

These hoses are intended for use in applications where reduction in amplitude of pump pressure pulsations is not required.

*2. **References***

2.1 Applicable Publications—The following publications form a part of the specification to the extent specified herein.

2.1.1 ASTM PUBLICATIONS—Available from ASTM, 100 Barr Harbor Drive, West Conshohocken, PA 19428-2959.

ASTM D 380—Methods of Testing Rubber Hose

ASTM D 413—Tests for Adhesion of Vulcanized Rubber (Friction Test)

*3. **Hose Construction***—The construction of this hose embodies a smooth bore inner tube of suitable synthetic rubber material, reinforced with two plies of braided fabric and covered with a synthetic rubber outer cover.

*4. **Dimensions***—Hose must be within the tolerances shown in Table 1B. In addition, the concentricity based on full indicator reading between the inside bore and the outer surface of the hose shall not exceed 0.076 cm (0.030 in).

*5. **Test Procedures***—Procedures described in ASTM D 380 shall be followed wherever applicable.

*6. **Qualification Tests***—To qualify hose under this document, all of the requirements shown in Section 9 must be met.

*7. **Inspection Tests***—Production shipments or lots of qualified hose shall be tested in accordance with Table 2 and shall conform to the applicable test requirements, but the user may test hose or hose assemblies from any or all such production shipments or lots to all the test requirements. Fourteen sample hose assemblies, selected at random, as listed in Table 2, are required to conduct a complete test. In the event of a failure, the test or tests that have failed shall be retested using twice the number of samples indicated in Table 2. Failure of any of the retested samples shall be cause for rejection of the entire lot.

TABLE 1A—HOSE DIMENSIONS (METRIC)

Nominal ID, cm	Nominal OD, cm	ID Tolerance, cm	OD Tolerance, cm	Working Pressure, max, MPa	Proof Pressure, MPa	Burst Strength, min, MPa	Tensile Strength, min, N
0.635	1.429	0.699/0.61	1.5/1.4	8.96	13.8	41.4	2001.7

TABLE 1B—HOSE DIMENSIONS (ENGLISH)

Nominal ID, in	Nominal OD, in	ID Tolerance, in	OD Tolerance, in	Working Pressure, max, psi	Proof Pressure, psi	Burst Strength, min, psi	Tensile Strength, min, lb
1/4	9/16	0.275/ 0.240	0.592/ 0.552	1300	2000	6000	450

TABLE 2—INSPECTION TESTS

Test	Samples Required
1. Length Change (9.7) followed by Bursting Strength (9.5)	3
2. Tensile (9.2)	3
3. Adhesion (9.4)	1
4. Low Temperature Flexibility (9.3)	1
5. Impulse (9.1)	6

*8. **Frequency of Testing for Inspection***—All inspection tests except impulse shall be performed on either a bulk hose lot or a coupled hose lot basis or tests may be split between a bulk hose lot and a coupled hose lot.

A coupled hose lot shall not exceed 10 000 hose assemblies and a bulk hose lot shall not exceed 6096 m (20 000 ft) of bulk hose. The lot size for impulse testing shall not exceed 30 480 m (100 000 ft) of bulk hose.

*9. **Test Requirements***

9.1 Impulse Test

9.1.1 TEST CONDITIONS

a. Oil Temperature—135 °C ± 2 °C (275 °F ± 5 °F)
b. Ambient Temperature—104 °C ± 11 °C (220 °F ± 20 °F)
c. Cycle Rate—30 to 40 per minute.
d. Cycle Data—Pressure rise time, 0.20 s ± 0.10 s. High pressure hold time, 0.65 s ± 0.20 s. Pressure drop time, 0.20 s ± 0.10 s.
e. Pressure Variation—0 to 0.69 MPa (0 to 100 psi) to maximum working pressure listed in Table 1B.

9.1.2 HYDRAULIC FLUID AND TEST FIXTURE—As specified by the original equipment manufacturer.

9.1.3 CYCLE LIFE—Samples submitted to this test shall exceed 100 000 cycles for inspection acceptance and 225 000 cycles for qualification testing, without failure.

9.2 Tensile Test—When tested in accordance with ASTM D 380, hose assemblies shall withstand a minimum tensile load as specified in Table 1 without the fittings pulling off or rupture of the hose.

9.3 Low Temperature Flexibility—Samples shall be subjected to a temperature of -40 °C ± 1 °C (-40 °F ± 2 °F) for a period of 24 h, after which the hose shall be flexed in the cold chamber through 180 degrees from the centerline around a mandrel whose diameter is eight times the nominal hose OD. Flexing shall be accomplished within 4 s. Hose shall not fracture or show any cracks, checks, or breaks in the tube or cover.

9.4 Adhesion Test—When tested in accordance with ASTM D 413, a pull of not less than 44.48 N (10 lb) shall be required to separate a 2.54 cm (1 in) wide ring section of the bond between any adjacent layers of the hose.

9.5 Bursting Strength—Samples shall meet the minimum bursting strength requirements shown in Table 1B.

9.6 Ozone Resistance—The outer cover of the hose shall show no cracking when examining the cover of the hose under 7X magnification, ignoring the areas immediately adjacent to or within the area covered by the binding.

Bend the hose around a cylinder, the diameter of which shall be seven times the nominal outside diameter of the hose, and bind the ends. The cylinder and binding shall be made of metal or materials that prevent the consumption of ozone. If the hose collapses when bent around the cylinder, provide for internal support of the hose.

Condition the hose, on the cylinder, for 24.0 h ± 0.5 h at room temperature, and then place it in an exposure chamber containing air mixed with ozone in the proportion of 50 pphm ± 5 ozone in air by volume, for 70 to 72 h. Ambient air temperature in chamber during test shall be 40 °C ± 3 °C (104 °F ± 5 °F). Examine the cover of the hose for cracks under 7X magnification, ignoring the areas immediately adjacent to or within the area covered by the binding.

9.7 Length Change—Hose shall not change in length more than +2%, -4% when pressure is increased from 0 MPa (0 psi) to the maximum working pressure shown in Table 1B.

9.8 Tensile Strength and Elongation

a. Original Tensile Strength of Cover—6.9 MPa (1000 psi) min
b. Original Tensile Strength of Tube—6.9 MPa (1000 psi) min
c. Original Elongation of Cover—175% min
d. Original Elongation of Tube—150% min

9.9 Dry Heat Resistance—After oven aging for 70 h at a temperature of 100 °C (212 °F), the reduction in tensile strength and elongation of specimens taken from tube and cover material shall not exceed the following values:

a. Original Tensile Strength—20%
b. Original Elongation—50%

9.10 Oil Resistance—After 70 h immersion in ASTM No. 3 oil at a temperature of 121 °C (250 °F), the reduction in tensile strength and elongation of specimens taken from the tube material shall not exceed the following values:

a. Original Tensile Strength—65%
b. Original Elongation—50%

In addition, the volume change of specimens taken from the tube and cover material shall not exceed 0 to +100%.

9.11 Identification Marking—Hose shall be identified with the SAE number, type, size of inside diameter in fractions, date code in days of the year, and last digit of the year (for example, 1707 represents the 170th day of 1987), and hose manufacturer's and/or coupling manufacturer's code marking. This marking shall appear on the outer cover of the hose at intervals of not greater than 25.4 cm (10 in). Additional identification may be added as agreed on by user and supplier.

9.12 100% Proof Pressure Test—Each hose assembly shall be proof pressure tested using air, oil, or water as the pressure medium. Hose shall be tested at the maximum working pressure when air is used or at the proof pressure shown in Table 1B when tested with oil or water. Care should be taken when testing with air due to its explosive nature at high pressure.

HIGH-TEMPERATURE POWER STEERING PRESSURE HOSE—SAE J2050 APR2001

SAE Standard

Report of the SAE Power Steering Hose Standards Committee approved February 1993. Revised by the SAE Automotive Brake and Steering Hose Standards Committee April 2001. Rationale statement available.

Foreword—This SAE Standard represents the minimum quality recognized by original equipment manufacturers and hose suppliers as essential for satisfactory and safe operation by the hose itself and other coacting parts of the power steering system. The original equipment manufacturer may, at his option, add or alter tests through OEM specifications.

*1. **Scope***—This SAE Standard covers two types of hose fabricated from textile reinforcement and synthetic rubber, assembled with end fittings for use in high-temperature automotive power steering applications as flexible connections within the temperature range of -40 to +150 °C (-40 to +302 °F) maximum and 10.3 MPa (1500 psi) maximum working pressure. These hoses are intended for use in applications where reduction in amplitude of pump pressure pulsation is required. Class A hose has a nominal OD of 19.84 mm (0.781 in). Class B hose is a lightweight hose with a nominal OD of 17.91 mm (0.705 in). This specification defines the minimum performance levels of a flexible connector in the hydraulic steering system to convey power steering fluid from the steering pump to the steering gear.

*2. **References***

2.1 Applicable Publications—The following publications form a part of this specification to the extent specified herein.

2.1.1 ASTM PUBLICATIONS—Available from ASTM, 100 Barr Harbor Drive, West Conshohocken, PA 19428-2959.

ASTM D 380—Standard Test Methods for Rubber Hose

ASTM D 413—Test Method for Rubber Property—Adhesion to Flexible Substrate

*3. **Hose Construction***—The construction of this hose embodies a smooth bore inner tube of suitable synthetic rubber material, reinforced with textile reinforcement and covered with a synthetic rubber outer cover. The tube shall be resistant to transmission and power steering fluids. The cover shall be abrasion, heat and weather resistant.

*4. **Dimensions***—See Table 1.

TABLE 1—DIMENSIONS

	Class A Standard	Class B Light Weight
ID	9.4/10.3 mm (0.370/0.405 in)	9.4/10.3 mm (0.370/0.405 in)
OD	19.05/20.62 mm (0.750/0.812 in)	17.27/18.54 mm (0.680/0.730 in)

Concentricity based upon full indicator reading between the inside bore and the outer surface of the hose shall not exceed 0.76 mm (0.030 in).

*5. **Test Procedure***—Procedures described in ASTM D 380 shall be followed wherever applicable.

*6. **Qualification Tests***—To qualify hose under this specification, all of the requirements shown under Section 9 must be met. The sample sizes listed in Table 2 represent minimums for validation of a production process. The manufacturer of the power steering hose assembly is responsible for conducting appropriate design verification exercises and for controlling the production processes such that any hose assembly provided for sale or use on a vehicle will be capable of meeting the performance requirements listed in Section 9 when subjected to the tests listed in Table 2, performed per the procedures and conditions described in Section 9.

*7. **Inspection Tests***—Production shipments or lots of qualified hose shall be tested in accordance with Table 2 and shall conform to the applicable test requirements, but the user may test hose or hose assemblies from any or all such production shipments or lots to all the test requirements. A minimum of seven sample hose assemblies, selected at random, as listed in Table 2, are required to conduct a complete test. In the event of a failure, the test or tests that failed shall be retested using a minimum of twice the number of samples indicated in Table 2. Failure of any of the retested samples shall be cause for rejection of the entire lot.

TABLE 2—INSPECTION TESTS

Title and Section Number	Minimum Sample Size
1. Volumetric Expansion (9.7) followed by Bursting Strength (9.5)	1
2. Tensile (9.2)	1
3. Adhesion (9.4)	1
4. Low-Temperature Flexibility (9.3)	1
5. Impulse (9.1)	3

*8. **Frequency of Testing for Inspection***—All inspection tests except Impulse shall be performed on either a bulk hose lot or a coupled hose lot basis, or test may be split between a bulk hose lot and a coupled hose lot.

A coupled hose lot shall not exceed 10 000 hose assemblies and a bulk hose lot shall not exceed 6096 m (20 000 ft) of bulk hose.

*9. **Test Requirements***

9.1 Impulse Test

9.1.1 TEST CONDITIONS—New hose assemblies shall be used for each test. The hose assemblies shall be clean and dry and allowed to stabilize at room temperature for a minimum of 24 h prior to testing.

Test equipment is to be capable of maintaining the following parameters:

a. Continuous flow of test fluid through the hoses at a rate of 6.1 L/m ±0.8 L/m (1.6 GPM ±0.2 GPM) per hose except at high pressure.
b. A system oil capacity sufficient to provide 4.7 to 9.4 L (1.25 to 2.50 gal) of oil per test hose.

Using new power steering fluid, the test hose assemblies shall be subjected to the following test conditions:

a. Cycle Pressure
    1. Low pressure—0 to 0.70 MPa (0 to 100 psi)
    2. High pressure—10.3 to 10.7 MPa (1500 to 1550 psi)
b. Cycle Rate—30/40 cycles per min.
c. Pressure Rise Time—0.2 s ±0.02 s.
d. Pressure Dwell Time—0.7 s ±0.05 s.
e. Oil Temperature (in hose)—150 °C ±3 °C (302 °F ±5 °F)
f. Ambient Temperature—150 °C ±6 °C (302 °F ±10 °F)
g. Test Cycle (repeated for the duration of the test)
    1. Hot Cycle—25 000 cycles
    2. Cool Down—Shut off machine and cool to a reservoir temperature of 82 °C (180 °F). After the initial cool down at 25 000 cycles, the cool down is to be repeated at 50 000 cycle intervals.

The hose assemblies should be inspected for leakage within the first 5 min of a machine start-up following a cool down.

h. Test Fluid—As specified by the original equipment manufacturers. Recommended fluids are:
    1. Exxon, Houston, TX—FN-1973CJ
    2. Texaco—Code 1831-PSF
i. Test Duration
    1. Performance Validation—200 000 cycles (min)
    2. Lot Approval—100 000 cycles (min)
j. Failure—Any fluid observed dripping from the hose during the test constitutes a failure.

9.2 Tensile Test—Hose assemblies shall withstand a minimum tensile load of 4480 N (1000 lb) without the fittings pulling off or rupture of the hose.

9.3 Low-Temperature Flexibility—Samples shall be subjected to a temperature of -40 °C ±1 °C (-40 °F ±2 °F) for a period of 24 h, after which the hose shall be flexed in the cold chamber through 180 degrees from the centerline around a mandrel whose diameter is eight times the nominal hose OD. Flexing shall be accomplished within 3 to 5 s. Hose shall not fracture or show any cracks, checks, or breaks in the tube or cover.

9.4 Adhesion Test—When tested in accordance with ASTM D 413, using the machine method, ring specimen, a pull of not less than 44.8 N (10 lb) shall be required to separate a 25 mm (1 in) wide ring section of the bond between any adjacent layers of the hose.

In case of repeated tearing of the rubber stock, instead of separating from the braid, no fewer than three tests will be run starting at locations approximately 120 degrees apart to assure uniform adhesion. A new test specimen will be used for each test. Take as a result of the test the average load at which tearing occurs and note as a tear adhesion. A stock tear value below the minimum is acceptable.

9.5 Bursting Strength—Samples shall meet a minimum bursting requirement of 41.4 MPa (6000 psi).

9.6 Ozone Resistance—The outer cover of the hose shall show no cracking when examining the cover of the hose under 7X magnification, ignoring the areas immediately adjacent to or within the area covered by the binding. Bend the hose around a cylinder, the diameter of which shall be eight times the nominal outside diameter of the hose and bind the ends. The cylinder and binding shall be made of metal or materials which prevent the consumption of ozone. If the hose collapses when bent around the cylinder, provide for internal support of the hose. Condition the hose, on the cylinder for 24.0 h ± 0.5 h at room temperature and then place in an exposure chamber containing air mixed with ozone in such quantities that a 50 mPa ± 5 mPa partial pressure of ozone is present at 40 °C ± 3 °C (104 °F ± 5 °F) for 70 to 72 h. Ambient air temperature in the chamber during test shall be 40 °C ± 3 °C (104 °F ± 5 °F).

9.7 Volumetric Expansion—Samples shall be installed on the test fixture in a manner which allows the hose to be straight but not under tension when test pressure is applied. Samples shall be preconditioned at 9.0 MPa ± 0.14 MPa (1300 psi ± 20 psi) for 30 s ± 5 s and allowed to recover at 0 MPa (0 psi) for 2 min ± 5 s prior to the test. Test pressure shall then be applied and held for 2 min ± 5 s. At the end of this period, the inlet valve shall be closed and the test fluid allowed to rise in the burette for a period of 1 min ± 5 s. The outlet valve shall then be closed and the reading taken. The average of three volumetric expansion readings per sample shall not exceed the values listed as follows:

a. Volumetric Expansion cc/m at 0 to 9.0 MPa (1300 psi)
   1. Maximum—46 cc/m (14 cc/ft)
   2. Minimum—10 cc/m (3 cc/ft)

9.8 100% Proof Pressure Test—Bulk Hose—Each bulk hose length shall be proof pressure tested using water as the pressure medium. Test pressure shall be 20.7 MPa (3000 psi) minimum and held for not less than 30 s nor more than 60 s.

NOTE—Bulk Hose is defined as straight random length hose intended for further processing into cut lengths.

9.9 Identification Marking—Hose shall be identified with the SAE number, class, size of inside diameter in fractions, a six-digit date code as shown in Figure 1 and hose manufacturer's and/or coupling manufacturer's code marking. This marking shall appear on the outer cover of the hose at intervals of not greater than 254 mm (10 in).

Example date June 7, 1992

6-digit date 060792 = 06 (month) 07 (day) 92 (year)

FIGURE 1—EXAMPLE OF IDENTIFICATION MARKING

Additional identification may be added as agreed upon by user and supplier.

HIGH-TEMPERATURE POWER STEERING RETURN HOSE—LOW PRESSURE—SAE J2076 APR2001

SAE Standard

Report of the SAE Power Steering Hose Standards Committee approved February 1993. Revised by the SAE Automotive Brake and Steering Hose Standards Committee April 2001. Rationale statement available.

Foreword—This SAE Standard represents the minimum quality recognized by original equipment manufacturers and hose suppliers as essential for satisfactory and safe operation by the hose itself and other coacting parts of the power steering system. The original equipment manufacturer may, at his option, add or alter tests through OEM specifications.

1. Scope—This SAE Standard covers hose fabricated from textile reinforcement and synthetic rubber, assembled with clamps and/or end fittings for use in high-temperature automotive power steering applications as flexible connections within the temperature range of –40 to +150 °C (–40 to +302 °F) maximum and 1.21 MPa (175 psi) maximum working pressure. This specification defines the minimum performance levels of a flexible connector in the hydraulic steering system to convey power steering fluid from the steering gear back to the pump/reservoir.

2. References

2.1 Applicable Publications—The following publications form a part of this specification to the extent specified herein. Unless otherwise indicated, the latest issue of SAE publications shall apply.

2.1.1 SAE PUBLICATION—Available from SAE, 400 Commonwealth Drive, Warrendale, PA 15096-0001.

SAE J962—Formed Tube Ends for Hose Connections

2.1.2 ASTM PUBLICATIONS—Available from ASTM, 100 Barr Harbor Drive, West Conshohocken, PA 19428-2959.

ASTM D 380—Standard Test Methods for Rubber Hose

ASTM D 413—Test Method for Rubber Property—Adhesion to Flexible Substrate

3. Hose Construction—The construction of this hose embodies a smooth bore inner tube of suitable synthetic rubber material, reinforced with textile reinforcement and covered with a synthetic rubber outer cover. The tube shall be resistant to transmission and power steering fluids. The cover shall be abrasion, heat and weather resistant.

4. Dimensions

a. ID—9.09 to 9.91 mm (0.358 to 0.390 in)
b. OD—15.88 to 17.48 mm (0.625 to 0.688 in)

Concentricity based upon full indicator reading between the inside bore and the outer surface of the hose shall not exceed 0.76 mm (0.030 in).

5. Test Procedure—Procedures described in ASTM D 380 shall be followed wherever applicable.

6. Qualification Tests—To qualify hose under this specification, all of the requirements shown under Section 9 must be met. The sample sizes listed in Table 1 represent minimums for validation of a production process. The manufacturer of the power steering hose assembly is responsible for conducting appropriate design verification exercises and for controlling the production processes such that any hose assembly provided for sale or use on a vehicle will be capable of meeting the performance requirements listed in Section 9 when subjected to the tests listed in Table 1, performed per the procedures and conditions described in Section 9.

7. Inspection Tests—Production shipments or lots of qualified hose shall be tested in accordance with Table 1 and shall conform to the applicable test requirements, but the user may test hose or hose assemblies from any or all such production shipments or lots to all the test requirements. A minimum of nine sample hose assemblies, selected at random, as listed in Table 1, are required to conduct a complete test. In the event of a failure, the test or tests that have failed shall be retested using a minimum of twice the number of samples indicated in Table 1. Failure of any of the retested samples shall be cause for rejection of the entire lot.

TABLE 1—INSPECTION TESTS

Title and Section Number	Minimum Sample Size
1. Length Change (9.6) followed by Bursting Strength (9.5)	1
2. Tensile (9.2)	1
3. Adhesion (9.4)	1
4. Low-Temperature Flexibility (9.3)	1
5. Impulse (9.1)	3
6. Kink Resistance (9.8)	1
7. Assembly Effort (9.9)	1

8. Frequency of Testing for Inspection—All inspection tests except Impulse shall be performed on either a bulk hose lot or a coupled hose lot basis, or test may be split between a bulk hose lot and a coupled hose lot.

A coupled hose lot shall not exceed 10 000 hose assemblies and a bulk hose lot shall not exceed 6096 m (20 000 ft) of bulk hose.

9. Test Requirements

9.1 Impulse Test

9.1.1 TEST CONDITIONS—New hose assemblies shall be used for each test. The hose assemblies shall be clean and dry and allowed to stabilize at room temperature for a minimum of 24 h prior to testing.

Test equipment is to be capable of maintaining the following parameters:

a. Continuous flow of test fluid through the hoses at a rate of 6.1 L/m ± 0.8 L/m (1.6 GPM ± 0.2 GPM) per hose except at high pressure
b. A system oil capacity sufficient to provide 4.7 to 9.4 L (1.25 to 2.50 gal) of oil per test hose

Using new power steering fluid, the test hose assemblies shall be subjected to the following test conditions:

a. Cycle Pressure
   1. Low Pressure—0 to 0.40 MPa (0 to 58 psi)
   2. High Pressure—1.20 to 1.35 MPa (174 to 196 psi)
b. Cycle Rate—30/40 cycles per min.
c. Pressure Rise Time—0.2 s ± 0.02 s
d. Pressure Dwell Time—0.7 s ± 0.05 s
e. Oil Temperature (in hose)—150 °C ± 3 °C (302 °F ± 5 °F)
f. Ambient Temperature—150 °C ± 6 °C (302 °F ± 10 °F)
g. Test Cycle (repeated for the duration of the test)
   1. Hot Cycle—25 000 cycles
   2. Cool Down—Shut off machine and cool to a reservoir temperature of 82 °C (180 °F).
      After the initial cool down at 25 000 cycles, the cool down is to be repeated at 50 000 cycle intervals.
      The hose assemblies should be inspected for leakage within the first 5 min of a machine start-up following a cool down.
h. Test Fluid—As specified by the original equipment manufacturers. Recommended fluids are:
   1. Exxon, Houston, TX—FN-1973CJ
   2. Texaco—Code 1831-PSF
i. Test Duration
   1. Performance Validation—200 000 cycles (min)
   2. Lot Approval—100 000 cycles (min)
j. Failure—Any fluid observed dripping from the hose during the test constitutes a failure.

9.2 Tensile Test—Hose assemblies shall withstand a minimum tensile load of 380 N (85 lb) without the fittings pulling off or rupture of the hose.

9.3 Low-Temperature Flexibility—Samples shall be subjected to a temperature of –40 °C ± 1 °C (–40 °F ± 2 °F) for a period of 24 h, after which the hose shall be flexed in the cold chamber through 180 degrees from the centerline around a mandrel whose diameter is eight times the nominal hose OD. Flexing shall be accomplished within 3 to 5 s. Hose shall not fracture or show any cracks, checks, or breaks in the tube or cover.

9.4 Adhesion Test—When tested in accordance with ASTM D 413, using the machine method, ring specimen, a pull of not less than 44.8 N (10 lb) shall be required to separate a 25 mm (1 in) wide ring section of the bond between any adjacent layers of the hose.

In case of repeated tearing of the rubber stock, instead of separating from the braid, no fewer than three tests will be run starting at locations approximately 120 degrees apart to assure uniform adhesion. A new test specimen will be used for each test. Take as a result of the test the average load at which tearing occurs and note as a tear adhesion. A stock tear value below the minimum is acceptable.

9.5 Bursting Strength—Samples shall meet a minimum bursting requirement of 6.90 MPa (1000 psi).

9.6 Length Change—Hose shall not change more than +2%, –6% when pressurized from 0 to 1.21 MPa (175 psi).

9.7 Ozone Resistance—The outer cover of the hose shall show no cracking when examining the cover of the hose under 7X magnification, ignoring the areas immediately adjacent to or within the area covered by the binding. Bend the hose around a cylinder, the diameter of which shall be eight times the nominal outside diameter of the hose and bind the ends. The cylinder and binding shall be made of metal or materials which prevent the consumption of ozone. If the hose collapses when bent around the cylinder, provide for internal support of the hose. Condition the hose on the cylinder for 24.0 h ± 0.5 h at room temperature and then place in an exposure chamber containing air mixed with ozone in such quantities that a 50 mPa ± 5 mPa partial pressure of ozone is present at 40 °C ± 3 °C (104 °F ± 5 °F) for 70 to 72 h. Ambient air temperature in the chamber during the test shall be 40 °C ± 3 °C (104 °F ± 5 °F).

9.8 Kink Resistance—The change in OD of the hose at the center of the loop shall not exceed 20% when the end of a 230 mm (9.0 in) length of hose is placed in a locating fixture having two holes at 18 to 19 mm (0.709 to 0.748 in) diameter, 25 mm (1 in) deep and 115 mm (4.5 in) between centerlines of the hose.

9.9 Assembly Effort—The force required to install a 76 mm (3 in) length of hose at a rate of 50 mm/min (2 in/min) over an insert shall not exceed 133 N (30 lb). The insert used shall be as defined by SAE J962.

9.10 100% Proof Pressure Test—Bulk Hose—Each bulk hose length shall be proof pressure tested using water as the pressure medium. Test pressure shall be 1.7 MPa (250 psi) minimum and held for not less than 30 s nor more than 60 s.

NOTE—Bulk Hose is defined as straight random length hose intended for further processing into cut lengths.

9.11 Identification Marking—Hose shall be identified with the SAE number, size of inside diameter in fractions, a six-digit date code as shown in Figure 1 and hose manufacturer's and/or coupling manufacturer's code marking. This marking shall appear on the outer cover of the hose at intervals of not greater than 254 mm (10 in).

Example date June 7, 1992

6-digit date 060792 = 06 (month) 07 (day) 92 (year)

FIGURE 1—IDENTIFICATION MARKING

Additional identification may be added as agreed upon by user and supplier.

POWER STEERING PRESSURE HOSE—WIRE BRAID —SAE J190 MAY1998

SAE Standard

Report of SAE Nonmetallic Materials Committee approved August 1970. Revised by the SAE Nonmetallic Materials Committee May 1998. Rationale statement available.

Foreword—This Document has also changed to comply with the new SAE Technical Standards Board format. All Sections are numbered. References were added as Section 2. Metric has been added throughout the document.

1. Scope—This specification covers hose fabricated from wire braid and synthetic rubber, assembled with end fittings for use in automotive applications up to 10.3 MPa (1500 psi) maximum pressure, as flexible connections within the temperature range of -40 °C to 121 °C (-40 °F to +250 °F) average, 13.5 °C (275 °F) maximum peaks.

The specification in this SAE Standard originated in the SAE-ASTM Technical Committee on Automotive Rubber (other than tires). They represent the correlation of the best information available from research investigation and production experience on the minimum constructional and performance characteristics essential for new power steering assemblies used as original or replacement equipment. This standard applies to passenger cars. It may prove useful to truck manufacturers, but it is not to be presented as present practices.

They also represent the minimum quality recognized by original equipment manufacturers and hose suppliers as essential for satisfactory and safe operation by the hose itself and other coacting parts of the power steering system. The original equipment manufacturer may, at his option, add or alter tests through OEM specifications.

2. References

2.1 Applicable Publications—The following publications form a part of the specification to the extent specified herein.

2.1.1 ASTM PUBLICATIONS—Available from ASTM, 100 Barr Harbor Drive, West Conshohocken, PA 19428-2959

ASTM D 380—Methods of Testing Rubber Hose
ASTM D 413—Tests for Adhesion of Vulcanized Rubber (Friction Test)
ASTM D 571—Testing Automotive Hydraulic Brake Hose
ASTM D 1149—Test for Accelerated Ozone Cracking of Vulcanized Rubber

3. Hose Construction—The construction of this hose embodies a smooth bore inner tube of suitable synthetic rubber material, reinforced with one ply of wire braid and covered with a synthetic rubber outer cover.

4. Dimensions—Hose must be within the tolerances shown in Tables 1A and 1B. In addition, the concentricity, based upon full indicator reading, between the inside bore and the outer surface of the hose shall not exceed 0.076 cm (0.030 in).

5. Test Procedures—Procedures described in ASTM D 380 shall be followed wherever applicable.

6. Qualification Tests—To qualify hose under this specification, all of the requirements shown under Test Requirements must be met.

7. Inspection Tests—Production shipments or lots of qualified hose shall be tested in accordance with Table 2 and shall conform to the applicable test requirements, but the user may test hose or hose assemblies from any or all such production shipments or lots to all the test requirements. Fourteen sample hose assemblies, selected at random, as listed in Table 2 are required to conduct a complete test. In the event of a failure, the test or tests which have failed shall be retested using twice the number of samples indicated in Table 2. Failure of any of the retested samples shall be cause for rejection of the entire lot.

8. Frequency of Testing for Inspection—All inspection tests except Impulse shall be performed on either a bulk hose lot or a coupled hose lot basis or tests may be split between a bulk hose lot and a coupled hose lot.

A coupled hose lot shall not exceed 10,000 hose assemblies and a bulk hose lot shall not exceed 6096 m (20 000 ft) of bulk hose. The lot size for Impulse testing shall not exceed 30 480 (100 000 ft) of bulk hose.

9. Test Requirements

9.1 Impulse Test

9.1.1 TEST CONDITIONS

a. Oil Temperature—135 °C ± 2 °C (275 °F ± 5 °F).
b. Ambient Temperature—104 °C ± 11 °C (220 °F ± 20 °F).
c. Cycle Rate—30 to 40 per minute.
d. Cycle Data—Pressure rise time, 0.20 s ± 0.10 s. High pressure hold time, 0.65 s ± 0.20 s. Pressure drop time, 0.20 s ± 0.10 s.
e. Pressure Variation—0 to 0.69 MPa (0 to 100 psi) to maximum working pressure listed in Table 1B.

9.1.2 HYDRAULIC FLUID AND TEST FIXTURE——As specified by the original equipment manufacturer.

9.1.3 CYCLE LIFE——Samples submitted to this test shall exceed 100 000 cycles for inspection acceptance and 225 000 cycles for qualification testing, without failure.

9.2 Tensile Test—When tested in accordance with ASTM D 571, hose assemblies shall withstand a minimum tensile load as specified in Table 1B without the fittings pulling off or rupture of the hose.

9.3 Low Temperature Flexibility—Hose and/or hose assemblies shall be subjected to -40 °C ± 1 °C (-40 °F ±2 °F) for 24 h. After this time and while still at -40 °C ± 1 °C (-40 °F ± 2 °F), the samples shall be flexed over a mandrel having a diameter equal to twice the minimum bend radius specified in Table 1B in 4 s or less. Hose shall be bent through 180 degrees over the mandrel. After flexing, the sample shall be allowed to warm to room temperature and be visually examined for cover cracks and subjected to the proof test. There shall be no cover cracks or leakage.

TABLE 1A—HOSE DIMENSIONS (METRIC)

Nominal ID, cm	Nominal OD, cm	ID Tolerance, cm	OD Tolerance, cm	Wire OD, cm	Working Pressure, max, MPa	Proof Pressure, MPa	Burst Strength, min, MPa	Tensile Strength, min, N	Bend Radius, min, cm
0.952	1.984	1.011/0.932	2.062/1.905	1.567/1.450	10.3	13.8	62	4448.2	12.7
1.27	2.302	1.349/1.232	2.383/0.223	1.905/1.748	10.3	13.8	55.2	5337.9	17.78

TABLE 1B—HOSE DIMENSIONS (ENGLISH)

Nominal ID, cm	Nominal OD, cm	ID Tolerance, cm	OD Tolerance, cm	Wire OD, cm	Working Pressure, max, MPa	Proof Pressure, MPa	Burst Strength, min, MPa	Tensile Strength, min, N	Bend Radius, min, cm
3/8	25/32	0.398/0.367	0.812/0.750	0.617/0.571	1500	2000	9000	1000	5
1/2	29/32	0.531/0.485	0.938/0.875	0.750/0.688	1500	2000	8000	1200	7

9.4 Adhesion Test—When tested in accordance with ASTM D 413, a pull of not less than 44.48 N (10 lb) shall be required to separate a 2.54 cm (1 in) wide ring section of the bond between the cover and the reinforcement.

9.5 Bursting Strength—Samples shall meet the minimum bursting strength requirements shown in Table 1B.

9.6 Ozone Resistance—Test procedure and apparatus shall be in accordance with ASTM D 1149, where applicable. A specimen of the hose shall be bent around a mandrel having an outside diameter seven times the nominal outside diameter of the hose under test. The two ends of the hose shall be tied where they cross one another with enameled copper or aluminum wire. After mounting, the specimens shall be permitted to rest in a relatively ozone-free atmosphere for 24 hr at room temperature. The mounted specimen shall be placed in a suitable ozone test chamber that is maintained at an ozone concentration of 50 ± 5 parts ozone per 100 million parts of air (by volume) and a chamber ambient temperature of 38 °C ± 1 °C (100 °F ± 2 °F).

After 72 hr of exposure, specimens shall be removed from the chamber and permitted to cool to room temperature and then, while still on the mandrel, shall be visually inspected for signs of cracking under 7X magnification. There shall be no evidence of cracking of the cover.

9.7 Length Change—Hose shall not change in length more than +2%, -4% when pressure is increased from 0 MPa (0 psig) to maximum working pressure shown in Table 1B.

9.8 Tensile Strength and Elongation

a. Original Tensile Strength of Tube—6.9 MPa (1000 psi) min
b. Original Elongation of Cover—175% min
c. Original Elongation of Tube—100% min

9.9 Dry Heat Resistance—After oven aging for 70 hr at a temperature of 100 °C (212 °F), the reduction in tensile strength and elongation of specimens taken from the tube and cover material shall not exceed the following values:

a. Original Tensile Strength—20%
b. Original Elongation—50%

9.10 Oil Resistance—After 70 h immersion in ASTM No. 3 oil at a temperature of 121 °C (250 °F), the reductions in tensile strength and elongation of specimens taken from the tube material shall not exceed the following values:

a. Original Tensile Strength—65%
b. Original Elongation—50%

In addition, the volume change of specimens taken from the tube material shall not exceed 0 to +100%.

9.11 Identification Marking—Hose shall be identified with the SAE number, size of inside diameter in fractions, date code in days of the year and last digit of the year (for example, 1707 represents the 170th day of 1967), and hose manufacturer's and/or coupling manufacturer's code marking. This marking shall appear on the outer cover of the hose at intervals of not greater than 25.4 cm (10 in). Additional identification may be added as agreed upon by user and supplier.

9.12 100% Proof Pressure Test—Each hose assembly shall be proof pressure tested using air, oil, or water as the pressure medium. Hose shall be tested at the maximum working pressure when air is used or at the proof pressure shown in Table 1B when tested with oil or water. Care should be taken when testing with air due to its explosive nature at high pressures.

TABLE 2—INSPECTION TESTS

Test	Samples Required
1. Length Change (paragraph 9.7) followed by Bursting Strength (paragraph 9.5)	3
2. Tensile (paragraph 9. 2)	3
3. Adhesion (paragraph 9.4)	
4. Low Temperature Flexibility (paragraph 9.3)	1
5. Impulse (paragraph 9.1)	6

(R) REFRIGERANT 12 AUTOMOTIVE AIR-CONDITIONING HOSE—SAE J51 AUG1998 SAE Standard

Report of the SAE Nonmetallic Materials Committee, approved September 1960, revised by the SAE Coolant Hose Committee May 1989, and revised by the SAE Air-Conditioning Hose and Hose Assembly Subcommittee of the SAE Coolant Hose Committee August 1998. J51 JUL88 was not included in the SAE Handbook due to technical changes.

Foreword—This Document has also changed to comply with the new SAE Technical Standards Board format. References were added as Section 2.

1. Scope—This SAE Standard covers reinforced hose, or hose assemblies, intended for conducting liquid and gaseous dichlorodifluoromethane (refrigerant 12) in automotive air-conditioning systems. The hose shall be designed to minimize permeation of refrigerant 12 and contamination of the system and to be serviceable over a temperature range of –30 to 120 °C (–22 to 248 °F). Specific construction details are to be agreed upon between user and supplier.[1]

NOTE—SAE J2064 is the Standard for refrigerant 134a hose. For refrigerant 134a use, refer to SAE J2064

2. References

2.1 Applicable Publications—The following publications form a part of this specification to the extent specified herein. Unless otherwise specified, the latest issue of SAE publications shall apply.

2.1.1 SAE PUBLICATION—Available from SAE, 400 Commonwealth Drive, Warrendale, PA 15096-0001.

SAE J343 JUN87—Tests and Procedures for SAE 100R Series Hydraulic Hose and Hose Assemblies

SAE J2064—R134a Refrigerant Automotive Air-Conditioning Hose

2.1.2 ASTM PUBLICATION—Available from ASTM, 100 Barr Harbor Drive, West Conshohocken, PA 19428-2959.

ASTM D 380—Methods of Testing Rubber Hose

3. Manufacture—The following is a list of common constructions and standard sizes of R12 hose, but is not meant to exclude other sizes and constructions.

3.1 Size—Standard dimensions are given in Tables 1A and 1B.

3.2 Type A1 and A2—Rubber, Textile Reinforced—The hose shall be built having a seamless oil-resistant synthetic rubber tube. The reinforcement shall consist of textile yarn, cord, or fabric adhered to the tube and cover. The outer cover shall be heat and ozone-resistant synthetic rubber. It is recommended that the cover be pinpricked.

NOTE—Commercial product normally offered for Type A1 hose has been a one braid reinforcement of textile yarn with a smaller OD than Type A2 hoses. Type A2 hose has been a two braid hose. Hose fittings for Type A1 and A2 hoses are not normally interchangeable.

3.3 Type B1 and B2—Rubber, Wire Reinforced—The hose shall be built having a seamless oil-resistant synthetic rubber tube. The reinforcement shall consist of steel wire adhered to the rubber tube. The cover shall consist of a heat-resistant textile yarn impregnated with a synthetic rubber cement.

NOTE—Type B1 hose is currently not being manufactured. Commercial product normally offered for Type B1 hose has been a one-braid reinforcement of wire with unique ID and OD dimensions. Type B2 hose has been a one-braid reinforcement of wire with unique ID and OD dimensions conforming to those specified in SAE 100R5 hose and compatible with SAE 100R5 hose fittings. Hose fittings for Type B1 and Type B2 are not normally interchangeable.

3.4 Type C—Thermoplastic, Textile Reinforced—The hose shall have a thermoplastic tube. The reinforcement shall consist of suitable textile yarn. The outer cover shall be heat and ozone resistant. It is recommended that the cover be pin-pricked.

3.5 Type D—Thermoplastic, Textile Reinforced, Rubber Covered—The hose shall consist of textile yarn, cord, or fabric adhered to the tube and cover. It is recommended that the cover be pin-pricked.

4. Hose Identification—The hose shall be identified with the SAE number, type, and size of the inside diameter in metric mm equivalents or fraction of inches or both, and hose manufacturer's code marking. This marking shall appear on the outer cover of the hose at intervals not greater than 380 mm (15 in).

5. Testing—The test procedures described in the current issue of ASTM D 380 shall be followed whenever applicable. Tests referenced in this specification are laboratory tests intended to establish a performance standard.

5.1 Test Conditions—The temperature of testing room shall be maintained at 23 °C ± 2 °C (73 °F ± 3.6 °F). The temperature of the test hose or hose assemblies shall be stabilized for 24 h at the testing room temperature prior to testing.

5.2 Permeation Tests—Hose and hose assemblies shall not permit effusion of refrigerant 12 at a rate greater than that listed in Table 2 when tested at the specified temperature. Hose and hose assemblies intended for high-pressure side service (discharge and liquid line applications) shall be tested at 100 °C ± 2 °C (212 °F ± 3.6 °F). Hose and hose assemblies intended for low-pressure side service (suction line applications) shall be tested at 80 °C ± 2 °C (176 °F ± 3.6 °F).

1. Tests referenced in this specification are laboratory tests, utilized to establish a performance standard.

TABLE 1A—REFRIGERANT 12 AUTOMOTIVE AIR-CONDITIONING HOSE DIMENSIONS(1)(2)(3)—INSIDE DIAMETER

Size mm	Size in	Type A1, A2, B1 Max mm	Type A1, A2, B1 Max in	Type A1, A2, BA Min mm	Type A1, A2, B1 Min in	Type C Max mm	Type C Max in	Type C Min mm	Type C Min in	Type B2, D(4) Max mm	Type B2, D(4) Max in	Type B2, D(4) Min mm	Type B2, D(4) Min in
4.8	3/16					5.1	0.202	4.6	0.182	5.4	0.214	4.8	0.188
6.4	1/4	7.0	0.275	6.2	0.245	6.7	0.265	6.1	0.240				
8	5/16	8.6	0.337	7.8	0.307	8.3	0.327	7.6	0.300	8.7	0.343	8.0	0.313
9.5	3/8					9.9	0.390	9.1	0.360				
10	13/32	11.1	0.436	10.2	0.401	10.7	0.423	9.9	0.389	11.1	0.437	10.3	0.406
13	1/2	13.6	0.535	12.4	0.490	13.2	0.520	12.2	0.480	13.7	0.539	12.7	0.500
16	5/8	16.8	0.660	15.6	0.615	16.5	0.650	15.2	0.600	16.9	0.667	15.9	0.625
22	7/8									23.3	0.917	22.2	0.825
29	1-1/8									29.8	1.172	28.6	1.125

1. Fitting compatibility-fittings for thermoplastic hose may not necessarily be interchangeable. Therefore, it is recommended that fittings for hose be properly matched. Fittings and/or hose manufacturers' recommendations should be followed.
2. Concentricity based on total indicator reading between inside bore of hose and outer surface of hose shall not exceed the following values:

Types A1, A2, B1, B2, and D:

Sizes 6.4 mm (1/4 in) and under	0.8 mm (0.030 in)
Sizes over 6.4 mm to 22 mm (1/4 to 7/8 in)	1.0 mm (0.040 in)
Sizes over 22 mm (7/8 in)	1.3 mm (0.050 in)

Type C

Sizes 6.4 mm (1/4 in) and under	0.5 mm (0.020 in)
Sizes over 6.4 mm to 13 mm (1/4 to 1/2 in)	0.6 mm (0.025 in)
Sizes over 13 mm (1/2 in)	0.8 mm (0.030 in)

3. These are common hose sizes, but are not meant to exclude other sizes.
4. Dimensions for 3/16 in size apply only to Type B2 hose.

TABLE 1B—REFRIGERANT 12 AUTOMOTIVE AIR-CONDITIONING HOSE DIMENSIONS(1)(2)—OUTSIDE DIAMETER

Size mm	Size in	Type A1 Max mm	Type A1 Max in	Type A1 Min mm	Type A1 Min in	Type A2 Max mm	Type A2 Max in	Type A2 Min mm	Type A2 Min in	Type B1 Max mm	Type B1 Max in	Type B1 Min mm	Type B1 Min in	Type C(2) Max mm	Type C(2) Max in	Type B2, D(3) Max mm	Type B2, D(3) Max in	Type B2, D(3) Min mm	Type B2, D(3) Min in
4.8	3/16													8.3	0.328	13.7	0.539	12.7	0.500
6.4	1/4	15.1	0.594	13.5	0.532					16.5	0.648	15.3	0.602	11.4	0.450				
8	5/16	19.1	0.750	17.5	0.688	19.8	0.781	18.3	0.719	18.8	0.742	17.7	0.696	13.5	0.530	17.6	0.695	16.7	0.656
9.5	3/8													15.2	0.600				
10	13/32	23.0	0.906	21.4	0.844	23.8	0.937	22.2	0.875	21.2	0.835	20.0	0.789	16.1	0.635	20.0	0.789	18.9	0.743
13	1/2	25.4	1.000	23.8	0.937	26.2	1.031	24.6	0.969	23.8	0.937	22.2	0.875	18.8	0.740	24.0	0.945	22.8	0.899
16	5/8	28.5	1.124	27.8	1.062	29.4	1.156	27.8	1.094	27.0	1.062	25.4	1.080	23.4	0.920	28.0	1.101	26.8	1.055
22	7/8															32.2	1.266	30.6	1.203
29	1-1/8															38.9	1.531	37.3	1.469

1. Fitting compatability-fittings for thermoplastic hose may not necessarily be interchangeable. Therefore, it is recommended that fittings for hose be properly matched. Fittings and/or hose manufacturers' recommendations should be followed.
2. Concentricity based on total indicator reading between inside bore of hose and outer surface of hose shall not exceed the following values:
   Types A1, A2, B1, B2, and D:
   - Sizes 6.4 mm (1/4 in) and under — 0.8 mm (0.030 in)
   - Sizes over 6.4 mm to 22 mm (1/4 to 7/8 in) — 1.0 mm (0.040 in)
   - Sizes over 22 mm (7/8 in) — 1.3 mm (0.050 in)

   Type C
   - Sizes 6.4 mm (1/4 in) and under — 0.5 mm (0.020 in)
   - Sizes over 6.4 mm to 13 mm (1/4 to 1/2 in) — 0.6 mm (0.025 in)
   - Sizes over 13 mm (1/2 in) — 0.8 mm (0.030 in)
3. Dimensions for 3/16 in size apply only to Type B2 hose.

The permeation test is designed to measure, by loss of mass, the rate of effusion of refrigerant 12 through the hose wall. The apparatus required consists of canisters with internal volumes of 475 to 525 cm^3 (29 to 32 in^3) and a 21 MPa (3000 psi) minimum burst pressure with appropriate fittings to connect to the hose assemblies, halogen detector, circulation air oven capable of maintaining uniform test temperature throughout the test periods, and a weighing scale capable of mass measurements of 0.1 g accuracy.

5.2.1 PROCEDURE—Four hose assemblies, having a free hose length of 1 m are required. Three of the hose assemblies shall be used for determining the loss of refrigerant and the fourth assembly shall be run as an empty plugged blank to be used as a means of determining the mass loss of the hose body alone.

Measure the free length of hose in each assembly at zero gage pressure to the nearest 1 mm (0.04 in). Connect each of the four hose assemblies to a canister and obtain the total mass of each test unit including end plugs to the nearest 0.1g.

TABLE 2—ALLOWABLE PERMEATION RATE(1)

Test Temperature °C	Test Temperature °F	Reference Pressure MPa	Reference Pressure psig	Maximum Allowable Loss of Refrigerant 12 kg/m²year(1) Types B2, A1, A2, B1	Maximum Allowable Loss of Refrigerant 12 kg/m²year(1) Types C, D	Maximum Allowable Loss of Refrigerant 12 lb/ft²year(1) Types B2, A1, A2, B1	Maximum Allowable Loss of Refrigerant 12 lb/ft²year(1) Types C, D
100	212	3.24	470	46.5	13.2	10	3
80	176	2.21	320	29	9.7	6	1.98

1. These rates reflect specific temperature and pressure conditions and do not reflect normal life permeation rates.

Load three of the test units with 0.6 mg of liquid refrigerant 12 per mm^3 of each test unit's volume to a total variance of ±5 g. Check the loaded test units with a halogen detector at a sensitivity of 11 g/year (1lb/40 years) to be sure that they do not leak. Any suitable method for safely loading may be used.

Two suggested methods are as follows:

5.2.1.1 *Method I*—Hose assemblies may be conveniently loaded by conditioning the hose assemblies, connected canisters, and refrigerant 12 cylinder in a cold box for 4 h minimum at a temperature below the boiling point of the refrigerant 12. Using the density of the refrigerant 12 at the conditioning temperature, the proper load weight may be calculated in terms of volume at the temperature, they may be loaded by measuring the calculated volume of liquid refrigerant 12 with a graduate. The filled hose assemblies and connected canisters should be capped while still at the conditioning temperature, but may be removed from the cold box to complete the tightening to ensure proper seal.

5.2.1.2 *Method II*—The hose assemblies and connected canisters may be loaded at room temperature by transferring the refrigerant 12 under pressure through suitable valves and connections. A suitable apparatus consists of a refrigerant 12 cylinder, liquid accumulator, piston pump, and controls for metering the required charge.

Place the three loaded and one blank test units in the air oven at the specified test temperature for a period of 30 min ± 5 min to drive off surface moisture. Do not bend the hose in a curve with a diameter smaller than 20 times the outside diameter of the hose while in the oven. Check the loaded test units for leakage and weigh all test units not less than 15 min or more than 30 min after removal from the oven. Record the mass obtained as the original mass.

Place the test units back in the oven at the specified temperature for 24 h. At the end of the 24-h period, remove the test units; weigh in the same manner as previously specified, and return to the oven. If a loss of 20 g or more occurs, discontinue the test, check for leaks, and repeat test procedure.

Consider the first 24-h period as the preconditioning period. Disregard the mass loss during this period in final calculations. 72 h after the preconditioning weighing, weigh in the same manner as previously described. Calculate the 72-h mass loss. Determine the effusion rate by subtracting the corresponding mass loss of the blank from that of the loaded test unit. Express the effusion rate in kg/m^2/year or lb/ft^2/year. Calculate the rate of loss of refrigerant 12 mass for the loaded test units as follows in Equation 1:

$$R = \left[\frac{(A-B)}{L_1} - \frac{(C-E)}{L_2}\right] \cdot \frac{K}{D} \qquad \text{(Eq. 1)}$$

where:

A = Initial mass after preconditioning period of loaded test unit, g
B = Final mass after 72-h period of loaded test unit, g
C = Initial mass after preconditioning period of blank test unit, g
D = Nominal hose inside diameter, mm

E = Final mass after 72-h period of blank test unit, g
K = 39.7
R = Rate of refrigerant 12 mass loss, kilograms per square meter per year
L_1 = Free hose length of loaded test unit, m
L_2 = Free hose length of blank test unit, m

or where:
D = Nominal hose inside diameter, in
K = 12.3
R = Rate of refrigerant 12 mass loss, pounds per square foot per year
L_1 = Free hose length of loaded test unit, in
L_2 = Free hose length of blank test unit, in

At the conclusion of the test, the refrigerant charge in each specimen should be exhausted to a suitable reclamation container.

5.3 Integrity test—The hose shall show no signs of tube splitting causing rupture when tested at 107 °C ± 2 °C (225 °F ± 3.6 °F) for 24 h when loaded with refrigerant 12 as described in the Permeation Test. Three test units are required.[2] This test may be conducted as a separate test or as part of the Permeation Test by running the 24-h preconditioning period at 107 °C ± 2 °C (225 °F ± 3.6°F).

At the conclusion of the test, the refrigerant charge in each specimen should be exhausted to a suitable reclamation container.

5.4 Aging Test—The hose shall show no cracks or other disintegration when tested as specified after aging at 120 °C ± 2 °C (248 °F ± 3.6 °F) for 168 h. The mandrel used shall have a diameter eight times the nominal OD for Types A1, A2, B1, B2, and D, and shall have a diameter twice the minimum bend radius shown in Table 3 for Type C. The test unit shall have free hose length not less than 300 mm (12 in) or more than 1000 mm (39 in).

TABLE 3—MINIMUM BEND RADIUS FOR TYPE C HOSE

Size mm	Size in	Minimum Bend Radius mm	Minimum Bend Radius in
4.8	3/16	51	2.0
6.4	1/4	76	3.0
8	5/16	89	3.5
9.5	3/8	102	4.0
10	13/32	114	4.5
13	1/2	127	5.0
16	5/8	165	6.5

5.4.1 PROCEDURE—Coil the uncapped hose assembly around the mandrel of the designated size. Place in a circulating air oven for the time and at the temperature specified. After removal from the oven, allow the hose assembly to cool to room temperature, then open the hose assembly to a straight length and examine the hose externally for cracks or other disintegration. Place the hose assembly under an internal hydrostatic pressure of 2.4 MPa (350 psi) for a period of 5 min. Report any leakage through the hose as evidence of cracking.

5.5 Cold Test—The hose shall show no evidence of cracking or breaking when tested as specified. The mandrel used for Types A1, A2, B1, B2, and D shall have a diameter eight times the nominal OD of the hose and for Type C shall have diameter twice the minimum bend radius shown in Table 3. The test hose assembly shall have a free hose length not less than 450 mm (18 in) or more than 1000 mm (39 in).

5.5.1 PROCEDURE—Load the test hose assembly to 70% of capacity with refrigerant 12 at room temperature. For convenience, the hose assembly and refrigerant 12 may be chilled below the boiling point of the refrigerant 12 in order that the refrigerant 12 may be handled in the liquid state. Place the loaded hose assembly in an air oven 70 °C ± 2 °C (158 °F ± 3.6 °F) for 48 h. Remove hose assembly from the air oven and allow it to cool to room temperature. Allow the liquid to remain in the hose assembly. Place the hose assembly in a straight position along with designated size mandrel in a cold chamber at –30 °F (–22 °F) for 24 h. The cold chamber shall be capable of maintaining a uniform atmosphere of cold dry air or a mixture of air and carbon dioxide at the specified temperature with a tolerance of ±2 °C (±3.6 °F). Without removing the hose assembly from the cold chamber, bend it through 180 over mandrel of the designated size at a uniform rate within a time period of 4 to 8 s. Allow the hose assembly to warm to room temperature and exhaust the refrigerant 12 to a suitable reclamation container. Place the hose assembly under an internal hydrostatic pressure of 2.4 MPa (350 psi) for a period of 5 min. Report any leakage through the hose as evidence of cracking.

5.6 Vacuum Test—The collapse of the outside diameter of the hose shall not exceed 20% of the original outside diameter when subjected to a reduced pressure (vacuum) of 81 kPa (24 in of mercury) for 2 min.

5.6.1 PROCEDURE—The test hose assembly shall have a free hose length not less than 610 mm (24 in) nor more than 1000 mm (39 in). Bend the hose assembly to a "U" shape with the inside radius of the base of the "U" being five times the nominal outside diameter of the hose. Apply a reduced pressure (vacuum) of 81 kPa (24 in of mercury) to the bent hose assembly for 2 min. At the end of the 2-min period, while the hose is still under reduced pressure, measure the outside diameter of the hose at the base of the "U," to determine the minimum diameter in any plane.

5.7 Length Change—All hose types shall not contract in length more than 4% or elongate more than 2% when subjected to a pressure of 2.4 MPa (350 psi). Test in accordance with ASTM D 380.

5.8 Bursting Strength—The minimum bursting strength for all hose and hose assemblies except the 5/8 ID Types A1 and A2 shall be 12 MPa (1750 psi). 5/8 ID Types A1 and A2 are intended for low pressure side service and shall have minimum bursting strengths of 8.5 MPa (1250 psi). Test in accordance with ASTM D 380.

5.9 Proof Test—All hose shall satisfactorily withstand a hydrostatic proof test with a minimum hydrostatic pressure equal to 50% of the minimum required burst strength for a period not less than 30 s or more than 5 min.

5.10 Extraction Test—The extractable of the inside surface of the hose tube shall not exceed 118 g/m^2 (76 mg/in^2) and any extractable shall be oil or soft/greasy in nature. The test hose assembly shall have a free hose length not less than 450 mm (18 in) or more than 1000 mm (39 in).

5.10.1 PROCEDURE—Fill the hose assembly to capacity with a suitable solvent and then empty it immediately to remove any surface material. Load the hose assembly to approximately 70% capacity with refrigerant 12 at room temperature. For convenience, the hose assembly and refrigerant 12 may be chilled below the boiling point of refrigerant 12 in order that the refrigerant 12 may be handled in the liquid state. Place the loaded hose assembly to –34 °C (–30 °F) or colder and pour the liquid refrigerant 12 into a weighed vacuum flask, chilled to –30 °C (–22 °F) or colder, then attach flask to R12 recovery unit and recover all R12. After the refrigerant 12 has evaporated, condition the beaker at approximately 70 °C (158 °F) for 1 h to remove condensed moisture, then weigh the beaker again. Report the extract in terms of grams per square meter (milligrams per square inch) of the hose inner surface based on the nominal inside diameter of the base.

At the conclusion of the test, the refrigerant charge in each specimen should be exhausted to a suitable reclamation container.

5.11 Tensile Test of Hose Assembly—The minimum force required to separate the hose from the coupling shall not be less specified in Table 4. The test hose assembly shall have a minimum free hose length of 300 mm (12 in). Test in accordance with ASTM D 380.

TABLE 4—TENSILE STRENGTH OF HOSE ASSEMBLY

Size mm	Size in	Types A1, A2, C, D kg	Types A1, A2, C, D lb	Types B1, B2 kg	Types B1, B2 lb
4.8	3/16	91	200	91	200
6.4	1/4	113	250	181	400
8	5/16	159	250	272	600
9.5	3/8	204	450		
10	13/32	227	500	329	725
13	1/2	249	550	329	725
16	5/8	249	550	329	725
22	7/8	249	550	329	725
29	1-1/8	249	550	329	725

5.12 Ozone Test—This test is not applicable to hoses of Types B1 and B2. When the hose is bent around a mandrel with a diameter 8 times the nominal outside diameter of the hose and exposed for 70 h to ozone air atmosphere in which the ozone partial pressure is 50 MPa ± 5 MPa at 40 °C ± 2 °C (104 °F ± 3.6 °F), the outer cover of the hose shall show no cracks when examined under 7X magnification. The test hose shall be about 250 mm (10 in) longer than the mandrel circumference. Test in accordance with ASTM D 380.

2. Failure of this test by a weight loss exceeding 20% of the original refrigerant 12 mass.

5.13 Cleanliness Test—The bore of all hose and hose assemblies shall be clean and dry. When subjected to this test, there shall not be more than 270 mg/m^2 (25 mg/ft^2) of foreign material. The test hose shall not be less than 300 mm (12 in).

5.13.1 PROCEDURE—Bend the hose or hose assembly to a "U" shape, the legs of the "U" being of equal length. Position the hose in a vertical plane and fill the hose to capacity with a suitable solvent. Then filter the suitable solvent through a prepared Gooch crucible, sintered glass crucible, or 0.8 µm filter of known weight. After drying at approximately 70 °C (158 °F) for 20 min, determine by weight difference the insoluble contamination.

5.14 Impulse Test—A minimum of two hose assemblies shall be installed in a test fixture and then subjected to a pulsating pressure from 2.6 MPa ± 170 kPa (375 psi ± 25 psi) at 30 to 40 cycles per min using a petroleum base hydraulic oil such as refrigerant oil, power steering oil, or automatic transmission oil having viscosity at 107 °C ± 2 °C (225 °F ± 3.6 °F) of 5.0 to 10.0 cSt, at 107 °C ± 2 °C (225 °F ± 3.6 °F) for a minimum of 150 000 cycles with no leakage or failure. For Types A1, A2, B1, B2, and D, the minimum bend radius should be five times the nominal OD of the hoses. For Type C hoses, see Table 3.

Test in accordance with SAE J343 JUN87.

TRANSMISSION OIL COOLER HOSE—SAE J1532 FEB1995 SAE Standard

Report of the SAE Fuel, Oil, and Emission Hose Committee approved October 1988, revised April 1989, completely revised June 1993, and revised February 1995. Rationale statements available.

1. Scope—This SAE Standard covers four types of hose for use with automatic transmission fluid: A, B, AT, and BT. Type A and Type B are for use within a temperature range of -40 °C to 125 °C (-40 °F to 257 °F) while types AT and BT are for use within a temperature range of -40 °C to 150 °C (-40 °F to 302 °F). Recommended maximum operating pressure for Type A and Type AT hose is 1.7 MPa (250 psi) while recommended maximum operating pressure for Type B and Type BT hose is 1.0 MPa (150 psi). The lower pressure (Types B and BT) hose is for auxiliary cooler applications only. The reference fluid for tests requiring the use of automatic transmission fluid shall be Dexron-II E/Mercon or equivalent.

2. References

2.1 Applicable Publications—The following publications form a part of this specification to the extent specified herein. The latest issue of SAE publications shall apply.

2.1.1 SAE PUBLICATIONS—Available from SAE, 400 Commonwealth Drive, Warrendale, PA 15096-0001.

SAE J343—Tests and Procedures for SAE 100R Series Hydraulic Hose and Hose Assemblies

2.1.2 ASTM PUBLICATIONS—Available from ASTM,100 Barr Harbor Drive, West Conshohocken, PA 19428-2959.

ASTM D 380—Test Methods for Testing Rubber Hose

ASTM D 413—Test Methods for Rubber Property—Adhesion to Flexible Substrate

ASTM D 1149—Test Method for Rubber Deterioration—Surface Ozone Cracking in a Chamber (Flat Specimens)

3. Dimensions—The dimensions of this hose are listed in Table 1. Previous designations for metric nominal hose size are listed as alternative designations in parentheses. Concentricity based on total indicator reading between the bore and outer surface cannot exceed 0.8 mm (0.03 in).

TABLE 1—DIMENSIONS

Nominal Hose Size mm (alt)	Nominal Hose Size in	Inside Diameter mm	Inside Diameter in	Outside Diameter mm	Outside Diameter in
8 (7.9)	5/16	7.62/8.64	0.300/0.340	13.5/15.1	0.531/0.594
9 (8.7)	11/32	8.43/9.45	0.332/0.372	14.3/15.9	0.563/0.625
10 (9.5)	3/8	9.22/10.24	0.363/0.403	15.1/16.7	0.594/0.657
13 (12.7)	1/2	12.12/ 13.28	0.476/0.523	19.0/20.6	0.748/0.811

4. Qualification Tests

4.1 Original Burst Test—When hydrostatically tested in accordance with ASTM D 380, two hose samples with a minimum of 460 mm (18.1 in) in length, shall not burst or leak below the burst pressure defined in Table 2.

TABLE 2—BURST PRESSURE

Nominal Hose Size mm	Nominal Hose Size in	Type A and Type AT MPa	Type A and Type AT psi	Type B and Type BT MPa	Type B and Type BT psi
8	5/16	6.9	1000	4.1	600
9	11/32	6.9	1000	4.1	600
10	3/8	6.2	900	4.1	600
13	1/2	6.9	1000	4.1	600

4.2 Ozone Test—Test procedure and apparatus shall be in accordance with ASTM D 1149. A hose specimen of sufficient length shall be bent around a mandrel of non-ozone absorbing material with diameter as specified in Table 3. Both ends shall be tied at their crossing with enameled copper or aluminum wire. After mounting, the specimen shall be allowed to rest in an ozone-free atmosphere for 24 h at room temperature of 23 °C ± 2 °C (73.4 °F ± 3.6 °F). The mounted specimen shall be placed in a test chamber with an ozone partial pressure of 100 mPa ± 5 mPa at a temperature of 40 °C ± 2 °C (104 °F ± 3.6 °F). After 70 to 72 h of exposure, the specimen shall be removed, allowed to cool to a temperature of 23 °C ± 2 °C (73.4 °F ± 3.6 °F) and then visually inspected under 7X magnification. There shall be no evidence of surface cracking except for the area immediately adjacent to the wire, which shall be ignored.

4.3 Automatic Transmission Fluid Resistance Test—Type A and Type B hose shall be filled with reference fluid and aged for 168 h at 125 °C ± 2 °C (257 °F ± 3.6 °F). Type AT and Type BT hose shall be filled with reference fluid and aged for 70 h at 150 °C ± 2 °C (302 °F ± 3.6 °F), six specimens of aged hose shall then be subjected to the tests described as follows so that each specimen is subjected to one and only one of the tests.

TABLE 3—TEST FIXTURE DIMENSIONS

Nominal Hose Size mm	Nominal Hose Size in	Mandrel Diameter, Ozone Test (mm)	Mandrel Diameter, Cold Flex (mm)	Bend Radius, Impulse (mm)
8	5/16	108–121	135–151	31.8 minimum
9	11/32	114–127	143–159	36.0 minimum
10	3/8	121–134	151–167	40.2 minimum
13	1/2	152–165	190–206	50.8 minimum

a. Vacuum Collapse Test—Measure the O.D. of the hose along its narrowest dimension with calipers. Seal one end air tight and connect the other to a vacuum source. Then expose to a vacuum of 508 mm (20 in) of Hg for 30 s and measure the O.D. of the hose along its narrowest dimension under vacuum. The O.D. of the hose must not collapse more than 25% when compared to the O.D. of the hose before exposure of vacuum.

b. Kink Resistance—Hose shall not kink when tested as follows: Use a board approximately 20 mm thick with hole diameter, center distance and sample length as shown in Table 4. Insert one end of the hose into the board with the end flush on the opposite side of the board. Carefully bend the hose along its natural curvature and insert the other end carefully into the second hole until it projects 65 mm out the other side. After the hose has been in this position for 5 min, a steel ball having the diameter specified in Table 4 must be able to roll from one end of the hose to the other.

TABLE 4—KINK RESISTANCE DIMENSIONS

Nominal Hose Size mm	Nominal Hose Size in	Hose Sample Length (mm)	Hole Center Distance (mm)	Diameter of Hole (mm)	Diameter of Ball (mm)
8	5/16	275	45	15.5-16.0	3.9-4.0
9	11/32	275	50	16.0-16.5	4.3-4.4
10	3/8	300	75	17.0-17.5	4.7-4.8
13	1/2	300	100	21.0-21.5	6.2-6.3

c. Burst Test—When hydrostatically tested in accordance with ASTM D 380, two hose samples, a minimum of 460 mm (18.1 in) in length, shall not burst or leak below the burst pressure defined in Table 2.

d. Cold Flexibility—The hose shall be placed in a cold box in a straight position for 70 h at -40 °C ± 2 °C (-40 °F ± 3.6 °F). While still in the cold box, the hose shall be bent 180 degrees around a mandrel having the diameter specified in Table 3 and stabilized at -40 °C ± 2 °C (-40 °F ± 3.6 °F) within 4 to 8 s. The hose shall not fracture and shall not show any cracks, checks, or breaks in the tube or cover.

e. Adhesion—The minimum force required to separate the reinforcement from cover and tube shall be 1.4 N/mm of width (8.0 lb/in) as tested against the machine method in ASTM D 413.

4.4 Hot Oil Circulation Test—Reference fluid shall be circulated through Type A and Type B hose at 125 °C ± 3 °C (257 °F ± 5.4 °F) for 1008 h (42 days) at a pressure of 0.34 MPa ± 0.02 MPa (50 psi ± 3 psi). Reference fluid shall be circulated through Type AT and Type BT hose at 150 °C ± 3 °C (302 °F ± 5.4 °F) for 1008 h (42 days) at a pressure of 0.34 MPa ± 0.02 MPa (50 psi ± 3 psi). The hose shall not leak or burst.

4.5 Accelerated Impulse Test—Impulse testing shall be conducted in accordance with the procedure outlined in SAE J343. The test fluid shall be reference fluid, the test pressure shall be 1.03 MPa ± 0.10 MPa (150 psi ± 15 psi), the low pressure shall not exceed 0.14 MPa (20 psi), the impulse rate shall be 30 to 40 cpm, and the minimum bend radius shall be as specified in Table 3. Type A and Type B hose shall be tested at 125 °C ± 3 °C (257 °F ± 5.4 °F). Type AT and Type BT hose shall be tested at 150 °C ± 3 °C (257 °F ± 5.4 °F). The hose must not burst or leak before a minimum of 150 000 cycles for Type A and Type AT hose or a minimum of 50 000 cycles for Type B and Type BT hose.

4.6 Identification Marking—The hose shall be identified with the SAE number, type, nominal size, date code, and manufacturer's code marking. This marking shall appear at least once per length of hose repeating at intervals of no greater than 300 mm (12 in). Additional identification may be added as agreed upon by user and supplier.

(R) WINDSHIELD WASHER TUBING—SAE J1037 AUG2001 SAE Standard

Report of the SAE Nonmetallic Materials Committee approved September 1973. Revised by the SAE Coolant Hose Committee December 1987 and completely revised August 2001. Rationale statement available.

1. Scope—This SAE Standard covers nonreinforced, extruded, flexible tubing intended primarily for use as fluid lines for automotive windshield washer systems which conform to the requirements of SAE J942.

2. References

2.1 Applicable Publications—The following publications form a part of the specification to the extent specified herein. Unless otherwise indicated, the latest revision of SAE publications shall apply.

2.1.1 SAE PUBLICATIONS—Available from SAE, 400 Commonwealth Drive, Warrendale, PA 15096-0001.

SAE J942—Passenger Car Windshield Washer Systems
SAE J1231—Formed Tube Ends for Hose Connections

2.1.2 ASTM PUBLICATIONS—Available from ASTM, 100 Barr Harbor Drive, West Conshohocken, PA 19428-2959.

ASTM D 380—Methods of Testing Rubber Hose
ASTM D 573—Test for Rubber—Deterioration in an Air Oven
ASTM D 925—Test Method for Rubber Property—Staining of Surfaces
ASTM D 1149—Test Method for Rubber Deterioration—Surface Ozone Cracking in a Chamber
ASTM D 2240—Test Method for Rubber Property Durometer Hardness

3. Dimensions—Typical available sizes are noted in Table 1. The Nominal Tube Size is for reference purposes only. Tubing should be made to the ID Dimensions and Tolerances shown in Table 1.

4. Requirements—The following tests shall be conducted on full sections of tubing, except when noted otherwise. All test values indicated herein are based on samples conditioned at standard laboratory test conditions of 23 °C ± 2 °C and 50% ±5% relative humidity for not less than 24 h prior to testing and tested under the same conditions unless otherwise specified.

TABLE 1—TUBE ID DIMENSIONS AND TOLERANCES(1)

Nominal Tube Size mm	Nominal Tube Size in	ID Dimension mm	Tolerance mm
3	1/8	2.54	±0.25
4.5	3/16	3.96	±0.40
6	1/4	5.56	±0.40

1. Dimensions and tolerances, others than those shown in Table 1, must be agreed upon by both the manufacturer and customer.

4.1 Hardness Durometer A (ASTM D 2240)—70 points ±5 points.

4.2 Tensile Strength

a. Tensile Strength—7.0 MPa, minimum
b. Elongation—200%, minimum

4.2.1 TEST METHOD—Tubing 250 mm long is fastened to the jaws of a tensile tester by means of knots tied in both ends with two washers located between the knots and the washers fastened in the jaws. The jaw separation rate shall be 500 mm ±25 mm per minute until failure occurs. If the tubing fails in the knots or within 25 mm of the knots, then the tests should be rerun until failure occurs in the section between the knots. To obtain the cross-sectional area of tubing, an optical comparator or similar instrument may be used.

4.2.2 ALTERNATE TEST METHOD—If the tubing continues to fail in the knot, the tensile strength and elongation may be obtained by testing of cured slabs according to ASTM D 380. The test method used should be recorded with the results.

4.3 Burst Pressure (ASTM D 380)—0.70 MPa, minimum

4.4 Formed Tube End or Connector Pull-Off Force

4.4.1 TEST METHOD—150 mm specimen lengths of tubing shall be installed on the respective size beaded tube or plastic connector fitting as described in SAE J1231. The beaded tube ends or plastic connectors used shall be clean and dry. The tubing specimens shall be as received with no preparation of the bore. If a lubricant is required to facilitate installation, only isooctane or similar evaporative petroleum derivative may be used. After installation, the specimens shall be allowed to stabilize at standard laboratory test temperature for 48 h. Using a suitable tensioning device at a pull rate of 500 mm per min ±25 mm per min, the rubber tubing shall not be pulled from the fitting with less than the specified force in Table 2.

TABLE 2—PULL-OFF FORCE(1)

Nominal Tube Size mm	Beaded Tube Fitting Dimension SAE J1231 Fitting OD Dimension E mm	Beaded Tube Fitting Dimension SAE J1231 Fitting Bead Diameter Dimension F mm	Pull-Off Force N
3	3.17	3.77	22
4.5	4.78	5.59	44
6	6.35	7.37	66

1. For Tube Sizes other than the ones in Table 2, refer to SAE J1231. If the Tube Size is not included in SAE J1231, it is recommended that the Beaded Tube Fitting OD should be 20% greater than the Tube ID Dimension and the Bead Diameter should be 35% greater than the Tube ID Dimension. For Tube Sizes other than those in Table 2, the manufacturer and customer shall agree upon the Pull-Off Force.

4.5 Vacuum Collapse Test—30%, maximum.

The collapse of the OD of the tubing under internal vacuum of 610 mm of mercury for 5 min shall be 30% max. The test shall be made with the tubing curved to a radius equal to five times the maximum OD.

4.6 Wax Bloom—There shall be no visible evidence of wax or any other contaminants exuding from the inside or outside diameter of the tubing.

4.6.1 TEST METHOD—Condition a 150 mm section of tubing for 45 min at –40 °C. Remove the specimen from the cold chamber and permit recovery to room temperature for 1 h. The tubing shall then be twisted 360 degrees for 10 successive cycles, after which the center 50 mm section shall be compressed 10 successive cycles by finger pressure or utilization of a compression device to full closure of the ID. The tubing shall then be sectioned longitudinally and examined for evidence of wax bloom or other contaminants.

4.7 Tear Test—The tubing shall not tear when expanded to a minimum internal diameter of two times the nominal ID by forcing the tubing over a 30 degree tapered, clean metal rod which has been lubricated with a silicone parting agent. The metal rod shall have a finish of 20 rms maximum.

4.8 Formed Tube End Pull-Off Force After Sequential Heat Aging/Ozone Exposure

4.8.1 TEST METHOD—150 mm specimen lengths of tubing shall be installed on formed tube ends or plastic connector as described in Table 2. The tubing shall be heat aged as in accordance with ASTM D 573 for 70 h at 125 °C. After 24 h stabilization period at standard laboratory test conditions, the heat aged tubing shall be exposed in an ozone test chamber as described in 4.10. At the end of the exposure, the specimens shall be allowed to cool to standard laboratory test conditions for minimum of 16 h. Using a suitable tensioning device at a pull rate of 500 mm per min ± 25 mm per min, the rubber tubing shall not be pulled from the formed tube end with less than the specified force in Table 3.

TABLE 3—PULL-OFF FORCE AFTER SEQUENTIAL HEAT AGING/OZONE EXPOSURE(1)

Nominal Tube Size mm	Pull-Off Force N
3	18
4.5	35
6	53

1. For dimensions other than those in Table 3, the Pull-Off Force should be 80% of the unaged Pull-Off Force as agreed upon by the manufacturer and customer.

4.9 Cold Resistance—Shall not show fractures, cracks, checks, or breaks.

4.9.1 TEST METHOD—The tubing shall be subjected to a temperature of –40 °C for a period of 5 h. After aging, the tubing shall be flexed in the cold chamber through 180 degrees from the centerline in each direction to a diameter 10 times the maximum OD of the tube at each extreme of the cycle for five cycles. The rate of cycling shall be approximately one cycle in 4 s.

4.10 Ozone Resistance (ASTM D 1149)—Rating of 0.

4.10.1 Test Method—Elongate the specimen around a wooden or aluminum mandrel of random selection to attain approximately 25% elongation. Condition the specimen on the mandrel 24 h at room temperature in an ozone-free atmosphere. Then hang the specimen(s) in an ozone box with an ozone partial pressure of 50 mPa ± 5 mPa for 70 h at 40 °C ± 1 °C. Examine for rating using 7X-power glass.

4.11 Heat Aging—After being subjected to dry air aging in accordance with ASTM D 573 for 70 h at 125 °C, the tubing must then meet the following test requirements:

a. Vacuum Collapse: 30% max (tested to 4.5)
b. Cold Resistance: Shall not crack, etc. (tested to Method 4.9.1)
c. Hardness: Durometer A Change: +15 points, max
d. Tensile Change: –20% max
e. Elongation Change: –50% max
f. Tear Resistance: Must not tear (tested to 4.7)
g. Ozone Resistance: ASTM D 1149 – Rating of 0

4.12 Stain Test (Water Solution)—When tested as described as follows, slight staining of the paint is permitted, providing it can be removed by employing the usual cleaning materials.

4.12.1 Test Method—Cut a 150 mm length of tubing into small pieces and place in 200 ml of a 50% aqueous solution of windshield washer solution and reflux for 4 h. Cool the resulting liquid to room temperature. Pour out on a surface of a freshly prepared white paint panel, convertible and vinyl top materials of your production, covering about 6.45 cm^2 surface of each specimen. Expose specimens to ultraviolet radiation (RSM Sunlamp per ASTM D 925-Method B) for 24 h. Cool and examine. Make a visual assessment of the degree of staining relative to a reference sample (protected from irradiation).

(R) ACCELERATED EXPOSURE OF AUTOMOTIVE INTERIOR TIRM COMPONENTS USING A CONTROLLED IRRADIANCE WATER COOLED XENON-ARC APPARATUS—SAE J1885 MAR1992

SAE Standard

Report of the SAE Textile and Flexible Plastics Committee approved August 1987. This report is related to ISO-DP 105-B06, Draft Method 1149. Completely revised by the SAE Textile and Flexible Plastics Committee March 1992.

This document is equivalent to ISO/DIS 105-B06 option 5.

1. Scope—This test method specifies the operating procedures for a controlled irradiance, water cooled xenon-arc apparatus used for the accelerated exposure of various automotive interior trim components.

Test durations, as well as any exceptions to the sample preparation and performance evaluation procedures contained in this document, are covered in material specifications of the different automotive manufacturers.

2. References

2.1 Applicable Publications—The following publications form a part of this specification to the extent specified herein. The latest issue of SAE publications shall apply.

2.1.1 SAE PUBLICATIONS—Available from SAE, 400 Commonwealth Drive, Warrendale, PA 15096-0001.

SAE J1545 JUN86—Instrumental Color Difference Measurement for Exterior Finishes, Textiles, and Colored Trim

2.1.2 ASTM PUBLICATIONS—Available from ASTM, 100 Barr Harbor Drive, West Conshohocken, PA 19428-2959.

ASTM G 26—Standard Practice for Operating Light-Exposure Apparatus (Xenon-Arc Type) With and Without Water for Exposure of Nonmetallic Materials

2.1.3 OTHER PUBLICATIONS

AATCC Evaluation Procedure 1 (1987)

3. Definitions

3.1 Black Panel Thermometer, n.—A temperature measuring device, the sensing unit of which is a stainless steel panel coated with black material designed to absorb most of the radiant energy encountered in fade/weathering testing.

NOTE—This device provides an estimation of the maximum temperature a specimen may attain during exposure to natural or artificial light.

3.2 Blue Wool Lightfastness Standard, n.—One of a group of dyed fabrics used to determine the amount of light, or combined light, heat, and moisture to which a specimen is exposed during fade/weathering testing.

3.3 Center Wavelength, n.—The specified wavelength for bandpass filters; the wavelength midway between the half power points e.g., 340 nm ± 2 nm.

3.4 Color Change, n.—As used in fade/weathering testing, a change in color of any kind (whether a change in hue, saturation, or lightness).

3.5 Half Power Bandpass, n.—The interval between wavelengths at which transmittance is 50% of peak. (It should not exceed 20 nm for a narrow bandpass filter.)

3.6 Irradiance, Controlled, n.—The maintenance by closed loop feedback of a preselected irradiance throughout a designated exposure interval.

3.7 Irradiance, Spectral, n.—The radiant energy within a specified wavelength interval that falls upon a unit area of exposed surface (W/m^2 x nm)

3.8 Irradiance, Total, n.—Radiant energy integrated over all wavelengths falling upon a unit area of exposure at a point in time expressed in watts per square meter (W/m^2).

3.9 Irradiation, n.—See radiant exposure.

3.10 Long-Arc Xenon, n.—A xenon arc in which the length of the arc between electrodes is greater than the diameter of the envelope enclosing the arc.

3.11 Peak Wavelength, n.—The wavelength of peak transmission, e.g., 340 nm.

3.12 Radiant Exposure, n.—The time integral of irradiance expressed in joules per square meter (J/m^2).

3.13 Radiant Exposure, Spectral, n.—The integration of spectral irradiance with respect to time.

3.14 Reference Fabric, n.—One or more blue wool lightfastness standards selected for exposure as a check on a test apparatus and operating conditions.

3.15 Reference Plastic, n.—A clear polystyrene plastic standard selected for exposure as check on a test apparatus and operating conditions. This reference material is normally used for long-term exposures.

3.16 Sample, Laboratory, n.—A portion of material taken to represent the lot sample, or the original material, and used in the laboratory as a source of test specimens.

3.17 Specimen, n.—A specific portion of a material or a laboratory sample upon which a test is performed or which is selected for that purpose.

3.18 Spectral Power Distribution, n.—The variation of energy due to the source over the wavelength span of the emitted radiation.

4. Significance and Use

4.1 This test method is designed to simulate extreme environmental conditions encountered inside vehicle due to sunlight, heat, and humidity for the purpose of predicting the performance of automotive interior trim materials.

5. Equipment

5.1 A more complete description of the following equipment may be found in ASTM G 26.

5.2 The equipment employed utilizes a water cooled xenon-arc lamp as the source of radiation and should be one of the following:

5.2.1 TYPE AH[1]—A controlled irradiance apparatus in which the radiant energy source is vertically located at the center axis of a specimen rack. The specimen rack shall rotate at 1 rpm ± 0.1 rpm and shall be of the three-tiered, inclined type having a center segment of 648 mm ± 6 mm (25.5 in ± 0.25 in) outside diameter centered on the xenon-arc lamp. The top and bottom segments shall be 511 mm ± 6 mm (20 in ± 0.25 in) outside diameter, positioned 28 degrees ± 2 degrees from the vertical. Each segment shall accommodate 152 mm (6 in) specimen holders. The apparatus shall provide for automatic control of temperature, relative humidity, and irradiance at 340 nm.

5.2.2 TYPE BH[1]—A controlled irradiance apparatus in which the radiant energy source is vertically located at the central axis of the following two racks:

5.2.2.1 The specimen rack shall rotate at 1 rpm ± 0.1 rpm and shall be of the three-tiered, inclined type having a center segment of 965 mm ± 6 mm (38 in ± 0.25 in) outside diameter centered on the xenon-arc lamp. The top and bottom segments shall be 842 mm ± 6 mm (33.16 in ± 0.25 in) outside diameter, positioned 22 degrees ± 2 degrees from the vertical. Each tier shall accommodate 152 mm (6 in) specimen holders. The apparatus shall provide for automatic control of temperature, relative humidity, and irradiance at 340 nm. All specimen exposure openings may be used.

5.2.2.2 The specimen rack shall rotate at 1 rpm ± 0.1 rpm and shall be of the two-tiered, inclined type, 965.2 mm ± 6 mm (38 in ± 0.25 in) outside diameter in the center. The top and bottom segments shall be 872.5 mm ± 6 mm vertical. The rack shall be positioned so that the exposure area is centered on the xenon lamp. Each tier shall accommodate 254 mm (10 in) long specimen holders. The apparatus shall provide for automatic control of temperature, relative humidity, and irradiance at 340 nm. When using this two-tiered specimen rack, test specimens shall not be placed in positions 1 and 8. (See Figure 1.)

5.2.3 The xenon-arcs employed shall be of the "long-arc" water cooled type. They shall employ cylindrical inner and outer optical filters to direct the flow of cooling water and to provide a selected spectral power distribution.

5.2.4 Distilled or deionized water (solids content less than 20 ppm) shall be recirculated past the burner at a flow rate sufficient to remove excess heat. Passing water through a cartridge demineralizer installed in the recirculation line just ahead of the lamp minimizes contamination of the quartz envelope of the burner. A heat exchange unit shall be used to cool the recirculated lamp water.

6. Apparatus Set-Up

6.1 To insure repeatability of tests, maintain and calibrate the apparatus to manufacturer's specifications, and as described in Appendicies A, B, and C. Appendix A contains additional maintenance instructions and replacement schedules, and Appendix B and C describe the use of reference materials to determine

1. The Ci35 Xenon-Arc Weather Ometer® or equivalent with factory installed air heater meets the requirements of Type AH. The Ci65 Xenon-Arc Weather-Ometer® or equivalent with factory installed air heater meets the requirements of Type BH. These apparatuses are available from Atlas Electric Devices Company, 4114 North Ravenswood Avenue, Chicago, IL 60613.

if the xenon-arc apparatus is operating within the desired range. Appendix C provides an alternative to the method described in Appendix B using a polystyrene reference plastic suitable for use during long-term exposures and requires less frequent interruption of machine operation. Contractual agreement will determine which method(s) will be used.

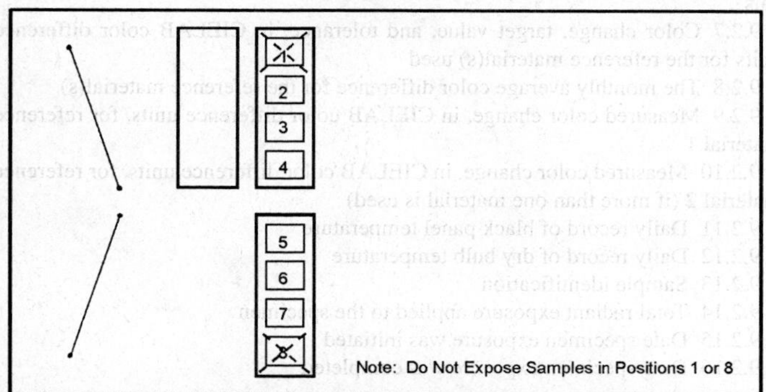

FIGURE 1—TWO-TIER INCLINED SPECIMEN RACK C165

6.1.1 The input voltage must be between 215 to 250 V.

6.1.2 Water for humidification and lamp cooling must be purified so that it is free of silica and has no more than 20 ppm total dissolved solids.

6.1.3 Remove and cap the specimen spray unit. Turn off the rack spray unit with the valve provided.

NOTE—While the specimen spray can be turned off through a switch on the control panel, it is recommended that the specimen spray assembly be removed and the pipe capped to prevent accidental spraying of the test samples.

6.1.4 Fit the xenon-arc burner with quartz inner filter and Type S borosilicate outer filter.

6.1.5 Set the operation switches as follows in Table 1:

TABLE 1—OPERATION SWITCH SETTINGS

Switch	Setting
Black Panel Ambient Air	Black Panel
Wattage Adjustment	Automatic
Countdown Switch	Irradiation
Lamp Ignition	On
Fixed Air Valve	Off
Humidifier	On
Water Heater	On
Air Heater	On(1)
Specimen Spray	Off
Rack Spray	Off

1. The Air Heater selector switch, under the cover labeled "Circuit Breakers/Mode Switches," should be set to Light/Dark Cycle. If proper humidity during the light cycle cannot be maintained, set to Dark Cycle. Only one air heater should be used on devices equipped with two air heaters. The test chamber High Temperature Adjust switch should be set to 72 °C.

6.1.6 Set the thumb wheel controls as follows in Table 2:

TABLE 2—THUMB WHEEL CONTROL SETTINGS

	Dark Cycle	Light Cycle
Automatic Irradiance	—	0.55 w/m² at 340 nm
Black Panel Temperature	38 °C	89 °C
Wet Bulb Depression(1)	0 °C	12 °C (Nominal)
Conditioning Water	40 °C	63 °C
"A" Series Equipment		
Automatic Dry Bulb Temperature(2)		62 °C
Cycle Programmer		Program 2 or 3

1. NOTE—The wet bulb depression setting indicated is a suggested setting to obtain the specified humidity level. It may be necessary to adjust this setting due to ambient conditions in the room containing the equipment.
2. Set Light Cycle dry bulb control switch to automatic.

6.1.7 Set cycle that provides 3.8 h light and 1.0 h dark.

6.1.8 Operate the equipment to maintain the conditions in Table 3. If the actual operating conditions do not agree with the machine settings after the equipment has stabilized, discontinue the test and identify the cause of the disagreement.

TABLE 3—Equipment Operating Conditions

	Dark Cycle	Light Cycle
Automatic Irradiance		0.55 w/m² ± 0.01 w/m² at 340 nm
Black Panel Temperature	38 °C ± 2 °C	89 °C ± 3 °C
Dry Bulb Tolerance(1)	38 °C ± 2 °C	62 °C ± 2 °C
Relative Humidity	95% ± 5%	50% ± 5%
Conditioning Water	40 °C ± 4 °C	63 °C ± 4 °C
Radiant Exposure	See Applicable Specification	See Applicable Specification

1. Note—It may be necessary to adjust the blower speed to maintain the specified dry bulb temperature.

6.1.9 Adjust the temperature of the lamp cooling water to provide sufficient cooling, but prevent condensation from forming on the lamp assembly. Suggest 60 °C for cooling water, and 70 °C for high temperature water cut-out.

7. *Test Procedure*

7.1 Prepare the specimens to be exposed to fit the specimen holder being used.

7.2 Specimen sizes must conform to the size of the specimen holder(s)[2] supplied by the manufacturer for use with the equipment. Specimens that exceed these sizes may not give proper exposure results. Instructions for mounting parts or portions of a part can be obtained from the responsible engineering group.

7.3 Back interior textiles (body cloth, carpet, vinyl coated fabrics, etc.) with white cardboard.[3] Specimens other than interior textiles that do not completely fill the exposure area of the specimen holder are also backed with white cardboard.

7.4 Insert specimen in holder and secure. Under no circumstances should the face side of the sample be closer to the arc than the front side of the specimen holder.

7.5 Fill all unused slots with specimen holders filled with white cardboard[3] to maintain desired air flow. Cardboard blanks should be changed when noticeable physical distortion occurs.

7.6 Expose specimens, beginning at the end of a dark cycle, for the required radiant exposure (kilojoules per square meter [kJ/m²]) measured at the central wavelength of 340 nm. See applicable material specification.

NOTE—Care should be taken to avoid mixing potentially incompatible specimens in the same machine load, i.e., textiles should not be exposed together with foam backed textiles, foams, or plastics.

Once exposure has been initiated, equipment operation should not be interrupted more than once daily. Additional interruptions, e.g., opening the chamber door during the course of daily operation, may cause variation in test results.

8. *Evaluating and Reporting the Degree of Fade*

8.1 The degree of fade should be evaluated and reported as specified between the contractual parties. One or more of the following methods may be specified:

8.1.1 INSTRUMENTAL MEASUREMENT

8.1.1.1 Color difference values in CIELAB units are obtained by instrumentally measuring the specimen before and after a specified amount of radiant exposure. The procedure used for specimen measurement will conform to that specified in Appendix B.

8.1.2 VISUAL ASSESSMENT

2. Specimen holders SL-3T, CD-3T, SL, CD, and CD-4 have been found to be suitable. Frames other than these can be agreed upon between the contractual parties.
3. Franklin, Grain long-felt side up 110/500 white index, Stock Number 06506 made by Union Camp or 9016 White Bristol Card Stock have been found suitable for this purpose. Franklin white index is usually available from local office supply or art supply stores. Weight of card stock should be sufficient to prevent warping.

8.1.2.1 Assign colorfastness ratings using the AATCC Gray Scale for Color Change in accordance with AATCC Evaluation Procedure 1 (1987).

8.1.2.2 Using the viewing conditions specified in AATCC Evaluation Procedure 1 (1987), quantify the color change using the following terminology:

a. NONE—No change in hue, lightness, or saturation.
b. SLIGHT—A change in lightness and/or saturation which can be determined only upon close examination but no change in hue.
c. NOTICEABLE—A change in lightness and/or saturation which can easily be seen and/or a change in hue.
d. SEVERE—An extreme change in lightness, saturation, and/or hue.

9. Exposure Report

9.1 A copy of the Exposure Control/Report Form (Figure 2)[4] indicating the color change of the exposed reference material in CIELAB color difference units must accompany each exposed specimen being submitted for approval. If any one of the color difference data points is outside the specified tolerance (control limits), the cause and corrective action must be indicated in the space provided.

9.2 The Exposure Control/Report Form shall include the following additional information:

4. Copies of the Exposure Control/Report Form can be obtained from any automotive company using this procedure.

9.2.1 Laboratory Name
9.2.2 Type and serial number of exposure equipment
9.2.3 Month and Year of equipment operation represented by the control chart
9.2.4 Test method
9.2.5 Reference material(s) used
9.2.6 Frequency of operation verification, e.g., daily, three, or seven day intervals
9.2.7 Color change, target value, and tolerance, in CIELAB color difference units for the reference material(s) used
9.2.8 The monthly average color difference for the reference material(s)
9.2.9 Measured color change, in CIELAB color difference units, for reference material 1
9.2.10 Measured color change, in CIELAB color difference units, for reference material 2 (if more than one material is used)
9.2.11 Daily record of black panel temperature
9.2.12 Daily record of dry bulb temperature
9.2.13 Sample identification
9.2.14 Total radiant exposure applied to the specimen
9.2.15 Date specimen exposure was initiated
9.2.16 Date specimen exposure was completed

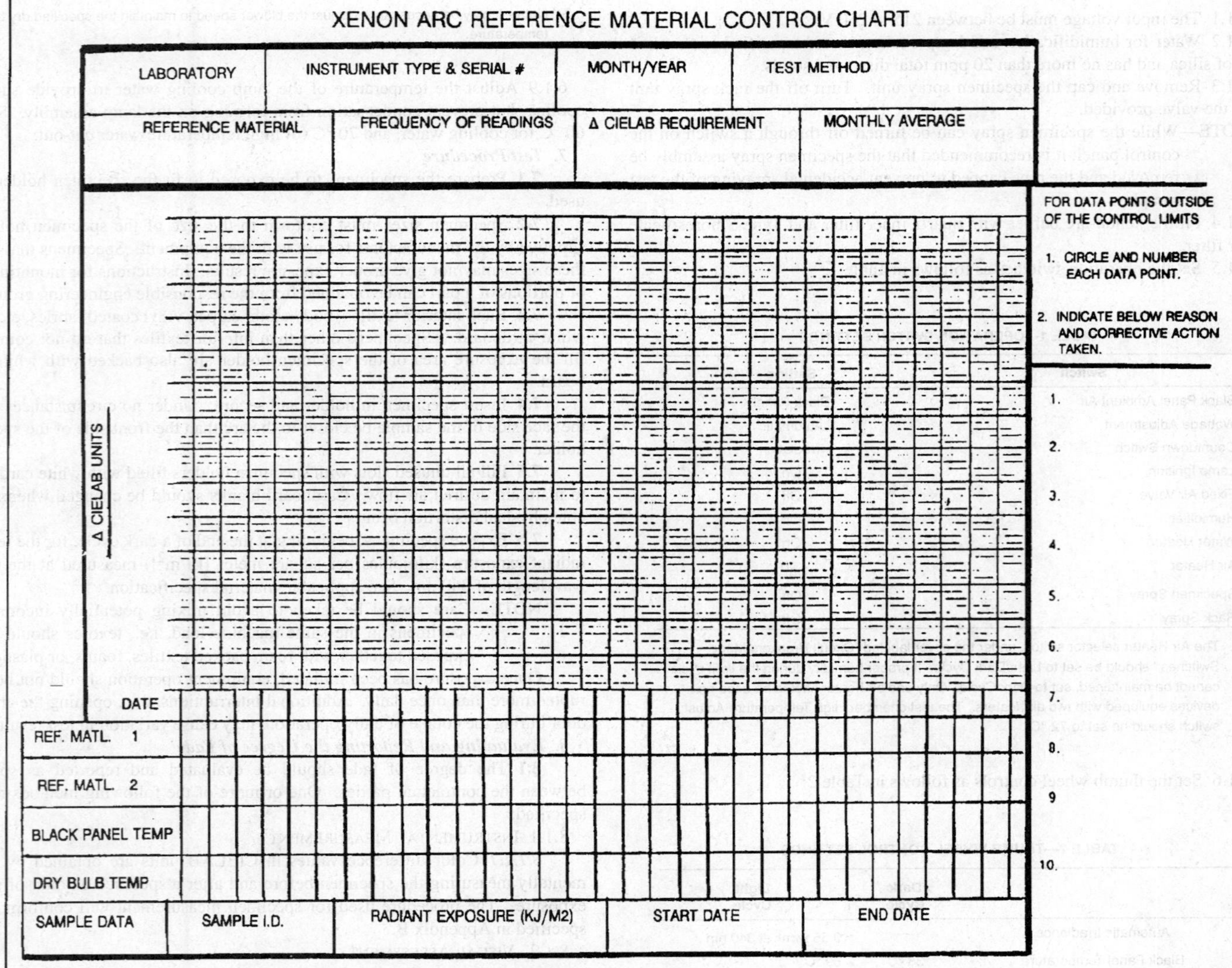
XENON ARC REFERENCE MATERIAL CONTROL CHART

LABORATORY	INSTRUMENT TYPE & SERIAL #	MONTH/YEAR	TEST METHOD
REFERENCE MATERIAL	FREQUENCY OF READINGS	Δ CIELAB REQUIREMENT	MONTHLY AVERAGE

Δ CIELAB UNITS

FOR DATA POINTS OUTSIDE OF THE CONTROL LIMITS

1. CIRCLE AND NUMBER EACH DATA POINT.
2. INDICATE BELOW REASON AND CORRECTIVE ACTION TAKEN.

1.
2.
3.
4.
5.
6.
7.
8.
9
10.

DATE

REF. MATL. 1

REF. MATL. 2

BLACK PANEL TEMP

DRY BULB TEMP

SAMPLE DATA	SAMPLE I.D.	RADIANT EXPOSURE (KJ/M2)	START DATE	END DATE

FIGURE 2—EXPOSURE CONTROL/REPORT FORM

APPENDIX A

A.1 Maintenance

A.1.1 Test Chamber—The frequency of cleaning will vary with water quality. However, the chamber must be cleaned at least once a month with a stainless steel cleaning agent and flushed with deionized water. Do NOT use cleaning agents containing chlorine.

A.1.2 Conditioning Chamber—The frequency of cleaning will vary with water and air quality in the laboratory. However, the chamber must be drained once a month and flushed with deionized water to remove sediment.

A.1.3 Lamp Assembly—Frequency of cleaning will vary with water quality. However, at least once each week wipe the outer surface of the outer filter with alcohol and a soft cloth. If deposits cannot be removed, replace the filter.

A.1.4 Quartz Light Rod—Clean weekly the end of the light rod with alcohol and soft cloth.

A.1.5 Black Panel Sensor—Polish weekly using a good quality automotive polish.

A.2 Replacement Schedule

A.2.1 Lamp Assembly and Related Parts

A.2.1.1 Replace the inner filter when the specified irradiance level can no longer be achieved or after a maximum of 1000 h of operation, and also whenever the burner tube is replaced.

A.2.1.2 Replace the outer filter when the specified irradiance level can no longer be achieved or after a maximum of 1000 h of operation.

A.2.1.3 Replace the burner tube when the specified irradiance level can no longer be achieved even after the outer filter has been replaced.

A.2.1.4 Replace the interference filter located in the light monitoring system after 9000 light-on hours or 18 months of use, whichever comes first. The interference filter may require replacement sooner if the wattage level does not return to "normal" after the burner tube and outer filter have been replaced.

A.2.2 Replace the black panel sensor when local surface luster can no longer be maintained, or when bare metal can be seen.

A.2.3 Inspect wet bulb wick weekly and replace when discoloration or mineral deposits are observed.

A.3 Calibration Checks

A.3.1 Check the switches and thumb wheel controls daily to insure proper settings.

A.3.2 Calibrate the apparatus once each week following the procedures detailed in the operating manual provided by the manufacturer. If contractual agreement is to use L-4 Blue Wool as the reference material, Thursday is the suggested calibration day.

A.3.2.1 Weekly calibration records are maintained using the recording form provided (Figure A1). Set points may differ depending on the model of apparatus used. Refer to the operating manual provided with the equipment for the exact requirements.[5]

A.3.2.2 The use of the "substitution temperature calibration PC board" is a requirement for the weekly calibration of the apparatus. This method of temperature calibration replaces the use of the hot and cold water method which may be detailed in the operating manual provided with the equipment at the time of purchase. Complete adherence to the manufacturer's instructions for calibration using this "PC Board" is mandatory.

5. Copies of the calibration record chart can be obtained from any automotive company using this procedure.

RECORD OF EQUIPMENT CALIBRATION

Company/Area: ____________ Equipment Type: ____________

Model Number: ____________ Serial Number: ____________

Calibration Lamp Serial Number: ____________ Calibration lamp Calibration Date: ____________

DATE									
XENON LAMP OPERATING HOURS									
INNER FILTER OPERATING HOURS									
OUTER FILTER OPERATING HOURS									
CALIBRATION LAMP OPERATING HOURS									
CALIBRATION POINTS	Set Point	First Value	Final Value	First Value	Final Value	First Value	Final Value	First Value	Final Value
WATTAGE REGULATOR	Min: Max:								
LIGHT ROD ADJUSTMENT									
IRRADIANCE ZERO	0.00								
IRRADIANCE THUMBWHEEL SPAN	-0.10vdc								
INTEGRATOR ZERO									
INTEGRATOR REFERENCE									
INTEGRATOR SPAN									
IRRADIANCE THUMBWHEEL (LOW AND SPAN ADJUST)	Min: Max:								
CALIBRATION LAMP	Irradiance Wattage								
BLACK PANEL TEMPERATURE	Min: 0.0 Max:100.0								
DRY BULB TEMPERATURE	Min: 0.0 Max:100.0								
WET BULB TEMPERATURE	Min: 0.0 Max:100.0								
DEPRESSION	Min: 0.0 Max:100.0								
CONDITIONING WATER	Min: 0.0 Max:100.0								

FIGURE A1—EQUIPMENT CALIBRATION RECORD

APPENDIX B

B.1 Scope

B.1.1 This Appendix describes the procedure for using AATCC Blue Wool Lightfastness Standards as reference fabrics for the purpose of determining whether the xenon-arc apparatus is operating within the desired range.

B.1.2 Color difference values in CIELAB units are obtained by instrumentally measuring the reference fabrics before and after a specified amount of radiant exposure.

B.1.3 AATCC L-2[6] Blue Wool Lightfastness Standards shall be exposed daily and/or an AATCC L-4[6] Blue Wool Lightfastness Standard shall be used to monitor a continuous three day operating cycle as agreed upon between contractual parties.

B.2 Procedure

B.2.1 Instruments used to determine color difference for this procedure require capability for providing CIELAB color values using illuminant D-65, 10 degree observer data. If an instrument with diffuse geometry is used, the specular component of reflectance shall be included in the measurement. (Refer to SAE J1545, 3.6 for details).

NOTE—An aperture diameter smaller than 20 mm cannot be used for these measurements.

B.2.2 Calibrate the instrument to be used for the color measurements to the manufacturers recommendations.

B.2.3 Back the reference fabric to be measured with white cardboard.[7] Condition the backed reference fabric in a standard atmosphere (50% RH ± 5% RH and 21 °C ± 1 °C) for a minimum of 2 h. Insert one layer of unexposed material of the lightfastness standard between the reference fabric and cardboard backing prior to measurement.

NOTE—The reference fabrics are light sensitive. Therefore, the piece used as the backing layer during measurement will need to be replaced when noticeable color change has occurred (after approximately 50 uses).

B.2.4 Place the reference fabric against the sample port of the instrument in such a way that a smooth surface of the face of the fabric is presented for measurement.

B.2.5 After taking an initial reading in CIELAB units, rotate the reference fabric 90 degrees and take a second reading. Average the readings and store as the standard measurement for the identified piece of reference fabric. REMOVE THE BACKING FABRIC AND PLACE IN A LIGHT TIGHT CONTAINER FOR LATER USE.

NOTE—The measurement obtained in B.2.5 cannot be used for different pieces of reference fabric. Each individual piece must be conditioned and measured prior to exposure.

B.2.6 Place the cardboard backed reference fabric (single layer) in a specimen holder and secure on the specimen rack adjacent to the black panel thermometer (see Figures B1 and B2).

B.2.7 Always start the exposure apparatus at the end of the dark cycle. Expose the L-2 reference fabric for 37.6 kJ/m^2 at 340 nm or the L-4 reference fabric for 112.8 kJ/m^2 at 340 nm as agreed upon by contractual parties.

B.2.8 After the specified radiant exposure, remove the reference fabric and the white cardboard backing and allow them to condition at 21 °C ± 1 °C and 50% ± 5% relative humidity for a minimum of 1 h.

B.2.9 Repeat the color measurement steps specified in B.2.2 through B.2.5 on the exposed reference fabric(s) and using the previously stored pre-exposure measurement, determine the Delta L*, a*, b*, and E*.

B.2.10 Compare the Delta E* value determined to that specified in Table B1:

TABLE B1—COLORIMETRIC SPECIFICATIONS FOR TOTAL COLOR CHANGE OF BLUE WOOL LIGHTFASTNESS STANDARDS(1)

Lightfastness Standard	Delta E
AATCC L02 (Lot 4)	900 ± 0.50
AATCC L-2 (Lot 5)	9.90 ± 0.55
AATCC L-4 (Lot 4)	6.70 ± 0.50

1. The stated color difference values may change when new lots of the reference materials are produced. The target values desired should be confirmed by the contractual automotive company.

B.2.11 If the Delta E* value does not fall within the limits specified in B.2.10, do not resume the test until the reason has been determined and resolved.

B.2.12 As each group of test specimens completes its specified radiant exposure, record and report the color change information in terms of Delta E*, values of the reference fabric piece(s) used during the test period on the Exposure Control/Report (Figure 2).

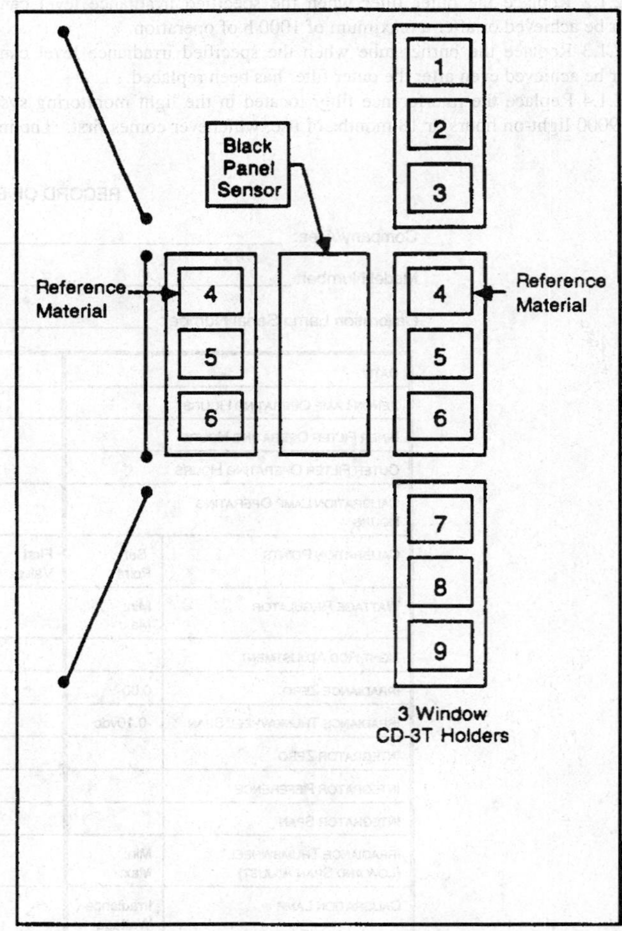

NOTE—Expose reference materials in position 4, either to the right or left of the black panel thermometer.

FIGURE B1—REFERENCE MATERIAL PLACEMENT THREE-TIER INCLINE SPECIMEN RACK

6. AATCC L-2 and L-4 Blue Wool Lightfastness Standards may be obtained from AATCC, P.O. Box 12215, Research Triangle Park, North Carolina 277009.
7. Franklin, Grain long-felt side up, 110/500 white index made by Union Camp or 9016 White Bristol Card Stock have been found suitable for this purpose. Franklin white index is usually available from local office supply or art supply stores and is also available from Dilliard Paper Company.

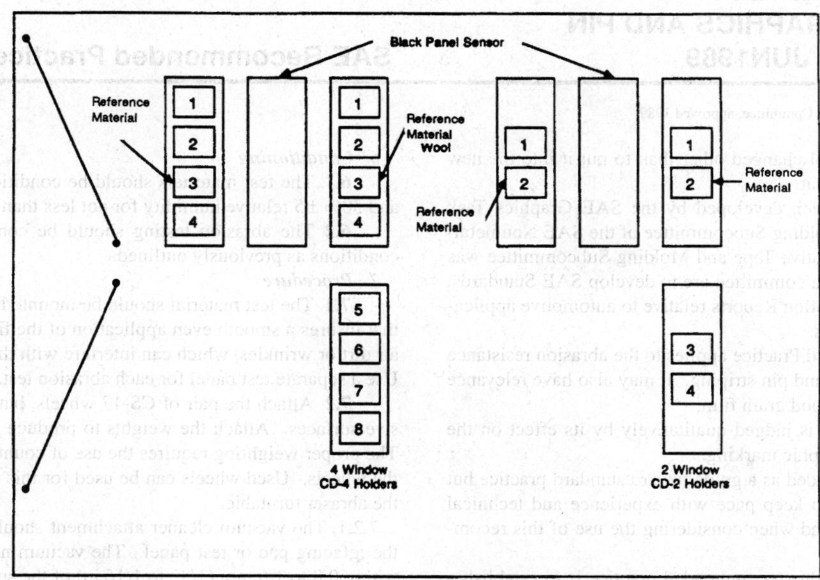

NOTE—Expose reference materials in position 3 when using the 4 window holder and in position 2 when using the 2 window holder. Location either to the right or left of the black panel thermometer is accepted.

FIGURE B2—REFERENCE MATERIAL PLACEMENT TWO-TWO INCLINE SPECIMEN RACK

APPENDIX C

C.1 Scope

C.1.1 This Appendix describes an alternate procedure for using a clear Polystyrene Lightfastness Standard[8] as a reference standard for the purpose of determining whether the xenon-arc apparatus is operating properly. This lightfastness standard is used during testing of rigid plastics and other miscellaneous materials requiring long exposures.

C.1.2 Color difference values in CIELAB units are obtained by instrumentally measuring the reference plastic before and after a specified amount of radiant exposure.

C.1.3 The polystyrene lightfastness standard may be exposed for an equivalent kilojoule period of 2 to 7 days.

C.2 Procedure

C.2.1 Instruments used to determine color difference for this procedure require a capability for operation which includes the specular component and providing CIELAB color values using illuminant D-65, 10 degree observer data. No substitutions are permitted. Measurements in either the transmission or reflectance mode may be used.

NOTE—An aperture diameter smaller than 20 mm cannot be used for these measurements.

C.2.2 Calibrate the instrument to be used for the color measurements in accordance with the manufacturer's recommendations.

C.2.3 Reflectance Mode

C.2.3.1 Place a piece of unexposed reference plastic, backed with a white calibration tile against the sample port of the instrument.

C.2.3.2 Take an initial reading and store it as the standard measurement for the identified piece of reference plastic.

C.2.4 Transmission Mode:

C.2.4.1 Place a piece of unexposed reference plastic in the proper location for measuring transmittance as recommended by the manufacturer of the instrument in use.

C.2.4.2 Place the white tile used for calibration against the outer sample port of the instrument.

C.2.4.3 Take an initial measurement and store it as the standard measurement for the identified piece of reference plastic.

C.2.5 Place the premeasured piece of reference plastic in a specimen holder and secure on the specimen rack adjacent to the black panel thermometer. See Figures B1 and B2.

C.2.6 Expose the reference plastic for an equivalent kilojoule period of 2 to 7 days.

C.2.7 After the radiant exposure, remove the reference plastic from the apparatus.

C.2.8 Repeat the color measurement steps specified in C.2.3 or C.2.4 on the exposed reference plastic and using the previously stored pre-exposure measurement, determine the Delta L*, a*, b*, and E* color difference values.

C.2.9 Compare the Delta b* value determined to those indicated in Table C1 for TESTFABRICS LOT #1. See Table C1.

C.2.10 If the Delta b* value does not fall within duration of exposure, do not resume the test until the reason has been determined and resolved.

C.2.11 As each group of test specimens completes its specified radiant exposure, record and report the color change information in terms of Delta b* values of the reference plastic piece(s) used during the test period on the Exposure Control/Report Form (see Figure 2).

8. Polystyrene Plastic Lightfastness Standard may be obtained from Testfabrics, Inc., 200 Blackford Avenue, P.O. Box 420, Middlesex, NJ 08846 (201) 469-6446.

TABLE C1—COLORMETRIC SPECIFICATIONS FOR CHANGE IN YELLOWNESS OF THE REFERENCE PLASTIC AT VARIOUS EXPOSURE LEVELS(1)

kJ	Reflectance Delta B −10%	Reflectance Delta B Target	Reflectance Delta B +10%	Transmission Delta B −10%	Transmission Delta B Target	Transmission Delta B +10%
75.2	3.24	3.60	3.96	1.44	1.60	1.76
112.8	4.59	5.10	5.61	2.07	2.30	2.53
150.4	5.94	6.60	7.26	2.79	3.10	3.41
188.0	7.29	8.10	8.91	3.42	3.80	4.18
225.6	8.64	9.60	10.56	4.14	4.60	5.06
263.2	10.17	11.30	12.43	4.77	5.30	5.83

1. Data for lots other than that specified may be obtained from the supplier or contractual automotive company.

ABRASION RESISTANCE TESTING—VEHICLE EXTERIOR GRAPHICS AND PIN STRIPING—SAE J1847 JUN1989

SAE Recommended Practice

Report of the SAE Decorative Tapes and Moldings Committee, approved 1989.

Foreword—This Document has not changed other than to put it into the new SAE Technical Standards Board Format.

This recommended practice has been developed by the SAE Graphics Task Force of the Decorative Tapes and Molding Subcommittee of the SAE Nonmetallic Materials Committee. The Decorative Tape and Molding Subcommittee was formed in 1984. The objectives of the committee are to develop SAE Standards, Recommended Practices, and Information Reports relative to automotive applications of decorative tapes and moldings.

1. Scope—This SAE Recommended Practice applies to the abrasion resistance testing of decorative tapes, graphics, and pin striping. It may also have relevance to certain vehicle labels and plastic wood grain film.

The resistance to abrasive damage is judged qualitatively by its effect on the legibility, pattern, and color of the graphic marking.

This recommended practice is intended as a guide toward standard practice but may be subject to frequent change to keep pace with experience and technical advances. This should be kept in mind when considering the use of this recommended practice.

1.1 Purpose—The purpose of this recommended practice is to establish a uniform practice for testing the abrasion resistance of decorative tapes and moldings.

2. References—There are no referenced publications specified herein.

3. Significance and Use—The plastic decorative tapes and graphic marking films are subject to the abrasive forces of wiping, cleaning, automatic washes, and various exterior environments.

4. Apparatus

4.1 Abrader—A Teledyne Taber Abraser, Model 174, or its equivalent, complete with vacuum accessory. The abraser should be capable of using "Calibrase" type abrasive wheels under 250, 500, and 1000 g loads.

4.2 Abrasive Wheels—"Calibrase" brand, grade CS-17 wheels as supplied by Teledyne Taber.

4.3 Resurfacing Pads—150 grit silicon carbide sand paper or equivalent, Teledyne Taber part number S-11.

4.4 Test Panel—A clean cold rolled steel panel, 102 mm (4 in) square. A 6.0 mm (1/4 in) hole is centrally located in the panel. The panel thickness should be approximately 1.0 mm (0.04 in). The Teledyne Taber catalog number for such panels is S-16.

5. Test Samples—The test specimens should be of sufficient size to cover the entire surface of the test panel. When the specimen size is too small to cover an entire panel, this should be noted and the material should be mounted to maintain a contiguous test surface.

6. Conditioning

6.1 The test materials should be conditioned at 23 °C ± 2 (73.4 °F ± 3.6) and 50% ±5 relative humidity for not less than 40 h prior to testing.

6.2 The abrasion testing should be conducted under standard laboratory conditions as previously outlined.

7. Procedure

7.1 The test material should be mounted on the steel test panel in a manner that insures a smooth even application of the film. There should be no entrapped air dirt or wrinkles, which can interfere with the even abrasion of the test surface. Use a separate test panel for each abrasion test.

7.2 Attach the pair of CS-17 wheels, but do not handle them by their abrasive surfaces. Attach the weights to produce a 500 g load on the panel surface. The proper weighting requires the use of counterweights to balance the weight of the wheels. Used wheels can be used for this purpose. Mount a refacing pad on the abraser turntable.

7.2.1 The vacuum cleaner attachment should be used to remove residue from the refacing pad or test panel. The vacuum nozzle height should be adjusted to within 0.8 to 1.6 mm (1/32 to 1/16 in) of the surface.

Set the vacuum to a setting of 80 or higher. The vacuum is used only during the refacing process and not during actual testing.

7.2.2 New wheels should be refaced for 100 cycles or until a uniform surface is achieved, whichever is greater. Reface previously used wheels for 25 cycles. Reface the wheels for 25 cycles before abrading each test sample. After refacing, brush any residue from the wheels; however, be certain not to touch the surface of the refaced wheels.

7.2.3 Discard the refacing pad after using once.

7.3 Mount the test panel on the turntable; lower the abrasive wheels carefully onto the test surface. Start the abraser. Expose the test panel to abrasion for the number of cycles specified or until the specified end point is reached. Remove any residue from the test panels with a soft brush. Label each test panel on the film surface with the number of cycles to which it was exposed. Reface the wheels between tests in order to remove abraded materials that collect during the test.

7.4 The failure definition is left to the discretion of the tester or specifier. Failures may be determined by appearance after testing to a specified number of cycles. A loss in legibility or wear through to a second surface can be considered a failure point. Abrasion resistance can also be measured by the weight loss of the sample after testing or as the number of abrasion cycles until initial wear through.

ACCELERATED EXPOSURE OF AUTOMOTIVE INTERIOR TRIM COMPONENTS USING A CONTROLLED IRRADIANCE AIR-COOLED XENON-ARC APPARATUS —SAE J2212 MAR1993

SAE Recommended Practice

Report of the SAE Textiles and Flexible Plastics Committee approved March 1993.

Foreword—This Document has not changed other than to put it into the new SAE Technical Standards Board Format. The Definition Section has been changed to Section 3.

1. Scope

1.1 This SAE Recommended Practice specifies the operating procedures for a controlled irradiance, air-cooled xenon-arc apparatus used for the accelerated exposure of various automotive interior trim components.

1.2 Test durations, as well as any exceptions to the sample preparation and performance evaluation procedures contained in this document, are covered in material specifications of the different automotive manufacturers.

2. References

2.1 Applicable Publications—The following publications form a part of the specification to the extent specified herein. Unless otherwise indicated the latest revision of SAE publications shall apply.

2.1.1 SAE PUBLICATIONS—Available from SAE, 400 Commonwealth Drive, Warrendale, PA 15096-0001.

SAE J1545—Instrumental Color Difference Measurement for Exterior Finishes, Textiles, and Colored Trim

2.1.2 AATCC PUBLICATIONS—Available from AATCC, P.O. Box 12215, Research Triangle Park, NC 27709.

AATCC Evaluation Procedure 1 (1987)—Gray Scale for Color Change (AATCC Technical Manual)

2.1.3 ASTM PUBLICATIONS—Available from ASTM, 100 Barr Harbor Drive, West Conshohocken, PA 19428-2959.

ASTM G 26—Standard Practice for Operating Light-Exposure Apparatus (Xenon-Arc Type) With and Without Water for Exposure of Nonmetallic Materials (ASTM Standards Vol. 14.02)

2.1.4 CIE PUBLICATIONS—Available from Commission Internationale de Leclairage, 52 Bd Malesherbes, F-75008 Paris, France

CIE DO.85 (1989)

3. Definitions

3.1 Black Standard Thermometer, n.—A temperature-measuring device which uses a resistance thermometer with good heat-conducting properties, fitted to the reverse side of a metal plate. The metal plate is fixed to a plastic plate so that it is thermally insulated. It is coated with a black layer.

3.2 Blue Wool Lightfastness Standard, n.—One of a group of dyed fabrics used to determine the amount of light, or combined light and heat, to which a specimen is exposed during fade/weathering testing.

3.3 Wavelength Range, n.—The specified wavelength range for bandpass filters; for example, 300 to 400 nm.

3.4 Color Change, n.—As used in fade/weathering testing, a change in color of any kind (whether a change in hue, saturation, or lightness).

3.5 Irradiance, Controlled, n.—The maintenance by closed loop feedback of a preselected irradiance throughout a designated exposure interval.

3.6 Irradiance, Spectral, n.—The radiant energy within a specified wavelength interval that falls upon a unit area of exposed surface ($W/m^2/nm$).

3.7 Irradiance, Total, n.—Radiant energy integrated over all wavelengths falling upon a unit area of exposure at a point in time expressed in watts per square meter (W/m^2).

3.8 Irradiation, n.—See Radiant Exposure.

3.9 Long-Arc Xenon, n.—A xenon-arc in which the length of the arc between electrodes is greater than the diameter of the envelope enclosing the arc.

3.10 Radiant Exposure, n.—The time integral of irradiance expressed in joules per square meter (J/m^2).

3.11 Radiant Exposure, Spectral, n.—The integration of spectral irradiance with respect to time.

3.12 Reference Fabric, n.—One or more blue wool lightfastness standards selected for exposure as a check on a test apparatus and operating conditions.

3.13 Reference Plastic, n.—A clear polystyrene standard selected for exposure as a check on a test apparatus and operating conditions. This reference material is normally used for long-term exposures.

3.14 Sample, Laboratory, n.—A portion of material taken to represent the lot sample, or the original material, and used in the laboratory as a source of test specimen(s).

3.15 Specimen, n.—A specific portion of a material or a laboratory sample upon which a test is performed or which is selected for that purpose.

3.16 Spectral Power Distribution, n.—The variation of energy due to the source over the wavelength span of the emitted radiation.

4. Significance and Use

4.1 This test method is designed to simulate extreme environmental conditions encountered inside a vehicle due to sunlight, heat, and humidity for the purpose of predicting the performance of automotive interior trim materials.

5. Equipment

5.1 A more complete description of the apparatuses listed as follows may be found in ASTM G 26.

5.2 Air-Cooled Type[1]—The apparatus employed shall use an air-cooled xenon-arc lamp as the source of radiation and should be as follows:

5.2.1 GENERAL—An apparatus using three lamps based on xenon-arc technology that meets the conditions specified in Section 6 is acceptable as long as the filter/optical systems reproduce the spectral distribution of the lamp output and filter system specified in this document. Also, all temperature and humidity must be identical to the conditions specified in Section 6.

5.2.1.1 Spectral Power Distribution—The spectral distribution shown in Table 1 (based on CIE Publication No. 85 (1989) Table No. 4) specifies acceptable ranges within wavebands to describe the lamp output defined in this document.

TABLE 1—RELATIVE SPECTRAL IRRADIANCE

Wavelength	Relative Spectral Irradiance &
290 to 400	100
below 290	0(1)
> 290 to 320	5.4 ± 1.8
> 320 to 360	38.2 ± 4.6
> 360 to 400	56.4 ± 9.0

1. Xenon arcs operating according to the method emit a small amount of radiation below 290 nm. In some cases, this may cause degradation reactions which do not occur in natural sunlight exposures.

5.2.1.2 Specimen holders should revolve around the arc, with the sample plane describing a spherical or cylindrical surface. A slight tilting of the upper and lower sample holders can provide uniformity satisfactory to eliminate the need to reposition specimens in the sample rack and allows use of the complete sample holder.

5.2.1.3 Testing temperatures should be calibrated using a Black Standard Thermometer unit that is mounted so that the face of the unit is subjected to the same influences as the test specimens.

5.2.1.4 A blower unit in the base of the apparatus shall provide a flow of air through the test chamber and over the test specimens. Control of the specimen, test chamber, and the black standard temperature should be accomplished by thermostatic control of the chamber temperature and adjustment of the air flow rate to obtain the specified black standard temperature.

5.2.1.5 Relative humidity in the test chamber should be measured and controlled by a hygrometer. Water should be vaporized and diffused to enrich the air with moisture and produce the required humidity.

6. Apparatus Set-Up

6.1 To insure repeatability of tests, maintain and calibrate the apparatus to manufacturer's specifications, and as described in Appendices A, B, and C. Appendix A contains additional maintenance instructions and replacement schedules and Appendices B and C describe the use of reference materials to determine if the xenon-arc apparatus is operating within the desired range. Appendix C provides an alternative to the method described in Appendix B using a polystyrene reference plastic suitable for use during long-term exposure and requires less fre-

1. Model XENOTEST® 1200 CPS or equivalent with chamber air heater and variable fan speed controller meets the requirements of this test method. This apparatus is available from Heraeus DSET Laboratories, Inc., 45601 N. 47th Avenue, Phoenix, AZ 85027-7042.

quent interruption of machine operation. Contractual agreement will determine which method(s) will be used.

6.1.1 The input voltage must be between 200 to 240, 380, or 400 to 440 V based on manufacturer's specifications.

6.1.2 Water for humidification and lamp cooling must be purified so that it is free of silica and has no more than 20 ppm total dissolved solids.

6.1.3 Install 3 sections of Suprax filter system, or equivalent to match 5.2.1.1.

6.1.4 Program the microprocessor for the test conditions in Table 2. Program other functions to be OFF.

TABLE 2—MICROPROCESSOR PROGRAM

Parameter	Program Light	Program Dark
Irradiance Level	80 W/m²	0 W/m²
Irradiance	ON	OFF
Rel. Humidity	50%	95%
Chamber Temperature	62 °C	38 °C
Phase Time	228 min	60 min
Phase No.	1	2
Number of filters	Window Glass0	
Number of filters	Suprax 1/33	
Number of filters	Suprax 1/60	

6.1.5 Operate the equipment to maintain the conditions in Table 3. If the actual operating conditions do not agree with the machine settings after the equipment has stabilized, discontinue the test and identify the cause of the disagreement.

TABLE 3—EQUIPMENT OPERATING CONDITIONS

Parameter	Cycle Light	Cycle Dark
Automatic Irradiance	80W/m² ± 1 W/m² @ 300 to 400 nm	—
Black Standard Temperature	97 °C ± 3 °C	—
Chamber Temperature	62 °C ± 2 °C	38 °C ± 2 °C
Relative Humidity	50 % ± 5%	95 % ± 5%
Radiant Exposure	See applicable specifications	

NOTE— It may be necessary to adjust the blower speed to maintain the temperature difference between the black standard and the chamber temperatures.

7. Test Procedure

7.1 Prepare the specimens to be exposed to fit the specimen holder being used.

7.2 Specimen sizes must conform to the size of the specimen holder(s) supplied by the manufacturer for use with the equipment. Specimens that exceed these sizes may not give proper exposure results. Instructions for mounting parts or portions of a part can be obtained from the responsible engineering group.

7.3 Back interior textiles (body cloth, carpet, vinyl coated fabrics, etc.) with white cardboard[2]. Specimens other than interior textiles do not completely fill the exposure area of the specimen holder and are also backed with white cardboard.

7.4 Insert specimen in holder and secure. Under no circumstances should the face side of the sample be closer to the arc than the front side of the specimen holder.

7.5 Fill all unused slots in specimen holders with stainless steel blanks to maintain desired air flow.

2. Six-ply white card stock, lined on both sides, manufactured by the Beverage Paper Company or equivalent has been found suitable for this purpose. This part is available as stock No. GJ003 from the Dilliard Paper Company, P.O. Box 7550, Norfolk, VA 23509. Weight of card stock should be sufficient to prevent warping.

7.6 Expose specimens, beginning with the light cycle, for the required radiant exposure (Megajoules per square meter [MJ/m²]) measured in the wavelength range of 300 to 400 nm. See applicable material specification.

NOTE—Care should be taken to avoid mixing potentially incompatible specimens in the same machine load, i.e., textiles should not be exposed together with foam backed textile, foams, or plastics.

Once exposure has been initiated, equipment operation should not be interrupted more than once daily. Additional interruptions, e.g., opening the chamber door during the course of daily operation, may cause variation in test results.

8. Evaluating and Reporting the Degree of Fade

8.1 The degree of fade should be evaluated and reported as specified between the contractual parties. One or more of the following methods may be specified:

8.1.1 INSTRUMENTAL MEASUREMENT

8.1.1.1 Color difference values in CIELAB units are obtained by instrumentally measuring the specimen before and after a specified amount of radiant exposure. The procedure used for specimen measurement will conform to that specified in Appendix B.

8.1.2 VISUAL ASSESSMENT

8.1.2.1 Assign colorfastness ratings using the AATCC Gray Scale for Color Change in accordance with AATCC Evaluation Procedure 1 (1987).

8.1.2.2 Using the viewing conditions specified in AATCC Evaluation Procedure 1 (1987), quantify the color change using the following terminology:

a. NONE—No change in hue, lightness, or saturation.

b. SLIGHT—A change in lightness and/or saturation which can be determined only upon close examination but no change in hue.

c. NOTICEABLE—A change in lightness and/or saturation which can easily be seen and/or change in hue.

d. SEVERE—An extreme change in lightness, saturation, and/or hue.

9. Report

9.1 A copy of the Exposure Control/Report Form (Figure 1)[3] indicating the color change of the exposed reference material in CIELAB color difference units must accompany each exposed specimen being submitted for approval. If any one of the color difference data points is outside the specified tolerance (control limits), the cause and corrective action must be indicated in the space provided.

9.2 The Exposure Control/Report Form shall include the following additional information:

9.2.1 Laboratory name

9.2.2 Type and serial number of exposure equipment

9.2.3 Month and Year of equipment operation represented by the control chart

9.2.4 Test method

9.2.5 Reference material(s) used

9.2.6 Frequency of operation verification, e.g., daily, three, or seven day intervals

9.2.7 Color change, target value, and tolerance, in CIELAB color difference units for the reference material(s) used

9.2.8 The monthly average color difference for the reference material(s)

9.2.9 Measured color change, in CIELAB color difference units, for reference material 1

9.2.10 Measured color change, in CIELAB color difference units, for reference material 2 (if more than one material is used)

9.2.11 Daily record of black standard temperature

9.2.12 Daily record of chamber temperature

9.2.13 Sample identification

9.2.14 Total radiant exposure applied to the specimen

9.2.15 Date specimen exposure was initiated

9.2.16 Date specimen exposure was completed

3. Copies of the Exposure Control/Report Form can be obtained from any automotive company using this procedure.

APPENDIX A

A.1 Maintenance

A.1.1 Test Chamber—The frequency of cleaning will vary with water quality. However, the chamber must be cleaned at least once a month and flushed with deionized water. Do NOT use cleaning agents containing chlorine.

A.1.2 Conditioning Chamber—The frequency of cleaning will vary with water and air quality in the laboratory. However, the water reservoir must be drained once a month and flushed with deionized water to remove any deposits.

A.1.3 Optical Assembly—Frequency of cleaning will vary with water quality. However, at least once each week wipe the outer surface of the filter with reagent grade alcohol and a soft cloth. If deposits cannot be removed, the filter should be disassembled and cleaned as necessary.

A.1.4 Black Standard Sensor—Polish monthly using a good quality automotive polish.

A.2 Replacement Schedule

A.2.1 Lamp Assembly and Related Parts—Replace lamps as required by the manufacturer specifications. To adequately control both low wavelength UV and the infrared component of the lamps spectral irradiance, lamps should be rotationally replaced so that individual lamps do not exceed 1500 h. For systems with more than 1 lamp, a rotational replacement schedule is recommended.

A.3 Calibration Checks

A.3.1 Check the calibration of the exposure chamber as instructed by the manufacturer, or when the control materials deviate from the specified ranges. (Record these values on the form shown in Figure A1).

EQUIPMENT CALIBRATION REPORT

Company/Area: ______

Equipment Type: **Model #:** **Serial #:**

Filter Combination: ______ **Test Specification:**

	Date						
CALIBRATION	**SET POINT**	**BEFORE ADJUSTM.**	**AFTER ADJUSTM.**	**BEFORE ADJUSTM.**	**AFTER ADJUSTM.**	**BEFORE ADJUSTM.**	**AFTER ADJUSTM.**
Irradiance	**W/m²**						
	UV sensor serial #						
PLC Readout indicates power to lamp	**as indicated**						
Black Standard Temperature (BST)	**°C**						
	BST serial #						
Chamber Temperature	**Ambient**						
	65°C						
Humidity (% RH)	**35%**						
	80%						
Operating Hours	**Total**						
	Lamp 1						
	Lamp 2						
	Lamp 3						

FIGURE A1—EQUIPMENT CALIBRATION REPORT

APPENDIX B

B.1 Scope

B.1.1 This appendix describes the procedure for using AATCC blue wool lightfastness standards as reference fabrics for the purpose of determining whether the xenon-arc apparatus is operating properly.

B.1.2 Color difference values in CIELAB units are obtained by instrumentally measuring the reference fabrics before and after a specified amount of radiant exposure.

B.1.3 AATCC L-2[4] Blue Wool Lightfastness Standard shall be exposed daily. An AATCC L-4[4] Blue Wool Lightfastness Standard shall be used to monitor continuous three day operating cycle as agreed upon between contractual parties.

B.2 Procedure

B.2.1 Instruments used to determine color difference for this procedure require capability for providing CIELAB color values using illuminant D-65, 10 degree observer data. If an instrument with diffuse geometry is used, the specular component of reflectance shall be included in the measurement. (Refer to SAE J1545, 3.6 for details.)

NOTE—An aperture diameter smaller than 20 mm cannot be used for these measurements.

B.2.2 Calibrate the instrument to be used for the color measurements to the manufacturer's recommendations.

B.2.3 Back the reference fabric to be measured with white cardboard[5]. Condition the backed reference fabric in a standard atmosphere (50% RH ± 5% RH and 21 °C ± 1 °C) for a minimum of 2 h. Insert one layer of unexposed material of the same lightfastness standard between the reference fabric and cardboard-backing prior to measurement.

NOTE—The reference fabrics are light-sensitive. Therefore, the piece used as the backing layer during measurement will need to be replaced when noticeable color change has occurred (after approximately 50 uses).

B.2.4 Place the reference fabric against the sample port of the instrument in such a way that a smooth surface is presented for measurement.

B.2.5 After taking an initial reading in CIELAB units, rotate the reference fabric 90 degrees and take a second reading. Average the readings and store them as the standard measurement for the identified piece of reference fabric. REMOVE THE BACKING FABRIC AND PLACE IN A LIGHT TIGHT CONTAINER FOR LATER USE.

4. AATCC L-2 and L-4 Blue Wool Lightfastness Standards may be obtained from AATCC, P.O. Box 12215, Research Triangle Park, NC 27709.

5. Six-ply white card stock, lined on both sides, manufactured by the Beverage Paper Company or equivalent has been found suitable for this purpose. This part is available as stock No. GJ003 from the Dilliard Paper Company, P.O. Box 7550, Norfolk, VA 23509. Weight of card stock should be sufficient to prevent warping

B.2.6 Place the cardboard backed reference fabric (single layer) in specimen holder(s) and secure on specimen rack adjacent to the black standard thermometer (if used).

B.2.7 Always start the exposure apparatus at the beginning of the light cycle. Expose the L-2 reference fabric for 5.47 MJ/m^2/@ 300 to 400 nm or the L-4 reference fabric for 16.42 MJ/m^2/300 to 400 nm as agreed upon by contractual parties.

B.2.8 After the specified radiant exposure, remove the reference fabric and the white cardboard backing and allow them to condition at 21 °C ± 1 °C and 50% ± 5% relative humidity for a minimum of 1 h.

B.2.9 Repeat the color measurement steps specified in B.2.2 through B.2.5 on the exposed area of the reference fabric(s) and using the previously stored pre-exposure measurement, determine the delta L*, a*, b*, and E*.

B.2.10 Compare the delta E* value determined to that specified in Table B1:

TABLE B1—COLORIMETRIC SPECIFICATIONS FOR TOTAL COLOR CHANGE OF BLUE WOOLD LIGHTFASTNESS STANDARDS

Lightfastness Standards	delta E
AATCC LJ-2 (Lot 5)	11.0 ± 0.60
AATCC L-4 (Lot 4)	6.90 ± 0.50

NOTE—The stated color difference values may change when new lots of the reference materials are produced. The target values desired should be confirmed by the contractual automotive company.

B.2.11 If the delta value does not fall within the following tolerances, do not resume the test until the reason has been determined and resolved.

B.2.12 As each group of test specimens completes its specified radiant exposure, record and report the color change information in terms of delta E* values of the reference fabric piece(s) used during the test period on the Exposure Control Report Form (Figure B1).

EXPOSURE CONTROL/REPORT FORM

LABORATORY	INSTRUMENT TYPE & SERIAL #	MONTH/YEAR	TEST METHOD
REFERENCE MATERIAL	FREQUENCY OF READINGS	Δ CIELAB REQUIREMENT	MONTHLY AVERAGE

Δ CIELAB UNITS

FOR DATA POINTS OUTSIDE OF THE CONTROL LIMITS

1. CIRCLE AND NUMBER EACH DATA POINT.
2. INDICATE BELOW REASON AND CORRECTIVE ACTION TAKEN.

1.

2.

3.

4.

5.

6.

7.

8.

9.

10.

DATE

REF. MAT'L 1

REF. MAT'L 2

BLACK STANDARD TEMP.

CHAMBER TEMP.

SAMPLE DATA	SAMPLE I.D.	RADIANT EXPOSURE *(KJ/M2)*	START DATE	END DATE

FIGURE B1—EXPOSURE CONTROL REPORT FORM

APPENDIX C

C.1 Scope

C.1.1 This Appendix describes an alternate procedure for using a clear Polystyrene Lightfastness Standard[6] as a reference standard for the purpose of determining whether the xenon-arc apparatus is operating properly. This lightfastness standard is used during testing of rigid plastics and other miscellaneous materials requiring long exposures.

C.1.2 Color difference values in CIELAB units are obtained by instrumentally measuring the reference plastic before and after a specified amount of radiant exposure.

C.1.3 The polystyrene lightfastness standard may be exposed for equivalent megajoule periods from 2 to 7 days.

6. The Polystyrene Plastic Lightfastness Standard may be obtained from Testfabrics, Inc., 200 Blackford Avenue, P.O. Box 420, Middlesex, NJ 08846, Phone # (908) 469-6446.

C.2 Procedure

C.2.1 Instruments used to determine color difference for this procedure require a capability for operation which includes the specular component and providing CIELAB color values using illuminant D-65, 10 degree observer data. No substitutions are permitted. Measurements in either the transmission or reflectance mode may be used.

NOTE—An aperture diameter smaller than 20 mm cannot be used for these measurements.

C.2.2 Calibrate the instrument to be used for the color measurements in accordance with the manufacturer's recommendations.

C.2.3 Reflectance Mode

C.2.3.1 Place a piece of unexposed reference plastic, backed with a white calibration tile against the sample port of the instrument.

C.2.3.2 Take an initial reading and store it as the standard measurement for the identified piece of reference plastic.

C.2.4 Transmission Mode

C.2.4.1 Place a piece of unexposed reference plastic in the proper location for measuring transmittance as recommended by the manufacturer of the instrument in use.

C.2.4.2 Place a white tile used for calibration against the outer sample port of the instrument.

C.2.4.3 Take an initial measurement and store it as the standard measurement for the identified piece of reference plastic.

C.2.5 Place the pre-measured piece of reference plastic in a specimen holder and secure on the specimen rack adjacent to the black standard thermometer (if used).

C.2.6 Expose the reference plastic for an equivalent Megajoule period of 2 to 7 days.

C.2.7 After the radiant exposure, remove the reference plastic from the apparatus.

C.2.8 Repeat the color measurement steps specified in C.2.3 or C.2.4 on the exposed reference plastic and using the previously stored pre-exposure measurement, determine the delta L*, a*, b*, and E* color difference values.

C.2.9 Compare the delta b* value determined to those indicated in Table C1 for the polystyrene chips supplied in TESTFABRICS LOT #1:

TABLE C1—COLORIMETRIC SPECIFICATIONS FOR CHANGE IN YELLOWNESS OF THE REFERENCE PLASTIC AT VARIOUS EXPOSURE LEVELS

KJ/m^2 340 nm[(1)]	MJ/m^2 (300-400 nm)	Reflectance delta B −10%	Reflectance delta B Target	Reflectance delta B +10%	Transmission delta B −10%	Transmission delta B Target	Transmission delta B +10%	Days
75.2	10.94	2.27	2.52	2.77	1.20	1.20	1.32	2
112.8	16.42	3.31	3.68	4.05	1.75	1.75	1.93	3
150.4	21.89	4.35	4.83	5.31	2.30	2.30	2.53	4
188.0	27.36	5.48	6.09	6.70	2.90	2.90	3.19	5
225.6	32.83	6.62	7.35	8.08	3.50	3.50	3.85	6
263.2	28.30	7.75	8.61	9.47	4.10	4.10	4.51	7

NOTE— Data for lots other than that specified may be obtained from the supplier or contractual automotive company.

1. The values listed as KJ/m^2 at 340 nm are for reference only. This method measures and controls over the waveband of 300 to 400 nm. It is not proper to calculate ratios of 300 to 400 nm versus 340 nm using the data presented.

C.2.10 If the delta b* value does not fall within ±10% of that specified for the stated duration of exposure, do not resume the test until the reason has been determined and resolved.

C.2.11 As each group of test specimens completes its specified radiant exposure, record and report the color change information in terms of delta b* values of the reference plastic piece(s) used during the test period on the Exposure Control/Report Form (see Figure B1).

SURFACE MATCH VERIFICATION METHOD FOR PRESSURE SENSITIVE ADHESIVELY ATTACHED COMPONENTS—SAE J2215 DEC1991

SAE Recommended Practice

Report of the SAE Mountig Tape Subcommittee of the SAE Decorative Tape and Molding Committee approved December 1991. Rationale statement available.

Foreword—This Document has not been changed other to put it into the new SAE Technical Standards Board Format.

This SAE Recommended Practice has been developed by the SAE Mounting Tape Subcommittee of the SAE Decorative Tape and Molding Committee. The Mounting Tape Subcommittee was formed in 1984. The objectives of this committee are to develop SAE Standards, Recommended Practices, and Information Reports relative to automotive applications of decorative tapes and adhesive mounting tapes.

1. Scope—This SAE Recommended Practice applies to evaluation of the conformance match condition existing between two surfaces. Evaluation of this conformance may be especially useful in bonded applications although it may also have relevance to bolted adjacent surface joint conditions.

Since good bonding surface conformity is necessary for providing optimal bond performance with pressure sensitive adhesives, the purpose of this document is to provide a method of evaluating the conformance match of the mating surfaces.

This document is intended as a guide toward standard practice but may be subject to frequent change to keep pace with experience and technical advances. This should be kept in mind when considering the use of this document.

Tool types, materials, application tools, and component contact area evaluation methods are included as part of this document.

In most cases a visual evaluation of contact performance may be satisfactory; however, for greater accuracy a measurement tool may be used. When reporting a contact value the mode of evaluation (e.g., visual, measurement tool) should be indicated.

1.1 Purpose—The purpose of this document is to establish a uniform practice for testing the surface match conformance which exists between two surfaces.

2. References—There are no referenced publications specified herein.

3. Definitions

3.1 Test Surface—The component surface applied to the CCS tool to evaluate match (moldings, nameplates, claddings, emblems, etc.).

3.2 Contact Pattern—Size, configuration, and location of contacted areas occurring within the test surface.

4. Significance and Use—The adhesive contact demonstrated by the component applied to a clear surface is an excellent indication of the degree of conformance existing between the component and its target surface.

A component's surface contacts a clear surface representation of the component's mating surface during application. This provides an index of the surface conformance match existing between the component and its target application area. In addition, these clear representative surfaces are useful for validating application tool component placement processes.

5. Apparatus

5.1 Clear Coordinated Surface (CCS)—A transparent polymer accurately representing a specific surface, providing an edge or outline scribe, (or equivalent) location index, and displaying test surface contacted and uncontacted areas.

NOTE—Tools may be constructed from Blehm BP-4228 or equivalent. Surfaces to be matched (e.g., prototype, pilot, production, etc.) should be agreed upon by the participating parties.

5.2 Measurement Tool—Such as a Compensating Polar Planimeter, or equivalent, is used for measurement of contacted and uncontacted areas.

6. Conditioning—At the time of application, test surface, CCS tool surface, as well as surrounding ambient temperatures shall be 23 °C ± 2 °C (72 °F ± 4 °F).

7. Procedure

7.1 Tool Surface Preparation—Immediately prior to application clean CCS tool surface with a clean lintfree cloth moistened with isopropyl alcohol.

NOTE—For repeated use and ease of repositioning, CCS tool application surface may be treated using a material such as Johnson Paste Wax, or equivalent. Surface treatments must not adversely affect tool clarity or component contact.

Contamination of component or tool mating surfaces at any time throughout the component application stage is considered unacceptable.

7.2 Component—Loose Application Method—Immediately prior to application, remove any release liners from the component and loose apply (plant on) the component to the tool assuring proper alignment with indexing or aligning features.

7.3 Pressurization—Using a 4.5 kg (10 lb) roller, make two passes at an approximate rate of 50 mm/s (2 in/s) along the central axis of any contact surfaces, through the component center, or as agreed upon by the participating parties.

NOTE—Assure any pressurizing device is guided along as freely as possible avoiding any additional normal forces. Roller rates and paths taken on the component surface must remain as consistent as possible between application in order to minimize contact pattern effects. Avoid imposing any additional weight on the applied component (weight of tool, etc.) prior to measurement of contact pattern.

7.4 Tool Surface Contact Evaluation—Observe the test surface through the tool, distinguishing contacted from uncontacted areas. Note the contact pattern.

7.5 Measurement of Contact Surface—Within 60 min of application of component to tool, calculate the percentage of contact area by using the following formula:

$$\frac{\text{Total Contacted Area}}{\text{Total Available Mating Surface Area}} \times 100\% = \%\ \text{Contact} \qquad \text{(Eq. 1)}$$

NOTE—Measurement directly to the CCS tool surface or a photograph is considered acceptable.

7.6 Component Removal—Avoid damaging the tool surface during removal.

ACCELERATED EXPOSURE OF AUTOMOTIVE EXTERIOR MATERIALS USING A CONTROLLED IRRADIANCE WATER-COOLED XENON ARC APPARATUS—SAE J1960 AUG2003

SAE Standard

Report of the SAE Weathering Test Standardization of Exterior Materials Committee approved June 1989 and revised November 2001. Rationale statement available. Revised by the SAE Textiles and Flexible Plastics Committee August 2003. Rationale statement available.

1. Scope

1.1 This test method specifies the operating procedures for a controlled irradiance, water cooled xenon arc apparatus used for the accelerated exposure of various automotive materials.

1.2 The sample preparation, test durations, and performance evaluation procedures are covered in material specifications of the different automotive manufacturers.

2. References

2.1 Applicable Publications—The following publications form a part of the specification to the extent specified herein. Unless otherwise indicated, the latest revision of SAE publications shall apply

2.1.1 SAE PUBLICATION—Available from SAE, 400 Commonwealth Drive, Warrendale, PA 15096-0001.

SAE J1545—Instrumental Color Difference Measurement for Exterior Finishes, Textiles, and Colored Trim

2.1.2 ASTM PUBLICATION—Available from ASTM, 100 Barr Harbor Drive, West Conshohocken, PA 19428-2959.

ASTM D 859—Standard Test Method for Silica in Water

ASTM D 4517—Standard Test Method for Low-Level Total Silica in High-Purity Water by Flameless Atomic Absorption Spectroscopy

ASTM G 155—Standard Practice for Operating Xenon Arc Light Apparatus for Exposure of Non-Metallic Materials

3. Definitions

3.1 Black Panel Thermometer, n

3.1.1 A temperature measuring device, the sensing unit of which is coated with black enamel designed to absorb most of the radiant energy encountered in fade/weathering testing.

3.1.1.1 This device provides an estimation of the maximum temperature a specimen might attain during exposure to natural or artificial light.

3.2 Center Wavelength, n—The specified wavelength for bandpass filters; the wavelength midway between the half power points (e.g., 340 nm ±2 nm).

3.3 Color Change, n—As used in fade-weathering testing, a change in color of any kind (whether a change in hue, saturation, or lightness).

3.4 Half Power Bandpass, n—The interval between wavelengths at which transmittance is 50% of peak. (It should not exceed 20 nm for a narrow bandpass filter.)

3.5 Irradiance, n. (E)—The incident radiant flux per unit area of a surface. ($W\ m^{-2}$)

3.6 Irradiance, Controlled, n—The maintenance by closed loop feedback of a preselected irradiance throughout a designated exposure interval.

3.7 Irradiance, Spectral, n—(E_λ) Irradiance per wavelength interval. ($Wm^{-2}\ nm^{-1}$).

3.8 Irradiance, Total, n—($W\ m^{-2}$) Irradiance integrated over all wavelengths of a light source on an exposed surface.

3.9 Irradiation, n—See radiant exposure.

3.10 Long-Arc Xenon, n—A xenon arc in which the length of the arc between electrodes is greater than the diameter of the envelope enclosing the arc.

3.11 Peak Wavelength, n—The wavelength of peak transmission (e.g., 340 nm).

3.12 Radiant Exposure, n—The time integral of irradiance (Jm^{-2}).

3.13 Radiant Exposure, Spectral, n—The time integral of spectral Irradiance ($Jm^{-2}\ nm^{-1}$).

3.14 Reference Plastic, n—A clear polystyrene plastic standard selected for exposure as a check on a test apparatus and operating conditions.

3.15 Sample, Laboratory, n—A portion of material taken to represent the lot sample, or the original material, and used in the laboratory as a source of test specimens.

3.16 Specimen, n—A specific portion of a material or a laboratory sample on which a test is performed or that is selected for that purpose.

3.17 Spectral Power Distribution, n—The relative power emitted by a source as a function of wavelength.

4. Significance and Use

4.1 This test method is designed to accelerate extreme environmental conditions encountered outside a vehicle such as sunlight, heat, and moisture (in the form of humidity, condensation or rain) for the purpose of predicting the weatherability of automotive materials.

5. Apparatus

5.1 A more complete description of the apparatuses listed below may be found in ASTM G 155.

5.2 The apparatus employed utilizes a water-cooled xenon arc lamp as the source of radiation and should be one of the following:

5.2.1 TYPE AH—A controlled irradiance apparatus in which the radiant energy source is vertically located at the central axis of a specimen rack. The specimen rack shall rotate at 1 rpm ±0.1 rpm and shall be of the three-tiered, inclined type having a center segment of 648 mm ±6 mm (25.5 in ±0.25 in) outside diameter centered on the xenon arc lamp. The top and bottom segments shall be 511 mm ± 6 mm (20 in ±0.25 in) outside diameter, positioned 28 degrees ±2 degrees from the vertical. Each segment shall accommodate 152 mm (6 in) specimen holders. The apparatus shall provide for control of dry bulb and black panel temperature, relative humidity, and irradiance at 340 nm[1].

5.2.2 TYPE BH—A controlled irradiance apparatus in which the radiant energy source is vertically located at the central axis of one of the following two racks:

5.2.2.1 The specimen rack shall rotate at 1 rpm ±0.1 rpm and shall be of the three-tiered, inclined type having a center segment of 965 mm ±6 mm (38 in ± 0.25 in) outside diameter centered on the xenon arc lamp. The top and bottom segments shall be 842 mm ±6 mm (33.16 in ±0.25 in) outside diameter, positioned 22 degrees ±2 degrees from the vertical. Each tier shall accommodate 152 mm (6 in) specimen holders. The apparatus shall provide for automatic control of temperature, relative humidity, and irradiance at 340 nm[1]. All specimen exposure openings may be used.

5.2.2.2 The specimen rack shall rotate at 1 rpm ±0.1 rpm and shall be of the two-tiered, inclined type, 965.2 mm ±6 mm (38 in ±0.25 in) outside diameter in the center. The top and bottom segments shall be 872.5 mm ±6 mm (34.35 in ± 0.25 in) outside diameter positioned 11 degrees ±2 degrees from the vertical. The rack shall be positioned so that the exposure area is centered on the xenon lamp. Each tier shall accommodate 254 mm (10 in) long specimen holders. The apparatus shall provide for automatic control of temperature, relative humidity, and irradiance at 340 nm[1]. When using this two-tiered specimen rack, the test specimens shall not be placed in positions 1 and 8 (see Figure 1).

5.2.3 The xenon arc employed shall be of the "long-arc" water-cooled type. It shall employ cylindrical inner and outer optical filters to direct the flow of cooling water and to provide a selected spectral power distribution.

5.2.4 Distilled or deionized water shall be recirculated past the burner at a flow rate sufficient to remove excess heat. Passing water through a cartridge demineralizer installed in the recirculation line just ahead of the lamp minimizes contamination of the quartz envelope of the burner. A heat exchange unit shall be used to cool the recirculated lamp water.

6. Apparatus Setup

6.1 To insure repeatability of tests, maintain and calibrate the apparatus to manufacturer's specifications and as described in Appendix A and B. Appendix A contains additional maintenance instructions and replacement schedules, and Appendix B describes the use of a reference plastic to determine if the xenon arc apparatus is operating properly within the desired range.

6.1.1 The input voltage must be between 215 to 250 V.

6.1.2 Water for lamp cooling must be purified so that it is free of silica and has no more than 20 ppm total dissolved solids.

6.1.2.1 Water used for the specimen spray and humidification system shall leave no objectionable deposits or stains on the exposed specimens. It is strongly recommended that the water contain a maximum of 1-ppm solids and a maximum

1. The Ci35, Ci35A Xenon Arc Weather-Ometer® or equivalent with factory installed air heater meets the requirements of Type AH. The Ci65 and Ci65A Xenon Arc Weather-Ometer® or equivalent with factory installed air heater meets the requirements of Type BH.

of 0.2-ppm silica. Silica levels should be determined using ASTM procedures D 859 or D 4517. A combination of deionization and reverse osmosis treatment can effectively produce water with the desired purity.

6.1.3 Install the specimen spray and the rack spray units.

6.1.4 Fit the xenon arc burner with a quartz inner filter and a "Type S" borosilicate outer filter.

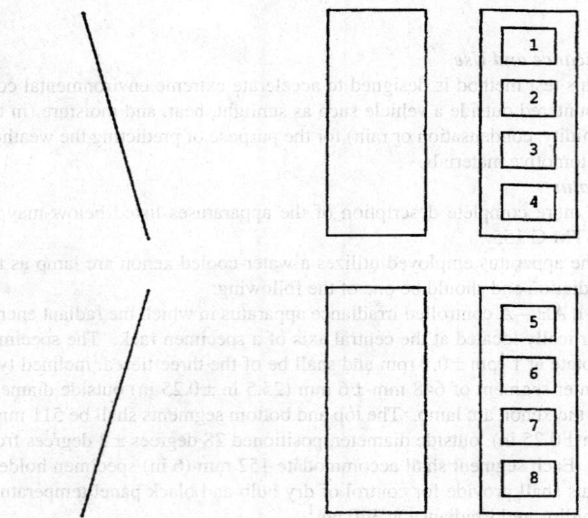

FIGURE 1—TWO-TIERED INCLINE SPECIMEN RACK

6.1.5 Set the operation switches/controls as follows in Table 1:

TABLE 1—OPERATION SWITCHES/CONTROLS

SWITCH	SETTING
Black panel/ambient air	Black panel
Wattage adjustment	Automatic
Irradiation/timed	Irradiation
Countdown meter	Set to required kJ m^{-2} nm^{-1} at 340 nm
Lamp ignition	On
Lamp cooling water	On
Fixed air valve	Off
Humidifier	On
Water heater	On
Air heater	On
Specimen spray	On
Rack spray	On
Under the circuit breakers/mode switch cover, set the following:	
Air heater on cycle	Light-on cycle
Rack spray light cycle	Off
Test chamber/high temperature adjust.	75 °C

If the proper humidity cannot be achieved, set the air heater switch to dark-on cycle.

6.1.6 Set the thumb wheel controls as follows in Table 2:

TABLE 2—THUMB WHEEL CONTROLS

Controls	Dark Cycle	Light Cycle
Automatic/irradiance	—	0.55 W m^{-2} nm^{-1} at 340 nm
Black panel temperature	38 °C	70 °C
Wet bulb depression (see 6.1.6.1)(See 6.1.6.1)	0.00 °C	12 °C
Conditioning water	40 °C	45 °C

6.1.6.1 These are suggested settings to obtain the specified humidity level. Because of ambient conditions in the room containing the apparatus, it may be necessary to adjust the wet bulb depression and/or the conditioning water temperature settings.

6.1.7 Choose the program cycle which provides 120 min of light and 60 min of dark in the following cycle: 40 min of light followed by 20 min of light and front specimen spray, followed by 60 min of light, followed by 60 min of dark with both back and front spray and repeating. The test cycle is shown in Table 3.

NOTE—Users of instruments that employ a program logic controller (PLC) should consult their manual for the appropriate program cycle. Others should use a #180 cam.

TABLE 3—TEST CYCLE

Cycle Segment	Light	Dark	Spray	Inner Filter	Outer Filter
1	N/A	60 min	Front and back	Quartz	S-Boro
2	40 min	N/A	None	Quartz	S-Boro
3	20 min	N/A	Front	Quartz	S-Boro
4	60 min	N/A	None	Quartz	S-Boro

6.1.8 Operate the apparatus to maintain the following tolerances listed in Table 4. If the actual operating conditions do not agree with the machine settings after the equipment has stabilized, discontinue the test and correct the cause of the disagreement before continuing.

NOTE 1—To maintain dry bulb tolerance, blower speed adjustment may be required.

NOTE 2—For instruments equipped with automatic blower control, for this test manufacturer recommends that the control be switched to the manual mode.

TABLE 4—TOLERANCES

Controls	Dark Cycle	Light Cycle
Automatic irradiance	—	±0.01 W m^{-2}
Black panel	±2 °C	±2 °C
Dry bulb	38 °C ±2 °C	47 °C ±2 °C
Relative humidity	95% ±5%	50% ±5%
Conditioning water	±4 °C	±4 °C
Radiant exposure	See applicable specification.	See applicable specification.

6.1.8.1 The tolerances do not apply during the spray portion of the cycle.

6.1.9 Adjust the temperature of the lamp cooling water to provide sufficient cooling but prevent condensation from forming on the lamp assembly. Suggest 50 °C for cooling water and 70 °C for high temperature cut out.

7. Test Procedure

7.1 Prepare a specimen to be exposed to fit the specimen holder being used.

7.1.1 Specimen sizes must conform to the size of the approved specimen holder. Specimens that exceed these sizes may not give proper exposure results. The correct means of mounting odd sized specimens can be obtained from the automotive company for which the material is being tested.

7.1.2 Approved frames for the three-tier rack are the SL-3T and the CD-3T only.

7.1.3 Approved frames for the two-tier rack are the SL, CD, SL-X, and the CD-4 only.

7.2 Insert the specimen in the specimen holder and attach the spring-loaded holding device.

NOTE—If the apparatus has an inclined panel rack (supplied with attached clips), the samples must fit the provided spaces.

7.3 Fill all unused slots with an inert non-reflective material to maintain desired airflow. Anodized aluminum panels are an example.

NOTE—High reflectance material may effect the operation of the equipment. Refer to the manufacturer's instructions for proper operation of the equipment.

7.4 After setting up the instrument to run for the required radiant exposure (kJm^{-2}) at 340 nm, start the test at the beginning of a dark cycle. See applicable material specification.

7.5 Report the change in color or any other property as outlined in SAE J1545.

7.6 Exposure report.

7.6.1 A copy of the exposure report (Figure 2) must be included with each exposed specimen being submitted for approval.

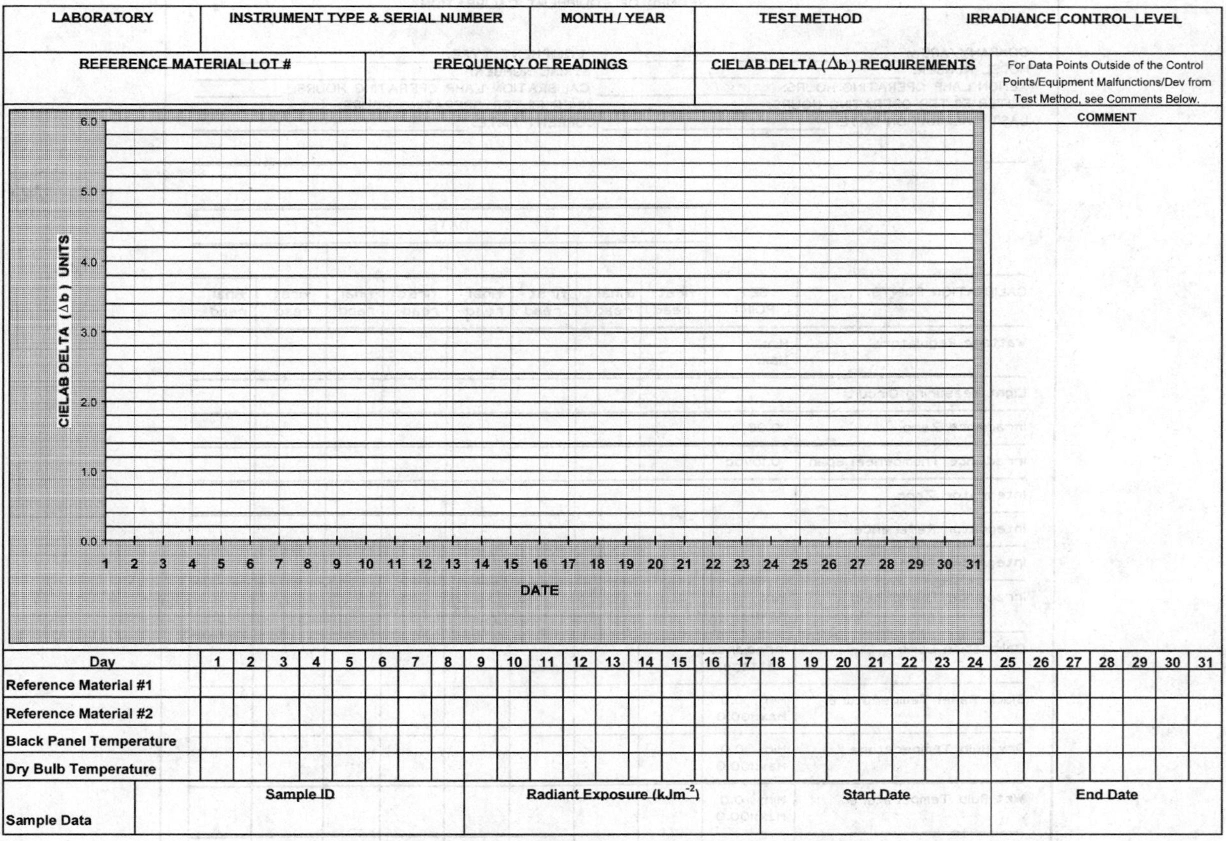

XENON ARC REFERENCE MATERIAL CONTROL CHART

LABORATORY	INSTRUMENT TYPE & SERIAL NUMBER	MONTH / YEAR	TEST METHOD	IRRADIANCE CONTROL LEVEL

REFERENCE MATERIAL LOT #	FREQUENCY OF READINGS	CIELAB DELTA (Δb) REQUIREMENTS	For Data Points Outside of the Control Points/Equipment Malfunctions/Dev from Test Method, see Comments Below.
			COMMENT

Day	1	2	3	4	5	6	7	8	9	10	11	12	13	14	15	16	17	18	19	20	21	22	23	24	25	26	27	28	29	30	31
Reference Material #1																															
Reference Material #2																															
Black Panel Temperature																															
Dry Bulb Temperature																															

Sample Data	Sample ID	Radiant Exposure (kJm^{-2})	Start Date	End Date

FIGURE 2—XENON ARC REFERENCE MATERIAL CONTROL CHART

APPENDIX A
MAINTENANCE INSTRUCTIONS AND REPLACEMENT SCHEDULES

A.1 Maintenance

A.1.1 Test Chamber—The frequency of cleaning will vary with water quality. However, the chamber should be cleaned at least once a month with a stainless steel cleaning agent and flushed with deionized water. Do NOT use cleaning agents containing chlorine.

A.1.2 Conditioning Chamber—The frequency of cleaning will vary with the water and air quality in the laboratory. However, the chamber should be drained once a month and flushed with deionized water to remove sediment.

A.1.3 Lamp Assembly—Frequency of cleaning will vary with water quality. However, at least once each week wipe the outer surface of the outer filter with alcohol and a soft cloth. If deposits cannot be removed, replace the filter.

A.1.4 Quartz Light Rod—Clean weekly the end of the light rod with alcohol and a soft cloth.

A.1.5 Black Panel Sensor—Polishing monthly, using a good quality automotive polish, should be adequate. The need for more frequent polishing may indicate a problem. For resolution, contact the manufacturer.

A.1.6 Spray Nozzles—Check daily for any signs of clogging. If continual clogging occurs, additional filters may be necessary in the distilled water lines supplying the instrument.

A.2 Replacement Schedule

A.2.1 Lamp assembly and related parts.

A.2.1.1 Replace the inner filter when the specified irradiance level can no longer be achieved or after a maximum of 1000 h of operation.

A.2.1.2 Replace the outer filter when the specified irradiance level can no longer be achieved or after a maximum of 1000 h of operation.

A.2.1.3 Replace the burner tube when the specified irradiance level can no longer be achieved or when the black panel temperature can no longer be controlled.

A.2.1.4 Replacement of the interference filter located in the light monitoring system after 9000 h of operation in the light cycle or 18 months of use, whichever comes first. Earlier replacement may become necessary if after replacement of lamp and filters, the wattage level does not return to normal. Refer to the operators manual.

A.2.2 Replace the black panel sensor when local surface luster can no longer be maintained or when bare metal can be seen.

A.2.3 Inspect the wet bulb wick weekly and replace when discoloration or mineral deposits are observed.

A.3 Calibration Checks

A.3.1 Check daily the switches and thumb wheel controls for proper settings.

A.3.2 Calibrate the apparatus every two weeks following the procedures detailed in the operating manual provided by the manufacturer. It is suggested that the calibration be performed on the same day of the week.

A.3.3 When proof of calibration is required, contact specific Automotive manufacturers for the appropriate reporting forms.

A.3.4 Calibration records are maintained using the recording form as provided in Figure A1. Set point may differ depending on the model of apparatus used. Refer to the operating manual provided with the equipment for the exact requirements.

A.3.5 The use of the "Temperature Calibration PC Board," provided by the manufacturer, is a requirement for the every two week calibration of the apparatus. This replaces the biweekly use of the hot and cold-water method which may be outlined in the instrument's operating manual. Complete adherence to the manufacturer's instructions for calibration using this "PC board" is mandatory.

RECORD OF EQUIPMENT CALIBRATION

COMPANY/AREA: ____________ EQUIPMENT TYPE: ____________
MODEL NUMBER: ____________ SERIAL NUMBER: ____________
XENON LAMP OPERATING HOURS: ____________ CALIBRATION LAMP OPERATING HOURS: ____________
OUTER FILTER OPERATING HOURS: ____________ INNER FILTER OPERATING HOURS: ____________
LAST CALIBRATION DATE: ____________ CURRENT DATE: ____________

CALIBRATION POINTS	SET POINT	DATE							
		first read	final read	first read	final read	first read	final read	first read	final read
Wattage Regulator	Min: Max:								
Light Measuring Circuit									
Irradiance Zero	0.00								
Irradiance Thumbwheel Span	0.10vdc								
Integrator Zero									
Integrator Reference									
Integrator Span									
Irradiance Thumbwheel	Min: Max:								
Calibration Lamp	Irradiance Wattage								
Black Panel Temperature	Min: 0.0 Max:100.0								
Dry Bulb Temperature	Min: 0.0 Max:100.0								
Wet Bulb Temperature	Min: 0.0 Max:100.0								
Depression	Min: 0.0 Max:100.0								
Conditioning Water	Min: 0.0 Max:100.0								

FIGURE A1—EQUIPMENT CALIBRATION RECORD

APPENDIX B
PROCEDURE FOR DETERMINING COLORFASTNESS TO LIGHT

B.1 Scope

B.1.1 Appendix B describes the procedure for using a clear polystyrene lightfastness standard as a reference plastic for the purpose of determining whether the xenon arc apparatus is operating properly.

B.1.2 The color difference values in CIELAB units are obtained by instrumentally measuring the reference plastic before and after a specified amount of radiant exposure.

B.1.3 The clear polystyrene lightfastness standard may be exposed for equivalent kilojoule periods from two to seven days. The reference plastic may be obtained from Test Fabrics, Inc., 415 Delaware Avenue, West Pittston, PA 18643, Phone 570-603-0432.

B.2 Procedure

B.2.1 The instruments used to determine color difference for this procedure requires a capability for providing CIELAB illuminant D-65, 10 degree observer, specular included readings. No substitutions are permitted. Either a transmission or a reflection mode may be used.

B.2.2 Calibrate the instrument to be used for the color measurements to the manufacturers instructions.

B.2.3 Reflection Mode

B.2.3.1 Place a piece of unexposed reference plastic backed with the white tile used for calibration against the sample port of the instrument.

NOTE—IN ORDER TO PRESERVE THE SURFACE OF THE WHITE CALIBRATION TILE, IT IS RECOMMENDED THAT A SECOND CALIBRATION TILE BE PURCHASED FOR THESE MEASUREMENTS.

B.2.3.2 Take an initial reading. Save this reading and store it as your standard reading.

B.2.4 Transmission Mode

B.2.4.1 Place a piece of unexposed reference plastic in the proper location as instructed by the manufacturer.

B.2.4.2 Place the white tile used for calibration against the outer sample port of the instrument.

NOTE—IN ORDER TO PRESERVE THE SURFACE OF THE WHITE CALIBRATION TILE, IT IS RECOMMENDED THAT A SECOND CALIBRATION TILE BE PURCHASED FOR THESE MEASUREMENTS.

B.2.4.3 Take an initial reading. Save this reading and store it as your standard reading.

B.2.5 Place a piece of reference plastic in a specimen holder and attach the spring-loaded holding device.

B.2.6 Secure it on the specimen rack adjacent to the black panel thermometer Figure B1 and Figure B2.

B.2.7 Always start the exposure apparatus at the beginning of the dark cycle and expose the reference plastic for an equivalent radiant dosage period of two to seven days.

B.2.8 After the radiant exposure, remove the reference plastic from the apparatus.

B.2.9 Examine the surfaces for water spotting. If spotting is found, carefully remove it using a piece of water-saturated white cheese cloth. Thoroughly dry the reference plastic using another piece of white cheese cloth.

B.2.9.1 Care must be taken not to scratch the surface of the reference plastic as the measurement could be affected.

B.2.10 Repeat the color measurement steps specified in B.2.3 or B.2.4 on the exposed area of the reference plastic and determine the delta L*, a*, b*, and E*.

B.2.11 Compare the delta b* reading to the graph chart for the cycle used.

B.2.11.1 The supplier is to provide graph charts with each purchase of the polystyrene chip.

B.2.12 If the delta b* value does not fall within the predetermined value as established by the supplier, immediately run another polystyrene per Section B.2 for the shortest time interval. If the polystyrene reference standard continues to be out of specification, discontinue testing until the problem is corrected.

B.2.13 The polystyrene standard is to be run after every calibration (every two weeks) for the specified amount of kilojoules or hours. As each group of test specimens completes its specified radiant exposure, record and report as required by the customer the delta b* values and the mean and standard deviation of the reference plastic used during the test period.

B.2.14 The intent of the polystyrene is to monitor the performance of the test. It is for Statistical Process Control (SPC) purposes. A point outside of the range does not necessarily invalidate the test.

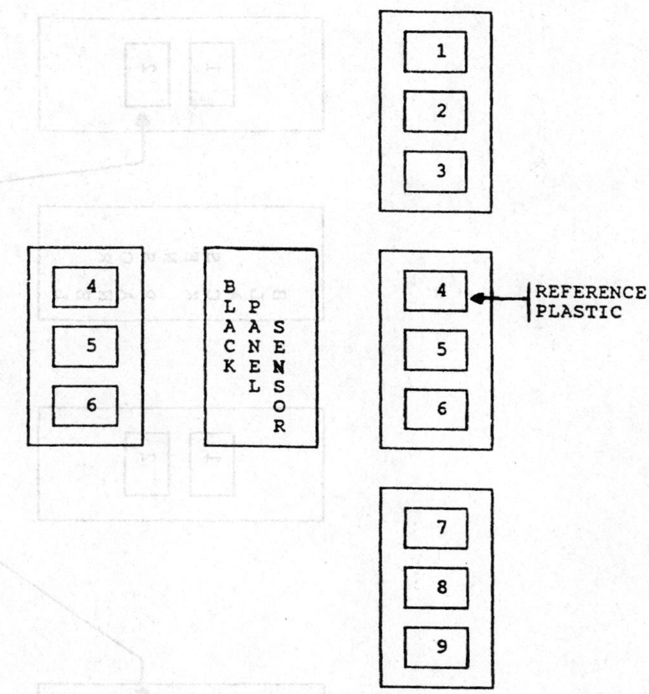

NOTE: Expose Reference Plastic in position #4. Position holder to the right of the Black Panel Sensor.

FIGURE B1—THREE-TIER INCLINE SPECIMEN RACK

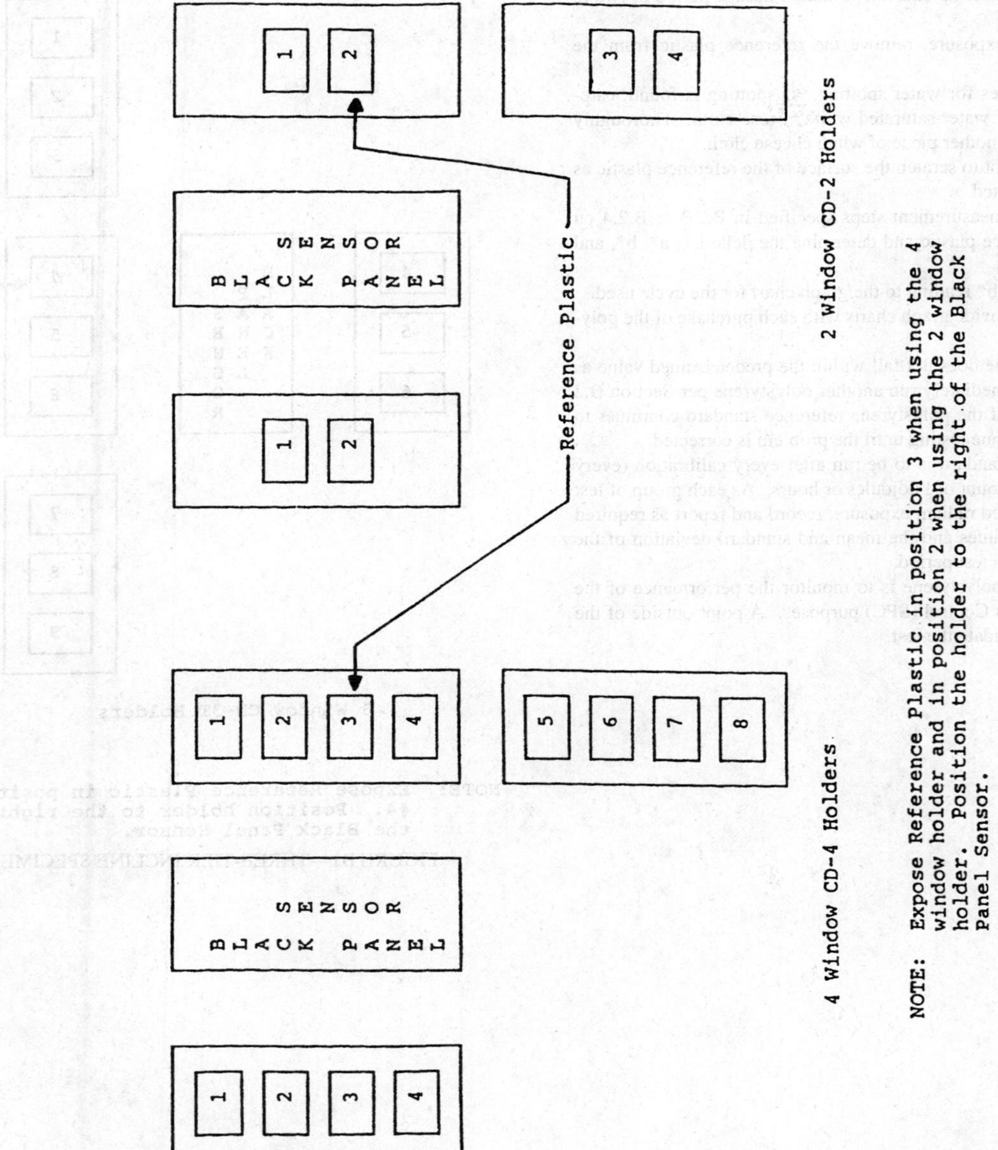

FIGURE B2—TWO-TIER INCLINE SPECIMEN RACK CI65 ONLY

(R) OUTDOOR WEATHERING OF EXTERIOR MATERIALS —SAE J1976 MAR2002

SAE Standard

Report of the SAE Weathering Test Standardization of Exterior Materials Committee approved June 1989. Completely revised by the SAE Weathering Test Standards Committee February 1994. Completely revised by the SAE Textiles and Flexible Plastics Committee March 2002. Rationale statement available.

1. Scope

1.1 This test method specifies the exposure rack(s), black box(es), and instrumentation, which shall be used for the outdoor weathering of materials for automotive exterior application.

1.2 All dimensions are nominal unless otherwise noted.

1.3 A list of approved exposure test sites is generally available from specified automotive manufacturers.

1.4 Sample preparation, exposure duration, and performance evaluation procedures not presented in this method are covered in material specifications of the different automotive manufacturers.

1.5 This method includes three procedures:

1.5.1 PROCEDURE A—Exposure in a rack without backing; or, as required, (1) expanded metal backing, or (2) backed plywood at a fixed angle of 5 degrees from the horizontal facing the equator.

1.5.2 PROCEDURE B—Exposure in an unheated black box at a fixed angle of 5 degrees from the horizontal facing the equator. For non-rigid specimens, see note below.

1.5.3 PROCEDURE C—Exposure at angles other than 5 degrees as specified in PROCEDURE A AND PROCEDURE B.

1.5.3.1 Special Tests—These are established on an as-needed basis to duplicate end-use conditions. Examples are in-service position of large assemblies or components that cannot be accommodated in a 5 degrees exposure rack.

NOTE—If required for nonrigid specimens, use expanded metal backing for unbacked exposures. Expose specimens in a rack with plywood backing 13 mm to 19 mm (1/2 in to 3/4 in) that have an end-use application in a backed configuration.

2. References

2.1 Applicable Publications—One or more of the following documents may be required for materials evaluation before and after exposure. Evaluation procedures shall be specified by the different automotive manufacturers:

2.1.1 SAE PUBLICATIONS—Available from SAE, 400 Commonwealth Drive, Warrendale, PA 15096-0001

SAE J400—Test for Chip Resistance of Surface Coatings

SAE J1545—Instrumental Color Difference Measurements for Exterior Finishes, Textiles, and Colored Trim

2.1.2 ASTM PUBLICATIONS—Available from ASTM, 100 Barr Harbor Drive, West Conshohocken, PA 19428.

ASTM G 147—Standard Practice for Conditioning and Handling of Nonmetallic Materials for Natural and Artificial Weathering Tests

ASTM D 523—Standard Test Method for Specular Gloss

ASTM D 610—Standard Method for Evaluating Degree of Rusting on Painted Steel Surfaces

ASTM D 714—Standard Method for Evaluating Degree of Blistering of Paints

ASTM D 772—Standard Method for Evaluating Degree of Flaking (Scaling) of Exterior Paints

ASTM D 2794—Standard Method for Resistance of Organic Coatings to the Effect of Rapid Deformation (Impact)

ASTM D 3002—Standard Practice for Evaluation of Coatings for Plastics

ASTM D 3359—Standard Method for Measuring Adhesion by Tape Test

ASTM D 3363—Standard Test Method for Film Hardness by Pencil Test

ASTM D 3924—Standard Specifications for Standard Environment for Conditioning and Testing Paint, Varnish, Lacquer, and Related Materials

ASTM D 4060—Standard Test Method for Abrasion Resistance of Organic Coatings by the Taber Abraser

ASTM D 4214—Standard Test Method for Evaluating Degree of Chalking of Exterior Paint Films

ASTM E 313—Standard Test Method for Index of Whiteness and Yellowness of Near-White Opaque Materials

2.1.3 ISO PUBLICATIONS—Available from ANSI, 25 West 43rd Street, New York, NY 10036-8002.

ISO 9223—Corrosion of metals and alloys—Corrosivity of atmospheres—Measurement of pollution

ISO TS16949 – Quality Systems – Automotive Suppliers – Particular requirements for the application of ISO 9001:1994

ISO 17025 – General requirements for the competence of testing and calibration laboratories

3. Significance and Use

3.1 This method shall be used to test the weather resistance of all materials intended for automotive exterior applications. Those materials covered by government specifications are exempt from this document.

3.2 Since the natural environment varies considerably during any twelve-month period with respect to location, different results may be expected among sites located within the same climate classification or region.

3.2.1 Exposures can be conducted in any type of climate. However, to obtain results from the most severe outdoor environment, exposures are often conducted in locations that receive high levels of solar radiation, temperature, and moisture. Typically, these conditions are found in hot desert and subtropical or tropical climates, such as Phoenix, Arizona and Miami, Florida, respectively. Known attributes of the use environment should be represented by the locations selected for outdoor durability evaluation. For example, if the use environment for the product being evaluated will include freeze/thaw cycling, specimen exposure in a northern temperate climate is recommended. In addition, exposures are often conducted in areas where specimens are subjected to salt air (seashore) or industrial pollutants.

3.2.2 The relative durability of materials in natural exposures can be very different depending on the location of the exposure because of differences in ultraviolet (UV) radiation, time of wetness, temperature, pollutants, and other factors. Therefore, it cannot be assumed that results from exposure in a single location will be useful for determining relative durability in a different location. Exposures in several locations with different climates which represent a broad range of anticipated service conditions are recommended.

3.2.3 Because of year-to-year climatological variations, results from a single exposure test cannot be used to predict the absolute rate at which a material degrades. Several years of repeat exposures are needed to get an "average" test result for a given location.

3.2.4 Solar ultraviolet radiation varies considerably as a function of time of year. This can cause large differences in the apparent rate of degradation in many polymers. Comparing results for material exposed for short periods (less than one year) is not recommended unless materials are exposed at the same time in the same location.

4. Location

4.1 The rack and/or black boxes shall be placed in an area free from objects likely to shade the test specimens during exposure. The area beneath and in the immediate vicinity of the test fixtures should be characterized by low reflectance and be typical of the ground cover in that climatological area. The lowest section of the racks or black boxes shall be at a sufficient height above ground to avoid contact with vegetation and to prevent damage during area maintenance. A minimum height of 46 cm (18 in) above the ground is recommended or at a sufficient height to avoid contact with vegetation and to prevent damage that might occur during area maintenance, whichever is greater.

5. Construction

5.1 Panel Exposure Racks – Procedure A (Coating Systems)

5.1.1 The exposure racks and hardware used in Procedure A shall be constructed of anodized aluminum or an approved equivalent. The racks shall be designed for unbacked exposure.

NOTE—Clear anodized aluminum alloy No. 6061T6 and 6063T6 have been found suitable for construction of racks and frames for use in all geographic locations.

5.1.2 When required, the racks shall be fitted with a 65 mm (2.5 in) shield to provide an unexposed area on the test piece. A typical panel rack and fitted shield for exposing coating systems is shown in Figure 1.

5.1.3 When required, expanded metal backing shall be 0.03 cm (0.012 in) thick, flattened mesh 5005 H34 aluminum expanded metal, with an opening size of 0.270 x 0.690 cm (0.106 in x 0.272 in).

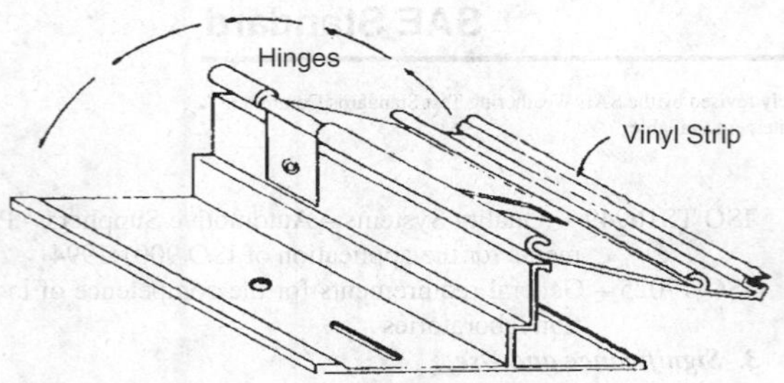

Panel Flap Assembly

Harrison Open Backed Exposure Rack

A. 1.52 m – 152 mm x 3.66 m x 102 mm (5 ft 6 in x 12.0 ft x 4 in) aluminum frame anodized welded fabrication.
B. Panel base and flap assemblies (or masks) 12 ft 0 in in length are adjustable for any size panel.
C. Vinyl strip in edge of panel flap insures fine demarcation line.
D. Support post for ground or roof mountings are provided.
E. Arms for frame angle position are adjustable from vertical to five degrees.
F. Fabrications are available for strong panel exposure.

FIGURE 1—TYPICAL PANEL RACK AND FITTING SHIELD

5.1.4 For backed exposures, use exterior grade plywood to form a solid surface to which the specimens are directly attached. A minimum of 13 mm (1/2 in) thick exterior grade plywood has been found satisfactory for use in arid environments. A maximum of 19 mm (3/4 in) thick exterior grade plywood has been found satisfactory for use in sub-tropical environments. Medium-density overlay (MDO) or high-density overlay (HDO) are satisfactory substrates and require less frequent replacement than plywood with no overlay. The edges of the plywood should be sealed to prevent delamination. Replace the plywood when there is any evidence of delamination or fiber separation.

5.2 Black Boxes – Procedure B (Coating Systems Only)

5.2.1 Black boxes used in Procedure B shall be constructed of corrosion-resistant metal. Exterior surfaces shall be coated with a high-temperature, flat black paint. The interior of boxes constructed of materials with minimal reflectance properties shall remain uncoated.

NOTE—No. 3003 aluminum sheet has been found suitable for black boxes for use in all geographic locations. Krylon High Temperature, flat black bar-b-que paint has been found suitable for painting the outside of the boxes.

5.2.2 The black box shall have a minimum of 4 weep holes for drainage.

5.2.3 There are two sizes of black boxes currently in use as illustrated in Figures 2A, 2B, and 3. The dimension of the box used must be included in the exposure report.

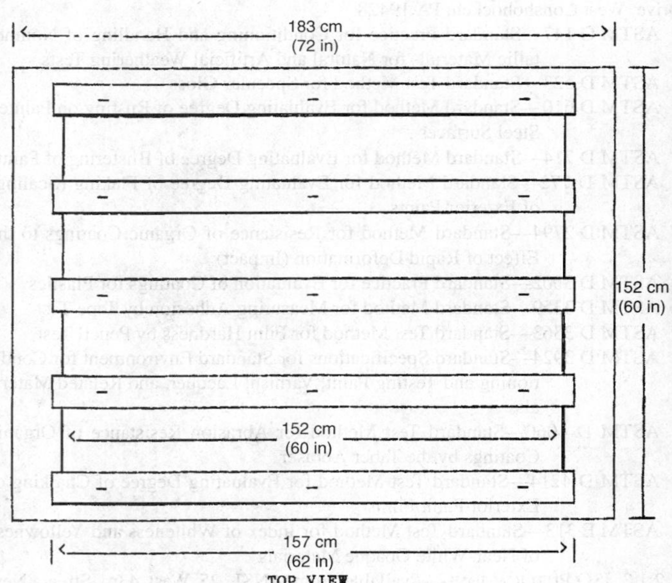

FIGURE 2A—SMALL BLACK BOX

FRONT VIEW

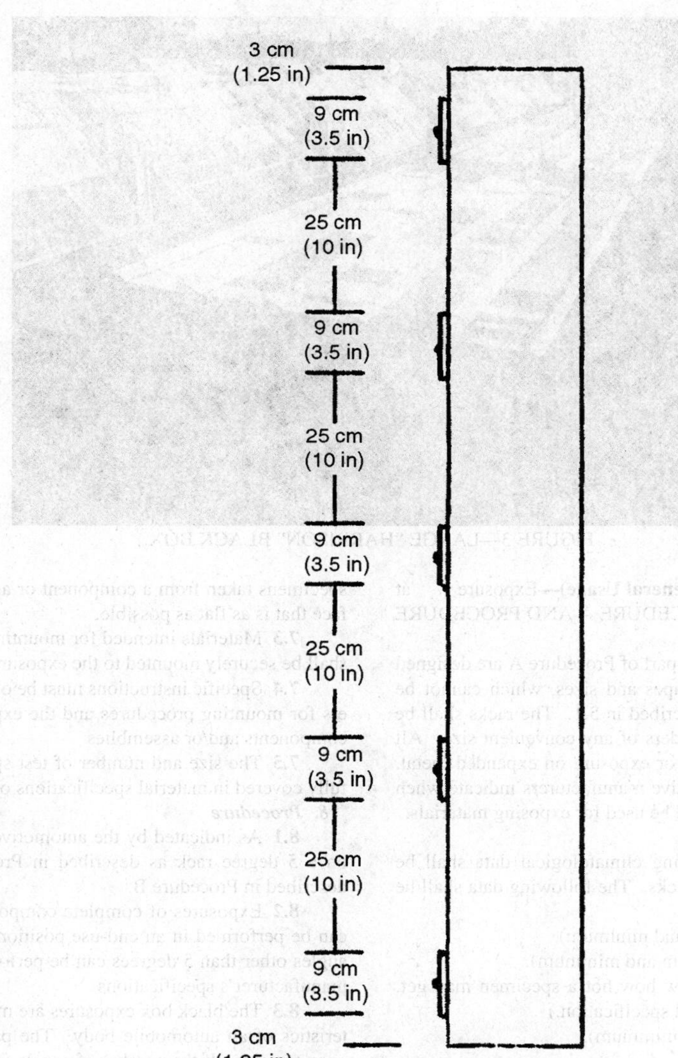

END VIEW

FIGURE 2B—SMALL BLACK BOX

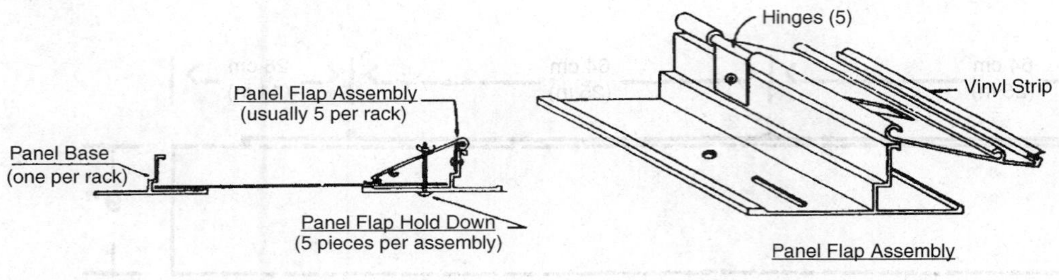

Harrison Black Box

A. 1.52 m – 152 mm x 3.66 m x 229 mm (5 ft 6 in x 12 ft 0 in x 9 in) aluminum anodized frame welded fabrication.
B. Panel base and flap assemblies (or masks) 12 ft 0 in in length are adjustable for any size panel.
C. Vinyl strip in edge of panel flap insures fine demarcation line.
D. Support post for ground or roof mountings are provided.
E. Arms for frame angle position are adjustable from vertical to five degrees.

FIGURE 3—LARGE "HARRISON" BLACK BOX

5.3 Exposure Racks – Procedure C (General Usage)—Exposure at angles other than 5 degrees as specified in PROCEDURE A AND PROCEDURE B.

5.3.1 General usage exposure racks used as a part of Procedure A are designed to accommodate any samples, such as odd shapes and sizes, which cannot be placed in the coating system exposure rack described in 5.1. The racks shall be constructed to hold specimens or specimen holders of any convenient size. All racks shall be designed for unbacked exposure or exposure on expanded metal. Materials specifications for the various automotive manufacturers indicate when expanded metal or an approved substitute should be used for exposing materials.

6. *Instrumentation*

6.1 Instruments for recording the following climatological data shall be located in the immediate area of the exposure racks. The following data shall be available upon request:

6.1.1 Ambient temperature (daily maximum and minimum).

6.1.2 Black-panel temperature (daily maximum and minimum).

NOTE—(Black panel temp is needed to know how hot a specimen may get. Refer to the applicable OEM material specification.)

6.1.3 Relative humidity (daily maximum and minimum).

6.1.4 Total time of wetness

6.1.5 Solar radiation, T (total).

6.1.6 Solar radiation, UV (total ultraviolet = 300 – 385 nm)

6.1.7 Solar radiation, CSW (centered selected wavelength), optional.

7. *Test Specimens*

7.1 The coating system for metal, and materials applied directly to coated metal (decorative taped, logos, side molding, emblems, etc.) are to be applied to 100 x 300 mm (4 x 12 in) type J1008--1010 steel panels. The preparation of the panels shall be as specified by the various automotive manufacturers or as agreed upon by contractual parties.

7.2 Materials other than those covered (plastic substrates, aluminum, etc) in 7.1 must be of suitable size, which shall be determined by the evaluation procedures that the specimens will be subjected to after exposure. Test samples or specimens taken from a component or assembly should present an exposure surface that is as flat as possible.

7.3 Materials intended for mounting on backed or expanded metal surfaces shall be securely mounted to the exposure rack.

7.4 Specific instructions must be obtained from the automotive manufacturers for mounting procedures and the exposure method for large parts of, or full components and/or assemblies.

7.5 The size and number of test specimens that are to be exposed is more fully covered in material specifications of the various automotive manufacturers.

8. *Procedure*

8.1 As indicated by the automotive manufacturers, place the test specimen on a 5 degree rack as described in Procedure A, or a 5 degree black box as described in Procedure B.

8.2 Exposures of complete components as described in 1.5.3 Procedure C can be performed in an end-use position as directed by the client. Exposures at angles other than 5 degrees can be performed in accordance with the automotive manufacturer's specifications.

8.3 The black box exposures are meant to simulate the air heat sink characteristics of an automobile body. The panels to be tested must cover the entire open top side. If the number of panels to be exposed is not sufficient to cover the entire opening, black-painted sheet metal panels must be used to fill the open areas.

8.4 During exposure, all test panels and/or specimens are to be rinsed monthly with water at the end of the morning dew formation. Water used for monthly rinsing shall leave no objectionable deposits or stains on the exposed specimens. It is strongly recommended that the water contain a maximum of 1 ppm solids, and a maximum of 0.2 ppm silica.

8.5 Prior to evaluation, coating systems only are to be prepared as follows:

8.5.1 Unless otherwise specified, wash left side of panel (51 mm/2 in) using a mild dishwashing non-ionic soap and deionized water solution (ratio 0.05/99.95) and a clean, dirt-free soft, non-abrasive cloth or sponge. Caution should be taken to make sure the cloth or sponge is free of dirt or panel degradation to avoid scratching of the test specimens.

8.5.2 Rinse immediately with deionized water and allow to air dry or use clean compressed air.

8.5.3 After washing and drying, polish the top 100 mm of the washed half of the panel using a non-abrasive automotive polish. A standard wax is not suitable.

8.6 All other materials, decorative tapes, logos, moldings, emblems, coated fabrics (vinyl top), uncoated plastics, etc., are to be washed only using the procedure described in 8.5.1 and 8.5.2 unless by contractual agreement with specific automotive manufacturers.

9. Report (see Figure 4)—This information shall be available upon request. The Exposure Report may include all or part of the following information:

9.1 Exposure site
9.2 Material
9.3 Substrate
9.4 Procedure A, B or C (include dimension of black box if used)
9.5 Exposure dates
9.6 Solar radiation, T (total)
9.7 Solar radiation, TUV (total ultraviolet)
9.8 Solar radiation, CSW (centered selected wavelength), optional
9.9 Total time of wetness

NOTE—Manufacturer, type, and calibration records for instruments used to obtain data for 9.6, 9.7, 9.8, and 9.9 shall be available upon request from the testing laboratory.

9.9.1 If time of wetness measurements are reported, the manufacturer, test method, and type of instrument used to obtain data shall be included in the report. In dry climates such as Arizona, time of wetness may be determined using ISO 9223.

Exposure Site : ____________________

Material : ____________________

Procedure A or B
Dimension of Black Box, if used : ____________________

Exposure Dates : ____________________

Radiant Exposure, Total : ____________________ **MJ/m²**

Radiant Exposure, UV : ____________________ **MJ/m²**

Radiant Exposure, CSW : ____________________ **MJ/m²**

Total Time of Wetness : ____________________

Remarks (include manufacturer and type of instrument used to obtain radiant exposure data):

____

Signature: ____________________ **Date:** ____________________
Company: ____________________

FIGURE 4—SAE J1976 EXPOSURE REPORT FORM

INSTRUMENTAL COLOR DIFFERENCE MEASUREMENT FOR EXTERIOR FINISHES, TEXTILES AND COLORED TRIM—SAE J1545 JUN1986

SAE Recommended Practice

Report of the SAE Nonmetallic Materials Committee approved June 1986.

Foreword—This Document has not changed other than to put it into the new SAE Technical Standards Board Format.

1. Scope—The practice applies to parts and materials used in vehicle manufacture which are intended to be acceptable color matches to a specified color standard. This practice is intended for use with parts or materials which are opaque or nearly so and does not apply to transparent materials. Materials covered by this practice include topcoat paint finishes, interior soft trim, interior and exterior hard trim, and exterior film.

1.1 Purpose—The intent of this practice is to precisely specify procedures for instrumental color difference measurement of colored parts or colored materials incorporated in the manufacture of vehicles. The recommended practice provides a consistent engineering practice for determination of color difference, for numerical communication of color difference, and for determination of acceptance or rejection compared to numerical tolerances. The practice is intended to be used as a specification and means of communication for color part acceptance in a buyer-seller agreement.

2. References

2.1 Applicable Publications—The following publications form a part of this specification to the extent specified herein. Unless otherwise indicated, the latest issue of SAE publications shall apply.

2.1.1 ASTM E 284-81a—Standard Definitions of Terms Relating to Appearance of Materials

2.1.2 Commission International de l'Éclairage, International Lighting Vocabulary, Bureau Central de la CIE, Paris, 1970, 3rd ed., Publications CIE No. 17 [E-1.1.] 1970. CIE publications are available from Dr. Klaus D. Mielenz, Secretary, U.S. National Committee, CIE, Room B-306, Metrology Bldg., National Bureau of Standards, Gaithersburg, MD 20899.

2.1.3 ASTM E 105-58—Probability Sampling of Materials

2.1.4 Commission International de l'Éclairage, Colorimetry, Bureau Central de la CIE, Paris, 1970, Publication CIE No. 15 (E-1.3.1.) 1971.

2.1.5 Commission International de l'Éclairage, Recommendations on Uniform Color Spaces—Color Difference Equations Psychometric Color Terms, Bureau Central de la CIE, Paris, 1978, Supplement No. 2 to CIE Publication No. 15 (E-1.3.1) 1971/(TC-1.3.) 1978.

2.1.6 Rolf G. Kuehni, "CIELAB Color Difference and LIghtness, Hue and Chroma Components for Objective Color Control", Detroit Colour Council Technical Bulletin No. 1. Available from Detroit Colour Council, c/o Matteson-Ridolfi Co., 14450 King Road, Riverview, MI 48192.

2.1.7 ASTM D 1729-82—Visual Evaluation of Color Differences of Opaque Materials

2.1.8 One source for color performance standards is British Ceramic Research Association Instrument Performance Standards, available from Hemmendinger Color Lab, RD 1, Box 213, Pequest Bend, Belvidere, NJ 07823.

2.1.9 One source for external verification is Color and Appearance Proficiency Testing, service available from Collaborative Testing Services, 8343-A Greensboro Dr., McLean, VA 22102.

2.1.10 F. J. J. Clarke, R. McDonald, B. Rigg. "Modifications to the JPC 79 Colour-difference Formula", J. Soc. Dyers and Colourists, 100, 128-132 (1984).

2.1.11 "Farbtoleranzen Fuer Automobillackierungen, Unilackierungen", DIN 6175, Teil 1. Entwurf Dezember 1984, Beuth Verlag Gumbh, Berlin 30, Federal Republic of Germany.

2.2 Related Publications—The following publications are provided for information purposes only and are not a required part of this document.

2.2.1 ASTM Committee E-12—ASTM Standards on Color and Appearance Measurement, 1st Edition, 1984

2.2.2 ASTM D 3134-74—Selecting and Defining Color and Gloss Tolerances of Opaque Materials and for Evaluating Conformance

2.2.3 Commission International de l'Éclairage, Colorimetry, Second Edition, Final Draft (April 1983), Publication CIE No. 15.2 (TC-1.3).

2.2.4 Collaborative Testing Services, "Color and Appearance, Report No. 50," 1984. Reports the results of inter-laboratory color difference measurements of automobile fabrics.

2.2.5 R. W. Harold, K. Loughrey, T. Mabon, "Benefits of the Sample Averaging Technique," Hunterlab Application Notes, 4 No. 3, March 21, 1985

2.2.6 Wolfgang Budde, "The Gloss Trap in Diffuse Reflectance Measurements," Color Research and Application 5, 73-75 (1980).

2.2.7 Strocka and Brockes, "Comparison of the CIE (1931) 2° and the CIE (1964) 10° Colorimetric Standard Observer with Individual Observers in the Assessment of Metameric Matches," Proc. Intern. Color Meeting, Color 69, Stockholm 1969, Vol. 2, pp 785-793

2.2.8 Brian P. Hake, "Comparison of CIELAB, JPC79 and CMC (2:1) Color Difference Equations Performance on Automotive Exterior Paints and Grained Interior Plastics," Symposium on Color and Appearance Instrumentation, Pittsburgh, April 1985

3. Definitions—Except for terms specifically defined in this document, terminology used in this report follows the definitions reported by ASTM (2.1.1) and the Commission International de l'Éclairage (2.1.2) 1970.

3.1 Product, Lot, Sample, Reading, Measurement:

3.1.1 PRODUCT—A product is the group of all parts or material having the same color, composition and physical form.

3.1.2 LOT—A lot is the customary unit of production of a product comprising one or more individual product units. For example, a lot of plastic parts might comprise 500 individual product units and a lot of paint material might comprise one 5000 gallon batch of paint.

3.1.3 SAMPLE—A sample is an individual product unit chosen from the product lot. The sample or group of samples chosen shall be representative of the color difference properties of the product lot (2.1.3).

3.1.4 READING—A reading is a single instrumental color difference assessment made in one particular location and in one particular orientation within a sample.

3.1.5 MEASUREMENT—A measurement is the estimate of the sample color difference relative to a standard determined from one reading or the mean of multiple readings as specified by the procedure of this recommended practice.

3.2 Standards

3.2.1 OFFICIAL STANDARD—An official standard is a physical standard that is an acceptable match to the concept color. The official standard physically represents the color target for visual and colorimetric evaluation of all products referenced to that official standard. Where feasible, the official standard should have the same composition and construction as the reference and working standards.

3.2.2 REFERENCE STANDARD—A reference standard is a physical standard used to calibrate working standards. Reference standards shall have the same composition and construction as the working standards and the composition and construction shall be representative of samples of the product. Reference standards are instrumentally referenced to the official standard.

3.2.3 WORKING STANDARD—A working standard is a physical standard in routine use. Working standards are made of material identical to the reference standard and are instrumentally referenced to the reference standard.

3.3 Instruments

3.3.1 MASTER INSTRUMENT—The master instrument is an instrument that is used to establish the basic references among various levels of standards and among other instruments. This instrument is the normal arbiter in any situation not adequately resolved at a lower level. This instrument should generally be a spectrophotometer and is usually retained by the organization which issues the standards.

3.3.2 SECONDARY INSTRUMENT—A secondary instrument is any other instrument used for color difference measurement of the product by reference to the standards.

4. Basic Color Measurements Specifications

4.1 Standard Observer—The standard observer for colorimetric determination should be the CIE 1964 supplementary standard colorimetric observer (2.1.4) 1971, referred to as the 10° standard observer. If the design of the color measuring instrument used precludes use of the 10° standard observer, the CIE 1931 standard colorimetric observer (2.1.4), referred to as the 2° standard observer, may be used. See Appendix B1.1.

4.2 Standard Illuminant—The standard illuminant for colorimetric determination should be CIE standard illuminant D65 [CIE No. 15 (E-1.3.1.) 1971]. If the design of the color measuring instrument used precludes use of CIE standard illuminant D65, CIE standard illuminant (2.1.4) may be used. No other illuminant may be used. See Appendix B1.1.

4.3 Uniform Color Space—The uniform color space for determination of color difference shall be the CIE 1976 ($L^*a^*b^*$) space (2.1.5). This space may be abbreviated, CIELAB. The conversion to CIELAB coordinates for colors with tristimulus value ratios (X/X_n, Y/Y_n, Z/Z_n) less than or equal to 0.01 shall follow the equations in the appendix to the CIELAB specification (2.1.5).

4.4 Color Difference—The color difference between sample and standard shall be determined by three component color difference scales. The three component color difference scales shall be lightness difference (DL^*), CIE 1976 a, b chroma difference (DC^*_{ab}) and CIE 1976 a, b hue difference (DH^*_{ab}) (2.1.5 and 2.1.6). The abbreviations DL^*, DC^*, DH^* respectively are recommended .[1]

4.5 Color Difference Tolerance—Tolerances for color difference assessment shall be specified by upper and lower tolerances on each of the color difference scales; DL^*, DC^*, DH^*. A sample is rated acceptable by the color difference assessment if its measured color difference values relative to the color standard are within the specified tolerances for DL^*, DC^* and DH^*. A sample is rated unacceptable by the color difference assessment if its measured color difference values relative to the color standard are outside the specified tolerances for DL^*, DC^*, DH^* on one or more of the color difference scales.

4.5.1 TOLERANCE APPLICATION—Often there will be some difference in color values between a reference standard and the official standard and between a working standard and a reference standard (see 6.1.2)(see 6.1.2). The color tolerances as applied to each level of standards should be adjusted to account for these differences. For example, if the DL^* tolerances were ±2 and the reference standard measured +1 L^* unit higher than the official standard, the DL^* tolerances as referenced to that reference standard should be adjusted to +1 and −3 DL^* units. See Figure 1.

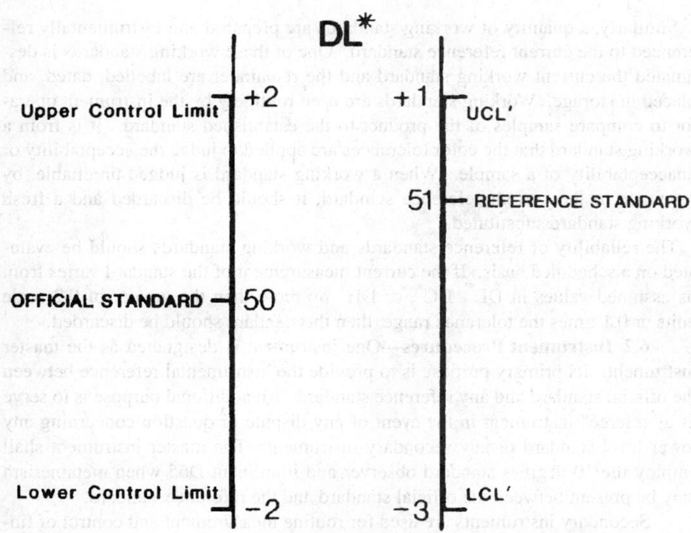

FIGURE 1—EXAMPLE OF THE MODIFICATION OF THE UPPER AND LOWER TOLERANCES OF A REFERENCE STANDARD TO ALLOW FOR THE COLOR DIFFERENCE OF THE REFERENCE STANDARD RELATIVE TO THE OFFICIAL STANDARD.

4.6 Color Measuring Instrument—The instrument used for color difference measurement shall be either a spectrophotometer or a tristimulus colorimeter. The instrument geometry, unless otherwise specified under Section 7, shall conform to one of the four sets of illuminating and viewing conditions specified by the CIE (2.1.4). The instrument geometries are identified by the convention: illuminating geometry/viewing geometry. The four allowed instrument geometries with their abbreviations are 45°/normal (45/0), normal/45 degrees (0/45), diffuse/normal (d/0) and normal/diffuse (0/d). If a diffuse geometry (d/0 or 0/d) instrument is used, the specular component of reflectance shall be included in the measurement. The angle between the sample normal and the illuminating beam in 0/d geometry and the angle between the sample normal and the viewing beam in d/0 geometry shall not exceed 10°.

4.6.1 EFFECT OF INSTRUMENT DESIGN ON COLOR DIFFERENCE MEASUREMENT—Instruments of differing designs and especially of differing illuminating and viewing geometries do not necessarily result in equivalent color difference values for all sample differences. The result depends on sample characteristics and instrument design. For this reason, the color difference tolerances for a product may need to have different values with different instrument designs.

4.6.2 EFFECT OF APPEARANCE ON COLOR DIFFERENCE MEASUREMENT—Appearance characteristics other than color may influence color difference measurement. Examples of these characteristics include gloss, texture, luster, transparency, pile height, and other surface characteristics. For this reason, it is necessary to assure that the sample and standard have similar appearance characteristics.

4.7 Sample-Color Difference Measurement Variability—The variability of sample-color difference measurements depend on the variability within the color sample and the variability of the color measurement instrument. In order for the color difference acceptability decision to be valid, the standard errors of the mean estimates of the DL^*, DC^*, and DH^* values must be small fractions of their respective DL^*, DC^*, and DH^* tolerances. Sample color difference acceptability decisions made under this document shall require that the standard error of the mean estimate for each color difference scale be less than the greater of 0.2 scale units or 0.1 times the tolerance range. The tolerance range is the upper tolerance minus the lower tolerance.

4.7.1 DETERMINATION OF THE STANDARD DEVIATION OF SAMPLE COLOR DIFFERENCE MEASUREMENT—For each product measured under this document, the standard deviations of the sample color difference measurement must be determined once. The sample shall be a representative sample of the product. The color difference measurements shall conform to the measurement practices appropriate for the color sample as specified in Section 7. The standard deviations for DL^*, DC^*, and DH^* measurements shall be determined from at least 10 color difference readings of randomly selected areas of the sample. The sample-color difference measurement standard deviations are represented by S_{DL^*}, S_{DC^*} and S_{DH^*}. The defining equation for standard deviation is shown in Equation 1:

$$S = \left[\frac{\sum_i (X_i - \bar{X})^2}{N-1}\right]^{0.5} \quad \text{(Eq. 1)}$$

where:

S is the standard deviation
N is the number of sample readings
$\bar{X}$ is the mean of N sample readings
X_i is an individual sample reading for the ith reading

4.7.2 STANDARD ERROR OF THE MEAN ESTIMATE—The standard error of the mean estimate (S_e) is equal to the standard deviation divided by the square root of the number of sample readings (N). See Equation 2.

$$S_e = S/(N)^{0.5} \quad \text{(Eq. 2)}$$

where:

N is the sampling number. The standard error of the mean esimate is a measure of the uncertainty in the estimate of the mean of multiple sample readings.

4.7.3 STANDARD ERROR OF THE MEAN ESTIMATE WITH A SINGLE MEASUREMENT—If the standard errors of the estimates ($S_{eDL}*$, $S_{eDC}*$, $S_{eDH}*$) with one sample reading do not exceed the greater of 0.2 scale units or 0.1 times their respective tolerance ranges, then a single color difference measurement is valid under this practice. In this case, N=1, and the standard error of the estimate is equal to the standard deviation. See Equation 3.

$$S_e = S \text{ if } N = 1 \quad \text{(Eq. 3)}$$

Samples taken from future lots of the same product and measured with the same instrument and procedures shall require one sample reading.

4.7.4 STANDARD ERROR OF THE MEAN ESTIMATE WITH MULTIPLE MEASUREMENTS—If the standard errors of the mean estimates with a single measurement exceed the greater of 0.2 scale units or 0.1 times the tolerance range, then multiple measurements are required. Averaging multiple measurements in varying areas of the sample can reduce the standard error of the mean to acceptable levels.

1. Capital D indicates a differential colorimetric value (sometimes referred to as a delta, Greek symbol Δ).

The sampling number required to meet the standard error of the mean estimate criterion is determined by rearranging Equation 2. See Equation 4:

$$N = (S/S_{e,g})^2 \quad \text{(Eq. 4)}$$

For each color difference scale, determine the sampling number by substituting the sample-color difference measurement standard deviation (S) and the standard error of the mean estimate goal ($S_{e,g}$) into Equation 4. The standard error of the estimate goal is the greater of 0.2 scale units or 0.1 times the tolerance range. Round each sampling number to the next larger integer value. The product sampling number shall be the largest of the sampling numbers for the DL^*, DC^*, and DH^* color difference measurement scales. Samples taken from future lots of the same product and measured with the same instrument and procedures shall require that all sample color difference measurements be the mean of N readings in varying sample areas.

4.7.5 ADDITIONAL INFORMATION—Appendix A, provides additional information on sample color difference measurement variability including the rationale for this procedure and an example calculation.

4.8 Report—The user shall report the standard observer, standard illuminant, instrument geometry, the standard error of the mean estimate and the sampling number employed in instrumental color difference measurements made under this document.

5. *Tolerance Determination*

5.1 General Tolerance Concepts—A tolerance is the permissible variation of an object in some characteristic. Tolerances are agreed upon between buyer and seller and could be part of the purchasing contract. In reference to this document, color tolerances of automotive materials are separately expressed in terms of the three perceptual variables; hue, chroma, and lightness. (See 4.5.) The reference material is the agreed-upon standard material.

Tolerances are normally the sum of the variability in the material manufacturing process and the method used to assess the tolerance. For colored materials, especially materials that need to match or harmonize, the over-riding factor for tolerances is the degree of mismatch that can be visually tolerated in the application. Tolerances are, therefore, usually set by visual methods.

5.2 Procedures for Visual Determination of Tolerances—Visual tolerances shall be set up by preparing and judging color samples differing in defined ways.

Since tolerances are expressed relatively in terms of differences and are likely to change only slowly across color space, tolerance experience developed for one color may be applied to other colored materials of similar construction having similar hue, chroma, and lightness.

The viewing situation has an important influence on color tolerances. Therefore, the viewing conditions should simulate the end use application. Appearance and width of the line separating the two color fields to be compared shall be similar to the appearance and width of the line separating the colored fields in the final application.

Color samples should be selected which exhibit increasing visual distances from the standard in the hue, chroma, and lightness variables. The differences represented by pairs of standard and sample are visually assessed by a panel of observers. The visual conditions of assessment shall generally conform to ASTM D 1729-82 (2.1.7).

Tolerances shall be set based on the visual judgements and the measured and calculated hue, chroma, lightness differences between pairs of samples.

6. *Standards and Instruments*

6.1 Standards Procedures—Standards are used for colorimetric control of the product and to maintain the validity of the test procedure.

6.1.1 STANDARDS—The composition and construction of reference standards, working standards, and the product to be colorimetrically controlled with these standards shall be identical. Normally, the official standard will also have identical composition and construction to the reference standards, working standards and product. In those cases where an official standard in the material of the product is not developed, it is permissible to calibrate the reference standard to an official standard of the same color in another similar product form. For example, an ABS molded part reference standard could be calibrated to a polypropylene molded part official standard. See Figure 2.

6.1.2 STANDARDIZATION PROCEDURE—A quantity of reference standards is prepared and instrumentally referenced to the official standard. See 4.5.1. At this point, the official standard should be labelled, dated, and placed in storage. Proper storage requires that the standards are stored so as to preserve their color by minimizing the influence of factors such as light, temperature, and contamination. A quantity of reference standards should be retained by both the customer and the supplier. These, also, should be labelled, dated, and placed in storage. One of these reference standards at a time should be designated as the current reference standard and this standard should be used until it is deemed unreliable for this purpose. At such time, it should be discarded and a fresh reference standard employed. Unreliability would generally be determined by reference to other reserved reference standards or, ultimately, to the official standard.

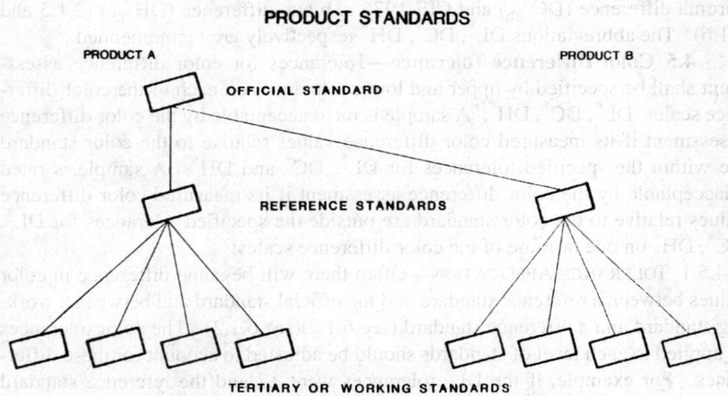

FIGURE 2—NETWORK SHOWING THE RELATIONSHIPS BETWEEN OFFICIAL, REFERENCE, AND WORKING STANDARDS. FOR PRODUCT A, THE OFFICIAL REFERENCE AND WORKING STANDARDS HAVE THE SAME COMPOSITION AND CONSTRUCTION AS THE PRODUCT. AN OFFICIAL STANDARD WAS NOT PREPARED FOR PRODUCT B. IN THIS CASE, THE REFERENCE AND WORKING STANDARDS HAVE THE SAME COMPOSITION AND CONSTRUCTION AS THE PRODUCT.

Similarly, a quantity of working standards are prepared and instrumentally referenced to the current reference standard. One of these working standards is designated the current working standard and the remainder are labelled, dated, and placed in storage. Working standards are used routinely by the instrument operator to compare samples of the product to the established standard. It is from a working standard that the color tolerances are applied to judge the acceptability or unacceptability of a sample. When a working standard is judged unreliable, by reference to the current reference standard, it should be discarded and a fresh working standard substituted.

The reliability of reference standards and working standards should be evaluated on a scheduled basis. If the current measurement of the standard varies from its assigned values in DL^*, DC^*, or DH^* by more than the greater of 0.2 scale units or 0.1 times the tolerance range, then the standard should be discarded.

6.2 Instrument Procedures—One instrument is designated as the master instrument. Its primary purpose is to provide the instrumental reference between the official standard and any reference standard. An additional purpose is to serve as a "referee" instrument in the event of any dispute or question concerning any lower level standard or any secondary instrument. The master instrument shall employ the 10 degrees standard observer and illuminant D65 when metamerism may be present between the official standard and the reference standard.

Secondary instruments are used for routine measurement and control of finished product. They also serve to determine the relationship between reference and working standards as well as to determine the reliability of a particular reference or working standard. The network of instruments and standards is illustrated in Figure 3.

6.3 System Maintenance—A color control program is a complex scheme involving product, instruments, standards, procedures, and personnel. Any measurement is only an approximation of the exactly current state of the material and the instrument being used. Care should be used in both the setup of the program and the necessary maintenance of the program to insure consistent and reliable results. Proper attention to certain areas, including the use of unbiased external resources, should be considered to insure the integrity of any color control program. The intent of this section is to recommend certain practices that should insure this integrity.

6.3.1 INSTRUMENT VERIFICATION PROCEDURE—Instrument performance standards which are independent of the product standards should be used to periodically verify the performance of master and secondary instruments. Instrument performance standards are available from the instrument manufacturer or from an independent source (2.1.8)

6.3.2 External Verification Service—Outside resources are useful in the verification process (2.1.9). They provide an unbiased reference as to the performance of both the instruments and personnel involved in the program.

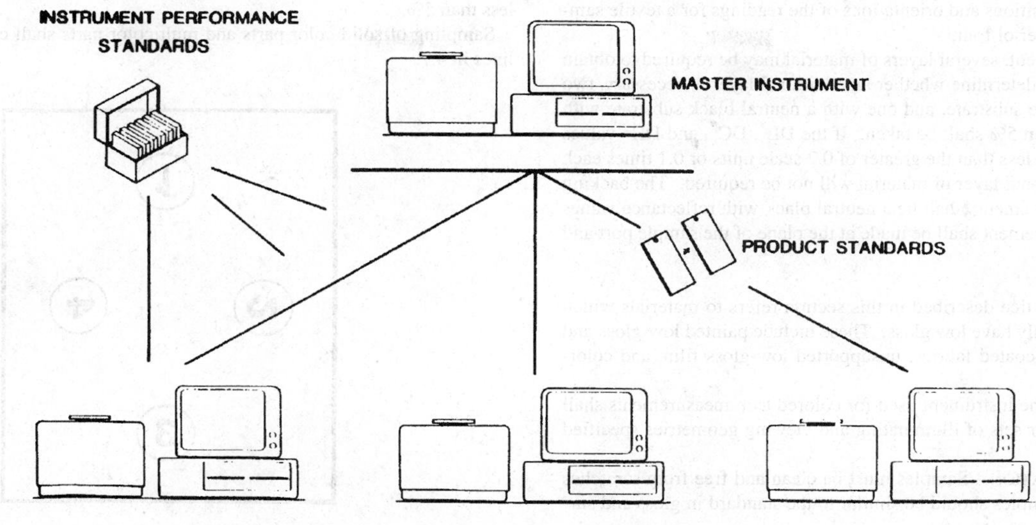

FIGURE 3—NETWORK SHOWING THE RELATIONSHIPS BETWEEN MASTER AND SECONDARY INSTRUMENTS AND INSTRUMENT PERFORMANCE AND PRODUCT STANDARDS.

7. Measurement Practices

7.1 Exterior Finishes

7.1.1 Scope—The practice described in this section refers to high-gloss exterior paints and decorative films.

7.1.2 Instrument—The instrument used in measuring high-gloss exterior finishes shall conform to the requirement of 4.6. When a single illuminating/viewing geometry is used to measure finishes containing oriented flake type pigments, it is possible that the sample and standard will not match for other measurement geometries. Visually the observed effect is that sample may match standard at some viewing angle and not match at others. For these applications, multiple geometry measurements will provide better control of geometric differences. See B.1.3.

7.1.3 Sample Preparation—Samples of exterior finishes should be prepared using appropriate substrate, primer and film thickness as specified for the end use of the product. For other than production parts, sample size should be at least 3 x 5 in (75 x 125 mm). Samples must be clean and free from scratches and other defects in the area to be measured. The sample should be similar to the standard in gloss and texture.

7.1.4 Sample Presentation—Sample and standard should be oriented in the same direction. When making multiple measurements, care must be taken to avoid the edges of the panel because of the tendency for excessive film build in these areas. The number of measurements required shall be determined as described in 4.7.

7.2 Textiles

7.2.1 Scope—The practice described in this section refers to colored fibrous materials. These products include but are not limited to body cloth, headlining cloth, carpet, webbing, straps, and flocking.

7.2.2 Instrument—The instrument used for textile measurements shall conform to one of the four sets of illuminating and viewing geometries specified in 4.6.

7.2.3 Sample Preparation—Textile samples must be prepared before presentation to an instrument. Samples must be clean and free from lint, creases, and other distortions. A lint roller or brush should be used to clean the samples. Pile fabrics and carpet must be oriented in the natural direction of pile lay. Once the direction is identified, a lint roller or brush should be used to orient the pile.

Textile samples and standards should be similar in luster, texture, and physical form. For multicolored pattern textiles, the individual components of the pattern should be visually similar to those of the standard. Figure 4 shows two samples that are visually different but numerically the same. Color difference readings between these two samples would be meaningless.

The size of textile samples should be approximately 200 x 250 mm (8 x 10 in). If this is not possible, as may be the case for webbing and straps, a 250 mm (10 in) length of the standard width should be used.

FIGURE 4—HYPOTHETICAL EXAMPLE OF A MULTICOLOR SAMPLE AND STANDARD. WHILE THE MEAN COLOR DIFFERENCE SCALE READINGS ARE WITHIN TOLERANCE, THE SAMPLE IS UNACCEPTABLE BECAUSE THE INDIVIDUAL COMPONENTS OF THE PATTERN DO NOT VISUALLY MATCH THE INDIVIDUAL COMPONENTS OF THE STANDARD PATTERN.

7.2.4 Sample Presentation—Multiple readings are required to account for variation in color and to minimize the influence of directionality. Accordingly, the determinations of standard deviation (4.7.1) and sampling number (4.7.4) are modified for textile samples. The standard deviation is determined from 12 sample readings with each reading in a different position and with the 12 readings evenly apportioned to sample orientations of 0°, 90°, 180°, and 270° in relation to an arbitrarily selected reference direction on the sample. In order to minimize the influence of directionality for all illuminating/viewing geometries, equal numbers of each of the four directional orientations must be used. Therefore, the allowed sampling numbers for textiles are 4, 8, 12, 16, etc. The textile sampling number shall be the sampling number (4.7.4) raised to the next larger multiple of four. The textile sample measurement shall comprise the specified number of readings in N different positions with N/4 of the readings in each of the four orientations. Figure 5 illustrates the positions and orientations of the readings for a textile sample with a sampling number of four.

If the sample is translucent, several layers of material may be required to obtain a valid measurement. To determine whether an additional layer is necessary, two readings, one with a white substrate, and one with a neutral black substrate with reflectance values less than 5% shall be taken. If the DL^*, DC^*, and DH^* values of the two readings are all less than the greater of 0.2 scale units or 0.1 times each tolerance range, an additional layer of material will not be required. The backing for all textile color measurements shall be a neutral black with reflectance values less than 5%. The measurement shall be made at the plane of the sample port and without any cover glass.

7.3 Colored Trim

7.3.1 SCOPE—The practice described in this section refers to materials which are pigmented and generally have low gloss. These include painted low-gloss and semi-gloss parts, leather, coated fabrics, unsupported low-gloss film, and color-impregnated plastics.

7.3.2 INSTRUMENT—The instrument used for colored trim measurements shall conform to one of the four sets of illuminating and viewing geometries specified in 4.6.

7.3.3 SAMPLE PREPARATION—Samples must be clean and free from scratches and other distortions. Samples should be similar to the standard in gloss and surface texture.

When measuring multicolor patterned materials and parts, the individual color components should be similar in pattern and general color. Multicolor parts must not be compared in measurement to solid color parts.

7.3.4 SAMPLE PRESENTATION—For materials of a directional nature, sample and standard should be oriented in the same direction. Materials and parts described in this section are presumed to be essentially opaque. If some light transmission is likely, use a neutral black sample backing with reflectance values less than 5%.

Sampling of solid color parts and multicolor parts shall conform to the guidelines in 4.7.

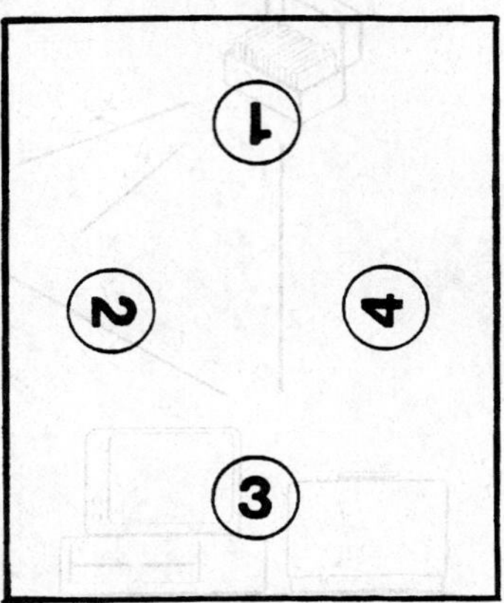

FIGURE 5—FOR TEXTILE SAMPLE MEASUREMENT, A MINIMUM MEASUREMENT IS THE MEAN OF FOUR READINGS WITH EACH READING TAKEN WITH A DIFFERENT SAMPLE AREA AND SAMPLE ORIENTATION AS ILLUSTRATED.

APPENDIX A
SAMPLE COLOR MEASUREMENT VARIABILITY

A.1 Rationale—When a sample color difference measurement is made, the color difference values obtained are estimates of the sample color difference values. Because of variability within the sample and because of instrument variability, repeat sample color difference readings will form a distribution of values. A single reading, therefore, is a sample from this distribution and the uncertainty of the reading is related to the standard deviation of repeat sample readings. In Figure A1(a), notice that for a sample mean estimate value there is a distribution of possible sample estimate values. In this example, notice that while the sample estimate has an acceptable value, because of the uncertainty of the estimate there is some probability (cross-hatched area of Figure A1(a) that a single sample color difference reading is unacceptable.

Not all sample-color difference measurements will have the same uncertainty. In Figure A1(b), two sample estimate distributions with identical mean estimate values but varying uncertainties, as observed by the breadth of their distributions, are shown. For uncertainty distribution A there is a much higher probability that a single sample reading is acceptable than for uncertainty distribution B. This despite the fact that both distributions give identical mean estimates. Clearly, we would prefer to have low sample measurement uncertainty. However, it is not possible to obtain errorless estimates. As a practical compromise, there will be infrequent, incorrect decisions (conditions where the mean estimate is within the tolerance but individual estimates are outside the tolerance or the inverse condition) if the uncertainty of the estimate is a small fraction of the range of the tolerance values. The uncertainty of measurement is defined by the standard error of the mean estimate. The requirement is that the standard error of the mean estimate not exceed the greater of 0.2 scale units or 0.1 times the tolerance range.

How do we proceed if the standard error of the mean estimate exceeds the goal value? The mean of multiple sample readings has lower uncertainty than a single reading. By increasing the number of sample readings included in the measurement, the standard error of the mean estimate can be reduced to an acceptable level. Figure A1(c) shows uncertainty distributions for a single reading (B1), the mean of four readings (B4), and the mean of nine readings (B9). The procedure determines the minimum sampling number which will reduce the standard error of the mean estimate to an acceptable level.

A.2 Hypothetical Example—The standard error of the mean estimate and sampling number are determined for a red molded trim plastic. A representative sample is selected. Ten readings of DL^*, DC^*, and DH^* are made according to the procedures reported in 7.3.. Each reading is made on a separate area of the sample. Table A1 indicates the ten individual sample readings and the calculated means and standard deviations for the DL^*, DC^*, and DH^* readings.

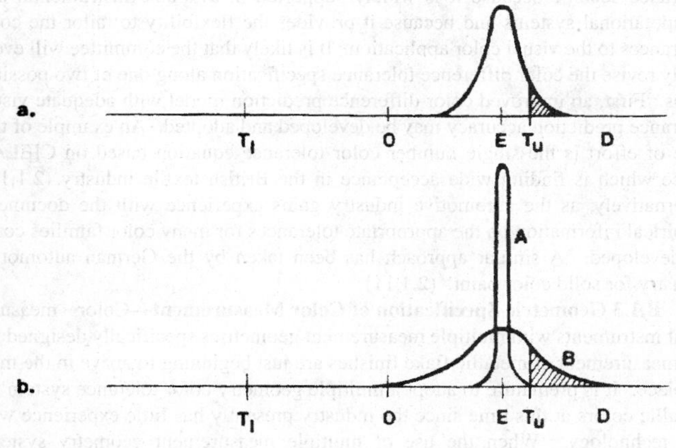

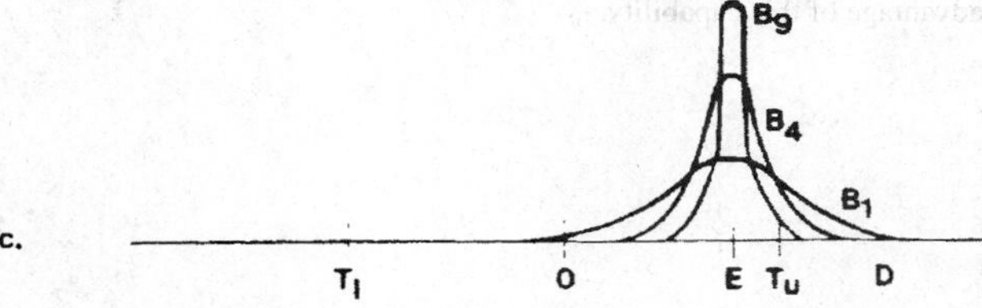

a. Distribution of sample readings. The shaded area represents the probability that a sample reading is outside the tolerance.

b. Two sample reading distributions with low (A) and high (B) standard deviations.

c. Distributions of sample measurement estimates with one reading (B1), the mean of four readings (B4), and the mean of nine readings (B9).

FIGURE A1—THE INFLUENCE OF SAMPLE READING VARIABILITY ON COLOR ACCEPTABILITY DECISIONS. THE SYMBOLS ARE LOWER TOLERANCE (T_L), UPPER TOLERANCE (T_U), COLOR DIFFERENCE SCALE (D), ZERO POINT OF THE SCALE (O), AND SAMPLE COLOR DIFFERENCE MEAN ESTIMATE (E).

TABLE A1—EXAMPLE CALCULATION OF THE MEANS AND STANDARD DEVIATIONS FOR DL*, DC*, AND DH* SAMPLE MEASUREMENTS

Reading	Color Difference Scales DL*	Color Difference Scales DC*	Color Difference Scales DH*
1	–1.42	0.79	–0.18
2	–0.12	0.14	–0.02
3	–0.62	0.65	0.25
4	–1.13	0.89	0.22
5	–0.71	0.68	0.04
6	–0.22	0.21	0.30
7	–0.47	0.30	–0.01
8	–0.77	1.25	0.19
9	–0.18	0.91	0.21
10	–0.09	0.55	0.21
Mean	–0.57	0.64	0.12
Std. Dev.	0.45	0.35	0.15

The standard errors of the estimates and product sampling numbers are determined as follows (refer to Table A2):

a. Calculate the standard deviations of sample color difference readings for DL*, DC*, and DH* (line 1). Taken from Table A1.
b. Calculate the tolerance range, the upper tolerance minus the lower tolerance (lines 2, 3, 4).
c. Multiply the tolerance range by 0.1 (line 5).
d. The goal for standard error of the mean estimate is the larger of 0.2 units or 0.1 times the tolerance range (line 6).
e. Compare the standard deviation for each color difference scale to its corresponding goal for standard error of the mean estimate. In this case, the standard deviations for the DL* and DC* scales exceed their goals and, therefore, multiple readings are required. Proceed to determine the sampling number.
f. Calculate the sampling number for each color scale (line 7). See Equation A1.

$$N = (S/S_{e,g})^2 \qquad \text{(Eq. A1)}$$

g. Round the sample averaging numbers to the next larger integer values (line 8).
h. The product sampling number (N_p) is the largest of the individual sampling numbers (line 9).
i. Calculate the standard error of the mean estimate for each color difference scale with the product sample averaging number. See Equation A2.

$$S_e = S/(N_p)^{0.5} \qquad \text{(Eq. A2)}$$

Color difference assessments made under this document for all future lots of this product shall be based on the mean of four readings of DL*, DC*, and DH*, with each reading taken from a different area of the sample. The standard error of the mean estimate for each color difference scale and the product sampling number shall be reported with the color difference measurements.

TABLE A2—EXAMPLE CALCULATION OF THE STANDARD ERROR OF THE MEAN ESTIMATE AND THE PRODUCT SAMPLING NUMBER

Line	Quantity	Symbol	Color Difference Scales DL*	Color Difference Scales DC*	Color Difference Scales DH*
1	Standard Deviation	S	0.45	0.35	0.15
2	Upper Tolerance		+2.0	+1.0	+0.5
3	Lower Tolerance		–2.0	–1.0	–0.5
4	Tolerance Range		4.0	2.0	1.0
5	0.1 x Tolerance Range		0.4	0.2	0.1
6	Goal for Standard Error of the Mean Estimate	Se, g	0.4	0.2	0.2
7	Sampling Number	N	1.27	3.06	0.56
8	Round to the Next Larger Integer	N	2	4	1
9	Product Sample Averaging Number	Np	4	4	4
10	Standard Error of the Mean Estimate	Se	0.23	0.18	0.08

A.3 Practical Means to Reduce the Product Sampling Number—It is advantageous to reduce the product sampling number in order to reduce the expense of testing. Users should be aware that the product sampling number may be reduced by increasing the product tolerance range or by decreasing either the sample's color variability or the instrument's measurement variability. A negotiated increase in the color tolerance range to values greater than 2.0 will reduce the number of readings required. For samples which do not intentionally have a multicolor pattern, improvement in the color uniformity of the sample will reduce the within sample variability and reduce the product sample averaging number.

For products which have a multicolor pattern, the within sample variability may be reduced by choosing an instrument using a relatively large sample measurement area. The product sample averaging number may also be reduced by decreasing the color difference measurement variability. Selection of precise color difference measurement instruments and careful maintenance of the instrument's calibration are important means to reducing color difference measurement variability.

APPENDIX B
FUTURE REVISIONS TO THE RECOMMENDED PRACTICE

***B.1 Future Revisions to the Recommended Practice*—**This document represents the committee's development of the best system for instrumental colorimetry in the automotive industry in terms of available color technology. We believe the procedure is sound and that it will serve the automotive industry for many years. However, revision of the document will be needed from time to time to incorporate improvements in available color measurement instruments or advances in color theory. In particular, we believe that the technical opportunity to improve the document in three areas will develop over the next ten years. Users of this practice should be aware of the potential for change in these areas.

B.1.1 Observer and Illuminant—The committee chose to allow the 2° standard observer and illuminant C as alternatives to the 10 degrees standard observer and illuminant D65 so that tristimulus colorimeters employing the former conditions would be allowed instruments under this document. There would be considerable value to requiring all instruments to employ the 10° standard observer and illuminant D65. Particularly with metameric sample pairs, the use of a single allowed observer-illuminant combination would reduce one major source of measurement variability. If 10°-D65 filter colorimeters become widely available or the industry moves to predominant use of spectrophotometers, the committee expects to standardize on the 10 degrees standard observer and illuminant D65 as the only allowed observer and illuminant.

B.1.2 Color Difference Tolerance—There is extensive activity within the automotive industry and in other industries aimed at developing improved models of acceptable color tolerances. The committee chose to adopt the DL*, DC*, DH* tolerance scheme because it is widely supported in available instrumental and computational systems and because it provides the flexibility to tailor the color tolerances to the visual color application. It is likely that the committee will eventually revise the color difference tolerance specification along one of two possible paths. First, an improved color difference prediction model with adequate visual tolerance prediction accuracy may be developed and adopted. An example of this type of effort is the single number color tolerance equation based on CIELAB space which is finding wide acceptance in the British textile industry (2.1.10). Alternatively, as the automotive industry gains experience with the document, empirical information on the appropriate tolerances for many color families could be developed. A similar approach has been taken by the German automotive industry for solid color paint. (2.1.11)

B.1.3 Geometric Specification of Color Measurement—Color measurement instruments with multiple measurement geometries specifically designed for the measurement of metallic flake finishes are just beginning to arrive in the marketplace. It is premature to adopt a multiple geometry color tolerance system for metallic colors at this time since the industry presently has little experience with this technology. When the use of multiple measurement geometry systems becomes more widely adopted for process control and quality control of metallic color, it may be appropriate to revise the measurement practices for finishes to take advantage of this capability.

ACCELERATED EXPOSURE OF AUTOMOTIVE EXTERIOR MATERIALS USING A SOLAR FRESNEL REFLECTOR APPARATUS—SAE J1961 MAR2002

SAE Standard

Report of the SAE Weathering Test Standardization for Exterior Materials Committee approved December 1988. Completely revised by the SAE Weatherization of Exterior Parts Committee June 1994. Completely revised by the SAE Textiles and Flexible Plastics Committee March 2002. Rationale statement available.

1. Scope

1.1 This test method specifies the operating procedures for using a solar fresnel reflector apparatus for the accelerated exposure of various automotive materials.

1.2 Sample preparation, test durations, and performance evaluation procedures are covered in material specifications of the different automotive manufacturers.

2. References

2.1 Applicable Publications—The following publications form a part of this specification to the extent specified herein.

2.1.1 ASTM PUBLICATIONS—Available from ASTM, 100 Barr Harbor Drive, West Conshohocken, PA 19428-2959.

ASTM D 859—Test Methods for Silica in Water

ASTM D 4517—Test Method for Low-Level Total Silica in High Purity Water by Flameless Atomic Absorption Spectroscopy

ASTM E 891—Standard Tables for Terrestrial Direct Normal Solar Spectral Irradiance for Air Mass 1.5

ASTM G 90—Standard Practice for Performing Accelerated Outdoor Weathering of Nonmetallic Materials Using Concentrated Natural Sunlight

ASTM G 147—Standard Practice for Conditioning and Handling of Nonmetallic Materials for Natural and Artificial Weathering Tests

2.2 Related Publication—The following publication is provided for information purposes only and is not a required part of this specification.

2.2.1 ASTM PUBLICATION—Available from ASTM, 100 Barr Harbor Drive, West Conshohocken, PA 19428-2959.

ASTM E 903—Test Method for Solar Absorptance, Reflectance, and Transmittance of Materials Using Integrating Spheres

3. Definitions

3.1 Black Panel Thermometer, n.—A temperature measuring device, the sensing unit of which is covered with a black coating designed to absorb most of the radiant energy encountered in fade/weathering testing.

NOTE—This device provides an estimation of the maximum temperature a specimen may attain during exposure to natural or artificial light.

3.2 Irradiance, Spectral, n.—The radiant power within a specified wavelength interval that falls upon a unit area of exposed surface (W/m^2).

3.3 Irradiance, Total, n.—Radiant power integrated over all wavelengths falling upon a unit area of exposure at a point in time expressed in watts per square meter (W/m^2).

3.4 Irradiation, n.—See radiant exposure.

3.5 Radiant Exposure, n.—The time integral of irradiance expressed in joules per square meter (J/m^2).

3.6 Radiant Exposure, Spectral, n.—The integration of spectral irradiance with respect to time.

3.7 Reference Materials, n.—One or more light fastness standards selected for exposure as a check on a test apparatus and operating conditions.

3.8 Sample, Laboratory, n.—A portion of material taken to represent the lot sample, or the original material, and used in the laboratory as a source of test specimens.

3.9 Specimen, n.—A specific portion of a material or a laboratory sample upon which a test is performed or selected for that purpose.

3.10 Spectral Power Distribution, n.—The variation of power due to the source over the wavelength span of the emitted radiation.

4. Significance and Use—This test method is designed to simulate extreme environmental conditions encountered outside a vehicle due to sunlight, heat, and moisture (in the form of humidity, condensation, or rain) for the purpose of predicting the performance of automotive materials.

5. Apparatus

5.1 The testing apparatus shall be a fresnel-reflecting device possessing 10 flat mirrors which focus direct sunlight onto an air-cooled sample area. A more complete description of the apparatus may be found in ASTM G 90. See Figure 1.

NOTE—The apparatus shall be operated in dry, sunny climates receiving approximately 3500 to 4000 h of sunshine per year and an average annual relative humidity of approximately 25 to 35%.

5.2 If mirror reflectance cannot be measured directly, the apparatus shall be provided with a mounting area for affixing a removable optical-mirror sample. This sample shall possess a minimum area of 2580 mm^2 (4 in^2). The essential requirement is that the optical-mirror specimen be manufactured from the same batch and lot as the mirror stock-material used to irradiate the target sample area. This sample shall be labelled with a number which identifies which mirrors the sample applies to. The optical mirror sample is mounted at the same time as are the mirrors used to irradiate the sample area, and its specular, spectral reflectance is periodically measured.

5.3 A black panel thermometer may optionally be mounted onto the sample exposure area to assist in monitoring expected maximum sample temperatures. The device shall be constructed by affixing the sensing element to the front surface of a metal panel measuring 5 x 13 x 0.16 cm (2 x 5 x 0.06 in) or any other convenient size. The sensor can be attached using a thermally conductive epoxy such as Part Number EC-286 from Therm-X of California or equivalent. The front surface of the panel shall be then coated with DuPont 93 005 Delux® Super Black Enamel, or other glass black automotive coating.

NOTE—ASTM Committee G03 on Durability is currently addressing the issue of Black Panel thermometers as a result of widely different temperature data reported by commercial testing agencies.

5.4 Water Quality

5.4.1 The purity of water used for specimen spray is very important. Without proper treatment to remove cations, anions, organics, and particularly silica, exposed panels will develop spots or stains that do not occur in exterior exposures.

5.4.2 Water used for specimen spray shall leave no objectionable deposits or stains on the exposed specimens. It is strongly recommended that the water contain a maximum of 1 ppm solids and a maximum of 0.2 ppm silica. Silica levels should be determined using the procedures defined in ASTM D 859 or ASTM D 4517. Prepackaged analysis kits are commercially available that are capable of detecting silica levels of less than 200 parts per billion (ppb). A combination of deionization and reverse osmosis treatment can effectively produce water with the desired purity. If the spray water used is above 1 ppm solids, the solids and silica levels must be reported.

6. Calibration and Maintenance

6.1 At least every six months, measure the specular reflectance of each mirror in two places along the mirror's centerline using a portable specular reflectometer with narrow-band-pass filters centered at 310 nm wavelength: (1) 15 cm (6 in) from the north edge, and (2) 15 cm (6 in) from the south edge. Visibly inspect each mirror and measure any additional areas which appear non-uniform. Update the value of P_s employing actual average values of specular reflectance. Replace individual mirrors if the average 310 nm specular reflectance is less than 0.65 (65%).

6.2 If measurement of specular reflectance of the mirrors used in exposure devices is not practical, mount small, representative specimens of the mirror material. Place the representative specimens next to the mirror locations described in 5.1. These representative specimens must be of the same material and lot number as the mirrors used in the instrument. The representative specimens must also be installed at the same time as the mirrors. At least every six months, measure the specular reflectance of the representative specimens at 310 nm. Replace individual mirrors if the average 310 nm specular reflectance of the representative specimens is less than 0.65 (65%).

6.3 Mirrors shall be checked for mirror focus monthly in accordance with the procedure specified in ASTM G 90 and refocused if required at that time.

6.4 The safety mechanism used to protect samples in the event of a power outage shall be checked monthly to make sure it operates properly in all positions.

6.5 Clean mirrors (and removable mirror samples) at intervals necessary to maintain the reflectance specified in 6.1. To maintain optimum specular reflectance, it is recommended that mirrors be cleaned on an established frequency to minimize the effects of surface deposits that may alter spectral irradiance at the target area.

6.6 Clean black panel thermometers at an interval necessary to maintain optical performance.

A FRESNEL-REFLECTING MIRROR
B WATER SPRAY NOZZLE
C AIR TUNNEL
D SQUIRREL CAGE BLOWER
E AIR SWITCH
F SOLAR CELL TRACKER
G SPECIMENS ON TARGET BOARD
H CENTER OF ROTATION
J REVERSIBLE MOTOR/GEAR DRIVE
K CLUTCH
L ALTITUDE ADJUSTMENT MAST
M MIRROR BED/FRAME
N ANCHORS
P A-FRAME

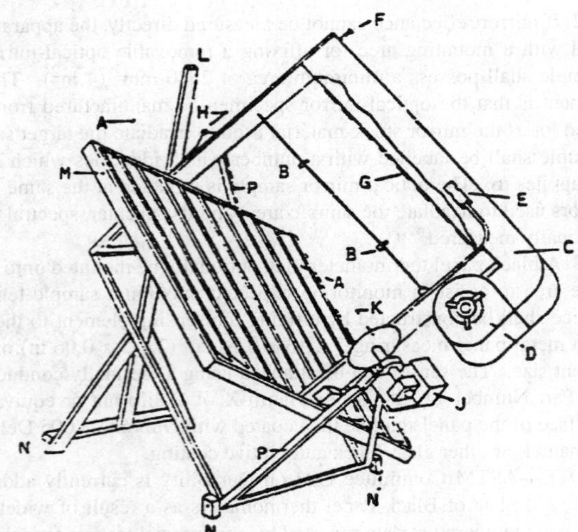

FIGURE 1—SCHEMATIC OF FRESNEL REFLECTING CONCENTRATOR ACCELERATED WEATHERING MACHINE (SINGLE AXIS TRACKING)

A AIR PLENUM
B AIR BLOWER
C ROTOR ASSEMBLY
D TURN TABLE ASSEMBLY
E A-FRAME ASSEMBLY
F MIRROR
G GEAR BOX, ELEV DRIVE
H CONTROL BOX
I GEAR BOX, AZIMUTH DRIVE
J AIR FLOW SWITCH
K WATER SPRAY NOZZLE
L CLUTCH DISC, ELEV DRIVE
M SOLAR CELLS/SHADOW HAT
N SAMPLE PROTECTION DOOR
O DOOR RELEASE MECHANISM
P AIR DEFLECTOR

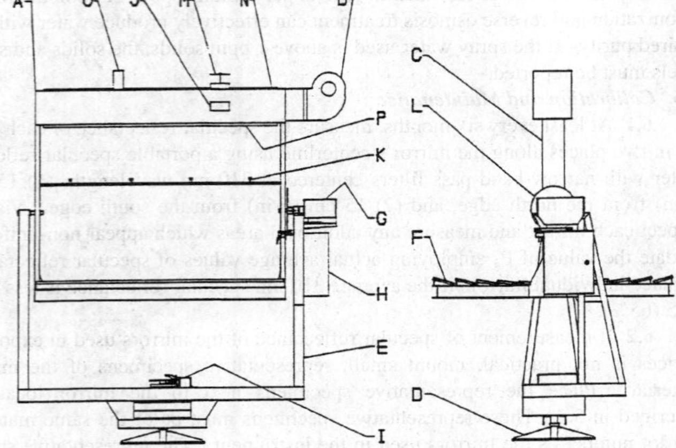

FIGURE 2—DUAL AXIS TRACKING

7. *Test Procedures*

7.1 To insure repeatability of test, maintain the apparatus in accordance with Section 6 and the manufacturer's specifications.

7.1.1 Conditioning and handling of test, control, reference, and file specimens shall be according to ASTM G 147.

7.2 Mount samples in the exposure area using one of two methods:

7.2.1 NONINSULATED EXPOSURE—Mount samples into sample holders constructed of a corrosion-resistant metal such as stainless steel or aluminum in an unbacked configuration such that panels can lose heat from back-side cooling.

7.2.2 INSULATED EXPOSURE—Mount samples into sample holders such that samples are backed with an insulating water-resistant material such as 13 mm (1/2-in) thick exterior plywood.

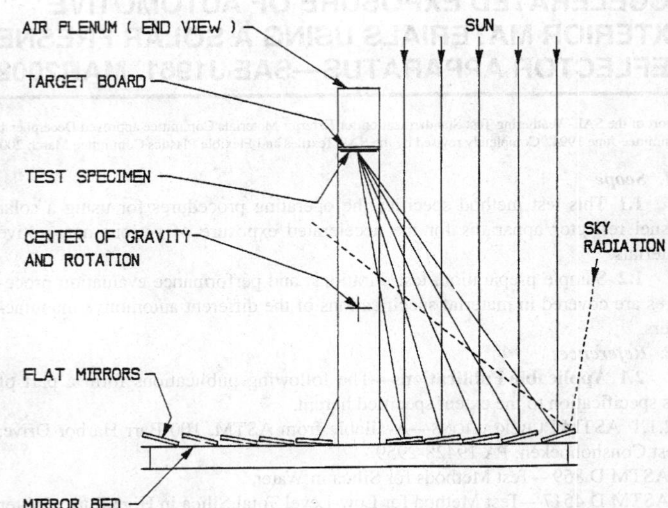

FIGURE 3—ACCELERATED EXPOSURE OF AUTOMOTIVE EXTERIOR MATERIALS USING A SOLAR FRESNEL REFLECTOR APPARATUS EXPOSURE REPORT FORM

7.3 Coated metal specimens shall be mounted using either of the two mounting methods in accordance with the schedule in Table 1:

TABLE 1—MOUNTING CONDITIONS

Time Period	Mounting Condition
November 1 – March 31	Insulated
April 1 – October 31	Noninsulated

7.4 Specimens which are not coated metal shall be mounted for a noninsulated exposure.

7.5 If a black panel thermometer is mounted onto the sample area with the test samples to be exposed, it shall be mounted using the same mounting condition as the test samples.

7.6 Apparatus shall be set up to provide conditions in accordance with one of the cycles in Table 2:

TABLE 2—SPRAY CYCLES

Cycle Number	Description
1	3 min spray, 12 min dry (night spraying only) 7 p.m. to 5 a.m.
2	No sprays

7.7 Expose samples for a predetermined amount of ultraviolet radiant exposure measured in J/m^2. Determine the solar radiant exposure of the test specimens in accordance with Equations 1 and 2:

$$H_s = M\rho_s \sum_{i=1}^{N} H_d \quad \text{(Eq. 1)}$$

$$\rho_s = \frac{\rho}{M} \sum_{i=1}^{M} \cos\theta_i \quad \text{(Eq. 2)}$$

where: θρ

H_s = solar radiant exposure, J/m^2

M = number of mirrors

ρ_s = the cosine corrected specular reflectance

ρ = the average energy-weighted specular reflectance of the mirrors

N = number of days of exposure

θ_I = the angle of incidence of the irradiance from each mirror at the specimen target area

H_d = direct-normal daily solar radiant exposure measured in a 6 degrees field of view

To determine the ultraviolet (295 to 385 nm) solar radiant exposure, H_d in Equation 1 shall be determined as the integration of irradiance with respect to time. Irradiance shall be measured using two ultraviolet radiometers.[1]

A black-painted permanent shading disk (see Figure 4) is positioned over one radiometer in order to provide a diffuse-only measurement (excluding 6 degrees field of view). H_d is determined using Equation 3:

$$H_d = H - H_{do} \qquad \text{(Eq. 3)}$$

where:

H_d = hemispherical daily solar radiant exposure

H_{do} = diffuse-only daily solar radiant exposure (excluding direct-normal radiant exposure in a 6 degrees field of view)

The two ultraviolet radiometers shall be calibrated at the same time at least annually against a standard source of spectral irradiance. Instrument calibration constants shall be checked by mounting both instruments at the same orientation for at least 1 h under clear sky conditions. If a difference of more than 2% exists between instruments, they shall be recalibrated.

At least monthly, for 1 h under clear sky conditions, both instruments shall be tracked off-altitude approximately 15 degrees with no shading on the normally shaded instrument's diffuser. If the radiant exposure readings from the two instruments differ by more than 2%, the radiometers shall be recalibrated. Historical radiation data shall be checked on an annual basis to compare results of present radiation measurements.

The measurement of reflectance (ρ) shall be the power-weighted specular reflectance in the wavelength region of 295 to 385 nm, calculated using the air mass 1.5 spectrum and procedure outlined in ASTM E 891.

1. Available as model TUVR from Eppley Laboratories, 12 Sheffield Avenue, Newport, RI 02840, or equivalent.

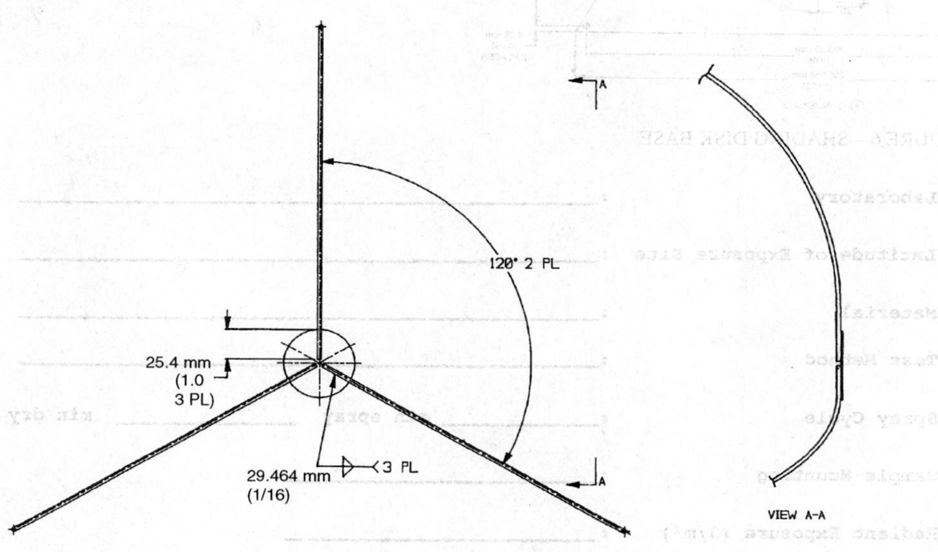

FIGURE 4—SHADING DISK AND SUPPORT BARS

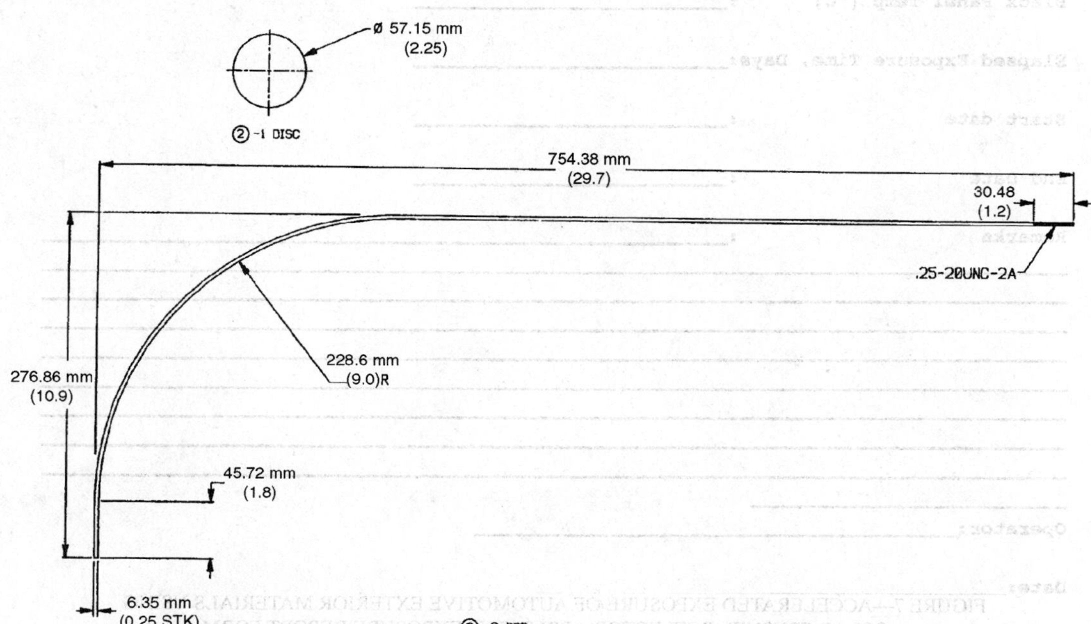

FIGURE 5—SHADING DISK SUPPORT BAR

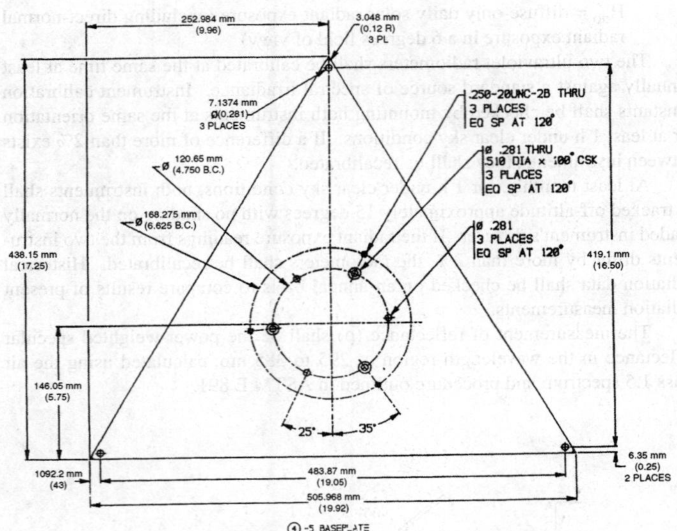

FIGURE 6—SHADING DISK BASE

8. ***Report***—See Figure 7.

8.1 The report shall include the following:

8.1.1 Laboratory

8.1.2 (Accurate Identification of all specimens)

8.1.3 Material

8.1.4 Test method

8.1.5 Operating cycle

8.1.6 Sample mounting (insulated or non-insulated)

8.1.7 Ultraviolet radiant exposure, J/m^2

8.1.8 Black panel temperature, if recorded, °C (°F)

8.1.9 (Dates of Exposure)

Laboratory :____________________

Latitude of Exposure Site :____________________

Material :____________________

Test Method :____________________

Spray Cycle :________ **min spray** ________ **min dry**

Sample Mounting :____________________

Radiant Exposure (J/m²) :____________________

Inst. Used to Measure Radiant Exposure :____________________

Black Panel Temp (°C) :____________________

Elapsed Exposure Time, Days:____________________

Start date :____________________

End Date :____________________

Remarks :____________________

Operator:____________________

Date:____________________

FIGURE 7—ACCELERATED EXPOSURE OF AUTOMOTIVE EXTERIOR MATERIALS USING A SOLAR FRESNEL REFLECTOR APPARATUS EXPOSURE REPORT FORM

ACCELERATED EXPOSURE OF AUTOMOTIVE EXTERIOR MATERIALS USING A CONTROLLED IRRADIANCE AIR-COOLED XENON-ARC APPARATUS—SAE J2019 JAN1994

SAE Standard

Report of the SAE Weathering Test Standardization of Exterior Materials Committee approved January 1994.

Foreword—This Document has not changed other than to put it into the new SAE Technical Standards Board format.

1. Scope

1.1 This SAE Standard specifies the operating procedures for a controlled irradiance, air-cooled xenon-arc apparatus used for the accelerated exposure of various automotive exterior materials.

1.2 The sample preparation, test durations, and performance evaluation procedures are covered in material specifications of the different automotive manufacturers.

2. References

2.1 Applicable Publications—The following publications form a part of this specification to the extent specified herein. The latest issue of SAE publications shall apply.

2.1.1 SAE PUBLICATION—Available from SAE, 400 Commonwealth Drive, Warrendale, PA 15096-0001.

SAE J1545—Instrumental Color Difference Measurement for Exterior Finishes, Textiles and Colored Trim

2.1.2 ASTM PUBLICATIONS—Available from ASTM, 1916 Race Street, Philadelphia, PA 19103-1187.

ASTM G 26—Standard Practice for Operating Light Exposure Apparatus (Xenon Arc Type) With and Without Water for Exposure of Nonmetallic Materials

ASTM D 859—Test Methods for Silica in Water

ASTM D 4517—Test Method for Low-Level Total Silica in High Purity Water by Flameless Atomic Absorption Spectroscopy

2.1.3 CIE PUBLICATION—Available from Commission International de L'eclairage, 52 Bd Malesherbes, F-75008 Paris, France.

Publication No. 85 (1989): Technical Report — Solar Spectral Irradiance

3. Definitions

3.1 Black Standard Thermometer, N—A temperature measuring device, which uses a resistance thermometer with good heat-conducting properties, fitted to the reverse side of a metal plate. The metal plate is fixed to a plastic plate so that it is thermally insulated. It is coated with a black layer.

3.2 Color Change, N—As used in fade-weathering testing, a change in color of any kind (whether a change in hue, saturation, or lightness).

3.3 Irradiance, N (E)—The incident radiant flux per unit area of a surface (W/m^2.

3.4 Irradiance, Controlled, N—The maintenance by closed loop feedback of a preselected irradiance throughout a designated exposure interval.

3.5 Irradiance, Spectral, N—The radiant energy within a specified wavelength interval that falls on a unit area of exposed surface (W/m^2/nm).

3.6 Irradiance, Total, N—Radiant energy integrated over all wavelengths falling on a unit area of exposure at a point in time expressed in watts per square meter (W/m^2).

3.7 Irradiation, N—See radiant exposure.

3.8 Long-arc Xenon, N—A xenon arc in which the length of the arc between electrodes is greater than the diameter of the envelope enclosing the arc.

3.9 Radiant Exposure, N—The time integral of irradiance (J/m^2).

3.10 Radiant Exposure, Spectral, N—The integration of spectral irradiance with respect to time (J/m^2/nm).

3.11 Reference Plastic, N—A clear polystyrene plastic standard selected for exposure as a check on a test apparatus and operating conditions.

3.12 Sample, Laboratory, N—A portion of material taken to represent the lot sample or the original material, and used in the laboratory as a source of test specimens.

3.13 Specimen, N—A specific portion of a material or a laboratory sample on which a test is performed or that is selected for that purpose.

3.14 Spectral Power Distribution, N—The variation of energy due to the source over the wavelength span of emitted radiation.

3.15 Wavelength Range, N—The specified wavelength range for bandpass filters; for example, 300 to 400 nm.

4. Significance and Use—This test method is designed to simulate extreme environmental conditions encountered outside a vehicle such as sunlight, heat, and moisture (in the form of humidity, condensation, or rain) for the purpose of predicting the weatherability of automotive materials.

5. Equipment—A more complete description of the apparatuses listed as follows may be found in ASTM G 26.

5.1 Air-Cooled Type[1]—The apparatus employed shall use an air-cooled xenon-arc lamp as the source of radiation and should be as follows:

5.1.1 GENERAL—An apparatus using three lamps based on xenon-arc technology that meets the conditions specified in Section 6 is acceptable as long as the filter/optical systems reproduce the spectral distribution of the lamp output and filter system specified in this document. Also, all temperature and humidity must be identical to the conditions specified in Section 6.

5.1.1.1 Spectral Power Distribution—The spectral distribution shown in Table 1 (based on CIE Publication No. 85 (1989) Table 4) specifies acceptable ranges within wavebands to describe the lamp output defined in this standard.

TABLE 1—RELATIVE SPECTRAL IRRADIANCE

Wavelength	Relative Spectral Irradiance %
290 to 400	100
below 290	0 (1)
> 290 to 320	5.4 ± 1.8
> 320 to 360	38.2 ± 4.6
> 360 to 400	56.4 ± 9.0

1. Xenon arcs operating according to the method emit a small, but significant, amount of radiation below 295 nm. This radiation can cause degradation reactions which do not occur in actual outdoor exposures.

5.1.1.2 Specimen holders shall revolve around the arc, with the sample plane describing a spherical or cylindrical surface. A slight tilting of the upper and lower sample holders can provide uniformity satisfactory to eliminate the need to reposition specimens in the sample rack and allows use of the complete sample holder.

5.1.1.3 Testing temperatures shall be calibrated using a Black Standard Thermometer unit that is mounted so that the face of the unit is subjected to the same influences as the test specimens.

5.1.1.4 A blower unit in the base of the apparatus shall provide a flow of air through the test chamber and over the test specimens. Control of the specimen, test chamber, and the black standard temperature shall be accomplished by thermostatic control of the chamber temperature and adjustment of the air flow rate to obtain the specified black standard temperature.

5.1.1.5 Relative humidity in the test chamber shall be measured and controlled by a hygrometer. Water should be vaporized and diffused to enrich the air with moisture and produce the required humidity.

6. Apparatus Setup

6.1 To insure repeatability of tests, maintain and calibrate the apparatus to manufacturer's specifications, and as described in Appendices A and B. Appendix A contains additional maintenance instructions and replacement schedules and Appendix B describes the use of reference plastic to determine if the xenon-arc apparatus is operating within the desired range.

6.1.1 The input voltage must be between 200 to 240, 340 to 420, or 400 to 440 V based on manufacturer's specifications.

6.1.2 Water used for the specimen spray and humidification system shall leave no objectionable deposits or stains on the exposed specimens. It is strongly recommended that the water contains a maximum of 1 ppm solids and a maximum of 0.2 ppm silica. Silica levels should be determined using ASTM D 859 or ASTM D 4517. A combination of deionization and reverse osmosis treatment can effectively produce water with the desired purity.

6.1.3 Install both front panel and sample cooling (back side of specimen) spray nozzles.

6.1.4 Install three sections of Suprax filter system, or equivalent to match 5.1.1.1.

6.1.5 Program the microprocessor for the test conditions in Table 2. Program other functions to be OFF.

1. Model XENOTEST® 1200 CPS or equivalent with chamber air heater and variable fan speed controller meets the requirements of this test method. This apparatus is available from Heraeus DSET Laboratories, Inc., 45601 N. 47th Avenue, Phoenix, AZ 85027-7042.

Other similar instruments may be used provided that they (a) can be demonstrated to produce results equivalent to those from the instruments described above, and (b) are mutually agreed to by interested parties.

TABLE 2—MICROPROCESSOR PROGRAM

Parameter	Program Dark	Program Light	Program Light	Program Light
Phase No.	1	2	3	4
Phase Time	60 min	40 min	20 min	60 min
Chamber Temperature	38°C	47°C	47°C	47°C
Relative Humidity	---	50%	---	50%
Irradiance	OFF	ON	ON	ON
Panel Spray	OFF	OFF	ON	OFF
Sample Cooling	ON	OFF	OFF	OFF
Irradiance Level	0 W/m^2	80 W/m^2	80 W/m^2	80 W/m^2
Number of Filters	Window Glass 0			
Number of Filters	Suprax 1/3 3			
Number of Filters	Suprax 1/6 0			

6.1.6 Operate the equipment to maintain the conditions in Table 3. If the actual operating conditions do not agree with the machine settings after the equipment has stabilized, discontinue the test and identify the cause of the disagreement.

TABLE 3—EQUIPMENT OPERATING CONDITIONS

Parameter	Cycle Light	Cycle Dark
Automatic Irradiance	80 W/m^2 ± 1 W/m^2 @ 300–400 nm	---
Black Standard Temperature	77°C ± 2°C	---
Chamber Temperature	47°C ± 2°C	38°C ± 2°C
Relative Humidity	50% ± 5%	95% ± 5%
Radiant Exposure	See applicable specifications	

NOTE 1— The above tolerances are relative to equipment operation and are not intended to indicate tolerances from absolute calibrations.

NOTE 2— It may be necessary to adjust the blower speed to maintain the temperature difference between the black standard and the chamber temperatures.

6.1.7 The tolerances do not apply during the spray portion of the cycle.

6.1.8 Adjust the temperature of the core cooling water to provide sufficient cooling but prevent condensation from forming on lamp assembly.

7. *Test Procedure*

7.1 Prepare the specimens to be exposed to fit the specimen holder being used.

7.2 Specimen sizes must conform to the size of the specimen holder(s) supplied by the manufacturer for use with the equipment. Specimens that exceed these sizes may not give proper exposure results. Instructions for mounting parts or portions of a part can be obtained from the automotive company for which the material is being tested.

7.3 Insert specimen in holder and secure. Under no circumstances should the face side of the sample be closer to the arc than the front side of the specimen holder.

7.4 Fill all unused slots in specimen holders with unpolished stainless steel blanks to maintain desired air flow.

7.5 Expose specimens, beginning with the dark cycle, for the required radiant exposure (Megajoules per square meter [MJ/m^2]) measured in the wavelength range of 300 to 400 nm. See applicable material specification.

7.6 Report the degree of fade or other changes as outlined in SAE J1545.

7.7 Exposure Report

7.7.1 A copy of the exposure report, Figure 1, must be included with each exposed specimen being submitted for approval.

EXPOSURE CONTROL/REPORT FORM

LABORATORY | INSTRUMENT TYPE & SERIAL # | MONTH/YEAR | TEST METHOD

REFERENCE MATERIAL | FREQUENCY OF READINGS | Δ CIELAB REQUIREMENT | MONTHLY AVERAGE

Δ CIELAB UNITS

DATE

REF. MAT'L 1

REF. MAT'L 2

BLACK STANDARD TEMP.

CHAMBER TEMP.

SAMPLE DATA | SAMPLE I.D. | RADIANT EXPOSURE (KJ/M2) | START DATE | END DATE

FOR DATA POINTS OUTSIDE OF THE CONTROL LIMITS

1. CIRCLE AND NUMBER EACH DATA POINT.
2. INDICATE BELOW REASON AND CORRECTIVE ACTION TAKEN.

1.

2.

3.

4.

5.

6.

7.

8.

9.

10.

FIGURE 1—EXPOSURE CONTROL REPORT FORM

APPENDIX A

A.1 Maintenance

A.1.1 Test Chamber—The frequency of cleaning will vary with water quality. However, the chamber must be cleaned at least once a month and flushed with deionized water. Do NOT use cleaning agents containing chlorine.

A.1.2 Conditioning Chamber—The frequency of cleaning will vary with water and air quality in the laboratory. However, the water reservoir must be drained twice a month and flushed with deionized water to remove any deposits.

A.1.3 Optical Assembly—Frequency of cleaning will vary with water quality. However, at least once each week wipe the outer surface of the filter with reagent grade alcohol and a soft cloth. If deposits cannot be removed, the filter should be disassembled and cleaned as necessary.

A.1.4 Black Standard Sensor—Polish monthly using a good quality automotive polish.

A.2 Replacement Schedule

A.2.1 Lamp Assembly and Related Parts—Replace lamps as required by the manufacturer specifications. To adequately control both low wavelength UV and the infrared component of the lamps spectral irradiance, lamps should be replaced so that individual lamps do not exceed manufacturer's recommendations. For systems with more than one lamp, a rotational replacement schedule is recommended.

A.3 Calibration Checks

A.3.1 Check the calibration of the exposure chamber as instructed by the manufacturer, or when the control materials deviate from the specified ranges. (Record these values on the form shown in Figure A1.)

EQUIPMENT CALIBRATION REPORT

Company/Area: ____________

Equipment Type: ____________ **Model #:** ____________ **Serial #:** ____________

Filter Combination: ____________ **Test Specification:** ____________

	Date						
CALIBRATION	**SET POINT**	**BEFORE ADJUSTM.**	**AFTER ADJUSTM.**	**BEFORE ADJUSTM.**	**AFTER ADJUSTM.**	**BEFORE ADJUSTM.**	**AFTER ADJUSTM.**
Irradiance	W/m²						
	UV sensor serial #						
PLC Readout indicates power to lamp	as indicated						
Black Standard Temperature (BST)	°C						
	BST serial #						
Chamber Temperature	Ambient						
	65°C						
Humidity (% RH)	35%						
	80%						
Operating Hours	Total						
	Lamp 1						
	Lamp 2						
	Lamp 3						

FIGURE A1—EQUIPMENT CALIBRATION REPORT

APPENDIX B
PROCEDURE FOR DETERMINING COLORFASTNESS TO LIGHT

B.1 Scope

B.1.1 Appendix B describes the procedure for using a clear polystyrene lightfastness standard as a reference plastic for the purpose of determining whether the xenon-arc apparatus is operating properly.

B.1.2 The color difference values in CIELAB units are obtained by instrumentally measuring the reference plastic before and after a specified amount of radiant exposure.

B.1.3 The clear polystyrene lightfastness standard may be exposed for equivalent kilojoule or megajoule periods from two to seven days. The reference plastic may be obtained from Test Fabrics, Inc., 200 Blackford Ave., P.O. Box 420, Middlesex, NJ 08846, (908) 469-6446.

B.2 Procedure

B.2.1 The instruments used to determine color difference for this procedure requires a capability for providing CIELAB illuminant D-65, 10 degree observer, specular included readings. No substitutions are permitted. Either a transmission or a reflection mode may be used.

B.2.2 Calibrate the instrument to be used for the color measurements to the manufacturer's instructions.

B.2.3 Reflection Mode

B.2.3.1 Place a piece of unexposed reference plastic backed with the white tile used for calibration against the sample port of the instrument.

NOTE—In Order To Preserve The Surface Of The White Calibration Tile, It Is Recommended That A Second Calibration Tile Be Purchased For These Measurements.

B.2.3.2 Take an initial reading. Save this reading and store it as your standard reading.

B.2.4 Transmission Mode

B.2.4.1 Place a piece of unexposed reference plastic in the proper location as instructed by the manufacturer.

B.2.4.2 Place the white tile used for calibration against the outer sample port of the instrument.

NOTE—In Order To Preserve The Surface Of The White Calibration Tile, It Is Recommended That A Second Calibration Tile Be Purchased For These Measurements.

B.2.4.3 Take an initial reading. Save this reading and store it as your standard reading.

B.2.5 Place a piece of reference plastic in a specimen holder and attach the spring-loaded holding device.

B.2.6 Always start the exposure apparatus at the beginning of the dark cycle and expose the reference plastic for an equivalent kilojoule or megajoule period of two to seven days.

B.2.7 After the radiant exposure, remove the reference plastic from the apparatus.

B.2.8 Examine the surfaces for water spotting. If spotting is found, carefully remove it using a piece of water-saturated white cheesecloth. Thoroughly dry the reference plastic using another piece of white cheesecloth.

B.2.8.1 Care must be taken not to scratch the surface of the reference plastic as the measurement could be affected.

B.2.9 Repeat the color measurement steps specified in B.2.3 or B.2.4 on the exposed area of the reference plastic and determine the delta L*, a*, b*, and E*.

B.2.10 Compare the delta b* value determined to the graph or table for the cycle used. This graph or table is supplied with the control material by the manufacturer. The values may change with lot number.

B.2.11 If the delta b* value does not fall within the predetermined value (± 10%), do not resume the test until the reason has been determined and resolved.

B.2.12 As each group of test specimens completes its specified radiant exposure, record and report as required by the customer the delta b* values and the mean and standard deviation of the reference plastic used during the test period.

ACCELERATED EXPOSURE OF AUTOMOTIVE EXTERIOR MATERIALS USING A FLUORESCENT UV AND CONDENSATION APPARATUS—SAE J2020 FEB2003

SAE Standard

Report of the SAE Weathering Test Standardization of Exterior Materials Committee approved June 1989. Completely revised by the SAE Textiles and Flexible Plastics Committee May 1995 and revised February 2003. Rationale statement available.

1. Scope

1.1 This test method specifies the operating conditions for a fluorescent ultraviolet (UV) and condensation apparatus used for the accelerated exposure of various automotive exterior components.

1.2 Specimen preparation, test duration, and performance evaluation procedures are addressed by each automotive manufacturer's material specifications.

1.3 This SAE Standard may involve hazardous materials, operations, and equipment. This document does not purport to address all of the safety problems associated with its use.

It is the responsibility of whoever uses this document to consult and establish appropriate and health practices and determine the applicability of regulatory limitations prior to use.

1.4 Significance and Use—This test method is designed to simulate extreme environmental conditions encountered on the outside of an automobile due to sunlight, heat, and to provide an acceleration of exposure for the purpose of predicting the performance of exterior automotive materials.

1.5 Unless otherwise specified, all dimensions reported in this method are nominal.

2. References

2.1 Applicable Publications—The following publications form a part of this specification to the extent specified herein.

2.1.1 ASTM PUBLICATIONS—Available from ASTM, 100 Barr Harbor Drive, West Conshohocken, PA 19428-2959.

ASTM E 207—Standard Test Method for Thermal EMF Test of Single Thermoelement Materials By Comparison with a Reference Thermo-element of Similar EMF-Temperature Properties

ASTM E 220—Method for Calibration of Thermocouples by Comparison Techniques

ASTM G 113—Standard Terminology Relating to Natural and Artificial Weathering Tests of Nonmetallic Materials

ASTM G 154—Standard Practice for Operating Fluorescent Light Apparatus for UV Exposure of Nonmetallic Materials

2.1.2 CIE PUBLICATION—Available from Commission Internationale de L'eclairage, 52 Bd Malesherbes, F-75008 Paris, France.

CIE Publication No. 85—Solar spectral irradiance (1989)

2.1.3 ISO PUBLICATION—Available from ANSI, 25 West 43rd Street, New York, NY 10036-8002.

ISO 9370—Plastics—Instrumental determination of radiant exposure in weathering tests—General guidance and basic test method

2.2 Related Publication—The following publication is provided for information purposes only and is not a required part of this specification.

2.2.1 ASTM PUBLICATION—Available from ASTM, 100 Barr Harbor Drive, West Conshohocken, PA 19428-2959.

ASTM G 151—Standard Practice for Exposing Nonmetallic Materials in Accelerated Test Devices that Use Laboratory Light Sources

3. Definitions—The terminology found in ASTM G 113 may be appropriate to this procedure.

3.1 Black Panel Thermometer, n—A temperature measuring device consisting of a metal panel, having a black coating which absorbs all wavelength uniformly, with a thermal sensitive element firmly attached to the center of the exposed surface. The black panel thermometer is used to control an artificial weathering device and to provide an estimate of the maximum temperature of specimens exposed to a radiant energy source.

3.2 Irradiance, n—The radiant power per unit area incident on a receiver, typically reported in watts per square meter, W/m^2.

3.3 Irradiance, Spectral, n—The distribution of irradiance as a function of wavelength ($W/m^2/nm$).

3.4 Spectral Power Distribution (SPD), n—The absolute or relative radiant power emitted by a source, or incident upon a receiver as a function of wavelength.

3.5 Fluorescent UV Lamp, n—A lamp in which the irradiance from a low pressure mercury arc is transformed to a higher wavelength UV by a phosphor. The spectral power distribution of a fluorescent lamp is determined by the emission spectrum of the phosphor and the UV transmittance of the glass tube.

4. Apparatus

4.1 A more complete description of the apparatus may be found in ASTM G 154.

4.1.1 Test Chamber, constructed of corrosion-resistant materials enclosing eight fluorescent UV lamps, a heated water pan, test specimen racks, and provisions for controlling and indicating operating times and temperatures.

4.2 Lamps shall be rapid start, medium bi-pin fluorescent UV type with a length of 1200 mm, and a nominal rating of 40 W when operated from a ballast providing a controlled current of 430 mA at 102 V.

4.2.1 The lamps shall be one of the following types:

a. UVB lamps with a peak emission of 313 nm as described in Table 3 of ASTM G 154. A representative spectral power distribution of this lamp is shown in Figure 1.

NOTE—In devices that do not automatically control irradiance, "FS-40" or "F40UVB" type lamps have historically been used. In devices that automatically control irradiance, UVB-313 lamps may be used.

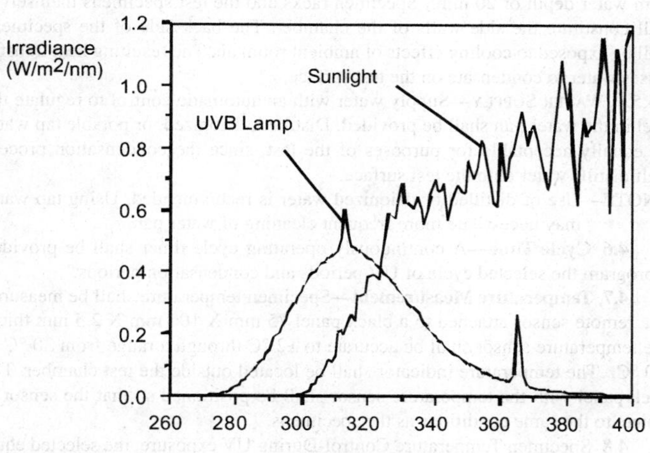

FIGURE 1—UVB LAMPS REPRESENTATIVE SPECTRAL POWER DISTRIBUTION

4.2.2 Other fluorescent UV lamps meeting the size and electrical characteristics in 4.2 may be used by prior agreement, provided that the lamp and spectral power distribution are reported in conformance with the Report section. Use of lamps other than those specified in 4.2 may result in significant differences in test results.

a. UVA lamps with a peak emission of 340 nm as described in Table 1 of ASTM G 154. A representative spectral power distribution of this lamp is shown in Figure 2.

4.3 Lamp Spacing and Arrangement—The lamps shall be mounted in two banks of four lamps each. The lamps in each bank shall be mounted in a flat plane on 70 mm centers.

4.3.1 Lamp manufacturing techniques typically result in a slight gradient in light output from one end of a lamp to the other end. To compensate for this, each lamp shall be positioned so that it is reversed 180 degrees from those mounted above it and below it.

NOTE—This can be accomplished by using the manufacturer's stamps which are generally located on the same end of every lamp.

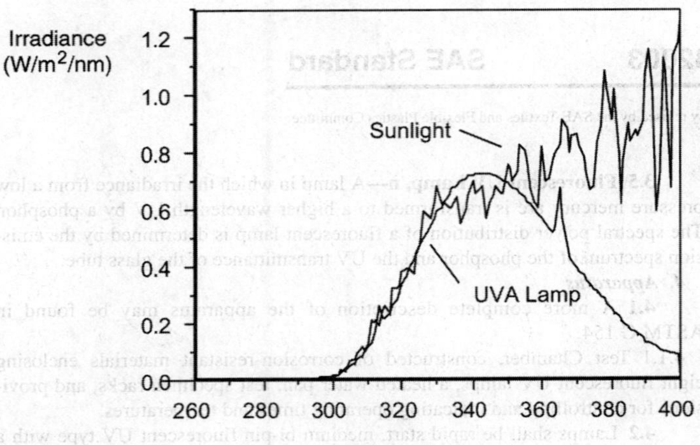

FIGURE 2—UVA LAMPS REPRESENTATIVE SPECTRAL POWER DISTRIBUTION

4.4 Test Specimens—The test specimens shall be mounted in stationary racks with the plane of the surface parallel to the plane of the lamps at a distance of 50 mm from the nearest surface of the lamps.

4.5 Condensation Mechanism—Water vapor shall be generated by heating a water pan extending under the entire specimen area and containing a minimum water depth of 20 mm. Specimen racks and the test specimens themselves shall constitute the side walls of the chamber. The back side of the specimens shall be exposed to cooling effects of ambient room air. The resulting heat transfer causes water to condensate on the test surface.

4.5.1 WATER SUPPLY—Supply water with an automatic control to regulate the level in the water pan shall be provided. Distilled, deionized, or potable tap water are equally acceptable for purposes of the test, since the condensation process itself distills water onto the test surface.

NOTE—Use of distilled or deionized water is recommended. Using tap water may necessitate more frequent cleaning of water pan.

4.6 Cycle Time—A continuously operating cycle timer shall be provided to program the selected cycle of UV periods and condensation periods.

4.7 Temperature Measurement—Specimen temperature shall be measured by a remote sensor attached to a black panel 75 mm X 100 mm X 2.5 mm thick. The temperature sensor shall be accurate to ±2 °C through a range from 30 °C to 100 °C. The temperature indicator shall be located outside the test chamber. The black panel with the temperature sensor shall be positioned so that the sensor is subject to the same conditions as the specimens.

4.8 Specimen Temperature Control-During UV exposure, the selected equilibrium temperature shall be maintained within ±3 °C of set-point temperature by supplying heated air to the test chamber. During condensation exposure, the selected equilibrium temperature shall be maintained within ±3 °C of set-point temperature by heating the water in the water pan. The UV and condensation temperature controls shall be independent of each other.

4.9 Test Chamber Location

4.9.1 The apparatus shall be located in an area maintained between 18 °C and 27 °C. Ambient temperature shall be measured at a maximum distance of 150 mm from the plane of the specimen door of the apparatus and 150 mm from the chamber air intake. Control of ambient temperature is particularly critical for proper operation of apparatus stacked one above the other, because the heat generated from one unit could interfere with the operation of adjacent units.

4.9.2 The apparatus shall be located at least 300 mm from walls or other apparatus. Nearby heat sources, such as ovens or heated test apparatus, shall be avoided or shielded.

4.9.3 The room where the apparatus is located shall be ventilated to remove the heat and moisture produced and to maintain the temperatures specified in 4.9.1.

4.10 To insure repeatability of test results, maintain and calibrate the apparatus to the manufacturer's specifications as described in Appendix A.

5. Test Specimens

5.1 Specimen size shall be either 50 mm X 75 mm, 75 mm X 100 mm, 75 mm X 150 mm, 100 mm X 150 mm, or as agreed upon by concerned parties.

NOTE—Because of the geometry of some specimen holders, the previous sizes may cause some problems if, after inspection, they are replaced in a different orientation than the original. For example, improper replacement of 75 mm X 150 mm panel into a commonly used holder can cause the end 1/3's to be shielded (i.e., exposed less than the center 1/3).

5.1.1 For simultaneous exposures of original and repair coatings on one test specimen, 100 mm X150 mm specimens have been found useful. In this situation, each coating should cover one half of the specimen and be 50 mm X 150 mm area.

5.2 Replicate specimens are desirable to provide a record of degradation at different time intervals. Retention of unexposed specimens in a controlled environment is recommended as it is difficult to mask a specimen to prevent exposure to condensation.

5.3 For specimens of insulating materials, such as plastics or foams, maximum specimen thickness should be 30 mm to allow adequate heat transfer for condensation. Report any thickness greater than this in the test report.

5.4 To provide rigidity, flexible specimens should be attached to a backing panel made of aluminum, 0.635 mm thick, 3003 H14 alloy.

5.5 Holes in specimens larger than 2 mm and any openings larger than 1 mm around irregularly shaped specimens shall be sealed to prevent loss of water vapor. Porous specimens, such as textiles, shall be backed with a vapor barrier such as metal.

6. Procedure

6.1 Mount the test specimens in the specimen racks with the test surfaces facing the lamp. When the test specimens do not completely fill the racks, the empty spaces must be filled with panels to maintain the test conditions within the chamber.

6.2 The test specimens shall be exposed within an area 210 mm in height by 900 mm wide on each side of the apparatus located as shown in Figure 3.

NOTE—To avoid areas of variability in the specimen exposure area, do not use the extreme right- and left-hand specimen holders on the apparatus.

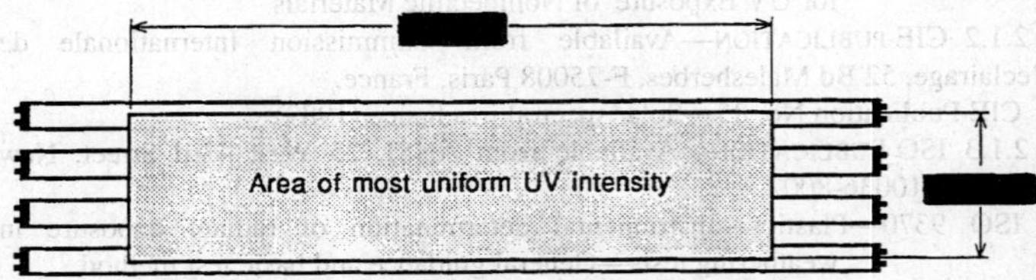

FIGURE 3—AREA OF MOST UNIFORM UV INTENSITY

6.3 Set Condensation Cooling Timer to 15 min, if applicable. Report any variations in the test report Figure 4.

6.4 Initiate all exposures at the beginning of the condensation cycle.

6.5 Program the Cycle Timer to achieve the following test conditions: 8 h UV light exposure at 70 °C, alternating with 4 h condensation exposure at 50 °C.

6.5.1 Operating continuously, repeating the cycle, except for servicing the instrument and inspection of specimens. Inspect specimens weekly during the condensation cycle for evidence of condensation.

6.6 In order to minimize any effect from temperature or UV light variation, specimens shall be repositioned periodically. As a minimum, specimens must be rotated horizontally once each week by (a) moving the two extreme right-hand specimen holders to the far left of the exposure area and (b) sliding the remaining specimen holders to the right (see Figure 5).

ACCELERATED EXPOSURE OF AUTOMOTIVE EXTERIOR MATERIALS USING A FLUORESCENT UV AND CONDENSATION APPARATUS

Material Test Date: ____________________

Material Identification: ____________________

____

Total Hours Exposure: ____________________

Test Cycle

_______ hours UV at _______ °C
_______ hours Condensation at _______ °C

UV Light Source

Lamp Type: ____________________ Supplier: ____________________

Lot Number: ____________________ Peak Emission: ____________________

Total Time Meter at Start of Test: ____________________ Total Time Meter at End of Test: ____________________

Frequency of Sample Rotation: ____________________

Apparatus Model: ____________________

Special Test Conditions: ____________________

____

Remarks: ____________________

____

Name/Signature: ____________________

Date: ____________________

Attach measurements of irradiance. Include all individual measurements and the average irradiance throughout the exposure test.

FIGURE 4—EXPOSURE REPORT FORM

6.7 UV Irradiance

6.7.1 UV irradiance shall be maintained within a specified range by one of the methods shown in Appendix A.

6.7.2 For UVB lamps, the irradiance level shall be 0.48 ± 15% W/m^2/nm at 310 nm (0.41 to 0.55 W/m^2/nm at 310 nm). If the irradiance deviates beyond this tolerance, terminate the test until the cause of the deviation has been determined and corrected.

NOTE—The previous edition of SAE J2020 specified an irradiance level of 0.43 W/m^2/nm at 310 nm (0.37 to 0.49 W/m^2/nm at 310 nm). The new 0.48 irradiance level is not an increase from the previously specified 0.43 irradiance level. The 0.48 target irradiance level is based on more precise radiometer calibration in accordance with B.1.3.1 of SAE J2020.

6.7.2.1 Other irradiance levels can be used by mutual agreement between contracting parties.

6.7.3 For UVA lamps, the irradiance level shall be mutually agreed upon by contracting parties.

NOTE—For devices that automatically control irradiance, target irradiance levels between the range of 0.67 to 0.77 W/m^2/nm at 340 nm are commonly used. CIE Publication No. 85, Table 4, states that noon summer sunlight, air mass 1.0, is 0.68 W/m^2/nm at 340 nm.

6.8 Expose specimens for the required time. See material/manufacturer specification for specific requirements.

7. Report

7.1 The report shall include the following:

7.1.1 Laboratory

7.1.2 Material

7.1.3 Test Method

7.1.4 The supplier and model of fluorescent UV/Condensation apparatus

7.1.5 The name of the supplier of the fluorescent UV lamp. The manufacturer's designation for the lamp, the lot number or date code, and the wavelength (nm) at which peak emission occurs. For example: FS-40, C6 lot, 313 nm.

7.1.6 Cycle of UV exposure time and temperature, condensation time and temperature. For example: 8 h UV/70 °C, 4 h Condensation/50 °C.

7.1.7 Total hours exposure time

7.1.8 Results of UV irradiance measured and the intervals at which it was measured during the exposure test as specified in Appendix A.

7.1.9 Any special conditions of test

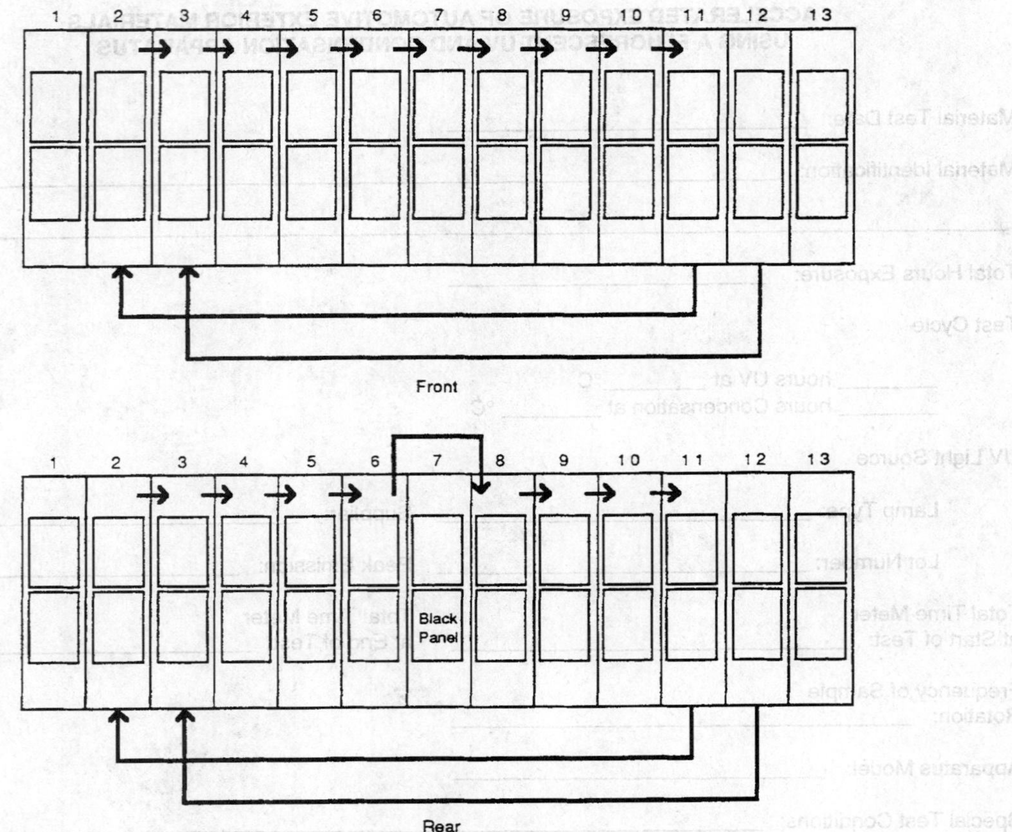

FIGURE 5—HORIZONTAL SPECIMEN HOLDER ROTATION

APPENDIX A
REQUIRED PERIODIC MAINTENANCE

A.1 Maintenance and Calibration of Test Apparatus

A.1.1 The test apparatus requires periodic maintenance to maintain uniform exposure conditions. Perform required maintenance and calibration in accordance with manufacturer's instructions.

A.2 Maintenance of Irradiance

A.2.1 Maintenance of proper UV irradiance can be achieved by any of the two methods specified as follows. Regardless of the method used for regular monitoring and control, the system should be measured every six months using the procedure specified in Appendix B.

A.2.2 Method 1, Automatic Feedback-Loop Method—The system consists of a programmable controller that continuously monitors the UV intensity. A feedback loop system maintains the programmed irradiance level by adjusting power to the UV lamps.

A.2.2.1 Every 425 h ± 25 h of lamp operation, measure light output and calibrate the system as recommended by the manufacturer.

A.2.2.2 Replace all of the lamps in the unit when they can no longer maintain the center point of the desired range.

A.2.2.3 Using the procedure in B.1.3, re-calibrate the calibration radiometer every 6 months.

A.2.3 Method 2, Manual Irradiance Measurement Method—This system uses constant output ballasts which do not compensate for variability in light output caused by lamp aging, temperature, or lot-to-lot variability.

NOTE—Many fluorescent lamps age significantly with extended use. Follow the apparatus manufacturer's instructions on the procedure necessary to maintain desired irradiance.

A.2.3.1 At a minimum, operators should measure lamp irradiance every two weeks (336 total hours) to assure that the irradiance is within the specified range. If the light intensity is below 0.48 ± 15% $W/m^2/nm$ at 310 nm (0.41 to 0.55 $W/m^2/nm$ at 310 nm) replace one lamp in each bank and rotate the others as shown in Figure A1.

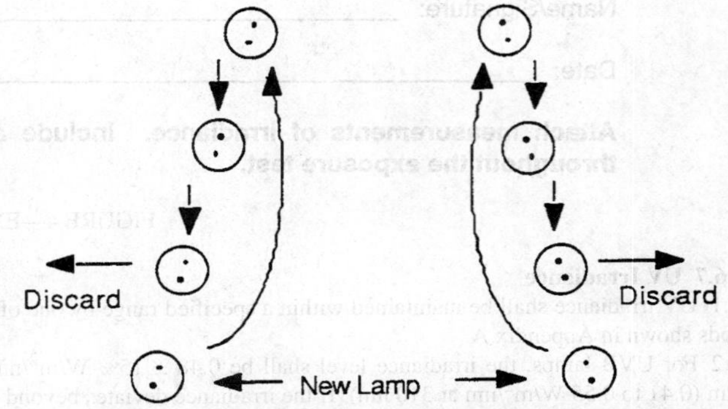

FIGURE A1—LAMP ROTATION/REPLACEMENT PROCEDURE

A.2.3.2 Using the procedure in B.1.3, re-calibrate the calibration radiometer every 6 months.

A.3 Thermometer Calibration—The Black Panel thermometer shall be calibrated every 6 months. The thermometer or thermocouple which indicates test temperature shall be calibrated by immersing the sensing element and a liquid-in-glass thermometer in water heated to approximately 70 °C and comparing the two temperatures as in ASTM E 220 or by using the calibration method specified in ASTM E 207.

A.4 The rate of deterioration caused by exposure in this apparatus may be monitored by exposing weathering reference materials.

A.5 Water Pan Maintenance—Drain the water and clean the pan every 6 months or more frequently if local water conditions warrant it. Heavy scum or residue on the top of the water can inhibit water vaporization.

APPENDIX B
MEASUREMENT OF IRRADIANCE

B.1 Equipment Needed

B.1.1 The instrumentation required to measure irradiance is a radiometer and, in addition, for the manual method, special specimen holders with measurement ports.

B.1.2 Special Specimen Holders with Measurement Port—Follow the manufacturer's instructions to measure in the prescribed locations shown in Figure B1. Maintain temperature integrity within the chamber so that the measurements are not affected.

B.1.3 The Radiometer—The radiometer used to measure irradiance must have a detector which can be placed in the specimen plane of the apparatus. The detector must have some spectral response at 310 nm but no response between 400 and 600 nm.

B.1.3.1 RADIOMETER CALIBRATION—In order to obtain good inter-instrument agreement, the radiometer must be calibrated via a special procedure using a Fluorescent UV and Condensation Apparatus, the type of lamps used in the test and a spectroradiometer. The spectroradiometer used for this calibration procedure must itself be calibrated traceable to the National Institute of Standards and Technology (NIST), have a double grating monochromator, with a half bandwidth of 2 nm or less, and a cosine receptor that is within ±4% of the cosine between ±60 degrees of normal incidence as specified in ISO 9370.

B.1.3.2 RADIOMETER CALIBRATION PROCEDURE

a. Stabilize the Fluorescent UV and Condensation Apparatus for 2 h with the air heater turned off.
b. Place the input optics of the spectroradiometer in the center of the top window of the middle panel holder and record the irradiance at 310 nm. The units shall be W/m^2/nm.
c. Remove the spectroradiometer and replace it with the detector of the radiometer to be calibrated. If the radiometer has an adjustable read-out, adjust the calibration potentiometer to match the irradiance measured in step "b." If the radiometer cannot be adjusted, calculate a calibration factor to use in converting the radiometer reading to the proper irradiance value in W/m^2/nm.

B.1.3.3 Re-calibrate the radiometer on a semi-annual basis. More frequent calibration may be necessary if the equipment is used on a frequent basis or if the equipment has been handled with less delicate care. One method to determine if more frequent calibration is necessary is to compare the "working" radiometer's output to that of a reference radiometer which is used only for inter-instrument comparisons. When a difference in values occurs, the "working" unit must be re-calibrated.

B.2 Irradiance Measurement Procedure

B.2.1 There are two measurement procedures described as follows. The first is for apparatus without automatic control of irradiance. The second is for testers with a feedback-loop automatic irradiance control system.

B.2.2 Calibrate the radiometer in accordance with B.1.3.2.

B.2.3 Calibrate the Fluorescent UV and Condensation Apparatus black panel thermometer in accordance with Section A.4.

B.2.4 Stabilize the test chamber for a minimum of 2 h on the UV cycle at a black panel temperature of 70 °C.

B.2.5 Manual Measurement Method—This applies to apparatus that do not have automatic feedback-loop control of irradiance.

B.2.5.1 Place three measurement panel holders on each side of the test chamber at specimen holder positions 2, 6, and 12 as shown in Figure B2.

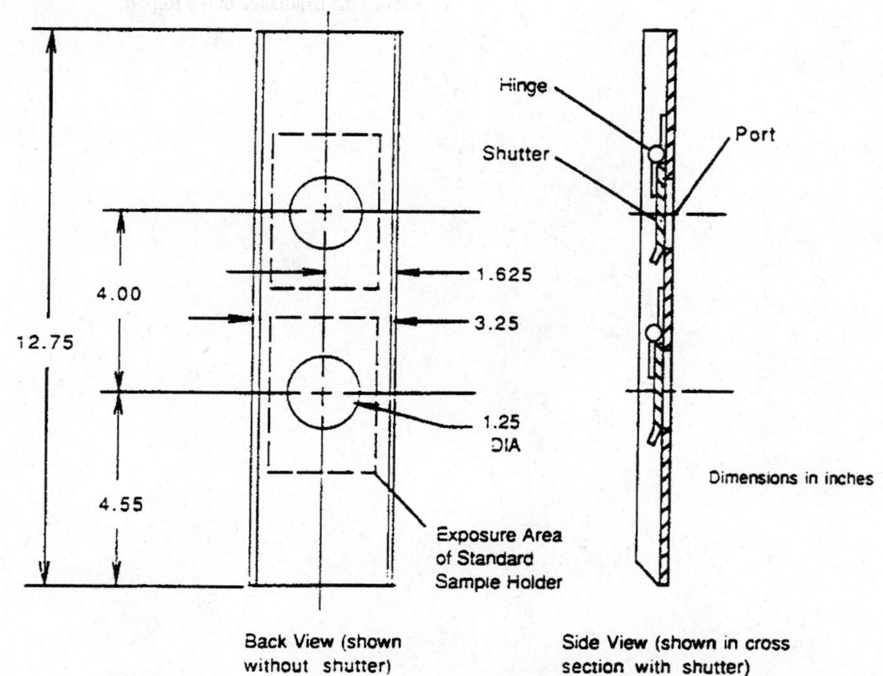

FIGURE B1—SPECIAL SAMPLE HOLDER WITH MEASUREMENT PORT

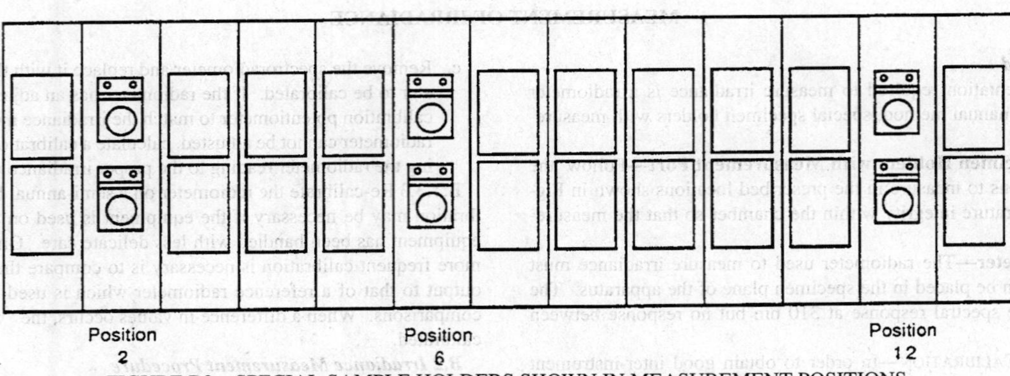

FIGURE B2—SPECIAL SAMPLE HOLDERS SHOWN IN MEASUREMENT POSITIONS

B.2.5.2 After the measurement panels are in place and the temperature has reached 70 °C, stabilize the test chamber for another 5 min. Make sure all doors are closed during the stabilization period.

B.2.5.3 Open the door on one side of the tester. Take measurement by opening the viewing shutter and placing the sensor in the port and against the panel. Record the irradiance reading. Immediately after each reading, close the shutter to prevent heat loss from the chamber. Close the door on one side before proceeding to the other side. After closing the door from the previous side, observe a stable 70 °C temperature for 5 min again before measurements on the opposite side are taken. Record the measured values.

B.2.6 Automatic Measurement Method—This applies to apparatus that are equipped with an automatic feedback-loop irradiance control system.

B.2.6.1 These systems have internal radiometers that continually monitor the irradiance in the tester. The measured irradiance is continuously displayed on the apparatus' control panel.

B.2.6.2 Calibrate the system as shown in A.2.1.

B.2.6.3 Observe and record the irradiance displayed on the front control panel display.

B.3 Acceptability Range

B.3.1 For purposes of this method, each side of the test chamber is considered as a single unit. The irradiance of each side of a test chamber shall be characterized by the average of the 6 readings described in B.2.5.3 or the readings corresponding to one side of a tester as described in B.2.5.3. The irradiance units are $W/m^2/nm$ at 310 nm. Compare the irradiance to the requirements in 6.7. Record the irradiance in the Report.

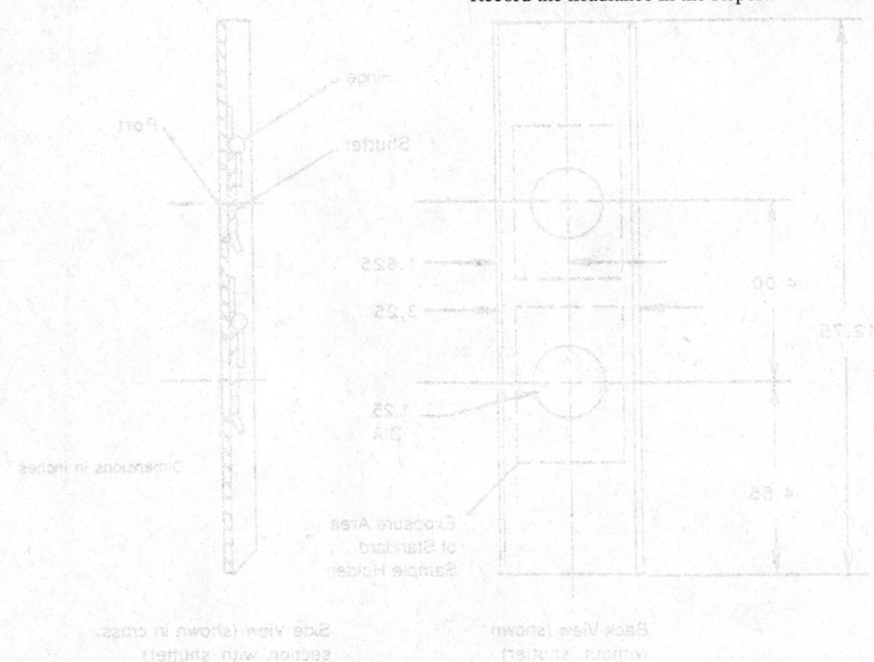

ACCELERATED EXPOSURE OF AUTOMOTIVE INTERIOR TRIM COMPONENTS USING A CONTROLLED IRRADIANCE XENON-ARC APPARATUS—SAE J2412 NOV2003 SAE Recommended Practice

Report of the SAE Textiles and Flexible Plastics Committee approved November 2003. Rationale available upon request

1. Scope

1.1 This test method specifies the operating procedures for a controlled irradiance, xenon arc apparatus used for the accelerated exposure of various automotive interior trim components.

1.2 This is a performance standard based on the test parameters of SAE J1885.

1.3 Test duration as well as any exceptions to the sample preparation and performance evaluation procedures contained in this document, are covered in material specifications of the different automotive manufacturers.

1.4 Equipment qualified to perform this test is determined by material test comparison between instruments approved for SAE J1885 and those intending to perform SAE J2412. A specific test protocol to compare new test equipment to those previously approved must be done by material test comparison by the contractual parties. The interested contractual companies shall identify details of the test protocol and the materials to be tested. At the time of publication of this test method, the committee is developing a 'Protocol To Verify New Test Apparatus' identified as SAE J2413.

1.5 Any deviations to this test method, such as filter combinations, is to be agreed upon by contractual parties.

2. References

2.1 Applicable Documents

The following publications form a part of this specification to the extent specified herein. The latest issue of SAE publications shall apply.

2.1.1 SAE PUBLICATIONS

Available from SAE, 400 Commonwealth Drive, Warrendale, PA 15096-0001.

SAE J1767—Instrumental Color Difference Measurement for Colorfastness of Automotive Interior Trim Materials.

SAE J1885—Accelerated Exposure of Automotive Interior Trim Components Using a Controlled Irradiance Water Cooled Xenon-Arc Apparatus.

2.1.2 ASTM PUBLICATIONS

Available from ASTM, 100 Barr Harbor Drive, West Conshohocken, PA19428-2959.

ASTM D859—Standard Test Method for Silica in Water

ASTM D4517—Standard Test Method for Low-Level Total Silica in High-Purity Water by Flameless Atomic Absorption Spectroscopy

ASTM G113—Standard Terminology Relating to Natural and Artificial Weathering Tests of Non-Metallic Materials.

ASTM G130—Standard Test Method for Calibration of Narrow and Broad-Band Ultraviolet Radiometers Using Spectroradiometer

ASTM G147—Standard Practice for Conditioning and Handling of Nonmetallic Materials for Natural and Artificial Weathering Tests.

ASTM G151—Standard Practice for Exposing Non-Metallic Materials in Accelerated Test Devices that use Laboratory Light Sources.

ASTM G155—Standard Practice for Operating Xenon Arc Light Apparatus for Exposure of Non Metallic Materials

2.1.3 RELATED PUBLICATIONS

American Association of Textile Chemists and Colorists (AATCC) P.O. Box 12215, Research Triangle Park, North Carolina 27709

AATCC - Evaluation Procedure 1

AATCC - L-2 Blue Wool Lightfastness Standard

AATCC - L-4 Blue Wool Lightfastness Standard

Testfabrics, Inc., 415 Delaware Ave., P.O. Box 26, West Pittston, PA18643

Polystyrene Plastic Lightfastness Standard

3. Terminology

3.1 Black Panel Thermometer, n

A temperature measuring device, the sensing unit of which is coated with black enamel designed to absorb most of the radiant energy encountered in fade/weathering testing.

3.2 Black Standard Thermometer, n

See ASTM G 147 for definition.

NOTE—These devices provide an estimation of the maximum temperature a specimen might attain during exposure to natural or artificial light.

3.3 Definitions applicable to this standard can be found in ASTM G 151.

4. Significance and Use

4.1 This test method is designed to simulate extreme environmental conditions encountered inside vehicle due to sunlight, heat, and humidity for the purpose of predicting the performance of automotive interior trim materials.

5. Apparatus

5.1 The equipment manufacturer is responsible for the approval of the equipment and for providing the proof of compliance of the critical test parameters, including the different spectral power distributions (SPDs) that are required by contractual parties. Materials used for the compliance testing should include the approved lots of standard reference materials, such as the Testfabrics polystyrene and/or the AATCC L4 & L2 Blue Wools as appropriate. It is the responsibility of the instrument manufacturer to provide all necessary data to demonstrate compliance of each model type with this specification. At the minimum, the data should include (1) all the pertinent spectral power distribution (SPD) data for 250 nm - 800 nm, and (2) repeatability and reproducibility data for the current approved lots of standard reference materials. Contractual parties should agree upon the instrument model prior to testing.

NOTE—In normal practice, different instruments may give different results. The result depends on sample characteristics and instrument design. Refer to ASTM G155 Section 4.3 and 4.4 for more information.

5.2 The apparatus employed utilizes a xenon-arc lamp(s) as the source of radiation. The specimens shall be mounted in a manner to expose the specimens to the uniform conditions of the test chamber. The instrument must have the means to automatically control irradiance, Black Panel temperature, chamber temperature and relative humidity. Contractual parties shall agree upon the manufacturer and model of the instrument before testing begins.

5.2.1 A more complete description of the apparatus can be found in ASTM G151 and ASTM G155.

5.3 The apparatus must have an uninsulated black panel thermometer as described in ASTM G151 unless otherwise agreed upon by contractual parties.

5.4 Manufacturers of exposure devices shall assure that the irradiance at any location in the area used for specimen exposures is at least 70% of the maximum irradiance measured in this area.

5.4.1 If irradiance at positions farthest from the center of the exposure area is between 70% and 90% of that measured at the center, place specimens only in exposure area where irradiance is at least 90% of the maximum irradiance.

6. Apparatus Set-Up

6.1 To minimize variability maintain and calibrate the apparatus to manufacturer's specifications. Appendix B and C describe the use of reference materials to determine if the xenon-arc apparatus is operating within the desired range.

6.1.1 The water for humidification or other purposes shall leave no objectionable deposits or stains on the exposed specimens. The water cannot have more than 1 ppm solids and it must have less than 0.2 ppm silica. Silica levels should be determined using ASTM procedures D 859 or D 4517. A combination of deionization and reverse osmosis treatment can effectively produce water with the desired purity.

6.1.2 If applicable, to prevent accidental spraying of the test samples, turn off all water spray assemblies.

6.1.3 Fit the xenon-arc burner with an Extended UV Filter to provide a spectral power distribution (SPD) indicated in Appendix D, Table D1 and Figure D1.

6.1.4 The equipment manufacturer is responsible for the approval of the equipment and the SPD required by the different Original Equipment Manufacturers (OEM). The use of the approved lot of polystyrene and other materials provided by the OEM's as control materials will determine the approval of the equipment. It is also the responsibility of the instrument manufacturer to provide all the necessary data to demonstrate compliance of each model type with this specification. At the minimum, the data should include (1) all the pertinent spectral power distribution (SPD) data for 250 nm – 800 nm, and (2) repeatability and reproducibility data for the current approved lot of the polystyrene standard reference material.

6.1.5 Operate the equipment to alternating cycles as described in Table #1.

TABLE 1—TARGET VALUES AT CONTROL PANEL SENSOR

Controls	Dark Cycle		Light Cycle	
	Target	Tolerance	Target	Tolerance
Automatic Irradiance	None		Contractual Agreement (See Note 1)	± 0.02
Black Panel Temperature	38 °C	± 3 °C	70 °C	± 3 °C
Dry Bulb Temperature	38 °C	± 3 °C	47 °C	± 3 °C
Relative Humidity	95%	± 5%	50%	± 5%
Radiant Exposure	Not applicable		Contractual Agreement	
Cycle Duration	1 hour (See Note 2)	± 6 minutes	3.8 hours (See Note 2)	± 6 minutes

Note 1: 0 .55 Wm^{-2} nm^{-1} at 340 nm is the default irradiance for the equipment listed in J1885. Equipment monitoring a broad band rather than the narrow band will have different target values than those listed in Table 1. Other values, higher or lower, agreed upon by contractual parties can be used but they invalidate the values listed for the polystyrene reference material shown in Appendix B.

Note 2: Other cycle times may be used upon contractual agreement, if, for example, an irradiance different than the specified default value is specified.

7. ***Test Procedure***

7.1 Prepare the specimens to be exposed to fit the specimen holder being used. Refer to ASTM G147 for conditioning and handling of specimens.

7.2 Specimen sizes must conform to the size of the approved specimen holder(s). Specimens that exceed these sizes may not give proper exposure results. The correct means of mounting odd sized specimens can be obtained from the contractual parties for which the material is being tested. Distance from the light source is a major factor on the amount of irradiance received and the surface temperature of the sample and hence the exposure results obtained from the test. It is important to follow the manufacturer guidelines to obtain uniform light exposure on the specimens.

7.3 Interior textiles shall be backed (body cloth, carpet, vinyl coated fabrics, etc.) with white cardboard[1]. Specimens other than interior textiles that do not completely fill the exposure area of the specimen holder shall be backed with white cardboard.

7.4 Fill all unused slots with an inert non-reflective material to maintain desired air flow. (e.g., white cardboard panels[1]). Cardboard blanks should be changed when noticeable physical distortion occurs.

7.5 Program the weathering device for the specified radiant exposure *($kJ \cdot m^{-2} \cdot nm^{-1}$ @ 340nm for example)*, and ensure that the test begins at the beginning of the light cycle. See applicable material specification. This is to accommodate scheduling of reference materials.

7.6 For some instruments and/or materials, periodic repositioning of specimens during the exposure period may be needed to ensure that each receives an equal amount of radiant exposure. Reposition specimens as agreed upon by contractual parties if no data is available for that material.

NOTE—Care should be taken to avoid mixing potentially incompatible specimens in the same machine load, i.e., textiles should not be exposed together with foam backed textiles, foams, or plastics.

NOTE—Once exposure has been initiated, equipment operation should not be interrupted more than once daily. Additional interruptions, e.g., opening the chamber door during the course of daily operation, may cause variation in test results.

8. ***Evaluating and Reporting***

8.1 The degree of fade should be evaluated and reported as specified between the contractual parties. One or more of the following methods may be specified:

8.1.1 INSTRUMENTAL MEASUREMENT

8.1.1.1 Color difference values in CIELAB units are obtained by instrumentally measuring the specimen before and after a specified amount of radiant exposure. The procedure used for specimen measurement will conform to that specified in Appendix B.

8.1.2 VISUAL ASSESSMENT

8.1.3 Assign colorfastness ratings using the AATCC Gray Scale for Color Change in accordance with AATCC Evaluation Procedure 1.

8.1.4 Using the viewing conditions specified in AATCC Evaluation Procedure 1, quantify the color change using the following terminology:

a. NONE - No change in hue, lightness or saturation.
b. SLIGHT - A change in lightness and/or saturation which can be determined only upon close examination but no change in hue.
c. NOTICEABLE - A change in lightness and/or saturation which can be easily seen and/or a change in hue.
d. SEVERE - An extreme change in lightness, saturation and/or hue.

9. ***Exposure Report***

9.1 A copy of the Exposure Control/Report Form (Figure 1) indicating the color change of the exposed reference material in CIELAB color difference units must accompany each exposed specimen being submitted for approval. If any one of the color difference data points is outside the specified tolerance (control limits), the cause and corrective action must be indicated in the space provided.

9.2 The Exposure Control/Report Form shall include the following additional information:

1. Laboratory Name
2. Type and serial number of exposure equipment
3. Month and Year of equipment operation represented by the control chart
4. Test method
5. Reference material(s) used. Include lot number(s).
6. Frequency of operation verification, e.g., daily, three or seven day intervals

[1] Franklin, Grain long-felt side up 110/500 white index, Stock Number 06506 or 9016 White Bristol Card Stock have been found suitable for this purpose. Franklin white index is usually available from local office supply or art supply stores. Weight of card stock should be sufficient to prevent warping.

7. Color change, target value, and tolerance, in CIELAB color difference units for the reference material(s) used
8. The monthly average color difference for the reference material(s)
9. Measured color change, in CIELAB color difference units, for reference material 1.
10. Measured color change, in CIELAB color difference units, for reference material 2 (if more than one material is used)
11. Daily (except weekends and holidays) record of black panel temperature (BPT) or black standard temperature (BST). These readings should be taken after the machine has reached equilibrium in a partial segment, example light/dark.
12. Daily (except weekends and holidays) record of dry bulb temperature or chamber temperature. These readings should be taken after the machine has reached equilibrium in a particular segment, example light/dark.
13. Irradiance control level.

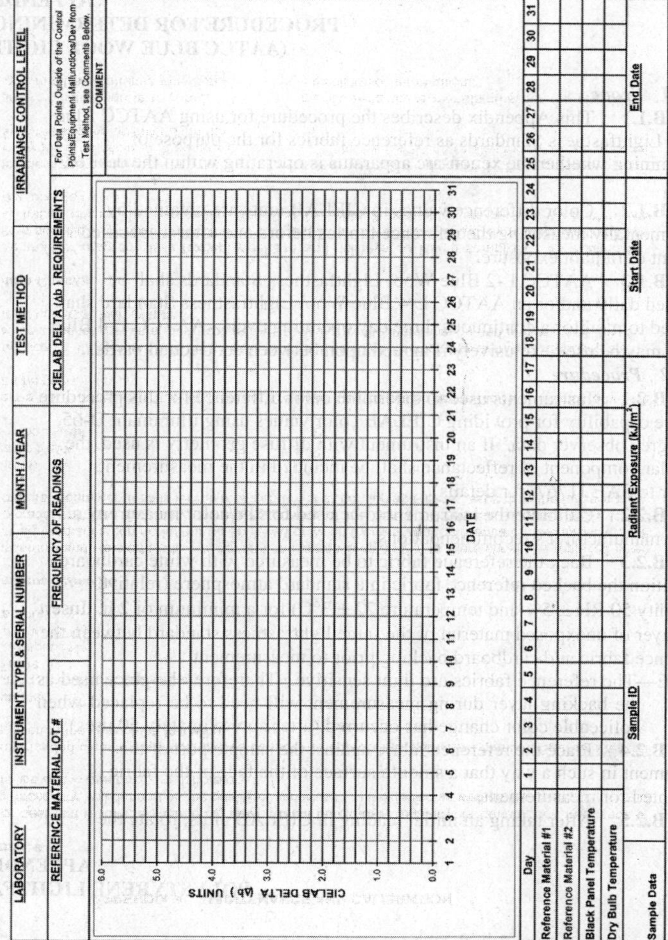

FIGURE 1—XENON ARC REFERENCE MATERIAL CONTROL CHART

APPENDIX A
MAINTENANCE AND CALIBRATION

A.1 Maintenance

A.1.1 NOTE—For best test results, a weathering device must be cleaned regularly. In general, the frequency of cleaning necessary, will depend on the quality of water used in the device as well as the quality of air used in the device and is present in the laboratory.

A.1.2 For recommended cleaning practice, please consult the appropriate instruction manual. Special attention must be given to the care of the following:

Test Chamber
Conditioning Chamber (if applicable)
Xenon Filters
Optical Components
Black Sensor (BPT)
Xenon lamp(s)

A.2 Replacement Schedule

A.2.1 Lamp Assembly and Related Parts

In general, the xenon lamp and/or its filters should be replaced when the specified irradiance can no longer be achieved or when there is visual evidence of deterioration, such as discoloration of filter assembly, increasing opacity of the burner. Otherwise, adhere strictly to the manufacturers recommendations for the replacement of all consumable items, especially the following:

Xenon Lamp
Xenon lamp filters
Optical components

A.2.2 Replace the Black Panel sensor when local surface luster can no longer be maintained, or when any bare metal can be seen.

A.2.3 Where applicable, inspect wet bulb wick weekly and replace when discoloration or mineral deposits are observed. In all cases, observe manufacturer's instructions for the maintenance and proper operation of the devices' humidification system.

A.3 Calibration Checks

A.3.1 Check controls or program daily (except weekend and holidays) to insure compliance to required test parameters specified in Table 2 and other critical test parameters. Also, on a daily (except weekend and holidays) basis, ensure the parameters specified in Table 2 and other critical test parameters are accurately recorded.

A.3.2 Calibrate the apparatus every two weeks following the procedures detailed in the operating manual provided by the manufacturer. If contractual agreement is to use L-4 Blue Wool as the reference material, Thursday is the suggested calibration day.

A.3.3 When proof of calibration is required, contact the specific Automotive manufacturer for the appropriate reporting forms. Use manufacturers' forms for recording calibration information.

APPENDIX B
PROCEDURE FOR DETERMINING COLORFASTNESS TO LIGHT (AATCC BLUE WOOL LIGHTFASTNESS STANDARDS)

B.1 Scope

B.1.1 This Appendix describes the procedure for using AATCC Blue Wool Lightfastness Standards as reference fabrics for the purpose of determining whether the xenon-arc apparatus is operating within the desired range.

B.1.2 Color difference values in CIELAB units are obtained by instrumentally measuring the reference fabrics before and after a specified amount of radiant exposure.

B.1.3 AATCC L-2 Blue Wool Lightfastness Standards shall be exposed daily and/or an AATCC L-4 Blue Wool Lightfastness Standard shall be used to monitor a continuous three day operating cycle. AATCC L-4 Blue Wool may be used exclusively if agreed upon between contractual parties.

B.2 Procedure

B.2.1 Instruments used to determine color difference for this procedure require capability for providing CIELAB color values using illuminant D-65, 10 degree observer data. If an instrument with diffuse geometry is used, the specular component of reflectance shall be included in the measurement. (Refer to SAE J1767, for details).

B.2.2 Calibrate the instrument to be used for the color measurements to the manufacturer's recommendations.

B.2.3 Back the reference fabric to be measured with white cardboard. Condition the backed reference fabric in a standard atmosphere (relative humidity 50 RH ± 5% and temperature 22 ± 3°C) for a minimum of 2 h. Insert one layer of unexposed material of the same lightfastness standard between the reference fabric and cardboard backing prior to measurement.

NOTE—The reference fabrics are light sensitive. Therefore, the piece used as the backing layer during measurement will need to be replaced when noticeable color change has occurred (after approximately 50 uses).

B.2.4 Place the reference fabric against the sample port of the instrument in such a way that a smooth surface of the face of the fabric is presented for measurement.

B.2.5 After taking an initial reading in CIELAB units, rotate the reference fabric 90 degrees and take a second reading. Average the readings and store as the standard measurement for the identified piece of reference fabric. REMOVE THE BACKING FABRIC AND PLACE IN A LIGHT TIGHT CONTAINER FOR LATER USE.

NOTE—The measurement obtained in B.2.5 cannot be used for different pieces of reference fabric. Each individual piece must be conditioned and measured prior to exposure.

B.2.6 Place the cardboard backed reference fabric (single layer) in a specimen holder and secure on the specimen rack adjacent to the Black Panel thermometer.

B.2.7 Always start the exposure apparatus at the end of the dark cycle. Expose the L-2 reference fabric and/or the L-4 reference fabric as agreed upon by contractual parties.

B.2.8 After the specified radiant exposure, remove the reference fabric and the white cardboard backing and allow them to condition at (relative humidity 50 RH ± 5% and temperature 22 ± 3°C) for a minimum of 1 hour.

B.2.9 Repeat the color measurements steps specified in B.2.2 through B.2.5 on the exposed reference fabric(s) and using the previously stored pre-exposed measurement, determine the Delta L*, a*, b* and E* values.

B.2.10 Compare the Delta E* value determined to that specified in the AATCC chart supplied.

NOTE—The supplier (AATCC) is to provide the determined values with each purchase of reference fabric as furnished to them by IFAI Transportation Division.

B.2.11 If the Delta E* value does not fall within the limits specified, do not resume the test until the reason has been determined and resolved.

B.2.12 As each group of test specimens completes its specified radiant exposure, record and report the color change information in terms of Delta E*, values of the reference fabric piece(s) used during the test period on the Exposure Control/Report Form (Figure 1).

APPENDIX C
POLYSTYRENE LIGHTFASTNESS STANDARDS

C.1 Scope

C.1.1 This Appendix describes a procedure for using a Polystyrene Lightfastness Standard as a reference standard for assisting in determining whether the xenon-arc apparatus is operating properly.

NOTE—The Delta B values provided with the standard are based on the J1885 test method. They do not apply to tests that use higher or lower irradiance levels or that use different filter combinations other than the extended UV filters. Weathering instruments that monitor UV in a broadband rather than a narrowband should apply the equivalent broadband radiant dosages in order to use the target values supplied. Note that the broadband (300 nm – 400 nm) equivalent for 0.55 $Wm^{-2} nm^{-1}$ at 340 nm is approximately 60 Wm^{-2}).

C.1.2 Color difference values in CIELAB units are obtained by instrumentally measuring the reference plastic before and after a specified amount of radiant exposure.

C.1.3 The polystyrene lightfastness standard may be exposed to a radiant dosage (*$kJ \cdot m^{-2} \cdot nm^{-1}$ for example*), which is equivalent to a period of 2 to 7 days.

C.2 Procedure

C.2.1 Instruments used to determine color difference for this procedure require a capability for operation which includes the specular component and provides CIELAB color values using illuminant D-65, 10 degree observer data. No substitutions are permitted. Measurements in either the transmission or reflectance mode may be used.

C.2.2 Calibrate the instrument to be used for the color measurements in accordance with the manufacturer's recommendations.

C.2.3 Reflectance Mode

C.2.3.1 Place a piece of unexposed reference plastic, backed with a white calibration tile against the sample port of the instrument.

NOTE—Take precautions to avoid any interference from ambient light.

C.2.3.2 Take an initial reading and store it as the standard measurement for the identified piece of reference plastic.

NOTE—In order to preserve the surface of the White Calibration Tile, it is recommended that a second calibration tile be purchased for these measurements.

C.2.3.3 Place the pre-measured piece of reference plastic in a specimen holder and secure on the specimen rack adjacent to the black panel thermometer.

C.2.4 Transmission Mode

C.2.4.1 Place a piece of unexposed reference plastic in the proper location for measuring transmittance as recommended by the manufacturer of the instrument in use. If there is no specific recommendation, then place the chip as close to the detector as possible.

C.2.4.2 Place the white tile used for calibration against the outer sample port of the instrument.

C.2.4.3 Take an initial measurement and store it as the standard measurement for the identified piece of reference plastic.

C.2.5 Place the pre-measured piece of reference plastic in a specimen holder and secure on the specimen rack adjacent to the black panel thermometer.

C.2.6 Always start the exposure apparatus at the end of the dark cycle and expose the reference plastic to a radiant exposure (*$kJ \cdot m^{-2} \cdot nm^{-1}$ @ 340nm for example*) for an equivalent period of two to seven days.

C.2.7 After the radiant exposure, remove the reference plastic from the apparatus.

C.2.8 Repeat the color measurement steps specified in C.2.3 or C.2.4 on the exposed reference plastic and using the previously stored pre-exposure measurement, determine the Delta b* values.

C.2.9 Compare the Delta b* reading to the chart for the cycle used.

C.2.9.1 The supplier (Testfabrics) of the reference plastic is to provide the charts as supplied by IFAI Transportation Division with each purchase of the polystyrene standard.

C.2.10 If the Delta b* value does not fall within the predetermined value, as established by the supplier, immediately run another polystyrene standard per section 2.12.

C.2.11 As each group of test specimens completes its specified radiant exposure, record and report the color change information in terms of Delta b* values of the reference plastic piece(s) used during the test period.

C.2.12 Run the polystyrene standard after every calibration (every two weeks) for the specified amount of kilojoules. If the reference material is out of specification, run another polystyrene standard at the shortest time interval (for example: 75.2 kJ/m2 or 112.8 kJ/m2 for a three day weekend). If the polystyrene reference standard continues to be out of specification, discontinue testing until the problem is corrected.

NOTE—In order to preserve the surface of the White Calibration Tile, it is recommended that a second calibration tile be purchased for these measurements.

C.2.13 The intent of the Polystyrene is to monitor the performance of the test. It is for Statistical Process Control (SPC) purposes. A point outside of the range does not necessarily invalidate the test.

APPENDIX D
REPRESENTATIVE SPECTRAL POWER DISTRIBUTION (SPD) FOR EXTENDED UV FILTER

D.1 Scope

D.1.1 This appendix consists of reference tables and a figure

TABLE D1 (PART 1)—IRRADIANCE IN W/m^2 BASED ON 81 SPD's FOR XENON-ARCS WITH EXTENDED UV FILTERS NORMALIZED TO EXACTLY 0.55 $W m^{-2}$ AT 340 nm

bandpass	average	standard deviation	min	max	lower 95% confidence limit	upper 95% confidence limit
250-260	0.00	0.00	0.00	0.02	0.00	0.01
261-270	0.00	0.00	0.00	0.03	0.00	0.01
271-280	0.04	0.02	0.01	0.10	0.00	0.08
281-290	0.22	0.08	0.09	0.42	0.07	0.38
291-300	0.73	0.16	0.36	1.16	0.41	1.04
301-310	1.60	0.20	1.04	2.19	1.19	2.00
311-320	2.72	0.19	2.13	3.26	2.34	3.10
321-330	3.91	0.14	3.48	4.29	3.63	4.18
331-340	5.06	0.04	4.95	5.18	4.97	5.15
341-350	6.10	0.10	5.91	6.33	5.90	6.30
351-360	7.06	0.22	6.48	7.67	6.61	7.51
361-370	7.97	0.33	7.19	8.83	7.32	8.62
371-380	8.65	0.48	7.55	9.77	7.68	9.62
381-390	9.17	0.59	7.99	10.57	8.00	10.34
391-400	10.67	0.70	9.17	13.29	9.26	12.08
300-400	63.10	1.97	58.30	68.17	59.16	67.04

NOTES:

1. The ultraviolet irradiance for Extended UV Filters is 11% and the visible to near infrared irradiance is 89% relative to the irradiance in the wavelength range 290 nm - 800nm (as given in CIE Publication No.85:1989). These values measured on specimen plane will vary by as much as 30% when performing a test due to the reflectance properties and number of samples.

2. For Extended UV spectrum, lamp is operated at 0.55 $W.m^{-2}$ @340 nm. Wide band, 300 nm - 400 nm, equivalence is approximately 60.0 $W.m^{-2}$.

3. The SPD data contained in Table D1 was developed using the "rectangular" integration technique. The data is based on 81 spectra for the 250 nm - 400 nm bandpass and the same 37 spectra used for the 400 nm - 800 nm region. The formula for the rectangular method is shown below.

   Formula used for calculating irradiance using rectangular integration in indicated bandpass when spectra at 2 nm increments are used

$$I_{x,y} = 2 \times \sum_{n=x}^{n=y} i_n$$

Where:

$I_{x,y}$	=	total irradiance in bandpass with lower wavelength x and upper wavelength y
x	=	lower wavelength limit
y	=	upper wavelength limit
i_n	=	irradiance at wavelength n within the indicated bandpass between x and y

Other integration techniques can be used to evaluate SPD data but may give different results.

When comparing spectral power distribution data to Table D1, the same integration technique, rectangular, should be applied.

TABLE D1 (PART 2)—SPD TABLE FOR 400 NM - 800 NM AT 50 NM BANDPASSES BASED ON 37 SPDS

			suggested spec			
bandpass	average	std dev	min	max	lower 95% confidence limit	upper 95% confidence limit
400-450	57.47	5.13	47.20	67.74	47.20	67.74
451-500	73.71	6.22	61.28	86.15	61.28	86.15
501-550	66.26	7.40	51.46	81.06	51.46	81.06
551-600	67.61	7.43	52.75	82.48	52.75	82.48
601-650	64.85	7.69	49.46	80.24	49.46	80.24
651-700	60.52	6.14	48.25	72.80	48.25	72.80
701-750	57.06	6.17	44.72	69.40	44.72	69.40
751-800	48.44	7.39	33.66	63.22	33.66	63.22

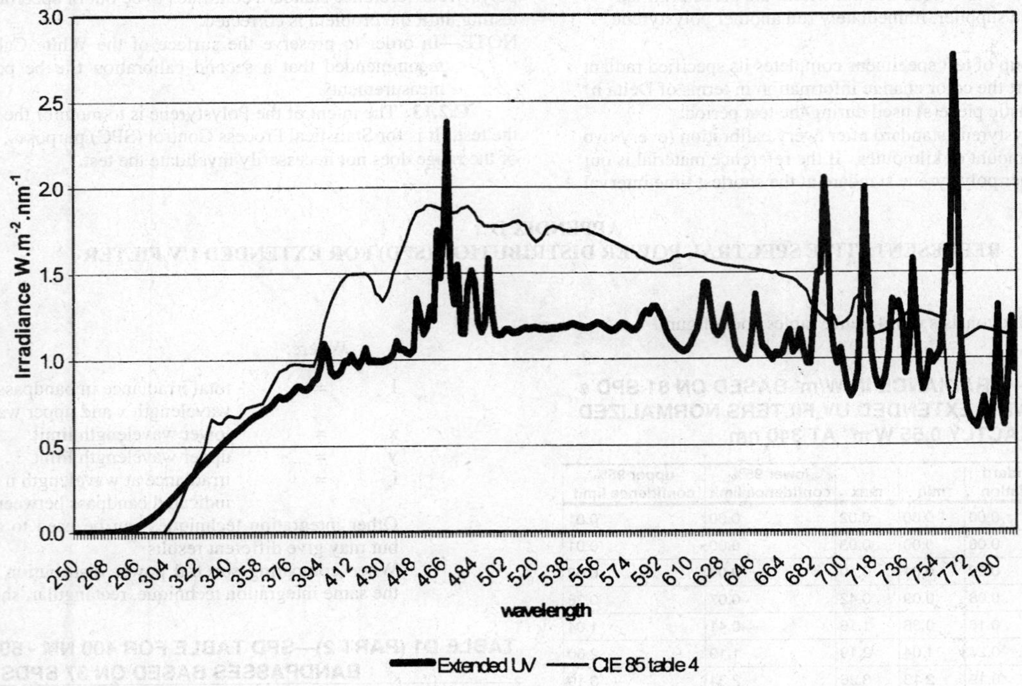

FIGURE D1—EXTENDED UV FILTER VS. SUNLIGHT SPECTRAL POWER DISTRIBUTION (SPD)

HOSE GAUGE EVALUATION PROCEDURE—SAE J2666 NOV2003

SAE Standard

Report of the SAE Non-Hydraulic Hose Committee approved November 2003.

1. Scope—The Gauge Evaluation Procedure Task Force was formed by the Non-Hydraulic Hose Committee to develop a gauge evaluation procedure to be used when evaluating the capability of gauges used for hose measurement. The use of a standard method for gauge evaluation will help users easily compare equipment capability. The information provided in this recommendation is based on the methods used to produce the data presented in SAE J1759 and J2605.

2. References

2.1 Applicable Publications—The following publications form a part of this specification to the extent specified herein. Unless otherwise indicated, the latest version of SAE publications shall apply.

2.1.1 SAE PUBLICATIONS—Available from SAE, 400 Commonwealth Drive, Warrendale, PA 15096-0001.

SAE J1759—SAE Hose Measurement Study, Issued 2000-10. Summary of a GR&R study completed using plug gauges, PI tapes, and calipers.

SAE J2605—SAE Non-Contact Hose Measurement Study 1, Issued 2001-8. Summary of a GR&R study completed using the LOTIS QC-20 Hose Measurement Device.

2.2 Related Publication—The following publication is provided for information purposes only and is not a required part of this document.

2.2.1 AIAG PUBLICATION—Available from Automotive Industry Action Group, Suite 200, 262 Lahser Road, Southfield, MI 48034.

(MSA) Manual-Measurement Systems Analysis Manual

3. Procedure—The following procedure enumerates the important features of a gauge capability study and is modeled after SAE J1759 and J2605. This procedure is to be used for equipment that provides variable output data.

3.1 Metric measurement shall be used.

3.2 Clearly define the types of hoses the study will include. Ideally, the study should include a range of parts, i.e., straight, curved, material, etc.

3.3 Define what dimensions or features the study will include, i.e., inside diameter, outside diameter, wall thickness, wall thickness variation, etc. Use the same tolerance levels as previous studies to simplify comparisons.

3.4 The study must include 3 operators, 3 test locations, and 3 different gauges (one at each testing location). Minimum of 3 sets of parts with 10 samples in each set. The parts are transferred from location to location to complete the study. Clearly mark which end of the hose is used for the measurement and the depth at which the measurement is taken, if applicable.

3.5 Select one of the test locations to perform the GR&R calculations.

3.6 Use standard GR&R calculations (AIAG using the Anova method):

Compute the average GR&R over the 3 test locations - each location provides GR&R for one system and 3 operators for each measurement similar to SAE J1759.

Compute the GR&R from each location/system and measurement – Use this data to compute an average GR&R.

Compute a composite GR&R using the results from the first operator from each test location/system. This is useful as an additional measure of gauge capability (more stringent because it includes any gauge offsets between systems).

3.7 The study must include a **detailed** test procedure with sufficient detail that any operator that has been trained to use the specific equipment can duplicate the study.

3.8 The study should reference any previous or similar gauge studies like SAE J1759 and J2605.

3.9 The study can include both electronic and manual recording of data.

4. Conclusion—The use of the procedures outlined in this document will allow gauging equipment users to compare results between different gauging methods and equipment from different gauge manufacturers.

MULTI-DIMENSIONAL THERMAL PROPERTIES OF INSULATED HEAT SHIELD MATERIAL SYSTEMS—SAE J2609 DEC2003

SAE Standard

Report of the SAE Formed Heat Shield Committee approved December 2003 .

1. Scope

This test method measures the system material properties of an insulated formed heat shield under in-vehicle conditions. While the material properties of the individual components can often be determined via existing test methods, the system properties of the entire composite is typically much harder to ascertain (especially for multi-layer shields). System material properties include thermal conductivity in the lateral or in-plane (x) direction, thermal conductivity through the thickness or perpendicular (y), surface emissivity on the top and bottom sides of the shield and specific heat of the shield material.

1.1 All properties are determined for the entire shielding material specimen as a composite of the entire structure. Properties are determined using a testing apparatus that allows for two-dimensional heat flow through the specimen. Due to this, the material property results from this test method may not agree with one-dimensional heat flow type testing methods, but is representative of most heat shield materials performance tested with a centralized heat source. Therefore, material property results from this test method may be more suited for multi-dimensional analytical studies.

1.2 This standard sets forth the general guidelines to construct and operate the testing apparatus to acquire a satisfactory set of test data. Designs conforming to this standard are included and must *not* be deviated from for sensitivity reasons that will be discussed in more detail later. Test parameters that cannot be deviated from include, but are not limited to; specimen size, distance between the source and the specimen, source diameter and environmental conditions around the apparatus.

1.3 This method ultimately determines the shield material properties by using the test data along with an analytical scheme, see Section 8.1.

1.4 This test method will evaluate both isotropic and anisotropic insulated shielding materials. This may also include multi-layer shielding structures which include embossed/corrugated solids, porous, fibrous, granulated and coated materials.

1.5 Limitations

This test method does have limitations in the type of insulated shielding materials that can be evaluated. However, many of the limitations apply to materials that would not typically be suitable in a heat shielding function or the properties can be derived by simpler one-dimensional hot plate methods (SAE J1361, ASTM C 177).

Limitations include:

a) Materials where the radiant transmissivity through the material cannot be assumed as zero. Materials of this type are classified as translucent or transparent.

b) Materials that do *not* have an insulating characteristic in at least one axis; (*i.e.,* single wall stamped metal shielding). This includes shielding materials where lateral thermal conductivity (x) and thermal conductivity through the thickness (y) are the same and considered high (in the order of 25 W/m-C) when compared to metallic materials. These types of single sheet metallic shields are not included in the standard because the properties of these materials are typically well known and do not require a procedure to determine them.

c) Materials where the lateral thermal conductivity (x) is less than the thermal conductivity through the thickness (y).

d) Testing exposes the shielding material to temperatures up to 250°C. Materials with limits below this level should *not* use this method.

1.6 Safety

This method involves a test apparatus that exposes the operator to very high temperatures. This standard does not purport to address all of the safety concerns, if any, associated with its use. It is the responsibility of the user of this standard to establish appropriate safety and health practices and determine the applicability of regulatory limitations prior to use.

1.7 The attached Appendix A provides a detailed discussion of the analytical technique used in calculating the insulated shielding material properties from the test data. The Appendix A also presents the theoretical sensitivity study of the analytical method.

1.8 This test method requires two specific pieces of test instrumentation. A portable emissometer as outlined in ASTM C1371 and a radiosity meter or infrared camera with the ability to set the emissivity to 1.0.

2. References

2.1 Related Publications

The following publications are for informational purposes only. The **ShieldProp** and **ShieldTherm** programs, available free from ThermoAnalytics at http://www.thermoanalytics.com/products/shieldtherm/index.html were written specifically to solve the equations for this standard and give examples.

2.1.1 SAE PUBLICATIONS

Available from SAE, 400 Commonwealth Drive, Warrendale, PA 15096-0001.

SAE J1361—Hot Plate Method for Evaluating Heat Resistance and Thermal Insulation Properties of Materials

2.1.2 ASTM PUBLICATIONS

Available from ASTM, 100 Barr Harbor Drive, West Conshohocken, PA 19428-2959.

ASTM C177—Standard Test Method for Steady-State Heat Flux Measurements and Thermal Transmission Properties by Means of the Guarded-Hot Plate Apparatus

ASTM C1371—Standard Test Method for Determination of Emittance of Materials Near Room Temperature Using Portable Emissometers

3. Summary

This method describes a testing procedure and equipment, coupled with a computer analyses to directly measure or calculate the base material properties of an insulated shielding specimen. These material properties include thermal conductivity in the lateral or in-plane (x) direction, thermal conductivity through the thickness (y), surface emissivity on the top and bottom sides of the shield, density, and specific heat of the shield material.

3.1 Figure 1 is a slice through the thickness of a shield to illustrate a typical multi-dimensional heat flow through an insulated shielding specimen with a centralized heat source. This arrangement is very typical of actual in-vehicle usage and is the basis for this test method.

3.2 This test method is designed to induce a multi-dimensional heat flow pattern into the insulated shield test specimen. After collecting temperature data on both the shielding material and ambient with a predetermined arrangement, the following composite shield material properties can be calculated: thermal conductivity in the lateral or in-plane (x) direction, thermal conductivity through the thickness (y), and specific heat of the shield. Surface emissivity on the top and bottom sides of the shield are obtained through the use of ASTM Standard C 1371 and not analytically calculated as part of this test method, although, it is a required piece of data for the analytical software program. Also, heat source radiosity is a required input to the analytical software program. Both surface emissivity of the shield, heat source radiosity and floor radiosity are obtained through the use of additional equipment as outlined in Section 4. Since specific heat is one of the properties the test method calculates, the test procedure and the data collected will be done in a transient mode.

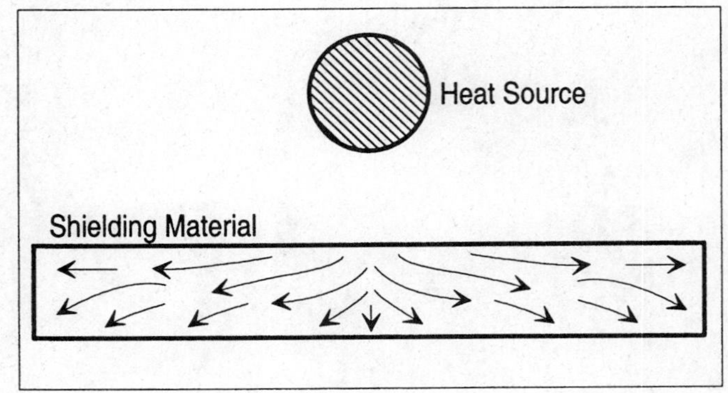

FIGURE 1—MULTI-DIMENSIONAL HEAT FLOW THROUGH SHIELDING MATERIAL WITH CENTRAL HEAT SOURCE

3.3 Figure 2 illustrates the main components of the test set-up. Two shield specimen sizes are required to be tested independently during this method, 22.5 cm x 45 cm and 45 cm square. Both are required to satisfy the sensitivity requirements of the analytical calculation. The insulated shield test specimen is thermocoupled on the top and the bottom, identically, in the arrangement displayed in Figures 3 and 4. It is important that the thermocouples be completely shielded from direct radiant energy from the heat source. Also, an ambient thermocouple, similarly shielded, is set to measure the ambient air temperature in the test area that would represent T_∞. The ambient thermocouple is intended to measure the average temperature of the air at a distance sufficiently outside the convective boundary layer of the shield specimen. A cylindrical heat source of 5.08 cm in diameter is positioned 25.4 mm above and centered on the specimen. The heat source is held at a constant, average temperature of 400° C (as measured across the length of the test specimen) during the entire transient test. As soon as the heat source is at steady state, the insulated shield specimen is moved quickly into position and the data collection is started.

3.4 Data collection is started and continued until steady state is reached on the insulated shield test specimen. Data sampling rates should be a least one per minute. Data should continue to be taken, after the specimen has reached steady state, for at least ten minutes. Data is saved to a predetermined comma delimited (.csv) format, Table 1.

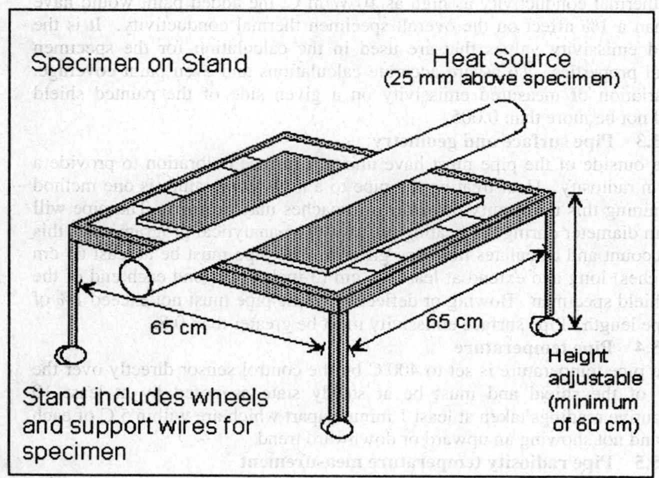

FIGURE 2—MAIN COMPONENTS OF EXPERIMENTAL SETUP

TABLE 1—EXPERIMENTAL RESULTS, FORMAT OF THE CSV DATA FILE

Column #	Test Data
1	Time (seconds)
2	Temp Heat Source (C)
3	Temp Room Ambient (C)
4	Temp Top of Specimen (center, #1 position)
5	Temp Top of Specimen (#2 position)
6	Temp Top of Specimen (#3 position)
7	Temp Top of Specimen (#4 position)
8	Temp Top of Specimen (#5 position)
9	Temp Bottom of Specimen (center, #1 position)
10	Temp Bottom of Specimen (#2 position)
11	Temp Bottom of Specimen (#3 position)
12	Temp Bottom of Specimen (#4 position)
13	Temp Bottom of Specimen (#5 position)

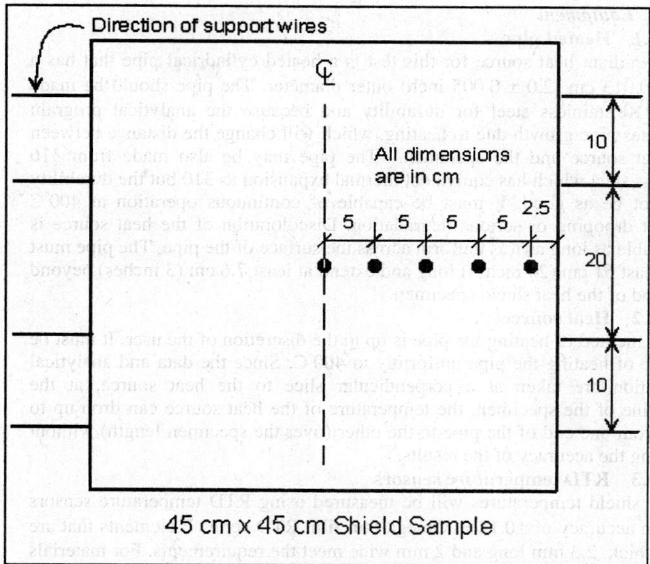

FIGURE 3—THERMOCOUPLE ARRANGEMENT ON 45 cm SAMPLE

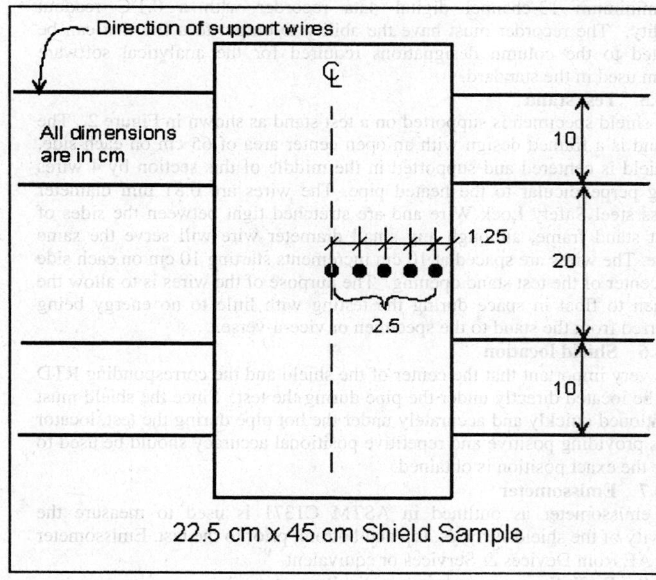

FIGURE 4—THERMOCOUPLE ARRANGEMENT ON 22.5 cm SAMPLE

3.5 Both the 22.5 cm and 45 cm width specimen sizes are tested using the same procedure and the data saved to separate .csv files.

3.6 The data is read into an available analytical software program that calculates the base material properties of the insulated shield material.

4. *Equipment*

4.1 Heated pipe

The radiant heat source for this test is a heated cylindrical pipe that has a 5.08 ±0.013 cm (2.0 ± 0.005 inch) outer diameter. The pipe should be made from 310 stainless steel for durability and because the analytical program calculates pipe growth due to heating, which will change the distance between the heat source and the specimen. The pipe may be also made from 316 stainless steel which has equivalent thermal expansion as 310 but the durability may not be as good. It must be capable of continuous operation at 400°C without drooping or serious degradation. Discoloration of the heat source is acceptable as long as it is uniform across the surface of the pipe. The pipe must be at least 61 cm (24 inches) long and extend at least 7.6 cm (3 inches) beyond each end of the heat shield specimen.

4.2 Heat source

The method of heating the pipe is up to the discretion of the user. It must be capable of heating the pipe uniformly to 400°C. Since the data and analytical calculation are taken at a perpendicular slice to the heat source, at the centerline of the specimen, the temperature of the heat source can drop up to 25°C from one end of the pipe to the other (over the specimen length) without affecting the accuracy of the results.

4.3 RTD temperature sensors

The shield temperatures will be measured using RTD temperature sensors with an accuracy of ±0.12%. Omega thin film RTD series F elements that are 1 mm thick, 2.3 mm long and 2 mm wide meet the requirements. For materials where the temperature sensors cannot be tack welded directly to the surface, special epoxies can be used. Omegabond OB-500 air-dry cement (Omega Engineering Inc., Stanford, Connecticut) or equivalent should be used.

4.4 Temperature recorder

A minimum 13-channel digital data recorder with a 0.1°C readout capability. The recorder must have the ability to output to a file that can be formatted to the column designations required for the analytical software program used in the standard.

4.5 Test stand

The shield specimen is supported on a test stand as shown in Figure 2. The test stand is a framed design with an open center area of 65 cm on each side. The shield is centered and supported in the middle of this section by 4 wires running perpendicular to the heated pipe. The wires are 0.81 mm diameter stainless steel Safety Lock Wire and are stretched tight between the sides of the test stand frame, although any small diameter wire will serve the same purpose. The wires are spaced at 10 cm increments starting 10 cm on each side of the center of the test stand opening. The purpose of the wires is to allow the specimen to float in space during the testing with little to no energy being transferred from the stand to the specimen or vice-a-verse.

4.6 Shield location

It is very important that the center of the shield and the corresponding RTD sensor be located directly under the pipe during the test. Since the shield must be positioned quickly and accurately under the hot pipe during the test, locator devices providing positive and repetitive positional accuracy should be used to be sure the exact position is obtained.

4.7 Emissometer

An emissometer as outlined in ASTM C1371 is used to measure the emissivity of the shield surfaces, top and bottom, prior to the test. Emissometer Model AE from Devices & Services or equivalent.

4.8 Radiation pyrometer or radiosity meter

A meter capable of measuring the pipe radiosity temperature using an emissivity setting of 1.0 is necessary. The Oakton Model U-35629-30 Infrapro sold by Cole-Palmer or equivalent will suffice.

4.9 Analytical software

Any analytical software program capable of performing the methods described in Section 8.2, see Section 2 Related References for software.

4.10 Computer

The minimum requirements should be based on the software selected in Section 4.9. The minimum requirements to use the software in the first reference of section 2 are as follows: IBM PC compatible computer, 125 MB RAM, 200 MHz, 3 MB Hard Disk Space, Windows 95 or higher.

5. *Test requirements*

5.1 Specimen

There are two test specimens used for this standard: 45x45cm square and 22.5x45 cm rectangle with a tolerance of ±0.5 cm. The test specimens must be flat (except for any surface embossment pattern, etc.) and its materials and construction must be representative of the final production part, except for any edge treatments. The specimen must be free of any visible defects that would affect the test results. Samples should not contain crimped or rolled edges. Edges of this type help short circuit the energy to the back side of the specimen and do not give a representative performance of the material. The analytical software in Related References section 2.0 does not assume a short circuit; therefore under these conditions, less effective thermal conductivity values will result from this phenomenon.

5.2 Specimen surface condition

The surface emissivity of each shield will be measured four times. The first and second measurements will be taken in the as received (new) condition on both the top and the bottom of the shield specimen. These are the values that will be used to satisfy the surface emissivity property requirement. Then for testing and calculation purposes, the specimen will be painted with a high temperature flat black on the top and high temperature flat gray on the bottom and measured a third (top) and fourth (bottom) time. The emissivity on the top should be greater than 0.8 and on the bottom in the range of 0.5 to 0.7. The shield will only be tested under the heat source in the painted condition. For an accurate value of emissivity to be obtained in both the as received and painted conditions, multiple measurements over the surface should be taken and averaged. The specimen is painted and tested to satisfy the calculation assumption of a uniform emissivity over the surface of the specimen. The paint does not change the results of the thermal conductivity values calculated. Using the assumption that the paint is 5 microns thick and the base specimen has a thermal conductivity as high as 10 W/m C, the added paint would have less than a 1% affect on the overall specimen thermal conductivity. It is the painted emissivity values that are used in the calculation for the specimen thermal properties. To assure accurate calculations and even paint coverage, the variation of measured emissivity on a given side of the painted shield should not be more than 0.005.

5.3 Pipe surface and geometry

The outside of the pipe must have uniform surface coloration to provide a uniform radiosity. Heat-treating the pipe to a high temperature is one method of obtaining this uniformity but other approaches may be used. The pipe will grow in diameter during the heating process. The analytical program takes this into account and calculates this pipe growth. The pipe must be at least 61 cm (24 inches) long and extend at least 7.6 cm (3 inches) beyond each end of the heat shield specimen. Bowing or deflection of the pipe must not exceed 1% of the pipe length. Pipe surface emissivity must be greater than 0.8.

5.4 Pipe temperature

The pipe temperature is set to 400°C by the control sensor directly over the center of the shield and must be at steady state as noted by at least 10 consecutive readings taken at least 1 minute apart which are within 5°C of each other and not showing an upward or downward trend.

5.5 Pipe radiosity temperature measurement

The radiosity temperature is the temperature of the pipe as measured by radiation methods assuming that the emissivity is 1.0. This measurement will be taken at the middle of the pipe directly over the center of the specimen.

5.6 Shield temperature measurement

The shield temperatures will be measured at the locations shown in Figures 3 & 4 on both the top and bottom of the shield using RTD temperature sensors. The wires from the RTD mounting location will run parallel to the heated pipe for at least 3 cm to minimize interference with the shield gradient. The preferred method of mounting the sensors to the shield surface is by tack welding, however if the surface of the specimen does not allow this, special epoxies may be used. For materials where the temperature sensors cannot be tack welded directly to the surface, special epoxies can be used. Omegabond OB-500 air-dry cement (Omega Engineering Inc., Stanford, Connecticut) or equivalent should be used. The temperatures will be recorded to an accuracy of 0.1° C.

5.7 Temperature recording

All temperatures are to be recorded simultaneously to avoid errors since this is a transient test. Recorders that do rapid sequential recording are acceptable. Manual recording of the data is not acceptable since this causes skewing of the data, which will cause errors in the calculated material properties. The recording device must be able to record in 0.1° C increments.

5.8 Distance pipe to specimen

The distance between the top of the shield and the bottom of the pipe must be 25.4 ± 1.5 mm while the setup is in the cold position. Adjustments to the pipe or the shield stand must be made prior to the start of the test to assure the correct distance. An inside caliper measurement tool can be used for this placement. The analytical program calculates the pipe growth due to heating, which will change the distance between the heat source and the specimen.

5.9 Distance specimen to floor

The specimen must be held at least 60 cm above the floor.

5.10 Ambient airflow

Test in a "passive hood" environment. External airflow must not influence test measurements. There can be no forced airflow anywhere in the region of the test setup.

5.11 Ambient air temperature

A standard K-Type thermocouple shall be mounted at least 60 cm away from the pipe and at approximately the same height as the pipe to measure the room air temperature.

6. Calibration

6.1 The instrument manufacturer or certified agent should calibrate all recorders to National Institute for Science and Technology (NIST) for accuracy claimed and the appropriate label displayed on the instrument. Calibration by the test facility is appropriate if substantiated by data measured by calibrated instruments traceable to NIST.

7. Procedure

7.1 Prepare two specimens of the same material. One 45 x 45 cm and one 22.5 x 45 cm. Measure the length and width of each specimen to be sure that it meets the specifications in Section 5.

7.2 Weigh the specimens in grams. Measure the thickness of the specimens using a micrometer. Multiple measurements (minimum of 4 for simple construction and 10 for complex structures) should be taken to assure that a "total surface area" average thickness can be derived.

7.3 Using the emissometer, measure the emissivity of the specimens on the top and bottom surfaces in the as-received condition (prior to painting). Since surface emissivity can change over the surface of the specimen, multiple readings over the surface of the specimen should be taken and averaged. These readings should be recorded as the as-received measurements.

7.4 Install the RTD temperature sensors per Figures 3 and 4. The preferred method of mounting the sensors to the shield surface is by tack welding, however if the surface of the specimen does not allow this, Appendix B presents a study that evaluated different epoxy materials for adhering the sensors and how well they performed.

7.5 For testing and calculation purposes, the specimens will be painted with a high temperature flat black on the top (facing the heat source) and high temperature flat gray on the bottom. After the paint has dried, measure the emissivity again using the emissometer. (The averaged readings must agree within 0.005 to ensure uniform paint coverage.) The emissivity will be measured on both the top and bottom of the specimen. The shield will only be tested under the heat source in the painted condition.

7.6 With the specimen in place under the heat source and the heat source cold, measure the distance from the top of the specimen to the bottom of the pipe. Adjust this distance until the shield is 25.4 mm below the heat source. When the heat source is centered over the specimen, install locators on the floor so that when the test stand is rolled out, the correct position will be known.

7.7 Remove the specimen from under the heat source. Having the test stand on wheels will allow easy movement of the specimen during the test. Turn on the heat source and bring the pipe to steady state at 400°C.

7.8 Quickly but carefully roll the test stand with the specimen on it under the pipe so that the center RTD sensor is directly below the heat source pipe (use the floor locators) with the pipe 25.4 mm above the specimen. Using the data acquisition system, start recording the temperature data immediately.

7.9 Record the 13 columns of data as specified in Table I, at least one-minute intervals. Continue taking data until the specimen has reached steady state. Steady state is achieved when the temperatures on the specimen do not increase more than 1 °C during a two-minute period. The data will be recorded and stored in a file in a comma delimited (.csv) format as described in Table I.

7.10 Measure the floor radiosity temperature directly beneath the specimen. Use either the IR pyrometer (emissivity set to 1.0) or the radiosity meter.

7.11 Using the IR pyrometer (emissivity set to 1.0) or the radiosity meter, manually measure the radiosity temperature of the heat source at the center of the specimen. Record this measurement as the Pipe Radiosity Temperature.

7.12 Shut down the test and repeat step 7.2 thru 7.11 with the other specimen size. Data sets from both specimen sizes, 45 x 45 cm and 22.5 x 45 cm, are required for the calculation. Due to the natural repeatability issues of any experiment as outlined in Appendix C, it is prudent to repeat this test on the same specimen multiple times to gain confidence that the results are representative of the average material.

8. Calculation

8.1 From the data, the calculation of the properties of interest; normal (through thickness) conductivity, lateral (in-plane) conductivity, specific heat, and density is somewhat complex. The equations are given in Appendix A and can be solved using any mathematical computer program using the method described below or the software in the first reference of section 2 written specifically for this standard.

8.2 Solving the System of Equations

First, the steady state equations are solved to determine conductivities. Afterwards, the transient equations are solved for specific heat. The ten steady state equations and four unknowns (k_x, k_y, h_T, and h_B) constitute a 10 x 4 overdetermined system of equations. Overdetermined systems cannot, in general, be satisfied exactly, and thus the standard procedure is to solve the system in a least-squares sense. The Normal Equations method is used to find the least-squares solution to the system [1].

9. Report

9.1 The report file includes all of the inputted data from the program and the calculated material properties: normal (through thickness) conductivity, lateral (in-plane) conductivity, specific heat and density.

9.2 A complete description of the specimen including all input data (including but not limited to the top and bottom emissivity) to the computer program plus special construction methods and any other pertinent information related to the material.

APPENDIX A
EQUATION SOLUTION AND SENSITIVITY ANALYSES

A.1 Introduction

This appendix is provided to describe both the method used to solve the equations and the sensitivity analysis that ultimately helped define many of the test setup parameters, see Section 2. References.

A.2 Symbols

A	Element surface area
A_c	Element cross-sectional area
C_p	Specific heat
$F_{i\text{-}j}$	View factor (surface i to surf. j)
h	Convection coefficient
J	Radiosity emitted
k_x	Lateral conductivity
k_y	Normal conductivity
m	Mass
T	Temperature
t_s	Specimen thickness
t	time
w_e	Element width
w_s	Specimen width
ε	Emissivity
σ	Stefan-Bolzman constant

Subscripts

A	Ambient air
T	Top of specimen
B	Bottom of specimen
P	Radiant heat source
W	Room walls
s	Specimen
e	Element
1	Centermost element
5	Outermost element

A.3 System of equations

The shield specimen is divided into nine elements on each side. Due to symmetry, four of the nine elements are redundant; hence, only five elements on each side need to be considered. An RTD temperature sensor is located at the center of each of the ten unique elements. The elements are designated as 1T, 2T, 3T, 4T 5T, 1B, 2B, 3B, 4B, and 5B. A "T" indicates that an element is on the top, a "B" indicates that an element is on the bottom, a "1" indicates that an element is on the shield centerline, and a "5" indicates that an element is on the edge. An energy balance can be formed for each element.

The energy balance for element 1T is

$$0 = \varepsilon_T A\left(\sigma T_{1T}^4 - J_P F_{1T-P} - J_W F_{1T-W}\right) + 2k_x \frac{A_c}{w_e}(T_{1T} - T_{2T}) + h_T A(T_{1T} - T_A) + k_y \frac{A}{t_s}(T_{1T} - T_{1B})$$

The energy balance for element iT (where i = 2, 3, or 4) is

$$0=\varepsilon_T A\left(\sigma T_{iT}^4-J_P F_{iT-P}-J_W F_{iT-W}\right)+k_x\frac{A_c}{w_e}\left(2T_{iT}-T_{(i-1)T}-T_{(i+1)T}\right)+h_T A\left(T_{iT}-T_A\right)+k_y\frac{A}{t_s}\left(T_{iT}-T_{iB}\right)$$

The energy balance for element 5T is

$$0=\varepsilon_T A\left(\sigma T_{5T}^4-J_P F_{5T-P}-J_W F_{5T-W}\right)+k_x\frac{A_c}{w_e}\left(T_{5T}-T_{4T}\right)+h_T A\left(T_{5T}-T_A\right)+k_y\frac{A}{t_s}\left(T_{5T}-T_{5B}\right)$$

The energy balance for element 1B is

$$0=\varepsilon_B A\left(\sigma T_{1B}^4-J_W\right)+2k_x\frac{A_c}{w_e}\left(T_{1B}-T_{2B}\right)+h_B A\left(T_{1B}-T_A\right)+k_y\frac{A}{t_s}\left(T_{1B}-T_{1T}\right)$$

The energy balance for element iB (where i = 2, 3, or 4) is

$$0=\varepsilon_B A\left(\sigma T_{iB}^4-J_W\right)+k_x\frac{A_c}{w_e}\left(2T_{iB}-T_{(i-1)B}-T_{(i+1)B}\right)+h_B A\left(T_{iB}-T_A\right)+k_y\frac{A}{t_s}\left(T_{iB}-T_{iT}\right)$$

The energy balance for element 5B is

$$0=\varepsilon_B A\left(\sigma T_{5B}^4-J_W\right)+k_x\frac{A_c}{w_e}\left(T_{5B}-T_{4B}\right)+h_B A\left(T_{5B}-T_A\right)+k_y\frac{A}{t_s}\left(T_{5B}-T_{5T}\right)$$

Because the system is nominally two-dimensional, view factors are evaluated using two-dimensional analytical formulas.

The aforementioned equations form a 10X4 matrix, which we multiplied each side of the matrix equation by the transpose of this matrix, $A^TAX=A^TB$, allowing for reduction to a 4X4 system of equations with an equivalent solution through Gaussian elimination.

The transient energy balance for element 1T is

$$m_{1T}C_p\frac{T_{1T}^{i+1}-T_{1T}^{i-1}}{t_{i+1}-t_{i-1}}=\varepsilon_T A\left(\sigma T_{1T}^4-J_P F_{1T-P}-J_W F_{1T-W}\right)+2k_x\frac{A_c}{w_e}\left(T_{1T}-T_{2T}\right)+h_T A\left(T_{1T}-T_A\right)+k_y\frac{A}{t_s}\left(T_{1T}-T_{1B}\right)$$

where the temperatures on the right hand side are at time *i*.

The transient energy balance for element iT (where i = 2, 3, or 4) is

$$m_{iT}C_p\frac{T_{iT}^{i+1}-T_{iT}^{i-1}}{t_{i+1}-t_{i-1}}=\varepsilon_T A\left(\sigma T_{iT}^4-J_P F_{iT-P}-J_W F_{iT-W}\right)+k_x\frac{A_c}{w_e}\left(2T_{iT}-T_{(i-1)T}-T_{(i+1)T}\right)+h_T A\left(T_{iT}-T_A\right)+k_y\frac{A}{t_s}\left(T_{iT}-T_{iB}\right)$$

The transient energy balance for element 5T is

$$m_{5T}C_p\frac{T_{5T}^{i+1}-T_{5T}^{i-1}}{t_{i+1}-t_{i-1}}=\varepsilon_T A\left(\sigma T_{5T}^4-J_P F_{5T-P}-J_W F_{5T-W}\right)+k_x\frac{A_c}{w_e}\left(T_{5T}-T_{4T}\right)+h_T A\left(T_{5T}-T_A\right)+k_y\frac{A}{t_s}\left(T_{5T}-T_{5B}\right)$$

The transient energy balance for element 1B is

$$m_{1B}C_p\frac{T_{1B}^{i+1}-T_{1B}^{i-1}}{t_{i+1}-t_{i-1}}=\varepsilon_B A\left(\sigma T_{1B}^4-J_W\right)+2k_x\frac{A_c}{w_e}\left(T_{1B}-T_{2B}\right)+h_B A\left(T_{1B}-T_A\right)+k_y\frac{A}{t_s}\left(T_{1B}-T_{1T}\right)$$

The transient energy balance for element iB (where i = 2, 3, or 4) is

$$m_{iB}C_p\frac{T_{iB}^{i+1}-T_{iB}^{i-1}}{t_{i+1}-t_{i-1}}=\varepsilon_B A\left(\sigma T_{iB}^4-J_W\right)+k_x\frac{A_c}{w_e}\left(2T_{iB}-T_{(i-1)B}-T_{(i+1)B}\right)+h_B A\left(T_{iB}-T_A\right)+k_y\frac{A}{t_s}\left(T_{iB}-T_{iT}\right)$$

The transient energy balance for element 5B is

$$m_{5B}C_p\frac{T_{5B}^{i+1}-T_{5B}^{i-1}}{t_{i+1}-t_{i-1}}=\varepsilon_B A\left(\sigma T_{5B}^4-J_W\right)+k_x\frac{A_c}{w_e}\left(T_{5B}-T_{4B}\right)+h_B A\left(T_{5B}-T_A\right)+k_y\frac{A}{t_s}\left(T_{5B}-T_{5T}\right)$$

The transient set of equations creates a 10X1 matrix and the same solution method is used to determine the value for specific heat.

A.4 Solving the system of equations

Typically, the energy balance equations are solved to find the temperature distribution and/or history, so that there is one unknown temperature for each equation. Although the system is nonlinear, numerous techniques are available which can easily provide the steady or transient solution. What is needed here is sometimes described as solving the equations "backwards." Knowing the temperatures, we need to determine the unknown values: k_x, k_y, C_p, and any others that are not directly measured.

First, the steady state equations are solved to determine conductivities. Afterwards, the transient equations are solved for specific heat. It was decided that the direct measurement of temperature, radiosity, and emissivity, and the subsequent calculation of conductivity, specific heat, and convection coefficients provides the most reasonable balance between cost and sensitivity. For example, while numerical calculation of radiosity from the other known data is possible, it would significantly increase sensitivity. The ten steady state equations and four unknowns (k_x, k_y, h_T, and h_B) constitute a 10 x 4 overdetermined system of equations. Overdetermined systems cannot, in general, be satisfied exactly, and thus the standard procedure is to solve the system in a least-squares sense. The Normal Equations method is used to find the least-squares solution to the system [1].

The equations are solved for both sizes of heat shields and the eigenvalues for the solutions are determined. Check the eigenvalues for both size shields and select the one that is the most stable to use for the property calculations.

A.5 Sensitivity studies

The sensitivity of the procedure to perturbations in the input data was studied. Such perturbations may be introduced through measurement errors or normal variability in the experimental setup from site to site. The sensitivity studies were performed analytically for a given specimen of known conductivities in one of two ways:

1. the steady equations are solved for the temperatures and radiosities,
2. a temperature or radiosity value is perturbed to simulate measurement error,
3. the equations are solved in a least-squares sense to estimate conductivities,

or

1. a geometric parameter is perturbed from its nominal value to simulate variability in the experimental setup,
2. the steady equations are solved for the temperatures and the radiosities,
3. the geometric parameters are returned to their nominal values,
4. the equations are solved in a least-squares sense to estimate conductivities.

The percent error in the estimated conductivities is the propagated error due to the perturbation. It is a measure of sensitivity to the given perturbation. For example, an inaccurate measurement of emissivity by 1% could cause a 5% error in the estimated values of conductivity.

The results of the steady-state sensitivity studies are presented in Tables A1-A20. The percentage shown at the top and bottom of each box is the error in computing k_y and k_x, respectively. For example, for a shield with $k_x = 0.5$ and $k_y = 0.1$, Table A1 shows that a temperature mis-measurement at location 1T will cause a 2.6% and 5.3% error in the calculation of k_y and k_x, respectively. For one who carefully follows the standard setup and tolerance requirements, a bound on the error is given in Tables A1-A10. Only the most sensitive (Table A1) and least sensitive (Table A2) elements to temperature measurement accuracy are shown. The average error and maximum error are shown in Tables A9 and A10, respectively. The purpose of Tables A12-A20 is to give the user some understanding of why parameters were specified the way they were, why tolerances are as small as they are, and why two shield specimens are required.

The results shown in each box of Tables A1-A10 & A14-A20 correspond to the width (22.5 cm or 45 cm) which is expected to have a lower sensitivity. The software from the Related References section 2.0 performs this step automatically by comparing the minimum eigenvalue of the normal equations [2] as soon as the data from both the 22.5 cm and the 45 cm specimens are available. Table A11 shows, for each case, which specimen width (22.5 cm or 45 cm) was chosen by the software. The propagated error using only a 22.5 cm specimen is provided in Table A12, whereas the propagated error using only a 45 cm specimen is given in Table A13. For large values of k_x, the error associated with the 45 cm specimen is much smaller than that associated with the 22.5 cm specimen. On the other hand, the error associated with the 22.5 specimen is less than that associated with the 45 cm specimen for large values of k_y and small values of k_x. Since the conductivities are unknown before testing, data from both a 22.5 cm and a 45 cm specimen are necessary to satisfy sensitivity requirements.

Tables A14 and A15 are provided to illustrate the importance of achieving the error tolerances required by this standard. First, very accurate RTD temperature sensors, which are accurate within ±0.12%, are required in Section 4.3. If the RTD sensors were replaced with less accurate type-K thermocouples, which are only accurate to the larger of ±1.1°C and ±0.375%, the material properties would be computed to a lower accuracy. This is shown in Table A14 which can be compared to Table A1. Second, the vertical distance from the top of the shield to the bottom of the heat source is required to be 25.4 mm ± 1.5 mm in Section 5.8

The user is required to know whether the specimen in question is isotropic or anisotropic. The large errors in Table A16 (as compared to Table A10) show why the anisotropic model is not usable for isotropic specimens.

The sensitivity also depends on the nominal values of various parameters: H, h_T, h_B, J_p, ε_T, and ε_B.

Thus a significant effort was made to use parameter design to reduce the sensitivity of the system. The results showed that, in general, sensitivity can be reduced by increasing ε_T or J_p. See Tables A17 and A18, respectively. Emissivity is a parameter because the specimen can be painted to achieve a specific value. Heat source radiosity J_p increases to the fourth power of T_p. The results further showed that as either H or convection coefficients are reduced the sensitivity is likewise reduced. See Tables A19 and A20, respectively. However, H was not reduced beyond 25.4 mm to keep the heat source thermal boundary layer sufficiently far from the specimen. The convection coefficients can be reduced, to that corresponding to natural convection from a heated plate, by minimizing forced airflow over the shield.

The analysis considers neither the error or sensitivity due to numerical truncation nor that due to neglecting spatial variation of convection coefficients.

A.6 References

[1] B. N. Datta, *Numerical Linear Algebra and Applications*, Pacific Grove, California: Brooks/Cole Publishing Company, 1995.

[2] J. V. Beck, *Parameter Estimation in Engineering and Science*, New York: John Wiley & Sons, 1977.

TABLE A1—PROPAGATED ERROR DUE TO A TEMPERATURE MISMEASUREMENT AT LOCATION 1T OF ±0.12%.

k_y \ k_x	0.1	0.5	2	10	40	200
0.1	3.6% 3.6%	2.6% 5.3%	1.7% 1.7%	1.0% 1.0%	0.7% 0.8%	0.1% 1.4%
0.5		4.8% 4.8%	3.2% 1.4%	1.8% 0.8%	1.5% 0.7%	1.3% 1.4%
2			7.8% 7.8%	4.8% 0.8%	3.8% 1.2%	3.1% 1.3%
10				13.7% 13.7%	13.9% 1.3%	10.5% 1.2%

TABLE A2—PROPAGATED ERROR DUE TO A TEMPERATURE MISMEASUREMENT AT LOCATION 2B OF ±0.12%.

k_y \ k_x	0.1	0.5	2	10	40	200
0.1	0.4% 0.4%	0.3% 0.1%	0.2% 0.0%	0.1% 0.0%	0.3% 0.0%	1.7% 0.1%
0.5		0.4% 0.4%	0.5% 0.1%	0.4% 0.0%	0.2% 0.1%	0.5% 0.2%
2			0.5% 0.5%	1.3% 0.0%	0.9% 0.1%	0.1% 0.2%
10				0.3% 0.3%	2.9% 0.2%	0.1% 0.1%

TABLE A3—PROPAGATED ERROR DUE TO A MISMEASUREMENT OF THE SHIELD THICKNESS BY ±0.127 mm.

k_y \ k_x	0.1	0.5	2	10	40	200
0.1	2.4% 2.4%	2.5% 2.5%	2.5% 2.5%	2.5% 2.5%	2.5% 2.5%	2.5% 2.5%
0.5		2.1% 2.1%	2.5% 2.5%	2.5% 2.5%	2.5% 2.5%	2.5% 2.5%
2			1.3% 1.3%	2.5% 2.5%	2.5% 2.5%	2.5% 2.5%
10				0.3% 0.3%	2.5% 2.5%	2.5% 2.5%

TABLE A4—PROPAGATED ERROR DUE TO SHIELD WIDTH (NOMINALLY 22.5 OR 45 cm) TOO LARGE OR TOO SMALL BY 1% (REDISTRIBUTING THE TEMPERATURE SENSORS)

k_y \ k_x	0.1	0.5	2	10	40	200
0.1	10.5% 10.5%	6.7% 25.9%	3.8% 8.5%	1.4% 3.7%	0.4% 2.8%	0.5% 2.2%
0.5		6.1% 6.1%	3.0% 7.5%	1.2% 3.4%	0.5% 2.6%	0.1% 2.2%
2			3.8% 3.8%	1.2% 3.3%	0.6% 2.6%	0.0% 2.1%
10				2.1% 2.1%	0.6% 2.6%	0.1% 2.1%

TABLE A5—PROPAGATED ERROR DUE TO HEAT SOURCE DIAMETER (NOMINALLY 50.8 mm) TOO LARGE OR TOO SMALL BY 0.127 mm.

k_y \ k_x	0.1	0.5	2	10	40	200
0.1	1.0% 1.0%	0.6% 2.2%	0.3% 0.5%	0.0% 0.1%	0.1% 0.1%	0.2% 0.1%
0.5		0.5% 0.5%	0.2% 0.4%	0.0% 0.0%	0.1% 0.1%	0.1% 0.1%
2			0.2% 0.2%	0.0% 0.0%	0.1% 0.1%	0.1% 0.1%
10				0.0% 0.0%	0.1% 0.1%	0.1% 0.1%

TABLE A6—PROPAGATED ERROR DUE TO SPECIMEN-TO-SOURCE DISTANCE (NOMINALLY 25.4 mm) TOO LARGE OR TOO SMALL BY 0.127 mm.

k_y \ k_x	0.1	0.5	2	10	40	200
0.1	3.3% 3.3%	2.1% 7.7%	1.3% 2.3%	0.6% 0.8%	0.4% 0.5%	0.1% 0.3%
0.5		1.9% 1.9%	1.1% 2.0%	0.6% 0.7%	0.4% 0.5%	0.2% 0.3%
2			1.2% 1.2%	0.6% 0.7%	0.4% 0.4%	0.3% 0.3%
10				0.6% 0.6%	0.4% 0.4%	0.3% 0.3%

TABLE A7—PROPAGATED ERROR DUE TO MISMEASUREMENT OF HEAT-SOURCE RADIOSITY TEMPERATURE BY ±0.5°C OR ±0.5% (WHICHEVER IS LARGER).

k_y \ k_x	0.1	0.5	2	10	40	200
0.1	3.3% 3.3%	2.3% 8.3%	1.8% 3.1%	1.4% 1.6%	1.3% 1.4%	1.3% 1.3%
0.5		2.1% 2.1%	1.5% 2.8%	1.3% 1.6%	1.3% 1.4%	1.2% 1.3%
2			1.8% 1.8%	1.3% 1.5%	1.3% 1.3%	1.2% 1.3%
10				1.4% 1.4%	1.3% 1.3%	1.2% 1.3%

TABLE A8—PROPAGATED ERROR DUE TO MISMEASUREMENT OF ROOM-WALL RADIOSITY TEMPERATURE BY ±3°C OR ±3% (WHICHEVER IS LARGER).

k_y \ k_x	0.1	0.5	2	10	40	200
0.1	2.0% 2.0%	0.5% 15.1%	0.4% 4.0%	0.2% 0.9%	0.2% 0.9%	0.2% 0.3%
0.5		1.9% 1.9%	0.6% 3.8%	0.3% 0.9%	0.3% 0.9%	0.2% 0.3%
2			1.4% 1.4%	0.3% 0.9%	0.2% 0.3%	0.2% 0.3%
10				0.6% 0.6%	0.2% 0.3%	0.2% 0.3%

TABLE A9—AVERAGE PROPAGATED ERROR WITH PRESENT SETUP.

k_y \ k_x	0.1	0.5	2	10	40	200
0.1	2.2% 2.2%	1.5% 4.7%	1.0% 1.4%	0.6% 0.6%	0.4% 0.5%	0.9% 0.5%
0.5		2.3% 2.3%	1.5% 1.3%	0.8% 0.6%	0.6% 0.5%	0.7% 0.5%
2			3.1% 3.1%	2.0% 0.6%	1.5% 0.5%	1.1% 0.5%
10				4.7% 4.7%	5.6% 0.5%	3.6% 0.5%

TABLE A10—MAXIMUM PROPAGATED ERROR USING PRESENT SETUP.

k_y \ k_x	0.1	0.5	2	10	40	200
0.1	10.5% 10.5%	6.7% 25.9%	3.8% 8.5%	1.4% 3.7%	1.3% 2.8%	4.2% 2.2%
0.5		6.1% 6.1%	3.2% 7.5%	1.8% 3.4%	1.5% 2.6%	2.4% 2.2%
2			7.8% 7.8%	4.8% 3.3%	3.8% 2.6%	3.4% 2.1%
10				13.7% 13.7%	13.9% 2.6%	11.7% 2.1%

TABLE A11—PREFERRED SPECIMEN WIDTH (IN cm) BASED ON EXPECTED SYSTEM SENSITIVITY.

k_y k_x	0.1	0.5	2	10	40	200
0.1	22.5	22.5	22.5	22.5	45	45
0.5		22.5	22.5	22.5	45	45
2			22.5	22.5	22.5	45
10				22.5	22.5	45

TABLE A12—MAXIMUM PROPAGATED ERROR USING ONLY A 22.5 cm WIDE SPECIMEN.

k_y k_x	0.1	0.5	2	10	40	200
0.1	10.5% 10.5%	6.7% 25.9%	3.8% 8.5%	1.4% 3.7%	3.6% 2.7%	47.2% 4.6%
0.5		6.1% 6.1%	3.2% 7.5%	1.8% 3.4%	2.3% 2.7%	15.0% 4.6%
2			7.8% 7.8%	4.8% 3.3%	3.8% 2.6%	8.6% 4.6%
10				13.7% 13.7%	13.9% 2.6%	14.5% 4.8%

TABLE A13—MAXIMUM PROPAGATED ERROR USING ONLY A 45 cm WIDE SPECIMEN.

k_y k_x	0.1	0.5	2	10	40	200
0.1	7.8% 7.8%	6.0% 40.9%	4.2% 12.3%	1.7% 4.5%	1.3% 2.8%	4.2% 2.2%
0.5		5.6% 5.6%	4.3% 10.7%	2.4% 4.1%	1.5% 2.6%	2.4% 2.2%
2			11.6% 11.6%	7.2% 3.9%	3.9% 2.5%	3.4% 2.1%
10				19.8% 19.8%	18.2% 2.5%	11.7% 2.1%

TABLE A14—PROPAGATED ERROR DUE TO A TEMPERATURE MISMEASUREMENT AT LOCATION 1T OF ±1.1°C OR ±0.375% (WHICHEVER IS GREATER).

k_y k_x	0.1	0.5	2	10	40	200
0.1	13.6% 13.6%	10.0% 20.5%	6.7% 7.1%	4.3% 4.3%	3.8% 4.2%	1.9% 9.3%
0.5		19.2% 19.2%	13.6% 6.5%	8.6% 4.2%	8.3% 4.1%	8.7% 9.9%
2			32.1% 32.1%	22.8% 4.4%	20.4% 8.2%	20.7% 9.9%
10				54.9% 54.9%	55.8% 8.9%	51.6% 9.9%

TABLE A15—PROPAGATED ERROR DUE TO SPECIMEN-TO-SOURCE DISTANCE (NOMINALLY 25.4 mm) TOO LARGE OR TOO SMALL BY 1.5875 mm.

k_y k_x	0.1	0.5	2	10	40	200
0.1	42% 42%	27% 98%	17% 29%	8% 10%	5% 6%	2% 4%
0.5		24% 24%	13% 25%	7% 9%	5% 6%	3% 4%
2			15% 15%	7% 8%	5% 5%	3% 4%
10				7% 7%	5% 5%	3% 4%

TABLE A16—MAXIMUM PROPAGATED ERROR OF AN ISOTROPIC SPECIMEN USING AN ANISOTROPIC ANALYTICAL MODEL.

k_y k_x	0.1	0.5	2	10	40	200
0.1	8% 118%					
0.5		5% 22%				
2			9% 7%			
10				20% 3%		

TABLE A17—MAXIMUM PROPAGATED ERROR USING AN UNPAINTED SPECIMEN HAVING AN EMISSIVITY OF 0.20 ON BOTH SIDES.

k_y k_x	0.1	0.5	2	10	40	200
0.1	17.8% 17.8%	6.9% 12.9%	2.8% 5.3%	1.8% 3.0%	1.8% 2.5%	10.0% 2.8%
0.5		8.9% 8.9%	5.3% 4.9%	2.9% 2.9%	2.6% 2.4%	5.3% 2.8%
2			11.4% 11.4%	8.5% 2.9%	7.7% 2.5%	7.7% 2.7%
10				23.0% 23.0%	27.4% 2.6%	27.6% 2.7%

TABLE A18—MAXIMUM PROPAGATED ERROR WITH HEAT SOURCE NOMINALLY SET AT 300°C, RATHER THAN 500°C.

k_y k_x	0.1	0.5	2	10	40	200
0.1	6.5% 6.5%	6.1% 36.9%	3.2% 10.3%	1.7% 3.4%	1.7% 2.8%	8.1% 2.3%
0.5		8.6% 8.6%	4.6% 10.0%	2.5% 3.2%	2.3% 2.8%	4.3% 3.2%
2			10.8% 10.8%	7.2% 3.1%	6.1% 2.6%	6.1% 2.2%
10				19.9% 19.9%	21.9% 2.5%	21.6% 2.2%

TABLE A19—MAXIMUM PROPAGATED ERROR WITH THE HEAT SOURCE NOMINALLY LOCATED 50.8 mm, RATHER THAN 25.4 mm, ABOVE SPECIMEN.

k_y k_x	0.1	0.5	2	10	40	200
0.1	9.5% 9.5%	7.6% 64.5%	5.0% 9.9%	2.0% 4.3%	1.3% 3.1%	5.1% 2.4%
0.5		8.1% 8.1%	4.3% 8.8%	2.5% 4.0%	1.8% 3.0%	2.8% 2.4%
2			11.0% 11.0%	6.9% 3.9%	4.9% 2.9%	4.1% 2.3%
10				20.7% 20.7%	21.0% 3.0%	14.2% 2.3%

TABLE A20—MAXIMUM PROPAGATED ERROR WITH FORCED-AIR COOLING (H_T = H_B = 25 W/M^2 K).

k_y k_x	0.1	0.5	2	10	40	200
0.1	17.1% 17.1%	15.0% 41.5%	7.4% 12.6%	2.3% 4.6%	2.9% 2.9%	3.5% 2.3%
0.5		17.9% 17.9%	6.6% 11.4%	2.2% 4.4%	1.8% 2.9%	1.9% 2.3%
2			8.8% 8.8%	4.6% 4.1%	2.9% 2.8%	2.6% 2.3%
10				11.8% 11.8%	10.3% 2.8%	9.5% 2.9%

APPENDIX B
THERMOCOUPLE ATTACHMENT METHODS

B.1 Abstract

Epoxy can be used as an alternative attachment method when spot or tack welding (preferred methods) are unavailable or impractical. This appendix presents the results of the experiments performed to determine the best epoxy as a method of thermocouple attachment. Four different epoxy types were evaluated and compared to a welded thermocouple (standard). The four different epoxy types are described within this report along with recommendations.

B.2 Introduction

One of the most accepted and effective methods of attaching thermocouples to a metal surface is by the means of spot welding. This method insures the first junction of the thermocouple is in constant contact with the surface throughout the test. Special equipment is required to weld the thermocouples to the surface depending on the material type (steel or aluminum). This special equipment may not be available at all test locations and therefore alternate methods of attachment are required.

Epoxy type adhesives are one of the most widely used alternative attachment methods. The thermocouple would be placed on the surface of the material and the epoxy would be poured over the thermocouple and allowed to dry. This attachment method adheres well to porous surfaces such as SMC or plastic. With Metal surfaces, which are normally smooth, the adhesion properties of many epoxies fail. Also, the temperature monitored by the thermocouple is sometimes misleading due to the thermal conductivity properties of the epoxy.

This report covers the testing performed to determine the best epoxy material to use as an alternative thermocouple attachment method for metal surfaces. Material types and procedures are discussed along with recommendations. The materials will be judged on the ability to track the performance of a spot-welded thermocouple along with their adhesion properties.

B.3 Materials and procedures.

Epoxy materials discussed and tested are:

1. Omega Engineering Inc.
   Stanford, Connecticut
   Omegabond OB-300 air dry cement
2. Omega Engineering Inc.
   Stanford, Connecticut
   Omegabond OB-400 air dry cement
3. Omega Engineering Inc.
   Stanford, Connecticut
   Omegabond OB-500 air dry cement
4. ITW Devcon
   Danvers, Massachusetts
   Titanium Putty

A sample of each epoxy material was used to adhere a K-type thermocouple to steel and aluminum sample according to manufacturer's directions. All the thermocouples have been placed in a row along with a spot welded thermocouple for comparison. The heat source was set to a temperature of 400°C. After verifying the heat source reached steady state, the epoxy samples were placed under a heat source and monitored during the temperature cycle. All temperature data was recorded, see Figures B1 and B2 below.

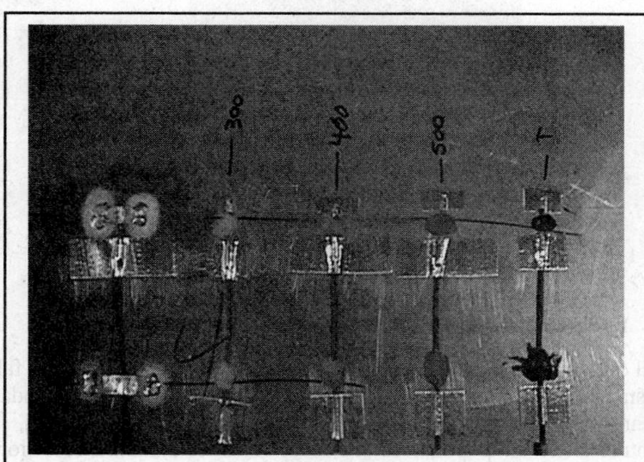

FIGURE B1—EPOXY SAMPLES

FIGURE B2—TEST SETUP

B.4 Results

Each of the epoxy-covered thermocouples is compared to the spot welded thermocouple for accuracy and rise time. The results of the tests are as follows:

The Omegabond OB-300 had difficulty adhering to the material samples and therefore could not be evaluated. The adhering problems we had with this material were evaluation enough to eliminate this material from the study.

The Omegabond OB-400 showed temperatures hotter than the control thermocouple. Also, when attaching the thermocouple to the aluminum sample, the bond showed signs of cracking. When adhering the thermocouple to a steel sample, the OB-400 adhesion weakened and the thermocouple came loose of the sample.

The Omegabond OB-500 demonstrated the best characteristics of all the Omegabond materials. The temperature rise and stabilization closely followed the control thermocouple for both the aluminum sample as well as the steel. The OB-500 adhesion bond showed no signs of weakening and or cracking.

The titanium putty by ITW Devcon showed much cooler temperatures than the control thermocouple. Also the rise time is much slower. The adhesion properties are very good for porous surfaces but showed signs of weakening on the smooth samples used in this study. The bond on the steel surface came loose during the test.

B.5 Conclusion

As the results of the testing were examined it was concluded that the Omegabond OB-500 is the best choice to use as an alternate attachment method. The OB-500 matched the results most closely to the spot welded thermocouple on repeated tests and was within the specified parameters. It also proved to have the best adhesion properties out of all the epoxy materials tested. It would be recommended to use the Omegabond 500 as an alternative attachment method when spot welding or tig welding is not available.

APPENDIX C
REPEATABILITY

No measurement can yield one absolutely true value. Rather, the best we can hope for is a best estimate. In addition, we can collect enough information to tell us how sure we can be of our best estimate. Experimental data collected in a given experiment are frequently normally distributed around a mean value.

In order to verify the repeatability of this test standard, two samples were created and tested twenty times. One sample, an air gap heat shield, consisted of a 4mm air gap located between two pieces of 1.5mm sheet steel, and the other sample consisted of a 4mm layer of fiberglass between two pieces of 1.5mm sheet steel. Twenty tests were run on each of these two samples in order to gain the necessary data to create this appendix. The intent of this study was to test using very relaxed methods in order to introduce a high amount of experimental setup error, verify that the results were repeatable, and assess the robustness of the standard from large external noise factors. All distances were measured with a rule instead of highly accurate calipers. The thermocouples were K-Type instead of the more accurate RTDs sensors.

The twenty samples were used to calculate the mean and standard deviation for both samples and the results were then compiled and plotted below. Twenty samples, according to Devore [1], are sufficient for calculating a standard deviation of a population. Consequently, we used these twenty samples and assumed a normal distribution for the resulting properties in order to explain the results in an easy to understand manner. The histograms are given in Figures C1 and C2.

The normal thermal conductivity histograms best represented a normal distribution, while the lateral thermal conductivity histograms were only slightly skewed to the right, and the specific heat histograms were normal in shape.

Table C1 illustrates the values for the average and standard deviation for all of the population of tests for the Steel air gap shield.

TABLE C1—CONDUCTIVITIES FOR STEEL AIR GAP SHIELD

Calculated shield material properties	Average	Standard Deviation
Normal thermal conductivity (ky)	0.203	0.0205
Lateral thermal conductivity (kx)	7.747	1.389
Specific heat (Cp)	264.2	43.60

The standard deviation is seen to be an order of magnitude less than that of the average for the normal thermal conductivity, while the lateral thermal conductivity standard deviation is roughly five times smaller than that of the average, and the specific heat standard deviation value is approximately six times smaller than that of the average. This demonstrates that the normal thermal conductivity calculation is more repeatable than the other two.

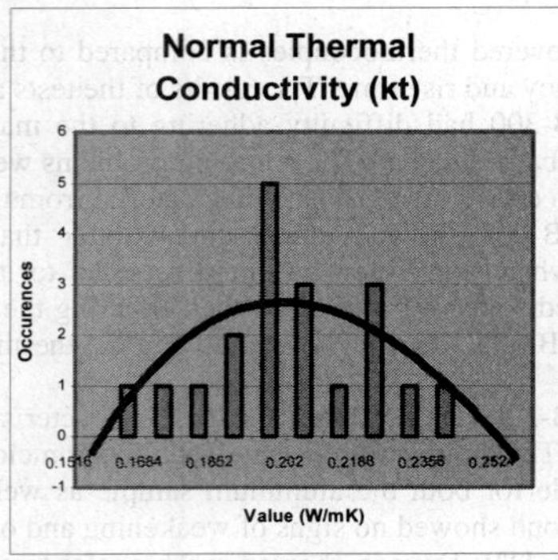

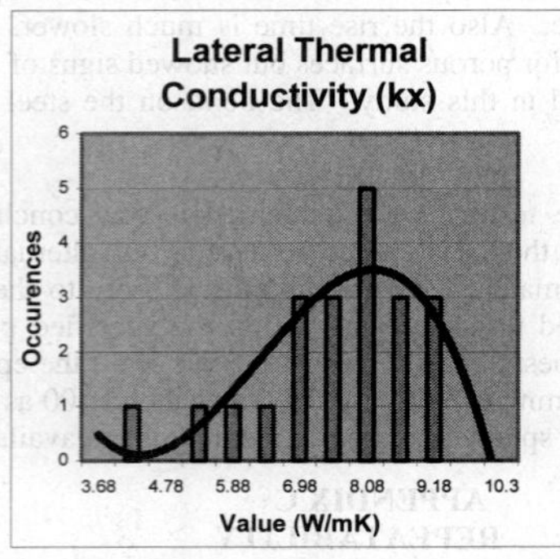

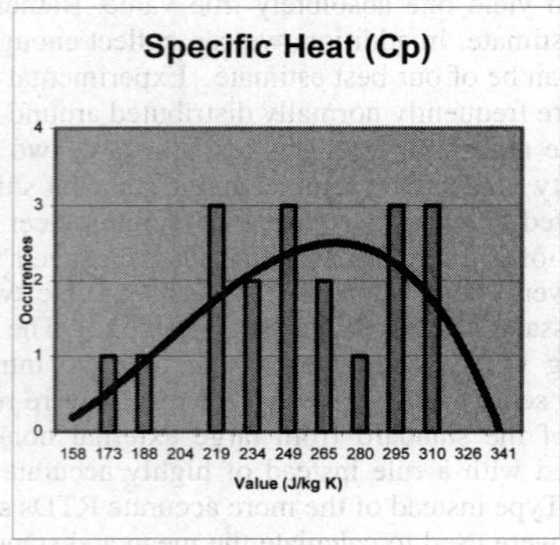

FIGURE C1—STEEL AIR GAP SHIELD

Table C2 illustrates the values for the average and standard deviation for all of the population of tests for the Steel fiberglass gap shield.

TABLE C2—CONDUCTIVITIES FOR STEEL FIBERGLASS GAP SHIELD

Calculated shield material properties	Average	Standard Deviation
Normal thermal conductivity (ky)	0.0317	0.00535
Lateral thermal conductivity (kx)	6.659	1.023
Specific heat (Cp)	237.3	24.05

The standard deviation is seen to be almost an order of magnitude less than that of the average for the normal thermal conductivity, while the lateral thermal conductivity standard deviation is about six and one half times smaller than that of the average, and the specific heat standard deviation value is an order of magnitude smaller than that of the average. This demonstrates that the specific heat calculation is more repeatable than the other two. On average this set of twenty tests were slightly more repeatable than the air gap shield results.

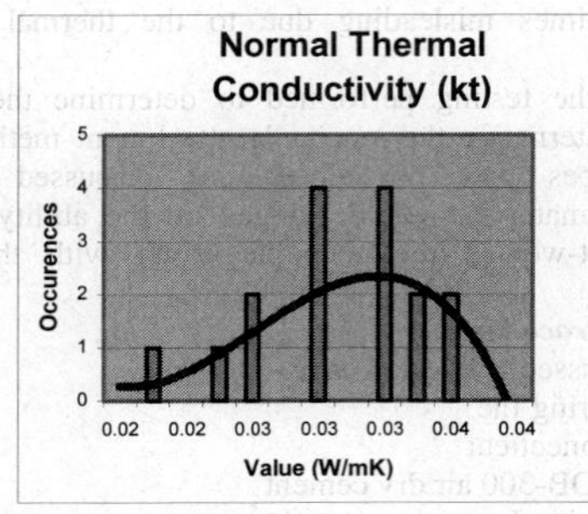

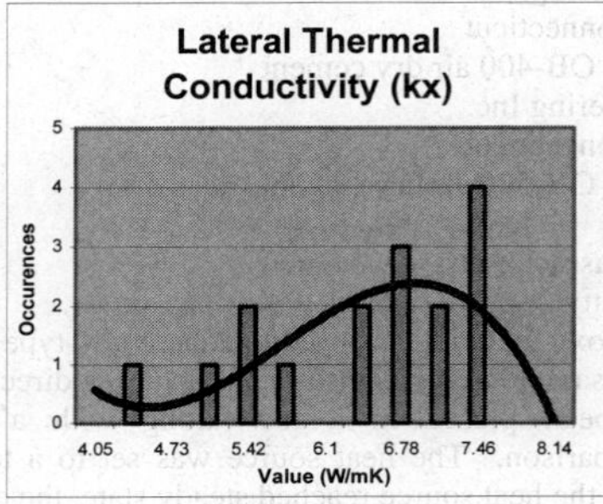

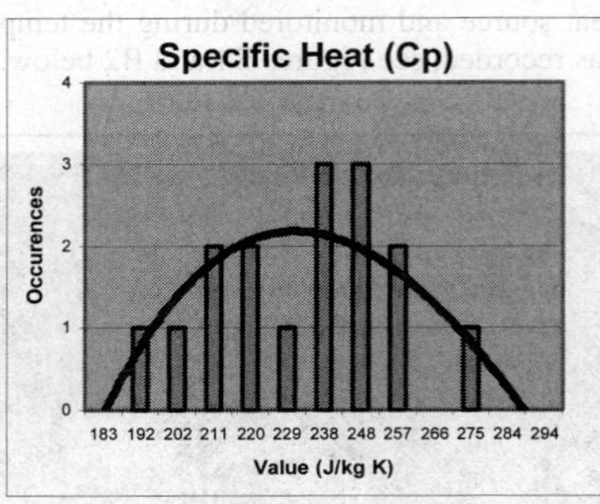

FIGURE C2—STEEL FIBERGLASS GAP SHIELD

A normal distribution assumption illustrates that 68% of the population falls within one standard deviation, 95% of the population falls within two standard deviations, and 99.7% falls within three standard deviations, [Devore, 1]. In order to capture all of the population, one must use three standard deviations. In other words, the average ± three standard deviations would include all of the population of tests that were run while the average ± two standard deviations would include 95% of the population.

Using one standard deviation as acceptable for test repeatability studies, the test results would show that the proposed standard is accurate to within ± 10-15% for all material properties. If 99.7% of the population is necessary then the repeatability of this standard is less.

Due to the natural repeatability issues of any experiment as outlined in this Appendix C, it is prudent to repeat this test standard on the same specimen multiple times to gain confidence that the results are representative of the average material.

C.1 References

[1] Devore, Jay L., *Probability and Statistics for Engineering and the Sciences,* Third Edition, Brooks/Cole Publishing Company, 1991.

FIBERBOARD CREASE BENDING TEST—SAE J119 FEB1987 SAE Standard

Report of the SAE Nonmetallic Materials Committee approved September 1969, completely revised January 1982, and reaffirmed February 1987.

Foreword—This Document has not changed other than to put it into the new SAE Technical Standards Board Format.

1. Scope—This test method is designed to determine the suitability of a painted or unpainted fiberboard for application involving creasing and bending. The specific purpose of the test is to determine whether a given material, properly creased, can be bent along the impressed crease without objectionable failure on the surface of the bend.

2. Reference

2.1 Applicable Publication—The following publications form a part of the specification to the extent specified herein. Unless otherwise indicated the latest revision of SAE publications shall apply.

2.1.1 SAE PUBLICATION—The following publication forms a part of the specification to the extent specified herein. Unless otherwise indicated the latest revision of SAE publications shall apply.

SAE J315 JAN 85—Fiberboard Test Procedure

3. Equipment Required

3.1 Press with adequate tonnage to crease the test specimen to the desired configuration.

3.2 Matched male and female die sections, selected for the caliper of sample to be tested and for the desired end result(see 5) (see Section 5).

4. Test Specimen

4.1 Size—Minimum of 100 x 300 mm or as determined by the size of the test die.

4.2 Condition Prior to Testing—See SAE J315 (see Section 4) unless otherwise specified.

5. Creasing Rule (Male Die Section)

5.1 The thickness of the creasing rule (T_2) is designated commercially by the printer's point system (1 point equals approximately 0.36 mm), Figure 1.

BRDA Disclaimer: As is implied in the bulletin (BRDA Technical Bulletin 12), these procedures and the instrument(s) utilized were developed specifically for multi-ply folding boxboard manufactured by a continuous wet-forming process in a caliper range up to 0.040 in. Although the same principles may apply in the creasing and bending of laminated, single-ply, or convolute-formed paperboard, this caveat should be noted, especially as to caliper.

5.2 Commercially available in either flat or round face and in the following thicknesses (round face rule should be used unless otherwise specified):

TABLE 1—

Standard Creasing Rule Thickness	Standard Creasing Rule Thickness
2 points	10 points
3 points	12 points
4 points	5 mm
6 points	6 mm
8 points	

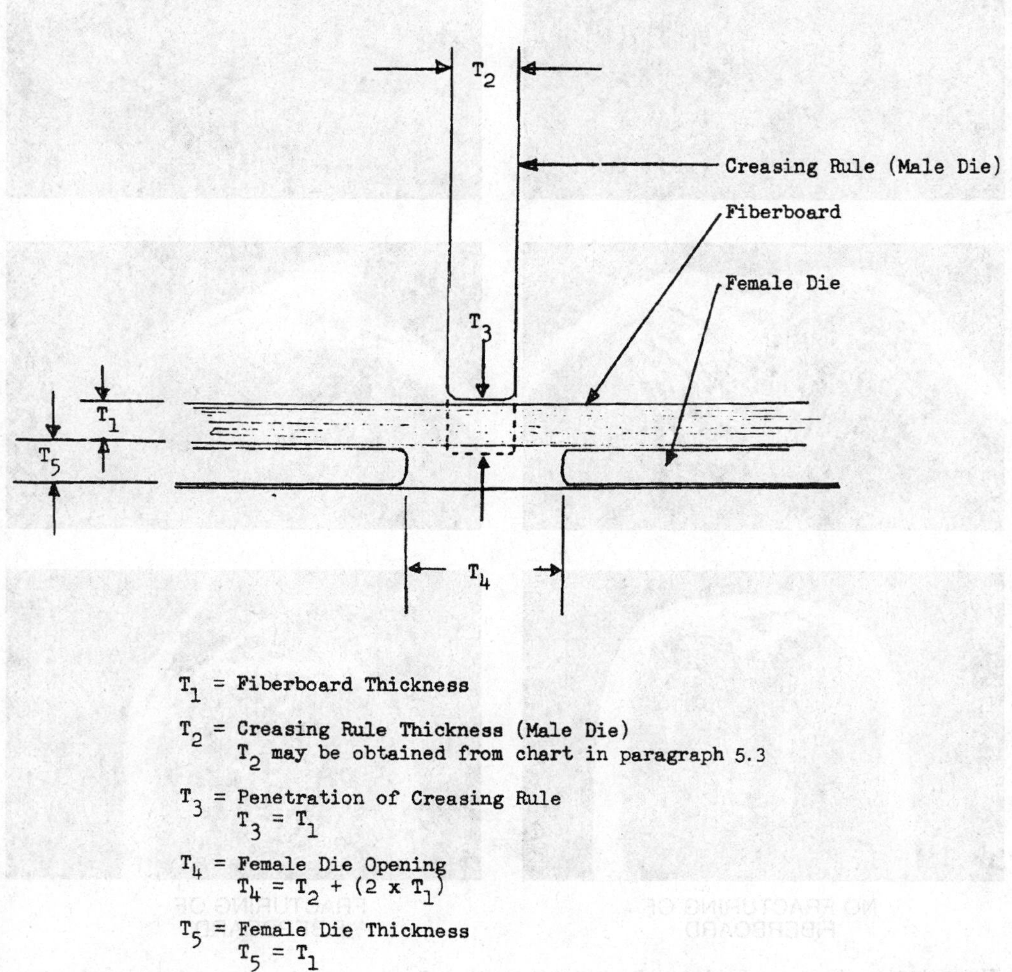

FIGURE 1—

5.3 For the normal range of bending fiberboards, the following may serve as a guide in the selection of creasing rule:

Fiberboard Thickness mm	Creasing Rule
0.76	3–6 points
1.02	3–6 points
1.26	4–8 points
1.52	6–10 points
1.78	8–12 points
2.03	10 points5 mm
2.28	12 points6 mm

5.4 Penetration of the creasing rule (T_3) should be such that it equals the thickness of the fiberboard, Figure 1.

6. *Female Die Section*

6.1 The female die opening (T_4) may be determined by adding the creasing rule thickness to twice the caliper of the test specimen, Figure 1.

6.2 Depth (T_5) should be equivalent to the caliper of the test specimen unless otherwise specified, Figure 1.

6.3 Both female die section and creasing rule should extend beyond the edges of the test specimen.

7. *Procedure*

7.1 Matched male and female die sections should be determined by the caliper of the test specimen (see 5.3) and mounted in press (see 3.1). Stops should be provided so that penetration of male creasing rule is as specified in 5.4.

7.2 Insert test specimen in die and crease with one stroke of press. Using separate specimens, crease both with the grain and across the grain and on one or both sides as specified.

7.3 The test die or dies should encompass the range of rule thicknesses recommended for the caliper of board being tested (see 5.3). Three or four rules of different thicknesses can be incorporated into the same die to aid in determining the proper rule thickness for creasing that board.

When using a die with multiple scores, the creases should not be closer than 76 mm on centers or less than 25 mm from the edges of the test specimen parallel to the creasing rule.

8. *Evaluation*

8.1 The recommended practice is to bend sides of specimen away from male side of die. In actual practice, the design of the part may require bending both ways.

8.2 The specimen should be bent through an angle of 180 deg. The specimen should be bent not to exceed 180 deg with the parallel face kept the minimum distance of board thickness apart, unless otherwise specified. See Figure 2.

8.3 The specimen should be usually evaluated after bending. The appearance of fractures on the fiberboard and/or the paint coating should be reported.

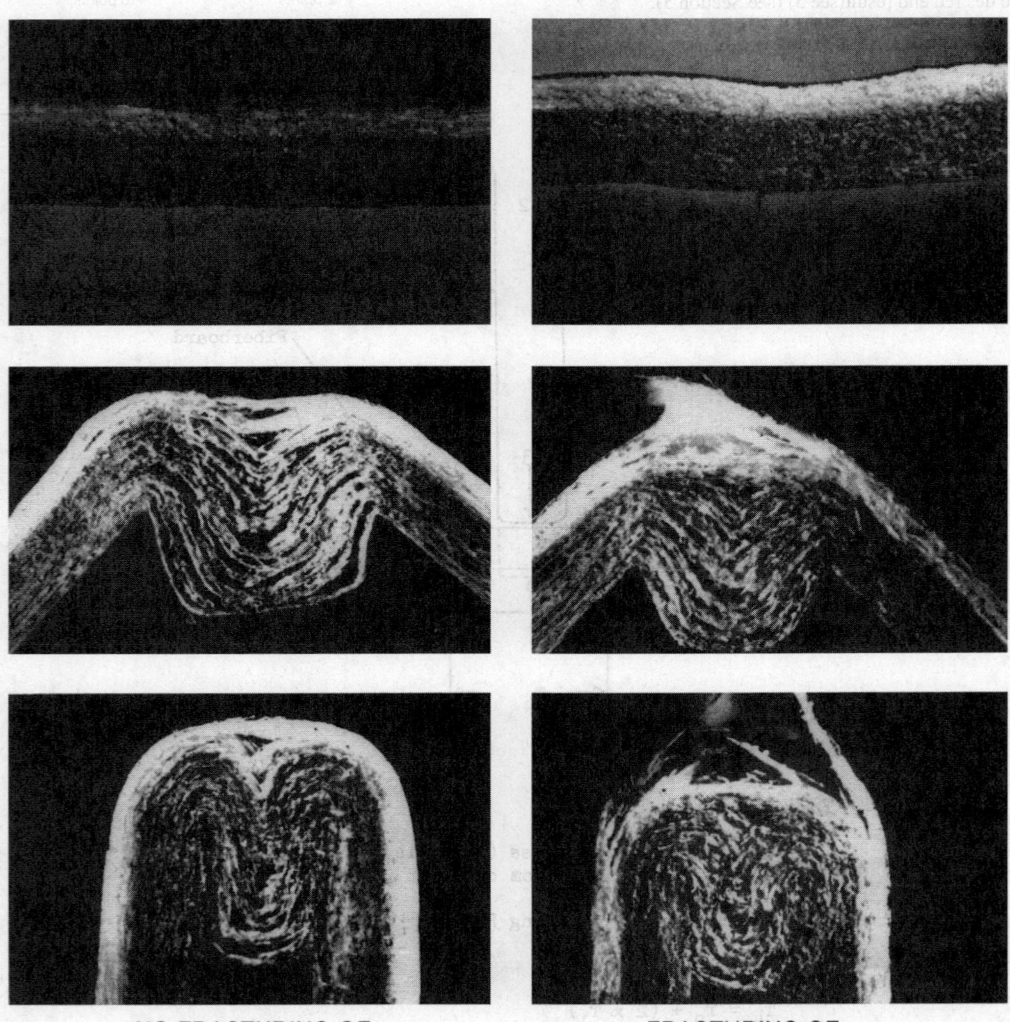

These photographs were provided by Boxboard Research & Development Association from studies of the scoring and folding qualities of multi-ply folding boxboard performed by Arthur D. Little, Inc. for the Association.

FIGURE 2—

FUELS AND LUBRICANTS

12 Fuels and Lubricants

EFFECTIVE DATES OF NEW OR REVISED TECHNICAL REPORTS—SAE J301 MAR1999

SAE Recommended Practice

Report of the SAE Lubricants Division approved January 1935 and completely revised by the SAE Fuels and Lubricants Division June 1987. Reaffirmed by the SAE Fuels and Lubricants Division March 1993 and March 1999.

*1. **Scope***—The final approval date for Fuels and Lubricants technical reports is shown following the J-report number. This approval date is the date of final approval by the Fuels and Lubricants Division. It is effective immediately subsequent to divisional approval for *newly issued Standards, Recommended Practices*, and *Information Reports*, and also for *revised Information Reports* and the *SAE J1146 Recommended Practice*. In the case of *revised* or *cancelled Standards* or *Recommended Practices* (used to define product quality), an 18-month optional grace period exists before they become fully effective.

2. Reference

2.1 Applicable Publication—The following publication forms a part of the specification to the extent specified herein. Unless otherwise indicated, the latest version of SAE publications shall apply.

2.1.1 SAE PUBLICATION—Available from SAE, 400 Commonwealth Drive, Warrendale, PA 15096-0001.

SAE J1146—The Automotive Lubricant Performance and Service Classification Maintenance Procedure

ENGINE OIL PERFORMANCE AND ENGINE SERVICE CLASSIFICATION (OTHER THAN "ENERGY CONSERVING") —SAE J183 JAN2002

SAE Standard

Report of the SAE Fuels and Lubricants Technical Committee approved June 1970. Revised by the SAE Fuels and Lubricants Division June 1989. Revised by the SAE Fuels and Lubricants Technical Committees 1 and 2 June 1990. Revised by the SAE Fuels and Lubricants Technical Committee 2—Heavy-Duty Type Engine Oils, June 1991. Completely revised by the SAE Fuels and Lubricants Technical Committee 1—Automotive Engine Oils, April 1996. Revised by the SAE Fuels and Lubricants Technical Committee 1—Automotive Engine Oils, June 1999. Rationale statement available. Revised by the SAE Fuels and Lubricants Technical Committee 1—Automotive Engine Oils, January 2002.

1. Scope—This SAE Standard outlines the engine oil performance categories and classifications developed through the efforts of the Alliance of Automobile Manufacturers (AAM), American Petroleum Institute (API), the American Society for Testing and Materials (ASTM), the Engine Manufacturers Association (EMA), International Lubricant Standardization and Approval committee (ILSAC) and SAE. The verbal descriptions by API and ASTM, along with prescribed test methods and limits are shown for active categories in Table 1 and obsolete categories in Table A1. Appendix A is a historical documentation of the obsolete categories.

For purposes of this document, active categories are defined as those (a) for which the required test equipment and test support materials, including reference engine oils and reference fuels, are readily available, (b) for which ASTM or the test developer monitors precision for all tests, and (c) which are currently available for licensing by API EOLCS.

The current processes for initiating new classifications were developed through the cooperative efforts of the AAM, API, ASTM, EMA, ILSAC, and SAE. New API "S" and ILSAC classifications are added using the procedure defined in API 1509 Appendix C. New API "C" categories are developed through agreement among EMA, API, and ASTM.

2. References

2.1 Applicable Publications—The following publications form a part of this specification to the extent specified herein. The latest issue of SAE publications shall apply.

2.1.1 SAE PUBLICATIONS—Available from SAE, 400 Commonwealth Drive, Warrendale, PA 15096-0001.

SAE J300—Engine Oil Viscosity Classification
SAE J304—Engine Oil Tests
SAE J312—Automotive Gasolines
SAE J1297—Alternative Automotive Fuels
SAE J1423—Classification of Energy-Conserving Engine Oil for Passenger Cars, Vans, and Light-Duty Trucks
Engine Oil/Catalyst and Oxygen Sensor Compatibility Task Force Status Report, dated October, 1985.

2.1.2 API PUBLICATION—Available from American Petroleum Institute, 1220 L Street N.W., Washington, DC 20005.

API Publication 1509—Engine Oil Licensing and Certification System

2.1.3 ASTM PUBLICATIONS—Available from ASTM, 100 Barr Harbor Drive, West Conshohocken, PA 19428-2959.

ASTM D 92—Standard Test Method for Flash and Fire Points by Cleveland Open Cup
ASTM D 93—Standard Test Methods for Flash-Point by Pensky-Martens Closed Cup Tester
ASTM D 130—Test Method for Detection of Copper Corrosion from Petroleum Products by the Copper Strip Tarnish Test
ASTM D 892—Standard Test Method for Foaming Characteristics of Lubricating Oils
ASTM D 2887—Standard Test for Boiling Range Distribution of Petroleum Fractions by Gas Chromatography
ASTM D 4814—Standard Specification for Automotive Spark-Ignition Engine Fuel
ASTM D 4485—Standard Performance Specification for Performance of Engine Oils
ASTM D 4684—Standard Test Method for Determination of Yield Stress and Apparent Viscosity of Engine Oils at Low Temperature
ASTM D 4951—Standard Test Method for Determination of Additive Elements in Lubricating Oils by Inductively Coupled Plasma Atomic Emission Spectrometry
ASTM D 5119—Standard Test Method for Evaluation of Automotive Engine Oils in the CRC L-38 Spark-Ignition Engine
ASTM D 5133—Test Method for Low Temperature, Low Shear Rate, Viscosity/Temperature Dependence of Lubricating Oils Using a Temperature-Scanning Technique
ASTM D 5185—Standard Test Method for Determination of Additive Elements, Wear Metals, and Contaminants in Used Lubricating Oils by Inductively Coupled Plasma Atomic Emission Spectrometry
ASTM D 5293—Standard Test Method for Apparent Viscosity of Engine Oils Between –5 and –30 °C Using the Cold-Cranking Simulator
ASTM D 5302—Standard Test Method for Evaluation of Automotive Engine Oils for Inhibition of Deposit Formation and Wear in a Spark-Ignition Internal Combustion Engine Fueled with Gasoline and Operated at Low-Temperature, Light-Duty Conditions
ASTM D 5480—Test Method for Motor Oil Volatility by Gas Chromatography
ASTM D 5533—Standard Test Method for Evaluation of Automotive Engine Oils in the Sequence IIIE, Spark Ignition Engine
ASTM D 5800—Standard Test Method for Evaporation Loss of Lubricating Oils by the Noack Method
ASTM D 5844—Test Method for Evaluation of Automotive Engine Oils for Inhibition of Rusting (Sequence IID)
ASTM D 5862—Standard Test Method for Evaluation of Engine Oils in Two-Stroke Cycle Turbo-Supercharged 6V92TA Diesel Engine
ASTM D 5966—Standard Test Method for Evaluation of Engine Oils for Roller Follower Wear in Light-Duty Diesel Engine
ASTM D 5967—Standard Test Method for Evaluation of Diesel Engine Oils in T-8 Diesel Engine
ASTM D 5968—Standard Test Method for Evaluation of Corrosiveness of Diesel Engine Oil
ASTM D 6082—Standard Test Method for High Temperature Foaming Characteristics of Lubricating Oils
ASTM D 6202—Standard Test Method for Measurement of the Effects of Automotive Engine Oils on the Fuel Economy of Passenger Cars and Light-Duty Trucks in the Sequence VIA Spark Ignition Engine
ASTM D 6278—Standard Test Method for Shear Stability of Polymer Containing Fluids Using a European Diesel Injector Apparatus
ASTM D 6483—Standard Test Method for Evaluation of Diesel Engine Oils in T-9 Diesel Engine
ASTM E 178—Recommended Practice for Dealing with Outlying Observations
ASTM RR:D-2-1219—Supporting Data for D 4485, Performance Specification for Automotive Engine Oils (Multicylinder Engine Test Procedure for the Evaluation of Lubricants—Mack T-6)
ASTM RR:D-2-1220—Supporting Data for D 4485, Performance Specification for Automotive Engine Oils (Multicylinder Engine Test Procedure for the Evaluation of Lubricants—Mack T-7)
ASTM RR:D-2-1222—Supporting Data for D 4885, Performance Specification for Automotive Engine Oils (Test Method for Measurement of Lubricating Oil Performance in Two-Stroke Cycle Turbo-Supercharged Diesel Engines)
ASTM RR:D-2-1273—1Y540 Engine 1K Test Procedure
ASTM RR:D-2-1319—Test Method for the Determination of Lubricating Oi Performance in Turbo-Supercharged Two-Cycle Diesel Engines—Detroit Diesel 6V92TA
ASTM RR:D-2-1320—Single Cylinder Piston Deposit Test - CAT 1 M-PC
ASTM RR:D-2-1321—Single Cylinder Piston Deposit Test - CAT 1N
ASTM RR:D-2-1379—Engine Oil Aeration Test
ASTM RR:D-2-1439—Standard Test Method for Evaluation of Diesel Engine Oil on the Mack T-9 Diesel Engine Test
ASTM RR:D-2-1440—Cummins M-11 High Soot Test for Evaluating Heavy Duty Diesel Engine Oil in Regards to Wear, Sludge, and Oil Filter Plugging
ASTM RR:D-2-1441—Research Report on the Caterpillar 1P.
ASTM STP 315—Multicylinder Test Sequences for Evaluating Automotive Engine Oils

ASTM STP 509—Single Cylinder Engine Tests for Evaluating Performance of Crankcase Lubricants

2.1.4 CRC PUBLICATION—Available from Coordinating Research Council, 219 Perimeter Center Parkway, Atlanta, GA 30346.

CRC Modified Supplemental Diesel Engine Rating Manual No. 15

2.1.5 FEDERAL PUBLICATION—Available from The Standardization Documents Order Desk, Building 4D, 700 Robbins Avenue, Philadelphia, PA 19111-5094.

Federal Test Method Standard 791C—Lubricants, Liquid Fuels and Related Products; Methods of Testing

Federal Test Method Standard 791C, Method 3470—Homogeneity and Miscibility of Oils

2.1.6 ILSAC PUBLICATION—Available from American Automobile Manufacturers Association, 730 Second Avenue, Suite 300, Detroit, MI 48202.

ILSAC GF-1—The ILSAC Minimum Performance Standard for Passenger Car Engine Oils

ILSAC GF-2—Minimum Performance Standard for Passenger Car Engine Oils

2.1.7 DEPARTMENT OF DEFENSE PUBLICATIONS—Available from The Standardization Documents Order Desk, Building 4D, 700 Robbins Avenue, Philadelphia, PA 19111-5094.

Department of Defense Publication—CID-A-A-52039—Lubricating Oil, Automotive Engine, API Service SH

Department of Defense Publication—CID-A-A-52306—Lubricating Oil, Heavy-Duty Diesel Engine

2.1.8 AMERICAN CHEMISTRY COUNCIL (ACC), PETROLEUM ADDITIVES PANEL PUBLICATION—Available from American Chemistry Council, 1300 Wilson Boulevard, Arlington, VA 22209.

ACC Publication—Product Approval Code of Practice

2.1.9 GENERAL MOTORS CORPORATION PUBLICATION—Available from General Motors Corporation, CPE Engineering Standards, W-3, Warren, MI 48090.

GM9099-P—Engine Oil Filterability Test

2.1.10 COORDINATING EUROPEAN COUNCIL PUBLICATION—Available from the Coordinating European Council, CEC Secretariat, Madou Plaza - 25th Floor, Place Madou 1, B-1030 Brussels, Belgium.

CEC L-40-A-93—Evaporative Loss of Lubricating Oils

2.1.11 JAPAN PETROLEUM INSTITUTE PUBLICATION—Available from the American Automobile Manufacturers Association, 7430 Second Avenue, Suite 300, Detroit, MI 48202.

JPI 55-41-93 (Method B)—Determination of Evaporation Loss of Engine Oils

2.1.12 CHRYSLER CORPORATION/TANNAS COMPANY PUBLICATION—Available from Tannas Company, 4800 James Savage Road, Midland, MI 43642.

Thermo-Oxidation Engine Oil Simulation Test (Method 33)

3. The API Engine Oil Licensing and Certification System provides a communications tool for both engine manufacturers and oil marketers to describe a complex series of performance specifications to the user through a simple designation of several letters or symbols. This simplifies the oil marketer's job of communicating the applications for which his oil is suitable by using the same designations on his containers. More importantly, the consumer can easily link the engine manufacturer's recommendation with the information on the oil marketer's label to assist him in selecting the proper oil for his engine.

3.1 API Engine Oil Licensing and Certification System—The API Engine Oil Licensing and Certification System was developed through the cooperative efforts of AAM and API to assist engine manufacturers, oil marketers, and consumers to specify, market, and purchase engine oils using simple designations that describe the minimum performance standards for engine oils. The system embodies several different types of classifications including the API "S" series which describes engine oil standards primarily for gasoline engine service, the API "C" series which defines standards for diesel engines, and the ILSAC GF Series, "Minimum Performance Standard for Passenger Car Engine Oils."

3.2 Table 1, which summarizes the active Engine Oil Performance and Engine Service Categories, was prepared from information developed by API, ILSAC, AAM, EMA, and ASTM. These categories include API Classifications SH and SJ, ILSAC GF-2, and API categories CF, CF-2, and CF-4, CG-4, and CH-4. API service category SH is only available for licensing when used in conjunction with an active API "C" category. In such cases, the "C" service category must precede SH in the API Service Symbol. In some instances, an engine manufacturer may specify an engine oil that meets more than one engine service category, such as CG-4/SH. Oils which can support the performance claims for more than one API service category may be so designated. API licensed oils may display the appropriately licensed symbol(s).

3.3 Engine oils with newer classifications may not always provide satisfactory performance where older classifications are recommended. For example, CH-4 oils may not perform adequately in applications in which a CF-2 rated oil is recommended. The ASTM Engine Oil Description and the API Engine Service Description provide some guidance for substituting products with newer classifications where older ones are recommended. If there is any doubt, the equipment manufacturer should be consulted.

3.4 Some engine manufacturers may specify an Engine Service Category as the basis for their recommendation, but also have additional requirements. These requirements may include certain physical or chemical properties, or supplemental engine tests. Efforts should be made to determine the complete set of requirements for an application before selecting or recommending a lubricant.

3.5 Details regarding many of these test techniques, including descriptions of their objectives or significance may be found in SAE J304, ASTM STP 315, and STP 509, and Federal Test Method Standard 791. Some service categories have required test protocol. Where applicable, test results are considered valid only if the tests are run in calibrated stands monitored by the ASTM Test Monitoring Center and the test protocol meets all requirements of the ACC Product Approval Code of Practice when applicable.

3.6 Oils identified as ILSAC GF-2 and some oils identified as SH or SJ may be used in engines that contain catalysts, oxygen sensors, or other emission control devices where recommended by the equipment manufacturer. ILSAC GF-2 and some API SJ service category oils have phosphorus levels restricted to 0.10% by mass maximum. Some SH service category oils have phosphorus levels restricted to 0.12% by mass maximum. To minimize emission control system deterioration, it may be advantageous to use oils with limited phosphorus and optimized alkaline earth metal combinations, but which do not compromise engine durability.

There are much data indicating phosphorus can significantly reduce the performance and life of catalysts. The data also demonstrate this effect can be modified by the detergent package. However, no industry test is currently available for evaluating the impact of engine oil formulations on emission control systems. ASTM initiated a program in 1995 to develop such a performance test. A satisfactory test to discriminate oil performance in this area has not been finalized; further work will be required. ILSAC has announced they plan to include a limit on phosphorus content and/or an actual catalyst compatibility test in ILSAC GF-4.

Informational guidance on this subject may be found in the ASTM Report title "Oil Protection of Emission System Test (OPEST)—Development of an ASTM Sequence VII Test," available from Southwest Research Institute; and in SAE Fuels and Lubricants Technical Subcommittee 1, Engine Oil/Catalyst and Oxygen Sensor Compatibility Task Force Status Report, dated October 1985.

3.7 In 1983, a standard was established to define the energy conserving features of motor oils. This characteristic is described in SAE J1423.

4. Obsolete Categories—When a new category is created, it may result in the immediate or eventual obsolescence of another category. The obsolescence of a category usually results from its loss of practical value and significance. WIthout the proper efforts to maintain test procedures, parts, and materials, a candidate oil cannot be satisfactorily evaluated to determine whether or not it meets all the requirements for that category. Once a category is no longer available for licensing by API EOLCS, or if one or more of the tests used to define it is no longer monitored by ASTM or the test developer, or if one of the tests which define it can no longer be run due to the lack of test stands, test parts, or test materials, the category is considered obsolete.

Table A1 in Appendix A summarizes the obsolete Engine Oil Performance and Engine Service Categories. These include API SA, SB, SC, SD, SE, SF, SG, CA, CB, CC, CD, CD-II, CE, and ILSAC GF-1.

TABLE 1A—ACTIVE ENGINE SERVICE CLASSIFICATIONS
API SERVICE CATEGORY SH[1]

API Engine Service Description	Test Methods	Rated or Measured Parameters	Primary Performance Criteria	Rating Scale
API Service Category SH was adopted in 1992 for use in describing engine oil first mandated in 1993. This oil is for use in service typical of gasoline engines in current and earlier passenger-car, van, and light-truck operation under vehicle manufacturers recommended maintenance procedures.	ASTM D 5844 Sequence IID	Average engine rust rating, min Number stuck lifters	8.5 None	0-10, 10=clean
Engine oils developed for this Service Category provide performance exceeding the minimum requirements for API Service Category SG, which Service Category SH is intended to replace, in the areas of controlling deposits, oil oxidation, wear, rust, and corrosion and must meet the engine-protection sequence test requirements of DOD CID A-A-52039A and ILSAC GF-1. In addition, all viscosity grades designated in DOD CID A-A-52039A (SAE 5W-30, 10W-30, and 15W-40) must meet the bench test requirements described in DOD CID A-A-52039A and ILSAC GF-1. (SAE 15W-40 does not have a phosphorus limitation and does not have to meet the GM filterability test.)	ASTM D 5533 Sequence IIE	Hours to 375% kinematic viscosity increase at 40 °C, min Average sludge rating, min Average piston skirt varnish rating, min Average oil ring land deposit rating, min Lifter sticking Scuffing and wear Cam or lifter scuffing Cam plus lifter wear, µm Average, max Maximum, max Ring sticking (Oil related)	64 9.2 8.9 3.5 None None 30 64 None	 0-10, 10=clean 0-10, 10=clean 0-10, 10=clean
Engine oils that meet the API Service Category SH designation have been tested in accordance with the ACC Code, may use the API Base Oil Interchangeability Guidelines and the API Guidelines for SAE Viscosity-Grade Engine Testing, and may be used where API Service Category SG and earlier Categories have been recommended. Engine Oils that meet these requirements may display API Service Category SH in the upper portion of the API Service Symbol. Energy Conserving and Energy Conserving II continue to be separate from API Service Category SH.	ASTM D 5302 Sequence VE	Average engine sludge rating, min Rocker arm cover sludge rating, min Average piston skirt varnish rating, min Average engine varnish rating, min Oil ring clogging, % max Oil screen clogging, % max Compression ring sticking (hot stuck) Cam wear, µm Average, max Maximum, max	9.0 7.0 6.5 5.0 Report 20.0 None 127 380	0-10, 10=clean 0-10, 10=clean 0-10, 10=clean 0-10, 10=clean

API Engine Service Description	Test Methods	Rated or Measured Parameters	5W-30	10W-30	15W-40
Oil meeting the performance requirements measured in the following gasoline engine tests and bench tests. Test Method D 5844, the Sequence IID gasoline engine test has been correlated with vehicles used in short-trip service prior to 1978, particularly with regard to rusting. Test Method D 5533, the Sequence IIIE gasoline engine test has been correlated with vehicles used in high temperature service prior to 1988, particularly with regard to oil thickening and valve train wear. Test Method D 5302, the Sequence VE gasoline engine test, has been correlated with vehicles used in stop-and-go service prior to 1988, particularly with regard to sludge and valve train wear. Test Method D 5119, the L-38 gasoline engine test, is used to measure copper-lead bearing weight loss under high-temperature operating conditions. In addition to passing performance in the engine test, specific viscosity grade shall also meet bench test requirements. The volatility of engine oils relates to engine oil consumption. The Engine Oil Filterability Test screens for the formation of precipitates that can cause oil filter plugging. Phosphorus compounds can cause glazing of automotive catalysts and exhaust gas oxygen sensors and, thereby, deactivate them. Control of the phosphorus level in the engine oil can reduce this tendency. The flash point can indicate if residual solvents and low boiling fractions remain in the finished oil. Foaming in engine oil can cause valve lifter collapse and a loss of lubrication due to the presence of air in the oil. The foam test indicates an oil's foaming tendency. The Homogeneity and Miscibility Test indicates the compatibility of an oil with standard test oils. The L-38 Shear Stability Test indicates the ability of an oil to resist permanent viscosity loss due to shearing in an engine. The SH category requires that candidate oils meet the performance requirements in this specification, and that the oils be tested in accordance with the protocols described in the American Chemistry Council Petroleum Additives Product Approval Code of Practice. The ACC Code requires advance registration of all engine tests, along with a test methodology (Multiple Test Acceptance Criteria) to get a more precise estimate of the oil's true performance.	ASTM D 5119 L-38	Bearing weight loss, mg, max		40	
	ASTM D 2887 or ASTM D 5800	Volatility, % loss at 371 °C, max, or wt % loss 1 h 250 °C, max	20 25	17 20	15 18
	GM EOFT (GM9099P)	Flow reduction, %, max	50	50	NR
	ASTM D4951 or ASTM D 5185	Phosphorous mass, %, max	0.12	0.12	NR
	ASTM D 92 or ASTM D 93	Flash Point, °C, min Flash Point, °C, min	200 185	205 190	215 200
	ASTM D 892 (Option A)	Foaming Tendency, Foaming/Settling, mL/mL, max Sequence I Sequence II Sequence III	 10/0 50/0 10/0	 10/0 50/0 10/0	 10/0 50/0 10/0
	ASTM D 6082	Foaming Tendency, Foaming/Settling, mL/mL, max	Report	Report	Report
	FTM 791C Method 3470.1	Homogeneity and Miscibility		Homogeneous with SAE Reference Oils	
	ASTM D 5119 L-38	Shear Stability, 10 h stripped viscosity		Must remain in original grade	

1. API Service Category SH cannot be used except with CF and/or CF-2 and/or CF-4 and/or CG-4 and/or CH-4 when displayed in the API Service Symbol, and the "C" Category must appear first.

TABLE 1B—ACTIVE ENGINE SERVICE CLASSIFICATIONS
API SERVICE CATEGORY SJ

API Engine Service Description	Test Methods	Rated or Measured Parameter	Primary Performance Criteria	Rating Scale
API Service Category SJ was adopted for use in describing engine oils available in 1996. These oils are for use in service typical of gasoline engines in current and earlier passenger-car, sport utility vehicle, van, and light truck operations under vehicle manufacturers' recommended maintenance procedures.	ASTM D 5844 Sequence IID	Average engine rust rating, min	8.5	0-10, 10=clean
		Number stuck lifters	None	
Engine oils that meet the API Service Category SJ designation may be used where API Service Category SH and earlier Categories have been recommended.	ASTM D 5533 Sequence IIIE	Hours to 375% kinematic viscosity increase at 40 °C, min	64	
		Average sludge rating, min	9.2	0-10, 10=clean
		Average piston skirt varnish rating, min	8.9	0-10, 10=clean
		Average oil ring land deposit rating, min	3.5	0-10, 10=clean
Engine oils that meet the API Service Category SJ designation have been tested in accordance with the ACC Code, may use the API Base Oil Interchangeability Guidelines and the API Guidelines for SAE Viscosity-Grade Engine Testing.		Lifter sticking	None	
		Scuffing and wear		
		Cam or lifter scuffing	None	
		Cam plus lifter wear, μm		
Engine oils that meet these requirements may display API Service Category SJ in the upper portion of the API Service Symbol.		Average, max	30	
		Maximum, max	64	
		Ring sticking (Oil related)	None	
	ASTM D 5302 Sequence VE	Average engine sludge rating	9.0	0-10, 10=clean
		Cam cover sludge rating, min	7.0	0-10, 10=clean
		Average piston skirt varnish rating, min	6.5	0-10, 10=clean
		Average engine varnish rating, min	5.0	0-10, 10=clean
		Oil ring clogging, % max	Report	
		Oil screen clogging, % max	20.0	
		Compression ring sticking (hot stuck)	None	
		Cam wear, μm		
		Average, max	127	
		Maximum, max	380	

API Engine Service Description	Test Methods	Rated or Measured Parameter	Primary Performance Criteria: 0W-20, 5W-20, 5W-30, 10W-30	Primary Performance Criteria: All Others
Oil meeting the performance requirements measured in the following gasoline engine tests and bench tests. Test Method D 5844, the Sequence IID, gasoline engine test has been correlated with vehicles used in short trip service prior to 1978, particularly with regard to rusting. Test Method D 5533, the Sequence IIIE gasoline engine test, has been correlated with vehicles used in high temperature service prior to 1988, particularly with regard to oil thickening and valve train wear. Test Method D 5302 the Sequence VE gasoline engine test, has been correlated with vehicles used in stop-and-go service prior to 1988, particularly with regard to sludge and valve train wear. Test Method D 5119, the L-38 gasoline engine test, is used to measure copper-lead bearing weight loss under high-temperature operating conditions. In addition to passing performance in the engine tests, specific viscosity grades shall also meet bench test requirements. The volatility of engine oils is one of several factors which relates to engine oil consumption. The Engine Oil Filterability Test screens for the formation of precipitates and gels which can cause oil filter plugging. Phosphorus compounds in excessive amounts can cause glazing of automotive catalysts and exhaust gas oxygen sensors and, thereby, deactivate them. Control of the phosphorus level in the engine oil may reduce this tendency. The flash point may indicate if residual solvents and low boiling fractions remain in the finished oil. Excessive foaming in engine oil can cause valve lifter collapse and a loss of lubrication due to the presence of air in the oil. The foam test indicates an oil's foaming tendency. The Homogeneity and Miscibility Test indicates the compatibility of an oil with standard test oils. The L-38 Shear Stability Test indicates the ability of an oil to resist permanent viscosity loss due to shearing in an engine. Newer engines designed to provide increased horsepower, improved driveability, and meet future federal emissions and fuel economy requirements may be sensitive to internal deposits caused by elevated engine operating temperatures. The TEOST test may be useful in determining the deposit control of oils recommended for these engines. The Gelation Index technique might identify engine oils susceptible to air binding and might provide low temperature protection not adequately measured by the Test Method D 4684, Determination of Yield Stress and Apparent Viscosity of Engine Oils at Low Temperature. The SJ category requires that candidate oils meet the performance requirements in this specification, and that the oils be tested in accordance with the protocols described in the American Chemistry Council Petroleum Additives Product Approval Code of Practice. The ACC Code requires advance registration of all engine tests, along with a test methodology (Multiple Test Acceptance Criteria) to get a more precise estimate of the oil's true performance.	ASTM D 5119 L-38	Bearing weight loss, mg, max	40	
	ASTM D 5800 or Simulated Distillation ASTM D 2887 (Extended) or ASTM D 5480	Evaporation loss, wt %, max	22	20
		Wt % off at 371 °C, max	17	15
	GM EOFT (GM9099P) (H)	Flow reduction, %, max	50	50
		Standard Procedure		
		Modified with 0.6% H_2O	Report	Report
		Modified with 0.6% H_2O	Report	Report
		Modified with 0.6% H_2O	Report	Report
		Modified with 0.6% H_2O	Report	Report
	ASTM D 4951 or ASTM 5185	Phosphorus, mass %, max	0.10	NR
	ASTM D 92 or	Flash Point, °C, min	200	215
	ASTM D 93	Flash Point, °C, min	185	200
	ASTM D 892 (Option A)	Foaming Tendency, Foaming/Settling, mL/mL, max		
		Sequence I	10/0	10/0
		Sequence II	50/0	50/0
		Sequence III	10/0	10/0
	ASTM D 6082	Static Foam, Foaming/Settling mL/mL, max	200/50	200/50
	FTM 791C Method 3470.1	Homogeneity and Miscibility	Homogeneous with SAE Reference Oils	
	ASTM D 5119 L-38	Shear Stability, 10 h stripped viscosity	Must remain in original SAE grade	
	High Temperature Deposits (TEOST)	Deposit wt, mg, max	6060	
	Gelation Index ASTM D 5133	max	12NR	

TABLE 1C—ACTIVE ENGINE SERVICE CLASSIFICATIONS
ILSAC CATEGORY GF-2

ASTM Engine Oil Description	Test Methods	Rated or Measured Parameter	Primary Performance Criteria	Rating Scale
The Alliance of Automobile Manufacturers (AAM) Association of the United States, Inc., and the Japan Automobile Manufacturers Association, Inc., (JAMA), through an organization called the International Lubricants Standardization and Approval Committee (ILSAC), jointly developed and approved an ILSAC GF-2 minimum performance standard for gasoline fueled passenger car engine oils. The standard specifies the minimum performance requirements (both engine sequence and bench tests) and chemical and physical properties for those engine oils that vehicle manufacturers deem necessary for satisfactory equipment performance and life.	ASTM D 5844 Sequence IID	Average engine rust rating min	8.5	0-10, 10=Clean
		Number stuck lifters	None	
	ASTM D 5533 Sequence IIIE	Hours to 375% increase in viscosity at 40 °C, min	64	
		Average sludge rating, min	9.2	0-10, 10=Clean
		Average piston skirt varnish rating, min	8.9	0-10, 10=Clean
		Average oil ring land deposit rating, min	3.5	0-10, 10=Clean
		Cam plus lifter wear, µm (in)		
		Average, max	30	
		Maximum, max	64	
		Ring sticking	No oil related	
		Oil Consumption, l, max	5.1 max	
	ASTM D 5302 Sequence VE	Average engine sludge rating	9.0	0-10, 10=Clean
		Cam cover sludge rating, min	7.0	0-10, 10=Clean
		Average piston skirt varnish rating, min	6.5	0-10, 10=Clean
		Average engine varnish rating, min	5.0	0-10, 10=Clean
		Oil ring clogging, % max	Rate & Report	
		Oil screen clogging, % max	20.0	
		Compression ring sticking (hot stuck)	None	
		Cam wear, µm		
		Average, max	127	
		Maximum, max	380	
		Piston undercrown deposits	Rate & Report	
		Ring land deposits	Rate & Report	
		Cylinder bore wear	Rate & Report	
	L-38	Bearing weight loss, mg, max	40	
	ASTM D 5119 Volatility Evaporation Loss CEC-L-40-A-93[(1)] or JPI 55-41-93	Evaporation loss, wt %, max	22	
	or Simulated Distillation ASTM D 2887 (extended) or ASTM D 5480	Wt % off at 371 °C, max	17	
	GM EOFT (GM9099P)[(2)]	Flow reduction, %, max	50	
	ASTM D 4951 or ASTM D 5185	Phosphorus, mass %, max	0.10	
	ASTM D 92 or	Flash Point, °C, min	200	
	ASTM D 93	Flash Point, °C, min	185	
	ASTM D 892 (Option A)	Foaming Tendency, Foaming/Settling, mL/mL, max		
		Sequence I	10/0	
		Sequence II	50/0	
		Sequence III	10/0	
	ASTM D 6082	Static Foam, Foaming/Settling[(3)] mL/mL, max	200/50	
	FTM 791B Method 3470	Homogeneity and Miscibility	Homogeneous with SAE Reference Oils	
	ASTM D 5119 L-38	Shear Stability, 10 h stripped viscosity	Must remain in original grade	
	ASTM D 6202 Sequence VIA	Estimated Fuel Economy Improvement, %, min	0W-20 and 5W-20 = 1.4 Other 0W-XX and 5W-XX = 1.1 10W-XX = 0.5	
	High Temperature Deposits (TEOST)	Deposit wt, mg, max	60	
	ASTM D 5293	Low temperature Cranking viscosity, –20 °C, mPa·s, max	3500	
	ASTM D 4684	Low temperature pumping viscosity, –30 °C, mPa·s, max	60 000	
	ASTM D 5133	Gelation Index[(4)], max	12.0	

1. Since the publication of ILSAC GF-2, ASTM D 5800, a tightened version of CEC-L-40-A-93 has been issued.
2. In addition, the GM EOFT is to be run with the following modifications (Rate and Report only). Dry ice is not to be used during sample preparation. Sample is to be placed in an oven at 70 °C for 6 h. Tests to be run at 0.6, 1.0, 2.0, and 3.0% water. Test formulation with the highest additive (DI/VI) combination. Read across results to all other base oil/viscosity grade formulations using same or lower concentration of identical additive (DI/VI) combination. Each different (DI/VI) combination must be tested.
3. Settling time determined after 1 min.
4. To be evaluated from –5 °C to temperature at which 40 000 cP is attained or –40 °C, whichever occurs first.

TABLE 1D—ACTIVE ENGINE SERVICE CLASSIFICATIONS
API SERVICE CATEGORY CF

API Engine Service Description	Test Methods	Rated or Measured Parameters	Primary Performance Criteria		
API Service Category CF denotes service typical of off-road indirect injected diesel engines and other diesel engines which use a broad range of fuel types including those using fuel with higher sulfur content, for example over 0.5% wt. Effective control of piston deposits, wear, and corrosion of copper-containing bearings is essential for these engine, which may be naturally aspirated, turbocharged, or supercharged. Oils designated for this service have been in existence since 1994. Oils designated for this service may also be used when API service category CD is recommended. Engine oils that meet the API Service Category CF designation have been tested in accordance with the ACC Code, may use the API Base Oil Interchangeability Guidelines and the API Guidelines for SAE Viscosity-Grade Engine Testing.	1M-PC	Top groove fill (TGF), % volume, max	70(1)		
		Weighted total demerits (WTD) max	240		
		Ring Side clearance loss mm, max	0.013		
		Piston ring sticking	none		
		Piston, ring, and liner scuffing	none		
			First-Test	**Two-Test Average**	**Three-Test Average(2)**
	ASTM D 5119 L-38	Bearing weight loss, mg, max	43.7	48.1	50.0

ASTM Engine Oil Description

Oil meeting the performance requirements in the following diesel and gasoline engine tests. The 1M-PC diesel engine test has been shown to provide correlation with engine oil performance when used in naturally aspirated, turbocharged, or supercharged indirect injection engines. Test Method D 5119, the L- 38 gasoline engine test, is used to measure copper-lead bearing weight loss. Licensing of the CF category requires that candidate oils meet the performance requirements of this specification, and that the oils be tested in accordance with the protocols described in the ACC Petroleum Additives Product Approval Code of Practice. The methodology detailed in the ACC Code will help ensure that an engine oil meets its intended performance specification.

1. If three or more tests are run, one complete test may be discarded.
2. In a three-test program, allowance is made for excluding one of the tests as an outlier. The basis for determining whether the test is an outlier is ASTM E 178.

TABLE 1E—ACTIVE ENGINE SERVICE CLASSIFICATIONS
API SERVICE CATEGORY CF-2

API Engine Service Description	Test Methods	Rated or Measured Parameters	Primary Performance Criteria		
API Service Category CF-2 denotes service typical of two-stroke cycle engines requiring highly effective control over cylinder and ring-face scuffing and deposits. Oils designated for this service have been in existence since 1994 and may also be used when API Service Category CD-II is recommended. These oils do not necessarily meet the requirements of CF or CF-4 unless the oils have specifically met the performance requirements of these categories.	1M-PC	Weighted total demerits (WTD)	100(1)		
			First-Test	**Two-Test Average**	**Three-Test Average(2)**
	ASTM D 5862 6V-92TA	Cylinder liner scuffing area, % max	45.0	48.0	50.0
		Cylinder liner port plugging area,			
		Average, % max	2	2	2
		Single Cylinder, % max	5	5	5
		Piston rings face distress demerits			
Engine Oils in the two-stroke cycle DD 6V92TA engine test since January 1, 1992, may be considered for this Service Category provided the tests were conducted in accordance with the test procedure as published in ASTM Research Report RR:D02-1319 or as revised by the ASTM Test Monitoring Center. All testing conducted since January 1, 1994, must be done in accordance with the most current test procedures. Engine oils that meet the API Service Category CF-2 designation have been tested in accordance with the ACC Code, may use the Base Oil Interchangeability Guidelines and the API Guidelines for Viscosity-Grade Engine Testing.		No. 1 (fire ring) max	0.23	0.24	0.26
		Average of No. 2 and 3	0.20	0.21	0.22
	ASTM D 5119 L-38	Bearing weight loss, mg, max	43.7	48.1	50.0

ASTM Engine Oil Description

Oil meeting the performance requirements in the following diesel and gasoline engine tests:

The 1M-PC diesel engine test has been shown to provide correlation with engine oil performance when used in naturally aspirated, turbocharged, or supercharged indirect injection engines with modified piston deposit rating methodology to relate to effective piston and ring groove deposit control for two-stroke cycle diesel engines.

Test Method D 5862, the 6V92TA diesel engine test has been correlated with two-stroke cycle diesel engines in heavy-duty service, particularly with regard to ring face distress and liner scuffing. Licensing of the API CF-2 category requires that candidate oils meet the performance requirements of this specification, and that the oils be tested in accordance with the protocols described in the ACC Petroleum Additives ACC Product Approval Code of Practice. The methodology detailed in the ACC Code will help ensure that an engine oil meets its intended performance specification.

1. API Category CF-2 allows the running of multiple tests. The results of all tests run are averaged to determine the final result for WTD. When three or more tests are run, one test may be removed as an outlier result and the average calculated from the remaining test results.
2. In a three-test program, allowance is made for excluding one of the tests as an outlier. The basis for determining whether the test is an outlier is ASTM E 178.

TABLE 1F—ACTIVE ENGINE SERVICE CLASSIFICATIONS
API SERVICE CATEGORY CF-4

API Engine Service Description	Test Methods	Rated or Measured Parameters	Primary Performance Criteria			Rating Scale
			Two-Test	Three-Test	Four-Test	
API Service Category CF-4 describes oils for use in high-speed, four-stroke cycle diesel engines. CF-4 oils exceed the requirements of the Service Category CE, are designed to replace CE oils, and provide improved control of oil consumption and piston deposits. CF-4 oils may be used in place of CC-CD oils. They are particularly suited for on-highway, heavy-duty truck applications.	1K[(1)(2)]	Weighted Demerits (WDK), max	332	339	342	
		Groove No. 1 (top) carbon fill (TGF), % volume, max	24	26	27	
		Top land heavy carbon (TLHC), % max	4	4	5	
		Oil Consumption, g/kW-h, (228-252 h) max	0.27	0.27	0.27	
		Piston ring sticking	None	None	None	
		Piston ring and liner scuffing	None	None	None	
				Individual Tests		
	ASTM D 5119 L-38	Bearing weight loss, mg, max		50		
	T-6	Merit rating, min		90		0-160
	or T-9	Top piston ring weight loss average, mg, max		150		
	ASTM D 6483	Liner wear, µm, max		40		
	T-7	Average rate of kinematic viscosity increase during last 50 h, cSt at 100 °C/h, max		0.040		
	or ASTM D 5967 (T-8A	Average rate of kinematic viscosity increase from 100 to 150 h, mm^2/s at 100 °C/h, max		0.20		
ASTM Engine Oil Description						
Oil meeting the performance requirements in the following diesel and gasoline engine tests: The 1K diesel engine test has been correlated with vehicles equipped with engines used in high-speed operation prior to 1989, particularly with regard to deposits, oil consumption, and ring wear. The T-6 has been correlated with vehicles equipped with engines used in high-speed operation prior to 1980, particularly with regard to deposits, oil consumption, and ring wear. The T-7 test has been correlated with vehicles equipped with engines operated largely under lugging conditions prior to 1984, particularly with regard to oil thickening. Test Method D 5968, the corrosion bench test, has been shown to predict corrosion of engine oil-lubricated copper, lead, or tin-containing components used in diesel engines. Test Method D 5290, the NTC-400 diesel engine test, has been correlated with vehicles equipped with engines in highway operation prior to 1983, particularly with regard to oil consumption control, deposits, and wear. Calibrated stands are no longer available due to unavailability of critical test parts. It has been demonstrated that the 1K test, in combination with Test Method D 5968, can be substituted for the NTC-400 test as an acceptable means to demonstrate performance against this category; however, data from NTC-400 tests, run in calibrated stands, can be used to support this category in accordance with the provisions of Specification D 4485-94. Test Method D 5119, the L-38 gasoline engine test is used to measure copper-lead bearing weight loss.	ASTM D 5968 Corrosion bench test	Copper mg/kg (ppm) increase, max		20		
		Lead, mg/kg (ppm) increase, max		60		
		Tin, mg/kg (ppm) increase		Report		
		Copper, Corrosion[(3)], max		3		

1. Caterpillar 1K reference oil, two, three, and four test limits are published twice per year by the ASTM Test Monitoring Center. Copies of these data may be obtained by contacting the Center of ASTM TMC, 4400 Fifth Avenue, Pittsburgh, PA 15213. Applicable reference oil data to which candidate oil data are to be compared are included with each engine test report.
2. A 1K test program with a minimum of two tests, acceptable according to the limits shown, is required to demonstrate performance for this category. ASTM D 4485-94 lists the NTC 400 (D5290) as a test method required to demonstrate performance for this category. Due to the lack of availability of critical test parts, the NTC 400 is no longer available as a calibrated test, and has been replaced in this category by the requirement for a second 1K test and the Bench Corrosion Test. Alternatively, instead of running a second 1K test and Bench Corrosion Test, data from the NTC 400 test, run in calibrated test stands can be used to support this category according to all provisions of ASTM D 4485-94, Table 3. Original NTC 400 limits were as follows:
   Camshaft roller follower pin wear: 0.051 mm max
   Crownland (top land) deposits, area covered with heavy carbon, % average: 15 max.
   Oil Consumption, g/s: Candidate oil consumption second order regression curve shall fall completely below the published mean curve for the applicable reference oil.
3. The rating system in Test Method D 130 is used to rate the copper coupon in the Test Method D 5968.

TABLE 1G—ACTIVE ENGINE SERVICE CLASSIFICATIONS API SERVICE CATEGORY CG-4

API Engine Service Description

API Service Category CG-4 describes oils for use in high-speed, four-stroke cycle diesel engines used in highway and off-road applications where the fuel sulfur content may vary from less than 0.05% weight to less than 0.5% weight. CG-4 oils provide effective control over high temperature piston deposits, wear, corrosion, foaming, oxidation, and soot accumulation. These oils are especially effective in engines designed to meet 1994 exhaust emission standards and may also be used in engines requiring API Service Categories CD, CE, and CF-4. Oils designated for API Service Category CG-4 have been in existence since 1995. Engine oils that meet the API Service Category CG-4 designation have been tested in accordance with the ACC Code, may use the API Base Oil Interchangeability Guidelines and the API Guidelines for SAE Viscosity-Grade Engine Testing.

ASTM Engine Oil Description

Oil meeting the performance requirements in the following diesel and gasoline engine tests:

The 1N diesel engine test has been used to predict piston deposit formation in four-stroke cycle, direct injection, diesel engines which have been calibrated to meet 1994 U.S. federal exhaust emissions requirements for heavy-duty engines operated on fuel containing less than 0.05% weight sulfur. Test Method D 5967, the T-8 diesel engine test, has been shown to generate soot-related oil thickening in a manner similar to 1992 emission-controlled heavy-duty diesel engines using mechanical injection control systems. Test Method D 5533, the Sequence IIIE gasoline engine test, has been correlated with vehicles used in high-temperature service prior to 1988, particularly with regard to oil thickening. Test Method D 5119, the L-38 gasoline engine test, is used to measure copper-lead bearing weight loss and viscosity loss due to shearing. Test Method D 5966, the roler follower wear test (RFWT), has been correlated with hydraulic roller cam follower pin wear in medium-duty indirect injection diesel engines used in broadly based field operations. The Engine Oil Aeration Test has been correlated with oil aeration in diesel engines equipped with hydraulically actuated electronically controlled, unit injectors, (HEUI) used in medium-duty service. Test method D 892, a foaming test, Sequences I, II, and III, has been shown to predict foaming of engine oils used in diesel engines. Test Method d 5968, the bench corrosion test, has been shown to predict corrosion of engine oil-lubricated copper, lead, or tin-containing components used in diesel engines. Licensing of the API CG-4 category requires that candidate oils meet the performance requirements of this specification, and that the oils be tested in accordance with the protocols described in the ACC Petroleum Additives Product Approval Code of Practice. The methodology detailed in the ACC Code will help ensure that an engine oil meets its intended performance specification.

Test Methods	Rated or Measured Parameters	Primary Performance Criteria		
		First-Test	**Two-Test**	**Three-Test**
1N	Weighted Demerits 1N (WDN),	286.2	311.7	323.0
	Top groove fill (TGF) % volume, max	20	23	25
	Top land heavy carbon (TLHC), % max	3	4	5
	Oil consumption, g/kW-h, (0-252 h) max	0.5	0.5	0.5
	Scuffing, piston-rings-liners	none	none	none[1]
	Stuck rings	none	none	none
ASTM D 5967 T8	Viscosity increase at 3.8% soot, cSt, max	11.5	12.5	13.0
	Filter plugging, differential pressure, kPa (psi), max	138 (20)	138 (20)	138 (20)
	Oil consumption, g/kW-h, max lb/bhp-h, max	0.304 (0.0005)	0.304 (0.0005)	0.304 (0.0005)
ASTM D 5533 Sequence IIIE	Hours to 375% viscosity increase, min	67.5	65.1	64.0
ASTM D 5119 L-38	Bearing weight loss, mg, max	43.7	48.1	50.0
	Used oil viscosity, cSt greater than SAE J300 lower limit for grade, min[2]	0.5	0.5	0.5
ASTM D 5966 (RFWT)	Wear, µm, max mils, max	11.4 (0.45)	12.4 (0.49)	12.7 (0.50)
D 892	Foaming characteristics			
	Foaming/settling[3] mL, max			
	Sequence I	10/0		
	Sequence II	20/0		
	Sequence III	10/0		
Engine Oil Aeration Test	Foam, vol %, max	10		
ASTM D 5968 Bench Corrosion Test	Copper, ppm increase, max	20		
	Lead, ppm increase, max	60		
	Tin, ppm increase, max	Report		
	Copper corrosion[4], max	3		

1. If three or more operationally valid tests have been run, the majority of these shall not have scuffing. The scuffing tests are considered uninterpretable, and all data from these tests are eliminated from averaging.
2. Limits do not apply to mono-grade oils.
3. Settling time is 10 min.
4. The rating system in Test Method D 130 is used to rate the copper coupon in the bench corrosion test.

TABLE 1H—ACTIVE ENGINE SERVICE CLASSIFICATIONS
API SERVICE CATEGORY CH-4

API Engine Service Description	Test Methods	Rated or Measured Parameters	Primary Performance Criteria		
			First-Test	Two-Test	Three-Test
API Service Category CH-4 describes oils for use in high-speed, four-stroke diesel engines designed to meet 1998 exhaust emissions standards as well as for previous model years. CH-4 oils are specifically compounded for use with diesel fuels ranging in sulfur content up to 0.5% weight. These oils are especially effective to sustain engine durability even under adverse applications that may stress wear control, high temperature stability, and soot handling properties. In addition, optimum protection is provided against non-ferrous corrosion, oxidative and insoluble thickening, foaming, and viscosity loss due to shear These oils also have the performance capability to afford a more flexible approach to oil drain intervals in accordance with the recommendations of the individual engine builders for their specific engines. CH-4 oils are superior in performance to those meeting API CF-4 and AP CG-4 and can effectively lubricate engines calling for those API Service Categories.	1P	WDP, max	350	378	390
		TGC, max	36	39	41
		TLC, max	40	46	49
		Average Oil Consumption, g/h (0-360 h), max	12.4	12.4	12.4
		Final Oil Consumption, g/h (312-360 h), max	14.6	14.6	14.6
		Scuffing, piston-rings-liner	None	None	None
	1K	WDK, max	332	347	353
		TGF, max	24	27	29
		TLHC, max	4	5	5
		Oil Consumption, g/kW-h (0-252h), max	0.5	0.5	0.5
		Scuffing, piston-ring-liner	None	None	None(1)
	T-9	Average Liner Wear, normalized to 1.75% soot, µm max	25.4	26.6	27.1
		Average Top Ring Weight Loss, mg max	120	136	144
		EOT Used Oil Lead Content less New Oil Lead content, ppm max	25	32	36
	ASTM D 5966 (RFWT)	Average Pin Wear, µm max (mils max)	7.6 (0.30)	8.4 (0.33)	9.1 (0.36)
	M11 HST	Rocker Pad Average Wt. Loss, normalized to 4.5% soot, mg max	6.5	7.5	8.0
		Oil Filter Differential Pressure at EOT, kPa max	79	93	100
		Engine Sludge, CRC Merits at EOT, min	8.7	8.6	8.5
	D 5967 Ext. T-8	Relative Viscosity at 4.8% Soot by TGA, max	2.1	2.2	2.3
		Viscosity increase at 3.8% Soot by TGA, cSt, max,	11.5	12.5	13.0
	D 5533	64 Hour Viscosity @ 40 °C, max increase from 10 minute sample, %	200	200	200
	EOAT	Aeration, Vol. % max	8.0	8.0	8.0
	D 5968 (275 °F HTC BT)	Used Oil Elemental Concentration, ppm above baseline, max			
		Copper	20		
		Lead	120		
		Tin	50		
		Specimen discoloration(2), max	3		
	D 892	Foaming/Settling(3), mL, max			
		Sequence I	10/0		
		Sequence II	20/0		
		Sequence III	10/0		
	D 5800 or D 2887 ext.		SAE 10W-30	SAE 15W-40	
		Weight % volatility loss at 250 °C, max	20	18	
		Weight % volatility loss at 371 °C, max	17	15	
	D 6278		SAE XW-30	SAE XW-40	
		Kinematic Viscosity after shearing, cSt min	9.3	12.5	

TABLE 1H—ACTIVE ENGINE SERVICE CLASSIFICATIONS
API SERVICE CATEGORY CH-4 (continued)

API Engine Service Description	Test Methods	Rated or Measured Parameters	Primary Performance Criteria
ASTM Engine Oil Description			
Oil meeting the performance requirements measured in the following diesel and gasoline engine tests and the requirements in the following bench tests:			
The 1K diesel engine test has been correlated with engines use in high speed operation prior to 1989, particularly with respect to aluminum piston deposits, oil consumption, and ring wear when fuel sulfur content is nominally 0.4% by weight. The 1P diesel engine test has been used to predict iron piston deposit formation and oil consumption in four-stroke-cycle, direct injection, diesel engines that have been calibrated to meet 1998 U.S. federal exhaust emissions requirements for heavy-duty engines operating on fuel containing less than 0.05% by weight sulfur. The T-9 diesel engine test has been correlated with vehicles equipped with engines used in high speed operation prior to 1998, particularly in regard to ring and liner wear and used oil lead content. Test Method D 5967 extended, the T-8E engine test, has been shown to generate soot related oil thickening in a manner similar to 1998 emissions-controlled heavy-duty diesel engines using electronic injection control systems. The M11 High Soot diesel engine test has been correlated with vehicles equipped with four-stroke-cycle diesel engine used in high speed operations prior to 1998, particularly with regard to soot related valve train wear, filter plugging, and sludge control. Test Method D 5966, the Roller Follower Wear Test, has been correlated with hydraulic roller cam follower pin wear in medium-duty indirect injection diesel engines used in broadly based field operations. Test Method D 5533, the Sequence IIIE gasoline engine test, has been correlated with vehicles used in high-temperature service prior to 1988, particularly with regard to oil thickening. The EOAT has been correlated with oil aeration in diesel engines equipped with HEUI used in medium-duty diesel engines. Test Method D 892, a foaming test, Sequences I, II, and III has been shown to predict foaming of engine oils in diesel engines. Test Method D 5968 opeated at 275 °F, the High Temperature Corrosion Bench Test (HTCBT), has been shown to predict the corrosion of engine oil-lubricated copper, lead, or tin-containing components used in diesel engines. Test Method D 6278, the Diesel Injector Shear Test, has been shown to correlate with permanent shear loss of engine oils in medium-duty direct injection diesel engines used in broadly based field operations. Test Method D 5800, Noack Volatility or, alternatively, Test Method D 2887, extended, is used to measure engine oil volatility loss under high temperature operating conditions. Licensing of the API CH-4 category requires that candidate oils meet the performance requirements in this specification, and that the oils be tested in accordance with the protocols described in the ACC Petroleum Additives Product Approval Code of Practice. The methodology detailed in the ACC Code will help ensure that an engine oil meets its intended performance specification.			

1. If three or more operationally valid tests have been run, the majority of these shall not have scuffing. The scuffed tests are considered uninterpretable, and all data from these tests are eliminated from averaging.
2. The rating system in Test Method D 130 is used to rate the copper coupon in the bench corrosion test.
3. Settling time is 10 min.

APPENDIX A
HISTORICAL ENGINE OIL PERFORMANCE AND ENGINE OIL SERVICE CLASSIFICATION FOR API CATEGORIES NO LONGER ACTIVE

A.1 Scope—The scope of this Appendix is to reference historical engine oil categories that are defined by obsolete test techniques. The American Petroleum Institute Lubricants Subcommittee has declared these categories to be obsolete.

Tables 1 and A1 summarize the Historical Engine Oil Performance and Engine Oil Service Classification for API Categories No Longer Active. This classification system is divided into two major categories, "S" and "C." This "S" category denotes gasoline engine services and historically was composed of service classifications SA, SB, SC, SD, SE, SF, and SG. The "C" category denotes commercial diesel engine services, and historically has been composed of service classifications CA, CB, CC, CD, CD-II, and CE.

A.2 History of Obsolete Engine Service Classifications—Prior to 1947, automotive engine oils were classified by SAE J300 in terms of viscosity only. In order to permit the recommendation of oils by classes which would include factors other than viscosity, the American Petroleum Institute adopted in 1947 a system which divided crankcase oils into three classes depending on the properties of the oil and the operating conditions under which it was intended to be used. In this system, crankcase oils were single grade oils classified as: Regular Type, Premium Type, or Heavy-Duty Type. Generally, the Regular Type oils were straight mineral oils, Premium Type contained oxidation inhibitors, and Heavy-Duty Type contained oxidation inhibitors plus detergent-dispersant additives.

These early service classifications did not recognize that diesel and gasoline engines might have different engine oil requirements or that the requirements for either type of engine are influenced significantly by the characteristics of the fuel burned and operating conditions, especially cold weather "start and stop" operation. Consequently, the API developed a new classification system based on the severity of engine service. This system was developed in 1952 and revised in 1955.

The API Engine Service Classification System described and classified, in general terms, the service conditions under which engines were operated. It included three categories for gasoline engines (ML=Motor Light, MM=Motor Medium, and MS=Motor Severe) and three for diesel engines (DG=Diesel General, DM=Diesel Medium, and DS=Diesel Severe). In 1960 the system was again modified and performance definitions were added to define the service categories by the adoption of the ASTM Multi-cylinder Sequence Tests (Sequence I, II, III, IV, and V). Detail regarding these categories was given in SAE J303, Internal Combustion Engine Service Classifications, which last appeared in the 1971 SAE Handbook.

Because the API Engine Service Classification lacked precise technical definitions of quality, gasoline and diesel engine oils were described using combinations of the API Service Classification, and individual company and military specifications. Supplementary quality definitions were found necessary and these supplemental definitions were incorporated into individual company specifications. This practice encouraged the development of special lubricants acceptable to only one equipment manufacturer. Also, the performance level indicated by each category changed periodically and thus it became necessary to include supplementary definitions in communications regarding engine oil.

It became apparent that more effective means must be found to communicate engine oil performance and engine service classification information between the automotive equipment manufacturer, the petroleum industry, and the customer. Accordingly, in 1969 and 1970, the API, ASTM, and SAE cooperated in establishing the present classification as a joint effort to provide these means.

In 1987, the Motor Vehicle Manufacturers Association (MVMA) and the Japan Automobile Manufacturers Association formed the International Lubricant Standardization and Approval Committee (ILSAC) to provide them with a greater voice in setting engine oil specifications. MVMA has since changed their name to the American Automobile Manufacturers Association (AAMA) and more recently reorganized as the Alliance of Automobile Manufacturers (AAM). AAM and API jointly manage the implementation of ILSAC standards. The first ILSAC standard, ILSAC GF-1, was commercialized in 1993.

A.2.1 API "S" Categories—The "S" categories were developed as a cooperative effort between the American Petroleum Institute (API), the American Society for Testing and Materials (ASTM) and SAE. In this system, SA was the base or minimum level and each increase in the alphabetic letter following the letter "S" indicated an increase in the engine oil performance requirements.

All of the engine oil performance and engine service categories starting with the letter "S" were originally intended for service lubrication of certain automotive internal combustion engines, based on a 4-stroke cycle, using reciprocating trunk pistons, utilizing spark ignition and powered by gasoline fuel.

For purposes of this standard, the term "gasoline fuel" means either hydrocarbon fuel derived from petroleum, or hydrocarbon fuel blended with alcohols and other oxygenated compounds, which complied with the then applicable industry standards. The then applicable industry standards include: American Society for Testing and Materials (ASTM) D 439 - Specification for Automotive Gasolines, ASTM D 4814 - Standard Specification for Automotive Spark-Ignition Engine Fuel, SAE Recommended Practice J312 - Automotive Gasolines, and SAE Information Report 1297 - Alternative Automotive Fuels.

A.2.2API "C" Categories—The "C" categories were devised as a result of joint efforts of the American Petroleum Institute (API), the Society of Automotive Engineers (SAE), and the American Society for Testing and Materials (ASTM). Originally, four categories were established, CA, CB, CC, and CD. At this time, CA was the base or minimum performance level, and each increase in the alphabet letter following the "C" indicated an increase in severity of service. Unlike the "S" categories in which each new addition has superseded the previous category, the "C" categories added after CD have branched to simultaneously accommodate several different types of engines with different types of lubrication needs. Some of these different and sometimes conflicting requirements include two-stroke versus four-stroke cycle and direct versus indirect fuel injection. For this reason, a higher letter designation following the "C" does not necessarily mean that the oil is better for a given application. For example, a CF-2 oil may not provide adequate service in an engine designed for a CE level oil.

A.2.3 ILSAC Categories—All ILSAC categories currently apply to gasoline powered passenger car engines. ILSAC designations contain a GF prefix followed by a number indicating the generation of the standard. The only ILSAC designation in the obsolete section is ILSAC GF-1. To date, ILSAC Standards and API "S" categories have closely matched one another with a few notable exceptions. ILSAC standards apply to the viscosity grades primarily recommended by the U.S. and Japanese auto manufacturers. ILSAC standards up to this time have also included requirements for fuel economy, which have been absent from API "S" categories. All ILSAC standards contain maximum phosphorus limits. Their API "S" counterparts match these restrictions only on certain SAE grades, currently 0W-20, 5W-20, 5W-30, and 10W-30. Except for the SAE viscosity grades designated to match the ILSAC phosphorus requirements, API "S" categories have no phosphorus content restrictions for any other SAE viscosity grades.

A.2.4 API Category SA (pre-1964)—This category has been declared TECHNICALLY OBSOLETE by both the SAE Fuels and Lubricants Technical Committee 1 and the Fuels and Lubricants Division.

A.2.4.1 BACKGROUND—The oils used in North America before 1931 were "additive-free" and such oils were referred to as either API Regular or SERVICE ML prior to 1971. The use of the terminology "SA" was adopted in 1971 to define an engine service category for engine oil which contained no performance additives.

In North America, mineral oils began to replace animal and vegetable oils for lubrication during the period 1885 to 1900. This service category identified mineral oils which contained no performance additives and were intended for the service lubrication of certain low performance gasoline-powered automotive engines typical of the period 1900 to 1930 in North America. Because these oils did not contain any detergent additives, they were also commonly referred to as "non-detergent." These "additive-free" mineral oils were only single or "straight" viscosity grade and the customer had to change the "weight" of the engine oil depending on the season of the year. High viscosity or "heavy weight" engine oil was generally preferred in the higher temperature summer months and lower viscosity or "weight" was needed in the colder temperatures to permit proper starting. While the correct terminology for these fluids is engine oils they also were commonly referred to as "motor oils." Since these mineral oils did not have additives, they were only able to provide the most basic lubrication protection. Such low performance oils were only suitable for automotive gasoline engine lubrication under the very mild operating conditions and maintenance intervals typical of this period in North America.

The typical high-production volume passenger car produced in the U.S. during 1900 to 1930, weighed 1000 kg (2200 lb) or less and was powered by a 4-cylinder engine of about 3.4 L (200 in^3) displacement. These engines would operate at about 1600 to 2500 revolutions per minute (rpm), with a compression ratio of about 4.5 to 1, and produce an output of 15 to 40 kW (20.1 to 53.6 hp). Such vehicles were capable of top speeds between 50 and 100 km/h (31.1 and 62.1 mph). Most of these low-cost engines had generous design clearances between moving parts. These high-production volume automotive engines had no oil pumps or oil filters and relied on a combination of gravity and splash for engine lubrication. Air cleaners were first introduced in 1922. In 1924, the first full pressure lubrication system with an oil filter became available on a high-production volume engine. The early air and oil filters used on automobiles were low performance and not really effective. Many of these engines had no water pump and relied on the thermosyphon circulation of water for engine cooling. These engines were not equipped with any emissions control technology.

During the early 1900s, the road system did not permit long periods of high-speed driving. In 1904, only 8.7% of 3.7 million kilometers (2.3 million miles) of U.S. roads were surfaced. This increased, in 1930, to 26% of 5.1 million kilometers (3.2 million miles). In 1900, only 4200 passenger cars were sold in the U. S.; but, by 1930, there were about 35 million passenger cars in operation in the U. S.

There were no formal performance standards or specifications established for automotive fuels during this period. Kerosene was the preferred product from the refining of petroleum. Gasoline was only a by-product of this refining process, which had no obvious use until the automobile came along. The production of gasoline exceeded the production of kerosene for the first time in 1915.

The rapid growth of automobile production and the subsequent demand for gasoline caught the petroleum industry without adequate capacity to manufacture enough naturally occurring "straight run" gasoline to meet the demand. In the 1920 to 1930 time period, many refiners raised the allowable distillation end point from 205 °C to 225 °C (401 °F to 437 °F) in an attempt to stretch the gasoline production to meet demand. In effect, this operational change added light kerosene to the normal gasoline production. This "heavier gasoline" caused excessive fuel dilution of the engine oil in the crankcase and also created hard starting problems. In addition, the light kerosene portion of the heavy gasoline was found to promote engine knock. To improve the performance and increase the supply of gasoline, refiners installed thermal cracking equipment to break down the heavy petroleum into a larger volume of lighter products, like gasoline. This allowed the refiners to market these higher octane products as "High Test" gasoline. The use of thermally cracked gasoline solved the capacity/octane issues, but caused the formation of unstable gum-like deposits in the fuel systems.

Many gasolines of this period, caused automotive engines to experience violent detonation or spark-knock, especially at low speeds. To help quantify this observed "knocking" phenomenon, an industry standard test procedure using a single cylinder test engine and reference fuels was developed. The term used to define the unit of knocking intensity was the octane number. The octane number of an unknown test fuel was defined as the volume of the high reference fuel (isooctane) which had to be added to the low reference fuel (normal heptane) to match the knock intensity of the unknown test fuel. Some of the early straight run gasolines were estimated to have Research Octane Numbers (RON) of 35 to 57. Thermally cracked gasolines had values of RON ranging between 72 to 82. Thus the two major gasoline blending components had widely differing engine knock performance characteristics. The wide variations in gasoline anti-knock quality and the concern about potential low-speed engine knock, forced designers to keep a ceiling on engine compression ratio of 4.5 to 1.

The use of fuel additives containing lead was found to help control the engine knock concern. Starting in 1923, lead anti-knock compounds were blended, upon customer request, into automotive fuel, at the gasoline dispensing pump. In 1926, Premium Ethyl gasoline, of 70 RON, was first available directly from the refinery with up to 0.8 cm^3/L (3 cm^3/gal) of Tetra Ethyl Lead (TEL) anti-knock already added. Some engine manufacturers quickly took advantage of this new opportunity to raise compression ratios. In 1924, the first medium priced high compression engine, with a 4.7 to 1 ratio, was introduced. This was followed, in 1928, by a model with a 6.1 to 1 compression ratio. This started a performance trend which saw both gasoline octane ratings and compression ratios rise in support of each other.

The early model automobiles were not designed for all season use and most were stored indoors during cold weather. Cold starting was not a significant concern and there was little interest in low viscosity engine oils. High viscosity oils were preferred to minimize oil consumption, handle high loads, and tolerate large amounts of crankcase fuel dilution.

The average per vehicle consumption of gasoline, for calendar year 1930, was estimated at 650 L (170 gal) based on published figures for gasoline sales and vehicle registrations. Typical gasoline mileage for high volume passenger cars in this period fell in the range of 8 to 13 km/L (19 to 28 mpg).

Even under these relatively mild engine operating conditions, automobile manufacturers recommended oil change intervals were relatively short for those engine oils which would have been defined as SA. A typical U.S. manufacturer's oil change service interval was 1600 km (1000 miles) during this period. However, the actual recommended service interval for oil change varied widely and ranged from as low as 25 km (16 miles) up to 3200 km (2000 miles) depending on the specific vehicle and its date of manufacture. The engines had high internal clearances and were poorly sealed. Therefore, they consumed and leaked large amounts of oil and required the constant addition (almost daily) of substantial amounts of make-up oil to maintain the proper oil level in the crankcase. This constant fresh oil addition, in effect, allowed the equipment manufacturer to stretch the oil change interval more than would have been prudent if the SA performance oil was used in a lower oil consumption, close tolerance engine. Such limited performance oils were only suited for automotive engine lubrication until about 1930.

A.2.4.2 Rationale for Obsolescence—The number of vintage automotive engines, in use, which could use such a limited performance category without harm is extremely small (far less than 0.1% of vehicles registered in the U.S.). The equipment design, fuel, and operating conditions, which existed at the time engine oils of this performance level were appropriate, are discussed in the background section. Modern equipment designs, fuels and operating conditions are different and more severe than those described in the background section and they require an improved lubricant technology to provide acceptable performance. Since API "S" Performance Categories alphabetically higher than SA are suitable for all gasoline powered automotive engine applications specifying SA, there is no further technical need for such products in the marketplace and such products are considered TECHNICALLY OBSOLETE for use in automotive engine lubrication.

A.2.4.3 Recommended Labeling Practice—SA performance oils do not provide adequate engine protection under modern vehicle operating conditions. If SA performance oils were used by an uninformed consumer in a modern automotive engine, there is a high probability its misapplication would cause harm to his engine and its emissions control devices which are required to comply with emission standards which did not exist at the time SA performance oils were used.

Therefore, it is reasonable and prudent for any marketer, who chooses to offer such a low performance, limited application oil to the consumer, to warn the consumer of the limitations of their product's application. This caution should be displayed on each oil container and on any overpack carton in legible and conspicuous type upon a contrasting background. In the case of engine oil sold in bulk, information indicating the product's limitations and application should be clearly and prominently included on the invoice. The following statement would be considered reasonable and prudent by experts in the field of automotive gasoline engine lubrication:

CAUTION—THIS OIL IS RATED API SA. IT CONTAINS NO ADDITIVES. IT IS NOT SUITABLE FOR USE IN MOST GASOLINE-POWERED AUTOMOTIVE ENGINES BUILT AFTER 1930. USE IN MODERN ENGINES MAY CAUSE UNSATISFACTORY ENGINE PERFORMANCE OR EQUIPMENT HARM.

A.2.5 API Category SB (pre-1964)—This engine service category has been declared TECHNICALLY OBSOLETE by both the SAE Fuels and Lubricants Technical Committee 1 and the Fuels and Lubricants Division.

A.2.5.1 Background—This engine service category identified engine oils typical of the time period 1931 to 1963 in North America. These oils, which had a low level of additive treatment, were also known as API Premium and SERVICE MM prior to 1971. The use of the terminology "SB" was adopted in 1971 to describe engine oils containing some minimum level of performance additives. These oils offered mild anti-scuff capability, some limited resistance to oil oxidation and some copper/lead bearing corrosion protection. These SB performance oils were inhibited, but contained no detergents and were also referred to as "non-detergent" oils.

These low-additive content oils were first marketed around 1930 in the U.S. and coincided with the introduction of solvent refining technology for lubricant base oil stocks. Solvent refining improved the viscosity index and the appearance of the base oil but removed some of the naturally occurring oxidation inhibitors. These oxidation inhibitors had to be replaced by man-made anti-oxidants to protect against rapid deterioration of the oil.

The additives used in SB performance oils were also influenced by the widespread use of tetraethyl lead (TEL) as a gasoline octane improver and knock suppressor. The use of TEL, with the associated halogen based scavengers, increased the corrosion and deposit tendencies in engines. The use of gasoline, containing TEL, initially formed combustion chamber deposits. Analysis showed these deposits were primarily composed of lead compounds. Spark plug fouling also occurred when highly conductive lead compounds deposited on the electrode. The addition of ethylene dibromide and ethylene dichloride to TEL helped to reduce these deposits. Fortunately, these halogen-based compounds acted as effective scavengers of lead based deposits, but also caused corrosion problems.

The use of tricresylphosphate (TCP) as a gasoline additive became popular in the 1950's. TCP was found to limit the formation of lead deposits and changed the character of these deposits. This helped prevent spark plug misfiring and preignition caused by combustion chamber deposits.

Gasoline antioxidants were first used in 1930 to help stabilize the fuel and prevent gum-like deposits in fuel lines, carburetor jets and on intake valves. During this period, other gasoline additives which came into use were rust inhibitors, metal deactivators, anti-icing compounds, and corrosion inhibitors. In addition, gasoline was sweetened by chemical treatment of certain sulfur compounds to improve its odor. This was accomplished by the removal of hydrogen sulfide and the conversion of mercaptan compounds into disulfides.

In 1934, leaded regular gasoline became widely available and was introduced at a research octane number (RON) of 70 and this gradually rose over the period to 92 RON. This permitted the first widespread availability of consistent anti-knock quality in gasoline fuels. A similar trend occurred for the leaded premium gasoline which rose from 75 to 100 RON, allowing typical engine compression ratios to increase from 4.0 to 9.5, with some exceeding 11.0.

Crankcase sludge became common during the winter of 1935. Sludge is an undesirable internal engine deposit, of pudding-like consistency, which can plug the inlet screen of the oil pick-up tube and oil passageways in an engine. Sludge is a stable emulsion of oil, water, and solids which can occur when a rich mixture of fuel and air is burned at low temperatures. The rich air-fuel mixture has a tendency to form soot. The soot can in turn promote sludge formation, and the low temperature helps the oil, soot, and water form a stable emulsion. The lead compounds, which are by-products of leaded gasoline combustion, can also help initiate and stabilize sludge formation. To minimize sludge formation, engine designers of this period set cooling system thermostats to keep the coolant immediately around the engine block, between 60 °C to 80 °C (140 °F to 180 °F). Designers also installed road draft tubes on the crankcase. This was intended to vent any water vapor and other gases which blow by the piston rings to the atmosphere. By 1962, atmospheric venting of the crankcase was replaced by closed ventilation and the blow-by gases and water vapor were drawn from the crankcase back into the combustion chamber. These systems, described as positive crankcase ventilation (PCV) systems, were among the first devices required to control automotive emissions.

The petroleum industry made major strides during this period to keep up with the increasing demand for automotive fuel. U.S. crude oil refining capacity grew from 600 million liters per day (3.8 million barrels per day) in 1931 to over 1.3 billion liters per day (8 million barrels per day) in 1956. Over the same interval, the percentage of U.S. crude oil converted into gasoline rose from 41% to more than 70%. Typically, "straight run" or natural gasoline is only 30% of crude oil. To increase the yield of gasoline from a barrel of crude oil beyond 30%, required the use of sophisticated refining processes. In addition, there was interest in increasing the octane value of gasoline. In simple terms, refining processes were used which either put together smaller petroleum molecules to form gasoline components, split larger petroleum molecules into smaller gasoline components, or rearranged existing gasoline molecules into shapes which had higher octane ratings. The most significant increase in the conversion of crude oil into gasoline was the introduction of catalytic cracking. This proved a major improvement over thermal cracking and increased the octane of this gasoline component to more than 90 RON. The use of catalytic reforming, isomerization, and alkylation provided small increases in gasoline yield, but primarily provided components with over 100 RON for production of premium gasolines.

Automotive engine oil technology was also advanced during this time period. The use of vacuum distillation, solvent dewaxing, and solvent treating permitted the production of high viscosity index lubricating oils from a wider range of crude oils. In 1955, approximately 2% of the total U.S. crude oil refined ended up as lubricating oil. Pour point depressants to improve low temperature flow and viscosity index improvers were developed early in this period. The previous developments permitted the production of the first "wax-free" motor oil in refinery sealed containers in 1934. Lower viscosity engine oils were introduced to improve cold weather starting performance. The 1930 to 1947 interval saw the development of several automotive engine oil additives including bearing corrosion inhibitors, detergents, dispersants, improved oxidation inhibitors, anti-foam agents, and corrosion inhibitors. The first synthetic oils were developed in 1947. During the 1950s, additional advancements included the first all season multi-viscosity engine oil, overbased detergents, ashless dispersants, and the widespread use of Zinc DialkylDithioPhosphate (ZDDP) as an anti-wear and anti-oxidant for engine oil.

The first use of a full flow oil filter on mass production vehicles occurred in 1946. In the U.S. by the end of 1963, approximately 60% of the engines were built as V-8s. During this period, the typical U.S. V-8 engines ranged from 120 to 300 kW (160 to 400 bhp) and 3.3 to 6.5 L (200 to 400 in^3) displacement. At the same time, V-8 fuel economy fell from 8.5 km/L (20 mpg) to 4.5 km/L (11 mpg). The increase in horsepower and engine speed required greater valve train contact pressures and spring loadings producing increased wear concerns. The combination of increases in displacement, compression ratios, horsepower, and fuel consumption produced increased combustion temperature and heat rejection. The result was an increase in crankcase oil temperatures from about 95 °C (203 °F) to a range of 120 °C to 150 °C (248 °F to 302 °F). When combined with decreasing oil volumes in the crankcase and longer drain intervals, the net effect was a significant increase in the severity of the engine oil operating conditions.

The automatic transmission was introduced in 1949 and by the late 1950s, luxury cars came with automatic transmissions, air conditioning, and other power options. During this period, vehicle weight rose from approximately 1400 to 3000 kg (3000 to 6500 lb). In 1961, vehicle warranties were extended from 90 days or 6500 km (4000 miles), to 2 years or 40 000 km (24 000 miles). It was common practice in 1940, for an engine to require an overhaul at 65 000 km (40 000 miles). By the end of this period, the mileage until overhaul had been extended to 150 000 km (100 000 miles). At the end of this period, the average engine was 4.5 L (280 in^3) and 135 kW (180 bhp) and operated at higher temperatures than prior designs. Engines of this period in the U.S. were not equipped with any emissions control technology until 1962.

In the 1930 to 1950 time period, the water used for engine coolant was commonly protected from winter freeze by adding methyl alcohol or denatured alcohol. By 1960, mixtures of ethylene glycol and water had become popular for use as an engine coolant. The addition of the proper amount of ethylene glycol to water produced a lowering of the freezing point of the coolant and a raising of the boiling point when compared to water/alcohol mixtures. This provided additional protection against both winter freeze and summer boil over. Since 1962, all U.S. based manufacturers have recommended ethylene glycol be used in the cooling system on a year round basis.

The existing U.S. highway system did not permit extended periods of sustained high-speed operation. Starting in 1930, 26% of the 5.2 million kilometers (3.2 million miles) of roads in the U.S. were surfaced. By 1963, surfaced roads had increased to 74% of 6 million kilometers (3.7 million miles). Construction of the U.S. interstate highway system had begun in 1956, and about 25 000 km (15 000 miles) were in operation by 1963, with almost 63 million passenger cars in operation. Under these operating conditions, U.S. manufacturers recommended oil change maintenance intervals ranged from 3000 km (2000 miles) to 2 months or 6500 km (4000 miles) using engine oils which would qualify as SB. During this period, the average annual per vehicle consumption was 20 to 25 L (21 to 26 qt) of engine oil and the corresponding consumption of gasoline rose from 2250 L (594 gal) in 1940, to 2450 L (647 gal) in 1963. Oils which would qualify as SB were not generally recommended for service in model years after 1963.

A.2.5.2 Rationale for Obsolescence—Most of the key performance tests used to define this category are OBSOLETE. Reference fuels, reference engine oils, and engine parts for most of these tests are no longer available and any performance claims to this category cannot be verified by independent engine testing. Some of the key performance tests have been obsolete since the early 1960s. With the changes in additives, refining processes, and base stocks which have occurred over time, it is unlikely historic test data would still support SB performance claims.

The number of vehicles and engines in use which could properly use such a limited performance category is very small (less than 1% of the vehicles registered in the U. S.).

Today's vehicles, fuels, maintenance intervals, and consumer operating conditions are significantly different from those listed in the background section when engine oils equivalent to SB were appropriate. Since API "S" Performance Categories alphabetically higher than SB, are suitable for SB performance applications, there is no further technical need for such products in the marketplace and such products are considered TECHNICALLY OBSOLETE.

A.2.5.3 Recommended Labeling Practice—Oils meeting SB performance do not provide adequate protection in modern automotive engines equipped with advanced emission control technology required to comply with more stringent emissions standards than existed at the time SB performance oils were used. There is a real probability uninformed consumers could improperly use SB quality oils in modern automotive engines and experience harm to their engine and vehicle emission control systems.

Therefore, it is both reasonable and prudent for any marketer who chooses to offer such a limited application oil to the consumer, to warn the consumer of the limitations of the product's application. This caution should be displayed on each engine oil container and the corresponding overpack carton in legible and conspicuous type upon a contrasting background. In the case of engine oil sold in bulk, such information should be clearly and prominently included on the invoice. The following statement is recommended for use on both packaged and bulk product and would be considered reasonable and prudent by experts in the field of automotive engine lubrication.

CAUTION—THIS OIL IS RATED API SB AND IS NOT SUITABLE FOR USE IN MOST GASOLINE-POWERED AUTOMOTIVE ENGINES BUILT AFTER 1963. USE IN MORE MODERN ENGINES MAY CAUSE UNSATISFACTORY PERFORMANCE OR EQUIPMENT HARM.

A.2.6 Category SC (1964 to 1967)—This category has been declared TECHNICALLY OBSOLETE by both the SAE Fuels and Lubricants Technical Committee 1 and the Fuels and Lubricants Division.

A.2.6.1 Background—This engine service category identified oils which contained performance additives typical of 1964 to 1967 in North America. This performance level was also known as SERVICE MS prior to 1971. The use of the terminology "SC" to define this performance level was adopted in 1971.

The additive treatment used in SC performance oils was necessary to meet the performance requirements of the new multicylinder engine sequence tests. These engine tests were introduced to provide better protection against low temperature sludge, deposits, rust, corrosion, and wear. The engine sequence tests were selected to be representative of the consumer driving conditions during this period.

Most engines built in this time period were equipped with closed positive crankcase ventilation emissions control systems, hydraulic valve lifters, and improved full flow oil filter designs. Approximately 70% of the engines produced in the U.S. during this period were of V-8 configuration with average displacements of 5.0 L (305 in^3) and around 170 kW (228 bhp). These engines were operated at compression ratios of 9.5 to 10.5 on leaded gasoline. Regular grade 92 RON was about 60% and premium grade 100 RON about 40% of total gasoline sales.

By 1967, 40 000 km (25 000 miles) of the U.S. interstate highway system were in operation and almost 75% of the 6 million kilometers (3.7 million miles) of roads were surfaced. There were 73 million passenger cars in operation in the U.S. Under normal operating conditions, U.S. manufacturer recommended oil change interval ranged between 2 months or 10 000 km (6000 miles) and 6 months or 10 000 km (6000 miles) using SC engine oils.

During this period, the average annual engine oil consumption was 14 to 17 L (15 to 18 qt). The corresponding consumption of gasoline rose from 2450 L (647 gal) in 1964, to 2600 L (687 gallons) in 1967. SC quality oils were not generally recommended for service in model years after 1967.

A.2.6.2 Rationale for Obsolescence—Most of the key performance tests used to define this category are OBSOLETE. Reference fuels, reference engine oils, and engine parts for most of these tests are no longer available and any performance claims to this category cannot be verified by independent engine testing. Some of the key performance tests have been obsolete since the early 1970s. With the corresponding changes in additives, refining processes, and base stocks, it is unlikely historic test data would still support SC performance claims.

The number of vehicles and engines in use which could properly use such a limited performance category is small (less than 1% of the vehicles registered in the U.S.). Today's vehicles, fuels, and consumer driving conditions are significantly different than those listed in the background section when SC performance oils were recommended. Since API "S" Performance Categories alphabetically higher than SC, are suitable for SC performance applications, there is no further need for such products in the marketplace and such products are considered TECHNICALLY OBSOLETE.

A.2.6.3 Recommended Labeling Practice—Oils meeting SC performance do not provide acceptable protection in modern automotive engines equipped with improved emission control technology required to comply with more stringent emissions standards than existed at the time SC oils were used. There is a real probability uninformed consumers could improperly use SC quality oils in their more modern automotive engines and experience harm to their engines and emission control systems.

Therefore, it is both reasonable and prudent for any marketer who chooses to offer such a limited application oil to the consumer to warn the consumer of the product's limited application. This caution should be displayed on each container and the corresponding overpack carton in legible and conspicuous type upon a contrasting background. In the case of engine oil sold in bulk, such information should be clearly and prominently included on the invoice. The following statement is recommended for use on both packaged and bulk product and would be considered reasonable and prudent by experts in the field of automotive engine lubrication.

CAUTION—THIS OIL IS RATED API SERVICE SC AND IS NOT SUITABLE FOR USE IN MOST GASOLINE-POWERED AUTOMOTIVE ENGINES BUILT AFTER 1967. USE IN MORE MODERN ENGINES MAY CAUSE UNSATISFACTORY PERFORMANCE OR EQUIPMENT HARM.

A.2.7 API Category SD (1968 to 1971)—This category has been declared TECHNICALLY OBSOLETE by both the SAE Fuels and Lubricants Technical Committee 1 and the Fuels and Lubricants Division.

A.2.7.1 BACKGROUND—This engine service category described oils which contained performance additives typical of the 1968 to 1971 time period in North America. This performance level was also known as SERVICE MS prior to 1971. The use of the terminology "SD" to define this performance level was adopted in 1971.

The additive treatment used in these oils was necessary to meet the performance requirements of the revised multicylinder engine sequence tests. These tests were revised to better address consumer needs related to maintaining the cleanliness of the positive crankcase ventilation valves during short trip, stop-and-go driving. Customer surveys indicated more than 50% of all passenger car trips, during this period, were 10 km (6 miles) or less (one way). The added emphasis of the tests was on low temperature operation and the prevention of rust and sludge under real world driving conditions.

Engines of this period were similar to previous designs (1964 to 1967) and equipped with closed positive crankcase ventilation emissions control systems, hydraulic valve lifters, and improved oil filters. However, 90% of the engines produced in the U.S. during this period were of V-8 configuration with an average displacement of 5.6 L (342 in^3) and 190 kW (255 bhp). These engines were operated at compression ratios of 9.5 to 10.5 on leaded gasoline. Regular grade 92 RON was about 60% and premium grade 100 RON about 40% of total gasoline sales.

By the end of this period, about 79% of the 6 million kilometers (3.7 million miles) of roads in the U.S. were surfaced and 50 000 km (31 000 miles) of the U. S. interstate highway system were complete. In 1971, there were 83 million passenger cars in operation in the U.S. During this period, imported vehicle sales rose from 7% to 15% of U. S. passenger car sales. The typical U.S. manufacturer recommended oil change interval was 4 months or 10 000 km (6000 miles) for SD performance oils under normal driving conditions. During this period, the average annual engine oil consumption was 11 to 12 L (12 to 13 qt) and the corresponding consumption of gasoline rose from 2650 L (700 gal) in 1968, to 2800 L (740 gal) in 1971. SD performance level oils were not generally recommended for service in model years after 1971.

A.2.7.2 RATIONALE FOR OBSOLESCENCE—Most of the key performance tests used to define this category are OBSOLETE. Reference fuels, reference engine oils, and engine parts for most of these tests are no longer available and any performance claims to this category cannot be verified by independent engine testing. Some of the key performance tests have been obsolete since the late 1980s. With the changes in additives, refining processes, and base stocks it is unlikely historic test data would still support SD performance claims.

The number of vehicles and engines in use which could use such a limited performance category is small (less than 3% of the vehicles registered in the U.S.). Today's vehicles, fuels, and customer driving conditions are significantly different from those listed in the background section, when SD performance oils were recommended. Since API "S" Performance Categories alphabetically higher than SD are suitable for SD performance applications, there is no further need for such products in the marketplace and such products are considered TECHNICALLY OBSOLETE.

A.2.7.3 RECOMMENDED LABELING PRACTICE—Oils meeting SD performance do not provide acceptable protection in modern automotive engines equipped with improved emission control technology required to comply with more stringent emissions standards than existed at the time SD performance oils were used. There is a real probability uninformed consumers could improperly use SD performance oils in their modern automotive engines and experience harm to their engines and vehicle emission control systems.

Therefore, it is both reasonable and prudent for any marketer who chooses to offer such a limited application oil to the consumer to warn the consumer of the product's limitations. This caution should be displayed on each container and the corresponding overpack carton in legible and conspicuous type upon a contrasting background. In the case of engine oil sold in bulk, such information should be clearly and prominently included on the invoice. The following statement is recommended for use on both packaged and bulk product and would be considered reasonable and prudent by experts in the field of automotive engine lubrication:

CAUTION—THIS OIL IS RATED API SERVICE SD. IT IS NOT SUITABLE FOR USE IN MOST GASOLINE-POWERED AUTOMOTIVE ENGINES BUILT AFTER 1971. USE IN MODERN ENGINES MAY CAUSE UNSATISFACTORY PERFORMANCE OR EQUIPMENT HARM.

A.2.8 API Category SE (1972 to 1979) —This category has been declared TECHNICALLY OBSOLETE by both the SAE Fuels and Lubricants Technical Committee 1 and the Fuels and Lubricants Division.

A.2.8.1 BACKGROUND—This performance category identified oils which contained performance additives typical of the 1972 to 1979 time period in North America. The additive treatment used in these oils was necessary to meet the SE performance requirements of the next revision of the multicylinder engine sequence tests. These engine tests were revised to better reflect consumer needs related to high-temperature engine oil thickening. The engine tests were given added emphasis to correlate with consumer use during long distance, high-speed driving typical of a summer vacation with vehicle trailer towing.

Automotive engines of this period were undergoing significant change in order to meet the increasingly stringent U.S. Government and California emission control requirements starting in 1972, and the U.S. Corporate Average Fuel Economy standards starting in 1978. Initially, changes were made to engine combustion to lower the total vehicle emissions of hydrocarbons and oxides of nitrogen. This included retarded spark ignition timing at low-rpm and the use of exhaust gas recirculation. In 1974, exhaust gas catalytic converters and electronic ignition became widespread.

The use of exhaust gas catalytic converters containing noble metal catalyst required the removal of both phosphorus and tetraethyl lead from gasoline to prevent contamination and subsequent catalyst poisoning. Most U.S. manufacturers stopped recommending the use of 100 RON premium leaded gasoline in 1971. Premium leaded grade dropped from 40% to 8% of total gasoline sales during this period. Unleaded regular gasoline was introduced in 1974 at 92 RON and rose to 93 RON by 1979.

The average displacement of domestic engines fell from 5.8 L (350 in^3) to around 4.4 L (269 in^3). The corresponding compression ratios were lowered from 9.5 to 8.0 to accommodate the use of lower octane fuel. Engine configurations changed dramatically over this period as V-8's fell from 88% to 56% of total U.S. produced engines, while 6-cylinder engines rose from 13% to 24% and 4-cylinder engines increased from 8% to 18% respectively of total U.S. production. Two popular customer options contributed to high engine operating temperature concerns. These options were air conditioning, which rose from 61% to 80% and automatic transmissions which averaged 90% of U.S. manufactured vehicles. The engine coolant for these vehicles was a 50% ethylene glycol/50% water mixture which, in combination with higher temperature thermostats and higher pressure radiator caps, permitted engine coolant operating temperature to approach 110 °C (230 °F) without boil over.

During this period, imported vehicles became a more significant factor in the North American market and rose from 15% to 22% of U.S. passenger car sales. The average import gasoline engine was 2.4 L (146 in^3), 8.3 compression ratio, 80 kW (107 bhp) and 5400 rpm.

By the end of this period, about 80% of the 6.3 million kilometers (3.9 million miles) of U.S. roads were surfaced and 68 000 km (42 000 miles) of the U.S. Interstate highway system were complete. In 1979, there were about 105 million passenger cars in operation in the U.S. The typical U.S. manufacturer recommended oil change interval was 6 months or 10 000 km (6000 miles) for SE performance oil, under normal operating conditions. The average annual engine oil consumption was 7 to 9 L (7 to 10 qt) and the corresponding consumption of gasoline fell from 2850 L (752 gal) in 1972, to 2300 L (608 gal) in 1979. Annual per vehicle gasoline consumption peaked during 1973 at 2900 L (766 gal). SE performance level oils were not generally recommended for service in model years after 1979 in North America.

A.2.8.2 RATIONALE FOR OBSOLESCENCE—Most of the key performance tests used to define this category are OBSOLETE. Reference fuels, reference engine oils, and engine parts for most of these tests are no longer available and any performance claims to this category cannot be verified by independent engine testing. Some of the key performance tests have been obsolete since the late 1980s. With the corresponding changes in additives, refining processes, and base stocks, it is unlikely historic test data would still be applicable for support of SE performance claims.

The number of vehicles and engines in use which could use such a limited performance category is low (less than 25% of the vehicles registered in the U.S.). Since API "S" Performance Categories alphabetically higher than SE, are suitable for SE performance applications, there is no further need for such products in the marketplace and such products are considered TECHNICALLY OBSOLETE.

A.2.8.3 RECOMMENDED LABELING PRACTICE—Oils meeting SE performance do not provide acceptable protection in modern automotive engines equipped with improved emission control technology required to comply with more stringent emissions standards than existed at the time SE performance oils were used. There is a real probability uninformed consumers could improperly use SE oils in their modern automotive engines and experience harm to their engines and/or vehicle emissions control systems.

Therefore, any marketer who chooses to offer such a limited application oil to the consumer has an obligation to provide clear information indicating the limitations of the product's legitimate application. Such information should be displayed on each container and the corresponding overpack carton in legible and conspicuous type upon a contrasting background. In the case of engine oil sold in bulk, such information should be clearly and prominently included on the invoice. The following statement is recommended for use on both packaged and bulk product and would be considered reasonable and prudent by experts in the field of automotive engine lubrication:

CAUTION—THIS OIL IS RATED API PERFORMANCE CATEGORY SE. IT IS NOT SUITABLE FOR USE IN MOST GASOLINE POWERED AUTOMOTIVE ENGINES BUILT AFTER 1979.

A.2.9 API Category SF (1980 to 1988)—This performance category identified oils which contained performance additives typical of the 1980 to 1988 time period in North America. The additive treatment used in these oils was necessary to meet the performance requirements of the multicylinder engine sequence tests which were revised to better reflect customer concerns related to wear. This added requirement was prompted by the change to higher speed (rpm), small displacement engines with overhead camshaft valve trains. Concerns, over extended maintenance intervals, and higher under hood temperatures were also addressed in the revised test requirements.

Vehicles of this period were undergoing significant change in order to meet the increasingly stringent U.S. Government and California emission control requirements and the U.S. Corporate Average Fuel Economy (CAFE) standards. Starting with the 1980 model year, the Federal Standard for allowable exhaust emissions was lowered. With the uncontrolled 1960 levels as the reference, the permitted levels of Hydrocarbons and Carbon Monoxide were lowered 96% and the oxides of Nitrogen were lowered 76%. The U.S. CAFE standard was raised from 8.5 km/L (20 mpg) in 1980, to 11 km/L (26 mpg) in 1988.

The average displacement of domestic engines fell from 4.2 L (256 in^3) to 3.4 L (207 in^3). The corresponding compression ratios were raised from 8.3 to 8.8. Average domestic power and revolutions per minute (rpm) both increased to 100 kW (134 bhp) and to 4430 rpm respectively. Engine configurations changed dramatically over this period as V-8's fell from 30% to 17% of total U.S. produced engines, while 6-cylinder engines remained constant at 35% and 4-cylinder engines increased from 29% to 48% of total U.S. production.

In 1980, imports comprised over 16% of all vehicles in operation in the U.S. market and in 1988, the imports represented 25% of total U.S. passenger car sales. The average displacement of import engines during this period was relatively stable going from 2.4 L (146 in^3) to 2.5 L (153 in^3). However, the compression ratio, rpm's, and power of these engines were all increased respectively from 8.4 to 9.2, 5100 rpm to 5500 rpm, and 80 to 110 kW (107 to 147 bhp).

In addition to the engine changes already discussed, this period saw the rapid evolution of modifications to both the vehicle and powertrain for both emissions and CAFE benefits. These included improvements in fuel metering and atomization, initially using throttle body fuel injection, then moving to port fuel injection and eventually sequential port fuel injection. These fuel metering improvements led to the virtual elimination of carburetors. Combustion also improved by advanced electronic engine controls and fast-burn combustion chamber designs. The drive for fuel efficiency was supported by low-friction piston rings, roller followers in the valve train and lower viscosity engine oils. Most vehicles were redesigned to front wheel drive, more efficient transmissions, improved aerodynamic designs, and use of light-weight materials of construction, resulting in the average vehicle weight declining from 1400 to 1100 kg (3000 to 2400 lb). The substitution of aluminum for downsized radiators, water pumps, and cylinder heads was typical of engine related weight reductions. Some vehicles used turbocharging and supercharging in an attempt to improve engine performance. Customer purchase of power options increased which further contributed to the high temperature concerns. By 1988, both air conditioning and automatic transmissions were installed in almost 90% of U.S. manufactured vehicles.

In 1983, 97 RON premium unleaded gasoline was introduced to respond to the performance needs of certain engines. The definition of "gasoline" was evolving. Alternatives to hydrocarbon fuels derived from petroleum were introduced for use as automotive fuels in passengers cars.

Alcohols and other oxygenated compounds were added as supplements to motor gasoline derived from petroleum. First, gasohol, a blend of motor gasoline and up to a maximum of 10 Vol % ethanol, became available. In 1981, gasohol represented 1 vol % of total gasoline sales and grew to 7% of sales by 1988. Automotive fuels containing up to 5 Vol % methanol, with the necessary cosolvents and additives, peaked at 3% of total gasoline sales in 1985. Gasoline containing methanol was almost non-existent in 1988. Gasoline blends containing a maximum of 15 Vol % Methyl Tertiary Butyl Ether (MBTE) were non-existent in 1980, but represented more than 10% of total gasoline sales by 1988.

By the end of this period, about 90% of the 6.3 million kilometers (3.9 million miles) of U.S. roads were surfaced and almost 70 000 km (43 000 miles) of the U.S. interstate highway system were complete. By 1988, there were 122 million cars in operation in the U.S. U.S. manufacturer recommended engine oil change interval was 12 months or 12 000 km (7500 miles) for SF performance oil, under normal driving conditions. During this period, the average annual engine oil consumption per vehicle was 6 to 7 L (6 to 7 qt) and the corresponding consumption of gasoline fell from 2300 L (607 gal) in 1980, to 1900 L (502 gal) in 1988. Oils of this SF performance level were not generally recommended for service in model years after 1988 in North America.

A.2.9.1 RATIONALE FOR OBSOLESCENCE—The Sequence V-D necessary to evaluate both anti-wear and anti-sludge characteristics for the SF performance rating was one of the key engine tests. As engine designs changed, it no longer was able to assess sludge prevention capability. In fact, there were a significant number of field problems related to sludging when customers used engine oils claiming to meet API service SF. It became obvious to the equipment manufacturers the sequence V-D test no longer correlated to the field. The V-D test was declared incapable of discriminating between good and poor sludge performance of engine oils in severe field service by ASTM and was declared OBSOLETE. Reference fuels, reference engine oils, and engine parts for this V-D test are no longer available and any performance claims to this category cannot be verified by independent engine testing. Since API "S" Performance Categories alphabetically higher than SF are suitable for SF performance applications, there is no need for such products in the marketplace and such products are considered TECHNICALLY OBSOLETE.

A.2.9.2 RECOMMENDED LABELING PRACTICE—Oils meeting SF performance do not provide acceptable engine protection against sludge build-up. There is a real probability consumers could improperly use SF performance oils in modern automotive engines and experience harm to their engines and/or vehicle emissions control systems.

Therefore, any marketer who chooses to offer such a limited application oil to the consumer should provide clear information indicating the product's limitations. Such information should be displayed on each container and the corresponding overpack carton in legible and conspicuous type upon a contrasting background. In the case of engine oil sold in bulk, such information should be clearly and prominently included on the invoice. The following statement is recommended for use on both packaged and bulk product and would be considered reasonable and prudent by experts in the field of automotive engine lubrication:

CAUTION—THIS OIL IS RATED API SERVICE CATEGORY SF. IT IS NOT SUITABLE FOR USE IN MOST GASOLINE POWERED AUTOMOTIVE ENGINES BUILT AFTER 1988. IT MAY NOT PROVIDE ADEQUATE PROTECTION AGAINST THE BUILD-UP OF ENGINE SLUDGE.

A.2.10 API CATEGORY SG (1987 to 1993)—This performance category identified engine oils formulated to protect passenger car gasoline engines of the 1987 to 1993 time period in North America. Two major engine tests, the Sequence IIIE and Sequence VE were instituted to evaluate oxidation and sludge respectively. Both tests also measure valve train wear. Engine oils meeting this standard generally had higher levels of dispersant than their API Category SF predecessors, primarily for Sequence VE performance.

During this time period, vehicles were undergoing important changes to improve fuel economy to meet federally mandated CAFE requirements and improvements in emissions control to meet federally imposed requirements. Also during this period substantial improvements in overall vehicle performance were made to improve customer satisfaction. Increased use of electronic controls improved the efficiency by which the timing and conditions for combustion could be controlled. Carburetors gave way to fuel injection and mass air flow sensors as means for controlling air/fuel ratios and yielded notable improvements in driveability. The increased use of oxygen sensors aided in controlling air/fuel mixtures. Knock sensors helped extract additional power from the engine without the damaging effects of knock.

This period was marked by a generally stable supply of gasoline, the one exception being the Gulf War. The combination of a generally improved economy compared to the prior decade, availability of relatively low cost gasoline, and a wave of offspring from the baby boomers led to demand for larger vehicles. Mini-vans, light trucks, and sport utility vehicles gained popularity during this time.

Manufacturer recommended oil change recommendations over this timeframe were relatively constant. 5000 km (3000 miles) or 3 months between oil changes was generally recommended for severe service and 12 000 km (7500 miles) or 6 months was typically for normal service. Oil change habits also underwent change. The growth of the fast oil change business made it economical and more convenient for consumers to have their oil changed for them rather than performing the service themselves. In addition to the convenience, it also relieved them of the problem of how to properly dispose of the used oil.

Gasoline also evolved. Mid-grade gasoline became a popular method for eliminating knock without having to pay the price of Premium. Gasoline vapor pressure and oxygenate content were varied seasonally in some locations to improve air quality. Virtually all gasoline contained detergent or was formulated to minimize fuel injector and exhaust valve fouling.

A.2.10.1 Rationale for Obsolescence—Motor oils tested under API Service SG guidelines were not subject to the rigorous surveillance required today. They were not tested registered through ACC, tested in certified stands, or subjected to Multiple Test Acceptance Criteria. Because of this, the actual performance of the oil can not be assured.

A.2.10.2 Recommended Labeling Practice—Oils meeting SG performance do not assure acceptable engine protection against sludge build-up, oxidation, or wear. There is a real probability consumers could improperly use SG performance oils in modern automotive engines and experience harm to their engines and/or vehicle emissions control systems.

Therefore, any marketer who chooses to offer such a limited application oil to the consumer should provide clear information indicating the product's limitations. Such information should be displayed on each container and the corresponding overpack carton in legible and conspicuous type upon a contrasting background. In the case of engine oil sold in bulk, such information should be clearly and prominently included on the invoice. The following statement is recommended for use on both packaged and bulk product and would be considered reasonable and prudent by experts in the field of automotive engine lubrication:

CAUTION—THIS OIL IS RATED API SERVICE CATEGORY SG. IT IS NOT SUITABLE FOR USE IN MOST GASOLINE POWERED AUTOMOTIVE ENGINES BUILT AFTER 1993. IT MAY NOT PROVIDE ADEQUATE PROTECTION AGAINST THE BUILD-UP OF ENGINE SLUDGE, OXIDATION, OR WEAR.

A.2.11 ILSAC GF-1 (1993 to 1997)—ILSAC GF-1 was developed to describe the performance attributes required for the lubrication of U.S. and Japanese passenger vehicle gasoline engines sold in North America. The standard closely resembles API category SH, providing the same requirements for engine protection. ILSAC GF-1 provided improved protection over prior API "S" categories in several key areas. Although the engine tests and associated limits were the same as for API SG, ILSAC GF-1 required that the qualification program be run under the ACC Code of Practice including registration prior to running tests, running in ACC approved test stands, and Multiple Test Acceptance Criteria. Although records do not exist, it is generally acknowledged that the ACC Code of Practice resulted in higher average level of performance for ILSAC GF-1 engine oils compared to API SG engine oils.

ILSAC GF-1 incorporated only 0W-XX, 5W-XX, and 10W-XX viscosity grades. Automakers preferred to restrict the standard to these grades to help educate the public and encourage them to use the proper viscosity grades for their engines. The intent was to match the ILSAC viscosity grades to those appearing in owners' manuals.

ILSAC GF-1 engine oils mandated fuel economy performance required neither by API category SG nor SH. This was built into the standards at the behest of automakers to promote the development of fuel economy technology to assist them in meeting CAFE requirements.

Phosphorus was limited in ILSAC GF-1 to provide protection to automobile emissions systems. Automakers provided substantial documentation that motor oil derived phosphorus could contribute to exhaust system catalytic converter deactivation. The oxidized phosphorus compounds formed a high melting point glaze on the catalyst surface, inhibiting ability to contact and convert the exhaust gas. It was also believed that the phosphorus could poison oxygen sensors in the same manner.

Volatility control was another new requirement over API category SG. This requirement was added to address concerns regarding high oil consumption with highly volatile engine oils. In addition to the possibility of running with a low oil level, high oil consumption was believed to contribute to fuel system and exhaust system deposits and a higher rate of phosphorus introduction into the exhaust system.

In addition, ILSAC GF-1 included most of the bench tests that appeared in the various automaker service fill specifications. This resulted in harmonization of a variety of diverse specifications.

A.2.11.1 Rationale for Obsolescence—Engine oils meeting ILSAC GF-1 do not provide the protection against high temperature deposits, volatility and foaming, may lead to unacceptably short catalyst life and do not provide all the protection against low temperature gelation required by modern automobile engines. ILSAC GF-1 oils were superseded by ILSAC GF-2 motor oils which provide these additional levels of protection.

A.2.12 API CATEGORY CA (1900 to 1961)—This category has been declared TECHNICALLY OBSOLETE by both the SAE Fuels and Lubricants Technical Committee 1 and the Fuels and Lubricants Division.

A.2.12.1 Background—The use of the terminology "CA" to define this performance level was adopted by the American Petroleum Institute (API) in 1971. Between 1952 and 1971, this performance level was known as Service DG.

This category was based on the performance requirements of MIL-L-2104 as set forth by the US Army.

CA service was typical of diesel engines operated in mild- to moderate-duty with high-quality fuels and occasionally included gasoline engines in mild service. It is not intended to protect against the harmful effects resulting from the use of diesel fuels with moderate to high levels of sulfur. Oils designed for this service provided protection from bearing corrosion and from ring deposits in some naturally aspirated diesel engines when used with fuels of such quality that they imposed no unusual requirements for wear and deposit protection. They were widely used in the late 1940s and the 1950s but should not be used in any engine unless specifically recommended by the equipment manufacturer.

CA oils met the performance requirements of the Caterpillar L-1 diesel and CRC L-38 gasoline engine tests. The L-1 (0.4% mass fuel sulfur) naturally aspirated diesel engine test provided a measurement of piston deposits. The L-38, or alternatively the L-4, gasoline engine test provided a measurement of copper-lead bearing weight loss and piston varnish under high-temperature operating conditions.

A.2.12.2 Rationale for Obsolescence—The CA category includes performance tests for which engine parts and/or test fuel and/or reference oils are no longer generally available. These tests are no longer being monitored by the test developer or by ASTM. An oil's performance in this category can no longer be evaluated.

Since API "C" categories alphabetically higher than CA are suitable for all diesel engine applications specifying CA, there is no further need for CA products in the marketplace and such products are considered TECHNICALLY OBSOLETE for use in diesel engines.

A.2.12.3 Recommended Labeling Practice—CA performance oils do not provide acceptable diesel engine protection under today's more stringent operating conditions. The use of CA oils by uninformed consumers would cause harm to their engines. Therefore, any marketer who chooses to offer such a limited application oil to the consumer has an obligation to provide clear information indicating the limitations of the product's legitimate application. Such information should be displayed on each container and the corresponding overpack carton in legible and conspicuous type upon a contrasting background. In the case of engine oil sold in bulk, such information should be clearly and prominently included on the invoice. The following statement is recommended for use on both packaged and bulk product and would be considered reasonable and prudent by experts in the field of automotive engine lubrication:

CAUTION—THIS OIL IS RATED API SERVICE CATEGORY CA. IT IS NOT SUITABLE FOR USE IN MOST DIESEL POWERED ENGINES BUILT AFTER 1959.

A.2.13 API CATEGORY CB (1949 to 1961)—This category has been declared TECHNICALLY OBSOLETE by both the SAE Fuels and Lubricants Technical Committee 1 and the Fuels and Lubricants Division.

A.2.13.1 Background—The use of the terminology "CB" to define this performance level was adopted by the American Petroleum Institute (API) in 1971. Between 1952 and 1971, this performance level was known as API Service DM.

This category was based on the performance requirements of MIL-L-2104, Supplement 1, as set forth by the US Army.

CB service was typical of diesel engines operated in mild- to moderate-duty with lower quality fuels which necessitated more protection from wear and deposits. The primary difference between category CA and CB is that CB provides better protection against the harmful effects of moderate to higher sulfur content diesel fuels. It occasionally had included gasoline engines in mild service. Oils designed for this service were introduced in 1949. Such oils provided necessary protection from bearing corrosion and from high- temperature deposits in some naturally aspirated diesel engines with higher sulfur diesel fuels. They were widely used in the 1950s but should not be used in any engine unless specifically recommended by the equipment manufacturer.

CB oils met the performance requirements of the Caterpillar L-1 (1.0% mass fuel sulfur) diesel engine test and CRC L-38. The L-1 naturally aspirated diesel engine test provided a measurement of piston deposits. The L-38 gasoline engine test, or alternatively the L-4, gasoline engine test provided a measurement of copper-lead bearing weight loss and piston varnish under high-temperature operating conditions.

A.2.13.2 Rationale for Obsolescence—The CB category includes performance tests for which engine parts and/or test fuel and/or reference oils are no longer generally available. These tests are no longer being monitored by the test developer or by ASTM. An oil's performance in this category can no longer be evaluated. Since API "C" categories alphabetically higher than CB are suitable for all diesel engine applications specifying CB, there is no further technical need for CB products in the marketplace and such products are considered TECHNICALLY OBSOLETE for use in diesel engine lubrication.

A.2.13.3 Recommended Labeling Practice—CB performance oils will not provide acceptable diesel engine protection under today's more stringent operating conditions. The use of CB oils by uninformed consumers would cause harm to their engines. Therefore, any marketer who chooses to offer such a limited application oil to the consumer has an obligation to provide clear information indicating the limitations of the product's legitimate application. Such information should be displayed on each container and the corresponding overpack carton in legible and conspicuous type upon a contrasting background. In the case of engine oil sold in bulk, such information should be clearly and prominently included on the invoice. The following statement is recommended for use on both packaged and bulk product and would be considered reasonable and prudent by experts in the field of automotive engine lubrication:

CAUTION—THIS OIL IS RATED API SERVICE CATEGORY CB. IT IS NOT SUITABLE FOR USE IN MOST DIESEL POWERED AUTOMOTIVE ENGINES BUILT AFTER 1961.

A.2.14 API CATEGORY CC (1961 to 1990)—This category has been declared TECHNICALLY OBSOLETE by both the SAE Fuels and Lubricants Technical Committee 1 and the Fuels and Lubricants Division.

A.2.14.1 Background—The use of the terminology "CC" to define this performance level was adopted by the American Petroleum Institute (API) in 1971. Between 1952 and 1971, this performance level was known as Service DM.

This category was based on the performance requirements of MIL-L-2104 and MIL-L-46152 as set forth by the US Army.

CC service was typical of certain naturally aspirated and turbocharged diesel engines operated in moderate- to severe-duty service and certain heavy-duty gasoline engines. Oils designed for this service provided protection from high-temperature deposits and bearing corrosion in these diesel engines and also from rust, corrosion, and low-temperature deposits in gasoline engines. They were introduced in 1961. They should not be used in any engine unless specifically recommended by the equipment manufacturer.

CC oils met the performance requirements in the following diesel and gasoline engine tests. The Caterpillar 1H2 diesel engine test was correlated with indirect injection engines used in moderate-duty operation, particularly with regard to piston and ring groove deposits. The L-38 gasoline engine test requirement provided a measurement of copper-lead bearing weight loss and piston varnish under high-temperature operating conditions. The LTD or Modified LTD gasoline engine test provided a measurement of sludge and varnish. The IID gasoline engine test had been correlated with engines used in short trip service prior to 1978, particularly with regard to rusting.

A.2.14.2 Rationale for Obsolescence—The CC category includes performance tests for which engine parts and/or test fuel and/or reference oils are no longer generally available. These tests are no longer being monitored by the test developer or by ASTM. An oil's performance in this category can no longer be evaluated. Since API "C" categories alphabetically higher than CC are suitable for all diesel engine applications specifying CC, there is no further technical need for CC products in the marketplace and such products are considered TECHNICALLY OBSOLETE for use in diesel engine lubrication.

A.2.14.3 Recommended Labeling Practice—CC performance oils will not provide acceptable diesel engine protection under today's more stringent operating conditions. The use of CC oils by uninformed consumers would cause harm to their engines. Therefore, any marketer who chooses to offer such a limited application oil to the consumer has an obligation to provide clear information indicating the limitations of the product's legitimate application. Such information should be displayed on each container and the corresponding overpack carton in legible and conspicuous type upon a contrasting background. In the case of engine oil sold in bulk, such information should be clearly and prominently included on the invoice. The following statement is recommended for use on both packaged and bulk product and would be considered reasonable and prudent by experts in the field of automotive engine lubrication:

CAUTION—THIS OIL IS RATED API SERVICE CATEGORY CC. IT IS NOT SUITABLE FOR USE IN MOST DIESEL POWERED AUTOMOTIVE ENGINES BUILT AFTER 1990.

A.2.15 API CATEGORY CD (1955 to 1995)

A.2.15.1 Background—The use of the terminology "CD" to define this performance level was adopted by the American Petroleum Institute (API) in 1971. Between 1952 and 1971, this performance level was known as Service DS. This category was based on the performance requirements of Caterpillar Series III and MIL-L-45199B, later MIL-L-2104-C, as set forth by the US Army.

CD service was typical of certain naturally aspirated and turbocharged diesel engines operated in moderate- to severe-duty service and some heavy-duty gasoline engines. These oils provided protection for engines operated on a wide range of fuel qualities, including high sulfur diesel fuel. Oils designed for this service provided protection from wear, high- and low-temperature deposits, bearing corrosion, rust, and corrosion.

Category CD oils were introduced in 1955. They served as the primary heavy-duty diesel engine oil for over-the-road trucks, as well as mining and construction applications for thirty years. With the advent of more advanced engine designs in the 1980s that required better dispersancy, oils rated only API CD category no longer protected many engines against oil thickening, wear, and piston deposits. Category CD oils were largely replaced by category CE oils for most commercial engines.

Category CD was also recommended for some passenger car diesel applications and for some turbocharged gasoline engines to provide protection against high-temperature deposits in turbocharger bearings. Category CD oils are no longer recommended by major gasoline or diesel passenger car vehicle manufacturers.

CD category oils should not be used in any engine unless specifically recommended by the equipment manufacturer.

A.2.15.2 Rationale for Obsolescence—The CD category includes performance tests for which engine parts and/or test fuel and/or reference oils are no longer generally available. Some tests are no longer monitored by the test developer or by ASTM. An oil's performance in this category can no longer be evaluated. Since API CF category oils are suitable for all diesel engine applications specifying CD, there is no further technical need for CD products in the marketplace and such products are considered TECHNICALLY OBSOLETE for use in diesel engine lubrication.

A.2.15.3 Recommended Labeling Practice—CD performance oils will not provide acceptable diesel engine protection under today's more stringent operating conditions. The use of CD oils by uninformed consumers would cause harm to their engines. Therefore, any marketer who chooses to offer such a limited application oil to the consumer has an obligation to provide clear information indicating the limitations of the product's legitimate application. Such information should be displayed on each container and the corresponding overpack carton in legible and conspicuous type upon a contrasting background. In the case of engine oil sold in bulk, such information should be clearly and prominently included on the invoice. The following statement is recommended for use on both packaged and bulk product and would be considered reasonable and prudent by experts in the field of automotive engine lubrication:

CAUTION—THIS OIL IS RATED API PERFORMANCE CATEGORY CD. IT IS NOT SUITABLE FOR USE IN MOST DIESEL POWERED AUTOMOTIVE ENGINES BUILT AFTER 1994.

A.2.16 API CATEGORY CD-II (1985 to 1995)

A.2.16.1 Background—The CD-II Service Category was introduced in 1985 to meet the needs of 2-stroke cycle diesel engines. It provided all the protection required of the API CD Category and had additional requirements that pertained specifically to 2-stroke cycle diesel engines. While most 4-stroke cycle diesel engines had by this time converted to SAE 15W-40 as the primary recommended viscosity grade, some SAE 15W-40 oils performed poorly in 2-stroke cycle engines. This problem was especially pronounced because many fleet managers that had both 2-stroke and 4-stroke cycle diesels wanted only one oil and the SAE 15W-40 grade frequently prevailed. Of greatest concern was the inability of some SAE 15W-40 oils to protect against cylinder liner scuffing.

Category CD-II incorporated the 6-V-53T 2-stroke cycle diesel engine test in which provided assurance that an oil had the ability to protect 2-stroke cycle diesel engines, particularly against piston ring and liner wear, deposits, and valve distress. Because of their extensive use in tactical vehicles, the U.S. Army had developed test procedures using it to evaluate the performance of engine oils in 2-stroke diesel engines. Much of this work was key in establishing and defining Category CD-II.

In 1994, Service Category CD-II was superseded by Service Category CF-2. Service Category CF-2 uses more relevant diesel engine tests.

CD-II category oils should not be used in any engine unless specifically recommended by the equipment manufacturer.

A.2.16.2 Rationale for Obsolescence—The CD-II category includes performance tests for which engine parts and/or test fuel and/or reference oils are no longer generally available. Some tests are no longer monitored by the test developer or by ASTM. An oil's performance in this category can no longer be evaluated. Since API CF-2 category oils are suitable for all diesel engine applications specifying CD-II, there is no further technical need for CD-II products in the marketplace and such products are considered TECHNICALLY OBSOLETE for use in diesel engine lubrication.

A.2.16.3 Recommended Labeling Practice—CD-II performance oils will not provide acceptable diesel engine protection under today's more stringent operating conditions. The use of CD-II oils by uninformed consumers would cause harm to their engines. Therefore, any marketer who chooses to offer such a limited application oil to the consumer has an obligation to provide clear information indicating the limitations of the product's legitimate application. Such information should be provided on each container and the corresponding overpack carton in legible and conspicuous type upon a contrasting background. In the case of engine oil sold in bulk, such information should be clearly and prominently included on the invoice. The following statement is recommended for use on both packaged and bulk product and would be considered reasonable and prudent by experts in the field of automotive engine lubrication:

CAUTION—THIS OIL IS RATED API PERFORMANCE CATEGORY CD-II. IT IS NOT SUITABLE FOR USE IN MOST DIESEL POWERED AUTOMOTIVE ENGINES BUILT AFTER 1994.

A.2.17 API CATEGORY CE (1985 to 1995)

A.2.17.1 Background—The CE Service Category was introduced in 1985 to meet the needs of more modern high- speed, high-output four-stroke cycle diesel engines. By the mid-1980s, emissions control had become an important criteria in diesel engine design. The resulting new piston configurations and combustion patterns altered the amounts and impact of combustion products on the engine and engine oil. In some cases, particularly low-speed high-load operation, some category CD oils failed to provide adequate soot control leading to excessive oil thickening and bore polishing. Some CD oils failed to provide adequate protection against high-temperature upper piston deposits in direct injected engines with narrow cutback pistons. These deposits frequently caused stuck rings and loss of oil consumption control.

By this time the CD Service Category performance level was approximately 30 years old. Oil testing capabilities needed to be updated to better represent service of the newer production engines.

Category CE oils were designed to meet the need for better soot control, oil consumption control, and high-temperature deposit prevention in 4-stroke cycle engines built in throughout most of the 1980s.

A.2.17.2 Rationale for Obsolescence—The CE category includes performance tests for which engine parts and/or test fuel and/or reference oils are no longer generally available. Some tests are no longer monitored by the test developer or by ASTM. An oil's performance in this category can no longer be evaluated. Since API CG-4 category oils are suitable for all diesel engine applications specifying CE, there is no further technical need for CE products in the marketplace and such products are considered TECHNICALLY OBSOLETE for use in diesel engine lubrication.

A.2.17.3 Recommended Labeling Practice—CE performance oils will not provide acceptable diesel engine protection under today's more stringent operating conditions. The use of CE oils by uninformed consumers would cause harm to their engines. Therefore, any marketer who chooses to offer such a limited application oil to the consumer has an obligation to provide clear information indicating the limitations of the product's legitimate application. Such information should be provided on each container and the corresponding overpack carton in legible and conspicuous type upon a contrasting background. In the case of engine oil sold in bulk, such information should be clearly and prominently included on the invoice. The following statement is recommended for use on both packaged and bulk product and would be considered reasonable and prudent by experts in the field of automotive engine lubrication:

CAUTION—THIS OIL IS RATED API PERFORMANCE CATEGORY CE. IT IS NOT SUITABLE FOR USE IN MOST DIESEL POWERED AUTOMOTIVE ENGINES BUILT AFTER 1994.

TABLE A1A—OBSOLETE ENGINE SERVICE CLASSIFICATIONS— API SERVICE CATEGORY SA

API Engine Service Description	Test Methods	Rated or Measured Parameter	Performance Limits
The category SA denotes service typical of older engines operated under such mild conditions that the protection afforded by compounded oils is not required. This category has no performance requirements, and oils in this category should not be used in any engine unless specifically recommended by the equipment manufacturer.	None	None	
ASTM Engine Oil Description			
No performance requirements have been established for this category since it describes oil containing no performance additives.			

TABLE A1B—OBSOLETE ENGINE SERVICE CLASSIFICATIONS— API SERVICE CATEGORY SB

API Engine Service Description	Test Methods	Rated or Measured Parameter	Performance Limits
The category SB denotes service typical of older engines operated under such mild conditions that only minimum protection afforded by compounding is desired. Oils designed for this service have been used since the 1930s and provide mild antiscuff capability and resistance to oil oxidation and bearing corrosion. They should not be used in any engine unless specifically recommended by the equipment manufacturer.	L-4 or L-38[1]	Bearing weight loss, mg, max	**L-4L-38** 500500
	Sequence IV	Cam scuffing	None
		Lifter scuff rating, max	2
ASTM Engine Oil Description			
Oil meeting the performance requirements of the following gasoline engine tests: The Sequence IV test has been correlated with vehicles used in consumer service prior to 1958, particularly with regard to valve train scuffing. Either the L-4 or the L-38 test provides a measurement of copper-lead bearing weight loss under high-temperature conditions.			

1. Test conditions or performance requirements changed since originally dictated.

TABLE A1C—OBSOLETE ENGINE SERVICE CLASSIFICATIONS—API SERVICE CATEGORY SC

API Engine Service Description	Test Methods	Rated or Measured Parameter	Performance Limits
The category SC denotes service typical of gasoline engines in 1964 through 1967 models of passenger cars and some trucks operating under engine manufacturers' warranties in effect during those model years. Oils designed for this service provide control of high- and low-temperature deposits, wear, rust, and corrosion in gasoline engines.			**IIAIIIA**
	Sequences IIA and IIIA	Average rust rating, min	8.2—
		Cam and lifter scuffing	—None
		Average cam plus lifter wear, mm (in) max	—0.064(0.0025)
ASTM Engine Oil Description		Average sludge rating, min	—9.5
		Average varnish rating, min	—9.7
Oil meeting the performance requirements measured in the following gasoline and diesel engines tests. The IIA and IIIA gasoline engine tests are run in series on the same oil change. The IIA has been correlated with vehicles used in short-trip service with regard to rusting, and the IIIA has been correlated with vehicles used in high-temperature service, primarily with regard to valve train wear. These correlations were developed with vehicles in use prior to 1958. The Sequence IV gasoline engine test has been correlated with vehicles used in consumer service prior to 1958, particularly with regard to valve train scuffing. The sequence V test has been correlated with vehicles used in stop-and-go service prior to 1957, primarily with regard to sludge, varnish, and valve tip wear. The L-38 gasoline engine test requirement provides a measurement of copper-lead bearing weight loss under high-temperature operating conditions.	Sequence IV	Cam scuffing	None
		Lifter scuff rating, max	2
	Sequence V	Total engine sludge rating, min	40
		Average piston skirt varnish rating, min	7.0
		Total engine varnish rating, min	35
		Average intake valve tip wear, mm (in) max	0.051(0.0020)
		Ring Sticking	None
		Oil ring clogging, %, max	20
		Oil screen plugging, %, max	20
	L-38	Bearing weight loss, mg, max	50

TABLE A1D—OBSOLETE ENGINE SERVICE CLASSIFICATIONS—API SERVICE CATEGORY SD

API Engine Service Description	Test Methods	Rated or Measured Parameter	Performance Limits
The category SD denotes service typical of gasoline engines in 1968 through 1970 models of passenger cars and some trucks operating under engine manufacturers' warranties in effect during those model years. This category may also apply to certain 1971 and/or later models as specified or recommended in the owner's manuals. Oils designed for this service provide more protection against high- and low-temperature engine deposits, wear, rust, and corrosion in gasoline engines than oils that are satisfactory for API Engine Service Category SC and may be used when API Engine Service Category SC is recommended.			**IIBIIIB**
	Sequences IIB and IIIB	Average rust rating, min	8.8—
		Cam and lifter scuffing	—None
		Average cam plus lifter wear, mm (in) max	—0.076 (0.0030)
		Average sludge rating, min	—9.6
		Average varnish rating, min	—9.6
ASTM Engine Oil Description	Sequence IV	Cam scuffing	None
		Lifter scuff rating, max	1
Oil meeting the performance requirements measured in the following gasoline and diesel engine tests: The IIB and IIIB gasoline engine tests are run in series on the same oil change. The IIB has been correlated with vehicles used in short-trip service with regard to rusting, and the IIIB has been correlated with vehicles used in high-temperature service, primarily with regard to valve train wear. These correlations were developed with vehicles in use prior to 1953. The Sequence IV gasoline engine test has been correlated with vehicles used in consumer service prior to 1958, particularly with regard to valve train scuffing. The Sequence VB test has been correlated with vehicles used in stop-and-go service prior to 1965, primarily with regard to sludge, varnish, and valve tip wear. The L-38 gasoline engine test requirement provides a measurement of copper-lead bearing weight loss under high-temperature operating conditions. The L-1 (1.0% mass fuel sulfur) or 1H diesel engine test requirements are alternatives that provide a measurement of high-temperature deposits. The Falcon gasoline engine test has been used to provide additional performance requirements with regard to rusting.	Sequence VB	Total engine sludge rating, min	42.5
		Average piston skirt varnish rating, min	8.0
		Total engine varnish rating, min	37.5
		Average intake valve tip wear, mm (in) max	0.038 (0.0015)
		Oil ring clogging, %, max	5
		Oil screen plugging, %, max	5
	L-38	Bearing weight loss, mg, max	40
			L-11H
	L-1 (0.85% min sulfur fuel) or 1H	Groove No. 1 (top) carbon fill, % vol, max	2530
		Groove No. 2 lacquer coverage, % area, max	—50
		Groove No. 2 and below	Essentially clean—
		Land No. 3 and below	—Essentially Clean
	Falcon	Average engine rust rating, min	9.0

**TABLE A1E—OBSOLETE ENGINE SERVICE CLASSIFICATIONS—
API SERVICE CATEGORY SE**

API Engine Service Description	Test Methods	Rated or Measured Parameter	Performance Limits		
			IIB	IIC	IID
The category SE denotes service typical of gasoline engines in passenger cars and some trucks beginning with 1972 and certain 1971 through 1979 models operating under engine manufacturers' warranties. Oils designed for this service provide more protection against oil oxidation, high-temperature engine deposits, rust, and corrosion in gasoline engines than oils that are satisfactory for API Engine Service Categories SD or SC and may be used when either of these categories is recommended.	Sequence IIB, IIC, or IID	Average engine rust rating, min	8.9	8.4	8.5
		Number stuck lifters	None	None	None
			IIIC		IIID
	Sequence IIIC or IIID	Viscosity increase at 37.78 °C (100 °F) and 40 test h, %, max	400		
		Viscosity increase at 40 °C and 40 test h, %, max	—		375
ASTM Engine Oil Description		Average engine ratings at 64 test h			
Oil meeting the performance requirements measured in the following gasoline engine tests: The IIB, IIC, and IID gasoline engine tests were correlated with vehicles used in short-term service prior to 1968, 1971, and 1978, respectively - particularly with regard to rusting. The IIIC and IIID gasoline engine tests were correlated with vehicles used in high-temperatures service prior to 1971 and 1978, respectively - particularly with regard to oil thickening and valve train wear. The VC and V-D gasoline engine tests were correlated with vehicles used in stop-and-go service prior to 1971 and 1978, respectively - particularly with regard to varnish and sludge. The L-38 gasoline engine test requirement provides a measurement of copper-lead bearing weight loss under high-temperature operating conditions.		Average sludge rating, min.	9.2		9.2
		Average piston skirt varnish rating, min	9.3		9.1
		Average oil ring land deposit rating, min	6.0		4.0
		Ring sticking	None		None
		Lifter sticking	None		None
		Scuffing and wear at 64 test h			
		Cam or lifter scuffing	None		None
		Cam plus lifter wear, mm (in)			
		Average	0.025 (0.0010)		0.102 (0.0040)
		Maximum	0.051 (0.0020)		0.254 (0.100)
				VC	V-D
	Sequence VC or V-D	Average engine sludge rating, min.		8.7	9.2
		Average piston skirt varnish rating, min.		7.9	6.4
		Average engine varnish rating, min		8.0	6.3
		Oil screen clogging, %, max		5	10.0
		Oil ring clogging, %, max		5	10.0
		Compression ring sticking		None	None
		Cam wear, mm (in)			
		Average, max		—	Rate and Report
		Maximum, max		—	Rate and Report
	L-38	Bearing weight loss, mg, max		40	

**TABLE A1F—OBSOLETE ENGINE SERVICE CLASSIFICATIONS—
API SERVICE CATEGORY SF**

API Engine Service Description	Test Methods	Rated or Measured Parameter	Performance Limits	
The category SF denotes service typical of gasoline engines in passenger cars and some trucks beginning with the 1980 through 1988 model years operating under engine manufacturers' recommended maintenance procedures. Oils developed for this service provide increased oxidation stability and improved antiwear performance relative to oils that meet the minimum requirements for API Service Category SE. These oils also provide protection against engine deposits, rust, and corrosion. Oils meeting API Service Category SF may be used when API Service Categories SE, SD, or SC are recommended.	Sequence IID	Average engine rust rating, min	8.5	
		Number stuck lifters	None	
	Sequence IIID	Viscosity Increase at 40 °C (64 test h)	375	
		Average sludge rating, min	9.2	
		Average piston skirt varnish rating, min	9.2	
		Average oil ring land deposit rating, min	4.5	
		Ring sticking	None	
ASTM Engine Oil Description		Lifter sticking	None	
		Scuffing and wear		
		Cam and lifter scuffing	None	
Oil meeting the performance requirements measured in the following gasoline engine tests: The IID gasoline engine test has been correlated with vehicles used in short-trip service prior to 1978, particularly with regard to rusting. The IIID gasoline engine test has been correlated with vehicles used in high-temperature service prior to 1978, particularly with regard to oil thickening and valve train wear. The V-D gasoline engine test has been correlated with vehicles used in stop-and-go service prior to 1978, particularly with regard to varnish, sludge, and valve train wear. The L-38 gasoline engine test requirement provides a measurement of copper-lead bearing weight loss under high-temperature operating conditions. NOTE (added in 1988): Many automobile manufacturers' warranty requirements for 1986-1988 gasoline engines include CC or CD requirements in addition to SF.		Cam plus lifter wear, min (in)		
		Average, max	0.102 (0.0040)	
		Maximum, max	0.203 (0.0080)	
	Sequence V-D	Average engine sludge rating, min	9.4	
		Average piston skirt varnish rating, min	6.7	
		Average engine varnish rating, min	6.6	
		Oil ring clogging, %, max	10.0	
		Oil screen clogging, %, max	7.5	
		Compression ring sticking	None	
		Cam wear, min (in)		
		Average, max	0.025 (0.0010)	
		Maximum, max	0.064 (0.0025)	
	L-38	Bearing weight loss, mg, max	40	
			1H	1H2
	1H or 1H2	Groove No. 1 (top) carbon fill, % vol, max	30	45
		Groove No. 2 lacquer coverage, % area, max	50—	
		Land No. 3 and below	Essentially Clean	—
		Weight total dements, max	—	140
		Ring side clearance Loss, mm (in) max[(1)]	—	0.013 (0.0005)

1. This refers to the piston groove and ring side clearances.

TABLE A1G—OBSOLETE ENGINE SERVICE CLASSIFICATIONS—
API SERVICE CATEGORY SG

API Engine Service Description

API Service Category SG denotes service typical of more recent gasoline engines and some diesel engines in recommended maintenance procedures. Engine oils designated by this API Category must meet the engine protection sequence test requirements of CID-A-A-52039 and ILSAC GF-1. In addition, all viscosity grades designated in DOD CID-A-A-52039 must meet the bench test requirements described in DOD CID-A-A-52039 and ILSAC GF-1. Engine oils that meet these requirements may display the API Service Category SG in the upper portion of the API Service Symbol. Engine oils that also meet the fuel efficiency requirements of DOD CID-A-A-52039 and ILSAC GF-1 may be designated as Energy Conserving II in the bottom portion of the API Service Symbol.

Test Methods	Rated or Measured Parameter	Primary Performance Criteria	Rating Scale
Sequence IID	Average engine rust rating, min	8.5	0-10, 10=clean
	Number stuck lifters	None	
Sequence IIIE	Hours to 375% kinematic viscosity increase at 40 °C, min	64	
	Average sludge rating, min	9.2	0-10, 10=clean
	Average piston skirt varnish rating, min	8.9	0-10, 10=clean
	Average oil ring land deposit rating, min	3.5	0-10, 10=clean
	Lifter sticking	None	
	Scuffing and wear		
	Cam or lifter scuffing	None	
	Cam plus lifter wear, μm (in)		
	Average, max	30 (0.0012)	
	Maximum, max	64 (0.0025)	
	Ring sticking (oil related)	None	
Sequence VE	Average engine sludge rating	9.0	0-10, 10=clean
	Cam cover sludge rating, min	7.0	0-10, 10=clean
	Average piston skirt varnish rating, min	6.5	0-10, 10=clean
	Average engine varnish rating, min	5.0	0-10, 10=clean
	Oil ring clogging, % max	Rate and Report	
	Oil screen clogging, % max	20.0	
	Compression ring sticking (hot stuck)	None	
	Cam wear, μm (in x 10^{-3})		
	Average, max	130 (5)	
	Maximum, max	380 (15)	

ASTM Engine Oil Description

Oil meeting the performance requirements measured in the following gasoline and bench tests: the IID gasoline engine test has been correlated with vehicles used in short-trip service prior to 1978, particularly with regard to rusting. Test Method D 5533, the IIIE gasoline engine test has been correlated with vehicles used in high-temperature service prior to 1988, particularly with regard to oil thickening and valve train wear. Test Method D 5302, the VE gasoline engine test has been correlated with vehicles used in stop-and-go service prior to 1988, particularly with regard to sludge and valve train wear. Test Method D 5119, the L-38 gasoline engine test is used to measure copper-lead bearing weight loss and piston varnish under high-temperature operating conditions. In addition to passing performance in the engine tests, specific viscosity grades shall also meet bench test requirements. The volatility of engine oils relates to engine oil consumption. The Engine Oil Filterability Test screens for the formation of precipitates that can cause oil filter plugging. Phosphorus compounds can cause glazing of automotive catalysts and exhaust gas oxygen sensors and, thereby, deactivate them. Control of the phosphorus level can reduce this tendency. The flash point can indicate if residual solvents and low-boiling fractions remain in the finished oil. Foaming in engine oil can cause valve lifter collapse and a loss of lubrication due to the presence of air in the oil. The foam test indicates an oil's foaming tendency. The Homogeneity and Miscibility Test indicates the compatibility of an oil with standard test oils. The L-38 Shear Stability Test indicates the ability of an oil to resist permanent viscosity loss due to shearing in an engine.

Test Methods	Rated or Measured Parameter	5W-30	10W-30	15W-40	Rating Scale
L-38	Bearing weight loss, mg, max		40		
	Piston skirt varnish rating, min		9.0		0-10, 10=clean
ASTM D 2887 or CEC L-40-T-87	Volatility, % loss at 371 °C, max	20	17	15	
	or wt % loss 1 h, 250 °C, max	25	20	18	
GM EOFT (GM9099P) (H)	Flow reduction, %, max	50	50	NR	
D 4951 or D 5185	Phosphorus mass, %, max	0.12	0.12	NR	
ASTM D 92 or ASMT D 93	Flash Point, °C, min	200	205	215	
		185	190	200	
ASTM D 892 (Option A)	Foaming Tendency, Foaming/Settling, mL/mL, max				
	Sequence I	10/0	10/0	10/0	
	Sequence II	50/0	50/0	50/0	
	Sequence III	10/0	10/0	10/0	
	Sequence IV	------------	Report	------------	
FTM 791 B Method 3470	Homogeneity & Miscibility	Homogeneous with SAE Reference Oils			
L-38	Shear Stability, 10 h stripped viscosity	Must remain in original grade			

TABLE A1H—OBSOLETE ENGINE SERVICE CLASSIFICATIONS—ILSAC CATEGORY GF-1

Description	Test Methods	Rated or Measured Parameter	Primary Performance Criteria	Rating Scale
The International Lubricants Standardization and Approval Committee (ILSAC) is a joint activity of the Japanese Automobile Manufacturers Association (JAMA) and the Alliance of Automobile Manufacturers (AAM). In 1990, ILSAC issued their first minimum performance standard for gasoline fueled passenger cars, ILSAC GF-1. This standard listed the requirements deemed necessary by vehicle manufacturers for satisfactory equipment life and performance.	Sequence IID	Average engine rust rating min	8.5	0-10, 10=Clean
		Number stuck lifters	None	
	Sequence IIIE	Viscosity increase at 40 °C (64 test h), % max	375	
		Average sludge rating, min	9.2	0-10, 10=Clean
		Average piston skirt varnish rating, min	8.9	0-10, 10=Clean
		Average oil ring land deposit rating, min	3.5	0-10, 10=Clean
		Lifter sticking		
		Scuffing and wear		
		Cam or lifter scuffing	None	
		Cam plus lifter wear, mm (in)		
		Average, max	30 (0.0012)	
		Maximum, max	64 (0.0025)	
		Ring sticking	No oil related	
		Oil Consumption, L, max	5.1 max	
	Sequence VE	Average engine sludge rating	9.0	0-10, 10=Clean
		Cam cover sludge rating, min	7.0	0-10, 10=Clean
		Avg. piston skirt varnish rating, min	6.5	0-10, 10=Clean
		Avg. engine varnish rating, min	5.0	0-10, 10=Clean
		Oil ring clogging, % max	Rate and Report	
		Oil screen clogging, % max	20.0	
		Compression ring sticking (hot stuck)	None	
		Cam wear, μm (in x 10^{-3})		
		Average, max	130 (5)	
		Maximum, max	380 (15)	
	L-38	Bearing weight loss, mg, max	40	
		Piston skirt varnish rating, min	9.0	0-10, 10=clean
	ASTM D 2887	Volatility, % loss at 371 °C, max	20 for 0W, 5W multigrades, 17 for all other multigrades	
	or CEC L-40-T-87	or wt % loss 1 h, 250 °C, max	or 25 for 0W, 5W multigrades, 20 for all other multigrades	
	GM EOFT (GM9099P) (H)	Flow reduction, % max	50	
	ASTM D 4951 or ASTM D 5185	Phosphorus, mass %, max	0.12	
		Flash Point, °C, min	200	
	ASTM D 92 or ASTM D 93	Flash Point, °C, min	185	
	ASTM D 892 (Option A)	Foaming Tendency, Foaming/Settling, mL/mL, max		
		Sequence I	10/0	
		Sequence II	50/0	
		Sequence III	10/0	
		Sequence IV	Report	
	FTM 791 B Method 3470	Homogeneity and Miscibility	Homogeneous with SAE Reference Oils	
	L-38	Shear Stability, 10 h stripped viscosity	Must remain in original grade	
	Sequence VI	Estimated Fuel Economy Improvement, %, min	2.7	
	ASTM D 5293	Low temperature Cranking viscosity, –20 °C, mPa·s, max	3500	
	ASTM D 4684	Low temperature pumping viscosity, –25 °C, mPa·s, max	30 000	

**TABLE A1I—OBSOLETE ENGINE SERVICE CLASSIFICATIONS—
API SERVICE CATEGORY CA**

API Engine Service Description	Test Methods	Rated or Measured Parameter	Performance Limits	
Service typical of diesel engines operated in mild- to moderate-duty with high-quality fuels and occasionally has included gasoline engines in mild services. Oils designed for this service provide protection from bearing corrosion and from ring belt deposits in some naturally aspirated diesel engines when using fuels of such quality that they impose no unusual requirements for wear and deposit protection. They were widely used in the late 1940s and 1950s but should not be used in any engine unless specifically recommended by the equipment manufacturer.			**L-4**	**L-38**
	L-4 or L-38(1)	Bearing weight loss, mg, max	120-135	50
		Piston skirt varnish rating, min	9.0	9.0
	L-1 (0.35% min sulfur fuel)	Groove No. 1 (top) carbon fill, % vol, max	25	
		Groove No. 2 and below	Essentially clean	
ASTM Engine Oil Description				
Oils meeting the performance requirements measured in the following diesel and gasoline engine tests. The L-1 (0.4% mass fuel sulfur) naturally-aspirated diesel engine test provides a measurement of piston deposits. The L-38 (or alternatively the L-4) gasoline engine test requirement provides a measurement of copper-lead bearing weight loss and piston varnish under high-temperature operating conditions.				

1. Test conditions or performance requirements changed since originally dictated.

**TABLE A1J—OBSOLETE ENGINE SERVICE CLASSIFICATIONS—
API SERVICE CATEGORY CB**

API Engine Service Description	Test Methods	Rated or Measured Parameter	Performance Limits
Service typical of diesel engines operated in mild- to moderate-duty, but with lower quality fuels which necessitate more protection from wear and deposits. Occasionally has included gasoline engines in mild service. Oils designed for this service were introduced in 1949. Such oils provide necessary protection from bearing corrosion and from high temperature deposits in normally aspirated diesel engines with higher sulfur fuels.			**L-4 L-38**
	L-4 or L-38(1)	Bearing weight loss, mg, max	120-135 50
		Piston skirt varnish rating, min	9.0 9.0
	L-1 (0.95% min sulfur fuel)	Groove No.1 (top) carbon fill, % vol, max	30
		Groove No. 2 and below	Essentially clean
ASTM Engine Oil Description			
Oils meeting the performance requirements measured in the following diesel and gasoline engine tests. The L-1 (1% mass fuel sulfur) naturally-aspirated diesel engine test provides a measurement of piston deposits. The L-38 (or alternatively the L-1) gasoline engine test requirement provides a measurement of copper-lead bearing weight loss and piston varnish under high-temperature operating conditions.			

1. Test conditions or performance requirements changed since originally dictated.

**TABLE A1K—OBSOLETE ENGINE SERVICE CLASSIFICATIONS—
API SERVICE CATEGORY CC**

API Engine Service Description	Test Methods	Rated or Measured Parameter	Performance Limits		
	L-38	Bearing weight loss, mg, max		50	
		Piston skirt varnish rating, min		9.0	
			LTD		**Modified**
The category CC denotes service typical of certain naturally aspirated, turbocharged, or supercharged diesel engines operated in moderate-to severe-duty service and certain heavy-duty gasoline engines. Oils designed for this service provide protection from high-temperature deposits and bearing corrosion in these diesel engines and also from rust corrosion, and low-temperature deposits in gasoline engines. These oils were introduced in 1961.	LTD or Modified LTD(1)(2)	Piston skirt varnish rating, min	7.5		7.5
		Total engine varnish rating, min	—		42
		Total engine sludge rating, min	35		42
		Oil ring plugging, %, max	25		10
		Oil screen clogging, %, max	25		10
ASTM Engine Oil Description			**IIA**	**IIBIIC**	**IID**
	Sequence IIA, IIB(1), IIC or IID	Average engine rust rating, min	8.2	8.2 7.6	7.7
Oil meeting the performance requirements measured in the following diesel and gasoline engine tests. The 1H2 diesel engine test has been correlated with indirect injection engines used in moderate-duty operation, particularly with regard to piston and ring groove deposits. The L-38 gasoline engine test requirement provides a measurement of copper-lead bearing weight loss and piston varnish under high-temperature operating conditions. The Modified LTD gasoline engine test provides a measurement of sludge and varnish. The IID gasoline engine test has been correlated with vehicles used in short-trip service prior to 1978, particularly with regard to rusting.			1H		IH2
	1H or 1H2	Groove No. 1 (top) carbon fill, % vol, max	30		45
		Groove No. 2 lacquer coverage, % area, max	50		—
		Land No. 3 and below	Essentially	Clean	—
		Weighted total demerits, max	—		140
		Ring side clearance Loss, mm (in) max	—		0.013 (0.0005)

1. Test conditions or performance requirements changed since originally dictated.
2. An oil can also satisfy this requirement by meeting or exceeding the Sequence VC or V-D deposit limits of the SE category.

TABLE A1L—OBSOLETE ENGINE SERVICE CLASSIFICATIONS— API SERVICE CATEGORY CD

API Engine Service Description	Test Methods	Rated or Measured Parameter	Primary Performance Criteria	Rating Scale
API Service Category CD denotes service typical of certain naturally aspirated, turbocharged, or supercharged diesel engines in which highly effective control of wear and deposits is vital or in which fuels of a wide quality range, including high sulfur fuels, are used. Oils designed for this service were introduced in 1955 and provide protection from bearing corrosion and from high-temperature deposits in these diesel engines.	1G2	Groove No. 1 (top) carbon fill, % vol, max	80	
		Weighted total demerits, max	300	
		Ring side clearances. Loss, mm (in) max[1]	0.013 (0.0005)	
ASTM Engine Oil Description	L-38	Bearing weight loss, mg, max	50	
Oil meeting the performance requirements measured in the following diesel and gasoline engine test: The 1G2 diesel engine test has been correlated with indirect injection engines used in heavy-duty operation, particularly with regard to piston and ring groove deposits. The L-38 gasoline engine test is used to measure copper-lead bearing weight loss and piston varnish under high-temperature operating conditions.		Piston skirt varnish rating, min	9.0	0-10,10=clean

1. This refers to losses in the piston groove and ring side clearances.

TABLE A1M—OBSOLETE ENGINE SERVICE CLASSIFICATIONS— API SERVICE CATEGORY CD-II

API Engine Service Description	Test Methods	Rated or Measured Parameter	Primary Performance Criteria	Rating Scale
API Service Category CD-II denotes service typical of two-stroke cycle diesel engines that require highly effective control of wear and deposits. Oils designed for this service also meet all performance requirements of API Service Category CD.	1G2	Groove No. 1 (top) carbon fill, % vol, max	80	
		Weighted total dements, max	300	
		Ring side clearance Loss, mm (in) max[1]	0.013 (0.0005)	
ASTM Engine Oil Description	L-38	Bearing weight loss, mg, max	50	
Oil meeting the performance requirements measured in the following diesel and gasoline engine tests: The 1G2 diesel engine test has been correlated with indirect injection engines used in heavy-duty operation, particularly with regard to piston and ring groove deposits. The 6V-53T diesel engine test has been correlated with vehicles equipped with two-stroke cycle diesel engines in high-speed operation prior to 1985, particularly with regard to ring and liner distress. The L-38 gasoline engine test requirement provides a measurement of copper-lead bearing weight loss and piston skirt varnish high-temperature operating conditions.		Piston skirt varnish rating, min	9.0	0-10, 10=clean
	6V-53T	Piston area		
		Weighted total demerits, average, max	400	
		Hot stuck rings	None	
		Face distress, Nos. 2 and 3 rings demerits, average, max	13.0	
		Liner and head area		
		Liner distress, average, % area, max	12.0	
		Valve distress	None	

1. This refers to losses in the piston groove and ring side clearances.

TABLE A1N—OBSOLETE ENGINE SERVICE CLASSIFICATIONS— API SERVICE CATEGORY CE

API Engine Service Description	Test Methods	Rated or Measured Parameter	Primary Performance Criteria	Rating Scale
API Service Category CE denotes service typical of certain turbocharged or supercharged heavy-duty diesel engines manufactured since 1983 and operated under high-load for both low- and high-speed operations. Oils designed for this service may also be used when API Engine service Category CD is recommended for diesel engines.	1G2	Groove No. 1 (top) carbon fill, % vol, max	80	
		Weighted total demerits, max	300	
		Ring side clearance Loss, mm (in), max[1]	0.013 (0.0005)	
ASTM Engine Oil Description	L-38	Bearing weight loss, mg, max	50	
Oil meeting the performance requirements of the following diesel and gasoline engine tests: The 1G2 diesel engine test has been correlated with indirect injection engines used in heavy-duty service, particularly with regard to piston and ring groove deposits. The T-6, T-7, and NTC-400 are direct injection diesel engine test. The T-6 has been correlated with vehicles equipped with engines used in high-speed operations prior to 1980, particularly with regard to deposits, oil consumption, and ring wear. The T-7 test has been correlated with vehicles equipped with engines operated largely under lugging conditions prior to 1984, particularly with regard to oil thickening. Test Method D 5290, the NTC-400 diesel engine test has been correlated with vehicles equipped with engines in highway operation prior to 1983, particularly with regard to oil consumption control, deposits, and wear. Test Method D 5119, the L-38 gasoline engine test requirement is used to measure copper-lead bearing weight loss.	T-6	Merit rating, min	90	0-160
	T-7	Average rate of viscosity increase during last 50 h, cSt @ 100 °C/h, max	0.040	
	NTC-400	Oil consumption	Candidate oil consumption second order regression curve must fall completely below the published mean plus one standard deviation curve for the applicable reference oil.[2]	
		Camshaft roller follower pin wear average, max, mm (in)	0.051 (0.002)	
		Crownland (top land) deposits, % area covered with heavy carbon, average, max	25	
		Piston deposits, third ring land, total CRC demerits for all six pistons, max	40	

1. This refers to losses in the piston groove and ring side clearances.
2. Applicable NTC-400 reference oil consumption curves are published twice per year by the ASTM Test Monitoring Center. Copies of these data may be obtained by contacting the Center of ASTM TMC, 4400 Fifth Avenue, Pittsburgh, PA 15213. Applicable reference oil data to which candidate oil data are to be compared are included with each engine test report.

INTERNATIONAL TESTS AND SPECIFICATIONS FOR AUTOMOTIVE ENGINE OILS—SAE J2227 APR2002

SAE Information Report

Report of the SAE Fuels and Lubricants Technical Committees 1 and 2—Passenger Car Type Engine Oils and Heavy-Duty Type Engine Oils approved June 1991, revised May 1992, completely revised May 1993, and revised June 1994 and August 1995. Revised by the SAE Fuels and Lubricants Technical Committee 1—Automotive Engine Oils, August 1996, July 1997, July 1998, June 1999, June 2000, and April 2002. Rationale statement available.

Foreword—Engine and laboratory tests are utilized to determine the performance of engine oils. The API, ASTM, and SAE have established engine tests and classifications to describe engine oil performance. Such tests are included in SAE J183, Engine Oil Performance and Engine Service Classification (Other Than "Energy Conserving"), SAE J304, Engine Oil Tests, and SAE J300, Engine Oil Viscosity Classification. Additionally tests to characterize the energy-conserving characteristics of engine oils is described in SAE J1423. Engine and laboratory tests apart from those described in these SAE documents are also established in Europe and Japan. The purpose of this document is to summarize the respective international tests and specifications utilized to characterize the performance of service fill automotive engine oils outside of North America. Since specifications are likely to change frequently, it is recommended that all specifications be confirmed with the appropriate manufacturer or Technical Society at the time that critical usage is contemplated.

1. Scope—This SAE Information Report lists engine and laboratory tests for service fill engine oils which are associated with specifications and classifications established outside of North America. These specifications and classifications include those developed prior to June 1, 2001, by International Technical Societies as well as individual original equipment manufacturers. The information contained within this report applies to engine oils utilized in gasoline and diesel powered automotive vehicles.

2. References

2.1 Applicable Publications—The following publications form a part of this SAE Information Report to the extent specified herein. The latest issue of SAE publications shall apply.

2.1.1 SAE PUBLICATIONS—Available from SAE, 400 Commonwealth Drive, Warrendale, PA 15096-0001.

SAE J183—Engine Oil Performance and Engine Service Classification (Other Than "Energy-Conserving")

SAE J300—Engine Oil Viscosity Classification

SAE J304—Engine Oil Tests

SAE J1423—Classification of Energy-Conserving Engine Oil for Passenger Cars, Vans, and Light-Duty Trucks

2.1.2 API PUBLICATION—Available from the American Petroleum Institute, 1220 L Street, Northwest, Washington, DC 20005. WEB Address: api.org/eolcs

API Publication 1509—Engine Oil Licensing and Certification System

2.1.3 ASTM PUBLICATION—Available from ASTM, 100 Barr Harbor Drive, West Conshohocken, PA 19428-2959.

ASTM D 4485—Standard Specification for Performance of Engine Oils

2.1.4 CEC PUBLICATIONS—Available from the Coordinating European Council, Boulevard du Souverain 165, B-1160, Brussels, Belgium.

CEC Annual Report

CEC Catalogue of Methods

2.1.5 ACEA PUBLICATIONS—Available from ACEA (Association of the European Automobile Manufacturers), 211 rue du Noyer, B-1040, Brussels.

ACEA European Oil Sequences, September 1998—Service Fill Oils for Gasoline Engines, Light Duty Diesel Engines, Heavy Duty Diesel Engines, Issue date 4th March 1998

2.1.6 GLOBAL PERFORMANCE SPECIFICATION—Available through the following web sites:

www.acea.be

www.engine-manufacturers.org

www.jama.or.jp

Global Performance Specification for Diesel Engine Oil (Global DHD-1)

2.1.7 INTERNATIONAL LUBRICANT STANDARDIZATION AND APPROVAL COMMITTEE STANDARDS—Available from the American Petroleum Institute, 1220 L Street Northwest, Washington, DC 20005 and contained within API Publication 1509.

International Lubricant Standardization and Approval Committee (ILSAC) Standards for Passenger Car Engine Oils

ILSAC GF-3

2.1.8 JASO PUBLICATIONS—Available from the Society of Automotive Engineers of Japan Inc., 10-2 Goban-cho, Chiyoda-ku, Tokyo 102, Japan. (M-336-97 presently available in Fall 1998 in Japanese only.)

JASO Standard M328-95—Valve Train Wear Test Procedure for Evaluating Automobile Gasoline Engine Oils

JASO Standard M331-91—Low and Medium Temperature Detergency Test Procedure for Evaluating Automobile Gasoline Engine Oils

JASO Standard M333-93—High Temperature Oxidation Stability Test Procedure for Evaluating Automobile Gasoline Engine Oils

JASO Standard M336-98—High Temperature and High Load Detergency Test Procedure for Evaluating Automobile Diesel Engine Oils

JASO Standard M354-99—Automobile Diesel Engine Oils—Valve Train Wear Test

2.1.9 MANUFACTURER PUBLICATIONS—Available from the respective European Original Equipment Manufacturers.

MAN Specifications 270, 271, 3275, 3277

Mercedes-Benz Betriebsstoff—Vorschriften

MTL 5044 Oil Category 1, 1*, 2 and 3

MWM Deutz Motor Technical Circular 0199-3002

MWM Deutz Motor Technical Circular 0199-2090

Perkins Engine Specification P.M.S. S.1.01—1983, TSD 3187-1998, PS No. 7294/SB019

Scania Specifications Fuels, Lubricants and Fluids 00.03-09

Scania LDF Specification

Volkswagen Specification VW 500 00, 501 01, 502 00, 503 00, 503 01, 505 00, 505 01, 506 00, 506 01

Volvo Drain Specification (VDS, VDS-2, and VDS-3)

3. European ACEA Sequences—Oil Sequences are established by the European Automobile Manufacturers Association (ACEA) to ensure that suitable lubricants are available to meet the minimum requirements of European vehicles. ACEA, which was formed in February 1991, is engaged in a broad range of activities including safety and environmental concerns and any regulations which have a direct impact on the European automobile industry. ACEA members are all the European motor vehicle manufacturers.

The ACEA Oil Sequences define laboratory tests and engine tests which lubricants must satisfy to achieve the minimum performance requirements established by European manufacturers. These sequences are divided into categories for gasoline, light-duty diesel and heavy-duty diesel engines. The categories are divided further into sub-groups which more precisely define the performance for specific applications.

ACEA Sequences use a two-digit number identifying the year of implementation. An issue number may also be included where requirements have been updated without a change in severity. For consumer use, the year of implementation and issue number is dropped and only a two-part code identifying the class (e.g., A) and the category number (e.g., A1) is used. As of September 1, 2000, all new claims to meet ACEA Sequences must be to the 1999 issue. The 1996 issue was withdrawn as of March 1, 2000 after which no claims to meet those requirements shall be made. The 1998 issue will be withdrawn as of March 1, 2002, after which no claims to meet these requirements shall be made.

Gasoline Sequences

3.1 A1-98—Oil intended for use in gasoline engines specifically designed to be capable of using low-friction, low-viscosity oils with a high-temperature/high-shear rate viscosity of 2.9 to 3.5 mPa·s. These oils may be unsuitable for use in some engines. Consult owner manual or handbook if in doubt.

3.2 A2-96 Issue 2—General purpose oil intended for use in most gasoline engines with normal drain intervals, although it may not be suitable for some high-performance engines.

3.3 A3-98—Stable stay-in-grade oil intended for use in high-performance gasoline engines and/or for extended drain intervals where specified by the engine manufacturer, and/or for year-round use of low-viscosity oils, and/or for severe-operating conditions as defined by the engine manufacturer.

Light-Duty Diesel Sequences

3.4 B1-98—Oil intended for use in car and light van diesel engines specifically designed to be capable of using low-friction, low-viscosity oils with a high-temperature/high-shear rate viscosity of 2.9 to 3.5 mPa·s. These oils may be unsuitable for use in some engines. Consult owner manual or handbook if in doubt.

3.5 B2-98—General purpose oil intended for use in most car and light van diesel engines (primarily indirect injection) with normal drain intervals, although it may not be suitable for some high-performance engines.

3.6 B3-98—Stable stay-in-grade oil intended for use in high-performance car and light van diesel engines (primarily indirect injection) and/or for extended drain intervals where specified by the engine manufacturer, and/or for year-round use of low-viscosity oils, and/or for severe-operating conditions as defined by the engine manufacturer.

3.7 B4-98—Oil intended primarily for use in car and light van direct injection diesel engines where special quality oils are required.

Heavy-Duty Diesel Sequences

3.8 E2-96 Issue 3—General purpose oil for naturally aspirated and turbocharged heavy-duty diesel engines, medium- to heavy-duty cycles and mostly normal oil drain intervals.

3.9 E3-96 Issue 3—This lubricant category provides effective control with respect to piston cleanliness, bore polishing, wear, soot handling and lubricant stability. It is therefore recommended for diesel engines meeting Euro 1 and Euro 2 emission requirements running under severe conditions. It is also suitable for extended oil drain intervals according to the manufacturer's recommendations.

3.10 E4-99—Stable stay-in-grade oil providing further control of piston cleanliness, wear, soot handling and lubricant stability compared to E3. It is recommended for highly rated diesel engines meeting Euro 1, Euro 2, and Euro 3 emission requirements and running under very severe conditions, e.g., significantly extended oil drain intervals according to the manufacturers recommendations.

3.11 E5-99—Stable, stay-in-grade oil providing effective control with respect to piston cleanliness and bore polishing. It further provides wear and turbocharger deposit control, soot handling, and lubricant stability compared to E3. It is recommended for highly rated diesel engines meeting Euro 1, Euro 2, and Euro 3 emission requirements and running under severe conditions, e.g., extended oil drains according to the manufacturers recommendations.

4. Global Performance Specification for Diesel Engine Oil (Global DHD-1)—The Global DHD-1 specification was jointly developed by the European Automobile Manufacturers Association (ACEA), Engine Manufacturers Association (EMA) and the Japan Automobile Manufacturers Association (JAMA). It is a performance specification for engine oils to be used in high speed, four stroke cycle heavy-duty diesel engines designed to meet 1998 and newer exhaust emission standards worldwide. Oils meeting this specification are compatible with certain older engines. Application of these oils is subject to the recommendation of individual engine manufacturers.

5. European Original Equipment Manufacturer Specifications—In addition to the performance requirements set by the ACEA Sequences, original equipment manufacturers in Europe have developed individual specifications for engine oils which may demand additional laboratory and engine performance testing. These specifications are based upon engine type, service, and application. For those specifications referencing ACEA Sequences, an update to ACEA 98 is anticipated.

5.1 MAN 270—Defines minimum laboratory and engine test requirements for naturally aspirated and turbocharged diesel engines both for stationary equipment and for vehicles. Quality level required is ACEA E2 covering monograde oils without VI improvers.

5.2 MAN 271—Defines minimum laboratory and engine test requirements for naturally aspirated and turbocharged diesel engines both for stationary equipment and for vehicles. Quality level required is ACEA E2 and covers multigrade oils (SAE 10W-40, 15W-40, and 20W-50).

5.3 MAN 3275—Defines minimum laboratory and engine test requirements for super high-performance turbocharged diesel engine oils for turbocharged and non-turbocharged engines whenever a higher performance level than MAN 270 or MAN 271 is required. Quality level is ACEA E3. Satisfactory performance in a MAN 500 Hour Engine Test is also required.

5.4 MAN 3277—Defines the minimum laboratory and engine test requirements for diesel oil operated under extended drain conditions. Quality level is ACEA E3 plus. Engine oils must pass additional requirements for wear and deposit control as well as an intake system deposit test.

5.5 MERCEDES-BENZ 227.0—Describes single-grade engine oils approved for passenger cars and commercial vehicles equipped with turbocharged and non-turbocharged diesel engines. For commercial vehicles, attention must be paid to oil drain intervals.

5.6 MERCEDES-BENZ 227.1—Describes multigrade engine oils approved for commercial vehicles equipped with turbocharged and non-turbocharged engines. Attention must be paid to oil drain intervals. Quality Level is similar to ACEA B2/E1, but with more requirements.

5.7 MERCEDES-BENZ 228.0—Describes single-grade engine oils approved for all Mercedes-Benz diesel engines including turbocharged commercial vehicle diesel engines operating with increased oil drain intervals.

5.8 MERCEDES-BENZ 228.1—Describes multigrade engine oils approved for all Mercedes-Benz diesel engines including turbocharged commercial diesel engines operating with increased oil drain intervals. Quality level is similar to ACEA B2/E2 plus more stringent requirements for bore polishing and cylinder wear.

5.9 MERCEDES-BENZ 228.2—Describes single-grade engine oils as in the case of Mercedes-Benz 228.0 which are also suited in given commercial vehicles for longer drain intervals compared to 228.0. Quality level is similar to ACEA B2/E3.

5.10 MERCEDES-BENZ 228.3—Describes multigrade engine oils as in the case of Mercedes-Benz 228.1 which are also suited in given commercial vehicles for longer drain intervals. Quality level is similar to ACEA B2/E3.

5.11 MERCEDES-BENZ 228.5—Describes multigrade engine oils approved for given Mercedes Benz commercial diesel engines in long distance delivery fleets and operating under extended oil drain intervals. Requirements include engine wear, sludge, and oil consumption protection in both pre-Euro II and Euro II engines.

Performance of 227.0 and 227.1, 228.0 and 228.1, 228.2 and 228.3 is equivalent. 228.5 is suitable for the longest drain intervals in commercial vehicles.

5.12 MERCEDES-BENZ 229.1—Describes multigrade engine oils approved for Mercedes-Benz passenger cars equipped with gasoline or diesel engines. Quality level is ACEA A2 or A3 and B2 or B3 as well as additional requirements for wear, piston cleanliness, engine sludge, and seal compatibility. Fuel economy and dielectric constant testing are also required to be reported.

5.13 MERCEDES-BENZ 229.3—Describes multigrade engine oils approved for Mercedes-Benz passenger cars equipped with gasoline or diesel engines. Quality level is ACEA A3, B3, and B-4 with additional requirements for deposit control, wear protection, and turbocharged direct injection diesel performance.

5.14 MTL 5044 Oil Category 1, 1*, 2, and 3—Defines the performance of both single- and multigrade engine oils recommended for MTU diesel engines. Quality level required is ACEA E1/E2 or API CF/CF-4 for Category 1, additional corrosion inhibition for Category 1*, ACEA E3 for Category 2 and ACEA E3+ for Category 3 oils.

5.15 MWM DEUTZ TR 0199-3002—Defines the performance of both single and multigrade engine oils recommended for all Deutz diesel engines and/or small-size Deutz MWM engines. Quality level required is API CC, CD, CE, and CCMC D-4, D-5.

5.16 MWM DEUTZ TR 0199-2090—Defines the performance of both single and multigrade engine oils recommended for big-size Deutz MWM engines. Quality level required is API CC, CD, CE, and CCMC D-4, D-5.

5.17 PERKINS P.M.S. S1.01—1983, TSD 3187—1990, PS No. 7294/SB019—Defines the performance of both single- and multigrade oils utilized in Perkins naturally aspirated and turbocharged diesel engines. P.M.S. S1.01-1983 applies to Peterborough engines, TSD 3187-1998, Shrewsbury engines, and PS No. 729H/SB019 Gardner Engines. TSD 3187-1998 requires ACEA E3-96 or E2-96 performance.

5.18 SCANIA Specification—Defines the performance of engine oils for naturally aspirated and turbocharged diesel engines to be used in maintenance programs.

5.19 SCANIA LDF—Defines the performance of SAE 5W-30, 5W-40, 10W-30, 10W-40, and 15W-40 engine oils intended for use at extended drain intervals in turbocharged engines meeting the European EC96 emission requirement. Engine oils must meet ACEA E3 plus field test requirements.

5.20 VOLKSWAGEN, VW 500 00, ISSUE 01/97—Defines laboratory and engine test requirements for service fill engine oils in VW, Audi, and SEAT gasoline engines. Basic quality level is ACEA A3 plus additional performance requirements for evaporative loss, seal compatibility, piston cleanliness, black sludge, and cam and tappet wear.

5.21 VOLKSWAGEN, VW 501 01, ISSUE 01/97—Defines laboratory and engine test requirements for service fill engine oils in VW, Audi, and SEAT gasoline and naturally aspirated diesel engines. Basic quality level is ACEA A2/A3 plus additional requirements for seal compatibility, piston cleanliness, black sludge, and cam and tappet wear.

5.22 VOLKSWAGEN 502 00—Defines laboratory and engine test requirements for service fill engine oils in VW, Audi, and SEAT gasoline engines. VW 502 00 defines an engine oil performance level higher than VW 501 01 and 500 00. Basic quality level is ACEA A2/A3 plus additional requirements for seal compatibility, piston cleanliness, ring sticking, viscosity increase, TBN decrease, sludge, and cam and tappet wear.

5.23 VOLKSWAGEN 503 00—Defines laboratory and engine test requirements for service fill extended drain engine oils with fuel saving properties in VW, Audi, and SEAT gasoline engines equipped with the "WIV" service interval computer. Basic quality level is ACEA A3 plus additional requirements for fuel economy, seal compatibility, piston cleanliness, ring sticking, viscosity increase, TBN decrease, sludge, and cam and tappet wear. These oils are not to be used in high performance turbocharged Audi engines.

5.24 VOLKSWAGEN 503 01—Defines laboratory and engine test requirements for service fill extended drain engine oils with fuel saving properties in turbocharged gasoline engines equipped with the "WIV" service interval computer. Basic quality level is ACEA A3 plus additional requirements for fuel economy, seal compatibility, piston cleanliness, ring sticking, viscosity increase, TBN decrease, sludge, and cam and tappet wear.

5.25 VOLKSWAGEN VW 505 00, ISSUE 01/97—Defines laboratory and engine test requirements for service fill engine oils in VW, Audi, and SEAT turbocharged passenger car and commercial diesel engines and with exhaust-driven supercharger with and without boost intercooling. Basic quality level is ACEA B2/B3 plus additional requirements for piston cleanliness, seal compatibility, and cam and tappet wear.

5.26 VOLKSWAGEN 505 01—Defines requirements for service fill and factory fill SAE 5W-40 engine oil to be used for all diesel engines, including those equipped with unit injectors but without "WIV" service interval computers.

5.27 VOLKSWAGEN 506 00—Defines laboratory and engine test requirements for service fill extended drain engine oils with fuel saving properties for all diesel engines except those fitted with unit injectors and fitted with "WIV" service interval computers. Basic quality level is ACEA A2/B2 plus additional requirements for fuel economy, seal compatibility, piston cleanliness, ring sticking, viscosity increase, TBN decrease, sludge, and cam and tappet wear.

5.28 VOLKSWAGEN 506 01—Defines laboratory and engine test requirements for service fill extended drain engine oils with fuel saving properties for all diesel engines including those fitted with unit injectors and fitted with "WIV" service interval computers. Basic quality level is ACEA B4 plus additional requirements for fuel economy, seal compatibility, piston cleanliness, ring sticking, viscosity increase, TBN decrease, sludge, cam and tappet wear and turbocharged direct injection diesel performance.

5.29 VOLVO DRAIN SPECIFICATION (VDS)—Defines the performance of SAE 15W-40 and SAE 10W-30 engine oils intended for turbocharged engines running under extended drain conditions. Volvo VDS-2 specification was introduced in 1992 and is recommended for all Volvo truck engines meeting the 1996 European emission requirements. VDS-2 covers SAE 5W-30, 5W-40, 10W-30, 10W-40, and 15W-40 grades. Volvo VDS-3 was introduced in 2000 and is intended for Euro 3 engines. Base requirement is ACEA E-5 or Global DHD-1. VDS-3 covers the same viscosity grades as VDS-2.

6. European Military Specifications—Laboratory and engine tests which are utilized to define the CCMC sequences are also incorporated in the development of various Military specifications throughout Europe.

7. International Lubricant Standardization and Approval Committee Standards—General Motors Corporation, Ford Motor Company, Daimler-Chrysler Corporation, the Engine Manufacturers Association (EMA) and the Japan Automobile Manufacturers Association, Inc (JAMA), through an organization called the International Lubricant Standardization and Approval Committee (ILSAC), have jointly developed and approved a minimum performance standard for gasoline-fueled passenger car engine oils. This standard, ILSAC GF-3, was published in October of 2000, includes the performance requirements and chemical and physical properties of those engine oils that vehicle manufacturers may deem necessary for satisfactory equipment life and performance. Included within the standard are both engine and bench test requirements, as well as additional requirements for fuel efficiency, catalyst compatibility (phosphorus content), and low-temperature viscosity.

8. Japanese Classifications and Specifications—Japanese vehicle manufacturers, in general, rely on the API Classification System to recommend engine oils for service fill applications. Additionally, "in-house" procedures are also required by many manufacturers. In October of 2000 a new diesel engine oil category, JASO DH-1, was introduced to address the increasing demands of heavy-duty diesel engines. This category employs test procedures developed by the Japanese Automobile Standards Organizations (JASO). JASO, which is comprised of automobile and truck manufacturers, oil and additive companies, and government authorities, has worked to unify the engine oil evaluation procedures in Japan. Five test procedures are currently established. Three of these procedures address lubricant performance in gasoline engines. The remaining two procedures evaluate diesel engine oil performance.

8.1 JASO Gasoline Engine Test Procedures

8.1.1 JASO M328-95—Specifies the test procedure for the evaluation of the wear resistance of valve trains of automobile gasoline engine oils.

8.1.2 JASO M333-93—Specifies the test procedure for the evaluation of the high-temperature oxidation stability of lubricating oils for automobile gasoline engines.

8.1.3 JASO M331-91—Specifies the test procedure for the evaluation of the low- and medium-temperature detergency of lubricating oils for automobile gasoline engines.

8.2 JASO Diesel Engine Test Procedure

8.2.1 JASO M336-98—Specifies the test procedure for the evaluation of the high-temperature and high-load detergency of lubricating oils for automobile diesel engines.

8.2.2 JASO M354-99—Specifies the test procedure for the evaluation of valve train wear performance of lubricating oils in automobile diesel engines.

9. European Engine Tests

9.1 Gasoline Engine Tests—A number of gasoline engine tests have been developed by the European CEC and original equipment manufacturers to evaluate the ability of engine oils to prevent piston deposits, sludge, varnish, rust and corrosion, and wear. These tests include procedures established by Volkswagen and Mercedes-Benz as well as tests which utilize Peugeot engines. Engine test conditions for these procedures are presented in Table 1. Table 2 provides procedure reference, performance evaluation factors, and test applications.

9.2 Diesel Engine Tests—Many diesel engine test procedures are established by the European CEC and original equipment manufacturers to evaluate diesel engine oil performance. Included in these are tests which utilize engines developed by Volkswagen, PSA, and Mercedes-Benz as well as procedures incorporating Petter and an MWM diesel engine. Engine test conditions for these procedures are provided in Table 3. Table 4 presents the respective procedure references, performance evaluation factors, and test applications.

10. ILSAC Engine Tests—The following engine tests are included within the GF-3 performance standard.

10.1 ASTM Sequence IIIF Test—Specifies the test procedure that evaluates the ability of engine oil to protect against valve train wear, piston deposits, and oil thickening under high temperature conditions.

10.2 ASTM Sequence IVA Test—Specifies the test procedure which measures the ability of engine oil to provide overhead cam and slider follower wear control.

10.3 ASTM Sequence VE Test—Specifies the test procedure which evaluates the ability of engine oil to protect against cam wear. This test is not required for engine oils that contain a minimum of 0.08% phosphorus in the form of ZDDP.

10.4 ASTM Sequence VG Test—Specifies the test procedure which evaluates the ability of engine oil to protect against sludge and varnish deposits in stop and go service.

10.5 ASTM Sequence VIB Test—Specifies the test procedure which evaluates the ability of engine oils to provide engine fuel efficiency improvement.

10.6 ASTM Sequence VIII Test—Specifies the test procedure which evaluates the ability of engine oil to protect agains copper-lead bearing weight loss and resist permanent viscosity loss.

In addition to the previous engine tests the ILSAC GF-3 standard also includes a test to ensure protection from engine rusting (ASTM Ball Rust test which replaces the ASTM Sequence IID test). The ASTM Sequence VIB Test is included as a requirement for API licensing of energy-conserving properties. Performance requirements for all other engine tests listed are identical to API SL. Fleet testing may also be requested. Test conditions and performance evaluation factors for ILSAC GF-3 engine tests can be referenced within SAE J183 and SAE J304.

11. Japanese Engine Tests

11.1 Gasoline Engine Tests—The engine test procedures developed within Japan for gasoline engine oil performance are referenced by JASO procedures M328-95, M333-93, and M331-91. These include tests developed by both Nissan and Toyota for valve train wear, high-temperature oxidation stability, and low and medium-temperature detergency. Engine test conditions are presented in Table 5. Table 6 provides procedure reference, performance evaluation factors, and test applications.

11.2 Diesel Engine Tests—The engine test procedure for diesel engine oil performance is referenced by JASO procedure M336-98 and M354-99. The M336-98 procedures utilizes the Nissan diesel engine and evaluates automobile diesel engine oil detergency under high-temperature and high-load conditions. The M354-99 procedure utilizes a Mitsubishi diesel engine and evaluates valve train wear protection. Engine test conditions are presented in Table 7. Table 8 provides procedure reference, performance evaluation factors, and test application.

12. Global DHD-1 Engine Tests—The engine test procedures for the Global DHD-1 specification are designed to measure the ability of engine oil to provide valve train and ring and liner protection, maintain piston and turbocharger cleanliness, protect against bore polishing, control viscosity increase and oxidation, reduce the effects of soot on engine durability, soot control, and prevent engine corrosion. The following engine tests are included within the specification.

12.1 Mitsubishi 4D34T4—Evaluates soot related valve train wear protection.

12.2 Mercedes Benz OM 441LA—Evaluates bore polish, piston cleanliness, and turbocharger deposit protection.

12.3 Caterpillar 1R—Evaluates lubricant peformance with regards to piston deposits, oil control, and scuffing resistance for ferrous pistons.

12.4 Cummins M11HST—Evaluates the ability of engine oil to prevent excessive filter pressure drop, excessive viscosity increase, valve train wear, bearing corrosion, and sludge deposit when subjected to high levels of soot.

12.5 Mack T-8E—Evaluates the ablity of engine oil to prevent excessive viscosity increase and filter plugging when it is contaminated with high levels of soot.

12.6 Mack T-9—Evaluates ring and liner wear with two piece ferrous/aluminum pistons as well as lead corrosion due to loss of total base number.

12.7 Engine Oil Aeration Test—Evaluates the engine oil's resistance to aeration.

12.8 Roller Follower Wear Test—Evaluates the ability of an engine oil to prevent wear of the axle shaft in roller follower hydraulic valve lifter assemblies equipped with needle bearings.

In addition to the previous, the Global DHD-1 category requires an ASTM IIIF test which is previously described.

13. Laboratory Test Procedures—In addition to the previously discussed engine test procedures, a series of laboratory tests are also employed as part of the ACEA, ILSAC, JASO DH-1, and Global DHD-1 performance criteria as well as original equipment manufacturers' specifications in Europe. The tests include evaluation for engine oil shear stability, high-temperature/high-shear viscosity, volatility, foaming tendency, cam and tappet wear, seal compatibility, engine oil filterability, flash point, high-temperature deposits, gelation index, corrosiveness, and homogeneity/miscibility. Table 9 provides a list of important procedures for the evaluation of both gasoline and diesel engine oils along with the respective applications.

TABLE 1—EUROPEAN GASOLINE ENGINE TEST CONDITIONS

Manufacturer	Engine No.	Engine Displacement cm^3	Cylinders	Fuel	Test Duration Hours	Test Duration Stages	Stages	Engine[1] Speed rpm	Oil Temp °C	Coolant Temp °C	Fuel Cons. kg/h	Fuel Cons. L/h	Air/Fuel Ratio	Engine[1] Load NM	Engine Load kW	Procedure
Peugeot (PSA)	TU3M	1360	4	Unleaded CEC RF 83-A-91	100	40 h 60 h		1500 3000	40 100	45 90	1.5 4.0		(2)	10 35		CEC-L-38-A-94
VW	1302	1285	4	Premium Fuel 0.15 g/l Lead Max Approved to DIN 51600	50			4200	100			15.0	(3)		31.5	DKA 6/79
VW	T4	1968	4	VW recommended	248	192 h Cycle 3 Stages	Stage 1 Stage 2 Stage 3	4300 4300 Idle	133 130 40	100 100 30				Full Load 75 —		PV 1449
						56 h Steady State		4300	130	100				75		
Mercedes Benz	M111	1998	4	Special fuel batch to batch approval	224	48 h		Alternating 750-1950	45 max	–4 to 40				Alternating 0-31.5		CEC-L-53-T-95
						1 h 75 h		1500-6000 3850 3750	100-140 123	98				95-194 WOT		
						100 h		780-5500	37-130	31-97				0-WOT		
Mercedes Benz	M111	1998	4	RF-89-X-94	24		Cyclic	Various	20 33 75 88	20 85 95 95				Alternating		CEC-L-54-T-96
Peugeot	TU3M	1360	4	RF-83-A-91	96	11 h 50 min 10 min		WOT Oil make up	150	110 max	16.5					CEC-L-55-T-95

1. WOT = Wide Open Throttle
2. As per manufacturer's recommendation: 0.8 to 1.5% Vol CO
3. As per manufacturer's recommendation: 2% ± 1% Vol CO

TABLE 2—EUROPEAN GASOLINE TEST PERFORMANCE EVALUATION FACTORS

Test	Procedure[1]	Piston Deposits	Sludge	Varnish	Wear	Other	Test Application
Peugeot TU3M	CEC-L-38-A-94				X		ACEA, A1, A2, A3 WV 502 00, 503 00, VW 503 01, 505 00
VW 1302	DKA 6/79	X		X	X	Oil Consumption	VW 500 00, 501 01, 505 00
VW-T4	PV 1449	X			X	Ring Sticking Viscosity Increase Total Base Number Decrease	VW 502 00, 503 00, 503 01, 506 00, 506 01, MB 229.3
Mercedes Benz M111	CEC-L-53-T-95		X		X		ACEA A1, A2, A3, VW 502 00, 503 00, 503 01, 505 00, MB 229.1, 229.3
Mercedes Benz M111	CEC-L-54-T-96					Fuel Economy	ACEA A1-98, B1-98, MB 229.3
Peugeot TU3M	CEC-L-55-T-95	X				Ring Sticking Viscosity Increase	ACEA A1, A2, A3, VW 502 00, 503 00, 503 01, 505 00

1. CEC Procedures available from the Coordinating European Council, Boulevard du Souverain 165, B-1160 Brussels, Belgium

TABLE 3—EUROPEAN DIESEL ENGINE TEST CONDITIONS

Test Manufacturer	Test Engine No.	Engine Displacement cm^3	Test Duration Hours	Test Duration Stages	Oil Change Period Hours	Engine Speed rpm	Fuel Rate mg/Stroke	Engine Power (kW)	Air-to-Engine Temperature °C	Air-to-Engine Pressure	Coolant Outlet Temperature °C	Oil-to-Bearing Temperature °C	Fuel Sulfur % Mass	Procedure[1]
Mercedes-Benz	OM 364LA	3972	300	1 h 0.5 h 50 h	Continuous Up to 5.2 kg	2400 1500/1000 2400	Variable	102 at full power	30	1550 mbar	105	126	0.25	CEC-L-42-T-99
Mercedes Benz	OM 441LA	11000	400	50 h cyclic 50 h steady		1900		max			105 105	123 min 123 min	0.05	CEC-L-52-T-97
Volkswagen TC Intercooled	1431	1600	50	---	None	4500	31.1	55 min	50	670 mbar	90	130	0.3	CEC-L-46-T-93
Volkswagen naturally aspirated diesel	1435	1588	50	---	None	4800	20 ± 1 mg/ stroke	40	28	Atmospheric	90	128	0.3	VW PV 1431
Volkswagen	1.9 TDi	1896	60	2.5 h 0.5 h	None	4150 Idle	39.5 5.6	81	28	920 mbar 14 mbar	90 30		0.3	CEC-L-78-T-97
Peugeot (PSA)	XUD11 BTE	2088	75	2 min	None	1000	---	0	---	Atmospheric	---	---	CEC RF-90-A-92	CEC-L-56-T-98
				27 min		4300	47.5	>80	60	710 mbar	100	110	0.25-0.3%	
Mercedes Benz	OM602 A	2497	200	14 stages	None	Alternating 0-5000	---	Minimum to maximum	30	800-825 mbar boost during stage 10 and 11	20-92	---	---	CEC-L-51-T-95

1. CEC Procedures available from the Coordinating European Council, Boulevard du Souverain 165, B-1160, Brussels, Belgium

TABLE 4—EUROPEAN DIESEL ENGINE TEST PERFORMANCE EVALUATION FACTORS

Test	Procedure Reference[1]	Piston Deposits	Rust and Corrosion	Sludge	Varnish	Wear	Other	Test Application
Mercedes-Benz OM 364A	CEC-L-42-A-92	X		X	X	X	Oil Cons. Bore Polishing	MB 227 and 228, MTU ACEA E2, E3
Peugeot (PSA) XUDII ATE	CEC-L-56-T-95	X					Viscosity Increase (Soot related)	ACEA B1, B2, B3 ACEA B4-98, MAN 3277, VW 505 00, 505 01, 506 00, 506 01
Mercedes Benz OM 602A	CEC-L-51-T-95	X		X		X	Viscosity Increase, Bore Polishing	ACEA B1, B2, B3, E2, E3 ACEA B4-98, E4-98, VW 505 00, MB 227, 228, 229
Mercedes Benz OM 441LA	CEC-L-52-T-97	X			X	X	Bore Polishing Turbocharger Deposits	ACEA E4, E5, MB 228.5, Global DHD-1
MWM KD12E	CEC-L-12-A-76	X			X			MAN 270/271, MTU, Perkins
Volkswagen TC Intercooled	CEC-L-46-T-93	X			X		Ring Sticking	VW 505 00, 505 01, 506 00, 506 01, ACEA B1, B2, B3
Volkswagen	PV 1435	X					Ring Sticking	VW 500 00, VW 501 01
Volkswagen Direct Injection	CEC-L-78-T-97	X					Ring Sticking Viscosity Increase	ACEA B4-98, VW 506 00, 506 01

1. CEC Procedures available from the Coordinating European Council, Boulevard du Souverain 165, B-1160, Brussels, Belgium

TABLE 5—JAPANESE GASOLINE ENGINE TEST CONDITIONS

Manufacturer	Engine No.	Engine Displacement cm^3	Engine Type	Test Duration Hours	Test Duration Stages	Engine Speed rpm	Oil Temp °C	Outlet Coolant Temp °C	Air/Fuel Ratio	Engine Load (N·m)	Spring Load	JASO[1] Procedure
Nissan	KA24E	2400	4 OHC	100	50 min 10 min	800 1500	50 58-63	50 55	14.6	15	standard	M328-95
Nissan	VG20E	1998	6 OHC	300[2] 200[3]	24 min 24 min 12 min	800 1800 3500	50 96 117	42 85 97	19.6 98.1 93.1			M331-91
Toyota	1G-FE	1988	6 OHC	96[2] 48[3]		4800	149	120	14.5	58.8		M333-93

1. Available from the Society of Automotive Engineers of Japan, Inc., 10-2 Goban-cho, Chiyoda-ku, Tokyo 102, Japan
2. High-grade oils
3. Regular-grade oils

TABLE 6—JAPANESE GASOLINE ENGINE TEST PERFORMANCE EVALUATION FACTORS

Test	Procedure Reference[1]	Evaluation Piston Rings	Evaluation Rust & Corrosion	Evaluation Sludge	Evaluation Varnish	Evaluation Wear	Evaluation Other
Nissan KA24E	M328-95					X	
Nissan VG20E	M331-91	X		X	X	X	
Toyota 1G-FE	M333-93	X		X	X	X	Viscosity Increase

1. Available from the Society of Automotive Engineers of Japan, Inc., 10-2 Goban-cho, Chiyoda-ku, Tokyo 102, Japan

TABLE 7—JAPANESE DIESEL ENGINE TEST CONDITIONS

Manufacturer	Engine No.	Engine Displacement cm^3	Test Duration Hours	Test Duration Stages	Oil Change Period	Engine Speed (rpm)	Fuel Rate mm^3/ Stroke Cycle	Engine Load	Air to Engine Temp °C	Spring Load	Coolant Outlet Temp °C	Oil Temp °C	Fuel Sulfur % Mass	JASO Procedure
Nissan Diesel	TD25	2494	200 h		100 h	4300	43				90	120	0.05–0.5	M336-98
Mitsubishi	4D34T4	3907	160		None - 200 g Replaced every 20 h	3200	96	Full	25		90	105	0.05 max	M354-99

TABLE 8—JAPANESE DIESEL ENGINE TEST PERFORMANCE EVALUATION FACTORS

Test	Procedure Reference[1]	Evaluation Piston Rings	Evaluation Rust & Corrosion	Evaluation Sludge	Evaluation Varnish	Evaluation Wear	Evaluation Other	Applicable Specification
Nissan TD25	M336-98	X		X	X	X	Combustion Chamber deposits	JASO DH-1
Mitsubishi 4D34T4	M354-99	X				X	Total valve train wear	JASO DH-1

1. Available from the Society of Automotive Engineers of Japan, Inc., 10-2 Goban-cho, Chiyoda-ku, Tokyo 102, Japan (M336-98 available Fall 1998. in Japanese)

TABLE 9—LABORATORY TEST PROCEDURES

Test	Reference[1]	Description	Applicable Specifications
Shear Stability	CEC-L-14-A-93	Evaluates the shear stability of polymer containing lubricating oils utilizing a diesel fuel injector rig. Shear stability is defined as a permanent percent drop in kinematic viscosity at 100 °C.	Volkswagen, Rover, Mercedes-Benz, ACEA, Global DHD-1
	ASTM D 6278-98		JASO DH-1
Volatility	CEC-L-40-A-93 DIN 51581 ASTM D 5800	Evaluates the volatility or evaporative loss tendency of lubricating oils. Volatility is expressed as a percentage of loss in mass after 1 h at 250 °C.	MAN, MTU, Volkswagen, Mercedes-Benz, ACEA, ILSAC GF-3, JASO DH-1, Global DHD-1
	ASTM D 6417	Evaluates the amount of motor oil volatilized at 371 °C	ILSAC GF-3
High-Temperature/ High-Shear Viscosity	CEC-L-36-A-90 ASTM D 4683 ASTM D 5481	Evaluates the dynamic viscosity of lubricating oils at 150 °C and 106 sec–1 shear rate.	Mercedes-Benz, Volkswagen, ILSAC GF-3, ACEA, Global DHD-1 ILSAC GF-3 ILSAC GF-3
Foaming Tendency	ASTM D 892	Evaluates the foaming characteristics of lubricating oils at specified temperatures.	ILSAC GF-3, ACEA, JASO DH-1, Global DHD-1
	ASTM D 6082	Evaluates the high temperature foaming characteristics of lubricating oils.	ILSAC GF-3, ACEA, Global DHD-1
Oil/Elastomer Compatibility	CEC-L-39-T-95	Evaluates the degree of compatibility of lubricating oils and cured elastomers used in the automotive industry. Elastomer materials include acrylics, nitriles, fluorinated, and silicones.	ACEA Global DHD-1
Filterability	GM 9099P	Evaluates the tendency of an oil to form a precipitate which can plug the oil filter.	ILSAC GF-3
Homogeneity and Miscibility	Federal Test Method Standard 791B, Method 3470	Evaluates if an oil is and will remain homogeneous and if it is miscible with certain standard reference oils after being submitted to a prescribed cycle of temperature ranges.	ILSAC GF-3
Gelation Index	ASTM D 5133	Evaluates the temperature at which an oil can become unsuitable because of insufficient flow of bulk oil in sump to the oil screen.	ILSAC GF-3
Sulfated Ash	ASTM D 874	Evaluates the sulfated ash of unused oils containing additives.	ACEA, VW, Mercedes Benz, Global DHD-1
Thermo-Oxidation Engine Oil Simulation Test	(TEOST MHT-4)	Evaluates high temperature deposit forming tendency of engine oils.	ILSAC GF-3
Ball Rust Test		Evaluates the ability of an oil to prevent the formation of rust	ILSAC GF-3
JPI Hot Tube Test	JPI-55-55-99	Evaluates hot surface deposit control	JASO DH-1
Corrosion Bench Test	ASTM D 5968-97 ASTM D 6594	Predicts corrosion of copper lead or tin containing components in diesel engines	JASO DH-1 Global DHD-1
Oxidation-Hot Surface	CEC L-85-T-99	Evaluates engine oil oxidation tendency	Global DHD-1

1. – CEC procedures available from the Coordinating European Council, Boulevard du Souverain 165, B-1160, Brussels, Belgium
   – DIN procedures available from DIN, Postfach 1107, D-1000 Berlin 30, W. Germany
   – ASTM procedures available from ASTM, 100 Barr Harbor Drive, West Conshohocken, PA 19428-2959
   – P-VW 5106 available from Volkswagen, Wolfsburg, Germany
   – GM 9099P available from General Motors Corporation, CPE-Engineering Standards, W-3, Warren, MI 48090-9010
   – Federal Test Method 791B available from the General Services Administration, Business Service Center, Region 3, Seventh and D Street, SW, Washington, DC 20025

ENGINE OIL VISCOSITY CLASSIFICATION—SAE J300 DEC1999 SAE Standard

Report of the Maintenance Division approved June 1911. Completely revised by the Fuels and Lubricants Division June 1989. Completely revised by the SAE Fuels and Lubricants Technical Committee 1—Passenger Car Type Engine Oils February 1991, revised February 1992, completely revised March 1993, and revised December 1994, December 1995, and April 1997. Revised by the SAE Fuels and Lubricants Technical Committee 1—Engine Lubrication, December 1999.

1. Scope—This SAE Standard defines the limits for a classification of engine lubricating oils in rheological terms only. Other oil characteristics are not considered or included.

2. References

2.1 Applicable Publications—The following publications form a part of this specification to the extent specified herein. Unless otherwise specified, the latest issue of SAE publications shall apply.

2.1.1 SAE PUBLICATIONS—Available from SAE, 400 Commonwealth Drive, Warrendale, PA 15096-0001.

SAE J510—Lubricants for Two-Stroke-Cycle Engines

SAE J1536—Two-Stroke-Cycle Engine Oil Miscibility/Fluidity Classification

2.1.2 ASTM PUBLICATIONS—Available from ASTM, 100 Barr Harbor Drive, West Conshohocken, PA 19428-2959.

ASTM D 97—Standard Test Method for Pour Point of Petroleum Oils

ASTM D 445—Standard Test Method for Kinematic Viscosity of Transparent and Opaque Liquids (and the Calculation of Dynamic Viscosity)

ASTM D 2500—Standard Test Method for Cloud Point of Petroleum Oils

ASTM D 3244—Standard Practice for Utilization of Test Data to Determine Conformance with Specifications

ASTM D 3829—Standard Test Method for Predicting the Borderline Pumping Temperature of Engine Oil

ASTM D 4683—Standard Test Method for Measuring Viscosity at High Temperature and High-Shear Rate by Tapered Bearing Simulator

ASTM D 4684—Standard Test Method for Determination of Yield Stress and Apparent Viscosity of Engine Oils at Low Temperature

ASTM D 4741—Standard Test Method for Measuring Viscosity at High Temperature and High-Shear Rate by Tapered-Plug Viscometer

ASTM D 5133—Standard Test Method for Low Temperature, Low Shear Rate, Viscosity/Temperature Dependence of Lubricating Oils Using a Temperature-Scanning Technique

ASTM D 5293—Standard Test Method for Apparent Viscosity of Engine Oils Between –30 and –5 °C Using the Cold-Cranking Simulator

ASTM D 5481—Standard Test Method for Measuring Apparent Viscosity at High-Temperature and High-Shear Rate by Multicell Capillary Viscometer

2.1.3 OTHER PUBLICATIONS

CEC L-36-A-90—The Measurement of Lubricant Dynamic Viscosity Under Conditions of High Shear Using the Ravenfield Viscometer

CRC Report No. 409—Evaluation of Laboratory Viscometers for Predicting Cranking Characteristics of Engine Oils at 0 °F and –20 °F, April 1968

Hodges and Rodgers, "Some New Aspects of Pour Depressant Treated Oils," Oil and Gas Journal, p. 89, October 4, 1947

McNab, Rodgers, Michaels, and Hodges, "The Pour Stability Characteristics of Winter Grade Motor Oils," Quarterly Transactions, Society of Automotive Engineers, Inc. Vol. 2, No. 1, p. 34, January 1948

2.2 Related Publications—The following publications are provided for information purposes only and are not a required part of this document.

ASTM Data Series DS 62—The Relationship Between High-Temperature Oil Rheology and Engine Operation—A Status Report

ASTM STP 1068—High-Temperature, High-Shear Oil Viscosity—Measurement and Relationship to Engine Operation

ASTM STP 1143—Low-Temperature Lubricant Rheology: Measurement and Relevance to Engine Operation

ASTM Research Report RR-D02-1442—Cold Starting and Pumpability Studies in Modern Engines

3. Significance and Use—The limits specified in Table 1 are intended for use by engine manufacturers in determining the engine oil viscosity grades to be used in their engines, and by oil marketers in formulating, manufacturing, and labeling their products. Oil marketers are expected to distribute only products which are within the relevant specifications in Table 1.

Disputes between laboratories as to whether a product conforms with any specification in Table 1 shall be resolved by application of the procedures described in ASTM D 3244. For this purpose, all specifications in Table 1 are critical specifications to which conformance based on reproducibility of the prescribed test method is required. The product shall be considered to be in conformance if the Assigned Test Value (ATV) is within the specification.

Two series of viscosity grades are defined in Table 1: (a) those containing the letter W and (b) those without the letter W. Single viscosity-grade oils ("single-grades") with the letter W are defined by maximum low-temperature cranking and pumping viscosities, and a minimum kinematic viscosity at 100 °C. Single-grade oils without the letter W are based on a set of minimum and maximum kinematic viscosities at 100 °C, and a minimum high-shear-rate viscosity at 150 °C. The shear rate will depend on the test method used. Multiviscosity-grade oils ("multi-grades") are defined by both of the following criteria:

a. Maximum low-temperature cranking and pumping viscosities corresponding to one of the W grades, and
b. Maximum and minimum kinematic viscosities at 100 °C and a minimum high-shear-rate viscosity at 150 °C corresponding to one of the non-W grades.

4. Low-Temperature Test Methods—The low-temperature cranking viscosity is measured according to the procedure described in ASTM D 5293 and is reported in centipoise (mPa·s). Viscosities measured by this method have been found to correlate with the ability of engines to start at low temperature.

The pumping viscosity is a measure of an oil's ability to flow to the engine oil pump and provide adequate oil pressure during the initial stages of operation. The pumping viscosity is measured in centipoise (mPa.s) according to the procedure in ASTM D 4684. This procedure uses the Mini-Rotary Viscometer to measure either the existence of yield stress or the viscosity in the absence of measured yield stress after the sample has been cooled through a prescribed slow cool (so-called TP1) cycle. This cooling cycle has predicted as failures several SAE 10W-30 and SAE 10W-40 engine oils which are known to have suffered pumping failures in the field after short-term (two days or less) cooling. These field failures are believed to be the result of the oil forming a gel structure that results in excessive yield stress and/or viscosity of the engine oil. The significance of the ASTM D 4684 method is projected from the preceding SAE 10W-30 and SAE 10W-40 data.

Limited test work has shown that in a few specific instances, stable pour point (Appendix A, Test Method for Stable Pour Point of Engine Oils), borderline pumping temperature (ASTM D 3829), and/or Scanning Brookfield method (ASTM D 5133) can provide additional information regarding low-temperature performance. It is suggested that these tests be conducted when formulating new engine oils, or when there are significant changes in base oil or additive components of existing products.

Because engine pumping, cranking, and starting are all important at low temperatures, the selection of an oil for winter operation should consider both the viscosity required for successful oil flow, as well as that for cranking and starting, at the lowest ambient temperature expected.

5. High-Temperature Test Methods—Kinematic viscosity at 100 °C is measured according to ASTM D 445, and the results are reported in centistokes (mm^2/s). Kinematic viscosities have been related to certain forms of oil consumption and have been traditionally used as a guide in selecting oil viscosity for use under normal engine operating temperatures. Also, kinematic viscosities are widely used in specifying oils for applications other than in automotive engines.

High-shear-rate viscosity measured at 150 °C and reported in centipoise (mPa·s) is widely accepted as a rheological parameter which is relevant to high-temperature engine performance. In particular, it is generally believed to be indicative of the effective oil viscosity in high-shear components of an internal combustion engine (for example, within the journal bearings and between the rings and cylinder walls) under severe operating conditions. While the specific temperature and shear rate conditions experienced by an oil in a particular application depend on mechanical design and operating parameters, the measurement conditions specified in Table 1 are representative of a wide range of engine operating conditions.

Many commercial engine oils contain polymeric additives for a variety of purposes, one of the most important of which is viscosity modification. Specifically, the use of such additives in creating multigrade oils is commonplace. However, oils containing a significant polymeric additive concentration, whether for viscosity modification or another lubricant function, are generally characterized by having a non-Newtonian, "shear thinning" viscosity (i.e., a viscosity which decreases with increasing shear rate).

TABLE 1—SAE VISCOSITY GRADES FOR ENGINE OILS(1)(2)

SAE Viscosity Grade	Low-Temperature (°C) Cranking Viscosity(3), cP Max	Low-Temperature (°C) Pumping Viscosity(4) cP Max with No Yield Stress(4)	Low-Shear-Rate Kinematic Viscosity(5) (cSt) at 100 °C Min	Low-Shear-Rate Kinematic Viscosity(5) (cSt) at 100 °C Max	High-Shear-Rate Viscosity(6) (cP) at 150 °C Min
0W	6200 at –35	60 000 at –40	3.8	—	—
5W	6600 at –30	60 000 at –35	3.8	—	—
10W	7000 at –25	60 000 at –30	4.1	—	—
15W	7000 at –20	60 000 at –25	5.6	—	—
20W	9500 at –15	60 000 at –20	5.6	—	—
25W	13 000 at –10	60 000 at –15	9.3	—	—
20	—	—	5.6	<9.3	2.6
30	—	—	9.3	<12.5	2.9
40	—	—	12.5	<16.3	2.9 (0W-40, 5W-40, and 10W-40 grades)
40	—	—	12.5	<16.3	3.7 (15W-40, 20W-40, 25W-40, 40 grades)
50	—	—	16.3	<21.9	3.7
60	—	—	21.9	<26.1	3.7

1. Notes—1 cP = 1 mPa•s; 1 cSt = 1 mm^2/s
2. All values are critical specifications as defined by ASTM D 3244 (see text, Section 3.)
3. ASTM D 5293
4. ASTM D 4684: Note that the presence of any yield stress detectable by this method constitutes a failure regardless of viscosity.
5. ASTM D 445
6. ASTM D 4683, CEC L-36-A-90 (ASTM D 4741), or ASTM D 5481.

To insure that polymer-containing oils do not create a situation in which the viscosity of the oil decreases to less than a specified limit, minimum values of high-shear-rate viscosity are assigned to each of the non-W viscosity grades in Table 1. A special situation exists regarding the SAE 40 grade. Historically, SAE 0W-40, 5W-40, and 10W-40 oils have been used primarily in light-duty engines. These multigrade SAE 40 oils must meet a minimum high-temperature, high-shear-rate viscosity limit of 2.9 cP.

In contrast, SAE 15W-40, 20W-40, 25W-40, and 40 oils have typically been used in heavy-duty engines. The manufacturers of such engines have required high-shear-rate viscosity limits consistent with good engine durability in high-load, severe service applications. Thus, SAE 15W-40, 20W-40, 25W-40, and single-grade 40 oils must meet a minimum high-temperature, high-shear-rate viscosity limit of 3.7 cP.

There are three acceptable methods for the measurement of high-shear-rate viscosity. For rotation viscometer methods ASTM D 4683 and CEC L-36-A-90 (ASTM D 4741), the shear rate is 1.0 x 10^6 s^{-1}. For the capillary viscometer method, ASTM D 5481, the shear rate is 1.4 x 10^6 s^{-1} at the wall. The latter shear rate has been found to provide high-shear-rate viscosities in the capillary viscometer that are equivalent to those obtained by the rotational viscometer methods.

6. Labeling—In properly describing the viscosity grade of an engine oil according to this document, the letters "SAE" must precede the grade number designation. In addition, for multigrade oil formulations this document requires that the W grade precede the non-W grade, and that the two grades be separated by a hyphen (i.e., SAE 10W-30). Other forms of punctuation or separation are not acceptable.

Most oils will meet the viscosity requirements of at least one of the W grades. Nevertheless, consistent with historic practice, any Newtonian oil may be labeled as a single-grade oil (either with or without a W). Oils which are formulated with polymeric viscosity index improvers for the purpose of making them multiviscosity-grade products are non-Newtonian and must be labeled with the appropriate multiviscosity grade (both W and high-temperature grade). Since each W grade is defined on the basis of maximum cranking and pumping viscosities as well as minimum kinematic viscosities at 100 °C, it is possible for an oil to satisfy the requirements of more than one W grade. In labeling either a W grade or a multiviscosity grade oil, only the lowest W grade satisfied may be referred to on the label. Thus, an oil meeting the requirements for SAE grades 10W, 15W, 20W, 25W, and 30 must be referred to as an SAE 10W-30 grade only.

The intent of the low-temperature portion of SAE J300 is to insure that if oil viscosity is sufficiently low for an engine to crank, the viscosity must also be low enough that the oil will flow after the engine starts. Accordingly, the cranking viscosity is the primary criterion for establishing the W grade. Specifically, an oil must meet the pumping viscosity requirement of the lowest W grade satisfied by the cranking viscosity. If the W grade defined by the pumping viscosity is higher than the lowest grade satisfied by the cranking viscosity, the oil does not meet the requirements of this document and is, therefore, inappropriate for use.

Similarly, the intent of the kinematic viscosity limits for each W grade is to insure that the viscosities of these oils are high enough at engine operating temperatures to provide adequate protection. Thus, if the kinematic viscosity at 100 °C does not meet the requirements of the lowest W grade satisfied by the cranking viscosity, then the oil does not meet the requirements of this document and is, therefore, inappropriate for use.

Some engine oils are prediluted, usually to assist in mixing with fuel when used in certain two-stroke-cycle engines. If any viscosity grade in SAE J300 is used to describe a prediluted engine oil, the grade indicated should relate to the viscosity of the oil in its undiluted state. In displaying SAE J300 viscosity grades of prediluted oils, containers should indicate that the SAE grade applies to the oil in its undiluted state.

More accurately, the rheological properties of two-stroke-cycle engine oils should be identified using the terminology and grades described in SAE J1536. Further information on prediluted oils is also provided in SAE J1510.

APPENDIX A
TEST METHOD FOR STABLE POUR POINT OF ENGINE OILS

Preface—Use ASTM D 4684 for the Determination of the Pumpability Viscosity Requirements in Table 1.

When formulating new engine oils or when there are significant changes in base oils or additives, the following stable pour point test method is suggested to check the characteristics of formulated engine oils using as formulation guidelines the previously established limits of –35 °C, max, for SAE 5W oils and –30 °C, max, for SAE 10W oils.

A.1 Scope

A.1.1 The test for stable pour point is primarily intended for use with engine lubricating oils. The potential for applicability to other lubricants is unknown.

A.2 Summary of Method

A.2.1 After preliminary warming, the sample is subjected to a controlled temperature/time cycle over five and one-half to seven days. The cycle was originally established to reproduce pour instability or reversion which has occurred during storage of oils in moderately cold cyclic ambient conditions. More recent work has shown relevance to engine oil pumpability failure. Oils exhibiting pour reversion are essentially "solid" resulting from wax gel formation, at temperatures significantly above their ASTM D 97 pour points.

NOTE—Refer to: McNab, Rodgers, Michaels, and Hodges, "The Pour Stability Characteristics of Winter Grade Motor Oils," Quarterly Transaction, Society of Automotive Engineers, Inc., Vol. 2, No. 1, p. 34, January 1948; Hodges and Rodgers, "Some New Aspects of Pour Depressant Treated Oils," Oil and Gas Journal, October 4, 1947, p. 89.

A.3 Definitions

A.3.1 Pour Stability Temperature—That specified temperature at which oil remains fluid on completion of an established temperature/time cycle.

A.3.2 Stable Pour Point—The lowest temperature at which oil remains fluid when subjected to the specified temperature/time cycle.

A.4 Apparatus

A.4.1 Test Jar—Identical to ASTM D 97 and D 2500 pour point/cloud point test jar.

A.4.2 Thermometer—ASTM E 1 6C with temperature range of +20 to –80 °C.

A.4.3 Cork or Rubber Stoppers—To fit test jar.

A.4.4 Any equipment suitable to heat sample uniformly to precondition test samples.

A.4.5 Cooling Bath—Low temperature with controller to follow temperature/time cycles from +15 to –45 °C. Spacing between test jars is to be about 15 mm with jars suspended so that cooling medium circulates around bottom and sides of jar.

A.4.6 Temperature Recorder—Two channels to record temperatures of bath and sample.

A.5 Procedure

A.5.1 Adjust cooling bath temperature to 15 °C with one temperature sensing bulb in the cooling bath medium.

A.5.2 Prepare two temperature measurement samples as follows:

A.5.2.1 Select a sample oil which is known to be fluid to at least –45 °C.

A.5.2.2 Fill each of two test jars with approximately 60 mL of selected oil sample. Identify these bottles as "Temperature Measurement Sample."

A.5.2.3 Prepare cork stopper to accommodate the standardized calibrated ASTM thermometer.

A.5.2.4 Insert stopper and thermometer into one jar so that thermometer immersion line is visible but not more than 3 mm above top of stopper. Place jar in center of cooling bath.

A.5.2.5 Prepare cork stopper to accommodate recorded temperature sensing bulb.

A.5.2.6 Insert stopper and one temperature sensing bulb in the second jar and position the bulb approximately 7 mm into the control oil sample. Place jar in center of cooling bath next to jar with thermometer.

A.5.2.7 Place the other temperature sensing bulb in cooling bath medium adjacent to the two control sample bottles.

A.5.3 Prepare samples of test oils using clean, dust-free test jars. Fill jar with about 60 mL of test oil.

A.5.4 Pretreat the test oil samples.

A.5.4.1 Heat sample in such a way as to maintain oil temperature at 80 °C for 2 h.

A.5.4.2 After allowing sample to cool to room temperature, stopper the jar with a clean, solid cork or rubber stopper.

A.5.4.3 Place test sample jars in cooling bath adjacent to control sample jars. All samples must be at same level if liquid bath is used.

A.5.5 Prepare bath for cyclic temperature test.

A.5.5.1 Temperature of bath should be 15 °C. Check thermometer and recorded temperature of temperature measurement sample.

A.5.5.2 If liquid bath is used, adjust level in bath to slightly above sample level in test jars.

A.5.5.3 Initiate the temperature cycle as indicated in Tables A1 and A2.

A.5.6 During the final cool down, check proper temperature control each day as follows:

A.5.6.1 Read the "Temperature Measurement Sample" thermometer. Return this sample to the center of the bath.

A.5.6.2 Compare this temperature with the recorded temperature.

A.5.6.3 Determine whether a correction is required in the reading of recorded temperature. Estimate the correct time to make the first pour stability determination at the correct thermometer temperature (±1 °C).

A.5.7 The stable pour point is determined during the final cool down in the temperature/time cycle as follows:

A.5.7.1 At the sample temperature of –12 °C, carefully remove the test jar vertically from the bath and carefully tilt only enough to ascertain whether the oil surface moves and is "fluid." If movement is detected while tilting, return the bottle to a vertical position and carefully replace in bath. Total time for this operation shall be less than 3 s. Use care in handling jars in and out of bath. Shaking can cause a change in the onset or rate of gelation. Handle jars by cork end only. If frosting occurs, wipe with a rag to prevent heating of sample.

A.5.7.2 If no movement of the oil is detected when the jar is tilted at 90 degrees (horizontal) for 5 s, the sample is "solid." Record the reading of the temperature measurement sample thermometer.

A.5.7.3 For oils which remain fluid, repeat step A.5.7.1 at successively lower temperatures, in 3 °C increments, until no movement of the oil is detected and the oil is "solid" by A.5.7.2, or until temperature cycle is complete.

A.6 Report

A.6.1 Report stable pour point as 3 °C higher than the temperature recorded in A.5.7.2. If the sample is still fluid at –41 °C, report stable pour point as less than or equal to –41 °C.

TABLE A1—CYCLE C, SOFT METRICATION

Total Time, h	Time, h	Direction and Temp., °C
0	0	Set at 15 °C
15	15	Down to –22 °C
17	2	Down to –23 °C
19	2	Up to –21 °C
21	2	Up to –18 °C
26	5	Up to –14 °C
31	5	Up to –12 °C
34	3	Up to –11 °C
50	16	at –11 °C
60	10	Up to 0 °C
62	2	At 0 °C
63	1	Down to –1 °C
66	3	Down to –3 °C
69	3	Down to –4 °C
73	4	Down to –5 °C
91	18	At –5 °C
94	3	Down to –6 °C
96	2	Down to –7 °C
168	72	Down to –41 °C

TABLE A2—CYCLE C, READING TIMES ON FINAL DROP

Approx. h to Test	Temperature, °C
91	–5
98	–8
106	–12
113	–15
119	–18
126	–21
132	–24
138	–27
145	–30
152	–33
158	–36
164	–39
168	–41

Report of the SAE Fuels and Lubricants Committee approved January 1942, completely revised by Technical Committee 2—Heavy-Duty Type Engine Oils of the Fuels and Lubricants Division June 1989. Completely revised by the SAE Fuels & Lubricants Technical Committee 2—Heavy-Duty Type Engine Oils February 1991 and June 1993, and revised March 1995. Revised by the SAE Fuels and Lubricants Technical Committee 1—Automotive Engine Oils February 1998 and June 1999. Rationale statement available.

1. Scope—The purpose of this SAE Information Report is to describe test conditions and performance evaluation factors for both diesel and gasoline engine tests. Specifically, the tests described in this document are used to measure the engine performance requirements for engine oils described by the API Service Categories described in API Publication 1509, ASTM D 4485, SAE J183 and SAE J1423 standards, U.S. military specifications, and ILSAC GF Standards.

2. References

2.1 Applicable Publications—The following publications form a part of the specification to the extent specified herein. Unless otherwise indicated the latest revision of SAE publications shall apply.

2.1.1 SAE PUBLICATIONS—Available from SAE, 400 Commonwealth Drive, Warrendale, PA 15096-0001.

2.1.1.1 SAE J183—Engine Oil Performance and Engine Service Classification (other than "Energy Conserving")

2.1.1.2 SAE J1423—Passenger Car and Light Duty Truck Energy-Conserving Engine Oil Classification

2.1.2 ASTM PUBLICATIONS—Available from ASTM, 100 Barr Harbor Drive, West Conshohocken, PA 19428-2959.

2.1.2.1 ASTM D 4485—Standard Specification for Performance of Engine Oils

2.1.2.2 ASTM Special Technical Publication 315I, Part I—Multicylinder Test Sequences for Evaluating Automotive Engine Oils

2.1.2.3 Research reports containing the Cummins M-11, Mack T-6, T-7, and T9, and Caterpillar 1K, 1M-PC, 1N, and 1P and the Navistar HEUI procedures are available from ASTM. None of these procedures has been published as an ASTM Standard Test Method.

2.1.2.4 ASTM D 5290—Standard Test Method for Measurement of Oil Consumption, Piston Deposits, and Wear in a Heavy-Duty High-Speed Diesel Engine—NTC-400 Procedure

2.1.2.5 ASTM D 5119—Standard Test Method for Evaluation of Automotive Engine Oils in the CRC L-38 Spark-Ignition Engine

2.1.2.6 ASTM D 5302—Standard Test Method for Evaluation of Automotive Engine Oils for Inhibition of Deposit Formation and Wear in a Spark-Ignition Internal Combustion Engine Fueled with Gasoline and Operated Under Low-Temperature, Light-Duty Conditions—Sequence VE Procedure

2.1.2.7 ASTM D 5533—Standard Test Method for Evaluation of Automotive Engine Oils in the Sequence IIIE, Spark-Ignition Engine

2.1.2.8 ASTM D 5862—Test Method for Evaluation of Engine Oils in the Two-Stroke Cycle Turbo-Supercharged 6V-92TA.

2.1.2.9 ASTM D 5966—Test Method for Evaluation of Engine Oils for Roller Follower Wear in Light-Duty Diesel Engine

2.1.2.10 ASTM D 5967—Test Method for Evaluation of Diesel Engine Oils in the T-8 Diesel Engine

2.1.2.11 ASTM D 6202—Standard Test Method for Measurement of the Effects of Automotive Engine Oils on the Fuel Economy of Passenger Cars and Light Duty Trucks in the Sequence VIA Spark Ignition Engine

2.1.3 API PUBLICATION—Available from American Petroleum Institute, 1220 L Street NW, Washington, DC 20005.

API 1509—Engine Oil Licensing and Certification System

2.1.4 INTERNATIONAL LUBRICANT STANDARDIZATION AND APPROVAL COMMITTEE (ILSAC) STANDARDS—Available from the Alliance of Automobile Manufacturers

2.2 Related Publications

2.2.1 MILITARY SPECIFICATIONS AND COMMERCIAL ITEM DESCRIPTIONS—Available from Standardization Documents Order Desk, Building 4D, 700 Robbins Avenue, Philadelphia, PA 19111-5094.

MIL-PRF-2104G—Lubricating Oil—Internal Combustion Engine—Tactical Service

MIL-L-6082E—Lubricating Oil—Aircraft Reciprocating Engine

MIL-PRF-21260E—Lubricating Oil—Internal Combustion Engine—Preservative and Break-in

MIL-L-22851D—Lubricating Oil—Aircraft Piston Engine (Ashless Dispersant)

MIL-PRF-46167C—Lubricating Oil—Internal Combustion Engine—Arctic Service

CID A-A-52039B—Lubricating Oil—Automotive Engine—API Service SH

CID A-A-52306A—Lubricating Oil—Heavy-Duty Diesel Engine

3. Test Applicability—Engine tests have been used for many years to determine performance characteristics of engine oils, and the development of new engine tests is an ongoing process. The included API service categories based on current tests are the SH, SJ, CF, CF-2, CF-4, CG-4, CH-4, and Energy Conserving categories. The current U.S. military specifications included are the MIL-PRF-2104G, MIL-L-6082E, MIL-PRF-21260E, MIL-L-22851D, and MIL-L-46167B specifications. The included current ILSAC Standard is GF-2.

4. Diesel Engine Tests—Many tests for piston ring sticking, piston ring and cylinder wear, valve train wear, oil consumption, oil thickening, and general deposit accumulation have been developed using single-cylinder and multicylinder compression ignition (diesel) engines. Current single-cylinder tests in use include the Caterpillar 1K, 1M-PC, 1N, and 1P. Current multicylinder tests include the Cummins M-11, Detroit Diesel 6V-92TA, Mack T-6, T-7, T-8, T-9, General Motors 6.5L (Roller Follower Wear Test) and the Navistar HEUI. (See Tables 1A, 1B, and 2.)

TABLE 1A—DIESEL ENGINE TEST CONDITIONS

	Engine Displacement cm^3	Engine Displacement in^3	Test Duration, h total	Test Duration, h each phase	Engine Speed, rpm	Fuel Rate, kW	Fuel Rate, btu/min	Load bmep, kPa	Load bmep, psi
6V-92TA	9 046	552	100	8.0	1200	≥653	≥37 326	2062	299
				8.0	2300	≥1130	≥64 265	1076	156
T-6	11 000	672	600	4.0	1400	523	29 756	1531	222
				4.0	1800	628	35 762	1420	206
				4.0	2100	697	39 641	1262	183
T-7	11 000	672	150		1200	514	29 235	1655	240
T-8	12 000	728	300(1)		1800	800	45 692	1459	212
T-9	11 931	728	500	75	1800	756	43 012	1475	214
				425	1250	657	37 370	2316	336
NTC-400(2)	14 000	855	200		2100	865	49 237	1289	187
M-11	10 824	660	200	50	1800	634	36 075	1575	228
				50	1600	634	36 075	1916	278
1K	2 400	149	252		2100	140.7(3)	7 995	1240	180
1M-PC	2 200	134	120		1800	102.8	5 850	972	141
1N	2 400	149	252		2100	140.7(2)	7 995	1 240	180
1P	2400	146	360		1800	132	7545	1496	217
RFWT	6 500	397	50		1000	106.1	6 033	620	90
HEUI	7300	444	20		3000	155	29 000	855	124

1. The test duration for category CG-4 is 250 h.
2. This test is obsolete and is included for historical purposes only.
3. Within the test this parameter is expressed in metric units, and the specified fuel rate is 8430 kJ/min.

TABLE 1B—DIESEL ENGINE TEST CONDITIONS

	Air-to-Engine Temperature °C	Air-to-Engine Temperature °F	Air-to-Engine Pressure Abs., kPa	Air-to-Engine Pressure Abs., inch Hg	Water Outlet Temperature °C	Water Outlet Temperature °F	Oil-to-Bearing Temperature °C	Oil-to-Bearing Temperature °F	Fuel Sulfur, % mass
6V-92TA	35	95	N/S	N/S	84	172–190	102	216	0.1–0.4
	35	95	97	29	84	172–190	111	232	0.1–0.4
T-6	66	150	98	29	87.8	190	112.8	235 max	0.1–0.3
	85	185	139	41	87.8	190	112.8	235 max	0.1–0.3
	99	210	156	46	87.8	190	112.8	235 max	0.1–0.3
T-7	113	135	102	30	85.0	185	112.8	235 max	0.40 max
T-8	43	109	186–199	55–59	85	185	100–107	212–225	0.03–0.05
T-9	43	110	287-300	85-89	85	185	100-107	212-225	0.03-0.05
	43	110	260-274	77-81	85	185	99-107	210-225	0.03-0.05
NTC-400[1]	143	290	142–169	42–50	85.0	185	121.1	250	0.40
M-11	46	115	280	83	88	190	115	239	0.03-0.05
	46	115	265	78	88	190	115	239	0.03-0.05
1K	127	260	240	71	93	199.4	107	224.6	0.38–0.42[2]
1M-PC	124	255	179	53	87.8	190	96	205	0.38–0.42[2]
1N	127	260	240	71	93	200	107	225	0.03–0.05
1P	60	140	272	81	90	194	130	266	0.03-0.05
RFWT	32	90	97	29	120	248	120	248	0.03–0.05
HEUI	29	84	235	70	100	212	120	248	0.03-0.05

1. This test is obsolete and is included for historical purposes only.
2. Sulfur must be of "Natural Origin."
N/S = not specified

TABLE 2—DIESEL ENGINE TEST REFERENCES, PERFORMANCE EVALUATION FACTORS, AND APPLICATIONS

Test	Procedure Reference See Section 2.1.2	Evaluation Deposits	Evaluation Wear	Evaluation Oil Consumption	Evaluation Other	Test Application (See 2.1.1 and 2.1.2.1)
6V-92TA	ASTM D 5862	X	X			API CF-2, MIL-PRF-2104G, MIL-PRF-46167C(1)
T-6	ASTM Research Report RR:D02:1219	X	X	X	Oil Thickening	API CF-4
T-7	ASTM Research Report RR:D02:1220				Oil Thickening	API CF-4
T-8	ASTM D 5967			X	Oil Thickening, Filter Plugging	API CG-4
T-9	ASTM Research Report RR:D02:1439		X			API CH-4
NTC-400(2)	ASTM D 5290	X	X	X		API CF-4(3)
M-11	ASTM Research Report RR:D02:1440	X	X		Filter Plugging	API CH-4
1K	ASTM Research Report RR:D02:1273	X		X		API CF-4
1M-PC	ASTM Research Report RR:D02:1320	X				API CF, CF-2, MIL-PRF-2104G, MIL-PRF-46167C, MIL-PRF-21260E
1N	ASTM Research Report RR:D02:1321	X		X		API CG-4, MIL-PRF-2104G, MIL-PRF-46167C, MIL-PRF-21260E
1P	ASTM Research Report RR:D02:1441	X			Oil Consumption	API CH-4
RFWT	ASTM D 5966		X			API CG-4, MIL-PRF-2104G, MIL-PRF-46167C, MIL-PRF-21260E
HEUI	ASTM Research Report RR:D02:1379				Oil Aeration	API CG-4, CH-4

1. A passing 6V-53T test may be substituted for the 6V-92TA requirement for MIL-PRF-46167C.
2. This test is obsolete and is included for historical purposes only.
3. Back-to-back passing 1K tests may be substituted for the NTC-400 requirement for API CF-4.

5. Gasoline Engine Tests—Lubricant performance is evaluated in gasoline engine tests in terms of rust and corrosion, sludge, varnish, piston ring zone deposits and condition, wear, bearing corrosion, and fuel efficiency. For those tests listed in SAE J183 and J1423, Table 3 gives the test conditions and Table 4 gives procedure references, evaluation factors, and the API performance categories, U.S. military specifications, and ILSAC Standards in which the tests are included.

TABLE 3—GASOLINE ENGINE TEST CONDITIONS

Test	Engine Type	Engine Displacement cm^3	Engine Displacement in^3	Time Total, h	Time Each Phase	Air-Fuel Ratio	Load kW	Load bhp	Fuel Flow kg/h	Fuel Flow lb/h	Speed, rpm	Temperature Coolant °C	Temperature Coolant °F	Temperature Oil °C	Temperature Oil °F
L-38	Single	700	42.5	40		14.0	Not Controlled	Not Controlled	2.04/ 2.27	4.5–5.0	3150	93.3	200	143.3(1)	290(1)
Sequence IID	V8	5740	350	32	28 h	13.0	18.6	25			1500	43.3	110	48.9	120
					2 h	13.0	18.6	25			1500	43.3	110	48.9	120
					2 h	16.5	74.6	100			3600	93.3	200	126.7	260
Sequence IIIE	V6	3800	231	64		16.5	50.6	67.8			3000	115.0	239	149.0	300.2
Sequence VE	OHC4	2290	140	288	2 h	(2)	24.98	33.5			2500	51.7	125	68.3	155
					75 min		24.98	33.5			2500	85.0	185	98.9	210
					45 min		0.75	1.0			750	46.1	115	46.1	115
Sequence VIA															
	V8	4600	280	50(3)	1.5 h	14.25–15.25	2.18	2.92			800	95	203	105	221
					1.5 h		2.18	2.92			800	60	140	70	158
					1.5 h		5.81	7.79			1500	60	140	70	158
					1.5 h		15.39	20.63			1500	60	140	70	158
					1.5 h		15.39	20.63			1500	45	113	45	113
					1.5 h		2.18	2.92			800	45	113	45	113

1. For MIL-L-6082E and MIL-L-22851D, the oil temperature is 135 °C (275 °F).
2. Equivalence ratio is controlled by monitoring carbon monoxide and oxygen concentrations.
3. Candidate oil testing alternates with reference and flush oils.

TABLE 4—GASOLINE ENGINE TEST REFERENCES, PERFORMANCE EVALUATION FACTORS, AND APPLICATIONS

Test	Procedure Reference (Reference 2.1.2)	Evaluation Rust and Corrosion	Evaluation Sludge	Evaluation Varnish	Evaluation Wear	Evaluation Other	Test Application (See References 2.1.1, 2.1.1.1, 2.1.1.2, 2.1.2.1)
L-38	ASTM D 5119					Bearing Weight Loss	API SH, API SJ, API CF, API CF-4, API CG-4, MIL-PRF-2104G, ILSAC GF-2, MIL-PRF-46167C, MIL-PRF-21260E
Sequence IID	ASTM STP 315I, Part I	X				Lifter Sticking	API SH, MIL-PRF-2104G, MIL-PRF-46167C, MIL-PRF-21260E, ILSAC GF-2
Sequence IIIE	ASTM D 5533		X	X	X	Oil Thickening, Ring Sticking	API SH, API SJ, ILSAC GF-2, MIL-L-2104F
Sequence IIIE	ASTM D 5533					Oil Thickening	API CG-4, API CH-4
Sequence IIIE	ASTM Research Report RR:D02:1225				X		MIL-PRF-2104G, MIL-PRF-21260E, MIL-PRF-46167G
Sequence VE	ASTM D 5302		X	X	X		API SH, MIL-PRF-2104G, MIL-PRF-46167C, ILSAC GF-2, MIL-PRF-21260E
Sequence VIA	ASTM Research Report RR:DO2:1364					Fuel Efficiency	Energy Conserving, ILSAC GF-2

6. Military Specifications and CIDs—MIL-L specifications have historically been used as both primary performance specifications, including engine testing, as well as a part of the procurement via Qualified Products Lists. Recently, there has been some movement to adopt a CID (Commercial Item Description) system in place of the MIL-L Specification/QPL system. The first example of this was the adoption of CID A-A-52039B for API Service Category SG oils, and the concurrent cancellation of MIL-L-46152E and the corresponding QPL-46152-14. CID-A-A-52039B defines oil requirements in terms of API Service Category SH, SAE viscosity grades, and various other bench tests. A similar example was the adoption of CID A-A-52306 for heavy-duty diesel oils used in wheeled vehicles (only) which formerly would have required MIL-L-2104 products. With the exception of L-38 stay-in-grade viscosity tests, these CIDs do not specify engine test requirements per se, other than via API categories. For this reason, CID information is not listed in this document in the tables concerned with test applications, Tables 2 and 4.

SAE J301—EFFECTIVE DATES OF NEW OR REVISED TECHNICAL REPORTS

The final approval date for Fuels and Lubricants technical reports is shown following the J-report number. This approval date is the date of final approval by the Fuels and Lubricants Division. It is effective immediately subsequent to divisional approval for *newly issued Standards, Recommended Practices, and Information Reports*, and also for *revised Information Reports* and the *SAE J1146 Recommended Practice*. In the case of *revised or cancelled Standards or Recommended Practices* (used to define product quality), an 18-month optional grace period exists before they become fully effective.

PHYSICAL AND CHEMICAL PROPERTIES OF ENGINE OILS—SAE J357 OCT99

SAE Information Report

Report of the SAE Fuels and Lubricants Technical Committee approved August 1969. Reaffirmed by the SAE Fuels and Lubricants Division June 1986. Completely revised by the SAE Fuels and Lubricants Technical Committee 1—Passenger Car Type Engine Oils, June 1991 and February 1995. Revised by the SAE Fuels and Lubricants Technical Committee 1—Engine Oils, May 1996 and October 1999. Rationale statement available.

Foreword—This document discusses a number of the physical and chemical properties of new and used engine oils. Where appropriate, standardized methods of test for these properties are indicated and a detailed listing included in the references section. This document provides those concerned with the design and maintenance of internal combustion engines with information relative to the terms used to describe engine lubricants.

This document may be used as a general guide to engine oil properties and as an outline for establishing oil quality inspection and maintenance programs.

1. Scope—This SAE Information Report reviews the various physical and chemical properties of engine oils and provides references to test methods and standards used to measure these properties. It also includes general references on the subject of engine oils, base stocks, and additives.

2. References

2.1 Applicable Publications—The following publications form a part of this specification to the extent specified herein. The latest issue of SAE, ASTM, API, and CEC publications shall apply.

2.1.1 SAE PUBLICATIONS—Available from SAE, 400 Commonwealth Drive, Warrendale, PA 15096-0001.

SAE J183—Engine Oil Performance and Engine Service Classification (Other than "Energy Conserving")
SAE J300—Engine Oil Viscosity Classification
SAE J304—Engine Oil Tests
SAE J1423—Classification of Energy-Conserving Engine Oil for Passenger Cars, Vans, and Light Duty Trucks
SAE J2227—International Tests and Specifications for Automotive Engine Oils

2.1.2 ASTM PUBLICATIONS—Available from ASTM, 100 Barr Harbor Drive, West Conshohocken, PA 19428-2959.

ASTM DS 39b—Viscosity Index Tables for Celsius Temperatures
ASTM D 56—Test Method for Flash Point by Tag Closed Tester
ASTM D 91—Test Method for Precipitation Number of Lubricating Oils
ASTM D 92—Test Method for Flash and Fire Points by Cleveland Open Cup
ASTM D 93—Test Methods for Flash Point by Pensky-Martens Closed Cup Tester
ASTM D 95—Test Method for Water in Petroleum Products and Bituminous Materials by Distillation
ASTM D 97—Test Methods for Pour Point of Petroleum Oils
ASTM D 156—Test Method for Saybolt Color of Petroleum Products (Saybolt Chromometer Method)
ASTM D 189—Test Method for Conradson Carbon Residue of Petroleum Products
ASTM D 287—Test Method for API Gravity of Crude Petroleum and Petroleum Products (Hydrometer Method)
ASTM D 322—Test Method for Gasoline Diluent in Used Gasoline Engine Oils by Distillation
ASTM D 341—Viscosity-Temperature Charts for Liquid Petroleum Products
ASTM D 445—Test Method for Kinematic Viscosity of Transparent and Opaque Liquids (the Calculation of Dynamic Viscosity)
ASTM D 482—Test Method for Ash from Petroleum Products
ASTM D 524—Test Method for Ramsbottom Carbon Residue of Petroleum Products
ASTM D 664—Test Method for Acid Number of Petroleum Products by Potentiometric Titration
ASTM D 874—Test Method for Sulfated Ash from Lubricating Oils and Additives
ASTM D 892—Test Method for Foaming Characteristics of Lubricating Oils
ASTM D 893—Test Method for Insolubles in Used Lubricating Oils
ASTM D 974—Test Method for Acid and Base Number by Color-Indicator Titration
ASTM D 1160—Test Method for Distillation of Petroleum Products at Reduced Pressure
ASTM D 1298—Standard Practice for Density, Relative Density (Specific Gravity) or API Gravity of Crude Petroleum and Liquid Petroleum Products by Hydrometer Method
ASTM D 1310—Test Method for Flash Point and Fire Points of Liquids by Tag Open Cup Apparatus
ASTM D 1500—Test Method for ASTM Color of Petroleum Products (ASTM Color Scale)
ASTM D 2270—Standard Practice for Calculating Viscosity Index from Kinematic Viscosity at 40 and 100 °C
ASTM D 2500—Test Method for Cloud Point of Petroleum Oils
ASTM D 2887—Test Method for Boiling Range Distribution of Petroleum Fractions by Gas Chromatography
ASTM D 2896—Test Method for Base Number of Petroleum Products by Potentiometric Perchloric Acid Titration
ASTM D 2982—Test Method for Detecting Glycol-Base Antifreeze in Used Lubricating Oils
ASTM D 3244—Standard Practice for Utilization of Test Data to Determine Conformance with Specifications
ASTM D 3524—Test Method for Diesel Fuel Diluent in Used Diesel Engine Oil by Gas Chromatography
ASTM D 3525—Test Method for Gasoline Diluent in Used Gasoline Engine Oils by Gas Chromatography
ASTM D 3607—Test Method for Removing Volatile Contaminants from Used Engine Oils by Stripping
ASTM D 3828—Test Methods for Flash Point by Small Scale Closed Tester
ASTM D 3829—Test Method for Predicting the Borderline Pumping Temperature of Engine Oil
ASTM D 3945—Standard Test Methods for Shear Stability of Polymer-Containing Fluids Using a Diesel Injector Nozzle
ASTM D 4055—Test Method for Pentane Insolubles by Membrane Filtration
ASTM D 4485—Standard Specification for Performance of Engine Oils
ASTM D 4530—Test Method for Determinatino of Carbon Residue (Micro Method)
ASTM D 4628—Test Method for Analysis of Barium, Calcium, Magnesium, and Zinc in Unused Lubricating Oils by Atomic Absorption Spectrometry
ASTM D 4683—Test Method for Measuring Viscosity at High Temperature and High Shear Rate by Tapered Bearing Simulator
ASTM D 4684—Test Method for Determination of Yield Stress and Apparent Viscosity of Engine Oils at Low Temperature
ASTM D 4739—Test Method for Base Number Determination by Potentiometric Titration
ASTM D 4741—Test Method for Measurement of Viscosity at High Temperature and High Shear Rate by Tapered Plug Viscometer
ASTM D 4927—Test Methods for Elemental Analysis of Lubricant and Additive Components—Barium, Calcium, Phosphorus, Sulfur, and Zinc by Wavelength-Dispersive X-Ray Fluorescence Spectroscopy
ASTM D 4951—Test Method for Determination of Additive Elements in Lubricating Oils by Inductively Coupled Plasma Atomic Emission Spectrometry
ASTM D 5002—Test Method for Density and Relative Density of Crude Oil by Digital Density Analyzer
ASTM D 5119—Test Method for Evaluation of Automotive Engine Oils in the CRC L-38 Spark Ignition Engine
ASTM D 5133—Test Method for Low Temperature, Low Shear Rate, Viscosity/Temperature Dependence of Lubricating Oils Using a Temperature-Scanning Technique
ASTM D 5185—Standard Test Method for Determination of Additive Elements, Wear Metals, and Contaminants in Used Lubricating Oils and Determination of Selected Elements in Base Oil by Inductively Coupled Plasma Atomic Emission Spectrometry (ICP-AES)
ASTM D 5293—Standard Test Method for Apparent Viscosity of Engine Oils Between −5°C and −30 °C Using the Cold-Cranking Simulator
ASTM D 5480—Test Method for Engine Oil Volatility by Gas Chromatography
ASTM D 5800—Test Method for Evaporation Loss of Lubricating Oils by the NOACK Method
ASTM D 6278—Test Method for Shear Stability of Polymer Containing Fluids Using a European Diesel Injector Apparatus

ASTM D 6417—Test Method for the Estimation of Engine Oil Volatility by Capillary Gas Chromatography

ASTM E 1131—Test Method for Compositional Analysis by Thermogravimetry

ASTM MNL 1—Manual on the Significance of Tests for Petroleum Products: 5th Edition

ASTM STP 1068—High Temperature/High Shear (HTHS) Oil Viscosity: Measurement and Relation to Engine Operation

ASTM STP 1143—Low Temperature Lubricant Rheology Measurement Relevance to Engine Operations

2.1.3 OTHER PUBLICATIONS

API Publication 1509, latest edition, plus revisions

Federal Test Method Standard No. 791C, Method 203.1, "Pour Stability of Lubricating Oils"

Federal Test Method Standard No. 791C, Method 3470.1, "Homogeneity and Miscibility of Oils"

American Society of Lubrication Engineers, 1951, "The Physical Properties of Lubricants"

General Motors Engineering Standard GM 9099P, "Engine Oil Filterability Test (EOFT)," May 1980

CEC L-40-A-93, "Evaporative Loss," NOACK (DIN 51581) Method

CEC L-14-A-93, "Evaluation of the Mechanical Shear Stability of Lubricating Oils Containing Polymers" Method

C.M. Georgi, "Motor Oils and Engine Lubrication," New York: Reinhold Publishing Corporation, 1950

William A. Gruse, "Motor Oils, Performance and Evaluation," New York: Reinhold Publishing Corporation, 1967

A. Schilling, "Automotive Engine Lubrication," Broseley, England: Scientific Publications (G.B.) Ltd., 1972

R.C. Gunderson and A.W. Hart, "Synthetic Lubricants," New York: Reinhold Publishing Corporation, 1962

Dieter Klamann, "Lubricants and Related Products," Weinheim: Verlag Chemie (F.R.G.) GmbH, 1984

M. Campen, D. Kendrick, and A. Markin, "Growing Use of Synlubes," Hydrocarbon Processing, February 1982

G.J. Schilling and G.S. Bright, "Fuel and Lubricant Additives—II. Lubricant Additives," Lubrication Vol 63, No. 2, 1977

N. Benfaremo and C.S. Liu, "Crankcase Engine Oil Additives," Lubrication Vol 76, No. 1, 1990

3. General Description of Engine Oil Components—Modern engine oils consist of (1) base stocks and (2) the additives that are necessary to produce the required finished product performance. These engine oil components will be described in the following sections.

3.1 Base Stocks—A variety of different processes are used in the manufacture of base stocks for engine oils. These processes are briefly described in the following paragraphs:

3.1.1 DISTILLATION—Crude oil as it comes from the ground is a highly complex mixture of hydrocarbon molecules of three basic types: paraffinic, naphthenic, and aromatic. Crude oils are classified according to the predominant type of hydrocarbon molecules they contain.

The first step in refining crude oil into useful products is the separation according to boiling range by atmospheric or vacuum distillation. The various fractions are then further processed into gaseous products, gasoline, diesel and burner fuels, lubricating oil stock, asphalt, etc. The lubricating oil stock is distilled into a series of fractions of different viscosity and volatility. Base oils produced using the distillation process include "NEUTRALS" and "BRIGHT STOCKS" (with neutrals generally being of lower viscosity than the bright stocks).

Historically, a nomenclature has evolved to identify neutral and bright stock fractions by their Saybolt viscosities. Neutral fractions are referred to by their nominal viscosity at 100 °F in Saybolt Universal Seconds (SUS). For example, a 150 neutral is a distillate fraction with a nominal viscosity of 29 mm^2/s (cSt) at 40 °C (150 SUS at 100 °F). Generally speaking, the viscosity for the distillate (neutral) fractions range from about 11 to 150 mm^2/s (cSt) at 40 °C (60 to 850 SUS).

In similar fashion, bright stocks are referred to by their nominal SUS viscosity at 210 °F rather than 100 °F. For example, a 150 bright stock is a residual fraction with a nominal viscosity of 30.6 mm^2/s (cSt) at 100 °C (150 SUS at 210 °F). For comparison purposes, if the viscosity of the bright stocks were measured at 40 °C rather than 100 °C, they would range from 140 to 1600 mm^2/s (cSt) (650 to 7400 SUS).

3.1.2 SOLVENT REFINING—The fractions resulting from vacuum distillation contain nitrogen and sulfur compounds, metal-containing compounds, and aromatic hydrocarbons of various structures. Many of these compounds can adversely affect the stability and performance properties of base stocks and the ability of various additives to enhance these properties for engine oil applications. These compounds can be removed through separation processes using solvents such as phenol, furfural, or N-methyl pyrrolidone. This processing step is commonly referred to as solvent extraction.

Waxy materials present in the base stock may crystallize and agglomerate or congeal at low temperatures and thereby impede low temperature flow. These materials may be removed by solvent dewaxing processes employing solvents such as methylethyl ketone or propane.

3.1.3 HYDROGEN PROCESSING—Hydrogen processing can occur separately or in conjunction with solvent processing. This processing can range in severity from hydrogen treating to hydrogen cracking of base stocks. Both hydrotreated and hydrocracked base stocks are typically composed of higher percentages of saturates and reduced sulfur contents relative to solvent refined base stocks. The various modern hydrogen processes are briefly described below.

3.1.3.1 Hydrotreating—Hydrotreating converts some of the unsaturated and aromatic molecules in the base stock into saturated molecules. In addition, significant desulfurization occurs along with some nitrogen removal. Mild hydrotreating, also known as hydrofinishing or hydrofining, is normally used to improve color and odor.

3.1.3.2 Hydrocracking—The hydrocracking process changes virtually all molecules through cracking, isomerization, and saturation reactions. Aromatics are converted to naphthenes, while many of the naphthene rings are broken open. Hydrocracking can replace solvent extraction, but other processes such as desphalting and dewaxing are still required.

3.1.3.3 Hydroisomerization—Base stocks may also be produced by isomerization of wax or high wax content fractions from the crude oil refining process. Normal paraffinic molecules are primarily being rearranged to isoparaffins, while some hydrocracking of molecules may occur. The feed for this process is normally sourced from the refinery's solvent dewaxing unit or from wax manufactured by Fischer Tropsch Process. Typically solvent dewaxing follows to meet pour point requirements.

3.1.3.4 Hydrodewaxing—Catalytic hydrodewaxing is an alternative to solvent dewaxing. Wax molecules are catalytically cracked to lower boiling-products and/or isomerized to isoparaffins. This step typically follows either a hydrocracking or solvent extraction step. Catalytic dewaxing does not produce the waxy by-products used as feed source for hydroisomerized base stocks.

3.1.4 OLIGOMERIZATION—Olefin oligomers are made by linking together a low molecular weight material, such as ethylene, to produce a specific olefin. The olefins are then chemically joined ("oligomerized") to produce a base stock of suitable molecular weight and viscosity. Olefin oligomers are all hydrocarbon structures, containing no sulfur, phosphorus, or metals. When specific 1-alkenes are used as feed, these materials are commonly known as poly-alpha-olefins (PAOs).

3.1.5 ESTERIFICATION—Esters are formed by chemically reacting an acid and an alcohol. The most common organic esters used as engine oil base stocks are dibasic acid esters and polyol esters. Dibasic esters, or diesters, are the reaction products of a dibasic acid, such as adipic acid, and an alcohol containing one reactive hydroxyl group, such as 2-ethylhexyl alcohol. By reacting a monobasic acid with an alcohol with two or more hydroxyl groups, polyol esters are produced. "Hindered" alcohols commonly used to produce polyol esters are trimethylolpropane (TMP) and pentaerythritol (PE).

3.1.6 RECYCLING AND RE-REFINING—Used lubricating oils have been involved in recycling processes for over 65 years. Recycling normally involves the removal of volatile components produced in use as well as water, insolubles, and dirt. Little, if any, additional processing is involved. The resulting oil is not normally considered to be suitable for use in modern engines. However, it is often blended with other materials and burned as a fuel.

Re-refined base stocks may be manufactured from used oil by re-refining processes. Re-refined stocks shall be substantially free from additives and contaminants introduced from the re-refining process or from previous use. Re-refined oils can undergo one or more of the following processes: water separation, additive separation, solvent extraction, hydrotreating, and re-fractionation. The resulting finished, re-refined oil is often virtually indistinguishable from good quality virgin base stocks. These re-refined oils may be suitable for use in modern engines when treated with appropriate additives.

3.2 Additive Agents—A lubricant additive agent is defined as a material designed to enhance the performance properties of the base stock or to impart to the base stock properties that do not naturally exist with the base stock. These additive agents are used at concentration levels ranging from several parts per million to greater than 10 volume percent. Generally, additives are materials that have been chemically synthesized to provide the desired performance features, and they frequently contain an oil-solubilizing hydrocarbon portion as part of the molecule. Some additive agents are naturally occurring materials that have undergone only minor modifications to obtain the desired property.

Additives can carry out their task of enhancing or imparting new properties to an oil in one of three ways—protection of engine surfaces, modification of oil properties, protection of base stocks. Engine protectors include seal swell agents, antiwear agents, antirust agents, corrosion inhibitors, detergents, dispersants, and friction modifiers. Oil modifiers include pour point depressants, antifoam agents, and viscosity index (VI) improvers. Base stock protectors include antioxidants and metal deactivators. Some additives possess multifunctional properties.

Additive combinations contribute performance features which are required to satisfy the lubrication needs of modern engines under the most severe conditions and currently recommended oil change intervals. If additives have been put into the base stock to increase its commercial value to those who will use it for formulating engine oil, care should be taken to identify such additives so that further additive treatments will be compatible.

4. Physical and Chemical Properties—Understanding and agreeing on the methods of measurement of the physical and chemical properties of base oils and formulated engine oils can assist the user, the oil refiner, and the formulator to define a consistently uniform product. These properties are often used to establish acceptable levels of additive components in finished oils. Although oil performance in the engine is related to base stock and additive composition, it is often difficult to assign a specific aspect of such performance totally to the use of a specific additive or base stock. Part of the reason is that some of the physical and chemical properties of the oil overlap in their influences on engine performance and durability and it is presently difficult to directly and unambiguously attribute such effects to either the chemical or the physical properties of the oil. Progress in developing this level of understanding is being made. Some of these performance characteristics of engine oils are discussed in SAE J183, SAE J300, SAE J1423, and SAE J2227. At the present time, oil physical and chemical properties can be related to engine performance and durability only with the guidance of engine manufacturers and with appropriate and jointly accepted engine and/or field tests successfully completed on that oil.

At low temperatures where cranking/starting and engine oil pumpability are matters of concern, the physical properties of the engine oil can be directly related to its effects on any particular engine. Engine cranking and starting and oil pumpability are also related to a variety of other factors including engine response to oil rheology, as well as to nonrheological factors such as battery power and fuel volatility.

While the physical and chemical properties of an oil at operating temperatures are not related to oil performance in a simple way, these individual properties are meaningful and are related to the oil's ability to fulfill its function as a lubricant. These and the low temperature properties will be discussed in the following sections.

4.1 Viscosity—Viscosity of the engine oil is one of its most important and most evident properties. If sufficiently high, it is the source of the phenomenon of hydrodynamic lubrication in which the viscosity of the oil forces the bearing surface to ride on a thin film of oil and, thus, protect the lubricated surface from wear. Chemical additives, fuel dilution, contaminants from within and outside of the engine, wax in the oil, oil oxidation, volatilization, and many other materials found in or added to the oil affect the viscosity in advantageous or disadvantageous ways.

4.1.1 DEFINITION—Viscosity is defined as the internal resistance to flow of any fluid. It is expressed as follows in Equation 1:

$$\text{Dynamic Viscosity} = \frac{\text{Force/Sheared Area}}{\text{Velocity/Film Thickness}} = \frac{\text{Shear Stress}}{\text{Shear Rate}} \quad \text{(Eq. 1)}$$

The unit of measure for dynamic viscosity is the millipascal second (mPa·s), although the centipoise (cP) is also commonly used. One mPa·s equals 1 cP. Oils that exhibit a constant viscosity at all shear rates in this equation are known as "Newtonian" oils. In the absence of polymeric additives, most single grade oils are in this category at temperatures above their cloud point.

Oils that exhibit a viscosity which varies with changing shear rates in this equation are known as "non-Newtonian" oils. Multiviscosity graded oils formulated with polymeric additives are generally in this category.

Another form of viscometric expression involves the use of kinematic viscometers in which the liquid is driven by its own hydrodynamic head. This head varies directly with the density of the oil at the temperature of measurement. The relationship between kinematic and dynamic viscosity is as follows in Equation 2:

$$\text{Kinematic Viscosity} = \text{Dynamic Viscosity/Density of Liquid} \quad \text{(Eq. 2)}$$

The unit of measurement for kinematic viscosity is the millimeter squared per second (mm^2/s), although the centistoke (cSt) is commonly used. One mm^2/s equals 1 cSt. Density effects should be eliminated either by measuring the dynamic viscosity or by measuring kinematic viscosity and density at the temperature of interest and converting the values to dynamic viscosity.

4.1.2 VISCOSITY INDEX (VI)—Viscosity decreases rapidly with increasing temperature. For most oils, the relationship between viscosity and temperature can be approximated by the following empirical relationship in Equation 3:

$$\text{loglog(kinematic viscosity + 0.7)} = A + B\ \text{(log absolute temperature)} \quad \text{(Eq. 3)}$$

where:

A and B are constants, specific for each oil

This relationship, which is an approximation of the MacCoull, Walther, Wright equation, forms the basis for special viscosity temperature charts published in ASTM D 341. These charts permit the plotting of viscosity-temperature data as straight lines over the temperature range in which the oils are homogeneous liquids. The slope of these lines is a measure of the change in viscosity with temperature. It is dependent on the chemical composition of the oil and is described by an empirical relationship called VI. The higher the VI, the smaller the change in viscosity with temperature (slope). ASTM D 2270 is used to determine VI values. ASTM DS 39b is based on ASTM D 2270 and allows for more convenient determination of VI.

For engine oils, a relatively smaller change in viscosity with temperature (high VI) is desirable to provide a wider range of operating temperatures over which a given oil will provide satisfactory lubrication. At low temperatures, a relatively low viscosity oil is desirable to permit adequate cranking speed during starting, and then adequate flow to the oil pump and the entire engine oiling system after starting.

At high temperatures in a running engine, the oil viscosity must be high enough to maintain adequate film thickness between rotating or rubbing parts to minimize wear. Using a higher viscosity oil generally reduces oil consumption (past piston rings and valve guides) and blowby, but increases friction associated with oil film shearing in the piston/piston ring cylinder wall interface and bearings.

4.1.3 VISCOSITY INDEX IMPROVERS—To extend the upper temperature limit at which an oil will still provide satisfactory lubrication, polymeric additives, called Viscosity Index (VI) improvers, are widely used. Engine oils properly formulated with VI improvers generally contain lower viscosity base stocks which provide better low temperature cranking/starting and pumpability properties. As the oil temperature increases, the viscosity of the oil containing a VI improver decreases more slowly than the same oil without a VI improper, thus increasing the VI. The result is an oil that can give good starting/pumping response and is also effective in providing a more viscous oil film at operating temperatures than could be obtained with a single grade oil providing equivalent startability at low temperatures.

Oils containing a polymeric VI improver exhibit a decrease in viscosity as the shear rate or stress is increased. Because the viscosity of such oils depends on shear stress, they are called "non-Newtonian oils." Such change generally lasts only as long as the oil is operated under such high shear stress. When the shear stress is relieved, the oil reverts to its previous viscosity. This reversible decrease in viscosity due to shear is called "temporary shear (or viscosity) loss." When certain critically high shear stresses are imposed on a VI improper in oil solution, the viscosity contribution of the VI improper to both low and high shear rate viscosity can be permanently reduced. This nonreversible reduction in viscosity is called "permanent shear (or viscosity) loss." The magnitude of these temporary and permanent losses is dependent on the type and molecular weight of the VI improper used, as well as the actual service conditions.

The permanent shear stability characteristics of engine oils are evaluated by comparing the stripped viscosity of an engine oil after 10 h in the CRC L-38 engine test to the new oil viscosity. Shear stability can also be measured using CEC L-14-A-93, ASTM D 3945, and ASTM D 6278.

4.1.4 VISCOSITY MEASUREMENT—The SAE J300 standard classifies oils into grades according to their kinematic viscosities measured at low shear rates and high temperature (100 °C), and their viscosities at high shear rate and high temperature (150 °C), and at both low and high shear rates at low temperatures (–5 to –35 °C).

Low shear rate kinematic viscosity is measured using ASTM D 445 and is reported in millimeters squared per second (mm^2/s), although the centistoke (cSt) is also commonly used. Kinematic viscosity is measured most commonly at 100 °C, and also at 40 °C if VI is to be determined.

At low temperature, the high shear rate viscosity is measured by ASTM D 5293. This is a multitemperature cold cranking simulator method. The low temperature, low shear rate viscosity is measured by ASTM D 4684. Both ASTM D 5293 and ASTM D 4684 report viscosities in millipascal seconds (mPa·s), although the centipoise (cP) is also commonly used. Results of both tests have been shown to correlate with engine starting and engine oil pumpability at low temperatures, although the precise correlation to modern engines has been questioned and is under active investigation with ASTM.

Oil viscosity at very high shear rates/stresses and at high temperatures (150 °C) is measured using ASTM 4683 or ASTM 4741 and is reported in millipascal seconds (mPa·s), although the centipoise (cP) is also commonly used. A comparable Capillary Viscometer method is currently being developed by ASTM. These methods are intended primarily to simulate operating conditions occurring in engine bearings.

4.2 Other Tests Pertinent to New and Used Oils

4.2.1 Cloud Point and Pour Point—The cloud point of a moisture-free oil is defined as the temperature at which a cloud or haze appears in the lower portion of the test oil when tested (i.e., cooled) by ASTM D 2500. The haze indicates the presence of some insoluble fractions, such as wax, at the temperature noted. In most applications, this haze will have little practical significance.

The pour point of an oil is defined as the lowest temperature at which the oil can be poured when tested by ASTM D 97. The pour point can be directly related to whether or not the oil can be poured from a container at low temperatures. Although pour point is a simple measure of wax crystal structure and low temperature viscosity, more precise and correlatable viscometric methods, such as ASTM D 3829 and ASTM D 4684, have been developed which better predict the ability of an oil to flow to the oil pump and throughout the system at low temperature. In actual practice, the oil in the crankcase will be a mixture of oil and small amounts of fuel fractions, the composition depending on several factors (see 4.3.4)(see 4.3.4).

Some oils display an increase in pour point when exposed to repeated cycling at temperatures below and above the pour point. Appendix B of SAE J300 (taken from Federal Test Method, Standard No. 791C, Method 203.1) describes a procedure, commonly called the stable pour point, for evaluating the tendency of the pour point to so increase. While no longer a mandatory procedure in the low temperature classification requirements of SAE J300, the measurement of the stable pour point continues to be recommended when significant changes in formulation or base stock sources are made.

4.2.2 Flash Point and Fire Point—The flash point of a petroleum product is the lowest temperature to which the product must be heated under specific conditions to give off sufficient vapor to form a mixture with air that can be ignited momentarily by a specified flame. Fire point is the lowest temperature to which a product must be heated under prescribed conditions to burn continuously when the mixture of vapor and air is ignited by a specified flame.

Flash and fire points are significant from the viewpoint of safety and should be related to the temperatures to which petroleum products will be subjected in storage, transportation, and use. Normally, engine oils will present no hazards in this respect but the minimum flash point that can be tolerated must be determined in each application. Flash point may also be used to indicate gross contamination of used oil by a volatile product such as gasoline or diesel fuel. Methods of obtaining this type of information are ASTM D 56, ASTM D 92, ASTM D 93, ASTM D 1310, and ASTM D 3828. ASTM D 92 and ASTM D 93 are the preferred methods for unused engine oils.

4.2.3 Distillation Data—The volatility characteristics of engine oils can be defined by several procedures.

Distillation is one method. Because engine oils are comprised of relatively high boiling point fractions, which would thermally crack in an atmospheric distillation, a reduced-pressure (vacuum) distillation method; i.e., ASTM D 1160, must be used. The use of gas chromatography is another method. ASTM D 2887, which gives boiling-range distribution data by gas chromatography, has gained acceptance and is often used in place of ASTM D 1160. ASTM D 2887 and CEC L-40-A-93 are both currently used to measure evaporative loss on volatility of engine oils. Neither of these methods are entirely satisfactory and new methods have been developed.

ASTM D 5800 and ASTM D 5480 may be used to measure engine oil volatility.

NOTE—An improved version of ASTM D 2887, designated ASTM D 6417, is being considered for final approval. ASTM D 6417 has not, as of this revision, been published as an official ASTM test but should be shortly. ASTM D 5800 and ASTM D 6417 have gained increased acceptance as the preferred standard methods to determine engine oil evaporative loss. Work done by several companies has shown a correlation between these methods and in-service oil consumption.)

4.2.4 Alkalinity And Acidity—The alkalinity or acidity characteristics of petroleum products can be measured by any one of several standardized methods. Methods currently used include ASTM D 664, ASTM D 974, ASTM D 2896, and ASTM D 4739. Changes in alkalinity or acidity with use give some indication of the nature of the changes taking place in the engine oil. For example, a reduction in base number can be ascribed to neutralization of basic additive components such as metal containing detergents as well as certain ashless dispersants. An increase in acid number may be ascribed to engine oil oxidation and/or contamination by products of combustion. Base number of a new oil is an indication of an oil's ability to resist the deleterious effects associated with high sulfur levels in diesel fuels. Different titration methods may yield different base numbers on the same oil. Therefore, caution is necessary in applying base number—oil performance relationships. For diesel engines, relationships have been published between base number of the new oil, change in base number during service, fuel sulfur content, and desired engine oil drain interval. The change in base number in service can be used under certain conditions to evaluate engine oil change interval practices. Both ASTM D 2896 and ASTM D 4739 methods are commonly used in these instances.

4.2.5 Carbon Residue—The base stock components of engine oils are mixtures of many compounds that differ widely in their physical and chemical properties. Some vaporize at atmospheric pressure without leaving an appreciable residue. When destructively distilled, the nonvolatile compounds may leave a carbonaceous material known as carbon residue. Two methods used for evaluating base stocks in this respect are ASTM D 189 and ASTM D 524. ASTM D 4530 is essentially equivalent to ASTM D 189 while minimizing sample size. Engine oils containing ash-forming constituents, such as the additives commonly used in formulating oils, may give misleading high carbon residues by either method. Carbon residue has little value as a guide for predicting deposit-forming tendencies in automotive engines, but may relate to intake port deposits in certain large, two stroke cycle, natural gas fueled stationary engines.

4.2.6 Ash Content—The amount of ash formed from burning engine oils may be obtained by ASTM D 482. However, ASTM D 874 is now the method most commonly used because it is a more accurate measure of ash-forming constituents. When tested by ASTM D 482, some metals are partially volatilized and lost, giving erroneously low values. The ash produced from burning new engine oils is principally related to the concentration of ash-producing additives in the oil. In addition to the additive contribution, the ash produced by used oils will also be a function of the amount of contaminants present in the engine oil. High values can also result from other contaminants, such as dirt, iron oxide, wear metals, and corrosion products. Ash forming substances in an oil may contribute to deposits on combustion chamber surfaces, spark plugs, and intake or exhaust valves, which can influence the combustion characteristics, exhaust valve sealing and certain driveability characteristics of an engine. However, the mechanism for the buildup of deposits in these areas is very complex and depends on many variables in addition to the ash content of the oil.

4.2.7 Compatibility—Engine oils are expected to be homogeneous and completely miscible with all other engine oils with which they might be mixed in service. When oils are mixed in any proportion, there should be no evidence of separation either of the additives or of the oils when the mixed oils are heated to a temperature as high as 232 °C and cooled to a temperature as low as the pour point of the mixture. The homogeneity and miscibility test currently used to evaluate engine oils is Federal Test Method Standard No. 791C, Method 3470.1.

4.2.8 Foaming—Oils with poor antifoaming characteristics have been shown to result in decreased oxidation resistance and reduced lubricant efficacy. A bench test for determining this quality is ASTM D 892.

4.2.9 Gravity, Color, Odor—Gravity (density) may be used to characterize the basic hydrocarbon type of the base stocks. Gravity and color are factors generally associated with the quality control of manufactured products rather than with performance characteristics. ASTM D 287 and ASTM D 1298 may be used to determine the gravity and density characteristics of oil. The color of engine oils may be specified by using ASTM D 156 or more commonly ASTM D 1500.

It is expected that engine oils will not produce offensive odors due to the nature of the base stocks or the additive agents with which the oil is compounded; nor should offensive odors or toxic vapors be generated during use of, or prolonged storage of, an engine oil. There are no standardized odor tests suitable for engine oils.

4.2.10 Elemental Analysis—Elemental analysis of engine oils is often used as a means of quality control. Instrumental analytical techniques, such as emission spectroscopy, ICP, atomic absorption spectroscopy, and X-ray emission spectroscopy, are useful in this respect. Similar analyses of used oils will provide information relative to the changes in the elemental content of the engine oil. These data can also give a measure of contamination by materials such as ingested dirt, coolant, or products of combustion, especially with engines using leaded gasoline. They also can provide information relative to the extent of wear in the engine. Concentrations of the following elements are commonly determined:

a. Additive elements such as barium, boron, calcium, copper, magnesium, molybdenum, nitrogen, phosphorus, silicon, sodium, sulfur, and zinc.
b. Contaminants such as lead, silicon, chlorine, bromine, and potassium.
c. Wear metals such as aluminum, chromium, copper, iron, lead, molybdenum, and tin.

4.2.11 INFRARED ANALYSIS—Infrared spectrophotometry techniques are valuable in identifying the chemical structures found in base stocks and additives. Changes in these structures can be determined by comparing results of analyses of new and used oils. In used oils, it is also possible to measure oxidation and/or nitration, and to identify the presence of contaminants (e.g., fuel dilution and fuel soot), water, antifreeze, and similar materials.

4.2.12 FILTERABILITY—The tendency of an oil to form gels or other filter plugging material in the presence of water can be evaluated by use of the General Motors Engineering Standard GM 9099P. This method is being considered for standardization by ASTM in the near future.

4.3 Tests Pertinent to Used Oils

4.3.1 USED OIL PROPERTIES—The analysis of a used engine oil may be of value in establishing the condition of the engine and may be helpful in estimating the remaining useful life of the oil. To be of most value, used oil analyses must be taken periodically during the drain interval and a trend line established. The conditions of usage also must be considered in evaluating used oil analyses.

4.3.2 INSOLUBLE CONTENT—Insoluble materials found in both new and used engine oils may be determined using ASTM D 91, or the more frequently used ASTM D 893. Use of these methods permits an evaluation of the contaminant content and buildup of insoluble materials through oxidation, etc. However, the results must be judged with care, because minor changes in the analytical procedure can produce different results. For example, the age and purity of the coagulant solutions specified in ASTM D 893 can affect the results obtained.

With modern highly dispersant oils, the determination of insolubles has become increasingly difficult. Use of coagulant in ASTM D 893 may be required to make accurate determinations. ASTM D 4055 measures all insolubles greater in size than 0.8 mm. However, current interlaboratory precision (reproducibility) is poor.

4.3.3 COOLANT (MOISTURE) CONTENT—Small quantities of water will frequently be found in used engine oil as contamination from products of combustion, leakage from the cooling system, or condensation from atmospheric moisture. ASTM D 95 defines a process for determining the water content of used oil. For a qualitative determination, a commonly used simple test is to heat a drop of oil on aluminum foil. A snapping or crackling sound indicates free or suspended water in the oil. Cooling system leakage can be suspected when water is found in the oil on cool down after operation for several hours under high temperature conditions, such as interstate highway driving. The presence of glycol can be a more definitive indication of leakage. Glycol is detected by distillation of the aqueous material, followed by chemical analyses or infrared spectrophotometry on the distillate. A less complicated procedure which is adaptable to field kit use and gives positive, trace, or negative results is ASTM D 2982. Some additives commonly used in formulating engine oils contain glycol at a level that will give a positive result. If the new oil gives a positive result, the test in its simple form will be inadequate for detecting coolant glycol in used oils and the oil supplier should be consulted for advice.

4.3.4 FUEL DILUTION—Engines in good mechanical condition and operated at normal temperatures will usually show a small amount of fuel dilution in the used engine oil. Typical fuel dilution values for an engine in good mechanical conditions operating at normal temperatures is 0.1 to 1.5% volume. Low operating temperatures, rich mixtures of fuel and air, and low ambient temperatures will promote fuel dilution, particularly if the engine is in poor mechanical condition or crankcase ventilation is inadequate. High dilution reduces oil viscosity and pour point. The presence of such dilution can cause accelerated wear and promote the formation of sludge, varnish, and rust. The presence of a high dilution level may indicate a need for engine maintenance. Dilution may be determined by ASTM D 322 or by ASTM D 3607. This latter method also produces a dilution-free sample for subsequent analyses. These methods are useful only with gasoline engines since the distillation range for diesel fuels in many cases overlaps that for the engine oils used in diesel engines. Procedures applicable to both diesel and gasoline engine oils are ASTM D 3524 and ASTM D 3525. For laboratories so equipped, ASTM D 2887 is also a suitable method for measuring fuel dilution.

The flash point may also be used to approximate fuel dilution. If the flash point test is utilized, it is extremely important to measure the flash point of the new (reference) oil to establish a correct baseline (see 4.2.2)(see 4.2.2). The infrared spectrophotometer may also be utilized as a test tool to approximate fuel dilution in used oil. Viscosity decrease may also indicate the presence of fuel dilution; however, high levels of soot contamination can mask such reductions.

4.3.5 SOOT CONTENT—Soot content of used diesel engine oils can cause a number of problems related to additive complexing and abnormal viscosity increases. The soot is formed by the combustion process and is especially serious when combustion is incomplete. Currently soot can be detected by ASTM E 1131. A qualitative indication of soot content can be made by viscosity measurement.

5. Performance Characteristics—In the operation of an internal combustion engine, engine oils are expected to lubricate, cool, seal, maintain cleanliness, and protect against wear and corrosion. An oil's ability to perform these functions depends on the combined effectiveness of its base stock and additives, as well as operating conditions, fuel quality, and the design and the mechanical condition of the engine. Although the physical and chemical tests described in the preceding sections can be used for quality control to insure manufacturing uniformity, they are not effective for accurately defining performance characteristics at operating loads and temperatures. Only actual performance evaluations in special laboratory engines and in field tests will define the capabilities of an engine oil. Laboratory diesel and gasoline engine tests that have become industry recognized for evaluating engine oils are described in SAE J304. SAE J183 and SAE J1423 classify oils according to performance criteria based on results from engine dynamometer tests. These criteria are generally correlated with field test results. Where other operational properties are of interest, specific tests must be developed using the equipment and conditions most relevant to a given situation.

Although the laboratory engine tests are necessary and valuable aids to engine oil development and evaluation, they have limitations. In many instances, the final proof-of-performance is established by field tests of the oil in actual vehicle service. While no industry standardized field test procedures are currently available, the SAE Lubricants Review Institute has furnished some guidelines in their procedures manual. The most meaningful results on a given oil are obtained by evaluation in the most severe type of service expected to be encountered by a particular engine oil.

6. Handling and Disposal of Used Oils—Continuous, long-term contact with used engine oil has caused skin cancer in laboratory animal tests. Proper protective clothing and equipment (gloves, etc.) should be used when handling used engine oil. Exposed skin areas should be washed thoroughly after exposure to used engine oil.

Clothing should be laundered regularly, especially after contact with used engine oil. In addition, proper disposal of used engine oil is very important. For more information on handling and disposal of used engine oil, contact your oil supplier, the American Petroleum Institute, or appropriate federal, state, or local government agencies.

7. Conclusions—The lubrication requirements for modern engines are extremely complex. Current engine oils are the result of extensive research and development aimed at meeting these requirements. It is not the objective of this document to treat the subject in detail. Rather, the purpose of this document is to define very briefly the terms frequently encountered in discussions of engine oils and engine oil performance for those technical people not directly associated with lubricants and lubricant development. For more detailed information on these matters, the reader is referred to the technical services offered by lubricant and additive manufacturers, appropriate engine manufacturer organizations, and pertinent literature available through the Society of Automotive Engineers, Society of Tribologists and Lubrication Engineers, American Society of Mechanical Engineers, American Petroleum Institute, American Society for Testing and Materials, etc. Information directly related to this document may be found in the listed references (see Section 2).

) CLASSIFICATION OF ENERGY CONSERVING ENGINE OIL FOR PASSENGER CARS, VANS, SPORT UTILITY VEHICLES, AND LIGHT-DUTY TRUCKS—SAE J1423 DEC2003

SAE Recommended Practice

Report of the SAE Fuels and Lubricants Technical Committee approved March 1984 and revised May 1988. Completely revised by the SAE Fuels and Lubricants Technical Committee 1—Passenger Car Type Engine Oils April 1990, revised February 1992, and completely revised August 1994 and May 1997. Completely revised by the SAE Fuels and Lubricants Technical Committee 1—Engine Lubrication December 2003.

Foreword

Automotive engine oils are classified by viscosity as described in SAE J300, Engine Oil Viscosity Classification, and by certain engine performance and service characteristics as described in SAE J183. This SAE Standard is a classification for engine oils that have Energy Conserving characteristics under certain operating conditions and are categorized as "Energy Conserving" or "Energy Conserving II." These Energy Conserving properties are supplemental to the performance requirements of the API service category or categories that are technically described in SAE J183.

1. Scope

This SAE Standard was developed cooperatively by SAE, ASTM, and API to define and identify Energy Conserving engine oils for passenger cars, vans, sport utility vehicles, and light-duty (3856 kg [8500 LB] GVW or less) trucks.

2. References

2.1 Applicable Publications

The following publications form a part of this specification to the extent specified herein. Unless otherwise indicated, the latest issue of SAE publications shall apply.

2.1.1 SAE PUBLICATIONS

Available from SAE, 400 Commonwealth Drive, Warrendale, PA 15096-0001.

SAE J183—Engine Oil Performance and Engine Service Classification (Other than "Energy Conserving")

SAE J300—Engine Oil Viscosity Classification

2.1.2 ASTM PUBLICATIONS

Available from ASTM, 100 Barr Harbor Drive, West Conshohocken, PA 19428-2959.

ASTM Research Report No. RR:D02:1364—"Sequence VIA Test Development," October 1995

ASTM Research Report No. RR:D02:1204—"Fuel Efficient Engine Oil Dynamometer Test Development Activities," Final Report, Part II, August 1985

ASTM Research Report No. RR: D02-1469 – Development of Standard Test Method for Measurement of the Effects of Automotive Engine Oils on the Fuels Economy of Passenger Cars and Light Duty Trucks in the Sequence VIB Spark Ignition Engine Test.

1986 Annual Book of ASTM Standards, D-2 Proposal P101 Method of Measuring Engine-Conserving Quality of Engine Oils In Vehicles

1986 Annual Book of ASTM Standards, D-2 Proposal P102 Classification for Energy Conserving Engine Oils

1988 Annual Book of ASTM Standards, D-2 Proposal P-205 Classification for Energy Conserving Engine Oils

ASTM Standard D 6202 – Test Method for Measurement of the Effects of Automotive Engine Oils on the Fuel Economy of Passenger Cars and Light-Duty Trucks in the Sequence VIA Spark Ignition Engine

2.1.3 API PUBLICATION

Available from American Petroleum Institute, 1220 L Street NW, Washington DC 20005.

API Publication No. 1509, 15th Edition—Engine Oil Licensing and Certification System

3. ASTM Definition, Test Procedure, and Passing Limits

ASTM has developed a definition, test procedures, and passing limits for Energy Conserving engine oils, based on the Sequence VIA, and VIB tests.

3.1 Definition

Energy Conserving engine oils are lubricants that demonstrate reduced fuel consumption when compared to specified ASTM reference oil(s) and run in the ASTM Sequence VIA or VIB procedures (See 3.3 and 3.3.1 and Figure 1 and Figure 2.)

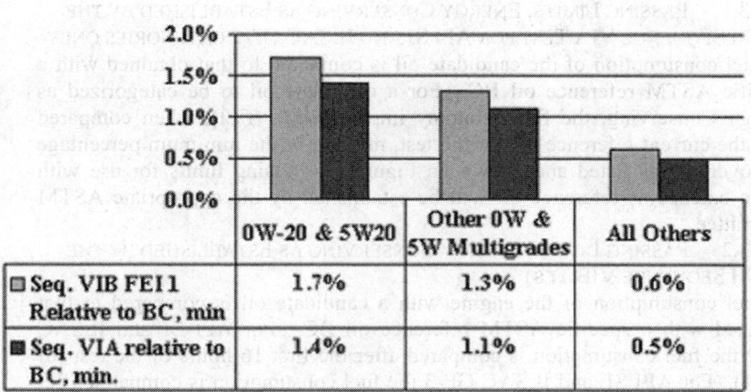

	0W-20 & 5W20	Other 0W & 5W Multigrades	All Others
Seq. VIB FEI 1 Relative to BC, min	1.7%	1.3%	0.6%
Seq. VIA relative to BC, min.	1.4%	1.1%	0.5%

FIGURE 1—ENERGY CONSERVING LIMITS IN CONJUNCTION WITH API SJ CATEGORY

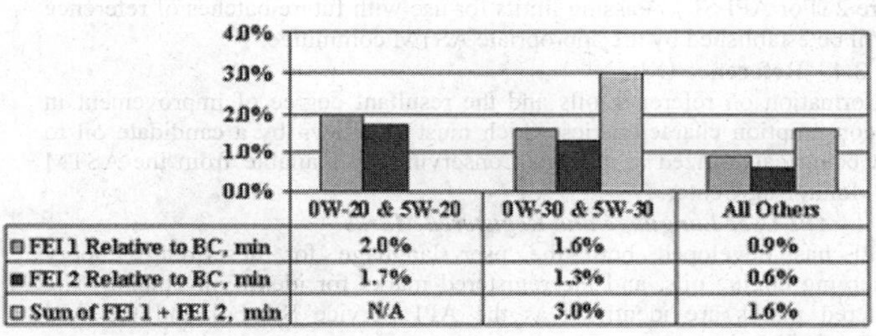

	0W-20 & 5W-20	0W-30 & 5W-30	All Others
FEI 1 Relative to BC, min	2.0%	1.6%	0.9%
FEI 2 Relative to BC, min	1.7%	1.3%	0.6%
Sum of FEI 1 + FEI 2, min	N/A	3.0%	1.6%

FIGURE 2—ENERGY CONSERVING LIMITS IN CONJUNCTION WITH API SL CATEGORY AND ILSAC GF-3

3.2 Test Procedures

The Sequence VIA and VIB test procedures are used to evaluate the Energy Conserving characteristics of engine oils. The procedures are intended for use in measuring the effects of engine oils on the fuel consumption of passenger cars, vans, sport utility vehicles, and light-duty (3856 kg [8500 lb] GVW or less) trucks. Two obsolete test methods, the Sequence VI and the ASTM Five-Car Test Method preceded these.[1,2]

3.2.1 The Sequence VIA test procedure is described in the ASTM Research Report No. RR:D02:1364 of October, 1995 and In ASTM Standard D 6202. The Sequence VIA procedure is used for evaluating engine oil service category SJ, and only to categorize the oil as Energy Conserving. The Energy Conserving designation under ILSAC GF-2 is based on the Sequence VIA test and became effective October 15, 1996. The Sequence VIA engine test fuel economy results have correlated to vehicles representative of circa 1996 production running under the current EPA Testing Cycle.

3.2.2 The Sequence VIB test procedure is described in the ASTM Research Report No. RR: D02: 1469. The Sequence VIB procedure evaluates the oil's effect on the engine fuel consumption after 16 hours of aging (FEI 1) and again after another 80 hours of aging (FEI 2) when compared to an ASTM reference oil BC. The Sequence VIB is used for evaluating engine oil service

[1] The Five-Car test was used to identify engine oils as energy–conserving; however, the test is now obsolete. The Five-Car Test Procedure is published as a proposal in Volume 05.03 of the 1986 Annual Book of ASTM Standards (D-2 Proposal P102)

[2] The Sequence VI test was used to identify engine oils as Energy Conserving and Energy Conserving II; however the test is now obsolete. The Sequence VI procedure is published as an ASTM Research Report No. RR: D02: 1204

category SL, and only to categorize the oil as Energy Conserving. The Energy Conserving designation under ILSAC GF-3 is based on the Sequence VIB test. Both API SL Energy Conserving and ILSAC GF-3 are effective July 1, 2001. The Sequence VIB engine test fuel economy results have correlated to vehicles representative of current production running under the current EPA Testing Cycle. The Sequence VIB test can also be used to evaluate engine oil Service Category SJ, and only to categorize the oil as Energy Conserving. This evaluation is performed after 16 hours of oil aging (FE1).

3.3 Passing Limits, Energy Conserving

3.3.1 PASSING LIMITS, ENERGY CONSERVING AS ESTABLISHED BY THE ASTM SEQUENCE VIA TEST FOR API SJ AND ILSAC GF-2 CATEGORIES ONLY

Fuel consumption of the candidate oil is compared to that obtained with a specific ASTM reference oil BC. For a candidate oil to be categorized as Energy Conserving, the fuel economy improvement, (FEI), when compared with the current reference oil for the test, must meet the minimum percentage improvement as listed and shown on Figure 1. Passing limits for use with future batches of reference oil will be established by the appropriate ASTM committee.

3.3.2 PASSING LIMITS, ENERGY CONSERVING AS ESTABLISHED BY THE ASTM SEQUENCE VIB TEST

Fuel consumption of the engine with a candidate oil is compared to that obtained with a specific ASTM reference oil BC. For API SJ and ILSAC GF-2 the fuel consumption is compared after the first 16 hours of the test (or FEI 1). For API SL and ILSAC GF-3 the fuel consumption is compared after 16 hours (FEI 1) and after 96 hours (FEI 2) of the test. For a candidate oil to be categorized as Energy Conserving, the fuel economy improvement when compared with the current reference oil for the test, must meet the minimum percentage improvement as listed and shown on Figure 1 (for API SJ) or on Figure 2 (For API SL). Passing limits for use with future batches of reference oil will be established by the appropriate ASTM committee.

3.4 Reference Oils

Information on reference oils and the resultant degree of improvement in fuel consumption characteristics which must be shown by a candidate oil to merit being categorized as Energy Conserving, is available from the ASTM Test Monitoring Center.

4. API User Language and Registered Marks

API has developed both the user language for describing Energy Conserving engine oils, and the registered marks for identifying them. The registered marks are identified as the API Service Symbol and the API Certification Mark.

4.1 API User Language

4.1.1 API Service Category SJ engine oils that also carry the classification Energy Conserving are formulated to improve the fuel economy of passenger cars, sport utilities, vans, and light-duty trucks powered by gasoline engines. These oils have produced a fuel economy improvement when compared with the standard reference oil (ASTM Reference OIL BC) used in the Sequence VIA and VIB tests. Energy Conserving may be defined by meeting the primary performance criteria in either the Sequence VIA or the Sequence VIB tests. (Figure 1)

4.1.2 API Service Category SL engine oils categorized as Energy Conserving are formulated to improve the fuel economy of passenger cars, sport utility vehicles, vans, and light-duty trucks powered by gasoline engines. These oils have produced a fuel economy improvement (FEI) both at the start and end of the Sequence VIB test when compared with the standard reference oil (ASTM Reference Oil BC) used in the Sequence VIB test. (Figure 2)

4.1.3 No energy conserving claims are permitted with API Service Category SH engine oils

4.2 Description of Registered Marks

API licenses two types of registered marks identified as the API Service Symbol and the API Certification Mark. Certain oils may meet the requirements of both the API Certification Mark and the API Category SJ, SL, and Energy Conserving. Examples of the two types of registered marks are shown in Figures 3 and 4.

4.3 API Service Symbol

API licenses the use of the API Service Symbol which is used for labeling engine oils with regard to API Service Categories, SAE Viscosity Grade, and Energy Conserving Categories as shown in Figure 3. The symbol consists of upper and lower annular segments, as well as a circular area in the center. These parts are reserved for the following uses:

4.3.1 UPPER SEGMENT

This segment of the symbol is to show only API service categories SH, SJ, SL, CF, CF-2, CF-4, CG-4, CH-4 and category CI-4as of September 5, 2002. The Energy Conserving categories may be used only in conjunction with API Service categories SJ or SL. API categories SH, SJ or SL cannot be used in the API Service Symbol at the same time. Effective August 1, 1997, Service Category SH becomes obsolete for stand alone use in the API Service Symbol and may only be used in conjunction with CF and/or CF-2 and/ or CF-4 and/or CG-4 and/or CH-4, and/or CI-4 and the C Category must always appear first. (Refer to 3.2.2 and 3.3.2.

NOTE—The letter combination SI was not used in the sequence of letter designators for API Service Categories due to the common association with "International Units" which is referred to as "SI" units. The letter combination SK was not used due to copyright restrictions.

4.3.2 CENTER AREA

This area is reserved to show only the appropriate SAE viscosity grade(s) as defined in the latest version of SAE J300.

4.3.3 LOWER SEGMENT

The lower segment is reserved to show only the categories "Energy Conserving" provided that the oil meets the ASTM requirements referred to in Section 3 of this document. If either of these designations is used in the lower segment of the symbol, the upper segment must show the appropriate API S-category or categories. If applicable, the appropriate C-category or categories may also be included. It should be clearly understood that the Energy Conserving characteristics of engine oils have not been defined for heavy-duty diesel engine applications and that the aforementioned designations apply only to S-categories displayed and do not apply to any C categories. (See Figure 3.)

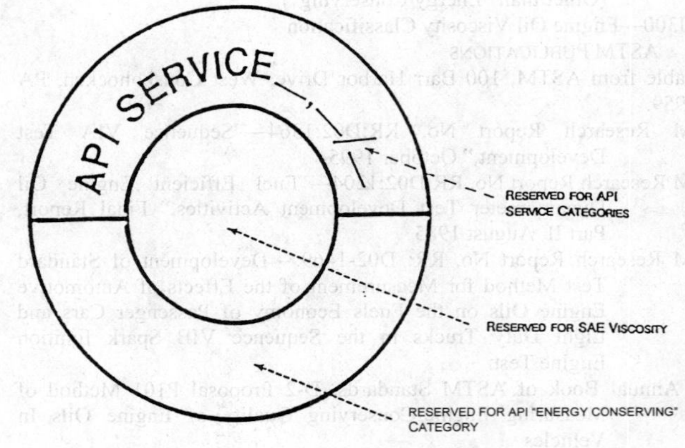

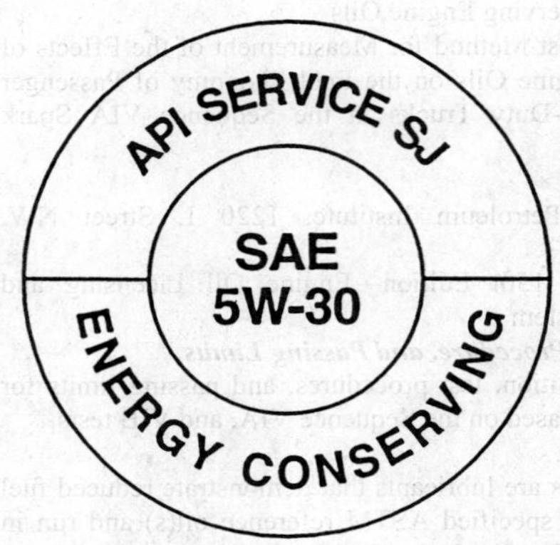

FIGURE 3—EXPLANATION AND EXAMPLE OF

THE API SERVICE SYMBOL

FIGURE 4—API CERTIFICATION MARK

4.3.4 NOTE

API will license oil marketers to use the symbol in which "Energy Conserving" should be displayed. It is the responsibility of the marketer to verify that the oil being labeled meets the requirements for the designations used in the service symbol, including the API service category or categories, the SAE viscosity grade or grades, and "Energy Conserving" category (if included) as specified in this document. For more information, see the latest version of API publication No. 1509 (paragraphs titled "API Service Symbol" and "Service Categories for Automotive Gasoline Engines" and "Service Categories for Commercial Diesel Engines.")

4.4 API Certification Mark

Each API Certification Mark is designed for identification of engine oils recommended for a general application (for example, gasoline, fuel flexible, light-duty diesel). The certification mark, shown in Figure 4, may be licensed only if an oil satisfies the requirements of the most recent and applicable ILSAC minimum performance standards. The certification mark remains the same for a given application even if a new engine oil performance standard is developed for the application. However, annual licenses are issued only for oils that meet the most recent standards.

4.4.1 NOTE

Beginning July 1, 2001, engine oils licensed for API SL were allowed to display the new service category in the upper portion of the API Service Symbol donut. Oils meeting the requirements of the VIB test and API Service Category SJ were allowed to display "Energy Conserving" in the lower portion of the API Service Symbol. Also oils meeting ILSAC GF-3 requirements may be licensed beginning July 1, 2001. API has not reached agreement on an obsolescence date for API SJ and for Energy Conserving defined by Sequence VIA results. The last date the API Certification Mark may be displayed on oils meeting ILSAC GF-2 criteria was March 31, 2002. It is the responsibility of the marketer to verify that the oil meets the requirements for the appropriate ILSAC performance level including Energy Conserving. For more information, see the latest version of API Publication No. 1509, Appendix Q "ILSAC Minimum Performance Standards for Passenger Car Engine Oils."

LUBRICANTS FOR TWO-STROKE-CYCLE GASOLINE ENGINES—SAE J1510 NOV2001

SAE Recommended Practice

Report of the SAE Fuels and Lubricants Technical Committee approved March 1983 and revised by the SAE Fuels and Lubricants Division October 1988. Completely revised by the SAE Fuels and Lubricants Technical Committee 6—Small Enine Lubricants August 1995. Reaffirmed by the SAE Fuels and Lubricants Technical Committee 1—Engine Lubricants of the SAE Fuels and Lubricants Division November 2001. Rationale statement available.

1. Scope—The information in this SAE Recommended Practice has been compiled by Technical Committee 1 (Engine Lubricants) of the SAE Fuels and Lubricants Division. The intent is to provide those concerned with the design and maintenance of two-stroke-cycle engines with a better understanding of the properties of two-stroke-cycle lubricants. Reference is also made to test procedures which may be used to measure the chemical and physical characteristics of these lubricants.

2. References

2.1 Applicable Publications—The following publications form a part of this specification to the extent specified herein. The latest issue of SAE publications shall apply.

2.1.1 SAE PUBLICATION—Available from SAE, 400 Commonwealth Drive, Warrendale, PA 15096-0001.

SAE J1536—Two-Stroke-Cycle Engine Oil Fluidity/Miscibility Classification

2.1.2 ASTM PUBLICATIONS—Available from ASTM, 100 Barr Harbor Drive, West Conshohocken, PA 19428-2959.

ASTM D 93—Test Methods for Flash Point by Pensky-Martens Closed Tester

ASTM D 874—Test Method for Sulfated Ash from Lubricating Oils and Additives

ASTM D 3607—Method for Removing Volatile Contaminants from Used Engine Oils by Stripping

ASTM D 4682-87—Specification for Miscibility with Gasoline and the Fluidity of Two-Stroke-Cycle Gasoline Engine Lubricants

3. Lubricant Classification—At the present time, two-stroke-cycle engine and lubricant manufacturers use a variety of engine and bench tests to define lubricant performance. For example, for several years the National Marine Manufacturers Association (NMMA) has been approving oils for water-cooled, two-stroke-cycle outboard engines. Products with this approval bear a NMMA TC-W3® or TC-W II® logo.

The value of a universal classification for all two-stroke-cycle lubricants is widely accepted. SAE, JASO, NMMA, ASTM, and CEC are currently developing such a system, encompassing several categories. It will aid in the correct labeling and application of these oils and will classify them according to their relative performance, but not necessarily their suitability in a given engine or application.

4. Engine Applications—Two-stroke-cycle engines are used in many applications with a broad range of specific power outputs. Water-cooled outboard engines with displacements to 4000 cc are not uncommon. At the other end of the scale are air-cooled engines for power tools, with displacements of 30 cc or less. In between are engines with various displacements and specific outputs. Typically, they are used to power motorbikes, lawn mowers, motorcycles, small tractors, chainsaws and other hand-held equipment, portable generators or pumps, snowmobiles, personal watercraft, etc.

5. Lubrication Systems—Two approaches to two-stroke-cycle engine lubrication are common:

a. Pre-mixing, in which the lubricant is added to the fuel either in the fuel tank or before it is put in the fuel tank
b. Injection, in which the lubricant is metered directly into the intake manifold or other points using a pump that is controlled by engine speed and/or throttle setting or where the lubricant is metered into the gasoline between the fuel tank and the engine

Use of oil injection systems is increasing. In addition to being more convenient, the injection system optimizes lubricant delivery rates over varying power and speed ranges.

6. Fuel:Oil Ratios—The ratio of fuel to oil depends on the engine, the application, and the lubricant. A fuel-to-oil ratio of 50:1 is often specified by both engine manufacturers and lubricant marketers for oils such as those used in large outboard engines. However, higher ratios, for example, 100:1, are sometimes recommended. Ratios as low as 16:1 are sometimes specified for use in air-cooled engines.

Variable ratios are characteristic of lube-injection systems. In one lube-injected snowmobile, for example, the ratio varies from 100:1 at idle to 24:1 at wide open throttle (WOT).

7. Lubricant Role—Two-stroke-cycle gasoline engines typically utilize "once through" lubrication. In any application, the lubricant is expected to protect the engine from wear, scuffing, ring sticking, piston deposits, and rust. It must do so without causing excessive plug fouling, pre-ignition, detonation, or exhaust system blockage. If the engine is lube-injected, the lubricant should continue to flow from the reservoir to the injection pump at the lowest ambient temperature expected in the application for which the lubricant is intended.

8. Oil Composition—With the wide variety of two-stroke-cycle engines and uses, one lubricant composition may not be optimum for all applications. However, two-stroke-cycle engine lubricants, like other lubricant classes, do have features in common. The base oils are most often petroleum derived but can be synthetic or part synthetic containing base fluid components such as ester and polyisobutene. Frequently, a portion of the base oil is a high viscosity component such as bright stock. Most oils contain an additive package to improve engine cleanliness. Many contain a hydrocarbon diluent to improve the miscibility (rate of mixing) with gasoline and the fluidity (flow) at low ambient temperatures. Some two-stroke-cycle engine lubricants also contain a pour depressant.

For some applications, for example, large outboard engines, where WOT operation for extended periods is common practice, the cleanliness additives must be essentially ashless to avoid pre-ignition and detonation. However, most lubricants, especially those designed for air-cooled engines, contain ash-forming components to control ring zone deposits at high-operating temperatures. Some modern air-cooled engines perform best with oils containing a mixture of ashless and ash-forming components.

9. Physical and Chemical Properties

9.1 Fluidity and Miscibility—The rheological requirements for two-stroke-cycle engine lubricants do not include viscosity exclusively. Lubricants must also have the ability to mix into gasoline and/or flow at the prevailing ambient temperature.

SAE J1536 and the supporting ASTM standard specification D 4682, describe four grades of two-stroke-cycle engine lubricants according to rheological properties.

9.2 Rust—The ability of the oil to prevent internal engine corrosion during shut-down is critical. The NMMA TC-W II® or TC-W3® standards provide a laboratory test procedure whereby the rust inhibiting properties of an oil in the presence of a brine solution can be established.

9.3 Stability and Compatibility—It is imperative that oils intended for use in lube-injected engines remain homogeneous over a broad range of ambient temperatures for extended periods of time. Otherwise, filter plugging and engine damage due to oil starvation may occur. Therefore, oils should be inspected to ensure that they are free of gel, sediment, particulates, immiscible liquids, etc. The NMMA TC-W3® specification requires that products demonstrate compatibility with commonly available two-stroke cycle outboard lubricants.

Lubricants must remain fluid when contaminated with small amounts of water. Lubricants which are individually satisfactory may not be so when mixed with other oils.

9.4 Pour Point—Two-stroke-cycle engine lubricants are usually pour depressed to ensure adequate dispensability over extended periods of time at lower ambient temperatures. The degree of pour depression, which varies depending on the intended applications, can be established using method ASTM D 97.

9.5 Solvent Content—The solvent content of a two-stroke-cycle engine lubricant can be established by using ASTM D 3607. However, because the solvent levels are considerably higher than the fuel contents of used oils, the stripping time should be extended 6 h.

9.6 Ash Content—The amount of ash formed from burning a two-stroke-cycle engine lubricant may be obtained by ASTM D 874. As noted in Section 8, some engines do not perform satisfactorily with ash-forming lubricants, while others benefit from them.

9.7 Elemental Analysis—The elemental analysis of lubricants containing ash-forming additives can be established using such techniques as emission spectroscopy, X-ray fluorescence, etc. The level of metal detergents can be determined using one of these methods.

The additive level of ashless two-stroke-cycle oils generally can be determined by an analysis for elemental nitrogen.

9.8 Flash Point—The flash point of solvent-diluted two-stroke-cycle engine lubricants can be quite low, for example, in the range of 40 to 65 °C (104 to 149 °F) by ASTM D 93. Such lubricants may be classified as "combustible liquids." This has obvious safety implications in terms of lubricant manufacturing, storage, packaging, or shipment.

9.9 Color—Many two-stroke-cycle engine lubricants are dyed to help establish that the oil has been mixed with gasoline prior to use. The intensity of the color should, therefore, be high enough to ensure a light, but readily visible, color after mixing. Because of the possibility of confusion with transmission fluids, it is recommended that a dye color other than red be used. Blue and green are common.

TWO-STROKE-CYCLE ENGINE OIL FUIDITY/MISCIBILITY CLASSIFICATION—SAE J1536 NOV2001

SAE Recommended Practice

Report of the SAE Fuels and Lubricants Division approved October 1988. Completely revised by the SAE Fuels and Lubricants Technical Committee 6—Small Engine Lubricants, August 1995. Revised by the SAE Fuels and Lubricants Technical Committee 1—Engine Lubricants of the SAE Fuels and Lubricants Division November 2001. Rationale statement available.

1. Scope—This SAE Recommended Practice is intended for use by engine manufacturers in determining the Fluidity/Miscibility Grades to be recommended for use in their engines, and by oil marketers in formulating and labeling their products.

2. References

2.1 Applicable Publications—The following publications form a part of this specification to the extent specified herein.

2.1.1 ASTM PUBLICATIONS—Available from ASTM, 100 Barr Harbor Drive, West Conshohocken, PA 19428-2959.

ASTM D 4682—Specification for Miscibility With Gasoline and Fluidity of Two-Stroke-Cycle Gasoline Engine Lubricants

ASTM D 4857—Test Method for Determination of the Ability of Lubricants to Minimize Ring Sticking and Piston Deposits in Two-Stroke-Cycle Gasoline Engines Other Than Outboards

ASTM D 4858—Test Method for Determination of the Tendency of Lubricants to Promote Preignition in Two-Stroke-Cycle Gasoline Engines

ASTM D 4859—Specification for Lubricants for Two-Stroke-Cycle Spark-Ignition Gasoline Engines—TC

ASTM D 4863—Test Method for Determination of the Lubricity of Two-Stroke Gasoline Engine Lubricants

3. The SAE Fluidity/Miscibility Grades defined in Tables 1 and 2 constitute a classification for two-stroke-cycle engine lubricating oils in rheological terms only. Other oil characteristics are not considered or included.

Fluidity and Miscibility are measured according to test procedures described in ASTM D 4682-87. These test procedures relate to the two common methods for introducing lubricating oils into two-stroke-cycle engines as defined in Table 3.

Most oils will meet the requirements of one of the grades. In labeling an oil with its Fluidity/Miscibility Grade, only the highest grade may be referred to on the label.

Listed are all documents which have been published in support of the Two-Stroke Engine Oil Fluidity/Miscibility Classification and the Two-Stroke Engine Oil Performance and Service Classification. In brief, they are:

a. Fluidity/Miscibility—SAE J1536 and ASTM D 4682
b. Performance/Service TC (Formerly TSC-3)—ASTM D 4859, 4857, 4858, 4863

TABLE 1—SAE MISCIBILITY GRADES FOR TWO-STROKE-CYCLE ENGINE OILS

Grade	Test Temperature °C(1)	Reference(2) Oil
1	0	VI-GG
2	–10	VI-FF
3	–25	VI-D
4	–40	VI-II

1. Both Miscibility and Brookfield tests must be run on a candidate oil at the temperature intended for qualification.
2. Miscibility revolutions on the candidate oil must not exceed those on the reference oil by more than 10% to qualify under a grade.

TABLE 2—SAE FLUIDITY GRADES FOR TWO-STROKE-CYCLE ENGINE OILS

Grade	Test Temperature °C(1)	Maximum Viscosity cP(2)	Reference Oil(3)	Reference Oil Limits cP(2)
1	0	3 500	N74B	3 250 - 3 600
2	–10	3 500	N38B	2 900 - 3 300
3	–25	7 500	N25B	7 600 - 8 700
4	–40	17 000	N14B	16 000 - 18 000

1. Both Miscibility and Brookfield tests must be run on a candidate oil at the temperature intended for qualification.
2. Brookfield viscosity in centipoise on the candidate oil must not exceed the maximum limit as shown for each temperature. The test must be monitored by running a reference oil with each set of tests (same freezer, same time), and the reference oil result must be within the set limits.
3. Available from Cannon Instrument Company,

TABLE 3—RHEOLOGICAL TEST PROCEDURES FOR TWO-STROKE-CYCLE ENGINE OILS

Test Procedure	Lubricating Oil Introduction By	Location
Miscibility	Mixture with fuel	In fuel tank or fuel line
Fluidity	Lube injection	Into air/fuel or fuel stream or at other points

TWO-STROKE-CYCLE GASOLINE ENGINE LUBRICANTS PERFORMANCE AND SERVICE CLASSIFICATION—SAE J2116 JUL2003

SAE Standard

Report of the SAE Fuels and Lubricants Technical Committee 6—Small Engine Lubricants approved October 1990. Rationale statement available. This standard contains API letter designation that are compatable with ISO nomenclature. Revised by the SAE Fuels and Lubricants Technical Committee 6—Small Engine Lubricants June 1993. Rationale statement available. Revised by the SAE Fuels and Lubricants Technical Committee 1—Engine Lubrication July 2003. Rationale statement available.

Foreword—This Document has also changed to comply with the new SAE Technical Standards Board format.

1. Scope—This SAE Standard was prepared by Technical Committee 1, Engine Lubrication, of SAE Fuels and Lubricants Council. The intent is to improve communications among engine manufacturers, engine users, and lubricant marketers in describing lubricant performance characteristics. The key objective is to ensure that a correct lubricant is used in each two-stroke-cycle engine.

1.1 Background—SAE J1510 previewed the cooperative effort of SAE, ASTM, API, and CEC in developing a universal classification for engine performance. SAE J1510 provides a great deal of information on the properties of two-stroke-cycle lubricants.

SAE J1536 is a classification in rheological terms only. SAE J1536 is a companion classification to SAE J2116. By use of both SAE J1536 and SAE J2116, any lubricant can be classified in terms of both rheology and engine performance.

2. References

2.1 Applicable Publications—The following publications form a part of the specification to the extent specified herein. Unless otherwise indicated the latest revision of SAE publications shall apply.

2.1.1 SAE PUBLICATIONS—Available from SAE, 400 Commonwealth Drive, Warrendale, PA 15096-0001.

SAE J1510—Lubricants for Two-Stroke-Cycle Gasoline Engines

SAE J1536—Two-Stroke-Cycle Oil Miscibility/Fluidity Classification

2.1.2 ASTM PUBLICATIONS—Available from ASTM, 100 Barr Harbor Drive, West Conshohocken, PA 19428-2959.

ASTM D 4681—Specification for Lubricants for Two-Stroke-Cycle Gasoline Engines (TSC-4)

ASTM D 4857—Test Method for Determination of the Ability of Lubricants to Minimize Ring Sticking and Piston Deposits in Two-Stroke-Cycle Gasoline Engines Other Than Outboards

ASTM D 4858—Test Method for Determination of the Tendency of Lubricants to Promote Preignition in Two-Stroke-Cycle Gasoline Engines

ASTM D 4859—Specification for Lubricants for Two-Stroke-Cycle Spark-Ignition Gasoline Engines - TC

ASTM D 4863—Test Method for Determination of Lubricity of Two-Stroke-Cycle Gasoline Engine Lubricants

2.1.3 NATIONAL MARINE MANUFACTURERS PUBLICATION—Available from NMMA, 401 North Michigan, Chicago, IL 60611.

TC-W3

3. Performance Characteristics—There are a number of engine test rating areas which are indicative of the contribution of a lubricant to the proper performance and durability of a two-stroke-cycle engine. In each category within this classification, the relevant rating areas are given numerical limits which permit assignment of a pass or fail to the performance of a lubricant. These areas include:

a. Ring sticking
b. Varnish (which may include piston skirts, lands, and undercrowns)
c. Preignition
d. Scuffing
e. Exhaust system blockage

Table 1 relates these performance characteristics to the critical lubrication requirements of each of the four Performance and Service categories. To assist in understanding the purpose of each category, normal engine service applications are also provided.

4. Performance Criteria—Table 2 summarizes the ASTM standard test methods, test engines, primary performance criteria, and status for each category.

TABLE 1—PERFORMANCE AND SERVICE CLASSIFICATION TWO-STROKE-CYCLE GASOLINE ENGINE LUBRICANTS CRITICAL LUBRICATION REQUIREMENTS AND NORMAL SERVICE

API Letter Designation	Critical Lubrication Requirements	Normal Engine Service Applications
TA	• Piston Scuffing • Exhaust System Blocking	Mopeds and other Extremely Small Engines (Typically <50 cc)
TB	• Piston Scuffing • Deposit-Induced Preignition • Power Loss due to Combustion Chamber Deposits	Motorscooters and other Highly Loaded Small Engines (Typically 50 cc to 200 cc)
TC	• Ring Sticking • Deposit-Induced Preignition • Piston Scuffing	Various High-Performance Engines (Not Outboards) (Typically 20 cc to 500 cc)
TD	• Piston Scuffing • Ring Sticking • Deposit-Induced Preignition	Outboard Engines

TABLE 2—PERFORMANCE AND SERVICE CLASSIFICATION TWO-STROKE-CYCLE GASOLINE ENGINE LUBRICANTS TEST METHODS AND PRIMARY CANDIDATE OIL PERFORMANCE CRITERIA

Letter Designation	Status	ASTM(1) Designation	Test Engine	Primary Performance Criteria	
TA	Obsolete(2) as of MAR93	Not yet assigned	Yamaha CE50S	Tightening—Method in preparation Exhaust Blocking—Method in preparation	
TB	Obsolete(3) as of MAR93	Not applicable	Vespa 125TS	Tightening—Method never developed Preignition—Method never developed Power Loss—Method never developed	
TC		D 4859	Covers Category TC comprehensively, including Primary Performance Criteria		
		D 4857	Yamaha RD 350B	Ring Sticking/Deposits In Two (crossover) test runs	
				Second Ring Sticking, Avg Prior to 1999	0.5 Max below ASTM Reference Oil Specified in D 4857
				1999 and later	0.5 Max below ASTM Reference Oil Specified in D 4857, after application of industry correction factor
				Piston Skirt Varnish, Avg.	0.5 Max below Reference Oil
				Plug Fouls	2 Max above Reference Oil
				Preignition (major)	1 Max per run

TABLE 2—PERFORMANCE AND SERVICE CLASSIFICATION TWO-STROKE-CYCLE GASOLINE ENGINE LUBRICANTS TEST METHODS AND PRIMARY CANDIDATE OIL PERFORMANCE CRITERIA (continued)

Letter Designation	Status	ASTM[1] Designation	Test Engine	Primary Performance Criteria	
				Exhaust Blocking	10% Max above Reference Oil
				Scuff/Seizure	None
				In one (without crossover) test run	
				Second Ring Sticking, Avg.	9.0 Min
				Piston Skirt Varnish, Avg.	Absolutely equal or better than Reference Oil
				Plug Fouls	1 Max
				Preignition	None
				Exhaust Blocking	5% Max above Reference Oil
				Scuff or other Lube-related damage	None
		D 4858	Yamaha CE50S	Preignition	
				Preignitions (major)	1 Max
				Other	See D 4859, Paras 6.4.2 and 6.4.3
		D 4863	Yamaha CE50S	Lubricity	
				Torque Drop	No more than reference oil within 90% confidence limit
TD	Obsolete[4] as of MAR83	D 4681[5]	OMC 90 HP	Outboard Lubrication	
				Accelerated Lubricity	No piston scuff or significant bore damage
				Top Ring Sticking, Avg.	Not more than 1.0 points below reference oil engine
				Piston Varnish, Avg.	Not more than 0.5 points below reference oil engine
				Preignition	No more in reference oil engine
				Plug Fouling	Max of one more than in reference oil engine
				Exhaust Port Blocking	Max of 10% more than in reference oil engine

1. Latest version of the ASTM designation should be used.
2. CEC withdrew support for this category.
3. Test sponsor no longer desired this oil category.
4. This category has been superseded and is no longer recommended by the National Marine Manufacturers Association.
5. The engine test in this Standard Specification is identical to that in National Marine Manufacturers (NMMA) TC-W3.

(R) AXLE AND MANUAL TRANSMISSION LUBRICANTS—SAE J308 JAN1996

SAE Information Report

Report of the SAE Lubricants Division approved February 1924. Completly revised by the SAE Fuels and Lubricants Technical Committee June 1989. Completely revised by the SAE Fuels and Lubricants Technical Committee3—Gear Lubricants, January 1996.

Foreword—This Document has not changed other than to put it into the new SAE Technical Standards Board Format.

In 1943, the U.S. Army Ordnance Department (currently U.S. Army Belvoir Research, Development and Engineering Center) began qualifying gear lubricants against U.S. Army Specification 2–105. This specification has gone through several revisions and is now identified as MIL-L-2105D. The American Petroleum Institute recognizes gear lubricants meeting this latter specification as API Service GL-5 (API GL-5).

In 1977, the U.S. Army terminated direct sponsorship of the qualification process and contracted with SAE to: (a) perform the reviewing activity, and (b) make recommendations relative to the acceptance of candidate products under the military gear lubricant specification. In accordance with its contract with SAE, the U.S. Army retains sole responsibility for approving and qualifying products to its specification.

Following termination of the U.S. Army sponsorship, the SAE Board of Directors established a Lubricants Review Institute (LRI), which in turn has established an LRI Gear Lubricant Review Committee. This committee developed procedures for submitting candidate lubricants for review as well as procedures for reviewing such lubricants. The LRI activities are reviewed by SAE Legal Counsel to ensure compliance with applicable federal and state laws. The LRI Gear Lubricant Review Procedures can be obtained from SAE headquarters in Warrendale, PA.

1. Scope—This SAE Information Report was prepared by the SAE Fuels and Lubricants Technical Committee for two purposes: (a) to assist the users of automotive equipment in the selection of axle[1] and manual transmission lubricants for field use, and (b) to promote a uniform practice for use by marketers of lubricants and by equipment builders in identifying and recommending these lubricants by a service designation.

2. References

2.1 Applicable Publications—The following publications form a part of the specification to the extent specified herein. Unless otherwise indicated the lastest revision of SAE publications shall apply.

2.1.1 SAE PUBLICATIONS—Available from SAE, 400 Commonwealth Drive, Warrendale, PA 15096-0001.

SAE J306—Axle and Manual Transmission Lubricant Viscosity Classification
LRI Gear Lubricant Review Procedures

2.1.2 ASTM PUBLICATIONS—Available from ASTM, 100 Barr Harbor Drive, West Conshohocken, PA 19428-2959.

ASTM D 130—Method for Detection of Copper Corrosion from Petroleum Products by the Copper Strip Tarnish Test
ASTM D 445—Test Method for Kinematic Viscosity of Transparent and Opaque Liquids (and the Calculation of Dynamic Viscosity)
ASTM D 471—Test Method for Rubber Property—Effect of Liquids
ASTM D 892—Test Method for Foaming Characteristics of Lubricating Oils
ASTM D 2983—Test Method for Oxidation Characteristics of Extreme Pressure Lubricating Oils
ASTM D 5182—Test Method for Evaluating the Scuffing (Scoring) Load Capacity of Oils
ASTM D 5579—Test Method for Evaluating the Thermal Stability of Manual Transmission Lubricants in a Cyclic Durability Test
ASTM D 5662—Test Method for Determining Automotive Gear Oil Compatibility with Typical Oil Seal Elastomers
ASTM D 5704—Test Method for Evaluation of the Thermal and Oxidative Stability of Lubricating Oils Used for Manual Transmissions and Final Drive Axles
ASTM STP 512—Laboratory Test Performance for Automotive Gear Lubricants Intended for API GL-5 Service (March, 1987)

2.1.3 API PUBLICATION—Available from American Petroleum Institute, 1220 L Street, Northwest, Washington, DC 20005.

API 1560 (July, 1995)—Lubricant Service Designation for Automotive Manual Transmissions and Axles

2.1.4 CRC PUBLICATIONS—Available from Coordinating Research Council Incorporated, 219 Perimeter Center Parkway, Suite 400, Atlanta, GA 30346-1301.

CRC L-12—Performance Test
CRC L-13—Performance Test
CRC L-19—Performance Test
CRC L-20—Performance Test
CRC L-21—Performance Test
CRC L-33—Performance Test
CRC L-37—Performance Test
CRC L-42—Performance Test
CRC L-60—Performance Test
Coordinating Research Council Manual 17

2.1.5 MILITARY PUBLICATION—Available from DODSSP, Subscription Services Desk, Building 4D, 700 Robbins Avenue, Philadelphia, PA 19111-5094.

MIL-L-2105D

3. Performance Characteristics—In axles and manual transmissions, gears and bearings of different designs are employed under a variety of service conditions. Therefore, the selection of a lubricant involves careful consideration of the performance characteristics required. The following sections describe performance characteristics of axle and manual transmission lubricants which are important in field service. A lubricant is a blend of base stocks and additives optimized for a particular service. Additive packages are available to enhance base stock performance for each performance characteristic.

3.1 Load-Carrying Capacity—One of the most important performance characteristics is load-carrying capacity. The load on gear teeth is a function of the contact area of, and the force applied to the surfaces in contact. Contact area is controlled by gear design; applied force is determined by the power needed to drive the equipment. The load-carrying capacity of a gear lubricant is defined by the maximum load which can be sustained by the lubricant without failure of gear teeth surfaces. If the load-carrying capacity is exceeded, the lubricant fails to protect the gears and the gear teeth become damaged. The most common forms of damage are adhesive wear (scuffing) and scoring.

Load-carrying capacity is determined by a fluid's viscosity at the operating temperature, and by additives. Gear lubricants compounded to achieve increased load-carrying capacity may be referred to as "extreme pressure" (EP) lubricants. However, when this term is applied to a gear lubricant, it means only that the load-carrying capacity of the lubricant is greater than that of untreated oil,[2] with no distinction as to how much greater it may be. The American Petroleum Institute (API) has developed a classification system which addresses this concern (See section 5).

3.2 Viscosity—Viscosity specifications are generally determined by equipment manufacturers. Refer to SAE J306 for axle and manual transmission lubricant viscosity classification information.

3.2.1 VISCOSITY LOSS—MULTIGRADE LUBRICANTS—Viscosity and film thickness are critical in both axle and transmission applications. Some multigrade gear lubricants are formulated with viscosity modifiers. Caution should be exercised when multigrade gear lubricants are used, since these may experience significant viscosity loss due to shear in field service. The shear stresses and shear rates encountered in gear applications can be significantly greater than those in most other lubricant applications.

3.3 Thermal Stability and Oxidation Resistance—Factors affecting thermal stability (cleanliness) and oxidation (thickening) characteristics while the lubricant is in service include ambient temperature, duty cycle, length of service, and the effects of contamination. Poor lubricant performance can result in oil thickening and/or the formation of deposits on parts. Even when lubricants are stored (prior to use), care should be exercised to ensure that they are not exposed to extreme temperatures and are kept free of contaminants. These precautions are intended to ensure optimum lubricant life.

Modern vehicle designs have resulted in significantly higher operating temperatures in axles and transmissions. Oils which do not have a high degree of thermal stability and oxidation resistance can form significant carbon and varnish deposits, which can cause premature seal failure.

1. Axle in this document is defined as a drive axle incorporating reduction gearing and/or differential gears.

2. Untreated oil is defined as either refined petroluem or synthetic lubricant base oil containing no supplemental performance additives.

For automotive axles and transmissions in mild service, the temperature of the lubricant may not be sufficiently high to cause significant oxidation. For vehicles operating in moderate to severe conditions of service such as passenger cars pulling trailers, or for trucks or buses in service where higher temperatures occur, thermal stability and oxidation resistance are important factors. Accordingly, only oils with a high degree of thermal stability and oxidation resistance should be used in these applications. The vehicle operator should consult the manufacturer's service guide for drain and refill recommendations.

3.4 Foaming—Excessive foaming may interfere with proper lubrication of gear and bearing surfaces and, consequently, should be avoided. Further, foaming can cause leakage via normal venting passages, thereby reducing lubricant sump volume.

3.5 Corrosion—Corrosion is a chemical reaction of a metal surface with an oil contaminant or a by-product of used oil degradation which produces a surface film and/or soluble metal salts. Corrosion of ferrous or copper-containing metals can result in a build-up of iron and copper in the oil, leading to decreased oxidation resistance (see 3.3). As defined by the Coordinating Research Council, corrosion is "a general alteration of the finished surfaces accompanied by roughing **not** attributable to mechanical action."

Excessive corrosion of heavy-duty components can lead to: (a) the reduction of designed contact areas, (b) an increase in insoluble debris, and (c) excessive movement ("play") of corroded components.

3.5.1 RUSTING—Rusting is a special case of corrosion of ferrous metals in the presence of water. Rust deteriorates or alters the original metal surface. It is evidenced by at least two of the following characteristics:

a. Color (usually red, yellow, brown, or black)
b. Depth (build-up or depression relative to adjacent areas)
c. Texture (such as etching or scale)

(See Coordinating Research Council Manual 17, Section 9—Miscellaneous)

3.6 Seal Compatibility—While the primary function of a gear lubricant is to protect gears and bearings, consideration must be given to the effect of a lubricant on seal elastomers used in the design of the component. Factors that can lead to early seal failure are loss of elongation or the ability to follow the shaft; change in hardness, which can lead to cracking; and volume change or swell, causing increased seal wear. Immersion testing, at conditions specific for axles and transmissions, may be used to establish the relative compatibility of the lubricant and the seal material.

4. Use and Handling of Gear Lubricants

4.1 Mixing Gear Lubricants—As a general practice, the mixing of lubricant types should be avoided. Specifically, mixing gear lubricants with engine oils can result in incompatibility due to reactions between the additive chemicals. Such reactions may result in a significant loss of performance or gear protection.

The mixing of MIL-L-2105 approved lubricants as in a top-up situation should not impair lubricant performance. MIL-L-2105 lubricants are required to demonstrate satisfactory storage stability when mixed with previously qualified gear lubricants.

5. API Gear Lubricant Classification—The following designations have been amended with the objective of improving user understanding of intended lubricant application. Refer to API Publication 1560, July 1995, for further information.

5.1 Inactive Categories—The following categories were declared inactive by SAE Technical Committee 3 on March 1, 1995. Oils may be marketed with these designations. However, ASTM does not plan to maintain the performance tests associated with these categories. In some cases these tests can no longer be run because parts or test installations are not available.

5.1.1 API GL-1 designates the type of service characteristic of manual transmissions operating under such mild conditions of low unit pressures and minimum sliding velocities, that untreated oil may be used satisfactorily. Oxidation and rust inhibitors, defoamers, and pour depressants may be used to improve the characteristics of lubricants intended for this service. Friction modifiers and extreme pressure additives shall not be used.

Due to the speeds and loads involved, untreated oil is generally not a satisfactory lubricant for many passenger car manual transmissions.[3] For some truck and tractor manual transmissions, untreated oils may be used successfully. In all cases, the transmission manufacturers' specific lubricant recommendations should be followed.

5.1.2 API GL-2 designates the type of service characteristic of automotive type worm-gear axles operating under such conditions of load, temperature, and sliding velocities, that lubricants satisfactory for API GL-1 service will not suffice.

Products suited for this type of service contain antiwear or very mild extreme-pressure agents which provide protection for worm gears.

5.1.3 API GL-3 designates the type of service characteristic of manual transmissions and spiral-bevel axles operating under mild to moderate to severe conditions of speed and load. These service conditions require a lubricant having load-carrying capacities greater than those that will satisfy API GL-1 service, but below the requirements of lubricants satisfying the API GL-4 service.

Gear lubricants designated for API GL-3 service are not intended for hypoid gear applications.

5.1.4 API GL-6 designates the type of service characteristic of gears designed with a very high pinion offset. Such designs typically require (gear) score protection in excess of that provided by API GL-5 gear oils. The original API GL-6 test equipment is obsolete.

5.2 Active Categories

5.2.1 API GL-4 designates the type of service characteristic of spiral-bevel and hypoid[4] gears in automotive axles operated under moderate-speeds and loads. These oils may be used in selected manual transmission and transaxle applications. (Users should consult axle/transmission manufacturers' specific lubricant recommendations.)

While this service designation is still used commercially to describe lubricants, some test equipment used for performance verification is no longer available. SAE is reviewing the performance requirements of this category.

5.2.2 API GL-5 designates the type of service characteristic of gears, particularly hypoids in automotive axles operated under high-speed and/or low-speed, high-torque conditions. Lubricants qualified under U.S. Military specification MIL-L-2105D (formerly MIL-L-2105C) satisfy the requirements of the API GL-5 service designation. Details of the API GL-5 performance tests are contained in ASTM Publication STP-512A.

5.2.3 API MT-1 designates lubricants intended for non-synchronized manual transmissions used in buses and heavy-duty trucks. Lubricants meeting API MT-1 provide protection against the combination of thermal degradation, component wear, and oil seal deterioration which is not provided by lubricants meeting only the requirements of API GL-4 and GL-5.

API MT-1 does not address the performance requirements of synchronized transmissions and transaxles in passenger cars and heavy-duty applications.

API MT-1 lubricants should not be mixed with engine oils in the same transmission unit.

Transmission manufacturers' specific lubricant quality recommendations should be followed.

5.3 Performance Tests—Table 1 lists lubricant tests which are used to evaluate the performance characteristics discussed in Section 3. Tests which are used to define the performance levels of active API Categories are noted.

Successful performance on such tests does not automatically ensure satisfactory performance under field service conditions.

5.3.1 REFERENCE OILS—Most tests used to define performance for the API gear oil categories are calibrated using selected reference oils. These oils are maintained by the ASTM Surveillance Panels which are responsible for the tests. The testing and inventory of these oils is carried out by the ASTM Test Monitoring Center. The oils are normally available only to laboratories which maintain or are qualifying test stands which are certified for LRI approval testing of oils. Information about reference oils can be obtained by contacting the Test Monitoring Center, 4400 Fifth Avenue, Pittsburgh, PA 15213 (Phone: 412-268-3315).

---

3. Automatic or semiautomatic transmissions, fluid couplings, torque converters, and tractor hydraulic systems usually require special lubricants. For the proper lubricant to be used, consult the equipment manufacturer or lubricant supplier.
4. Friction requirements for axles equipped with limited slip differentials are normally defined by the axle manufacturer.

TABLE 1—LUBRICANT TESTS FOR EVALUATING PERFORMANCE CHARACTERISTICS

Performance Characteristic	Test Method	Method Reference	Required for API Category	Note
Load Carrying Capacity	• Gear Distress - Low Speed, High Load	L-37	GL-5	4
		CRC L-20	GL-4	
	• Gear Scoring - High-Speed Shock Load	L-42	GL-5	4
		CRC L-19	GL-4	1
	• Spur Gear Scuffing Load	ASTM D 5182	MT-1	
Viscosity	• Kinematic Viscosity	ASTM D 445		2
	• Low Temperature (Brookfield) Viscosity	ASTM D 2983		2
Thermal Stability and Oxidation Resistance	• Thermal and Oxidative Stability Test	L-60	GL-5	4
	• Thermal and Oxidative Stability/Component Cleanliness	ASTM D 5704	MT-1	
	• High-Temperature Cyclic Durability	ASTM D 5579	MT-1	
Foaming	• Foaming Characteristics	CRC L-12	GL-4	1
		ASTM D 892	GL-5, MT-1	
Corrosion Resistance	• Copper Strip Tarnish Test	ASTM D 130	GL-4, GL-5, MT-1	
	• Corrosion Resistance in the Presence of Water	CRC L-13	GL-4	1
		CRC L-21	GL-4	1
		L-33	GL-5	4
Seal Compatibility	• Compatibility with Automotive Seal Materials	ASTM D 5662	MT-1	3
Lubricant Stability and Compatibility	• Storage Solubility Characteristics	FTM 3440.1	MT-1	
	• Compatibility Characteristics	FTM 3430.2	MT-1	

NOTE 1— Equipment no longer available. Impossible to conduct original test procedure. ASTM is considering replacement tests.
NOTE 2— Viscosity requirement varies by equipment manufacturer.
NOTE 3— ASTM D 5662 is a specific application of ASTM D 471.
NOTE 4— Test Method described in ASTM STP-512.

R) AUTOMOTIVE GEAR LUBRICANT VISCOSITY CLASSIFICATION—SAE J306 JUL1998

SAE Standard

Report of the SAE Lubricants Division, approved February 1924, last revised, SAE Fuels and Lubricants Division, March 1985. Reaffirmed by the SAE Fuels and Lubricants Technical Committee 3—Gear Lubricants October 1991 and completely revised July 1998.

1. Scope—This SAE Standard defines the limits for a classification of automotive gear lubricants in rheological terms only. Other lubricant characteristics are not considered.

2. References

2.1 Applicable Publications—The following publications form a part of this specification to the extent specified herein. The latest issue of ASTM and CEC publications shall apply.

2.1.1 ASTM PUBLICATIONS—Available from ASTM, 100 Barr Harbor Drive, West Conshohocken, PA 19428-2959.

ASTM D 445—Standard Test Method for Kinematic Viscosity of Transparent and Opaque Liquids (the Calculation of Dynamic Viscosity)

ASTM D 2983—Standard Test Method for Low-Temperature Viscosity of Automotive Fluid Lubricants Measured by Brookfield Viscometer

ASTM D 5293—Standard Test Method for Apparent Viscosity of Engine Oils Between –5 and –30°C Using the Cold-Cranking Simulator

2.1.2 CEC TEST METHODS—Available from Coordinating European Council, Madou Plaza, 25th Floor, Place Madou 1, B-1030 Brussels, Belgium

CEC Test Method CEC L-45-T-93—Viscosity Shear Stability of Transmission Lubricants (KRL – Tapered Roller Bearing Test Rig) Shear Stability Test, 1993.

3. Definitions—This SAE Standard is intended for use by equipment manufacturers in defining and recommending automotive gear, axle, and manual transmission lubricants, for oil marketers in labeling such lubricants with respect to their viscosity, and for users in following their owner's manual recommendations. The SAE viscosity grades shown in Table 1 constitute a classification for automotive gear, axle, and manual transmission lubricants in rheological terms only.

TABLE 1—AUTOMOTIVE GEAR LUBRICANT VISCOSITY CLASSIFICATION

SAE Viscosity Grade	Maximum Temperature for Viscosity of 150 000 cP, °C (1),(2)	Kinematic Viscosity at 100 °C, cSt(3) Minimum(4)	Kinematic Viscosity at 100 °C, cSt(3) Maximum
70W	–55(5)	4.1	—
75W	–40	4.1	—
80W	–26	7.0	—
85W	–12	11.0	—
80	—	7.0	<11.0
85	—	11.0	<13.5
90	—	13.5	<24.0
140	—	24.0	<41.0
250	—	41.0	—

Note—1 cP = 1 mPa s; 1 cSt = 1 mm²/s

1. Using ASTM D 2983.
2. Additional low-temperature viscosity requirements may be appropriate for fluids intended for use in light-duty synchronized manual transmissions. See text.
3. Using ASTM D 445
4. Limit must also be met after testing in CEC L-45-T-93, Method C (20 h).
5. The precision of ASTM D 2983 has not been established for determinations made at temperatures below –40 °C. This fact should be taken into consideration in any producer-consumer relationship.

This classification is based on the lubricant viscosity measured at both high and low temperatures. The high-temperature kinematic viscosity values are determined according to ASTM D 445, with the results reported in centistokes (cSt). The low-temperature viscosity values are determined according to ASTM D 2983 and these results are reported in centipoises (cP). These two viscosity units are related as follows in Equation 1:

$$\frac{\text{cP}}{\text{Density, g/cm}^3} = \text{cSt} \quad \text{(Eq. 1)}$$

Density is measured at the test temperature. This relationship is valid for Newtonian fluids; it is an approximation for non-Newtonian fluids.

High-temperature viscosity is related to the hydrodynamic lubrication characteristics of the fluid. Some gear lubricants may contain high molecular weight polymers, known as viscosity modifiers or viscosity index improvers, which function to increase the viscosity of the fluids. During use, these polymers may shear to a lower molecular weight, thereby resulting in a fluid with a lower viscosity than that of the new fluid. In order to ensure that the designated high-temperature viscosity grade is retained during use, lubricants must meet the 100 °C viscosity limits listed in Table 1 not only when new, but also following evaluation in CEC L-45-T-93, Viscosity Shear Stability of Transmission Lubricants, Method C (20 h).

Low-temperature viscosity requirements are related to the ability of the fluid to flow and provide adequate lubrication to critical parts under low ambient temperature conditions. The 150 000 cP viscosity value used for the definition of low-temperature properties is based on a series of tests in a specific rear axle design. These tests have shown that pinion bearing failure has occurred at viscosities higher than 150 000 cP and the Brookfield method was shown to give adequate precision at this viscosity level. However, it should be pointed out that other axle designs may tolerate higher viscosities or fail at lower viscosities.

Other applications may require additional low temperature limits. For example, shifting ease at low temperature in light-duty synchronized manual transmissions may be related to viscosity at higher shear rates than that provided by the Brookfield method. For such applications, use of the Cold Cranking Simulator (CCS) per ASTM D 5293 should be considered. A CCS viscosity of 5 000 cP, maximum, at –30 °C may ensure satisfactory low- temperature shiftability.

Automotive Gear lubricant SAE viscosity grades should not be confused with engine oil SAE viscosity grades. (Compare Table 1 in this report with Table 1 in SAE J300.) A gear lubricant and an engine oil having the same viscosity will have widely different SAE viscosity grade designations as defined in the two viscosity classifications. For instance, an SAE 75W gear lubricant can have the same kinematic viscosity at 100 °C as an SAE 10W engine oil; and an SAE 90 gear lubricant viscosity can be similar to that of an SAE 40 or SAE 50 engine oil.

4. Labeling—In properly describing the viscosity grade of an automotive gear lubricant according to this document, a lubricant may use one W grade numerical designation, one non-W grade numerical designation, or one W grade in combination with one non-W grade. In all cases, the numerical designation must be preceded by the letters "SAE." In addition, when both a W grade and a non-W grade are listed (multigrade) the W grade shall be listed first and the two designations shall be separated by a hyphen (i.e., SAE 80W-90). Other forms of punctuation or separation are not acceptable.

A lubricant which meets the requirements of both a low-temperature and a high-temperature grade is commonly known as a multiviscosity-grade lubricant. For example, an SAE 80W-90 lubricant must meet the low-temperature requirements for SAE 80W and the high-temperature requirements for SAE 90. Since the W grade is defined on the basis of maximum temperature for a Brookfield viscosity of 150 000 cP and minimum kinematic viscosity at 100 °C, it is possible for a lubricant to satisfy the requirements of more than one W grade. In labeling either a W grade or a multiviscosity grade lubricant, only the lowest W grade satisfied may be referred to on the label. Thus, a lubricant meeting the requirements of both SAE 75W and SAE 85W as well as SAE 90, would be labeled as an SAE 75W-90, and not SAE 75W-85W-90.

AUTOMOTIVE LUBRICATING GREASES —SAE J310 JAN2000

SAE Recommended Practice

Report of the SAE Fuels and Lubricants Technical Committee approved September 1951, and revised August 1987. Completely revised by the SAE Fuels and Lubricants Technical Committee 4—Lubricating Greases, April 1990 and June 1993, and revised May 1997 and January 2000.

1. Scope—This SAE Recommended Practice was developed by SAE, and the section "Standard Classification and Specification for Service Greases" cooperatively with ASTM, and NLGI. It is intended to assist those concerned with the design of automotive components, and with the selection and marketing of greases for the lubrication of certain of those components on passenger cars, trucks, and buses. The information contained herein will be helpful in understanding the terms related to properties, designations, and service applications of automotive greases.

2. References

2.1 Applicable Publications—The following publications form a part of this specification to the extent specified herein. Unless otherwise specified, the latest issue of SAE publications shall apply.

2.1.1 SAE PUBLICATIONS—Available from SAE, 400 Commonwealth Drive, Warrendale, PA 15096-0001.

SAE AMS 3217A—Standard Elastomer Stock - Test Slabs
SAE AMS 3217/2A—Test Slabs, Acrylonitrile Butadiene (NBR-L) - Low Acrylonitrile, 65-75
SAE AMS 3217/3B—Test Slabs, Chloroprene (CR) - 67-75

2.1.2 ASTM PUBLICATIONS—Available from ASTM, 100 Barr Harbor Drive, West Conshohocken, PA 19428-2959.

ASTM D 128—Analysis of Lubricating Grease
ASTM D 217—Cone Penetration of Lubricating Grease
ASTM D 566—Dropping Point of Lubricating Grease
ASTM D 942—Oxidation Stability of Lubricating Greases by the Oxygen Bomb Method
ASTM D 972—Evaporation Loss of Lubricating Greases and Oils
ASTM D 1092—Apparent Viscosity of Lubricating Greases
ASTM D 1263—Leakage Tendencies of Automotive Wheel Bearing Greases
ASTM D 1264—Water Washout Characteristics of Lubricating Greases
ASTM D 1403—Cone Penetration of Lubricating Grease Using One-Quarter and One-Half Scale Cone Equipment
ASTM D 1404—Test Method for Estimation of Deleterious Particles In Lubricating Grease
ASTM D 1478—Low-Temperature Torque of Ball Bearing Greases
ASTM D 1742—Oil Separation from Lubricating Grease During Storage
ASTM D 1743—Corrosion Preventive Properties of Lubricating Greases
ASTM D 1831—Roll Stability of Lubricating Grease
ASTM D 2265—Dropping Point of Lubricating Grease Over Wide-Temperature Range
ASTM D 2266—Wear Preventive Characteristics of Lubricating Grease (Four-Ball Method)
ASTM D 2509—Measurement of Load-Carrying Capacity of Lubricating Grease (Timken Method)
ASTM D 2595—Evaporation Loss of Lubricating Greases Over Wide-Temperature Range
ASTM D 2596—Measurement of Extreme-Pressure Properties of Lubricating Grease (Four-Ball Method)
ASTM D 3336—Test Method for Life of Lubricating Greases in Ball Bearings at Elevated Temperatures
ASTM D 3337—Test Method for Life and Torque of Lubricating Greases in Small Ball Bearings
ASTM D 3527—Life Performance of Automotive Wheel Bearing Grease
ASTM D 3704—Test Method for Wear Preventive Properties of Lubricating Greases Using the (Falex) Block on Ring Test Machine in Oscillating Motion
ASTM D 4048—Test Method for Detection of Copper Corrosion from Lubricating Grease
ASTM D 4049—Test Method for Determining the Resistance of Lubricating Grease to Water Spray
ASTM D 4170—Fretting Wear Protection by Lubricating Greases
ASTM D 4289—Compatibility of Lubricating Grease with Elastomers
ASTM D 4290—Leakage Tendencies of Automotive Wheel Bearing Grease Under Accelerated Conditions
ASTM D 4693—Low-Temperature Torque of Greased-Lubricated Wheel Bearings
ASTM D 4950—Standard Classification and Specification for Automotive Service Greases
ASTM D 5483—Test Method for Oxidation Induction Time of Lubricating Greases by Pressure Differential Scanning Calorimetry
ASTM D 5706—Test Method for Determining Extreme Pressure Properties of Lubricating Greases Using a High-Frequency, Linear-Oscillation (SRV) Test Machine
ASTM D 5707—Test Method for Measuring Friction and Wear Properties of Lubricating Grease Using a High-Frequency, Linear-Oscillation (SRV) Test Machine
ASTM D 5969—Test Method for Corrosion-Preventive Properties of Lubricating Greases in Presence of Dilute Synthetic Sea Water Environments
ASTM D 6138—Test Method for Determination of Corrosion Preventive Properties under Dynamic Wet Conditions (Emcor Test)
ASTM D 6184—Test Method for Oil Separation from Lubricating Grease (Conical Sieve Method)
ASTM D 6185—Practice for Evaluating Compatibility of Binary Mixtures of Lubricating Greases
ASTM MNL-1—Manual on Significant Petroleum Tests (Sixth Edition)

2.1.3 NGLI PUBLICATIONS—Available from NGLI, 4635 Wyandotte Street, Kansas City, MO 64112.

NGLI Recommended Practice for Lubricating Passenger Car Wheel Bearings
NGLI Recommended Practice for Lubricating Passenger Car Ball Joint Front Suspensions
NGLI Recommended Practice for Grease Lubricated Truck Wheel Bearings

3. Definition of Lubricating Grease—A lubricating grease is a solid to semi-fluid mixture of a liquid lubricant and a thickening agent. Additives to impart special properties or performance characteristics can be incorporated. The liquid component may be a mineral (petroleum) oil or a synthetic liquid; the thickener can be a metallic soap or soaps or a nonsoap substance such as an organophilic modified clay, a urea compound, carbon black, or other material. The viscosity of the fluid, the thickener concentration, and the chemical nature of the thickener can vary widely. The properties of the finished grease are influenced by the manufacturing process as well as by the materials used.

4. Basic Performance Requirements—Greases are most often used instead of fluids where a lubricant is required to maintain its original position in a mechanism, especially where opportunities for frequent relubrication may be limited or economically unjustifiable. This requirement may be due to the physical configuration of the mechanism, the type of motion, the type of sealing, or to the need for the lubricant to perform all or part of any sealing function in the prevention of lubricant loss or the entrance of contaminants. Because of their essentially solid nature, greases do not perform the cooling and cleaning functions associated with the use of a fluid lubricant. With these exceptions, greases are expected to accomplish all other functions of fluid lubricants.

A satisfactory grease for a given application is expected to:

a. Provide adequate lubrication to reduce friction and to prevent harmful wear of bearing components
b. Protect against corrosion.
c. Act as a seal to prevent entry of dirt and water.
d. Resist leakage, dripping, or undesirable throw off from the lubricated surfaces.
e. Resist objectionable change in structure or consistency with mechanical working (in the bearing) during prolonged service.
f. Not stiffen excessively to cause undue resistance to motion in cold weather.
g. Have physical characteristics suitable for the method of application.
h. Be compatible with elastomer seals and other materials of construction in the lubricated portion of the mechanism.
i. Tolerate some degree of contamination, such as moisture, without loss of significant characteristics.
j. Have suitable oxidation and thermal stability for the intended application.

5. Properties of Greases

5.1 Consistency—A measure of relative hardness. This property is commonly expressed in terms of the ASTM penetration or NLGI consistency number. The ASTM penetration is a numerical statement of the actual penetration of the grease sample, in tenths of a millimeter, by a standard test cone under stated conditions. The higher the penetration value, the softer the grease. The National Lubricating Grease Institute classifies greases according to their ASTM penetration as shown in Table 1.

The consistency of a grease is an important factor in its ability to lubricate, seal, and remain in place, and to the methods and ease by which it can be dispensed and applied. Most automotive greases are in the NLGI No. 1, 2, or 3 range, that is, ranging from soft to medium consistency.

5.2 Texture and Structure—The appearance and feel of greases. A grease may be described as smooth, buttery, fibrous, long- or short-fibered, stringy, tacky, etc. These characteristics are influenced by the viscosity of the fluid, type of thickener, proportion of each of these components, presence of certain additives, and process of manufacture. There are no standard test methods for quantitative definitions of these properties. Texture and structure are factors in the adhesiveness and ease of handling of a grease.

5.3 Structural Stability—The ability of a grease to retain its as-manufactured consistency and texture despite age, temperature, mechanical working, and other influences, or its ability to return to its original state when a transient influence is removed.

5.4 Mechanical Stability—The resistance of a grease to permanent changes in consistency due to the continuous application of shearing forces.

The stability of a grease is important to its ability to provide adequate lubrication and sealing and to remain properly in place during use.

5.5 Apparent Viscosity—The ratio of shear stress to rate of shear at a stated temperature and shear rate. Grease is by nature a plastic material. Therefore, the usual concept of viscosity valid for simple fluids (that is, internal resistance to flow) is not entirely applicable. The ratio of shear stress to shear rate varies as the shear rate changes. The apparent viscosity of most greases decreases with increase of either temperature or shear rate. Apparent viscosity greatly influences the ease of handling and dispensing a grease.

5.6 Dropping Point—The temperature at which the grease generally passes from a plastic solid to a liquid state, and flows through an orifice under standard test conditions. The dropping point is incorrectly regarded by some as establishing the maximum temperature for acceptable use. Performance at high temperature also depends on other factors such as duration of exposure, evaporation resistance, and design of the lubricated mechanism.

5.7 Oxidation Resistance—The resistance to chemical deterioration in storage and in service caused by exposure to air. It depends basically on the stability of the individual grease components, and can be improved by use of antioxidants. Oxidation resistance is important wherever long storage or service life is required or where high temperatures prevail even for short periods.

5.8 Protection Against Friction and Wear—A protection greatly influenced by the viscosity and type of the fluid component and by grease structural and consistency characteristics. This performance characteristic can be altered by use of additives.

5.9 Protection Against Corrosion—A protection of ferrous components achieved primarily by the inclusion of suitable additives in the grease. The effectiveness of the protection is influenced also by the chemical and physical properties, such as interactions with other additives, consistency and base oil viscosity (both of which will determine how effectively the grease will seal out corrosive and other undesirable material), and the interaction with water. The effect of water on the grease can be significant. Some greases are water resistant or waterproof, which means that they resist the washing effect of water and do not absorb it to any significant extent. Other greases can absorb varying amounts of water without appreciable damage to their structure or consistency, and may provide better rust protection than waterproof greases which can permit the accumulation of free water in bearings.

5.10 Bleeding or Oil Separation—The separation of liquid lubricant from a grease. Slight bleeding is regarded as desirable by some as indicative of good lubricating ability in rolling element bearings.

5.11 Color—A superficial grease property without performance significance.

TABLE 1—NLGI CONSISTENCY NUMBER

NLGI Consistency No.	ASTM Worked (60 Strokes) Penetration at 25 °C (77 °F) tenths of a millimeter(1)	NLGI Consistency No.	ASTM Worked (60 Strokes) Penetration at 25 °C (77 °F) tenths of a millimeter(1)
000	445 to 475	3	220 to 250
00	400 to 430	4	175 to 205
0	355 to 385	5	130 to 160
1	310 to 340	6	85 to 115
2	265 to 295		

1. ASTM D 217 Cone Penetration of Lubricating Grease.

5.12 Flow—There is, of course, the problem of getting grease to the bearings to be lubricated. Certain terms, by no means of strict, rigid interpretation, are used to describe the factors involved: feedability, pumpability, and dispensability.

5.12.1 FEEDABILITY OR SLUMPABILITY—The ability to flow to the suction of the grease-dispensing equipment or mechanism to be lubricated.

5.12.2 PUMPABILITY—The ability to flow through the grease-dispensing lines at a satisfactory rate, without the necessity of using excessively high pressure.

5.12.3 DISPENSABILITY—The ease with which a grease may be transferred from its container to the point of application. For practical purposes, it is a combination of feedability and pumpability.

5.13 Significance—Of these properties, oxidation resistance, protection against friction and wear, protection against corrosion, and structural stability are probably of most importance in automotive service as far as actual performance in bearings is concerned.

6. Grease Testing—Many of the previous grease properties are determined by tests which have been standardized or otherwise accorded industry recognition. These, in conjunction with simulated performance tests, permit some approximate judgment for the proper selection of greases for a given application. They are, however, not considered to be replacements for, or equivalent to, longtime service tests. A fuller discussion of grease tests and their significance can be found in Chapter 9 of ASTM MNL-1.

Table 2 shows some of the more important tests identified as to sponsor, title, and purpose.

7. Designation of Greases—Greases are commonly classified and designated according to chemical composition, such as lithium-soap grease; by broad type of usage, such as antifriction bearing grease or multipurpose grease; by specific properties such as high-temperature grease; by special additives, such as extreme-pressure grease or graphite grease; and by specific applications, such as automotive-wheel-bearing grease. SAE recognizes the following designations for greases used in servicing passenger cars, trucks, and buses according to their specific applications.

7.1 Wheel Bearing Grease—Designates lubricating greases of such composition, structure, and consistency as to be suitable for longtime use in antifriction wheel bearings. The properties and composition of greases used in ball-type wheel bearings can be significantly different than those used in tapered roller-type wheel bearings. Generally, ball-type wheel bearings used in modern automotive vehicles are not serviceable.

NOTE—Generally, these greases resist the deteriorating effects of temperature and the separating effects of centrifugal action. They have good antirust properties. They should not exhibit oil-soap separation or excessive softening which could result in leakage that could lead to braking failure.

For relubrication of serviceable wheel bearings, follow the manufacturer's recommendations. Generally, tapered-roller wheel bearings of light-duty vehicles (automobiles and small trucks) can be lubricated satisfactorily with greases meeting the requirements of NLGI categories GC or GC-LB. Consult manufacturer's recommendations for service lubrication of wheel bearings of heavy-duty vehicles. (Often, NLGI categories GA and GB can be used in wheel bearings of off-road vehicles or other applications requiring frequent lubrication.)

7.2 Universal Joint Grease—Designates lubricating greases of such composition, structure, and consistency as to be suitable for the lubrication of those types of automotive universal joints requiring grease lubrication.

NOTE—In many cases, the service relubrication of universal joints can be satisfied with NLGI categories LA or LB (Table 3). However, some designs, such as constant velocity joints, or some types of service, may require special greases. Manufacturers' recommendations or lubrication charts should be consulted.

7.3 Chassis Grease—Designates lubricating greases of proper consistency to be applied at periodic intervals in accordance with equipment manufacturers' recommendations, with grease guns through grease fittings, into the various parts of automotive chassis requiring grease lubrication.

NOTE—When no means are provided for periodic relubrication, the ability of a grease to retain its performance characteristics over long intervals of time and service becomes critical. This applies to seals as well because only seals in good condition can effectively prevent intrusion of water, dirt, and other contaminants, and minimize loss of grease by leakage.

For the service relubrication of chassis components, follow the manufacturer's recommendations. Generally, chassis components can be lubricated satisfactorily with greases meeting the requirements of NLGI categories LB or GC-LB. (Often, ASTM D 4950 Category LA can be used to lubricate chassis components of off-road vehicles or other applications requiring frequent lubrication.)

TABLE 2—GREASE TESTS

Test Designation	Test Purpose
ASTM D 128, Analysis of Lubricating Grease	Quantitative determination of specified constituents, such as soap, unsaponifiable matter (mineral oil), water, free alkali, free fatty acid, glycerine, and insolubles. Note—This procedure has a supplementary method useful for greases containing nonsoap thickeners or synthetic fluids.
ASTM D 217, Cone Penetration of Lubricating Grease	Measurement of consistency.
ASTM D 566, Dropping Point of Lubricating Grease	Determination of temperature at which grease generally passes from plastic to liquid state; not regarded as indicative of service suitability; limited to dropping points up to 260 °C (500 °F). (In this test, some greases may release oil before the grease flows which is defined as their dropping points.)
ASTM D 942, Oxidation Stability of Lubricating Greases by the Oxygen Bomb Method	Determination of resistance to oxidation under static conditions in a sealed system at elevated temperatures, not indicative of the stability of greases under dynamic service conditions, nor the stability of greases stored in containers for long periods, nor the stability of films of grease on machine parts.
ASTM D 972, Evaporation Loss of Lubricating Greases and Oils	Evaluation of weight loss by evaporation at temperatures up to 150 °C (300 °F).
ASTM D 1092, Apparent Viscosity of Lubricating Greases	Determination of apparent viscosity in temperature range of –54 to 38 °C (–65 to 100 °F); results relatable to ease of handling and dispensing.
ASTM D 1263, Leakage Tendencies of Automotive Wheel Bearing Greases	Evaluation of leakage tendencies from an unsealed wheel bearing assembly, run for 6 h at 104 °C (220 °F); permits screening candidate greases; not a replacement for longtime service tests. Note—Replaced by ASTM D 4290 in many updated specifications.
ASTM D 1264, Water Washout Characteristics of Lubricating Greases	Evaluation of resistance to water washout from rotating bearings at 38 °C (100 °F) and at 80 °C (175 °F) under prescribed conditions; not a replacement for actual service tests; not suitable for fibrous greases.
ASTM D 1403, Cone Penetration of Lubricating Grease Using One-Quarter and One-Half Scale Cone Equipment	Essentially same as ASTM D 217, using reduced-size apparatus to evaluate small grease samples, but limited to greases of NLGI No. 0 to 4 consistency.
ASTM D 1404, Test Method for Estimation of Deleterious Particles in Lubricating Grease	Detects and estimates abrasive particles in a lubricating grease sample placed between two plastic plates and counting the scratches that occur when they are rotated under load.
ASTM D 1478, Low-Temperature Torque of Ball Bearing Greases	Determination of the extent to which a grease retards the rotation of a slow-speed ball bearing when subjected to temperatures below –18 °C (0 °F). This method was developed using a test temperature of –54 °C (–65 °F) and greases with extremely low torque characteristics. Although higher test temperatures are commonly used, the precision statements may not apply to temperatures other than –54 °C (–65 °F) or to greases with torque characteristics different from those used to establish precision. Note—ASTM D 4693 is better suited for greases having higher torque characteristics.
ASTM D 1742, Oil Separation from Lubricating Grease During Storage	Determination of tendency of oil constituent to separate from parent grease while in containers; suitable for NLGI No. 1 or harder greases; results are indicative of oil separation in containers, but not of oil separation under dynamic service conditions.
ASTM D 1743, Corrosion Preventive Properties of Lubricating Greases	Determination of surface damage due to corrosion, such as pitting, etching, rusting, or black stains on raceways and rollers of tapered roller bearings which have been run-in and stored for a prescribed period at 52 °C (125 °F) and 100% relative humidity.
ASTM D 1831, Roll Stability of Lubricating Grease	Determination of changes to consistency after working in tester for 2 h at room temperature. Although test significance has not been determined, changes in worked penetration of a grease after rolling are believed to be an indication of shear stability under low shear conditions.
ASTM D 2265, Dropping Point of Lubricating Grease Over Wide-Temperature Range	Same purpose as ASTM D 566 but ASTM D 2265 is valid for temperatures up to 330 °C (625 °F).
ASTM D 2266, Wear Preventive Characteristics of Lubricating Grease (Four-Ball Method)	Determination of wear preventive characteristics of grease when a rotating loaded steel ball slides against three similar stationary steel balls, measured by wear-scar diameters on stationary balls after completion of test; not indicative of results in actual service, and cannot distinguish between extreme pressure (EP) and non-extreme pressure (non-EP) greases.
ASTM D 2509, Measurement of Load-Carrying Capacity of Lubricating Grease (Timken Method)	Determination of load-carrying ability of lubricating greases by Timken Lubricant and Wear Tester. In this device, a rectangular steel test block is forced against a rotating steel ring. Scar width and surface conditions are noted. Method differentiates between lubricants of various extreme-pressure levels; not a replacement for actual service tests.
ASTM D 2595, Evaporation Loss of Lubricating Greases Over Wide-Temperature Range	Evaluation of weight loss by evaporation at temperatures between 93 and 316 °C (200 and 600 °F).
ASTM D 2596, Measurement of Extreme-Pressure Properties of Lubricating Grease (Four-Ball Method)	Evaluation of load-carrying properties at high loads. Determines: a.Load-wear index (formerly mean-Hertz load) b.Weld point by Four-Ball EP Tester
ASTM D 3336, Test Method for life of Lubricating Greases in Ball Bearings at Elevated Temperatures	Evaluates the performance of lubricating greases in ball bearings operating under light loads at high speeds and elevated temperatures.
ASTM D 3337, Test Method for Life and Torque of Lubricating Greases in Small Ball Bearings	Determines lubricating-grease life in small bearings and measures the running torque at both low and high speeds. This test predicts relative grease life at high temperature in a reasonable testing time. It is not the equivalent of a long-time field-service test.
ASTM D 3527, Life Performance of Automotive Wheel Bearing Grease	Evaluation of the high-temperature life performance of wheel bearing grease.
ASTM D 3704, Test Method for Wear Preventive Properties of Lubricating Greases using the (Falex) Block on Ring Test Machine in Oscillating Motion	Determines wear properties of lubricating greases using the Falex block-on-ring friction and wear test machine.
ASTM D 4048, Test Method for Detection of Copper Corrosion from Lubricating Grease	Determines the corrosiveness of lubricating grease by rating the color changes of immersed copper strips.
ASTM D 4049, Test Method for Determining the Resistance of Lubricating Grease to Water Spray	Evaluates the Adherence of a grease on a metal surface when subjected to a water spray under prescribed laboratory conditions.
ASTM D 4170, Fretting Wear Protection by Lubricating Greases	Evaluation of fretting wear protection characteristic by measuring mass loss of ball thrust bearings oscillated under load; correlates with fretting protection performance of greases in wheel bearings of passenger cars shipped long distances.
ASTM D 4289, Compatibility of Lubricating Grease with Elastomers	Determination of hardness and volume changes in elastomers caused by contact with lubricating grease at elevated temperatures.
ASTM D 4290, Leakage Tendencies of Automotive Wheel Bearing Grease Under Accelerated Conditions	Evaluation of leakage tendency of a grease from unsealed wheel bearings run 20 h at 1000 rpm and thrust loaded to 111 N (25 lb force). Unlike ASTM D 1263, this method, which is conducted at a higher temperature, 160 °C (320 °F), differentiates among wheel bearing greases having distinctly different high-temperature leakage characteristics.

TABLE 2—GREASE TESTS (continued)

Test Designation	Test Purpose
ASTM D 4693, Low-Temperature Torque of Greased-Lubricated Wheel Bearings	Determination of the viscous resistance of a grease in a wheel bearing assembly rotated at low speed in a low-temperature environment; used to evaluate both wheel bearing and chassis greases for performance in low-temperature service. Note—Greases having torque characteristics that permit evaluation in both ASTM D 1478 and ASTM D 4693 will not give the same torque values in the two tests because of differences in bearings and test apparatus.
ASTM D 5483, Test Method for Oxidation Induction Time of Lubricating Greases by Pressure Differential Scanning Calorimetry	Determines the oxidation tendencies of lubricating greases by measuring the oxidation-induction time in a 3.5 MPa oxygen atmosphere at temperatures between 155 and 210 °C.
ASTM D 5706, Test Method for Determining Extreme Pressure Properties of Lubricating Greases Using a High-Frequency, Linear-Oscillation (SRV) Test Machine	Determines the extreme pressure properties of lubricating greases in the SRV test machine operating at high-frequency, linear-oscillation motion conditions. (Can be used to test fluid lubricants, as well.)
ASTM D 5707, Test Method for Measuring Friction and Wear Properties of Lubricating Grease Using a High-Frequency, Linear-Oscillation (SRV) Test Machine	Determines a lubricating grease's coefficient of friction and, from average wear scar dimensions, its ability to protect against wear when the test piece is subjected to high-frequency, linear-oscillation motion. (Can be used to test fluid lubricants, as well.)
ASTM D 5969, Test Method for Corrosion-Preventive Properties of Lubricating Greases in Presence of Dilute Synthetic Sea Water Environments	Determines the pass-fail rating of the corrosion-preventive properties of greases in tapered roller bearings exposed to any of various concentrations of dilute synthetic sea water and stored under wet conditions. (Similar to ASTM D 1743, which uses distilled water.)
ASTM D 6138, Test Method for Determination of Corrosion Preventive Properties under Dynamic Wet Conditions (Emcor Test)	Determines the relative corrosion-preventive ratings of lubricating greases in rotating ball bearings operating partially immersed in aqueous solution.
ASTM D 6184, Test Method for Oil Separation from Lubricating Grease (Conical Sieve Method)	Determines the tendency of oil to separate from lubricating grease held in a conical sieve at an elevated temperature (usually 100 °C for 30 h). This test method is not suitable for greases having a penetration greater than 340 (softer than NLGI No. 1 grade.) This standard test method is the ASTM equivalent of Federal Test Method (FTM) 791C Method 321.3.
ASTM D 6185, Practice for Evaluating Compatibility of Binary Mixtures of Lubricating Greases	A standard protocol to evaluate the compatibility of binary mixtures of lubricating greases by comparing the properties of three different mixture ratios relative to those of the neat constituent greases comprising the mixture. Initially, three test methods are used to evaluate the compatibility: a. Dropping Point (ASTM D 566 or D 2265), b. Shear Stability (ASTM D 217, 100 000-stroke worked penetration); and c. Storage Stability at Elevated Temperature (change in 60-stroke penetration measured by ASTM D 217.) Suggestions for additional tests are included if such are considered necessary for special or critical applications.

7.4 Multipurpose Grease—Designates lubricating greases of such composition, structure, and consistency to meet the performance requirements for chassis grease (more than 3200 km (2000 mile) service life), wheel bearing grease, universal joint grease, and other automotive uses of a miscellaneous nature, such as fifth-wheel service.

NOTE—Some chassis lubricants are satisfactory as multipurpose greases. The grease manufacturer should be consulted as to the multipurpose qualities of his product. Greases designated NLGI GC-LB are multipurpose greases by definition.

TABLE 3—SUMMARY OF NLGI AND ASTM DESIGNATION, DESCRIPTION, AND PERFORMANCE REQUIREMENTS FOR AUTOMOTIVE SERVICE GREASES

NLGI Letter Designation	NLGI Service Description	ASTM D 4950 Performance Description	ASTM D 4950 Performance Requirements
Chassis Service			
LA	Service typical of chassis components and universal joints in passenger cars, trucks, and other vehicles under mild duty only. Mild duty will be encountered in vehicles operated with frequent relubrication in noncritical applications.	The grease shall satisfactorily lubricate chassis components and universal joints where frequent relubrication is practiced (at intervals 3200 km or 2000 miles or less for passenger cars). During its service life, the grease shall resist oxidation and consistency degradation while protecting the chassis components and universal joints from corrosion and wear under lightly loaded conditions. NLGI 2 consistency greases are commonly recommended, but other grades may also be recommended.	Conform to requirements of Table 4.
LB	Service typical of chassis components and universal joints in passenger cars, trucks, and other vehicles under mild to severe duty. Severe duty will be encountered in vehicles operated under conditions which may include prolonged relubrication intervals, or high loads, severe vibration, exposure to water or other contaminants, etc.	The grease shall satisfactorily lubricate chassis components and universal joints at temperatures as low as –40 °C (–40 °F) and at temperatures as high as 120 °C (248 °F) over prolonged relubrication intervals (more than 3200 km or 2000 miles for passenger cars). During its service life, the grease shall resist oxidation and consistency degradation while protecting the chassis components and universal joints from corrosion and wear even when aqueous contamination and heavily loaded conditions occur. NLGI 2 consistency greases are commonly recommended, but other grades may also be recommended.	Conform to requirements of Table 4.
Wheel Bearing Service			
GA	Service typical of wheel bearings operating in passenger cars, trucks, and other vehicles under mild duty. Mild duty will be encountered in vehicles operated with frequent relubrication in noncritical applications.	The grease shall satisfactorily lubricate wheel bearings over a limited temperature range. Many products of this type are limited to bearing temperatures of –20 to 70 °C (–4 to 158 °F). No additional performance requirements are specified for these greases.	Conform to requirements of Table 5.

TABLE 3—SUMMARY OF NLGI AND ASTM DESIGNATION, DESCRIPTION, AND PERFORMANCE REQUIREMENTS FOR AUTOMOTIVE SERVICE GREASES (continued)

NLGI Letter Designation	NLGI Service Description	ASTM D 4950 Performance Description	ASTM D 4950 Performance Requirements
GB	Service typical of wheel bearings operating in passenger cars, trucks, and other vehicles under mild to moderate duty. Moderate duty will be encountered in most vehicles operated under normal urban, highway, and off-highway service.	The grease shall satisfactorily lubricate wheel bearings over a wide temperature range. The bearing temperatures may range down to 40 °C (–40 °F), with frequent excursions to 120 °C (320 °F). During its service life, the grease shall resist oxidation, evaporation, and consistency degradation while protecting the bearings from corrosion and wear. NLGI 2 consistency greases are commonly recommended, but NLGI 1 or 3 grades may also be recommended.	Conform to requirements of Table 5.
GC	Service typical of wheel bearings operating in passenger cars, trucks, and other vehicles under mild to severe duty. Severe duty will be encountered in certain vehicles operated under conditions resulting in high bearing temperatures. This includes vehicles operated under frequent stop-and-go service (buses, taxis, urban police cars, etc.), or under severe braking service (trailer towing, heavy loading, mountain driving, etc.).	The grease shall satisfactorily lubricate wheel bearings over a wide temperature range. The bearing temperatures may range down to –40 °C (–40 °F), with frequent excursions to 160 °C (320 °F) and occasional excursions to 200 °C (392 °F). During its service life, the grease shall resist oxidation, evaporation, and consistency degradation while protecting the bearings from corrosion and wear. NLGI 2 consistency greases are commonly recommended, but NLGI 1 or 3 grades may also be recommended.	Conform to requirements of Table 5.

TABLE 4—"L" CHASSIS GREASE CATEGORIES

Category	Test	Property	Acceptance Limit
LA	D 217	Consistency, worked penetration, mm/10	220 to 340[(1)]
	D 566 or D 2265	Dropping Point, °C, min	80
	D 2266	Wear Protection, scar diameter, mm, max	0.9
	D 4289	Elastomer SAE AMS 3217/3B Compatibility: volume change, % hardness change, Durometer-A points	0 to 40 –15 to 0
LB	D 217	Consistency, worked penetration, mm/10	220 to 340[(1)]
	D 566 or D 2265	Dropping Point, °C, min	150
	D 2266	Wear Protection, scar diameter, mm, max	0.6
	D 4289	Elastomer SAE AMS 3217/3B Compatibility: volume change, % hardness change, Durometer-A points	0 to 40 –15 to 0
	D 1742	Oil Separation, mass %, max	10
	D 1743	Rust Protection, rating, max	Pass
	D 2596	EP Performance: load wear index, kgf, min weld point, kgf, min	30 200
	D 4170	Fretting Protection, mass loss, mg, max	10[(2)]
	D 4693	Low-Temperature Performance, torque at –40 °C, N·m, max	15.5

1. Vehicle manufacturer's requirement may be more restrictive; grease containers should display NLGI Consistency Number as well as category designation.
2. The fretting wear requirement is significant in passenger car and light-duty truck service, but it has not been shown to be significant in heavy-duty truck applications.

7.5 Extreme Pressure or EP—Not a designation by usage, but is applied to greases with high load-carrying capacity, determined usually by the Timken method or the Four-Ball EP Test or similar. In some cases, the EP property results from a surface-active additive that imparts antiwear or antiseize properties beyond the capabilities of the usual fluid, thickener, or other finely dispersed lubricating solids in the grease. Extreme-pressure or wear-reducing properties may be incorporated in any of the usage types, most frequently those designated as multipurpose.

7.6 Greases for Other Vehicle Needs—Automotive equipment may require special greases not as yet designated by SAE. Examples of such applications are speedometer cables and brake adjustors.

TABLE 5—"G" WHEEL BEARING GREASE CATEGORIES

Category	Test	Property	Acceptance Limit
GA	D 217	Consistency, worked penetration, mm/10	220 to 340[(1)]
	D 566 or D 2265	Dropping Point, °C, min	80
	D 4693	Low-Temperature Performance, torque at –20 °C, N·m, max	15.5
GB	D 217	Consistency, worked penetration, mm/10	220 to 340[(1)]
	D 566 or D 2265	Dropping Point, °C, min	175
	D 4693	Low-Temperature Performance, torque at –40 °C, N·m, max	15.5
	D 1264	Water Resistance at 80 °C, %, max	15
	D 1742	Oil Separation, mass %, max	10
	D 1743	Rust Protection, rating, max	Pass
	D 2266	Wear Protection, scar diameter, mm, max	0.9
	D 3527	High-Temperature Life, hours, min	40
	D 4289	Elastomer SAE AMS 3217/2A Compatibility: volume change, % hardness change, Durometer-A points	–5 to +30 –15 to +2
	D 4290	Leakage Tendencies, g, max	24
GC	D 217	Consistency, worked penetration, mm/10	220 to 340[(1)]
	D 566 or D 2265	Dropping Point, °C, min	220
	D 4693	Low-Temperature Performance, torque at –40 °C, N·m, max	15.5
	D 1264	Water Resistance at 80 °C, %, max	15
	D 1742	Oil Separation, mass %, max	6
	D 1743	Rust Protection, rating, max	Pass
	D 2266	Wear Protection, scar diameter, mm, max	0.9
	D 3527	High-Temperature Life, hours, min	80
	D 4289	Elastomer SAE AMS 3217/2A Compatibility: volume change, % hardness change, Durometer-A points	–5 to +30 –15 to +2
	D 4290	Leakage Tendencies, g, max	10
	D 2596	EP Performance: load wear index, kgf, min weld point, kgf, min	30 200

1. Vehicle manufacturer's requirement may be more restrictive; grease containers should display NLGI Consistency Number as well as category designation.

8. Grease Application—Automotive greases are applied by hand packing, by hand- and power-operated pressure guns, and by hand- and power-operated central systems fitted to individual vehicles. In wheel-bearing lubrication, a bearing packing device should be used, as it is more effective, faster, and less wasteful of grease than hand packing. Mixing of different types of greases in wheel bearings should be avoided to preclude excessive thinning and leakage.

The prime consideration in applying greases is that of cleanliness of containers and dispensing and pumping equipment, and in the removal of surface grease and dirt accumulation from application points such as plugs and grease gun fittings. To preclude mixing, vehicle service manuals specify that wheel bearings and hubs must be cleaned to remove all old grease before new grease is installed.

Excessive dispensing pressures and pumping rates are to be avoided. They tend to cause seal deformation and rupture and are wasteful of lubricant.

Automotive servicing literature is voluminous on the subject of grease lubrication. Important sources are vehicle manufacturers' service bulletins, oil company bulletins and lubrication charts, and trade organization manuals, such as NGLI publications: "Recommended Practice for Lubricating Passenger Car Wheel Bearings," "Recommended Practice for Lubricating Passenger Car Ball Joint Front Suspensions," and "Recommended Practice for Grease Lubricated Truck Wheel Bearings."

8.1 Grease Mixing and Compatibility—It is well known that the mixing of two greases can produce a substance having performance characteristics markedly inferior to either of its constituent materials. Frequently, the use of an incompatible mixture will cause a lubrication failure. The consequences can range from relatively benign to disastrous, depending on the application and conditions. Seal materials and design can sometimes avert serious problems due to an incompatible grease mixture. For instance, grease-filled linkage joints will seldom experience dire consequences from an incompatible mixture because the boot seals can retain the grease mixture. On the other hand, wheel bearings are only partially filled with grease, and an incompatible mixture can flow away from the bearings regardless of the effectiveness the lip seals.

Not surprisingly, OEMs commonly warn their customers: do not mix greases under any circumstances, or in the case of wheel bearings, to completely remove all residual grease before installing new grease. Despite such admonitions, grease mixing does and will occur; in some circumstances it cannot be avoided. Compatibility cannot be reliably predicted from foreknowledge of grease composition. It needs to be judged on a case-by-case basis. ASTM has developed D 6185, Standard Practice for Evaluating Compatibility of Binary Mixtures of Lubricating Greases.

9. Grease Properties as Related to Types of Service—Service requirements determine the relative importance of the aforementioned grease properties for each kind of application and set the level of performance needed. Table 6 is a generalized summary of the grease properties of primary importance in the several fields of automotive use previously discussed. Certain properties, such as texture or structure, consistency, and apparent viscosity, are not included in the summary, because it is assumed they will be appropriate to the purposes of the individual grease types.

TABLE 6—RELATIVE IMPORTANCE OF LUBRICATING GREASE PROPERTIES FOR AUTOMOTIVE USES SHOWN[1]

Property	Wheel Bearings	Universal Joints	Chassis	Multipurpose Applications
Structural Stability (inc. Mechanical Stability)	H	M	H	H
High Dropping Point (High-Temp. Service)	H	M	M	H
Oxidation Resistance	H	M	H	H
Protection Against Friction and Wear	M	H	H	H
Protection Against Corrosion	M	M	H	M
Protection Against Washout	M	M	H	M

1. H = Highest, M = Moderate.

10. Standard Classification and Specification for Service Greases—After years of cooperative effort, SAE, NLGI, and ASTM developed a system for the designation, description, classification, and specification of greases for service relubrication. This system has been accepted by both the grease and automotive industries. It was first published in 1989 as ASTM D 4950. ASTM D 4950 is a grease specification expressly intended for service applications. Specifications for factory-fill greases are generally more restrictive and often contain additional performance requirements described by nonstandard tests. However, there is nothing in ASTM D 4950 to preclude its use by equipment manufacturers to describe initial-fill greases. The pertinent requirements are summarized in Table 3.

Automotive service greases are classified into two groups, those suitable for chassis relubrication (including universal joints), and those suitable for the relubrication of serviceable-type wheel bearings. These are further separated into performance categories: two Chassis Grease categories, LA and LB, and three Wheel Bearing Grease categories, GA, GB, and GC. Tables 4 and 5 list the requirements (Acceptability Limits) for the respective categories. These two tables do not constitute all of the requirements of ASTM D 4950. ASTM D 4950 also includes specific descriptions of the service applications and performance requirements, which are included in the standard to ensure the selection of greases suited to the intended application. For quick comparisons, a qualitative guide to the specified requirements is shown in Figure 1.

NLGI has developed a symbol (10.1) to be used to identify greases that conform to the requirements of ASTM D 4950. For greases meeting the requirements of both a Chassis Grease category and a Wheel Bearing category, multipurpose grease nomenclature may be used, provided the appropriate NLGI Designation for each group is included. This latter provision is essential to avoid confusion with commercial, nonautomotive, "multipurpose" greases.

ASTM D 4950 and the NLGI service descriptions and symbols were generated and will be maintained and expanded in accordance with SAE J1146.

10.1 NLGI Symbol for Automotive Service Greases—To provide a means of readily highlighting greases of the classification that meet the highest performance requirements, NLGI has proposed the use of a standardized identifying symbol. The symbol shall be used only with greases meeting the highest automotive grease performance requirements, i.e., categories GC or LB, or both, as illustrated in Figure 2. The NLGI symbol shall not be used with categories GA, GB, or LA. NLGI licenses grease packagers and marketers to use the symbol, whose size may be varied to meet packaging and labeling needs. It is the responsibility of the packager to verify that the product conforms to the requirements of the categories used in the symbol.

D 4950 AUTOMOTIVE SERVICE GREASE REQUIREMENTS

		SERVICE GREASE CATEGORIES				
		CHASSIS		WHEEL BEARING		
TEST	DESCRIPTION	LA	LB	GA	GB	GC
D 217	Penetration	√	√	√	√	√
D 566	Dropping Point	√	√	√	√	√
D 1264	Water Washout	—	—	—	√	√
D 1742	Oil Separation	—	√	—	√	√
D 1743	Rust Protection	—	√	—	√	√
D 2266	4-Ball Wear	√	√	—	√	√
D 2596	4-Ball EP	—	√	—		√
D 3527	High-Temperature Life	—	—	—	√	√
D 4170	Fretting Wear	—	√	—	—	—
D 4289	Elastomer Compatibility	√	√	—	√	√
D 4290	Leakage	—	—	—	√	√
D 4693	Low-Temperature Torque	—	√	√	√	√

FIGURE 1—GUIDE TO REQUIREMENTS FOR GREASE CATEGORIES

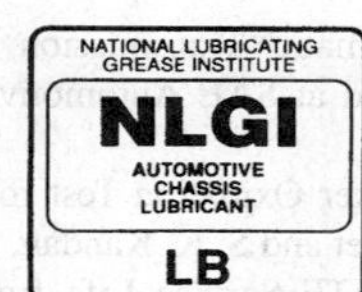

FIGURE 2—NLGI SYMBOL FOR LABELING AUTOMOTIVE LUBRICATING GREASES

FLUID FOR PASSENGER CAR TYPE AUTOMATIC TRANSMISSIONS—SAE J311 FEB2000

SAE Information Report

Report of the SAE Fuels and Lubricants Technical Committee approved January 1952. Revised by the SAE Fuels and Lubricants Division April 1986. Completely revised by the SAE Fuels and Lubricants Technical Committee 5—Fluids, February 1994. Revised by the SAE Fuels and Lubricants Technical Committee 3—Driveline and Chassis Lubrication February 2000.

1. Scope—This SAE Information Report details some of the equipment and procedures used to measure critical characteristics of automatic transmission fluid (ATF) used in current automatic transmissions. It is intended to assist those concerned with the design of transmission components, and with the selection and marketing of automatic transmission fluids for the use in passenger car and light-duty truck automatic transmissions. The information contained herein will be helpful in understanding the terms related to properties, designations, and service applications of automatic transmission fluids.

2. References

2.1 Applicable Publications—The following publications form a part of the specification to the extent specified herein. Unless otherwise indicated the lastest revision of SAE publications shall apply.

2.1.1 SAE PUBLICATION—Available from SAE, 400 Commonwealth Drive, Warrendale, PA 15096-0001.

SAE J110—Seals—Testing of Radial Lip

2.1.2 ASTM PUBLICATIONS—Available from ASTM, 100 Barr Harbor Drive, West Conshohocken, PA 19428-2959.

ASTM D 130—Method of Test of Copper Strip Corrosion by Petroleum Products
ASTM D 665—Rust-Preventing Characteristics of Inhibited Mineral Oil in the Presence of Water
ASTM D 892—Foaming Characteristics of Lubricating Oils
ASTM D 1275—Method of Test for Corrosive Sulfur in Electrical Insulating Oils
ASTM D 1748—Method of Test for Rust Protection by Metal Preservatives in the Humidity Cabinet
ASTM D 2882—Indicating the Wear Characteristics of Petroleum and Non-Petroleum Hydraulic Fluids in a Constant Volume Vane Pump

2.1.3 GM PUBLICATIONS—Available from General Motors Corporation, GM ATF Committee, 30500 Mound Road, M/C 480-106-160, Warren, MI 48090.

GM-6137M—DEXRON®-IIE Automatic Transmission Fluid Specification, General Motors Corporation, August 1992
GM-6417M—DEXRON®-III Automatic Transmission Fluid Specification, General Motors Corporation, December 1998

2.1.4 FORD MOTOR PUBLICATION—Available from Ford Motor Company, ATF Committee, 36200 Plymouth, Livonia, MI 48150.

MERCON®—Automatic Transmission Fluid Specification, Ford Motor Company, September 1, 1992
MERCON®-V—Automatic Transmission Fluid Specification, Ford Motor Company, February, 1996

2.2 Related Publications—The following publications are provided for information purposes only and are not a required part of this document.

2.2.1 SAE PUBLICATIONS—Available from SAE, 400 Commonwealth Drive, Warrendale, PA 15096-0001.

Design Practices—Passenger Car Automatic Transmissions, SAE Advances in Engineering, Vols. 1 and 2
SAE Paper 710838—Automatic Transmissions Fluid Viscosity Requirements, E. D. Davison and M. L. Haviland, presented at St. Louis, MO, 1971
SAE Paper 740051—Automotive Transmission Fluids—Some Aspects on Friction, E. J. Friihauf, presented at SAE Automotive Engineering Congress, Detroit, MI, February, 1974
SAE Paper 670051—Putting Automatic Transmission Clutch Friction Researchers on Speaking Terms, G. R. Smith, et al, presented at SAE Automotive Engineering Congress, Detroit, MI, January, 1967
SAE Paper 790019—Bridging the Gap Between DEXRON®-II and Type F ATF, H. E. Deen, et al; SAE Transactions for 1979, Vol. 88
SAE Paper 690768—Engine and Transmission Lubricant Viscosity Effects on Low Temperature Cranking and Starting, M. L. Haviland, SAE Transactions, Vol. 78 (1969)
SAE Paper 740053—DEXRON®-II Automatic Transmission Fluid Performance, M. L. Haviland, et al, presented at SAE Automotive Engineering Congress, Detroit, MI, February, 1974
SAE Paper 881673—The Aluminum Beaker Oxidation Test for MERCON® World-Wide Service ATF, P. A. Willermet and S. K. Kandah, 1988
SAE Paper 801363—The Prediction of ATF Service Life from Laboratory Oxidation Test Data, in SP 473, "Deterioration of Automotive Lubricants in Service," P. A. Willermet, et al; SAE Fuels and Lubricants Meeting, Baltimore, MD, October, 1980
SAE Paper 680438—Laboratory Methods for Predicting Viscosity Loss of Polymer Thickened Hydraulic Fluids, p. 74, R. L. Stambaugh and A. L. Preuss, Fuels and Lubricants, 1968 Paper, SAE Activity Proceedings, A P-1
SAE Paper 902148—Physical and Chemical Properties of a Typical Automatic Transmission Fluid, S. P. Kemp and J. L. Linden, 1990
SAE Paper 870356—Improving Transaxle Performance at Low Temperature with Reduced-Viscosity Automatic Transmission Fluids, J. L. Linden and S. P. Kemp, 1987
SAE Paper 922371—The Oxidation Stability of General Motors Proposed Factory-Fill Automatic Transmission Fluid, S. P. Kemp and J. L. Linden, 1992
SAE Paper 841214—Automatic Transmission Fluids—Properties and Performance, H. E. Deen and J. Ryer
SAE Paper 982674—Development and Introduction of Chrysler's New Automatic Transmission Fluid, D. W. Florkowski, T. E. King, A. P. Skrobul, J. L. Sumiejski, 1998

2.2.2 ASTM PUBLICATIONS—Available from ASTM, 100 Barr Harbor Drive, West Conshohocken, PA 19428-2959.

ASTM D 92—Flash and Fire Points by Cleveland Open Cup
ASTM D 445—Kinematic Viscosity of Transparent and Opaque Liquids (and the Calculation of Dynamic Viscosity)
ASTM D 808—Chlorine in New and Used Petroleum Products (Bomb Method)
ASTM D 971—Interfacial Tension of Oil Against Water by the Ring Method
ASTM D 1298—Density, Relative Density (Specific Gravity), or API Gravity of Crude Petroleum and Liquid Petroleum Products by Hydrometer Method
ASTM D 2717—Thermal Conductivity of Liquids
ASTM D 2766—Specific Heat of Liquids and Solids
ASTM D 2780—Solubility of Fixed Gases in Liquids
ASTM D 2983—Low-Temperature Viscosity of Automotive Fluid Lubricants Measured by Brookfield Viscometer
ASTM D 4951—Determination of Additive Elements in Lubricating Oils by Inductively Coupled Plasma Atomic Emission Spectrometry

2.2.3 DAIMLER CHRYSLER CORPORATION PUBLICATION—Available from Daimler Chrysler Corporation, Auburn Hills, MI 48326.

MS-9602—Automatic Transmission Fluid Specification, October, 1998

2.2.4 OTHER PUBLICATIONS

"Petroleum Refinery Engineering," 4th Edition by W. L. Nelson, New York, McGraw Hill Book Co., 1958, pp. 189–190
CRC Handbook of Lubrication, Volume II, Theory and Design, CRC Press, Inc., Boca Raton, Florida, 1984
J. B. Maxwell, "Data Book on Hydrocarbons," D Van Nostrand, New York, 1950

3. Definitions

3.1 Automatic Transmission Fluid—Automatic transmission fluid is a lubricating oil specifically designed for use in fully automatic transmissions. ATF consists of a base oil and an additive package which is added to enhance the properties of the base oil.

4. Basic Performance Requirements—Automatic transmission fluids are complex because they are intended to provide good transmission performance and durability, and serve a variety of functions: power transfer medium, hydraulic control fluid, heat-transfer medium, lubricant for sliding surfaces, gear lubricant, and lubricant for frictional surfaces. In order to ensure satisfactory performance in all intended applications under normal use and severe operating conditions, the fluid must satisfactorily meet the following requirements:

a. Miscibility with fluids used for initial OEM factory fill and with other OEM qualified fluids
b. Resistance to oxidation, including the formation of sludge and/or varnish
c. Operation from very low temperatures to very high temperatures
d. Component lubrication
e. Anti-foam performance
f. Protection against corrosion or rusting
g. Compatibility with elastomeric materials
h. OEM shift-feel characteristics
i. Stability of band and plate clutch friction characteristics over time and duty cycle at various temperatures
j. Anti-wear protection

5. Properties of Automatic transmission Fluids

5.1 Physical and Chemical Properties—The physical and chemical properties of an automatic transmission fluid are important transmission design criteria. The transmission design engineer must have data on these properties to solve the many momentum and heat transfer calculations required to design today's complex automatic transmissions. In general, air solubility, thermal expansion, and specific heat increase with increasing temperature; whereas, surface tension, specific gravity, viscosity, bulk modulus, density, thermal conductivity, and electrical conductivity decrease with increasing temperature.

5.1.1 TYPICAL VALUE

a. Brookfield Viscosity, cP
   –20 °C600 to 1200
   –40 °C8000 to 20 000
b. Kinemtic Viscosity, cSt
   40 °C33
   100 °C7.0
c. Thermal Conductivity, W/m·K
   40 °C0.158
   1000 °C0.149
d. Coefficient of Thermal Expansion, mL/mL C
   6×10^{-4}
e. Specific Gravity (Relative Density)
   40 °C0.8534
   100 °C0.8116
f. Specific Heat, J/kg·K
   40 °C2018
   100 °C2244
g. Density, g/cm^3
   40 °C0.853
   100 °C0.816
h. Bulk Modulus (Tangent Isothermal), MPa
   37.8 °C @ 6.9 MPa 1372
   37.8 °C @ 55.16 MPa2034
   37.8 °C @ 137.9 MPa2930

   93.3 °C @ 6.9 MPa1110
   93.3 °C @ 55.16 MPa1613
   93.3 °C @ 137.9 MPa2530
i. Electric Resistivity, Ohms/cm
   40 °C$8.05 \cdot 10^9$
   100 °C$1.44 \cdot 10^9$
j. Surface Tension, dynes/cm
   93 °C28.9
   135 °C25.5
k. Flash Point, °C — 190
l. Fire Point, °C — 210

5.2 Viscosity—Viscosity is the measure of a fluid's resistance to flow, and is one of the most important physical properties of a lubricant. The viscosity must be low enough at all operating temperatures to ensure adequate fluid flow and minimize viscous drag, but high enough at high temperatures to provide adequate fluid-film strength and prevent excessive internal transmission fluid leakage.

Viscosities chosen vary with the individual manufacturer, but are generally within the range of 6.5 to 8.5 cSt at 100 °C for fresh fluid. Both kinematic (centistokes) and absolute (centipoises) viscosities are determined on these fluids. The absolute viscosity divided by the density of the fluid equals the kinematic viscosity.

Fluid kinematic viscosity shall not fall below what is required for proper operation of the automatic transmission for which the fluid is used. Typical minimum viscosities during transmission operation range from 5 to 5.5 cSt at 100 °C.

Detailed discussion of fundamental principles and measuring equipment is available in current literature.

5.3 Chemical Content—An automatic transmission fluid consists of 85 to 90% base oil and 10 to 15% of a performance additive package containing chemical compounds necessary to impart the desired characteristics. The base oil may be naphthenic, paraffinic, hydro-treated or synthetic (or any combination) depending on the type of service, the needs of the transmission manufacturer and the oil company marketing plans for the automatic transmission fluid. The chemical compounds which form the additive package contain, in general: *dispersants* to control sludge and varnish; *corrosion inhibitors* to prevent the corrosion of bushings; thrust washers, and any other copper-based components; *anti-wear additives* to prevent wear of gears, bushings, washers, and other rubbing components; *friction modifiers* to improve shift-feel and friction material durability; *anti-oxidants* to control fluid degradation and increase fluid useful life; *pour point depressants* to lower the fluid pour point; *anti-foam additives* to reduce fluid foaming tendencies; *viscosity modifiers* to increase the viscosity index of the fluid; *seal swell additives* to insure elastomer compatibility and performance; and a *red dye* to identify the fluid as an automatic transmission fluid.

6. Oxidation and Thermal Stability—Oxidation is the chemical reaction of a substance with oxygen and is a major cause of automatic transmission fluid deterioration. The oxidation process involves the formation of free radicals, acidic compounds, and polar compounds which attack and degrade the ATF additive package, the ATF base oil, transmission elastomeric compounds, copper alloy components, and other sensitive transmission parts. Degrading an ATF can change the properties of the ATF significantly. Transmission designers must take such changes into consideration in the design of transmission components and fluid change interval recommendations.

The oxidation stability of ATF is affected by many parameters, such as: fluid temperature, aeration rate, additive system effectiveness, base oil type, and the presence of catalysts. Fluid temperature is probably the most critical parameter. Fluids used in automatic transmissions must be capable of operating at temperatures in excess of 150 °C in services such as trailer towing, and under conditions encountered in hot-weather high-density urban traffic.

Full-scale tests such as the DEXRON®-III Cycling Test and Oxidation Test, as well as bench tests such as the MERCON® Aluminum Beaker Oxidation Test (ABOT) are used for evaluating oxidation resistance of fluids.

7. Friction Characteristics—Fluid friction characteristics are important in automatic transmissions that utilize lubricated friction clutches and bands to change gear ratios. Extensive performance and durability testing is performed in actual transmissions and bench friction test apparatus. The General Motors and Ford Motor Company automatic transmission fluid specifications both require SAE No. 2 Friction Machine bench tests, dynamometer cycling tests, and vehicle shift-feel tests to characterize the fluid frictional properties and friction durability. No single fluid is known to provide the optimum friction requirements of all existing transmission types. The transmission designer must realize that the automatic transmission fluid formulator must compromise fluid friction properties of one clutch system to benefit another clutch system. For example, shifting clutches, in general, require a lower static coefficient of friction to maximize customer acceptance of the shift feel, whereas a holding clutch system (such as a forward clutch which is always engaged during forward motion) requires a higher static coefficient of friction to provide the necessary friction torque capacity and minimize clutch slippage. Maximizing the performance in one type of system compromises the performance in the other system.

Evolution of friction materials and consequent changes in reaction member surfaces, both clutch and band, has emphasized the friction-controlling role of automatic transmission fluid. Matching fluid friction characteristics properly with clutch and band materials is an important design consideration in all currently produced automatic transmissions.

8. Anti-Foam Characteristics—Suppression of the foaming tendency of fluids in an automatic transmission is essential to proper operation. Foaming of the transmission fluid can produce erratic pump, converter, and hydraulic control response; foaming frequently results in fluid loss through the vent or fill tube. Measurement of foaming tendency and foam stability is used for evaluating fluid suitability. Techniques for evaluation fluid foaming tendencies include transmission tests, bench tests such as ASTM D 892, and the DEXRON®-III Foam Test.

9. Fluid/Seal Compatibility—Automatic transmission fluid and transmission elastomeric materials must be compatible. Accepted design procedure involves the use of a reference elastomer to determine swell, shrink, and hardening tendencies of a candidate fluid. Seal materials must be selected to meet transmission performance requirements with established fluid formulations. Bench test procedures such as those outlined in the MERCON® and DEXRON®-III specifications are of value for screening purposes. Bench test devices for seal assemblies are also useful for determining compatibility; see SAE J110.

10. Score and Wear Resistance—Current automatic transmission fluids contain anti-wear additives which inhibit scoring and wear of rubbing surfaces. Anti-wear additives must be effective and compatible with the variety of materials used in transmissions. Many bench test devices exist for evaluation of fluid anti-wear performance. The most popular tests among OEMs are ASTM D 2882 using a Vickers Pump and the FZG test apparatus.

11. Corrosion Properties—Automatic transmission fluids generally contain corrosion inhibitors to assure protection of transmission components. As a result of the many components and materials involved, a variety of tests are used for evaluating moisture and/or chemical corrosion resistance of transmission fluids: ASTM D 1748, ASTM D 665, ASTM D 130, and ASTM D 1275.

AUTOMOTIVE GASOLINES—SAE J312 FEB2001 SAE Recommended Practice

Report of the SAE Lubricants Division approved January 1931, and revised by the SAE Technical Committee 7, Fuels and Lubricants Division, October 1988. Completely revised by the SAE Fuels and Lubricants Technical Committee 7—Fuels January 1993 and revised May 1997, July 1998, and February 2001. Rationale statement available.

Foreword—Automotive gasolines are used to fuel internal combustion spark-ignition engines. While gasolines discussed herein are used primarily in passenger car and highway truck service, they are also used extensively in off-highway utility vehicles and farm machinery, two-stroke and four-stroke cycle marine engines, and other spark-ignition engines employed in a variety of different service applications.

Automotive gasolines are essentially blends of numerous hydrocarbons derived from petroleum. To produce gasoline, refiners initially use fractional distillation of the crude oil to segregate those hydrocarbons in the gasoline boiling range, with finished gasolines encompassing a boiling range of about 30 to 225 °C (86 to 437 °F). They then use various processes to:

a. Increase the yield of gasoline from a barrel of crude oil by converting larger-molecule (higher-boiling) and smaller-molecule (lower-boiling) hydrocarbons to hydrocarbons in the gasoline boiling range; or
b. Convert low-octane hydrocarbons to high-octane hydrocarbons. The primary processes used by today's refiners are:
    1. Catalytic cracking, which converts higher-boiling hydrocarbons into hydrocarbons in the gasoline boiling range.
    2. Reforming, which converts low-octane hydrocarbons to higher-octane hydrocarbons.
    3. Alkylation, which converts gaseous hydrocarbons to high-octane liquid hydrocarbons.
    4. Isomerization, which upgrades the octane quality of light straightrun gasoline by converting straight-chain paraffins to their branched-chain isomers.
    5. Hydrocracking, in which cracking occurs in the presence of both hydrogen and a catalyst, to produce a less olefinic gasoline component.

Reforming was increasingly used during the 1970s and 1980s to replace the octane numbers lost by the requirement for unleaded gasoline in modern automobiles and the resulting reduction and eventual elimination of lead antiknock usage. Oxygenates such as ethanol and methyl tertiary-butyl ether (MTBE) are now contributing significant octane benefits. In 1995, the U.S. gasoline pool consisted of approximately 35% reformate, 34% catalytic crackate, 12% alkylate, 6% isomerate, 6% butanes, 3% MTBE, 2% light straightrun, 1% hydrocrackate, and 1% ethanol. (The term "pool" is often used to refer to the total of all gasoline produced in the country.)

Gasolines are blended to satisfy diverse automobile requirements. Antiknock rating, volatility, and other properties are balanced to provide satisfactory vehicle performance. Additives are used to provide or enhance specific performance features and have become increasingly important in late-model cars. Up to 10 vol% ethanol and up to 15 vol% ethers are used as blending agents in gasoline, as discussed in Section 9.

This SAE Recommended Practice summarizes the significance of the more important physical and chemical characteristics of automotive gasolines, and describes pertinent test methods for defining or evaluating these properties. Information on properties of automotive gasolines currently marketed in service stations throughout the United States can be found in semiannual reports issued by TRW Petroleum Technologies (formerly BDM Petroleum Technologies and the National Institute for Petroleum and Energy Research (NIPER)). The Alliance of Automobile Manufacturers (AAM), the successor to the American Automobile Manufacturers Association (AAMA), conducts semiannual surveys of gasoline quality in the U.S., and to a limited extent in Canada and Mexico. A number of proprietary surveys are also conducted.

1. Scope—This SAE Recommended Practice summarizes the composition of modern automotive gasolines, the significance of their physical and chemical characteristics, and the pertinent test methods for defining or evaluating these properties.

2. References

2.1 Applicable Publications—The following publications form a part of this standard to the extent specified herein. Unless otherwise indicated, the latest issue of SAE publications shall apply.

2.1.1 SAE PUBLICATIONS—Available from the Society of Automotive Engineers, 400 Commonwealth Drive, Warrendale, PA 15096-0001.

SAE J1082—Fuel Economy Measurements—Road Test Procedure
SAE J1297—Alternative Automotive Fuels
SAE J1498—Heating Value of Fuels
SAE J1829—Stoichiometric Air/Fuel Ratios of Automotive Fuels

2.1.2 ASTM PUBLICATIONS—Available from ASTM, 100 Barr Harbor Drive, West Conshohocken, PA 19428-2959.

ASTM D 56—Test Method for Flash Point by Tag Closed Tester
ASTM D 86—Test Method for Distillation of Petroleum Products
ASTM D 130—Test Method for Detection of Copper Corrosion from Petroleum Products by the Copper Strip Tarnish Test
ASTM D 240—Test Method for Heat of Combustion of Liquid Hydrocarbon Fuels by Bomb Calorimeter (High Precision Method)
ASTM D 287—Test Method for API Gravity of Crude Petroleum and Petroleum Products (Hydrometer Method)
ASTM D 381—Test Method for Existent Gum in Fuels by Jet Evaporation
ASTM D 445—Test Method for Kinematic Viscosity of Transparent and Opaque Liquids (and the Calculation of Dynamic Viscosity)
ASTM D 471—Test Method for Rubber Property—Effect of Liquids
ASTM D 525—Test Method for Oxidation Stability of Gasoline (Induction Period Method)
ASTM D 665—Test Method for Rust-Preventing Characteristics of Inhibited Mineral Oil in the Presence of Water
ASTM D 1266—Test Method for Sulfur in Petroleum Products (Lamp Method)
ASTM D 1298—Test Method for Relative Density (Specific Gravity) or API Gravity of Crude Petroleum and Liquid Petroleum Products by Hydrometer Method
ASTM D 1319—Test Method for Hydrocarbon Types in Petroleum Products by Fluorescent Indicator Adsorption
ASTM D 2382—Test Method for Heat of Combustion of Hydrocarbon Fuels by Bomb Calorimeter (High Precision Method)
ASTM D 2533—Test Method for Vapor/Liquid Ratio of Spark-Ignition Engine Fuel
ASTM D 2622—Test Method for Sulfur in Petroleum Products (X-Ray Spectrographic Method)
ASTM D 2699—Test Method for Research Octane Number of Spark-Ignition Engine Fuel
ASTM D 2700—Test Method for Motor Octane Number of Spark-Ignition Engine Fuel
ASTM D 3120—Test Method for Trace Quantities of Sulfur in Light Liquid Petroleum Hydrocarbons by Oxidative Microcoulometry
ASTM D 4052—Test Method for Density and Relative Density of Liquids by Digital Density Meter
ASTM D 4814—Standard Specification for Automotive Spark-Ignition Engine Fuel
ASTM D 4815—Test Method for Determination of MTBE, ETBE, TAME, DIPE, tertiary-Amyl Alcohol and C_1 to C_4 Alcohols in Gasoline by Gas Chromatography
ASTM D 4953—Test Method for Vapor Pressure of Gasoline and Gasoline-Oxygenate Blends (Dry Method)
ASTM D 5059—Test Methods for Lead in Gasoline by X-Ray Spectroscopy
ASTM D 5119—Test Method for Evaluation of Automotive Engine Oils in the CRC L-38 Spark-Ignition Engine
ASTM D 5188—Test Method for Vapor-Liquid Ratio Temperature Determination of Fuels (Evacuated Chamber Method)
ASTM D 5190—Test Method for Vapor Pressure of Petroleum Products (Automatic Method)
ASTM D 5191—Test Method for Vapor Pressure of Petroleum Products (Mini Method)
ASTM D 5302—Test Method for Evaluation of Automotive Engine Oils for Inhibition of Deposit Formation and Wear in a Spark-Ignition Internal Combustion Engine Fueled with Gasoline and Operated Under Low-Temperature, Light-Duty Conditions
ASTM D 5453—Test Method for the Determination of Total Sulfur in Light Hydrocarbons, Motor Fuels, and Oils by Ultraviolet Fluorescence
ASTM D 5482—Test Method for Vapor Pressure of Petroleum Products (Mini Method-Atmospheric)
ASTM D 5500—Test Method for Vehicle Evaluation of Unleaded Automotive Spark-Ignition Engine Fuel for Intake Valve Deposit Formation

ASTM D 5533—Test Method for Evaluation of Automotive Engine Oils in the Sequence IIIE, Spark-Ignition Engine

ASTM D 5598—Test Method for Evaluating Unleaded Automotive Spark-Ignition Engine Fuel for Electronic Port Fuel Injector Fouling

ASTM D 5844—Test Method for Evaluation of Automotive Engine Oils for Inhibition of Rusting (Sequence IID)

ASTM D 5845—Test Method for Determination of MTBE, ETBE, TAME, DIPE, Methanol, Ethanol and tert-Butanol in Gasoline by Infrared Spectroscopy

ASTM E 659—Test Method for Autoignition Temperature of Liquid Chemicals

ASTM Research Report D02-1347—Reformulated Spark-ignition Engine Fuel

2.2 Other Publications—The following publications are referenced throughout the document with parentheses.

1. R. V. Kerley and K. W. Thurston, "Knocking Behavior of Fuels and Engines," SAE Transactions, Vol. 64, p. 554, (1956)
2. K. Owen and T. Coley, "Automotive Fuels Reference Book," 2nd Edition, SAE (1995).
3. ASTM, "Manual on Significance of Tests for Petroleum Products: 6th Edition," MNL1 (1993).
4. W. A. Gruse, "Motor Fuels, Performance and Testing," Reinhold Publishing Corp., New York, (1967)
5. "Test Methods for Rating Motor, Diesel, Aviation Fuels," Annual Book of ASTM Standards, Vol. 05.04. See most recent edition.
6. L. M. Gibbs, "Transportation Fuels—Automotive Gasoline," Encyclopedia of Energy Technology and the Environment, John Wiley and Sons, Inc., (1995).
7. C. L. Dickson, P. W. Woodward, and P. L. Bjugstad, "Trends of Petroleum Fuels, 1987," NIPER-309, December 1987.
8. P. Dorn, A. M. Mourad, and S. Herbstman, "The Properties and Performance of Modern Automotive Fuels," SAE Paper 861178.
9. D. Godfrey and R. L. Courney, "Investigation of the Mechanism of Exhaust Valve Seat Wear in Engines Run on Unleaded Gasoline," SAE Paper 710356.
10. G. A. Schoonveld, et al., "Exhaust Valve Recession with Low-Lead Gasolines," SAE Paper 861550.
11. J. A. Garbak and G. E. Grinnell, "Effect of Using Unleaded and Low-Lead Gasoline Containing Non-Lead Additives on Agricultural Engines Designed for Leaded Gasoline," SAE Paper 871622.
12. G. A. Lavoie, C. S. Smith, and E. H. Schanerberger, "V/L Effect on Vapor Pressure Measurement of Full Boiling Range Fuels Using the Two-Part Injection Method," SAE Paper 930378.
13. "Evaluation of Expressions for Fuel Volatility," CRC Report No. 403.
14. R. L. Furey, "Volatility Characteristics of Gasoline-Alcohol and Gasoline-Ether Fuel Blends," SAE Paper 852116.
15. R. L. Furey and K. L. Perry, "Vapor Pressures of Mixtures of Gasolines and Gasoline-Alcohol Blends," SAE Paper 861557.
16. "1994 Intermediate-Temperature Cold-Start and Warmup Driveability Study," CRC Report No. 598, February 1996.
17. "CRC Low-and Intermediate-Temperature Driveability Program Using Gasoline-Alcohol Blends," CRC Report No. 568, February 1990.
18. "Effect of Volatility and Oxygenates on Driveability at Intermediate Ambient Temperatures," CRC Report No. 578, March 1992.
19. "1984 CRC Intermediate-Temperature Driveability Program Using Gasoline-Alcohol Blends," CRC Report No. 554.
20. "CRC Volatility Program on the Effect of Oxygenated Fuels and Altitude on Cold-Start Driveability at Low Ambient Temperature," CRC Report 569, January 1990.
21. "Assessment and Correlation of Customer and Rater Response to Cold-Start and Warmup Driveability," CRC Report No. 585, August 1993.
22. J. P. Doner, "A Predictive Study of the Occurrence of Meteorological Conditions Contributing to Automotive Carburetor Icing," CCL Report No. 3006, NTIS, September 1973.
23. "Two-Temperature Vapor Lock and High-Temperature Driveability Performance of 1982 Passenger Vehicles," CRC Report No. 538, December 1984.
24. "1983 CRC Two-Temperature Vapor Lock Program Using Gasoline-Alcohol Blends," CRC Report No. 550.
25. "CRC Vapor Lock Technique—Its Development and Application," SAE Transactions, p. 122 (1963).
26. "CRC Hot-Start and Driveaway Driveability Program at High and Intermediate Temperatures Using Gasoline-Alcohol Blends," CRC Report No. 555.
27. "Effects of RVP, T50, and Oxygenates on Hot-Start Driveability Performance at High and Low Altitude," CRC Report No. 584, March 1993.
28. J. P. Graham, A. T. Leard, and C. T. Valade, "Coordinating Research Council High and Intermediate Temperature Driveability Programs," SAE Paper 881671.
29. L. J. Clark, "The Causes and Control of Carburetor Foaming," SAE Paper 841400.
30. D. A. Barker, L. M. Gibbs, and E. D. Steinke, "The Development and Proposed Implementation of the ASTM Driveability Index for Motor Gasoline," SAE Paper 881668.
31. "Control of Air Pollution from New Motor Vehicles and New Motor Vehicle Engines: Certification and Test Procedures," Code of Federal Regulations, CFR40 Part 86, Subpart A, revised July 1, 1981.
32. R. S. Sickler and S.A. Pezda, "The Effect of Increasing Fuel Volatility on Exhaust Emissions," SAE Paper 860533.
33. R. L. Furey and J. B. King, "Evaporative and Exhaust Emissions from Cars Fueled with Gasoline Containing Ethanol or Methyl tert-Butyl Ether," SAE Paper 800261.
34. J. A. Gething and J. C. Horn, "Are Carbon Monoxide Exhaust Emission Reductions Proportional To Fuel Oxygen Content?" SAE Paper 890216.
35. P. A. Yaccarino, "The Effect of Oxygenated Fuel, Altitude and Temperature on CO Emissions," SAE Paper 892063.
36. W. J. Most, "Coordinating Research Council Study on Winter Exhaust Emissions with Gasoline/Oxygenate Blends," SAE Paper 892091.
37. M. R. Barusch, J. H. Macpherson, and G. H. Amberg, "Additives, Engine Fuel," Encyclopedia of Chemical Processing and Design, 2, pp. 1-77, Marcel Dekker, Inc., 1977.
38. P. Polss, "What Additives Do For Gasolines," Hydrocarbon Processing, February 1973.
39. L. M. Gibbs, "Gasoline Additives—When and Why," SAE Paper 902104.
40. D. L. Lenane and T. P. Stocky, "Gasoline Additives Solve Injector Deposit Problems," SAE Paper 861537.
41. R. C. Tupa and C. J. Dorer, "Gasoline and Diesel Fuel Additives for Performance/Distribution Quality—II," SAE Paper 861179.
42. Bill Bitting, et al., "Intake Valve Deposits—Fuel Detergency Requirements Revisited," SAE Paper 872117.
43. C. H. Jewett, et al., "Fuel Injector, Intake Valve and Carburetor Detergency Performance of Gasoline Additives," SAE Paper 872114.
44. "1982 CRC Fuel Rating Program: Road Octane Performance of Oxygenates in 1982 Model Cars," CRC Report No. 541, July 1985.
45. "Effect of Gasoline Octane Quality on Vehicle Acceleration Performance," CRC Report No. 574, July 1991.
46. Federal Register, Vol. 42, No. 124, p. 32958, June 28, 1977.
47. J. H. Currie, D. S. Grossman, and J. J. Gumbleton, "Energy Conservation with Increased Compression Ratio and Electronic Knock Control," SAE Paper 790173.
48. J. D. Benson, "Some Factors Which Affect Octane Requirement Increase," SAE Transactions, 84, p. 2582 (1975); SAE Paper 750933.
49. "1988 CRC Octane Number Requirement Survey," CRC Report No. 566, August 1989.
50. M. J. McNally, et al, "A CRC Program for Quantifying Performance of Knock-Sensor-Equipped Vehicles with Varying Octane Level Fuels," SAE Paper 892037; also, CRC Report No. 571, August 1990.
51. "1990 CRC Customer versus Rater Octane Number Requirement Program," CRC Report No. 586, October 1993.
52. "Vehicle Performance Effect of Octane on Knock-Sensor-Equipped Vehicles," CRC Report No. 597, November 1995.
53. J. C. Callison, "Octane Number Requirements of Vehicles at High Altitude," SAE Paper 872160.
54. J. C. Ingamells, R. K. Stone, H. J. Gerber, and G. H. Unzelman, "Effects of Atmospheric Variables on Passenger Car Octane Number Requirements," SAE Paper 660544.
55. "Effects of Altitude Changes on Octane Number Requirement of Late Model Cars," CRC Report No. 454, October 1973.
56. "1977 CRC Altitude Program," CRC Report No. 500, February 1979.
57. "1981 CRC Altitude Octane Requirement Program," CRC Report No. 523.
58. W. M. Steckle, "Vehicle Octane Number Requirements Versus Altitude—Another Look," SAE Paper 892035.
59. B. Y. Taniguchi, et al., "Injector Deposits—The Tip of Intake System Deposit Problems," SAE Paper 861534.
60. R. A. Lewis, et al., "A New Concept in Engine Deposit Control for Unleaded Gasolines," SAE of Japan Paper 830938.

61. R. C. Tupa, et al., "A Vehicle Test Technique for Studying PFI Deposits—A Coordinating Research Council Study," SAE Paper 890213.
62. B. D. Keller, J. H. Steury, and T. O. Wagner, "Seasonal Octane Specifications," SAE Paper 780668.
63. W. F. Biller, J. C. Callison, and T. Wusz, "Trends in Octane Number Requirement Increase," SAE Paper 892036.
64. "1994 CRC Octane Number Requirement Survey," CRC Report No. 596, November 1995.
65. J. A. Gething, "Performance-Robbing Aspects of Intake Valve and Port Deposits," SAE Paper 872116.
66. "AAMA International Fuel Survey—Motor Gasoline," Winter 1996, American Automobile Manufacturers Association, January 1996.
67. "AAMA International Fuel Survey—Motor Gasoline," Summer 1996, American Automobile Manufacturers Association, July 1996.
68. J. D. Benson, et al., "Effects of Gasoline Sulfur Level on Mass Exhaust Emissions—Auto/Oil Air Quality Improvement Research Program," SAE Paper 912323.
69. "A Program to Evaluate a Vehicle Test Method for Port Fuel Injector Deposit-Forming Tendencies of Unleaded Base Gasolines," CRC Report No. 565, February 1989.
70. "A Program to Evaluate a Bench Scale Test Method to Determine the Deposit Forming Tendencies of Port Fuel Injectors," CRC Report No. 592, April 1995.
71. "Literature Search on the Impact of Combustion Chamber Deposits on Engine Performance," CRC Report No. 595, August 1995.
72. G. T. Kalghatgi, "Deposits in Gasoline Engines—A Literature Review," SAE Paper 902105.
73. Title 13, California Code of Regulations, § 2257
74. Title 40, Code of Federal Regulations, Part 80.140 - 80.174
75. "1975 CRC Customer/Rater Knock Perception Study," CRC Report No. 492, July 1977.
76. "1978 CRC Customer Versus Rater Octane Number Requirement Program," CRC Report No. 514, April 1980.
77. "1990 CRC Customer Versus Rater Octane Number Requirement Program," CRC Report No. 586, October 1993.
78. "1995-97 CRC Study of Fuel Volatility Effects on Cold-Start and Warmup Driveability with Hydrocarbon, MTBE, and Ethanol Gasolines: Summary Report for Phases 1, 2, and 3," CRC Report No. 613, December 1998.

NOTE—SAE publications are available from SAE, 400 Commonwealth Drive, Warrendale, PA 15096-0001.

ASTM publications are available from American Society for Testing and Materials, 100 Barr Harbor Drive, West Conshohocken, PA 19428-2959.

CRC publications are available from Coordinating Research Council, 219 Perimeter Center Parkway, Atlanta, GA 30346.

*3. **Antiknock Quality***[1-8,66-67]—The antiknock quality of an automotive gasoline is of prime importance. If antiknock quality is too low, knock occurs. Knock results in a high-pitched metallic rapping noise. In addition to being audibly annoying, severe knock can cause burning of piston crowns and other engine damage. There is also evidence that knock increases the rate of engine wear. The potential durability, power, and fuel economy of a given engine is realized only when the gasoline antiknock quality is adequate. However, except for some vehicles equipped with knock sensors, there is no advantage in using a gasoline having antiknock quality higher than the engine requires. Section 11 contains additional details on knock sensors and other engine design factors affecting octane number requirement.

Knock depends on complex physical and chemical phenomena highly interrelated with engine design, engine operating conditions, and atmospheric conditions. It has not been possible to completely characterize the antiknock performance of gasoline by a single measurement. The antiknock performance of a gasoline is intimately related to the engine in which it is used and to the engine and transmission operating conditions. Furthermore, this relationship varies from one engine design to another and will be different among engines of the same design due to normal production variations.

The antiknock quality of a gasoline is measured by several methods. These employ single-cylinder laboratory engines and more realistic, but much less precise, multicylinder engines in cars on the road. The American Society for Testing and Materials (ASTM) has standardized the following two single-cylinder methods: ASTM D 2699 and ASTM D 2700.

Both of these test procedures employ a variable-compression-ratio engine. The Motor method operates at a higher speed and inlet mixture temperature than does the Research method. They relate the knocking characteristics of a test gasoline to standard fuels, which are blends of two pure hydrocarbons—isooctane (2,2,4-trimethylpentane) and n-heptane. These blends are called primary reference fuels. By definition, the octane number of isooctane is 100 and the octane number of n-heptane is zero. At octane levels below 100, the octane number of a given gasoline is the percentage by volume of isooctane in a blend with n-heptane that knocks with the same intensity at the same compression ratio as the gasoline when compared by one of the standardized engine test methods. The octane number of a gasoline greater than 100 is based on the milliliters of tetraethyllead required to be added to isooctane to produce knock with the same intensity as the reference gasoline. The number of milliliters of tetraethyllead in isooctane is converted to octane numbers greater than 100 by use of tables published by ASTM.

The octane number of a given blend of either isooctane and n-heptane or tetraethyllead in isooctane is, by definition, the same for the Research and Motor methods. However, because the Motor method involves more severe operating conditions, the Research and Motor octane numbers will rarely be the same for commercial gasolines. Therefore, when considering the octane number of a given gasoline, it is necessary to know the engine test method. Commercial gasoline typically will have an octane number approximately nine units lower by the Motor method than the Research method, illustrating the important effect of engine operating conditions on antiknock performance. The numerical difference between the Research and Motor octane numbers is called sensitivity. Research octane number is, in general, the better indicator of antiknock quality for engines operating at full throttle and low engine speed. Motor octane number is the better indicator at: (a) full throttle and high engine speed and (b) part throttle at low and high engine speeds. Run-on or afterrunning, where the engine continues to run after the ignition is turned off, correlates better with Research octane number.

In the past, the antiknock performance of gasolines in vehicles, or road octane number, could be determined directly by using primary reference fuels and manually controlling ignition timing to vary the knocking tendency of the engine. The most commonly used test methods were the CRC Modified Borderline (F-27) and Modified Uniontown (F-28) research techniques. When using these procedures, the knocking tendencies of test gasolines and reference fuels were compared at the lowest audible level of knock. The road octane number of a gasoline was defined as being equal to the octane number of the primary reference fuel blend that produced the same knock intensity while operating under the specified test conditions.

Modern vehicles equipped with computer-controlled ignition systems do not have provisions for manually varying ignition timing, and so the techniques described previously cannot be used to determine the road octane number of gasoline.

For most automotive engines and operating conditions, the road octane number of a gasoline will be between its Research and Motor octane numbers. The relationship between Research and Motor octane numbers used to predict the road antiknock quality of gasolines depends on the vehicles and operating conditions. The correlations between laboratory octane numbers and road octane numbers that have been developed usually employ a combination of Research and Motor octane numbers.

The average of Research (RON) and Motor (MON) octane numbers, abbreviated (R+M)/2, is considered to be a reasonable guide to a gasoline's road octane performance. U.S. Federal regulations require posting of the (R+M)/2 value on service station pumps. (R+M)/2 is also referred to as antiknock index and posted octane rating.

The tendency of gasolines to knock can be markedly decreased by the addition of very small quantities of chemical additives known as antiknock compounds. The lead alkyls (tetraethyllead, tetramethyllead, and physically and chemically reacted mixtures of these two materials) have been the most commonly used antiknock compounds. However, the use of lead antiknocks is banned for use in modern cars equipped with catalytic converters, and refiners have been forced to use refining processes and, more recently, oxygenated compounds to recover the lost octane numbers.

The Clean Air Act amendments of 1990 prohibit the use of leaded gasoline for highway vehicle use as of January 1, 1996, as discussed in more detail in Section 4.

Some leaded gasolines contained manganese in the form of methylcyclopentadienyl manganese tricarbonyl (MMT) for octane improvement. However, the use of MMT in unleaded gasolines was banned in the United States by the Environmental Protection Agency (EPA) from 1978 to 1995, but it was widely used in Canadian unleaded gasolines during that time and is still used at concentrations up to 0.018 g Mn/L. In 1995, a U.S. Court of Appeals ordered EPA to grant a Clean Air Act waiver to allow the use of MMT in unleaded gasolines in the U.S. at concentrations not to exceed 1/32 g Mn/gal (about 0.008 g Mn/liter).

4. Grades of Gasoline—Historically, leaded automotive gasolines have been classified into two grades: premium and regular, based on octane number. Superpremium, intermediate, subregular, and blends of high-octane and low-octane grades have also been marketed.

With the exception of one premium gasoline marketed on the east coast and southern areas of the United States, all automotive gasolines from the mid-1920's until 1970 contained lead antiknock compounds to increase antiknock quality. Because lead antiknock compounds were found to be detrimental to the performance of catalytic emission control systems then under development, United States passenger car manufacturers in 1971 began to build engines designed to operate satisfactorily on gasolines of nominal 91 Research octane number. Some of these engines were designed to operate on unleaded fuel, while others required leaded fuel or the occasional use of leaded fuel. The 91-RON level was chosen in the belief that unleaded gasoline at this level could be made available in quantities required using then current refinery processing equipment. Accordingly, unleaded and low-lead gasolines were introduced during 1970 to supplement the conventional leaded gasolines already available.

Beginning with the 1975 model year, most new car models were equipped with catalytic exhaust treatment devices as one means of compliance with the 1975 legal restrictions in the United States on automobile emissions. The need for gasolines that would not adversely affect such catalytic devices led to the large-scale availability and growing use of unleaded gasolines, with all late-model cars requiring unleaded gasoline.

The EPA regulations developed in response to the Clean Air Act Amendments of 1990 prohibit after December 31, 1995, the sale, supply, dispensing, transportation, or introduction into commerce of a fuel, for use in any motor vehicle, which is produced with the use of lead additives or which contains more than 0.05 g of lead per U.S. gallon (0.013 g/liter). These regulations define motor vehicle to include any self-propelled vehicle designed for transporting persons or property on a street or highway. The regulations do not prohibit the use of lead additives in fuel used in aircraft, racing cars, and nonroad engines, such as farm equipment engines and marine engines.

Table 1 lists the most common antiknock indexes of unleaded gasolines and gasoline-oxygenate blends in current practice and their applications. Generic designations for those grades of gasoline are regular (87), intermediate (89), and premium (91 and higher). However, some fuel marketers have their own designations for these and other grades, such as Plus, Super, Supreme, Ultimate, Ultra, and many others.

TABLE 1—AUTOMOTIVE UNLEADED GASOLINE ANTIKNOCK INDEXES IN CURRENT PRACTICE

Antiknock Index(1)(2)(3)(4)(5)(6) (R+M)/2	Application
87	Designed to meet antiknock requirements of most 1971 and later model vehicles
89	For vehicles with somewhat higher antiknock requirements
91 and higher	For vehicles with high antiknock requirements

1. EPA regulations require sale of at least one unleaded gasoline of at least 87 antiknock index at sea level in accordance with 40 CFR Part 80. The regulation also allows reductions in octane for altitude.
2. Unleaded gasoline having an antiknock index of at least 87 should also have a minimum motor octane number of 82 in order to adequately protect those vehicles which are sensitive to motor octane quality.
3. Reductions in vehicle antiknock requirements for altitude are shown in Figure 1.
4. Reductions in vehicle antiknock requirements for seasonal variations are shown in Figure 2.
5. Not all antiknock index levels listed in this table are available at all locations.
6. The Federal Trade Commission requires octane posting and certification in accordance with 16 CFR Part 306.

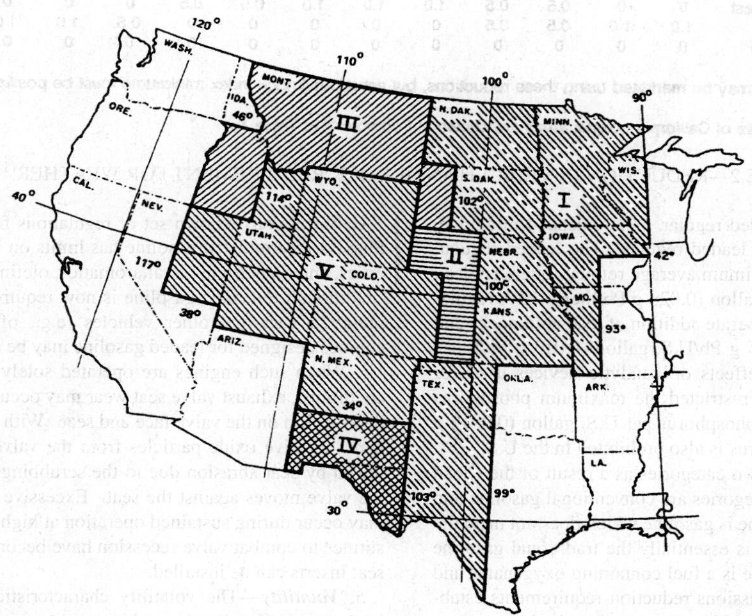

ASTM D 4814 Antiknock Index Reduction, (R+M)/2

Area	Less than 89	89 or Greater
I	0.7	0.5
II	1.5	1.5
III	2.2	1.5
IV	3.0	2.0
V	4.5	3.0

[1] **Fuel may be marketed using these reductions, but actual antiknock index minimums must be posted.**

[2] **While the reductions shown in this table apply to most pre-1985 vehicles, the control technology on many newer vehicles may cause them to have little or no reduced antiknock requirement at higher altitude.**

FIGURE 1—REDUCTION IN VEHICLE ANTIKNOCK REQUIREMENT FOR ALTITUDE(1)(2)

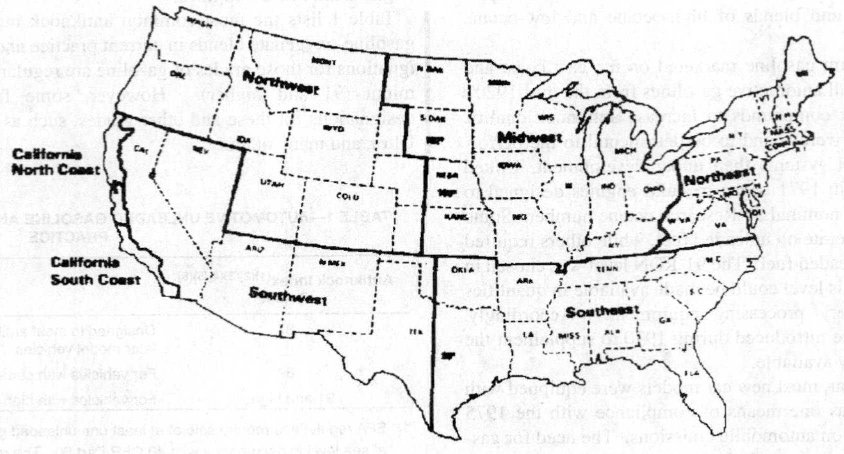

ASTM D 4814 Antiknock Index Reduction, (R+M)/2

	J	F	M	A	M	J	J	A	S	O	N	D
Northeast	1.0	0.5	0.5	0	0	0	0	0	0	0.5	0.5	1.0
Southeast	0.5	0	0	0	0	0.5	0.5	0.5	0.5	0	0	0.5
Midwest	1.0	0.5	0.5	0	0	0	0	0	0	0	0.5	1.0
Northwest	1.0	1.0	0.5	0.5	0	0	0	0	0	0.5	1.0	1.0
Southwest	1.0	0.5	0	0	0	0	0	0	0	0	0.5	1.0
California[2]												
No Coast	0.5	0.5	0.5	0.5	0.5	0.5	0.5	0.5	0	0	0.5	0.5
So Coast	0	0	0.5	0.5	1.0	1.0	1.0	0.5	0.5	0	0	0
Alaska	1.0	1.0	0.5	0.5	0	0	0	0	0	0.5	1.0	1.0
Hawaii	0	0	0	0	0	0	0	0	0	0	0	0

[1] Fuel may be marketed using these reductions, but actual antiknock index minimums must be posted.

[2] Details of California coastal areas are shown in Footnote 7 of Table 4.

FIGURE 2—REDUCTION IN VEHICLE ANTIKNOCK REQUIREMENT FOR WEATHER[(1)]

In 1994, gasoline sales were 69% unleaded regular, 11% unleaded midgrade, 20% unleaded premium, and less than 1% leaded regular. The leaded regular, before it was eliminated in 1996, had a maximum average refinery quarterly lead alkyl antiknock content of 0.10 g Pb/U.S. gallon (0.026 g Pb/liter). EPA regulations for unleaded gasoline prohibit the deliberate addition of lead antiknocks and allow the fuel to contain no more than 0.05 g Pb/U.S. gallon (0.013 g Pb/liter). Because phosphorus also causes adverse effects on catalytic devices used for automotive emission control, the EPA has restricted the maximum phosphorus content of unleaded gasoline to 0.005 g of phosphorus per U.S. gallon (0.0013 g P/liter). The deliberate addition of phosphorus is also prohibited in the U.S.

Gasolines, regardless of grade, fall into two categories as a result of the Clean Air Act Amendments of 1990. The two categories are conventional gasoline and reformulated gasoline. Conventional gasoline is gasoline which does not meet the requirements of reformulated gasoline and is essentially the traditional gasoline used for many years. Reformulated gasoline is a fuel containing oxygenates and certified to meet the specifications and emissions reduction requirements established by the Clean Air Act Amendments of 1990. Its use is required in automotive vehicles in extreme and severe ozone nonattainment areas and those areas that choose to require reformulated gasoline. Ozone nonattainment areas are those areas that do not meet the statutory maximum ambient ozone limits specified by the EPA. The program consists of two phases. Under Phase I, there was a "simple model" for 1995 through 1997 and a "complex model" that was required beginning in 1998, but could be used earlier. Phase II must use a "complex model." The primary requirements of the "simple model" were reduced vapor pressure and benzene content and a minimum oxygen content. (See 9.2 for the oxygen requirements.) The "complex model" retains the benzene and oxygen requirements of the simple model, and includes the following variable terms: vapor pressure, aromatics and olefins content, sulfur content, distillation terms, and specific oxygenates.

California has its own set of regulations for reformuated gasoline. California Phase 2 reformulated gasoline has limits on vapor pressure and distillation properties, and on benzene, total aromatics, olefins, sulfur, and oxygen contents.

Although unleaded gasoline is now required for all new cars sold in the U.S., pre-1975 cars and other vehicles (e.g., off-road and marine) equipped with engines designed for leaded gasoline may be subject to exhaust valve recession.[(9-11)] When such engines are operated solely on unleaded gasoline under severe conditions, exhaust valve seat wear may occur due to the lack of a protective lead-deposit film on the valve face and seat. With the resulting metal-to-metal contact, hard, abrasive oxide particles from the valve seat adhere to the valve face, followed by seat abrasion due to the scrubbing action of the imbedded particles as the valve moves against the seat. Excessive seat wear, and thus valve recession, may occur during sustained operation at high engine speeds and loads. Lead substitutes to combat valve recession have become commercially available, and hard seat inserts can be installed.

*5. **Volatility***—The volatility characteristics of a gasoline are also of prime importance. Gasoline is used in a great variety of engines with large variations in operating conditions and under a wide range of atmospheric temperatures and barometric pressures. These variations impose many limitations on the volatility of gasoline if it is to give satisfactory performance.

Gasolines that do not vaporize readily may cause hard starting of cold engines and poor vehicle driveability during warm-up and acceleration. Carbureted engines may also experience unequal distribution of fuel to the individual cylinders. Conversely, gasoline that vaporizes too readily in fuel pumps, lines, carburetors, or fuel injectors can cause decreased liquid fuel flow to the engine, resulting in rough engine operation or stalling. Fuels that vaporize too readily also may, if certain atmospheric conditions exist, cause ice formation in the carburetor, resulting in rough idle and stalling. A more volatile fuel also increases evaporative, refueling, and running loss emissions. Exhaust emissions and fuel economy are also related to fuel volatility to a limited extent.

5.1 Volatility Properties[3,12-15]—Since gasoline is a mixture of many hydrocarbons, it does not have a single boiling temperature. Therefore, one way to characterize automotive gasoline volatility is a distillation curve. This curve is a plot of temperature versus percentage of gasoline evaporated (see ASTM D 86). Figure 3 shows typical distillation curves for summer and winter gasolines.

Another measure of volatility is vapor pressure, which is the force per unit area exerted on the walls of a closed container by the vaporized portion of the liquid contained therein. For hydrocarbon mixtures, such as gasoline, the vapor pressure depends on the temperature and the ratio of vapor to liquid volume in the container. The vapor pressure of gasoline is typically measured at 37.8 °C (100 °F) in a chamber having a 4:1 ratio of vapor to liquid (see ASTM D 4953, ASTM D 5190, ASTM D 5191, and ASTM D 5482). Gasoline vaporization tendency may also be expressed in terms of vapor/liquid ratio (V/L) at temperatures approximating those found in critical parts of the fuel system (see ASTM D 2533 and ASTM D 5188).

ASTM D 4814 defines six volatility classes in terms of limits on vapor pressure, distillation temperatures, and driveability index as shown in Table 2, and six volatility classes based on V/L, as shown in Table 3. Table 4 shows the geographic and seasonal recommendations for use of gasoline meeting the specifications of each volatility class within the United States. Table 4 incorporates the U.S. EPA Phase II and reformulated gasoline limits on vapor pressure during the period May 1 through September 15.

For sea-level areas outside of the United States, ASTM has suggested the air temperatures in Table 5 for guidance in selecting the appropriate volatility class.

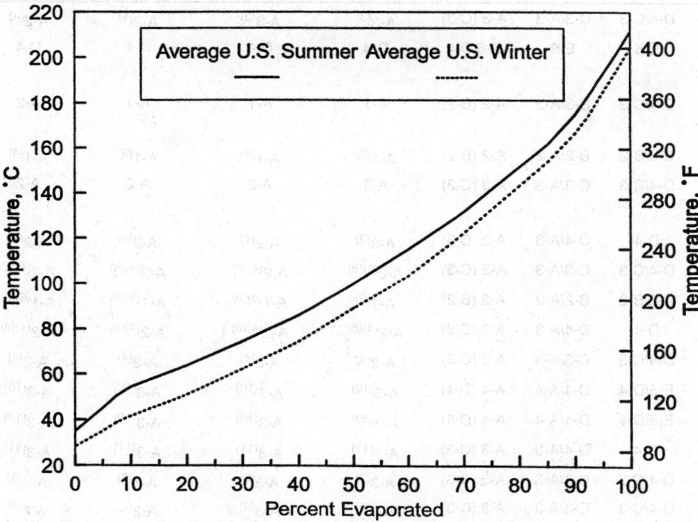

FIGURE 3—TYPICAL REGULAR GRADE UNLEADED GASOLINE DISTILLATION CURVES

TABLE 2—VAPOR PRESSURE AND DISTILLATION CLASS REQUIREMENTS

Vapor Pressure/ Distillation Class	Vapor Pressure[1] max, kPa (psi)	Distillation Temperatures, °C (°F) at % Evaporated[2] 10 vol %, max	Distillation Temperatures, °C (°F) at % Evaporated[2] 50 vol % min	Distillation Temperatures, °C (°F) at % Evaporated[2] 50 vol % max	Distillation Temperatures, °C (°F) at % Evaporated[2] 90 vol%, max	Distillation Temperatures, °C (°F) at % Evaporated[2] End Point, max	Distillation Residue, vol %, max	Driveability Index,[3] max, °C (°F) Derived[4][5]
AA	54 (7.8)	70 (158)	77(170)	121(250)	190(374)	225(437)	2	597 (1250)
A	62(9.0)	70(158)	77(170)	121(250)	190(374)	225(437)	2	597 (1250)
B	69(10.0)	65(149)	77(170)	118(245)	190(374)	225(437)	2	591 (1240)
C	79(11.5)	60(140)	77(170)	116(240)	185(365)	225(437)	2	586 (1230)
D	93(13.5)	55(131)	66(150)	113(235)	185(365)	225(437)	2	580 (1220)
E	102(15.0)	50(122)	66(150)	110(230)	185(365)	225(437)	2	569 (1200)

1. Consult EPA for approved test methods for compliance with EPA vapor pressure regulations.
2. At 101.3 kPa pressure (760 mm Hg).
3. Driveability Index (DI) = $1.5\ T_{10} + 3.0\ T_{50} + 1.0\ T_{90}$, where T_{10} = distillation temperature, °C (°F), at 10% evaporated; T_{50} = distillation temperature, °C (°F), at 50% evaporated; and T_{90} = distillaion temperture, °C (°F), at 90% evaporated.
4. The DI specification limits are applicable at the refinery or import facility as defined by 40 CFR Part 80.2 and are not subject to correction for precision of the test method.
5. Since DI is an index and has no units, the standard temperature converion from US Customary to SI units is not appropriate. The following equation is to be used to make the conversion: $DI_{°C} = (DI_{°F} - 176)/1.8$.

TABLE 3—VAPOR LOCK PROTECTION CLASS REQUIREMENTS

Vapor Lock Protection Class	Vapor-Liquid Ratio (V/L)[1][2] Test Temperature °C (°F)	Vapor-Liquid Ratio (V/L)[1][2] Max
1	60 (140)	20
2	56 (133)	20
3	51 (124)	20
4	47 (116)	20
5	41 (105)	20
6	35 (95)	20

1. At 101.3 kPa pressure (760 mm Hg).
2. The mercury confining fluid procedure of Test Method ASTM D 2533 shall be used for gasoline-oxygenate blends. Either glycerin or mercury confining fluid may be used for gasoline. ASTM Test Method D 5188 may be used for all fuels. The procedure for estimating temperature V/L (see Appendix X2 of ASTM D 4814) may only be used for gasoline.

TABLE 4—SCHEDULE OF SEASONAL AND GEOGRAPHICAL VOLATILITY CLASSES[1]—ASTM D 4814

NOTE 1—This schedule, subject to agreement between purchaser and seller, denotes the volatility properties of the fuel at the time and place of bulk delivery to the fuel dispensing facilities for the end user. For September 16 through April 30 (the time period not covered by EPA Phase II vapor pressure requirements), volatility properties for the previous month or the current month are acceptable for the end user from the 1st through the 15th day of the month. From the 16th day through the end of the month, volatility properties of the fuel delivered to the end user shall meet the requirements of the specified class(es). To ensure compliance with EPA Phase II vapor pressure requirements, vapor pressure for finished gasoline tankage at refineries, importers, pipelines, and terminals during May and for the entire distribution system, including retail stations, from June 1 to Sept. 15 shall meet only the current month's class. Shipments should anticipate this schedule.

NOTE 2—Where alternative classes are listed, either class or intermediate classes are acceptable; the option shall be exercised by the seller.

NOTE 3—See Appendix X2 of Research Report: D02-1347 (available from ASTM Headquarters) for detailed description of areas. Contact EPA for the latest information on areas requiring reformulated fuel.

State	Jan.	Feb.	March	April	May[2]	June	July	Aug.	Sept 1-15	Sept. 16-30	Oct.	Nov.	Dec.
Alabama	D-4	D-4	D-4/C-3	C-3/A-3	A-3 (C-3)	A-3[3]	A-3[3]	A-2[4]	A-2[4]	A-2/C-3	C-3	C-3/D-4	D-4
Alaska	E-6	E-6	E-6	E-6	E-6/D-4	D-4	D-4	D-4	D-4	D-4/E-6	E-6	E-6	E-6
Arizona[5]													
N 34° Latitude and E 111° Longitude	D-4	D-4	D-4/C-3	C-3/A-2	A-2 (B-2)	A-1	A-1	A-1	A-2	A-2/B-2	B-2/C-3	C-3/D-4	D-4
Remainder of State	D-4	D-4/C-3	C-3/B-2	B-2/A-2	A-2 (B-2)	A-1[6]	A-1[6]	A-1[6]	A-1[4]	A-1	A-1/B-2	B-2/C-3	C-3/D-4
Arkansas	E-5/D-4	D-4	D-4/C-3	C-3/A-3	A-3 (C-3)	A-3	A-2	A-2	A-2	A-2/C-3	C-3/D-4	D-4	D-4/E-5
California:[5][7]													
North Coast	E-5/D-4	D-4	D-4	D-4/A-3	A-3 (C-3)	A-3[3]	A-2[4]	A-2[4]	A-2[4]	A-2/B-2	B-2/C-3	C-3/D-4	D-4/E-5
South Coast	D-4	D-4	D-4/C-3	C-3/A-3	A-3 (C-3)	A-2[4][8]	A-2[4][8]	A-2[4][8]	A-2[4][8]	A-2/B-2	B-2/C-3	C-3/D-4	D-4
Southeast	D-4	D-4/C-3	C-3/B-2	B-2/A-2	A-2 (B-2)	A-1[6]	A-1[6][9]	A-1[6][9]	A-1[6][9]	A-1	A-1/B-2	B-2/C-3	C-3/D-4
Interior	E-5/D-4	D-4	D-4	D-4/A-3	A-3 (C-3)	A-2[4][8]	A-2[4][8]	A-2[4][8]	A-2[4][8]	A-2/B-2	B-2/C-3	C-3/D-4	D-4/E-5
Colorado	E-5	E-5/D-4	D-4/C-3	C-3/A-3	A-3 (C-3)	A-2[4]	A-2[4]	A-2[4]	A-2[4]	A-2/B-2	B-2/C-3	C-3/D-4	D-4/E-5
Connecticut	E-5	E-5	E-5/D-4	D-4/A-4	A-4 (D-4)	A-3[10]	A-3[10]	A-3[10]	A-3[10]	A-3/D-4	D-4	D-4/E-5	E-5
Delaware	E-5	E-5	E-5/D-4	D-4/A-4	A-4 (D-4)	A-3[10]	A-3[10]	A-3[10]	A-3[10]	A-3/C-3	C-3/D-4	D-4/E-5	E-5
District of Columbia	E-5	E-5/D-4	D-4	D-4/A-3	A-3 (C-3)	A-3[11]	A-3[11]	A-3[11]	A-3[11]	A-3/C-3	C-3/D-4	D-4/E-5	E-5
Florida	D-4	D-4	D-4/C-3	C-3/A-3	A-3 (C-3)	A-3[3]	A-3[3]	A-3[3]	A-3[3]	A-3/C-3	C-3	C-3/D-4	D-4
Georgia[5]	D-4	D-4	D-4/C-3	C-3/A-3	A-3 (C-3)	A-3[3]	A-3[3]	A-2[4]	A-2[4]	A-2/C-3	C-3	C-3/D-4	D-4
Hawaii	C-3	C-3	C-3	C-3	C-3	C-3	C-3	C-3	C-3	C-3	C-3	C-3	C-3
Idaho:													
N 46° Latitude	E-5	E-5	E-5/D-4	D-4/A-4	A-4 (D-4)	A-3	A-2	A-2	A-2	A-2/C-3	C-3/D-4	D-4/E-5	E-5
S 46° Latitude	E-5	E-5/D-4	D-4	D-4/A-3	A-3 (C-3)	A-2	A-2	A-2	A-2	A-2/B-2	B-2/C-3	C-3/D-4	D-4/E-5
Illinois:[5]													
N 40° Latitude	E-5	E-5	E-5/D-4	D-4/A-4	A-4 (D-4)	A-3[10]	A-3[10]	A-3[10]	A-3[10]	A-3/C-3	C-3/D-4	D-4/E-5	E-5
S 40° Latitude	E-5	E-5	E-5/D-4	D-4/A-3	A-3 (C-3)	A-3	A-3	A-3	A-3	A-3/C-3	C-3/D-4	D-4	D-4/E-5
Indiana[5]	E-5	E-5	E-5/D-4	D-4/A-4	A-4 (D-4)	A-3[10]	A-3[10]	A-3[10]	A-3[10]	A-3/C-3	C-3/D-4	D-4/E-5	E-5
Iowa	E-5	E-5	E-5/D-4	D-4/A-3	A-3 (C-3)	A-3	A-3	A-3	A-3	A-3/C-3	C-3/D-4	D-4/E-5	E-5
Kansas[5]	E-5	E-5/D-4	D-4/C-3	C-3/A-3	A-3 (C-3)	A-2[4]	A-2[4]	A-2[4]	A-2[4]	A-2/B-2	B-2/C-3	C-3/D-4	D-4/E-5
Kentucky	E-5	E-5/D-4	D-4	D-4/A-3	A-3 (C-3)	A-3[10]	A-3[10]	A-3[10]	A-3[10]	A-3/C-3	C-3/D-4	D-4/E-5	E-5
Louisiana	D-4	D-4	D-4/C-3	C-3/A-3	A-3 (C-3)	A-3[3]	A-3[3]	A-2[4]	A-2[4]	A-2/C-3	C-3	C-3/D-4	D-4
Maine[5]	E-5	E-5	E-5/D-4	D-4/A-4	A-4(D-4)	A-3	A-3	A-3	A-3	A-3/D-4	D-4	D-4/E-5	E-5
Maryland	E-5	E-5	E-5/D-4	D-4/A-4	A-4 (D-4)	A-3[10][11]	A-3[10][11]	A-3[10][11]	A-3[10][11]	A-3/C-3	C-3/D-4	D-4/E-5	E-5
Massachusetts	E-5	E-5	E-5/D-4	D-4/A-4	A-4 (D-4)	A-3[10]	A-3[10]	A-3[10]	A-3[10]	A-3/D-4	D-4	D-4/E-5	E-5
Michigan[5]	E-5	E-5	E-5/D-4	D-4/A-4	A-4 (D-4)	A-3	A-3	A-3	A-3	A-3/D-4	D-4	D-4/E-5	E-5
Minnesota	E-5	E-5	E-5/D-4	D-4/A-4	A-4 (D-4)	A-3	A-3	A-3	A-3	A-3/C-3	C-3/D-4	D-4/E-5	E-5
Mississippi	D-4	D-4	D-4/C-3	C-3/A-3	A-3 (C-3)	A-3	A-3	A-2	A-2	A-2/C-3	C-3	C-3/D-4	D-4
Missouri[5]	E-5	E-5/D-4	D-4	D-4/A-3	A-3 (C-3)	A-3[3]	A-2[4]	A-2[4]	A-2[4]	A-2/C-3	C-3/D-4	D-4	D-4/E-5
Montana	E-5	E-5	E-5/D-4	D-4/A-3	A-3 (C-3)	A-2	A-2	A-2	A-2	A-2/C-3	C-3/D-4	D-4/E-5	E-5
Nebraska	E-5	E-5	E-5/D-4	D-4/A-3	A-3 (C-3)	A-2	A-2	A-2	A-2	A-2/B-2	B-2/C-3	C-3/D-4	D-4/E-5
Nevada:													
N 38° Latitude	E-5	E-5/D-4	D-4	D-4/A-3	A-3 (C-3)	A-2[4]	A-2[4]	A-2[4]	A-2[4]	A-2/B-2	B-2/C-3	C-3/D-4	D-4/E-5
S 38° Latitude	D-4	D-4/C-3	C-3/B-2	B-2/A-2	A-2 (B-2)	A-1	A-1	A-1	A-1	A-1	A-1/B-2	B-2/C-3	C-3/D-4
New Hampshire	E-5	E-5	E-5/D-4	D-4/A-4	A-4 (D-4)	A-3[10]	A-3[10]	A-3[10]	A-3[10]	A-3/D-4	D-4	D-4/E-5	E-5
New Jersey	E-5	E-5	E-5/D-4	D-4/A-4	A-4 (D-4)	A-3[10]	A-3[10]	A-3[10]	A-3[10]	A-3/D-4	D-4	D-4/E-5	E-5
New Mexico:													
N 34° Latitude	E-5/D-4	D-4	D-4/C-3	C-3/A-2	A-2 (B-2)	A-1	A-1	A-2	A-2	A-2/B-2	B-2/C-3	C-3/D-4	D-4
S 34° Latitude	D-4	D-4/C-3	C-3/B-2	B-2/A-2	A-2 (B-2)	A-1	A-1	A-1	A-1	A-1/B-2	B-2/C-3	C-3/D-4	D-4
New York	E-5	E-5	E-5/D-4	D-4/A-4	A-4 (D-4)	A-3[10]	A-3[10]	A-3[10]	A-3[10]	A-3/D-4	D-4	D-4/E-5	E-5
North Carolina	E-5/D-4	D-4	D-4	D-4/A-3	A-3 (C-3)	A-3[3]	A-3[3]	A-2[4]	A-2[4]	A-2/C-3	C-3/D-4	D-4	D-4/E-5
North Dakota	E-5	E-5	E-5/D-4	D-4/A-4	A-4 (D-4)	A-3	A-2	A-2	A-2	A-2/C-3	C-3/D-4	D-4/E-5	E-5
Ohio	E-5	E-5	E-5/D-4	D-4/A-4	A-4 (D-4)	A-3	A-3	A-3	A-3	A-3/C-3	C-3/D-4	D-4/E-5	E-5

TABLE 4—SCHEDULE OF SEASONAL AND GEOGRAPHICAL VOLATILITY CLASSES[1]—ASTM D 4814 (continued)

NOTE 1—This schedule, subject to agreement between purchaser and seller, denotes the volatility properties of the fuel at the time and place of bulk delivery to the fuel dispensing facilities for the end user. For September 16 through April 30 (the time period not covered by EPA Phase II vapor pressure requirements), volatility properties for the previous month or the current month are acceptable for the end user from the 1st through the 15th day of the month. From the 16th day through the end of the month, volatility properties of the fuel delivered to the end user shall meet the requirements of the specified class(es). To ensure compliance with EPA Phase II vapor pressure requirements, vapor pressure for finished gasoline tankage at refineries, importers, pipelines, and terminals during May and for the entire distribution system, including retail stations, from June 1 to Sept. 15 shall meet only the current month's class. Shipments should anticipate this schedule.

NOTE 2—Where alternative classes are listed, either class or intermediate classes are acceptable; the option shall be exercised by the seller.

NOTE 3—See Appendix X2 of Research Report: D02-1347 (available from ASTM Headquarters) for detailed description of areas. Contact EPA for the latest information on areas requiring reformulated fuel.

State	Jan.	Feb.	March	April	May[2]	June	July	Aug.	Sept 1-15	Sept. 16-30	Oct.	Nov.	Dec.
Oklahoma	E-5/D-4	D-4	D-4/C-3	C-3/A-3	A-3 (C-3)	A-2	A-2	A-2	A-2	A-2/B-2	B-2/C-3	C-3/D-4	D-4/E-5
Oregon:													
E 122° Longitude	E-5	E-5/D-4	D-4	D-4/A-4	A-4 (D-4)	A-3	A-2	A-2	A-2	A-2/C-3	C-3/D-4	D-4	D-4/E-5
W 122° Longitude	E-5	E-5/D-4	D-4	D-4/A-4	A-4 (D-4)	A-3[3]	A-3[3]	A-3[3]	A-3[3]	A-3/C-3	C-3/D-4	D-4/E-5	E-5
Pennsylvania[5]	E-5	E-5	E-5/D-4	D-4/A-4	A-4 (D-4)	A-3[10]	A-3[10]	A-3[10]	A-3[10]	A-3/D-4	D-4	D-4/E-5	E-5
Rhode Island	E-5	E-5	E-5/D-4	D-4/A-4	A-4 (D-4)	A-3[10]	A-3[10]	A-3[10]	A-3[10]	A-3/D-4	D-4	D-4/E-5	E-5
South Carolina	D-4	D-4	D-4	D-4/A-3	A-3 (C-3)	A-3	A-3	A-2	A-2	A-2/C-3	C-3/D-4	D-4	D-4
South Dakota	E-5	E-5	E-5/D-4	D-4/A-3	A-3 (C-3)	A-2	A-2	A-2	A-2	A-2/B-2	B-2/C-3	C-3/D-4	D-4/E-5
Tennessee	E-5/D-4	D-4	D-4	D-4/A-3	A-3 (C-3)	A-3[3]	A-3[3]	A-2[4]	A-2[4]	A-2/C-3	C-3/D-4	D-4	D-4/E-5
Texas:[5]													
E 99° Longitude	D-4	D-4	D-4/C-3	C-3/A-3	A-3 (C-3)	A-3[3][11]	A-2[4][8]	A-2[4][8]	A-2[4][8]	A-2/B-2	B-2/C-3	C-3/D-4	D-4
W 99° Longitude	D-4	D-4/C-3	C-3/B-2	B-2/A-2	A-2 (B-2)	A-1[6]	A-1[6]	A-1[6]	A-1[6]	A-1/B-2	B-2/C-3	C-3/D-4	D-4
Utah	E-5	E-5/D-4	D-4	D-4/A-3	A-3 (C-3)	A-2[4]	A-2[4]	A-2[4]	A-2[4]	A-2/B-2	B-2/C-3	C-3/D-4	D-4/E-5
Vermont	E-5	E-5	E-5/D-4	D-4/A-4	A-4 (D-4)	A-3	A-3	A-3	A-3	A-3/D-4	D-4	D-4/E-5	E-5
Virginia	E-5	E-5/D-4	D-4	D-4/A-3	A-3 (C-3)	A-3[3][11]	A-3[3][11]	A-3[3][11]	A-3[3][11]	A-3/C-3	C-3/D-4	D-4/E-5	E-5
Washington:													
E 122° Longitude	E-5	E-5	E-5/D-4	D-4/A-4	A-4 (D-4)	A-3	A-2	A-2	A-2	A-2/C-3	C-3/D-4	D-4/E-5	E-5
W 122° Longitude	E-5	E-5	E-5/D-4	D-4/A-4	A-4 (D-4)	A-3	A-3	A-3	A-3	A-3/C-3	C-3/D-4	D-4/E-5	E-5
West Virginia	E-5	E-5	E-5/D-4	D-4/A-4	A-4 (D-4)	A-3	A-3	A-3	A-3	A-3/C-3	C-3/D-4	D-4/E-5	E-5
Wisconsin	E-5	E-5	E-5/D-4	D-4/A-4	A-4 (D-4)	A-3[10]	A-3[10]	A-3[10]	A-3[10]	A-3/C-3	C-3/D-4	D-4/E-5	E-5
Wyoming	E-5	E-5	E-5/D-4	D-4/A-3	A-3 (C-3)	A-2	A-2	A-2	A-2	A-2/B-2	B-2/C-3	C-3/D-4	D-4/E-5

1. For the period May 1 through September 15, the specified vapor pressure classes comply with 1992 U.S. EPA Phase II volatility regulations. EPA regulations (under the Phase II regulations) allow 1.0 psi higher vapor pressure for gasoline-ethanol blends containing 9 to 10 vol % ethanol for the same period.

2. Values in parentheses are permitted for retail stations and other end users.

3. Ozone Nonattainment Areas Requiring Volatility Class AA-3:
   See 40 CFR Part 81.305 for description of the geographic boundary for each area.

   Alabama—Jefferson and Shelby counties
   California*—Alameda, Contra Costa, Marin, Monterey, Napa, San Francisco, San Benito, San Mateo, Santa Clara, Santa Cruz, and Solano (part) counties
   Florida—Broward, Dade, Duval, Hillsborough, Palm Beach, and Pinellas counties
   Georgia*—Cherokee, Clayton, Cobb, Coweta, Dekalb, Douglas, Fayette, Forsyth, Fulton, Gwinnett, Henry, Paulding, and Rockdale counties
   Louisiana—Ascension, Beauregard, Calcasieu, East Baton Rouge, Grant, Iberville, Jefferson, Lafayette, Lafourche, Livingston, Orleans, Point Coupee, Saint Bernard, Saint Charles, Saint James, Saint Mary, and West Baton Rouge parishes
   Missouri—Franklin, Jefferson, Saint Charles, and Saint Louis counties, and the city of St. Louis
   North Carolina—Davidson, Davie (part), Durham, Forsyth, Gaston, Granville (part), Guilford, Mecklenburgh, and Wake counties
   Oregon—Clackamas, Marion (part), Multnomah, Polk (part), and Washington
   Tennessee—Davidson, Rutherford, Shelby, Sumner, Williamson, and Wilson Counties
   Texas—Hardin, Jefferson, Orange, and Victoria counties
   Virginia—Smyth county (part)
   *See footnote 5 for local vapor pressure limits.

4. Ozone Nonattainment Areas Requiring Volatility Class AA-2:
   See 40 CFR Part 81.305 for description of the geographic boundary for each area.

   Alabama—Jefferson and Shelby counties
   Arizona*—Maricopa County
   California—Alameda, Butte, Contra Costa, Fresno, Kern (part), Kings, Madera,Marin,Merced, Monterey, Napa, San Benito, San Francisco, San Joaquin, San Mateo, Santa Barbara, Santa Clara, Santa Cruz, Stanislaus, Tulare, and Yuba counties
   Colorado—Adams, Arapahoe, Boulder, Denver, Douglas, and Greeley counties (waived by EPA)
   Georgia*—Cherokee, Clayton, Cobb, Coweta, Dekalb, Douglas, Fayette, Forsyth, Fulton, Gwinnett, Henry, Paulding, and Rockdale counties
   Kansas*—Johnson and Wyandotte counties
   Louisiana—Ascension, Beauregard, Calcasieu, East Baton Rouge, Grant, Iberville, Jefferson, Lafayette, Lafourche, Livingston, Orleans, Point Coupee, Saint Bernard, Saint Charles, Saint James, Saint Mary, and West Baton Rouge parishes
   Missouri—Franklin, Jefferson, Saint Charles, and Saint Louis counties, and the city of St. Louis
   Nevada—Washoe County
   North Carolina—Davidson, Davie (part), Durham, Forsyth, Gaston, Granville (part) Guilford, Mecklenburgh, and Wake counties
   Tennessee—Davidson, Rutherford, Shelby, Sumner, Williamson, and Wilson counties
   Texas—Hardin, Jefferson, Orange, and Victoria counties
   Utah—Davis and Salt Lake counties
   *See footnote 5 for local vapor pressure limits

5. Federal Approved State Implementation Plan Areas Requiring More Restrictive Maximum Vapor Pressure Limits
   Note—Some areas are awaiting official EPA for the more restrictive local vapor pressure limits.

   Arizona—Maricopa County—48.2 kPa (7.0 psi) max May 31—Sep 30, 62.0 kPa (9.0 psi) max) Oct 1 — Mar 31
   California—48.26 kPa (7.00 psi) max Apr 1, May 1, or Jun 1—Sep 30 or Oct 31 depending on air basin
   Georgia—Barrow, Bartow, Butts, Carroll, Cherokee, Clayton, Cobb, Coweta, Dawson, Dekalb, Douglas, Fayette, Forsyth, Fulton, Gwinnett, Hall, Haralson, Henry, Jackson, Newton, Paulding, Pickens, Rockdale, Spalding, and Walton coutnies—48.2 kPa (7.0 psi) max Jun 1 — Sep 15**
   Illinois—Madison, Monroe, and Saint Clair counties area—49.6 kPa (7.2 psi) max Jun 1 — Sep 15**
   Indiana—Clark and Floyd counties area—53.8 kPa (7.8 psi) max May 1 terminal/Jun 1 retail — Sept 15**
   Kansas—Johnson and Wyandotte counties—49.6 kPa (7.2 psi) max Jun 1 — Sep 15**
   Maine—Androscoggin, Cumberland, Kennebec, Knox, Lincoln, Sagadahoc, and York counties—49.6 kPa (7.2 psi) max May 1 — Sep 15 (approval pending)
   Michigan—Livingston, Macomb, Monroe, Oakland, Saint Clair, Washtenaw, and Wayne counties—53.8 kPa (7.8 psi) max Jun 1 — Sep 15
   Missouri—Clay, Jackson, and Platte counties—49.6 kPa (7.2 psi) max Jun1 — Sep 15**
   Pennsylvania—Allegheny, Armstrong, Beaver, Butler, Fayette, Washington, and Westmoreland counties—53.8 kPa (7.8 psi) max Jun 1 — Sep 15
   Texas—El Paso County—48.2 kPa (7.0 psi) max May 1 terminal/June 1 retail — Sep 15
   Texas—Anderson, Angelina, Aransas, Atascosa, Austin, Bastrop, Bee, Bell, Bexar, Bosque, Bowie, Brazos, Burleson, Caldwell, Calhoun, Camp, Cass, Cherokee, Colorado, Comal, Cooke, Coryell, DeWitt, Delta, Ellis, Falls, Fannin, Fayette, Franklin, Freestone, Goliad, Gonzales, Grayson, Gregg, Grimes, Gaudalupe, Harrison, Hays, Henderson, Hill, Hood, Hopkins, Houston, Hunt, Jackson, Jasper, Johnson, Karnes, Kaufman, Lamar, Lavaca, Lee, Leon, Limestone, Live Oak, Madison, Marion, Matagorda, McLennan, Milam, Morris, Nacogdoches, Navarro, Newton, Neuces, Panola, Parker, Polk, Rains, Red River, Refugio, Robertson, Rockwall, Rusk, Sabine, San Jacinto, San Patricio, San Augustine, Shelby, Smith, Somervell, Titus, Travis, Trinity, Tyler, Upshur, VanZandt, Victoria, Walker, Washington, Wharton, Williamson, Wilson, Wise, and Wood Counties—48.2 kPa (7.0 psi) max May 1 terminal/June 1 retail — October 1 (approval pending)
   ** A 1.0 psi higher vapor pressure is allowed for gasoline-ethanol blends containing 9 to 10 vol% ethanol.

6. Ozone Nonattainment Areas Requiring Volatility Class AA-1:
   See 40 CFR Part 81.305 for description of the geographic boundary for each area.

   Arizona*—Maricopa County
   California*—Imperial and Kern (part) counties
   Texas*—El Paso County
   * See footnote 5 for local vapor pressure limits.

7. Details of State Climatological Division by county as indicated:

   California, North Coast—Alameda, Contra Costa, Del Norte, Humbolt, Lake, Marin, Mendocino, Monterey, Napa, San Benito, San Francisco, San Mateo, Santa Clara, Santa Cruz, Solano, Sonoma, Trinity
   California, Interior—Lassen, Modoc, Plumas, Sierra, Siskiyou, Alpine, Amador, Butte, Calaveras, Colusa, El Dorado, Fresno, Glenn, Kern (except that portion lying east of Los Angeles County Aqueduct), Kings, Madera, Mariposa, Marced, Placer, Sacramento, San Joaquin, Shasta, Stanislaus, Sutter, Tehama, Tulare, Tuolumne, Yolo, Yuba, Nevada
   California, South Coast—Orange, San Diego, San Luis Obispo, Santa Barbara, Ventura, Los Angeles (except that portion north of the San Gabriel Mountain range and east of the Los Angeles County Aqueduct)
   California, Southeast—Imperial, Riverside, San Bernadino, Los Angeles (that portion north of the San Gabriel Mountain range and east of the Los Angeles County Aqueduct), Mono, Inyo, Kern (that portion lying east of the Los Angeles County Aqueduct)

8. Federal RFG Areas Requiring Volatility Class AA-2
   See 40 CFR Part 81.305 for description of the geographic boundary for each area.
   No waiver for gasoline-ethanol blends

   California*—El Dorado (part), Los Angeles, Orange, Placer (part), Riverside (part), Sacramento, San Bernadino (part), San Diego, Solano (part), Ventura, and Yolo Counties
   Texas—Brasoria, Chambers, Collin, Dallas, Denton, Fort Bend, Galveston, Harris, Liberty, Montgomery, Tarrant, and Walter counties
   * See footnote 5 for local vapor pressure limits

9. Federal RFG Areas Requiring Volatility Class AA-1
   See 40 CFR Part 81.305 for description of the geographic boundary for each area.
   No waiver for gasoline-ethanol blends

   California* - Los Angeles (part), Riverside (part), and San Bernadino (part) counties
   *See footnote 5 for local vapor pressure limts.

10. Federal RFG Areas Requiring Volatility Class A-3
    See 40 CFR Part 81.305 for description of the geographic boundary for each area.
    No waiver for gasoline-ethanol blends

    Connecticut—All counties
    Delaware—All counties
    Illinois*—Cook, DuPage, Grundy (part), Kane, Kendall (part), Lake, McHenry, and Will counties
    Indiana*—Lake and Porter counties
    Kentucky—Boone, Bullitt (part), Campbell, Jefferson, Kenton, and Oldham (part) counties
    Maryland—Cecil County
    Massachusetts—All counties
    New Hampshire—Hillsborough, Merrimack, Rockingham, and Strafford counties
    New Jersey—All counties
    New York—Bronx, Dutchess, Essex (part), Kings, Nassau, New York, Orange, Putnam, Queens, Richmond, Rockland, Suffolk, and Westchester counties
    Pennsylvania—Bucks, Chester, Delaware, Montgomery, and Philadelphia counties
    Rhode Island—All counties
    Wisconsin—Kenosha, Milwaukee, Ozaukee, Racine, Washington, and Waukesha counties
    * See footnote 5 for local vapor pressure limits.

11. Federal RFG Areas Requiring Volatility Class AA-3
See 40 CFR Part 81.305 for description of the geographic boundary for each area.
No waiver for gasoline-ethanol blends

District of Columbia

Maryland—Anne Arundel, Baltimore, Calvert, Carroll, Charles, Frederick, Harford, Howard, Kent, Montgomery, Prince George's, and Queen Anne's counties

Texas—Brasoria, Chambers, Collin, Dallas, Denton, Fort Bend, Galveston, Harris, Liberty, Montgomery, Tarrant, and Waller counties

Virginia—Arlington, Charles City, Chesterfield, Fairfax, Hanover, Henrico, James City, Loudoun, Prince William, Stafford, and York counties and independent cities of Alexandria, Chesapeake, Colonial Heights, Fairfax, Falls Church, Hampton, Hopewell, Manassas, Manassas Park, Newport News, Norfolk, Posquoson, Portsmouth, Richmond, Suffolk, Virginia Beach, and Williamsburg

TABLE 5—GUIDANCE IN SELECTING THE APPROPRIATE VOLATILITY CLASS

Volatility Class	Daily Temperature, °C (°F) 10 Percentile 6-h Minimum	Daily Temperature, °C (°F) 90 Percentile 6-h Maximum
A	>16 (60)	Š43 (110)
B	>10 (50)	<43 (110)
C	>4 (40)	<36 (97)
D	>–7 (20)	<29 (85)
E	≤–7 (20)	<21 (69)

For areas above sea-level outside of the United States, the 10 percentile 6 h minimum temperature should be increased by 3.6 °C/1000 m (2 °F/1000 ft) of altitude and the 90 percentile 6 h maximum daily temperature for the area should be increased by 4.4 °C/1000 m (2.4 °F/1000 ft) before comparing it to the suggested sea-level temperature. This correction compensates for changes in fuel volatility caused by changes in barometric pressure due to altitude.

5.1.1 Effect of Government Regulations on Volatility—Federal and state government regulations on volatility have a significant effect on the gasoline produced by refiners. Summer gasoline vapor pressure was limited by EPA Phase I regulations to 9.0, 9.5, or 10.5 psi during the years 1989-1991. Phase II regulations, which became effective in 1992, impose maximum vapor pressure limits of 7.8 or 9.0 psi, depending on the geographic area and ambient ozone concentration.

Finally, in 1995, for ozone nonattainment areas requiring reformulated gasoline and for those areas opting into the program, the vapor pressure maximum limits for any gallon sold were set at 7.4 psi for Region 1 (southern tier states) and 8.3 psi for Region 2 (northern tier states). The regulations allowed averaging at 7.1 psi and 8.0 psi for the two areas. If manufactured such that every gallon meets the regulation, the corresponding limits are 7.2 psi and 8.1 psi. In addition, some states have more restrictive vapor pressure limits that have been approved by the EPA as part of the State Implementation Plan (SIP). The RFG and state regulations are shown in Table 4. For the latest information on vapor pressure requirements, the EPA should be contacted.

The use of oxygenates—alcohols and ethers—as blending agents with gasoline has increased as a result of the Clean Air Act Amendments of 1990 requiring oxygenated gasoline in the wintertime for carbon monoxide nonattainment areas beginning in November 1992. The addition of alcohols significantly affects fuel volatility, as discussed in Section 9.

5.2 Driveability[16-30]—Vehicle driveability is influenced by fuel volatility, ambient temperatures, and engine calibrations, such as fuel-air ratio, ignition timing, and exhaust gas recirculation. The main symptoms (malfunctions) of poor driveability are stalling, stumble, hesitation, and surge. Stalling is the inability of the engine to continue running. Stumble is a short, sharp reduction in acceleration after the vehicle is in motion. Hesitation is a temporary delay in acceleration when the throttle is opened. Surging is a cycling of engine power output.

5.2.1 Cold-Start Driveability—Any or all of the malfunctions listed in 5.2 can occur after a cold-start at any ambient temperature. Generally, the frequency of occurrences and the severity of malfunctions increase with decreasing ambient temperatures. Tests conducted by the CRC have shown that cold-start and cool-weather driveability are affected by changes in the 10%, 50%, and 90% evaporated temperatures of a gasoline. (See ASTM D 86.) A simple expression, called the driveability index, that predicts relative cold-start driveability performance fairly well is shown in Equation 1:

$$\text{Driveability Index} = 1.5(10\%\ \text{temperature}) + 3.0(50\%\ \text{temperature}) + 1.0(90\%\ \text{temperature}) \quad \text{(Eq. 1)}$$

Higher values mean lower volatility and poorer driveability. This expression shows that the 50% temperature has the largest effect but that the entire boiling range can influence driveability. The exact relationship is very vehicle dependent. Additional information on cold driveability may be obtained from references in 2.2.

A comprehensive 1995-97 CRC test program[78] has shown that gasolines containing 10% ethanol or 15% MTBE do not provide the same driveability performance as non-oxygenated gasolines having the same driveability index. The presence of oxygenates can cause increased driveability problems due to leaning of the air-fuel mixture. Driveability problems can also be manifested through increased intake charge cooling caused by the higher latent heat of vaporization in the case of alcohols. To more accurately predict vehicle performance of oxygenate blends, the CRC results show that an adjustment must be made to the DI formula. The modified DI equation can be written as follows:

$$DI_{mod} = 1.5(10\%\ \text{temperature}) + 3.0(50\%\ \text{temperature}) + (90\%\ \text{temperature}) + X \quad \text{(Eq. 2)}$$

5.2.2 Carburetor Icing—Carburetor icing is caused by vaporization of gasoline lowering the temperature of the air-fuel mixture, which causes moisture in the air to condense and freeze into ice on the throttle blade. The ice blocks the air flow when the throttle blade is returned to the closed, idle position causing the engine to stall.

The worst conditions for carburetor icing are high humidity and ambient temperatures between about –1 and 13 °C (30 and 55 °F). Above 13 °C (55 °F), the chances for forming ice are small, because more than 13 °C (23 °F) of cooling must occur. Below –1 °C (30 °F) there is very little moisture available in the air, even at 100% relative humidity, to form ice. Fuels that are more volatile cause more carburetor icing because they evaporate more completely in the carburetor, causing larger temperature decreases. Carburetor icing correlates with mid-range distillation temperature.

The Department of the Army completed a study in 1973 concerning the meteorological conditions that contribute to carburetor icing. Isopleth maps were proposed to identify geographical regions where carburetor icing is likely to occur.

Two types of gasoline additives have been used to control carburetor icing. Freezing point depressants reduce ice formation in the carburetor and gasoline by acting as an antifreeze. Surfactant additives are also effective by reducing adhesion between ice and metal surfaces.

The introduction of air intake heating and the gradual increase in underhood temperatures in many vehicles have nearly eliminated the problem in carbureted engines. Obviously, the almost universal use of fuel injection systems instead of carburetors in recent years has eliminated the problem for those vehicles.

5.2.3 Vapor Lock[23-25]—At high ambient temperatures, vapor lock and other hot driveability problems can occur. Vapor lock is defined as the inability of the fuel system to supply the required quantity of gasoline to the engine because of the formation of excessive vapor in the system. The effect of vapor lock may range from a condition of slightly lean air-fuel ratio to engine stalling due to lack of fuel.

Considerable test work has been conducted on vapor lock over a period of years. A vapor lock test was developed by CRC in 1958 and further refined in later test programs.

Expressions relating fuel volatility to vapor lock are of prime importance for specifying fuel properties for control of warm-engine driveability. A large number of volatility expressions have been developed over the years and CRC conducted studies to evaluate 17 of these in 1962 and 1964. One of these, the temperature at a vapor-liquid ratio of 20, is used in ASTM D 4814 as a control for vapor lock.

In carbureted vehicles, some design factors affecting vapor lock are: use of vapor return lines, fuel tank and line placement, and fuel pump location, pressure, and capacity. It is not known how well the temperature at V/L=20 correlates with vapor lock and other hot driveability problems in fuel-injected vehicles, where the fuel is under pressure from the tank to the fuel injectors.

5.2.4 Hot-Start and Driveaway[26-29]—Hot-starting characteristics of automobiles are defined as the ability or inability of a hot engine to start after an engine-off soak period. Hot driveaway problems of stalling, idle roughness, hesitation, and stumble can occur because of leaning due to vapor lock or richening due to the carburetor bowl foaming. Different techniques have been developed to evaluate two types of performance parameters—(a) hot-start and hot-driveaway and (b) vapor lock. The fuel property that has the greatest influence on hot-start and driveaway, in carbureted vehicles, is the temperature at V/L 20, but the limiting temperature for V/L 20 may be different for the two parameters and for individual vehicles.

5.2.5 DRIVEABILITY TEST TECHNIQUES—Many driveability procedures are used throughout the automotive and petroleum industries for vehicle and fuel testing. One set of procedures, those of the CRC, was developed cooperatively and is commonly used by both industries to determine the effects of fuel parameters on vehicle driveability. The three procedures used by CRC are: (a) The Cold-start and Warm-up driveability procedures for testing at low and intermediate ambient temperatures, generally below 26.7 °C (80 °F), (b) Hot-start and driveaway procedures, and (c) The Vapor Lock Procedure used for testing at ambient temperatures above 26.7 °C (80 °F).

5.3 Emissions[31-36]

5.3.1 EVAPORATIVE EMISSIONS—Fuel vapor emissions from a vehicle may include evaporative, running loss, and permeation emissions. The amount of gasoline vapor that will escape into the atmosphere depends on a variety of factors. Fuel system configuration and materials, fuel system and ambient temperatures, volume of vapor in the tank, evaporative emissions control system design, and fuel properties all contribute. The vapor pressure, as described in 5.1, is a fuel characteristic that has been found to be useful for predicting the amount of fuel vapor that will be generated in the tank.

5.3.2 EXHAUST EMISSIONS—Vehicle exhaust hydrocarbon and carbon monoxide emissions have been shown to either increase or decrease with increasing volatility. The direction of the response of exhaust emissions to volatility appears to depend on a combination of factors. These include the level of volatility tested, ambient temperature, and fuel system design and management method. Both vapor pressure and distillation characteristics have been shown to affect exhaust emissions.

5.3.3 REFUELING EMISSIONS—Emissions of hydrocarbons from the fuel tank during refueling are affected by the temperature of the dispensed fuel and tank fuel and by the vapor pressure of the fuels.

5.4 Fuel Economy—Fuel economy can be influenced by density and energy content of the fuel. Where fuel volatility changes result in a change of these properties, fuel economy can be affected. However, within practical limits, the effects of volatility on fuel economy are very small.

Both wintertime oxygenated gasoline and reformulated gasoline contain oxygenates which have lower heating values than gasoline boiling range hydrocarbons. Because of the lower energy content, fuel economy with oxygenated fuels will be on average 2% to 3% lower than that obtained with conventional gasoline.

6. Cleanliness[3,37-43,59-61,65,69-72]—In addition to providing acceptable antiknock quality and volatility characteristics, automotive gasolines must also provide for satisfactory engine cleanliness, both physical and chemical. The following properties have a direct bearing on the overall performance of a gasoline.

6.1 Workmanship and Contamination—A finished gasoline is essentially a blend of petroleum fractions visually free of undissolved water, sediment, and suspended matter. It is clear and bright when observed at 21 °C (70 °F). Physical contamination may occur during distribution of the fuel to the eventual power source. Control of such contamination is a matter requiring constant vigilance. Solid and liquid contamination can lead to restriction of fuel metering points, improper seating of inlet valves, corrosion, fuel line freezing, gel formation, and filter plugging.

6.2 Rust and Corrosion—Filter plugging and engine wear problems are reduced by minimizing rust and corrosion in fuel distribution and in vehicle fuel systems when engines are idle. Modifications of ASTM D 665, such as NACE Standard TM-0172-86, are used to measure rust protection of gasolines.

6.3 Sulfur Content and Copper Strip Corrosion—Crude petroleum contains sulfur compounds, some of which are removed during refining. Sulfur content is determined by ASTM D 1266, by ASTM D 2622, ASTM D 3120, or ASTM D 5453. Presence of corrosive sulfur compounds can be detected by ASTM D 130. ASTM D 4814 limits sulfur content of unleaded gasolines to a maximum of 0.10 mass percent and leaded gasolines to a maximum of 0.15 mass percent. Currently, average sulfur content of gasolines distributed in the United States is about 0.03 mass percent with the maximum reported values approaching the specification limits.

Sulfur oxides formed during combustion may be converted to acids that promote rusting and corrosion of engine parts and piston ring and cylinder wall wear. Sulfur oxides formed in the exhaust are undesirable atmospheric pollutants; however, the contribution of automotive exhaust to total sulfur oxide emissions is small. The fate of these sulfur compounds upon passage through the catalytic exhaust treatment devices and their possible contribution to sulfates, sulfuric acid, and hydrogen sulfide in automotive exhaust and the atmosphere is receiving careful study. Recent studies[68] have shown that the efficiency of catalytic converters is improved by reducing the sulfur content of gasoline.

6.4 Gum and Stability—During storage, gasolines may oxidize slowly in the presence of air, forming undesirable oxidation products called gum. The gum is usually soluble in the gasoline, but may appear as a sticky residue on evaporation. These residues may deposit on carburetor surfaces, port fuel injection pintles, intake manifolds, pistons, intake valves, stems, and guides. ASTM D 4814 limits gasoline to a maximum of 5 mg of solvent-washed gum per 100 mL of gasoline. ASTM D 381 is a test to determine the amount of unwashed and solvent-washed gum.

Automotive gasolines have a negligible gum content when manufactured, but may form gum during extended storage. ASTM D 525 is a test to indicate the tendency of a gasoline to form gum in storage. ASTM D 4814 has set a minimum limit of 240 min for oxidation stability by this method. It should be recognized, however, that the method's correlation may vary markedly under different storage conditions and with different gasoline blends. Most automotive gasolines contain special chemicals (antioxidants) to inhibit oxidation and gum formation. Some gasolines also may contain metal deactivators, which inhibit the catalytic oxidation caused by copper. Commercial gasoline is not designed for abnormally severe conditions of storage. Gasoline purchased for severe bulk storage conditions or for prolonged storage in vehicle fuel systems generally has additional amounts of antioxidant and metal deactivator added.

As gasolines oxidize, hydroperoxide content is increased and, in the presence of metal ions (especially copper), certain elastomers deteriorate and become unserviceable. Gasoline oxidation is retarded by the use of antioxidants and metal deactivators, but the selection of appropriate materials for hoses and other fuel system components, and avoidance of the use of copper in fuel systems play an important part in avoiding problems associated with oxidized gasoline.

To obtain the solvent washed gum content in ASTM D 381, the test sample is washed with *n*-heptane. If the gum is weighed before the washing step, it is reported as unwashed gum. The difference between the unwashed gum and solvent washed gum values indicates the presence of nonvolatile, *n*-heptane-soluble material in the fuel. Additional analytical testing is necessary to determine if the material is additive, carrier oil, diesel fuel, etc.

7. Other Properties—Many chemical and physical properties of gasoline, not directly controlled by specifications, are important considerations in combustion, fuel system design and calibration, and safe handling in storage and distribution systems. These properties are particularly important when comparing the performance of alternative fuels or alternative fuel components with gasoline.

7.1 Hydrocarbon Composition—The stoichiometry of gasoline combustion is determined by the ratio of hydrogen and carbon in gasoline, which in turn depends upon the types of hydrocarbons present. For more information on stoichiometry, see SAE J1829. The main hydrocarbon constituents are saturates (paraffins and naphthenes), olefins, and aromatics. These are identified using ASTM D 1319. The concentrations of these hydrocarbons in commercial gasolines typically cover the ranges of 12 to 54 volume percent for aromatics, 0 to 37% for olefins, and 35 to 85% for saturates. Nonstandardized analytical procedures are available that permit identification of specific compounds and the ultimate determination of carbon and hydrogen content. Carbon content varies from 85 to 88% and hydrogen content varies from 12 to 15% for most gasolines. Stoichiometric air-fuel ratios of commercial gasolines typically range from 14.3 for gasolines with high concentrations of aromatics to 14.8 for low-aromatic fuels.

7.2 Heating Value—The heating value of gasoline is a measure of its energy content and has a small effect on fuel economy. The heating value of commercial gasoline ranges from 42 to 44 MJ/kg (18 000 to 19 000 Btu/lb) and can be measured by ASTM D 240 or by ASTM D 2382. Volumetric heating value of gasolines generally varies directly with specific gravity, which is more convenient to measure than is heat of combustion. For more information on heating value, see SAE J1498. The relationship between specific gravity and fuel economy is quantified in SAE J1082, by the correction factor 1.0 + 0.8 (0.737—specific gravity). Typical extremes in specific gravity (or heating value) of commercial gasolines represent a fuel economy difference of about 3%. The addition of oxygenates to gasoline can lower the heating value up to 3.5%. The actual amount of reduction depends on the type and quantity of the oxygenate.

7.3 Gravity—Gravity is a term used to denote the density of gasolines. Two methods of expressing gravity—specific gravity and API gravity—are commonly used. Specific gravity is the ratio of the mass of a given volume of gasoline at a temperature of 15.6 °C (60 °F) to the mass of an equal volume of water at the same temperature. API gravity is based on an arbitrary hydrometer scale and is related to specific gravity as in Equation 2:

$$\text{Degrees API} = \frac{141.5}{\text{Sp. Gr. } (60\ °\text{F}/60\ °\text{F})} - 131.5 \qquad \text{(Eq. 3)}$$

Typically, automotive gasolines have specific gravities between 0.70 and 0.78, and API gravities between 50 and 70.

In the change to the SI metric system of measurement, API gravity and specific gravity are eliminated from usage. API gravity is to be replaced by absolute density (kg/m^3) at 15 °C and 101.325 kPa. Specific gravity is to be replaced by relative density at 15 °C and 101.325 kPa, where the reference fluids are water for liquids and air for gases.

The gravity, or density, of gasoline is determined by ASTM D 287, ASTM D 1298, or ASTM D 4052.

7.4 Viscosity and Surface Tension—Viscosity and surface tension of gasolines affect calibration of carburetors and metering orifices. Viscosity is measured by ASTM D 445. Surface tension is measured by nonstandard techniques. Both viscosity and surface tension vary with temperature. Viscosity variation due to temperature is greater than the variability caused by fuel compositions. Typical values for viscosity and surface tension at ambient and low temperatures are shown in Table 6:

TABLE 6—VISCOSITY AND SURFACE TENSION

Temperature	20 °C (68 °F)	–20 °C (–4 °F)
Viscosity, mm^2/s (cSt)	0.5-0.6	0.8-1.0
Surface Tension, N/m	20 x 10^{-3}	24 x 10^{-3}
dynes/cm	20	24

7.5 Fire Safety—Fire hazards of gasolines are related to the typical properties as follows:

a. Flash Point: –43 °C (–45 °F)
b. Autoignition Temperature: 260 °C (500 °F)
c. Flammability Limits, volume percent in air: 1.4 to 7.6
d. Vapor Pressure at 21 °C (70 °F): 28 to 55 kPa (4 to 8 psi)
e. Concentration in Saturated Air at 20 °C (68 °F), volume percent: 25 to 50

Flash point can be measured by use of ASTM D 56 and autoignition temperature by ASTM E 659. The flash point of automotive gasoline is so low that a flammable mixture should always be presumed to exist over the liquid. However, gasoline does not normally present an explosive hazard in covered storage tanks, because the saturated vapor above the liquid is too rich to ignite. Explosive conditions may occur at extremely low temperatures or during transfer operations. Recent legislated reductions in vapor pressure may increase the hazard potential.

7.6 Miscellaneous Properties—A number of other properties can be useful for assessing the performance of gasoline or for designing fuel-handling equipment. For average gasolines, they are:

a. Refractive Index, n_D at 20 °C (68 °F): 1.4 to 1.5
b. Coefficient of Expansion at 15.6 °C (60 °F) and 1 atm 0.00111/°C (0.0006/°F)
c. Electrical Conductivity, mhos/cm: 1 x 10^{-14}
d. Specific Heat, kJ/kg-K (Btu/lb-°F): 2.01 (0.48)

8. Additives[3,6,37-43,60]—Gasoline additives are used to enhance or maintain various performance features related to the satisfactory operation of engines, as well as to minimize gasoline handling and storage problems. These compounds complement refinery processing in attaining the desired level of product quality.

The first additives—antiknocks—were blended into gasoline in 1923, with oxidation inhibitors following about 1930. Since then, the use of additives has grown significantly. Table 7 lists the class, function, and type of additives currently used in commercial gasolines. Corrosion inhibitors are used in pipelines to inhibit iron corrosion and thus prevent rust contamination of the gasoline. Such contamination can increase friction, thereby reducing the flow rate through the pipeline. Metal deactivators, introduced in 1939, inhibit oxidation and gum formation that is catalyzed by copper in the gasoline or fuel system. Demulsifiers are usually used in combination with carburetor/injector detergents and deposit control additives to provide excellent water separation.

Carburetor/injector detergents and deposit control additives prevent and in some cases remove various deposits in the engine intake system. The detergents were introduced in 1954 to prevent and remove deposits from carburetor throttle bodies. The deposit control additives were introduced in 1970 to prevent and remove deposits not only from carburetors, but also from the intake manifold hot spots and runners and intake valves and ports. Both detergents and deposit control additives can control deposits in fuel injectors. The amount and location of performance depend on both the chemistry and concentration of the additive. When the concentration of the detergents was increased in 1985 to control port fuel injector deposits, some additives of this class tended to increase intake valve deposits.

TABLE 7—COMMERCIAL GASOLINE ADDITIVES

Class and Function[1]	Additive Type
Oxidation Inhibitors—minimize oxidation and gum formation	Aromatic amines and hindered phenols
Corrosion Inhibitors—inhibit ferrous corrosion in pipelines, storage tanks, and vehicle fuel systems	Carboxylic acids and carboxylates
Metal Deactivators—inhibit oxidation and gum formation catalyzed by ions of copper and other metals	Chelating agent
Carburetor/Injector Detergents—prevent and remove deposits in carburetors and port fuel injectors	Amines, amides, and amine carboxylates
Deposit Control Additives—remove and prevent deposits throughout fuel injectors, carburetors, intake ports and valves, and intake manifold	Polybutene amines and polyether amines
Demulsifiers—minimize emulsion formation by improving water separation	Polyglyol derivatives
Anti-Icing Additives—minimize engine stalling and starting problems by preventing ice formation in the carburetor and fuel system	Surfactants, alcohols, and glycols
Antiknock Compounds—improve octane quality of gasoline	Lead alkyls and methylcyclopentadienyl manganese tricarbonyl
Dyes—Identification of gasoline	Oil-soluble solid and liquid dyes

1. Some materials are multifunctional or multipurpose additives, performing more than one function.

Intake system deposits can affect vehicle power and driveability, exhaust emissions, fuel economy, and maintenance. Carburetor and fuel injector deposits can upset the air-fuel ratio. The degree of upset depends on the fuel management system and the location of deposits. Intake valve deposits also can upset the air-fuel ratio during cold start and adversely affect exhaust emissions even when warmed up, in some engine designs. If intake valve and port deposits are sufficiently heavy, maximum power can be reduced. Large deposits breaking away from the intake valves can cause mechanical problems.

8.1 Deposit Control Additive Regulations—Deposit control additives are required by law for use in all motor gasolines sold in the United States, except for some fuel-specific certifications. The state of California through its Air Resources Board (CARB) first mandated the use of these additives on January 1, 1992. The Clean Air Act Amendments (CAAA) of 1990 called for the U.S. EPA to promulgate rules for the use of deposit control additives in gasoline in the remaining 49 states effective January 1, 1995. There are differences between the CARB[73] and EPA[74] rules for using these compounds.

Deposit control additives for use under EPA rules are required to maintain intake valve (IVD) and port fuel injector (PFI) cleanliness. ASTM methods D 5500 and D 5598, respectively, must be used to demonstrate additive effectiveness. The EPA has provided for a number of additive certification options depending on the gasoline for which the additive is targeted.

Additive suppliers are required to register each additive and inform the EPA of any use restrictions pursuant to that certification. The additive supplier is also required to provide the gasoline marketer documentation on the use of any additive. This documentation must give blending instructions including the additive's Lowest Additive Concentration (LAC) in gallons of additive per 1000 gallons of gasoline treated. The gasoline marketer must be able to demonstrate that the required additive at the required treat rate has been blended into all retail gasoline that has left their terminal facility, using methodology defined in the EPAs rule as Volume Additive Reconciliation (VAR). Product transfer documents must accompany all nonretail transfer of additive or gasoline.

California's deposit control additive regulations have been amended from time to time. Effective July 17, 1999, PFI cleanup performance is no longer required. However, PFI keep-clean performance, with a maximum flow restriction of 5% for any injector, must still be demonstrated using ASTM D 5598. The IVD maximum limit has been changed from 100 to 50 mg per valve average, using ASTM D 5500. A combustion chamber deposit (CCD) limit has been added, allowing no more than 1300 mg average per cylinder in ASTM D 5500, or no more than 140% as much deposits with the additive as compared to fuel without the additive.

Unlike federal requirements, additives alone are not certified under California rules. Gasoline formulations that contain a deposit control additive are certified under CARB rules. The requirements for the additive portion of these formulations are similar to federal requirements. However, the holder of the certification in California is the gasoline supplier, whereas outside California, the additives are separately certified and the certificates are held by detergent suppliers. With the introduction of California Phase 2 reformulated gasoline, additives demonstrating performance in "80% cap limit" fuel may be used at that performance level in certification in any California gasoline formulation.

Due to the complexity of both the federal and state rules pertaining to deposit control additive usage, it is recommended that all gasoline marketers consult regulatory compliance experts to insure full adherence to all applicable requirements.

9. Oxygenates[8,14-15,17-20,33-36,44]—Since the introduction of ethanol as a blending component in U.S. gasolines in 1978, oxygenates have been used to improve octane quality, extend gasoline volume, and reduce crude oil imports. As a result of the passage of the Clean Air Act Amendments of 1990, oxygenates are now being used as a means of reducing vehicle carbon monoxide (CO) emissions during winter months in metropolitan areas that do not meet ambient CO emissions standards. Federal reformulated gasoline contains oxygenates to meet a year-round minimum oxygen requirement. See 9.2 for details on the federal regulations.

Ethanol is permitted in gasoline at concentrations not exceeding 10 volume-percent. It has enjoyed market success for a number of reasons: (a) the high price of crude oil in the late 1970s and early 1980s, (b) tax subsidies from federal and some state governments due to its agricultural source, (c) the need for unleaded octane quality, and (d) the requirement for oxygenated fuels in CO nonattainment areas.

Methanol was used in the early 1980s as a blend with tertiary-butyl alcohol (TBA), but methanol is not currently blended in commercial gasolines. There is very limited use in California of M85 (85% methanol plus 15% gasoline) and M100 (neat methanol) in vehicles specifically designed for those fuels. Ed85 (85% denatured ethanol plus 15% hydrocarbons) is being used in even fewer specially-designed vehicles in the Midwest, primarily as a demonstration of its feasibility.

One factor discouraging the use of alcohols in commercial gasolines is their low water tolerance. Since they have not been accepted by common carrier pipelines, blending has been done at the terminal or the refinery truck rack. Another factor is their effect on fuel volatility, which is discussed in 9.1

Besides ethanol, a second widely used oxygenate in U.S. gasolines is methyl tertiary-butyl ether (MTBE). First approved in 1979 by the EPA in concentrations up to 7 volume-percent, MTBE now is allowed up to 15 volume-percent. Tertiary-amyl methyl ether (TAME) has been used in Europe in commercial gasolines on a limited scale and is now appearing similarly in U.S. gasolines. Ethyl tertiary-butyl ether (ETBE) and diisopropyl ether (DIPE) also are being used on a limited scale. Ethers are attractive as oxygenated blending components because they have high Research octane values and do not have the water tolerance and volatility problems of alcohols.

For more information on gasoline-oxygenate blends, see SAE J1297.

9.1 Effect of Oxygenates on Volatility—One problem with the use of alcohols is their adverse effect on volatility when blended into gasolines. Ethanol and methanol severely distort the distillation curve of gasoline downward in the lower 50% of the curve. When added to gasoline, they also increase the vapor pressure of the gasoline. This led the EPA to approve a 1.0 psi allowance for gasolines containing 9 to 10 volume-percent ethanol during the summer volatility control period. There is no vapor pressure allowance for any other fuel blend. The vapor pressure allowance for ethanol blends does not apply to federal reformulated gasoline.

By comparison, MTBE blends into gasoline with very little effect on vapor pressure, but it significantly affects the 50% distillation temperature when used at 15 volume percent.

9.2 Government Regulations—The use of oxygenates in unleaded gasoline is controlled by federal regulations. The basic regulation is the "substantially similar" rule which was issued in 1981 and revised in 1991. This rule now allows aliphatic alcohols (except methanol) and/or aliphatic ethers to be blended into gasoline up to concentrations that would result in 2.7 mass-percent oxygen in the blends. Methanol alone is only allowed at concentrations up to 0.3 volume-percent. Also, up to 2.75 volume-percent methanol with an equal volume of butanol or higher molecular weight alcohol is allowed under the "substantially similar' rule. If the use of an oxygenate does not fall under the "substantially similar" rule, a waiver must be obtained from EPA before it can be used. To obtain a waiver, it must be demonstrated that the candidate oxygenate will not cause or contribute to a failure of any emission control device or system. Waivers have been issued by EPA for blends of gasoline and ethanol, ethanol with cosolvent, methanol with cosolvents, and MTBE. For the latest list of waivers, EPA should be contacted. In order to ensure an adequate supply of base gasoline for ethanol blending, EPA has ruled that gasoline containing up to 2.0 volume-percent MTBE can be blended with 10 volume-percent ethanol without violating the ethanol waiver.

Before they can be used, all oxygenates must be registered with EPA. Now, to continue to use an oxygenate, it must also have had a supplemental registration which requires specified additional data. These registered materials are subject to a three-tier toxicological testing program. A new oxygenate, which was not previously registered, will not be registered until information from the first two tiers of testing is available.

Beginning in November 1992, the Clean Air Act Amendments of 1990 required the use of oxygenated fuels in about 40 CO nonattainment areas during the winter months. The program is implemented by the states and varies among the states. If averaging is allowed, the average fuel oxygen content must be at least 2.7 mass percent, with a minimum oxygen content of 2.0 mass-percent in each gallon of gasoline. Without averaging, the minimum oxygen content of each gallon of fuel must be 2.7 mass-percent. Before this regulation came into effect, several high-altitude areas implemented wintertime oxygenated fuels progams to reduce ambient CO. The first program was established in 1987 for the Front Range area of the Rocky Mountains in Colorado (including Denver).

The Clean Air Act Amendments of 1990 also require the use of oxygenates in federal reformulated gasoline by establishing a minimum oxygen content requirement. Each gallon must contain at least 2.0 mass-percent oxygen, or if averaging is selected, each gallon must contain at least 1.5 mass-percent oxygen and must average 2.1 mass-percent oxygen. The maximum oxygen content can be as high 4.0 mass-percent for gasoline-ethanol blends and 2.9 mass-percent for gasoline-ether blends. See ASTM Research Report D02-1347 for more details on federal and California reformulated gasolines.

9.3 Calculation of Fuel Mass Oxygen Content

9.3.1 SCOPE—In the absence of a direct ASTM test method to measure the mass oxygen concentration of gasoline-oxygenate blends, the oxygen concentration of these fuels is to be determined indirectly by: (a) measuring the volume concentration of the oxygenates in the blend, (b) measuring the density or relative density of the blend, (c) converting the oxygenate concentrations from volume to mass concentrations, and (d) converting the mass oxygenate concentrations to mass oxygen concentrations using the oxygen mass fractions of the oxygenates present.

9.3.2 PROCEDURE—The following steps are used to determine the total mass oxygen concentration of gasoline-oxygenate blends.

a. Determine the volume concentrations of oxygenates in a gasoline-oxygenate blend (ASTM Test Method D 4815 or equivalent test method).
b. Determine the density or relative density of the gasoline-oxygenate blend (ASTM Test Methods D 287, D 1298, or D 4052).
c. The oxygen mass percent of the gasoline-oxygenate blend is calculated using the following general equation. The densities or relative densities and oxygen mass fractions of a number of pure oxygenates are provided in Table 8 for use in Equation 3. The choice of density or relative density must be the same as determined previously for the gasoline-oxygenate blend.

$$\text{Oxygen, Mass \%} = \frac{V_1 d_1 O_1 + V_2 d_2 O_2 + ...V_n d_n O_n}{V_b d_b} \times 100 \quad \text{(Eq. 4)}$$

where:

V_n = volume percent of oxygenates 1 through n
d_n = density or relative density of oxygenates 1 through n
O_n = mass fraction oxygen in oxygenates 1 through n
V_b = volume percent of gasoline-oxygenate blend = 100
d_b = density or relative density of gasoline-oxygenate blend

9.3.3 EXAMPLE CALCULATION—Assume that a gasoline-oxygenate blend is found to contain 9.5 volume percent ethanol and 2.0 volume percent methyl tertiary-butyl ether using Test Method D 4815 and that the relative density of the blend is measured to be 0.7450, 15.56/15.56 °C (60/60 °F).

Using the relative density and oxygen mass fraction data for ethanol and methyl tertiary-butyl ether from Table 8, the following mass percent oxygen is calculated for this gasoline-oxygenate blend. See Equation 4.

$$\text{Oxygen, Mass \%} = \frac{9.5 \times 0.7939 \times 0.3473 + 2.0 \times 0.7460 \times 0.1815}{100 \times 0.7450} \times 100 \quad \text{(Eq. 5)}$$

$$= 3.88$$

10. Special Test Fuels—Special fuels are used in test programs within the automotive and petroleum industries to ensure engine-fuel compatibility. Most special fuels can be classified as follows:

10.1 Antiknock Requirement Testing—In addition to primary reference fuels, full-boiling range reference fuels varying in Research and Motor octane numbers are used to determine antiknock requirements of vehicles. Full-boiling range means that the fuel is similar to commercial fuels, consisting of many hydrocarbons with different boiling points. The CRC sponsors preparation of these reference fuels biannually.

10.2 Driveability Testing—Gasolines with specific volatility specifications are used in controlled tests for evaluating vapor lock, evaporative control systems, tank filling, cold-starting, and warm-up. The CRC sponsors preparation of volatility test fuels for specific programs.

10.3 Emission Test Fuel[46]—The U.S. EPA and the California Air Resouces Board specify gasolines for emission testing.

10.4 Engine Oil Qualification—Gasolines are specified for engine oil qualification tests according to ASTM engine oil sequence tests described in ASTM D 5119, D 5302, D 5533, and D 5844.

TABLE 8—DENSITIES, RELATIVE DENSITIES, AND OXYGEN MASS FRACTIONS OF PURE OXYGENATES

Oxygenate	Density, g/mL 20 °C(68 °F)	Relative Density 15.56/15.56 °C (60/60 °F)	Oxygen Mass Fraction
Methyl Alcohol	0.7913	0.7963	0.4993
Ethyl Alcohol	0.7894	0.7939	0.3473
n-Propyl Alcohol	0.8038	0.8080	0.2662
Isopropyl Alcohol	0.7855	0.7899	0.2662
n-Butyl Alcohol	0.8097	0.8137	0.2158
Isobutyl Alcohol	0.8016	0.8058	0.2158
sec-Butyl Alcohol	0.8069	0.8114	0.2158
tertiary-Butyl Alcohol	0.7866(1)	0.7922(1)	0.2158
Methyl tertiary-Butyl Ether	0.7406	0.7460	0.1815
Ethyl tertiary-Butyl Ether	0.7399	0.7452	0.1566
tertiary-Amyl Methyl Ether	0.7707	0.7758	0.1566
tertiary-Hexyl Methyl Ether	0.7815	0.7860	0.1377
Diisopropyl Ether	0.7235	0.7282	0.1566

1. Extrapolated, below freezing temperature.

10.5 Fuel System Materials—Rubber-swelling test fluids for evaluating the compatibility of rubber or rubber-like fuel system components with gasolines are specified in ASTM D 471.

10.6 Flow Testing of Carburetors and Injectors—Special fluids are used in flow test stands. These fluids have carefully controlled density and viscosity, but have a narrower boiling range than commercial fuels.

11. Engine Octane Number Requirement[1-4,47,58,63-64]—The presence or absence of knock in an engine is determined by two factors—the antiknock quality (octane number) of the gasoline used and the octane number requirement (ONR) of the engine. If the octane number of the gasoline is higher than the engine's ONR, knocking does not occur.

The ONR of an engine depends on basic engine design and in-use operating conditions. The ONR of an engine is expressed in terms of reference fuels. The octane number of the highest octane quality fuel that produces audible knock, as judged by a trained rater, defines the ONR of the engine.

There are many factors in engine design and operation that affect the knocking tendencies of an engine and therefore its ONR. Engine design factors include compression ratio, ignition timing, air-fuel ratio, swirl, valve timing, volumetric efficiency, induction system heating, coolant temperature, exhaust gas recirculation rate, and combustion chamber design. In-use operating factors include atmospheric conditions (barometric pressure, temperature, and humidity), combustion chamber deposits, and operating conditions.

11.1 Engine Design Factors[1,47,50]

11.1.1 COMPRESSION RATIO—Figure 4 shows the approximate gasoline antiknock quality required to permit a given level of engine compression ratio. This curve was developed from data obtained from several engine programs where engine compression ratio was varied over a large range and other engine variables were optimized at each compression ratio. The relationship between octane number and compression ratio is not linear; instead, the allowable increase in compression ratio for each octane number is larger at high octane levels than at lower octane levels. The effect of compression ratio on ONR varies with different engines, being dependent on combustion chamber design, cylinder size, ignition timing, and other factors.

It should be noted that this curve was developed before such design factors as swirl, fast burn, and exhaust gas recirculation were adopted.

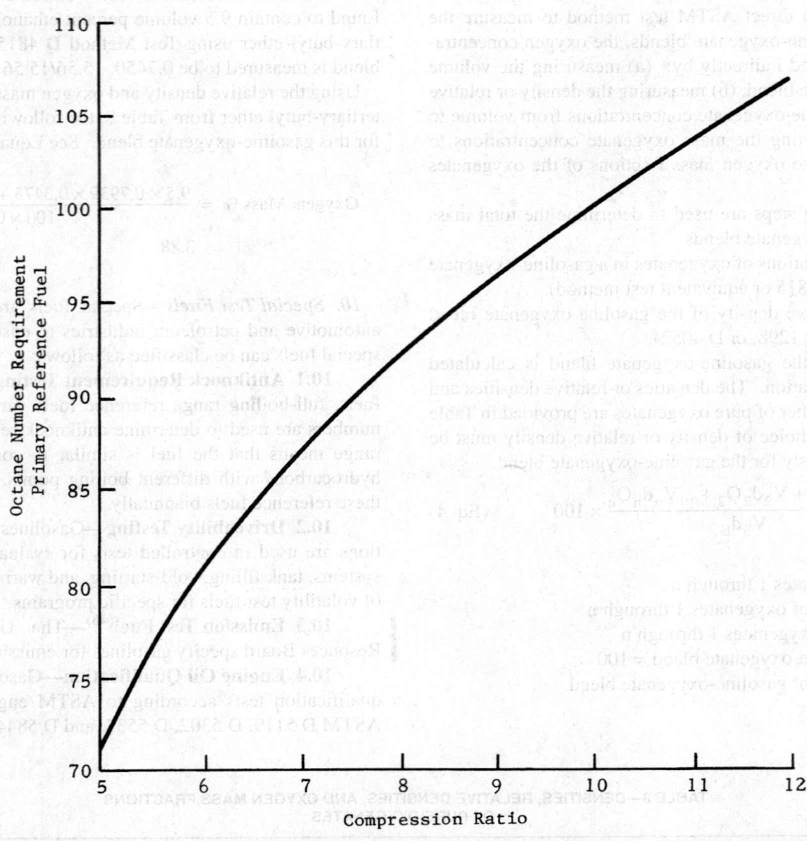

FIGURE 4—FUEL ANTIKNOCK QUALITY REQUIRED AS COMPRESSION RATIO IS INCREASED

11.1.2 IGNITION TIMING—Figure 5 shows the effects of changes in basic ignition timing on the ONR of five different 1978 vehicles when using commercial fuels. Although the specific effects of variations in ignition timing differ for each engine, all engines exhibit increases in ONR as the ignition timing is advanced. Thus, for a given engine, changes in basic ignition timing, modification of the distributor spark advance curve, variations in spark advance due to production tolerances of the distributor all or singly have a direct effect on the ONR of the engine.

Reduction of knock is currently achieved in some cars by using a system that retards the ignition timing when knock is detected. An engine-mounted vibration sensor, which generates a signal when excited by engine knock, retards the ignition until knock is reduced to an acceptable level. This system has the advantage of limiting the car's ONR to approximately the octane rating of the fuel being used. However, fuels with octane quality well below the design level will cause considerable ignition retard under knocking conditions. This results in reduced performance and fuel economy, especially for supercharged vehicles having control systems that both retard spark and reduce boost pressure.

Three CRC programs[50-52] have studied the effect of gasoline octane number on the acceleration performance of passenger cars and light-duty trucks. The tests were run under conditions of wide-open throttle and maximum throttle operation using CRC full boiling range octane test gasoline. For vehicles without knock sensors, acceleration performance was not affected by fuel octane. Vehicles with knock sensors generally experienced a loss in acceleration performance when fueled with gasoline that did not meet their octane requirements. Some knock sensor vehicles experienced improved acceleration performance when fueled with gasoline that exceeded their octane requirements. The loss of acceleration performance varied greatly among vehicles with knock sensors. High-performance vehicles with turbochargers typically showed larger losses than other types.

11.1.3 AIR-FUEL RATIO—Another factor affecting ONR is the ratio of air to fuel in the mixture supplied to each cylinder. In general, the maximum ONR will occur when the mass air-fuel ratio is about 14.5:1. Enriching or leaning the air-fuel mixture will decrease the ONR from this maximum value. Excessive enrichment or leaning of the air-fuel mixture will result in a substantial loss of power. Conventionally, enrichment for maximum power air-fuel ratio is used during full-throttle operation to reduce knocking during this critical condition and to provide better engine acceleration, hill climbing ability, and driveability. The air-fuel ratio on most late-model cars is controlled at part throttle by a closed-loop system using an oxygen sensor in the engine exhaust. This system maintains the air-fuel ratio at approximately stoichiometric which is very close to the maximum knock mixture ratio.

11.1.4 COMBUSTION-CHAMBER DESIGN—Variations in combustion-chamber design also influence ONR. The effect of such variations cannot be predicted as readily as the effect of the other variables previously mentioned. In general, however, those combustion chambers that provide high turbulence and/or the shortest path of flame travel from the spark plug to the last portion of the charge to burn have relatively lower ONR and, therefore, permit the use of a higher compression ratio for a given octane number gasoline.

11.1.5 TEMPERATURE CONTROL SYSTEMS—ONR is strongly influenced by combustion temperatures, which in turn are affected by coolant temperature, inlet air temperature, and intake manifold heat input. An increase in combustion temperature increases ONR. Thus, the coolant thermostat setting, air heater design, and the intake manifold heating system design are all important engine parameters.

11.2 In-Use Factors[(48-58, 62,71)]

11.2.1 ATMOSPHERIC OR CLIMATIC CONDITIONS—A vehicle's ONR is affected by changes in three atmospheric variables: barometric pressure, temperature, and humidity.

The ONR of most automotive engines built prior to the mid-1980s generally decreases with an increase in altitude because:

a. Reduced air density at higher altitudes results in lower combustion pressures and temperatures.
b. Fuel is metered according to the volume of air drawn into the engine. Since air density decreases with an increase in altitude, the fuel/air mixture becomes richer, reducing ONR.
c. Spark advance is controlled by manifold vacuum. Since ambient pressure decreases with an increase in altitude, lower manifold vacuum results in less spark advance and thus lower ONR.

CRC studies from 1965 to 1977 indicated that, on the average, a vehicle's ONR would drop about one to two octane numbers per 300 m (1000 ft) increase in altitude, as shown in Table 9. Reductions in antiknock index requirements for these older engines in high-altitude areas are shown in Figure 1.

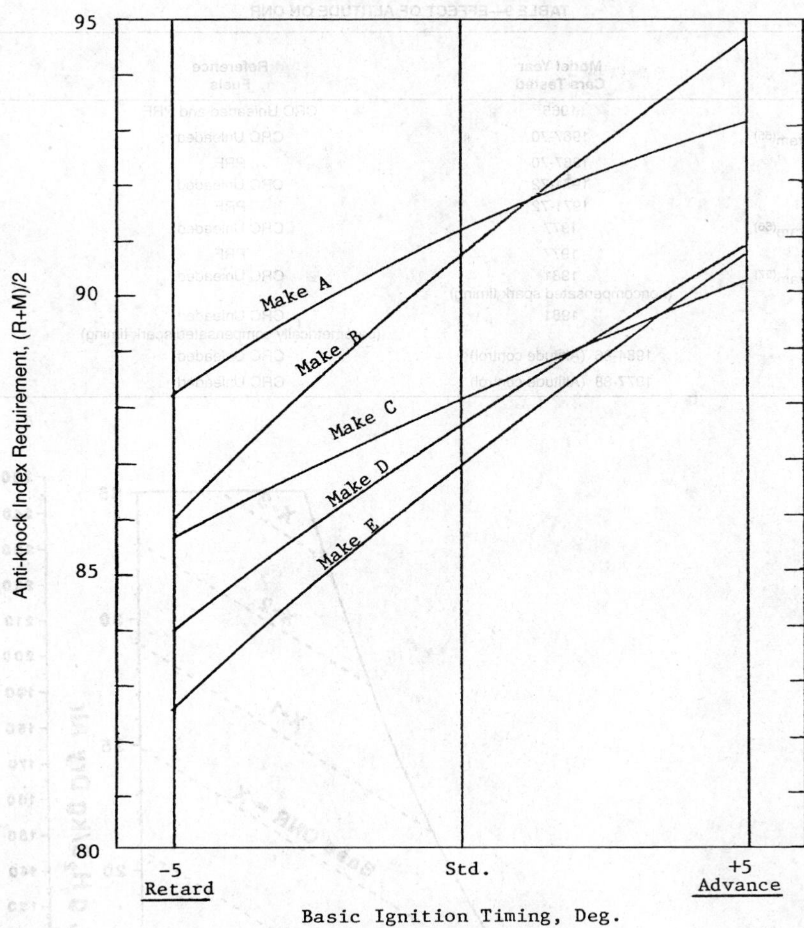

FIGURE 5—EFFECT OF IGNITION TIMING ON ONR

Since the mid-1980's, electronic controls that compensate spark timing and air-fuel ratio for changes in altitude (barometric pressure) have been increasingly used in vehicles. As shown in Table 9, these controls have significantly lowered the ONR reduction as altitude increases, with the two most recent studies showing an average altitude difference in ONR of only 0.2 and 0.5 (R+M)/2 per 300 m (1000 ft).

Studies using cars of different manufacturers, makes, and models indicate that, on the average, a 5.6 °C (10 °F) increase in atmospheric temperature raises a vehicle's ONR about 0.54 Motor octane number, while a 0.00065 kg (ten-grain) H_2O increase in absolute humidity lowers the ONR about 0.35 units. Because the octane number requirement response of a few vehicles varies markedly from average values, caution should be used in applying these corrections to individual vehicles. Results were obtained with full-boiling range gasolines blended to simulate the average of commercial fuels. Although knowledge of the independent effects of temperature and humidity on ONR is important, the primary concern is the simultaneous effect of these two weather variables. For example, Figure 6 shows that the most severe operating conditions occur during periods of hot, dry weather.

Because temperature and humidity of geographical areas are predictable from past weather records through the year, octane quality can be seasonally adjusted to closely match seasonal changes in vehicle ONR. Reductions in antiknock index for weather are shown in Figure 2.

11.2.2 COMBUSTION CHAMBER DEPOSITS AND OPERATING CONDITIONS—In addition to atmospheric factors, the in-use octane requirement of a particular motor vehicle is determined by: (a) its clean (new) engine ONR and (b) the octane requirement increase (ORI) occurring in service as deposits accumulate in the engine combustion chambers. When the octane requirements of a number of vehicles of the same make and model are considered, a range of values will be observed because of: (1) differences in clean-engine ONR resulting from manufacturing variations; (2) operating conditions encountered; and (3) fuel and lubricant use.

Combustion chamber deposits accumulate as vehicles are driven under a variety of speeds, loads, and temperatures. These deposits, which cling to combustion chamber surfaces, form as by-products of the burning of fuel and lubricating oil. By occupying volume within the combustion chamber, the deposits increase compression ratio somewhat. However, their major effect is to store heat from cycle to cycle and to act as barriers to the flow through the combustion chamber walls to the coolant. As a result of higher effective compression ratio, heat storage, and deposit insulating effects, knocking tendency typically increases during approximately the first 8000 to 24 000 km (5000 to 15 000 miles) that a vehicle is driven. After this time, deposit build-up generally reaches an equilibrium point and ONR stabilizes, assuming no significant mechanical or operating condition changes occur to upset equilibrium.

The net result of variable clean-engine octane requirement and in-use operating condition plus the variation in octane requirement determination among laboratories can be illustrated using data obtained from the annual octane number requirement surveys carried out by the CRC. Certain models are evaluated during these studies in numbers large enough to permit construction of a distribution curve for a given vehicle model. Figure 7 shows the distribution curves of percent satisfaction versus octane number for two car models from the 1988 ONR survey and typifies the variations in octane requirements that occur in in-use service on vehicles that have been operated for more than 9600 km (6000 miles).

11.2.3 MOTORIST EVALUATION—A further complication in assessing significant in-use octane requirement levels is the variation in ability to detect knock that exists from one motorist to another. In later model cars equipped with knock sensors, motorists may not be able to detect knock until after maximum spark timing retardation is reached. Because knock may not be detectable, acceleration performance may decrease as lower octane level fuels are used.

TABLE 9—EFFECT OF ALTITUDE ON ONR

Study	Model Year Cars Tested	Reference Fuels	ONR Difference Per 300 m (1000 ft)
Chevron/Ethyl[54]	1965	CRC Unleaded and PRF	1.5 RON
1972 CRC Altitude Program[55]	1967-70	CRC Unleaded	1.2 RON
	1967-70	PRF	1.2 RON
	1971-72	CRC Unleaded	1.9 RON
	1971-72	PRF	1.7 RON
1977 CRC Altitude Program[56]	1977	CRC Unleaded	1.1 RON
	1977	PRF	1.0 RON
1981 CRC Altitude Program[57]	1981 (noncompensated spark timing)	CRC Unleaded	1.7 RON
	1981	CRC Unleaded (barometrically compensated spark timing)	0.6 RON
Amoco[53]	1984-86 (Altitude control)	CRC Unleaded	0.2 (R+M)/2
Petro-Canada[58]	1977-88 (Altitude control)	CRC Unleaded	0.5 (R+M)/2

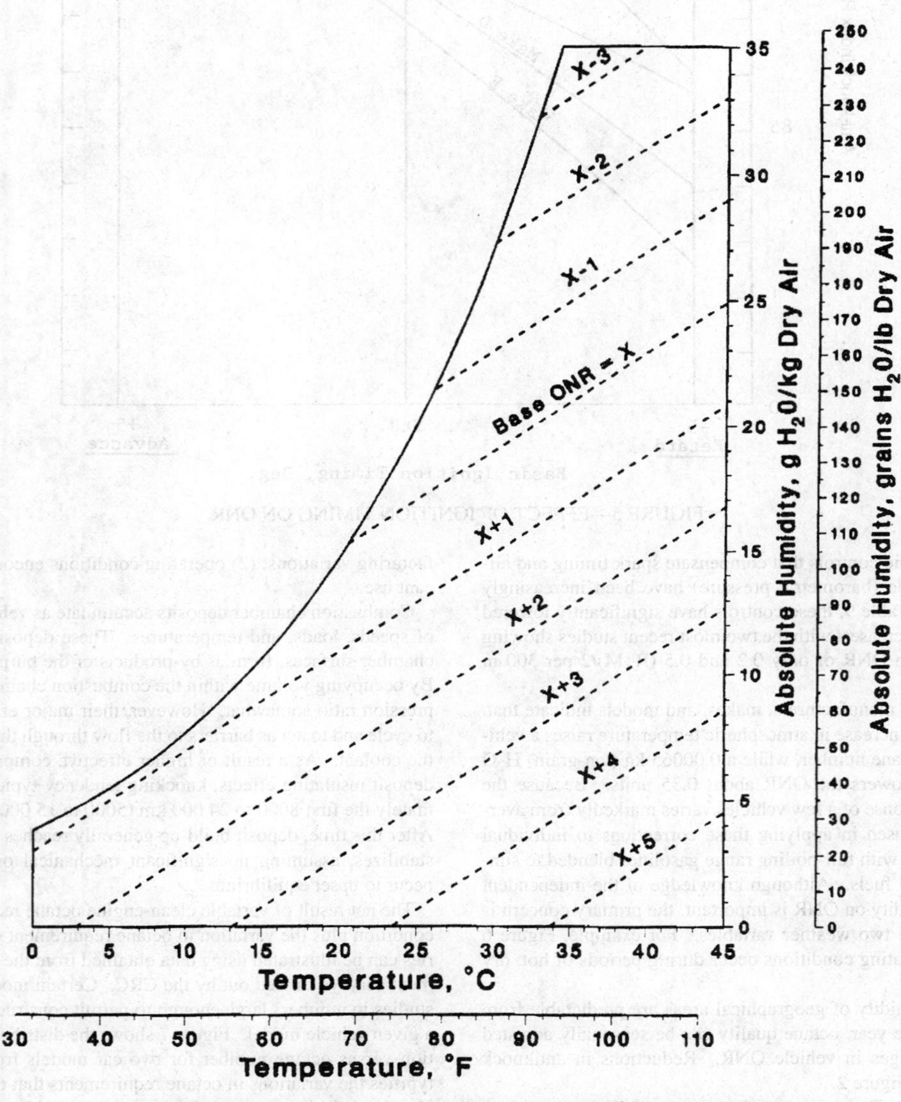

FIGURE 6—EFFECTS OF TEMPERATURE AND HUMIDITY ON ONR[62]
MON REQUIREMENT = X + 0.054(T, °F) – 0.035 (H)

To evaluate customer knock detection, the CRC has conducted studies in 1975, 1978, and 1990.[75-77] The results are summarized in Table 10. On average, motorists reported that knock was objectionable at levels about 4-6 (R+M)/2 octane numbers below their car's maximum octane requirement as determined by trained raters. That difference between average trained rater and customer requirements has narrowed with each successive study. There is a wide range of motorist sensitivity to knock. In the latest study,[77] about 10% of the customers were as sensitive or more sensitive than the trained raters, while another 10% had objection levels 10 or more octane numbers lower than the trained raters. This suggests that some motorists may not be able to hear knock. The average effect shown in Table 10 does not represent the entire customer population and should be used with caution. Knock sensors were found to have a significant effect on increasing the difference between the trained rater and customer ratings.

TABLE 10—Trained Rater Octane Requirement Minus Customer OBjection, (R+M)/2

1975 Study	1978 Study	1990 Study
5.9	4.8	3.8

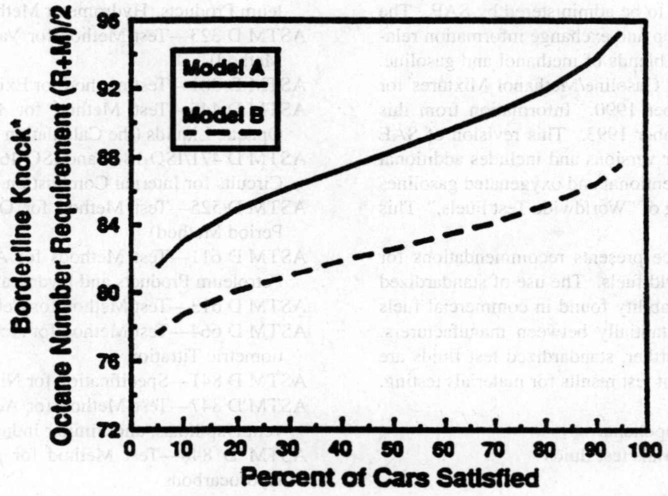

* Spark knock of lowest audible intensity of at least three pings and over a range of engine speed of at least 50 rpm, all being repeatable during subsequent accelerations.

FIGURE 7—DISTRIBUTION CURVES OF ONR FOR CARS OF A GIVEN MAKE AND MODEL ON AVERAGE COMMERCIAL REFERENCE FUELS[49]

(R) GASOLINE, ALCOHOL, AND DIESEL FUEL SURROGATES FOR MATERIALS TESTING—SAE J1681 JAN2000 SAE Recommended Practice

Report of the SAE Fuel Lines and Fittings Committee approved September 1993. Completely revised by the SAE Test Fluid Task Force of the SAE Fuel Supply Systems Forum January 2000.

Foreword—This SAE Recommended Practice is based on the product of the SAE Cooperative Research Program, Project Group 2 which has been extended to cover the current conventional and oxygenated gasolines and diesel fuels. SAE Cooperative Research Project Group 2 was formed by the Oxygenated Fuels Task Force, which is composed of OEM automotive engineering executives. The task of the Oxygenated Fuels Task Force is to identify and prioritize potential areas for pre-competitive cooperative research programs to be administered by SAE. The specific scope of Project Group 2 was to develop and exchange information relative to materials and test methods for use with blends of methanol and gasoline. An SAE Cooperative Research Report titled, "Gasoline/Methanol Mixtures for Materials Testing," was published in September 1990. Information from this report was published as SAE J1681 in September 1993. This revision of SAE J1681 provides information presented in earlier versions and includes additional fluids that can be used to simulate current conventional and oxygenated gasolines and diesel fuels. New in this revision is a listing of "Worldwide Test Fuels." This list is presented in Appendix G.

1. Scope—This SAE Recommended Practice presents recommendations for test fluids that can be used to simulate real world fuels. The use of standardized test fluids is required in order to limit the variability found in commercial fuels and fluids. Commercial fuels can vary substantially between manufacturers, batches, seasons, and geographic location. Further, standardized test fluids are universally available and will promote consistent test results for materials testing. Therefore, this document

a. Explains commercial automotive fuel components
b. Defines standardized components of materials test fluids
c. Defines a nomenclature for test fluids
d. Describes preparations for test fluids and
e. Recommends fluids for testing fuel system materials

The test fluid compositions specified in Section 7 of this document are recommended solely for evaluating materials. They are not intended for other activities, such as engine development, design verification, or process validation unless agreed upon by the contracting parties. The marketplace test fuels listed in Appendix B of this document can be used for engine, vehicle, or component testing.

Most marketplace fuels contain additives for such purposes as oxidation stability, intake and combustion chamber deposit control, anti-foaming, electrostatics, octane, etc., applied at a parts per million basis. It is not the intention of this document to include a surrogate for the potential effects of these additives. As far as this committee is aware, current additives do not adversely effect fuel system materials. Those contemplating new or improved additives for future application could use the basic test fluids or fuels from this document, inject such additives and use the resulting mixtures to assess whether these new additives might effect fuel system materials.

For the purposes of this document, the term FUEL is used in conjunction with fully blended hydrocarbon or hydrocarbon oxygenate mixtures for use in commercial automotive engines. The term FLUID is applied to mixtures of specific controlled components used to simulate the effects of fuels.

1.1 Purpose—The purpose of this document is to define standardized surrogate gasoline and diesel mixtures to be used in materials testing, and to publish these compositions. This document also promotes the use of its standardized test fluids to permit consistent results from materials testing and more uniform specification of materials. Formulations in this document are intended to exaggerate the effects of typical severe fuel on materials, as well as to allow the tests to be conducted in a reasonable amount of time.

2. References

2.1 Applicable Publications—The following publications form a part of this specification to the extent specified herein. Unless otherwise indicated, the latest version of SAE publications shall apply.

2.1.1 SAE PUBLICATIONS—Available from SAE, 400 Commonwealth Drive, Warrendale, PA 15096-0001.

SAE J1681 MAR93—Gasoline/Methanol Mixtures for Materials Testing
SAE J1748—Methods for Determining Physical Properties of Polymeric Materials Exposed to Gasoline/Oxygenate Fuel Mixture

2.1.2 ASTM PUBLICATIONS—Available from ASTM, 100 Barr Harbor Drive, West Conshohocken, PA 19428-2959.

ASTM D 56—Test Method for Flash Point by Tag Closed Tester
ASTM D 86—Test Method for Distillation of Petroleum Products
ASTM D 93—Flash Point by Pensky-Martens Closed Cup Tester
ASTM D 130—Test Method for Detection of Copper Corrosion from Petroleum Products by the Copper Strip Tarnish Test
ASTM D 156—Test Method for Saybolt Color of Petroleum Products (Saybolt Chromometer Method)
ASTM D 287—Test Method for API Gravity of Crude Petroluem and Petroleum Products (Hydrometer Method)
ASTM D 323—Test Method for Vapor Pressure of Petroleum Products (Reid Method)
ASTM D 381—Test method for Existent Gum in Fuels by Jet Evaporation
ASTM D 445—Test Method for Kinematic Viscosity of Transparent and Opaque Liquids (the Calculation of Dynamic Viscosity)
ASTM D 471/ISO 1817 and ISO 4639-3—Rubber Hoses and Tubing for Fuel Circuits for Internal Combustion Engines - Part 3, Oxidized Fuel
ASTM D 525—Test Method for Oxidation Stability of Gasoline (Induction Period Method)
ASTM D 611—Test Methods for Aniline Point and Mixed Aniline Point of Petroleum Products and Hydrocarbon Solvents
ASTM D 613—Test Method for Cetane Number of Diesel Fuel Oil
ASTM D 664—Test Method for Acid Numer of Petroleum Products by Potentiometric Titration
ASTM D 841—Specification for Nitration Grade Toluene
ASTM D 847—Test Method for Acidity of Benzene, Toluene, Xylenes, Solvent Napththas, and Similar Industrial Aromatic Hydrocarbons
ASTM D 848—Test Method for Acid Wash Color of Industrial Aromatic Hydrocarbons
ASTM D 849—Test Method for Carbon Strip Corrosion by Industrial Aromatic Hydrocarbons
ASTM D 850—Test Method for Distillation of Industrial Aromatic Hydrocarbons and Related Materials
ASTM D 853—Test Method for Hydrogen Sulfide and Sulfur Dioxide Content (Qualitative) of Industrial Aromatic Hydrocarbons
ASTM D 874—Test Method for Sulfated Ash from Lubricating Oils and Additives
ASTM D 891—Test Methods for Specific Gravity, Apparent, of Liquid Industrial Chemicals
ASTM D 1152-97—Standard Specification for Methanol (Methyl Alcohol)
ASTM D 1193—Specification for Reagent Water
ASTM D 1209—Test Method for Color of Clear Liquids (Platinum-Cobalt Scale)
ASTM D 1266—Test Method for Sulfur in Petroleum Products (Lamp Method)
ASTM D 1298—Test Method for Density, Relative Density (Specific Gravity), or API Gravity of Crude Petroleum and Liquid Petroleum Products by Hydrometer Method
ASTM D 1319—Test Method for Hydrocarbon Types in Liquid Petroleum Products by Fluorescent Indicator Adsorption
ASTM D 1353—Test method for Nonvolatile Matter in Volatile Solvents for Use in Paint, varnish, Lacquer, and Related Products
ASTM D 1363—Test method for Permanganate Time of Acetone and Methanol
ASTM D 1364—Test Method for Water in Volatile Solvents (Karl Fischer Reagent Titration Method)
ASTM D 1612—Test Method for Acetone in Methanol (Methyl Alcohol)
ASTM D 1613-96—Standard Test Method for Acidity in Volatile Solvents and Chemical Intermediates Used in Paint, Varnish, Lacquer and Related Products
ASTM D 1722—Test Method for Water Miscibility of Water-Soluble Solvents
ASTM D 2268—Test Method for Analysis of High-Purity n-Heptane and Isooctane by Capillary Gas Chromatography
ASTM D 2360—Test Method for Trace Impurities in Monocyclic Aromatic Hydrocarbons by Gas Chromatography
ASTM D 2500—Test Method for Cloud Point of Petroleum Oils
ASTM D 2622—Test Method for Sulfur in Petroleum Products by X-Ray Spectrometry

ASTM D 2699—Test Method for Research Octane Number of Spark-Ignition Engine Fuel

ASTM D 2700—Test Method for Motor Octane Number of Spark-Ignition Fuel

ASTM D 2709—Test Method for Water and Sediment in Middle Distillate Fuels by Centrifuge

ASTM D 3120—Test Method for Trace Quantities of Sulfur in Light Liquid Petroleum Hydrocarbons by Oxidative Microcoulometry

ASTM D 3231—Test Method for Phosphorus In Gasoline

ASTM D 3237—Test Method for Lead in Gasoline by Atomic Absorption Spectrometry

ASTM D 3606—Test Method for the Determination of Benzene and Toluene in Finished Motor and Aviation Gasoline by Gas Chromatography

ASTM D 4045—Test Method for Sulfur in Petroleum Products by Hydrogenolysis and Rateometric Colorimetry

ASTM D 4052—Test Method for Density and Relative Density of Liquids by Digital Density Meter

ASTM D 4176—Test Method for Free Water and Particulate Contamination in Distillate Fuels (Visual Inspection Procedures)

ASTM D 4294—Test Method for Sulfur in Petroleum Products by Energy-Dispersive X-Ray Fluorescence Spectroscopy

ASTM D 4530—Test Method for Determination of Carbon Residue (Micro Method)

ASTM D 4806—Standard Specification for Denatured Fuel Alcohol for Blending with Gasolines for Use as Automotive Spark Ignition Engine Fuel

ASTM D 4814—Specification for Automotive Spark-Ignition Engine Fuel

ASTM D 4815—Test Method for Determination of MTBE, ETBE, TAME, DIPE, tertiary-Amyl Alcohol and C_1 to C_4 Alcohols in Gasoline by Gas Chromatography

ASTM D 5191—Test Method for Vapor Pressure of Petroleum Products (Mini Method)

ASTM D 5254—Practice for Minimum Set of Data Elements to Identify a Ground-Water Site

ASTM D 5441—Test Method for Analysis of Methyl tert-Butyl Ether (MTBE) by Gas Chromatography

ASTM D 5453—Test Method for the Determination of Total Sulfur in Light Hydrocarbons, Motor Fuels and Oils by Ultraviolet Fluorescence

ASTM D 5797-96—Standard Specification for Fuel Methanol (M70 - M85) for Automotive Spark Ignition Engines

ASTM D 5798-98a—Standard Specification for Fuel Ethanol (Ed75 - Ed85) for Automotive Spark Ignition Engines

ASTM D 6423-99—Standard Test Method for Determination of pHe of Ethanol. Denatured Fuel Ethanol and Fuel Ethanol (Ed75-Ed85)

ASTM E 203—Test Method for Water Using Karl Fischer Reagent

ASTM E 298-98—Standard Test Method for Assay of Organic Peroxides

ASTM E 346—Test Methods for Analysis of Methanol

ASTM as PS122-99—Provisional Standard Specification for BioDiesel Fuel (B100) Blend Stock for Distillate Fuels

2.1.3 ARB PUBLICATION—Available from State of California Air Resources Board in Sacramento.

ARB MLD 16

2.1.4 CEC PUBLICATIONS—Available from Coordinating European Council for the Development of Performance Tests for Transportation Fuels, Lubricants and other Fluids, Madou Plaza - 25th Floor, Place Madou 1, B-1030 Brussels, Belgium

CEC-RF-01-A-80

CEC-RF-08-A-85

2.1.5 DIN PUBLICATION—Available from SAE, 400 Commonwealth Drive, Warrendale, PA 15096-0001.

DIN 51 604

2.1.6 FEDERAL PUBLICATIONS—Available from the Superintendent of Documents, U. S. Government Printing Office, Mail Stop: SSOP, Washington, DC 20402-9320. http:/www.access.gpo.gov/nara/cfr/cfr-table-search.html.

27 CFR 21.24

2.1.7 ISO PUBLICATION—Available from ANSI, 11 West 42nd Street, New York, NY 10036-8002.

ISO 1817—Rubber, vulcanized—Determination of the effect of liquids

2.1.8 NF PUBLICATIONS—Available from ????

NF EN 22719

NF ISO 3991

NF T 60-700

NF T 60-702

NF T 60-703

2.1.9 OTHER PUBLICATIONS

Mazich, Rossi, and Smith, "Macromolecules 25, 6929," (1992)

2.2 Related Publication—The following publication is for information purposes only and is not a required part of this specification.

SAE J1747—Recommended Methods for Conducting Corrosion Tests in Gasoline/Methanol Fuel Mixtures

3. Explanation of Commercial Automotive Fuel Components

3.1 General—Automotive fuels are made from many compounds that are derived from petroleum, natural gas, and biomass. Materials that come into contact with fuel components are affected in different ways. This document identifies the significant components of fuel mixtures and includes those components in recommended testing formulations. A discussion of the fuel components is offered.

3.2 Major Fuel Components

3.2.1 ALKANES—The alkane component group includes straight chain, branched chain, and cyclic aliphatic hydrocarbons. The alkanes are often referred to as paraffins and are derived from the naphtha fractions from a refinery or gas processing facility.

Polymeric materials can sorb alkanes, which can in turn cause swelling. Extensive earlier work on rubber materials was performed using the alkane isooctane (2,2,4 - trimethyl pentane).

3.2.2 AROMATICS—The aromatics group includes molecules based on the six-member ring compound benzene, and substituted benzenes, such as toluene, and xylenes. The aromatics also include molecules containing additional carbons in various configurations and positions on a benzene molecule.

Polymeric materials can undergo swelling and decomposition when exposed to high concentrations of aromatics. Extensive earlier work on rubber materials was performed using the aromatic toluene, generally in a mixture with the alkane isooctane.

3.2.3 OXYGENATES—The oxygenates in fuel blends include lower molecular weight alcohols, such as methanol (MeOH) and ethanol (EtOH). The oxygenates also include ethers such as methyl tertiary - butyl ether (MTBE), ethyl tertiary - butyl ether (ETBE), and tertiary-amyl methyl ether (TAME). The oxygenated compounds are manufactured to create useful fuel components starting with natural gas, certain natural gas liquids, certain refinery and petrochemical intermediates, and alcohols generated from biomass feeds that are readily available to the fuel industry.

Oxygenates in diesel fuel are currently limited to fatty acid methyl esters. In Europe, methyl esters are made from the trans-esterification of rapeseed oil with methanol predominate. These are referred to as rapeseed methyl esters (RME). In the US, vegetable oils (predominantly soybean oil), animal fats, and used cooking oils are reacted with either methanol or ethanol to form fatty acid alkyl esters. The US product is referred to as BioDiesel. These two products are currently being blended into commercial diesel fuels; however, volumes of these products in the market are still small.

Oxygenates can affect polymers (including elastomers and plastics) and polymer systems (including laminates and multi-layered components). Oxygenates and some compounds derived from these oxygenates can also affect metals, especially when moisture is present in the fuel.

3.3 Other Fuel Contaminants/Minor Fuel Components

3.3.1 GENERAL—During the manufacturing, transfer, storage, and use of fuels, many chemical reactions can occur to fuels and fuel components. The products of these reactions can in turn affect the properties of the materials that are in contact with the fuels.

Contaminated fuels can represent especially severe environments for polymer, elastomer, plastic, and metal fuel system parts. Several different types of contaminants commonly found in commercial fuels are added to the test fluids described in this document to increase the severity of the test fluids for more rapid materials testing.

3.3.2 ACIDS—Organic acids such as formic acid and acetic acid are present in certain fuels along with its corresponding alcohol (MeOH and EtOH, respectively. The acid is formed either in the alcohol production process or due to oxidation of the alcohol during handling, transfer, or storage. Ethanol may also contain trace amounts of sulfuric acid, a strong mineral acid that also originates in the production process.

Organic sulfur-containing acids and corresponding sulfur-containing esters can be formed by sulfur containing gasoline components that react with alcohols, notably ethanol and acetic acid/ethanol mixtures. These acids affect materials that are in contact with the fuel.

An acid/alcohol mixture with some water and salts present (see 3.3.4) is referred to as an "aggressive alcohol." Aggressive alcohol fluids are used in this document to test materials in harsh testing conditions.

3.3.3 PEROXIDES—Fuel hydrocarbons can undergo natural oxidation in the presence of heat and oxygen. Unsaturated hydrocarbons, such as olefins, degrade more easily. Organic peroxides form as a result of fuel oxidation (often referred to as auto-oxidation). These peroxides decompose to form free radicals that can chemically attack reactive sites (primarily at carbon double bonds but also hydrogen bonds to the carbon backbone) on polymers and elastomers in the fuel system. Other by-products of these degradation processes are acids that cause corrosion of metal components in the fuel system and gums and varnish that can coat the fuel system.

Although time and temperature alone are capable of decomposing peroxides, transition metals capable of a one electron transition, such as copper, will catalyze the decomposition of organic peroxides thereby accelerating this reaction.

3.3.4 IONIC COMPOUNDS—Sodium chloride or salt, is a compound that often makes its way into fuel systems. In fuels that contain moisture, the salt can adversely affect materials, especially metals.

Water has been mentioned in conjunction with several of the components. Water allows and contributes to many reactions concerning fuel components. Many of these reactions adversely affect materials in fuel systems.

3.3.5 SULFUR—Commercial gasolines contain varying amounts of sulfur in several forms. Prior to the introduction of reformulated gasoline, the average 1990 sulfur content in U. S. gasolines was 338 ppm. The ASTM D 4814 standard for gasoline allows up to 1000 ppm of total sulfur, the U. S. Federal RFG gasoline specification currently has no limit for total sulfur, and California CARB Phase 2 reformulated gasoline (RFG) regulations allow an average of 30 ppm of total sulfur. Similar restrictions on sulfur are becoming common around the world. In Europe, gasoline sulfur levels will be limited to 50 ppm after 2005.

One process in the refining and gasoline processing industry is the "sweetening" of gasoline components by converting mercaptans (R – S – H) to disulfides. Disulfide compounds are in the form of $R_1 – S – S – R_2$, where the groups R_1 and R_2 are generally C_1 to C_4 alkyl radicals. Disulfides can be converted to sulfonic and sulfinic acids in the presence of atmospheric oxygen and water.

Disulfides and their related sulfonic and sulfinic acid oxidation products have significant effects on metals, some elastomers, and some plastics. The stability of fuels and test fluids containing these sulfur compounds is not well understood. Further research is required before sulfur impurities can be recommended for addition to material testing fluid formulations of this document.

Commercial diesel fuels also contain varying amounts of sulfur. The 1996 average sulfur content in U. S. and European diesel fuels was 310 ppm while the application specifications limit sulfur to 500 ppm max. The trend to lower sulfur diesel is underway, with the 2005 European target sulfur content set at 50 ppm. Similar reductions on diesel fuel sulfur are becoming common around the world.

***4. Components of Materials Test Fluids*—**Due to the complexity and variability of commercial automotive fuels, they are not suitable for repeatable and reproducible material qualification testing. This document recommends the use of controlled test fluids to simulate commercial fuels. The components of these fluids are described in this section with further details in the appendices.

4.1 Hydrocarbon Fluids

4.1.1 GENERAL—The first component in the materials testing fluid formula is the hydrocarbon fluid. There are several hydrocarbon fluids recommended for materials testing. These test fluids are designed to simulate more severe, real world fuels as described in Section 3. Suppliers and specifications for the hydrocarbon fluids are presented in Appendix A.

4.1.2 FUEL C—Standard ASTM test fluids are described in ASTM D 471/ISO 1817. These fluids are commonly used as the hydrocarbon component of a test fluid. ASTM test fluids are composed of isooctane or mixtures of isooctane and toluene. The ratios of isooctane and toluene vary, and each mixture has a separate letter designation (A through D). Fuel A is 100% isooctane; Fuel B is 70% isooctane, balance toluene; Fuel C is 50% isooctane, balance toluene; and Fuel D is 60% isooctane, balance toluene.

The most notable ASTM test fluid is "Fuel C." Fuel C, as previously mentioned, is a mixture that contains 50 volume percent isooctane and 50 volume percent toluene. Fuel C has been the ASTM fuel most often associated with materials testing since 1980. Fuel C is designated with a "C" in the nomenclature of this document. Suppliers and specifications for isooctane and toluene components are presented in Appendix A.

4.1.3 SURROGATE FUEL C—Since isooctane is a relatively expensive compound, this doucment now allows use of certain isoparaffin solvents that are suitable substitutes for isooctane. Surrogate Fuel C is a mixture that contains 50 volume percent of the substitute isoparaffin solvent, and 50 volume percent toluene. The substituted isoparaffin fluid is designated as "SC" in the nomenclature of this document. Suppliers and specifications for the substitute isoparaffin solvents are also presented in Appendix A.

The user is cautioned to repeat tests using Fuel C if the results from using Fuel SC fall close to the borderline of allowable material tolerances.

A comparison and validation of two isoparaffin surrogates with isooctane can be found in Appendix F.

4.1.4 REFERENCE GASOLINES—Reference gasolines can be used in place of the hydrocarbon test fluids listed previously, when test fluids more representative of commercial fuels are required. For example, for component subsystem or system design validation, several reference gasolines that are produced for use in vehicles are being recommended for use as hydrocarbon fluids. Suppliers and specifications for the reference gasolines are presented in Appendix B.

4.1.5 REFERENCE DIESEL FUELS—Reference diesel fuel can be used in place of the hydrocarbon test fluids listed previously, when a diesel test fluid more representative of commercial diesel fuel is required. Reference diesel fuels that are produced for use in diesel engines are being recommended for use as the hydrocarbon fluid for component subsystem or system design validation.

Suppliers and specifications for the reference diesel fuel are also presented in Appendix B.

4.2 Oxygenates

4.2.1 GENERAL—The second (and optional third) formula components of this document are oxygenated compounds. The two oxygenates most commonly found in commercial gasoline fuels in the US are ethanol (EtOH) and methyl tertiary-butyl ether (MTBE). These oxygenates are used in US reformulated gasoline (RFG), California Phase II RFG, Oxy-Fuel and gasohol in the general range of 5 to 10% by volume for ethanol and 5 to 15% by volume for methyl tertiary-butyl ether. Other oxygenates that can be added to gasoline include methanol (MeOH), ethyl tertiary-butyl ether (ETBE), and tertiary-amyl methyl ether (TAME). Of these oxygenates, methanol is generally not found in commercial gasolines sold in the US ETBE and TAME are only occasionally used as the oxygenated component of gasoline at this time.

There are two oxygenates derived from agricultural sources that can be used in diesel fuel. They are rapeseed methyl esters (RME) in Europe and BioDiesel in the US. BioDiesel is composed of methyl and/or ethyl esters of vegetable oils, animal fats, used cooking oils, or combinations of the previous. In order to standardize testing soy methyl esters (SME) derived from the trans-esterification of soybean oil with methanol has been selected as the diesel oxygenate of choice to represent the US market. Soy is the most highly unsaturated of the available oils/esters, which make it potentially the most aggressive test fluid.

4.2.2 ETHANOL—The most common source for ethanol is from biomass (corn, grain, sugar cane, etc.) fermentation. Since there are multiple feed sources and several fermentation/purification processes, the minor components of biomass derived ethanols vary greatly. This document recommends the use of synthetic ethanol that has a recognized set of specifications shown in Appendix C. The ethanol and its associated denaturant specified in this document will help to minimize some of the variables in the use of ethanol as a test fluid component.

The document specifies the denaturant that is used in the synthetic ethanol. The denaturant specified is approved by the U. S. Bureau of Alcohol, Tobacco & Firearms (BATF), and will render the ethanol as "completely denatured." This denaturant is made primarily of heptane isomers, and was chosen so that the denaturant would have a minimal effect on the test fluid. At the same time, the chosen denaturant will allow the testing laboratory to avoid the expenditure of resources on the BATF record keeping requirements associated with non-denatured ethanol or "specially denatured" ethanols.

Ethanol derived from biomass contains a complex set of acid(s) and buffers associated with the acid(s). The buffering process is not fully understood at this time, but acetic acid that is found in biomass derived ethanol has been found to act as a buffer, tending to control the pH of the alcohol when strong acids such as sulfuric acid are present.

A new method analogous to pH, called pH_e, has been developed for use with ethanol. The method for measuring pH_e is ASTM D 6423-99. This method uses special pH electrodes and a pH meter recommended for use with ion specific electrodes to rank ethanols for acid strength on an arbitrary scale. The method was developed to overcome the shortcomings of ASTM D 1613 Acidity method which only measures buffering capacity and cannot distinguish between weak and strong acids. Many ethanol producers are currently using the ASTM D 6423 method to monitor and control strong acids in biomass derived ethanol. ASTM has successfully balloted pH_e specification limits of 6.5 to 9.0 for inclusion into ASTM D 4806.

4.2.3 Methyl Tertiary-Butyl Ether (MTBE)—MTBE is the most prevalent oxygenate/octane booster found in current gasoline formulations. MTBE is used worldwide as a replacement for tetraethyl lead, which is legally prohibited from many automotive fuels. Suppliers and specifications for the oxygenated components are presented in Appendix C.

4.2.4 Methanol—The methanol specified is synthetic commercial methanol derived from natural gas. The specifications for methanol found in ASTM D 1152 are recommended by this document. Suppliers and specifications for the oxygenated components are presented in Appendix C.

4.2.5 Fatty Acid Methyl-Esters—Rapeseed methyl esters (RME) are being used in European diesel fuels. The specifications are found in Appendix C. Fatty acid alkyl esters, referred to as BioDiesel, are starting to be introduced into the U.S. diesel fuel markets. A provisional specification for BioDiesel has been developed by ASTM as PS122-99. Soy methyl ester made to this specification is recommended by this document and can be found in Appendix C.

4.2.6 Other Oxygenates—Higher molecular weight alcohols (isopropyl alcohol and tertiary-butyl alcohol) and ethers (diisopropyl ether and ethyl tertiary-amyl ether) may also find some limited usage in commercial gasolines. However, the effects of alcohols on polymers, elastomers, and metals generally decrease as the molecular weight increases.

4.2.7 Alternative Spark Ignition Engine Fuels—Several alternative gasoline fuels are composed primarily of alcohols. The two most common alcohol blends are ethanol (70 to 85%) and methanol (70 to 85%), with the balance composed of a hydrocarbon mixture, such as unleaded gasoline. These alternative fuels currently make up a very small portion of the U. S. market and are specified in ASTM D 5798 and ASTM D 5797 respectively. Alternative fuels are currently used more extensively in markets outside of the U. S. Brazil, for example, uses a hydrated ethanol fuel containing 5 to 7% water and Brazilian gasohol containing approximately 25% anhydrous ethanol in gasoline.

In alternative fuels, more than one oxygenate may be added to a test fluid, but the use of multiple oxygenates is not common in U. S. commercial fuels. The nomenclature of this document (Section 5) provides for fuels containing multiple oxygenates.

4.3 Other Fuel Contaminants/Minor Fuel Components

4.3.1 General—The organic peroxide, aggressive alcohol, and aggressive water (for hydrocarbons) are the only minor components currently recommended by this document.

4.3.2 Aggressive Alcohol—An "Aggressive" alcohol contains the alcohol, salts, water, and a corresponding organic acid. Aggressive ethanol also contains sulfuric acid, a contaminant found in some commercial biomass derived ethanols. The specifications and suppliers for aggressive alcohol components are found in Appendix D. The formulations for making aggressive alcohols are found in Appendix E.

4.3.3 Corrosive Water for Metals Testing—Corrosive water for hydrocarbons is composed of Reagent Water and salt. Fluids C and SC (or C and SC with MTBE) are the only fluids that can contain Corrosive Water and are used for metals testing only. The formulation used in making corrosive water is also found in Appendix E.

4.3.4 Peroxides—Tertiary-butyl hydroperoxide (TBHP) is the recommended organic peroxide to be added into test fluids to simulate and create an oxidized fuel. TBHP is normally sold either as a 70% aqueous solution or as part of a hydrocarbon solution. In order to control the amount of TBHP added, the peroxide content of the TBHP solution must be known. This determination can be performed by the supplier and provided with the product, or the testing laboratory can perform it prior to use. The specifications and suppliers for TBHP are found in Appendix D.

Small amounts of copper, especially cuprous, (Cu^{+1}) compounds are often added to a test fluid that contains organic peroxides to accelerate the decomposition of peroxides into free radicals. Copper compounds are documented in the literature as promoters of free radicals, and their use offers an acceptable method to reduce testing time in sour fuel mixtures. Copper is often found in fuel systems in the form of electrical circuit components, fuel pump motor windings and armatures and in associated wiring. The specifications and suppliers for potentially useful copper compounds are found in Appendix D.

Copper addition to test fluids containing TBHP in prior work was accomplished using a cupric (Cu^{+2}) salt such as copper naphthenate. In the Cupric form, heat and time were required to convert some Cu^{+2} into Cu^{+1} in order to make it available as a catalyst in peroxide decomposition reactions. Results from current and prior testing using cupric salts as a promoter are considered valid. If a suitable cuprous (Cu^{+1}) compound which is both soluble and active can be found, its use will accelerate the formation of free radicals in the test fluid, which in turn accelerates the oxidation of the test fluid and generates quicker results.

It should be noted that adjustments in test time and/or temperature should be made if changing from a test fluid which either contained or did not contain the copper ion. For example, to duplicate tests conducted with the copper ion using a test fluid without the copper ion might require raising the test temperature 10 °C to 20 °C or increasing the exposure time by a factor of 2 to 4 at the same temperature.

4.3.5 Future Components—Components, such as sulfur compounds and other contaminants, may be considered in future revisions of this document. These components will be assigned designated formula nomenclatures and specifications.

5. Test Fluid Nomenclature

5.1 General—A recommended naming convention for test fluids and fuels is presented in this document. Using these abbreviations uniquely identifies the composition of each fluid. Uniform adaptation of this flexible nomenclature for other test fluids is encouraged.

5.2 Nomenclature Convention—The test fluid nomenclature includes the following items, in the specified order:

5.2.1 an abbreviation (X) designating the hydrocarbon fluid used,

5.2.2 an abbreviation (Y_n) designating the oxygenate(s) and the volume percentage(s) of oxygenate(s) used,

5.2.3 an optional suffix (S) designating an optional minor component added to make a more extreme fluid,

5.2.4 the letter "P" at the end indicating the presence of peroxide,

5.2.5 a subscript "A" following the (Y_n) component to designate the presence of minor components making that component aggressive toward the material being tested,

5.2.6 the letter "w" at the end indicating the presence of Corrosive Water.

5.3 Formulas

5.3.1 General Formula—The general formula for a material test fluid is:

$$X(Y_1\%)(Y_2\%)(Y_n\%)\ S \quad \text{(Eq. 1)}$$

where:

X = Hydrocarbon fluid
Y_1 = First optional oxygenate
Y_2 = Second optional oxygenate
Y_n = the nth optional oxygenate
% = Volume percent of oxygenate
S = optional minor constituent such as:
P = the presence of an organic peroxide contaminant which can be added to any fuel mixture.
$_A$ = a subscripted "A" following the alcohol component indicating the presence of an aggressive alcohol.
$_w$ = a lower case "w" component indicating the presence of Corrosive Water added to a hydrocarbon fluid or MTBE containing hydrocarbon fluid.

5.3.2 Hydrocarbon Nomenclature—Letter designations for the recommended hydrocarbon fluids in the nomenclature of this document are:

C = ASTM Fuel C (50% Toluene and 50% Isooctane)
SC = ASTM Surrogate Fuel C (50% Toluene and 50% substitute isoparaffin solvent)
D_{EPA2} = EPA Certification No. 2 low sulfur reference diesel fuel

Commercial reference gasoline names as shown in Appendix B and their industry abbreviations may be used as the hydrocarbon fluid nomenclature of this document.

5.3.3 Oxygenate Nomenclature—Letter designations for the more common oxygenates in the nomenclature of this document are:

M = methanol
E = ethanol
ME = methyl tertiary-butyl ether
EE = ethyl tertiary-butyl ether
TE = tertiary-amyl methyl ether
RME = rapeseed methyl esters
SME = soybean methyl esters (this is the recommended version of BioDiesel).

5.4 Examples—Examples utilizing this naming convention are presented as follows:

Example 1—C(E10) = 90 volume % Fuel C + 10 volume % ethanol.

Example 2—$SC(M25)_A$ = 75 volume % Surrogate Fuel C + 25 volume % aggressive methanol.

Example 3—C(E25)(ME15) = 60 volume % Fuel C + 25 volume % ethanol + 15 volume % methyl tertiary butyl ether.

EXAMPLE 4—C(ME15)P = 85 volume % Fuel C + 15 volume % methyl tertiary butyl ether + tertiarybutyl hydroperoxide (an auto-oxidized fuel).

EXAMPLE 5—C(E10)AP = 90 volume % Fuel C + 10 volume % aggressive ethanol + tertiary butyl hydroperoxide (an auto-oxidized fuel).

EXAMPLE 6—D_{EPA2} (RME20) = 80 volume % Certification diesel + 20 volume % rapeseed methylesters.

EXAMPLE—SCw = Surrogate Fuel C with Corrosive Water (for metals testing).

6. Preparation of Test Fluids

6.1 General—Each of the test fluids used in this document shall be made from components as specified in the appendices of this document.

Most of the test fluids are flammable liquids and should be stored, handled, and used only after consulting the appropriate Material Safety Data Sheets.

All liquid components of test fluids are specified in terms of volume percent. Test fluids should be well mixed before use. Inverting a closed container 24 times assures complete mixing.

Phase separated fluids should be handled such that the relative amounts of the two phases are not changed during transfer.

Fluids and/or components prepared in advance should be stored in tightly sealed containers to prevent evaporation or contamination.

Transfer of hydrocarbon fluids from container to container can generate static charges. The charges can discharge via a spark and cause subsequent ignition of the fluid or its vapor. Grounding methods for the containers are recommended.

Hydrocarbons and oxygenated compounds are volatile and release vapors. Vapor tight containers are recommended to prevent possible vapor ignition and personal exposure to the compounds present in the test fluids.

The following steps are recommended for preparing these blends:

a. Determine the volume of fluid to be blended.
b. Determine the volume or weight of each component required.
c. Add the required volumes of hydrocarbon and/or oxygenate(s).
d. Add the contaminants (peroxide solution, aggressive components, etc.).
e. Mix well before use.

Mixing can be accomplished with a stirrer that constantly mixes the fluid as components are added in the blending container.

6.2 Hydrocarbon Fluids

6.2.1 GENERAL—ASTM reference fluids and surrogate reference fluids should be premixed according to the formulations. Reference fluids are used as obtained from the suppliers.

6.2.2 CORROSIVE WATER—Corrosive water is used to make corrosive hydrocarbon fluids such as Cw and SCw, or corrosive MTBE containing hydrocarbon fluids such as SC(ME15)w and C(ME15)w.

A Corrosive Water stock solution provides 100 ppm chloride ion per liter of water. Previous versions of this document also included Na_2SO_4 and $NaHCO_3$. These two constituents have been judged to not contribute significantly to metal corrosion. In fact, it was determined that $NaHCO_3$ helped to neutralize acids that were added to make aggressive alcohol.

The detailed formulation used in making Corrosive Water is found in Appendix E.

6.3 Alcohols

6.3.1 GENERAL—Methanol and ethanol should be purchased to conform to the properties shown in Appendix C. Reagent Water is added to purchased alcohols prior to their use in materials testing fluid blends as described in this document. This is done to simulate the water content commonly found in fuel grade methanol and ethanol. The amount of water required is determined by difference between the total water content required and the water content of the product as received, determined by Karl Fisher titration.

6.3.2 METHANOL—Methanol used in materials testing fluids should be adjusted by adding Reagent Water to the methanol, as received, to obtain a test fluid component that contains 0.3 wt % total water content.

6.3.3 ETHANOL—Ethanol for use in materials testing fluids should be adjusted by adding Reagent Water to the ethanol, as received, to obtain a test fluid component that contains 1.0 wt % total water content.

Alcohols are hygroscopic, absorbing moisture from the air. For this reason, alcohol containers should be tightly sealed after the water content has been adjusted and measured.

6.3.4 AGGRESSIVE ALCOHOLS—Aggressive MeOH and EtOH formulations are stated in Appendix E.

6.4 Peroxides

6.4.1 GENERAL—It is recommended that the peroxide solution be refrigerated at approximately 7 °C (45 °F) to minimize decomposition. It is also recommended that the peroxide solution be analyzed periodically to determine the actual peroxide content over time.

6.4.2 TERTIARY-BUTYL HYDROPEROXIDE—Tertiary-butyl hydroperoxide (TBHP) in an aqueous solvent must conform to the properties shown in Appendix D. The weight percent of TBHP in solution should be provided by the supplier or be determined using ASTM E 298. In order to simulate an oxidized fuel, 50 millimoles (mMol) of TBHP is added per liter of the test fluid. The amount of TBHP solution required to obtain a concentration of 50 mMol TBHP per liter of test fluid is calculated using Equation 2:

$$\text{grams of TBHP solution to make 1.0 L of test fluid} = \frac{(50\,\text{mMol TBHP}) \times (90\ \text{mg/mMol TBHP})}{(\text{wt fraction of TBHP in solution}) \times (1000\ \text{mg/g})} \quad \text{(Eq. 2)}$$

According to this equation, 6.43 g of 70% TBHP solution is required per liter of test fluid.

6.4.3 COPPER ION—The use of copper compounds to create copper ions in solution is optional for this document. The specifications, and suppliers for organic copper salts are found in Appendix D. The final test fluid should contain 0.01 mg of Cu per liter.

If copper ions are used, simply dissolve the correct amount of one of the compounds listed in Appendix D.

The amount of copper compound required to give 0.01 g copper per liter of test fluid can be calculated from the Equation 3, where the weight percent copper is obtained from the suppliers specification for the copper compound or it is determined by testing:

$$(0.01\ \text{mg Cu}) \div [(\text{wt \% Cu in copper compound}) \times (0.01)] = \text{mg Cu compound to be used} \quad \text{(Eq. 3)}$$

The addition of copper should be made with adequate mixing immediately AFTER blending the TBHP into the test fluid. Mixing the cuprous ions into the concentrated TBHP solution is NOT recommended.

7. Recommended Fluids for Materials Testing

7.1 Fluids for Testing Fuel System Materials

7.1.1 GENERAL—While this document establishes a system of methods and nomenclature capable of creating and naming an infinite variety of potential test fluid recipes, it is not the intention that materials should be tested in all potential fluids. The test fluids that the document recommends as a minimum to evaluate all candidate materials are listed in this section.

The recommended fluids are designed to simulate typical, severe, real world conditions that can be encountered. The selected fluids are intended to:

a. Minimize the testing required to rigorously evaluate fuel system materials,
b. Reduce variability in test fluids listed in materials specifications, and
c. Standardize testing of fuel system materials.

The final choice of materials to be selected and the test fluids to be used to qualify these materials are dependent on the application as well as the specific design of the component. It will likely involve the cooperative efforts of the component engineer, materials engineer, and the suppliers.

7.1.2 FLUIDS TO QUALIFY MATERIALS FOR WORLDWIDE, BASIC, GASOLINE, AND DIESEL FUEL SYSTEM APPLICATIONS—The four test fluids that are representative of severe general gasoline fuels in marketplaces, worldwide include:

$C(M15)_A$ or $SC(M15)_A$,
C(ME15) or SC(ME15), and
CP or SCP
Cw or SCw for metals testing only (see 7.2.4)

Testing in these fluids alone is sufficient for qualifying materials for consideration in general fuel system applications.

Note that a fuel mixture containing methanol is recommended (CM15) whereas methanol is rarely found in commercial fuels. This fuel has been used for years in the automotive industry and continues to be a valid test fluid because methanol creates effects on materials which are representative of worst case marketplace fuels whether they contain methanol or not. Ethanol and higher alcohols, which may be more common in fuels, usually create significantly smaller effects on fuel system materials.

Diesel fuel is usually less chemically aggressive; therefore, materials qualified in these four test fluids can also be used in diesel fuel applications without being tested in additional fluids.

7.1.3 Fluids to Qualify Materials for Dedicated, Alcohol Based Fuel System Applications—Materials to be qualified for use in fuel systems intended for dedicated alcohol fueled vehicles (E100 to E85 or M100 to M85 fuels) must be tested in the following test fluids:

a. All fluids designated in 7.1.2, and
b. Either: $C(M85)_A$, $SC(M85)_A$, $C(E85)_A$, or $SC(E85)_A$ (depending on the intended marketplace alcohol fuel: ethanol or methanol).

7.1.4 Fluids to Qualify Materials for Alcohol Based, Flexible Fueled Vehicle Fuel System Applications—Materials to be qualified for use in fuel systems intended for flexible fueled vehicles (gasoline, E85, or M85) should be tested in the intended marketplace alcohol fuel (ethanol or methanol) as follows:

a. All fluids designated in 7.1.2,
b. $C(E15)_A$ or $SC(E15)_A$ (if applicable) and
c. $C(M30)_A$ or $SC(M30)_A$ or $C(E30)_A$ or $SC(E30)_A$ and
d. $C(M50)_A$ or $SC(M50)_A$ or $C(E50)_A$ or $SC(E50)_A$ and
e. $C(M85)_A$ or $SC(M85)_A$ or $C(E85)_A$, or $SC(E85)_A$ and
f. $C(M20)_A$(ME15) or $SC(M20)_A$(ME15) or $C(E20)_A$(ME15) or $SC(E20)_A$(ME15).

The purpose for testing with the six additional fluids indicated in this section is to identify the fluid composition that causes the greatest effect on the material being evaluated. The worst case fluid should then be used exclusively for all subsequent testing of that material. This allows all materials to be compared at their individual worst to indicate suitability for use in a particular application.

7.1.5 Fluids to Qualify Materials for Diesel Fuel Only Applications—Materials previously qualified in gasoline systems and tested in fluids designated in 7.1.2, will qualify for diesel fuel applications. To qualify for diesel fuel only applications, candidate materials need only be tested in D_{EPA2} (EPA certification No. 2 diesel fuel). Testing in RME or BioDiesel and their mixtures with diesel fuel may also be required.

7.1.6 Further Qualification of Materials in Marketplace Fuels—In addition to the basic fuel compatibility testing specified previously, component or automotive original equipment manufacturers may require further testing in marketplace representative fluids or fuels. These include:

a. Test fluids that simulate marketplace fuels which are all fluids designated in 7.1.2, and
b. Test fuels that represent typical marketplace fuels (see Appendix B):
   a. EPA certification gasoline
   b. California certification gasoline
   c. GM test fuel 1 (TF-1)
   d. GM test fuel 2 (TF-2)
   e. Brazilian Gasohol (with 25% Biomass Ethanol)
   f. D_{EPA2} (EPA certification No. 2 diesel fuel)
   g. D_{EPA2} (RME20) (20% RME in No. 2 reference diesel fuel)
   h. D_{EPA2} (SME20) (20% SME in No. 2 reference diesel fuel)

7.2 Material Qualification Testing for Fuel Compatibility

7.2.1 General—The purpose of this testing is initial screening of material coupon samples to determine their compatibility with intended marketplace fuels. Use of the test fluids outlined in 7.1 permits simplified testing with standardized chemicals and assures repeatable test results.

Careful attention should be paid to the mechanisms of failure or incompatibility discovered by this testing. For example, the aggressive fluid mixtures may cause one type of degradation while auto-oxidized (peroxide) fluid may cause another. If the extent of degradation is significant for each fluid, then both fluid types must be considered as worst case for further evaluations.

7.2.2 Polymers (Plastics and Thermoplastic Elastomers)—Flexural modulus and/or tensile modulus should be used as a screening test for polymers. The test fluid that causes the greatest reduction in modulus should be used for all subsequent testing and/or for inclusion in the specification of the material when intended for fuel system applications.

7.2.3 Elastomers (Rubber)—Swelling should be used as the screening test for elastomers. The test fluid that causes the greatest amount of swelling should be used for all subsequent testing and/or for inclusion in the specification of the material when intended for fuel system applications.

7.2.4 Metals and Their Protective Coatings—The primary concern for metals is corrosion. Test exposure of the material or component should reflect actual use conditions. Tests should include immersion of the material or component in the fluid and exposure of the material or component to the vapor phase above the fluid. Note that in some test fluids, phase separation can occur. Exposure to the water-rich "lower" phase may be the most difficult environment for metals. The test design should include exposure of the metal to such a water-rich phase if this circumstance exists. Test specimens should be examined for corrosion or any obvious chemical attack after exposure to the vapor phase, the fluid phase, and the water-rich phase.

Metals should be tested for resistance to corrosion by placing the test specimen in a container filled with enough mixture of fluid C or SC and Corrosive Water to expose the lower end to water phase and the top end to vapor phase. The test fluid mixture should contain enough Corrosive Water to create a second phase layer thick enough to contact the lower 10 to 20% of the test specimen. In addition, the container should be only partially filled with test fluid mixture so that the top 20 to 30% of the test specimen is exposed to vapor phase only. The Corrosive Water formulation is found in Appendix A.

7.2.5 Other Requirements—A material's properties, including its fuel compatibility, can be strongly influenced by the part design and the manufacturing processes used to convert the raw material into a finished component. The task of assessing fuel compatibility and suitability of a material for use in a fuel system is not complete unless the material is re-evaluated after conversion into the intended component using the test fluids or test fuels identified as worst case. However, as emphasized earlier in the document (see "Scope"), it is not intended that the TEST FLUIDS listed in this document be used for product or process validation of devices (e.g., fuel pumps, injectors, etc.) assembled from materials so qualified. Product validation should only be conducted using the TEST FUELS specified in this document.

*8. **Listing of Worldwide Test Fuels*** —Test fluids and fuels that have been used worldwide for materials testing are listed in Appendix G for reference only.

*9. **Summary of the Appendices***

Appendix A: Specifications for Hydrocarbon Fluids
- Specifications for ISOOCTANE AND TOLUENE
- Specifications for REFERENCE FUEL GRADE TOLUENE
- Specifications for TOLUENE Nitration Grade
- Specifications for ISOOCTANE (2,2,4 - trimethyl pentane)
- Specifications for MIXED OCTANE ISOMERS (Isopar C)
- Specifications for MIXED OCTANE ISOMERS (Soltrol 10)

Appendix B: Specifications and Suppliers for Reference Gasolines and Diesel Fuel
- Specifications for EPA CERTIFICATION GRADE GASOLINE
- Specifications for CARB PHASE 2 REFORMULATED CERTIFICATION GRADE GASOLINE
- Specifications for TF-1 GASOLINE
- Specifications for TF-2 GASOLINE
- Specifications for BRAZILIAN E 22 GASOLINE
- Specifications for EPA CERTIFICATION NO. 2 DIESEL FUEL

Appendix C: Suppliers and Specifications for Oxygenates
- Specifications for METHANOL, Commercial Grade
- Specifications for ETHANOL, Synthetic
- Specifications for METHYL TERTIARY-BUTYL ETHER, (MTBE), High Purity Grade
- Specifications for RAPESEED METHYL ESTERS (RME)
- Specifications for SOY METHYL ESTERS (SME)

Appendix D: Specifications and Suppliers of Other Chemicals For Materials Testing
- Specifications for TERTIARY-BUTYL HYDROPEROXIDE, 70% Solution
- Specifications for GLACIAL ACETIC ACID, ACS Reagent Grade
- Specifications for FORMIC ACID, ACS Reagent Grade
- Specifications for SODIUM CHLORIDE, Crystalline, ACS Reagent Grade
- Specifications for Copper Salts for Adding Copper Ions to Peroxide Test Fluids
- Specifications for SULFURIC ACID, 95 to 98%, ACS Reagent Grade
- Specifications for REAGENT WATER

Appendix E: Formulations for Aggressive Alcohols and Corrosive Water
- Aggressive Methanol
- Aggressive Ethanol
- Corrosive Water

Appendix F: Test Results Validating the Use of Isooctane Surrogates

Appendix G: Worldwide Test Fluids and Test Fuels

APPENDIX A
SPECIFICATIONS FOR HYDROCARBON FLUIDS

A.1 Specifications for ISOOCTANE AND TOLUENE from ASTM D 471—See Table A1.

TABLE A1—SPECIFICATIONS FOR ISOOCTANE AND TOLUENE FROM ASTM D 471

	ASTM Isooctane	ASTM n-Heptane	ASTM 80 O.N. Blend
ASTM-IP MOTOR OCTANE NO.(1)	—	—	NOMINAL ± 0.1
ISOOCTANE,(2) %	NOT LESS THAN 99.75	NOT GREATER THAN 0.10	
N-HEPTANE,(2) %	NOT GREATER THAN 0.10	NOT LESS THAN 99.75	—
LEAD CONTENT,(3) G/GAL	NOT GREATER THAN 0.002	NOT GREATER THAN 0.002	

1. Determined in accordance with ASTM D 2700-IP236.
2. Determined in accordance with ASTM D 2268.
3. To be determined in the certification test in accordance with ASTM D 3237-97.

A.2 Specifications for Reference Fuel Grade Toluene[1]

Toluene, %not less than 99.5[(1)(2)]

1. Determined in accordance with ASTM D 2360.
2. In addition to determining nonaromatic hydrocarbons, a calibration for trace benzene and trace xylenes must be made to aid in the determination of monocyclic aromatic hydrocarbons other than toluene.

1. Determined in accordance with ASTM D 2360.

A.3 Specifications for Toluene Nitration Grade—See Table A2.

TABLE A2—SPECIFICATIONS FOR TOLUENE NITRATION GRADE(1)

Parameter	Units	Conditions	Minimum	Maximum	Test Method
TOLUENE	wt /wt %		99.5		ASTM D 2360 MOD.
NITRATION TOLUENE			PASSES 99.5		ASTM D 841
DISTILLATION RANGE	°C	INCLUDING 110.6 °C	PASSES	1.0	ASTM D 850
NON AROMATICS	wt /wt %			1.5	ASTM D 2360 MOD.
SPECIFIC GRAVITY	—	15 °C (60 °F)	0.869	0.873	ASTM D 4052
COLOR	Pt - Co		0.869	20	ASTM D 1209
ACIDITY	—		NONE	20	ASTM D 847
ACID WASH COLOR	—		NONE	2	ASTM D 848
COPPER CORROSION	—		1 A	2	ASTM D 849
H2S + SO2	—		NONE		ASTM D 853
BENZENE	PPM			300	ASTM D 2360
NON-VOLATILE MATTER	MG. / 100 mL			1.0	ASTM D 1353
APPEARANCE	—		BRIGHT & CLEAR		ASTM D 4176 MOD.

1. U.S. Suppliers: Specified Fuels and Chemicals
Various Chemical Distributing Companies
Various Laboratory Supply Companies

Trade Name: Nitration Grade Toluene

A.4 Specifications for Isooctane (2,2,4, - trimethyl pentane)—See Table A3.

TABLE A3—SPECIFICATIONS FOR ISOOCTANE (2,2,4, - TRIMETHYL PENTANE)(1)

Parameter	Units	Conditins	Typical	Minimum	Maximum	Test Method
NON-VOLATILE MATTER	MG./1000 mL.		0.16			ASTM D 381
SULFUR CONTENT	PPM		<1			ASTM D 3120
LEAD	grams / gal.		0.000		0.002	ASTM D 3237
COMPOSITION	LV%					
2,2,4 TRIMETHYL PENTANE			99.95	99.75		ASTM D 2268
OTHER OCTANES			0.04			
n HEPTANE			0.01		0.1	

1. U.S. Suppliers: Phillips Petroleum Company
Specified Fuels and Chemicals
Various Chemical Distributing Companies
Various Laboratory Supply Companies

Trade Name: Isooctane, Primary Reference Fuel (PRF)

A.5 Specifications for Mixed Octane Isomers (Isopar C)—See Table A4.

TABLE A4—SPECIFICATIONS FOR MIXED OCTANE ISOMERS (ISOPAR C)[1]

Parameter	Units	Conditions	Typical	Minimum	Maximum	Test Method
ANILINE POINT	°C			77	80	ASTM D 611
	°F			170.6	176	
APPEARANCE				BRIGHT & CLEAR		ASTM D 4176 MOD.
AROMATICS	vol/vol %				0.02	ASTM D 1319
BULK ODOR	—			PASS		PANEL
COLOR	SAYBOLT UNITS			30		ASTM D 156
DISTILLATION						ASTM D 86
INITIAL B P	°C (°F)			96 (204.8)		
DRY POINT	°C (°F)				107 (224.6)	
NON-VOLATILE MATTER	MG. /100 mL				1.0	ASTM D 1353
SPECIFIC GRAVITY	—	15 °C (60 °F)		0.694	0.701	ASTM D 4052 / 1298
SULFUR CONENT	PPM				5	ASTM D 4045 MOD.
COMPOSITION	L V %					
2,2,4 TRIMETHYL PENTANE			79			TYPICAL G. C.
OTHER BRANCHED OCTANES			17			TYPICAL G. C.
BRANCHED HEPTANES			4			TYPICAL G. C.

1. U.S. Suppliers: Exxon Chemical Company
   Specified Fuels and Chemicals
   Various Chemical Distributing Companies
   Various Laboratory Supply Companies

   Trade Name: Isopar C

A.6 Specifications for Mixed Octane Isomers (Soltrol 10)—See Table A5.

TABLE A5—SPECIFICATIONS FOR MIXED OCTANE ISOMERS (SOLTROL 10)[1]

Parameter	Units	Conditions	Typical	Minimum	Maximum	Test Method
ANILINE POINT	° F		170.6			ASTM D 611
AROMATICS	vol/vol %		NIL			G.C.
BULK ODOR	- - -		PASS			PANEL
COLOR	SAYBOLT UNITS			30		ASTM D 156
DISTILLATION	°F					ASTM D 86
INITIAL B P	°F		204	200		
5%	°F		205	202		
10%	°F		206			
50%	°F		208			
90%	°F		212			
95%	°F		215	219		
DRY POINT	°F		218	220		
NON-VOLATILE MATTER	MG. / 100 mL		0.5		1.0	ASTM D 1353
SPECIFIC GRAVITY	- - -	15 °C (60 °F)		0.694	0.701	ASTM D 4052 / 1298
API GRAVITY	° API	60 °F	70.6			
SULFUR CONENT	PPM					ASTM D 4045 MOD.
	PPM		<1		10	ASTM D 3120
COMPOSITION	L V %					G. C.
2,2,4 TRIMETHYL PENTANE			62			
OCTANES			10			
HEPTANES			28			
REID VAPOR PRESSURE	PSIA	100 °F	2.2			ASTM D 323
FLASH POINT	° F		13			ASTM D 56
KARI - BUTANOL VALUE	—	27.9				

1. U.S. Suppliers: Phillips Petroleum Company
   Specified Fuels and Chemicals
   Various Chemial Distributing Companies
   Various Laboratory Supply Companies

   Trade Name: Soltrol 10

APPENDIX B
SPECIFICATIONS AND SUPPLIERS FOR REFERENCE GASOLINES AND DIESEL FUEL

B.1 Specifications and Suppliers for Reference Gasolines and Diesel Fuel—
See Tables B1 through B6.

TABLE B1—SPECIFICATIONS FOR EPA CERTIFICATION GRADE GASOLINE[(1)]
U.S. ENVIRONMENTAL PROTECTION AGENCY
40 CFR 86.307 (A) (1)

Parameter	Units	Specifications Minimum	Specifications Maximum	ASTM Test Method
OCTANE, RESEARCH		96		D 2699
PB (ORGANIC)	grams/U.S. gal	0.00	0.05	
DISTILLATION RANGE:				
IBP	°F	75	95	D 86
10 PCT POINT	°F	120	135	D 86
50 PCT POINT	°F	200	230	D 86
90 PCT POINT	°F	300	325	D 86
EP			415	D 86
SULFUR	wt %		0.1	D 1266
PHOSPHORUS	grams/U.S. gal		0.005	
RVP	psig	8.0	9.2	D 323
COMPOSITION:				
OLEFINS	%		10	D 1319
AROMATICS	%		35	D 1319
SATURATES	%		BALANCE	D 1319

1. U.S. Suppliers: Specified Fuels and Chemicals
BP/Amoco
Trade name: EEE
Indolene

TABLE B2—SPECIFICATIONS FOR CARB PHASE 2 REFORMULATED CERTIFICATION GRADE GASOLINE[(1)]
CALIFORNIA AIR RESOURCE BOARD REGULATIONS SECTION 2262, 2252 - 54

Parameter	Units	Specifications Minimum	Specifications Maximum	ASTM or ARB Test Method
SULFUR	ppm		80	D 2622
OXYGEN	vol %	1.80	2.7	D 4815
DISTILLATION RANGE:				
50 PCT POINT	° F		220	D 86
90 PCT POINT	° F		330	D 86
RVP	psig		7.0	D 323
COMPOSITION:				
OLEFINS	%		10.0	D 1319
AROMATICS	%		35	D 1319
BENZENE	vol %		1.2	D 3606 ARB MLD 16
PHOSPHORUS	grams/U.S. gal		0.005	D 3231
LEAD	grams/U.S. gal		0.05	D 3237
MANGANESE	grams/U.S. gal		0	—

1. U.S. Suppliers: Specified Fuels and Chemicals
Trade Name: C A RB Phase 2

TABLE B3—SPECIFICATIONS FOR TF-1 GASOLINE[(1)]

Parameter	Units	Specifications Minimum	Specifications Maximum	ASTM or ARB Test Method
SULFUR	ppm		500	D 2622, D 3120, or D 5453
METHANOL	VOL %		0	D 4815
ETHANOL	VOL %	9.5	10.5	D 4815
MTBE	VOL %		0	D 4815
DISTILLATION RANGE:				
10 PCT POINT	°F		158	D 86
50 PCT POINT	°F	170	250	D 86
90 PCT POINT	°F		374	D 86
END POINT	°F		437	D 86
RVP	psig	8.0	9.0	D 5191
COMPOSITION:				
OLEFINS	vol %		15.0	D 1319
AROMATICS	vol %	45.0	50.0	D 1319
GUM CONTENT, WASHED	mg/100mL		5.0	D 381
OXIDATION STABILITY	minutes	960		D 525
OCTANE (R+M/2)	- - -	91.0		D 2699/2700
WATER	vol %		0.1	D 2709
LEAD	grams/U.S. gal		0.005	D 3237
APPEARANCE	—	Clear, Bright, free	of undissolved water	Visual

1. U.S. Suppliers: Specified Fuels and Chemicals
Trade Name: General Motors Test Fuel 1 (TF-1)

TABLE B4—SPECIFICATIONS FOR TF-2 GASOLINE(1)

Parameter	Units	Specifications Minimum	Specification Maximum	ASTM or ARB Test Method
SULFUR	ppm		500	D 2622, D 3120, or D 5453
METHANOL	vol %	4.5	5.5	D 4815
ETHANOL	vol %	2.0	3.0	D 4815
MTBE	vol %		0	D 4815
DISTILLATION RANGE:				
10 PCT POINT	°F		158	D 86
50 PCT POINT	°F	170	250	D 86
90 PCT POINT	°F		374	D 86
END POINT	°F		437	D 86
RVP	psig	8.0	9.0	D 5191
COMPOSITION:				
OLEFINS	vol %		15.0	D 1319
AROMATICS	vol %	45.0	50.0	D 1319
GUM CONTENT, WASHED	mg/100 ml		5.0	D 381
OXIDATION STABILITY	minutes	960		D 525
OCTANE (R+M/2)	—	91.0		D 2699/2700
WATER	vol %		0.1	D 2709
LEAD	grams/U.S. gal		0.005	D 3237
APPEARANCE	—	Clear, Bright, free	of undissolved water	Visual

1. U.S. Suppliers: Specified Fuels and Chemicals
   Trade Name: Greneral Motors Test Fuel 2 (TF-2)

TABLE B5—SPECIFICATIONS FOR BRAZILIAN E 22 GASOLINE(1)

Parameter	Units	Specifications Minimum	Specifications Maximum	Typical	ASTM Test Method
SULFUR	ppm	350	650		D4294
ETHANOL	vol %	21.0	23.0		D4815
DISTILLATION RANGE:					D86
10 PCT POINT	°F		150	132	
50 PCT POINT	°F		220	162	
95 PCT POINT	°F			329	
END POINT	°F		400	358	
RVP	psig		9.0	7.0	D 5191
LEAD	g/gal			0.01	D 3237
COMPOSITION:					
AROMATICS	%		30	20	D 1319
OLEFINS	%		15.0	10.0	D 1319

1. NOTE—This fluid has been designed to be similar to Braziliam gasohol containing 22% biomass ethanol.

   U.S. Suppliers: Specified Fuels and Chemicals
   Trade Name: Brazilian E 22

TABLE B6—SPECIFICATIONS FOR EPA CERTIFICATION NO. 2 DIESEL FUEL(1)
U.S. ENVIRONMENTAL PROTECTION AGENCY
40 CFR 86.1313 (B) (2)

Parameter	Units	Specifications Minimum	Specifications Maximum	ASTM Test Method
CETANE NUMBER	—	42	48	D 613
DISTILLATION RANGE:				
IBP	°F	350	390	D 86
10 PCT POINT	°F	410	450	D 86
50 PCT POINT	°F	480	530	D 86
90 PCT POINT	°F	570	620	D 86
EP	°F	620	680	D 86
GRAVITY	° API	32	37	D 287
SULFUR	wt %	0.03	0.05	D 2622
COMPOSITION:				
AROMATICS	vol %	28	35	D 1319
PARAFFINS, NAPHTHENES, OLEFINS	vol %	BALANCE	BALANCE	D 1319
FLASHPOINT	°F	130		D 93
VISCOSITY	cSt	2.0	3.2	D 445

1. U.S. Suppliers: Specified Fuels and Chemicals
   Trade Name: Low Sulfur Reference Diesel - 4

APPENDIX C
SUPPLIERS AND SPECIFICATIONS FOR OXYGENATES

C.1 Suppliers and Specifications for Oxygenates—See Tables C1 through C5.

TABLE C1—SPECIFICATIONS FOR METHANOL, COMMERCIAL GRADE[1]

Parameter	Units	Conditions	Minimum	Maximum	Test Method
METHANOL	wt /wt Percent		99.85		ASTM E 346
SPECIFIC GRAVITY	—	20 °C/20 °C		0.7928	ASTM D 891
DISTILLATION RANGE	°C	Not More Than:		1.0	
DISTILLATION RANGE	°C	RANGE 64.6 ±		0.1	
COLOR	Apha			5	ASTM D 1209
ACIDITY	wt /wt Percent	AS ACETIC ACID		0.003	ASTM D 1613
ACETONE	wt /wt Percent			0.003	ASTM D 1612
NON-VOLATILE MATTER	wt /wt Percent			0.001	ASTM D 1353
PERMANGANATE TIME	Minutes	at 15 °C	50		ASTM D 1363
ETHANOL	wt./wt Percent			0.003	ASTM D 1612
WATER	vol/vol Percent			0.10	ASTM D 1364
HYDROCARBONS	Cloudiness		None		ASTM D 1722
	Opalescence		None		
APPEARANCE			Clear		VISUAL
APPEARANCE			Colorless		VISUAL

1. Meets:
   Federal Grade A,
   ASTM D 1152 and
   USP (NF XVI) Standards

   U.S. Suppliers; Specified Fuels and Chemicals
   Various Chemical Distributing Companies
   Various Laboratory Supply Companies

   Trade Name: Methanol

TABLE C2—SPECIFICATIONS FOR ETHANOL, SYNTHETIC[1]

Parameter	Units	Conditions	Minimum	Maximum	Test Method
ETHANOL	Proof	15.6 ° (60 °F)	199.8		
	wt Percent	16 °C (61 °F)	99.9		
WATER	vol/vol Percent			0.10	ASTM D 1364
SPECIFIC GRAVITY	—	15.6 °C (60 °F)		0.7942	ASTM D 4052
	—	20 °C (68 °F)		0.7910	
	—	77/77 °F		0.7876	
ACIDITY	wt/wt Percent	As Acetic Acid		0.0025	ASTM D 1613
COLOR	Pt - Co			10	ASTM D 1209
NON-VOLATILE MATTER	Grams Per 100 mL			0.0025	ASTM D 1353
PERMANGANATE TIME	Minutes	at 15 °C	30		ASTM D 1363
DENATURANT CDA 20:					
RUBBER HYDROCARBON SOLVENT	vol/vol Percent		2.0		27 CFR 21.24

1. U.S. Suppliers: Specified Fuels and Chemicals
   Various Chemical Distributing Companies
   Various Laboratory Supply Companies

   Trade Name: Ethyl Alcohol, USP, Dehydrated and Denatured to BATF CDA 20

TABLE C3—SPECIFICATIONS FOR METHYL TERTIARY-BUTYL ETHER, (MTBE) HIGH PURITY GRADE[1]

Parameter	Units	Conditions	Minimum	Maximum	Test Method
MTBE	wt /wt Percent		99.9		ASTM D 5441
WATER	wt /wt Percent			0.15	ASTM E 203
METHANOL	wt /wt Percent			0.05	ASTM D 5254
TERT BUTYL ALCOHOL	wt /wt Percent		None		ASTM D 5441
C4 HYDROCARBONS	wt/wt Percent		None		ASTM D 5441
C5 + HYDROCARBONS	wt /wt Percent		None		ASTM D 5441
UNKNOWNS	wt /wt Percent		None		ASTM D 5441
REID VAPOR PRESSURE	psia	100 °F		11.0	ASTM D 323

1. U.S. Suppliers: Lyondell Chemical Company
   Specified Fuels and Chemicals
   Various Chemical Distributing Companies
   Various Laboratory Supply Companies

   Trade Name: High Purity MTBE

TABLE C4—SPECIFICATIONS FOR RAPESEED METHYL ESTERS (RME)[1]

Parameter	Units	Minimum	Maximum	Test Method
ESTER CONTENT	wt %	98.9 ° (210 °F)		
IODINE NUMBER			120	ISO 3991
FLASH POINT (PMCC)	°C (°F)	210		ASTM D 93
ACID VALUE	mg KOH/gm		0.5	ASTM D 664
WATER CONTENT	wt %		0.2	ASTM D 2709

1. U.S. Suppliers: Specified Fuels and Chemicals
Various Laboratory Supply Companies

Trade Name: Rapeseed Methyl Esters

TABLE C5—SPECIFICATIONS FOR SOY METHYL ESTERS (SME)[1]
In accordance with ASTM PS121-99, Provisional Standard Specification for Biodiesel Fuel (B100) Blend Stock for Distillate Fuels

Parameter	Units	Minimum	Maximum	Test Method
ESTER CONTENT	wt %	96.5	—	
FLASH POINT (PMCC)	°C	100	—	ASTM D 93
WATER AND SEDIMENT	vol %		0.05	ASTM D 2709
KINEMATIC VISCOSITY, 40 °C	mm^2/s	1.9	6.0	ASTM D 445
SULFATED ASH	% mass	—	0,020	ASTM D 874
SULFUR	% mass	—	0.05	ASTM D 2622
COPPER STRIP CORROSION	-	—	No. 3	ASTM D 130
CETANE	-	40	—	ASTM D 613
CLOUD POINT	°C	report	—	ASTM D 2500
CARBON RESIDUE (100% SAMPLE)	% mass	—	0.050	ASTM D 4530
ACID NUMBER	mg KOH/gm	—	0.8	ASTM D 664
FREE GLYCERIN	% mass	—	0.020	GC
TOTAL GLYCERIN	% mass	—	0.240	GC

1. U.S. Suppliers: Specified Fuels and Chemicals
Various Laboratory Supply Companies
Ag Environmental Company

Trade Name: Soy Methyl Esters
Soy Diesel

APPENDIX D
SPECIFICATIONS AND SUPPLIERS OF OTHER CHEMICALS FOR MATERIALS TESTING SPECIFICATIONS FOR TERTIARY-BUTYL HYDROPEROXIDE,

D.1 Specifications and Suppliers of Other Chemicals for Materials Testing— See Tables D1 through D7.

TABLE D1—SPECIFICATIONS FOR TERTIARY-BUTYL HYDROPEROXIDE, 70% SOLUTION[1]

Parameter	Units	Conditions	Minimum	Maximum	Test Method
ACTIVE OXYGEN	wt. Percent		12.2		ASTM E 298
TERT. BUTYL HYDROPEROXIDE	wt Percent		69.0	71.0	ASTM E 298
DI ALKYL PEROXIDES	wt Percent			0.10	G. C.
KETONES	wt Percent		None	0.20	G. C.
OTHER HYDROPEROXIDES	wt Percent		None	1.00	G. C.
OTHER ORGANICS	wt Percent		None	0.40	G. C.
TERT BUTYL ALCOHOL	wt Percent		None	0.50	G. C.
WATER, FREE PHASE	vol Percent			0.7	Centrifuge
WATER BY DIFFERENCE	vol Percent		Balance		

1. U.S. Suppliers; Lyondell Chemical Company
Elf Atochem
Various Chemical Distributing Companies
Various Laboratory Supply Companies

Trade Name: TBHP, tert-Butyl Hydroperoxide 70% Solution

TABLE D2—SPECIFICATIONS FOR GLACIAL ACETIC ACID, ACS REAGENT GRADE(1)

Parameter	Units	Minimum	Maximum
ACETIC ACID	wt Percent	99.7	
ACETIC ANHYDRIDE	wt Percent		0.01
ACETALDEHYDE	Wt. Percent		0.005
COLOR	Apha		10
RESIDUE AFTER EVAPORATION	ppmw		10
HEAVY METALS (AS, PB)	ppmw		500
ACS SPECIFICATIONS		Passes	

1. U.S. Suppliers: Various Chemical Distributing Companies
Various Laboratory Supply Companies

Trade Name: Glacial Acetic Acid

TABLE D3—SPECIFICATIONS FOR FORMIC ACID, ACS REAGENT GRADE(1)

Parameter	Units	Minimum	Maximum
FORMIC ACID	wt Percent	88.0	
ACETIC ACID	wt Percent		0.4
ACETALDEHYDE	wt Percent		0.005
COLOR	Apha		15
RESIDUE AFTER EVAPORATION	ppmw		20
HEAVY METALS (AS, PB)	ppmw		5
ACS SPECIFICATIONS		Passes	

1. U.S. Suppliers: Various Chemical Distributing Companies
Various Laboratory Supply Companies

Trade Name: Formic Acid

TABLE D4—SPECIFICATIONS FOR SODIUM CHLORIDE, CRYSTALLINE, ACS REAGENT GRADE(1)

Parameter	Units	Minimum	Maximum
SODIUM CHLORIDE	wt Percent	99.0	
IODIDE	wt Percent		0.002
BROMIDE	wt Percent		0.01
SULFATE	wt Percent		0.003
RESIDUE INSOLUBLE MATTER	ppmw		50
ACS SPECIFICATIONS		Passes	

1. U.S. Suppliers: Various Chemical Distributing Companies
Various Laboratory Supply Companies

Trade Name: Salt
Table Salt
Sodium Chloride

TABLE D5—SPECIFICATIONS FOR COPPER SALTS FOR ADDING COPPER IONS TO PEROXIDE TEST FLUIDS

Parameter	AVAILABLE FROM
COPPER NAPTHENATE	AVAILABLE FROM HULS/VEBA
COPPER CYCLOHEXANEBUTYRATE	AVAILABLE FROM KODAK
CUPRIC ACETATE	AVAILABLE FROM BAKER CHEMICAL

TABLE D6—SPECIFICATIONS FOR SULFURIC ACID, 95 TO 98%, ACS REAGENT GRADE(1)

Parameter	Units	Minimum	Maximum
SULFURIC ACID	wt Percent	95.0	98.0
RESIDUE AFTER IGNITION	PPMw		4
COLOR	Apha		8
HEAVY METALS (AS PB)	PPMw		0.5

1. U.S. Suppliers: Various Chemical Distributing Companies
Various Laboratory Supply Companies

Trade Names: Concentrated Sulfuric Acid

TABLE D7—SPECIFICATIONS FOR REAGENT WATER(1)

Parameter	Units	Minimum	Maximum
CONDUCTIVITY	μ S/cm @ 25 °C		10
RESISTIVITY	mΩ-cm @ 25 °C	10	
SODIUM	μG / L		5
CHLORIDE	μG / L		5

1. Meets ASTM D 1193-91 Ty;e II grade

Trade Names: Reagent Water
Megaohm Water

APPENDIX E
FORMULATIONS FOR AGGRESSIVE ALCOHOLS AND CORROSIVE WATER AGGRESSIVE METHANOL

E.1 Formulations for Aggressive Alcohols and Corrosive Water—See Tables E1 through E3.

E.1.1 Aggressive Methanol—The components to make 1.0 L or 1.0 gal of Aggressive Methanol are shown in Table E1.

TABLE E1—AGGRESSIVE METHANOL

Component	Units	1.0 Liter	1.0 Gallon
METHANOL, COMMERCIAL GRADE	gm	792.4	2995.3
REAGENT WATER	gm	2.330	8.808
SODIUM CHLORIDE	gm	0.004	0.014
FORMIC ACID	gm	0.046	0.173

E.1.2 Aggressive Ethanol—The components to make 1.0 L or 1.0 gal of Aggressive Ethanol are shown in Table E2.

TABLE E2—AGGRESSIVE ETHANOL(1)

Component	Units	1.0 Liter	1.0 Gallon
ETHANOL, SYNTHETIC	gm	816.0	3084.5
DEIONIZED WATER	gm	8.103	30.631
SODIUM CHLORIDE	gm	0.004	0.014
SULFURIC ACID	gm	0.021	0.080
GLACIAL ACETIC ACID	gm	0.061	0.230

1. NOTE—To minimize esterification reactions, the sulfuric acid should be blended into the Reagent Water prior to mixing with ethanol

E.1.3 Corrosive Water—The components to make 1.0 L or 1.0 gal of Corrosive Water are shown in Table E3.

TABLE E3—CORROSIVE WATER(1)

Component	Units	1.0 Liter	1.0 Gallon
SODIUM CHLORIDE	gm	0.165	0.624
REAGENT WATER	gm	1000	3780

1. NOTE—All materials for these formulations are specified in Appendices C and D.

APPENDIX F
TEST RESULTS VALIDATING THE USE OF ISOOCTANE SURROGATES

F.1 Two isoparaffin surrogates, Soltrol 10 and Isopar C, were tested on materials and compared with isooctane. Solvent uptake tests on loosely crosslinked isoprene were performed to determine polymer swelling after exposure to these three hydrocarbons.

Swelling tests were performed on crosslinked isoprene with exposures of 42.5 and 66.5 hours, at 40 °C. Additional testing was done on High Density Polyethylene (HDPE) with exposure of 450 hours, at 40 °C and on Natural Rubber with exposure of 450 hours, at 40 °C.

The results of these tests are indicated in Table F1.

TABLE F1—COMPARISON OF THE EFFECT OF ISO-OCTANE VERSUS MIXED OCTANE ISOMERS ON NATURAL RUBBER

Material Solvent	Solvent Uptake, Weight Fraction(1) Crosslinked Polyisoprene	Solvent Uptake, Percent Weight Increase(2) High Density Polyethylene	Solvent Uptake, Percent Weight Increase(2) Natural Rubber
ISOOCTANE	2.07	5.96	72.7
SOLTROL 10	2.23	6.64	89.0
ISOPAR C	2.15	6.21	79.4
ASTM FUEL C	4.00	—	—
SURROGATE C1 (50% SOLTROL 10 + 50% TOLUENE)	4.09	—	—
SURROGATE C2 (50% ISOPAR C + 50% TOLUENE)	4.04	—	—

1. Weight fraction is defined as the difference in weight before and after exposure of the polymer to the solvent, divided by the original weight of the polymer tested. Polymer preparation is described by Mazich, Rossi, and Smith in Macromolecules 25, 6929 (1992). Testing courtesy of Ford Motor Company.
2. Testing performed on 1 x 2 in samples suspended in the test fluid. Testing courtesy of Solvay Automotive.

APPENDIX G
WORLDWIDE TEST FLUIDS AND TEST FUELS

G.1 Worldwide Test Fluids and Test Fuels—See Table G1.

TABLE G1—WORLDWIDE TEST FLUIDS AND TEST FUELS

Identification	Name	Major Ingredient	Paraffinic (vol %)	Olefinic (vol %)	Aromatic (vol %)	Oxygenate (vol %)	Other (vol %)
AUTO-OIL	U.S. Industry Avg. (Summer)	Full range distillate gasoline.	58 mixed C_4 - C_{10}	9.2 mixed	32 mixed	none	1.5 Benzene, 8.7 psig RVP 165 °C (330 °F) T90
U.S. EPA CERTIFICATION FUEL	Specified Fuels & Chem. EEE; Indolene Clear	Full range distillate gasoline.	64 mixed C_4 - C_{10}	4.6 mixed	29.9 mixed	none	.5 Benzene, 9.0 psig RVP 154 °C (309 °F) T90
CALIFORNIA PHASE II REFORMULATED		Full range distillate gasoline	74 mixed C_4 - C_{10}	4.0 mixed	22 mixed	15 MTBE or 5 Methanol or 7 Ethanol	.8 max. Benzene, 7.8 psig RVP, 143 °C (290 °F) T_{90}
ASTM D 471 ('79) / ISO 14469	Ref. Fuel A	Iso-Octane	100				
	Ref. Fuel B	Iso-Octane	70 Iso-Octane		30 Toluene		
	Ref. Fuel C		50 Iso-Octane		50 Toluene		
	Ref. Fuel D	Iso-Octane	60 Iso-Octane		40 Toluene		
	Ref. Fuel E	Toluene			100 Toluene		
	Ref. Fuel F	Grade #2 Diesel Fuel					
	Ref. Fuel G	Ref. Fuel D				15 anhydrous denatured Ethanol	
	Ref. Fuel H	Ref. Fuel C				15 anhydrous denatured Ethanol	
	Ref. Fuel I	Ref. Fuel C				15 anhydrous denatured Methanol	
	Ref. Fuel K	Ref. Fuel C				85 anhydrous denatured Methanol	
DIN 51 604	FAM A (11/82)	Toluene	30 Iso-Octane	15 Di-Isobutylene	50 Toluene	5 Ethanol	
	FAM B (03/84)	84.5 FAM A				15 Methanol	0.5 Water
	FAM C (03/84)	40 FAM A				58 Methanol	2.0 Water

TABLE G1—WORLDWIDE TEST FLUIDS AND TEST FUELS (continued)

Identification	Name	Major Ingredient	Paraffinic (vol %)	Olefinic (vol %)	Aromatic (vol %)	Oxygenate (vol %)	Other (vol %)
ISO 1817 (03/85)	Liquid A	ASTM Fuel A					
	Liquid B	ASTM Fuel B					
	Liquid C	ASTM Fuel C					
	Liquid D	ASTM Fuel D					
	Liquid E	Toluene			100 Toluene		
	Liquid F	Mixed paraffinic	80 C_{12} to C_{18}		20 1-Methylnaphthalene		
	Liquid 1	DIN FAM A					
	Liquid 2	DIN FAM B					
	Liquid 3	90 ASTM Fuel C				7 Ethanol 3 Methanol	
	Liquid 4	85 ASTM Fuel C				15 Methanol	
	CM(As specified)	ASTM Ref Fuel C				As specified Methanol	0.5 Aggressive water
	CM(As specified)P	ASTM Ref Fuel C				As specified Methanol	50 mmol/liter t-Butylhydro-peroxide plus 0.01 mg Cu^{+} ion
SAE J1681 (03/93) /J1748 (03/94)	CM0/CM0P	ASTM Ref Fuel C					"P" index = adding 50 mmol/liter t-Butylhydro-peroxide
	CM15/CM15P	ASTM Ref Fuel C				15 Methanol	plus .01 mg Cu+ ion
	CM30/CM30P	ASTM Ref Fuel C				30 Methanol	Aggressive Methanol = 995 mL Anhydrous Methanol + 5 mL
	CM50/CM50P		25 Iso-Octane		25 Toluene	50 Methanol	Aggressive water = Add to one liter of Distilled Water:
	CM85/CM85P	Aggressive Methanol	7.5 Iso-Octane		7.5 Toluene	85 Methanol	.028 mL organic acid normally in chosen alcohol + 990 mg NaCl + 888 mg Na_2SO_4 + 828 mg $NaHCO_3$.
CHRYSLER FLEX FUEL TESTING (03/91)	MS-8004 UnLeaded Fuel	Full range distillate gasoline					Specified Fuels & Chem. Hydrocarbon
	M15, M30, M85	85, 70, 15 MS-8004				15, 30, 85 Aggressive Methanol	Aggressive Methanol = 995 mL Anhydrous Methanol + 5 mL Aggressive water (990 mL Distilled Water + 10 mL Formic acid + 1.gm NaCl + .8 gm Na_2SO_4)
	Gasohol	90 MS-8004				10 Ethanol	
	Oxygenated Gasoline	85 MS-8004				15 MTBE	
	Oxidized Stale Gasoline	MS-8004					2.6 mL t-Butylhydroperoxide + 10.4 mL Laurylperoxide per liter of fuel.
FIAT 9.02137/01(04/95)	Gasoline + Alcohol (benzina alcolata)	90 Octane Super (Norm 55511)				3 Methanol + 5 Ethanol + 2 Iso-Propanol	
FORD - CURRENT	Auto-Oxidized gasoline FLTM AZ-105-01	ASTM Ref. Fuel C					mmol/liter Peroxide as specified by adding t-Butyl hydroperoxide + 0.01 mg Cu ions per liter.
	Fuel Compatibility FLTM AZ-105-02 (similar to SAE J1681)	ASTM Ref. Fuel C				As specified Methanol, Ethanol, MTBE or other	0.5 Aggressive Water (Add to one liter of Distilled Water: .028 ml organic acid normally in chosen alcohol + 990 mg NaCl + 888 mg Na_2SO_4 + 828 mg $NaHCO_3$)
	Permeation Test FLTM BP 114-02	85 ASTM Ref. Fuel C				15 Methanol	plus 5 mg NaCl + 0.05 mL Formic acid per liter of fuel.
GENERAL MOTORS (U.S.)	TF-1	U.S. EPA Certification Fuel		15 max.	adjusted to 45 - 50	10 Ethanol	Specified Fuels and Chemicals Hydrocarbons
	TF-2	U.S. EPA Certification Fuel		15 max.	adjusted to 45 - 50	5 Methanol + 2.5 Ethanol	Specified Fuels and Chemicals Hydrocarbons
	GM6264M (03/90) Sour Gasoline	ASTM Ref. Fuel B					50 Peroxide number by adding t-Butylhydroperoxide
	Brazil Worst Case	ASTM Fuel C	39.5 Iso-Octane		39.5 Toluene	20 Ethanol	1 Corrosive Water: Into 1 L Distilled Water, dissolve: ² 198 mg/L NaCl ² 148 mg/L Na_2SO_3 ² 1.67 mL/L Ethyl Acetate ² 1.33 mL/L Acetaldehyde ² 1.50 mL/L Acetic Acid
OPEL (GM EUROPE)	GME L 0001 (06/80)	FAM A					
	GME L 0003 (07/80)	FAM B					20 ppm Formic acid
NIPPONDENSO	Brazil Compatibility Test Fuel - Pumps & Injectors	Gasoline (?)				22 Ethanol	To each Liter of fuel add: ² 250 mg Peroxide ² 2000 ppm Water ² 14.2 mg Acetic Acid

TABLE G1—WORLDWIDE TEST FLUIDS AND TEST FUELS (continued)

Identification	Name	Major Ingredient	Paraffinic (vol %)	Olefinic (vol %)	Aromatic (vol %)	Oxygenate (vol %)	Other (vol %)
RENAULT	03-50-000/-A (11/91) Fluid A	ASTM Fuel A					
	03-50-000/-A (11/91) Fluid B	ASTM Fuel B					
	03-50-000/-A (11/91) Fluid C	ASTM Fuel C					
	03-50-000/-A (11/91) Fluid D	ASTM Fuel D					
	03-50-000/-A (11/91) Fluid E				100		
	03-50-000/-A (11/91) Fluid L	CEC-RF-08-A-85					DKA Premium, Unleaded Gasoline acc. German stVZO
	03-50-000/-A (11/91) Fluid N	ISO 1817/Liquid 3					
	03-50-000/-A (11/91) Fluid O	ISO 1817/Liquid 4					
	03-50-000/-A (11/91) Fluid T	CEC-RF-01-A-80					Premium leaded gasoline for European emission tests (supplier: Haltermann)
	03-50-000/-A (11/91) Fluid Y	90 ISO 1817, Liquid 3					
VOLVO	STD 1027.6131 (09/91) Test Liquid 1	ASTM Ref. Fuel C					
VOLKSWAGEN	50 TL-VW 703 Prüfkraftstoff	50 Iso-Octane				20 Ethanol	
	PV 3006 Testkraftstoff	CEC-RF-08-A-85					DKA Premium, Unleaded Gasoline acc. German stVZO (supplier: Haltermann)
	TL-VW 782 R-OK-N UnLeaded	Š55 mixed C4 - C10			≤10		4 ppm Cu(II) ion as $Cu(CH_3COO)_2$

DIESEL FUELS—SAE J313 OCT2002 SAE Standard

Report of the SAE Fuels and Lubricants Technical Committee, approved January 1955, and revised by the SAE Technical Committee 7—Fuels, of the SAE Fuels and Lubricants Division June 1989. Completely revised by the SAE Fuels and Lubricants Technical Committee 7—Fuels March 1992 and March 1998. Rationale statement available. Revised by the SAE Fuels and Lubricants Technical Committee 7—Fuels October 2002. Rationale statement available.

1. Scope—Automotive and railroad diesel fuels, in general, are derived from petroleum refinery products which are commonly referred to as middle distillates. Middle distillates represent products which have a higher boiling range than gasoline and are obtained from fractional distillation of the crude oil or from streams from other refining processes. Finished diesel fuels represent blends of middle distillates.

The properties of commercial distillate diesel fuels depend on the refinery practices employed and the nature of the crude oils from which they are derived. Thus, they may differ both with and within the region in which they are manufactured. Such fuels generally boil over a range between 163 and 371 °C (325 to 700 °F). Their makeup can represent various combinations of volatility, ignition quality, viscosity, sulfur level, gravity, and other characteristics. Additives may be used to impart special properties to the finished diesel fuel.

2. References

2.1 Applicable Publications—The following publications form a part of this specification to the extent specified herein. Unless otherwise specified, the latest issue of SAE publications shall apply.

2.1.1 SAE PUBLICATIONS—Available from SAE, 400 Commonwealth Drive, Warrendale, PA 15096-0001.

SAE J183—Engine Oil Performance and Engine Service Classification (Other Than "Energy-Conserving")

SAE J304—Engine Oil Tests

SAE J1498—Marine Circuit Breakers

SAE Paper 830594—1981 CRC Diesel Fuel Low-Temperature Operability Field Test, Coordinating Research Council Report 528 (September 1983), Summarized by M. L. McMillan and E. G. Barry, "Fuel and Vehicle Effects on Low-Temperature Operation of Diesel Vehicles—The 1981 CRC Field Test"

2.1.2 ASTM PUBLICATIONS—Available from ASTM, 100 Barr Harbor Drive, West Conshohocken, PA 19428-2959.

ASTM D 86—Method for Distillation of Petroleum Products

ASTM D 93—Test Method for Flash Point by the Pensky-Martens Closed Tester

ASTM D 97—Test Method for Pour Point of Petroleum Oils

ASTM D 129—Test Method for Sulfur in Petroleum Products by the Bomb Method

ASTM D 130—Method for Detection of Copper Corrosion from Petroleum Products by the Copper Strip Tarnish Test

ASTM D 240—Test Method for Heat of Combustion of Liquid Hydrocarbon Fuels by Bomb Calorimeter

ASTM D 287—Test Method for API Gravity of Crude Petroleum and Petroleum Products (Hydrometer Method)

ASTM D 445—Test Method for Kinematic Viscosity of Transparent and Opaque Liquids (and the Calculation of Dynamic Viscosity)

ASTM D 482—Test Method for Ash from Petroleum Products

ASTM D 524—Test Method for Ramsbottom Carbon Residue of Petroleum Products

ASTM D 611—Test Method for Aniline Point and Mixed Aniline Point of Petroleum Products and Hydrocarbon Solvents

ASTM D 613—Test Method for Ignition Quality of Diesel Fuels by the Cetane Method

ASTM D 665—Test Method for Rust-Preventing Characteristics of Inhibited Mineral Oil in the Presence of Water

ASTM D 975—Specification for Diesel Fuel Oils

ASTM D 976—Method for Calculated Cetane Index of Distillate Fuels

ASTM D 1266—Test Method for Sulfur in Petroleum Products and Liquefied Petroleum (LP) Gases (Lamp Method)

ASTM D 1298—Test Method for Relative Density (Specific Gravity)

ASTM D 1405—Method for Estimation of Net Heat of Combustion of Aviation Fuels

ASTM D 1552—Test Method for Sulfur in Petroleum Products (High Temperature Method)

ASTM D 1796—Test Method for Water and Sediment in Fuel Oils by Centrifuge Method (Laboratory Procedure)

ASTM D 2274—Test Method for Oxidation Stability of Distillate Fuel Oil (Accelerated Method)

ASTM D 2500—Test Method for Cloud Point of Petroleum Oils

ASTM D 2622—Test Method for Sulfur in Petroleum Products (X-Ray Spectographic Method)

ASTM D 3117—Test Method for Wax Appearance Point of Distillate Fuels

ASTM D 3338—Method for Estimation of Heat of Combustion of Aviation Fuels

ASTM D 4539—Filterability of Diesel Fuels by Low Temperature Flow Test (LTFT)

ASTM D 4737—Method for Calculated Cetane Index by Four Variable Equation

ASTM D 5452—Test Method for Particulate Contamination of Aviation Fuels by Laboratory Filtration

ASTM D 6078—Test Method for Evaluating Lubricity of Diesel Fuels by the Scuffing Load Ball-on-Cylinder Lubricity Evaluator

ASTM D 6079—Test Method for Evaluating Lubricity of Diesel Fuels by the High Frequency Reciprocating Rig (HFRR)

2.1.3 U.S. BUREAU OF STANDARDS

Miscellaneous Publication No. 97, 1929, Thermal Properties of Petroleum Products

2.1.4 OTHER PUBLICATIONS

1. U.S. Clean Air Act (1970)
2. Federal Register, March 5, 1980
3. Federal Register, March 15, 1985
4. U.S. Clean Air Act Amendments 1990
5. Govt. of Canada Gazette
6. Stockholm Club Emissions—Impact on European Truck Engines. H. D. Freeman—Ricardo Consulting Engineers Autotech 89
7. Worldwide Developments in Motor Vehicle Diesel Particulate Control. Michael P. Walsh, SAE 890168
8. Fuel Effects and Heavy Duty Diesel Particulate Control. J. C. Wall & S. K. Hoekman, SAE 841364
9. Recommended Federal On Highway Diesel Fuel Specifications to Assist Engine Manufacturers Meet 1991 and 1994 Particulate Standards Joint API/EMA/NPRA/NCFC Report, July 19, 1988
10. Federal Register, August 21, 1990
11. Investigation of the Effects of Fuel Composition and Injection and Combustion System Type on Heavy Duty Diesel Exhaust Emissions. Report from CRC VE-1 Project by Terry Ullman, March 1989
12. Study of Fuel Cetane Number and Aromatic Content Effects on Regulated Emissions from a Heavy Duty Diesel Engine. Report from CRC VE-1 Project by Terry Ullman, Robert Mason and Daniel Montalvo, September 1990
13. Gasoline and Diesel Fuel Qualification—A National Need, K. J. Springer, ASME Paper 90-ICE-19
14. Letter from EMA Fuels and Lubricants Committee to SAE Technical Committee 7-Fuels dated February 25, 1991
15. ISO/DIS 12156-1.3 Diesel Fuel-Measurement of Lubricity by HFRR, International Standards Organization, 1996 and CEC F-06-A-96 Measurement of Diesel Fuel Lubricity, CEC, 1966.

2.2 Related Publications

2.2.1 GENERAL PROPERTIES

1. Annual Book of ASTM Standards, "Petroleum Products, Lubricants, and Fossil Fuels," Volumes 05.01, 05.02, 05.03, and 05.04.
2. "Significance of Tests for Petroleum Products," ASTM Special Technical Publication Manual One (March 1989).
3. "Manual on Hydrocarbon Analysis," ASTM Special Technical Publication 332-A (1977).
4. H. R. Hultkrans, "Role of Diesel Fuel Properties in Diesel Fleet Economy," SAE Paper 650429.
5. R. Burt and K. A. Troth, "New CFR Cetane Rating Method is More Accurate than ASTM D 613 Method," SAE Paper 680464.
6. R. P. Lindeman, D. K. Lawrence, and T. O. Wagner, "Classification of Fuels that is Compatible with Fuel Availability," SAE Paper 680467.
7. G. K. Brower, "Diesel Fuel Specifications and Their Current Suitability," SAE Paper 700521.

8. "Update Proposed for Diesel Fuel Specs.," Automotive Engineering, Vol. 78, No. 11 (1970), pp. 34-40.
9. T. O. Wagner, "Economics of Manufacturing Automotive Diesel Fuel," SAE Paper 770758.
10. N. A. Henein and N. Y. Elias, "A Modified Cetane Scale for Low Ignition Quality Fuels," SAE Paper 780640.
11. E. G. Barry, F. J. Hills, and L. J. McCabe, "Diesel Fuel—Availability, Trends, and Performance," SAE Paper 790921.
12. D. E. Steere and T. J. Nunn, "Diesel Fuel Quality Trends in Canada," SAE Paper 790922.
13. "Distillate Fuel Stability and Cleanliness," ASTM Special Technical Publication 751 (1981).
14. D. K. Lawrence, D. A. Plautz, B. D. Keller, and T. O. Wagner, "Automotive Fuels—Refining Energy and Economics," SAE Paper 800225.
15. T. Currie and R. B. Whyte, "Broad Cut Fuels for Automotive Diesels," SAE Paper 811182.
16. C. L. Wong and D. E. Steere, "The Effects of Diesel Fuel Properties and Engine Operating Conditions on Ignition Delay," SAE Paper 821231.
17. J. W. Taracha and J. O. Cliffe, "The Effect of Cetane Quality on the Performance of Diesel Engines," SAE Paper 821232.
18. D. E. Steere, "Development of the Canadian Cetane Index," SAE Paper 841344.
19. M. C. Ingham, J. A. Bert, and L. J. Painter, "Improved Predictive Equations for Cetane Number," SAE Paper 860250.

2.2.2 Cold Weather Operation

20. W. F. Ellison and A. H. Scrimshaw, "Cold Weather Operation of Fuels and Lubricants in Western Canada," SAE Paper 650639.
21. B. L. Mickel and L. D. Fergesen, "Dimensions of Diesel Fuel Performance—Design, Depressants, and Response," SAE Paper 660371.
22. K. A. Beyreis, V. P. Catto, and E. S. Swanson, "Role of Flow Improvers in Solving Autodiesel Winter Fuel Problems," SAE Paper 660372.
23. T. J. Fallon, "Flow Improver Additives are Effective for Winterizing Diesel Fuels," SAE Paper 680537.
24. "Effects of Fuels and Fuel System Designs on Low Temperature Operability of Diesel Vehicles," Coordinating Research Council Report 463 (June 1973).
25. N. Feldman, "Operability of Automotive Diesel Equipment at Temperatures Below Fuel Cloud Point," SAE Paper 730677.
26. J. W. Muzatko, "Reducing Low Temperature Wax Plugging in Fuel Systems of the Diesel Passenger Car," SAE Paper 800222.
27. B. Y. Taniguchi and J. D. Benson, "Cold Weather Fuel Requirements of Oldsmobile Diesels," SAE Paper 800223.
28. J. W. Muzatko, K. A. Frost, and C. C. Bishop, "Winterization of Diesel Fuel Systems in Large Coal Mining Haul Trucks," SAE Paper 800224.
29. J. W. Frankenfield and W. F. Taylor, "Effects of Flow Improver Additives on Distillate Fuels from Oil Shale," SAE Paper 801376.
30. J. P. Marino, R. L. Elliott, M. F. Dooley, and D. H. Rehrer, "The Use of Flow Improvers in Extending the Low Temperature Operability of Diesel Fuels," National Petroleum Refiners Association Paper FL-80-81, November 1980.
31. D. E. Steere and J. P. Marino, "Low Temperature Field Performance of Flow Improved Diesel Fuels," SAE Paper 810024.
32. M. L. McMillan and S. R. Reddy, "Fuel and Fuel System Effects on Low Temperature Operation of Diesel Vehicles," SAE Paper 811180.
33. S. R. Reddy and M. L. McMillan, "Understanding the Effectiveness of Diesel Fuel Flow Improvers," SAE Paper 811181.
34. J. D. Rummel, "Development of a New Cold Filterability Test for Automotive Diesel Fuels," SAE Paper 821234.
35. T. R. Coley, "Low Temperature Operability of Diesels," SAE Paper 830596.
36. R. D. Tharby, "Experiences with Diesel Fuel Containing Cold Flow Improver Additives," SAE Paper 831753.
37. R. W. Fenstermaker and R. K. Riley, "Additives for Improving the Low-Temperature Filterability of Diesel Fuel Oils," SAE Paper 841350.
38. S. R. Reddy, "Increasing the Responsiveness of No. 2-D Diesel Fuels to Flow Improvers by Blending with Low-Wax Diluents," SAE Paper 841351.
39. J. Zielinski and F. Rossi, "Wax and Flow in Diesel Fuels," SAE Paper 841352.

2.2.3 Exhaust Emissions

40. H. W. Pearsall, "Measuring the Total Hydrocarbons in Diesel Exhaust," SAE Paper 670089.
41. G. McConnell and H. E. Howells, "Effect of Fuel Properties on Diesel Exhaust Gas Composition," SAE Paper 670091.
42. W. F. Marshall and R. D. Fleming, "Diesel Emissions as Related to Engine Variables and Fuel Characteristics," SAE Paper 710836.
43. E. Shamah and T. O. Wagner, "Fuel Quality or Engine Design: Which Controls Diesel Emissions?" SAE Paper 730168.
44. L. C. Broering and L. W. Holtman, "Effect of Diesel Fuel Properties on Emissions and Performance," SAE Paper 740692.
45. C. T. Hare, K. J. Springer, and R. L. Bradow, "Fuel and Additive Effects on Diesel Particulate-Development and Demonstration of Methodology," SAE Paper 760130.
46. F. J. Hills and C. G. Schleyerbach, "Diesel Fuel Properties and Engine Performance," SAE Paper 770316.
47. G. P. Gross and K. E. Murphy, "The Effects of Diesel Fuel Properties on Performance, Smoke, and Emissions," ASME Paper No. 78-DGP-26, presented at Energy Technology Conference, Houston (Nov. 1978).
48. D. B. Kittelson, D. F. Dolan, R. B. Diver, and E. Aufderheide, "Diesel Exhaust Particle Size Distributions—Fuel and Additive Effects," SAE Paper 780787.
49. L. E. Frisch, J. H. Johnson, and D. G. Leddy, "Effects of Fuels and Dilution Ratio on Diesel Particulate Emissions," SAE Paper 790417.
50. H. A. Burley and T. L. Rosebrock, "Automotive Diesel Engines—Fuel Composition vs. Particulates," SAE Paper 790923.
51. T. W. Ryan, J. O. Storment, B. R. Wright, and R. Waytulonis, "The Effects of Fuel Properties and Composition on Diesel Engine Exhaust Emissions—A Review," SAE Paper 810953.
52. R. A. Bouffard and M. Beltzer, "Light Duty Diesel Particulate Emissions—Fuel and Vehicle Effects," SAE Paper 811191.
53. D. L. Hilden, S. P. Bergin, H. A. Burley, R. D. Tharby, and I. P. Fisher, "The Effect of Hydrotreatment of Diesel Fuel Derived from Canadian Tar Sands on Particulate Exhaust Emissions," SAE Paper 821243.
54. B. B. Bykowski, C. T. Hare, and R. L. Mason, "Comparison of Petroleum and Alternate-Source Diesel Fuel Effects on Light-Duty Diesel Emissions," SAE paper 831712.
55. S. P. Bergin, "The Influence of Fuel Properties and Engine Load Upon the Carbon and Hydrocarbon Fractions of Particulate Emissions from a Light Duty Diesel Engine," SAE Paper 831736.
56. W. R. Wade and C. M. Jones, "Current and Future Light Duty Diesel Engines and Their Fuels," SAE Paper 840105.
57. R. M. Olree and D. L. Lenane, "Diesel Combustion—Cetane Number Effects," SAE Paper 840108.
58. J. C. Wall and S. K. Hoekman, "Fuel Effects on Heavy Duty Diesel Particulate Emissions," SAE Paper 841364.
59. C. T. Hare, "Study of the Effects of Fuel Composition, and Injection and Combustion System Type and Adjustment, on Exhaust Emissions from Light-Duty Diesels," Final Report No. SwRI-6741 on CRC-APRAC Project CAPE-32-80, April 1985.
60. E. G. Barry, L. J. McCabe, D. H. Gerke, and J. M. Perez, "Heavy-Duty Diesel Engine/Fuels Combustion Performance and Emissions—A Cooperative Research Program," SAE Paper 852078.

2.2.4 Lubricity

61. P. I. Lacey and S. A. Howell, "Fuel Lubricity Reviewed," SAE Paper 982567.
62. Manuch Nikanjam, et al., "ISO Diesel Fuel Lubricity Round Robin Program," SAE Paper 952372
63. P. I. Lacey and S. A. Howell, "Fuel Lubricity Reviewed," SAE Paper 982567.
64. Manuch Nikanjam, "Diesel Fuel Lubricity: On the Path to Specifications," SAE Paper 1999-01-1479.
65. P. I. Lacey and R. L. Mason, "Fuel Lubricity: Statistical Analysis of Literature Data, SAE Paper 2000-01-1917.
66. Manuch Nikanjam, et al., "Diesel Fuel Lubricity," 8th Annual Fuels & Lubes Asia Conference and Exhibition, February 2002.
67. P. I. Lacey, "Evaluation of Oxidation Corrosion in Diesel Fuel Lubricated Contacts," Tribology Transactions, Vol. 37, No. 2, pp. 253-260 (1994).
68. J. Davenport, R. Caprotti, and H. D. Chochrane, "Background, Development, and Validation of a Bench Test for Compatibility Between Diesel Fuel and Lubricating Oil," Esslingen Symposium (1991).
69. Seppo Mikkonen and Esko Tenhunen, "Deposits in Diesel Fuel—Injection Pumps Caused by Incompatibility of Fuel and Oil Additives," SAE Paper 872119.

70. Edward C. Mozdzen, Stephen W. Wall, and William D. Byfleet, "The No Harm Performance of Lubricity Additives for Low Sulfur Diesel Fuel," SAE Paper 982571.

71. R. Caprotti, "Harm Free Use of Diesel Additives," SAE paper 982569.

***3. Classification of Diesel Fuel Oils, ASTM D 975*[1]**—ASTM D 975, which includes five grades of fuel (Grade No. 1-D, Grade Low Sulfur No. 1-D, Grade No. 2-D, Grade Low Sulfur No. 2-D, and Grade 4-D), is intended as a statement of permissible limits of significant fuel properties used for classifying the wide variety of commercially available diesel fuels, in accordance with their service application. The classification chart contained in ASTM D 975 is shown here as Table 1.

1. References to ASTM Standards in this report are all to be construed as the most recent ASTM publications.

TABLE 1—DETAILED REQUIREMENTS FOR DIESEL FUEL OILS[(1),(2),(3)]

Grade of Diesel Fuel Oil	Flash Point, °C (°F) Min	Cloud Point, °C (°F) Max	Water and Sediment, Volume % Max	Carbon Residue on, 10 percent Residuum, % Max	Ash, weight % Max	Distillation Temperatures °C (°F) 90% Point Min	Distillation Temperatures °C (°F) 90% Point Max	Viscosity Kinematic cSt or mm²/s[(4)] at 40 °C Min	Viscosity Kinematic cSt or mm²/s[(4)] at 40 °C Max	Viscosity Saybolt, SUS at 100 °F Min	Viscosity Saybolt, SUS at 100 °F Max	Sulfur[(5)], weight % Max	Copper Strip Corrosion Max	Cetane Number [(6)] Min
No. 1-D A volatile distillate fuel oil for engines in service requiring frequent speed and load changes.	38 (100)	(7)	0.05	0.15	0.01	—	288 (550)	1.3	2.4	—	34.4	0.50	No. 3	40[(8)]
No. 1-DLS A volatile fuel oil required for on-highway operations in engines requiring frequent speed and load changes in the 49 State area of the USA (except Alaska).	38	(7)	0.05	0.15	0.01	—	288	1.3	2.4	—	34.4	0.050	No. 3	40[(9)]
No. 2-D A distillate fuel oil of lower volatility for engines in industrial and heavy mobile service.	52 (125)	(7)	0.05	0.35	0.01	282[(10)] (540)	338 (640)	1.9	4.1	32.6	40.1	0.50	No. 3	40[(8)]
No. 2-DLS A distillate fuel oil required for on-highway operations in engines in industrial and heavy mobile service in the 49 State area of the USA (except Alaska).	52	(7)	0.05	0.35	0.01	282[(10)]	338	1.9	4.1	32.6	40.1	0.05	No. 3	40[(9)]
No. 4-D A fuel oil for low and medium speed engines.	55 (130)	(7)	0.50	—	0.10	—	—	5.5	24.0	45.0	125.0	2.0	—	30[(8)]

1. To meet special operating conditions, modifications of individual limiting requirements may be agreed upon between purchaser, seller, and manufacturer.
2. The values in SI units are to be regarded as the standard. The values of U.S. customary units are for information only.
3. Nothing in this specification shall preclude observance of federal, state, or local regulations which may be more restrictive.
4. Millimeter squared per second (official SI unit) (Note: 1 cSt = 1 mm²/s).
5. In countries outside the USA, other sulfur limits may apply.
6. Where cetane number by Method D 613 is not available, Method D 976 may be used as an approximation. Where there is disagreement, Method D 613 shall be the referee method.
7. It is unrealistic to specify low-temperature properties that will ensure satisfactory operation on a broad basis. The tenth percentile minimum ambient temperatures for the months of October, November, December, January, February, and March are given in ASTM D 975 in maps for the 48 contiguous states and Alaska. This guidance is of a general nature; some equipment designs, use of flow improver additives, fuel properties, and/or operations may allow higher or require lower cloud point fuels. Appropriate low temperature operability properties should be agreed on between the fuel supplier and purchaser for the intended use and expected ambient temperatures.
8. Low-atmospheric temperatures as well as engine operation at high altitudes may require use of fuels with higher cetane ratings.
9. EPA requires minimum 40 Cetane Index (ASTM D 976-80) or 35% vol maximum aromatics content (ASTM D 1319).
10. When cloud point less than −12 °C (10 °F) is specified, the minimum flash point shall be 38 °C (100 °F), the minimum viscosity shall be 1.7 cSt, and the minimum 90% recovered temperature shall be waived.

4. National Survey of Diesel Fuels—Since the properties of diesel fuels can vary widely, surveys are conducted annually to provide data on the properties of fuels produced in the United States. In one survey, conducted annually, laboratory inspection data on diesel fuels are furnished voluntarily by the refiners. The results are tabulated according to five general regions of the country where the fuels are marketed. The average values reported are arithmetic, and are not weighed according to sales volume. These results have been compiled and published as Bureau of Mines reports from 1950 to 1974, U.S. Energy Research and Development Administration reports for 1975 and 1976, U.S. Department of Energy reports from 1977 to 1982, and National Institute for Petroleum and Energy Research reports from 1983 to 1999. TRW Petroleum Technologies now compiles and publishes the survey reports.

Before 1957, the data were tabulated in these reports according to ASTM grade. From 1957 to 1982, they were tabulated according to intended service type as follows:

Type C-B—Diesel fuel oils for city-bus and similar operations

Type T-T—Fuels for diesel engines in trucks, tractors, and similar service

Type R-R—Fuels for railroad diesel engines

Type S-M—Heavy-distillate and residual fuels for large stationary and marine diesel engines

Fuels that met the requirements for ASTM D 975, Grade No. 1-D or 2-D (see Table 1) were so indicated in these reports.

Since 1983, the data have been tabulated according to ASTM Grade No. 1-D or 2-D, and the intended service types (listed previously) have been so indicated. Beginning in 1995 the on-highway (low sulfur) Grade No. 1-D and Grade No. 2-D diesel fuels are reported separately.

The Alliance of Automobile Manufacturers conducts winter and summer surveys of diesel fuel quality in the U.S., and to a limited extent in Canada and Mexico. Fuel samples from 17 U.S. cities, four Canadian cities, and seven Mexican cities are collected and analyzed by an independent laboratory.

5. Significance and Methods of Measurement of Diesel Fuel Properties

5.1 Hydrocarbon Composition—The hydrocarbon composition of diesel fuel determines many other properties: the ignition quality, heating value, volatility, gravity, oxidation stability, etc. Thus, it directly affects the power and economy, wear, deposit formation, starting, and smoke performance of diesel engines.

Since diesel fuels are complex mixtures of many individual hydrocarbons, the measurement of their hydrocarbon composition is not simple. A number of procedures are used, and the reader is referred to current ASTM publications for suggested methods.

5.2 Ignition Quality—Engine performance factors which may be influenced by ignition quality of the fuel are: cold starting, warmup, combustion roughness, acceleration, deposits under idle and light load operation, and exhaust smoke density. In each of these cases, other fuel factors as well as engine factors can also affect performance. The ignition quality requirement of an engine depends on design, size, mechanical condition, operating conditions, atmospheric temperature, and altitude. Increase in ignition quality over the level required does not materially improve engine performance.

Ignition quality is measured by ASTM D 613. The ASTM cetane number of a diesel fuel is defined as the percentage by volume of normal cetane in a blend with heptamethylnonane required to match the ignition quality of the test fuel (ASTM Cetane Number = % n-cetane + (0.15) (% heptamethylnonane)). The method requires the use of a standard test engine equipped with accepted instrumentation and operated under prescribed conditions.

When a test engine is not available for determining cetane number, or when the quantity of sample is too small for an engine rating, this property may be approximated by the ASTM calculated cetane index methods provided in ASTM D 976 or ASTM D 4737.

In 1980, ASTM Committee D02.E0.02 concluded a study of the correlation between measured cetane number and calculated cetane index determined from various fuel properties. Data obtained by 17 laboratories on about 1200 diesel fuels, predominantly from the United States and Canada, were used to revise the cetane index formula and improve the correlation with cetane number. A nomograph from ASTM D 976-80, based on this revised formula, is shown in Figure 1. The method for determining the calculated cetane index from the API gravity or density and the mid-boiling point is indicated by the illustrative example on the nomograph.

A more recent test method developed for estimating the cetane quality of distillate fuels is ASTM Method D 4737. This method provides for estimating cetane number of distillate fuels from density and the 10, 50, and 90% distillation temperatures of the fuels. The relationship is given by the following equation:

$$\begin{aligned} CCI = {} & 45.2 + (0.0892)(T_{10N}) \\ & + [0.131 + (0.901)(B)][T_{50N}] \\ & + [0.0523 - (0.420)(B)][T_{90N}] \\ & + [0.00049][(T_{10N})^2 - (T_{90N})^2] \\ & + (107)(B) + (60)(B)^2 \end{aligned} \quad \text{(Eq. 1)}$$

where:

CCI = Calculated Cetane Index by Four Variable Equation

D = Density at 15 °C, determined by Test Method D 1298

DN = $D - 0.85$

B = $[e^{(-3.5)(DN)}] - 1$

T_{10} = 10% distillation temperature, °C, determined by Method D 86 and corrected to standard barometric pressure

T_{10N} = $T_{10} - 215$

T_{50} = 50% distillation temperature, °C, determined by Method D 86 and corrected to standard barometric pressure

T_{50N} = $T_{50} - 260$

T_{90} = 90% distillation temperature, °C, determined by Method D 86 and corrected to standard barometric pressure

T_{90N} = $T_{90} - 310$

The Calculated Cetane Index by Four Variable Equation is useful for estimating ASTM cetane number when a test engine is not available for determining this property directly. It may be conveniently employed for estimating cetane number when the quantity of sample available is too small for an engine rating. In cases where the ASTM cetane number of a fuel has been previously established, the Calculated Cetane Index by Four Variable Equation is useful as a cetane number check on subsequent samples of that fuel, provided the fuel's source and mode of manufacture remain unchanged.

Procedure: Determine the density of the fuel at 15 °C to the nearest 0.0001 kg/L, as described in Test Method D 1298.

Determine the 10, 50, and 90% distillation temperatures of the fuel to the nearest 1 °C, as described in Method D 86.

Calculation or Interpretation of Results: Compute the Calculated Cetane Index by Four Variable Equation using the equation given in Equation 1. The calculation is more easily performed using a computer or programmable hand calculator. Round the value obtained to the nearest one-tenth.

Calculated Cetane Index by Four Variable Equation can also be easily determined by means of the nomographs appearing in Figures 2 through 4. Figure 2 is used to estimate the cetane number of a fuel based on its density at 15 °C and its 50% distillation temperature. Figure 3 is used to determine a correction for the estimate from Figure 2 to account for deviations in the density and the 90% distillation temperature of the fuel from average values. Figure 4 is used to determine a second correction for the estimate from Figure 2 to account for deviations in the 10% and 90% distillation temperatures of the fuel from average values. The corrections determined from Figures 3 and 4 are summed algebraically with the cetane number estimate from Figure 2 to find the Calculated Cetane Index by Four Variable Equation. The method of using these nomographs is indicated by the illustrative example shown as follows and on Figures 2 through 4.

a. Measured Fuel Properties

ASTM Cetane Number	37.0
Density at 15 °C, kg/L	0.885
D 86 10% Dist. Temp., °C	234
D 86 50% Dist. Temp., °C	274
D 86 90% Dist. Temp., °C	323

b. Calculated Cetane Index

Estimate from Figure 1	34.0
Correction from Figure 2	+0.6
Correction from Figure 3	+2.5
	CCI = 37.1

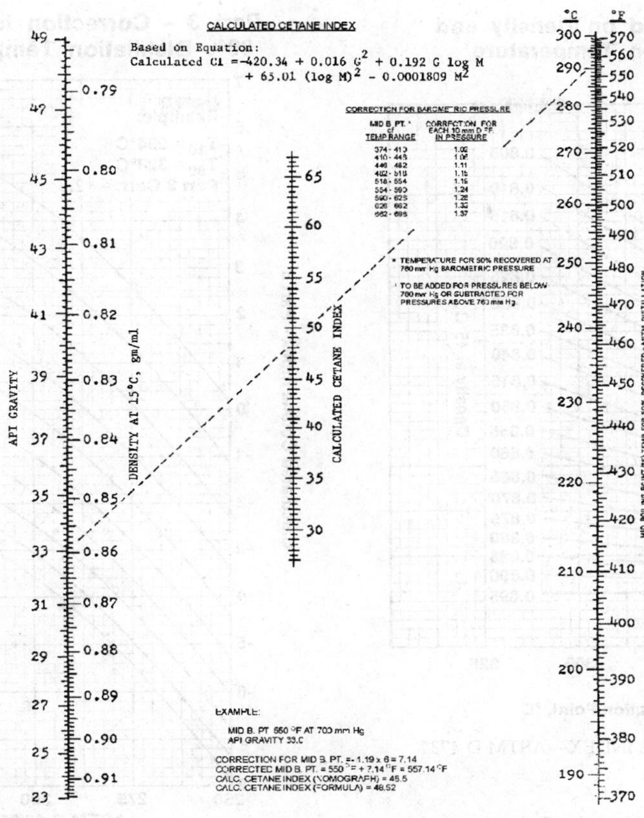

NOTE—The Calculated Cetane Index formula represents a useful tool for estimating cetane number. Due to inherent limitations in its application, Index values may not be a valid substitute for ASTM Cetane Numbers as determined in a test engine.

From ASTM D 976-80. Copies of the Nomograph for Calculated Cetane Index are available from ASTM, 100 Barr Harbor Drive, West Conshohocken, PA 19428-2959.

FIGURE 1—NOMOGRAPH FOR CALCULATED CETANE INDEX

The revised (D 976-80) cetane index method has not been adopted in Europe. Thus, the previous (D 976-66) method is published in Europe as Institute of Petroleum Designation 218/67(75), and is used there for estimating ignition quality.

The ASTM calculated cetane index is particularly applicable to straight-run fuels, catalytically cracked stocks, and blends of the two. Their application is limited as follows:

a. The ASTM calculated cetane index test methods are not applicable to fuels containing additives for raising cetane number.
b. ASTM D 976 is not applicable to pure hydrocarbons, synthetic fuels, alkylates, or coal-tar products.
c. The use of ASTM D 976 may result in substantial inaccuracies in correlation if used for crude oils, residuals, or products having a distillation end point below 260 °C (500 °F).
d. ASTM D 4737 is particularly applicable to straight-run and cracked stocks, and blends of the two. It can also be used for fuels containing nonpetroleum derivatives from tar sands and oil shale. The recommended range of application for this test method is as follows in Table 2:

TABLE 2—RECOMMENDED RANGE OF APPLICATION

Property	Recommended Range
ASTM Cetane Number	32.5 – 56.5
Density at 15 °C, kg/L	0.805 – 0.895
D 86 10% Dist. Temp., °C	171 – 259
D 86 50% Dist. Temp., °C	212 – 308
D 86 90% Dist. Temp., °C	251 – 363

The ASTM calculated cetane index text methods are not recommended as a substitute for actual measured cetane number in the preparation of fuel specifications. However, because good correlations can be established between cetane index test methods and cetane number for a given crude oil and processing scheme, cetane index test methods are often used for refinery control of diesel fuel ignition quality.

5.3 Heating Value—An important property of a diesel fuel is its heat of combustion, which is a measure of the energy available from the fuel. A knowledge of this value is essential when considering the thermal efficiency of equipment for producing power.

The gross heat of combustion at constant volume is determined by the bomb calorimeter, which measures the amount of heat actually released by burning a known quantity of fuel. ASTM D 240 is applicable to diesel fuels. In the determination of the heating value of fuels by the bomb calorimeter method, the water vapor formed is condensed, which results in the gross or higher heating value for the fuel. The net or lower heating value of fuel is determined by subtracting the latent heat of condensation of water vapor formed in the calorimeter process from the reported gross or higher heating value. It is customary to use the lower heating value for calculating thermal efficiency.

Heating values may be expressed as J/kg, J/L, Btu/lb, Btu/gal, cal/g, or cal/L. Since diesel engine fuel consumption is expressed on a kg/KW·h or lb/bhp·h basis and since diesel fuel is purchased on a liter or gallon basis, both weight and volume bases are of interest to the engine manufacturer and user.

When bomb calorimeter heating values are not available, it is customary to use empirical relationships which yield heating values sufficiently accurate for many purposes. One source of such empirical data is the U.S. Bureau of Standards Miscellaneous Publication No. 97, 1929, "Thermal Properties of Petroleum Products," by C. S. Cragoe. ASTM D 3338 and ASTM D 1405 contain equations for estimating heating value from physical and chemical properties.

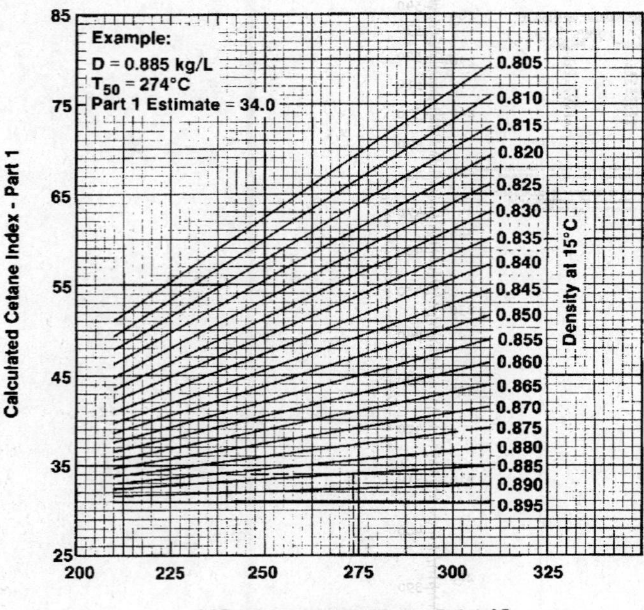

FIGURE 2—CALCULATED CETANE INDEX—ASTM D 4737

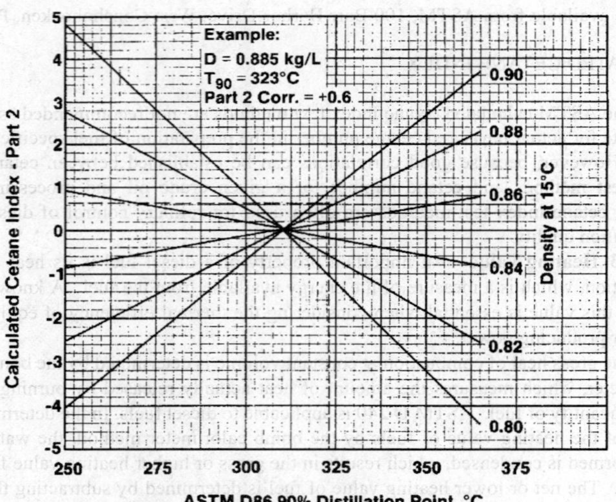

FIGURE 3—CALCULATED CETANE INDEX—ASTM D 4737

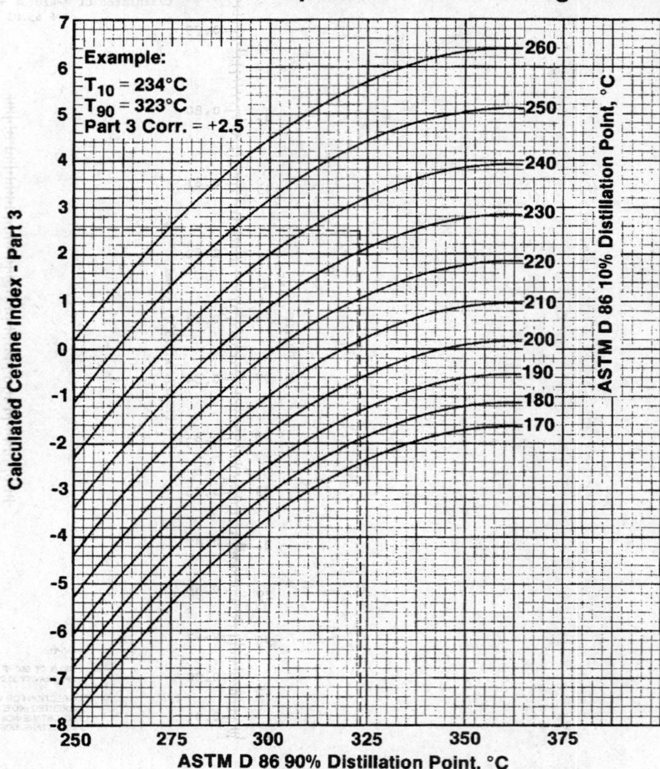

FIGURE 4—CALCULATED CETANE INDEX—ASTM D 4737

Two nomographs for estimating the heating value of fuels from empirical formulas and theoretical considerations are shown in Figures 5 and 6. In Figure 5, the gross or net heat of combustion may be estimated from the API gravity or density, and the aniline point (a measure of the aromatic and naphthenic components), as determined by ASTM D 611. In Figure 6, the gross heating value may be estimated from the API gravity or density, and the mid-boiling point temperature for 50% recovered by ASTM D 86.

Heating values determined from the various empirical relations may not agree precisely, nor will they necessarily indicate the true difference in heating value between two specific fuels. However, as average values, they do offer useful estimates for many purposes. A more extensive discussion of heating values is given in SAE J1498.

5.4 Volatility—Power and economy of diesel engines are insensitive to volatility directly, although less volatile fuels normally have a higher heating value (see Figure 6) and thus indirectly affect these performance factors. On the other hand, starting and warmup are favored by high front end volatility, and deposition, wear, and exhaust smoke in some engines are increased by high 90% and end points.

The volatility of No. 1-D and No. 2-D diesel fuels is normally measured by ASTM D 86.

5.5 Gravity/Density—Knowledge of fuel gravity/density, along with volatility, provides useful information about the composition of the fuel, which in turn relates to heating value (Figures 5 and 6), power and economy, deposition, wear, and exhaust smoke. It should be noted from Figures 5 and 6 that, for fixed aniline point and mid-boiling point, decreased API gravity (increased pound per gallon) increases the heating value per gallon, but decreases the heating value per pound. On the other hand, it should be understood that gravity is not the sole determining factor of heating value.

Gravity and density are normally measured by ASTM D 287 or by ASTM D 1298, or API Gravity of Crude Petroleum and Liquid Petroleum Products by Hydrometer Method.

It should be noted that in the change to the SI metric system of measurement, API gravity and specific gravity are to be eliminated from usage. API gravity is to be replaced by absolute density (kg/m^3) at 15 °C and 101.325 kPa. Specific gravity is to be replaced by relative density at 15 °C and 101.325 kPa where the reference fluids for liquids and gases are water and air respectively.

5.6 Viscosity—Diesel fuel viscosity can affect the performance of fuel injection systems. Low viscosity can result in excessive wear in some injection pumps and power loss due to pump and injector leakage. High viscosity can result in excessive pump resistance or filter damage. Fuel spray characteristics are also influenced by viscosity.

Diesel fuel viscosity is measured by ASTM D 445.

5.7 Cloud Point and Pour Point—Normal paraffins occur naturally in all diesel fuels. As the fuel is cooled, these components become less soluble, and begin to precipitate as wax crystals. The temperature at which a sufficient number of these wax crystals become large enough to make the fuel appear hazy or cloudy is called the "cloud point." Cloud point indicates the onset of filter plugging with some fuel system designs, and is expressed in increments of 1 °C (2 °F). As the fuel is further cooled, these wax crystals continue to precipitate and grow. The lowest temperature at which the fuel is observed to flow is called the "pour point." The pour point may indicate the lowest temperature at which fuel can be pumped, and is expressed in increments of 3 °C (5 °F). For fuels which do not contain a pour point depressant additive, the pour point is usually from 3 °C (5 °F) to 15 °C (25 °F) below the cloud point. Pour point depressant additives have no effect on the cloud point. The applicable measurement methods are ASTM D 2500 and ASTM D 97. ASTM D 3117 gives results which are closely related to cloud point.

A test widely used in Europe to predict low-temperature performance is the Cold Filter Plugging Point of Distillate Fuels (CFPP), IP Test Method No. 309/80. This test measures the lowest temperature at which less than 60 s is required for 20 mL of fuel to flow through a fine wire mesh screen having a nominal aperture of 45 µm. A 1981 CRC study has shown that CFPP does not correlate well with low temperature performance of North American fuels in North American equipment. Other tests have been proposed such as ASTM Method D 4539 (LTFT), which may show better correlation, and they are being evaluated within ASTM.

5.8 Flash Point—The flash point is the lowest fuel temperature at which application of a test flame causes the vapor above the sample to ignite momentarily under prescribed conditions. It is not directly related to engine performance, but is important in connection with legal requirements and safety precautions involved in fuel handling and storage. An abnormally low flash point may denote contamination with lighter products such as gasoline.

The usual method of measurement is ASTM D 93.

5.9 Sulfur Content—The effect of sulfur content on engine wear and deposits varies with engine and operating conditions. Higher sulfur contents than those stipulated in ASTM D 975 should be avoided because of these effects. In some engines, higher sulfur fuels may be used if a crankcase lubricant formulated to combat the effects of high sulfur is used along with an appropriate shortening of the oil drain intervals. Sulfur content of diesel fuels may also be limited by regulations directed at exhaust emission control.

Sulfur content may be measured by one of several methods: ASTM D 129 (prescribed in ASTM D 975), ASTM D 1552, ASTM D 1266, and ASTM D 2622.

5.10 Carbon Residue—Carbon residue may be related to the formation of deposits in diesel engine injection systems and combustion chambers.

Carbon residue is measured by ASTM D 524.

5.11 Ash—Ash forming materials may be present in diesel fuel either as suspended solids or soluble metallic compounds. Suspended solids and certain dissolved organometallic compounds containing sodium, vanadium, etc., may contribute to injector, fuel pump, and ring wear and also to rapid deterioration of engine parts exposed to high temperatures such as turbochargers and valves. Soluble metallic compounds may also contribute to engine deposits.

ASTM D 482 is commonly used to measure ash.

5.12 Copper-Strip Corrosion—Corrosion of copper, brass, or bronze parts of the fuel system can result from certain sulfur compounds in diesel fuel. ASTM D 130 is an indication of possible difficulties of this type.

5.13 Water and Sediment Content—Contamination of diesel fuel by water and sediment sometimes occurs during distribution of diesel fuels from the refinery to the users and during the use in diesel equipment. Control of such contamination is a matter requiring constant vigilance. In engines such contamination can lead to filter plugging and injection system wear, and may promote corrosion. ASTM D 1796 indicates the amount of these contaminants present in a sample.

5.14 Oxidation Stability—The products of oxidation of diesel fuel in storage can result in deposits, filter plugging, and lacquering of fuel pump and injector parts.

ASTM D 2274 is available as a measure of this property.

5.15 Rust Protection—Minimizing rust in fuel distribution and diesel equipment fuel handling systems when engines are idle minimizes filter plugging and wear problems. ASTM D 665 is a possible measure of rust protection of diesel fuels, although it has not been clearly correlated with field experience.

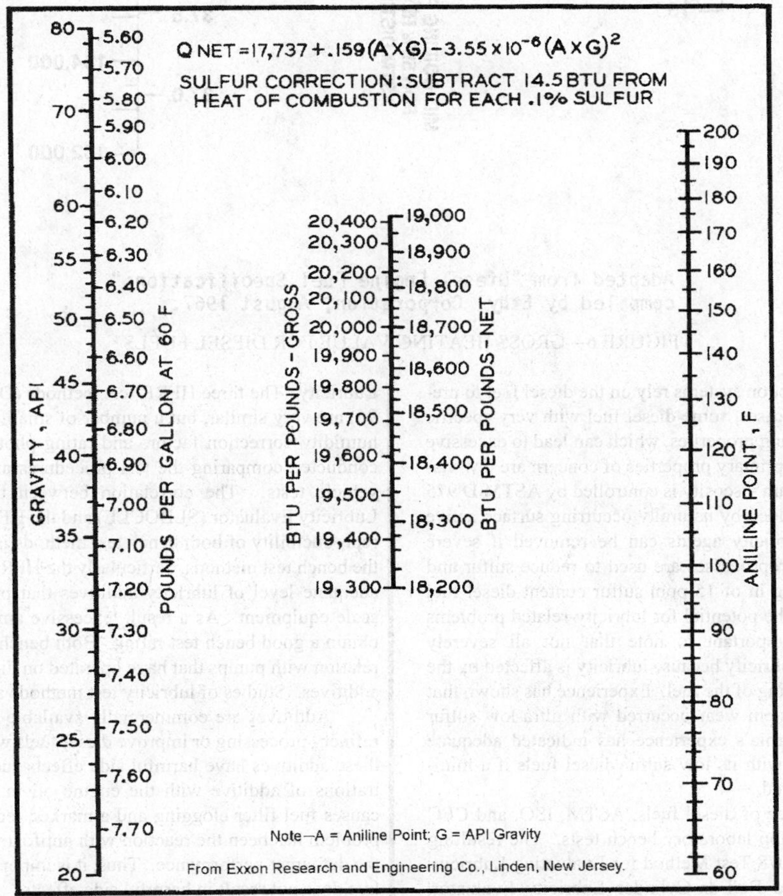

FIGURE 5—RELATION BETWEEN HEAT OF COMBUSTION AND ANILINE POINT AND GRAVITY OF DISTILLATE PETROLEUM FUELS

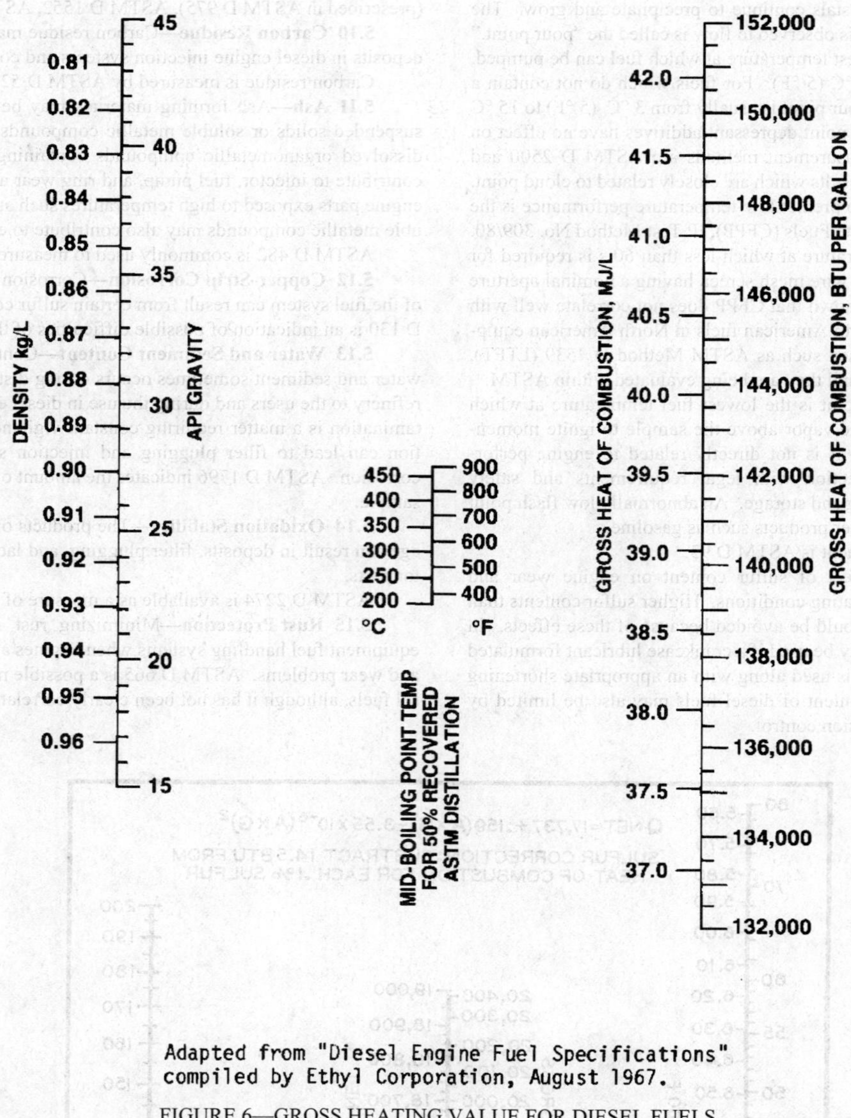

FIGURE 6—GROSS HEATING VALUE FOR DIESEL FUELS

5.16 Lubricity—Diesel fuel injection systems rely on the diesel fuel to prevent wear in moving parts. In limited cases, some diesel fuel with very specific properties can have insufficient lubricating properties, which can lead to excessive wear of fuel injectors and pumps. The primary properties of concern are low viscosity and lack of lubricity. The minimum viscosity is controlled by ASTM D 975 and historically lubricity has been provided by naturally occurring surface active materials. However, these natural lubricity agents can be removed if severe hydrotreating processing is used. Hydroprocesses are used to reduce sulfur and aromatics contents and with the phasing in of 15 ppm sulfur content diesel fuel beginning in 2006 in the U.S., there is the potential for lubricity-related problems with fuel injection systems. It is important to note that not all severely hydrotreated diesel fuel will have low lubricity because lubricity is affected by the crude oil, processing severity, and blending of the fuel. Experience has shown that in 1991 in Sweden, severe injector system wear occurred with ultra-low sulfur content diesel fuel. However, California's experience has indicated adequate lubricity performance can be achieved with its low sulfur diesel fuels if a minimum SLBOCLE level of 3000 is observed.

To assess the lubricity performance of diesel fuels, ASTM, ISO, and CEC have undertaken test programs to develop laboratory bench tests. The resulting published test methods are ASTM D 6078 Test Method for Evaluating Lubricity of Diesel Fuels by the Scuffing Load Ball-on-Cylinder Lubricity Evaluator, ASTM D 6079 Test Method for Evaluating Lubricity of Diesel Fuels by the High Frequency Reciprocating Rig (HFRR), ISO/DIS 12156-1.3 Diesel Fuel-Measurement of Lubricity by HFRR, and CEC F-06-A-96 Measurement of Diesel Fuel Lubricity. The three HFRR test methods (D 6079, ISO 12156, and CEC F-06-A-96) are very similar, but a number of small differences exist including the use of humidity correction factors and rating photographs. Several studies have been conducted comparing the test procedures among two types and with pump and vehicle tests. The correlation between the Scuffing Load Ball-on-Cylinder Lubricity Evaluator (SLBOCLE) and the HFRR test methods is poor. Further, the reproducibility of both bench test methods is large. Studies have also shown that the bench test methods, particularly the HFRR, predict negligible benefits from an adequate level of lubricity additives that provided acceptable durability in full scale equipment. As a result, excessive amounts of additive have to be used to obtain a good bench test rating. Both bench test methods have shown better correlation with pumps that have operated on diesel fuel that did not contain lubricity additives. Studies of lubricity test methods are continuing.

Additives are commercially available that will restore lubricity lost due to refinery processing or improve diesel fuels with poor lubricity. However, some of these additives have harmful side effects such as the interaction of high concentrations of additive with the engine oil in in-line fuel injection pumps, which causes fuel filter clogging and a marked reduction in pump efficiency. Another problem has been the reaction with antifoaming additives and the deactivation of the defoamer performance. Thus, it is important that the type and amount of additive does not result in harmful side effects.

A number of organizations have developed either diesel fuel lubricity specification limits or guidelines. For the HFRR the wear scar diameter limits range from a maximum of 400 to 600 microns at 60 °C. For the SLBOCLE specification limits range from a minimum of 2800 to a minimum of 3100 grams. ASTM is in the process of balloting a specification limit in ASTM D 975. ASTM believes that the inclusion of a single fuel specification in the main table for Grade No. 2-D requires further research because 1) the correlation of the data among the two test methods and the fuel injection equipment needs further clarification, 2) both methods in their current form do not apply to all fuel-additive combinations, and 3) the reproducibility values for both test methods are large. In the meantime, the following ASTM D 975 information may be of use and serve as a general guideline to fuel suppliers and users.

The following ASTM guidelines are generally accepted and may be used in the absence of a single test method and a single fuel lubricity value:

a. Fuels having a SLBOCLE lubricity value below 2000 g might not prevent excessive wear in injection equipment while fuels with values above 3100 g should provide sufficient lubricity in all cases.
b. If HFFR at 60 °C is used, fuels with values above 600 microns might not prevent excessive wear while fuels with values below 450 microns should provide sufficient lubricity in all cases.
c. More accurately, an industry-accepted long-term durability pump test, such as the ones used on a test stand or in a vehicle, can be used to evaluate the lubricity of a diesel fuel. A poor result in such a test indicates that the fuel has low lubricity and can cause excessive wear.

6. Relationships Among Properties—Certain properties of distillate diesel fuels, such as volatility, viscosity, gravity, ignition quality, cloud and pour points, and heating value, exhibit interrelationships. Low volatility, straight run fuels usually have lower API gravity, but higher viscosity, cetane number, cloud and pour points, and heating value than do fuels of higher volatility from similar crude sources. Since diesel fuels are composed of complex mixtures of many hydrocarbon compounds, the influence of hydrocarbon composition is also reflected in the interrelationships of these properties.

It has been established, through extensive experimental investigation, that certain properties of a fuel can be estimated with reasonable accuracy from two or more measured properties, such as volatility and API gravity.

A chart showing the approximate relationship between 50% and 90% recovery temperatures from the ASTM distillation, API gravity, cetane number, viscosity, cloud point, and net heating value is shown in Figure 7. These interrelationships may not be applicable to all distillate fuels produced from current crude oils by current refining processes. Because of these limitations, this chart should only be used to estimate fuel properties in the absence of complete data, and should not be used to establish specifications.

7. Diesel Fuel Additives—Commercial diesel fuels may contain a variety of additives to enhance or impart certain desirable properties. Among those which may be found in current fuels are ignition quality improvers, oxidation inhibitors, biocides, rust preventives, metal deactivators, pour point depressants, demulsifiers, smoke suppressants, detergent-dispersants, conductivity improvers, dyes, and de-icers.

Diesel fuel additives are shown by class and function in Table 3. As with any system in which a variety of additives may be used, care should be taken to avoid incompatibilities among additives and unanticipated interactions which may produce undesirable fuel effects.

8. Other Diesel Fuel Specifications

8.1 Commercial Fuels—ASTM D 975 is the specification most commonly used in the U.S. to describe and classify commercial diesel fuels. Other specifications have been established in the U.S. and in other countries. Selected property limits from some of the most widely used specifications for automotive type diesel fuels are shown in Tables 4 to 6. While these specifications are generally similar, they are not identical. The engine manufacturer, fuel supplier, and equipment user must all remain aware of these differences in different parts of the world.

8.2 Test Fuels—Specifications more stringent than those for commercial fuels have been established for special fuels used during exhaust emissions or performance testing. Selected property limits from three widely used test fuel specifications are shown in the right hand columns of 7.

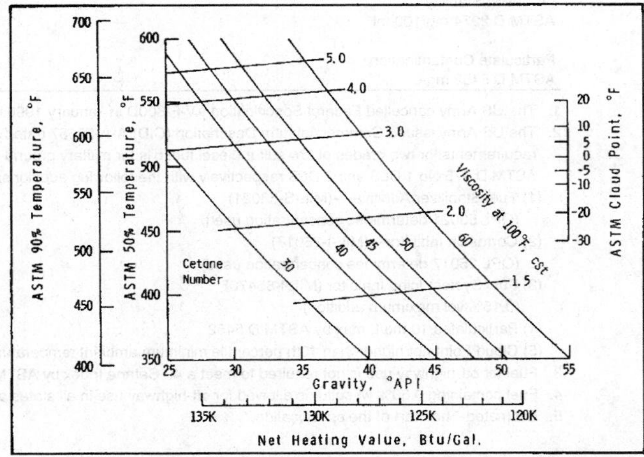

FIGURE 7—RELATED PROPERTIES OF DISTILLATE DIESEL FUELS ADAPTED FROM REFERENCE 8 IN 2.3.1

TABLE 3—COMMERCIAL DIESEL FUEL ADDITIVES—FUNCTION AND TYPE

Class for Function	Common Additive Type
1. Ignition Quality Improvers—Raise Cetane Number thereby promoting faster starts and less white smoke.	Alkyl nitrates.
2. Oxidation Inhibitors—Minimize oxidation and gum and precipitate formation, improve storage life.	Alkyl amines and amine-containing complex materials.
3. Biocides—Inhibit the growth of bacteria and fungi which feed on hydrocarbons, help prevent filter-clogging caused by these organisms.	Boron compounds, ethers of ethylene glycol, quaternary amine compounds.
4. Rust Preventives—Minimize rust formation in fuels systems and storage facilities.	Organic acids and amine salts. A widely used type is based on dimerized linoleic acid.
5. Metal Deactivator—Deactivates copper ions which are powerful oxidation catalysts.	N,N'-disalicylidene-1,2-propane diamine.
6. Pour Point Depressants—Reduce the pour point and improve low-temperature fluidity properties by modifying the wax crystal growth, structure, and/or agglomeration.	Generally consist of polymeric materials such as polyolefins, polyacrylates, polymethacrylates, modified polystyrenes, ethylene-vinyl acetate copolymers, and ethylene-vinyl chloride copolymers.
7. Demulsifiers and Dehazers—Improve the separation of water from distillate fuels and prevent haze.	Surface-active materials which increase the rate of water/oil separation. Usually quite complex mixtures.
8. Smoke Suppressants—Minimize exhaust smoke by catalyzing more complete combustion of carbonaceous materials or by helping to maintain fuel spray patterns.	Catalyst types are generally overbased barium compounds. Maintenance of spray patterns is helped by detergents.
9. Detergent-Dispersants—Promote engine fuel system cleanliness, help prevent nozzle deposit formation and injector sticking, interfere with precipitate agglomeration, thus maintaining optimum filtration characteristics.	These are usually surface-active agents. They are often polymeric materials containing amines and other functional groups.
10. Conductivity Improvers—Improve dissipation of electrostatic charge.	Amine salts, metallic salts, and polymeric compounds.
11. Dyes—Various identification purposes including tax status.	Oil-soluble solid and liquid dyes.
12. De-icers—Reduce the freezing point of small amounts of water to prevent fuel line plugging.	Low molecular weight alcohols (ethanol, isopropanol, and/or methanol), and ethylene glycol monomethyl ether or di-ethylene glycol monomethyl ether.

NOTE—Some materials may also be marketed as multifunctional or multipurpose additives, performing more than one of the functions.

TABLE 4—KEY PROPERTY LIMITS FROM U.S. AUTOMOTIVE DIESEL FUEL SPECIFICATIONS

Property	ASTM D 975 Grade 2-DLS	U.S. Federal VV-F-800 D and Grade DF-2 (U.S.)[(1)(2)],	NATO Standardization Agreement (STANAG) 7040, Military F-S4 Diesel Fuel
Cetane Number	40 min	40 min	45 min
Cetane Index,[(3)] or	40 min	43 min	N.R.
Aromatics Content, vol%	35 max		
Sulfur% wt or	0.05 max[(4)]	0.05 max[(4)]	0.30 max
Distillation °C			
50% Point		Report	Report
90% Point	282-338	338 max	357 max
End Point	—	370 max	370 max
Kinematic Viscosity cSt			
at 20 °C			1.8-9.5
at 40 °C	1.9-4.1	1.9-4.4	1.4-5.5[(5)]
Density at 15 °C g/mL	—	Report	0.820-0.860
Oxidation Stability ASTM D 2274 mg/100 ml	—	1.5 max	1.5 max
Particulate Contamination ASTM D 5452 mg/L	—	10 max	10 max

1. The US Army cancelled Federal Specification VV-F-800D in January 1996 but it is still used in civilian procurement in the USA.
2. The US Army issued Commercial Item Description (CID) A-A-52557 dated January 2/96 entitled, "Fuel Oil, Diesel, for Posts, Camps, and Stations" which covers requirements for two grades of low sulfur diesel fuel oils for military ground compression ignition and gas turbine engines. This specifies the fuel quality to be that of ASTM D 975 No 1 DLS and 2 DLS respectively with the following additions:
   (1) Fuel Stabilizer Additive —(MIL-S-53021)
   (QPL 53021 determines concentration used)
   (2) Corrosion Inhibitor—(MIL-I-25017)
   (QPL 25017 determines concentration used)
   (3) Fuel System Icing Inhibitor (MIL-I-85470)
   (0.15% vol maximum addition)
   (4) Particulates 10 mg/L max by ASTM D 5452
   (5) Cloud Point not higher than 10th percentile minimum ambient temperatures as shown for US locations in Appendix A2 in ASTM D 975
3. Fuel for off-highway use is not required to meet a 40 Cetane Index by ASTM D 976-80.
4. Fuel containing 0.50% wt sulfur is allowed for off-highway use in all states of the USA, except for California vehicular use.
5. Estimated—not part of the specification.

9. Cold Weather Operation

9.1 Fuel Selection—Proper attention to diesel fuel low-temperature properties is essential to minimizing fuel handling and engine operating problems in cold weather. The specific recommendations of equipment manufacturers should be followed explicitly. Most North American manufacturers of automotive diesel engines currently recommend the use of ASTM D 975, Grade No. 2-D fuel at ambient temperatures above –7 °C (+20 °F). At very low temperatures, they recommend the use of No. 1-D fuel (if available), which usually forms fewer wax crystals and thus has much lower cloud and pour points. Otherwise, they recommend the use of "winterized" or "climatized" No. 2-D fuel. Such fuels are made by diluting No. 2-D with No. 1-D or kerosene to lower the cloud and pour points as required. ASTM D 975 suggests that satisfactory operation should be achieved in most cases if the cloud point (or wax appearance point) is specified at 6 °C (10 °F) above the tenth percentile minimum ambient temperature for the area in which the fuel will be used.

A chart for estimating the cloud point of fuel blends is shown in Figure 8. Such blending is not efficient, as large amounts (20 to 30%) of diluent are required to achieve modest [6 °C (10 °F)] reductions in cloud point.

9.2 Additives—Additives, called pour point depressants, flow improvers, or wax modifiers, can change the size and/or shape of wax crystals as they form, and thus minimize cold weather problems. The additive type and concentration must be optimized for a specific fuel, and the additive must be thoroughly blended into the fuel at temperatures well above the cloud point. Therefore, such additives are most effective when blended by fuel suppliers rather than by equipment users. These additives will not lower the cloud point, but they can lower the temperature at which fuel filter plugging due to wax crystals occurs.

9.3 Minimum Vehicle Operating Temperature—Both vehicle fuel system design and fuel properties are important factors in determining the minimum temperature for acceptable vehicle operation. This temperature can be as high as the cloud point, or as low as the pour point. Thus, cloud point is a fail-safe but conservative predictor of field performance.

Laboratory filter plugging tests have been devised to correlate with vehicle performance, especially using additive-treated fuels. Results from such tests are highly dependent upon the fine wire mesh screen size and the sample cooling rate. A test widely used in Europe is the Cold Flow Plugging Point of Distillate Fuels (CFPP), IP Test Method No. 309/80. This test measures the lowest temperature at which less than 60 s is required for 20 mL of fuel to flow through a screen having a nominal aperture of 45 μm.

The Filterability of Diesel Fuels by Low Temperature Flow Test (LTFT), ASTM D 4539, was developed to correlate with field performance of North American fuels in North American equipment. This test measures the lowest temperature at which less than 60 s is required for 180 mL of fuel to flow through a screen having a normal aperture of 17 μm.

A 1981 CRC study (reference SAE Paper 830594) was conducted using four diesel passenger cars, three heavy-duty trucks, and eight fuels (three base fuels and five additive-treated versions of the base fuels). Of the individual laboratory tests, the LTFT provided the best correlation with overall vehicle performance, followed closely by cloud point and then less closely by CFPP. No single laboratory test was found which adequately predicted the performance of all fuels in all vehicles. Pour point was a poor predictor.

10. Exhaust Emissions—Historically, exhaust emission control of both light- and heavy-duty diesel engines was centered on visible smoke which was readily perceived by—and generally objectionable to—the public. Recent concern about the health impact of particulate emissions coupled with the nonattainment of ambient air quality standards—especially NO_x and the link between it and ground level ozone—caused the enactment of several U.S. Federal Laws (1)(2)(3)(4) to control both particulate and gaseous emissions from on-highway diesel engines. Similar laws have been enacted, or are under consideration for enactment, in Canada (5) and the European Economic Community (EEC). The stringent emissions levels required for the 1993/94 U.S. standards are considered to be technology forcing both in terms of engine design and fuel quality demands.

TABLE 5—KEY PROPERTY LIMITS FOR EUROPEAN AUTOMOTIVE DIESEL FUELS CEN EN 590-93 (EUROPEAN COMMON MARKET)

Property	Limits	
Generally Applicable Requirements		
Flash Point °C	55 min	ASTM D 93
Oxidation Stability mg/100 mL	2.5 max	ASTM D 2274
Sulfur Content% wt	0.05 max	
Particulate Matter mg/kg	24 max	
Water Content mg/kg	200 max	
Climatically Related Requirements—Temperate Areas		
Cetane Number ASTM D 613	49 min	
Cetane Index (ISO 4264)	46 min	
Density at 15 °C g/mL	0.820-0.860	
Viscosity cSt at 40 °C	2.0-4.50	
Distillation ASTM D 86		
% vol rec. at 350 °C	85 min	
% vol rec. at 370 °C	95 min	
CFPP °C Grade A	+5 max	
Grade B	0 max	
Grade C	–5 max	
Grade D	–10 max	
Grade E	–15 max	
Grade F	–20 max	

Climatically Related Requirements—Arctic Areas

Fuel Class	0	1	2	3	4
CFPP °C max	–20	–26	–32	–38	–44
Cloud Pt. °C max	–10	–16	–22	–28	–34
Density 15 °C min	0.80	0.80	0.80	0.80	0.80
g/mL max	0.845	0.845	0.840	0.840	0.840
Viscosity min	1.50	1.50	1.50	1.40	1.20
cSt at 10 °C max	4.00	4.00	4.00	4.00	4.00
Cetane No. min	47	47	46	45	45
Cetane Index min	46	46	46	43	43
Distillation					
% vol at 180 °C max	10	10	10	10	10
% vol at 340 °C min	95	95	95	95	95

Note—Cetane Index also requires the 10% and 50% vol recovered temperatures and is equivalent to ASTM D 4737. CFPP is Cold Filter Plugging Point Temperature Test IP 309.

TABLE 6—KEY PROPERTY LIMITS FOR CANADIAN, AUSTRALIAN, AND JAPANESE AUTOMOTIVE DIESEL FUEL SPECIFICATIONS GENERAL REQUIREMENTS

Property	Canada CAN 3-517 Grade B-LS	Australia AS 3570-1988	Japan JIS KK 2204-88 Grade 2
Density 15 °C	N.R.	0.82-0.87	N.R.
Distillation °C 90% vol max	360	357	350
Cetane Number min	40	45	45
Cetane Index min	40	45	45
Viscosity cSt 40 °C	1.7-4.1	1.9-5.5	2.0 min[(1)]
Sulfur% wt max	0.05	0.5	0.20
Oxidation Stability mg/100 mL ASTM D 2274	N.R.	2.5 max	N.R.
Cloud Point °C max	2.5% Low Temp. Map[(2)]	Winter Summer +7 Nth +15 Nth 0 W +6 W –1 E +4 E –4 S –4 S (Spec has map)	N.R.
Pour Point	N.R.	N.R. N.R.	–7.5
CFPP °C max	N.R.[(3)]	3 °C max below Cloud Point	–5.0
Electrical Conductivity ps/m	25 min	N.R.	N.R.

1. Viscosity at 38 °C—equivalent is about 2.1 cSt at 40 °C.
2. 2.5% Low End Design Temperature maps based on 25 year continuous hourly records.
3. Specification recognizes LTFT ASTM D 4539 as valid for defining low temperature operability.

N.R. means No Requirement in specification.

TABLE 7—KEY PROPERTY LIMITS FOR VARIOUS AUTOMOTIVE DIESEL EMISSION REFERENCE FUELS

Property	1994 EPA Exhaust Emission Testing Type 2-D	1995 California Exhaust Emission Testing Type 2-D	ECE European Reference Fuel Type RF-03-A-80
Density g/mL	0.840-0.865	0.830-0.860	0.835-0.845
Distillation °F			
IBP	340-400	340-420	N.R.
10%	400-460	400-490	N.R.
50%	470-540	470-560	474 min
90%	560-630	560-610	608-644
FBP	610-690	580-660	708 max
Viscosity cSt at 40 °C	2.0-3.2	2.0-4.1	2.5-3.5
Cetane No.	40-48	47-55(1)	51-57
Cetane Index(2)	40-48	N.R.	N.R.
Sulfur% wt	0.03-0.05	0.01-0.05	0.2-0.5
Aromatics% vol	27 min	8-12	N.R.
Polycyclic Aromatics% vol	N.R.	1.4 max	N.R.
Flash Point °F	130 min	130 min	130 min
Nitrogen Content ppmw	N.R.	100-500	N.R.

1. Natural Cetane Number without additives only allowed.
2. ASTM D 976-80 Cetane Index.

Notes (a) Federal Reference fuel is used for certifying all on-highway diesel engines destined for sale in the 49 states outside California. It can also be used to certify engines destined for sale in California if desired.

(b) California Reference fuel may be used to certify engines destined for use in California if desired.

TABLE 8—LIGHT-DUTY VEHICLES/ENGINES USA AND CANADA

Model Year	Jurisdiction	Emission Standards HC g/mi	Emission Standards CO g/mi	Emission Standards NO_x g/mi	Emission Standards Particulates g/mi
1988	US Federal	0.80	10.0	1.7	0.45
	California	0.50	9.0	1.0	
	Canada	0.80	9.0	1.7	0.26
1991	US Federal	0.80	10.0	1.7	0.13
	California	0.50	9.0	1.0	
	Canada	0.80	9.0	1.7	0.26
1994	US Federal	0.32	4.4	1.7	0.13
	California	0.40	9.0	1.5	
	Canada	0.80	9.0	1.7	0.13
1995-50K	US Federal	0.32	4.4	—	0.08
	California	0.32	4.4	0.7	0.08
	Canada				
1995-100K	US Federal	0.40	5.5	0.97	0.10
	California	0.40	5.5	0.97	—
	Canada				

TABLE 9—MEDIUM-DUTY VEHICLE—120 000 MILE EMISSION STANDARDS

Test Weight lb	Emission Standards g/mi NMHC	Emission Standards g/mi CO	Emission Standards g/mi NO_x	Emission Standards g/mi Particulates
3 751 - 5 750	0.46	6.4	0.98	0.10
5 751 - 8 500	0.56	7.3	1.53	0.12
8 501 - 10 000	0.66	8.1	1.81	0.15
10 000 - 14 000	0.86	10.3	2.77	0.18

10.1 Exhaust Emission Regulations—Key emission standards contained in various regulations for light- and heavy-duty on-highway diesel engines relevant to the USA, Canada, and the EEC are summarized as follows in Tables 8 to Table 12.

a. Light-Duty Vehicles/Engines USA and Canada
b. Medium-Duty Vehicles—California Air Resources Board (CARB) approved the proposed Medium-Duty Vehicle (MDV) emission standards for model year 1995 on June 4th 1990. This extends the light-duty chassis emissions test to include vehicles in the 8500 to 14 000 lb GVWR bracket. The final standards for diesel-powered vehicles are:

Alternatively, engines and incomplete vehicles may be tested using the EPA transient dynamometer test and then must comply with the following standards:

1. 120 000 mile Emission Standards g/BHP/h
   a. NMHC + NO_x —3.9
   b. CO —14.4
   c. Particulates—0.10

c. Heavy-Duty Engines—USA

More complete details and discussion of the development of both the light- and heavy-duty diesel emission standards can be found in the referenced literature (6)(7).

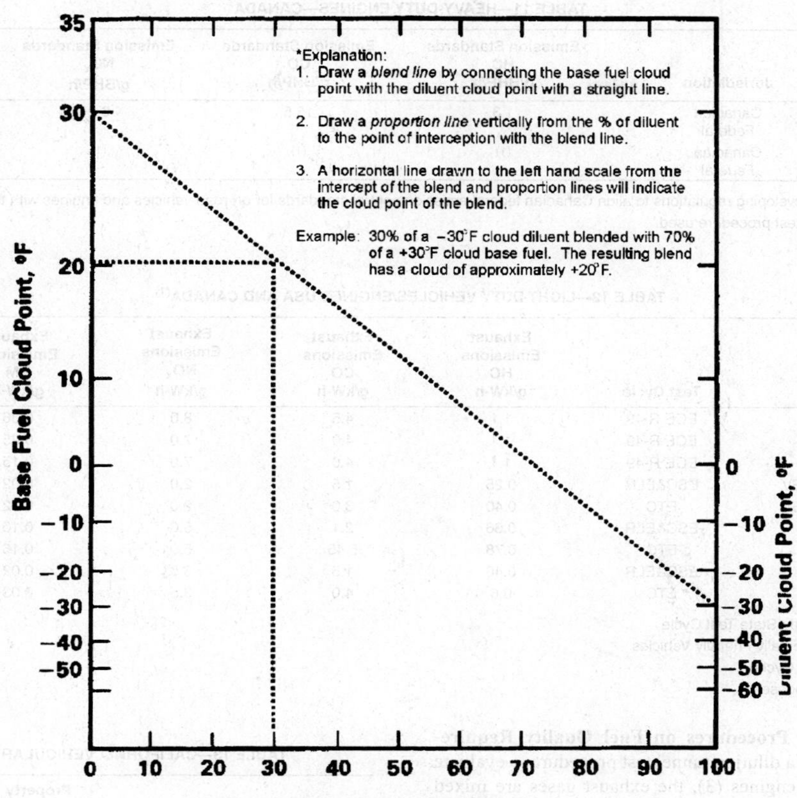

FIGURE 8—CHART FOR ESTIMATING THE CLOUD POINT OF FUEL BLENDS
From "Diesel Fuels and Low Temperatures," Amoco Oil Company, Product Information Sheet No. 304, December 1977

TABLE 10—HEAVY-DUTY ENGINES—USA

Model Year	Jurisdiction	Emission Standards HC g/bhp-h	Emission Standards CO g/bhp-h	Emission Standards NO_x g/bhp-h	Emission Standards NMHC +NO_x g/bhp-h	Emission Standards Particulates g/bhp-h	Smoke Opacity Accel %	Smoke Opacity Lug %	Smoke Opacity Peak %
1987	US Federal	1.3	15.5	10.7			20	15	50
	California	1.3	15.5	6.0		0.60	20	15	50
1988	US Federal	1.3	15.5	10.7		0.60	20	15	50
1990	US Federal	1.3	15.5	6.0		0.60	20	15	50
1991	US Federal	1.3	15.5	5.0		0.25	20	15	50
	California	1.3	15.5	5.0		0.10	20	15	50
1993	US Federal	1.3	15.5	5.0		0.25/0.10(1)	20	15	50
1994	US Federal	1.3	15.5	5.0		0.10/0.07(1)	20	15	50
	California	1.3	15.5	5.0		0.07	20	15	50
1996	California	1.3(1)	15.5(1)	4.0(1)		0.05(1)	20	15	50
1998	US Federal	1.3	15.5	4.0		0.10/0.05(1)	20	15	50
2004	US Federal	0.5(1)	15.5		2.4/2.5(2)	0.10/0.05(1)	20	15	50

1. Urban Bus Engines
2. 2.4 g/bhp-h HC+NO_x max. or 2.5 g/bhp-h HC+NO_x max. with a 0.5 max. limit.

NOTES—Emissions determined by US EPA transient test where:

$$\text{Transient Emissions} = \frac{1/7\,\text{Cold Emissions} + 6/7\ \text{Hot Emissions}}{1/7\ \text{Cold Work} + 6/7\ \text{Hot Work(BHP} - \text{h)}}$$

TABLE 11—HEAVY-DUTY ENGINES—CANADA

Model Year	Jurisdiction	Emission Standards HC g/BHP/h	Emission Standards CO g/BHP/h	Emission Standards NO_x g/BHP/h	Emission Standards Particulates g/BHP/h
1988	Canadian Federal	1.3	15.5	6.0	0.60
2004	Canadian Federal	(1)	(1)	(1)	(1)

1. Environmental Canada is developing regulations to align Canadian federal emission control standards for on-road vehicles and engines with those of the U.S. EPA.
NOTE—U.S. EPA transient test procedure used.

TABLE 12—LIGHT-DUTY VEHICLES/ENGINES USA AND CANADA(1)

Tier	Year	Test Cycle	Exhaust Emissions HC g/kW-h	Exhaust Emissions CO g/kW-h	Exhaust Emissions NO_x g/kW-h	Exhaust Emissions PM g/kW-h	Smoke
Euro I	1992	ECE R-49	1.1	4.5	8.0	0.36	
Euro II	1996	ECE R-49	1.1	4.0	7.0	0.25	
Euro II	1998	ECE R-49	1.1	4.0	7.0	0.15	
Euro III	1999 EEV	ESC&ELR	0.25	1.5	2.0	0.02	0.15
Euro III	1999 EEV	ETC	0.40	3.0	2.0	0.02	
Euro III	2000	ESC&ELR	0.66	2.1	5.0	0.10	0.8
Euro III	2000	ETC	0.78	5.45	5.0	0.16	
Euro IV	2005	ESC&ELR	0.46	1.5	3.5	0.02	0.5
Euro IV	2005	ETC	0.6	4.0	3.5	0.03	

1. ECE R-49 = European Steady-State Test Cycle
EEV = Enhanced Environmentally Friendly Vehicles
ESC = European Stationary Cycle
ELR = European Load Response

10.2 Impact of Emission Test Procedures on Fuel Quality Requirements—In conjunction with the use of a dilution tunnel test procedure to evaluate the particulate emissions from diesel engines (3), the exhaust gases are mixed with filtered air and cooled to a temperature which is below the acid dew point for sulfuric acid. Sulfates and their hydrates precipitate from the gas stream and are collected on the filters together with carbonaceous and soluble organic fraction (SOF) particulates. The significance of the sulfur content of the test fuel on exhaust particulates was quickly appreciated (8) and this led ultimately to the historic proposal (9) from:

The American Petroleum Institute (API)
The National Petroleum Refiners Association (NPRA)
The Engine Manufacturers Association (EMA)
The National Council of Farmers Coops (NCFC)

recommending that diesel fuel having a sulfur content of 0.05% weight maximum and a cetane index of 40 minimum by ASTM D 976-80, be available by October 1993 for the 1994 model year engines which would require such fuel to comply with mandated emission standards. The U.S. EPA has translated this agreement into a Final Rule (10) which was published in the Federal Register in August 1990.

In the USA, except for California, low sulfur diesel fuels meeting the requirements of:

a. Maximum Sulfur Content—0.05% wt
b. Minimum Cetane Index (ASTM D 976-80)—40.0 or
Maximum Aromatic Content (ASTM D 1319)—35.0% vol

have become mandatory for all on-highway operations in the 49 states area which excludes California from October 1, 1993.

In California, all fuel for vehicular use (on- and off-highway) has been required to meet the following criteria since October 1, 1993:

a. Maximum Sulfur Content—0.05% wt
b. Maximum Aromatics Content (ASTM D 1319)—10.0% vol

Farm equipment, locomotives, etc., can use conventional fuel.

In California, an alternate method of certifying diesel fuel for sale under Section 2282 of the California Code of Regulations Title 13, has been to demonstrate equivalent exhaust emissions in a specified test using a Detroit Diesel Series 60 engine operating on the reference fuel shown in Table 13. This is known as the designated alternative limit and this option has been used by several major refiners resulting in fuel blends being certified with the characteristics in Table 14:

TABLE 13—CALIFORNIA VEHICULAR REFERENCE DIESEL FUEL

Property	
Density g/mL	0.830–0.860
Distillation °F	
IBP	340–420
10% rec	400–490
50%	470–560
90%	550–610
FBP	580–660
Viscosity cSt at 40 °C	2.0–4.1
Cetane Number	48(1) min
Flash Point °F	130 min
Sulfur% wt	0.05 max
Nitrogen ppmw	10 max
Aromatics% vol	10.0 max
Polycyclic Aromatics% wt	1.4 max

1. Natural Cetane Number without additives only allowed.
Note—This fuel is used as a reference for emissions when testing designated alternative limit fuels in a specified heavy-duty diesel engine test.

From October 1, 1994 in Canada, all diesel sold through retail and cardlock outlets must meet the following criteria:

a. Maximum Sulfur Content—0.05% wt
b. Minimum Cetane Index (ASTM D 976-80)—40.0

In Canada, fuel supplied to a customer's own tankage for on-highway use can continue to contain up to 0.5% wt sulfur except in British Columbia where all fuel must be low sulfur (0.05% wt maximum).

In Canada, high sulfur diesel fuel must contain a green dye. In the USA, the IRS and EPA require addition of a red dye to all untaxed and high sulfur diesel fuels at a rate to provide the spectral equivalent of 3.0 lb/thousand barrels of solid dye Solvent Red 26.

TABLE 14—CERTIFIED CHARACTERISTICS

Refiner Blend	A 1	A 2	A 3	B 1	B 2
Cetane No.	58	59	55	55.2	56.2
Sulfur ppm	54	196	202	33	42
Aromatics% vol	19	19	15	21.7	24.7
Nitrogen ppm	484	466	341	20	40
Polyaromatics	2.22	4.39	3.6	4.6	4.0

Note—All values are maxima except Cetane number which is the minimum. Other compositions are in use commercially to meet Section 2282 but have not been disclosed publicly.

10.3 Impact of Fuel Quality Parameters on Heavy-Duty Diesel Exhaust Emissions—The initial focus, from a fuel quality and compositional perspective, was on the influence of fuel aromatic content, 90 vol% distilled temperature and the sulfur content, and more recently, the fuel cetane number, both natural and when improved with alkyl nitrate ignition improver additives. Some of these properties are quite strongly correlated and this fact must be taken into account when considering the results from programs aimed at identifying the effect of specific fuel parameters.

The most definitive and relevant work published on the subject to date are the reports from the Coordinating Research Council (CRC) VE-1 Project (11)(12) which has used three engines of differing design and size and has looked at fuel aromatic content, 90 vol% distilled temperature, sulfur content, natural cetane number, and additive-improved cetane number, in statistically designed experiments with closely tailored fuel sets.

Emission responses from the three engines were sufficiently different and the quantity of data limited so that universal models were not developed for the three engines as a group. Engine design features can be seen from the results to have a much greater effect on emissions of all regulated species than the fuel compositional changes.

From published data (11)(12)(13) and other information from regulatory agency hearings, the following conclusions can be drawn regarding the effects of fuel composition on diesel exhaust emissions in general:

a. Increases in fuel sulfur content directly increase particulate emissions.
b. As cetane number increases, CO and hydrocarbon emissions decrease.
c. As cetane number increases, NO_x emissions decrease with a somewhat higher rate for natural cetane over additive improved fuels.
d. As aromatic content is decreased NO_x emissions decrease.
e. Cetane number, both natural and additive-improved, and possibly aromatic content affect particulate emissions. Increasing cetane number particularly natural cetane number reduces particulates while increasing aromatics content increases particulates.
f. 90 vol% distilled temperature is significant for CO, NO_x, and HC but the effect is highly engine dependent being most significant for the indirect injection engine tested. The influence on CO emissions was in different directions for different engines.

10.4 Secondary Effects of Emissions Regulation on Diesel Fuel Quality—Diesel fuel which is produced by high-pressure, high-temperature hydrotreatment, and hydroconversion process, which are capable of effecting some limited aromatic saturation, can sometimes lack adequate lubricity performance even though they have sufficient viscosity. This subject is discussed in 5.16.

As a result of engine design changes, particularly the use of retarded timing to lower NO_x emissions, serious increases of white smoke emissions in cold operating conditions have been reported by several manufacturers. This appears to be related to marginal cetane quality and as a result the Engine Manufacturers Association, and this Fuels and Lubricants Committee has requested (14) consideration of raising the minimum cetane number specification to improve performance.

10.5 Emissions Regulations/Fuel Quality/Lubricant Quality Interactions—Mechanical and combustion improvements coupled with cleaner burning reformulated diesel fuels in the 1990s will alter the combustion by-products which the crankcase lubricant has to contend with. A crucial requirement for the crankcase lubricant will be its impact on the soluble organic fraction (SOF) of the particulates and also any effects which the lubricant or performance additives may have on aftertreatment devices, which are expected to be employed on 1994 engines and beyond. These aspects will be addressed in appropriate changes to SAE J183 and SAE J304.

TAMPER RESISTANCE FOR ADJUSTABLE PARAMETERS ON DIESEL FUEL INJECTION PUMPS—SAE J2317 SEP2002

SAE Recommended Practice

Report of the SAE Diesel Fuel Injection Equipment Standards Committee approved August 1996 and reaffirmed September 2002.

Foreword—Engine exhaust emission standards and test procedures enforced by various regulatory agencies has resulted in in-use emissions testing of certain vehicles or engines. Such testing has revealed that some diesel vehicles failing the smoke opacity test had adjustable parameters tampered with by the owner or an agent of the owner. To avoid non-compliance of an engine's exhaust emissions due to tampering, there have been various regulations developed designed to assure that the adjustable parameters which affect exhaust emissions will remain in-use within the original equipment manufacturer's intended settings.

It has been recognized that the impetus for developing designs that offer adequate tamper-resistance is with the manufacturer of the fuel injection pump (FIP). This SAE Recommended Practice is developed by the standards committee representing the interests of diesel fuel injection equipment (FIE) manufacturers, engine manufacturers, and the FIE service industry. The purpose of this document is to offer some design proposals which can be standardized in the FIE industry, are cost effective, and allow for servicing to be accomplished with a minimum of obstruction. The design proposals contained herein are designed in anticipation of approval by, specifically, the U.S. Environmental Protection Agency and the California Air Resources Board as to their being effective in discouraging tampering attempts and that the listing of applicable adjustable parameters is appropriate.

Described herein are designs which may be proprietary to the manufacturer and protected by patents. Information on the sources of fasteners shown can be obtained from SAE.

1. Scope—This SAE Recommended Practice defines a guideline for the fuel injection pump designer to select appropriate fastener designs which are considered to be tamper-resistant. It applies to fuel injection pumps used on diesel engines.

2. References

2.1 Applicable Publication—The following publication forms a part of this specification to the extent specified herein.

2.1.1 FEDERAL REGULATION—Available from the Superintendent of Documents, U.S. Government Printing Office, Washington, DC 20402.

Code of Federal Regulations, 40 CFR 86-090-22e

3. Definitions

3.1 Tamper-Resistance—The definition of this term is found in 40 CFR 86-090-22e.

4. Applicable Features—The following lists the features of an injection pump which may require tamper-resistance. Excluded from the list is low idle and high idle adjustments. These features are excluded because (a) it is unlikely that an owner would knowingly tamper with these settings beyond that which may be necessary for the normal resettings in use, (b) the changing of these settings from the factory settings do not generally result in significant exhaust emissions non-compliance, and (c) after sale in-use resetting of these features is often required for application adaptability and considered part of normal use.

4.1 Fuel Setting—An adjustment which can alter the fuel setting considered to be the basic setting of the FIP may need to be tamper-resistant.

4.2 Fuel Trimming—An adjustment which alters the fuel curve which results in modifying the engine torque curve may need to be tamper-resistant.

4.3 Advance Setting—An adjustment which can alter the FIP timing device (i.e., speed advance or load advance) may need to be tamper-resistant.

4.4 Aneroid or Aneroid Setting—An adjustment which can alter the FIP aneroid or any mechanism which can alter the aneroid operation may need to be tamper-resistant.

5. Adjustment Type—There are two types of adjustment which can employ tamper-resistant designs. One type is a design in which the adjustable feature is housed under a cover and the cover fastener is the item which is required to be tamper-resistant. The second design is an adjusting screw which is externally accessible. Adjusting screws are often secured from further movement with a lock nut.

5.1 Cover Screw—Cover screws may be considered tamper-resistant by the design of the head configuration. The preferred design is shown in Figure 1. The features of the design make use of a special keyed tool which is available only to authorized servicing facilities and not to the general public. The design shown uses a special design socket shape with a pin protruding from its center. The pin disables the engagement of a commercially available socket key. An alternate design which requires the use of a special socket wrench to be used is shown in Figure 2.

Additionally, an alternate cover screw design employs the use of a breakaway capscrew. This design utilizes an external drive that breaks away at a specified torque, thus preventing the use of wrenches or drivers for removal. Removal of the capscrew requires the use of a drill and screw extractor.

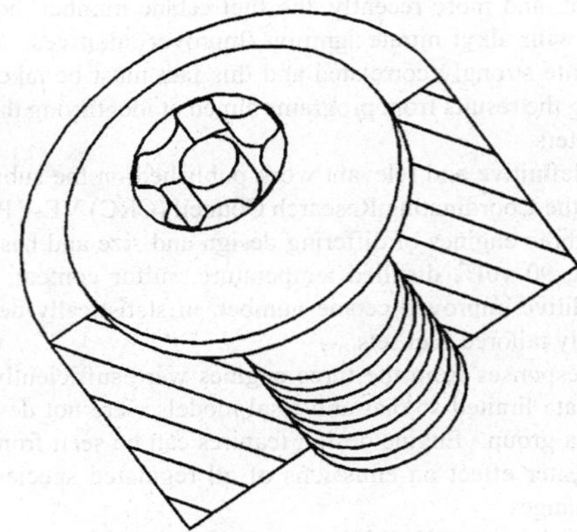

FIGURE 1—KEYED CAPSCREW

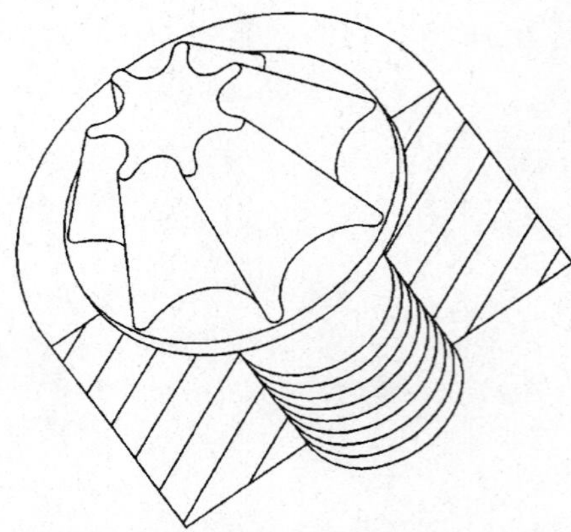

FIGURE 2—SPECIAL SOCKET CAPSCREW

5.2 Cover Screw for Seal Wire—This design, as shown in Figure 3, utilizes a breakaway hex and a ring that prevents the use of standard wrenches. It can further be used by the manufacturer and manufacturer's service representative to place their seal on a tag and wire.

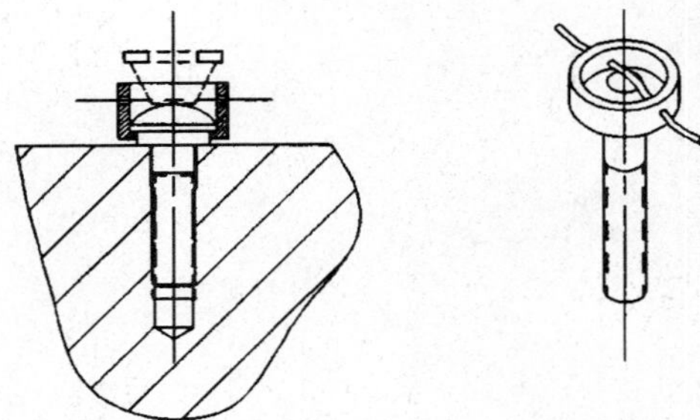

FIGURE 3—BREAKAWAY CAPSCREW

5.3 Adjusting Screw with Lock Nut—An adjusting screw with its lock nut can be made tamper-resistant by one of two designs. The "special nut design" as shown in Figure 4 has the nut recessed in an area such that its outside surface is inaccessible. The nut incorporates a design feature requiring the use of a special tool which is only available to authorized servicing dealers.

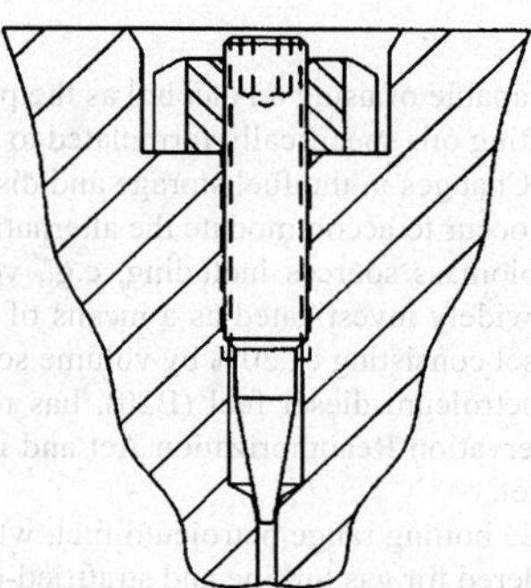

FIGURE 4—SPECIAL NUT AND ADJUSTING SCREW

The "covered access design" also contains the screw and nut in a recess. Access is denied by placing a cover over the adjustment making the recessed area inaccessible as shown in Figure 5.

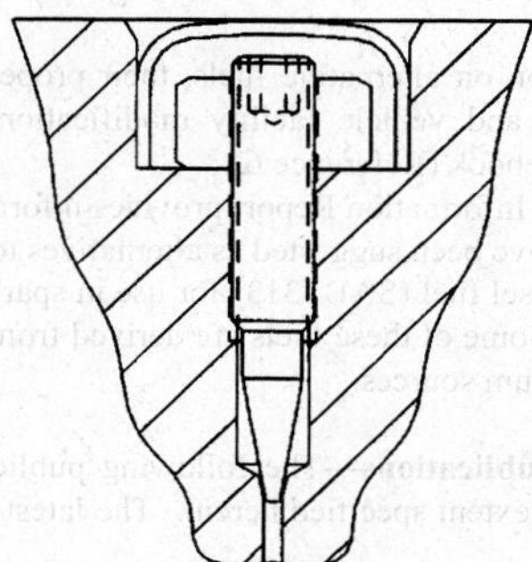

FIGURE 5—COVERED ACCESS

The "covered access design" can be employed on an adjustment which may not be recessed. Access is denied by virtue of the cover design itself. Such designs are shown in Figures 6 and 7.

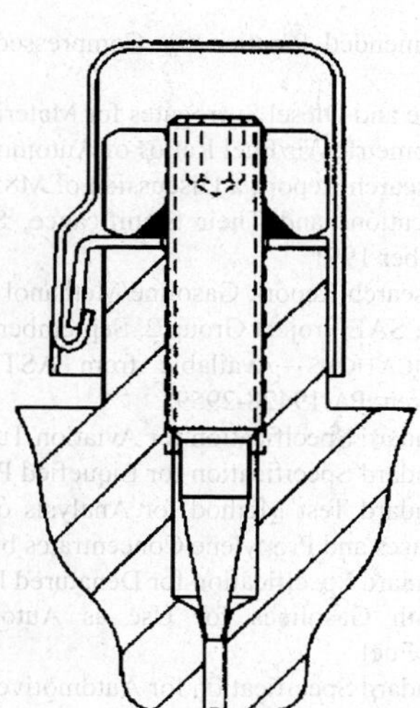

FIGURE 6—IRREVERSIBLE CAP

An alternate design is that shown in Figure 7 contains the snap-ring in the outside diameter of the cap. The cap is more fully recessed into a bore until the snap-ring engages with a groove located on the inside surface of the bore.

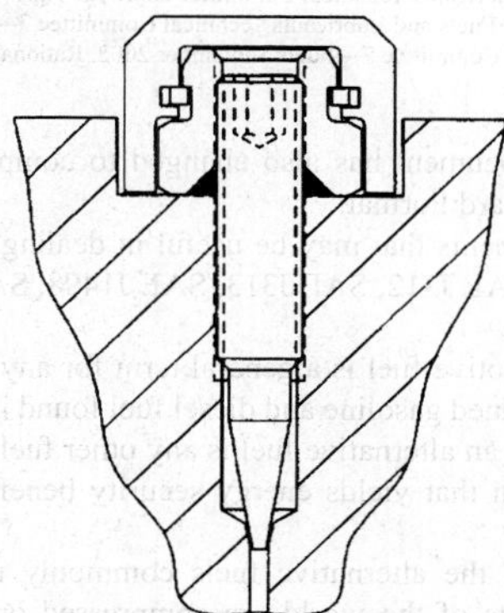

FIGURE 7—SNAP-RING CAP

5.4 Adjusting Screw without Lock Nut—An adjusting screw may be secured without the use of a lock nut. In this case, the threaded cavity into which the adjusting screw is fitted may be plugged with the same type fastener used for tamper-resistant covers. This design is shown in Figure 8.

In an alternate design, the upper portion of the cavity into which the adjusting screw is fitted is bored to accept a pressed steel ball. The placement of the steel ball into the cavity makes the adjusting screw inaccessible.

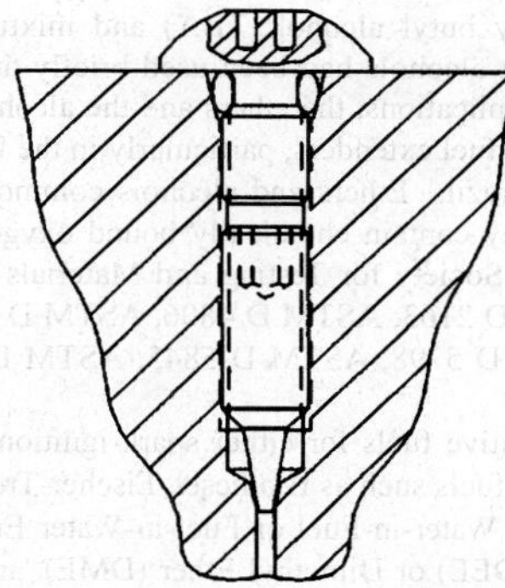

FIGURE 8—PLUGGED ADJUSTING SCREW

5.5 Tampering Evidence—A sealing lacquer may be used with any of the designs shown in this document to provide the manufacturer or the manufacturer's service representative with evidence that tampering has been attempted.

(R) ALTERNATIVE AUTOMOTIVE FUELS—SAE J1297 SEP2002

SAE Information Report

Report of the SAE Fuels and Lubricants Technical Committee approved April 1980, and revised by the SAE Fuels and Lubricants Technical Committee 7—Fuels June 1989. Completely revised by the SAE Fuels and Lubricants Technical Committee 7—Fuels June 1990, March 1993, and October 2000. Rationale statement available. Revised by SAE Fuels and Lubricants Technical Committee 7—Fuels September 2002. Rationale statement available.

Foreword—This Document has also changed to comply with the new SAE Technical Standards Board Format.

Relevant SAE documents that may be useful in dealing with alternative automotive fuels include: SAE J312, SAE J313, SAE J1498, SAE J1515, SAE J1616, and SAE J1829.

An alternative automotive fuel is a general term for any automotive fuel other than conventionally refined gasoline and diesel fuel found in the commercial marketplace. Additionally, an alternative fuel is any other fuel determined to be substantially not petroleum that yields energy security benefits and environmental benefits.

Other than gasoline, the alternative fuels commonly used in spark-ignition engines in various parts of the world are compressed or liquefied natural gas (CNG or LNG), primarily methane; propane, frequently referred to as LPG (liquefied petroleum gas); hydrous ethyl alcohol (ethanol), particularly in Brazil; gasohol (Reference 1) — a blend, as typically used in the United States, of 90% by volume gasoline and 10% by volume denatured, nominally anhydrous ethanol; fuel methanol (M70-M85) containing small percentages of hydrocarbons; fuel ethanol (Ed75-Ed85) containing small percentages of hydrocarbons; and reformulated gasolines containing methyl tertiary butyl ether (MTBE), ethanol, ethyl tertiary butyl ether (ETBE), diisopropyl ether (DIPE), or tertiary amyl methyl ether (TAME). Although gasohol and reformulated gasoline are not considered as alternative fuels but contain blending components that individually are considered as alternative fuels, they have been included in this report for completeness. Gasoline containing tertiary butyl alcohol (TBA) and mixtures of methanol and higher molecular weight alcohols had been used briefly during the early 1980s. In the gasoline blend applications, the ethers and the alcohols have been used as octane improvers and as fuel extenders, particularly in the United States, Western Europe, Canada, and Brazil. Ethers and alcohols commonly are referred to as oxygenates, because they contain chemically bound oxygen. Applicable documents of the American Society for Testing and Materials are: ASTM D 1655[1], ASTM D 1835, ASTM D 2163, ASTM D 4806, ASTM D 4814, ASTM D 4815, ASTM D 5797, ASTM D 5798, ASTM D 5845, ASTM D 5983, and ASTM D 6751.

Other possible alternative fuels for either spark-ignition or compression-ignition engines include Biofuels such as Biodiesel, Fischer-Tropsch (F-T) or Gas-to-Liquid Synthetic Fuels, Water-in-Fuel or Fuel-in-Water Emulsions, other ethers such as Diethyl Ether (DEE) or Dimethyl Ether (DME), and other alcohols, particularly methanol, which is widely used as a racing fuel. The use of such fuels is being encouraged in the United States by federal and state legislative and regulatory activities including the U.S. Alternative Motor Fuels Act of 1988, the U.S. Clean Air Act Amendments of 1990, environmental regulations adopted by California in 1990, the U.S. Energy Policy Act of 1992, and the U.S. Energy Conservation Reauthorization Act of 1998.

The near-neat alcohols have been evaluated extensively in many countries in vehicles equipped with engines which have been retrofitted or specifically designed to use these alternative fuels. From these efforts, a mixture of 85% by volume methanol or denatured ethanol and 15% by volume hydrocarbons or gasoline, referred to as M85 or Ed85, respectively, have evolved as the preferred fuels for spark-ignition engines by some. Gasoline or a hydrocarbon mixture is used in either M85 or Ed85 to enhance vehicle startability and, as a safety feature, to increase the visibility of burning methanol or ethanol. So-called flexible fuel vehicles (FFVs) have been developed which can be fueled by either M85 and gasoline alone or, Ed85 and gasoline alone (Reference 2). Fuel methanol and fuel ethanol without added hydrocarbon or gasoline (that is, M100 or Ed100), often referred to as neat alcohols, have also been evaluated in many countries in vehicles equipped with modified compression-ignition (CI) type engines (Reference 3) as well as those equipped with spark-ignition engines. Both the FFVs and at least one M100 CI engine have reached the commercial production stage of development (References 4, 5). Blends of natural gas liquids, ethanol, and biomass derived co-solvents are also being evaluated for both spark-ignition and compression-ignition engine applications.

Engines made to be capable of using an alcohol as the primary fuel component will require new lubricating oils specifically formulated to provide optimum durability of such engines. Changes in the fuel storage and distribution infrastructure can also be expected to occur to accommodate the alternative fuels.

Fuels derived from biomass sources including, e.g., vegetable oils and their derivatives, have been widely investigated as a means of extending diesel fuels. One such fuel, a biodiesel consisting of 20% by volume soy methyl ester blended with 80% by volume petroleum diesel fuel (B20), has recently been approved under the Energy Conservation Reauthorization Act and is being actively evaluated as an alternative fuel.

In another area, a wide boiling range petroleum fuel, which has been used as a jet fuel, has been considered for gas turbine and stratified-charge engines.

The Department of Defense (DOD) has implemented the Single Fuel on the Battlefield policy which mandates that all combat and tactical diesel fueled ground vehicles and equipment are to use an aviation kerosene (i.e., JP-8 or JP-5) in place of diesel fuel (Reference 55a). This policy allows both aviation and ground materiel systems to use the same common fuel which significantly reduces the logistics of fuel supply and distribution. Thus, JP-8 and JP-5 have become alternative fuels for DOD's diesel fueled ground vehicle and equipment fleet.

Additional information on alternative fuels, their properties, storage and dispensing considerations and vehicle facility modifications can be found in a recently published guidebook (Reference 6).

1. Scope—This SAE Information Report provides information on certain fuels that are being used or have been suggested as alternatives to motor gasoline (SAE J312) or automotive diesel fuel (SAE J313) for use in spark-ignition or compression-ignition engines. Some of these fuels are derived from petroleum while others are from non petroleum sources.

2. References

2.1 Applicable Publications—The following publications form a part of this specification to the extent specified herein. The latest issue of SAE publications shall apply.

2.1.1 SAE Publications—Available from SAE, 400 Commonwealth Drive, Warrendale, PA 15096-0001.

SAE J312—Automotive Gasolines
SAE J313—Diesel Fuels
SAE J1498—Heating Value of Fuels
SAE J1515—Impact of Alternative Fuels on Engine Test and Reporting Procedures
SAE J1616—Recommended Practice for Compressed Natural Gas Vehicle Fuel
SAE J1681—Gasoline and Diesel Surrogates for Materials Testing
SAE J1829—Stoichiometric Air/Fuel Ratios of Automotive Fuels
SAE Cooperative Research Report, a Discussion of M85 (85% Methanol) Fuel Specifications and Their Significance, SAE Project Group 3, September 1991
SAE Cooperative Research Report, Gasoline/Methanol Mixtures for Materials Testing, SAE Project Group 2, September 1990

2.1.2 ASTM Publications—Available from ASTM, 100 Barr Harbor Drive, West Conshohocken, PA 19428-2959.

ASTM D 1655—Standard Specification for Aviation Turbine Fuels
ASTM D 1835—Standard Specification for Liquefied Petroleum (LP) Gases
ASTM D 2163—Standard Test Method for Analysis of Liquefied Petroleum (LP) Gases and Propylene Concentrates by Gas Chromatography
ASTM D 4806—Standard Specification for Denatured Fuel Ethanol for Blending With Gasolines for Use as Automotive Spark-Ignition Engine Fuel
ASTM D 4814—Standard Specification for Automotive Spark-Ignition Engine Fuel
ASTM D 4815—Standard Test Method for Determination of MTBE, ETBE, TAME, DIPE, Tertiary Amyl Alcohol, and C_1 to C_4 Alcohols in Gasoline by Gas Chromatography
ASTM D 5797—Standard Specification for Fuel Methanol M70 — M85 for Automotive Spark-Ignition Engines

1. References to ASTM Standards in this document are to most recent publications.

ASTM D 5798—Standard Specification for Fuel Ethanol Ed75 — Ed85 for Automotive Spark-Ignition Engines

ASTM D 5845—Standard Test Method for Determination of MTBE, ETBE, TAME, DIPE, Methanol, Ethanol, and tert-Butanol by Infrared Spectroscopy

ASTM D 5983—Specification for Methyl Tertiary Butyl Ether (MTBE) for Downstream Blending for Use in Automotive Spark-Ignition Engine Fuel

ASTM D 6751—Standard Specification for Biodiesel Fuel (B100) Blend Stock for Distillate Fuels

2.1.3 LITERATURE REFERENCES CITED

1. American Society for Testing and Materials, 1985 Annual Book of Standards, Vol. 05.01, "Information Document on Gasohol," Philadelphia, PA.
2. "Development of Alternative Motor Fuels Pushed," Oil and Gas Journal, May 9, 1988, p. 24.
3. "Methanol Fuel Looks Good Again," Machine Design, December 10, 1987, p. 22.
4. New Fuels Report, January 13, 1992, p. 1.
5. S. P. Miller, "DDC's Production 6V-92TA Methanol Bus Engine," Paper 911631 presented at SAE Future Transportation Technology Conference and Exposition, Portland, Oregon, August 5–7, 1991.
6. Richard L. Bechtold, "Alternative Fuels Guidebook," ISBN 0-7680-0052-1, 1997, Society of Automotive Engineers, Warrendale, PA.
7. Letter from R. D. Wilson, Director, EPA Office of Mobile Sources, to B. G. Henneke, Jr., President, Energy Fuels Development Corp., December 15, 1986.
8. Letter from R. D. Wilson, Director, EPA Office of Mobile Sources, to W. Wells III, Vice President, Chemical Fuels Corp., March 27, 1987.
9. A. E. Felt and R. V. Kerley, "Anti-Knock Compounds Applied to LP-Gas," presented at 65th Annual Meeting of American Society for Testing and Materials, New York, NY, June 23, 1962.
10. N. E. Gallopoulos, "Alternative Fuels for Reciprocating Internal Combustion Engines." Reprinted from "Alternative Hydrocarbon Fuels: Combustion and Chemical Kinetics." Edited by Craig T. Bowman and Jorgen Birkeland, Vol. 62, 1978, of Progress in Astronautics and Aeronautics.
11. Ana Rodriguez-Forker,et al., Butane/Propane Mixtures as Fleet Fuels," Automotive Engineering International Magazine, December 1999, p. 41.
12. "Alternative Fuels for Spark Ignition Engines," Automotive Engineering, December 1983, Vol. 91, Number 12, pp. 30–33.
13. Chemical & Engineering News, January 15, 1990, p. 6.
14. Norman L. Kline, "German Military Fuels and Lubricants," Paper 460170 presented at the SAE German Engineering Evaluation Meeting, Detroit, MI March 1946.
15. Charles L. Gray, "Alternative Fuels and Air Quality," presented at the Conference on Air Quality Issues: Changing America's Motor Fuel Business, Denver, CO, January 27, 1988.
16. Octane Week, July 17, 1989, p. 7.
17. "Federal Highway Administration's Highway Statistics 1998, Section 1 — Motor Fuel," Website - http:/www.fhwa.dot.gov/ohim/hs98/mfpage.htm.
18. Octane Week, June 27, 1988, p. 1.
19. Alcohol Outlook, May, 1989, p. 5.
20. New Fuels Report, February 11, 1991, p. 12.
21. Federal Register, Vol. 54, No. 68, April 11, 1989, p. 14426.
22. Alcohol Week, May 11, 1987, p. 3.
23. B. C. Davis, "Distribution and Market Experience With Methanol Blends," presented at the First International Conference on Fuel Methanol, New York City, NY, May 10, 1983.
24. R. T. Johnson and B. Y. Taniguchi, "Methyl Tertiary-Butyl Ether—Evaluation as a High Octane Blending Component for Unleaded Gasoline," presented at Meeting of American Chemical Society, Miami, FL September 1978.
25. Chemical and Engineering News, The American Chemical Society, Washington, DC, June 25, 1979.
26. Octane Week, July 17, 1989, p. 7.
27. Alcohol Outlook, February 1991, p. 15.
28. Herb Short, "Multi-Ether Processes Boost Gasoline Octane," Chemical Engineering, June 23, 1986, p. 34.
29. "Fina, Total Bring On Line Commercial TAME Plant in UK," Oil & Gas Journal, October 19, 1987.
30. "Elf's TAME Unit Boosts Gasoline Octane," Oil & Gas Journal, November 21, 1988, p. 41.
31. Octane Week, May 13, 1991, p. 3.
32. G. H. Unzelman, "Ethers Have Good Gasoline-Blending Attributes," Oil & Gas Journal, April 10, 1989, p. 33.
33. C. M. Shiblom, et al., "Use of Ethyl-t-Butyl Ether (ETBE) as a Gasoline Blending Component," Paper 902132 presented at the SAE Fuels and Lubricants Meeting, Tulsa, OK, October 1990.
34. "New Process Produces Alternative Oxygenate From Propylene," Oil & Gas Journal, May 25, 1992, p. 39.
35. W. H. Douthit, "Performance and Utility of Gasoline Containing Oxygenates as Viewed by a Petroleum Refiner," 1983 Proceedings—Refining Department at 48th Mid-year API Meeting, May 1983, Vol. 62, pp. 202–209.
36. W. L. Miron, R. A. Ragazzi, T. W. Hollman, and G. L. Gallagher, "Ethanol-Blended Fuel as a CO Reduction Strategy at High Altitude," Paper 860530 presented at the SAE International Congress and Exposition, Detroit, MI, February 24–28, 1986.
37. L. R. Smith, "Additional Mini-Canister Evaluation," EPA Report No. 460/3-85-010, December 1985.
38. N. D. Brinkman, N. E. Gallopoulos, and M. W. Jackson, "Exhaust Emissions, Fuel Economy, and Driveability of Vehicles Fueled With Alcohol-Gasoline Blends," SAE Transactions, Vol. 84 (1975), Paper 750120.
39. A. W. Crowley, et al., "Methanol-Gasoline Blends—Performance in Laboratory Tests and in Vehicles," Paper 750419 presented at SAE Automotive Engineering Congress and Exposition, Detroit, MI, February 24–28, 1975.
40. P. A. Yaccarino, "Hot Weather Driveability and Vapor-Lock Performance With Alcohol-Gasoline Blends," Paper 852117 presented at the SAE Fuels and Lubricants Meeting, Tulsa, OK, October 1985.
41. C. W. Turner, "Engine Wear Rate and Material Compatibility With Methanol Fuel Study," Report TE 83-14 Transportation Energy Division EMR Canada, August 1983.
42. J. L. Keller, G. M. Nakaguchi, and J. C. Ware, "Methanol Fuel Modifications for Highway Vehicle Use," DOE Report No. EY-76-K-04-3683, May 16, 1978.
43. "Alcohols—A Technical Assessment of Their Application as Fuels and Fuel Components," Publication No. 4261, Second Edition, July 1988, American Petroleum Institute, Washington, DC.
44. H. W. Marbach, Jr., E. A. Frame, E. C. Owens, and D. W. Naegeli, "The Effects of Alcohol Fuels and Fully Formulated Lubricants on Engine Wear," Paper 811199 presented at the SAE Fuels and Lubricants Meeting, Tulsa, OK, October 1981.
45. F. D. Rossini, K. S. Pitzer, R. L. Arnett, R. M. Braun, and G. C. Pimental, "Selected Values of Physical and Thermodynamic Properties of Hydrocarbons and Related Compounds," 1953, Carnegie Press, Carnegie Institute of Technology, Pittsburgh, PA.
46. R. C. Wilhoit and B. J. Zwolinski, "Physical and Thermodynamic Properties of Aliphatic Alcohols," Journal of Physical and Chemical Reference Data, Vol. 2, 1983, Supplement No. 1, American Chemical Society and the American Institute of Physics.
47. J. A. Harrington and R. M. Pilot, "Combustion and Emission Characteristics of Methanol," Paper 750420 presented at SAE Automotive Engineering Congress and Exposition, Detroit, MI, February 23–27, 1976.
48. N. D. Brinkman, "Vehicle Evaluation of Neat Methanol—Compromises Among Exhaust Emissions, Fuel Economy, and Driveability," Proceedings of the Fourth International Symposium on Automotive Propulsion Systems, NATO/CCMS Vol. 2, 1977, Session 4.
49. E. R. Fanick, L. R. Smith, and T. M. Baines, "Safety Related Additives for Methanol Fuel," Paper 841378 presented at the SAE Fuels and Lubricants Meeting, Baltimore, MD, October 1984.
50. H. W. Marbach, Jr., E. A. Frame, E. C. Owens, D. W. Naegeli, and B. D. Wielgos, "The Effects of Lubricant Composition on SI Engine Wear With Alcohol Fuels," Paper 831702 presented at the SAE Fuels and Lubricants Meeting, San Francisco, CA, October 1983.
51. R. J. Wineland, "An Update on the Ford Flexible Fuel Vehicle Program," presented at the Fifth Windsor Workshop on Alternative Fuels, Windsor, Ontario, Canada, June 12–14, 1989.
52. J. M. Colucci and J. J. Wise, "The Auto/Oil Quality Improvement Research Program—What Is It and What Has It Learned?" presented at the XXIV FISITA Congress, London, England, June 7–11, 1992.

53. L. Hudson, "Retrofit of a DDC 8V-71 Bus Engine: Methanol With Avocet Ignition Enhancer," presented at the Fifth Windsor Workshop on Alternative Fuels, Windsor, Ontario, Canada, June 12–14, 1989.
54. M. D. Jackson, "Transit Bus Operation With Methanol Fuel," Paper 850216 presented at the SAE International Congress, Detroit, MI, February, 1985.
55. "Alcohols and Ethers—A Technical Assessment of Their Application as Fuels and Fuel Components," Publication No. 4261, Section 6.5.2.12, Draft Third Edition, November 1999, American Petroleum Institute, Washington, DC.
56. Alcohol Week, January 18, 1988, p. 7.
57. T. Fleisch, et al., "A New Clean Diesel Technology: Demonstration of ULEV Emissions on a Navistar Diesel Engine with DME," SAE Paper 950061, 1995.
58. P. E. Kapus, et al., "ULEV Potential of a DI/TCI Diesel Passenger Car Engine Operating on DME," SAE Paper 952754, 1995.
59. V. I. Golovitchev, et al., "Net Dimethyl Ether: is it Really Diesel Fuel of Promise?," Paper 982537 presented at the SAE International Fall Meeting and Exposition, San Francisco, CA, October, 1998.
60. John B. Hansen, et al., "Large Scale Manufacture of Dimethyl Ether—A New Alternative Diesel Fuel from Natural Gas," Paper 950063 presented at the SAE International Congress and Exposition, Detroit, MI, February, 1995.
61. Brent Bailey, et al., "Diethyl Ether (DEE) as a Renewable Diesel Fuel," Paper 972978 presented at the SAE International Fuels and Lubricants Meeting and Exposition, Tulsa, OK, October, 1997.
62. Keith D. Vertin, et al., "Methylal and Methylal-Diesel Blended Fuels for Use in Compression-Ignition Engines," Paper 1999-01-1958 presented at the SAE International Fuels and Lubricants Meeting and Exposition, Dearborn, MI, May, 1999.
63. Frank J. Liotta, Jr., et al., "The Effect of Oxygenated Fuels on Emissions from a Modern Heavy-Duty Diesel Engine., SAE Paper 932734, 1993.
64. Noboru Miyamoto, et al., "Improvement of Diesel Combustion and Emissions with Addition of various Oxygenated Agents to Diesel Fuels," Paper 962115 presented at the SAE International Fuels and Lubricants Meeting and Exposition, San Antonio, TX, October 1996.
65. J. C. Dart, "Methanol Fuel—Technology, Markets, and Future Prospects," Energy Progress Vol. 3, No. 3, September 1983, pp. 127–132.
66. W. M. Scott, "Alternative Fuels for Automotive Diesel Engines," Future Automotive Fuels, Plenum Press, New York, NY, 1977, pp. 263–290.
67. A. W. Schwab, M. O. Babgy, and B. Freedman, "Preparation and Properties of Diesel Fuels from Vegetable Oils," Fuel, Vol. 66, October 1987, p. 1372.
68. W. T. Tierney, E. M. Johnson, and N. R. Crawford, "Energy Conservation, Optimization of the Vehicle-Fuel Refinery System," Paper 750673 presented at SAE Fuels and Lubricants Meeting, Houston, TX, June 3–5, 1975.
69. Department of Defense (DOD) Directive 4140.25, "DOD Management Policy for Energy Commodities and Related Services," April 20, 1999.
70. F. J. Salzano and C. Braun, "Hydrogen Energy Assessment," March 1977, National Center for Analysis of Energy Systems, Brookhaven National Laboratory, Upton, NY.
71. W. J. D. Escher, "Hydrogen-Fueled Internal Combustion Engine—A Technical Survey of Contemporary U.S. Projects," TEC-75/605, September 1975, Escher Technology Associates, St. Johns, MI.
72. R. B. Cole, "The Performance of Hydrogen-Fueled Reciprocating Engines," Proceedings of the Fourth International Symposium on Automotive Propulsion Systems, NATO/CCMS, Vol. 2, 1977, Session 6.
73. R. E. Billings, "Hydrogen's Potential as a Vehicular Fuel for Transportation," Tenth Intersociety Energy Conversion Engineering Conference, Newark, DE, August 18–22, IEEE Catalogue No. 75 CHO 983-7TAB.
74. F. B. Simpson, J. H. Lofthouse, and D. R. Swope, "Modification Techniques and Performance Characteristics of Hydrogen-Powered IC Engines—State of the Art, 1975," Proceedings of the First World Hydrogen Energy Conference, The University of Miami, FL, Vol. 3, 1976, pp. 6C/75-6C/95.
75. D. J. Richeard and N. D. Thompson, "A Review of the Potential for Bio-Fuels as Transporation Fuels., Paper 932778 presented at the SAE Fuels and Lubricants Meeting and Exposition, Philadelphia, PA, October, 1993.
76. Montagne, "Introduction of Rapeseed Methyl Ester in Diesel Fuel—The French National Program," Paper 962065 presented at the SAE International Fuels and Lubricants Meeting and Exposition, San Antonio, TX October, 1996.
77. Gunter H. Hohl, "Rape Oil Methyl ester (RME) and Used Cooking Oil Methyl Ester (UOME) as Alternative Fuels," SAE Paper 962755, 1996.
78. Sherri W. Goodman, Deputy Under Secretary of Defense (Environmental Security), Memorandum to all Military Services dated December 14, 1999, Subject: Using Biodiesel to Meet Alternative Fueled Vehicle Requirements.
79. M. Norman, William Kelly, Masami Manabe, and K. Krieger, "Diesel Fuel Injection (FIE) Equipment Manufacturers Common Position Statement on Fatty Acid Methyl Ester Fuels (FAME) as a Replacement or Extender for Diesel Fuels," issued June 2000.
80. U. S. Army Tank-Automotive Research, Development and Engineering Center Purchase Description PD-B20-01, "B20, Biodiesel Fuel Blend," issued September 8, 2000, Warren, MI.
81. Paul B. Harder, "DOE Test Demonstrates French Fry Oil as Diesel Substitute," Diesel Progress North American Edition Magazine, February 1999, p. 38.
82. Keith Owen and Trevor Coley, "Automotive Fuels Reference Book, Second Edition," Chapter 19.6, 1995, Society of Automotive Engineers, Warrendale, PA.
83. Leo L. Stavinoha,et al., "Alternative Fuels: Gas to Liquids as Potential Military Fuels," SAE Paper 2000-01-3422, presented at the SAE International Truck and Bus Meeting and Exposition, Portland, OR, December 2000.
84. Mark A. Agee, "Fuels for the Future," Energy Frontiers International Conference on Gas Conversion: Projects, Technologies and Strategies, San Francisco, CA, October 1999.
85. Peter V. Snyder, Branch J. Russell, and Paul F. Schubert, "The Case for Synthetic Fuels: Enabling Technology for Advanced Engines," Clean Fuels 2000 - The Race to Produce New Fuels and Engines, San Diego, CA, February 2000.
86. Leo L. Stavinoha, et al., "Alternative Fuels: Development of a Biodiesel B20 Purchase Description," SAE Paper 2000-01-3428 presented at the SAE International Truck and Bus Meeting and Exposition, Portland, OR, December 2000.
87. Mark A. Agee, "Taking GTL Conversion Offshore," 1999 Offshore Technology Conference, Houston, TX, May 1999.
88. G. E. Fodor, et al., "Army's Fire Resistant Diesel Fuel," SAE Paper 790926, 1979.
89. B. R. Wright, et al., "Final Review of United States Army Fire Resistant Fuel Program," Belvoir Fuels and Lubricants Research Facility Technical Report BFLRF-244, Accession Number A194304, December 1987.
90. Allyson Barnes, et al., "Evaluation of Water-Blend Fuels in a City Bus and an Assessment of Performance with Emission Control Devices," SAE Paper 2000-01-1915, presented at the SAE International Spring Fuels and Lubricants Meeting and Exposition, Paris, France, June 2000.
91. Mike Brezonick, "Cat-Lubrizol Efforts Highlights Increasing Focus on Fuel," Diesel Progress North American Edition Magazine, October 1999, p. 22.
92. Frederic Barnaud, Pierre Schmelzle, and Phillippe Schulz, "AQUAZOLE: An Original Emulsified Water-Diesel Fuel for Heavy Duty Applications," SAE Paper 2000-01-1861 presented at the SAE International Spring Fuels and Lubricants Meeting and Exposition, Paris, France, June 2000.
93. P. Saengbangpla, "Butanol as Alternative Fuel in Spark Ignition Engine," SAE Paper 958426, 1995.
94. S. Frigo, et al., "Feasibility of Using Wood Flash-Pyrolysis Oil in Diesel Engines," Paper 982529 presented at the SAE International Fuels and Lubricants Meeting and Exposition, San Francisco, CA, October, 1998.
95. "Alternatives to Traditional Transportation Fuels 1998 - Tables, and Vehicles Supplied - Tables 14-19," Website - http://www.eia.doe.gov.
96. "Protection of Environment," 1999 Code of Federal Regulation Title 40, Volume 11, Part 79 - Registration of Fuels and Fuel Additives, Subpart F - Testing Requirements for Registration, Section 79.59, pages 22-24.
97. U.S. Department of Defense Commercial Item Description A-A-59693, "Diesel Fuel, Biodiesel Blend (B20)," issued September 7, 2001.

3. Legislation Impacting Alternative Fuels

3.1 U.S. Legal Restrictions on Blending Alternative Fuels Into Unleaded Gasoline—The Office of Transportation and Air Quality (formerly The Office of Mobile Sources) within the Environmental Protection Agency (EPA) has been involved since its formation with the use of alternative transportation fuels in the United States. EPA's responsibilities under the Clean Air Act also have necessitated a significant regulatory role dealing with transportation fuels. In particular, Section 211 of the Clean Air Act requires EPA to play a key role in the introduction of new fuels and fuel additives. EPA mandated the introduction of unleaded gasoline to permit the use of catalytic converters on 1975 and later model year automobiles. More recently, EPA has regulated the use of alternative fuel components in motor vehicles, which use unleaded gasoline. EPA's responsibility is to assure that fuel components used in unleaded gasoline will not harm the effectiveness of vehicle emission control systems.

The U.S. Federal Legislation (U.S. Clean Air Act [42 U.S.C., 7545 Section 211 (f)(1)A]) prohibits introduction into commerce, or increases in concentration in use, of any fuel or fuel additive for general use for post-1974 model-year light-duty motor vehicles which is not "substantially similar" to the fuel or fuel additive utilized in the emission certification of such vehicles.

EPA considers (Federal Register, Vol. 56, No. 28, February 11, 1991, p. 5352) the fuels or fuel additives to meet the "substantially similar" requirement if the following criteria are met:

a. The fuel must contain carbon, hydrogen, oxygen, and nitrogen, and/or sulfur, exclusively, in the form of some combination of the following:
   1. Hydrocarbons
   2. Aliphatic ethers
   3. Aliphatic alcohols other than methanol
   4. Up to 0.3% methanol by volume; up to 2.75% methanol by volume with an equal volume of butanol, or higher molecular weight alcohol
   5. A fuel additive at a concentration of no more than 0.25% by weight which contributes no more than 15 ppm sulfur by weight to the fuel
b. The fuel must contain no more than 2.0% oxygen by weight, except fuels containing aliphatic ethers and/or alcohols (excluding methanol) must contain no more than 2.7% oxygen by weight.

NOTE—This rule limits the oxygen content of "substantially similar" unleaded gasoline to (1) 2.0% by weight for blends of aliphatic alcohol mixtures containing methanol, or similar mixtures which also contain ethers, and (2) 2.7% by weight for blends of aliphatic ethers and/or alcohols other than methanol.

c. The fuel must possess, at the time of manufacture, all of the physical and chemical characteristics of an unleaded gasoline as specified by ASTM D 4814-88 for at least one of the Seasonal and Geographical Volatility Classes specified in the standard.

NOTE—As stated in EPA's ruling, "EPA is not adopting ASTM D 4814-88 in its entirety, but is continuing unchanged the provision" relating to volatility classes as set forth in their original rule in Federal Register, Vol. 46, No. 144, July 28, 1981. EPA provided the following explanatory statement at that time: "Lastly, EPA feels that the fuel should meet ASTM standards in general, that is, not necessarily for every geographic location and time of year. Compliance with the detailed requirements of the ASTM volatility specifications is not the intent of this interpretation; rather it is EPA's intent to ensure that gasolines resemble certification fuels in general. Therefore, EPA has removed from the interpretive rule the requirement that all fuels must meet ASTM specifications for all areas and times of year. This will eliminate the requirement that each refiner must assure that every gallon of gasoline sold in an area meets the ASTM standards for the area and time of year. Such a requirement would have reduced manufacturing and distribution flexibility."

d. The fuel additive must contain only carbon, hydrogen, and any one or all of the following elements: oxygen, nitrogen, and/or sulfur.

Fuels or fuel additives which are not "substantially similar" may only be used if a waiver of this prohibition is obtained from EPA. Manufacturers of not "substantially similar" fuels and fuel additives must apply for such a waiver and must establish to the satisfaction of EPA that the fuel or additive does not cause or contribute to a failure of any emission control device or system over the useful life of the vehicle for which it was certified. If the EPA Administrator has not acted to grant or deny the waiver application within one hundred eighty days after its receipt, the waiver is treated as granted. A summary of waivers granted by EPA for fuels and fuel additives, which do not comply with the "substantially similar" requirements, is presented in Table 1. EPA should be consulted for the details and status of its latest waivers.

e. The fuel and fuel additive must be registered.

Since 1975, under Section 211 (b) of the Clean Air Act, it has been unlawful to introduce into commerce any gasoline or diesel fuel and their respective additives unless they are registered with EPA. Any fuel or fuel additive, which was registered as of May 27, 1994, had to have supplemental registration with additional data by November 27, 1994, in order to continue marketing the product. The registered products are then subject to a three-tier toxicological testing program. Tier 1 requires manufactures to provide emissions characteristics, exposure analyses, and a literature search. If insufficient data exists, under Tier 2 manufacturers are required to conduct a 90-day subchronic toxicity test on rodents with additional health effects testing for carcinogenicity/mutagenicity, teratogenicity, reproductive toxicity, toxicity, and neurotoxicity.

All Tier 1 requirements had to be submitted by May 1997. Tier 2 requirements must be submitted by January 2004. Tier 3 testing may be required at EPA's discretion after reviewing the Tier 1 and Tier 2 submissions. A fuel or fuel additive which has not been previously registered, but is compositionally similar to a registered material can be registered as a registrable fuel or fuel additive and marketed. A new fuel or additive, which was not registered as of May 27, 1994, will not be registered until all Tier 1 and Tier 2 information is made available.

To develop the information, a consortium of about 150 companies was formed. API is the agent for contracting the testing for the consortium. The oxygenates to be tested are ethanol, TBA, MTBE, ETBE, TAME, and DIPE. None of the waivered oxygenates containing methanol have undergone a supplemental registration. However, any of the previously registered waivered gasoline-methanol-cosolvent blends can be used after a supplemental registration is made and the required additional information submitted.

Normally, EPA does not permit any oxygenate-containing fuel to be used as a base gasoline for the blending of other oxygenates if the finished blend were to exceed the applicable oxygen limitation of the "substantially similar" rule (i.e., 2.0% or 2.7% oxygen, depending on the presence or absence of methanol). However, because of concerns that the widespread use of MTBE can lead to its inadvertent commingling in a base gasoline (thus restricting the use of other oxygenates), an exception was made in the case of waiver 5 of Table 1 (Methanol/C_2–C_8 Alcohols) which allows up to 2% by volume of MTBE in the base fuel "if the MTBE is present only as a result of commingling in transport and storage, not purposely added as an additional component." Likewise, under the same proviso, EPA has extended this allowance to use base gasolines containing no more than 2% by volume MTBE in the case of ethanol blends (waiver 1) (Reference 7) and Methanol/C_2-C_4 Alcohol blends (waiver 4) (Reference 8).

NOTE—The legislation identified as follows, in 3.2 to 3.9, either specifically require use of alternative fuels, or require the purchasing of AFVs which in turn require alternative fuels for their operation.

3.2 Energy Policy Act of 1992 (Public Law 102-486)—Congress passed The Energy Policy Act known as EPACT on October 24, 1992, which was to increase United States energy security by establishing National goals for energy efficiency and fossil fuel use reduction. EPACT included legislation establishing purchase and use of Alternative Fueled Vehicles (AFVs) for certain types of vehicle fleets and allowed the use of alternative fuels to satisfy their requirements. Additionally, it provided incentives to manufacturers of AFVs and encouraged conversion of gasoline and diesel powered vehicles to alternative fuels. This law also set a National goal of 30 percent penetration of alternative fuels including ethanol into the light-duty vehicle market by 2010. Title III under the EPACT defined "alternative fuel" as any of the following which have been approved under EPACT: methanol, denatured ethanol, and other alcohols, mixtures containing 85% by volume or more of methanol, denatured ethanol, and other alcohols with gasoline or other fuels, compressed natural gas (CNG), liquefied natural gas (LNG), liquefied petroleum gas (LPG), hydrogen, coal-derived liquid fuels, fuels other than alcohol derived from biological materials including neat 100% biodiesel, P-series fuel, solar fuel, electricity, and any other fuel substantially not petroleum that would yield substantial energy security benefits and substantial environmental benefits.

3.3 Energy Conservation Reauthorization Act of 1998 (Public Law 105-388)—Congress passed The Energy Conservation Reauthorization Act known as ECRA on November 13, 1998. This legislation amended Title III of the EPACT to allow fleets that were required to purchase AFVs under Titles III, IV, and V of EPACT to meet these requirements, in part, through the use of biodiesel fuel use credits. The new law allocated one EPACT AFV acquisition credit to a fleet or covered person for every 1 703.4 liters (450 gallons) of biodiesel contained in biodiesel blends of at least 20% by volume biodiesel. The fuel had to be purchased for use by the fleet or covered person in vehicles owned or operated by the entity that weighed more than 8 500 pounds gross vehicle weight.

3.4 Executive Order 12759 Federal Energy Management—This Executive Order signed April 17, 1991 directed all federal agencies to develop energy efficiency goals for facilities and for vehicles, to procure energy efficient goods and products, and to procure AFVs. More specifically, agencies operating 300 or more commercial type vehicles were to develop a plan to reduce motor vehicle gasoline and diesel consumption by at least 10 percent by 1995 in comparison with fiscal year 1991. Additionally, agencies were to ensure that the maximum number practicable of vehicles acquired annually were to be AFVs as required by the Alternative Motor Fuels Act of 1988.

3.5 Executive Order 12844 Federal Fleet Conversion Task Force—This Executive Order signed April 21, 1993, tasked the federal agencies to exercise leadership in the use of AFVs. Each agency was required to adopt aggressive plans to substantially exceed the AFV purchase requirements that had been established by the EPACT.

3.6 Executive Order 13123 Greening the Government Through Efficient Energy Management—This Executive Order signed June 3, 1999, required the Federal Government to significantly improve its energy management in order to save taxpayer dollars and reduce emissions that contribute to air pollution and global climate change. Section 205 required that each agency reduce the use of petroleum by switching to less greenhouse gas intensive non petroleum energy sources. Section 405 required that each agency improve the operation of mobile equipment, implement life-cycle cost effective energy efficiency measures, and consider enhanced use of alternative or renewable-based fuels.

3.7 Executive Order 13134 Developing and Promoting Biobased Products and Bioenergy—This Executive Order signed August 12, 1999, established the Interagency Council on Biobased Products and Bioenergy. This Council was tasked to develop a comprehensive national strategy that would stimulate the creation and early adoption of technologies needed to make biobased products and bioenergy cost-competitive in the commercial marketplace. The strategic plans included biomass used in the production of energy that encompassed both liquid and gaseous fuels.

3.8 Biodiesel Fuel Use Credit Interim Rule—This rule became effective June 18, 1999, and allows covered fleets to allocate AFV acquisition credits towards meeting EPACT requirements through the purchasing of biodiesel fuel. One biodiesel fuel use credit, counted as one AFV acquisition credit, will be allocated to fleets and covered persons for each purchase of 450 gallons of neat biodiesel fuel, where neat biodiesel fuel is 100% biodiesel (B100). A fleet to be allocated a biodiesel fuel use credit may also purchase biodiesel blends, such as B20 (20% by volume biodiesel and 80% by volume petroleum diesel fuel). However, in purchasing biodiesel blends, a fleet may only count the biodiesel portion of the blend towards the allocation of a biodiesel fuel use credit.

3.9 Executive Order 13149 Greening the Government Through Federal Fleet and Transportation Efficiency—This Executive Order signed April 21, 2000, superseded Executive Order 13031, and requires the Federal Government to increase its leadership in the reduction of petroleum consumption through improvements in fleet fuel efficiency and the use of alternative fuel vehicles (AFVs) and alternative fuels. Reduced petroleum use and the displacement of petroleum by alternative fuels will help promote markets for more alternative fuels and fuel efficient vehicles, encourage new technologies, enhance the United States' energy self-sufficiency and security, and ensure a healthier environment through the reduction of greenhouse gases and other pollutants in the atmosphere.

4. Petroleum Gases—Of the petroleum gases, only methane and propane are practical automotive fuels. Methane is available as natural gas and additional methane can be made from non-petroleum sources such as coal, municipal wastes, or biomass. Propane is available in commercial quantities, although the amount is limited to that produced along with natural gas and crude petroleum and as a by-product of refinery reforming and cracking processes. Ethane is fully utilized for chemicals manufacture, and butane is already used in gasoline as a blending agent and in some liquefied petroleum gas (LPG).

Methane and propane have both advantages and disadvantages as automotive fuels relative to gasoline. They have good octane quality, are clean burning, easy to meter, and generally produce lower vehicle exhaust emissions (References 9, 10) but are more difficult to store than gasoline.

Methane can be stored as a compressed gas or as a liquid if cooled to very low temperatures. Present automotive use of methane is has been confined almost entirely to compressed natural gas (CNG), but there has been a slow but incremental increase in the use of liquefied natural gas (LNG) as a vehicular fuel. Use of CNG is expanding somewhat, but vehicular storage and general availability will continue to be limiting. SAE has published a Recommended Practice for Compressed Natural Gas Vehicle Fuel (SAE J1616 FEB94) which gives the more important physical and chemical characteristics of CNG vehicle fuel and describes the test methods for defining these characteristics. It establishes acceptable compositional limits for natural gas to be used in vehicles.

Propane can be stored as a liquid at pressures of approximately 1.4 MPa (200 psi) at normal ambient temperature; however, special equipment is needed to assure good pressure reduction and gasification. Specifications for propane as a motor fuel are given in ASTM D 1835.

The present supply of methane and/or propane is inadequate for large-scale automotive use. Additional methane could be made from coal or other non petroleum sources with new facilities. The ability to increase the domestic supply of propane is very limited. Imports would be necessary to increase the supply significantly.

In addition to those gaseous fuels mentioned above, there has been a recent interest in using mixtures of butane and propane for municipal fleets. Using these mixtures, levels of improved fuel economy were realized due to the contribution of butane (Reference 11).

5. Alcohols and Other Oxygenated Compounds

5.1 Background—Until the late 1970s, oxygenates were looked upon as potential alternatives or supplements to gasoline but were judged too expensive for extensive commercial use. With the escalation of crude oil prices in the 1970s and the concern about the security of foreign crude oil supply, interest in domestic, "renewable" alternatives such as alcohols increased. In addition, the growing production of unleaded gasoline coupled with the introduction of unleaded premium and the more severe legal restrictions on lead concentration in gasoline, made it difficult for some refineries to meet their octane requirements.

Use of oxygenates in fuels is also dependent on policies of importing and exporting nations. This includes such things as tax incentives, balance of payments, employment, availability of indigenous natural resources, etc. For example, in Brazil, where sugar cane is abundant, ethanol is widely used as a gasoline alternative (References 12, 13). As one of the first oxygenates for transportation fuel, ethanol synthesized from the fermentation of agricultural products was used before the turn of the century. Later, during World War I, both methanol and ethanol appeared as motor fuels. Germany, faced with a serious shortage of petroleum, used mixtures of alcohol and benzene with whatever gasoline was available. However, during World War II when Germany again faced a very severe shortage of petroleum crude, alcohols were only used by the civilian sector as the German military preferred synthetic fuels produced from coal using hydrogenation, Fischer-Tropsch synthesis, or coal carbonization and gassification (Reference 14). For many years, some refineries added alcohol to gasoline, principally methanol, isopropanol, and isobutanol in low percentages, as de-icer additives. It was not until the energy crisis of 1973–74 in the United States triggered a revived interest in substitute alcohols that once again fermentation ethanol increased in popularity. Primarily as the result of favorable state and federal tax exemptions, sales of gasohol (90% by volume gasoline, 10% by volume denatured ethanol) in the United States grew from about 1% of the gasoline market in 1981 to 7 percent in 1985; its market penetration has remained at about 7% through mid-1989 (References 15, 16). However, recent data as of 1998 (Reference 17) has shown the ethanol usage to have increased to 10.8%. Further, about 25% of the ethanol blends contain less than the 10 % by volume ethanol which expands the percentage of blends containing ethanol. It should be noted however that the EPACT of 1992 expanded the definition of gasohol effective January 1, 1993. Prior to EPACT, gasohol was defined as a blend of gasoline and at least 10% by volume of fuel alcohol. Under the expanded EPACT, three (3) types of gasohol were defined: [1] 10% gasohol, which corresponds to the definition before the Act; [2] 7.7 percent gasohol, which contains at least 7.7% alcohol but less than 10%; and [3] 5.7 percent gasohol which contains at least 5.7% alcohol but less than 7.7% (Reference 17).

TABLE 1—EPA WAIVERS IN EFFECT FOR NOT "SUBSTANTIALLY SIMILAR" UNLEADED GASOLINE BLENDS

Oxygenate	Principal Waiver Conditions[1]	Federal Register (FR) Notice of Waiver
1. Ethanol	10 volume % as gasohol	Waiver application April 6, 1979, FR Volume 44, page 20777. EPA did not grant or deny waiver request within 180 days of receipt.
	Allows blends less than 10 volume % ethanol	Interpretive ruling of April 5, 1982. FR Volume 47, No. 65, page 14596.
2. Methanol/Gasoline Grade t-Butyl Alcohol (GTBA)	Methanol/GTBA not to exceed one to one ratio; concentration of oxygen not to exceed 3.5 by weight %. Blend must meet ASTM D 439[2] specification limits.	November 16, 1981. FR Volume 46, No. 220, page 56361.
3. Ethanol/Methyl Isobutyl Ketone/C_5 + Alcohols	5 gal of ethanol denatured with methyl isobutyl ketone and 1/4 gal stabilizer blended with 45 gal of unleaded gasoline. The stabilizer consists of C_5, C_6, and C_8 alcohols and raffinates from coal liquefaction. Blend must meet ASTM D 439[2] specification limits.	May 24, 1982. FR Volume 47, No. 100, page 22404.
4. Methanol/C_2-C_4 Alcohols	A maximum of 3.7 weight % fuel oxygen with a maximum of 5 volume % methanol and a minimum of 2.5 volume % cosolvent alcohol(s) with a proprietary corrosion inhibitor. Cosolvent is any one or mixture of ethanol, propanols, or butanols. Blend must meet ASTM D 439[2] specification limits.	May 19, 1987. FR Volume 52, No. 96, page 18736.
5. Methanol/C_2-C_8 Alcohols	A maximum of 3.7 weight % fuel oxygen with a maximum of 5 volume % methanol and a minimum of 2.5 volume % cosolvent alcohol(s). Cosolvent is any one or mixture of C2 to C8 alcohols, subject to restrictions on the C5 to C8 alcohols content. Blend must meet specified ASTM D 439[2] and P-176[3] requirements.	October 28, 1988. FR Volume 53, No. 209, page 43768.
6. Methyl t-Butyl Ether	Allows up to 15 volume %. Blend must meet ASTM D 4814 specification limits.	September 1, 1988. FR Volume 53, No. 170, page 33846.

1. In unleaded gasoline. Refer to the Federal Register for other waiver conditions and legal requirements.
2. ASTM has replaced the D 439 gasoline Standard with ASTM D 4814, which covers both gasoline and gasoline-oxygenate blends.
3. ASTM Proposed Specification P-176 has been adopted as a standard and designated as ASTM D 4814.

Environmental considerations have led to many regulatory initiatives requiring increasing use of oxygenates. Thus, some areas within the United States adopted mandates to use oxygenates in gasoline in the wintertime as a strategy to reduce carbon monoxide exhaust emissions (References 18, 19). The Clean Air Act Amendments of 1990 extended this wintertime mandate, effective in 1992, to all geographical areas of the U.S. which fail to comply with federal standards for atmospheric carbon monoxide. Effective 1995, the Amendments also required oxygenates in gasoline year-round in areas having the highest exceedances of the federal ozone standards. In California, state agencies are assisting in the establishment of a market for methanol fuel, e.g., through a program, which is has been adding M85 (85% by volume methanol, 15% by volume gasoline) dispensers at a growing number of retail gasoline stations (Reference 20). However, this trend has reversed itself as no new M85 cars have been purchased in California in recent years. There have been, and continue to be, several fleet tests around the world to demonstrate advances in vehicle and engine technology that permit the use of alcohol fuels, especially methanol and more recently Ed85 (85% by volume denatured ethanol, 15% by volume gasoline). Some of this work has been done with modified CI engines, particularly in buses. However, most of the development work and fleet testing has been done with vehicles equipped with spark-ignition engines, and recent emphasis has been on vehicles capable of running on either gasoline or alcohol (M85 and/or Ed85) alone or in any combination (Reference 2). Such vehicles have been referred to as flexible fuel vehicles, variable fuel vehicles and fuel flexible vehicles, or FFVs or VFVs. The fuel flexibility of these vehicles permits travel beyond the range of available alcohol refueling sites.

Methanol and its mixtures with gasoline have more severe effects on some metals and nonmetals than gasoline alone. This can affect the durability of some fuel system components in vehicles as well as within the storage and distribution infrastructure. With this in mind, a standard set of gasoline-methanol blend recipes has been developed for the purpose of evaluating the durability of elastomer, plastic, and metal parts that may be exposed to gasoline-methanol fuel mixtures. These recipes use ASTM Reference Fuel "C" (50% by volume toluene, 50% by volume iso-octane) as the hydrocarbon component (see SAE Cooperative Research Report, "Gasoline/Methanol Mixtures for Materials Testing" and SAE J1681-Gasoline and Diesel Surrogates for Materials Testing). Although the recipes were developed specifically for evaluation involving gasoline-methanol mixtures such as M85, similar recipes could be used to evaluate the effects of other oxygenates.

In view of the progress toward the development of methanol-fueled engines, the EPA has promulgated their "Standards for Emissions From Methanol-Fueled Motor Vehicles and Motor Vehicle Engines" (Reference 21). ASTM has since published ASTM D 5797 – Standard Specification for Fuel Methanol M70 – M85 for Automotive Spark-Ignition Engines (1996). Additional information on M85 properties is available in SAE Cooperative Research Report: "A Discussion of M85 (85% Methanol) Fuel Specifications and Their Significance."

As a result of the recent increase in vehicles using Ed85, ASTM has also published ASTM D 5798 – Standard Specification for Fuel Ethanol Ed75 – Ed85 for Automotive Spark-Ignition Engines (1999).

5.2 Key Oxygenate Components—The most important oxygenates now used in various alternative fuel applications are methanol, ethanol, and methyl tertiary butyl ether (MTBE). As already noted both methanol and ethanol have been used as neat or near-neat fuels and as gasoline blending components. While higher alcohols can be used, only methanol and ethanol are readily produced in large quantities. Although almost all of the methanol manufactured in several countries now is made from natural gas, methanol can be synthesized from a variety of materials such as coal, municipal wastes, and biomass. Virtually all of the ethanol used for fuel purposes is derived from the direct fermentation of sugars, but it can be made from petroleum sources or by the fermentation of starches and cellulose after chemical or enzymatic pretreatment.

Compared to a market share of 7% for gasoline-ethanol blends since 1985, the market penetration by gasoline blends containing up to 5% methanol reached a peak of about 3% in the United States in 1985, and has since dropped to near zero because of market forces (Reference 15), and because none of the methanol waivers have been supplementally registered under Section 211 (b) of the Clean Air Act. Western Germany and other European countries similarly have seen a decline in the use of gasoline blends containing up to 3% by volume methanol (Reference 22). When methanol has been used as a gasoline blending component, higher alcohols (ethanol, isopropanol, and butanols) have been used as cosolvents. The use of cosolvents with methanol have been shown to improve water tolerance and materials compatibility, and to alter volatility effects (Reference 19). While methanol blending has declined, methanol continues to be an important alternative fuel because of increasing interest in its use as a neat fuel.

In the mid-1960s, the petroleum industry, in anticipation of reduced use of lead antiknocks, began research with oxygenated hydrocarbons as high-octane blending components. MTBE attracted the most attention, because of the phase stability of its blends, and because it can be manufactured from readily available raw materials, isobutene and methanol, at moderate reaction temperatures and pressures (References 24, 25). During the 1980s, MTBE became the fastest growing chemical commodity, and the use of MTBE in gasoline steadily increased in the United States, Europe, Japan, and Canada. In the United States, the market penetration of gasoline blends containing varied amounts (2 to 11% by volume) of MTBE grew from zero in 1981 to 10% in 1987 (Reference 12) and was still growing as of 1989 (Reference 26). Unleaded gasoline is now permitted to contain up to 15% by volume MTBE (see Table 1). However, there had been some recent concern as to MBTE affecting the quality of ground water.

The most recent entry to the field of commercial oxygenates (Reference 27), though not as a single component, is tertiary-amyl methyl ether (TAME). Thus, processes producing mixtures of TAME and, primarily, light hydrocarbons started up in West Germany in 1986, the U.K. in 1987, and France in 1988. MTBE is part of the mixture produced in the German plant (References 28, 29, 30). Although plans were previously reported to produce TAME at several locations in the U.S. (Reference 31), there are at least two TAME plants currently operating in the United States and gasoline surveys have shown TAME being used in numerous locations. There is also a growing interest in ethyl tertiary butyl ether (ETBE) (References 32, 33), tertiary hexyl methyl ether (THEME), and diisopropyl ether (DIPE) (Reference 34), but there is as yet no commercial source of these oxygenates. However, gasoline surveys have also shown DIPE is being used, but this is probably a by-product in manufacturing isopropyl alcohol.

5.3 Properties of Oxygenated Blending Components—Table 2 lists some of the properties of oxygenates that have been used or are being considered for use as components in gasoline-oxygenate blends (References 32, 35). The high octane quality of oxygenates is of particular importance. A common hydrocarbon used as an octane enhancer is toluene and therefore it is often used for comparison in assessing the value of oxygenates. The blending octane values of many oxygenates in unleaded gasoline are higher than that of toluene. It should be noted that blending octane values can vary with concentration and with gasoline base stock octane and composition. The values in Table 2 should be considered for relative comparisons only.

TABLE 2—PROPERTIES OF OXYGENATED COMPOUNDS FOR USE IN GASOLINE-OXYGENATE BLENDS

Property or Feature	Gasoline (Typical Properties)	Toluene	Methyl t-Butyl Ether	t-Amyl Methyl Ether	Ethyl t-Butyl Ether	Diiso-propyl Ether	t-Butyl Alcohol	Isoprop-anol	Ethanol	Methanol	Methanol With Cosolvent
Chemical formula	Mixed C_4 to C_{12} Hydrocarbons	C_7H_8	$CH_3OC_4H_9$	$CH_3OC_5H_1$ 1	$C_2H_5OC_4H$ 9	$C_3H_7OC_3H$ 7	$(CH_3)3CO$ H	$(CH_3)_2CHO$ H	CH_3CH_2OH	CH_3OH	50% Methanol 50% GTBA[(1)]
Molecular Weight	95-115	92	88	102	102	102	74	60	46	32	--
Oxygen, wt %	--	0	18.2	15.7	15.7	15.7	21.6	26.6	34.7	49.9	35
Specific Gravity 60 °F/60 °F	0.72-0.78	0.8692	0.7447	0.776	0.745	0.730	0.7892	0.7900	0.7939	0.7965	0.7889
BONV[(2)] in 87 (R + M)/2 UL gasoline											
RON	--	111	116	111	118	110	103	118	129	133	114
MON	--	95	103	98	102	97	91	98	102	105	96
(R + M)/2	--	103	110	105	110	103	97	108	115	119	105
Net Heat of Combustion BTU/Gal[(3)]	115 000	126 000	94 000	101 000	97 000	100 000	93 000	86 000	76 000	57 000	75 000
Latent Heat of Vaporization, BTU/Gal[(3)]	800	1130	860	900	830	900	1700	2100	2600	3300	2500
Stoichiometric A/F Ratio, Mass Air/Mass Fuel	14.6	13.5	11.7	12.1	12.1	12.1	11.1	10.4	9.0	6.4	8.8

1. Gasoline-grade t-Butyl Alcohol
2. BONV = Blending octane value = [ONB-ONG (1-X)]/X
3. BTU/Gal = 279 J/L

5.4 Gasoline-Oxygenate Blend Performance—Gasoline-oxygenate blends are being marketed for use in conventional SI engine-powered automobiles. Thermal efficiency can increase in cars with rich fuel/air mixture calibrations; however, fuel economy measured in miles per gallon generally decreases, approximately in proportion to the oxygen content of the blends. The improvements in thermal efficiency are of lesser magnitude than the reduced energy content of the blends.

Exhaust emissions effects of gasoline-oxygenate blends are small, and generally occur only in vehicles operating without oxygen sensor feedback to control fuel/air metering. Under these conditions, exhaust emissions could change to the same extent they would have changed using gasoline, if the fuel/air mixture were adjusted to an equivalently leaner mixture strength. Hydrocarbon and, more significantly, carbon monoxide emissions are reduced, particularly for pre-1981 cars, but the improvement is not enough to obviate the need for emission controls (Reference 36). NOx emissions are not much different with alcohol blends, being somewhat higher for cars set rich and somewhat lower for cars set lean. Aldehyde emissions increase slightly.

Adding lower molecular weight alcohols to gasoline increases its volatility. The amount of butane and sometimes other light hydrocarbons in the blend must be reduced to obtain the equivalent vapor pressure of an "all hydrocarbon" gasoline. With regard to evaporative emissions of gasoline containing oxygenates, the fuel volatility can be tailored to approximate the losses of typical straight hydrocarbon gasolines. However, the long-term effects of certain alcohols on the efficiency of evaporative emission control equipment, namely, a charcoal-filled canister, have not been quantified. The effect of gasoline-alcohol blends on canister performance is not well defined, but there are data to suggest that humidity and the type charcoal used may have more significant effects (Reference 37).

Driveability may be degraded depending on the oxygen content of the fuel, just as it would if gasoline alone were used with equivalently lean carburetion (References 38, 39). Driveability effects can be reduced by appropriate adjustments to fuel volatility (Reference 40).

Durability of fuel system components with gasoline-alcohol blends is dependent upon the alcohol used, its concentration, and the use of a corrosion inhibitor. Studies have shown generally acceptable materials compatibility with ethanol up to 10% by volume and methanol concentrations up to 5% by volume with appropriate cosolvents. Higher dosages have degraded certain plastics, elastomers, metals, and vehicle finishes (References 41, 42). In order to avoid corrosion problems, proper amounts of effective corrosion inhibitors must be used (Reference 43). There are pH requirements for both the finished blends and the component oxygenates. Engine wear studies with blends containing up to 10% by volume ethanol have not shown any unusual problems (Reference 44).

All low molecular weight alcohols have a strong affinity for water. If gasoline-alcohol blends are contaminated with sufficient quantities of water, serious product loss, fuel system materials compatibility problems, degradation of vehicle performance and environmental problems can result. The low molecular weight alcohols have limited solubility in gasoline compared to their solubility in water. Solubility of alcohols in gasoline decreases with decreasing temperature and generally increases with decreasing gasoline paraffin content (Reference 43). If a gasoline-alcohol blend is saturated with water, a reduction in ambient temperature may cause the alcohol and gasoline to separate into two layers. Water concentrations above the saturation limit will cause immediate separation. Gasoline-methanol blends are most prone to phase separation when contaminated with water. The same problem may occur with gasoline-ethanol blends. Distribution facilities (and vehicle fuel tanks) handling gasoline-alcohol blends must be kept as free of water as possible using good housekeeping practices. In contrast to the alcohols, MTBE is completely miscible with gasoline, even at very low temperatures, and is not susceptible to phase separation when its blends are contacted by water.

5.5 Neat Alcohol Fuel Performance—If neat or near-neat alcohol fuels are used in vehicles specifically designed for their use, potential advantages could outweigh disadvantages in certain situations. An example might be a large fleet, where both vehicles and fuel distribution facilities could be designed as a coordinated system, and where fuel production could be justified by the local supply pattern of raw materials and energy. In Brazil, 100% ethanol (Ed100) is used commercially in large volumes (Reference 13). Methanol has been evaluated at concentrations ranging from 85% by volume (M85) to 100% (M100) in various programs in the United States, Canada, Germany, New Zealand, and Sweden, and M85 commercialization is has been underway in California.

Volume-based fuel consumption is higher with neat or near-neat alcohol fuels than with gasolines, which is a direct result of the lower energy contents of the oxygenates (References 45, 46). Methanol, for instance, has about half the energy content per unit volume of gasoline, and ethanol about two-thirds. Nevertheless, both methanol and ethanol have relatively high octane values, (R + M)/2, of approximately 99 versus 87 for typical unleaded regular gasoline. This permits these alcohols to be used in spark-ignition engines with higher compression ratios to attain a higher thermal efficiency compared to gasoline. Alcohol fuels also allow an engine to operate on leaner fuel/air mixtures. Exhaust emissions of hydrocarbons (or unburned fuel) and of carbon monoxide is practically the same when methanol and gasoline are compared at the same relative mixture strength (equivalence ratio). Even with catalyst aftertreatment, aldehyde emissions are significantly higher with methanol. Emissions of nitrogen oxides are generally lower with methanol, especially at very lean mixtures where operation without misfire would not be practical with gasoline (References 47, 48). Starting methanol-fueled engines below 10 °C (50 °F) requires either a volatile auxiliary fuel or a volatile additive in the methanol as a starting aid, such as isopentane or dimethyl ether. Even with these aids, starting below −12 °C (10 °F) is difficult (References 39, 48). Up to 15% by volume unleaded gasoline is used in the case of M85, not only to improve starting, but also as a safety feature to improve the luminosity of burning methanol, which otherwise is difficult to see (Reference 49). Addition of gasoline to methanol also narrows the conditions required for flammability, e.g., within a fuel tank, and imparts taste and odor to discourage ingestion of the methanol, which is highly toxic. The addition of up to 15% by volume unleaded gasoline used for Ed85 follows the same rationale as was given for M85, improving cold starting and improving the luminosity of burning ethanol. Engine wear rates can be higher when neat alcohol fuels are used especially in cold climates. Special motor oil formulations are required to provide needed wear protection (Reference 50).

The small number of available methanol and ethanol refueling sites limits the range and, thus, the utility of dedicated methanol-fueled and ethanol-fueled vehicles. This led to the development of the spark-ignition FFVs capable of running on both M85 and gasoline or any M85-gasoline combination, or Ed85 and gasoline or any Ed85-gasoline combination. The engines of such vehicles are equipped with dielectric sensors or other such devices in the fuel system to detect the ratio of alcohol to gasoline so the fuel rate and ignition timing can be electronically adjusted for satisfactory engine operation (Reference 51). Although studies have been made, the overall impact of these vehicles on air quality, relative to gasoline-fueled vehicles, has not yet been conclusively determined (Reference 52).

5.6 Oxygenate Fuels for Diesel Engines—Although alcohols including methanol have inherently high autoignition temperatures and long ignition delay times and are not good diesel fuel substitutes for current conventional compression-ignition (CI) engines, techniques are being developed that permit the use of methanol fuel in modified CI engines. Two basic approaches currently receiving the greatest attention are the use of an ignition-improving additive at very high concentrations (e.g., up to 7.5% by volume) with minimal engine modification (Reference 53), and more extensive engine modification, including the use of glow plugs or spark-assistance for operation on M100, without added ignition improver (Reference 54). These approaches have been evaluated in commercial demonstration programs, including city transit bus and line haul trucking operations, in the United States, Canada, and other countries involving use of M100, M85, Ed95 and Ed85. However, the additive treatment approach does not offer an economic incentive for converting engines to operate on M100 (Reference 55). One engine reportedly ready for commercial production uses glow plugs for starting and warm-up to operate on either M85 or M100 (Reference 5). The engine, equipped with a catalytic converter, satisfied both Federal and California emissions standards. Other techniques for using methanol in Cl engines that have been investigated include: fumigation, or the carburetion of methanol into the Cl engine intake airstream (References 65, 66); the use of a dual injection system to deliver diesel fuel at low speeds and loads and predominantly methanol at higher speeds and loads; and the use of methanol emulsions in diesel fuel.

Ethanol has been evaluated in a bus demonstration program in France, but there is a much greater emphasis on methanol as a fuel for CI engines in most parts of the world (Reference 56).

In addition to M100 and Ed100 being evaluated as potential diesel fuels, other oxygenates have been tested in CI engines. Testing has been done to demonstrate that Dimethyl Ether (DME) performed satisfactorily in a variety of CI engines that had undergone modifications to the fuel delivery and injection systems to accommodate this gaseous fuel (References 57, 58, 59). Nearly soot-free combustion and efficiency near or equal to diesel fuel has been demonstrated in the laboratory. Because of this, the potential for manufacturing DME from natural gas on a commercial basis was explored (Reference 60). An effort was also initiated to investigate the potential for Diethyl Ether (DEE) for use as a transportation fuel (Reference 61). Although DEE has long been known as a cold starting aid, little was known as to its potential as either a blending component or as a neat fuel. DEE is a renewable pathway for oxygenating diesel fuel from the biomass ethanol process. Like with DME, engine modifications would be required prior to considering DEE as a replacement fuel. However, based upon preliminary engine testing, DEE is not as effective as DME in reducing particulate emissions when blended with diesel fuel.

There have been other oxygenates evaluated for use with diesel fuel that were designed to reduce exhaust emission from CI engines. Substantial reductions of particulate matter emission were demonstrated with using 10 to 30% by volume blends of Methylal which is also know as dimethoxymethane (Reference 62). Other investigators have found similar reductions in exhaust emission with using 1 to 5% by volume of different glycol ethers such as digylme, dimethyl carbonate, diethylene glycol dimethyl ether, etc. (References 63, 64).

Vegetable oils and their ester derivatives have been extensively evaluated as direct substitutes for diesel fuel. Problems with alternatives such as these include excessively high viscosity, a tendency to form coke and deposits, and the relatively high cost of the materials and processing (Reference 67). Additional discussion on vegetable oils and their esters is found under Biobased Fuels.

6. Wide-Boiling-Range Fuels—Wide-boiling-range fuels have been used or proposed as a way to reduce refinery process energy and cost and to increase the supply of petroleum fuels (Reference 68). Such products have much broader distillation limits than gasoline or diesel fuel, but have neither the octane quality to function properly in present spark-ignition engines or the cetane quality for proper operation in compression-ignition engines. The only fuel of this type used extensively in the past is was JP-4, described by Specification MIL-DTL-5624 (Turbine Fuel, Aviation, Grades JP-4, JP-5, and JP-5/JP-8 ST), or its civilian counterpart, Jet B, described in ASTM D 1655. However, DOD has since converted from JP-4 to JP-8 and no longer uses JP-4. JP-8 is described by Specification MIL-DTL-83133 (Turbine Fuels, Aviation, Kerosene Type, NATO F-34 (JP-8), NATO F-35, and JP-8+100). This in consonance with DOD's implementation of the One Fuel Forward or Single Fuel on the Battlefield policy which mandates the use of an aviation kerosene fuel (JP-8 or JP-5 which is described by MIL-DTL-5624) for supporting the Air Land Battle conflicts (Reference 69). JP-4 was originally developed as a maximum-volume fuel for military use under wartime conditions. Typically, Jet B is simply distilled from crude oil with a few of the major compositional changes required for gasoline. To produce Jet B in large quantities, some cracking of heavy crude fractions would be necessary, as is now done for gasoline and diesel fuel. The boiling range of Jet B covers the heavier part of motor gasoline and the lighter part of No. 1- and No. 2-Diesel fuels. Jet B and similar wide-boiling-range fuels have low octane number, perhaps 40 Motor Octane Number (MON) versus 80–90 MON for gasoline, and low cetane numbers, 20–30 compared to 40 min for diesel fuels. While used primarily in jet aircraft, Jet B and fuels of even broader boiling range have been considered for land-based vehicles powered by gas turbines or stratified-charge engines.

7. Hydrogen—Hydrogen has been studied as an alternative fuel largely because of its clean-burning characteristics and other possible performance advantages (References 70, 71, 72, 73, 74). The use of hydrogen would require revolutionary changes in fuel manufacturing, distribution, and handling systems. At present, application of hydrogen to vehicles as motor fuel is in the research stage, and problems in its use are not clearly defined. Safety and methods for storage of hydrogen fuel will require additional investigation. To be competitive and cost effective, key problems must be solved in engine combustion, fuel delivery, and practical storage.

Hydrogen has almost three times the heat content of gasoline by weight, but in liquid form has only one-quarter the heat content of gasoline by volume. Hydrogen can be handled as a compressed gas, as a cryogenic liquid, or as a chemically unstable hydride. A hydrogen-rich mixture can also be generated on board the vehicle. Although such systems are being promoted, none is now practical or economical for vehicle use. High cost storage problems and safety considerations represent substantial deterrents to the use of hydrogen as a vehicle fuel.

8. Fuel From Synthetic Crudes—Synthetic crudes can be prepared from coal, shale and tar sands, and heavy oil deposits. Liquid fuels similar to gasoline and diesel fuel can be refined from the crude by currently available processes. However, compared with petroleum, these synthetic crudes are of low quality and must be extensively upgraded before they can be refined into useful products. Characteristics of the synthetic crudes and the products made from them are highly dependent on how the crudes are manufactured and upgraded.

It should be noted however that during the Carter administration (1976-1980), there was a considerable effort on the part of DOD to develop capabilities for utilizing military fuels refined from synthetic crudes (syncrudes). This was in consonance with his Energy Plan announced in July 1979 which was designed to reduce our dependence on foreign imports through an unprecedented commitment of natural, economic, and human resources to a crash program of synthetic fuels production. As part of this initiative, the Synthetic Fuels Corporation was established to facilitate this initiative. These syncrudes were those produced from shale, coal liquefaction, and tar sands. The products refined from the shale were those that received the most attention and plans were subsequently made to have complete military installations converted to the synthetic fuels as a means to validate the acceptance of the synthetic fuels, both for aircraft and for ground vehicles. However, the production of large amounts of the shale syncrude never materialized due to political changes, loss of government subsidies, and the return to normal prices for a barrel of crude oil.

Large scale commercial production of synthetic crudes from the Athabasca Tar Sands in Northern Alberta Canada has been carried out since 1975. It should be noted however that crude oil from the Athabasca Tar Sands is technically not considered to be a syncrude, but instead is viewed as a bitumin. Current production is about 300 000 b/d and is being expanded over the next five years to about 650 000 b/d. Considerable amounts of these syncrudes are exported into the nearby northern areas of the United States where the low sulfur content, high distillate fuel yield, and freedom form any residual fractions are sought after desirable properties.

Along with very low sulfur content and high distillate fuel yield, synthetic crude for the Canadian Tar Sands has relatively low cetane number quality for the diesel fuel fractions (e.g., around 34 cetane number). Further upgrading or dilution with higher cetane number conventional crude are operational practices used by various refiners. However, significant quantities of the 34 cetane number diesel fractions are used directly by the Canadian Railways to power both their two stroke and four stroke CI engine systems.

Initially, these syncrudes were produced by various coking processes followed by hydrotreatment, but later production utilized hydrocracking technologies which increased crude yield and quality while avoiding the generating of high sulfur content coke for which there is no market.

9. Biobased Fuels—Biobased fuels are those, which are, derived from commercial or industrial products that utilize any biological products, renewable domestic agriculture (plant, animal and marine), or forestry materials. They are essentially produced in two principal ways: [1] production of alcohols through fermentation processes and, [2] use of vegetable oils, either raw, or more typically after esterification to improve their suitability as fuels (Reference 75). Under the production of alcohols, ethanol has been the principal focus. However, there has been some interest in converting ethanol with iso-butylene to ETBE. More recently, the P-Series Fuel became approved under EPACT. This fuel is a blend of butanes, pentanes, ethanol, and methyltetrahydrofuran.

With vegetable oils, the main focus of attention in Europe has been the use of Rape Seed Methyl Ester (RME). Esterified vegetable oils such as RME are collectively known as Fatty Acid Methyl Esters (FAME). In France, a four year testing program was successfully completed using 5% by volume of RME in diesel fuel (Reference 76). As a result, major countries within the European Union (EU) such as France, United Kingdom, Finland, and Poland are limiting use of RME to 5% by volume maximum in diesel fuel. In France, there is a requirement to advise purchasers/consumers if the fuel contains RME in excess of 5% by volume. Although there are no clear indications of economic or environmental benefits, field tests are continuing in other European countries such as Austria where they are testing the RME as a neat fuel (100% RME) and not as a blend (Reference 77). Some centrally fueled captive fleets (i.e., mostly city buses) in France are understood to be using as much as 30% by volume FAME under controlled conditions. Specifications or standards for biodiesel fuel have since been issued by several countries in Europe; namely, Germany's DIN 51606 as well as those of France, Austria, and Italy.

In the United States, the focus on vegetable oils has been with the soybean methyl ester (SME). Results thus far have been very favorable and a number of demonstration fleets are operating with 20% by volume SME in diesel fuel, or B20 (e.g., Florida Power and Light, Beltsville Agricultural Research Center in MD, Medford Township School System in NJ, etc.). As B20 has been approved under the EPACT and is part of the Biodiesel Fuel Use Credit Ruling, there is obviously a greater incentive for using this alternative fuel. A Department of Defense Memorandum was issued in December 1999 to provide guidance regarding potential use of B20 in DOD administrative vehicles as a means to meet alternative fueled vehicle requirements and gain EPACT credits (Reference 78). Currently, there have been approximately forty major commercial fleets that have started to purchase and use B20 in the last eighteen months to acquire EPACT credits as a result of the Biodiesel Fuel Use Credit Ruling.

ASTM has recently approved the D 6751 Standard Specification for Biodiesel Fuel (B100) Blend Stock for Distillate Fuels (1999). The specification defines Biodiesel as a fuel composed of mono-alkyl esters of long chain fatty acids derived from vegetable oils or animal fats, designated B100.

The Diesel Fuel Injection Equipment (FIE) Manufacturers have recently published a document titled "Diesel Fuel Injection Equipment Manufacturers Common Position Statement on Fatty Acid Methyl Ester Fuels as a Replacement or Extender for Diesel Fuel", to address the application concerns for using Biodiesel (Reference 79). It states that although there is much experience in Europe with 5% by volume blends, 20% by volume blends (i.e., B20) are acceptable for use provided both the biodiesel base stock meets the ASTM D 6751 standard specification and the resultant B20 blend meets all the ASTM D 975 specification limits for Grade 2-D diesel fuel and all the specification limits for Grade 1-D diesel fuel except for the 90% off distillation temperature and the viscosity at the point of use. For blends exceeding 20% by volume and up to 100% Biodiesel, the same stipulations mentioned above remain for fuel acceptability with the additional requirement that appropriately fitted FIE would be required (i.e., FIE with a biodiesel kit of parts if required by the manufacturer). It further explains that poor quality or aged Biodiesel that no longer meets the ASTM specification can cause deposits and corrosion which could reduce the service life of fuel injection equipment.

The U.S. Army issued a Purchase Description PD-B20-01 titled "B20, Biodiesel Fuel Blend" on September 8, 2000 to facilitate use of B20 by the DOD and the other Federal Agencies (Reference 80). The Purchase Description has been converted to a Commercial Item Description. The Commercial Item Description A-A-59693 titled "Diesel Fuel, Biodiesel Blend (B20)" was approved and issued on September 7, 2001 (Reference 97). The effort that led to the development of the Purchase Description and the more recent Commercial Item Description has been documented in a recent SAE paper (Reference 86).

In addition to SME and RME as possible alternative biofuels, other oilseed products that have been investigated include methyl esters of safflower oil, sunflower oil, palm oil, canola oil (which is a close cousin to rapeseed oil), and hydrogenated soy ethyl ester (HySEE). Animal products such as esterified beef tallow have also been evaluated as potential biofuels. Additionally, there has been some interest in the United States and Europe in utilizing waste or used cooking oil that has been esterified. In Austria, disposal of used cooking oils and cooking fats presented environmental problems which were resolved with their conversion to Used Oil Methyl Esters (UOME). They have reported successful operation with the use of UOME as an alternative fuel (Reference 77). Recent testing in this country by the Department of Energy involved over-the-road heavy-duty truck operation on a biodiesel fuel formulated from 50% by volume "yellow grease" (used french fry oil) and 50% by volume diesel fuel. Results obtained have shown great promise, and the effort is continuing (Reference 81).

10. Synthetic Hydrocarbon Fuels—Synthetic hydrocarbon fuels are those fuels which are synthesized from low molecular weight gaseous or liquid hydrocarbons. The Fischer Tropsch Process (F-T) for synthesizing hydrocarbons from carbon monoxide and hydrogen was discovered in 1923. The first commercial large scale production of synthetic hydrocarbon fuels occurred in Germany prior to and during World War II as a result of their shortage of crude oil (Reference 14). Eighty-five percent of their aviation gasoline was produced by hydrogenation of coal and coal tars. They also used the F-T to produce their gasoline and diesel fuel for ground vehicles and equipment.

In South Africa, the SASOL Process has been used commercially since 1955 to produce synthetic gasoline and diesel fuel (Reference 82). The F-T process has recently taken on renewed interest in light of the proposed emission regulations designed to reduce sulfur levels in both gasoline and diesel fuels by 2004 and beyond. The F-T chemistry initially involves converting natural gas (or coal as in the case of the SASOL Process) to a synthesis or producer gas which is then reassembled into liquid fuel fractions (or oil) and water by iron or cobalt catalysts. The feed stock could be anything which can be made into the producer or synthesis gas such as biomass, recycled rubber, plastics, etc. This conversion has been referred to as Gas-to-Liquid (GTL) technology and is receiving considerable interest as all fuel products produced from the GTL technology are environmentally clean and cold be an answer to the federal demands for stricter vehicle emissions. It was recently reported (Reference 84) that there are at least some twelve GTL projects in operations or in various stages of development at this time.

A new application of the GTL technology designed to produce high quality fuels has been the Shell Middle Distillate Synthesis Process (SMDS). The products produced, primarily kerosene and middle distillates, are completely paraffinic and free of sulfur and nitrogen. It should be noted that since these GTL fuels have no aromatics, certain problems could be created with fuel-wetted elastomer components that depend upon aromatic compounds to generate minimal swelling for positive sealing.

Synthetic GTL diesel fuel has been tested in Class 8 trucks and buses with no detectable performance difference when compared to conventional diesel fuel. Substitution of the GTL diesel fuel resulted in significant reduction in exhaust emissions. Additionally, GTL diesel fuels have been used as commercial-scale blend stocks to upgrade conventional diesel fuel for meeting California diesel fuel emission standards. Additional engine testing of GTL synthetic diesel fuels in a variety of engines has been reported (Reference 60i) which all show significant reductions in emission levels. More recently, GTL fuels have been identified as potential fuels for the 21st Century Truck program (Reference 83).

The appeal of GTL technology in producing synthetic fuels takes on even greater importance as there exists the future possibility of tapping the limitless deposits of natural gas found in hydrates on the ocean floor. This combined with scenarios for potential off-shore GTL production applications (Reference 87) make the production of environmentally clean synthetic fuels clearly a worthwhile challenge and opportunity.

Additionally, a process has been investigated in New Zealand for producing gasoline from methanol. This provides yet another alternative to GTL technology for producing synthetic fuels.

11. Water-Fuel Emulsions—The emulsifying of water with petroleum fuels has been investigated by many over the past several decades as a means to improve the combustion of heavier fuels. During the 1970s and into the mid 1980s, the United States Army was involved in an extensive effort to develop a "Fire Resistant Fuel" as one of the solutions to the threat of fire that all armored vehicles were continually exposed to. This effort led to the development of a new fuel formulation consisting of 10% by volume distilled water, 6% by volume surfactant, and the remaining 84% by volume being diesel fuel. This produced a "Water-in-Fuel Microemulsion" that took on the appearance of neat diesel fuel; that is, it was not milky white in appearance as would typically be the case for a macroemulsion (Reference 88). The resultant microemulsion took on essentially all the physical and chemical characteristics of the neat diesel fuel and was extremely effective in eliminating the pool burning that typically follows the initial mist fireball that occurs when vehicles are impacted by projectiles. Further, this microemulsion fuel did not require any engine modifications for its use and could be used interchangeably with conventional diesel fuels in all CI engines. However, the required purity of the water (the hardness had to be approximately 50 ppm or less) needed to insure adequate stability of the microemulsion became a logistical problem, and the Army was unable to field this new fuel (Reference 89).

Three different water-fuel emulsions have since surfaced and have been undergoing extensive field testing and evaluation. Product A is a water and petroleum blend typically containing approximately 20 to 30% by volume water, 70 to 80% by volume petroleum products (e.g., naphtha, gasoline, diesel fuel, or fuel oil), and approximately 0.5% by volume of a proprietary surfactant and additive package (Reference 90). Tests results with Product A have reportedly shown reductions in CO and NOx emissions when used in spark-ignition engines. This water-fuel emulsion is being tested in several locations not only in transportation fuels, but also in the heavier fuels used in power utility operations. More recently, water-fuel emulsions have been shown as a means to reduce the emissions of diesel fueled engines for compliance with the planned implementation of EPA's Tier 2 emission standards. Product B, the second water-fuel emulsion to have evolved has been shown to reduce both NOx emissions and particulates (Reference 91). Product B is a white, water-in-fuel emulsion that maintains the chemical and physical characteristics of diesel fuel. It contains approximately 10 to 20% by volume water (depending upon the customer's needs), 80 to 90% by volume diesel fuel, and 4.7 to 7.6 liters (1.25 to 2 gallons) of surfactant and additives per 378.5 liters (100 gallons) of emulsified fuel. Product B is currently being field tested in several locations in the United States and in Europe. The third water-fuel emulsion, Product C is being promoted in Europe and is currently undergoing field evaluation (Reference 92). Expectations are that Product C will be tested in 1,000 city buses and 2 000 trash-hauling trucks by next year. Product C is 13% by volume water (municipal source), 2 to 3% by volume surfactant and additives, and the remaining 85% by volume being diesel fuel refined to the European Standard CEN EN590 Testing has shown that using Product C reportedly also reduces NOx emissions and particulates

However, use of these water-fuel emulsions is not without some penalty. They cannot be used in spark-ignition engines without some internal engine modifications and should not be viewed as a "drop-in" replacement fuel. Because of the surfactant qualities of the emulsifier systems, the water-fuel emulsion tends to clean up the interior surfaces of fuel systems which increases the level of contamination brought to the fuel filters. As water has no heat content, increased fuel is needed to compensate for the reduced power due to the lower heating value of the water-fuel emulsion. This obviously will increase overall fuel consumption. The presence of intentionally-added water in fuel can cause operability problems in areas where cold temperatures persist. The production of the water-fuel emulsion itself must be essentially at or near the point of use since these alternative fuels cannot be pipelined. As such, mixing devices must be made available to combine the water and the emulsifier-additive packages with the appropriate fuel. Once prepared, the question of the stability of the water-fuel emulsion continues to be raised.

12. Other Possible Alternatives—Other materials such as ammonia, acetylene, powdered coal, and hydrazine have been suggested as possible alternative automotive fuels (Reference 10), but their wide-scale use is unlikely. Butanol has also been proposed as an alternative fuel for spark-ignition engines (Reference 93), and wood flash-pyrolysis oils have been investigated for use in CI engines (Reference 94).

Another alternative is solar fuel that derives its energy from the sun using photovoltaic cells that convert the solar energy into electrical energy. Although the use of solar power alone to operate a vehicle is a far term goal for the automotive industry requiring considerable research, efforts have been underway to develop that capability. One such approach is a solar-hydrogen-powered car, which is being pursued by scientists at the National Renewable Energy Laboratory in Golden CO. They have developed a one-step device that uses solar power to convert water into a hydrogen fuel. Although this technology has been known for years, commercial development remains unrealistic.

13. Alternative Fuel Utilization—DOE's Energy Information Administration (EIA) compiles data on the annual estimated consumption of alternative fuels in the United States. It also provides the estimated numbers of alternative fueled vehicles that are in use as well as those planned to be manufactured (Reference 95).

EIA's estimated consumption of Alternative Fuels and Oxygenates in the United States for 1998 gives values in terms of "thousand gasoline-equivalent gallons", and these are then compared to the estimated consumption for traditional gasoline and diesel fuels. For the consumption of Fuels and Oxygenates for 1998, the following thousand gasoline-equivalent gallon values were given: LPG, 914 221.7 thousand liters (241 583 thousand gallons); CNG, 277 203.5 thousand liters (73 251 thousand gallons); LNG, 20 219.5 thousand liters (5 343 thousand gallons); M85, 4 586.6 thousand liters (1 212 thousand gallons); M100, 1 699.2 thousand liters (449 thousand gallons); Ed85, 6 535.5 thousand liters (1 727 thousand gallons); Ed95, 223.3 thousand liters (59 thousand gallons); electricity, 4 548.7 thousand liters (1 202 thousand gallons); MTBE, 11 033 495.2 thousand liters (2 915 600 thousand gallons); and ethanol in gasohol, 3 466 415.7 thousand liters (916 000 thousand gallons). The total for Alternative Fuels and Oxygenates is 15 729 148.8 thousand liters (4 156 426 thousand gallons) which can be compared to the total for gasoline being 464 897 053.9 thousand liters (122 849 000 thousand gallons), and the total for diesel fuel being 127 399 707.6 thousand liters (33 665 360 thousand gallons).

For the numbers of AFVs, EIA separates the AFVs by fuel type and lists these as LPG, CNG, LNG, M85, M100, Ed85, Ed95, and electricity. The listings of onroad AFVs currently in use are grouped in terms of those being used by Federal agencies, by State agencies, by fuel providers, and by buses operated by school, transit, and intercity organizations. For 1998, the total numbers by specific fuel type were: LPG, 21 699 or 31.65%; CNG, 33 746 or 49.22%; LNG, 637 or 0.93%; M85, 3.357 or 4.90%; M100, 17 or 0.03%, Ed85, 8 057 or 11.75%; Ed95, 13 or 0.02%; and electricity, 1 026 or 1.50%. The totals for all were 68 557.

EIA's estimation for numbers of AFVs to be in use by 2000 and the average annual growth rate percentage by fuel types were: LPG, 270 000 or 2.5%; CNG, 101 991 or 20.3%; LNG, 1 682 or 44.2%; M85, 18 725 or 18.4%; M100, 200 or -8.4%; Ed85, 30 017 or 90.6%; Ed95, 14 or -11.7%; and electricity, 7 590 or 21.4%. The minus percentages reflect a negative growth.

In addition to the EIA information, there is further recognition by EPA as to anticipated use of alternative fuels. This is contained in their Code of Federal Regulations (CFR) Title 40, Volume 11, Part 79 – Registration of Fuels and Fuel Additives (Reference 96). Under Subpart F – Testing Requirements of Registration, Section 79.55 provides Base Fuel Specifications and includes Base Fuel Properties for Methanol, Ethanol, Methane, and Propane as well as for Gasoline and Diesel Fuel.

***14. Notes*—SAE J301—Effective Dates of New or Revised Technical Reports**

The final approval date for Fuels and Lubricants technical reports is shown following the J-report number. This approval date is the date of final approval by the Fuels and Lubricants Division. It is effective immediately subsequent to divisional approval for newly issued Standards, Recommended Practices, and Information Reports, and also for revised Information Reports and the SAE J1146 Recommended Practice. In the case of revised or cancelled Standards or Recommended Practices (used to define product quality), an 18-month optional grace period exists before they become fully effective.

RECOMMENDED PRACTICE FOR COMPRESSED NATURAL GAS VEHICLE FUEL—SAE J1616 FEB1994SAE Recommended Practice

Report of the SAE Fuels and Lubricants Technical Committee 7—Fuels, approved February 1994. Rationale statement available.

Foreword—This document has been changed to comply with the SAE Technical Standards Board format. Definitions have changed to Section 3. All other section numbers have changed accordingly.

1. Scope—Compressed Natural Gas (CNG) is a practical automotive fuel, with advantages and disadvantages when compared to gasoline. It has a good octane quality, is clean burning, easy to meter, and generally produces lower vehicle exhaust emissions. CNG is used to fuel internal combustion engines. Natural gas is normally compressed form 20 690 to 24 820 kPa (3000 to 3600 psig) to increase its energy density thereby reducing its on-board vehicle storage volume for a given range and payload.

The properties of natural gas are influenced by (1) the processing of natural gas by the production and transmission companies and (2) the regional gas supply, storage, and demand balancing done by distribution companies often in concert with pipeline companies to maintain uninterrupted service throughout the year, e.g., peakshaving with propane-air (see U.S. Bureau of Mines Publication 503).

Information on the properties of distribution system natural gas and its variability has been included in Figure 1 and can be found in GRI-92/0123. The analysis in this reference summarizes the expected composition of natural gas in 26 cities. Composition can vary hourly under certain operating conditions in certain areas of the country. Thus the data should generally be considered representative for the areas mentioned with due consideration for local variation.

Natural gas is comprised chiefly of methane (generally 88 to 96 mole percent) with the balance being a decreasing proportion of non-methane alkanes (i.e., ethane, propane, butanes, etc.).

Other components found in natural gas are nitrogen (N_2), carbon dioxide (CO_2), water, oxygen, and trace amounts of lubricating oil (from compressors) and sulfur found as hydrogen sulfide (H_2S) and other sulfur compounds. Before entering the transmission system, it is processed to meet limits on hydrogen sulfide, water, condensibles of heavier hydrocarbons, inert gases such as carbon dioxide and nitrogen, and energy content. Mercaptan odorants (e.g., tertiary butyl mercaptan) are added by local distribution companies (LDC's) for safety reasons to detect the presence of natural gas which otherwise would be odorless.

Water content and other corrosion precursors, heavier hydrocarbons which may condense within the fuel container, particulate matter, oil and energy content need to be controlled in order to minimize corrosion and provide satisfactory low-temperature vehicle operation, performance, and emissions levels.

The provisions contained in this SAE Recommended Practice are intended to protect the interior surfaces of the fuel container and other vehicle fuel system components such as fuel injector and exhaust catalyst elements from the onset of corrosion, poisoning, the deposition of liquids or large dust particles, or the formation of water, ice particles, frost, or hydrates. The provisions contained in this document are not intended to address the composition of natural gas as delivered to a fueling station, but rather at the outlet of the fueling station as delivered into the containers on the vehicle. Limits on gas composition constituents currently not included in this document may be added when data are available to substantiate them.

1.1 Purpose—This document presents the more important physical and chemical characteristics of compressed natural gas vehicle fuel and describes pertinent test methods for defining or evaluating these properties.

In order for compressed Natural Gas Vehicles (NGVs) to effectively provide satisfactory and safe operation for users, there is a need to address specific issues relative to the use of natural gas as a vehicle fuel. The two primary areas relate to (1) compressed storage of natural gas and (2) vehicle fuel system and engine performance issues. These provisions have been derived through a joint effort of the SAE TC-7 Natural Gas Vehicle Task Force and the Technology Committee of the Natural Gas Vehicle Coalition.

NOTE—This document is intended as a guide and is subject to change to keep pace with experience and technical advances. The following are separate documents that are not part of the document, but are added as an Informative Appendix (Appendix A).

Background Statement—Summarizes the development of the maximum water content provision for SAE J1616.

Excerpts from ANSI AGA/NGV2—Basic Requirements for Compressed Natural Gas Vehicle Fuel Containers Bibliography of SAE Publications and Other Publications.

Rationale Document for SAE J1616.

2. References

2.1 Applicable Publications—The following publications form a part of this specification to the extent specified herein. The latest issue of SAE publications shall apply.

2.1.1 SAE Publications—Available from SAE, 400 Commonwealth Drive, Warrendale, PA 15096-0001.

SAE Paper 902069—Ambient Temperature and Driving Cycle Effects on CNG Motor Vehicle Emissions, Gabelle, P., Crews, W., Perry, N., Lenning, J., Knapp, K. T., Ray, W.D., Snow, R.

SAE Paper 920593—The Impact of Natural Gas Fuel Composition on Fuel Metering and Engine Operational Characteristics, King, S.R.

2.1.2 ANSI Publication—Available from ANSI, 11 West 42nd Street, New York, NY 10036-8002.

ANSI AGA/NGV2, 1992—Basic Requirements for Compressed Natural Gas Vehicle (NGV) Fuel Containers

2.1.3 ASHRAE Publication—Available from ASHRAE, 1791 Tullie Circle NE, Atlanta, GA 30329.

ASHRAE Handbook

2.1.4 ASTM Publications—Available from ASTM, 100 Barr Harbor Drive, West Conshohocken, PA 19428-2959.

ASTM D 1142-90—Test Method for Water Vapor Content of Gaseous Fuels by Measurement of Dew Point Temperature

ASTM D 1945-91—Test Method for Analysis of Natural Gas by Gas Chromatography

ASTM D 3588-91—Standard Method for Calculating Calorific Value and Specific Gravity "Relative Density" of Gaseous Fuels

ASTM D 4084-88—Test Method for Analysis of H_2S in Gaseous Fuels (Lead Acetate Reaction Method)

2.1.5 Administration Publication—Available from National Climatic Data Center, Federal Building, Asheville, NC 28001.

Climatography of the U.S. No. 20, Climatic Summaries for Selected Sites, 1951–80

Comparative Climatic Data for the United States through 1991, U.S. Dept. of Commerce's National Oceanic and Atmospheric Administration

2.1.6 GRI Publications—Available from Gas Research Institute, 8600 West Byr Mawr Avenue, Chicago, IL 60631.

GRI-91/1011,92/0123—Variability of Natural Gas Composition in Select Major Metropolitan Areas of the United States, Final Report, March 1992, Liss, W.E. and Thrasher, W.R.

GRI-92/0150—Effect of Gas Composition on Octane Number of Natural Gas Fuels, Kubesh, J.

Gas Engineers Handbook, Industrial Press Inc., New York, 1965

2.1.7 NFPA Publication—Available from National Fire Protection Agency, 1 Batterymarch Park, P.O. Box 9101, Quincy, MA 02269-9101.

NFPA 52 1992 Edition—Compressed Natural Gas (CNG) Vehicular Fuel Systems

2.1.8 U.S. Bureau Of Mines Publication—Available from U.S. Bureau of Mines, Department of the Interior, 1849 C Street NW, Washington, DC 20250.

U.S. Bureau of Mines Publication 503, Copyright 1952

2.2 Related Publications—The following publications are provided for information purposes only and are not a required part of this document.

2.2.1 GRI Publication—Available from Gas Research Institute, 8600 West Byr Mawr Avenue, Chicago, IL 60631.

GRI 92/0158, 1992—Proceedings of the Gas Research Institute Natural Gas Vehicle Fuel Composition Workshop Held February 13, 1992, Rosemont, IL

2.2.2 ISO Publications—Available from ANSI, 11 West 42nd Street, New York, NY 10036-8002.

ISO 6326-2-1981—Gas analysis—Determination of sulfur compounds in natural gas—Part 2: Gas chromatographic method using and electrochemical detector for the determination of odoriferous sulfur compounds

ISO 6570-3-1989—Natural gas—Determination of potential hydrocarbon liquid content—Part 3, Volumetric method

ISO 6977-1983—Natural gas—Detection of water and methanol content, gas chromatograph method

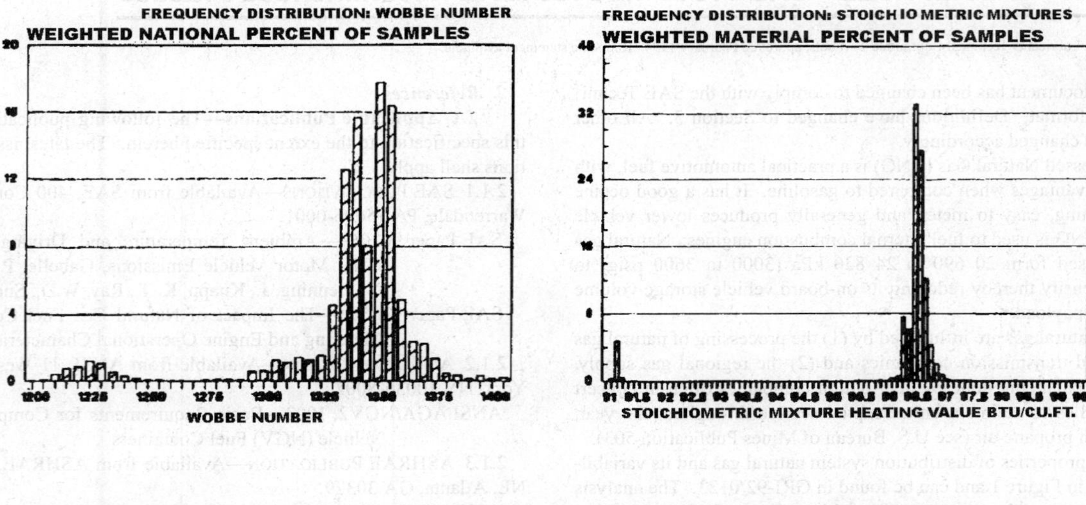

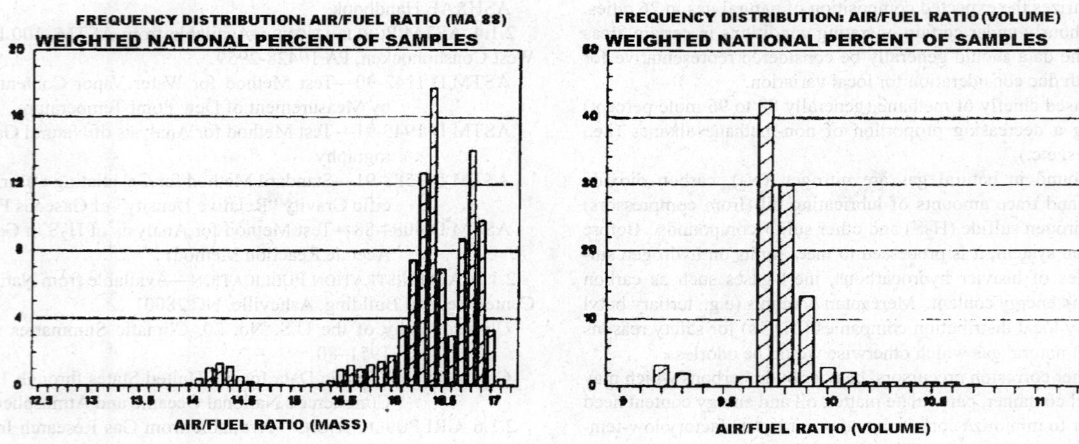

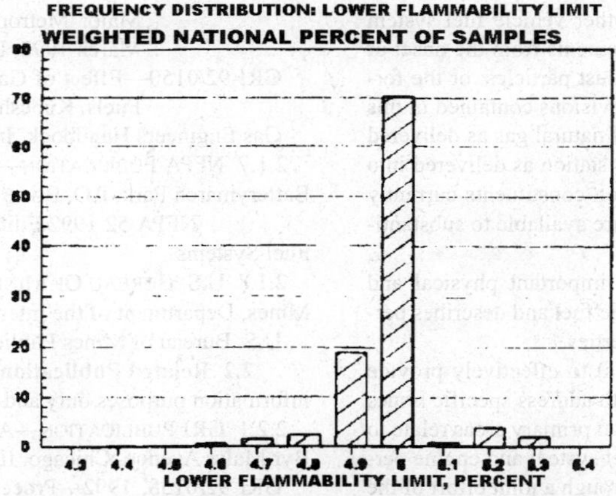

FIGURE 1—NATIONAL WEIGHTED DISTRIBUTIONS

3. *Definitions*

3.1 Dew Point Temperature—The temperature, referenced to a specific pressure, at which water vapor or other vapor phase components begin to condense.

3.2 Pressure Water Dew Point (At Container Pressure)—The water dew point temperature of the gas at the maximum anticipated pressure in the fuel storage container(s) of the CNG vehicular fuel system (usually measured in the fueling station storage container(s) prior to pressure reduction). When presenting or referencing dew point, the value shall be given in terms of the container pressure; e.g., –20 °C, (–4 °F) dew point at 24 820 kPa (3600 psig).

3.3 Pressure Hydrocarbon Dew Point (At Container Pressure)—The hydrocarbon dew point temperature of the gas at the maximum anticipated container(s) pressure of the CNG vehicular fuel system (usually measured in the fueling station storage container(s) prior to pressure reduction). When presenting or referencing dew point, the value shall be given in terms of the container pressure; e.g. –20 °C (–4 °F) dew point at 24 820 kPa (3600 psig).

3.4 Micrometre—A metric measure with a value of 10^{-6} m or 0.000001 m (also referred to as "micron"). The ANSI spelling of "micrometre" for dimension and "micrometer" for the measuring tool is used in this document.

3.5 (PPM)—Represents parts per million and can be given on a volume or mass basis. The abbreviation shall be ppm (v/v) for volume, or m/m for mass: e.g., 1.0 ppm (v/v), which corresponds to 1.0 m^3 (CO_2 or other limited constituent) per million (1 000 000) m^3 of natural gas at standard conditions of pressure and temperature. There are numerous "standard conditions" in use in the gas industry. For purposes of this document, the values being adopted by ISO of 101.325 kPa (14.7 psig) and 288.15 K (15 °C or 59 °F) are used.

3.6 Specific Gravity—Also known as relative density, is the ratio of the density of natural gas (kg/m^3) to the density of air measured at standard conditions of pressure and temperature.

3.7 Wobbe Index (WI)—Also known as Wobbe Number (WN), is a measure of fuel energy flow rate through a fixed orifice under given inlet conditions.

4. Properties Related to Containers and Vehicle Fuel System Corrosion—Natural gas for vehicle fuel use is typically stored in a high-density gaseous state at CNG fueling stations at peak tank pressures of 24 820 to 34 480 kPa (3600 to 5000 psig) and on board vehicles at peak tank pressures of 20 690 to 24 820 kPa (3000 to 3600 psig) in cylinders made of metal (e.g., steel or aluminum), metal liners with resin-reinforced filament winding, or non-metallic liners with resin-reinforced filament winding. It is essential that all safety factors must provide adequate safety margin for rupture pressure as well as resistance to corrosion, fatigue, fire, vibration, and mechanical damage. Cylinder failures can be caused by corrosion or corrosion-related damage, i.e., stress corrosion cracking (essentially hydrogen embrittlement) or corrosion fatigue.

Specific fuel components can impact cylinder integrity. The most critical potential issue is crack growth due to corrosion fatigue. This process occurs due to the combined action of corrosion agents in natural gas—hydrogen sulfide, carbon dioxide, water (or water vapor)—and the pressure cycling associated with periodically expending and replenishing the fuel storage cylinder. Complementary discussion of issues related to compressed gas storage is available in Appendix A.

4.1 Pressure Water Dew Point Temperature—The pressure water dew point temperature of the fuel should be compatible with the specific geographical location in which the vehicle will operate and should be set such that condensation of water will not occur in the storage cylinder at the maximum operating container pressure. The local dew point temperature of the fuel should be defined as 5.6 °C (10 °F) below the monthly lowest dry-bulb temperature as found in U.S. Dept. of Commerce's National Oceanic and Atmospheric Administration Publication: "Comparative Climatic Data for the United States through 1991," at the maximum operating container pressure. Data for specific states/cities can be found in the Department's "Climatography of the U.S. No. 20: Climatic Summaries for Selected Sites, 1951–80." The margin of 5.6 °C (10 °F) is intended to provide some allowance for expansion cooling as gas flows throughout the fuel system components. Expansion cooling will generally lead to greater temperature decreases than 5.6 °C (10 °F). Hence, freezing in the fuel system may occur if the fuel gas is not extremely dry. It should be noted that current hydromatic devices have been found to be inherently inaccurate below 1.6×10^5 kg/m^3 (1 lb/mmscf). Future engineering development programs are expected to better define the appropriate specification in this regard.

The fuel provider or station operator should determine the most appropriate method to maintain the pressure water dew point limit. Future changes to NFPA-52 will address specific safety requirements.

Pressure water dew point is determined by ASTM D 1142-90.

4.2 Hydrogen Sulfide Concentration—Given that the corrosive environment is controlled via the limited water concentration per 3.1, no limitations are required on the concentration of hydrogen sulfide for this purpose. However, the total content of sulfur compounds, including odorants, should be limited to 1.0 grain per 2.83 m^3 (100 ft^3) [8 to 30 ppm mass] to avoid excessive exhaust catalyst poisoning.

Hydrogen sulfide concentration is determined by ASTM D 4084-88.

4.3 Carbon Dioxide Concentration—Given that the corrosive environment is controlled via the limited water concentration per 3.1, no limitations are required on the concentration of carbon dioxide (CO_2) for this purpose. However, a limit of 3.0% CO_2 by volume is recommended to help maintain stoichiometry.

Carbon dioxide concentration is determined by ASTM D 1945-91.

4.4 Methanol Concentration—No methanol shall be added to natural gas at the CNG fueling station. Methanol can cause corrosion of natural gas cylinders and deterioration of fuel system components. Methanol is not needed if the pressure water dew point temperature of the stored gas is controlled to the recommended limits.

There is no applicable test method for determining methanol concentration at this time.

4.5 Oxygen Concentration—Given that the corrosive environment is controlled via the limited water concentration per 3.1, no limitations are required on the concentration of oxygen for the control of corrosion. At no time shall the oxygen level produce a mixture within the flammability limits of the fuel. Flammability limits at ambient conditions are readily known and published in documents such as the Gas Engineers Handbook. Information about flammability limits at the temperature and pressure conditions to which the onboard cylinders or ground storage containers are subjected have not been documented. Current auto industry experience indicates closed-loop engine controls can be used to maintain stoichiometry using pipeline quality gas.

Oxygen concentration is determined by ASTM D 1945–91. Flammability limits can be calculated using U.S. Bureau of Mines Publication 503.

4.6 Particulate and Foreign Material—Particulate concentration should be minimized to avoid contamination, clogging, and erosion of fuel system components. The fuel should be processed with a filter rated at 5 μm (micron) nominal (i.e., 98% efficiency) particle size. CNG fuel delivered to the vehicle should have particulate matter content equal to or less than 5 μm in size.

There is no applicable test method for determining particulate concentration at present.

4.7 Oil Content—Lubricating oils are often present in natural gas at trace levels due to carryover from pipeline compressors, or on-site fueling station compressors. Excessively high levels of lubricating oil entrained or absorbed in natural gas can condense and may create vehicle operational problems (e.g., liquids in the fuel pressure regulator). Additional data are required to determine acceptable lubricating oil levels as well as standardized test procedures for quantifying lubricating oil content. However, it must be understood that levels adversely affecting NGV performance are unacceptable by definition. Lubricated compressor oil levels should be monitored, and coalescing filters may be installed downstream of the compressor discharge to control oil.

4.8 Pressure Hydrocarbon Dew Point Temperature—Some locally distributed natural gases may contain mixtures of propane and air used to meet peak demand requirements. Propane therefore is the predominant condensable hydrocarbon of concern. Propane has a comparably low vapor pressure and if present in significant quantities will form a liquid phase at elevated pressures and low temperatures. Fuel variability due to revaporization of this liquid condensate at reduced tank pressures can lead to reduced vehicle performance. To minimize these occurrences, the composition of natural gas should be such that the original gaseous storage volume will form less than 1% of a liquid condensate at the lowest ambient temperatures and gas storage pressures between 5517 to 8275 kPa (800 to 1200 psig) at which maximum condensation occurs, depending on gas composition.

Figure 2 shows the maximum allowable concentration of propane in mole percent that corresponds to a 1% liquid condensation volume for various low ambient temperatures and gas storage pressure conditions. The amount of propane shall be compatible with the specific geographical region or temperatures in which the vehicle will operate and shall be set such that less than 1% hydrocarbon condensate will form at the dry-bulb temperatures as found in U. S. Department of Commerce Publications: "Comparative Climatic Data for the United States Through 1991." Data for specific states/cities can be found in the Department's "Climatography of the U.S. No. 20: Climatic Summaries for Selected Sites, 1951–80."

Propane concentration is determined by ASTM D 1945–91.

4.9 Natural Gas Odorant—Natural gas introduced into any CNG fueling station or vehicle shall have a distinctive odor potent enough for its presence to be detected down to a concentration in air of not over 1/5 of the lower limit of flammability. This is approximately 1.0% gas in air by volume.

5. Vehicle Fuel System and Engine Performance—Some chemical and physical properties not currently limited by this document are important considerations in vehicle fuel system, and engine performance. Theoretical and laboratory results cannot fully define all pertinent fuel properties that impact engine operation characteristics. A complete list of fuel properties requires a more substantial level of field experience. Currently, there is insufficient field data on NGV's to specify limits on all properties. However, laboratory results do indicate how certain parameters impact engine operational characteristics and future fuel composition limits are anticipated. An overview of the characteristics of natural gas as an engine fuel is provided in SAE Paper 902069.

5.1 Engine Performance—SAE Paper 920593 describes in detail the causes and effects of varying composition on fuel metering and engine operational characteristics.

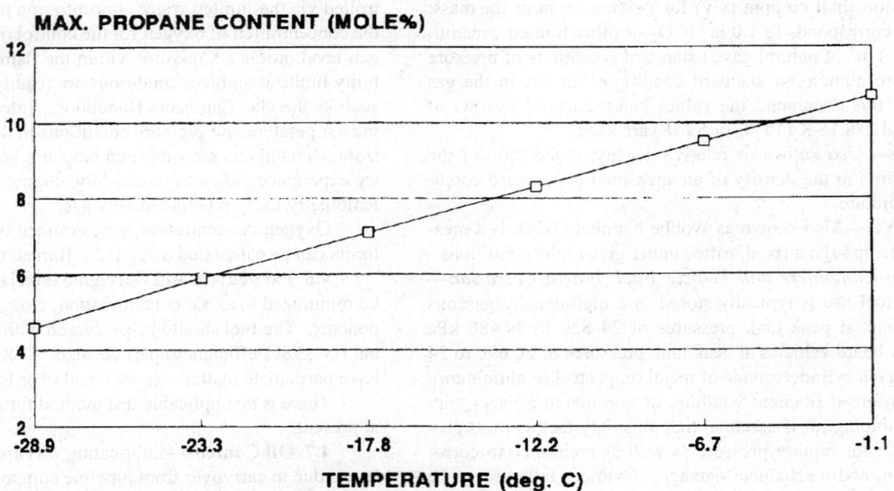

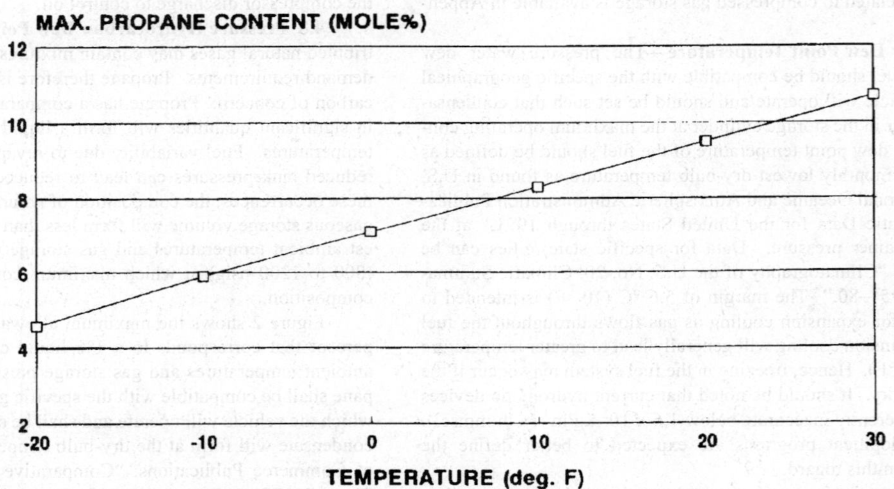

FIGURE 2—MAXIMUM PROPANE CONTENT (MOLE % PROPANE IN GAS FOR MAX. 1% HC CONDENSATION)

5.1.1 WOBBE INDEX—Natural gas can be characterized by Wobbe Index (WI). The Wobbe Index is a measure of the fuel energy flow rate through a fixed orifice under given inlet conditions. Mathematically, the Wobbe Index is expressed as shown in Equation 1:

$$\mathrm{WI} = \frac{\text{(dry, higher heating value)}}{\text{(specific gravity)}^{1/2}} \qquad \text{(Eq. 1)}$$

Dry denotes essentially no water vapor in the gas fuel. A change in Wobbe Index may affect the power output and performance of the engine. Since most present natural gas metering systems are based on orifices, variations in Wobbe Index of the gas will produce similar variations in the air-fuel ratio. Variability in this parameter most significantly impacts engines that are not equipped with closed-loop controls.

In recommending a Wobbe Index range, it is important to consider the practicality of supplying gas meeting a narrow criteria. As documented by Liss and Thrasher in GRI-91/1011, 92/0123, major gas pipelines already maintain reasonably tight control over Wobbe Index of delivered gas. Figure 1 shows the Wobbe Index distribution for a national sample. As the figure shows, there are essentially two distributions: one between 1200 and 1250 and the other between 1300 and 1420. Alterations or further tightening of these ranges for NGV use would not be practical, given foreseen NGV fuel demand.

At this time, a Wobbe Index range of 48.5 to 52.9 MJ/m^3 (1300 to 1420 BTU/ft^3) is recommended; however, a Wobbe Index range of 44.7 to 46.6 MJ/m^3 (1200 to 1250 BTU/ft^3) has been found to be acceptable for use on current equipment in high altitude areas. The recommended range, typical of most natural gas, would allow maximum variation from nominal air-fuel ratio of about ±3.7%, which is comparable to the range in variation in gasoline density, and should not present significant control problems. The engine control systems for NGV's are presently under development. It is not well understood whether Wobbe Index adequately characterizes these control systems. Flow through a Pintle type injector at sonic flow regimes is an example. Hence, the Wobbe Index limits may need to be reconsidered in the near future.

The Wobbe Index of natural gas can be determined through the measurement of heating value and specific gravity (i.e., relative density) by ASTM D 3588–91. Wobbe Index is then calculated using Equation 1.

5.1.2 KNOCK RATING—The resistance of a fuel to autoignition (sometimes referred to as detonation or combustion knock) is a fundamental fuel characteristic. No recognized test method presently exists for determination of the Motor Octane Number (MON) of natural gas. A methodology has been developed by Southwest Research Institute (SAE Paper 920593 and GRI 92/0150) which shows a close correlation between hydrogen - carbon ratio and MON antiknock performance. The results of these analyses suggest that the MON of natural gas ranges from 115 to 124.

5.2 Driveability—The Pressure Water Dew Point criterion as specified is expected to be adequately rigorous to eliminate operational problems that the presence of condensed water can cause. Use of natural gas with high water content can result in the formation of water, ice particles, frost, or hydrates at low ambient temperatures. If permitted to enter the vehicle fuel system, this may interfere with consistently smooth natural gas flow, and has been known to result in driveability problems due to clogging or freeze up of gas lines, fittings, valves, regulators, fuel injectors, and the like.

APPENDIX A

A.1 Informative Background Statement—Initially, the NGV Coalition's Fuel Cylinder Task Group had recommended in ANSI AGA/NGV2 a water vapor criteria of –45.6 °C (–50 °F) or lower pressure water dew point. The Task Group had agreed that the coverage in the proposed NGV2 standard is predicated entirely on absense of liquid water, i.e., a pressure water dew point of –45.6 °C (–50 °F) or lower. The Task Group's recommendation was based on existing industry design experience for compressed gas cylinders, which is mandatory by DOT cylinder regulations and exemptions. In addition, the Task Group's consideration involved review of pertinent compressed gas cylinder corrosion research performed by Southwest Research Institute (U.S.) and Powertech Labs (Canada). This review of corrosion research also involved reports from the National Association of Corrosion Engineers (NACE).

Over the course of several meetings, the Gas Composition Subcommittee and the Fuel Cylinder Task Group arrived at an acceptable compromise to the –45.6 °C (–50 °F) criterion, which then appeared in proposed NGV2 and the Society of Automotive Engineer's proposed Recommended Practice for Compressed Natural Gas Vehicle Fuel Composition, SAE J1616. It was acknowledged that the present specification of 5.6 °C (10 °F) below the 99% winter design temperature was more realistic and feasible as a criterion than a –45.6 °C (–50 °F) water pressure dew point specification. With this compromise, the Task Group's goal of establishing a suitable internal environment for NGV2-certified containers was realized.

Subsequently, the Coalition's Gas Composition Subcommittee considered local seasonal or monthly adjustment of the pressure water dew point criterion, and agreed that the ASHRAE 99% winter design temperature reference should be replaced with the lowest dry-bulb temperatures found in the U. S. National Oceanic and Atmospheric Administration Publication: "Comparative Climatic Data for the United States Through 1991."

The ANSI AGA/NGV2 Standard is included in NFPA 52-1992, under vehicle fuel container coverage. The NGV2 Standard has been approved by ANSI to ensure approval of its proposed reference in NFPA 52-1992. In addition, SAE J1616 is included in NFPA 52-1992 as an informational, non-mandatory text "Note,", under "gas quality" coverage. The "gas quality" coverage in NFPA 52-1988 was retained for the 1992 edition.

Several vehicle OEM's are unanimous in pressing for at least as tight or a tighter limit in the context of the gas composition Recommended Practice, SAE J1616, to protect NGV fuel system components, particularly fuel injectors, from the internal formation of condensed water, ice, or frost.

A.2 Excerpts from ANSI AGA/NGV2 Basic Requirements for Compressed Natural Gas Vehicle Fuel Containers "Rationale Document" Pertinent to SAE J1616—The dew point limit is intended to relieve NGV operators in warm climates of the extreme water vapor limits needed in colder areas. The ASHRAE Handbook is an authoritative publication, readily available, upon which to base a location-specific standard. The 99.0% winter design temperature is exceeded during 99.0% of the total hours of the months of December, January, and February. Natural gas storage containers have considerable thermal mass, and the lowest container temperature cannot be below atmospheric ambient unless gas has been withdrawn. The margin of 5.6 °C (10 °F) is intended to allow for expansion cooling of the container.

It is intended that the pressure used for the dew point determination be the "service pressure," as defined in NGV2 as follows:

"Service pressure. The settled pressure post adjustment per ASHRAE at a uniform gas temperature of 21 °C (70 °F) and full gas content. It is the pressure for which the equipment has been constructed, under normal conditions. Also referred to as nominal pressure or working pressure."

In addition, methanol injection at the fuel station is prohibited because of the corrosive effects of methanol and the extreme difficulty of monitoring the methanol content in the compressed gas. The methanol delivered in the pipeline is not considered sufficient to harm the cylinders, but much greater amounts might be added at the fueling compressor. Methanol injection will not be necessary to prevent hydrate formation if the dew point is controlled.

The water content of natural gas stored in NGV2 containers must be controlled to prevent the formation of liquid water in the container. The proposed NGV2 standard permits significant economic advantages when compared to the existing DOT specifications and exemptions for gas cylinders, but these advantages, and their regulatory acceptance, depend upon an interior service environment free of liquid water.

The Task Group has editorially revised the gas composition coverage to correlate with the proposed SAE Recommended Practice on Natural Gas Vehicle Fuel. In the absence of an ASTM natural gas fuel specification, the SAE Recommended Practice, once approved by SAE probably will be referenced by the three major automakers in their NGV owner manuals. These will probably require compliance to ensure the continued validity of warranties for the NGV's which they will produce and sell.

The NGV2 Standard required only periodic visual external inspection as assurance that the container condition has not deteriorated at an unsafe level. The hydrostatic expansion retest is excluded from NGV2 because neither general corrosion nor undetected overheating which would cause a reduction in the pressure retention capability of the container are expected. These two sources of strength loss are the reasons for the inclusion of the hydrostatic expansion retest for DOT cylinders. The presence of liquid water in the container raises the issue of general corrosion and therefore coverage tolerant of the presence of water would require the addition of hydrostatic expansion retest to NGV2.

The NGV2 Standard requires no internal visual inspection during the 15-year service life. This is somewhat more ambitious than the 10-year retest/reinspection interval for DOT-3AA steel cylinders used in dry gas service. Twenty-two years experience with the 10-year retest interval in dry gas service has shown that interior deterioration is not a problem with the current DOT restriction of –46.7 °C (–52 °F) dew point. This experience forms the basis for the NGV2 reinspection criterion.

The NGV2 standard requires only 5000 fatigue cycles to the maximum allowable working pressure plus 13 000 cycles to service pressure. The total of 18 000 cycles is the estimate of worst case service fatigue cycles and contains no additional safety factor. Present DOT specification cylinders have cycle lives on the order of 50 000 at maximum allowable operating pressure and 500 000 at service pressure. The two most common composite compressed natural gas cylinders, E8725 and E8965, have demonstrated cycle lives in excess of 20 000 and 50 000 at these same pressures. The presence of liquid water in the NGV2 containers raises the issue of corrosion fatigue and will require the application of fatigue safety factors of between four and twenty. Increasing the fatigue requirements to allow for liquid water corrosion fatigue will drive up the cost of all except plain metal containers, limiting the weight benefits and feasibility of the lighter composite designs.

The NGV2 standard reduces the safety factor for metal and hoop wrapped metal containers from 2.5:1 to 2.25:1. This 10% reduction corresponds to the safety factor of DOT 3AA "+" marked cylinders and DOT-3HT high tensile steel aircraft cylinders. Although DOT specifications do not require that only dry gas be used in "+" marked 2.25:1 safety factor cylinders, the reinspection criteria requires removal from 2.25 safety factor service if local or pitting corrosion are present. Water accumulation in compressed natural gas containers may be expected to cause such corrosion.

The Task Group is aware of no definitive study of the effects of methanol injection on local corrosion, general corrosion or corrosion fatigue of compressed natural gas containers. Industry experience with methanol fuel systems give cause for concern regarding methanol attack in both metallic and nonmetallic compressed natural gas containers. Existing NGV fueling technology requires the use of methanol injection to achieve reliable mechanical operation in the presence of liquid water. Methanol is not needed if the pressure dew point of the stored gas is controlled.

The final issue concerns the potential for use of higher strength, more efficient steels in compressed natural gas cylinders. Today, there are DOT industrial gas cylinders in service with minimum tensile strengths 50% greater than the minimum tensile strength of DOT-3AA cylinders. These more efficient designs cannot be contemplated as long as the gas contained may be wet.

The conclusion of the Task Group is that substantial cost and weight penalties will result from modifications to the NGV2 standard unless the gas to be stored is dry. In addition, the corrosion damage mechanisms are not well defined, and a large investment in both basic and specific research would be necessary to establish adjustment factors between design qualification tests performed with noncorrosive fluids and actual service with a corrosive wet gas. The variability of natural gas quality, both geographically and seasonally, further complicates any such research effort.

Gas quality assurance is not easy from either a Quality Assurance (QA) system standpoint or a technical analysis standpoint. Neither the individual fuel station operator nor the gas distribution company supplying the fuel station can by themselves maintain a complete QA program. Therefore, such a QA program must be the joint responsibility of both parties. The QA program could condition the gas either before or after compression, but monitoring of the quality should be done after compression to detect contamination by defective cooling systems on the compressors. In all cases, the responsibility for maintaining the dispensed gas at the required dew point should rest with the party responsible for final sale of the gas dispensed into a container covered by the NGV2 standard.

As a result of the reference change from ASHRAE winter design temperature to the monthly lowest dry-bulb temperature reference, the ANSI AGA/NGV2 standard will need to be revised to be consistent with SAE J1616.

A.3 Bibliography—The following publications are provided for information purposes only and are not referenced in this document.

A.3.1 SAE Publications—Available from SAE, 400 Commonwealth Drive, Warrendale, PA 15096-0001.

SAE J1297—Alternative Automotive Fuel

SAE Paper 811386—"Keeping the Vehicle Moving - A Practical Study of Identical Vehicles Using Alternative Fuels," Freshwater, M.A., Turner, D., Milkins, E.E.

SAE Paper 831066—"NGFVs - How Large is the Potential Market?," Sprafka, Robert J., Tison, Raymond R., Vitous, William J.

SAE Paper 831071—"The Practical and Economic Considerations of Converting HIghway Vehicles to Use Natural Gas as a Fuel," Bechtold, Richard L., Timbario, Thomas J., Tison, Raymond R., Sprafka, Robert J.

SAE Paper 831076—"A Team Effort in Compressed Natural Gas Fleet Conversion," Hutton, Jerrold L., Shaffer, Paul

SAE Paper 831078—"Safety Issues Surrounding the Use and Operation of Compressed Natural Gas Vehicles," Tison, Raymond R., Sprafka, Robert J., Bechtold, Richard L., Timbario, Thomas J.

SAE Paper 852277—"The Development of Ford's Natural Gas Powered Ranger," Adams, Tim G.

SAE Paper 861578—"Interchangeability of Gaseous Fuels - Importance of the Wobbe Index," Klimstra, J.

SAE Paper 872165—"Catalytic Converters for Natural Gas Fueled Engines - A Measurement and Control Problem," Klimstra, J.

SAE Paper 881656—"Methanol vs. Natural Gas Vehicles - A Comparison of Resource Supply, Performance, Emissions, Fuel Storage, Safety, Costs, and Transitions," Deluchi, Mark A., Johnston, Robert A., Sperling, Daniel.

SAE Paper 892067—"Fuel Choice for Dual-Fuel Vehicles - An Analysis of the Canadian Natural Gas Vehicle Survey," Green, David, L.

SAE Paper 892133—"Natural Gas Vehicles - A Review of the State of the Art," Weaver, C.S.

SAE Paper 892136—"New Zealand Experience with Natural Gas Fueling of Heavy Transport Engines," Raine R.R., McFeaters, J.S., Elder, S.T., Stephenson, J.

SAE Paper 892141—"Carburetors for Gaseous Fuels - On Air-to-Fuel Ratio, Homogeneity, and Flow Restriction," Klimstra, J.

SAE Paper 901498—"The Dynamixer - A Natural Gas Carburetor System for Lean Burn Vehicle Engines," Klimstra, J., August 1990.

SAE Paper 902068—"Low Emissions Engines for Heavy-Duty Natural Gas-Powered Urban Vehicles - Development Experience," Hundleby, G.E., and Thomas, J.R.

SAE Paper 902137—"The Chemical Origin of Fuel Octane Sensitivity," Leppard, W.R.

SAE Paper 912364—"Natural Gas as a Stationary Engine and Vehicular Fuel," Liss, W.E. and Thrasher, W.R.

SAE P-129—Compressed Natural Gas Conference Proceedings

A.3.2 Other Publications

"Alternative Fuels for Reciprocating Internal Combustion Engines," Reprinted for "Alternative Hydrocarbon Fuels: Combustion and Chemical Kinetics," Volume 62, 1978 of Progress in Astronautics and Aeronautics, Callopoulos, N.E.

"Effects of Natural Gas Contaminants on Stress Corrosion of Compressed Natural Gas Fuel Storage Cylinders," Paper #98, The NACE Annual Conference and Corrosion Show, Lyle, F.E. Jr., March 1991

"Control of Corrosion Fatigue in NGV Fuel Cylinders," Hudak, S., GRI Report-89/0239.

"Variable Gas Composition Experiments," Presentation to Gas Research Institute Gas Engine Technical Advisory Committee, Rosemont, IL, Ryan, T.W., May 1991, "Effects of Gas Composition on Engine Performance and Emissions," Ryan, T.W., and Callahan, T., GRI Report - 92/0054.

"Evaluation of Antiknocking Property of Gaseous Fuels by Means of Methane Number and its Practical Application to Gas Engines," ASME Paper 72-DPG-4, Leiker, M. et al.

"Combustion and Chemical Kinetics," Edited by Craig T. Bowman and Jorgen Birkeland, Vol. 62, 1978, of Progress in Astronautics and Aeronautics.

"1991 GRI Baseline Projection of U.S. Energy Supply and Demand to 2010," Gas Research Institute, April, 1991.

"Analysis of Natural Gas, 1917–1988," U.S. Bureau of Mines, Amarillo, TX, 1989.

"Engineering Data Book, Volume I and II," Tenth Edition, Gas Processors Suppliers Association, 1987.

"Natural Gas Quality in Canada," Report for British Columbia Research, Clapham Common Services, IBI Group, 1985.

"Equilibrium Moisture Content of Natural Gases," Bukacek, R.F., Institute of Gas Technology Research Bulletin 8, Chicago, IL 1955.

"LNG and Propane-Air Peakshaving Storage and Deliverability," Issue Brief 1990–9, American Gas Association, July, 1990.

"Gas Quality Specifications for Compressed Natural Gas Vehicle Fuel," Gas Quality, Elsevier Science Publishers, Wiley, F.V., Amsterdam, 1986.

"Exhaust Gas Oxygen Sensor Characteristics on Natural Gas Fuel-Draft," GRI Report-91/0148, Snyder, C., and King, S.R., May 1991.

"Design and Development of the Waukesha Lean Burn Control System," ASME Internal Combustion Engine Division, Publication Vol. 9, pp 97–104, Moss, D.W. and Wang, D.Y., 1989.

"A Procedure for Calculating Fuel Gas Blend Knock Rating for Large-Bore Gas Engines and Predicting Engine Operation," ASME Paper 85-DPG-5, Schaub, F.S. and Hubbard, R.L., October 1985.

"Internal Combustion Engine Fundamentals," McGraw-Hill, New York, Heywood, J.B., 1988.

STOICHIOMETRIC AIR-FUEL RATIOS OF AUTOMOTIVE FUELS—SAE J1829 OCT2002

SAE Recommended Practice

Report of the SAE Fuels and Lubricants Division approved June 1987. Completely revised by the SAE Fuels and Lubricants Technical Committee 7—Fuels May 1992 and reaffirmed December 1997 and October 2002.

1. Scope—The mass of air required to burn a unit mass of fuel with no excess of oxygen or fuel left over is known as the stoichiometric air-fuel ratio. This ratio varies appreciably over the wide range of fuels—gasolines, diesel fuels, and alternative fuels—that might be considered for use in automotive engines.

Although performance of engines operating on different fuels may be compared at the same air-fuel ratio or same fuel-air ratio, it is more appropriate to compare operation at the same equivalence ratio, for which a knowledge of stoichiometric air-fuel ratio is a prerequisite.

This SAE Recommended Practice summarizes the computation of stoichiometric air-fuel ratios from a knowledge of a composition of air and the elemental composition of the fuel without a need for any information on the molecular weight of the fuel.

2. References

2.1 Applicable Publications—The following publications form a part of this specification to the extent specified herein.

N.E. Holden and R.L. Martin, "Pure and Applied Chemistry," 56, 663 (1984).

U.S. Standard Atmosphere, 1976, National Oceanic and Atmospheric Administration; National Aeronautics and Space Administration; United States Air Force, Washington, DC, October 1976.

W.R. Pierson, Chemtech, May 1976, p. 332.

L.M. Horsley, "Azeotropic Data III," Advances in Chemistry Series 116, American Chemical Society, Washington.

O.T. Zimmerman and I. Lavine, "Industrial Research Services Psychrometric Tables and Charts," 1945.

A. Wexler, "Humidity and Moisture—Measurement and Control in Science and Industry," Vol. 1, p. 97, Reinhold Publishing Corp., New York, NY, 1965.

3. Equivalence Ratios—When the actual air-fuel ratio supplied to the engine is higher than the stoichiometric air-fuel ratio, there is excess air and the engine is operating "lean." Conversely, when the air-fuel ratio is lower than stoichiometric, fuel combustion will be incomplete and engine operation is "rich."

The ratio of the actual fuel-air ratio to the stoichiometric fuel-air ratio is the fuel-air equivalence ratio. (See Equation 1.)

$$\frac{(\text{Fuel/Air})_{\text{actual}}}{(\text{Fuel/Air})_{\text{stoichiometric}}} = \text{fuel-air equivalence ratio} = (\text{phi} = \Phi) \quad \text{(Eq. 1)}$$

The inverse of the fuel-air ratio is the air-fuel ratio. The ratio of the actual air-fuel ratio to the stoichiometric air-fuel ratio is the air-fuel equivalence ratio. (See Equation 2.)

$$\frac{(\text{Air/Fuel})_{\text{actual}}}{(\text{Air/Fuel})_{\text{stoichiometric}}} = \text{air-fuel equivalence ratio} = \text{lambda} = \lambda \quad \text{(Eq. 2)}$$

When the term "equivalence ratio" is used, it is necessary to indicate whether the fuel-air equivalence ratio (Equation 1) or the air-fuel equivalence ratio (Equation 2) is intended. The air-fuel equivalence ratio has frequently been labeled as "excess air ratio."

4. Atomic Weights and Composition of Fuels and Air—The following atomic weights of elements present in many fuels are:

Carbon—12.011
Hydrogen—1.00794 ± 0.00007
Oxygen—15.9994 ± 0.0003
Nitrogen—14.0067
Sulfur—32.066 ± 0.006

These atomic weights have been adopted by the Commission on Atomic Weights and Isotropic Abundances of the International Union of Pure and Applied Chemistry.[1]

The composition of air is shown in Table 1.

In the computations as follows, the atomic weights and mass of air containing one mass unit of oxygen are rounded to five significant digits. Measured values of actual air-fuel ratios and elemental analyses are seldom more precise than four significant digits.

TABLE 1—MOLECULAR WEIGHTS AND ASSUMED FRACTIONAL VOLUME—COMPOSITION OF SEA LEVEL DRY AIR

Gas Species	Fractional Volume(1)	Molecular Weight kg/mole	Relative Mass(2)
N_2	0.78084	28.0134	21.873983
O_2	0.209476	31.9988	6.702981
Ar	0.00934	39.948	0.373114
CO_2	0.000314	44.0098	0.013819
Ne	0.00001818	20.179	0.000365
He	0.00000524	4.002602	0.000021
Kr	0.00000114	83.80	0.000092
Xe	0.000000087	131.29	0.000011
CH_4	0.000002	16.04276	0.000032
H_2	0.0000005	2.01588	0.000001
			28.964419

Thus, $\frac{\text{Mass of Air}}{\text{Mass of Oxygen}} = \frac{28.964419}{6.702981} = 4.3211$ (3)

1. Data from Table 3 of Reference 2 in Section 2.
2. Relative mass = fractional volume × molecular weight.
3. Calculated form 1983 IUPAC Atomic Weights, Reference 1 in Section 2.

5. Calculation of Stoichiometric Air-Fuel Ratios of Hydrocarbons—The stoichiometric oxidation of pure compounds such as methane and ethane can be expressed by balanced chemical equations, (see Equations 3 and 4):

$$\text{Methane: } CH_4 + 2O_2 \rightarrow CO_2 + 2H_2O \quad \text{(Eq. 3)}$$

$$\text{Ethane: } C_2H_6 + 3.5O_2 \rightarrow 2CO_2 + 3H_2O \quad \text{(Eq. 4)}$$

Thus, the stoichiometric oxygen/methane mass ratio is shown in Equation 5:

$$(\text{oxygen/methane})_{\text{stoich}} = \frac{15.999 \times 2 \times 2}{(12.011 \times 1) + (1.0079 \times 4)} = \frac{63.996}{16.043} = 3.9891 \quad \text{(Eq. 5)}$$

Similarly, the stoichiometric oxygen/ethane mass ratio is shown in Equation 6:

$$(\text{oxygen/ethane})_{\text{stoich}} = \frac{15.999 \times 3.5 \times 2}{(12.011 \times 2) + (1.0079 \times 6)} = \frac{111.99}{30.069} = 3.7245 \quad \text{(Eq. 6)}$$

A general equation applicable to all hydrocarbons and mixtures thereof can be expressed in terms of the amount of hydrogen per carbon atom, that is, the atomic ratio of hydrogen to carbon (H/C). Thus (see Equation 7),

$$(\text{oxygen/hydrocarbon})_{\text{stoich}} = \frac{15.999\ [2 + 0.5\ \text{H/C}]}{[(12.011 \times 1) + (1.0079\ \text{H/C})]} \quad \text{(Eq. 7)}$$

The bracketed term in the numerator, namely, [2 + 0.5 H/C], indicates that 2 atoms of oxygen are needed to oxidize each atom of carbon to carbon dioxide plus another 0.5 atom of oxygen is needed to oxidize each atom of hydrogen to water.

For illustration, Equation 5 can then be rewritten as shown in Equation 8:

$$(\text{oxygen/methane})_{\text{stoich}} = \frac{15.999[2 + (0.5 \times 4)]}{[(12.011 \times 1) + (1.0079 \times 4)]} = 3.9891 \quad \text{(Eq. 8)}$$

1. See Reference 1 in Section 2.

and Equation 6 can be rewritten as shown in Equation 9:

$$(\text{oxygen/ethane})_{\text{stoich}} = \frac{15.999[2+(0.5\times 3)]}{[(12.011\times 1)+(1.0079\times 3)]} = 3.7245 \quad \text{(Eq. 9)}$$

The stoichiometric oxygen-hydrocarbon ratio can readily be converted to stoichiometric air-fuel ratio by multiplying by the mass of air containing unit mass of oxygen, (see Equation 10):

$$(\text{oxygen/hydrocarbon})_{\text{stoich}} \times (\text{mass air/mass oxygen}) = (\text{air/hydrocarbon})_{\text{stoich}} = (\text{Air/Fuel})_{\text{stocih}} \quad \text{(Eq. 10)}$$

For automotive engine applications, the analysis of dry air can be regarded as essentially constant throughout the lower atmosphere. As shown in Table 1, the mass of air per unit mass of oxygen is shown in Equation 11:

$$\text{mass air/mass oxygen} = 28.964/6.7030 = 4.3211 \quad \text{(Eq. 11)}$$

Combining Equations 7, 10 and 11 leads to the general relationship as shown in Equation 12:

$$(\text{Air/Fuel})_{\text{stoich}} = (A/F)_s = 4.3211 \times \frac{15.999\ [2+(0.5)\ (H/C)]}{(12.011\times 1)+(1.0079\ H/C)} \quad \text{(Eq. 12)}$$

which applies to all hydrocarbons and mixtures thereof.

6. Calculation of Stoichiometric Air-Fuel Ratios of Oxygenates—Equation 12 can be modified to include not only all hydrocarbons but also all oxygenated compounds and blends with hydrocarbons. This modification includes the addition of quantities expressed in terms of the oxygen-to-carbon atomic ratio, O/C, to both the numerator and denominator of Equation 12. Thus, the general equation now becomes Equation 13:

$$(A/F)_s = 4.3211 \times \frac{15.999\ [2+(0.5)\ (H/C)-(O/C)]}{[(12.011\times 1)+(1.0079)\ (H/C)+(15.999)\ (O/C)]} \quad \text{(Eq. 13)}$$

The quantity added to the numerator reflects that the total oxygen required is decreased by the oxygen-to-carbon atomic ratio since oxygen is present in the fuel and need not be supplied by the air.

The stoichiometric air-fuel ratio of a mixture can be determined either by calculation from the known composition or by the chemical analysis of the mixture.

If the H/C, O/C and mass of each component in a mixture are known, the $(A/F)_s$ of each component can be calculated and summed for the amount of each component present. Thus (see Equation 14):

$$\Sigma(A/F)_2 = \frac{[\text{mass } F_1 \times (A/F_1)_s] + [\text{mass } F_2 \times (A/F_2)_s] + \dots \text{mass } F_n \times (A/F_n)_s]}{[\text{mass } F_1 + \text{mass } F_2 + \dots F_n]} \quad \text{(Eq. 14)}$$

In many cases, however, the composition of the fuel may be unknown. The H/C and O/C ratios of the mixture can then be determined by a precision combustion analysis. In such an analysis, the mass % hydrogen and mass % carbon are usually calculated from the weights of water and carbon dioxide produced from combustion and the mass % of oxygen may be determined by difference, (see Equation 15):

$$\text{mass \% oxygen} = 100\% - (\text{mass \% carbon} + \text{mass \% hydrogen}) \quad \text{(Eq. 15)}$$

The atomic ratios of hydrogen to carbon (H/C) and of oxygen to carbon (O/C) can be calculated from mass percentages as follows in Equations 16 and 17:

$$\frac{H}{C} = \left(\frac{\text{mass \% hydrogen}}{1.0079}\right) / \left(\frac{\text{mass \% carbon}}{12.011}\right) = \frac{\%H}{\%C} \times \frac{12.011}{1.0079} = \frac{\%H}{\%C} \times 11.917 \quad \text{(Eq. 16)}$$

$$\frac{O}{C} = \left(\frac{\text{mass \% oxygen}}{15.999}\right) / \left(\frac{\text{mass \% carbon}}{12.011}\right) = \frac{\%O}{\%C} \times \frac{12.011}{15.999} = \frac{\%O}{\%C} \times 0.75073 \quad \text{(Eq. 17)}$$

These values for the mixture can then be inserted into general Equation 13 to obtain the stoichiometric air-fuel ratio of the blend containing carbon and hydrogen or carbon, hydrogen, and oxygen.

7. Calculation of Stoichiometric Air-Fuel Ratios of Fuels Containing Sulfur—Sulfur (at.wt. = 32.066) forms numerous oxides, e.g., SO or S_2O_3, SO_2, SO_3, SO_4, and S_2O_7. Of these, SO_2 predominates in the exhaust gas of internal combustion engines.[2]

General Equation 13 can be modified further to include sulfur containing fuels. For this purpose, a quantity is added to the denominator, representing the mass added by the sulfur per carbon atom and a quantity is added to the numerator indicating that two oxygen atoms are required to burn the sulfur to SO_2.

Thus, Equation 13 becomes (see Equation 18):

$$(A/F)_s = \frac{4.3211 \times 15.999\ [2+(0.5)(H/C)-(O/C)+2(S/C)]}{[(12.011\times 1)+(1.0079)(H/C)+(15.999)(O/C)+(32.066)(S/C)]} \quad \text{(Eq. 18)}$$

If engine exhaust gases containing excess oxygen either from "lean" operation or from injection of air into the exhaust manifold is passed over a catalyst used for emission control, additional oxidation of SO_2 to SO_3 can result. In this case, three atoms of oxygen are needed to oxidize the sulfur and the numerator quantity should be changed from 2(S/C) to 3(S/C).

8. Calculation of Stoichiometric Air-Fuel Ratios of Fuels Containing Nitrogen—Nitrogen (at.wt. = 14.007), like sulfur, forms numerous oxides, e.g., NO, NO_2, NO_3, N_2O, and N_2O_5. The major product in automotive engine exhaust is nitric oxide, NO. Thus, a quantity is added to the denominator representing the mass added by the nitrogen per carbon atom and a quantity is added to the numerator indicating that one oxygen atom is required to burn the nitrogen atom to NO. Equation 18 then becomes (see Equation 19):

$$(A/F)_s = \frac{4.3211 \times 15.999\ [2+(0.5)(H/C)-(O/C)+2(S/C)+1(N/C)]}{[(12.011\times 1)+(1.0079)(H/C)+(15.999)(O/C)+(32.066)(S/C)+(14.007)(N/C)]} \quad \text{(Eq. 19)}$$

Equation 19 is then the general equation for calculating the stoichiometric air-fuel ratio of fuels containing carbon and hydrogen along with oxygen, sulfur, and nitrogen. In summary, in this equation:

H/C = atomic hydrogen-to-carbon ratio
O/C = atomic oxygen-to-carbon ratio
S/C = atomic sulfur-to-carbon ratio
N/C = atomic nitrogen-to-carbon ratio

and

12.011 = atomic weight of carbon
1.0079 = atomic weight of hydrogen
15.999 = atomic weight of oxygen
32.066 = atomic weight of sulfur
14.007 = atomic weight of nitrogen
4.3211 = weight of air per unit weight of oxygen

It should be noted that Equation 19 assumes that sulfur oxidizes to SO_2 and nitrogen to NO which is generally applicable to internal combustion engines. However, these approximations should be verified for engines optimized for different operating conditions for alternative fuels that may become available. In general, however, the effect on stoichiometric air-fuel ratio is expected to be small since the atomic ratios of S/C and N/C for most fuels are usually small. The user should recognize that during combustion, oxygen will also combine with nitrogen from the air to form oxides of nitrogen.

In vehicles equipped with reducing catalysts, generally part of the "three-way catalysts," the oxides of nitrogen from the engine are reduced to nitrogen and therefore the nitrogen term in the numerator, 1 N/C, should be eliminated if the overall stoichiometry of engine plus catalysts is considered.

9. Calculation of Stoichiometric Air-Fuel Ratios of Fuels Containing Water—Some alternative automotive fuels may contain appreciable quantities of water. For example, the ethanol-water azeotrope which contains 4 mass percent water[3] has been used as a spark-ignition engine fuel and a microemulsion of 10 volume percent of water in diesel fuel has been considered as a fire-resistant fuel for military use.

---

2. See Reference 3 in Section 2.
3. See Reference 4 in Section 2.

The water adds to the weight of fuel without adding to the amount of oxygen required for combustion. Therefore, the stoichiometric air-fuel ratio of the wet fuel will differ from that of the dry fuel. However, Equation 13 will apply to the wet fuel if the H/C and O/C atomic ratios were determined for that wet fuel.

10. Fuels Without Carbon Atoms—Several substances which do not contain carbon atoms, such as ammonia and hydrazine, have been investigated as potential alternative fuels for automotive engines. For such fuels, the equations listed previously do not apply. However, the same principles can be used; namely, the calculations can be based on a "per nitrogen atom" basis.

11. Effect of Humidity in Air—Stoichiometric air-fuel ratios should always be calculated on the basis of the mass of dry air required to burn a unit mass of fuel as is done in the preceding equations. However, it may also be desirable to determine the required mass of ambient air which usually contains water vapor. The mass of water vapor present can be determined from measured temperatures and relative humidities of the ambient air using psychrometric charts.[4,5]

At room temperature and humidity, the relative mass of water vapor to dry air is small. For example, at 21 °C (70 °F) and 50% relative humidity, the damp air will contain 0.008 mass unit of water vapor for each 1.000 mass unit of dry air. The actual mass of ambient air at 21 °C (70 °F) and 50% relative humidity required for stoichiometric burning will therefore be 1.008 times higher than the mass of dry air computed in the preceding equations.

4. See Reference 5 in Section 2.
5. See Reference 6 in Section 2.

APPENDIX A

A.1 The method described previously is applicable to wet fuels as well as dry fuels as shown by the following two methods of calculating the stoichiometric air-fuel ratio of the ethanol-water azeotrope. The first method calculates the $(A/F)_s$ from the elemental composition of the wet fuel and the second calculates it from the elemental composition of the dry fuel and then corrects the $(A/F)_s$ by adding the weight of water to the dry fuel.

In the illustration, the following values are used:

a. The ethanol-water azeotrope consists of 96.0 mass percent of ethanol and 4.0 mass percent of water.[6]
b. The atomic weights to five significant figures are:
   1. Carbon = 12.011
   2. Hydrogen = 1.0079
   3. Oxygen = 15.999

A.1.1 Method 1—In the absence of direct measurement of the elemental analysis of the azeotrope, the carbon, hydrogen, and oxygen contents are calculated in this example from the known composition of the azeotrope and its constituents.

A.1.1.1 Weight of elements in 96.0 g of ethanol (C_2H_5OH) (see Table A1):

TABLE A1—WEIGHT OF ELEMENTS IN 96.0 G OF ETHANOL (C_2H_5OH)

	Relative Weight	Weight Fraction	g in 96.0 g
Carbon — 2 × 12.011 =	24.022	0.52144	50.058
Hydrogen— 6 × 1.0079 =	6.0474	0.13127	12.602
Oxygen — 1 × 15.999 =	15.999	0.34729	33.340
mol. wt. =	46.068	Σ = 1.00000	Σ = 96.000

A.1.1.2Weight of elements in 4.0 g of water (H_2O) (see Table A2):

TABLE A2—WEIGHT OF ELEMENTS IN 4.0 G OF WATER (H_2O)

	Relative Weight	Weight Fraction	g in 96.0 g
Carbon — 0			
Hydrogen— 2 × 1.0079 =	2.0158	0.11190	0.4476
Oxygen — 1 × 15.999 =	15.999	0.88810	3.5524
mol. wt. =	18.0148	Σ = 1.00000	Σ = 4.0000

A.1.1.3Weight of elements in 100 g of azeotrope (see Table A3).

TABLE A3—WEIGHT OF ELEMENTS IN 100 G OF AZEOTROPE

	From Ethanol	From Water	Total
Carbon	50.058	—	50.058
Hydrogen	12.602	0.4476	13.050
Oxygen	33.340	3.5524	36.892
	96.000	4.0000	100.000

6. See Reference 4 in Section 2.

A.1.1.4 Thus, a direct measurement of the elemental composition of the azeotrope should be:

a. % carbon = 50.058
b. % hydrogen = 13.050
c. % oxygen = 36.892

A.1.1.5 Calculation of H/C and O/C atomic ratios (see Equations A1 and A2):

$$(\%H/\%C) \times 11.917 = (13.050/50.058) \times 11.917 = 3.1067 \quad \text{(Eq. A1)}$$

$$(\%O/\%C) \times 0.75073 = (36.892/50.058) \times 0.75073 = 0.55328 \quad \text{(Eq. A2)}$$

A.1.1.6 Using H/C and O/C from A.1.1.5 in Equation 13 (see Equation A3):

$$(A/F)_s = 4.3211 \times \frac{15.999\ [2 + (0.5)(H/C) - (O/C)]}{[(12.011 \times 1) + (1.0079)(H/C) + (15.999)(O/C)]} \quad \text{(Eq. A3)}$$

$$(A/F)_s = 4.3211 \times \frac{15.999\ [2 + (0.5)\ (3.1067) - (0.55328)]}{(12.011 \times 1) + (1.0079)\ (3.1067) + (15.999)\ (0.55328)}$$

$$= 69.133 \times [3.0001/23.994]$$

$$(A/F)_2 = 8.6438 \text{ of azeotrope}$$

A.1.2 Method 2—The direct measurement of the elemental composition of pure dry ethanol as shown in A.1.1.11 should be 52.144% carbon, 13.127% hydrogen and 34.729% oxygen. A fuel with this analysis would have H/C and O/C ratios as follows in Equations A4 and A5:

$$(\%H/\%C) \times 11.917 = (13.127/52.144) \times 11.917 = 3.0 \quad \text{(Eq. A4)}$$

$$(\%O/\%C) \times 0.75073 = (34.729/52.144) \times 0.75073 = 0.5 \quad \text{(Eq. A5)}$$

In this example, the composition of C_2H_5OH is known and H/C and O/C would also be readily available from the formula. Substituting the previous values in Equation 13, (see Equation A6):

$$(A/F)_2 = 4.3211 \times \frac{15.999\ [2 + (0.5)\ (3) - (0.5)]}{[(12.011 \times 1) + (1.0079)\ (3) + (15.999)\ (0.5)]} \quad \text{(Eq. A6)}$$

$$= 69.133 \times [3/23.034]$$

$$= 9.0040 \text{ for pure dry ethanol}$$

Thus, 1 g of ethanol requires 9.0040 g of air and 96.0 g of ethanol requires 96.0 x 9.0040 = 864.38 g of air. The azeotrope includes 4.0 g of water which does not require any air. Thus, 100.0 g of azeotrope also requires 864.38 g of air. The stoichiometric air-fuel ratio of the azeotrope is then (864.38)/100.0 or 8.6438, which agrees with the value of 8.6438 obtained by Method 1.

A.2 Summary—The stoichiometric air-fuel ratio of wet fuels can be determined by two methods:

a. Calculate from elemental analysis of wet fuel.
b. Determine amount of water and elemental analysis of dry fuel. Calculate from analysis of dry fuel and add amount of water to weight of fuel without adding to air.

HEATING VALUE OF FUELS—SAE J1498 FEB1998 SAE Information Report

Report of the SAE Fuels and Lubricants Division approved May 1987 and revised by the SAE Fuels & Lubricants Technical Committee 7—Fuels October 1988. Completely revised by the SAE Fuels and Lubricants Technial Committee 7—Fuels May 1990 and revised February 1998. Rationale statement available.

1. Scope—The heating value or heat of combustion is a measure of the energy available from the fuel. The fraction or percentage of the heat of combustion that is converted to useful work is a measure of the thermal efficiency of an engine. Thus, a knowledge of the heat of combustion of the fuel is basic to the engineering of automotive engines. This SAE Information Report provides information on the standardized procedures for determining the heat of combustion of fuels that may be used for automotive engines.

2. References

2.1 Applicable Publications—The following publications form a part of this specification to the extent specified herein. Unless otherwise indicated, the latest version of SAE publications shall apply.

2.1.1 SAE PUBLICATIONS—Available from SAE, 400 Commonwealth Drive, Warrendale, PA 15096-0001.

SAE J313—Diesel Fuels
SAE TSB 003—Rules for SAE Use of SI (Metric) Units

2.1.2 OTHER PUBLICATIONS

1. J. M. Sturtevant, "Calorimetry", Chapter VII, Vol. I, Part V of "Physical Methods of Chemistry", Edited by A. Weissberger and B. W. Rossiter, Wiley-Interscience, New York, NY, 1971.
2. ASTM Methods cited throughout the text are available in the latest volume of the Annual Book of ASTM Standards as shown as follows. These volumes are available from ASTM, 100 Barr Harbor Drive, West Conshohocken, PA 19428-2959.

Method	Volume
D 86	05.01
D 240	05.01
D 1018	05.01
D 1405	05.01
D 1826	05.05
D 1945	05.05
D 1946	05.05
D 2015	05.05
D 2163	05.01
D 2421	05.01
D 2650	05.02
D 3286	05.05
D 3338	05.02
D 3588	05.05
D 3701	05.02
D 4529	05.02
D 4809	05.03
D 4868	05.03
E 380	14.02
E 711	11.04

3. F.D. Rossini, K. S. Pitzer, R. L. Arnett, R. M. Braun, and G. C. Pimental, "Selected Values of Physical and Thermodynamic Properties of Hydrocarbons and Related Compounds", pp. 445–463, Carnegie Press, Carnegie Institute of Technology, Pittsburgh, PA, 1953.
4. ASTM Data Series Publication DS4B, "Physical Constants of Hydrocarbon and Non-Hydrocarbon Compounds", ASTM, West Conshohocken, PA, 1991.
5. "Reference Data for Hydrocarbons and Petro-Sulfur Compounds", Phillips Petroleum Company Bulletin No. 521, Bartlesville, Oklahoma.
6. R. C. Wilhoit and B. J. Zwolinski, "Physical and Thermodynamic Properties of Aliphatic Alcohols", Journal of Physical and Chemical Reference Data, Vol. 2, Supplement No. 1, 1973, American Chemical Society and the American Institute of Physics.
7. E. S. Domalski, "Selected Values of Heats of Combustion and Heats of Formation of Organic Compounds Containing the Elements of C, H, N, O, P, and S", Journal of Physical and Chemical Reference Data, Vol. 1, No. 2, pp. 221–278, 1972, American Chemical Society and the American Institute of Physics.
8. "Technical Data Book - Petroleum Refinery", 3rd Edition, American Petroleum Institute, Washington, DC, 1977.
9. J. D. Cox and G. Pilcher, "Thermochemistry of Organic and Organometallic Compounds", Academic Press, 1970.

3. Measurement Of Heat Of Combustion—Heats of combustion can be determined to high precision by burning a known amount of the sample completely in pure oxygen in a calibrated calorimeter. The heat of combustion is the product of the temperature rise and the total heat capacity of the calorimeter and its contents. For precision measurements, corrections are applied for energy added to initiate combustion and for the energy involved in the formation of extraneous products such as nitric acid and sulfuric acid.

Calorimeters of various types have been developed to obtain heats of combustion of gases, liquids, or solids to various levels of precision (Reference 1). For evaluation of fundamental thermodynamic properties, precision of calorimetric measurements of the highest order is required since the results are obtained as small differences in large quantities. For heats of combustion of fuel mixtures, lower precisions are usually sufficient for many purposes and less sophisticated techniques are usually used.

Heats of combustion or calorific values of gaseous fuels are usually measured in flame calorimeters in which the sample and oxygen react at constant pressure. Heats of combustion of solid and liquid fuels are usually measured in bomb calorimeters at constant volume.

4. Units Of Measurement—In the SI system of measurement, the heat of combustion is expressed in joules per kilogram. For materials generally used as fuels, the heat of combustion is of such magnitude that it is customarily expressed in terms of a multiple of the basic unit, namely in megajoules per kilogram, MJ/kg. Where the molecular weight is known as in pure compounds, it is sometimes expressed in terms of megajoules per mole, MJ/mole.

A large body of literature is available - and still accumulating - in terms of other, non-SI units such as calories per gram or British Thermal Units (Btu) per pound. The following factors can be used in converting these other units to SI units as in Table 1:

TABLE 1—Units of Measurement

To Convert From	To	Multiply by
Calorie (International Table)	Joule (J)	4.186 800
British Thermal Unit (IT)	Joule (J)	1055.056
Calorie/Gram	Megajoules/kilogram (MJ/kg)	0.004 186 800
Btu/pound	Megajoules/kilogram (MJ/kg)	0.002 326 000
Pound (Avoirdupois)	Kilogram (kg)	0.453 592 4
Btu/cubic foot	Megajoules/cubic meter (MJ/m^3)	0.037 258 95

SAE TSB 003 and ASTM E 380 list conversion factors for units other than those included here. In any conversions, the number of digits retained should not exceed that implied by the precision of the original quantity.

Many fuels are sold by volume. Heating values are, therefore, frequently expressed in terms of heat units on a volume basis. Thus, the heating values of gaseous fuels are given in terms of heat units per cubic foot or per cubic meter and those of liquid fuels are frequently given in terms of heat units per gallon or per liter. These terms can be computed to a mass basis using the density in appropriate units at the appropriate temperature and pressure.

5. Types of Heating Values—Four types of heating values may be defined according to the assumed state of water as a combustion product (gaseous or liquid) and according to the nature of the assumed combustion process (constant volume or constant pressure). Gross (liquid water) and net (gaseous water) heating values differ by the heat of vaporization of the water in the combustion product mixture. Constant volume and constant pressure heating values differ by the heat equivalent of the work represented by the volume change at constant pressure caused by the change in the number of moles during combustion. Numerical differences between constant volume and constant pressure combustion are small and normally neglected for fuels. Tables of heating values usually list gross and net values at constant pressure.

ASTM D 4809 defines the gross heat of combustion, Q_g, as follows:

"The gross heat of combustion at constant volume of a liquid or solid fuel containing only the elements carbon, hydrogen, oxygen, nitrogen, and sulfur is the quantity of heat liberated when a unit mass of the fuel is burned in oxygen in an enclosure of constant volume, the products of combustion being gaseous carbon dioxide, nitrogen, sulfur dioxide, and liquid water, with the initial temperature of the fuel and the oxygen and the final temperature of the products at 25 °C."

ASTM D 4809 also defines the net heat of combustion, Q_n, as:

"The net heat of combustion at constant pressure of a liquid or a solid fuel containing only the elements carbon, hydrogen, oxygen, nitrogen, and sulfur is the quantity of heat liberated when a unit mass of the fuel is burned in oxygen at a constant pressure of 0.101 MPa (1 atm), the products of combustion being carbon dioxide, nitrogen, sulfur dioxide, and water, all in the gaseous state, with the initial temperature of the fuel and the oxygen and the final temperature of the products of combustion at 25 °C."

These two types are interrelated by Equation 1:

$$Q_n \text{ (net, 25 °C)} = Q_g \text{ (gross, 25 °C)} - 0.2122 \times H \qquad \text{(Eq. 1)}$$

where:

Q_n (net, 25 °C) = net heat of combustion at constant pressure, MJ/kg
Q_g (gross, 25 °C) = gross heat of combustion at constant volume, MJ/kg
H = mass % hydrogen in sample.

NOTE—The percentage of hydrogen in the sample may be determined in accord with ASTM D 1018 or with ASTM D 3701 (IP 338).

The net heat of combustion is also known as the "lower heating value, (LVH)". It is the value customarily used in calculating thermal efficiency of engines since the exhaust gases are emitted at nearly the same pressure as that of the air and fuel supplied to the inlet system and since they contain water in the uncondensed or vapor state.

6. Standard Conditions—Whenever heats of combustion are reported, the temperature, pressure, and physical state (solid, liquid, gas) of the reactants and products should be included. By international convention, a standard state of 25 °C and 1 atm pressure is currently in use. It should be noted that in the change to the SI system of measurement, the standard state pressure is being changed to 1 bar, which is 100 kPa, instead of 1 at which is 101.3250 kPa. Few data are yet available at 1 bar pressure. This change will have negligible effect on the practical heating value of fuels.

Many data in the technical literature are given at temperatures other than the standard reference temperature of 25 °C. These can be converted to 25 °C (77 °F) by correcting for the difference between the total heat capacity of the products of the combustion and the total heat capacity of the reactants at constant pressure. ASTM DS 4B, p. 62 (Reference 4) provides the details of such corrections when the heat capacities are known. ASTM D 2382 provides a series of empirical correction factors that can be used for petroleum fuels when the heat capacities are unknown. Equation 2 applies to such corrections:

$$Q_g \text{ (gross, 25 °C)} = Q_g \text{ (gross, t °C)} + A \text{ (t °C} - 25 \text{ °C)} \qquad \text{(Eq. 2)}$$

where:

A = correction factor

Although heating values of gaseous fuels are usually expressed in terms of heating units per cubic foot, the amount of gas contained in a cubic foot has not been completely standardized throughout the gas industry. In ASTM D 1826, the standard cubic foot is regarded to be the quantity of gas that will fill one cubic foot at a standard pressure of 14.73 psia (71.92 kg/m^2) and a standard temperature of 60 °F (15.56 °C) when in equilibrium with water.

7. Heating Values of Pure Compounds—The heats of combustion of pure compounds, particularly hydrocarbons, have been measured with great precision because of their significance in elucidating structures and the chemical, physical, and thermodynamic properties of organic molecules. Major compilations of such data have been published (References 2 to 9) showing centimeter-gram-second metric and/or U.S. inch-pound units at standard state conditions of 25 °C and 1 atm pressure.

8. Heating Values of Mixtures—Heating values of mixtures of nonpolar liquids and gases, which do not react, are generally additive for practical purposes and can be computed from the known amounts and heating values of each component. When any of the components are polar liquids, solids, or gases that interact with each other, the heats of combustion may no longer be additive and, therefore, should be measured calorimetrically.

If water is present in the fuel as is frequently the case with such fuels as oxygenated fuels and coals, the total net heating value of the wet fuel will be lower than that of dry fuel. In this case, some of the heat of burning the fuel will be spent in evaporating the water present with the fuel.

9. Standardized Methods for Measuring Heating Values—A variety of methods for measuring or estimating the heating values of fuels have been standardized by technical societies. The methods published by ASTM include statements of precision which are included here as guides to the usefulness of the method in proposed applications. A statement on precision, i.e., repeatability and reproducibility, provides information on the degree of mutual agreement between individual measurements while a statement on accuracy provides information on the agreement of the measurements with an accepted reference value. In general, 95% of the measurements can be expected to lie within the precision limits stated in the method when conducted properly. However, readers are cautioned to examine each of the methods for full information including the range of materials included in the interlaboratory comparison on which the method is based.

It should also be noted that the precision of the methods for computing heats of combustion from measured values of other properties such as aniline point and gravity are dependent upon the precision of these measured values rather than on the computation process.

9.1 Gaseous Fuels—The heat of combustion of a gaseous fuel can be measured directly or can be calculated from the composition of the mixture and the heats of combustion of its individual constituents provided that there is no chemical reaction between the constituents.

ASTM D 1826 is a standardized procedure for measuring the heat of combustion of gases in the natural gas range of 900 to 1200 Btu/standard ft^3 with a precision of 0.3 to 0.5%. In this procedure, the test gas is burned in a stream of air and the temperature rise of the air stream is measured. The water is condensed to the liquid state and the gross heat of combustion is obtained.

ASTM D 3588 is applicable to all common types of utility gaseous fuels for which suitable methods of analysis are available. This includes dry natural gas, reformed gas, oil gas (both high and low Btu), propane-air, carbureted water gas, and coke oven and retort coal gas. The calorific values are calculated from the molar composition and the respective ideal gas values for the components. These values must then be converted to the real gas basis by means of compressibility summation factors which are listed in ASTM D 3588 for most of the lower molecular weight hydrocarbons and gaseous nonhydrocarbons.

The following ASTM documents are helpful in determining the molar composition of the gaseous fuels:

a. ASTM D 1945—Method for Analysis of Natural Gas by Gas Chromatography
b. ASTM D 1946—Method for Analysis of Reformed Gas by Gas Chromatography
c. ASTM D 2163 (IP 264)—Method for Analysis of Liquefied Petroleum (LP) Gases and Propane Concentrates by Gas Chromatography
d. ASTM D 2421—Test Method for Interconversion of Analysis of C_5 and Lighter Hydrocarbons to Gas-Volume, Liquid-Volume, or Weight Basis
e. ASTM D 2650—Test Method for Chemical Composition of Gases by Mass Spectrometry

9.2 Liquid Fuels—Heats of combustion of liquid fuels and solid fuels as well, are usually measured in a bomb calorimeter equipped with either an isothermal or an adiabatic type jacket.

a. ASTM D 240 describes a method which is particularly applicable to hydrocarbons of both low and high volatility. The precision of this method is as follows:
   1. Repeatability—0.13 MJ/kg (55 Btu/lb)
   2. Reproducibility—0.40 MJ/kg (175 Btu/lb)
b. ASTM D 4809 was designed specifically for use with aviation turbine fuels but is also directly applicable to such fuels as gasolines, kerosenes, No. 1 and 2 fuel oil, No. 1D and 2D diesel fuel and No. 0-GT, 1-GT, and 2-GT gas turbine fuels. The precision of the method varies with the type of fuel and can be summarized in Table 2:

TABLE 2—ASTM D 4809 Test Method Precision

	Gross Heat of Combustion MJ/kg	Gross Heat of Combustion Btu/1b	Net Heat of Combustion MJ/kg	Net Heat of Combustion Btu/lb
Repeatability:				
All Fuels	0.097	42	0.096	41
Nonvolatile Fuels	0.096	41	0.099	43
Volatile Fuels	0.100	43	0.091	39
Reproducibility:				
All Fuels	0.228	98	0.324	139
Nonvolatile Fuels	0.239	103	0.234	101
Volatile Fuels	0.207	89	0.450	193

9.3 Solid Fuels—ASTM has standardized three procedures for the determination of the gross heating value of solid fuels:

1. ASTM D 2015—Test Method for Gross Calorific Value of Solid Fuel by the Adiabatic Bomb Calorimeter
2. ASTM D 3286—Test Method for Gross Calorific Value of Solid Fuel by the Isothermal-Jacket Bomb Calorimeter
3. ASTM E 711—Test Method for Gross Calorific Value of Refuse-Derived Fuel (RDF-3) by the Bomb Calorimeter

The precision of these three methods is listed in Table 3:

TABLE 3—Test Method Precision

	Repeatability MJ/kg	Repeatability Btu/lb	Reproducibility MJ/kg	Reproducibility Btu/lb
ASTM D 2015	0.116	50(1)	0.233	100(1)
ASTM D 3286	0.116	50	0.233	100
ASTM E 711	not determined	not determined	not determined	not determined

1. Dry basis

9.4 Heterogeneous Fuels—Heterogeneous fuels such as emulsions of diesel fuel and water, microemulsions of vegetable oils and alcohols, and slurries of coals in liquids have received some attention as possible fuels for automotive engines. However, no calorimetric methods for measuring the heats of combustion of such fuels have yet been standardized by ASTM. It is expected that ASTM D 4809 can be used for such measurements, possibly in modified form, but no estimate of precision can be given. Special care is required to ensure that the sample taken for such measurements is representative of the fuel ingested into the engine.

When water is present as in a fuel/water emulsion or as moisture associated with the fuels such as coals, alcohols, and esters, some of the net heat of combustion of the dry fuel will be spent in evaporating the water.

10. Empirical Methods For Estimating Heats Of Combustion—Several empirical methods have been developed for estimating the heat of combustion where experimental measurements are unavailable or cannot be made conveniently and where estimates may be satisfactory. Such empirical estimates are based on observed correlations between accurately measured properties and the heats of combustion of representative samples of compounds or fuels typical of a particular class of fuels. The correlations may change when the composition of the class of fuel changes as a result of changes in crude oil supply and in refinery practice. The estimates may be in error by large amounts even within the same class of fuels as well as with fuels of other classes. Some automotive fuels now contain oxygenated compounds to help meet mandates requirements for the control of atmospheric carbon monoxide and ozone, to enhance octane level, and to augment the total fuel supply. The oxygen in such fuels adds to the mass and volume of these fuels without adding to the heat of combustion. Thus, the heat of combustion per unit mass and unit volume will be lowered in proportion to the mass percent oxygen. Also, some oxygenated fuels have an increased propensity to absorb atmospheric moisture which will reduce the heat of combustion as well. However, to date experimental methods for estimating the heat of combustion of such fuels has not been standardized and therefore direct measurement is advisable. Whenever possible, heats of combustion should be measured.

ASTM D 1405 (IP 193) and ASTM D 4529 provide estimates of the heat of combustion of certain aviation fuels. These fuels include aviation gasolines, aircraft turbine, and jet engine fuels of limited boiling ranges and compositions. They are liquid hydrocarbons derived from normal refining processes and conventional crude oils. Both methods are based upon an empirical relationship between aniline point, density, sulfur content, and heat of combustion for fuels of these types. When values of densities, aniline points, and sulfur are obtained in replicate determination on a fuel sample, they may show some variation; consequently, heats of combustion estimated from them using the empirical relationship may also vary. For a given fuel, estimates (95% confidence) are considered suspect if duplicate results obtained by the same operator differ by more than 0.012 MJ/kg or if results submitted by each of two laboratories differ by more than 0.035 MJ/kg.

ASTM D 3338 provides a correlation between the net heat of combustion and gravity, aromatic content, and average volatility of aviation gasolines, aircraft turbine, and jet engine fuels. When a second set of measured values of aromatic content, gravity, and distillation data are used to obtain estimates from the empirical relationship of this method, the estimates are considered suspect if duplicate results obtained by the same operator differ by more than 0.021 MJ/kg (or 9 Btu/lb) or if results submitted by each of two laboratories differ by more than 0.046 MJ/kg (or 20 Btu/lb).

D 4868 covers the estimation of heating values from density, sulfur, water, and ash content. It is applicable to a variety of petroleum fuels derived by normal refining processes from conventional crude oil and which have densities in the range of 750 to 1000 kg/m^3. It is not applicable to pure hydrocarbons or fuels of high aromatic content. The precision for the fuels used in the development of this method is:

a. Repeatability—0.05 MJ/kg
b. Reproducibility—0.15 MJ/kg

A variety of other nonstandardized correlations for hydrocarbon fuels have been published. SAE J313 shows several correlations for diesel fuels that have been developed for relating

a. Gravity, aniline point, and heat of combustion
b. Density, mid-boiling point, and heat of combustion
c. 50 and 90% recovery temperatures from the ASTM D 86 distillation, API gravity, cetane number, viscosity, cloud point, and net heating value

No estimate of precision is available for these methods.

NONMETALLIC FUEL SYSTEM TUBING WITH ONE OR MORE LAYERS—SAE J2260 NOV1996

SAE Standard

Report of the SAE Fuel Lines and Fittings Standards Committee approved November 1996.

1. Scope—This SAE Standard covers the minimum requirements for multilayer, nonmetallic tubing as manufactured as a liquid-carrying or vapor-carrying component for use in gasoline, alcohol blends with gasoline, or diesel fuel systems. Monowall tubing (one layer construction) is also covered by this document. The construction has one or more layers of polymer-based compounds in the wall, primarily for the purpose of improvement in permeation resistance to hydrocarbons found in various fuels. The construction can have a straight-wall configuration or can have a wall that is partially convoluted or corrugated. It may have an innermost layer with improved electrical conductivity for use where such a characteristic is desired; also, the improved electrical conductivity can apply to the entire wall construction, if the tubing is a monowall. This document is intended to cover tubing for any portion of a fuel system which operates above –40 °C, and below 115 °C, and up to a maximum working gage pressure of 690 kPa. The peak intermittent temperature is 115 °C. For long-term continuous usage, the temperature shall not exceed 90 °C.

In some cases, a distinction is made in the criteria that apply to tubing used to carry liquid fuel compared to tubing used to carry fuel vapor. The term "fuel vapor" can also apply to evaporative emissions and refers to a condition where the fuel content is in vapor form (very low concentration) and operates at a working gage pressure that does not exceed 17 kPa. The fuel vapor, or evaporative emissions, may contain small quantities of liquid fuel, which are present primarily as a result of vapor condensation.

2. References

2.1 Applicable Publications—The following publications form a part of this specification to the extent specified herein. Unless otherwise indicated, the latest issue of SAE publications shall apply.

2.1.1 SAE PUBLICATIONS—Available from SAE, 400 Commonwealth Drive, Warrendale, PA 15096-0001.

SAE J1645—Information Report Covering Electrostatic Charge in Fuel Systems (FEB94 and latest)
SAE J1681—Gasoline/Methanol Mixtures for Material Testing
SAE J1737 (DRAFT)—Recommended Practice for Measurement of Permeation Resistance by the Recirculation Technique
SAE J1960—Accelerated Exposure of Automotive Exterior Materials Using a Controlled Irradiance Water-Cooled Xenon-Arc Apparatus
SAE J2027—Standard for Protective Covers for Gasoline Fuel Lines
SAE J2044—SAE Quick Connector Specifications for Liquid Fuel Systems
SAE J2045—Tube/Hose Assemblies

2.1.2 ISO PUBLICATIONS—Available from ANSI, 11 West 42nd Street, New York, NY 10036-8002.

ISO 527—Plastics—Determination of tensile properties
ISO 4639-3—Rubber tubing and hoses for fuel circuits for internal combustion engines specification—Part 3: Oxidized fuels

2.2 Related Publications—The following publications are for information purposes only and are not a required part of this document.

2.2.1 SAE PUBLICATIONS—Available from SAE, 400 Commonwealth Drive, Warrendale, PA 15096-0001.

SAE J30—Fuel and Oil Hoses
SAE J2043—Standard for Nonmetallic Fuel System Tubing

2.2.2 ASTM PUBLICATIONS—Available from ASTM, 100 Barr Harbor Drive, West Conshohocken, PA 19428-2959.

ASTM D 412—Test Methods for Rubber Properties in Tension
ASTM D 4000—Classification System for Specifying Plastic Materials
ASTM D 4066—Specification for Nylon Injection and Extrusion Materials

3. Installation, Assembly, and Handling Recommendation

3.1 End Fittings—End fittings are to be assembled to the tubing with a procedure which does not permit mechanical damage to the tubing that results in decreased performance. Requirements of such end fittings are covered in SAE J2044 documentation. Assemblies manufactured with such end fittings must meet all of the requirements of the SAE J2045 specification.

3.2 Support and Routing—When installed in a vehicle this tubing shall be routed and supported so as to:

a. Prevent chafing, abrasion, kinking, or other mechanical damage.
b. Be protected against road hazards by installation in a protected location or by providing adequate shielding in vulnerable areas.
c. Be protected from heat by proper clearance or the addition of insulation and/or heat shielding (refer to SAE J2027), for use in applications where temperatures may briefly exceed the upper limits of 115 °C.

3.3 Handling—Tubing ends should be protected during handling and storage to prevent internal contamination.

4. Construction—Tubing shall consist of an extrusion of one or more layers within the body of the wall. The dimensions and tolerances of the one or various layers shall be expressed in millimeters and the general material name should be called out on the drawing. In those specific cases where material specifications exist for a given tubing construction, they shall be identified for the entire wall or for each individual layer.

4.1 Materials—The materials used in the construction of the tubing have different requirements depending on their location within the wall. The various materials used may also use plasticizers, colorants, impact modifiers, and other additives to enhance performance provided the tubing produced complies to the requirements of this standard.

If monowall tubing is used, then the material used must meet all exposure criteria described in this document.

4.1.1 OUTER LAYER—Materials used in the outer layer must conform to the exposure test described in 7.5. There may be additional environments to which the tubing construction will be exposed; the end user should be consulted for what additional requirements may be appropriate. Refer to 4.3 for comments on color.

4.1.2 INNER LAYER—Materials used in the inner layer must conform to the fuel exposure tests described in 7.7 and 7.8. There may be other fuels to which the tubing construction will be exposed. The end user should be consulted for what additional requirements there may be.

The materials used in the inner layer should also be able to withstand contact with road chemicals. This is the case because the inner layer of the tubing can be exposed to such an environment at the "ends" that are attached to the various connection points in a fuel system. It is for this reason that the ends of the tubing are also exposed to the chemical resistance test in 7.5.

4.2 Regrind—Small amounts of regrind may be used in the manufacture of tubing. Tubing containing the selected percentage of regrind that will be used in production must meet all the performance criteria in this document.

4.2.1 USE OF REGRIND OF A SPECIFIC RESIN—Use of regrind material blended with virgin resin in a specific layer of the MLT (or in the wall of the monowall tubing) is permissible only when the manufacturer has identified a specific percentage of the regrind that will be used. In this case, that regrind can be used to blend with the virgin resin of the same type only in the specific layer where that material is used (or tubing wall, in the case of monowall tubing). Such regrind being blended shall contain no contaminants of any other material.

All performance criteria in this document must be met by conducting all tests on tubing that contains the specific regrind percentage in the particular designated layer. Once the performance of a multilayer tubing containing regrind material blended in a specific layer has been validated, acceptance of such tubing applies only to the specific resin in the specific layer and only to that manufacturer involved. Any regrind percentage up to or equal to the level approved can be used.

If regrind is used in the portions of the tube that is outermost or innermost, there could be a deleterious effect that could result in the tubing's ability to perform in the external environment (i.e., heat-aging) or in fuel exposure in the very long term. Testing in this specification includes exposure tests only up to 1000 h, involves only certain fuels, and is conducted at only mildly aggressive temperatures (40 °C). The end user should be consulted for guidance on how tests for the presence of regrind in the innermost or outermost portions of the tubing should be conducted. Longer term exposures or more aggressive test parameters than those indicated in the specification may be advisable to confirm there is no negative effect.

It is recommended that no more than 10% regrind is blended in the innermost or outermost layer; that percentage also applies to monowall tubing. If regrind is blended in other layers, it is recommended that no more than 20% regrind is used.

4.2.2 USE OF REGRIND RESIN OR MLT IN A SEPARATE LAYER—It's possible to use regrind of resin or regrind of completed multilayer tubing (MLT) as an additional and separate layer in the construction of an MLT; to do so, the following criteria must be met:

a. It is used only in a separate layer that is in addition to the number of layers in the construction of the MLT being produced.
b. The regrind layer should not be the innermost or outermost layer of the tubing construction.
c. It is recommended to use a maximum thickness of 10% (of the total tubing wall thickness) for the regrind layer.

For a construction that contains an additional and separate layer of regrind resin or regrind MLT, all performance criteria of this specification must be met. The testing done shall be on tubing that contains the specific type of regrind layer in the specific, identified position within the wall. Once the performance of such an MLT has been validated, acceptance of such a construction applies only to that layer configuration and only to the specific manufacturer involved. Any layer thickness of that regrind layer up to (or equal) to the specific thickness approved can be utilized.

4.3 Color—The normal color of the outside layer of tubing covered under this document is black, although alternative colors are permissible. Fuel system tubing shall be labeled in a contrasting color with the legend repeated every 500 mm or less along the entire length of tubing in legible block capital letters.

The color of the outside layer of the MLT constructions covered by this document is usually black. They can be another color, chosen for purposes of color-coding for routing through the vehicles. For whatever color is chosen, the following criteria must be met:

a. The tubing color and the label color chosen must be such that there is sufficient contrast with the color of the printing to achieve easy readibility.
b. Material used in outside layer may be extensively exposed to sunlight during storage or use. The material should be U.V. stabilized to withstand such expected exposure (either with an additive or by the inherent characteristics of the material). Requirements necessary to adequately resist sunlight exposure will depend strongly on the application. The end user must be consulted for specific standards to be met. As a general guideline, also refer to SAE J1960.

4.4 Identification—The following minimum information, in the order listed, is required. Additional information and/or another lay line may be added: SAE J2260 - D-T-P.

a. "D" refers to the reference size or nominal tubing diameter (OD) in mm from Tables A1 or A2A located in the Appendix.
b. "T" refers to the type of tube.
   1. Type NF—This is an MLT construction that is "non-conductive" by 7.9 and passes all requirements of this specification for carrying liquid fuel.
   2. Type CF—This is an MLT construction that is "conductive" by 7.9 and passes all requirements of this specification for carrying liquid fuel.
   3. Type NV—This is an MLT construction that is "non-conductive" by 7.9 and passes all requirements of this specification for carrying fuel vapor.
   4. Type CV—This is an MLT construction that is "conductive" by 7.9 and passes all requirements of this specification for carrying fuel vapor.
c. "P" refers to the permeation category (for the 4 types of tubing indicated previously) as determined by the procedures described in 7.10. It shall be a single digit that is identified from 7.10.2.
d. If it is not practical to print on the outside of the tubing (convoluted tubing or tubing with an outside surface that is not smooth, for example), then the labeling will be done by a tag or loop of tape permanently attached to the outside circumference of the tubing. Such labeling must be repeated every 500 mm or less along the entire length.
   For convoluted or corrugated tubing, the necessary printing can be done by the labeling or tagging procedure that is described. An acceptable alternative is to print the necessary wording only on each straight end section.

5. Dimensions—Tubing of various sizes and routed with certain bend radii are described in this specification. The end user should be consulted for specific requirements. What is detailed in this specification are recommended dimensions, tolerances, etc., based on common practices within the automotive industry and by participants in the fuel system business.

5.1 Tubing Sizes and Dimensions

5.1.1 DIAMETERS—For liquid fuel lines, the typical nominal OD's of the tubing used are in the range up to 10 mm. Lines that are over 10 mm nominal OD are typically used for fuel vapor. The end user should be consulted for specific requirements. The details on diameters are found in Tables A1, A2A and A2B.

5.1.2 WALL THICKNESS—Wall thicknesses vary for different tubing sizes and for the various classes of materials that are used in the construction of the tubing. Typical wall thicknesses for straight wall tubing are 1 mm ± 0.1 mm for nominal OD sizes up to 10 mm; the wall is thicker for larger OD sizes.

There are numerous factors that can have an influence on the wall thickness that is selected:

a. Higher required burst pressure could mean a thicker wall is required
b. As walls become thicker, the minimum bend radius increases
c. For MLT constructions with elastomeric covers, the critical dimension is the ID. The wall thickness is determined by the materials utilized and the requirements of the application
d. Tubing wall thickness may differ for convoluted/corrugated wall (refer to Section 6)

The result of all these factors is that the end user must be consulted to determine all requirements. The wall thickness is then determined by those requirements and the materials selected for the various layers of the multilayer tubing or for the monowall tubing.

Details on the suggested wall thicknesses are found in Tables A1, A2A, and A2B.

5.1.3 DIMENSIONAL TOLERANCES—Recommended tolerances of the various dimensions suggested for the tubing described in this document are found in Tables A1, A2A, and A2B. Actual tolerances used are determined by manufacturing capability and the requirements of the end user.

5.2 Minimum Bend Radius—When a tubing is routed as part of a vehicle system, there are occasional "free-state" bends that occur. Care must be taken to ensure that such bends do not occur at radii that are so tight that the inside dimensions of the tubing distort excessively. The end user should be consulted to determine the actual minimum bend radius that the tubing will encounter in a specific application. That detail should then be compared to the bend radius details described in 7.3.1. If the actual minimum bend radius is smaller than indicated by the appropriate table in 7.3.1, then the procedure of 7.3.2 should be followed to verify if the actual minimum bend of the application imposes a problem.

For the purposes of the performance measurements described in 7.3.3, the smaller of the two possible bend radii should be used (smaller of the appropriate calculation of Table 1/Table 2 or the required bend radius of actual application).

6. Convoluted or Corrugated Tubing—Tubing that has an OD over 10 mm may not be flexible enough for some applications. One way to resolve this concern is to use multilayer tubing with a wall that has a convoluted or corrugated configuration for all or portions of its length. There are certain criteria that must be met if such tubing is used; they are listed as follows:

a. The normal size of this tubing shall be the same as straight-wall tubing whose inside-diameter dimensions are the same as the effective inside diameter of the corrugated/convoluted tubing (e.g., a 12 mm convoluted tubing has an effective inside diameter of 9 mm (see Table A1)).
b. For the parts of the tubing that are not convoluted or corrugated, the size and dimensions that are used will be the same as described in 5.1.
c. At each end of the convoluted or corrugated tubing, there will be a straight section (sometimes called a cuff) that is a minimum of 30 mm in length. This section is the part of the tubing used to join the tubing to connectors, nipples, and other attachment elements. The dimensions of this cuff will correspond to those identified on Tables A1, A2A, and A2B.
d. Wall thickness of the convoluted/corrugated portions of the tubing may differ from those indicated in Table A1. This is due to the manufacturing process. Wall thickness deviations should be identified, and discussed with the end user. Performance test results will be used to gain agreement from the end user that such "routinely occurring" variations in wall thickness are acceptable.
e. Tubing with a convoluted or corrugated wall configuration is typically used in vapor or evaporative emissions applications. It is possible that such convoluted or corrugated tubing can be used in liquid fuel applications. Any tubing used in liquid fuel applications must meet the requirements called for in 7.9. In addition, the end user must be consulted and the final application must be carefully tested to determine that no unacceptable electrostatic charge situation develops (refer to SAE J1645).

7. Performance Requirements—All tests described in this standard are to be performed on the completed product (tubing). It must meet all applicable criteria described in this specification. Differences in performance criteria between liquid fuel and fuel vapor applications are indicated in the procedure or acceptance criteria of each section. If no distinction is made, both liquid and vapor fuel lines must meet the entire requirement as written.

The tubing shall meet the following performance tests with a ±3 S capability. Tubing shall be conformance tested no sooner than 24 h after production.

All test temperatures specified may vary by ±2 °C, unless otherwise specified. All times are minimum unless otherwise specified.

7.1 Room Temperature Burst Test

7.1.1 Initial Burst Test Measurement—Tubing shall be stabilized for 1/2 to 3 h at 23 °C and tested by increasing pressure of a fluid inside the tubing at a rate of 7 MPa/min ± 1 MPa/min. Continue at that rate until tubing bursts. Any type of fitting can be used during this burst test. If the connectors blow out of the tubing before the required level of burst pressure is reached, the data from that particular sample should be discarded. Additional clamps over the existing connectors or fittings may be utilized, if necessary, to ensure that the tubing sample fails by bursting.

The end user shall be consulted to establish the maximum pressure that can be encountered system in which the tubing will be used.

7.1.1.1 Acceptance Criteria—Minimum burst pressure of any one sample shall be 8 times the maximum pressure that can be encountered in the system in which the tubing will be used.

NOTE—If the maximum pressure is not known, then the measured burst pressure is recorded so it can be reported and compared to the requirements of a specific liquid or vapor system at some future time.

7.1.2 Burst Test Measurements After Exposures—An additional acceptance criteria is the comparison of the burst pressure test values of the tubing before exposure compared to the tubing after exposure, as detailed in Section 7. All values for burst test measured after exposure must be equal to or greater than 75% of the value of burst test measured on the tube prior to the exposure test. This criteria applies to the tests described in 7.5, 7.6, 7.7, and 7.8.

7.2 High Temperature Burst Test

7.2.1 The test procedure described in 7.1.1 shall be performed at a temperature of 115 °C.

NOTE—The fluid used in this burst test shall also be at the same temperature.

The end user shall be consulted to establish the maximum pressure that can possibly be encountered in the specific liquid or vapor system in which the tubing will be used.

7.2.1.1 Acceptance Criteria—Minimum burst pressure shall be three times the maximum pressure that can be encountered in the system in which the tubing will be used.

NOTE—If the maximum pressure is not known, then the high temperature burst pressure is recorded so it can be reported and compared to the requirements of a specific liquid or vapor system at some future time.

7.3 Resistance to Kinking

7.3.1 Calculation of Minimum Bend Radius—The formulae shown in Tables 1 and 2 shall be used to determine the minimum bend radius for tubing with dimensions as indicated in Tables A1, A2A, and A2B.

TABLE 1—MINIMUM BEND RADII FOR VARIOUS MLT SIZES

Reference Size of Tubing (From Tables A1, A2A and A2B)	Minimum Bend Radius
<8 mm	6 X Reference Size OD
8 £ OD < 12 mm	7.5 X Reference Size OD
12 £ OD < 18 mm	8.5 X Reference Size OD
Š18 mm	10 X Reference Size OD

TABLE 2—MINIMUM BEND RADII FOR VARIOUS SIZES OF MLT (WITH ELASTOMERIC OUTER LAYER)

Reference Size of Tubing (From Tables A1, A2A, and A2B)	Minimum Bend Radius
<6 mm	8 X Reference Size ID
6 £ ID < 9 mm	10 X Reference Size ID
9 £ ID < 14 mm	12 X Reference Size ID
Š14 mm	13 X Reference Size ID

Tubing that is part of this document can be bent at a tighter radii than the formulae shown in Tables 1 and 2. The procedure to determine this is described in the following section. The performance criteria that must be met for any tubing configured at the minimum bend radius is described in 7.3.3

7.3.2 Procedure to Determine Minimum Bend Radius—The following procedure can be used to determine if a tubing can be bent in a tighter radius than is indicated by the formula in Table 1 or Table 2 and to approximate what that bend radius may be. The procedure is shown in Figure 1.

The tubes are to be bent in a free state until they form a coil, the free ends are then grasped, wrapped over the first loop of tubing to form a two-layered coil of tubing. The tubing is drawn down to the smallest coil diameter possible within 1 min and without kinking the tubing. The measurement of the minimum bend radius is made by taking 1/2 the measured value of the inside diameter (inside wall to inside wall of coil of tubing). The length of tubing used for this test shall vary with different diameters of the tubing. The length shall be enough so that the procedure shown in Figure 1 can be accomplished with at least 100 mm of tubing extending beyond the circle on both sides.

It is important to note that the radius measured by this procedure is an approximation. The performance test of 7.3.3 must be passed to confirm that the estimated bend radius can be achieved without kinking.

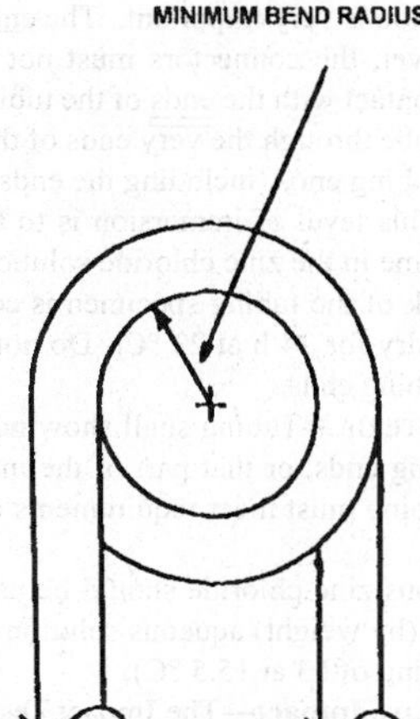

FIGURE 1—ILLUSTRATION OF PROCEDURE FOR DETERMINING MINIMUM BEND RADIUS

7.3.3 Resistance to Kinking—Test Procedure—This test procedure is to determine if a tube can meet the minimum bend radius dimensions from Table 1, Table 2, or from the procedure of 7.3.2.

First step is to identify the minimum bend radius dimension that is to be tested for a specific tubing diameter. A tubing test specimen shall then be cut to length equal to: (1.2xp) x minimum radius.

The tubing specimen shall then be placed in a fixture as shown in Figure 2. When installing the tube, it shall be bent in the same plane and direction as its free state curvature. Place the tube, installed on the fixture, into an oven at 115 °C and soak for 1 h. Remove the fixture from the oven and pass the specified steel ball through the tube on the fixture. Tubing and fixture can be allowed to cool to room temperature for easier handling.

The diameter of the ball shall be determined by Equation 1:

Ball diameter (mm) = 0.4 x minimum tubing ID ± 0.05 mm (Eq. 1)

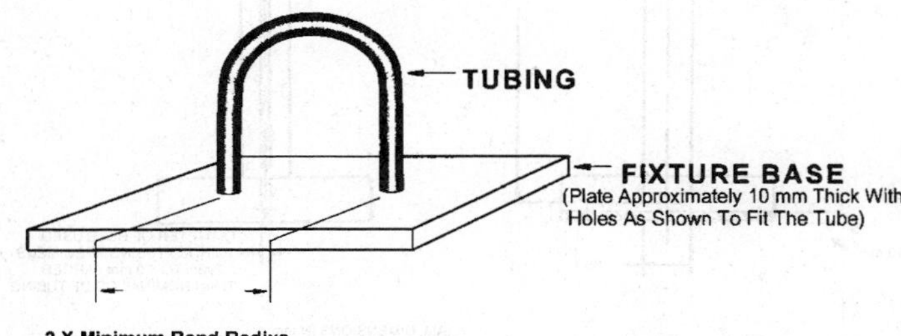

FIGURE 2—KINKING RESISTANCE TEST FIXTURE

7.3.3.1 Acceptance Criteria—Restriction of the passage of the ball constitutes a failure.

7.4 Burst Test on Kinked Tubing—Tubing shall be stabilized for 1/2 to 3 h at 23 °C. Completely bend tubing so it is kinked and two lengths of tubing on either side of kink touch along entire length. Straighten tubing completely. Repeat so tubing is kinked a total of five times at same position tubing.

7.4.1 ACCEPTANCE CRITERIA—Tubing must meet requirements of the Room Temperature Burst Test (see 7.1.2).

7.5 Resistance to Zinc Chloride—Cut tubing specimen to be tested to a length as described in the second paragraph of 7.3.3. The connectors or fittings that will be used in the burst pressure testing of 7.1 are then inserted in each end of the tubing. The tubing is then bent in a half circle and mounted onto a fixture that is similar to that shown in Figure 2. The dimensions of the fixture, spacing of the means of mounting the connectors, radius of curvature are dependent on the diameter of the tubing. Other details described in 7.3 are to be used for guidance.

When the tubing specimen (and its two connectors/fittings) is appropriately mounted in the fixture, invert it so the curved part is down and immerse the tubing specimen into a 50% (by weight) aqueous solution of zinc chloride at 23 °C for 200 h.

Depth of the immersion is very important. The entire tubing specimen must be fully immersed; however, the connectors must not be fully immersed. The zinc chloride must be in contact with the ends of the tubing, but should not be able to enter the inside of the tube through the very ends of the connectors. This simulates the exposure of the tubing ends (including the ends of each layer) to the road chemical environment. This level of immersion is to be maintained throughout the entire 200 h soaking time in the zinc chloride solution.

When the 200 h soak of the tubing specimen is completed, remove it from the solution and allow to dry for 24 h at 23 °C. Do not wipe off excess solution from any surface or the tubing ends.

7.5.1 ACCEPTANCE CRITERIA—Tubing shall show no evidence of cracking on the outside diameter, tubing ends, or that part of the inner surface that is visible from the tubing ends. Tubing must meet requirements of the Room Temperature Burst Test (see 7.1.2).

NOTE—Fresh, anhydrous zinc chloride should be used to make up a concentration of 50% (by weight) aqueous solution (specific gravity of 1.576 or a Baumé rating of 53 at 15.5 °C).

7.6 Cold Temperature Impact—The Impact Test Apparatus is pictured in Figure 3. The impact head weighs 0.912 kg ± 0.003 kg. It is in the form of bar with a diameter of 31.75 mm and its end has a spherical radius of 15.88 mm. The test apparatus allows the impact head to fall 305 mm ± 3 mm. The 305 mm ± 3 mm distance is measured from the bottom of the weight to the center of the tube specimen. When the mass is released, it must fall freely in the fixture. The maximum radius of curvature of the edge of the supporting platform is 1.3 mm. The supporting platform should be 10 mm ± 1 mm thick.

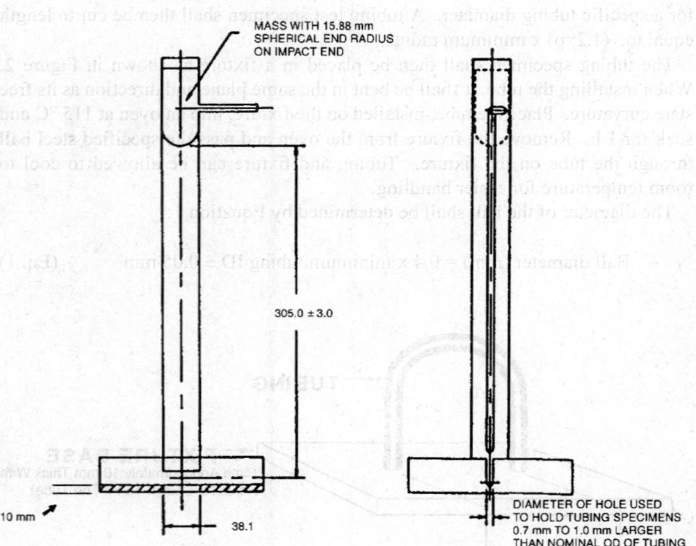

FIGURE 3—COLD IMPACT TEST FIXTURE

7.6.1 PREFERRED PROCEDURE—Expose the test samples and the impact test apparatus to –40 °C for 4 h. Place each sample in the supporting platform of the apparatus and allow the impact head to fall on it. Impact should occur with both apparatus and specimens inside the cold chamber.

7.6.2 OPTIONAL PROCEDURE—If the impact test cannot be done inside the cold chamber, the apparatus and the specimens can be removed from the chamber by the following procedure:

a. The apparatus is removed from the chamber for up to a 3 min period. During that period, impact tests of several tubing specimens can be completed. At the end of that 3 min period, the apparatus is returned to the chamber for additional temperature soak (–40 °C) of at least 25 min duration. After that additional soak at temperature, the apparatus can be removed again for an additional set of cold impact of tubing specimens (within a 3 min period). This procedure is repeated until all test specimens have been impacted properly.
b. All test specimens are kept in the cold chamber until immediately before impact in the apparatus. When a tubing specimen is removed, it must be impacted in the apparatus within 5 s of its removal from the cold temperature environment.

NOTE—The temperature of the ambient air where these impacts occur shall not be higher than 23 °C.

7.6.3 ACCEPTANCE CRITERIA—After impact of a tubing specimen, it is allowed to return to 23 °C. The tubing specimen is then subjected to Room Temperature Burst requirements of 7.1.2. All criteria of that section must be met.

7.7 Methanol Fuel Resistance

7.7.1 PROCEDURES—There are two procedures that can be followed for exposing the test specimens to methanol fuel; the preferred to follow is the recirculation method of 7.7.1.1. Test fuel for this procedure shall be CM-15 (refer to SAE J1681 for details on composition). Needs of end user may require that another test fuel be used (such as TF-2, FAMB, etc.). Therefore, a different methanol-containing test fuel may be used in this procedure but it would be only for that specific application. For purposes of comparison and unless otherwise specified for a certain situation, the test fuel shall be CM-15. Length of the tubing specimens tested shall be 0.3 m or longer. At least 5 specimens should be tested to allow subsequent testing identified in the acceptance criteria section (7.7.2).

7.7.1.1 Recirculation Method—Methanol-blend fuel should be continuously circulated through the tubing specimens for a minimum of 1000 h (approximately 42 days). The temperature of the fuel must be maintained at 40 °C. Composition of the fuel should be measured and adjusted periodically to ensure that the methanol content of the fuel is maintained at 15% ± 3% (frequency of the checking of the composition is determined primarily by the size of the liquid fuel reservoir that's used in the recirculation process). Methanol content shall be measured every 3 days after the start of test until it is established that the rate of methanol content change is less than the ±3% within a week's time. The frequency of checking methanol content can then be decreased to once per week. If these tests are done frequently and a history of how often the methanol should be checked can be substantiated from previous test specimens, then that established schedule can be utilized. Methanol content shall always be checked at least once per week. If the methanol content of the fuel goes outside of the limits, the test fuel should be replaced with a new mixture with the correct level of methanol.

7.7.1.2 Optional Method—(To be followed only if recirculation procedure is not available.)

Plug one end of tubing to be tested, then fill with the test fuel. Plug the other end of the tubing in such a manner that it can be periodically removed. Expose the filled tubing to a temperature of 40 °C for 42 days continuously. The test fuel must be replaced with fresh test fuel every 3 days.

7.7.2 ACCEPTANCE CRITERIA—After 42 days exposure to the methanol fuel at 40 °C, the tubing is then tested for cold impact resistance per 7.6. The cold soak must be started immediately after emptying the tubing of the methanol blend fuel (to avoid any drying out of the tubing). All criteria of that section must be met.

NOTE—Section 7.6 also includes the burst requirements of 7.1.2.

The tubing that was exposed to the methanol fuel shall also be tested for layer adhesion (see 7.11.2) and for electrical resistance (see 7.9.1). The acceptance criteria of those two sections must be met.

7.8 Auto-Oxidized Gasoline

7.8.1 PROCEDURES—There are two procedures that can be followed for exposing the tubing test specimens to auto-oxidated gasoline; the preferred one to follow is the recirculation method of 7.8.1.1. The auto-oxidized gasoline must be maintained at a peroxide number of 90 (for determination of peroxide number, refer to ISO 4639-3 Annex A; base fuel for auto-oxidized gasoline formulation shall be ASTM fuel C). The temperature of the test fuel shall be maintained at 40 °C. At least 5 specimens should be tested to allow for subsequent testing identified in the acceptance criteria section (7.8.2). Length of the specimens tested shall be 0.3 m or longer.

7.8.1.1 Recirculation Method—(Refer to SAE J1737 for details of procedure.)

Auto-oxidized gasoline (with the required peroxide number) should be recirculated continuously through the tubing being tested for a period of 1000 h (approximately 42 days). Composition of the fuel should be measured periodically to ensure that the peroxide number is maintained at 90 ± 5 (frequency of the checking of the composition is determined primarily by the size of the liquid fuel reservoir that's used in the recirculation process). It is recommended that the peroxide number (P/N) be measured on the first and seventh day after the test begins. Based on the rate of change of P/N over that period of time, a schedule for frequency of measurement of P/N should be established (no less than once every 10 days, however). If the P/N goes outside the limits, the test fuel should be entirely replaced with a new mixture with the correct P/N.

7.8.1.2 Optional Method—(To be followed only if recirculation procedure is not available.)

Plug one end of the tubing specimen, then fill with auto-oxidized gasoline (with peroxide number of 90). Plug the other end of the tubing in such a manner that it can be periodically removed. Expose the filled tubing to a temperature of 40 °C for 42 days continuously. The auto-oxidized gasoline must be replaced with "fresh" auto-oxidized gasoline every 3 days in order to maintain the peroxide number at 90 ± 5.

7.8.2 ACCEPTANCE CRITERIA—After 42 days of continuous exposure to the auto-oxidized gasoline at 40 °C, the tubing specimen is then tested for cold impact resistance per 7.6. The cold soak must be started immediately after emptying the tubing of the auto-oxidized gasoline (to avoid drying out of the tubing). All criteria of that section must be met.

NOTE—Section 7.6 also includes the burst requirements of 7.1.

The tubing that was exposed to the auto-oxidized fuel shall also be tested for layer adhesion (see 7.11.2) and for electrical resistance (see 7.9.2). The acceptance criteria of those two sections must be met.

7.9 Electrical Resistance—In many liquid fuel carrying lines a certain level of conductivity is required. An acceptable conductivity level can be verified by setting a maximum allowable surface resistivity, derived from the resistance measurement procedure described in 7.9.2.

7.9.1 SAE DOCUMENT—SAE J1645 describes the situation surrounding the electrostatic charging that can exist in a fuel system. Although that report is not a specific standard, it does suggest certain guidelines in such areas as grounding, assemblies, and tubing configurations that should be followed. When developing a system to carry liquid fuel, care must be taken to consider all aspects of the system from an electrostatic charge perspective. The final system should be tested in close conjunction with the needs of the end user to insure that all necessary criteria are met.

7.9.2 SURFACE RESISTIVITY—The test apparatus consists of a resistance meter (MEG-CHECK 2100A R-meter from Associates Research Inc. or equivalent) and a set of copper pins (diameter approximately 0.1 mm larger than ID of tubing).

7.9.2.1 Test Procedure

a. All tests are conducted at 23 °C ± 2 °C and 50% ± 5% relative humidity.
b. Measure sample length. Record as 'L_o' (mm).
c. Measure inner diameter of sample. Record as 'd' (mm).
d. Insert the copper pins to full depth in ends of tube assuring a tight fit. Measure the depth of the copper pin 'a' (mm). Attach the leads to the resistance meter as shown in Figure 4.
e. Record the resistance R (ohms).
f. Calculate Equation 2:

$$\text{Surface Resistivity (ohms/sq)} = \frac{R(\pi d)}{(L_0 - 2a)} \quad \text{(Eq. 2)}$$

g. Measure the resistance and record the associated surface resistivity of tubing specimens before any exposure testing.

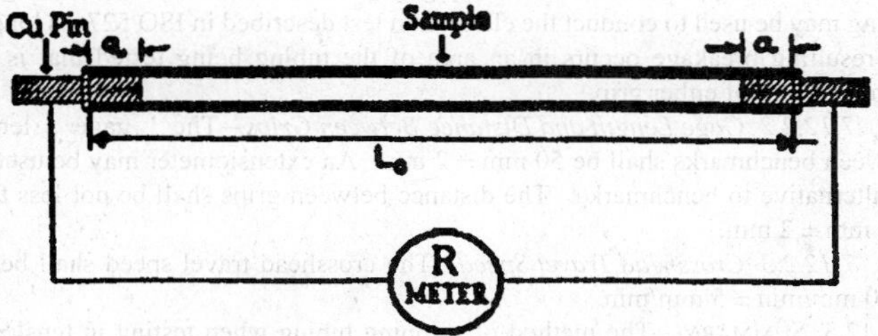

FIGURE 4—SCHEMATIC OF RESISTANCE MEASUREMENT FIXTURE

7.9.2.2 Surface resistivity (W/square) shall also be obtained from tubing samples that have been subjected to certain tests or exposures described in the specification. In each case, it is the exposure test only that is included in this section. The burst test or other subsequent procedure is not included in requirements of this section.

Section 7.4—Full Kink Procedure
Section 7.6—Cold Impact Test
Section 7.7—Methanol Fuel Exposure
Section 7.8—Sour Gasoline Exposure

For each of these four tests, the resistance of the tubing specimen is measured after the exposure by the same procedure as 7.9.2.1. The result obtained is recorded and compared to the result obtained on the same tubing specimen before the exposure test. A different tubing specimen is used in each of the exposure tests. Acceptance criteria indicated in 7.9.2.3 must be met.

7.9.2.3 Acceptance Criteria—There are two types of acceptance criteria for the level of surface resistivity level measured.

7.9.2.3.1 Surface Resistivity Level—The surface resistivity derived from measured resistance values measured on test specimens both before and after exposure testing shall not be greater than 10^6 W/square.

7.9.2.3.2 Maximum Change in Measured Surface Resistance Level—When the level of surface resistivity measured on each test specimens after exposure testing is compared to the level measured on the same test specimen before exposure testing, the maximum difference in surface resistivity between the two for each exposure test shall not be greater than a change of two orders of magnitude.

7.10 Permeation Resistance—The procedure to be followed for determining level of permeation resistance is described in SAE J1737. The test fuel to be used will depend on the requirements of the end use application. Typical comparison tests are made among various multilayer tubing constructions by use of alcohol-content fuels (CE-10 and CM-15 are most common).

Permeation is expressed in grams/(meter^{2}Þday). It is also possible to relate that rate of permeation to the permeation that could occur in grams per day per meter of tubing (by calculating the inside circumference of the tubing that is wetted by the fuel).

7.10.1 DETERMINATION OF PERMEATION RESISTANCE—For determination of permeation resistance for use on a specific vehicle or in a specific subsystem, the test fuel can relate more closely to the specific fuel that is used in testing of whole vehicles or vehicle subsystems for compliance to emissions requirements.

Permeation resistance testing must be conducted until steady state is achieved (refer to SAE J1737). The value determined is expressed in grams/(meter^{2}Þday). Acceptance criteria is to be determined by the end user.

It is important to realize that the permeation rate in grams/(meter^{2}Þday) is much larger than the permeation rate per meter of tubing, because it takes many meters of the tubing to equal a square meter. In the case of 8 mm tubing with a 6 mm ID, for example, 53.05 m of tubing are required to reach a total inside surface area of 1 m^2. The calculation is shown in Equation 3:

$$1\ \text{m}^2 \text{ of tubing inside surface} = \text{circumference of the inside of tubing x length in meters} \quad \text{(Eq. 3)}$$

a. A sample calculation for 8 mm tubing with a 1 mm wall thickness:
1 m^2 = p x (6 x 10^{-3} m) x length in meters
1 m^2 = 0.01885 x length in meters
1 m^2 = 53.05 m of length

7.10.2 GENERAL CLASSIFICATION OF PERMEATION RESISTANCE—For purposes of general identification, the equilibrium level of permeation rate shall be measured by following the procedure described in SAE J1737. The steps that must be followed are:

a. Use test fuel that is a blend of ASTM Fuel C and 15% methanol (CM-15 by SAE J1681).
b. Use test temperature of 60 °C and test proessure of 200 kPa.
c. Units reported from the measurement shall be grams/(meter^2·day) and shall be reported as a whole number by following all the guidelines of 8.3 of SAE J1737.
d. Care must be taken that the permeation rate measured is at steady-state as defined and discussed in 3.3 of SAE J1737 (see also 7.10.3 of this document).
e. A minimum of five specimens must be tested by this procedure. After the high and low value of those five separate measurements are discarded, the average of the remaining 3 measurements shall be the number used to describe the permeation rate of the tubing being tested. The average shall be rounded off to a whole number by following the guidelines of 8.3 of SAE J1737.
f. The whole number value of permeation determined from the previous step shall be used to identify the permeation category from Table 3. That category number is the digit "P" that is marked on the tubing for identification purposes that is described in 4.4.

TABLE 3—DETERMINING CATEGORY OF PERMEATION PERFORMANCE

Category Number	Permeation Measurement of Tubing as Determined by Steps of 7.10.2 (grams/m^2·day)
1	0 - 25
2	25 - 50
3	50 - 100
4	100 - 200
5	200 - 400
6	over 400

7.10.3 Time to Reach Equilibrium Permeation Resistance—When measuring permeation resistance, experience has shown that it can take several hundreds of hours to achieve steady-state or equilibrium levels. Based on experience with the test conditions and fuel indicated in 7.10.2, the following general guideline should be followed.

This time to reach equilibrium is the continuous exposure time to the identified test conditions. It is a summation of the preconditioning step and time in the permeation test unit (refer to SAE J1737, Section 7.2). If temperatures are lower than 60 °C or test fuels are "less active" than those containing methanol, the overall time will be longer than shown in Table 4.

TABLE 4—ESTIMATING TIME TO ACHIEVE EQUILIBRIUM PERMEATION MEASUREMENT

Range of Measured Permeation Resistance Level (grams/meter^{2}PDay) (M-15 Fuel @ 60 °C)	Suggested Time
0 -25	over 1000 h
25 – 50	1000 h
50 – 100	800 h
100 – 200	600 h
200 – 400	500 h
Over 400	400 h

7.11 Layer Adhesion—When the tubing has been manufactured with 2 or more layers, those various layers must properly adhere to one another initially and after fuel exposure. (If tubing being tested is a monowall construction, then the tests of 7.11 are not necessary.)

7.11.1 Initial Adhesion Test—This test is designed for straight-wall MLT. If the spiral cut test cannot be applied to the particular construction, then the adhesion test described in 7.11.2 will still apply.

7.11.1.1 Procedure—Cut a sample of tubing into a helical coil whose length is at least five times the circumference of the tubing. The width of the strip should be no less than 70% of the outer diameter of the tubing. (Figure 5 shows an example of a suitable tool for producing such a cut.) Suspend a weight from the end of the strip using an alligator clip or some other suitable means. Increase the weight until the helical coil is "unspiraled" into a flat ribbon (minimum weight is 2 kg). To aid in the unspiraling process, the weight can be turned by hand.

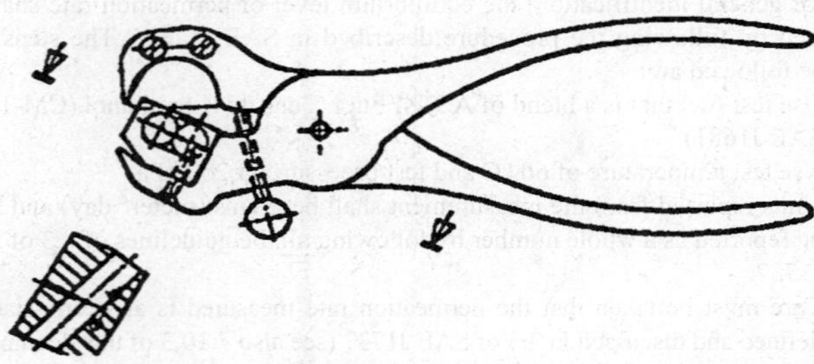

FIGURE 5—EXAMPLE OF SUITABLE TOOL FOR SPIRAL CUT ADHESION TEST

7.11.1.2 Acceptance Criteria—No visible signs of delamination should occur between layers (excluded from this is the point on the strip where the weight is attached).

7.11.2 Adhesion Test After Fuel Exposure—After each of the two fuel exposure procedures described in 7.7 and 7.8, each specimen must be examined for layer adhesion.

7.11.2.1 Procedure—Tubing specimen shall be cut to length and then shall be bent into a "U" shape at the minimum bend radius (refer to 7.3 for details of length and radius). Each tubing end is then inserted into a fixture that secures the specimen in the desired bend radius and allows the specimen to be laid flat on a horizontal surface. The tubing is then cut in half lengthwise in the bend area for at least 120 degrees of the required 180 degree bend. The cut goes through both vertical portions of the tubing wall and is made parallel to the surface upon which the bent tubing is resting. The cut removes the "top half" of the tubing, leaving behind a "U-shaped" cross section of the tubing for the required length of the cut (at least 120 degrees of the 180 degree bend). Refer to Figure 6.

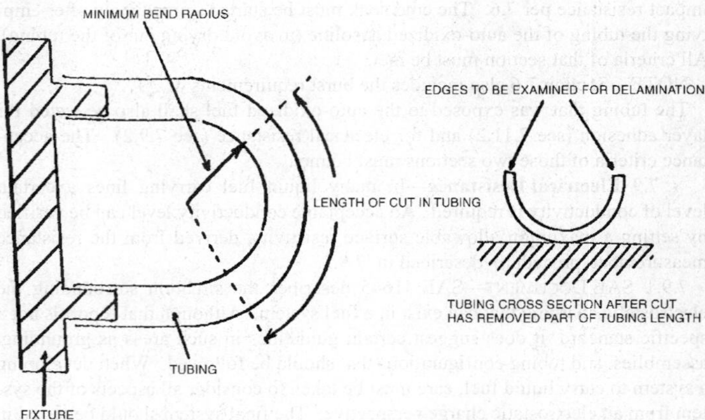

FIGURE 6—ILLUSTRATION OF PROCEDURE FOR LAYER ADHESION TEST AFTER FUEL EXPOSURE

7.11.2.2 Acceptance Criteria—Examine the exposed edges of the cut portion of the tubing while it remains in the fixture. There shall be no evidence of delamination between the layers in the area of the cut.

7.12 Tensile Strength, Elongation—This is an optional test. The acceptance criteria are to be agreed upon by producer and end user.

The procedure to be followed is described in 7.12.1 through 7.12.3. The gripping procedure that is suggested for use in the tests is described in 7.12.2.1. Other gripping fixtures/procedures may be used provided that the resulting breakage during the tensile elongation test is in the approximate center of the test specimen. If breakage occurs outside the gage length (see 7.12.2.2) the elongation test result will be considered invalid.

7.12.1 Test Methods Summary—This test method covers tension testing of plastic fuel tubing. It follows the general practices of ISO 527. Method "A" of ISO 527 for dumbbell and straight specimens is the method choice with the following modifications listed in 7.11.2.1.

7.12.2 Modifications to ISO 527

7.12.2.1 Grips and Fixtures—Any grip procedure or fixture for holding the tubing may be used to conduct the elongation test described in ISO 527, as long as the resulting breakage occurs in an area of the tubing being tested that is not within 25 mm of either grip.

7.12.2.2 Gage Length and Distance Between Grips—The gage length between benchmarks shall be 50 mm ± 2 mm. An extensiometer may be used as an alternative to benchmarks. The distance between grips shall be not less than 100 mm ± 2 mm.

7.12.2.3 Crosshead Travel Speed—The crosshead travel speed shall be set at 50 mm/min ± 5 mm/min.

7.12.3 Summary—The method of gripping tubing when testing in tension is critical to optimizing repeatability. The previous modifications to ISO 527 listed in 7.11.2, enhance this repeatability.

APPENDIX A

A.1 Tables A1, A2A, and A2B are listings of the various tubing sizes, wall thicknesses, and tolerances that should be used for the tubing covered in this document.

TABLE A1—TUBING DIMENSIONS (METRIC SIZES)[1]

Reference Sizes OD Dimension (mm)	ID of Tubing (mm)	Wall Thickness
5	3.0	1.0
6	4.0	1.0
8	6.0	1.0
10	8.0	1.0
12	9.0	1.5
15	12.0	1.5
18	14.0	2.0
20	16.0	2.0
22	18.0	2.0

1. Tolerances are ±0.1 mm for reference sizes 10 mm and less. For over 10 mm reference size, the tolerance is ±0.15 mm.

TABLE A2A—TUBING DIMENSIONS (INCH SIZES)— TYPICAL EXTRUDED TUBING

Reference Sizes (Nominal Tubing Diameter OD)	ID of Tubing (mm)	Wall Thickness (mm)
1/4 in (6.35 mm)	3.89 to 4.14 mm	0.98 to 1.41
5/16 in (7.93 mm)	6.20 to 6.50 mm	0.90 to 1.15
3/8 in (9.53 mm)	7.90 to 8.20 mm	0.90 to 1.15

TABLE A2B—TUBING DIMENSIONS (INCH SIZES)— MLT WITH ELASTOMERIC COATING

Reference Sizes (Nominal Tubing Diameter)	ID of Tubing Metric (mm)	ID of Tubing Decimal (in)	Wall Thickness Metric (mm)	Wall Thickness Decimal (in)
3/8 in (9.53 mm)	8.9 ± 0.3	3.50 ± 0.012	3.5 ± 0.5	0.138 ± 0.020
7/16 in (11.12 mm)	9.9 ± 0.3	0.390 ± 0.012	3.5 ± 0.5	0.138 ± 0.020
1/2 in (12.7 mm)	11.7 ± 0.3	0.460 ± 0.012	3.5 ± 0.5	0.138 ± 0.020
5/8 in (15.88 mm)	14.5 ± 0.3	0.570 ± 0.012	3.5 ± 0.5	0.138 ± 0.020

LOW-PERMEATION FUEL FILL AND VENT TUBE—SAE J2405 AUG1997

SAE Standard

Report of the SAE Fuel, Oil, and Emission Hose Committee approved August 1997.

1. Scope—This SAE Standard covers the minimum requirements for a low-permeation tubing (100 $g/m^2 \cdot day$ or less) for use as a low pressure (14.5 kPa) liquid- or vapor-carrying component for use in gasoline or diesel fuel filler, vent, and vapor systems. The construction shall be designed to be functional over a temperature range of –40 °C to 100 °C for the T1 designation, or –40 °C to 125 °C for the T2 designation.

2. References

2.1 Applicable Publications—The following publications form a part of the specification to the extent specified herein. Unless otherwise indicated the latest revision of SAE publications shall apply.

2.1.1 SAE PUBLICATION—Available from SAE, 400 Commonwealth Drive, Warrendale, PA 15096-0001.

SAE J1737—Recommended Practice for Measurement of Permeation Resistance by the Recirculation Technique

2.1.2 ASTM PUBLICATIONS—Available from ASTM, 100 Barr Harbor Drive, West Conshohocken, PA 19428-2959.

ASTM D 380—Methods of Testing Rubber Hose

ASTM D 413—Test Methods for Rubber Property: Adhesion to Flexible Substrate

ASTM D 471—Test for Rubber Property: Effect of Liquids

ASTM D 1149—Test Method for Rubber Deterioration: Surface Ozone Cracking in a Chamber (Flat Specimens)

2.2 Related Publications—The following publications are provided for information purposes only and are not a required part of this document.

2.2.1 SAE PUBLICATIONS—Available from SAE, 400 Commonwealth Drive, Warrendale, PA 15096-0001.

SAE J30—Fuel and Oil Hoses

SAE J1645—Fuel System Electrostatic Charge

SAE J1681—Gasoline/Methanol Mixtures for Material Testing

SAE J2260—Nonmetallic Fuel System Tubing With One or More Layers

2.2.2 ASTM PUBLICATIONS—Available from ASTM, 100 Barr Harbor Drive, West Conshohocken, PA 19428-2959.

ASTM D 257—DC Resistance or Conductance of Insulating Materials

ASTM D 412—Test for Rubber Properties in Tension

ASTM D 573—Test for Rubber: Deterioration in an Air Oven

2.2.3 RMA PUBLICATION—Available from Rubber Manufacturers Association, 1400 K Street, NW, Suite 900, Washington, DC 20005.

RMA IP-2—Method for Measuring Electrical Resistance of Hose

3. Construction—The construction typically consists of a smooth bore or laminated tube of one or more synthetic rubber compound(s) and/or thermoplastic material(s) resistant to chemical attack, swelling, and permeation by gasoline, alcohol extended gasoline, or diesel fuel. It may also be covered with a suitable oil, ozone, and heat-resistant synthetic rubber compound or thermoplastic. The specific construction details are to be agreed between the supplier and the original purchaser.

4. Dimensions

4.1 The ends of the tube shall be square within 3.0 mm for sizes up to but excluding 25.4 mm ID, 6.4 mm for sizes 25.4 mm through 50.8 mm ID, and 9.5 mm for sizes over 50.8 mm ID. Reference Table 1.

4.2 When tubing is supplied in specific cut or long lengths, the length tolerances shall be as in Table 2.

4.3 End squareness shall be measured as the angle between a plane intersecting the long and short extremes of the tube end and a plane perpendicular to the tube axis. The allowable maximum out-of-squareness is specified in Table 1.

5. When a tube is supplied as a preformed item, the tolerance shall be as follows:

5.1 Squareness of Ends—The tolerance on squareness of ends of preformed parts shall be a minimum 15% of the nominal tube OD on all sizes through 25.4 mm ID, 6.3 mm for sizes over 25.4 mm ID through 50.8 mm ID, and 9.5 mm for sizes over 50.8 mm ID. End squareness shall be measured as described in 4.1.

5.2 Arms Lengths—Measured from end to intersection of nearest centerline. Each end shall be as described in Section 4. These tolerances apply also to the length of an expanded end.

5.3 General Layout—Dimensions locating bend intersections are to establish the theoretical centerline of the tube. Actual outside contour of the tube must be held within 4.8 mm in all planes with respect to the theoretical outside contour. To check contour, tube ends should first be placed in nominal position (it may have to be flexed to correct any distortion caused by handling after vulcanization in the producing plant or in shipment) in a checking fixture made in accordance with user requirements from which contour deviation can be measured. Allowance shall be provided in the end-mounting area of the fixture for the arm length tolerances which are applicable.

When the ID of an end of the tube is enlarged, the wall gauge of the enlarged end normally changes. Allowable change should be +0.8 –0.5 mm. The wall gauge within bends of a preformed tube may differ from the gauge in straight portions. The difference shall not exceed 33%.

TABLE 1—DIMENSIONS AND TOLERANCES

Nominal Size mm	Inside Diameter mm	Outside Diameter(1) mm	End Out-of Squareness Angle, Deg(2)
4.0	4.0 ± 0.4	9.1 ± 0.6	14.5
4.8	4.8 ± 0.4	10.3 ± 0.6	14.4
5.6	5.6 ± 0.4	11.1 ± 0.6	14.3
6.4	6.4 ± 0.4	12.7 ± 0.6	14.2
7.0	7.0 ± 0.4	13.5 ± 0.6	14.1
7.9	7.9 ± 0.4	14.3 ± 0.6	14.0
8.7	8.7 ± 0.4	15.1 ± 0.6	14.0
9.5	9.5 ± 0.4	15.9 ± 0.6	13.9
11.1	11.1 ± 0.6	18.3 ± 0.8	13.7
12.7	12.7 ± 0.6	19.8 ± 0.8	13.5
15.9	15.9 ± 0.8	23.8 ± 0.8	13.1
19.1	19.1 ± 0.8	28.6 ± 0.8	12.7
25.4	25.4 ± 0.8	34.9 ± 1.6	12.0
31.8	31.8 ± 1.0	not specified(3)	11.2
38.1	38.1 ± 1.0	not specified(3)	10.4
44.5	44.5 ± 1.0	not specified(3)	9.7
50.8	50.8 ± 1.0	not specified(3)	8.9
57.2	57.2 ± 1.0	not specified(3)	8.1
63.5	63.5 ± 1.0	not specified(3)	7.4

1. Concentricity based on total indicator reading between the inside bore and the outer surface of the tube shall not exceed the values given as follows:
   Sizes 6.4 mm and under:0.762 mm
   Sizes over 6.4 mm up to 12.7 mm:1.016 mm
   Sizes over 12.7 mm:1.270 mm
2. These values were determined by the equation:
   A = 15 degrees – K X D
   where:
   A = Maximum out-of-squareness angle
   K = 0.12 degree per mm of diameter (a slope factor derived from linear best-fit previous squareness requirement)
   D = Nominal inside diameter in millimeters
3. The wall gauge for sizes 31.8 mm to 50.8 mm shall be between 4.3 to 5.9 mm, and for sizes 57.2 mm to 63.5 mm, between 4.3 to 6.4 mm.

TABLE 2—CUT OR LONG LENGTH TOLERANCES

Length m	Precision mm	Commercial mm
0-0.3	± 3.0	+ 9.5/–3.0
over 0.3-0.6	± 4.8	+9.5/–4.8
over 0.6-0.9	±6.3	+12.7/-6.3
over 0.9-1.2	±9.5	+12.7/-9.5
over 1.2-1.8	±12.7	+19.0/-12.7
over 1.8	±1%	+2%/0%

6. ***Tests***—Procedures described by ASTM D 380 are to be followed. All temperature tolerances are ±2 °C unless otherwise specified.

6.1 Qualification Testing—In order to qualify under this specification, tube or the assembly must meet all the applicable test requirements of Section 7. Tube for testing will be 12.7 mm ID or agreed upon between supplier and user. The construction must be representative of constructions of all other sizes. The impermeable layer thickness cannot be reduced with other sizes.

6.2 Frequency of Testing for Qualification—Qualification testing to be performed once each year except for permeation testing which only needs to be tested initially.

6.3 Inspection Testing—ON tube or the assembly, the following inspection tests shall apply: (7.1) burst, (7.2) vacuum collapse, (7.11.1) original adhesion, (7.12) kink resistance, and (7.6) electrical conductivity (if required).

6.4 Frequency of Testing for Inspection and Quality Acceptance Standards—Quality acceptance standards to be agreed upon between supplier and the original purchaser.

7. ***Test Requirements***

7.1 Burst Test (Inspection Test on all sizes)—The minimum burst shall be 350 kPa per ASTM D 380.

7.2 Vacuum Collapse Test (Inspection Test on all sizes)—For straight tube, a 1 m length of tube or the assembly shall be held in a straight line. On preformed parts, the vacuum collapse test shall be performed on the finished part. No diameter shall decrease by more than 20% during application of vacuum for a minimum of 15 s and not more than 60 s. Tube sizes as listed in Table 3 shall be subjected to the corresponding vacuum pressure:

TABLE 3—VACUUM COLLAPSE MINIMUM PRESSURES

Tube ID Size	Vacuum Pressure
<12.7 mm	81 kPa
12.7 to 25.4 mm	34 kPa
>25.4 mm to 44.5 mm	14.3 kPa
>44.5 mm	limit to be agreed upon between supplier and manufacturer

7.3 Low-Temperature Flexibility (Qualification Test)—Fill tube with Reference Fuel C and seal both ends. Allow it to condition at 23 °C for 168 h. Drain the fuel. Immediately expose the tube along with a mandrel that is 10 times the nominal OD to a temperature of –40 °C for 24 h. Bend the tube or sample around the mandrel while keeping both at the prescribed temperature. It shall not fracture and shall not show cracks, checks, or breaks in any of the layers of construction.

7.4 Original Material Properties (Qualification Test)—The test procedure and apparatus shall be in accordance with ASTM D 412, where applicable.

a. Original Tensile Strength of Cover—7 MPa min
b. Original Tensile Strength of tube or Laminated Tube—7 MPa min
c. Original Elongation of Cover—150% min
d. Original Elongation of Tube or Laminated Tube—150% min

7.5 Heat Resistance (Qualification Test)—Expose a 300 mm length tube for 1000 h at the prescribed test temperature. The test temperature for a T1 construction is 100 °C and 125 °C for the T2 construction. Remove the tube from the oven and allow to cool to room temperature for a minimum of 2 h. Bend it over a mandrel having a diameter of 10 times the nominal OD within 4 s. Examine it, both inside and outside. The tube shall show no cracks or breaks.

7.6 Electrical Conductivity (Inspection Test on all sizes)—The purpose is to provide a conductive pathway to dissipate any static electrical buildup. This test is required only for tube that will be designated as electrically conductive.

An entire tube (maximum length 610 mm) will be used for this test, unless its length exceeds 610 mm, at which time the length for test shall be 610 mm. Insert a brass, steel, or copper plug or fitting into each end. Place clamps on each end of the tube and firmly tighten. Attach the ohmmeter electrodes to the plugs at each end. Measure the resistance between the plugs while applying 550 V DC (±50 V). The maximum resistance allowable is 10 MΩ.

NOTE 1—The diameter of the plug or fitting should be close to the ID of the tube.

NOTE 2—The tube while under test should be placed on a nonconductive surface.

NOTE 3—Ohmmeter must have the capability of measuring resistance from 10^{-1} to 10^{3} MΩ at 550 V DC.

7.7 Oil Resistance (Qualification Test)—After immersion in IRM 903 oil for 70 h, at 125 °C per ASTM D 471, the volume change of a sample taken from the outer layer (or tube, in the case of a monolayer tube) shall not exceed +60%.

7.8 Fuel Resistance (Qualification Test)—After immersion in ASTM Reference Fuel C for 48 h, at 23 °C per ASTM D 471, the physical values of the specimens taken from the tube or inner tube, when taken from a laminated tube, shall not exceed the change in value as follows:

a. Tensile Change:–45% max
b. Elongation Change:–45% max
c. Volume Change:0 to 50%

NOTE—If a laminated tube is used, the inner tube must be separated and tested alone. If a satisfactory test specimen cannot be provided from the inner tube, then a lab prepared test slab is acceptable.

7.9 Test for Extractables in Tube (Qualification Test)

a. Apparatus and Reagents

ASTM Reference Fuel C (50 Toluene—50 Isooctane percent by volume)
Methanol, 99% minimum purity
Gooch crucible
Glass fiber filter, Grade 934AH
Beaker—100 mL
Heating unit

b. Specimens—Tube under test shall be 300 mm long; plugged at both ends with metal (aluminum or steel) plugs to retain the fluid. Calculate inside surface area based on the actual inside diameter of the tube for its total effective length. The total effective length of tube with end plugs inserted shall be 274 mm.

c. Procedure—Record tube actual inside diameter, length, and inside surface area. Preferred method is with plug gauges to nearest 0.025 mm. Fill tube with ASTM Reference Fuel C. Allow to stand for 24 h at temperature of 23 °C.

NOTE—Solubility of waxy hydrocarbon is affected by temperature.

Take up residue with 30 mL of room temperature 23 °C ± 2 °C methanol. Filter this solution on the tared crucible, rinsing beaker twice with 10 mL of 23 °C ± 2 °C methanol. Place crucible in tared beaker and dry in a 65 to 90 °C oven for 1 h to insure complete evaporation of methanol. Weigh the crucible and tared beaker and determine mass of extractables expressed as g/m^2 using inside surface area of tube in contact with Reference Fuel C. Value for total waxy extractables shall be less than 2.50 g/m^2.

7.10 Ozone Resistance—The test procedure and apparatus shall be in accordance with ASTM D 1149, where applicable.

a. Sample Preparation—For straight tube, sufficient length shall be bent around a mandrel with OD eight times the nominal OD of the specimen. The two ends shall be tied at their crossing with enameled copper or aluminum wire.

b. For preformed parts, prepare a specimen by cutting a strip of tube 12.7 mm x 100 mm long and tie specimen (cover out) around a 12.0 mm diameter mandrel.

c. After mounting, the specimen shall be allowed to rest in an ozone-free atmosphere for 24 h at 23 °C. The mounted specimen shall be placed in a test chamber containing ozone at 100 mPa ± 5 mPa at a temperature of 40 °C for 70 h. Remove the specimen from the chamber, allow to cool to a temperature of 23 °C. The specimen cover shall be visually inspected under 7X magnification and must meet a "0" rating except for the area immediately adjacent to the wire, which shall be ignored.

NOTE—This test applies to the cover only and cracks in the exposed tube or cut edges of the cover shall be ignored.

7.11 Adhesion

7.11.1 ORIGINAL ADHESION (INSPECTION TEST ON ALL SIZES)—Cut 25 mm samples out of the tube in the transverse direction. The number of samples to be tested is dependent on the construction of the tube but should be enough to test the adhesion between all adjacent layers. When tested in accordance with ASTM D 413, Machine Method, Strip Specimen—Type A, 180° Peel, the minimum force required to separate the two layers shall be 1.4 N/mm or stock tear.

7.11.2 AGED ADHESION (QUALIFICATION TEST)

a. Sample conditioning

1. Use tube from the permeation test (7.13)
2. Alternate method

Plug one end of the tube to be tested. Fill with test fuel CM15.

Plug the other end in such a manner that it can be periodically removed.

Expose the filled tube to a temperature of 40 °C for 1000 h continuously.

Change the fuel every 168 h.

b. Cut 25 mm samples in the transverse direction. The number of samples to be tested is dependent on the construction but should be enough to test the adhesion between all adjacent layers.
c. Condition the test samples in a 70 °C oven for 24 h followed by 2 h at 23 °C.
d. Test for adhesion in accordance with ASTM D 413, Machine Method, Strip Specimen—Type A, 180° Peel, the minimum force required to separate the two layers shall be 1.0 N/mm or stock tear.

7.12 Kink Resistance (Inspection Test on all applicable sizes)

NOTE—This test is not applicable for tube of 12.7 mm ID nor for formed tube.

This test should be performed on a straight length of tube. When tested to the following procedure, a ball having a diameter equal to one-half the nominal inside diameter of the tube shall pass freely through the tube. Use fixture consisting of a 19-mm thick board or plate with holes and center distances shown in Table 4. Condition 300-mm long specimens of tube for 2 h at room temperature – 23 °C. Insert one end of tube into board with end flush with opposite side of board. Carefully bend tube along its natural curvature and insert the other end carefully into the second hole until it projects 63 mm out the other side. After tube has been in this position for 5 min, insert a steel ball having a diameter equal to one-half the tube nominal ID. The ball must pass freely from one end to the other.

TABLE 4—KINK RESISTANCE

Tube Inside Diameter mm	Tube Center Distance mm	Hole Diameter mm
6.3	19.0	14.3
7.9	25.4	15.9
9.5	76.2	19.0
12.7	127.0	23.0

7.13 Permeation Resistance—(Initial qualification test only)

NOTE—After completion of this test, save tube if performing adhesion testing.

a. Test Method—The test procedure and apparatus shall be in accordance with SAE J1737.
b. Test Conditions—CM15 will be used as the fuel source at a temperature of 40 °C and a pressure of 14.5 kPa. The suggested ID is 12.7 mm and the construction shall be representative of planned production tube.
c. Precondition the tube for 664 h at 40 °C, changing the fuel every 168 h followed immediately by permeation testing for a minimum of 336 h at 40 °C.
d. A minimum of 3 specimens must be tested by this procedure. The median of the three measurements shall be used to describe the permeation rate.
e. Units reported from the measurement shall be grams/meter^2/day and shall be reported as a whole number by following all the guidelines of Section 8.3 of SAE J1737.

8. Marking—The outer surface will be printed with the designation SAE J2405XYTZ along with any other identification agreed upon between user and manufacturer, repeated every 300 mm. The "X" designation (Table 5) shall indicate the range that the permeation rate falls within. The "Y" designation will be either "E" for electrically conductive or "N" for non-conductive tube. The "Z" designation will be either 1 for 100 °C heat resistance or 2 for 125 °C heat resistance.

TABLE 5—MARKING DESIGNATIONS

"X" Designation	Permeation Range	"Y" Designation	Electrical Conductivity	"Z" Designation	Temperature
A	0–25	E	Conductive	T1	100 °c
B	25–50	N	Non-conductive	T2	125 °C
C	50–100				

NOTE— Some examples of the markings follow:

SAE J2405ANT1—This tube is designed to meet the 0 to 25 g/m^2 day permeation range.
It will meet the 100 °C heat requirement and is not electrically conductive.

SAE J2405ANT2—This tube is designed to meet the 0 to 25 g/m^2 day permeation range.
It will meet the 125 °C heat requirement and is not electrically conductive.

SAE J2405AET2—This tube is designed to meet the 0 to 25 g/m^2 day permeation range.
It will meet the 125 °C heat requirement and is electrically conductive.

PERFORMANCE REQUIREMENTS FOR FUEL SYSTEM TUBING ASSEMBLIES—SAE J2045 FEB1998

SAE Standard

Report of the SAE Fuel Lines and Fittings Standards Committee approved October 1992. Completely revised by the SAE Fuel Supply Systems Committee February 1998.

TABLE OF CONTENTS

1. Scope—This SAE Standard encompasses the recommended minimum requirements for non-metallic tubing and/or combinations of metallic tubing to non-metallic tubing assemblies manufactured as a liquid- and/or vapor-carrying systems designed for use in gasoline, alcohol blends with gasoline, or diesel fuel systems. This SAE Standard is intended to cover tubing assemblies for any portion of a fuel system which operates above –40 °C (–40 °F) and below 115 °C (239 °F), and up to a maximum working gage pressure of 690 kPa (100 psi). The peak intermittent temperature is 115 °C 239 °F). For long-term continuous usage, the temperature shall not exceed 90 °C (194 °F). It should be noted that temperature extremes can affect assemblies in various manners and every effort must be made to determine the operating temperature to which a specific fuel line assembly will be exposed, and design accordingly.

The applicable SAE standards should be referenced when designing liquid-carrying and/or vapor-carrying systems which are described in this document.

Wherever possible or unless stated otherwise, systems tested to this document shall be in the final design intent configuration.

2. References

2.1 Applicable Publications—The following publications form a part of the specification to the extent specified herein. Unless otherwise indicated the latest revision of SAE publications shall apply.

2.1.1 SAE PUBLICATIONS—Available from SAE, 400 Commonwealth Drive, Warrendale, PA 15096-0001

SAE J30—Fuel and Oil Hoses, Sections 10 and 11
SAE J517—Hydraulic Hose
SAE J526—Welded Low Carbon Steel Tubing
SAE J1645—Fuel System Electrostatic Charge
SAE J1681—Gasoline/Oxygenate Mixtures for Materials Testing
SAE J1737—Procedure/Fuel Permeation Losses
SAE J2027—Protective Covers for Non-metallic Gasoline Fuel Injection Tubing
SAE J2044—Fluid Coupling for Gasoline Fuel Injection Fuel Supply & Vapor Systems
SAE J2260—Non-metallic Fuel System Tubing with 1 or more layers

2.2 Other Publications

Code of Federal Regulations Title 40 part 86

3. Routing Recommendations— Fuel tube/hose assemblies shall be routed and supported as to;

a. Prevent chafing, abrasion, kinking, or other mechanical damage.
b. Be protected against road hazards or provided with adequate shielding in locations that are vulnerable to physical and/or chemical hazards.
c. Be protected where temperatures may exceed the limits of –40 °C to +90 °C by the addition of adequate insulation and/or shielding.
d. To assure maintenance of design intent routings of liquid fuel and/or fuel vapor assemblies, appropriate retaining/mounting devices must be incorporated for proper assembly and subsequent vehicle service operation, maintaining interfaces for temperature and environmental control for durability.
e. Route tube assemblies in an environment which minimizes heat input to the assemblies and the liquid fuel and/or fuel vapor which they contain.

4. Technical Requirements

4.1 Leak Resistance

4.1.1 TESTING DEVICE—A device capable of applying the recommended internal pressure specified for both liquid fuel and fuel vapor line assemblies. Test is intended to be performed on liquid fuel/fuel vapor assemblies that duplicate the design intended for vehicle application, including applicable end fittings and/or connections.

4.1.2 SAMPLE PREPARATION—All tests are to be conducted at room temperature.

4.1.3 PROCEDURE

a. Attach tube assemblies to test fixture which simulates vehicle installation where at all possible.
b. Apply internal pressure (see Appendix A) at one end of the assembly, allowing sufficient time for system to stabilize before determining leak rate.
c. At test completion, test media should be exhausted through opposite end of assembly to which it was pressurized to insure obstruction and/or blockage was not present in the liquid fuel/fuel vapor line assembly, as well as blowout any potential residue which may have been present.
d. After test, remove assembly from test fixture.

4.1.4 ACCEPTANCE CRITERIA—Design target for maximum leakage allowed, are per specified guidelines (see Appendix A). Final acceptance criteria to be jointly determined by producer and end user.

4.2 Fitting Pull-Off—(room temperature and elevated temperature)

4.2.1 TESTING DEVICE—A device suitable for applying a tensile load at a constant rate of 50 mm/min, elongating tube or hose assemblies up to 400% of their initial length, and measuring the maximum load achieved up to a load of 900 N minimum.

4.2.2 SAMPLE PREPARATION—All tests are to be conducted at room temperature (room temperature fitting pull-off) and at 115 °C for high-temperature fitting pull-off.

4.2.3 PROCEDURE

a. The test specimen shall consist of a direct connection coupling between the flexible tubing/hose and fitting or tube with enough length of hose and/or tube on either side of specimen to permit adequate gripping in the test apparatus. Specimens may be cut from the production intent part or made for this est utilizing production intent product and processes, such as component assembly devices and tube forming techniques.
b. Grip the test specimen in the tensile-loading device and apply a tensile load at a speed of 50 mm/min until one of the following events occur;
   1. The fitting or tube separates from the flexible tubing
   2. One of the test specimen components break, fracture, or rupture
   3. A maximum load is reached whereby the flexible tubing reaches its maximum tensile/elongation load capability
c. For elevated temperature pull-off tests, grip the test specimen in the tensile-loading device and heat test chamber to 115 °C (239 °F) prior to applying the 50 mm/min tensile load. Test chamber should be instrumented with a thermocouple to insure test environment reaches 115 °C prior to applying the tensile load.
d. Measure and record the greatest load achieved before one of the events listed (2) occurs, and the type of event (failure mode).

4.2.4 ACCEPTANCE CRITERIA

a. Room Temperature—450 N minimum (fuel assemblies) or 222 N minimum (vapor assemblies)
b. 115 °C Temperature—115 N minimum (fuel assemblies) or 65 N minimum (vapor assemblies)

4.3 Flow Restriction

4.3.1 TESTING DEVICE—A spherical ball half the size of the nominal flexible tubing material inner diameter.

4.3.2 SAMPLE PREPARATION—Testing is to be performed at room temperature.

4.3.3 PROCEDURE

a. Bend or preform tubing, utilizing intended production processing method, to the shape and contour required by its design application. It is not recommended to include connectors or tubing ends for this test since geometry constraints of these components may interfere with performing this test (i.e., lack of flow through feature, restrictions, etc.)

b. Pass the spherical ball through the preformed tube.

4.3.4 ACCEPTANCE CRITERIA—The spherical ball must pass freely through the preformed tube.

4.4 Internal Cleanliness

4.4.1 TESTING DEVICE(S)—Testing devices must be utilized which can safely and accurately flush the interior of the tubing assembly with solvent, effectively remove any contaminants and foreign material from the interior surface, and accurately measure that material and its weight. (See Figure 1.)

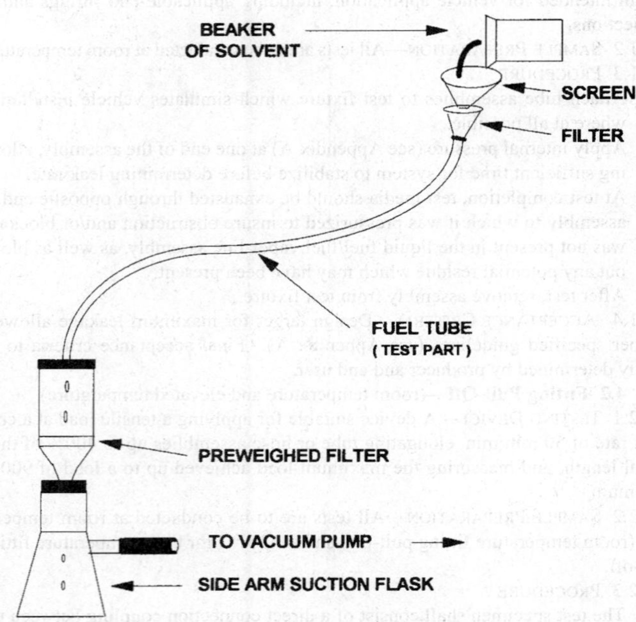

FIGURE 1—EXAMPLE

4.4.2 SAMPLE PREPARATION—Testing is to be performed at room temperature.

4.4.3 PROCEDURE

a. Pre-dry filter device, then cool in a desiccant cabinet.
b. Pre-weigh filter device which will be used in collecting potential contaminants and foreign material in fuel line assembly. Filter must be capable of collecting a contaminant which is 240 micron in size or larger.
c. Set up test specimen in test device/apparatus.
d. Turn on vacuum pump (if applicable or utilized).
e. Pour an amount of solvent (equivalent to at least the volume of the assembly) through the tube assembly. Solvent which is dispensed into the fuel line assembly should be pre-filtered.
f. Dispense solvent which has passed through the fuel line assembly into a pre-weighed filter, followed by a collection device to contain the solvent. Dry filter to dissipate solvent absorbed by filter.
g. Weigh filter to determine weight gain, which is an indicator of contaminant and/or foreign material collected from tube assembly. Record value obtained in grams per tube.

4.4.4 ACCEPTANCE CRITERIA—Total contaminant collection should not exceed 0.15 g/s meter (flexible tubing assembly) or 0.25 g/s meter (flexible tubing assembly with steel tubing attached) of interior surface area.

4.5 Internal Fuel Resistance

4.5.1 TESTING DEVICE(S)—Apparatus capable of safely storing fuel filled test specimens at elevated temperature (up to 60 °C) and controlling the ambient temperature to within ±2 °C.

4.5.2 SAMPLE PREPARATION—Prepare samples and conduct testing to temperatures as described in SAE J2260, 7.7 and 7.8.

4.5.3 TEST PROCEDURE—Per SAE J2260, 7.7 and 7.8, except conduct on finished assemblies or samples which consist of design intent interfaces and components.

4.5.4 ACCEPTANCE CRITERIA—Assemblies must meet 4.1, 4.2 (room temperature only), 4.8, and 4.10 (conductive systems only) of SAE J2045 upon completion of internal fuel resistance exposures. End user should be consulted for any potential additional requirements beyond SAE J2260 baseline fuels.

4.6 Life Cycle

4.6.1 TESTING DEVICE—Life cycle test chamber capable of performing the pressure, vibration, and temperature cycles with test fluid as outlined in SAE J2044, 6.5.

4.6.2 SAMPLE PREPARATION—Prepare samples as described in 6.5 of SAE J2044 on finished assemblies or samples which consist of production intent interfaces and components.

4.6.3 TEST PROCEDURE—Per SAE J2044, 6.5 (both liquid-fuel and/or fuel-vapor applications)

4.6.4 ACCEPTANCE CRITERIA—Test assemblies must exhibit no fluid leaks through entire test duration. At completion of test, visually inspect assemblies and components to insure no fractures, cracks, or unusual wear has occurred. Test assemblies must then meet the air leak test, 4.1 of SAE J2045.

4.7 Flame/Heat Resistance

4.7.1 TESTING DEVICE—Device capable of performing the burn-through resistance test as outlined in SAE J2027, 5.2.8.

4.7.2 SAMPLE PREPARATION—Prepare samples and conduct testing to temperatures as outlined in 5.2.8 of SAE J2027.

4.7.3 TEST PROCEDURE—Per SAE J2027, 5.2.8 on finished test samples, which consist of design intent interfaces/components.

4.7.4 ACCEPTANCE CRITERIA

a. Flame/heat resistance of the assembly shall meet the burn-through resistance requirements of the individual coverstock material chosen for the design.
b. Burn through of the assembly shall be no less than the time specified in the burn test referenced in SAE J2027.
c. Insulating ability of the assembly can be altered or modified per SAE J2027 to attain desired end result.

4.8 Burst—(room temperature and elevated temperature)

4.8.1 TESTING DEVICE—A test apparatus capable of applying a pulse free hydrostatic pressure at a uniform rate of increase of 7000 kPa/min (1000 psi/min).

For high-temperature burst testing, test apparatus must also be capable of heating test fluid to the test temperature of 115 °C (239 °F) and maintaining test temperature to within ±3 °C (±5 °F).

Fluid bath (silicon oil or equivalent) or hot-air exposure are recommended means to employ in conducting this test.

Test apparatus must also be capable of filling test specimens with hydraulic fluid to conduct room and high-temperature burst testing.

4.8.2 SAMPLE PREPARATION—Sample tubing, representative of the production design intent, shall be cut to a length 31 to 46 cm (12 to 18 in) and assembled with the proper, production design intent connectors. Test assemblies shall be processed and assembled in the manner applicable to the production design intent process. Samples are then conditioned for 24 h minimum at room temperature.

4.8.3 TEST PROCEDURE

a. Room Temperature
   1. Fill burst test apparatus and test specimen with burst fluid.
   2. Secure test assembly to burst test apparatus in the same manner which the test assembly will be secured for end use.
   3. Apply pressure at a 7000 kPa/min rate of increase until the test specimen fails.
b. Elevated Temperature (115 °C)
   1. Fill burst test apparatus and test specimen with burst fluid.
   2. Secure test assembly to burst test apparatus in the same manner which the test assembly will be secured for end use.
   3. Heat both the test specimen and test fluid to 115 °C (bath chamber or oven) and allow to stabilize at 115 °C.
   4. Once the test specimen and test fluid have reached a stabilized pressure of 115 °C, apply pressure at a 7000 kPa/min rate of increase until the test specimen fails.

4.8.4 ACCEPTANCE CRITERIA

a. Room Temperature—Minimum burst value must equal 8 times the average vehicle system working pressure (vehicle application)
b. 115 °C Temperature—Minimum burst value must equal 3 times the average vehicle system working pressure (vehicle application)

4.9 Pressure Drop/Flow Resistance

4.9.1 TESTING DEVICE—A device capable of applying an internal air pressure for fuel line and/or vapor line applications to ±7 kPa increment from a nominal set-point pressure which is to be jointly determined by producer and end user (as well as test need and applicability). Matched fittings that duplicate production design intent shall be used.

4.9.2 SAMPLE PREPARATION—All tests are to be conducted at room temperature.

4.9.3 TEST PROCEDURE

a. Attach test assemblies to the test fixture.
b. Apply air pressure at 1035 kPa (fuel) or 69 kPa (vapor) at one end of the assembly, allow flow to reach a steady state, then measure pressure drop across assembly.
c. After test, remove assembly from test fixture and examine for cracking, deformation, or damage to connectors.

4.9.4 ACCEPTANCE CRITERIA—Maximum pressure drop allowed across entire assembly for fuel and /or vapor line assemblies must be determined by end user.

4.10 Electrical Resistance

4.10.1 BACKGROUND—SAE J1645 is a document that covers electrostatic charge issues as they pertain to the fuel system. It is a recommended practice that:

1. Explains the phenomenon,
2. Outlines design factors that can be used to mitigate a charging situation that may develop,
3. Describes general techniques to be followed to determine aspects of a fuel system assembly's performance in handling the electrostatic charge situation,
4. Identifies cautions that relate to the various testing elements,
5. Delineates specific test procedures that can be followed.

That document should serve as a guideline for measurement of the electrical resistance of a fuel system assembly. Numerous other steps and tests may be pertinent to the performance of the assembly; the end user should be consulted for the various details of the document that should be followed.

If there are no inputs from the end user for performance of a fuel system assembly (in the sense of handling electrostatic charge), then the following general steps should be completed.

NOTE—These steps only relate to assemblies designed to handle liquid fuel. Electrostatic charge is not typically an issue for systems designed to handle fuel vapor.

4.10.2 TESTING DEVICE—A device capable of measuring electrical resistance as described in 7.1 of SAE J1645 shall be used. Such a device should be capable of using a 9-V and 500-V source as the drive for the measurement of the level of ohms.

4.10.3 SAMPLE PREPARATION—All tests are to be conducted at 23 °C ± 2 °C and at 50% ± 5% relative humidity. Measurements are to be conducted on the liquid fuel line assembly which has completed all process steps per production design-intent application (including end fittings, attachment clips, etc.).

4.10.4 TEST PROCEDURE—Measure the D.C. resistance using the ohmmeter (referenced in 4.10.2) from one extreme end of the fuel systems assembly to the other end for each of the fuel lines involved. If at all possible, measurements of the assembly attached to the vehicle should also be done.

4.10.5 ACCEPTANCE CRITERIA

a. Assembly Alone—D.C. resistance between any metal or conductive fuel system component in direct contact with the liquid fuel during vehicle operation shall not exceed 1 000 000 Ω measured using a 500-V source (this is the " tip-to-tip " resistance measurement of the full assembly).
b. Assembly on the Vehicle—The D.C. resistance between metal or conductive fuel system components in direct contact with the fuel during refueling or vehicle operation and the vehicle chassis should not exceed 10 Ω, measured from bare metal on the component to bare metal on the chassis using a 9-V ohmmeter, if the ground path consists of a mechanically fastened ground strap, metal bracket, or other hard metal connection. The D.C. resistance between any metal or conductive fuel system component in direct contact with the fuel during refueling or vehicle operation and the vehicle chassis should not exceed 1 000 000 Ω measured using a 500-V source, if the ground path is through a conductive plastic housing, plastic bracket, or other plastic connection.

4.11 Assembly Hydrocarbon Loss (Mini-S.H.E.D.)

4.11.1 TEST DEVICES—A testing device/set-up capable of recirculating fuel through the liquid-fuel and/or fuel-vapor assembly at a determined pressure and temperature (fuel soak/pre-condition cycle).

A testing device/set-up capable of measuring HC emission loss from liquid-fuel and/or fuel-vapor assembly at a determined pressure and temperature cycle (mini-S.H.E.D. determination).

4.11.2 SAMPLE PREPARATION—Test assemblies shall be representative of the production intent design, utilizing the appropriate flexible tubing, connectors, and rigid tubing, along with the appropriate connecting interfaces to the connectors.

4.11.3 TEST PROCEDURE

a. Testing to be conducted with fuel composition and test temperature conditions as determined and agreed to by the end item user for both pre-conditioning and mini-S.H.E.D. requirements.
b. Test assemblies shall be representative of the production intent design, however, can be made in a straight length configuration whereby entire test assembly and connector interface(s) can be contained within test cell.
c. Conduct an assembly leak test as described in SAE J2045, 4.1.
d. Pre-condition (i.e., soak) test assemblies by recirculating required test fuel. Soak time shall be consistent with time found necessary to achieve steady-state permeation value during hose permeation measurement per SAE J2260, 7.10.
e. Following pre-condition (soak) portion of test, conduct the hydrocarbon loss portion of test (mini- S.H.E.D.) S.H.E.D. test fuel, temperature, and test duration conditions are to be jointly determined between producer and end user.

4.11.4 ACCEPTANCE CRITERIA—Final acceptance criteria to be jointly determined by producer and end user. Test values to be expressed in total grams of hydrocarbron loss per 24 h period.

4.12 Chemical Resistance

4.12.1 TEST DEVICE—A testing device/set-up capable of performing external chemical resistance exposure tests as outlined in 6.2 and 6.3 of SAE J2044.

4.12.2 SAMPLE PREPARATION—Samples are to be tested as described in 6.2 and 6.3 of SAE J2044 on production design intent test assemblies.

4.12.3 TEST PROCEDURE

a. Assemble test assemblies with production design intent flexible tubing, along with production design intent quick connectors, rigid tubing, etc. Test assemblies may be constructed on short lengths to accommodate testing with various test fluids.
b. Insert mating tube ends to quick connectors and/or cap mating tube ends (for rigid tubing attachments) as described in 6.2 and 6.3 of SAE J2044.
c. Expose test assembly externally in the test fluids for the described exposure durations specified (6.2 and 6.3 of SAE J2044).

4.12.4 ACCEPTANCE CRITERIA—Test assemblies must meet 4.1 and 4.8 at the completion of each fluid exposure.

5. Validation Testing Recommendations—See Table 1.

TABLE 1—SAE J2045 TABLE SUMMARY

Section	Requirement	Acceptance Criteria	Suggested Sample Size D.V.[1]	Suggested Sample Size P.V.[2]	Suggested Sample Size I.P.[3]
4.1	LEAK RESISTANCE	maximum leakage as described in SAE J2045 Appendix A (Leak Resistance Guidelines) * non-enhanced evaporative systems * enhanced evaporative systems	 30 30	 100% 100%	 100% 100%
4.2	FITTING PULL-OFF (room temperature and 115 °C)	Liquid Fuel: 450 N (room temp.) and 155 N (115 °C elevated temp.) **Fuel Vapor:** 222 N (room temp.) and 65 N (115 °C elevated temp.)	 30 30	 10 10	1/lot/ connector (RT only)
4.3	FLOW RESTRICTION	ball size 1/2 the nominal inside hose diameter must pass freely through entire hose assembly	30	30	5/lot
4.4	INTERNAL CLEANLINESS	0.15 g/square area max insolubles	N/R	10	1/lot
4.5	INTERNAL FUEL RESISTANCE	must meet 4.1, 4.2, 4.8, and 4.10 (conductive systems only) of SAE J2045 upon completion of SAE J2260 fuel exposures	10	N/R	N/R
4.6	LIFE CYCLE	no leakage during life cycle test and meet 4.1, 4.2, and 4.8 of SAE J2045 at test completion	10	10[4]	N/R
4.7	FLAME/HEAT RESISTANCE	per applicable SAE J2027 application reference	6	6[4]	N/R
4.8	BURST	**Room Temperature:** 8x average working system pressure **115 °C Elevated Temperature:** 3X average working system pressure	 10 10	 10[4] 10[4]	 N/R N/R
4.9	PRESSURE DROP	to be determined by end user	10	10[4]	N/R
4.10	ELECTRICAL RESISTANCE	as described in 4.10 of SAE J2045	5	5[4]	N/R
4.11	ASSEMBLY HYDROCARBON LOSS	to be jointly determined between producer and end user	6	6[4]	N/R
4.12	CHEMICAL RESISTANCE	meet 4.1 and 4.8 of SAE J2045 at completion of each exposure	10	10[4]	N/R

1. D.V. = Design Validation (design proveout)
2. P.V. = Production Validation (production process proveout)
3. I.P. = In Process (ongoing process verification)
4. * = P.V. not required providing basic design features have not changed since D.V. which could influence performance features

APPENDIX A

TABLE A1—LEAK RESISTANCE GUIDELINES

Vehicle Compliance	System Description	Leak Test Pressure	Leak Test Gas	Maximum Leak Rate	Comments
Non-Evaporative Emission Vehicles	Fuel Vapor Line Assemblies	69 kPa ± 7 kPa (10 psi ± 1 psi)	Air	5 cc minute	
	Liquid Fuel Line Assemblies	1035 kPa ± 35 kPa (150 psi ± 5 psi)	Air	8 cc minute	
Evaporative Emission Vehicles	Fuel Vapor Line Assemblies	69 kPa ± 7 kPa (10 psi ± 1 psi)	Helium	5×10^{-6} cc/s	sensitivity of helium leak-testing device must be a minimum of 10^{-6} cc/s final acceptance criteria to be jointly determined by producer and end user
	Liquid Fuel Line Assemblies	345 kPa ± 35 kPa (50 psi ± 5 psi)	Helium	5×10^{-6} cc/s	see above

IMPACT OF ALTERNATIVE FUELS ON ENGINE TEST AND REPORTING PROCEDURES—SAE J1515 JUN1995 SAE Information Report

Report of the SAE Engine Committee approved March 1988. Reaffirmed by the SAE Powerplant Forum Committee June 1995.

Foreword—This Document has not changed other than to put it into the new SAE Technical Standards Board Format.

In the past, several major disruptions have occurred in the normal distribution of petroleum derived fuels at the consumer level. With the realization that stable consumer supplies of petroleum fuels might not be assured in the future, efforts were increased to investigate the utilization of nonpetroleum derived fuels for automotive engines.

Up until this time, the generally accepted automotive fuels were petroleum-derived gasoline for SI (Spark Ignition) engines, and petroleum-derived diesel fuel for CI (Compression Ignition) engines. Fuels other than these have generally been considered "alternative fuels." A review of the literature will show that various investigators have considered alcohols, vegetable oils, gaseous fuels, hydrogen, shale oil, and coal products, among others as "alternative fuels" in various engines. As time passes, the label of "alternative" tends to become less meaningful as some fuels drop by the wayside while others move into the realm of practicality. In Brazil, production vehicles are designed to operate on ethanol, and in this case, it could be argued that ethanol is no longer an "alternative fuel." Because of this changing climate, the case could be made that there are no "alternative fuels"—just "new fuels" or "different fuels." However, because the term "alternative fuels" appears rather entrenched in the technical literature, it can only be suggested that one be aware of the changing climate and use an expanded definition of fuels when dealing with research in automotive engines.

These different fuels may present a variety of problems concerning testing(1) and evaluating the performance of an engine when compared to the baseline performance with the conventional fuel for that engine. These problems include identifying common terms, determining the fuel properties, determining the health and safety factors associated with use of the fuel, testing the engine, and calculating and reporting the results. Further, if the experimental results are to be compared to the results of others in the field, the variety of techniques that may have been used to obtain and report the data may preclude a legitimate comparison. This variety of reporting techniques may be further confused by different assumptions that may have been made in analyzing the data (not the least of which is—"What is meant by 'fuel' when determining fuel rates?"). In addition, important nonproprietary information relating to the fuel or energy accounting data may be lacking, leading to difficulties in interpreting the results of others.

The purpose of this SAE Information Report is to provide guidance for those newly entering the field of alternative fuels as well as those currently involved with testing and reporting engine results with both conventional and alternative fuels. It is hoped that use of this document with its suggested guidelines will allow more convenient and complete comparisons of results between investigations involving different fuels.

1. Scope—The guidelines in this SAE Information Report are directed at laboratory engine dynamometer test procedures with alternative fuels, and they are applicable to four-stroke and two-stroke cycle spark ignition (SI) and diesel (CI) engines (naturally aspirated or pressure charged, with or without charge air cooling). A brief overview of investigations with some alternative fuels can be found in SAE J1297. Other SAE documents covering vehicle, engine, or component testing may be affected by use of alternative fuels. Some of the documents that may be affected can be found in Appendix A. Guidelines are provided for the engine power test code (SAE J1349) in Appendix D. The principles of these guidelines may apply to other procedures and codes, but the effects have not been investigated.

The report is organized into four technical sections, each dealing with an important aspect of testing or reporting of results when using alternative fuels. The first (Section 3) deals with such issues as what is a "fuel" in the context of engine operation. The next (Section 4) is concerned with identifying fuel properties. The third technical section (Section 5) covers the testing considerations and calculations for alternative fuels. The final technical section (Section 6) provides some guidelines for reporting the results so that sufficient information is given in a form that allows convenient comparison of the results from different investigations.

1. Health and safety issues when using these alternative fuels in the transportation sector may not be well understood. When using, storing, or transporting such fuels, the investigator should be aware of all potential safety issues. A primary source of safety related information would be the manufacturer of the fuel or fuel additive.

2. References

2.1 Applicable Publications—The following publications form a part of this specification to the extent specified herein. The latest issue of SAE publications shall apply.

2.1.1 SAE PUBLICATIONS—Available from SAE, 400 Commonwealth Drive, Warrendale, PA 15096-0001.

SAE TSB 003—Rules for SAE Use of SI (Metric Units)
SAE J30—Fuel and Oil Hoses
SAE J35—Diesel Smoke Measurement Procedure
SAE J177—Measurement of Carbon Dioxide, Carbon Monoxide, and Oxides of Nitrogen in Diesel Exhaust
SAE J215—Continuous Hydrocarbon Analysis of Diesel Emissions
SAE J245 (CANCELLED)—Engine-Rating Code—Spark Ignition
SAE J254—Instrumentation and Techniques for Exhaust Gas Emissions Measurement
SAE J255—Diesel Engine Smoke Measurement
SAE J312—Automotive Gasolines
SAE J313—Diesel Fuels
SAE J607—Small Spark Ignition Engine Test Code
SAE J816 (CANCELLED)—Engine Test Code—Spark Ignition and Diesel
SAE J905—Fuel Filter Test Methods
SAE J1003—Diesel Engine Emission Measurement Procedure
SAE J1082—Fuel Economy Measurement—Road Test Procedure
SAE J1088—Test Procedure for the Measurement of Exhaust Emissions from Small Utility Engines
SAE J1094—Constant Volume Sampler System for Exhaust Emissions Measurement
SAE J1130—Determination of Emission from Gas Turbine Powered Light Duty Surface Vehicles
SAE J1228—Marine Engine Rating Code
SAE J1243—Diesel Emission Production Audit Test Procedure
SAE J1256—Fuel Economy Measurement—Road Test Procedure—Cold Start and Warm-Up Fuel Economy
SAE J1297—Alternative Automotive Fuels
SAE J1312—Procedure for Mapping Engine Performance—Diesel and Spark Ignition Engines
SAE J1349—Engine Power Test Code—Spark Ignition and Diesel
SAE J1350—Selection and Application Guidelines for Diesel, Gasoline, and Propane Fired Liquid Cooled Engine Pre-Heaters
SAE J1376—Fuel Economy Measurement Test (Engineering Type) for Trucks and Buses
SAE J1498—Heating Values of Fuels
SAE J1829—Stoichiometric Air/Fuel Ratios of Automotive Fuels

2.1.2 ASTM PUBLICATIONS—Available from ASTM, 100 Barr Harbor Drive, West Conshohocken, PA 19428-2959.

ASTM D 2/P 176
ASTM D 56—Test Method for Flash Point by Tag Closed Tester
ASTM D 93—Test Method for Flash Point by Pensky-Martens Closed Tester
ASTM D 129/IP 61—Test Method for Sulfur in Petroleum Products (General Bomb Method)
ASTM D 240—Test Method for Heat of Combustion of Liquid Hydrocarbon Fuels by Bomb Calorimeter
ASTM D 323—Test Method for Vapor Pressure of Petroleum Products (Reid Method)
ASTM D 439—Specification for Automotive Gasoline
ASTM D 445—Kinematic Viscosity of Transparent and Opaque Liquids (and the Calculation of Dynamic Viscosity), Method of Test for
ASTM D 613—Test Method for Ignition Quality of Diesel Fuels by the Cetane Method
ASTM D 909—Test Method for Knock Characteristics of Aviation Gasolines by the Supercharge Method
ASTM D 976—Methods for Calculated Cetane Index of Distillate Fuels
ASTM D 1018—Test Method for Hydrogen in Petroleum Fractions
ASTM D 1072—Test Method for Total Sulfur in Fuel Gases
ASTM D 1266/IP 107—Test Method for Sulfur in Petroleum Products (Lamp Method)

ASTM D 1298—Test Method for Relative Density (Specific Gravity) or API Gravity of Crude Petroleum and Liquid Petroleum Products by Hydrometer Method

ASTM D 1405—Method for Estimation of Net Heat of Combustion of Aviation Fuels

ASTM D 1480—Test Method for Density and Relative Density (Specific Gravity) of Viscous Materials by Bingham Pyconometer

ASTM D 1552—Test Method for Sulfur in Petroleum Products (High-Temperature Method)

ASTM D 1685—Test Method for Traces of Thiophene in Benzene by Spectrophotometry

ASTM D 1826—Test Method for Calorific Value of Gases in Natural Gas Range by Continuous Recording Calorimeter

ASTM D 2015—Test Method for Gross Calorific Value of Solid Fuel by the Adiabatic Bomb Calorimeter

ASTM D 2382—Test Method for Heat of Combustion of Hydrocarbon Fuels by Bomb Calorimeter (High Precision Method)

ASTM D 2385—Test Method for Hydrogen Sulfide in Mercaptan Sulfur in Natural Gas (Cadmium Sulfate Iodometric Titration Method)

ASTM D 2420—Test Method for Hydrogen Sulfide in Liquified Petroleum (LP) Gases (Lead Acetate Method)

ASTM D 2421—Standard Method for Interconversion of Analysis of C_5 and Lighter Hydrocarbons to Gas-Volume, Liquid-Volume, or Weight Basis

ASTM D 2504—Test Method for Noncondensible Gases in C_3 and Lighter Hydrocarbon Products by Gas Chromatography

ASTM D 2551—Test Method for Vapor Pressure of Petroleum Products

ASTM D 2622—Test Method for Sulfur in Petroleum Products (X-Ray Spectrographic Method)

ASTM D 2623—Test Method for Knock Characteristics of Liquified Petroleum (LP) Gas by the Motor (LP) Method

ASTM D 2699—Test Method for Knock Characteristics of Motor Fuels by the Research Method

ASTM D 2700—Test Method for Knock Characteristics of Motor and Aviation Fuels by the Motor Method

ASTM D 2725—Test Method for Hydrogen Sulfide in Natural Gas (Methylene Blue Method)

ASTM D 2747—Test Method for Trace Quantities of Total Sulfur in Volatile Organic Liquids (Oxy-Hydrogen Combustion Method)

ASTM D 2784—Test Method for Sulfur in Liquified Petroleum Gases (Oxy-Hydrogen Burner or Lamp)

ASTM D 2785—Test Method for Trace Quantities of Total Sulfur (Wickbold and Beckman Combustion Apparatus)

ASTM D 2885—Test Method for Research and Motor Method Octane Ratings Using On-Line Analyzers

ASTM D 2886—Test Method for Knock Characteristics of Motor Fuels by the Distribution Octane Number (DON) Method

ASTM D 3031—Test Method for Total Sulfur in Natural Gas by Hydrogenation

ASTM D 3120—Test Method for Trace Quantities of Sulfur in Light Liquid Petroleum Hydrocarbons by Oxidative Microcoulometry

ASTM D 3227/IP 342—Test Method for Mercaptan Sulfur in Gasoline, Kerosene, Aviation Turbine and Distillate Fuels (Potentiometric Method)

ASTM D 3228—Test Method for Total Nitrogen in Lubricating Oils by Modified Kjeldahl Method

ASTM D 3230—Test Method for Salts in Crude Oil (Electrometric Method)

ASTM D 3235—Test Method for Solvent Extractables in Petroleum Wax

ASTM D 3246—Test Method for Sulfur in Petroleum Gas by Oxidative Microcoulometry

ASTM D 3286—Test Method for Gross Calorific Value of Coal and Coke by the Isothermal-Jacket Bomb Calorimeter

ASTM D 3343—Method for Estimation of Hydrogen Content of Aviation Fuels

ASTM D 3431—Test Method for Trace Nitrogen in Liquid Petroleum Hydrocarbon (Microcoulometric Method)

ASTM D 3505—Test Method for Density or Relative of Pure Liquid Chemicals

ASTM D 3588—Method for Calculating Calorific Value and Specific Gravity (Relative Density) of Gaseous Fuel

ASTM D 3701/IP338—Test Method for Hydrogen Content of Aviation Turbine Fuels by Low Resolution Nuclear Magnetic Resonance Spectrometry

ASTM D 3703—Test Method for Peroxide Number of Aviation Turbine Fuels

ASTM D 4045—Test Method for Sulfur in Petroleum Products by Hydrogenolysis and Rateometric Colorimetry

ASTM D 4046—Test Method for Alkyl Nitrate in Diesel Fuels by Spectrophotometry

ASTM D 4052—Test Method for Density and Relative Density of Liquids by Digital Density Meter

ASTM D 4084—Method for Analysis of Hydrogen Sulfide in Gaseous Fuels (Lead Acetate Reaction Rate Method)

ASTM D 4175—Standard Terminology Relating to Petroleum, Petroleum Products, and Lubricants

ASTM D 4292—Vibrated Bulk Density of Calcined Petroleum Coke, Test Method for

ASTM D 4294—Test Method for Sulfur in Petroleum Products by Non-Dispersive X-Ray Fluorescence Spectrometry

ASTM D 4529—Test Method for Estimation of Net Heat of Combustion of Aviation Fuels

ASTM E 147—Specification for Apparatus for Microdetermination of Nitrogen by Kjeldahl Method

ASTM E 148—Specification for Apparatus for Microdetermination of Nitrogen by Dumas Method

ASTM E 191—Specification for Apparatus for Microdetermination of Carbon and Hydrogen in Organic and Organo-Metallic Compounds

ASTM E 258—Test Method for Total Nitrogen in Organic Materials by Modified Kjeldahl Method

ASTM E 379—Specification for Apparatus for Direct Microdetermination of Oxygen in Organic Compounds

ASTM E 711—Test Method for Gross Calorific Value of Refuse Derived Fuel (RDF-3) by the Bomb Calorimeter

2.1.3 FEDERAL PUBLICATIONS—Available from The Superintendent of Documents. U.S. Government Printing Office, Washington, DC 20402.

Title 27 of the U.S. Code of Federal Regulations Part 21
Title 27 of the U.S. Code of Federal Regulations Part 19, Subpart B
Title 29 of the U.S. Code of Federal Regulations Part 1910.1200
Title 40 of the U.S. Code of Federal Regulations Part 86

2.1.4 OTHER PUBLICATIONS

The Handbook of Chemistry and Physics
U.S. Standard Atmosphere, 1976
1983 IUPAC Atomic Weights
U.S. Federal and State of California Emission Regulations for Heavy-Duty Vehicles
40 CFR 86.345
U.S. Clean Air Act
1977 Clean Air Act Amendments
U.S. EPA Report No. EPA460/3-83-009
40 CFR 86, Subparts B, D, E, F, G, K, N, and P

*3. **Common Terms***—Terms commonly used to report engine performance and test conditions are listed as follows. Included in this list are a few terms that have been adopted by ASTM through ASTM's broad consensus procedures. These terms are identified as ASTM terms, and are repeated here for two reasons. One is simply for convenience. The other is to highlight the limitations within the ASTM terms, and to counsel against the misuse of ASTM terms.

Most ASTM Test Methods explicitly state the class or range of substances for which the procedures and terms are valid. Departures from these procedures create a risk that both the procedure and the term may be invalidated. For example, ASTM limits the term "Cetane Number" to the performance of diesel fuel during a standardized engine test. To evaluate vegetable oil with this standardized test, and to discuss the performance of the vegetable oil with the term "Cetane Number" would be inappropriate. The preferred use of terminology would be to discuss the performance characteristic (for example, ignition delay) of the vegetable oil when tested by a *Modified* Cetane Number *Test Method.*

Once again, these terms are listed only for the expressed purpose of establishing consistency in reporting engine performance or describing testing parameters and conditions relating to that performance. Use of the term descriptions listed here outside of that context is inappropriate.

3.1 Alcohol—a class of organic compounds characterized by the presence of a hydroxyl group attached to an alkyl hydrocarbon structure.

3.2 Cetane Number—A measure of the ignition performance of a diesel fuel obtained by comparing it to reference fuels in a standardized engine test (1984) (ASTM term, see ASTM D 4175).

3.3 Colloidal Suspension (Colloid)—A suspension of finely divided particles approximately 5 to 10 000 angstroms (0.5 nm to 1 μm) in size that are dispersed in a continuous medium (for example, a gaseous, liquid, or solid substance), that do not settle or settle very slowly, and are not readily filtered.

3.4 Denaturants—Any material authorized under Title 27 of the U.S. Code of Federal Regulations Part 21 for addition to spirits in the production of denatured spirits (from Title 27 U.S. Code or Federal Regulations Part 19, Subpart B). These materials are agents used to make ethanol unfit for human consumption without impairing its usefulness for a specific intended purpose. Denaturants vary depending on the end-use of the alcohol.

3.5 Emission Test Fuel—Gasoline or diesel fuels with controlled properties used for engine and emission testing. The specifications for U.S. Emission Test Fuel can be found in Title 40 of the U.S. Code of Federal Regulations Part 86. There are separate requirements for Light-Duty gasoline and diesel vehicles, and for Heavy-Duty gasoline and diesel engines.

3.6 Emulsion—A fluid formed by the suspension of a very finely divided immiscible liquid in the continuous phase of another liquid.

3.7 Ethanol or Ethyl Alcohol—An alcohol of formula C_2H_5OH.

3.8 Equivalence Ratio—A ratio of the actual fuel-air ratio (f/a) divided by the chemically correct (stoichiometric) fuel-air ratio $(f/a)_s$. This ratio is equivalent to the stoichiometric air-fuel ratio $(a/f)_s$ divided by the actual air-fuel ratio (a/f). The Greek letter "phi" or symbol "φ" is commonly used to designate the equivalence ratio. Equivalence ratio is the preferred method to describe mixture strength.

$$\varphi = \text{phi} = \frac{(f/a)}{(f/a)_s} = \frac{(a/f)_s}{(a/f)} \quad \text{(Eq. 1)}$$

3.9 Excess Air Ratio—A ratio of the air supplied to the air required for stoichiometric combustion. Referred to by the Greek letter "lambda" or symbol "λ", the excess air ratio is equivalent to the inverse of the equivalence ratio. Excess air ratio is not a preferred method to describe mixture strength.

$$\lambda = \text{lambda} = \frac{\text{Air(actual)}}{\text{Air(stoich)}} = \frac{1}{\text{phi}} \quad \text{(Eq. 2)}$$

3.10 Flammability Limits—The limits of volume percentage composition of mixtures of fuel and air, within which flame propagation takes place when the mixture is ignited. The lower limit of flammability corresponds to the minimum amount of combustible fuel and the upper limit to the maximum amount of combustible fuel capable of conferring flammability on the mixture. Flammability limits are dependent on pressure, temperature, ignition energy, and combustor design, and are usually given at standard atmospheric conditions.

3.11 Flash Point—The lowest temperature at which vapors arising from a combustible substance will ignite momentarily (that is, flash) on application of an ignition source under specified conditions. ASTM has several Test Methods for determining the flash point of various substances. The conditions and statement of the term "Flash Point" vary slightly between Test Methods.

3.12 Fuel—Any solid, liquid, or gaseous substance which contains chemical energy that is released during the combustion process in an engine for the purpose of producing mechanical work is defined as fuel. Any other substance, combustible or noncombustible (for example, water), which is mixed with or added to the base combustible substance to modify the combustion process or to control emissions, or is inherently present in the base substance should be included as fuel in the calculation of fuel and energy consumption. For the energy consumption calculations prescribed in this document, fuel scavengers, corrosion inhibitors, lubricating oil, etc., which when combined, change the heating value by less than 0.25%, need not be considered as fuel. Recirculated exhaust products are not considered fuel.

3.13 Heating Value—The energy liberated when a unit mass of fuel is completely oxidized and the temperature of the reactants is equal to the products. For the lower (or net) heating value, the water produced is assumed to be in a gaseous phase; while for the higher (or gross) heating value, the water is assumed to be in the liquid phase. For a more detailed discussion of heating value, refer to 4.2.2.

3.14 Kerogen—The substantially organic material in oil shale, consisting primarily of carbon and hydrogen with quantities of sulfur, nitrogen, and oxygen, which upon pyrolysis will yield gas and raw shale oil.

3.15 Manufacturer's Designated Fuel (MDF)—The fuel or fuels specified by the engine manufacturer for ordinary engine operation. All other fuels are considered alternative fuels unless redesignated by the engine manufacturer for a particular engine or class of engines.

3.16 Material Safety Data Sheet (MSDS)—Written or printed material concerning a hazardous chemical which is prepared in accordance with paragraph (g) of Title 29 of the U.S. Code of Federal Regulations, Part 1910.1200.

3.17 Methanol or Methyl Alcohol—An alcohol of formula CH_3OH.

3.18 Octane Number—(for spark ignition engine fuels)—Any one of several numerical indicators of resistance to knock obtained by comparison with reference fuels in standardized engine or vehicle tests (1986) (ASTM Term, see ASTM D 4175).

3.19 Oil Shale—A sedimentary rock containing a relatively high (5 to 30%) content of kerogen from which shale oil can be produced by heating.

3.20 Oxygenate—An oxygen-containing organic compound, which may be used as a fuel or fuel supplement; for example, various alcohols and ethers (1984) (ASTM Term, see ASTM D 4175).

3.21 Oxygenated Fuel—A class of fuels with chemically bound oxygen (for example, oxygenates) such as alcohols, vegetable oils, esters, or ethers.

3.22 Phase—A portion of a physical system (solid, liquid, or gas) that is homogeneous throughout, has definable boundaries, and can be separated physically from the other phases. The act of separating different phases is commonly termed "phase separation."

3.23 Proof—The ethyl alcohol content of a liquid at 15.56 °C (60 °F), stated as twice the percent of ethyl alcohol by volume (from Title 27 U.S. Code of Federal Regulations Part 19, Subpart B).

3.24 Slurry—A mixture of a pulverized solid and a liquid carrier that behaves as a liquid.

3.25 Specific Energy Consumption (SEC)—The ratio of the rate of fuel energy supplied divided by the rate of work done by the engine, (kJ/s)/kW, which is also the inverse of thermal efficiency. The values to be used for fuel energy units are lower or net heating values. SEC can be reported as either Brake or Indicated consumption.

3.26 Stoichiometric Fuel-Air Ratio—The ratio of the mass of fuel to the mass of air of a stoichiometric mixture of fuel and air. The inverse is the stoichiometric air-fuel ratio.

3.27 Stoichiometric Mixture—The chemically correct mixture of fuel (fuel as defined in this report) and air or oxidizer that will enable complete oxidation of the combustible components of the fuel with no excess oxygen.

3.28 Surfactant—A surface active agent which can enhance emulsification, dispersion, or demulsification by modifying the liquid surface tension.

3.29 Thermal Efficiency—The ratio of the rate of work done by an engine divided by the rate of fuel energy supplied, kW/(kJ/s). The inverse of thermal efficiency is Specific Energy Consumption. The values to be used for fuel energy units are lower or net heating values. Thermal efficiency can be reported as either Brake Thermal Efficiency (BTE or ηb) or Indicated Thermal Efficiency (ITE or ηi).

3.30 Vapor Pressure—The pressure exerted when a solid or liquid substance is in equilibrium with its own vapor. The vapor pressure is a function of the substance and of the temperature. ASTM has several Test Methods that determine the vapor pressure under specified conditions for a number of substances (See 4.2.3.3)(see 4.2.3).

3.31 Vegetable Oil—Any oil from plant origin as distinguished from animal (origin) oil, including the fixed oils of plants (for instance, glyceryl esters of various fatty acids) which are also known as glycerides, specifically triacylglycerols.

3.32 Volatility—The tendency of a substance to evaporate readily at ordinary temperatures and pressures. An indirect quantification of this quality can usually be determined through various ASTM Test Methods which measure the distillation curve, the flammability or flash point, the vapor/liquid ratio, and the vapor pressure of the substance (See 4.2.3.4)(see 4.2.3).

4. Fuel Composition and Properties

4.1 Background—Because limits for the composition and physical properties have generally been established for commercial automotive fuels, they have not been of great concern during engine testing, unless specific tests were directed toward particular fuel properties. With the increased interest in and use of alternative fuels, more concern must now be directed towards a broader scope of fuel properties.

Therefore, before proceeding to test an engine, one should first investigate the chemical composition and physical properties of the fuel to be used. This step is necessary for physical compatibility with the facility and the engine. The elemental composition is also needed to determine the stoichiometric fuel-air ratio of the fuel for proper engine adjustments, as well as for performance comparisons and reporting of results. In addition to the fuel composition, other properties of the fuel such as heating value, volatility, viscosity, and density (among others) are necessary to properly compare and report engine performance.

4.2 Determining Fuel Properties

4.2.1 ELEMENTAL AND CHEMICAL COMPOSITION—It is necessary to know the composition of any fuel in terms of mass percent C, H, O, N, S, and any other elements which could react during combustion if the stoichiometric fuel-air ratio and equivalence ratio are to be calculated. The exact values of the elemental mass percentages should be determined and reported for the particular fuel used. Note also that the contributions to the elemental mass percentage from fuel additives should be included if they affect the energy content by more than 0.25%. In addition, a determination of the quantity of additives and trace compounds or elements in the fuel (such as corrosion inhibitors, chloride levels, iodine number, peroxide number, etc.) may be necessary in order to select corrosion-resistant components for the fuel system.

Carbon, hydrogen, and oxygen content can be determined analytically by a variety of micro-combustion techniques. In addition, Appendix B lists a number of ASTM Test Methods for analysis of nonhydrocarbon constituents. There are also a number of nonstandardized micro-analytical techniques for nitrogen and sulfur. Researchers are advised to consult their laboratory for the details of precision errors and bias errors when applied to the particular fuel used. Researchers should also note that many times, ASTM Test Methods are valid only for a specific class or range of substances (for example, petroleum products). Use of such procedures for other substances (for example, nonpetroleum products) requires a careful examination of the procedure by the researcher, and an analysis of the errors that could occur by such a modified procedure. The method of modification (if any) and error analysis used should be reported.

4.2.2 HEATING VALUES OF FUELS—The heating value or heat of combustion is a measure of the energy available from the complete oxidation of a fuel. Because the fraction of the heat of combustion that is converted to useful work is a measure of the thermal efficiency of an engine, a knowledge of the heat of combustion of any fuel used is essential when quantifying the performance of an automotive engine.

4.2.2.1 The measurement, calculation, reporting, and use of heating values of fuels is covered in detail in the SAE Handbook under SAE J1498. For the purpose of performing engine tests using alternative fuels, the following interpretations and concepts from SAE J1498 are emphasized here:

4.2.2.1.1 Only the lower or net heating value should be used for all energy input calculations.

4.2.2.1.2 Since heats of combustion are not always additive when compounds are mixed, calorimetric measurements are recommended when dealing with alternative fuels or mixtures of alternatives with traditional petroleum fuels.

4.2.2.1.3 Empirical methods for estimating heats of combustion are based on observed correlations, accurately measured properties, and the heats of combustion of a particular class of fuels. Because such estimates may be in error by large amounts even within the same class of fuels, they are not substitutes for precisely measured heats of combustion, particularly for alternative fuels. For comparing engine results, empirical estimates should be avoided.

4.2.2.2 The need to accurately characterize the heating value of the baseline fuel should not be overlooked when performance comparisons are being made between two fuels. Typically, but not always, automotive gasoline or diesel fuel would be the baseline fuel. The precepts in SAE J1498 along with SAE J312 and SAE J313 should be used in determining the heating value of the baseline fuel.

4.2.3 PHYSICAL PROPERTIES—ASTM has many Test Methods for determining the physical properties of substances. However, most ASTM Test Methods explicitly state the class or range of substances for which the procedures are valid. Departures from these substances, or modifications to these procedures, run the risk of erroneous results. Since some alternative fuels are not covered by ASTM Test Methods, use of such procedures for substances other than those specified by ASTM requires a careful examination of the procedure, and an analysis of the errors that could occur by such a modified procedure. The modifications (procedure or substance) should be clearly reported.

4.2.3.1 Density—Density measurements should be performed in a manner that will allow calculation of the mass per unit volume of the fuel, in the form that the fuel is introduced to the engine. For pure liquid or pure gaseous fuels, density measurements should not create any unique problems with the caveat that ASTM Test Methods may not address the particular substance under consideration. For example, the scope of the glass hydrometer method (ASTM D 1298) includes liquid petroleum products, and liquid mixtures of petroleum products and nonpetroleum products, but does not include pure nonpetroleum products. However, ASTM D 3505 may apply to these substances. ASTM D 1480 apparently can be used for any material that is fluid between 20 and 100 °C. Determining the density of powdered solid fuels may be more difficult, particularly since the density may vary with handling techniques. ASTM D 4292 provides one method of sample preparation, but the scope of this method only includes calcined petroleum coke. Determining the density of fuels consisting of any combination of gaseous, liquid, or solid substances could pose significant conceptual and physical measurement problems.

4.2.3.2 Flash Point—ASTM has established several Test Methods for determining the flash point of substances. One difference between these Test Methods includes the physical characteristics of the substance. For example, ASTM D 56 can be used for liquids that have viscosities below certain values at specific temperatures and flash below 93 °C, and do not contain suspended solids or form a surface film. Higher viscosity liquids and those containing suspended solids generally fit the criteria for ASTM D 93. Care should be taken to insure that the proper procedure is used for the substance to be tested in the engine.

4.2.3.3 Vapor Pressure—Vapor pressure of many pure organic or inorganic compounds can be found in reference books such as *The Handbook of Chemistry and Physics* (a CRC publication). The limitation on this data is that it applies only to pure compounds. For substances where the exact composition is not known, ASTM has developed several Test Methods. These Test Methods have limitations on their applicability as well. For example, the scope of ASTM D 2551 only includes air-containing, volatile, nonviscous *petroleum* products at preselected vapor-to-liquid ratios and temperatures. The scope is further limited to substances that have a vapor pressure between 0.5 and 17 lbf/in^2 (3.4 to 117.2 kPa). Vapor Pressure of Petroleum Products by the Reid Method (ASTM D 323) or Reid Vapor Pressure (RVP) is another common procedure. The scope of this Test Method is limited to gasoline, volatile crude oil, and other volatile petroleum products. Specifically excluded from ASTM D 323 are liquified petroleum gases and oxygenated fuels. For fuels containing alcohols, a dry method and an automatic method described in ASTM D-2 P-176 has been proposed as a future ASTM Test Method. Because of the various limitations on methods to determine vapor pressure, identifying an accepted standard procedure for fuel consisting of certain combinations of gaseous, liquid, or solid substances may be difficult.

4.2.3.4 Volatility—The volatility characteristics of a substance can be determined by a number of different measures. For this reason, the method used to measure volatility generally depends on the specific concern of interest. For instance, the flash point would be a volatility concern in safety issues. The vapor pressure of the substance at different temperatures might also be a safety concern if the possibility exists of forming a combustible mixture within the test cell (or other confined space) due to spills or leaks. Within the engine and fuel delivery system, the volatility of the substance can affect the fuel distribution in some induction systems, the degree of wall wetting, cold starting capabilities, and vapor lock to name just a few of the possible effects. ASTM has various Test Methods to measure different volatility characteristics of certain substances. Included are Test Methods to measure distillation curves, flash points, vapor/liquid ratios, and vapor pressures. SAE J312 and ASTM D 439 provide some insight on the significance of these different volatility characteristics relative to automotive gasoline. Flash point and vapor pressure are also briefly discussed in this section of this document. It is important to select the appropriate volatility measure for the concern at hand.

4.2.3.5 Viscosity—Viscosity measurements for pure liquid fuels should not create any unique conceptual measurement problems. ASTM D 445 describes one method for measuring kinematic viscosity, but the scope of the Test Method only includes transparent and opaque petroleum products. Measuring viscosity of fuels consisting of gas and a liquid, a liquid and solid, or some other combination could pose significant measurement problems.

4.3 Determining Stoichiometric Fuel-Air Ratio—The stoichiometric fuel-air ratio is needed to calculate the operating equivalence ratio so that engine performance can be compared at the same equivalence ratio. Changes in stoichiometric fuel-air ratio must also be known in advance of engine experiments when sizing or making adjustments to fuel injection or carburetion systems.

The stoichiometric fuel-air ratio can be calculated from knowledge of the fuel composition with the assumption that combustion occurs with dry air of the composition found in Table 1. It is further assumed that the fuel can be represented by the formula in Equation 3.

TABLE 1—MOLECULAR WEIGHTS AND ASSUMED FRACTIONAL VOLUME—COMPOSITION OF SEA LEVEL DRY AIR

Gas Species	Fractional Volume (1)	Molecular Weight kg/kmole (2)	Relative Mass (3)	Oxygen Normalized Volume Ratio (4)
N_2	0.78084	28.0134	21.873983	3.7276 E+00
O_2	0.209476	31.9988	6.702981	1.000 E+00
Ar	0.00934	39.948	0.373114	4.4587 E–02
CO_2	0.000314	44.0098	0.013819	1.4990 E–03
Ne	0.00001818	20.179	0.000365	8.6788 E–05
He	0.00000524	4.002602	0.000021	2.5015 E–05
Kr	0.00000114	83.80	0.000092	5.4422 E–06
Xe	0.000000087	131.29	0.000011	4.1532 E–07
CH_4	0.000002	16.04276	0.000032	9.5476 E–06
H_2	0.0000005	2.01588	0.000001	2.3869 E–06
			28.964419	4.7738

1. Data from Table 3 of "U.S. Standard Atmosphere, 1976," National Oceanic and Atmospheric Administration; National Aeronautics and Space Administration; United States Air Force, Washington, DC, October 1976.
2. Calculated from 1983 IUPAC Atomic Weights, N.E. Holden and R.L. Martin, Pure and Applied Chemistry, 56, 663 (1983).
3. Relative mass = fractional volume X molecular weight.
4. The ratio of the fractional volume of each gas species relative to oxygen.

$$\text{Fuel} = C_xH_yO_zN_vS_w \quad \text{(Eq. 3)}$$

where:

x = the atoms of carbon per mole of fuel
y = the atoms of hydrogen per mole of fuel
z = the atoms of oxygen per mole of fuel
v = the atoms of nitrogen per mole of fuel
w = the atoms of sulfur per mole of fuel

Ash is not included in the fuel, since it is not common practice to give molar analysis of ash contained in fuels.

The basic chemical equation for combustion of the fuel identified in Equation 3 is provided in Equation 4 and Equation 5. Note that species other than those in Equation 3 are assumed to be nonreactive with the oxygen or the nitrogen in the air. As indicated in Equation 5, the products of stoichiometric fuel combustion are assumed to be CO_2, H_2O, N_2, and SO_2. (Note also that these products may be subject to interpretation if exhaust gas analysis is used to compute the operating equivalence ratio because of assumptions about the final form of the nitrogen and sulfur compounds.) Should an unusual fuel be encountered that is not consistent with these assumptions, the following equations should not be used, and the basic chemical balance (Equation 3, Equation 4, and Equation 5) should be re-formulated for the fuel under test. Such reformulations should be reported.

$$C_xH_yO_zN_vS_w + (q)[O_2 + 3.7276N_2 + 0.044587\,Ar] = PROD \quad \text{(Eq. 4)}$$

$$PROD = (a)CO_2 + (b)H_2O + (c)SO_2 + [(q)(3.7276) + (v/2)]\,N_2 + (q)(0.044587)Ar \quad \text{(Eq. 5)}$$

where:

q = [x + (0.25) y + w–(0.5)z] = the moles of oxygen necessary for stoichiometric combustion

The fundamental form of the stoichiometric fuel-air ratio is given by Equation 6.

$$(f/a)_s = MW_f/(q)(MW_a) \quad \text{(Eq. 6)}$$

where:

MW_f = Molecular weight of the fuel in the reactants of Equation 4
$MW_a = 138.2703 = (28.964419)^{\#}(4.7738)^{\#}$
= The mass of air containing one molecular weight of oxygen
NOTE—# From Table 1.

If the number of atoms for each element in the fuel is easily obtainable, which might be the case for some pure component fuels, determining the stoichiometric fuel-air ratio by Equation 6 can be rather straight forward. However, many fuels are not pure compounds, and a precise number of atoms for each element may be difficult or impractical to determine; for example, where a blend of hydrocarbons is used or where hydrocarbons are blended with alcohols. Further, for these nonpure compound fuels, the fuel analysis typically available is one which determines the mass fractions of the elements—not the number of atoms. Therefore, in these more common situations, Equation 7 is preferred for calculation of the stoichiometric fuel-air ratio.

$$(f/a)_s = (0.7232)/[(\%C/12.011) + 0.25(\%H/1.00794) + (\%S/32.066) - 0.5(\%O/15.9994)] \quad \text{(Eq. 7)}$$

where:

%C = (FC)(100) = the mass percentage of carbon in the fuel
%H = (FH)(100) = the mass percentage of hydrogen in the fuel
%S = (FS)(100) = the mass percentage of sulfur in the fuel
%O = (FO)(100) = the mass percentage of oxygen in the fuel
0.7232 = (1/138.2703)(100)

and where:

FC = the mass fraction of carbon in the fuel
FH = the mass fraction of hydrogen in the fuel
FS = the mass fraction of sulfur in the fuel
FO = the mass fraction of oxygen in the fuel

Although the amounts of any nonreactive species that may be contained in the fuel (for example, water) do not appear explicitly in Equation 7, their effects are included accurately, provided that the percentages appearing in Equation 7 are determined on the total fuel sample which includes the nonreactive species. In other words, the sum of the percentages in Equation 7 does not necessarily have to equal 100.

If the fuel being used contains a significant amount of ash, the researcher should consider the possibility that some forms or a certain portion of the ash is reactive. If any of the ash is reactive, then Equation 7 would not be applicable.

An alternative calculation for the stoichiometric fuel-air ratio can be found in SAE J1829. The procedure in SAE J1829 which uses a ratio technique (hydrocarbon/carbon, oxygen/carbon, etc.) allows some flexibility in the selection of the combustion products of fuel nitrogen and fuel sulfur. For example one equilibrium product allowed in SAE J1829 from the combustion of fuel nitrogen is NO. In an engine, the amount of NO produced is affected by many variables such as compression ratio, combustion chamber shape, and ignition timing. Because it would be difficult to separate any NO produced by fuel nitrogen from that produced by high temperature air reactions, and to preclude the possibility of the stoichiometric fuel-air ratio changing with engine design or operating conditions, the convention of fuel nitrogen going to N_2 and fuel sulfur going to SO_2 should ALWAYS be used when reporting engine performance on different fuels. If these assumptions are used in the equations found in SAE J1829 (fuel nitrogen to N_2 and fuel sulfur to SO_2), there is essentially no difference in the results between SAE J1829 and Equation 7.

5. *Impact of Fuel on Test Procedures and Calculations*

5.1 Background—SAE has developed several specific test codes that deal with reciprocating engine test procedures and performance calculations (SAE J607, J1312, J1349)[2], emissions measurement (SAE J177, J215, J254, J1003, J1088, J1094, J1130, J1243)[2], and vehicle fuel economy (SAE J1082, J1256, J1376)[2]. These codes and procedures have historically focused on tests with conventional distillate fuels. When using alternative fuels, a broader range of physical and chemical fuel properties must be addressed as outlined in Section 4. For safety considerations and to give better assurance of a proper comparison of the engine performance with alternative fuels, engine personnel need to become better acquainted with the technical details of the fuel chemistry and combustion reactions than has been the case for engine tests with conventional distillate fuels.

5.2 Test Procedure for Alternative Fuel Utilization—If an engine has been designed to operate on a specific alternative fuel, then many technical concerns with the test facility and the fuel supply may have been addressed and the focus can immediately be on the performance, emissions, and calculated results. However, many alternative fuel investigations occur with existing engine designs. In these situations, facility and fuel supply questions must be addressed before testing.

5.2.1 HEALTH AND SAFETY—An initial fuel property assessment should focus on health and safety. These aspects are foremost considerations for personnel handling the fuel or conducting the test, the end consumer or vehicle operator, and others in contact with the environment around the operating engine. The possible toxicity of the fuel vapors to the respiratory system, liquids to the skin, or combustion products to either must be investigated. Combustion of even trace elements or compounds could cause harmful exhaust. Explosion hazards can occur from volatile fuels with low ignition temperatures, combinations of fuels causing combustible vapors where individually there is no concern, or unstable mixtures self-igniting. In addition, health hazards for combinations of fuels can in some cases be greater than those exhibited by the individual fuels or components. If the health and safety related fuel properties are not known or incomplete, they should be determined before testing. Since many alternative fuels are by-products from the production of other chemicals, details of chemical composition of the fuels may not be readily available. A source of safety information should be the facility Safety Officer (who should be consulted); fuel composition and other related safety information should be available from the fuel manufacturer by means of a Material Safety Data Sheet (MSDS)[3]. Other sources of health and safety information are described in Appendix C.

5.2.2 FACILITY CONSIDERATIONS—Safety considerations previously may establish special facility or handling requirements such as automatic fire protection systems, special test area ventilation or personal protective clothing, etc. One of the first engine test facility considerations is to determine the amount of fuel required, that is, the size of the cell fuel tank, the bulk tank, special transportation requirements, etc. This can be determined by the test duration, heating values of the alternative fuel(s), projected combustion efficiency, and the average energy consumption rate of the conventional fuel. For test consistency, the total quantity of fuel required may need to be prepared or stored as a single batch with limits dictated by the weathering performance of the fuel (for example, loss of volatile components, oxidation stability, etc.).

Containment of the fuel is an important aspect, since incompatibilities between the fuel and equipment may cause changes in fuel uniformity or composition that could result in poor test consistency. Assessment of fuel compatibility with tank, lines, valves, seals, pumps, coolers, etc., should include a detailed review of every component of the supply system from the delivery container to the combustion chamber.

Fuel viscosity, stoichiometry, and melting points will determine whether supply lines or pumps need to be sized differently or special temperature controls added. Care should be taken when heating fuels to reduce viscosity such that an unsafe fuel condition is not created or that degradation of the fuel does not occur. Extra energy added to the engine fuel handling system to overcome adverse fuel properties should be taken into consideration in calculations of performance comparisons. (See Section 6.)

5.2.3 ENGINE FUEL SYSTEM(S) CONSIDERATIONS—The objectives of the particular alternative fuel test will determine if fuel system modifications are needed. The simplest approach is to utilize the conventional fuel system if compatible, and to document the change in power or performance that occurs with the alternative fuel. Possible overloading of the engine or drivetrain, or shortage of power for the application should then be addressed.

If the test is to demonstrate equivalent engine or application performance with the alternative fuels, then the fuel system setting, fuel metering, metering control, or even the entire system may need to be changed for equal energy input rate. In this case, the flexibility to operate on conventional fuels when they are available may not be able to be retained unless an independent secondary system is added for the alternative fuel. However it should be noted that if a dual fuel or pilot fuel system is used, care should be taken to avoid overloading or overfueling the engine.

5.2.4 PERFORMANCE AND EMISSIONS TEST—Instrumentation and procedures described in SAE codes and listed in 5.1 should be consulted when performing engine tests. Additional guidance can be found in Appendices A to E of this document. Deviations from these procedures for specific test goals should be outlined clearly in the report on the test results. Additional instrumentation may be required to accurately determine total energy input (that is, voltage and current of auxiliary pumps or heaters necessary for proper use of a specific alternative fuel, unique density, volume, or mass fuel rate measuring requirements, etc.). Since combustion characteristics can be drastically influenced by an alternative fuel, in-cylinder dynamic combustion pressure measurements (when available) are most valuable in determining the direction for preliminary engine adjustment or modification. Simultaneous exhaust gas emission measurements further enhance this understanding when these measurements are correlated to inlet fuel rates and fuel chemistry.

Emissions (both regulated and unregulated) also are ultimately necessary to determine environmental impact of a final configuration. The possibility of unexpected problems that could alter the emission results should be a major concern when testing with alternative fuels. Some of these concerns are discussed in Appendix E.

5.2.5 CALCULATION OF RESULTS—Calculation procedures to determine the results obtained from testing with alternative fuels generally require only the inclusion of additional terms or changes to constants in the standard equations found in SAE codes listed in 5.1. However, some required changes are more broad based, such as determining the energy accounting system with which to report the results. Formal test reports should document or reference changes made to standard calculations, and methods used for energy input accounting, including the boundaries or limits of the accounting technique.

Specific guidance on calculation changes for engine dynamometer performance testing is given in Appendix D. Similar guidance on emission measurements is given in Appendix E.

5.2.6 OTHER CONSIDERATIONS—Alternative fuel engine tests can contribute to technical information and understanding in many different areas. Areas that are sometimes investigated are (a) whether combustion can occur, if so (b) the quality of combustion, (c) emissions from the fuel or combustion, (d) health and safety, immediate or long-term, (e) materials compatibility with engine components or lubricants, (f) specific or overall operating performance, (g) appropriate lubricant properties and their possible effect on engine performance, (h) steady-state dynamometer performance or transient operation, (i) cold starting, local ambient, or expected extremes, (j) structural impact, (k) short-term wear or extended life, (l) specific application performance or all applications, etc. These areas as well as many others have generally been defined or investigated for conventional fuels. Testing an alternative fuel in one or several of these areas may not imply acceptable results in other areas. The overall assessment of an alternative fuel may require a more comprehensive understanding and testing program than a normal development program with conventional fuels.

6. *Performance Comparisons*

6. Performance Comparisons—Due to the different properties of alternative fuels, special care must be exercised when comparing the performance of engine and vehicular systems operated on nonpetroleum fuels. It is useful in this regard to specify recommended parameters for reporting operating conditions, engine performance, and emissions results.

6.1 Engine Performance Parameters—Engine performance tests should be conducted as closely as possible in accordance with recommended procedures to be found in the SAE Handbook for the size and type of engines at hand. Necessary changes should be documented where specific SAE codes and procedures do not address specific test goals. It is recommended that speed be reported in revolutions per minute (rpm) and that load be reported as mean effective pressure in units of kPa. Maximum values of speed and loads should also be given. Other engine parameters, such as displacement and number of cylinders, should be reported so that parameters given previously can be converted into power and torque.

---

2. See Appendix A for complete SAE titles. Note also that SAE continually updates the documents listed in the SAE Handbook, therefore, the latest version should be consulted.
3. Material Safety Data Sheets are required to be available by U.S. Federal Regulation (29 CFR 1910.1200). See Appendix C for additional information.

Acceptable practice for multicylinder engines is to report performance parameters on a brake basis, that is, brake power, brake mean effective pressure, etc. In the case of the development of new engine systems for the combustion of alternative fuels, initial work is often performed on single-cylinder engines. In this case, engine friction data are usually available either from motoring tests or as determined from brake power and measured pressure-volume diagrams. Since single-cylinder engines typically have lower mechanical efficiencies than multi-cylinder engines, the use of both indicated and brake mean effective pressure and associated parameters is recommended for single-cylinder tests.

6.2 Efficiency—For engines operating on alternative fuels, it is recommended that comparisons be made on the basis of thermal efficiency on a brake or indicated basis, in agreement with the guidelines from the previous paragraph. In reporting the thermal efficiency, it should be clearly stated which heating value of the fuel is used, and the physical state of the fuel in the heating value tests. Specific energy consumption, as described in Section 3, is also an acceptable measure of efficiency. Again, the heating value used should be clearly stated.

In the calculation of engine efficiency, care must be taken to include all of the input energy to the engine. For example, if engine-mounted systems are used which change the chemical structure of the fuel and the systems require external energy sources for start-up or continuous operation and if the energy supplied to operate the systems is not supplied by the fuel input to the engine, this additional energy must be added to the fuel energy supplied when determining the thermal efficiency of the engine. Also, any energy supplied to the engine or associated fuel processing system which is stored before a test and then depleted during a test, such as a battery which is charged before a test and then discharged during a test, must also be included in the energy supply to the engine. In other words, if a system is essential for the operation of the engine, or is an "on-board" fuel processing system, or is used to supplement the power output of the engine, the energy consumed should be included in the calculation of thermal efficiency.

6.3 Exhaust Emissions—Exhaust emissions should be reported on a basis which gives a true comparison of the effects of the fuel used. For engine tests it is recommended that emissions be reported on a brake or indicated specific basis in terms of grams emitted per hour per unit of power (g/kW-h)[4]. The emission index, typically grams of emitted substance per kilogram (kg) of fuel consumed, is also a satisfactory parameter for reporting emission results. If the emissions are a weighted average, the test cycle and weighting procedures should be described.

6.4 Fuel Composition—Fuel composition should be reported on a basis that allows a true comparison of and evaluation of the fuel used. It is preferred that blend fractions of common fuels as well as elemental fractions be reported on a mass basis. If reported on a different basis (for example, volume or energy split), sufficient information should be included that will allow a determination of the mass fractions (where possible ASTM D 2421 should be used). In addition to the basic composition information, the phase of the fuel (liquid, gas, or solid) as used by the engine should be clearly evident in the report of the results.

6.5 Mixture Strength—Since many alternative fuels have stoichiometric fuel-air ratios which are significantly different from the typical values for pure hydrocarbon fuels, special care should be exercised when reporting mixture strength. The recommended parameter is the fuel-air equivalence ratio as defined in Section 3 and 4.3. In reporting the properties of the fuel, the stoichiometric fuel-air ratio of the fuel tested should be given, but the equivalence ratio should be the only parameter used for the actual comparison of mixture strength.

4. The U.S. Federal and State of California Emission Regulations for Heavy-Duty Vehicles require emissions to be reported in the non-SI unit of g/BHP-h.

APPENDIX A
SAE HANDBOOK DOCUMENTS THAT MAY BE AFFECTED BY USE OF ALTERNATIVE FUELS[5]

A.1 Power Test Codes[6]

SAE J607—Small Spark Ignition Engine Test Code
SAE J1228—Marine Engine Rating Code
SAE J1312—Procedure for Mapping Engine Performance—Diesel and Spark Ignition Engines
SAE J1349—Engine Power Test Code—Spark Ignition and Diesel

A.2 Emissions

SAE J35—Diesel Smoke Measurement Procedure
SAE J177—Measurement of Carbon Dioxide, Carbon Monoxide, and Oxides of Nitrogen in Diesel Exhaust
SAE J215—Continuous Hydrocarbon Analysis of Diesel Emissions
SAE J254—Instrumentation and Techniques for Exhaust Gas Emissions Measurement
SAE J255—Diesel Engine Smoke Measurement
SAE J1003—Diesel Engine Emission Measurement Procedure
SAE J1088—Test Procedure for the Measurement of Exhaust Emissions from Small Utility Engines
SAE J1094—Constant Volume Sampler System for Exhaust Emissions Measurement
SAE J1130—Determination of Emission from Gas Turbine Powered Light Duty Surface Vehicles
SAE J1243—Diesel Emission Production Audit Test Procedure

A.3 Fuels

SAE J312—Automotive Gasolines
SAE J313—Diesel Fuels
SAE J1297—Alternative Automotive Fuels
SAE J1498—Heating Values of Fuels
SAE J1829—Stoichiometric Air/Fuel Ratios of Automotive Fuels

A.4 Vehicle Fuel Economy

SAE J1082—Fuel Economy Measurement—Road Test Procedure
SAE J1256—Fuel Economy Measurement—Road Test Procedure—Cold Start and Warm-Up Fuel Economy
SAE J1376—Fuel Economy Measurement Test (Engineering Type) for Trucks and Buses

A.5 Other

SAE J30—Fuel and Oil Hoses
SAE J905—Fuel Filter Test Methods
SAE J1350—Selection and Application Guidelines for Diesel, Gasoline, and Propane Fired Liquid Cooled Engine Pre-Heaters

6. Note SAE J245 and J816 have been superseded by SAE J1349.

APPENDIX B
ASTM TEST METHODS THAT MAY BE USEFUL FOR CHARACTERIZING FUEL PROPERTIES[7]

B.1 ASTM Number

ASTM D 4175—Standard Terminology Relating to Petroleum, Petroleum Products, and Lubricants

B.2 Fuel Properties

ASTM D 56—Test Method for Flash Point by Tag Closed Tester
ASTM D 93—Test Method for Flash Point by Pensky-Martens Closed Tester
ASTM D 323—Test Method for Vapor Pressure of Petroleum Products (Reid Method)
ASTM D 613—Test Method for Ignition Quality of Diesel Fuels by the Cetane Method
ASTM D 909—Test Method for Knock Characteristics of Aviation Gasolines by the Supercharge Method
ASTM D 976—Methods for Calculated Cetane Index of Distillate Fuels
ASTM D 1298—Test Method for Relative Density (Specific Gravity) or API Gravity of Crude Petroleum and Liquid Petroleum Products by Hydrometer Method

5. This list may not cover all of the SAE Handbook documents that could be affected by use of Alternative Fuels. The more obvious documents are listed here. Note also that SAE continually updates the documents listed in the SAE Handbook and the latest version should be consulted.

7. This list may not cover all of the ASTM Test Methods or procedures that may be of use in characterizing fuel properties. For further information, consult *the most current* "Annual Book of ASTM Standards." Additionally, most ASTM Test Methods explicitly state the class or range of substances for which the procedures are valid. Departures from these substances or modifications to the procedures run the risk of erroneous results. However, if departures or modifications are made, they should be well documented, and the documentation should include an estimation of potential errors in the results.

ASTM D 2623—Test Method for Knock Characteristics of Liquified Petroleum (LP) Gas by the Motor (LP) Method

ASTM D 2699—Test Method for Knock Characteristics of Motor Fuels by the Research Method

ASTM D 2700—Test Method for Knock Characteristics of Motor and Aviation Fuels by the Motor Method

ASTM D 2885—Test Method for Research and Motor Method Octane Ratings Using On-Line Analyzers

ASTM D 2886—Test Method for Knock Characteristics of Motor Fuels by the Distribution Octane Number (DON) Method

ASTM D 4052—Test Method for Density and Relative Density of Liquids by Digital Density Meter

B.3 Heating Value

ASTM D 240—Test Method for Heat of Combustion of Liquid Hydrocarbon Fuels by Bomb Calorimeter

ASTM D 1405—Method for Estimation of Net Heat of Combustion of Aviation Fuels

ASTM D 1826—Test Method for Calorific Value of Gases in Natural Gas Range by Continuous Recording Calorimeter

ASTM D 2015—Test Method for Gross Calorific Value of Solid Fuel by the Adiabatic Bomb Calorimeter

ASTM D 2382—Test Method for Heat of Combustion of Hydrocarbon Fuels by Bomb Calorimeter (High Precision Method)

ASTM D 3286—Test Method for Gross Calorific Value of Coal and Coke by the Isothermal-Jacket Bomb Calorimeter

ASTM D 3588—Method for Calculating Calorific Value and Specific Gravity (Relative Density) of Gaseous Fuels

ASTM D 4529—Test Method for Estimation of Net Heat of Combustion of Aviation Fuels

ASTM E 711—Test Method for Gross Calorific Value of Refuse Derived Fuel (RDF-3) by the Bomb Calorimeter

B.4 Fuel Composition

ASTM D 129/IP 61—Test Method for Sulfur in Petroleum Products (General Bomb Method)

ASTM D 1018—Test Method for Hydrogen in Petroleum Fractions

ASTM D 1072—Test Method for Total Sulfur in Fuel Gases

ASTM D 1266/IP 107—Test Method for Sulfur in Petroleum Products (Lamp Method)

ASTM D 1552—Test Method for Sulfur in Petroleum Products (High-Temperature Method)

ASTM D 1685—Test Method for Traces of Thiophene in Benzene by Spectrophotometry

ASTM D 2385—Test Method for Hydrogen Sulfide in Mercaptan Sulfur in Natural Gas (Cadmium Sulfate Iodometric Titration Method)

ASTM D 2420—Test Method for Hydrogen Sulfide in Liquified Petroleum (LP) Gases (Lead Acetate Method)

ASTM D 2421—Standard Method for Interconversion of Analysis of C_5 and Lighter Hydrocarbons to Gas-Volume, Liquid-Volume, or Weight Basis

ASTM D 2504—Test Method for Noncondensible Gases in C_3 and Lighter Hydrocarbon Products by Gas Chromatography

ASTM D 2622—Test Method for Sulfur in Petroleum Products (X-Ray Spectrographic Method)

ASTM D 2725—Test Method for Hydrogen Sulfide in Natural Gas (Methylene Blue Method)

ASTM D 2747—Test Method for Trace Quantities of Total Sulfur in Volatile Organic Liquids (Oxy-Hydrogen Combustion Method)

ASTM D 2784—Test Method for Sulfur in Liquified Petroleum Gases (Oxy-Hydrogen Burner or Lamp)

ASTM D 2785—Test Method for Trace Quantities of Total Sulfur (Wickbold and Beckman Combustion Apparatus)

ASTM D 3031—Test Method for Total Sulfur in Natural Gas by Hydrogenation

ASTM D 3120—Test Method for Trace Quantities of Sulfur in Light Liquid Petroleum Hydrocarbons by Oxidative Microcoulometry

ASTM D 3227/IP 342—Test Method for Mercaptan Sulfur in Gasoline, Kerosene, Aviation Turbine and Distillate Fuels (Potentiometric Method)

ASTM D 3228—Test Method for Total Nitrogen in Lubricating Oils by Modified Kjeldahl Method

ASTM D 3230—Test Method for Salts in Crude Oil (Electrometric Method)

ASTM D 3235—Test Method for Solvent Extractables in Petroleum Wax

ASTM D 3246—Test Method for Sulfur in Petroleum Gas by Oxidative Microcoulometry

ASTM D 3343—Method for Estimation of Hydrogen Content of Aviation Fuels

ASTM D 3431—Test Method for Trace Nitrogen in Liquid Petroleum Hydrocarbon (Microcoulometric Method)

ASTM D 3701/IP338—Test Method for Hydrogen Content of Aviation Turbine Fuels by Low Resolution Nuclear Magnetic Resonance Spectrometry

ASTM D 3703—Test Method for Peroxide Number of Aviation Turbine Fuels

ASTM D 4045—Test Method for Sulfur in Petroleum Products by Hydrogenolysis and Rateometric Colorimetry

ASTM D 4046—Test Method for Alkyl Nitrate in Diesel Fuels by Spectrophotometry

ASTM D 4084—Method for Analysis of Hydrogen Sulfide in Gaseous Fuels (Lead Acetate Reaction Rate Method)

ASTM D 4294—Test Method for Sulfur in Petroleum Products by Non-Dispersive X-Ray Fluorescence Spectrometry

ASTM E 147—Specification for Apparatus for Microdetermination of Nitrogen by Kjeldahl Method

ASTM E 148—Specification for Apparatus for Microdetermination of Nitrogen by Dumas Method

ASTM E 191—Specification for Apparatus for Microdetermination of Carbon and Hydrogen in Organic and Organo-Metallic Compounds

ASTM E 258—Test Method for Total Nitrogen in Organic Materials by Modified Kjeldahl Method

ASTM E 379—Specification for Apparatus for Direct Microdetermination of Oxygen in Organic Compounds

APPENDIX C
POTENTIAL SOURCES OF HEALTH AND SAFETY INFORMATION[8]

C.1 One source of health and safety related information is standard reference books (three are listed in the bibliography—there may be others). In addition, many countries may have government agencies which have promulgated standards, regulations, or which have related information for exposure, handling, storage, transport, or disposal of particular fuels or fuel components. The primary agencies in the U.S.A. are OSHA—Occupational Safety and Health Administration, Dept. of Labor; NIOSH—National Institute for Occupational Safety and Health, Dept. of Health and Human Services; DOT—Department of Transportation; and EPA—Environmental Protection Agency. Another source of information are the codes of Fire Protection Associations such as the National Fire Protection Association in the U.S.A.

C.2 To distinguish between the various U.S. Federal Agencies in general terms, OSHA can be described as a regulatory Administration primarily concerned with setting exposure limits for various substances in the work place. NIOSH primarily makes available research data on toxicology and exposure levels to OSHA for OSHA's regulation process. DOT (in this context) deals mainly with the interstate transportation of various substances. The EPA is concerned with emission hazards from the transportation, storage, and use of the fuel or fuel components, as well as the hazards that may occur from disposal (water supplies, land fill, etc.).

8. The information provided in this Appendix is not to be taken as endorsement of any particular reference nor is it to be implied that with a review of these references the obligation to investigate health and safety related issues is necessarily complete. The information listed is intended only as a guideline with which to start the investigation.

OSHA Standards can be found in a set of books called the Code of Federal Regulations (CFR) which are published and updated each year by the U.S. Federal Government. These books are labeled by "Title" numbers, and are available in most major university libraries. OSHA information is in Title 29. The most relevant portions of Title 29 are in Part 1910 (Subpart Z-Toxic and Hazardous Substances), Section 1000 (Air Contaminants), and Section 1200 (Hazard Communication). The correct references would be 29 CFR 1910.1000 and 29 CFR 1910.1200.

Section 1200 includes the Federal requirements for Material Safety Data Sheets (MSDS). The sheets are required by regulation to be provided to "manufacturing purchasers" by "chemical manufacturers" or "importers" (as defined in Section 1200) for each hazardous chemical (also defined in Section 1200). The sheets include labeling information, physical and chemical characteristics, physical hazards, health hazards, primary route of entry, permissible exposure limits, whether it is listed as a carcinogen, general precautions, control measures, emergency procedures, and a phone number for additional information.

EPA standards and regulations are contained in Title 40 of the Code of Federal Regulations.

C.3 Reference Books

C.3.1 Condensed Chemical Dictionary—G.G. Hawley, Van Nostrand Reinhold—(use latest edition).

C.3.2 Dangerous Properties of Industrial Materials—N.I. Sax, Van Nostrand Reinhold—(use latest edition).

C.3.3 Handbook of Toxic and Hazardous Chemicals—M. Sitting, Noyes Publications—(use latest edition).

C.3.4 Safe Handling and Testing of Alternative Fuels—U.S. Department of Energy, Number DOE/CS/-56051-6 UC-96, January of 1982.

C.3.5 Additional sources (that is, reference books and databases) can be found in Appendix C to 29 CFR 1910.1200.

C.4 Databases—The databases referenced are primarily computer records of chemicals and their physical, environmental, and toxicological properties. Both public and commercial databases are available. Most require a fee for use in addition to a computer terminal and trained personnel.

There are also many commercial literature search companies that, for a fee, will access or provide access to private as well as public databases. As would be expected, the information available from the different sources may overlap. To aid in identifying such sources, those that are currently available to Environmental Protection Agency personnel through the EPA library system are listed in Tables C1 and C2. There may be other sources that may be more convenient, useful, relevant, etc. Information on locating additional sources should be available through the local public or university library.

TABLE C1—CHEMICAL INFORMATION DATABASES

Data Base	Description	Source Code [1]
CAS On-line	Chemical Abstract Service. Records of chemical abstracts covering journals, books, etc., from all areas of chemistry and chemical engineering worldwide through STN International.	10
CIS	Chemical Information Service. A collection of scientific and regulatory databases pertaining to chemistry.	2, 3
DIALOG	Dialog Information Service, Inc. An umbrella-like collection of many databases; includes hazardous waste information.	4
MSDS	Material Safety Data Sheets on various substances.	7
HAZARDLINE	Regulatory, health, and precautionary information on more than 78 000 industrial chemicals. This database is available through a number of sources, including NLM, BRS, and OHS.	1, 6, 7
NLM	National Library of Medicine. Includes a collection of specialized hazardous waste databases.	1, 4, 5
	a. TOXLINE—Covers pharmacological, biochemical, physiological, environmental, and toxicological effects of drugs on other chemicals.	
	b. TOXNET—A new NLM Toxicology Network.	
OHM/TADS	Oil and Hazardous Materials/Technical Assistance Data System. Overall data files covering transportation combustibility, toxicity to humans and animals, odor disposal, and hazards, among other topics.	2
OHS	Occupational Health Services. Contains some 5000 chemical profiles, including names, CERCLA [2] information, disposal information, and other materials.	7
RTECS	Registry of Toxic Effects of Chemical Substances (RTECS), U.S. Department of Health and Human Services, CDC, NIOSH, Cincinnati, OH 49226.	2, 5, 8
SDS	Systems Development Corp. A collection of databases including those with scientific and technical material.	9

1. Table C2, other sources may be available. Consult your local public or university library.
2. Comprehensive Environmental Response Compensation and Liability Act (Superfund).

TABLE C2—DATA BASE SOURCES [1]

Source Code [2]	Source
1	BRS Information Technologies, 1200 Rt. 7 Latham, NY 12110; 800/345-4BRS.
2	Chemical Information Systems, a subsidiary of Fein Marquart Assoc., 7215 York Road, Baltimore, MD 21212; 301/321-8840; 800/247-8737.
3	ICI, Information Consultants, Inc., 1133-15th Street, NW, Suite 300, Washington, DC 20005; 202/822-5200.
4	DIALOG - Information Services, Inc., 3460 Hillview Ave., Palo Alto, CA 94304; 415/858-3785; 800/3DIALOG.
5	Medlars Management Section, National Library of Medicine, 8600 Rockville Pike, Bethseda, MD 20894; 1301/496-6193; outside of Maryland 1800/638-8480.
6	Mead Data Central, P.O. Box 933, Dayton, OH 45401; 513/865-6800; 800/227-4908.
7	OHS (Occupational Health Services), 400 Plaza Drive, P.O. Box 1505, Secaucus, NJ 07094; 201/865-7500; 800/223-8978.
8	Printed RTECS is generally available through the Superintendent of Documents, U.S. GPO, Washington, DC 20402; 202/783-3238. Yearly microfiche updates are available through the GPO. Computer tapes are available through the National Technical Information Service (NTIS), Port Royal Road, Springfield, VA 22161; 703/487-4650.
9	SDC Information Services, 2525 Colorado Avenue, Santa Monica, CA 90406; 213-453-6194; in California - 800/352-6689; outside of California - 800/421-7229.
10	STN-Columbus, c/o Chemical Abstracts Service, P.O. Box 02228, Columbus, OH 43202; 614/421-3600; inside Ohio - 800/848-6538; outside Ohio - 800/848-6533.

1. Other sources may be available; consult your local public or university library.
2. From Table C1.

C.5 National Fire Protection Agency (NFPA) Codes—(Battery March Park, Quincy, MA 00269)

National Fire Protection codes are mainly concerned with combustion of flammable substances at atmospheric pressure. Codes that may be relevant are listed as follows:

C.5.1 Hazardous Chemical Data, No. 49.

C.5.2 Combustion Engines and Gas Turbines, No. 37.

C.5.3 Flammable and Combustible Liquids Classification, No. 321.

C.5.4 Flammable and Combustible Liquids Code, No. 30.

C.5.5 Laboratories Using Chemicals, No. 45.

C.5.6 Flammable Liquids, Gases, and Volatile Solids, No. 325M.

C.5.7 Manual of Hazardous Chemical Reactions, No. 491M.

APPENDIX D
GUIDELINE FOR ADJUSTMENTS TO POWER TEST CODE CALCULATIONS WHEN USING ALTERNATIVE FUELS

D.1 Introduction—If published engine test results from various sources are more directly comparable, the selection of the best engine and alternative fuel option to meet the job requirements specified by the manufacturer or the end user can be more efficient. The partial list of affected SAE documents in Appendix A is a focus to help the reader recognize breadth of scope of the requirements. This appendix focuses on both the general and the specific modifications that might be required in the performance calculations for SAE J1349. Similar modifications should be considered when using SAE J607, J1228, J1312, or J1376, or when performing unique tests outside of the scope of the various test codes. SAE TSB 003 (SI units of measure) is a further guide for uniformity of results.

D.2 General Guidance

D.2.1 Airflow—measurement with alternative fuels should pose no special problems, unless a vapor fuel is aspirated into the air stream before airflow measurement is performed. In this case, caution should be used to obtain the correct airflow measurement, and in subsequent calculations. Volume flow measurements need to be converted to mass flow for fuel-air ratio calculations.

D.2.2 Barometer—corrections for humidity and the humidity calculation shall be in accordance with SAE J177.

D.2.3 Energy Rate—for alternative fuels includes the energy in the actual mass fuel flow plus any auxiliary equipment power not utilized by the engine when running on conventional fuels.

D.2.3.1 FUEL ENERGY RATE—requires a knowledge of the fuel's lower heating value and the mass rate of fuel flow. The mass rate of fuel flow is preferably determined by a mass/time measurement.

Mass fuel rate (F) is simply ...

$$F = (m_f)/(\Delta t) \quad \text{(Eq. D1)}$$

where:

m_f = mass of fuel consumed, g
Δt = time, s

If a volume/time fuel measurement system is used, the density of the fuel at the measured fuel temperature must be included ...

$$F = [(1000)(V_f)(d)]/(\Delta t) \quad \text{(Eq. D2)}$$

where:

V_f = volume of fuel, L or m^3
d = density of fuel, kg/L or kg/m^3

The fuel energy rate then is:

$$FER = (F)(LHV) \quad \text{(Eq. D3)}$$

where:

FER = fuel energy rate, kJ/s
F = fuel rate, g/s
LHV = fuel lower heating value, MJ/kg

D.2.3.2 OTHER ENERGY—required to change viscosity, vaporize, pump, inject, maintain solution, assist ignition, etc., if it is not engine driven, must be included in fuel (energy) consumption results for comparison to engines running on other alternative or conventional fuels.

D.2.3.3 TOTAL ENERGY RATE

$$TER = FER + OE \quad \text{(Eq. D4)}$$

where:

TER = total energy rate to the engine, kJ/s—note that one kJ/s equals one kW
FER = fuel energy rate, kJ/s
OE = other energy, kW or kJ/s

D.2.4 Specific Energy Consumption

$$BSEC = TER/bp \quad \text{(Eq. D5)}$$

$$ISEC = TER/ip \quad \text{(Eq. D6)}$$

where:

bp = brake power, kW
ip = indicated power, kW
BSEC = brake specific energy consumption, (kJ/s)/kW
ISEC = indicated specific energy consumption, (kJ/s)/kW

D.2.5 Stoichiometric Fuel-Air Ratio—is a function of the fuel type, and varies according to the fuel composition. See 4.3 for stoichiometric determination. Stoichiometric (f/a) ratio calculations in 40 CFR 86.345 (Subpart D), SAE J1088 (paragraph 5.2.2 and Appendices A, B, and C), and J177 (Sections 5 and 6) must be modified to include molecular fuel oxygen, nitrogen, or sulfur when present, and are generally not adequate for alternative fuels (see Appendix E for additional insight).

D.2.6 Thermal Efficiency

$$BTE = 100[bp/TER] = 100[1/BSEC] \quad \text{(Eq. D7)}$$

$$ITE = 100[ip/TER] = 100[1/ISEC] \quad \text{(Eq. D8)}$$

where:

BTE = brake thermal efficiency (%)
ITE = indicated thermal efficiency (%)
NOTE—The fractional thermal efficiency is the inverse of the specific of the specific energy consumption.

D.3 Specific Guidance for SAE J1349

D.3.1 Power Correction—factors for nonstandard ambient or inlet test conditions shall be determined in accordance with SAE J1349 except for the computation of the mass fuel rate per stroke per unit of engine displacement, or "q" in mg/L-cycle, for diesel engines. The term, which was developed for typical diesel fuels, must be stated on an energy basis because of the varied heating values associated with alternative fuels. (SAE J1498 provides additional information on heating values of fuels.)

$$q = [(120\,000\,F)/(DN)](LHV_A/LHV_B)\,mg/L-cycle \quad \text{(Eq. D9)}$$

for a four-stroke engine (constant 120 000 would be 60 000 for a two-stroke engine).

where:

F = fuel rate, g/s
D = engine displacement, L
N = engine speed, r/min
LHV_A = lower heating value of alternative or off-spec fuel, MJ/kg
LHV_B = lower heating value of spec diesel fuel, MJ/kg

This corrects the mass flow of the alternative fuel to the mass flow of a typical diesel fuel that would provide the same energy input. Thus modified, "q" can be used in the standard engine factor and in the corrected brake power calculations as specified by SAE J1349.

APPENDIX E
GUIDELINES FOR ADJUSTMENTS TO EMISSION MEASUREMENT CALCULATIONS WHEN USING ALTERNATIVE FUELS

E.1 Overview—The U.S. Environmental Protection Agency has published regulations with specified emissions test procedures and equipment performance requirements. These regulations apply to gasoline and diesel powered light-duty passenger cars and trucks, and heavy-duty gasoline and diesel engines that are being operated on either gasoline or diesel fuels (Title 40, Code of Federal Regulations, Part 86). SAE also has several standard emission measurement procedures (see Appendix A). Regulated emissions from the classes of vehicles and engines described include hydrocarbons (HC), [9] carbon monoxide (CO), oxides of nitrogen (NO_x), and diesel particulate and smoke. All other emissions (for example, PNA, BaP, formaldehyde ([9]), and sulfates) are considered unregulated emissions. The U.S. Clean Air Act and the 1977 Clean Air Act Amendments imply compliance with applicable regulations, but there are no specific procedures for measuring emissions when using alternative fuels([9]).

Because the chemical composition of the alternative fuel used will influence the exhaust emission species, procedures developed for gasoline and diesel fuels may not have adequate safeguards to prevent erroneous or incomplete emission measurements. The possibility of unexpected problems that could alter the emissions results should be a major concern when testing with alternative fuels. The following possible problem areas illustrate some of these concerns:

E.1.1 Emissions Analyzers—The limitations of the emissions analyzers should be identified for the particular alternative fuel under test. For example, current flame ionization detectors (FIDs) have a different voltage to concentration response for different classes of organic matter (OM)[9] compounds. When calibrated in accordance with procedures for gasoline and diesel fueled vehicles or engines, these instruments may not be capable of accurately measuring the compound of interest in the exhaust of an engine running on an alternative fuel.

The probable difference in species composition of the engine exhaust may produce a different instrument response. The instrument, therefore, may not produce a reading representative of the actual concentration, resulting in erroneous emission measurement.

Other analyzers for either regulated or unregulated emissions may also be affected by the change in species or a change in the ratio of species in the exhaust of an alternative fueled engine when compared to one fueled by either gasoline or diesel fuel.

New species that may be in the exhaust which were not present in the exhaust with typical gasolines and diesel fuels could also interfere with the measurement of the species desired. Changes in concentration of well known interfering species such as water could cause problems. High water concentrations might, under some circumstances, overwhelm water traps in the CO and CO_2 analyzers such that the extra water would be measured as increases in CO and CO_2. In chemiluminescent NO_x analyzers, additional water may increase the amount of quench and reduce the NO_x reading.

In some cases, mathematical corrections can be made after the measurement of data to modify the emissions readings from the instrument to compensate for errors known to result from the use of an alternative fuel. In addition to evaluating the potential impact that the alternative fuel may have on the instruments, and attempting to alleviate these effects, emission data from alternative fueled engines should clearly indicate whether any correction to the data has been made, and the technique used to derive the correction factor.

E.1.2 Sample Handling Systems—A change in concentration or a change in type of exhaust emissions species due to the use of alternative fuels may affect the proper transport of the sample to the emissions analyzer. For example, some alternatively fueled engines may produce significantly more water than current gasoline or diesel fueled engines. This may lead to the need for heated lines, or in the case of CVS testing, higher dilution ratios to prevent water condensation when alternative fuels are used. The use of an alternative fuel may also cause the unburned fuel emissions to change such that increased sample system temperature and reduced transport time are necessary to prevent these new species of unburned fuel emissions from condensing in the sample system. Some alternative fuels may produce compounds that are more corrosive to the sample transport hardware, or react with the other constituents in the exhaust gas. In this case, different system materials may be needed and extremely short transport times may be required to minimize the time available for reactions.

E.1.3 New Emissions—An alternative fuel may create a class of emissions that are not normally associated with the particular type of engine being tested. For example, the use of some forms of alternative fuels in SI engines might possibly create high levels of particulates that are not normally associated with an SI engine.

E.1.4 Calculations—Equations for calculating the exhaust emissions rates and indexes from the basic emissions measurements and concentrations will most likely need to be modified because of the different composition of the alternative fuel. General guidance can be found in "Calculation of Emissions and Fuel Economy When Using Alternative Fuels" (U.S. EPA Report No. EPA460/3-83-009) by Southwest Research Institute.

E.2 Examples of Affected SAE and U.S. Federal Procedures—Emission results from SAE Standards and Recommended Practices as well as from Governmental Emission Regulations may be affected when an alternative fuel is used and the procedure is based on an analysis that assumes gasoline or diesel is the fuel being used. These procedures may need modification in order to obtain results that are more realistic when an alternative fuel is being tested.

Emissions data reduction techniques that compute mass emissions flow rates partly or totally from concentrations of exhaust constituents without measured exhaust mass flow depend on knowledge of the fuel composition. Some procedures assume "standard" information about the fuel, which is then assumed to be a "typical" gasoline or diesel fuel. For example, the atomic H/C ratio may be assumed to be a constant 1.85. Results of such an analysis would not be valid for an alternative fuel that deviated from this assumption. Carbon balance computations and emissions rates based on a carbon balance analysis would be in error.

E.2.1 SAE J177, Section 5 and Paragraph 6.4—The dry-to-wet basis conversion factor is for $CH_{y/x}$ hydrocarbon fuel only. Oxygen-bearing fuels will require a different formulation for the dry-to-wet basis conversion factor.

E.2.2 SAE J1088

E.2.2.1 PARAGRAPH 5.2.2—The use of alternative fuels with molecular compositions different from a $CH_{y/x}$ formulation will require more comprehensive derivations for the stoichiometric fuel/air ratio, mass emissions rates, and wet-to-dry basis conversion factor.

E.2.2.2 APPENDICES A, B, AND C—The factor describing the mass of carbon per unit mass of fuel is for a fuel in form of $CH_{y/x}$, where $y/x = 1.85$.

This factor is not valid for fuels with significantly different atomic H/C ratios and/or molecular composition.

E.2.3 SAE J1094a

E.2.3.1 PARAGRAPH 5.4—The computation of fuel economy from exhaust emissions is based on an assumed fuel of $CH_{y/x}$ (where $y/x = 1.85$) and a specific gravity of 0.7404. The 2423 g C/gallon fuel is only valid for these assumptions, and the specific fuel they represent. Results of this analysis applied to an alternative fuel would be in error.

E.2.4 40 CFR 86, Subparts B, D, E, F, G, K, N, and P—All formulations for computation of mass emissions rates by the carbon balance method, wet-to-dry basis conversions, stoichiometric f/a ratio calculations, and calculated f/a ratios are for a fuel of form $CH_{y/x}$. If an alternative fuel varies significantly from the $CH_{y/x}$ assumption, errors in the computations will result unless the calculation techniques are modified.

9. A Notice of Public Rulemaking (NPRM) for emission standards and test procedures for methanol fueled Light Duty Vehicles (LDV) and trucks (LDT) was published by the U.S. EPA on August 29, 1986 in the *Federal Register*. For methanol, vehicle emission levels of formaldehyde are proposed to be included in the measure of organic matter, and therefore could be considered a regulated emission component.

LUBRICATING OIL, AIRCRAFT PISTON ENGINE (ASHLESS DISPERSANT)—SAE J1899 JUN2000 SAE Standard

Report of the SAE Fuels and Lubricants Technical Committee 8—Aviation Piston Engine Fuels and Lubricants approved June 1991, completely revised October 1995, and revised June 2000.

1. Scope—This SAE Standard establishes the requirements for lubricating oils containing ashless dispersant additives to be used in four-stroke cycle, reciprocating piston aircraft engines. This document covers the same lubricating oil requirements as the former military specification MIL-L-22851. Users should consult their airframe or engine manufacturers manuals for the latest listing of acceptable lubricants.

1.1 Classification—The lubricating oils shall be furnished in the following grades as in Table 1:

1.2 Commercial Products—Commercial products sold under this document must meet all of the requirements of Sections 3 and 4 of this document with the following exceptions:

a. Qualification samples and test results do not have to be submitted to Naval Air Warfare Center (NAWC), but must be retained by the manufacturer for a period of at least three years.
b. Individual products acceptance lists for commercial aviation piston engine oils will be maintained by each of the original aircraft engine manufacturers.
c. The detailed sampling and inspection procedural requirements of 4.4.2.2 through 4.4.3.2 do not apply.
d. Commercial products do not have to meet the packaging requirements of Section 5.

TABLE 1—VISCOSITY GRADE COMPARISON TABLE

SAE Grade	Military Grade	Commercial Grade	NATO Code Number
30	none	65	none
40	Type III	80	0—123
50	none	100	none
60	Type II	120	0—128
Multi-Grade	none	none	none

NOTE—The Military Grade designations are being phased-out in favor of the NATO Code Numbers. Commercial Grade designations are being replaced by the SAE Grade classifications.

2. References

2.1 Applicable Publications—The following publications form a part of this specification to the extent specified herein. The latest issue of SAE publications shall apply.

2.1.1 GOVERNMENT DOCUMENTS

2.1.1.1 Specifications and Standards—The listed publications and standards form a part of this specification to the extent specified herein. Unless otherwise specified, the issues of these documents shall be those listed in the issue of the Department of Defense Index of Specifications and Standards (DODISS) and supplement thereto cited in the solicitation (see 6.2)(see 6.2). The military specifications are listed for reference only and are not current.

2.1.1.1.1 Specifications

Military

MIL-L-6082—Lubricating Oil, Aircraft Piston Engine (Non-Dispersant Mineral Oil), canceled Nov. 1995

MIL-L-22851—Lubricating Oil, Aircraft Piston Engine (Ashless Dispersant), canceled Nov. 1995

2.1.1.1.2 Standards

Federal

FED-STD-313—Material Safety Data Sheets, Preparation and the Submission of

FED-STD-791—Lubricants, Liquid Fuels and Related Products; Methods of Testing

Military

MIL-STD-290—Packaging, Packing and Marking of Petroleum and Related Products

(Unless otherwise indicated, copies of federal and military specifications, standards, and handbooks are available from DODSSP, Subscription Services Desk, Building 4D, 700 Robbins Avenue, Philadelphia, PA 19111-5094.)

2.1.1.2 Other Government Publications—The following other Government publications form a part of this specification to the extent specified herein. Unless otherwise specified, the issues shall be those in effect on the date of the solicitation.

Naval Air Systems Command

Navair 17-15-BF-62—Fluid Analysis Spectrometer, Type A/E 35U-3, Operation Instructions and Maintenance Instructions

(Application for copies should be addressed to the Naval Air Technical Services Facilities, 700 Robbins Avenue, Philadelphia, PA 19111-5098.)

(Copies of specifications, standards, other Government documents and publications required by contractors in connection with specific acquisition functions should be obtained from the contracting activity or as directed by the contracting activity.)

2.2 Other Publications—The following publications form a part of this specification to the extent specified herein. Unless otherwise specified, the issues of the documents which are DOD adopted shall be those listed in the issue of the DODISS specified in the solicitation. Unless otherwise specified, the issues of documents not listed in the DODISS shall be the issue of the nongovernment documents which is current on the date of the solicitation (see 6.2)(See 6.2).

2.2.1 SAE PUBLICATIONS—Available from SAE, 400 Commonwealth Drive, Warrendale, PA 15096-0001.

SAE J300—Engine Oil Viscosity Classification

SAE J1787—Measurement of the Total Ash Content of Aviation Piston Engine Oils by a Calculation Method

2.2.2 AMERICAN SOCIETY FOR TESTING AND MATERIALS (ASTM)—Available from the American Society for Testing and Materials, 100 Barr Harbor Drive, West Conshohocken, PA 19428-2959.

ASTM D 92—Flash and Fire Points by Cleveland Open Cup

ASTM D 93—Flash Point by Pensky-Martens Closed Cup Tester

ASTM D 97—Pour Point of Petroleum Oils

ASTM D 129—Sulfur in Petroleum Products (General Bomb Method

ASTM D 130—Detection of Copper Corrosion from Petroleum Products by the Copper Strip Tarnish Test

ASTM D 445—Kinematic Viscosity of Transparent and Opaque Liquids (and the Calculation of Dynamic Viscosity)

ASTM D 482—Ash from Petroleum Products

ASTM D 664—Neutralization Number by Potentiometric Titration

ASTM D 892—Foaming Characteristics of Lubricating Oils

ASTM D 1298—Density, Relative Density (Specific Gravity), or API Gravity of Crude Petroleum and Liquid Petroleum Products by Hydrometer Method

ASTM D 1552—Sulfur in Petroleum Products (High-Temperature Method)

ASTM D 2270—Calculating Viscosity Index from Kinematic Viscosity at 40 and 100 °C

ASTM D 2273—Trace Sediment in Lubricating Oils

ASTM D 2622—Sulfur in Petroleum Products (X-ray Spectrographic Method)

ASTM D 4052—Density and Relative Density of Liquids by Digital Density Method

ASTM D 4057—Manual Sampling of Petroleum and Petroleum Products

ASTM D 4177—Automatic Sampling of Petroleum and Petroleum Products

ASTM D 4683—Measuring Viscosity at High Temperature and High Shear Rate by Tapered Bearing Simulator

ASTM D 4684—Determination of Yield Stress and Apparent Viscosity of Engine Oils at Low Temperature

ASTM D 4741—Measuring Viscosity at High Temperature and High Shear Rate by Tapered-Plug Viscometer

ASTM D 4927—Elemental Analysis of Lubricant and Additive Components—Barium, Calcium, Phosphorus, Sulfur, and Zinc by Wavelength—Dispersive X-Ray Fluorescence Spectroscopy

ASTM D 5119—Single Cylinder Engine Test

ASTM D 5293—Evaluation of Automotive Engine Oils Between −5 and −30 °C Using the Cold-Cranking Simulator

ASTM D 5949—Pour Point of Petroleum Products (Automatic Pressure Pulse Method)

ASTM D 5950—Pour Point of Petroleum Products (Automatic Tilt Method)

ASTM D 5985—Pour Point of Petroleum Products (Rotational Method)

2.2.3 AMERICAN NATIONAL STANDARDS INSTITUTE (ANSI)—Application for copies should be addressed to the American National Standards Institute, 11 West 42nd Street, New York, NY 10036-8002.

ANSI Z129.1—American National Standard for the Precautionary Labeling of Hazardous Industrial Chemicals

2.2.4 AMERICAN SOCIETY FOR QUALITY CONTROL (ASQC)—Available from the American Society for Quality Control, P.O. Box 12233, Research Triangle Park, NC 27709.

ASQC-Z1.4—Sampling Procedures and Tables for Inspection by Attributes (DoD Accepted)

2.2.5 ORDER OF PRECEDENCE—In the event of a conflict between the text of this specification and the references cited herein (except for associated detail specifications, specification sheets, or MS standards), the text of this specification takes precedence. Nothing in this specification, however, shall supersede applicable laws and regulations unless a specific exemption has been obtained.

3. Requirements

3.1 Qualification—The lubricating oils furnished under this specification shall be products which are authorized by the qualifying activity for listing on the applicable qualified products list at the time for opening of bids (see 4.3 and 6.2.2)(see 6.2.2). Detailed information on the procedures to be followed when submitting a candidate lubricating oil are available from the Naval Air Systems Command, AIR-4.4.5, Fuels and Lubricants Division, Building 2360, 22229 Elmer Road, Unit 4, Patuxent River, MD 20670. Interim qualification approval will be granted upon the successful completion of all specification requirements with the exception of the 12-month storage stability test.

3.1.1 READ-ACROSS APPROVALS—Read-across approvals will only be granted to different grades of oil which are composed of varying percentages of the same base stocks blended with identical additive packages (adjustments in VI improver and pour point depressant concentration will be permitted). Complete chemical and physical property test results shall be submitted for each grade of oil for which qualification is requested. L-38 tests shall be performed on the lightest and heaviest single grade oils to be blended from the same basestock materials (neutral and bright stock). All single grade oils blended from the same basestock materials and meeting SAE viscosity classification standards between the two tested products will be granted qualification approval based on similarity. The 150 h engine test will be run on an SAE 50 grade oil unless the use of another grade is acceptable to the approving agency. The flight test will be run on the appropriate single grade(s) for the environmental conditions encountered. No read-across approvals will be granted to multi-grade oils.

3.1.2 REQUALIFICATION—Requalification shall be required in the event any change is made in the source or composition of the lubricant, the ingredients used, the manufacturing processes, or the plant location.

3.2 Materials—The lubricating oils shall be derived from petroleum fractions, synthetically prepared compounds or a combination of the two types of products compounded with such functional additives as dispersants, oxidation inhibitors, antifoam agents, viscosity index improvers, and pour point depressants necessary to meet specified requirements. Crude source(s) and the types of processing used in the manufacture of the base stocks shall be identified in accordance with Appendix A. Exceptions to these requirements shall be directed to the qualifying activity. If re-refined materials are used the manufacturer must demonstrate the consistency of the products to the qualifying activity.

3.3 Chemical and Physical Properties—The finished lubricating oil shall conform to the physical and property requirements specified in Tables 2A and 2.

3.4 Sulfur—The sulfur content of the oil shall not exceed the value shown for each grade in Tables 2A and 2. For quality conformance inspection, the sulfur content shall be within ±0.15% mass of the qualification value or within a 0.3% mass range selected by the manufacturer to bracket the qualification value.

3.5 API Gravity—The American Petroleum Institute (API) gravity of the oil shall be determined but not limited on qualification inspection. For quality conformance inspection, the gravity shall be within ±1.0 °API of the qualification value, or within a 2.0 °API range selected by the manufacturer to bracket the qualification value.

3.6 Workmanship—The lubricating oil shall be a homogeneous blend when examined visually at room temperature (25 °C ± 3 °C) in a well-lighted room or daylight. It shall exhibit no separation or fallout of the additive package. Any jelly-like substance or very viscous material observed in the bottom of the container will be considered evidence of additive fallout.

3.7 Storage Stability

3.7.1 FOURTEEN-DAY STORAGE TEST—When stored as specified in 4.5.1.1, the oil shall show no separation.

3.7.2 TWELVE-MONTH STORAGE TEST—When stored as specified in 4.5.1.2, the oil shall show no separation.

3.8 Performance Requirements

3.8.1 L-38 ENGINE TEST—The fully formulated oil shall meet the requirements of Table 3 when tested in the L-38 engine in accordance with ASTM D 5119. The test shall be run with the oil gallery temperature controlled at 135 °C ± 1 °C (275 °F ± 2 °F).

3.8.2 ENGINE TEST—All candidate lubricating oils shall demonstrate satisfactory performance in a 150 h engine endurance test run on a Textron Lycoming TIO-540-J2BD engine in accordance with Appendix B. Results of this engine test shall be acceptable to the qualifying activity. For read-across approvals, only one engine test is required as defined in 3.1.1.

3.8.2.1 Engine Test Exclusion—At the discretion of the qualifying activity, this engine test requirement may be waived. Manufacturers requesting this waiver shall provide sufficient data to the qualifying activity to either verify that the candidate oil formulation does not represent a significant change from an existing qualified formulation or demonstrate the performance of the oil in an equivalent manner.

3.8.3 FLIGHT TEST—After satisfactory completion of the 150 h engine test requirement, all candidate oils shall demonstrate satisfactory performance when flight tested as specified in Appendix C. Flight tests shall be performed in accordance with current Federal Aviation Administration (FAA) advisory material. If the terms of 3.8.2.1 apply, the flight test shall not be required.

3.9 Material Safety Data Sheets—When applying for qualification, the manufacturer shall submit to the qualifying activity Material Safety Data Sheets prepared in accordance with FED-STD-313 (see 6.5).

4. Quality Assurance Provisions

4.1 Responsibility for Inspection—Unless otherwise specified in the contract or purchase order, the contractor is responsible for the performance of all inspection requirements as specified herein. Except as otherwise specified in the contract or purchase order, the contractor may use his own or any other facility suitable for the performance of the inspection requirements specified herein, unless disapproved by the Government. The Government reserves the right to perform any of the inspections set forth in the specification where such inspections are deemed necessary to assure supplies and services conform to prescribed requirements.

4.1.1 RESPONSIBILITY FOR COMPLIANCE—All items shall meet all requirements of Sections 3 and 5. The inspection set forth in this document shall become a part of the contractor's overall inspection system or quality program. The absence of any inspection requirements in the specification shall not relieve the contractor of the responsibility of assuring that all products or supplies submitted to the Government for acceptance comply with all requirements of the contract. Sampling inspection, as part of manufacturing operations, is an acceptable practice to ascertain conformance to requirements; however, this does not authorize submission of known defective material; either indicated or actual, nor does it commit the Government to accept defective material.

4.2 Classification of Inspections—The inspection requirements specified herein are classified as follows:

a. Qualification inspection (see 4.3)(see 4.3).
b. Quality assurance inspection (see 4.4)(see 4.4).

4.3 Qualification Inspection—The qualification inspection shall consist of a review of and concurrence with the manufacturer's test results (see 4.3.2)(see 4.3.2) by NAVAIR's field activity, the Naval Air Warfare Center (NAWC). Additional testing of the qualification inspection sample shall be performed by NAPC to confirm compliance with the requirements of Tables 2A and 2.

TABLE 2A—CHEMICAL AND PHYSICAL PROPERTY REQUIREMENTS FOR FINISHED LUBRICANT

Characteristic (Limits) SAE GRADE	30	40	50	60	Multi-grade	Test Method
Viscosity, cSt,						ASTM D 445
@ 100 °C, Min	9.3	12.5	16.3	21.9	(1)	
@ 100 °C, Less than	12.5	16.3	21.9	26.1	(1)	
Viscosity Index, Min	100	100	95	95	100	ASTM D 2270
Flash Point, °C, Min	220	225	243	243	220	ASTM D 92
Flash Point, °C	report	report	report	report	report	ASTM D 93
Pour Point, °C, Max	−24	−22	−18	−18	—	ASTM D 97 ASTM D 5949 ASTM D 5950 ASTM D 5985
Sulfur, Mass %, Max	0.6	0.8	1.0	1.2	0.6	ASTM D 129 ASTM D 1552 ASTM D 2622
Viscosity, Low Temp., Pumping	—	—	—	—	(1)	ASTM D 4684
Viscosity, Low Temp., Cold Crank Sim., cP, Min	—	—	—	—	(1)	ASTM D 5293
Viscosity, High Temp., High Shear, at 150 °C, cP, Min	3.3	3.7	3.7	3.7	(1)	ASTM D 4683 ASTM D 4741
All Grades						
Viscosity, cSt,						ASTM D 445
@ 40 °C		report				
Total Acid Number,						ASTM D 664
mg KOH/g, Max(2)		1.0				
Density, @ 15 °C, kg/L		report				ASTM D 4052
Gravity, @ 60 °F, °API(3)		report				ASTM D 1298, ASTM D 4052
Ash Content,(4)						ASTM D 482, SAE J1787
Mass %, Max		0.011				
Trace Sediment,						ASTM D 2273
mL/100 mL Oil, Max		0.005				
Copper Strip Corrosion,(5)						ASTM D 130
Max Rating						
3 h @ 100 °C		1				
3 h @ 204 °C		3				
Foaming Tendency/Stability						ASTM D 892
Seq. I						
Aerated Vol., mL, Max		50				
Vol. after 10 min, mL, Max		0				
Seq. II						
Aerated Vol., mL, Max		50				
Vol. after 10 min, mL, Max		0				
Seq. III						
Aerated Vol., mL, Max		50				
Vol. after 10 min, mL, Max		0				

1. Oil shall meet the viscosity requirements of SAE J300 for the designated grade.
2. Titrate to a pH 11 end point.
3. API gravity may be computed from the relative density measured by ASTM D 4052.
4. ASTM D 482 is required for qualification. Either ASTM D 482 or SAE J1787 may be used for quality Assurance testing.
5. Conduct the test in accordance with ASTM D 130 but at the temperature specified.

TABLE 2B—CHEMICAL AND PHYSICAL PROPERTY REQUIREMENTS FOR FINISHED LUBRICANT

Characteristic (Limits) SAE Grade		All Grades	Test Method
Compatibility with other oils(1)		pass	FTM 791 Method 3470
Elastomer Compatibility(2)			FTM 791 Method 3604
% swelling, acceptable range:			
after 72 h			
Material	Test Temp.		
AMS 3217/1	70 °C (158 °F)	−5 to +5	
AMS 3217/4	150 °C (302 °F)	−5 to +5	
AMS 3217/5	150 °C (302 °F)	−5 to +5	
US Navy			
Silicone Rubber	121 °C (250 °F)	0 to +20	
Trace Metal Content, ppm, Max(3)			(see 4.5.2)(see 4.5.2)
Iron (Fe)		5	
Silver (Ag)		2	
Aluminum (Al)		7	
Chromium (Cr)		5	
Copper (Cu)		3	
Magnesium (Mg)		3	
Nickel (Ni)		3	
Lead (Pb)		5	
Silicon (Si)		25	
Tin (Sn)		10	
Titanium (Ti)		2	
Molybdenum (Mo)		4	

1. Reference oils may be obtained from NAWC.
2. The elastomer compatibility test shall be performed in accordance with Fed Test Method Std 791 Method 3604 with the following exception: The specific materials which shall be tested and the temperature at which the test is to be conducted are those listed in this table.
3. Required for qualification and for U.S. Government procurements.

TABLE 3—L-38 ENGINE TEST REQUIREMENTS AT 40 h (END OF TEST)(1)

End of Test Characteristic	Limit Single Grade	Limit Multigrade	Test Method
BEARING			
Bearing Weight Loss, Total, mg, Max	500	500	ASTM D 5119
USED OIL			
Viscosity, % Change, Max @ 40 °C	−15 to +10	report	ASTM D 445
Viscosity, @ 100 °C	—	(2)	ASTM D 445
Total Acid Number, Change, Max(3)	2.0	2.0	ASTM D 664

1. L-38 engine test is to be run in accordance with ASTM D 5119, Part IV with an oil gallery temperature of 135 °C ± 1 °C (275 °F ± 2 °F).
2. Stripped viscosity of the 10 h sample shall remain in original SAE grade.
3. Titrate to a pH 11 end point.

4.3.1 QUALIFICATION INSPECTION SAMPLE—All qualification and NAWC testing shall be conducted on the same homogeneous batch of oil. In addition, the qualification inspection test samples for testing by NAWC shall consist of a 3.8 L (1 gal) sample of each grade of blended base oil without additives and a 38 L (10 gal) sample of each grade of the finished oil for which qualification approval is sought. Material Safety Data Sheets completed in accordance with FED-STD-313 shall also be included with the test samples. At the direction of the Naval Air Systems Command, AIR-4.45, these samples should be forwarded to the Naval Air Warfare Center, AIR-4.4.5 at an address to be specified at the time of sample submission. The sample should be plainly identified by a securely attached durable tag or label marked with the following information:

QUALIFICATION INSPECTION SAMPLE
LUBRICATING OIL, AIRCRAFT PISTON ENGINE, ASHLESS DISPERSANT

Type of Sample: ______ (basestock or finished oil)
Name of Manufacturer ______
Product Code Number ______
Batch Number ______
Date of Manufacture ______
Submitted by ______ (name) on (date)
for qualification inspection in accordance with SAE J1899 under authorization of (reference authorizing letter) (see 6.2.2).

FIGURE 1—QUALIFICATION INSPECTION SAMPLE

4.3.2 TEST RESULTS—The manufacturer shall present a certified copy of the test report to NAWC. The report shall contain complete test data showing the results of all tests required by this specification with the exception of the 12-month storage stability test and the trace metal content. Photographs of the test parts from the L-38 engine shall be included along with data on the test oil's viscosity (measured at 40 °C) and TAN at 0, 10, 20, 30, and 40 h into the test (including the stripped 40 °C viscosity of the 10 h sample for multigrade oils.) The test report shall also include complete formulation data, including the brand name and manufacturer of each of the additives used, the concentration of each additive in the finished oil, the percentages of neutral and bright stock, as well as the crude oil sources and type of processing used in the manufacture of these base stock components.

4.4 Quality Assurance Inspection—Quality assurance inspection shall consist of all the tests in Table 4. Oil manufacturers shall retain a copy of each batch test report in their files for at least three years. A copy of the test report on each batch of oil produced for the U.S. Government shall be forwarded to Naval Air Systems Command.

4.4.1 LOT FORMATION

4.4.1.1 Bulk Lot—A bulk lot is considered as an indefinite quantity of homogeneous mixture of material in a single isolated container or manufactured by a single plant run (not exceeding 24 h) through the same processing equipment, with no change in ingredient material.

4.4.1.2 Packaged Lot—A packaged lot is considered as an indefinite number of 208 L (55 gal) drums or smaller unit packages of identical size and type filled with a homogeneous mixture of material manufactured by a single plant run (not exceeding 24 h) through the same processing equipment, with no change in ingredient material.

4.4.2 SAMPLING

4.4.2.1 Sampling for Verification of Product Quality—Each bulk and packaged lot of material shall be sampled at random in accordance with ASTM D 4057 or ASTM D 4177 for verification of product quality as specified in 4.4.

4.4.2.2 Sampling for Examination of Filled Containers—Each packaged lot of containers shall be sampled in accordance with ASQC-Z1.4, for leakage, fill, closure, and preparation for shipment (packaging, packing, marking) in accordance with Section 5.

4.4.2.3 Sampling for Examination of Sedimentation of Filled and Sealed Containers—Samples of filled and sealed 0.95 L (1 qt) containers shall be taken at such periodic levels as to be representative of each day of operation. The number of samples to be taken each day shall be in accordance with ASQC-Z1.4, when tested against the sedimentation requirement of Table 4.

4.4.3 INSPECTION

4.4.3.1 Inspection of Material—Inspection shall be performed in accordance with Method 9601 of FED-STD-791.

4.4.3.2 Examination of Filled Containers—Examine samples taken in accordance with 4.4.2.2 for compliance with MIL-STD-290 with regard to fill, closure, sealing, leakage, packaging, packing, and marking requirements. Reject any container having one or more defects or under the required fill. If the number of defective or unfilled containers exceeds the acceptance number for the appropriate plan of ASQC-Z1.4, reject the lot represented by the sample.

4.5 Test Methods—Tests shall be performed in accordance with the applicable methods listed in Tables 2A, 2, 3, and 4, and Appendicies B and C.

4.5.1 STORAGE STABILITY

4.5.1.1 Fourteen-Day Storage Test—A clean, capped, or stoppered 0.95 L (1 qt) glass bottle shall be half filled with test oil and stored on alternate days ±1 h at 5 °C ± 1 °C (40 °F ± 2 °F) and −18 °C ± 1 °C (0 °F ± 2 °F) by daily transferring from one cold box to another. Examine the sample for evidence of additive separation immediately after removal from the 5 °C storage. Note optical clarity and invert the bottles to see if deposits adhere to the bottom. Also slowly pour 10 to 15 mL of cold oil over the lip of the bottle and observe carefully any unevenness in fluid texture. Deposits or suspended material may be present even though the sample is optically clear, because of similar refractive indices. The test cycle shall be repeated for 14 days except for weekend periods where the sample may remain at one temperature condition for up to 72 continuous hours.

4.5.1.2 Twelve-Month Storage Test—A 1 gal sample shall be stored in a clean, capped, or stoppered wide-mouth glass container for a period of 12 months at 25 °C ± 3 °C (77 °F ± 5 °F) away from light. At the end of the storage period the oil shall then be examined visually for separation of components.

TABLE 4—QUALITY ASSURANCE TEST REQUIREMENTS FOR FINISHED LUBRICANT

Characteristic (Limits) SAE Grade	30	40	50	60	Multi-Grade	Test Method
Viscosity, cSt,						ASTM D 445
@ 100 °C, Min	9.3	12.5	16.3	21.9	(1)	
@ 100 °C, Less Than	12.5	16.3	21.9	26.1	(1)	
Flash Point, °C Min	220	225	243	243	220	ASTM D 92
Sulfur, Mass % Max[(2)]	0.6	0.8	1.0	1.2	0.6	ASTM D 129, ASTM D 1552, ASTM D 2622
Pour Point, °C Max	−18	−15	−12	−9	—	ASTM D 97, ASTM D 5949, ASTM D 5950, ASTM D 5985
Viscosity, Low Temp., Cold Crank Sim.	—	—	—	—	(1)	ASTM D 5293
			All Grades			
Viscosity, cSt, @ 40 °C			Report			ASTM D 445
Viscosity Index, Min.			85			ASTM D 2270
Total Acid Number, mg KOH/g, Max[(3)]			1.0			ASTM D 664
Density @ 15 °C, kg/L			Report			ASTM D 4052
Gravity @ 60 °F, °API[(4)]			Report			ASTM D 1298, ASTM D 4052
Ash Content[(5)] Mass % Max			0.011			ASTM D 482, SAE J1787
Trace Sediment ml/100 mL Oil, Max.			0.005			ASTM D 2273
Copper Strip Corrosion, Max Rating 3 h @ 100 °C			1			ASTM D 130
Foaming Tendency/Stability						ASTM D 892
Sequence 2						
Aerated Volume, mL, max			50			
Volume after 10 min, mL, max			0			
Trace Metal Content, ppm, Max[(6)]						See 4.5.2
Iron (Fe)			5			
Silver (Ag)			2			
Aluminum (Al)			7			
Chromium (Cr)			5			
Copper (Cu)			3			
Magnesium (Mg)			3			
Nickel (Ni)			3			
Lead (Pb)			5			
Silicon (Si)			25			
Tin (Sn)			10			
Titanium (Ti)			2			
Molybdenum (Mo)			4			

1. Oil shall meet the viscosity requirements of SAE J300 for the designated grade.
2. See 3.4 for conformance limit range.
3. Titrate to a pH 11 end point.
4. API gravity may be computed from the relative density measured by ASTM D 4052, see 3.5 for conformance limit range.
5. ASTM D 482 is required for qualification. Either ASTM D 482 or SAE J1787 may be used for Quality Assurance Testing.
6. Required for U.S. Government procurements only.

4.5.2 TRACE METAL CONTENT—The trace metal content of the oil shall be determined with a Joint Oil Analysis Program (JOAP) approved atomic emission spectrometer. Using JOAP spectrometric calibration standards, the spectrometer shall be standardized in accordance with 4-32, 4-33, 4-46, and 4-47 of NAVAIR 17-15-BF-62 publication. Immediately after standardizing the spectrometer, five determinations for trace metal content shall be determined on the oil. The average of the five determinations shall be reported. Samples requiring trace metal content determinations may be sent to: Department of Defense, Technical Support Center, Joint Oil Analysis Program, 296 Farrar Road, Pensacola, FL 32508-5010.

5. Packaging (For Military Procurements)

5.1 Preservation and Packing—For acquisition purposes, the packaging requirements shall be as specified in the contract order (see 6.2.1.1).

5.2 Marking—All unit, intermediate, and shipping containers shall be marked in accordance with the contract order. All unit and intermediate packs of toxic and hazardous chemicals and materials shall also be labeled in accordance with the applicable laws, statutes, regulations, or ordinances, including Federal, State, and Municipal requirements. In addition, unit or intermediate containers, including unit containers that serve as shipping containers, such as pails and drums, shall be marked with the applicable precautionary information detailed in ANSI Z129.1.

6. Notes—This section contains information of a general or explanatory nature that may be helpful, but is not mandatory.

6.1 Intended Use—The lubricating oil covered by this specification is intended for use in four cycle piston aircraft engines and covers the same lubricating oil requirements as the former military specification MIL-L-22851. Users should consult their engine manufacturers manuals for the latest listing of acceptable lubricants.

6.2 Military Procurements

6.2.1 ORDERING DATA

6.2.1.1 Acquisition Requirements—Procurement documents should specify the following:

a. Title, number, and date of this specification;
b. Grade of lubricating oil required (see 1.2)(see 1.2);
c. Type and size of containers required (see 5.1)(see 5.1);
d. Level of packing required (see 5.1)(see 5.1);
e. Quantity desired;
f. Submittal of test results (see 4.4)(see 4.4).

6.2.2 QUALIFICATION—With respect to products requiring qualification, awards shall be made only for the products which are, at the time set for opening of bids, qualified for inclusion in applicable Qualified Products List whether or not such products have actually been so listed by that date. The attention of the contractors is called to these requirements, and manufacturers are urged to arrange to have the products that they propose to offer to the Federal Government tested for qualification in order that they may be eligible to be awarded contracts or purchase orders for the products covered by this specification. The activity responsible for the Qualified Products List is Commander, Naval Air Systems Command, AIR-4.4.5, Fuels and Lubricants Division, Building 2360, 22229 Elmer Road, Unit 4, Patuxent River, MD 20670. Information pertaining to qualification of products may be obtained from that activity.

6.2.3 INTERNATIONAL STANDARDIZATION AGREEMENT*—Certain provisions of this specification are the subject of an international standardization agreement with NATO (STANAG 1135). When amendment, revision, or cancellation of this specification is proposed which will affect or violate the international agreement concerned, the preparing activity shall take appropriate reconciliation action through international standardization channels, including department standardization offices, if required.

6.3 Revisions—Revisions or changes to this document must have concurrence from the Naval Air Systems Command.

6.4 Material Safety Data Sheets*—Contracting officers will identify those activities requiring copies of completed Material Safety Data Sheets prepared in accordance with FED-STD-313. The pertinent Government mailing addresses for submission of data are listed in paragraph 4 of FED-STD-313.

APPENDIX A
BASE STOCK CRUDE OIL SOURCE AND PROCESSING DESCRIPTIONS

A.1 When applying for qualification, refiners shall provide the following information about the crude oil and the processing used in the manufacture of each base stock blended into their product:

a. Name of original base stock refiner or processor;
b. Location of refinery or processing plant, by city and state (U.S.), province (Canada), or country;
c. General crude source shall be identified as follows:

ACI—Alaskan Cook Inlet
ANS—Alaskan North Slope
DE—Diester (Including Manufacturing Source)
GE—Germany
MC—Mid Continent
MW—Middle East
MW—Mid West
MXA—Maya
MXO—Mexican
NA—North Africa
PA—Pennsylvania
PAO—Polyalpha Olefin (Including Manufacturing Source)
PE—Polyol Ester (Including Manufacturing Source)
VEN—Venezuelan
WC—West Coast
WCA—Western Canada
WT—West Texas
OC—Other (Please provide brief description)

d. General crude refining processes (nonsynthetics only) shall be defined as follows:

SC—Straight Distillation
VD—Vacuum Distallation
SR—Solvent Refining
MH—Mild Hydrogenation
SH—Severe Hydrogenation
HP—Hydrocracked
OP—Other (Please provide brief description)

APPENDIX B
ENGINE TEST REQUIREMENTS FOR SAE J1899/MIL-L-22851 AVIATION PISTON ENGINE LUBRICANT

B.1 References (Latest Applicable Publication Applies)

a. Society of Automotive Engineers Standard, SAE J1899, Lubricating Oil, Aircraft Piston Engine (Ashless Dispersant).
b. Code of Federal Regulations (CFR) 14, Federal Air Regulation Part 33.49 Endurance test, Subpart D Block Test, Reciprocating Aircraft Engines.
c. Overhaul Manual, Textron Lycoming Direct Drive Engine, Publication Number 60287-23.
d. Operator's Manual, Textron Lycoming TIO-540 Series Aircraft Engines, Publication Number 60278-23.
e. Parts Catalog, Textron Lycoming TIO-540-J2BD Engine, Publication Number PC315.
f. Overhaul Manual for Aircraft Systems Turbochargers, Publication Number TP20-0128.
g. Service Table of Limits and Torque Value Recommendations, Textron Lycoming, Publication Number SSP1776.
h. Overhaul Manual for Aircraft System Valves and Controllers, Publication Number TP20-0129.
i. Code of Federal Regulations (CFR) 14, Federal Air Regulation Part 33.57 General Conduct of Block Tests.

B.2 Enclosures

a. TIO-540-J2BD Engine Instrumentation Data (Tables B1 and B2)
b. Figures B1 and B2
   1. Objective: To conduct an engine test that will evaluate the quality of aviation piston engine oils (described in B.1a) prior to being subjected to flight test evaluations.
   2. Introduction:
      a. Qualified oils under SAE J1899 are synthetic or petroleum base lubricating oil blends containing additives to impart oxidative stability and dispersant properties. Laboratory and bench tests are performed under B.1a to determine the chemical and physical properties of the lubricants.

b. Flight evaluations are also performed according to B.1a to determine the oil's performance under actual engine operating conditions.
c. This directive identifies the equipment, procedure, and requirements for a full scale piston engine test to evaluate aviation engine lubricating oils.

B.3 Approach

a. The engine used in this test is the Textron Lycoming TIO-540-J2BD or an equivalent model with the approval of the Naval Air Systems Command (NAVAIR). It shall be run in the 150 h endurance test described in B.1b without the turbocharger test requirements and along with the exceptions and amendments described herein.
1. Prior to the engine test, the engine is to be assembled using original manufacturer parts.
2. All the critical parts are to be measured during the initial build-up. These dimensions shall be compared with the respective post test engine dimensions to determine the amount of wear which has occurred.
3. Engine hardware shall also be visually inspected after the test and the presence of carbonaceous deposits shall be described and recorded.
4. The test may be run at ambient pressure altitude in place of the critical altitude and 8000 ft pressure altitude requirement as noted in reference B.1.b.
5. It is not necessary to load each accessory drive and mounting attachment as noted in reference B.1.b.
6. NOTE: A TIO-540-J2BD Engine test run in strict compliance with reference B.1.b may be used to qualify lubricant without these listed exceptions.

b. Lubricant properties shall be examined periodically throughout the test to determine oil degradation.
c. All measured items shall meet the requirements contained herein.

TABLE B1—TIO-540-J2BD ENGINE INSTRUMENTATION DATA(1)

Parameter	I.D. Tags	Range	Limit
Temperature (°F)			
Oil, In (gallery)	TIS	0–400	245 Max(2)
Oil, Out (to cooler)	TOO	0–500	Record
Air, Compressor Inlet	TAI	0–200	32–104
Air, Compressor Outlet	TATE	0–500	400 Max
Air, Test Cell	TATC	0–200	32–104
Exhaust Gas, Turbocharger Inlet	TETI	0–2000	1650 Max
Cylinder Head (at each Cyl.)	TCH (1–6)	0–800	500 Max
Fuel Inlet	TFI	0–200	100 Max
Pressure			
Oil, Engine Gallery	POEG	0–200	55–95(2)(3)
Oil, Pump Exit Engine (psig)	POPE	0–300	Record2
Oil, Filter Outlet (psig)	POFO	0–200	Record(4)
Air, Dry Manifold, Std. Location (in Hg)	PAM	0–100	49.0 Max(2)
Air, Barometric, Test Cell (in Hg)	PBTC	0–40	Record(5)
Fuel, at Engine Fuel Pump Inlet (psig)	PFUP	0–200	–2 to +65
Flow			
Fuel (lb/h)	FF	0–300	250 Max
Speed (rpm)			
Engine	ERPM	0–4000	2575 Max
Other			
Test Time, h	TET	0–200	150
Test Time, h	TOT	0–200	

1. The test instrumentation shall be calibrated before each test so that reported data shall have static accuracy within the following limits:
   Temperature within 2 °F
   Pressure within 2%
   Flow within 0.2%
   Speed within 0.2%
2. Measured at the location specified in B.6d.
3. Values stated are for normal operation after engine warm-up. The minimum idle pressure is 25 psig and the maximum warm-up pressure is 115 psig.
4. The oil filter outlet pressure should not drop more than 18 psi below the oil pump exit pressure.
5. Barometric pressure.

TABLE B2—150 H TEST OPERATING CONDITIONS, TIO-540-J2BD[1]

Test Period	Cumulative Time, h	Cycles/ Period	Cycle Time, h	BHR	RPM	Manifold Pressure[2]	Fuel Flow lb/h	Oil Temp. °F	Cyl. Head Temp. °F
1	0 to 30	10	0.08	350	2575	43.0	240–250	140–245	350–475
			0.08	210	2200	record	86–90	140–245	350–475
2	30 to 50	4	2.5	350	2575	43.0	240–250	215–225	350–475
			2.5	210	2200	record	86–90	215–225	350–475
3	50 to 70	10	1.5	350	2575	43.0	240–250	215–225	350–475
			0.5	263	2340	record	130–135	140–245	350–475
4	70 to 90	10	1.5	350	2575	43.0	240–250	235–245	500 Min[3]
			0.5	245	2290	record	120–125	140–245	350–475
5	90 to 110	10	1.5	350	2575	43.0	240–250	235–245	500 Min[3]
			0.5	228	2240	record	102–109	140–245	350–475
6	110 to 130	10	1.5	350	2575	43.0	240–250	235–245	500 Min[3]
			0.5	210	2180	record	86–90	140–245	350–475
7	130 to 150	10	1.5	350	2575	43.0	240–250	235–245	500 Min[3]
			0.5	175	2050	record	79–84	140–245	350–475

1. The engine is to be shut down a minimum of 0.5 h between each cycle.
2. Measured at 60 °F. For nonstandard conditions, use power charts to set the manifold pressure to corrected values.
3. Starting at cycle 7, the hottest cylinder head shall maintain a minimum temperature of 500 °F. The temperature of the remaining cylinder heads shall be within 50 °F of the hottest cylinder head for the remainder of the test at all maximum power conditions.

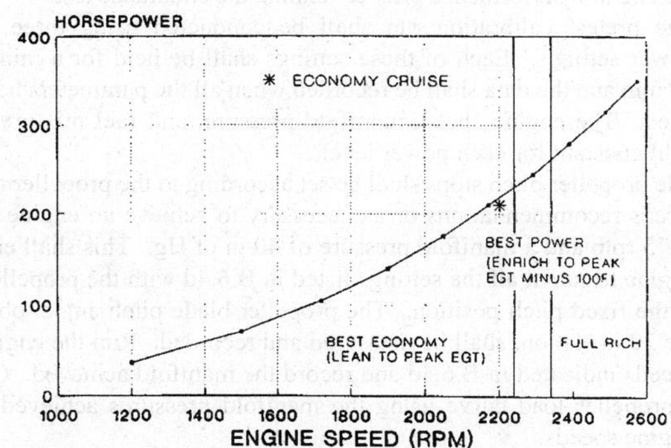

FIGURE B1—HORSEPOWER VERSUS ENGINE SPEED

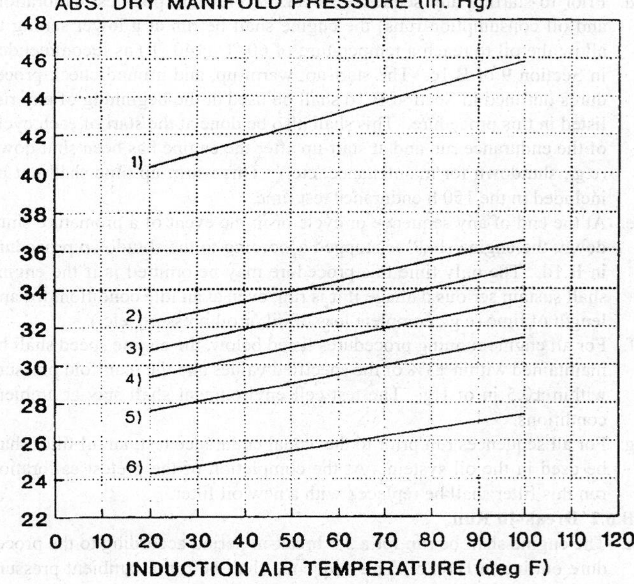

FIGURE B2—POWER CHART AT SEA LEVEL

B.4 Equipment

a. Engine:
   1. The TIO-540-J2BD engine is manufactured by Textron Lycoming, Williamsport Division, Textron Inc., Williamsport, Pennsylvania. It is an internal combustion, air cooled, turbocharged piston engine.
   2. It is equipped with a continuous flow type fuel injection system and shall run on aviation grade gasoline with a minimum octane rating of 100LL.
   3. The engine is a six-cylinder opposed design with a displacement of 8873.6 cm^3 (541.5 in^3). At maximum power it shall develop 350 Horsepower at sea level through critical altitude (4626 m [15 000 ft]).
   4. The engine is provided with a wet sump oil system having a capacity of 11.36 L (12 qt).
   5. Accessories supplied with the engine are the fuel pump, the starter, and the alternator. Two additional accessory drives are supplied on this model engine and need not be loaded during the test.

b. Test Stand: The test stand shall consist of an aircraft type dynafocal engine mounting system, Piper model number 01272-2, identical to that used on the Piper PA31-350 (manufactured by Piper Aircraft Corp., Vero Beach, Florida) or equivalent. This system shall then be attached to a suitable test bed.

c. Power Absorber:
   1. This engine drives a propeller directly off the engine crankshaft. For this test setup a flight propeller shall be used to absorb engine power. The propeller shall be a three-blade variable pitch type, Hartzell model number HC3YR-2UF/FC8468-6R manufactured by Hartzell Propeller Inc., Piqua, Ohio, or equivalent representative propeller in a fixed position. Used in conjunction with this propeller shall be the Hartzell propeller governor model number F624Z or equivalent. This propeller and governor are similar to those used on the Piper PA31-350.
   2. With this type of installation auxiliary air may be required to cool the engine to the specified limits. The flight propeller alone may not provide sufficient cooling air to the engine in a test cell environment.
   3. Alternate means of absorbing engine power, e.g., club propellers or dynamometers are acceptable for this test method.

d. Instrumentation:
   1. The test location shall be equipped with the necessary instrumentation and associated hardware to record the required data. The minimum required instrumentation is listed in Table B1. Also listed are the ranges and the limits of these parameters. The system shall acquire data from thermocouples, pressure taps, flow meters, and tachometer. The instrumentation shall also be equipped with suitable alarms and controls to permit safe operation.

2. Data shall be recorded periodically throughout the entire test. This includes the break-in, pre and post test calibration, and oil consumption runs along with the endurance test run. The data shall be recorded either by hand or by data acquisition system.

e. Fuel: All testing shall be conducted using grade 100LL aviation fuel manufactured to ASTM D 910 Standards.

f. The test installation shall incorporate a suitably sized air-oil separator connected to the oil breather exit of the engine.

B.5 Location—The engine test shall be conducted by a testing source approved by NAVAIR. To become an approved source, an operator must have successfully completed a similar FAA monitored 150 h aircraft engine type test, conducted per reference B.1b.

B.6 Procedure

B.6.1 Introduction

a. The engine shall be run using the power settings outlined in B.1b. The test shall run for a total of 150 h. A daily engine log shall be maintained summarizing all the daily activities.

b. Prior to performing the 150 h endurance test a break-in, an oil consumption run, and a pretest calibration run shall be performed. The time spent on these sequences shall not be included as part of the 150 h of test time. All nontest time accumulated during the 150 h endurance test plus the pre- and post-test run time and any miscellaneous running should not exceed 20 h. All miscellaneous running time shall be documented.

c. After 150 h of testing has been completed the engine shall be subjected to a post-test calibration run. At this time any change in engine performance which has occurred during the test shall be determined and recorded.

d. Prior to starting any sequence (break-in, pre- and post-test calibration, and oil consumption runs) the engine shall be run at a lower setting to allow the oil to reach a temperature of 60 °C (140 °F) as recommended in Section 9 of B.1c. The start-up, warm-up, and ground check procedures outlined in Section B.1d shall be used at the beginning of any run listed in this procedure. This shall also be done at the start of each cycle of the endurance run and at start-up after the engine has been shut down (e.g., shutdown for maintenance, etc.). This warm-up time shall not be included in the 150 h endurance test time.

e. At the end of any sequence or cycle or in the event of a premature shutdown, the engine shall be stopped according to the shutdown procedure in B.1d. The only time this procedure may be omitted is if the engine shall sustain serious damage if it is run, even at an idle condition, for any length of time (e.g., complete loss of oil or oil pressure, etc.).

f. For all engine running procedures listed below, the engine speed shall be maintained within ±3% of the specified values and the manifold pressure within ±0.5 in of Hg. The test cell environment shall stay at ambient conditions.

g. For all sequences run prior to the actual endurance test, an oil filter shall be used in the oil system. At the completion of the pretest calibration run this filter shall be replaced with a new oil filter.

B.6.2 Break-In Run

a. The engine shall be run for a 3 h break-in period according to the procedure outline in B.6.2b. This sequence shall be run at ambient pressure with the mixture setting adjusted to full rich. Record the data once at each power setting. The oil used during this run shall be a SAE J1966.

b. The break-in run shall be conducted as follows:

1. 0.25 h at 1200 rpm.
2. 0.25 h at 1500 rpm.
3. 0.25 h at 1720 rpm.
4. 0.25 h at 1900 rpm.
5. 0.33 h at 2050 rpm.
6. 0.33 h at 2170 rpm with a manifold pressure of 32 in of Hg.
7. 0.33 h at 2290 rpm with a manifold pressure of 36 in of Hg.
8. 0.33 h at 2390 rpm with a manifold pressure of 38 in of Hg.
9. 0.33 h at 2490 rpm with a manifold pressure of 41 in of Hg.
10. 0.33 h at 2575 rpm with a manifold pressure of 43 in of Hg.
11. Adjust the turbocharger density controller as per Lycoming Service Instruction Number 1187.
12. Shut down the engine according to the shutdown procedure in B.1d.

During the break-in run, the engine temperatures, pressures, and speeds shall remain within the normal operating limits specified by the manufacturer for the power setting selected. If a fixed pitch (club propeller) type of power absorber is used, the break-in run manifold pressure for condition (j) shall be met. For all other conditions the test profile manifold pressure shall be monitored but not controlled.

c. Drain the used break-in oil from the engine, oil lines, and oil cooler. Remove the oil filter and replace it with a new one. Fill the crankcase with a clean charge of the candidate oil and proceed to the oil consumption run.

B.6.3 Oil Consumption Run

a. This sequence shall be run for 2 h at maximum continuous power and speed (2575 rpm with a manifold pressure of 43 in of Hg), at sea level pressure, and have an oil temperature of 93 °C ± 6 °C (200 °F ± 10 °F). During this run record data every 15 min. After the engine has been shut down and the oil has drained down into the engine sump (approximately one-half hour), add enough test oil to bring the level to the full mark. Determine the oil consumption from the amount of oil added and record this quantity. The oil consumption shall not exceed 0.95 L per hour (1.0 qt per hour), if this value is exceeded the engine shall be rejected for testing.

b. Drain the used oil from the engine, oil lines, and the oil cooler. Fill the engine with a clean charge of candidate oil to flush out any residual break-in lubricant. Proceed to the pretest calibration run.

B.6.4 Pretest Calibration Run

a. Prior to endurance testing a calibration run shall be conducted. The engine shall not be used if its performance does not meet the required power settings listed in B.6.4c. With the data obtained from the calibration run described as follows, construct a propeller load curve for the engine to be used in testing. This propeller load curve shall also be used as a record of the engine's performance prior to running the endurance test.

b. The pretest calibration run shall be conducted using three different power settings. Each of these settings shall be held for a minimum of 10 min and the data shall be recorded when all the parameters have stabilized. The engine speed, manifold pressure, and fuel mixture shall be held constant for each power level.

c. The propeller pitch stops shall be set according to the propeller manufacturer's recommendations or as necessary to achieve an engine speed of 2575 rpm and a manifold pressure of 40 in of Hg. This shall enable the engine to run at all the settings listed in B.6.4d with the propeller blades at the fixed pitch position. The propeller blade pitch angle, obtained at the 30 in station, shall be measured and recorded. Run the engine at the speeds indicated in B.6.4d and record the manifold achieved. Construct a propeller load curve using the manifold pressures achieved at these engine speeds.

d. The following instrument settings shall be used for the pretest calibration run:

1. All power levels below shall be run with the fuel mixture at the settings specified in Figure B1;
2. 2575 rpm at 40 in of Hg manifold pressure;
3. 2400 rpm and record manifold pressure;
4. 2200 rpm and record manifold pressure;
5. Shut down the engine according to the shutdown procedure in B.1d.

e. If an alternate power absorber is used, a similar propeller load curve shall be constructed to measure engine power. The alternate device selected shall allow the engine to operate at the speeds and manifold pressures specified by the manufacturer for the ambient conditions present. These values and limits are contained in B.1d. If the engine's performance does not meet the minimum acceptable limits, it will not be considered acceptable for use.

f. Drain the used oil from the engine, oil lines, and the oil cooler. Replace the slave oil filter with a new test oil filter. Install a fresh charge of test oil and proceed to the endurance test.

B.6.5 FAR 33.49 Endurance Test

a. The test procedure listed below is similar to that as described in B.1b. The test consists of seven portions for which the engine is run at various power settings. The total test duration is 150 h as indicated in Table B2.

b. Use Figure B2 as a guideline to set the manifold pressure and engine speed to achieve the desired power settings. Figure B1 shows the recommended fuel mixture setting for the desired engine speed and horsepower. Holding the engine speed and the manifold pressure constant, adjust the fuel mixture as necessary to obtain the setting shown in Figure B1. The fuel flow shall remain within the specified limits shown in Figure B2.

c. During 50 h of the endurance test at least one cylinder shall be operated at or above the limiting cylinder head temperature, 260 °C (500 °F). The other cylinders shall not be lower than 28 °C (50 °F) below the limiting cylinder head temperature. This 50 h of test time shall be conducted with the engine set at maximum continuous power and speed. For test method consistency this phase shall take place during the last 50 h of testing at the maximum continuous power setting. Start at test portion 4 cycle 7, as given in B.6.5d.

d. The 50 h of test time mentioned above shall also be run with the oil inlet temperature maintained within ±3 °C (±5 °F) of the limiting oil inlet temperature, 118 °C (245 °F). Adjust the cooling equipment for the engine is necessary to achieve this temperature. If it is necessary the oil lines and sump may be insulated. The remainder of the test shall be conducted with the oil inlet temperature of 104 °C ± 3 °C (220 °F ± 5 °F).

e. The test procedure shall be run as follows with a minimum of one-half hour separation between cycles. The delay between cycles is to permit evaluation of the lubricant's resistance to the formation of carbonaceous materials during static hot soak conditions. Test data is to be recorded once during the last 5 min of each power setting in portion 1. In portions 2 through 7 record the data at approximately 15 min intervals during each power setting. Allow the engine to run for at least 10 min after a setting change (in portions 2 through 7) before taking an instrument reading. (All horsepower values are corrected to sea level standard day conditions at the stated speed.)

1. Portion 1, 0 to 30 h (10 cycles):

Each test cycle shall include the 0.16 h (10 min) sequence as follows, repeated 18 times in a 3 h period:

a. 0.08 h at maximum continuous power with maximum continuous speed (350 horsepower at 2575 rpm).

b. 0.08 h at economy cruise (210 horsepower at 2200 rpm).

2. Portion 2, 30 to 50 h (4 cycles):

Each test cycle is 5 h run as follows:

a. 2.5 h at maximum continuous power with maximum continuous speed (350 horsepower at 2575 rpm).

b. 2.5 h at maximum best economy cruising power (210 horsepower at 2200 rpm).

3. Portion 3, 50 to 70 h (10 cycles):

Each test cycle is 2 h run as follows:

a. 1.5 h at maximum continuous power with maximum continuous speed (350 horsepower at 2575 rpm).

b. 0.5 h at 75% maximum continuous power with 91% maximum continuous speed (263 horsepower at 2340 rpm).

4. Portion 4, 70 to 90 h (10 cycles):

Each test cycle is 2 h run as follows:

a. 1.5 h at maximum continuous power with maximum continuous speed (350 horsepower at 2575 rpm).

b. 0.5 h at 70% maximum continuous power with 89% maximum continuous speed (245 horsepower at 2290 rpm).

5. Portion 5, 90 to 110 h (10 cycles):

Each test cycle is 2 h run as follows:

a. 1.5 h at maximum continuous power with maximum continuous speed (350 horsepower at 2575 rpm).

b. 0.5 h at 65% maximum continuous power with 87% maximum continuous speed (228 horsepower at 2240 rpm).

6. Portion 6, 110 to 130 h (10 cycles):

Each test cycle is 2 h run as follows:

a. 1.5 h at maximum continuous power with maximum continuous speed (350 horsepower at 2575 rpm).

b. 0.5 h at 60% maximum continuous power with 84.5% maximum continuous speed (210 horsepower at 2180 rpm).

7. Portion 7, 130 to 150 h (10 cycles):

Each test cycle is 2.0 h run as follows:

a. 1.5 h at maximum continuous power with maximum continuous speed (350 horsepower at 2575 rpm).

b. 0.5 h at 50% maximum continuous power with 79.5% maximum continuous speed (175 horsepower at 2050 rpm).

NOTE—Proceed to the post-test calibration run.

B.6.6 Post-Test Calibration Run—This sequence shall be conducted after the endurance test has been completed. The data obtained here shall be compared to the pretest calibration data to determine the loss of engine performance due to the endurance test. The procedure performed shall use the same method as that employed in the pre-test calibration run (B.6.4), except that the propeller blade angle shall be fixed at the angle established in the pre-test run. Changes in performance will be displayed by the differences in the manifold pressures needed to achieve a specified engine speed in the pre- and post-test calibration runs.

B.6.7 Oil Sampling

a. Oil samples shall be taken from the sampling valve (B.6.8g) on the engine crankcase within 10 min after the engine is shut down. The samples shall be taken every 25 test hours or at the end of the next cycle nearest the 25 h interval (unless otherwise specified). When taking oil samples drain 50 mL of oil into a clean beaker to clear the sample line then take a clean sample bottle and draw the required sample amount. Return the original 50 mL of oil to the oil sump.

b. Draw a 100 mL sample of the lubricant for laboratory analysis. This analysis shall consist of viscosity at 40 °C (104 °F) and 100 °C (212 °F) (per ASTM D 445), total acid number determination (per ASTM 664, titrate to a pH of 11) and trace metal content determination (by spectrometric oil analysis).

c. Identify the oil sample with the test number, engine model number, engine serial number, oil time, engine time, test portion and cycle number, oil code number, and the date drawn.

d. The oil samples are to be taken before any make-up oil is added to the oil sump.

B.6.8 Engine Assembly

a. The engine is to be built up according to the assembly procedure outlined in B.1d and e. Engine parts are to be replaced as recommended in B.1c during the engine overhaul. Certain parts shall be replaced that are not listed in B.1c. This is to be done for the purpose of rating consistency. These parts are as follows: pistons, valves, and valve guides, piston pin plugs, camshaft, valve lifters, spark plugs, cylinders, crankshaft gear, crankshaft to camshaft idler gear, rocker arm shafts, rocker arm bushings, and the turbocharger. The turbocharger may be reconditioned as long as it meets with the manufacturer's specifications for new equipment (B.1f) and is fitted with a new bearing. A preassembly hydraulic leak down test shall be performed on each lifter unit and the data recorded.

b. The piston ring gap shall be at the service maximum (B.1g).

c. The turbocharger shall be sent to the manufacturer or to an overhaul facility approved by the manufacturer for inspection and overhaul. It shall be installed on the engine according to the procedures listed in B.1f and h.

d. The engine crankshaft bearings shall be weighed prior to being installed in the engine. The bearings shall be clean, dry, and free of any grease, oil, or preservative before weighing. Do not handle clean unweighed bearings with bare hands. Wear clean rubber gloves (e.g., surgical gloves) or use a clean pair of tweezers to handle the bearings. Weigh bearings on a scale with an accuracy of 0.001 g. Record the weight of each bearing and the position where it is installed in the engine.

e. Prior to each engine assembly specific engine parts are to be measured and their dimensions recorded. These same parts shall be measured after the test has been completed and compared to the original dimensions. This comparison shall be used to determine the amount of wear that has occurred during the test. B.1g lists all the required items to be measured prior to overhaul, with their respective dimensions and clearances. Some of these parts are of particular importance in determining the outcome of the test. The dimensions of these items and the items listed in B.1g shall be recorded upon assembly of the engine for comparison with post test dimensions. Listed below are the critical items to be measured:

1. Crankshaft journals, main, and rod;
2. Bearings, main, and rod inside diameter;
3. Tappet bore, case inside diameter;
4. Tappet body, outside diameter;
5. Tappet plunger assembly and body;
6. Camshaft journal and bore;
7. Connecting rod bushing, inside diameter;
8. Piston pin hole in piston, inside diameter;
9. Piston pin, outside diameter;
10. Piston ring and piston, side clearance, all rings;
11. Piston ring, gap, all rings;
12. Piston pin plug hole in piston, inside diameter;
13. Piston pin plug, outside diameter;
14. Piston, outside diameter, lands, and skirts;
15. Cylinder barrel bore at 2,4, and 6 in stations as measured from the bottom of the cylinder;

16. Valve stem, intake and exhaust, outside diameter (3 places), and length;
17. Valve guide, intake and exhaust, inside diameter (3 places);
18. Valve rocker shaft, outside diameter;
19. Valve rocker bushing, intake and exhaust, inside diameter;
20. Oil pump impeller, diameter, and side clearance;
21. Accessory drive bushings, inside diameters;
22. Accessory drive journals, outside diameters.

f. If a constant speed propeller is used, the condition of its oil wetted parts shall be documented prior to use. The propeller shall be inspected and assembled as described in the manufacturer's overhaul manuals.

g. In order to reduce the possibility of oil loss during sample acquisition, the crankcase drain plug should be replaced with an appropriate sampling valve.

h. After the break-in run is completed perform a compression check on each cylinder. Record the cylinder pressure for comparison with the post-test compression check.

B.6.9 Servicing and Maintenance

a. The oil level should be checked after each cycle and not allowed to drop below 9.46 L (10 qt). Add test oil as necessary to keep the system full (11.36 L, 12 qt). An oil test log shall be maintained by recording the amount of oil added to or removed from the engine during the test. This data shall be used for the determination of engine oil consumption.

b. After 75 h of testing, the used test oil shall be drained from the engine, oil lines, and oil cooler. This shall be performed in portion 4 between cycles 3 and 4 of the endurance test. The amount of oil drained shall be recorded on the oil test log. Allow sufficient time for the oil to completely drain from the engine (approximately one-half hour). Store the oil in a sealable metal container and mark the container as per B.6.7c. Remove the oil filter and replace it with a new one. The filter is to be drained, placed in a sealed container, and retained for later examination. Any oil removed with the filter housing shall be measured and the amount recorded on the oil test log. The engine shall be recharged to the 11.36 L (12 qt) level with new test oil which shall be used for the remainder of the test. The spark plugs shall be inspected, cleaned, and regapped if necessary, at 75 h of test time.

c. Maintenance during the test shall be allowed as long as it is in accordance with B.1i and it shall be reported in the test log.

d. Prior to engine disassembly a post test cylinder compression check shall be performed.

B.6.10 Test Completion

a. Perform post-test calibration run.

b. Drain oil and retain a 3.8 L (1 gal) sample and the oil filter.

c. Remove any disassemble engine as per B.1c. Take care not to disturb any carbonaceous deposits that have formed during the test.

B.7 Post-Test Inspection Requirements

a. Introduction: After the engine has been disassembled, it shall be inspected. The engine's moving and respective stationary parts shall be measured to determine the amount of wear that has occurred throughout the test. The oil wetted areas in the engine shall be visually examined to determine the amount and the type of carbonaceous deposits that have formed. Color photographs of lubricant wetted areas, as designated by NAVAIR, shall be taken prior to engine cleaning. Disassembly and inspection of the engine shall be witnessed by a NAVAIR designated representative.

b. Deposit Inspection

1. Visual: The oil wetted surfaces in the engine shall be visually inspected for carbonaceous deposits at the end of the test. These deposits shall be rated according to their type and severity (e.g., light varnish, medium carbon, heavy sludge, etc.). All the inspections and ratings shall be reviewed by NAVAIR. A comparison shall be made between the relative rated areas in the test engine and the engine from the reference test. With this method if any of the areas have more severe deposits than those found in the reference test, the oil may be rejected for qualification under the SAE J1899 Standard. Ratings shall be conducted according to the Coordinating Research Council manuals and procedures. Photographs shall be taken of all post test lubricant wetted areas prior to cleaning to insure a pictorial documentation of the deposits. Photographs and deposit ratings of the reference oil are available from the cognizant activity.
2. Measurements: The side clearance and end gap of each piston ring shall be measured prior to part cleaning. The exhaust and intake valve guides shall also be measured prior to cleaning to determine the amount of deposits that may be present. A post-test hydraulic leak down check shall be performed on each lifter unit and the results compared to pre-test results.

c. Post-Cleaning Dimensional Inspection:

1. Following disassembly and parts cleaning all the engine parts that had been measured before the test shall now be measured as part of the post-test inspection. These parts shall be cleaned in accordance with Section 3 of B.1c. The parts shall be measured by the same methods used during the engine assembly (B.6h[5]) and the measurements recorded. This procedure shall insure that the relative dimensions are measured consistently. All the components shall be within the manufacturer's maximum and minimum dimensions and clearances or below the service maximums, where applicable (B.1g).
2. The engine bearings shall be weighted after the test to determine the amount of metal loss during the test. Using the same procedure in B.6h(4) determine the weight of each bearing and record it with the respective pre-test weight. Insure that the bearings are thoroughly cleaned prior to weighing. This includes all carbonaceous deposits that may have formed during the test. From this determine the weight loss of each bearing.
3. All nonconforming measurements shall be highlighted with an asterisk (*). Following the measurement table a summary of the discrepant parts, if any, shall be provided identifying the part by number, nomenclature, and the nature of the failure (e.g., worn beyond service limits).

d. Propeller Inspection: After the completion of the post test calibration run the propeller shall be removed and disassembled as necessary for rating all the oil wetted areas. Any abnormal deposits shall be cause for rejecting the candidate oil for qualification under this specification. Propeller disassembly and inspection shall be carried out using the manufacturer's overhaul instructions. The condition of the oil wetted parts shall be described as noted in B.7b.

e. Turbocharger Inspection: As part of the engine inspection the oil wetted areas of the turbocharger shall be rated for deposits. The bearing and shaft shall be checked for excessive wear by dimensional measurement. Any abnormal deposits or wear may be cause for rejecting the candidate oil for qualification under this specification. Turbocharger disassembly and inspection shall be carried out using the manufacturer's overhaul instructions. The condition of the oil wetted parts shall be described as noted in B.7b.

f. Oil Degradation:

1. The oil properties shall be examined throughout the test to determine the amount of degradation that has occurred. The change in physical and chemical properties of the oil (determined by the methods described in B.6.7b) shall be recorded. The engine test facility is responsible for reporting the lubricant analysis. The analysis shall be conducted by a certified laboratory or other facility as approved by the cognizant activity. The test report shall include a table of the data acquired and computations of the percent viscosity change and total acid number change. The table shall start with the new oil (zero time) and proceed through the 25 h incremental samples to the test completion.
2. After removal of the 100 mL samples for laboratory analysis, 3.8 L (1 gal) of the remaining oil drained at 75 h and 3.8 L (1 gal) taken at test completion shall be held for additional analysis.

g. Oil Filter Inspection: The two engine oil test filters shall be opened, inspected, photographed, their conditions recorded, and the elements compared. The filter elements shall be retained.

B.8 Report Requirements—After the completion of the engine inspection one copy of the test report shall be submitted to the Naval Systems Command within sixty (60) days. The report shall contain the following information as a minimum:

a. Identification of the candidate oil;
b. Test summary;
c. Oil consumption log;
d. Used oil analysis;
e. Dimensional inspection tables;
f. Deposit inspection records and photographs;
g. Daily engine test log;
h. Copy of data sheets;
i. Propeller condition report;
j. Turbocharger condition report.

B.9 Miscellaneous

a. NAVAIR Contact: In the event that any problems occur during testing, contact:

Naval Air Systems Command
Fuels and Lubricants Division
22229 Elmer Road, Unit 4
Patuxent River, MD 20670
301-757-3421

b. Federal Aviation Administration Approval: If concurrent Federal Aviation Administration (FAA) approval is desired, the applicant shall make suitable arrangements with the appropriate FAA regional office. Coordination of the testing with Federal Aviation Administration requirements is encouraged.

APPENDIX C
FLIGHT EVALUATION REQUIREMENTS

C.1 Objective—Flight evaluations are to be conducted on all new formulations of SAE J1899 aviation piston engine oils to determine their acceptability for general use.

C.2 Introduction

a. Federal Aviation Administration Approval: The applicant shall make suitable arrangements with the engine manufacturer to obtain FAA approval.
b. The flight evaluation of candidate oils is the last step for the complete qualification of new products to the SAE J1899 specifications. Prior to entering this phase of the qualification process, candidate oils shall have met all the physical, chemical, and bench test requirements of the specification. In addition, the candidate shall also have satisfactorily completed a 150 h engine test.
c. In the flight evaluation, the lubricant is subjected to actual flight environments for a specified duration. During the program, lubricant samples are periodically analyzed for changes in physical and chemical composition. At the completion of the evaluation, key parts are measured and visually examined. Based on the results obtained, a determination is made on the acceptability of the candidate lubricant and a recommendation is forwarded to NAVAIR for action.

C.3 Approach—The flight evaluation is performed in nonmilitary aircraft and is arranged for, and conducted by, the lubricant supplier. Prior to program initiation, the lubricant supplier shall provide an outline of the proposed evaluation to NAVAIR for approval. The outline shall, as a minimum, address all the criteria contained in this document. The periodic used oil analysis shall be provided. When engines have completed the specified operating intervals, the required inspections shall be witnessed by NAVAIR personnel or their appointed representatives.

C.4 Equipment

a. Engines: The flight evaluation is to be conducted on a minimum of two turbocharged engines. One engine shall be from Textron-Lycoming and the other from Teledyne-Continental. Acceptable engine models are listed in Table C1. The engines used should be new, rebuilt, or freshly original equipment manufacturer (OEM) overhauled units. However, engines having less than 200 h of total time since new or since their last overhaul are acceptable.
b. Propellers: All engines used in the flight evaluation shall have oil-actuated variable pitch propellers. The propellers shall be in suitable condition to permit a performance assessment of the lubricant in the unit.

C.5 Procedure

a. The lubricant supplier shall submit a general flight evaluation test plan, which includes the identification of the test location, to the Naval Air Systems Command for approval prior to initiating the program.
b. The lubricant supplier is responsible for insuring that, as a minimum, 500 h are obtained on each of the required engines. A suitable number of evaluation engines should be included in the program to insure that the 500 flight hour requirements are met on at least one of each type of engine.
c. Oil consumption records and oil property data shall be maintained on all flight evaluation engines. The data is to be available throughout the evaluation period and is to be summarized at the completion of the test. Approximately 475 mL (one pint) oil samples shall be obtained at 50 h ± 5 h intervals. The oil samples shall be obtained before fresh oil is added to the engine and shall be taken within one-half hour after engine shutdown. The oil samples shall be analyzed for viscosity at 100 °C, and for total acid number per the methods listed in Tables 2A and 2 of this document. The sample shall also be examined by spectrographic oil analysis for wear metal content.
d. Oil changes are to be conducted per the engine manufacturer's recommendations. The oil filters shall be replaced and inspected as per C.6e at each oil change.
e. All normal engine maintenance records shall be documented and be available for review throughout the evaluation interval.
f. A differential pressure compression check shall be performed and recorded on each engine in the program upon its inception and approximately 100 h intervals until completion.

C.6 Inspection Requirements

a. At the completion of the specified operational period the engine is to be disassembled to the degree required and inspected. The disassembly is to be witnessed by NAVAIR personnel or an appointed representative. Parts are to be measured using approved standard practices. Critical dimensions and acceptable tolerances and wear limits shall meet the requirements listed in the engine manufacturer's overhaul information.
b. The disassembled parts are to be color photographed and their condition rated in accordance with the Coordinating Research Council rating manuals and procedures prior to cleaning and measurement. Any lubricant related deposit shall be photographed and recorded.
c. At the completion of the evaluation all cylinders shall be removed and inspected. The critical items to be inspected and measured are listed in Table C2.
d. The variable pitch propeller shall be disassembled to the extent that the oil activated mechanisms and seals can be visually rated.
e. The oil filter elements and/or screens removed during the flight evaluation shall be visually examined for wear debris and carbonaceous material and their conditions recorded if abnormal.
f. The periodic oil samples are to be identified with the aircraft model and registration number, engine model and serial number, engine total time, oil identification, and date drawn. The periodically obtained oil samples shall be tested for viscosity and total acid number per C.5c and the values reported in table and graphic format.
g. Complete spectrographic wear metal analysis data shall be reported for each engine in the program. The used oil values obtained are for engine operational health monitoring and lubricant wear property information only. The data are not specifically limited, but are indicative of potential wear problems which may require additional engine disassembly and inspection.
h. A general description of the engine flight-use profile shall be provided in the final report. A log shall be maintained, containing general information regarding the ambient environmental conditions involved over the duration of the program.
i. Any engine or propeller malfunctions which occur during the flight evaluation on the candidate lubricant, which may be lubricant related, shall be reported to the Naval Air Systems Command. The cause of the problem and corrective actions employed shall be included in the final report.
j. If any of the inspections or measurements are unusual or indicate incipient problems, further inspection may be required. At the discretion of the Naval Air Systems Command, a continuation of the flight evaluation may be required for a duration to be specified by them.

TABLE C1—ACCEPTABLE ENGINE MODELS

1. Textron Lycoming

   360 and 540 series of turbocharged engines

2. Teledyne Continental Motors

   360, 470, and 520 series of turbocharged engines

NOTE 1— All engines used shall be air cooled, have variable pitch propellers, and at least one engine from each manufacturer shall be turbocharged.
NOTE 2— Additional type aircraft engines may be added.

TABLE C2—INSPECTION REQUIREMENTS

Visual Descriptions	
1.	Crankcase general condition
2.	Cylinder, valves, and valve guides
3.	Piston Assembly
4.	Camshaft lobes and lifters
5.	Propeller oil wetted components
6.	Oil filter element and/or screens
7.	Pushrod ends and overall condition
8.	Connecting rod bearings and corresponding shafts
9.	Cylinder head dome and valve seat area
10.	Rocker box cover, cylinder top deck, rocker arms, rocker shaft, and valve springs
Measurements	
1.	Connecting rod bushing, crankshaft end, inside diameter
2.	Connecting rod bushing, piston pin end, inside diameter
3.	Crankshaft connecting rod journal, outside diameter
4.	Piston pin, hole
5.	Piston pin, diameter
6.	Piston pin plug hole in piston, inside diameter (if used)
7.	Piston pin plug, outside diameter
8.	Piston ring side clearance (before and after cleaning)
9.	Piston ring gap (before and after cleaning)
10.	Piston diameter
11.	Cylinder barrel bore
12.	Valve stems, intake and exhaust, outside diameter
13.	Valve guides, intake and exhaust, inside diameter, measured in three locations
14.	Valve rocker arm shaft, intake and exhaust, outside diameter
15.	Valve rocker bushings, intake and exhaust, inside diameter

C.7 Report Requirements

a. For each engine in the evaluation program, a final report summarizing the results of the program shall be provided to the Naval Air Systems Command within 60 days following the inspection. The report, as a minimum, shall contain information from C.6a through C.6j.

C.8 Miscellaneous

a. Contacts: Questions on this requirement may be addressed to:
Naval Air Systems Command
AIR-4.4.5, Building 2360
22229 Elmer Road, Unit 4
Patuxent River, MD 20670
301-757-3421

MEASUREMENT OF THE TOTAL ASH CONTENT OF AVIATION PISTON ENGINE OILS BY A CALCULATION METHOD—SAE J1787 JUL2000

SAE Recommended Practice

Report of the SAE Fuels and Lubricants Technical Committee 8—Aviation Piston Engine Fuels and Lubricants approved October 1995 and revised July 2000. Rationale statement available.

1. Scope—This SAE Recommended Practice describes an empirical method for determining the theoretical ash content of aviation piston engine lubricating oils by calculating the equivalent weight of metallic oxides formed at 775 °C based on the metallic elemental concentration.

The calculation method of ash determination may be used as an alternate to ASTM D 482 for application to the standards for aviation piston engine lubricating oils.

1.1 Field of Application—This procedure is recommended for use in the qualification, manufacturing, and quality assurance testing of aviation piston engine lubricating oils where the ash content is limited to a maximum of 0.011%.

1.2 Background

1.2.1 The ash content as measured by ASTM D 482 has very poor precision and repeatability for lubricants having low ash content. The precision statement for the method states that the reproducibility of a sample in the range of 0.001 to 0.079% ash content is 0.005%. Further, the bias of the test cannot be determined and there is no standard reference material containing a known level of ash for this method. This poor precision has led to numerous problems concerning the actual ash content of products on many occasions. The test method is valuable when run by experienced operators, but can provide dubious information if run under the general conditions stated in the method. For example, to obtain repeatable results, a platinum crucible must always be used in place of the silica or porcelain crucibles listed as equivalent substitutes. Meticulous care and procedural knowledge must be used by experienced operators for the method to be productive.

1.2.1.1 The notes provided in ASTM D 482 also suggest that this method may not be appropriate for oils containing ashless additives or for oils containing certain phosphorous compounds which may now be in use in aviation lubricants. For oils containing additives an alternate method, ASTM D 874, is suggested. However, ASTM D 874 includes additional restrictions and reservations which question the suitability of that method as an acceptable alternate or replacement for ASTM D 482 for low ash containing lubricating oils.

1.2.1.2 These contradictions have led to the development of a "calculated ash content" method as a recommended alternative for use with aviation piston engine oils. This procedure is based on the ideal conversion of selected metallic elements to their theoretical oxide weights and then summing the components to obtain a total value. The seven metallic elements chosen were selected as being those most likely to be present in lubricant manufacturing and packaging plants. As such they would also be the most likely contaminants to be found in the aviation lubricants specified.

2. References

2.1 Applicable Publications—The following publications form a part of this specification to the extent specified herein. Unless otherwise indicated, the latest issue of SAE publications shall apply.

2.1.1 SAE PUBLICATION—Available from SAE, 400 Commonwealth Drive, Warrendale, PA 15096-0001.

SAE J1899—Lubricating Oil, Aircraft Piston Engine (Ashless Dispersant)

2.1.2 ASTM PUBLICATIONS—Available from ASTM, 100 Barr Harbor Drive, West Conshohocken, PA 19428-2959.

ASTM D 482—Standard Test Method for Ash from Petroleum Products

ASTM D 874—Standard Test Method for Sulfated Ash from Lubricating Oils and Additives

2.2 Related Publications—The following publications are provided for information purposes only and are not a required part of this document.

2.2.1 SAE PUBLICATION—Available from SAE, 400 Commonwealth Drive, Warrendale, PA 15096-0001.

SAE J1966—Lubricating Oil, Aircraft Piston Engine (Nondispersant Mineral Oil)

2.2.2 ASTM PUBLICATIONS—Available from ASTM, 100 Barr Harbor Drive, West Conshohocken, PA 19428-2959.

ASTM D 4628—Standard Test Method for Analysis of Barium, Calcium, Magnesium and Zinc in Unused Lubricating Oils by Atomic Absorption Spectrometry

ASTM D 4951—Standard Test Method for Determination of Additive Elements in Lubricating Oils by Inductively Coupled Plasma Atomic Emission Spectrometry

3. Test Requirements

3.1 Measurements

3.1.1 The concentration of the selected metallic elements are determined by the appropriate ASTM test method listed in Section 2. The measurements for iron, copper, and silicon have no specified ASTM method and therefore are to be determined using standard accepted laboratory methods. For military qualification purposes, the trace metal content for iron, copper, and silicon shall be obtained using the procedure noted in 4.5.2 of SAE J1899. The values are recorded as parts per million (ppm) of each element. The elements to be measured are listed in Table 1.

TABLE 1—ELEMENTS TO BE MEASURED

Element	Oxide Conversion Factors
Magnesium	1.66×10^{-4}
Zinc	1.24×10^{-4}
Calcium	1.40×10^{-4}
Sodium	1.35×10^{-4}
Iron	1.43×10^{-4}
Copper	1.25×10^{-4}
Silicon	2.14×10^{-4}

3.2 Calculations

3.2.1 The concentration of each metal element is then converted to its equivalent oxide mass by multiplying the obtained element's ppm value by the corresponding oxide conversion factor shown in Table 1. The product for each conversion is reported individually as "metal oxide, percent mass" for each element. The sum of these combined metal oxide masses are then computed.

4. Report

4.1 The ash content for the sample is then recorded as required by the standard or specification. The result is reported as the "Calculated Ash Value" of the sample tested.

LUBRICATING OILS, AIRCRAFT PISTON ENGINE (NON-DISPERSANT MINERAL OIL)—SAE J1966 JUN2000 SAE Standard

Report of the SAE Fuels and Lubricants Technical Committe 8 approved December 1989. Completely revised by the SAE Fuels and Lubricants Technical Committee 8—Aviation Piston Engine Fuels and Lubricants June 1991 and October 1995, and revised June 2000.

1. Scope—This SAE Standard establishes the requirements for nondispersant, mineral lubricating oils to be used in four-stroke cycle piston aircraft engines. This document covers the same lubricating oil requirements as the former military specification MIL-L-6082. Users should consult their airframe or engine manufacturers manuals for the latest listing of acceptable lubricants.

1.1 Classification—The lubricating oils shall be furnished in the viscosity grades as per Table 1:

TABLE 1—VISCOSITY GRADE COMPARISON TABLE

SAE Viscosity Table	Military Grade	Commercial Grade	NATO Code Number
30	1065	65	0—113
40	1080	80	none
50	1100	100	0—117
60	1120	120	none
Multi-Grade	none	none	none

NOTE—The Military Grade designations are being phased out in favor of the NATO Code Numbers, when available, or the SAE viscosity grade classifications. Commercial grade designations are being phased out in favor of the SAE viscosity grade classifications.

1.2 Commercial Products—Commercial products sold under this document must meet all of the requirements of Sections 3 and 4 of this document with the following exceptions:

a. Qualification samples and test results do not have to be submitted to Naval Air Warfare Center (NAWC), but must be retained by the manufacturer for a period of at least three years.
b. Individual products acceptance lists for commercial aviation piston engine oils will be maintained by each of the original aircraft engine manufacturers.
c. The detailed sampling and inspection procedural requirements of 4.4.2.2 through 4.4.3.2 do not apply.

2. References

2.1 Applicable Publications—The following publications form a part of the specification to the extent specified herein. Unless otherwise indicated, the latest revision of SAE publications shall apply.

2.1.1 GOVERNMENT DOCUMENTS

2.1.1.1 The following publications form a part of this document to the extent specified herein. Unless otherwise specified, the issues of these documents shall be those numbers listed in the issue of the Department of Defense Index of Specifications and Standards (DODISS) and supplement thereto, cited in the solicitation (see 6.2). The military specifications are listed only for reference and are not current.

Specifications

(Unless otherwise indicated, copies of federal and military specifications, standards, and handbooks are available from the Standardization Documents Order Desk, Building 4D, 700 Robbins Avenue, Philadelphia, PA 19111-5094.)

(Copies of specifications, standards, other Government documents and publications required by contractors in connection with specific acquisition functions should be obtained from the contracting activity or as directed by the contracting activity.)

2.1.1.1.1 Military

MIL-L-6082—Lubricating Oil, Aircraft Piston Engine, Non-Dispersant Mineral Oil, Cancelled November 1995

MIL-L-22851—Lubricating Oil, Aircraft Piston Engine, Ashless Dispersant, Cancelled November 1995

Standards

2.1.1.1.2 Federal

FED-STD-313—Material Safety Data Sheets, Preparation and the Submission of

FED-STD-791—Lubricants, Liquid Fuels and Related Products; Methods of Testing

2.1.1.1.3 Military

MIL-STD-290—Packaging, Packing and Marking of Petroleum and Related Products

2.2 Related Publications—The following publications form a part of this document to the extent specified herein. Unless otherwise specified, the issues of the documents which are DOD adopted shall be those listed in the issue of the DODISS specified in the solicitation. Unless otherwise specified, the issues of documents not listed in the DODISS shall be the issue of the nongovernment documents which is current on the date of the solicitation (see 6.2).

2.2.1 SAE PUBLICATIONS—Available from SAE, 400 Commonwealth Drive, Warrendale, PA 15096-0001.

SAE J300—Engine Oil Viscosity Classification

SAE J1787—Measurement of the Total Ash Content of Aviation Piston Engine Oil by a Calculation Method

SAE J1899—Lubricating Oil, Aircraft Piston Engine, Ashless Dispersant

2.2.2 AMERICAN SOCIETY FOR TESTING AND MATERIALS (ASTM)—Available from ASTM, 100 Barr Harbor Drive, West Conshohocken, PA 19428-2959.

ASTM D 92—Flash and Fire Points by Cleveland Open Cup

ASTM D 93—Flash Point by Pensky-Martens Closed Cup Tester

ASTM D 97—Pour Point of Petroleum Oils

ASTM D 129—Sulfur in Petroleum Products (General Bomb Method)

ASTM D 130—Detection of Copper Corrosion from Petroleum Products by the Copper Strip Tarnish Test

ASTM D 445—Kinematic Viscosity of Transparent and Opaque Liquids (and the Calculation of Dynamic Viscosity)

ASTM D 482—Ash from Petroleum Products

ASTM D 664—Neutralization Number by Potentiometric Titration

ASTM D 892—Foaming Characteristics of Lubricating Oils

ASTM D 1298—Density, Relative Density (Specific Gravity), or API Gravity of Crude Petroleum and Liquid Petroleum Products by Hydrometer Method

ASTM D 1552—Sulfur in Petroleum Products (High-Temperature Method)

ASTM D 2270—Calculating Viscosity Index from Kinematic Viscosity at 40 and 100 °C

ASTM D 2273—Trace Sediment in Lubricating Oils

ASTM D 2622—Sulfur in Petroleum Products (X-Ray Spectrographic Method)

ASTM D 4052—Density and Relative Density of Liquids by Digital Density Method

ASTM D 4057—Manual Sampling of Petroleum and Petroleum Products

ASTM D 4177—Automatic Sampling of Petroleum and Petroleum Products

ASTM D 4683—Measuring Viscosity at High Temperature and High Shear Rate by Tapered Bearing Simulator

ASTM D 4684—Determination of Yield Stress and Apparent Viscosity of Engine Oils at Low Temperature

ASTM D 4741—Measuring Viscosity at High Temperature and High Shear Rate by Tapered-Plug Viscometer

ASTM D 4927—Elemental Analysis of Lubricant and Additive ComponentsæBarium, Calcium, Phosphorus, Sulfur and Zinc by Wavelength—Dispersive X-Ray Fluorescence Spectroscopy

ASTM D 5119—Evaluation of Automotive Engine Oils in the CRC L-38 Spark-Ignition Engine

ASTM D 5293—Apparent Viscosity of Engine Oils Between -5 and -30 °C Using the Cold-Cranking Simulator

ASTM D 5949—Pour Point of Petroleum Products (Automatic Pressure Pulse Method)

ASTM D 5950—Pour Point of Petroleum Products (Automatic Tilt Method)

ASTM D 5985—Pour Point of Petroleum Products (Rotational Method)

2.2.3 AMERICAN NATIONAL STANDARDS INSTITUTE (ANSI)—Available from ANSI, 11 West 42nd Street, New York, NY 10036-8002.

ANSI Z129.1—American National Standard for the Precautionary Labeling of Hazardous Industrial Chemicals

2.2.4 AMERICAN SOCIETY FOR QUALITY CONTROL (ASQC)—Available from the American Society for Quality Control, P.O. Box 12233, Research Triangle Park, NC 27709.

ASQC-Z1.4—Sampling Procedures and Tables for Inspection by Attributes (DoD Addopted)

2.2.5 ORDER OF PRECEDENCE—In the event of a conflict between the text of this document and the references cited herein (except for associated detail specifications, specification sheets, or MS standards), the text of this document shall take precedence. Nothing in this document, however, shall supersede applicable laws and regulations unless a specific exemption has been obtained.

3. Requirements

3.1 Qualification—The lubricating oils furnished under this document shall be products which are authorized by the qualifying activity for listing on the applicable qualified products list at the time for opening of bids (see 4.3 and 6.2.2). Detailed information on the procedures to be followed when submitting a candidate lubricating oil are available from the Naval Air Systems Command, AIR-4.4.5, Fuels and Lubricants Division, Building 2360, 22229 Elmer Road, Unit 4, Patuxent River, MD 20670.

3.1.1 READ-ACROSS APPROVALS—Read-across approvals will only be granted to different grades of oil that are composed of varying percentages of the same base stocks blended with identical additive packages (adjustments in pour point depressant concentration will be permitted). Complete chemical and physical property test results shall be submitted for each grade of oil for which qualification is requested. L-38 tests shall be performed on the lightest and heaviest single SAE grade oils to be blended from the same base stock materials (neutral and bright stock). All single grade oils blended from the same base stock materials and meeting SAE viscosity classification standards between the two tested products will be granted qualification approval based on similarity. No read-across approvals will be granted for multi-grade oils.

3.1.2 REQUALIFICATION—Requalification will be required in the event any change is made in the source or composition of the lubricant, the ingredients used, the manufacturing processes, or the plant location.

3.2 Materials—The single grade lubricating oils shall be refined petroleum products and may contain pour point depressants up to a maximum amount of 1.0% by weight as well as an antioxidant in an amount not to exceed 0.5% by weight. In addition to these materials, multi-grade oil may also contain a viscosity index improver. Silicone antifoam additives may be used up to a maximum of 25 parts per million. Crude source(s) and the types of processing used in the manufacture of the base stocks shall be identified in accordance with Appendix A. If re-refined materials are used, the manufacturer must demonstrate the consistency of the products to the qualifying agency.

3.3 Chemical and Physical Properties—The finished lubricating oil shall conform to the physical and chemical property requirements specified in Table 2.

3.4 Sulfur—The sulfur content of the oil shall not exceed the value shown for each grade in Table 2. For quality conformance inspection, the sulfur content shall be within ±0.15% mass of the qualification value or within a 0.3% mass range selected by the manufacturer to bracket the qualification value.

TABLE 2—CHEMICAL AND PHYSICAL PROPERTY REQUIREMENTS FOR FINISHED LUBRICANT

Characteristic (Limits) SAE Grade	30	40	50	60	Multi-Grade	Test Method
Viscosity, cSt,						ASTM D 445
@ 100 °C, Min	9.3	12.5	16.3	21.9	(1)	
@ 100 °C, Less Than	12.5	16.3	21.9	26.1	(1)	
Flash Point, °C Min	220	225	243	243	220	ASTM D 92
Flash Point, °C	Report	Report	Report	Report	Report	ASTM D 93
Sulfur, Mass % Max	0.6	0.8	1.0	1.2	0.6	ASTM D 129, ASTM D 1552, ASTM D 2622
Pour Point, °C Max	−18	−15	−12	−9	—	ASTM D 97 ASTM D 5949 ASTM D 5950 ASTM D 5985
Viscosity, Low Temp., Pumping	—	—	—	—	(1)	ASTM D 4684
Viscosity, Low Temp., Cold Crank Sim.	—	—	—	—	(1)	ASTM D 5293
Viscosity, High Temp., High Shear, at 150 °C, cP, Min	3.3	3.7	3.7	3.7	(1)	ASTM D 4683 ASTM D 4741
			All Grades			
Viscosity, cSt, @ 40 °C			report			ASTM D 445
Viscosity Index, Min.			85			ASTM D 2270
Total Acid Number, mg KOH/g, Max(2)			0.10			ASTM D 664
Density @ 15 °C, kg/L			report			ASTM D 4052
Gravity @ 60 °F, °API(3)			report			ASTM D 1298, ASTM D 4052
Ash Content(4) Mass % Max			0.011			ASTM D 482, SAE J1787
Trace Sediment ml/100 mL Oil, Max.			0.005			ASTM D 2273
Copper Strip Corrosion, Max Rating						ASTM D 130
3 h @ 100 °C			1			
3 h @ 204 °C(5)			3			
Foaming Tendency/Stability						ASTM D 892
Sequence 1						
Aerated Volume, mL, max			50			
Volume after 10 min, mL, max			0			
Sequence 2						
Aerated Volume, mL, max			50			
Volume after 10 min, mL, max			0			
Sequence 3						
Aerated Volume, mL, max			50			
Volume after 10 min, mL, max			0			
Compatibility(6)			pass			FTM 791, Method 3470

1. Oil shall meet the viscosity requirements of SAE J300 for the designated grade.
2. Titrate to a pH 11 end point.
3. API gravity may be computed from the relative density measured by ASTM D 4052.
4. ASTM D 482 is required for qualification. Either ASTM D 482 or SAE J1787 may be used for Quality Assurance Testing.
5. Conduct the test in accordance with ASTM D 130 but at the temperature specified.
6. Only required for qualification. Reference oils may be obtained from NAWC.

3.5 API Gravity—The American Petroleum Institute (API) gravity of the oil shall be determined but not limited on qualification inspection. For quality conformance inspection, the gravity shall be within ±1.0 °API of the qualification value, or within a 2.0 °API range selected by the manufacturer to bracket the qualification value.

3.6 Workmanship—The lubricating oil shall be a homogeneous blend when examined visually at room temperature (25 °C ± 3 °C) in a well-lighted room or daylight. It shall exhibit no separation or fallout of the additives. Any jelly-like substance or very viscous material observed in the bottom of the container will be considered evidence of additive fallout.

3.7 Bench Performance Requirements (L-38 Engine Test)—The finished lubricating oil shall meet the requirements of Table 3 when tested in the L-38 engine in accordance with ASTM D 5119. The test shall be run with the oil gallery temperature controlled at 135 °C ± 1 °C (275 °F ± 2 °F).

3.8 Material Safety Data Sheets—When applying for qualification, the manufacturer shall submit to the qualifying activity Material Safety Data Sheets prepared in accordance with FED-STD-313 (see 6.4).

4. Quality Assurance Provisions

4.1 Responsibility for Inspection—Unless otherwise specified in the contract or purchase order, the contractor is responsible for the performance of all inspection requirements as specified herein. Except as otherwise specified in the contract or purchase order, the contractor may use his own or any other facility suitable for the performance of the inspection requirements specified herein, unless disapproved by the Government. The Government reserves the right to perform any of the inspections set forth in the document where such inspections are deemed necessary to assure supplies and services conform to prescribed requirements.

4.1.1 RESPONSIBILITY FOR COMPLIANCE—All items shall meet all requirements of Sections 3 and 5. The inspection set forth in this document shall become a part of the contractor's overall inspection system or quality program. The absence of any inspection requirements in the document shall not relieve the contractor of the responsibility of assuring that all products or supplies submitted to the Government for acceptance comply with all requirements of the contract. Sampling inspection, as part of manufacturing operations, is an acceptable practice to ascertain conformance to requirements; however, this does not authorize submission of known defective material, either indicated or actual, nor does it commit the Government to accept defective material.

4.2 Classification of Inspections—The inspection requirements specified herein are classified as follows:

a. Qualification inspection (see 4.3).
b. Quality assurance inspection (see 4.4).

4.3 Qualification Inspection—The qualification inspection shall consist of a review and acceptance of the manufacturer's test results (see 4.3.2) by the Naval Air Systems Command and its field activity, the NAWC. Additional testing of the qualification inspection sample by the NAWC will be performed to confirm compliance with the requirements of Table 2.

4.3.1 QUALIFICATION INSPECTION SAMPLE—All qualification and NAWC testing must be conducted on the same homogeneous batch of oil. The qualification inspection test samples to be tested by NAWC shall consist of a 3.8 L (1 gal) sample of each grade of blended base oil without additives and a 38 L (10 gal) sample of each grade of the finished oil for which qualification approval is sought. Material Safety Data Sheets completed in accordance with FED-STD-313 shall also be included with the test samples. At the direction of the Naval Air Systems Command, AIR-4.4.5, these samples should be forwarded to the Naval Air Warfare Center, (AIR-4.4.5), at an address to be specified at the time of sample submission. The sample should be plainly identified by a securely attached durable tag or label marked with the following information:

SAMPLE FOR QUALIFICATION INSPECTION
LUBRICATING OIL, AIRCRAFT PISTON ENGINE,
(NONDISPERSANT MINERAL OIL)
Type of sample (base stock or finished oil)
Name of manufacturer
Product code number
Batch number
Date of manufacture
Submitted by (name) (date) for qualification inspection in accordance with SAE J1966 under authorization of (reference authorizing letter) (see 6.2.2).

4.3.2 TEST RESULTS—The manufacturer shall forward a certified copy of the test report to the NAWC. The report shall contain complete test data showing the results of all tests required by this document. Photographs of the test parts from the L-38 engine will be included along with data on the test oil's viscosity (measured at 40 °C), and TAN, properties at 0, 10, 20, 30, and 40 h into the test (including the stripped 40 °C viscosity of the 10 h sample for multi-grade oils). The test report shall also include complete formulation data including the brand name and manufacturer of each of the additives used, the concentration of each additive in the finished oil, the percentages of neutral and bright stock used in the blending of the base stock, as well as the crude oil sources and type of processing used in the manufacture of these base stock components.

4.4 Quality Conformance Inspection—Quality assurance inspection shall consist of all the tests included in Table 4. Oil manufacturers must retain a copy of each batch test report in their files for at least three years. A copy of the test report on each batch of oil produced for the U.S. Government shall be forwarded to Naval Air Systems Command.

4.4.1 LOT FORMATION

4.4.1.1 Bulk Lot—A bulk lot is considered as an indefinite quantity of homogeneous mixture of material in a single isolated container or manufactured by a single plant run (not exceeding 24 h) through the same processing equipment, with no change in ingredient material.

4.4.1.2 Packaged Lot—A packaged lot is considered as an indefinite number of 208 L (55 gal) drums or smaller unit packages of identical size and type filled with a homogeneous mixture of material manufactured by a single plant run (not exceeding 24 h) through the same processing equipment, with no change in ingredient material.

4.4.2 SAMPLING

4.4.2.1 Sampling for Verification of Product Quality—Each bulk lot of material shall be sampled at random in accordance with ASTM D 4057 or ASTM D 4177 for verification of product quality as specified in 4.4.

4.4.2.2 Sampling for Examination of Filled Containers—Each packaged lot of containers shall be sampled in accordance with ASQC-Z1.4 for leakage, fill, closure, and preparation for shipment (packaging, packing, marking) in accordance with Section 5.

4.4.2.3 Sampling for Examination of Sedimentation of Filled and Sealed Containers—Samples of filled and sealed 0.95 L (1 qt) containers shall be taken at such periodic intervals as to be representative of each day of operation. The number of samples to be taken each day shall be in accordance with ASQC-Z1.4, when tested against the sedimentation requirement of Table 3.

4.4.3 INSPECTION

4.4.3.1 Inspection of Material—Inspection shall be performed in accordance with Method 9601 of FED-STD-791.

4.4.3.2 Examination of Filled Containers—Examine samples taken in accordance with 4.4.2.2 for compliance with MIL-STD-290 with regard to fill, closure, sealing, leakage, packaging, packing, and marking requirements. Reject any container having one or more defects or under the required fill. If the number of defective or unfilled containers exceeds the acceptance number for the appropriate plan of ASQC-Z1.4, reject the lot represented by the sample.

TABLE 3—L-38 ENGINE TEST REQUIREMENTS AT 40 h (END OF TEST)(1)

End of Test Characteristic	Limit Single Grade	Limit Multigrade	Test Method
BEARING			
Bearing Weight Loss, Total, mg, Max	500	500	ASTM D 5119
USED OIL			
Viscosity, % Change, Max, @ 40 °C	–5 to +10	report	ASTM D 445
Viscosity, @ 100 °C	—	(2)	ASTM D 445
Total Acid Number Change, Max(3)	2.0	2.0	ASTM D 664

1. L-38 engine test is to be run in accordance with ASTM D 5119 with an oil gallery temperature controlled at 135 °C ± 1 °C (275 °F ± 2 °F).
2. Stipped viscosity of the 10 hour sample shall remain in original SAE grade.
3. Titrate to a pH 11 end point.

TABLE 4—QUALITY ASSURANCE TEST REQUIREMENTS FOR FINISHED LUBRICANT

Characteristic (Limits) SAE Grade	30	40	50	60	Multi-Grade	Test Method
Viscosity, cSt,						ASTM D 445
@ 100 °C, Min	9.3	12.5	16.3	21.9	(1)	
@ 100 °C, Less Than	12.5	16.3	21.9	26.1	(1)	
Flash Point, °C Min	220	225	243	243	220	ASTM D 92
Sulfur, Mass % Max[2]	0.6	0.8	1.0	1.2	0.6	ASTM D 129, ASTM D 1552, ASTM D 2622
Pour Point, °C Max	–18	–15	–12	–9	—	ASTM D 97, ASTM D 5949, ASTM D 5950, ASTM D 5985
Viscosity, Low Temp., Cold Crank Sim.	—	—	—	—	(1)	ASTM D 5293
			All Grades			
Total Acid Number, mg K0H/g, Max[3]			0.10			ASTM D 664
Density @ 15 °C, kg/L			report			ASTM D 4052
Gravity @ 60 °F, °API[4]			report			ASTM D 1298, ASTM D 4052
Ash Content[5] Mass % Max			0.011			ASTM D 482, SAE J1787
Trace Sediment ml/100 mL Oil, Max.			0.005			ASTM D 2273
Copper Strip Corrosion, Max Rating 3 h @ 100 °C			1			ASTM D 130
Foaming Tendency/Stability Sequence 2						ASTM D 892
Aerated Volume, mL, max			50			
Volume after 10 min, mL, max			0			

1. Oil shall meet the viscosity requirements of SAE J300 for the designated grade.
2. See 3.4 for conformance limit range.
3. Titrate to a pH 11 end point.
4. API gravity may be computed from the relative density measured by ASTM D 4052.
5. ASTM D 482 is required for qualification. Either ASTM D 482 or SAE J1787 may be used for Quality Assurance Testing.

4.5 Test Methods—Tests shall be performed in accordance with the applicable methods of Tables 2, 3, and 4.

5. Packaging (For Military Procurements)

5.1 Preservation and Packing—For acquisition purposes, the packaging requirements shall be as specified in the contrct order (see 6.2.1.1).

5.2 Marking—All unit, intermediate, and shipping containers shall be marked in accordance with the contract order. All unit and intermediate packs of toxic and hazardous chemicals and materials shall also be labeled in accordance wit the applicable laws, statutes, regulations, or ordinances, including Federal, State, and Municipal requirements. In addition, unit or intermediate containers, including unit containers that serve as shipping containers, such as pails and drums, shall be marked with the applicable precautionary information detailed in ANSI Z129.1.

6. Notes—This section contains information of a general or explanatory nature that may be helpful but is not mandatory.

6.1 Intended Use—The lubricating oil covered by this document is intended for use in four cycle piston aircraft engines where the dispersant additives found in SAE J1899 (formerly military specification MIL-L-22851) oil are not needed or desired. This document covers the same lubricating oil requirements as the former military specification MIL-L-6082. Users should consult their airframe or engine manufacturers manuals for the latest listing of acceptable lubricants.

6.2 Military Procurements

6.2.1 ORDERING DATA

6.2.1.1 Acquisition Requirements—Procurement documents should specify the following:

a. Title, number, and date of this document.
b. Grade of lubricating oil required (see 1.2).
c. Type and size of containers required (see 5.1).
d. Level of packing required (see 5.1).
e. Quantity desired.
f. Submittal of test results (see 4.4).

6.2.2 QUALIFICATION—With respect to products requiring qualification, awards will be made only for the products that are at the time set for opening of bids, qualified for inclusion in the applicable Qualified Products List whether or not such products have actually been so listed by that date. The attention of the contractors is called to these requirements, and manufacturers are urged to arrange to have the products that they propose to offer to the federal government tested for qualification in order that they may be eligible to be awarded contracts of purchase orders for the products covered by this document. The activity responsible for the Qualified Products List is Commander Naval Air Systems Command, AIR-4.4.5, Fuels and Lubricants Division, Buidling 2360, 22229 Elmer Road, Unit 4, Patuxent River, MD 20670. Information pertaining to qualification of products may be obtained from that activity.

6.2.3 INTERNATIONAL STANDARDIZATION AGREEMENT—Certain provisions of this document are the subject of an international standardization agreement with NATO (STANAG 1135). When amendment, revision, or cancellation of this document is proposed, which will affect or violate the international agreement concerned, the preparing activity will take appropriate reconciliation action through international standardization channels, including departmental standardization offices, if required.

6.3 Revisions—Revisions or changes to this document must have concurrence from the Naval Air Systems Command.

6.4 Material Safety Data Sheets—Contracting officers will identify those activities requiring copies of completed Material Safety Data Sheets prepared in accordance with FED-STD-313. The pertinent Government mailing addresses for submission of data are listed in Section 4 of FED-STD-313.

APPENDIX A
BASE STOCK CRUDE OIL SOURCE AND PROCESSING DESCRIPTIONS

A.1 When applying for qualification, refiners shall provide the following information about the crude oil and the processing used in the manufacture of each base stock blended into their product:

a. Name of original base stock refiner or processer.
b. Location of refinery or processing plant, by city and state (U.S.), province (Canada), or country.
c. General crude source shall be identified as follows:
   - ACI—Alaskan Cook Inlet
   - ANS—Alaskan North Slopte
   - GE—Germany
   - MC—Mid Continent
   - ME—Middle East
   - MW—Mid West
   - MXA—Maya
   - MXO—Mexican
   - NA—North Africa
   - NS—North Sea
   - PA—Pennsylvania
   - VEN—Venezuelan
   - WC—West Coast
   - WCA—Western Canada
   - WT—West Texas
   - OC—Other (Please provide brief description)
d. General crude refining processes shall be defined as follows:
   - SD—Straight Distillation
   - VD—Vacuum Distillation
   - SR—Solvent Refining
   - MH—Mild Hydrogenation
   - SH—Severe Hydrogenation
   - HP—Hydrocracked
   - OP—Other (Please provide brief description)

LUBRICATING OIL, INTERNAL COMBUSTION ENGINE, MILITARY COMBAT/TACTICAL SERVICE—SAE J2359 NOV1998 SAE Standard

Report of the SAE Military/industry Lubricants Committee approved November 1998. Rationale statement available.

1. Scope—This SAE Standard covers engine military oils suitable for lubrication of reciprocating internal combustion engines of both spark-ignition and compression-ignition types, and for power transmission fluid applications in combat/tactical service equipment (see 7.1). This document is equivalent to MIL-PRF-2104G when all requirements are met.

1.1 Classification—The lubricating oils shall be of the following viscosity grades shown in Table 1 (see 7.1):

TABLE 1—VISCOSITY GRADES

SAE Viscosity Grade	Military Symbol	NATO Code
10W	OE/HDO-10	0-237
30	OE/HDO-30	0-238
40	OE/HDO-40	—
15W-40	OE/HDO-15/40	0-1236

2. References

2.1 Applicable Publications—The following publications form a part of this specification to the extent specified herein. Unless otherwise specified, the latest issue of SAE publications shall apply.

In the event of a conflict between the text of this document and the references cited herein, the text of this document takes precedence. Nothing in this document, however, supersedes applicable laws and regulations unless a specific exemption has been obtained

2.1.1 SAE PUBLICATIONS—Available from SAE, 400 Commonwealth Drive, Warrendale, PA 15096-0001.

SAE J183—Engine Oil Performance and Engine Service Classification (Other than "Energy-Conserving")

SAE J300—Engine Oil Viscosity Classification

2.1.2 ALLISON TRANSMISSION DIVISION (ATD) PUBLICATION—Available from EG&G Stationary Testing, Attn: ATF/Specialty Lab (C-4), 5904 Bandera Road, San Antonio, TX 78283-1993.

TES-228—C-4 Fluid Specification

2.1.3 ANSI PUBLICATION—Available from ANSI, 11 West 42nd Street, New York, NY 10036-8002.

ANSI Z1.4—Sampling Procedures and Tables for Inspections by Attributes

2.1.4 AMERICAN SOCIETY FOR QUALITY CONTROL (ASQC) PUBLICATION—Available from American Society for Quality Control, 611 East Wisconsin Avenue, Milwaukee, WI 53201-4606.

ASQC Z1.4—Sampling Procedures and Tables for Inspections by Attributes

2.1.5 ASTM PUBLICATIONS—Available from ASTM, 100 Barr Harbor Drive, West Conshohocken, PA 19428-2959.

ASTM D 92—Flash and Fire Points by Cleveland Open Cup
ASTM D 94—Saponification Number of Petroleum Products
ASTM D 97—Pour Point of Petroleum Oils
ASTM D 129—Sulfur in Petroleum Products (General Bomb Method)
ASTM D 130—Detection of Copper Corrosion from Petroleum Products, by the Copper Strip Tarnish Test
ASTM D 287—API Gravity of Crude Petroleum and Petroleum Products (Hydrometer Method)
ASTM D 445—Kinematic Viscosity of Transparent and Opaque Liquids (and the Calculation of Dynamic Viscosity)
ASTM D 524—Ramsbottom Carbon Residue of Petroleum Products
ASTM D 664—Standard Test Method for Acid Number of Petroleum Products by Potentiometric Titration
ASTM D 808—Chlorine in New and Used Petroleum Products (Bomb Method)
ASTM D 874—Sulfated Ash from Lubricating Oils and Additives
ASTM D 892—Foaming Characteristics of Lubricating Oils
ASTM D 1091—Phosphorus in Lubricating Oils and Additives
ASTM D 1317—Chlorine in New and Used Lubricants (Sodium Alcoholate Method)
ASTM D 1500—ASTM Color of Petroleum Products (ASTM Color Scale)
ASTM D 1552—Sulfur in Petroleum Products (High-Temperature Method)
ASTM D 2270—Calculating Viscosity Index from Kinematic Viscosity at 40 and 100 C
ASTM D 2622—Sulfur in Petroleum Products (X-Ray Spectrographic Method)
ASTM D 2887—Boiling Range Distribution of Petroleum Fractions by Gas Chromatography
ASTM D 2896—Base Number of Petroleum Products by Potentiometric Perchloric Acid Titration
ASTM D 3228—Total Nitrogen in Lubricating Oils and Fuel Oils by Modified Kjeldahl Method
ASTM D 3951—Standard Practice for Commercial Packaging
ASTM D 4047—Phosphorus in Lubricating Oils and Additives by Quinoline Phosphomolybdate Method
ASTM D 4057—Manual Sampling of Petroleum and Petroleum Products
ASTM D 4177—Automatic Sampling of Petroleum and Petroleum Products
ASTM D 4294—Sulfur in Petroleum Products by Non-Dispersive X-Ray Fluorescence Spectrometry
ASTM D 4485—Standard Specification for Performance of Engine Oils
ASTM D 4624—Measuring Apparent Viscosity by Capillary Viscometer at High Temperature and High-Shear Rates
ASTM D 4628—Analysis of Barium, Calcium, Magnesium, and Zinc in Unused Lubricating Oils by Atomic Absorption Spectrometry
ASTM D 4629—Trace Nitrogen in Liquid Petroleum Hydrocarbons by Syringe/Inlet Oxidative Combustion and Chemiluminescence Detection
ASTM D 4683—Measuring Viscosity at High Temperature and High Shear Rate by Tapered Bearing Simulator
ASTM D 4684—Determination of Yield Stress and Apparent Viscosity of Engine Oils at Low Temperature
ASTM D 4739—Base Number Determination by Potentiometric Titration
ASTM D 4741—Measuring Viscosity at High Temperature and High Shear Rate by Tapered-Plug Viscometer
ASTM D 4927—Elemental Analysis of Lubricants and Additive Components - Barium, Calcium, Phosphorus, Sulfur, and Zinc by Wavelength-Dispersive X-Ray Fluorescence Spectroscopy
ASTM D 4951—Determination of Additive Elements in Lubricating Oils by Inductively Coupled Plasma Atomic Emission Spectrometry
ASTM D 4998—Evaluating Wear Characteristics of Tractor Hydraulic Fluids
ASTM D 5119—Evaluation of Automotive Engine Oils in the CRC L-38 Spark-Ignition Engine
ASTM D 5185—Determination of Additive Elements, Wear Metals and Contaminants in Used Lubricating Oils by Inductively-Coupled Plasma Atomic Emission Spectrometry
ASTM D 5480—Motor Oil Volatility by Gas Chromatography
ASTM D 5533—Evaluation of Automotive Engine Oils in the Sequence IIIE, Spark-ignition Engine
ASTM D 5800—Evaporation Loss of Lubricating Oil at the NOACK Method
ASTM D 5862—DDC 6V92TA Test Procedure
ASTM D 5950—Pour Point, Automatic
ASTM D 5966—Roller Follower Wear Test
ASTM D 5967—Evaluation of Diesel Engine Oils in the Mack T-8 Diesel Engine
ASTM D 5968—Corrosion Bench Test
ASTM Special Publication (STP) 315H includes:
Caterpillar 1M-PC Test Procedure—ASTM Research Report D02-1320
Caterpillar 1N Test Procedures—ASTM Research Report D02-1321
HEUI Engine Oil Aeration Test

2.1.6 CATERPILLAR INC., ENGINE DIVISION (CAT.) PUBLICATION—Available from Caterpillar, Component Development, Technical Center - C, P.O. Box 1875, Peoria, IL 61656-1875.

Caterpillar TO-4, Fluid Requirements, VC 70.

2.1.7 GOVERNMENT PUBLICATIONS

2.1.7.1 Military and Federal Publications—Available from the Standardization Documents Order Desk, Building 4D, 700 Robbins Avenue, Philadelphia, PA 19111-5094.

MIL-PRF-2104—Lubricating Oil, Internal Combustion Engine, Military Combat/Tactical Service

MIL-L-21260—Lubricating Oil, Internal Combustion Engine, Preservative and Break-In

MIL-L-46167—Lubricating Oil, Internal Combustion Engine, Arctic

FED-STD-313—Material Safety Data, Transportation Data and Disposal Data for Hazardous Materials Furnished to Government Activities

FED-STD-791—Lubricants, Liquid Fuels and Related Products; Methods of Testing

NATO STANAG 2835

NATO STANAG 2845

2.1.7.2 U.S. Department of Labor (DOL) (OSHA)—Available from OSHA Publication Office, Room S-4203, 200 Constitution Avenue, NW, Washington, DC 20210.

OSHA 29 CFR 1910.1200—Hazard Communication; Interpretation Regarding Lubricating Oils

2.1.7.3 US Mobility Technology Center—Available from US Army Tank Automotive and Armament Command, Attn: AMSTRA-TR-0/210, Warren, MI 48397-5000.

Guide for the Qualification of Engine and Gear Lubricants

3. Definitions

3.1 Bulk Lot—An indefinite quantity of a homogeneous mixture of one grade of oil offered for acceptance in a single, isolated container; or manufactured in a single plant run (not exceeding 24 h), through the same processing equipment, with no change in the ingredient materials.

3.2 Packaged Lot—An indefinite number of 208.175 L (55-gal drum) or smaller unit containers of identical size and type, offered for acceptance, and filled with a homogeneous mixture of one grade of oil from a single, isolated container; or filled with a homogeneous mixture of one grade of oil manufactured in a single plant run (not exceeding 24 h), through the same processing equipment, with no change in the ingredient materials.

4. Requirements

4.1 Qualification

4.1.1 QUALIFICATION—GENERAL—Engine lubricating oils furnished under this specification shall be products that are qualified by the qualifying activity (see 7.4) for listing on the applicable qualified products list at the time of contract award (see 5.1.1 and 7.4). Qualification will be granted by the qualifying activity (see 7.4) to any manufacturer (original or reblender) of lubricating oils provided a "Manufacturing Facility Survey" (MFS) has been accepted as described in the "Guide for Qualification of Engine and Gear Lubricants." Each manufacturing facility intended for the manufacture of products under this specification shall have a MFS. This is a one time requirement provided there is no change in facilities, blending method or equipment. Companies requesting rebrand approvals do not need an MFS to be qualified. The qualifying activity (see 7.4) may waive complete qualification testing or may require only partial qualification testing of SAE 40 grade oil if the contractor states in a written affidavit that the product has been formulated with base stocks, refining treatment, and additives the same as those used in the formulation of SAE 30 grade oil qualified under this specification.

4.1.2 QUALIFICATION PERIOD—Each viscosity grade of oil which satisfies all the requirements of this specification shall be qualified for a period not exceeding four years from the date of its original qualification. The qualification period for each SAE 40 grade oil qualified in accordance with 4.1 shall not exceed that of the SAE 30 grade used in the qualification procedure. When the qualification period has expired, or whenever there is a change in the base stock, in the refining treatment or in the additives used in the formulation, each product must be retested if the contractor wishes to maintain the formulation as a qualified product and be eligible to bid on government solicitations for this material.

4.1.3 TOLERANCES—The engine lubricating oil supplied under contract shall have the same base stocks and additives components, at the appropriate concentrations, as when qualified. The finished oil properties shall fall within permissible tolerances assigned by the qualifying activity to the properties listed in 4.5, of the product receiving qualification. The values resulting after the application of tolerances shall not exceed the maximum nor fall below the minimum limits specified herein (see Table 2 and 4.4.1 through 4.4.11).

4.1.4 POUR-POINT DEPRESSANT—No changes shall be made in either the type or concentration of the pour-point depressant after qualification testing and approval unless:

a. The oil is retested for conformity to the pour-point, stable pour point, borderline pumping temperature and all viscosities (see Table 2).
b. The qualifying activity (see 7.4) is informed of the proposed change(s) and of the retesting.
c. The qualifying activity approves the proposed change(s) in writing.

4.1.5 MATERIAL SAFETY DATA SHEETS—When applying for qualification, the manufacturer shall submit to the qualifying activity (see 7.4) a sample of the product tested (see 4.4.2.1) and include Material Safety Data Sheets prepared in accordance with FED-STD-313. When FED-STD-313 is at variance with the OSHA 29 CFR 1910.1200, the CFR shall take precedence, modify, and supplement FED-STD-313.

4.2 Materials—The engine lubricating oils shall be derived from petroleum fractions, synthetically prepared compounds or a combination of the two types of products. They may be virgin, refined stocks, or a combination thereof. The stocks shall be compounded with such functional additives (detergents, dispersants, oxidation inhibitors, corrosion inhibitors, etc.) as are necessary to meet the specified requirements. The stocks used shall not be considered carcinogenic or potentially carcinogenic as defined under the Hazard Communication Standard 29 CFR 1910.1200.

4.3 Physical and Chemical Requirements

4.3.1 REQUIREMENTS FOR FINISHED OIL—The oils shall conform to the requirements specified in Table 2 and 4.4.1 through 4.4.10.2.

4.3.2 REQUIREMENTS FOR BASE STOCK—(Optional for non-military procurement)—A 180 mL production sample of each base stock component used in formulating the finished oil, accompanied by the following property data, shall be submitted annually to the qualifying activity.

a. Viscosity
   at 100 °C, centistokes (mm^2/s)
   at 40 °C, centistokes (mm^2/s)
b. Viscosity index
c. Gravity, API @ 60 °F
d. Pour point, °C
e. Carbon residue, mass %
f. Sulfated ash, mass %
g. Total acid number
h. Elemental content, mass %
i. Nitrogen, mass %
j. Chlorine, mass %
k. Sulfur, mass %
l. Color
m. Boiling point distribution, °C
   @ 1%, 5%, 10%, 50%, & 90% points
n. Saponification number
o. Flash point

4.4 Performance Requirements—The oils shall conform to the respective requirements specified in 4.4.1 through 4.4.11.

4.4.1 FOAMING—All grades of oil shall demonstrate the following foaming characteristics when tested in accordance with 5.1.2, Table 3 (ASTM D 892).

a. Initial test at 24 °C ± 0.5 °C. Not more than 10 mL of foam shall remain immediately following the end of the 5-min blowing period. No foam shall remain at the end of the 10-min settling period.
b. Intermediate test at 93.5 °C ± 0.5 °C. Not more than 20 mL of foam shall remain immediately following the end of the 5-min blowing period. No foam shall remain at the end of the 10-min settling period.
c. Final test at 24 °C ± 0.5 °C. Not more than 10 mL of foam shall remain immediately following the end of the 5-min blowing period. No foam shall remain at the end of the 10-min settling period.
d. Test at 150 °C ± 0.5 °C. Not more than 50 mL of foam shall remain immediately following the end of the blowing period. No foam (0) shall remain at the end of the 1-min settling period. Option A is not allowed (CG-4 requirement).

4.4.2 STABILITY AND COMPATIBILITY

4.4.2.1 Stability—The oils shall show no evidence of separation or color change when they are tested in accordance with 5.1.2, Table 3 (FED-STD-791, Method 3470). A 1 L sample of the finished lubricant to be qualified and used for this test shall be provided to the qualifying activity (see 7.4) at the time of qualification.

4.4.2.2 Compatibility—The oils shall be compatible with oils previously qualified under MIL-PRF-2104, MIL-L-21260, and MIL-L-46167. The oils shall show no evidence of separation when they are tested against selected reference oils in accordance with 5.1.2, Table 3 (FED-STD-791, Method 3470).

4.4.3 OXIDATION AND WEAR PROTECTION CHARACTERISTICS—The oils shall protect internal loaded engine components against excessive wear and oxidation. Satisfactory performance in this respect shall be demonstrated when the oils are tested according to multiple test criteria and rated in accordance with 5.1.2, Table 3 (ASTM D 5533) and exhibit test results (single or average) meeting the criteria in Table 4:

TABLE 2—FINISHED OIL REQUIREMENTS

Property	SAE Grade 10W	SAE Grade 30	SAE Grade 40	SAE Grade 15W-40
Kinematic viscosity, cSt,				
@ 100 °C min.	5.6	9.3	12.5	12.5
max.	<7.4	<12.5	<16.3	<16.3
@ 40 °C[(1)]	X	X	X	X
Viscosity apparent, cP @ °C[(2)]				
min.	3500@–25	—	—	3500@–20
max.	3500@–20	—	—	3500@–15
High-temperature/high-shear viscosity, min.	X	2.9	3.7	3.7
Pumpability, 60 000 cP, max. @ temperature, °C	–30	—	—	–25
Viscosity index, min.	X	80	80	X
Pour point, °C, max.	–30	–18	–15	–25
Stable pour point, °C, max.[(3)]	–30	—	—	–25
Flash point, °C, min.	205	220	225	215
Evaporative loss, %	18	—	—	15
Other properties[(1)]				
Gravity	X	X	X	X
Carbon residue	X	X	X	X
Sulfur	X	X	X	X
Sulfated ash	X	X	X	X
Total acid number	X	X	X	X
Base number	X	X	X	X
Phosphorus	X	X	X	X
Nitrogen	X	X	X	X
Metallic components	X	X	X	X

1. Value shall be reported ('X' indicated report).
2. Report the measured apparent viscosity for grades 10W and 18W-40 oils at the minimum and maximum temperatures.
3. After being coled down to its pour point, the oil shall regain its homogeneity on standing at a temperature not more than 6 °C above the pour point. However, it should not exceed the indicated limits.

4.4.4 ROLLER FOLLOWER WEAR TEST ASTM D 5966—The oils shall protect internal loaded diesel engine components against excessive wear caused by the presence of soot. Satisfactory performance in this respect shall be demonstrated when the oils are tested according to multiple test criteria and rated in accordance with 5.1.2, Table 3 (6.2 L test) and exhibit averaged test results meeting the criteria in Table 5:

4.4.5 BEARING CORROSION AND SHEAR STABILITY

4.4.5.1 Bearing Corrosion—The oils shall be non-corrosive to alloy bearings. Satisfactory performance in this respect shall be demonstrated when the oils are tested in accordance with 5.1.2, Table 3 (ASTM D 5119) and exhibit test results meeting the criteria in Table 6:

4.4.5.2 Shear Stability—SAE 15W-40 grade oil shall demonstrate shear stability by exhibiting a viscosity at 100 °C of 13.0 cSt minimum, on any of the samples taken, when tested in accordance with 5.1.2.2.

4.4.6 RING-STICKING, WEAR, AND ACCUMULATION OF DEPOSITS—The oils shall prevent the sticking of piston rings and port clogging, and shall minimize the wear of cylinders, rings and loaded engine components such as cam shaft lobes, cam followers, valve rocker arms, rocker arm shafts, and the oil pump and fuel injection pump drive gears.

4.4.6.1 Four-Stroke Cycle Diesel Engine—Low Sulfur Fuel—Satisfactory performance shall be demonstrated when the oils that meet the criteria of 5.1.1.7 are tested with low-sulfur fuel and rated in accordance with 5.1.2, Table 3 (Caterpillar 1N) and exhibit test results meeting the following criteria: (Only one test is required. However, the test limits are adjusted according to the number of tests submitted and equivalency to original limits.) See Table 7.

4.4.6.2 Four-Stroke Cycle Diesel Engine—Higher Sulfur Fuel—Satisfactory performance shall be demonstrated when the oils are tested with higher-sulfur fuel and rated in accordance with 5.1.2, Table 3 (Caterpillar 1M-PC) and exhibit test results meeting the following criteria: (Only one test is required, however, when three or more tests are run, one test may be discarded and the average calculated from the remaining test results. This average result must meet the criteria in Table 8.

4.4.6.3 Two-Stroke Cycle Diesel Engine—Satisfactory performance shall be demonstrated when the oils are tested and rated in accordance with 5.1.2, Table 3 (ASTM D 5862) and exhibit test results meeting the criteria in Table 9: (Only one test is required. However, if more than one test is run, the test limits are adjusted according to the number of tests run, maximum of three tests, and equivalency to original limits.)

4.4.7 FRICTION RETENTION CHARACTERISTICS AND WEAR—The oils shall maintain a stable coefficient of friction and shall minimize distress and wear during use in power shift transmissions and other cooled friction compartments or hydraulic systems such as steering and disconnect clutches.

4.4.7.1 Slip Time and Torque—Satisfactory performance shall be demonstrated when the oils are tested and rated in accordance with 5.1.2, Table 3 (ATD C-4) and exhibit test results meeting the nominal criteria in Table 10, as adjusted to accommodate slight changes in individual friction plate batches:

4.4.7.2 Friction Coefficient and Wear—Satisfactory performance shall be demonstrated when the oils are tested and rated in accordance with 5.1.2, Table 3 (Caterpillar VC 70) and a test on each sequence exhibit results meeting the nominal criteria in Table 11 as adjusted to accommodate slight changes in individual fluoroelastomer batches and performance of the reference oil:

TABLE 3—TEST METHODS

Test	Test Methods FED-STD-791	Test Methods ASTM	Test Methods SAE
Viscosity, Kinematic		D 445	
Viscosity, Apparent(1)			J300
High Temperature/High Shear		D 4624, D 4683(2), D 4741	
Viscosity Index		D 2270	
Pour Point		D 97(2), D 5950	
Stable Pour Point	203		
Pumpability		D 4684	
Flash Point		D 92	
Evaporative Loss		D 5480(2), D 5800	
Gravity, API		D 287	
Carbon Residue		D 524	
Color		D 1500	
Acid Number		D 664	
Base Number		D 2896, D 4739(2)	
Phosphorus		D 1091(2), D 4047, D 4927, D 4951, D 5185	
Chlorine		D 808(2), D 1317	
Sulfur		D 129, D 1552(2), D 2622, D 4294, D 4927, D 4951, D 5185	
Nitrogen		D 3228(2), D 4629	
Saponification Number		D 94	
Sulfated Residue		D 874	
Boiling Range Distribution		D 2887	
Metallic Components		D 4628, D 4927, D 4951(2), D 5185	
Foaming		D 892	
Engine Oil Aeration		HEUI	
Stability and Compatibility	3470(3)		
Oxidation and Wear Characteristics		D 5533 (III E)	
Dispersancy Characteristics		D 5967 (Mack T-8)	
Bearing Corrosion and Shear Stability		D 5119 (L-38)	
Ring-Sticking, Wear, and Deposits			
Four-Stroke Cycle Diesel Engine-LS		Caterpillar 1N	
Four-Stroke Cycle Diesel Engine-HS		Caterpillar 1M-PC	
Two-Stroke Cycle Diesel Engine		D 5862 (DDC 6V92TA)	
Friction Retention Characteristics and Wear:			
Slip Time and Wear		ATD C-4(4)	
Friction Coefficient and Wear		Caterpillar VC-70(5)	
Seal Compatibility		ATD C-4(6)	
Metal Corrosion	5308		
Copper Corrosion		D 130	
Roller Follower Wear Test		D 5966	

1. Obtain the apparent viscosity using the method of test set forth by SAE J300.
2. Denotes preferred method.
3. See 5.1.2.1 for clarifying instructions.
4. Use procedure described in item 8 and 9 of C-4 specification.
5. Use test SEQs 1220 and FRRET (VC-70) described in the Caterpillar TO-4 specification.
6. Use procedure in item 5 of C-4 specification.

TABLE 4—ASTM D 5533 LIMITS (III E)

Average Rating at 64 h	1 test	2 Tests	3 Tests
Viscosity increase, Hours to 375% avg max	67.5	65.1	64.0
Oil ring land deposits, avg. min	2.6	2.6	2.6
Piston skirt varnish, avg. min	8.7	8.7	8.7
Sludge, avg. min	9.0	9.0	9.0
Stuck rings, avg. max	None	None	None
Stuck lifter, avg max	None	None	None
Scuffing and wear at 64 h			
Cam or lifter scuffing	None	None	None
Cam plus lifter wear, µm			
Average (avg max.)	64	64	64
Maximum (Avg)	145	145	145

TABLE 5—ASTM D 5966 LIMITS (ROLLER FOLLOWER WEAR TEST)

	1 Test	2 Test	3 Test
Pin Wear, µm, avg. max.	11.4	12.4	12.7
mils, avg. max	0.45	0.49	0.50

TABLE 6—ASTM D 5119 LIMITS (L-38)

	1 Test	2 Test	3 Test
Bearing weight loss, milligrams (max.)	43.7	48.1	50.0

TABLE 7—1N TEST LIMITS

	1 Test	2 Tests	3 Tests
Top groove filling, % avg. max	20	23	25
WDN, demerits, avg. max	286	311.7	323.0
Top land heavy carbon, %, avg. max	3	4	5
Oil consumption, g/Kw-h, avg. max	0.5	0.5	0.5
Scuffing, piston-rings-liners, avg max	None	None	None
Stuck rings, avg. max	None	None	None

TABLE 8—1M-PC TEST LIMITS

Top groove filling, % max.	70
WTD, avg, max.	240
Ring Side Clearance Loss, mm, max	0.013
Piston Ring Sticking	None
Piston, Ring, and Liner Scuffing	None

TABLE 9—ASTM D 5862 (DDC 6V92TA)

	1 Test	2 Tests	3 Tests
Piston, average % area			
Skirts tin removed	Report	Report	Report
Wrist pin slipper bushing copper exposed	Report	Report	Report
Average ring face distress, demerits (max.)			
Fire ring, AVG	0.33	0.34	0.36
Nos. 2 and 3 compression rings, avg	0.28	0.29	0.30
Broken rings, avg	None	None	None
Cylinder liner area			
Average liner distress, % area (avg max.)	60.0	63.5	65.0
Port plugging, % area, (avg max.)			
Average	2	2	2
Single cylinder	5	5	5

TABLE 10—C-4 FRICTION TEST LIMITS

	Graphite 0-5500 cycles	Paper 0-10 000 cycles	Paper 10 000
Slip time at cycles, s (max.)	0.74	0.67	Report
Mid-point coefficient (min.)	0.097	0.080	Report

TABLE 11—VC-70 TEST Limits

	Sequence 1220	Sequence FRRET
Average dynamic coefficient, %	90-140	—
@ 3000 cycles	—	85-130
@ 8000 cycles	—	90-125
@ 15 000 cycles	—	90-125
@ 25 000 cycles	—	95-125
Average static coefficient, %	91-127	—
Disc wear, mm (max)	0.04	—
Energy limit, %	25	—

4.4.8 SEAL COMPATIBILITY—The oils shall minimize deterioration of seal and friction materials.

4.4.8.1 Effect on Seals—Satisfactory performance shall be demonstrated when the oils are tested and rated in accordance with 5.1.2, Table 3 (ATD C-4) and exhibits test results meeting the nominal criteria in Table 12, as adjusted to accommodate slight changes in individual elastomer batches:

TABLE 12—C-4 SEALS TEST LIMITS

Buna N:	
Volume changes, %	0 to +5
Hardness changes, points	0 ± 5
Polyacrylate:	
Volume changes, %	0 to +10
Hardness change, points	0 to +5
Silicone:	
Volume changes, %	0 to +5
Hardness changes, points	0 to −10
Fluoroelastomer:	
Volume changes, %	0 to +4
Hardness change, points	4 to +4
Ethyl Acrylic:	
Volume changes, %	+12 to +28
Hardness change, points	−6 to −18

4.4.9 DISPERSANCY CHARACTERISTICS—Satisfactory performance shall be demonstrated when the oils are tested and rated in accordance with 5.1.2, Table 3 ASTM D 5967 (Mack T-8) and exhibits test results meeting the criteria in Table 13:

TABLE 13—ASTM D 5967 TEST LIMITS (MACK T-8)

	1 test	2 test	3 test
Viscosity increase, cSt max			
from min. corrected to 3.8% Soot by TGA	11.5	12.5	13.0
Oil Consumption, gm/Bhp-h, max.	0.0005	0.0005	0.0005

4.4.10 METAL AND COPPER CORROSION

4.4.10.1 Metal Corrosion—Satisfactory performance shall be demonstrated when the oils are tested and rated in accordance with 5.1.2, Table 3 (Corrosion Bench Test ASTM D 5968) and exhibits test results meeting the following criteria:

a. Cu ppm max—20
b. Pb, ppm, max—60

4.4.10.2 Copper Corrosion, ASTM D 130—Satisfactory performance shall be demonstrated when the oils are rated in accordance with 5.1.2, Table 3 (Copper Corrosion, ASTM D 130). The copper coupons used in 4.4.10.1 shall be rated according to ASTM D 130 and the oil shall exhibit copper strip discoloration not exceeding ASTM No. 3 when compared to ASTM Copper Strip Corrosion Standard.

4.4.11 HEUI ENGINE OIL AERATION TEST—Satisfactory performance shall be demonstrated when the oils are tested in accordance with 5.1.2, Table 3 (HEUI) and exhibit test results meeting the following criteria:

a. HEUI A Foam Stability @ 20 h % max – 10

4.5 Other Requirements and Tolerances for Quality Conformance Testing—The following physical and chemical properties shall be tested in accordance with the appropriate methods listed in 5.1.2 to insure that purchased products are of the same compositions as the respective qualification samples and to identify the products. No specific values or limits are assigned in qualification testing, except as otherwise specified in Table 2 and 4.4.1 through 4.4.10.2, but test results shall be reported for all properties listed. The qualifying activity (see 7.4) shall establish specific values and tolerances for subsequent quality conformance testing of the finished lubricant for these properties (see 7.3 and 7.4):

a. Viscosity, apparent and kinematic
b. High-temperature/high-shear
c. Viscosity index
d. Pour point
e. Pumpability
f. Flash point
g. Gravity, API at 60 °F
h. Chlorine
i. Carbon residue
j. Foaming
k. Phosphorus
l. Sulfur
m. Sulfated ash
n. Metallic components
o. Nitrogen

5. Verification

5.1 Classification of Inspections—The inspection requirements specified herein are classified as follows:

a. Qualification inspections (see 5.1.1).
b. Conformance inspections (see 5.1.3).

5.1.1 QUALIFICATION INSPECTIONS—Qualification inspections consist of tests for all of the requirements specified in Section 4 and may be conducted in any plant or laboratory that follows the ASTM procedures and referencing requirements where appropriate. Qualification inspections shall be performed on each viscosity grade except as specified in 5.1.1.1 through 5.1.1.8.

5.1.1.1 Stable Pour-Point—The stable pour-point test (FED-STD-791, Method 203) shall be required only on SAE grades 10W and 15W-40 oils.

5.1.1.2 Shear Stability—Shear stability shall be required for only SAE 15W-40 grade oil.

5.1.1.3 Modified Formulations—SAE 40 grade oils based on the formulation of an SAE 30 grade oil qualified under this specification may be qualified in accordance with 4.4.1.

5.1.1.4 Oxidation and Wear Protection—The qualifying activity (see 7.4), may waive ASTM D 5533 testing of the candidate oil when acceptable supporting ASTM D 5533 wear evaluations for formulations similar in additive technology to the candidate lubricant are presented to substantiate the wear protection characteristics.

5.1.1.5 Ring-Sticking, Wear, and Accumulation of Deposits—The two-stroke cycle diesel engine test ASTM D 5862 (DDC 6V92TA) shall be required only for SAE grades 30, 40, and 15W-40 oils. Requirements for this test may be waived for oils formulated with a specific additive technology (detergent, dispersant, inhibitor system) provided satisfactory performance is demonstrated for the technology used in conjunction with various base stock-viscosity improver additive combinations. Satisfactory performance shall be demonstrated by conducting the following acceptable two-stroke cycle diesel engine tests:

a. One test each of three SAE 15W-40 grade oils formulated using the additive system, a viscosity index improver additive but with base stocks of different manufacture.
b. One test each of an SAE 15W-40 grade oil formulated using the additive system, a base stock employed in 5.1.1.5.a for each viscosity index improver additive to be used in conjunction with the additive system.

5.1.1.6 Friction Retention Characteristics and Wear—Test for friction retention characteristics and wear shall be required only for SAE grades 10W, 30, and 15W-40 oils. The qualifying activity (see 7.4) may waive testing for those requirements when acceptable supporting friction retention characteristics and wear evaluations for formulations similar in additive technology to the candidate lubricant are presented to substantiate these performance requirements.

The 1N test shall be required only on 15W/40.

5.1.1.7 Four-Stroke Cycle Diesel Engine (1N)—Low Sulfur Fuel

5.1.1.8 HEUI Engine Oil Aeration—The HEUI test shall be required only when a satisfactory sequence IV foam test (SEQ IV D892) is not available.

5.1.2 QUALIFICATION INSPECTION METHODS—Perform tests in accordance with Table 3 and with 5.1.2.1 through 5.1.2.2, as applicable.

5.1.2.1 Stability and Compatibility—Determine the stability and compatibility of the oils by the procedures for "Homogeneity and Miscibility" given in FED-STD-791, Method 3470, as explained in 5.1.2.1.1 and 5.1.2.1.2. The procedures in 5.1.2.1.1 and 5.1.2.1.2 should be performed at the same time.

5.1.2.1.1 Stability—Determine the stability by subjecting an unmixed sample of oil to the prescribed cycle of temperature changes, then examine the sample for conformance to the requirements of 4.4.2.1. Record the test results on a copy of the "Homogeneity and Miscibility Test" form in the column marked "None".

5.1.2.1.2 Compatibility—Determine the compatibility of the oil with other oils previously qualified under MIL-L-2104, MIL-L-21260, and MIL-L-46167 by subjecting separate mixtures of the oil with selected reference oils designated by the qualifying activity (see 7.4) to the prescribed cycle of temperature changes, then examine the mixtures for conformance to the requirements of 4.4.2.2. Record the test results on the same copy of the "Homogeneity and Miscibility test" form (see 5.1.2.1) in the appropriate columns marked "1-30", "2-30", etc. Reference oils for conducting compatibility tests are to be obtained from the SAE, 400 Commonwealth Drive, Warrendale, PA 15096.

5.1.2.2 Shear Stability—Determine the shear stability of SAE 15W-40 grade oil by the following method:

a. Weigh 25 g of used oil, obtained every 10 h of testing in accordance with ASTM D 5119.
b. Filter the sample through a 0.5 µm filter pad.
c. Determine the kinematic viscosity at 100 °C of the filtered sample using ASTM D 445. Check the resulting viscosity for conformance to the requirements of 4.4.5.2.

5.1.3 CONFORMANCE INSPECTIONS—Inspections for conformance of individual lots (see 7.5) shall consist of tests for the following requirements using the test method listed in Table 3. The results obtained when using the test methods in Table 3 must fall within the tolerances/specific values (see 4.1.3 and 7.3) assigned at time of qualification:

a. Viscosities
b. High-temperature/high-shear
c. Viscosity index
d. Pour point
e. Pumpability
f. Flash point
g. Gravity, ° API
h. Carbon residue
i. Foaming
j. Phosphorus
k. Sulfur
l. Nitrogen
m. TAN
n. TBN
o. Sulfated ash
p. Metallic components

5.2 Sampling

5.2.1 SAMPLING FOR THE EXAMINATION OF FILLED CONTAINERS—Take a random sample of filled containers from each lot in accordance with ANSI Z1.4 or ASQC Z1.4.

5.2.2 SAMPLING FOR TESTS—Take samples from bulk or packaged lots (see 7.5) for tests in accordance with ASTM D 4057 or D 4177, as appropriate.

5.3 Inspection—Perform inspection in accordance with FED-STD-791, Method 9601. In addition to the inspection, the manufacturer shall provide certification of non-carcinogenicity as specified in 4.2 (i.e., materials are not considered carcinogenic or potentially carcinogenic).

5.3.1 EXAMINATION OF FILLED CONTAINERS—Examine samples taken in accordance with 5.2.1 with regard to fill, closure, sealing, and leakage. Reject any container having one or more defects or under the required fill. If the number of defective or under filled containers exceeds the acceptance number for the appropriate sampling plan of ANSI Z1.4, reject the lot (see 7.5) represented by the sample.

6. Packaging

6.1 Packing—For acquisition purposes, the packaging requirements shall be as specified in the contract or order (see 7.2). When actual packaging of material is to be performed by DoD personnel, these personnel need to contact the responsible packaging activity to ascertain requisite packaging requirements. Packaging requirements are maintained by the inventory control point's packaging activity within the Military Department of Defense Agency, or within the Military Department's System Command. Packaging data retrieval is available from the managing Military Department's or Defense Agency's automated packaging files, CD-ROM products, or by contacting the responsible packaging activity.

6.2 Marking—Unless specified in the contract or order (see 7.2), marking shall be in accordance with MIL-STD-129.

7. General Requirements

7.1 Intended Use—The SAE 10W (OE/HDO-10) grade oil is not to be used in high-output, two-cycle compression-ignition engines. The lubricating oils, except as mentioned previously, covered by this specification are intended for the crankcase lubrication of reciprocating spark-ignition and compression-ignition engines used in all types of military combat/tactical ground equipment and for the crankcase lubrication of two-cycle, four-cycle, high-speed, high-output, supercharged compression-ignition engines used in all ground equipment. The oils are also intended for the same application in power transmissions, hydraulic systems, and non-hypoid gear units of engineer/construction equipment, materials handling equipment and combat/tactical ground equipment. The lubricating oils covered by this specification meet service classifications API CG-4, CF of SAE J183 and are intended for all conditions of operational service, as defined by appropriate lubrication orders, when temperatures are above –25 °C. Recommended ambient temperature ranges for specific grade oils are shown in Figure 1.

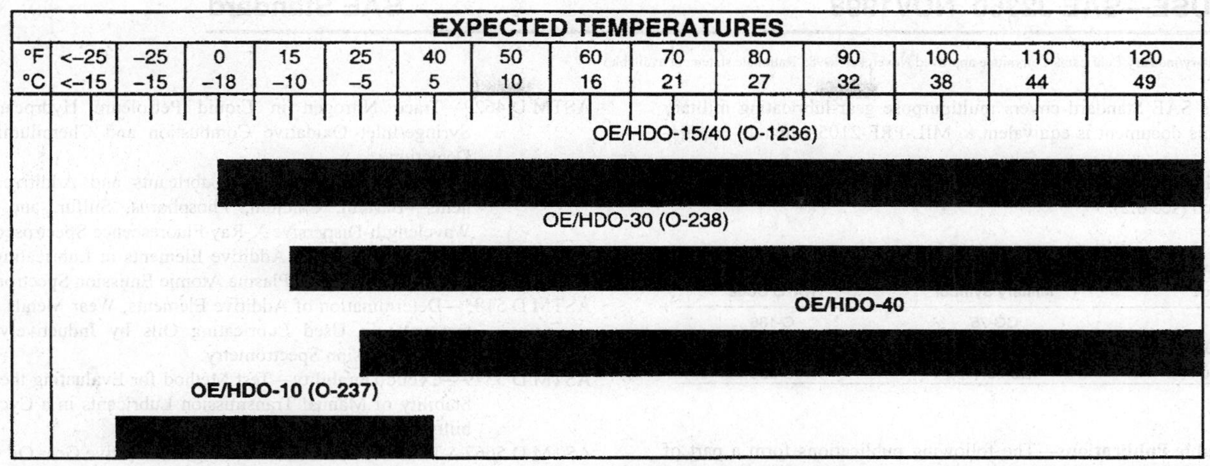

NOTE—For power transmission, hydraulic system, and nonhypoid gear box applications, lubricants may be used at all temperature above the low-temperature recommendation shown in Figure 1.

FIGURE 1—RECOMMENDED AMBIENT TEMPERATURE RANGES FOR USAGE OF ENGINE OILS

7.2 Acquisition Requirements—Acquisition documents should specify the following:

a. Title, number, and date of this specification.
b. Issue of DoDISS to be cited in the solicitation, and if required, the specific issue of individual documents referenced (see 2.1.1).
c. Military grade of oil required (see 1.1).
d. Certification of non-carcinogenicity (see 4.2).
e. Quantity of oil required.
f. Type and size of containers required (see 6.1).
g. Marking requirements (see 6.2).

7.3 Other Requirements and Tolerances for Conformance Inspections—Definite numerical values are not specified for certain of the physical and chemical properties listed in 4.5, and for which corresponding test methods are given in Section 5. Values of some properties vary from one brand of oil to another for the same grade. These values are influenced by the source of the base stock, the identities and quantities of additives, etc. Definite numerical values are not always functionally important except, for some properties, within specified maximum and minimum limits. It is not possible (or necessary) to assign restrictive values in the specification before the testing of qualification samples. During qualification, test values will be determined which are characteristics of a particular product and which can serve thereafter to identify the product. Using the results of qualification testing, the qualifying activity (see 7.4) can set values, including permissible tolerances, for future quality conformance testing.

7.4 Qualification—Lubricating oils covered under this standard must be submitted for qualification. Awards will be made only for products which are, at the time of contract award, qualified for inclusion in the applicable qualified products list whether or not such products have actually been so listed by that date. The attention of the contractors is called to this requirement, and manufacturers are urged to arrange to have the products that they propose to offer to the Federal Government tested for qualification in order that they may be eligible to be awarded contracts or orders for the products covered by this specification. The activity responsible for the qualified products list is the U. S. Army Tank Automotive and Armament Command, Attn: AMSTRA-TR-D/210, Warren, MI 48397-5000, and information pertaining to qualification of products may be obtained from that activity. Additionally, qualification information may be obtained by contacting the Performance Review Institute, Attn: Secretary of the LRI, 161 Thornhill Road, Warrendale, PA 15086, (724) 772-1616.

7.5 Part or Identifying Number (PIN)—The PINs to be used for oil acquired to this performance specification shall consist of; a "M" prefix and specification number, a single digit "Dash Number" taken from Figure 2 and Table 14 which indicates the container size, and the viscosity grade of the lubricant.

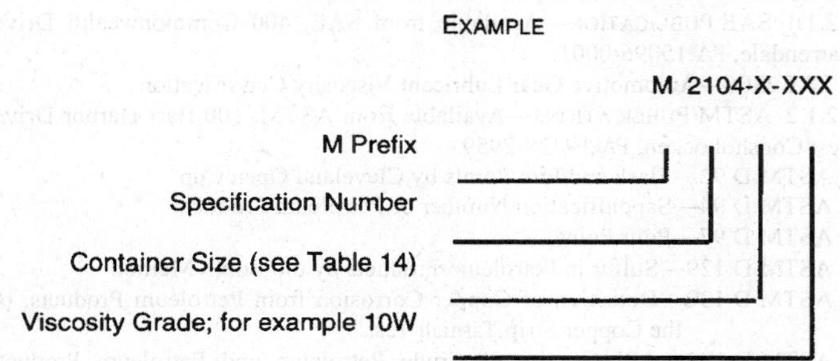

FIGURE 2—EXAMPLE OF PIN

TABLE 14—DASH NUMBER DESIGNATIONS FOR USE IN PIN NUMBERS

Dash number	Container size
1	946 mL (1-qt)
2	3.785 L (1-gal)
3	18.925 L (5-gal pail)
4	208.175 L (55-gal drum)

7.6 International Standardization Agreement—Certain provisions of this specification are subject of international standardization agreement STANAGs 2845 and 1135. When amendment, revision, or cancellation of this specification is proposed which would affect or violate the international agreement concerned, the preparing activity will take appropriate reconciliation action through international standardization channels, including departmental standardization office, if required.

7.7 Changes from Previous Issue—Marginal notations not used in this revision to identify changes with respect to the previous issue due to the extensiveness of the changes.

7.8 Key Words—Combat service, Heavy duty diesel, Internal combustion engine, Lubricating oil, Tactical service

LUBRICATING OIL, GEAR MULTIPURPOSE (METRIC) MILITARY USE—SAE J2360 NOV1998

SAE Standard

Report of the SAE Military/industry Lubricants Committee approved November 1998. Rationale statement available.

1. Scope—This SAE Standard covers multipurpose gear-lubricating military oils (see 6.1). This document is equivalent to MIL-PRF-2105 when all requirements are met.

1.1 Classification—The gear lubricating oils shall be of the following grades, as specified (see 6.2).

TABLE 1—VISCOSITY GRADES

SAE Grade	Military Symbol	NATO Code
75W	GO-75	O-186
80W-90	GO-80/90	O-226
85W-140	GO-85/140	O-228

2. References

2.1 Applicable Publications—The following publications form a part of this specification to the extent specified herein. Unless otherwise specified, the latest issue of SAE publications shall apply.

In the event of a conflict between the text of this specification and the references cited herein, (except for associated detail specifications, specifications sheets, or MS standards), the text of this specification shall take precedence. Nothing in this specification, however, shall supersede applicable laws and regulations unless a specific exemption has been obtained.

2.1.1 SAE PUBLICATION—Available from SAE, 400 Commonwealth Drive, Warrendale, PA 15096-0001.

SAE J306—Automotive Gear Lubricant Viscosity Classification

2.1.2 ASTM PUBLICATIONS—Available from ASTM, 100 Barr Harbor Drive, West Conshohocken, PA 19428-2959.

ASTM D 92—Flash and Fire Points by Cleveland Open Cup
ASTM D 94—Saponification Number of Petroleum Products
ASTM D 97—Pour Point
ASTM D 129—Sulfur in Petroleum Products by the Bomb Method
ASTM D 130—Detection of Copper Corrosion from Petroleum Products, by the Copper Strip Tarnish Test
ASTM D 287—API Gravity of Crude Petroleum and Petroleum Products (Hydrometer Method)
ASTM D 445—Kinematic Viscosity of Transparent and Opaque Liquids (Kinematic and Dynamic Viscosity)
ASTM D 524—Ramsbottom Carbon Residue of Petroleum Products
ASTM D 664—Standard Test Method for Acid Number of Petroleum Products by Potentiometric Titration
ASTM D 808—Chlorine in New and Used Petroleum Products (Bomb Method)
ASTM D 874—Sulfated Ash from Lubricating Oils and Additives
ASTM D 892—Foaming Characteristics of Lubricating Oils
ASTM D 893—Insolubles in Used Lubricating Oils
ASTM D 1091—Phosphorus in Lubricating Oils and Additives
ASTM D 1500—ASTM Color of Petroleum Products (ASTM Color Scale)
ASTM D 1552—Sulfur in Petroleum Products (High-Temperature Method)
ASTM D 2270—Calculating Viscosity Index from Kinematic Viscosity at 40 and 100 °C
ASTM D 2622—Sulfur in Petroleum Products (X-Ray Spectrographic Method)
ASTM D 2887—Boiling Range Distribution of Petroleum Fractions by Gas Chromatography
ASTM D 2983—Low-Temperature Viscosity of Automotive Fluid Lubricants Measured by Brookfield Viscometer
ASTM D 3228—Total Nitrogen in Lubricating Oils and Fuel Oils by Modified Kjeldahl Method
ASTM D 4047—Phosphorus in Lubricating Oils and Additives by Quinoline Phosphomolybdate Method
ASTM D 4057—Manual Sampling of Petroleum and Petroleum Products
ASTM D 4177—Automatic Sampling of Petroleum and Petroleum Products
ASTM D 4294—Sulfur in Petroleum Products by Non-Dispersive X-Ray Fluorescence Spectrometry
ASTM D 4628—Analysis of Barium, Calcium, Magnesium and Zinc in Unused Lubricating Oils by Atomic Absorption Spectrometry
ASTM D 4629—Trace Nitrogen in Liquid Petroleum Hydrocarbons by Syringe/Inlet Oxidative Combustion and Chemiluminescence Detection
ASTM D 4927—Elemental Analysis of Lubricants and Additive Components—Barium, Calcium, Phosphorus, Sulfur, and Zinc by Wavelength-Dispersive X-Ray Fluorescence Spectroscopy
ASTM D 4951—Determination of Additive Elements in Lubricating Oils by Inductively-Coupled Plasma Atomic Emission Spectrometry
ASTM D 5185—Determination of Additive Elements, Wear Metals and Contaminants in Used Lubricating Oils by Inductively-Coupled Plasma Emission Spectrometry
ASTM D 5579—Cyclic Durability—Test Method for Evaluating the Thermal Stability of Manual Transmission Lubricants in a Cyclic Durability Test
ASTM D 5662—Test Method for Determining Automotive Gear Oil Compatibility with Typical Oil Seal Elastomers
ASTM D 5704—Test Method for Evaluating the Thermal and Oxidative Stability of Lubricants used for Manual Transmissions and Final Drive Axles
ASTM D 5760—Standard Specifications for Peformance of Normal Transmission Gear Lubricants
ASTM D 6121—L-37 Test—Performance Test for Evaluating the Load Carrying Capacity of Automotive Gear Lubricants Under Conditions of Low Speed and High Torque
ASTM Special Technical Publication (STP) 512A including:
L-33 Test—Performance Test for Evaluating the Moisture Corrosion Tendencies of Automotive Gear Lubricants
L-42 Test—Performance Test for Evaluating the Load Carrying Capacity of Automotive Gear Lubricants Under Conditions of High Speed Shock Loading

2.1.3 DEPARTMENT OF LABOR (OSHA)—Available from OSHA Publication Office, Room S-4203, 200 Constitution Avenue, NW, Washington, DC 20210.

OSHA 29 CFR 1910.1200—Hazard Communication Interpretation Regarding Lubricating Oils

2.1.4 GOVERNMENT DOCUMENTS

2.1.4.1 Federal and Military—Available from U.S. Army Tank Automotive and Armament Commands, Attn: AMSTA-TR-D/210, Warren, MI 48397-5000.

FED-STD-791—Lubricants, Liquid Fuels and Related Products; Methods of Testing
FED-STD-313—Material Safety Data Sheets Preparation and the Submission of
MIL-PRF-2105—Lubricating Oil Gear Mulitpurpose Metric
MIL-STD-105—Sampling Procedures and Table for Inspection by Attributes
MIL-STD-290—Packaging of Petroleum and Related Products
NATO STANAG 1135
NATO STANAG 2845

3. Requirements

3.1 Qualification

3.1.1 QUALIFICATION—GENERAL—Gear oils furnished under this specification shall be products which are qualified for listing on the applicable qualified products list at the time for opening of bids (see 4.5.1 and 6.4).

3.1.2 COMPANION LUBRICANTS—When companion gear lubricants in grades SAE 80W-90 and SAE 85W-140 are submitted for qualification, testing prescribed in 3.4.7 is not required on the SAE 85W–140 Grade, provided the additive type and concentration used, base stock source and refining treatment are identical for both products. Additionally, testing prescribed in 3.4.9 is required only on the grade with the poorer carbon varnish rating result in the ASTM D 5704 (L-60-1) test.

3.1.3 QUALIFICATION PERIOD—Each grade of oil which satisfies all the requirements of this specification will be qualified for a period not to exceed five years from the date of its original qualification. The qualification period for each grade SAE 85W-140 oil qualified in accordance with 3.1.2 shall not exceed that of the companion grade SAE 80W-90 product used in the qualification procedure.

3.1.4 REQUALIFICATION—When the qualification period has expired, each product must be requalified if the supplier wishes to maintain the formulation as a current product and be eligible to bid on prospective procurements. If a product is submitted for requalification and there has been no change in the specification requirements, the qualifying activity may, at its discretion, waive complete retesting or require only partial retesting of the product to determine its continued acceptability. Whenever there is a change in the base stock, refining treatment, or additives used in the formulation, requalification will be required. When the proposed changes are minor and may not be expected to significantly affect performance, the qualifying activity may, at its discretion, waive complete requalification or may require only partial requalification in order to determine the significance and acceptability of the proposed changes.

3.1.5 TOLERANCES—The gear oil supplied under contract shall be identical, within permissible tolerances assigned by the qualifying activity, to the product receiving qualification. The values resulting after application of tolerances shall fall within the maximum and minimum limits specified herein (see Table 2 and 3.4.1 through 3.4.10).

3.1.6 MATERIAL SAFETY DATA SHEETS—When applying for qualification, the manufacturer shall submit to the qualifying activity (see 6.4) a sample of the product tested and include material safety data sheets prepared in accordance with FED-STD-313 and OSHA 29 CFR 1910.1200. When FED-STD-313 is at variance with the CFR, 29 CFR 1910.1200 shall take precedence, modify and supplement FED-STD-313.

TABLE 2—FINISHED OIL REQUIREMENTS

Property[1]	SAE 75W	SAE 80W-90	SAE 85W-140
Viscosity	Per SAE J306	Per SAE J306	Per SAE J306
Channel Point, °C, max	–45	–35	–20
Flash Point, °C, min	150	165	180
Gravity, API	X	X	X
Viscosity Index	X	X	X
Pour Point, °C	X	X	X
Pentane Insolubles, % wt	X	X	X
Sulfur, % wt	X	X	X
Phosphorus, % wt	X	X	X
Nitrogen, % wt	X	X	X
Boron, % wt	X	X	X
Zinc, % wt	X	X	X
Potassium, % wt	X	X	X
Chlorine, % wt	X	X	X
Organo-metallic components, % wt	X	X	X

1. Values shall be reported for all requirements (X indicates report).

3.2 Materials—The gear lubricating oil shall be derived from petroleum fractions, synthetically prepared compounds or a combination of the two types of products. They may be virgin or rerefined stocks or combination thereof. The stocks shall be compounded with such functional additives (extreme pressure agents, corrosion inhibitors, friction modifiers, etc.) as are necessary to meet the performance requirements specified in this standard. The stocks used shall not be considered carcinogenic or potentially carcinogenic as defined under the Hazardous Communication Standard OSHA 29 CFR 1910.1200.

3.2.1 POUR POINT DEPRESSANTS—Not more than 2.0% (by volume) of any type of pour point depressant or combination thereof is allowed in the final formulation.

3.3 Physical and Chemical Requirements

3.3.1 REQUIREMENTS FOR FINISHED OIL—The oils shall conform to the requirements specified in Table 2 and 3.4.1 through 3.4.10.

3.3.2 REQUIREMENTS FOR BASE STOCK—A one liter sample of each base stock component used in formulating the finished oil, accompanied by the following property data, shall be submitted to the qualifying activity (see 6.4) at the time of qualification. Annually thereafter, a one liter production sample of each base stock component used in formulating the finished oil, accompanied by the property data, shall be submitted to the qualifying activity.

a. Viscosity, Kinematic
   at 100 °C, centistokes (mm^2/s)
   at 40 °C, centistokes (mm^2/s)
b. Viscosity Index
c. Gravity, °API
d. Flash point, °C
e. Pour point, °C
f. Carbon residue, mass %
g. Sulfated ash, mass %
h. Saponification number
i. Elemental content, mass %
j. Nitrogen, mass %
k. Chlorine, mass %
l. Sulfur, mass %
m. Color
n. Boiling point, °C at 1%, 5%, 10%, 50% & 90% points
o. Total acid number

3.4 Performance Requirements—The oils shall conform to the requirements specified in 3.4.1 through 3.4.10.

3.4.1 CHANNEL POINT—The gear oil shall be non-channeling at the temperature indicated by Table 2 when tested in accordance with Table 3 (method 3456, FED-STD-791).

3.4.2 FOAMING—All grades of oil shall demonstrate the following foaming characteristics when tested in accordance with 4.6, Table 3 (ASTM D 892).

a. Initial test at 24 °C ± 0.5 °C—Not more than 20 mL of foam shall remain immediately following the 5-min blowing period.
b. Intermediate test at 93.5 °C ± 0.5 °C—Not more than 50 mL of foam shall remain immediately following the 5-min blowing period.
c. Final test at 24 °C ± 0.5 °C—Not more than 20 mL of foam shall remain immediately following the 5-min blowing period.

3.4.3 STORAGE STABILITY—The gear oil shall demonstrate the following characteristics for separated solid material, liquid material, or a combination of the two materials when tested in accordance with 4.6, Table 3 (Method 3440, FED-STD-791).

TABLE 3—TEST METHOD

Test	ASTM Test Method	FED-STD-791 Method No.
Viscosity, Kinematic	D 445	
Viscosity, Apparent	D 2983	
Viscosity, Index	D 2270	
Channel Point		3456
Flash Point	D 92	
Gravity, API	D 287	
Pour Point	D 97	
Pentane Insolubles	D 893	
Carbon Residue	D 524	
Color	D 1500	
Total Acid Number	D 664	
Saponification Number	D 94	
Boiling Range Distribution	D 2887	
Sulfated Ash	D 874	
Sulfur	D 1552[1], D 2622, D 129, D 4294 D 4927, D 4951, D 5185	
Phosphorus	D 1091[1], D 4047, D 4927, D 4951, D 5185	
Chlorine	D 808	
Nitrogen	D 3228[1], D 4629	
Metallic Components	D 4628, D 4927, D 4951[1] D 5185	
Foaming	D 892	
Storage Stability		3440
Compatibility[2]		3430
Copper Corrosion	D 130	
Moisture Corrosion[3]	L-33	
Thermal and Oxidative Stability[3] and Deposition Characteristics	D 5704 (L-60-1)	
Gear Scoring[3],[4]	L-42	
Gear Distress and Deposits[3]	D 6121 (L-37)	
Cyclic Durability	D 5579 (Mack Cyclic Durability)	
Elastomer Compatibility	D 5662	

1. Denotes preferred method.
2. See 4.6.1.
3. In accordance with ASTM STP 512A.
4. See 4.6.2.

3.4.3.1 Solid Material—When the separated material is solid, the average increase in the weight of each centrifuge tube and residue over the initial weight of the clean tube shall not exceed 0.25 mass percent of the additive material originally contained in the sample.

3.4.3.2 Liquid Material—When the separated material is liquid, it shall not exceed 0.50 volume percent of the additive material originally contained in the sample.

3.4.4 COMPATIBILITY—The gear oil shall be compatible with other gear lubricants previously qualified under this specification or MIL-PRF-2105 and/or MIL-L-2105 when tested against selected reference oils in accordance with 4.6, Table 3 (Method 3430, FED-STD-791) and 4.6.1.

3.4.5 MOISTURE CORROSION—The oil shall prevent or minimize corrosion to gear unit components in the presence of moisture. Satisfactory performance shall be demonstrated when the oil is tested in accordance with 4.6, Table 3 (ASTM STP 512A, L-33 Test) and exhibits test results of one percent or less rust on the test cover plate and no rust on gear teeth, bearings, and functional components.

3.4.6 THERMAL AND OXIDATIVE STABILITY—The oil shall resist thermal and chemical oxidation. Satisfactory performance shall be demonstrated when the oil is tested in accordance with 4.6, Table 3 (ASTM D 5704, L-60-1 Test) for 50 h and meets the criteria in Table 4. A maximum of three tests may be conducted. If more than one test is conducted, the average of any two test results must meet the limits described in Table 4, and the results from the third test, if conducted, may be excluded.

TABLE 4—ASTM D 5704, L-60-1 TEST LIMITS

Parameters	Limits
Kinematic Viscosity Increase %, @100 °C, cSt	100 max
N-Pentane Insolubles, wt %	3.0 max
Toluene Insolubles, wt %	2.0 max
Carbon/Varnish Rating	7.5 min
Sludge Rating	9.4 min

3.4.7 LOAD-CARRYING, EXTREME-PRESSURE, AND DEPOSITION CHARACTERISTICS—The oil shall prevent or minimize gear distress and lubricant deposits under conditions of high-speed and shock-loading and conditions of high-speed, low-torque and low-speed, high-torque operation.

3.4.7.1 Gear Scoring—Satisfactory performance shall be demonstrated when the oil is tested in duplicate in accordance with 4.6, Table 3 (ASTM STP 512A, L-42 Test) and exhibits scoring less than or equal to Reference Oil TMC 114, or most recent approved blend, under conditions of high-speed and shock-loading.

3.4.7.2 Gear Distress and Deposits—Satisfactory performance shall be demonstrated when the oil is tested in accordance with 4.6, Table 3 (ASTM D 6121, L-37 Test) using untreated and phosphate-treated gear assemblies and prevents gear-tooth ridging, rippling, pitting, welding, spalling, and excessive wear or other surface distress and objectionable deposits and does not produce excessive wear, pitting or corrosion of bearing rollers, or races under conditions of high-speed, low-torque and low-speed, high-torque and meets the criteria in Table 5.

TABLE 5—ASTM D 6121, L-37 TEST LIMITS

Category	ASTM Rating	Comments
Ridging	8 or greater	Compare overall appearance to closest gear on rating board
Rippling	8 or greater	Same as above
Wear	5 or greater	Same as above
Spalling/ Pitting	9.3 or greater	At heel end of pinion tooth only—elsewhere not allowed
Scoring	10	Not allowed

3.4.8 COPPER CORROSION—The oil shall minimize copper corrosion. Satisfactory performance shall be demonstrated when the oil is tested in accordance with 4.6, Table 3 (ASTM D 130) for 3-h at 121 °C ± 1 °C and exhibits copper strip discoloration not exceeding ASTM No. 2a when compared to ASTM Copper Strip Corrosion Standard.

3.4.9 CYCLIC DURABILITY—Satisfactory performance shall be demonstrated when the oil is tested in accordance with 4.6, Table 3 (ASTM D 5579, Cyclic Durability). The number of tests conducted shall be in accordance with Section 6.3 of ASTM D 5760. The test evaluates the thermal stability of gear lubricants when subjected to cyclic operating conditions of high-low range and high temperature. The oil shall avoid deteriorating the synchronizer performance by preventing two unsynchronized shifts from occurring at cycles equal to or lower than the mean of the prior five passing reference oil results in the same test stand.

3.4.10 ELASTOMER COMPATIBILITY—The gear lubricants shall minimize deterioration of elastomer materials. Satisfactory performance shall be demonstrated when the oils are tested and rated in accordance with 4.6, Table 3 (ASTM D 5662, Elastomer Compatibility) and exhibit test results meeting the nominal criteria in Table 6 as adjusted to accommodate slight changes in individual elastomer batches:

TABLE 6—ASTM D 5662 ELASTOMER COMPATIBLITY TEST LIMITS

Parameters	Minimum	Maximum
Polyacrylate @150 °C, 240 h:		
Elongation Change, %	No limit	−60
Hardness Change, points	−35	+5.0
Volume Change, %	−5	+30
Fluoroelastomer @ 150 °C, 240 h		
Elongation Change, %	No limit	−75
Hardness Change, points	−5	+10
Volume Change, %	−5	+15

3.5 Other Requirements and Tolerances for Quality Conformance Testing—The following physical and chemical properties shall be tested in accordance with the appropriate methods listed in 4.6 to ensure that purchased products are of the same compositions as the respective qualification samples and to identify the products. No specific values or limits are assigned in qualification testing, except as otherwise specified in Table 2 and 3.4.1 through 3.4.10, but test results shall be reported for all properties listed. The qualifying activity (see 6.4) shall establish specific values and tolerances for subsequent quality conformance testing of the finished lubricant for these properties (see 6.3 and 6.4):

a. Viscosity
b. Viscosity Index
c. Pour point
d. Flash point
e. Gravity, °API
f. Channel point
g. Copper corrosion
h. Pentane insolubles
i. Sulfur
j. Phosphorus
k. Nitrogen
l. Chlorine
m. Boron
n. Potassium
o. Zinc
p. Metallic components

4. *Quality Assurance Provisions*

4.1 Responsibility for Inspection—Unless otherwise specified in the contract or purchase order, the contractor is responsible for the performance of all inspection requirements as specified herein. Except as otherwise specified in the contract or purchase order, the contractor may use his own or any other facilities suitable for the performance of the inspection requirements specified herein, unless disapproved by the Government. The Government reserves the right to perform any of the inspections set forth in the specification where such inspections are deemed necessary to assure supplies and services conform to prescribed requirements.

4.1.1 RESPONSIBILITY FOR COMPLIANCE—All items must meet all requirements of Sections 3 and 5. The inspection set forth in this specification shall become a part of the contractor's overall inspection system or quality program. The absence of any inspection requirements in the specification shall not relieve the contractor of the responsibility of assuring that all products or supplies submitted to the Government for acceptance comply with all requirements of the contract. Sampling in quality conformance does not authorize submission of known defective material, either indicated or actual, nor does it commit the Government to acceptance of defective material.

4.2 Lot

4.2.1 BULK LOT—A bulk lot is an indefinite quantity of a homogeneous mixture of one grade of oil offered for acceptance in a single, isolated container; or manufactured in a single plant run (not to exceed 24 h), through the same processing equipment, with no change in the ingredient materials.

4.2.2 Packaged Lot—A packaged lot is an indefinite number of 55-gal drums or smaller unit containers of identical size and type, offered for acceptance, and filled with a homogeneous mixture of one grade of oil from a single, isolated container; or filled with a homogeneous mixture of one grade of oil, manufactured in a single plant run (not to exceed 24 h), through the same processing equipment, with no change in the ingredient materials.

4.3 Sampling

4.3.1 Sampling for the Examination of Filled Containers—Take a random sample of filled containers from each lot in accordance with MIL-STD-105, at inspection level II.

4.3.2 Sampling for Tests—Take samples from bulk or packaged lots for tests in accordance with ASTM D 4057 or D 4177.

4.4 Inspection—Perform inspection in accordance with Method 9601 of FED-STD-791.

4.4.1 Examination of Filled Containers—Examine samples taken in accordance with 4.3.1 for compliance with MIL-STD-290 with regard to fill, closure, sealing, and leakage. Reject any container having one or more defects or under the required fill. If the number of defective or underfilled containers exceeds the acceptance number for the appropriate sampling plan of MIL-STD-105, reject the lot represented by the sample.

4.5 Classification of Tests

a. Qualification tests (see 4.5.1).
b. Quality conformance tests (see 4.5.2).

4.5.1 Qualification Tests—Qualification tests consist of tests for all of the requirements specified in Section 3 and may be conducted in any plant or laboratory approved by the qualifying activity (see 6.4). These tests have been correlated with field performance. New lubricant technology must have demonstrated correlation with field performance for these tests to apply as required by the qualifying activity. The Lubricant Review Institute Procedures outline the requirements for field testing. Copies of these procedures may be obtained by contacting the Secretary of the LRI at the Performance Review Institute. Once correlation has been demonstrated, only the tests specified herein will be required for further qualification. In addition the manufacturer shall provide certification of noncarcinogenicity (i.e., materials are not considered carcinogenic or potentially carcinogenic) and shall provide material safety data sheets.

4.5.2 Quality conformance Tests—Tests for quality conformance of individual lots shall consist of tests for all of the requirements in Section 3, except for the following (see Table 3):

a. Requirements for base stocks
b. Storage stability
c. Compatibility
d. Moisture corrosion
e. Thermal oxidation stability
f. Load-carrying, extreme-pressure, and deposition characteristics
g. Cyclic Durability
h. Elastomer Compatibility

4.6 Test Methods—Perform tests in accordance with Table 3, 4.6.1, and 4.6.2.

4.6.1 Compatibility—Determine compatibility by subjecting separate mixtures of the oil with six selected reference oils designated by the qualifying activity to the procedure specified by method 3430 of FED-STD-791.

4.6.2 Gear Scoring—For grade SAE 75W oil, the L-42 gear scoring test shall be modified such that the sequence II (high-speed) portion of the test shall be commenced at a temperature of 79 °C and sequence IV (shock-loading) run with water sprays on commencing at 93 °C with a maximum rise of 5.5 to 8.3 °C.

4.7 Inspection of Packaging

4.7.1 Quality Conformance Inspection of Pack

4.7.1.1 Unit of Product—For the purpose of inspection, a complete pack prepared for shipment shall be considered a unit of product.

4.7.1.2 Inspection Lot—The inspection lot shall be as defined in 4.2 packed for shipment.

4.7.1.3 Sampling—Samples for examination of packaging shall be selected at random from each inspection lot in accordance with procedures prescribed in MIL-STD-105.

4.7.1.4 Examination—Samples selected in accordance with 4.7.1.3 shall be examined for the defects listed as follow:

a. 101—Unit container not as specified and not in accordance with the requirements of MIL-STD-290.
b. 102—Intermediate container when required, not as specified in MIL-STD-290.
c. 103—Quantity and arrangement of unit containers packed in intermediate containers not as specified in MIL-STD-290.
d. 104—Exterior container not as specified in MIL-STD-290.
e. 105—Quantity and arrangement of intermediate containers packed in exterior containers not as specified in MIL-STD-290.
f. 106—Marking not as specified in MIL-STD-290.

5. Packaging

5.1 Packing and Marking—Packing and marking shall be as specified by the procuring agency.

6. Notes—General Requirements

6.1 Intended Use—The gear lubricants covered by this specification exceed American Petroleum Institute (API) Service Classification GL-5 and MT-1 and are intended for automotive gear units, heavy-duty industrial type enclosed gear units, steering gear units, heavy-duty nonsynchronized class 7 and 8 heavy duty truck manual transmissions, and fluid lubricated universal joints of automotive equipment. The lubricants covered by this specification are intended for use as defined by appropriate lubrication orders when ambient temperatures are above –54 °C. Recommended ambient temperature ranges for use of specific viscosity grade lubricants are shown by Figure 1.

6.2 Ordering Data—Acquisition documents should specify the following information:

a. Title, number, and date of this specification.
b. Date of issue of DoDISS applicable to this contract and exceptions thereto.
c. Grade of oil required (see 1.1).
d. Quantity of oil required.
e. Type and size of containers required (see 5.1).
f. Level of packaging required (see 5.1).

6.3 Other Requirements and Tolerances for Quality Conformance Testing—Definite numerical values are not specified for certain of the physical and chemical properties listed in 3.5, and for which corresponding test methods are given in Section 4. Values of some properties vary from one commercial brand of oil to another for the same grade. These values are influenced by the source of the base stock, the identities and quantities of additives, etc. Definite numerical values are not always functionally important except, for some properties, within specified maximum and minimum limits. It is not possible (or necessary) to assign restrictive values in the specification before the testing of qualification samples. During qualification, test values will be determined which are characteristic of a particular product and which can serve thereafter to identify the product. Using the results of qualification testing, the qualifying activity (see 6.4) can set values, including permissible tolerances, for future quality conformance testing.

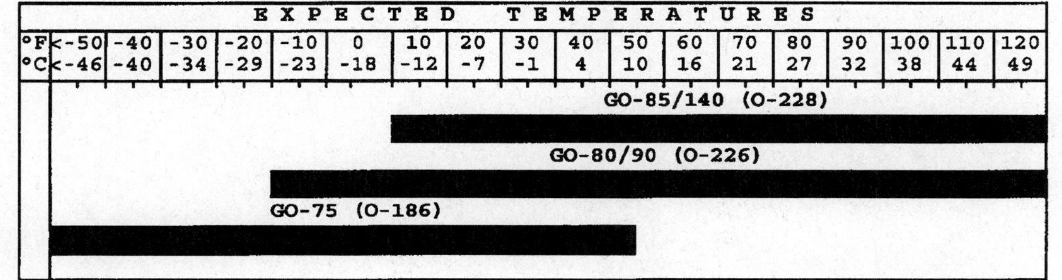

FIGURE 1—RECOMMENDED AMBIENT TEMPERATURE RANGES FOR USAGE OF GEAR LUBRICANTS

6.4 Qualification—Lubricating oils covered under this standard must be submitted for qualification. Awards will be made only for products which are at the time set for opening of bids, qualified for inclusion in the applicable qualified products list (QPL) whether or not such products have actually been so listed by that date. The attention of the contractors is called to these requirements, and manufacturers are urged to arrange to have the products that they propose to offer to the Federal Government tested for qualification in order that they may be eligible to be awarded contracts or purchase orders for the products covered by this specification. The activity responsible for the qualified products list is the US Army Tank Automotive and Armament Command, ATTN: AMSTA–TR–D/210, Warren, MI 48397-5000, and information pertaining to qualification of products may be obtained from this activity. Additionally, qualification information may be obtained by contacting the Performance Review Institute, Attn: Secretary of the LRI, 161 Thornhill Road, Warrendale, PA 15086, (724) 772-1616.

6.5 Material Safety Data Sheets—Contracting officers will identify those activities requiring copies of completed Material Safety Data Sheets prepared in accordance with 3.1.5. The pertinent government mailing addresses for submission of data are listed in appendix B of FED-STD-313.

6.6 Military Part Number—Gear lubricants furnished under this specification shall be identified by a military part number consisting of; a "M" prefix and specification number, a single digit "Dash Number" taken from Table 7 which indicates the container size, and the viscosity grade of the lubricant. The military part number from Grade 80W-90 lubricant to be furnished in 1-pt containers is shown in the example in Figure 2:

TABLE 7—DASH NUMBER DESIGNATIONS FOR USE IN MILITARY PART NUMBERS

Dash Number	Container size
1	1-pt
2	1-qt
3	1-gal
4	5-gal
5	55-gal drum
6	bulk

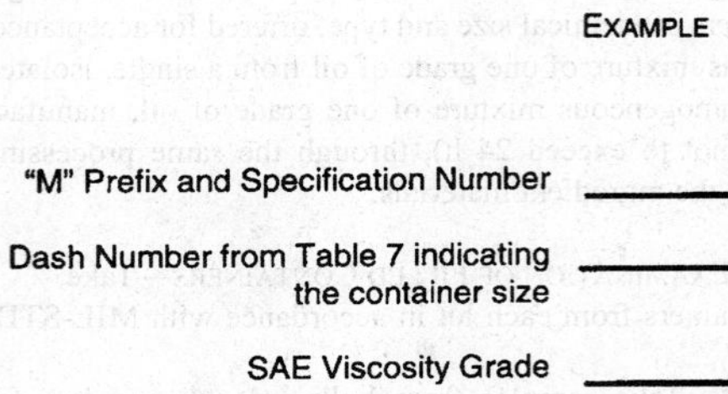

EXAMPLE

M2105-1- 80W90

"M" Prefix and Specification Number

Dash Number from Table 7 indicating the container size

SAE Viscosity Grade

FIGURE 2—EXAMPLE MILITARY PART NUMBER

6.7 Subject Term (Key Word) Listing

a. Axles
b. Gear
c. Heavy-Duty
d. Enclosed Gears
e. Steering Units
f. Non-Synchronized
g. Manual Transmissions

6.8 International Standardization Agreements—Certain provisions of this specification are the subject of international standardization agreements STANAGs 2845 and 1135. When amendment, revision, or cancellation of this specification is proposed which would affect or violate the international agreement concerned, the preparing activity will take appropriate reconciliation action through international channels, including departmental standardization offices, if required.

6.9 Changes from Previous Issue—Asterisks (or vertical lines) are not used in this revision to identify changes with respect to the previous issue due to the extensiveness of the changes.

LUBRICATING OIL, INTERNAL COMBUSTION ENGINE, PRESERVATION BREAK-IN—SAE J2361 NOV1998

SAE Standard

Report of the SAE Military/industry Lubricants Committee approved November 1998. Rationale statement available.

1. Scope—This SAE Standard covers military engine oils suitable for preservation, break-in, and lubrication of reciprocating internal combustion engines of both spark-ignition and compression-ignition types and of power transmission fluid applications in equipment used in combat/tactical service (see 7.1). This document is equivalent to MIL-L-21260 when all requirements are met.

1.1 Classification—The lubricating oils shall be of the following SAE viscosity grades (see 7.2):

TABLE 1—VISCOSITY GRADES

SAE Viscosity Grade	Military Symbol	NATO Code
10W	PR-10	C-640
30	PE-30	C-642
40	PE-40	—
15W-40	PE-15/40	—

2. References

2.1 Applicable Publications—The following publications form a part of this specification to the extent specified herein. Unless otherwise specified, the latest issue of SAE publications shall apply.

In the event of a conflict between the text of this document and the references cited herein, the text of this document takes precedence. Nothing in this document, however, supersedes applicable laws and regulations unless a specific exemption has been obtained.

2.1.1 SAE PUBLICATIONS—Available from SAE, 400 Commonwealth Drive, Warrendale, PA 15096-0001.

SAE J183—Engine Oil Performance and Engine Service Classification (Other than "Energy-Conserving")

SAE J300—Engine Oil Viscosity Classification

2.1.2 ALLISON TRANSMISSION DIVISION (ATD) PUBLICATION—Available from EG&G Stationary Testing, Attn: ATF/Specialty Lab (C-4), 5904 Bandera Road, San Antonio, TX 78283-1993.

TES-228—C-4 Fluid Specification

2.1.3 ANSI PUBLICATION—Available from ANSI, 11 West 42nd Street, New York, NY 10036-8002.

ANSI Z1.4—Sampling Procedures and Tables for Inspections by Attributes

2.1.4 AMERICAN SOCIETY FOR QUALITY CONTROL (ASQC) PUBLICATION—Available from American Society for Quality Control, 611 East Wisconsin Avenue, Milwaukee, WI 53201-4606.

ASQC Z1.4—Sampling Procedures and Tables for Inspections by Attributes

2.1.5 ASTM PUBLICATIONS—Available from ASTM, 100 Barr Harbor Drive, West Conshohocken, PA 19428-2959.

ASTM D 92—Flash and Fire Points by Cleveland Open Cup

ASTM D 94—Saponification Number of Petroleum Products

ASTM D 97—Pour Point of Petroleum Oils

ASTM D 129—Sulfur in Petroleum Products (General Bomb Method)

ASTM D 130—Detection of Copper Corrosion from Petroleum Products, by the Copper Strip Tarnish Test

ASTM D 287—API Gravity of Crude Petroleum and Petroleum Products (Hydrometer Method)

ASTM D 445—Kinematic Viscosity of Transparent and Opaque Liquids (and the Calculation of Dynamic Viscosity)

ASTM D 524—Ramsbottom Carbon Residue of Petroleum Products

ASTM D 664—Standard Test Method for Acid Number of Petroleum Products by Potentiometric Titration

ASTM D 808—Chlorine in New and Used Petroleum Products (Bomb Method)

ASTM D 874—Sulfated Ash from Lubricating Oils and Additives

ASTM D 892—Foaming Characteristics of Lubricating Oils

ASTM D 1091—Phosphorus in Lubricating Oils and Additives

ASTM D 1317—Chlorine in New and Used Lubricants (Sodium Alcoholate Method)

ASTM D 1500—ASTM Color of Petroleum Products (ASTM Color Scale)

ASTM D 1552—Sulfur in Petroleum Products (High-Temperature Method)

ASTM D 2270—Calculating Viscosity Index from Kinematic Viscosity at 40 and 100 C

ASTM D 2622—Sulfur in Petroleum Products (X-Ray Spectrographic Method)

ASTM D 2887—Boiling Range Distribution of Petroleum Fractions by Gas Chromatography

ASTM D 2896—Base Number of Petroleum Products by Potentiometric Perchloric Acid Titration

ASTM D 3228—Total Nitrogen in Lubricating Oils and Fuel Oils by Modified Kjeldahl Method

ASTM D 3951—Standard Practice for Commercial Packaging

ASTM D 4047—Phosphorus in Lubricating Oils and Additives by Quinoline Phosphomolybdate Method

ASTM D 4057—Manual Sampling of Petroleum and Petroleum Products

ASTM D 4177—Automatic Sampling of Petroleum and Petroleum Products

ASTM D 4294—Sulfur in Petroleum Products by Non-Dispersive X-Ray Fluorescence Spectrometry

ASTM D 4624—Measuring Apparent Viscosity by Capillary Viscometer at High Temperature and High-Shear Rates

ASTM D 4628—Analysis of Barium, Calcium, Magnesium, and Zinc in Unused Lubricating Oils by Atomic Absorption Spectrometry

ASTM D 4629—Trace Nitrogen in Liquid Petroleum Hydrocarbons by Syringe/Inlet Oxidative Combustion and Chemiluminescence Detection

ASTM D 4683—Measuring Viscosity at High Temperature and High Shear Rate by Tapered Bearing Simulator

ASTM D 4684—Determination of Yield Stress and Apparent Viscosity of Engine Oils at Low Temperature

ASTM D 4741—Measuring Viscosity at High Temperature and High Shear Rate by Tapered-Plug Viscometer

ASTM D 4927—Elemental Analysis of Lubricants and Additive Components - Barium, Calcium, Phosphorus, Sulfur, and Zinc by Wavelength-Dispersive X-Ray Fluorescence Spectroscopy

ASTM D 4951—Determination of Additive Elements in Lubricating Oils by Inductively Coupled Plasma Atomic Emission Spectrometry

ASTM D 4998—Evaluating Wear Characteristics of Tractor Hydraulic Fluids

ASTM D 5119—Evaluation of Automotive Engine Oils in the CRC L-38 Spark-Ignition Engine

ASTM D 5185—Determination of Additive Elements, Wear Metals and Contaminants in Used Lubricating Oils by Inductively-Coupled Plasma Atomic Emission Spectrometry

ASTM D 5480—Motor Oil Volatility by Gas Chromatography

ASTM D 5533—Evaluation of Automotive Engine Oils in the Sequence IIIE, Spark-ignition Engine

ASTM D 5800—Evaporation Loss of Lubricating Oils by the NOACK Method

ASTM D 5862—DDC 6V92TA Test Procedure

ASTM D 5966—Roller Follower Wear Test

ASTM D 5967—Evaluation of Diesel Engine Oils in the Mack T-8 Diesel Engine

ASTM D 5968—Corrosion Bench Test

ASTM Special Publication (STP) 315H includes:

Caterpillar 1M-PC Test Procedure—ASTM Research Report D02-1320

Caterpillar 1N Test Procedures—ASTM Research Report D02-1321

HEUI Engine Oil Aeration Test

2.1.6 CATERPILLAR INC., ENGINE DIVISION (CAT.) PUBLICATION—Available from Caterpillar, Component Development, Technical Center - C, P.O. Box 1875, Peoria, IL 61656-1875.

Caterpillar TO-4, Fluid Requirements, VC 70.

2.1.7 GOVERNMENT PUBLICATIONS

2.1.7.1 Military and Federal Publications—Available from the Standardization Documents Order Desk, Building 4D, 700 Robbins Avenue, Philadelphia, PA 19111-5094.

MIL-PRF-2104—Lubricating Oil, Internal Combustion Engine, Combat/Tactical Service

MIL-L-46167—Lubricating Oil, Internal Combustion Engine, Arctic

FED-STD-313—Material Safety Data, Transportation Data and Disposal Data for Hazardous Materials Furnished to Government Activities

FED-STD-791—Lubricants, Liquid Fuels and Related Products; Methods of Testing

NATO STANAG 1135

NATO STANAG 2845

2.1.7.2 U.S. Department of Labor (DOL) (OSHA)—Available from OSHA Publication Office, Room S-4203, 200 Constitution Avenue, NW, Washington, DC 20210.

OSHA 29 CFR 1910.1200—Hazard Communication; Interpretation Regarding Lubricating Oils

2.1.7.3 US Mobility Technology Center—Available from U.S. Army Tank Automotive and Armament Command, Attn: AMSTRA-TR-D/210, Warren, MI 48397-5000.

Guide for the Qualification of Engine and Gear Lubricants

3. Definitions

3.1 Bulk Lot—An indefinite quantity of a homogeneous mixture of one grade of oil offered for acceptance in a single, isolated container; or manufactured in a single plant run (not exceeding 24 h), through the same processing equipment, with no change in the ingredient materials.

3.2 Packaged Lot—An indefinite number of 208.175 L (55-gal drum) or smaller unit containers of identical size and type, offered for acceptance, and filled with a homogeneous mixture of one grade of oil from a single, isolated container; or filled with a homogeneous mixture of one grade of oil manufactured in a single plant run (not exceeding 24 h), through the same processing equipment, with no change in the ingredient materials.

4. Requirements

4.1 Qualification

4.1.1 QUALIFICATION—GENERAL—Qualification will be granted by the qualifying activity (see 7.4) to any manufacturer (original or reblender) of lubricating oils provided a "Manufacturing Facility Survey" (MFS) has been accepted as described in the "Guide for Qualification of Engine and Gear Lubricants". Each manufacturing facility intended for the manufacture of products under this specification shall have a MFS. This is a one time requirement provided there is no change in facilities, blending method or equipment. Companies requesting rebrand approvals do not need an MFS to be qualified. Engine lubricating oils furnished under this specification shall be products which are qualified for listing on the applicable qualified products list at the time of contract award (see 5.1.1 and 7.4). The qualifying activity (see 7.4) may waive complete qualification testing or may require only partial qualification testing of SAE 40 grade oil if the contractor states in a written affidavit that the product has been formulated with base stocks, refining treatment, and additives the same as those used in the formulation of SAE 30 grade oil qualified under this specification.

4.1.2 QUALIFICATION PERIOD—Each viscosity grade of oil which satisfies all the requirements of this specification shall be qualified for a period not exceeding four years from the date of its original qualification. The qualification period for each SAE 40 grade oil qualified in accordance with 4.1.1 shall not exceed that of the SAE 30 grade used in the qualification procedure. When the qualification period has expired, or whenever there is a change in the base stock, in the refining treatment or in the additives used in the formulation, each product must be retested if the contractor wishes to maintain the formulation as a qualified product and be eligible to bid on government solicitations for this material.

4.1.3 TOLERANCES—The engine lubricating oil supplied under contract shall have the same base stocks and additives components, at the appropriate concentrations, as when qualified. The finished oil properties shall fall within permissible tolerances assigned by the qualifying activity to the properties listed in 4.5, of the product receiving qualification. The values resulting after the application of tolerances shall not exceed the maximum nor fall below the minimum limits specified herein (see Table 2 and 4.4.1 through 4.4.14).

4.1.4 POUR-POINT DEPRESSANT—No changes shall be made in either the type or concentration of the pour-point depressant after qualification testing and approval unless:

a. The oil is retested for conformity to the pour-point, stable pour point, borderline pumping temperature and all viscosities (see Table 2).

b. The qualifying activity (see 7.4) is informed of the proposed change(s) and of the retesting.

c. The qualifying activity approves the proposed change(s) in writing.

4.1.5 MATERIAL SAFETY DATA SHEETS—When applying for qualification, the manufacturer shall submit to the qualifying activity (see 7.4) a sample of the product tested (see 4.4.2.1) with Material Safety Data Sheets prepared in accordance with FED-STD-313. When FED-STD-313 is at variance with the OSHA 29 CFR 1910.1200, the CFR shall take precedence, modify and supplement FED-STD-313.

4.2 Materials—The engine lubricating oils shall be derived from petroleum fractions, synthetically prepared compounds or a combination of the two types of products. They may be virgin, rerefined stocks, or a combination thereof. The stocks shall be compounded with such functional additives (detergents, dispersants, oxidation inhibitors, corrosion inhibitors, etc.) as are necessary to meet the specified requirements. The stocks used shall not be considered carcinogenic or potentially carcinogenic as defined under the Hazard Communication Standard OSHA 29 CFR 1910.1200.

4.3 Physical and Chemical Requirements

4.3.1 REQUIREMENTS FOR FINISHED OIL—The oils shall conform to the requirements specified in Table 2 and 4.4.1 through 4.4.14.

TABLE 2—FINISHED OIL REQUIREMENTS

Property	SAE Grade 10W	SAE Grade 30	SAE Grade 40	SAE Grade 15W-40
Kinematic viscosity, cSt,				
@ 100 °C min.	5.6	9.3	12.5	12.5
max.	<7.4	<12.5	<16.3	<16.3
@ 40 °C[1]	X	X	X	X
Viscosity apparent, cP @ °C[2]				
min	3500@−25	—	—	3500@−20
max	3500@−20	—	—	3500@−15
High-temperature/high-shear viscosity, min		2.9	3.7	3.7
Pumpability, 60 000 cP, max. @ temperature, °C	−30	—	—	−25
Viscosity index, min	X	80	80	X
Pour point, °C, max	−30	−18	−15	−25
Stable pour point, °C, max[3]	−30	—	—	−25
Flash point, °C, min	205	220	225	215
Evaporative loss, %	18	—	—	15
Other properties[1]				
Gravity	X	X	X	X
Carbon residue	X	X	X	X
Sulfur	X	X	X	X
Sulfated ash	X	X	X	X
Total acid number	X	X	X	X
Base number	X	X	X	X
Phosphorus	X	X	X	X
Nitrogen	X	X	X	X
Metallic components	X	X	X	X

1. Value shall be reported ("X" indicated report).
2. Report the measured apparent viscosity for grades 10W and 15W-40 oils at the minimum and maximum temperatures.
3. After being cooled down to its pour point, the oil shall regain its homogeneity on standing at a temperature not more than 6 °C above the pour point. However, it should not exceed the indicated limits.

4.3.2 REQUIREMENTS FOR BASE STOCK—(Optional for non-military procurement) A 180 mL production sample of each base stock component used in formulating the finished oil, accompanied by the following property data, shall be submitted annually to the qualifying activity.

a. Viscosity
   @ 100 °C, centistokes (mm^2/s)
   @ 40 °C, centistokes (mm^2/s)
b. Viscosity index
c. Gravity, °API @ 60 °F
d. Pour point, °C
e. Carbon residue, mass %
f. Sulfated ash, mass %
g. Total acid number
h. Elemental content, mass %
i. Nitrogen, mass %
j. Chlorine, mass %
k. Sulfur, mass %
l. Color
m. Boiling point distribution, °C
   @ 1%, 5%, 10%, 50%, & 90% points
n. Saponification number
o. Flash Point

4.4 Performance Requirements—The oils shall conform to the respective requirements specified in 4.4.1 through 4.4.13.

4.4.1 FOAMING—All grades of oil shall demonstrate the following foaming characteristics when tested in accordance with 5.1.2, Table 3 (ASTM D 892).

a. Initial test at 24 °C ± 0.5 °C. Not more than 10 mL of foam shall remain immediately following the end of the 5-min blowing period. No foam shall remain at the end of the 10-min settling period.
b. Intermediate test at 93.5 °C ± 0.5 °C. Not more than 20 mL of foam shall remain immediately following the end of the 5-min blowing period. No foam shall remain at the end of the 10-min settling period.
c. Final test at 24 °C ± 0.5 °C. Not more than 10 mL of foam shall remain immediately following the end of the 5-min blowing period. No foam shall remain at the end of the 10-min settling period.
d. Test at 150 °C ± 0.5 °C. Not more than 50 mL of foam shall remain immediately following the end of the blowing period. No foam (0) shall remain at the end of the 1-min settling period. Option A is not allowed (CG-4 requirement).

TABLE 3—TEST METHODS

TEST	Test Methods FED-STD-791	Test Methods ASTM	Test Methods SAE
Viscosity, Kinematic		D 445	
Viscosity, Apparent[1]			J300
High Temperature/High Shear		D 4683[2], D 4624, D 4741	
Viscosity Index		D 2270	
Pour Point		D 97	
Stable Pour Point	203		
Pumpability		D 4684	
Flash Point		D 92	
Evaporative Loss		D 5480[2], D 5800	
Gravity, API		D 287	
Carbon Residue		D 524	
Color		D 1500	
Acid Number		D 664	
Base Number		D 2896	
Phosphorus		D 1091[2], D 4047, D 927, D 4951, D 5185	
Chlorine[2]		D 808[2], D 1317	
Sulfur[3]		D 129, D 1552[2], D 2622, D 4294, D 4927, D 4951, D 5185	
Nitrogen		D 3228[2], D 4629	
Saponification Number		D 94	
Sulfated Residue		D 874	
Boiling Range Distribution		D 2887	
Metallic Components		D 4628, D 4927, D 4951[2], D 5185	
Foaming		D 892	
Stability and Compatibility	3470[3]		
Engine Oil Aeration		HEUI	
Corrosion Protection (Humidity Cabinent)	5329		
Oxidation and Wear Characteristics		D 5533 (III E)	
Dispersancy Characteristics		D 5967 (Mack T-8)	
Bearing Corrosion and Shear Stability		D 5119 (L-38)	
Ring-Sticking, Wear, and Deposits			
Four-Stroke Cycle Diesel Engine-LS		Caterpillar 1N	
Four-Stroke Cycle Diesel Engine-HS		Caterpillar 1M-PC	
Two-Stroke Cycle Diesel Engine		D 5862 (DDC 6V92TA)	
Friction Retention Characteristics and Wear:			
Slip Time and Wear		ATD C-4[4]	
Friction Coefficient and Wear		Caterpillar VC-70[5]	
Seal Compatibility		ATD C-4[6]	
Metal Corrosion	5308		
Copper Corrosion		D 130	
Roller Follower Wear Test		D 5966	

1. Obtain the apparent viscosity using the method of test set forth by SAE J300, Appendix A.
2. Denotes preferred method
3. See 5.1.2.1 for clarifying instructions.
4. Use procedure described in item 8 and 9 of C-4 specification.
5. Use test SEQs 1220 and FRRET (VC-70) described in the Caterpillar TO-4 specification.
6. Use procedure in item 5 of C-4 specification.

4.4.2 STABILITY AND COMPATIBILITY

4.4.2.1 Stability—The oils shall show no evidence of separation or color change when they are tested in accordance with 5.1.2, Table 3 (FED-STD-791, Method 3470). A 1 L sample of the finished lubricant to be qualified and used for this test shall be provided to the qualifying activity (see 7.4) at the time of qualification.

4.4.2.2 Compatibility—The oils shall be compatible with oils previously qualified under MIL-L-2104, MIL-L-21260, and MIL-L-46167. The oils shall show no evidence of separation when they are tested against selected reference oils in accordance with 5.1.2, Table 3 (FED-STD-791, Method 3470).

4.4.3 OXIDATION AND WEAR PROTECTION CHARACTERISTICS—The oils shall protect internal loaded engine components against excessive wear and oxidation. Satisfactory performance in this respect shall be demonstrated when the oils are tested according to multiple test criteria and rated in accordance with 5.1.2, Table 3 (ASTM D 5533) and exhibit test results (single or average) meeting the criteria in Table 4:

TABLE 4—ASTM D 5533 LIMITS (III E)

Average rating @ 64 h	1 Test	2 Tests	3 Tests
Viscosity increase, Hours to 375% avg max	67.5	65.1	64.0
Oil ring land deposits, avg. min	2.6	2.6	2.6
Piston skirt varnish, avg. min	8.7	8.7	8.7
Sludge, avg. min	9.0	9.0	9.0
Stuck rings, avg. max	None	None	None
Stuck lifter, avg max	None	None	None
Scuffing and wear at 64 h			
Cam or lifter scuffing	None	None	None
Cam plus lifter wear, μm			
Average (avg max)	64	64	64
Maximum (Avg)	145	145	145

4.4.4 ROLLER FOLLOWER WEAR TEST ASTM D 5966—The oils shall protect internal loaded diesel engine components against excessive wear caused by the presence of soot. Satisfactory performance in this respect shall be demonstrated when the oils are tested according to multiple test criteria and rated in accordance with 5.1.2, Table 3 (6.2 L test) and exhibit averaged test results meeting the criteria in Table 4:

TABLE 5—ASTM D 5966 LIMITS (ROLLER FOLLOWER WEAR TEST)

		1 Test	2 Tests	3 Tests
Pin Wear,	μm, avg. max.	11.4	12.4	12.7
	mils, avg. max	0.45	0.49	0.50

4.4.5 BEARING CORROSION AND SHEAR STABILITY

4.4.5.1 Bearing Corrosion—The oils shall be non-corrosive to alloy bearings. Satisfactory performance in this respect shall be demonstrated when the oils are tested in accordance with 5.1.2, Table 3 (ASTM D 5119) and exhibit test results meeting the criteria in Table 6:

TABLE 6—ASTM D 5119 LIMITS (L-38)

	1 Test	2 Tests	3 Tests
Bearing weight loss, milligrams (max.)	43.7	48.1	50.0

4.4.5.2 Shear Stability—SAE 15W-40 grade oil shall demonstrate shear stability by exhibiting a viscosity at 100 °C of 13.0 cSt minimum, on any of the samples taken, when tested in accordance with 5.1.2.2.

4.4.6 RING-STICKING, WEAR, AND ACCUMULATION OF DEPOSITS—The oils shall prevent the sticking of piston rings and port clogging, and shall minimize the wear of cylinders, rings, and loaded engine components such as cam shaft lobes, cam followers, valve rocker arms, rocker arm shafts, and the oil pump and fuel injection pump drive gears.

4.4.6.1 Four-Stroke Cycle Diesel Engine—Low Sulfur Fuel—Satisfactory performance shall be demonstrated when the oils are tested with low-sulfur fuel and rated in accordance with 5.1.1.7, Table 3 (Caterpillar 1N) and exhibit test results meeting the criteria in Table 7. (Only one test is required. However, the test limits are adjusted according to the number of tests submitted and equivalency to original limits.)

TABLE 7—1N TEST LIMITS

	1 Test	2 Tests	3 Tests
Top groove filling, % avg. max	20	23	25
WDN, demerits, avg. max	286	311.7	323.0
Top land heavy carbon, %, avg. max	3	4	5
Oil consumption, g/Kw-h., avg. max	0.5	0.5	0.5
Scuffing, piston-rings-liners, avg max	None	None	None
Stuck rings, avg. max	None	None	None

4.4.6.2 Four-Stroke Cycle Diesel Engine—Higher Sulfur Fuel—Satisfactory performance shall be demonstrated when the oils are tested with higher-sulfur fuel and rated in accordance with 5.1.2, Table 3 (Caterpillar 1M-PC) and exhibit test results meeting the criteria in Table 8. (Only one test is required, however, when three or more tests are run, one test may be discarded and the average calculated from the remaining test results. This average result must meet the criteria in Table 8.)

TABLE 8—1M-PC LIMITS

Top groove filling, % max.	70
WTD, avg, max.	240
Ring Side Clearance Loss, mm, max	0.013
Piston Ring Sticking	None
Piston, Ring, and Liner Scuffing	None

4.4.6.3 Two-Stroke Cycle Diesel Engine—Satisfactory performance shall be demonstrated when the oils are tested and rated in accordance with 5.1.2, Table 3 (ASTM D 5862) and exhibit test results meeting the criteria in Table 9. (Only one test is required. However, if more than one test is run, the test limits are adjusted according to the number of tests run, maximum of three tests, and equivalency to original limits.)

TABLE 9—ASTM D 5862 LIMITS (DDC 6V92 TA)

	1 Test	2 Tests	3 Tests
Piston, average % area			
Skirts tin removed	Report	Report	Report
Wrist pin slipper bushing copper exposed	Report	Report	Report
Average ring face distress, demerits (max)			
Fire ring, AVG	0.33	0.34	0.36
Nos. 2 and 3 compression rings, avg	0.28	0.29	0.30
Broken rings, avg	None	None	None
Cylinder liner area			
Average liner distress, % area (avg max)	60.0	63.5	65.0
Port plugging, % area, (avg max)			
Average	2	2	2
Single cylinder	5	5	5

4.4.7 FRICTION RETENTION CHARACTERISTICS AND WEAR—The oils shall maintain a stable coefficient of friction and shall minimize distress and wear during use in power shift transmissions and other cooled friction compartments or hydraulic systems such as steering and disconnect clutches.

4.4.7.1 Slip Time and Torque—Satisfactory performance shall be demonstrated when the oils are tested and rated in accordance with 5.1.2, Table 3 (ATD C-4) and exhibit test results meeting the nominal criteria in Table 10, as adjusted to accommodate slight changes in individual friction plate batches:

TABLE 10—C-4 FRICTION TEST LIMITS

	Graphite 0-5500 cycles	Paper 0-10 000 cycles	Paper 10 000
Slip time at cycles, s (max)	0.74	0.67	Report
Mid-point coefficient (min)	0.097	0.080	Report

4.4.7.2 Friction Coefficient and Wear—Satisfactory performance shall be demonstrated when the oils are tested and rated in accordance with 5.1.2, (see 3)Table 3 (Caterpillar VC 70) and a test on each sequence exhibit results meeting the nominal criteria in Table 11, as adjusted to accommodate slight changes in individual fluoroelastomer batches and performance of the reference oil:

TABLE 11—VC-70 TEST LIMITS

	Sequence 1220	Sequence FRRET
Average dynamic coefficient, %	90-140	—
@ 3000 cycles	—	85-130
@ 8000 cycles	—	90-125
@ 15 000 cycles	—	90-125
@ 25 000 cycles	—	95-125
Average static coefficient, %	91-127	—
Disc wear, mm (max)	0.04	—
Energy limit, %	25	—

4.4.8 SEAL COMPATIBILITY—The oils shall minimize deterioration of seal and friction materials.

4.4.8.1 Effect on Seals—Satisfactory performance shall be demonstrated when the oils are tested and rated in accordance with 5.1.2, Table 3 (ATD C-4) and exhibits test results meeting the nominal criteria in Table 12, as adjusted to accommodate slight changes in individual elastomer batches:

TABLE 12—C-4 SEALS TEST LIMITS

Buna N:	
Volume changes, %	0 to +5
Hardness changes, points	0 ± 5
Polyacrylate:	
Volume changes, %	0 to +10
Hardness change, points	0 to +5
Silicone:	
Volume changes, %	0 to +5
Hardness changes, points	0 to –10
Fluoroelastomer:	
Volume changes, %	0 to +4
Hardness change, points	–4 to +4
Ethyl Acrylic:	
Volume changes, %	
Hardness change, points	—

4.4.9 DISPERSANCY CHARACTERISTICS—Satisfactory performance shall be demonstrated when the oils are tested and rated in accordance with 5.1.2, Table 3 ASTM D 5967 (Mack T-8) and exhibits test results meeting the criteria in Table 13:

TABLE 13—ASTM D 5967 TEST LIMITS (MACK T-8)

	1 Test	2 Tests	3 Tests
Viscosity increase, cSt max			
from min. corrected to 3.8% Soot by TGA	11.5	12.5	13.0
Oil Consumption, gm/Bhp·h, max.	0.0005	0.0005	0.0005

4.4.10 METAL AND COPPER CORROSION

4.4.10.1 Metal Corrosion—Satisfactory performance shall be demonstrated when the oils are tested and rated in accordance with 5.1.2, Table 3 (Corrosion Bench Test, ASTM D 5968) and exhibits test results meeting the following criteria:

a. Cu, ppm, max—20
b. Pb, ppm, max—60

4.4.10.2 Copper Corrosion, ASTM D 130—Satisfactory performance shall be demonstrated when the oils are rated in accordance with 5.1.2, Table 3 (Copper Corrosion, ASTM D 130). The copper coupons used in 4.4.10.1 shall be rated according to ASTM D 130 and the oil shall exhibit copper strip discoloration not exceeding ASTM No. 3 when compared to ASTM Copper Strip Corrosion Standard.

4.4.11 CORROSION-PROTECTION (HUMIDITY CABINET)—After performance of the test procedure specified in 5.1.2.3 (a minimum of 720 h of exposure in a humidity cabinet), not more than three corrosion spots, none of which exceeds 1 mm in length, width or diameter, shall be evident on any of the test panels.

4.4.12 CORROSION-PROTECTION (SALT WATER IMMERSION)—After performance of the test procedure specified in 5.1.2.4 (20 h of immersion in synthetic salt water), a total of not more than three corrosion spots, none of which exceeds 1 mm in length, width, or diameter, shall be evident on the three test panels.

4.4.13 ACID NEUTRALIZATION—After performance of the test procedure specified in 5.1.2.5, a total of not more than three corrosion spots, none of which exceeds one millimeter in length, width, or diameter, shall be evident on the three test panels. In addition, there shall be no evidence of staining or other attack on any of the three test panels.

4.4.14 HEUI ENGINE OIL AERATION TEST—Satisfactory performance shall be demonstrated when the oils are tested in accordance with 5.1.2, Table 3 (HEUI) and exhibit test results meeting the following criteria:

a. HEUI A Foam Stability @ 20 hours % max—10

4.5 Other Requirements and Tolerances for Quality Conformance Testing—The following physical and chemical properties shall be tested in accordance with the appropriate methods listed in 5.1.2 to insure that purchased products are of the same compositions as the respective qualification samples and to identify the products. No specific values or limits are assigned in qualification testing, except as otherwise specified in Table 2 and 4.4.1 through 4.4.13, but test results shall be reported for all properties listed. The qualifying activity (see 7.4) shall establish specific values and tolerances for subsequent quality conformance testing of the finished lubricant for these properties (see 7.3 and 7.4):

a. Viscosity, apparent and kinematic
b. High-temperature/high-shear
c. Viscosity index
d. Pour point
e. Pumpability
f. Flash point
g. Gravity, °API @ 60 °F
h. Carbon residue
i. Foaming
j. Phosphorus
k. Sulfur
l. Sulfated ash
m. Metallic components
n. Nitrogen
o. Chlorine

5. Verification

5.1 Classification of Inspections—The inspection requirements specified herein are classified as follows:

a. Qualification inspections (see 5.1.1).
b. Conformance inspections (see 5.1.3).

5.1.1 QUALIFICATION INSPECTIONS—Qualification inspections consist of tests for all of the requirements specified in Section 4 and may be conducted in any plant or laboratory that follows the ASTM procedures and referencing requirements where appropriate. Qualification inspections shall be performed on each viscosity grade except as specified in 5.1.1.1 through 5.1.1.8.

5.1.1.1 Stable Pour-Point—The stable pour-point test (FED-STD-791, Method 203) shall be required only on SAE grades 10W and 15W-40 oils.

5.1.1.2 Shear Stability—Shear stability shall be required for only SAE 15W-40 grade oil.

5.1.1.3 Modified Formulations—SAE 40 grade oils based on the formulation of an SAE 30 grade oil qualified under this specification may be qualified in accordance with 4.1.1.

5.1.1.4 Oxidation and Wear Protection—The qualifying activity (see 7.4), may waive ASTM D 5533 testing of the candidate oil when acceptable supporting ASTM D 5533 wear evaluations for formulations similar in additive technology to the candidate lubricant are presented to substantiate the wear protection characteristics.

5.1.1.5 Ring-Sticking, Wear, and Accumulation of Deposits—The two-stroke cycle diesel engine test (DDC 6V92TA) shall be required only for SAE grades 30, 40, and 15W-40 oils. Requirements for this test may be waived for oils formulated with a specific additive technology (detergent, dispersant, inhibitor system) provided satisfactory performance is demonstrated for the technology used in conjunction with various base stock-viscosity improver additive combinations. Satisfactory performance shall be demonstrated by conducting the following acceptable two-stroke cycle diesel engine tests:

a. One test each of three SAE 15W-40 grade oils formulated using the additive system, a viscosity index improver additive but with base stocks of different manufacture.
b. One test each of an SAE 15W-40 grade oil formulated using the additive system, a base stock employed in 5.1.1.5(a) for each viscosity index improver additive to be used in conjunction with the additive system.

5.1.1.6 Friction Retention Characteristics and Wear—Test for friction retention characteristics and wear shall be required only for SAE grades 10W, 30, and 15W-40 oils. The qualifying activity (see 7.4) may waive testing for those requirements when acceptable supporting friction retention characteristics and wear evaluations for formulations similar in additive technology to the candidate lubricant are presented to substantiate these performance requirements.

5.1.1.7 Four-Stroke Cycle Diesel Engine (1N)—Low Sulfur Fuel—The 1N test shall be required only on 15W/40.

5.1.1.8 HEUI Engine Oil Aerations—The HEUI test shall be required only when a satisfactory sequence IV foam test (SEQ IV D 892) is not available.

5.1.2 QUALIFICATION INSPECTION METHODS—Perform tests in accordance with Table 3 and with 5.1.2.1 through 5.1.2.2, as applicable.

5.1.2.1 Stability and Compatibility—Determine the stability and compatibility of the oils by the procedures for "Homogeneity and Miscibility" given in FED-STD-791, Method 3470, as explained in 5.1.2.1.1 and 5.1.2.1.2. The procedures in 5.1.2.1.1 and 5.1.2.1.2 should be performed at the same time.

5.1.2.1.1 Stability—Determine the stability by subjecting an unmixed sample of oil to the prescribed cycle of temperature changes, then examine the sample for conformance to the requirements of 4.4.2.1. Record the test results on the "Homogeneity and Miscibility Test" form in the column marked "None".

5.1.2.1.2 Compatibility—Determine the compatibility of the oil with other oils previously qualified under MIL-L-2104, MIL-L-21260, and MIL-L-46167 by subjecting separate mixtures of the oil with selected reference oils designated by the qualifying activity (see 7.4) to the prescribed cycle of temperature changes, then examine the mixtures for conformance to the requirements of 4.4.2.2. Record the test results on the same copy of the "Homogeneity and Miscibility test" form (see 5.1.2.1) in the appropriate columns marked "1-30", "2-30", etc. Reference oils for conducting compatibility tests are to be obtained from the SAE, 400 Commonwealth Drive, Warrendale, PA 15096.

5.1.2.2 Shear Stability—Determine the shear stability of SAE 15W-40 grade oil by the following method:

a. Weigh 25 g of used oil, obtained every 10 h of testing, in accordance with ASTM D 5119, into a 50 mL three-necked round bottom flask equipped with a thermometer, gas inlet tube, stirrer, and distillation side arm.
b. Heat the sample at 120 °C ± 5 °C in a vacuum of 100 mm of mercury with a nitrogen sparge for 1 h.
c. Filter the stripped sample through a 0.5 µm filter pad.
d. Determine the kinematic viscosity at 100 °C of the filtered sample using ASTM D 445. Check the resulting viscosity for conformance to the requirements of 4.4.5.2.

5.1.2.3 Corrosion-Protection (Humidity Cabinet)—Test the corrosion-protection properties of the oils in a humidity cabinet for 30 days (720 h) in accordance with method 5329, FED-STD-791. Three test panels conforming to the requirements of Method 5329, FED-STD-791 are to be used. This test shall be conducted only in a laboratory designated by the qualifying activity (see 7.4).

5.1.2.4 Corrosion-Protection (Salt-Water Immersion)—Test the corrosion-protection properties of the oils in salt water in accordance with 5.1.2.4.1 through 5.1.2.4.4. This test shall be conducted only in a laboratory designated by the qualifying activity (see 7.4).

5.1.2.4.1 Test Panels—Make three test panels of the composition specified in Method 5329, FED-STD-791. Each panel shall measure 76 x 51 x 1.6 mm and shall contain a hole 6.4 mm in diameter, whose center is on the mid-line of the panel, 6.4 mm from one of the 51 mm edges. Round all corners and edges of the panels completely.

5.1.2.4.2 Preparation of Test Panels—Clean and sand-blast the test panels in accordance with Method 5320, FED-STD-791. Immerse the panels in the oil sample at 25 °C ± 3 °C. Agitate the oil gently for 1 min. Suspend the panels on glass hooks and allow the oil to drain for 20 h in a dust-free area maintained at 25 °C ± 3 °C and a maximum relative humidity of 50%.

5.1.2.4.3 Preparation of Synthetic Sea Water—Prepare synthetic sea water with chemicals conforming to American Chemical Society (ACS) specifications for analytical reagents and distilled water. The composition of the synthetic sea water shall be as specified in Table 14. Adjust the pH of the salt solution to a value between 8.0 and 8.2 by the addition of 5% solution of sodium carbonate. If the salt solution is kept in stock, check the pH and adjust it before each test, if necessary, to the same value.

TABLE 14—FORMULA FOR SYNTHETIC SEA WATER

Ingredient	Grams per liter of solution
Magnesium, chloride hexahydrate	11.0
Anhydrous calcium chloride	1.2
Anhydrous sodium sulfate	4.0
Sodium Chloride	25.0

5.1.2.4.4 Procedure—Immerse each of the oil-coated test panels separately in a tall-form beaker containing synthetic sea water at 25 °C ± 3 °C for 20 h. Immerse the panels in a vertical position to a depth of 10 to 16 mm above the panel. Support the panels by inserting them in slots cut in the faces of cylindrical hardwood blocks, 54 mm in diameter and 25.4 mm in height. Each slot shall measure 3 mm deep and 2 mm wide. Precondition the blocks before initial use by immersing them for 48 h in synthetic sea water at 25 °C ± 3 °C. Cover each beaker with a watch glass before the start of the 20-h immersion period. After immersion, rinse with acetone, and finally rinse with aliphatic naphtha. Allow the panels to dry at 25 °C ± 3 °C and inspect them immediately for conformance to 4.4.12. To differentiate between gray discoloration and rust, illuminate each panel with a 100-W "daylight" electric bulb and view its surface at an angle of 20 degrees to 40 degrees with the plane of the panel. Corrosion occurring within 3 mm of any edge of the panel, within 3 mm of the edge of the hole in any panel, or within 6 mm of the line of contact of the panel and the upper surface of the slot in the support block shall be considered in the evaluation of the test results.

5.1.2.5 Acid Neutralization—Clean and sand-blast three test panels which shall be of the material, design, and dimensions specified in 5.1.2.4.1. Handling each panel separately with forceps, immerse the panel completely for not more than one second in a 0.1% ± 0.01% aqueous solution of hydrobromic acid. Within 1 s after removal from the acid solution, immerse the panel completely, with agitation, in a sample of the oil to be tested, maintained at a temperature of 25 °C ± 3 °C and contained in a 500-mL tall-form beaker. Transfer the panel from the hydrobromic acid solution immediately, without draining the excess acid solution. Immerse the panel in the oil sample and remove it a total of 12 times in 60 s. Change the position of the tips for each immersion to assure access of the oil to all surfaces of the panel. Place the panel in a slotted wooden block (see 5.1.2.4.4) and allow it to stand in the air at 25 °C ± 3 °C for a period of 4 h. Following this 4-h standing period, remove the remaining oil film from the panel with naphtha and examine the panel for the extent of corrosion. Corrosion, staining, or other attack occurring within 3 mm of any edge of the panel, or within 3 mm of the line of contact between the panel and the upper surface, or within 3 mm of the line of contact between the panel and the upper surface of the slot in the wooden block, shall not be considered for evaluation of the test results. This test shall be conducted only in a laboratory designated by the qualifying activity (see 7.4).

5.1.3 CONFORMANCE INSPECTIONS—Inspections for conformance of individual lots (see 7.5) shall consist of tests for the following requirements using the test method listed in Table 3. The results obtained when using the test methods in Table 3 must fall within the tolerances/specific values (see 4.1.3 and 7.3) assigned at time of qualification:

a. Viscosities
b. High-temperature/high-shear
c. Viscosity index
d. Pour point
e. Pumpability
f. Flash point
g. Gravity, °API
h. Carbon residue
i. Foaming
j. Phosphorus
k. Sulfur
l. Nitrogen
m. TAN
n. TBN
o. Sulfated ash
p. Metallic components

5.2 Sampling

5.2.1 SAMPLING FOR THE EXAMINATION OF FILLED CONTAINERS—Take a random sample of filled containers from each lot in accordance with ANSI Z1.4/ ASQC Z1.4.

5.2.2 SAMPLING FOR TESTS—Take samples from bulk or packaged lots (see 7.5) for tests in accordance with ASTM D 4057 or D 4177, as appropriate.

5.3 Inspection—Perform inspection in accordance with FED-STD-791, Method 9601. In addition to the inspection, the manufacturer shall provide certification of non-carcinogenicity as specified in 4.2 (i.e., materials are not considered carcinogenic or potentially carcinogenic) and shall provide Material Safety Data Sheets.

5.3.1 EXAMINATION OF FILLED CONTAINERS—Examine samples taken in accordance with 5.2.1 with regard to fill, closure, sealing, and leakage. Reject any container having one or more defects or under the required fill. If the number of defective or under filled containers exceeds the acceptance number for the appropriate sampling plan of ANSI Z1.4/ASQC Z1.4, reject the lot (see 7.5) represented by the sample.

6. Packaging

6.1 Packing—For acquisition purposes, the packing requirement shall be as specified in the contract or order (see 7.2). When actual packaging of material is to be performed by DoD personnel, these personnel need to contact the responsible packaging activity to ascertain requisite packaging requirements. Packaging requirements are maintained by the Inventory Control Point's Packaging Command. Packaging data retrieval is available from the managing Military Department's or Defense Agency's automated packaging files, CD-ROM products, or by contacting the responsible packaging activity.

6.2 Marking—Unless otherwise specified (see 7.2), marking shall be as specified in contract or order.

7. General Requirements

7.1 Intended Use—The SAE 10W (OE/HDO-10)grade oil is not to be used in high-output, two-cycle compression-ignition engines. The lubricating oils, except as mentioned previously, covered by this specification are intended for the preservative, break-in and operational use until the first scheduled oil change of all spark-ignition and compression-ignition engines used in all types of military combat/tactical ground equipment and for the crankcase lubrication of two-cycle, four-cycle, high-speed, high-output, supercharged compression-ignition engines used in all ground equipment. The oils are also intended for the same application in power transmissions, hydraulic systems, and non-hypoid gear units of engineer/construction equipment, materials handling equipment and combat/tactical ground equipment. The lubricating oils covered by this specification meet service classifications API CG-4, CF of SAE J183 and are intended for all conditions of operational service, as defined by appropriate lubrication orders, when temperatures are above –25 °C. Recommended ambient temperature ranges for specific grade oils are shown in Figure 1.

7.2 Acquisition Requirements—Acquisition documents should specify the following:

a. Title, number, and date of this specification.
b. Issue of DoDISS to be cited in the solicitation, and if required, the specific issue of individual documents referenced.
c. Military grade of oil required (see 1.1).
d. Certification of non-carcinogenicity (see 4.2).
e. Quantity of oil required.
f. Type and size of containers required (see 6.1).
g. Marking requirements (see 6.2).

7.3 Other Requirements and Tolerances for Conformance Inspections—Definite numerical values are not specified for certain of the physical and chemical properties listed in 4.5, and for which corresponding test methods are given in Section 5. Values of some properties vary from one brand of oil to another for the same grade. These values are influenced by the source of the base stock, the identities and quantities of additives, etc. Definite numerical values are not always functionally important except, for some properties, within specified maximum and minimum limits. It is not possible (or necessary) to assign restrictive values in the specification before the testing of qualification samples. During qualification, test values will be determined which are characteristics of a particular product and which can serve thereafter to identify the product. Using the results of qualification testing, the qualifying activity (see 7.4) can set values, including permissible tolerances, for future quality conformance testing.

7.4 Qualification—Lubricating oils covered under this standard must be submitted for qualification. Awards will be made only for products which are, at the time of contract award, qualified for inclusion in the applicable qualified products list whether or not such products have actually been so listed by that date. The attention of the contractors is called to this requirement, and manufacturers are urged to arrange to have the products that they propose to offer to the Federal Government tested for qualification in order that they may be eligible to be awarded contracts or orders for the products covered by this specification. The activity responsible for the qualified products list is the U. S. Army Tank Automotive and Armaments Command, ATTN: AMSTRA-TR-D/210, Warren, MI, 48392-5000, and information pertaining to qualification of products may be obtained from that activity. Additionally, qualification information may be obtained by contacting the Performance Review Institute, Attn: Secretary of the LRI, 161 Thornhill Road, Warrendale, PA 15086, (724) 772-1616.

7.5 Military Part Number—Preservative/engine oils furnished under this performance specification shall be identified by a military part number consisting of; a "M" prefix and specification number, a single digit "Dash Number" taken from Table 15 which indicates the container size, and the viscosity grade of the lubricant. See Figure 2 and Table 15.

7.6 Subject term (key word) listing

a. Combat service
b. Heavy-duty diesel
c. Internal combustion engine
d. Tactical service
e. Engine oil
f. Track vehicle
g. Wheel vehicle

7.7 International Standardization Agreement—Certain provisions of this specification are subject of international standardization agreement STANAGs 2845 and 1135. When amendment, revision, or cancellation of this specification is proposed which would affect or violate the international agreement concerned, the preparing activity will take appropriate reconciliation action through international standardization channels, including departmental standardization office, if required.

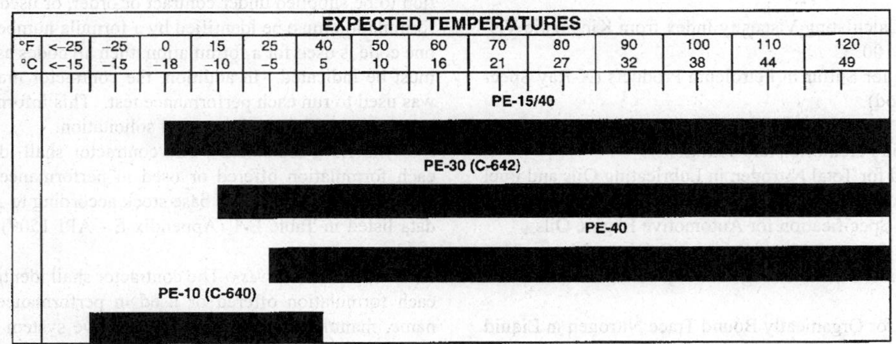

NOTE—For power transmission, hydraulic system and non-hypoid gear box applications, lubricants may be used at all temperature above the low temperature recommendation shown in Table 15.

FIGURE 1—RECOMMENDED AMBIENT TEMPERATURE RANGES FOR USAGE OF ENGINE OILS

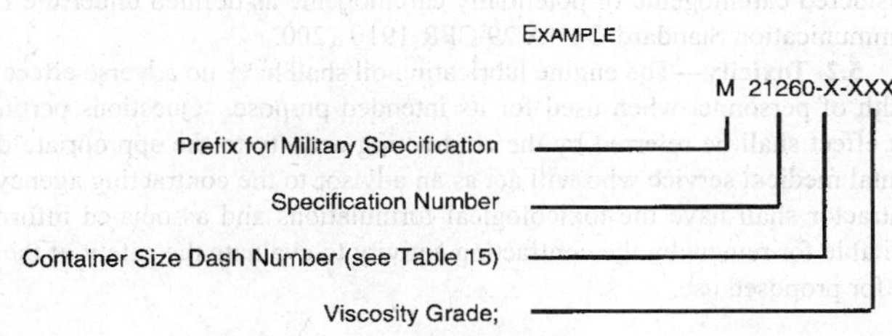

FIGURE 2—EXAMPLE OF MILITARY PART NUMBER

TABLE 15—DASH NUMBER DESIGNATIONS FOR USE IN MILITARY PART NUMBERS

Dash number	Container size
1	946 mL (1-quart)
2	3.785 L (1-gal)
3	18.925 L (5-gal pail)
4	208.175 L (55-gal drum)

7.8 Changes from Previous Issue—Marginal notations not used in this revision to identify changes with respect to the previous issue due to the extensiveness of the changes.

LUBRICATING OIL, AUTOMOTIVE ENGINE, API SERVICE SJ FOR MILITARY ADMINISTRATIVE SERVICE—SAE J2362 NOV1998 SAE Standard

Report of the SAE Military/industry Lubricants Committee approved November 1998. Rationale statement available.

1. Scope

1.1 General—This SAE Standard describes lubricating oils meeting the API SJ performance category, SAE J300, the International Lubricant Standardization and Approval Committee (ILSAC) GF-2 Standard, and bear the API Certification Mark (starburst symbol) in accordance with API 1509. These oils are suitable for the lubrication of spark-ignition engines (gasoline engines). This document is equivalent to the military's Commercial Item Description A-A-52039 when all requirements are met.

1.2 Intended Use—The products described in this document are intended for use in administrative type, commercial vehicles equipped with spark-ignition, gasoline consuming engines.

2. References

2.1 Applicable Publications—The following publications form a part of this specification to the extent specified herein. Unless otherwise specified, the latest issue of SAE publications shall apply.

2.1.1 SAE PUBLICATIONS—Available from SAE, 400 Commonwealth Drive, Warrendale, PA 15096-0001.

SAE J183—Engine Oil Performance and Engine Service Classification (Other Than "Energy-Conserving")

SAE J300—Engine Oil Viscosity Classification

2.1.2 API PUBLICATION—Available from the American Petroleum Institute, Marketing Department, Program Manager, ESCS Program, 1220 L Street NW, Washington, DC 20005.

API 1509—The API Engine Oil Licensing and Certification System

2.1.3 ASTM PUBLICATIONS—Available from ASTM, 100 Barr Harbor Drive, West Conshohocken, PA 19428-2959.

ASTM D 97—Test Methods for Pour Point of Petroleum Oils

ASTM D 287—Test Method for API Gravity of Crude Petroleum and Petroleum Products (Hydrometer Method)

ASTM D 445—Test Method for Kinematic Viscosity of Transparent and Opaque Liquids (and the Calculation of Dynamic Viscosity)

ASTM D 524—Test Method for Ramsbottom Carbon Residue of Petroleum Products

ASTM D 664—Standard Test Method for Acid Number of Petroleum Products by Potentiometric Titration

ASTM D 874—Test Method for Sulfated Ash from Lubricating Oils and Additives

ASTM D 2270—Method for Calculating Viscosity Index from Kinematic Viscosity at 40 and 100 °C

ASTM D 2622—Test Method for Sulfur in Petroleum Products (X-Ray Spectrographic Method)

ASTM D 2896—Test Method for Total Base Number of Petroleum Products by Potentiometric Perchloric Acid Titration

ASTM D 3228—Total Method for Total Nitrogen in Lubricating Oils and Fuel Oils by Modified Kjeldahl Method

ASTM D 4485—Performance Specification for Automotive Engine Oils

ASTM D 4628—Test Method for Analysis of Barium, Calcium, Magnesium, and Zinc in Unused Lubricating Oils by Atomic Absorption Spectrometry

ASTM D 4629—Test Method for Organically Bound Trace Nitrogen in Liquid Petroleum Hydrocarbons by Oxidative Combustion and Chemiluminescence Detection

ASTM D 4739—Test Method for Base Number Determination by Potentiometric Titration

ASTM D 4927—Test Methods for Elemental Analysis of Lubricant and Additive Components—Barium, Calcium, Phosphorus, Sulfur, and Zinc by Wavelength-Dispersive X-Ray Fluorescence Spectroscopy

ASTM D 4951—Determination of Additive Elements in Lubricating Oils by Inductively Coupled Plasma Atomic Emission Spectrometry

ASTM D 5185—Test Method for Determination of Additive Elements, Wear Metals, and Contaminants in Used Lubricating Oils by Inductively Coupled Plasma Atomic Emission Spectrometry

2.1.4 ILSAC PUBLICATION—Available from American Automobile Manufacturers Association, 7430 Second Avenue, Suite 300, Detroit, MI 48202.

ILSAC GF-2

2.1.5 GOVERNMENT PUBLICATION—Available from Standardization Documents Order Desk, Building 4D, 700 Robbins Avenue, Philadelphia, PA 19120.

FED-STD-313—Material Safety Data, Transportation Data and Disposal Data for Hazardous Materials Furnished to Government Activities

2.1.6 U.S. DEPARTMENT OF LABOR (DOL) (OSHA)—Available from the OSHA Publication Office, Room S-4203, 200 Constitution Avenue, NW, Washington, DC 20210.

OSHA 29 CFR 1910.1200—Hazard Communication; Interpretation Regarding Lubricating Oils

3. Classification

3.1 Viscosity Grades—The lubricating oils shall be of the following viscosity grades:

a. SAE 5W-30
b. SAE 10W-30

4. Salient Characteristics

4.1 Materials—The engine lubricating oils shall be derived from petroleum fractions, synthetically prepared compounds or a combination of the two types of products. They may be virgin, rerefined stocks, or a combination thereof. The stocks shall be compounded with such functional additives (detergents, dispersants, oxidation inhibitors, corrosion inhibitors, etc.) as are necessary to meet the specified requirements (see Sections 5 and 6).

4.2 Performance—The engine lubricants shall have an "SJ" API performance level as identified in SAE J183 and ASTM D 4485, shall carry the American Petroleum Institute (API) donut symbol, the API Certification Mark (starburst symbol).

4.3 Physical and Chemical Requirements—The lubricating oils shall meet all the physical and chemical properties required for the API Certification Mark and SAE J300. In addition, the lubricating oils must have those properties indicated in Table 1 when tested in accordance with the respective test method (ASTM test procedures are listed where applicable). Section 4.3.1 is required only for military contracts unless otherwise requested.

4.3.1 FORMULATION DATA—The contractor shall provide the name, type, percent, and manufacturer of all base stocks and additive packages for each formulation to be supplied under contract or order, or used in performance testing. Each formulation must be identified by a formula number or oil code, and if more than one code is used for a formulation, then all codes associated with that formulation must be indicated. In addition, the contractor must identify which formulation was used to run each performance test. This information shall be provided to the contracting officer at the time of solicitation.

4.3.1.1 Base Stocks—The contractor shall identify all base stocks used in each formulation offered or used in performance testing by base stock name, manufacturer, and type of base stock according to Appendix E of API 1509. The data listed in Table E-1 (Appendix E - API 1509) shall be included for all base stocks.

4.3.1.2 Additives—The contractor shall identify all additive systems used in each formulation offered or used in performance testing by additive package name, manufacturer, and type of additive system (i.e. Detergent Inhibitor (DI), Viscosity Improver Type (OCP, SIP, PMA, etc.), Pour Point Depressant, etc.). If there are read-across between different formulations, then an explanation on how the additive systems relate to one another must be provided.

5. Regulatory Requirements

5.1 Hazard Communication Standard—The stocks used shall not be considered carcinogenic or potentially carcinogenic as defined under the Hazard Communication Standard OSHA 29 CFR 1910.1200.

5.2 Toxicity—The engine lubricating oil shall have no adverse effect on the health of personnel when used for its intended purpose. Questions pertinent to this effect shall be referred by the contracting activity to the appropriate departmental medical service who will act as an advisor to the contracting agency. The contractor shall have the toxicological formulations and associated information available for review by the contracting activity to evaluate the safety of the material for proposed use.

TABLE 1—LUBRICATING OIL PROPERTIES

Property[1]	SAE 5W–30	SAE 10W–30	ASTM Test Procedures
Viscosity Kinematic, cSt (mm^2/s) @ 40 °C	1	1	D 445
Viscosity Index	1	1	D 2270
Pour-Point, °C max.	–36	–30	D 97
Stable Pour Point, °C,[2] max.	–36	–30	FED-STD-791, Method 203
Gravity, API	1	1	D 287
Carbon Residue, mass %	1	1	D 524
Sulfur, mass %	1	1	D 2622, D 4927, D 4951[3], D 5185
Sulfated Ash, mass %	1	1	D 874
Total Acid Number,	1	1	D 664
Base Number,	1	1	D 2896, D 4739[3]
Nitrogen	1	1	D 3228[3], D 4629
Metallic components, mass %	1	1	D 4628, D 4927, D 4951[3], D 5185

1. Typical values for all physical and chemical properties required in Table 1, API 1509, and SAE J300 shall be provided at the time of solicitation or contract as specified by the contracting officer.
2. After being cooled below its pour point, the oil shall regain its homogeneity on standing at a temperature not more than 6 °C above the pour point, but not to exceed the previously stated values.
3. Denotes preferred method.

5.3 Recovered Material—The offeror/contractor is encouraged to use recovered materials in accordance with Public Law 94-580 to the maximum extent possible. When re-refined base stocks are sought, the minimum content to be used in the formulation shall be indicated in the contract or solicitation.

6. Quality Assurance Provisions

6.1 Contractor Certification—The contractor shall certify and maintain substantiating evidence, that the product offered meets the salient characteristics of this document, and that the product conforms to the producer's own drawings, specifications, standards, quality assurance practices, and the information provided in 6.4.

6.2 Market Acceptability (MA)—The contractor shall provide products which have a proven market record based on the number of items sold, length of time the product has been on the market, and reliability and performance of the products as required under the contract or solicitation.

6.3 Inspection and Test—The inspection and testing of products to be supplied under the document shall be as specified in the contract or order.

6.4 Pre-Review Process—Awards will be made only for products which have been pre-reviewed by the Lubricant Review Institute Engine Oil Review Committee. The attention of the contractors is called to the requirement and manufacturers are urged to arrange to have their products pre-reviewed in order that they may be eligible to be awarded contracts or order covered by this document. Copies of the Lubricant Review Institute Procedures are available from the Society of Automotive Engineers, Inc., 400 Commonwealth Drive, Warrendale, PA 15096-0001, Attention: Secretary of the Lubricant Review Institute.

7. Packaging

7.1 Preservation, Packaging, Packing, Labeling, and Marking—Preservation, packaging, labeling, and marking shall be as specified in the contract or order. The container will be as specified in the contract or order.

8. Notes

8.1 Ordering Data—The procuring agency should specify the preferred options permitted herein and include the following information in procurement documents:

a. Title, number, and date of this item description.
b. SAE grade of oil required.
c. Quantity of oil required.
d. Type and unit of issue required.
e. The certification requirement as indicated in 5.1 must be included in the solicitation/contract.
f. When this document is used for procurement, the inspection and test clause must appear in the solicitation.
g. Market Acceptability requirements must appear in the solicitation.

8.2 National Stock Numbers (NSN)—The following NSN's are for use by the Government and do not constitute a requirement on the contractor, unless required by the contract or order. The lubricating oils provided under this CID can be ordered using the following NSNs in Table 2:

TABLE 2—NATIONAL STOCK NUMBERS

National Stock Numbers	SAE Viscosity Grade	Unit Issue
9150-01-320-3706	5W-30	Box 12 1-qt plastic bottles
9150-01-348-1596		55-gal drum
9150-01-227-8210	10W-30	Box 12 1-qt plastic bottles
9150-01-230-9749		5-gal plastic container
9150-01-230-9748		55-gal drum
The following NSNs are for Rerefined Oil Only		
9150-01-413-6897	10W-30	Box 12 1-qt plastic bottles
9150-01-413-6892		5-gal plastic container
9150-01-413-6990		55-gal drum

LUBRICATING OIL FOR WHEELED MILITARY VEHICLES WITH HEAVY-DUTY DIESEL ENGINES—SAE J2363 NOV1998 SAE Standard

Report of the SAE Military/industry Lubricant Committee approved November 1998. Rationale statement available.

1. Scope

1.1 General—This SAE Standard describes lubricating oils meeting the API performance categories CF, CF-2, and CG-4, and the SAE J300. These oils are suitable for the lubrication of wheeled vehicles with compression-ignition (diesel) engines. This document is equivalent to the military's Commercial Item Description A-A-52306 when all requirements are met.

1.2 Intended Use—The lubricating oils described by this document are only intended for use in the engines of Tactical Wheeled vehicles equipped with compression-ignition engine systems. It is not a replacement for SAE J2359 (Lubricating Oil, Internal Combustion Engine, Military Combat/Tactical Service), nor is it intended for use in transmissions or hydraulic systems.

2. References

2.1 Applicable Publications—The following publications form a part of this specification to the extent specified herein. Unless otherwise specified, the latest issue of SAE publications shall apply.

2.1.1 SAE PUBLICATIONS—Available from SAE, 400 Commonwealth Drive, Warrendale, PA 15096-0001.

SAE J300—Engine Oil Viscosity Classification

SAE J2359—Lubricating Oil, Internal Combustion Engine, Military Combat/ Tactical Service

2.1.2 API PUBLICATION—Available from American Petroleum Institute, Marketing Department Program Manager, ESCS Program, 1220 L Street NW, Washington, DC 2005.

API 1509—The API Engine Oil Licensing and Certification System

2.1.3 ASTM PUBLICATIONS—Available from ASTM, 100 Barr Harbor Drive, West Conshohocken, PA 19428-2959.

ASTM D 92—Test Method for Flash and Fire Points by Cleveland Open Cup

ASTM D 97—Test Methods for Pour Point of Petroleum Oils

ASTM D 287—Test Method for API Gravity of Crude Petroleum and Petroleum Products (Hydrometer Method)

ASTM D 445—Test Method for Kinematic Viscosity of Transparent and Opaque Liquids (and the Calculation of Dynamic Viscosity)

ASTM D 524—Test Method for Ramsbottom Carbon Residue of Petroleum Products

ASTM D 664—Standard Test Method for Acid Number of Petroleum Products by Potentiometric Titration

ASTM D 874—Test Method for Sulfated Ash from Lubricating Oils and Additives

ASTM D 1091—Test Methods for Phosphorus in Lubricating Oils and Additives

ASTM D 2270—Method for Calculating Viscosity Index from Kinematic Viscosity at 40 and 100 °C

ASTM D 2622—Test Method for Sulfur in Petroleum Products (X-Ray Spectrographic Method)

ASTM D 2896—Test Method for Total Base Number of Petroleum Products by Potentiometric Perchloric Acid Titration

ASTM D 3228—Test Method for Total Nitrogen in Lubricating Oils and Fuel Oils by Modified Kjeldahl Method

ASTM D 4047—Test Method for Phosphorus in Lubricating Oils and Additives by Quinoline Phosphomolybdate Method

ASTM D 4628—Test Method for Analysis of Barium, Calcium, Magnesium, and Zinc in Unused Lubricating Oils by Atomic Absorption Spectrometry

ASTM D 4629—Test Method for Organically Bound Trace Nitrogen in Liquid Petroleum Hydrocarbons by Oxidative Combustion and Chemiluminescence Detection

ASTM D 4739—Test Method for Base Number Determination by Potentiometric Titration

ASTM D 4927—Test Methods for Elemental Analysis of Lubricant and Additive Components—Barium, Calcium, Phosphorus, Sulfur, and Zinc by Wavelength-Dispersive X-Ray Fluorescence Spectroscopy

ASTM D 4951—Determination of Additive Elements in Lubricating Oils by Inductively Coupled Plasma Atomic Emission Spectrometry

ASTM D 5185—Test Method for Determination of Additive Elements, Wear Metals, and Contaminants in Used Lubricating Oils by Inductively Coupled Plasma Atomic Emission Spectrometry

2.1.4 GOVERNMENT PUBLICATIONS—Available from the Standardization Documents Order Desk, Building 4D, 700 Robbins Avenue, Philadelphia, PA 19111-5094.

FED-STD-313—Material Safety Data, Transportation Data and Disposal Data for Hazardous Materials Furnished to Government Activities

FED-STD-791—Lubricants, Liquid Fuels and Related Products; Methods of Testing

2.1.5 U.S. DEPARTMENT OF LABOR (DOL) (OSHA)—Available from the OSHA Publication Office, Room S-4203, 200 Constitution Avenue, NW, Washington, DC 20210.

OSHA 29 CFR 1910.1200—Hazard Communication; Interpretation Regarding Lubricating Oils

3. Classification

3.1 Viscosity Grades—The lubricating oils shall be of the grades in Table 1:

TABLE 1—VISCOSITY GRADES

Viscosity Grade	Performance Level
SAE 15W-40	CF, CF-2, CG-4
SAE 30	CF, CF-2
SAE 40	CF, CF-2

4. Salient Characteristics

4.1 Materials—The engine lubricating oils shall be derived from petroleum fractions, synthetically-produced fractions, or a combination of the two types of products. They may be virgin or re-refined stocks or a combination thereof. The stocks shall be compounded with such functional additives (detergents, dispersants, oxidation inhibitor, corrosion inhibitors, etc.) as necessary to meet the specified requirements (see Sections 5 and 6).

4.2 Performance—The engine lubricants shall meet the SAE J300, the American Petroleum Institute (API) performance level identified herein and described in API Publication 1509. The lubricating oils shall carry the API donut symbol and shall meet all the requirements and characteristics for the performance level herein specified (see 3.1).

4.2.1 STORAGE AND COMPATIBILITY—The oils shall show no evidence of separation or color change when they are tested in accordance with FED-STD-791 (FTMS) Method 3470 and using designated reference oils as required by the test. Reference oils can be obtained from SAE. A test report for each formulation offered must be provided at the time of solicitation.

4.3 Physical and Chemical Requirements—The lubricating oils shall meet all the physical and chemical properties required for all the previously specified performance levels (see 3.1), SAE J300, and those in Table 2. Typical values are to be provided for each salient physical and chemical property listed in Table 2 for each formulation offered at the time of solicitation and for those properties required to meet the performance level herein specified (see 3.1), and SAE J300. Section 4.3.1 is required only for military contracts unless otherwise requested.

4.3.1 FORMULATION DATA—The contractor shall provide the name, type, percent, and manufacturer of all base stocks and additive packages for each formulation to be supplied under contract or order, or used in performance testing. Each formulation must be identified by a formula number or oil code, and if more than one code is used for a formulation, then all codes associated with that formulation must be indicated. In addition, the contractor must identify which formulation was used to run each performance test. This information shall be provided to the contracting officer at the time of solicitation.

4.3.1.1 Base Stocks—The contractor shall identify all base stocks used in each formulation offered or used in performance testing by base stock name, manufacturer, and type of base stock according to Appendix E of API 1509. The data listed in Table E-1 (Appendix E - API 1509) shall be included for all base stocks.

4.3.1.2 Additives—The contractor shall identify all additive systems used in each formulation offered or used in performance testing by additive package name, manufacturer, and type of additive system (i.e., Detergent Inhibitor (DI), Viscosity Improver Type (OCP, SIP, PMA, etc.), Pour Point Depressant, etc.). If there are read-across between different formulations, then an explanation on how the additive systems relate to one another must be provided.

5. Regulatory Requirements

5.1 Hazard Communication Standard—The stocks used shall not be considered carcinogenic or potentially carcinogenic as defined under the Hazard Communication Standard OSHA 29 CFR 1910.1200.

TABLE 2—LUBRICATING OIL PROPERTIES

Property	SAE 15W-40	SAE 30	SAE 40	ASTM Test Procedure or Federal Test Method Standard (FTMS)
Viscosity Kinematic, cSt @ 40 °C	X	X	X	D 445
Viscosity Index	X	X	X	D 2270
Pour Point, °C max.	–25	–18	–15	D 97
Stable Pour Point, °C max.	–25	—	—	FTMS 203
Flash Point, °C min.	215	220	225	D 92
Gravity, °API	X	X	X	D 287
Carbon Residue, Mass %	X	X	X	D 524
Sulfated Ash, Mass %	X	X	X	D 874
Total Acid Number	X	X	X	D 664
Base Number	X	X	X	D 2896, D 4739(1)
Phosphorus, Mass %	X	X	X	D 1091(1), D 4047, D 5185, D 4927, D 4951
Sulfur, Mass %	X	X	X	D 2622, D 4927, D 4951(1), D 5185
Nitrogen, Mass %	X	X	X	D 3228(1), D 4629
Metallic Components, Mass %	X	X	X	D 4628, D 4927, D 4951(1), D 5185

X = Report Typical Value.

1. Denotes preferred method.

5.2 Toxicity—The engine lubricating oil shall have no adverse effect on the health of personnel when used for its intended purpose. Questions pertinent to this effect shall be referred by the contracting activity to the appropriate departmental medical service who will act as an advisor to the contracting agency. The contractor shall have the toxicological formulations and associated information available for review by the contracting activity to evaluate the safety of the material for proposed use.

5.3 Recovered Material—The offeror/contractor is encouraged to use recovered materials in accordance with Public Law 94-580 to the maximum extent possible. When re-refined base stocks are sought, the minimum content to be used in the formulation shall be indicated in the contract or solicitation.

6. Quality Assurance Provisions

6.1 Contractor Certification—The contractor shall certify and maintain substantiating evidence, that the product offered meets the salient characteristics of this document, and that the product conforms to the producer's own drawings, specifications, standards, quality assurance practices, and the information provided in 6.4.

6.2 Market Acceptability (MA)—The contractor shall provide products which have a proven market record based on the number of items sold, length of time the product has been on the market, and reliability and performance of the products as required under the contract or solicitation.

TABLE 3—LUBRICANT TOLERANCES

Property	Tolerance Range(1)
Kinematic Viscosity @ 100 °C	X ± 1.00 cSt, but must fall within the herein specified limits.
Kinematic Viscosity @ 40 °C	X ± 10 cSt.
Apparent Viscosity, cP; @ –15 °C and @ –20 °C	SAE 15W-40 must meet requirement according to SAE J300
High Temperature/High Shear	SAE 15W-40 must meet requirement according to SAE J300
Pumpability @ –25 °C	SAE 15W-40 must meet requirement according to SAE J300
Viscosity Index	SAE grades 30 and 40 shall be ≥80.
Pour Point	Must meet requirement indicated in the physical and chemical requirements.
Flash Point	Meet requirement indicated in the physical and chemical requirements.
Gravity, °API	X ± 1.0 °API
Total Base Number	X ± 1 TBN number
Sulfur	0.90 x (typical value); minimum and 1.20 x (typical value), maximum
Nitrogen	0.90 x (typical value); minimum
Other Elements: Zinc, Phosphorus, Calcium, Magnesium, Barium, Sodium, Copper, Boron, and Molybdenum.	0.90 x (typical value); minimum, and 1.20 x (typical value); maximum

1. Tolerances will be calculated from the accepted typical physical and chemical properties provided at the time of the solicitation for each formulation identified.

6.3 Inspection and Test—The inspection and testing of products to be supplied under the document shall use the following tolerances. These will be used to determine acceptability of the physical and chemical properties of SAE grade products supplied under contract unless otherwise specified. The typical properties of the offered product(s) (see 4.3) will be used to assign tolerances according to Table 3. In no case will tolerances assigned, based on the typical properties provided, be outside the established limits indicated, including the SAE J300 viscosity requirements. The inspection and testing of products to be supplied under the document shall be specified in the contract or order.

6.4 Pre-Review Process—Awards will be made only for products which have been pre-reviewed by the Lubricant Review Institute Engine Oil Review Committee. The attention of the contractors is called to the requirement and manufacturers are urged to arrange to have their products pre-reviewed in order that they may be eligible to be awarded contracts or orders for the products covered by this document. Copies of the Lubricants Review Institute Engine Oil procedures are available from the Society of Automotive Engineers, Inc., 400 Commonwealth Drive, Warrendale, PA 15096-0001, Attention: Secretary of the Lubricant Review Institute.

7. Packaging

7.1 Preservation, Packaging, Packing, Labeling, and Marking—Preservation, packaging, labeling, and marking shall be as specified in the contract or order. The container will be as specified in the contract or order.

8. Notes

8.1 Ordering Data—The procuring agency should specify the preferred options permitted herein and include the following information in procurement documents:

a. Title, number, and date of this document.
b. SAE grade of oil required.
c. Quantity of oil required.
d. Type and unit of issue required.
e. The certification requirement as indicated in 5.1 must be included in the solicitation/contract.
f. When this document is used for procurement, the inspection and test clause must appear in the solicitation.
g. Market Acceptability requirements must appear in the solicitation.

8.2 National Stock Numbers (NSN)—The following NSN's are for use by the Government and do not constitute a requirement on the contractor, unless required by the contract or order. The lubricating oils provided under this document can be ordered using the NSN's in Table 4:

TABLE 4—NATIONAL STOCK NUMBERS

National Stock Numbers	SAE Viscosity Grade	Unit Issue
9150-01-352-2962	15W-40	5 gal plastic container
9150-01-351-9018		55 gal drum
9150-01-351-9016	30	Box 12 1-qt. plastic bottles
9150-01-352-8090		5 gal plastic container
9150-01-351-9015		55 gal drum
9150-01-352-8091	40	55 gal drum

EMISSIONS

13 Emissions

MEASUREMENT OF INTAKE AIR OR EXHAUST GAS FLOW OF DIESEL ENGINES—SAE J244 AUG1992

SAE Recommended Practice

Report of the SAE Automotive Emissions and Air Pollution Committee approved May 1971, completely revised by the SAE Automotive Emissions Committee June 1983. Completely revised by the SAE Diesel Emissions Standards Committee August 1992.

1. Scope—This procedure establishes recommendations on the measurement of diesel engine intake air flow under steady-state test conditions. The measurement methods discussed have been limited to metering systems and associated equipment found in common usage in the industry, specifically, nozzles, laminar flow devices, and vortex shedding. The procedure establishes accuracy goals as well as explains proper usage of equipment. The recommendations concerning diesel engine exhaust mass flow measurements are minimal in scope.

1.1 Purpose—This SAE Recommended Practice is intended to provide guidance for the proper measurement of combustion air flow into diesel engines as utilized in engine test cell environments.

2. References

2.1 Applicable Publications—The following publications form a part of the specification to the extent specified herein. Unless otherwise indicated the lastest revision of SAE publications shall apply.

1. SAE J177—Measurement of Carbon Dioxide, Carbon Monoxide, and Oxides of Nitrogen in Diesel Exhaust.
2. ASME PTC 19.5:4-1959—"Flow Measurement."
3. "Fluid Meters, Their Theory and Application," ASME, Sixth Edition, New York, 1971.
4. ISA 1979, ISBN 87664-453-3, Tutorial, "Test Measurement Accuracy."
5. Voss, L. R., and Hollyer, R. N., "GMR True Radius Nozzles," General Motors Research Laboratories, Warren, MI, January 1961.
6. "Tables of Thermal Properties of Gases," National Bureau of Standards Circular 564, 1960.

3. Definitions—Symbols and Abbreviations

3.1 Abbreviations

abs—Absolute
cal—Calibration
exh—Exhaust
rpm—Revolutions per minute
vol—Volume
mo—Moist

3.2 Symbols—SI Units (English Units)

B—Barometric pressure, kPa (in Hg); abs
C—Coefficient of discharge
D—Upstream pipe diameter, mm (in)
E—Velocity of approach factor
Fa—Area thermal expansion factor
MW—Molecular weight, kg/kg-mole (lbm/lbm-mole)
N_H—Hodgson's number
N_R—Reynolds number
P—Pressure, kPa (in Hg)
Q—Volume flow rate, m^3/s (ft^3/s)
RU—Universal gas constant, 8314.4 J/kg-K (1545.3 ft-lb/lbm mole °R)
R—Gas constant, specific gas, J/kg-K (ft-lbf/lbm-°R)
SW—Swept volume, m^3 (ft^3)
T—Temperature, Kelvin (°Rankine)
U—Uncertainty
V—Velocity, m/s (ft/s)
Y—Expansion factor
Z—Compressibility factor
b—Bias error
d—Nozzle throat diameter, mm (in)
e—Vapor pressure, kPa (in Hg, abs)
f—Frequency, Hz
k—Ratio of specific heats
m—Mass flow per unit time, kg/s (lbm/s)
t—Ambient temperature, °Celsius (°Fahrenheit)
μ—Viscosity, absolute, centipoise
β—Ratio of nozzle throat diameters (throat or orifice to pipe diameter)
ρ—Density, kg/m^3 (lbm/ft^3)
σ—Precision error
Y—Ratio of specific heats, 1.40 for air
ΔP—Pressure differential, kPa (in H_2O)

3.3 Subscripts

A—absolute
d—Dry
dt—Dry at test conditions
t—Test
mo—Moist
(test)—Test conditions
(cal)—Calibration conditions
L—Leakage
v—Vapor
1—Location point at meter inlet
2—Location point at meter outlet

4. Principal Equipment

4.1 Component Description—Components necessary for measurements are as described as follows and as in Figure 1:

a. Filter — Only as required by flow meter.
b. Flow meter — As described in Section 5.
c. Nonpulsating blower — Optional, to restore pressure loss due to flow meter and temperature control.
d. Temperature control — Optional.
e. Restriction valve — To control engine inlet air pressure.
f. Plenum — See 4.2.
g. Engine.
h. Pressure sensors, P_1, P_2, P_3, and P_4.
i. Temperature sensors, T_1, T_2, T_3, and T_4.
j. Chamber to engine line may be flexible. Should be minimum length; diameter selected on basis of maximum velocity not to exceed 90 m/s.
k. Restriction valve — Optional, to control engine back pressure. Locate the valve at usual muffler position. However, if muffler location is unknown, it is recommended that the valve be located 20 diameters of exhaust pipe from the engine exhaust flange.

4.2 Plenum Chamber Volume—Due to the nature of diesel engines, pressure pulsations in the air measurement system may be present. In general, pulsations in the systems have adverse effects on most air flow metering devices and must be controlled for proper air flow measurements. A plenum chamber between the meter and the engine air intake can help isolate the meter by attenuating the pulsations.

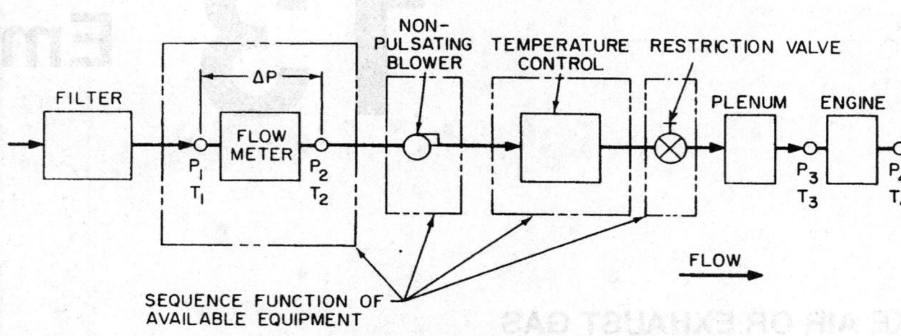

FIGURE 1—COMPONENT FIGURATION

4.2.1 The minimum recommended plenum chamber volume should conform to Equation 1:

$$\text{vol} = \frac{K \times SW}{\text{rpm} \times \sqrt{\text{Stroke/Rev}}} \quad \text{(Eq. 1)}$$

where:

vol	=	Volume of plenum chamber	m^3	in^3
SW	=	Swept volume of one cylinder	L	in^3
rpm	=	Lowest engine speed at which air flow measurements are to be made	rpm	rpm
Stroke/Rev	=	Number of intake strokes per engine revolution		
K	=	Dimensionless constant.		
		Suggested values are:		
		Naturally aspirated diesel w/nozzle	180	180 000
		Naturally aspirated diesel w/o nozzle	90	90 000
		Other meters and engines	90	90 000

4.2.2 The plenum may be excluded if test data show that the engine and flow meter are insensitive to the plenum chamber volume. The check, as follows, may help determine the effect of the pressure pulsations.

a. The frequency of the pulsations should be determined at a point between the flow meter and the plenum chamber.
b. Low-pressure transducers or microphones can be used to sense the pulsations with their output fed into a narrow-band frequency analyzer or FFT (Fast Fourier Transform analyzer).
c. Determine the effect of the pulsations by Equation 2:

$$N_H = \frac{\text{Vol} \cdot f \cdot \Delta P \cdot K_H}{Q \cdot P_A} \quad \text{(Eq. 2)}$$

where:

			Metric	English
N_H	=	Hodgson Number	m^3	ft^3
Vol	=	Volume of the flow system (piping between the pulsation source and the meter)		
f	=	Frequency of the pulsations	H_Z	H_Z
Q	=	Average volume rate of flow	m^3/s	ft^3/min
ΔP	=	Average pressure drop in the system from pulsation sources to the meter		
P_A	=	Average absolute pressure at the meter	kPa	in Hg
K_H	=	Units conversion	1.0	4.42

d. The Hodgson Number(N_H should be larger than 2 to minimize the errors due to pulsations. For air flow measurement systems the effects of pulsations must be minimized by isolating the meter from the source, since there is no known correction factor.
e. With vortex-shedding meters it is important that the pulsation frequencies near the meter shedding frequencies be minimized in amplitude.

5. Measurement Systems—Whenever possible, a flow measuring system per 4.1 should be used. The flow meter, nonpulsating blower, plenum, temperature control, and restriction valve may be combined in a single unit.

5.1 Flow Nozzle—The smooth approach nozzle is one of the most commonly used meters for diesel-engine air flow measurements. Classed as a head-type meter, it has a converging inlet section which blends smoothly into a reduced cylindrical cross-section or throat. The purpose of the convergent inlet is to direct the air to the throat in a well-defined, uniform manner. The reduced cross-section appreciably accelerates the flowing air and produces a differential pressure between the entrance and the throat. The convergent section can be of several forms. The ASME long and short radius nozzle, as well as the true-radius nozzle (see Appendix A), are examples of some of these forms. Each of these types of nozzles has similar but slightly different flow characteristics that are accounted for in their coefficient of discharge factors. Otherwise the flow calculations for each type of nozzle are the same. It is assumed for this document that the meters will be used to measure diesel-engine air flow at or near normal room temperatures and pressures. If temperature or pressure extremes are anticipated, it is recommended that a fluid metering handbook be consulted. Common installations are shown in Figures 2 to 4.

5.1.1 NOZZLE SELECTION—Commercial nozzles are available to cover most testing needs. Selection of several nozzles of different throat diameters will usually be needed to cover the flow range of most engines.

5.1.2 CALIBRATION—Each nozzle and its adjacent sections should be calibrated over its entire flow range. Systems that conform to Figure 2 can delete the pipe sections; and, if standard ASME nozzles are used, calibration can be substituted with discharge coefficient equations presented in 7.2.2. The accuracy of the air flow measurement depends directly on the accuracy of the calibration (see 7.2 for sources of error). The accuracy goal should be dictated by the uses of the data. Diesel engine inlet air flow is used in several basic engine performance calculations and can be required to be within 2% of reading.

There is more than one acceptable method used to calibrate nozzle flow meters. The volumetric tank system described in Appendix B is the preferred method. An alternate method is to place the nozzle flow meter to be calibrated in series with a previously calibrated flow meter and record related data throughout their mutual range. The data to be recorded are described in Section 7.

Recalibration and leak checking of the system are recommended whenever any changes are made to adjacent pipe sections or when any wear or contamination occurs to the nozzle in its approaching section or in the throat. With care in use and cleaning, a nozzle flow meter should not need periodic recalibration.

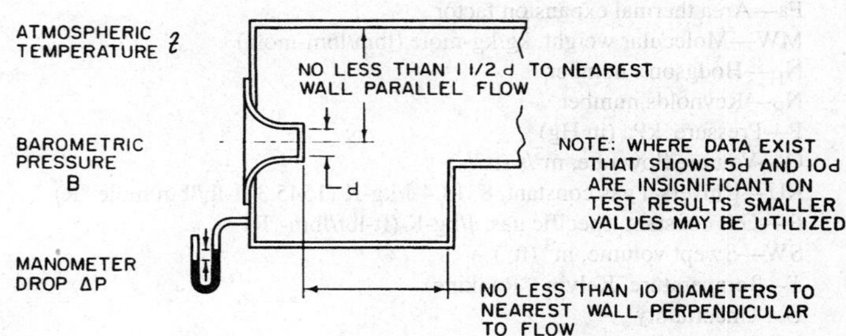

FIGURE 2—NOZZLE DISCHARGING FROM ATMOSPHERE INTO A VESSEL

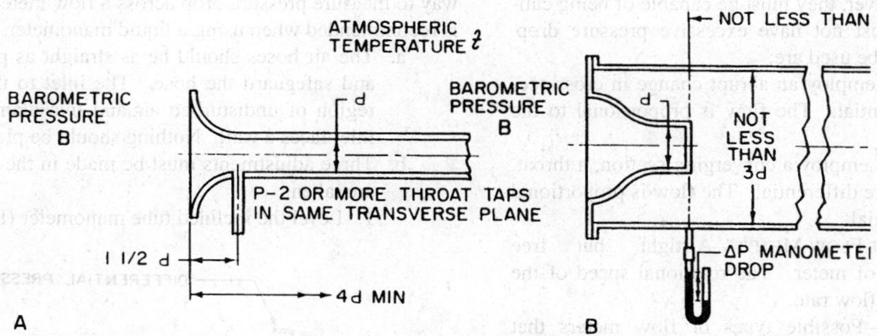

FIGURE 3—NOZZLE DISCHARGING FROM ATMOSPHERE INTO A PIPE

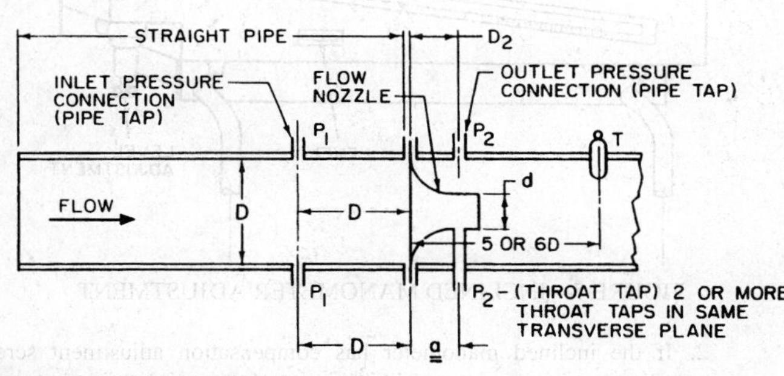

FIGURE 4—NOZZLE IN A PIPE

5.2 Laminar Flow Meter—The metering element consists of a large number of narrow flow passages arranged in parallel (Figure 5). The structure must be sufficiently rigid to assure fixed geometry in normal handling between calibration tests. The meter size must be selected such that the flow through the metering element is laminar in nature under all test conditions. When the flow is laminar, the pressure drop across the meter is directly proportional to the gas velocity through the meter and the time average pressure drop is directly proportional to the time average volumetric flow rate. The meter can be used to measure slightly pulsating flows when the peak flow rates are well within the laminar range, and a true time average pressure drop can be read. In principle, for the same accuracy, a laminar flow meter can be used over a broader flow range than head-type meters, since the flow is directly proportional to the pressure drop rather than the square root of the pressure drop. Although the laminar flow meter has some desirable features, it requires cleaning and frequent periodic recalibration to maintain its accuracy.

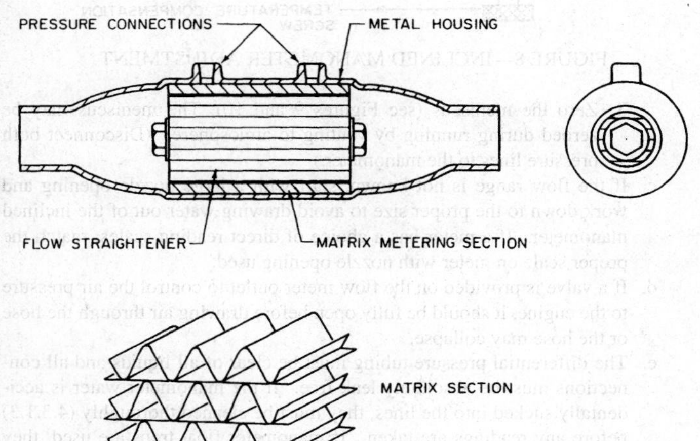

FIGURE 5—GENERAL CONSTRUCTION OF LAMINAR FLOW ELEMENT

5.2.1 METER SELECTION—Commercial meters are available that are designed to optimum proportions to assure laminar flow, if the manufacturer's installation recommendations are followed. Flow straighteners and viscous dampers in the pressure taps should be used when recommended by the manufacturers.

5.2.2 CALIBRATION—Each flow meter should be calibrated over its entire flow range. If the installation deviates from that recommended by the flow meter manufacturer, the flow meter should be calibrated with its adjacent piping. The accuracy of the air flow measurement is dependent directly on the accuracy of the calibration. The accuracy goal should be determined by the uses of the data. Diesel engine inlet air flow is used in several basic engine performance calculations and can be required to be within 2% of reading.

There is more than one acceptable method used to calibrate laminar flow meters. The volumetric tank system described in Appendix B is the preferred method. An alternate method is to place the flow meter to be calibrated in series with a previously calibrated flow meter and record related data throughout their mutual flow range. The data to be recorded are described in Section 7.

Recalibration of the flow meter is recommended on a periodic basis because the metering section can have a change in coefficient due to a build-up of material on the interior walls. Care in upstream filtering and periodic cleaning can help minimize the need for recalibration.

5.3 Vortex Shedding Meters—Vortex shedding meters are those which detect the rate at which a continuous series of eddies are formed in the wake of a nonstreamlined body in a flow field. Boundary layer separation occurs alternately on one side of the body and then the other. The rate at which the vortices are shed has been shown to be a function only of the fluid velocity for Reynolds numbers above 1000 to 2000. Sensing of the vortex shedding frequency can be performed by several techniques and varies depending on the manufacturer and application.

5.3.1 METER SELECTION—Commercial units are available to cover a wide range of flows. Careful sizing and selection may enable the use of a single device over the entire flow range of the engine, since turn-down ratios of 10:1 and 20:1 can be achieved with an accuracy of 1% of reading.

5.3.2 CALIBRATION—Commercial vortex meters are generally supplied with a single calibration coefficient to be used over the entire flow range. This calibration should be verified with the meter installed as it will be used in an engine test. The accuracy goal should be determined by the uses of the data. Diesel engine inlet air flow is used in several basic engine performance calculations and can be required to be within 2% of reading. When the air flow measurements are to be this accurate, it is recommended to correct for changes in the calibration coefficient rather than using a single number.

The calibration data can be represented by a power series polynomial using a least-squares regression technique. Care should be taken that the resulting equation accurately represents the calibration data. This is best done by graphically displaying the equation and the original data on the same plot. The equation should not be used to compute flows outside the range of calibration. Generally a second- or third-order polynomial will provide an equation that will represent the calibration data within 1/2% (see 7.4.1 for a reference calculation).

There is more than one accepted technique for calibrating vortex flow meters. The necessity to calibrate the flow meter in its installation makes it desirable to place a calibrated flow meter such as a nozzle system in series and record related data throughout their mutual flow range. The data to be recorded are described in Section 7.

5.4 Other Flow Meters—Other types of flow meters may be used in addition to the previously named types. However, they must be capable of being calibrated to the required accuracy and must not have excessive pressure drop. Examples of other flow meters that could be used are:

5.4.1 ORIFICE METERS—These meters employ an abrupt change in cross-sectional area to produce a pressure differential. The flow is proportional to the square root of this pressure differential.

5.4.2 VENTURI METERS—These meters employ a converging section, a throat, and diverging section to produce a pressure differential. The flow is proportional to the square root of this pressure differential.

5.4.3 ROTARY POSITIVE DISPLACEMENT FLOW METER—Airtight, but free moving, impellers characterize this type of meter. The rotational speed of the impellers is proportional to the volume of flow rate.

5.4.4 MISCELLANEOUS FLOW METERS—Possible types of flow meters that could be used, but are not commonly used, are hot wire anemometers, mechanical anemometers, heat injection meters, chamber gas meters, and variable area meters.

6. Measurement System Preparation

6.1 Test for Airtightness of Air Metering System—Care must be exercised to prevent unmetered air from entering the engine. Even small leaks result in substantial errors when the flow rates are in the 20 to 200 kg/h (50 to 500 lb/h) range. Air leaks can be present in any of the air metering system's sections Figure 1. The following is an acceptable method for establishing the leakage rate for typical metering systems:

a. Cap both ends of the assembly (Figure 1) and pressurize or evacuate the system, depending on how it is used in normal operation, to about 3 kPa gage (12 in H_2O). Shut off the air supply and record the time for the pressure gage to reach about 1.5 kPa (6 in H_2O).
b. Calculate the leakage rate with the following formula:

$$m_\ell = \frac{K_\ell \cdot \Delta P \cdot Vol}{Time} \quad \text{(Eq. 3)}$$

where:

m_ℓ = mass flow of leak
vol = volume of system
time = time for pressure change
ΔP = amount of pressure change
K_ℓ = unit conversion constant

c. Acceptable leakage rate for this procedure is 0.5% of the lowest air flow rate to be measured during testing.

An alternate technique for measuring leak rate is to seal both ends of the system and directly measure the leak rate with the installation shown in Figure 6. The system is pressurized to its maximum operating pressure or depressurized to its minimum operating pressure depending on normal operation using the throttling valve to regulate flow. The leakage rate is read directly off the flow meter since the "make-up" air flowing into the system to maintain the system at constant pressure is equal to the air leaking out of the system.

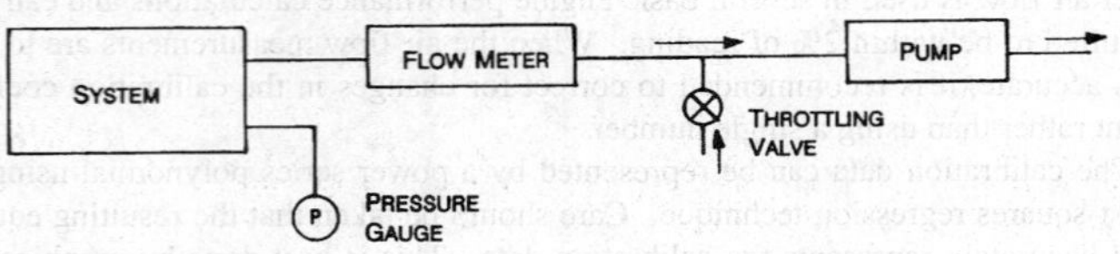

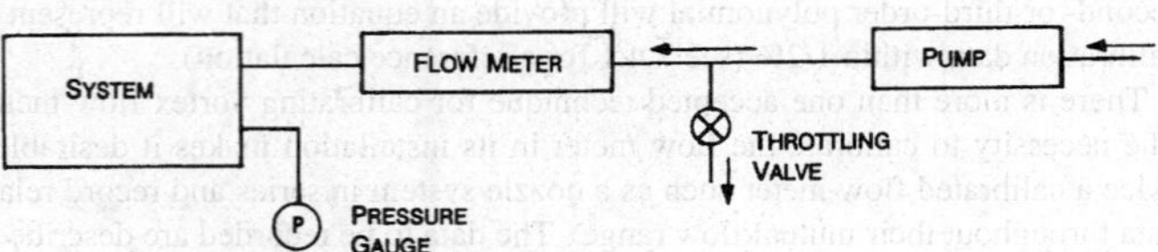

FIGURE 6—INSTALLATION FOR MEASURING LEAK RATE

6.2 Inclined Manometer Operation—There is more than one acceptable way to measure pressure drop across a flow meter. The procedure described here is recommended when using a liquid manometer.

a. The air hoses should be as straight as possible to reduce pressure drop and safeguard the hose. The inlet to the meter should be placed in a region of undisturbed air and five diameters clearance provided if the inlet faces a wall. Nothing should be placed in front of the air nozzle.
b. Three adjustments must be made in the order listed before any readings are taken:
   1. Level the inclined tube manometer (Figure 7).

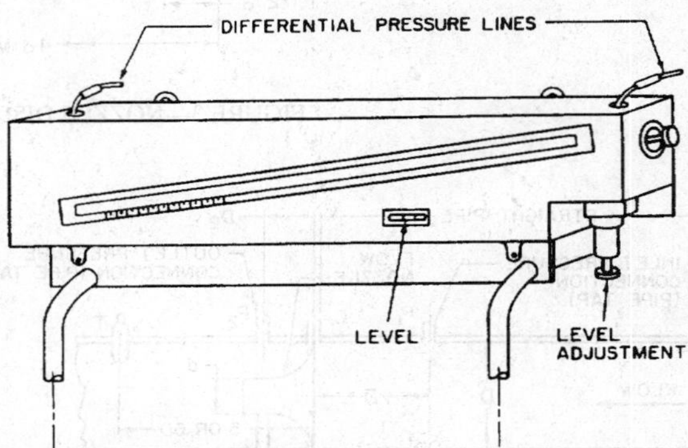

FIGURE 7—INCLINED MANOMETER ADJUSTMENT

   2. If the inclined manometer has compensation adjustment screws, adjust settings to agree with the current meter inlet air temperature and absolute pressure per the manufacturer's instructions. (Figure 8 shows one example of a compensating manometer.)

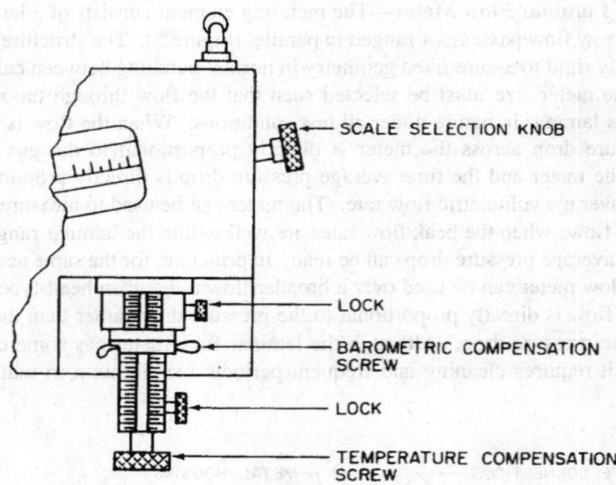

FIGURE 8—INCLINED MANOMETER ADJUSTMENT

   3. Zero the meniscus (see Figures 9 and 10). The meniscus may be zeroed during running by venting to atmosphere. (Disconnect both pressure lines to the manometer.)
c. If the flow range is not known, start with a large nozzle opening and work down to the proper size to avoid drawing water out of the inclined manometer. If a meter has a choice of direct reading scales, match the proper scale on meter with nozzle opening used.
d. If a valve is provided on the flow meter outlet to control the air pressure to the engine, it should be fully open before drawing air through the hose or the hose may collapse.
e. The differential pressure tubing must be clear of all liquids and all connections must be absolutely leak free. If the manometer water is accidentally sucked into the lines, they must be cleaned thoroughly (4.3.1.3) before any readings are taken. If manometer float traps are used, they must drain back completely after being wetted by fluid.

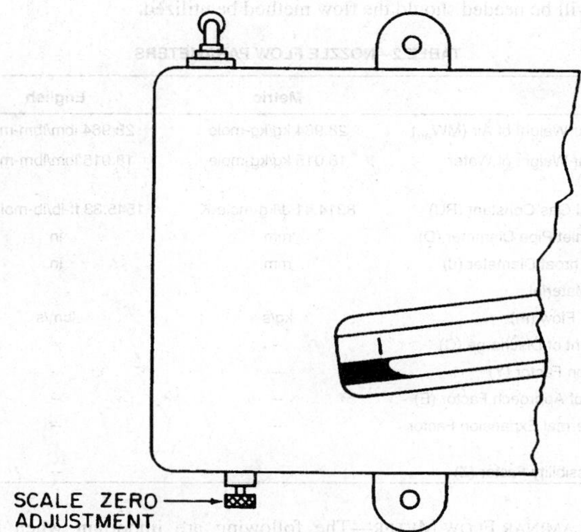

FIGURE 9—INCLINED MANOMETER ADJUSTMENT

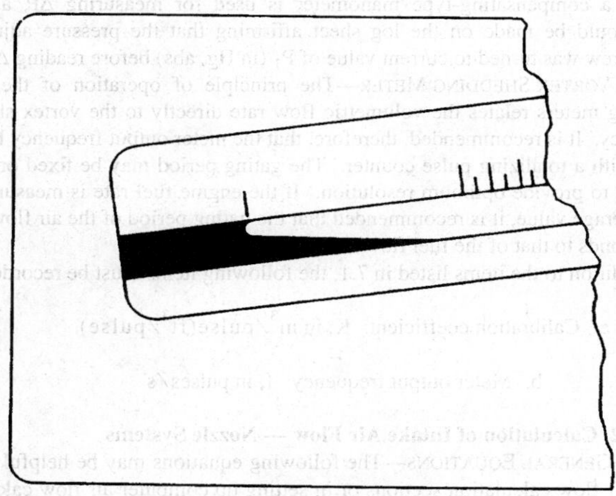

FIGURE 10—INCLINED MANOMETER ADJUSTMENT

f. The pressure differential (ΔP) must be measured directly, using an inclined manometer or micromanometer graduated to permit resolution of 0.1% of the smallest ΔP to be measured. The zero reading must be checked after readings are taken on the lower 25% of the manometer scale (it is recommended that the lower 10% of scale be avoided where possible), and must be less than 0.1% of the lowest value of ΔP measured.

6.2.1 MAINTENANCE

a. Manometers must be cleaned periodically to remove wall deposits. This is particularly important for inclined manometers where errors can be caused by changes in the force of adhesion between the liquid and the tube wall.
b. Inclined manometers should be calibrated with a deadweight tester or micromanometer after cleaning to assure accuracy and verify the use of the correct fluid and wetting agents.

6.3 Flow Nozzles—There are certain standard operating criteria which should be observed if maximum accuracy is to be obtained.

a. Fluid flow velocity should be in the turbulent region, but below sonic velocity. Calculations will be simplified and mistakes minimized by restricting the ΔP range of 0.25 to 2.5 kPa (1 to 10 in H_2O).
b. When a wide range of flows is to be encountered, the measuring element should be changed when necessary to remain within pressure differential limits.
c. For maximum accuracy, the element should be sized to produce as high a pressure differential as possible. However, if the ΔP exceeds the range specified in 4.3.2.1(a), then the adiabatic expansion factor should be considered to account for gas expansion at the nozzle throat.

6.3.1 PRESSURE MEASUREMENT—Since all flow measurements depend on the pressure drop across the nozzle, the following is recommended for accuracy:

a. Inlet Pressures
   1. If the nozzle is installed at the inlet of a plenum chamber (Figure 2), or at the inlet of a pipe (Figure 3), no inlet pressure connections are required and the atmospheric pressure is considered to be the inlet pressure.
   2. If the nozzle is installed in a continuous pipe (Figure 4), the inlet pressure connections shall be placed at one pipe diameter preceding the entrance plane of the nozzle.
b. Outlet Pressures
   1. If the nozzle is installed at the inlet of a plenum chamber (Figure 2), the outlet pressure shall be considered to be pressure in the chamber.
   2. If the nozzle is installed at the inlet of a pipe (Figure 3A), the outlet pressure throat taps shall be located 1-1/2 pipe diameters following the entrance plane. If the nozzle is installed at the inlet of a pipe (Figure 3B), the outlet pressure throat tap should be located in the same plane as the nozzle exit per Figure 3B.
   3. If the nozzle is located in a continuous pipe (Figure 4) and outlet pressure connection is a pipe tap, it shall be located one-half pipe diameter following the nozzle entrance plane. If the outlet pressure connection is a throat tap, there shall be two or more taps located one-half pipe diameter following the nozzle entrance plane if the nozzle is a high β series, or 1–1/2 pipe diameters following the nozzle entrance plane if the nozzle is a low β series. (See ASME PTC 19.5:4-1959 and Appendix B for nozzle specifications.)
c. Pressure Differential Measurement—The difference between the nozzle inlet and outlet pressure (ΔP) must be read directly from the scale of a manometer. The manometer may be calibrated in pressure units or to read in flow units directly. See 4.3.3.2(f) for requirements.

6.4 Laminar Flow Meter

6.4.1 INSTALLATION REQUIREMENTS

a. An air filter is recommended, and is usually required in most applications upstream of the meter. Laminar flow meters must be protected from airborne dirt and oily vapors.
b. Instrumentation must be provided to measure P_1, T_1, and ΔP. See Figure 1. Commercial meter manufacturers usually provide proper instrumentation locations on the meters for these purposes.
c. If a compensating-type manometer is used (see Figures 7 and 8) to measure ΔP, the steps recommended by the meter manufacturer must be inserted in the appropriate order in 6.2. The pressure adjustment must compensate for losses upstream of the metering element such as filters, pipe elbows, etc.

6.4.2 MAINTENANCE

a. Filters must be replaced as recommended by the meter manufacturer or when the total pressure loss through the intake system exceeds test requirements.
b. Frequent calibrations are required to assure accuracy.
c. Cleaning is required only when there is a large shift in flow between calibration periods. The meter should be cleaned by the manufacturer or by following the manufacturer's cleaning instructions.

6.5 Vortex Shedding Meters

6.5.1 INSTALLATION REQUIREMENTS—Due to the nature of the vortex shedding phenomenon and the sensing devices used, it is important that the velocity profile entering the metering section be uniform, fully developed and free of large-scale turbulence. This dictates the following requirements:

a. The piping both before and after the metering section shall be of the same diameter as the metering section.
b. The inside of the piping should be reasonably smooth and free of surface irregularities such as weld beads or gasket protrusions. All upstream surface irregularities should be less than 1/2% of the nominal pipe diameter.
c. The length of the straight pipe required before the meter section depends on the type of transition or obstruction. The user should follow standard installation recommendations for ASME orifice meters or the table in Figure 11.
d. Any air inlet restriction control device should be installed at least five diameters downstream of the meter section.
e. Deviations from these installation recommendations should be used only if the user has experimentally verified that the accuracy of the meter has not been affected by the installation. Compensation for an apparent calibration shift is not recommended because this is usually caused by instability.

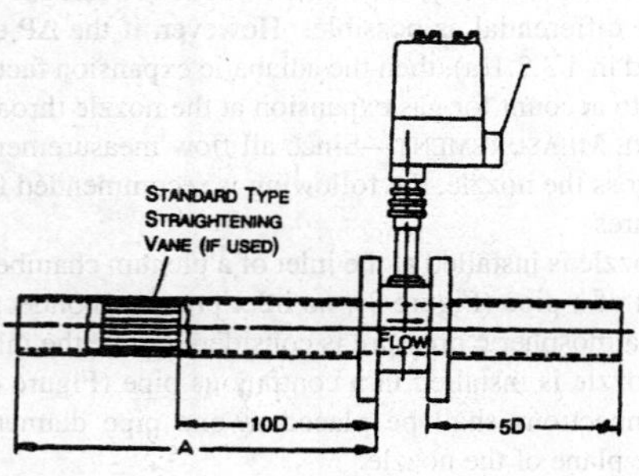

Upstream Fitting or Obstruction	Recommended Dimension A Without Vanes	Recommended Dimension A With Vanes
90-degree Elbow	20 D	15 D
Two 90-degree Elbows Same Plane	25 D	15 D
Two 90-degree Elbows Different Planes	40 D	15 D
Reduction in Pipe Diameter	20 D	15 D
Expansion in Pipe Diameter	40 D	20 D
Valve Partially Closed or Regulator	Recommend Motor Upstream	Recommend Motor Upstream

FIGURE 11—INSTALLATION OF VORTEX SHEDDING METER

6.5.2 PRESSURE MEASUREMENT—Instrumentation shall be provided for monitoring the static pressure at the meter. The pressure tap should be located between two and six diameters upstream of the meter section.

6.5.3 TEMPERATURE MEASUREMENT—Instrumentation shall be provided for monitoring the air temperature at the meter. The sensor should be located between two and ten diameters downsteam of the meter section.

7. Air Flow Measurement

7.1 General Measured Data—Table 1 lists the data recommended to be obtained at test time to measure engine intake air flow with the common air meters.

TABLE 1—RECOMMENDED DATA MEASUREMENTS

	Metric	English
Engine Speed	rpm	rpm
Fuel Flow Rate	kg/s	lbm/s
Atmospheric Conditions		
Barometric Pressure (Pa)	kPa	in Hg
Dry Bulb Temp	°C	°F
Wet Bulb or Dew Point	°C	°F
Water Vapor Pressure (P_v)	kPa	in Hg
Pressures		
Flow Meter Inlet (P_1)	kPa	in Hg
Flow Meter Outlet (P_2)	kPa	in Hg
Differential Across Flow Meter (ΔP)	kPa	in H_2O
Temperatures		
Flow Meter Inlet (T_1)	K	°R
Flow Meter Outlet (T_2)	K	°R

The following meter specific parameters should be recorded:

Air meter — Make and Model Number
Serial Number
Calibration Date

7.1.1 FLOW NOZZLE —For nozzle-type air meters, the parameters shown in Table 2 will be needed should the flow method be utilized.

TABLE 2—NOZZLE FLOW PARAMETERS

	Metric	English
Molecular Weight of Air (MW_{air})	28.964 kg/kg-mole	28.964 lbm/lbm-mole
Molecular Weight of Water (MW_{H2O})	18.015 kg/kg-mole	18.015 lbm/lbm-mole
Universal Gas Constant (RU)	8314.41 J/kg-mole-K	1545.33 ft-lb/lb-mole-°R
Nozzle Inlet Pipe Diameter (D)	mm	in
Nozzle Throat Diameter (d)	mm	in
Nozzle Material		
Air Mass Flow (m)	kg/s	lbm/s
Coefficient of Discharge (C)	--	--
Expansion Factor (Y)	--	--
Velocity of Approach Factor (E)	--	--
Area Thermal Expansion Factor (Fa)	--	--
Compressibility Factor (Z)	--	--

7.1.2 LAMINAR FLOW METER—The following are important when using a laminar flow meter:

a. Pressure (P_1), temperature (T_1), and ΔP must be measured at the taps provided at the inlet and exit of the metering element by the manufacturer.
b. If a compensating-type manometer is used for measuring ΔP, an entry should be made on the log sheet affirming that the pressure adjustment screw was turned to current value of P_1 (in Hg, abs) before reading ΔP.

7.1.3 VORTEX SHEDDING METER—The principle of operation of the vortex shedding meters relates the volumetric flow rate directly to the vortex shedding frequency. It is recommended, therefore, that the meter output frequency be measured with a totalizing pulse counter. The gating period may be fixed or can be selected to provide optimum resolution. If the engine fuel rate is measured as a time average value, it is recommended that the gating period of the air flow meter corresponds to that of the fuel flow measurement.

In addition to the items listed in 7.1, the following items must be recorded:

a. Calibration coefficient: K; in $m^3/\text{pulse}(ft^3/\text{pulse})$ (Eq. 4)

b. Meter output frequency: f; in pulses/s (Eq. 5)

7.2 Calculation of Intake Air Flow — Nozzle Systems

7.2.1 GENERAL EQUATIONS—The following equations may be helpful for use in the air flow calculation sections or in setting up computer air flow calculation routines.

a. Water vapor pressure (P_v): See SAE J177 for humidity calculation equations, or determine the vapor pressure from a psychometric chart.
b. Ambient pressure (absolute, upstream of meter):

$$P_{abs} = B + P_1 \text{ ; kPa(inHg), abs} \quad \text{(Eq. 6)}$$

c. Molecular weight of air-water vapor mixture:

$$MW_{mo} = \left[\frac{MW_{air} \cdot (P_{abs} - P_v) + MW_{H_2O} \cdot P_v}{P_{abs}}\right] \text{; kg/kg-mole (lbm/lbm-mole)} \quad \text{(Eq. 7)}$$

d. Gas constant of mixture:

$$R_{mo} = Ru/MW_{mo} \text{ ; J/kg-k (ft-lbf/lbm-°R)} \quad \text{(Eq. 8)}$$

e. Density of mixture:

$$P_{mo} = \frac{P_{abs}}{K_p \cdot R_{mix} \cdot T_{pabs}} \text{ ; kg/m}^3 \text{ (lbm/ft}^3\text{)} \quad \text{(Eq. 9)}$$

where:
$K_p = 1.000 \times 10^{-3}$; SI units
$K_p = 1.414 \times 10^{-2}$; English units

f. Viscosity of air:

$$\mu = V_L + (NV^*(V_H - V_L)) \quad \text{(Eq. 10)}$$

where:

N = $3.895635 \times 10^{-4} + (1.083746 * NT) + (-8.467568 \times 10^{-2} \times (NT^{-2}))$
NT = $(T_t - T_L)/(T_H - T_L)$
T_t = Temperature of air at test conditions

Temperature Units	T_L	T_H
degree C	−17.78	87.78
degree F	0.0	190.00
degree K	255.37	360.93
degree R	459.69	649.69

Viscosity Units (μ)	V_L	V_H
Centipoise	1.626699E-2	2.212111E-2
lbm/sec-ft	1.093095E-5	1.425330E-5

NOTE—Equation 10 is with ± 0.01% of NBS data over the range of -18 to 88 °C (0 to 190 °F).

g. Reynolds number:

$$N_R = \frac{K_{NR} \cdot \dot{m}}{\pi \cdot d \cdot \mu} \quad \text{(Eq. 11)}$$

where:

$K_{NR} = 4.0 \times 10^6$ (SI Units)
$K_{NR} = 48.0$ (English Units)

7.2.2 NOZZLE CALIBRATION

a. Calibrated Nozzle System—From the calibration data of the flow nozzle a table or curve should be constructed of ΔP versus air mass flow (or volume flow—if it is referenced to the calibration air density). If the air flow is being used in computerized data reduction routines, the calibration data may be represented by a power series least-squares polynomial equation. It generally takes fourth- to eighth-order equations to accurately fit the calibration curve. The calibration data may also be plotted on log-log coordinates in which case a linear curve is obtained. It is recommended that the calibration data for one nozzle not be used for other similar-sized nozzles unless it has been shown that the flow characteristics, meter surface finish, and throat diameters are identical. If the nozzle is used at air densities other than that at which the measurement system was calibrated, the air flow determined from the calibration chart or equation must be multiplied by the correction factor shown in 7.2.4.2.
b. Uncalibrated Nozzle System—If the nozzle has unknown flow characteristics or is to be used in a measurement system not conforming to the recommendations shown in Figures 2, 3, or 4, then the measurement system must be calibrated. If the nozzle was made according to the specifications for the ASME long-radius nozzle or the true-radius nozzle, and it is installed in a flow measurement system equivalent to one of those shown in Figures 2, 3, or 4, then as a second alternative to calibration the air flow can be calculated using the General Flow Equation. The General Flow Equation will produce calculation results within about ± 2%.

7.2.3 GENERAL FLOW EQUATION—CALCULATED NOZZLE FLOW—The General Flow Equation for nozzles is the result of combining several fundamental flow principles such as conservation of energy, ideal gas relationships, flow continuity, etc., into a basic equation that describes the flow of ideal gases through a nozzle. However, in order to account for the real world characteristics of gases, such as compressibility, viscosity, etc., the basic equation is generalized by including various factors that account for the differences between ideal and real gases. Since these modifying factors affect the basic equation in various degrees, the user must determine which factors are significant enough to be included in the flow calculation after considering the desired calculation accuracy, the repetitiveness of the calculation, and the availability of computers.

a. General Flow Equation:

$$\dot{m}_{mo} = Kg \cdot C \cdot Y \cdot E \cdot Fa \cdot d^2 \sqrt{\frac{\rho_{mo} \cdot \Delta P}{Z}} \quad \text{(Eq. 12)}$$

where:

$Kg = 3.5124 \times 10^{-5}$ (9.9702×10^{-2})

b. Coefficient of Discharge:

$$C = \frac{\text{Actual Rate of Flow}}{\text{Theoretical Rate of Flow}} \quad \text{(Eq. 13)}$$

The coefficient of discharge should in all cases be taken into account in the General Flow Equation 12 since its absence introduces a 1 to 4% calculation error for typical nozzles used for measuring diesel engine air flows. In other cases the error may be as great as 8% for the flow nozzles. The coefficient of discharge can best be determined by calibrating the nozzle as in Appendix B, and dividing the actual mass flow rate determined from the calibration procedure by the theoretical mass flow rate from Equation 12 with the C set equal to one. If the nozzle in use was made according to the specifications for an ASME long-radius nozzle or a true-radius nozzle (see Appendix A), as a second alternative to an actual calibration of the nozzle, one of the coefficient of discharge equations as follows can be used:

1. ASME Long-Radius Nozzle

$$C = 0.19436 + (0.152884 \times (\ln N_R)) - (0.0097785 \times (\ln N_R)^2) + (2.093 \times 10^{-4} \times (\ln N_R)^3) \quad \text{(Eq. 14)}$$

2. True-Radius Nozzle

$$C = 1 - \frac{8.36}{\sqrt{N_R}} \quad \text{(Eq. 15)}$$

c. Expansion Factor — Y:

$$Y = \left[r^{(2/\gamma)} \left(\frac{\gamma}{\gamma - 1}\right) \left(\frac{1 - r(\gamma - 1/\gamma)}{1 - r}\right) \left(\frac{1 - \beta^4}{1 - (\beta^4 \cdot r^{(2/\gamma)})}\right) \right]^{1/2} \quad \text{(Eq. 16)}$$

where:

$$r = 1 - \frac{\Delta P}{P_A} \text{ or } \left(\frac{P_A - \Delta P}{P_A}\right)$$

P_A = ambient absolute pressure (upstream of meter)
ΔP = nozzle pressure drop (same units as P_A)
γ = ratio of specific heats (1.40 for air)

$$\beta = \frac{d}{D} = \frac{\text{diameter of nozzle throat}}{\text{diameter of approach pipe}}$$

The density of compressible fluids changes when passing through a flow nozzle. The effect of this density change is accounted for in the expansion factor. The change in fluid density will be proportional to the pressure differential across the nozzle, therefore, the higher the ΔP the more compensation that takes place. Ignoring the expansion factor can introduce over a 1% calculation error in the 0.25 to 2.5 kPa (1 to 10 in H_2O) ΔP range. If the nozzle system in use is like that shown in Figure 2, D (in the Beta calculation) becomes very large, in which case assume a value of D of at least 10 times the nozzle throat diameter.

d. Velocity of Approach Factor:

$$E = \frac{1.0}{\sqrt{1 - \beta^4}}\ ;\ \beta = \frac{d}{D} \quad \text{(Eq. 17)}$$

In most diesel-engine air flow measurement systems using flow nozzles, the air drawn into the nozzle will most likely be initially at rest or close to it. In such cases (very small Beta (β)) the velocity of approach factor is very close to one and can be omitted from calculations. However, if the nozzle is used in a system in which the air is piped to the nozzle (as in Figure 4), this factor should be evaluated by the user to determine if it is significant enough to take into account. In general, if the Beta (β) factor is greater than 0.25, it is recommended that the velocity of approach factor be included in air flow calculations using the General Flow Equation.

e. Area Thermal Expansion Factor:

$$\text{(Metric)} \quad F_a = \frac{[1.0 + (A \cdot T_C) + (B \cdot T_C^2)]^2}{[1.0 + (A \cdot T_{CR}) + (B \cdot T_{CR}^2)]^2} \quad \text{(Eq. 18)}$$

$$\text{(English)} \quad Fa = \frac{\left[1.0 + C\left(\frac{T_F - 32}{1000}\right) + D\left(\frac{T_F - 32}{1000}\right)^2\right]^2}{\left[1.0 + C\frac{(T_{FR} - 32)}{1000} + D\left(\frac{T_{FR} - 32}{1000}\right)^2\right]^2}$$

where:

Factor = A 2.2644×10^{-5} for (Aluminum) 1.1182×10^{-5} for (Steel)
Factor = B 9.720×10^{-9} for (Aluminum) 5.2585×10^{-9} for (Steel)
Factor = C 1.258×10^{-2} for (Aluminum) 6.212×10^{-3} for (Steel)
Factor = D 3.00×10^{-3} for (Aluminum) 1.623×10^{-3} for (Steel)
T_c and T_F — Meter temperature at test conditions in °C and °F, respectively.
T_{CR} and T_{FR}—Meter temperature at reference conditions in °C and °F, respectively.

If a nozzle is used at a temperature other than that at which it was calibrated, or at which the throat diameter was measured, the temperature difference will cause the area of the nozzle throat to change. The amount of error due to the change in area for aluminum nozzles will be about 0.1% for every 22 °C (40 °F) change from the reference temperature and even less for steel nozzles. For typical diesel engine air flow measurements made at normal room temperatures this factor may be omitted.

f. Compressibility Factor—Z—One of the fundamental equations used to derive the General Flow Equation was the ideal gas law. All real gases deviate from the ideal gas relationship by an amount called the compressibility factor, or Z. Under normal room temperatures and pressures, the compressibility factor is about 0.9997 or about 0.03% correction to the flow calculation. Under normal conditions this factor is ignored, but if temperature or pressure extremes are encountered the effect of this factor should be investigated in a fluid metering handbook.

7.2.4 Ambient Conditions—Record the ambient environmental conditions surrounding the flow nozzle at its operating conditions. Included in these readings shall be the following items:

a. Barometric Pressure — P_B: The pressure should be made in the same area that the nozzle is located.
b. Air Meter Pressure (upstream of nozzle) — P_1: This pressure is made one pipe diameter (D) upstream of the nozzle. If the nozzle is used as shown in Figure 2, $P_1 = 0$.
c. Air Meter Temperature — T_1 or T_2: Record the temperature of the air five to six pipe diameters downstream of the nozzle. If an upstream location is desired, it must be located at least 200 temperature-probe diameters upstream of the nozzle. The temperature probe must not interfere with the flow patterns surrounding the nozzle, both upstream or downstream.
d. Air Meter Pressure Differential — ΔP: Record the pressure drop across the nozzle.
e. Humidity Parameters: Record either wet bulb or dry bulb or dew point temperatures of the air flowing through the nozzle. If these parameters are unavailable, assume a water vapor pressure (P_v) of 2 kPa (0.6 in Hg) for use in the calculations. This is equivalent to 50% relative humidity at 29 °C (85 °F).

7.2.4.1 Calculations—Calibrated Nozzle Systems—For calibrated nozzle systems, the air flow determined from the calibration curve or equation must be corrected according to the correction factors that follow. Correcting observed air flow values with these correction factors also applies in cases where: (a) the manometer was calibrated to read flow directly, but is of the fixed gradient type, or (b) the manometer was calibrated to read out in pressure units at the actual test conditions.

$$K_f = (\rho_{mo}/\rho_{cal})^{1/2}; \text{ for flow in mass units} \quad \text{(Eq. 19)}$$

$$K_f = (\rho_{cal}/\rho_{mo})^{1/2}; \text{ for flow in volume units} \quad \text{(Eq. 20)}$$

where:

actual air flow = observed air flow x K_f
ρ_{mo} = observed wet air density at test conditions
ρ_{cal} = air density at which nozzle (or manometer) was calibrated

7.2.4.2 Calculations—Uncalibrated Nozzle Systems—For uncalibrated nozzle systems the General Flow Equation should be utilized. If the nozzle was constructed according to ASME standards, or equivalent, the Coefficient of Discharge equations of 7.2.3(b) may be used. Should the value of C be unknown, or the nozzle made to an unknown design, the meter should be calibrated. If this is not practical, assume a value of C of 0.98 and consider the resulting calculated air flow value as approximate. The following calculation sequence is recommended:

a. Determine the water vapor pressure — P_v.
b. Determine the ratio of specific heats (ℓ = 1.40 for air).
c. Determine the pipe diameter (D) upstream of the nozzle. If the nozzle is used as in Figure 2 (no upstream pipe), assume a pipe diameter of at least 10 times the (largest) nozzle throat diameter.
d. Calculate the Beta ratio. $\beta = d/D$
e. Calculate the ambient pressure (abs) upstream of the nozzle (Equation 6).
f. Calculate as required for calculation accuracy:
   Y — Expansion Factor
   E — Velocity of Approach Factor
   Fa — Area of Thermal Expansion Factor
   Z — Compressibility Factor
g. Assume a coefficient of discharge (C) of 0.98. Utilizing this value in the General Flow Equation (Equation 12), calculate an approximate air mass flow value. With experience better estimates for the value of C should be made and used at this point.
h. Calculate the viscosity of the air entering the nozzle (Equation 10).
i. Calculate the Reynolds Number (N_R) (Equation 11) using the approximate air mass flow rate determined from (g).
j. Calculate the actual Coefficient of Discharge (C) from the appropriate equation (Equation 14 or 15).
k. Calculate the actual air mass flow rate (m) by using the actual (C) value in the General Flow Equation (Equation 12).
l. The actual volume flow rate may be calculated according to the following equation:

$$Vol(Q) = \dot{m}/\rho_{mo}\ ;\ m^2/s(ft^3/s) \quad \text{(Eq. 21)}$$

7.2.5 Sources of Error—The elemental sources of error are listed in Table 3. The recommended technique to estimate the error of a nozzle air flow measurement is to take the RSS (Root-Sum-Squared) of the elemental bias errors (error components that remain fixed during a test) and the RSS of the elemental precision errors (error components that vary randomly during a test) and add them using the equation:

$$U = b + 2\sigma \quad \text{(Eq. 22)}$$

where:

U = measurement uncertainty
b = RSS of elemental bias errors
σ = RSS of elemental precision errors (σ is equivalent to one sample standard deviation of the random error)

See Reference 3 for detailed explanation of uncertainty technique.

Other sources of error are considered negligible when following recommended practice.

The estimated error of a direct reading (mass flow) inclined manometer includes all sources of error in Table 3 and U = 1.8%–1.9% rdg.

Using the equations presented in 7.2.1, calculations can be made to minimize error sources 2, 3, and 8, thereby improving the estimated uncertainty to U = +1.2%/–1.4% rdg.

TABLE 3—SOURCES OF ERROR—NOZZLE AIR FLOW MEASUREMENTS

Source of Error	Error in Flow Measurement Bias (b)	Error in Flow Measurement Precision (2σ)
1. Calibration (Recommended Tolerance)	± 0.5% rdg	
2. Variation of CΔ and Y over 8:1 Range [1]	±0.3% rdg	
3. Density Changes Due to Humidity (20 to 90% RH)		±0.5% rdg
4. Pressure Drop - P(b = 0.5%, 2σ = 0.5% min rdg)	±0.25% min rdg	±0.25% min rdg
5. Ambient Pressure - P_A(b = 0.2 kPa (0.06 Hg), 2σ = 0.2 kPa)	±0.1% rdg	±0.1% rdg
6. Temperature - T(b = 1 °C (2 °F), 2σ = 1 °C)	±0.15% rdg	±0.15% rdg
7. System Leaks (Recommended Tolerance)	−0.5% min rdg	
8. Scale Conformance to Flow Equation (for Direct Reading Manometers)	1% rdg	

1. Can be eliminated using equations presented in 7.2.1.

7.3 Laminar Flow Meter

7.3.1 BASIC FLOW EQUATION—The mass air flow relationship can be simplified to:

$$m_t = \frac{\rho_{1t}}{\rho_{1cal}} \cdot \frac{\mu_{cal}}{\mu_{1t}} \cdot m_{cal} \quad \text{(Eq. 23)}$$

where:

m_{cal} = a function of ΔP across the meter read from the calibration data at ΔP(test)

μ = viscosity of air (Eq. 10)

ρ = density of air (Eq. 9)

NOTE—Density may be either wet or dry, but must be consistent.

7.3.2 CALCULATION WITH STANDARD INSTRUMENTATION

a. Air flow $m_{(cal)}$ corresponding to the observed $\Delta P_{(test)}$ is found from a calibration curve (Figure 12) or calibration curve fit equation.

b. Calculate density and viscosity correction factor using:

$$cf = \frac{\rho_{1(test)}}{\rho_{1(cal)}} \times \frac{\mu_{1(cal)}}{\mu_{1(test)}} \quad \text{(Eq. 24)}$$

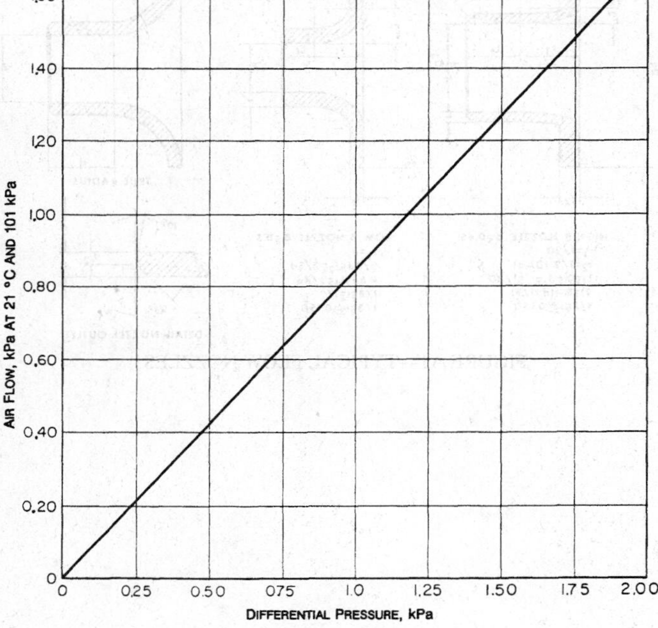

FIGURE 12—EXAMPLE OF LAMINAR FLOW METER CALIBRATION CHART

c. Calculate mass flow rate:

$$m_{test} = m_{cal} \bullet CF \quad \text{(Eq. 25)}$$

7.3.3 CALCULATION STEPS WITH COMPENSATING INSTRUMENTATION—The manufacturer's instructions must be followed depending on the scale of the compensating manometer used.

a. For a manometer reading values of corrected ΔP, the value of $m_{(test)}$ is read directly from the appropriate calibration curve.

b. For a manometer reading values of kg/s, the value of $m_{(test)}$ is read directly. (Corrections must be made if there is any shift from the original meter calibration.)

7.3.4 SOURCES OF ERROR—The elemental sources of error are listed in Table 4. The recommended technique to estimate the error of a laminar air flow measurement is to take the RSS of the elemental bias errors (error components that remain fixed during a test) and the RSS of the elemental precision errors (error components that vary randomly during a test) and add them using the equation:

$$U = b + 2\sigma \quad \text{(Eq. 26)}$$

where:

U = measurement uncertainty

b = RSS of elemental bias errors

σ = RSS of elemental precision errors (σ is equivalent to the sample standard deviation of the random error)

Other sources of error are considered negligible when following recommended practice.

The estimated error of a direct reading manometer includes all the errors listed in Table 4 and results in U = +2%/−2.2% rdg. Using the equations, correcting for humidity and calculating flow, can minimize error sources 2 and 7, thereby improving the estimated uncertainty to U = +1.2%/−1.4% rdg.

TABLE 4—SOURCES OF ERROR—LAMINAR FLOW MEASUREMENTS

Source of Error	Error in Flow Measurement Bias (b)	Error in Flow Measurement Precision (2σ)
1. Calibration Data	±0.5% rdg	
2. Density Changes Due to Humidity (20 to 90% RH)		±1% rdg
3. Pressure Drop, ΔP(b = ±0.5%, 2σ = ± 0.5% min rdg)	±0.5% min rdg	±0.25% min rdg
4. Temperature (b = ±1 °C, 2σ = ±1 °C)	±0.3% rdg	±0.3% rdg
5. Pressure, P_1(b = ±0.2 kPa, 2σ = ±0.2 kPa)	±0.2% rdg	±0.2% rdg
6. System Leaks (Recommended Tolerance)	−0.5% min rdg	
7. Scale Conformance to Flow Equation (for Direct Reading Manometers	±0.5% rdg	

7.4 Vortex Shedding Meter—The vortex shedding principle results in a simple linear relationship between volumetric flow rate (Q) and vortex shedding frequency (f).

$$Q = K \times f;\ m^3/s(ft^3/s) \quad \text{(Eq. 27)}$$

7.4.1 ALTERNATE CALIBRATION—If calibration facilities are available and machine computation of flow rates is performed, additional accuracy can sometimes be obtained by using a least-squares curve fit to the calibration data. In this case the flow equation takes the more complex form of a polynomial, for example:

$$Q = K1 + K2{*}f + K3{*}f^2 \quad \text{(Eq. 28)}$$

where:

K1, K2, K3 are the coefficients derived from a second-order least-squares curve fit.

7.4.2 SOURCES OF ERROR—The elemental sources of error are listed in Table 5. The recommended technique to estimate the error of a vortex shedding flow measurement is to take the RSS of the elemental bias errors (error components that remain fixed during a test) and the RSS of the elemental precision errors (error components that vary randomly during a test) and add them using the equation:

$$U = b + 2\sigma \quad \text{(Eq. 29)}$$

where:

U = measurement uncertainty

b = RSS of elemental bias errors

σ = RSS of elemental precision errors (σ is equivalent to the sample standard deviation of the random error)

Other sources of error are considered negligible when following recommended practice. It is stressed that the installation requirements outlined in 6.5.1 must be followed to assure a uniform flow profile. Flow profile variations in duct work can cause errors in excess of 2% of reading.

The estimated error of a vortex shedding flow measurement without humidity corrections includes all of the errors listed in Table 5 and results in U = +1.8%/−2% rdg. If humidity corrections are made to the data, error 2 is minimized, improving the measurements to U = +1.1%–1.3% rdg.

TABLE 5—SOURCES OF ERROR—VORTEX SHEDDING FLOW MEASUREMENT

Source of Error	Error in Flow Measurement Bias (b)	Error in Flow Measurement Precision (2σ)
1. Calibration	±0.5% rdg	
2. Density Changes Due to Humidity (20 to 90% RH)		±1% rdg
3. Pressure, P_1 (b = ±0.2 kPa, 2σ = ±0.2 kPa)	±0.2 rdg	±0.2% rdg
4. Temperature, T_1 (b = ±1 °C, 2σ = ±1 °C)	±0.3% rdg	±0.3% rdg
5. System Leaks (Recommended Tolerance)	−0.5% min rdg	
6. Nonlinearity of Flow Coefficient (20:1 Range)	±0.5% min rdg	

8. Exhaust Gas Flow Calculation—(See 8.1 for alternate method.) In the general case, the mass flow out of an engine equals the mass flow into the engine. Therefore, exhaust mass flow rate equals the intake air mass flow rate plus the fuel mass flow rate. Typical units for mass flow rate would be kg/h, kg/min, or kg/s. The basic equation is:

$$\dot{m}_{exh} = \dot{m}_{air} + \dot{m}_{fuel} \quad \text{(Eq. 30)}$$

An exception to the previous relationship would be any air flow into the engine which was diverted before the exhaust system to leave the engine by an auxiliary path. Such a flow would have to be measured and subtracted from the intake air flow in order to calculate the exhaust mass flow (see Figure 13).

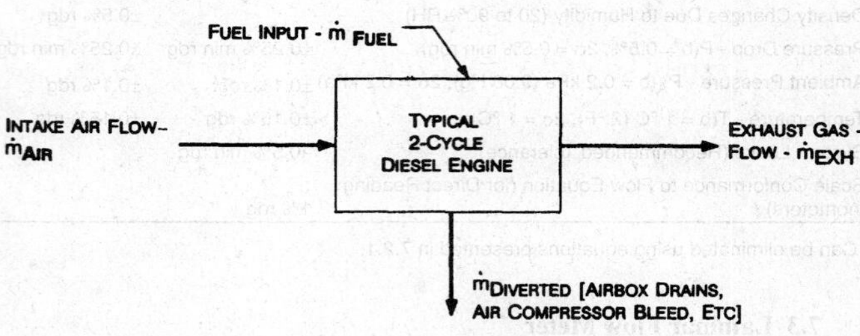

FIGURE 13—MASS BALANCE FOR 2-STROKE/CYCLE ENGINE

8.1 Alternate Method of Obtaining Exhaust Mass Flow—When it is desired to measure exhaust mass flow, the technique in Appendix C is recommended. Due to the nature of the exhaust gas, it is recommended that the flow meter be cleaned for each use. If this is impractical, the meter may be calibrated in place in a "dirty," but stable condition. Knowledge of the molecular weight of the exhaust becomes a factor in obtaining the best results with this method.

APPENDIX A
FLOW NOZZLES

A.1 Description—Several types of flow nozzles are available. Three common types are illustrated in Figure A1. The simplest type is the true radius nozzle. The true radius nozzle is a simple circular contour whose radius of curvature is equal to the diameter of the cylindrical section.

A.2 Calibration Technique—Essentially, the only absolute method of calibrating a system is to weigh the quantity of fluid flowing through in a unit time. When gases are involved, "weighing" becomes more complicated, and an expandable tank with the gas enclosed must be employed. Knowing the change in volume of the tank, the pressure, the temperature inside the tank, the mass rate of flow can be determined. (See Appendix B.) It is recommended that the nozzle be calibrated in the same or similar plenum chamber that it is to be used in. This will minimize the variations in the nozzle coefficients caused by different piping conditions.

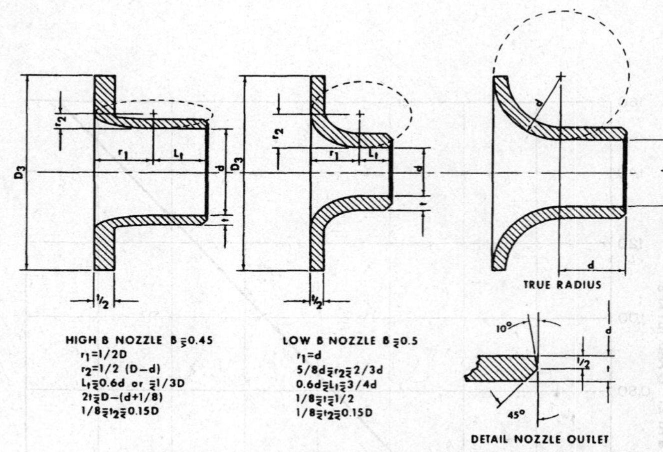

FIGURE A1—TYPICAL FLOW NOZZLES

APPENDIX B
CALIBRATION TECHNIQUE FOR VOLUME FLOW RATE METERS

B.1 A volumetric tank is a quantity-type measuring instrument for the calibration of air flow nozzles or meters. It passes a definite quantity of air in a measured time, from which the air flow rate can be calculated.

A generally used type of volumetric tank (Figure B1) consists of two concentric cylinders, each closed at one end. One is stationary and opens upward, while the other, vertically movable and opening downward, fits into a circular water well around the stationary cylinder. Access is provided to the volume included between the two, and air can be passed into or out of this volume, causing the movable cylinder to rise or fall. The movable cylinder is light, counterbalanced, relatively free from friction, and movable by very small pressure differences. The timed motions of the upper cylinder and a knowledge of the volumes associated with these motions may be used to compute the rate of air flow into or out of the apparatus. Corrections for density can be made if taps are placed in the manually operated hood to measure the wet and dry bulb temperatures and static pressure of the air. When the upper tank descends and air flows from the measured volume, the liquid height of the water seal will increase as the result of displacement of water by the upper tank. This effect will cause some error in measurement of the displaced volume if not corrected in one of two ways.

a. A given overflow level of the water may be maintained when the tank is in its "up" position, and the rise in level of water may be corrected by altering the calibration of the volumetric scale.
b. A constant stream of overflow water may be utilized to maintain the liquid level, regardless of the position of the upper movable tank.

In operation, when the manually operated cylindrical hood is in its "up" position, air enters the underhood area at the air intake. The measured volume tank is slightly out of balance, so that when the manually operated hood is in its "up" position, the tank may move slowly upward to the extreme position shown. Flow control valves are set to control the flow of air through the unit to be calibrated. For a given position of these valves, when the hood is manually lowered into the water seal, air is pumped from the measured volume tank, at a rate determined by the respective positions of the valves. The volumetric quantity of air as read on the scale for a given time measures the rate of air flow through the unit being calibrated.

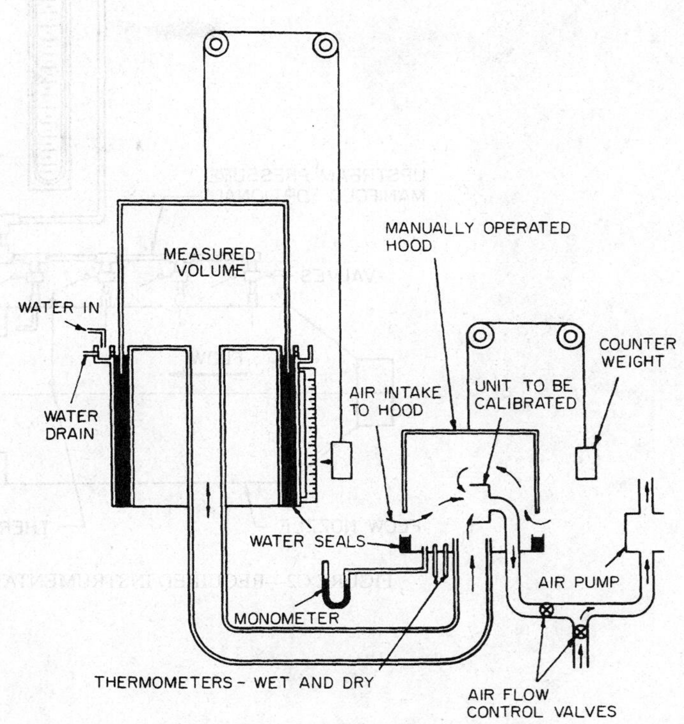

FIGURE B1—VOLUMETRIC TANK

APPENDIX C
EXHAUST MASS FLOW MEASUREMENT

C.1 Scope—The necessary equipment and metering system required to measure the exhaust mass flow of a diesel engine at a steady-state operating condition is presented in this procedure. One of the fundamental parameters controlling the accuracy of this measurement is the knowledge of the exhaust molecular weight. Air, water vapor, and CO_2 will comprise almost all of the exhaust mass. In order to determine the exhaust molecular weight, additional instrumentation and analytical methods would be required to determine the proportions of each. This is felt to be beyond the scope of this procedure. The measurement of exhaust mass flow rate is usually more easily assessed by adding the engine fuel and air intake mass flow rates (see 6.2).

C.2 Equipment and Operating Procedure for Measuring Exhaust Gas Flow

C.2.1 Instruments

a. Flow nozzle (ASME long radius)
b. Manometers (inclined and "U" tube types)
c. Thermocouples
d. Plenum chamber
e. Barometer

C.2.2 Component Description—See Figure C1.

a. Engine
b. Restriction valve — Optional to control engine back pressure
c. Plenum (two required) — See Figure C2.
d. Pressure sensors, P_1, P_2
e. Temperature sensors, T_1, T_2
f. Flow nozzle — See Figure C3

C.3 Operating Procedures—The same procedures apply to exhaust mass flow measurement as to intake air measurement as to intake air measurement with flow nozzles, as described in Section 5. The main exception will be the molecular weight used in the calculations. Since accurate knowledge of the exhaust molecular weight would be difficult to obtain without additional instrumentation and analytical methods, assume a molecular weight of 29 for use in the calculations. Based upon this, the resulting exhaust mass flow rates should be considered approximate.

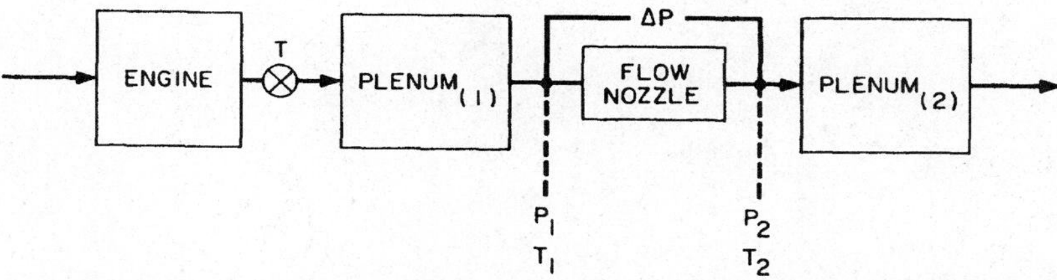

FIGURE C1—COMPONENT CONFIGURATION FOR EXHAUST MEASUREMENT

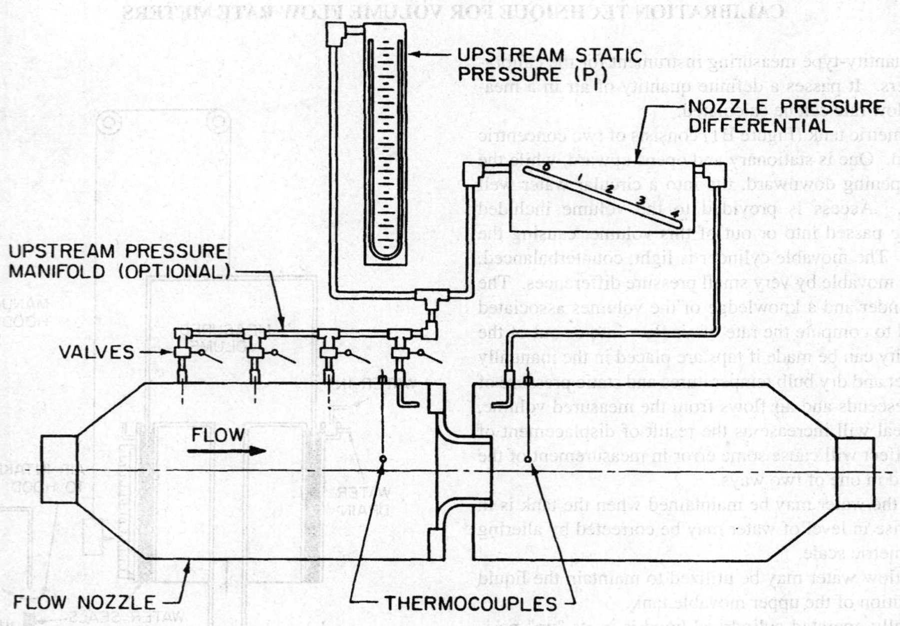

FIGURE C2—REQUIRED INSTRUMENTATION FOR EXHAUST FLOW MEASUREMENT

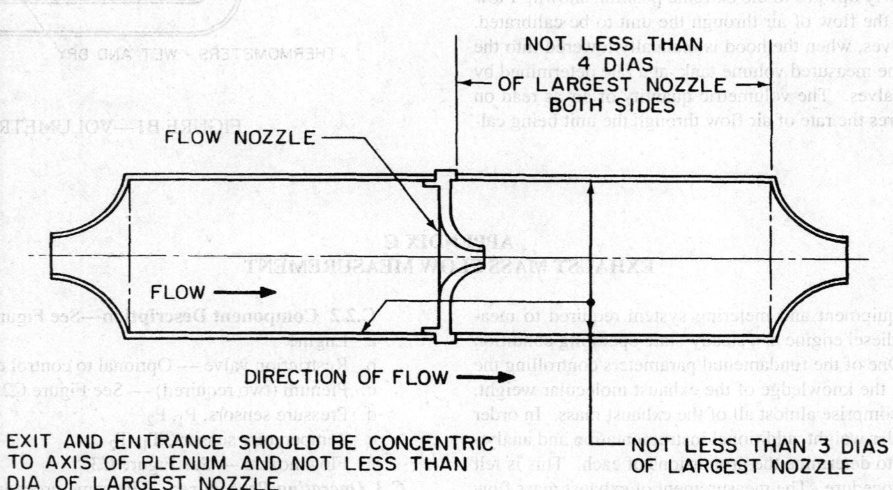

FIGURE C3—DETAILS OF PLENUM

SNAP-ACCELERATION SMOKE TEST PROCEDURE FOR HEAVY-DUTY DIESEL POWERED VEHICLES —SAE J1667 FEB1996

SAE Recommended Practice

Report of the SAE Heavy-Duty In-Use Emission Standards Committee approved February 1996.

Foreword. This Document has not changed other than to put it into the new SAE Technical Standards Board Format.

TABLE OF CONTENTS

1. Scope—This SAE Recommended Practice applies to vehicle exhaust smoke measurements made using the Snap-Acceleration test procedure. Because this is a non-moving vehicle test, this test can be conducted along the roadside, in a truck depot, a vehicle repair facility, or other test facilities. The test is intended to be used on heavy-duty trucks and buses powered by diesel engines. It is designed to be used in conjunction with smokemeters using the light extinction principle of smoke measurement.

This procedure describes how the snap-acceleration test is to be performed. It also gives specifications for the smokemeter and other test instrumentation and describes the algorithm for the measurement and quantification of the exhaust smoke produced during the test. Included are discussions of factors which influence snap-acceleration test results and methods to correct for these conditions. Unless otherwise noted, these correction methodologies are to be considered an integral part of the snap-acceleration test procedure.

1.1 Purpose—This document provides a procedure for assessing smoke emissions from in-use vehicles powered by heavy-duty diesel engines. Testing conducted in accordance with this procedure, in combination with reference smoke values, is intended to provide an indication of the state of maintenance and/or tampering of the engine and fuel system relative to the parameters which affect exhaust smoke. The procedure is expected to be of use to regulatory and enforcement authorities responsible for controlling smoke emissions from heavy-duty diesel-powered vehicles, and to heavy-duty vehicle maintenance and repair facilities. However, the procedure as written does not replicate the federal engine certification smoke cycle, and is intended to identify gross emitters. Regulatory agencies using this procedure must establish pass/fail criteria since SAE by-laws prohibit assignment of such criteria.

2. References

2.1 Applicable Publications—The following publications form a part of this specification to the extent specified herein. Unless otherwise specified, the latest issue of SAE publications shall apply.

2.1.1 SAE PUBLICATIONS—Available from SAE, 400 Commonwealth Drive, Warrendale, PA 15096-0001.

SAE J1349—Engine Power Test Code—Spark Ignition and Compression Ignition—Net Power Rating

SAE J1995—Engine Power Test Code—Spark Ignition and Compression Ignition—Gross Power Rating

2.2 Related Publications. 2.2.1 SAE PUBLICATIONS. Available from SAE, 400 Commonwealth Drive, Warrendale, PA 15096-0001.

SAE J255a—Diesel Engine Smoke Measurement

SAE J1243—Diesel Emission Production Audit Test Procedure

2.2.2 ISO PUBLICATION. Available from ANSI, 11 West 42nd Street, New York, NY 10036-8002.

ISO CD 11614—Apparatus for the Measurement of the Opacity of the Light Absorption Coefficient of Exhaust Gas from Internal Combustion Engines

2.2.3 FEDERAL PUBLICATION. U. S. Government, DOD SSP, Subscription Service Division, Building 4D, 700 Robbins Avenue, Philadelphia, PA 19111-5094

Code of Federal Regulations (CFR), Title 40, Part 86, Subpart I—Emission Regulation for New Diesel Heavy-Duty Engines: Smoke Exhaust Test Procedure

2.3 Other Publications

Procedures for Demonstrating Correlation Among Smokemeters

3. Definitions

3.1 Diesel Smoke—Particles, including aerosols, suspended in the exhaust stream of a diesel engine which absorb, reflect, or refract light.

3.2 Transmittance (T)—The fraction of light transmitted from a source which reaches a light detector.

3.3 Opacity (N)—The percentage of light transmitted from a source which is prevented from reaching a light detector. See Equation 1.

$$\text{Opacity \%} = 100*(1 - \text{Transmittance}) \quad \text{(Eq. 1)}$$

3.4 Effective Optical Path Length (L) or (EOPL)—The length of the smoke obscured optical path between the smokemeter light source and detector. Note that portions of the total light source to detector path length which are not smoke obscured do not contribute to the effective optical path length.

3.5 Smoke Density (K)—(also known as "Light Extinction Coefficient" and "Light Absorption Coefficient") A fundamental means of quantifying the ability of a smoke plume or smoke containing gas sample to obscure light. By convention, smoke density is expressed on a per meter basis (m^{-1}). The smoke density is a function of the number of smoke particles per unit gas volume, the size distribution of the smoke particles, and the light absorption and scattering properties of the particles. In the absence of blue or white smoke, the size distribution and the light absorption/scattering properties are similar for all diesel exhaust gas samples and the smoke density is primarily a function of the smoke particle density.

3.6 Beer-Lambert Law—A mathematical equation describing the physical relationships between the smoke density (K) and the smoke parameters of transmittance (T), and effective optical path length (L). Because smoke density (K) cannot be measured directly, the Beer-Lambert equation is used to calculate (K), when opacity (N) and EOPL (L) are known.

3.7 Smoke Opacimeter—A type of smokemeter designed to measure the opacity of a plume or sample of smoke by means of a light extinction principle.

3.8 Full-Flow End-of-Line Smokemeter—A smokemeter which measures the opacity of the full exhaust plume as it exits the tailpipe. The light source and detector for this type of smokemeter are located on opposite sides of the smoke plume and in close proximity to the open end of the tailpipe. When applying this type of smokemeter, the effective optical path length is a function of the tailpipe design.

3.9 Sampling Type Smokemeter (Also called Partial Flow Smokemeter)—A smokemeter which continually samples a representative portion of the total exhaust flow and directs it to a measurement cell. With this type of smokemeter, the effective optical path length is a function of the smokemeter design.

3.10 Smokemeter Measurement Zone—The effective length between the smokemeter light source and light detector through which exhaust gases pass and interact with the smokemeter light beam.

3.11 Smokemeter Response Time—See 6.3 and Appendix A.

3.12 Smokemeter Linearity—A measure of the maximum absolute deviation of values measured by the smokemeter from the reference values.

4. Special Notes and Conventions

4.1 The term smokemeter is a broad term which applies to all smoke-measuring devices regardless of the smoke-sensing technique employed. Throughout this document, the term smokemeter will refer only to opacimeter type smokemeters.

4.2 To fully describe the light obscuration properties of a smoke sample (i.e., smoke density), opacity (N) must always be associated with an EOPL. Whenever specific smoke opacity values are referenced in this document, the associated effective optical path length is understood to be 0.127 m (5 in).

5. Snap-Acceleration Test—The complete Snap-Acceleration process consists of five phases. These phases are:

a. Vehicle Preparation and Safety Check
b. Test Preparation and Equipment Set-up
c. Driver Familiarization and Vehicle Preconditioning
d. Execution of the Snap-Acceleration Test
e. Calculation and Reporting of Final Results

5.1 Vehicle Preparation and Safety Check—Prior to conducting the snap-acceleration test, the following items must be completed:

a. If the vehicle is equipped with a manual transmission, the transmission must be placed in neutral and the clutch must be released.
If the vehicle is equipped with an automatic transmission, the transmission must be placed in the park position, if available, or otherwise in the neutral position.
b. The vehicle wheels must be chocked or the vehicle must be otherwise restrained to prevent the vehicle from moving during the testing.
c. Vehicle air conditioning should be turned off.
d. If the engine is equipped with an engine brake, it must be deactivated during the snap-acceleration testing.
e. All devices installed on the engine or vehicle which alter the normal acceleration characteristics of the engine and have the effect of temporarily lowering snap-acceleration test results, or preventing the test from being successfully completed, shall be deactivated prior to testing.
f. Verify the speed-limiting capability of the engine governor using the following procedure:
With the engine at low idle, slowly depress the engine throttle and allow the engine speed to gradually increase toward its maximum governed high idle speed. As the engine speed increases, carefully note any visual or audible indications that the engine or vehicle may be of questionable soundness. If there are no indications of problems, allow the engine speed to increase to the point that it is possible to verify that the speed-limiting capability of the governor is functioning. Should there be any indication that the speed-limiting capability of the governor is not functioning, or that potential engine damage, or unsafe conditions for personnel or equipment may occur, the throttle should immediately be released and the snap-acceleration testing of the vehicle shall be aborted.
g. The vehicle should be inspected for exhaust leaks. Severe leaks in the system may cause the introduction of air into the exhaust stream which may cause erroneously low test results.
h. Users must be cautioned regarding the observance of blue or white smoke in the exhaust. Blue smoke can be an indicator of unburned hydrocarbons (possible oil burning or malfunctioning nozzle), and white smoke can be an indicator of water vapor (possible internal coolant leaking conditions).

5.2 Test Preparation and Equipment Set-up

5.2.1 Ambient Air Test Conditions—Ambient air conditions can affect snap-acceleration smoke test results. To ensure reliable results, the correction factors in Appendix B should be applied to snap-acceleration testing results to account for normal changes in ambient conditions. However, these correction factors must be applied under the following conditions.

a. Altitude—Greater than 457 m (1500 ft) above sea level.
b. Air Temperature—Above or below the range of 2 to 30 x °C (36 to 86 x °F).
c. Wind—Excessively windy conditions should be avoided. Winds are excessive if they disturb the size, shape, or location of the vehicle exhaust plume in the region where exhaust samples are drawn or where the smoke plume is measured. The effect of wind may be eliminated or reduced by locating the vehicle in a wind-sheltered area or by using measuring equipment designs which preclude wind effects on the smoke in the measuring or sampling zones.
d. Dry Air Density—If the correction factors referenced in Appendix B are used, the useful range of dry air densities are: 0.908 to 1.235 kg/m^3 (0.0567 to 0.0771 lbm/ft^3). This range of dry air densities is based on air densities experienced during ambient conditions testing.
e. Humidity—No visible humidity (including fog, rain, and snow) in the region where exhaust samples are drawn or the smoke plume is measured. Some equipment designs preclude the effects of these conditions.

5.2.2 Smokemeter Installation—The smokemeter and other test equipment used for snap-acceleration tests shall meet the specifications of 6.1 through 6.5. The general installation procedures specified by the smokemeter manufacturer shall be followed when preparing to test a vehicle.

In addition, these special installation procedures shall be followed:

a. If the test results are to be reported in units of smoke opacity, the rated power of the engine should be determined. The rated power is needed to define the standard effective optical path length used to correct the as-measured smoke opacity to standard conditions as described in Appendix C. The rated power should be available from the tune-up label fixed to the engine or from literature supplied to the owner by the engine manufacturer. In some cases, particularly under roadside test conditions, it may not be possible to readily determine the rated engine power. In these cases, it is recommended that the OD of the vehicle tailpipe section be determined and used as the standard effective optical path length for the purposes of the Beer-Lambert corrections described in Appendix C. If the rated engine power becomes available after the test is run, the test result should be recorrected as necessary using Equation C3 and the appropriate standard effective optical path length from Table C1.
Sampling in or immediately downstream of bends such as curved stack outlets in the exhaust pipe may cause some variability between individual Snap-Acceleration cycle readings.
b. For Full Flow End-of-Line Type Smokemeters—The axis of the smokemeter light beam shall be perpendicular to the axis of the exhaust flow. The centerline of the light beam axis should be located as close as possible, but in no case further than 7 cm (2.76 in) from the exhaust outlet. Appendix D provides additional guidance for smokemeter replacement.
Determine the effective optical path length used to make the smoke measurements. For straight tailpipes of circular cross section, the effective optical path length is equal to the tailpipe ID, and for tubing construction can be reasonably approximated by the tailpipe OD. Appendix D provides guidance for determining the as-measured effective optical path length when irregular tailpipe configurations are encountered. The as-measured effective optical path length is required to convert measured smoke values to standard corrected smoke values using the procedures described in Appendix C.
c. For Sampling Type Smokemeters—The probe of the sampling type smokemeter shall be inserted into the exhaust tailpipe with the open end facing upstream and into the exhaust flow.
The clearance between the inside edge of the open end of the sample probe and the tailpipe wall must be at least 5 mm (0.197 in).
Only the probe and sampling pipe, or tubing, specified by the manufacturer of the smokemeter shall be used for the smoke sampling. Manufacturer's recommendations regarding the length of the sample line shall be adhered to.
d. Multiple Exhaust Outlets—When testing vehicles equipped with multiple exhaust outlets, such as dual exhaust systems originating from a single manifold or single pipe, it is normally not necessary to measure the smoke from each exhaust outlet. The following approach is suggested.
If there is no discernible difference in the exhaust smoke exiting from each multiple exhaust outlet, the smoke should be measured from the exhaust outlet that provides the most convenient meter installation. A visual observation of one or more preliminary snap-acceleration test cycles should be sufficient to make this determination.
Should there be a discernible difference in the smoke exiting from the multiple exhaust outlets, install the smokemeter and conduct the snap-acceleration test on the exhaust outlet that visually appears to have the highest smoke level.

5.2.3 A tachometer to measure the engine speed may be installed and calibrated per the manufacturer's recommendations. A tachometer provides useful data regarding idle RPM, maximum engine RPM, the time necessary for the operator to accelerate the engine from idle to maximum RPM, and the time the engine speed was held at maximum RPM. This information helps to ensure repeatability between test cycles.

5.3 Driver Familiarization and Vehicle Preconditioning

5.3.1 Prior to the preconditioning test, the vehicle should be operated under load for at least 15 min to ensure that the engine is warmed-up. Alternatively, vehicle water and oil temperature gages may be checked to verify that the engine is within its normal operating temperature range.

5.3.2 SNAP-ACCELERATION CYCLE—The vehicle operator shall be instructed on the proper execution of the snap-acceleration test sequence. It is of critical importance that the vehicle operator fully understand the proper movement of the vehicle throttle during the testing.

With the vehicle conditioned as in 5.1 and with the engine warmed-up and at low idle speed:

a. The operator shall move the throttle to the fully open position as rapidly as possible.
b. The operator shall hold the throttle in the fully open position until the time the engine reaches its maximum governed speed, plus an additional 1 to 4 s.
c. Upon completion of the 1 to 4 s with the engine at its maximum governed speed, the operator shall release the throttle and allow the engine to return to the low idle speed.
d. Once the engine reaches its low idle speed, the operator shall allow the engine to remain at idle for a minimum of 5 s, but no longer than 45 s, before initiating the next snap-acceleration test cycle. The time period at low idle allows the engine's turbocharger (if so equipped) to decelerate to its normal speed at engine idle. This helps to reduce the smoke variability between snap-acceleration cycles.
e. Steps (a) through (d) shall be repeated as necessary to complete the preliminary snap-acceleration cycles and the snap-acceleration test cycles described in 5.3.3 and 5.4.2.

5.3.3 PRELIMINARY SNAP-ACCELERATION TEST CYCLES—The vehicle shall receive at least three preliminary snap-acceleration test cycles using the sequence described in 5.3.2. The preliminary cycles allow the vehicle operator to become familiar with the proper throttle movement, and also remove any loose soot which may have accumulated in the vehicle exhaust system during prior operation.

If smoke measurements are made during the preliminary cycles, the preliminary cycles can also provide the opportunity to check for proper operation of the smoke measurement system, and to check if the test validation criteria of 5.4.4 can be met. In this case, the data-processing unit and the smokemeter zero and full scale should first be set according to 5.4.1 and 5.4.2.

5.4 Execution of the Snap-Acceleration Test

5.4.1 DATA PROCESSING UNIT SET-UP—Before snap-acceleration testing can proceed, the smokemeter data processing unit must be properly set up. The operating instructions supplied by the processing unit manufacturer should be consulted for specific set-up procedures; however, the following functional steps must be accomplished.

a. If a multi-mode test system is used, the appropriate mode for snap-acceleration testing must be selected.
b. The desired smoke output units (opacity or smoke density) must be selected.
c. If the Beer-Lambert corrections as described in Appendix C are to be performed within the data-processing unit, values must be supplied for the standard and as-measured effective optical path lengths if opacity output is desired and for the as-measured effective optical path lengths if smoke density output is desired. Appendices C and D provide guidance in determining these input values.
d. If a red LED smokemeter light source is used and light source wavelength corrections are to be performed within the data-processing unit, the appropriate selections must be made to trigger these calculations (see Appendix C).
e. If the ambient condition corrections described in Appendix B are to be performed automatically by the data-processing unit, the appropriate ambient parameters must be input.
f. Any additional test identification information consistent with the needs of the test program and capabilities of the data-processing unit should be supplied at this time. Normally this would include the test date, test operator, vehicle identification, and other such information.

5.4.2 SMOKEMETER ZERO AND FULL SCALE—Prior to conducting smoke measurements, the zero and full scale readings of the smokemeter shall be verified. (Some meter systems may automatically perform the zero and full scale checks. For other meters, this sequence will need to be done manually.) Should optional recording devices be part of the test set-up, this equipment should also be checked for proper operation and calibration.

a. Smokemeter Warm-up—Prior to any zero and/or full-scale checks or adjustments, the smokemeter shall be warmed up and stabilized according to the manufacturer's recommendations. If the smokemeter is equipped with a purge air system to prevent sooting of the meter optics, this system should also be activated and adjusted according to the manufacturer's recommendations.
b. Smokemeter Zero—With the smokemeter in the Opacity readout mode, and with no blockage of the smokemeter light beam, adjust the readout to display 0.0% ± 1.0% opacity.
c. Smokemeter Full Scale—With the smokemeter in the Opacity readout mode, and all light prevented from reaching the detector, adjust the readout of the smokemeter to display 100.0% ± 1.0% opacity.

NOTE—For Smokemeter readouts in units of Smoke Density (K).

Smoke density (K) is a calculation based upon opacity and EOPL. The opacity scale offers two truly definable calibration points, namely 0% opacity and 100% opacity. The upper end of the smoke density scale is infinite, which makes this point on the K scale undefined. Because of this, the preferred method to set the zero and full scale of the meter when measuring in either smoke density (K) or opacity (N) units is to set the meter to the opacity readout mode and make the zero and full-scale adjustments as described in 5.4.2 (a) to (c). The smoke density would then be correctly calculated based upon the measured opacity and, of course, the EOPL, when the meter is returned to the smoke density readout mode for testing.

However, if this technique is not possible, it is acceptable to set the zero and span of the smokemeter in units of smoke density (K) with the use of a neutral density filter of known value. Should this be the case, the smokemeter zero and span shall be set as follows:

d. Smokemeter Zero—With the smokemeter in the Smoke Density (K) readout mode, and with no blockage of the smokemeter light beam, adjust the readout to display 0.00 m^{-1} ± 0.10 m^{-1}.
e. Smokemeter Span (If required by the smokemeter manufacturer)—With the smokemeter in the Smoke Density (K) readout mode, place a neutral density filter of known value between the light emitter and detector. The neutral density filter shall meet the accuracy requirements of 6.2.10 and have a known nominal value in the range of 1.5 to 5.5 m^{-1}. Adjust the smokemeter readout to display the filter nominal value, ±0.10 m^{-1}.

NOTE—Neutral density calibration filters are precision devices and can easily be damaged during use. Handling should be minimized and, when required, should be done with care to avoid scratching or dirtying of the filter.

5.4.3 SNAP-ACCELERATION TEST CYCLES—Within 2 min of the execution of the preliminary snap-acceleration cycles, conduct three snap-acceleration test cycles, actuating the vehicle throttle in the manner and sequence described in 5.3.2 (a to e).

Determine the corrected maximum 0.5 s average smoke values for each of the three snap-acceleration cycles using the smoke data processing algorithms described in Appendices A and C.

At the conclusion of the test sequence, and where needed as per manufacturer's recommendation, determine the degree of smokemeter zero shift by eliminating all exhaust from between the smokemeter light source and detector and noting the smokemeter display.

5.4.4 TEST VALIDATION CRITERIA—The test results from 5.4.3 shall be considered valid only after the following criteria have been met.

a. The post-test smokemeter zero shift values shall not exceed:
   1. ±2.0% opacity—For smoke measurements made in opacity.
   2. ±0.15 m^{-1}—For smoke measurements made in smoke density (K).
b. The arithmetical difference between the highest and lowest corrected maximum 0.5 s average smoke values from the three test cycles shall not exceed:
   1. 5.0% opacity—For smoke measurements made in opacity.
   2. 0.50 m^{-1}—For smoke measurements made in smoke density (K).

5.4.5 INVALID TESTS—Should the smoke test data from 5.4.3 not meet the test validation criteria of 5.4.4, the following items should be checked as possible causes for the invalid test results:

a. If the engine did not meet the operating temperature requirements, run the engine/vehicle under load for at least 15 min or until the vehicle oil and water temperature gages indicate that normal engine operating temperatures have been achieved. Return to 5.2.2 (Smokemeter Installation) and repeat the test sequence.
b. If improper or inconsistent application of the vehicle throttle is suspected, re-instruct the vehicle operator as to the proper execution of the snap-acceleration test, especially the movement of the vehicle throttle, as detailed in 5.3.2. Continue on with the procedure at this point and repeat the preliminary test cycles and the snap-acceleration test sequence while observing the vehicle operator.

c. Check the smokemeter, its installation on the tailpipe, and any support instrumentation for possible malfunctions. Correct as necessary and then return to 5.3.3 (Preliminary Snap-Acceleration Test Cycles), and repeat the test sequence.

d. If the post-test smokemeter zero check was exceeded due to positive zero drift, the probable cause is soot accumulation on the smokemeter optics. It is recommended that the snap-acceleration test sequence be repeated and while doing so, the smokemeter zero may be readjusted during the low idle period between each of the snap-acceleration test cycles. If the measured low idle smoke level of the vehicle is less than 2.0% opacity or 0.20 m^{-1} smoke density, it is permissible to re-zero the meter while it remains exposed to the vehicle exhaust. If the idle smoke level exceeds these limits, it is necessary to discontinue exposure to exhaust before rezeroing the meter.

It is not necessary to complete an invalid test before employing the rezeroing technique discussed previously. If comparison of the low idle smoke readings shows an increasing trend from one test cycle to the next, sooting of meter optics can be suspected and the rezeroing technique can immediately be used.

If it is not possible to rezero the meter, the meter optics should be cleaned per the smokemeter manufacturer's recommended procedures and the test sequence should be repeated beginning at 5.3.3 (preliminary snap-acceleration test cycles). If zero drift and rezeroing difficulties persist, it is recommended that the meter purge air system (if so equipped) be checked for proper operation.

e. If the procedure has been repeated in accordance with the requirements stated in 5.4.5 (a to d), and the test results still cannot be obtained that conform with the test validation criteria, then it is likely that the engine is in need of service.

5.5 Calculation and Reporting of Final Test Result—If the validation criteria of 5.4.4 are met, the data shall be deemed valid and the test complete. The average of the corrected maximum 0.5 s average smoke values from the three snap-acceleration test cycles shall be computed and reported as the final test result. (See Appendix A.)

6. Test Instrumentation Specifications—This section provides specifications for the required and optional test equipment used in the snap-acceleration test.

6.1 General Requirements for the Smoke Measurement Equipment—The snap-acceleration smoke test requires the use of a smoke measurement and data-processing system which includes three functional units. These units may be integrated into a single component or provided as a system of interconnected components. The three functional units are:

a. A full-flow end-of-line or a sampling type smokemeter meeting the specifications of 6.2 through 6.4.

b. A data-processing unit capable of performing the functions described in Appendices A and C.

c. A printer and/or electronic storage medium to record and output the individual corrected maximum 0.5 s average smoke values from each snap-acceleration test cycle, and the final average snap-acceleration test result.

6.2 Specific Requirements for the Smoke Measurement Equipment

6.2.1 LINEARITY—±2% opacity or ±0.30 m^{-1} density.

6.2.2 ZERO DRIFT RATE—Not to exceed ±1% opacity/hour.

6.3 Instrument Response Time Requirements

6.3.1 OVERALL INSTRUMENT RESPONSE TIME REQUIREMENT—The overall instrument response time (t) shall be: 0.500 s ± 0.015 s. It is defined as the difference between the times when the output of the smokemeter reaches 10% and 90% of full scale when the opacity of the gas being measured is changed in less than 0.01 s. It shall include all the physical, electrical, and filter response times. Mathematically, it is represented by Equation 2. (See Appendix A for a more detailed methodology and an example calculation.)

$$t = SQRT(t_p^2 + t_e^2 + t_F^2) \quad \text{(Eq. 2)}$$

where:

t_p = The physical response time
t_e = The electrical response time
t_F = The filter response time

6.3.2 PHYSICAL RESPONSE TIME (t_p)—This is the difference between the times when the output of a rapid response receiver (with a response time of not more than 0.01 s) reaches 10% and 90% of the full deviation when the opacity of the gas being measured is changed in less than 0.1 s.

The physical response time is defined for the smokemeter only and excludes the probe and sample line. However, on some in-use smokemeter systems, the probe and sample line may significantly affect the overall response time of the system. If necessary, this shall be taken into account for any particular smokemeter system.

For full-flow type smokemeters, the response time is a function of the velocity of flow in the vehicle exhaust pipe and the path length across the detector (detector diameter). It can be assumed equal to a negligible 0.01 s. For sampling type smokemeters where the measuring zone is a straight section of pipe of uniform diameter, the physical response can be estimated by Equation 3:

$$t = 0.8*V/Q \quad \text{(Eq. 3)}$$

where:

Q = The rate of flow of gas through the measuring zone
V = The volume of the measuring zone

For such instruments, the speed of the gas through the measuring zone shall not differ by more than 50% from the average speed over 90% of the length of the measuring zone.

For all smokemeters, if the physical response calculates greater than 0.2 s, then the response time shall be measured.

6.3.3 ELECTRICAL RESPONSE TIME (t_e)—It is defined as the time needed for the recorder output to go from 10% of the maximum scale to 90% of the maximum scale value when a fully opaque screen is placed in front of the photo cell in less than 0.01 s, or the LED is turned off. This is to include all of the effects of recorder output response time.

6.3.4 FILTER RESPONSE TIME (t_F)—Filtering of the smoke signal will be necessary on most smokemeters to achieve an overall response time of 0.500 s ± 0.015 s. Most smokemeters have a very fast electrical response time, but physical response times will vary from one device to the next depending on design and gas flow.

Appendix A specifies the recommended second-order digital filtering algorithm to be used.

6.3.5 DETERMINATION OF THE PEAK SMOKE VALUE—An algorithm in Appendix A shall be used to determine the reported peak exhaust smoke levels.

6.4 Smokemeter Light Source and Detector

6.4.1 LIGHT SOURCE—The light source shall be an incandescent lamp with a color temperature in the range of 2800 to 3250 °K, or a green light emitting diode (LED) with a spectral peak between 550 and 570 nm.

Alternatively, a red LED may be used provided that the appropriate light wavelength correction is made as described in Appendix C.

6.4.2 LIGHT DETECTOR—The light detector shall be a photocell or a photodiode (with a filter, if necessary). In the case of an incandescent light source, the detector shall have a peak spectral response in the range of 550 to 570 nm, and shall have a gradual reduction in response to values of less than 4% of the peak response value below 430 nm and above 680 nm.

6.4.3 The rays of the light beam shall be parallel within a tolerance of 3 degrees of the optical axis. The detector shall be designed such that it is not affected by direct or indirect light rays with an angle of incidence greater than 3 degrees to the optical axis.

6.4.4 Any method such as purge air which is used to protect the light source and detector from direct contact with exhaust soot shall be designed to minimize any unknown effect on the effective optical path length of the measured smoke (see C.5.1). For full-flow end-of-line smokemeters, the protection feature must not cause the smoke plume to be distorted by more than 0.5 cm. For sampling type smokemeters, the meter manufacturer must account for any effect of the protection feature in specifying the effective optical path length of the meter.

6.4.5 The sampling and digitization rate of the data processing units shall be at least 20 Hz (i.e., at least 10 data samples per 0.5 s interval). Additionally, the product of the data sampling time increment (seconds) and one half the data sample rate (Hz) rounded to the next higher integer value must be within the range of 0.500 to 0.510 s.

6.5 Specifications for Auxiliary Test Equipment

6.5.1 NEUTRAL DENSITY FILTERS—Any neutral density filter used in conjunction with smokemeter calibration, linearity measurements, or setting span shall have its value known to within 0.5% opacity or 0.04 m^{-1}. The filter's named value must be checked for accuracy at least yearly using a reference traceable to a national standard.

6.5.2 If altitude correction (i.e., the altitude is greater than 457 m (1500 ft)) then:

a. Equipment used to measure barometric pressure must be accurate within ±0.30 kPa (±0.089 in-Hg)

b. Ambient dry bulb temperature must be accurate within ±2 °C (±3.6 °F)

6.5.3 Measurement of the following parameters is optional; however, if measured, the specified accuracy requirements should be met:

a. Ambient Dry Bulb Temperature—±2 °C (±3.6 °F)

b. Dew Point Temperature—±2 °C (±3.6 °F)

c. Engine Speed—±100 rpm

6.5.4 Optional Recording Devices—A supplemental chart recorder or other collection media may be used provided that the device(s) does not affect the smoke measurement.

7. Smokemeter Maintenance and Calibration—The smokemeter should be maintained and serviced per the manufacturer's recommendations. In addition to the zero and span adjustments to be made prior to each snap-acceleration test (5.4.2), the linearity of the meter response should be periodically checked as per manufacturer's recommendations in the range of measurement interest using neutral density filters meeting the requirements of 6.5.1. Non-linearities in excess of 2% opacity or 0.30 m^{-1} smoke density should be corrected prior to resuming testing with the meter.

APPENDIX A
SECOND-ORDER FILTER ALGORITHM USED TO CALCULATE A MAXIMUM 0.500 S AVERAGE SMOKE VALUE

A.1 Introduction—This appendix explains how to create and use the recommended Bessel low-pass digital filter algorithm in a smokemeter to filter out the high-frequency smoke readings which are produced during a snap-acceleration test. This appendix in particular describes the methodology used to design a low-pass second-order Bessel filter with a response time as needed for a particular smokemeter application. This appendix also describes the procedure for determining the final snap-acceleration test. Two example calculations detailing the selection of Bessel filter coefficients and their use are also provided in this appendix to illustrate the concepts more clearly.

The digital Bessel filter described in this appendix is a second-order (2-pole) low-pass digital filter algorithm. It is the recommended filter to be used for designing smokemeters with 0.500 s overall response times as required in 6.3. The Bessel filter type was chosen because it allows passage of all signals which do not change very much with time, but effectively blocks all signals with higher-frequency components. Its linear-phase characteristics also enable it to approximate a constant time delay over a limited frequency range. Transient waveforms can also be passed with minimal distortion when it is used as a running average type filter. A digital approach was chosen due to the relative ease of implementing a software algorithm in most smokemeters. However, analog Bessel filters using the appropriate electronic circuits may also be used.

A.2 Definitions

- B = Bessel parameter constant. It equals [Sqrt(5)-1]/2
- f_c = Bessel cutoff frequency used to control the filtered response
- t_e = Electrical response time of the smokemeter (seconds)
- t_F = Filter response time (seconds)
- t_{Fd} = Desired filter response time (seconds)
- t_p = Physical response time of the smokemeter (seconds)
- t_{10} = The test time when the output response to an input step response is equal to 10% of the step input
- t_{90} = The test time when the output response to an input step response is equal to 90% of the step input
- Δ_t = Time between two stored opacity values (i.e., sampling period (seconds))
- X_i = Bessel filter input at sample number (i)
- X_{i-1} = Bessel filter input at sample number (i-1)
- X_{1-2} = Bessel filter input at sample number (i-2)
- Y_i = Bessel filter output at sample number (i)
- Y_{i-1} = Bessel filter output at sample number (i-1)
- Y_{i-2} = Bessel filter output at sample number (i-2)

A.3 Designing a Bessel Low-Pass Filter—Designing the 0.500 s Bessel low-pass digital filter is a multistep process which may involve several iterative calculations to determine coefficients. This section provides a method for determining the desired amount of filtering for smokemeters with different electrical and physical response times, or different sample rates. Bessel filters can be designed to accommodate filter designs having response times ranging from 0.010 to 0.500 s, and digitization rates of 50 Hz and higher.

It is recommended that all Bessel filter calculations be performed in opacity units for the sake of consistency between smokemeters. If smokemeter output in units of density need to be reported, the Beer-Lambert law may be used to convert the final opacity results to density results, and perform any necessary stack size correction. This conversion should be done only after all Bessel filter equations have been performed due to the non-linearity of the Beer-Lambert law.

A.3.1 Calculating the Desired Filter Response Time (t_{Fd})—Prior to designing a digital Bessel filter, it is necessary to determine the physical response time (t_p) and the electrical response time (t_e) for the relevant smokemeter. These parameters are necessary in order to determine how much electronic filtering is necessary to achieve an overall 0.500 s response time. For some partial flow smokemeters this may require experimental data. For other smokemeters the procedures and equations in 6.3 may be used.

Once the values of t_p and t_e are known, the desired filter response time (t_{Fd}) can be determined by using Equation A1.

$$t_{Fd} = SQRT[0.500^2 - (t_p^2 + t_e^2)] \quad \text{(Eq. A1)}$$

A.3.2 Estimating Bessel Filter Cutoff Frequency (f_c)—The Bessel filter response time (t_F) is defined as the time in which the output signal (Y_i) reaches 10% (Y_{10}) and 90% (Y_{90}) of a full-scale input step (X_i) which occurs in less than 0.01 s. The difference in time between the 90% response (t_{90}) and the 10% response time (t_{10}) defines the response time (t_F). Thus,

$$(t_F) = (t_{90}) - (t_{10}) \quad \text{(Eq. A2)}$$

For the filter to operate properly, the filter response time (t_F) should be within 1% of the desired response time (t_{Fd}), that is, $[(t_F) - (t_{Fd})] < [0.01 * (t_{Fd})]$.

To create a filter where t_F approximates t_{Fd}, the appropriate cutoff frequency (f_c) must be determined. This is an iterative process of choosing successively better values of (f_c) until $[(t_F) - (t_{Fd})] < [0.01 * (t_{Fd})]$.

The first step in the process is to calculate a first guess value for f_c using Equation A3.

$$f_c = \pi/(10*t_{Fd}) \quad \text{(Eq. A3)}$$

The values of B, Ω, C, and K are then calculated using Equation A4 through A7.

$$B = 0.618034 \quad \text{(Eq. A4)}$$

$$\Omega = 1/[\tan(\pi*\Delta t*f_c)] \quad \text{(Eq. A5)}$$

$$C = 1/[1 + \Omega*sqrt(3*B) + B*\Omega^2] \quad \text{(Eq. A6)}$$

$$K = 2 * C * [B*\Omega^2 - 1] - 1 \quad \text{(Eq. A7)}$$

Δt = Time between two stored opacity values (i.e., sampling period (seconds)).

The values of K and C are then used in Equation A8 to calculate the Bessel filter response to the given step input. Because of the recursive nature of Equation A8, the values of X and Y listed as follows are used to begin the process.

$$Y_i = Y_{i-1} + C*[X_i + 2*X_{i-1} + X_{i-2} - 4*Y_{i-2}] + K*(Y_{i-1} - Y_{i-2}) \quad \text{(Eq. A8)}$$

where:

X_i = 100

X_{i-1} = 0

X_{i-2} = 0

Y_{i-1} = 0

Y_{i-2} = 0

As shown in the example (A.7.1), calculate Y_i for successive values of X_i = 100 until the value of Y_i has exceeded 90% of the step input (X_i). The difference in time between the 90% response (t_{90}) and the 10% response (t_{10}) defines the response time (t_F) for that value of (f_c). Since the data are digital, linear interpolation may be needed to precisely calculate t_{10} and t_{90}.

If the response time is not close enough to the desired response time {that is, if $[(t_F)-(t_{Fd})] > [0.01*(t_{Fd})]$}, then the iterative process must be repeated with a new value of (f_c). The variables (t_F) and (f_c) are approximately proportional to each other, so the new (f_c) should be selected based on the difference between (t_F) and (t_{Fd}) as shown in the example calculations (A.5.1).

A.4 Using the Bessel Filter Algorithm—The proper cutoff frequency (f_c) is the one that produces the desired filter response time (t_{Fd}). Once this frequency has been determined through the iterative process, the proper Bessel filter algorithm coefficients for Equation A4 through A7 are specified. Equation A8 and the coefficients can then be programmed into the smokemeter to produce the desired filter.

The Bessel filter equation (Equation A8) is recursive in nature. Thus, it needs some initial input values of X_{i-1} and X_{i-2} and initial output values Y_{i-1} and Y_{i-2} to get the algorithm started. These may be assumed to be 0% opacity. A detailed example calculation is shown in A.7.3.

A.5 Determining the Maximum 0.500 s Averaged Smoke Value—The maximum smoke value for a snap-acceleration test cycle (Y_{max}) is then selected from among the individual Y_i values computed using Equation A8 (after suitable Beer-Lambert and light source wavelength corrections are applied). This is the final test result for the test cycle and is used in combination with the results from the other snap-acceleration cycles in the test to determine a final snap-acceleration test result.

In equation form:

$$Y_{max} = \text{Maximum}(Y_i) \quad \text{(Eq. A9)}$$

A.6 Determination of the Final Test Result—If the test validation criteria of 5.4.4 have been met, the final snap-acceleration test result shall be computed by taking the simple average of the three corrected maximum 0.500 s averaged smoke values obtained from the three snap-acceleration test cycles.

$$A = (Y_{max,\,1} + Y_{max,\,2} + Y_{max,\,3})/3 \quad \text{(Eq. A10)}$$

A.7 Example of Incorporating a Bessel Filter Into a Smokemeter Design—This example illustrates how a full flow meter with a fast physical and electrical response time can implement the Bessel filter algorithm. The sample smokemeter has the following characteristics:

a. Physical Response Time = 0.020 s
b. Electrical Response Time = 0.010 s
c. Sampling Rate = 100 Hz
d. Sampling Period = 0.01 s

A.7.1 First Iteration to Estimate Bessel Function Cutoff Frequency (f_c)—This section displays the initial calculations which are performed to estimate the correct value of the cutoff frequency (f_c).

The results from Equation A1 indicate that the desired filter response (t_{Fd}) is 0.4995 (for simplicity, a value of 0.50 will be used in the sample calculations). This may be typical of a full flow meter with a very fast electrical and physical response time. It suggests that most of the desired 0.500 s filtering will be performed by the digital filter rather than the instrument.

$$t_{Fd} = 0.4995 = \text{SQRT}[0.500^2 - (0.020^2 + 0.010^2)] \quad \text{(Eq. A11)}$$

By inserting the correct values of Δt and t_F into Equations A2 through A7, the Bessel function coefficients are determined. These are shown in Table A1.

TABLE A1—INITIAL BESSEL COEFFICIENTS

Equation A1	t_F	0.500
Equation A2	f_c	0.6283
Equation A4	B	0.618
Equation A5	Ω	50.6555063
Equation A6	C	0.00060396
Equation A7	K	0.91427037
	Δt	0.01

The Bessel coefficients can now be inserted into Equation A8 along with the step input function (i.e., an input of 0% opacity to 100% opacity in 0.01 s) to illustrate the effect of the Bessel filter on the step response as a function of time. The input step function is shown as X_i in Table A2. To simulate the step response, input $X_I = 100$. This will create the sudden jump from 0 to 100%.

The Bessel filtered output is shown as Y_i in Table A2. The two output points which are of interest are the 10% response point and the 90% response point. These are the values where Y_i first exceeds 10% and 90%.

Since the output Y_i is digital, the exact 10% and 90% points must be interpolated from Table A2. The four points which bound the 10% and 90% points are indicated by an "X" in the Index column of Table A2. These are index numbers 9, 10, and 64, 65.

For this specific case, the following interpolation formulas are used to calculate the values of $t_{10\%}$ and $t_{90\%}$.

$$t_{10\%} = 0.01*[9 + (10 - 8.647)/(10.260 - 8.647)] = 0.0984\,\text{s} \quad \text{(Eq. A12)}$$

$$t_{90\%} = 0.01*[64 + (90 - 89.834)/(90.427 - 89.834)] = 0.6428\,\text{s} \quad \text{(Eq. A13)}$$

Now calculate the difference between $t_{90\%}$ and $t_{10\%}$ and see if it is close enough to t_F (close enough means within 1% or in this case 0.005).

$$0.6428 - 0.0984 = 0.5444\,\text{s} \quad \text{(Eq. A14)}$$

The calculation shows that the response time of the filter is 0.5444 s using a value of f_c of 0.6283. The difference between this value and the desired value of 0.50 is 0.0444 which is about 10% greater than desired. Thus, another attempt to reach the desired response time will have to be made. Since 0.5444 is about 10% too high, use a cutoff frequency (f_c) which is 10% larger for the second iteration.

A.7.2 Second Iteration to Estimate Bessel Function Cutoff Frequency (f_c)—For the second iteration, a value of 0.690 is chosen for the value of f_c. This is approximately 10% higher than the value previously used. When this value is used, the Bessel function coefficients in Table A3 are obtained.

The filter responses Y_i were also recalculated for the step input X_i. The entire table of inputs (X_i) and responses (Y_i) (analogous to Table A2) is not shown. However, the values of t_{10} and t_{90} and the difference between were calculated and are shown in Table A4. In this case, the difference between the filter response time and the desired filter response time of 0.50 s is 0.0049. This is less than the 1% difference criteria (0.005 s). Thus, the value of 0.692 for the frequency cutoff (f_c) is the correct one for this smokemeter application.

A.7.3 Sample Calculation of the Bessel Filter Opacity Response—Once the appropriate value for the cutoff frequency (f_c) has been determined, then Equations A4 through A8 are used to calculate the Bessel filtered opacity values (Y_i) for any given input opacity values (X_i). The maximum filtered response is then selected and reported as the smoke reading for that particular snap-acceleration cycle.

TABLE A2—INITIAL SIMULATION OF THE BESSEL FILTER EFFECT (USED TO DETERMINE f_c)

	Index	Time	X_i	X_{i-1}	X_{i-2}	Y_i	Y_{i-1}	Y_{i-2}
	0	0.00	100	0	0	0.060	0.000	0.000
	1	0.01	100	100	0	0.297	0.060	0.000
	2	0.02	100	100	100	0.754	0.297	0.060
	3	0.03	100	100	100	1.414	0.754	0.297
	4	0.04	100	100	100	2.256	1.414	0.754
	5	0.05	100	100	100	3.264	2.256	1.414
	6	0.06	100	100	100	4.423	3.264	2.256
	7	0.07	100	100	100	5.715	4.423	3.264
	8	0.08	100	100	100	7.128	5.715	4.423
X	9	0.09	100	100	100	8.647	7.128	5.715
X	10	0.10	100	100	100	10.260	8.647	7.128
	11	0.11	100	100	100	11.956	10.260	8.647
	12	0.12	100	100	100	13.723	11.956	10.260
	13	0.13	100	100	100	15.552	13.723	11.956
	14	0.14	100	100	100	17.432	15.552	13.723
	15	0.15	100	100	100	19.355	17.432	15.552
	16	0.16	100	100	100	21.312	19.355	17.432
	17	0.17	100	100	100	23.297	21.312	19.355
	18	0.18	100	100	100	25.301	23.297	21.312
	19	0.19	100	100	100	27.319	25.301	23.297
	20	0.20	100	100	100	29.344	27.319	25.301
	21	0.21	100	100	100	31.372	29.344	27.319
	22	0.22	100	100	100	33.396	31.372	29.344
	23	0.23	100	100	100	35.413	33.396	31.372
	24	0.24	100	100	100	37.417	35.413	33.396
	25	0.25	100	100	100	39.406	37.417	35.413
	26	0.26	100	100	100	41.375	39.406	37.417

TABLE A2—INITIAL SIMULATION OF THE BESSEL FILTER EFFECT (USED TO DETERMINE f_c) (continued)

	Index	Time	X_i	X_{i-1}	X_{i-2}	Y_i	Y_{i-1}	Y_{i-2}
	27	0.27	100	100	100	43.322	41.375	39.406
	28	0.28	100	100	100	45.244	43.322	41.375
	29	0.29	100	100	100	47.138	45.244	43.322
	30	0.30	100	100	100	49.001	47.138	45.244
	31	0.31	100	100	100	50.833	49.001	47.138
	32	0.32	100	100	100	52.631	50.833	49.001
	33	0.33	100	100	100	54.394	52.631	50.833
	34	0.34	100	100	100	56.119	54.394	52.631
	35	0.35	100	100	100	57.807	56.119	54.394
	36	0.36	100	100	100	59.457	57.807	56.119
	37	0.37	100	100	100	61.067	59.457	57.807
	38	0.38	100	100	100	62.637	61.067	59.457
	39	0.39	100	100	100	64.166	62.637	61.067
	40	0.40	100	100	100	65.654	64.166	62.637
	41	0.41	100	100	100	67.102	65.654	64.166
	42	0.42	100	100	100	68.508	67.102	65.654
	43	0.43	100	100	100	69.873	68.508	67.102
	44	0.44	100	100	100	71.198	69.873	68.508
	45	0.45	100	100	100	72.481	71.198	69.873
	46	0.46	100	100	100	73.724	72.481	71.198
	47	0.47	100	100	100	74.927	73.724	72.481
	48	0.48	100	100	100	76.090	74.927	73.724
	49	0.49	100	100	100	77.215	76.090	74.927
	50	0.50	100	100	100	78.300	77.215	76.090
	51	0.51	100	100	100	79.348	78.300	77.215
	52	0.52	100	100	100	80.358	79.348	78.300
	53	0.53	100	100	100	81.331	80.358	79.348
	54	0.54	100	100	100	82.269	81.331	80.358
	55	0.55	100	100	100	83.171	82.269	81.331
	56	0.56	100	100	100	84.039	83.171	82.269
	57	0.57	100	100	100	84.872	84.039	83.171
	58	0.58	100	100	100	85.673	84.872	84.039
	59	0.59	100	100	100	86.442	85.673	84.872
	60	0.60	100	100	100	87.180	86.442	85.673
	61	0.61	100	100	100	87.887	87.180	86.442
	62	0.62	100	100	100	88.564	87.887	87.180
	63	0.63	100	100	100	89.213	88.564	87.887
X	64	0.64	100	100	100	89.834	89.213	88.564
X	65	0.65	100	100	100	90.427	89.834	89.213
	66	0.66	100	100	100	90.994	90.427	89.834
	67	0.67	100	100	100	91.536	90.994	90.427
	68	0.68	100	100	100	92.053	91.536	90.994
	69	0.69	100	100	100	92.546	92.053	91.536
	70	0.70	100	100	100	93.016	92.546	92.053

TABLE A3—FINAL BESSEL COEFFICIENTS

Equation A1	t_F	0.500
Equation A2	f_c	0.6292
Equation A4	B	0.618000
Equation A5	Ω	45.991292
Equation A6	C	0.000729
Equation A7	K	0.905717
	Δt	0.01

TABLE A4—BOUNDARY RESPONSE TIMES (SECOND ITERATION)

$t_{10\%}$	0.09145
$t_{90\%}$	0.5856
$\Delta\ t_{90\%} - t_{10\%}$	0.4951

Table A5 shows a sample calculation for an actual snap-acceleration smoke event collected at 100 Hz. Only 100 (1 s) readings and calculated values are shown so as to reduce the length of the table. The Bessel coefficients shown in Table A3 are used with Equation A8 to calculate the Bessel filter responses (Y_i) to the raw smoke inputs (X_i).

TABLE A5—BESSEL FILTER EXAMPLE

Time	X_i	X_{i-1}	X_{i-2}	Y_i	Y_{i-1}	Y_{i-2}
0.00	0.00	0.00	0.00	0.000	0.000	0.000
0.01	0.00	0.00	0.00	0.000	0.000	0.000
0.02	0.30	0.00	0.00	0.000	0.000	0.000
0.03	0.60	0.30	0.00	0.001	0.000	0.000
0.04	0.50	0.60	0.30	0.004	0.001	0.000
0.05	0.40	0.50	0.60	0.007	0.004	0.001
0.06	0.30	0.40	0.50	0.012	0.007	0.004
0.07	0.10	0.30	0.40	0.017	0.012	0.007
0.08	0.00	0.10	0.30	0.021	0.017	0.012
0.09	0.00	0.00	0.10	0.026	0.021	0.017
0.10	0.00	0.00	0.00	0.029	0.026	0.021
0.11	0.00	0.00	0.00	0.033	0.029	0.026
0.12	0.00	0.00	0.00	0.036	0.033	0.029
0.13	0.20	0.00	0.00	0.039	0.036	0.033
0.14	0.40	0.20	0.00	0.042	0.039	0.036
0.15	0.40	0.40	0.20	0.045	0.042	0.039
0.16	0.30	0.40	0.40	0.049	0.045	0.042
0.17	0.30	0.30	0.40	0.054	0.049	0.045
0.18	0.70	0.30	0.30	0.059	0.054	0.049
0.19	0.80	0.70	0.30	0.066	0.059	0.054
0.20	0.70	0.80	0.70	0.073	0.066	0.059
0.21	0.40	0.70	0.80	0.082	0.073	0.066
0.22	0.20	0.40	0.70	0.091	0.082	0.073
0.23	0.20	0.20	0.40	0.100	0.091	0.082
0.24	0.30	0.20	0.20	0.108	0.100	0.091
0.25	0.50	0.30	0.20	0.116	0.108	0.100
0.26	0.40	0.50	0.30	0.124	0.116	0.108
0.27	0.20	0.40	0.50	0.133	0.124	0.116
0.28	0.00	0.20	0.40	0.140	0.133	0.124
0.29	0.40	0.00	0.20	0.147	0.140	0.133
0.30	0.30	0.40	0.00	0.154	0.147	0.140
0.31	0.20	0.30	0.40	0.161	0.154	0.147
0.32	0.20	0.20	0.30	0.167	0.161	0.154
0.33	0.10	0.20	0.20	0.172	0.167	0.161
0.34	0.10	0.10	0.20	0.177	0.172	0.167
0.35	0.30	0.10	0.10	0.182	0.177	0.172
0.36	0.70	0.30	0.10	0.186	0.182	0.177
0.37	1.10	0.70	0.30	0.192	0.186	0.182
0.38	2.60	1.10	0.70	0.200	0.192	0.186
0.39	3.50	2.60	1.10	0.215	0.200	0.192
0.40	7.10	3.50	2.60	0.239	0.215	0.200
0.41	10.20	7.10	3.50	0.281	0.239	0.215
0.42	15.90	10.20	7.10	0.350	0.281	0.239
0.43	21.80	15.90	10.20	0.458	0.350	0.281
0.44	28.10	21.80	15.90	0.619	0.458	0.350
0.45	34.40	28.10	21.80	0.846	0.619	0.458
0.46	39.90	34.40	28.10	1.149	0.846	0.619
0.47	44.80	39.90	34.40	1.537	1.149	0.846
0.48	50.30	44.80	39.90	2.016	1.537	1.149
0.49	52.70	50.30	44.80	2.590	2.016	1.537
0.50	56.40	52.70	50.30	3.259	2.590	2.016
0.51	58.80	56.40	52.70	4.020	3.259	2.590
0.52	61.50	58.80	56.40	4.873	4.020	3.259
0.53	63.40	61.50	58.80	5.812	4.873	4.020
0.54	64.70	63.40	61.50	6.832	5.812	4.873
0.55	65.00	64.70	63.40	7.928	6.832	5.812
0.56	66.20	65.00	64.70	9.091	7.928	6.832
0.57	66.40	66.20	65.00	10.313	9.091	7.928
0.58	68.30	66.40	66.20	11.589	10.313	9.091
0.59	67.00	68.30	66.40	12.911	11.589	10.313
0.60	66.30	67.00	68.30	14.271	12.911	11.589
0.61	66.40	66.30	67.00	15.659	14.271	12.911
0.62	65.90	66.40	66.30	17.068	15.659	14.271
0.63	66.10	65.90	66.40	18.491	17.068	15.659
0.64	63.50	66.10	65.90	19.921	18.491	17.068

TABLE A5—BESSEL FILTER EXAMPLE (continued)

Time	X_i	X_{i-1}	X_{i-2}	Y_i	Y_{i-1}	Y_{i-2}
0.65	63.40	63.50	66.10	21.349	19.921	18.491
0.66	61.20	63.40	63.50	22.768	21.349	19.921
0.67	59.90	61.20	63.40	24.170	22.768	21.349
0.68	59.40	59.90	61.20	25.549	24.170	22.768
0.69	58.20	59.40	59.90	26.900	25.549	24.170
0.70	56.60	58.20	59.40	28.218	26.900	25.549
0.71	54.70	56.60	58.20	29.499	28.218	26.900
0.72	53.80	54.70	56.60	30.737	29.499	28.218
0.73	53.40	53.80	54.70	31.930	30.737	29.499
0.74	51.70	53.40	53.80	33.075	31.930	30.737
0.75	50.80	51.70	53.40	34.171	33.075	31.930
0.76	48.80	50.80	51.70	35.214	34.171	33.075
0.77	48.30	48.80	50.80	36.203	35.214	34.171
0.78	45.80	48.30	48.80	37.135	36.203	35.214
0.79	45.30	45.80	48.30	38.009	37.135	36.203
0.80	44.30	45.30	45.80	38.823	38.009	37.135
0.81	42.00	44.30	45.30	39.579	38.823	38.009
0.82	42.20	42.00	44.30	40.274	39.579	38.823

TABLE A5—BESSEL FILTER EXAMPLE (continued)

Time	X_i	X_{i-1}	X_{i-2}	Y_i	Y_{i-1}	Y_{i-2}
0.83	39.90	42.20	42.00	40.910	40.274	39.579
0.84	39.20	39.90	42.20	41.485	40.910	40.274
0.85	39.10	39.20	39.90	42.002	41.485	40.910
0.86	36.90	39.10	39.20	42.462	42.002	41.485
0.87	36.50	36.90	39.10	42.865	42.462	42.002
0.88	35.20	36.50	36.90	43.211	42.865	42.462
0.89	34.50	35.20	36.50	43.503	43.211	42.865
0.90	34.90	34.50	35.20	43.743	43.503	43.211
0.91	32.70	34.90	34.50	43.934	43.743	43.503
0.92	32.10	32.70	34.90	44.075	43.934	43.743
0.93	31.50	32.10	32.70	44.169	44.075	43.934
0.94	30.50	31.50	32.10	44.216	44.169	44.075
0.95	30.70	30.50	31.50	44.220	44.216	44.169
0.96	30.20	30.70	30.50	44.184	44.220	44.216
0.97	29.30	30.20	30.70	44.110	44.184	44.220
0.98	26.90	29.30	30.20	43.999	44.110	44.184
0.99	25.80	26.90	29.30	43.848	43.999	44.110
1.00	25.30	25.80	26.90	43.660	43.848	43.999

APPENDIX B
CORRECTIONS FOR AMBIENT TEST CONDITIONS

B.1 Introduction—Adjustment of snap-acceleration smoke values for the influence of ambient measurement conditions is an important and integral part of the SAE J1667 smoke measurement procedure. Testing has shown at-site ambient environmental conditions to be among the most influential testing factors that affect as-measured snap-acceleration smoke results. The ambient environmental factors incurred at the point of measurement in the form of altitude, barometric pressure, air temperature, and humidity have been combined into the single parameter of dry air density in order to provide a means of accounting for the influence of these factors on snap-acceleration test results. This appendix details procedures and offers guidelines for performing this important adjustment to snap-acceleration smoke values.

As will be summarized in Section B.7, the adjustment equations provided in this appendix were derived from an extensive snap-acceleration smoke test program involving a wide variety of heavy-duty diesel powered vehicles. One of the main conclusions of this test program was that each of the engines powering the test vehicles displayed different degrees of sensitivity to changes in air density. These differences were likely due to the different combustion and smoke control technologies employed by these engines at the time of their manufacture.

The air density adjustment equations provided in this appendix reflect the best fit nominal sensitivity of the sample of engines/vehicles evaluated. Some engines were more sensitive, and some were less sensitive, to the air density changes than predicted by the adjustment equations. In light of this, applying the correction equations to specific engines/vehicles of unknown air density sensitivity, the adjustment equations can only be considered approximate. It is recommended that regulatory agencies adopting this procedure in enforcement programs make some allowance for the fact that the air density sensitivity of individual vehicles tested in the program will, in general, not be known precisely and may be different than indicated by the nominal adjustment.

B.1.1 Reference Conditions—To perform an air density adjustment to an observed smoke value, it is necessary to define a reference air density which is used as the basis for the adjustment. The reference dry air density which was selected is:

1.1567 kg/m^3 (0.0722 lbm/ft^3)

This dry air density is the reference density specified in SAE J1349 and J1995, which specify the net and gross power rating conditions for diesel engines.

B.1.2 Precautions

a. The air density extremes encountered during the smoke test program (see Section B.7) used to derive the adjustment equations ranged from a low of 0.908 kg/m^3 (0.0567 lbm/ft^3) to a high of 1.235 kg/m^3 (0.0771 lbm/ft^3). The adjustment equations provided in this appendix should not be used outside of this range of air density.
b. The results from the study used to develop these correction factors suggested that at high temperatures above 32 °C (90 °F) and at low altitude sites around 412 m (1350 ft) in elevation there appeared to be a systematic temperature effect present that may not be accounted for by these correction factors. Residuals (the difference between measured values and calculated values) at these sites tend to decrease in value with increasing temperature. This may suggest the need for further adjustments to the equations to account for these temperature trends.
c. The air density adjustment equations presented here were developed specifically for use with snap-acceleration smoke values obtained using the procedures, equipment, and analysis techniques described in this document. The adjustment equations are not recommended for use with snap-acceleration smoke values obtained using peak-reading type smokemeters, or other smoke measurement procedures.

B.2 Symbols

A = Final avg. snap-acceleration test result, in units of opacity (%) or smoke density K(m^{-1}), from Equation A4. "A" is equivalent to N_t or K_t, depending on the smoke units being used.
BARO = Barometric pressure, absolute, kPa (in-Hg).
c = Regression coefficient for ambient condition adjustment equation.
DBT = Dry bulb temperature, ambient temperature measured in conjunction with WBT, °C (°F).
DPT = Dew point temperature, °C (°F).
F = Ferrel's equation, saturation pressure adjustment factor.
K = Smoke density (extinction coefficient), per meter (m^{-1}).
N = Smoke opacity, in percent (%).
r = Air density (dry), kg/m^3 (lbm/ft^3).
Dr = Dry air density differential between actual test conditions or reference conditions, and base conditions.
RH = Relative humidity, percent (%).
SPT = Water saturation pressure at the ambient temperature, kPa (in-Hg).
SPWBT = Water saturation pressure at the wet bulb temperature, kPa (in-Hg).
T = Ambient temperature, if different from the DBT, °C (°F).
WBT = Wet bulb temperature, °C (°F).
WVP = Water vapor pressure, kPa (in-Hg).

NOTE—Pressure units given in in-Hg are referenced to 0 °C.

subscripts

abs = absolute temperature. T + 273.15 Kelvin (T + 459.67 °R)
base = base dry air density. The air density upon which the ambient conditions correction regression efficients are based.
ref = at reference dry air density conditions, 1.1567 kg/m^3 (0.0722 lbm/ft^3).
t = at non-reference dry air density, usually actual test dry air density.

B.3 Snap-Acceleration Smoke Adjustment Methods. This appendix contains snap-acceleration adjustment equations that account for the air density effects on snap-acceleration smoke. The measured vehicle smoke value (A) is adjusted to the reference air density (ρ_{ref}). The measured smoke value (A), along with the actual dry air density (ρ_t) at the time of the test, are used in Section B.4 for opacity units or Section B.5 for smoke density units to compute the smoke level (N_{ref} or K_{ref}) at the reference air density (ρ_{ref}).

B.4 Adjustment of Snap-Acceleration Smoke Opacity (N) Values for the Effects of Changes in the Dry Air Density. The approach for adjusting smoke opacity values for the effects of changes in the dry air density is to convert the smoke opacity value, N_t, to smoke density units (K), adjust the smoke density value according to the procedures described in Section B.5, and then re-convert the adjusted smoke density value back into smoke opacity units as N_{ref}.

To adjust a snap-acceleration smoke opacity value for the effects of changes in the dry air density:

a. Convert the smoke opacity value to the equivalent smoke density units using the following equation:

$$K = (-1/L) * \ln(1-(N/100)) \quad \text{(Eq. B1)}$$

where:

K = Smoke density (m-1).
L = Optical path length of the smoke measurement, in meters (m). If L is not known, assume a value of 0.127 m.
N = Smoke opacity value to be converted, usually Nt.

b. Adjust the resulting smoke density value, calculated in step 1, according to the procedures described in Section B.5 to produce K_{ref}.

c. Convert the resulting adjusted smoke density value calculated in Section B.5 to equivalent smoke opacity units according to the following equation:

$$N = (1-e^{-KL})*100 \quad \text{(Eq. B2)}$$

where:

N = Ambient conditions adjusted smoke opacity value, N_{ref}.
K = Ambient conditions adjusted smoke density value, K_{ref}, determined in Section B.5.
L = Optical path length value used in Equation B1.

NOTE—It is important to use the same value of L (optical path length) for the conversion to smoke density units and for the re-conversion back to smoke opacity units. The actual value of L is not critical; however, it must be a positive non-zero value.

B.5 Adjustment of Snap-Acceleration Smoke Density (K) Values for the Effects of Changes in the Dry Air Density. The base air density (ρ_{base}) parameter used in this section should not be confused with the reference air density (ρ_{ref}). The base air density is the ambient condition used to develop the adjustment regression coefficient used in this section. The adjustment equations in this section provide for the reference air density to be different from the base air density used in the regression analysis of the ambient conditions test data.

To adjust a measured snap-acceleration smoke density value to reference air density conditions:

a. Calculate the air density differences using ρ_{ref} and ρ_{base}:

$$\Delta\rho_1 = \rho_{ref} - \rho_{base} \quad \text{(Eq. B3)}$$

$$\Delta\rho_2 = \rho_t - \rho_{base} \quad \text{(Eq. B4)}$$

b. Calculate the adjusted snap-acceleration smoke density value, K_{ref}, at the reference dry air density, using Equation B5, and the appropriate values for coefficient c and r from Table B1.

$$K_{ref} = K_t * \frac{(c*\Delta\rho_1^{\ 2}+1)}{(c*\Delta\rho_2^{\ 2}+1)} \quad \text{(Eq. B5)}$$

TABLE B1—SMOKE DENSITY ADJUSTMENT CONSTANTS

Air Density Units	c	ρ_{base}	
kg/m^3	21.1234	1.2094	(metric)
lbm/ft^3	5420.0671	0.0755	(English)

c. Substituting the values in Table B1 for c and ρ into Equation B3 through B5 produces Equation B6 and B7 for K_{ref}.

Metric Units ρ (kg/m^3)

$$K_{ref} = \frac{K_t}{19.952\ \rho_t^{\ 2} - 48.259\ \rho_t + 30.126} \quad \text{(Eq. B6)}$$

English Units ρ (lbm/ft^3)

$$K_{ref} = \frac{K_t}{5119.55\ \rho_t^{\ 2} - 773.05\ \rho_t + 30.126} \quad \text{(Eq. B7)}$$

B.6 Calculation of Dry Air Density—In order to correct the smoke values using the equations in Sections B.4 or B.5, it is first necessary to determine the dry air density at the test conditions. This can be done by measuring the barometric pressure (BARO), the ambient air temperature (T or DBT), and either the dew point temperature (DPT), or the wet and dry bulb temperatures (WBT and DBT), or the relative humidity (RH). From these measurements the dry air density may be determined from the following equation.

$$\rho = (u*(BARO - WVP))/(T_{abs}) \quad \text{(Eq. B8)}$$

where:

TABLE B2—

	Metric	English
ρ, Air Density (dry)	kg/m^3	lbm/ft^3
Units conversion (u)	3.4836	1.3255
Barometric Pressure (BARO)	kPa	in-Hg
Water Vapor Pressure (WVP)	kPa	in-Hg
Ambient Temperature (T_{abs})	Kelvin	°R

The barometric pressure and the ambient temperature must be measured at the test conditions of interest. The water vapor pressure may be calculated as described in B.6.1, or obtained from a psychrometric chart.

NOTE—Exclusion of the water vapor pressure term in Equation B8 (calculation of dry air density) is permissible, thus eliminating the need to measure DPT, WBT, or RH and calculate the WVP. However, the user should be aware that this results in a bias error, usually towards a smaller adjustment factor applied to the smoke values. In addition, it should be noted that as the ambient temperature increases, the amount of water the air can hold increases rapidly, and thus, the potential impact of this error also increases. The examples in Section B.6 illustrate the impact of ignoring the water vapor pressure in the adjustment equations.

B.6.1 Calculation of Water Vapor Pressure (WVP)—The method of calculating the water vapor pressure is dependent upon the instrumentation used to determine the moisture in the ambient air. The most common methods utilized are by the measurement of the dew point temperature (DPT), the measurement of the wet bulb/dry bulb temperatures, and by the measurement of the relative humidity (RH). From these measurements, the vapor pressure of the air may be determined.

B.6.1.1 CALCULATION OF WVP FROM DEW POINT TEMPERATURE—This procedure uses a dimensionless (normalized) polynomial for the vapor pressure calculation. This allows calculations to be performed in any units, utilizing the same polynomial coefficients. In using this technique, the input and output parameters to the polynomial are normalized and un-normalized, respectively, with the supplied support equations.

a. Calculate the normalized dew point temperature (NT) from the measured dew point temperature (DPT).

$$NT = (DPT - TL)/(TH - TL) \quad \text{(Eq. B9)}$$

NOTE—

TABLE B3—

Temperature Units	TL	TH
°C	-30.0	+40.0
°F	-22.0	+104.0

NOTE—DPT, TL, and TH must be in the same temperature units. Equation B9 applies over a dew point temperature range of -30 to +40 °C (-22 to +104 °F).

b. Calculate the normalized water vapor pressure (NP) at the normalized dew point temperature (NT).

$$NP = -4.959658E\text{-}5 + (4.956773E\text{-}2*NT) + (9.455172E\text{-}2*NT^2) + (4.199096E\text{-}1*NT^3) + (-7.549164E\text{-}2*NT^4) + (5.114628E\text{-}1*NT^5) \quad \text{(Eq. B10)}$$

c. Un-normalize the saturation pressure (NP) to produce the WVP at the dew point temperature, DPT, in the units of choice.

$$WVP = PL + (NP*(PH - PL)) \quad \text{(Eq. B11)}$$

TABLE B4—

Pressure Units	PL	PH
kPa	5.0951E-2	7.375
in-Hg	1.5046E-2	2.178

NOTE—WVP, PL, and PH must be in the same pressure units.

B.6.1.2 CALCULATION OF WVP FROM WET BULB/DRY BULB TEMPERATURES—This procedure uses a dimensionless (normalized) polynomial for the vapor pressure calculation. This allows calculations to be performed in any units, utilizing the same polynomial coefficients. In using this technique, the input and output parameters to the polynomial are normalized and un-normalized, respectively, with the supplied support equations.

a. Calculate the normalized wet bulb temperature (NT) from the measured wet bulb temperature (WBT).

$$NT = (WBT - TL)/(TH - TL) \quad \text{(Eq. B12)}$$

TABLE B5—

Temperature Units	TL	TH
°C	-30.0	+40.0
°F	-22.0	+104.0

NOTE—WBT, TL, and TH must be in the same temperature units. Equation B12 applies over a wet bulb temperature range of -30 to +40 °C (-22 to +104 °F).

b. Calculate the normalized saturation pressure (NP) at the normalized wet bulb temperature (NT).

$$NP = -4.959658E\text{-}5 + (4.956673E\text{-}2*NT) + (9.455172E\text{-}2*NT^2) + (4.199096E\text{-}1*NT^3) + (-7.549164E\text{-}2*NT^4) + (5.114628E\text{-}1*NT^5) \quad \text{(Eq. B13)}$$

c. Un-normalize the saturation pressure (NP) to produce the saturation pressure at the wet bulb temperature, SPWBT, in the units of choice.

$$SPWBT = PL + (NP*(PH - PL)) \quad \text{(Eq. B14)}$$

TABLE B6—

Pressure Units	PL	PH
kPa	5.0951E-2	7.375
in-Hg	1.5046E-2	2.178

NOTE—SPWBT, PL, and PH must be in the same pressure units.

d. Using Ferrel's equation, calculate the adjustment factor (F).

Metric Units—WBT in °C

$$F = 3.67E\text{-}4*(1 + (1.152E\text{-}3*WBT)) \quad \text{(Eq. B15)}$$

English Units—WBT in °F

$$F = 3.67E\text{-}4*(1 + (6.4E\text{-}4*(WBT - 32))) \quad \text{(Eq. B16)}$$

e. Calculate the Water Vapor Pressure (WVP).

Metric Units—SPWBT, BARO in kPa; DBT, WBT in °C.

$$WVP = SPWBT - (1.8*F*BARO*(DBT - WBT)) \quad \text{(Eq. B17)}$$

English Units—SPWB, BARO in in-Hg; DBT, WBT in °F.

$$WVP = SPWBT - (F*BARO*(DBT - WBT)) \quad \text{(Eq. B18)}$$

B.6.1.3 CALCULATION OF WVP FROM RELATIVE HUMIDITY AND AMBIENT TEMPERATURE—This procedure uses a dimensionless (normalized) polynomial for the vapor pressure calculation. This allows calculations to be performed in any units, utilizing the same polynomial coefficients. In using this technique, the input and output parameters to the polynomial are normalized and un-normalized, respectively, with the supplied support equations.

a. Calculate the normalized ambient temperature (NT) from the measured ambient temperature (T).

$$NT = (T - TL)/(TH - TL) \quad \text{(Eq. B19)}$$

TABLE B7—

Temperature Units	TL	TH
°C	-30.0	+40.0
°F	-22.0	+104.0

NOTE—T, TL, and TH must be in the same temperature units. Equation B19 applies over an ambient temperature range of -30 to +40 °C (-22 to +104 °F).

b. Calculate the normalized saturation pressure (NP) at the normalized ambient temperature (NT).

$$NP = -4.959658E\text{-}5 + (4.956673E\text{-}2*NT) + (9.455172E\text{-}2*NT^2) + (4.199096E\text{-}1*NT^3) + (-7.549164E\text{-}2*NT^4) + (5.114628E\text{-}1*NT^5) \quad \text{(Eq. B20)}$$

c. Un-normalize the saturation pressure (NP) to produce the saturation pressure at the ambient temperature, SPT, in the units of choice.

$$SPT = PL + (NP*(PH - PL)) \quad \text{(Eq. B21)}$$

TABLE B8—

Pressure Units	PL	PH
kPa	5.0951E-2	7.375
in-Hg	1.5046E-2	2.178

NOTE—SPT, PL, and PH must be in the same pressure units.

d. Calculate the WVP at the measured relative humidity, RH. WVP will be in the same units as SPT.

$$WVP = SPT*(RH/100) \quad \text{(Eq. B22)}$$

***B.7 Examples of Adjustments to Ambient Smoke Values*—**The following hypothetical examples may assist in applying the ambient correction equations. Both metric and English unit based examples are provided. Also included for reference are the applicable equation numbers used in this appendix.

Example 1

Situation—A vehicle tested for smoke at a moderate elevation produces an average snap-acceleration smoke value of 60% opacity (the (A) value reported from Equation B3).

Task—From the ambient conditions measurements, determine the adjusted smoke opacity (N_{ref}) at the reference air density (ρ_{ref}).

Ambient measurements	Equation Constants
Smoke (A) = 60% opacity	c = 54.200671
(BARO) = 27.00 in-Hg	TL = -22 x °F
(T) = 77 x °F	TH = 104 x °F
(RH) = 50%	PL = 1.5046E-2 in-Hg
	PH = 2.178 in-Hg
	EOPL = 0.127 m
	(ρ_{ref}) = 0.0722 lbm/ft^3
	(ρ_{base}) = 0.0755 lbm/ft^3

Calculations:

(Eq.B19)	NT	= (77 - (-22))/(104 - (-22)) = 0.785714
(Eq.B20)	NP	= 0.425334 (polynomial)
(Eq.B21)	SPT	= 1.5046E-2 + 0.425334 * (2.178 - 1.5046E-2) = 0.935024
(Eq.B22)	WVP	= 0.935024 * (50.0/100) = 0.4675
(Eq.B8)	ρ_{dry}	= (1.3255 * (27.0 - 0.4675))/(77 + 459.67) = 0.06553
(Eq.B1)	K_t	= 7.215
(Eq.B3)	$\Delta\rho 1$	= 0.0722 - 0.0755 = -0.0033
(Eq.B4)	$\Delta\rho 2$	= 0.06553 - 0.0755 = -0.00996
(Eq.B5)	K_{ref}	= 4.966
(Eq.B2)	N_{ref}	= 46.8%

Result—A vehicle with a snap-acceleration smoke level of 60% opacity at a dry air density of 0.0655 lbm/ft^3 would be projected to produce a smoke value of 46.8% opacity at the reference dry air density of 0.0722 lbm/ft^3.

It should be noted that if the RH measurement had not been performed and the effect of WVP ignored, the resulting impact would have changed N_{ref} from 46.8% to 49.5% opacity.

Example 2

Situation—A vehicle tested for smoke at a moderate elevation produces an average snap-acceleration smoke density of 7.2 m^{-1} (the (A) value reported from Equation B3).

Task—From the ambient conditions measurements, determine the adjusted smoke density (K^{ref}) at the reference air density (ρ_{ref}).

Ambient measurements	Equation Constants
Smoke (A) = 7.2 m^{-1}	c = 0.211234
(BARO) = 88.50 kPa	TL = -30 °C
(T) = 20 °C	TH = 40 °C
(DPT) = 10 °C	PL = 5.0951E-2 kPa
	PH = 7.375 kPa
	(ρ_{ref}) = 1.1567 kg/m^3
	(ρ_{base}) = 1.2094 kg/m^3

Calculations:

(Eq.B9)	NT	= (10 – (–30))/(40 – (–30)) = 0.571428
(Eq.B10)	NP	= 0.160612 (polynomial)
(Eq.B11)	WVP	= 5.0951E-2– (0.160612 * (7.375 – 5.0951E-2)) = 1.2272
(Eq.B8)	ρ_{dry}	= (3.4836 * (88.5 – 1.227))/(20 + 273.15) = 1.0370
(Eq.B3)	$\Delta\rho_1$	= 1.1567– 1.2094 = –0.0527
(Eq.B4)	$\Delta\rho_2$	= 1.0370 – 1.2094 = –0.17230
(Eq.B5)	K_{ref}	= 4.684 m-^{1}

Result—A vehicle with a snap-acceleration smoke density of 7.2 m^{-1} at a dry air density of 1.0370 kg/m^3 would be projected to produce a smoke density of 4.684 (m^{-1}) at the reference dry air density of 1.1567 kg/m^3.

***B.8 Snap-Acceleration/Air Density Field Test Program*—**The snap-acceleration smoke adjustment equations of this appendix were derived using data from a smoke test program designed to study the effects of ambient conditions on snap-acceleration smoke levels. The test program was conducted during the summer of 1993 and involved measuring the snap-acceleration levels of several heavy-duty diesel-powered vehicles, as the vehicles traveled an out and back route over a wide range of elevations on Interstate 80, in California. The vehicles were tested for snap-acceleration smoke with several types of smokemeters using the SAE J1667 test procedures and data analysis algorithm. Eight tests were performed at six different elevations along the route. At two of the elevations, tests were performed on both the outbound and return legs of the test route. The range of the ambient test conditions encountered during the test program are shown in Table B9.

TABLE B9—TEST PROGRAM AMBIENT EXTREMES

Units	min	max
Metric		
Elevation	12 m	2207 m
Air Density (dry)	0.906 kg/m^3	1.235 kg/m^3
Air Density (wet)	0.915 kg/m^3	1.240 kg/m^3
Barometer	78.3 kPa	101.7 kPa
Ambient Temp.	11.7 °C	37.2 °C
Specific Humidity	0.6 gm/kg	12.7 gm/kg
English		
Elevation	40 ft	7240 ft
Air Density (dry)	0.0567 lbm/ft^3	0.0771 lbm/ft^3
Air Density (wet)	0.0571 lbm/ft^3	0.0774 lbm/ft^3
Barometer	23.11 in-Hg	30.03 in-Hg
Ambient Temp.	53 °F	99 °F
Specific Humidity	4 grains	89 grains

A total of 24 diesel-powered vehicles were tested in the program, with the number, type, and manufacturer of the diesel engines powering these vehicles providing a fairly representative sample of the engines in the general U.S. heavy-duty vehicle population. Engines manufactured by Caterpillar, Cummins, Detroit Diesel (both 2 and 4 cycle), and Mack were included in the test sample, as were engines with both mechanical and electronic injection control systems. There was one naturally aspirated engine in the test sample with the rest being turbocharged. The manufacturing dates of the engines covered a range from 1971 to 1993 with about 46% of the engines manufactured in the 1985-1989 period and about 33% manufactured between 1990 and 1993.

Four different manufacturers of smokemeters (Bosch, Caltest, Sun, and Wager) participated in the test program. The smokemeters included full flow end-of-line (EOL) and sampling type smokemeters. Both peak-reading meters and prototype meters which were programmed to perform the SAE J1667 half-second averaging algorithm were included in the testing.

The data from the testing program were assembled into a single data base so that standard mathematical and statistical procedures could be utilized to query for relationships among the various test parameters. Data from the peak-reading meters and data which did not meet the SAE J1667 test validation criteria, as given in 5.4.4, were excluded from the analyses. Dry air density, barometric pressure, and altitude all produced significant correlations with the snap-acceleration smoke values, with dry air density providing the better correlation.

The data from this test program were also used to quantify the repeatability of the test procedure. This was done in two ways. In the first method, the average of the ambient condition corrected smoke values was computed for each vehicle, test day and smokemeter combination. The deviations of the individual corrected smoke values from this average were then computed and used to provide a measure of the repeatability of the test procedure over the full range of ambient conditions encountered in the test program and allowed by the procedure. When this was done for all the data in the test program data base, 91% of the deviations from average were less than 6% opacity.

In the second method, only the data taken at the two elevations where repeat tests were run were utilized. For each vehicle/meter combination the two test results obtained at these test locations created a data pair which differed only slightly in ambient dry air density. (Since the elevation was the same for both points in the data pair, the only source of air density differences was the change in ambient conditions which occurred in the few hours between the two tests.) All these smoke values were corrected to the standard reference air density using the methods described in this appendix and the deviation of the corrected smoke values was noted for each data pair. For 90% of the pairs, the deviations were less than 3% opacity.

The difference in the repeatabilities quantified by the two methods reflects the imprecision of applying the ambient condition corrections to specific vehicles over wide ranges of air density.

APPENDIX C
APPLICATION OF CORRECTIONS TO MEASURED SMOKE VALUES

C.1 Introduction—Fundamentally, all smoke opacimeters measure the transmittance of light through a smoke plume or a sample of gas which contains smoke particles. Typically, however, it is desired to quantify and report the exhaust smoke emissions in units of either smoke opacity (N) or smoke density (k). Furthermore, if the smoke level is reported as smoke opacity, then is it also necessary to report the associated effective optical path length to fully specify the smoke level of the vehicle. This is because measured smoke opacity is a function of the effective optical path length (EOPL) used to make the measurement. For example, an engine that yielded a 20% opacity when tested with a tailpipe which caused the EOPL to be 76 mm would have measured opacities of 26%, 31%, and 36%, respectively, when tested with larger tailpipes which caused the EOPL to be 102, 127, and 152 mm. Therefore, to facilitate comparisons of smoke opacity data from different sources and with smoke standards which may be developed, opacity values must be reported at standard effective optical path lengths.

When smoke is measured using an effective optical path length which is different than the standard path length, the measured smoke values must be converted to opacity at the standard path length using the appropriate Beer-Lambert relationship. Similarly, if it is desired to report the test results in units of smoke density, it is necessary to use the Beer-Lambert relationship to convert the measured opacity results to smoke density.

Finally, if smoke measurements are made using a smokemeter having a red LED light source, a wavelength correction is necessary to account for the fact that the ability of diesel smoke to absorb light depends on the wavelength of the light.

This appendix describes how measured smoke values are to be corrected to the desired reporting units using the Beer-Lambert relationships and how the light source wavelength corrections are to be made.

C.2 Definitions and Symbols

C.2.1 Diesel Smoke—Particles, including aerosols, suspended in the exhaust stream of a diesel engine which absorb, reflect, or refract light.

C.2.2 Transmittance (T)—The fraction of light transmitted from a source which reaches a light detector.

C.2.3 Opacity (N)—The percentage of light transmitted from a source which is prevented from reaching a light detector.

C.2.4 Effective Optical Path Length (L)—The length of the smoke obscured optical path between the smokemeter light source and light detector. Note that portions of the total light source to detector path length which are not smoke obscured do not contribute to the effective optical path length.

C.2.5 Smoke Density (k)—A fundamental means of quantifying the ability of a smoke plume or a smoke-containing gas sample to prevent the passage of light. By convention, smoke density is expressed on a per meter basis (m^{-1}).

C.2.6 W—The wavelength of the smokemeter light source.

C.2.7 Subscripts

C.2.7.1 m—Refers to the as-measured condition

C.2.7.2 s—Refers to values corrected to a standard condition

C.3 Beer-Lambert Relationships—The Beer-Lambert Law defines the relationship between transmittance, smoke density, and effective optical path length as shown in Equation C1.

$$T = e^{-kL} \quad \text{(Eq. C1)}$$

From the definitions of transmittance and opacity, the relationship between these parameters may be defined as shown in Equation C2.

$$N(\%) = 100*(1-T) \quad \text{(Eq. C2)}$$

From Equations C1 and C2 the following important relationships can be derived:

$$N_s = 100*(1-((1-(N_m/100))(L_s/L_m))) \quad \text{(Eq. C3)}$$

$$k = -(1/L_m)*(\ln(1-(N_m/100))) \quad \text{(Eq. C4)}$$

To achieve proper results in applying Equations C1 and C4, the effective optical path lengths (L and L_m) must be expressed in units of meters (m). It is recommended that the effective optical path lengths used in Equation C3 also be expressed in meters (m); however, any length unit may be used as long as L_s and L_m are expressed in the same measurement unit.

C.4 Use of Beer-Lambert Relationships—Conversion from as-measured smoke values to appropriate reporting units is a two-step process. Since, as noted in Section C.1, the basic measurement unit of all smokemeters is transmittance, the first step in all cases is to convert from transmittance (T) to opacity at the as-measured effective optical path length (N_m) using Equation C2. Since all opacimeters do this internally, this step is transparent to the user.

The second step of the process is to convert from N_m to the desired reporting units as follows:

a. If the test results are to be reported in opacity units, Equation C3 must be used to convert from opacity at the as-measured effective optical path length to opacity at the standard effective optical path length. (In the event that the measured and standard effective optical path lengths are identical, N_s is equal to N_m and this secondary conversion step is not required.)
b. If the test results are to be reported in units of smoke density, then Equation C4 must be applied.

C.5 Effective Optical Path Length Input Values—In order to apply conversion Equation C4, it is necessary to input the as-measured effective optical path length (L_m). To use Equation C3, values must be input both for L_m and for L_s, the standard effective optical path length. This section provides guidance on the determination of these input values.

C.5.1 Determination of L_m—For full-flow end-of-line type smokemeters, L_m is a function of the vehicle tailpipe design. For straight tailpipes with a circular cross section, L_m is equal to the tailpipe ID. For tailpipes constructed of common tubing, the tubing OD may be used to approximate the tubing ID. Appendix D provides guidance in determining L_m for other tailpipe configurations.

For sampling type smokemeters, L_m is a fixed function of the meter measurement cell and purge air system design. Specification data supplied by the meter manufacturer should be consulted to determine the appropriate value for L_m when this type of smokemeter is used.

Typically, it is necessary to determine L_m within ±5 mm to achieve corrected smoke results that are accurate within ±2% opacity or ±0.2 m^{-1} smoke density.

C.5.2 Determination of L_s—To ensure meaningful smoke data comparisons, smoke opacity results should be reported at the standard effective optical path lengths, L_s shown in Table C1. Table C1 is constructed such that the standard effective optical path length increases with the engine power rating and approximates exhaust tailpipe sizes commonly used in vehicle applications. In cases where the engine rated power cannot be determined, the actual tailpipe OD usually provides a good approximation of L_s and may be used in lieu of Table C1.

TABLE C1—STANDARD EFFECTIVE OPTICAL PATH LENGTHS

Related Engine Power kW	Rated Engine Power BHP	Standard Effective Optical Path length mm	Standard Effective Optical Path Length in
Less than 75	Less than 101	51	2
75 to 149	101 to 200	76	3
150 to 224	201 to 300	102	4
225 or More	301 or more	127	5

When testing vehicles with multiple exhaust outlets, the total rated engine power must be used with Table C1 to determine the standard effective optical path length. The rated engine power must not be divided by the number of exhaust outlets when using Table C1. If this error is made, it will result in reported smoke opacity values which are erroneously low.

C.6 Sequencing of Beer-Lambert Corrections

C.6.1 Preferred Method—To achieve the highest degree of accuracy, the Beer-Lambert conversion calculations described in Section C.4 should be performed on each instantaneous measured smoke value before any further data-processing takes place. To perform the calculations in this manner during snap-acceleration testing requires significant data-processing capacity since the minimum smoke data-processing rate is 20 Hz. In addition, the ability to input values for L_m and L_s to the data-processing unit is required.

C.6.2 Alternate Methods—In some cases, users may wish to use data-processing systems which are not capable of performing the Beer-Lambert corrections using the preferred method in C.6.1. In these cases, either of the following alternate techniques may be employed; however, users are cautioned that there will be some loss of accuracy.

a. The appropriate Beer-Lambert conversion equations as defined in Section C.4 may be applied after instantaneous smoke values have been averaged using the procedures described in Appendix A. The snap-acceleration test error that results from the use of this method will, in most cases, be less than 1% opacity or 0.15 m^{-1} smoke density, but could be somewhat higher when the snap-acceleration test generates a very high and sharp smoke spike.

b. Appropriate Beer-Lambert conversions may be performed manually on as-measured average smoke values by using the alignment chart shown in Figure C1. In this method, an as-measured smoke opacity (N_m) is located on the vertical column which most closely represents the as-measured effective optical path length (L_m). The user then reads horizontally across the chart to the column which represents the standard effective optical path length (L_s) if a smoke opacity output is desired, or to the smoke density column if a density output is desired. The user then reads the desired output by interpolating the scale of the target column. For example, if an opacity value of 40% were measured using an effective optical path length of 102 mm (4 in), the chart could be used to determine that the equivalent opacity at a path length of 127 mm (5 in) is approximately 47% and that the associated smoke density is about 5.0 m^{-1}.

Since the alignment chart was developed using Equations C3 and C4, the fundamental accuracy of this method is the same as alternate method (a). However, when the as-measured effective optical path length is not equal to one of the values which appear as one of the vertical chart scales the utility and/or accuracy of this method is reduced. This method also introduces the potential for small errors due to resolution and readability of the non-linear chart scales.

C.7 Smokemeter Light Source Wavelength Corrections—The ability of diesel smoke to absorb light is wavelength dependent (i.e., diesel smoke does not have neutral spectral density). For this reason, smokemeters using different light sources will respond differently to the same smoke sample, and corrections are required to achieve comparable results.

Since most smokemeters today use either a green LED or an incandescent light source, with an equivalent peak spectral emissivity, this will be the standard for reporting snap-acceleration test results. Smoke measurements made with meters using red LED light sources must be corrected using the following equations.

$$N_s = 100*(1-((1-(N_m/100))(w_m/w_s))) \quad \text{(Eq. C5)}$$

$$K_s = (-1/L)*\ln((1-(N_m/100))(w_m/w_s)) \quad \text{(Eq. C6)}$$

where:

Ws = the wavelength of a standard green LED light source = 570 nm
Wm = the wavelength of a red LED light source = 660 nm

It is preferred that the wavelength corrections, like the Beer-Lambert corrections, be applied to each instantaneous measured smoke value. However, if this is not possible, and if small errors are acceptable, the wavelength corrections may be applied after average smoke values are obtained as described in Appendix A.

Light source wavelength corrections using Equations C5 and C6 should be applied when the meter is used to measure diesel smoke, but should not be used when the meter is being calibrated using a neutral density filter.

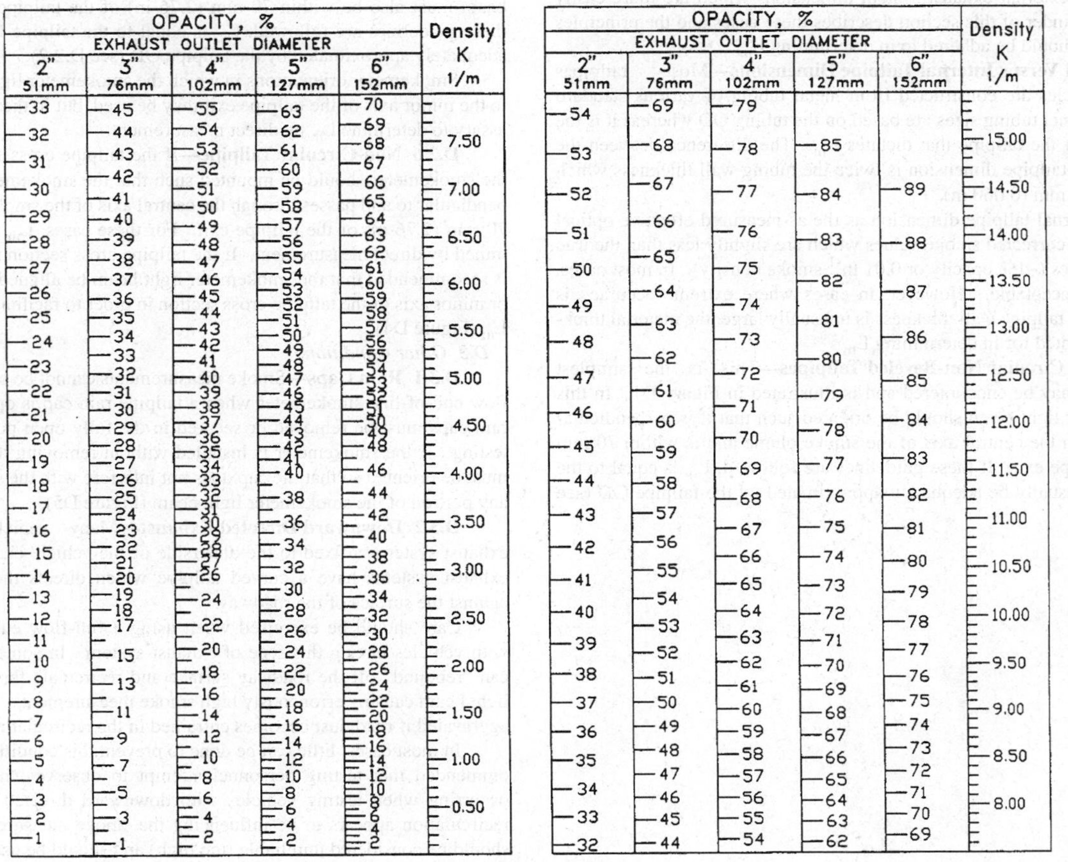

OPACITY, %
EXHAUST OUTLET DIAMETER
2" 51mm | 3" 76mm | 4" 102mm | 5" 127mm | 6" 152mm | Density K 1/m

FIGURE C1—ALIGNMENT CHART

APPENDIX D
EXHAUST SYSTEMS AND SPECIAL APPLICATIONS

D.1 Introduction—In order to report snap-acceleration test results at standard conditions, the Beer-Lambert effective optical path length corrections described in Appendix C must be applied to the as-measured smoke values. A required input for the Beer-Lambert corrections is the as-measured effective optical path length (L_m). When a sampling type smokemeter is used, L_m is a function of the meter design and is expected to be supplied by the meter manufacturer. When a full-flow end-of-line smokemeter is used, L_m is a function of the vehicle exhaust system and the way the meter is mounted on the tailpipe. Users of full-flow smokemeters must, therefore, determine L_m for each test conducted on a case by case basis.

Recognizing the wide variety of exhaust systems that may be encountered when conducting vehicle tests, this appendix provides guidelines which will assist full-flow smokemeter users in determining L_m. This appendix also includes suggestions for mounting full-flow meters on specific types of vehicular exhaust systems. Following these suggestions will facilitate the determination of L_m and will insure that proper smoke measurement principles are adhered to.

D.2 Determination of the As-Measured Effective Optical Path Length (L_m)

D.2.1 General Comments—The effective optical path length has been defined as "the length of the smoke obscured path between the smokemeter light source and detector." Portions of the light source to detector path length which are not smoke obscured do not contribute to the effective optical path length. If the smokemeter light beam is located sufficiently close to the exhaust outlet (within 7 cm or 2.76 in) the cross section of the smoke plume as it passes by the smokemeter is essentially the same as the tailpipe outlet and the effective optical path length is equal to the internal distance across the tailpipe outlet along the line of orientation of the smokemeter light beam. In general, this distance should be determined by direct measurement of the tailpipe outlet, and to achieve corrected smoke results which are within ±2% opacity or ±0.2 m^{-1} smoke density, this measurement should be made within ±5 mm (±0.197 in).

It is often difficult, particularly in roadside testing applications, to gain access to and obtain direct measurements of the tailpipe outlets on many vehicles. Fortunately, for many common tailpipe designs L_m can be determined with sufficient accuracy from external exhaust system dimensions which are more easily measured. The remainder of this section describes these cases and the principles and procedures that should be adhered to in determining L_m.

D.2.2 External Versus Internal Tailpipe Dimensions—Most tailpipes encountered on vehicles are constructed from metal tubing of various standard nominal sizes. Nominal tubing sizes are based on the tubing OD whereas it is the internal dimension of the tailpipe that dictates L_m. The difference between the external and internal tailpipe dimension is twice the tubing wall thickness which is typically about 1.5 mm (0.060 in).

Use of the external tailpipe dimension as the as-measured effective optical path length results in corrected smoke values which are slightly less than the true corrected smoke values (~1% opacity or 0.01 m^{-1} smoke density). In most cases, this small error is acceptable. However, in cases where extreme accuracy is required or where the tailpipe wall thickness is unusually large, the material thickness should be accounted for in determining L_m.

D.2.3 Straight Circular Non-Beveled Tailpipes—This is the simplest tailpipe design that may be encountered and is illustrated in Figure D1. In this case, the smokemeter light beam should be oriented such that it is perpendicular to and passes through the central axis of the smoke plume and is within 70 mm (2.76 in) of the tailpipe exit. If these guidelines are followed, L_m is equal to the tailpipe ID and can usually be adequately approximated by the tailpipe OD (see D.2.2).

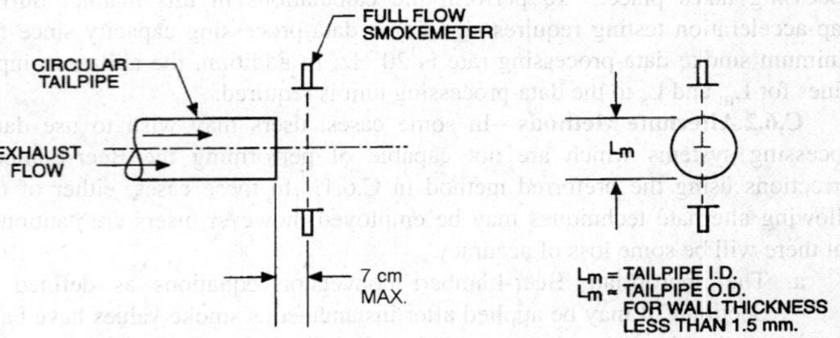

FIGURE D1—STRAIGHT CIRCULAR NON-BEVELED TAILPIPE

D.2.4 Straight Circular Beveled Tailpipes—A beveled tailpipe is formed when the outlet of the tailpipe is not cut off square (perpendicular) to the axis of the exhaust flow. When this type of tailpipe is encountered, there is only one recommended smokemeter mounting orientation. The axis of the smokemeter light beam should be perpendicular to and passing through the central axis of the smoke plume and should be parallel to the minor axis of the elliptical shape of the tailpipe exit. The smokemeter light beam must also be within 70 mm (2.76 in) of the tailpipe outlet (Figure D2). If these guidelines are followed, L_m is equal to the tailpipe ID and can usually be adequately approximated by the tailpipe OD (see D.2.2).

D.2.5 Curved Circular Tailpipes—When the central axis of the tailpipe is curved at the approach to the exit, the tailpipe is said to be curved and the cross section of the tailpipe outlet is non-circular. To avoid erroneously low readings when this type of tailpipe is encountered, the smokemeter should be mounted such that the axis of the smokemeter light beam is perpendicular to and passing through the central axis of the smoke plume (not necessarily the centerline of the pipe) and is parallel to the minor axis of the tailpipe exit. The smokemeter light beam must also be within 70 mm (2.76 in) of the tailpipe exit (Figure D3). If these guidelines are followed, L_m is equal to the tailpipe ID and can usually be adequately approximated by the tailpipe OD (see D.2.2).

Smokemeter orientations in which the smokemeter light beam is not parallel to the minor axis of the tailpipe exit may be used, but in these cases it will be necessary to determine L_m by direct measurement.

D.2.6 Non-Circular Tailpipe—If the tailpipe cross section is non-circular, the smokemeter should be mounted such that the smokemeter light beam is perpendicular to and passes through the central axis of the smoke plume and is within 70 mm (2.76 in) of the tailpipe exit. For these cases, L_m will need to be determined by direct measurement. If the tailpipe cross section is an oval or ellipse, it is recommended that the smokemeter light beam be aligned with either the major or minor axis of the tailpipe cross section in order to facilitate the measurement of L_m (Figure D4).

D.3 Other Conditions

D.3.1 Rain Caps—Smoke measurements cannot be performed using a full-flow end-of-line smokemeter when a tailpipe rain cap is operational. If present, rain caps must be removed or secured in the fully open position prior to smoke testing. If the smokemeter is installed without removing the rain cap, the meter must be oriented so that the cap does not interfere with the smoke plume or block any portion of the smokemeter light beam (Figure D5).

D.3.2 Downward Directed Exhaust—Many vehicles have horizontal exhaust systems affixed to the underside of the vehicle chassis. Typically these exhaust systems have a curved tailpipe which directs the exhaust flow down against the surface of the roadway.

Care should be exercised when using a full-flow end-of-line smokemeter with vehicles having this type of exhaust system. In some cases, exhaust gases can "rebound" off the roadway surface and recirculate through the smokemeter light beam causing erroneously high smoke measurements. This condition can be aggravated if road dust becomes entrained in the recirculating exhaust flow.

In most cases, little can be done to prevent this condition; however, it is recommended that testing personnel attempt to observe whether recirculation is occurring when testing vehicles with downward directed exhaust systems. If recirculation appears to be influencing the smoke measurement, the test results should be considered unreliable (too high) and should be used with caution.

RECOMMENDED SMOKEMETER ORIENTATION

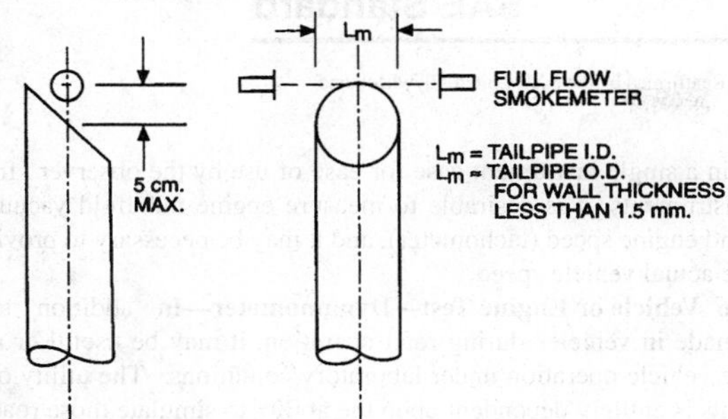

SMOKEMETER ORIENTATIONS WHICH ARE NOT RECOMMENDED

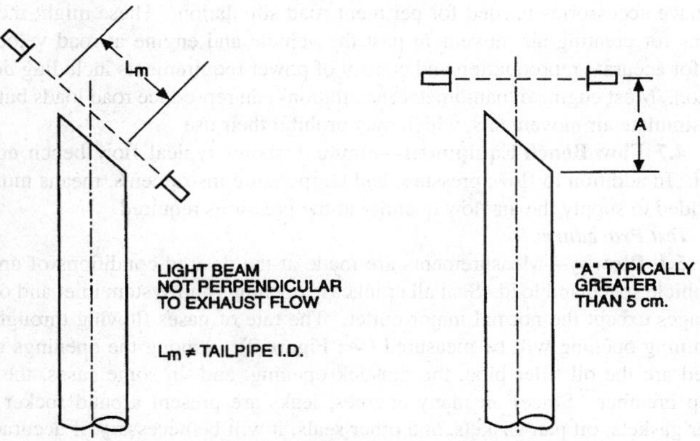

FIGURE D2—STRAIGHT CIRCULAR BEVELED TAILPIPE

RECOMMENDED SMOKEMETER ORIENTATION

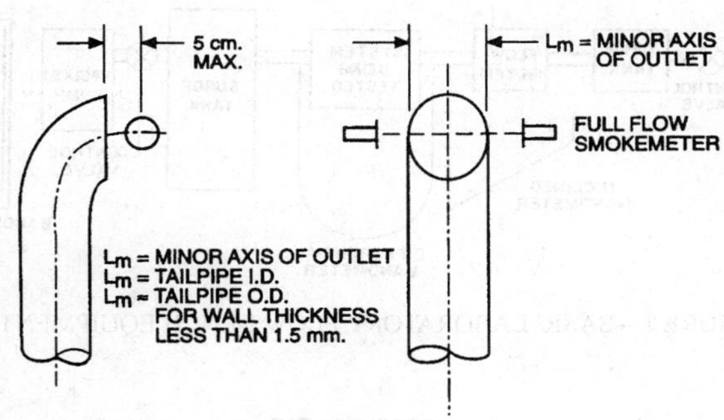

ACCEPTABLE SMOKEMETER ORIENTATION

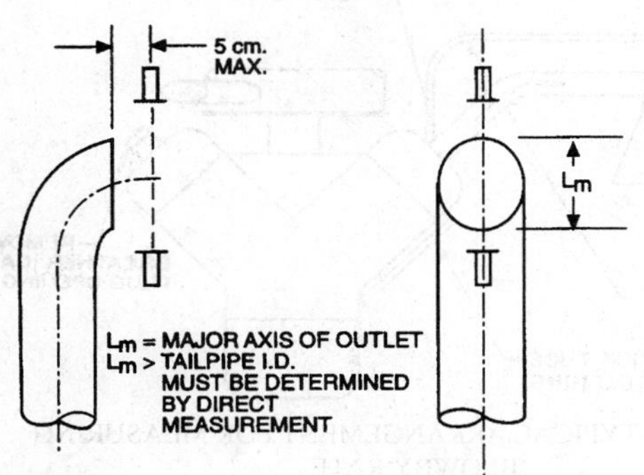

FIGURE D3—CURVED CIRCULAR TAILPIPE

RECOMMENDED SMOKEMETER ORIENTATIONS

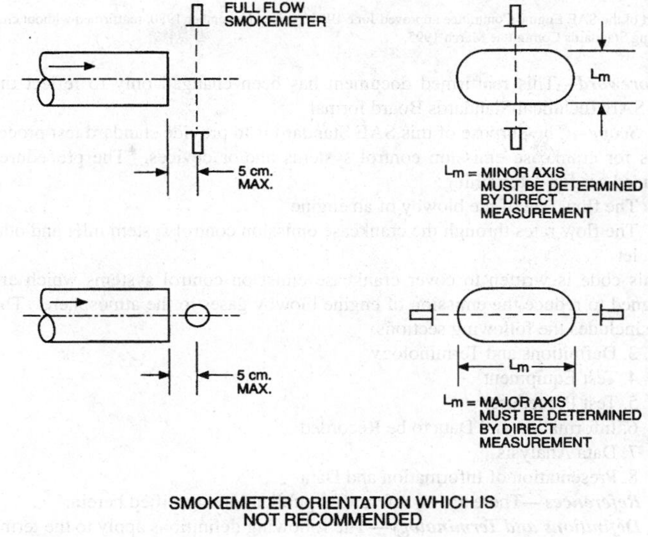

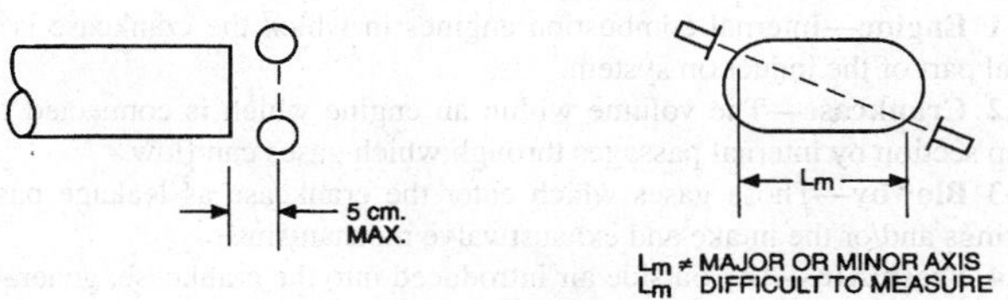

SMOKEMETER ORIENTATION WHICH IS NOT RECOMMENDED

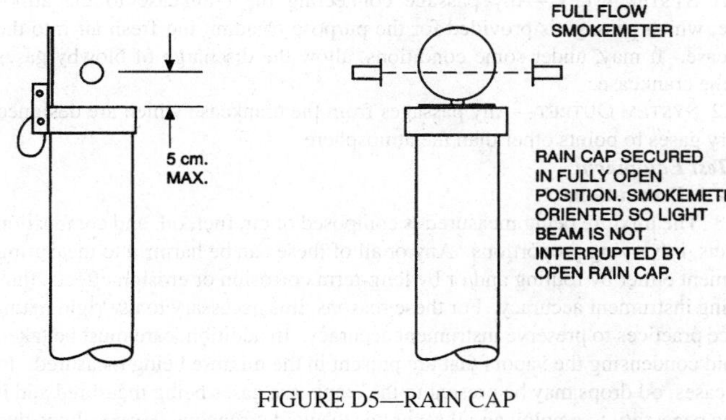

FIGURE D4—NON-CIRCULAR TAILPIPE

FULL FLOW SMOKEMETER

5 cm. MAX.

RAIN CAP SECURED IN FULLY OPEN POSITION. SMOKEMETER ORIENTED SO LIGHT BEAM IS NOT INTERRUPTED BY OPEN RAIN CAP.

FIGURE D5—RAIN CAP

CRANKCASE EMISSION CONTROL TEST CODE —SAE J900 MAR1995

SAE Standard

Report of the SAE Engine Committee approved June 1964, revised November 1980, reaffirmed without change August 1985. Reaffirmed by the SAE Clutch, Flywheel, and Housing Standards Committee March 1995.

Foreword—This reaffirmed document has been changed only to reflect the new SAE Technical Standards Board format.

1. Scope—The purpose of this SAE Standard is to provide standard test procedures for crankcase emission control systems and/or devices. The procedures included are for determining:

a. The flow rate of the blowby of an engine
b. The flow rates through the crankcase emission control system inlet and outlet

This code is written to cover crankcase emission control systems which are designed to reduce the emission of engine blowby gases to the atmosphere. The code includes the following sections:

3. Definitions and Terminology
4. Test Equipment
5. Test Procedures
6. Information and Data to be Recorded
7. Data Analysis
8. Presentation of Information and Data

2. References—There are no referenced publications specified herein.

3. Definitions and Terminology—The following definitions apply to the terms indicated as they are used in this code.

3.1 Engine—Internal combustion engines in which the crankcase is not a principal part of the induction system.

3.2 Crankcase—The volume within an engine which is connected to the oil sump section by internal passages through which gases can flow.

3.3 Blowby—Those gases which enter the crankcase as leakage past the piston rings and/or the intake and exhaust valve mechanisms.

3.4 Fresh Air—Any outside air introduced into the crankcase, generally to aid in ventilation (purging of blowby gases from the crankcase).

3.5 Crankcase Emission Control System—A system of passages designed to convey gases from and/or to the crankcase of an engine. The system may or may not include means to regulate the flow(s).

3.5.1 SYSTEM INLET—Any passage connecting the crankcase to the atmosphere; which passage is provided for the purpose of admitting fresh air into the crankcase. It may, under some conditions, allow the discharge of blowby gases from the crankcase.

3.5.2 SYSTEM OUTLET—Any passages from the crankcase which are designed to carry gases to points other than the atmosphere.

4. Test Equipment

4.1 Precautions

4.1.1 The mixture being measured is composed of air, fuel, oil, and combustion products, in varying proportions. Any or all of these can be harmful to measuring equipment either by fouling and/or by long-term corrosion or erosion effects, thus reducing instrument accuracy. For these reasons, it is necessary to use rigid maintenance practices to preserve instrument accuracy. In addition, care must be taken to avoid condensing the vapors that are present in the mixture being measured. In some cases, oil drops may be present in the crankcase gases being measured and it may be necessary to employ an oil separator to avoid erroneous flow readings due to oil accumulations in the flowmeter.

4.1.2 The flow restrictions of the measurement equipment can greatly affect the volume of flow. For this reason, it is necessary to use some means such as a make-up blower to compensate for the restrictive effect.

4.1.3 The pressures created by actual vehicle movement and engine operation, as well as the system design, will affect flow rates on many types of emission control systems. Therefore, it will be necessary for laboratory tests to simulate the vehicle insofar as it affects the system.

4.2 Flow Measurement Instrumentation—A suitable meter such as a rotometer, viscous flow meter, flow orifice, venturi, or integrating gas meter should be used. Meter accuracy should be within ±5%.

4.3 Pressure Measurement Instrumentation—Suitable manometers or pressure gages should be used. Accuracy should be within ±5%.

4.4 Temperature Measurement Instrumentation—A suitable instrument such as a liquid filled, gas filled, or resistance thermometer, or a thermocouple may be used. Accuracy must be within ±1 °C.

4.5 Vehicle Test—Road—For vehicle tests, it is convenient to mount the flow, pressure, and temperature measuring instruments as well as the make-up blower in a single instrument case for ease of use by the observer. In addition to these instruments, it is desirable to measure engine manifold vacuum (pressure gage) and engine speed (tachometer), and it may be necessary to provide means to measure actual vehicle speed.

4.6 Vehicle or Engine Test—Dynamometer—In addition to measurements made in vehicles during road operation, it may be useful or necessary to simulate vehicle operation under laboratory conditions. The utility of such measurements is entirely dependent upon the ability to simulate those road conditions which may influence the performance of the particular crankcase emission control system under test or the quantity of blowby created by the engine. Most chassis dynamometers are custom installations and any particular installation may or may not have accessories needed for pertinent road simulation. These might include means for creating air movement past the vehicle and engine at road velocities and for accurate reproduction and control of power requirements including deceleration. Most engine dynamometer installations can reproduce road loads but few can simulate air movements, which may prohibit their use.

4.7 Flow Bench Equipment—Figure 1 shows typical flow bench equipment. In addition to flow, pressure, and temperature instruments, means must be provided to supply the air flow quantity at the pressures required.

5. Test Procedures

5.1 Blowby—Measurements are made at the desired conditions of engine or vehicle speed and load. Seal all crankcase openings and system inlet and outlet passages except the normal major outlet. The rate of gases flowing through the remaining opening will be measured (see Figure 2). Among the openings to be sealed are the oil filler pipe, the dipstick opening, and, in some cases, the fuel pump breather. Since, on many engines, leaks are present around rocker arm cover gaskets, oil pan gaskets, and other seals, it will be necessary, if accuracy is required, to account for the escape of blowby through them or to reduce the error by keeping the crankcase at ambient pressure with a blower installed as illustrated in Figure 3.

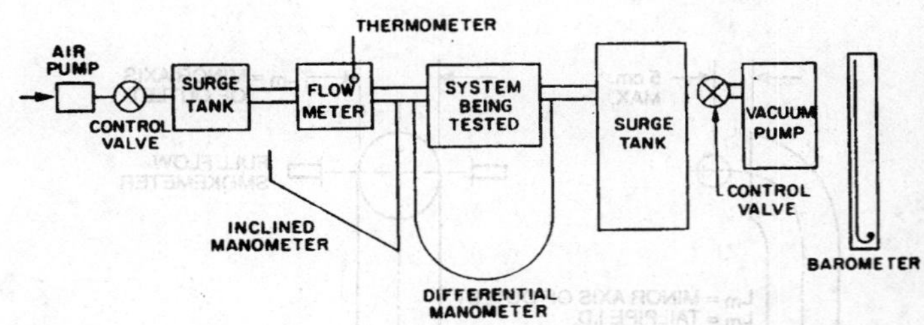

FIGURE 1—BASIC LABORATORY FLOW BENCH EQUIPMENT

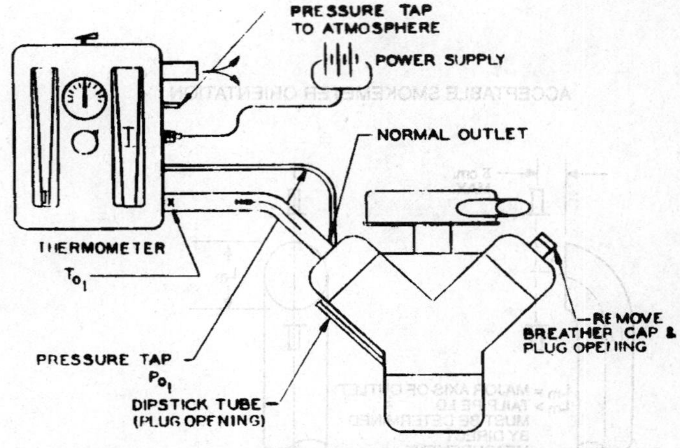

FIGURE 2—TYPICAL ARRANGEMENT FOR MEASURING BLOWBY RATE

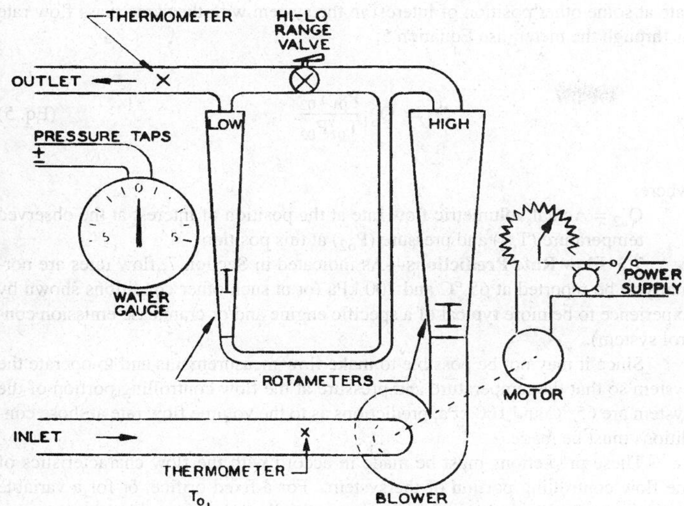

FIGURE 3—SCHEMATIC OF TYPICAL TWO ROTOMETER BALANCING TYPE INSTRUMENT

5.2 Crankcase Emission Control System Flow Rates—For the purpose of this code, the outlet flow rate is defined as follows in Equation 1[1]:

$$\text{Inlet flow rate} + \text{Blowby flow rate} = \text{Outlet flow rate}^{1} \qquad \text{(Eq. 1)}$$

If only two of the three rates can be measured directly, the other can be obtained by difference; however, in the interest of accuracy, it may be necessary to determine the smallest of these quantities by the pressure differential method given in footnote 1.

Figure 4 illustrates an installation of a control system where it is difficult to measure the fresh air flow into the crankcase directly and relatively easy to measure the outlet flow.

Figure 5 shows a different type of system installed that makes outlet flow difficult to measure, since the control valve is inserted directly into the rocker arm cover. The fresh air inflow is measurable through the passage between the breather cap and the crankcase, or through the hose connecting the carburetor air cleaner and the oil filler cap.

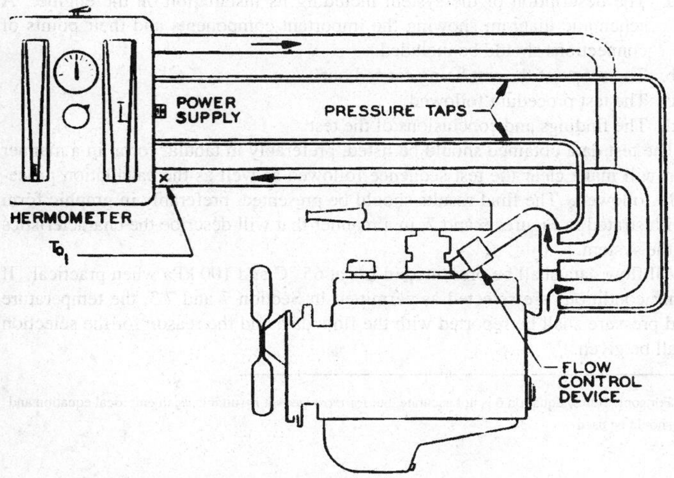

FIGURE 4—TYPICAL INSTALLATION FOR MEASURING SYSTEM OUTFLOW

1. This follows from the law of conservation of mass, that is, "mass flow in" plus "blowby mass flow" equals "mass flow out."

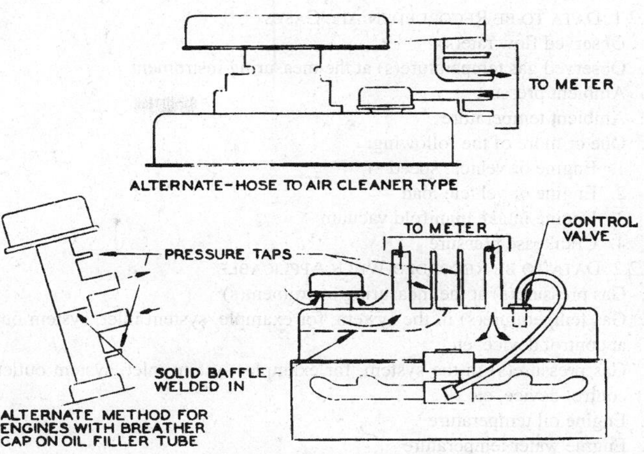

FIGURE 5—TYPICAL METHOD OF MEASURING FRESH AIR INLET RATE

Expressed mathematically, this is:

$$Q_{I}\rho_{I} + Q_{BB}\rho_{BB} = Q_{OUT}\rho_{OUT} \qquad \text{(Eq. 2)}$$

Then, if all of these densities (ρ) are identical:

$$Q_{I} + Q_{BB} = Q_{OUT} \qquad \text{(Eq. 3)}$$

Therefore, all volume flow rates, expressed in L/s, must be reported at the same temperature and pressure for this to hold true.

Flow rates through the oil filler cap in Figure 5 and through the control valve in Figure 4 may be estimated by measuring the inlet and outlet pressures across them during vehicle operation and then reproducing these pressures in the laboratory where flow can be measured.

5.2.1 MEASUREMENT AT SYSTEM OUTLET—Flow rate shall be measured on the engine for which the system was designed by installing the equipment such as shown in Figure 3 to a typical system outlet shown in Figure 4. With systems incorporating a modulating device, the flow rate measuring equipment should be used on the inlet side of the device (see Figure 4). If the capacity of the emission control system is influenced by the blowby rate of the engine, air may be added to the crankcase at such a location and manner to produce a volume of flow through the system equivalent to the desired blowby rate.

5.2.2 MEASUREMENT AT SYSTEM INLET—If the flow rate at the system inlet will not be materially affected by the installation of measuring equipment, its value may be measured directly. Flow rate shall be measured on the engine for which the system was designed by installing the equipment such as is shown in Figure 3 to a typical system inlet as shown in Figure 5.

The flow may be positive (inward) or negative (outward).

6. Information and Data to be Recorded

6.1 Information

6.1.1 GENERAL

a. Laboratory performing test
b. Date of test
c. Description of test equipment, including method of power absorption

6.1.2 VEHICLE DESCRIPTION

a. Manufacturer
b. Model year
c. Body style
d. Transmission

6.1.3 ENGINE DESCRIPTION

a. Manufacturer
b. Configuration—type and number of cylinders
c. Displacement
d. Carburetor—number of venturies
e. Condition—New________ or Hours________ or Kilometers________

6.1.4 CRANKCASE VENTILATION SYSTEM DESCRIPTION

a. Manufacturer
b. Part or system identification number
c. Principle of operation

6.2 Data

6.2.1 DATA TO BE RECORDED IN ALL CASES

a. Observed flow rate(s)
b. Observed gas temperature(s) at the measuring instrument
c. Ambient pressure
d. Ambient temperature
e. One or more of the following:
   1. Engine or vehicle speed
   2. Engine or vehicle load
   3. Engine intake manifold vacuum
   4. Crankcase pressure

6.2.2 DATA TO BE RECORDED WHEN APPLICABLE

a. Gas pressure(s) at the measuring instrument(s)
b. Gas temperature(s) in the system, for example, system inlet, system outlet, at control device, etc.
c. Gas pressure(s) in the system, for example, system inlet, system outlet, at control device, etc.
d. Engine oil temperature
e. Engine water temperature

*7. **Data Analysis***—For purposes of uniformity, flow rates should be reported at 65 °C and 100 kPa. In order to report flow rates at these conditions it may be necessary to perform one or more of the following computations:

a. A meter correction to convert an observed flow meter reading to actual flow rate through the meter.
b. A calculation of the volume flow rate in a portion of the system which is of interest and in which the temperature and/or pressure are different from the existing at the meter.
c. A prediction of the flow rate at temperature and pressure conditions other than those at which observed measurements were made.

For engines and/or crankcase emission control systems which exhibit a gas temperature and/or pressure in the outlet portion of the crankcase emission control system (for example, control valve) significantly different from 65 °C and/or 100 kPa, the flow rate shall be measured at or predicted at the different temperature and/or pressure.

7.1 Meter Correction—Flow meters are calibrated at specific temperatures and pressures which may not prevail at the time an observation is made. Any observed flow reading must be corrected to a value corresponding with the actual temperature and pressure existing at the flow meter.

This correction will depend upon the particular flow measuring instrument being used. As an example, for an orifice meter or rotometer, the observed reading may be corrected by the following general relationship:

$$Q_{a1} = Q_o\sqrt{\frac{P_c T_{01}}{T_c P_{01}}} \quad \text{(Eq. 4)}$$

where:

Q_{a1} = Actual volumetric flow rate through the meter at the observed temperature and pressure at the meter inlet, mm^3/min
Q_o = Observed meter reading
P_{o1} = Observed absolute gas pressure at the meter entrance
P_c = Absolute gas pressure corresponding with the gas density upon which the flow meter calibration is based
T_{o1} = Observed absolute gas temperature (degrees K) at the meter entrance
T_c = Absolute gas temperature (degrees K) corresponding with the gas density upon which the flow meter calibration is based

Equation 4 is typical for rotometers; however, exceptions have been noted. For these exceptions and for other types of flow measuring instruments, the manufacturer's recommendations should be followed.

7.2 Flow Rate Adjustments—If it is desired to determine the volume flow rate at some other position of interest in the system with the same mass flow rate as through the meter, use Equation 5:

$$Q_{a2} = Q_{a1}\frac{P_{01} T_{02}}{T_{01} P_{02}} \quad \text{(Eq. 5)}$$

where:

Q_{a2} = Actual volumetric flow rate at the position of interest at the observed temperature (T_{o2}) and pressure (P_{o2}) at this position

7.3 Flow Rate Predictions—As indicated in Section 7, flow rates are normally to be reported at 65 °C and 100 kPa (or at such other conditions shown by experience to be more typical of a specific engine and/or crankcase emission control system).

Since it may not be possible to make flow measurements and to operate the system so that the temperature and pressure at the flow controlling portion of the system are 65 °C and 100 kPa, predictions as to the volume flow rate at those conditions must be made.

These predictions must be made in accord with the flow characteristics of the flow controlling portion of the system. For a fixed orifice, or for a variable orifice valve in which the orifice size is essentially uninfluenced by gas temperature or pressure, Equation 6 may be used for this prediction with an accuracy consistent with the accuracy of the measurements being made [2].

$$Q_p = Q_{a2}\sqrt{\frac{P_{02} T_p}{T_{02} P_p}} \quad \text{(Eq. 6)}$$

where:

Q_p = Predicted volumetric flow rate at T_p and P_p
T_p and P_p = 338 K absolute temperature (65 °C) and 100 kPa absolute pressure or other typical conditions described previously

Certain crankcase emission control systems (such as a diaphragm-type pressure regulator) are so designed as to have flow characteristics significantly affected by crankcase temperatures and pressures. For such systems, the observed flow rates can only be adjusted, as in 7.2, to the actual gas temperatures and pressures existing at the control valve. Flow rates at other temperature and pressure conditions cannot be predicted as previously outlined. It is recommended that for such systems the outlet flow rate be determined by summation of the blowby rate and inlet flow rate as discussed in 5.2.

*8. **Presentation of Information and Data***—The information and data are to be presented as follows:

a. The description of the system including its installation on the engine. A schematic diagram showing the important components and their points of connections should be included.
b. The scope of the test being carried out.
c. The test procedure followed.
d. The findings and conclusions of the test.

The test data obtained should be listed, preferably in tabular form, in a manner that will make clear the test sequence followed as well as the calculation procedure followed. The final results should be presented, preferably in graphic form as illustrated in Figures 6 and 7, in a manner that will describe the characteristics of the system.

All flow data shall be presented in L/s at 65 °C and 100 kPa when practical. If other conditions are selected as permitted in Section 7 and 7.3, the temperature and pressure shall be reported with the flow data and the reason for the selection shall be given.

2. For sonic flows, Equation 6 is not accurate, but for most cases it is suitable as an empirical equation and should be used.

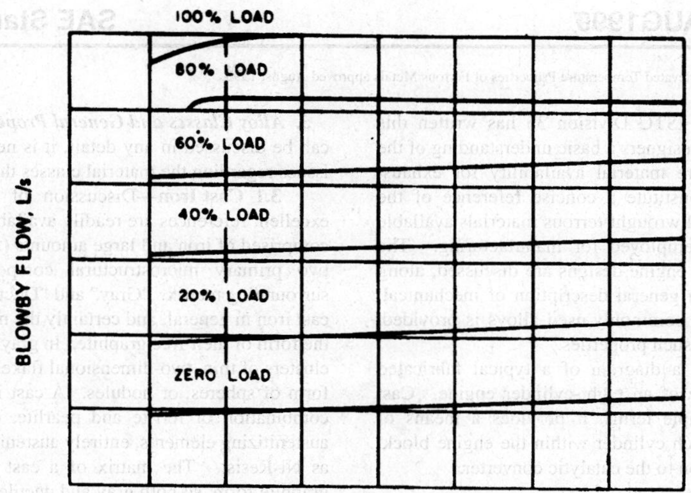

FIGURE 6—TYPICAL ENGINE BLOWBY CURVES

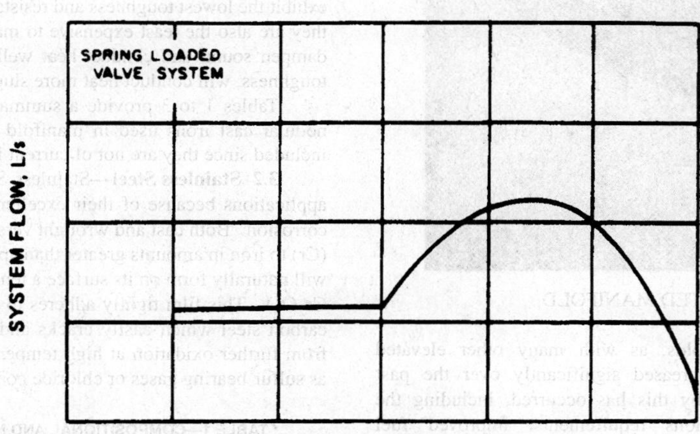

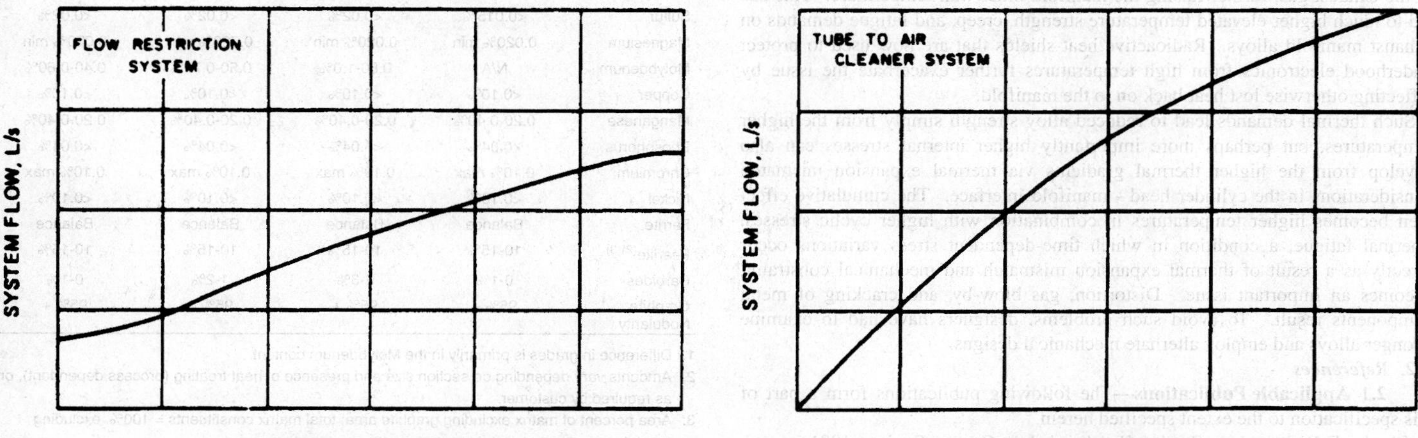

FIGURE 7—EXAMPLES OF DATA PLOTTED FROM TYPICAL SYSTEMS

HIGH TEMPERATURE MATERIALS FOR EXHAUST MANIFOLDS—SAE J2515 AUG1999

SAE Standard

Report of the SAE Iron and Steel Technical Division 35—Elevated Temperature Properties of Ferrous Metals approved August 1999.

1. Scope—A subcommittee within SAE ISTC Division 35 has written this report to provide automotive engineers and designers a basic understanding of the design considerations and high temperature material availability for exhaust manifold use. It is hoped that it will constitute a concise reference of the important characteristics of selected cast and wrought ferrous materials available for this application, as well as methods employed for manufacturing. The different types of manifolds used in current engine designs are discussed, along with their range of applicability. Finally, a general description of mechanical, chemical, and thermophysical properties of commonly-used alloys is provided, along with discussions on the importance of such properties.

1.1 Background—Figure 1 provides a diagram of a typical fabricated exhaust manifold, in this case for one side of an eight-cylinder engine. Cast versions are similar in geometry. In simple terms, it provides a means of containing exhaust gases generated from each cylinder within the engine block, combining the volume, and passing the gas on to the catalytic converter.

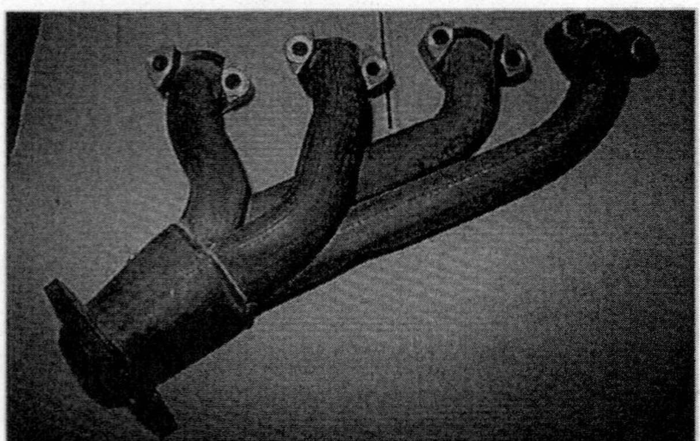

FIGURE 1—FABRICATED MANIFOLD

Operating demands on exhaust manifolds, as with many other elevated temperature engine components, have increased significantly over the past decade. There are numerous reasons why this has occurred, including the usually-cited reasons of tighter emissions requirements, improved fuel efficiencies, and design toward higher specific engine power (kW/kg), with a cumulative end-effect yielding higher exhaust gas temperatures. Techniques used to meet emissions requirements, such as the addition of air injection systems and the use of controlled variations in air-fuel ratios, have changed overall hydrocarbon levels, and, under certain conditions, have increased the emissivity of the exhaust gas, further raising the manifold inner wall temperature. This has led to much higher elevated temperature strength, creep, and fatigue demands on exhaust manifold alloys. Radioactive heat shields that are now used to protect underhood electronics from high temperatures further exacerbate the issue by reflecting otherwise lost heat back on to the manifold.

Such thermal demands lead to reduced alloy strength simply from the higher temperatures, but perhaps more importantly higher internal stresses can also develop from the higher thermal gradients via thermal expansion mismatch considerations in the cylinder head - manifold interface. The cumulative effect then becomes higher temperatures in combination with higher cyclic stresses. Thermal fatigue, a condition in which time-dependent stress variations occur directly as a result of thermal expansion mismatch and mechanical constraint, becomes an important issue. Distortion, gas blow-by, and cracking of metal components result. To avoid such problems, designers have had to examine stronger alloys and employ alternate mechanical designs.

2. References

2.1 Applicable Publications—The following publications form a part of this specification to the extent specified herein.

Charles F. Walton, *Iron Casting Handbook*, Iron Casting Society, 1981

Stephen I. Karsay, *Ductile Iron I Production*, QIT – Fer et Titane, Inc., 1992

Michael F. Burditt, *Ductile Iron Handbook*, American Foundrymen's Society, Inc., 1992

3. Alloy Classes and General Properties—Before manifold design and use can be discussed in any detail, it is necessary to review some of the more basic issues regarding the material classes that are used to make them.

3.1 Cast Iron—Discussion of cast iron metallurgy will be brief, as excellent references are readily available.[1,2,3]. In very basic terms, cast irons are comprised of iron and large amounts (>1% by weight) of carbon (C), and contain two primary microstructural components, a free graphite phase and the surrounding matrix. "Gray" and "Ductile" iron, two of the most common types of cast iron in general, and certainly the most typical for exhaust manifolds, differ in the form of their free graphite. In gray cast iron, graphite is present in the form of clusters of thin, two-dimensional flakes, while in ductile (nodular) iron it is in the form of spheres, or nodules. A cast iron matrix can be ferritic, pearlitic, some combination of ferrite and pearlite, or, with addition of suitable amounts of austenitizing elements, entirely austenitic. Austenitic matrix irons are also known as Ni-Resist. The matrix of a cast iron can be varied independently of the graphite form, so both gray and ductile irons can be ferritic, pearlitic, or austenitic. The different graphite forms and matrix microstructures are created by using special alloying additions and inoculation practices. Silicon (Si) and carbon provide the primary influence on graphite type and amount. The combination of graphite form and matrix microstructure give each type of cast iron its characteristic mechanical and physical properties. For instance, flake graphite alloys (gray iron) typically exhibit the lowest toughness and resistance to crack growth of all the cast irons, but they are also the least expensive to make, and the graphite flakes very effectively dampen sound and conduct heat well. Nodular, or ductile irons exhibit better toughness, will conduct heat more sluggishly, and are more expensive to produce.

Tables 1 to 3 provide a summary of important properties associated with nodular cast irons used in manifold production. Gray iron properties are not included since they are not of current interest.

3.2 Stainless Steel—Stainless Steels are selected for elevated temperature applications because of their excellent strength and resistance to oxidation and corrosion. Both cast and wrought versions are available. Additions of Chromium (Cr) to iron in amounts greater than approximately 12% will result in an alloy that will naturally form on its surface a tenacious chrome oxide passive film (chromia, Cr_2O_3). This film tightly adheres to the base alloy (in contrast to "red rust" on carbon steel which easily cracks and spalls) and protects the underlying metal from further oxidation at high temperature, or corrosion from other factors such as sulfur-bearing gases or chloride containing aqueous solutions.

TABLE 1—COMPOSITIONAL AND MICROSTRUCTURAL CHARACTERISTICS OF DUCTILE CAST IRON

	Ferritic Ductile	Si-Mo Ductile Grade A(1)	Si-Mo Ductile Grade B(1)	Si-Mo Ductile Grade C(1)
Carbon	3.80%	3.45%	3.45%	3.45%
Silicon	2.70-3.00%	4.00%	4.00%	4.00%
Sulfur	<0.015%	<0.02%	<0.02%	<0.02%
Magnesium	0.020% min	0.020% min	0.020% min	0.020% min
Molybdenum	N/A	0.80-1.0%	0.50-0.70%	0.40-0.60%
Copper	<0.10%	<0.10%	<0.10%	<0.10%
Manganese	0.20-0.40%	0.20-0.40%	0.20-0.40%	0.20-0.40%
Phosphorus	<0.04%	<0.04%	<0.04%	<0.04%
Chromium	0.10% max	0.10% max	0.10% max	0.10% max
Nickel	<0.10%	<0.10%	<0.10%	<0.10%
Ferrite	Balance	Balance	Balance	Balance
Pearlite(2)(3)	10-15%	10-15%	10-15%	10-15%
Carbides	0-1%	2-3%	1-2%	0-1%
Graphite Nodularity	95% +	95% +	95% +	95% +

1. Difference in grades is primarily in the Molybdenum content.
2. Amounts vary depending on section size and presence of heat treating (process dependent), or as required by customer.
3. Area percent of matrix excluding graphite area; total matrix constituents = 100%, excluding graphite.

1. Charles F. Walton, *Iron Castings Handbook*, Iron Casting Society, 1981
2. Stephen I. Karsay, *Ductile Iron I Production*, QIT - Fer et Titane Inc., 1992
3. Michael F. Burditt, *Ductile Iron Handbook*, American Foundrymen's Society Inc., 1992

TABLE 2—ELEVATED TEMPERATURE MECHANICAL PROPERTIES OF DUCTILE CAST IRON

	Ferritic Ductile	Si-Mo Ductile Grade A (0.8-1.0% Mo)	Si-Mo Ductile Grade B (0.6-0.8% Mo)	Si-Mo Ductile Grade C (0.4-0.6% Mo)
Elongation	16-20%	10-14%	12-16%	14-18%
Tensile Strength	MPa	MPa	MPa	MPa
22 °C (72 °F)	565	601	592	588
316 °C (600 °F)	490	535	524	518
427 °C (800 °F)	386	414	407	404
538 °C (1000 °F)	248	293	282	276
649 °C (1200 °F)	90	123	115	111
704 °C (1300 °F)	61	83	78	75
Yield Strength	MPa	MPa	MPa	MPa
22 °C (72 °F)	331-365	468	462	459
316 °C (600 °F)		409	404	401
427 °C (800 °F)		379	370	366
538 °C (1000 °F)		263	253	249
649 °C (1200 °F)		92	83	79
704 °C (1300 °F)		71	66	63
Elongation 22 °C (72 °F)	16-20%	8-12%	10-13%	11-14%
Compressive Strength (MPa)	234	356	354	353
Modulus Elasticity	170 GPa	145-170 GPa	145-170 GPa	145-170 GPa

TABLE 3—PHYSICAL PROPERTIES OF DUCTILE CAST IRON

	Ferritic Ductile	Si-Mo Ductile Grade A	Si-Mo Ductile Grade B	Si-Mo Ductile Grade C
Thermal Conductivity (W/K x cm)				
20 °C	0.33	N/A	N/A	N/A
100 °C	0.40	0.25	0.25	0.25
400 °C	0.33	0.27	0.27	0.27
1000 °C	0.24	0.25	0.25	0.25
Coefficient of Thermal Expansion Temp (°C)	$x10^{-6}$/°C			
20-100	11.2			
20-200	12.2			
20-300	12.8			
20-400	13.1			
20-500	13.5			
20-600	13.7			
20-760	14.8			
20-871	15.3			
Density (at 20 °C)	6.9 g/cc	6.9 g/cc	6.9 g/cc	6.9 g/cc
DBTT[1] Charpy Impact Properties	At 22 °C notched 13.5–19.0 j	N/A	N/A	N/A
Notched: –10 °C to –65 °C as tensile increases	notched, ductile fracture: 16.3-21.7 j			
	un-notched, ductile fracture: 94.9-135.6 j			
Un-notched: –60 °C to –10 °C as tensile increases	un-notched, brittle fracture: 2.7-4.0 j			
Creep Strength Temp °C	MPa @ 0.0001%/h rate	N/A	N/A	N/A
427	96.5			
538	27.7			
649	3.09			
Hardness (HB)	143-217	192	192	192
Fatigue Strength Endurance Limit				
Un-notched	193 MPa	N/A	N/A	N/A
V-notched	117 MPa	N/A	N/A	N/A
Poisson's ratio	0.28	0.28	0.28	0.28

1. Ductile to Brittle Transition Temperature

Iron with the addition of 11% to 30% Cr comprises a host of ferritic stainless steels. These alloys are primarily characterized as having a BCC structure, are ferromagnetic, and are less expensive than their austenitic counterparts. High temperature oxidation resistance tends to be very good to excellent, partly because the thermal expansion coefficient of the alloys and chromia are similar, limiting scaling of the chromia during cyclic thermal conditions. While considering the ferritics for welded fabrications, it is important to maintain extremely low levels of carbon and nitrogen so that matrix chromium levels are not depleted by the formation of chromium carbonitrides. Improved weldability, formability, and corrosion resistance will result when these interstitial elements are controlled to low levels. Ferritic stainless steels are preferred in fabricated exhaust systems due to their cost advantage over the nickel (Ni) containing austenitics. Another important advantage is the low coefficient of thermal expansion (~40% less than austenitics) which minimizes stresses generated from thermal growth at operating temperatures.

Nickel, when added to stainless steels in percentages ranging from 6% to as high as 35%, will lead to an FCC or austenitic structure at room temperature. These austenitic stainless steels typically possess much better deep drawability, weldability, and elevated temperature strength than the ferritic grades. The austenitic alloys with moderate additions of other refractory elements, e.g, Molybdenum (Mo), Niobium (Nb), Titanium (Ti), exhibit even better corrosion resistance and further enhanced elevated temperature properties. Austenitic stainless steels exhibit superior elevated thermal mechanical properties in comparison to ferritic, pearlitic, and martensitic cast irons, as well as ferritic stainless steels.

Both ferritic and austenitic stainless steels are susceptible to the formation of internal chromium rich carbides at high temperature by a reaction between the chromium and carbon/nitrogen in the alloy. This is otherwise known as sensitization. Sensitization can lead to severely reduced corrosion resistance, because the local concentration of chromium near these carbide particles can be reduced to well below the nominal alloy level. If time and temperature are insufficient to allow back diffusion (or "healing") into the area near the carbides, chromium-depleted regions will exist adjacent to the carbide network. If the network is continuous, a path of lower corrosion resistance will exist through the material. Sensitization can also lead to reduced strength and fracture resistance, particularly with the ferritic stainless grades. A common means of mitigating sensitization is by employing "stabilization" of the base alloy. This term refers to the addition of small levels of refractory elements, that are more reactive with carbon and nitrogen than chromium, e.g., Ti and Nb, to tie up the interstitial carbon/nitrogen, thus preventing further reaction with Cr. Thus, the chromium carbide formation that could occur during high temperature exposure is minimized. This is the primary method used to address the sensitization of ferritic stainless steels which are put into service in the as-welded condition.

The temperature ranges in which austenitic alloys become susceptible to sensitization are different than the ferritic counterparts. In the as-welded form, corrosion resistance in austenitics can be achieved through the use of low carbon chemistries (e.g., 304L) or by stabilization (e.g., 321 or 347). Applications in which austenitic stainless steels are put into service at sensitization temperatures require additional consideration.

Physical, chemical, and mechanical properties of some of the more commonly-used wrought stainless steels are shown in Tables 4 to 6. Additional elevated temperature properties are listed in Table 7.

TABLE 4—PHYSICAL PROPERTIES AT ROOM TEMPERATURE

Product Designation	Density g/cc	Young's Mod. GPa	Therm. Cond. W/m/K	CTE[(1)] cm/cm/°C	Cost $/lb
409	8	206	25	14	1
439	8	196	24	13	1
444	7			13	1.75[(2)]
441	8	206	24	12	1
468	8	200	25	14	1
304	8	193	16	20	2
309	8	200	16	20	3
321	8	193	16	20	2
601	8	207	11	17	8

1. Coefficient of thermal expansion.
2. Indicates estimated value.

TABLE 5—CHEMISTRY OF COMMONLY-USED STAINLESS STEELS

Product Designation	Composition, Weight Percent C	Composition, Weight Percent Ni	Composition Weight Percent Cr	Composition Weight Percent Fe	Others	Type
409	0.08 max	0.5 max	11	88.4	Ti = 6 x C min to 0.75 max	Ferritic
439	0.07	0.5	18	Balance	Ti = 0.20 + 4(C+N) min to 1.0 max	Ferritic
444 (18Cr 2Mo)	0.02	0.4	18	Balance	2Mo, 0.02N	Ferritic
441	0.02	0.3	18	Balance	0.7Nb, 0.3Ti	Ferritic
468	0.009	0.22	18.25	Balance	0.25Cb, 0.1Ti	Ferritic
304	0.03	10	19	Balance	2Mn, 1.0Si, P, S	Austenitic
309	0.06	13	23	Balance	1.75Mn, 0.5Si, 0.02P, 0.002 S	Austenitic
321	0.08 max	10	18	72	Ti = 5xC min to 0.7 max	Austenitic
601	0.05	60.5	23	14.4	1.4Al	Ni Base

TABLE 6A—ELEVATED TEMPERATURE MECHANICAL PROPERTIES OF STAINLESS STEELS—YIELD STRENGTH

Grade	409	439	444	441	468
Temp. (°C)	YS (MPa)	YS (MPa)	YS (MPa)	YS (MPa)	YS (MPa)
21	255	290	358	345	290
260	172	255	262		
538	117	193	207	175	152
649	83			145	117
760	28			47	
816	24	41	34	40	62

TABLE 6A—ELEVATED TEMPERATURE MECHANICAL PROPERTIES OF STAINLESS STEELS—YIELD STRENGTH

Grade	409	439	444	441	468
Temp. (°C)	YS (MPa)	YS (MPa)	YS (MPa)	YS (MPa)	YS (MPa)
871	17	28	34	29	34

TABLE 6B—ELEVATED TEMPERATURE MECHANICAL PROPERTIES OF STAINLESS STEELS—TENSILE STRENGTH

Grade	409	439	444	441	468
Temp. (°C)	TS (MPa)	TS (MPa)	TS (MPa)	TS (MPa)	TS (MPa)
21	407	455	476	510	476
538	241	262	338	372	276
649	159	124	283	303	207
704	76	69	241	145	159
760	41	41	145	62	83
816	28	28	83	48	48
871	21	21	69	34	41

TABLE 6C—TENSILE STRENGTH DATA: (300 AND 600 SERIES STAINLESS STEEL)

Grade	304L	309	321	IN601	IN625
Temp (°C)	TS (MPa)	TS (MPa)	TS (MPa)	TS (MPa)	TS (MPa)
21	676	620	586	0	931
204		528	459		862
427		517	457		820
538	434	483	444		
649	324	393	385	538	765
704	248				
732			286		
760	193			290	
816	145	207	179		
871	114			138	276
982		76		76	138
1093		48		48	

TABLE 6D—YIELD STRENGTH DATA: (300 AND 600 SERIES STAINLESS STEEL)

Grade	304	309	321	601	625
Temp (°C)	YS (MPa)	YS (MPa)	YS (MPa)	YS (MPa)	YS (MPa)
21	241	290	216		469
204	159	241	162		296
427	131	207	134		283
538		165	131		
649	107	152	131	172	283
732			131	193	
760					
816	90		117		
871		128		131	276
982				62	138
1093				28	

TABLE 7—ADDITIONAL MECHANICAL PROPERTIES

Product Description	Hardness HRB	Charpy Impact Toughness[(1)] Joules	Stress Rupture MPa 100 h 816 °C	Stress Rupture MPa 1000 h 816 °C	Stress Rupture MPa 10 000 h 816 °C
409	68	44	10.3	6.2	
439	73			6.2	
444	95 max				
441	80				
468	78		13.7		
304	88 max	203		20.6	10.3
309	95 max			41.3	24.1
321	80	144		31.0	20.6

TABLE 7—ADDITIONAL MECHANICAL PROPERTIES

Product Description	Hardness HRB	Charpy Impact Toughness[(1)] Joules	Stress Rupture MPa 100 h 816 °C	Stress Rupture MPa 1000 h 816 °C	Stress Rupture MPa 10 000 h 816 °C
601	81	139		44.8	27.5

1. Dependent on materials processing history. Sources: Allegheny Ludlum and Armco product Literature.

3.3 Weldability—The chemical makeup, microstructure, mechanical, and physical properties of ductile irons can vary greatly. A correspondingly large number of welding electrode compositions are available for welding ductile irons, such as pure nickel, iron-nickel alloys, and stainless steel. Electrode selection is just one important factor in specifying an appropriate welding process to produce a high strength weldment. Heat treatment before and/or after welding may be specified to prevent possible microstructure changes. For example, formation of martensite or iron carbide will adversely affect the ductility and strength of the heat affected zone of the weldment. Maintaining thermal expansion compatibility between the filler metal and base alloy is also an important consideration. Historically, many foundries have used welding as a method of repair to recover otherwise scrap castings as salable product.

Both ferritic and austenitic stainless steels can be welded. To limit contamination of the molten weld metal with interstitial carbon, nitrogen, extremely clean practices and the use of shielded welding methods such as Gas Metal Arc Welding (GMAW) or Gas Tungsten Arc Welding (GTAW) are preferred. When employing filler metal welds on austenitic alloys, it is common practice to use alloys richer in chromium and nickel than the base alloy. For ferritic stainless alloys, high nickel fillers with similar thermal expansion coefficients are sometimes used.

Due to stringent emission requirements and vehicle packaging constraints, current designs favor the positioning of the catalytic converter as close as possible to the exhaust manifold. Welding a fabricated stainless steel exhaust manifold to a stainless steel converter shell is a common and well understood practice. Cast iron manifolds have several advantages over fabricated manifolds, not the least of which is cost. Unfortunately, a method of welding cast iron to stainless steel has not yet been developed. Thus, a weld joint between these two dissimilar metals continues to pose a challenge for manufacturing in high volume.

3.4 Machinability—As cast iron alloys become more highly alloyed (usually with matrix strengthening elements such as Mo, Nb, and Si) to achieve their desired microstructure and properties, unique machining challenges arise. Machine tool selection becomes critical as the increased alloying promotes carbides and decreases tool life. This creates quality and cost problems for tooling selection and machining parameters. In addition, machining equipment must be more robust in order to handle the higher clamping force and torque required to machine these alloys. Austenitic alloys, both Ni-Resist cast iron and cast stainless steels, are known to be very difficult to machine. Figure 2 summarizes relative machinability of some manifold alloys.

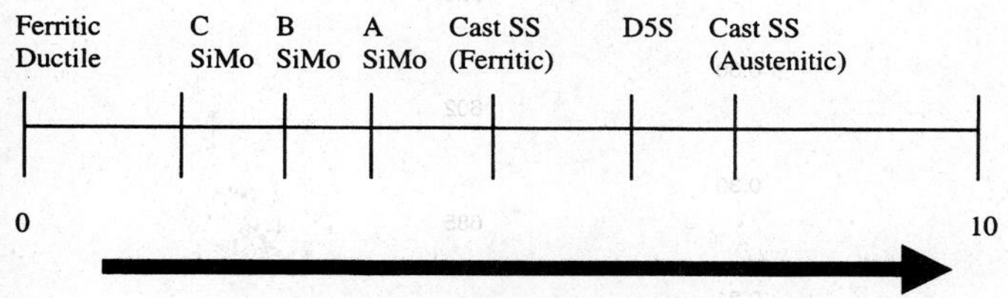

FIGURE 2—RELATIVE MACHINABILITY IN VARIOUS MATERIALS

4. Alloy Selection for Manifold Design—Gray cast iron was the material of choice in exhaust manifold design for many years. In the 1970s, the first applications of air injection systems (AIR) were used to reduce hydrocarbon and carbon monoxide emissions from engines by oxidizing the HC and CO to CO_2 and H_2O. However, the exothermic nature of these oxidation reactions increased the temperature of the exhaust gas. Gray iron was unable to meet the design criteria for service life in this environment, in terms of both strength at temperature and scaling resistance. Designs began incorporating alloys with higher maximum use temperatures, including compacted graphite and ferritic ductile irons, high silicon, and Si-Mo ferritic ductile irons, and austenitic ductile iron. High silicon ductile iron and austenitic ductile iron are two of the casting alloys formerly used to produce exhaust manifolds. High silicon ductile irons are essentially alloys of the Ferritic D4512 type, but with a silicon content of 4 to 6%. The silicon addition increases the ferrite-to-austenite transition temperature, extending the service temperature at which a manifold can be used to 900 °C. Increased silicon imparts good high temperature scaling resistance and serves as a ferrite strengthener, but beyond 5%, Si significantly degrades impact strength and ductility between room temperature and 450 °C. The resulting casting brittleness makes higher silicon ductile irons undersirable for high volume production.

Austenitic ductile irons, also known as Ni-Resist ductile irons, are a family of ductile irons displaying an austenitic matrix at room temperature by alloying with large amounts of nickel. The grade most commonly used for exhaust manifolds, D-5S, contains 36% nickel and 2% chromium. D-5S can be used at service temperatures to 925 °C, and has excellent scaling resistance and thermal stability. However, Ni-Resist ductile irons require special foundry practices and tooling, due to their austenitic matrix, and are significantly more expensive than conventional ductile irons because of their high nickel content.

The microstructures of gray irons used in the past for exhaust manifolds were typically all pearlitic, and thus, high strength. This was possible because operating temperatures were well below that which causes the cementite phase to either coarsen to a spheroidal structure or decompose to ferrite + graphite. The microstructure of current D4512-type ductile iron is essentially ferritic, because this is the stable phase at application temperatures. High silicon-molybdenum ductile iron is basically D4512 type with added silicon and molybdenum for improved high temperature properties. Its microstructure is also essentially ferritic.

The exhaust manifold is the only major engine component that is not actively cooled. Therefore, alloys used for this application must withstand high heat loads and should absorb as little heat as possible from the exhaust gas during start up, to avoid delays in catalytic converter warm up and function. Manifold alloys should be dimensionally stable at high temperature. They should also attenuate noise as efficiently as possible, yet be light to limit vehicle weight. For these reasons, thermophysical properties are of equal importance as mechanical properties when considering alloys for manifold use.

More recently, wrought and cast stainless steels have been used. Figure 3 illustrates generally accepted maximum temperatures of use for these various alloys.

Stainless steel fabrications and castings are used when exhaust gas temperatures exceed 870 °C, an increasingly common occurrence. Fabricated manifolds, both single wall and dual wall air-gap designs, typically use Ferritic or Austenitic grades. The increased emissions and performance requirements of future engines call for high temperature cast stainless steel manifolds. Properties of cast and wrought stainless steels are shown in Tables 4 to 7. Cast Stainless manifolds are made from Ferritic, Duplex, or Austenitic grades. The relative selection preference for selecting these materials, based on properties required in the application is shown in Table 8.

- Gray Iron **(1)**
- Compacted Graphite Iron **(2)**
- Ductile Iron (D4512) **(3)**
- Hi Silicon ductile Iron **(4)**
- Hi Silicon -Molybdenum Ductile Iron **(5)**
- Austenitic Ductile Iron (D5S) **(6)**
- Fabricated Stainless Steel **(7)**
- Cast Stainless Steel **(8)**

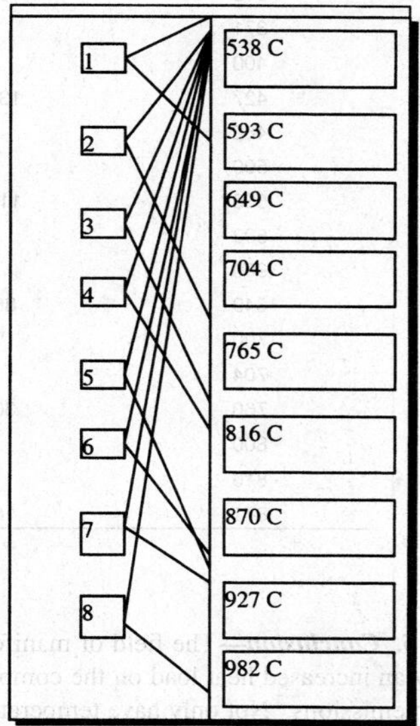

FIGURE 3—TEMPERATURE LIMITS OF THE VARIOUS EXHAUST MANIFOLD ALLOYS IN USE

TABLE 8—RELATIVE SELECTION PREFERENCE

	Austenitic	Ferritic
Cost		Preferred
Coefficient of Thermal Expansion		Preferred
Thermal Conductivity	Preferred	
Elevated Temperature Strength	Preferred	
Oxidation Resistance		Preferred
Fracture Toughness	Preferred	
Weldability	Preferred	
Formability	Preferred	
Hot Salt Corrosion		Preferred

As shown in Figure 1, exhaust manifold alloy demand changes as the exhaust gas temperature increases. Future applications will likely see an increase in the use of thin-walled exhaust manifolds because of the following benefits:

a. Lower mass for improved fuel economy
b. Higher engine output through leaner, more controlled combustion
c. Increased exhaust gas temperature, due to more fuel-efficient engines
d. Turbocharging and Supercharging
e. Consumer demand for higher performance engines
f. More extensive shielding to protect under-hood components
g. Consumer demand for lower emissions

It is likely that future engines will require exhaust manifolds to operate at or above 900 °C. Current materials used to make exhaust manifolds, such as Si-Mo ductile iron, CB-30 duplex cast stainless steel or ferritic wrought stainless steels will not provide adequate life at these temperatures.

Cast ferritic stainless steels are currently undergoing development for thin-wall exhaust manifolds. These alloys have a low coefficient of thermal expansion compared with Si-Mo ductile irons or cast austenitic stainless alloys. They are weldable, and exhibit good oxidation resistance to about 940 °C. The nominal composition of this cast alloy is 12.0% Cr, 1.8% Si, and 0.03% C, with small amounts of Nb and Ti as stabilizers. Results of oxidation tests conducted in synthetic exhaust gas for this 12% Chromium cast alloy are compared to wrought 409 and 439 stainless steel in Table 9. Further development of these alloys is ongoing and some details of such materials are presented in Table 10.

TABLE 9—WEIGHT GAIN (g/m^2) AFTER 96 h OF OXIDATION AT VARIOUS TEMPERATURES IN SYNTHETIC EXHAUST GAS

Temperature °C	Type 409	Type 439	12% Cr 1.8% Si
650	3.9	1.9	1.3
700	6.1	2.4	1.5
750	7.8	3.3	1.8
800	11.5	4.3	2.8
850	18.3	6.1	4.6
900	149.8	20.6	9.0

TABLE 10—PROPERTIES OF DEVELOPMENTAL CAST STAINLESS STEEL - 12% Cr

Temperature °C	Yield Strength MPa	Tensile Strength MPa	Elastic Modulus 10^3 MPa	Poisson's Ratio	Specific Heat W/kg °K	Elongation %
21	233		20.6	0.28	451	5
93	200		19.4			
100					493	
148				0.29		
200					528	
204	172		18.9			5
260				0.29		
300					560	
315	168		18.3			
371				0.30		
400					602	
427	132		17.5			
482				0.30		
500					685	
538	110	241	16.4			5
593				0.31		
600					801	
649	86	157	15.4			6.5
700					990	
704				0.32		
760	30	42	11.4			
800						
816				0.33		
871	16	21	6.9			

5. Conclusion—The field of manifold development has been driven primarily by an increased heat load on the component brought about by stricter regulations on emissions. Not only have temperatures increased, but through thermal expansion and mechanical constraints, operational stresses have also increased, and often in a time-dependent manner. Demands on materials have become significant. Potential failure modes are numerous: creep or rupture from insufficient static strength at temperature, thermal fatigue, and alloy loss from static or cyclic oxidation are three of the major ones.

The goal set forth by the subcommittee writing this document was to provide an introductory and central reference of exhaust manifold design, manufacture, and alloy selection. Publication comes at a time of very active work in the field, and it would not be surprising if within a few short years it become somewhat incomplete. It is certainly not intended (at this point) to be an all-encompassing reference, although a very comprehensive bibliography is provided to guide the reader to further and more detailed work. Certainly as the document is revised in the coming years, newer and perhaps more detailed information will be added.

APPENDIX A
BIBLIOGRAPHY
REFERENCE LISTING BY MATERIAL AND TOPIC

A.1 Cast Iron (Reference Number

a. Applications—#1, 8, 18, 36, 95, 96, 100, 101, 102, 143, 148, 149
b. Mechanical Properties—#2, 3, 4, 5, 8, 10, 13, 21, 25, 28, 29, 30, 31, 33, 35, 37 to 53, 55, 56, 57, 62, 65, 66, 67, 68, 70, 72 to 79, 81 to 100
c. Thermal Performance—#2, 4, 5, 21, 24, 28 to 33, 41 to 44, 68 to 70, 75 to 79, 82 to 87, 89, 90, 98, 104 to 133, 142, 152 to 157
d. Microstructure—#27, 40, 65, 74, 78, 81, 82, 85, 86, 89, 128, 135, 136

A.2 Cast Stainless Steel

a. Applications—#2, 6, 7, 15, 19, 20, 59, 144
b. Mechanical/Thermal Performance—#2, 7, 11, 19, 20, 58, 59

A.3 Stainless Steel

a. #2, 6, 7, 11, 12, 14 to 20, 22, 23, 27, 34, 58 to 61, 63, 64, 69 to 71, 80, 143, 144, 151, 152

A.4 Other Topics

a. Coatings—#1
b. Other High Temperature Applications—#22, 25, 54, 72, 73, 102

TABLE A1—REFERENCE LISTING BY NUMBER

Ref	Author	Title	Document	Pages
1	Itoh, K., Ohtsuka, K.	Development of Ceramic Coated Exhaust Manifolds for Heavy Duty Diesel Engines	SAE Transactions 910399 1991	1-14
2	Akiyama, K., Otsuka, K.	Analysis of Thermal Resistance of Engine Exhaust Parts	SAE Transactions 910430 1991	63-71
3	Spear, W.	Engineering Properties of Low Coefficient Austenitic Ductile Iron for Engine Appl.	SAE Transactions 870374 1987	1-9
4	Fontaine, P.	Ni-Resist Type D5S—An Improved Material for Turbocharger Housings	SAE Transactions 800016 1980	1-21
5	Roy, A., Hage, F.	Performance of Heat Resistant Alloys in Emission-Control Systems	SEA Transactions 740093 1974	1-6
6	Unknown	Hitachi Develops Super Heat Resistant Material	Japan Autotech Report Vol 155, Nov. 5, 1992	16
7	Ike, M., Akiyama, K.	Development of Heat Resistant Cast Steel for Exhaust Manifolds	JSAE Review Vol. 11, No. 4 Oct. 1990	82-90
8	Mianji, C., Renfang, W.	Properties and Application of Compacted Vermicular Graphite Cast Iron in Vehicle Component	Korean SAE 912535 Vol. 1, Oct. 1991	713-718
9	Mianji, C., Refang, W.	Mass Production of Compacted Vermicular Graphite Cast Iron Exhaust Manifold	Academic Press 1410-1414 1985 Conference Bejing, China	1410-1414
10	Rickard, J.	An Engineering Cast Iron for Service at Temperatures Exceeding 800 °C	British Foundryman 77, (6) July 1984 ISSN 0007-0718	313-317
11	Ike, M., Akiyama, K.	Development of Heat Resistant Cast Steel for Exhaust Manifolds	Int'l Jnl of Mat'ls and Prod. Tech. Vol 6 n 3 1991	243-258
12	Loria, E.	Cyclic Oxidation of Chromized "Steels" & Competitive "Materials" at 850 to 815 °C	Jnl of Materials Energy Systems V8 n2 Sept. 1986	132-141
13	Lalich, M.	Compacted Graphite Cast Iron—It's Properties and Production with a New Alloy	Modern Casting V66 n7 July 1976	50-52
14	Watanabe, R.	Heat-Resistant Ferritic Cast Steel Having Excellent Thermal Fatigue Resistance	U.S. Patent 5,096,514 Mar. 17, 1992	1-8
15	Fujikawa, H., Kohso, M.	Heat Resistant Steels for Exhaust Gas Cleaning Systems of Automobiles	Patent—Sumitomo Search No. 39 Sept. 1989	87-96
16	Unknown	Armco 12SR (Ferritic Stainless Steel)	Alloy Digest SS-424 Feb. 86	1-2
17	Staff	Stainless Steel Thrives on Tough Prod Applications	Modern Metals 38 (2) Mar. '82	47-51
18	Staff	Thin Engine Manifolds Cut Pollution	Engineer Dec. 5, 1991	37
19	Miyazaki, A., Ujiro, T.	150 Development of Heat Resistant Ferritic Stainless Steel for Exhaust Manifold	JSAE Conference Proc. 921 1992-5(169-172)	1-10
20	Miyazaki, A., Tada, M.	143 Effect of Alloying Elements on High Temperature Property of Ferritic Stainless Steels for Ex. Manifolds	JSAE Conference Proc. 936 1993-10(201-204)	1-11
21	Wojnar, L., Dziadur, W.	Fracture of Ferritic Ductile Iron at Elevated Temperature	Conf. ECF6-Fracture Control of Engr. Struct. Vol. III, June 1986	1941-1946
22	Ernst, P., Uggowitzer, P.	Improved Boron Containing 12% Cr Steels with High Creep Rupture Strength for Steam Turbine & Other	E.I. Conf. No. 11073 D. Reidel Publ. (USA) 1986	1357-1369
23	Asbury, F.	Factors Influencing Long-Term Creep of Type 316 Steel at 600 Degree C	Mat'l Science and Technology Nov. 1986 Vol. 2	1123-1130
24	Tanaka, Y., Ikawa, K.	Transformation Superplasticity in Ductile Cast Iron	Trans. JIM (Japan) V17n2 1976	73-82
25	Smith, G.	Cast Metals for Structural & Pressure Containment Appl.	Conf. ASME MPC11 1979	57-67
26	Chijiiwa, K., Mayashi, M.	Tensile Fracture of Cast Iron at High Temperatures	Imono 53 (4) Apr. 1981	161-169
27	Vodarek, V.	Effect of Microstructure on Creep Duct. Of AISI 316	Kovove Monthly V27nl 1989	23-39
28	Toor, P.	An Experimental Investigation of Strain Cycling Behavior of Flake Graphite Iron at Elevated Temp.	Lockheed-Georgia Publ.	57-67
29	Drapkin, B., Ahukov, A.	The Initial Stage in Thermal Fatigue Failure of Cast Iron	Mat'l Science & Heat Treat Vol. 15 n11-12 Nov. 1973	964-966
30	Kinosshita, M.	Thermal Stress Fatigue & Low Cycle Fat. of Cast Iron	Fracture 1969 Paper 58	667-676
31	Tsuda, M., Saito, M.	Characteristics of Thermal Expansion & Oxidation at High Temperature of Cast Irons with Graphite Shape	Technology Report Kansai Univ. N25 May 1984	111-124
32	Lewis, D., Stevens, C.	High Temperature Oxidation of 30% Cr Cast Irons	J Iron Steel Inst v207 Dec '69	1599-06
33	Titran, R.	Creep-Rupture Behavior of Developmental Cast Iron Base Alloy for Use up to 800 Deg. C	NASA TM-100167 Tech Memo pp 12 1987	1-15

TABLE A1—REFERENCE LISTING BY NUMBER (continued)

Ref	Author	Title	Document	Pages
34	Cleeton, M.	Development of Stamped Steel Exhaust Manifolds—A Materials Supplier Program	SAE 810034 1981	1-7
35	Randon, J.	Fatigue Crack Propagation at Elevated Temperature	EMAS Ltd. June 1989 Conf.	117-134
36	Unknown	Hitachi Metals Develops New Alloy for Ex. Manifolds	Comline Transport Aug. '89	6
37	Fusani, G. Hugony, E.	Contribution Spermentale Conoscenze Delle G'Allumino	Metall'gia Italia v79 n7-8 '87	537-548
38	Beckert, E., Guedes, L.	Ferrous Fundidos Nodulares com 4% de Silicio	Metall'gia - ABM v46n392 '90	539-550
39	Schuyten, J.	Heat Resistant Nodular Iron	Casting Engr. Spring 1978	17-23
40	Guerin, L., Gagne, M.	Effect of Mn, Cu & Sn on the Microstructure and Properties of Ductile Iron Castings	AFS Library Search 871134 British Foundryman 1987	336-344
41	Ugol'nikov, V.	Creep of Gray Cast Iron	Russian Cast'g Prod. Feb. '75	54-55
42	Dawson, J., Sage, A.	High Strength Cast Irons Containing Vanadium Annealed Ductile Irons and High Carbon Gray Irons	AFS Library Search 900206 British Foundryman Oct '89	479-490
43	Janowak, J.	SiMo Ductile Iron for Elevated Temp. Service	Climax P28-1	1-34
44	Baxter, D.	Tensile Testing at Extreme Temperatures	Advanced Mat'l & Proc. 2/91	22-29
45	Kane, R., Taraborelli, R.	Selecting Alloys to Resist Heat & Corrosion	Adv. Mat'l & Proc. 4/93	22-28
46	Rohrig, K.	Low Alloy Graphitic Cast Irons—GG, GGV & GGG	Konst'en + Giessen 12(1) '87	29-47
47	Palmer, K.	High Temperature Properties of Cast Irons	BCIRA Publication	217-238
48	Palmer, K.	High Temperature Properties of Cast Irons	Jnl Iron & Steel Feb. 1971	39-46
49	Rukadikar, M., Reddy, G.	Influence of Chemical Comp. & Micro on Thermal Conductivity of Alloyed Pearlitic Flake Graphite Iron	Chapman & Hall 1986 0022-2461/86	4403-4410
50	Spear, W.	High Silicon Austenitic Ductile Iron for Elev. Temp.	INCO	129-134
51	Farrell, R.	Ferritic Ductile Irons for Elevated Temp. Applications	Euro Patent 0 214 812 '87	1-20
52	Czech, M., Jakowluk, A.	Badanie Wytrymalosci na Pelazanie Zeliwe	Archiwum Rudowy 33 '86	2-25
53	Bechet, S.	Fundiciones empleadas a alta temperatura	Technica Metal' gca 247 1981	9-24
54	Ohtani, R., Kitamura, T.	Cracking Behavior of Heat Resistant Steels, Alloys and a Carbon-Fibre Reinforced Polymer at Elev. Temp.	Mat'l Science & Engr. A143(1991)	213-222
55	Unknown	New Super Alloys Used in Turbochargers	Jidosha Gijutsu Oct. '87	1150-55
56	Dinescu, L.,	Oboseala Terminca a Fontelor ... si Nodular	Metalurgica 37 1985 n2	90-93
57	Dinescu, L.,	Oboseala Terminca a Fontelor ... Si Nodular	Metalurgica 37 1985 n2	39-43
58	Miyazaki, A., Tada, M.	Effect of Alloying Elements on High Temperature Property of Ferritic Stainless Steels for Ex. Manifolds	JSAE 930668 SAE 938305 1993	1-22
59	Hohiyo, N., Shimamoto, T.	Development of Stainless Cast-Steel Exhaust Manifold	Mitsubishi Motors Publ.	1-18
60	Sikka, V	Development of Mod. 9 Cr-1 Mo Steel for Elev. Temp.	ORNL/DOE	317-327
61	Sikka, V	Development of Mod. 9 Cr-1 Mo Steel for Elev. Temp.	ORNL/DOE	413-423
62	Nechtelberger, L.	Elasticity Modulus & Creep of Flake Graphite Iron	Lit. Priozvodsto N11 1986	1-4
63	Desport, J., Bennet, M.	Investigation by Fractography of High Temperature Oxidation of 20% Cr-Ni-Nb Stainless Steel	Oxidation of Metals Vol. 29 No. 3/4 1988	327-346
64	Fields, R., Ashby, M.	Fracture Mechanics in Pure Iron, Two Austenitic Steels and One Ferritic Steel	Met. Trans A Vol. 11A Feb. 1980	333-347
65	Frediksson, H., Sunnerkrantz, P.	Relationship Between Structure & Thermal fatigue in Cast Iron	Materials Science & Tech. Vol 4, March 1988	222-226
66	Petrichenko, A.	Stress-Rupture Strength of Mg Cast Iron	Russian Engr, Jnl V L 11 n7	71-72
67	Kozhinskii, L.	Effect of Cr & Ti on Creep & Relax of Cast Iron	Metal Term Obr No. 6 1970	67-69
68	Drapkin, B.	Initial Stage in Thermal Fatigue Failure of Cast Iron	Metal Term Obr No. 11 1973	40-41
69	Matera, R.	Evaluation of Creep Damage in Mn-Cr Austenitic Steel	Scripta Metallurgica v23 '89	65-70
70	Kitagawa, M.	Fatigue Life Evaluation of Turbocharger Comp.	Ishikawajima-Harma Ind.	103-107
71	Minimai, Y.	Creep Rupture Prop. of 18% Cr-8%Ni-Ti-Nb & Type 347H Austenitic Stainless Steels	Kawasaki 8410-009	231-242
72	Sahoo, M., Dion, J.L.	Thermal Shock Resistance of Mold Materials for Permanent Mold Casting of Copper-Base Alloys	AFS Transactions, Vol. 97 1989	749-758
73	Chiesa, F., Mucciardi, F.	Thermal Behavior of Permanent Molds During Production of Aluminum Castings	AFS Transactions, pp. 90-93	459-466
74	Shieh, C.S., Din, T.A.	Effect of Nodule Size and Silicon Content on Tensile Deformation Behavior of Austempered Spheroidal Graphite Cast Iron at Elevated Temperatures	AFS Transactions, pp. 801-812 1985	365-371
75	Pam, E.N., Chen, S.P.	Influence of metallurical Parameters on Low Thermal Expansion Austenitic Cast Irons	AFS Transactions Vol. 98 1990	293-303
76	Gundlach, R. B., Whelan, E.P.	Critical Temperatures in Ferritic Ductile Irons	AFS Transactions, Vol. 57, 69 1959	713-718
77	Noguchi, T., Muroga, T., Minoya, K.	Thermal Deformation Characteristics of Low Thermal Expansion Cast Irons with Various Graphite Shapes	AFS Transactions, pp. 27-90	287-293
78	Rukadikar, M.C.	Prediction of Thermal Fatigue Life of Pearlitic Flake Graphite Cast Irons by Means of Quantitative Assessment of Microstructure and Chemical Composition	AFS Transactions, Vol. 95, 1987	627-636
79	Rukadikar, M.C., Reddy, G.P.	Elevated Temperature Strength and Modulus of Elasticity of Alloyed Pearlitic Flake Graphite Cast Irons	AFS Transactions, Vol. 86, 1978	351-360
80	Iwabuchi, Y., Axekoshi, K.	Properties of 12% Cr Heat Resisting Cast Steel for Upper-High Pressure and High Temperature Turbine Casting	AFS Transactions, pp. 87-1989	211-216
81	Rukadikar, M.C.	Prediction of Flake Graphite Cast Irons Thermal Fatigue Life	AFS Transactions, Vol 91 1983	217-226
82	Park, Y.J., Gundlach, R.B.	Effects of Molybdenum on Thermal Fatigue Resistance of Ductile and Compacted Graphite Irons	AFS Transactions, Vol. 87 1989	267-272
83	Wright, R.N.	Elevated Temperature Brittleness of Ferritic Ductile Iron	AFS Transactions, Vol. 61 1953	853-864

TABLE A1—REFERENCE LISTING BY NUMBER (continued)

Ref	Author	Title	Document	Pages
84	Park, Y.J., Gundlach, R.B.	Thermal Fatigue Resistance of Gray and Compacted Graphite Irons	AFS Transactions, Vol. 86, 1978	415-422
85	Ziegler, K.R., Wallace, J.F.	The Effect of Matrix Structure and Alloying on the Properties of Compacted Graphite Iron	AFS Transactions, Vol. 60, 1952	735-748
86	Gundlach, R.B.	The Effects of Alloying Elements on the Elevated Temperature Properties of Gray Irons	AFS Transactions, Vol. 87 1989	389-421
87	Altstetter, J.D.	Compacted Graphite Iron: Its Properties and Automotive Applications	AFS Transactions, Vol 84, 1976	959-970
88	Ruff, G.F., Vert, T.C.	Investigation of Compacted Graphite Iron Using a High Sulfur Gray Iron Base	AFS Transactions, Vol. 86, 1978	459-560
89	Shea, M.M.	Influence of Composition and Microstructure on Thermal Cracking of Gray Cast Iron	AFS Transactions, Vol. 4, 78	23-30
90	Roehrig, K.	Thermal Fatigue of Gray and Ductile Irons	AFS Transactions, Vol.	75-88
91	Church, N.L.	An Austenitic Ductile Iron for Elevated Temperature Applications	AFS Transactions, Vol. 38,72	67-72
92	Sponseller, D.L.	Development of Low-Alloy Ductile Irons for Service at 1200-1500 F	AFS Transactions, Vol. 76 1968	353-368
93	Janowak, Jay F.	Technical Advances in Cast Iron Metallurgy	AFS Transactions, Vol. 65 1957	1-15
94	Torkington, Donald L.	Ductile Iron for Elevated Temperature Service	Foundry M&T 1983	24-30
95	Drake, Justin R.	Cast Iron for Future Diesel Engines	Modern Casting 1982	46-47
96	Unknown	Selecting Materials for High Temp Exhaust Manifold Applications	Modern Casting Jan. 1990	49
97	Murthy, V.S.R.	Alloying CG Irons with Copper and Nickel	Foundry M&T July 1986	50-51
98	Unknown	Behavior of Castings at Elevated Temperatures	Casting Engineering & Foundry World	17-20
99	Janowak, Jay F.	Silicon-Molybdenum	Molybdenum Mosaic	19-21
100	Dodd, John	Advanced Technology Creates New Markets for Iron Castings	Summer 1981	45-53
101	Janowak, Jay F., Panasiewicz, Jim	Chrysler's Laser Sports Car Uses Molybdenum Technology	Casting Engineering & Foundry World	19-22
102	Campo, E.	High Temperature Structural Materials for Gas Turbines	Metallurgical Science & Technology	31-47
103		Which Cast?	BCIRA Broadsheet 1	1-2
104	Smith, L.W.L.	Thermal Conductivity of Unalloyed Cast Irons	BCIRA Broadsheet 203	1-2
105	Garden, R.L.	Thermal Expansion of Cast Iron at Temperatures up to 500 °C	BCIRA Broadsheet 203-4	1-2
106	Grant, J.W.	Thermal Expansion of Unalloyed Flake or Nodular Graphite Cast Irons at Temperatures Above 500 deg. C	BCIRA Broadsheet 203-6	4-6
107	Umino, S.	Specific Heat-Capacity of Cast Irons	BCIRA Broadsheet 203-7	1-2
108	Gilbert, G.N.J.	Effects of Silicon in Nodular (SG) Iron	BCIRA Broadsheet 211-1	3-7
109	Maitland, R.J.	4-6% Silicon Nodular Irons for High-Temperature Service	BCIRA Broadsheet 219-2	1-2
110	Dearden, A.	Cracking and Distortion Due to Thermal Cycling	BCIRA Broadsheet 240	1-3
111	Gilbert, G.N.J.	Growth and Scaling of Unalloyed Engineering Cast Irons in Air at Temperatures up to 650 deg. C	BCIRA Broadsheet 241	173-176
112	Fallon, M.	The High Silicon and Silicon-Molybdenum Ductile Irons	BCIRA Technology Nov. 1993	10-12
113	Keynes, Milton	Creep Rupture Properties at 350 deg. C	BCIRA Library	3-4
114	Fallon, Martin	Heat and Corrosion Resistant Grades of Austenitic Ductile Iron	BCIRA Technology July 1993	8-14
115	Palmer, K.B.	The Mechanical and Physical Properties of Engineering Grades of Cast Irons up to 500 deg. C	BCIRA Report 1717	417-425
116	Palmer, K.B.	The Effect of 0.5 percent Molybdenum on the Creep Properties of Ferritic Nodular Graphite Cast Irons at 400 deg. C and 450 deg. C	BCIRA Report 1711	361-367
117	Palmer, K.B.	High Temperature Tensile Properties of a Compacted Graphite Iron	BCIRA Report 1566	79-82
118	Smith, L.W.L.	The Short-Time High-Temperature Tensile Properties of Malleable Irons	BCIRA Report 1458	103-121
119	Palmer, K.B.	Creep and Stress-to-Rupture Properties of Eight Unalloyed Cast Irons at 350 deg. C	BCIRA Report 1403	43-56
120	Palmer, K.B., Robson, K.	The Effect of 0.5% Molybdenum on the Creep Properties of Ferritic Nodular Graphite Cast Irons at 400 deg. C and 450 deg. CC — A Progress Report	BCIRA Report 1347 Sept. 1979	467-471
121	Palmer, K.B.	Design with Cast Irons at High Temperatures—1: Growth and Scaling	BCIRA Report 1248 Nov. 1976	589-609
122	Palmer, K.B.	Design with Cast Irons at High Temperatures—2: Tensile, Creep and Rupture Properties	BCIRA Report 1251 Jan. 1977	31-50
123	Palmer, K.B.	The High Temperature Tensile Properties of Nodular Graphite Cast Irons	BCIRA Report 464 June 1957	637-659
124	Hughes, I.C.H.	Growth and Scaling of Cast Iron	BCIRA Vol. 8 Jan. 1960	6-28
125	Latona, Martin, Wallace, J.F.	Literature Search on the High Temperature Properties of Ductile Iron	DIS Ductile Iron Society Report	1-56
126	Speich, G.R., Schwoeble, A.J.	Elastic Module of Gray and Nodular Cast Iron	Journal of Applied Mechanics	821-826
127	Benedicts, C.	Thermal Conductivity/Ferrous Metals	Watmough AFS 5F	75-123
128	Tanaka, Yuichi	Relationship Between Heat Transfer Properties and Numerical Indexes of Graphite Shape in Compacted/Vermicular Graphite Cast Irons	Muroran Institute of Technology	1-2
129	Torkington, Donald L.	Ductile Irons for Elevated Temperature Service	Metal Progress, May 1981	1-7
130	Doane, D.V.	The Effects of Alloying on the Elevated Temperature Properties of Nodular Iron	Cast Iron with Nodular Graphite, 1968	1-41
131	Toor, M.	An Experimental Investigation of Low Cycle Fatigue Behavior of Nodular Cast Iron at Elevated Temperature	Effects of Cyclic Thermal Stress, 1945, Vol. 76	193-199
132	Dodd, John	Ductile Iron Alloyed with Molybdenum	Cast Ferrous Alloys, 1949	15-35
133	Dodd, John	Gray and Nodular Alloyed and High-Strength Irons	Foundry Trade Journal, 1949	1-5
134	Sankov, I.I.	Magnesium-Treated Cast Iron Brake Drums	Russian Castings Production	242-243
135	Lerner, Yu. S.	Structure and Properties of Nodular Cast Iron Alloyed with Molybdenum	Russian Castings Production	293-294
136	Lerner, Yu. S.	Structure and Properties of Nodular Cast Iron with Increased Si Contents	Russian Castings Production	191-192
137	Dodd, J.	Gray and Nodular Alloyed and High-Strength Irons	Foundry Trade Journal, Nov. 1979	978-991

TABLE A1—REFERENCE LISTING BY NUMBER (continued)

Ref	Author	Title	Document	Pages
138	Bevan, John E.	Ductile Iron for High-Temperature Service	Climax Molybdenum	151-152
139	Barr, Robert	Ferritic Nodular Irons for Elevated Temperature Service	Journal of Molybdenum Technology Vol. 5 1982	1
140	Janowak, Jay	The Effect of Silicon/Molybdenum	Molybdenum Mosaic	1-5
141	Fairhurst, W., Rohrig, K.	High-Silicon Nodular Irons	Foundry Trade Journal Mar. 1979	657-678
142	Noguchi, T., Yasuki, T., Nakakubo, T., Atsumi, T.	Thermal Stress and Deformation Analysis of the Exhaust Manifold of an Internal-Combustion Engine	Int'l Jnl of Materials and Product Technology, Vol. 2, 1987	156-167
143	Ashworth, R.	Materials Requirements for Modern Exhaust Systems	Steel Time International July 1993	36-38
144	Franson, Ivan A.	Stainless Steel for Automotive Exhaust	Advanced Materials & Processes Mar. 1994	18-19
145	Dipl. Ing. Erich Nechtelberger	The Properties of Cast Iron up to 500 deg. C	Technology Limited	1
146	Winters, Drew	Cast Irons Old Gray Head Finds a Fountain of Youth	Ward's Auto World Nov. 1991	46-47
147	Powers, Roger K.	Nippondenso Develops 2-Stroke Fuel Injection	Ward's Engine Update	8-11
148	Louckes, Theodore N.	Nissan's Tokyo Display Includes New Engines	Ward's Engine and Vehicle Technology Update	1
149	Otsuka, Koki/Hitachi Metals	Evaluation of Well-Known Heat Resistant Cast Irons for an Exhaust manifold	JSAE Academic Proceedings, Oct. 1989	1-12
150	Takenouchi, Masaru	Development of Ferritic Stainless MIG Welding Wire Applied on Exhaust Manifold with Welded Structure of Cars (sic)	Denki Seiko, Vol. 61 Nov. 1990	1-11
151	Akiyama, Shun-ichior	Development of New Stainless Steels for Automotive Exhaust Systems < Recommendation of a Few Materials Developed Recently in Nippon Stainless Steel	Nihon Stainless Technical Report No., 26, 1991	1-13
152	Chijiiwa, Denji	High Temperature Tensile Fractography of Cast Iron	Journal of the Japan Foundrymen's Society, Vol. 51	1-15
153	Dietrich, Herman	Process to Increase the Resistance and Reduction of the Creep Expansion of Austenitic Cast Iron	Influence of Heat Treatment, 1989	1-21
154	Unknown	Improvement of the Creep Rupture Behavior Ferritic Cast Iron with Ball Graphite Through Alloying	Unknown	1-15
155	Ota, Ken-ichiro	High Temperature Oxidation of Cast Iron (FC20) by Cyclic Heating	Boshaki Gijutsu (Corrosion Engineering)38, 1989	1-14
156	Kato, Yozo	The Effect of Cyclic Strain Aging on the Fatigue Strength of Spheroidal Graphite Cast Iron at Elevated Temperatures	JSME Vol. 52, Aug. 1986	1-19
157	Kazuo, Yasue, Yasuo Yamada	Thermal Fatigue Strength of Cast Iron	Nagoya Kogyo Gijutsu Shikenjo 36-12, 1987	1-15

R) INSTRUMENTATION AND TECHNIQUES FOR EXHAUST GAS EMISSIONS MEASUREMENT —SAE J254 SEP1993

SAE Recommended Practice

Report of the SAE Automotive Emissions and Air Pollution Committee approved June 1971. Completely revised by the SAE Automotive Emissions Committee, Exhaust Emissions Measurement Subcommittee, August 1984. Completely revised by the SAE Light-Duty Emission Standards Committee September 1993.

Foreword—This Document has also changed to comply with the new SAE Technical Standards Board format.

1. Scope—This SAE Recommended Practice establishes uniform laboratory techniques for the continuous and bag-sample measurement of various constituents in the exhaust gas of the gasoline engines installed in passenger cars and light-duty trucks. The report concentrates on the measurement of the following components in exhaust gas: hydrocarbons (HC), carbon monoxide (CO), carbon dioxide (CO_2), oxygen (O_2), and nitrogen oxides (NO_x). NO_x is the sum of nitric oxide (NO) and nitrogen dioxide (NO_2). A complete procedure for testing vehicles may be found in SAE J1094.

This document includes the following sections:

1. Scope
2. References
3. Emissions Sampling Systems
4. Emissions Analyzers
5. Data Analysis
6. Associated Test Equipment
7. Test Procedures

1.1 Purpose—The purpose of this document is to describe means for the analysis of exhaust emissions. This procedure has been developed after thorough review and consideration of test techniques in use in laboratories of federal and state governments, and the automobile and petroleum industries.

2. References

2.1 Applicable Publications—The following publications form a part of this specification to the extent specified herein. The latest issue of SAE publications shall apply.

2.1.1 SAE PUBLICATIONS. Available from SAE, 400 Commonwealth Drive, Warrendale, PA 15096-0001.

SAE J1094—Constant Volume Sampler System for Exhaust Emissions Measurement

SAE J1263—Road Load Measurement and Dynamometer Simulation Using Coastdown Techniques

3. Definitions

3.1 Bag Sample—Ambient air or vehicle exhaust collected during various segments of the driving test cycle for analysis.

3.2 Calibrating Gas—A precisely analyzed gas of known concentration, used to determine the response curve of an analytical instrument.

3.3 Chemiluminescent Analyzer—An analytical method for determining the NO_x concentration in exhaust gas.

3.4 Chassis Dynamometer—A laboratory-power absorption unit, capable of simulating the inertia and road-load power developed by a vehicle.

3.5 Cooler—A device capable of sufficient refrigeration to maintain condenser temperatures in the analytical train at 2 °C ± 1 °C (35 °F ± 2 °F).

3.6 Curb Weight—The weight of the vehicle in operational status, with all standard and commonly installed optional equipment, and the gas tank filled to nominal capacity.

3.7 Detector—That component in an analytical instrument which responds to a particular exhaust gas constituent.

3.8 Driver's Aid—An instrument intended to guide the vehicle driver in operating the vehicle in accordance with the specified acceleration, idle, deceleration, and cruise operating modes of a specific driving procedure.

3.9 Exhaust Emissions—Any substance (but normally limited to pollutants) emitted to the atmosphere from any opening downstream from the exhaust point of the combustion chamber of an engine.

3.10 Flame Ionization Detection Analyzer (FID)—An analytical instrument used for determining the carbon concentration of hydrocarbons in a gas sample.

3.11 Hang-up—The absorption-desorption of sample (mainly higher molecular weight hydrocarbons) from the surface of the sample system that can cause a delay in instrument response and lower concentration at the analyzer, followed by higher readings in subsequent tests.

3.12 Inertia Masses—A series of rotating masses on a chassis dynamometer, used to simulate the test mass of a vehicle.

3.13 Loaded Vehicle Mass—The manufacturer's estimated mass of a vehicle in operating condition. For the purpose of emission testing, it is the curb mass of a light-duty vehicle plus 136 kg (300 lb).

3.14 Lox-Service Cleaning—Process where sampling system plumbing is cleaned thoroughly prior to flowing liquid oxygen (LOX). Hydrocarbon contamination is removed by rinsing with a solvent that will not generate emission constituents.

3.15 Mode—A particular event (for example, acceleration, deceleration, cruise, or idle) of a test cycle.

3.16 Nondispersive Infrared (NDIR) Analyzer—An analytical instrument currently used to determine CO and CO_2 in exhaust gas.

3.17 Probe—A device inserted into some portion of an engine or vehicle system in order to obtain a representative gas or liquid sample.

3.18 Reference Cell—That portion of the NDIR instrument which contains the reference gas for comparison with the sample.

3.19 Response Curve (Calibration Curve)—A line drawn through at least six points established by calibration gases, which determines the analytical instrument's sensitivity to unknown concentrations.

3.20 Sample Bag—A container made of nonabsorbent material, used to collect ambient and exhaust samples.

3.21 Sample Cell—That portion of the analytical instrument through which the sample gas being analyzed passes.

3.22 Sampling, Bag—A technique for collecting a sample of exhaust gas during a period of a test cycle and storing it for future analysis.

3.23 Sampling, Continuous—A technique in which a portion of the exhaust is continuously withdrawn for immediate analysis.

3.24 Span Gas—A single calibrating gas blend routinely used to adjust the calibration of an analyzer just prior to its use.

3.25 Test Cycle—A sequence of engine or vehicle operating modes, usually designed to simulate road usage of the vehicle.

3.26 Zero Gas (Zero Air)—A pure gas, such as nitrogen or air, used to determine the zero point of an analyzer's response curve.

4. Emissions Sampling Systems

4.1 Continuous (Undiluted Exhaust Gas)—Figure 1 shows a typical sampling system for the continuous measurement of exhaust-gas products emitted from the tailpipe of a vehicle. Such a system generally consists of sample probes, sample lines, coolers, particulate filters, positive displacement pumps, flow regulators and flow meters, and desiccators.

4.1.1 SAMPLE PROBE. The sample probe is the inlet to the sample system. It is recommended that this probe be constructed of stainless steel tubing, typically 6 mm (0.25 in) OD; it is usually part of a fixture which adapts to the end of the tailpipe of the vehicle. To minimize induction of ambient air, the end of the probe is extended into the tailpipe 30 to 45 cm (12 to 18 in) (if possible). The most desirable probe location is parallel to the exhaust flow, facing upstream. The sample probe fixture may slip over the outside of the tailpipe and be used with either a flexible adaptor (silicone rubber) or thermosetting-fiberglass-backed adhesive tape. This arrangement provides a seal which does not allow dilution of the exhaust gas with ambient air. Design of the probe fixture should also allow for unrestricted exit of the remaining exhaust gas (that which is not inducted into the probe) to either an exhausting system or another test apparatus such as a constant volume sampler (see SAE J1094). A valve should be located at or near the tailpipe fixture to allow purging of the sample probe and the rest of the analysis system with prepurified dry nitrogen gas or clean, dry air. The test probe for engine dynamometer testing should be located to approximate the sampling location in an actual exhaust system of the vehicle.

In work with single-cylinder engines, or with the exhaust of a single cylinder of a multicylinder engine operating over a transient duty cycle, the proper probe location is difficult to define because of a varying degree of stratification of the concentrations of the various exhaust products which exist along the length of the exhaust pipe.

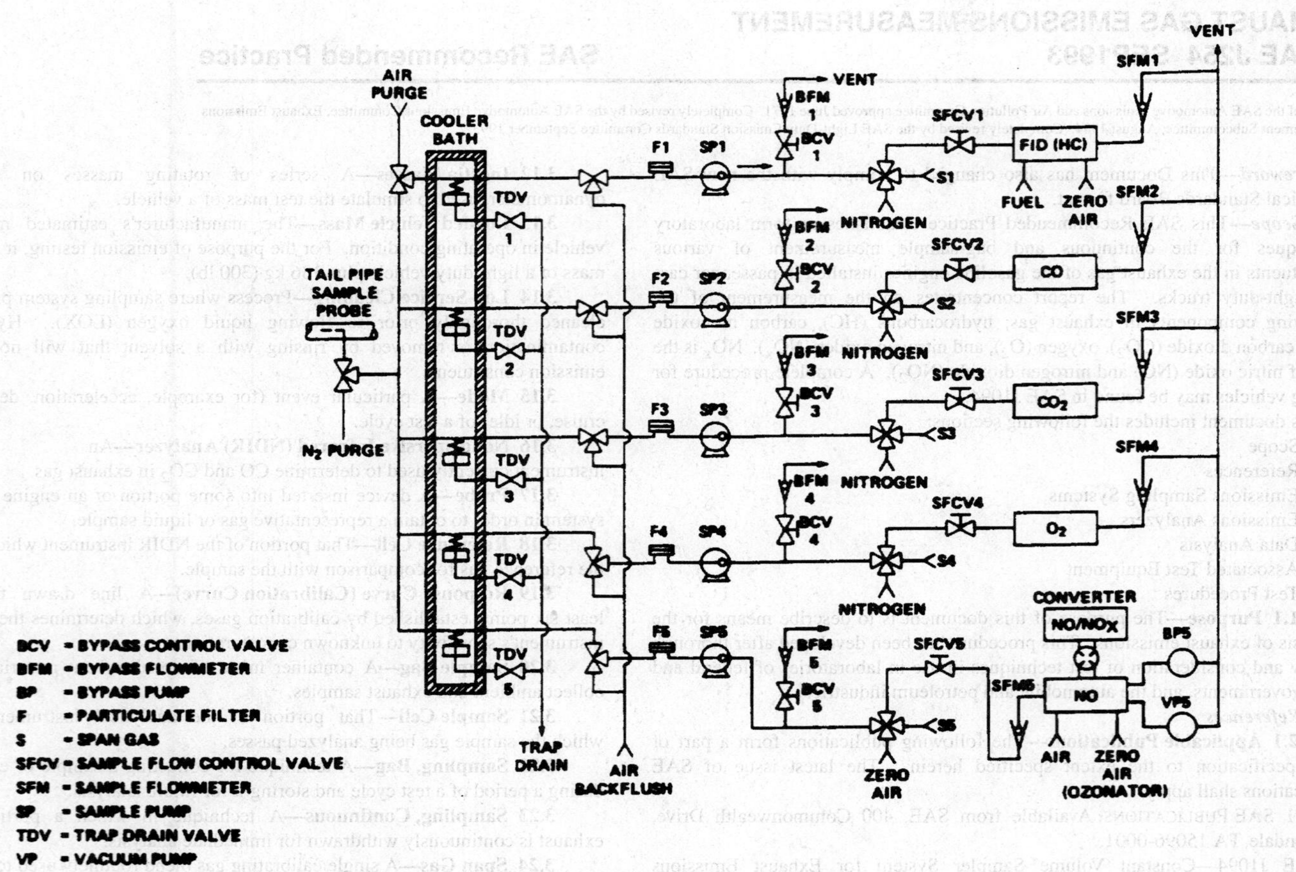

FIGURE 1—A CONTINUOUS UNDILUTED EXHAUST GAS ANALYSIS SYSTEM

4.1.2 Sample Line—The sample line carries the exhaust gas inducted into the sample probe to the condensers which are usually located close to the analysis system. This line is typically 6 mm (0.25 in) OD and should be made of stainless steel or Teflon (or equivalent). Teflon tubing with a flexible outside protective covering is recommended because it practically eliminates the hang-up from this part of the sampling system. If the ID is 6 mm (0.25 in), it can easily be joined to 6 mm (0.25 in) OD stainless steel tubing. The length of this sample line should be kept to a minimum, since its length is directly related to the delay time of the entire system; in many cases, it will be found to be responsible for the major portion of the delay time. Excessive delay times usually result when the line from the sample probe to the cooler is too long, or the sample flow rate is too low. Room restrictions may prohibit the use of short sample lines; therefore, other means, such as increasing the sample flow rate or simply determining the extent of the delay and accounting for it when processing the data, may have to be used. All tubes connecting the various components of the sampling system should be either stainless steel or Teflon, and should also be as short as possible.

4.1.3 Cooler—The cooler condenses and removes the water contained in the exhaust gas sample. This is required because many analyzers have a strong response to water vapor, and also to prevent condensation of water in the analyzers.

There are a number of acceptable cooler configurations. Two types which have proved effective are the ice-bath cooler and the refrigerated-water bath. Both of these utilize a cooling coil of 6 mm (0.25 in) OD [uncoiled length is approximately 3 m (10 ft)] which empties into a trap with a volume not to exceed 60 to 80 cm^3 (4 to 5 in^3) for each leg of the analysis system. Figure 1. A drain and toggle valve are provided to remove the water collected in each trap. The cooling coils are usually clustered in a common, insulated chest which can be filled with ice and water, or a water glycol solution, which can be kept near 2 °C (36 °F) with an electrically-powered refrigeration system. Keeping the coolant slightly above 0 °C (32 °F) eliminates water freezing in the trap. A mixer in the coolant helps to maintain a constant temperature. (Corrections for water removed may be needed. (see 6)See Section 6.)

4.1.4 Sample Filter—Borosilicate glass fiber filters of approximately 7 cm in diameter with an appropriate holding fixture of low internal volume should be used (one in each leg of the sample system, Figure 1), to remove any particulate matter which may be present. These filters also tend to stop water droplets which may have passed the cooler. Contaminated filters can result in excessive hangup and should be changed frequently (as often as each test, and if experience indicates the need, even during a test).

4.1.5 Sample Pumps. A pump that supplies a constant flow rate (typically 20 L/min with pump inlet and outlet at atmospheric pressure) can be used in each leg of the analysis system to pull the sample from the probe and then push the sample through the analyzer. Arrangements with a single-sample pump are also possible. To minimize hangup, pumps with stainless steel metal bellows or Teflon coated diaphragms should be used. Carbon vane or piston pumps which may introduce a hydrocarbon lubricant into the sample gas are to be avoided. The pump and motor should be mounted to eliminate the transmission of mechanical vibrations to the connecting sample lines and analyzers. An effective means of accomplishing this is to use short, flexible Teflon tubing (stainless steel braided for safety), to carry the sample gas to and from the pump, and to isolate the pump and motor with shock mounts. Small mechanical vibration of the analyzers may affect their output.

4.1.6 Flow Control And Measurement—The pump for each analyzer should be allowed to pull as much sample as it can through the sample system to reduce the lag time required to move the sample from the tailpipe to the analyzer. An optional means of increasing the sample flow rate is to use a sample flow bypass. Immediately following each pump, a bypass line allows sample gas to be dumped to a waste system with the remaining 5 L/min proceeding through the analyzer. The bypass flow is regulated by an adjustable needle valve (stainless steel), and monitored with a rotameter-type flowmeter with at least 10 L/min capacity using a stainless steel or inert material float. [High sample rates for raw (undiluted) exhaust analysis should not be used simultaneously with dilute CVS-type analysis, as the raw sample flow will cause an error in the mass emissions obtained from the CVS calculations.]

4.1.7 Extreme care must be taken to assure that all sample system connections are leak free.

4.2 Emissions Sampling Systems--Bag Analysis—These tests yield average emission values for various periods of a complete test by a single measurement of each bag sample. The analysis can determine whether a vehicle will pass surveillance or compliance tests. SAE J1094 describes this technique. Figures 2 and 3 show a six-bag sample gathering system and an analytical system, respectively.

In this constant volume (variable dilution) proportional sampling technique, a sampling pump draws a constant volume flow rate, for example, 8.5 m^3/min (300 scfm). This flow consists of the total exhaust of a vehicle with the remainder made up of dilution air. The technique allows for monitoring of continuous emissions on a mass basis and also, with the addition of a second pump, provides an aggregate total mass sample from a vehicle operated through an entire test cycle.

5. Emissions Analyzers

5.1 Nondispersive Infrared Analyzer—NDIR analyzers shown in Figure 4 are primarily used to determine concentrations of CO and CO_2 in exhaust gas. Although not recommended, NDIR analyzers can also be used to measure NO and HC.

5.1.1 THEORY—The NDIR analyzer detects the infrared energy absorption differential between two gas-filled columns. The gas whose concentration is to be determined is flowed through the sample column. The reference column is filled with a nonabsorbing gas such as dry air. In a nondispersive instrument, no attempt is made to separate the infrared energy into discrete wavelengths, but rather to make use of the principle that gas molecules absorb discrete bands of infrared energy.

The infrared radiation is passed through the sample and reference columns into a detector that has two cells which are physically separated by a flexible, metal diaphragm. These two detector cells contain the same gas that is to be analyzed. When the gas in the detector receives infrared energy, the pressure increases in that cell because the absorbed energy heats the gas. With no infrared absorbing gas in the sample column, both cells of the detector receive the same amount of energy and the pressure in the two cells is identical. However, if a gas sample is flowing in the sample column, some of the infrared energy will be absorbed by the gas. This means less energy will arrive at the sample cell side of the detector and the pressure in that cell will be less. This will cause the flexible metal diaphragm to move. The metal diaphragm is used as one plate of a variable plate capacitor in a tuned electric circuit.

To make the diaphragm oscillate, thus creating a detector output signal, a chopper blade driven by a synchronous motor periodically interrupts the sample and reference energy beams in the range of 5 to 10 Hz. In some cases, the 5 to 10 Hz signal can modulate a carrier frequency of 10 MHz or so, which is demodulated to obtain a DC signal that is more practical. The amplitude of the diaphragm oscillation, which is a measure of the concentration of the gas, is converted from a variable capacitance into an AC signal, amplified, and synchronously rectified to give a DC output signal.

5.1.2 INTERFERENCES—Since exhaust gas is a multicomponent gas mixture, several gases in it may have absorption bands that overlap the absorption bands for CO and CO_2. To make an NDIR analyzer insensitive to interfering gases, an optical filter, or a cell charged with the interfering gas, may be used to filter out unwanted portions of the infrared absorbing spectrum.

Various sample detection system configurations have been used to alleviate undesirable interference signals occurring in the low CO concentration ranges. Individual design variations are described in 5.1.3.

5.1.3 ANALYZER DESIGN VARIATIONS—The analyzer shown in Figure 4A produces infrared radiation from two separate energy sources. This radiation is beamed separately through a chopper. The beams pass through a combination filter cell and optical filter assembly that reduces the interference effects of water vapor and other interfering gases.

The analyzer shown in Figure 4B has dual collimated infrared radiation sources. The response of the detector to other infrared absorbing components in the sample stream is minimized by the stacked nature of its construction. The detector has two sets of chambers. The infrared beams enter the first set of chambers, pass through them by means of a transparent bottom into the second set of chambers. The signal detected in the first chamber consists of a large part of the IR absorption signal of the components of interest in the sample stream and a small part of the IR absorption signal of the other components. The second chamber signal provides a much lower-level absorption signal of the component of interest, but approximately the same signal from the interfering components. The interfering gas signal from the lower chamber is electronically subtracted from the upper chamber signal of interest. To further minimize interference, optical filters are placed in front of the detector to cut out those IR beams in the radiation sources which are not necessary for detecting the IR absorption of the component of interest.

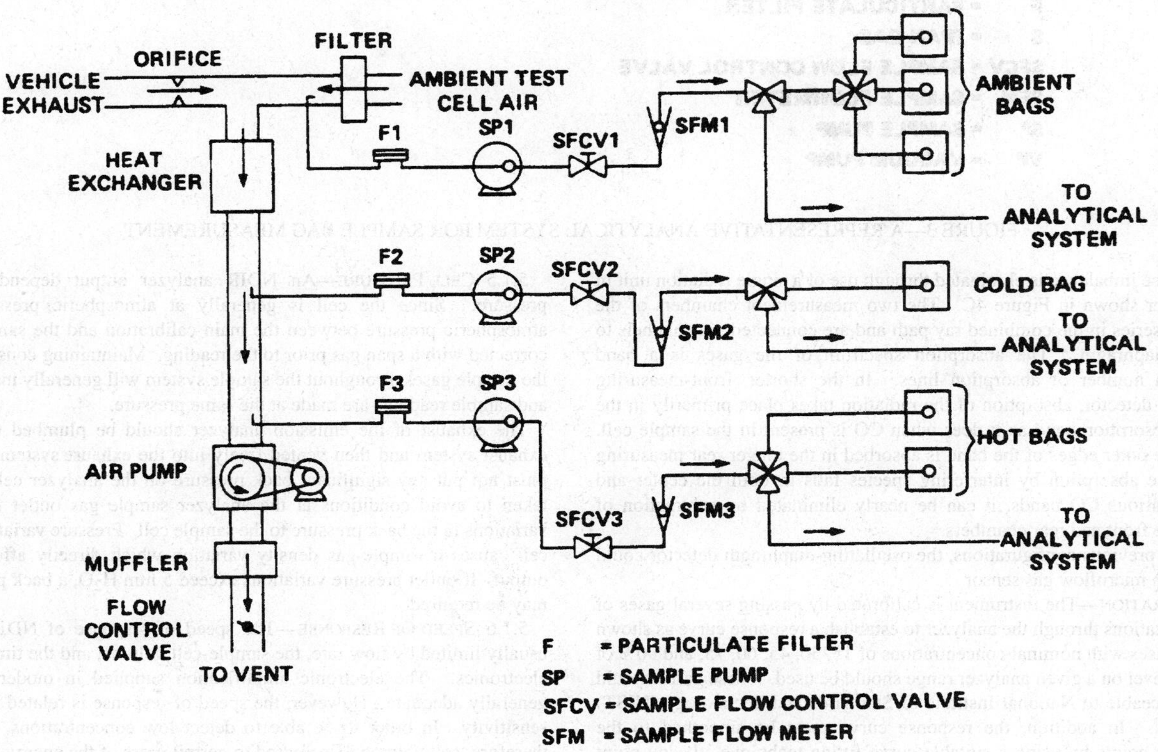

FIGURE 2—A REPRESENTATIVE SIX-BAG EMISSIONS SAMPLE GATHERING SYSTEM (CONSTANT VOLUME SAMPLER)

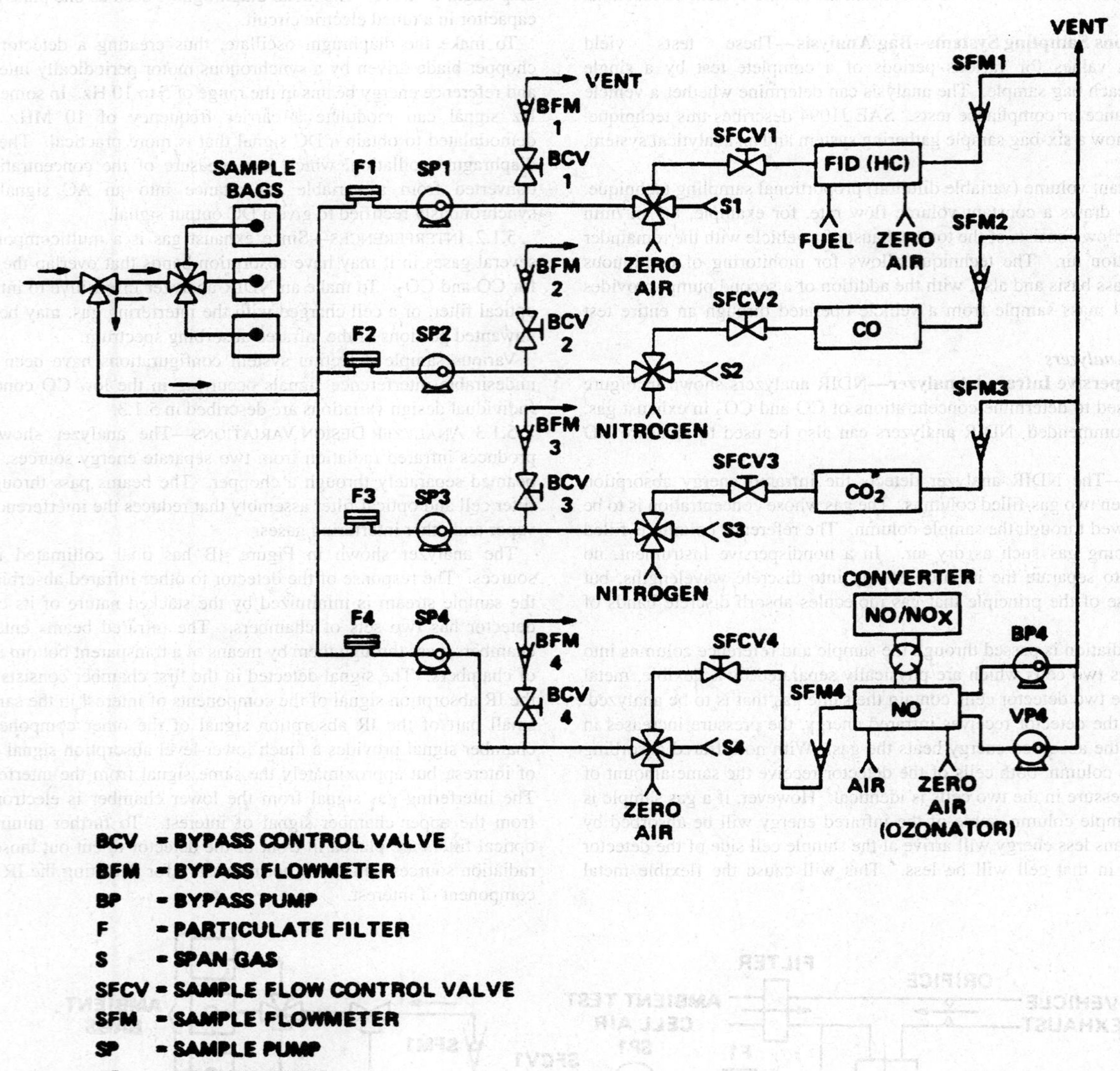

FIGURE 3—A REPRESENTATIVE ANALYTICAL SYSTEM FOR SAMPLE BAG MEASUREMENT

Infrared source imbalance is eliminated through use of a single radiation unit in the CO analyzer shown in Figure 4C. The two measurement chambers of the detector are in series in the combined ray path and are connected via channels to the detector diaphragm. The absorption spectrum of the gases is a band composed of a number of absorption lines. In the shorter, front-measuring chamber of the detector, absorption of the radiation takes place primarily in the center of the absorption band as it does when CO is present in the sample cell. Radiation in the outer edges of the band is absorbed in the longer rear measuring chamber. Since absorption by interfering species falls in both the center and edges of the various CO bands, it can be nearly eliminated by subtraction of signals from the front and rear chambers.

In any of the previous configurations, the oscillating-diaphragm detector could be replaced by a microflow gas sensor.

5.1.4 CALIBRATION—The instrument is calibrated by passing several gases of known concentrations through the analyzer to establish a response curve as shown in Figure 5. Gases with nominal concentrations of 15, 30, 45, 60, 75, and 90% of the maximum level on a given analyzer range should be used. These gases should have values traceable to National Institute of Standards and Technology (NIST) reference gases. In addition, the response curve must be smoothed to the calibration data points by using a suitable curve fitting technique. If any point does not fall on a smooth curve, it must be considered suspect; that calibration standard gas should not be used until its concentration can be verified. Cylinder contamination, mislabeling, or some other reason may have resulted in an error.

5.1.5 CELL PRESSURE—An NDIR analyzer output depends upon the cell pressure. Since the cell is generally at atmospheric pressure, changes in atmospheric pressure between the main calibration and the sample readings are corrected with a span gas prior to the reading. Maintaining constant flow rates of the sample gases throughout the sample system will generally insure that the span and sample readings are made at the same pressure.

The exhaust of the emission analyzer should be plumbed to the laboratory exhaust system and then vented freely into the exhaust system. This plumbing must not put any significant back pressure on the analyzer cell. Care must be taken to avoid conditions at the analyzer sample gas outlet that could create variations in the back pressure to the sample cell. Pressure variation in the sample cell causes a sample-gas density variation which directly affects the analyzer output. If outlet pressure variations exceed 5 mm H_2O, a back pressure regulator may be required.

5.1.6 SPEED OF RESPONSE—The speed of response of NDIR instruments is usually limited by flow rate, the sample-cell volume, and the time constant of the electronics. The electronic amplification supplied in modern instruments is generally adequate. However, the speed of response is related to the instrument sensitivity. In order to be able to detect low concentrations, path length, and therefore, cell volume is increased to permit more of the energy to be absorbed in the sample. This means that as the cell volume is increased, the flow must be increased to maintain the same speed of response.

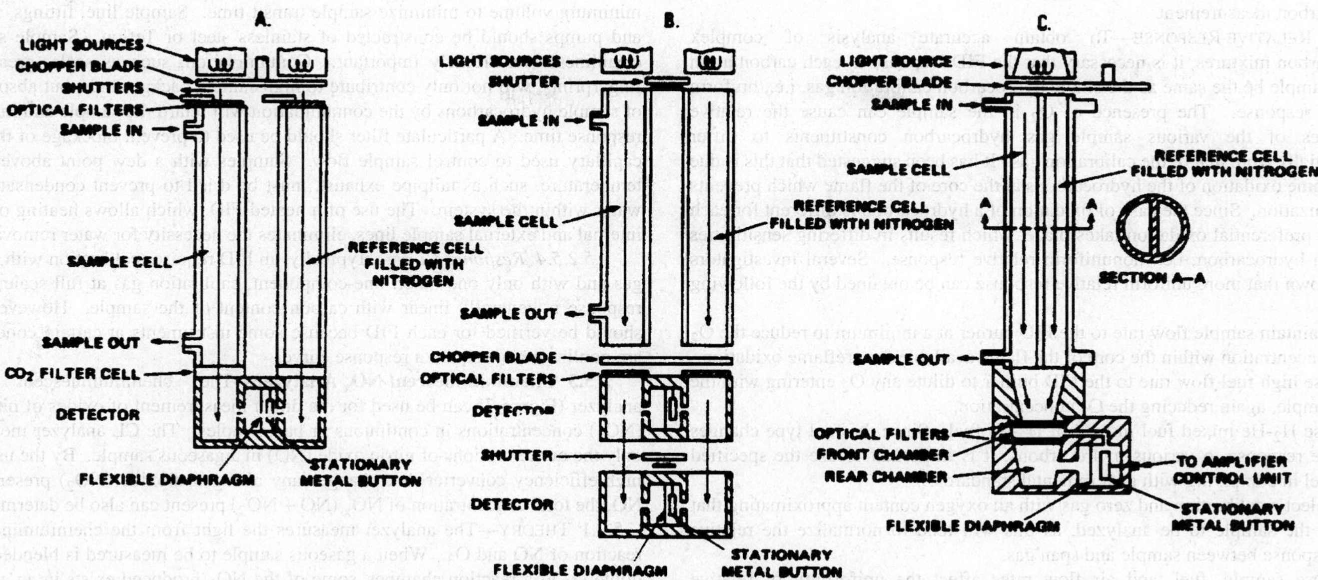

FIGURE 4—THREE NONDISPERSIVE INFRARED ANALYZERS SHOWING DIFFERENT DESIGNS USED TO MINIMIZE THE EFFECTS OF INTERFERING GASES

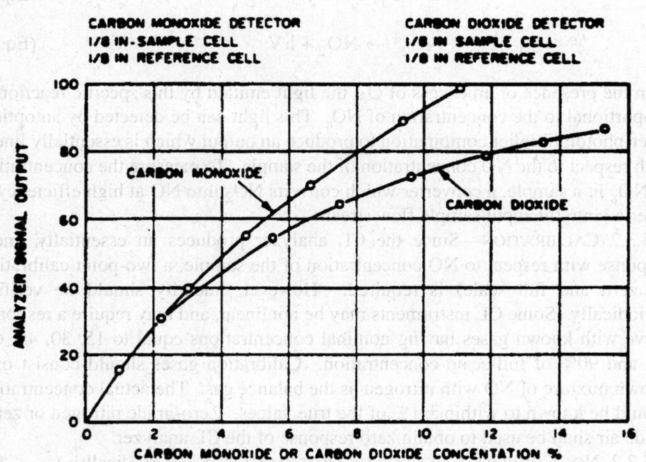

FIGURE 5—TYPICAL NDIR ANALYZER RESPONSE CURVES TO CARBON MONOXIDE AND CARBON DIOXIDE

5.1.7 Response—The response of NDIR CO and CO_2 instruments is nonlinear due to energy absorption characteristics as approximately described by Beer's law Figure 5. The output of the instrument can be made linear using appropriate linearizing circuits. Beer's law states that the exponential output signal, E, is related to the sample gas concentration, c, by the expression;

$$E = A(1 - e^{-kcx}) \quad \text{(Eq. 1)}$$

where A is the amplification factor, k is the gas absorption factor for a particular gas, and x is the length of the sample cell. This expression is useful in qualifying an instrument, but because of detector characteristics and characteristics of the signal conditioning by the electronics, it should not be used in place of a multipoint calibration. Even with linear instruments, at least 6 calibration gases spread evenly over each range of the instrument must be used to verify the linearity of the instrument.

5.1.8 Signal Noise—Noise is the unwanted part of the signal that degrades instrument accuracy. Noise can be caused by many things, but the most common are:

a. Cell misalignment
b. Low detector signal output
c. Dirty cells
d. Poor electrical connections
e. Improper chopper blade alignment and synchronization
f. Pressure fluctuations from changes in flow rate

Connecting an active filter between the first stage of signal amplification and the phase inverting network of the analyzer signal conditioner reduces the noise level considerably, with little effect on response time. Care should be taken when making this type of modification.

5.2 Flame Ionization Detector—Hydrocarbons—The flame ionization detector (FID) is used to measure the total hydrocarbon content of complex-hydrocarbon mixtures on a carbon-mass basis. This measurement can be converted to a hydrocarbon-mass basis by assumption of a specific carbon to hydrogen ratio.

5.2.1 Description—The burner of a typical FID is similar to that shown in Figure 6. A small stream of fuel, hydrogen diluted with an inert gas, is premixed with the sample gas and burned at the outlet of the jet in a diffusion flame with air.

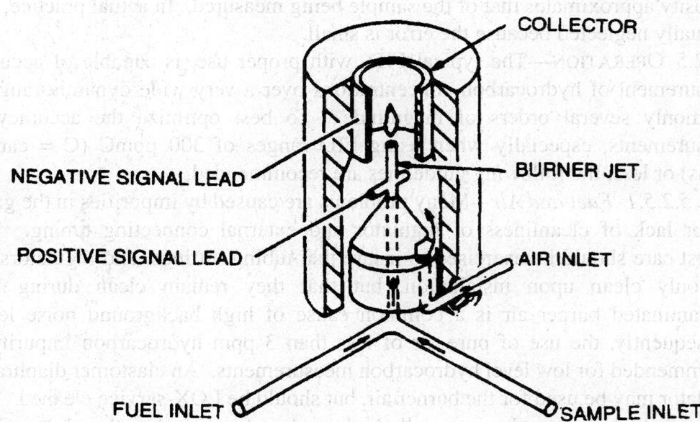

FIGURE 6—TYPICAL BURNER OF FLAME IONIZATION DETECTOR

The FID operates on the principle that the introduction of a gas sample containing hydrocarbon into a hydrogen diffusion flame will increase the concentration of ions within the flame. This increase in ionization is almost directly proportional to the mass flow rate of carbon atoms into the flame. A DC voltage between the burner tip and a collector electrode, which surrounds the flame, collects the ions within the flame, causing current to flow through the associated electronic measuring circuits.

5.2.2 Interferences—Under normal operating conditions, a FID has no significant response to any non-organic carbon constituent found in exhaust gas.

The presence of O_2 in the sample, though, can interfere with the accuracy of the hydrocarbon measurement.

5.2.3 RELATIVE RESPONSE—To obtain accurate analysis of complex hydrocarbon mixtures, it is necessary that the FID response to each carbon atom in the sample be the same as the single hydrocarbon calibration gas, i.e., uniform relative response. The presence of O_2 in the sample can cause the relative responses of the various sample gas hydrocarbon constituents to differ substantially from that of the calibration gas. It has been suggested that this is due to preflame oxidation of the hydrocarbons at the core of the flame which prevents later ionization. Since the ease of oxidation of a hydrocarbon is different for each species, preferential oxidation takes place, which results in differing sensitivities for each hydrocarbon, i.e., nonuniform relative response. Several investigators have shown that more uniform relative response can be obtained by the following steps.

a. Maintain sample flow rate to the FID burner at a minimum to reduce the O_2 concentration within the core of the flame available for preflame oxidation.
b. Use high fuel flow rate to the FID burner to dilute any O_2 entering with the sample, again reducing the O_2 concentration.
c. Use H_2-He mixed fuel instead of H_2-N_2 fuel. Since the fuel type changes the response to various hydrocarbons, it is important to use the specified fuel in complying with governmental standards.
d. Select a calibration and zero gas with an oxygen content approximating that of the sample to be analyzed, as this will tend to normalize the relative response between sample and span gas.

Because sample, fuel, and air flow rates affect the uniformity of relative response of a FID to the various exhaust hydrocarbons, good correlation between FID's of the same model will occur only when their flow rates are the same. To establish correlation between dissimilar FID's, it may be necessary to actually determine their relative response to several major hydrocarbon species and normalize them by adjustment of sample, fuel, and air flow rates for equal relative response. As an initial guide in setting flow rates, the following is recommended:

a. Sample Flow — 3 to 5 cm^3/min
b. Fuel Flow — Adjusted for maximum response
c. Air Flow — 3-1/2 to 4 times the fuel flow rate

The response of the FID to the carbon in oxygen-containing organic compounds (such as alcohols, ethers, and aldehydes) will usually be less than to the carbon in hydrocarbons.

5.2.4 VISCOSITY—The response of an FID is directly proportional to the volumetric sample flow to the FID burner. Therefore, a stringent control of sample flow rate is mandatory. Because most FID's use a pressure-regulated capillary flow control system, the sample flow to the burner is dependent on both sample pressure and viscosity. Any change in sample viscosity will, therefore, result in an inversely proportional change in apparent reading, though pressure has remained constant. It is, therefore, necessary to use a calibration gas whose viscosity approximates that of the sample being measured. In actual practice, this is usually neglected because the error is small.

5.2.5 OPERATION—The typical FID, with proper use, is capable of accurate measurement of hydrocarbon concentrations over a very wide dynamic range—commonly several orders of magnitude. To best optimize the accuracy of measurements, especially when using FID ranges of 300 ppmC (C = carbon atoms) or less, the following guidelines are recommended.

5.2.5.1 Fuel and Air—Many problems are caused by impurities in the gases and/or lack of cleanliness of regulator and external connecting tubing. The utmost care should be exercised to insure that tubing, fittings, and regulators are not only clean upon installation, but that they remain clean during use. Contaminated burner air is a common cause of high background noise level. Consequently, the use of pure air of less than 3 ppm hydrocarbon impurity is recommended for low level hydrocarbon measurements. An elastomer diaphragm regulator may be used for the burner air, but should be LOX-service cleaned. The hydrogen fuel gas must be essentially hydrocarbon-free, i.e., less than 1 ppmC. A metal diaphragm LOX-service cleaned fuel regulator is required. It is also important that supply gases and lines be maintained at a relatively constant temperature as temperature fluctuation will result in absorption-desorption of hydrocarbons which will appear as analyzer drift.

5.2.5.2 Calibration Gases—As with the fuel and air, care should be exercised to insure that all lines, fittings, and regulators used with the calibration gases are contamination-free. LOX-service cleaned, metal diaphragm regulators are especially recommended for low concentration (less than 300 ppmC) calibration gases and the zero gas.

As discussed previously, it is important that the calibration and zero gases have approximately the same oxygen content and viscosity as the sample gas.

5.2.5.3 Sample Lines—The sampling system should be kept short with minimum volume to minimize sample transit time. Sample line, fittings, filters, and pumps should be constructed of stainless steel or Teflon. Sample system cleanliness is extremely important. Contamination, such as scale, grease, or fingerprints, will not only contribute to high sample backgrounds, but absorption of sample hydrocarbons by the contamination will retard the sample and increase response time. A particulate filter should be used to prevent blockage of the fine capillary used to control sample flow. Samples with a dew point above room temperature, such as tailpipe exhaust, must be dried to prevent condensation of water within the system. The use of a heated FID, which allows heating of both internal and external sample lines, eliminates the necessity for water removal.

5.2.5.4 Response Curve—Typically, an FID requires calibration with a zero gas and with only one other, one-component, calibration gas at full scale, since response is generally linear with carbon content of the sample. However, this should be verified for each FID because some instruments at certain conditions are nonlinear and require a response curve.

5.3 Chemiluminescent NO_x Analyzer—The chemiluminescent (CL) analyzer (Figure 7) can be used for the direct measurement of oxides of nitrogen (NO_x) concentrations in continuous or bag samples. The CL analyzer measures only the concentrations of nitric oxide (NO) in a gaseous sample. By the use of a high-efficiency converter that changes any nitrogen dioxide (NO_2) present into NO, the total concentration of NO_x (NO + NO_2) present can also be determined.

5.3.1 THEORY—The analyzer measures the light from the chemiluminescent reaction of NO and O_3. When a gaseous sample to be measured is blended with dilute O_3 in a reaction chamber, some of the NO_2 produced exists in an excited state (NO_2^*). The excited NO_2^* can return to its ground energy state by emitting a photon according to the following equations:

$$NO + O_3 \rightarrow NO_2^* + O_2 \quad \text{(Eq. 2)}$$

$$NO_2^* \rightarrow NO_2 + hV \quad \text{(Eq. 3)}$$

In the presence of an excess of O_3, the light emitted by this specific reaction is proportional to the concentration of NO. This light can be detected by an optical filter-photomultiplier combination to produce an output which is essentially linear with respect to the NO concentration of the sample. To measure the concentration of NO_x in a sample, a converter which converts NO_2 into NO at high efficiency is inserted into the input sample flow stream.

5.3.2 CALIBRATION—Since the CL analyzer produces an essentially linear response with respect to NO concentration of the sample, a two-point calibration (at zero and full scale) is required. However, linearity should be verified periodically. Some CL instruments may be nonlinear, and may require a response curve with known gases having nominal concentrations equal to 15, 30, 45, 60, 75, and 90% of full-scale concentration. Calibration gases should consist of a known mixture of NO with nitrogen as the balance gas. The actual concentration should be known to within ± 1% of the true values. Zero-grade nitrogen or zero-grade air shall be used to obtain zero response of the CL analyzer.

5.3.3 NO_x CONVERTER EFFICIENCY DETERMINATION—Periodically, the efficiency of the NO_x converter should be measured using the apparatus illustrated in Figure 8 to determine the NO_2 to NO conversion efficiency. Efficiency checks should be made using an NO span gas concentration appropriate to the instrument range to be used. Appropriate adjustments to the converter temperature should be made to obtain converter efficiency between 97 and 100%. The following procedure is to be used for determining the values for Equation 4.

a. Attach the NO/N_2 supply at C2, the O_2 supply at C1 and the analyzer inlet connection to the efficiency detector at C3 as shown in Figure 8. At low concentrations of NO, air may be used in place of O_2 to facilitate control of the NO_2 generated during Step d and to minimize the fire hazard.
b. With the variable transformer off, place the NO_2 converter in the bypass mode and close valve V3. Open valve V2 until sufficient flow and stable readings are obtained at the analyzer. Zero and span the analyzer output to indicate the value of the NO concentration being used. Record this concentration.
c. Open valve V3 (on/off flow control solenoid valve for O_2) and adjust valve V1 (O_2 supply metering valve) to blend enough O_2 to lower the NO concentration (b) about 10%. Record this concentration.
d. Turn on the ozonator and increase its supply voltage until the NO concentration of (c) is reduced to about 20% of (b). NO_2 is now being formed from the NO + O_2 reaction. There must always be at least 10% unreacted NO at this point. Record this concentration.

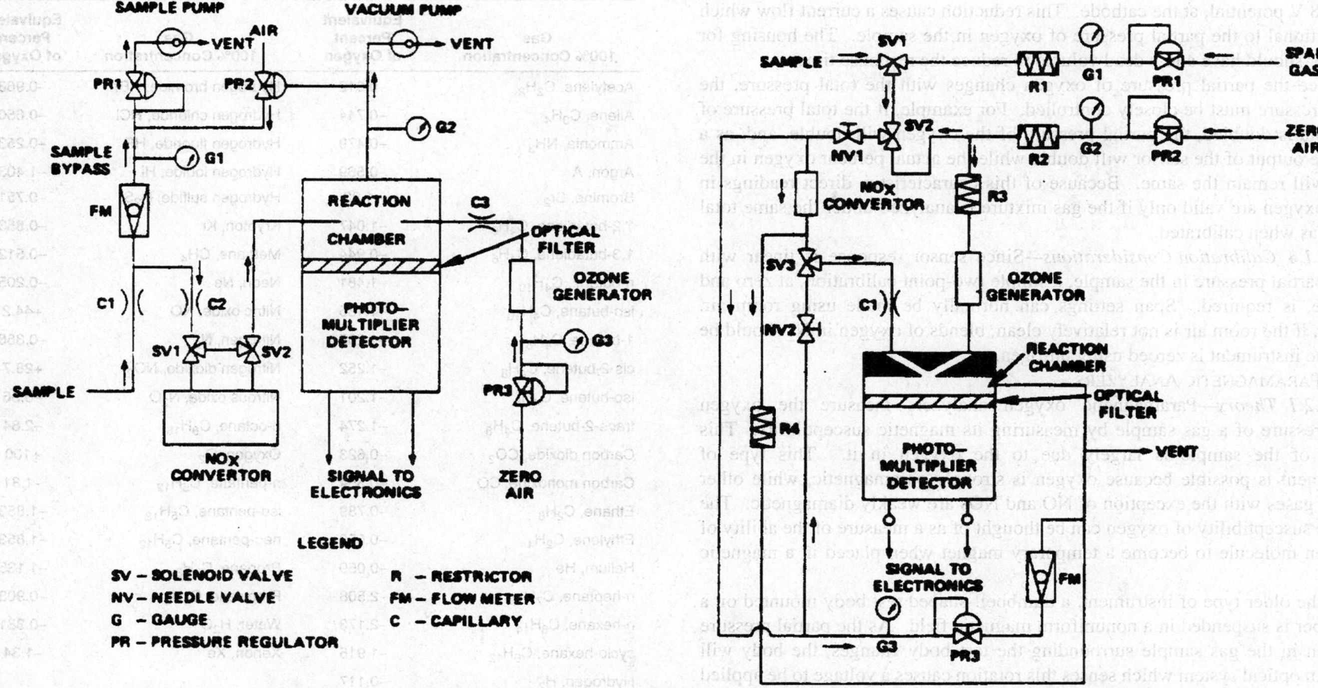

FIGURE 7—SCHEMATICS OF TWO CHEMILUMINESCENT ANALYZERS SHOWING A LOW PRESSURE TYPE (LEFT) AND AN ATMOSPHERIC PRESSURE TYPE (RIGHT)

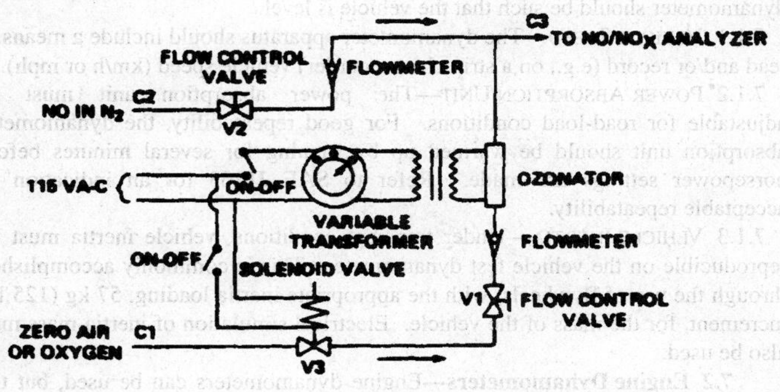

FIGURE 8—NO_X GENERATOR FOR CONVERTER EFFICIENCY DETERMINATION

e. When a stable reading has been obtained from (d), place the NO_x converter in the converter mode. The analyzer now indicates the total NO_x concentration. Record this concentration.

f. Turn off the ozonator and allow the analyzer reading to stabilize. The mixture NO + O_2 is still passing through the converter. This reading is the total NO_x concentration of the dilute NO span gas used at step (c). Record this concentration.

g. Close valve V3. The NO concentration should be equal to or greater than the reading of (b). Calculate the efficiency of the NO_x converter by substituting the concentrations obtained during the test into the equation:

$$\% \text{ Efficiency} = \frac{[(3)-(4)]-[(6)-(5)]}{[(3)-(4)]} \qquad \text{(Eq. 4)}$$

5.3.4 VISCOSITY—The response of a CL analyzer is directly proportional to the volumetric sample flow to the CL analyzer reaction chamber, making stringent control of sample flow rate mandatory. Because most CL analyzers use a pressure-regulated capillary flow control system, the sample flow to the reaction chamber is dependent on both sample pressure and viscosity. Any change in sample viscosity will result in an inversely proportional change in apparent reading, though pressure has remained constant. It is necessary to use a calibration gas whose viscosity approximates that of the sample being measured.

5.3.5 OPERATION—Prior to use, the CL analyzer should be calibrated with gases of known concentration. Pass zero gas through the analyzer and adjust the dark current suppression or amplifier zero control for zero instrument response. A known concentration of NO span gas is then applied and the photomultiplier high voltage supply or the amplifier gain is adjusted for the proper corresponding instrument response.

5.3.6 ANALYZER PERFORMANCE IMPROVEMENT—Output signal drift is often encountered in analyzers using photomultiplier tubes (PMT). This drift is a characteristic of the PMT referred to as fatigue. Fatigue can be reduced in certain analyzers by providing illumination to the PMT during prolonged periods when there is no chemiluminescent reaction. A light emitting diode may be inserted into the reaction chamber to illuminate the PMT while the analyzer isn't being used for testing. Use of light during analyzer idle periods has been shown to reduce warmup drift and increase analyzer-to-analyzer correlation in certain instances.

Interference from H_2O and CO_2 quenching in atmospheric pressure CL analyzers can be reduced by moving the sample capillary further upstream from the reaction chamber, reducing sample flow rate, and increasing the ozone flow rate.

5.4 Oxygen Analyzers

5.4.1 POLAROGRAPHIC ANALYZERS

5.4.1.1 Theory—Polarographic oxygen analyzers operate on the principle that different gases are chemically reduced at different applied voltage potentials. Of the gases normally found in exhaust gas, oxygen is reduced at the lowest potential and can, therefore, be readily measured. The instrument actually measures the partial pressure of oxygen in the sample, but for fixed operating conditions, it can be calibrated in other units such as percent oxygen by volume.

The analyzer consists of two basic units, a sensor and an amplifier. The sensor, which detects oxygen content, normally consists of a gold cathode insulated from a silver anode between which a potential of approximately 0.8 V is applied. The anode is electrically connected to the cathode by a potassium chloride gel. The entire anode-cathode assembly is separated from the sample by a Teflon gas-permeable membrane.

5.4.1.2 Interferences—There are other gases, such as SO_2, Cl_2, Br_2, I_2, and NO_2 which will reduce at 0.8 V. These gases are not usually found in exhaust gas in sufficient concentrations relative to O_2 to give a significant interference.

5.4.1.3 Continuous Operation—In operation, the sensor is placed in the sample stream and oxygen diffuses through the Teflon membrane and is reduced, by the 0.8 V potential, at the cathode. This reduction causes a current flow which is proportional to the partial pressure of oxygen in the sample. The housing for the sensor should have a low dead volume to reduce the response time.

Since the partial pressure of oxygen changes with the total pressure, the system pressure must be closely controlled. For example, if the total pressure of the sample is doubled, the partial pressure of the oxygen will double, and, as a result, the output of the sensor will double while the actual percent oxygen in the sample will remain the same. Because of this characteristic, direct readings in percent oxygen are valid only if the gas mixture is analyzed under the same total pressure as when calibrated.

5.4.1.4 Calibration Considerations—Since sensor response is linear with oxygen partial pressure in the sample, a simple two-point calibration, at zero and full scale, is required. Span settings can normally be made using room air. However, if the room air is not relatively clean, blends of oxygen in N_2 should be used. The instrument is zeroed using nitrogen.

5.4.2 PARAMAGNETIC ANALYZERS

5.4.2.1 Theory—Paramagnetic oxygen analyzers measure the oxygen partial pressure of a gas sample by measuring its magnetic susceptibility. This property of the sample is largely due to the oxygen in it. This type of measurement is possible because oxygen is strongly paramagnetic, while other common gases with the exception of NO and NO_2 are weakly diamagnetic. The magnetic susceptibility of oxygen can be thought of as a measure of the ability of an oxygen molecule to become a temporary magnet when placed in a magnetic field.

In the older type of instrument, a dumbbell-shaped test body mounted on a quartz fiber is suspended in a nonuniform magnetic field. As the partial pressure of oxygen in the gas sample surrounding the test body changes, the body will rotate. An optical system which senses this rotation causes a voltage to be applied to the test body to maintain it in a null position. This voltage is the output voltage of the amplifier circuit, and is the voltage required to hold the test body stationary against the forces exerted by the magnetic field.

This instrument, because it depends on the physical movement of a relatively large mass, does not have the speed of response necessary to measure dynamic changes in oxygen content, such as may occur when analyzing exhaust gas. Therefore, it is not recommended for use during cyclic operation. However, it can be used to measure oxygen either at steady-state conditions or in collected samples of exhaust gas.

The newer type of paramagnetic oxygen analyzer measures the pulsating pressure variation at the pole of an electromagnet with a pulsating magnetic field. The pulsating pressure is caused by the attraction of oxygen to the electromagnet when it is energized. This type of instrument has a faster response time than the dumbbell type instrument. Because these oxygen analyzers measure the partial pressure of oxygen, an instrument calibrated in percent oxygen must be operated at the same system pressure at which it is calibrated to obtain reliable analytical results.

5.4.2.2 Interferences—Although the instrument response caused by most gases other than oxygen is comparatively slight, it is not in all cases negligible, as can be seen in Table 1. Therefore, in making oxygen measurements in exhaust gas, correction should be made for the interfering compounds such as CO_2, CO, and NO. Equation 5.

$$\text{Interference} = \text{Equivalent } \%\, O_2 \times \text{observed concentration} \times 0.01 \quad \text{(Eq. 5)}$$

5.4.2.3 Calibration Consideration—Instrument response is linear with oxygen partial pressure in the sample; therefore, only a one-point calibration is required. Span settings can normally be made on room air. However, if the room air is not relatively clean, blends of oxygen in N_2 should be used. The instrument is normally zeroed on nitrogen.

6. Data Analysis—Data from the individual analyzers are typically collected by a computer. The computer uses predetermined calibration curves to calculate net concentration for each sample bag and concentration for individual modes of the test cycle. With additional information, the computer can also calculate emission mass and emission mass per unit distance driven.

The computer needs to be programmed for the separate time lags for each analyzer. This is because the recorder response for measuring exhaust gas concentrations will always lag the engine's operation because of a variable exhaust system delay and a fixed sample system delay.

Whenever water is removed from a gas stream with a cold trap, all concentrations must be corrected for the water removed if concentrations of the original wet stream are desired.

TABLE 1—OXYGEN EQUIVALENTS OF COMMON GASES

Gas 100% Concentration	Equivalent Percent of Oxygen	Gas 100% Concentration	Equivalent Percent of Oxygen
Acetylene, C_2H_2	−0.612	Hydrogen bromide, HBr	−0.968
Allene, C_3H_4	−0.744	Hydrogen chloride, HCl	−0.650
Ammonia, NH_3	−0.479	Hydrogen fluoride, HF	−0.253
Argon, A	−0.569	Hydrogen iodide, HI	−1.403
Bromine, Br_2	−1.83	Hydrogen sulfide, H_2S	−0.751
1,2-butadiene, C_4H_6	−1.047	Krypton, Kr	−0.853
1,3-butadiene, C_4H_6	−0.944	Methane, CH_4	−0.512
n-butane, C_4H_{10}	−1.481	Neon, Ne	−0.205
iso-butane, C_4H_{10}	−1.485	Nitric oxide, NO	+44.2
1-butene, C_4H_8	−1.205	Nitrogen, N_2	−0.358
cis-2-butene, C_4H_8	−1.252	Nitrogen dioxide, NO_2	+28.7
iso-butene, C_4H_8	−1.201	Nitrous oxide, N_2O	−0.56
trans-2-butene, C_4H_8	−1.274	n-octane, C_8H_{18}	−2.84
Carbon dioxide, CO_2	−0.623	Oxygen, O_2	+100
Carbon monoxide, CO	−0.354	n-pentane, C_5H_{12}	−1.81
Ethane, C_2H_6	−0.789	iso-pentane, C_5H_{12}	−1.853
Ethylene, C_2H_4	−0.553	neo-pentane, C_5H_{12}	−1.853
Helium, He	−0.059	Propane, C_3H_8	−1.135
n-heptane, C_7H_{16}	−2.508	Propylene, C_3H_6	−0.903
n-hexane, C_6H_{14}	−2.173	Water, H_2O	−0.381
cyclo-hexane, C_6H_{12}	−1.915	Xenon, Xe	−1.34
Hydrogen, H_2	−0.117		

7. Associated Test Equipment

7.1 Chassis Dynamometers—Chassis dynamometers should be of the power absorption type with variable inertia load capabilities. Installation of the dynamometer should be such that the vehicle is level.

7.1.1 VEHICLE SPEED—The dynamometer apparatus should include a means to read and/or record (e.g., on a strip chart recorder) vehicle speed (km/h or mph).

7.1.2 POWER ABSORPTION UNIT—The power absorption unit must be adjustable for road-load conditions. For good repeatability, the dynamometer absorption unit should be warmed up by running for several minutes before horsepower settings are made. Refer to SAE J1263 for an indication of acceptable repeatability.

7.1.3 VEHICLE INERTIA—Under transient conditions, vehicle inertia must be reproducible on the vehicle test dynamometer. This is commonly accomplished through the use of flywheels, with the appropriate inertia loading, 57 kg (125 lb) increment, for the mass of the vehicle. Electrical simulation of inertia mass may also be used.

7.2 Engine Dynamometers—Engine dynamometers can be used, but the exhaust emission results will not necessarily correlate with those from chassis dynamometer tests. Carburetor air inlet temperature or engine soak temperatures during engine dynamometer tests must approximate those obtained with a chassis dynamometer.

7.3 Cooling System—For a vehicle undergoing exhaust emissions testing on a chassis dynamometer, engine cooling is maintained by the vehicle's normal water-cooling system and a fixed-speed cooling fan. The cooling fan should have a capacity of 150 m^3/min ± 8 m^3/min (5300 cfm ± 300 cfm).

The cooling fan should be located immediately in front of the vehicle's normal cooling air inlet with the hood or engine compartment lid open. Additional cooling to maintain the equivalent of road temperatures may be used.

8. Test Procedures

8.1 Vehicle (Engine) Preparation and Test—Preparation and preconditioning usually includes engine break-in, a preconditioning test drive, and a temperature equilibration (soak) period.

For test reproducibility, all parameters must be kept the same. Some important parameters for preconditioning, soaking, and testing are:

a. engine driving cycles
b. test fuel
c. test area temperature and humidity
d. engine tune-up to manufacturer's specifications
e. previous vehicle (engine) history
f. charcoal vapor storage canister(s) loading
g. condition of crankcase oil

R) CONSTANT VOLUME SAMPLER SYSTEM FOR EXHAUST EMISSIONS MEASUREMENT —SAE J1094 JUN92

SAE Information Report

Report of the SAE Automotive Emissions Committee approved June 1974 and completely revised by the SAE Automotive Emissions Committee April 1978. Editorial change November 1978. Completely revised by the SAE Exhaust Emissions Measurement Standards Committee June 1992.

Foreword—This Document has also changed to comply with the new SAE Technical Standards Board format.

Development of CVS System—Constant volume sampler (CVS) systems have been used since the late 1950s. The engine exhaust to be sampled is diluted with ambient air so that the total combined flow rate of exhaust and dilution air mix is nearly constant for all engine operating conditions. The CVS system is sometimes called a variable dilution sampler. Recently constant volume sampler systems have been abbreviated PDP-CVS or CFV-CVS. The PDP-CVS system is the older system that uses a positive displacement pump to maintain a constant total flow. The CFV-CVS system uses a critical flow venturi to maintain a nearly constant total flow. Some of the newer CFV systems no longer use a heat exchanger to bring the mix of engine exhaust and dilution air to a constant temperature, but instead monitor the mix temperature continuously in order to calculate the total flow accurately. These CFV systems are not constant volume samplers, but since they are used to measure emissions, the units are discussed here.

Hydrocarbons in the dilution air were recognized from the first as a problem in the CVS procedure. Studies were initiated on the feasibility of removing the unwanted hydrocarbons. As a result, the installation of charcoal filters in the dilution air system was chosen as the most practical solution. On a long-term basis, charcoal does not remove the hydrocarbon materials but it does stabilize their concentration level during a given test and thereby permit the collection of an accurate background sample.

1. Scope—This SAE Information Report describes uniform laboratory techniques for employing the constant volume sampler (CVS) system in measuring various constituents in the exhaust gas of gasoline engines installed on passenger cars and light trucks. The techniques described relate particularly to CVS systems employing positive displacement pumps. This is essentially an almost obsolete system relative to usage in industry and government. Current practice favors the use of a critical flow venturi to measure the diluted exhaust flow. In some areas of CVS practice, alternative procedures are given as a guide toward development of uniform laboratory techniques.

The report includes the following sections:

2. References

2.1 Applicable Publications—The following publications form a part of the specification to the extent specified herein. Unless otherwise indicated the lastest revision of SAE publications shall apply.

2.1.1 SAE PUBLICATION—Available from SAE, 400 Commonwealth Drive, Warrendale, PA 15096-0001.

SAE J1506—Emission Test Driving Schedules

2.1.2 FEDERAL PUBLICATIONS—Available from the Superintendent of Documents, U. S. Government Printing Office, Washington, DC 20402.

1975 Federal Test Procedure: 40 CFR 86 Subpart B

The Federal Register

3. Definitions—The following definitions apply to the term indicated as the term is used in this document.

3.1 Analytical Train—A general term to define the entire system required to sample and analyze a particular constituent in exhaust gas. Typically, this train will include items such as tubing, condenser, particulate filter, sample pump, analytical instrument, and flow meter.

3.2 Calibration Curve—Normally, the dependent variable y, the concentration of the calibration gas, is plotted as a function of the independent variable x, the instrumental voltage. For nonlinear analyzers, a polynomial of degree no greater than the fourth power is used. Sufficient data points should be used to adequately define the analyzer response. The calibration curve should agree to within 1% of the measured data point.

3.3 Calibration Frequency—Analyzers should be checked at least monthly to determine if significant change has occurred in the calibration. In addition, the calibration should be verified when a problem is suspected and when large gain shifts are observed.

3.4 Calibrating Gas—A gas mixture of accurately known concentration which is used periodically to calibrate the analytical instruments. Usually, calibration requires a number of mixtures of different concentrations. Calibrating gases are usually divided into groups such as National Institute of Standards and Technology (NIST) standard reference gases, golden standards, primary standards, and working gases. The naming of the working gases should be traceable to the NIST standard reference gases. A standard gas divider is normally used to blend a gas with a zero (or near zero) gas to generate a calibration curve. It provides a significant reduction in calibration gas cylinders.

3.5 Chassis Dynamometer—A laboratory power absorption unit capable of simulating to a limited degree the road operation of a vehicle. The dynamometer should possess the capability to simulate the inertia and road load power developed by a vehicle.

3.6 Chemiluminescent (CL) Analyzer—An instrument which measures nitric oxide by measuring the intensity of chemiluminescent radiation from the reaction of nitric oxide with ozone. The addition of a converter will permit the measurement of the oxides of nitrogen.

3.7 Chock—A block or wedge that prevents movement of the wheels of a vehicle.

3.8 Coastdown—The procedure used to determine the total horsepower absorbed by a dynamometer at 80 km/h (50 mph). The time required for the rolls to coast down from 88 to 72 km/h (55 to 45 mph) is observed.

3.9 Constant Volume Sampler (CVS)—A device for collecting samples of diluted exhaust gas. The exhaust gas is diluted with air in a manner that keeps the total flow rate of exhaust gas and dilution air constant throughout the test. The device permits measuring mass emissions on a continuous basis and also, through use of a second pump, allows a proportional mass sample to be collected.

3.10 Converter—A thermal or catalytic reaction device which usually precedes the chemiluminescent analyzer and converts oxides of nitrogen to nitric oxide. The converter may also convert ammonia and other nitrogen containing compounds to nitric oxide.

3.11 Counter—A mechanical and/or electrical device that totalizes the number of revolutions of the CVS for each test phase.

3.12 Curve Fitting—See calibration curve, Lagrangian fit, polynomial fit.

3.13 Detector—That Component in an analytical instrument which is sensitive to a particular gas.

3.14 Dilution Air—Ambient air which is passed through filters to stabilize the background hydrocarbon concentration and which is used to dilute the vehicle exhaust.

3.15 Dilution Factor—Based on stoichiometric equation for fuel with composition $CH_{1.85}$, the dilution factor is defined as:

$$\frac{13.4}{CO_2 + (HC + CO) \times 10^{-4}} \quad \text{(Eq. 1)}$$

where:

CO_2 is equal to the concentration in dilute exhaust sample in mole percent, HC in ppm carbon equivalent, and CO in ppm corrected for water vapor and CO_2 extraction.

3.16 Dilution Ratio—The ratio of CVS volume to exhaust volume, usually found by dividing the undiluted exhaust CO_2 concentration by the dilute CO_2 concentration.

3.17 Driver Aid—An instrument used to guide the vehicle driver in operating the vehicle in accordance with the specified acceleration, deceleration, and cruise operating modes of a specific driving procedure.

3.18 Exhaust Emissions—Substances emitted to the atmosphere from any opening downstream from the exhaust port of a motor vehicle engine.

3.19 Fifth Wheel—A calibrated wheel, axle, and tachometer generator assembly that can be used to determine the true speed of the vehicle (by towing the wheel assembly), or true speed of the dynamometer rolls (by permitting the rolls to drive the fifth wheel assembly).

3.20 Filter Cell—That portion of the NDIR instrument which is filled with a particular gas in order to reduce interference signals.

3.21 Flame Ionization Detector (FID)—A device containing a hydrogen-in-air diffusion flame that produces an electrical current approximately proportional to the mass of the carbon component of the hydrocarbons entering the flame per unit time.

3.22 Hang-up—The absorption-desorption of sample (mainly higher molecular weight hydrocarbons) from the surfaces of the sample system that can cause instrument response delay and lower concentration at the analyzer, followed by higher readings in subsequent tests.

3.23 Heat Exchanger—An air-to-air or air-to-water heat exchanger, which is used to control the temperature of the dilution air-exhaust gas mixture.

3.24 Horsepower

3.24.1 ABSORBED HORSEPOWER—Total power absorbed by the absorption unit of the dynamometer and by the frictional components of the dynamometer.

3.24.2 ABSORBED HORSEPOWER AT 80.5 KM/H (50 MPH) ROAD LOAD—The dynamometer setting values for various inertia weight vehicles published in the Federal Register.

3.24.3 FRICTIONAL HORSEPOWER—Power absorbed by the frictional components of the dynamometer.

3.24.4 INDICATED HORSEPOWER—Power values indicated by the power meter of the dynamometer.

3.24.5 INDICATED HORSEPOWER AT 80.5 KM/H (50 MPH) ROAD LOAD—The dynamometer setting values, determined by calibration, that correspond to the dynamometer setting values published in the Federal Register.

3.25 Inertia Weights—A series of rotating disks used on a chassis dynamometer to simulate to the nearest 57, 113, or 227 kg (125, 250, or 500 lb) increments of the test weight of a vehicle during accelerations and decelerations. The inertia weights have no effect during steady states.

3.26 Lagrangian Fit—A computer technique used to interpolate polynomial curves generated from a set of data points (calibration points): N data points are required to generate a curve to N—1 degree. A feature of this technique is that the interpolated curve goes through each data point exactly.

3.27 Laminar Flow Element (LFE)—A flow rate measuring device that has a linear relationship between flow rate and pressure drop.

3.28 Light-Duty Truck—Any motor vehicle rated at 8,500 pounds GVWR or less which has a vehicle curb weight of 6,000 pounds or less and which has a basic vehicle frontal area of 45 square feet or less, which is:

a. Designed primarily for purposes of transportation of property or is a derivation of such a vehicle, or
b. Designed primarily for transportation of persons and has a capacity of more than 12 persons, or
c. Available with special features enabling off-street or off-highway operation and use.

3.29 Light-Duty Vehicle—A passenger car or passenger car derivative capable of seating 12 passengers or less.

3.30 Loaded Vehicle Weight—The curb weight of a light-duty vehicle plus 136 kg (300 lb).

3.31 Mixing Device—A device that is used in the main flow stream of a CVS to promote mixing of the exhaust gas with the dilution air.

3.32 Mode—A particular operating condition (for example, acceleration, cruise, deceleration, or idle) of a test cycle.

3.33 Nondispersive Infrared (NDIR) Analyzer—An instrument to determine carbon monoxide, carbon dioxide, nitric oxide, and hydrocarbons in exhaust gas. Now primarily being used for carbon monoxide and carbon dioxide determinations.

3.34 Normalizing Gas (Span Gas)—A single calibrating gas blend routinely used in calibration of each analytical instrument.

3.35 Optical Filter—That portion of the NDIR instrument which eliminates wavelength regions where interference signals are obtained.

3.36 Oxides of Nitrogen—The sum total of the nitric oxide and nitrogen dioxide in a sample expressed as equivalent mass of nitrogen dioxide.

3.37 Ozonator—An electrical device that generates ozone from oxygen or air.

3.38 Parts Per Million Carbon—The mole fraction of hydrocarbon measured on a methane equivalence basis.

3.39 Polynomial Fit—A technique of generating a calibration curve from a set of points.

3.40 Positive Displacement Pump—A CVS blower, gas pump, or constant displacement pump that delivers a metered amount of air per revolution measured at inlet conditions.

3.41 Probe—A sample line inserted into the exhaust stream of a vehicle or engine in such a manner as to obtain a homogeneous or well-mixed exhaust sample.

3.42 Reference Cell—That portion of the NDIR instrument that is usually filled with air (sometimes nitrogen) and provides the reference signal to the detector.

3.43 Remote Filter Box—Particular CVS design that has the dilution air filters and mixing chamber housed in a separate cabinet which can be located close to the tailpipe of the test vehicle.

3.44 Sample Cell—That portion of the NDIR instrument which contains the flowing sample gas.

3.45 Stratification—Variation in concentration of a sample stream when samples are taken at different points on a cross section of the mixed CVS stream just ahead of the CVS positive displacement pump.

3.46 Tailpipe Pressure—The static pressure measured at the tailpipe when a CVS is connected to a test vehicle.

4. Test Facilities and Equipment

4.1 Sampler—CVS systems can exist in a variety of physical configurations but all of them permit measuring emissions of vehicles:

4.1.1 BASIC EQUIPMENT—The principal component of a CVS is either the positive displacement pump (PDP) of the older models or the critical flow venturi (CFV) of more recent designs. The positive displacement pump consists of a pair of symmetrical rotating, two-lobe impellers driven in opposite directions and encased by a housing. A critical flow venturi CVS has a CVS compressor unit that is used in conjunction with the critical flow venturi. Figure 1 shows a sketch of a CFV-CVS.

4.1.1.1 A dilution air filter system consisting of a particle (dust) filter, a charcoal filter to stabilize hydrocarbons, and a second particle filter to remove airborne particles and trap charcoal particles.

4.1.1.2 A flexible coupling to the tailpipe of the test car brings in undiluted exhaust gas to the mixing chamber.

4.1.1.3 A mixing chamber combines the automotive exhaust from the test car and the dilution air into a homogeneous (nonstratified) mixture.

4.1.1.4 A heat exchanger is used to control the temperature of the exhaust gas dilution air mixture. The heat exchanger should be capable of controlling the temperature of the dilute exhaust gas ±5.6 °C (±10 °F) during testing. In some models of CVS, a temperature controller regulates both the flow of cooling water or hot water (from a hot water heater) through the heat exchanger to control mixture temperature. In other models of CVS, the dilution air is preheated so that the temperature controller regulates the flow of cooling water through the heat exchanger in order to control the mixture temperature.

4.1.1.5 A secondary heater system maintains the heat exchanger at a temperature to prevent water condensation.

4.1.1.6 A sampling system transfers the exhaust-air mixture from the CVS to the bag at a constant flow rate. The minimum sample flow rate should be 0.28 m^3/h (10 ft^3/h). Each sampling system consists of fiberglass filter, a diaphragm type pump, a flow control valve, and a flow meter or other gas measuring device. All of the surfaces in contact with the sample air or air-gas mixture are stainless steel or other nonreactive material.

4.1.1.7 A similar sampling system collects dilution air from a point just downstream of the air filter and transfers it to a separate bag.

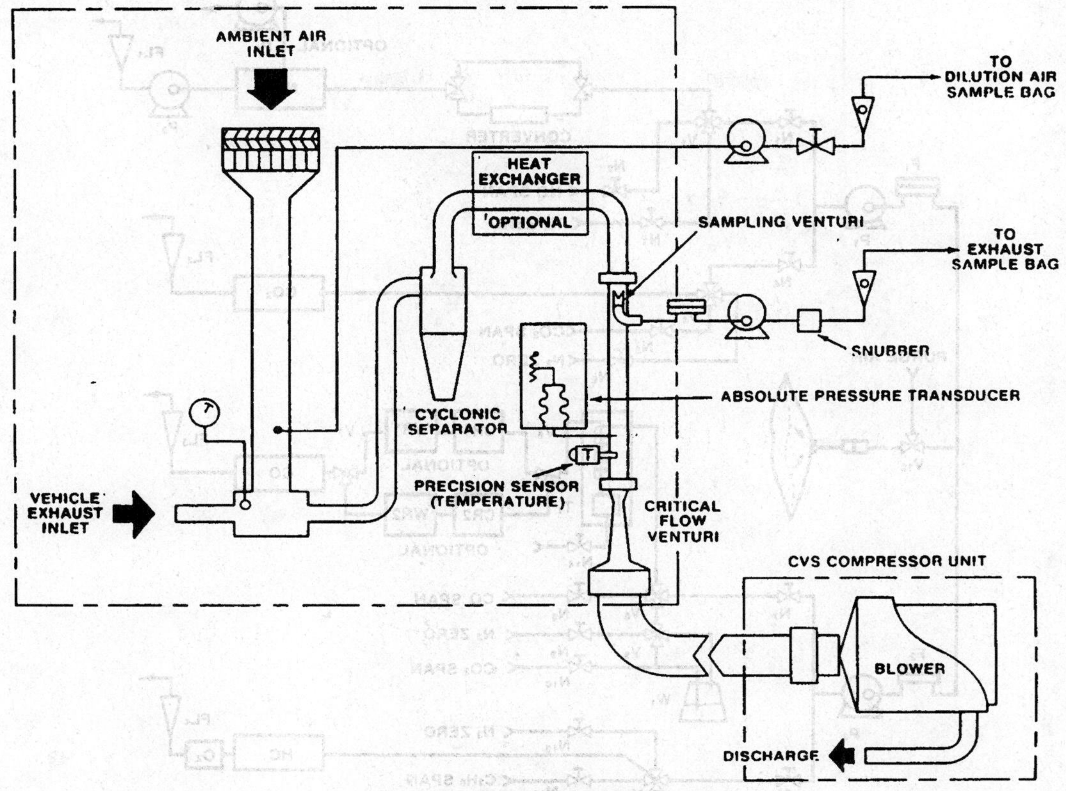

FIGURE 1—CFV—CVS SAMPLER UNIT

4.1.1.8 An evacuation and purge pump to remove the excess sample from the bags and purge the bags with clean air.

4.1.1.9 A set of bags (sample and background) and appropriate controls is needed for each of the test phases.

4.1.2 SUPPLEMENTARY EQUIPMENT—In addition to the above basic equipment, the following items can be added for operating convenience:

4.1.2.1 A muffler located after the CVS pump to reduce the noise.

4.1.2.2 A four-speed motor, transmission, or other suitable means for driving the positive displacement pump will permit a choice of different dilution ratios.

4.1.2.3 An optional remote control operating station containing the counter, the operations logic module, and the various control function switches and indicator lights that permit convenient operator control at a distance from the CVS console.

4.1.2.4 Optional modal analysis at the analytical bench during the filling of the bag is made possible through the use of a separate sampling probe(s). One probe is used if continuous modal analysis is conducted using diluted exhaust.[1] The second probe in this case is used to monitor diluted CO_2 which is used as a tracer gas to determine engine flow. Tail pipe sample should either be returned to the CVS bulk stream if the amount withdrawn is a significant fraction of total exhaust flow (greater than 1%), or the loss in tail pipe sample should be corrected mathematically.

4.2 Analysis Instrumentation—Bag Analysis

4.2.1 SCHEMATIC—Figure 2 is a sketch of the sampling and analysis train that is a typical flow schematic for the bag analysis of engine exhaust using the CVS.

4.2.2 COMPONENT DESCRIPTION—The following components are suggested for the CVS bag sampling and analytical systems for the analysis of carbon monoxide (CO), hydrocarbons (HC), nitrogen oxides (NO_x), carbon dioxide (CO_2), and oxygen (O_2):

4.2.2.1 NDIR analyzers for measurement of CO and CO_2 with cells of appropriate length for concentration ranges being measured. Typical ranges are shown in Table 1.

4.2.2.2 Chemiluminescent (CL) NO analyzer is equipped with a bypass and NO_2 to NO converter for the measurement of NO_x with concentration range selection as shown in Table 1.

4.2.2.3 FID for measurement of HC. The instrument employed should be capable of measuring HC for ranges shown in Table 1.

4.2.2.4 Oxygen analyzer for measurement of O_2 with range of measurement as shown in Table 1.

4.2.2.5 Valves V_{12} used to direct the sample or purge air to the analyzers.

4.2.2.6 Valves V_1, V_4, V_8 (optional), V_9, and V_{10} used to direct the sample, zero gas, or span gas streams to the analyzers.

4.2.2.7 Filters F_1 and F_2 for removing particulate materials from the sample prior to analysis. A glass fiber filter of at least 7 cm diameter is suitable.

4.2.2.8 Pumps P_1 and P_2 to move the sample through the system. Pumps should have stainless steel or aluminum chambers with diaphragms and valves made from or covered with an inert material, such as Teflon. Free air capacity should be approximately 1.1 m^3/h (40 ft^3/h). Pumps P_3 for bypass flow of chemiluminescent analyzer and vacuum pump P_4 (optional depending upon the design of the chemiluminescent analyzer) for evacuation of the chemiluminescent reactor chamber.

4.2.2.9 Needle valves N_1, N_4, N_7, and N_{11} to regulate sample gas flow to the analyzers.

4.2.2.10 Needle valves N_2, N_5, N_8, and N_{12} to regulate span gas flow to the analyzers.

4.2.2.11 Optional valve V_9 used to direct CO_2 span gas through the water bubbler for checking the performance of drier and absorber system or to check the H_2O and CO_2 interference rejection characteristics of the CO analyzer. Needle valve N_2 is used to regulate CO_2 flow.

4.2.2.12 Needle valves N_3, N_6, N_9, N_{13}, and N_{15} to regulate zero gas flow to the analyzers.

4.2.2.13 Flow meters FL_1, FL_2, FL_3, and FL_4 to indicate span gas, zero gas, and sample flow to the analyzers.

1. Two probes are required if continuous modal analysis is conducted using undiluted exhaust.

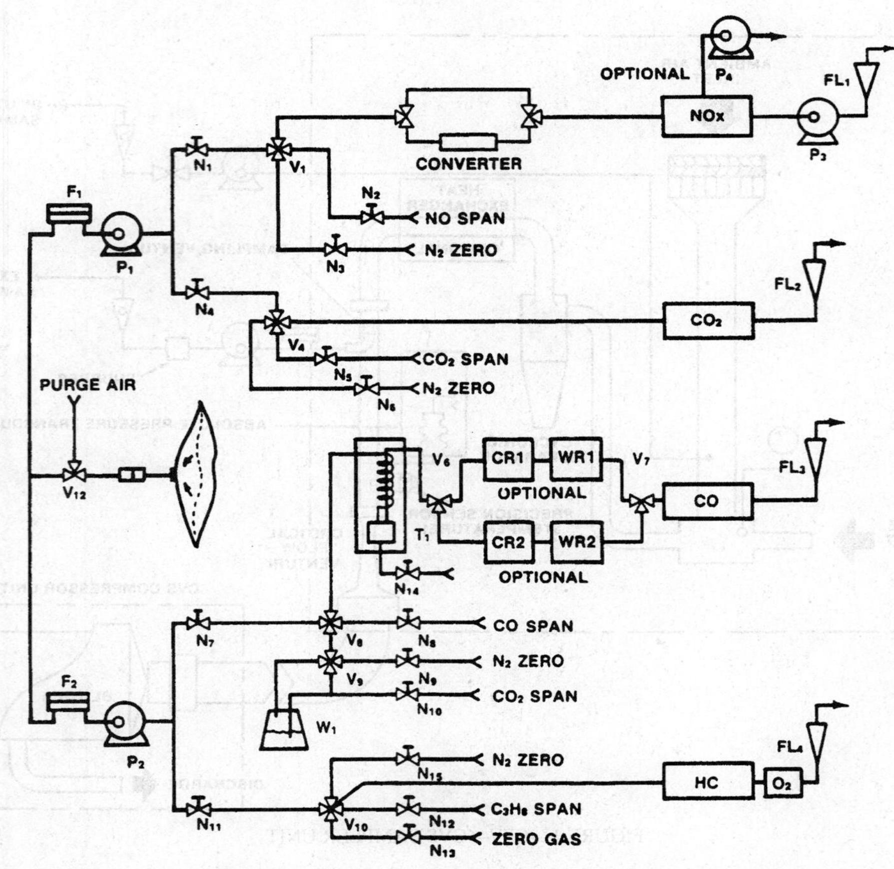

FIGURE 2—BAG SAMPLING AND ANALYSIS TRAIN

TABLE 1—TYPICAL LOW RANGES FOR ANALYSIS OF HC, CO, CO_2, NO_x, AND O_2 IN SPARK IGNITION ENGINE EXHAUST

Component	Ranges CVS Bag Sample	Ranges Undiluted Exhaust Gas
HC	0–300 ppmC	0–500 ppmC
CO	0–100 ppm	0–0.3%
NO_x		
1975	0–250 ppm	0–2500 ppm
1976	0–10 ppm	0–250 ppm
CO_2	0–2.0%	0–15%
Dilute CO_2	—	0–5%
O_2	0–21%	0–10%

4.2.2.14 Water trap T_1, if necessary, to partially remove water and a valve N_{14} to allow the trap to be drained.

4.2.2.15 Optional[2] sample conditioning columns CR_1 and CR_2 containing Ascarite to remove CO_2 from the CO analysis stream, and WR_1 and WR_2 containing indicating $CaSO_4$ or indicating silica gel to remove the remainder of the water. Equivalent drying techniques such as diffusion driers may be used. These optional sample conditioning techniques must be used if the CO instrument is subject to CO_2 or water interference. However, several CO analyzers are commercially available that have negligible CO_2 and water interference and their use is strongly recommended.

4.2.2.16 Optional valves V_6 and V_7 to permit switching from exhausted absorbing columns to fresh columns.

4.2.2.17 Optional water bubbler W_1 to allow saturation of CO_2 span gas to check the efficiency of the absorbing columns in the CO system.

4.2.2.18 Optional methane analyzer with a range of 0 to 50 ppmC.

4.3 Analysis Instrumentation—Modal Analysis (Undiluted Exhaust Gas)

4.3.1 GENERAL—Figure 3 is a schematic drawing of the sampling and analysis train that is recommended for the modal analysis of spark ignition engine exhaust using the CVS. The system is very similar to that required for bag analysis, with the exception that water traps are required on all instrument sampling steams and an additional CO_2 analyzer is required. In addition, instruments of only approximately 1/10 the sensitivity of those used for bag analysis are needed. This system is based upon measuring continuously undiluted exhaust gas concentrations of HC, CO, NO_x, and CO_2 and the diluted exhaust CO_2 concentration.

The undiluted and diluted exhaust CO_2 concentrations are used to calculate a dilution factor which, in conjunction with the total diluted volume, can be used to calculate the vehicle exhaust volume. With the calculated exhaust volume and the undiluted exhaust concentrations, the modal mass emissions of each pollutant can be calculated as described in 6.2.2.

2. The criteria for CO interference by CO_2 and water is given in the Code of Federal Regulations (40 CFR 86.122): A CO instrument will be considered to be essentially free of CO_2 and water vapor interference if its response to a mixture of 3% CO_2 in N_2, which has been bubbled through water at room temperature (68 to 86 °F), produces an equivalent CO response, as measured on the most sensitive CO range, which is less than 1% of full scale CO concentration on instrument ranges above 300 ppm CO or less than 3 ppm on instrument ranges below 300 ppm CO.

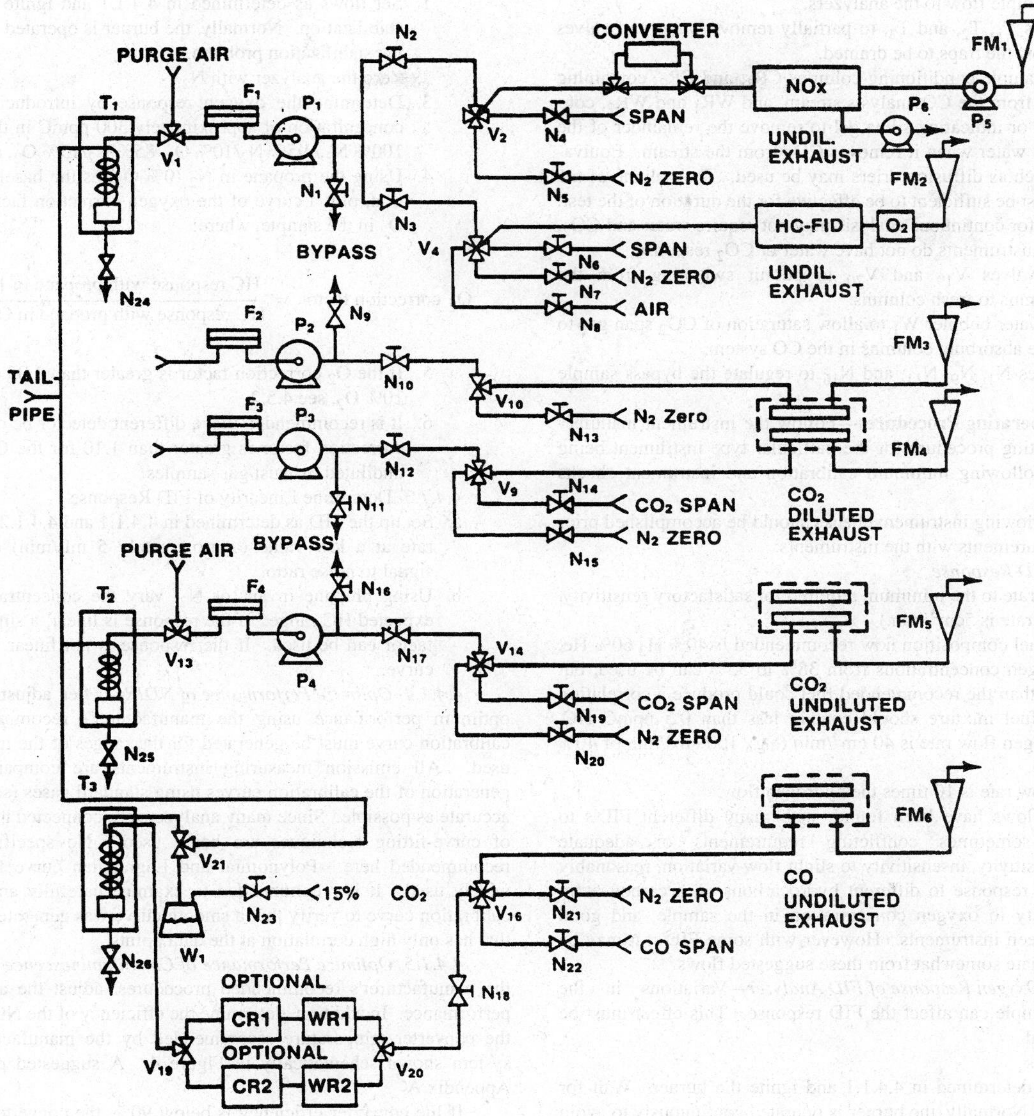

FIGURE 3—MODAL SAMPLING AND ANALYSIS TRAIN

4.3.2 COMPONENT DESCRIPTION—The following components are recommended for the analytical systems for the modal analysis of CO, HC, NO_x, CO_2, and O_2.

4.3.2.1 NDIR analyzers for measurement of CO and CO_2 with cells of appropriate length for the concentration ranges being measured. Typical ranges are shown in Table 1.

4.3.2.2 The CO_2 analyzer for the measurement of CO_2 in the diluted exhaust stream can be modified to the extent that the reference cell is replaced with a second sampling cell through which dilution air is passed during sampling. This feature will automatically correct the measured CO_2 in the diluted exhaust for the amount of CO_2 in the dilution air.

4.3.2.3 Chemiluminescent (CL) NO analyzer equipped with a bypass and a NO_2 to NO converter for the measurement of NO_x with the concentration range selection as shown in Table 1.

4.3.2.4 FID for measurement of HC. The instrument should be capable of measuring HC for the ranges shown in Table 1.

4.3.2.5 Oxygen analyzer for measurement of O_2 with range of measurement shown in Table 1.

4.3.2.6 Valves V_1 and V_{13} used to direct the sample of purge air to the analyzers or to purge air to the blowout traps.

4.3.2.7 Valves V_2, V_4, V_9, V_{10}, V_{14}, and V_{16}, used to direct the sample, zero gas, or span gas streams to the analyzers. Valve V_4, is used to direct the span gas to the O_2, sensor.

4.3.2.8 Filters F_1, F_2, F_3, and F_4, for removing the particulate from the sample prior to analysis. A glass fiber type of at least 7 cm in diameter is suitable.

4.3.2.9 Pumps P_1, P_2, P_3, and P_4, to move the sample through the system. Pump P_5, for bypass flow of the chemiluminescent analyzer and vacuum pump P_6 (optional dependent on design of chemiluminescent analyzer) for evacuation of the chemiluminescent reactor chamber. Pumps should have stainless steel or aluminum chambers with diaphragms and valves made from or covered with an inert material, such as Teflon. Free air capacity should be approximately 1.1 m^3/h (40 ft^3/h).

4.3.2.10 Needle valves N_2, N_3, N_{10}, N_{12}, N_{17}, and N_{18}, to regulate sample gas flow to the analyzers.

4.3.2.11 Needle valves N_4, N_6, N_{14}, N_{19}, and N_{22}, to regulate span gas flow to the analyzers.

4.3.2.12 Optional valve V_{21}, used to direct CO_2, span gas through the water bubbler for checking the performance of the absorbers in the CO analyzer stream. Needle valve N_{23}, (optional) is used to regulate CO_2, flow.

4.3.2.13 Needle Valves N_5, N_7, N_{13}, N_{15}, N_{20}, and N_{21}, to regulate zero gas flow to the analyzers.

4.3.2.14 Flow meters FM_1, FM_2, FM_3, FM_4, FM_5, and FM_6, to indicate span gas, zero gas, and sample flow to the analyzers.

4.3.2.15 Water traps T_1, T_2, and T_3, to partially remove water and valves N_{24}, N_{25}, and N_{26}, to allow the traps to be drained.

4.3.2.16 Optional sample conditioning columns CR_1, and CR_2, containing Ascarite to remove CO_2, from the CO analysis stream, and WR_1 and WR_2, containing indicating $CaSO_4$ or indicating silica gel to remove the remainder of the water. Ascarite produces water when it removes CO_2 from the stream. Equivalent drying techniques such as diffusion driers may be used. The volume of the conditioning columns must be sufficient to be effective for the duration of the test. Some operational ranges for continuous analysis may not require water and CO_2, removal. Some new CO instruments do not have water or CO_2 response.

4.3.2.17 Optional valves V_{19} and V_{20} to permit switching from the exhausted absorbing columns to fresh columns.

4.3.2.18 Optional water bubbler W_1 to allow saturation of CO_2 span gas to check the efficiency of the absorbing columns in the CO system.

4.3.2.19 Need valves N_1, N_9, N_{11}, and N_{16} to regulate the bypass sample flow.

4.4 Instrument Operating Procedures—Follow the instrument manufacturer's start-up and operating procedure for the particular type instrument being used. In addition, the following minimum calibration and instrument checks should be included.

4.4.1 INITIAL—The following instrument checks should be accomplished prior to making emission measurements with the instruments:

4.4.1.1 Optimize FID Response

a. Set sample flow rate to the minimum required for satisfactory sensitivity. (Suggested flow rate is $5 cm^3/min$.)
b. Present burner fuel composition now recommended is 40% H_2 60% He. However, hydrogen concentrations from 38% to 55% can be used, but the use of other than the recommended fuel could produce a correlation problem. The fuel mixture should contain less than 0.5 ppmC HC. Suggested hydrogen flow rate is 40 cm^3/min (e.g., 100 cm^3/min of 40% H_2/60% He fuel).
c. Suggested air flow rate is 10 times the hydrogen flow.
d. The suggested flows have been found, with many different FID's to reconcile the sometimes conflicting requirements of adequate hydrocarbon sensitivity, insensitivity to slight flow variation, reasonably uniform relative response to different hydrocarbons on a carbon atom basis, insensitivity to oxygen concentration in the sample, and good correlation between instruments. However with some FID's, it may be necessary to deviate somewhat from these suggested flows.

4.4.1.2 Determine Oxygen Response of FID Analyzer—Variations in the oxygen content of the sample can affect the FID response. This effect must be determined and minimized.

a. CVS bag analysis
   1. Set flows as determined in 4.4.1.1 and ignite the burner. Wait for stabilization. Normally, the burner is operated continuously to avoid the stabilization problem.
   2. Zero the analyzer on HC free air.
   3. Determine the oxygen response by introducing propane gas at a concentration of approximately 30 ppmC in the following diluents: 100% N_2, 95% N_2/5% O_2, 90% N_2/10% O_2, 85% N_2/15% O_2, and 100% air.
   4. Using the propane in the air gas as the baseline for no O_2 correction, plot a curve of the oxygen correction factor versus the percent O_2 in the sample:

$$O_2 \text{ correction factor } = 1.0 - \frac{(A - B)}{B} \quad \text{(Eq. 2)}$$

where:

A = HC response in N_2/O_2 blends
B = HC response in air

   5. Check the effect of O_2 using a propane concentration of 50 ppmC. If it is significantly different from the 30 ppmC correction data, establish a curve and apply the O_2 correction on a prorated basis as a function of HC concentration.
   6. If the O_2 correction factor is less than 0.96 over the normal O_2 range encountered in CVS sampling, see 4.5.2.
   7. It is recommended that a different detector be obtained if the oxygen correction factor is less than 0.90 for the O_2 range found in CVS samples.

b. Modal Analysis—Undiluted Exhaust Gas
   1. Set flows as determined in 4.4.1.1 and ignite the burner. Wait for stabilization. Normally, the burner is operated continuously to avoid the stabilization problem.
   2. Zero the analyzer with N_2.
   3. Determine the oxygen response by introducing propane gas at a concentration of approximately 300 ppmC in the following diluents: 100% N_2,/ 95% N_2/10% O_2, 85% N_2/15% O_2, and 100% air.
   4. Using the propane in N_2 (0% O_2) as the baseline for no O_2 correction, plot a curve of the oxygen correction factor versus the percent O_2 in the sample, where:

$$O_2 \text{ correction factor } = \frac{\text{HC response with propane in 100\% } N_2}{\text{HC response with propane in } O_2 \text{blends}} \quad \text{(Eq. 3)}$$

   5. If the O_2 correction factor is greater than 1.05 over the range of 0 to 10% O_2, see 4.5.2.
   6. It is recommended that a different detector be obtained if the oxygen correction factor is greater than 1.10 for the O_2 range found in the undiluted exhaust gas samples.

4.4.1.3 Determine Linearity of FID Response

a. Set up the FID as determined in 4.4.1.1 and 4.4.1.2. Set the sample flow rate at a low value (approximately 5 mL/min) consistent with good signal to noise ratio.
b. Using propane in air, or N_2, vary the concentration of HC over the expected HC range. If the response is linear, a simple linear calibration factor can be used. If the response is not linear, prepare a calibration curve.

4.4.1.4 Optimize Performance of NDIR—After adjusting the analyzers for optimum performance using the manufacturer's recommended procedures, a calibration curve must be generated for the ranges of the instrument that will be used. All emission measuring instruments are comparative devices. The generation of the calibration curves using standard gases (see 4.5.1) should be as accurate as possible. Since many analyzers are connected to computers, a variety of curve-fitting techniques are being used. No specific technique will be recommended here. Polynomial and Lagrangian curve fitting techniques are widely used. It is recommended to examine carefully an accurate plot of the calibration curve to verify that a smooth curve was generated, rather than a curve that has only high correlation at the data points.

4.4.1.5 Optimize Performance of Chemiluminescence NO Analyzer—Using the manufacturer's recommended procedures, adjust the analyzer for optimum performance. In addition, determine the efficiency of the NO_2 to NO converter, at the converter temperature recommended by the manufacturer, using the flow system shown schematically in Figure 4. A suggested procedure is given in Appendix A.

If the converter efficiency is below 90%, the converter temperature should be increased and the efficiency rechecked. Converter temperature should be set at a minimum required for near 100% conversion efficiency.

Care must be used to prevent condensation due to pressure buildup in the NO_x sample train between the sample pump and the analyzer. This has been found to be a critical area of the NO_x sample train, since condensation causes a lowering of the measured NO_x concentration and, therefore, an incorrect NO_x emission measurement.

4.4.2 MONTHLY—The following checks are to be made monthly or more frequently if there is any doubt regarding the accuracy of the analyses.

4.4.2.1 Calibrate the NDIR analyzers using the same gas flow rates as when sampling exhaust.

a. Allow 2 h warmup of analyzers.
b. Tune analyzer.
c. Set zero and span using prepurified N_2 and the 100% range calibration gas.
d. Recheck zero and repeat step 4.4.21(c), if necessary.
e. Calibrate each analyzer with calibrating gases that are approximately 15, 30, 45, 60, 75, and 90% of each range used. The concentration of the standard gases should be known with at least ±2% accuracy. If the analyzer proves to be nonlinear, use an eight point calibration with a set of calibration gases spread approximately uniformly over the analyzer range in question.
f. Compare values with previous curves. Any significant change reflects some problem in the system. Locate and correct the problem and recalibrate.

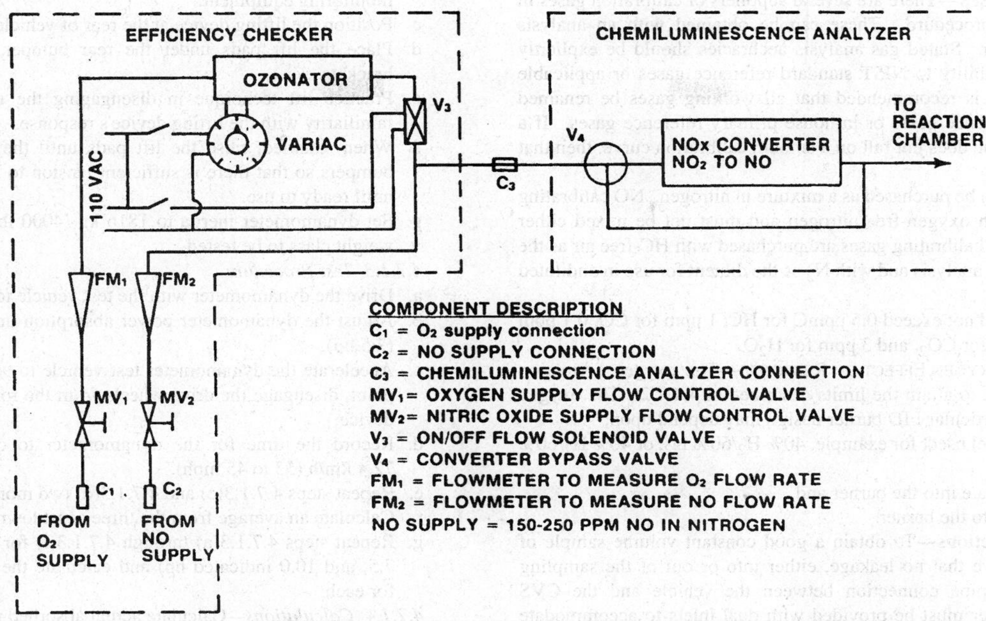

FIGURE 4—FLOW SCHEMATIC OF CONVERTER EFFICIENCY ANALYSIS SYSTEM

4.4.2.2 Check FID analyzer O_2 response and HC response.

a. Ignite the burner and then set the fuel, air, and sample flow rates as determined in 4.4.1.1 and 4.4.1.2.
b. Introduce HC free air zero gas (CVS bag analysis) or N_2 (Modal-undiluted exhaust gas analysis) and zero analyzer.
c. Check O_2 effect on the response by introducing the calibration gases of propane in air, propane in N_2, and propane in 90% N_2/10% O_2.
d. Compare the O_2 response values with the previous curves. Any significant change (±10%) indicates a change in the burner operating characteristics. Check the burner system and measure the flows. If the change in the response cannot be resolved, establish a new O_2 response curve as per 4.4.1.2.
e. Check the calibration curve or response data as per 4.4.1.3.

4.4.2.3 Calibrate chemiluminescent analyzer using same flow rates as when sampling exhaust.

a. Set the sample flow and oxygen flow to the recommended settings.
b. Turn the ozone generator on and allow a 10 min warmup period.
c. Using nitrogen, zero the meter on the most sensitive range or the range to be used by means of the dark current suppression adjustment.
d. Set the span, using 100% range calibration gas on the range to be used.
e. Calibrate the analyzer with gases blended in N_2 that are approximately 25, 50, 75, and 100% of the range being used.
f. Check the values with the previous curves. Any significant change reflects some problem in the system. Locate and correct the problem and recalibrate.
g. Caution. The correct standby position for the NO_x converter is dependent on the converter type. See manufacturer's instructions.
h. Caution. Some NO_2 to NO converters can be rendered useless for many hours if they are allowed to sample rich exhaust gas (even momentarily) where high levels of CO, low levels of O_2, and free H_2 are present.

4.4.3 WEEKLY—Check the converter of the chemiluminescent analyzer using the procedure outlined in 4.4.1.5.

4.4.4 DAILY—Prior to daily testing carry out the following:

4.4.4.1 NDIR Analyzers—Normally, power is left on the NDIR analyzers continuously. Only the chopper motors are turned off. In some cases, more dependable performance has been achieved by leaving the chopper motors on.

a. Zero on prepurified N_2.
b. Introduce span gas and set the gain to match the calibration curves. Use the same flow rate for calibration, span gas, and exhaust gas to avoid correction for the sample cell pressure change. Use span gas having a concentration of the constituent being measured that will result in 75 to 95% of full-scale deflection. If the gain has shifted significantly, check the tuning: if necessary, check the calibration.
c. Check nitrogen zero and repeat steps 4.4.4.1(a) and 4.4.4.1(b), if necessary.
d. Repeat steps 4.4.4.1(a) through 4.4.4.1(c) prior to each exhaust gas analysis.
e. Span and zero should be rechecked after bag measurements.

4.4.4.2 FID Analyzer

a. Ignite the burner and then set the fuel, air, and sample flow rates as determined in 4.4.1.1 and 4.4.1.2.
b. Introduce zero gas (HC-free air for CVS analyzers, N_2 for undiluted exhaust gas analyzers) and zero analyzer.
c. Introduce HC span gas (propane in HC-free air for CVS analyzers, propane in N_2 for undiluted exhaust gas analyzers) of appropriate concentration to result in a response of at least 50% of full-scale on the range anticipated for use. If the calibration curve and span value disagree adjust the span potentiometer of the FID. Sample flow for zero and span must be the same as that used for analyzing exhaust sample.
d. Repeat steps 4.4.4.2(a) through 4.4.4.3(c) prior to each exhaust gas analysis.
e. Span and zero should be rechecked after bag measurements.

4.4.4.3 Chemiluminescent Analyzer—Normally power is left on continuously. Operate converter in standby mode as recommended by the manufacturer. Vacuum pumps are normally kept on continuously on those model analyzers using vacuum pumps. The ozonator should not be left on continuously for safety reasons. Vacuum pump and ozone problems can be minimized by replacing the pump oil with perfluorinated polyether fluid.

a. Turn on the sample pumps.
b. Set O_2 (in some models air is used) and sample flows using nitrogen.
c. Turn on ozone generator and allow a 10 min warmup.
d. With the converter in the NO mode, adjust the dark current suppression to zero the meter on the most sensitive range or the range to be used, using prepurified N_2.
e. Introduce span gas and set gain to match the calibration curves. Use a span gas having an NO concentration that will result in 75 to 95% of full-scale deflection.
f. Check dark current suppression and repeat steps 4.4.4.3(d) and 4.4.4.3(e) if necessary.
g. Span and zero should be rechecked after bag measurements.

4.4.4.4 Oxygen Analyzer

a. Introduce oxygen-free nitrogen and set zero.
b. Introduce air and set O_2 span. This is usually done concurrently when setting the zero on the FID analyzer.
c. Sample flow for zero and span must be the same as that used when analyzing exhaust gas samples.

4.5 Supplementary Discussion

4.5.1 CALIBRATION GASES—There are several suppliers of calibration gases in the ranges used in this procedure. These can be obtained with an analysis accuracy of ±2% or better. Stated gas analysis accuracies should be explicitly defined in terms of traceability to NIST standard reference gases or applicable gravimetric standards. It is recommended that all working gases be renamed using NIST standard reference gases or in-house primary reference gases. If a reference gas cylinder value does not fall on a smooth calibration curve, then that cylinder must not be used.

The CO and CO_2 gas can be purchased as a mixture in nitrogen. NO calibrating gas should be diluted with oxygen-free nitrogen and must not be mixed either with CO or CO_2. Propane calibrating gases are purchased with HC-free air as the diluent for use in CVS bag analysis and with N_2 as the diluent for use in undiluted exhaust gas analysis.

Zero gas impurity should not exceed 0.5 ppmC for HC, 1 ppm for CO, 0.1 ppm for NO, 400 ppm (0.04%) for CO_2, and 3 ppm for H_2O.

4.5.2 REDUCING THE OXYGEN EFFECT ON RESPONSE—The oxygen correction for FID should be reduced to attain the limits described in 4.4.1.2. The oxygen effect on response for a particular FID burner design may depend upon:

a. The type of burner fuel used, for example, 40% H_2/60% N_2, or 40% H_2/60% He
b. On the sample flow rate into the burner and
c. The air and fuel rate to the burner.

4.6 Tailpipe Connections—To obtain a good constant volume sample of exhaust gas it is imperative that no leakage, either into or out of the sampling system, occur at the tailpipe connection between the vehicle and the CVS sampler. The CVS sampler must be provided with dual inlets to accommodate vehicles with dual exhaust systems. When a vehicle with a single exhaust is being tested, the second sampler inlet must be tightly capped to prevent leakage.

Piping between the sampler and the vehicle should be kept to a minimum length and be of adequate diameter. (See Section 5 for more detail on this subject.) The actual connection between the vehicle tailpipe and the flexible tubing of the CVS can be made in one of two ways:

a. A flanged fitting such as a Marmon coupling. One end of this coupling is welded to the flexible piping from the CVS and a mating section is welded to the exhaust pipe(s) of each vehicle to be tested.
b. A silicone rubber boot clamped to the exhaust pipe and inlet plumbing to the CVS.

The first method, a flanged fitting, should be used whenever possible. However, when fittings cannot be welded to each vehicle to be tested, the silicon boot alternative has to be used. The main drawback of the silicone boot is that the hot exhaust gas causes rapid deterioration of the silicone. When vehicles with advanced control devices are tested, the very hot exhaust gases produced by these systems may cause the boot to crack internally after a single test.

4.7 Chassis Dynamometer

4.7.1 PROCEDURE FOR DYNAMOMETER ABSORBED POWER CALIBRATION—The following procedure describes one method for determining the absorbed power of a chassis dynamometer. The measured absorbed power includes dynamometer frictional power as well as the power absorbed by the power absorption unit. The dynamometer is driven above the test speed range to 96 km/h (60 mph). The device used to drive the dynamometer (in most cases a vehicle) is then disengaged from the dynamometer and the roll(s) allowed to coast down. The kinetic energy of the system is dissipated by the dynamometer friction and absorption unit. This method neglects the variations in roll bearing friction due to the drive axle weight of the vehicle and also neglects the variations in friction due to different inertia weights. The difference in coastdown time of the free (rear) roll relative to the drive (front) roll may be neglected in the case of dynamometers with paired rolls.

4.7.1.1 Equipment

a. Fifth wheel, tachometer generator, or other device to measure the speed of the front roll.
b. Hydraulic jack or other equipment to lift vehicle's drive wheels from the rolls.
c. Timing device to measure the time it takes the rolls speed to decrease from 88.5 to 72.4 km/h (55 to 45 mph) with 0.01 s accuracy.
d. Pair of chocks, vehicle tie-downs, and other safety devices used to assure safe operation of a vehicle on the rolls.

4.7.1.2 Preparation

a. Place the vehicle on the dynamometer rolls and set chocks against the front wheels. Tie-downs should be slack enough to allow the vehicle to be lifted from the rolls.
b. Verify the calibration of the fifth wheel, tach generator, or other speed monitoring equipment.
c. Position the lifting device at the rear of vehicle.
d. Place the lift pads under the rear bumper, adjacent to the bumper brackets.
e. Practice lift technique in disengaging the rear wheels to develop a familiarity with the lifting device's response.
f. When satisfied, raise the lift pads until they are in contact with the bumpers so that there is sufficient tension to keep the lift pads in place until ready to use.
g. Set dynamometer inertia to 1816 kg (4000 lb) or to the more common weight class to be tested.

4.7.1.3 Test Procedure

a. Drive the dynamometer with the test vehicle to 80.5 km/h (50 mph).
b. Adjust the dynamometer power absorption unit to an indicated 1.9 kW (2.5 hp).
c. Accelerate the dynamometer test vehicle to 96 km/h (60 mph). At this point, disengage the drive wheels from the rolls by means of the lifting device.
d. Record the time for the dynamometer to coast down from 88.5 to 72.4 km/h (55 to 45 mph).
e. Repeat steps 4.7.1.3(c) and 4.7.1.3(d) two more times.
f. Calculate an average from the three coastdown times.
g. Repeat steps 4.7.1.3(a) through 4.7.1.3(f) for 3.7, 5.6, and 7.4kW (5.0, 7.5, and 10.0 indicated hp) and calculate the average coastdown times for each.

4.7.1.4 Calculations—Calculate actual absorbed road horsepower from:

$$HP_{act} = \frac{1}{2}\,\frac{W_1}{32.2}\,\frac{(V_1^2 - V_2^2)}{550t} = \frac{0.06073\ W_1}{t} \qquad \text{(Eq. 4)}$$

Where:

W_i = equivalent inertia, lb
V_1 = initial velocity, ft/s (55 mph — 80.67 ft/s)
V_2 = final velocity, ft/s (45 mph — 66.00 ft/s)
t = elapsed time for rolls to coast down from 55 to 45 mph (88 to 72 km/h)

4.7.1.5 Belt Drive Dynamometers—The procedure outlined previously has been applied extensively to belt drive dynamometers. The next step is to plot the indicated road load power at 80 km/h (50 mph) versus the actual road power at 80 km/h (50 mph). See Figure 5.

The Federal Register advises running coastdowns at the inertia weight most frequently used. Common practice is to run coastdowns at either all inertia weight settings of a dynamometer or at least all inertia weights that are used for testing.

4.7.1.6 Direct-Drive Dynamometers—The same procedure can be used for direct-drive dynamometers as for belt drive dynamometers and should be used for manual loading calibration of these units. However, automatic loading features of the new direct-drive dynamometers can improve the coastdown procedure.

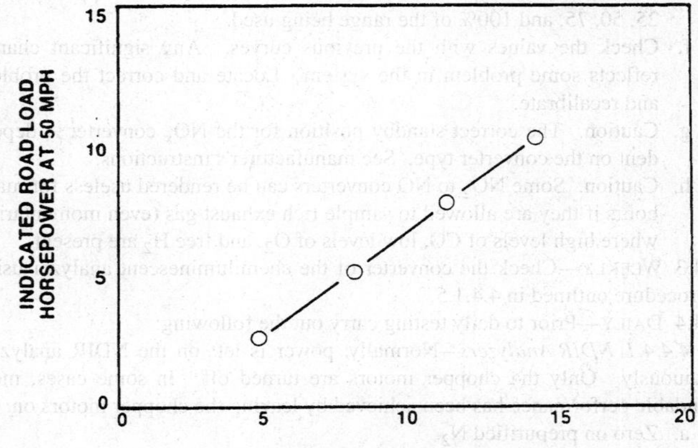

FIGURE 5—DYNAMOMETER CALIBRATION CURVE

The direct-drive dynamometer procedure sets up the dynamometer for operation at the desired operating points rather than finding a linear range for each inertia weight. This procedure is rapid and reproducible in both running coastdowns and in operation. It is recommended that a plot of frictional horsepower versus inertia weight be made for each set of coastdown data. These plots can aid in determination that the coastdown data is valid.

In Figure 6, the frictional power is plotted as a function of inertia weight for nine automatic loading direct-drive dynamometers. The data show that the frictional powers are confined to an approximate 745 kW (1 hp) band. On these plots, the "over 5500" values are plotted at 6000 for convenience.

An example of the effect of recalibration is shown in the frictional power versus inertia weight plot in Figure 7. A dynamometer recalibration indicated a shift of over 0.3 kW (0.5 hp) friction. A recalibration showed that a speed calibration error had been made. After correction, a typical shift of less than 0.3 kW (0.5 hp) was observed.

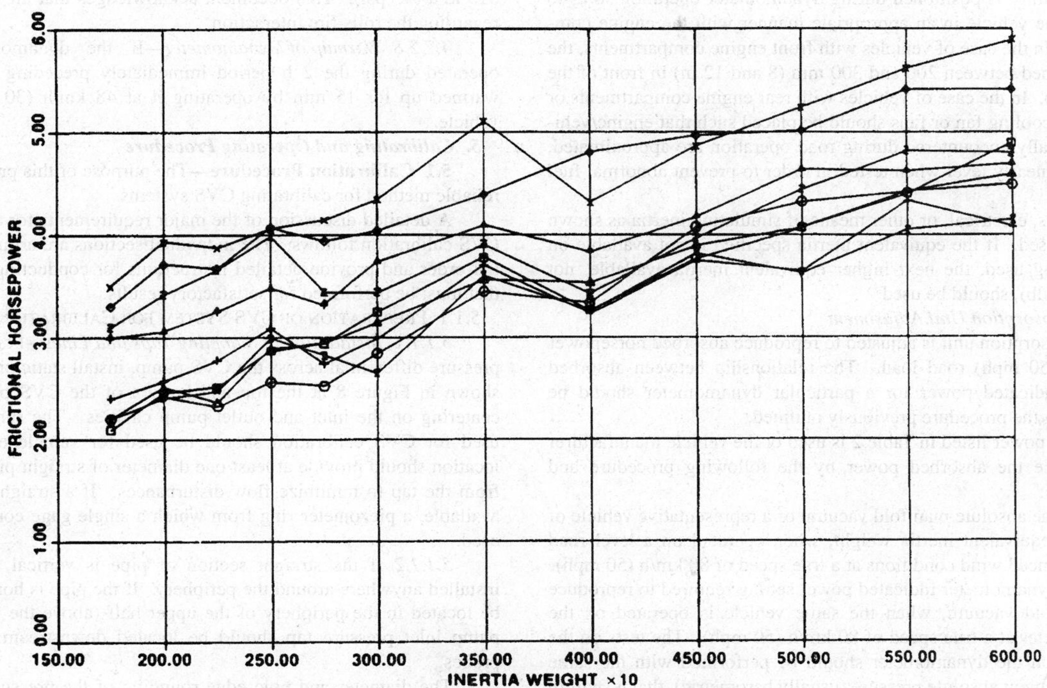

FIGURE 6—TYPICAL FRICTIONAL HORSEPOWERS

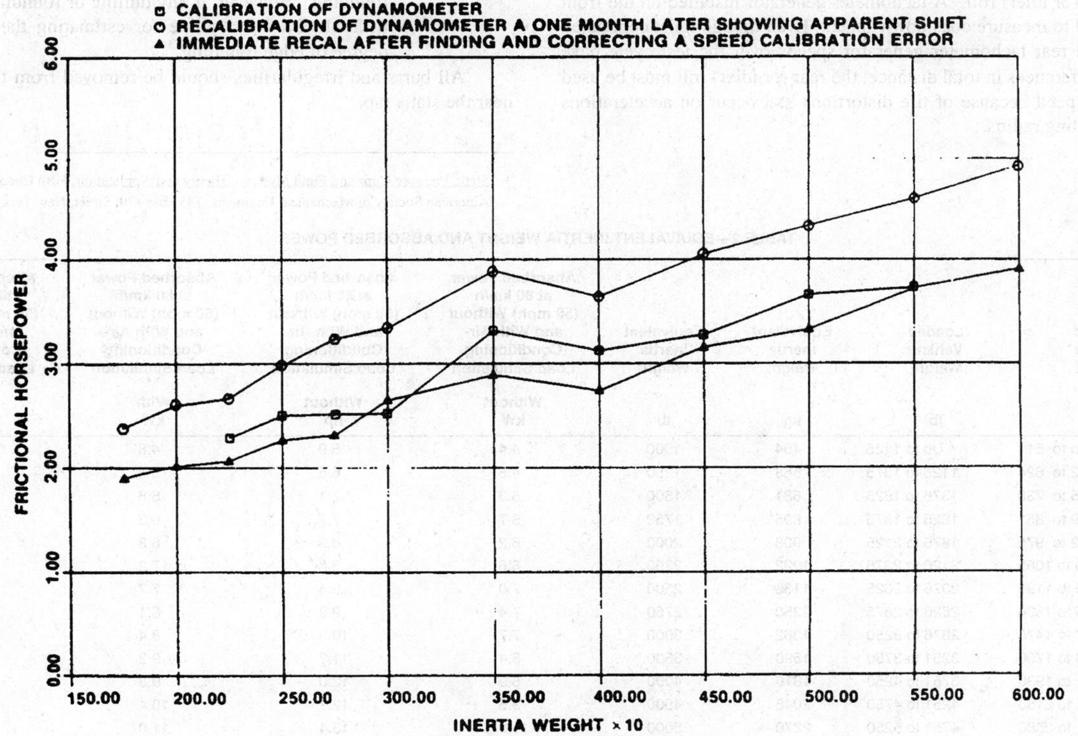

FIGURE 7—EFFECT OF RECALIBRATION

4.7.2 DYNAMOMETER PROCEDURE

4.7.2.1 The vehicle shall be tested from a cold start. Engine startup and operation over the driving schedule make a complete test run. Exhaust emissions are diluted with air to a constant volume and a portion is sampled continuously during each of the three test phases. The composite samples, collected in three bags, are analyzed for HC, CO, NO_x, and CO_2. Three parallel samples of dilution air are similarly analyzed. CO_2 is measured because it is needed in determining the carbon balance fuel economy.

4.7.2.2 A fixed-speed cooling fan with a nominal capacity not to exceed 150 m^3/min (5300 ft^3/min) is positioned during dynamometer operation so as to direct cooling air to the vehicle in an appropriate manner with the engine compartment cover open. In the case of vehicles with front engine compartments, the fan is squarely positioned between 200 and 300 mm (8 and 12 in) in front of the cooling air inlets (grill). In the case of vehicles with rear engine compartments or if special designs, the cooling fan or fans should be placed such that engine/vehicle temperatures normally encountered during road operation are approximated. The vehicle should be nearly level when tested in order to prevent abnormal fuel distribution.

4.7.2.3 Flywheels, electrical, or other means of simulating inertia as shown in Table 2 should be used. If the equivalent inertia specified is not available on the dynamometer being used, the next higher equivalent inertia available, not exceeding 113 kg (250 lb), should be used.

4.7.2.4 Power Absorption Unit Adjustment

a. The power absorption unit is adjusted to reproduce absorbed horsepower at 80 km/h (50 mph) road load. The relationship between absorbed power and indicated power for a particular dynamometer should be determined by the procedure previously outlined.
b. The absorbed power listed in Table 2 is used or the vehicle manufacturer may determine the absorbed power by the following procedure and request its use:
   1. Measure the absolute manifold vacuum of a representative vehicle of the same equivalent inertia weight, when operated on a level road under balanced wind conditions at a true speed of 80 km/h (50 mph).
   2. Note the dynamometer indicated power setting required to reproduce the manifold vacuum, when the same vehicle is operated on the dynamometer at a true speed of 80 km/h (50 mph). The tests on the road and on the dynamometer should be performed with the same vehicle ambient absolute pressure (usually barometric), that is, within ±5 mm of Hg.
   3. The absorbed power values are listed in Table 2.

4.7.2.5 The vehicle speed must be measured by a tachometer generator installed on the rear (or idler) roll. A tachometer generator installed on the front (or drive) roll is used to measure coastdown speed. Even though most conducted integrating front and rear tachometer generator speeds over the test cycle have shown only small differences in total distance, the rear (or idler) roll must be used to measure vehicle speed because of tire distortions that occur on accelerations which change the rolling radius.

4.7.2.6 The Federal Register recommends that minimum throttle action should be used to maintain the proper speed-time relationship. When using a two-roll dynamometer, a truer speed-time trace may be obtained by minimizing the rocking of the vehicle in the rolls. The rocking of the vehicle changes the tire rolling radius on each roll. The rocking may be minimized by restraining the vehicle horizontally (or nearly so) by using a cable and winch. Care must be used to prevent tightening this cable too much as this could cause vehicle to be pulled off rolls.

4.7.2.7 Drive wheel tires must be inflated to a cold gage pressure of 310 kPa (45 psi). This document acknowledges that all is not fully understood regarding the rolls-tire interaction.

4.7.2.8 Warmup of Dynamometer—If the dynamometer has not been operated during the 2 h period immediately preceding the test, it should be warmed up for 15 min by operating it at 48 km/h (30 mph) using a nontest vehicle.

5. Calibrating and Operating Procedure

5.1 Calibration Procedure—The purpose of this procedure is to provide a reliable method for calibrating CVS systems.

A detailed discussion of the major requirements for conducting an accurate CVS calibration follows. The individual sections are arranged in proper sequential order and provide detailed instructions for conducting the necessary checks that must be performed for satisfactory results.

5.1.1 PREPARATION OF CVS SYSTEM FOR CALIBRATION

5.1.1.1 Installation of Sampling Taps and Lines—For measurement of the pressure differential across the CVS pump, install static pressure taps of the type shown in Figure 8 at the top and bottom of the CVS pump drive head plate, centering on the inlet and outlet pump cavities. The same static pressure taps used for CVS calibration should be used for vehicle emission testing. The location should provide at least one diameter of straight pipe up and downstream from the tap to minimize flow disturbances. If a straight length of pipe is not available, a piezometer ring from which a single gage connection is led may be used.

5.1.1.2 If the straight section of pipe is vertical, the static tap can be installed anywhere around the periphery. If the pipe is horizontal, the tap should be located in the periphery of the upper half (above the pipe center-line). The pump inlet pressure tap should be located downstream from the gas sample probes.

The diameter and hole edge rounding of the pressure tap should conform with the recommendations shown in Table 3.

NOTE—It is realized that it will seldom be practical and, generally, it will be impossible actually to measure the radius of the hole-edge rounding. However, if any dulling or rounding is done, the values in Table 3 offer a guide for estimating the maximum desirable degree of edge rounding.[3]

All burrs and irregularities should be removed from the inner wall surface near the static tap.

3. Static Pressure Cups and Fluid Meters—Theory and Application, Fifth Chapter, Section A3, pp. 18–19. American Society of Mechanical Engineers, 345 East 47th Street, New York, New York 10017.

TABLE 2—EQUIVALENT INERTIA WEIGHT AND ABSORBED POWER

Loaded Vehicle Weight kg	Loaded Vehicle Weight lb	Equivalent Inertia Weight kg	Equivalent Inertia Weight lb	Absorbed Power at 80 km/h (50 mph) Without and With Air-Conditioning Load Simulation Without kW	Absorbed Power at 80 km/h (50 mph) Without and With Air-Conditioning Load Simulation Without hp	Absorbed Power at 80 km/h (50 mph) Without and With Air-Conditioning Load Simulation With kW	Absorbed Power at 80 km/h (50 mph) Without and With Air-Conditioning Load Simulation With hp
Up to 511	Up to 1125	454	1000	4.4	5.9	4.8	6.5
512 to 624	1126 to 1375	568	1250	4.8	6.5	5.4	7.2
625 to 738	1376 to 1625	681	1500	5.3	7.1	5.8	7.8
739 to 851	1626 to 1875	895	1750	5.7	7.7	6.3	8.5
852 to 975	1876 to 2125	908	2000	6.2	8.3	6.8	9.1
976 to 1085	2126 to 2375	1022	2250	6.6	8.8	7.2	9.7
1086 to 1195	2376 to 2625	1135	2500	7.0	9.4	7.7	10.3
1196 to 1306	2626 to 2875	1250	2750	7.4	9.9	8.1	10.9
1307 to 1475	2876 to 3250	1362	3000	7.7	10.3	8.4	11.3
1476 to 1700	3251 to 3750	1590	3500	8.4	11.2	9.2	12.3
1701 to 1930	3751 to 4250	1816	4000	8.9	12.0	9.8	13.2
1931 to 2150	4251 to 4750	2045	4500	9.5	12.7	10.4	14.0
2151 to 2380	4751 to 5250	2270	5000	10.0	13.4	11.0	14.7
2381 to 2610	5251 to 5750	2500	5500	10.4	13.9	11.4	15.3
2611 or more	5751 or more	2500	5500	10.7	14.4	11.8	15.8

5.1.1.3 The sample probes should be made of stainless steel and be the design haown in Figure 8. They should be faced upstream directly into the flow. All sample lines leading from the probes should be routed upward. This will allow any water which may condense to drain out of the line and thereby prevent hydraulic blockage. (Similar precautions should be taken when installing static pressure lines).

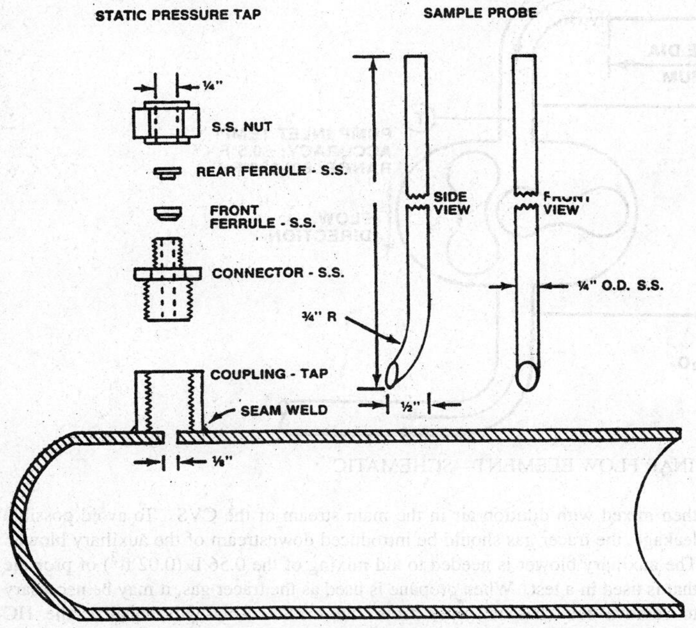

FIGURE 8—STATIC PRESSURE TAP FITTINGS AND PROBE DESIGN

5.1.2 FLANGE GASKETS—When installing the plumbing on the inlet side of the pump, compression of the gasket may cause a decrease in its inside diameter. If this occurs, it will affect the restriction on the pump and may affect the accuracy of the static pressure reading if the gasket protrusion is upstream of the static tap. Therefore, when assembling the plumbing insure that the gasket ID as installed is not smaller than the pipe ID.

The placement of modal analysis probes relative to the bag sample probe can also disrupt sampling. It has been shown that the backflushing of a modal analysis cart through a probe can significantly affect the bag sampling probe sample during a CVS calibration verification with propane injection.

TABLE 3—PRESSURE TAP HOURS

Nominal Inside Pipe Diameter cm	Nominal Inside Pipe Diameter in	Pressure Hole Diameter mm	Pressure Hole Diameter in	Hole-Edge Radius mm	Hole-Edge Radius in
Under 5	Under 2	6.4 ± 3.2	1/4 ± 1/8	About 0.4	About 1/64
5 to 7.5	2 to 3	9.5 ± 3.2	3/8 ± 1/8	Less 0.8	Less 1/32
10 to 20	4 to 8	12.7 – 3.2 + 6.4	1/2 – 1/8 + 1/4	Less 0.8	Less 1/32
25 +	10 +	19.0 + 6.4	3/4 + 1/4	Less 1.6	Less 1/16

5.1.3 PRIMARY CVS CALIBRATION WITH LAMINAR FLOW ELEMENT

5.1.3.1 This procedure utilizes a laminar flow element and a variable restriction device to generate a pump performance curve (flow rate as a function of pressure differential). Figure 9 is a schematic of the test layout and instruments required to perform this calibration. The volumetric flow is determined by a laminar flow element (LFE) placed upstream of the CVS pump (as shown in Figure 9) to avoid introducing flow disturbances in the LFE. A straightener section of 10 times the exit diameter is added to the outlet of the LFE. This is followed by an adjustable restriction valve. Since the LFE and the pump are in series, it is necessary that all connections between these two items be free of leakage. It is advisable to plug all openings and pressure test the system to insure that the system is free of leaks.

Some LFE have straightener sections built into the device. This obviates the use of a straightener section. However, these LFEs are subject to calibration shifts if they are disassembled for cleaning. If these units are cleaned, they should be recalibrated.

When conducting calibration, the restriction device should be used to generate data points above and below the normal CVS system operating pressure. Data should be obtained beginning with the pump inlet depression corresponding to LFE as the only restriction. Pump inlet depression should be increased by increments of 500 to 1250 Pa (2 to 5 in H_2O) until 6 to 8 data points are determined. Usually, it is difficult to get points below the normal CVS system operating pressure unless the heat exchanger is removed from the system. Most calibrations are done with the heat exchanger in the system.

The following listing of the data to be recorded, unit conversions, and calculations will be followed by a sample calculation and a computer print-out.

5.1.3.2 Data Recorded

a. LFE inlet depression, = Pa (in H_2O)
b. Delta P LFE, Pa (in H_2O)
c. LFE inlet temperature, °C (°F)
d. Pump inlet depression, Pa (in H_2O)
e. Pump inlet temperature, °C (°F)
f. Delta P pump, Pa (in H_2O)
g. Barometric pressure, Pa (in Hg)
h. Pump rpm. A pump revolutions counter should be used and elapsed test time should be measured.

5.1.3.3 Conversion of Units

a. Convert in H_2O to in Hg pressure:

$$\text{LFE inlet depression (in Hg)} = \text{LFE inlet depression (in } H_2O) \times 0.07355 \text{ in Hg/in } H_2O \quad \text{(Eq. 5)}$$
$$\text{Pump inlet depression (in Hg)} = \text{Pump inlet depression (in } H_2O) \times 0.07355 \text{ in Hg/in } H_2O$$

b. Convert from degrees Fahrenheit to degrees Rankine:

$$\text{LFE inlet temperature (R)} = \text{LFE inlet temperature } (°F) + 460 \quad \text{(Eq. 6)}$$
$$\text{Pump inlet temperature (R)} = \text{pump inlet temperature } (°F) + 460$$

c. Conversion to absolute pressure:

$$\text{Absolute pressure (in Hg) at LFE inlet} = \text{barometric pressure (in Hg)} - \text{LFE inlet depression (in Hg)} \quad \text{(Eq. 7)}$$
$$\text{Absolute pressure (in Hg) at pump inlet} = \text{barometric pressure (in Hg)} - \text{pump inlet depression (in Hg)}$$

5.1.3.4 Calculations

a. Determine air viscosity correction factor for LFE inlet air temperature from LFE correction curve obtained from LFE manufacturer.
b. Determine pressure correction factor for LFE inlet pressure from LFE correction table obtained from LFE manufacturer.
c. Determine uncorrected volume flow rate from curve supplied by LFE manufacturer and pressure drop. Then determine corrected volume flow rate by multiplying uncorrected volume flow rate × air viscosity correction factor × pressure correction factor.
d. Using Ideal Gas Law, convert the volume flow rate at LFE standard conditions (530 R, 29.92 in Hg) to the volume flow rate at the pump inlet temperature and pressure:

$$\text{pump ft}^3/\text{min} = \text{LFE ft}^3/\text{min} \times \frac{29.92}{\text{pump abs inlet pressure (in Hg)}} \times \frac{\text{Pump inlet temperature (R)}}{530} \quad \text{(Eq. 8)}$$

e. Determine pump ft^3/rev by dividing ft^3/min by the pump rpm.
f. Plot pump ft^3/rev versus the square root of pump delta P. Determine the first degree equation of the line by the least squares method.

5.1.3.5 Example of Calculations for LFE CVS calibration, using typical data from a 400 ft^3/min LFE.

5.1.3.5.1 Data Recorded

a. LFE inlet depression = 1.00 in H_2O
b. Delta P of LFE = 6.520 in H_2O
c. LFE inlet temperature = 75.5 °F
d. Pump inlet depression = 37.8 in H_2O
e. Pump inlet temperature = 78.0 °F
f. Delta P pump = 60.0 in H_2O
g. Barometric pressure = 29.34 in Hg
h. Pump rpm = 1421

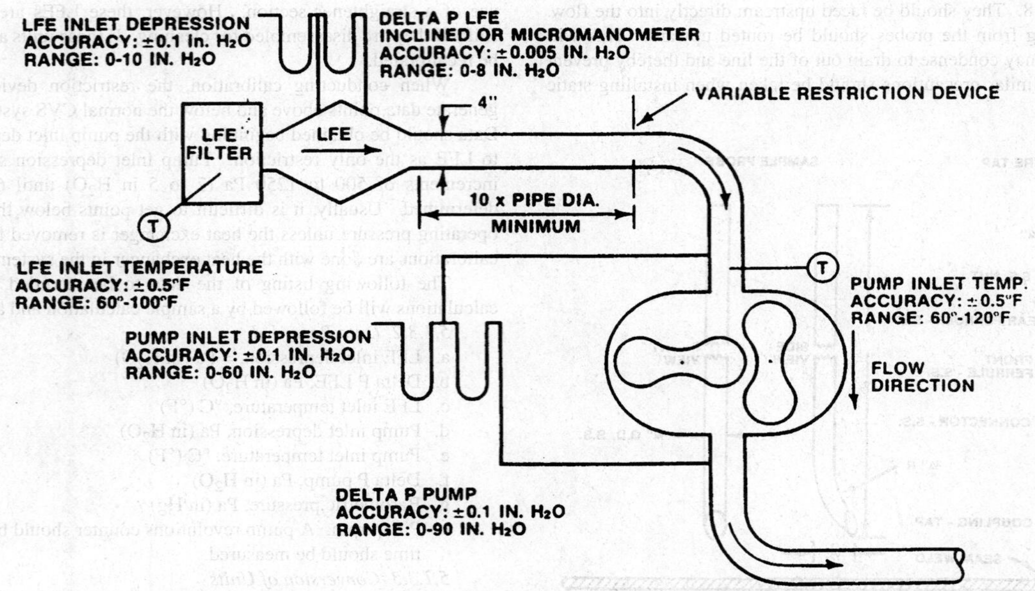

FIGURE 9—CVS CALIBRATION WITH LAMINAR FLOW ELEMENT—SCHEMATIC

5.1.3.5.2 Conversion of Units

a. LFE inlet depression = 0.07355 in Hg
b. Pump inlet depression = 2.78 in Hg
c. LFE inlet temperature = 535.5 R
d. Pump inlet temperature = 538 R
e. LFE inlet, absolute pressure = 29.27 in Hg
f. Pump inlet, absolute pressure = 26.56 in Hg

5.1.3.5.3 Calculations

a. Air viscosity correction factor at 75.5 °F (from LFE manufacturer's curve) = 1.006.
b.
$$\text{Pressure correction factor} = \frac{29.27}{29.92} = 0.9783 \quad \text{(Eq. 9)}$$
c. Uncorrected flow rate (from LFE manufacturer's curve) = 342.8 ft^3/min.
d. Corrected volume flow rate = 342.8 × 1.006 × 0.9783 = 337.4.
e.
$$\text{Pump ft}^3/\text{min} = 337.4 \times \frac{29.92}{26.56} \times \frac{538}{530} = 385.8 \quad \text{(Eq. 10)}$$
f.
$$\text{Pump ft}^3/\text{rev} = \frac{385.8}{1421} = 0.2715 \quad \text{(Eq. 11)}$$

5.1.4 Gas Stratification Check

5.1.4.1 With the CVS operating in its testing configuration, introduce a tracer gas, such as 100% propane, into the vehicle exhaust inlet of the CVS system as shown in Figure 10. The tracer gas should be introduced at a rate that will give a bag sample which produces at least a 3/4 full-scale deflection on the HC range normally used for reading bags. The use of a continuous HC analyzer on the dilute continuous sampling probe makes this rate determination simple. The continuous analyzer is needed for the profile determination of 5.1.4.2.

5.1.4.2 Starting with the sample probe inlet opening at one side of the dilute stream, run a cross-sectional profile of the pipe, sampling at 13 mm (0.5 in) intervals (wall to wall). Record the concentration at each sampling point location. Conduct a second cross-sectional profile at 90 degrees to the first profile. If concentrations from wall to wall vary more than 1%, there is incomplete mixing.

5.1.5 Independent CVS System Verification

5.1.5.1 Introduction—The system verification technique involves the introduction of a measured quantity of a tracer such as propane (or CO) at the tailpipe sampling location. If all components of the system are functioning properly, the quantity of tracer calculated from that collected in the sample bag should agree closely with the quantity which was injected. A measured amount of tracer gas partially diluted with air from a small auxiliary blower (Figure 11) is then mixed with dilution air in the main stream of the CVS. To avoid possible leakage, the tracer gas should be introduced downstream of the auxiliary blower. The auxiliary blower is needed to aid mixing of the 0.56 L (0.02 ft^3) of propane that is used in a test. When propane is used as the tracer gas, it may be necessary to remove the charcoal filter from the CVS. This will equalize the HC background in the two dilution air streams.

5.1.5.2 Equipment

a. CVS system to be checked.
b. A container of instrument grade tracer gas.
c. Analytical balance with a capacity to weigh the charged gas container and flow regulator with a resolution of 0.01 g.
   Instead of the weighing technique, flow measurement techniques can be used to determine the amount of tracer gas injected into the CVS. These include: wet test meter, rotameter, and critical flow orifice.
d. A tracer gas flow regulator which is capable of adjustment to yield bag concentrations which are normally encountered during testing.
e. An auxiliary blower of 0.005 to 0.014 m^3/s (10 to 30 ft^3/min) capacity.
f. Analyzers to measure tracer gas.

5.1.5.3 Procedure

a. Turn on CVS and allow stream pressure and temperature to stabilize.
b. Weigh gas container with the flow regulator connected and record weight.
c. Purge the gas sample bags with dilution air.
d. Simultaneously, activate CVS mixture and dilution air bag sampling and the positive displacement pump revolution counter.
e. After 30 s, begin injecting tracer gas into the CVS. Set tracer gas flow rate to yield sample stream concentrations approximating those encountered during vehicle testing.
f. Record CVS data during tracer gas injection:
   1. Average pump inlet temperature, °C (°F)
   2. Average pump inlet pressure, Pa (in H_2O)
   3. Average pump differential pressure, Pa (in H_2O)
g. After 14 min 30 s total elapsed time, stop the tracer gas injection.
h. After 15 min total elapsed time, stop the CVS mixture and dilution air bag samples and the pump revolution counter simultaneously. Record total CVS pump revolutions.
i. Analyze gases in the CVS mixture and dilution air sample bags. Record concentrations.
j. Weigh tracer gas container and record weight.
k. Determine the injected weight of tracer gas by subtracting weight measured in step 5.1.5.3(j) from weight measured in step 5.1.5.3(b). Record difference.

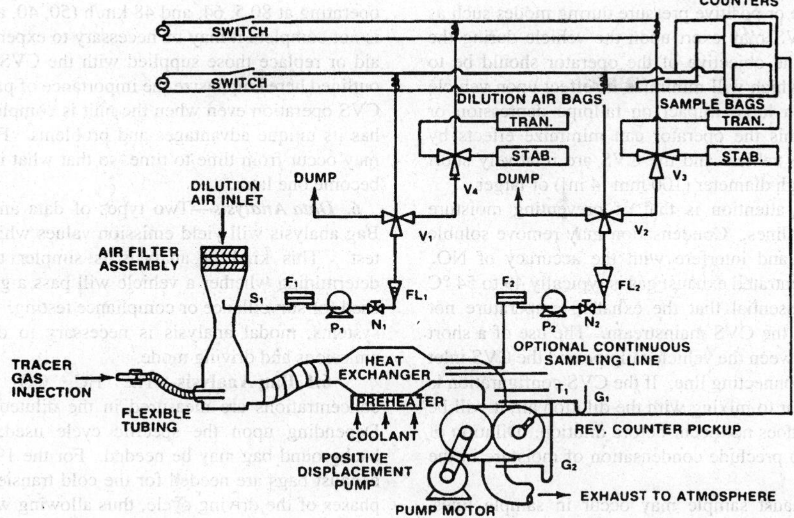

FIGURE 10—EXHAUST GAS SAMPLING SYSTEM

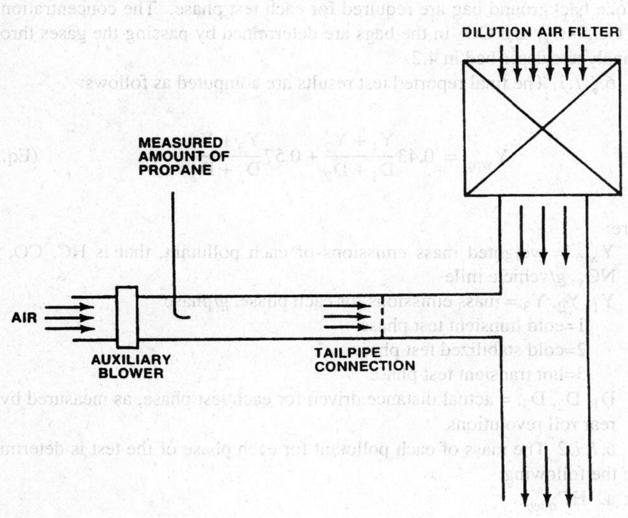

FIGURE 11—CVS SYSTEM VERIFICATION

5.1.5.4 Calculations

a. Determine the mass of injected tracer gas indicated by the CVS using the following formula:

$$\text{Calculated mass} = V_{mix} \times \text{density} \times \text{conc} \quad \text{(Eq. 12)}$$

where:

$$V_{mix} = K_1 \times V_0 \times N \times \frac{P_p}{T_p}$$

$$K_1 = \frac{528R}{29.92 \text{ in Hg}}$$

V_o = volume of gas pumped by the positive displacement pump, ft^3/rev at ambient conditions.
This volume is dependent on the pressure differential across the positive displacement pump.

N = number of revolutions of the positive displacement pump during the test while samples are being collected

P_p = absolute pressure of the dilute exhaust entering the positive displacement pump, that is, barometric pressure minus the pressure depression below atmospheric of the mixture entering the positive displacement pump

T_p = average temperature of dilute exhaust entering positive displacement pump during test while samples are being collected, R

Density = Ideal Gas Law density of tracer gas, g/ft^3 at 68 °F and 29.92 in Hg pressure.

Example—Propane = 51.91 g/ft^3
CO = 32.97 g/ft^3

Conc = concentration of gas in sample bag minus concentration of gas in background bag.

b. Compare the measured tracer gas weight to the calculated tracer gas weight and determine the percent difference, based upon the measured weight and determine the percent difference, based upon the measured weight.

c. If the difference is greater than ±2% investigate possible sources of error and repeat the verification.

5.1.5.5 Critical Flow Orifice—A simpler alternative to the gravimetric procedure described in 5.1.5.3 for CVS system verification is the use of a critical flow orifice (CFO). The advantage of a calibrated CFO is that the weighting steps are replaced by a single determination of a high pressure level reading. The CVS measurement is compared to the CFO measurement using the CFO as the measurement as the standard. Again, if the percent difference is greater than ±2%, investigate possible sources of error and repeat the verification.

5.2 Operating Procedure—A wide variety of CVS configurations are currently available. The detailed operating procedure for each configuration will be unique, and will depend upon the nature of the test being performed. Requirements for hot and cold weighting and inclusion of multiple background bags all necessitate changes in the detailed operating procedure. Furthermore, the required degree of operator attention to the CVS console during performance of an emission test varies from installation to installation. Fully automated systems require almost no attention to detail. Once the test is initiated, all functions including the diverting of exhaust gas into the appropriate sample bags at the correct times and even changing of the paper filters are all accomplished automatically. Other units may require the operator to perform each of these operations manually. As a result of these many factors (configuration of equipment, interfacing equipment for automatic control, and test procedure), no attempt will be made here to provide a detailed step-by-step procedure. Any such procedure would be specific for a particular unit and test objective, rather than of universal value. Each operator should, of course, follow the instructions of the CVS manufacturer and/or systems designer as well as the test procedure outlined in the appropriate governmental regulations. The remainder of this section will be devoted to items which may be best described as "good operating practice" and are more universally applicable.

First, it should be pointed out that the concept of CVS sampling is still evolving. Areas of uncertainty still exist. Such an area is that of defining the acceptable "tailpipe depression" at idle or positive pressure during modes such as acceleration and cruise, which the CVS may exert upon the vehicle during the performance of an emissions test. The objective of the operator should be to employ his given CVS unit in a way which will minimize its effect upon vehicle operation. Actual CVS design has a large impact on tailpipe depression or pressurization. Above and beyond this the operator can minimize effects by insuring that connections between the vehicle and the CVS are relatively short (1.5 to 1.8 m [5 to 6 ft]), of large enough diameter (100 mm [4 in]) or larger.

A second area which deserves attention is that of preventing moisture condensation in the CVS or sampling lines. Condensation may remove soluble gas species from the sample stream and interfere with the accuracy of NO_x measurements. The dew point of concentrated exhaust gas is typically 49 to 54 °C (120 to 130 °F). Therefore, it is essential that the exhaust temperature not approach this range before dilution in the CVS mainstream. The use of a short (1.5 to 1.8 m [5 to 6 ft]) connection between the vehicle tailpipe and the CVS inlet will help prevent condensation in the connecting line. If the CVS configuration is such that the exhaust gas is cooled prior to mixing with the dilution air, it will be necessary to insure that condensation does not occur before dilution. Dilution of the exhaust gas should be sufficient to preclude condensation of moisture in the main flow stream.

Condensation of the dilute exhaust sample may occur in sample lines, pumps, filters, and meters, particularly when the relative humidity of the dilution air exceeds 50%. Unless bubbles appear in the flow meters, this condensation may be difficult to detect. Dampness in the paper filters in the sample streams is an indication that condensation is occurring. If condensation is a problem, it may be necessary to install drain lines to divert the condensation back into the main flow path of the CVS upstream of the positive displacement pump. Better approaches to avoid the condensation problem are to match the sample pump capacity more closely to the sampling system and to use back-pressure regulated sample pumps to reduce the maximum pressure to which the sample is exposed and thus reduce the tendency for condensation to occur.

Deposits will slowly build up in the CVS. These are most likely to occur in the heat exchanger. Good operating practice dictates regularly scheduled cleaning. Increase of depression at the pump inlet is a good indicator of deposit buildup. Even though the CVS flow conditions are corrected for the changing operating conditions, the deposit buildup is not uniform and consequently can cause stratification at the sample probe. Deposit buildup will be a function of the number and type of tests. For a very active testing program, monthly cleaning would be recommended.

CVS pumps have been known to seize. Usually, this is due to deposits and moisture that remain in a CVS after a series of intermittent tests. This problem can be avoided by connecting the CVS outlet to a laboratory exhaust system that has sufficient capacity to rotate the blower slowly when the CVS is off. The laboratory exhaust is effective in removing the moisture.

Foreign objects can enter the CVS inlet and effectively destroy mixing or cause severe stratification. Large mesh screens have been used effectively to prevent foreign objects from reaching the mixing area and the heat exchanger.

The dilution air filter is not intended to remove all hydrocarbons from the inlet air, but rather to stabilize their level. Precautions should be taken to insure that the dilution air is not contaminated with excessive HC vapor from spilled gasoline, etc. The dilution air filter package is normally a set of three 600 × 600 mm (24 × 24 in) filters. The first is a dust filter, the second a charcoal filter, and the third filter is to remove charcoal particles from the dilution air stream. These filters can become loaded with dirt. An acceptable method for determining the useful life of these filters is to monitor the pressure drop across the filter when the CVS blower is operating at high speed. When the pressure drop across the three filters reaches 125 Pa (0.5 in H_2O), the filter set should be changed. If desired the charcoal could be reactivated and reused.

A detailed calibrating procedure appears in another section. It should be noted that, while this procedure is intended to uncover mechanical and flow problems which may exist, it is not a cure-all. Actual operating conditions are somewhat different from calibrating conditions. For example, the temperature and flow rate entering the CVS during calibration is different than the temperature and flow rate of exhaust entering during vehicle emission testing. The degree of stratification under actual test conditions could differ from that observed during calibration. Mixing difficulties at other than calibrating conditions will lead to a situation where, even though a CVS checks out during the calibration, during actual operation the mass obtained by integrating the continuous diluted exhaust stream concentration does not agree with that collected in the bags. When a situation like this is observed, it will be necessary to repeat the stratification check outlined in the calibrating procedure with exhaust gas supplied by a vehicle operating at 80.5, 64, and 48 km/h (50, 40, and 30 mph) steady-states. If mixing is not complete it may be necessary to experiment with unique mixing devices to aid or replace those supplied with the CVS unit. Considerations such as those outlined here emphasize the importance of paying careful attention to each step of CVS operation even when the unit is completely automated. Each configuration has its unique advantages and problems. Furthermore, changes in a given unit may occur from time to time, so that what is not a problem at one moment may become one later.

*6. **Data Analysis***—Two types of data analysis are possible, bag and modal. Bag analysis will yield emission values which are the composite for a complete test. This kind of analysis is simpler to perform, and is satisfactory for determining whether a vehicle will pass a given test. Therefore, bag analysis is used for surveillance or compliance testing. For development of emission control systems, modal analysis is necessary to determine the relationships between emissions and driving mode.

6.1 Bag Analysis—The HC, CO, NO_x (NO + NO_2), and CO_2 concentrations are measured in the diluted exhaust and the background bags. Depending upon the specific cycle used, more than one exhaust and one background bag may be needed. For the 1975 Federal Test Procedure, separate exhaust bags are needed for the cold transient, cold stabilized, and hot transient phases of the driving cycle, thus allowing weighting factors to be applied to the cold and hot transient phases of the test. It is good practice to use a separate background bag for each sample bag used, in case the background concentrations change during a test.

6.1.1 Exhaust Emission Calculations—One diluted exhaust sample bag and one background bag are required for each test phase. The concentrations of HC, CO, NO_x, and CO_2 in the bags are determined by passing the gases through the analyzers described in 4.2.

6.1.1.1 The final reported test results are computed as follows:

$$Y_{wm} = 0.43\frac{Y_1 + Y_2}{D_1 + D_2} + 0.57\frac{Y_3 + Y_2}{D_3 + D_2} \quad \text{(Eq. 13)}$$

where:

Y_{wm} = weighted mass emissions of each pollutant, that is HC, CO, and NO_x, g/vehicle mile

Y_1, Y_2, Y_3 = mass emissions for each phase, g/phase

1=cold transient test phase

2=cold stabilized test phase

3=hot transient test phase

D_1, D_2, D_3, = actual distance driven for each test phase, as measured by the rear roll revolutions

6.1.1.2 The mass of each pollutant for each phase of the test is determined from the following:

a. HC_{mass}:

$$HC_{mass} = V_{mix} \times density_{HC} \times \frac{HC_{conc}}{1\,000\,000} \quad \textit{(Eq. 14)}$$

b. CO_{mass}:

$$CO_{mass} = V_{mix} \times density_{CO} \times \frac{HC_{conc}}{1\,000\,000} \quad \text{(Eq. 15)}$$

c. NO_{xmass}:

$$NO_{x_{mass}} = V_{mix} \times density_{NO_2} \times \frac{NO_{x_{conc}}}{1\,000\,000} \times Kh \quad \text{(Eq. 16)}$$

d. CO_{2mass}:

$$CO_{2_{mass}} = V_{mix} \times density_{CO_2} \times \frac{CO_{2_{conc}}}{100} \quad \text{(Eq. 17)}$$

6.1.1.3 Meaning of Symbols

HC_{mass} = hydrocarbon emission, g/test phase

$Density_{HC}$ = density of hydrocarbons in the exhaust gas, assuming an average carbon-to-hydrogen ratio of 1:1.85, g/ft^3 at 20 °C (68 °F) and 101 kPa (29.92 in Hg) pressure (16.33 g/ft^3)[4]

HC_{conc} = hydrocarbon concentration of the dilute exhaust sample corrected for background, ppm carbon equivalent, that is equivalent propane × 3

$HC_{conc} = HC_e - HC_d(1-1/DF)$

HC_e = hydrocarbon concentration of the dilute exhaust sample as measured, ppm carbon equivalent

HC_d = hydrocarbon concentration of the background as measured, ppm carbon equivalent

CO_{mass} = carbon monoxide emissions, g/test phase

$Density_{CO}$ = density of carbon monoxide, g/ft^3 at 20 °C (68 °F) and 101 kPa (29.92 in Hg) pressure (32.97 g/ft^3)

CO_{conc} = carbon monoxide concentration of the dilute exhaust sample corrected for background, water vapor, and CO_2 extraction, ppm

$CO_{conc} = CO_e - CO_d(1-1/DF)$

CO_e = carbon monoxide concentration of the dilute exhaust sample corrected for water vapor and carbon dioxide extraction, ppm. The calculation assumes the hydrogen-carbon ratio of the fuel is 1.85:1

$CO_e = (1-0.01925\ CO_{2e} - 0.000323\ R)\ COe_m$

($CO_e = COe_m$, if instrument has no CO_2 or H_2O response)

CO_{em} = carbon monoxide concentration of the dilute exhaust sample as measured, ppm

CO_{2e} = carbon dioxide concentration of the dilute exhaust sample, mol %

R = relative humidity of the dilution air, %

CO_d = carbon monoxide concentration of the background air corrected for water vapor extraction, ppm

$CO_d = (1-0.000323\ R)COd_m$

($CO_d = COe_m$, if instrument has no H_2O response)

COd_m = carbon monoxide concentration of the background air sample as measured, ppm

NOx_{mass} = oxides of nitrogen emissions, g/test phase

$DensityNO_2$ = density of oxides of nitrogen in the exhaust gas, assuming they are in the form of nitrogen dioxide, g/ft^3 at 20 °C (68 °F) and 101 kPa (29.92 in Hg) pressure (54.16 g/ft^3)

NOx_{conc} = oxides of nitrogen concentration of the dilute exhaust sample corrected for background, ppm

$NOx_{conc} = NOx_e - NOx_d(1-1/DF)$

NOx_e = oxides of nitrogen concentration of the dilute exhaust sample as measured, ppm

NOx_d = oxides of nitrogen concentration of the background as measured, ppm

$CO2_{mass}$ = carbon dioxide emissions, g/test phase

$Density_{CO}$ = density of carbon dioxide, g/ft^3 at 68 °F (20 °C) and 29.92 in Hg (101 kPa) pressure (51.81 g/ft^3)

$CO2_{conc}$ = carbon dioxide concentration of the dilute exhaust sample corrected for background, %

$CO2_{conc} = CO_2e - CO_{2d}(1-1/DF)$

$CO2_e$ = carbon dioxide concentration of the dilute exhaust sample as measured, %

$CO2_d$ = carbon dioxide concentration of the background as measured %

$$DF = \frac{13.4}{CO_{2e} + (HC_e + CP_e)10^{-4}} \qquad \text{(Eq. 18)}$$

V_{mix} = total dilute exhaust volume, ft^3/test phase corrected to standard conditions (528 R, 101 kPa) (68 °F, 29.92 in Hg)

$V_{mix} = V_o \times N \times (P_p/29.92)(528/T_n)$

V_o = volume of gas pumped by the positive displacement pump, ft^3/rev. This volume is dependent upon the pressure differential across the positive displacement pump

N = number of revolutions of the positive displacement pump during the test phase while samples are being collected

P_p = absolute pressure of the dilute exhaust entering the positive displacement pump, in Hg, that is, barometric pressure minus the pressure depression below atmospheric of the mixture entering the positive displacement pump

T_p = average temperature of dilute exhaust entering the positive displacement pump during test while samples are being collected

P_b = barometric pressure, in Hg

T_w = wet bulb temperature, °F

T_d = dry bulb temperature, °F

P_w = saturation water vapor pressure, in Hg at wet bulb temperature (Eq. 19)

$$P_w = -4.14438\ 10^{-3} + 5.76645\ 10^{-3}T_w - 6.32788\ 10^{-5}T_w^{\ 2} + 2.12294\ 10^{-6}T_w^{\ 3} - 7.85415\ 10^{-9}T_w^{\ 4} + 6.55263\ 10^{-11}T_w^{\ 5}$$

This equation is a least squares fit of the Keenan and Keyes "steam table." It reproduces steam table values within ±0.001 in HG for tempertures of 20 to 110 °F.

P_d = saturation water vapor pressure in Hg at dry bulb temperature. Same equation as for P_w except T_d is used instead of T_w.

A = experimentally derived constant for use in Ferrel's equation as recommended by NIST

$A = 3.67\ 10^{-4}\ [(1 + 0.00064\ (T_w - 32))]$

P_v = partial pressure of water vapor, in Hg (found from Ferrel's equation)

$P_v = P_w - A\ P_b\ (T_d - T_w)$, Ferrel's equation

H = absolute humidity, grains H_2O/lb dry air

$$H = \frac{4347.8\ P_v}{P_b - P_v} \qquad \text{(Eq. 20)}$$

K_h = humidity correction factor

$$K_h = \frac{1}{1 - 0.0047(H - 75)} \qquad \text{(Eq. 21)}$$

R = relative humidity, %

$$R = \frac{P_v}{P_d} \times 100 \qquad \text{(Eq. 22)}$$

6.2 Modal Analysis—Modal analysis is necessary for the development of emission controls because it relates cause and effect. The cause is the particular engine system at a specific operating point. The effect is the resulting emissions. Mode of operation can be defined as an idle, cruise, acceleration, and deceleration. The length of a mode could be several minutes or as short as 1 s. At least two methods of modal analysis are available: continuous analysis of diluted vehicle exhaust, and continuous analysis of undiluted exhaust using the CO_2 tracer technique.

6.2.1 CONTINUOUS ANALYSIS USING DILUTED VEHICLE EXHAUST—Any driving schedule can be broken down into arbitrary modes such as idle, acceleration, cruise, and deceleration. For each mode, the mass emission of each pollutant can be computed using the equations of 6.1.1.2 modified slightly. The modifications are: The HC, CO, and NO_x masses will be in grams per mode. Generally, a computer will be advantageous for performing the large amount of calculation required for continuous modal analysis.

6.2.1.1 Calculation of V_{mix} for One Mode—The diluted exhaust volume, ft^3/mode, can be calculated as in 6.1.1.3, except that N should be taken as the number of pump revolutions for the individual mode being calculated. The number of pump revolutions can be sensed with magnetic or photocell pickups and fed into the computer. For short modes, it may be necessary to measure partial pump revolutions in order to obtain sufficient accuracy.

6.2.1.2 Calculation of HC_{conc}, CO_{conc}, and NOx_{conc}—These quantities have the same meaning as in 6.1.1.2, except that they now are the average concentrations for each mode. The output of the HC, CO, NO_x, and CO_2 analyzers can be continuously monitored by a computer, with suitable provisions for time delays between the vehicle driver's mode changes and the corresponding analyzer output change. The computer can be programmed to time average the concentrations for the specified intervals corresponding to the individual modes, and make the required corrections. However, it is difficult to measure the background HC, CO, NO_x, and CO_2 concentrations continuously in the dilution air unless separate analyzers are available, which is not usually the case. Therefore, some approximation may be necessary, such as measuring the background before and after the test and assuming a linear relation in between, or collecting an average background dilution air sample for the entire test.

4. Density of emissions are based on Ideal Gas Law. Density is equal to 1.17714 times the molecular weight.

6.2.2 Modal Analysis Using CO_2 Tracer Method—There are many inherent difficulties in continuously analyzing diluted vehicle exhaust, primarily because of the very low diluted concentrations obtained for some modes. These problems can be avoided by continuously measuring the undiluted exhaust concentrations of HC, CO, NO_x, and CO_2. If the undiluted exhaust CO_2 concentration is also measured continuously, it is possible to calculate the vehicle exhaust volume for each mode. From the exhaust volume and the undiluted exhaust concentrations, the modal mass of each pollutant can be calculated. Actually, any constituent of the exhaust can be used as the tracer, but CO_2 is a good choice because it occurs in the largest and most constant concentration and, therefore, is easiest to measure accurately even after dilution.

6.2.2.1 Exhaust Modal Mass Flow Calculation Using CO_2 Tracer Method—Assume that the modal average undiluted exhaust HC, CO, NO_x, and CO_2 concentrations are measured, and that the modal average CO_2 concentrations are measured in the diluted exhaust stream. The diluted exhaust volume ft^3/mode, V_{mix}, can be calculated as described in 6.2.1.1. Assuming a constant for background CO_2, the average exhaust dilution ratio for each mode can be calculated as follows:

$$DR = \frac{CO_2 \text{ exhaust} - CO_2 \text{ background}}{CO_2 \text{ CVS} - CO_2 \text{ background}} \quad \text{(Eq. 23)}$$

The undiluted exhaust volume, ft^3/mode, is:

$$V_{und} = V_{mix}/DR \quad \text{(Eq. 24)}$$

The modal mass is given by following:

$$HC_{\text{modal mass}} = HC_{\text{conc und}} \times V_{und} \times \frac{\text{density}_{HC}}{10^6} \quad \text{(Eq. 25)}$$

$$CO_{\text{modal mass}} = CO_{\text{conc und}} \times V_{und} \times \frac{\text{density}_{CO}}{10^6} \quad \text{(Eq. 26)}$$

$$NOx_{\text{modal mass}} = NOx_{\text{conc und}} \times V_{und} \times \frac{\text{density}_{NO_2}}{10^6} \quad \text{(Eq. 27)}$$

The upper portion of Figure 12 shows only a hot transient modal mass output. Several pages may be required for a complete test. The mass emissions for individual modes can then be summed for the complete test, and these values compared with the mass emissions computed from the bags. Theoretically, the total of the modal masses should be equal to the mass emissions calculated from the bag data. In practice, there will not usually be perfect agreement, but the bags should agree with the modal total for each phase within a few percent. Figure 13 is an example of a computer mass summary. The weighted mass values of Figure 13 can be compared to the weighted modal data of Figure 12. Figure 14 shows the results of the bag versus modal NO_x comparison when the chemiluminescent NO_x analyzer was used.

6.3 Background—The exhaust dilution inherent in the operation of the constant volume sampler results in low concentrations of pollutants being presented to analyzers. Under some conditions, such as testing vehicles with very low emission levels, the diluted exhaust concentrations are not far above the background level of pollutants found in the dilution air. Therefore, it is important that background levels of pollutants be taken into account when measuring vehicle emissions.

Figure 15 is a partial schematic diagram of a constant volume sampler. Equations 28, 29, and 30 apply:

$$V_E + V_D = V_{mix} \quad \text{(Eq. 28)}$$

where:

V_E = volume of vehicle exhaust
V_D = volume of dilution air
V_{mix}= volume of diluted exhaust

$$V_E C_E + V_D C_D = V_{mix} C_{mix} \quad \text{(Eq. 29)}$$

where:

C_E = concentration of a given pollutant in the undiluted exhaust
C_D = concentration of same pollutant in the dilution air (background)
C_{mix} = concentration of the same pollutant in the diluted exhaust

$$V_E C_E = V_{mix} C_{mix} - V_D C_D = V_{mix} C_{mix} - (V_{mix} - V_E) C_D \quad \text{(Eq. 30)}$$
$$V_E C_E = V_{mix}(C_{mix} - C_D) + V_E C_D$$

Equation 30 expresses the correct way of calculating the true mass emission of the test vehicle, which is the quantity, $V_E C_E$. However, the application of Equation 30 requires that V_E be measured, which is not done in practice. An approximation to the correct value of $V_E C_E$ can be obtained by neglecting the $V_E C_D$ term in the right-hand side of Equation 30. The background concentration is merely subtracted from the diluted exhaust concentration of the same pollutant. This method may be satisfactory if the background concentration and/or V_E is small compared to V_{mix}. However, for very low emitting vehicles whose diluted exhaust concentrations approach the background concentrations, it is necessary to apply Equation 309 more rigorously, which requires the determination of either vehicle exhaust volume or the dilution air flow. The procedure of 6.1.1 may be used, wherein the exhaust dilution factor is estimated by means of Equation 31 derived for the case of stoichiometric combustion:

$$DF = \frac{13.4}{CO_{2_e} + (HC_e + CO_e)\,10^{-4}} \quad \text{(Eq. 31)}$$

Then V_E is approximately equal to V_{mix} divided by DF. With V_E known, Equation 30 can be used. This technique avoids the need to measure either the exhaust flow or the dilution air flow, and may be satisfactory for all but the most rigorous testing. Equation 30 is applicable to continuous modal analysis as well as to bag samples.

6.4 Fuel Economy Calculation from Exhaust Emissions—It is possible to calculate fuel economy from a vehicle's exhaust emissions using a form of carbon balance. The carbon in the fuel can be calculated as follows:

$$\text{Fuel density, g/gal} = 8.331 \times 0.740 \times 453.6 = 2796 \quad \text{(Eq. 32)}$$

8.331 lb/gal = density of water
0.740 = specific gravity of typical gasoline
453.6 g/lb = conversion factor
Weight fraction of carbon in fuel, assuming fuel of composition

$$CH_{1,85} = 12.011/(12.011 + [1.85 \times 1.008]) = 0.866 \quad \text{(Eq. 33)}$$

12.011 = atomic weight of carbon
1.008 = atomic weight of hydrogen

Grams of carbon per gallon of fuel = (fuel density, g/gal)wt% C in fuel) = 2796 x 0.866 = 2421 (Eq. 34)

The carbon in the exhaust can be calculated as follows:
Mass C in HC = (HC g/mile) (wt% C in HC molecule, assume $HC_{1,85}$)
= (HC g/mile) (0.866)
Mass C in CO = (CO g/mile) (wt% C in CO molecule)
= (CO g/mile) (12.011/12.011 + 16)
= (CO g/mile) (0.429)
Mass C in CO_2 = (CO2 g/mile) (wt% C in CO_2 molecule)
= (CO_2 g/mile) (12.011)/(12.011 + [2 x 16])
= (CO_2 g/mile) (0.273)

Total mass of C in the exhaust, g/mile = 0.866 HC g/mile + 0.429 CO g/mile + 0.273 CO_2 g/mile. The vehicle fuel economy can be calculated as follows:

$$\text{miles/gal} = (\text{g C/gal fuel})(\text{g/mile C in exhaust}) = \frac{2421}{0.866HC + 0.429CO + 0.273CO_2} \quad \text{(Eq. 35)}$$

where:

HC, CO, and CO_2 represent the grams/mile of these respective exhaust emissions for the vehicle.

Different values for fuel density and/or fuel H/C ratio will yield a slightly different equation.

—TAILPIPE CONC—TAILPIPE MASS—

TIME	HC	CO	NO	CO2	O2	CO2D	HC	CO	NOX	CO2	X-VOL	D/M
<	219	.422	56	1.82	16.3	.19	.010	.13	.003	.9	.9	.0
I 20	383	.644	64	10.05	6.2	.81	.134	1.52	.026	37.2	7.1	.0
A 11	55	.019	588	11.53	4.8	2.92	.035	.08	.429	76.9	12.9	.0
C 84	25	.086	218	11.45	5.0	2.12	.088	2.04	.888	426.1	71.8	.0
D 10	6	.013	107	10.90	5.8	.97	.001	.02	.024	22.8	4.0	.0
CYCLE 1 (GRAMS/MILE)							.398	5.62	2.037	837.9	96.8	D/M= 0 VIOL .0 SEC
I 39	9	.012	74	10.53	6.3	.89	.006	.06	.061	79.4	14.5	.0
A 42	41	.559	301	12.62	2.8	3.66	.113	10.38	.961	368.2	56.3	.0
C 95	5	.013	680	10.87	5.7	3.10	.031	.54	4.868	711.0	126.2	.0
D 33	17	.012	183	9.77	7.2	1.00	.013	.06	.161	78.6	15.5	.0
CYCLE 2 (GRAMS/MILE)							.083	5.63	3.087	631.2	212.6	D/M= 0 VIOL .0 SEC
I 13	5	.010	103	10.69	6.1	.89	.001	.02	.029	27.5	5.0	.0
A 20	9	.072	442	12.37	3.6	3.61	.012	.65	.686	175.5	27.4	.0
C 17	3	.011	520	10.39	6.5	1.92	.002	.05	.430	78.5	14.6	.0
D 14	3	.012	130	10.06	6.8	.92	.001	.02	.043	30.3	5.8	.0
CYCLE 3 (GRAMS/MILE)							.044	2.01	3.219	844.9	52.7	D/M= 0 VIOL .0 SEC
I 5	4	.011	102	10.66	6.1	1.01	.000	.01	.012	11.9	2.2	.0
A 13	14	.369	342	12.90	2.5	3.97	.013	2.24	.357	123.2	18.4	.0
D 14	3	.021	173	11.43	5.1	1.11	.001	.04	.061	36.6	6.2	.0
CYCLE 4 (GRAMS/MILE)							.099	16.22	3.053	1218.0	26.8	D/M= 0 VIOL .0 SEC
I 18	3	.013	103	10.70	6.0	.92	.001	.03	.041	39.0	7.0	.0
A 17	19	.674	362	12.88	2.3	4.16	.024	5.65	.522	169.6	25.4	.0
C 27	1	.014	557	10.33	6.5	1.63	.001	.09	.627	106.3	19.9	.0
D 14	1	.012	118	10.05	6.8	.87	.000	.02	.037	28.8	5.5	.0
CYCLE 5 (GRAMS/MILE)							.058	12.92	2.738	767.1	57.8	D/M= 0 VIOL .0 SEC

TEST LENGTH: 507.1

*** MODAL TEST SUMMARY ***

COLD TRANSIENT

GRAMS	HC	CO	NOX	CO2	EX-VOL	D/M
IDLE	1.092	18.64	.190	237	47.7	.0
ACCEL	1.096	35.32	2.530	1037	159.3	.6
CRUISE	2.101	32.88	6.568	1741	293.6	.0
DECEL	.034	.25	.310	196	36.6	.4
TOTAL	4.324	87.10	9.598	3211	537.1	1.0

EQUIVALENT MASS BAG RESULTS					F-ECON
GRAMS/MI	1.201	24.19	2.666	892	9.50

COLD STABILIZED

GRAMS	HC	CO	NOX	CO2	EX-VOL	D/M
IDLE	.017	.20	.273	291	53.6	.0
ACCEL	.075	3.72	4.388	1375	230.8	.0
CRUISE	.016	.81	2.719	1172	212.4	.0
DECEL	.027	1.18	.544	418	75.6	.0
TOTAL	.135	5.91	7.924	3257	572.3	.0

EQUIVALENT MASS BAG RESULTS					F-ECON
GRAMS/MI	.034	1.52	2.032	835	10.59

HOT TRANSIENT

GRAMS	HC	CO	NOX	CO2	EX-VOL	D/M
IDLE	.153	1.76	.172	196	36.8	.0
ACCEL	.196	18.99	2.955	913	140.4	.0
CRUISE	.122	2.72	6.812	1322	232.5	.0
DECEL	.016	.17	.326	197	37.1	.0
TOTAL	.487	23.64	10.266	2628	446.8	.0

EQUIVALENT MASS BAG RESULTS					F-ECON
GRAMS/MI	.135	6.57	2.852	730	11.98

WEIGHTED TOTAL

EQUIVALENT MASS BAG RESULTS					F-ECON
GRAMS/MI	.303	7.58	2.387	818	10.68

FIGURE 12—EXAMPLE OF HOT TRANSIENT MODAL DATA AND MODAL TEST SUMMARY

*** MASS BAG RESULTS ***

BAG	HC	CO	NOX	CO2
C.T. ZERO CK.	.4	1.3	.0	.03
C.T. SPAN SPEC	92.2	1580.0	80.0	3.43
C.T. SPAN CK.	92.5	1578.6	80.1	3.43
C.T. MID SPEC	36.8	450.0	16.1	2.13
C.T. MID-SP CK	38.5	465.4	18.0	2.08
#1 (C.T. SAMP)	32.6	1337.3	75.7	2.59
#4 (C.T. AMB)	2.4	6.7	.5	.07
C.S. ZERO CK	.2	1.0	.0	.03
C.S. SPAN SPEC	92.2	1580.0	80.0	3.43
C.S. SPAN CK	92.7	1570.9	80.5	3.41
C.S. MID SPEC	36.8	450.0	16.1	2.13
C.S. MID-SP CK	38.4	466.8	18.2	2.07
#2 (C.S. SAMP)	3.4	42.5	45.4	1.63
#5 (C.S. AMB)	2.6	5.0	.5	.07
H.T. ZERO CK	.4	1.2	.0	.03
H.T. SPAN SPEC	92.2	1580.0	80.0	3.43
H.T. SPAN CK	92.2	1584.4	80.5	3.42
H.T. MID SPEC	36.8	450.0	16.1	2.13
H.T. MID-SP CK	38.2	466.2	18.0	2.06
#3 (H.T. SAMP)	7.2	369.8	88.8	2.08
#6 (H.T. AMB)	3.0	4.3	.5	.07

*** EPA MASS TEST RESULTS ***

GRAMS	HC	CO	NOX	CO2
COLD TRANS.	3.62	105.9	10.29	3166
COLD STAB.	.22	5.1	10.38	3309
HOT TRANS.	.55	28.9	12.00	2508

GRAMS/MILE	HC	CO	NOX	CO2	ECON
COLD TRANS.	1.007	29.41	2.860	879.4	9.55
COLD STAB.	.057	1.31	2.662	848.6	10.43
HOT TRANS.	.152	8.03	3.334	696.7	12.50
WEIGHTED TOTAL	.279	8.95	2.887	813.4	10.71

FUEL	COLD-74	HOT-74	TOT-75
ECON	9.99	11.34	10.69

*** TEST VARIABLES ***

TEST DATE	7-27-74	TEST NO.	4H 26 6012	TEST TIME	1887.4		
DRY BULB	77	WET BULB	67	BAROMETER	29.21	ODOMETER	15278
VEH NO.	403	MODEL NO.	3D57	CID	360	TRANS	A

	COLD TRANS.	COLD STAB.	HOT TRANS.
DILUTION FACTOR	4.902	8.194	6.323
RELATIVE HUMIDITY (%)	60	60	60
HUM. CORR. FACTOR	1.047	1.047	1.047
CVS REVOLUTIONS	8870	15070	8800
MAX. CVS TEMPERATURE (DEG. F)	103	104	102
MIN. CVS TEMPERATURE (DEG. F)	88	90	85
AVG. CVS TEMPERATURE (DEG. F)	96	99	95
MAX. INLET DEPR. (IN. H2O)	8.3	8.1	8.5
MIN. INLET DEPR. (IN. H2O)	7.1	7.7	7.4
AVG. INLET DEPR. (IN. H2O)	7.7	7.9	7.9
MAX. PRESSURE DIFF. (IN. H2O)	14.0	13.9	14.4
MIN. PRESSURE DIFF. (IN. H2O)	12.8	13.5	13.3
AVG. PRESSURE DIFF. (IN. H2O)	13.4	13.7	13.8
AVG. CVS FLOW (CU. FT/REV)	.299	.299	.299
TOTAL CVS VOL. (STD. CU. FT.)	2411	4072	2395
AVG. MODAL CO2 RATIO	4.33	7.04	5.20

FIGURE 13—EXAMPLE OF BAG DATA

6.4.1 WEIGHTED FUEL ECONOMY—""Weighted" fuel economy is the carbon balance fuel economy based on weighted emission values found from the 1975 Federal Test Procedure. This weighted fuel economy is identical to the fuel economy that would be obtained if the fuel economies were calculated for each of the three phases of the 75 FTP, and then weighted in the same manner as the emissions. The proof follows: Subscript w refers to the 75 FTP weighted emissions, subscript 1, 2, and 3 refer to the 75 FTP phase. The distance for phase 1 and phase 3 is 3.59 miles, and the distance for phase 2 is 3.91 miles. The weighting factor for phase 1 is 0.43 and for phase 3 is 0.57. (See Equations 36, 37, 38, 39, 40, 41, and 42.)

$$FE_w = \frac{2421}{0.866\ HC_w + 0.429\ CO_w + 0.273\ CO_2} \quad \text{(Eq. 36)}$$

$$HC_w = \frac{0.43(3.59)HC_1 + 3.91HC_2 + 0.57(3.59)HC_3}{7.5} \quad \text{(Eq. 37)}$$

$$CO_w = \frac{0.43(3.59)CO_1 + 3.91CO_2 + 0.57(3.59)CO_3}{7.5} \quad \text{(Eq. 38)}$$

$$CO_{2_w} = \frac{0.43(3.59)CO_{21} + 3.91CO_{22} + 0.57(3.59)CO_{23}}{7.5} \quad \text{(Eq. 39)}$$

Substituting Equations 37, 38, and 39 into Equation 36 and rearranging terms gives equation 40:

$$FE_w = \frac{2421(7.5)}{\begin{array}{c}0.43(3.59)(0.866\ HC_1 + 0.429\ CO_1 + 0.273\ CO_{21}) + \\ (3.91)(0.866\ HC_2 + 0.429\ CO_2 + 0.273\ CO_{22}) + \\ 0.57(3.59)(0.866\ HC_3 + 0.429\ CO_3 + 0.273\ CO_{23})\end{array}} \quad \text{(Eq. 40)}$$

The carbon balance formula applied to the emissions for each test phase is given by Equation 40:

$$FE_n = \frac{2421}{0.866\ HC_n + 0.429\ CO_n + 0.273\ CO_{2_n}} \quad \text{(Eq. 41)}$$

where:

n indicates the test phase. Substituting Equation 41 into Equation 40 gives Equation 42:

$$FE^w = \frac{7.5}{0.43\frac{3.59}{FE_1} + \frac{3.91}{FE_2} + 0.57\frac{3.59}{FE_3}} \quad \text{(Eq. 42)}$$

The denominator is simply the gallons for each test phase weighted in the same manner as emissions.

6.4.2 FUEL ECONOMY CYCLE—The carbon balance fuel economy can be determined from any cycle, where emissions have been measured and are expressed in grams/mile. EPA has developed a Highway Fuel Economy Test Schedule. The driving sequence for this cycle is shown in SAE J1506.

7. *Safety Recommendations*

7.1 Dynamometer—The test vehicle should be restrained on the dynamometer by using tie-downs or other suitable means. The maximum speed and acceleration/deceleration rates of the dynamometer must not be exceeded.

7.2 Calibration Gas Cylinders

7.2.1 HANDLING—Gas cylinders must not be moved unless the safety cap is securely screwed on the cylinder. Gas cylinders must always be supported by chains or other suitable means when in use, transported, or in storage.

7.2.2 TOXIC OR DANGEROUS GASES—Gases such as CO and NO_x must be used in an area with adequate ventilation. An ambient CO monitor for the emissions laboratory area is suggested.

7.3 Vehicle Fuel (Gasoline)—Vehicle fuel must always be contained in safety containers.

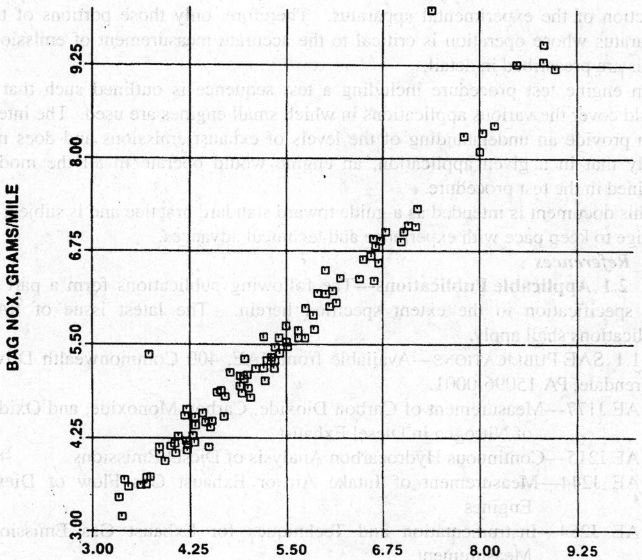

FIGURE 14—BAG NO_X VERSUS MODAL NO_X

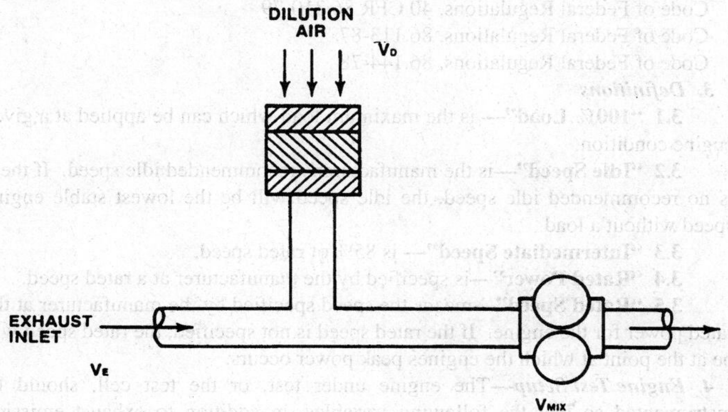

FIGURE 15—CONSTANT VOLUME SAMPLER SCHEMATIC

(R) TEST PROCEDURE FOR THE MEASUREMENT OF GASEOUS EXHAUST EMISSIONS FROM SMALL UTILITY ENGINES—SAE J1088 FEB1993

SAE Recommended Practice

Report of the SAE Engine Committee approved June 1974, revised June 1983. Completely revised by the SAE Small Engine and Powered Equipment Committee February 1993.

Foreword—This Document has also changed to comply with the new SAE Technical Standards Board format.

1. Scope—This SAE Recommended Practice specifies a uniform procedure for the evaluation of gaseous exhaust emissions from small utility engines typically less than 20 kW. Details of engine test setup and exhaust gas analysis techniques are specified with the intent of providing a uniform and reproducible method of measurement.

The intent has been to allow as much flexibility as possible in the physical construction of the experimental apparatus. Therefore, only those portions of the apparatus whose operation is critical to the accurate measurement of emissions levels are prescribed in detail.

An engine test procedure including a test sequence is outlined such that it would cover the various applications in which small engines are used. The intent is to provide an understanding of the levels of exhaust emissions and does not imply that in a given application, an engine would operate in all the modes outlined in the test procedure.

This document is intended as a guide toward standard practice and is subject to change to keep pace with experience and technical advances.

2. References

2.1 Applicable Publications—The following publications form a part of this specification to the extent specified herein. The latest issue of SAE Publications shall apply.

2.1.1 SAE PUBLICATIONS—Available from SAE, 400 Commonwealth Drive, Warrendale, PA 15096-0001.

SAE J177—Measurement of Carbon Dioxide, Carbon Monoxide, and Oxides of Nitrogen in Diesel Exhaust
SAE J215—Continuous Hydrocarbon Analysis of Diesel Emissions
SAE J244—Measurement of Intake Air or Exhaust Gas Flow of Diesel Engines
SAE J254—Instrumentation and Techniques for Exhaust Gas Emissions Measurement
SAE J313—Diesel Fuels
SAE Paper 650507—Air Fuel Ratios From Exhaust Gas Analysis, R.S. Spindt

2.1.2 FEDERAL REGULATIONS—Available from The Superintendent of Documents, U.S. Government Printing Office, Washington, DC 20402.

Code of Federal Regulations, 40 CFR 86.310-79
Code of Federal Regulations, 86.113-87
Code of Federal Regulations, 86.144-78

3. Definitions

3.1 "100% Load"— is the maximum load which can be applied at a given engine condition.

3.2 "Idle Speed"—is the manufacturer's recommended idle speed. If there is no recommended idle speed, the idle speed will be the lowest stable engine speed without a load.

3.3 "Intermediate Speed"— is 85% of rated speed.

3.4 "Rated Power"—is specified by the manufacturer at a rated speed.

3.5 "Rated Speed"—means the speed specified by the manufacturer at the rated power for the engine. If the rated speed is not specified, the rated speed will be at the point at which the engines peak power occurs.

4. Engine Test Setup—The engine under test, or the test cell, should be instrumented so that the following variables, in addition to exhaust emission levels, can be measured:

a. Inlet air temperature
b. Inlet air humidity (Test cell)
c. Barometric pressure (Test cell)
d. Fuel mass flow rate
e. Engine speed
f. Engine brake torque output

Throughout the course of a test, exhaust composition will be measured through use of an analytical train and instrumentation system to be described subsequently.

Suggested engine setup and exhaust gas analysis systems are illustrated in Figures 1, 2, and 3, respectively. Engine test cell ambient conditions shall remain within the following tolerances:

a. Ambient Air Temperature—20 to 30 °C

4.1 Air and Fuel Flow Measurement—Emissions measurements are made on a molar basis and results are given in terms of concentration. General practice at present is to quote emissions in mass terms. Conversion of concentrations into mass should be based on the fuel flow technique. For all engines it is recommended to use the Fuel Flow Method as described in 7.2.2.1. The following paragraphs give recommended procedures for measuring air and fuel flow.

4.1.1 FUEL FLOW MEASUREMENT—Fuel flow rate measurement instrumentation must have a combined accuracy of ±2% of the reading.

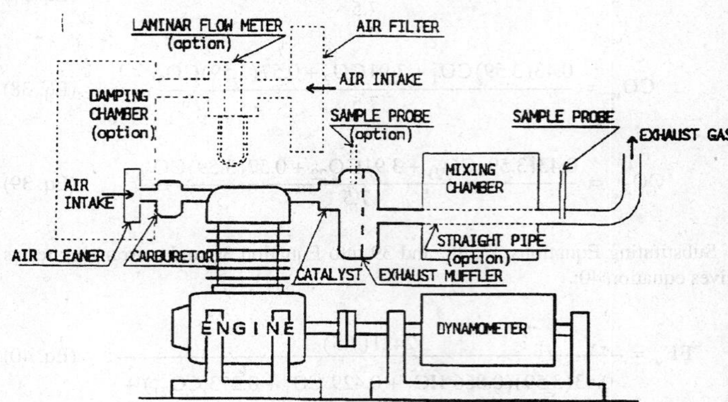

FIGURE 1—ENGINE SETUP FOR EMISSIONS TEST

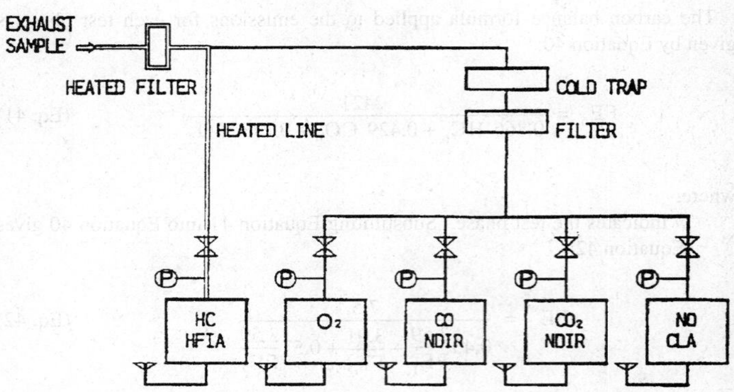

FIGURE 2—EXHAUST GAS ANALYTICAL SYSTEM WITH CLA

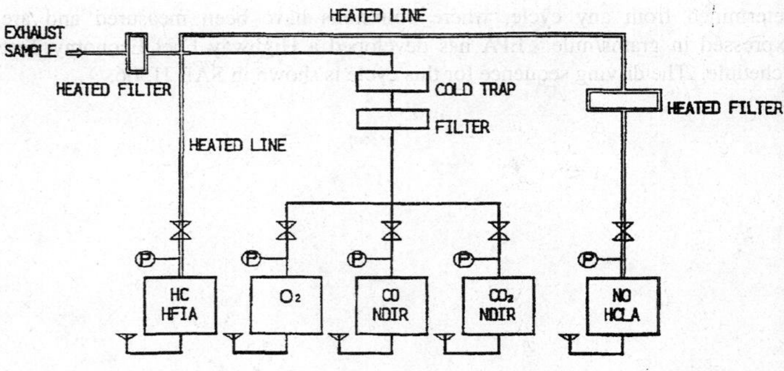

FIGURE 3—EXHAUST GAS ANALYTICAL SYSTEM WITH HCLA

4.1.2 Inlet Air Flow Measurement (Optional)—Figure 1 shows in schematic form an optional inlet airflow measurement system. The measurement system shown consists of a laminar flow meter used in conjunction with a pressure wave damping chamber. The damping chamber may consist of any vessel having an internal volume not less than 100 times the displacement per cylinder under test. The damping chamber should be installed between the airflow metering element and the engine air inlet, thus serving to isolate the meter from the engine. One of a number of alternate airflow measurement systems may be substituted for the preferred system described previously. Such systems should adhere to the practices specified by SAE J244.

If the airflow element reduces the engine airflow because of excessive pressure drop, greater than 100 Pa, an auxiliary blower can be used to compensate for the effect of the air meter. If a blower is used, engine inlet pressure should be measured and controlled to ±50 Pa of barometer readings.

4.2 Exhaust Gas Sampling System—The exhaust gas sampling system consists of the exhaust system normally supplied with the engine, an exhaust sampling probe, and an exhaust mixing chamber. Figure 1 shows a typical sampling system. Figure 4 shows the sample probe and typical hole spacings.

4.2.1 Exhaust Sample Probe—The sample probe shall be a straight, closed end, stainless steel, multi-hole probe. The Inside Diameter (ID) shall not be greater than the ID of the sample line. The wall thickness of the probe shall not be greater than 1 mm. The fitting that attaches the probe to exhaust conduit shall be as small as practical in order to minimize heat loss from the probe.

There shall be a minimum of three holes in the probe. The spacing of the radial planes for each hole in the probe must be such that they cover approximately equal cross-sectional areas of the exhaust conduit. The angular spacing of the holes must be approximately equal. The angular spacing of any two holes in one plane may not be 180 degrees ± 20 degrees (i.e., section C-C of Figure 4). The holes should be sized such that each has approximately the same flow. If only three holes are used, they may not all be in the same radial plane.

The probe shall extend radially across the exhaust conduit. The probe must pass through the approximate center and must extend across at least 80% of the diameter of the conduit.

The exhaust sample probe information given previously was taken from the Code of Federal Regulations, 40 CFR 86.310-79.

4.2.2 Exhaust Mixing Chamber—The mixing chamber is located in the exhaust system between the muffler and the sample probe. Its purpose is to ensure complete mixing of the engine exhaust before sample extraction so that a truly representative average exhaust sample is obtained. The internal volume of the mixing chamber must be not less than 10 times the cylinder displacement of the engine under test and should be of roughly equal dimensions in height, width, and depth.

To minimize dropout of heavy hydrocarbon fractions in the exhaust mixing chamber during part throttle, light load operation, the chamber size should be kept as small as practical, consistent with the 10 times cylinder displacement minimum size limitation. Restricting the size of the chamber will keep internal turbulence as high as possible, thus promoting thorough mixing of the exhaust gas. The chamber should be coupled as close as possible to the engine.

The exhaust line leaving the chamber should extend a sufficient length beyond the sample probe location to eliminate possible sampling errors due to strong exhaust pulsations pulling air back into the exhaust system. The exhaust line should be of sufficient size to hold exhaust back pressure to a minimum. The temperature of the inner surface of the mixing chamber must be maintained above the dew point of the exhaust gases. A temperature range of 175 to 400 °C is recommended. It is suggested that surface thermocouples or other suitable monitoring devices be installed in the mixing chamber to ensure operation at the proper temperatures.

4.2.3 Alternate Exhaust Gas Sampling Systems—One of a number of exhaust gas sampling methods may be substituted for the preferred method described in 4.2.2 and seen in Figure 1 if it can be shown the alternate method provides a homogeneous representative exhaust gas sample and avoids dilution by aspiration of ambient air. If a mixing chamber is not used, the exhaust sampling probe shall be located in the exhaust conduit downstream of the exhaust valve or exhaust port of a single-cylinder engine or downstream of the final junction of the exhaust manifold of a multi-cylinder engine. If the exhaust sample probe is located in the muffler, it should be positioned in the high-pressure side of the muffler. If the engine is equipped with an exhaust catalytic convertor, the exhaust sample probe shall be located downstream from the catalytic element but not so close to the exhaust outlet as to ingest air from the atmosphere due to pressure pulsations in the exhaust.

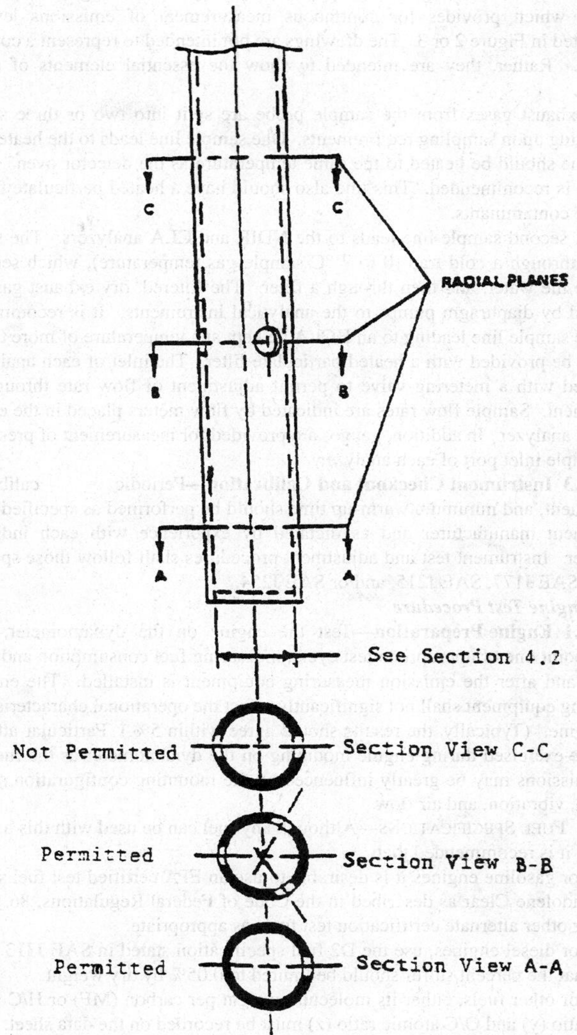

FIGURE 4—EXHAUST SAMPLE PROBE

5. Exhaust Gas Analysis

5.1 Analytical Methods—The following instruments will be used to measure exhaust concentrations of the species listed as follows: (The instrument should be capable of an accuracy of 2% of point value or 1% of full scale, whichever is less.)

5.1.1 Unburned Hydrocarbons—Heated flame ionization detector (FID).

Operation of the analyzer should conform to the procedure specified in SAE J215. If SAE J215 is not applicable to a specific instrument, the manufacturer's recommendations should be followed. An oven temperature in the range of 175 to 200 °C is recommended for both 2-stroke cycle and 4-stroke cycle engines.

5.1.2 Carbon Monoxide—Nondispersive infrared analyzer (NDIR).

Operation of the infrared analyzer should conform to the practice specified in SAE J254 and/or SAE J177.

5.1.3 Carbon Dioxide—Nondispersive infrared analyzer (NDIR).

Operation of this analyzer should follow recommendations given in SAE J254 and/or SAE J177.

5.1.4 Oxides Of Nitrogen—Chemiluminescent Analyzer (CLA). Heated Chemiluminescent Analyzer (HCLA).

Recommendations for operation of the chemiluminescent analyzer are given in SAE J177 practices.

If the operating recommendations given in the SAE J177 practices are not applicable to the particular make of chemiluminescent analyzer being used, follow instrument manufacturer's recommendations.

5.1.5 Oxygen—Polarograph Or Paramagnetic—Oxygen measurement may provide an indication of air leaks in the system. Operation should conform to SAE J254.

5.2 Exhaust Sample Preparation and Analysis—A suggested analytical system which provides for continuous measurement of emissions levels is illustrated in Figure 2 or 3. The drawings are not intended to represent a complete system. Rather, they are intended to show the essential elements of such a system.

Exhaust gases from the sample probe are split into two or three streams depending upon sampling requirements. One sample line leads to the heated FID. This line should be heated to the same temperature as the detector oven. 175 to 200 °C is recommended. This line also should have a heated particulate filter to remove contaminants.

A second sample line leads to the NDIR and CLA analyzers. The sample passes through a cold trap (0 to 7 °C sample gas temperature), which serves to remove the water, and then through a filter. The filtered, dry exhaust gases are pumped by diaphragm pumps to the analytical instruments. It is recommended that the sample line leading to an HCLA be kept at a temperature of more than 60 °C and be provided with a heated particulate filter. The inlet of each analyzer is provided with a metering valve to permit adjustment of flow rate through that instrument. Sample flow rates are indicated by flow meters placed in the exhaust of each analyzer. In addition, gauges are provided for measurement of pressure at the sample inlet port of each analyzer.

5.3 Instrument Checkout and Calibration—Periodic calibration, adjustment, and minimum warm-up time should be performed as specified by the instrument manufacturer and as dictated by experience with each individual analyzer. Instrument test and adjustment procedures shall follow those specified within SAE J177, SAE J215, and/or SAE J254.

6. Engine Test Procedure

6.1 Engine Preparation—Test the engine on the dynamometer, under mode point one of appropriate test cycle, measuring fuel consumption and power before and after the emission measuring equipment is installed. The emission sampling equipment shall not significantly affect the operational characteristics of the engine. (Typically, the results should agree within 5%.) Particular attention must be exercised during engine mounting on the dynamometer as the fuel flow and emissions may be greatly influenced by the mounting configuration such as friction, vibration, and air flow.

6.1.1 FUEL SPECIFICATIONS—Although any fuel can be used with this test procedure, it is recommended that:

a. For gasoline engines it is desirable to use an EPA certified test fuel such as Indolene Clear as described in the Code of Federal Regulations, 86.113-87 or other alternate certification test fuels as appropriate.
b. For diesel engines, use the D2 fuel specification stated in SAE J313 except that the percent sulfur should be limited to 0.05% by dry weight.
c. For other fuels, either its molecular weight per carbon (MF) or H/C atomic ratio (y) and O/C atomic ratio (z) must be recorded on the data sheet.

For some nonoxygenated fuels Table 1:

TABLE 1—NONOXYGENATED FUELS

Fuel	y	z	MF
gasoline	1.85	0	13.88
diesel	1.80	0	13.83
methane	4.00	0	16.04
propane	2.67	0	14.69

6.1.2 LUBRICATING OIL—During all engine tests, the engine should employ a lubricating oil consistent with the engine manufacturer's specifications for that particular engine. For 2-stroke-cycle engines, the fuel-oil mixture ratio should conform to the engine manufacturer's recommendations.

6.1.3 ENGINE RUN-IN PRIOR TO BEGINNING ENGINE EXHAUST EMISSION TESTS—The engine should be run-in in accordance with the manufacturer's instructions.

6.1.4 ENGINE START-UP—Prior to starting the emissions tests, the engine should be allowed to warm up in accordance with the manufacturer's instructions. Before proceeding with the tests, the carburetor and engine adjustments should be set to the manufacturer's recommendations.

6.2 Exhaust Emission Test Sequence Measurement Procedure—The test sequence is a series of steady-state operating modes. Standard sequences are presented in Figure 5. Additional operating modes may be added for more comprehensive emission mapping. It should be understood that once coupled to the end product, the engine may seldom operate in some of the modes shown in Figure 5. Modes are to be performed in the numerical order specified for the appropriate test cycle. At the manufacturer's option, testing may be performed with locked throttle in a fixed position or using the engine governor. During the idle, no load mode, the engine may or may not be coupled to the dynamometer. In either case, test records should indicate which method was selected.

Once engine speed and load are set for a mode, the engine shall be run for a sufficient period of time to achieve thermal stability. The goal is to stabilize all engine parameters affecting emissions production and performance output before recorded measurement begins. Temperatures of combustion chamber components are good indicators of engine stability. After thermal stability is achieved, emissions measurements are initiated.

All data used to calculate emissions shall be averaged for a period of at least 2 min. Longer averaging times may be required to ascertain the true time averaged emissions if data variability over time is significant. Discrete data sampling must occur sufficiently fast to ensure accurate measurement of time averages. Data sample intervals should be less than 1/2 the response time of the fastest instrument. At the completion of the measurement, the engine is set to the next mode.

Mode	1	2	3	4	5	6	7	8	9	10	11
Speed	–rated speed–					–intermediate speed–					idle
Mode points A cycle						1	2	3	4	5	6
Load % A cycle						100	75	50	25	10	0
Mode points B cycle	1	2	3	4	5						6
Load % B cycle	100	75	50	25	10						0
Mode points C cycle	1										2
Load % C cycle	100										0

NOTE—It is recommended that the mode points be run (as numbered) in order of decreasing temperature (highest to lowest power mode).

Choosing an Appropriate Test Cycle—If the primary end use of an engine model is known then the test cycle may be chosen based on the examples given in the cycle description. If the primary end use of an engine model is uncertain, then an appropriate test cycle should be chosen based upon the engine specifications. Both compression ignition and spark ignition engines may be tested in any of the three cycles, whichever is most appropriate.

A Cycle—Non-handheld intermediate speed applications such as, but not limited to: walk behind rotary or reel lawn mowers, front or rear engine riding lawn mowers, rotary tillers, edger trimmers, waste disposers, lawn sweepers, sprayers, snow removal equipment.

B Cycle—Non-handheld rated speed applications such as, but not limited to: portable generators, pumps, welders, air compressors. Rated speed applications may also include lawn and garden equipment which operates at engine rated speed.

C Cycle—Handheld rated speed applications such as, but not limited to: edge trimmers, string trimmers, blowers, vacuums, chain saws.

FIGURE 5—STANDARD SEQUENCES

7. Data Reduction and Presentation of Results

7.1 Engine Performance—The following engine operating and performance parameters should be presented for each test in the units indicated in Table 2.

TABLE 2—ENGINE OPERATING AND PERFORMANCE PARAMETERS

Parameter	Units - SI
Air flow rate (Optional)	g/h
Fuel flow rate	g/h
Engine speed	r/min
Engine torque output	N·m
Power output	kW
Air inlet temperature	°C
Air humidity	mg/kg
Coolant temperature (liquid cooled)	°C
Exhaust mixing chamber surface temperature (Optional)	°C
Exhaust sample line temperature	°C
Total accumulated hours of engine operation	h
Barometric pressure	kPa

7.2 Exhaust Species Concentrations

7.2.1 INITIAL MOLAR CONCENTRATIONS—In all HC designation the C is expressed in C1.

Concentrations of each of the exhaust species will be measured in the following units:

Unburned Hydrocarbons (HC)	Molar ppm C1 (in wet exhaust)
CO_2	Mole percent (in dry exhaust)
CO	Mole percent (in dry exhaust)
NO	Molar ppm (in dry or wet exhaust measured by chemiluminescent analyzer)
O_2	Mole percent (in dry exhaust)

7.2.2 Conversion To Mass Emission Rates—Conversion to mass terms should be wet species concentration data, but care must be taken that all data are reported on the same basis. Since engine emissions are discharged to the atmosphere in the wet state, it would seem reasonable to report emissions concentrations on a wet basis.

For this reason, the conversion equations given as follows are written for use with wet concentration data. A suggested method for converting dry concentration data into wet terms is given in Appendix A.

Two methods may be used to calculate mass rate of discharge. One method makes use of both air and fuel flow data. The other method is based upon fuel flow alone.

7.2.2.1 Fuel Flow Method—These equations are based on the same assumptions used for the combined air/fuel method. A correction for the mass effect of humidity on NOx species concentration is included in the equations. The error introduced by neglecting the effect of humidity on other exhaust species concentrations in insignificant when the overall accuracy of measurement is considered and, therefore, is considered as part of the experimental error.

$$\text{HC, g/h} = \text{MHCexh/MF} * \text{Fuel, g/h} / (\text{TC}) * \text{HC, ppmC w} * 1/10000 \quad \text{(Eq. 1)}$$

$$\text{CO, g/h} = \text{MCO/MF} * \text{Fuel, g/h} / (\text{TC}) * \text{CO, \% w} \quad \text{(Eq. 2)}$$

$$\text{NOx, g/h} = \text{MNOx/MF} * \text{Fuel, g/h} / (\text{TC}) * \text{NOx, ppm w} * \text{KH} * 1/10000 \quad \text{(Eq. 3)}$$

where:

1. (TC) = CO, % wet + CO_2, % wet + HC, % wet
2. If fuel is in lb/h, divide by 0.002205
3. MHCexh = MF, molecular weight of fuel = 12.011 + 1.008 * y + 15.999 * z

NOTE—This assumes that the exhaust hydrocarbons are identical to unburned fuel.)

4. MF = molecular weight of fuel
5. MCO = molecular weight of CO = 28.01
6. MNOx = molecular weight of NO_2 (NOx) = 46.01
7. y = H/C hydrogen/carbon atomic ratio of the fuel

z = O/C oxygen/carbon atomic ratio of the fuel

8. KH = Federal factor for correcting the effect of humidity on NO_2 formation

$$= \frac{1}{[1 - 0.0329 * (H - 10.71)]} \text{ (Gasoline)} \quad \text{(Eq. 4)}$$

$$= \frac{1}{[1 - 0.0182 * (H - 10.71)]} \text{ (Diesel)} \quad \text{(Eq. 5)}$$

where:

H = grams of moisture per kilogram of dry air

The humidity correction factor given previously was taken from the code of Federal Regulations, 40 CFR 86.144-78. This correction factor has not been verified for small engines. Moreover, the NOx emissions for small engines are low and the KH factor approaches one in a laboratory test environment. The KH factor for two-stroke cycle engines should be set to "1" regardless of humidity.

7.2.2.2 Air and Fuel Flow Method—The following equations may be used to calculate mass emissions when both air and fuel flows are measured.

$$\text{HC, g/h} = (\text{airflow, g/h} + \text{fuel flow, g/h}) \times \frac{\text{MHCexh}}{\text{ME}} \times \text{HC, ppmC w} \times 1/1000000 \quad \text{(Eq. 6)}$$

$$\text{CO, g/h} = (\text{airflow, g/h} + \text{fuel flow, g/h}) \times \frac{\text{MCO}}{\text{ME}} \times \text{CO, \% wet} \times 1/100 \quad \text{(Eq. 7)}$$

$$\text{NOx, g/h} = (\text{airflow, g/h} + \text{fuel flow, g/h}) \times \frac{\text{MNO}_2}{\text{ME}} \times \text{NOx, ppm w} \times \text{KH} \times 1/1000000 \quad \text{(Eq. 8)}$$

where:

1. If airflow or fuel flow are in lb/h rather than g/h, divide by 0.002205
2. ME, molecular weight of exhaust is calculated using the equation specified as follows
3. Refer to 7.2.2.1 for molecular weight information and humidity correction factor KH

The following equation may be used to determine the molecular weight of the exhaust:

$$\begin{aligned}\text{mol wt exh} = {} & \frac{13.88 \times \text{HC ppm C1}_W}{10^6} + \frac{28.01 \times \text{CO\%}_w}{10^2} \quad \text{(Eq. 9)} \\ & + \frac{44.01\ \text{CO}_2\%_W}{10^2} + \frac{46.01 \times \text{NOx ppm}_W}{10^6} + \frac{32.00 \times \text{O}_2\%_W}{10^2} \\ & + \frac{2.016 \times \text{H}_2\%_W}{10^2} + 18.01 \times (1 - \text{K}) + \{28.01 \times [100 - \frac{\text{HCppm C1}_W}{10^4} \\ & - \text{CO\%}_W - \text{CO}_2\%_W - \frac{\text{NOxppm}_W}{10^4} - \text{O}_2\%_W - (\text{H}_2\%_W) - 100 \times (1 - \text{K})]\}/10^2\end{aligned}$$

where:

$$K = \frac{1}{1 + 0.005 \times (\text{CO\%}_d + \text{CO}_2\%_d) \times y - 0.01 \times \text{H}_2\%_d} \quad \text{(Eq. 10)}$$

$$\text{H}_2\%_d = \frac{0.5 \times y \times \text{CO\%}_d \times (\text{CO\%}_d + \text{CO}_2\%_d)}{\text{CO\%}_d + 3 \times \text{CO}_2\%_d} \quad \text{(Eq. 11)}$$

y = H/C atomic ratio of test fuel

For two-stroke cycle engines, we assume no residual free H_2 and modify K by deleting the H_2 term.

In some cases it may not be practical to measure fuel flow. The fuel/air ratio, however, can be determined from the exhaust products of nonoxygenated fuels using the Spindt method (SAE Paper 650507). With this information available, the term (airflow) x (1 + F/A) may be substituted for the (airflow + fuel flow) term in the preceding equations. This substitution is valid for 4-stroke cycle engines only. It does not apply to 2-stroke cycle engines.

7.3 Additional Information—The following additional information should be supplied with the results of each test series:

a. Engine model, displacement, and power rating
b. Type of fuel used
c. Type of lubricant used
d. Fuel-oil ratio used for 2-stroke-cycle engines
e. Type of dynamometer used
f. Make and model of exhaust gas analysis instrumentation

APPENDIX A

A.1 When FID (flame ionization detector) is used in HC analysis and a chemiluminescent analyzer utilizing a wet sample is used for NO analysis, the combustion water is not removed and, therefore, measurements are made with reference to the wet exhaust. When NDIR and chemiluminescent analyzer requiring a dry sample are used for species analysis, water vapor is removed prior to the concentration measurement and the results are on a dry basis. The following equation may be used to determine the correction factor to be used in converting dry measurements to a wet basis.

$$K = \frac{1}{1 + 0.005 \times (\text{CO\%}_d + \text{CO}_2\%_d) \times y - 0.01 \times \text{H}_2\%_d} \quad \text{(Eq. A1)}$$

where:

$$\text{H}_2\%_d = \frac{0.5 \times y \times \text{CO\%}_d \times (\text{CO\%}_d + \text{CO}_2\%_d)}{\text{CO\%}_d + 3 \times \text{CO}_2\%_d} \quad \text{(Eq. A2)}$$

y = H/C atomic ratio of test fuel

Therefore: Species concentration, wet = K x species concentration, dry

For two-stroke-cycle engines, we assume no residual free H_2 and modify K by deleting the H_2 term.

(R) METHANE MEASUREMENT USING GAS CHROMATOGRAPHY—SAE J1151 DEC91

SAE Recommended Practice

Report of the SAE Automotive Emissions Committee approved August 1976, completely revised June 1983, and reaffirmed October 1988. Completely revised by the SAE Exhaust Emissions Measurement Standards Committee December 1991.

Foreword—This Document has also changed to comply with the new SAE Technical Standards Board Format. The Definition Section has changed to Section 3 and Abbreviations changed to Section 4.

1. Scope—This SAE Recommended Practice describes instrumentation for determining the amount of methane in air and exhaust gas.

1.1 Purpose—This document provides a means for a batch measurement of the methane concentration in light-duty vehicle exhaust samples. Nonmethane hydrocarbon concentration can be obtained by subtracting the methane concentration from the total hydrocarbon concentration obtained by a separate measurement made in accordance with accepted practices such as SAE J1094, J254, or a current Federal Test Procedure.[1]

2. References

2.1 Applicable Publications—The following publications form a part of this specification to the extent specified herein. The latest issue of SAE publications shall apply.

2.1.1 SAE PUBLICATIONS—Available from SAE, 400 Commonwealth Drive, Warrendale, PA 15096-0001.

SAE J254—Instrumentation and Techniques for Exhaust Gas Emissions Measurement

SAE J1094—Constant Volume Sampler System for Exhaust Emissions Measurement

SAE J1145—Emissions Terminology and Nomenclature

SAE 770141—Optimization of a Flame Ionization Detector for Determination of Hydrocarbon in Diluted Automotive Exhausts. G.D. Reschke, Vehicle Emission Laboratory, General Motors Proving Ground

3. Definitions

3.1 Vehicle Emission Terms— Defined in SAE J1145.

3.2 Carrier Gas—A gas that acts as a passive vehicle to transport the sample through a gas chromatograph column.

3.3 Gas Chromatography—A separation technique in which a sample in the gaseous state is carried by a flowing gas (carrier gas) through a tube (column) containing stationary material. The stationary material performs the separation by means of its differential affinity for the components of the sample.

4. Abbreviations and Symbols

°C —degree(s) Celsius
CH_4 —methane
CO —carbon monoxide
CO_2 —carbon dioxide
cm —centimeter(s)
CVS —constant volume sampler
FID —flame ionization detector
g —gram
GC —gas chromatograph(ic)
h —hour(s)
HC —hydrocarbon(s)
ID —inside diameter
in —inch(s)
kPa —kilopascal
NMHC —nonmethane hydrocarbon(s)
min —minute(s)
m —meter(s)
mm —millimeter(s)
µm —micrometer(s)
O_2 —oxygen
OD —outside diameter
ppm —parts per million
ppm C —parts per million carbon
psig —pound(s) per square inch, gage
s —second(s)
scfh —standard cubic foot per hour
SAE —Society of Automotive Engineers, Inc.
SS —stainless steel
% —percent

1. See Code of Federal Regulations, Title 40 Protection of Environment, Part 86, Subpart B, Emission Regulations for 1977 and Later Model Year New Light-Duty Vehicles and New Light-Duty Trucks; Test Procedures (40 CFR 86.101 et seq.) (as possibly amended by the Federal Register).

5. Sections—The remainder of this document is divided into the following sections:

6. Equipment
7. Principle of Operation
8. Instrument Operating Procedure
9. Instrument Performance Specifications
10. Maintenance

6. Equipment

6.1 Safety Precautions—Flammable FID fuel (containing hydrogen) and potentially toxic 2% CO in exhaust gas are vented from this instrument at low flow rates of approximately 80 cm^3/min (0.2 scfh). At these low flow rates, there should not normally be a hazard from these gases, but precautions should be observed to insure dilution of these potentially hazardous vented gas streams.

The instrument uses flammable fuel and the precautions specified by the manufacturer should be observed.

The sample bypass line in the instrument has a flow of about 2000 cm^3/min (4 scfh) of automotive exhaust gas. This flow should be discharged outside of the building or into an adequately ventilated area.

6.2 Instrument—A gas chromatograph is used to separate the methane from the other constituents of an exhaust gas sample. The concentration of methane is determined with a FID. A typical suitable gas chromatograph is described in this section.

6.3 Component Description—The schematic diagram in Figure 1 shows a typical gas chromatograph assembled to routinely determine methane. The following components are typically used.

6.3.1 VALVE, V1—Sample injection and switching valve, should be low dead volume, gas tight, and heatable to at least 150 °C.

6.3.2 VALVE, V2—Used to provide supplementary fuel to the FID burner.

6.3.3 VALVE, V3—Used to select span gas, sample, or no flow.

6.3.4 VALVE, V4—Used as a restrictor to match the flow resistance of the Porapak N column.

6.3.5 VALVE, V5—Used as a restrictor to match the flow resistance of the Molecular Sieve column. This valve allows equalizing backflush and foreflush flow rates through the Porapak column.

6.3.6 VALVE, V6—Used as a restrictor for controlling the rate of sample flow to fill the sample loop.

6.3.7 PRESSURE REGULATOR, PR1, AND PRESSURE GAGE, G1—To control flow rate of the fuel which is also the carrier gas.

6.3.8 PRESSURE REGULATOR, PR2, AND PRESSURE GAGE, G2—Back-pressure regulator for controlling the rate of sample flow to the sample loop in conjunction with valve V6. Should be adjusted in the pressure range from 7 to 34 kPa (1 to 5 psig).

6.3.9 GC COLUMN—Porapak N, 180/300 µm (equivalent to 50/80 mesh), 610 mm (2 ft) length x 2.16 mm (0.085 in) ID x 3.18 mm (1/8 in) OD SS, to separate air, CH_4, and CO from the other sample constituents. The column is conditioned 12 h or more at 150 °C with carrier gas flowing prior to initial use. Valve V1 should be in the fill/backflush position during the conditioning.

6.3.10 GC COLUMN—Molecular Sieve Type 13X, 250/350 µm (equivalent to 45/60 mesh), 1220 mm (4 ft) length x 2.16 mm (0.085 in) ID, 3.18 mm (1/8 in) OD SS, to separate methane from oxygen, nitrogen, and CO. The column is conditioned 12 h or more at 150 °C with carrier gas flow prior to initial use. Valve V1 should be in the fill/backflush position during the conditioning.

6.3.11 SAMPLE LOOP—A sufficient length of SS tubing to obtain approximately 1 cm^3 volume.

6.3.12 OVEN—To maintain columns and valves at a stable temperature for analyzer operation, and to condition columns at 150 °C.

6.3.13 VALVE ACTUATOR—To actuate sample injection and switching valve.

6.3.14 VALVE PROGRAMMER—Timing unit to control valve actuator.

6.3.15 DRYER—To remove water and other contaminants which might be present in the carrier gas, a filter dryer containing Molecular Sieve is used. If it is a visual indicating type, the dryer is replaced when the need is indicated. Otherwise, it is replaced or reconditioned monthly. If the dryer has a metal body, it can be reconditioned after removing it from the instrument by flowing approximately 50 cm^3/min of dry nitrogen through the dryer while it is heated to 150 °C in an oven for 12 h.

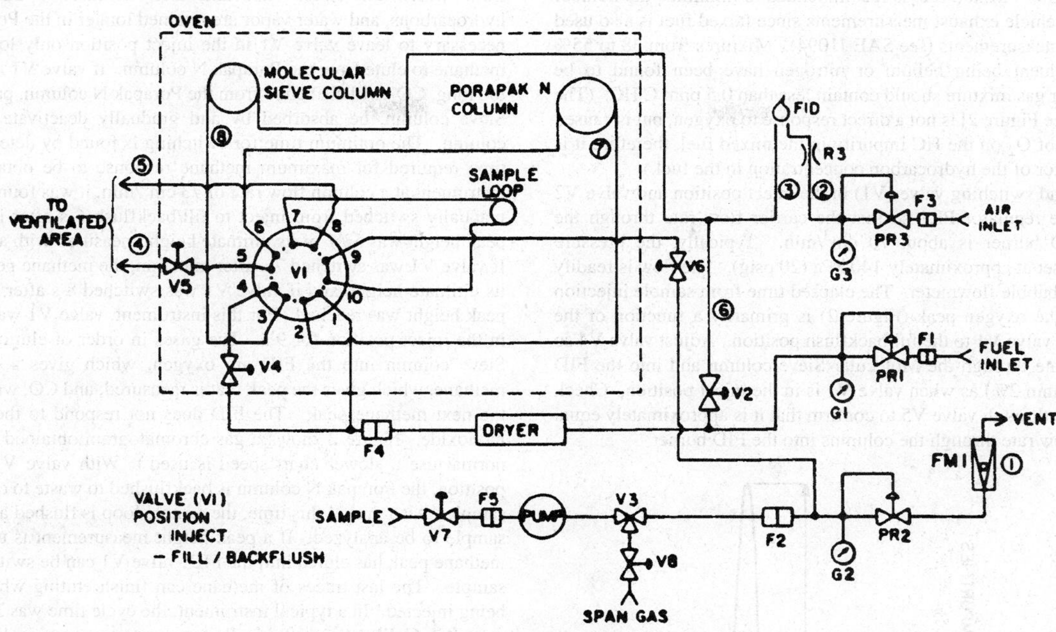

FIGURE 1—INSTRUMENT TO MEASURE METHANE

6.3.16 RESTRICTOR, R3—For controlling the rate of air flow to FID.

6.3.17 PRESSURE REGULATOR, PR3—Used with pressure gage, G3, and restrictor, R3, to control air flow to FID.

6.3.18 FILTERS F1, F3, F4—Sintered metal filters to prevent grit from entering the instrument.

6.3.19 FILTERS F2, F5—Sintered metal filters in the sample stream to prevent grit from entering the pump or instrument. Should be of sufficiently large area to have a pressure drop of less than 15 kPa (2 psi) at the bypass flow rate used of approximately 2000 cm^3/min (4 scfh).

6.3.20 PUMP—Used to bring sample to gas chromatograph.

6.3.21 VALVE, V7—Used with flowmeter, FM1, to regulate bypass sample flow rate. The bypass sample flow rate should be fast enough to flush out the entire sample line in a time less than the GC analysis time so that while an analysis is being made, the sample loop is filled with the next sample and is ready for the next analysis cycle. A typical bypass flow rate would be 2000 cm^3/min (4 scfh).

6.3.22 VALVE, V8—Used with flowmeter, FM1, to equalize bypass flow rates of span gas and sample.

6.3.23 RECORDER—The recorder or other readout device should have an input compatible with the FID analyzer output, an accuracy (including the effects of deadband and linearity) of ±0.25% of full scale or better, a span step response time of 0.4 s or less, and a chart speed of approximately 25 mm/min (1 in/min).

6.3.24 FID—The flame ionization detector generates an electrical current proportional to the flow rate of methane throughout the burner. The associated electrometer amplifier acts as a current to voltage converter and should have an electronic time constant of less than 0.20 s.

7. Principle of Operation—The instrument (Figure 1) measures the methane concentration in a sample swept from a fixed volume sample loop by a carrier gas stream when the valve (V1) is in the inject position. The carrier gas can be blended FID fuel. The stream enters the Porapak N gas chromatographic column which temporarily retains NMHC, CO_2, and water, and passes air, methane, and CO to the Molecular Sieve column. As soon as all of the methane elutes from the Porapak N column and has passed through valve V1 toward the Molecular Sieve column, the Porapak N column is backflushed to waste by switching the valve (V1) to the fill/backflush position. Switching V1 also starts filling the sample loop with the next sample. The Molecular Sieve column separates the methane from the air and CO before passing it to the FID. The FID produces a signal peak proportional to the methane concentration in the sample. As soon as the methane peak passes through the FID, valve V1 can be switched back to the inject position to inject the next sample. A complete cycle, from injection of one sample to injection of a second, can be made in 30 s. Automation of injection and backflush switching assures reproducible peak times and shapes and is easily accomplished.

8. Instrument Operating Procedure

8.1 In general, the manufacturer's instructions for operation of the instrument or gas chromatograph should be followed.

8.2 Component Assembly—The assembly of the components for the instrument is shown in Figure 1. The sample and switching valve V1, restrictor valves V4 and V5, sample loop, and the two GC columns are installed in the oven. The outlet of valve V5 and the outlet from valve V1, port 8 must discharge directly into an open area at atmospheric pressure where there can be no effluent build-up. The other components are connected outside the oven with all connecting tubing of minimum length. After all of the connections have been made, as indicated in Figure 1, leak check the fittings and the instrument is ready for adjustment of operating parameters.

8.3 Initial Adjustment of Operating Parameters—The timing sequence is determined by the flow rates of the carrier gas, the gas holdup volume of the system, and the column temperature. Typical flow rates at several instrument locations identified by the encircled numerals in Figure 1 are given in Table 1. The following procedure would typically be followed to determine satisfactory flow rates of the assembled system and the switching times of the valves.

TABLE 1—TYPICAL FLOW RATES

Location (Figure 1)	Valve V1 Position Inject Flow Rate - cm3/min (room pressure and temp.)	Valve V1 Position Fill/Backflush Flow Rate - cm3/min (room pressure and temp.)
1. Sampler Bypass Vent	2000	2000
2. Burner Air	400	400
3. Total Burner Fuel(1)	100	100
4. Backflush	60	60
5. Sample	95	90
6. Makeup Fuel(1)	30	30
7. Porapak N Column(1)	70(2)	60
8. Molecular Sieve Column(1)	70(2)	70(2)

1. Fuel: 40% H_2/60% He.
2. These flow rates were measured at location 3 with valve V2 closed.

8.3.1 Set the initial operating parameters. Record oven temperature, gas pressures, and flow rates for later reference.

8.3.1.1 Sample—Adjust the flow of span gas or sample with V8 or V7 so that the flow discharged to the vent is about 2000 cm^3/min (4 scfh). Adjust back-pressure regulator PR2 so that gage G2 reads from 7 to 34 kPa (1 to 5 psig). Readjust span gas or sample bypass flow to 2000 cm^3/min. With valve V1 in the fill/backflush position, adjust valve V6 so that the flow from port 8 of valve V1 is 80 to 100 cm^3/min.

8.3.1.2 Carrier Gas—Mixed fuel is recommended to minimize the number of gases required for vehicle exhaust measurements since mixed fuel is also used for total hydrocarbon measurements (see SAE J1094). Mixtures from 38 to 55% hydrogen with the diluent being helium or nitrogen have been found to be acceptable. The carrier gas mixture should contain less than 0.5 ppm C HC. (The oxygen peak height [see Figure 2] is not a direct response to oxygen, but is caused by a synergistic effect of O_2 on the HC impurity in the mixed fuel, therefore it is an approximate indicator of the hydrocarbon concentration in the fuel.)

With sampling and switching valve (V1) in the inject position and valve V2 closed, adjust pressure regulator PR1 so that the carrier flow rate through the columns into the FID burner is about 70 cm^3/min. Typically, the pressure regulator PR1 will be set at approximately 140 kPa (20 psig). The flow is readily measured with a soap bubble flowmeter. The elapsed time from sample injection to the appearance of the oxygen peak (Figure 2) is primarily a function of the carrier flow rate. Turn valve V1 to the fill/backflush position. Adjust valve V4 so that the carrier flow rate through the Molecular Sieve column and into the FID burner is the same (within 2%) as when valve V1 is in the inject position. Check the backflush flow rate through valve V5 to confirm that it is approximately equal (within 30%) to the flow rate through the columns into the FID burner.

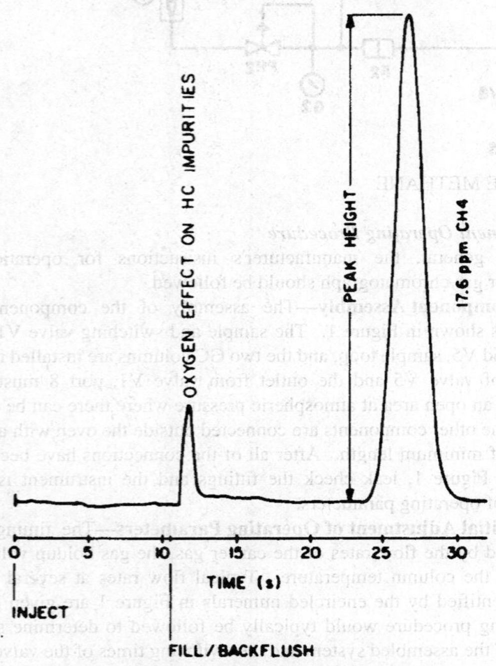

FIGURE 2—TYPICAL GAS CHROMATOGRAM

8.3.1.3 Column Conditioning—With valve V1 in fill/backflush position and carrier gas flowing, adjust oven temperature to 150 °C and condition columns for a minimum of 12 h. After conditioning, adjust oven temperature to about 55 °C.

8.3.1.4 Additional Fuel—Open valve V2 to provide a total hydrogen flow to the FID burner of about 40 cm^3/min (for example, 100 cm^3/min of 40% H_2/60% He fuel).

8.3.1.5 Air (Should Contain Less Than 0.5 ppm C HC)—Set the pressure regulator PR3 so that the air flow to the FID burner is approximately ten times the hydrogen flow.

8.3.1.6 Column Oven Temperature—The column oven should be maintained at a constant temperature. A temperature of about 55 °C will allow an analysis time of 30 s. The temperature can be adjusted between 35 and 75 °C in order to give a desired analysis time. Allow time for oven temperature to stabilize before making measurements. The temperature control setting that maintains 150 °C for use in conditioning the GC columns should be ascertained before column installation.

8.3.2 TIMING SEQUENCE—The analysis starts with valve V1 in the fill/backflush position. In this position, the sample loop is flushed and filled with sample (flow rate 80 to 100 cm^3/min). With a typical instrument, it was found that if the sample select valve, V3, selected the next sample at least 6 s before sample injection, the sample loop was fully flushed and, hence, a longer flush and fill time gave the same analytical results. The sample is injected by switching valve V1 into the inject position. The sample passes into the Porapak N column from which air elutes first and then methane. Carbon dioxide, higher hydrocarbons, and water vapor are retained longer in the Porapak N column. It is necessary to leave valve V1 in the inject position only long enough for all the methane to elute from the Porapak N column. If valve V1 is in the inject position too long, CO_2 will also elute from the Porapak N column, pass onto the Molecular Sieve column, be absorbed by and gradually deactivate the Molecular Sieve column. The optimum time for switching is found by determining the minimum time required for maximum methane response to be obtained. With a typical instrument at a column flow rate of 73 cm^3/min, it was found that if valve V1 was manually switched from inject to fill/backflush 6 s after injection, the methane peak height was 53% of its ultimate height measured with a later valve switching. If valve V1 was switched 7 s after injection, the methane peak height was 95% of its ultimate height, and if valve V1 was switched 8 s after injection, the ultimate peak height was reached. For this instrument, valve V1 was programmed to stay in the inject position for 9 s. The gases in order of elution from the Molecular Sieve column into the FID are oxygen, which gives a small peak; nitrogen; methane, which gives the peak that is measured; and CO, which elutes well before the next methane peak. The FID does not respond to the nitrogen and carbon monoxide. Figure 2 shows a gas chromatogram obtained with this system. (In normal use a slower chart speed is used.) With valve V1 in the fill/backflush position, the Porapak N column is backflushed to waste to clean it out for the next sample. Also during this time, the sample loop is flushed and filled with the next sample to be analyzed. If a peak height measurement is used, after most of the methane peak has eluted into the FID, valve V1 can be switched to inject the next sample. The last traces of methane can finish eluting while the next sample is being injected. In a typical instrument, the cycle time was 30 s.

8.4 Calibration—Typically, analyzer response is linear (not necessarily passing through the origin) with the methane content of the sample. However, this should be verified for each analyzer prior to its introduction into service and at monthly intervals thereafter. The linearity should also be verified whenever the FID burner is serviced and whenever the fuel carrier gas supply is changed. A series of four or more calibration gases, containing methane of known concentration in air, covering the range of concentrations within which sample gases may be expected to fall, should be used for calibration. Optionally, a flow blender may be used to blend a single calibration gas with zero grade air to provide a series of intermediate calibration gases. The methane impurity of the zero grade air should be determined and considered in the calculation of the methane concentration of the intermediate gases. Obtain the least-squares straight line regression of the methane concentration in the calibration gas as a function of methane peak height (or, if used, peak area). It is recommended that the datum point obtained with zero grade air should not be included in the regression. The reason is that if the methane concentration in the zero grade air is lower than the methane concentration in the carrier gas, the sample of zero grade air will produce a negative methane peak. Many peak height or peak area measuring schemes cannot correctly determine the height or area of the negative peak. For each range calibrated, if the deviation of the calibration points from the regression line is 2% or less, or within 0.1 ppm methane, of the value of each data point (excluding zero), then linearity is confirmed and a linear equation may be used to determine the methane concentration. Otherwise, attempt to find and correct the cause of the nonlinearity. If necessary, the best fit nonlinear equation which represents the data to within 2% (or 0.1 ppm methane) of each point may be used to determine the concentration.

8.5 Emission Measurement Procedure—Each series of sample and dilution air bags from one vehicle test should be preceded with a measurement of zero gas and span gas. If the instrument output for these gases is not the same as during the last calibration, an electrical or computational correction to the instrument output should be made. Recheck zero. Six methane analyses can be made in 4 min. A measurement of zero gas and span gas following the test series which is within 2% of full scale from the initial values will confirm that there was no substantial instrument drift during the measurement of the test samples. The instrument should be located near the CVS in order to minimize the length of tubing. Samples are pumped directly from the bag via a Teflon or stainless steel tube to the sample inlet.

8.6 Data Analysis—The methane peak height is used as a measure of the amount of methane. Peak height is the distance from the peak maximum to the peak baseline. The peak baseline is defined as the plateau immediately preceding the peak. (Alternatively, the methane peak area, as determined with an integrator, can be used as a measure of the amount of methane.) Methane concentrations are measured directly, NMHC concentrations can be determined by the difference between an independent total hydrocarbon concentration measurement and the methane concentration.

8.6.1 METHANE—The following example for a linear analyzer illustrates the method of calculation:

Span—18.9 ppm C methane—50.0 chart divisions
Bag Analysis
Methane—25.0 chart divisions
Bag Concentration Calculation
Methane—18.9 × (25.0/50.0) = 9.45 ppm C

For calculating the mass of methane by a method analogous to that used in the Federal Test Procedure[2] for hydrocarbons, the methane density at 20 °C (68 °F) and 101.32 kPa (760 mm Hg) pressure should be taken to be 0.667 kg/m^3 (18.89 g/ft^3).

8.6.2 NONMETHANE HYDROCARBON—The response of the total HC FID to the methane component of the mixed hydrocarbon sample is subtracted from the total hydrocarbon response of the FID to yield the determination of the nonmethane hydrocarbon concentration.

The total HC FID response to the carbon in methane is typically greater than its response to the carbon in propane. It has been shown (SAE J254 AUG84, paragraph 4.2; SAE 770141) that the FID relative response can be changed by varying fuel diluent (N_2 or He) and the flow rates of sample, fuel, and combustion air to the FID. With conditions where methane reads high relative to propane, olefins and aromatics will read low relative to propane — the higher the methane response, the lower the olefin response. The under-response of the FID to olefins will not be compensated for when the true methane effect is subtracted out. Therefore, the total HC FID should have a reasonably uniform response to the different hydrocarbons in the sample.

Using 40% hydrogen/60% helium FID fuel flowing at 100 cm^3/min, a 5 cm^3/min sample flow rate into the burner, and a 400 cm^3/min air flow rate, the FID response to methane can be only 7% higher than to propane.

The following example for a linear analyzer illustrates the method of calculation:

Span—18.9 ppm C methane—50.0 chart divisions
Bag Analysis
Methane—25.0 chart divisions
Total HC—82.56 ppm C
Total HC FID response to methane relative to FID response to propane (FID calibrated with propane)—1.07
Bag Concentration Calculations
Methane—18.9 × (25.0/50.0) = 9.45 ppm C
NMHC—total HC (ppm C) - (methane response × methane [ppm C])
= 82.56 – (1.07 × 9.45) = 72.45 ppm C

The exhaust sample and the dilution-air bags should be analyzed and the NMHC concentrations used for calculation of mass emissions as directed in the Federal Test Procedure[3] for hydrocarbon.

Note that, in general, the sum of the methane mass emissions and the calculated NMHC mass emissions will not exactly equal the total calculated HC mass emissions. This is because the FID measures carbon mass and not hydrocarbon mass. The relation between these two masses depends on the hydrogen/carbon ratio of the hydrocarbons in the exhaust gas and this is not determined for each sample. Instead, a nominal value for the hydrogen/carbon ratio is assumed in the Federal regulations.

9. Instrument Performance Specifications

9.1 Baseline Noise—The instrument shall be run for 20 min with valve V1 remaining in the fill/backflush position. The peak-to-peak noise and drift of the baseline shall not exceed the equivalent of 0.16 ppm methane. (With a typical instrument, the peak-to-peak noise and drift was 0.07 ppm methane.)

9.2 Precision—A span gas containing about 20 ppm methane in air shall be read at least 25 times. Wait one cycle period (typically 30 s) between starting the flow of span gas and the first rotation of valve V1 into the inject position. The standard deviation of the series of span gas readings shall not exceed 0.10 ppm methane. (With a typical instrument the standard deviation of a series of span gas readings was 0.02 ppm methane.) Since the first reading of the series is most apt to show an offset, the magnitude of the difference between the first determination of the series and the mean of the series shall be no greater than 0.14 ppm methane or 3.3 standard deviations, whichever is greater.

9.3 Column Resolution—The methane retention time (see 10.2.1) divided by the peak width at half height (see 10.2.2) shall exceed 10.5 (In Figure 2 this quotient is 11.5.)

10. Maintenance

10.1 Valve V1 Position—Except when actually injecting a sample, valve V1 should be kept in the fill/backflush position so as to minimize possible contamination of the Molecular Sieve column by effluent from the Porapak N Column.

10.2 Column Performance

10.2.1 The methane retention time, which is the elapsed time from sample injection (sample injection is when valve V1 rotates from the fill/backflush position to the inject position) to the appearance of the methane peak maximum, should be measured when the instrument is placed in service and at weekly intervals thereafter. A change in the retention time from its initial value gives an indication that the column has deteriorated or that the initial conditions have changed. If the retention time has changed by more than 10%, the cause should be identified and corrected. Check oven temperature. Check or condition the dryer as described in 6.3.15. Check the carrier gas flow rates against the flow rates initially measured as described in 8.3.1.2. Check for leaks. Condition the columns as described in 6.3.9 and 6.3.10.

10.2.2 Time the width of the methane peak at half of its peak height using a stopwatch or a gas chromatogram obtained with the recorder running at a fast speed of at least 0.3 m/min (1 ft/min). Perform this test when the instrument is first placed in service and at monthly intervals thereafter. A change in the peak width at half height of more than 15% suggests that the cause be identified as in 10.2.1.

10.3 Dryer Conditioning—If an indicating type dryer is used, it should be checked monthly and replaced if exhaustion is indicated. If a non-indicating type dryer is used, it should be replaced or reconditioned monthly. (See 6.3.15.)

2. See Code of Federal Regulations, Title 40 Protection of Environment, Part 86, Subpart B, Emission Regulations for 1977 and Later Model Year New Light-Duty Vehicles and New Light-Duty Trucks; Test Procedures (40 CFR 86.101 et seq.) (as possibly amended by the Federal Register).
3. See Code of Federal Regulations, Title 40 Protection of Environment, Part 86, Subpart B, Emission Regulations for 1977 and Later Model Year New Light-Duty Vehicles and New Light-Duty Trucks; Test Procedures (40 CFR 86. 101 et seq.) (as possibly amended by the Federal Register).

14 Sound Level

MAXIMUM SOUND LEVEL POTENTIAL FOR MOTORCYCLES—SAE J47 JUL1998

SAE Recommended Practice

Report of the Vehicle Sound Level Committee and Motorcycle Committee, approved May 1975. Revised by the Motorcycle Committee June 1986. Rationale statement available. Revised by the Motorcycle Sound Level Subcommittee of the Motorcycle Committee and the Specialized Vehicle and Equipment Sound Level Committee, October 1993. Reaffirmed by the Motorcycle Committee, July 1998. Rationale statement available.

***Foreword*—**This Reaffirmed Document has been changed only to comply with the new SAE Technical Standards Board Format. The Definitions Section has been changed to Section 3. All other section numbers have changed accordingly.

***1. Scope*—**This SAE Recommended Practice establishes the test procedure, environment, and instrumentation for determining the maximum sound level potential for motorcycles under wide open throttle acceleration and closed throttle deceleration.

2. References

2.1 Applicable Publications—The following publications form a part of this specification to the extent specified herein. Unless otherwise indicated, the latest issue of SAE publications shall apply.

2.1.1 SAE PUBLICATIONS—Available from the Society of Automotive Engineers, Inc., 400 Commonwealth Drive, Warrendale, PA 15096-0001.

SAE J184—Qualifying a Sound Data Acquisition System
SAE J213—Definitions, Motorcycles
SAE J331—Sound Levels for Motorcycles
SAE J1349—Engine Power Test Code—Spark Ignition and Diesel

2.1.2 ANSI PUBLICATION—Available from the American National Standards Institute, 11 West 42nd Street, New York, NY 10036-8002.

ANSI S1.4-1983—Sound Level Meters, Specifications for

3. Definitions

3.1 Rated Engine Speed—The speed in revolutions per minute at which the engine delivers maximum net brake power output as defined in SAE J1349, as determined by the manufacturer.

3.2 Manual Clutch—A clutch which must be disengaged by the operator to prevent engine stalling when the vehicle's forward motion is stopped.

3.3 Longitudinal Plane of Symmetry—As defined in SAE J213.

***4. Instrumentation*—**The following instrumentation shall be used where applicable.

4.1 A sound level meter which meets the Type 1 or Type S1A requirements of ANSI S1.4-1983. As an alternative to making direct measurements using a sound level meter, a microphone or sound level meter may be used with a magnetic tape recorder or a graphic level recorder or other indicating equipment, provided that the system meets the requirements of SAE J184.

4.2 An acoustic calibrator with accuracy of ±0.5 dB. (See 8.6.4(see 8.6.4).)

4.3 An engine speed tachometer, or other means of determining engine speed, with steady-state accuracy of ±3% at 60% and 100% of rated engine speed.

4.4 A speedometer with steady-state accuracy of ±3% at a vehicle speed of 100 km/h, or the vehicle maximum speed, whichever is less.

4.5 An anemometer with steady-state accuracy of ±10% at a wind speed of 5.0 m/s.

4.6 An acceptable wind screen may be used with the microphone. To be acceptable, the screen shall not affect the microphone response more than ±1 dB for frequencies of 4000 to 10 000 Hz, taking into account the orientation of the microphone.

5. Test Site

5.1 The test site (Figure 1) shall be a flat open space accommodating a straight vehicle path and the following points:

5.1.1 ON THE VEHICLE PATH

A—Microphone target point
B—End point—a point 7.5 m beyond the microphone target point
C—Acceleration point—a point at least 7.5 m before to the microphone target point established by the method described in 6.2(see 6.2) and 6.3(see 6.3).
D—A point 15 m before the microphone target point
E—A point 15 m beyond the microphone target point

5.1.2 OFF THE VEHICLE PATH

F—Microphone point—a point 15 m from the centerline of the vehicle path on the perpendicular line which passes through the microphone target point.

5.2 The measurement area within the test site shall be a triangular area defined by the microphone point (F) and the points D and E. The surface of the ground within at least this area shall be portland cement or bituminous asphalt concrete, dry and free from snow, soil, or other extraneous material.

5.3 The test site shall be free of large sound-reflecting surfaces (other than the ground) such as parked vehicles, signboards, buildings, or hillsides, located within 30 m of the measurement area.

5.4 The vehicle path shall be relatively smooth portland cement or bituminous asphalt concrete, dry and free of extraneous material such as gravel, snow, or ice and of sufficient length for acceleration, deceleration, and stopping of the vehicle.

5.5 The microphone of the sound measurement system shall be located above the microphone point. The microphone shall be positioned 1.2 m ± 0.02 m above the ground plane. The microphone's reference axis shall be perpendicular to the vehicle path. (See 8.6.1.)

5.6 The test site layout in Figure 1, for the purposes of clarity, illustrates an approach from left to right. Sound level measurements are to be made on both sides of the vehicle; therefore, it will be necessary to establish either a second microphone point on the opposite side of the vehicle path with a corresponding measurement and clear area, or use approaches from both directions with corresponding acceleration points and end points.

6. Procedure

6.1 Overview—The intention of this test is to have the vehicle under test reach the end point under its maximum noise conditions—at wide open throttle and at rated engine speed, or as close to rated engine speed as the powertrain and conditions permit. Vehicles with a manual clutch approach the acceleration point at a steady engine speed. All other vehicles begin accelerating from the acceleration point using a standing start procedure. Each vehicle uses a different acceleration point in the test. The acceleration point for each vehicle is established by, basically, running the test procedure in the reverse direction in order to determine how to run the test in the normal direction.

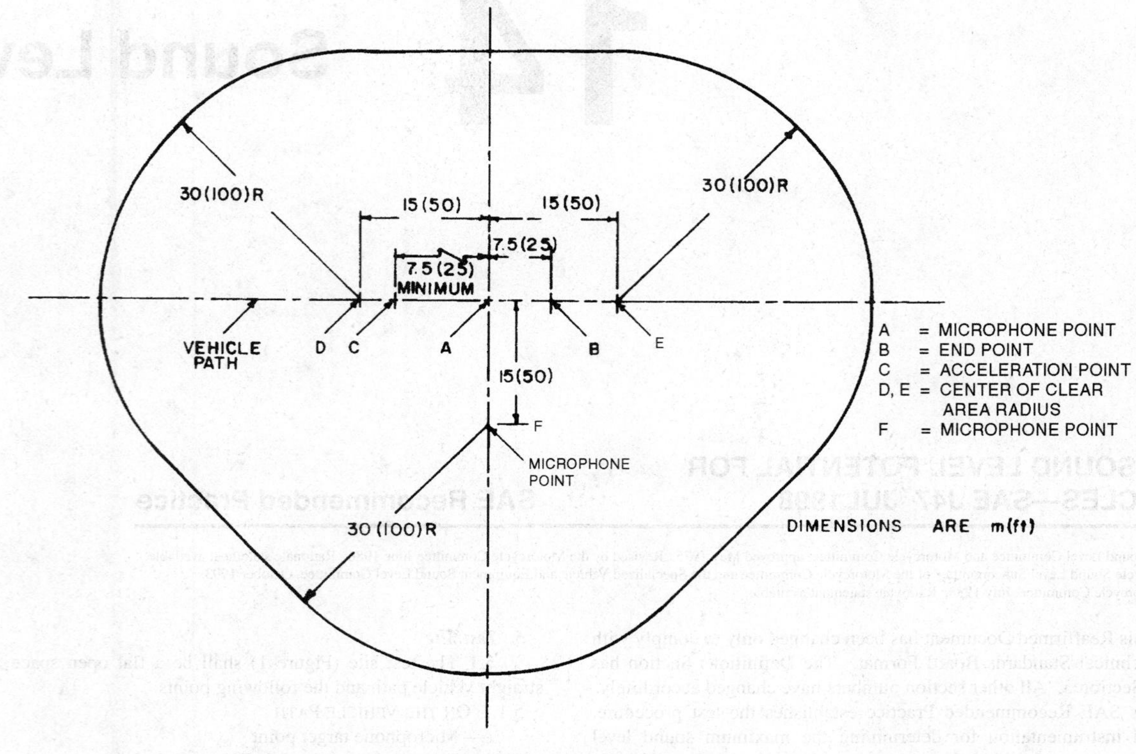

FIGURE 1—TEST SITE

6.2 To establish the acceleration point for vehicles with a manual clutch—the end point shall be approached in first gear from the direction opposite to the direction of the test run at a constant speed corresponding to 60% of rated engine speed. When the front of the vehicle reaches the end point, the throttle shall be rapidly and fully opened to accelerate the motorcycle past the microphone target point under wide open throttle. By trial, the lowest transmission gear shall be selected that will result in the vehicle traveling the shortest distance from the end point to the place where rated engine speed is reached, but which is not less than 7.5 m past the microphone target point. The location of the front of the vehicle on the vehicle path when rated engine speed is attained shall be acceleration point for test runs to be made in the opposite direction.

6.2.1 When the procedure described in (see 6.1)6.1 results in an unusual operating condition such as wheel spin with which the rider is not comfortable, the next higher gear shall be selected for the test, and the procedure rerun to establish the new acceleration point. In any event, the procedure shall result in the vehicle being at the end point when rated engine speed is attained.

6.3 Vehicles without a manual clutch shall use a standing start acceleration, starting from the end point, to establish the acceleration point. With the front of the vehicle at the end point and with the transmission in the lowest selectable range, the throttle shall be rapidly and fully opened to accelerate the motorcycle past the microphone target point under wide open throttle.

6.3.1 For vehicles that allow for operator selection of transmission gear ratio, the lowest transmission gear shall be selected, by trial, that will result in the vehicle traveling the shortest distance from the end point to the place where rated engine speed is reached, but which is not less than 7.5 m past the microphone target point. The location of the front of the vehicle on the vehicle path when rated engine speed is attained shall be the acceleration point for test runs to be made in the opposite direction.

6.3.2 For vehicles that do not allow for operator selection of transmission gear ratio, the location of the front of the vehicle on the vehicle path immediately before the place where the first transmission upshift occurs which is not less than 7.5 m past the microphone target point, shall be the acceleration point for the test runs to be made in the opposite direction.

6.3.2.1 For vehicles with continuously variable transmissions, the location of the front of the vehicle on the vehicle path where the vehicle speed reaches its maximum or 100 km/h, whichever is lower, shall be the acceleration point for test runs to be made in the opposite direction.

6.3.3 If the speed at the acceleration point established in 6.3.1(see 6.3.1) or (see 6.3.2)6.3.2 is over 100 km/h, then the procedure to establish the acceleration point shall be rerun and the location of the front of the vehicle on the vehicle path where the vehicle speed reaches 100 km/h, shall be the acceleration point for test runs to be made in the opposite direction.

6.4 For the test under acceleration, the same basic procedure shall be used as was used in establishing the acceleration point, except that test runs shall be made in the opposite direction. The rider shall rapidly and fully open the throttle when the front of the vehicle reaches the acceleration point to accelerate the motorcycle past the microphone target point under wide open throttle. Full acceleration shall continue until the applicable ending conditions determined according to 6.2(see 6.2) or 6.3(see 6.3) are achieved, which should be the end point, at which time the throttle shall be rapidly and fully closed.

6.5 Sufficient preliminary runs shall be made before measurements begin to familiarize the rider with the motorcycle under test and to establish the engine operating conditions. The engine temperature shall be within the normal operating range prior to each run.

6.6 The longitudinal plane of symmetry of the test vehicle shall be on the vehicle path for all test runs.

6.7 Unless it is apparent that maximum noise occurs under acceleration, the following test shall be performed to establish maximum sound levels under deceleration.

6.7.1 For the test under deceleration for vehicles tested under 6.2(see 6.2), the vehicle shall approach the end point from the reverse direction at rated engine speed in the gear selected for the test under acceleration. At the end point, the throttle shall be rapidly and fully closed and the vehicle shall be allowed to decelerate to an engine speed of one half of rated engine speed.

6.7.2 For the test under deceleration for vehicles tested under 6.3(see 6.3), a standing start procedure shall be used. The starting point shall be a point on the vehicle path which is the same distance from the end point as the acceleration point, except in the opposite direction. With the front of the vehicle at this point, the throttle shall be rapidly and fully opened to accelerate the motorcycle to the end point under wide open throttle. When the front of the vehicle reaches the end point, the throttle shall be rapidly and fully closed and the vehicle shall be allowed to decelerate to a vehicle speed which is one-half that achieved at the end point.

7. Measurements

7.1 The sound level meter shall be set for fast response and for the A-weighting network.

7.2 The ambient sound level (including wind effects) at the test site, due to sources other than the vehicle being measured, shall be at least 10 dB lower than the peak sound level produced by the vehicle under test.

7.3 Measurements shall be made only when the wind speed is below 5.0 m/s.

7.4 The following measurements shall be made for both the acceleration and, if conducted, deceleration test modes:

7.4.1 Measurements shall be taken for both sides of the vehicle.

7.4.2 The meter shall be observed during each test as the vehicle is accelerating or decelerating. The highest sound level observed for each side during each test run shall be recorded.

7.4.3 Sufficient test runs shall be made until at least four recorded measurements for each test mode and each side of the vehicle are within a 2 dB range. The sound level for that side and test mode shall be the arithmetic average of the first four measurements within a 2 dB range.

7.5 The sound level reported for the vehicle shall be the sound level of the side and test mode with the highest average sound level.

8. General Comments

8.1 Technically competent personnel should select equipment, and the test should be conducted only by trained and experienced persons familiar with the current techniques of sound measurement.

8.2 While making sound level measurements, not more than one person other than the rider and the observer reading the meter shall be within 15 m of the vehicle or microphone. The additional person shall be directly behind the meter observer on a line through the microphone and the observer.

8.3 The test rider should be fully conversant with and qualified to ride the machine under test, and be familiar with the test procedure.

8.4 It should be noted that error in the engine speed indicator as well as error due to operator response time may result in sound level measurement error.

8.5 Tachometers having steady-state accuracy within 3% of actual engine speed at 60% and 100% of the rated engine speed are commercially available and are included on some motorcycles as original equipment. This class of tachometers is regarded as being sufficiently accurate for general sound level measurements. In circumstances where very accurate sound level measurements are necessary, accurate engine speed determination is essential, and consideration must be given to the accuracy and response time of the engine speed measurement system. Special care must be taken not to exceed rated engine speed. Exact engine speed measurement must be based on the time interval for not less than one complete engine cycle; i.e., two crankshaft revolutions for a four-stroke engine.

8.6 Proper use of all test instrumentation is essential in obtaining valid measurements. Operating manuals or other literature furnished by the instrument manufacturer should be referred to for both recommended operation of the instrument and precautions to be observed. Specific items to be considered are:

8.6.1 The type of microphone, its directional response characteristics, and its orientation relative to the ground plane and source of noise.

8.6.2 The effects of ambient weather conditions (i.e., temperature, humidity, and barometric pressure) on the performance of all instruments.

8.6.3 Proper signal levels, terminating impedances, and cable lengths on multi-instrument measurement systems.

8.6.4 Proper acoustical calibration procedures, including the influence of extension cables, etc., shall be followed. Field calibration shall be made immediately before and after each test sequence. Internal calibration is acceptable for field use, provided that external calibration is accomplished immediately before or after field use.

8.7 This procedure, SAE J47, was developed primarily as a tool to determine the maximum sound level potential for motorcycles, and in no way intends to represent the way in which a motorcycle is driven on the public highways. The procedure SAE J331 was developed to yield noise from a new motorcycle under operating conditions more similar to motorcycles accelerating rapidly up to cruising speed on an expressway on-ramp.

SOUND LEVELS FOR MOTORCYCLES —SAE J331 JAN2000

SAE Recommended Practice

Report of the SAE Vehicle Sound Level Committee and Motorcycle Committee, approved May 1975 and completely revised by the SAE Motorcyle Committee May 1987. Reaffirmed by the SAE Motorcycle Sound Level Subcommittee of the SAE Motorcycle Committee October 1992 and January 2000.

1. Scope—This SAE Recommended Practice establishes the test procedure, environment, and instrumentation for determining the sound levels of motorcycles under full throttle acceleration and closed throttle deceleration.

2. References

2.1 Applicable Publications—The following publications form a part of the specification to the extent specified herein. Unless otherwise indicated, the latest revision of SAE publications shall apply.

2.1.1 SAE PUBLICATIONS—Available from SAE, 400 Commonwealth Drive, Warrendale, PA 15096-0001.

SAE J47—Maximum Sound Level Potential for Motorcycles
SAE J184—Qualifying a Sound Data Acquisition System
SAE J213a—Definitions—Motorcycles
SAE J1349—Engine Power Test Code—Spark Ignition and Diesel

2.1.2 ANSI PUBLICATION—Available from ANSI, 11 West 42nd Street, New York, NY 10036-8002.

ANSI S1.4-1983—Specification for Sound Level Meters

3. Definitions

3.1 Manual Transmission—A transmission having multiple discrete gear ratios which are individually selectable by the vehicle operator.

3.2 Automatic Transmission—A transmission which does not have multiple discrete gear ratios individually selectable by the vehicle operator.

3.3 Rated Engine Speed—The engine speed in revolutions per minute at which the engine delivers its maximum net brake power as defined in SAE J1349 as determined by the manufacturer.

3.4 Longitudinal Plane of Symmetry—As defined in SAE J213a.

4. Instrumentation

4.1 The following instrumentation shall be used where applicable:

4.1.1 A sound level meter which meets the Type 1 or Type S1A requirements of ANSI S1.4-1983. As an alternative to making direct measurements using a sound level meter, a microphone or sound level meter may be used with a magnetic tape recorder and/or a graphic level recorder or other indicating instrument, provided that the system meets the requirements of SAE J184.

4.1.2 An acoustic calibrator with an accuracy of ±0.5 dB (see 9.6.4).

4.1.3 An engine speed tachometer, or other means of determining engine speed, with a steady-state accuracy of ±3% at 60% and 100% of rated engine speed.

4.1.4 A speedometer with steady-state accuracy of ±3% at a vehicle speed of 50 km/h (31 mph).

4.1.5 An anemometer with steady-state accuracy of ±10% at a wind speed of 5.5 m/s (12 mph).

4.1.6 An acceptable windscreen may be used with the microphone. To be acceptable, the screen shall not affect the microphone response more than ±1 dB for frequencies of 4000 to 10 000 Hz, taking into account the orientation of the microphone.

5. Test Site

5.1 The test site (Figure 1) shall be a flat open space accommodating a straight vehicle path and the following points:

On the vehicle path—

(A) The microphone target point

(B) Acceleration point—a point 7.5 m (24 ft 7 in) prior to the microphone target point

(C) End point—a point 30 m (98 ft) beyond the microphone target point

(D) A point 15 m (49 ft 2 in) prior to the microphone target point

(E) A point 15 m (49 ft 2 in) beyond the microphone target point

Off the vehicle path—

(F) Microphone point—a point 15 m (49 ft 2 in) from the vehicle path on the perpendicular line which passess through the microphone target point

5.2 The measurement area (G) within the test site shall be a triangular area defined by the microphone point (F) and the points D and E. The surface of the ground within the measurement area shall be Portland cement or bituminous asphalt concrete, dry and free from snow, soil, or other extraneous material.

5.3 The test site shall be free of large sound reflecting surfaces (other than the ground) such as parked vehicles, signboards, buildings, or hillsides, located within 30 m (98 ft) of the measurement area.

5.4 The vehicle path shall be on relatively smooth Portland cement or bituminous asphalt concrete, dry and free of extraneous material such as gravel, snow, or ice and of sufficient length for acceleration, deceleration, and stopping of the vehicle (see 7.1.4).

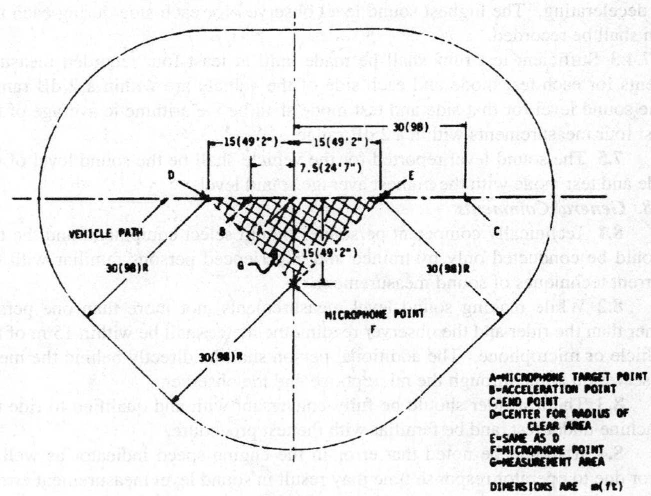

FIGURE 1—TEST SITE

5.5 The microphone of the sound level measurement system shall be located above the microphone point. The microphone shall be positioned 1.2 m ± 0.02 m (3 ft 11-1/4 in ± 3/4 in) above the ground plane. The microphone's reference axis shall be perpendicular to the vehicle path. (Also see 9.6 and 9.6.1.)

5.6 The test site layout in Figure 1, for purposes of clarity, illustrates an approach from left to right. Sound level measurements are to be made on both sides of the vehicle; therefore, it will be necessary to establish either a sound microphone location on the opposite side of the vehicle path with a corresponding clear area, or to use approaches from both directions with corresponding acceleration points and end points.

6. Test Mass

6.1 At the start of the test series, the vehicle shall be filled with fuel to not less than 75% capacity and other fluids to a nominal, full capacity.

6.2 The combined mass of the test rider and test equipment used on the vehicle shall be not more than 90 kg (198.5 lb) or less than 75 kg (165.4 lb).

If necessary, the vehicle/rider shall be laden with additional mass to compensate for any difference between the actual driver/equipment mass and the required 75 kg (165.4 lb) minimum.

7. Procedure

7.1 The following test shall be performed with sufficient runs (see 8.4) to establish maximum sound levels under acceleration:

7.1.1 Vehicles with manual transmissions shall proceed along the vehicle path in second gear at a constant approach speed which shall correspond to an engine speed of 60% of rated engine speed or a speed of 50 km/h (31 mph) whichever is slower. When the front of the vehicle reaches the acceleration point, the throttle shall be rapidly and fully opened to accelerate the motorcycle along the vehicle path until the front of the vehicle reaches the end point, or until rated engine speed is reached, at which time the throttle shall be rapidly and fully closed.

7.1.2 Vehicles with automatic transmissions shall use a standing start procedure. The front of the vehicle shall be at the acceleration point and with the transmission in the lowest selectable range, the throttle shall be rapidly and fully opened to accelerate the motorcycle along the vehicle path, until the front of the vehicle reaches the end point, or until rated engine speed is reached, at which time the throttle shall be rapidly and fully closed.

7.1.3 The maximum engine speed attained during each run shall be recorded.

7.1.4 Wheel slip or front wheel lifting which affects the maximum sound level shall be avoided.

7.2 Unless it is apparent that maximum noise occurs during acceleration, the following test shall be performed with sufficient runs to establish maximum sound levels under deceleration:

7.2.1 For the test under deceleration, the vehicle shall approach the end point from the reverse direction in the gear used and at the average maximum engine speed attained in the test under acceleration. When the front of the vehicle reaches the end point, the throttle shall be rapidly and fully closed and the vehicle allowed to decelerate along the vehicle path until one half of rated engine speed or the point 15 m (49 ft 2 in) past the microphone target point is reached, whichever comes later.

7.3 Before measurements begin, sufficient preliminary runs shall be made to familiarize the rider with the vehicle and to allow the engine to reach normal operating temperature. The engine temperature shall be within the normal operating range prior to each run.

7.4 The longitudinal plane of symmetry of the test vehicle shall remain on the vehicle path for all test runs.

8. Measurements

8.1 The sound level meter shall be set for fast response and for the A-weighting network.

8.2 The ambient sound level (including wind effects) at the test site, due to sources other than the vehicle being measured, shall be at least 10 dB lower than the peak sound level produced by the vehicle under test.

8.3 Measurements shall be made only when the wind speed is below 5.5 m/s (12 mph).

8.4 The following measurements shall be made for both the acceleration and, if conducted, deceleration test modes:

8.4.1 Measurements shall be taken for both sides of the vehicle.

8.4.2 The meter shall be observed during each test as the vehicle is accelerating and decelerating. The highest sound level observed for each side during each test run shall be recorded.

8.4.3 Sufficient test runs shall be made until at least four recorded measurements for each test mode and each side of the vehicle are within a 2 dB range. The sound level for that side and test mode shall be the arithmetic average for the first four measurements within a 2 dB range.

8.5 The sound level reported for the vehicle shall be the sound level of the side and test mode with the highest average sound level.

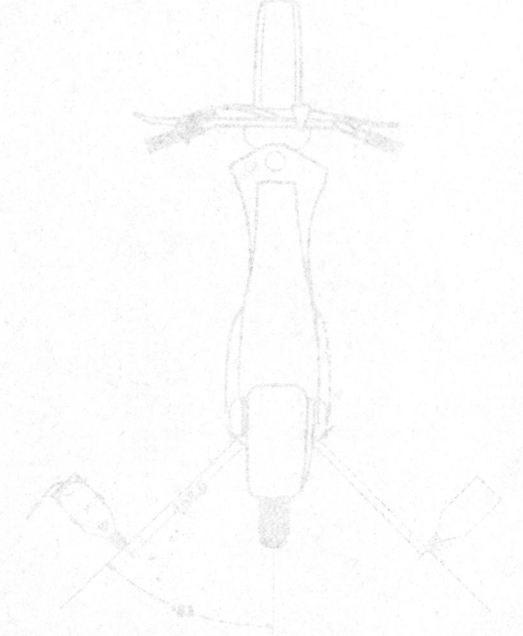

9. General Comments

9.1 Technically competent personnel should select the equipment, and the test should be conducted only by trained and experienced persons familiar with the current techniques of sound measurement.

9.2 While making sound level measurements, not more than one person other than the rider and the observer reading the meter shall be within 15 m (49 ft 2 in) of the vehicle or microphone. The additional person shall be directly behind the meter observer on a line through the microphone and the observer.

9.3 The test rider should be fully conversant with and qualified to ride the machine under test, and be familiar with the test procedure.

9.4 It should be noted that error in the engine speed indicator as well as error due to operator response time may result in sound level measurement error.

9.5 Tachometers having steady-state accuracy within 3% of actual engine speed at 60% and 100% of the rated engine speed are commercially available and are included on some motorcycles as original equipment. This class of tachometers is regarded as being sufficiently accurate for general sound level measurements. In circumstances where very accurate sound level measurements are necessary, accurate engine speed determination is essential, and consideration must be given to the accuracy and response time of the engine speed measurement system. Special care must be taken not to exceed rated engine speed. Exact engine speed measurement must be based on the time interval for not less than one complete engine cycle; for example, two crankshaft revolutions for a four-stroke engine.

9.6 Proper use of all test instrumentation is essential in obtaining valid measurements. Operating manuals or other literature furnished by the instrument manufacturer should be referred to for both recommended operation of the instrument and precautions to be observed. Specific items to be considered are:

9.6.1 The type of microphone, its directional response characteristics, and its orientation relative to the ground plane and source of noise.

9.6.2 The effects of ambient weather conditions (for example, temperature, humidity, and barometric pressure) on the performance of all instruments.

9.6.3 Proper signal levels, terminating impedances, and cable lengths on multi-instrument measurement systems.

9.6.4 Proper acoustical calibration procedures, including the influence of extension cables, etc., shall be followed. Field calibration shall be made immediately before and after the test series described in 8.4.3. Internal calibration is acceptable for field use, provided that external calibration is accomplished immediately before or after field use.

MEASUREMENT OF EXHAUST SOUND LEVELS OF STATIONARY MOTORCYCLES—SAE J1287 JUL1998

SAE Standard

Report of the SAE Motorcycle Committee approved June 1980 and completely revised June 1988. Rationale statement available. Reaffirmed by the SAE Motorcycle Sound Level Subcommittee of the SAE Motorcycle Committee June 1993. Reaffirmed by the SAE Motorcycle Committee July 1998. Rationale statement available.

Foreword—This Reaffirmed Document has been changed only to comply with the new SAE Technical Standards Board Format. The Definitions Section has changed to Section 3. All other section numbers have been changed accordingly.

1. Scope—This SAE Standard establishes the test procedure, environment, and instrumentation for determining the sound levels of motorcycles under stationary conditions. This test will measure primarily exhaust noise and does not represent the optimum procedure for evaluating total vehicle noise. For this purpose, SAE J331 or SAE J47 is recommended.

2. References

2.1 Applicable Publications—The following publications form a part of this specification to the extent specified herein. Unless otherwise indicated, the latest issue of SAE publications shall apply.

2.1.1 SAE PUBLICATIONS—Available from SAE, 400 Commonwealth Drive, Warrendale, PA 15096-0001.

SAE J47—Maximum Sound Level Potential for Motorcycles
SAE J184—Qualifying a Sound Data Acquisition System
SAE J213—Definitions—Motorcycles
SAE J331—Sound Levels for Motorcycles
SAE J1349—Engine Power Test Code—Spark Ignition and Diesel
SAE TSB 002 JUN86—Preparation of SAE Technical Reports

2.1.2 ANSI PUBLICATION—Available from ANSI, 11 West 42nd Street, New York, NY 10036-8002.

ANSI S1.4-1983—Specification for Sound Level Meters

3. Definitions

3.1 Field Calibration—Calibration of the sound level meter using an external sound level calibrator, an internal calibration means, or any other method which will ensure the accuracy of sound level meter readings.

3.2 Longitudinal Plane Of Symmetry—As defined in SAE J213.

3.3 Rated Engine Speed—The engine speed in revolutions per minute at which the engine delivers its maximum Net Brake Power as defined in SAE J1349, as determined by the manufacturer.

4. Instrumentation—The following instrumentation shall be used:

4.1 A sound level meter meeting the Type 1, Type S1A, Type 2, or Type S2A requirements of ANSI S1.4-1983.

4.1.1 As an alternative to making direct measurements using a sound level meter, a microphone or sound level meter may be used with a magnetic tape recorder and/or a graphic level recorder or other indicating instrument, provided the system meets the requirements of SAE J184.

4.2 A sound level calibrator with an accuracy of ±0.5 dB (see 7.9).

4.3 A windscreen which does not affect microphone response more than ±1 dB for frequencies of 63 to 4000 Hz and ±1.5 dB for frequencies of 4000 to 10 000 Hz.

4.4 An engine speed tachometer or other means of determining engine speed, with a steady-state accuracy of ±3% at the test speed.

4.5 An anemometer with steady-state accuracy of ±10% at 9 m/s (20 mph).

5. Test Site

5.1 The test site shall be a flat, open surface free of large sound-reflecting surfaces (other than the ground) such as parked vehicles, signboards, buildings, or hillsides located within 5 m (16 ft) of the motorcycle being tested and the location of the microphone.

5.2 The surface of the ground within the area described in 5.1 shall be paving or hard-packed earth, level within an average slope of 40 mm/m (0.5 in/ft), and shall be free of loose or powdered snow, plowed soil, grass of a height greater than 150 mm (6 in), trees, or other extraneous material.

6. Procedure

6.1 A rider shall sit astride the motorcycle in normal riding position with both feet on the ground. If this is not possible because of the seat height of the motorcycle, and for three-wheeled motorcycles, the rider shall sit in the normal riding position with one or both feet on the footrests. If necessary, an assistant may hold the motorcycle by the forks, front wheel, or handlebars so that it is stationary with its longitudinal plane of symmetry vertical. In the alternative, the rider may use a box, rock, or other object to rest his feet upon to steady the motorcycle, as long as the motorcycle longitudinal plane of symmetry is vertical and stationary.

The rider shall run the engine with the gearbox in neutral at a speed equal to one-half of the rated engine speed.

6.1.1 If no neutral is provided, the motorcycle shall be operated either with the rear wheel(s) at least 50 mm (2 in) clear of the ground or with the drive chain or belt removed, or with the clutch, if the motorcycle is so equipped, disengaged.

6.2 The engine of the motorcycle under test shall be at normal operating temperature during the test.

7. Measurements

7.1 The sound level meter shall be set for the A-weighting network and should be set for slow dynamic response. (See Appendix A, Section A.5.)

7.2 Tests shall be made on each side of the motorcycle having an exhaust outlet.

7.3 The microphone shall be located behind, 0.5 m ± 0.01 m (20 in ± 1/2 in) from, and within 0.01 m (1/2 in) of the same height as the exhaust outlet and at a 45 degrees ± 10 degrees angle to the normal line of travel of the motorcycle. If there is more than one exhaust outlet per side, the microphone shall be located with reference to the rearmost outlet.

The longitudinal axis of the microphone shall be in a plane parallel to the ground plane. The axis of the microphone shall be oriented as specified for free field response by the manufacturer (see Figure 1).

7.4 No wire or other rigid means of distance measurement shall be attached to the sound measuring system.

7.5 The sound level recorded shall be that measured during steady-state operation at the engine speed (±200 rpm) determined in Section 6 measured on the loudest side of the motorcycle (if outlet located on both sides — see 7.2). The test speed in rpm shall also be recorded.

7.6 The ambient sound level (including wind effects) at the test site due to sources other than the motorcycle being measured shall be at least 10 dB lower than the sound level produced by the motorcycle under test.

7.7 Wind speed at the test site during the test shall be less than 9 m/s (20 mph).

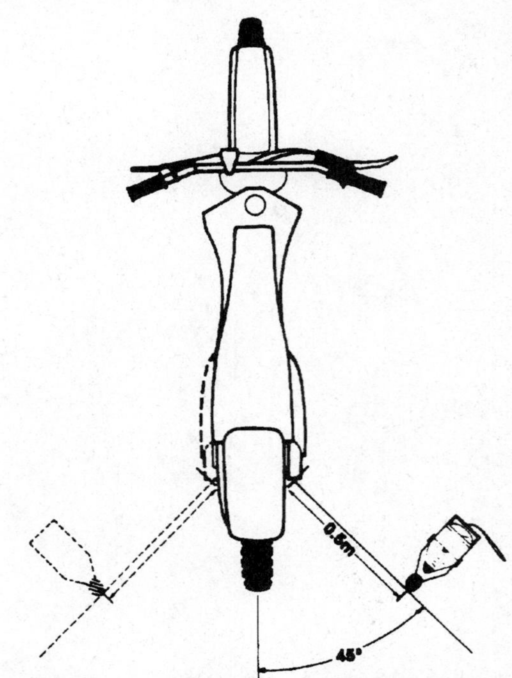

FIGURE 1—SOUND LEVEL AND MICROPHONE LOCATION AND ORIENTATION

7.8 While making sound level measurements, not more than one person other than the rider, the measurer, and the assistant (if necessary) (see 6.1) shall be within 3 m (10 ft) of the motorcycle under test or the microphone, and that person shall be directly behind the measurer on a line through the microphone and the measurer.

7.9 Calibration of the sound level meter using the sound level calibrator (see 4.2) shall be made immediately before the first test of each test day and should be made at the end of each test day. Field calibration should be made at intervals of no more than 1 h.

8. General Comments

8.1 It is essential that persons conducting the test be knowledgeable of the test procedure and use of the instrumentation.

8.2 Proper use of all test instruments is essential to obtain valid measurements. Operating manuals or other literature furnished by the instrument manufacturer should be referred to, for both recommended operation of the instrument and precautions to be observed.

8.3 Specific Items for Consideration

8.3.1 The type of microphone, its directional response characteristics, and its orientation relative to the source of sound.

8.3.2 The effects of ambient weather conditions on the performance of all instruments (that is, temperature, humidity, and barometric pressure).

8.3.3 Proper acoustical calibration procedure to include the influence of extension cables, etc.

8.4 Although either Type 1 or Type 2 sound level meters may be used with this procedure, it is suggested that a Type 1 instrument be considered as it generally has lesser overall tolerance which can result in more accurate measurements.

8.5 The use of the word "shall" in the procedure is to be understood as obligatory. The use of the word "should" is to be understood as advisory. The use of the word "may" is to be understood as permissive.

APPENDIX A

This procedure can be adapted to a variety of uses, which may include exhaust system certification, enforcement of in-use motorcycle standards, and use by motorcycle competition bodies to ensure some silencing of race vehicles. As provided in TSB 002, this Appendix adds supplementary engineering reference data and educational material and is not an integral part of the basic technical report. Accordingly, a description of the variations used shall be reported along with test results obtained using the variations provided in this Appendix. Such results shall not be reported as having been obtained according to the standard conditions of this document. Some of these uses may require less precision than is called for in the procedure. Accordingly, the following changes may be made for convenience with the realization that accuracy may suffer.

A.1 Enforcement Testing

When used for enforcement, this procedure is intended to be a pass-fail test. A ±1.5 dB variation due to changes in test conditions, motorcycles, and instruments can occur. Test to test variations within this limit shall be considered acceptable. If limits are to be set according to this procedure, these variations should be considered when limits are chosen.

In enforcement situations, it is often easier to use one-half of the redline speed (redline speed is the lowest numerical engine speed included in the red zone on the motorcycle tachometer) rather than the test speed specified in 6.1. One-half of redline speed is a higher test speed than one-half of rated rpm; thus, the measured sound level will be higher, and a 3 dB tolerance must be added to the applicable sound level limit.

While site tolerances may be relaxed somewhat without serious degradation of precision in the method, site parameters, as described in Section 5, should be as closely adhered to as possible. It is unlikely that useful results will be obtained if, for instance, any other motorcycle or other vehicle or person is within 6 ft of the test motorcycle, or if the motorcycle is tested while it is loaded in a pickup truck or on a trailer.

A.2 Instrumentation

Type 1 instrumentation, which generally can provide the most accurate measurements, should be used when the need for accuracy is great, such as certification of exhaust systems, or enforcement action which may result in some form of penalty.

Type 2 instrumentation could be appropriate for some enforcement work, such as a preliminary screening test, or for general data gathering. On the other hand, instrumentation which is less precise than Type 1 or Type 2 may be appropriate in cases such as at a racetrack or motorcycle park, when the primary interest is securing some noise reduction from the motorcycles operated within, and not measuring for the purpose of meeting specific maximum noise limits. Selection of equipment should reflect the need for accuracy (particularly considering any consequences) balanced against cost. Caution should be exercised, however, when selecting equipment which does not conform with ANSI standards. Experience with consumer electronic types of sound level meters indicates most such meters do not possess operating characteristics of sufficient accuracy or consistency to yield meaningful results. Meters which meet obsolete ANSI S1.4 Type 3 specifications, however, are sufficiently accurate for less demanding applications such as racetrack enforcement.

A.3 Procedure

When making comparison measurements where a single variable is to be evaluated, such as comparing the sound level of two different exhaust systems on the same vehicle, selection of the correct engine speed according to 6.1 is not critical as long as the same engine speed is used for each test.

A.4 Racing Motorcycles

This procedure may be used for sound testing of racing motorcycles. An appropriate test speed for both four-stroke and two-stroke high-performance competition motorcycles for which the rated engine speed is not known is determined from Equation A1:

$$\text{Test Speed} = \frac{306\ 000}{\text{stroke in millimeters}} \text{ or } \left(\frac{12\ 000}{\text{stroke in inches}}\right) \quad \text{(Eq. A1)}$$

A.5 Dynamic Response

Use of slow dynamic response is specified, but fast dynamic response may be used. Because of the essentially constant nature of the sound level, either mode is acceptable; the meter is easier to read when slow response is used.

A.6 Wind Speed

If it is not possible to delay testing until the specified wind conditions prevail, testing can be performed in higher winds. In this case, the motorcycle should be positioned so that the prevailing wind direction is parallel to the normal direction of travel of the motorcycle.

A.7 Alternate Engine Speed

If the rated engine speed for a particular motorcycle is unknown, then the test speed shall be calculated from either Equations A2 or A3:

$$\text{For four-stroke engines} = \frac{250\ 000}{\text{stroke in millimeters}} \text{ or } \left(\frac{9800}{\text{stroke in inches}}\right) \quad \text{(Eq. A2)}$$

$$\text{For two-stroke engines: } \frac{200\ 000}{\text{stroke in millimeters}} \text{ or } \left(\frac{7900}{\text{stroke in inches}}\right) \quad \text{(Eq. A3)}$$

INSTRUMENTATION FOR MEASURING ACOUSTIC IMPULSES WITHIN VEHICLES —SAE J247 FEB1987

SAE Recommended Practice

Report of the SAE Automotive Safety Committee approved May 1971, last revised August 1974, and reaffirmed by the SAE Vehicle Sound Level Committee February 1987. Rationale statement available.

Foreword—This Reaffirmed Document has been changed only to reflect the new SAE Technical Standards Board Format. Definitions changed to Section 3. All other section numbers have changed accordingly.

1. Scope—The purpose of this SAE Recommended Practice is to provide guidelines for selection and application of instrumentation for proper measurement of acoustic impulses within vehicles, as typified by those generated during the deployment of a passive restraint system. The objective is to achieve uniformity in instrumentation practice and reporting of test measurements. Use of this recommended practice should provide a basis for meaningful comparisons of test results from different sources.

2. References

2.1 Applicable Publications—The following publications form a part of the specification to the extent specified herein. Unless otherwise indicated the lastest revision of SAE publications shall apply.

2.1.1 SAE PUBLICATION—Available from SAE, 400 Commonwealth Drive, Warrendale, PA 15096-0001.

SAE J941 MAR81—Passenger Car Driver's Eye Range

2.1.2 ANSI PUBLICATIONS—Available from ANSI, 11 West 42nd Street, New York, NY 10036-8002.

ANSI S1.1 - 1960 (R1976)—Acoustic Terminology

ANSI S1.13 - 1971 (R1976)—Methods for the Measurement of Sound Pressure Levels

3. Definitions

3.1 Transducer—Microphone, pressure transducer, or other device along with integral conditioning used for pressure transduction.

3.2 Full-Scale—Maximum usable range of an instrument or system.

3.3 Data Channel—All of the instrumentation from and including a single transducer up to and including any display or analysis device or procedure that may alter the frequency content of the data. (Long cables, in particular, are not to be neglected.)

3.4 Data Channel Full-Scale—The valid range of a data channel, in terms of the input variable, determined by the component in the channel with the lowest full-scale level.

3.5 Mean Ear Location (MEL)—With reference to Figure 4 of SAE J941 MAR81 the mean ear location (MEL) is defined as a point 10 in. (25.4 cm) inboard from the X–Z plane, 3.5 in. (8.9 cm) rearward of line Z–Z, and 0.5 in. (1.3 cm) below line X–X.

3.6 Initiation Time—That instant in time when the deployment signal is applied to the passive restraint system. (See Figure 1.)

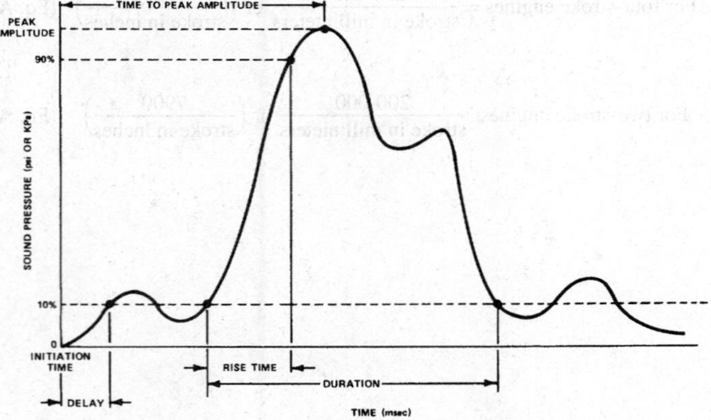

FIGURE 1—WAVEFORM DEFINITIONS

3.7 Peak Amplitude—The maximum value of sound pressure attained, expressed in pounds per square inch (kilopascals). It may also be expressed as sound pressure level in decibles (dB).

3.8 Risetime—The time difference between the occurrence of 90% peak amplitude (in psi or kPa) and the immediately prior occurrence of 10% peak amplitude, expressed in milliseconds.

3.9 Duration—The time difference between occurrences of 10% of peak amplitude (in psi or kPa) immediately before and following the occurrence of peak amplitude, expressed in milliseconds.

3.10 Delay—The time difference between "initiation time" and the initial occurrence of 10% of peak amplitude.

3.11 Sound Pressure Level—Twenty times the logarithm to the base 10 of the ratio of the pressure of a sound to a reference pressure equal to 20 µPa, expressed in decibels. Figure 2 relates peak sound pressure level, in dB, to peak sound pressure, in psi (kPa).

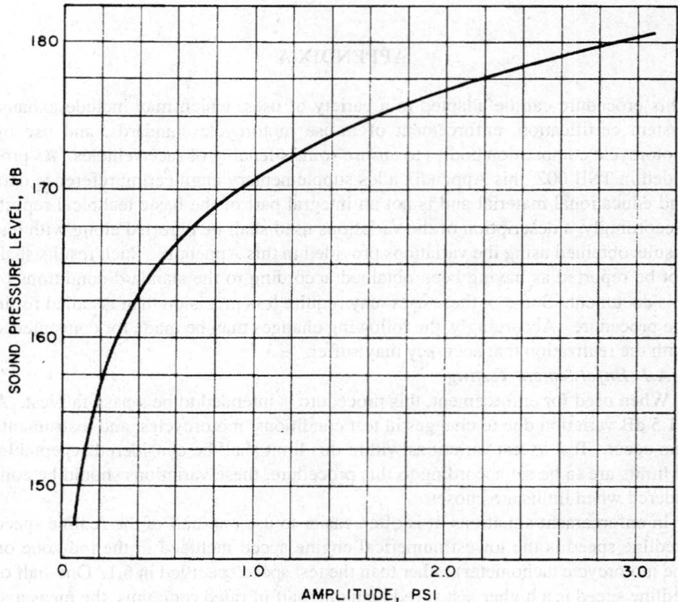

FIGURE 2—PEAK AMPLITUDE VERSUS PEAK SOUND PRESSURE LEVEL

4. Data Channel Specifications—Data channels should conform to the following specifications:

4.1 Maximum Sound Pressure—The data channels should be capable of measuring peak sound pressure levels of 180 dB. However, data channel full-scale may be set lower, depending on anticipated peak amplitudes.

4.2 Frequency Response—The amplitude response, as a function of frequency, is specified in Figure 3.

4.3 Amplitude Linearity—Maximum deviation of the calibration curve from the straight line through its end points should not exceed 1 dB.

4.4 Harmonic Distortion—Not more than 10% at 177 dB peak sound pressure level.

4.5 Overshoot—Not more than 10% for a step pressure input.

4.6 Signal-to-Noise Ratio—At least 40 dB.

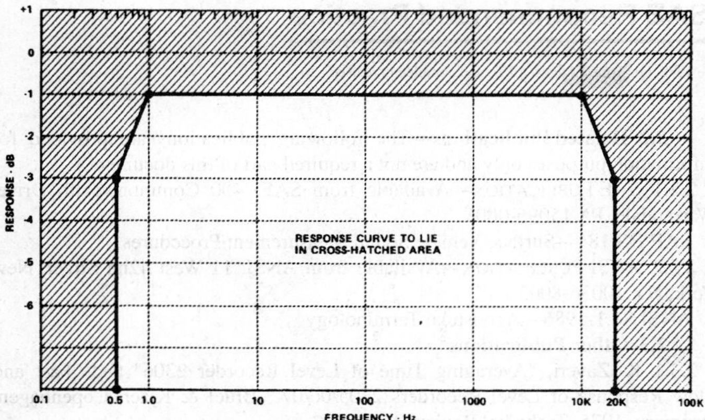

FIGURE 3—DATA CHANNEL FREQUENCY RESPONSE

5. Calibration Guidelines

5.1 Laboratory Calibrations—Laboratory calibrations should be conducted on a periodic basis, to documented procedures, and with standards and test equipment traceable to the National Bureau of Standards.

5.1.1 Frequency response tests should be conducted at an amplitude equal to full-scale.

5.1.2 Amplitude linearity checks should be made at full-scale and at −20, −40, −60 dB.

5.1.3 Whenever it is impossible to include the transducer in tests under 5.1.1 and 5.1.2, the transducers may be simulated and voltage insertion calibration techniques used. However, the transducers should then be calibrated for amplitude and frequency response according to the manufacturers' recommendations and then installed and the data channel checked with an acoustic calibrator at the highest level possible.

5.1.4 Checks should be made to determine the effects of any anticipated test site conditions (for example, temperature, barometric pressure, mechanical shock, acceleration, photographic lighting, electrical interference, etc.).

5.2 Test-Site Calibrations—Test-site calibrations are end-to-end data channel calibrations.

5.2.1 Closed-coupler acoustic calibration techniques should be used to check the operation and calibration of the transducer.

5.2.2 Calibrations should be conducted at a level equal to or greater than 50% (−6 dB) of data channel full-scale. Voltage insertion techniques using transducer laboratory calibration data may be used.

5.2.3 Several seconds of ambient noise should be recorded to establish the noise floor at the time of the test.

6. Test Guidelines—The following are suggested when conducting acoustic impulse tests:

6.1 Instrumentation used should be properly documented showing latest laboratory calibration dates.

6.2 Test-site calibrations should be conducted before and after each test.

6.3 "Initiation time" (±1 ms) should be recorded along with the acoustic data.

6.4 A time reference (for example, 1 kHz sine or square wave) should be recorded along with the data. This is useful to avoid timing errors when time scaling is employed.

6.5 Data channel full-scale should be selected so that anticipated maximum sound pressures will be within −12 to −2 dB of it.

6.6 Open-window tests should be conducted under free field conditions or out of doors away from walls.

6.7 Care should be exercised to isolate the transducers mechanically, consistent with the test vehicle environment. When the transducer is subjected to accelerations, output compensation may be required.

7. Transducer Locations—At least two locations should be monitored. One is the mean ear location (MEL) for the driver, and the other is a point symmetrical about the vehicle centerline to the MEL for the passenger. It is suggested that additional transducers be located within the vehicle at locations where high sound pressure levels are anticipated (for example, 2 in. (5 cm) out from ears adjacent to closed windows). Whatever locations are selected, they should be described in detail.

8. Data Presentation—The statement of test results should contain at minimum, the following information:

8.1 Pressure-Time Display—For each data channel, there should be a graphical display (oscillograph, computer plot, etc.) of sound pressure (psi or kPa) or sound pressure level (dB) as a function of time (ms). A calibration level should also be displayed.

8.2 Tabulation of Pressure-Time Parameters

8.2.1 Peak amplitude (express in both psi (kPa) and dB).

8.2.2 Time of occurrence of peak amplitude (ms after "initiation time").

8.2.3 Risetime.

8.2.4 Duration.

8.2.5 Delay.

8.3 Vehicle Configuration—A description of the vehicle body size and style, vented area present, restraint system configuration, number and type of dummies, if used, and whether windows were open or closed.

8.4 Instrumentation Documentation—List of instrumentation used, giving manufacturer, model, serial number, and date of last laboratory calibration for all data channels and test-site calibrators.

8.5 Special Conditions—Any nonstandard test conditions, analysis techniques, instrumentation, or additional transducer locations.

9. General Comments

9.1 Magnetic tape recorders used as part of a data channel should meet or exceed the IRIG specifications for an FM intermediate band recorder, operating at a speed of 60 in./s (150 cm/s) or greater. Tape speed compensation is recommended.

9.2 If a recorder is used to speed scale the data for playback on a relatively low frequency device, the upper frequency response limits of the devices in the data channel after the recorder may be divided by the speed scaling factor (that is, record speed/playback speed).

9.3 Data channel low frequency response may be severely limited by insufficient transducer-preamplifier time constants.

9.4 Data channel high frequency response may be severely limited by capacitive loading due to long output cables.

9.5 It is recognized that the frequency response and the dynamic range required by the prior sections may be difficult to achieve in a single instrumentation system. Accordingly, it is acceptable to use more than one transducer and/or parallel recording at different gain settings to achieve the total data channel requirements.

(R) QUALIFYING A SOUND DATA ACQUISITION SYSTEM—SAE J184 NOV1998

SAE Recommended Practice

Report of the SAE Motor Vehicle Council Sound Level Committee approved September 1970, completely revised June 1978, reaffirmed August 1987, and completely revised November 1998. Rationale statement available.

1. Scope—Various SAE vehicle sound level measurement procedures require use of a sound level meter which meets the Type 1 or Type 2 requirements of ANSI S1.4-1983 (see 2.1.1.1), or an alternative system which can be proved to provide equivalent test data. The purpose of this SAE Recommended Practice is to provide a procedure for determining if a sound data acquisition system (SDAS) has electro-acoustical performance equivalent to such a meter. By assuring equivalent performance of the test instrumentation, the equivalence of test data is assured.

Two general configurations of sound data acquisition systems will be encompassed (see Figure 1). The first configuration consists of instrument sections which perform as a sound level meter. The second configuration is a system which records data for later processing. The intent of this document is to establish guidelines which permit the test engineer to insure equivalence of sound data acquisition systems to a sound level meter. It requires that the test engineer have a working knowledge of the characteristics of the sound data being measured.

The scope of the document includes the system performance requirements for the entire sound measurement system. It provides the methods needed to verify Type 1 or Type 2 instruments. However, it also provides a method to qualify an SDAS that does not meet the requirements in their entirety, but can be used provided knowledge of the test data is obtained and an iterative process is followed in qualifying the SDAS. The system need only be qualified for the dynamic characteristics and weighting mode in which it is to be used. The scope of this document does not include qualification of system components for harmonic distortion, tape recorder wow and flutter, etc. However, these factors must be considered when determining system performance, especially where spectral information is sought. The references in Section 2 should be consulted for general performance requirements and precautions regarding instrumentation for acoustical measurements.

2. References

2.1 Applicable Publications—The following publications form a part of the specification to the extent specified herein.

2.1.1 ANSI PUBLICATIONS—Available from ANSI, 11 West 42nd Street, New York, NY 10036-8002.

2.1.1.1 ANSI S1.4-1983 and S1.4A-1985—Specification for Sound Level Meters

2.1.1.2 ANSI S1.11-1986—Specification for Octave, Half-Octave, and Third-Octave Band Filter Sets

2.1.2 IEC PUBLICATION—Available from International Electrotechnical Commission, 3 rue de Verambe, P.O. Box 131, 1211 Geneva 20, Switzerland.

2.1.2.1 IEC publication 651-1993—Sound Level Meters

2.2 Related Publications—The following publications are provided for information purposes only and are not a required part of this document.

2.2.1 SAE PUBLICATION—Available from SAE, 400 Commonwealth Drive, Warrendale, PA 15096-0001.

SAE HS 184—Surface Vehicle Sound Measurement Procedures

2.2.2 ANSI PUBLICATION—Available from ANSI, 11 West 42nd Street, New York, NY 10036-8002.

ANSI S1.1-1986—Acoustical Terminology

2.3 Other Publications

2.3.1 K. Zaveri, "Averaging Time of Level Recorder 2306" and "Fast and Slow Response of Level Recorders 2305/06/07," Bruel & Kjaer, Copenhagen, Denmark, 1975, Technical Review, Issue 2.

2.3.2 P. Hedegaard, "General Accuracy of Sound Level Meter Measurements," Bruel & Kjaer, Copenhagen, Denmark, 1977, Technical Review, Issue 4.

2.3.3 C. G. Wahrmann and J. T. Brock, "On the Averaging Time of RMS Measurements," Bruel & Kjaer, Copenhagen, Denmark, 1975, Technical Review, Issues 2 and 3.

2.3.4 Arnold P.G. Peterson and Ervin E. Gross, Jr., "Handbook of Noise Measurements," 7th Edition, General Radio Company, West Concord, MA, 1972.

2.3.5 R. B. Randall, "Frequency Analysis," Bruel & Kjaer, Copenhagen, Denmark, 1987.

3. Definitions

3.1 Data Signal Range—Twenty times the logarithm (to base 10) of the ratio of highest RMS signal amplitude to lowest RMS signal amplitude for a specific test condition; unit is decibel (dB).

3.2 Dynamic Range—Twenty times the logarithm (to base 10) of the ratio of the instrumentation system maximum signal amplitude to system noise floor amplitude; unit is decibel (dB).

3.3 Frequency Response—Twenty times the logarithm (to base 10) of the ratio of output signal amplitude to input signal amplitude over a specified frequency range as a function of signal frequency; unit is decibel (dB). For a complete sound data acquisition system, it is the indicated sound level minus the sound pressure level at the microphone.

3.4 Full Scale—The maximum undistorted signal level for each instrument.

3.4.1 Full scale for an amplifier is the maximum output signal level. Input full scale can change with amplifier gain.

3.4.2 Full scale for a tape recorder is the maximum signal amplitude defined in 3.6.

3.4.3 Full scale for an indicating instrument is defined as the input voltage for maximum indication.

3.4.4 Full scale for any system component is the maximum output signal level which allows for undistorted signals defined in this recommended practice.

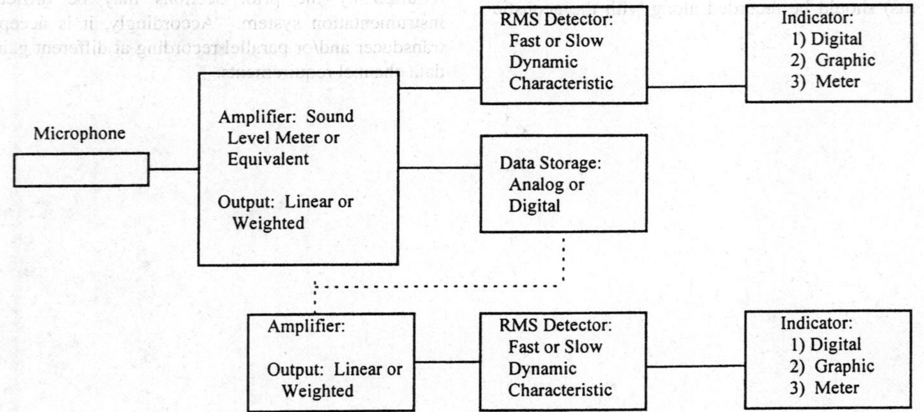

FIGURE 1—SOUND DATA ACQUISITION SYSTEM

3.5 Indicator—A device used to provide a visual display of signal amplitude.

3.5.1 DIGITAL— A numeric or alpha-numeric display of the measured signal amplitude.

3.5.2 GRAPHIC—A trace recording of the measured signal amplitude on a scaled chart.

3.5.3 METER—Electrically driven needle or other device (possibly digital) which deflects over a calibrated scale as a function of the measured signal amplitude.

3.6 Maximum Signal Amplitude—The signal amplitude below which the harmonic distortion is less than 3% over the operating frequency range.

3.7 Restricted System—Any data acquisition or analysis instrumentation that meets the requirements as specified herein, but only over a limited frequency range.

3.8 Signal Crest Factor—Twenty times the logarithm (to base 10) of the ratio of the peak signal amplitude to the RMS signal amplitude; unit is decibel (dB).

3.9 Signal-to-Noise Ratio—Twenty times the logarithm (to base 10) of the ratio of the data signal amplitude to system noise floor amplitude; unit is decibel (dB).

3.10 System Noise Floor—The broad band electrical noise inherent in instrument circuits with proper input/output terminations.

3.11 Test Apparatus—Equipment used for qualifying, but not part of the Sound Data Acquisition System.

3.12 Digital Signal Processing Terminology—Additional terminology referring to digital systems can be found in Appendix E of ANSI S1.11-1986.

4. System Performance Requirements

4.1 Frequency Response (Amplitude)—The continuous frequency response (linear or A-weighted) of a Type 1 or Type 2 Sound Data Acquisition System shall meet the tolerances in Table 1.

TABLE 1—SYSTEM TOLERANCE LIMITS AND FREQUENCY RESPONSE WEIGHTING FOR A-WEIGHTING

Nominal Frequency Hz	A-Weighting Response (dB)	Tolerance Limits on Response in dB Type 1	Tolerance Limits on Response in dB Type 2
10	–70.4	±4	+5.0, –∞
12.5	–63.4	±3.5	+5.0, –∞
16	–56.7	±3.0	+5.0, –∞
20	–50.5	±2.5	±3.0
25	–44.7	±2.0	±3.0
31.5	–39.4	±1.5	±3.0
40	–34.6	±1.5	±2.0
50	–30.2	±1.0	±2.0
63	–26.2	±1.0	±2.0
80	–22.5	±1.0	±2.0
100	–19.1	±1.0	±1.5
125	–16.1	±1.0	±1.5
160	–13.4	±1.0	±1.5
200	–10.9	±1.0	±1.5
250	–8.6	±1.0	±1.5
315	–6.6	±1.0	±1.5
400	–4.8	±1.0	±1.5
500	–3.2	±1.0	±1.5
630	–1.9	±1.0	±1.5
800	–0.8	±1.0	±1.5
1000	+0	±1.0	±1.5
1250	+0.6	±1.0	±1.5
1600	+1	±1.0	±2
2000	+1.2	±1.0	±2
2500	+1.3	±1.0	±2.5
3150	+1.2	±1.0	±2.5
4000	+1	±1.0	±3
5000	+0.5	±1.5	±3.5
6300	–0.1	+1.5, –2.0	±4.5
8000	–1.1	+1.5, –3.0	±5.0
10 000	–2.5	+2.0, –4.0	+5.0, –∞
12 500	–4.3	+3.0, –6.0	+5.0, –∞
16 000	–6.6	+3.0, –∞	+5.0, –∞
2 0000	–9.3	+3.0, –∞	+5.0, –∞

4.1.1 A Restricted System (linear or weighted) shall meet the tolerances in the continuous frequency range from 1/6 octave above to 1/6 octave below the range specified. For measured data, the total sound level of all bands outside the Restricted range shall be at least 15 dB lower than the overall measured level.

4.1.2 When other weighting networks are used, the frequency response and tolerance of the respective network as specified in ANSI S1.4-1983 shall apply.

4.1.3 Data recorded using a Restricted System shall be designated by type, weighting, dynamic characteristic, and frequency response. For example: Type 1, A, Fast, 100 Hz - 4 kHz.

4.2 Linearity

4.2.1 SYSTEM LINEARITY—For a single range attenuator setting, the linearity error for measurements over the data signal range shall not exceed the tolerances indicated in Table 2, unless limited by a Restricted system.

TABLE 2—SYSTEM LINEARITY REQUIREMENTS

Type 1	within ±0.7 dB	31.5 to 8000 Hz
	within ±1.0 dB	20 to 12 500 Hz
Type 2	within ±1.0 dB	31.5 to 8000 Hz
	within ±1.5 dB	20 to 12 500 Hz

4.2.2 RANGE ATTENUATOR LINEARITY—All settings of the sensitivity range control, either manual or automatic, shall introduce errors less than those specified in Table 2 for a sine wave with respect to a reference signal. If more than one sensitivity range is provided, it is recommended that the ranges be at 10 dB increments.

4.3 Dynamic Characteristic

4.3.1 FAST—The system dynamic response is tested with a 1000 Hz signal instantaneously increased by a minimum of 20 dB to the reference signal level for a duration of 200 ms. The maximum indication shall be within –2.0 to 0 dB with respect to the reference signal for a Type 1 system and within –3.0 to 0 dB for a Type 2 system. Overshoot for a continuous 20 dB increasing step change in level shall be between 0 and +1.1 dB for both Type 1 and Type 2.

4.3.2 SLOW—The system dynamic response is tested with a 1000 Hz signal, instantaneously increased by a minimum of 20 dB to the reference signal level for a duration of 500 ms. The maximum indication will be within –3.1 to –5.1 dB with respect to the reference signal for Type 1 and within –2.1 to –6.1 for Type 2. Overshoot for a continuous 20 dB increasing step change in level shall be 0 to +1.6 dB for both Type 1 and Type 2.

4.3.3 IMPULSE—The system dynamic response is tested with a 1000 Hz signal, instantaneously increased by a minimum of 20 dB to the reference signal level for a duration of 20 ms. The maximum indication will be within –5.1 to –2.1 dB with respect to the reference signal for Type 1 and within –5.6 to –1.6 dB for Type 2.

4.3.4 REFERENCE SIGNAL—The previous requirements apply for a reference signal 4.0 dB below full scale, on a logarithmically scaled indicator. For scales which are linear in dB, such as a graphic level recorder, 63% of maximum indicator deflection corresponds to 4.0 dB below full scale on a logarithmically scaled indicator.

CAUTION—Significant sound level reading variations are possible between systems measuring the same sound even though the system performs within the limits specified in 4.3.1, 4.3.2, and 4.3.3. The dynamic response performance is a function of the indicator ballistics and the detector averaging time which may differ between instruments. Since 4.3.1, 4.3.2, and 4.3.3 do not specify ideal design center circuit performance, a dynamic response model based on a single pole filter is suggested in Section A.1. Ideally, the dynamic response of the indicator should be an order of magnitude faster than the RMS detector dynamic response.

Fast and Slow decay times and additional performance tests for impulse are covered in Sections A.2 and A.3.

4.4 RMS Accuracy—The Sound Data Acquisition System RMS conversion must be within ±0.5 dB of the true RMS value for all signals with crest factors up to and including 10 dB. For test method, see Section A.4.

4.5 Dynamic Range—The Sound Data Acquisition System dynamic range is governed by three factors, the data signal crest factor, the data signal amplitude range, and the system signal-to-noise ratio. The system signal-to-noise ratio must be at least 15 dB to insure that inherent instrument noise does not contribute more than 0.2 dB to the measured level. The system selected for measurement must have a total dynamic range that at least equals the sum of these three factors. Any bandpass filtering or weighting of the data after recording may require a wider dynamic range of the Sound Data Acquisition System. The system noise floor including that of the filter must be 15 dB below the minimum filtered data signal value.

5. Component Requirements

5.1 Microphone—Microphones must meet the directional characteristics described in either ANSI S1.4–1983 or IEC 651-1993 and be used in accordance with the standard chosen. Note that the orientation of the microphone may in some cases affect measurements. This may be the case in the presence of strong components above several kHz.

5.2 Tape Recorders and Other Storage Systems—Generally, wow and flutter requirements will be met if the tape recorder meets the other requirements of this document in the data acquisition environment. In general, wow and flutter are not measurable in digital storage systems.

5.2.1 The brand and type of tape used for data acquisition must be tested with the system recorder to qualify overall recorder performance.

5.3 RMS Detector—Ideally, the RMS detector should control the dynamic response of the Sound Data Acquisition System in the Fast and Slow modes. Practically, the characteristics of the indicating instrument (in particular, analog meters or graphic recorders, where a needle or pen must be physically moved) may influence the dynamic response. When the RMS detector controls the dynamic response, the single pole filter time constants selected shall be 125 ms for Fast and 1 s for Slow (see Section A.1). For Impulse mode, the rise time constant is 35 ms and the decay time constant is 1.5 s. This is more fully described in Section A.3

Note that some systems may provide a selection of averaging time rather than time constant. In those cases the averaging time shall be 250 ms for Fast, 2 s for Slow, 70 ms for the impulse rise time and 3 s for the impulse decay time.

5.4 RMS Indicator Requirements—The indicating instrument shall comply with Section 4, System Performance Requirements. The resolution for the various types of indicators shall be as follows.

5.4.1 GRAPHIC—The scale shall be graduated in no more than 2 dB steps. A resolution of 1 dB steps over a range of, at least, 15 dB is preferred.

5.4.2 DIGITAL—The digital indicator resolution should be at least 0.1 dB. In order to meet the requirements of 4.3.1, 4.3.2, and 4.3.3 for noise of a transient nature, a Hold circuit should be incorporated.

5.4.3 METER—If a meter is used as the readout indicator, the scale shall be graduated in steps not greater than 1 dB over a range of at least 15 dB.

*6. Test Procedures—*The entire system, without microphone, must be used in the final qualification procedures. All components must be terminated with the correct impedance, including all connecting cables used to collect data. It may be desirable to check the frequency response, linearity, and dynamic range of individual instruments, such as tape recorders, before performing the system test.

6.1 System Frequency Response—The test oscillator amplitude frequency response shall be verified flat (±0.2 dB with a previously calibrated indicator). Corrections for deviation in oscillator output will be used to adjust the system frequency response. The microphone frequency response corrections must be added to obtain the total system frequency response.

6.1.1 LINEAR SYSTEM RESPONSE—The system frequency response must be checked with the previous calibrated oscillator (see Figure 2). The check shall be performed at a level which is 5 dB below full scale (to allow for the tolerance in Table 1) and at least 15 dB above the system noise floor.

6.1.2 A-WEIGHTED SYSTEMS RESPONSE—When an A-Weighted frequency response is measured, the system internal signal gain, immediately after the A-Weighting network, may be increased by 20 dB for the frequency response verification below 100 Hz and an additional 20 dB for verification below 30 Hz.

6.2 RMS Detector Performance Test—Two methods of testing the RMS detector are outlined in Section A.4. Either of the methods may be used to test the RMS detector.

6.3 System Noise Check—The complete system electronic noise floor should be measured with the microphone removed and replaced with the manufacturers recommended impedance. In some test environments, it may be advisable to also measure the system noise floor with the microphone in place, but acoustically isolated from the sound source and at the actual measurement location during a representative test sequence.

7. General Comments:

7.1 Environmental Responses—Care should be taken to ensure that the instrumentation is operated in an acceptable environment. Refer to the manufacturer's specifications for the effect of temperature, humidity, atmospheric pressure, vibration, and magnetic and electrostatic fields on each component piece of equipment. ANSI S1.4-1983 lists the required tolerance for which manufacturer data are not available.

7.2 Dynamic Characteristic and Time Constant—The combined effects of circuit electronics and any indicator ballistic properties on sound data can be termed Dynamic Characteristic. These parameters can vary widely and still meet the requirements of ANSI S1.4-1983 for Fast, Slow, and Impulse. In an effort to minimize variables in sound level meters, the dynamic performance characteristics must be understood. Section A.1 deals with the system dynamic characteristics in terms of a single pole RC filter with a precise time constant.

7.3 Windscreens—The spectrum of sound being measured and, to a lesser extent, the angle of incidence of source to microphone have an effect on the accuracy of Sound Data Acquisition Systems which utilize a windscreen. The windscreen can significantly alter the signal between 1000 Hz and 4000 Hz. Windscreen corrections on data may be provided by the manufacturer or by on-off comparison measurements under very carefully controlled conditions. Wind induced noise is often insignificant on weighted data, particularly with the wind speed limitations imposed in SAE sound level measurement procedures. It should be noted that contaminants such as dirt and oil may affect the response of the windscreen. Their characteristics may also change with use.

7.4 Frequency Weighting—A-weighting the signal before recording for later processing can reduce the need for unnecessary wide dynamic range because dominating low frequency data will be attenuated.

7.5 Digital Systems—Digital systems require additional components that must be properly designed/selected to meet the requirements of Section 6. Some of the design considerations include sampling frequency, aliasing, and quantization error. The additional components include antialiasing filters, sample and hold circuits, and analog to digital converters. A complete set of design guidelines to cover all of these topics falls outside of the scope of this document. A discussion of all of these topics can be found in Appendix E of ANSI S1.11-1986 (see 2.1.1.2).

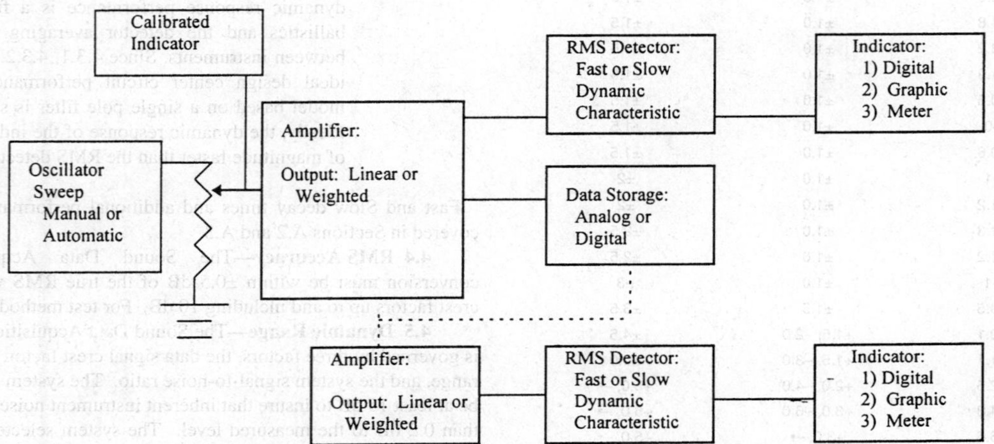

FIGURE 2—FREQUENCY RESPONSE QUALIFICATION

8. Notes

8.1 Rationale Statement—Many years have passed since SAE J184 was last revised. In the intervening years the basic rationale for the document itself has not changed, there are many instances where a system is required to provide results equivalent to those obtained with a sound level meter. In fact, this may now be the most common way of making measurements in a wide variety of situations.

Since SAE J184 was last revised, however, equipment has changed a great deal. With each passing year there are fewer people using chart recorders or electromechanical meters. There is still a desire, however, to duplicate measurements made with Type 1 and Type 2 sound level meters. In fact, over 30 SAE standards specify that either a sound level meter be used (meeting the requirements of ANSI S1.4-1983) or an equivalent system meeting the requirements of SAE J184.

This revision of SAE J184 is intended to bring it up to date with the current specifications outlined in ANSI S1.4-1983 and IEC 651-1993. In addition, sections have been added to incorporate digital technology. It was originally intended to add quite a few sections regarding the design of digital systems that would meet the requirements of SAE J184. After much discussion, however, it was decided that a proper treatment would be quite lengthy and was beyond the scope of SAE J184. In addition, SAE J184 specifies the performance of the system. These performance requirements must be met regardless of whether the analysis system is analog or digital. In fact, though the measurement systems have evolved considerable over the years, the desire to provide a sound data acquisition system that has the characteristics of a Type 1 or Type 2 sound level meter has not changed.

8.2 Relationship to ANSI and IEC Standards—This document follows both the ANSI and the IEC sound level meter standards. In general, there are very small differences between the IEC and the ANSI documents. The largest difference is the requirement of a random incidence microphone in the ANSI standard and a free field microphone in the IEC document. The approach of SAE J184 is that either of these is acceptable as long as the guidelines in the appropriate standard are followed.

SAE J184 permits a restricted frequency range in those cases in which it is known that no significant energy exists outside of the measurement band. This is not allowed in either the ANSI or IEC standards

In the few cases where there are differences between the ANSI and IEC standards, the ANSI sound level meter standard, S1.4-1983, has been followed.

8.3 Keywords—Acoustics, instrumentation, noise, calibration, sound level meter, SLM, sound data acquisition system, SDAS, microphone, detector, RMS, frequency response, windscreen, digital, dynamic range, impulse.

APPENDIX A

Preface—The following sections are intended to provide information for further verification of the system dynamic characteristic. These supplement the requirements of ANSI S1.4-1983 and are intended for better characterization of the SDAS.

A.1 System Dynamic Characteristic—The single point specification for dynamic characteristics of 4.3.1 and 4.3.2 is broad enough to allow significant variations between systems in measurement of transient data. To alleviate this potential problem, this document is suggesting that a simple first order system be adopted as the model for system response. The following suggested model does not intend to supersede the previous requirements, but to provide a model such that evaluation of all transient data will be made on a uniform basis. The single tone burst response specification of 4.3.1 and 4.3.2 meets the design center values of the model at the tone burst lengths specified.

Figure A1 is a block diagram of an RMS detector and indicator. The dynamic response to step changes in level is defined by Equations A1 and A2:

$$e_0 = e_{in}(1 - e^{-T/RC})^{1/2} \quad \text{for increasing signal levels} \qquad \text{(Eq. A1)}$$

$$e_0 = e_{in}(e^{-T/RC})^{1/2} \quad \text{for decreasing signal levels} \qquad \text{(Eq. A2)}$$

e_0 and e_{in} in volts
T—Time from beginning of step change
RC—Electrical time constant of the circuit

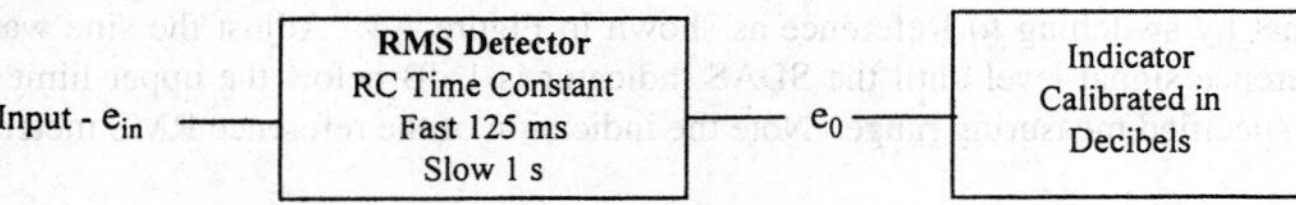

FIGURE A1—RMS DETECTOR INDICATOR

The RC time constant shall be 0.125 s for Fast and 1 s for Slow (as shown in Table A1) and these time constants shall determine the system dynamic response. This requires the indicator response to be approximately ten times faster than the time constant.

A.2 Dynamic Characteristic Decay Performance—The indicator decay for Fast from an indication 4.0 dB below full scale shall be at least 10 dB in 0.5 s when the signal is removed. Under the same test conditions, the indicator decay for Slow will be at least 10 dB in 3.0 s.

A.3 Impulse Mode—Figure A2 is a block diagram of an impulse detector indicator.

A.3.1 Frequency Response—When a continuous test signal is applied, the indication in impulse mode shall be the same as the indication in Fast and Slow within 0.1 dB between 31.5 Hz and 8 kHz.

A.3.2 Single Burst Response

A.3.2.1 The tone burst indications in Table A2 shall be met for a single sinusoidal burst with frequency of 2 kHz and a duration T.

TABLE A1—DYNAMIC PERFORMANCE TO INCREASING STEP INPUT CHANGES

Time Constant	Duration of Step Change, ms	Response Referred to Continuous Level e_0	Response Referred to Continuous Level dB
Fast	Continuous	1.00	0.00
125 ms	200	0.89	–1.00
	100	0.74	–2.60
	50	0.57	–4.80
	20	0.38	–8.30
	5	0.20	–14.10
Slow	Continuous	1.00	0.00
1 s	2000	0.93	–0.60
	1000	0.80	–2.00
	500	0.63	–4.10
	200	0.43	–7.40
	50	0.22	–13.10

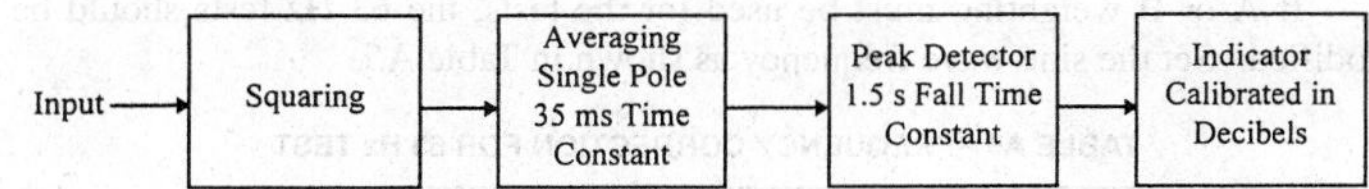

FIGURE A2—IMPULSE DETECTOR/INDICATOR

TABLE A2—SINGLE BURST RESPONSE

T in ms	Indication dB below Full Scale	Tolerance dB Type 1	Tolerance dB Type 2
Continuous	0	Ref	Ref
20	–3.6	±1.5	±2.0
5	–8.8	±2.0	±3.0
2	–12.6	±2.0	No test

A.3.2.2 When the burst duration is held constant at 2 ms and the input amplitude is increased by 10 dB, the indication must increase by 10 dB ± 1 dB for a Type 1 system. For a Type 2 system, the test shall be performed with a burst duration of 5 ms and an amplitude step of 5 dB. The indication shall increase by 5 dB ± 1 dB.

A.3.3 Multiple Burst Response

A.3.3.1 The following indications of Table A3 shall be met for continuous sequence of sinusoidal bursts having a frequency of 2 kHz, a duration of 5 ms, and a repetition frequency F.

TABLE A3—MULTIPLE BURST RESPONSE

F in Hz	Indication dB below Full Scale	Tolerance dB Type 1	Tolerance dB Type 2
Continuous	0	Ref	Ref
100	–2.7	±1.0	±2.0
20	–7.6	±2.0	±2.0
2	–8.8	±2.0	±3.0

A.3.3.2 When the repetition rate is held at 2 Hz, and the input amplitude is increased by 5.0 dB, the indication must increase by 5.0 dB ± 1 dB.

A.3.4 Impulse Decay Performance

A.3.4.1 When the continuous signal is suddenly decreased to zero, the indication must decrease by 2.9 dB per second ± 0.5 dB per second for Type 1 instruments and 2.9 dB per second ± 1.0 dB per second for Type 2 instruments.

A.4 RMS Detector Tests

A.4.1 RMS Detector Test Method 1—Connect the equipment as shown in Figure A3. The R value shall be 1% or less than the Detector Indicator System (DIS) input impedance. The DIS input may be applied through a suitable network replacing the microphone, or in series with the microphone if acoustic pickup can be made negligible. Perform the tests indicated in Table A4.

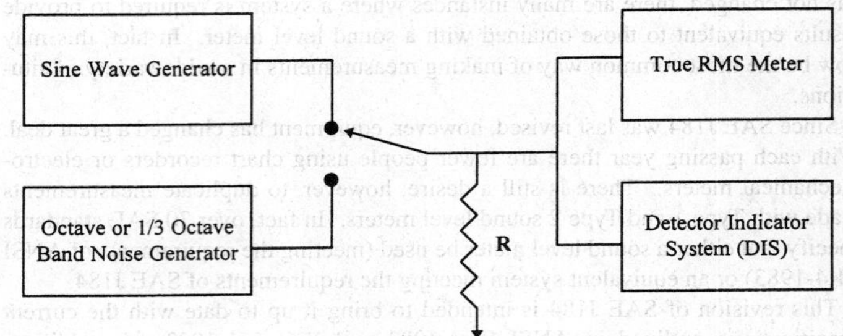

FIGURE A3—RMS DETECTOR TEST METHOD 1

TABLE A4—RMS DETECTOR TEST REQUIREMENTS

	Frequency Hz	Input	Indicated Value dB below Full Scale	Function	Averaging Time
Test 1	1000 Hz	Sine Wave	–1.0	Set	Fast
	1000 Hz Band	Noise	–1.0 ± 0.5	Read	Fast
Test 2	1000 Hz	Sine Wave	–10.0	Set	Fast
	1000 Hz Band	Noise	–10.0 ± 0.5	Read	Fast
Test 3	6300 Hz	Sine Wave	–1.0	Set	Fast
	6300 Hz Band	Noise	–1.0 ± 0.5	Read	Fast
Test 4	6300 Hz	Sine Wave	–10.0	Set	Fast
	6300 Hz Band	Noise	–10.0 ± 0.5	Read	Fast
Test 5	63 Hz	Sine Wave	–1.0	Set	Slow
	63 Hz Band	Noise	–1.0 ± 0.5	Read	Slow
Test 6	63 Hz	Sine Wave	–10.0	Set	Slow
	63 Hz Band	Noise	–10.0 ± 0.5	Read	Slow

For each test, adjust the sine wave generator level and the DIS gain controls for the required indicated value. Adjust the noise generator average RMS value to equal the sine wave generator RMS value as indicated on the True RMS meter. The DIS average reading must be within ±0.5 dB of the sine wave reading.

Use C or Flat weighting in Tests 3 to 6. If neither C nor Flat is provided, signals should be connected to the linear electronics section of the DIS between the weighting networks and the detection system.

If A or B weighting must be used for the tests, the 63 Hz tests should be modified. Set the sine wave frequency as shown in Table A5.

TABLE A5—FREQUENCY CORRECTION FOR 63 Hz TEST

Weighting	Octave	1/3 Octave
A	67.4 Hz	63.6 Hz
B	64.9 Hz	63.4 Hz

For Tests 5 and 6, the average meter deflection may be determined by averaging 50 instantaneous deflection readings taken at least 2 s apart.

Alternatively, if provided, use a longer averaging time. The meter fluctuations must be less than ±0.25 dB using this method.

The 1/3 octave or octave bands of noise should be derived from a gaussian noise source that is pink over the range from at least 20 Hz to 20000 Hz, within ±1 dB. The filters must meet the Class II or III requirements of ANSI S1.11-1986. Pink means a spectrum level downward slope of 3 dB/Octave applied to gaussian random noise. Above 20 kHz, the slope must fall at this rate or faster.

A.4.2 RMS Detector Test Method 2—The RMS accuracy is tested by comparing the indication for a reference sine wave to a continuous sequence of rectangular pulses and a sequence of tone bursts. The reference sine wave frequency shall be 2 kHz. The rectangle test pulses shall have durations of 200 µs and rise times of less than 10 µs. The tone burst test signal shall consist of an integer number of sine waves (2 kHz) starting and ending at zero crossing. The repetition frequency shall be 40 Hz.

The reference sine wave and test signals shall have identical RMS values. The signals are compared using a weighting network prior to the reference meter identical to the sound level meter weighting within the tolerances of Table 1. The C-weighting characteristic or Flat shall be used. If the instrument has only A– or B–weighting, test with tone bursts only.

The test signal is connected to the electrical input of the sound level meter. The test is performed in Slow dynamic characteristic, or in Fast if Slow is not available.

Both positive and negative going pulses are used in the rectangular pulse test. The test shall be performed at 1 dB below the upper limit of the specified measuring range and at intervals of 10 dB below this level down to the lowest level that produces an indication of more than 3 dB on the indicator.

A.4.2.1 RECTANGULAR PULSE TEST— Apply the 2000 Hz sine wave reference signal by switching to Reference as shown in Figure A4. Adjust the sine wave reference signal level until the SDAS indicator is 1 dB below the upper limit of the specified measuring range. Note the indication of the reference RMS meter.

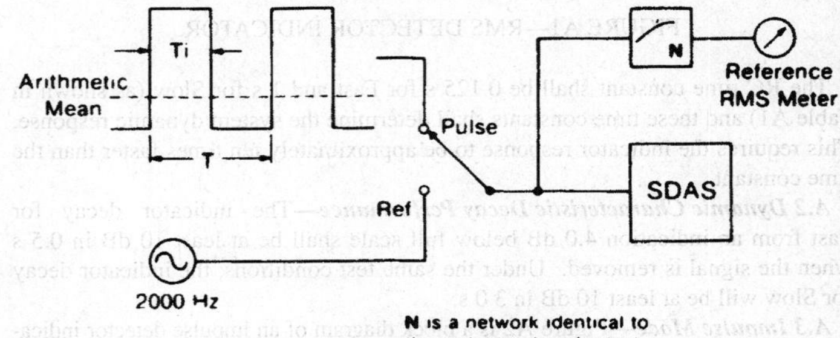

FIGURE A4—RECTANGULAR PULSE TEST

Apply the appropriate rectangular pulse sequence as shown in Table A6 by switching to Pulse. Adjust the pulse generator amplitude for the same indication on the reference RMS meter. The SDAS indication must be within the limits shown in Table A5.

TABLE A6—RECTANGULAR PULSE TEST VALUES

SLM Type	Crest Factor 10 dB Ti ms	Crest Factor 10 dB T ms	Crest Factor 10 dB Accuracy dB	Crest Factor 14 dB Ti ms	Crest Factor 14 dB T ms	Crest Factor 14 dB Accuracy dB	Crest Factor 20 dB Ti ms	Crest Factor 20 dB T ms	Crest Factor20 dB Accuracy dB
Type 1 Impulse	0.2	2.0	±0.5	0.2	5.2	±1.0	0.2	20.2	±1.5
Type 1	0.2	2.0	±0.5	—	—	—	—	—	—
Type 2	0.2	2.0	±1.0	0.2	5.2	±1.0	—	—	—
Impulse Type 2	0.2	2.0	±1.0	—	—	—	—	—	—

A.4.2.2 TONE BURST TEST—The rectangular pulse generator of A.4.2.1 is replaced by a tone burst generator and the procedure repeated using the values given in Table A7.

TABLE A7—TONE BURST TEST VALUES

SLM Type	Ti ms	T ms	Accuracy dB	Ti ms	T ms	Accuracy dB	Ti ms	T ms	Accuracy dB
Type 1 Impulse	5.55	25	±0.5	2.0	25	±1.0	0.5	25	±1.5
Type 1	5.55	25	±0.5	—	—	—	—	—	—
Type 2	5.55	25	±1.0	2.0	25	±1.0	—	—	—
Impulse Type 2	5.55	25	±1.0	—		—	—	—	—

APPENDIX B

B.1 Use of Fast Fourier Transform Analyzers—In general, Fast Fourier Transform (FFT) analyzers will not be able to meet those parts of this document that refer to the dynamic characteristic of the system. If a user is interested in using an FFT analyzer, particular care should be taken to insure that the requirements of 4.3, 4.4, 5.3 and Appendix A are met.

APPENDIX C

C.1 Dynamic Range—In an ideal situation the sound data acquisition system is adjusted so that the largest signal that can be accommodated without overload corresponds exactly to the peak level found in the signal. The RMS value of the signal lies below this peak by a value that is defined as the crest factor of the signal. Therefore, the greater the crest factor, the larger the amount of dynamic range that must be reserved for peaks in the signal. In practice, the precise crest factor is never known and it is impossible to adjust the input range of the sound data acquisition system to the precise peak of the signal. The amount of dynamic range reserved for the crest factor will, therefore, always have to be greater than the actual crest factor of the signal. It is not unusual to find that the crest factor is on the order of 10 dB for many common noise measurements.

Any fluctuations in the signal amplitude over time must also be accounted in the dynamic range of the instrument. These fluctuations might be quite small when measuring, for instance, a constant speed turbine whine or they may be quite large when measuring an automobile engine accelerating from 1000 to 4000 rpm.

APPENDIX D

D.1 Type 0 Characteristics—In some cases, greater precision may be required than that specified for the Type 1 system in this procedure. For those cases, the user is referred to Type 0 systems as specified in ANSI S1.4-1983 and IEC 651-1993. This type of performance is not currently required in any SAE standard that refers to SAE J184.

SOUND LEVEL FOR PASSENGER CARS AND LIGHT TRUCKS—SAE J986 MAY1998

SAE Recommended Practice

Report of the Vehicle Noise Committee approved July 1967 and revised by the Vehicle Sound Level Committee October 1988. Rationale statement available. Completely revised by the Light Vehicle Exterior Sound Level Standards Committee and the Vehicle Sound Level Standards Forum Committee August 1994. Revised by the SAE Light Vehicle Exterior Sound Level Committee and the SAE Vehicle Sound Level Standards Forum Committee May 1998. Rationale statement available.

Foreword—This Document has also changed to comply with the new SAE Technical Standards Board format. Definitions has been changed to Section 3. All other Sections have changed.

1. Scope—This SAE Standard establishes the test procedure, environment, and instrumentation for determining the exterior sound level for passenger cars, multipurpose vehicles, and light trucks having a gross vehicle mass rating of 4540 kg or less. The test procedure is characterized by having fixed initial conditions, i.e., an as-specified initial vehicle speed and gear selection at a fixed start point on the test site. Full-throttle acceleration and closed-throttle deceleration of the vehicle are included in this procedure.

Sound levels determined in accordance with this document are dependent on the performance capability of the test vehicle, as influenced by power-to-mass ratio and overall powertrain gear ratio.

2. References

2.1 Applicable Publications—The following publications form a part of this specification to the extent specified herein. The latest issue of SAE publications shall apply.

2.1.1 SAE PUBLICATIONS—Available from SAE, 400 Commonwealth Drive, Warrendale, PA 15096-0001.

SAE J184—Qualifying a Sound Data Acquisition System

SAE J1349—Engine Power Test Code—Spark Ignition and Diesel

2.1.2 ANSI PUBLICATIONS—Available from 11 West 42nd Street, New York, NY 10036-8002.

ANSI S1.4-1983—Specification for Sound Level Meters

ANSI S14A-1985—Sound Level Meters

2.1.3 U.S. Environmental Protection Agency Noise Advisory Circular: A/C No. 3, January 27, 1978

3. Definitions

3.1 Curb Mass—The mass of the vehicle with standard equipment, optional equipment, and fluids filled to capacity.

3.2 Multi-fuel Vehicle—A vehicle, such as a dual- or bi-fuel vehicle, equipped to operate on more than one type of fuel, e.g., either compressed natural gas or gasoline.

3.3 Variable Fuel Vehicle—A vehicle equipped to operate on a variety of fuel blends, e.g., a mixture of gasoline and methanol.

3.4 Rated Engine Speed—The engine speed at which the engine delivers rated power output as defined in SAE J1349, as determined by the manufacturer.

3.5 Throttle Control—The driver operated pedal (or other control) which connects through some mechanism to the engine fuel metering device (carburetor, fuel injectors, fuel distributor, or equivalent device) and thereby controls the engine power output.

NOTE—For the purpose of this document, depression of the throttle control acts to increase engine speed and release of the throttle control acts to reduce engine speed.

4. Vehicle Operation

4.1 The test mass of the vehicle, including the driver and equipment, shall not exceed 125 kg over the curb mass (fuel level may be reduced as needed to ensure that this requirement is met).

4.2 The powertrain and exhaust system temperatures shall be within the normal operating range throughout each test run. A 1 min stabilizing period with the engine at idle speed and the transmission in neutral is required prior to each test run.

NOTE—Usually a vehicle brought to normal engine coolant temperature through moderate driving operations is adequately conditioned for testing.

4.3 Vehicle tires shall be inflated to the proper pressure in accordance with the manufacturer's recommendations.

4.4 Preliminary runs to familiarize the driver and to establish the vehicle operating conditions should be made before taking sound level measurements.

4.5 Acceleration Test—The acceleration test is the primary test mode and must be conducted first to obtain information necessary to conduct the deceleration test.

4.5.1 For this test, the vehicle shall approach the measurement area along the vehicle path with the vehicle speed stabilized at 48 km/h ± 1.2 km/h. The highest-numerical-ratio transmission gear shall be used that will result in the front of the vehicle reaching or passing the entry point of the end zone before rated engine speed is attained. It is recommended that the approach speed be held constant for a distance of at least 7.5 m prior to reaching the start point.

When the front of the vehicle reaches the start point ± 1.5 m, the throttle control shall be fully depressed as rapidly as possible and the vehicle allowed to accelerate until the engine reaches rated engine speed. The test run is then terminated and the throttle control may be released.

Should rated engine speed not be attained in the end zone, the test run is nonetheless terminated when the front of the vehicle reaches the end of the end zone. The maximum engine speed attained should be noted. (See 4.5.1).

4.5.2 When vehicles equipped with automatic transmissions downshift from the gear ratio determined in accordance with 4.5.1, the downshift shall be prevented by one of the following methods:

a. The approach speed of the vehicle may be increased to a maximum of 60 km/h.

b. Maintain the speed at 48 km/h, with the fuel supply to the engine limited to 95% of the supply necessary for full load.

NOTE—This condition shall be satisfied in the case of a spark-ignition engine when the angle of the butterfly valve is 90% of full travel, and in the case of a compression-ignition engine when the movement of the feedrack of the injection pump is limited to 90% of its stroke.

c. The downshift mechanism may be disabled as recommended by the vehicle manufacturer.

d. Establish an electronic program that will maintain the gear selected and prevent changes to any other gear ratio.

4.5.3 If the vehicle is equipped with all-wheel drive that can be engaged or disengaged by operator control, the position used for normal urban driving shall be used.

4.5.4 If the vehicle is equipped with a multi-mode exhaust system that can be switched between modes by operator control, the vehicle shall be tested in each mode and the mode yielding the highest sound level shall be recorded.

4.5.5 If the vehicle is equipped with two or more driving modes (e.g., "normal" and "performance") affecting transmission shift schedules that can be engaged by operator control, the vehicle shall be tested in each mode and the mode yielding the highest sound level shall be recorded.

4.5.6 If the vehicle is equipped for operation on variable fuels or fuel mixtures, or if the vehicle is equipped for multiple (dual- or bi-) fuel operation, the vehicle shall be tested using each fuel or fuel mixture unless prior testing has established that the maximum sound level is produced when using a particular fuel or fuel mixture, in which case the vehicle shall be tested using that fuel or fuel mixture only.

4.5.7 If the vehicle is equipped with two or more multi-mode systems yielding a large number of possible combinations then a sufficient number of combinations shall be tested to establish a sound level range. Henceforth, a combination deemed to produce the highest sound levels in the sound level range shall be tested, and these data shall be recorded.

4.6 Deceleration Test—The deceleration test shall also be conducted unless prior testing has established that the maximum sound level is produced in the acceleration test mode.

4.6.1 The maximum engine speed attained in the acceleration test is to be used as the approach speed for the deceleration test (if conducted). This approach speed will be rated engine speed or the average of the terminal engine speed values at the end of the end zone as determined in 5.4.1.

4.6.2 For this test, the vehicle shall approach the measurement area along the vehicle path in the same gear used for the acceleration test with the engine speed stabilized at the speed determined according to 4.5.1. It is recommended that the approach speed be held constant for a distance of at least 7.5 m prior to reaching the start point. When the front of the vehicle reaches the start point ±1.5 m, the throttle control shall be completely released as rapidly as possible and the vehicle allowed to decelerate until the engine speed drops to one-half the approach speed or the front of the vehicle reaches the end of the end zone.

5. Measurements

5.1 The sound level meter shall be set for fast (F) exponential time-averaging and for the A-weighted network.

5.2 The ambient sound level at the test site due to sources other than the vehicle being measured, including wind effects, shall be at least 10 dB lower than the sound level produced by the vehicle under test. To improve the repeatability of the measurement, a 15 dB signal to ambient level is preferred.

5.3 Measurements shall be made only when the wind speed does not exceed 19 km/h.

5.4 The sound level meter or indicating instrument shall be observed during the constant-speed approach and acceleration or deceleration test phases specified in 4.4 or 4.5. The highest sound level occurring during this observation period shall be recorded. If a sound peak is obviously out of character with the general sound levels observed, the measurement shall be discarded.

5.4.1 If an instantaneous sound level "spike" occurs at depression of the throttle control at the start of the acceleration test due to momentary loss of tire traction (tire "chirp"), the "spike" shall be disregarded.

5.5 Measurements are to be made on each side of the vehicle, four consecutive valid measurements within 2 dB are achieved. The arithmetic average of these four measurements is the reported level for that side of the vehicle. The figure reported for the vehicle is the highest side average.

5.6 The reported sound level shall be that for the side of the vehicle having the highest sound level, as determined according to 5.5, from either the acceleration test mode or the deceleration test mode (if conducted).

6. Instrumentation

6.1 The instrumentation necessary to conduct this test shall meet the minimum performance requirements specified as follows.

6.2 The sound level meter shall meet the Type 1 or S1A requirements of ANSI S1.4-1983 and S1.4A-1985.

6.2.1 As an alternative to making direct measurements using a sound level meter, a microphone or sound level meter may be used with a magnetic tape recorder and/or a graphic level recorder or other indicating instrument providing the system is in conformance with SAE J184.

6.3 The sound level calibrator shall be accurate to ±0.5 dB (see 8.3.4)(see 8.3.4).

6.4 Engine and vehicle speed shall be measured with instruments having an accuracy of ±2% at the speeds required for the measurements being made (see 8.4)(see 8.4).

6.5 The anemometer shall be accurate to ±10% at 19 km/h wind speed.

6.6 A microphone windscreen may be used, provided that it does not affect the microphone response more than ±1 dB for frequencies from 20 to 4000 Hz and ±1.5 dB for frequencies from 4000 to 10 000 Hz.

7. Test Site

7.1 The test site shall be a flat, open space free of large reflecting surfaces such as parked vehicles, signboards, buildings, or hillsides located within 30 m of the measurement area. The measurement area, which is defined as the plane surface fixed by the point at the microphone location and the end points of the end zone on the far side of the traffic lane in both directions of vehicle travel, shall be flat to within ±0.05 m. The entire plane may slope toward or away from the microphone for drainage. The vehicle path shall be of minimal grade end-to-end to avoid variations in vehicle loading. To minimize measurement variability, it is recommended that a two-sided site have both measurement areas in the same uniform plane. See 7.5 and 7.6, Figure 1,(see 7.5) and Appendix A for flatness measurement procedure.

7.2 The surface of the measurement area shall be concrete or nonporous asphalt, dry, and free from snow, soil, or other extraneous material.

7.3 The test site shall include a vehicle path of relatively smooth concrete or asphalt, dry, and free of extraneous materials such as gravel and of sufficient length for acceleration, deceleration, and stopping of the vehicle.

7.4 The test site surface sound absorption coefficient (normal incidence), as measured in situ by the impedance tube method, shall be 0.10 or less.

7.5 The microphone shall be located 15 m from the centerline of the vehicle path and 1.2 m above the ground plane. The reference axis of the microphone shall lie in the vertical plane containing the perpendicular to the vehicle path through the microphone location.

7.6 The following fixed points and zones shall be established on the vehicle path:

7.6.1 The start point, 7.5 m ahead of the perpendicular to the vehicle path through the microphone location.

7.6.2 The end zone, starting at 7.5 m beyond, and ending at 38 m beyond the perpendicular to the vehicle path through the microphone location.

7.7 If it is desired to measure the sound level for both sides of the vehicle during each test run, another microphone location, measurement area, and clear area shall be established laterally opposite, meeting the requirements of 7.1, 7.2, and 7.5.

8. General Comments

8.1 It is recommended that persons technically trained and experienced in current sound measurement techniques, select the test instrumentation and conduct the tests.

8.2 When making sound level measurements, not more than one person other than the observer reading the meter shall be within 15 m of the vehicle or microphone, and that person shall be directly behind the observer reading the meter, on a line through the microphone and the observer.

8.3 Proper use of all test instrumentation is essential to obtain valid measurements. Operating manuals or other literature furnished by the instrument manufacturer should be referred to for both recommended operation of the instrument and precautions to be observed. Specific items to be considered are:

8.3.1 The type of microphone, its directional response characteristics, and its orientation relative to the ground plane and the sound source.

8.3.2 The effects of ambient weather conditions on the performance of all instruments (for example, temperature, relative humidity, and barometric pressure).

8.3.3 Proper signal levels, terminating impedances, and cable lengths on multi-instrument systems.

8.3.4 Proper acoustical calibration procedures, to include the influence of extension cables, etc. Field calibration shall be made immediately before and after each test sequence. Internal calibration is acceptable for field use, provided that external calibration is accomplished immediately before and after field use.

8.4 Many tachometers in common use have an appreciable time lag in response during vehicle acceleration. The use of such a tachometer without suitable correction could result in the attainment of higher than intended engine speed and possible effects on measured sound levels.

8.5 Vehicles used for tests shall not be operated in a manner such that the break-in procedure specified by the manufacturer is violated.

8.6 It should be recognized that variations in measured sound levels may occur due to variations in test site, ambient weather differences (temperature, wind, and their gradients), test equipment differences, and inherent differences between nominally identical vehicles.

APPENDIX A

A.1 Procedure for determining measurement area flatness (refer to 7.1).

1. Establish a 1.5 m x 1.5 m square grid on the measurement area (Figure A1). If the test site is double sided, the operation may be performed either for the total plane of the combined measurement areas or separately for each of the measurement areas. (It is recommended, to minimize measurement variability, that a two-sided site have both measurement areas in the same uniform plane.)
2. Measure the relative elevation of each of the grid points using a surveying level and an elevation rod calibrated in at least 6 mm increments.
3. Analyze the relative elevation data to determine a "best fit" plane based on two-dimensional linear regression analysis.
4. Calculate the deviations, in centimeters, of the actual site elevation from the best fit plane.
5. If the difference between maximum positive and negative deviations is greater than 10 cm, then the site exceeds the ±5 cm flatness requirement.

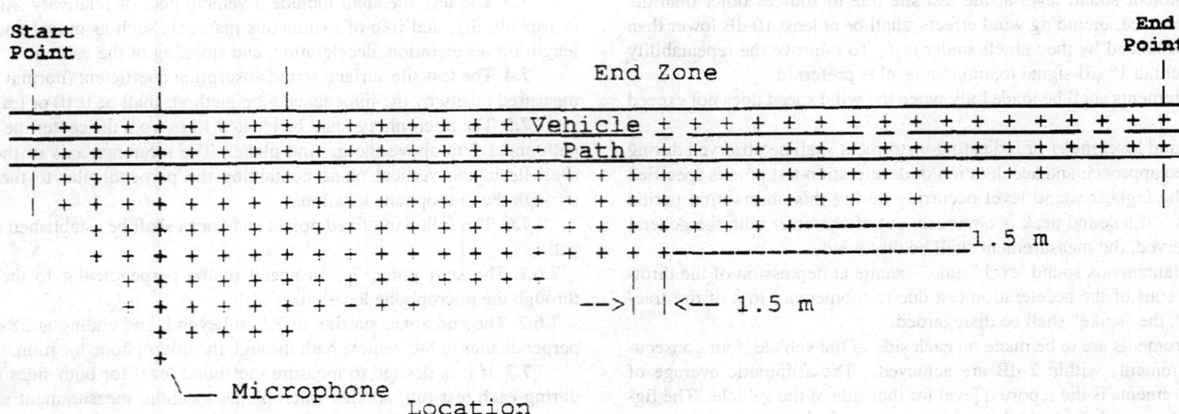

Not to scale.

Source: U.S. Environmental Protection Agency Noise Advisory Circular: A/C No. 3, January 27, 1978.

FIGURE A1—MEASUREMENT AREA FLATNESS TEST GRID

MEASUREMENT OF INTERIOR SOUND LEVELS OF LIGHT VEHICLES—SAE J1477 MAY2000

SAE Recommended Practice

Report of the SAE Vehicle Sound Level Committee approved January 1986. Reaffirmed by the SAE Motor Vehicle Council Sound Level Committee May 2000.

Foreword—This Document has not changed other than to put it into the new SAE Technical Standards Board Format. References were added as Section 2. All other section numbers changed accordingly.

1. Scope—This SAE Recommended Practice establishes the test procedure, environment, instrumentation, and data analyses for comparing interior sound level of passenger cars, multipurpose vehicles, and light trucks having gross vehicle weight rating (GVWR) of 4540 kg (10 000 lb) or less.

The test procedure is characterized by having fixed initial conditions (specified initial vehicle speed and gear selection at the starting point on the test site) to obtain vehicle interior sound measurement during road load operation over various road surfaces at specified constant speeds.

The measurement data so derived is useful for vehicle engineering development and analysis.

1.1 Operation—Perform a standard series of tests at 60, 70, 80, 90, and 100 km/h (38, 44, 50, 56, 63 mph) on smooth (within normal construction practice) level asphalt or equivalent road surface.

Perform special tests at desired speeds on designated road surfaces, and/or with special noise producing systems operating, as desired.

2. References

2.1 Applicable Publications—The following publications form a part of the specification to the extent specified herein. Unless otherwise indicated, the latest revision of SAE publications shall apply.

2.1.1 SAE PUBLICATION—Available from SAE, 400 Commonwealth Drive, Warrendale, PA 15096-0001.

SAE J184—Qualifying a Sound Data Acquisition System

2.1.2 ANSI AND ISO PUBLICATIONS—Available from ANSI, 11 West 42nd Street, New York, NY 10036-8002.

ANSI S1.4—American National Standard Specification for Sound Level meters

ISO 5128—Acoustics, measurement of noise inside motor vehicles

2.2 Related Publications—The following publications are provided for information purposes only and are not a required part of this document.

2.2.1 SAE PUBLICATION—Available from SAE, 400 Commonweatlh Drive, Warrendale, PA 15096-0001.

SAE J986—Sound Level for Passenger Cars and Light Trucks

2.2.2 OTHER PUBLICATIONS—Available from McGraw-Hill Book Company, New York.

Beranek, Leo L., Noise and Vibration Control, p. 554, 1971.

3. Instrumentation—The following instrumentation shall be used:

3.1 Two sound level meters which meet the type 1 or S1A requirements of the American National Standard Specifications for Sound Level Meters, S1.4.

3.2 Two condenser type omni-directional microphones.

3.3 A two-channel audio tape recorder (if analyses described in 8.2 are to be obtained) conforming to the requirements of SAE Recommended Practice J184a, Qualifying a Sound Data Acquisition System.

3.4 A sound level calibrator accurate to ±0.5 dB.

3.5 An anemometer accurate to ±10% at 18 km/h (11 mph).

3.6 Instrumentation to measure the vehicle speed accurate to ±2% for a desired test condition.

4. Test Site

4.1 The test site shall be a flat open space free of large reflecting surfaces which affect the sound level. No passing vehicles may be in the vicinity of the test vehicle while measurements are being made.

4.2 The test site shall include a vehicle path of sufficient length for safe acceleration, deceleration, and stopping of the vehicle.

4.3 The test road surfaces shall be hard, as smooth and level as possible, and of uniform surface texture[1]. The test road surfaces shall be in good repair and free of local extraneous material such as sand, gravel, snow, water, leaves, etc.

1. It should be noted that road surface texture differences may produce variability in test results.

5. Vehicle Preparation—The test vehicle shall be properly prepared for the test.

5.1 During the test, all operating conditions of the engine shall correspond to the specifications provided by the manufacturer, for example, fuel, lubricating oil, temperature, and ignition timing.

5.2 The tires shall be of a type specified by the vehicle manufacturer as being appropriate to the conditions under which the vehicle is normally used. The cold tire pressure shall be as recommended by the vehicle manufacturer.

5.3 Exhaust system, suspension, and steering including front end alignment and wheel(s) balance shall be checked and corrected as required to conform to the manufacturer's specifications.

5.4 All the windows and ventilating systems shall be tightly closed. Accessories such as windshield wipers and selectable ventilating fans shall not be operated for the standard test. Special tests, such as with an air- conditioning unit operating at higher blower speed, may be specified. Any system which operates automatically and affects the sound level reading must be identified in the test report, preferably with data for the different operating modes.

5.5 Operate the test vehicle for 8 km (5 mile) at 90 km/h (55 mph) to warm up the engine and tires immediately before the test.

6. Microphone Positions—The noise inside a vehicle may vary considerably with location. Therefore, measuring points should be selected in sufficient number and in such a manner that the distribution of the noise in the vehicle is adequately represented with respect to driver and passenger locations.

One measuring point shall be at the driver's position.

The microphone shall be no closer than 0.15 m (6 in) from walls or upholstery.

The microphone shall be oriented so that the direction of the manufacturer's recommended free field orientation is the same as the direction in which a person occupying the seat would be looking, or if such direction is not defined, in the driving direction. If a different orientation is used, it shall be reported.

The microphone used during the tests shall be mounted in such a way that it is not affected by vibrations of the vehicle. The mounting shall prevent excessive (more than about 20 mm) amplitudes relative to the vehicle.

6.1 Microphone position with respect to a seat (see Figure 1).

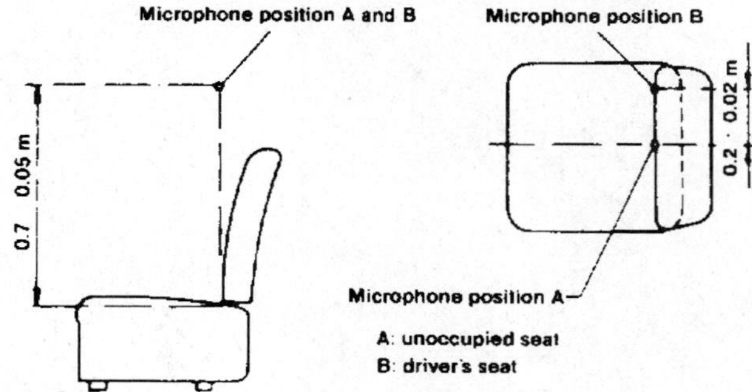

FIGURE 1—MICROPHONE POSITION WITH RESPECT TO A SEAT.

The vertical coordinate of the microphone shall be 0.7 m ± 0.05 m (28 in ± 2 in) above the intersection of the unoccupied seat surface and the surface of the back of the seat (see Figure 1). The horizontal coordinate shall be the middle plane (or plane of symmetry) of the unoccupied seat. At the driver's seat, with the driver present, the horizontal coordinate shall be 0.2 m ± 0.02 m (8 in ± 1 in) to the right from the middle plane of the seat.

Adjustable seats shall be set in the mid position of the horizontal and vertical range of adjustment. If the back rest of the seat is adjustable, it shall be set as near to the vertical position as possible.

Adjustable head rests shall be set at the mid position.

7. Measurements

7.1 The sound level meters shall be set for the fast dynamic response and for the A-weighting network.

7.2 Observe the sound level meter or indicating instrument while the vehicle is proceeding at each constant speed for at least 30 s. Where a sound level meter only is used, the applicable reading shall be the average sound level observed during the run.

7.3 If a tape recorder is used as part of the measuring equipment, it may be necessary to include suitable pre-emphasis and de-emphasis networks for recording and reproduction to provide an adequate signal-to-noise ratio over the whole frequency range of interest. For analysis of the data, refer to 8.2.

7.4 For all measurements of A-weighted sound pressure levels, the lower limit of the dynamic range set by the background noise[2] and by the inherent noise level of the measuring equipment shall be at least 10 dB below the A-weighted sound pressure levels of the vehicle noise.

7.5 The ambient air temperature, in which the vehicle is operating, shall be in the range –5 °C to +35 °C (23 °F to 95 °F). The wind speed along the test track measured at a height of approximately 1.2 m (47 in) shall not exceed 18 km/h (11 mph). The other meteorological conditions shall be such that they do not influence the measurements. The ambient temperature, speed of the wind, and the direction of the wind relative to the test track shall be stated.

7.6 Repeat 7.1, 7.2, 7.3, 7.4, and 7.5 for special road surface or system operation as desired by engineering development requirements.

8. Analyses

8.1 Interior sound levels, expressed in dBA at specified vehicle speeds for a given road surface, are widely accepted for evaluating vehicle interior noise.

8.2 When a tape recorder is used during measurements and a one-third octave frequency analyzer is used to obtain the frequency spectrum, the following parameters may be obtained:

2. Defined as the interior sound level at the desired microphone location in the stationary vehicle with engine off.

8.2.1 Overall average "A" weighted sound level;
8.2.2 Overall average unweighted sound level;
8.2.3 Total Stevens Mark VII sones;
8.2.4 Perceived "phons";
8.2.5 Preferred octave band speech interference level;
8.2.6 Total percent speech intelligibility;
8.2.7 Composite rating of preference.

9. General Comments

9.1 Technically competent personnel should select equipment, and tests should be conducted only by qualified persons familiar with the current technique of sound measurements.

9.2 While making sound level measurements, only the driver and instrumentation operator shall be in the vehicle.

9.3 Proper use of all test instrumentation is essential to obtain valid measurements. Operating manuals or other literature furnished by the instrument manufacturer should be referred to for both recommended operation of the instrument and precautions to be observed. Specific items to be considered are:

9.3.1 Proper signal levels, terminating impedances, and cable lengths on multi-instrument measurement systems.

9.3.2 Proper acoustical calibration procedure, to include the influence of extension cables, etc. Field calibration shall be made immediately before and after each test sequence. Internal calibration means is acceptable for field use, provided the external calibration is accomplished immediately before and after field use.

9.4 Vehicles used for tests shall not be operated in a manner such that the break-in procedure specified by the manufacturer is violated.

9.5 It should be recognized that variations in measured sound levels may occur due to variations in test site, ambient weather differences (temperature, wind, and their gradients), test equipment differences, and inherent differences between nominally identical vehicles, for example, squeaks, rattles, etc.

9.6 It is important to note that the test procedure is particularly written for the measurement of interior sound levels of light vehicles, while ISO Standard 5128 is a generalized interior noise test procedure.

MEASUREMENT OF LIGHT VEHICLE EXHAUST SOUND LEVEL UNDER STATIONARY CONDITIONS—SAE J1169 MAY1998

SAE Standard

Report of the SAE Vehicle Sound Level Committee, approved January 1977, completely revised September 1985, and reaffirmed February 1987. Rationale statement available. Completely revised by the SAE Vehicle Sound Level Forum Committee and the SAE Light Vehicle Exterior Sound Level Standards Committee March 1992. Revised by the SAE Sound Level Standards Forum Committee and the SAE Light Vehicle Exterior Sound Level Committee May 1998. Rationale statement available.

Foreword—This Document has also changed to comply with the new SAE Technical Standards Board format.

1. Scope—This SAE Standard establishes the test procedure, environment, and instrumentation to be used for measuring the exhaust sound level for passenger cars, multipurpose vehicles, and light trucks under stationary conditions.

Measurements are taken under steady-state conditions. In this respect, this procedure differs from ISO 5130 which includes measurements under the dynamic conditions of an engine deceleration.

This sound level measurement procedure has been developed as a guide for governmental agencies establishing vehicle in-service sound level regulations and enforcement measurement procedures. It is directed at the assessment of vehicle exhaust noise and is not intended to determine maximum vehicle sound levels. (See Appendix A.)

2. References

2.1 Applicable Publications—The following publications form a part of the specification to the extent specified herein. Unless otherwise indicated the latest revision of SAE publications shall apply.

2.1.1 SAE PUBLICATIONS—Available from SAE, 400 Commonwealth Drive, Warrendale, PA 15096-0001.

SAE J184—Qualifying a Sound Data Acquisition System

2.1.2 ANSI PUBLICATIONS—Available from ANSI, 11 West 42nd Street, New York, NY 10036-8002.

ANSI S1.4-1983—Specification for Sound Level Meters

ANSI S1.40-1984—Specification for Acoustical Calibrators

2.1.3 ISO PUBLICATIONS—Available from ANSI, 11 West 42nd Street, New York, NY 10036-8002.

ISO 5130-1982-15—Acoustics—Measurement of noise emitted by stationary road vehicles—Survey method

3. Instrumentation

3.1 The instrumentation necessary to conduct this test shall meet the minimum performance requirements specified as follows.

3.2 A sound level meter meeting the Type 1, S1A requirements of ANSI S1.4-1983.

3.2.1 As an alternative to making direct measurements using a sound level meter, a microphone or sound level meter may be used with a magnetic tape recorder and/or a graphic level recorder or indicating instrument, provided the system meets the requirements of SAE J184.

3.2.2 The sound level meter shall be set for the slow exponential time-averaging characteristics and for A-weighting network.

3.3 The calibration of the sound level meter shall be checked and adjusted according to the manufacturer's instructions using a calibrator meeting the requirements of ANSI S1.40-1984 at the start of measurements and rechecked and recorded at the end of them. (See 8.2.)

If the calibration readings of the sound level meter change by more than 0.5 dB during a series of measurements, the test shall be considered invalid.

3.4 A microphone windscreen may be used, provided that it does not affect the microphone response more than ±1 dB for frequencies from 20 to 4000 Hz and ±1.5 dB from 4000 to 10 000 Hz.

3.5 Engine speed shall be measured with an instrument having an accuracy of ±2% or better at the speeds required for the measurements being performed.

4. Test Environment

4.1 A suitable test site shall be out-of-doors and consist of a level concrete, asphalt, or similar hard material flat surface, free from snow, grass, loose soil, ashes, or other sound absorbing material. It shall be an open space free from large reflecting surfaces, such as parked vehicles, buildings, billboards, trees, shrubbery, parallel walls, people, etc., within a 3 m (10 ft) radius from the microphone location and any point on the vehicle.

4.1.1 As an alternative to outside testing a large hemi-anechoic chamber may be used.

4.2 The ambient sound level (including wind effects) from sources other than the vehicle being tested shall be at least 10 dB below that produced by the test vehicle.

5. Microphone Orientation

5.1 The microphone shall be located at a distance of 0.5 m from the reference point on the exhaust gas outlet pipe (refer to Figure 1) and at an angle of 45 degrees (+0, –10 degrees) to the flow axis of the pipe termination (refer to Figure 2). The microphone shall be at the height of the reference point, but not less than 0.2 m from the ground surface. The reference axis of the microphone shall lie in a plane parallel to the ground surface and shall be directed toward the reference point on the exhaust gas outlet. (See also 5.2, 5.3, and 8.5.)

5.1.1 If two microphone locations are possible, the location furthest laterally from the vehicle longitudinal centerline shall be used.

5.1.2 If the flow axis of the outlet pipe is at 90 degrees to the vehicle longitudinal centerline, the microphone shall be located at the point, determined in accordance with 5.1, which is furthest from the engine.

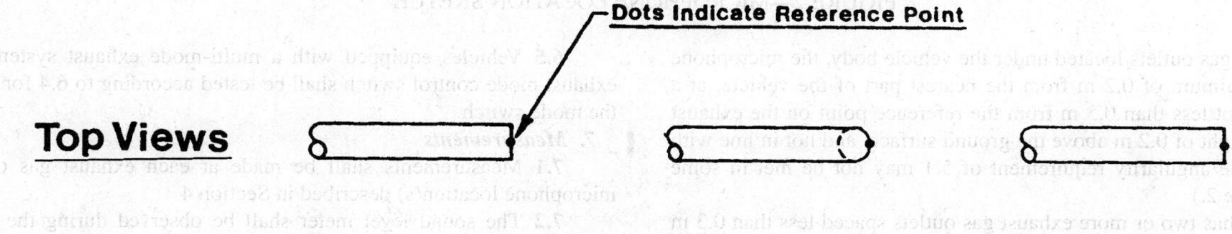

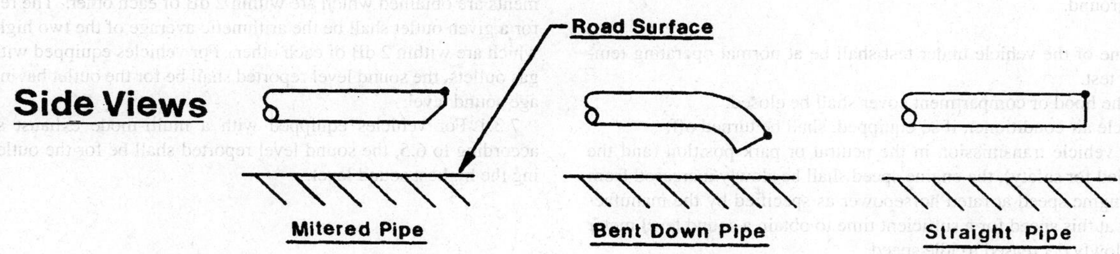

FIGURE 1—OUTLET PIPE DETAILS

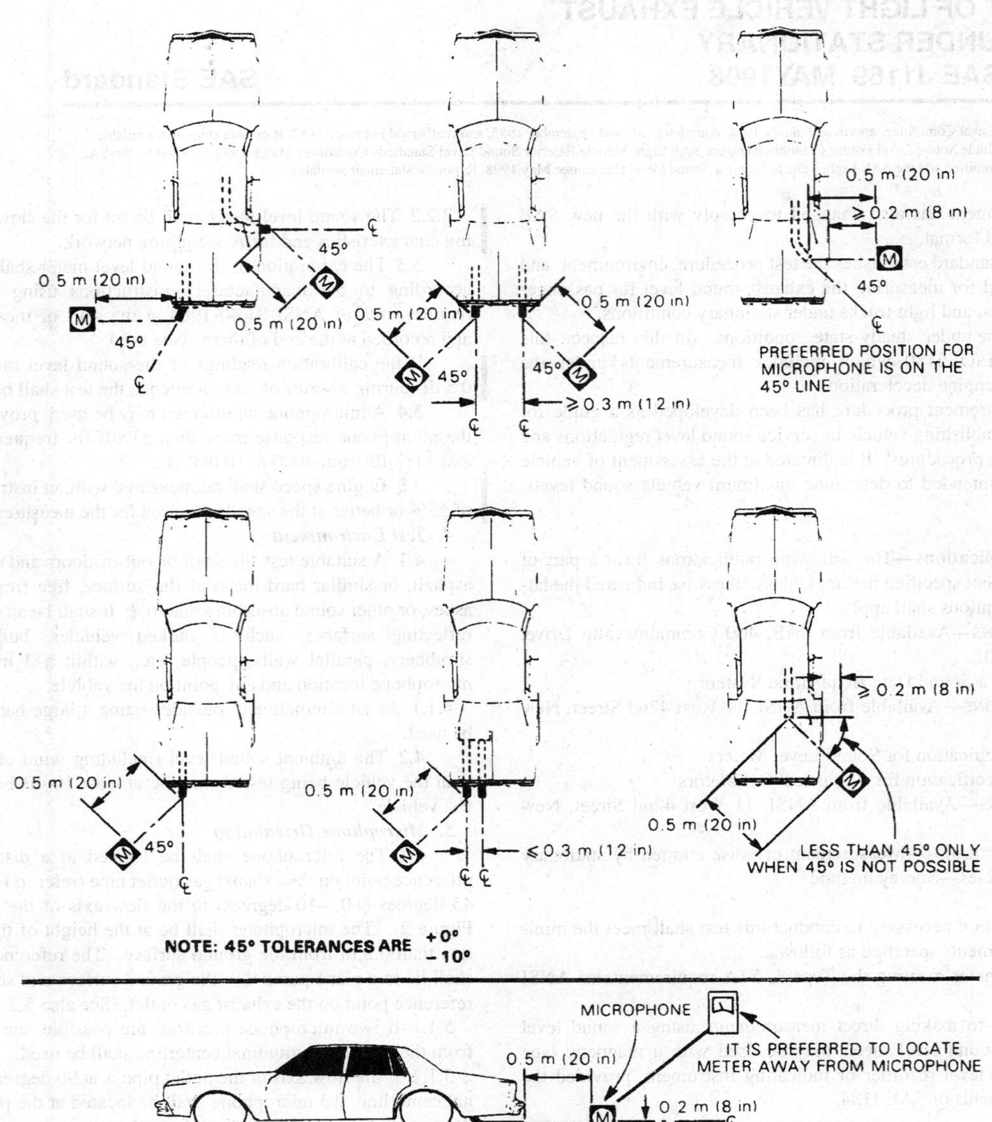

FIGURE 2—MICROPHONE LOCATION SKETCH

5.2 For exhaust gas outlets located under the vehicle body, the microphone shall be located a minimum of 0.2 m from the nearest part of the vehicle, at a point closest to, but not less than 0.5 m from the reference point on the exhaust gas outlet, and at a height of 0.2 m above the ground surface, and not in line with exhaust gas flow. The angularity requirement of 5.1 may not be met in some cases. (Refer to Figure 2.)

5.3 If a vehicle has two or more exhaust gas outlets spaced less than 0.3 m apart and connected to a single silencer, only one measurement shall be made. The microphone shall be located relative to the outlet furthest from the vehicle longitudinal centerline, or, when such outlet does not exist, to the outlet which is highest above the ground.

6. Procedure

6.1 The engine of the vehicle under test shall be at normal operating temperature during the test.

6.2 The engine hood or compartment cover shall be closed.

6.3 The vehicle air conditioner, if so equipped, shall be turned off.

6.4 With the vehicle transmission in the neutral or park position (and the parking brake applied for safety), the engine speed shall be slowly increased from idle to 3/4 of the engine speed at rated horsepower as specified by the manufacturer, held constant at this speed for a sufficient time to obtain a sound level meter reading, and then slowly decreased to idle speed.

6.5 Vehicles equipped with a multi-mode exhaust system and a manual exhaust mode control switch shall be tested according to 6.4 for each position of the mode switch.

7. Measurements

7.1 Measurements shall be made at each exhaust gas outlet, using the microphone location(s) described in Section 4.

7.2 The sound level meter shall be observed during the constant engine speed operation of the vehicle, as described in 6.4. The recorded reading shall be the highest sound level observed.

7.3 The tests shall be repeated at each exhaust gas outlet until two measurements are obtained which are within 2 dB of each other. The reported sound level for a given outlet shall be the arithmetic average of the two highest measurements which are within 2 dB of each other. For vehicles equipped with multiple exhaust gas outlets, the sound level reported shall be for the outlet having the highest average sound level.

7.3.1 For vehicles equipped with a multi-mode exhaust system and tested according to 6.5, the sound level reported shall be for the outlet and mode yielding the highest sound level.

8. General Comments

8.1 It is recommended that persons technically trained and experienced in current sound measurement techniques select the test instrumentation and conduct the tests.

8.2 Instrument manufacturer's recommended calibration practice shall be followed. External acoustic calibration shall be performed immediately before and after each period of field use.

8.3 It should be recognized that variations in measured sound levels may occur due to variations in test sites, atmospheric conditions and test equipment.

8.4 Caution should be exercised when measuring rear-and mid-engine vehicles because engine and cooling fan noise may prevent accurate measurements of exhaust noise.

8.5 Instrument manufacturer's specifications for orientation of the microphone relative to the sound source and the location of the observer relative to the microphone shall be followed. The test may be performed with a hand-held sound level meter. However, it is recommended that the sound level meter or microphone be mounted on a stand or fixture for stability. When possible, it is preferable to use a microphone extension cable and to locate measurement or recording devices away from the microphone.

APPENDIX A

A.1 General—This appendix contains a discussion of the rationale for revision of SAE J1169 FEB87 and and explanation of the changes including revisions to existing sections. This revision permits evaluation of exhaust system sound level performance in accordance with existing regulatory requirements in the U.S. for light vehicle exhaust equipment. These requirements specify measurements at steady-state conditions which causes this SAE Standard to differ from ISO 5130 which requires measurements to be taken during an engine deceleration.

A.2 Rationale—This revision of SAE J1169 differs from the SAE J1169 FEB87 revision in that it provides for performing the stationary exhaust system sound level test at 3/4 of rated engine speed instead of the 3000 r/min specified in the FEB87 revision.

The test engine speed of 3/4 of rated engine speed is in accord with existing regulatory practices in the U.S. for stationary exhaust system sound level testing. In 1977, when SAE J1169 was initially approved, 3000 r/min provided a reasonable approximation of the light vehicle industry volume-weighted mean engine speed at rated power as specified by the manufacturer. This meant that personnel performing the stationary test did not need access to engine specifications data since one criterion was applied to all vehicles.

Subsequent automotive advancements have resulted in a proliferation of smaller displacement engines and higher speeds, some above 6000 r/min, at rated horsepower. Therefore, in order to establish uniform conditions for the stationary exhaust system sound level test the test criterion of 3/4 of the engine speed at rated horsepower is adopted in this document. This information is available from various sources for use by personnel performing the test.

A.3 Differences—The differences between this revision and SAE J1169-FEB87 are explained in general, citing only the reasons for additions, deletions, or changes to existing text.

In keeping with SAE metrication objectives, only metric measurements are specified throughout this document.

A.3.1 Section 1.1—This section is revised by adding a new second paragraph and editorial revisions to the third paragraph.

A.3.2 Section 2—This section was added as the Reference Section to comply with SAE Electronic Capture Guidelines.

A.3.3 Section 3.2.1—This section is revised only to update for the revision status of the reference SAE J184 document.

Section 3.2.2—For conformity with other regulations, the reference to the S.L.M. previously in Measurements 7.1 has been moved to instrumentation, Section 3.

A.3.4 Section 3.3—This section is revised to incorporate the ANSI specification for acoustic calibrators.

A.3.5 Section 3.4—This section is revised to incorporate specific technical requirements for use of a microphone windscreen.

Section 3.4.1—This section revised to improve the precision of the measurement.

A.3.6 Section 3.5—This section is revised to specify changes to accuracy requirements for devices used to measure engine speed.

A.3.6.1This section revised to improve the precision of measurement.

A.3.7 Section 4.1—This section is revised by adding the word 'suitable' as a test site descriptor.

A.3.8 Section 6.4—This Section is revised by changing the required engine speed for testing from a constant 3000 rpm to '3/4 of the engine speed at rated horsepower as specified by the manufacturer'.

A.3.9 Section 6.5—This section is new and is added to include requirements for testing of vehicles with dual-mode mufflers wherein engine or vehicle speed conditions, or, if provided, a manual override switch, determine if exhaust gases are expelled through one or two exhaust or two outlets.

A.3.10 Section 7.4.1—This section is new to specify the reported test result for vehicles equipped with dual-mode muffler systems.

A.3.11 Section 8.2—This section is updated to delete unnecessary calibration requirements.

A.3.12 Section 8.3—This section is updated to delete 'operator skill' as a test variable since a trained and knowledgeable person should be performing the test. Also, the statement referring to a 2 dB variability is deleted to avoid the possible inference that it is a specification for this test.

A.3.13 Section 8.5—This section is revised to expand the caution to include the possibility of measurement contamination by noise from mid- as well as rear-engine vehicle engines.

A.3.14 Section 9.2—This section is new to include reference to the ANSI 1.40 specification for sound level meter calibrators.

A.3.15 Section 9.3—This section is renumbered from the original section 8.2 and revised only to update the revision status of the reference SAE J184 document.

A.3.16 Section 9.4—This section is new to include reference to the ISO 5130 stationary test standard.

MEASUREMENT OF LIGHT VEHICLE STATIONARY EXHAUST SYSTEM SOUND LEVEL ENGINE SPEED SWEEP METHOD—SAE J1492 MAY1998

SAE Recommended Practice

Report of the SAE Vehicle Sound Level Standards Forum Committee and the SAE Light Vehicle Exterior Sound Level Committee approved March 1992 and revised May 1998. Rationale statement available.

1. Scope—This SAE Recommended Practice establishes the test procedure, environment, and instrumentation to be used for measuring the exterior exhaust sound level for passenger cars, multipurpose vehicles, and light trucks under stationary conditions providing a continuous measure of exhaust system sound level over a range of engine speeds.

This sound level measurement procedure has been developed for use in engineering evaluation of the sound level performance of passenger car and light truck exhaust systems. It provides the means for detecting exhaust system resonances with the potential to affect both exterior and interior sound quality.

This document incorporates certain provisions of ISO 5130-1982-02-15, for measuring the sound level of exhaust systems. (See Appendix A.)

2. References

2.1 Applicable Publications—The following publications form a part of this specification to the extent specified herein. The latest issue of SAE publications shall apply.

2.1.1 SAE PUBLICATION—Available from SAE, 400 Commonwealth Drive, Warrendale, PA 15096-0001.

SAE J184—Qualifying a Sound Data Acquisition System

2.1.2 ANSI PUBLICATIONS—Available from ANSI, 11 West 42nd Street, New York, NY 10036-8002.

ANSI S1.4-1983—Specification for Sound Level Meters

ANSI S1.40-1984—Specification for Acoustical Calibrators

2.1.3 ISO PUBLICATION—Available from ANSI, 11 West 42nd Street, New York, NY 10036-8002.

ISO 5130-1982-02-15—Acoustics—Measurement of noise emitted by stationary road vehicles—Survey method

3. Instrumentation

3.1 The instrumentation necessary to conduct this test shall meet minimum performance requirements as specified herein.

3.2 A sound level meter meeting the Type and S1A requirements of ANSI S1.4-1983.

3.2.1 The sound level meter shall be set for the fast exponential time-averaging characteristic, (see 6.5)and A-weighting network.

3.2.2 As an alternative to making direct measurements using a sound level meter, a microphone or sound level meter may be used with a magnetic tape recorder and/or a graphic level recorder or indicating instrument, provided the system meets the requirements of SAE J184.

3.3 The calibration of the sound level meter shall be checked and adjusted according to the manufacturer's instructions using a calibrator meeting the requirements of ANSI S1.40-1984 at the start of measurements and rechecked and recorded at the end of them. (See 8.2.)(see 8.2)

If the calibration readings of the sound level meter change by more than 0.5 dB during a series of measurements, the test shall be considered invalid.

3.4 A microphone windscreen may be used, provided that it does not affect the microphone response more than ±1 dB for frequencies from 20 to 4000 Hz and ±1.5 dB from 4000 to 10 000 Hz.

3.5 Engine speed shall be measured with an instrument having an accuracy of ±2% or better at the speeds required for the measurements being performed.

4. Test Environment

4.1 A suitable test site shall be out-of-doors and consist of a level concrete, asphalt, or similar hard material flat surface, free from snow, grass, loose soil, ashes, or other sound absorbing material. It shall be in an open space free from large reflecting surfaces, such as parked vehicles, buildings, billboards, trees, shrubbery, parallel walls, people, etc., within a 3 m radius from the microphone location and any point on the vehicle.

4.1.1 As an alternative to outside testing, a large hemi-anechoic chamber may be used.

4.2 The ambient sound level (including wind effects) from sources other than the vehicle being tested shall be at least 10 dB below that produced by the test vehicle.

5. Microphone Orientation

5.1 The microphone shall be located at a distance of 0.5 m from the reference point on the exhaust outlet pipe (refer to Figure 1) and at an angle of 45 degrees (+0, –10 degrees) to the flow axis of the pipe termination (refer to Figure 2). The microphone shall be at the height of the reference point, but not less than 0.2 m from the ground surface. The reference axis of the microphone shall lie in a plane parallel to the ground surface and shall be directed toward the reference point on the exhaust outlet. (see 5.2)(See 5.2 and 5.3) (see 5.3).

5.1.1 If two microphone locations are possible, the location furthest laterally from the vehicle longitudinal centerline shall be used.

5.1.2 If the flow axis of the exhaust outlet pipe is at 90 degrees to the vehicle longitudinal centerline, the microphone shall be located at the point, determined in accordance with 5.1, which is furthest from the engine.

5.2 For exhaust outlets located under the vehicle body, the microphone shall be located a minimum of 0.2 m from the nearest part of the vehicle, at a point closest to, but not less than 0.5 m from, the exhaust outlet, and at a height of 0.2 m above the ground surface, and not in line with exhaust flow. The angularity requirement of 5.1 may not be met in some cases. (Refer to Figure 2.)

5.3 If a vehicle has two or more exhaust outlets spaced less than 0.3 m apart and connected to a single silencer, only one measurement shall be made. The microphone shall be located relative to the outlet furthest from the vehicle longitudinal centerline, or when such outlet does not exist, to the outlet which is highest above the ground.

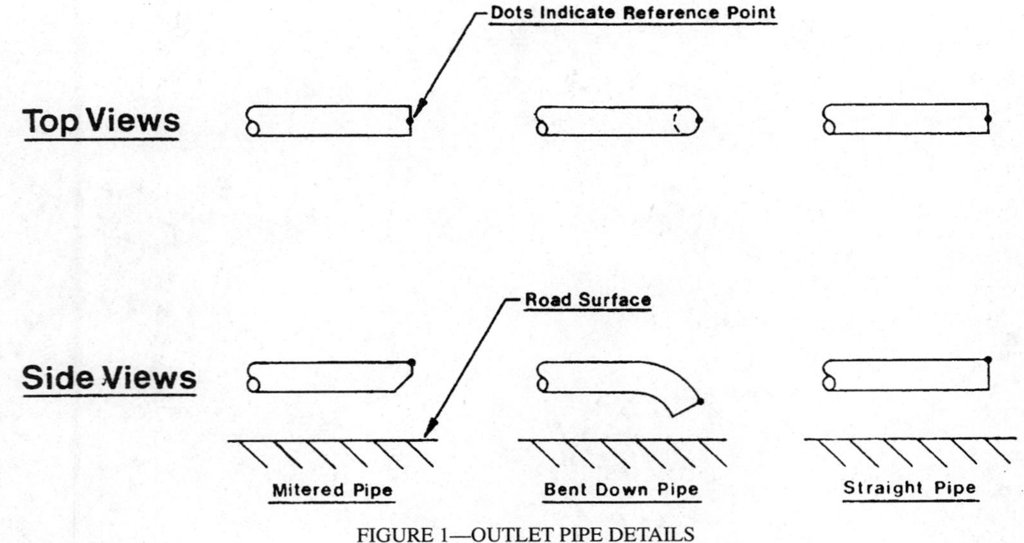

FIGURE 1—OUTLET PIPE DETAILS

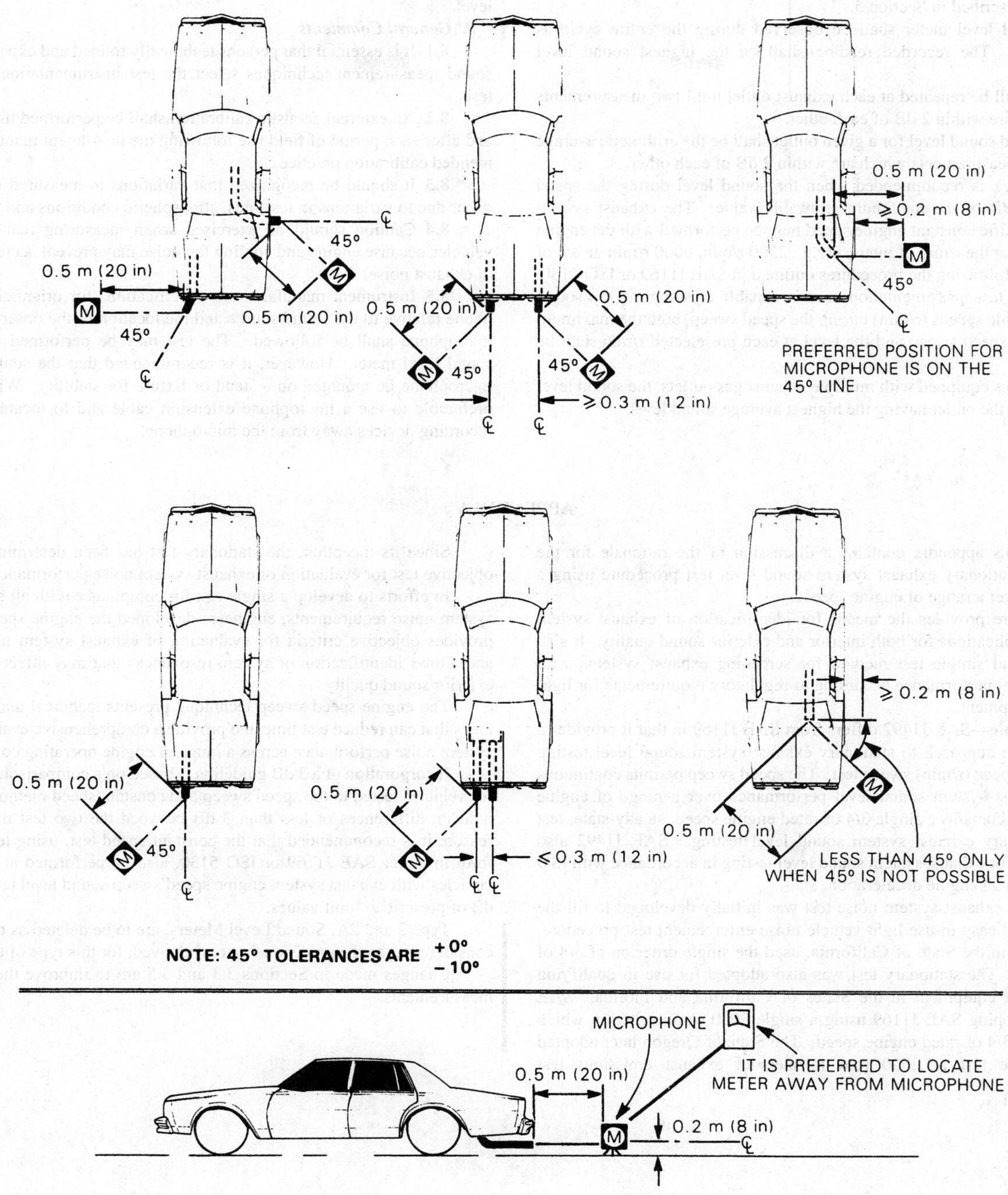

FIGURE 2—MICROPHONE LOCATION SKETCH

6. Procedure

6.1 The engine of the vehicle under test shall be at normal operating temperature during the test.

6.2 The engine hood or compartment cover shall be closed.

6.3 The vehicle air conditioner, if so equipped, shall be turned off.

6.4 The vehicle transmission shall be in the neutral or park position and the parking brake applied for safety.

6.5 Test Operation

6.5.1 The sound level meter shall be set for the fast exponential time-averaging characteristic.

6.5.2 The engine speed shall be gradually increased from idle to 3/4 of the engine speed at rated horsepower and held constant at that speed for 1 to 2 s. Then the throttle shall be rapidly released and the engine allowed to return to idle. Measure the sound level during this entire cycle.

NOTE—The change from idle up to 3/4 rated engine speed should occur over a 10 to 15 s interval. Some engines exhibit sensitivity to the rate of increase. The longer time interval tends to reduce run-to-run variability.

6.5.3 Vehicles equipped with a multi-mode exhaust system and a manual exhaust mode control switch shall be tested according to 6.5.2 with the mode switch in all positions.

7. Measurements

7.1 Measurements shall be made at each exhaust outlet, using the microphone location(s) described in Section 5.

7.2 The sound level meter shall be observed during the entire cycle as described in 6.5.2. The recorded reading shall be the highest sound level observed.

7.2.1 The test shall be repeated at each exhaust outlet until two measurements are obtained which are within 2 dB of each other.

7.2.2 The reported sound level for a given outlet shall be the arithmetic average of the two highest measurements which are within 2 dB of each other.

7.2.3 A spot check is recommended when the sound level during the speed sweep is within 3 dB of the maximum allowable value. The exhaust system sound level at a specific constant engine speed may be performed with the engine speed held constant at the r/min of interest (e.g., 2500 r/min, 3000 r/min or 3/4 of rated engine speed) following the procedures outlined in SAE J1169 or ISO 5130.

7.3 When the test instrumentation used is capable of sampling the sound level at selected engine speeds (r/min) during the speed sweep, both the maximum level for the engine speed sweep and the level at each preselected r/min shall be recorded.

7.4 For vehicles equipped with multiple exhaust gas outlets, the sound level reported shall be for the outlet having the highest average sound level.

7.4.1 For vehicles equipped with a multi-mode exhaust system, the sound level reported shall be for the outlet and the mode yielding the highest average sound level.

8. General Comments

8.1 It is essential that persons technically trained and experienced in current sound measurement techniques select the test instrumentation and conduct the tests.

8.2 An external acoustic calibration shall be performed immediately before and after each period of field use following the instrument manufacturer's recommended calibration practice.

8.3 It should be recognized that variations in measured sound levels may occur due to variations in test sites, atmospheric conditions and test equipment.

8.4 Caution should be exercised when measuring rear- and mid-engine vehicles because engine and cooling fan noise may prevent accurate measurement of exhaust noise.

8.5 Instrument manufacturer's specifications for orientation of the microphone relative to the sound source and the location of the observer relative to the microphone shall be followed. The test may be performed with a hand-held sound level meter. However, it is recommended that the sound level meter or microphone be mounted on a stand or fixture for stability. When possible, it is preferable to use a microphone extension cable and to locate measurement or recording devices away from the microphone.

APPENDIX A

A.1 General—This appendix contains a discussion of the rationale for the development of a stationary exhaust system sound level test procedure using a continuous sweep over a range of engine speeds.

This test procedure provides the means for identification of exhaust system resonances with implications for both interior and exterior sound quality. It also provides a quick and simple test method for screening exhaust systems with respect to sound level performance according to regulatory requirements for light vehicle exhaust equipment.

A.1.1 Rationale—SAE J1492 differs from SAE J1169 in that it provides a more comprehensive approach to stationary exhaust system sound level testing utilizing an engine speed (r/min) sweep test. The speed sweep permits continuous evaluation of exhaust system sound level performance over a range of engine speeds. SAE J1169 contains a single 3/4 of rated engine speed, steady-state, test criterion for stationary exhaust system sound level testing. SAE J1492 also includes provisions for exhaust system sound level testing in accordance with ISO 5130 which includes an engine deceleration.

The stationary exhaust system noise test was initially developed to fill the need for a quick and easy in-use light vehicle noise enforcement test procedure. The test, as applied in the State of California, used the single criterion of 3/4 of rated engine speed. The stationary test was also adopted for use in qualifying replacement exhaust equipment in the States of California and Florida. SAE responded by developing SAE J1169 using a single 3000 r/min criterion which has been revised to 3/4 of rated engine speed. The State of Oregon later adopted the stationary noise test at 2500 rpm in biennial exhaust emissions test regulations.

Since its inception, the stationary test has been determined to be a valid, objective test for evaluation of exhaust system noise performance.

In efforts to develop a single test for compliance with all stationary exhaust system noise requirements, engineers developed the engine speed sweep test. It provides objective criteria for evaluation of exhaust system noise performance and allows identification of system resonances that may affect both interior and exterior sound quality.

The engine speed sweep technique presents technical and practical advantages that can reduce test time and provide a comprehensive evaluation of exhaust system noise performance across a range of engine operating conditions.

Incorporation of a 3 dB guideline is based on a comparison of empirical data for vehicles tested to the speed sweep and constant speed methods. These results indicate differences of less than 3 dB between the two test methods. For this reason, it is recommended that the constant speed test, using test procedures set forth in either SAE J1169 or ISO 5130, also be performed at critical r/min for vehicles with exhaust system engine speed sweep sound level test results within 3 dB of prescribed limit values.

Type 2 and 2A, Sound Level Meters, are to be deleted as they are no longer considered to be the precision devices received, for this type of test.

Changes made in Sections 3.3 and 3.5 are to improve the precision of the measurements.

EXTERIOR SOUND LEVEL FOR HEAVY TRUCKS AND BUSES—SAE J366 APR2001

SAE Standard

Report of the SAE Vehicle Sound Level Committee approved July 1969, completely revised November 1984, and reaffirmed February 1987. Reaffirmed by the SAE Heavy Truck Sound Level Subcommittee of the SAE Vehicle Sound Level Committee April 2001. Rationale statement available.

Foreword—This Document has not changed other than to put it into the new SAE Technical Standards Board Format. Scope is Section 1, References are Section 2. All other section numbers have changed accordingly.

1. Scope—This SAE Standard establishes the test procedure, environment, and instrumentation for determining the maximum exterior sound level for highway motor trucks, truck tractors, and buses. The test results obtained by this test procedure give an objective measure of the maximum noise level emitted by vehicles under a prescribed condition. A subjective rating of the annoyance caused by vehicles in use may not be directly related to this type of noise level measurement.

2. References

2.1 Applicable Publications—The following publications form a part of the specification to the extent specified herein. Unless otherwise indicated, the latest revision of SAE publications shall apply.

2.1.1 SAE PUBLICATION—Available from SAE, 400 Commonwealth Drive, Warrendale, PA 15096-0001.

SAE J184 MAR85—Qualifying a Sound Data Acquisition System

2.1.2 ANSI PUBLICATION—Available from ANSI, 11 West 42nd Street, New York, NY 10036-8002.

ANSI S1.4-1983—Specification for Sound Level Meters

3. Instrumentation—The following instrumentation shall be used, where applicable, for the measurement required:

3.1 A sound level meter which meets the Type 1 or S1A requirements of American National Standard, Specification for Sound Level Meters, S1.4-1983.

3.1.1 As an alternative to making direct measurements using a sound level meter, a microphone or sound level meter may be used with a magnetic tape recorder and/or a graphic level recorder or indicating instrument, providing the system meets the requirements of SAE J184 MAR85, Qualifying a Sound Data Acquisition System.

3.2 A sound level calibrator accurate within ±0.5 dB. (See 6.2.3.)

3.3 An engine-speed tachometer accurate within ±2% of full scale.

3.4 An anemometer having an accuracy of ±10% at 19 km/h (12 mile/h) wind speed.

3.5 A windscreen, which if used does not affect the microphone response more than ±1 dB for frequencies from 20–4000 Hz, and ±1.5 dB for frequencies from 4000-10 000 Hz.

4. Test Site

4.1 A suitable test site shall consist of a level open space free of large reflecting surfaces such as parked vehicles, signboards, buildings, or hillsides, located within 30 m (100 ft) of either the vehicle path or the microphone. See Figure 1.

4.2 The microphone shall be located 15.2 m ± 0.1 m (50 ft ± 4 in) from the centerline of the vehicle travel and 1.2 m ± 0.1 m (4 ft ± 4 in) above the ground plane. The microphone point is defined as the point of intersection of the vehicle path and the normal to the vehicle path drawn from the microphone.

The microphone shall be oriented with respect to the source so that the sound strikes the diaphram at an angle at which the microphone was designed to have the flattest frequency response over the frequency range 100 Hz to 10 kHz.

4.3 An acceleration point shall be established on the vehicle path 15.2 m (50 ft) before the microphone point.

4.4 An end point shall be established on the vehicle path 30.4 m (100 ft) from the acceleration point and 15.2 m (50 ft) from the microphone point.

4.5 The end zone is the last 12.2 m (40 ft) of vehicle path prior to the end point.

4.6 The measurement area shall be the triangular area formed by the acceleration point, the end point, and the microphone location.

4.7 The reference point on the vehicle, to indicate when the vehicle is at any of the points on the vehicle path, shall be the front of the vehicle, except as follows:

4.7.1 If the horizontal distance from the front of the vehicle to the exhaust outlet is more than 5080 mm (200 in), tests shall be run using both the front and rear of the vehicle as reference points.

4.7.2 If the engine is located rearward of the center of the chassis, the rear of the vehicle shall be used as the reference point.

4.8 During measurement, the surface of the ground within the measurement area shall be free from snow, long grass, loose soil, ashes, and other porous sound-absorbing materials.

4.9 Because bystanders have an appreciable influence on meter response when they are in the vicinity of the vehicle or microphone, not more than one person, other than the observer reading the meter, shall be within 15 m (50 ft) of the vehicle path or instrument, and that person shall be directly behind the observer reading the meter, on a line through the microphone and observer.

4.10 The ambient sound level (including wind effects) coming from sources other than the vehicle being measured shall be at least 10 dB lower than the level of the tested vehicle.

4.11 The vehicle path and measurement area shall be relatively smooth, dry concrete or sealed asphalt, free of extraneous material such as gravel.

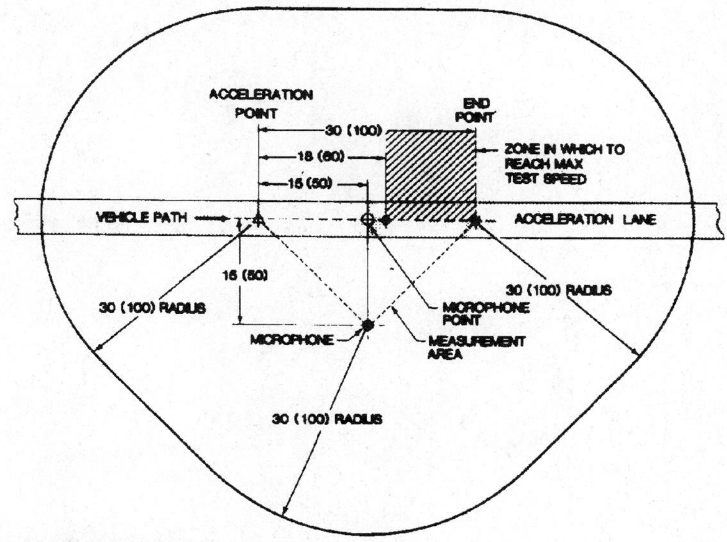

FIGURE 1—MINIMUM UNIDIRECTIONAL TEST SITE (SEE 4.1)

5. Procedure

5.1 Vehicle Operation—Full throttle acceleration and closed throttle deceleration tests are to be used. A beginning engine speed and proper gear ratio must be determined for use during measurements.

5.2 Maximum Test Speed—The term maximum test speed as used in this document is defined as: For ungoverned engines, this is the rated engine speed as specified by the engine manufacturer. For governed engines, the maximum engine speed attained during the test, when wide open throttle is maintained past the end point.

5.2.1 Select the highest rear axle and/or transmission gear ("highest gear" is used in the usual sense; it is synonymous to the lowest numerical ratio) and an initial vehicle speed such that a wide-open throttle the vehicle will accelerate from the acceleration point:

a. Starting at no more than two thirds (67%) of maximum rated engine speed.
b. Reaching maximum test speed within the end zone.
c. Without exceeding 55 km/h (35 mile/h) before reaching the end point.

5.2.1.1 Should maximum test speed be attained before reaching the end zone, decrease the approach rpm in 100 rpm increments until maximum test speed is attained within the end zone.

5.2.1.2 Should maximum test speed not be attained until beyond the end zone, select the next lower gear until maximum test speed is attained within the end zone.

5.2.1.3 Should the lowest gear still result in reaching maximum test speed beyond the permissible end zone, increase the approach rpm in 100 rpm increments until the maximum test speed is reached within the end zone.

5.2.2 For the acceleration test, approach the acceleration point using the engine speed and gear ratio selected in 5.2.1 and at the acceleration point rapidly establish wide-open throttle. The vehicle reference shall be as indicated in 4.7. Acceleration shall continue until maximum test speed is reached.

5.2.3 Wheel slip which affects maximum sound level must be avoided.

5.2.4 For the deceleration test, approach the microphone point at maximum test speed in the gear selected for the acceleration test. At the microphone point, close the throttle and allow the vehicle to decelerate to one-half of maximum test speed. The vehicle reference shall be as indicated in 4.7. If the vehicle is equipped with an exhaust brake, this deceleration test is to be repeated with the brake full on immediately following closing of the throttle.

5.3 Measurements

5.3.1 The meter shall be set for fast response and the A-weighting network.

5.3.2 The meter shall be observed during the period while the vehicle is accelerating or decelerating. The applicable reading shall be the highest sound level obtained for the run. The observer is cautioned to rerun the test if unrelated peaks should occur due to extraneous ambient noises. Readings shall be taken on both sides of the vehicle.

5.3.3 The sound level for each side of the vehicle shall be the average of the two highest readings which are within 2 dB of each other. Report the sound level for the side of the vehicle with the highest average.

6. General Comments—Measurements shall be made only when wind speed is below 19 km/h (12 mile/h).

6.1 It is strongly recommended that technically trained personnel select the equipment and that tests are conducted only by qualified personnel trained in the current techniques of sound measurement.

6.2 Proper use of all test instrumentation is essential to obtain valid measurements. Operating manuals or other literature furnished by the instrument manufacturer should be referred to for both recommended operation of the instrument and precautions to be observed. Specific items to be considered are:

6.2.1 The effects of ambient weather conditions on the performance of all instruments (for example, temperature, humidity, and barometric pressure).

6.2.2 Proper signal levels, terminating impedances, and cable lengths on multi-instrument measurement systems.

6.2.3 Proper acoustical calibration procedure, to include the influence of extension cables, etc.

6.3 Field calibration shall be made immediately before and after each test sequence. Internal calibration means is acceptable for field use, provided that external calibration (i.e., sound level calibrator) is accomplished immediately before or after field use.

6.4 The engine coolant shall be brought to within the manufacturer's recommended operating temperature range prior to and during testing.

6.5 A 2 dB variation in sound level may typically occur due to variations in test site, temperature gradient, test equipment, and inherent differences in nominally identical vehicles.

6.6 The sound level of a diesel engine may be dependent on the fuel's cetane level. A diesel fuel with a cetane number between 42–50 is recommended. For gasoline-fueled engines, a fuel grade consistent with the engine manufacturer's recommendation should be used.

(R) SOUND LEVEL FOR TRUCK CAB INTERIOR—SAE J336 JUN2001

SAE Recommended Practice

Report of the SAE Vehicle Sound Level Committee approved June 1968 and completely revised October 1988. Rationale statement available. Reaffirmed by the SAE Truck and Bus Cab and Occupant Environment Committee June 2001.

Foreword—This Document has not changed other than to put it into the new SAE Technical Standards Board Format. References were changed from Section 5 to Section 2. All other section numbers have changed accordingly.

1. Scope—This SAE Recommended Practice describes the equipment and procedure for determining the truck cab interior sound level over the upper half of the engine speed range. This practice applies to motor trucks and truck-tractors and does not include construction and industrial machinery.

2. References

2.1 Applicable Publications—The following publications form a part of the specification to the extent specified herein. Unless otherwise indicated, the latest revision of SAE publications shall apply.

2.1.1 SAE PUBLICATIONS—Available from SAE, 400 Commonwealth Drive, Warrendale, PA 15096-0001.

SAE J184—Qualifying a Sound Data Acquisition System

SAE J1349—Engine Power Test Code—Spark Ignition and Diesel

2.1.2 ANSI PUBLICATION—Available from ANSI, 11 West 42nd Street, New York, NY 10036-8002.

ANSI S1.4-1983—Specifications for Sound Level Meters.

2.1.3 ISO PUBLICATION—Available from ANSI, 11 West 42nd Street, New York, NY 10036-8002.

ISO 5128—Acoustics Measurement of Noise Inside Motor Vehicle.

2.1.4 FMVSS—Available from the Superintendent of Documents, U. S. Government Printing Office, Mail Stop: SSOP, Washington, DC 20402-9320.

Title 49 CFR 393.94—Vehicle Interior Noise Levels.

3. Instrumentation—The following instrumentation shall be used:

3.1 A sound level meter which meets the Type 1 or S1A requirements of American National Standard, Specification for Sound Level Meters, S1.4-1983.

3.1.1 As an alternative to making direct measurements using a sound level meter, a microphone or sound level meter may be used with a data recorder and/or a graphic level recorder or other indicating instrument, provided that the system used meets the requirements of SAE J184.

3.2 A sound level calibrator accurate within ±0.5 dB. (See 5.2.3.)

3.3 An engine-speed tachometer accurate within ±2% of full scale.

3.4 An anemometer accurate to ±10% at 19 km/h (12 mph).

4. Test Procedure—The following procedure is to be used for the purpose of this SAE Recommended Practice:

4.1 Establish a seat reference point at the intersection of the tangent lines to the predominant surfaces of the undeflected cushion and backrest at the lateral center of the seat (or intended operator location). Adjust the seat to the midpoint of its horizontal and vertical travel.

Locate the microphone, oriented vertically upward, at a point 740 mm (29 in) vertically above the seat reference point and 250 mm (10 in) laterally to the right (to the left for right-hand drive vehicles) of the seat reference point.

Position the driver so that his ear is reasonably aligned with, and approximately 150 mm (6 in) laterally from, the microphone. Seat adjustment may be made to meet this provision.

4.2 Sound level tests may be conducted with or without a trailer or body on the vehicle. The configuration shall be recorded.

4.3 The engine coolant shall be within the manufacturer's recommended operating temperature range during testing.

4.4 Vehicle windows and vents shall be in the fully closed position with all accessories "off."

4.5 The tests shall be conducted on a smooth, dry concrete or asphalt road surface. No large sound-reflecting surfaces should be within 15 m (50 ft) of the test vehicle. Wind speed should not exceed 19 km/h (12 mph). The test personnel should be aware that the direction of the wind relative to the vehicle may have an influence on the measurement.

4.6 Select a transmission and/or axle gear ratio so that approximately 80 km/h (50 mph) is obtained at rated engine speed. "Rated engine speed" is defined as the engine speed at which the engine delivers "Rated Power," as defined in SAE J1349 as specified by the engine manufacturer.

4.7 For each test run, accelerate the vehicle in the selected gear ratio of 4.6 at wide-open throttle from a beginning engine speed of one-half rated engine speed up to rated engine speed. A minimum of four test runs shall be made.

4.8 The applicable reading shall be the highest A-weighted sound level observed during each test run of 4.7. The meter shall be set for "fast exponential-time-averaging" for these measurements. The test run shall be repeated until four sound level readings are obtained with a total range of 2 dB, or less. The reported sound level shall be the average of the four highest readings within a total range of 2 dB, or less. The observer is cautioned to rerun a test run if unrelated peaks should occur because of sounds that are not caused by the vehicle.

4.8.1 If a data-recording system is used, make recordings during each test run. Record a calibration signal of known acoustic level immediately prior to, or following, each sequence of test recordings. For analysis of the test run recordings, use the calibration signal to establish playback gain and thus calibrate the analysis system. Set the level indicating instrument for "fast exponential-time-averaging" or equivalent for analysis of the recorded data.

5. General Comments

5.1 It is strongly recommended that technically qualified personnel select the equipment, and that tests are conducted only by persons trained in the current techniques of sound measurement.

5.2 Proper use of all test instrumentation is essential to obtain valid measurements. Operating manuals or other literature furnished by the instrument manufacturer should be referred to for both recommended operation of the instrument and precautions to be observed. Specific items to be considered are:

5.2.1 The effects of ambient weather conditions on the performance of all instruments (that is, temperature, humidity, and barometric pressure).

5.2.2 Proper signal levels, terminating impedances, and cable lengths on multi-instrument measurement systems.

5.2.3 Proper acoustical calibration procedure, to include the influence of extension cables, etc. Field calibration shall be made immediately before and after each test sequence. Internal calibration means is acceptable for field use, provided the external calibration is accomplished immediately before or after field use.

5.2.4 The microphone shall be supported in such a manner that mechanical vibration will not influence the sound level measurements.

5.3 The sound level of a diesel engine may be dependent on the fuel's cetane level. A diesel fuel with a cetane number between 42–50 is recommended. For gasoline-fueled engines, a fuel grade consistent with the engine manufacturer's recommendation should be used.

5.4 It is recommended that the ambient temperature be reported with the test results because ambient temperature may influence the measured sound level. If the relationship between the measured sound level and the ambient temperature is known, and the test results are to be corrected to a reference ambient temperature, 25 °C (77 °F) is recommended as the reference ambient temperature. If the test result is corrected, it must be reported as a "corrected sound level" at the reference ambient temperature of 25 °C (77 °F).

5.5 For repeated development tests where the relative change in sound level is a desired quantity, the position of the microphone in the truck cab, and the position of the driver relative to the microphone (see 4.1) should remain constant.

5.6 Road surfaces, such as those with concrete joints, which add significant noise, should be avoided.

MEASUREMENT OF EXTERIOR SOUND LEVELS FOR HEAVY TRUCKS UNDER STATIONARY CONDITIONS —SAE J1096 MAY2000

SAE Recommended Practice

Report of the SAE Vehicle Sound Level Committee approved March 1976, and reaffirmed February 1987. Rationale statement available. Reaffirmed by the SAE Heavy Truck Sound Level Standards Committee and the SAE Vehicle Sound Level Forum Committee February 1993. Rationale statement available. Reaffirmed by the SAE Motor Vehicle Council Sound Level Committee May 2000.

1. Scope—This SAE Recommended Practice establishes the test procedure, environment, and instrumentation for determining the maximum exterior sound level of highway motor trucks and truck tractors over 4540 kg gross vehicle weight rating (GVWR) with governed engines under stationary vehicle conditions. The basic procedure involves a full throttle engine acceleration and a closed throttle deceleration with the engine inertia as the load.

2. References

2.1 Applicable Publications—The following publications form a part of the specification to the extent specified herein. Unless otherwise indicated, the latest revision of SAE publications shall apply.

2.1.1 SAE PUBLICATION—Available from SAE, 400 Commonwealth Drive, Warrendale, PA 15096-0001.

SAE J184—Qualifying a Sound Data Acquisition System

2.1.2 ANSI PUBLICATIONS—Available from ANSI, 11 West 42nd Street, New York, NY 10036-8002.

ANSI S1.4-1983 and S1.4A-1985—Specification for Sound Level Meters

ANSI S1.40-1984—Specification for Acoustical Calibrators

2.1.3 ISO PUBLICATION—Available from ANSI, 11 West 42nd Street, New York, NY 10036-8002.

ISO 5130-1982—Acoustics—Measurements of noise emitted by stationary road vehicles—Survey method

2.1.4 DOT PUBLICATION—Available from The Superintendent of Documents, U.S. Government Printing Office, Washington, DC 20402.

DOT/BMCS Title 40, Part 325, Subpart E—Exterior Noise Regulation for Commercial Vehicles

3. Instrumentation—The following instrumentation shall be used, where applicable, for the measurement required.

3.1 A sound level meter which satisfies the Type 1 or S1A requirements of American National Standard Specification for Sound Level Meters, ANSI S1.4-1983 and S1.4A-1985.

3.2 As an alternative to making direct measurements using a sound level meter, a microphone or sound level meter may be used with a magnetic tape recorder and/or a graphic level recorder or other indicating instrument, providing the system meets the requirements of SAE J184.

3.3 A sound level calibrator, accurate to ±0.5 decibel (dB) which satisfies the requirements of ANSI S1.40-1984.

3.4 A windscreen may be used. The windscreen shall not affect the microphone response more than ±1 dB for frequencies of 20 to 4000 Hz or ±1-1/2 dB for frequencies of 4000 to 10 000 Hz (see 6.1). (See 6.1).

3.5 An engine-speed tachometer accurate to within ±2% of full scale.

4. Test Site—The following test site requirements shall be considered necessary to perform effective measurements for this stationary procedure.

4.1 A suitable test site shall consist of a flat open space free of large reflecting surfaces, such as parked vehicles, signboards, buildings, or hillsides, located within 30 m of either the vehicle or the microphone. See Figure 1.

4.2 The measurement area (defined as shown in Figure 1, including the area under the test vehicle) shall be surfaced with concrete, asphalt, or similar hard nonporous material, and shall be free of snow, grass, soil, ashes, or other sound-absorbing materials. Trailers or semitrailers are to be neglected when determining the measurement area.

4.3 The microphone shall be located 15 m from the centerline of the vehicle and 1.2 m above the ground plane as shown in Figure 1. The microphone shall be located on a line perpendicular to the vehicle centerline and in line with the rear of the cab.

4.4 Because bystanders have an appreciable influence on meter response when they are in the vicinity of the vehicle or microphone, not more than one person, other than the observer reading the meter, shall be within 15 m of the vehicle or instrument, and that person shall be directly behind the observer reading the meter, on a line through the microphone and the observer.

4.5 The ambient sound level (including wind effects) coming from sources other than the vehicle being measured shall be at least 10 dB lower than the level of the tested vehicle.

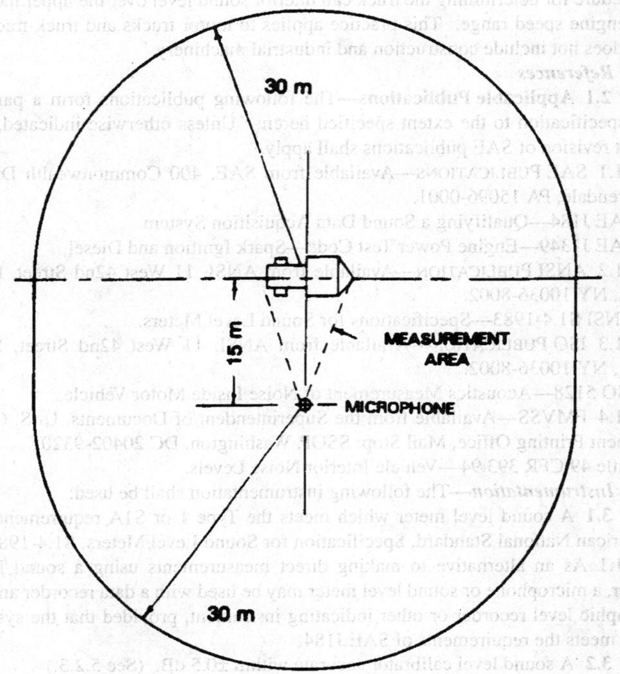

FIGURE 1—TEST SITE CONFIGURATION

5. Procedure

5.1 The vehicle shall be tested in a stationary position with maximum engine acceleration and deceleration with no external load applied.

5.1.1 The engine governor and throttle delay (if one is installed) shall be set to the manufacturer's specifications.

5.1.2 The vehicle engine coolant temperature shall be raised to the normal operating range.

5.1.3 The vehicle shall be positioned at the test site as shown in Figure 1, with the main transmission in neutral and the clutch engaged.

5.1.4 The engine shall be accelerated, by rapidly establishing full throttle, from a low idle condition to the maximum governed speed. After the engine speed has been stabilized (3 to 5 s), the engine shall be decelerated at closed throttle to low idle speed.

5.2 Measurements

5.2.1 The sound level meter shall be set for fast response and the A-weighing network. Equivalent settings shall be used with other instruments.

5.2.2 The meter shall be observed during the entire engine acceleration-deceleration cycle. The applicable reading shall be the highest sound level obtained during this cycle. Unrelated peaks due to extraneous ambient noises should be ignored.

5.2.3 The sound level for each side of the vehicle shall be the average of the first two highest readings which are within 1 dB of each other. Report the sound level for the side of the vehicle with the highest average value.

6. General Comments

6.1 Measurements shall be made only when wind speed is below 19 km/h. The microphone windscreen may be used to minimize effects of wind gusts and other changes in wind speed. See 4.5.

6.2 It is strongly recommended that persons technically trained and experienced in the current techniques of sound measurement select the equipment and conduct the tests.

6.3 Proper use of all test instrumentation is essential to obtain valid measurements. Operating manuals or other literature furnished by the manufacturer should be referred to for both recommended operation of the instrument and precautions to be observed. Specific items to be considered are:

6.3.1 The effects of ambient weather conditions on the performance of all instruments (for example, temperature, humidity, and barometric pressure).

6.3.2 The effects of proper signal levels, terminating impedances, and cable lengths on multi-instrument measurement systems.

6.3.3 Proper acoustical calibration, to include the influence of extension cables, etc.

6.4 Field calibration shall be made immediately before and after each test sequence. Internal calibration means are acceptable for field use, provided that external calibration is accomplished immediately before or after field use.

6.5 The sound level of a vehicle with a diesel engine may be dependent on the fuel's cetane level. A diesel fuel with a cetane number between 42 to 50 is recommended. In vehicles with gasoline-fueled engines, a fuel grade consistent with the engine manufacturer's recommendations should be used.

APPENDIX A

A.1 The Department of Transportation/Bureau of Motor Carrier Safety exterior noise regulation for commercial vehicles has a stationary test procedure (Title 40, Part 325, Subpart E) that is similar to this SAE test procedure.

The intent of the two test procedures and the resultant sound levels are in general the same. However, there are procedural differences that can result in different measured sound levels. The Department of Transportation/Bureau of Motor Carrier Safety test procedure allows for a greater deviation from ideal test conditions than this SAE test procedure.

ISO 5130-1982 is an International Standard for the determination of noise emitted by stationary road vehicles in use, the noise being measured in close proximity to the exhaust outlet. The ISO 5130 test method is not similar to this SAE test procedure.

(R) SOUND LEVEL OF HIGHWAY TRUCK TIRES —SAE J57 MAY2000

SAE Recommended Practice

Report of the SAE Vehicle Sound Level Committee approved July 1973, revised June 1976, editorial change July 1978, and reaffirmed February 1987. Rationale statement available. Completely revised by the SAE J57 Review Subcommittee of the SAE Tire Noise Sound Level Standards Committee June 1994. Reaffirmed by the SAE Motor Vehicle Council Sound Level Committee May 2000.

Foreword—This SAE Recommended Practice establishes a test procedure for measuring the sound level produced by tires intended primarily for highway use on motor trucks, truck tractors, trailers and semitrailers, and buses.

TABLE OF CONTENTS

1. Scope

1.1 This procedure provides for the measurement of the sound generated by a test tire, mounted on a single-axle trailer, operated at multiple speeds.

1.2 The procedure describes test practices for both United States and International practices.

1.3 Specifications for the instrumentation, the test site, and the operation of the test apparatus are set forth to minimize the effects of extraneous sound sources and to define the basis of reported sound levels.

2. References

2.1 Applicable Publications—The following publications pertain to noise measurement and tire noise. The references not directly cited in the text are suggested background information for individuals performing tire noise testing.

2.1.1 SAE PUBLICATION—Available from SAE, 400 Commonwealth Drive, Warrendale, PA 15096-0001.

SAE J184—Qualifying a Sound Data Acquisition System

2.1.2 ANSI PUBLICATION—Available from ANSI, 11 West 42nd Street, New York, NY 10036-8002.

ANSI S1.4 & S1.4A—Specification for Sound Level Meters

2.1.3 ISO PUBLICATION—Available from ANSI, 11 West 42nd Street, New York, NY 10036-8002.

ISO 10844—Acoustics—Test surface for road vehicle noise measurement

2.2 Related Publications—The following publications are provided for information purposes only and are not a required part of this publication.

2.2.1 SAE PUBLICATIONS—Available from SAE, 400 Commonwealth Drive, Warrendale, PA 15096-0001.

SAE Publication SP-373—Truck Tire Noise

SAE Paper 740607—Effect of Road Surface and Bed Clearance on Truck Tire Noise, Thurman, G.R

SAE Paper 740606—Regulatory Implications of Truck Tire Noise Studies, Close, W.H.

SAE Paper 850969—Vehicle Sound Measurement—20 Years of Testing, Howell, T.M. and Schumacher, R.F.

SAE Paper 800282—Relative Influence of Pavement Texture and Tire Type on Pavement/Tire Noise, Osman, M.M. and May, D.N.

SAE P-70—Proceedings from the SAE Highway Noise Symposium, Nov., 1976

2.2.2 ACOUSTICAL SOCIETY OF AMERICA PUBLICATIONS—Available from Acoustical Society of America, 500 Sunnyside Boulevard, Woodbury, NY 11797-2999.

J. Acoust. Soc. Am., 76(4), October 1984, pp. 1150–1160, "Effects of Environmental Variables on Truck Noise Emission and Noise Propagation to Test Microphones," Hemdal, J.F., Baker, R.N., and Saha, P.

J. Acoust. Soc. Am., Vol. 58, No. 1, July 1975, pp. 39–50, "Tire-Road Interaction Noise," Leasure, W.A. and Bender, E.K.

2.2.3 DOT PUBLICATIONS—Available from the United States Department of Transportation.

DOT HS-AS-60031, January 1979, US DOT, "Effects of Load, Inflation Pressure, and Tire Deflection on Truck Tire Noise Levels," Kilmer, R.D., Codoff, M.A., Mathews, D.E., and Shoemaker, C.O.

DOT Report No. DOT-TST-76-4, August 1975, "Automobile Tire Noise: Results of a Pilot Study and Review of the Open Literature," Leasure, W.A., Mathews, D.E., and Codoff, M.A.

2.2.4 TIRE AND RIM ASSOCIATION PUBLICATION—Available from The Tire and Rim Association, Inc., 175 Montrose West Ave., Suite 150, Copley, OH 44321.

The Tire and Rim Association Yearbook, latest edition

3. Instrumentation

3.1 The following instrumentation shall be used for the measurements as required:

a. A sound level meter which satisfies the Type 1 or S1A requirements of American National Standard Specification for Sound Level Meters, S1.4 or S1.4A (latest revision) or its ISO equivalent.
   1. As an alternative to making direct measurements using a sound level meter, a microphone may be used with a magnetic or digital tape recorder and/or a graphic level recorder or other indicating instrument, providing the system meets the requirements of SAE J184 (latest revision).

b. An acoustical calibrator, having an accuracy of ±0.5 dB, for establishing the calibration of the sound level meter and associated instrumentation.

c. An anemometer having an accuracy of ±10% at 18 km/h (11 mph).

4. Test Site

4.1 The test site shall be located on a flat area which is free of reflecting surfaces (other than the ground), such as parked vehicles, trees, or buildings within 30 m (100 ft) of the measurement area.

4.2 The vehicle path, within the Test Zone, shall meet the requirements of ISO 10844. The vehicle path shall be dry and free of extraneous material.

4.3 The microphone shall be located at a height of 1.2 m (4 ft) above the ground plane. The normal to the vehicle path from the microphone shall establish the microphone point on the vehicle path. The distance from the microphone to the microphone point shall be as follows:

a. 15 m (50 ft) for testing representative of United States practices. See Table 1 and Figure 1.

b. 7.5 m (25 ft) for testing representative of International practices. See Table 2 and Figure 2.

TABLE 1—CRITICAL DIMENSIONS FOR UNITED STATES PRACTICES (J57 TEST A)

	SI Units	U.S. Customary Units
Distance Between Centerline of Veh. Path and Microphone	15 m	50 ft
Microphone Height	1.2 m	4 ft
Test Zone Length	30 m	100 ft
Low Speed Pass	56 km/h ± 1 km/h	35 mph ± 0.6 mph
High Speed Pass	80 km/h ± 1 km/h	50 mph ± 0.6 mph

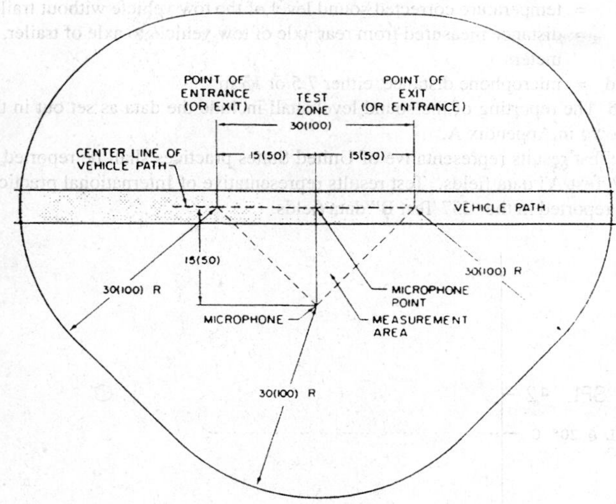

FIGURE 1—TEST SITE (U.S. PRACTICE)
(VEHICLE MAY BE RUN IN EITHER DIRECTION)

TABLE 2—CRITICAL DIMENSIONS FOR INTERNATIONAL PRACTICES (J57 TEST B)

	SI Units	U.S. Customary Units
Distance Between Centerline of Veh. Path and Microphone	7.5 m	25 ft
Microphone Height	1.2 m	4 ft
Test Zone Length	20 m	66 ft
Low Speed Pass	60 km/h ± 1 km/h	37 mph ± 0.6 mph
High Speed Pass	80 km/h ± 1 km/h	50 mph ± 0.6 mph

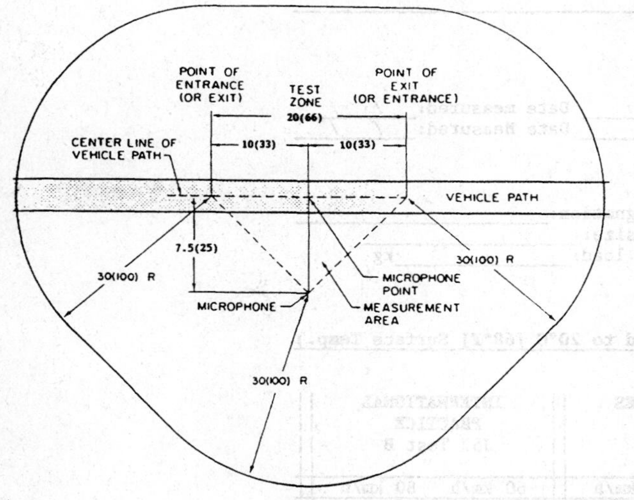

FIGURE 2—TEST SITE (INTERNATIONAL PRACTICE
(VEHICLE MAY BE RUN IN EITHER DIRECTION)

4.4 The measurement area is the triangular area formed by the point of entrance into the test zone, point of exit from the test zone, and the microphone. The test zone is established as follows:

a. The test zone extends 15 m (50 ft) on either side of the microphone point along the vehicle path for testing representative of United States practices. See Table 1 and Figure 1.

b. The test zone extends 10 m (33 ft) on either side of the microphone point along the vehicle path for testing representative of International practices. See Table 2 and Figure 2.

4.5 The measurement area (excluding vehicle path) should be surfaced with concrete, asphalt, or similar hard material, having a Coefficient of Absorption not exceeding 0.10 measured as specified in ISO 10844, and in any event, should be free of snow, grass, soil, ashes, or other sound-absorbing materials.

4.6 The ambient sound level (including wind effects) at the test site shall be at least 10 dB below the level of the subject tires operated in accordance with the test procedure.

4.7 The wind speed in the measurement area shall be less than 18 km/h (11 mph).

4.8 The ambient air temperature of the test location shall be between 10 and 30 °C (50 and 86 °F) throughout the test.

4.9 Test surface temperature shall be between 5 and 40 °C (41 and 104 °F) throughout the test.

4.9.1 The surface reference temperature shall be 20 °C (68 °F). The reported sound levels shall be corrected to this temperature by means of the procedure set forth in 7.5.

5. *Test Apparatus*

5.1 The test apparatus shall consist of two parts:

a. Tow Vehicle

1. The rolling noise of the towing vehicle can be minimized by appropriate measures (low-noise tires, shielding, aerodynamic skirting, etc.) to a point at which the sound level for the tow vehicle alone is at least 3 dB(A) lower than for the tow vehicle-trailer combination with the subject tires.

b. Trailer

1. The trailer shall be a single-axle frame trailer with drawbar and a facility for varying wheel load. Superstructures or paneling are to be avoided in order to minimize vehicle-specific influences.
2. An axle assembly consisting of a single axle with one test tire on each end shall be rigidly suspended from the trailer.

5.2 The test apparatus shall be operated in a coasting mode with the tow vehicle power turned off.

6. *Tires*

6.1 Before measurements are started, a tire break-in period of at least 80 km (50 miles) at typical highway speeds is required.

6.2 Tires should be at normal operating temperature during the test.

6.3 Tires shall be singly mounted on the test trailer.

6.4 The tires shall be inflated to 85% of the pressure corresponding to the maximum single tire load that is molded on the sidewall, and loaded to 70% of the maximum single tire load that is molded on the sidewall.

7. *Procedure*

7.1 The tow vehicle shall be used to attain sufficient speed prior to entering the test zone, such that, when the tow vehicle engine is switched off and the vehicle and trailer are coasting into the test zone, the trailer speed at the microphone point will be as listed in 7.1.1.

7.1.1 The trailer speed at the microphone point shall be:

a. Refer to Table 1 for testing representative of United States practices.

b. Refer to Table 2 for testing representative of International practices.

7.2 The sound level meter shall be set for fast dynamic response and the A-weighting network.

7.3 There shall be at least five measurements for each test speed. The observer shall record the highest level attained during each pass. Measurement shall continue until five levels for each speed are recorded which are within ±0.5 dB(A) of their arithmetic average. This arithmetic average is to be used for the temperature correction calculations in 7.5.

7.3.1 Alternatively, each pass may be recorded on magnetic or digital tape, or any other generally accepted recording device, and subsequently analyzed with a sound level meter, graphic level recorder, or acoustic frequency analyzer. The reported data from this analysis must comply with 7.3 and the environmental conditions required to qualify the test results shall be recorded.

7.4 The surface temperature of the vehicle path shall be measured immediately after the completion of the test passes which compose the arithmetic average of 7.3.

7.5 The arithmetic average of the measured sound pressure levels will be corrected to the surface reference temperature specified in 4.9.1. Two levels shall be measured, one at a surface temperature within the range specified in 4.9 and above the reference temperature, and a second at a surface temperature within the range and below the reference temperature. As demonstrated in Figure 3, the predicted level at the reference temperature is obtained through linear interpolation.

7.5.1 An alternative correction method may be used if ambient conditions preclude obtaining measured levels at surface temperatures both above and below the reference temperature. In this case, a least-squares linear regression line may be calculated for correction of levels to the surface reference temperature. To insure adequate separation of the data points, the regression line shall be calculated based on at least three surface temperatures differing from one another by at least 2 °C (3.6 °F) and covering a range of at least 5 °C (9 °F). The calculated slope and intercept of the regression line shall be reported with the sound pressure level corrected to the surface reference temperature.

7.6 Determination of the tow vehicle noise must be made prior to reporting test tire sound levels. The tow vehicle sound level must be corrected to the surface reference temperature by the method outlined in 7.5.

7.7 The subject tires' sound levels reported are the difference between the sound pressure level of the tow vehicle-trailer combination and the sound pressure level of the tow vehicle alone. This is represented by Equation 1:

$$L_{tire} = 10 \log_{10}[10^{(Ltp/10)} - 10^{(Lt'/10)}] \quad \text{(Eq. 1)}$$

where:

L_{tire} = temperature corrected sound level of the subject tire (this is the level reported)

Ltp = temperature corrected sound level of the test pass (tow vehicle and trailer assembly)

Lt' = temperature corrected sound level of the tow vehicle without trailer, corrected for drawbar length as shown in Equation 2:

$$Lt' = Lt - 10 \log_{10}[(d^2 + Md^2)/Md^2] \quad \text{(Eq. 2)}$$

where:

Lt = temperature corrected sound level of the tow vehicle without trailer

d = distance measured from rear axle of tow vehicle to axle of trailer, in meters

Md = microphone distance, either 7.5 or 15 m

7.8 The reporting of the sound level shall include the data as set out in the form shown in Appendix A.

7.8.1 Test results representative of United States practices shall be reported in the "J57 Test A" data fields. Test results representative of International practices shall be reported in the "J57 Test B" data fields.

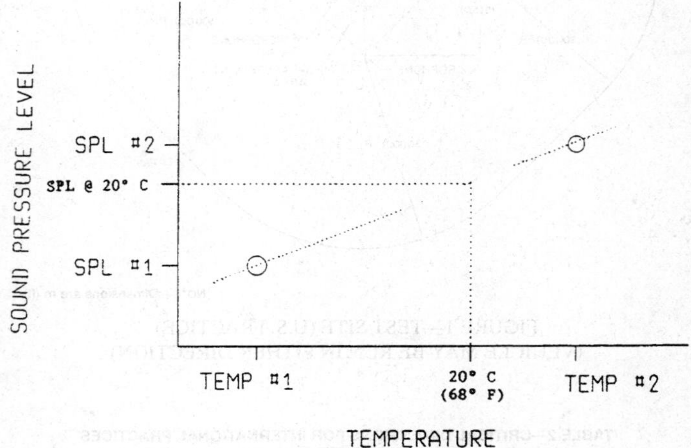

FIGURE 3—TEMPERATURE ADJUSTMENT EXAMPLE

APPENDIX A

A.1 J57 Test Report Form

TIRE NOISE MEASUREMENT ACCORDING TO SAE J57

BACKGROUND DATA
Performing organization:____________________
Test location:____________________
Test date: ___/___/___

ROAD SURFACE
Vehicle Path: Absorption coefficient:________ **Date measured:** ___/___/___
Meas. Area: Absorption coefficient:________ **Date Measured:** ___/___/___

TIRE
Manufacturer:__________ **Designation:**__________
Size:__________ **Rim size:**__________
Max. Single Load:______ **kg** **Test load:**______ **kg**
Test inflation:______ **kPa**

RESULTS (All reported noise levels corrected to 20°C [68°F] Surface Temp.)

	UNITED STATES PRACTICE J57 Test A		INTERNATIONAL PRACTICE J57 Test B	
NOMINAL TEST SPEEDS:	56 km/h dB(A)	80 km/h dB(A)	60 km/h dB(A)	80 km/h dB(A)
TOW VEHICLE & TRAILER: (L_{tp})				
TOW VEHICLE ONLY: (L_t)				
TIRE NOISE LEVEL: (L_{tire})				

(R) MEASUREMENT OF NOISE EMITTED BY ACCELERATING HIGHWAY VEHICLES —SAE J1470 JUN1998

SAE Standard

Report of the SAE Vehicle Sound Level Committee, Light Vehicle Exterior Sound Level Subcommittee, approved October 1984 and reaffirmed February 1987. Rationale statement available. This SAE Recommended Practice is equivalent to ISO Standard 362-1981 except for the differences detailed in the Appendix and includes the modifications adopted by WP29 in ECE R51. Completely revised by the SAE Vehicle Sound Level Forum Committee and the SAE Light Vehicle Exterior Sound Level Standards Committee March 1992, and completely revised June 1998. Rationale statement available.

1. Scope—This SAE Standard is equivalent to ISO Standard 362 - 1997 except for the differences detailed in Appendix A, and includes the modifications adopted by WP 29 in ECE R51 Revision 1 and EEC 92/97 and EEC 96/20.

This document specifies an engineering method for measuring the noise emitted by accelerating highway vehicles of all types (except motorcycles) in intermediate gears with full utilization of the available engine power.

The method is designed to meet the requirements of simplicity and reproducibility of results under realistic vehicle operating conditions.

Measurements relate to operating conditions of the vehicle which give the highest noise level consistent with urban driving and which lead to reproducible noise emissions. Therefore, an acceleration test at full throttle from a stated engine or vehicle speed is specified.

The test method calls for an acoustical environment which can only be obtained in an extensive open space. Such conditions can usually be provided for:

a. Measurements at the manufacturing stage
b. Measurements at official testing stations

Measurements must be carried out in an acoustical environment which fulfill the requirements stated in this document. It should be noted that spot checking of vehicles chosen at random can rarely be made in an ideal acoustical environment. If measurements have to be carried out on the road in an acoustical environment which does not fulfill the requirements stated in this document, it should be recognized that the results obtained may deviate appreciably from the results obtained using the specified conditions.

The results obtained by this method give an objective measure of the noise emitted under prescribed conditions of test. However, it is necessary to consider the fact that the subjective appraisal of the annoyance of different classes of motor vehicles is not simply related to the indications of a sound level meter. The motorcycles are covered in other SAE documents that prescribe an operating mode that is more representative of actual use.

2. References

2.1 Applicable Publications—The following publications form a part of this specification to the extent specified herein. Unless other indicated, the latest issue of SAE publications shall apply.

2.1.1 SAE PUBLICATIONS—Available from SAE, 400 Commonwealth Drive, Warrendale, PA 15096-0001.

SAE J184—Qualifying a Sound Data Acquisition System
SAE J1349—Engine Power Test—Spark Ignition and Diesel
SAE 951361—Paper from the SAE Noise & Vibration Conference Report, P-291, Volume 2, SAE and ISO Noise Test Site Variability

2.1.2 ANSI PUBLICATIONS—Available from ANSI, 11 West 42nd Street, New York, NY 10036-8002.

ANSI S1.4-1983 and S1.4A-1985—Specification for Sound Level Meters
ANSI S1.40-1984—Specification for Acoustical Calibrators

2.1.3 ECE PUBLICATIONS—Available from United Nations Economic Commission for Europe, Palais Des Nations, CH-1211, Geneva 10, Switzerland.

ECE R51—Uniform Provisions Concerning the Approval of Motor Vehicles Having at Least Four Wheels with Regard to Their Noise Emission

2.1.4 IEC PUBLICATIONS—Available from ANSI, 11 West 42nd Street, New York, NY 10036-8002.

IEC Publication 60651: 1979—Sound Level Meters
IEC Publication 60942: 1988—Sound Calibrators

2.1.5 ISO PUBLICATIONS—Available from ANSI, 11 West 42nd Street, New York, NY 10036-8002.

ISO 362-1981—Acoustics—Measurement of noise emitted by accelerating road vehicles—Engineering method
ISO 1176-1974—Road vehicles—Masses—Vocabulary and Codes
ISO 1585-1982—Road vehicles—Engine test code—Net power
ISO 3833-1977—Road vehicles—Types—Terms and definitions
ISO 10844:1994—Acoustics—Specification of test tracks for purpose of measuring noise emitted by road vehicles

2.1.6 EUROPEAN ECONOMIC COMMUNITY - EEC REFERENCE—Available from European Commission, Rue de la Loi 200, B-1049 Brussel, Belguim.

EC- 92/97/EEC—Council Directive of 10 November 1992 from the Official Journal of the European Communities
EC- 96/20/EEC—Council Directive of 27 March 1996 from the Official Journal of the European Communities

3. Definitions—For the purpose of this document, the following definitions apply.

3.1 Automatic Downshift—A gear change to a lower gear (higher numerical ratio) which occurs outside the control of the driver.

NOTE—An automatic downshift may be initiated, for example, by a change of pressure on or position of the accelerator control, thereby activating a special program which effects downshifts to gears which are lower than those normally used in urban driving.

3.2 Forced Downshift—A gear change to a lower gear (higher numerical ratio) which can be initiated at the will of the driver. A forced downshift may be initiated, for example, by a change in the position of the throttle pedal, thereby activating an external switch which affects the downshift.

3.3 Kickdown—A forced downshift to the lowest possible gear (first or low gear).

3.4 Intermediate Result—The value calculated from the test series measurements and used to determine the reported value.

3.5 Curb Mass—Complete shipping mass of a vehicle fitted with all equipment necessary for normal operation plus the mass of the following elements:

a. Lubricants, coolant (if needed), washer fluid,
b. Fuel (tank filled to at least 90% of the capacity specified by the manufacturer),
c. Optional equipment if included as standard parts for the vehicle such as: spare wheel(s), wheel chocks, fire extinguisher(s), spare parts, and tool-kit.

NOTE—The definition of curb mass may vary from country to country, but in this document, it refers to the definition contained in ISO 1176. The mass values listed are US equivalent to the metric requirement: 1 Metric Tonne = 1.1 tons.

3.6 Rated Engine Speed, S—That engine speed at which the engine develops its rated maximum net power as stated by the manufacturer.

NOTE—The test engine speed for governed engines is typically the maximum full load governed speed which is up to 500 rpm higher than the engine speed at maximum net power. The use of net rated power speed or maximum governed speed may vary from one regulatory group to another.

3.7 Vehicle Categories

3.7.1 CATEGORY M—Motor vehicles with at least four wheels used for the carriage of passengers:

M1—Vehicles used for the carriage of passengers and comprising no more than eight seats in addition to the driver's seat.

M2—Vehicles used for the carriage of passengers and comprising more than eight seats in addition to the driver's seat, and having a maximum mass not exceeding 5.5 tons.

M3—Vehicles used for the carriage of passengers and comprising more than eight seats in addition to the driver's seat, and having a maximum mass that exceeds 5.5 tons.

3.7.2 CATEGORY N—Motor vehicles with at least four wheels used for the carriage of goods:

N1—Vehicles used for the carriage of goods and having a maximum authorized total mass not exceeding 3.85 tons.

N2—Vehicles used for the carriage of goods and having a maximum authorized total mass exceeding 3.85 tons but not exceeding 13.2 tons.

N3—Vehicles used for the carriage of goods and having a maximum authorized total mass exceeding 13.2 tons.

4. Instrumentation

4.1 Instrumentation for Acoustical Measurements—The sound level meter system including the windscreen recommended by the manufacturer shall meet Type 1 or Type S1A requirements of ANSI S1.4-1983. A microphone windscreen may be used, provided that it does not affect the microphone response by more than ±1dB for frequencies from 20 to 4000 Hz and ±1.5 dB for frequencies from 4000 to 10 000 Hz.

The sound level meter shall be set for the frequency weighting "A" and the time weighting "F."

The calibration of the sound level meter shall be checked and adjusted according to the manufacturer's instructions using a sound level meter calibrator meeting the requirements of ANSI S1.40-1984 (for example, a pistonphone) at the beginning of the measurements and rechecked and recorded at the end of them. (See 7.3.4)

If the readings of the sound level meter obtained from these calibrations change by more than 0.5 dB during a series of measurements, the test shall be considered invalid.

Compliance of the sound level meter with ANSI S1.4-1983, Type 1, shall be verified at intervals of not more than 2 years. The compliance of the sound calibration device with the requirements of ANSI S1.40-1984 shall be verified once a year. These compliance verification evaluations shall be performed by a laboratory which is authorized to perform calibrations traceable to the appropriate standards.

As an alternative to making direct sound level measurements using a sound level meter, a microphone or sound level meter may be used with a magnetic tape recorder, or other indicating instrument providing the system is in conformance with SAE J184. When using a system that includes a periodic monitoring of the A-weighted sound level, a reading should be made at a time interval not greater than 30 ms.

4.2 Instrumentation for Speed Measurements—Engine speed and vehicle speed shall be measured during the approach with instruments having an accuracy of 2% or better at the speeds required for the measurements being performed.

4.3 Other Instrumentation—The meteorological instrumentation used to monitor the environmental conditions shall include the following:

a. A temperature measuring device which shall be accurate within ±1 °C.
b. A wind speed measuring device which shall be accurate within ±1.0 m/s.

5. Acoustical Environment, Meteorological Conditions, and Background Noise

5.1 Test Site—The test site shall be such that hemispherical divergence exists between the noise source and the microphone to within ±1dB.

This condition is deemed to be satisfied if the following requirements are met:

a. Within a radius of 50 m around the center of the track, the space shall be free of large reflecting objects such as fences, rocks, bridges, or buildings. (See Figure 1.)
b. The entire test track and the surface of the site up to 10 m from the center "0" of the track shall consist of concrete, non-porous or sealed asphalt, or similar hard material and be free of absorbing materials such as powdery snow, or ashes. (See Figure 1.)
c. When this procedure is used for compliance and type approval of vehicle sold in non-US markets, the surface must be constructed according to the requirements given in ISO 10844. The surface shall also meet the performance criteria contained in ISO 10844.
d. In the vicinity of the microphone, there shall be no obstacle that could influence the acoustical field and no person shall be between the microphone and the noise source. The meter observer shall be positioned so as not to influence the meter reading.

A primary concern regarding the test site is flatness of the measurement area. The measurement area shall be flat within ±0.05 m, particularly in that portion of this area between the vehicle path centerline and the microphone location and to a distance of 15 m before and after the intersection of the vehicle path and the perpendicular to it passing through the microphone location. (See Figure 1.)

5.2 Meteorological Conditions—The meteorological instrumentation should be positioned adjacent to the test area at a height representative of the site, except the specific location as follows.

It is recommended that the measurements be made when the ambient air temperature is within the range from 0 °C to 40 °C.

It is recommended that tests should not be carried out if the wind speed, including gusts, at microphone height exceeds 5 m/s, during the sound measurement interval.

It is recommended that a value representative of air temperature, wind speed and direction, relative humidity, and barometric pressure, and track temperature be recorded during the sound measurement interval.

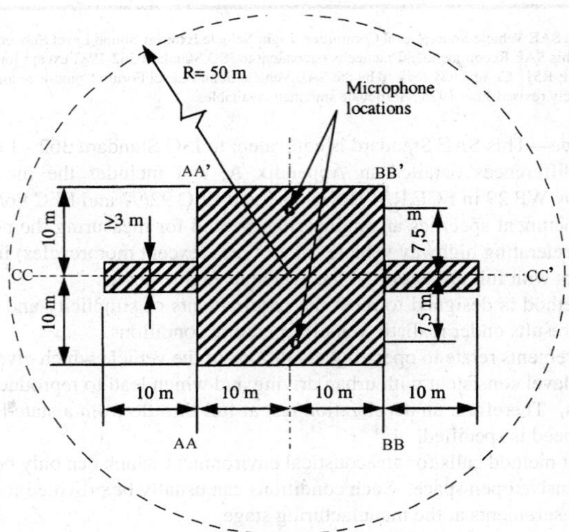

FIGURE 1—TEST SITE DIMENSIONS - SHADED AREA ("TEST AREA") IS THE MINIMUM AREA TO BE COVERED WITH A SURFACE COMPLYING WITH ISO 10844.

5.3 Background Noise—It is recommended the background noise (including any wind noise) be 15 dB(A) below the sound produced by the vehicle under test, but it shall be at least 10 dB(A)

6. Test Procedure

6.1 Microphone Positions—The distance from the microphone positions to the reference centerline CC (see Figure 1) on the test track shall be 7.5 m ± 0.05 m.

The microphone shall be located 1.2 m ± 0.02 m above the ground level. Unless otherwise indicated by the manufacturer of the sound level meter, its reference axis for free field conditions (see ANSI S1.4-1983) shall be horizontal and directed perpendicularly towards the path of the vehicle (centerline CC) on the microphone line.

6.2 Number of Measurements—At least four measurements shall be made on each side of the vehicle.

6.3 Readings to be Taken—The maximum sound pressure level indicated during each passage of the vehicle when operated as specified in 5.5.1 shall be recorded. If a sound peak obviously out of character with the general sound level is observed, the measurement shall be discarded.

The results shall be considered valid if the differences between four consecutive measurements made on the side of the vehicle which gives the highest sound pressure level do not exceed 2 dB. If not, additional runs shall be made until four consecutive measurements on either side are within 2 dB of each other. The spread of results between runs may be reduced if there is a 1-minute wait, at idle in neutral, between runs.

Average the results of each side separately. The intermediate result is the higher of the two averages.

The final reported value for the vehicle is as indicated as follows:

a. For vehicles in categories M1 and N1 tested in a single gear: the intermediate result.
b. For vehicles in categories M1 and N1 tested in two gears: the arithmetic average of the intermediate results for each gear.
c. For vehicles in all categories other than M1 and N1 tested in multiple gears: the highest intermediate result from the gear ranges tested.
d. For vehicles tested at multiple speeds in all categories: the highest intermediate result.

6.4 Conditions of the Vehicles—Measurements shall be made on vehicles unladen (that is - at curb mass) plus the driver and instrumentation, and except for the case of nonseparable vehicles, without trailer or semitrailer.

The vehicle shall be equipped with components that are representative of the intended production unit including engine, driveline, and noise control systems.

The tires used for the test shall be selected by the vehicle manufacturer. They shall correspond to one of the tire sizes designated for the vehicle by the vehicle manufacturer and shall be inflated to the pressure(s) recommended by the manufacturer for the vehicle in its unladen (curb mass) condition. In the case of M1 to N3 vehicles, some European countries allow the use of tires with a tread depth to as low as 1.6 mm, on any part of the tread.

The powertrain and exhaust system temperatures shall be within the normal operating range throughout each test run.

NOTE—Usually, a vehicle brought to its normal engine coolant temperature through moderate driving conditions is adequately conditioned for testing.

6.5 Operating Conditions

6.5.1 GENERAL CONDITIONS—The vehicle shall approach line AA with the path of its centerline following as closely as possible the centerline CC as specified in 6.5.2.1 to 6.5.2.3 as appropriate.

When the front of the vehicle reaches line AA, within ±1.5 m, the throttle shall, as rapidly as possible, be opened as fully as will ensure maximum acceleration without operating kickdown (if any), and held until the rear of the vehicle reaches line BB; the throttle shall then be closed as rapidly as possible.

Any trailer which is not readily separable from the towing vehicles shall be ignored when considering the crossing of line BB.

If the vehicle is fitted with more than two-wheel drive, it shall be tested in the drive which is intended for normal road use.

If the vehicle incorporates equipment which is not normally in operation on the road, such as a concrete mixer, a compressor, etc., this equipment shall not be in operation during the test.

NOTE—It is recommended that supplementary measurements be made with the equipment operating.

6.5.2 SPECIAL CONDITIONS

6.5.2.1 *Vehicles Without Transmission Range Selection*—The vehicle shall approach line AA at a uniform vehicle speed corresponding to one of the following:

a. 50 km/h, or
b. An engine rotational speed equal to 3/4 of the speed, n, which is the rated engine speed, or
c. 3/4 of the engine maximum rotational speed allowed by the governor at full load conditions of the engine,

whichever is the lowest.

6.5.2.2 *Manual Transmission Vehicle*

a. Approach Speed—The vehicle shall approach the line AA' at a steady vehicle speed corresponding to the lower of the following speed with a tolerance ±1 km/h, except where the controlling factor is engine speed the tolerance shall be the larger of ±2% or 50 rpm:
   1. 50 km/h;
   2. The vehicle speed corresponding to an engine speed equal to three-quarters of the rated speed S in the case of vehicles of category M1, and in the case of vehicles of the other categories having an engine power not greater than 225 kW;
   3. The engine speed corresponding to an engine speed equal to half the rated engine speed S in the case of vehicles not belonging to category M1 and having an engine power greater than 225 kW.
b. Choice of Gear Ratios for M1 and N1—Vehicles in categories M1 and N1 equipped with a manually operated gearbox having not more than four forward gear ratios shall be tested in second gear.

   Vehicles in these categories equipped with a manually operated gearbox having more than four forward gear ratios shall be tested in second and third gears successively. Only overall gear ratios intended for normal road use are considered. The final reported value is that determined in 6.3.

   If during the test in second gear, the engine speed exceeds the rated engine speed S, before the rear of the vehicle reaches the line BB, the test shall be repeated with the approach engine speed reduced by steps of 5% of S until the engine speed attained no longer exceeds S. If during the test in second gear, the approach engine speed has been reduced to the idle speed, and the engine attains the rated engine speed S before the rear of the vehicle reaches the line BB, then the test shall be performed only in third gear and the relevant measurement reported as in 7.5.

   However, vehicles in category M1 having more than four forward gears and equipped with an engine developing a maximum power greater than 140 kW, and whose permissible maximum-power/maximum-mass ratio exceeds 75 kW/ (1 metric ton) 1.2 ton, or 62.5 kW/ ton may be tested in third gear only, provided that the vehicle speed change during the acceleration is greater than 11 km/h over a distance of 20 m plus the vehicle length.
c. Choice of Gear Ratios in Categories other than M1, N1—Vehicles other than those in categories M1 and N1 in which the total number of forward gear ranges is x (including the ranges obtained by combining the transmission ratios and the gear ratios added by means of an auxiliary transmission or multiple ratio drive axle) shall be tested, sequentially, using the range equal to or higher than x/n, where n=2 for vehicle having a rated engine power not greater than 225 kW and n=3 for vehicles having a rated engine power greater than 225 kW.

   The initial test will be carried out using the range which is gear (x/n) or the next higher gear range if (x/n) in not an integer. The testing shall continue from the gear (x/n) to the next higher gear.

   Shifting up gear ranges from (x/n) shall be terminating when in the gear X in which the rated engine speed is reached just before the rear of the vehicle has passed the line BB'.

   <u>Sample Calculation for Testing</u>—A vehicle has an engine with a power rating of 230 kW and thedrivetrain has 16 forward ranges available consisting of a primary transmission with 8 ratios and an auxiliary transmission with 2 ratios. The 230 kW engine has a divisor of 3, then calculation is (x/n) = (8 x 2)/3 = 16/3 = 5–1/3. The initial test gear range is 6th (includes the ratios from both the main transmission and auxiliary which is 6th out of the 16 total gear ranges), with the next gear range is 7th up to range X.

   In the case of vehicles having different overall gear ratios (including a different number of gear ranges), the representativity of the type by the test vehicle is determined as follows:
   1. If the highest sound pressure level is obtained between the range x/n and range X, the vehicle selected is deemed representative of its type for those vehicles which include the same gear ratios in the same ranges.
   2. If the highest sound pressure level is obtained at range x/n, the vehicle selected is deemed representative of its type only for those vehicles which have a lower overall gear ratio at range x/n.
   3. If the highest sound pressure level is obtained at range X, the vehicle selected is deemed representative of its type only for those vehicles which have a higher overall gear ratio than the gear ratio at range X.

   However the vehicle, under test, is deemed representative of its type also, if at the applicant's request, the tests are extended over more ratios and the highest sound pressure level is obtained at a ratio that is between the extreme ratios tested.

6.5.2.3 *Automatic Transmission Vehicle*—Two cases may occur:

a. Vehicles without a manual selector shall be tested at various uniform approach speeds of 30, 40, and 50 km/h or at 3/4 of the maximum vehicle speed specified by the manufacturer if this value is lower. The condition yielding the highest sound pressure level , as determined in 6.3, shall be reported.
b. Automatic Transmission Vehicles Categories M and N—If a vehicle is equipped with an automatic transmission with a manual selector, conduct the test with the selector in the position recommended by the manufacturer for normal driving.

   The vehicle shall approach the line AA' at a steady speed corresponding to the lower of the following speeds with a tolerance ±1 km/h; in cases where the controlling factor is engine speed, the tolerance shall be the larger of ±2% or ±50 rpm:
   1. 50 km/h;
   2. The vehicle speed corresponding to 3/4 of the rated engine speed, S, in the case of vehicles of category M1, and in the case of vehicles of the other categories having an engine power not greater than 225 kW;
   3. The speed corresponding to half the rated engine speed S in the case of vehicles not belonging to category M1 and having an engine power greater than 225 kW.
c. Prevention of Downshift—Some vehicles equipped with an automatic transmission (two or more discrete ratios) may downshift to a gear ratio not normally used in urban driving, as defined by the manufacturer. A gear ratio not used for urban driving includes a gear ratio intended for slow movement, parking or braking. In these cases, the operator may select any of the following modifications:
   1. Increase the vehicle speed v of the vehicle to a maximum of 60 km/h in order to avoid such a downshift.

2. Maintain the vehicle speed v at 50 km/h and limit the fuel supply to the engine to 95% of the supply necessary for full load[1]. This condition is considered to be satisfied when:
   a. n the case of a spark-ignition engine, the angle of the throttle opening is 90% of the full angle.
   b. In the case of a compression-ignition engine, the fuel supply to the injection pump is limited to 90% of its maximum supply.
3. Establish and use an electronic control that will prevent a downshift to gears lower than those used in normal urban driving as defined by the manufacturer.

   In all cases, the special selector's positions for slow movements, parking, or braking shall be excluded.

   If the vehicle is fitted with an auxiliary manual transmission or multi-gear axle, the position used for normal urban driving shall be used.

7. General Comments

7.1 It is recommended that persons technically trained and experienced in current sound measurement techniques select the test instrumentation and conduct the tests.

7.2 When making sound level measurements, not more than one person other than the observer reading the meter shall be within 15 m of the vehicle or microphone, and that person shall be directly behind the observer reading the meter, on a line through the microphone and the observer.

7.3 Proper use of all test instrumentation is essential to obtain valid measurements. Operating manuals or other literature furnished by the instrument manufacturer should be referred to for both recommended operation of the instrument and precautions to be observed. Specific items to be considered are:

7.3.1 The type of microphone, its directional response characteristics, and its orientation relative to the ground plane and the sound source.

7.3.2 The effects of ambient weather conditions on the performance of all instruments (for example, temperature, relative humidity, and barometric pressure).

7.3.3 Proper signal levels, terminating impedances, and cable lengths on multi-instrument measurement systems.

7.3.4 Proper acoustical calibration procedures, to include the influence of extension cables, etc. Field calibration shall be made immediately before and after each test sequence. Internal calibration is acceptable for field use, provided that external calibration using a sound level meter calibrator meeting the requirements of ANSI S1.40-1984 is accomplished immediately before and after field use.

7.4 Many tachometers in common use have an appreciable time lag in response during vehicle acceleration. The use of such a tachometer without suitable correction could result in the attainment of higher than intended engine speed and possible effects on measured sound levels.

7.5 Vehicles used for tests shall not be operated in a manner such that the break-in procedure specified by the manufacturer is violated.

7.6 It should be recognized that variations in measured sound levels may occur due to variations in test site, ambient weather differences (temperature, wind, and their gradients), test equipment differences, and inherent differences between nominally identical vehicles.

7.7 Vehicles with diesel engines should be tested using Number 1D or Number 2D diesel fuel possessing a cetane rating from 42 to 50 inclusive (recommended by the manufacturer for use by the purchaser.)

7.8 Vehicles with gasoline engines shall use the grade of gasoline recommended by the manufacturer for use by the purchaser.

7.9 Measurement Uncertainty—Measurements made in conformity with this document results in levels that are influences by climatic conditions. The climatic conditions can affect the performance of the vehicle powertrain, modify the level from the tires, and disturb the propagation path of the sound. In addition, the use of the asphalt test surface specified in ISO 10844 has reduced, but not eliminated, the variations traditionally encountered from different site. Tests of a vehicle at the same site, in similar climatic conditions will result in sound levels that are within ±1 dB. However, testing over the entire range of temperature and wind conditions allowed in this document may result in greater variation. This document encourages the measurement and reporting of additional environmental conditions, to develop a better understanding of the effect of these factors on the measurement. The test temperature range and the wind speed limit as well as the tolerance on vehicle operation provides some reduction of the variations. See Appendix A.

1. This condition shall be satisfied in the case of a spark-ignition engine when the angle of the butterfly valve is 90% of full travel, and in the case of a compression-ignition engine when the movement of the feed-rack of the injection pump is limited to 90% of its stroke.

8. Test Report

8.1 —In the event preparation of a formal test report is required, the report shall contain the following information:

8.1.1 Reference to this document;

8.1.2 Details of the test site, site orientation, the testing surface conditions and weather conditions including wind speed and air temperature. Wind direction, barometric pressure, humidity and track surface temperature are optional measurements and should also be recorded if available date, and test personnel;

8.1.3 The measurement equipment (including windscreen);

8.1.4 The measured A-weighted sound pressure level typical of the background noise;

8.1.5 The identification of the vehicle, its engine, its transmission system including available transmission ratios, size and type of tires, tire pressure, tire tread depth, test mass, and vehicle length;

8.1.6 The transmission gears or gear ratios used during the test;

8.1.7 The vehicle and engine speeds at the beginning of the period of acceleration, and the location of the beginning of the acceleration;

8.1.8 The vehicle speed and engine speed at the end of the acceleration;

8.1.9 The auxiliary equipment, where appropriate, and its operating conditions; and

8.1.10 The A-weighted sound pressure level values measured, from all valid runs, listed according to the side of the vehicle and the direction of the vehicle movement on the test site.

APPENDIX A
RATIONALE

Preface

SAE J1470 has been changed to recognize the updates that have occurred in the ISO 362 procedure. While the procedure conforms to the test cycles used in the majority of the European countries as well as the United States State and Local requirements, it is important that the actual regulations of a specific country be reviewed to insure that this procedure meets the specific country law.

This procedure compliments other SAE procedures that measure the vehicle under maximum operating mode compared to this more typical urban driving cycle which utilizes intermediate gear ratios. The procedure does not include motorcycles which are covered by other SAE procedures.

1. Scope—This section has been updated to highlight the importance of the procedure being used in the manufacturing and official testing facilities but acknowledges the limitations of the use of a local street or large asphalt areas such as routine parking lot construction facilities. This section also indicates that the motorcycle procedure developed by the SAE Motorcycle committee is more representative of actual use than the cycle used in the ISO procedure. Therefore, the ISO section for motorcycles is not included in this SAE procedure.

2. Applicable Documents—This section has been expanded and updated to include the recent data contained in engineering reports and test procedures that are representative of current technology for vehicle passby testing. Section 3.1 adds reference to a SAE report for a cooperative research project comparing the traditional SAE and ISO surface. The ISO surface tends to de-emphasize the tire/road noise during the acceleration compared to the sealed SAE surface. 2.1.5 adds the ISO reference for the test surface construction and performance measurements.

2.1.6—Adds reference to the common market regulation which is the pattern for some of the vehicle gear selector criteria.

3. Definitions—This section contains the modified definitions that clarify the terminology specific to the procedure that were not used in previous procedures or have a specific meaning to the procedure.

3.1—Modified the automatic downshift definition introducing the idea for allowing the vehicle manufacturer to develop data verifying the appropriate urban gear for the powertrain being tested.

3.4—The intermediate result term introduced to identify the value determined from one or more series of runs to be combined for the reported value. The procedure requires multiple runs in some cases prior to determining a reported value.

3.5—Defines the mass of the vehicle configuration that is being tested, and notes the difference between U.S. and British terms for mass.

3.6—Clarifies the engine speed used to determine the approach and conditions of the test run. For use in U.S. jurisdiction, it is the same as SAE net rated hp engine speed. In addition there is a note regarding the difference between “net rated RPM” and “governed engine speed”.

3.7—Defines the vehicle categories at function use, capacity, and mass. These classifications determine the test protocol to be used in the measurements.

4. Instrumentation for Acoustical Measurements—This section has been modified to include the new requirements for verifying the conformance of the acoustic equipment. The intent and the effect is to improve the calibration practice that identify a potential problem in the measurement equipment. It also includes the recommended sampling rate for equipment that used a digital processing technique. This section also adds the requirements for the accuracy of the meteorological equipment that reports the variables that have been shown to effect the sound measurement.

4.1—Adds the requirement for use of a wind screen during the measurement and limits the allowable influence of the wind screen on the measurement. Engineering data supports the need for wind protection even at the limited wind speed allowed. Use of the windscreen helps improve the repeatability of the measurements.

This section also requires a verification of the acoustical test equipment. The requirement allows for calibration by a qualified laboratory. The requirement forces a reference to a traceable standard. It is not so rigid as to force a government approval but allows any laboratory meeting the quality and standards tractability to perform the verification. This section further specifies the need for a digital sampling rate, fast enough to maintain the accuracy of the instrument system.

4.2—Instrument specifications defines the performance expected over the range of measurements. New analog, digital, and hybrid instruments have improved measurement techniques. The devices may have extended ranges that exceed the range typically used and the single reference to full scale or a (%) of full scale may oversimplify the measurement accuracy. The user must be knowledgeable of the instruments used and verify the performance in the range used.

5.1 Test Site—The test surface in all SAE procedures has been specified as a highly reflective uniform asphalt plane. The ISO committee has developed a new surface specification that reduces some of the variation that has occurred in the test sites used. The ISO 10844 construction material and installation technique as well as the performance criteria of macrotexture, residual voids, and absorption characteristics have improved on the site uniformity. However, the SAE surface specification with the application of a surface sealer provides a similar uniformity in the test site surface. The surface texture for the ISO specification has resulted in a reduction in the tire road noise component of the vehicle noise. As a result, the ISO surface is better for measurement of vehicles at lower regulated levels where the objective is to measure powertrain noise and de-emphasize the tire/road noise component.

5.1.c—This paragraph notes the need for a special surface construction when applying this procedure for vehicles exported to some countries. Because of the surface characteristics, the tire/road noise is often lower on this surface than the SAE surface. The performance criteria of the ISO 10844 minimizes the test surface absorption. The ISO surface with an absorption coefficient of less than 0.1 can be characterized as comparable to the SAE sealed surface which also has an absorption coefficient of approximately 0.04. The correlation of the surfaces was shown in SAE Noise and Vibration Conference 951361.

5.1.d—This paragraph requires the surface to be constructed in a uniform plane. A measurement area with surface flatness deviations tends to increase run-to-run variations.

5.2—The recommendation for testing in a limited temperate range is the result of years of data collection where individual product lines are significantly influenced by temperature changes. The lower limit allows fairly nonrestricted testing but recognizes the vehicle performance and instrument changes at the lower temperatures. Again, this procedure does not prevent measurement outside this range but makes test personnel aware of the need to consider temperature in the measurement variability. The recommendation for measuring the other atmospheric quantities again raises the need to be aware of the typical measurement environment. It does not prevent measuring sound level in any conditions.

6. Test Procedure—This section includes a number of major changes that modified the operating conditions of the vehicle to include the current practice in many countries for vehicle approval testing.

6.1—The microphone position and height tolerance were added to encourage an actual measurement of the locations and discourage rough approximation that could alter measurements. Recent studies verify the significance of site/transducer geometry.

6.2—The procedure adds 2 runs to the required measurements which help verify the repeatability of the test runs.

6.3—This section along with the new requirements on the testing, attempt to obtain a better representative number without an overly complex process. The measurement outdoors of a variable source are influenced by a number of uncontrollable factors. This method improves the measurement by helping mitigate some of the variables. The addition of the 1 minute, added to SAE J986 in the late 60's, helps reduce some of the engine temperature increases that have been observed during repeated test runs.

The procedure requires testing some vehicles more than once typically in multiple gears or at multiple speeds. To distinguish between a result from one series of runs from the final result, the term "intermediate result" has been used. The reported test results are a combination or selection of intermediate results as identified in 6.3, a, b, c, and d.

6.4—Specifies the mass of the vehicle and conditions of the powertrain and related components. This section also defines the conditions of the vehicle tire tread and inflation pressure. The reduced tire tread depth decrease the dominance of tire noise in the powertrain measurement cycle for products being designed for some non-U.S. markets.

6.5—This section is completely revised to identify the vehicle operating modes currently representative of urban driving. This cycle allows for testing in an intermediate ratio or ratios that are typical of urban traffic. The concept of using intermediate gears preclude the use of the lowest range in an automatic transmission. This procedure offers an option to be used to prevent the new automatic transmission (with electronic controls) from downshifting into the lowest range, highest ratio or other ratios not normally used in urban driving.

In 6.5.2.2.c, the (n) values indicated (n=2 and n=3) were determined from earlier procedure development work. The exact origin has not been explained or reviewed by the latest ISO Working Group.

8. Test Report—This section relates the information that should be contained in the final report of the total vehicle test. The test technician must determine the importance of this information, to the measurements taken. Site orientation, environmental conditions, vehicle performance, and instrumentation used, all help identify the vehicle test condition during the test conducted. This rigorous test identification can help explain sound level changes on identical products.

A.1 Measurement Uncertainty

This document has been modified, in relation to ISO 362:1997, to improve the repeatability and reproducibility of the measurements. The procedure still does not require a higher level of precision for some test parameters, because there is insufficient data to justify tighter tolerance or limits on these requirements.

The use of the asphalt surfacing specified in ISO 10844 has reduced the variation typical in earlier measurements. However, ISO and Society of Automotive Engineers (SAE) test programs, have indicated that there is still some variation in sound level measurements of identical vehicles on surfaces meeting the site qualifications. In addition to the site variation, there are vehicle and measurement variations attributable to climatic conditions. A reduction of the temperature range to 10 °C to 30 °C generally produces better agreement in the results. Likewise one should be aware that temperature, humidity and atmospheric pressure can have a significant influence on engine performance and microphone response. There is also a level of uncertainty introduced by the wind disturbance of the propagation path.

More precise calibration, better instrument specifications, and test operation criteria in this revised document reduces the variations in sound levels. Also, the variations that will occur may be easier to explain since the document now requires or recommends important meteorological parameters be recorded. However, there remains variations that cannot be accounted for within the allowed ranges. Tests from one site to another and during different, but accepted, climatic conditions will normally vary around ±1 dB, but in extreme cases, variations of ±2 dB may occur. Test data of identical products should be evaluated taking into account these factors if the measurements are found to be out of the range that would be anticipated from previous measurements.

NOTE—Some regulatory organizations specify a reduction of the measured level, by 1 dB, to account for this type of variation. However, such modification of measured levels are out of the scope of the ISO engineering standards. The variations also support the idea of rounding the measured level to the nearest integer in cases where the test parameters are not closely controlled. Engineering comparisons where meteorological and other parameters are restricted or controlled, will reduce this variation to where reporting levels to the nearest 0.1 dB is significant.

(R) VEHICULAR TRAFFIC SOUND SIGNALING DEVICES—SAE J377 MAR2001

SAE Standard

Report of the SAE Vehicle Sound Level Committee approved April 1969, reaffirmed February 1987. Revised by the SAE Sound Signalling Subcommittee of the SAE Motor Vehicle Sound Level Forum May 1998. Completely revised by the SAE Sound Signaling (Horn) Subcommittee of the SAE Motor Vehicle Sound Level Committee March 2001. Rationale statement available.

TABLE OF CONTENTS

1. Scope—General—This SAE Standard establishes the minimum operational life cycles, environmental requirements, and sound level output for traffic horns (electric) on new automotive vehicles. Test equipment, environment, and procedures are specified.

1.1 Intended Usage and Life Expectation—The horns meeting this specification are intended to be used on automotive vehicles, in defined climatic conditions and environments.

Any device functioning as a horn, is intended to perform its function, to this specification for at least 10 years or 250 000 km (150 000 miles).

For the purposes of this specification, this life shall be interpreted as:

Nominal Duty Cycles—50 000 cycles of 1.0 s ON, 4.0 s OFF. plus

Chirp Duty Cycles—40 000 cycles of 0.03 s ON, 1.97 s OFF. plus

Long Duty Cycles—200 cycles of 30 s ON, 60 s OFF; plus

Continuous Duty Cycles—5 cycles of 3.0 min. ON, 10 min. OFF.

These cycles shall be intermixed during testing as follows:

16 chirp duty cycles after each 20 nominal cycles;

2 long duty cycles after each 500 nominal cycles;

1 continuous duty cycle after the first long duty cycle and then every 10 000 normal cycles thereafter.

These duty cycles shall be modified for Combined Environment Testing as shown in the Combined Environment section.

2. References

2.1 Applicable Publications—The following publications form a part of this specification to the extent specified herein. Unless otherwise indicated, the latest issue shall apply.

2.1.1 SAE PUBLICATIONS—Available from SAE, 400 commonwealth Dr. Warrendale PA 15096-0001

SAE J184—Qualifying a Sound Data Acquisition System

SAE J726—Air Cleaner Test Code

2.1.2 AIAG PUBLICATION—Available from Automotive Industry Action Group, 26200 Lahser Road, Suite 200, Southfield, MI 48034.

AIAG QS9000 Quality Systems

2.1.3 ANSI PUBLICATION—Available from ANSI, 11 West 42nd Street, New York, NY 10036-8002.

ANSI S1.4-1983 and S1.4A-1985—Specification for Sound Level Meters

2.1.4 ASTM PUBLICATION—Available from ASTM, 100 Barr Harbor Drive, West Conshohocken PA 19428-2959.

ASTM B117-85—Testing for Salt Spray (Fog)

2.1.5 ECE PUBLICATION—Available from United Nations Economic Commission for Europe, Palais Des Nations, CH-1211, Geneva 10, Switzerland.

ECE Regulation R28 - Uniform provisions concerning the approval of audible warning devices and of motor vehicles with regard to their audible signals.

2.1.6 EEC PUBLICATION—Available from European Economic Community Council

EEC Directive of 70/388/EEC, 27 July 1970, relating to audible warning devices for motor vehicles.

2.1.7 IEC PUBLICATIONS—Available from International Electrotechnical Commission, 3, rue de Verambe, P.O. Box 131, 1211 Geneva 20, Switzerland.

IEC Publication 60068-2-27—Basic environmental testing procedures Part 2: test Ea and guidance: Shock

IEC Publication 529: 1989—Degrees of protection provided by enclosures (IP Code)

IEC Publication 60068-2-64—Environmental testing Part 2: Test Fh: Vibration, braod-band random

IEC Publication 60651: 1979—Sound Level Meters

IEC Publication 60942: 1988—Sound Calibrators

2.1.8 ISO PUBLICATIONS—Available from ANSI, 11 West 42nd Street, New York, NY 10036-8002.

ISO 10844: 1994—Acoustics - Test surface for road vehicle noise measurements

ISO 9001—Quality Systems

2.1.9 USCAR PUBLICATION—Available from USCAR, Suite 300, 1000 Town Center Bldg., Southfield Michigan, 48075.

USCAR Connector Drawing 150-S-002-A01

2.1.10 US GOVERNMENT DOCUMENTS—Available from ???

US EPA-40-CFR Ch1, Part 205 Test Surface

US FMVSS 302 Flammability

2.2 Related Publications—The following publications are provided for information purposes only and are not a required part of this document.

2.2.1 SAE PUBLICATION—Available from SAE, 400 Commonwealth Drive, Warrendale, PA 15096-0001.

SAE 951361—Paper from the SAE Noise & Vibration Conference Report, P-291, Volume 2, SAE and ISO Noise Test Site Variability

2.2.2 ANSI PUBLICATION—Available from ANSI, 11 West 42nd Street, New York, NY 10036-8002.

ANSI S1.40-1984—Specification for Acoustical Calibrators

3. Definitions—For purposes of this specification the following terms will be used:

3.1 Sound Signaling Device—A device that makes an audible sound of sufficient amplitude to alert people in the vicinity of the vehicle. For purposes of this document, the more common term "horn" will be used.

3.2 Horn Subsystem—The Horn Subsystem will be considered to include the horn or horn assembly, the horn attachments, the driver-controlled actuation device (steering column horn pad), any control devices between the actuation device and the horn (e.g., relay), and the related portions of any other horn actuation interfaces (e.g., electronic modules, wiring).

This document addresses only the horn or horn assembly as defined as follows. Unless otherwise specified, or defined by context, the term horn shall always be construed in the broadest context to include all pieces of the deliverable part, including, but not limited, to multiple horns, bracket(s), jumper harness(es), and connector(s).

3.3 Horn—A device for making an audible tone for signaling persons in the vicinity of the vehicle, or annunciating the occurrence of some event on or in the vehicle. Where multiple horn units are supplied with a common bracket, the units will meet their requirements both individually and as a horn assembly. Excluded from this specification are sirens and other special signaling devices.

3.4 Disk Horn—A horn that produces the majority of its acoustical energy by use of a shaped metallic disc attached to the primary vibrating diaphragm.

3.5 Trumpet Horn—A horn that produces its acoustical energy by a diaphragm operating on an air column which is tuned to the diaphragm frequency. The air column (trumpet) is usually spiraled or otherwise bent to fit within the diameter of the basic horn.

3.6 Bracket—A connecting piece that interfaces between the audio-producing assembly (horn) and the vehicle mounting point. Due to acoustic and/or packaging reasons the bracket can consist of several parts or layers. The bracket is usually supplied as an integral part of the delivered horn, and may be an acoustic part of the horn system.

4. Test Environment

4.1 On-Vehicle

4.1.1 TEST EQUIPMENT DEFAULTS—The following instrumentation defaults shall apply where applicable:

Sound Levels shall be measured with a meter or measurement system that meets the requirements of ANSI S1.4 or IEC 60651. The meter shall be set for the A weighting scale and the Fast response. If a system other than a single sound level meter is used the system performance should be verified following the recommendations of SAE J184.

A microphone wind screen, if used must not affect the microphone response more than ±1 dB for frequencies from 20 to 4000 Hz, and ±1.5 dB from 4000 to 10 000 Hz.

When using a system that includes a periodic monitoring of the A-weighted sound level, a reading should be made at a time interval not greater than 30 ms.

At the beginning and at the end of a complete measurement session, but not less than once per day, the entire measurement system shall be checked by means of a sound calibrator that fulfills the requirements for sound calibrators of at least precision Class 1 according to IEC 60942. Without any adjustment, the difference between the readings of two consecutive checks shall be less than or equal to 0.5 dB. If this value is exceeded the results of the measurements obtained after the previous satisfactory check shall be discarded.

Wind velocity shall be measured with an anemometer accurate to ±10% at 20 km/h (12 mph).

Measurement instruments, not otherwise specified, shall be accurate to one order of magnitude (1 decimal point) greater than the stated requirement.

Measurement instruments must be calibrated to a recognized standard as often as manufacturer recommends, but not less than once per year.

4.1.2 TEST ENVIRONMENT DEFAULTS—The test site shall be a smooth dry asphalt or concrete surface with an acoustic absorption of less than 0.10 in the frequency range from 400 to 1600 Hz. Surfaces that meet the requirements of ISO 10844 or the U.S. Federal EPA surface per 40 CFR Ch1 Part 205 will meet this requirement.

The location of the microphone within the test site shall also meet the following:

a. Free of reflecting surfaces within 30.5 m,
b. No one except microphone operator in test field,
c. Wind velocity less than 20 km/h (12 mph).

Microphone shall be swept in a vertical path from a height of 0.5 m to 1.5 m to use the maximum sound pressure level occurring in that path.

Microphone shall be located at a distance of 7 m in front of, and on the longitudinal centerline of the vehicle.

Ambient sound level, including wind effects, coming from sources other than the vehicle being measured, shall be at least 10 dB(A) lower than the level of the horn(s) being tested. When engine noise makes the 10 dB differential impossible, the test may be run and the measurement may be corrected according to the principles for combining decibel signal levels; provided the result is identified as having been corrected, the correction method is identified, and the observed data is provided.

Ambient temperature shall be between 13 °C and 30 °C. If the temperature is outside this range the test may be conducted if agreed to by all parties.

Measurements shall be made with the vehicle stationary and the engine running at idle. The engine shall have been running for 30 min prior to the test with no headlamp or other heavy electrical loads activated. For reference purposes the battery voltage shall be recorded before and after the test and shall be in the range of the vehicle manufacturer's specification.

NOTE—The requirement to test with engine running differs from the engine off requirement of ECE R28. Under this requirement, all horns are tested at the vehicle level with the horn powered as it would be on the road, regardless of whether it is DC, AC, or air powered. It provides a more accurate representation of how the horn will sound in actual usage, and makes the measurement independent of the nominal vehicle system voltage.

Duration of the horn activation shall not exceed 5 s, with not less than 20 s between activations.

The vehicle operator should be seated in/on the vehicle in normal operating position for a stationary vehicle. Enclosed vehicles should have the windows closed during the test.

4.2 Component Level

4.2.1 TEST EQUIPMENT DEFAULTS—The following instrumentation defaults shall apply where applicable:

Sound Levels shall be measured with a meter or measurement system that meets the requirements of IEC 60651. The meter shall be set for the A weighting scale and the Fast response.

Measurement instruments, not otherwise specified, shall be accurate to one order of magnitude (1 decimal point) greater than the stated requirement.

Measurement instruments must be calibrated to a recognized standard as often as manufacturer recommendations but not less than once per year.

The power supply shall be capable of supplying a continuous output current of at least 200% of the nominal current for the quantity of units being tested simultaneously. Output regulation shall not allow voltage to deviate more than 1.0 V from zero to maximum load (including surges) and shall recover 63% of its maximum excursion within 5.0 ms. Ripple shall not exceed 100 mV peak-to-peak.

4.2.2 TEST ENVIRONMENT DEFAULTS—Unless otherwise specified all tests shall be run at 13.0 V DC ± 0.3 V DC.

Source Resistance including all wiring to a "device under test" shall be not more than 0.1 Ohm. For single terminal, case grounded horns, the case ground path resistance must be included.

For horns that have been designed to operate on a different voltage or with a different circuit resistance, the voltage and resistance specified by the vehicle manufacturer shall be used.

Voltage measurements shall be made at, or within 80 mm, of the horn harness connector terminals.

Ambient temperature shall be between 13 °C and 30 °C.

Airflow up to 10 m/s is permitted.

Production wiring and connections shall be used. Terminals shall be changed periodically to assure terminal wear does not affect test results.

The horn shall be mounted with its production bracket to a sturdy base of mass at least 30 times the mass of the horn assembly. Mounting hardware and torque shall be consistent with the horn manufacturer's recommendations.

In the case of multiple horns mounted to a single bracket, each horn should be tested on its intended bracket with the other horn, but with only one horn connected. If necessary, individual horns may be rotated on the bracket such that their speaking axes are pointing toward the measurement microphone, as long as such rotation does not adversely influence their operation.

Alternatively a horn may be tested with the horn mounted on a standardized bracket defined by the horn manufacturer. Horns intended to be mounted to a bracket integral to the vehicle, shall be tested with the horn mounted on a standardized bracket defined by the horn manufacturer.

Sound Pressure Level measurements shall be conducted in a "Sound Attenuation Chamber" that is substantially anechoic in the frequency range of 20 to 2000 Hz. The materials and dimensions of the chamber shall be such that the sound pressure level will decrease 6 dB(A) at each doubling distance between the horn and the microphone, or which has been calibrated to simulate a free field environment.

The horn and microphone shall face each other along the axis of maximum sound level at a distance of 2.0 m ± 0.1 m.

Unless otherwise specified, maximum time of activation shall be 3 s, with at least 20 s OFF between activations. Shorter off times may be used at the option of the horn manufacturer.

4.3 Test Samples—Component Level Test Samples shall be selected from normal production, at random from pieces that have been subjected to all normal processing and handling.

Test Samples shall be allocated among the various tests as indicated in the test matrix (see Appendix A).

Vehicle level tests shall be performed on vehicle(s) which are production intent in all areas that might affect emitted sound pressure level, and with horns that are production qualified.

4.4 Failure Determination—A component level test failure will be determined should any sample fail to meet the specification, regardless of age or accumulated cycles.

Unless otherwise specified all test samples shall be checked for proper performance before and after each test segment, and after a complete test sequence. Performance shall be determined by a minimum of one (1) actuation of 15 s ON and 15 s OFF, and a minimum of three (3) actuations of 1 second ON and 1 s OFF. Sound Pressure Level shall be measured during any of the 1 s cycles. Failure shall be defined as a reduction in sound pressure level from the as-built condition of 5 dB(A) or greater, a change in fundamental frequency which results in the unit being outside its manufacturing tolerance by more than 20 Hz, or a significant change in perceived tone quality.

A vehicle level test failure will be determined should the vehicle fail to produce a sound level in the specified range.

5. On Vehicle Performance Requirements—The Horn(s), when mounted to the vehicle in its designed position, and tested under the default test environment, shall produce a sound level of 93 to 104 dB(A) (see note) at a distance of 7 m. Sound pressure level must satisfy this requirement with all horns with which the vehicle is equipped operating. Optionally, a series of three readings may be taken and the average of the readings used for the determination.

NOTE—112 dB(A) is the upper limit for vehicles sold under ECE R28. 104 dB(A) is the upper limit for vehicles sold in Brazil. 104 dB(A) is also the upper limit for vehicles sold in the U.S. based on converting the New York City Code to common dimensions. Vehicles destined for countries that do not subscribe to ECE R28 requirements must be tested to those countries' requirements. EEC 70/388 is equivalent to ECE R28. There are no nationally required measurements for U.S. or Canadian vehicles, except as recommended or stated previously.

6. Component Mechanical Requirements

6.1 Dimensional and Visual—Parts shall be inspected for visual defects in appearance, manufacture, or assembly. Rattles and tightness of attachments shall be included in the inspection. Dimensions, mass, and finishes shall be as specified in the controlling documents.

6.2 Mounting—Each Horn of a horn/bracket assembly shall withstand a torque of 8 Nm, applied about its axis in such a direction as would try to loosen the horn from its bracket.

6.3 Terminations—The preferred connection for nominal 12 V DC systems shall meet the requirements of USCAR drawing 150-S-002-1-A01. For reference, portions of that drawing are reproduced in Appendix C. The polarity of the connector shall be Pin A = Gnd, Pin b = B+. For voltages other than 12 V DC, unique keying shall be incorporated into this connector.

Individual contacts of the termination interface shall withstand force of 50 N applied in each direction (push and pull) to dislodge the contact from its connector body or other attachment.

When terminals are contained in a connector body, the connector body shall withstand the following forces without permanent deformation or impairing the function or sealing of the connection system:

a. A linear force of 50 N applied in any direction to the open end of the connector body. (Figure 1A)
b. A torque of 2.5 Nm applied to the connector body around three mutually orthogonal axes. (Figure 1B).

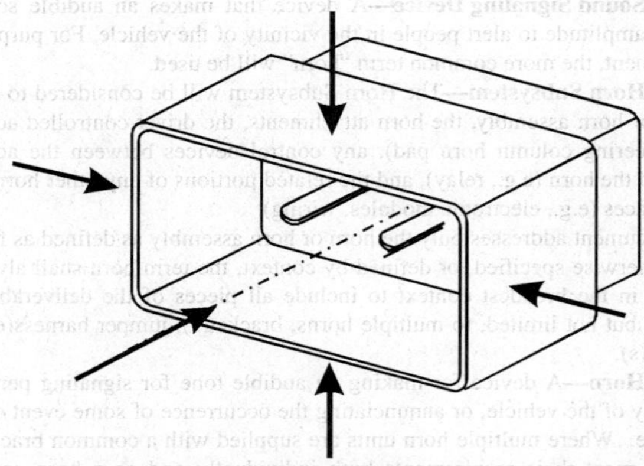

FIGURE 1A—FORCE TEST DIRECTIONS

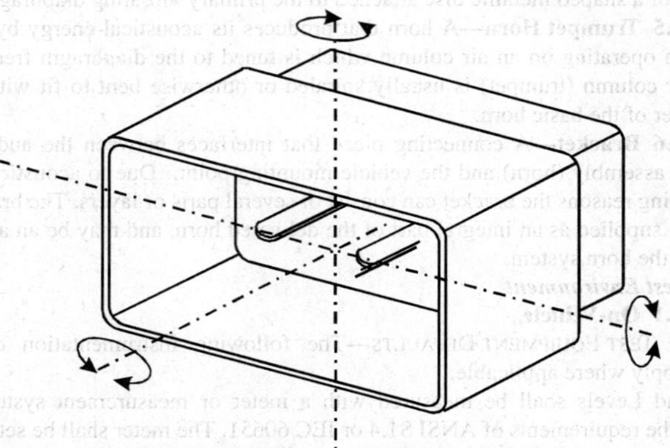

FIGURE 1B—TORQUE TEST DIRECTIONS

6.4 Materials—The horn or any supplied components shall not use any materials that are restricted or prohibited under any National or Local regulations, for the locations in which the using vehicle is expected to be sold or operated.

When intended for use inside the passenger compartment, materials used in the construction of any parts covered by this document shall meet the requirements of US FMVSS302.

6.5 Recycleability—Parts made of materials covered by any national regulations for recycleability shall be appropriately labeled.

6.6 Serviceability/Adjustments—The only service shall be by replacement of the horn or horn assembly. No customer or dealer adjustments shall be required or provided.

6.7 Identification—For part identification, the parts will include the following identification applied in such a manner as to be externally visible.

6.7.1 CUSTOMER'S PART NUMBER—Part number shall be applied as specified in the drawings. Additional manufacturer's designations may be included but shall not be applied in a way as to be confused with the final part number. In particular, manufacturer's identification of piece parts or sub-assemblies should be applied to be concealed or on less visible surfaces.

6.7.2 DATE OF MANUFACTURE—A "date code" shall be applied as a final operation indicating successful completion of tests. The date code shall include the year and day, shift, manufacturing line, and location as applicable. The date code may be in any format, but such format shall be publicly available.

6.7.3 SOURCE—The source of the part shall be identified by company name or logo.

6.7.4 REGULATORY IDENTIFICATION—Identification required by various governmental agencies shall be provided, (including but not limited to component type certifications and recycleability markings).

6.7.5 FREQUENCY—Each horn shall be marked with its nominal fundamental frequency, and or the musical note equivalent of the nominal fundamental frequency. In lieu of the actual fundamental frequency an abbreviated designation, such as *L* for *low* or *H* for *high*, is acceptable.

7. Component Electrical and Acoustic Requirements

7.1 Polarity, Connection Sequence—Horns shall be designed to have the polarity as specified by the drawing. The use of the mounting as a ground return shall be allowed only if specified by the drawing. In all devices, any exposed metallic case, shell or bracket is to be at vehicle ground potential, whether used as part of the energizing circuit or not.

The polarity of the preferred connector is specified in Appendix C.

The horn shall not be damaged by the sequence of connection to any of its terminals.

7.2 Operating Voltage Range—Horns shall be designed to work within specific ranges of voltage.

For horns designed to operate in nominal voltage systems other than 12 V DC, the voltage range shall be specified on the drawings or other documents. All references in this document, which is based on a nominal 12 V DC system, shall be adjusted by the drawings or other documents to the alternative voltage system values.

For 12 V DC nominal systems, horns shall be designed to work with voltages in the range of 9 to 16 V DC.

a. 9.0 to 11.5 V DC Performance variation allowed
b. 11.5 to 15.0 V DC Meet all parameters.
c. 15.0 to 16.0 V DC Performance variation allowed

For this requirement, the unit will be operated 5 times at 13.5 V DC, noting tone quality (clear tone, fundamental frequency stability, and sound pressure level stability). The horn will then be operated 5 times at 11.7 V DC, and 5 times at 14.8 V DC, noting no appreciable difference in tone quality. The horn will then be operated 5 times at 9.0 V DC and 5 times at 16.0 V DC, noting tone quality. The horn will then be operated 5 times at 13.5 VDC noting tone quality. Each cycle shall be approximately 10 s ON for this test. OFF time shall be at the discretion of the supplier. Allowable performance variation shall be limited to a change of sound pressure level of ±5 dB(A), and/or a change in fundamental frequency of ±20 Hz. Tone stability is required, but some loss of tone clarity may be accepted.

7.3 Grounding, Insulation Resistance—Except where the case is used as a ground return path, the case shall be isolated from any terminal by a minimum of 1 Mohm when tested at 500 V DC ±10 V DC for 60 s.

7.4 Parasitic Loads—If designed to be supplied continuously with vehicle power and operated by a separate trigger signal or control connection, each unit's parasitic current shall be no more than allowed by the applicable drawing.

7.5 Readiness, Response Time—The horn shall be in a constant state of readiness. It shall not require any wake-up or warm-up time. When tested at a component level, at 18 °C to 28 °C, the horn shall produce an audible output upon application of a signal of at least 25 ms duration at 9 V DC. Full sound pressure level shall be produced upon application of 13 V DC for greater than 200 ms. For this test the sound pressure meter should be set to the *Impulse* setting if available.

7.6 Current—Horns shall be nominally rated at no greater than 6.0 A per horn at 13.0 V DC. Actual maximum current shall be as specified on the drawing. For three-terminal horns, the control (trigger) circuit maximum current shall be as specified on the drawing.

7.7 Fundamental Frequency—Fundamental frequency of a horn shall be as specified on the drawing.

7.8 Sound Pressure Level and Harmonics—Sound pressure level and harmonic structure of each horn shall be certified to meet the applicable requirements of United Nations Economic Commission for Europe Regulation Number 28 (ECE R28) as amended.

Horns so qualified must carry the appropriate markings.

7.9 Variability—Each horn shall produce a steady tone. For this requirement, the horn shall be operated at an ambient temperature between 13 °C and 30 °C and a nominal voltage of 13 V DC for 5 cycles of 1 min ON and then sufficient OFF time to return to ambient temperature. During the ON time, the fundamental frequency and sound pressure level shall be subjectively evaluated as being essentially unvarying.

7.10 Electromagnetic Compatibility—The horn shall not produce energy that would interfere with any other components or systems in the vehicle. Specific requirements shall be specified on the drawing or in related documents.

8. Component Environmental Requirements

8.1 Temperature—The horn shall be designed to withstand storage temperatures of –40 °C to +100 °C. This requirement shall be tested by exposing the horn to 5 cycles of temperature as follows:

a. 30 min rising from ambient to +100 °C,
b. 47 h (±30 min) dwell at +100 °C,
c. 3 h max dropping to –40 °C,
d. 47 h (±30 min) dwell at –40 °C
e. 1 h max rising from –40 °C to ambient.

At completion of each cycle, the horn shall operate without degradation when actuated 5 times at 13 V DC for 2 s ON and 10 s OFF.

8.2 Thermal Shock—The horn shall operate without degradation after exposure to 10 cycles of thermal shock of +85 °C to –40 °C and back to +85 °C, with a minimum dwell time at each temperature of 1 h and a maximum transition time of 2 min.

8.3 Humidity—Two separate tests shall be performed. Operating Humidity shall be performed as part of the test matrix sequence. Non-Operating Humidity shall be performed on a separate group of 10 horns as specified as follows.

8.3.1 HUMIDITY, OPERATING—The horn shall operate in high humidity environments. For this test, Disk horns shall be mounted with the plane of the diaphragm vertical; Trumpet horns shall be mounted with the plane of the diaphragm horizontal and the trumpet below the motor housing. The horn shall be placed in a chamber stabilized at 38 °C and 95% relative humidity for 10 days. For 12 h per day the horns shall be energized for 3 s every 10 min.

8.3.2 HUMIDITY, NON-OPERATING—The horn shall operate without degradation after sitting dormant in high humidity environments.

Terminal resistance and functional characteristics will be measured before and after test. Five (5) of the horns will be mounted with the plane of the diaphragm horizontal and the diaphragm below the motor housing. Five (5) of the horns will be mounted with the plane of the diaphragm vertical, and if a trumpet is included, axis of the mouth of the trumpet shall point between vertically down and 45 degrees from vertically down. The horns will be placed in a chamber with 95% humidity at ambient temperature, raised to 40 °C at maximum speed and maintained for 4 h. Increase temperature to 80 °C in 40 min and maintain 4 h. Decrease temperature to 40 °C in 40 min and repeat cycle for a total of 10 cycles without operating the horn.

8.4 Frost—The horn shall operate without degradation after being subjected to frost. For this test the horn shall be stabilized for 4 h at –20 °C, then transferred to 10 °C and 95% RH. After 10 min operate 20 times for 3 s ON and 10 s OFF. Repeat the test 5 times on each horn.

8.5 Vibration—The horn, when tested with its intended bracket, shall withstand random vibration in each of 3 mutually perpendicular axes, without damage or degradation of performance. The direction of one of the 3 axes shall be normal to the bracket mounting plane. Optionally, under customer direction, for validating horns that include brackets, the horns may be tested only in vehicle mounting position. During this test the horn(s) is to be connected to a representative harness connector(s) so that it can be operated during the test.

Perform test according to IEC 60068-2-64, random vibration, method 1 or 2. The vibration shall be from 10 to 1000 Hz, applied for 8 h in each axis (24 h total) with power levels and spectral density specified by the following:

RMS acceleration value = 20.9 m/s^2

TABLE 1—POWER SPECTRAL DENSITY

Frequency	$\frac{(m/s^2)^2}{Hz}$
10	7
50	3.5
60	1.75
1000	0.06

As a development test only, production intent units (with bracket) shall be evaluated for their resonant frequency.

Each tested horn shall be checked after such test for any rattles, noise, or lack of original clear tone when operated 20 times at 13 V DC, 3 s ON and 10 s OFF.

8.6 Shock/Drop—The horn with its intended bracket shall withstand the shock loading encountered during shipping and handling, installation, and during normal operation. Each tested horn shall be checked after such test for any rattles, noise, or lack of original clear tone when operated 20 times at 13 V DC, 3 s ON and 10 s OFF.

8.6.1 SHOCK—The horn shall withstand 3000 shocks in each direction along each of the 3 primary axes (9000 shocks total) without visible damage or degradation of performance. Each shock shall be 20 g peak acceleration, half sine wave of 18 ms duration tested in accordance with IEC 68-2-27. Optionally, under customer direction, for validating horns that include brackets, the horns may be tested only in vehicle mounting position.

8.6.2 DROP—The horn, in its delivered state with bracket, shall be capable of withstanding a 1.0 m drop onto a solid concrete floor when released in 6 orthogonal directions. When no obvious damage is visible, no degradation of performance is allowed. Minor cosmetic damage is acceptable.

8.7 Contaminants—The horn shall withstand the following contaminants with the unit mounted both with the diaphragm vertical (trumpet mouth opening down if applicable), and with the diaphragm horizontal, trumpet or disk below the diaphragm.

a. Gasoline (unleaded)Commercial
b. Diesel FuelCommercial
c. Engine OilCommercial 10W30
d. Power Steering FluidCommercial
e. Ethylene GlycolCommercial 50% by volume
f. Windshield Washer FluidAll Commercial types
g. Automatic Transmission FluidAll Commercial types
h. Car Wash DetergentsAll Commercial types
i. Brake FluidAll Commercial types

Each contaminant will be tested on a different sample. A connector representative of the harness connection will be installed prior to and during these tests.

Test is to be accomplished by pouring an adequate amount of material over the unit to completely coat the appropriate surfaces. Allow the unit to stand for 24 h.

The sound of the horn shall be clear and the allowable drop in sound pressure level shall be less than 5 dB(A). The horn shall function properly when subjected to 20 actuations of 3 s ON, 10 s OFF at 13 V DC. There shall be no loss of electrical or mechanical integrity that could result in shorting, shorting to ground, or unintentional operation of the horn.

8.8 Corrosion—Horns shall be capable of operating in regions of the world where corrosive salt environments exist. Horns are to be tested in accordance with ASTM B 117 for 168 h. Each hour the horn shall be operated 20 cycles of 1 s ON and 4 s OFF during this test.

Following the exposure, visible corrosion (red rust) shall not be greater than 10% of the exposed metal surface.

Following the exposure, there shall be no more than 5 dB(A) loss in sound pressure, or significant change in perceived tone quality.

8.9 Dust—Horns shall be capable of operating in regions of the world where dust environments exist. Horns are to be tested for 8 h in a chamber per IEC 529-IP6 except with 6 kg/m^{3}concentration of dust conforming to SAE J726 Coarse Grade. Agitate the dust for 5 s in each 20 min in such a manner that the dust is uniformly diffused throughout the chamber. Operate the horn(s) 1 s ON, 29 s OFF throughout the test.

8.10 Water Impingement—The horn shall not be damaged by splash from rain or road, or by pressure washers.

At end of test, the horns shall function without degradation when operated 5 times, 1 s ON, 29 s OFF. The horns shall be disassembled after these tests. There shall be no evidence of water intrusion into the motor housing or sealed connection interfaces.

8.10.1 SIMULATED RAIN ENVIRONMENT—The horn shall be subjected for 5 days to a simulated rain environment. The horn, if a trumpet type, shall be mounted with the trumpet mouth down. The environment shall consist of either nozzles aimed at 5 surfaces (not the trumpet mouth), or a moving array of nozzles oscillating at no less than 5 s/cycle, that will wet the same surfaces. Water must not be directed into the trumpet mouth. The spray shall operate for 2 h, and rest for 10 h, repeated twice per day for 5 days. The horn is to be operated continuously for 1 s ON and 29 s OFF during the first hour of each spray cycle.

8.10.2 HIGH PRESSURE WASHER—The horn shall withstand, without damage or degradation, a water jet of 8 to 10 MPa, 14 to 16 l/min, for 120 s aimed at all surfaces and edges, except the trumpet mouth, from a distance of 0.5 m and using a 30 degree fan nozzle.

8.11 Water Immersion—The horn shall not be damaged by full contact with water. This shall be tested by an immersion test. This test shall be accomplished by immersion to 30 cm in 5% salt water at ambient temperature for 5 min. At the conclusion of the test the horn shall operate without degradation when actuated 20 times for 3 s ON. For trumpet style horns the horns shall be immersed with the mouth pointing down.

As a development test the horn should be temperature conditioned for 1 h in air at 85 °C, then immersed to 30 cm in 5% salt water at 0 °C for 1 h, and followed by 1 h at ambient. This sequence shall be repeated 25 times. The horn should be operated at least once prior to each heating cycle to verify functionality and tone. The horn shall be disassembled and inspected for water entry. Entry of water into the horn or any sealed connection shall be evaluated by the customer.

8.12 Altitude—The horn shall be designed to work at all altitudes from –85 m to +3700 m relative to mean sea level. This requirement need be demonstrated only once per horn family. Demonstration shall consist of operating a horn in a pressure controlled chamber. The horn sound shall be subjectively evaluated for clear tone with the chamber pressure set at 56 kPa and again with the pressure set at 106 kPa.

8.13 Combined Environments—Reliability and durability shall be demonstrated by subjecting a minimum of 22 random sample of horns/assemblies to a life test by operating the horn using the usage profile specified in 1.1 Intended Usage and Life Expectation, and the environmental profile defined by Appendix B. The demonstration will be accomplished by running the samples to failure, or three (3) times life, whichever comes first.

Six (6) of the samples shall be mounted with the plane of the diaphragm horizontal, trumpet/disk below. Six (6) of the samples shall be mounted with the plane of the diaphragm vertical and centerline of bracket horizontal, (if trumpet type, trumpet mouth vertical and below centerline). Six (6) of the samples shall be mounted with the plane of the diaphragm vertical and centerline of bracket vertical, (if trumpet type, trumpet mouth vertical and below centerline). Four (4) of the samples shall be mounted, at supplier option, in any of the orientations described previously. One (1) horn of each orientation (3 total) shall be properly connected, but shall be operated only at the beginning and end of test to verify performance. End of test for the three silent horns shall be defined as the length of time for the other horns to reach one times life. All other horns shall be operated in accordance with the usage profile.

The test schedule shall be modified, if necessary, to assure that:

a. No continuous duty cycles occur above 75 °C, and
b. At least one long cycle group occurs during a 65 °C segment, and
c. At least one long cycle group occurs during a –40 °C segment.

The test schedule may be modified, at the supplier's option, to increase the OFF time between cycles at any temperature above 50 °C.

Vibration during this test shall be random with the Power Spectral Density (PSD) according to 8.5 Vibration, but with a maximum power level of 1 g RMS.

Sound Pressure measurements and tone quality evaluations shall be made at least every 10 000 Normal Duty Cycles, when the temperature is at ambient, and shall include an evaluation of both chirp and normal activation modes.

For purposes of this test, failure shall be defined as:

a. A loss of greater than 5 dB in sound pressure level
b. A change in frequency which results in a fundamental frequency outside the normal manufacturing tolerance of greater than 5 Hz.
c. Failure of the horn to operate for more than 5 times in succession at any time during the demonstration.

9. Validation

9.1 Development Testing

9.1.1 PURPOSE—Development tests are tests used to evaluate specific areas of design. They are a tool for evaluating original designs, design alternatives, proposed improvements, cost reduction proposals, or for field problem analysis. Development tests may be severe. Development tests often accelerate testing by exaggerating specific environments. Failures under a development test are expected. Such failure does not necessarily indicate inadequacy of design. Any failures must be evaluated and the results and any action documented to the customer. Any development tests included herein are for reference only and are not a part of the part approval. Additional development test requirements will vary from customer to customer.

9.2 Design Validation and Durability Testing—Validation tests are those tests required to demonstrate that the component or system of components can meet the requirements of this specification for the life of the component. These validation tests must be satisfactorily completed before use on a production vehicle.

Design validation shall consist, unless otherwise specified, of the tests stated in this specification. Sample sizes and test sequence shall be in accordance with the test matrix of Appendix A.

Where a basic horn family has been validated as separate components, the test schedule for assemblies consisting of those validated components, together with brackets and/or jumper harnesses may be abbreviated to include only those parameters related to the assembly differences.

When new parts differ from parts previously tested and fully qualified under this specification by details that affect only mounting and orientation, and which can be shown analytically to not affect performance, re-testing under this paragraph may be modified or waived.

9.3 Annual Re-validation/Re-certification—At least once per year, a minimum of 10 samples shall be placed on an automated cycle test, and cycled until failure, or three (3) times life, whichever comes first. The test shall be the same as that specified for the Combined Environment as specified above.

10. Reliability—The Reliability requirements have been incorporated in the testing specified previously. No additional testing is required.

11. Quality Assurance—The supplier shall be certified to a system recognized and accepted by the customer (e.g., ISO 9001, AIAG QS 9000).

12. Authority and Revision History

12.1 Authority—This document has been developed by the SAE Sound Signaling (Horn) sub-committee of the SAE Motor Vehicle Sound Level Committee. It is intended to be a common specification that will meet the requirements of vehicle manufacturers and governmental agencies worldwide.

APPENDIX A
TEST MATRIX AND TEST PROFILES

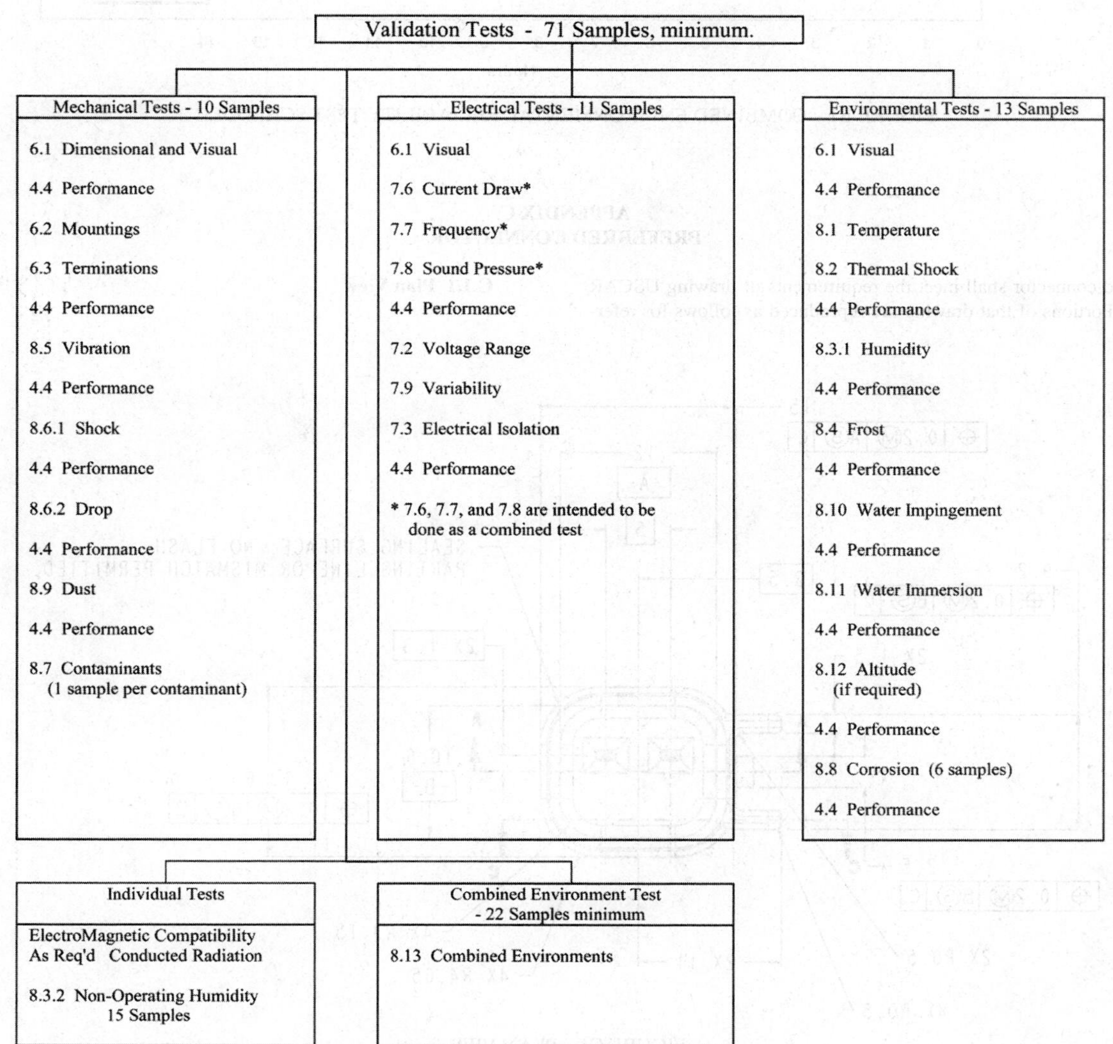

FIGURE A1—TEST MATRIX AND TEST PROFILES

APPENDIX B
COMBINED ENVIRONMENT PROFILE

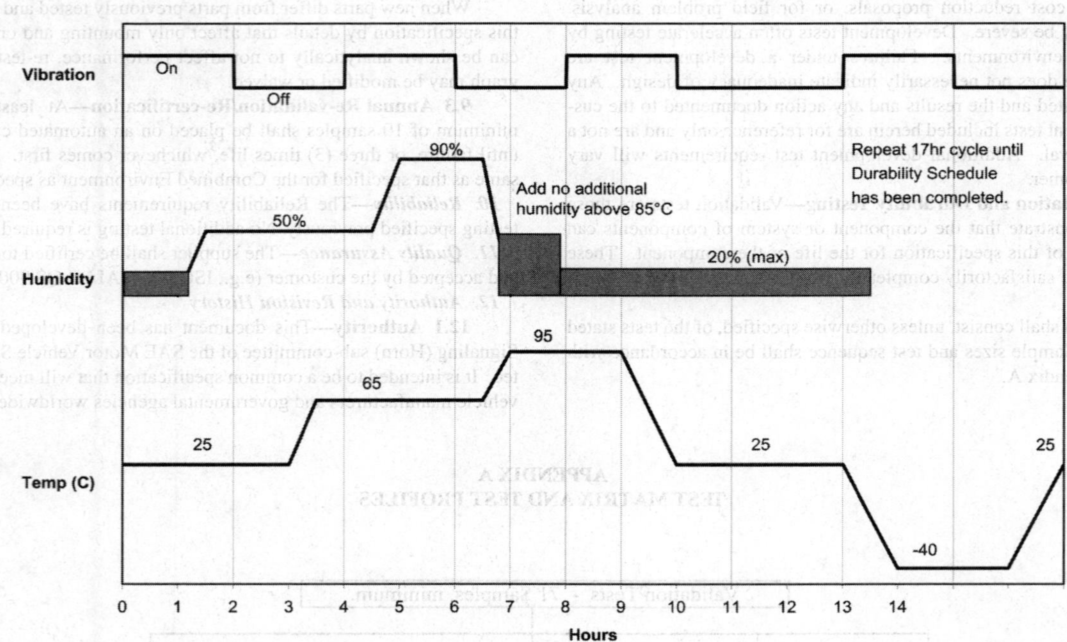

FIGURE B1—COMBINED ENVIRONMENTAL RELIABILITY TEST SCHEDULE

APPENDIX C
PREFERRED CONNECTOR

C.1 The preferred connector shall meet the requirements of drawing USCAR 150-S-002-1-A01. Portions of that drawing are reproduced as follows for reference.

C.1.1 Plan View

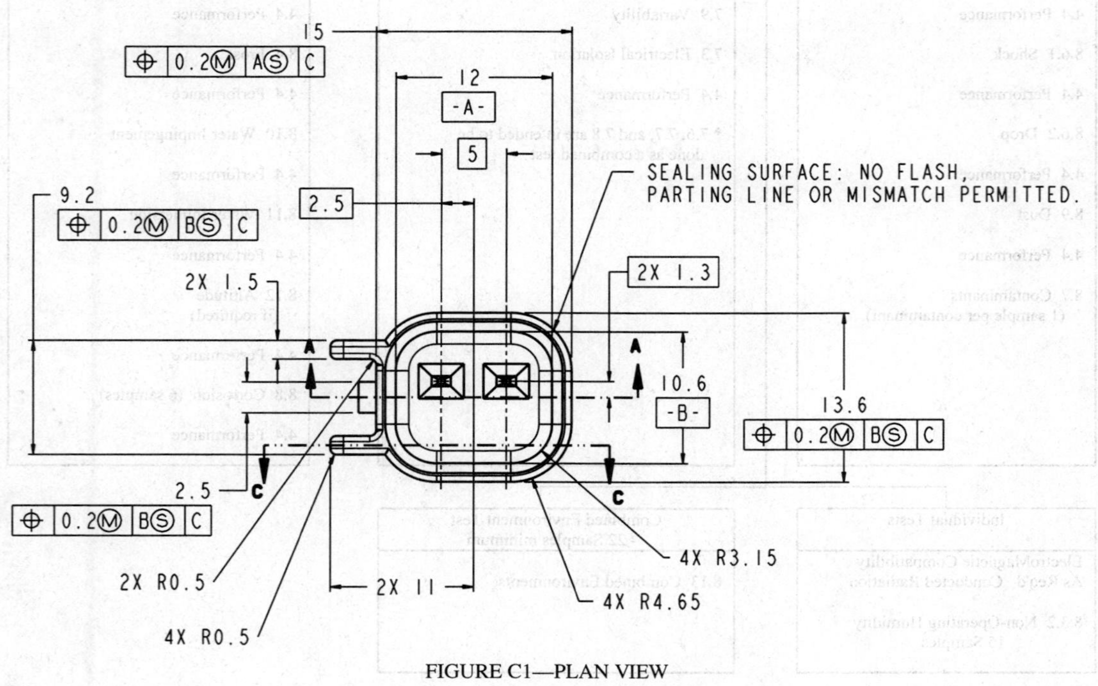

FIGURE C1—PLAN VIEW

C.1.2 Section A-A

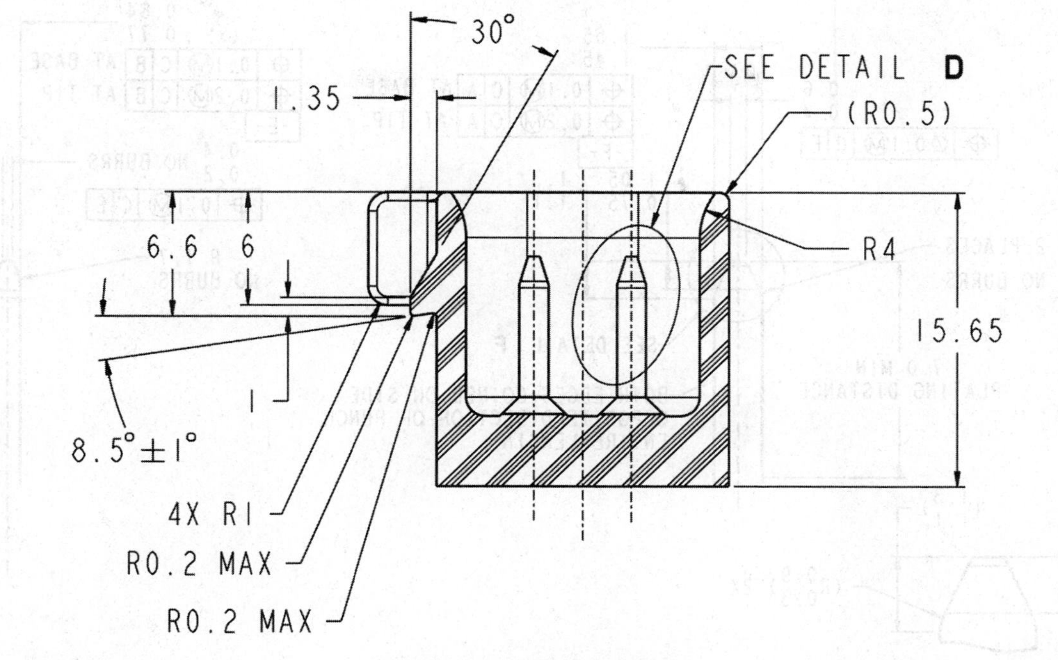

FIGURE C2—SECTION A-A

C.1.3 Section B-B

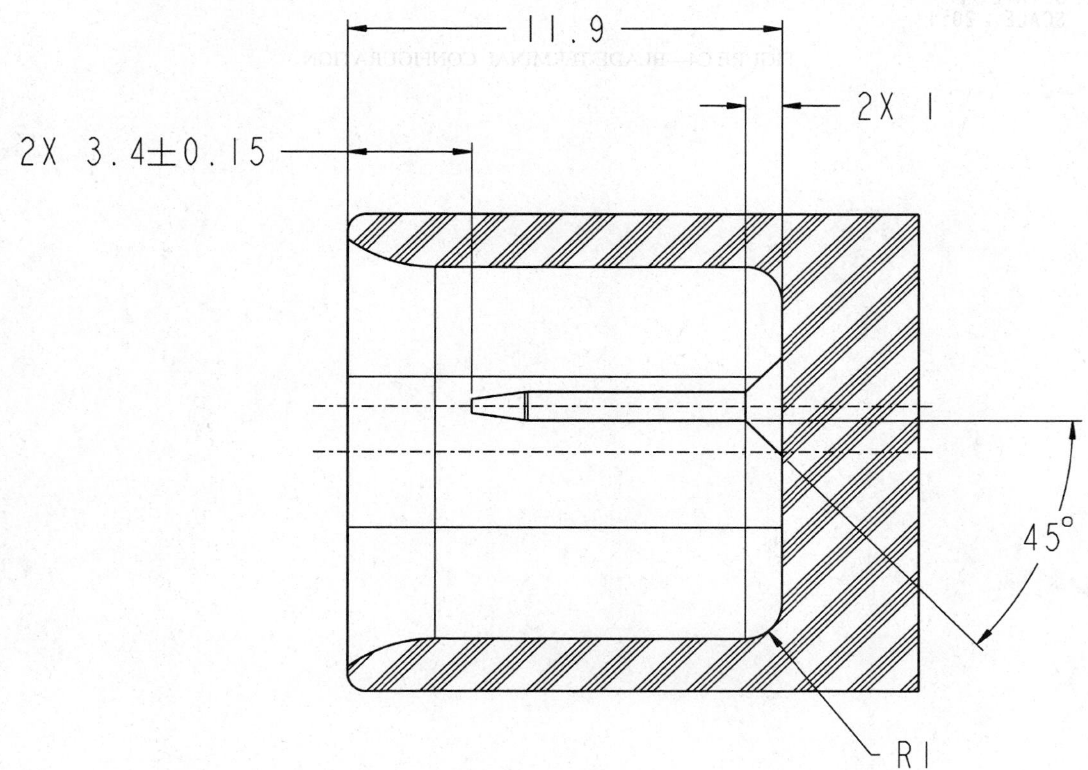

FIGURE C3—SECTION B-B

C.1.4 Blade Terminal Configuration

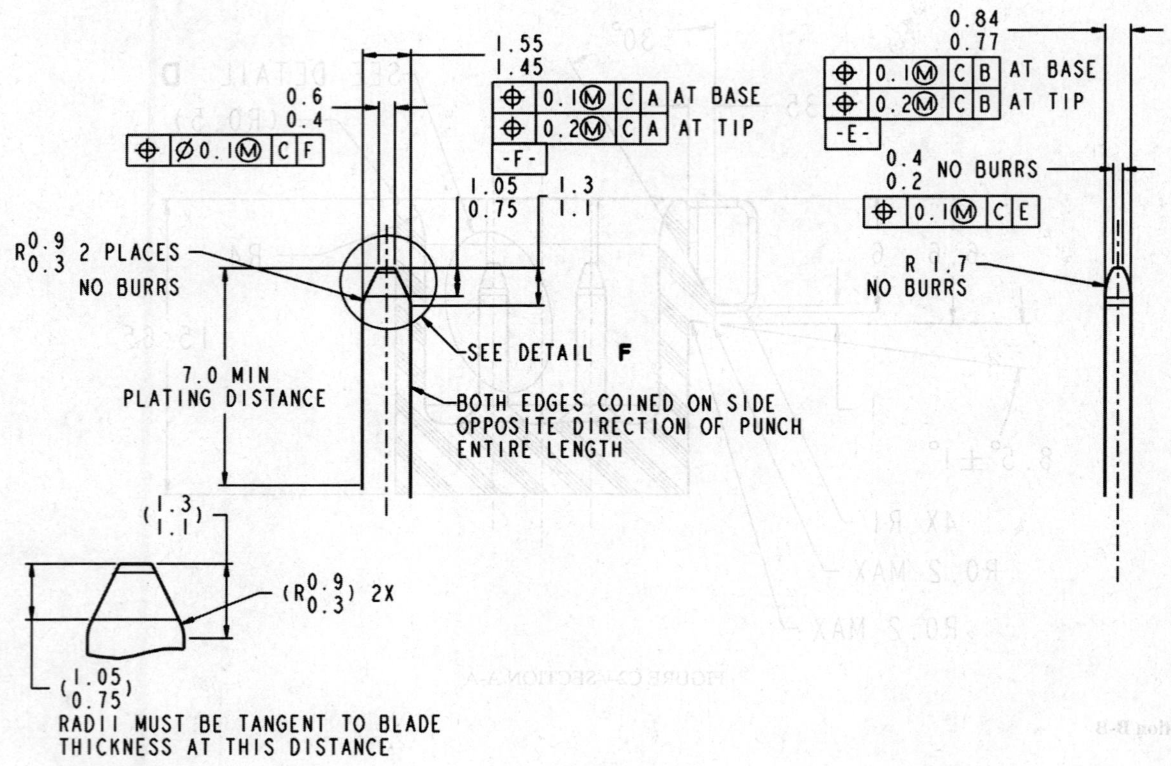

FIGURE C4—BLADE TERMINAL CONFIGURATION

R) MAXIMUM EXTERIOR SOUND LEVEL FOR SNOWMOBILES—SAE J192 MAR2003

SAE Recommended Practice

Report of the SAE Vehicle Sound Level Committee, approved September 1970, last revised November 1973, reaffirmed without change March 1985. Completely revised by the SAE Snowmobile Subcommittee of the SAE Special Purpose Vehicle, Engine and Equipment Technical Committee March 2003. Rationale statement available.

Foreword—This SAE Recommended Practice is intended as a guide toward standard practice, but may be subject to frequent change to keep pace with experience and technical advances.

*1. **Scope***—This SAE Recommended Practice establishes the instrumentation, test site, and test procedure for determining the maximum exterior sound level for snowmobiles.

*2. **References***

2.1 Applicable Publications—The following publications form a part of the specification to the extent specified herein. Unless otherwise indicated, the latest revision of SAE publications shall apply.

2.1.1 SAE PUBLICATION—Available from SAE, 400 Commonwealth Drive, Warrendale, PA 15096-0001.

SAE J184— Qualifying a Sound Data Acquisition System

2.1.2 ANSI PUBLICATION—Available from ANSI, 25 West 43rd Street, New York, NY 10036-8002.

ANSI S1.4—Specification for Sound Level Meters

2.2 Related Publications—The following publications are provided for information purposes only and are not a required part of this document.

2.2.1 ANSI PUBLICATIONS—Available from ANSI, 25 West 43rd Street, New York, NY 10036-8002.

ANSI S1.1—Acoustical Terminology

ANSI S1.13—Methods of Measurements of Sound Pressure Levels

*3. **Instrumentation***—The following instrumentation shall be used for the measurements required.

3.1 A sound level meter which meets the Type 1 requirements of ANSI S1.4.

3.1.1 As an alternative to making direct measurements using a sound level meter, a microphone or sound level meter may be used with an audio recorder and/or a graphic level recorder or other indicating instrument provided the system meets the requirements of SAE J184.

3.1.2 The microphone shall be used with an acceptable windscreen. To be acceptable, the screen must not affect the microphone response by more than ±1 dB for frequencies of 20 to 4000 Hz or ±1 1/2 dB for frequencies of 4000 to 10 000 Hz.

3.2 A sound level calibrator with an accuracy of ±0.1 dB.

3.3 An engine speed tachometer or other means of determining engine speed with a steady-state accuracy of ±3% at the prescribed test speed.

3.4 Thermometer.

3.5 Barometer.

3.6 Sling psychrometer, or dew point apparatus.

3.7 Windvane.

3.8 Anemometer.

*4. **Test Site***

4.1 A suitable test site shall be a level, open space free from the effects of large sound reflecting surfaces. Parked vehicles, signboards, or other obstacles must not be located within 30 m (100 ft) of either the vehicle path or the microphone. (See Figure 1.)

4.2 The microphone shall be located 15 m (50 ft) from the centerline of the snowmobile path and 1.2 m (4 ft) above the snow or turf. The normal to the vehicle path from the microphone shall establish the microphone point on the snowmobile path.

4.3 The measurement area shall be the triangular area formed by the start point, the end point, and the microphone location.

4.4 The surface of the ground within the measurement area, including the snowmobile path, shall be covered with a maximum of 75 mm (3 in) loose snow over a base consisting of at least 50 mm (2 in) of snow sufficiently compacted to support the snowmobile without significant penetration. An alternate surface of turf, primarily grass, up to a maximum of 75 mm (3 in) in height may be used, which, except for the snowmobile path, shall be free of visible droplets of water.

4.5 The reference point of the snowmobile, to indicate where the snowmobile is on the snowmobile path, shall be the front of the ski(s).

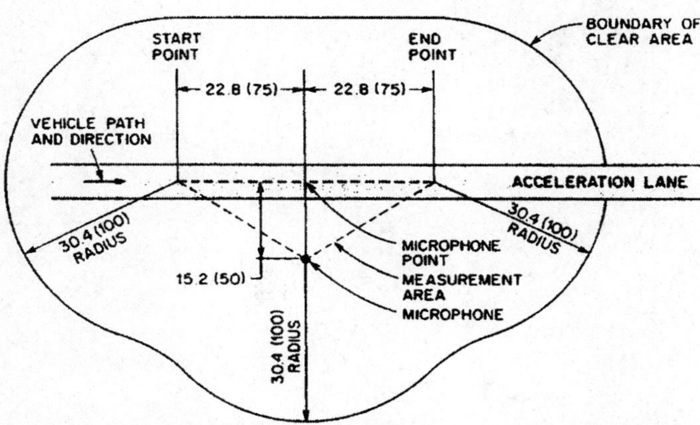

FIGURE 1—UNIDIRECTIONAL TEST SITE LAYOUT

4.6 While making sound level measurements, not more than one person, other than the observer reading the meter, shall be within 15 m (50 ft) of the snowmobile or microphone, and that person shall be directly behind the observer reading the meter, on a line through the microphone and the observer.

4.7 The ambient A-weighted sound level (including wind effects), coming from sources other than the snowmobile being measured, shall be at least 10 dB lower than the level of the test snowmobile.

*5. **Procedure***

5.1 Snowmobile Operation—A full-throttle acceleration test as specified as follows, is the basis for establishing maximum noise capabilities of the snowmobile.

5.1.1 For the test, approach the starting point at a steady speed of 24 km/h (15 mph). When the starting point is reached, smoothly and rapidly open the throttle fully. Maintain wide open throttle until the end point is reached. The centerline of the snowmobile must not deviate more than 1 m (3 ft) from either side of the centerline of the snowmobile path. Record the maximum engine speed reached.

If the snowmobile is unable to attain a speed of 24 km/h (15 mph) on approach to the start point, pass the start point at wide open throttle, and maintain wide open throttle until the end point is passed.

5.2 The sound level meter shall be set for slow response and A-weighting network.

5.2.1 The applicable reading shall be the highest sound level indicated for the run, between the start point and the end point, ignoring unrelated peaks due to extraneous noises.

5.2.2 Test runs shall be repeated until three readings within a 2 dB range per snowmobile side have been obtained. The sound level for each side of the snowmobile shall be the average of all three readings, rounded to the nearest integer. The sound level reported shall be that for the side of the snowmobile with the highest readings.

5.3 During the test period, the atmospheric temperature, barometric pressure, humidity, wind speed, and wind direction shall be recorded at intervals not exceeding 1 h.

*6. **General Comments***

6.1 It is recommended that persons technically trained and experienced in the current techniques of sound measurements select the equipment and conduct the tests.

6.2 The operation of recording and measuring equipment is likely to be affected by temperature near or below 0 °C (32 °F); hence, special precautions must be taken to ensure the reliability of sound level meter readings and/or recordings.

6.3 Proper acoustical calibration procedure shall account for the influence of extension cables, etc. Field calibration shall be made immediately before and after each test sequence. Internal calibration means are acceptable for field use, provided that external calibration is accomplished immediately before and after field use.

6.4 Instrument manufacturer's specifications for the proper use of the test equipment shall be adhered to.

6.5 Measurements shall be made only when the wind speed is below 19 km/h (12 mph) and the barometric pressure is between 93 and 103 kPa (27.5 and 30.5 in Hg).

6.6 The vehicle manufacturer's recommendations governing the proper operation of the vehicle shall be followed.

6.7 The method has been found to have a measurement uncertainty of ±2 dB.

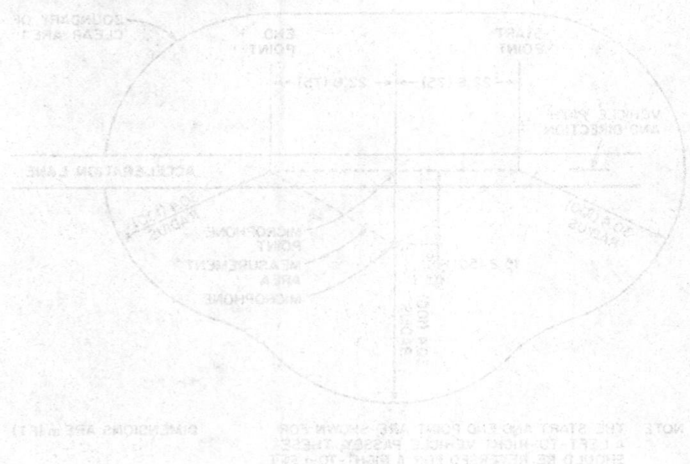

OPERATOR EAR SOUND LEVEL MEASUREMENT PROCEDURE FOR SNOW VEHICLES —SAE J1160 MAR1983

SAE Recommended Practice

Report of the SAE Off-Road Sound Level Committee approved October 1976, editorial change February 1977, reaffirmed without change March 1983. Rationale statement available.

Foreword—This Document has not changed other than to put it into the new SAE Technical Standards Board Format.

*1. **Scope***—This recommended practice establishes the instrumentation, test site and test procedure for determining the operator ear sound level for snowmobiles.

*2. **References***

2.1 Related Publications—The following publications are provided for information purposes only and are not a required part of this document.

2.1.1 SAE PUBLICATION—Available from SAE, 400 Commonwealth Drive, Warrendale, PA 15096-0001.

SAE J184—Qualifying a Sound Data Acquisition System

2.1.2 ANSI PUBLICATIONS—Available from ANSI, 11 West 42nd Street, New York, NY 10036-8002.

ANSI S1.1—1960 (R-1971)—Acoustical Terminology
ANSI S1.2—1962 (R-1971)—Method for the Physical Measurement of Sound
ANSI S1.4—1971—Specification for Sound Level Meters
ANSI S1.13—1971—Methods for the Measurement of Sound Pressure Levels

*3. **Instrumentation***—The following instrumentation shall be used, where applicable, for the measurements required:

3.1 A precision sound level meter which meets the Type 1 requirements of American National Standard Specification for Sound Level Meters (S1.4-1971).

3.1.1 As an alternative to making direct measurements using a sound level meter, a microphone or sound level meter may be used with a magnetic tape recorder and/or a graphic level recorder or other indicating instrument providing the system meets the requirements of SAE J184—Qualifying a Sound Data Acquisition System.

3.1.2 The microphone shall be used with a wind screen that will not affect the microphone response by more than ±1 dB for frequencies of 20–4000 Hz or ± 1.5 dB for frequencies of 4000–10 000 Hz at zero wind speed conditions.

3.2 An acoustic calibrator (accuracy within ±0.5 dB).

3.3 A calibrated engine speed tachometer (accuracy within ±2% at clutch control rpm).

3.4 A calibrated vehicle speed indicating system (accuracy within ±5% at test speeds).

3.5 A thermometer (accuracy within ±1 °C [2 °F]).

3.6 A barometer (accuracy within ±1%).

3.7 A psychrometer or dew point apparatus.

3.8 An anemometer (accuracy within ±10%).

3.9 A windvane or other device for measurement of wind direction.

*4. **Test Site***

4.1 A suitable test site is a level open space free from the effects of large sound reflecting surfaces. Parked vehicles, signboards or other obstacles must not be located within 30.4 m (100 ft) of the vehicle path.

4.2 The vehicle path shall be covered with snow. A maximum of 7.5 cm (3 in) of loose snow is permitted. As an alternative, a surface of turf, primarily grass not exceeding 7.5 cm (3 in) in height, may be used.

4.3 The start point and the end point shall be 45.7 m (150 ft) apart on the vehicle path.

4.4 The ambient sound level at the location specified in paragraph 6.1 (including wind effects) due to sources other than the vehicle being tested shall be at least 10 dB (A) lower than the noise level with the vehicle operating under test conditions.

*5. **Procedure***

5.1 Vehicle Operation—Constant speed and acceleration runs as specified below are the basis for determining sound level of the snowmobile.

5.1.1 CONSTANT SPEED—The vehicle shall be operated at constant speeds of 24 ± 3 km/h (15 ± 2 mile/h) and 48 ± 3 km/h (30 ± 2 mile/h). The vehicle shall be accelerated to test speed before the start point is reached and shall be operated in a straight line from the start point to the end point with the throttle held as steady as possible.

5.1.2 ACCELERATION—The vehicle shall be accelerated from a standing start by establishing wide-open throttle at the start point and wide-open throttle shall be maintained until the end point is reached.

5.1.3 The vehicle shall be at a stabilized operating temperature. At wide-open throttle the engine shall operate within ±5% of its clutch control rpm.

*6. **Measurements***

6.1 The microphone shall be located 25 cm (10 in) to the right and left of the vertical centerline of the operator's head (also centerline of the vehicle) and 51 cm (20 in) to the rear of the rear most point of the handle bars and 76 cm (30 in) above the seat.

6.2 The microphone wind screen is necessary when making measurements on an open, fast moving vehicle. To verify that valid data is being obtained, measure the air velocity at the microphone position while operating the vehicle at the selected speed. The air velocity on the microphone can be minimized by running with the wind. Consult data similar to that shown in Figure 1 to determine the wind generated noise for the microphone and wind screen being used. If the wind generated noise level is at least 10 dB (A) less than the level being measured, the reading will be valid.

6.3 The meter shall be set for *slow* response and the A-weighted network.

6.4 Measurements shall be made only when the ambient wind speed is below 19 km/h (12 mile/h) and the absolute barometric pressure is between 93 and 103 kPa (27.5 and 30.5 in of mercury).

6.5 The applicable reading shall be the highest sound level observed during the run, between the start point and the end point, ignoring unrelated peaks due to extraneous noises.

6.6 Acceleration test runs shall be repeated until three readings within a 2 dB range per vehicle side have been obtained. The acceleration sound level for each side of the vehicle shall be the average of all three readings, rounded to the nearest integer.

6.7 The sound levels shall be reported as a plot for each side of the vehicle of dB (A) versus observed vehicle speed. The constant speed levels shall be plotted at 24 km/h (15 mile/h) and 48 km/h (30 mile/h). The acceleration level shall be plotted at speeds ≥ 72 km/h (45 mile/h).

6.8 The atmospheric temperature, pressure, humidity, wind speed, and direction shall be recorded at the beginning and end of each test sequence. Also record test surface conditions.

*7. **General Comments***

7.1 It is recommended that persons technically trained and experienced in the current technique of sound measurement select the equipment and conduct the tests.

7.2 Proper use of all test instrumentation is essential to obtain valid measurements. Operating manuals or other literature furnished by the instrument manufacturer should be referred to for both recommended operation of the instrument, and precautions to be observed. Specific items to be considered are:

7.2.1 The type of microphone and its orientation relative to the source of noise.

7.2.2 The effects of ambient weather conditions on the performance of all instruments (for example, temperature, humidity, and barometric pressure). Special caution should be exercised when the sound level meter is exposed to low temperatures for extended periods of time.

7.2.3 Proper signal levels, terminating impedances, and cable lengths on multi-instrument measurement systems.

7.2.4 RFI (Radio Frequency Interference) from the snow vehicle itself.

7.2.5 Proper acoustical calibration procedure, to include the influence of extension cables, etc. Field calibration shall be made immediately before and after each test sequence. Either an external or internal calibration means is acceptable for field use, provided that external calibration is accomplished immediately before and after field use.

7.3 The vehicle manufacturer's recommendation governing the proper operation of the vehicle shall be followed.

OPERATIONAL SOUND LEVEL MEASUREMENT PROCEDURE FOR SNOW VEHICLES —SAE J1161 MAR1983

SAE Recommended Practice

Report of the SAE Off-Road Sound Level Committee approved November 1976. Rationale statement available.

1. Scope—This recommended practice establishes the instrumentation, test site, and test procedure for determining the exterior operational sound level for snowmobiles.

2. References

2.1 Applicable Publications—The following publications form a part of the specification to the extent specified herein. Unless otherwise indicated the lastest revision of SAE publications shall apply.

2.1.1 SAE PUBLICATION—Available from SAE, 400 Commonwealth Drive, Warrendale, PA 15096-0001.

SAE J184 JUN78—Qualifying a Sound Data Acquistion System

2.1.2 ANSI PUBLICATION—Available from ANSI, 11 West 42nd Street, New York, NY 10036-8002.

ANSI S1.4 1971—Specification for Sound Level Meters

2.2 Related Publications—The following publications are provided for information purposes only and are not a required part of this document.

2.2.1 ANSI PUBLICATIONS—Available from ANSI, 11 West 42nd Street, New York, NY 10036-8002.

ANSI S1.1—1960 (R-1971)—Acoustical Terminology

ANSI S1.2—1962 (R-1971)—Method for the Physical Measurement of Sound

ANSI S1.3—1971—Methods for the Measurement of Sound Pressure Levels

3. Instrumentation—The following instrumentation shall be used, where applicable, for the measurements required:

3.1 A precision sound level meter which meets the Type 1 requirements of American National Standard Specification for Sound Level Meters (S1.4-1971).

3.1.1 As an alternate to making direct measurements using a sound level meter, a microphone or sound level meter may be used with a magnetic tape recorder and/or graphic level recorder or indicating meter providing the system meets the requirements of SAE J184, Qualifying a Sound Data Acquisition System.

3.1.2 The microphone shall be used with a windscreen that will not affect the microphone response by more than ±1 dB for frequencies of 20–4000 Hz or ±1.5 dB for frequencies of 4000–10 000 Hz at zero wind speed conditions.

3.2 An acoustic calibrator (accuracy within ±0.5 dB).

3.3 A calibrated vehicle speed indicating system (accuracy within ±5% at test speed).

3.4 A thermometer (accuracy within ±1 °C [2 °F]).

3.5 A barometer (accuracy within ±1%).

3.6 A psychrometer or dew point apparatus.

3.7 An anemometer (accuracy within ±1%).

3.8 A windvane or other device for the measurement of wind direction.

4. Test Site

4.1 A suitable test site is a level open space free from the effects of large sound reflecting surfaces. Parked vehicles, signboards, and other obstacles must not be located within 30.4 m (100 ft) of either the vehicle path or the microphone (Figure 1).

4.2 The microphone shall be located 15.2 m (50 ft) from the centerline of the vehicle path and 120 cm (48 in) above the snow or turf. The normal to the vehicle path from the microphone shall establish the microphone point on the vehicle path.

4.3 The measurement area shall be the triangular area formed by the start point, the end point, and the microphone location.

4.4 The surface of the ground within the measurement area, including the vehicle path, shall be covered with a maximum of 7.5 cm (3 in) loose snow over a base consisting of at least 5 cm (2 in) of snow sufficiently compacted to support the snowmobile without penetration. As an alternative, a surface of turf, primarily grass up to a maximum of 7.5 cm (3 in) in height may be used, which, except for the vehicle operating path, shall be free of visible droplets of water.

4.5 The reference point of the vehicle, to indicate when the vehicle is at any of the points on the vehicle path, shall be the front of the vehicle skis.

4.6 While making sound level measurements, not more than one person, other than the observer reading the meter and the test driver, shall be within 15.2 m (50 ft) of the vehicle path or microphone and that person shall be directly behind the observer reading the meter on a line through the microphone and observer.

4.7 The ambient A-weighted sound level (including wind effects) coming from sources other than the vehicle being measured, shall be at least 10 dB lower than the noise level with the vehicle operating under test conditions.

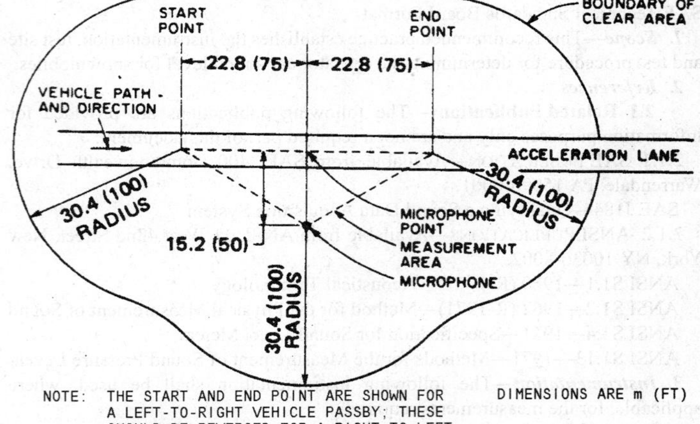

FIGURE 1—UNIDIRECTIONAL TEST SITE LAYOUT

5. Procedure

5.1 Vehicle Operation—A constant speed as specified below is the basis for determining the operational sound level of the snowmobile.

5.1.1 Before reaching the start point, accelerate the vehicle to the speed of 24 ± 3 km/h (15 ± 2 mile/h). Maintain this constant speed with throttle held as steady as possible through to the end point. The centerline of the vehicle must not deviate more than 1 m (3 ft) from either side of the centerline of the vehicle path.

6. Measurements

6.1 The sound level meter shall be set for slow response and the A-weighted network.

6.2 The applicable sound level reading shall be the highest indicated for the run, between the start point and the end point, ignoring unrelated peaks due to extraneous noise.

6.3 During the test period, the atmospheric temperature, pressure, humidity, wind speed, and wind direction shall be recorded at intervals not to exceed 1 h. Also record test surface conditions.

6.4 Test runs shall be repeated until three readings within a 2 dB range per vehicle side have been obtained. The sound level for each side of the vehicle shall be the average of all three readings, rounded to the nearest integer. The sound level reported shall be that for the side of the vehicle with the highest average.

7. General Comment

7.1 It is recommended that persons technically trained and experienced in the current technique of sound measurement select the equipment and conduct the tests.

7.2 The operation of recording and measuring equipment is likely to be affected by low temperatures. Where measurements are undertaken at temperatures near or below 0 °C (32 °F), special precautions must be taken to ensure the reliability of sound meter readings and/or recordings.

7.3 Instrument manufacturers' specifications for the proper use of all the test equipment shall be adhered to.

7.4 Measurements shall be made only when the wind speed is below 19 kg/h (12 mile/h) and absolute barometric pressure is between 93 and 103 kPa (27.5 and 30.5 in of mercury).

7.5 The vehicle manufacturers' recommendation governing the proper operation of the vehicle shall be followed.

7.6 Proper acoustical calibration procedure shall include the influence of extension cables, etc. Field calibration shall be made immediately before and after each test sequence. Internal calibration means is acceptable for field use, provided external calibration is accomplished immediately before and after field use.

7.7 A 2 dB tolerance over the sound level limit shall be included to provide for variations in test sites, temperature gradients, wind velocity gradients, test equipment, and inherent differences in nominally identical vehicles.

SHORELINE SOUND LEVEL MEASUREMENT PROCEDURE FOR RECREATIONAL MOTORBOATS—SAE J1970 SEP2003

SAE Recommended Practice

Report of the SAE Marine Sound Level Subcommittee of the SAE Marine Technical Committee and the SAE Specialized Vehicle and Equipment Sound Level Committee approved December 1991. Rationale statement available. Revised by the SAE Marine Technical Committee September 2003. Rationale statement available.

1. Scope—This SAE Recommended Practice establishes the procedure for measuring the sound level of recreational motorboats at a position on the shore under conditions other than stationary mode operation. It is intended as a guide toward standard practice and is subject to change to keep pace with experience and technical advances.

1.1 Purpose—This document specifies guidelines for sound level measurements made from the shoreline of recreational boating areas and is intended for recreational motorboats only.

2. References

2.1 Applicable Publications—The following publications form a part of the specification to the extent specified herein. Unless otherwise indicated, the latest revision of SAE publications shall apply.

2.1.1 ASA Publications—Available from Acoustical Society of America, http://asa.aip.org, or from ANSI, 25 West 43rd Street, New York, NY 10036-8002, http://www.ansi.org.

ANSI S1.4—Specification for Sound Level Meters

2.2 Related Publications—The following publications are provided for information purposes only and are not a required part of this document.

2.2.1 SAE Publications—Available from SAE, 400 Commonwealth Drive, Warrendale, PA 15096-0001.

SAE J34—Exterior Sound Level Measurement Procedure for Pleasure Motorboats

SAE J2005—Stationary Sound Level Measurement Procedure for Recreational Motorboats

2.2.2 ASA Publications—Available from Acoustical Society of America, http://asa.aip.org, or from ANSI, 25 West 43rd Street, New York, NY 10036-8002, http://www.ansi.org.

ANSI S1.1—Acoustical Terminology

ANSI S1.13—Measurement of Sound Pressure Levels in Air

3. Instrumentation—The following instrumentation shall be used for the measurement required.

3.1 A sound level meter which meets ANSI Standard S1.4 Type 1 or Type 2 specification for Sound Level Meters.

3.2 A microphone windscreen that does not affect the overall reading by more than ± 0.5 dB(A).

3.3 A sound level calibrator. (see 5.3)

4. Procedure

4.1 Measurement Site—A suitable site is the shore of a body of water or dock projecting out from the shore into the body of water, or a raft or a boat moored to a dock or anchored so that the sound level meter or microphone is not more than 6 m (20 ft) from shore. If the measurement is made from a dock, care should be taken to minimize the effect of sound waves reflected from the dock. The area around the microphone and boat being measured shall be free of large obstructions or reflective surfaces, such as buildings, high embankments, sea walls, hills, large piers, or large tree trunks >0.3 m (1 ft) in diameter breakwaters, etc., for a minimum distance of 3 m (10 ft).

4.2 Boat Operation

4.2.1 The applicable reading does not require that the boat be at any specific distance from the shoreline or microphone.

4.2.2 This measurement procedure shall not be used during the 30 s time period following engine start-up and/or preceding engine shutdown.

4.3 Measurements

4.3.1 The microphone shall be placed 1.2 to 1.5 m (4 to 5 ft) above the water, and no less than 0.6 m (2 ft) above the surface of the shore, dock, or platform. If on a dock or platform, the microphone shall be placed near or beyond the end of the dock or platform. If the measurement is made from a boat, the microphone shall be held at a height of not less than 0.6 m (2 ft) above the surface of the water. A suitable boat for this purpose is of open hull construction.

4.3.2 The meter shall be set for slow response and the A-weighting network.

4.3.3 The observer reading the meter shall not be closer than arm's length from the microphone. Only one other person may be within 15 m (50 ft) of the microphone when measuring from the dock or shoreline, and that person shall be directly behind the observer reading the meter.

4.3.4 The applicable reading shall be the highest sound level measured during a period when the background sound level is at least 10 dB lower than the maximum allowable sound level. Background sound level includes wind effects, noise from boats other than the one being measured, wave action, boat wakes, and other extraneous noises. Readings due to hull slaps which create intermittent sound levels shall be disregarded.

4.3.5 The observer shall record the applicable reading and the background sound levels taken immediately before and immediately after the applicable reading.

4.3.6 When sound level readings are taken from inside a boat, 3 dB shall be subtracted from the reading to better correlate with shoreline readings.

5. General Requirements

5.1 The measurements shall be conducted only by persons qualified by training to perform these measurements.

5.2 Proper use of all test instrumentation is essential to obtain valid measurements. Operating manuals or other literature furnished by the instrument manufacturer should be consulted for both recommended operation of the instrument, and precautions to be observed.

5.3 Proper acoustical calibration shall comprise the complete measurement system including extension cables, etc. Field calibration shall be performed immediately before and after each test sequence.

5.4 A measurement shall be invalid if changes in the background sound level affect the applicable reading.

5.5 The use of the word "shall" in the procedure is to be understood to be mandatory. The use of the word "should" is to be understood as advisory. The use of the word "may" is to be understood as permissive.

APPENDIX A

A.1 This procedure may be used for the measurement of sound emitted by recreational motorboats in use on waterways where sound level restrictions apply. Sound level is a function of the exhaust system, the boat hull, the manner of boat operation, e.g., distance from shore, engine speed and trim angle, and other factors. Background information is included in the SAE J1970 Rationale Statement.

STATIONARY SOUND LEVEL MEASUREMENT PROCEDURE FOR PLEASURE MOTORBOATS —SAE J2005 DEC1991

SAE Recommended Practice

Report of the SAE Marine Sound Level Subcommittee of the SAE Marine Technical Committee and the SAE Specialized Vehicle and Equipment Sound Level Committee approved December 1991. Rationale statement available.

1. Scope—This SAE Recommended Practice establishes the procedure for determining if pleasure motorboats have effective exhaust muffling means when operating in the stationary mode. It is intended as a guide toward standard practice and is subject to change to keep pace with experience and technical advances.

1.1 Purpose—This document specifies guidelines for stationary sound level measurements for boats with above- water exhaust systems.

2. References

2.1 Applicable Publication—The following publications form a part of this specification to the extent specified herein.

2.1.1 ANSI PUBLICATION—Available from the American National Standards Institute, Inc., 11 West 42nd Street, New York, NY 10036-8002.

ANSI S1.4-1983 and S1.4A-1985—Specifications for Sound Level Meters

2.2 Related Publications—The following publications are provided for information purposes only and are not a required part of this document.

2.2.1 SAE PUBLICATION—Available from SAE, 400 Commonwealth Drive, Warrendale, PA 15096-0001.

SAE J34—Exterior Sound Level Measurement Procedure for Pleasure Motorboats

2.2.2 ANSI PUBLICATIONS—Available from the American National Standards Institute, Inc., 11 West 42nd Street, New York, NY 10036-8002.

ANSI S1.1-1960(1976)—Acoustical Terminology

ANSI S1.13-1971(R1986)—Methods for the Measurement of Sound Pressure Levels

3. Instrumentation—The following instrumentation shall be used for the measurement required:

3.1 A sound level meter which meets ANSI Standard S1.4-1983 Type 1 or Type 2 Specification for Sound Level Meters.

3.2 A microphone windscreen that does not affect the overall reading by more than ±0.5 dB(A).

3.3 A sound level calibrator. (See 5.3.)

4. Procedure

4.1 Measurement Site—A suitable site is a body of water free of large obstructions or reflective surfaces such as buildings, boats other than those involved in this procedure, large embankments or breakwaters, etc. for a minimum distance of 8 m (25 ft) from the boat being measured. The boat being tested shall either be moored to a dock or lashed to another boat. If moored to a dock, the dock shall be of open construction so that it presents a minimum of reflecting surfaces. If the measurement is made in open water, the boat being evaluated shall be lashed to the measurement boat to prevent relative motion and to allow positioning of the microphone in the prescribed location. The measurement boat shall be positioned to minimize reflected sound.

4.2 Boat Operation—The engine shall be operated at low idle speed within the engine manufacturer's recommended operating range, in neutral gear if so equipped. For motorboats without a neutral gear, the engine shall be operated at its lowest operational speed. The engine shall be operated for a sufficient amount of time to allow water to flow through the exhaust system before taking measurements.

4.3 Measurements

4.3.1 The microphone shall be placed at a distance of 1.2 to 1.5 m (4 to 5 ft) above the water and no closer than 1 m (3.3 ft) from the vertical projection of any part of the boat in the area adjacent to the exhaust outlet(s).

4.3.2 The meter shall be set for slow response and the A-weighting network.

4.3.3 The observer reading the meter shall not be closer than arm's length from the microphone to minimize sound reflections.

4.3.4 The applicable reading shall be the average sound level measured during a period when the background sound level is at least 10 dB lower than the measured sound level. Background sound level includes wind effects, noise from boats other than the one being measured, wave action, boat wakes, and other extraneous noises. Peak readings of intermittent sound levels created by wave slaps or changes in sound level due to wave action and/or engine speed variation shall not be included in the applicable reading.

4.3.5 The observer shall record the applicable reading and the background sound levels taken immediately before and immediately after the applicable reading.

5. General Requirements

5.1 The measurements shall be conducted only by persons qualified by training to perform these measurements.

5.2 Proper use of all test instrumentation is essential to obtain valid measurements. Operating manuals or other literature furnished by the instrument manufacturer should be consulted for both recommended operation of the instrument, and precautions to be observed.

5.3 Proper acoustical calibration shall comprise the complete measurement system including extension cables, etc. Field calibration shall be performed immediately before and after each test sequence.

5.4 A measurement shall be invalid if changes in the background sound level affect the applicable reading.

5.5 The use of the word "shall" in the procedure is to be understood to be mandatory, while the word "should" is to be understood as advisory.

APPENDIX A

This procedure has been developed as a guide for governmental agencies to enforce the requirement for effective muffling means in pleasure motorboats. The measured level is not an indication of maximum operational sound levels.

In most applications involving thru-transom exhaust the microphone location should be 1 m (3.3 ft) aft of the intersection of the vertical plane of the aft-most part of the transom and the vertical plane of the port-most or starboard-most part of the gunnel at the specified height of 1.2 to 1.5 m (4 to 5 ft) above the surface of the water with the microphone oriented toward the exhaust outlet(s).

Care must be taken to avoid erroneous readings due to sound reflections by proper positioning of the enforcement boat such that minimal extension of the enforcement hull protrudes into the area surrounding the microphone during measurements. Only one enforcement boat shall be in the area where measurements are being taken.

Sound level limits should generally have tolerance band to compensate for variations in test sites, boats, and weather conditions. Background information is included in the SAE J2005 Rationale Statement.

(R) EXTERIOR SOUND LEVEL MEASUREMENT PROCEDURE FOR PLEASURE MOTORBOATS—SAE J34 JUN2001

SAE Recommended Practice

Report of the SAE Vehicle Sound Level Committee approved April 1973 and last revised by Specialized Vehicle and Equipment Sound Level Committee April 1977. It is strongly recommended that the user of this document obtain a copy of the companion document from SAE Headquarters. Completely revised by the SAE Marine Sound Level Subcommittee of the Marine Technical Committee and the Specialized Vehicle and Equipment Division Sound Level Committee December 1991. Rationale statement available. Revised by the SAE Marine Sound Level Subcommittee of the SAE Marine Technical Committee and the Specialized Vehicle and Equipment Division Sound Level Committee June 2001. Rationale statement available.

1. Scope—This SAE Recommended Practice establishes the procedure for measuring the maximum exterior sound level of pleasure motorboats while being operated under wide open throttle conditions. It is intended as a guide toward standard practice and is subject to change to keep pace with experience and technical advances.

2. References

2.1 Applicable Publication—The following publication forms a part of this specification to the extent specified herein.

2.1.1 ANSI PUBLICATION—Available from ANSI, 11 West 42nd Street, New York, NY 10036-8002.

ANSI S1.4-1983—Type 1 Specification for Sound Level Meters

2.2 Related Publications—The following publications are provided for information purposes only and are not a required part of this document.

2.2.1 ANSI PUBLICATIONS—Available from ANSI, 11 West 42nd Street, New York, NY 10036-8002.

ANSI S1.1-1960(1976)—Acoustical Terminology

ANSI S1.13-1971(R1986)—Methods for the Measurement of Sound Pressure Levels

ANSI S1.4A-1985—Specifications for Sound Level Meters

3. Instrumentation—The following instrumentation shall be used for the measurement required.

3.1 A sound level meter which meets ANSI Standard S1.4-1983 Type 1 Specification for Sound Level Meters.

3.2 A microphone windscreen that does not affect the overall reading by more than ±0.5 dB(A).

3.3 A sound level calibrator. (See (see 5.3)5.3.)

3.4 A wind speed anemometer.

3.5 An engine speed tachometer.

4. Procedure

4.1 Measurement Site—A suitable site is the shore of a body of water or a dock projecting out from the shore into the body of water. If the measurement is made from a dock, the dock shall be of open construction so that it presents a minimum of reflecting surfaces. The area around the microphone and boat being measured shall be free of large obstructions or reflective surfaces, such as buildings, high embankments, sea walls, hills, large piers, or breakwaters, etc. for a minimum distance of 30 m (100 ft). Three markers (buoys or posts) shall be placed in line, 50 m (165 ft) apart, to mark the course the boat is to follow while being tested. The site should be set up similar to that shown in Figure 1.

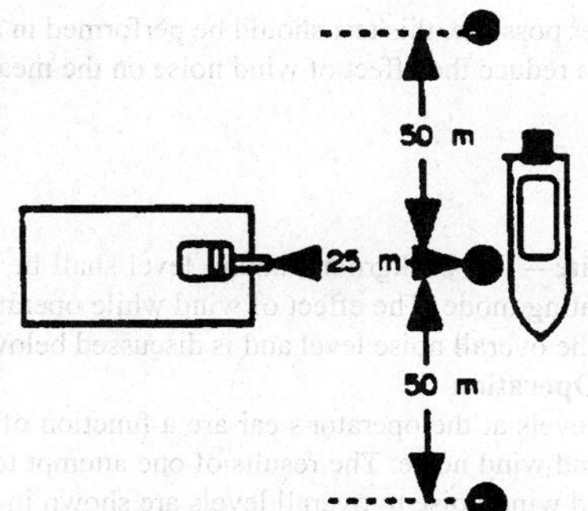

FIGURE 1—MEASUREMENT SITE DIAGRAM

4.2 Boat Operation

4.2.1 The boat shall pass all three markers within a distance of 3 m (10 ft) maximum on a straight course at full throttle with the engine operating at the midpoint of the manufacturer's recommended full throttle rpm range.

4.2.2 The engine speed tolerance shall be ±100 rpm if this falls within the recommended full throttle speed range. If a single top speed rpm is recommended, the tolerance shall be +0, −100 rpm.

4.2.3 For boats with motors or drive systems which are equipped with adjustable trim, the trim angle shall be adjusted so that the propeller thrust is parallel to the plane of the hull.

4.2.4 Boats which are sold with the power units installed (e.g., inboards and stern drives) shall be tested in this combination. Outboard motorboats shall be tested with a motor or motors for which the boat is rated.

4.3 Measurements

4.3.1 The microphone shall be placed 25 m (82.5 ft) from the line determined by the three markers, normal to the line and opposite the center marker. It shall be positioned 1.2 to 1.5 m (4 to 5 ft) above the water, and no less than 0.6 m (2 ft) above the surface of the shore, dock, or platform. If on a dock or platform the microphone shall be placed near or beyond the end of the dock or platform.

4.3.2 The meter shall be set for fast response and the A-weighting network.

4.3.3 The observer reading the meter shall not be closer than arm's length from the microphone. Only one other person may be within 15 m (50 ft) of the microphone and that person shall be directly behind the observer reading the meter.

4.3.4 The meter shall be observed during the entire pass-by with the boat passing within 0.5 to 1 m (~ 1 to 3 ft) on the far side of all three markers. The applicable reading shall be the highest sound level measured during the pass-by provided that the background sound level is at least 10 dB lower than the boat being measured. A measurement shall be invalid if changes in the background sound level affect the applicable reading. Background sound level includes wind effects, noise from boats other than the one being measured, wave action, boat wakes, and other extraneous noises. Peak readings due to hull slaps which create intermittent sound levels shall be disregarded.

4.3.5 Measurements shall be made only when the wind speed is below 19 km/h (13 mph).

4.3.6 The observer shall record the applicable reading and the background sound levels taken immediately before and immediately after the applicable reading.

4.3.7 At least two measurements shall be made for each side of the boat. The sound level for each side of the boat shall be the average of the first two readings for each side which are within 1 dB of each other. The sound level reported shall be that of the louder side of the boat.

5. General Requirements

5.1 The measurements shall be conducted only by persons qualified by training to perform these measurements.

5.2 Proper use of all test instrumentation is essential to obtain valid measurements. Operating manuals or other literature furnished by the instrument manufacturer should be consulted for both recommended operation of the instrument and precautions to be observed.

5.3 Proper acoustical calibration shall comprise the complete measurement system including extension cables, etc. Field calibration shall be performed immediately before and after each test sequence.

5.4 The use of the word "shall" in the procedure is to be understood to be mandatory. The use of the word "should" is to be understood as advisory. The use of the word "may" is to be understood as permissive.

APPENDIX A

A.1 The intent of this procedure is to provide manufacturers of marine equipment with a standardized set of conditions and method of measurement of the maximum sound level of boats and motors. When performing this procedure, the boat is typically operated at maximum speed at the measurement distance from the shoreline, requiring skilled operators and a quiet, safe location which is devoid of other boat traffic during testing. Background information is included in the Rationale Statement.

OPERATOR SOUND LEVEL EXPOSURE ASSESSMENT PROCEDURE FOR PLEASURE MOTORBOATS—SAE J1281 MAR1985

SAE Standard

Report of the SAE Specialized Vehicle and Equipment Sound Level Committee approved November 1979, reaffirmed without change March 1985.

1. Scope—This SAE Recommended Practice establishes the procedure for assessing operator sound level exposure for pleasure motorboats under 20 m (65 ft) in length when operated under typical conditions, an describes the instrumentation, test site, and boat operation for making valid measurements.

2. References

2.1 Applicable Publications—The following publications form a part of the specification to the extent specified herein. Unless otherwise indicated the latest revision of SAE publications shall apply.

2.1.1 ANSI PUBLICATIONS—Available from ANSI, 11 West 42nd Street, New York, NY 10036-8002.

ANSI S 1. 1- 1960 (R 197 1)—Acoustical Terminology
ANSI SIA-1971 (R1976)—Specification for Sound Level Meters.
ANSI SI.2-1962 (R1976)—Method for Physical Measurement of Sound.
ANSI SI.13-1971—Methods for the Measurement of Sound Pressure Levels.

3. Instrumentation—The following instrumentation shall be used fo the measurement required:

3.1 A precision sound level meter which meets Type I or Type S I requirements of American National Standard Specification for Sound Level Meters, SIA-1971 (R1976).

3.1.1 The microphone shall be used with an acceptable foam win screen. To be acceptable, the wind screen shall not affect the overall reading by more than –0.5 dB for the sound source that is being measured

3.2 A sound level calibrator accurate to 0.5 dB. (See 4.2.3.)

3.3 A wind speed anemometer accurate to within 1017o at 19 km/h

3.4 An engine speed tachometer accurate to within 517o of full-scal reading.

4. Procedure

4.1 Test Site—A suitable test site is a flat, calm body of water, larg enough to allow full speed runs. The area around the boat shall be fre of large obstructions, such as buildings, boats, hills, large piers or breakwa ter, bridges, etc. for a minimum distance of 30 m (100 ft). The backgroun sound level with the engine not operating (including wind effects) shal be at least 10 dB lower than the measured level of the boat being tested

4.2 Boat Operation

4.2.1 The boat shall be operated in a straight line at a constant engin speed of two-thirds of the midpoint of the manufacturer's recommende full throttle rpm range. If a single top speed rpm is recommended, th engine shall be operated at two-thirds of the specified value.

4.2.2 Boats which are sold with the power units installed (for example inboards and stern drives, shall be tested in this combination. Outboar motorboats shall be tested with a motor or motors for which the boa is rated.

4.2.3 Propulsion systems which are sold with adjustable trim shall b tested at the trim angle appropriate for the engine/boat combination a the test speed.

4.3 Measurements

4.3.1 The microphone shall be positioned on the inboard side of th operator's head at a distance of 250 mm (10 in) from the plane of th vertical centerline of the operator's head and in the plane of the operator' ear.

4.3.2 The operator shall be in a seated position during the measure ments if a seat is provided.

4.3.3 For boats with multiple operator stations, measurements shal be taken at all stations. The highest sound level shall be reported.

4.3.4 The sound level meter shall be set for slow response and th A-weighting network.

4.3.5 The meter shall be observed while the boat proceeds in a straight line. When the sound level reading stabilizes within -LI dB, determine the central tendency of the indicator to the nearest 0.5 dB. This readin~ is the sound level to be recorded for the measurement station. Care should be taken to avoid higher than normal readings which may be the result of unusual boat motion due to waves or wakes.

5. General Requirements

5.1 It is strongly recommended that technically trained personne select the equipment, and that the tests be conducted only by person trained in the current techniques of sound measurements.

5.2 Proper use of all test instrumentation is essential to obtain valid measurements. Operating manuals and other literature furnished by the instrument manufacturer, should be referred to for both recommended operation of the instrumentation, and precautions to be observed. Specific items to be considered are:

5.2.1 The type of microphone and its orientation relative to the domi nant sources of noise.

5.2.2 The effects of ambient weather conditions on the performance of all instruments (for example, temperature, humidity, and barometric pressure).

5.2.3 Proper acoustical calibration procedure, to include the influence of extension cables, etc. Field calibration shall be made immediately before and after each test sequence. Either an external calibrator or internal calibration means is acceptable for field use, provided that external calibration is accomplished immediately before and after field use.

5.3 Because bystanders may have an appreciable influence on meter response when they are in the vicinity of the microphone, not more than one person other than the observer reading the meter and the boat driver shall be within 3 m (10 ft) of the microphone, and no person shall be in a position so as to affect the propagation of sound from the source(s) to the microphone.

5.4 Measurements shall be made only when the wind speed is below 19 km/h (12 mph) in the vicinity of the test site.

5.5 Boats sold with convertible tops should be tested with the top down, since measurements taken with the top up are found to be inconsistent and spatially dependent.

5.6 Whenever possible, this test should be performed in a boat with a windshield in position to reduce the effect of wind noise on the measurement.

APPENDIX A

Preface—The purpose of this Appendix is to assess operator's ear exposure levels and is based on use cycle data which are utilized to predict long term average sound level or L, This technique takes into consideration the typical manner in which a pleasure motorboat is operated and predicts the equivalent sound level to which the operator is exposed.

A.1 Scope—The purpose of this recommended practice is to establish a procedure for assessing the operator sound level exposure during normal operation of pleasure motorboats. The Motorboat Act of 1940 specifies that a pleasure motorboat is any vessel 65 ft in length or less, which is propelled by machinery and is used primarily for noncommercial use. Motor vessels larger than 65 ft in length are generally utilized for commercial applications and consequently do not fall within the scope of this procedure.

The exposure level attained utilizing this procedure represents the level of a constant sound having the same sound energy as the time-varying sound produced as a result of typical boat operation.

A.2 Instrumentation—This paragraph is typical of other SAE Standards of this type.

A.3 Procedure

A.3.1 Test Site—The background sound level shall be measured with the boat in a non-operating mode. The effect of wind while operating a boat at speed may contribute to the overall noise level and is discussed below.

A.3.2 Boat Operation

A.3.2.1 Sound levels at the operator's ear are a function of propulsion system noise, hull noise, and wind noise. The results of one attempt to ascertain the contribution of hull and wind noise to overall levels are shown in Figure A1 The test consisted of towing a 17 ft boat with an outboard motor mounted in place on the transom while allowing the propeller to free-wheel. The tow boat was powered by two 150 bhp outboard motors and utilized a 300 ft tow cable between boats. Sound levels were measured in the towed boat in dB(A) at various boat speeds, and in octave bands in dB(L) at maximum speed only (Figure A2). The test was repeated with a 15 ft boat of similar construction (fiberglass hull with V-bottom) and make. Sound levels measured at maximum towing speeds were 82.0 and 86.0 dB(A) at a distance of 2.4 m (8 ft) forward of the engine centerline for the 17 and 15 ft boats respectively. Consequently, it is apparent that sound level measurements performed in a typical pleasure motorboat can be substantially influenced by hull and/ or wind noise.

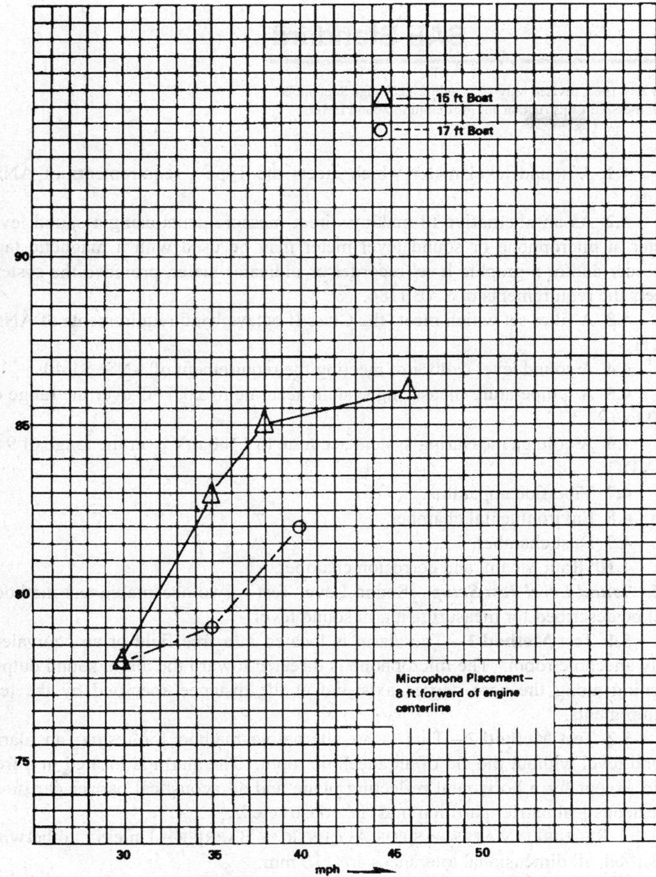

FIGURE A1—TOWED BOAT TEST—BOAT NOISE VERSUS SPEED

Operator exposure levels are a direct function of boat usage. A nationwide survey conducted by the Boating Industry Associations on pleasure motorboats (outboards and stern drives) illustrates that boats are typically operated over a wide rpm range. Figure A-3 summarizes the use cycle data as obtained by the survey. Note that the use cycle data is divided into increments of the rpm range and that different horsepower categories have different usage data.

Determination of operator exposure level requires knowledge of noise levels to which the operator is exposed and the time interval of exposure. Sound levels are measured for each rpm shown in the use cycle data and the level at each interval and the percentage of time spent at each speed are substituted into the following equation to compute L_{eq}.

$$L_{eq} = 10\log\sum_{1}\left(f_i \cdot 10^{\frac{L_i}{10}}\right) \qquad \text{(Eq. A1)}$$

where:

f_i = the % of time at each rpm (from use cycle data) ($0 \leq fi \leq 1$)
L_i = sound level in dB(A) at the corresponding rpm

A variety of outboard and stern drive engine/boat combinations were tested, measuring sound level at the operator's ear at each rpm in the cycle data. The data was analyzed and the L_{eq} computed for each configuration.

It was found that the L_{eq} for the average boat corresponded to a throttle setting of 6676 of the midpoint of the manufacturer's recommended full throttle rpm range for outboards and 687o for stern drives. Noise levels were measured at two-thirds of the midpoint of the maximum rpm range and were compared to the calculated L_{eq} values. The average deviation of the measured values from the calculated L_{eq} values was found to be :±:0.9 dB(A) for outboards and -LO.7 dB(A) for stern drives. Consequently, the method of determining the exposure level for the operator of a pleasure motorboat is to measure the noise level at two-thirds of the midpoint of the maximum rated rpm. The results are, on the average, within experimental error of the laborious method of measuring the sound level in each rpm band and calculating by L_{eq} by means of the above formula.

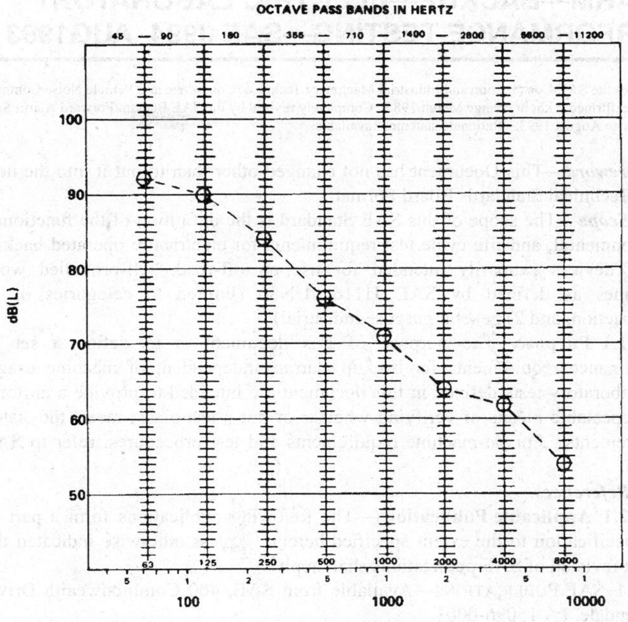

Key: O----O 17 ft V-Bottom Hull at 40 mph

Microphone Placement—8 ft forward of engine centerline, 30 in above deck

FIGURE A2—TOWED BOAT NOISE—OCTAVE BAND ANALYSIS OF IN-BOAT NOISE

	% Time at rpm				
% Max rpm	**0–10 hp**	**10.1–44.9 hp**	**45–64.9 hp**	**65 hp and Above**	**Stern Drive**
0.0–10.0	1	18	7	26	33
10.1–20.0	6	14	18	16	8
20.1–30.0	22	11	10	8	16
30.1–40.0	34	8	8	7	9
40.1–50.0	5	11	8	7	6
50.1–60.0	2	18	8	9	5
60.1–70.0	3	8	12	8	4
70.1–80.0	5	3	8	8	6
80.1–90.0	17	5	15	7	7
90.1–100.0	5	4	5	4	6

FIGURE A3—BOAT USAGE DATA

A.3.2.2 The effect of hull construction on operator exposure level presents some problems which must be recognized. Prediction of outboard motor noise levels by the manufacturer of either the engine or the boat is impossible, since neither manufacturer is aware of the combination which will eventually be in the hands of the consumer. An example of this variation is a 10 bhp outboard motor on one boat producing an L_{eq} of 81.5 dB(A) while on another boat the L_{eq} was 84.0 dB(A). It is speculated that for larger outboard motors and stern drives, the variation could be considerably greater since different hull configurations could produce speed differences of 20 mph or more in addition to structural response effects. Consequently, a large variation in L_{eq} is possible using the same engine in different hull configurations.

A.3.3 Measurements—The objective of performing the measurements is to determine the maximum exposure level which is representative and repeatable.

A.3.3.1 Placement of the microphone adjacent to the inboard ear is an attempt to reduce the effects of wind noise.

Positioning of the microphone should take into account the location of the noise source and proper orientation of the microphone sensitive axis.

A.4 General Requirements—Most of the comments in this section are typical of other SAE Standards of this type.

(R) ALARM—BACKUP—ELECTRIC LABORATORY PERFORMANCE TESTING—SAE J994 AUG1993

SAE Standard

Report of the SAE Construction and Industrial Machinery Technical Committee and Vehicle Noise Committee approved July 1967, revised May 1974, editorial change September 1980, reaffirmed without change March 1985. Completely revised by the SAE Backup/Forward Alarm Subcommittee of the SAE Construction and Agricultural Sound Level Committee August 1993. Rationale statement available.

Foreword—This Document has not changed other than to put it into the new SAE Technical Standards Board Format.

*1. **Scope***—The scope of this SAE Standard is the definition of the functional, environmental, and life cycle test requirements for electrically operated backup alarm devices primarily intended for use on off-road, self-propelled work machines as defined by SAE J1116 JUN86 (limited to categories of 1) construction, and 2) general purpose industrial).

1.1 Purpose—The purpose of this document is to define a set of performance requirements for backup alarms, independent of machine usage. The laboratory tests defined in this document are intended to provide a uniform and repeatable means of verifying whether or not a test alarm meets the stated requirements. For on-machine requirements and test procedures, refer to SAE J1446.

*2. **References***

2.1 Applicable Publications—The following publications form a part of the specification to the extent specified herein. Unless otherwise indicated the lastest revision of SAE publications shall apply.

2.1.1 SAE PUBLICATIONS—Available from SAE, 400 Commonwealth Drive, Warrendale, PA 15096-0001.

SAE J184—Qualifying a Sound Data Acquisition System
SAE J1116—Categories of Off-Road Self-Propelled Work Machines
SAE J1446—On-Machine Alarm Test and Evaluation Procedure for Construction and General Purpose Industrial Machinery

2.1.2 ANSI PUBLICATIONS—Available from ANSI, 11 West 42nd Street, New York, NY 10036-8002.

ANSI S1.4—Specification for Sound Level Meters
ANSI S1.11—Specification for Octave Band and Fractional Octave Band Analog and Digital Filter Sets
ANSI S1.40—Specification for Acoustical Calibrators

2.1.3 ASTM PUBLICATION—Available from ASTM, 100 Barr Harbor Drive, West Conshohocken, PA 19428-2959.

ASTM B 117—Method of Salt Spray (Fog) Testing

2.1.4 MIL SPECIFICATION—Available from Defense Printing Service, Detachment Office, 700 Robbins Avenue, Building 4D, Philadelphia, PA 19111-5094.

MIL-STD-810B—Environmental Test Methods 510 and 514.1

2.2 Related Publications—The following publications are provided for information purposes only and are not a required part of this document.

2.2.1 SAE PUBLICATIONS—Available from SAE, 400 Commonwealth Drive, Warrendale, PA 15096-0001.

SAE J1105—Performance, Test and Application of Electric Forward Warning Horn
SAE J1211—Recommended Environmental Practices for Environmental Electronic Equipment

2.2.2 ANSI PUBLICATIONS—Available from ANSI, 11 West 42nd Street, New York, NY 10036-8002.

ANSI S1.1 - 1960 (R1976)—Acoustical Terminology
ANSI S1.13 (R1986)—Methods for the Measurement of Sound Pressure Level

2.2.3 GENERAL MOTORS CORPORATION MATERIALS—Available from GM AC Rochester/GMC, P.O. 1360, Flint, MI 48501-8054.

AC fine and AC coarse dust

*3. **Definitions***

3.1 Free Field—A free field, for the purposes of this document, is defined as a space with no reflecting surface within 15 m of the sound source in any direction.

3.2 Horizontal Reflecting Plane—A horizontal reflecting plane is defined as flat ground with a surface no rougher than an asphalt road. A paved parking lot with no reflecting surfaces within 15 m would be an acceptable horizontal reflecting plane for the tests outlined in this document.

3.3 Zero Degree Axis—A line known as the "zero degree axis" is defined to correspond to the centerline of the sound producer, perpendicular to and extending outward from the output face of the alarm.

*4. **Instrumentation***—It is recommended that persons technically trained and experienced in current techniques of sound measurement select the equipment.

4.1 A sound level meter which meets the Type I requirements of ANSI S1.4.

4.2 As an alternative to making direct measurements using a sound level meter, a microphone or sound level meter may be used with a magnetic tape recorder and/or a graphic level recorder or indicator meter, provided the system meets the requirements of SAE J184.

4.3 A filter set which meets the Class II octave band requirements of ANSI S1.11.

4.4 A sound level calibrator meeting the requirement of ANSI S1.40.

4.5 A temperature measuring system accurate to ±0.5 °C over the range of –40 to +85 °C.

4.6 A voltage measuring system accurate to ±100 mV over the range of 9 to 36 VDC.

4.7 Vibration apparatus.

4.8 Environmental chamber.

4.9 Dust chamber.

4.10 Rain, steam, and corrosion chamber.

*5. **Sound Level Test Setup***—Sound Level Test - Two acceptable test methods will be described for measuring alarm sound level.

5.1 Test Method 1—The alarm is located in a free field or an equivalent fully anechoic room. The microphone is directed toward the alarm sound output opening along the zero degree axis and at the distance specified by the test requirements.

5.2 Test Method 2—This is an alternative method for testing an alarm sound level without the aid of an anechoic room. The alarm is located in a free field except for a horizontal reflecting plane and an acoustical barrier partition. The acoustical barrier partition must be constructed.

5.2.1 REQUIRED MATERIALS FOR ACOUSTICAL BARRIER—Unless otherwise specified, all dimensional tolerances are ±10 mm.

a. Two pieces of particle board 900 mm x 1200 mm x 16 mm ± 2 mm thick
b. Two Tripods adjustable to 1200 mm high
c. Three each 200 mm x 200 mm x 90 degree sheet metal shelf brackets.
d. Two sections of sound absorbing foam of dimensions 1200 mm x 1350 mm and a thickness of 50 mm or greater. The sound absorbing foam should have an absorption efficiency of at least 50% at 50 Hz rising to at least 75% at 1000 Hz and greater.

5.2.2 CONSTRUCTION OF ACOUSTICAL BARRIER—Using the three 200 mm shelf brackets and screws, center and attach one of the 900 mm x 1200 mm particle boards perpendicular to the other 900 mm x 1200 mm base board to yield a 900 mm high wall as shown in Figure 1. Two brackets should be located 150 mm from the outside edge on one side of the upright board. The third bracket should be mounted in the center on the other side of the upright board. Cover the exposed particle board with the sound absorbing foam as shown in Figure 1.

5.2.3 ALARM AND MICROPHONE LOCATIONS—Secure the alarm and microphone to their tripods. Position the alarm and microphone on opposite sides of and equidistant from the sound barrier at a height of 1200 mm above the horizontal reflecting plane. The distance between the two devices is specified in 6.3 of the Functional Test Requirements.

5.3 Allowable Background Noise Level—While the sound level test is in progress, the sound level due to all sources other than the alarm device shall be at least 10 dB lower than the sound level of the alarm. This precaution reduces the effect of background noise on the sound level test results.

5.4 Sound Level Meter Settings—The sound level meter shall be set for fast response or equivalent and have the A-weighting network installed when checking sound levels.

5.5 Instrumentation Precautions—Proper usage of all test instrumentation is essential to obtain valid measurements. Operating manuals or other literature furnished by the instrument manufacturer should be referred to for both recommended operation of the instrument and precautions to be observed. Specific items to review include:

5.5.1 THE MICROPHONE—The type of microphone, its directional response characteristics, and its orientation relative to the ground plane and source of noise.

5.5.2 MULTI-INSTRUMENT SYSTEMS—Proper signal levels, terminating impedances, and cable lengths on multi-instrument measurement systems should be observed.

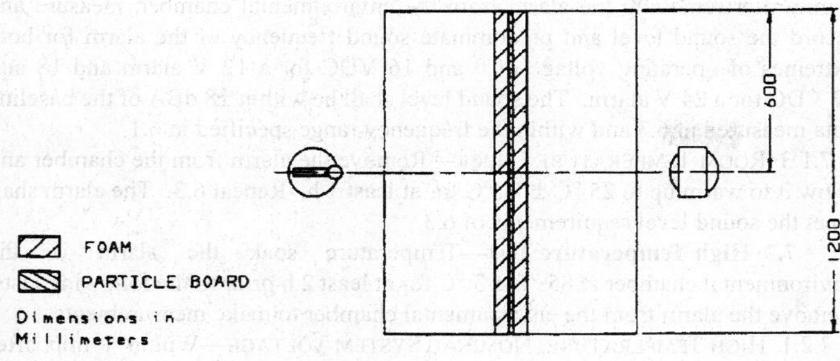

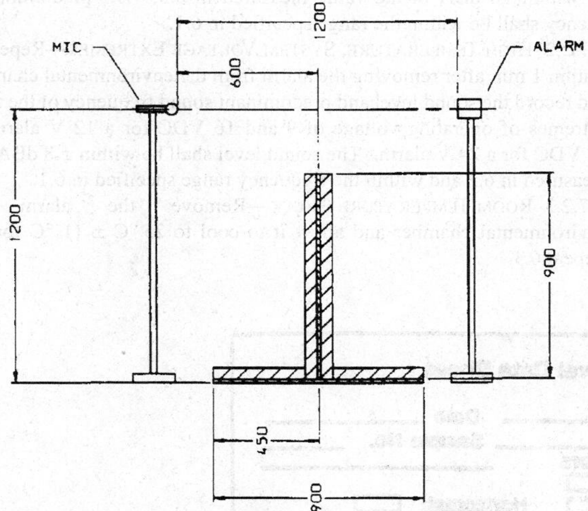

FIGURE 1—ACOUSTICAL BARRIER DIMENSIONS FOR TEST METHOD 2

5.5.3 CALIBRATION—Proper acoustical calibration procedure, including the influence of extension cables, etc. Field calibration should be made immediately before and after each test sequence. Internal calibration means are acceptable for field use, provided that external calibration is accomplished immediately before or after field use.

5.5.4 THE WEATHER—The effects of ambient weather conditions on the performance of all instruments (for example, temperature, humidity, and barometric pressure). Instrumentation can be influenced by low temperatures and caution should be exercised.

5.5.5 WINDSCREENS—When using a windscreen, it should be calibrated for the type of noise source being measured and data corrected if necessary. It is recommended that measurements be made only when the wind speed is below 19 km/h.

6. Functional Test Requirements—Unless otherwise specified, data measurements will be taken during a minimum test period of 1 min operation at ambient temperature of 25 °C ± 11 °C and supply voltage of 14 VDC ± 0.2 VDC for a nominal 12 V alarm and 28 VDC ± 0.2 VDC for a nominal 24 V alarm.

6.1 Predominant Sound Frequency—Measure and record the predominant sound frequency of the alarm. The predominant sound frequency shall be checked with a third octave passband filter set. The acceptable frequency range is 700 to 2800 Hz.

6.2 Cyclic Pulsation Rate and Duty Cycle—Measure and record the rate of cyclic sound level pulsations from the alarm and the duration of the "on" and "off" intervals. The cycles of sound level pulsations from the alarm shall be of the order of 1 to 2 per second. The duration of the "on" interval shall be equal to that of the "off" interval within ±20%.

6.3 Sound Level—Measure and record the sound level of the alarm using the methods of 5.1 or 5.2. The microphone shall be placed on the zero axis of the alarm at a distance of 1.2 m from the front face of the alarm. The sound level shall be any of the following:

Type A - 112 dB(A)
Type B - 107 dB(A)
Type C - 97 dB(A)
Type D - 87 dB(A)
Type E - 77 dB(A)
Type F - Other
(Sound level rating in dBA must be imprinted on the alarm.)

Unless otherwise stated, the tolerance on sound level measurements is ±4 dB(A).

6.4 Sound Level Change With Voltage—Measure and record the sound level at the extreme operating voltages of 9 and 16 VDC for a nominal 12 V system and 18 and 32 VDC for a nominal 24 V system. The sound level shall not vary more than ±8 dB from the values given in 6.3.

6.5 Off-Axis Sound Levels

6.5.1 HORIZONTAL MOUNTING SURFACE—All sound level measurements are made at a radius of 1.2 m from the sound producer. The initial measurement is on the zero degree axis. Twelve additional measurements are taken at 15 degree intervals from –90 to +90 degrees through the horizontal plane as shown in Figure 2.

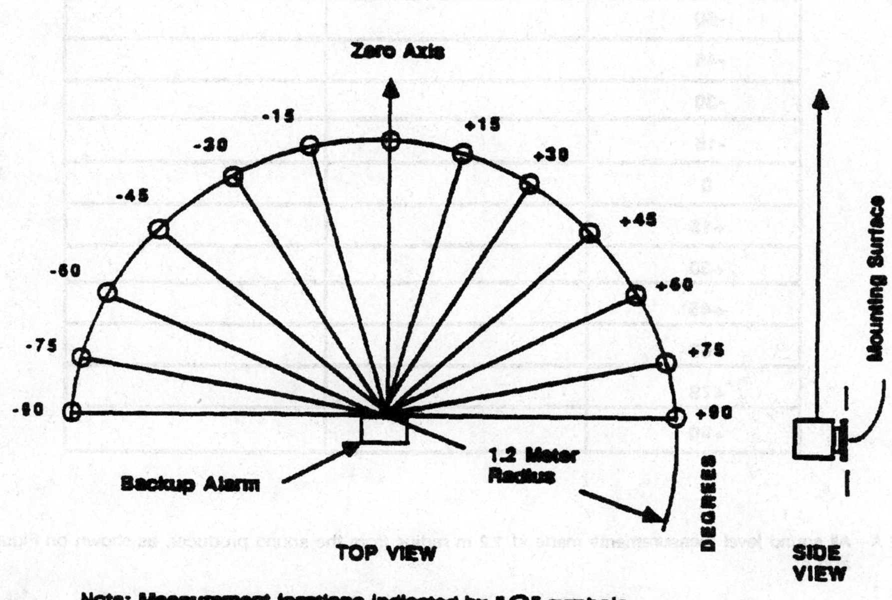

FIGURE 2—BACKUP ALARM SOUND LEVEL MEASUREMENT LOCATIONS—MOUNTING SURFACE HORIZONTAL

For each location described previously, measure the sound level using either Test Method 1 or Test Method 2 of Section 5. Record the data in Column 2, the form shown in Figure 3. The values recorded in Column 3 of the form are obtained by subtracting the sound level at the zero degree axis from the sound level at each angular position. The data from Column 3 is plotted on the chart of Figure 4 to obtain the profile of sound variation as a function of direction from the alarm. Fill in the blanks and check the appropriate boxes at the tops of the form and the profile sheets.

6.5.2 VERTICAL MOUNTING SURFACE—The alarm is next rotated 90 degrees about the zero axis, as shown in Figure 5. Repeat the procedure of 6.5.1.

This document does not specify any limitations on sound variation as a function of direction from the alarm but does require that the sound variation profiles be made available upon request.

7. Environmental Tests—Unless otherwise specified, all data measurements will be taken during a minimum test period of 1 min operation at temperatures specified and supply voltage of 14 VDC ± 0.2 VDC for a nominal 12 V system and 28 VDC ± 0.2 VDC for a nominal 24 V system.

7.1 Low Temperature Test—Temperature soak the alarm in the environmental chamber at 40 °C ± 3 °C for at least 2 h prior to the following tests. Remove the alarm from the environmental chamber to make measurements.

7.1.1 LOW TEMPERATURE, NOMINAL SYSTEM VOLTAGE—Within 1 min after removing the alarm from the environmental chamber, measure and record the sound level and predominate sound frequency of the alarm. The sound level must be within ±8 dBA of the baseline data measured in 6.3. The predominate sound frequency must be within the range specified in 6.1.

7.1.2 LOW TEMPERATURE, SYSTEM VOLTAGE EXTREMES—Repeat 7.1. Within 1 min after removing the alarm from the environmental chamber, measure and record the sound level and predominate sound frequency of the alarm for both extremes of operating voltage of 9 and 16 VDC for a 12 V alarm and 18 and 32 VDC for a 24 V alarm. The sound level shall be within ±8 dBA of the baseline data measured in 6.3 and within the frequency range specified in 6.1.

7.1.3 ROOM TEMPERATURE CHECK—Remove the alarm from the chamber and allow it to warm up to 25 °C ± 11 °C for at least 1 h. Repeat 6.3. The alarm shall meet the sound level requirements of 6.3.

7.2 High Temperature Test—Temperature soak the alarm in the environmental chamber at 85 °C ± 3 °C for at least 2 h prior to the following tests. Remove the alarm from the environmental chamber to make measurements.

7.2.1 HIGH TEMPERATURE, NOMINAL SYSTEM VOLTAGE—Within 1 min after removing the alarm from the environmental chamber, measure and record the sound level and predominate sound frequency of the alarm. The sound level shall be within ±8 dBA of the value measured in 6.3. The predominate sound frequency shall be within the range specified in 6.1.

7.2.2 HIGH TEMPERATURE, SYSTEM VOLTAGE EXTREMES—Repeat 7.2. Within 1 min after removing the alarm from the environmental chamber, measure and record the sound level and predominant sound frequency of the alarm for both extremes of operating voltage of 9 and 16 VDC for a 12 V alarm and 18 and 32 VDC for a 24 V alarm. The sound level shall be within ± 8 dBA for the value measured in 6.3 and within the frequency range specified in 6.1.

7.2.3 ROOM TEMPERATURE CHECK—Remove the alarm from the environmental chamber and allow it to cool to 25 °C ± 11 °C for at least 1 h. Repeat 6.3.

Backup Alarm Sound Level Data Sheet

Manufacturer: ____________ **Date** ________
Alarm Name & Model No.: ____________ **Sample No.** ________
Zero Axis Sound Level (dBA) at 1.2 Meters ________
Test Method 1 ☐ **Test Method 2** ☐
Alarm Mounting Postion: Vertical ☐ **Horizontal:** ☐

Angle (Degrees)	Recorded Sound Level (See Note A) (dbA)	Sound Level Deviation (See Note B) (dbA)
-90		
-75		
-60		
-45		
-30		
-15		
0		0
+15		
+30		
+45		
+60		
+75		
+90		

NOTE A—All sound level measurements made at 1.2 m radius from the sound producer, as shown on Figures 2 and 4.

NOTE B—Subtract sound level measured at 0 degree axis from sound level measured at angle.

FIGURE 3—BACKUP ALARM SOUND LEVEL DATA SHEET

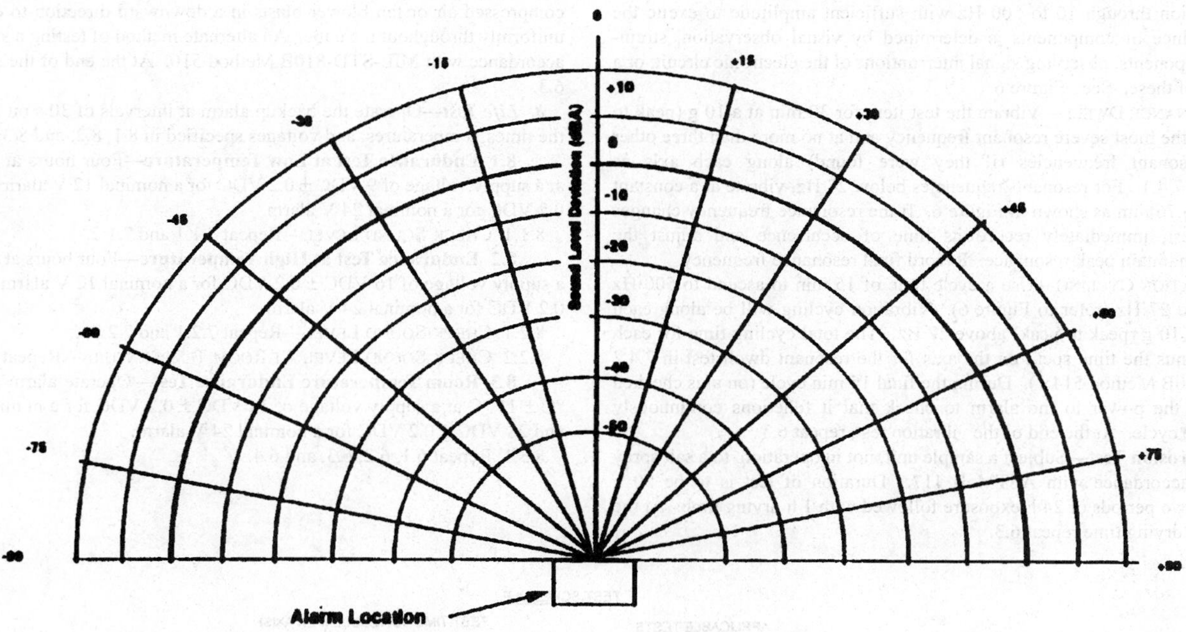

FIGURE 4—SOUND LEVEL DIRECTIONALITY CHART

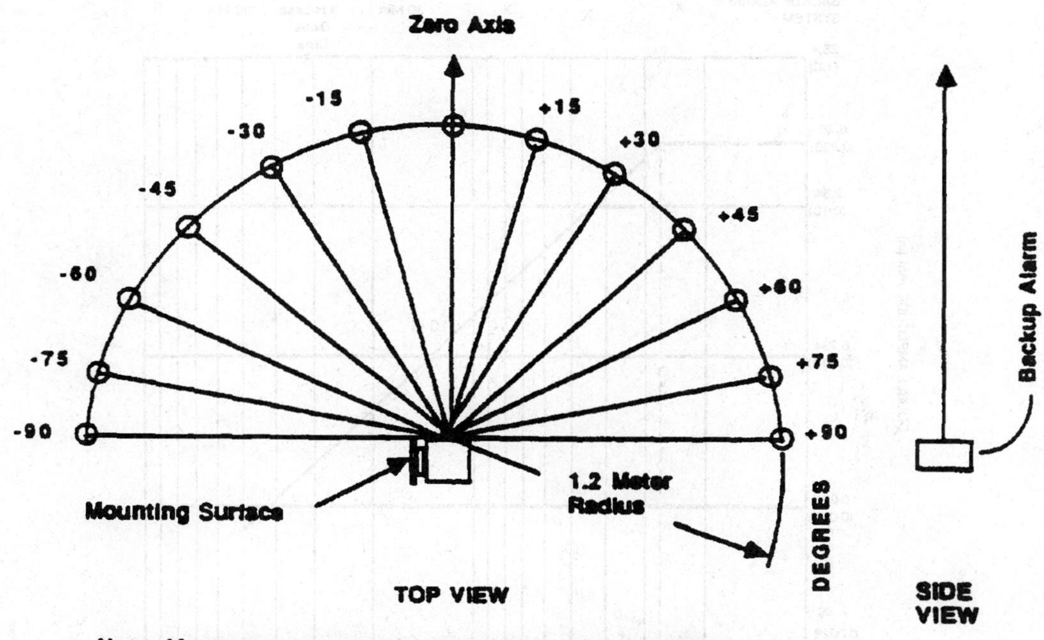

FIGURE 5—BACKUP ALARM SOUND LEVEL MEASUREMENT LOCATIONS—
MOUNTING SURFACE VERTICAL

7.3 Rain Test—Mount a sample alarm, not in operation, such that the zero axis of the alarm is horizontal. Subject all exposed sides of the alarm item to simulated blown rain for at least 2 h with a precipitation rate of 2.5 mm water per minute delivered at an angle of 45 degrees from a nozzle with a solid cone spray. Within 1 min after removal from the rain test, measure and record the sound level of the alarm. The sound level shall meet the requirements of 6.3.

7.4 Vibration Test—A sample alarm, as mounted on the supports supplied, shall be bolted to the table of the vibration test machine and the test conducted as follows with the alarm in operation.

7.4.1 RESONANCE SEARCH—Determine and record the resonant frequencies of the test item for each position (x-y-z axis) by slowly varying the frequency of applied vibration through 10 to 500 Hz with sufficient amplitude to excite the item. Resonance of components is determined by visual observation, strain-gaging of components, observing signal interruptions of the electronic circuit, or a combination of these. See Figure 6.

7.4.2 RESONANCE DWELL—Vibrate the test item for 30 min at a 10 g (peak to peak) level at the most severe resonant frequency and at no more than three other significant resonant frequencies (if they were found) along each axis as determined in 7.4.1. For resonant frequencies below 27 Hz, vibrate at a constant amplitude of 6.76 mm as shown in Figure 6. If the resonance frequency changes during this test, immediately record its time of occurrence and adjust the frequency to maintain peak resonance. Record final resonance frequency.

7.4.3 VIBRATION CYCLING—Use a cycle time of 15 min to ascend to 500 Hz and descend to 27 Hz (refer to Figure 6). Vibration cycling will be along each axis (x-y-z) at 10 g (peak to peak) above 27 Hz. The total cycling time for each axis is 3 h minus the time spent on the axis for the resonant dwell test in 7.4.2 (MIL-STD-810B Method 514.1). During the final 15 min cycle (on axis checked last), connect the power to the alarm to check that it functions continuously throughout the cycle. At the end of the vibration test, repeat 6.3.

7.5 Corrosion Test—Subject a sample unit, not in operation, to a salt spray (fog) test in accordance with ASTM B 117. Duration of test is to be 50 h consisting of two periods of 24 h exposure followed with 1 h drying time. At the end of the last drying time repeat 6.3.

7.6 High Pressure Hot Water Test—Direct a spray of hot water and detergent solution, consisting of 2 oz of Tri-Sodium Phosphate per gallon of water, at 85 °C temperature, 1000 psi pressure and 5 gal/min flow rate through a 15 degree spray angle nozzle, at the alarm sound opening at a distance of 300 mm. Direct the spray back and forth across the alarm sound opening for 10 s followed by a 30 s drain time. Repeat the spray and drain cycle for a total of 50 cycles. At the end of the last drain period, repeat 6.3.

7.7 Dust Test—Mount a sample alarm in its normal operating position, at least 150 mm from the wall in a cubical box with inside measurements of 900 mm on each side. The box shall contain 4.5 kg of AC dust of 50% fine and 50% coarse particles. For 5 h agitate the dust every 15 min for a 2 s period with compressed air or fan blower blasts in a downward direction to diffuse the dust uniformly throughout the cube. An alternate method of testing a sample unit is in accordance with MIL-STD-810B Method 510. At the end of the dust test, repeat 6.3.

8. Life Test—Operate the backup alarm at intervals of 30 s on and 30 s off for the times, temperatures, and voltages specified in 8.1, 8.2, and 8.3.

8.1 Endurance Test at Low Temperature—Four hours at –40 °C ± 3 °C at a supply voltage of 9 VDC ± 0.2 VDC for a nominal 12 V alarm and 18 VDC ± 0.2 VDC for a nominal 24 V alarm.

8.1.1 CHECK SOUND LEVEL—Repeat 7.1.1 and 7.1.2.

8.2 Endurance Test at High Temperature—Four hours at 85 °C ± 3 °C at a supply voltage of 16 VDC ± 0.2 VDC for a nominal 12 V alarm and 32 VDC ± 0.2 VDC for a nominal 24 V alarm.

8.2.1 CHECK SOUND LEVEL—Repeat 7.2.1 and 7.2.2.

8.2.2 CHECK SOUND LEVEL AT ROOM TEMPERATURE—Repeat 6.3 and 6.4.

8.3 Room Temperature Endurance Test—Operate alarm for 100 h at 25 °C ± 11 °C at a supply voltage of 14 VDC ± 0.2 VDC for a nominal 12 V alarm and 28 VDC ± 0.2 VDC for a nominal 24 V alarm.

8.3.1 Repeat 6.1, 6.2, 6.3, and 6.4.

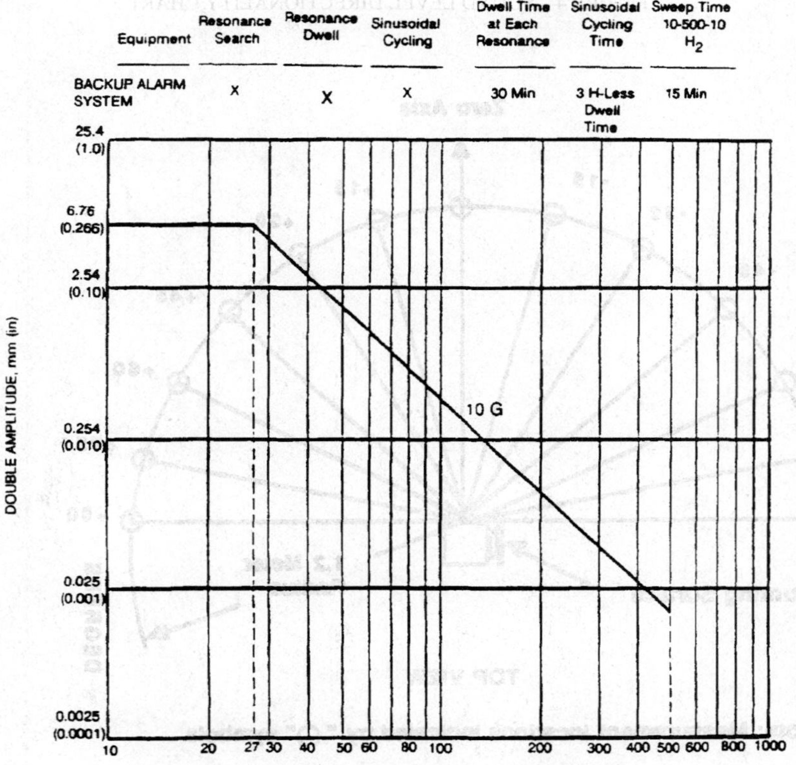

FIGURE 6—VIBRATION TEST

DISCRIMINATING BACK-UP ALARM SYSTEM STANDARD—SAE J1741 JUN1999

SAE Standard

Report of the Construction and Agricultural Backup/Forward Alarm Subcommittee of the SAE Construction and Agricultural Sound Level Technical Committee approved June 1999.

Foreword—This document is intended for use as a test procedure, to enable qualification of a Discriminating Back-Up Alarm System installed on an of-road, self-propelled, work machine, as defined by SAE J1116, limited to categories: (a) Construction, and (b) General purpose industrial.

The systems described within are intended to supplement the machine's warning equipment and operating procedures and not replace them.

1. Scope—This SAE Standard describes methods for evaluating the performance of the systems detection device, the minimum detection areas behind the machine, the visual and audible information presented to the operator and ground personnel, and the systems fault detection requirements. Also included are operator system function tests and maintenance procedures.

1.1 Purpose—The purpose of this document is to establish performance requirements for a Discriminating Back-Up Alarm System.

2. References

2.1 Applicable Publications—The following publications form a part of this specification to the extent specified herein. Unless otherwise indicated, the latest issue of SAE publications shall apply.

2.1.1 SAE PUBLICATIONS—Available from SAE, 400 Commonwealth Drive, Warrendale, PA 15096-001.

SAE J833—Human Physical Dimensions

SAE J994—Alarm—Backup—Electric Laboratory Performance Testing

SAE J1116—Categories of Off-Road Self-Propelled Work Machines

SAE J1446—On-Machine Alarm Test and Evaluation Procedure for Construction and General Purpose Industrial Machinery

2.1.2 FEDERAL PUBLICATION—U. S. Government, DOD SSP, Subscription Service Division, Building 4D, 700 Robbins Avenue, Philadelphia, PA 19111-5094.

Federal Register CFR 30 Part 77.410—Mobile Equipment—Automatic Warning Devices

2.1.3 ISO PUBLICATION—Available from ANSI, 11 West 42nd Street, New York, NY 10036-8002.

ISO 5006—Earth-moving machinery—Operator's field of view

2.2 Related Publication—The following publications are provided for information purposes only and are not a required part of this document.

2.2.1 ISO PUBLICATION—Available from ANSI, 11 West 42nd Street, New York, NY 10036-8002.

ISO 9533—Earth-moving machinery—Machine-mounted forward and reverse audible warning alarm—Sound test method

3. Definitions

3.1 Detection Time—Time required for discriminating back-up alarm system to detect an object or person in the detection zone and activate all warning systems.

3.2 Discriminating Back-Up Alarm System—A system which causes a back-up alarm to sound only if an object or person is within the detection zone.

3.3 Free-Field—A level area with no vertical reflecting surface within the detection zone being tested.

3.4 Hazard Zone—(Danger Zone) includes Operator Masked Zone and Detection Zone, see Figure 1.

3.5 Machine Width—Maximum width of machine including wheels or tracks and rear-mounted attachments.

3.6 Object—Solid body similar in size or larger than test body.

3.7 Operator Masked Zone(s)—Area to the rear of the machine which is obscured by part(s) of the machine from the operator's view including the use of rear view mirrors. (As defined in ISO 5006.) Operator's size being small as defined by SAE J833.

3.8 Detection Zone—Area to the rear of the machine within which an object or person moving or stationary will be detected by the discriminating back-up alarm system, see Figure 1.

3.9 Sensor—A device which senses the presence of a person or object within the detection zone.

3.10 Test Body—Person or object that will provide equivalent results, not exceeding dimensions in Figure 2, dressed in long sleeve shirt and long pants of heavy felt cloth, sitting. (See Figure 2.)

3.11 Travel Mode—Mode when machine exceeds 15 km/h.

3.12 Zone Depth—Length of detection zone, measured from rear of machine on zero axis.

4. General Comments

4.1 The sensing system must be capable of meeting the requirements of this document under all anticipated environmental conditions (e.g., rain, snow, dust, high wind, etc.). Sensing method must not pose health hazards to the ground worker or test person.

5. Detection of Zone Type Selection

5.1 Selection—The selection of the correct zone for a machine type will be made based on the depth of the operator masked zone, maximum rearward speed of the machine, intended use of the equipment, or any combination of these and other equipment specific factors. Note that in some cases, the operator masked zone may extend out to infinity. In these cases, the maximum depth detection ZONE 4 must be used to allow for the maximum possible advance warning.

5.2 Measuring Zone Depth—The zone depth is measured from the rearmost point on the basic machine, with no implements, along the machine's longitudinal centerline.

5.3 Minimum Zone Depth—Minimum zone depth must equal or exceed the operators masked zone depth, or default to ZONE 4 calculated as follows in Equation 1:

$$C = (D/W + R)*V \qquad \text{(Eq. 1)}$$

where:

C = Detection zone depth in meters
W = Walking Speed = 1.34 m/s
D = Distance to clear moving machine = 1/2 width of machine in meters
R = Human reaction time = 2 s
S = Machine rearward speed in km/h
V = S/3.6 = machine rearward speed in m/s
Minimum distance behind the machine to activate the alarm = rate x time

5.4 Detection Zone Shape—Detection zone shape to be a truncated fan, with the base of the fan equal to the machine width including tires or track, and a fan-out angle of 5 degrees from the perpendicular to the rear of the machine, beginning from the corners of the overall machine width points. (See Figures 1 and 3.)

6. Detection Zones—The detection zones in Table 1 are incorporated into this specification. (See Figure 1.)

TABLE 1—DETECTION ZONES[1]

Zone Type	Detection Zone Depth (Meters)	In-Cab Operator Audible Alarm(s) Pulse/s	Back-Up Alarm Level dB(A) at 1.2 m per SAE J994
4	16	1	112
3	8	1	112
2	4	2	107
1	2	4	102

1. Tolerance of ±10% for zone depth and pulse rate.

7. System—The system will consist of the following elements.

7.1 Sensors—A sensor/detection system for the specific Zone type.

7.2 In-Cab Annunciators—Cab installed audible and visual operator annunciators.

7.3 Back-Up Alarm—External back-up alarm mounted on the machine so as to meet the requirements of SAE J1446.

7.4 Wiring—Interconnecting wiring and cabling as required for installation.

7.5 Combining Functions—Elements may be combined or consolidated into different physical modules provided the discrete functions of the elements are present in the overall system and function as specified.

7.6 Sensor System

7.6.1 Sensor systems shall be capable of 100% detection of the test body as defined in 9.4 for their specified zone, when tested in accordance with 9.5. Inadvertent activation of the alarms shall be less than 10% when tested in accordance with 9.6.

DETECTION ZONE PARAMETERS

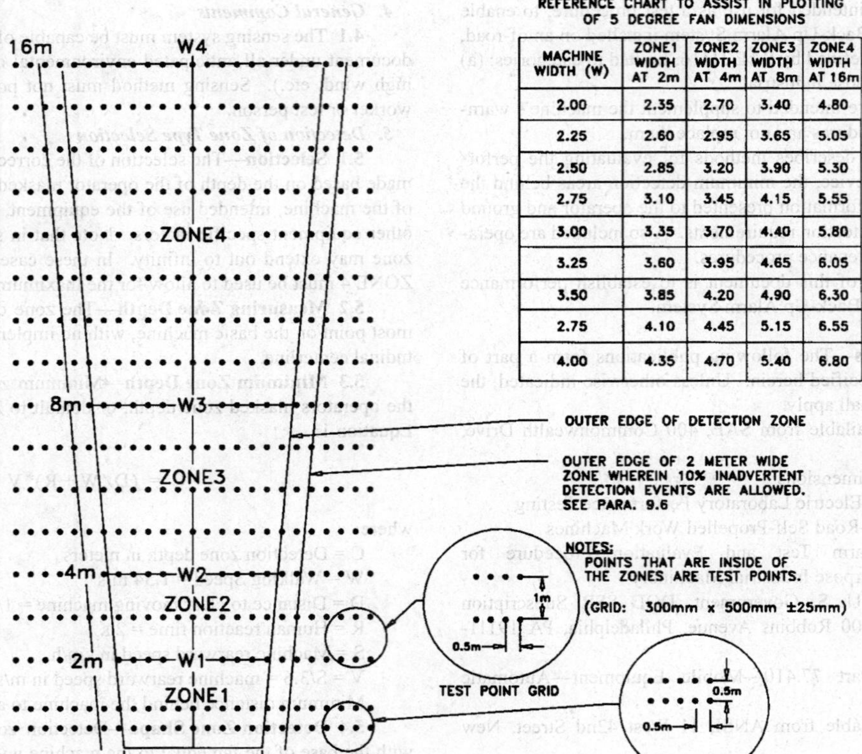

REFERENCE CHART TO ASSIST IN PLOTTING OF 5 DEGREE FAN DIMENSIONS

MACHINE WIDTH (W)	ZONE1 WIDTH AT 2m	ZONE2 WIDTH AT 4m	ZONE3 WIDTH AT 8m	ZONE4 WIDTH AT 16m
2.00	2.35	2.70	3.40	4.80
2.25	2.60	2.95	3.65	5.05
2.50	2.85	3.20	3.90	5.30
2.75	3.10	3.45	4.15	5.55
3.00	3.35	3.70	4.40	5.80
3.25	3.60	3.95	4.65	6.05
3.50	3.85	4.20	4.90	6.30
2.75	4.10	4.45	5.15	6.55
4.00	4.35	4.70	5.40	6.80

FIGURE 1—DETECTION ZONES

TEST BODY DIMENSIONS

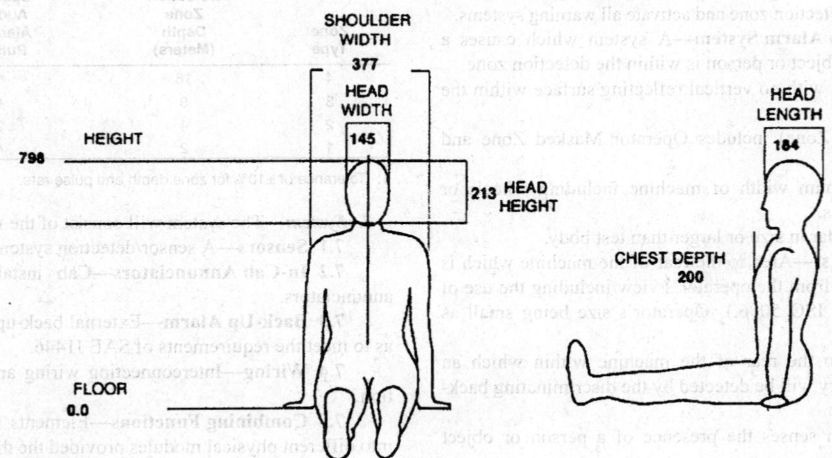

NOTES:

Position body facing away from vehicle.
Cover figure with felt cloth to simulate clothing.
Dimensions shown are in mm.
Dimensions are maximums for test person.

FIGURE 2—TEST BODY DIMENSIONS

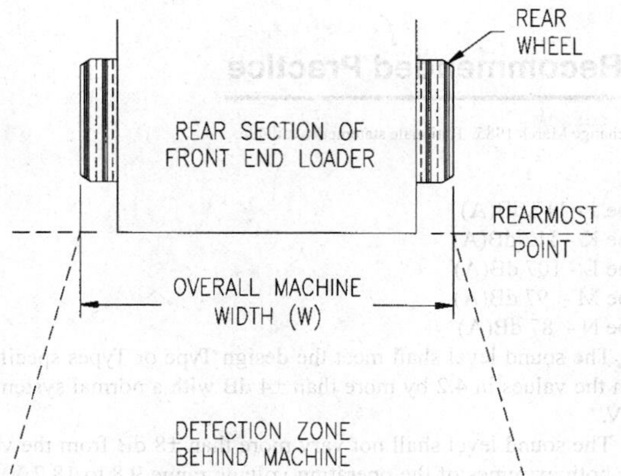

FIGURE 3—DETECTION ZONE BEHIND MACHINE

7.6.2 SENSOR LOCATION—Sensors shall be located as required to fulfill the detection zone requirements.

7.6.3 Detection time for the sensor to detect and energize the appropriate annunciator shall be 200 ms maximum.

7.7 Cab Installed Operator Warning Signals

7.7.1 AUDIBLE WARNING SIGNALS IN-CAB

a. The in-cab warning signal shall be audible under all anticipated working conditions. More than one warning signal may be used if multiple detection zones are employed.
b. Operator audible alarm shall activate only when reverse gear is engaged and will sound with the pulse rate synchronized with the operator visual warning light upon detection.

7.7.2 VISUAL WARNING SIGNALS IN-CAB

a. The in-cab warning signal shall be yellow, mounted in direct view of the operator, and be visible in direct sunlight. More than one warning signal may be used if multiple detection zones are employed.
b. A green system status light shall be provided to inform the operator that the system is powered and functional.

7.8 External Back-Up Alarm

7.8.1 The back-up alarm selected for use with the Discrimination System and machine, shall have been qualified for use on the machine by having met the performance requirements of SAE J994, and on-machine installation shall conform to SAE J1446.

7.8.2 The back-up alarm shall sound within 10 ms of being activated.

7.8.3 When reverse gear is selected, the back-up alarm shall be activated for a minimum of 3 s or 2 beeps.

7.8.4 In reverse gear when an object is detected, the back-up alarm shall activate.

7.8.5 In reverse exceeding 15 km/h, the back-up alarm shall activate.

8. Function of the System

8.1 The Discriminating Back-up Alarm System shall be activated under the following conditions (see Table 2):

a. Machine is in reverse mode
b. The machine travel speed is at or below 15 km/h
c. Operator warning devices shall be activated only upon object detection within the prescribed zone

TABLE 2—OPERATING MATRIX
REFER TO APPLICABLE SECTION FOR DETAILED OPERATING CHARACTERISTICS

Machine Condition	Operator Yellow Warning Light	Operator Audible In-Cab Alarm	External Back-Up Alarm	Operator Green Status Light
Engine Off	Off	Off	Off	Off
Engine Running	Sensing	Off	Off	On
Machine Forward Gear	Sensing	Off	Off	On
Machine Reverse at 15 km/h or less	Sensing	Sensing	Sensing	On
System Malfunction Forward	On Max Rate	On Max Rate	On	Flashing
System Malfunction Reverse	On Max Rate	On Max Rate	On	Flashing

8.2 The external back-up alarm shall, as a minimum, be activated under the following conditions:

a. For a minimum of 2 s, upon selecting the machines reverse travel mode from neutral or forward travel modes
b. The machines travel speed exceeds 15 km/h

8.3 Travel Mode—In reverse, exceeding 15 km/h, the system shall shift into a "travel mode." During this travel mode, the external back-up alarm will be activated continuously. In this mode, the internal audible and visual operator annunciators will only activate if an object is detected in the detection zone.

8.4 Monitoring Mode—The system shall be powered and monitoring when the machine engine is running. During this monitoring mode, the in-cab annunciators are active regardless of the direction of movement.

8.5 Active Mode—The system shall be active at selection of reverse gear and will sound the machine's external back-up alarm for a minimum of 2 s.

8.6 System Check Mode(s)

8.6.1 POWER-UP MONITORING—Upon starting the machine, the system shall self-test for function and confirm by a short audible signal, followed by an in-cab steady green status indicator light. The system check shall be automatic on power-up.

8.6.2 OPERATOR TEST MODE—An operator test mode will be provided by the system manufacturer, allowing the operator to exit the cab and walk around the rear of the machine to confirm proper system operation as demonstrated by activation of the external backup alarm when the operator is in the detection zone.

8.6.3 PERMANENT MONITORING—The warning system shall have a permanent monitoring capability with the following minimum requirements:

8.6.3.1 Optical/Audible Failure SIgnal if the Operation of the System is Impaired—A system malfunction will result in:

a. Operating status indication light (green) flashing at 2 Hz (±0.5 Hz)
b. All in-cab warning signals being activated at maximum pulse repetition rate
c. External alarm(s) activated whenever the machine is in reverse gear

8.6.3.2 Minimum Monitoring Requirements

a. Each wire between the electronic control unit, in-cab display and the sensor(s) should be monitored for:
    1. Wire break
    2. Short circuit
    3. Correct operation of the system

9. Test Procedures

9.1 Tests should be performed with major attachments mounted in a normal carry position on the machine to reflect the actual configuration during rearward travel on the worksite.

9.2 It is recommended that persons technically trained and experienced in general test techniques select the test instrumentation and conduct these tests.

9.3 Test Area—During all tests, all personnel should be forward of the rear of the machine, away from the detection zone. Test area should be open space with machine on a smooth surface and no significant physical objects within 5 machine lengths. No special test instrumentation is required.

9.4 Test Body Requirements—A test body with dimensions not exceeding a small person as defined by SAE J833, black felt covered, in sitting position. (See Figure 2.)

9.5 Object Detection Tests—100% detection is required. Static position the test body sequentially at 500 mm centers along each of the zone maximum detection range lines for which the system is being tested and at points 500 mm away from the rear of the rearmost part of the machine, 1 m from the rearmost part of the machine then at 1 m intervals outward. Detection must occur for all points. If the system fails to detect a location, move the test body 70 mm to the left or right and retest. If detection then occurs, the system is considered to have detected at that point. (See Figure 2.)

9.6 Inadvertent Detection Tests

9.6.1 Place the test body 2 m outside the 5 degree fan along the left and right detection zones sequentially starting at 500 mm from the rear of the machine then at 1 m and extending in 1 m increments away from the machine parallel to the respective edge of the detection zone. Log the number of locations and the number of detections.

9.6.2 Place a 1.2 m x 2.4 m sheet of 12 mm plywood at twice the selected zone depth perpendicular to the ground on the machine's centerline and facing the rear of the machine with the short edge against the ground. The system should not detect this object. Move the sheet 10 m to the left and right of the centerline and test. The system shall not detect this object.

9.6.3 Place 5 cinder/concrete blocks minimum dimensions 200 x 200 x 400 mm with the long edge on the ground in a line parallel to the rear face of the machine at the center of the detection zone. This simulates curbs and stones. Detection must not occur.

9.6.4 The system is deemed to have passed the inadvertent detection if the object was detected in fewer than 10% of the locations.

HORN—FORWARD WARNING—ELECTRIC—PERFORMANCE, TEST, AND APPLICATION —SAE J1105 SEP1989

SAE Recommended Practice

Report of the SAE Off-Road Sound Level Committee approved May 1975, editorial change September 1980, reaffirmed without change March 1985. Rationale statement available. Reaffirmed by the SAE Con-Ag Sound Level Committee September 1989.

Foreword—This Reaffirmed Document has not changed other than to put it into the new SAE Technical Standards Board Format.

1. Scope—This document establishes the following criteria for electrically operated forward warning horns on mobile construction machinery:

a. Forward warning horn performance requirements
b. Measurement technique for horn performance requirements
c. Laboratory environmental tests
d. Horn activation on the vehicle

2. References

2.1 Applicable Publications—The following publications form a part of the specification to the extent specified herein. Unless otherwise indicated the latest revision of SAE publications shall apply.

2.1.1 SAE PUBLICATION—Available from SAE, 400 Commonwealth Drive, Warrendale, PA 15096-0001.

SAE J184 AUG87—Qualifying a Sound Data Acquisition System

2.1.2 ANSI PUBLICATIONS—Available from ANSI, 11 West 42nd Street, New York, NY 10036-8002.

ANSI S1.4—1983—Specifications for Sound Level Meters

ANSI S1.11—1966 (R1976)—Specification for Octave, Half-Octave, and Third-Octave Band Filter Sets

2.1.3 MILITARY PUBLICATION—U. S. Government, DOD SSP, Subscription Service Division, Building 4D, 700 Robbins Avenue, Philadelphia, PA 19111-5094

Military Standard (MIL-STD-810B)—Environmental Test Methods 510 and 514.1

2.1.4 ASTM PUBLICATION—Available from ASTM, 100 Barr Harbor Drive, West Conshohocken, PA 19428-2959.

ASTM B 117—Method of Salt Spray (Fog) Testing

2.2 Related Publications

2.2.1 SAE PUBLICATION—Available from SAE, 400 Commonwealth Drive, Warrendale, PA 15096-0001.

SAE J994 MAR85—Alarm—Back-Up—Electric—Performance, Test, and Application

2.2.2 ANSI PUBLICATIONS—Available from ANSI, 11 West 42nd Street, New York, NY 10036-8002.

ANSI S1.1—1960 (R1976)—Acoustical Terminology

ANSI S1.2—1971 (R1976)—Physical Measurement of Sound

ANSI S1.13—1971 (R1986)—Methods for the Measurement of Sound Pressure Levels

2.3 Other Publications

AC Fine and AC Coarse Dust Available from AC Div. General Motors Corp.

3. Forward Warning Horn System—The forward warning horn system (complete system) for purposes of this document consists of a horn and an actuating switch (see Figure 1).

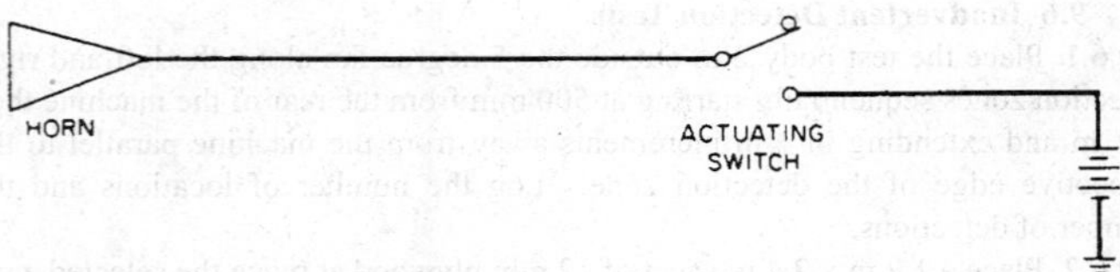

FIGURE 1—FORWARD WARNING HORN SYSTEM SCHEMATIC

4. Forward Warning Horn Performance Requirements—The performance requirements apply at ambient temperature of 77 °F ± 20 (25 °C ± 11) and at normal operating voltage of a 14 or 28 V battery system (nominal 12 and 24 V battery systems) unless otherwise stated and measured as in 5.2 to 5.3.27.

4.1 The predominant sound frequency of the horn shall fall within the frequency range of 710 to 2800 Hz.

4.2 The sound level of the horn shall be measured according to 5.2 and shall be any of the following with tolerances as stated in 4.3, 4.4, and 4.5:

Type J - 117 dB(A)
Type K - 112 dB(A)
Type L - 107 dB(A)
Type M - 97 dB(A)
Type N - 87 dB(A)

4.3 The sound level shall meet the design Type or Types specified and not vary from the values in 4.2 by more than ±4 dB with a normal system voltage of 14 or 28 V.

4.4 The sound level shall not vary more than ±8 dB from the values given in 4.2 for both extremes of the operating voltage range 9.8 to 18.2 V and 19.6 to 36.4 V for 14 and 28 V systems respectively.

4.5 The sound level shall not vary more than ±8 dB from a baseline measurement (determined as specified in 5.3.15) at −40 °F ± 5 (−40 °C ± 3) and 165 °F ± 5 (74 °C ± 3) when the alarm is in the appropriate environmental chamber.

5. Laboratory Measurement Technique

5.1 Instrumentation and Test Facilities

5.1.1 A sound level meter which meets the Type 1 requirements of the ANSI S1.4-1983.

5.1.2 As an alternative to making direct measurements using a sound level meter, a microphone or sound level meter may be used with a magnetic tape recorder and/or a graphic level recorder or indicating meter providing the system meets the requirements of SAE J184.

5.1.3 A filter set which meets the Class II Octave Band requirements of ANSI S1.11-1966 (R1976).

5.1.4 A sound level calibrator

5.1.5 A temperature measuring system

5.1.6 A voltage measuring system

5.1.7 Vibration apparatus

5.1.8 Environmental chamber

5.1.9 Dust chamber

5.1.10 Rain, steam, and corrosion chamber

5.2 Measurements

5.2.1 The horn and a microphone shall be located in a free field 4 ft (1.2 m) above a horizontal reflecting plane or laboratory equivalent, with the microphone 4 ft (1.2 m) from the horn along its 0 deg axis. The 0 deg axis must be parallel to the horizontal reflecting plane. For determination of the sound levels in the appropriate environmental chamber for the extreme temperature tests, 5.2.5. (A free field is defined as an area with no vertical reflecting surface within 17 ft (5 m). A horizontal reflecting plane is defined as the finished concrete in a laboratory or the equivalent when conducting testing in the field.)

5.2.2 The ambient sound level, due to all sources other than the horn, shall be at least 10 dB lower than the A-weighted sound level of the alarm.

5.2.3 The sound level meter shall be set for slow response or equivalent and A-weighting network to check sound level.

5.2.4 The predominant sound level output shall be checked with octave band filters only to determine that the frequency is within acceptable limits. All other sound level checks shall be made using the A-weighting network.

5.2.5 The sound level shall be determined and recorded for the forward warning horn (Type J, K, L, M, or N) when it is actuated in the environmental test chamber at 77 °F ± 20 (25 °C ± 11) and at extreme temperature as specified in 4.5.

5.3 Data Acquisition

5.3.1 All data measurements will be taken during a minimum test period of 5 s operation at ambient temperature of 77 °F ± 20 (25 °C ± 11) and normal battery system voltage of 14 or 28 V unless either temperature or voltage is stated otherwise. The data must be correlated with performance requirements where specified. If requirements are not met at any step in testing, a decision will be necessary to determine if testing should be continued.

5.3.2 Measure and record the predominant sound frequency of the horn. Correlate data with performance requirements in 4.1.

5.3.3 Measure and record the sound level of the horn. Correlate the data with performance requirements and tolerance from 4.3.

5.3.4 Measure and record the sound level change between extremes of operating voltage range 9.8 to 18.2 V and 19.6 to 36.4 V for 14 or 28 V systems respectively. Correlate the data with performance requirements and tolerance specified in 4.4.

5.3.5 Perform the vibration tests as specified in 6.1 to 6.1.3.

5.3.6 Repeat 5.3.3 and 5.3.4.

5.3.7 Perform rain tests as specified in 6.2.

5.3.8 Repeat 5.3.3 and 5.3.4.

5.3.9 Perform corrosion test as specified in 6.3.

5.3.10 Repeat 5.3.3 and 5.3.4.

5.3.11 Perform steam test as specified in 6.4.

5.3.12 Repeat 5.3.3 and 5.3.4.

5.3.13 Perform dust test as specified in 6.5.

5.3.14 Repeat 5.3.3 and 5.3.4.

5.3.15 Measure and record the sound level of the horn in the environmental chamber to obtain baseline data under conditions specified in 5.3.1.

5.3.16 Measure and record the sound level of the horn in the environmental chamber at –40 °F ± 5 (–40 °C ± 3) after the complete system has been at this temperature for at least 1 h immediately prior to this test. The sound level should be within ±8 dB of the baseline data measured in 5.3.15.

5.3.17 Measure and record the sound level of the horn in the environmental chamber at –40 °F ± 5 (–40 °C ± 3) for both extremes of the operating voltage range 9.8 to 18.2 V and 19.6 to 36.4 V for 14 or 28 V systems, respectively, after the complete system has been at the above temperature for at least 1 h immediately prior to the test. No specified sound level is required, but the horn is to be operational and register a reading on the meter above the existing ambient sound level.

5.3.18 Operate the complete system at –40 °F ± 5 (–40 °C ± 3) in the environmental chamber for 5000 sound pulsation cycles as specified in 6.6.1 and 6.6.2.

5.3.19 Repeat 5.3.16 and 5.3.17.

5.3.20 Repeat 5.3.15 for the environmental chamber that is to be used for the high temperature evaluation.

5.3.21 Measure and record the sound level of the horn in the environmental chamber at 165 °F ± 5 (74 °C ± 3), after the complete system has been at this temperature for 1 h immediately prior to this test. The sound level should be within ±8 dB of that measured in 5.3.20.

5.3.22 Measure and record the sound level of the horn in the environmental chamber at 165 °F ± 5 (74 °C ± 3) at both extremes of the operating range 9.8 to 18.2 V and from 19.6 to 36.4 V for 14 or 28 V systems, respectively, after the complete system has been at the above temperature for 1 h immediately prior to the test. No specified sound level is required, but the horn is to be operational and register a reading on the meter above the existing ambient sound level.

5.3.23 Operate the complete system at 165 °F ± 5 (74 °C ± 3) in the environmental chamber for 5000 sound pulsation cycles as specified in 6.6.1 and 6.6.3.

5.3.24 Repeat 5.3.21 and 5.3.22.

5.3.25 Repeat 5.3.3 and 5.3.4.

5.3.26 Operate the complete system for 40 000 sound pulsation cycles as specified in 5.6.1 and 5.6.4.

5.3.27 Repeat 5.3.1, 5.3.2, 5.3.3, and 5.3.4.

*6. **Laboratory Environmental Tests***—Sound level output shall be measured during a minimum test period of 5 s according to the requirements of 4.3, 4.4, and 4.5 in the sequence under Data Acquisition 5.3.1 to 5.3.27. The unit shall then be examined. Any unit showing evidence of material physical weakness, displacement or ruptured parts, shall be considered to have failed. The environmental tests are listed in the recommended test sequence.

6.1 Vibration Test—A sample unit, (complete system) as mounted on the supports supplied, shall be bolted to the table of the vibration test machine and the test conducted as follows with the horn in operation as specified in 6.6.1.

6.1.1 RESONANCE SEARCH—Determine and record the resonant frequencies of the test item for each position (x-y-z axis) by slowly varying the frequency of applied vibration through 10 to 500 Hz with sufficient amplitude to excite the item. Resonance of components is determined by visual observation, strain gaging of components, observing signal interruptions of the electronic circuit, or a combination of the above (see Figure 2).

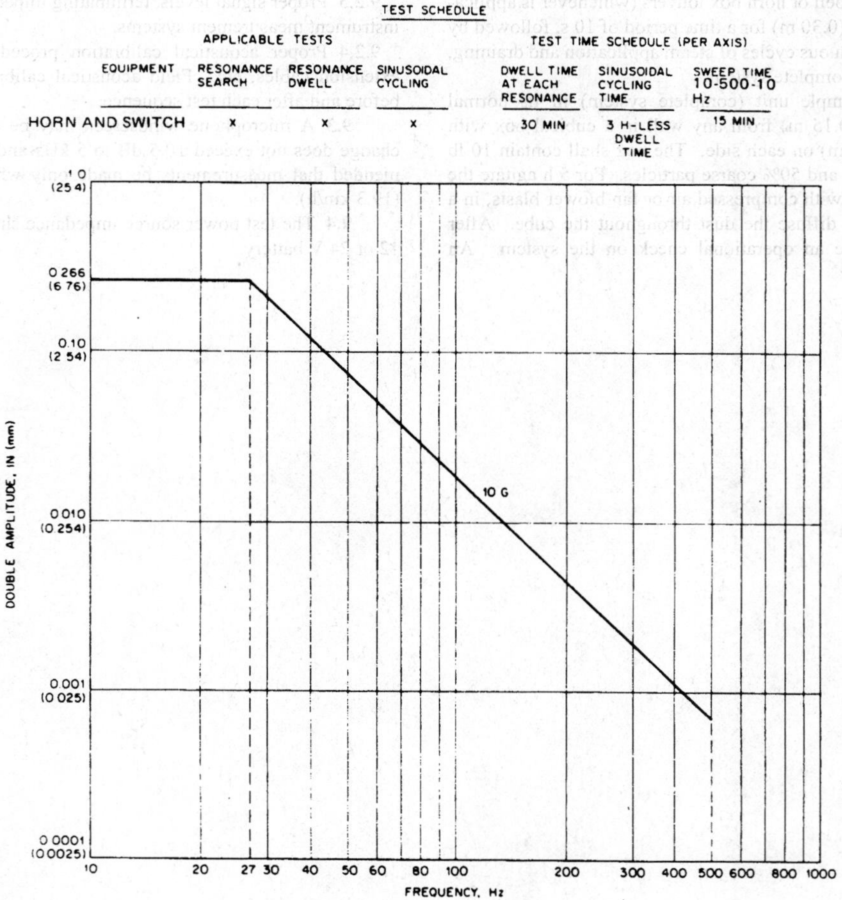

FIGURE 2—VIBRATION TEST

6.1.2 RESONANCE DWELL—Vibrate the test item for 30 min at a 10G (peak-to-peak) level at the most severe resonant frequency and at no more than three other significant resonant frequencies for 30 min, respectively (if they were found) along each axis (x-y-z) as determined in the Resonance Search in 6.1.1. For resonance frequencies below 27 Hz, the 10G (peak-to-peak) level may be allowed to decrease to a minimum of 2G (peak-to-peak) at 10 Hz to facilitate testing with equipment with inadequate capacity to maintain 10G (peak-to-peak) down to 10 Hz. If resonance frequency changes during this test, immediately record its time of occurrence and adjust frequency to maintain peak resonance. Record final resonant frequency.

6.1.3 VIBRATION CYCLING—Use a cycle time of 15 min to ascend to 500 Hz and descend to 10 Hz (see Figure 2). Vibration cycling will be along each axis (x-y-z) at 10G (peak-to-peak) above 27 Hz. Below 27 Hz, the G level may be allowed to decrease to a minimum of 2G (peak-to-peak) at 10 Hz to facilitate testing with equipment with inadequate capacity to maintain 10G (peak-to-peak) down to 10 Hz. The total cycling time for each axis is 3 h minus the time spent on that axis for the Resonant Dwell test in 6.1.2 (Reference MIL-STD-810B Method 514.1). During the final 15 min test period (on the axis checked last) connect the power to the horn and cycle it as per 6.6.1 to check that it is still operational.

6.2 Rain Test—Mount a sample unit (complete system), not in operation, in its normal operating position with all drain holes open. Subject all exposed sides of the test item to simulated blown rain for at least 2 h with a precipitation rate of 0.1 in (0.0025 m) water per minute delivered at an angle of 45 deg from a nozzle with a solid cone spray. During the final 1 min of the blown rain test, connect the power to the horn and cycle it as per 6.6.1 to check that it is still operational. Allow horn to drain for 1 h and immediately make an operational check on the complete system.

6.3 Corrosion Test—Subject a sample unit (complete system), not in operation, to a salt spray (fog) test in accordance with ASTM B 117. Duration of test is to be 50 h consisting of two periods of 24 h exposure followed with 1 h drying time. Immediately following the second 1 h drying period, make an operational check on the complete system.

6.4 Steam Test—Direct a spray of steam-cleaning detergent compound (Trisodium Phosphate) at the horn bell or horn box louvers (whichever is applicable) from a nozzle located at 12 in (0.30 m) for a time period of 10 s, followed by a 30 s drain period. After 50 continuous cycles of steam application and draining, make an operational check on the complete system.

6.5 Dust Test—Mount a sample unit (complete system) in its normal operating position, at least 6 in (0.15 m) from any wall in a cubical box with inside measurements of 3 ft (0.90 m) on each side. The box shall contain 10 lb (4.536 kg) of AC dust of 50% fine and 50% coarse particles. For 5 h agitate the dust every 15 min for a 2 s period with compressed air or fan blower blasts, in a downward direction, to uniformly diffuse the dust throughout the cube. After completion of the dust test, make an operational check on the system. An alternate method of testing a sample unit may be in accordance with MIL-STD-810B Method 510.

6.6 Life Cycle Test

6.6.1 Operate the forward warning horn with sound pulsation cycles of 1 s on and 4 s off intervals of the actuation switch at a normal battery voltage of either 14 or 28 V:

6.6.2 5000 sound pulsation cycles at –40 °F ± 5 (–40 °C ± 3)

6.6.3 5000 sound pulsation cycles at 165 °F ± 5 (75 °C ± 3)

6.6.4 40 000 sound pulsation cycles at 77 °F ± 20 (25 °C ± 11)

7. Vehicle Application—The job requirements, along with local, state, or national codes, should dictate whether a forward warning horn shall be used on mobile construction machinery.

8. General Requirements

8.1 The forward warning horn shall be mounted on the equipment so that the sound is projected forward. It shall be protected or constructed as to withstand severe wear and tear, adverse weather, and unfavorable environmental conditions.

8.2 The sound of the forward warning horn shall be distinctive when compared to the sound of the back-up alarm that is on the vehicle.

9. General Comments

9.1 It is recommended that persons technically trained and experienced in current techniques of sound measurement select the equipment and conduct the tests.

9.2 Proper usage of all test instrumentation is essential to obtain valid measurements. Operating manuals, or other literature furnished by the instrument manufacturer, should be referred to for both recommended operation of the instrument and precautions to be observed. Specific items include:

9.2.1 The type of microphone, its directional response characteristics, and its orientation relative to the ground plane and source of noise.

9.2.2 The effects of ambient weather conditions on the performance of all instruments (for example, temperature, humidity, and barometric pressure). Instrumentation can be influenced by low temperatures and caution should be exercised.

9.2.3 Proper signal levels, terminating impedances, and cable lengths on multi-instrument measurement systems.

9.2.4 Proper acoustical calibration procedure, to include the influence of extension cables, etc. Field acoustical calibration shall be made immediately before and after each test sequence.

9.3 A microphone windscreen may be used provided that the sensitivity change does not exceed ±0.5 dB to 5 kHz and ±2.0 dB to 12 kHz. It is recommended that measurements be made only when wind speed is below 12 mph (19.3 km/h).

9.4 The test power source impedance should closely approximate that of a 12 or 24 V battery.

R) SOUND MEASUREMENT—OFF-ROAD WORK MACHINES —OPERATOR—SINGULAR TYPE—SAE J919 APR1995

SAE Standard

Report of the SAE Construction and Industrial Machinery Technical Committee approved May 1966. Revised by the SAE Construction, Agricultural, and Off-Road Sound Level Technical Committee June 1986. Completely revised by the SAE Earthmoving Sound Level Subcommittee of the SAE ConAg Sound Level Committee April 1995. Rationale statement available.

Foreword—This Document has not changed other than to put it into the new SAE Technical Standards Board Format.

1. Scope—This SAE Standard describes the instrumentation and procedures to be used in measuring sound levels at the operator station for self-propelled sweepers as defined in SAE J2130 and self-propelled off-road work machines in categories 1, 2, 4, and 5, of SAE J1116.

This SAE document is applicable to machines that have operator stations where the operator can either stand or sit and will be either transported by, or walk with the machine during its operation. The sound levels obtained using this procedure are repeatable and representative of the higher range of sound levels generated by machines under actual field operating conditions. Due to variability of field operating conditions, this data is not intended to be used for operator noise exposure evaluations. Measurement and calculation of the operator's sound exposure should follow SAE J1166.

2. References

2.1 Applicable Publications—The following publications form a part of this specification to the extent specified herein. Unless otherwise specified, the latest issue of SAE publications shall apply.

2.1.1 SAE PUBLICATIONS—Available from SAE, 400 Commonwealth Drive, Warrendale, Pa. 15096-0001.

SAE J184 AUG87—Qualifying a Sound Data Acquisition System
SAE J732 JUN92—Specification Definitions—Loaders
SAE J833 MAY89—USA Human Physical Dimensions
SAE J1116 JUN86—Categories of Off-Road Self-Propelled Work Machines
SAE J1166 MAY90—Sound Measurement—Off-Road Self-Propelled Work Machines Operator-Work Cycle
SAE J2130—Identification of Self-Propelled Sweepers

2.1.2 ANSI AND IEC DOCUMENTS—Available from ANSI, 11 West 42nd Street, New York, NY 10036-8002.

ANSI S1.4-1983—Specifications for Sound Level Meters
IEC 804-1985—Integrating Sound Level Meter

2.2 Related Publications—The following publications are provided for information purposes only and are not a required part of this document.

2.2.1 SAE PUBLICATION—Available from SAE, 400 Commonwealth Drive, Warrendale, PA 15096-0001.

SAE J1262—Sound Measurement—Trenching Machines

2.2.2 ISO PUBLICATION—Available from ANSI, 11 West 42nd Street, New York, NY 10036-8002.

ISO 6394—Acoustics—Measurement of airborne noise emitted by earthmoving machinery—Operator's position—Stationary test condition

3. Instrumentation

3.1 A sound level meter which meets the Type 1 requirements of ANSI S1.4-1983 shall be used. Alternatively an integrating sound level meter may be used if it meets IEC 804-1985 requirements. If an integrating sound level meter is used for dynamic measurements, it must have a slow characteristic and max hold.

3.2 As an alternative to making direct measurements using a sound level meter, a microphone or sound level meter may be used with a magnetic tape recorder and/or graphic level recorder or indicating instrument, providing the system meets the requirements of SAE J184 for the frequency range that is of primary concern. The deviations in the magnetic tape recorder frequency response from flat response, especially at lower frequencies, must not affect the overall reading by more than ±0.5 dB(A).

3.3 An acoustical calibrator (accuracy within ±0.5 dB—see 5.2.4(see 5.2.4)) shall be used to ensure correct calibration of the sound level meter(s).

3.4 The use of a windscreen may be required under some test conditions (refer to 4.2), otherwise its use is optional, providing that it does not affect the A-weighted sound level of the source being measured by more than ±0.5 dB(A) under zero wind speed conditions. (Also refer to 5.2.2.)

3.5 An anemometer or other device for measurement of ambient wind speed and direction shall be used, if the machine to be tested has no operator enclosure or will be operated in the open configuration—doors and/or windows open during machine operation. The accuracy is ±10% at the highest wind speed. (see 5.2.2)(See 5.2.2.)

3.6 A speed indicator for determination of machine power source(s) rpm shall be used (accuracy within ±2% of the indicated reading).

3.7 A thermometer for measurement of ambient temperature (accuracy within ±1 °C) shall be used.

3.8 A barometer shall be used for measuring atmospheric pressure (accuracy within ±1 kPa of the indicated reading).

4. Procedure

4.1 Test Site

4.1.1 The test area shall consist of a smooth, uniform plane that has open space free of uncompacted snow, tall grass, and large reflecting surfaces such as a signboard, building, or vertical earth and rock embankment within 15 m of the machine being measured (see 5.2.5) (see 5.2.5).

4.1.2 Steel wheel and crawler machines shall be tested with the machines on a level surface of compacted earth or gravel. The moisture content should be low enough to prevent the material from sticking to the wheels or tracks. Other types of machinery may be tested with the machinery on a level surface of either hard-packed earth, gravel, concrete, or asphalt. The level surface should not have over ±1% grade in the direction of travel.

4.2 Environmental, Operator, and Machine Guidelines

4.2.1 No person other than the operator shall be in the operator's station area of the machine.

4.2.2 The ambient sound level measured at the microphone location (including wind effects), due to sources other than machinery being measured, shall be at least 10 dB(A) lower than the level of the machine being tested.

4.2.3 An operator shall be selected whose physical dimensions are as close as possible to a 50th percentile person (Reference SAE J833):

a. Standing Height—With shoes 1715 mm (5th percentile—1550 mm and 95th percentile—1880 mm)
b. Sitting Height—880 mm (5th percentile—800 mm and 95th percentile—960 mm)
c. Head Width—145 to 165 mm (5th percentile—145 mm and 95th percentile—165 mm)

An operator with physical dimensions that fall outside the 5th percentile to the 95th percentile range should not be permitted to operate the machine during this sound evaluation test.

4.2.4 The microphone shall be located 200 mm ± 20 mm from the median plane of the head and in line with the eyes and to the side of the head where the equivalent continuous A-weighted sound pressure level is highest. The microphone should either point in the direction of the operator's vision (head mounted) or upward (shoulder mounted). It is envisioned that a head-mounted or shoulder-mounted microphone will be remote mounted via a cable. Microphones mounted on the machinery should point in the forward direction of travel. Care shall be taken to isolate the microphone from vibrations or movements which could affect the measurements.

If more than one operating position is located on the machine, sound levels at all positions will be measured and the highest value reported.

NOTE—A 13 mm nominal diameter microphone is recommended.

4.2.5 When the test machine has a fully enclosed operator's station, measurements are to be taken with windows, doors, and vents in a fully closed position and the appropriate climatizing accessories in operation. For air circulation fan(s) with two positions, the high speed shall be used. If more than two operating speeds are available, the air conditioning and/or pressurizing ventilating system(s) shall be operated at midrange speed. If the air conditioning and/or pressure ventilating system(s) has(have) a recirculation and outside air position, the control shall be set for outside air. The test machine shall also be tested under a fully open configuration—all doors, windows, and vents open if they are designed to be open during machine operation. Climatizing accessory fans shall be off for the fully open configuration.

4.2.6 The machine shall be at a stabilized operating temperature during the test and must be operated in a manner such that the break-in procedure specified by the manufacturer is not violated.

4.3 Tests Required—Machines that are used primarily in a mobile mode shall be tested per 4.3.1.1, 4.3.1.2, 4.3.1.3, 4.3.1.4, and 4.3.2. Combined machines (such as loaders with a backhoe), shall be tested per 4.3.1.1, 4.3.1.2, 4.3.1.3, 4.3.1.4, and 4.3.2 when in the loader mode and tested per 4.3.1.1, 4.3.1.2, 4.3.1.3, and 4.3.1.4 when in the backhoe mode.

Rubber-tired and tracked excavators shall be tested in a stationary test mode only per 4.3.1.1, 4.3.1.2, 4.3.1.3, and 4.3.1.4.

4.3.1 STATIONARY TESTS WITH GROUND PROPULSION TRANSMISSION SHIFT SELECTOR IN NEUTRAL POSITION

4.3.1.1 Operate mobile machine power source(s) at no load and at a stabilized maximum governed speed (high idle). All major component drive systems shall be in neutral position.

4.3.1.2 Operate all power sources at no load and rated speed with all major component drive systems in neutral position.

4.3.1.3 Operate mobile machine power source(s) at no load with all major component drive systems in neutral position through the cycle low idle—maximum governed speed (high idle)—low idle as rapidly as possible, but allow the engine to stabilize for at least 10 s at the maximum governed speed (high idle) before it is permitted to return to low idle. It is recommended that care be taken to ensure stabilized combustion chamber surface temperatures prior to this test sequence. For some types of engines, such as engines with pre-combustion chambers, repeatability of sound levels may be affected. Between cycles, a cool down period of 5 min is recommended.

4.3.1.4 With the power source(s) at the maximum governed speed (high idle), or manufacturer's recommended operating speed at no load in a stabilized condition, activate the appropriate hydraulic circuits, mechanical, electrical, hydrostatic, or torque converter drive systems to cycle the major components or component from the most retracted and/or lowered position to fully extended and/or maximum height position and then back to the original position. The component cycled must have controls at the operator's station. This cycling should be done as fast as practical, taking into consideration all the pertinent safety factors, and be accomplished without exceeding relief valve settings. For short cycle hydraulic operation, the system may be feathered. For safety reasons and undesirability of change of location of major noise source(s) in relation to other major components of the machine, a major portion of the mobile machine, such as the tractor of a scraper unit, or the upper rotational structure of an excavator shall not be moved, or scraper elevator placed in operation during this stationary machine test.

For units such as nonriding trenching machines without power steering or hydraulic controls, this section shall be omitted. In no case shall the digging chain (wheel) or vibratory plow drives be engaged for this test or other tests in this document. For self-propelled street sweepers, the brooms may be lowered and raised for this portion of the test.

4.3.2 CONSTANT SPEED MOVING TEST—Machines shall be operated in a forward intermediate gear ratio at no load. The power source(s) shall be operated at maximum governed speed (high idle). Intermediate is intended to mean second gear ratio for machines with three or four gear ratios, third gear ratio for machines with five or six gear ratios, fourth gear ratio for machines with seven or eight gear ratios, etc. (Gear ratio refers to overall gear reductions.) If there is a problem with a transmission shifting up or down in this phase of the test, one gear lower or higher may be used to eliminate the problem. Machines with hydrostatic, electric drive, or other type drives shall be operated at approximately one-half maximum ground speed with the governor control set in maximum (high idle) position at no load. If this operating condition cannot be attained because of the interaction of the power source(s) and drive controls, then the ground speed may be increased or decreased so as to still permit the power source(s) governor control to be set in maximum (high idle) position. Machines that have major noise-generating components which are normally in use at this ground speed shall have these major components in operation during this test. For self-propelled street sweepers, these components include water systems, brooms, and blower or conveying systems.

4.3.3 Machines that have a major attachment that is normally used for the main operating function shall be equipped with this attachment. Examples of this are: buckets on loaders, brooms on sweepers, dozers on either wheel or crawler tractors, and back fill blades, digging booms (wheel), direct burial plows, and backhoes on trenching machines. For all tests, except component cycling, these attachments shall be in a minimum transport position of 160 to 320 mm for dozers, scrapers, etc. For trenching machines and sweepers these attachments shall be in their normal transport position, for example, backfill blade or brooms fully raised; plow, boom, or wheel fully raised and restrained (if appropriate). Loaders and trenchers with loaders shall use carry position as specified by SAE J732.

4.4 Measurements

4.4.1 The microphone shall be located next to the operator's right or left ear as stated in 4.2.4 for all operating conditions.

4.4.2 All sound level measurements shall be taken using the A-weighting network. For dynamic power source(s) and component cycling, the sound level meter shall be set for slow dynamic characteristic (see 3.1)(see 3.1). For the stabilized test conditions of maximum governed engine speed (high idle), rated engine speed, and intermediate gear constant speed moving, the time weighted average sound level (Leq) may be used in place of the slow dynamic characteristic.

4.4.3 The ambient temperature, atmospheric pressure, and A-weighted sound level shall be measured and recorded at the operator's station with the machine shut down. If the machine has a fully enclosed operator's station, these measurements shall be taken with the tested enclosure configuration. The ambient wind speed and direction shall be measured for all applicable tests.

4.4.4 The stabilized maximum governed power source(s) speed (high idle) at no load shall be measured and recorded.

4.4.5 The power source(s) speed shall be monitored during the rated speed test.

4.4.6 The gear ratio and approximate ground speed during the moving tests shall be recorded.

4.4.7 The sound level meter needle movement, digital readout, or graphic level recorder trace shall be observed during each test sequence. The highest value observed for all tests disregarding sounds of short duration that are out of character with the test on the machine (example: impact sound such as bucket rap against stops) shall be recorded for each test sequence. For a digital type readout, the meter must be frequently reset so the out-of-character sound levels for the test sequence are not included if the maximum hold mode is being used.

4.4.8 For the stabilized test condition of maximum governed speed (high idle) or rated speed, a single reading shall be recorded.

4.4.9 For power source(s) cycling, component cycling, and constant speed moving test conditions, a minimum of three valid readings shall be taken for each measuring point.

4.4.10 NUMBER OF SIMULATED WORK CYCLES—Three simulated work cycles shall be carried out resulting in three measurements to be taken at the microphone position.

It is necessary to have two of the readings at the microphone within a 2 dB range of each other. If these results are not obtained, additional simulated work cycles shall be taken to meet this requirement. Operational procedures may require correction to achieve this.

4.4.11 DETERMINATION OF MEASUREMENT RESULT—Report, as the value of the equivalent continuous A-weighted sound pressure level, the arithmetic mean of the highest values that are within a 2 dB range of each other.

5. General Comments

5.1 It is recommended that persons technically trained and experienced in the current techniques of sound measurements select the instrumentation and conduct the tests. Dedicated attention to detail and a thorough understanding of the machine and the instrumentation and operational requirements shall be prerequisite of all personnel attached to the evaluation program.

5.2 Proper use of all test instrumentation is essential to obtain valid measurements. Operating manual or other literature furnished by the instrument manufacturer should be referred to for both recommended operation of the instrument and precautions to be observed.

5.2.1 The effects of ambient weather conditions on the performance of all instruments (for example: temperature, humidity, barometric pressure, and stray magnetic fields) should be known. Instrumentation can be influenced by low temperature and caution should be exercised.

5.2.2 It is recommended that the wind speed of the air over the microphone not exceed 20 km/h. Caution should be used in making measurements with higher wind speeds.

A microphone windscreen shall not be used except when it is required to reduce wind-induced noise that is within 15 dB(A) of the sound level of the source being measured. When a windscreen is used, it shall not affect the sound level of the source being measured by more than ±0.5 dB(A) under zero wind speed conditions.

NOTE—In practice, windscreens are seldom required to reduce A-weighted wind noise, with the possible exception of microphone locations in the fan blast of the machine.

5.2.3 Proper signal levels, terminating impedances, and cable lengths on multi-instrument measurement systems should be known.

5.2.4 Proper acoustical calibration procedure, to include the influence of extension cables, etc., should be performed. Field acoustical calibration shall be made immediately before and after the testing of each machine or at least every 4 h. The calibration before and after shall not vary by more than ±0.5 dB for tests to be valid.

5.2.5 The overall effect due to an alternate test environment on the sound level measurement shall not exceed ±1.0 dB(A) from the sound level measurement made at the test site described in 4.1.1.

5.3 It should be recognized that variations in measured sound levels may occur due to variations in test site, ambient weather differences (temperature, wind, and their gradients), test equipment differences, and inherent differences between nominally identical machines.

SOUND MEASUREMENT—OFF-ROAD SELF-PROPELLED WORK MACHINES OPERATOR-WORK CYCLE —SAE J1166 OCT1998

SAE Standard

Report of the SAE Off-Road Machinery Sound Level Committee approved December 1976. Revised by the SAE Construction, Agricultural, and Off-Road Machinery Sound Level Technical Committee July 1987, and completely revised May 1990. Revised by the SAE Earthmoving Machinery Sound Level Subcommittee of the SAE Construction, Agricultural, and Off-Road Machinery Sound Level Technical Committee October 1998. Rationale statement available.

1. Scope—This SAE Standard sets forth the procedures to be used in measuring sound levels and determining the time weighted sound level at the operator's station(s) of specified off-road self-propelled work machines. This document applies to the following work machines which have operator stations as specified in SAE J1116:

Crawler Loader
Wheel Loader
Dumper
Tractor Scraper
Grader
Crawler Tractor with Dozer
Wheel Tractor with Dozer
Pad Foot Wheel Compactor with Dozer
Backhoe
Hydraulic Excavator
Log Skidder
Excavator and Wheel Feller-Buncher
Pipelayer
Roller/Compactor
Trencher
Sweeper

The instrumentation requirements and specific work cycles for these machines are described. The method used to calculate the time weighted average sound level at the operator station(s) is specified for $L_{eq(5)}$, or optional exchange rates, during continuous operation in a work cycle. A method to relate the time weighted average sound level at the operator station(s) to operator sound exposure is also provided.

2. References

2.1 Applicable Publications—The following publications form a part of the specification to the extent specified herein. Unless otherwise indicated the latest revision of SAE publications shall apply.

2.1.1 SAE PUBLICATIONS—Available from SAE, 400 Commonwealth Drive, Warrendale, PA 15096-0001.

SAE J833—USA Human Physical Dimensions
SAE J919—Sound Measurement—Earthmoving Machinery-Operator—Singular Type Test
SAE J2130—Identification of Self-Propelled Sweepers

2.1.2 IEC PUBLICATIONS—Available from International Electrotechnical Commission, 3, rue de Verambe, P.O. Box 131, 1211 Geneva 20, Switzerland.

IEC 651 (1979)—Sound Level Meters
IEC 804 (1985)—Integrating-Averaging Sound Level Meter

2.2 Related Publications—The following publications are provided for information purposes only and are not a required part of this document.

2.2.1 SAE PUBLICATIONS—Available from SAE, 400 Commonwealth Drive, Warrendale, PA 15096-0001.

SAE J49—Specification Definitions—Hydraulic Backhoes
SAE J727—Nomenclature—Crawler Tractor
SAE J728—Component Nomenclature—Scrapers
SAE J729—Nomenclature—Dozer
SAE J731—Component Nomenclature—Loader
SAE J869—Component Nomenclature—Construction Two- and Four-Wheel Tractors
SAE J870—Component Nomenclature—Graders
SAE J1016—Component Nomenclature—Dumpers
SAE J1017—Nomenclature—Rollers/Compactors
SAE J1057—Identification Terminology of Earthmoving Machines
SAE J1110—Component Nomenclature—Articulated Rubber Tired Log Skidder
SAE J1112—Specifications and Definitions Skidder-Grapple
SAE J1116—Categories of Off-Road Self-Propelled Work Machines
SAE J1254—Component Nomenclature—Feller Buncher
SAE J1262—Sound Measurement—Trenching Machines
SAE J1295—Identification Terminology—Specification Definitions Pipelayer and Side Boom—Tractor or Loader Mounted
SAE J1382—Specification Definitions and Nomenclature for Trenching Machines

3. Data Acquisition and Reduction System

3.1 The dynamic range of the system shall include +20 dB to –10 dB of the $L_{eq(5)}$ value that is determined.

NOTE—To determine if the appropriate instrumentation is available for the initial test, the highest value from SAE J919 can be substituted for $L_{eq(5)}$.

3.2 An exchange of 5 dB increase in sound level for halving of the time period shall be applied to the sound level data, unless otherwise noted.

3.3 The A-weighting network (reference IEC 651-1979) shall be applied to the input signal by the system.

3.4 The system shall meet the requirements of IEC 804-(1985) (except use a 5 dB exchange rate instead of an equal energy 3 dB exchange rate), or include a sound level meter meeting requirements of IEC 651-(1979) plus a direct integrating exposure accumulating system. If made up of separate instrument components, the system shall comply with SAE J184 for a frequency range of interest.

3.5 Examples of sound data acquisition and reduction systems are:

3.5.1 Extended range audio-dosimeter (cutoff level at least 15 dB below measured value).

3.5.2 Sound level meter, tape recorder, signal converter, and direct integrating exposure accumulating system.

3.5.3 Integrating-averaging sound level meter (reference IEC 804-(1985)).

3.5.4 Sound level meter, signal converter, and direct integrating exposure accumulating system.

3.5.5 Microphone, power supply signal, converter, and direct integrating exposure accumulating system.

3.6 The acoustical calibrator shall have an accuracy of ±0.5 dB.

3.7 The use of a windscreen may be desired under some test conditions (refer to 5.2.2); otherwise its use is optional, providing that it does not affect the A-weighted sound level of the source being measured by more than ±0.5 dB(A) under zero wind speed conditions.

3.8 Alternate exchange rates can be used by using the appropriate instrumentation and referencing the formula in Appendix E.

4. Measurement of Other Physical Parameters

4.1 The wind speed shall be determined with an accuracy of ±10% at the highest wind speed encountered. (See 7.2.3.)

4.2 The engine rotational speed shall be determined with an accuracy of ±2% of the indicated reading.

4.3 The temperature shall be determined with an accuracy of ±1 °C of the indicated reading.

4.4 The barometric pressure shall be determined with an accuracy of ±1.1 kPa of the indicated reading.

5. Test Procedure

5.1 General Test Site Requirements—The recommended test site should be a uniform plane of earth or other appropriate surface as noted in test cycle Section 8 with a grade not exceeding 3% in any direction, free of surface undulations that would restrict machinery operation. All earthen material in the test area should have a density of approximately 1800 kg/m^3. The test surface shall be free of snow, tall grass, or large rocks. For machines with an operator station that will be tested in an open configuration, the test area within 10 m of the test machine shall be free of reflecting surfaces such as signboards, buildings, or earth embankments. Haul roads must be in a condition to allow the machinery to operate at the specified speeds. Where machinery configurations or location is such that it is impractical to use a test site as described, sites with other conditions such as field job sites may be used. In such cases, a description of the test site conditions must be included in the data report to qualify the sound level data.

5.2 Environment, Operator, and Machine Guidelines

5.2.1 No person other than the operator shall be in the operator station area on machines with or without a cab.

5.2.2 The ambient sound level (including wind noise) due to sources other than the machinery being measured, shall be at least 10 dB(A) below the lowest sound level generated by the machine under test on the work cycle.

5.2.3 The environmental conditions such as humidity, temperature, vibration, stray electromagnetic fields, etc., shall be within the limits specified by the manufacturer of the test instrumentation.

5.2.4 The operator shall be positioned at the machines normal operating location as recommended by the manufacturer during the primary work function of the machine. The operator shall have a height physical dimension that falls within the 5th to 95th percentile as described by SAE J833 (800 mm to 960 mm for a sitting operator; 1550 mm to 1880 mm for a standing operator.)

5.2.5 The microphone shall be located 200 mm ± 20 mm to the right of the centerline of the operator's head unless the engine of the machinery is located on the left side of the operator. For machinery with the engine on the left side of the operator, the microphone shall be located on the left side. The face of the microphone should be in line with the ear canal. The microphone should either point in the direction of the operator's vision (head mounted) or upwards (shoulder mounted). It is envisioned that for a head mounted or shoulder mounted microphone, it will be remote mounted via a cable.

5.2.6 The machine shall be at a stabilized operating temperature during the test and must be operated in a manner such that the operating procedures specified by the manufacturer are not violated.

5.2.7 Tire pressures, track tension adjustment, fluid levels, governor setting, pressure valve relief settings, etc., must be within the manufacturer's specifications.

5.3 Sound exposure work cycles for the machinery defined in this document are described in Section 8.

For machinery categories not listed, elements of common field uses may be used for determining the time weighted average sound level at the operator's station(s). The test conditions shall meet criteria similar to that implied by the defined work cycles. Work cycles not specifically included in this document shall be fully described in the test report.

5.4 Test machines that have a major attachment which is normally used for the main operating function shall be equipped with this attachment. Examples of this are the standard capacity buckets on loaders and excavators and dozers on crawler and wheel tractors and on compactors.

5.5 Measurements and Reported Data

5.5.1 The ambient temperature and atmospheric pressure for the test site shall be determined.

5.5.2 The stabilized maximum governed engine speed (high idle) at no load shall be determined.

5.5.3 When the test machine is equipped with a fully enclosed and climatized operator's station(s), the test shall only be conducted under the closed condition and with the climatizing air circulation fan(s) in operation. For air circulation fan(s) with two speed positions, the high speed shall be used. On fan(s) with three or more speed positions, the intermediate speed shall be used. Intermediate is defined as the third highest of a four or five speed position arrangement. If the operator's station is equipped with air circulation controls that will permit either recirculated or outside air, the position for outside air should be used. When the machine is not equipped with climatization, a closed test and a fully open test (all doors, windows, and vents open if they are designed to be open during machine operation) shall be conducted.

5.5.4 The ambient sound level should be measured at the start and end of the test.

5.5.5 The ambient wind speed should be measured prior to starting the test at the test site.

5.5.6 The machine operation on the work cycle shall be repeated until the number of cycles or time requirements given in Table 1 are met before data is processed.

TABLE 1—TEST INTEGRATION TIME

Instrumentation	Minimum Required Test Time for ±0.25 dB(A) Accuracy in Calculation
Any system meeting IEC 804 (1985) or IEC 651-Type 1	3 cycles or 10 min
Any system meeting IEC 651-Type 2 with a resolution to 0.1% dosage	15 min
Any system meeting IEC 651-Type 2 with a resolution to 1% dosage	2 h

Work cycles used in the calculations for the first two systems must not vary in time more than ±10% of the average time of the cycles used for calculation of $L_{eq(5)}$.

NOTE—The machine operator should be allowed to run a number of practice work cycles before the test period begins to develop proficiency to repeat the cycles in less than ±10% elapsed time difference. The cycle time shall be monitored during the test so that incorrect work cycles can either be eliminated or the test restarted.

5.5.7 The reported result for this document shall be the time weighted average sound level at the operator's work station(s), $L_{eq(5)}$ (unless a different exchange is noted).

6. Calculation of an Operator's Sound Exposure—An operator's sound exposure is the value determined from the result reported in 5.5.7 which has been corrected by the actual work time of the operator, the output duty cycle of the machinery, and the effect of other noise sources. To determine the sound exposure, data on the actual duty cycle of the operator is required. If the machinery is run at reduced output for portions of the work shift, the time ratio, and equivalent sound level for the periods of reduced output must be determined. For other noise sources, the time duration as a ratio of the work shift and their equivalent sound level must be determined. See Appendix D for the method to calculate the sound exposure.

7. General Comments

7.1 It is recommended that persons technically trained and experienced in the current techniques of sound measurement select the instrumentation and evaluate the results.

7.1.1 The test engineer must be familiar with the required operation of the machine during the work cycle. Proper instructions must be given to the machine operator. Grade stakes or cone markers may be helpful in indicating travel distances or turn angles. Dry runs may be desirable to familiarize the machine operator with the required technique.

7.1.2 The machine operator must be familiar with the machine and proficient enough to work the machine as intended.

7.1.3 The test engineer must judge if the machine operator complies with the requirements of the work cycles.

7.2 Proper use of all test instrumentation is essential to obtain valid measurements.

7.2.1 The effects of ambient weather conditions on the performance of all instruments (temperature, humidity, and barometric pressure) should be known. Instrumentation can be influenced by temperature extremes or significant changes in temperature.

7.2.2 Vibration isolation of the microphone is essential particularly when the microphone is mounted on the machine. Care must be taken to ensure that spurious signals are not induced on the microphone output by vibration, electromagnetic pickup, or other sources. Nonacoustically generated signals shall be at least 10 dB below the acoustic signal. The microphone can be capped, (use of a dummy microphone or use of the calibrator in the off mode) to check for nonacoustical signals.

7.2.3 The wind speed at the microphone location shall not exceed 20 km/h prior to the start of the test.

7.2.4 When multi-instrument measurement systems are used, caution shall be exercised. The effect of cable length and terminating impedances on the signal levels shall be considered. They shall not affect the data.

7.2.5 Calibration shall be made immediately before and at the end of the test. The calibration shall include the effects of cable length.

7.3 The calibration of a dosimeter must produce a count 20 times ±8% of the lowest increment of the readout.

8. Sound Exposure Work Cycle

8.1 Crawler Loader—See Figure 1.

8.1.1 MATERIAL—The material should be earth that is slightly moist. The moisture content must be low enough so that the material does not stick to or pack in the track system. It should be free of large stones greater than 80 mm in diameter and not exceed 1/2 sand, gravel, or crushed rock. The soil can be clay or loam. The compaction of the material should not exceed that which allows grouser penetration. The material to be loaded shall be in a loose stockpile of height appropriate for the size of the machine.

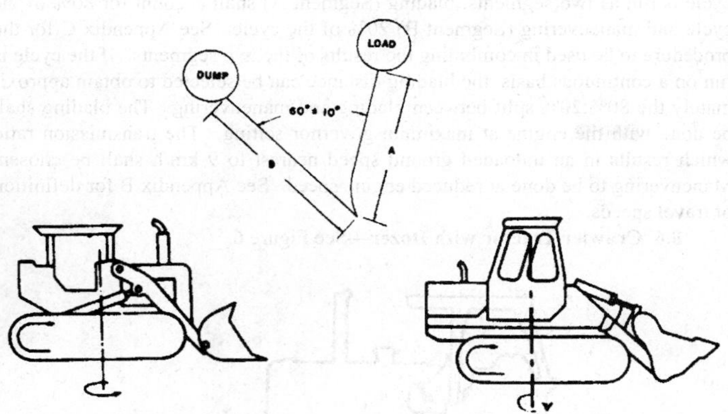

FIGURE 1—CRAWLER LOADER OPERATOR SOUND EXPOSURE WORK CYCLE

8.1.2 Machine Operation—The cycle is simulated truck loading from a stockpile. The machinery shall be operated at maximum governor setting considering all the safety requirements that are necessary on the test site. For machines with manual transmissions, changing the gear ratio during the cycle is not typically done. For machines where it is practical to change gear ratios, the machinery shall be operated in the speeds specified. See Appendix B for definition of travel speeds.

a. Load at low travel speed.
b. In reverse, back straight and start to raise the bucket, then commence turning until an angle of 60 degrees ± 10 degrees is made. Then move forward at intermediate speed while continuing to raise the bucket. The bucket should reach kickout height or the typical bucket dump height at the same time that the machine reaches the point for dumping into the phantom truck body.
c. Bring machine to a stop, then dump bucket.
d. Lower bucket while reversing from the dump point and move forward to the stockpile to complete the cycle.

The total travel distance for each type of machinery will be determined by the time required to raise the bucket from the position it has when loaded to the dumping height. The reverse travel distance shall be such that the bucket has been raised to 1/2 of its height. The remaining lifting should then be done while moving forward. The lengths A and B in the drawing shall be approximately equal.

8.2 Wheel Type Loader—See Figure 2.

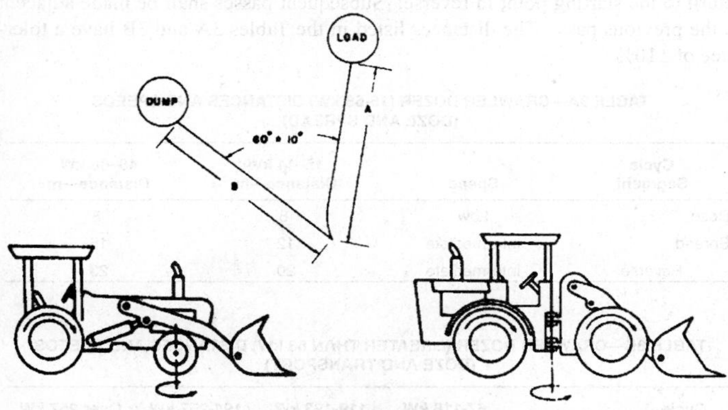

FIGURE 2—WHEEL TYPE LOADER OPERATOR SOUND EXPOSURE WORK CYCLE

8.2.1 Material—The material should be earth that is slightly moist. The moisture content should be low enough so that the material does not stick in the bucket. It should be free of large stones greater than 80 mm in diameter. It can contain varying proportions of sand, small stones, crushed rock, clay, and loam. The material to be loaded shall be in a loose stockpile of height appropriate for the size of the machine.

8.2.2 Machine Operation—The cycle is simulated truck loading from a stockpile. The machinery shall be operated at maximum governor setting considering all of the safety requirements that are necessary on the test site. The work cycle is structured for articulated frame automatic transmission machinery. Skid steer, rear wheel steer, front axle steer, and machinery with manual transmissions will require slight alteration of the work cycle in that the bucket lifting operation commences at a different point in the cycle, and that transmission gear ratio changes may not be made. See Appendix B for definition of travel speeds.

a. Load at low travel speed.
b. In reverse, back straight and start to raise the bucket, then commence turning until an angle of 60 degrees ± 10 degrees is made. Then move forward at intermediate speed while continuing to raise the bucket. The bucket shall reach kickout height or the typical bucket dump height at the same time that the machine reaches the point for dumping into the phantom truck body.
c. Bring the machine to a stop, then dump bucket.
d. Lower the bucket while reversing from the dump point and move forward to the stockpile to complete the cycle.

The total travel distance for each type of machinery will be determined by the time required to raise the bucket from the position it has when loaded to the dumping height. The reverse travel distance should be such that the bucket has been raised no more than 1/2 of its dumping height. The remaining lifting should then be done while moving forward. The lengths A and B in the drawing shall be approximately equal.

8.3 Dumper—See Figure 3 and Table 2.

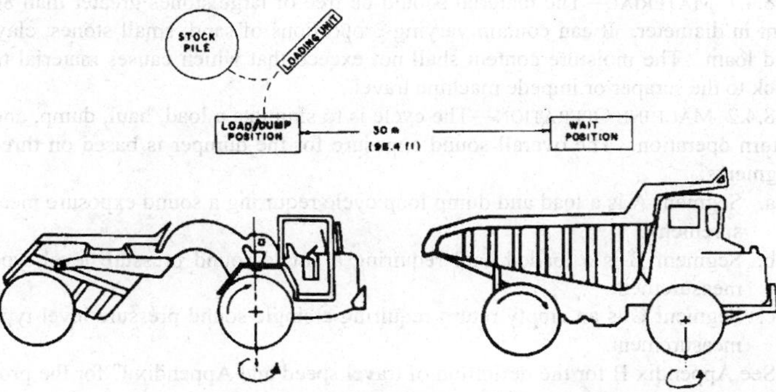

FIGURE 3—DUMPER OPERATOR SOUND EXPOSURE WORK CYCLE

TABLE 2—DUMPER CYCLE DISTANCES AND SPEEDS

Cycle Segment	Speed	Cycle Parameters
Wait	Neutral—Low Idle	2 min at 30 m from load area
Back into load area	Low	30 m
Load	Neutral—Low Idle	—
Forward to wait area	Low	30 m
Back to dump area	Low	30 m
Dump	Neutral—High Idle	—
Forward to wait area	Low	30 m

8.3.1 Material—The material can be any combination of earth including shot rock.

8.3.2 Machine Operation—The cycle is to simulate a load and haul application of the dumper. Machinery suitably sized for loading the dumper is required. The overall sound exposure for the dumper is based on three segments:

a. Segment A is a wait, load, and dump cycle requiring a sound exposure measurement.
b. Segment B is a loaded haul requiring a single sound pressure level type measurement.
c. Segment C is an empty return requiring a single sound pressure level type measurement.

See Appendix B for definition of travel speeds and Appendix C for the procedure to combine the results from the three parts of the test.

8.3.2.1 Segment A—Wait, Load, and Dump Cycle—45% of Total

8.3.2.2 Segment B—Loaded Haul—40% of Total—The transmission shall be in intermediate speed with the governor control in the maximum speed position. When the engine speed is at rated engine speed as a result of any combination of load, grade, attempted acceleration, or braking, the sound level shall be recorded.

NOTE—Since this may be a singular-type test, it is possible to determine the required value as the engine accelerates in intermediate speed into and through the rated speed range. This will reduce the need for a special test area.

8.3.2.3 Segment C—Empty Return—15% of Total—The transmission shall be in high speed with the engine speed controlled to 3/4 of maximum governed engine speed (high idle) when the sound level is recorded.

8.4 Tractor Scraper—See Figure 4.

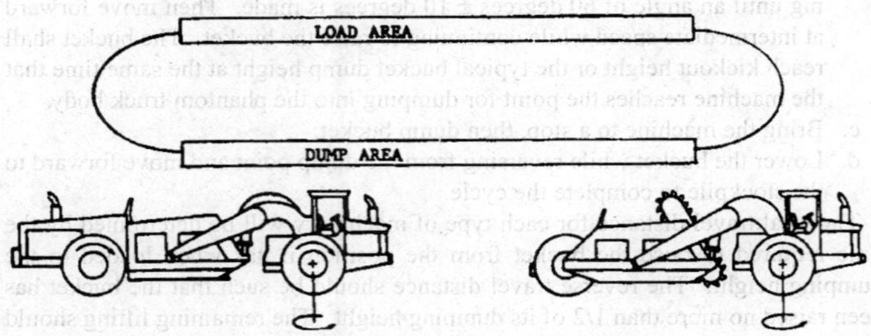

FIGURE 4—TRACTOR SCRAPER-OPEN BOWL AND ELEVATING OPERATOR SOUND EXPOSURE WORK CYCLE

8.4.1 MATERIAL—The material should be free of large stones greater than 80 mm in diameter. It can contain varying proportions of sand, small stones, clay, and loam. The moisture content shall not exceed that which causes material to stick to the scraper or impede machine travel.

8.4.2 MACHINE OPERATION—The cycle is to simulate a load, haul, dump, and return operation. The overall sound exposure for the dumper is based on three segments:

a. Segment A is a load and dump loop cycle requiring a sound exposure measurement.
b. Segment B is a loaded haul requiring a single sound pressure level type measurement.
c. Segment C is an empty return requiring a single sound pressure level type measurement.

See Appendix B for the definition of travel speed and Appendix C for the procedure to combine the results from the three parts of the test.

8.4.2.1 Segment A—Load and Dump Loop Cycle—35% of Total—For the loading operation, open bowl scrapers shall be pushed with an appropriately-sized push tractor(s). The scraper shall be operated on as tight a loop cycle as is possible for its size. The borrow pit depth and stockpile height shall not exceed the distance from the center of the drive axle to the ground.

8.4.2.2 Segment B—Loaded Haul—35% of Total—The transmission shall be in intermediate speed with the governor control in the maximum speed position. When the engine speed is at rated engine speed as a result of any combination of load, grade, attempted acceleration, or braking, the sound level shall be recorded.

NOTE—Since this may be a single sound pressure level type test, it is possible to determine the required value as the engine accelerates in intermediate speed into and through the rated speed range. This will reduce the need for a special test area.

8.4.2.3 Segment C—Empty Return—30% of Total—The transmission shall be in high speed with the engine speed controlled to 3/4 of maximum governed engine speed (high idle).

This is also a single sound pressure level type test.

8.5 Grader—See Figure 5.

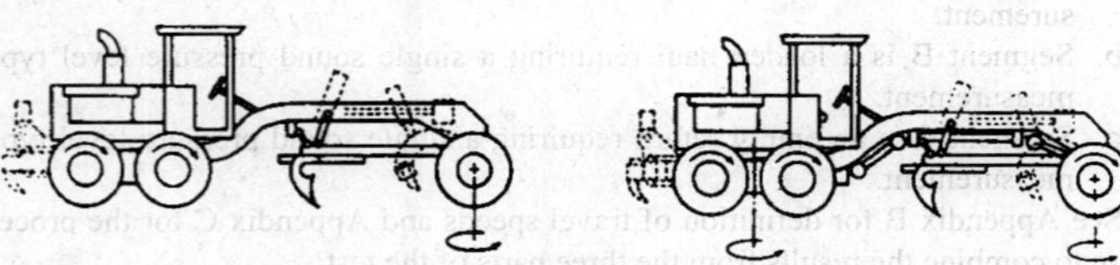

FIGURE 5—GRADER OPERATOR SOUND EXPOSURE WORK CYCLE

8.5.1 MATERIAL—The material should be a hard packed composite of sand, gravel, small stones, clay, and loam. The stones shall not exceed 50 mm in diameter. The surface moisture can be high to keep the dust level down, but the subsurface shall be dry.

8.5.2 MACHINE OPERATION—The cycle is to be haul road maintenance, cutting the hard packed material rather than just carrying a blade of loose material. The cycle can be run as two separate segments or as one continuous cycle. If the cycle is run as two segments, blading (Segment A) shall account for 80% of the cycle and maneuvering (Segment B) 20% of the cycle. See Appendix C for the procedure to be used in combining the results of the two segments. If the cycle is run on a continuous basis, the blading distance can be selected to obtain approximately the 80%:20% split between blading and maneuvering. The blading shall be done with the engine at maximum governor setting. The transmission ratio which results in an unloaded ground speed nearest to 9 km/h shall be chosen. Maneuvering to be done at reduced engine speed. See Appendix B for definition of travel speeds.

8.6 Crawler Tractor with Dozer—See Figure 6.

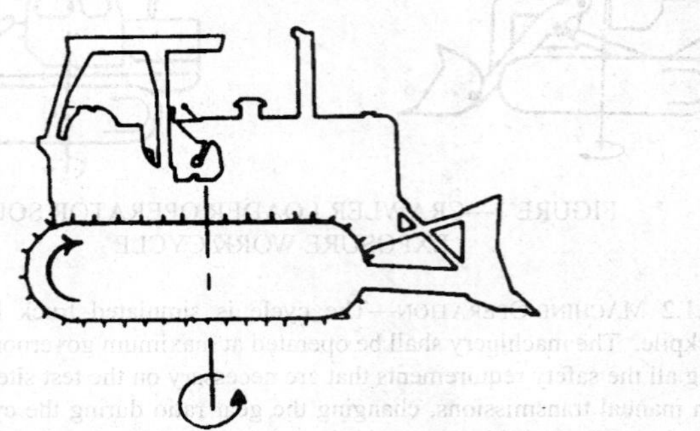

FIGURE 6—CRAWLER TRACTOR WITH DOZER OPERATOR SOUND EXPOSURE WORK CYCLE

8.6.1 MATERIAL—The material should be earth that is slightly moist. The moisture content must be low enough so that the material does not stick or pack in the track system. The material should be free of stones greater than 80 mm in diameter and not exceed 1/2 sand, gravel, or crushed rock. The soil can be clay or loam.

8.6.2 MACHINE OPERATION—The cycle consists of a continuous operation of dozing, spreading, or transporting and reversing over a specified distance. The machinery shall be operated at maximum governor setting considering all the safety requirements that are necessary on the test site. For machinery with manual transmissions, changing the transmission gear ratio is not typically done. For such machinery, the most appropriate gear ratio shall be used throughout the cycle. See Appendix B for definition of travel speeds.

The machinery shall be operated so as to fully load, but not overload, the dozer blade over the dozing distance. A constant load shall then be transported over the specified transport distance. For the dozers required to spread the material, the spreading shall commence at the start of the spread distance and continue with an ever decreasing blade load until the end of the spread distance. Dozers shall return to the starting point in reverse. Subsequent passes shall be made adjacent to the previous pass. The distances listed in the Tables 3A and 3B have a tolerance of ±10%.

TABLE 3A—CRAWLER DOZER (15-66 kW) DISTANCES AND SPEEDS (DOZE AND SPREAD)

Cycle Segment	Speed	15–44 kW Distance—m	45–66 kW Distance—m
Doze	Low	8	8
Spread	Intermediate	12	15
Reverse	Intermediate	20	23

TABLE 3B—CRAWLER DOZER (GREATER THAN 66 kW) DISTANCES AND SPEEDS (DOZE AND TRANSPORT)

Cycle Segment	Speed	67-118 kW Distance—m	119-193 kW Distance—m	194-257 kW Distance—m	Over 257 kW Distance—m
Doze	Low	9	12	15	18
Spread	Intermediate	15	18	23	27
Reverse	Intermediate	24	30	38	45

8.7 Wheel Tractor With Dozer—See Figure 7.

8.7.1 MATERIAL—The material should be earth that is slightly moist. The moisture content must be low enough so that the machinery does not lose traction. The material should be free of stones greater than 80 mm in diameter. It can contain varying proportions of sand, small stones, clay, and loam.

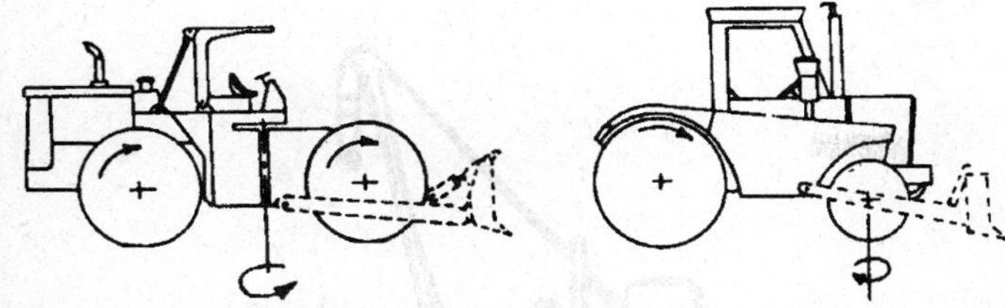

FIGURE 7—WHEEL TRACTOR WITH DOZER OPERATOR SOUND EXPOSURE WORK CYCLE

8.7.2 MACHINE OPERATION—The cycle consists of a continuous operation of dozing, spreading, and reversing over a specified distance. The machinery shall be operated at maximum governor setting considering all the safety requirements that are necessary on the test site. The machinery should be operated so as to fully load, but not overload, the dozer blade over the doze distance and then commence spreading at the start of the spread distance and continue with ever decreasing blade load until the end of the spread distance. The machine shall return to the starting point in reverse. Subsequent passes should be made adjacent to previous passes. Distances listed in Table 4 have a tolerance of ±10%. See Appendix B for definition of travel speeds.

TABLE 4—WHEEL TRACTOR DOZER DISTANCES AND SPEEDS

Cycle Segment	Speed	Under 119 kW Distance—m	119–193 kW Distance—m	194–257 kW Distance—m	Over 257 kW Distance—m
Doze	Low	9	12	15	18
Spread	Intermediate	15	18	23	27
Reverse	Intermediate	24	30	38	45

8.8 Pad Foot Wheel Compactor With Dozer—See Figure 8.

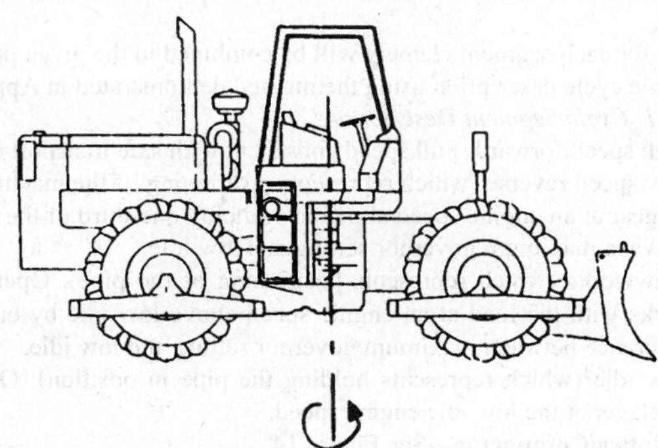

FIGURE 8—PAD FOOT WHEEL COMPACTOR WITH DOZER OPERATOR SOUND EXPOSURE WORK CYCLE

8.8.1 MATERIAL—The material should be free of stones greater than 80 mm in diameter. It can contain varying proportions of sand, small stones, crushed rock, clay, and loam. The moisture content shall not exceed that which causes the material to stick to the blade or compaction wheels. The material may be uneven so that the dozer blade is alternately loaded and unloaded.

8.8.2 MACHINE OPERATION—The cycle consists of a continuous operation of dozing, spreading, and reversing over a specified distance. The machinery shall be operated at maximum governor setting considering all the safety requirements that are necessary on the test site. In the doze portion, the blade should be loaded and in the spread portion unloaded. The machine shall return to the starting point in reverse. Subsequent passes shall be made adjacent to previous passes. Distances listed in Table 5 have a tolerance of ±10%. See Appendix B for definition of travel speeds.

TABLE 5—PAD FOOT WHEEL COMPACTOR WITH DOZER DISTANCES AND SPEEDS

Cycle Segment	Speed	Distance—m
Doze and Compact	Low	9
Spread and Compact	Intermediate	15
Reverse and Compact	Intermediate	24

8.9 Backhoe Loader—See Figure 9.

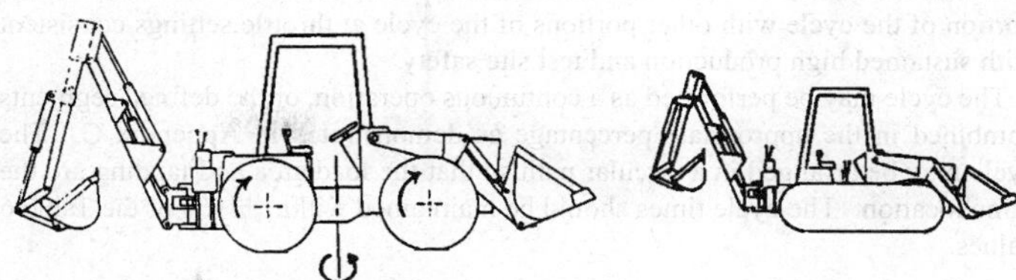

FIGURE 9—BACKHOE LOADER OPERATOR EXPOSURE WORK CYCLE

8.9.1 MATERIAL—The material should be compacted or virgin soil. It may contain varying proportions of sand, rock, clay, and loam. The material shall be free of large rock that would impede loading of the bucket.

8.9.2 BACKHOE OPERATION—The engine shall be operated at the manufacturer's recommended engine speed or if there is no manufacturer's recommendation, then the engine shall be operated at 85% ± 2% of rated speed. The cycle shall be a typical trenching operation. The cycle shall consist of digging at 1/2 to 2/3 of the maximum digging depth with the standard dipper stick. The swing arc shall be 50 degrees ± 10 degrees. Removed material may be stockpiled alongside the trench.

8.9.3 COMBINED BACKHOE/LOADER OPERATION—Many machines are commonly equipped to perform both loader and/or backhoe operations. For combined operator exposure, the backhoe operation shall represent 80% of the total $L_{eq(5)}$ and the remaining 20% shall be derived from the loader sound exposure work cycle. (8.1.2 for Crawler Loader and 8.2.2 for Wheel Loader.) See Appendix C to combine operator's sound exposures.

8.10 Hydraulic Excavator—See Figure 10.

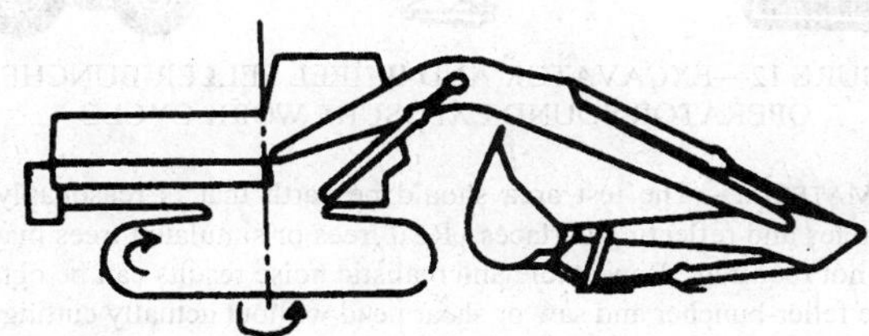

FIGURE 10—HYDRAULIC EXCAVATOR OPERATOR SOUND EXPOSURE WORK CYCLE

8.10.1 MATERIAL—The material should be compacted or virgin soil. It may contain varying proportions of sand, rock, clay, and loam. The material shall be free of large rock that would impede loading of the bucket.

8.10.2 MACHINE OPERATION—The machinery shall be operated at maximum governor setting considering all of the safety requirements that are necessary at the test site. The cycle shall be a typical trenching operation. The cycle shall consist of digging at 1/2 to 2/3 of the maximum digging depth with the standard stick. The swing arc shall be 50 degrees ± 10 degrees. Removed material may be stockpiled alongside the trench.

8.11 Skidder—See Figure 11.

FIGURE 11—SKIDDER OPERATOR SOUND EXPOSURE WORK CYCLE

8.11.1 MATERIAL—The test area should be earth that is reasonably free of obstacles and reflecting surfaces. Log loads should consist of at least three and not more than five separate logs which must be gathered to form a load which is approximately 80% of the advertised load.

8.11.2 MACHINE OPERATION—The cycle in a log skidding operation includes hooking up logs (or gathering with grapple), skidding 182 m, and positioning (decking) the logs with the front blade at the destination (landing). The cycle also includes a return trip without load to the "woods" of 182 m. An approximate cycle time for a hydraulic grapple skidder is 9 min and a cable skidder is 15 min. The machinery will be operated at maximum safe speed for the skid and return portion of the cycle with other portions of the cycle at throttle settings consistent with sustained high production and test site safety.

The cycle may be performed as a continuous operation, or the defined segments combined in the appropriate percentage as demonstrated in Appendix C. The cycle may be arranged in a circular path so that the load area and landing are the same location. The cycle times should be maintained within ±10% of the Table 6 values.

TABLE 6—SKIDDER SEGMENT TIMES AND PERCENTAGES

Cycle Segment	Gear	Hyd. Grapple Time—Percentage	Cable Time—Percentage
Gather or hookup logs	N	24	41
Skid 182 m	1F&2F	23	14
Maneuver at Landing	1F	12	7
Unhook Logs	N	0	14
Deck	1F&1R	12	7
Return to Woods 182 m	1F&2F	17	10
Maneuver to Stump	1F&1R	12	7
Total		100%	100%
		(9 min)	(15 min)

8.12 Excavator and Wheel Feller-Buncher—See Figure 12.

FIGURE 12—EXCAVATOR AND WHEEL FELLER-BUNCHER OPERATOR SOUND EXPOSURE WORK CYCLE

8.12.1 MATERIAL—The test area should be earth that is reasonably free of large obstacles and reflecting surfaces. Real trees or simulated trees may be cut, but this is not required. Repeatable and realistic noise results can be obtained by cycling the feller-buncher and saw or shear head without actually cutting at a rate simulating felling and bunching 3 to 5 trees per minute.

8.12.2 MACHINE OPERATION—The feller-buncher may operate in a wooded area or an open area. The complete cycle includes maneuvering or repositioning to reach standing trees, clamping on and cutting individual trees, then swinging or transporting to lay the tree(s) in a pile. After clearing the trees within easy reach, the excavator feller-buncher is repositioned to reach more trees. The machine shall be operated at maximum governor setting considering all the safety requirements that are necessary on the test site.

The cycle may be performed as a continuous operation, or the defined segments combined in the appropriate percentage as demonstrated in Appendix C. The cycle times should be maintained within ±3% of Tables 7A and 7B values for the cycle breakdown.

TABLE 7A—EXCAVATOR FELLER-BUNCHER CYCLE SEGMENT PERCENTAGES

Cycle Segment	Time—Percentage
Swing & Maneuver Unit Empty	20
Position Head & Cut Tree(s)	45
Swing & Drop Tree(s)	35
Total	100%

TABLE 7B—WHEEL FELLER-BUNCHER CYCLE SEGMENT PERCENTAGES

Cycle Segment	Time—Percentage
Move to tree(s)	35
Cut & Accumulate Tree(s)	40
Move to Pile & Drop Tree(s)	25
Total	100%

8.13 Pipelayer—See Figure 13.

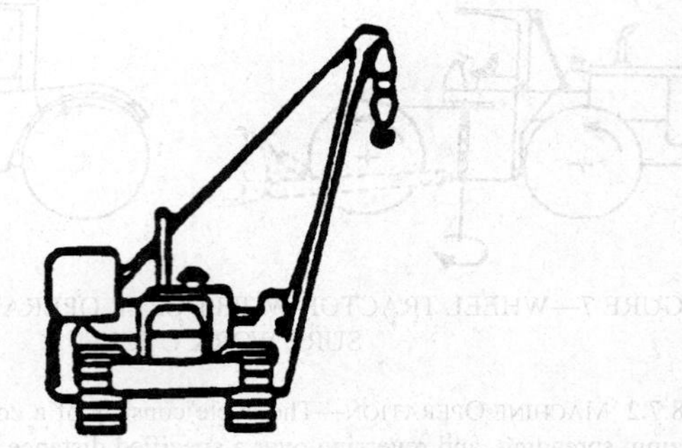

FIGURE 13—PIPELAYER OPERATOR EXPOSURE WORK CYCLE

8.13.1 MATERIAL—The test area should be level compacted earth that is reasonably free of large obstacles and reflecting surfaces. The load will be typical mainline pipe for the machine capacity, or an equivalent concentrated weight.

8.13.2 MACHINE OPERATION—The three job functions (mainline, string-out, and shuttle-to-bender) cover the work description of the vast majority of all pipelayers on large pipe jobs. The pipelayer will be operated under cycle segments as described in Table 8.

TABLE 8—PIPELAYER JOB FUNCTION VERSUS CYCLE SEGMENT PERCENTAGES

Cycle Segment	Mainline Time—Percentage	String-out Time—Percentage	Shuttle-to-bender Time—Percentage
High Forward	3 (without load)	7 (without load)	32 (with load)
Low Reverse	2 (without load)	—	—
Drawworks	5 (with load)	7 (with load)	3 (with load)
Low Idle	90	86	65
Total	100%	100%	100%

The $L_{eq(5)}$ for each segment element will be combined in the given percentages for the suitable cycle description using the method demonstrated in Appendix C.

8.13.2.1 Cycle Segment Descriptions

a. High speed forward: Full speed consistent with safe transport operation.
b. Low speed reverse (which represents positioning of the machine): Lowest gear at an engine speed above low idle by one-third of the difference between maximum governor setting and low idle.
c. Drawworks (which represents positioning of the pipe): Operate drawworks with the load at an engine speed above low idle by one-third of difference between maximum governor setting and low idle.
d. Low idle (which represents holding the pipe in position): Operate the pipelayer at the low idle engine speed.

8.14 Roller/Compactor—See Figure 14.

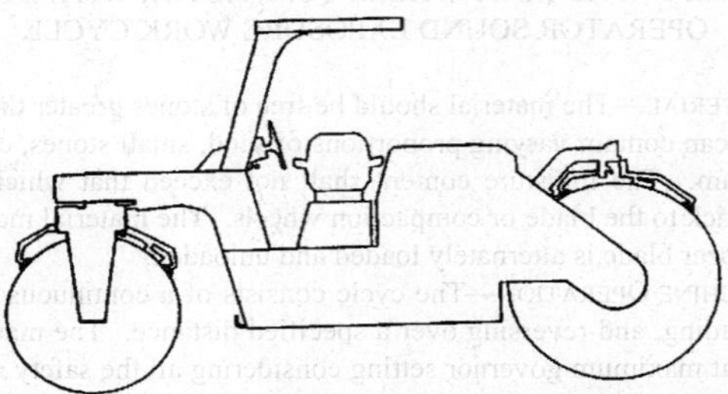

FIGURE 14—ROLLER/COMPACTOR OPERATOR SOUND EXPOSURE WORK CYCLE

8.14.1 MATERIAL—For vibratory smooth or pad foot rollers/compactors, the material should be uncompacted soil, free of stones greater than 40 mm in diameter. For static (nonvibratory) rollers/compactors, the material should be a 50 mm layer of sand or clay over compacted soil. The moisture content shall not exceed that which causes the material to stick to the rolls or tires. The test area should be level.

8.14.2 MACHINE OPERATION—The machine should be ballasted per manufacturer's instructions. Scrapers should be operating. Water spray should be off. For machines with hand throttles, 80% of maximum governor setting should be set. For machines with foot throttles, wide open throttle should be used. Travel speed for machines with infinitely variable transmissions should be half maximum ground speed. Machines equipped with manual transmissions should be operated in intermediate gear at half maximum ground speed. The cycle consists of forward and reverse travel over a distance of 30 m, and operated per Table 9. For vibratory machines, the vibratory mechanism should be run at manufacturer's recommended amplitude and at maximum frequency. No more than four passes should be made over a given area. The cycle may be performed as a continuous operation, or the defined segments may be combined in the appropriate percentage as demonstrated in Appendix C. The cycle times should be maintained within ±3% of Table 9 values for the cycle breakdown. If the roller is equipped with a leveling blade, the blade shall be in the transport position.

TABLE 9—ROLLER/COMPACTOR WORK SEGMENT PERCENTAGES

Cycle Direction	Segment Vibrator Operation	Static Time—Percentage	Vibratory Time—Percentage
Forward	Off	50	25
Forward	On	—	25
Reverse	Off	50	—
Reverse	On	—	50
Total		100%	100%

8.15 Trencher—See Figure 15.

FIGURE 15—TRENCHER OPERATOR SOUND EXPOSURE WORK CYCLE

8.15.1 MATERIAL—The material should be compacted or virgin soil. It may contain varying proportions of sand, small stones, clay, and loam. The material shall be free of large rock that would impede the trencher chain, wheel, or direct burial plow.

8.15.2 MACHINE OPERATION—The trencher engine shall be operated at the manufacturer's recommended engine speed, or if there is no manufacturer's recommendation, then the engine shall be operated at the maximum governor setting. Table 10 gives the appropriate cycle segment percentages. The trenching cycle segment shall consist of digging at full depth with the standard chain, wheel, or direct burial plow blade. See Appendix B for definitions of travel speeds.

TABLE 10—CHAIN, WHEEL, DIRECT BURIAL PLOW, and Walk-Along TRENCHER—CYCLE SEGMENT PERCENTAGES

Cycle Segment	Speed	Chain Time-Percentage	Wheel Time-Percentage	Direct Burial Plow Time-Percentage	Walk-Along Trencher Time-Percentage
Maneuver	Low	10	15	10	10
Trench/Plow	Low	60	85	70	90
Backfill/ Backtrack	Intermediate	30	—	20	—
Total		100%	100%	100%	100%

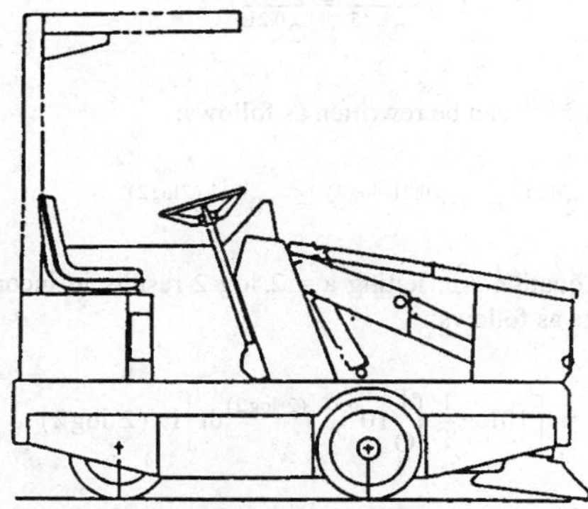

FIGURE 16—SWEEPER OPERATOR SOUND EXPOSURE WORK CYCLE

8.15.3 COMBINED TASK OPERATION—Many trenching machines are equipped to perform both trenching and other associated operations such as: backhoe excavation and provide hydraulic power. Each separate tool operation shall be measured for an individual task $L_{eq(5)}$. Where possible, the task description from other sections of this document will be used. For combined operator exposure, the trenching operation in Table 10 shall represent 75% of the total $L_{eq(5)}$, and the remaining 25% shall be the associated task $L_{eq(5)}$. Other percentage combinations may be calculated, but shall be documented. See Appendix C to combine operator's task sound exposures.

8.16 Sweeper—Refer to SAE J2130 for identification of self-propelled sweepers.

8.16.1 MATERIAL—The sweep test shall be conducted on a paved surface in an area that is reasonably free of large obstacles and reflecting surfaces.

8.16.2 MACHINE OPERATION—Normal sweeper operation is a ground debris collection operation with the machine moving forward in automatic or "drive". The sweeper truck engine shall be operated at an rpm to maintain a machine ground speed of 4 to 8 kph. If the sweeper is equipped with a water system, it shall be operating during this test. If equipped with an auxiliary engine, it shall operate at maximum rpm. The blower and/or conveying system shall operate at maximum rpm. All brooms shall operate at maximum rpm. The main broom may be a poly-type but the side brooms must be equipped with steel inserts. Indoor sweepers may have poly-type side brooms.

APPENDIX A

A.1 Definition of $L_{eq(5)}$—$L_{eq(5)}$ is defined as the equivalent value of a time varying sound level calculated on the 5 dB increase in level for halving of time. It can be calculated:

$$L_{eq(5)} = 16.61 \log_{10} \sum_{i=i}^{n} \frac{\%t_i}{100}(2^{0.2L_i}) \qquad \text{(Eq. A1)}$$

$\%t_i$ is the percentage of time at the L_i sound level in dB(A). Derivation of this equation is given.

Let L_{eq} be defined as the equivalent value of a time varying sound level. This can be expressed simply as:

$$Eq = \frac{1}{T} \int_O^T f(x)\,dt \qquad \text{(Eq. A2)}$$

Since sound pressure levels are measured in decibels, the mathematics must follow the laws associated with logarithms. The transformation of Equation A2 to equivalent sound level is as follows:

$$L_{eq} = 10 \log \frac{1}{T} \int_O^T 10^{L/10}\,dt \qquad \text{(Eq. A3)}$$

Equation A3 can be written in several forms which are more convenient to work with:

$$L_{eq} = 10 \log \frac{1}{T} \int_O^T 10^{0.1L}\,dt \qquad \text{(Eq. A4)}$$

or,

$$L_{eq} = 10\log\left[\frac{1}{T}\int_O^T (10^{0.1L})^a\,dt\right]^{1/a} \quad \text{(Eq. A5)}$$

Equations A3 and A4 will produce the equivalent sound level on the equal energy basis. In Equation A5, if a is equal to 1, the equal energy value will be determined.

In this document, the interest is to calculate the equivalent sound level based on a 5 dB doubling rate for halving of time. Equal energy doubling is a 10 log 2 dB doubling rate for halving of time. The 5 dB doubling rate for halving of time can be expressed as follows:

$$T = \frac{1}{2^{L/5}} = \frac{1}{2^{0.2L}} \quad \text{(Eq. A6)}$$

The expression $2^{0.2L}$ can be rewritten as follows:

$$2^{0.2L} = 10^{(0.2L\ \log 2)} = 10^{0.1L(2\log 2)} \quad \text{(Eq. A7)}$$

Returning to Equation A5, letting a = 2 log 2 results in incorporation of the 5 dB doubling rate as follows:

$$L_{eq(5)} = \left[10\log\frac{1}{T}\int_O^T 10^{0.1L\ (2\log 2)}\,dt\right]^{1/(2\log 2)} \quad \text{(Eq. A8)}$$

Simplifying, using laws of mathematics and Equation A7 results in:

$$L_{eq(5)} = \left(\frac{10}{2\log 2}\right)\log\frac{1}{T}\int_O^T 2^{0.2L}\,dt \quad \text{(Eq. A9)}$$

Further simplification yields:

$$L_{eq(5)} = 16.61\log\frac{1}{T}\int_O^T 2^{0.2L}\,dt \quad \text{(Eq. A10)}$$

Because the data being calculated per this document will typically be discrete dB values in either whole, half, or other width dB cells, the summation form is easier to use than the integral form.

Equation A10 can be rewritten as follows:

$$L_{eq(5)} = 16.61\log\sum_{i=i}^{n}\frac{\%t_i}{100}(2^{0.2L_i}) \quad \text{(Eq. A11)}$$

NOTE—The time weighting and cutoff in an instrument can affect the measured levels. The calculated time weighted average sound level with 5 dB exchange rate per SAE J1166 may not agree with the data from dosimeter type instruments. Many dosimeters have a slow dynamic time constant in the RMS detector and a cutoff level (below which data is not included in the result). The resulting difference would be most noticeable on impact type sounds.

APPENDIX B

B.1 Definition of Low, Intermediate, and High Speeds—Low speed means first gear or the lowest gear of a transmission system with up to five gear ratios. For transmission systems with six or more gear ratios, low speed means the second gear ratio.

Intermediate speed means second gear on the three or four gear ratio transmission system, third gear on a five or six gear ratio system, fourth gear ratio on a seven or eight gear ratio system, etc., for more gear ratio systems.

High speed means the upper gear ratio on a gear ratio transmission system, unless the highest gear ratio is considered only a transporting gear ratio. For those cases, the second highest gear ratio shall be considered as the highest gear ratio.

If there is a problem with automatic transmissions shifting up or down during the rated speed and load tests, one gear lower or higher may be used in an effort to alleviate the problem.

For hydrostatic, electric drive, or other type drive machinery, low speed means 1/4 of the maximum specified ground speed, intermediate speed means 1/2 of maximum specified ground speed, and high speed means maximum attainable ground speed. For these types of drive systems, the engine should be operated with the governor control in the maximum (high idle) position like for the gear ratio system. If this condition cannot be met because of the interaction of the engine and drive controls, then the ground speed may be increased or decreased, example—change in load, grade, or rolling resistance—may be utilized so as to still permit the engine governor control to be set in the maximum (high idle) position.

APPENDIX C

C.1 Calculation of Work Machine Operator Sound Exposure—The equivalent sound level $L_{eq(5)}$ shall be determined for cycle segments as described in Appendix A. This value shall then be considered for calculation purposes as L Segment A, etc., for various segments of the cycle and account for the appropriate percentage part of the total cycle as described in Section 8. The L Segment A, L Segment B, and L Segment C are combined using the appropriate cycle percentage in Equation C1.

$$L_{eq(5)} = 16.61\log_{10}\left[\frac{(A\%)}{100}(2^{0.2L\ \text{Segment A}}) + \frac{(B\%)}{100}(2^{0.2L\ \text{Segment B}}) + \frac{(C\%)}{100}(2^{0.2L\ \text{Segment C}})\right]\ (12) \quad \text{(Eq. C1)}$$

...for various segments or parts of the cycle as described in the appropriate paragraph in Section 8. The $L_{eq(5)}$ of each cycle segment shall be considered for calculation purposes as L_{eq} Part (A), L_{eq} Part (B), L_{eq} Part (C), etc. The L_{eq} parts are combined using the appropriate cycle percentage as shown in the cycle description.

APPENDIX D

D.1 Calculation of an operator's sound exposure is as follows:

$$\text{Operator's exposure} = 16.61\log_{10}\left[\begin{array}{l} A\left[2^{0.2L_{eq5}\ \text{of the machinery}}\right] \\ +B\left[2^{0.2\ \text{Level of other noise sources}}\right]\end{array}\right] \quad \text{(Eq. D1)}$$

A is the ratio of the operator's actual exposure time to the total time on the work shift. The actual exposure time does not include breaks, lunch time, or any other time the operator was not operating the machine. If the machinery is operated at reduced output for periods of time, these can be added in as $A_1, A_2, A_3 \ldots A_n$. The ratio of time and an equivalent sound level for these periods must be determined by time studies and additional sound level measurements. B is the ratio of the time during which additional noise sources are present in regard to the operator's total time on the work shift. If several additional noise sources are present, these can be added as $B_1, B_2, B_3 \ldots B_n$. The ratio of time and equivalent sound level for these noise sources must be known.

The calculation can expand according to the variations to:

(Eq. D2)

$$\text{Operator Exposure} = 16.61\ \log_{10}[A[2^{0.2L_{eq(5)}}] + A_1[2^{0.2L_1}] + A_2[2^{0.2L_2}] + A_3[2^{0.2L_3}] + \dots A_n[2^{0.2L_n}] + B[2^{0.2L_s}] + B_1[2^{0.2L_{s1}}] + B_2[2^{0.2L_{s2}}] + B_3[2^{0.2L_{s3}}] + \dots + B_n[2^{0.2L_{sn}}]]$$

APPENDIX E

E.1 Calculation of Operator Sound Exposure with Alternate Exchange Rates is as follows:

$$L_{eq(R)} = \frac{R}{\log_{10}2}\log_{10}\sum_{i=1}^{N}\frac{\%_i}{[(100}10^{\left(\frac{\log_{10}2L_i}{R}\right)})] \quad \text{(Eq. E1)}$$

where:

R = Exchange rate

L_i = Sound level of increment (in histogram distribution)

i = Different increments of percent time as in Appendix A.

APPENDIX F

F.1 See Figure F1.

SAE J1166
Earthmoving Machinery Operator
Work Cycle
Sound Level Test Report

Type of Machine ____________ Model ____________ S/N ____________

Work cycle used ____________

If not listed in this practice, describe cycle ____________

____

____

Cycle $L_{eq(5)}$ ________ dB(A)

Combined data system meets ________ Hz to ________ Hz

Instruments: Sound Level Meters, Recorders, Converters, Graphic Level Recorders, Integrating Systems, and Dosimeters

Manf./Model ____________ S/N ____________

Manf./Model ____________ S/N ____________

Manf./Model ____________ S/N ____________

Manf./Model ____________ S/N ____________

Manf./Model ____________ S/N ____________

Manf./Model ____________ S/N ____________

Manf./Model ____________ S/N ____________

Calibrator: Manf./Model ____________ S/N ____________

Certification Date ____________ Laboratory ____________

Other Comments: ____________

Data Author ____________ Date ____________

____

* If other than $L_{eq(5)}$, note exchange rate associated with this data.

FIGURE F1—EARTHMOVING MACHINERY OPERATOR WORK CYCLE SOUND LEVEL TEST REPORT

SOUND POWER LEVEL MEASUREMENTS OF WORK MACHINES—STATIC AND IN-PLACE DYNAMIC METHODS—SAE J1805 JAN2003

SAE Standard

Report of the SAE Construction Agricultural Sound Level Committee approved April 1987. Rationale statement available. Completely revised by the SAE Earthmoving Sound Level Subcommittee of the SAE Sound Level Technical Committee April 1993. Rationale statement available. Revised by the SAE Construction and Agricultural Sound Level Subcommittee SC1—Earthmoving Machinery January 2003. Rationale statement available.

1. Scope—This SAE Standard is used to determine the exterior A-weighted equivalent sound power level of static and in-place dynamic machines (dozer, loader, excavator, and backhoe) similar to the sound power obtained in ISO 6393 static and ISO 6395 dynamic sound power test procedures. Additional machine types, specifically sweepers and scrubbers, covered by SAE J2130 have been added, and other work machine types covered by SAE J1116 may be added with appropriate cycle descriptions and machine preparation. The recommended test procedures include conventional integrating sound pressure level methods or the sound intensity method using paired microphones. The sound intensity methodology provides a practical indoor alternative and permits measurement in the factory environment. The procedures in this document assume that the dominant sources are not highly sensitive to load (i.e., cooling fan, engine, track system). This test can be used as a substitute for the ISO 6393 static and ISO 6395 dynamic sound power tests for many machine types.

The requirements for the machine setup and operation, and the microphone array and hemispherical measurement surface are given in this document. This document shall be used in conjunction with instrumentation manufacturer's recommendations and SAE J/ISO 9614-1. The accompanying sound intensity procedure clarification is provided pending more widespread understanding of sound intensity.

2. References

2.1 Applicable Publications—The following publications form a part of this specification to the extent specified herein. Unless otherwise indicated, the latest issue of SAE publications shall apply.

2.1.1 SAE PUBLICATIONS—Available from SAE, 400 Commonwealth Drive, Warrendale, PA 15096-0001.

SAE J184 NOV1998—Qualifying a Sound Data Acquisition System

SAE J1116 MAR1999—Categories of Off-Road Self-Propelled Work Machines

SAE J2101/ISO 4872-1978—Acoustics—Measurement of Airborne Noise Emitted by Construction Equipment Intended for Outdoor Use—Method for Determining Compliance with Noise Limits

SAE J2130 OCT1997—Self-Propelled Sweepers and Cleaning Equipment

SAE J/ISO 9614-1:1993—Acoustics—Determination of sound power levels of noise sources using sound intensity—Part 1: Measurement at discrete points

2.1.2 ANSI AND ISO PUBLICATIONS—Available from ANSI, 25 West 43rd Street, New York, NY 10036-8002.

ANSI S1.4-1983 (R1997) (1997)—Specifications for Sound Level Meters ANSI S 1.4A-1985—Amendment to ANSI S 1.4-1983

ANSI S 1.40 (1984)—Specification for Acoustic Calibrators

ISO 6165-1997—Earth-Moving Machinery—Basic Types—Vocabulary

ISO 6393:1998—Acoustics—Measurement of exterior noise emitted by earth-moving machinery—Stationary test conditions

ISO 6395:1996—Acoustics—Measurement of exterior noise emitted by earth-moving machinery—Dynamic test conditions (includes Amend.1:1996)

2.1.3 IEC PUBLICATIONS—Available from International Electrotechnical Commission, 3 rue de Verambe, P.O. Box 131, 1211 Geneva 20, Switzerland.

IEC Publication 60651 (1979)—Sound Level Meters

IEC 60942 (1997)—Sound Calibrators

B&K Technical Review No. 4-1985, Validity of Intensity Measurements in Partially Diffuse Sound Fields, Svend Grand, M.Sc.

2.2 Related Publications—The following publications are provided for information purposes only and are not a required part of this document.

2.2.1 SAE PUBLICATIONS—Available from SAE, 400 Commonwealth Drive, Warrendale, PA 15096-0001.

SAE J1057 SEP88—Identification Terminology of Earthmoving Machines

SAE J1349 JAN90—Engine Power Test Code—Spark Ignition and Compression Ignition—Net Power Rating

SAE J/ISO 9614-2:1993—Acoustics—Determination of sound power levels of noise sources using sound intensity—Part 2: Measurement by scanning

SAE Technical Paper 850991—In-Place Dynamic Sound Power Test Method

2.2.2 ISO PUBLICATION—Available from ANSI, 25 West 43rd Street, New York, NY 10036-8002.

ISO 1585-1992—Road Vehicles—Engine Test Code—Net Power

ISO 3744:1994—Acoustics—Determination of sound power levels of noise sources using sound pressure—Engineering method in an essentially free field over a reflecting plane

2.2.3 IEC PUBLICATION—Available from International Electrotechnical Commission, 3 rue de Verambe, P.O. Box 131, 1211 Geneva 20, Switzerland.

IEC Publication 60804 (1985)—Integrating—Averaging Sound Level Meters, plus amendments

3. Instrumentation

3.1 The integrating sound pressure level system is used in conjunction with a free field over a reflecting plane (4.1.1).

3.1.1 The integrating sound level meter must permit the determination of the value of the A-weighted sound pressure level, energy averaged, over a time period dependent on the machine test cycle.

3.1.2 Any alternate system in place of a meter must perform the same functions required in 3.1.1.

3.1.3 The components of the measuring instrumentation system shall meet the Type 1 requirements given in the relevant clauses of IEC Publication 60651 (1979) and ANSI S1.4-1983 (R1997). Systems shall be qualified according to SAE J184 for the frequency range of interest.

3.1.4 The acoustic calibrator used for calibration prior to and after the test sequence shall have an accuracy within ± 0.5 dB and meet the requirements of ANSI S1.40-1984 or IEC 60942 (1997).

3.1.5 A microphone windscreen shall not be used except when it is required to reduce wind induced noise that is within 15 dB of the sound level of the source being measured. When a windscreen is used, it shall not affect the sound level of the source being measured by more than ± 0.5 dB(A) under zero wind speed conditions.

3.2 The sound intensity measurement system frequency response, linearity, A-weighting, and crest factor specifications shall conform to the Type 1 requirements of ANSI S1.4-1983 (R1997) or of SAE J184 NOV1998 for the frequency range of interest. (Until completion of the ANSI document, literature and software support from the major acoustic instrumentation manufacturers will aid in effective implementation of a sound intensity system.) The following is provided as interim information only:

3.2.1 A sound intensity system usually employs two closely spaced (paired) microphones, appropriate signal conditioning components, and a computerized analysis system. The sound intensity probe has a measurement axis that passes through the diaphragm center of both microphones (whether positioned side-by-side or end-to-end).

The intensity measurement interprets the phase information from each channel to determine the cosine value of the sound intensity vector relative to the probe axis. Sound energy passing through each surface segment is then the product of the intensity vector and the measurement surface segment perpendicular to the probe axis.

The total sound power is the summation of the surface segments times their respective intensity vectors.

3.2.2 Microphone spacing determines the useful frequency range of interest. A nominal spacing of 20 mm is suggested, but can be modified to better match the frequency characteristics of the machine being measured (see Table 1).

3.2.3 Low-frequency bias errors caused by phase-mismatching of the two microphones may be reduced by the following:

3.2.3.1 Phase Matched Instrumentation—The phase error between the two channels shall be less than 0.5 degree (dependent on frequency—see B&K Technical Review No. 4—1985).

3.2.3.2 Channel Switching—Electrically or physically switching channels halfway through each measurement.

3.2.3.3 On-Site Phase Calibration—Apply a random noise signal in a close coupled chamber or standing wave tube (refer to manufacturers' recommendations) simultaneously to both channels. The intensity program then calculates the phase mismatch between channels and applies a correction to the data.

TABLE 1—USABLE FREQUENCY RANGE FOR MICROPHONE SPACING

Usable Frequency Range with Phase Mismatch Microphone Spacing	Usable Frequency Range with Phase Mismatch 0.1 degree	Usable Frequency Range with Phase Mismatch 0.3 degree
6 mm	50 - 10 000 Hz	200 - 10 000 Hz
12 mm	40 - 5000 Hz	125 - 5000 Hz
20 mm	30 - 3500 Hz	100 - 3500 Hz
50 mm	10 - 1250 Hz	31 -1250 Hz

3.2.3.4 A combination of 3.2.3.1 and 3.2.3.2 or 3.2.3.3.

3.2.4 A-weighting for a sound intensity system shall be accomplished digitally on the calculated intensity vector frequency spectrum for data within the accuracy of standard industrial practice.

3.3 The anemometer or other device used in measurement of ambient wind speed and direction shall be accurate within ± 10% at 20 km/h.

3.4 The engine speed indicator shall be accurate within ± 2% of the indicated reading.

3.5 The ambient temperature measurement shall be accurate within ± 1 °C.

4. Procedure

4.1 Test Site—A nonabsorbing reflecting plane is required.

4.1.1 For sound pressure level instrumentation, a free field is required above the reflecting plane. There shall be no sound-reflecting obstacles within a distance from the source equal to three times the radius of the measuring hemisphere.

4.1.2 For sound intensity instrumentation the presence of reflecting objects is less critical, but no absorbing object or additional noise source other than the machine being measured shall be inside the measurement surface. This system permits measurements in most factory environments.

4.2 Measurement Surface—Size and shape depend on the instrumentation selected and the machine dimensions:

4.2.1 For sound pressure level instrument systems the measurement surface is a hemisphere with the radius determined by the length of the main body of the basic machine structure, excluding major attachments such as dozer blades, buckets, and booms. The radius (r) of the measurement hemisphere surface is given in Table 2 according to the basic length (ℓ).

TABLE 2—HEMISPHERE RADIUS RECOMMENDATION

Basic Length (ℓ) of the Machine	Radius (r) of Hemispherical Measurement Surface
$\ell \leq 1.5$ m	4 m
1.5 m $\leq \ell \leq$ 4 m	10 m
$\ell >$ 4 m	16 m

As a guideline for larger machines, over 6.5 m, the hemisphere radius should be 2.5 times the length of the basic machine not including attachments.

4.2.2 For sound intensity systems, rectangular and spherical surfaces are convenient for calculating surface segments and reproducibility. Though not required by this document, a hemispherical measurement surface is described to show the process and demonstrate the factors to be considered: perpendicular orientation of probe axis and the minimum number of surface segments. The measurement hemisphere radius should be large enough to enclose the machine and its moving attachments. A semicylindrical surface with hemispherical ends has proven satisfactory for long machines.

4.3 Measurement Surface and Microphone Positioning

4.3.1 For sound pressure level instrument systems, the measurement surface shall be a hemisphere of radius (r) given in Table 2. Location coordinates of the microphone positions are given in Table 3 and Figure 1.

TABLE 3—COORDINATES OF THE MICROPHONE LOCATION POINTS

Location No.	Figure No.	X/r[1]	Y/r	Z/r	Z
1	2	0.70	0.70	—	1.5 m
2	4	−0.70	0.70	—	1.5 m
3	6	−0.70	−0.70	—	1.5 m
4	8	0.70	−0.70	—	1.5 m
5	10	−0.27	0.65	0.71	—
6	12	0.27	−0.65	0.71	—

1. The positive X axis is the machine primary direction of travel.

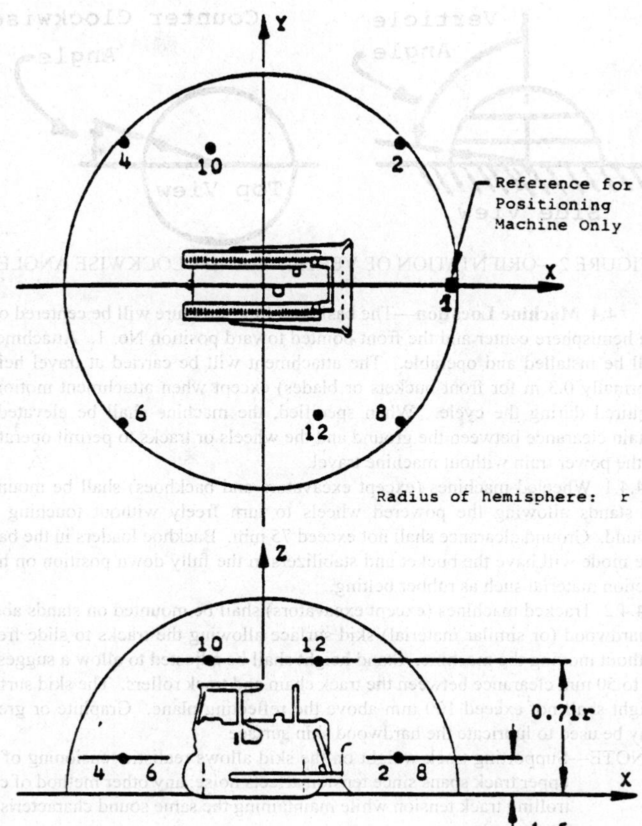

FIGURE 1—HEMISPHERE MEASUREMENT SURFACE FOR SOUND PRESSURE

4.3.2 For sound intensity systems the microphone probe axis shall be held perpendicular to the measurement surface. Two general methods are currently in use with their respective merits. Close scanning or area scanning will provide more information than just sound power but is more complex and labor intensive. Though not excluded, close scanning will not be detailed further. Fixed microphone locations at a sufficient number of representative surface segments must be further from the machine which results in lost detail, but simply and accurately determines sound power.

A hemispherical measurement surface is easily understood and implemented. Microphone positioning is most easily accomplished by a quarter arc boom pivoted to rotate above the hemisphere center. The arc boom provides the correct orientation of the microphone probe toward the hemisphere center located on the reflecting plane. Microphone repositioning becomes the simple horizontal rotation of the supporting arc boom to the next position (until the microphone probe must be moved higher along the arc boom for the upper layers). The suggested 24 microphone position array is described (at least 20 positions shall be used on a close enclosing hemisphere to ensure accuracy). The area is obtained by multiplying the hemisphere radius squared by the microphone location segment area factor given in Table 4 and illustrated in Figure 2. To qualify the number of surface segments necessary for a different measurement surface shape, continue doubling the number of surface segments until the change with each increase is less than 0.5 dB sound power.

TABLE 4—MICROPHONE LOCATION SEGMENT AREA FACTORS

Segments per Layer	Elevation Vertical Angle	Counterclockwise Angle Relative to Front	Segment Area Factor Multiply by (r) Squared
Bottom - 12	75 degree	Start @ 0, inc. 30 degree	0.270
Middle - 8	45 degree	Start @ 0. inc. 45 degree	0.248
Upper - 4	15 degree	Start @ 45, inc. 90 degree	0.263

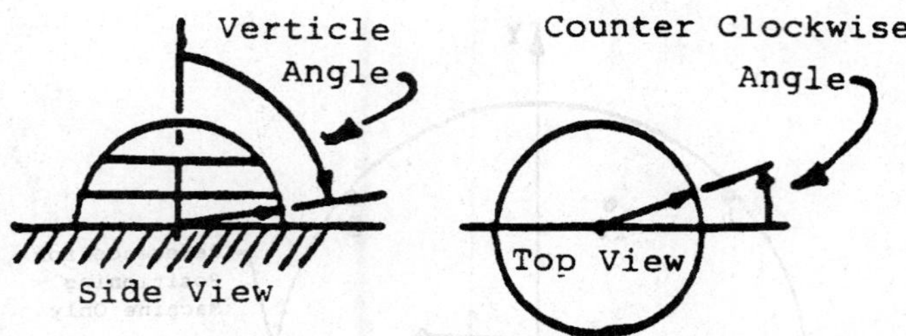

FIGURE 2—ORIENTATION OF VERTICAL AND CLOCKWISE ANGLES

4.4 Machine Location—The basic machine structure will be centered over the hemisphere center and the front pointed toward position No. 1. Attachments will be installed and operable. The attachment will be carried at travel height (normally 0.3 m for front buckets or blades) except when attachment motion is required during the cycle. When specified, the machine shall be elevated to obtain clearance between the ground and the wheels or tracks to permit operation of the power train without machine travel.

4.4.1 Wheeled machines (except excavators and backhoes) shall be mounted on stands allowing the powered wheels to turn freely without touching the ground. Ground clearance shall not exceed 75 mm. Backhoe loaders in the backhoe mode will have the bucket and stabilizers in the fully down position on high friction material such as rubber belting.

4.4.2 Tracked machines (except excavators) shall be mounted on stands above a hardwood (or similar material) skid surface allowing the tracks to slide freely without moving the machine. Stand height shall be adjusted to allow a suggested 25 to 50 mm clearance between the track chain and track rollers. The skid surface height shall not exceed 100 mm above the reflecting plane. Graphite or grease may be used to lubricate the hardwood skin surface.

NOTE—Supporting track weight on the skid allows realistic tensioning of the upper track spans since tension affects noise; any other method of controlling track tension while maintaining the same sound characteristics is allowed.

The hardwood skid may be permanent or installed on a plate for temporary use. Proper care in making the plate and shimming it on the reflecting plane will reduce plate noise contribution to insignificance.

4.4.3 Wheeled and tracked excavator machines shall be in contact with the reflecting plane or protecting rubber belting or any other nonabsorptive material.

4.5 Machine Operation—The machine shall be operated at a stabilized running temperature for the prevailing ambient condition. All engines on a multi-engined machine shall be operated concurrently. Sound data on the machine shall be measured under the two operating conditions as follows:

4.5.1 STATIC CONDITION—The machine will be operated at the manufacturer's specified rated engine speed under no-load condition with the transmission in neutral.

4.5.2 IN-PLACE DYNAMIC CONDITION—Machine operations are described in Appendices A through E. For machine types not listed use the dynamic cycle in the EU Sound directive or devise a cycle to characterize machine work and describe the cycle along with the data.

4.6 Climatic Conditions—Ambient wind and temperature shall be measured at a height of 2 m above the ground and recorded. Measurements shall not be conducted outdoors when precipitation is falling or when the test surface is covered with snow or temperature is below –10 °C or above +50 °C or if the wind velocity exceeds 8 m/s.

4.7 Measurements

4.7.1 Criteria for A-weighted background noise measured at the microphone positions shall be as follows:

4.7.1.1 For sound pressure level instruments, background noise shall be at least 10 dB below the measured level of the machine under test.

4.7.1.2 For sound intensity systems, background noise can equal that of the machine as long as no other noise source is within the measurement hemisphere. If background noise within 5 dB of the vector measurement is present, it shall be constant within 2 dB during the measurement and during the entire data accumulation.

4.7.2 INTEGRATION PERIOD—Shall be the duration of one cycle unless the event being simulated is a drive-through or static rated speed test, in which case, a single integration period of 20 to 30 s at each microphone location is recommended. It is recommended that three correctly executed cycles be measured at each microphone location. The surface segment measurements will be used to obtain the surface energy average sound pressure level $\overline{L}_{pAeq}$. The measurements from each surface segment will be energy-averaged together for comparison. The average of the highest two (within 2 dB of each other) will be used to obtain the surface energy average sound pressure level $\overline{L}_{pAeq}$.

4.7.3 NUMBER OF DYNAMIC CYCLES—Three dynamic cycles shall be carried out resulting in three measurements to be taken at each of the six microphone positions. Calculate the three sets of data obtained at all microphone positions. If two of the three values so obtained do not differ by more than 1 dB, further measurements are not necessary. If this is not the case, continue taking measurements until two values within 1 dB of each other are obtained. Report, as the value of the A-weighted sound power level, the arithmetic mean of the two highest values that are within 1 dB of each other.

4.8 Calculations

4.8.1 For sound pressure level systems, the surface energy average sound pressure level L_{pAeq} shall be calculated from each set of measured values of the energy average A-weighted equivalent continuous sound pressure level from all six microphone locations based on an energy average. The sound power level is obtained by adding an area factor, 10 log (S/S_o), and the environmental factor K.

$$L_{WAeq} = \overline{L}_{pAeq} + 10\log(S/S_o) - K \quad \text{decibels Ref: 1pW} \qquad \text{(Eq. 1)}$$

where:

S is the area of the measurement surface in square meters.
Ref: S_o = 1 m. ($S = 2\pi r^2$ for a hemispherical measurement surface.)
(See Table 5.)

TABLE 5—AREA FACTOR FOR STANDARD RADIUS HEMISPHERES

Radius	10 Log(S/S_0)
4 m	20 dB
10 m	28 dB
16 m	32 dB

Annex A of SAE J2101/ISO 4872-1978 shall be used to determine the environmental factor K or to determine if the reflecting plane is suitable. For test sites, which consist of a hard, flat surface such as asphalt or concrete and with no sound-reflecting obstacles within a distance from the source equal to three times the greatest distance from the source center to the lower measurement points, it may be assumed that the environmental correction factor K is less than or equal to 0.5 dB and is, therefore, negligible.

4.8.2 For sound intensity systems, the products of the sound intensity vectors times the represented perpendicular surface segments are summed. The surface correction factor K may be ignored if less than 0.5 dB. The total is sound power in decibels.

4.9 Information to be Recorded

4.9.1 MACHINERY UNDER TEST—The machine manufacturer, model number, arrangement, major attachments, engine speed at rated speed no-load condition, and maximum governed engine speed (during the in-place dynamic test only) shall be recorded. The machine operation will be specified either as a base mode operation under the appendix, or detailed to include gear selection, attachment operation, engine speeds, and if tracked, the track tension adjustment.

4.9.2 INSTRUMENTATION—State the instruments used during the tests to include name, type, manufacturer, and serial number.

4.9.3 ACOUSTICAL DATA—The measurement surface radius, microphone placement, average background sound pressure level, machine energy averaged sound pressure level or energy average sound intensity, and calculated sound power level, in A-weighted decibels, for the static and in-place dynamic test conditions.

4.10 Information to be Reported

4.10.1 The machine manufacturer, model number, arrangement, major attachments, engine speed at rated speed no-load condition for the static test, and maximum governed engine speed for the in-place dynamic test shall be recorded. For tracked machines, the track tension adjustment will be reported. The machine operation will be specified either as a base mode operation under the appendix, or detailed to include gear selection, attachment operation, and engine speeds.

4.10.2 The sound power level in A-weighted decibels for both the static and in-place dynamic test conditions rounded to the nearest decibel.

5. General Comments

5.1 It is recommended that persons trained and experienced in the current techniques of sound measurements select the instrumentation and conduct the tests. Attention to detail and a thorough understanding of the machine and test instrumentation operational requirements shall be prerequisites of all personnel attached to the evaluation program.

5.2 Proper use of all test instrumentation is essential to obtain valid measurements. Operating manuals or other literature furnished by the instrument manufacturer should be referred to for both recommended operation of the instrument and precautions to be observed.

5.2.1 The effects of ambient weather conditions on the performance of all instruments (for example: temperature, humidity, barometric pressure, and stray magnetic fields) must be known. Instrumentation can be influenced by low or high temperature, and caution should be exercised.

5.2.2 Proper signal levels, terminating impedances, and cable lengths on multi-instrument measurement systems must be known.

5.2.3 Proper acoustical calibration procedure, to include the influence of extension cables, etc., should be performed. Field acoustical calibration shall be made immediately before and after the testing of each piece of earthmoving machinery. The calibration before and after shall not vary by more than ± 0.5 dB for tests to be valid.

5.2.4 The overall effect due to an alternate test environment on the sound level measurement shall not exceed ±1.0 dB(A) from the sound power measurement made at the test site described in 4.1.

5.3 It should be recognized that variations in measured sound levels may occur due to variations in test site, ambient weather differences (temperature, wind, and their gradients), test equipment differences, and inherent differences between nominally identical machines.

APPENDIX A
EXCAVATORS (HYDRAULIC OR ROPE OPERATED)

Preface—(This appendix forms an integral part of the document.)

A.1 Definition (in Accordance with ISO 6165)—A self-propelled crawler or wheeled machine with an upper structure capable of a minimum of 360-degree rotation, which excavates, elevates, swings, and dumps material by the action of a bucket fitted to the boom and arm or telescoping boom, without moving the chassis or undercarriage during any one cycle of the machine.

A.2 Safety and Operation—All relevant safety precautions and the manufacturer's operating instructions shall be followed during the test.

Any signal devices, such as forward warning horn or backup alarm, shall not be activated during the test.

A.3 Setting-Up of the Machine—The excavator shall be equipped with the bucket, such as hoe, shovel, grab type, or dragline, designated for the manufacturer's production version. Engine and hydraulic systems shall be warmed to normal operating conditions for the prevailing ambient temperature. The engine governor control shall be set to the maximum position (high idle). All actuating movements shall be carried out at maximum velocity but without activating relief valves or contacting end-of-travel mechanical barriers. The excavator shall be located on a hard reflecting plane as specified in 4.1.

A.4 Operation of the Machine

A.4.1 Basic Machine Cycle—The dynamic cycle, without moving material, as described in A.4.2 to A.4.5, comprises three 90-degree swings to the left of the operator and back, with the machine positioned so the center of rotation of the upper structure of the excavator (which is defined as the machine center for the purpose of locating the machine) shall coincide with the center of the hemisphere shown in Figure 1. The longitudinal axis of the machine shall coincide with the x-axis and the front of the machine shall face position 1.

Each swing shall be from the x-axis to the y-axis, and back to the x-axis. A single cycle consists of three continuous 90-degree swings to the left and back while moving the front end attachment through a complete sequence for each 90-degree swing and back.

A.4.2 Hoe Attachment—The aim of the dynamic cycle is to simulate trench excavation and dumping the material adjacent to the trench. At the beginning of the cycle, the boom and arm shall be adjusted to place the bucket at 75% of the maximum reach with the bucket 0.5 m above the ground surface. The cutting edge of the bucket in the rolled forward position shall be at an angle of 60 degrees to the test site measurement surface.

First raise the boom and simultaneously retract the arm so that the bucket remains 0.5 m above the test site for 50% of the remaining boom and arm travel distance. Then roll back or curl the bucket. Lift the bucket by raising the boom and continue to retract the arm to simulate the adequate clearance (30% of maximum bucket lift height) needed to swing across the edge of the trench. Execute a 90-degree swing to the left of the operator. Raise the boom during the swing and extend the arm until the bucket has reached 60% of maximum boom lift height. Then uncurl the arm until it is 75% extended. Roll forward or uncurl the bucket until the cutting edge is vertical. Execute a return swing to the starting position with the boom being lowered and bucket being curled.

Repeat the sequence of events two more consecutive times in order to complete a single dynamic cycle.

NOTE—The single dynamic cycle is repeated three times to meet the requirements of three dynamic cycles as defined in 4.7.3.

A.4.3 Shovel Bucket Attachment—The aim of the work cycle is to simulate excavation at the height of a high wall. At the beginning of the cycle, with the bucket cutting edge parallel to the ground, the bucket shall be 0.5 m above the test site in the 75% retracted position.

First extend the bucket 75% of travel while maintaining the original bucket orientation. Then roll back or curl the bucket and raise it to 75% of maximum lift height and 75% of dipper arm extension. Execute a 90-degree swing to the left of the operator and at the end of the swing actuate the bucket dump mechanism. Execute a return swing to the starting position with the bucket 0.5 m above the test site in the 75% retracted position.

Repeat the sequence of events two more consecutive times in order to complete a single dynamic cycle.

NOTE—The single dynamic cycle is repeated three times to meet the requirements of three dynamic cycles as defined in 4.7.3.

A.4.4 Grab Type Attachment—The aim of the work cycle is to simulate excavation of a pit. At the beginning of the cycle, the grab shall be open and 0.5 m above the test site.

First close the grab. Then raise the grab to half of the maximum lift height. Execute a 90-degree swing to the left of the operator. Open the grab. Execute a return swing while lowering the attachment to the starting position.

Repeat the sequence of events two more consecutive times in order to complete a single dynamic cycle.

NOTE—The single dynamic cycle is repeated three times to meet the requirements of three dynamic cycles as defined in 4.7.3.

A.4.5 Dragline Attachment—The aim of the work cycle is to simulate excavation of a layer in a trench and dumping of the material adjacent to the trench. For the duration of the cycle, the boom shall be positioned at an angle of 40 degrees. The bucket shall hang vertically under the end of the boom and 0.5 m above the test site with drag chains not touching the ground.

First retract the bucket to bring it as close as possible to the machine while maintaining the distance of 0.5 m above the test site. When the bucket has been retracted, execute a 90-degree swing to the left of the operator. Simultaneously, raise the bucket to 75% of maximum lift height and extend to maximum reach in the loaded bucket position. Execute a return swing. Simultaneously, actuate the bucket dump and retract the bucket to the starting position.

Repeat the sequence of events two more consecutive times in order to complete a single dynamic cycle.

NOTE—The single dynamic cycle is repeated three times to meet the requirements of three dynamic cycles as defined in 4.7.3.

APPENDIX B
TRACTORS WITH DOZER EQUIPMENT

Preface—(This appendix forms an integral part of the document.)

B.1 Definition (in Accordance with ISO 6165)—A self-propelled crawler or wheeled machine used to exert a push or pull force through mounted equipment.

B.2 Safety and Operation—All relevant safety precautions and the manufacturer's operating instructions shall be followed during the test.

Any signal devices, such as forward warning horn or backup alarm, shall not be activated during the test.

B.3 Setting-Up of the Machine—The tractor shall be equipped with the dozer designated for the manufacturer's production version. Engine and hydraulic systems shall be warmed to normal operating conditions for the prevailing ambient temperature.

B.4 Operation of the Machine

B.4.1 The machine shall be positioned and elevated at the center of the hemisphere as defined in 4.4.

The machine shall be operated with the dozer in a lowered carry position 0.3 m ± 0.05 m above the ground plane of the hemisphere. The machine shall be operated at maximum governed engine speed (high idle) in a constant simulated forward and reverse travel mode. The simulated forward travel velocity shall be close to but not exceeding 4 km/h for crawler and steel-wheeled machines and 8 km/h for rubber-tired wheeled machines. The matching gear ratio shall be used in the reverse travel mode, regardless of the velocity. For the majority of machines, this will be first forward and first reverse. Hydrostatic drive machines may use a range of 3.5 to 4 km/h (crawler or steel-wheeled) and 7 to 8 km/h (rubber-tired) because of difficulty in setting ground speed controls for exact travel speeds.

These modes of operation are nonstop with no movement of the dozer equipment. If the lowest gear results in a velocity higher than the specified velocity, it shall be used with the engine operating at maximum governed speed (high idle). For hydrostatic drive machines with the engine at maximum governed engine speed (high idle), the ground speed control shall be set to match to specified velocities stated.

NOTE—Three separate forward and reverse cycles should be carried out to meet the requirements of three dynamic cycles as defined in 4.7.3.

B.4.2 Calculation for Combined Simulated Forward and Reverse Travel Mode Cycles—Since the forward and reverse modes of operation are two distinct modes, both the time and sound pressure level shall be measured as separate entities for each travel direction. The formula to be used for the calculation of the equivalent continuous A-weighted sound pressure level, $L_{pAeq,T}$, in decibels, for the combined dozer cycle is given by the following:

$$L_{pAeq,\,T} = 10\log\frac{V_1V_2}{V_1+V_2}\left[\left(\frac{1}{V_1}\times 10^{0.1L_{pAeq,\,1}}\right)+\left(\frac{1}{V_2}\times 10^{0.1L_{pAeq,\,2}}\right)\right] \quad \text{(Eq. B1)}$$

where:

V_1 is the velocity for the simulated forward travel mode.

V_2 is the velocity for the simulated reverse travel mode.

$L_{pAeq,1}$ and $L_{pAeq,2}$ are the quantities determined during the measurements at V_1 and V_2 velocities.

Use 1/V (where V represents velocity) for the inplace dynamic test instead of time used for the moving test to proportion the duration of forward and reverse travel.

APPENDIX C
LOADERS

Preface—(This appendix forms an integral part of the document.)

C.1 Definition (in Accordance with ISO 6165)—A self-propelled crawler or wheeled machine with an integral front-mounted bucket-supporting structure and linkage, which loads or excavates through forward motion of the machine, and lifts, transports, and discharges material.

C.2 Safety and Operation—All relevant safety precautions and the manufacturer's operating instructions shall be followed during the test.

Any signal devices, such as forward warning horn or backup alarm, shall not be activated during the test.

C.3 Setting-Up of the Machine—The loader shall be equipped with the bucket designated for the manufacturer's production version. Engine and hydraulic systems shall be warmed to normal operating conditions for the prevailing ambient temperature.

All activating movements shall be carried out at maximum velocity but without relief valves or contacting end-of-travel mechanical barriers.

C.4 Operation of the Machine

C.4.1 The machine shall be positioned and elevated at the center of the hemisphere, on a stand, as defined in 4.4.

The machine shall be operated with an empty bucket in a lowered carry position 0.3 m ± 0.05 m above the ground plane of the hemisphere. The machine shall be operated at maximum governed engine speed (high idle) in a constant simulated forward and reverse travel mode. The simulated forward travel velocity shall be close to but not exceeding 4 km/h for crawler machines and 8 km/h for wheeled machines. The matching gear ratio shall be used in the reverse travel mode, regardless of the velocity. For the majority of machines, this will be first forward and first reverse. Hydrostatic drive machines may use a range of 3.5 to 4 km/h (crawler) and 7 to 8 km/h (rubber-tired) because of difficulty in setting ground speed controls for exact travel speeds.

These modes of operation are with no movement of the bucket. If the lowest gear results in a velocity higher than the specified velocity, it shall be used with the engine operating at maximum governed speed (high idle). For hydrostatic drive machines with the engine at maximum governed engine speed (high idle), the ground speed control shall be set to match the specified velocities stated.

NOTE—Three separate forward and reverse cycles should be carried out to meet the requirements of three dynamic cycles as described in 4.7.3.

C.4.2 Calculation for Simulated Travel Modes—Since the simulated forward and reverse modes of operation are two distinct modes, both the time and sound pressure level shall be measured as separate entities for each travel direction. The formula to be used for the calculation of the equivalent continuous A-weighted sound pressure level, $L_{pAeq,3}$, in decibels, for the combined loader travel cycle is given by the following:

$$L_{pAeq,\,3} = 10\log\frac{V_1V_2}{V_1+V_2}\left[\left(\frac{1}{V_1}\times 10^{0.1L_{pAeq,\,1}}\right)+\left(\frac{1}{V_2}\times 10^{0.1L_{pAeq,\,2}}\right)\right] \quad \text{(Eq. C1)}$$

where:

V_1 is the velocity for the simulated forward travel mode.

V_2 is the velocity for the simulated reverse travel mode.

$L_{pAeq,1}$ and $L_{pAeq,2}$ are the quantities determined during the measurements at V_1 and V_2 velocities.

Use 1/V (where V represents velocity) for the inplace dynamic test instead of time used for the moving test to proportion the duration of forward and reverse travel.

C.4.3 Stationary Hydraulic Mode—The engine shall be operated at its maximum governed speed (high idle). The transmission control shall be set to neutral. Raise the bucket from the carry position to 75% of maximum lift height and then return to carry position three times. This sequence of events is considered to be a single cycle for the stationary hydraulic mode.

NOTE—The single cycle is repeated three times to meet the requirements of three dynamic cycles as defined in 4.7.3 $L_{pAeq,4}$ is the energy average L_{eq}.

C.4.4 Calculation for Combined Cycles in Travel and Stationary Hydraulic Modes—Calculate the combined equivalent continuous A-weighted sound pression level, $L_{pAeq,T}$, in decibels, for a total loader cycle using the following equation:

$$L_{pAeq,\,T} = 10\log[0.5\times 10^{0.1L_{pAeq,\,3}} + 0.5\times 10^{0.1L_{pAeq,\,4}}]\ldots \quad \text{(Eq. C2)}$$

where:

$L_{pAeq,3}$ is the quantity determined in the travel mode over the specified travel path.

$L_{pAeq,4}$ is the quantity determined with the loader in the stationary hydraulic mode.

APPENDIX D
BACKHOE LOADERS

Preface—(This appendix forms an integral part of the document.)

D.1 Definition—A self-propelled wheeled machine with a main structural support designed to carry both a front-mounted bucket loading mechanism and a rear-mounted backhoe. When used in the backhoe mode, the machine normally digs below ground level with bucket motion towards the machine. The backhoe lifts, swings, and discharges material while the machine is stationary. When used in the loader mode, the machine loads or excavates through forward motion of the machine, and lifts, transports, and discharges material.

D.2 Safety and Operation—All relevant safety precautions and the manufacturer's operating instructions shall be followed during the test.

Any signal devices, such as forward warning horn or backup alarm, shall not be activated during the test.

D.3 Setting-Up of the Machine—The backhoe loader shall be equipped with the backhoe and bucket designated for the manufacturer's production version. Engine and hydraulic systems shall be warmed to normal operating conditions for the prevailing ambient temperature.

For backhoe operation, the engine governor control shall be set to the maximum position (high idle) or to the position specified for use by the manufacturer. All actuating movements shall be carried out at maximum velocity but without activating relief valves or contacting end-of-travel mechanical barriers.

D.4 Operation of the Machine

D.4.1 Test Site Measurement Surface—For all operating modes of backhoe loaders the test site measurement surface shall be a hard reflecting plane, as specified in 4.1.

D.4.2 Backhoe Operation of the Machine—Carry out backhoe mode of operation of the machine in accordance with the procedures specified in A.4.1 and A.4.2, except substitute 45 degrees for each 90-degree angle specified in these subclauses.

D.4.3 Loader Operation of the Machine—Carry out this operation in accordance with the procedure specified in Section C.4 and with the bucket of the backhoe in a carry position.

D.4.4 Calculation for Combined Cycles in Backhoe and Loader Modes of Operation—Calculate the combined equivalent A-weighted sound pressure level, $L_{pAeq,T}$, in decibels, for a total backhoe loader cycle using the following equation:

$$L_{pAeq,\,T} = 10\log[0.8 \times 10^{0.1L_{pAeq,\,backhoe}} + 0.2 \times 10^{0.1L_{pAeq,\,loader}}] \quad \text{(Eq. D1)}$$

where:

$L_{pAeq,backhoe}$ is the quantity determined in the backhoe mode of operation.

$L_{pAeq,loader}$ is the quantity determined in the loader mode of operation.

APPENDIX E
SWEEPER/SCRUBBER

Preface—(This appendix forms an integral part of the document).

E.1 Definition (In Accordance with SAE J2130)—Sweepers; are self propelled machines primarily designed to sweep material from highways, parking lots, industrial and commercial areas, construction sites, and road re-paving work. These machines can move material to a hopper or other type of container attached to the machine by mechanical or pneumatic means, or by combinations of each.

Scrubbers; are self-propelled machines that use a washing system to remove material. The washing system consists of a tank of cleaning solution, a method for applying the cleaning solution to the surface and a collection system to recover the cleaning solution.

Combination sweepers/scrubbers; are self-propelled machines that incorporate both a sweeping and a scrubbing system.

E.2 Safety and Operation—All relevant safety precautions and the manufacturer's operating instructions shall be followed during the test. Any signal devices, such as forward warning horn or backup alarm, shall not be activated during the test.

E.3 Setting-Up of the Machine—The machine shall be equipped with standard brushes and other consumable cleansing mechanisms in an 'as-new' condition. In the case of machines with IC engines, the engine governor shall be set to the maximum position (high idle). Machines using other forms of prime mover, the system shall be set to run in the maximum condition.

E.4 Operation of the Machine—The machine shall be positioned as defined in 4.4 above a hard reflective surface. The engine/prime mover shall be set to operate at the manufacturer's maximum condition. Brushes shall be in their working position, set at normal ground pressure and operating at their highest speed. In the case of pneumatic conveyance systems, the distance between the mouth or inlet of the system and the ground level shall not exceed 25 mm. When the machine is positioned in the test condition and the mechanism is unable to achieve the required dimension, then a suitable substrate shall be provided and positioned to replicate a typical paved road surface. Machines with mechanical conveyance mechanisms, the mechanisms shall be set to work at their maximum speeds. In the case of Scrubbers, a suitable substrate shall be provided and positioned whereby the scrubbing mechanism and retrieval system shall work in the normal operating function. The machine's transmission shall be set to propel it at a speed of 4 km/h using the lowest gear ratio combination. Where machines are not capable of 4 km/h then the highest speed attainable shall be used.

NOTE—Three separate measurements of the simulated forward working travel should be carried out to meet the requirements of three dynamic cycles as defined in 4.7.3.

OPERATOR EAR SOUND LEVEL MEASUREMENT PROCEDURE FOR SMALL ENGINE POWERED EQUIPMENT—SAE J1174 MAR1985

SAE Recommended Practice

Report of the SAE Specialized Vehicle and Equipment Sound Level Committee approved October 1977, reaffirmed without change March 1985. Rationale statement available.

Foreword—This Reaffirmed Document has been changed only to reflect the new SAE Technical Standards Board Format.

1. Scope—This SAE Recommended Practice establishes the instrumentation and procedure to be used in measuring the operator ear sound level for engine powered equipment under 15 kW (20 bhp). The sound levels obtained by using this procedure are representative of the sound levels generated by the equipment under typical operating conditions. It is intended to include equipment such as lawn mowers, snow blowers, and tillers. It is not intended to include equipment designed primarily for operation on highways or within factories or buildings, or vehicles such as motorcycles, snowmobiles, and pleasure motorboats that are covered by other SAE Standards or Recommended Practices.

This procedure does not cover chain saws.

This SAE Recommended Practice may also be used when measuring the operator ear sound level of similar equipment powered by electricity or other power sources.

2. References

2.1 Applicable Publications—The following publications form a part of the specification to the extent specified herein. Unless otherwise indicated the latest revision of SAE publications shall apply.

2.1.1 SAE Publication—Available from SAE, 400 Commonwealth Drive, Warrendale, PA 15096-0001.

SAE J833a—Human Physical Dimensions

2.1.2 ANSI Publication—Available from ANSI, 11 West 42nd Street, New York, NY 10036-8002

ANSI S1.4-1971—Specification for Sound Level Meters

2.1.3 ASTM Publication—Available from ASTM, 100 Barr Harbor Drive, West Conshohocken, PA 19428-295

ASTM C423-66—Method of Test for Sound Absorption of Acoustical Materials in Reverberation Rooms

2.2 Related Publications

2.2.1 ANSI Publication—Available from ANSI, 11 West 42nd Street, New York, NY 10036-8002

ANSI S1.1-1960—Acoustical Terminology

ANSI S1.13-1971—Methods of Measurement of Sound Pressure

3. Instrumentation—The following instrumentation shall be used for the measurement required.

3.1 A precision sound level meter which meets the Type 1 requirements of American National Standard Specification for Sound Level Meters, S1.4-1971.

3.2 A sound level calibrator (see 5.3.3).

3.3 The microphone shall be used with a foam windscreen. The windscreen shall not affect the overall reading by more than ±0.5 dB(A) for the sound source that is being measured (see 5.4).

3.4 An anemometer or other device for measurement of ambient wind speed.

3.5 An engine speed indicator (accuracy ±1% of full range).

3.6 A thermometer for measurement of ambient temperature.

4. Procedure

4.1 Test Site—The test area shall consist of a flat open space free from the effects of signboards, buildings, or hillsides for at least 15 m (50 ft) from the measurement zone.

4.1.1 The minimum dimensions of the measurement zone are 1.0 m (3.3 ft) wider than the equipment being tested and 10 m (33 ft) long for moving tests. (See Figure 1.)

4.1.2 The entire surface of the measurement zone shall be a synthetic surface mounted to 19 mm (¾ in) exterior plywood or 13 mm (½ in) marine plywood with a suitable adhesive.

The acoustical properties tested per ASTM C423-66 after mounting shall be as shown in Table 1.

4.1.3 The observer reading the sound level meter shall be at least 2 m (6.6 ft) from the equipment being tested and not affect the measured sound level. One other person may be directly behind the observer reading the meter. All others, except the operator of the equipment being tested, shall be at least 7 m (23 ft) from the equipment.

4.1.4 The A-weighted sound level, (including wind effects) due to sources other than the equipment being measured, shall be at least 10 dB lower than the level of the equipment being measured.

TABLE 1—ACOUSTICAL PROPERTIES

Hz	Sound Absorption Coefficient
125	0.00-0.06
250	0.07-0.12
500	0.15-0.28
1000	0.28-0.34
2000	0.38-0.47
4000	0.40-0.62

4.2 Equipment Operation

4.2.1 All equipment shall be tested in either a traveling or stationary mode as specified in 4.2.2 to 4.2.6. Tests in the traveling mode shall be performed as the equipment moves along the centerline of the measurement zone at the closest operating speed to 5 km/h (3 mph). Tests in the stationary mode shall be made at the center of the measurement zone. Then engine(s) or motor(s) shall be set at the equipment manufacturer's maximum specified rpm. Then all mechanisms necessary for the equipment to perform its intended function shall be engaged.

4.2.2 Mowing Equipment—Test in a traveling mode. The cutting height of the blade shall be set at the closest available position to 50 mm (2 in).

4.2.3 Walk-Behind Tillers—Test in a stationary mode those units that are intended to be propelled by the tines. Units propelled by other means shall be tested in the traveling mode.

4.2.4 Walk-Behind Snow Blowers—Test in a traveling mode.

4.2.5 Garden Tractors With Attachments Other Than Mowers—Test in the traveling mode except those units with attachments that are intended for stationary use. These shall be tested in the stationary mode as stationary equipment.

4.2.6 Miscellaneous Equipment—Test either in a traveling or stationary mode according to its intended use.

4.3 Measurements

4.3.1 The sound level meter shall be set for *slow* response and the A-weighted network.

4.3.2 The ambient wind speed relative to the source and microphone, ambient temperature, equipment manufacturer's maximum specified engine rpm, engine rpm at test condition, and ambient A-weighted sound level shall be measured and recorded.

4.3.3 Walk-Behind Equipment (for Both Traveling and Stationary Modes)—With an operator present, the microphone shall be supported independent of the equipment being tested. The microphone shall be located 1.7 m (66 in) above the test surface, 250 mm (10 in) to the right and left of the centerline of the operator's position, and 200 mm (8 in) to the rear of the rear-most point of the handle, with the handle in the forward-most position.

4.3.4 Ride-On Equipment—With an operator present, the microphone shall be supported independent of the equipment being tested. The microphone shall be located 760 mm (30 in) above the loaded seat, 250 mm (10 in) to the right and left of the centerline of the operator's position, and 100 mm (4 in) forward of the seat back, with the seat adjusted to its center position.

4.3.5 Hand-Held Equipment—A standing operator shall hold the equipment under test and orient it in a normal operating position. The microphone shall be located 250 mm (10 in) to the right and left of the centerline of the operator, 1.7 mm (66 in) above the test surface, and 300 mm (12 in) to the rear of the rear-most point of the rear handle. Record equipment orientation.

4.3.6 Stationary Equipment—Stationary equipment normally requiring an operator shall be tested with an operator at the normal operator station. If the operator is standing, the microphone shall be located 1.7 mm (66 in) above the test surface and 460 mm (18 in) from the outer-most vertical surfaces of the equipment being tested, and 250 mm (10 in) to the right and left of the centerline of the operator. If the operator is seated, located the microphone as in 4.3.4. Record the exact microphone position relative to the equipment.

4.3.7 The sound level meter shall be observed for a minimum of 5 s or until a stabilized reading is obtained. Record the maximum sound level to the nearest 0.5 dB(A) and document the microphone position. The reported sound level shall be the highest repeatable sound level observed during the test.

5. General Requirements

5.1 It is recommended that the equipment operator size be within the SAE J833a dimensions for 5-95 percentile man.

5.2 It is strongly recommended that persons technically trained and experienced in the current techniques of sound measurement select the equipment and conduct the tests.

5.3 Proper use of all test instrumentation is essential to obtain valid measurements. Operating manuals or other literature furnished by the instrument manufacturer, should be referred to for both recommended operation of the instrument and precautions to be observed. Specific items to be considered are:

5.3.1 The type of microphone, its directional response characteristics, and its orientation relative to the noise source.

5.3.2 The effects of ambient weather conditions on the performance of all instruments (temperature, humidity, and barometric pressure). Instrumentation can be influenced by low temperature and caution should be exercised.

5.3.3 Proper acoustical calibration procedure shall include the influence of extension cables. Field calibration shall be made immediately before and after each test sequence. Internal calibration means is acceptable for field use, provided that external calibration is accomplished immediately before and after field use.

5.4 It is recommended that measurements be made only when wind speed is below 19 km/h (12 mph).

5.5 It is recommended that care be taken in selecting a test site and placing the synthetic test surface so that test surface vibrations do not contribute to the sound level readings.

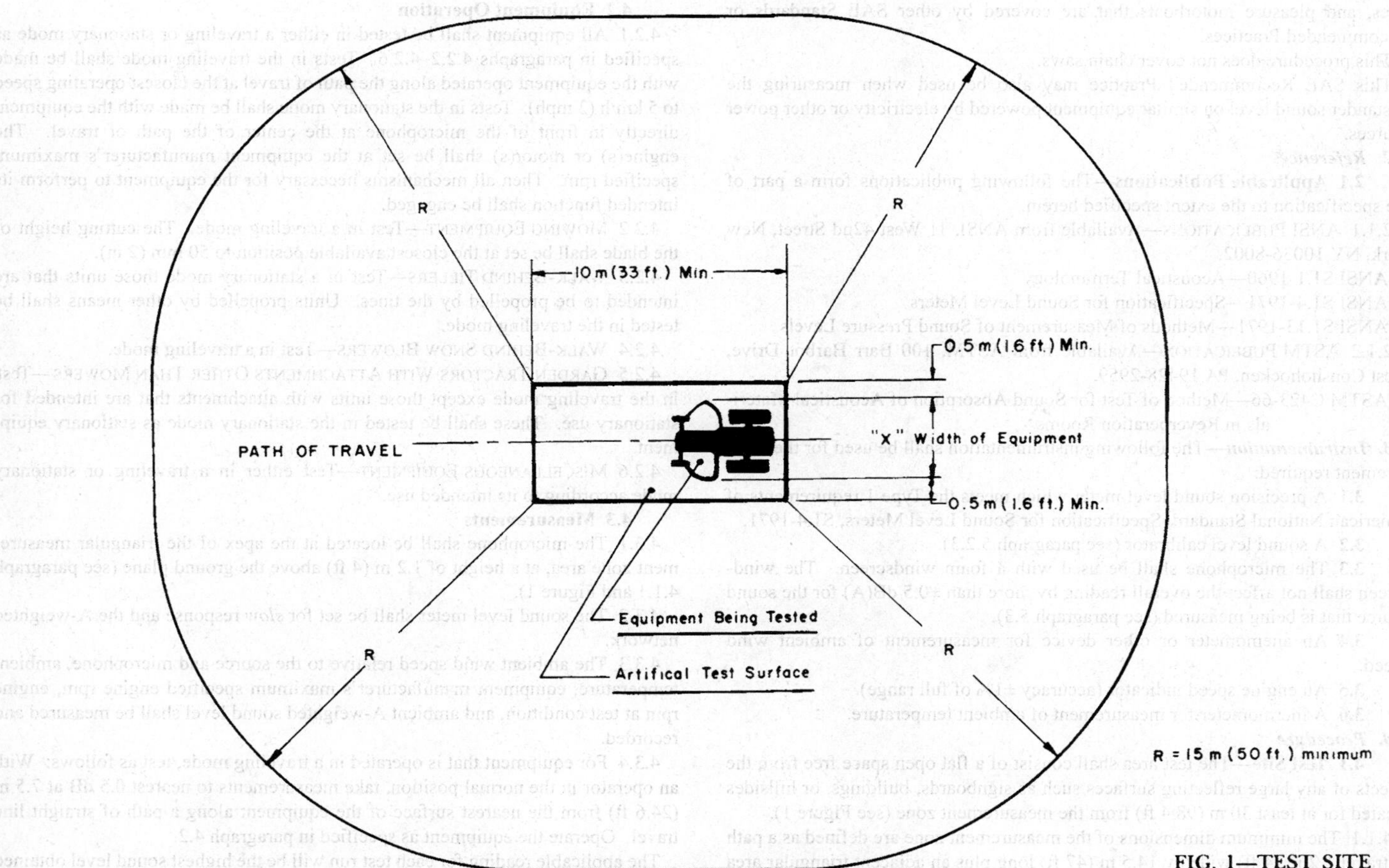

FIG. 1—TEST SITE

FIGURE 1—TEST SITE

BYSTANDER SOUND LEVEL MEASUREMENT PROCEDURE FOR SMALL ENGINE POWERED EQUIPMENT—SAE J1175 MAR1985

SAE Recommended Practice

Report of the SAE Specialized Vehicle and Equipment Sound Level Committee approved October 1977, reaffirmed without change March 1985. Rationale statement available.

Foreword—This Reaffirmed Document has been changed only to reflect the new SAE Technical Standards Board Format.

1. Scope—This SAE Recommended Practice establishes the instrumentation and procedure to be used in measuring the bystander sound level of engine powered equipment under 15 kW (20 bhp) typical of their normal operation. It is intended to include equipment such as lawn mowers, snow blowers, and tillers. It is not intended to include equipment designed primarily for operation on highways or within factories and buildings, or vehicles such as motorcycles, snowmobiles, and pleasure motorboats that are covered by other SAE Standards or Recommended Practices.

This procedure does not cover chain saws.

This SAE Recommended Practice may also be used when measuring the bystander sound level on similar equipment powered by electricity or other power sources.

2. References

2.1 Applicable Publications—The following publications form a part of the specification to the extent specified herein.

2.1.1 ANSI PUBLICATIONS—Available from ANSI, 11 West 42nd Street, New York, NY 10036-8002.

ANSI S1.1-1960—Acoustical Terminology

ANSI S1.4-1971—Specification for Sound Level Meters

ANSI S1.13-1971—Methods of Measurement of Sound Pressure Levels

2.1.2 ASTM PUBLICATION—Available from ASTM, 100 Barr Harbor Drive, West Conshohocken, PA 19428-2959.

ASTM C423-66—Method of Test for Sound Absorption of Acoustical Materials in Reverberation Rooms

3. Instrumentation—The following instrumentation shall be used for the measurement required:

3.1 A precision sound level meter which meets the Type 1 requirements of American National Standard, Specification for Sound Level Meters, S1.4-1971.

3.2 A sound level calibrator (see paragraph 5.2.3).

3.3 The microphone shall be used with a foam windscreen. The windscreen shall not affect the overall reading by more than ±0.5 dB(A) for the sound source that is being measured (see paragraph 5.3).

3.4 An anemometer or other device for measurement of ambient wind speed.

3.5 An engine speed indicator (accuracy ±1% of full range).

3.6 A thermometer for measurement of ambient temperature.

4. Procedure

4.1 Test Site—The test area shall consist of a flat open space free from the effects of any large reflecting surfaces such as signboards, buildings, or hillsides located for at least 30 m (98.4 ft) from the measurement zone (see Figure 1).

4.1.1 The minimum dimensions of the measurement zone are defined as a path of travel 1.2 m (4 ft) wide by 14.5 m (47 ft) long plus an adjacent triangular area having a base along the edge of the path of travel and the apex 7.5 m (24.6 ft) from the midpoint of the base.

4.1.2 The entire surface of the measurement zone shall be synthetic surface mounted to 19 mm (¾ in) exterior plywood or 13 mm (½ in) marine plywood with a suitable adhesive.

Acoustical properties tested per ASTM C423-66 after mounting on plywood shall be:

TABLE 1—

Hz	Sound Absorption Coefficients
125	0.00–0.06
250	0.07–0.12
500	0.15–0.28
1000	0.28–0.34
2000	0.38–0.47
4000	0.40–0.62

4.1.3 The observer reading the sound level meter shall be at least 2 m (6.6 ft) directly behind the microphone. One other person may be directly behind the observer reading the meter. All others, except the operator of the equipment being tested, shall be at least 15 m (50 ft) from the equipment path or instrumentation.

4.1.4 The A-weighted sound level (including wind effects), due to sources other than the equipment being measured, shall be at least 10 dB lower than the level of the equipment being measured.

4.2 Equipment Operation

4.2.1 All equipment shall be tested in either a traveling or stationary mode as specified in paragraphs 4.2.2–4.2.6. Tests in the traveling mode shall be made with the equipment operated along the path of travel at the closest operating speed to 5 km/h (3 mph). Tests in the stationary mode shall be made with the equipment directly in front of the microphone at the center of the path of travel. The engine(s) or motor(s) shall be set at the equipment manufacturer's maximum specified rpm. Then all mechanisms necessary for the equipment to perform its intended function shall be engaged.

4.2.2 MOWING EQUIPMENT—Test in a traveling mode. The cutting height of the blade shall be set at the closest available position to 50 mm (2 in).

4.2.3 WALK-BEHIND TILLERS—Test in a stationary mode those units that are intended to be propelled by the tines. Units propelled by other means shall be tested in the traveling mode.

4.2.4 WALK-BEHIND SNOW BLOWERS—Test in a traveling mode.

4.2.5 GARDEN TRACTORS WITH ATTACHMENTS OTHER THAN MOWERS—Test in the traveling mode except those units with attachments that are intended for stationary use. These shall be tested in the stationary mode as stationary equipment.

4.2.6 MISCELLANEOUS EQUIPMENT—Test either in a traveling or stationary mode according to its intended use.

4.3 Measurements

4.3.1 The microphone shall be located at the apex of the triangular measurement zone area, at a height of 1.2 m (4 ft) above the ground plane (see paragraph 4.1.1 and Figure 1).

4.3.2 The sound level meter shall be set for *slow* response and the A-weighted network.

4.3.3 The ambient wind speed relative to the source and microphone, ambient temperature, equipment manufacturer's maximum specified engine rpm, engine rpm at test condition, and ambient A-weighted sound level shall be measured and recorded.

4.3.4 For equipment that is operated in a traveling mode, test as follows: With an operator in the normal position, take measurements to nearest 0.5 dB at 7.5 m (24.6 ft) from the nearest surface of the equipment along a path of straight line travel. Operate the equipment as specified in paragraph 4.2.

The applicable reading for each test run will be the highest sound level obtained from the equipment as it moves along the line of travel. The equipment shall be run at least three times in each direction. Report, to nearest 0.5 dB, the average of 2 highest readings from the loudest side which are within 1 dB of each other.

4.3.5 For equipment that is operated in a stationary mode, test as follows: With the operator in normal position, orient the equipment to obtain the maximum sound level. Take measurements to nearest 0.5 dB at 7.5 m (24.6 ft) from the nearest surface of the equipment. Operate the equipment as specified inn paragraph 4.2. Report the highest reading to the nearest 0.5 dB.

5. General Requirements

5.1 It is strongly recommended that persons technically trained and experienced in the current techniques of sound measurement select the equipment and conduct the tests.

5.2 Proper use of all test instrumentation is essential to obtain valid measurements. Operating manuals or other literature furnished by the instrument manufacturer should be referred to for both recommended operation of the instrument and precautions to be observed. Specific items to be considered are:

5.2.1 The type of microphone, its directional response characteristics, and is orientation relative to the ground plane and source of noise.

5.2.2 The effects of ambient weather conditions on the performance of all instruments (for example, temperature, humidity, and barometric pressure). Instrumentation can be influenced by low temperature and caution should be exercised.

5.2.3 Proper acoustical calibration procedure to include the influence of extension cables. Field calibration shall be made immediately before and after each test sequence. Internal calibration means is acceptable for field use, provided that external calibration is accomplished immediately before and after field use.

5.3 It is recommended that measurements be made only when wind speed is below 19 km/h (12 mph).

5.4 It is recommended that care be taken in selecting a test site and placing the synthetic test surface so that test surface vibrations do not contribute to the sound level readings.

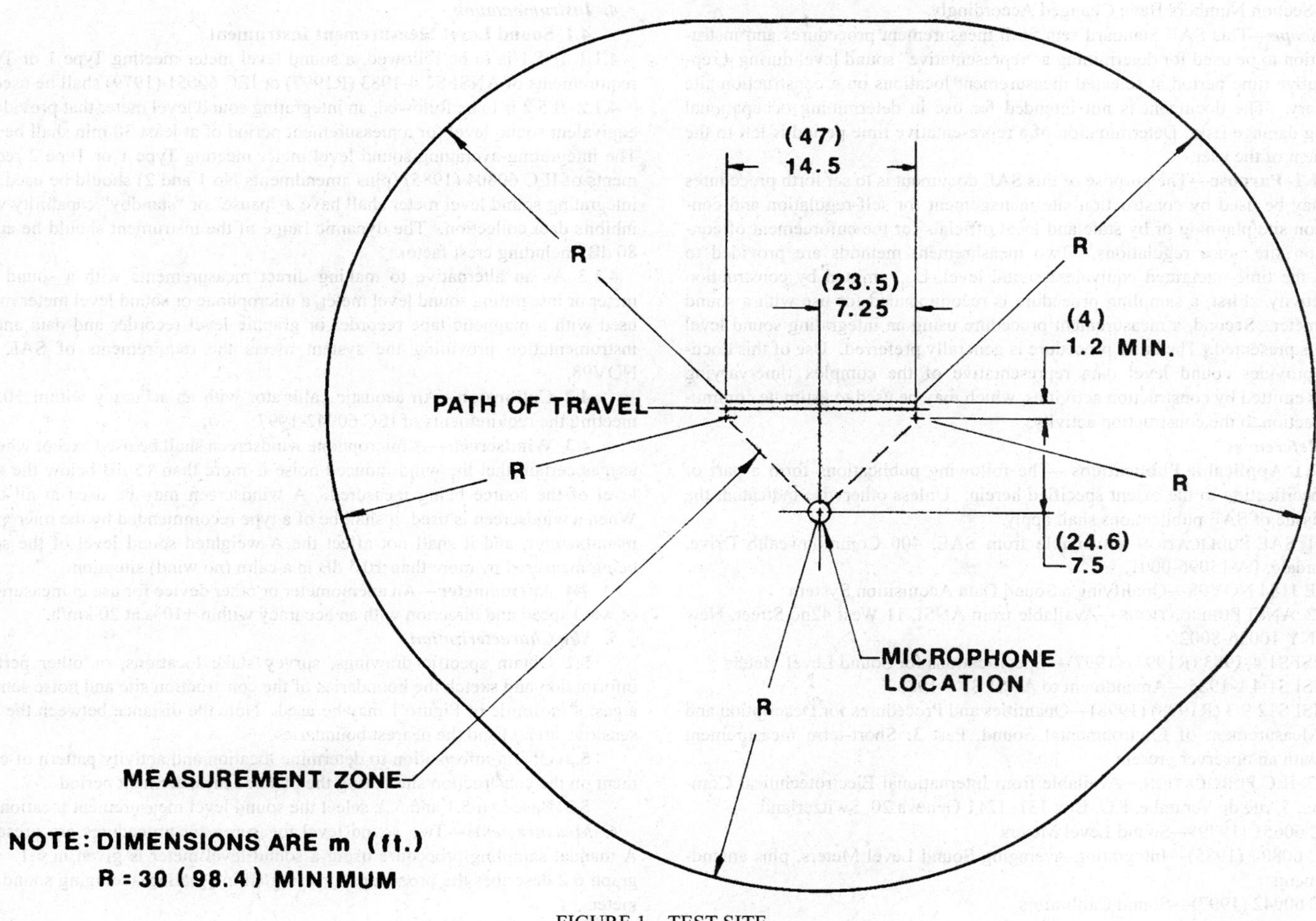

FIGURE 1—TEST SITE

(R) SOUND MEASUREMENT—CONSTRUCTION SITE —SAE J1075 JUN2000

SAE Standard

Report of the SAE Construction, Agricultural, and Off-Road Machinery Sound Level Committee approved April 1978, and revised March 1987. Completely revised by the SAE Construction Site Sound Level Subcommittee of the SAE Construction and Agricultural Sound Level Committee June 1993. Rationale statement available. Completely revised by the SAE Earthmoving Sound Level Subcommittee of the SAE Construction and Agricultural Sound Level Committee June 2000. Rationale statement available.

Foreword—This Document Has Also Changed To Comply With The New Sae Technical Standards Board Format. Definitions Have Changed To Section 3. All Other Section Numbers Have Changed Accordingly.

1. Scope—This SAE Standard sets forth measurement procedures and instrumentation to be used for determining a "representative" sound level during a representative time period at selected measurement locations on a construction site boundary. The document is not intended for use in determining occupational hearing damage risk. Determination of a representative time period is left to the judgment of the user.

1.1 Purpose—The purpose of this SAE document is to set forth procedures that may be used by construction site management for self-regulation and construction site planning or by state and local officials for the enforcement of construction site noise regulations. Two measurement methods are provided to obtain the time-integrated equivalent sound level, L_{eq}, emitted by construction site activity. First, a sampling procedure is recommended for use with a sound level meter. Second, a measurement procedure using an integrating sound level meter is presented. The latter procedure is generally preferred. Use of this document provides sound level data representative of the complex time-varying sounds emitted by construction activities, which may be used to estimate community reaction to the construction activity.

2. References

2.1 Applicable Publications—The following publications form a part of this specification to the extent specified herein. Unless otherwise indicated, the latest issue of SAE publications shall apply.

2.1.1 SAE PUBLICATION—Available from SAE, 400 Commonwealth Drive, Warrendale, PA 15096-0001.

SAE J184 NOV98—Qualifying a Sound Data Acquisition System

2.1.2 ANSI PUBLICATIONS—Available from ANSI, 11 West 42nd Street, New York, NY 10036-8002.

ANSI S1.4-1983 (R1997) (1997)—Specifications for Sound Level Meters

ANSI S1.4A-1985—Amendment to ANSI S1.4-1983

ANSI S12.9/3 (R1998) (1998)—Quantities and Procedures for Description and Measurement of Environmental Sound, Part 3: Short-term measurement with an observer present

2.1.3 IEC PUBLICATION—Available from International Electrotechnical Commission, 3, rue de Verambe, P.O. Box 131, 1211 Geneva 20, Switzerland.

IEC 60651 (1979)—Sound Level Meters

IEC 60804 (1985)—Integrating-Averaging Sound Level Meters, plus amendments

IEC 60942 (1997)—Sound Calibrators

3. Definitions

3.1 Construction Site—That area within the defined boundaries of the project. This includes defined boundary lines of the project itself, plus any staging area outside those defined boundary lines used expressly for construction or demolition.

3.2 Construction Site Boundaries—The outermost limit lines of the construction site.

3.3 Noise Sensitive Area—Property such as that used for public, commercial, religious, or educational purposes, or home dwellings, parks, and other special-purpose areas in the vicinity of a construction site where the background sound is less than the construction site sound level.

3.4 Background Noise—Total acoustical and electrical noise from all sources in a system that interferes with the production, transmission, detection, measurement, or recording of a signal.

NOTE—In many cases, the acoustical noise is the background sound.

3.5 Background Sound—The all-encompassing sound typically associated with the environment in a given area, being composed of sounds from many sources far and near, when the construction site is inactive.

3.6 Representative Sound Level, L_A—The average of sound level samples obtained in accordance with the procedures.

3.7 Equivalent (or Time-Average) Sound Level, L_{eq}—Equivalent or time-average sound is the square root of the time-average of instantaneous sound pressure squared. It is also termed the root-mean-square sound. Equivalent sound level is 10 times the common logarithm of the square of the ratio of the equivalent or time-average sound to the reference sound, p_o, of 20 µPa.

4. Instrumentation

4.1 Sound Level Measurement Instrument

4.1.1 If 5.1 is to be followed, a sound level meter meeting Type 1 or Type 2 requirements of ANSI S1.4-1983 (R1997) or IEC 60651 (1979) shall be used.

4.1.2 If 5.2 is to be followed, an integrating sound level meter that provides the equivalent sound level for a measurement period of at least 30 min shall be used. The integrating-averaging sound level meter meeting Type 1 or Type 2 requirements of IEC 60804 (1985) (plus amendments No 1 and 2) should be used. The integrating sound level meter shall have a "pause" or "standby" capability which inhibits data collection. The dynamic range of the instrument should be at least 80 dB, including crest factor.

4.1.3 As an alternative to making direct measurements with a sound level meter or integrating sound level meter, a microphone or sound level meter may be used with a magnetic tape recorder or graphic level recorder and data analysis instrumentation providing the system meets the requirements of SAE J184 NOV98.

4.2 Calibrator—An acoustic calibrator with an accuracy within ±0.5 dB meeting the requirements of IEC 60942-1997.

4.3 Windscreen—A microphone windscreen shall be used except when the user is certain that the wind-induced noise is more than 15 dB below the sound level of the source being measured. A windscreen may be used at all times. When a windscreen is used, it shall be of a type recommended by the microphone manufacturer, and it shall not affect the A-weighted sound level of the source being measured by more than ±0.5 dB in a calm (no wind) situation.

4.4 Anemometer—An anemometer or other device for use in measurement of wind speed and direction with an accuracy within ±10% at 20 km/h.

5. Site Characterization

5.1 Obtain specific drawings, survey stake locations, or other pertinent information and sketch the boundaries of the construction site and noise sensitive areas; a facsimile of Figure 1 may be used. Note the distance between the noise sensitive area(s) and the nearest boundaries.

5.2 Obtain information to determine location and activity pattern of equipment on the construction site during the planned measurement period.

5.3 Based on 5.1 and 5.2, select the sound level measurement location(s).

6. Measurements—Two sound level measurement procedures are presented. A manual sampling procedure using a sound level meter is given in 6.1. Paragraph 6.2 describes the procedure for using an integrating-averaging sound level meter.

NOTE—ANSI S12.9/3-1993 (R1998), meets the requirements of this document and provides a more detailed method to measure L_{eq} corrected for background sound.

6.1 Manual Sampling with Sound Level Meter—Sound level measurements at construction site boundary adjacent to noise sensitive areas shall be taken with a sound level meter in the following manner for any representative 30 min period of construction activity:

6.1.1 Calibrate the sound level meter before and after each measurement period using an acoustic calibrator, per manufacturer's instructions. If calibration shifts by more than 0.5 dB, the measurements shall be repeated after correction of the shift problem.

6.1.2 Locate the microphone at the location selected in 5.3 at approximately 1.5 m above the ground and, if practical, at least 3 m from sound reflecting structures. If circumstances dictate, measurements may be made at other heights and closer to sound reflecting structures providing these facts are noted on a data sheet similar to Figure 1.

6.1.3 Set the sound level meter to the A-weighting network and slow response. Observe the sound level meter during a 10 s ± 2 s sampling period at the start of each consecutive 30 s period. Record the maximum value observed during each sample period, L_A, on a data sheet such as shown in Figure 2. Take 60 valid readings where a valid reading is one in which the measurements are not affected by intrusive noise sources external to the construction site, such as aircraft, emergency signals, and surface transportation; make a note on the data sheet for each invalid reading.

CONSTRUCTION SITE SKETCH FORM

1. **Measurer** ____________________

2. **Date** ____________ **Temperature** ____________ **Wind Velocity** ____________

3. **Construction Site: Location** ____________________
   Description ____________________

4. **Sound Level Meter: Mfr.** ____________ **Model** ____________ **S/N** ____________

5. **Remarks:** ____________________
   ____

6. **Site sketch showing site boundaries, noise sensitive areas, measurement locations, and major pieces of construction equipment in operation, with distances between the above items; also show wind direction:**

FIGURE 1—SAMPLE SITE SKETCH DATA SHEET

Measurer: ____________ **Date:** ____________ **Time:** ____________
Construction Site: ____________ **Measurement Point:** ____________
Remarks: ____________

Instructions:

1. **Select A-weighting network and "slow" response on meter.**
2. **Calibrate meter using acoustic calibrator and install windscreen.**
3. **Observe for 10 s ± 2 s at the start of each minute and each one-half minute for 30 min, and record maximum level for each observation period.**

	L_A	Remarks		L_A	Remarks
1.			31.		
2.			32.		
3.			33.		
4.			34.		
5.			35.		
6.			36.		
7.			37.		
8.			38.		
9.			39.		
10.			40.		
11.			41.		
12.			42.		
13.			43.		
14.			44.		
15.			45.		
16.			46.		
17.			47.		
18.			48.		
19.			49.		
20.			50.		
21.			51.		
22.			52.		
23.			53.		
24.			54.		
25.			55.		
26.			56.		
27.			57.		
28.			58.		
29.			59.		
30.			60.		

4. **Determine $\overline{L_A}$: Circle L_A values within 6 dB of maximum value.**
   $\overline{L_A}$ = number of circled values/sum of circled values = n/sum = __/__ = __
5. **Determine L_{eq}:**
   n/60 = __ Correction (Table 1) = __ L_{eq} = $\overline{L_A}$ - Correction = __

FIGURE 2—MANUAL SAMPLING DATA SHEET

6.1.4 On/off-highway vehicles, such as dump trucks, truck/mixers, etc., which occasionally enter, operate on, and leave the site, shall be considered as part of the construction activity while within the site boundaries. However, off-site pass-by of such vehicles in the area of measurement location shall be considered as intrusions, and handled as outlined in 6.1.3.

6.1.5 Determine the representative sound level, L_A, using:

$$\overline{L_A} = \sum_{i-1}^{n} (L_A)_i / n \qquad \text{(Eq. 1)}$$

where:

L_A = The arithmetic average of the $(L_A)_i$
n = The number of $(L_A)_i$ values used for computing the arithmetic average

$(L_A)_i$ includes those sound level samples that fall within a range from the maximum sample level to 6 dB below the maximum sample level. For example, if the maximum sample level was 70 dB, all sound level samples between 64 and 70 dB would be valid $(L_A)_i$.

6.1.6 Determine a correction to be applied to L_A to approximate L_{eq} for the measurement period: divide n by 60, read the corresponding correction from Table 1, and subtract this value from L_A.

Then,

$$L_{eq} = L_A - \text{Correction} \qquad \text{(Eq. 2)}$$

6.2 Sampling With an Integrating Sound Level Meter—Equivalent sound level measurements at the construction site boundary adjacent to noise sensitive areas shall be taken with an integrating sound level meter in the following manner:

TABLE 1—CORRECTIONS TO L_A TO OBTAIN L_{eq}

n/60(1) greater than	n/60(1) less than or equal to	Correction, dB(2)
0.8	1.0	0
0.7	0.8	1
0.6	0.7	2
0.5	0.6	3
0.4	0.5	4
0.3	0.4	5
0.2	0.3	7
0	0.2	10

1. n is the number of samples used in the calculation of L_A.
2. Subtract L_A to obtain L_{eq}.

6.2.1 Calibrate the integrating sound level meter before and after each measurement period, using an acoustic calibrator. Equivalent sound level measurements at the construction site boundary adjacent to noise sensitive areas shall be taken with an integrating sound level meter in the following manner:

6.2.2 Locate the microphone at approximately 1.5 m above the ground and, if practical, at least 3 m from sound reflecting structures. When circumstances dictate, measurements may be made at other heights and closer to sound reflecting structures, providing these facts are noted on a data sheet similar to Figure 1.

6.2.3 Set the integrating sound level meter to the A-weighting network and slow response (if no slow response switch is present, note that fact in the reporting described in 6.3.1). Estimate what the anticipated maximum and minimum levels will be during the measurement period and set the range of the meter to include these extremes (for example, 40 to 120 dB is a typical range for construction site activity).

6.2.4 Start the integrating sound level meter and maintain it in a data collection state for 30 min, exclusive of periods deleted due to intrusions per 6.2.5.

6.2.5 If during the measurement period the levels are affected by intrusive noise sources external to the construction site, such as aircraft, emergency signals, and surface transportation, activate the pause or standby switch to inhibit data collection until the intrusion is over.

6.2.6 Record the L_{eq} value at the conclusion of the 30 min measurement period (exclusive of deleted time periods).

6.3 Information to be Reported

6.3.1 Name of measurer, date, time, construction site, location, type of construction, wind velocity and direction, ambient temperature, sound level meter manufacturer, model, and serial number shall be reported.

6.3.2 A site sketch showing construction site boundaries, major pieces of construction equipment operating during the measurement, noise sensitive areas, measurement locations, and distances between these features shall be prepared.

6.3.3 The sound level samples, representative sound level, and equivalent sound level at each measurement location shall be reported. Background levels, if measured per 7.1, shall also be reported with the time of measurement and a description of background sound sources and events excluded from the sound level measurement.

7. General Comments

7.1 It is often desirable to obtain the background sound level at the measurement locations when the construction site is inactive, such as before start-up, during the luncheon break, or after shut-down. The procedures in 6.1 or 6.2 should be used. Include all nonconstruction related noise sources, but exclude intrusive sources, such as emergency signals and aircraft or vehicles passing very close to the microphone, unless such occurrences are representative of typical background sound level conditions at the measurement point.

7.2 Only persons technically trained and experienced in the current techniques of sound measurements should select the equipment and conduct the tests.

7.3 Proper usage of all test instrumentation is essential to obtain valid measurements. Operating manuals or other literature furnished by the instrument manufacturer should be referred to for both the recommended operation of the instrument and precautions to be observed. Specific items to be considered are:

7.3.1 The type of microphone, its directional response characteristics, and its orientation relative to the ground plane and source of noise.

7.3.2 The effects of ambient weather conditions on the performance of all instruments (for example, temperature, humidity, and barometric/pressure). Instrumentation can be influenced by low temperature and high humidity, and caution should be exercised.

7.3.3 Proper signal levels, terminating impedances, and cable lengths on multi-instrument measurement systems.

7.3.4 Proper acoustical calibration procedure including the influence of extension cables, etc. Internal calibration means is acceptable for field use, provided that external calibration is accomplished immediately before or after field use.

7.4 It is recommended that measurements be made only when wind speed is below 20 km/h. If wind gusts go above 20 km/h, discard those samples taken when the wind is above 20 km/h and take additional samples.

7.5 Measurements should not be made if significant changes occur in extraneous, nonconstruction related noise-making activities or work patterns during the sampling period. Example of changes in noise-making activities or work patterns that may affect the data are:

7.5.1 Nearby noise sources, such as power mowers, pavement breakers, or power saws.

7.5.2 Changes in vehicular traffic flow, such as detouring of traffic or shift change periods near industrial plants.

7.6 It is suggested that, if available, earphones with an impedance recommended by the meter manufacturer be used to ensure that the sound level values are not affected by electromagnetic interference, wind, or humidity.

(R) SOUND MEASUREMENT—OFF-ROAD WORK MACHINES—EXTERIOR—SAE J88 APR1995

SAE Standard

Report of the SAE Vehicle Sound Level Committee approved November 1972, revised by the SAE Construction, Agricultural and Off-road Machinery sound Level Technical Committee, June 1986. Completely revised by the SAE Earthmoving Sound Level Subcommittee by the SAE ConAg Sound Level Committee April 1995. Rationale statement available.

Foreword—This Document has also changed to comply with the new SAE Technical Standards Board format.

1. Scope—This SAE Standard sets forth the instrumentation and procedure to be used in measuring the exterior sound levels for self-propelled sweepers as defined in SAE J2130 and self-propelled off-road work machines in categories 1, 2, 4, and 5 of SAE J1116.

This document does not address the operation of safety devices such as backup alarms, horns, or accessories. The sound levels obtained by using the test procedures set forth in this document are repeatable and are representative of the higher range of sound levels generated by machines under actual field operating conditions. Due to variability of field operating conditions, this data is not intended to be used for construction site boundary noise evaluations.

2. References

2.1 Applicable Publications—The following publications form a part of the specification to the extent specified herein. Unless otherwise indicated the latest revision of SAE publications shall apply.

2.1.1 SAE PUBLICATIONS—Available from SAE, 400 Commonwealth Drive, Warrendale, PA 15096-0001.

SAE J184 AUG87—Qualifying a Sound Data Acquisition System
SAE J732—Specification Definitions—Front End Loader
SAE J1116 JUN86—Categories of Off-Road Self-Propelled Work Machines
SAE J1382 AUG85—Classification, Nomenclature, and Specification Definitions for Trenching Machines
SAE J2130—Identification of Self-Propelled Sweepers

2.1.2 ANSI PUBLICATION—Available from ANSI, 11 West 42nd Street, New York, NY 10036-8002.

ANSI S1.4-1983—Specification for Sound Level Meters

2.1.3 IEC PUBLICATION—Available from International Electrotechnical Commission, 3, rue de Verambe, P.O. Box 131, 1211 Geneva 20, Switzerland.

IEC 804-1985—Integrating Sound Level Meters

2.2 Related Publications—The following publications are provided for information purposes only and are not a required part of this document.

2.2.1 SAE PUBLICATION—Available from SAE, 400 Commonwealth Drive, Warrendale, PA 15096-0001.

SAE J1262—Sound Measurement—Trenching Machines

2.2.2 ANSI PUBLICATION—Available from ANSI, 11 West 42nd Street, New York, NY 10036-8002.

ANSI S1.40-1984—Specification for Acoustical Calibrators

3. Instrumentation

3.1 A sound level meter which meets the Type 1 requirements of ANSI S1.4-1983 shall be used. Alternatively an integrating sound level meter may be used if it meets IEC 804-1985 requirements. If an integrating sound level meter is used for dynamic measurements, it must have a slow dynamic characteristic, and max hold.

3.2 As an alternative to making direct measurements using a sound level meter, a microphone or sound level meter may be used with a magnetic tape recorder and/or graphic level recorder or indicating instrument, providing the system meets the requirements for SAE J184 for the frequency range that is of primary concern. The deviations in the magnetic tape recorder frequency response from flat response, especially at lower frequencies, must not affect the overall reading by more than ±0.5 dB(A).

3.3 An acoustical calibrator (accuracy within ±0.5 dB(A)—see 5.2.4) shall be used to ensure correct calibration of the sound level meter(s).

3.4 The use of a windscreen may be required under some test conditions. Refer to 4.1.3, otherwise its use is optional, providing that it does not affect the A-weighted sound level of the source being measured by more than ±0.5 dB(A), under zero wind speed conditions. (Also refer to 5.2.2.)

3.5 An anemometer or other device for measurement of ambient wind speed and direction shall be used. The accuracy is ±10% at the highest recommended wind speed. (See 5.2.2.)

3.6 A speed indicator shall be used for determination of machine power source(s) rpm (accuracy within ±2% of the indicated reading).

3.7 A thermometer for measurement of ambient temperature (accuracy within ±1 °C) shall be used.

3.8 A barometer shall be used to measure atmospheric pressure (accuracy within ±1 kPa of the indicated reading).

4. Procedure

4.1 Test Site—The test area shall consist of a flat open space free of any large reflecting surfaces, such as a signboard, building, or hillside, located within 30 m of either the microphone or the machinery being measured (see Figure 1).

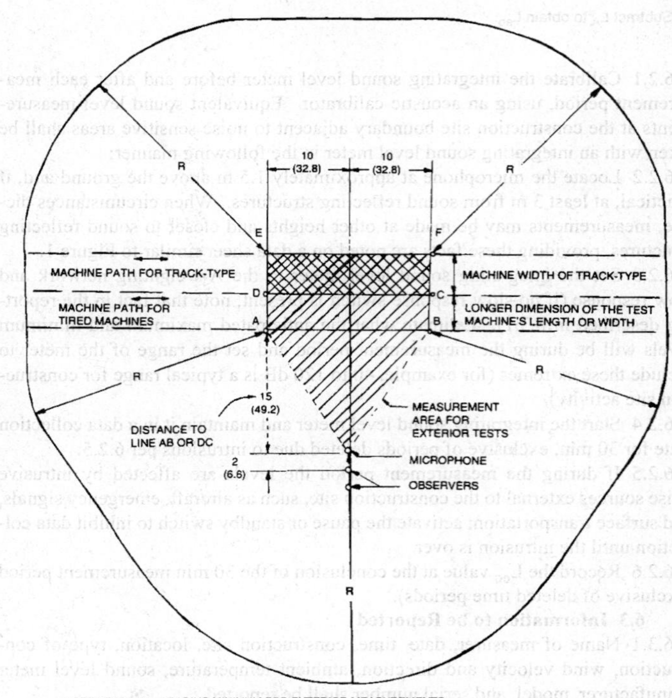

FIGURE 1—TEST SITE CONFIGURATION

4.1.1 The minimum measurement area (see Figure 1) shall consist of the triangle formed by the microphone location, points A and B, and the rectangle formed by points A, B, C, and D. Both designated areas shall be smooth concrete or smooth and sealed asphalt or a similar hard and smooth surface. The rectangle formed by points C, D, E, and F shall consist of hard-packed earth. The planes between the microphone location and line AB and planes encompassed by points A, B, C, F, E, and D shall form a continuous, uniform plane. If a minimum measurement area test site is used, it will require reorientation of the machine for each major surface measurement during the stationary tests, and the moving tests will have to be run in opposite directions. The other option is to have a larger measurement area test site and relocate the microphone for the series of prescribed test conditions with the machine in one position for stationary tests and driving by in only one direction for moving tests.

4.1.2 Because bystanders may have an appreciable influence on the meter response when they are in the vicinity of the earthmoving machinery or microphone, not more than one person, other than the observer reading the meter, shall be within 17 m of the earthmoving machinery and 2 m of the measuring microphone, and that person shall be directly behind the observer who is reading the meter, on a line through the microphone and the observer (see Figure 1).

4.1.3 The ambient sound level due to sources other than the machinery being measured (including wind effects) shall be at least 10 dB(A) lower than the sound level of the machinery being measured. (See 4.3.3.)

4.1.4 The surface between and under the machinery and microphone shall be smooth and free of acoustically absorptive material, such as snow or grass.

4.1.5 For all stationary tests, the machine shall be located on the hard surface area formed by points A, B, C, and D in Figure 1.

4.1.6 Moving Tests

4.1.6.1 For moving tests of all rubber-tired machines, the path of travel shall be across the area defined by points A, B, C, and D in the directions shown in Figure 1.

4.1.6.2 For moving tests of all steel wheel or track type machines, the path of travel shall be across the area defined by C, D, E, and F in the directions shown in Figure 1.

4.2 Tests Required—Machines that are used primarily in a mobile mode shall be tested per 4.2.1.1, 4.2.1.2, 4.2.1.3, 4.2.1.4, and 4.2.2.

Combined machines (such as loaders with a backhoe) shall be tested per 4.2.1.1, 4.2.1.2, 4.2.1.3, 4.2.1.4, and 4.2.2.

Rubber-tired and tracked excavators shall be tested in a stationary test mode only per 4.2.1.1, 4.2.1.2, 4.2.1.3, and 4.2.1.4.

4.2.1 Stationary tests with ground propulsion transmission shift selector in neutral position.

4.2.1.1 Operate mobile machine power source(s) at no-load with all component drive systems in neutral position and maximum governed speed (high idle at no load) at a stabilized condition.

4.2.1.2 Operate machine power source(s) at no-load and at manufacturer's specified rated speed with all component drive systems in neutral position.

4.2.1.3 Operate mobile machine power source(s) at no-load with all major component drive systems in neutral position through the cycle low idle—maximum governed speed (high idle)—low idle as rapidly as possible, but allow the engine to stabilize for at least 10 s at the maximum governed speed (high idle) before it is permitted to return to low idle. It is recommended that care be taken to ensure stabilized combustion chamber surface temperatures prior to this test sequence. For some types of engines, such as engines with precombustion chambers, repeatability of sound levels may be affected. Between cycles, a cool-down period of 5 min is recommended.

4.2.1.4 With the power source(s) at the maximum governed speed (high idle) or manufacturer's recommended operating speed at no-load in a stabilized condition, activate the appropriate hydraulic circuits, mechanical, electrical, hydrostatic, or torque converter drive systems to cycle the major components or component from the most retracted and/or lowered position to fully extended and/or maximum height position, and then back to original position. The component cycled must have controls at the operator's station. This cycling should be done as fast as practical, taking into consideration all the pertinent safety factors, and be accomplished without exceeding relief valve settings. For short cycle hydraulic operation, the system may be feathered.

For safety reasons and undesirability of change of location of major noise source(s) in relation to other major components of the machine, a major portion of the mobile machine, such as the tractor of a scraper unit, or the upper rotational structure of an excavator shall not be moved, or scraper elevator placed in operation during this stationary machine test.

For units such as nonriding trenching machines without power steering or hydraulic controls, this section shall be omitted. In no case shall the digging chain (wheel) or vibratory plow drives be engaged for this test or other tests in this document. For self-propelled street sweepers, the brooms may be lowered and raised for this portion of the test.

4.2.2 Constant Speed Moving Test—Machines shall be operated in a forward intermediate gear ratio at no-load at a location as specified in 4.1.6.1 or 4.1.6.2. The power source(s) shall be operated at maximum governed speed (high idle). Intermediate is intended to mean second gear ratio for machinery with three or four gear ratios, third gear ratio for machinery with five or six gear ratios, fourth gear ratio for machinery with seven or eight ratios, etc.

If there is a problem with the transmission shifting up or down in this phase of the test, one gear lower or higher may be used to eliminate the problem. Machines with hydrostatic, electric drive, or other type drives shall be operated at approximately one-half its maximum ground speed with the governor control set in maximum (high idle) position at no-load. If this operating condition cannot be attained because of the interaction of the power source(s) and drive controls, then the ground speed may be increased or decreased so as to still permit the power source(s) governor control(s) to be set in the maximum (high idle) position. Machines that have major noise-generating components which are normally in use at this ground speed, shall have these major components in operation during this test. For self-propelled street sweepers, these components include water systems, brooms, and blower or conveying systems.

4.2.3 Machines that have a major attachment that is normally used for the main operating function shall be equipped with this attachment. Examples of this are buckets on loaders, brooms on sweepers, dozers on either wheel or track-type tractors, and backfill blades, digging booms (wheel), direct burial plows, or backhoes on trenchers. For all tests, except component cycling, these attachments shall be in a minimum transport position of 160 to 320 mm for dozers, scrapers, etc. For loaders and trenchers with loaders, use carry position as specified by SAE J732. For machinery equipped with a ripper, such as on a wheel or track-type tractor, or a backhoe, such as on a front end loader, these attachments shall be in the transport position. For trenching machines and self-propelled sweepers these attachments shall be in their normal transport position, for example, backfill blade or brooms fully raised; plow, boom, or wheel fully raised and restrained (if appropriate).

4.3 Measurements

4.3.1 The microphone shall be located at a height of 1.2 m above the ground plane.

4.3.2 All sound level measurements shall be taken using the A-weighting network. For dynamic power source(s) cycling, component cycling, and constant speed moving test conditions, the sound level meter shall be set for slow dynamic characteristic (see 3.1). For the stabilized test condition of maximum governed speed (high idle) or rated engine speed, the time weighted average sound level (Leq) may be used in place of the slow dynamic characteristic.

4.3.3 The ambient wind speed and direction, ambient temperature, atmospheric pressure, and ambient A-weighted sound level shall be measured and recorded at the height of 1.2 m and within at least 3 m of one specified location of the microphone as shown in Figure 1.

4.3.4 The stabilized maximum governed power source(s) speed shall be measured and recorded.

4.3.5 The power source(s) speed(s) shall be monitored during the rated speed test per 4.2.1.2.

4.3.6 The gear ratio and approximate ground speed during the moving test shall be recorded.

4.3.7 The sound level meter needle movement, digital readout, or graphic level recorder trace shall be observed during each test sequence. The highest value observed for all tests disregarding sounds of short duration that are out of character with the test on the machine (example—impact noise such as bucket rap against stops) shall be recorded for each test sequence. For a digital-type readout, the meter must be frequently reset so the out-of-character sound levels for the test sequence are not included if the maximum hold mode is being used.

4.3.8 For the stabilized test condition, of maximum governed speed (high idle) or rated speed, a single reading shall be recorded at each measuring point.

4.3.9 For power source(s) cycling, component cycling, and the constant speed moving test conditions a minimum of three valid readings shall be taken for each measuring point. If for each specific test mode none of the readings are within 2 dB of each other, then additional readings shall be taken until there are two that are within 2 dB of each other. The recorded sound level for each measuring point shall be the average of those two values that are within 2 dB of each other. If there are two pairs of readings that are within 2 dB of each other, record the average of the higher pair. The final recorded sound level for each test mode shall be the highest reading for the stabilized test condition at each measuring point and the highest average for the cyclic or moving tests at each measuring point.

4.3.10 Number of Simulated Work Cycles—Three simulated work cycles shall be carried out resulting in three measurements to be taken at each microphone position.

It is necessary to have two of the readings at the microphone within a 2 dB range of each other. If these results are not obtained, additional simulated work cycles shall be taken to meet this requirement. Operational procedures may require correction to achieve this.

4.3.11 Determination of Measurement Result—Report, as the value of the continuous A-weighted sound pressure level, the arithmetic mean of the highest values that are within a 2 dB range of each other for each microphone position.

4.3.12 For stationary tests, record the sound level obtained at a distance of 15 m from each major surface, normal to the centers of the four major surfaces of the equipment at the microphone height. Generally, four major surfaces refer to front, rear, and sides of an imaginary box that would just fit over the machine but does not include attachment items such as buckets, dozers, backfill blades, backhoes, rippers, and booms (see Figure 2). These attachments should not be removed for the tests, but are not considered in defining major surfaces (see SAE J1382). In the case of an excavator, the upper (revolving superstructure) fore-and-aft centerline should be in line with the lower fore-and-aft centerline. Operate the machine in a manner as specified in 4.2.1.1, 4.2.1.2, 4.2.1.3, and 4.2.1.4.

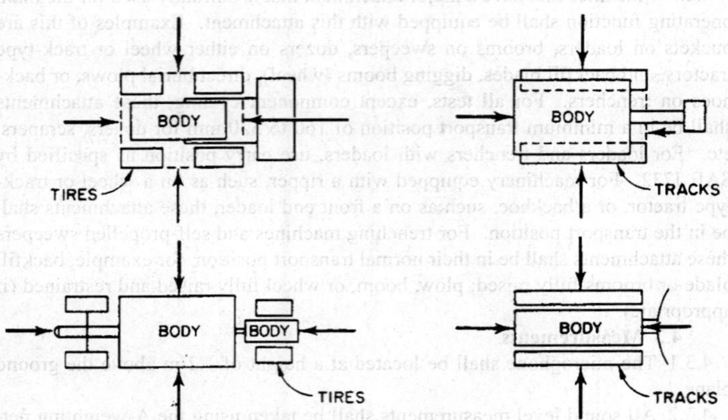

FIGURE 2—MAJOR SURFACE OUTLINES

4.3.13 For moving tests, take measurements at a distance of 15 m from each major surface, measured in a direction normal to both major side surfaces which are parallel to the machine path, as shown in Figure 1. Operate the machine in a manner specified in 4.2.2.

4.3.14 The reported sound level for each of the stationary test modes (per 4.2.1.1, 4.2.1.2, 4.2.1.3, and 4.2.1.4) shall be the arithmetical average of the recorded sound levels at each of the four measuring points.

The reported sound level for the moving test (per 4.2.2) shall be the arithmetical average of the recorded sound levels at each of the two measuring points. The reported sound levels for a given machine shall be included in the report format as shown in Appendix A.

5. General Comments

5.1 It is recommended that persons technically trained and experienced in the current techniques of sound measurements select the instrumentation and conduct the tests. Dedicated attention to detail and a thorough understanding of the machine and test instrumentation operational requirements shall be prerequisite of all personnel attached to the evaluation program.

5.2 Safety and Operation—All relevant safety precautions and the manufacturer's operating instructions shall be followed during the test. Any signal devices, such as forward-warning horn or backup alarm, shall not be activated during the test.

Proper use of all test instrumentation is essential to obtain valid measurements. Operating manuals or other literature furnished by the instrument manufacturer should be referred to for both recommended operation of the instrument and precautions to be observed.

5.2.1 The effects of ambient weather conditions on the performance of all instruments (for example—temperature, humidity, barometric pressure, and stray magnetic fields) should be known. Instrumentation can be influenced by low temperature or significant changes in temperature, and caution should be exercised.

5.2.2 It is recommended that the wind speed of the air over the microphone not exceed 20 km/h. Caution should be used in making measurements with higher relative velocities.

A microphone windscreen shall not be used except when it is required to reduce wind induced noise that is within 15 dB(A) of the sound level of the source being measured. When a windscreen is used it shall not affect the sound level of the source being measured by more than ±0.5 dB(A) under zero wind speed conditions.

Note—In practice, windscreens are seldom required to reduce A-weighted wind induced noise, with the possible exception of microphone locations in the fan blast of the machine.

5.2.3 Proper signal levels, terminating impedances, and cable lengths on multi-instrument measurement systems should be known.

5.2.4 Proper acoustical calibration procedure, to include the influence of extension cables, etc., should be performed. Field acoustical calibration shall be made immediately before and after the testing of each machine or at least every 4 h. The calibration before and after shall not vary by more than ±0.5 dB for the tests to be valid.

5.3 It should be recognized that variations in measured sound levels may occur due to variations in test site, ambient weather differences (temperature, wind, and their gradients), test equipment differences, and inherent differences between nominally identical machines.

SOUND MEASUREMENT—SELF-PROPELLED AGRICULTURAL EQUIPMENT—EXTERIOR—SAE J1008 JAN1987

SAE Recommended Practice

Report of the SAE Construction, Agricultural and Off-Road Machinery Sound Level Technical Committee approved May 1978 and revised January 1987.

Foreword—This Document has also changed to comply with the new SAE Technical Standards Board format.

1. Scope—This SAE Recommended Practice sets forth the instrumentation and procedures to be used in measuring exterior sound levels of self-propelled agricultural field equipment of 15 kW (20 net engine hp) or greater. It is not intended to cover operation of safety devices (such as alarms), or equipment used primarily in stationary operation. The sound levels obtained by using this test procedure are repeatable and representative of the higher range of sound levels generated by the machine in normal road transport. The sound levels are not intended to represent the average or equivalent sound levels over a field use cycle.

2. References

2.1 Applicable Publications—The following publications form a part of the specification to the extent specified herein. Unless otherwise indicated the latest revision of SAE publications shall apply.

2.1.1 SAE PUBLICATION—Available from SAE, 400 Commonwealth Drive, Warrendale, PA 15096-0001.

SAE J184 MAR85—Qualifying a Sound Data Acquisition System

2.1.2 ANSI PUBLICATIONS—Available from ANSI, 11 West 42nd Street, New York, NY 10036-8002.

ANSI S1.1-1960 (1971)—Acoustical Terminology
ANSI S1.2-1962 (R 1971)—Physical Measurement of Sound
ANSI S1.4-1983—Specifications for Sound Level Meters
ANSI S1.13-1971—Methods for the Measurement of Sound Pressure Levels

2.1.3 ISO PUBLICATION—Available from ANSI, 11 West 42nd Street, New York, NY 10036-8002.

ISO 362 1981—Measurement of Noise Emitted by Vehicles

2.2 Other Publications

O.E.C.D. —Standard Code for the Official Testing of Agricultural Tractors
EEC Directive 74/151/EEC Annex VI

3. Instrumentation

3.1 A sound level meter which meets the Type 1 requirements of American National Standard Specification for Sound Level Meters, S1.4-1983.

3.2 As an alternative to making direct measurements with a sound level meter, a microphone or sound level meter may be used with a magnetic tape recorder and/or graphic level recorder or other indicating instruments, providing the measurement system meets the intended accuracy of SAE J184 MAR85, Qualifying a Sound Data Acquisition System, for the frequency range of concern. The inaccuracies in the magnetic tape recorder frequency response, especially at lower frequencies, must not affect the overall reading by more than ±0.5 dB(A). The frequency range over which the alternate measurement system meets the requirements of SAE J184 MAR85 shall be specified in the test report.

3.3 An acoustic calibrator - accuracy within ±0.5 dB (see 5.2.5).

3.4 A microphone windscreen that does not affect the overall reading by more than ±0.5 dB(A) shall be used.

3.5 An anemometer or other device for measurement of ambient wind speed. Recommended accuracy is 10% at the highest wind speed allowed. (See 5.2.4.)

3.6 A thermometer for measurement of ambient temperature - recommended accuracy ±1°C (1.8°F).

3.7 A barometer for measurement of atmospheric pressure - recommended accuracy ±1 kPa (0.3 in Hg).

4. Procedure

4.1 Test Site

4.1.1 The test area shall consist of a flat, open space, free of large vertical or near vertical reflecting surfaces such as signboards, buildings, or hillsides, located within 30 m (100 ft) of either the microphone or machine being tested.

4.1.2 The minimum measurement area (see Figure 1) shall consist of the triangle formed by the microphone location, and points A and B; and the rectangle formed by points A, B, C, and D. The measurement area may be surfaced with concrete, asphalt, or similar reflective materials, and shall not be covered with powdery snow, high grass, loose soil, or ashes. The measurement surface should be described in the test report.

4.1.3 Since bystanders have appreciable influence on propagation of sound waves, not more than one person, other than the observer recording data; and the machine operator shall be within 15 m (49 ft) of the machine or microphone, and that person shall be directly behind the observer recording data, on a line through the microphone and observer (see Figure 1).

4.1.4 The ambient sound level (including wind effects) shall be at least 10 dB(A) lower than the sound level of the machine being tested (see 5.2.4).

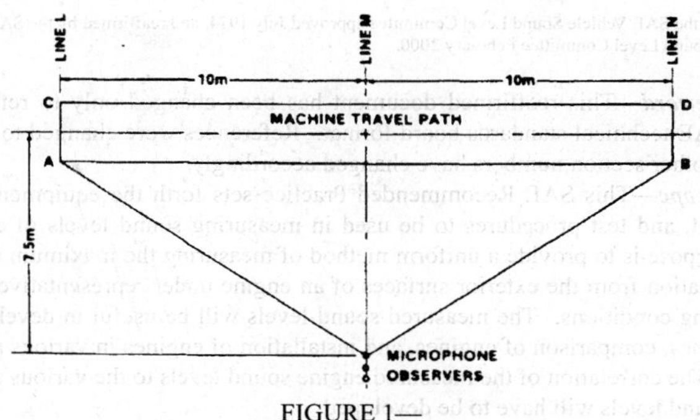

FIGURE 1—

4.2 Machine Operating Condition

4.2.1 All tests will be conducted with the machine in normal road transport configuration. Harvesting machinery will be tested with harvesting heads removed, if clearance to the microphone is less than 3 m (10 ft).

4.2.2 The machine shall be allowed to reach at least minimum operating engine and transmission temperatures before testing.

4.2.3 The machine shall approach line L (or Line N) headed toward Line M Figure 1 at a steady speed of three quarters of maximum engine speed used in normal road transport. When the front of the machine reaches Line L (or Line N), the throttle shall be fully opened as rapidly as possible and held there until the rear of the machine passes Line N (or Line L), and then closed as rapidly as possible. The highest transmission gear or variable speed ratio that will permit reaching rated engine speed within the area between Lines L and N shall be used.

4.3 Measurement

4.3.1 The microphone shall be located at a height of 1.2 m (4 ft) above the ground plane.

4.3.2 The sound level meter shall be set for fast response and the A-weighting network. When using alternative measurement systems (see 3.2), the final resulting data shall be A-weighted with fast response characteristics.

4.3.3 The ambient wind speed, ambient temperature, atmospheric pressure, and ambient A-weighted sound level shall be measured and recorded at the microphone locations used for testing.

4.3.4 Measurement shall be made at a distance of 7.5 m (25 ft) measured in a direction normal to the centerline of the travel path (see Figure 1). Tests shall be made in both directions of travel without changing microphone location.

4.3.5 The sound level meter needle movement or readout shall be observed during the test at the specified microphone location. The highest value observed shall be recorded for each test. Each test shall be repeated until there are two readings within 2 dB(A) of each other. The reported value shall be the average of these two values that are within 2 dB(A) of each other. If there are two pairs of readings that are within 2 dB(A) of each other, the average of the higher pair shall be reported. The final reported exterior sound level of the machine shall be the average sound level for the side having the highest readings.

5. General Comments

5.1 It is recommended that persons technically trained and experienced in the current techniques of sound level measurements select the instrumentation and conduct the test.

5.2 Proper usage of all test instrumentation is essential to obtain valid measurements. Operating manuals or other literature furnished by the instrument manufacturer should be referred to for both recommended operation of the instruments and precautions to be observed.

5.2.1 The effects of environmental conditions on the performance of all instruments (for example: temperature, humidity, barometric pressure, stray magnetic fields) should be known. Instrumentation can be influenced by low temperature or significant changes in temperature, and caution should be exercised.

5.2.2 The microphone should be oriented, with respect to the source, so that the sound strikes the diaphragm at the angle for which the microphone has the flattest frequency response characteristic over the frequency range of interest.

5.2.3 Proper signal levels, terminating impedances, and cable lengths on multi-instrument measurement systems should be observed.

5.2.4 It is recommended that the relative wind velocity of the air mass over the microphone not exceed 20 km/h (12 mph).

5.2.5 Proper acoustical calibration procedure, to include the influence of extension cables, etc. should be performed. Field acoustical calibration shall be made immediately before and after each test sequence on a machine.

ENGINE SOUND LEVEL MEASUREMENT PROCEDURE—SAE J1074 FEB2000

SAE Recommended Practice

Report of the SAE Vehicle Sound Level Committee approved July 1974, and reaffirmed by the SAE Vehicle Sound Level Committee February 1987. Reaffirmed by the SAE Vehicle Sound Level Committee February 2000.

Foreword—This reaffirmed document has been changed only to reflect the new SAE technical standards board format. References were changed to section 2. All other section numbers have changed accordingly.

1. Scope—This SAE Recommended Practice sets forth the equipment, environment, and test procedures to be used in measuring sound levels of engines. The purpose is to provide a uniform method of measuring the maximum acoustical radiation from the exterior surfaces of an engine under representative engine operating conditions. The measured sound levels will be useful in development of engines, comparison of engines, and installation of engines in various applications. The correlation of the measured engine sound levels to the various application sound levels will have to be developed.

2. References

2.1 Applicable Publications—The following publications form a part of the specification to the extent specified herein. Unless otherwise indicated, the latest revision of SAE publications shall apply.

2.1.1 SAE PUBLICATION—Available from SAE, 400 Commonwealth Drive, Warrendale, PA 15096-0001.

SAE J184 FEB87—Qualifying a Sound Data Acquisition System

2.1.2 ANSI PUBLICATIONS—Available from ANSI, 11 West 42nd Street, New York, NY 10036-8002.

ANSI S1.4-1983 and S1.4A-1985—Specification for Sound Level Meters

ANSI S1.11-1986—Octave, Half-Octave, and Third-Octave Band Filter Sets

2.1.3 OTHER PUBLICATION

Leo L. Beranek, "Noise and Vibration Control," New York: McGraw-Hill Book Co., 1971, Chap. 9.

3. Engine Classifications

3.1 Bare Engine—An engine equipped with only the built-in accessories essential to its operation, such as flywheel, fuel pump, oil pump, water pump, and intake and exhaust manifolds. The sound from the exhaust, intake, flywheel housing opening, test stand, and dynamometer shall be minimized in order to measure the sound level of the basic or bare engine: although for aircooled engines where the cooling air flows from the flywheel housing opening, the flywheel housing opening should not be covered. The exhaust and intake sounds shall be minimized by using remote mufflers and air cleaners, with heavy, acoustically treated piping to bare engine manifolds. Watercooled engines should not use a cooling fan. Isolation type engine mounts should be used to minimize the vibrations to the engine test equipment.

3.2 Fully Equipped Engine—An engine equipped with all mounted accessories necessary to perform its intended function unaided. The accessories shall be specified and described. If the sound from the exhaust, intake, and cooling systems are included, the systems should be specified and described. The sound from the flywheel housing opening, test stand, and dynamometer shall be minimized: although for aircooled engines where the cooling air flows from the flywheel housing opening, the flywheel housing opening should not be covered. The effect of the cooling fan airflow on the microphone should also be minimized (see 8.3).

4. Instrumentation—The following instrumentation shall be used, where applicable, for the measurement required:

4.1 A sound level meter which meets the Type 1 or S1A requirements of American National Standard Specification for Sound Level Meters, S1.4-1983 and S1.4A-1985.

4.2 An octave band filter set which meets the Class II requirements of American National Standard Specifications for Octave, Half-Octave, and Third-Octave Band Filter Sets, S1.11-1986.

4.3 As an alternative to making direct measurements using a sound level meter and octave band analyzer, a microphone or sound level meter may be used with a magnetic tape recorder and/or a graphic level recorder or other indicating instrument, providing the system meets the requirements of SAE J184 FEB87, Qualifying a Sound Data Acquisition System.

4.4 An acoustic calibrator (see 8.4).

4.5 An engine speed indicator, accurate to ±1% or ±10 rpm, whichever is greater.

4.6 An anemometer (if outside tests are being performed).

4.7 A windscreen may be used (see 8.3). The windscreen must not affect the microphone response more than ±1 dB for the frequencies of 20 to 4000 Hz or ±1-1/2 dB for frequencies of 4000 to 10 000 Hz.

5. Environment—The engine sound levels shall be measured in an environment such that results are equivalent to those obtained in a free field above a reflecting plane. Measurements may be made at a flat open space or in a calibrated acoustically treated test cell.

5.1 If a flat open space is used, it shall be free of the effect of large reflecting surfaces, such as signboards, buildings, or hillsides located within 30.4 m (100 ft) of either the engine or microphone. The surface within 15.2 m (50 ft) of either the engine or microphone shall be free from snow, grass, loose soil, or other acoustical absorption materials. The area directly between the engine and the microphone shall be concrete, non-porous or sealed asphalt paving extending at least 3.0 m (10 ft) in all directions from the line between the engine and the microphone.

5.2 If an acoustically treated test cell is used, it must be calibrated for comparison to the flat open space for each octave band, A-weighted, and linear (or C-weighted) sound pressure level. The measurements from test cells and outdoor test sites may not be directly comparable without a correction factor, because of a reverberant sound field contribution to the test cell measurements. The test cell correction factor and method of determining the correction factor should be reported with the measured engine sound levels (see 2.1.3).

5.3 The ambient sound pressure levels (including wind effects) coming from sources other than the engine being measured shall be at least 10 dB below the level of the tested engine.

5.4 Because bystanders have an appreciable influence on meter response when they are in the vicinity of the engine or microphone, not more than one person, other than the observer reading the meter, shall be present, and that person shall be directly behind the observer reading the meter, on a line through the microphone and the observer. If the meter operator or engine/dynamometer operator are in the test cell, they should be to the rear of the engine or at the maximum allowable distance from the engine or microphones.

6. Measurements

6.1 The microphone shall be located 1.0 m (3.3 ft) from the longitudinal centers of the vertical planes forming the smallest rectangle which completely encloses the bare engine. Measurements shall be made on both sides and in front of the engine at the height of the exhaust manifold, but not less than 1.0 m (3.3 ft) above the floor. A survey of the A-weighted sound level shall be made at this microphone height and distance from the rectangular box. If the survey indicates a reading(s) more than 3 dB above the highest reading at the three specified locations, the sound level at this location(s) shall be also reported. The microphone positions thus referred to the bare engine shall be used for tests on fully equipped engines.

6.1.1 If the flat open space is used for optional correlation with most of the SAE sound level measurements of vehicles, additional sound measurements may be made with the microphone located at a height of 1.2 m (4 ft) above the surface and at 15.2 m (50 ft) from the center of the engine.

6.1.2 If the flat open space is used for optional correlation with most ISO sound level measurements, additional sound measurements may be made with the microphone located at a height of 1.2 m (4 ft) and 7.5 m (25 ft) from the center of the engine or 7.0 m (23 ft) from major surfaces.

6.2 The sound level meter or other indicating instrument shall be set for slow response. At each of the microphone locations, the following measurements shall be made:

a. The sound level using the A-weighting network.
b. The sound pressure level using the linear or C-weighting network; the network used shall be reported.
c. The octave band sound pressure levels for center frequencies of 63 to 8000 Hz at the microphone location having the highest A-weighted sound level, as determined in 6.1.
d. The reported data shall be identified as to the microphone location.

The reported sound pressure level shall be the average of two or more readings that are within 2 dB of each other.

7. Engine Operation—The engine shall be previously checked for rated performance and proper tune-up and shall be operated at the following steady conditions after reaching normal operating conditions:

a. Rated speed and load.
b. For governed engines, maximum governed speed at no load; for ungoverned engines, rated speed at no load.
c. Speed and load resulting in peak torque.
d. Recommended low idle speed.

8. General Comments

8.1 It is essential that technically trained personnel select the equipment and that the tests be conducted only by persons trained in the current techniques of sound measurement.

8.2 Instrument manufacturer's specifications for orientation of the microphone relative to the source of sound and the location of the observer relative to the meter should be followed. The microphone or sound level meter temperatures should be monitored to prevent overheating from the exhaust manifold.

8.3 It is recommended that measurements be made only when wind speed is below 19 km/h (12 mph). The microphone windscreen may be used to minimize the effects of wind gusts and other changes in wind velocity.

8.4 Instrument manufacturer's recommended calibration should be made at appropriate times. Field calibrations should be made immediately before and after each test sequence. Either an external calibration or internal calibration means is acceptable for field use, provided that external calibration is accomplished before or after the field test.

8.5 If a tape recorder is used, record a calibration tone of a known sound pressure level on the tape, using the same microphone and the same recorder attenuation settings immediately before and after the series of recordings.

8.6 The sound level of a diesel engine may be dependent on the fuel's cetane level. A diesel fuel with a cetane number between 42 and 50 is recommended. For gasoline-fueled engines, a fuel grade consistent with the engine manufacturer's recommendations should be used.

MEASUREMENT PROCEDURE FOR DETERMINATION OF SILENCER EFFECTIVENESS IN REDUCING ENGINE INTAKE OR EXHAUST SOUND LEVEL —SAE J1207 FEB2000

SAE Recommended Practice

Report of the SAE Vehicle Sound Level Committee approved May 1978, and reaffirmed February 1987. Reaffirmed by the SAE Exhaust and Intake Silencer Subcommittee of the SAE Vehicle Sound Level Committee February 2000.

Foreword—This Reaffirmed Document has not changed other than to put it into the new SAE Technical Standards Board Format. References were changed to Section 2. All other section numbers have changed accordingly.

1. Scope—This SAE Recommended Practice sets forth the instrumentation, environment, and test procedures to be used in measuring the silencer system effectiveness in reducing intake or exhaust sound level of internal combustion engines. The system shall include the intake or exhaust silencer, related piping, and components. This procedure is intended for engine-dynamometer testing and is not necessarily applicable to vehicle testing (see Appendix A). The effect of the exhaust or intake system on the sound level of the overall machine must be determined using other procedures. This procedure may be successively applied to various silencer configurations to determine relative effectiveness for that engine. Insertion loss for individual silencers may be calculated through measurement of the silenced and unsilenced system.

2. References

2.1 Applicable Publications—The following publications form a part of the specification to the extent specified herein. Unless otherwise indicated, the latest revision of SAE publications shall apply.

2.1.1 SAE PUBLICATION—Available from SAE, 400 Commonwealth Drive, Warrendale, PA 15096-0001.

SAE J184 FEB87—Qualifying a Sound Data Acquisition System

2.1.2 ANSI PUBLICATIONS—Available from ANSI, 11 West 42nd Street, New York, NY 10036-8002.

ANSI S1.4-1983 and S1.4A-1985—Specifications for Sound Level Meters

ANSI S1.13-1971 (R1986)—Methods for the Measurement of Sound Pressure Levels

3. Instrumentation—The following instrumentation shall be used for the measurement required:

3.1 A sound level meter which meets the Type 1 or S1A requirements of American National Standard, Specification for Sound Level Meters, S1.4-1983 & S1.4A-1985.

3.2 As an alternative to making direct measurements using a sound level meter, a microphone or sound level meter may be used with a magnetic tape recorder and/or a graphic level recorder or other indicating instrument, providing the system meets the requirements of SAE J184 FEB87, Qualifying a Sound Data Acquisition System.

3.3 A sound level calibrator having an accuracy within ±0.5 dB. (See 7.2.4.)

3.4 A windscreen may be used. The windscreen must not affect the microphone response more than ±1 dB for frequencies of 20 to 4000 Hz or ±1.5 dB for frequencies of 4000 to 10 000 Hz. (See 7.3.)

3.5 If outside tests are being performed, an anemometer or other means for determination of ambient wind speed having an accuracy within ±10% at 19 km/h (12 mph).

3.6 A thermometer or other means for determination of ambient and engine intake air temperature, having an accuracy within ±1 °C (±2 °F).

3.7 A thermometer or other means for determination of fuel temperature at the fuel pump inlet having an accuracy within ±1 °C (±2 °F).

3.8 A barometer or other means for determination of ambient and engine intake air barometric pressure, having an accuracy within ±0.5% of the actual value.

3.9 A psychrometer or other means for determination of ambient and engine intake air relative humidity, having an accuracy within ±5% of the actual value.

3.10 An engine dynamometer with engine speed and torque (or power) indicators having an accuracy within ±2% of the rated engine speed and torque (or power).

3.11 A flowmeter or other means for determination of engine fuel rate having an accuracy within ±1% of the rated fuel flow.

4. Environment—The silencer shall be measured in an environment such that results are equivalent to those obtained in a free field above a reflecting plane. Measurements may be made at a flat open space or in an acoustically equivalent test site as described in Appendix B.

4.1 The flat open space or equivalent test site shall be free from the effect of a large reflecting surface, such as a building or hillside, located within 30 m (100 ft) of either the silencer opening or microphone. The area directly between the silencer opening and the microphone shall be concrete or sealed asphalt with a maximum deviation of ±0.05 m (±2 in) from a plane extending at least 3.0 m (10 ft) in all directions from all points on the line segment between the silencer outlet and the microphone.

4.2 The ambient A-weighted sound level (including wind effects and other noise sources such as the engine) shall be at least 10 dB lower than the level being measured.

4.3 Not more than one person other than the observer reading the meter shall be within 15 m (50 ft) of the silencer opening or microphone, and that person shall be directly behind the observer who is reading the meter, on a line through the microphone and the observer, or behind the silencer under test.

5. Procedure

5.1 The silencer shall be tested on the engine and silencer system for which data will be reported.

5.2 The specified silencer system configuration shall provide for measurement of the acoustical radiation from the surface of the silencer or silencers, connecting pipes, and the acoustical outlet of the system. This does not include piping from the engine to the silencer. The silencer system should be oriented in the same relative position to the ground as for the actual application. Any deviation must be reported with the test data. All system connections are to be free from leaks that will measurably affect test results. For determining the insertion loss, the unsilenced system shall include a pipe of physical length equal to the silencer.

5.3 The engine power and fuel rate shall be measured at full load from two-thirds of rated speed to governed speed, or to rated speed on ungoverned engines, to determine whether the engine is within the engine manufacturer's performance specifications prior to proceeding with this test procedure.

5.4 The engine shall be operated in the following modes after reaching normal operating conditions:

a. Steady-state Mode—Rated engine speed and full load.
b. Varying Speed Full Load Mode—Engine speed to be slowly varied from rated speed to two-thirds of rated speed at wide open throttle.

For governed engines only:

c. Acceleration Mode—Accelerate the engine from idle to governed speed until the engine speed stabilizes and return to idle by rapidly opening and closing the throttle under no load conditions.

6. Measurements

6.1 The microphone shall be located at a height of 1.2 m (4 ft) above the ground plane and at a horizontal distance of 15 m (50 ft) from the centerline of the opening of the silencer system. For a multiple-opening system, the midpoint of the line (or centroid of the plane) connecting the openings shall be used as the reference point for the microphone distance measurement. Other optional distances such as 7.5 m (25 ft) may be used and must be reported. The angular location of the microphone relative to the silencer system opening shall be recorded.

6.2 The sound level meter shall be set for fast dynamic response and for the A-weighting network.

6.3 For the procedure specified in 5.3 and 5.4, report:

a. Engine power and fuel rate as determined in 5.3.
b. Ambient wind speed, ambient temperature, ambient barometric pressure, ambient relative humidity, and ambient a-weighted sound levels for the test site.
c. Maximum A-weighted sound level measured for each test mode in 5.4.
d. Torque (or power), engine speed, engine intake air temperature, barometric pressure, and relative humidity at which the maximum sound level was obtained.
e. Any deviations from recommended test procedure as described in 5.2.
f. The angular location and distance of the microphone relative to the silencer opening.
g. Description of the test configuration, including all critical dimensions.

7. General Comments

7.1 It is essential that persons technically trained and experienced in the current techniques of sound measurement select the equipment and conduct the tests.

7.2 Proper use of all test instrumentation is essential to obtain valid measurements. operating manuals or other literature furnished by the instrument and manufacturer should be referred to for both recommended operation of the instrument and precautions to be observed. specific items to be considered are:

7.2.1 The type of microphone, its directional response characteristics, and its orientation relative to the ground plane and source of noise.

7.2.2 The effects of ambient weather conditions on the performance of all instruments (for example, temperature, humidity, and barometric pressure). instrumentation can be influenced by low temperature and caution should be exercised.

7.2.3 Proper signal levels, terminating impedances, and cable lengths on multi-instrument measurement systems.

7.2.4 Proper acoustical calibration procedure, to include the influence of extension cables, etc. Field calibration shall be made immediately before and after each test sequence. Internal calibration means is acceptable for field use, provided that external calibration is accomplished immediately before and after field use.

7.3 Measurements shall be made only when wind speed is below 19 km/h (12 mph).

7.4 It is recommended that a drawing or photograph of the test configuration be included in the reported results.

APPENDIX A

A.1 A typical test layout may include an engine-dynamometer located in an acoustically isolated test cell adjacent to the test site. The piping from the engine to the silencer should extend from the isolated test cell to the test site. The silencer system should be oriented in the same relative position to the ground as for the actual application. All piping between the engine and silencer should be acoustically treated to meet the requirements of 4.2. The sound level measured during the test should include outlet sound as well as shell sound from the silencer and connecting pipes, but not including the piping from the engine to the silencer. The test site may consist of a flat open space or acoustically equivalent indoor or outdoor test site.

APPENDIX B

B.1 If a facility other than a flat open space (see 4.1) is used, the A-weighted sound level from a broad band sound source must not deviate over the test distance from the response in a free field above a reflecting plane more than ±1 dB. Measurement considerations in American National Standard, Methods for the Measurement of Sound Pressure Levels, ANSI S1.13-1971 (R1986), shall be used.

THREADS, FASTENERS, AND COMMON PARTS

15 Threads

DRYSEAL PIPE THREADS—SAE J476a JUN1961

SAE Standard

Report of the SAE Miscellaneous Division approved March 1921 and last revised by the SAE Screw Threads Committee June 1961. Values in Table 1 conform to those in Table 9, Limits on Crest and Root of proposed American Standard, Dryseal Pipe Threads, ASA B2.2

Foreword—This Document has not changed other than to put it into the new SAE Technical Standards Board Format.

TABLE OF CONTENTS

1. Scope—The Dryseal American Standard Taper Pipe Thread, the Dryseal American Fuel Internal Straight Pipe Thread and the Dryseal American Intermediate Internal Straight Pipe Thread covered by this standard conform with the American Standard ASA-B2.2. The Dryseal SAE-Short Taper Pipe Thread in this standard conforms with the Dryseal American Standard Taper Pipe Thread except for the length of thread, which is shortened for increased clearance and economy of material.

The significant feature of the Dryseal thread is controlled truncation at the crest and root to assure metal to metal contact coincident with or prior to flank contact. Contact at the crest and root prevents spiral leakage and insures pressure-tight joints without the use of a lubricant or sealer.

Lubricants, if not functionally objectionable, may be used to minimize the possibility of galling in assembly.

2. References

2.1 Applicable Publications—The following publications form a part of the specification to the extent specified herein. Unless otherwise indicated the latest revision of SAE publications shall apply.

2.1.1 SAE PUBLICATIONS—Available from SAE, 400 Commonwealth Drive, Warrendale, PA 15096-0001.

ASAB2.2—Dryseal Pipe Threads
SAE Standards Screw Threads

3. Truncation—Dryseal American Standard External And Internal Pipe Threads For Pressure-Tight Joints Without Lubricant Or Sealer

3.1 Thread Form—The angle between the flanks of the thread is 60 deg when measured on an axial plane and the line bisecting this angle is perpendicular to the axis of both the taper and straight threads.

Diametral taper of tapered threads is 0.75 in. ± 0.06 in. per 12.00 in. of length.

Although the crests and roots of the Dryseal threads are theoretically flat, they may be rounded provided their contour is within the limits specified in Table 1.

3.2 Thread Series Symbols—The identification symbols which have been adopted for designating the various Dryseal Pipe Thread Series are as follows:

NPTF for Dryseal American Standard Taper Pipe Thread.
PTF—SAE for Dryseal SAE Short Taper Pipe Thread.
NPSF for Dryseal American Fuel Internal Straight Pipe Thread.
NPSI for Dryseal American Intermediate Internal Straight Pipe Thread.

Where: N stands for American Standard [formerly American (National) Standard].

P stands for Pipe
T stands for Taper
F stands for Fuel
S stands for Straight
I stands for Intermediate

3.3 Thread Designation—Dryseal pipe threads are designated by specifying in sequence the nominal size, number of threads per inch, form (Dryseal), and symbol of the thread series.

EXAMPLE—1/8—27 DRYSEAL NPTF
1/8—27 DRYSEAL PTF—SAE SHORT
1/8—27 DRYSEAL NPSF
1/8—27 DRYSEAL NPSI

3.4 Straight Pipe Threads—An assembly with straight internal pipe threads and taper external pipe threads is frequently more advantageous than an all taper thread assembly, particularly in automotive and other allied industries where economy and rapid production are paramount considerations. Dryseal threads are not used on assemblies in which both components have straight pipe threads.

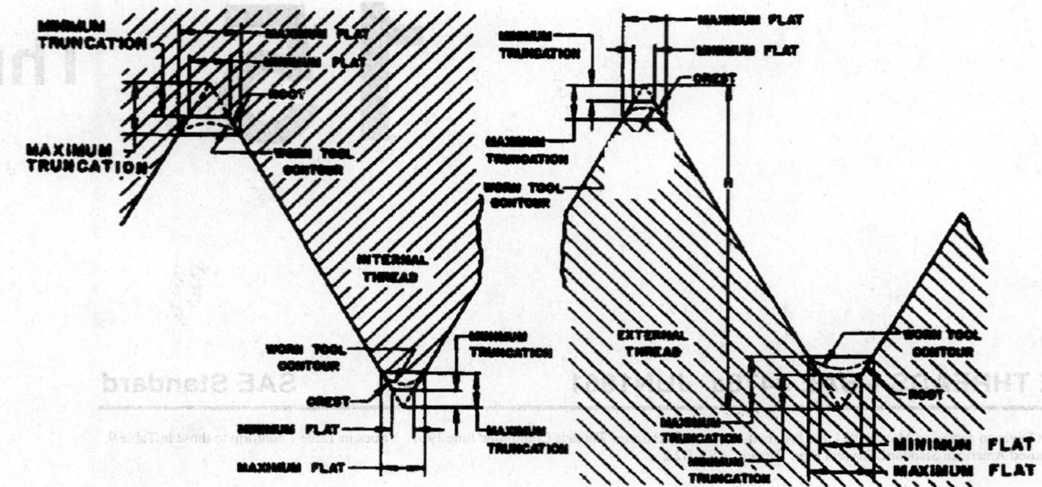

FIGURE 1—

TABLE 1—LIMITS ON CREST AND ROOT TRUNCATION

Threads per in.		Depth of Sharp-V Thread, H in.	Truncation Min Formula	Truncation Min in.	Truncation Max Formula	Truncation Max in.	Equalivalent Width of Flat(1) Min Formula	Equivalent Width of Flat(1) Min in.	Equivalent Width of Flat(1) Max Formula	Equivalent Width of Flat(1) Max in.
27	Crest	0.03208	0.047p	0.0017	0.094p	0.0035	0.054p	0.0020	0.108p	0.0040
	Root		0.094p	0.0035	0.140p	0.0052	0.108p	0.0040	0.162p	0.0060
18	Crest	0.04811	0.047p	0.0026	0.078p	0.0043	0.054p	0.0030	0.090p	0.0050
	Root		0.078p	0.0043	0.109p	0.0061	0.090p	0.0050	0.126p	0.0070
14	Crest	0.06186	0.036p	0.0026	0.060p	0.0043	0.042p	0.0030	0.070p	0.0050
	Root		0.060p	0.0043	0.085p	0.0061	0.070p	0.0050	0.098p	0.0070
11-1/2	Crest	0.07531	0.040p	0.0035	0.060p	0.0052	0.046p	0.0040	0.069p	0.0060
	Root		0.060p	0.0052	0.090p	0.0078	0.069p	0.0060	0.103p	0.0090
8	Crest	0.10825	0.042p	0.0052	0.055p	0.0069	0.048p	0.0060	0.064p	0.0080(2)
	Root		0.055p	0.0069	0.076p	0.0095	0.064p	0.0080	0.088p	0.0110

1. The major diameter of plug gages and minor diameter of ring gages used for gaging dryseal threads shall be truncated an amount sufficient to produce a flat width as shown in Appendix C, Tables C1-1 to C12-1 inclusive.
2. There is reason to doubt the correctness of the 8 threads per in. flat widths on account of the volume of metal to be displaced.

4. Dryseal American Standard Taper Pipe Thread (NPTF)—This series applies to both the external and internal threads of all full length and is suitable for pipe joints in practically every type of service. These threads are generally conceded to be superior for strength and seal. Use of the tapered internal thread in hard or brittle materials having thin sections will minimize trouble from fracture. Dimensional data for (NPTF) threads is given in Table 2. See Appendix D for limitations of assembly of NPTF threads with other series Dryseal pipe threads.

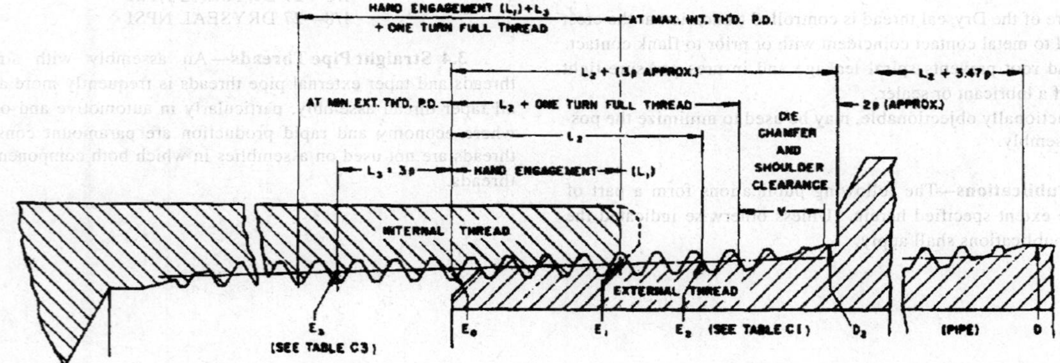

FIGURE 2—

TABLE 2—BASIC DIMENSIONS OF DRYSEAL AMERICAN STANDARD TAPER PIPE THREAD[1]

NPTF Size 1	Pitch, P in. 2	Pitch Diameter at End of External Thread, E_0 in. 3	Pitch Diameter at End of Internal Thread, E_1 in. 4	Hand Engage-ment, L_1 in. 5	Hand Engage-ment, L_1 Thread 6	Length of Full Thread,[2] L_2 in. 7	Length of Full Thread[2], L_2 Thread 8	Vanish Threads V Plus Full Thread Tolerance Plus Shoulder Clearance (V + 1p + 1/2 p) in. 9	Vanish Threads V Plus Full Thread Tolerance Plus Shoulder Clearance (V + 1p + 1/2 p) Thread 10	Shoulder Length L_2 + (3p Approx) in. 11	External Thread for Draw (L_2 - L_1) in. 12	External Thread for Draw (L_2 - L_1) Thread 13	Length of Internal Full Thread,[3] (L_1 + L_3) in. 14	Length of Internal Full Thread[3] (L_1 + L_3) Thread 15	OD of Fitting, D_2 in. 16	OD of Pipe, D
1/16-27	0.03704	0.27118	0.28118	0.160	4.32	0.2611	7.05	0.1139	3.075	0.3750	0.1011	2.73	0.2711	7.32	0.315	0.3125
1/8 -27	0.03704	0.36351	0.37360	0.1615	4.36	0.2639	7.12	0.1112	3.072	0.3750	0.1024	2.76	0.2726	7.36	0.407	0.405
1/4 -18	0.05556	0.47739	0.49163	0.2278	4.10	0.4018	7.23	0.1607	2.892	0.5625	0.1740	3.13	0.3945	7.10	0.546	0.540
3/8 -18	0.05556	0.61201	0.62701	0.240	4.32	0.4078	7.34	0.1547	2.791	0.5625	0.1678	3.02	0.4067	7.32	0.681	0.675
1/2 -14	0.07143	0.75843	0.77843	0.320	4.48	0.5337	7.47	0.2163	3.028	0.7500	0.2137	2.99	0.5343	7.48	0.850	0.840
3/4 -14	0.07143	0.96768	0.98887	0.339	4.75	0.5457	7.64	0.2043	2.860	0.7500	0.2067	2.89	0.5533	7.75	1.060	1.050
1 -11-1/2	0.08696	1.21363	1.23863	0.400	4.60	0.6828	7.85	0.2547	2.929	0.9375	0.2828	3.25	0.6609	7.60	1.327	1.315
1-1/4 -11-1/2	0.08696	1.55713	1.58338	0.420	4.83	0.7068	8.13	0.2620	3.013	0.9688	0.2868	3.30	0.6809	7.83	1.672	1.660
1-1/2 -11-1/2	0.08696	1.79609	1.82234	0.420	4.83	0.7235	8.32	0.2765	3.180	1.0000	0.3035	3.49	0.6809	7.83	1.912	1.900
-11-1/2	0.08696	2.26902	2.29627	0.436	5.01	0.7565	8.70	0.2747	3.159	1.0312	0.3205	3.69	0.6969	8.01	2.387	2.375
2-1/2 -8	0.12500	2.71953	2.76216	0.682	5.46	1.1375	9.10	0.3781	3.025	1.5156	0.4555	3.64	1.0570	8.46	2.893	2.875
3 -8	0.12500	3.34062	3.38850	0.766	6.13	1.2000	9.60	0.3781	3.025	1.5781	0.4340	3.47	1.1410	9.13	3.518	3.500

1. See general specifications preceding tables.
   For gaging methods, gages, cut thread blanks, taps, drilled hole sizes, hole depths, and full thread lengths, see Appendixes A, B, and C.
2. External thread tabulated full thread lengths include chamfers not exceeding one and one-half pitches (threads) length.
3. Internal thread tabulated full thread lengths do not include countersink beyond the intersection of the pitch line and the chamfer cone (gaging reference point).

5. Dryseal SAE Short External Taper Pipe Thread (PTF—SAE Short External) For Assembly With Dryseal American Intermediate Internal Straight (Table 6) or Dryseal American Standard Taper (Table 2) Pipe Threads—External threads of this series conform in all respects with the NPTF threads except that the full thread length has been shortened by eliminating one thread from the small end. These threads are primarily intended for assembly with NPSI internal threads but may also be used with NPTF internal threads. They are not designed for and at extreme tolerance limits may not assemble with PTF—SAE Short or NPSF internal threads. Dimensional data for PTF—SAE Short External Threads is given in Table 3. See Appendix D for limitations of assembly of PTF—SAE Short external threads with other series Dryseal pipe threads.

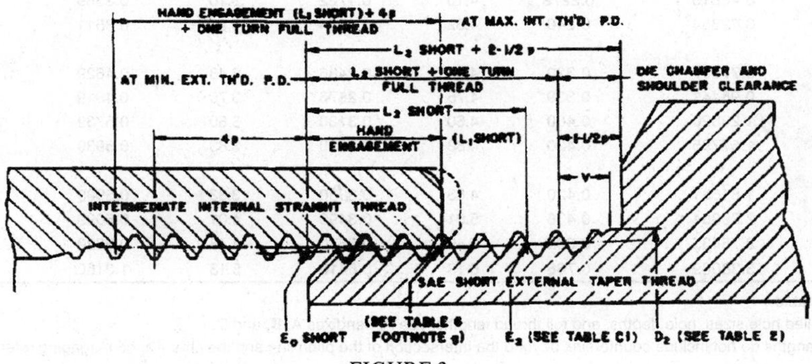

FIGURE 3—

TABLE 3—BASIC DIMENSIONS OF DRYSEAL SAE SHORT EXTERNAL TAPER PIPE THREAD[1]

PTF—SAE Short Size 1	Pitch, P in. 2	Pitch Diameter at End of External Thread, E_0 Short in. 3	L_1 in. 4	L_1 Thread 5	Hand Engage-ment, L_1 Short in. 6	Hand Engage-ment, L_1 Short Thread 7	Length of Full Thread,[2] L_2 Short in. 8	Length of Full Thread,[2] L2 Short Thread 9	Vanish Threads V Plus Full Thread Tolerance Plus Shoulder Clearance (V + 1p + 1/2 p) in. 10	Vanish Threads V Plus Full Thread Tolerance Plus Shoulder Clearance (V + 1p + 1/2 p) Thread 11	Min Shoulder Length (L_2 Short +2-1/2 p) in. 12	External Thread for Draw (L_2 Short—L1 Short) in. 13	External Thread for Draw (L_2 Short—L1 Short) Thread 14	Length of Internal Full Thread,[3] (L_1 Short + 4p) in. 15	Length of Internal Full Thread [3], (L_1 Short + 4p) Thread 16
1/16-27	0.03704	0.27349	0.160	4.32	0.1230	3.32	0.2241	6.05	0.0926	2.50	0.3167	0.1011	2.73	0.2711	7.32
1/8 -27	0.03704	0.36582	0.1615	4.36	0.1244	3.36	0.2268	6.12	0.0926	2.50	0.3194	0.1024	2.76	0.2726	7.36
1/4 -18	0.05556	0.48086	0.2278	4.10	0.1722	3.10	0.3462	6.23	0.1389	2.50	0.4851	0.1740	3.13	0.3945	7.10
3/8 -18	0.05556	0.61548	0.240	4.32	0.1844	3.32	0.3522	6.34	0.1389	2.50	0.4911	0.1678	3.02	0.4067	7.32
1/2 -14	0.07143	0.76289	0.320	4.48	0.2486	3.48	0.4623	6.47	0.1786	2.50	0.6409	0.2137	2.99	0.5343	7.48
3/4 -14	0.07143	0.97214	0.339	4.75	0.2676	3.75	0.4743	6.64	0.1786	2.50	0.6528	0.2067	2.89	0.5533	7.75
1 -11-1/2	0.08696	1.21906	0.400	4.60	0.3130	3.60	0.5958	6.85	0.2174	2.50	0.8132	0.2828	3.25	0.6609	7.60
1-1/4 -11-1/2	0.08696	1.56256	0.420	4.83	0.3330	3.83	0.6198	7.13	0.2174	2.50	0.8372	0.2868	3.30	0.6809	7.83
1-1/2 -11-1/2	0.08696	1.80152	0.420	4.83	0.3330	3.83	0.6365	7.32	0.2174	2.50	0.8539	0.3035	3.49	0.6809	7.83
2 -11-1/2	0.08696	2.27445	0.436	5.01	0.3490	4.01	0.6695	7.70	0.2174	2.50	0.8869	0.3205	3.69	0.6969	8.01
2-1/2 -8	0.12500	2.72734	0.682	5.46	0.5570	4.46	1.0125	8.10	0.3125	2.50	1.3250	0.4555	3.64	1.0570	8.46
-8	0.12500	3.34844	0.766	6.13	0.6410	5.13	1.0750	8.60	0.3125	2.50	1.3875	0.4340	3.47	1.1410	9.13

1. See general specifications preceding tables.
   For gaging methods, gages, cut thread blanks, taps, drilled hole sizes, hole depths, and full thread lengths, see Appendixes A, B, and C.
2. External thread tabulated full thread lengths include camfers not exceeding one and one-half pitches (threads) lengths.
3. Internal thread tabulated full thread lengths do not include countersink beyond the intersection of the pitch line and the camfer cone (gaging reference point).

6. Dryseal SAE Short Internal Taper Pipe Thread (PTF—SAE Short Internal) For Assembly With American Standard External Taper Pipe Thread (Table 2)—Internal Threads of this series conform in all respects with the NPTF threads except that the full thread length has been shortened by eliminating one thread from the large end. These threads are primarily intended for assembly with NPTF external threads. They are not designed for and at extreme tolerance limits may not assemble with PTF—SAE Short external threads. Dimensional data for PTF—SAE Short Internal Threads is given in Table 4. See Appendix D for limitations of assembly of PTF—SAE Short internal threads with other series Dryseal pipe threads.

Trouble-free assemblies and pressure-tight joints without the use of lubricant or sealer can best be assured where both components are threaded with NPTF (full length) threads. This should be considered before specifying PTF—SAE Short External or Internal Thread.

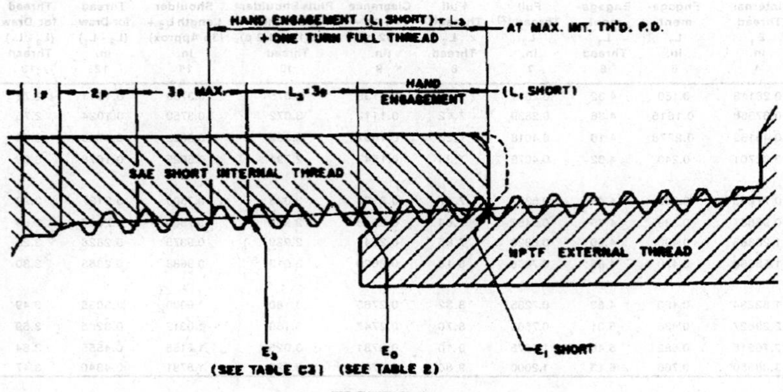

FIGURE 4—

TABLE 4—BASIC DIMENSIONS OF DRYSEAL SAE SHORT INTERNAL TAPER PIPE THREAD(1)

PTF—SAE Short Size 1	Pitch P in. 2	Pitch Diameter at End of Internal Thread E_1 Short in. 3	L_1 in. 4	L_1 Thread 5	Hand Engagement(2) L_1 Short 6	Hand Engagement(2) L_1 Short Thread 7	Length of Internal Full Thread(2) (L_1 Short + L_3) in. 8	Length of Internal Full Thread(2) (L_1 Short + L_3) Thread 9	Hole Depth for SAE Short Tap (Table B3) in. 10
1/16-27	0.03704	0.27887	0.160	4.32	0.1230	3.32	0.2341	6.32	0.4564
1/8 -27	0.03704	0.37129	0.1615	4.36	0.1244	3.36	0.2356	6.36	0.4578
1/4 -18	0.05556	0.48815	0.2278	4.10	0.1722	3.10	0.3389	6.10	0.6722
3/8 -18	0.05556	0.62354	0.240	4.32	0.1844	3.32	0.3511	6.32	0.6844
1/2 -14	0.07143	0.77397	0.320	4.48	0.2486	3.48	0.4629	6.48	0.8915
3/4 -14	0.07143	0.98441	0.339	4.75	0.2676	3.75	0.4819	6.75	0.9105
1 -11-1/2	0.08696	1.23320	0.400	4.60	0.3130	3.60	0.5739	6.60	1.0956
1-1/4 -11-1/2	0.08696	1.57795	0.420	4.83	0.3330	3.83	0.5939	6.83	1.1156
1-1/2 -11-1/2	0.08696	1.81691	0.420	4.83	0.3330	3.83	0.5939	6.83	1.1156
2 -11-1/2	0.08696	2.29084	0.436	5.01	0.3490	4.01	0.6099	7.01	1.1316
2-1/2 -8	0.12500	2.75435	0.682	5.46	0.5570	4.46	0.9320	7.46	1.6820
3 -8	0.12500	3.38069	0.766	6.13	0.6410	5.13	1.0160	8.13	1.7660

1. See general specification preceding table.
   For gaging methods, gages, taps, drilled hole sizes, hole depths, and full thread lengths, see Appendixes A, B, and C.
2. Internal thread tabulated full thread lengths do not include countersink beyond the intersection of the pitch line and the chamfer cone (gaging reference point).

7. Dryseal American Standard Fuel Internal Straight Pipe Thread (NPSF) For Assembly With Dryseal American Standard External Taper Pipe Thread (Table 2)—Threads of this series are straight (cylindrical) instead of tapered. They are generally used in soft or ductile materials which will adjust at assembly to the taper of external threads but may also be used in hard or brittle materials where the section is heavy. These threads are primarily intended for assembly with full length NPTF external taper threads. Dimensional data for NPSF threads is given in Table 5. See Appendix D for limitations of assembly of NPSF internal threads with other series Dryseal pipe threads.

TABLE 5—DRYSEAL AMERICAN STANDARD FUEL INTERNAL STRAIGHT PIPE THREAD LIMITS (1)

NPSF Size 1	Pitch Diameter(2) Max(3)(4) 2	Pitch Diameter(2) Min(4)(5) 3	Minor Diameter(6) Min 4	Desired Min Length of Full Thread(7) in. 5	Desired Min Length of Full Thread(7) Thread 6
1/16-27	0.2803	0.2768	0.2482	0.31	8.44
1/8 -27	0.3727	0.3692	0.3406	0.31	8.44
1/4 -18	0.4904	0.4852	0.4422	0.47	8.44
3/8 -18	0.6257	0.6205	0.5776	0.50	9.00
1/2 -14	0.7767	0.7700	0.7133	0.66	9.19
3/4 -14	0.9872	0.9805	0.9238	0.66	9.19
1 -11-1/2	1.2365	1.2284	1.1600	0.78	8.98

1. See general specifications preceding tables.
   For gaging methods, gages, taps, drilled hole sizes, hole depths, and full thread lengths, see Appendixes A, B, and C.
2. The pitch diameter of the tapped hole as indicated by the taper plug gage is slightly larger than the values given due to the gage having to enter approximately 3/8 turn to engage first full thread.
3. Column 2 is the E_1 pitch diameter of thread at large end of internal thread (Table 2) plus (larger) 5/8 thread taper.
4. Taps specified in Table B4 produce tapped holes to the above limits in cast iron, steel, and brass. In zinc and similar soft metals, they produce tapped holes approximately 0.001 smaller. Plug-gage turns engagement should be reduced accordingly.
5. Column 3 is Column 2 reduced by 1-1/2 turns.
6. As the Dryseal American Standard pipe thread form is maintained, the major and minor diameters of the internal thread vary with the pitch diameter.
7. Internal thread tabulated full thread lengths do not include countersink beyond the intersection of the pitch line and the chamfer cone (gaging reference point).

8. Dryseal American Intermediate Internal Straight Pipe Thread (NPSI) For Assembly With Dryseal SAE Short External Taper (Table 3) or American Standard Taper Pipe Thread (Table 2)—Threads of this series are straight (cylindrical) instead of tapered. They are generally used in hard or brittle materials where the section is heavy and where there is little expansion at assembly with the external taper threads. These threads are primarily intended for assembly with PTF—SAE Short External Taper Threads, but will also assemble with full length NPTF External Taper Threads. Dimensional data for NPSI threads is given in Table 6. See Appendix D for limitations of assembly of NPSI internal threads with other series Dryseal pipe threads.

TABLE 6—DRYSEAL AMERICAN INTERMEDIATE INTERNAL STRAIGHT PIPE THREAD LIMITS(1)

NPSF Size 1	Pitch Diameter(2) Max(3),(4) 2	Pitch Diameter(2) Min(3),(5) 3	Minor Diameter(6) Min 4	Desired Min Length of Full Thread(7) in. 5	Desired Min Length of Full Thread(7) Thread 7
1/16-27	0.2826	0.2791	0.2505	0.31	8.44
1/8 -27	0.3750	0.3715	0.3429	0.31	8.44
1/4 -18	0.4938	0.4886	0.4457	0.47	8.44
3/8 -18	0.6292	0.6240	0.5811	0.50	9.00
1/2 -14	0.7812	0.7745	0.7180	0.66	9.19
3/4 -14	0.9917	0.9850	0.9283	0.66	9.19
1 -11-1/2	1.2420	1.2338	1.1655	0.78	8.98

1. See general specifications preceding tables.
For gaging methods, gages, taps, drilled hole sizes, hole depths, and full thread lengths, see Appendixes A, B, and C.
2. The pitch diameter of the tapped hole as indicated by the taper plug gage is slightly larger than the values given due to the gage having to enter approximately 3/8 turn to engage first full thread.
3. Column 2 is the same as the E_1 pitch diameter of thread at large end of internal thread (Table 2) minus (small) 3/8 thread taper.
4. Taps specified in Table B5 produce tapped holes to the above limits in cast iron, steel, and brass. In zinc and similar soft metals, they produce tapped holes approximately 0.001 smaller. Plug-gage turns engagement should be reduced accordingly.
5. Column 3 is Column 2 reduced by 1-1/2 turns.
6. As the Dryseal American Standard pipe thread form is maintained, the major and minor diameters of the internal thread vary with the pitch diameter.
7. Internal thread tabulated full thread lengths do not include countersink beyond the intersection of the pitch line and the chamfer cone (gaging reference point).

APPENDIX A
SUPPLEMENTARY THREAD INFORMATION

A.1 Terminology—For definitions of terms relating to size of parts, geometrical elements, or dimensions of threads see SAE Standards Screw Threads, Appendix A—Terminology.

A.2 Dryseal American Standard And SAE Short External Taper Pipe Thread Blanks, Cut Threads

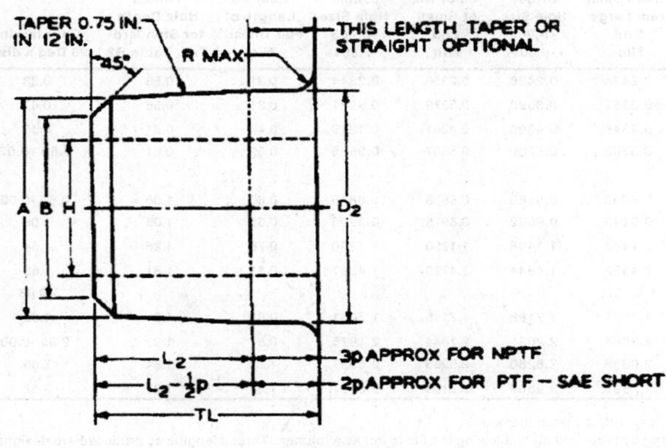

FIGURE A1—

A.2.1 Formulas for Diameter and Length of Thread—Basic diameter and length of thread for different sizes given in Tables 2, 3, and 4, are based on the following formulas:

Basic pitch diameter of thread at small end of NPTF External Thread.

$$E_0 = D - (0.05D + 1.1)p \quad \text{(Eq. A1)}$$

Basic pitch diameter of thread at small end of PTF—SAE Short External Thread.

$$E_0\text{Short} = D - (0.05D + 1.037)p \quad \text{(Eq. A2)}$$

Basic pitch diameter of thread at large end of NPTF Internal Thread.

$$E_1 = E_0 + (0.0625 X L_1 \text{ Basic}) \quad \text{(Eq. A3)}$$

Basic pitch diameter of thread at large end of PTF—SAE Short Internal Thread.

$$E_1\text{Short} = E_0 + (0.0625 X L_1 \text{ Short}) \quad \text{(Eq. A4)}$$

Basic length of NPTF external full and effective length thread.

$$L_2 = (0.8D + 6.8)p \quad \text{(Eq. A5)}$$

Basic length of PTF—SAE Short external full and effective length thread.

$$L_2\text{Short} = (0.8D + 5.8)p \quad \text{(Eq. A6)}$$

Basic length of NPTF internal full and effective length thread = L_1 Basic + L_3
Basic length of PTF—SAE Short internal full and effective length thread = L_1 Short + L_3

Where

D = outside of diameter of pipe

P = pitch of thread in inches

NPSG (for oil and grease cup) is Dryseal American Standard Pipe Thread Form—use NPSF tap drill sizes.

The drilled hole sizes given above for Dryseal straight and taper internal pipe threads are the diameters produced by drills which are closest to the minimum minor diameters as shown in Table A2.

They represent the diameters of the holes which would be cut with a twist drill correctly ground when drilling a material without tearing or flow of metal. This is approximately the condition obtained when a correctly sharpened twist drill is cutting a hole in SAE 1112 or 1113 steel, or SAE 72 brass. When Dryseal taps are used, these holes produce an acceptable pipe thread with the required thread height.

When flat drills are used, the width of the cutting edge may have to be adjusted to produce a hole of the required diameter.

When hard metals and other similar materials are to be drilled and tapped, it may be found necessary to use a drill of slightly smaller diameter to produce a hole of a size that will make it possible for the tap to cut an acceptable pipe thread with the required thread height.

When soft metals and other similar materials are to be drilled and tapped, it may be found necessary to use a drill of slightly larger diameter to produce a hole of a size that will allow for a flow of the metal or material without loading the tap or tearing the material and make it possible for the tap to produce an acceptable pipe thread with the required thread height.

TABLE A1—DIMENSIONS OF DRYSEAL AMERICAN STANDARD EXTERNAL TAPER PIPE THREAD BLANKS (CUT THREADS)

Size	OD at Large End NPTF at L_2 Length D_2 PTF—SAE Short at L_2 - 1/2p Length (Basic Thread One Turn Large with Max Truncation) +0.003 - 0.000	OD at Small End, A NPTF (Basic Thread Two Turns Large with Max Truncation) +0.003 - 0.000	OD at Small End, A PTF-SAE Short (Basic Thread 2-1/2 Turns Lare with Max Truncation) +0.003 - 0.000	Chamfer Dia[1], B (Minor Dia[1] at Small End)	Min Length from Small End to Shoulder, TL NPTF L_2 + (3p Approx)	Min Length from Small End to Shoulder, TL PTF-SAE Short L_2 Short + (2-1/2p Approx)	Corner Radius, R Max	Recommended Hole Size[2], H
1/16-27	0.315	0.301	0.302	0.23	0.38	0.3167	0.03	0.12
1/8 -27	0.407	0.393	0.394	0.32	0.38	0.3194	0.03	0.19
1/4 -18	0.546	0.523	0.525	0.42 +0.00	0.56	0.4851	0.06	0.28
3/8 -18	0.681	0.658	0.660	0.55	0.56	0.4911	0.06	0.41
1/2 -14	0.850	0.820	0.822	0.68 -0.02	0.75	0.6409	0.08	0.56
3/4 -14	1.060	1.029	1.031	0.89	0.75	0.6528	0.08	0.72
1 -11-1/2	1.327	1.289	1.292	1.12	0.94	0.8132	0.09	0.94
1-1/4 -11-1/2	1.672	1.633	1.636	1.46 +0.00	0.97	0.8372	0.09	1.25
1-1/2 -11-1/2	1.912	1.872	1.875	1.70	1.00	0.8539	0.09	1.47
2 -11-1/2	2.387	2.345	2.348	2.17 -0.03	1.03	0.8869	0.09	1.94
2-1/2 -8	2.893	2.829	2.833	2.59	1.52	1.3250	0.12	2.31
3 -8	3.518	3.450	3.454	3.21	1.58	1.3875	0.12	2.91

1. External pipe threads shall be chamfered from a diameter (rounded to a two-place decimal) obtained by subtracting 0, .016 in. for sizes below 1 in. and 0.025 in. for larger sizes from the minimum minor diameter at small end to produce a length of chamfered or partial thread equivalent to 1 to 1-1.2 times the pitch (rounded to a three-place decimal).
2. The hole sizes recommended respresent a desirable maximum, strength of wall being considered. However, as considerations otherthan wall strength frequently control the hole size in specific applications, the recommendations should not be construed as a requirement of this SAE Standard.

A.3 Pipe-Thread Drilled Hole Sizes For Dryseal American Standard Internal Pipe Thread—It should be understood that this table of drilled hole sizes is intended to help only the occasional user of drills in the application of this SAE Standard. When internal pipe threads are produced in larger quantities in a particular type of material and with specially designed machinery, it may be found to be more advantageous to use a drilled hole size not given in the table, even one requiring a nonstandard diameter drill size.

TABLE A2—PIPE-THREAD DRILLED HOLE SIZES

Size	Straight Pipe Thread Fuel (NPSF) Minor Dia[1] Min	Straight Pipe Thread Fuel (NPSF) Drilled Hole Size +0.003 -0.001	Straight Pipe Thread Intermediate (NPSI) Minor Dia[2] Min	Straight Pipe Thread Intermediate (NPSI) Drilled Hole Size +0.003 -0.001	Straight Pipe Thread Desired Length of Full Thread Min	Straight Pipe Thread Hole Depth for Plug End Tap, Tables B4 and B5	Taper Pipe Thread NPTF (Not Reamed) 2 FF Thread[3] Minor Dia 2 Thread Small from Large End Min	Taper Pipe Thread NPTF (Not Reamed) 2 FF Thread[2] Drilled Hole Size +0.003 =0.001	Taper Pipe Thread NPTF (Not Reamed) 4 FF Thread [2] Minor Dia 4 Thread Small from Large End Min	Taper Pipe Thread NPTF (Not Reamed) 4 FF Thread[2] Drilled Hole Size +0.003 -0.001	Taper Pipe Thread NPTF[4] (Taper Reamed) Desired Minor Dia at Small End Min	Taper Pipe Thread NPTF[4] (Taper Reamed) Drilled Hole Size +0.003 -0.001	Taper Pipe Thread Desired Length of Full Thread Min	Taper Pipe Thread Hole Depth for Standard Tap, Table B2	Countersink 90 Deg x dia[4]
1/16-27	0.2482	0.2500	0.2505	0.2500	0.31	0.47	0.2480	0.2460	0.2434	0.2420	0.2356	0.2344	0.31	0.56	0.33
1/8 -27	0.3406	0.3437	0.3429	0.3437	0.31	0.47	0.3403	0.3390	0.3357	0.3320	0.3279	0.3281	0.31	0.56	0.42
1/4 -18	0.4422	0.4440	0.4457	0.4440	0.47	0.72	0.4417	0.4375	0.4348	0.4300	0.4241	0.4219	0.47	0.81	0.55
3/8 -18	0.5776	0.5781	0.5811	0.5781	0.50	0.72	0.5771	0.5781	0.5702	0.5700	0.5587	0.5625	0.50	0.81	0.69 +0.02
1/2 -14	0.7133	0.7187	0.7180	0.7187	0.66	0.94	0.7127	0.7031	0.7038	0.6960	0.6873	0.6875	0.66	1.06	0.85 -0.00
3/4 -14	0.9238	—	0.9283	—	0.66	0.94	0.9232	0.9219	0.9143	0.9062	0.8976	0.8906	0.66	1.06	1.06
1 -11-1/2	1.1600	—	1.1655	—	0.78	1.16	1.1593	1.1562	1.1484	1.1406	1.1290	1.1250	0.78	1.25	1.34
1-1/4 -11-1/2	—	—	—	—	—	—	1.5041	1.5000	1.4932	1.4844	1.4725	1.4687	0.81	1.31	1.68 +0.03
1-1/2 -11-1/2	—	—	—	—	—	—	1.7430	1.7344	1.7321	1.7188	1.7115	1.7031	0.81	1.31	1.92
2 -11-1/2	—	—	—	—	—	—	2.2170	2.2187	2.2061	2.2031	2.1844	2.1875	0.81	1.31	2.39 -0.00
2-1/2 -8	—	—	—	—	—	—	2.6488	2.6406	2.6336	2.6250	2.5983	2.5937	1.25	1.84	2.89
3 -8	—	—	—	—	—	—	3.2751	3.2656	3.2595	3.2500	3.2194	3.2187	1.34	1.91	3.52

1. Minimum minor diameter for internal straight pipe threads is based upon minimum pitch diameter and minimum truncation and will vary with the pitch diameter.
2. NPTF (taper reamed) drilled hole sizes are recommended for taper reaming before tapping. They also are used without taper reami ng by taper drilling or allowing the tap to act as a reamer. Thread lengths so produced are designated "Full or Complete Thread" on drawings.
3. NPTF (not reamed) drilled hole sizes are recommended for taper tapping without reaming. [NPTF (2 FF thread)] minimum minor diam eter two threads small from large end and closest drilled hole sizes are recommended only for low pressure use. [NPTF (4 FF thread)] minimum minor diameter four threads small from large end and closest drilled hole sizes are recommended for all pressures. Thread lengths so produced are designated "Effective Thread" on drawings.
4. Internal pipe threads shall be countersunk 90 deg included angle to a diameter (rounded to a two-place decimal) obtained by adding 0.016 in. for sizes below 1 in. and 0.025 in. for larger sizes to the maximum major diamter at large end.

APPENDIX B
DRYSEAL PIPE THREAD TAPS AND CHASERS

B.1 General Information—While production taps will usually be purchased to specification, occasions may arise requiring adaptations of taps, dies, or chasers at hand.

American Standard Taper Taps, Dies, or Chasers (NPT) may be adapted for producing the Dryseal American Standard Taper Pipe Threads (NPTF) by truncating the outside diameter of taps and the inside diameter of dies or chasers the amount necessary to obtain flats shown in Table B1 for producing the limits on the product specified in Table 1. The pitch diameter of taps and dies or chasers so modified will remain standard. American Standard Coupling Straight Pipe Taps (NPSC) used for tapping the American Standard Coupling Straight Pipe Thread (NPSC), with the exception of one size only, may be adapted for tapping the Dryseal American Intermediate Straight Pipe Thread (NPSI) by truncating the outside diameter the amount necessary to obtain flats shown in Table B3 for producing the limits on the product shown in Table 1. The exception is the 1/4-18 size which has a minimum pitch diameter under that required. With the exception of one size only, taps designed to other standards cannot be adapted for tapping the Dryseal American Fuel Straight Pipe Thread (NPSF). The exception is the 1/8-27 American Standard Grease Fitting Tap (NPSG) which, if made in conformity with Tap Manufacturers' Standards of 1939 to 1941 issue, may be used without change for tapping of the 1/8-27 Dryseal American Fuel Straight Pipe Thread (NPSF).

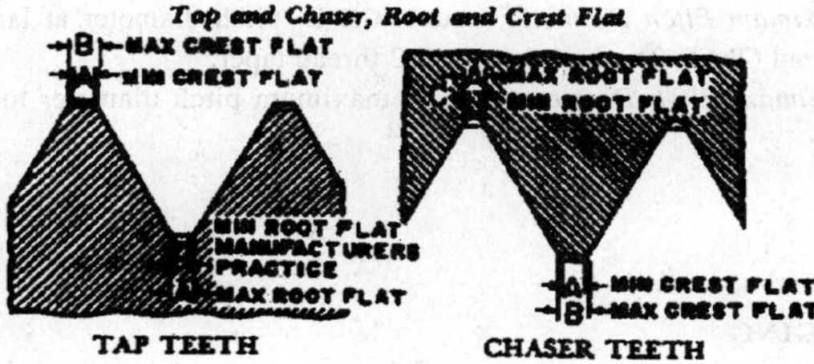

FIGURE B1—

TABLE B1—WIDTH OF FLATS

Threads per in.	A	B	C
27	0.004	0.005	0.002
18	0.005	0.006	0.003
14	0.005	0.006	0.003
11-1/2	0.006	0.008	0.004
8	0.008	0.010	0.006[1]

1. There is reason to doubt the correctness of the 8 threads per in. flat widths because of the volume of metal to be displaced.

B.2 Chamfer—2 to 3 threads.

B.3 Lead Tolerance—A maximum lead error of ±0.0005 in. in 1-in. of thread is permitted.

B.4 Angle Tolerance—Error in half angle of ±30 min is permitted.

B.5 Taper Tolerance—A maximum taper error of ±1/32 in. per ft is permitted.

B.6 Marking—In addition to regular markings, Dryseal American Standard Taper Taps will be marked NPTF.

TABLE B2—DRYSEAL TAPER PIPE TAPS FOR DRYSEAL AMERICAN STANDARD INERNAL TAPER PIPE THREAD, GROUND THREAD LIMITS

PTF Size	Gage[1] Measure Min	Gage[1] Measure Max	Major Dia Flat Min	Major Dia Flat Max	Minor Dia Flat[2] Max
1/16-27	0.250	0.375	0.004	0.005	0.004
1/8 -27	0.250	0.375	0.004	0.005	0.004
1/4 -18	0.397	0.521	0.005	0.006	0.005
3/8 -18	0.392	0.516	0.005	0.006	0.005
1/2 -14	0.517	0.641	0.005	0.006	0.005
3/4 -14	0.503	0.627	0.005	0.006	0.005
1 -11-1/2	0.584	0.772	0.006	0.008	0.006
1-1/4 -11-1/2	0.592	0.780	0.006	0.008	0.006
1-1/2 -11-1/2	0.605	0.793	0.006	0.008	0.006
2 -11-1/2	0.573	0.761	0.006	0.008	0.006
2-1/2 -8[3]	0.831	1.019	0.008	0.010	0.008
3 -8[3]	0.831	1.019	0.008	0.010	0.008

1. Distance small end of tap projects beyond face of American Standard Thin-Ring Gage.
2. Minor diameter as specified or sharper.
3. There is reason to doubt the correctness of the 8 threads per in. flat widths because of volume of metal to be displaced.

TABLE B3—DRYSEAL TAPER PIPE TAPS FRO DRYSEAL SAE SHORT INTERNAL TAPER PIPE THREAD, GROUND THREAD LIMITS

PTF—SAE Short Size	Gage[1] Measure Min (6p)	Gage Measure Max (7p)	Major Dia Flat Min	Major Dia Flat Max	Minor Dia Flat[2] Max
1/16-27	0.222	0.259	0.004	0.005	0.004
1/8 -27	0.222	0.259	0.004	0.005	0.004
1/4 -18	0.333	0.389	0.005	0.006	0.005
3/8 -18	0.333	0.389	0.005	0.006	0.005
1/2 -14	0.429	0.500	0.005	0.006	0.005
3/4 -14	0.429	0.500	0.005	0.006	0.005

1. Distance small end of tap projects beyond face of American Standard Thin-Ring Gage.
2. Minor diameter as specified or sharper.

B.7 Chamfer—1-1/2 to 2 threads.

B.8 Marking—In addition to regular markings, Dryseal SAE Short Taper Taps will be marked PTF—SAE Short.

B.9 Tolerances—Same as for Dryseal American Standard Taper Taps.

TABLE B4—DRYSEAL STRAIGHT PIPE TAPS FOR DRYSEAL AMERICAN FUEL INTERNAL STRAIGHT PIPE THREADS, GROUND THREAD LIMITS

NPSF Size	Pitch Diameter Basic	Pitch Diameter Min	Pitch Diameter Max	Major Dia Flat[1] Min	Major Dia Flat[1] Max	Minor Dia Flat[2] Max	Major Dia Basic	Major Dia Min	Major Dia Max
1/16-27	0.2812	0.2772	0.2777	0.004	0.005	0.004	0.3108	0.3008	0.3018
1/8 -27	0.3748	0.3696	0.3701	0.004	0.005	0.004	0.4044	0.3932	0.3942
1/4 -18	0.4899	0.4859	0.4864	0.005	0.006	0.005	0.5343	0.5239	0.5249
3/8 -18	0.6270	0.6213	0.6218	0.005	0.006	0.005	0.6714	0.6593	0.6603
1/2 -14	0.7784	0.7712	0.7717	0.005	0.006	0.005	0.8356	0.8230	0.8240
3/4 -14	0.9889	0.9817	0.9822	0.005	0.006	0.005	1.0460	1.0335	1.0345
1 -11-1/2	1.2386	1.2295	1.2305	0.006	0.008	0.006	1.3082	1.2933	1.2943

1. For reference only. Major-diameter flats specified may be slightly larger or smaller with extreme combinations of pitch diametee, major diameter, and half angle.
2. Minor diameter as specified or sharper.

B.10 Chamfer—Plug end 3 to 5 threads, intermediate end 2 to 3 threads, bottom end 1-1/2 to 2 threads.

B.11 Lead Tolerance—A maximum lead error of ±0.0005 in. in 1 in. of thread is permitted.

B.12 Angle Tolerance—Error in half angle of ±30 min permitted.

B.13 Marking—In addition to regular markings, Dryseal American Fuel Straight Pipe Taps will be marked NPSF.

B.14 Maximum Major Diameter equals minimum pitch diameter plus sharp-V thread height minus twice tool crest minimum truncation.

B.15 *Minimum Major Diameter* equals maximum major diameter minus tolerance.

B.16 *Maximum Pitch Diameter* equals the E_1 pitch diameter at large end of internal thread (Table 2) minus (small) 1-1/2 threads taper.

B.17 *Minimum Pitch Diameter* equals maximum diameter minus tolerance.

TABLE B5—DRYSEAL STRAIGHT PIPE TAPS FOR DRYSEAL AMERICAN INTERMEDIATE INTERNAL STRAIGHT PIPE THREAD, GROUND THREAD LIMITS

NPSF Size	Pitch Diameter Basic	Pitch Diameter Min	Pitch Diameter Max	Major Dia Flat(1) Min	Major Dia Flat(1) Max	Minor Dia Flat(2) Max	Major Dia Basic	Major Dia Min	Major Dia Max
1/16-27	0.2812	0.2795	0.2800	0.004	0.005	0.004	0.3108	0.3031	0.3041
1/8 -27	0.3748	0.3719	0.3724	0.004	0.005	0.004	0.4044	0.3955	0.3965
1/4 -18	0.4899	0.4894	0.4899	0.005	0.006	0.005	0.5343	0.5274	0.5284
3/8 -18	0.6270	0.6248	0.6253	0.005	0.006	0.005	0.6714	0.6628	0.6638
1/2 -14	0.7784	0.7757	0.7762	0.005	0.006	0.005	0.8356	0.8275	0.8285
3/4 -14	0.9889	0.9862	0.9867	0.005	0.006	0.005	1.0460	1.0380	1.0390
1 -11-1/2	1.2386	1.2349	1.2359	0.006	0.008	0.006	1.3082	1.2987	1.2997

1. For reference only. Major-diameter flats specified may be slightly larger or smaller with extreme combinations of pitch diameter, major diameter, and half angle.
2. Minor diameter as specified or sharper.

B.18 Chamfer— Plug end 3 to 5 threads, intermediate end 2 to 3 threads, bottom end 1-1/2 to 2 threads.

B.19 Lead Tolerance— A maximum lead error of ±0.0005 in. in 1 in. of thread is permitted.

B.20 Angle Tolerance— Error in half angle of ±30 min permitted.

B.21 Marking— In addition to regular markings, American Intermediate Straight Pipe Taps will be marked NPSI.

B.22 *Maximum Major Diameter* equals minimum pitch diameter plus sharp-V thread height minus twice tool crest minimum truncation.

B.23 *Minimum Major Diameter* equals maximum major diameter minus tolerance.

B.24 *Maximum Pitch Diameter* equals the E_1 pitch diameter at large end of internal thread (Table 2) minus (small) 1/2 thread taper.

B.25 *Minimum Pitch Diameter* equals maximum pitch diameter minus tolerance.

APPENDIX C
DRYSEAL PIPE-THREAD GAGING

C.1 General Information— There are three accepted methods of checking Dryseal pipe threads with threaded plug and ring gages. The methods separately described in the following sections are:

Section I—Position Method of Gaging with Basic Notch Gages.
Section II—Limit Method of Gaging with Step-Limit Gages.
Section III—Turns-Engagement Method of Gaging with Basic-Notch or Step-Limit Gages.

All methods of gaging external Dryseal threads involve the use of two ring thread gages, the (L_1) thin-ring thread gage for checking the pitch diameter over the hand engagement or (L_1) thread length and the (L_2) full-thread ring gage for checking the pitch diameter over the full thread length to insure adequate threads for wrench tightening.

All methods of gaging internal Dryseal threads involve the use of two plug thread gages, the (L_1) plug thread gage for checking the pitch diameter over the hand engagement or (L_1) thread length and the (L_3) plug thread gage for checking pitch diameter of the thread beyond the hand engagement length.

As indicated in the separate descriptions of the various gaging methods, coordination of the two ring thread gages for external threads and coordination of the two plug thread gages for internal threads control and check thread taper and length. The gages cannot be correlated, however, for external threads of minimum pitch diameter or internal threads of maximum pitch diameter unless the length of the threads is one thread longer than basic full thread length.

Working gages shall not be used where worn beyond the basic dimensions by more than 1/2 turn (thread). Proper allowance shall be made for any variation from basic when using a gage.

The threads of tools and the threads of a percentage of the product or casts in the case of internal threads should be projected as a check on thread form and truncation. Although projection is strongly recommended, the truncation at major diameter of internal thread and minor diameter of external thread may be checked respectively with special plug and ring gages with thread angle reduced to clear the flank of the threads; and the truncation at minor diameter of internal taper thread and major diameter of external taper thread may be checked respectively with plain taper plug gages and plain taper ring gages. Internal straight thread truncation at minor diameter may be checked with plain plug gages.

C.2 Section I—Position Method of Gaging with Basic Notch Gages— The position method of gaging Dryseal threads with plug thread and ring thread gages is a visual check of the position of the gages in relation to the product. It involves estimating the position of a notch or step on the thread gages in relation to the gaging point of the product within the allowable tolerance.

While the method is the same as that used for years past in checking conventional pipe threads without the Dryseal feature, the gages are different with respect to truncation of threads, the crests of the threads at the minor diameter of the ring gages and the major diameter of the plug gages being truncated to a greater extent to clear the increased truncation of the product thread. Another distinction is that the Dryseal (L_2) ring is counterbored larger than the thread diameter at the small end a distance equal to the (L_1) thread length minus one pitch. Conventional rings and plugs, however, may be converted to Dryseal by grinding the crests to conform with the width of flats specified for Dryseal gages, and grinding a counterbore in the (L_2) ring gage.

The gages are turned or screwed hand-tight into or onto the threaded product, the position of the gage notch in relation to the product reference point being noted to determine whether the standoff exceeds the allowable tolerance. Allowance must be made for excessive chamfer at the small end of external threads and the large end of internal threads, the product reference point in the first instance being the beginning of the first thread on the chamfer, and in the second instance being the intersection of the pitch diameter cone and the chamfer cone.

C.2.1 External Threads—Dryseal American Standard External Taper Pipe Threads (NPTF) are gaged with the NPTF (L_1) basic-notch Dryseal ring thread gages (Table C1) and the NPTF (L_2) basic-notch Dryseal ring thread gages (Table C1). Threads are within the allowable tolerance when the product reference point is flush with the gage reference point within a tolerance of plus (small) one turn, minus (large) one turn. As a check on taper, the (L_1) and (L_2) ring thread gages shall gage the same within 1/2 turn.

Dryseal SAE Short External Taper Pipe Threads PTF—SAE Short, which are one thread shorter at the small end than standard full thread length, are gaged with the NPTF (L_1) basic-notch Dryseal ring thread gages (Table C1) and the NPTF (L_2) basic-notch Dryseal ring thread gages (Table C1). Threads are within the allowable tolerance when the product reference point is flush with the gage reference point within a tolerance of plus zero, minus (large) 1-1/2 turns. As a check on taper, the (L_1) and (L_2) ring thread gages shall gage the same within 1/2 turn.

C.2.2 Internal Threads—Dryseal American Standard Internal Taper Pipe Threads (NPTF) are gaged with the NPTF (L_1) basic-notch Dryseal plug thread gages (Table C2) and the NPTF (L_3) basic-notch Dryseal plug thread gages (Table C3). Threads are within the allowable tolerance when the product reference point is flush with the gage notch within the following tolerances:

Plus (large) 1 turn, minus (small) 1 turn.

As a check on taper, the (L_1) and the (L_3) plug thread gages shall gage the same with relation to their respective notches within 1/2 turn.

Dryseal SAE Short Internal Taper Pipe Threads PTF—SAE Short, which are one thread shorter at the large end than standard full thread length, are gaged with the NPTF (L_1) basic-notch Dryseal plug thread gages (Table C2) and the NPTF (L_3) basic-notch Dryseal plug thread gages (Table C3). Threads are within the allowable tolerance when the product reference point is flush with the gage notch within the following tolerances:

Plus (large) 0 turns, minus (small) 1-1/2 turns.

Dryseal American (National) Standard Fuel Internal Straight Pipe Threads (NPSF) are gaged with the NPTF (L_1) basic-notch Dryseal plug thread gages (Table C2). Threads are within the allowable tolerance when the product reference point is flush with the gage notch within the following tolerances:

Plus (large) 0 turns, minus (small) 1-1/2 turns.

As depth gages without regard to gage notches, any of the (L_3) Dryseal plug thread gages may be used to check the full thread length of internal straight pipe threads.

Dryseal American (National) Standard Intermediate Internal Straight Pipe Threads (NPSI) are gaged with the NPTF (L_1) basic-notch Dryseal plug thread gages (Table C2). Threads are within the allowable tolerance when the product reference point is flush with the gage notch within the following tolerances:

Plus (large) 1 turn, minus (small) 1/2 turn.

As depth gages without regard to gage notches, any of the (L_3) Dryseal plug thread gages may be used to check the full thread length of internal straight pipe threads.

C.3 Section II—Limit Method of Gaging with Step-Limit Gages—The limit-gage or step-limit method of checking threaded product with plug thread and ring thread gages is a visual check of the position of the gages in relation to the product. Plug and ring gages with maximum and minimum limit notches are provided for the different thread types: NPTF, PTF—SAE Short, NPSF, and NPSI. The location of the limit notches on the 1/8- and 1/4-in. plugs eliminates the necessity for gaging correction.

The gages are turned or screwed hand-tight into or onto the threaded product, the position of the product reference point in relation to the limit notches on the gage being noted. Allowance must be made for excessive chamfer at the small end of external threads and the large end of internal threads, the product reference point in the first instance being the beginning of the first thread on the chamfer, and in the second instance being the intersection of the pitch diameter cone and the chamfer cone.

C.3.1 External Threads—Dryseal American Standard External Taper Pipe Threads (NPTF) are gaged with the NPTF (L_1) step-limit Dryseal ring thread gages (Table C4) and the NPTF (L_2) step-limit Dryseal ring thread gages (Table C8). Threads are within the allowable tolerance when the product reference point is on or between the limit notches. As a check on taper, the (L_1) and the (L_2) Dryseal ring thread gages shall gage the same in relation to their respective notches within 1/2 turn.

Dryseal SAE Short External Taper Pipe Threads PTF—SAE Short, which are one thread shorter at the small end than standard full thread length, are gaged with the PTF—SAE (L_1 Short) step-limit Dryseal ring thread gages (Table C8) and the PTF—SAE (L_2 Short) step-limit ring thread gages (Table C9). Threads are within the allowable tolerance when the product reference point is on or between the limit notches. As a check on taper, the (L_1 Short) and the (L_2 Short) Dryseal ring thread gages shall gage the same with relation to their respective notches within 1/2 turn.

C.3.2 Internal Threads—Dryseal American Standard Internal Taper Pipe Threads (NPTF) are gaged with the NPTF (L_1) step-limit Dryseal plug thread gages (Table C6) and the NPTF (L_3) step-limit Dryseal plug thread gages (Table C7). Threads are within the allowable tolerance when the product reference point is on or between the limit notches. As a check on taper, the (L_1) and (L_3) Dryseal plug thread gages shall gage the same with relation to their respective notches within 1/2 turn.

Dryseal SAE Short Internal Taper Pipe Threads PTF—SAE Short, which are one thread shorter at the large end than standard full thread length, are gaged with the PTF—SAE (L_1 Short) step-limit Dryseal plug thread gages (Table C10) and the PTF—SAE (L_3 Short) step-limit Dryseal plug thread gages (Table C11). Threads are within the allowable tolerance when the product reference point is on or between the limit notches. As a check on taper, the (L_1 Short) and (L_3 Short) Dryseal plug thread gages shall gage the same with relation to their respective notches within 1/2 turn.

Dryseal American Standard Fuel Internal Straight Pipe Threads (NPSF) are gaged with the NPSF (L_1 Short) step-limit Dryseal plug thread gages (Table C10). Threads are within the allowable tolerance when the product reference point is on or between the limit notches. As depth gages without regard to limit notches, any of the (L_3) Dryseal plug thread gages may be used to check the full thread length of internal straight pipe threads.

Dryseal American Standard Intermediate Internal Straight Pipe Threads (NPSI) are gaged with the NPSI (L_1) step-limit Dryseal plug thread gages (Table C12). Threads are within the allowable tolerance when the product reference point is on or between the limit notches. As depth gages without regard to limit notches, any of the (L_3) Dryseal plug thread gages may be used to check the full thread length of internal straight pipe threads.

C.4 Section III—Turns-Engagement Method of Gaging with Basic-Notch or Step-Limit Gages—Theturns en-gagement method of checking threaded product with plug thread and ring thread gages is a tactual check of the position of the gages in relation to the product. In checking by this method, either the basic-notch or the step-limit gages may be used. The gages are turned or screwed into or onto the threaded product and the turns to remove the gages are counted. This method compensates for gage chamfer and eliminates the variable of product chamfer.

C.4.1 Basic Turns Engagement of Ring Gages—The basic turns engagement of the (L_1) ring thread gages (Tables C1, C4, and C8) with Dryseal external taper pipe threads is the product of the (L_1) thread length of the ring gage used and the threads per inch, minus one turn to compensate for chamfer of the external threads and chamfer of the ring gages. (See accompanying tabulation of basic turns engagement.)

The basic turns engagement of the (L_2) ring thread gages (Tables C1, C5, and C9) with Dryseal external taper pipe threads is the product of the (L_2) thread length and the threads per inch, minus 1-1/4 turns to compensate for chamfer of the external threads and the chamfer and taper of the ring gages. (See accompanying tabulation of basic turns engagement.)

C.4.2 External Threads—Dryseal American Standard External Taper Pipe Threads (NPTF) by the turns-engagement method may be gaged with any combination of (L_1) and (L_2) Dryseal ring thread gages (Tables C1, C4, C5, C8, and C9). Nominal turns engagement equals basic turns engagement. The tolerance is plus (small) 1 turn, minus (large) 1 turn. As a check on taper, the difference in turns engagement with the (L_1) and the (L_2) Dryseal ring thread gages shall be within 1/2 turn of the difference between the basic turns engagement of the ring gages.

Dryseal SAE Short External Taper Pipe Threads PTF—SAE Short, which are one thread shorter at the small end than standard full thread length, may be gaged by the turns-engagement method with any combination of (L_1) and (L_2) Dryseal ring thread gages (Tables C1, C4, C5, C8, and C9). Nominal turns engagement is one turn less than basic turns engagement. The tolerance is plus (small) 1 turn, minus (large) 1/2 turn. As a check on taper, the difference in turns engagement with the (L_1) and the (L_2) Dryseal ring thread gages shall be within 1/2 turn of the difference between the basic turns engagement of the ring gages.

C.4.3 Basic Turns Engagement of Plug Gages—The basic turns engagement of the (L_1) Dryseal plug thread gages (Tables C2, C6, C10, and C12) and Dryseal internal pipe threads is the product of the (L_1) thread length (Table 2) and the threads per inch, minus 1/2 turn to compensate for chamfer on plug gages. (See accompanying tabulation of basic turns engagement.)

The basic turns engagement of the (L_3) Dryseal plug thread gages (Tables C3, C7, and C11) with Dryseal internal pipe threads is the (L_1) thread length (Table 2) plus three threads multiplied by the threads per inch, minus 3/4 turn to compensate for chamfer and taper on plug gages. (See accompanying tabulation of basic turns engagement.)

C.4.4 Internal Threads—Dryseal American Standard Internal Taper Pipe Threads (NPTF) are gaged with any combination of (L_1) and (L_3) Dryseal plug thread gages (Tables C2, C3, C6, C7, C10, C11, and C12). The nominal turns engagement equals basic turns engagement. The tolerance is plus (large) 1 turn, minus (small) 1 turn. As a check on taper, the difference in turns engagement of the (L_1) and the (L_3) Dryseal plug thread gages shall not be less than 2-1/4 turns nor more than 3-1/4 turns.

Dryseal SAE Short Internal Taper Pipe Threads PTF—SAE Short, which are one thread shorter at the large end than standard full thread length, are gaged with any combination of (L_1) and (L_3) Dryseal plug thread gages (Tables C2, C3, C6, C7, C10, C11, and C12). The nominal turns engagement is one turn less than basic turns engagement. The tolerance is plus (large) 1 turn, minus (small)

1/2 turn. As a check on taper, the difference in turns engagement of the (L_1) and the (L_3) Dryseal plug thread gages shall not be less than 2-1/4 turns nor more than 3-1/4 turns.

Dryseal American Standard Fuel Internal Straight Pipe Threads (NPSF) are gaged with any of the (L_1) Dryseal plug thread gages (Tables C2, C6, C10, and C12). The nominal turns engagement is one turn less than basic turns engagement. The tolerance is plus (large) 1 turn, minus (small) 1/2 turn. As depth gages without regard to limit notches, any of the (L_3) Dryseal plug thread gages may be used to check the full thread length of internal straight pipe threads.

Dryseal American Standard Intermediate Internal Straight Pipe Threads (NPSI) are gaged with any of the (L_1) Dryseal plug thread gages (Tables C2, C6, C10, and C12). The nominal turns engagement equals basic turns engagement. The tolerance is plus (large) 1 turn, minus (small) 1/2 turn. As depth gages without regard to limit notches, any of the (L_3) Dryseal plug thread gages may be used to check the full thread length of internal straight pipe threads.

C.5 Dryseal American Taper Pipe Thread (L_1 And L_2) Ring Gages

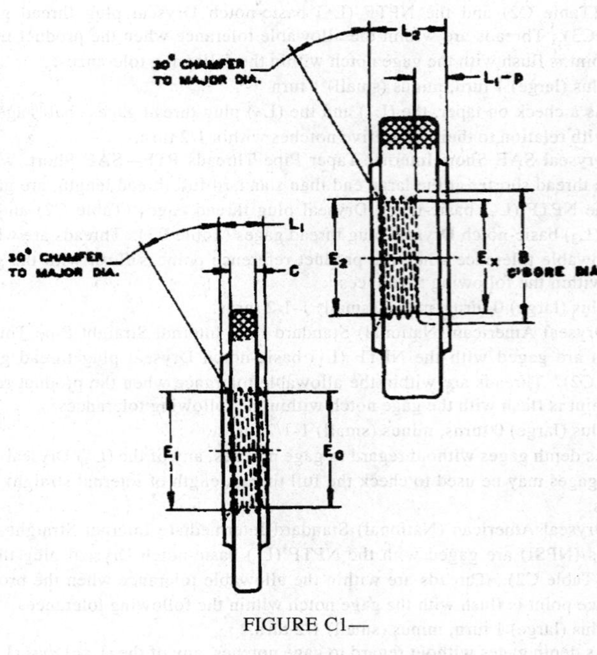

FIGURE C1—

BASIC TURNS ENGAGEMENT[1]

Size	Thread Gage L_1 Rings Basic-Notch, Table C1	Thread Gage L_1 Rings Step-Limit, Tables C4 and C8	Thread Gage All L_2 Rings	Thread Gage All L_1 Plugs	Thread Gage All L_3 Plugs
1/16-27	3.32	3.32	5.80	3.82	6.57
1/8 -27	3.36	3.36	5.87	3.86	6.61
1/4 -18	3.10	3.10	5.98	3.60	6.35
3/8 -18	3.32	3.32	6.09	3.82	6.57
1/2 -14	3.48	3.48	6.22	3.98	6.73
3/4 -14	3.75	3.75	6.39	4.25	7.00
1 -11-1/2	3.60	3.60	6.60	4.10	6.85
1-1/4 -11-1/2	3.83	3.83	6.88	4.33	7.08
1-1/2 -11-1/2	3.83	3.83	7.07	4.33	7.08
2 -11-1/2	4.01	4.01	7.45	4.51	7.26
2-1/2 -8	4.46	4.46	7.85	4.96	7.71
3 -8	5.13	5.13	8.35	5.63	8.38

1. Derivation of nominal turns engagement and tolerance for the different thread types, NPTF, PTF—SAE Short, NPSF, and NPSI, is explained in the accompanying text.

TABLE C1—BASIC DIMENSIONS OF DRYSEAL AMERICAN TAPER PIPE THREAD (L_1 AND L_2) BASIC-NOTHC RING GAGES

Size	(L_2) Basic-Notch Full-Ring Gaues L_2	(L_2) Basic-Notch Full-Ring Gaues Pitch Dia, E_2	(L_2) Basic-Notch Full-Ring Gaues Minor Dia at Large End(1)	(L_2) Basic-Notch Full-Ring Gaues Pitch Dia at L_1 - p, E_x	(L_2) Basic-Notch Full-Ring Gaues Minor Dia at L_1 - p(1)	(L_2) Basic-Notch Full-Ring Gaues L_1 - p	(L_2) Basic-Notch Full-Ring Gaue s B	(L_1) Basic-Notch Thin-Ring Gaues L_1	(L_1) Basic-Notch Thin-Ring Gaues Pitch Dia, E_1	(L_1) Basic-Notch Thin-Ring Gages Minor Dia at Large End(1)	(L_1) Basic-Notch Thin-Ring Gages Pitch Dia, E_0	(L_1) Basic-Notch Thin-Ring Gages Minor Dia at Small End(1)
1/16-27	0.26113	0.28750	0.27024	0.27886	0.26160	0.12296	0.38	0.1600	0.28118	0.26392	0.27118	0.25392
1/8 -27	0.26385	0.38000	0.36274	0.37129	0.35403	0.12446	0.47	0.1615	0.37360	0.35634	0.36351	0.34625
1/4 -18	0.40178	0.50250	0.47661	0.48816	0.46227	0.17224	0.59	0.2278	0.49163	0.46574	0.47739	0.45150
3/8 -18	0.40778	0.63750	0.61161	0.62354	0.59765	0.18444	0.72	0.2400	0.62701	0.60112	0.61201	0.58612
1/2 -14	0.53371	0.79179	0.75850	0.77396	0.74067	0.24857	0.88	0.3200	0.77843	0.74514	0.75843	0.72514
3/4 -14	0.54571	1.00179	0.96850	0.98440	0.95111	0.26757	1.09	0.3390	0.98887	0.95558	0.96768	0.93439
1 -11-1/2	0.68278	1.25630	1.21577	1.23320	1.19267	0.31304	1.34	0.4000	1.23863	1.19810	1.21363	1.17310
1-1/4 -11-1/2	0.70678	1.60130	1.56077	1.57794	1.53741	0.33304	1.69	0.4200	1.58338	1.54285	1.55713	1.51660
1-1/2 -11-1/2	0.72348	1.84130	1.80077	1.81690	1.77637	0.33304	1.94	0.4200	1.82234	1.78181	1.79609	1.75556
2 -11-1/2	0.75652	2.31630	2.27577	2.29084	2.25031	0.34904	2.50	0.4360	2.29627	2.25574	2.26902	2.22849
2-1/2 -8	1.13750	2.79062	2.73237	2.75434	2.69609	0.55700	2.94	0.6820	2.76216	2.70391	2.71953	2.66128
3 -8	1.20000	3.41562	3.35737	3.38068	3.32243	0.54100	3.56	0.7660	3.38850	3.33025	3.34062	3.28237

1. Minor diameter is based on crest minimum truncation of 0.20 p.

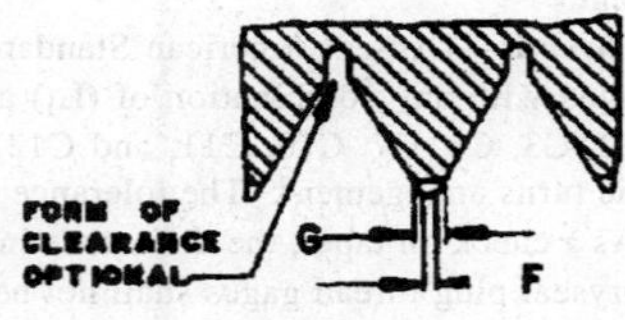

FIGURE C2—

TABLE C1-1—THREAD FLATS

Threads per in.	F	G
27	0.0086	0.0107
18	0.0128	0.0160
14	0.0165	0.0206
11-1/2	0.0201	0.0251
8	0.0289	0.0361

C.5.5 Marking—In addition to the regular markings, Dryseal American Standard Taper Thread Thin-Ring Gages will be marked NPTF (L_1) and Full-Ring Gages will be marked NPTF (L_2) on the entering side of gage.

C.5.6 Thread Form—The threads in all particulars excepting truncation shall conform to American Standard Taper Pipe Thread practice. Crests of threads at the minor diameter of ring gages and major diameter of plug gages shall be truncated 0.20p minimum to 0.25p maximum producing the minimum and maximum widths of flats specified in Table C1-1.

All other thread dimensions shall be within tolerances specified for the Dryseal American Standard Pipe Thread Working Plug Gages (ASA B2.2). Other gage details shall conform to American Gage Design Standards published in Commercial Standard CS8.

C.6 Dryseal American Taper Pipe Thread (L_1) Plug Gages Taper Lock Design Range 1/8 To 3 in., Inclusive

C.6.1 Marking—In addition to the regular markings, Dryseal American Standard Taper Pipe Thread (L1) Plug Gages will be marked NPTF (L_1).

C.6.2 Thread Form—The threads in all particulars excepting truncation shall conform to American Standard Taper Pipe Thread practice. Crests of threads at the minor diameter of ring gages and major diameter of plug gages shall be truncated 0.20p minimum to 0.25p maximum producing the minimum and maximum widths of flats specified in Table C2-1.

All other thread dimensions shall be within tolerances specified for the Dryseal American Standard Pipe Thread Working Plug Gages (ASA B2.2). Other gage details shall conform to American Gage Design Standards published in Commercial Standard CS8.

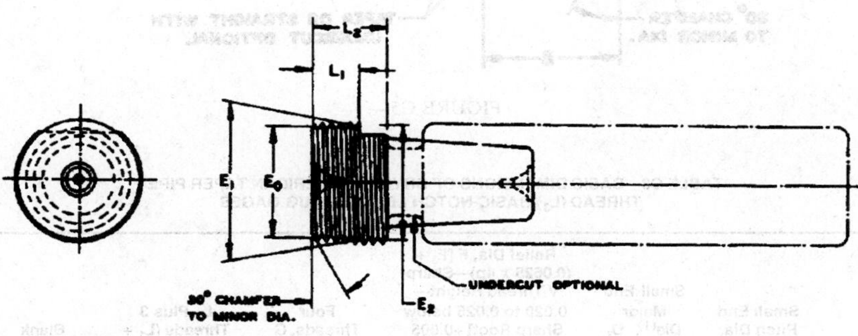

FIGURE C3—

TABLE C2—BASIC DIMENSIONS OF DRYSEAL AMERICAN TAPER PIPE THREAD (L_1) BASIC-NOTCH PLUG GAGES

Size	L_1	L_2	Small End Pitch Dia, E_0	Small End Major Dia[1]	Gaging Notch Pitch Dia, E_1	Gaging Notch Major Dia[1]	Large End Pitch Dia, E_2	Large End Major Dia[1]
1/16-27	0.1600	0.26113	0.27118	0.28844	0.28118	0.29844	0.28750	0.30476
1/8 -27	0.1615	0.26385	0.36351	0.38077	0.37360	0.39086	0.38000	0.39726
1/4 -18	0.2278	0.40178	0.47739	0.50328	0.49163	0.51752	0.50250	0.52839
3/8 -18	0.2400	0.40778	0.61201	0.63790	0.62701	0.65290	0.63750	0.66339
1/2 -14	0.3200	0.53371	0.75843	0.79170	0.77843	0.81170	0.79179	0.82506
3/4 -14	0.3390	0.54571	0.96768	1.00095	0.98887	1.02214	1.00179	1.03506
1 -11-1/2	0.4000	0.68278	1.21363	1.25416	1.23863	1.27916	1.25630	1.29683
1-1/4 -11-1/2	0.4200	0.70678	1.55713	1.59766	1.58338	1.62391	1.60130	1.64183
1-1/2 -11-1/2	0.4200	0.72348	1.79609	1.83662	1.82234	1.86287	1.84130	1.88183
2 -11-1/2	0.4360	0.75652	2.26902	2.30955	2.29627	2.33680	2.31630	2.35683
2-1/2 -8	0.6820	1.13750	2.71953	2.77778	2.76216	2.82041	2.79062	2.84887
3 -8	0.7660	1.20000	3.34062	3.39887	3.38850	3.44675	3.41562	3.47387

1. Major diameter is based upon crest minimum truncation of 0.20 p.

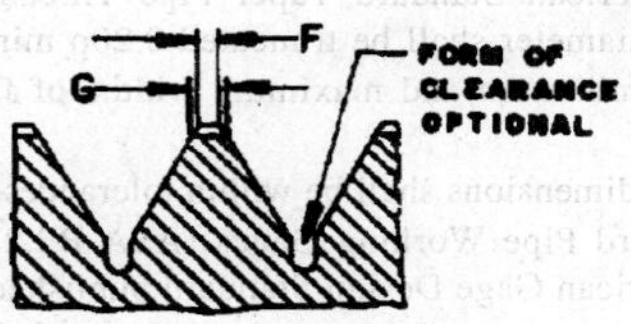

FIGURE C4—

TABLE C2-1—THREAD FLATS

Threads per in.	F	G
27	0.0086	0.0107
18	0.0128	0.0160
14	0.0165	0.0206
11-1/2	0.0201	0.0251
8	0.0289	0.0361

C.7 Dryseal American Taper Pipe Thread (L_3) Length Plug Gages

C.7.1 Marking—In addition to the regular markings, Dryseal American Standard Taper Pipe Thread (L_3) Plug Gages will be marked NPTF (L_3).

C.7.2 Thread Form—The threads in all particulars excepting truncation shall conform to American Standard Taper Pipe Thread practice. Crests of threads at major diameter shall be truncated 0.20p minimum to 0.25p maximum, producing the minimum and maximum widths of flat specified in Table C3-1.

All other thread dimensions shall be within tolerances specified for the Dryseal American Standard Pipe Thread Working Plug Gages (ASA B2.2). Other gage details shall conform to American Gage Design Standards published in Commercial Standard CS8.

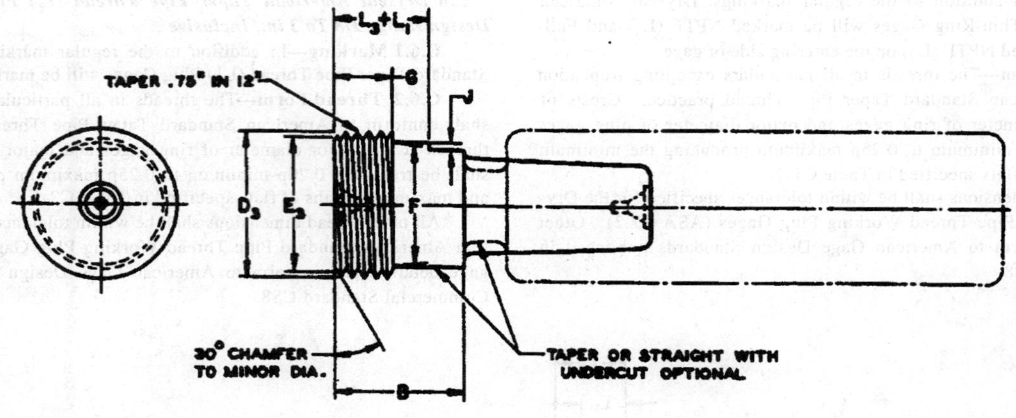

FIGURE C5—

TABLE C3—BASIC DIMENSIONS OF DRYSEAL AMERICAN TAPER PIPE THREAD (L_3) BASIC-NOTCH LENGTH PLUG GAGES

Size	Small End Pitch Dia, E_3	Small End Major Dia[1], D_3	Relief Dia, F [E_3 + (0.0625 x 4p)—Sharp-V Thread Height—0.020 to 0.025 below Sharp Root] +0.005 -0.000	Four Threads, G (L_3 + p)	L_1 Plus 3 Threads (L_1 + L_3)	Blank Length, B	Notch Depth, J +0.005 -0.000
1/16-27	0.2642	0.2815	0.216	0.1482	0.2711	0.38	0.030
1/8 -27	0.3566	0.3738	0.309	0.1482	0.2726	0.41	0.030
1/4 -18	0.4670	0.4928	0.409	0.2222	0.3945	0.50	0.030
3/8 -18	0.6016	0.6275	0.542	0.2222	0.4067	0.56	0.030
1/2 -14	0.7451	0.7783	0.676	0.2857	0.5343	0.69	0.040
3/4 -14	0.9543	0.9876	0.886	0.2857	0.5533	0.72	0.040
1 -11-1/2	1.1973	1.2379	1.118	0.3478	0.6609	0.88	0.050
1-1/4 -11-1/2	1.5408	1.5814	1.462	0.3478	0.6809	0.88	0.050
1-1/2 -11-1/2	1.7798	1.8203	1.701	0.3478	0.6809	0.88	0.050
2 -11-1/2	2.2527	2.2932	2.174	0.3478	0.6969	0.88	0.050
2-1/2 -8	2.6961	2.7543	2.590	0.5000	1.0570	1.50	0.050
3 -8	3.3172	3.3754	3.214	0.5000	1.1410	1.50	0.050

1. Major diameter is based upon crest minimum truncation of 0.20 p.

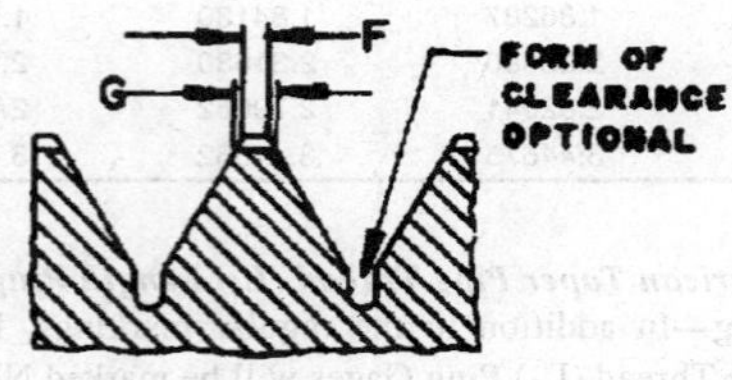

TABLE C3-1—THREAD FLATS

Threads per in.	F	G
27	0.0086	0.0107
18	0.0128	0.0160
14	0.0165	0.0206
11-1/2	0.0201	0.0251
8	0.0289	0.0361

C.8 Dryseal American Standard Taper Pipe Thread (L_1) Step-Limit Thin-Ring Gages

C.8.1 Marking—In addition to the regular markings, Dryseal American Standard Taper Thread Ring Gages will be marked NPTF (L_1) on the entering side of gage.

C.8.2 Thread Form—The threads in all particulars excepting truncation shall conform to American Standard Taper Pipe Thread practice. Crests of threads at the minor diameter shall be truncated 0.20p minimum to 0.25p maximum, producing the minimum and maximum widths of flat specified in Table C4-1.

All other thread dimensions shall be within tolerances specified for the Dryseal American Standard Pipe Working Gages (ASA B2.2). Other gage details shall conform to American Gage Design Standard published in Commercial CS8.

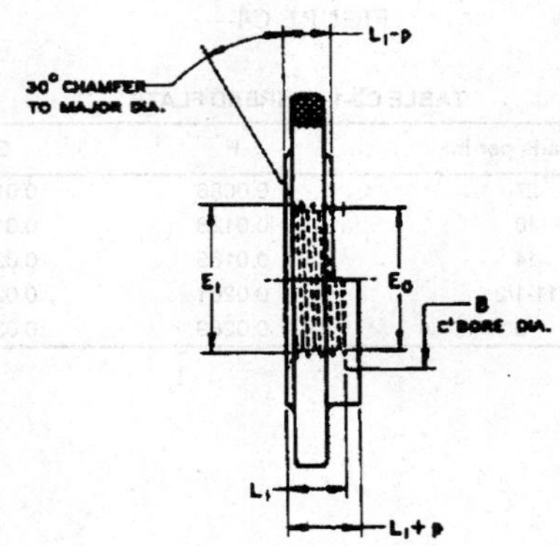

TABLE C4—BASIC DIMENSIONS OF DRYSEAL AMERICAN STANDARD TAPER PIPE THREAD (L_1) STEP-LIMIT THIN-RING GAGES

Size	(L_1) Step-Limit Thin-Ring Gages L_1	(L_1) Step-Limit Thin-Ring Gages Max Pitch Dia Gaging Step L_1 - p	(L_1) Step-Limit Thin-Ring Gages Min. Pitch Dia Gaging Step L_1 + p	(L_1) Step-Limit Thin-Ring Gages Pitch Dia, E_1	(L_1) Step-Limit Thin-Ring Gages Minor Dia at Large End	(L_1) Step-Limit Thin-Ring Gages Pitch Dia of Small End Counterbore E_0	(L_1) Step-Limit Thin-Ring Gages Minor Dia at Small End Counterbore[1]	(L_1) Step-Limit Thin-Ring Gages B
1/16-27	0.1600	0.12296	0.19704	0.28118	0.26392	0.27118	0.25392	0.38
1/8 -27	0.1615	0.12446	0.19854	0.37360	0.35634	0.36351	0.34625	0.47
1/4 -18	0.2278	0.17224	0.28336	0.49163	0.46574	0.47739	0.45150	0.59
3/8 -18	0.2400	0.18444	0.29556	0.62701	0.60112	0.61201	0.58612	0.72
1/2 -14	0.3200	0.24857	0.39143	0.77843	0.74514	0.75843	0.72514	0.88
3/4 -14	0.3390	0.26757	0.41043	0.98887	0.95558	0.96768	0.93439	1.09
1 -11-1/2	0.4000	0.31304	0.48696	1.23863	1.19810	1.21363	1.17310	1.34
1-1/4 -11-1/2	0.4200	0.33304	0.50696	1.58338	1.54285	1.55713	1.51660	1.69
1-1/2 -11-1/2	0.4200	0.33304	0.50696	1.82234	1.78181	1.79609	1.75556	1.94
2 -11-1/2	0.4360	0.34904	0.52296	2.29627	2.25574	2.26902	2.22849	2.50
2-1/2 -8	0.6820	0.55700	0.80700	2.76216	2.70391	2.71953	2.66128	2.94
3 -8	0.7660	0.64100	0.89100	3.38850	3.33025	3.34062	3.28237	3.56

1. Minor diameter is based on crest minimum truncation of 0.20 p.

All other thread dimensions shall be within tolerances specified for the Dryseal American Standard Pipe Working Gages (ASA B2.2). Other gage details shall conform to American Gage Design Standard published in Commercial Standard CS8.

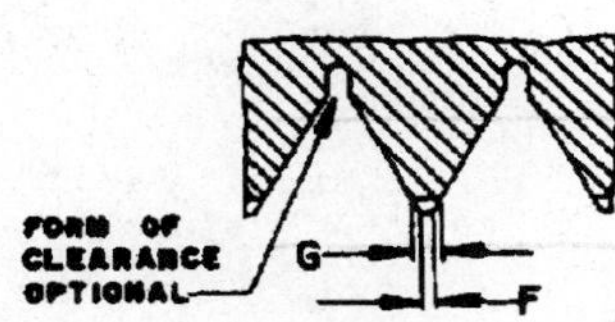

FIGURE C6—

TABLE C4-1—THREAD FLATS

Threads per in.	F	G
27	0.0086	0.0107
18	0.0128	0.0160
14	0.0165	0.0206
11-1/2	0.0201	0.0251
8	0.0289	0.0361

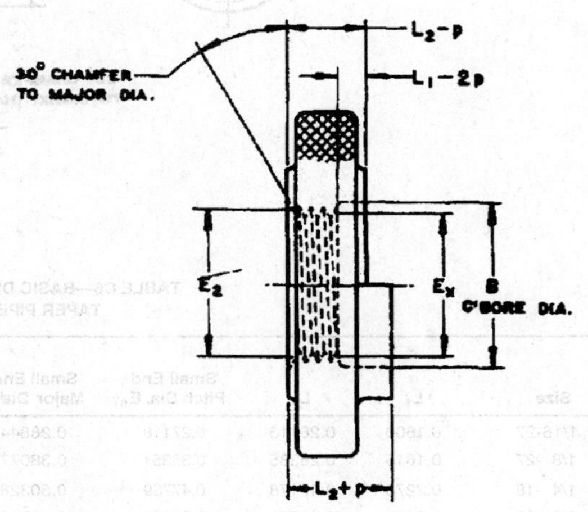

FIGURE C7—

C.9 Dryseal American Standard Taper Pipe Thread (L_2) Step-Limit Full-Ring Gages

C.9.1 Marking—In addition to the regular markings, Dryseal American Standard Taper Pipe Thread Ring Gages will be marked NPTF (L_2) on the entering side of gage.

C.9.2 Thread Form—The threads in all particulars excepting truncation shall conform to American Standard Taper Pipe Thread practice. Crests of threads at the minor diameter shall be truncated 0.20p minimum to 0.25p maximum, producing the minimum and maximum widths of flat specified in Table C5-1.

TABLE C5—BASIC DIMENSIONS OF DRYSEAL AMERICAN STANDARD TAPER PIPE THREAD (L_2) STEP-LIMIT FULL-RING GAGES

Size	(L_2) Step-Limit Full-Ring Gages L_2	(L_2) Step-Limit Full-Ring Gages Max Pitch Dia Gaging Step L_2 - p	(L_2) Step-Limit Full-Ring Gages Min Pitch Dia Gaging Step L_2 + p	(L_2) Step-Limit Full-Ring Gages Pitch Dia, E_2	(L_2) Step-Limit Full-Ring Gages Minor Dia at Large End[1]	(L_2) Step-Limit Full-Ring Gages Pitch Dia at L_1 from Min Pitch Dia Gaging Step (E_x)	(L_2) Step-Limit Full-Ring Gages Minor Dia at Small End Counterbore	(L_2) Step-Limit Full-Ring Gages L_1 - 2p	(L_2) Step-Limit Full-Ring Gages B
1/16-27	0.26113	0.22409	0.29817	0.28750	0.27024	0.27886	0.26160	0.08592	0.38
1/8 -27	0.26385	0.22681	0.30089	0.38000	0.36274	0.37129	0.35403	0.08742	0.47
1/4 -18	0.40178	0.34622	0.45734	0.50250	0.47661	0.48816	0.46227	0.11668	0.59
3/8 -18	0.40778	0.35222	0.46334	0.63750	0.61161	0.62354	0.59765	0.12888	0.72
1/2 -14	0.53371	0.46228	0.60514	0.79179	0.75850	0.77396	0.74067	0.17714	0.88
3/4 -14	0.54571	0.47428	0.61714	1.00179	0.96850	0.98440	0.95111	0.19614	1.09
1 -11-1/2	0.68278	0.59582	0.76974	1.25630	1.21577	1.23320	1.19267	0.22608	1.34
1-1/4 -11-1/2	0.70678	0.61982	0.79374	1.60130	1.56077	1.57794	1.53741	0.24608	1.69
1-1/2 -11-1/2	0.72348	0.63652	0.81044	1.84130	1.80077	1.81690	1.77637	0.24608	1.94
2 -11-1/2	0.75652	0.66956	0.84348	2.31630	2.27577	2.29084	2.25031	0.26208	2.50
2-1/2 -8	1.13750	1.01250	1.26250	2.79062	2.73237	2.75434	2.69609	0.43200	2.94
3 -8	1.20000	1.07500	1.32500	3.41562	3.35737	3.38068	3.32243	0.51600	3.56

1. Minor diameter is based on crest minimum truncation of 0.20 p.

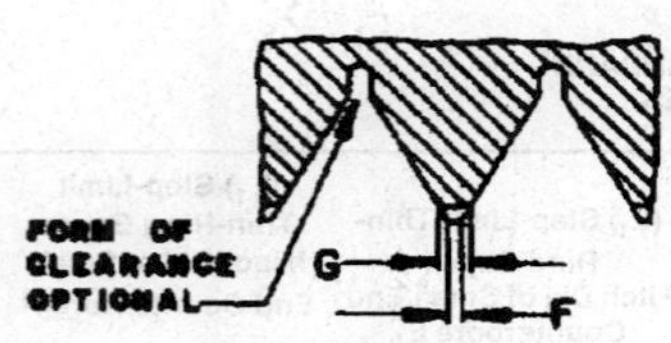

FIGURE C8—

TABLE C5-1—THREAD FLATS

Threads per in.	F	G
27	0.0086	0.0107
18	0.0128	0.0160
14	0.0165	0.0206
11-1/2	0.0201	0.0251
8	0.0289	0.0361

C.10 Dryseal American Standard Taper Pipe Thread (L_1) Step-Limit Plug Gages

C.10.1 Marking—In addition to the regular markings, Dryseal American Standard Taper Pipe Thread (L_1) Plug Gages will be marked NPTF (L_1).

C.10.2 Thread Form—The threads in all particulars excepting truncation shall conform to American Standard Taper Pipe Thread practice. Crests of threads at major diameter shall be truncated 0.20p minimum to 0.25p maximum, producing the minimum and maximum widths of flat specified in Table C6-1.

All other thread dimensions shall be within tolerances specified for the Dryseal American Standard Pipe Thread Working Plug Gages (ASA B2.2). Other gage details shall conform to American Gage Design Standards published in Commercial Standards CS8.

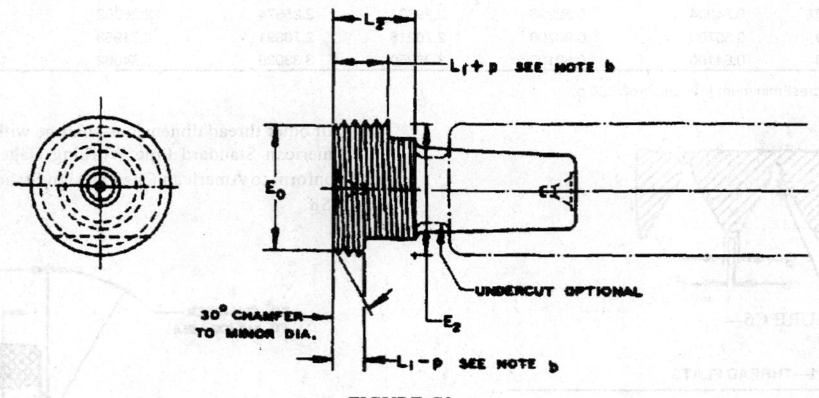

FIGURE C9—

TABLE C6—BASIC DIMENSIONS OF DRYSEAL AMERICAN STANDARD TAPER PIPE THREAD (L_1) STEP-LIMIT PLUG GAGES

Size	L_1	L_2	Small End Pitch Dia, E_0	Small End Major Dia(1)	Min Pitch Dia Gaging Step(2) L_1 - p	Min Pitch Dia Gaging Step(2) Pitch Dia	Max Pitch Dia Gaging Step(2) L_1 + p	Max Pitch Gaging Step(2) Pitch Dia	Large End Pitch Dia, E_2	Large End Major Dia(1)
1/16-27	0.1600	0.26113	0.27118	0.28844	0.12296	0.27887	0.19704	0.28350	0.28750	0.30476
1/8 -27	0.1615	0.26385	0.36351	0.38077	0.12446	0.37129	0.19854	0.37592	0.38000	0.39726
1/4 -18	0.2278	0.40178	0.47739	0.50328	0.17224	0.48816	0.28336	0.49510	0.50250	0.52839
3/8 -18	0.2400	0.40778	0.61201	0.63790	0.18444	0.62354	0.29556	0.63048	0.63750	0.66339
1/2 -14	0.3200	0.53371	0.75843	0.79172	0.24857	0.77397	0.39143	0.78289	0.79179	0.82508
3/4 -14	0.3390	0.54571	0.96768	1.00097	0.26757	0.98441	0.41043	0.99333	1.00179	1.03508
1 -11-1/2	0.4000	0.68278	1.21363	1.25416	0.31304	1.23320	0.48696	1.24407	1.25630	1.29683
1-1/4 -11-1/2	0.4200	0.70678	1.55713	1.59766	0.33304	1.57795	0.50696	1.58882	1.60130	1.64183
1-1/2 -11-1/2	0.4200	0.72348	1.79609	1.83662	0.33304	1.81691	0.50696	1.82778	1.84130	1.88183
2 -11-1/2	0.4360	0.75652	2.26902	2.30955	0.34904	2.29084	0.52296	2.30171	2.31630	2.35683
2-1/2 -8	0.6820	1.13750	2.71953	2.77778	0.55700	2.75435	0.80700	2.76997	2.79062	2.84887
3 -8	0.7660	1.20000	3.34062	3.39887	0.64100	3.38069	0.89100	3.39631	3.41562	3.47387

1. Major diameter is based on crest minimum truncation of 0.20 p.
2. Maximum and minimum pitch-diameter steps are gaging limits. Notch formulas on drawing apply to all sizes.

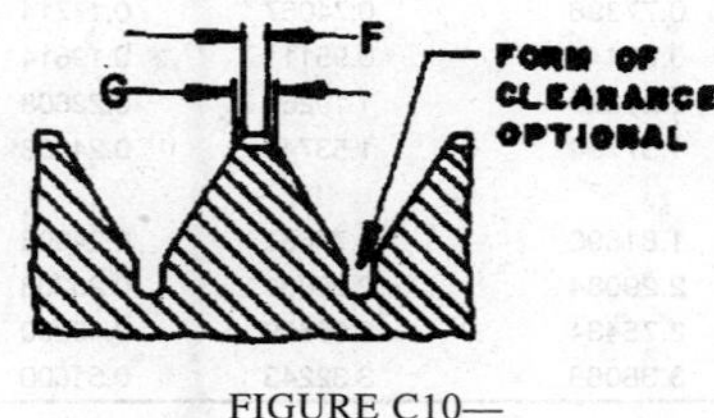

FIGURE C10—

TABLE C6-1—THREAD FLATS

Threads per in.	F	G
27	0.0086	0.0107
18	0.0128	0.0160
14	0.0165	0.0206
11-1/2	0.0201	0.0251
8	0.0289	0.0361

C.11 Dryseal American Standard Taper Thread (L_3) Length Step-Limit Plug Gages

C.11.1 Marking—In addition to the regular markings, Dryseal American Standard Taper Pipe Thread (L_3) Plug Gages will be marked PTF (L_3).

C.11.2 Thread Form—The threads in all particulars excepting truncation shall conform to American Standard Taper Pipe Thread practice. Crests of threads at major diameter shall be truncated 0.20p minimum and 0.25p maximum, producing the minimum and maximum widths of flat specified in Table C7-1.

All other thread dimensions shall be within tolerances specified for the Dryseal American Standard Pipe Thread Working Gages (ASA B2.2). Other gage details shall conform to American Gage Design Standards published in Commercial Standard CS8.

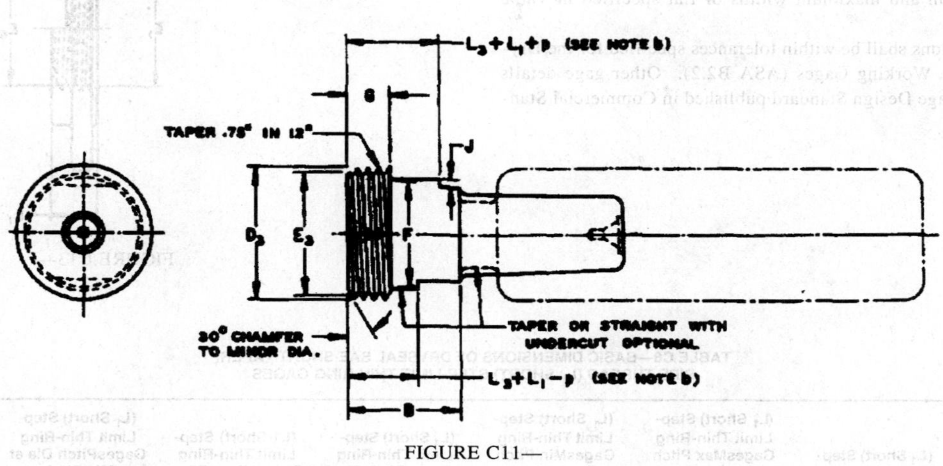

FIGURE C11—

TABLE C7—BASIC DIMENSIONS OF DRYSEAL AMERICAN STANDARD TAPER THREAD (L_3) LENGTH STEP-LIMIT PLUG GAGES

Size	Small End Pitch Dia, E_3	Small End Major Dia,[1] D_3	Relief Dia, F [E_3 + (0.0625x4p)—Sharp-V Thread Height—0.020 to 0.025 below Sharp Root] +0.005 -0.000	Four Threads, G (L_3 + p)	Pitch Dia Gaging Step[2] Plus 3 Threads (L_3 + L_1 - p) Min	Pitch Dia Gaging Step[2] Plus 3 Threads (L_3 + L_1 - p) Max	Blank Length B	Notch Depth, J +0.005 -0.000
1/16-27	0.2642	0.2815	0.216	0.1482	0.2341	0.3082	0.38	0.030
1/8 -27	0.3566	0.3738	0.309	0.1482	0.2356	0.3097	0.41	0.030
1/4 -18	0.4670	0.4928	0.409	0.2222	0.3389	0.4500	0.50	0.030
3/8 -18	0.6016	0.6275	0.542	0.2222	0.3511	0.4622	0.56	0.030
1/2 -14	0.7451	0.7783	0.676	0.2857	0.4628	0.6057	0.69	0.040
3/4 -14	0.9543	0.9876	0.886	0.2857	0.4818	0.6247	0.72	0.040
1 -11-1/2	1.1973	1.2379	1.118	0.3478	0.5739	0.7478	0.88	0.050
1-1/4 -11-1/2	1.5408	1.5814	1.462	0.3478	0.5939	0.7678	0.88	0.050
1-1/2 -11-1/2	1.7798	1.8203	1.701	0.3478	0.5939	0.7678	0.88	0.050
2 -11-1/2	2.2527	2.2932	2.174	0.3478	0.6099	0.7838	0.88	0.050
2-1/2 -8	2.6961	2.7543	2.590	0.5000	0.9320	1.1820	1.50	0.050
-8	3.3172	3.3754	3.214	0.5000	1.0160	1.2660	1.50	0.050

1. Major diameter is based upon crest minimum truncation of 0.20 p.
2. Maximum and minimum pitch-diameter steps are gaging limits. Notch formulas on drawing apply to all sizes.

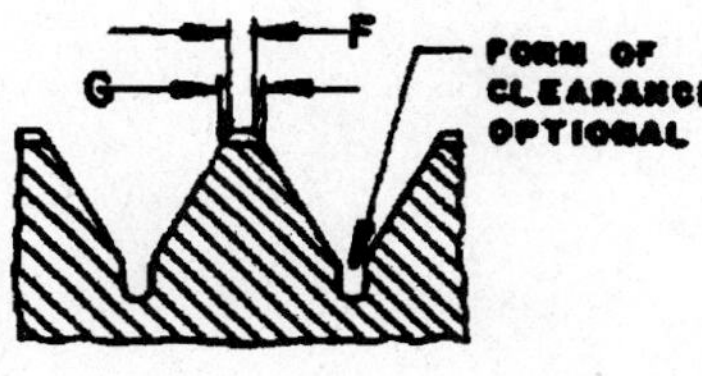

FIGURE C12—

TABLE C7-1—THREAD FLATS

Threads per in.	F	G
27	0.0086	0.0107
18	0.0128	0.0160
14	0.0165	0.0206
11-1/2	0.0201	0.0251
8	0.0289	0.0361

C.12 Dryseal SAE Short Taper Pipe Thread (L_1 Short) Step-Limit Thin-Ring Gages

C.12.1 Marking—In addition to the regular markings, Dryseal SAE Short Taper Pipe Thread Ring Gages will be marked PTF—SAE Short (L_1 Short) on the entering side of gage.

C.12.2 Thread Form—The threads in all particulars excepting truncation shall conform to American Standard Taper Pipe Thread practice. Crests of threads at the minor diameter shall be truncated 0.20p minimum to 0.25p maximum, producing the minimum and maximum widths of flat specified in Table C8-1.

All other thread dimensions shall be within tolerances specified for the Dryseal American Standard Pipe Working Gages (ASA B2.2). Other gage details shall conform to American Gage Design Standard published in Commercial Standard CS8.

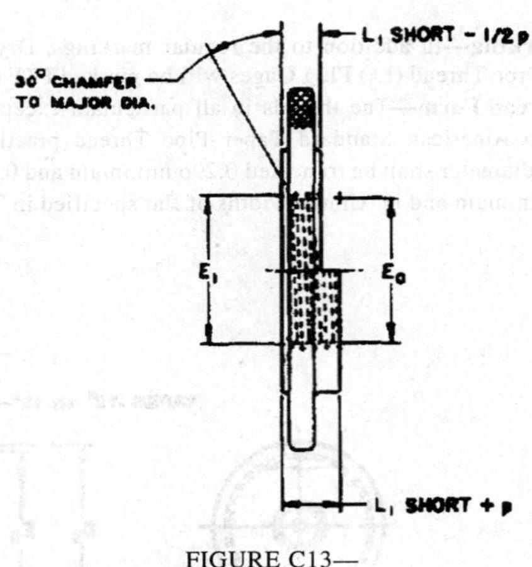

FIGURE C13—

TABLE C8—BASIC DIMENSIONS OF DRYSEAL SAE SHORT TAPER PIPE THREAD (L_1 SHORT) STEP-LIMIT THIN-RING GAGES

Size	(L_1 Short) Step-Limit Thin-Ring GagesL_1 Short	(L_1 Short) Step-Limit Thin-Ring GagesMax Pitch Dia Gaging StepL_1Short - 1/2 p	(L_1 Short) Step-Limit Thin-Ring GagesMin Pitch DiaGaging StepL_1Short + p	(L_1 Short) Step-Limit Thin-Ring GagesPitch Dia E_1	(L1 Short) Step-Limit Thin-Ring GagesMinor Diaat Large End(1)	(L_1 Short) Step-Limit Thin-Ring GagesPitch Dia at Min Pitch DiaGaging StepE_0	(L_1 Short) Step-Limit Thin-Ring GagesMinor Diaat Small End(1)
1/16-27	0.12296	0.10444	0.16000	0.28118	0.26392	0.27118	0.25392
1/8 -27	0.12446	0.10594	0.16150	0.37360	0.35634	0.36351	0.34625
1/4 -18	0.17224	0.14446	0.22780	0.49163	0.46574	0.47739	0.45150
3/8 -18	0.18444	0.15666	0.24000	0.62701	0.60112	0.61201	0.58712
1/2 -14	0.24857	0.21286	0.32000	0.77843	0.74514	0.75843	0.72514
3/4 -14	0.26757	0.23186	0.33900	0.98887	0.95558	0.96768	0.93439
1 -11-1/2	0.31304	0.26956	0.40000	1.23863	1.19810	1.21363	1.17310
1-1/4 -11-1/2	0.33304	0.28956	0.42000	1.58338	1.54285	1.55713	1.51660
1-1/2 -11-1/2	0.33304	0.28956	0.42000	1.82234	1.78181	1.79609	1.75556
2 -11-1/2	0.34904	0.30556	0.43600	2.29627	2.25574	2.26902	2.22849
2-1/2 -8	0.55700	0.49450	0.68200	2.76216	2.70391	2.71953	2.66128
3 -8	0.64100	0.57850	0.76600	3.38850	3.33025	3.34062	3.28237

1. Minor diameter is based on crest minimum truncation of 0.20 p.

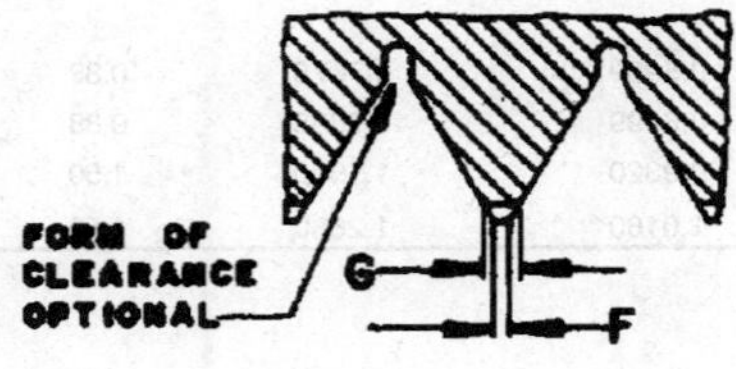

FIGURE C14—

TABLE C8-1—THREAD FLATS

Threads per in.	F	G
27	0.0086	0.0107
18	0.0128	0.0160
14	0.0165	0.0206
11-1/2	0.0201	0.0251
8	0.0289	0.0361

C.13 Dryseal SAE Short Taper Pipe Thread (L_2 Short) Step-Limit Full-Ring Gages

C.13.1 Marking—In addition to the regular markings, Dryseal SAE Short Taper Pipe Thread Ring Gages will be marked PTF—SAE Short (L_2 Short) on the entering side of gage.

C.13.2 Thread Form—The threads in all particulars excepting truncation shall conform to American Standard Taper Pipe Thread practice. Crests of threads at the minor diameter shall be truncated 0.20p minimum to 0.25p maximum, producing the minimum and maximum widths of flat specified in Table C9-1.

All other thread dimensions shall be within tolerance specified for the Dryseal American Standard Pipe Working Gages (ASA B2.2). Other gage details shall conform to American Gage Design Standard published in Commercial Standard CS8.

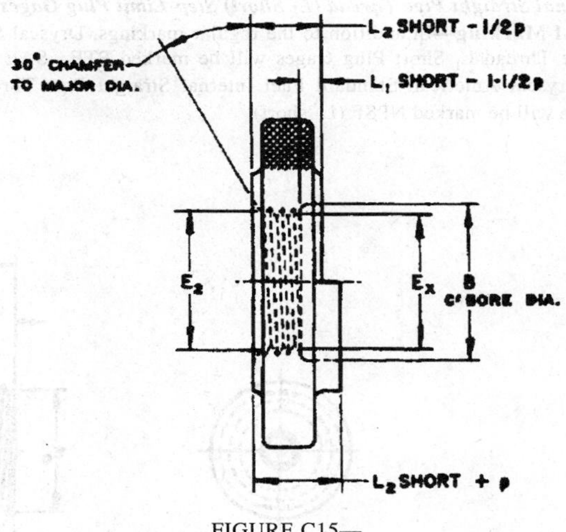

FIGURE C15—

TABLE C9—BASIC DIMENSIONS OF DRYSEAL SAE SHORT TAPER PIPE THREAD (L SHORT) STEP-LIMIT FULL-RING GAGES

Size	L_2 Short	(L_2 Short) Step-Limit Full-Ring Gages Max Pitch Dia Gaging Step L_2 Short - 1/2p	(L_2 Short) Step-Limit Full-Ring Gages Max Pitch Dia Gaging Step L_2 Short + p	(L_2 Short) Step-Limit Full-Ring Gages Pitch Dia E_2	(L_2 Short) Step-Limit Full-Ring Gages Minor Dia at Large End[(1)]	(L_2 Short) Step-Limit Full-Ring Gages Pitch Dia at L_1 Short - 1-1/2p from Min Pitch Dia Gaging Ste, E_x	(L_2 Short) Step-Limit Full-Ring Gages Minor Dia at Small End Counterbore	(L_2 Short) Step-Limit Full-Ring Gages L_1 Short -1-1/2p	(L_2 Short) Step-Limit Full-Ring Gages B
1/16-27	0.2241	0.20557	0.26113	0.28750	0.27024	0.27886	0.26160	0.06740	0.38
1/8 -27	0.2268	0.20829	0.26385	0.38000	0.36274	0.37129	0.35403	0.06890	0.47
1/4 -18	0.3462	0.31845	0.40178	0.50250	0.47661	0.48816	0.46227	0.08891	0.59
3/8 -18	0.3522	0.32445	0.40778	0.63750	0.61161	0.62354	0.59765	0.10111	0.72
1/2 -14	0.4623	0.42657	0.53371	0.79179	0.75850	0.77396	0.74067	0.14143	0.88
3/4 -14	0.4743	0.43857	0.54571	1.00179	0.96850	0.98440	0.95111	0.16043	1.09
1 -11-1/2	0.5958	0.55235	0.68278	1.25630	1.21577	1.23320	1.19267	0.18260	1.34
1-1/4 -11-1/2	0.6198	0.57635	0.70678	1.60130	1.56077	1.57794	1.53741	0.20260	1.69
1-1/2 -11-1/2	0.6365	0.59305	0.72348	1.84130	1.80077	1.81690	1.77637	0.20260	1.94
2 -11-1/2	0.6695	0.62609	0.75652	2.31630	2.27577	2.29084	2.25031	0.21860	2.50
2-1/2 -8	1.0125	0.95000	1.13750	2.79062	2.73237	2.75434	2.69609	0.36950	2.94
3 -8	1.0750	1.01250	1.20000	3.41562	3.35737	3.38068	3.32243	0.45350	3.56

1. Minor diameter is based on crest minimum truncation of 0.20 p.

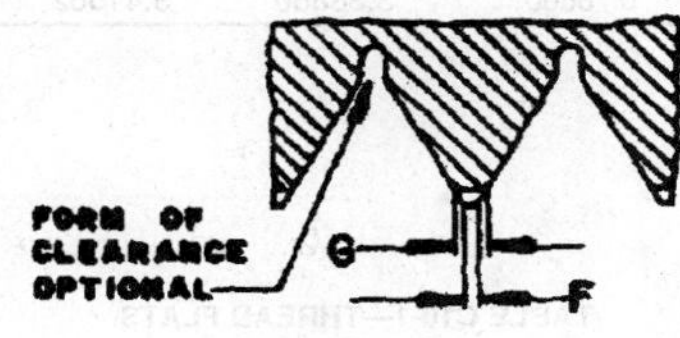

FIGURE C16—

TABLE C9-1—THREAD FLATS

Threads per in.	F	G
27	0.0086	0.0107
18	0.0128	0.0160
14	0.0165	0.0206
11-1/2	0.0201	0.0251
8	0.0289	0.0361

C.14 Dryseal SAE Short Taper Pipe Thread And Dryseal American Standard Fuel Internal Straight Pipe Thread (L_1 Short) Step-Limit Plug Gages

C.14.1 Marking—In addition to the regular markings, Dryseal SAE Short Taper Pipe Thread L_1 Short Plug Gages will be marked PTF—SAE Short (L_1 Short). Dryseal American Standard Fuel Internal Straight Pipe Thread Taper Plug Gages will be marked NPSF (L_1 short).

C.14.2 Thread Form—The threads in all particulars excepting truncation shall conform to American Standard Taper Pipe Thread practice. Crests of threads at major diameter shall be truncated 0.20p minimum to 0.25p maximum, producing the minimum and maximum widths of flat specified in Table C10-1.

All other thread dimensions shall be within tolerances specified for the Dryseal American Standard Pipe Thread Working Plug Gages (ASA B2.2). Other gage details shall conform to American Gage Design Standards published in Commercial Standard CS8.

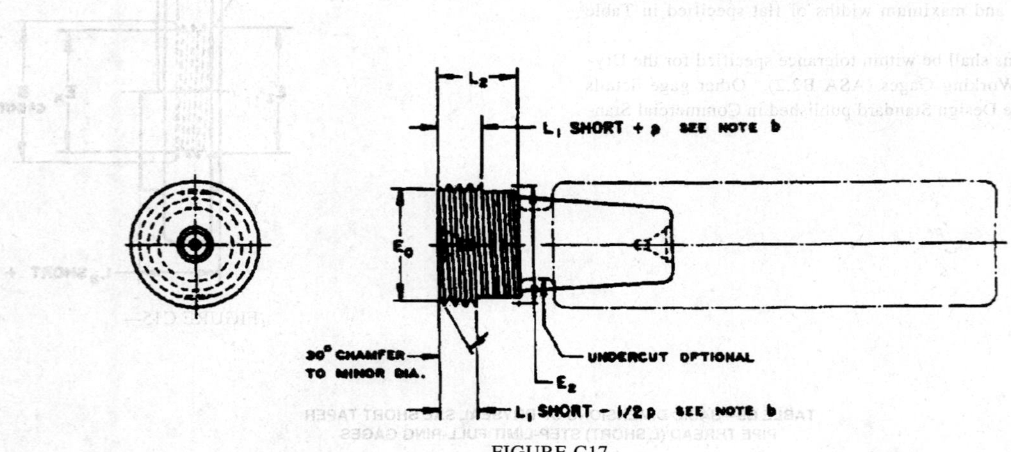

FIGURE C17—

TABLE C10—BASIC DIMENSIONS OF DRYSEAL SAE SHORT TAPER PIPE THREAD AND DRYSEAL AMERICAN STANDARD FUEL INTERNAL STRAIGHT PIPE THREAD (L_1 SHORT) STEP-LIMIT PLUG GAGES

Size	L_1 Short	L_2	Small End Pitch Dia, E_0	Small End Major Dia(1)	Min Pitch Dia Gaging Step(2) L_1 Short 1/2 p	Min Pitch Dia Gaging Step(2) Pitch Dia	Max Pitch Dia Gaging Step(2) L_1 Short + p	Max Pitch Dia Gaging Step(2) Pitch Dia	Large End Pitch Dia, E_2	Large End Major Dia(1)
1/16-27	0.12296	0.26113	0.27118	0.28844	0.10444	0.27771	0.16000	0.28118	0.28750	0.30476
1/8 -27	0.12446	0.26385	0.36351	0.38077	0.10594	0.37013	0.16150	0.37360	0.38000	0.39726
1/4 -18	0.17224	0.40178	0.47739	0.50328	0.14446	0.48642	0.22780	0.49163	0.50250	0.52839
3/8 -18	0.18444	0.40778	0.61201	0.63790	0.15666	0.62180	0.24000	0.62701	0.63750	0.66339
1/2 -14	0.24857	0.53371	0.75843	0.79170	0.21286	0.77174	0.32000	0.77843	0.79179	0.82506
3/4 -14	0.26757	0.54571	0.96768	1.00095	0.23186	0.98218	0.33900	0.98887	1.00179	1.03506
1 -11-1/2	0.31304	0.68278	1.21363	1.25416	0.26956	1.23048	0.40000	1.23863	1.25630	1.29683
1-1/4 -11-1/2(3)	0.33304	0.70678	1.55713	1.59766	0.28956	1.57523	0.42000	1.58338	1.60130	1.64183
1-1/2 -11-1/2(3)	0.33304	0.72348	1.79609	1.83662	0.28956	1.81419	0.42000	1.82234	1.84130	1.88183
2 -11-1/2(3)	0.34904	0.75652	2.26902	2.30955	0.30556	2.28812	0.43600	2.29627	2.31630	2.35683
2-1/2 -8(3)	0.55700	1.13750	2.71953	2.77778	0.49450	2.75044	0.68200	2.76216	2.79062	2.84887
3 -8(3)	0.64100	1.20000	3.34062	3.39887	0.57850	3.37678	0.76600	3.38850	3.41562	3.47387

1. Major diameter is based on crest minimum truncation of 0.20 p.
2. Maximum and minimum pitch-diameter steps are gaging limits. Notch forumlas on drawing apply to all sizes.
3. For reference only above 1-11-1/2 NPSF.

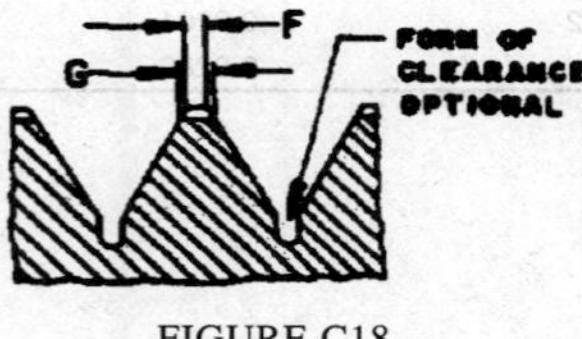

FIGURE C18—

TABLE C10-1—THREAD FLATS

Threads per in.	F	G
27	0.0086	0.0107
18	0.0128	0.0160
14	0.0165	0.0206
11-1/2	0.0201	0.0251
8	0.0289	0.0361

C.15 Dryseal Sae Short Taper Pipe Thread (L_3 Short) Length Step-limit Plug Gages

C.15.1 Marking—In addition to the regular markings, Dryseal SAE Short Taper Pipe Thread (L_3) Plug Gages will be marked PTF—SAE Short (L_3 Short).

C.15.2 Thread Form—The threads in all particulars excepting truncation shall conform to American Standard Taper Pipe Thread practice. Crests of threads at major diameter shall be truncated 0.20p minimum to 0.25p maximum, producing the minimum and maximum widths of flat specified in Table C11-1.

All other thread dimensions shall be within tolerances specified for the Dryseal American Standard Pipe Thread Working Plug Gages (ASA B2.2). Other gage details shall conform to American Gage Design Standards published in Commercial Standard CS8.

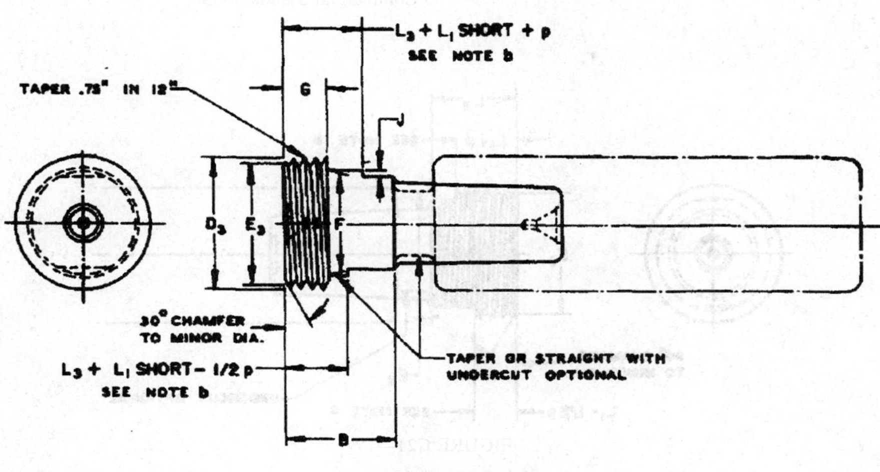

FIGURE C19—

TABLE C11—BASIC DIMENSIONS OF DRYSEAL SAE SHORT TAPER PIPE THREAD (L_3 SHORT) LENGTH STEP-LIMIT PLUG GAGES

Size	Small End Pitch Dia, E_3	Small End Major Dia[1], D_3	Relief Dia, F [E_3 + (0.0625 x 4p) - Sharp-V Thread Height - 0.020 to 0.025 below Sharp Root] +0.005 - 0.000	Four Threads, (G) (L_3 + p)	Pitch Dia Gaging Step[2] Plus 3 Threads (L_3 + L_1 Short - 1/2 p) Min	Pitch Dia Gaging Step[2] Plus 3 Threads (L_3 + L_1 Short - 1/2 p) Max	Black Length, (B)	Notch Depth, (J) +0.005 -0.000
1/16-27	0.2642	0.2815	0.216	0.1482	0.2156	0.2711	0.38	0.030
1/8 -27	0.3566	0.3738	0.309	0.1482	0.2171	0.2726	0.41	0.030
1/4 -18	0.4670	0.4928	0.409	0.2222	0.3111	0.3945	0.50	0.030
3/8 -18	0.6016	0.6275	0.542	0.2222	0.3233	0.4067	0.56	0.030
1/2 -14	0.7451	0.7783	0.676	0.2857	0.4271	0.5343	0.69	0.040
3/4 -14	0.9543	0.9876	0.886	0.2857	0.4462	0.5533	0.72	0.040
1 -11-1/2	1.1973	1.2379	1.118	0.3478	0.5304	0.6609	0.88	0.050
1-1/4 -11-1/2	1.5408	1.5814	1.462	0.3478	0.5504	0.6809	0.88	0.050
1-1/2 -11-1/2	1.7798	1.8203	1.701	0.3478	0.5504	0.6809	0.88	0.050
2 -11-1/2	2.2527	2.2932	2.174	0.3478	0.5644	0.6969	0.88	0.050
2-1/2 -8	2.6961	2.7543	2.590	0.5000	0.8695	1.0570	1.50	0.050
3 -8	3.3172	3.3754	3.214	0.5000	0.9535	1.1410	1.50	0.050

1. Major diameter is based upon crest minimum truncation of 0.20 p.
2. Maximum and minimum pitch-diameter steps are gaging limits. Notch formulas on drawing apply to all sizes.

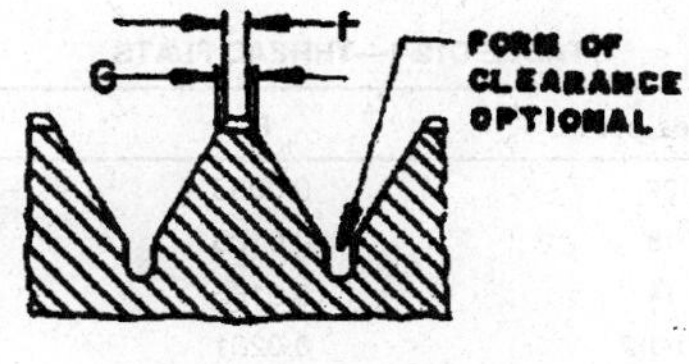

FIGURE C20—

TABLE C11-1—THREAD FLATS

Threads per in.	F	G
27	0.0086	0.0107
18	0.0128	0.0160
14	0.0165	0.0206
11-1/2	0.0201	0.0251
8	0.0289	0.0361

C.16 Dryseal American Intermediate Internal Straight Pipe Thread (L_1) Step-Limit Plug Gages Taper lock design, range 1/8 to 1 in., inclusive

C.16.1 Marking—In addition to the regular markings, Dryseal American Intermediate Internal Straight Pipe Thread Taper Plug Gages will be marked NPSI (L_1).

C.16.2 Thread Form—The threads in all particulars excepting truncation shall conform to American Standard Taper Pipe Thread practice. Crests of threads at major diameter shall be truncated 0.20p minimum to 0.25p maximum, producing the minimum and maximum widths of flat specified in Table C12-1.

All other thread dimensions shall be within tolerances specified for the Dryseal American Standard Pipe Thread Working Plug Gages (ASA B2.2). Other gage details shall conform to American Gage Design Standards published in Commercial Standard CS8.

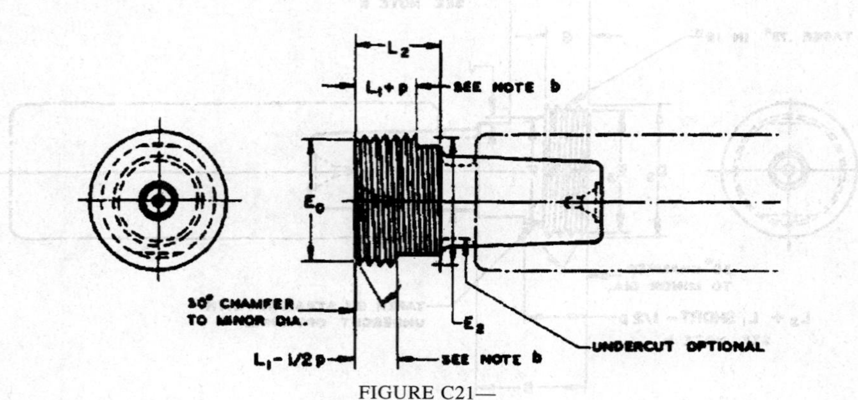

FIGURE C21—

TABLE C12—BASIC DIMENSIONS OF DRYSEAL AMERICAN INTERMEDIATE INTERNAL STRAIGHT PIPE THREAD (L_1) STEP-LIMIT PLUG GAGES

Size	L_1	L_2	Small End Pitch Dia, E_0	Small End Major Dia[(1)]	Min Pitch Dia Gaging Step[(2)] L_1 - 1/2p	Min Pitch Dia Gaging Step[(2)] Pitch Dia	Max Pitch Dia Gaging Step[(2)] L_1 + p	Max Pitch Dia Gaging Step[(2)] Pitch Dia	Large End Pitch Dia, E2	Large End Major Dia[(1)]
1/16-27	0.1600	0.26113	0.27118	0.28844	0.14148	0.28002	0.19704	0.28350	0.28750	0.30476
1/8 -27	0.1615	0.26385	0.36351	0.38077	0.14298	0.37245	0.19854	0.37592	0.38000	0.39726
1/4 -18	0.2278	0.40178	0.47739	0.50328	0.20002	0.48989	0.28336	0.49510	0.50250	0.52839
3/8 -18	0.2400	0.40778	0.61201	0.63790	0.21222	0.62527	0.29556	0.63048	0.63750	0.66339
1/2 -14	0.3200	0.53371	0.75843	0.79170	0.28428	0.77620	0.39143	0.78289	0.79179	0.82506
3/4 -14	0.3390	0.54571	0.96768	1.00095	0.30328	0.98664	0.41043	0.99333	1.00179	1.03506
1 -11-1/2	0.4000	0.68278	1.21363	1.25416	0.35652	1.23592	0.48696	1.24406	1.25630	1.29683
1-1/4 -11-1/2[(3)]	0.1200	0.70678	1.55713	1.59766	0.37652	1.58066	0.50696	1.58882	1.60130	1.64183
1-1/2 -11-1/2[(3)]	0.1200	0.72348	1.79609	1.83662	0.37652	1.81962	0.50696	1.82778	1.84130	1.88183
2 -11-1/2[(3)]	0.4360	0.75652	2.26902	2.30955	0.39252	2.29355	0.52296	2.30170	2.31630	2.35683
2-1/2 -8[(3)]	0.6820	1.13750	2.71953	2.77778	0.61950	2.75825	0.80700	2.76997	2.79062	2.84887
3 -8[(3)]	0.7660	1.20000	3.34062	3.39887	0.70350	3.38459	0.89100	3.39631	3.41562	3.47387

1. Major diameter is based on crest minimum truncation of 0.20 p.
2. Maximum and minimum pitch-diameter steps are gaging limits. Notch formulas on drawing apply to all sizes.
3. For reference only.

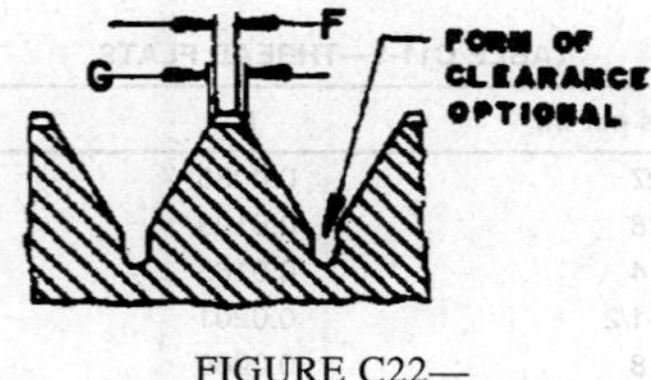

FIGURE C22—

TABLE C12-1—THREAD FLATS

Threads per in.	F	G
27	0.0086	0.0107
18	0.0128	0.160
14	0.0165	0.0206
11-1/2	0.0201	0.0251
8	0.0289	0.0361

APPENDIX D
SPECIAL SHORT, SPECIAL EXTRA SHORT, FINE, AND SPECIAL DIAMETER PITCH COMBINATION DRYSEAL PIPE THREADS

D.1 General Information—The SAE Dryseal Pipe Thread Series are based on thread length. Full thread lengths and clearances for Dryseal Standard and SAE Short Series are shown in Tables 2, 3, and 4 of the standard and the differences between them are described in the text under the series headings. These full thread lengths and clearances should be used in design applications wherever possible.

Design limitations, economy of material, permanent installation or other limiting conditions may not permit the use of either of the full thread lengths and shoulder lengths in the preceding tables for the above thread series. To meet these conditions two special thread series have been established as shown in Figure 1. The deviations from standard practice are described below.

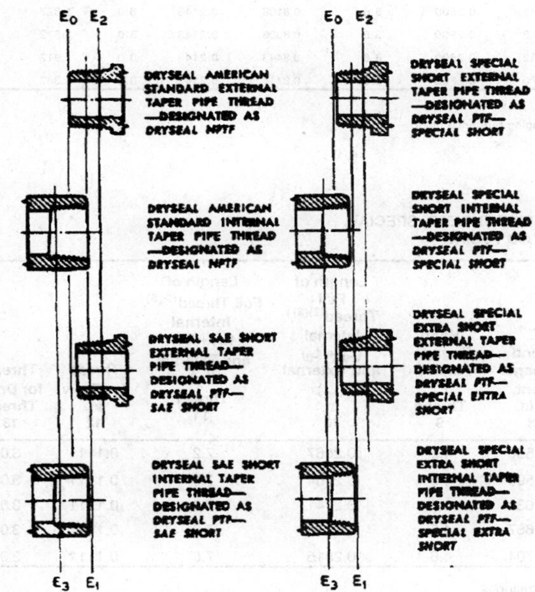

FIGURE D1—THREAD LENGTH AND DESIGNATION

D.2 Dryseal Special Short Taper Pipe Thread (PTF—SPL Short)—Threads of this series conform in all respects to the PTF—SAE Short threads except that the full thread length has been further shortened by eliminating one thread at the large end of external threads or eliminating one thread at the small end of internal threads. Gaging is the same as for PTF—SAE Short except the L_2 ring thread gage for external thread length and taper or the L_3 plug thread gage for internal thread length and taper cannot be used. Tolerance must be altered and co-ordinated as described in paragraph on Limitation of Assembly. The designation of this series thread is for example:

1/8—27 DRYSEAL PTF—SPL Short

D.3 Dryseal Special Extra Short Taper Pipe Thread (PTF—SPL Extra Short)—Threads of this series conform in all respects to the PTF—SAE Short threads except that the full thread length has been further shortened by eliminating two threads at the large end of external threads or eliminating two threads at the small end of internal threads. Gaging is the same as for PTF—SAE Short except the L_2 ring thread gage for external thread length and taper or the L_2 plug thread gage for internal thread length and taper cannot be used. Tolerance must be altered and co-ordinated as described in paragraph on Limitation of Assembly. The designation of this series thread is for example:

1/8—27 DRYSEAL PTF—SPL Extra Short

D.4 Limitation of Assembly—Standard combinations and applications of the various series Dryseal Pipe Threads are given in the preceding thread descriptions. However, where special combinations are used, additional considerations as outlined below must be observed. These should be designated with the suffix "SPL" and gaging tolerance should be specified.

PTF—SPL Short External	Maya[(1)]	PTF—SAE Short Internal
PTF—SPL Extra Short External	Assemble With	NPSF Internal
		PTF—SPL Short Internal
PTF—SPL Short Internal	May[(1)]	PTF—SPL Extra Short Internal
PTF—SPL Extra Short Internal	Assemble With	PTF—SAE Short External

1. Only when the external thread or the internal thread or both are held closer than the standard tolerance, the external toward the minimum and the internal toward the maximum pitch diameter to provide a minimum of one turn hand engagement. At extreme tolerance limits the shortened full thread lengths reduce hand engagement and threads may not start.

PTF—SPL Short External	Maya[(1)]	NPTF or NPSI Internal
PTF—SPL Extra Short External	Assemble With	
PTF—SPL Short Internal	May[(1)]	NPTF Externall
PTF—SPL Extra Short Internal	Assemble With	

1. Only when both the internal thread and the external thread are held closer than the standard tolerance, the internal toward the minimum and the external toward the maximum pitch diameter to provide a minimum of two turns or wrench make up and sealing. At extreme tolerance limits the shortened full thread lengths reduce wrench makeup and threads may not seal.

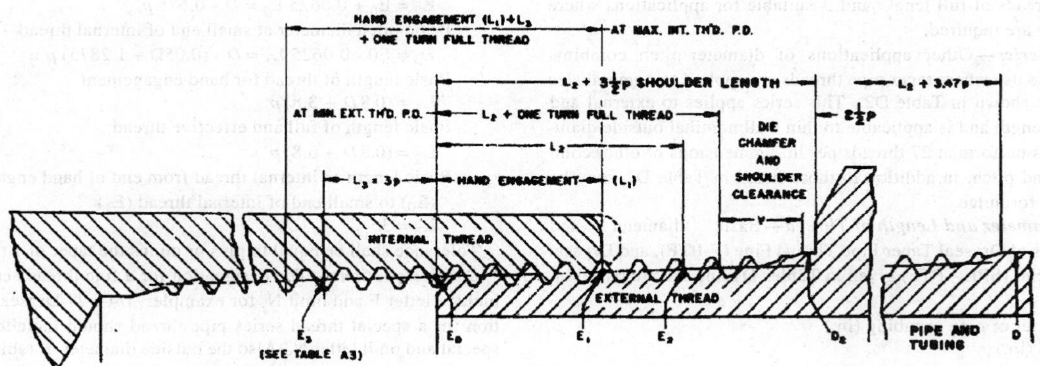

FIGURE D2—

TABLE D1—BASIC DIMENSIONS OF DRYSEAL TAPER PIPE THREAD, FINE, F-PTF

F-PTF Size (Fine) 1	Pitch, p in. 2	Pitch Dia at Small End of External Thread, E_0 in. 3	Pitch Dia at Large End of Internal Thread, E_1 in. 4	Pitch Dia at Large End of External Thread, E_2 in. 5	Pitch Dia at Small End of Internal, E_3 in. 6	Hand Engagement, L_1 in. 7	Hand Engagement, L_1 Thread 8	Length of Full Thread,(1)(2) Internal ($L_1 + L_3$) and External (L_2) in. 9	Length of Full Thread,(1)(2) Internal ($L_1 + L_3$) and External (L_2) Thread 10	Vanish Threads-V Plus Full Thread Tolerance Plus Shoulder Clearance (V + 1p + 1/2p) in. 11	Vanish Threads-V Plus Full Thread Tolerance Plus Shoulder Clearance (V + 1p + 1/2p) Thread 12	Shoulder Length, L_2 + 3-1/2p in. 13	Thread for Draw in. 14	Thread for Draw Thread 15	OD of Fitting, D2 in. 16	OD of Pipe, D in. 17
1/4-27	0.03704	0.49826	0.50807	0.51501	0.49132	0.157	4.23	0.268	7.23	0.1296	3.5	0.3975	0.1111	3.0	0.546	0.540
3/8-27	0.03704	0.63301	0.64307	0.65001	0.62607	0.161	4.34	0.272	7.34	0.1296	3.5	0.4015	0.1111	3.0	0.681	0.675
1/2-18	0.05556	0.77655	0.79205	0.80249	0.76613	0.248	4.47	0.415	7.47	0.1944	3.5	0.6096	0.1667	3.0	0.850	0.840
3/4-18	0.05556	0.98597	1.00210	1.01247	0.97555	0.258	4.64	0.424	7.64	0.1944	3.5	0.6189	0.1667	3.0	1.060	1.050
1 -14	0.07143	1.23173	1.25342	1.26679	1.21834	0.347	4.85	0.561	7.85	0.2500	3.5	0.8109	0.2143	3.0	1.327	1.315
1-1/4-14	0.07143	1.57550	1.59837	1.61181	1.56211	0.366	5.13	0.581	8.13	0.2500	3.5	0.8306	0.2143	3.0	1.672	1.660
1-1/2-14	0.07143	1.81464	1.83839	1.85176	1.80125	0.380	5.32	0.594	8.32	0.2500	3.5	0.8443	0.2143	3.0	1.912	1.900
2 -14	0.07143	2.28794	2.31338	2.32675	2.27455	0.407	5.70	0.621	8.70	0.2500	3.5	0.8714	0.2143	3.0	2.387	2.375

1. External thread tabulated full thread lengths include chamfers not exceeding one and one-half pitches (threads) length.
2. Internal thread tabulated full thread lengths do not include countersink beyond the intersection of the pitch line and the chamfer cone (gaging reference point).

TABLE D2—BASIC DIMENSIONS OF DRYSEAL TAPER PIPE THREAD, SPECIAL, SPL-PTF, FOR THIN WALL NOMINAL SIZE OD TUBING

Tubing Dia(1) D in. 1	Threads per in. 2	Pitch,p in. 3	Pitch Dia at Small End of External Thread, E_0 in. 4	Pitch Dia at Large End of Internal Thread, E_1 in. 5	Pitch Dia at Large End of External Thread, E_2 in 6	Pitch Dia at Small End of Internal Thread, E_3 in. 7	Hand Engagement, L_1 in. 8	Hand Engagement, L_1 Thread 9	Length of Full Thread(2)(3), Internal ($L_1 + L_3$) and External (L_2) in. 10	Length of Full Thread(2)(3), Internal ($L_1 + L_3$) and External (L_2) Thread 11	Thread for Draw in. 12	Thread for Draw Thread 13
1/2	27	0.03704	0.45833	0.46806	0.47500	0.45139	0.1556	4.2	0.2667	7.2	0.1111	3.0
5/8	27	0.03704	0.58310	0.59306	0.60000	0.57616	0.1593	4.3	0.2704	7.3	0.1111	3.0
3/4	27	0.03704	0.70787	0.71806	0.72500	0.70093	0.1630	4.4	0.2741	7.4	0.1111	3.0
7/8	27	0.03704	0.83264	0.84306	0.85000	0.82570	0.1667	4.5	0.2778	7.5	0.1111	3.0
1	27	0.03704	095740	0.96805	0.97500	0.95046	0.1704	4.6	0.2815	7.6	0.1111	3.0

1. This denotes nominal outside diameter of tubing and should not be confused with nominal pipe diameter and thread designations.
2. External thread tabulated full thread lengths include chamfers not exceeding one and one-half pitches (threads) length.
3. Internal thread tabulated full thread lengths do not include countersink beyond the intersection of the pitch line and the chamfer cone (gaging reference point).

D.5 Fine Thread Series—The need for finer pitches for nominal pipe sizes has brought into use applications of 27 threads per in. to 1/4 and 3/8 in. pipe sizes. There may be other needs which require finer pitches for larger pipe sizes. It is recommended that the existing threads per in. be applied to the next size larger pipe size for a fine thread series such as shown in Table D1. This series applies to external and internal threads of full length and is suitable for applications where threads finer than NPTF are required.

D.6 Special Thread Series—Other applications of diameter-pitch combinations have also come into use where taper pipe threads are applied to nominal size thin wall tubing such as shown in Table D2. This series applies to external and internal threads of full length and is applicable to thin wall nominal outside diameter tubing. The pitch is uniform at 27 threads per in. Dimensions of other combinations of diameter and pitch, in addition to those listed in Table D2, may be developed by the use of formulae.

D.7 Formulae for Diameter and Length of Thread—Basic diameter and length of thread for sizes of Dryseal Taper Pipe Thread Fine (F-PTF), and Dryseal Taper Pipe Thread Special (SPL—PTF) given in Tables D1 and D2 are based on the following formulae:

D = outside diameter of pipe or tubing (in.)
p = pitch of thread (in.)
Diameter taper = 0.75 in. per 12.00 in. of length

Basic pitch diameter at small end of external thread

$E_0 = D - (0.05D + 1.1)p$

Basic pitch diameter at large end of internal thread

$E_1 = E_0 + 0.0625\ L_1 = D - 0.8625\ p$

Basic pitch diameter at large end of external thread

$E_2 = E_0 + 0.0625\ L_2 = D - 0.675\ p$

Basic pitch diameter at small end of internal thread

$E_3 = E0 - 0.0625\ L_3 = D - (0.05D + 1.2875)\ p$

Basic length of thread for hand engagement

$L_1 = (0.8D + 3.8)\ p$

Basic length of full and effective thread

$L_2 = (0.8D + 6.8)\ p$

Basic length of internal thread from end of hand engagement (E_0) to small end of internal thread (E_3)

$L_3 = 3p$

Tolerance shall be equal to plus or minus the taper of 1 thread on the diameter.

D.8 Designations—The designation for a fine thread series pipe thread should include letter F and omit N, for example: 1/4—27 Dryseal F-PTF. The designation for a special thread series pipe thread should include abbreviation SPL for special and omit letter N. Also the outside diameter of tubing should be given, for example: 1/2—27 Dryseal SPL-PTF, OD 0.500.

APPENDIX E
SUPERSEDED GAGE DIMENSIONS AND GAGING PRACTICE FOR 1/8 AND 1/4 SIZE DRYSEAL PIPE THREADS

In this standard, the L_1 dimensions for the 1/8—27 and 1/4—18 sizes have been revised to correct for a disproportionate number of threads for hand engagement.

In the previous issue of this standard, the values of L_1 hand engagements in the tables of basic dimensions for the product were corrected, but the values in the tables of basic dimensions for gages were left unaltered since users were able to apply existing gages by modifying gaging practices and this allowed gage manufacturers an opportunity to reduce existing inventories. In this issue of the standard, the L_1 hand engagement dimensions affecting gages in Tables 1, C2 and C3 have been revised to agree with the product dimensions for future gage procurement.

Therefore, it should be noted that where basic-notch thread gages having superseded dimensions (see TableE1) are being used for gaging the 1/8—27 and 1/4—18 sizes, the formerly observed deviations from specified gaging practice should be applied as follows:

Internal threads gaged by the Position Method should be 1/2 turn smaller for the 1/8—27 size and 1/2 turn larger than the 1/4—18 size than the specified tolerances given in Appendix C.

External threads gaged by the Turns Engagement Method should be 1/2 greater for the 1/8—27 size and 1/2 turn less for the 1/4—18 size than the basic turns specified in Appendix C.

Table E1 lists the dimensions derived from the superseded L_1 dimensions of 0.1800 in. for the 1/8—27 size and 0.2000 in. for the 1/4—18.

TABLE E1—BASIC DIMENSIONS OF SUPERSEDED BASIC-NOTCH GAGES

Size	Pitch Dia at L_1 - P (E_x)	Minor Dia at L_1 - p	L_1 - p	L_1	Pitch Dia (E_1)	Minor Dia at Large End	Major Dia at Gaging Notch	3 Threads Plus L_1 ($L_3 + L_1$)
1/8-27	0.37244	0.35518	0.14296	0.1800	0.37476	0.35750	0.39202	0.2911
1/4-18	0.48642	0.46053	0.14444	0.2000	0.48989	0.46400	0.51578	0.3667

16 Fluid Conductor Fasteners

RECOMMENDED PRACTICES FOR DESIGN AND EVALUATION OF PASSENGER AND LIGHT TRUCK COOLANT HOSE CLAMPED JOINTS—SAE J1697 NOV2003

SAE Recommended Practice

Report of the SAE Hose/Hose Clamp Performance and Compatibility Committee approved July 1996 and revised November 2003. Rationale statement available.

TABLE OF CONTENTS

1. Scope—This SAE Recommended Practice covers recommended practices for design and evaluation of hose clamped joints primarily in automotive applications. It is intended to: (a) evaluate current joint designs, (b) compare existing designs, (c) aid in the development of new designs, (d) give objective results once weights are set, (e) rate the overall design and individual sections of design, and (f) encourage future research by industry and the OEM's.

2. References

2.1 Related Publications—The following publications are provided for information purposes only and are not a required part of this document.

2.1.1 SAE PUBLICATIONS—Available from SAE, 400 Commonwealth Drive, Warrendale, PA 15096-0001.

SAE J1508—Hose Clamp Specifications

SAE J1610—Test Method for Evaluating the Sealing Capability of Hose Connection with a PVT Test Facility

3. Abstract—Design of hose-clamped coolant joints is not an exact science, therefore precise formulas and methods cannot accurately predict performance. However, theoretical and philosophical constructs based on empirical data and industry experience can be used to develop standard practices for evaluating automotive hose-clamped coolant joints. This document allows individual users to define key parameters that are important to their products and educate the industry about hose clamped coolant joints.

Five major components of designing a robust hose-clamped joint are: (a) sealability, (b) hose assembly, (c) hose blow-off, (d) assembly of clamps over hose/fitting, and (e) serviceability of the clamp. Depending on the function of the joint and the priority of the design, one category may be more important than another. In automotive coolant joint designs, sealability and hose assembly are the main concerns. Since most of the coolant joints are "low" pressure, hose blow-off ranks third. To satisfy the end customer, coolant joints must not leak. In addition the hose must be able to be assembled. In other words, the effort to push the hose fully on the joint must not be higher than is consistently manageable by the assembly operator. Therefore both sealability and hose assembly conditions must be met. Until recently it was thought that either one or the other of the criteria could be met while sacrificing the other.

Assembly and serviceability are also legitimate concerns when variation and proliferation exist. Variation in the clamp assembly as well as the type of clamp is inversely related to the robustness of the joint. As the variation of the assembly decreases, the potential for the joint to seal increases. Serviceability is important because the clamping mechanism must be accessible to the general public or easily substituted with other standard products.

4. Methodology—A weighting system is used to rank choices in the design process. The weights are arbitrarily set by the user to target key system requirements for that particular user. The process works best with a computer program but is not required to use the procedure. The design choices are ranked from 1 to 5 where 1 is the worst choice and 5 is the best choice for that particular section. In the event that a given design does not match any of the listed choices, the most applicable match should be chosen.

a. 1 Poor Design—20% (1/5)
b. 2 Average to Poor Design—40%
c. 3 Average Design—60%
d. 4 Average to Good Design—80%
e. 5 Good Design—100%

NOTE—It must be noted that some sections may indicate excellent designs but due to the interactions and dependencies, the total joint will suffer. In the following example it is suggested that the designer has only two concerns: sealability and hose assembly. A 40% weight is assigned to sealability and a 60% weight is assigned to hose assembly. Therefore hose assembly is the most important joint design criterion.

For the sealability part of this example, only interference and residual load are considered important with weights of 30% and 70%, respectively. Therefore with the weights chosen it is understood that residual load is felt to contribute the most towards sealing a coolant joint.

For the hose assembly part of this example, only interference to the fitting and wall thickness are considered important with 60% and 40% weights, respectively. Therefore it is similarly understood that interference to the fitting plays the largest part in hose assembly.

In the first design iteration sealability of the joint is rated at 54% while hose assembly is rated at 56%. In the second design it is shown that both sealability and hose assembly ratings have been increased to 68% and 72%, respectively.

The conclusion is that the second design is better in preventing leaks and is easier to assemble than the prior design. **However, keep in mind that most coolant joints are more complex than in the following example.**

4.1 Example

.4 Sealability

.3 Interference

- 1 Line to Line
- 2 0 < 2.5% Interference
- 3 2.5 < 5.0 Interference
- 4 5 - 10% Interference
- 5 > 10 % Interference

Design 1 selection: 2
Design 2 selection: 2

.7 System Pressure (PSI)

- 1 > 80 PSI
- 2 51 - 80 PSI
- 3 31 - 50 PSI
- 4 16 - 30 PSI
- 5 0 - 15 PSI

Design 1 selection: 3
Design 2 selection: 4

.6 Hose Assembly

.6 Interference to Fitting

- 1 > 10% Interference
- 2 5 - 10 % Interference
- 3 2.5 < 5% Interference
- 4 0 < 2.5% Interference
- 5 Line to Line

Design 1 selection: 4
Design 2 selection: 4

.4 Wall Thickness

- 1 6.0 mm
- 2 5.3 mm
- 3 4.8 mm
- 4 4.3 mm
- 5 3.8 mm

Design 1 selection: 1
Design 2 selection: 3

Calculations Design 1
Rating for Sealability = .4x.3x2 + .4x.7x3 = 1.08/2.0 = **54%**
Rating for Hose Assembly = .6x.6x4 + .6x.4x1 = 1.68/3.0 = **56%**
Total Joint Rating = 1.08 + 1.68 = 2.76/5.0 = 55.2%

Calculations Design 2
Rating for Sealability = 68%
Rating for Hose Assembly = 72%

FIGURE 1A—EXAMPLE OF SEALABILITY AND HOSE ASSEMBLY

.40	SEALABILITY
.30	- Interference
.20	- Pressure
.17	- Surface Finish
.16	- Roundness
.07	- Sealing Length
.06	- Temperature
.02	- Adhesion
.02	- Bead Geometry and Diameter

.25	HOSE ASSEMBLY
.26	- Bead Diameter
.20	- Interference to Fitting
.10	- Hose Durometer
.08	- Wall Thickness
.08	- Angle of Installation
.08	- Reach to Install
.06	- Lead End Diameter of Fitting
.05	- Ramp Angle
.05	- Column Strength of Hose
.04	- Lubrication

.20	HOSE BLOW-OFF
.30	- Pressure
.20	- Interference Fit
.15	- Bead Diameter
.15	- Bead Design
.12	- Clamp Type
.08	- Type of Assembly Lubrication

.10	ASSEMBLY OF CLAMPS OVER HOSE/FITTING
.30	- Number of Different Assembly Tools
.30	- Operator Sensitivity
.20	- Calibration of Tools
.15	- Rpm of Air Tools
.05	- Stray Assembly Lubricant (Slip Agents)

.05	SERVICEABILITY OF CLAMP
.40	- Tool Availability
.20	- Clamp Reuse
.20	- Clamp Availability
.15	- Adjustability
.05	- Corrosion

FIGURE 1B—EXAMPLE OF SEALABILITY AND HOSE ASSEMBLY (CONTINUED)

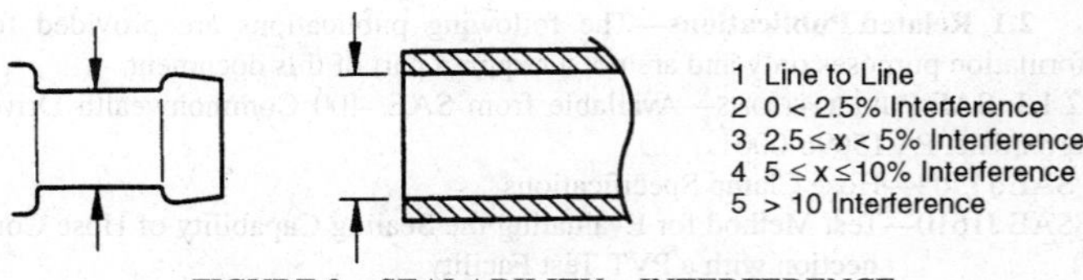

FIGURE 2—SEALABILITY—INTERFERENCE

5. *Sealability*

5.1 Interference—Interference of the inside diameter of the hose to the sealing surface (shank) of the fitting is one of the most important criteria in designing a sealed system. There is a direct relationship between hose to fitting interference and push-on force. As the interference increases so will the push-on force. The relationship between interference and push-on will also change with hose material, reinforcement type and construction. Minimum design requirements should always have a line to line fit between inner diameter of the hose and the shank of the fitting. Clearance fits of any magnitude can lead to joint leaks. More interference has been proven to provide better sealing than less interference or a clearance fit. The greater the interference (provided the joint can still be assembled), the better probability of the sealed joint. Interference is calculated as shown in Equation 1:

$$((\text{Shank OD} - \text{Hose ID}) / \text{Hose ID}) * 100 \quad \text{(Eq. 1)}$$

5.1.1 HOSE/SHANK INTERFERENCE (% OF INSIDE DIAMETER)—(See Figure 2.)

5.2 Clamp Force Throughout Temperature Range (Residual Load)—Residual pressure, along with hose to fitting interference, is one of the most important factors in designing a leak-free joint. Load around the diameter of the clamp (pressure) is required after the system has come to equilibrium. As the pressure increases the higher the clamping force needs to be to prevent leakage. Products that can maintain continuous pressure on the hose, even after the hose has set, will have a greater potential to seal. The impact of clamping pressure on sealing will be reduced if imperfections in the fitting exist. Initial load is not a complete indicator of how the joint will behave over time. Note that excessive clamp pressures can damage some hoses and fitting.

Incorrect sizing of the clamp can result in lower initial and residual loads. Development testing should determine the minimum pressure from the clamp required to seal the joint taking into consideration production processes.

5.3 Pressure—System operating pressures define the type of clamping system the joint requires. Low pressure systems will allow the most flexibility in the design of the joint and will be easier to seal. As the pressure increases the hose design requirements may also change. Higher pressure applications will require different reinforcements and constructions. Pressure is also important with respect to the friction between the hose and the fitting and the hose and the clamp.

5.3.1 MAXIMUM JOINT PRESSURE (PSI)

a. 1 > 80 PSI
b. 2 51 to 80 PSI
c. 3 31 to 50 PSI
d. 4 16 to 30 PSI
e. 5 0 to 15 PSI

5.4 Surface Finish—The surface finish of the fitting is important in the sealing process. Although rough finishes can contribute to a joint leak under some conditions, a certain degree of "grabbiness" by the fitting is required to prevent blow-off. Finishes that are too smooth will be harder to push on the fitting. Similarly if a boundary layer of fluid is allowed between the hose and a "too smooth" fitting, a blow-off condition is likely to occur. The more consistent the sealing surface, the better the chance the joint has to seal.

5.4.1 SURFACE FINISH OF FITTING (RA)
a. 1 Sand Cast (50 - 25)
b. 2 Sand Cast (24 - 6.3)
c. 3 Die Cast (6.2 - 2.1)
d. 4 Molded Plastic (2.0 - 0.8)
e. 5 Machined, Tubing, (0.8 - 0.2)

5.5 Roundness—Parting lines are direct leak paths. Larger parting lines have a higher probability of causing a joint leak than joints with smaller, faintly visible parting lines. Depressions or crevices below the contact surface will also cause leaks. Mismatch of dies or molds may create a leak path at low temperatures. When using self-adjusting type clamps, lack of roundness, in the sense of being elliptically shaped, causes lack of sealing pressure on certain areas of the fitting much more than when using screw type clamps.

5.5.1 ROUNDNESS OF FITTING SEALING SURFACE
a. 1 > 0.50 mm Major Surface Imperfection
b. 2 0.28 to 0.50 mm Machined Imperfections
c. 3 0.178 to 0.254 mm No visual as produced imperfections
d. 4 0.076 to 0.152 mm Radial Removal of Discontinuities
e. 5 < 0.076 mm Turned Surfaces

5.6 Sealing Length—Longer sealing lengths provide a more robust design and assembly process. If the sealing length is not long enough, there is a greater potential that the clamp will be mis-aligned. In production settings, where accurate placement of the clamp cannot be guaranteed (assuming loose assembly), there is a greater possibility that the clamp will be placed either on the bead of the fitting or the hose stop. If the clamp is "tilted" a leak may develop.

5.6.1 SEALING LENGTH OF FITTING—See Figure 3.

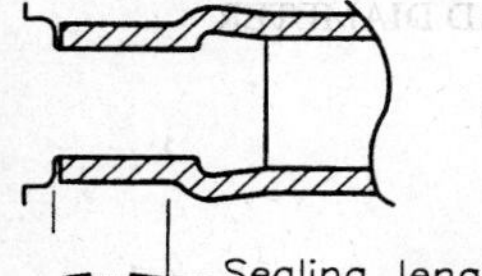

FIGURE 3—SEALABILITY—SEALING LENGTH

5.7 Temperature—Systems with a constant ambient or higher temperature will seal better than joints that have a constant cold temperature or fluctuating cold/hot temperatures. Greater rates of temperature changes may promote system leaks.

5.7.1 TEMPERATURE
a. 1 Constant Cold
b. 2 Fluctuating Cold Environment
c. 3 Fluctuating Cold/Hot Environment
d. 4 Constant Ambient Temperature
e. 5 Constant Hot Temperature

5.8 Adhesion—Any adhesion of the hose to the fitting aids in the sealing process and reduces the responsibility of the clamp. Joints that do not adhere over time rely more heavily on the clamp, hose interference, etc., to seal the joint. Not all EPDM hose bonds to copper brass.

5.8.1 ADHESION OF HOSE TO FITTING
a. 1 Paint/other that forms a lube
b. 2 Non-Dissipating Lubricant
c. 3 Clean/Smooth surface
d. 4 Paint that forms a bond
e. 5 Copper-Brass fitting to EPDM Hose

5.9 Bead Geometry and Diameter
a. 1 < 360 Degree Bead
b. 2 360 bead, 0 < 3% Interference
c. 3 360 bead, 3 to 5% Interference
d. 4 360 bead, 5 to 10% Interference
e. 5 360 bead, > 15% Interference

6. Hose Assembly

6.1 Bead Diameter—As the bead height increases the push-on force over the bead also increases. Although the larger bead aids in blow-off forces, it makes the joint more difficult to assemble.

6.1.1 BEAD DIAMETER OF FITTING—See Figure 4.

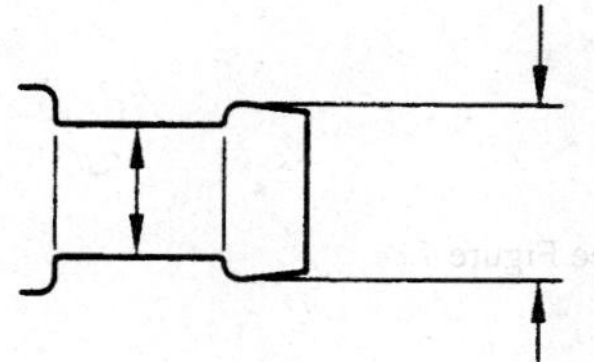

FIGURE 4—HOSE ASSEMBLY—BEAD DIAMETER

6.2 Interference to Fitting—Greater interference between the hose and the sealing surface of the fitting provides a better seal; however, the push-on forces (and efforts) increase also. In general, the greater the interference the greater the push-on forces.

6.2.1 INTERFERENCE TO FITTING—See Figure 5.

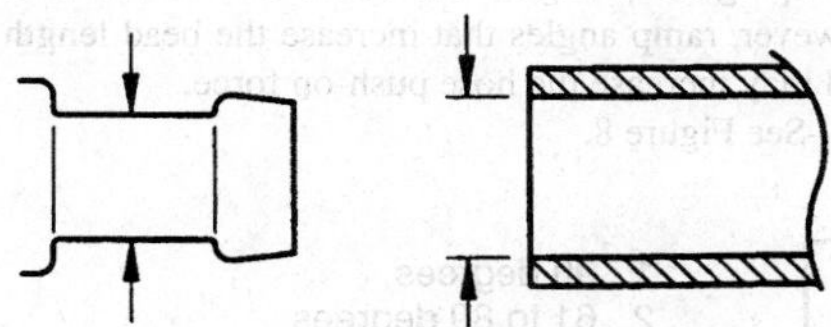

FIGURE 5—HOSE ASSEMBLY—INTERFERENCE TO FITTING

6.3 Hose Durometer—Higher durometer hose is less compliant than lower durometer hose and will have higher push-on forces. Lower durometer materials will allow the translation of the pressure of the clamp directly to the sealing surface. Lower durometer hose will allow the joint to be designed with more interference. Note that hose column strength may be reduced by using lower durometer rubbers and consequently lead to more difficult installation.

6.3.1 HOSE TUBE DUROMETER (SHORE A)
a. 1 71 to 80
b. 2 61 to 70
c. 3 51 to 60
d. 4 40 to 50
e. 5 < 40*

6.4 Wall Thickness—The wall thickness variation of a hose (thick on one side and thin on the other) can affect the distribution of pressure as applied by the clamp. The push-on force required to assemble the joint is affected by the wall thickness. Smaller wall thicknesses will allow easier installation and better transmission of load to the sealing surface.

6.4.1 WALL THICKNESS (FOR 15 TO 46 MM ID HOSES)
a. 1 6.0 mm
b. 2 5.3 mm
c. 3 4.8 mm
d. 4 4.3 mm
e. 5 3.8 mm

6.5 Angle of Installation—The angle of installation of the hose to the fitting will affect the push-on effort of the operator. The straighter the angle of installation the easier the joint is to assemble.

6.5.1 ANGLE OF INSTALLATION—See Figure 6.

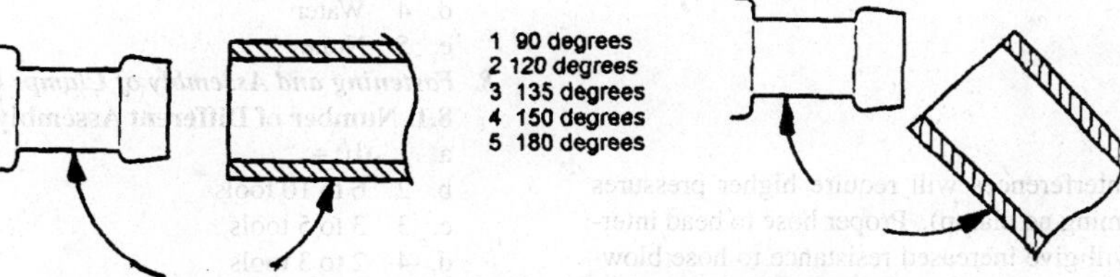

FIGURE 6—HOSE ASSEMBLY—ANGLE OF INSTALLATION

6.6 Reach to Install—Long overhead reaches to install hoses are more difficult than short horizontal reaches. Difficult to install joints have a higher probability of being assembled incorrectly.

6.6.1 REACH TO INSTALL

a. 1 Long Reach, Overhead
b. 2 Long Reach, Horizontal
c. 3 Average Reach, Horizontal
d. 4 Short Reach, Overhead
e. 5 Short Reach, Horizontal

Long Reach is > 1 foot from body
Short Reach is < 1 foot from body

6.7 Lead End Diameter of Fitting—See Figure 7.

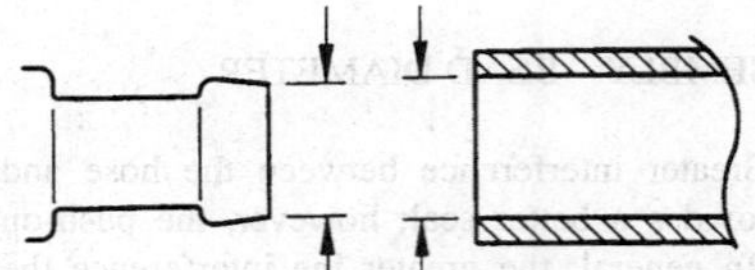

FIGURE 7—HOSE ASSEMBLY—LEAD END DIAMETER OF FITTING

6.8 Ramp Angle—Steep sloping ramp angles make assembly of the hose to the fitting more difficult. However, ramp angles that increase the bead length also increase the surface area and may increase the hose push-on force.

6.8.1 RAMP ANGLE OF BEAD—See Figure 8.

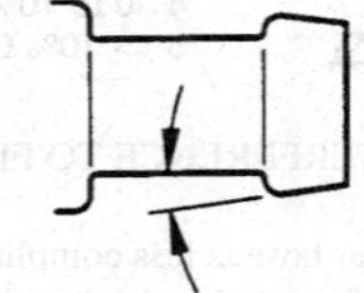

FIGURE 8—HOSE ASSEMBLY—RAMP ANGLE

6.9 Column Strength—For a given material and construction, hoses with a larger wall thickness will have a greater tendency to resist buckling during the installation of the hose. Reinforcement type (i.e., braid, spiral, knit, etc.) and configuration (i.e., angle, loops-needles, etc.) are very important parameters in push-on forces required to install the hose.

6.9.1 COLUMN STRENGTH OF HOSE

a. 1 3.8 mm
b. 2 4.3 mm
c. 3 4.8 mm
d. 4 5.3 mm
e. 5 6.0 mm

6.10 Type of Assembly Lubrication—Lubrication aids in the assembly of the hose to the fitting in some cases. Typically lubricants are used because the interference between the hose and the fitting causes a high installation (push-on) force. Although interference is good for the seal of the joint, the related push-on forces must be kept manageable for production environments. Time and temperature will affect the dissipation of lubricants. Use of any type of nondissipating lubricant may increase the potential for hose blow-off.

6.10.1 LUBRICATION

a. 1 None
b. 2 Water
c. 3 Water and Glycol
d. 4 Partially Dissipating
e. 5 Dissipating

7. Hose Blow-Off

7.1 Pressure—Joints with higher system pressures will have a greater probability of blowing off than joints with lower pressures.

7.1.1 SYSTEM PRESSURE (PSI)

a. 1 > 80 PSI
b. 2 51 to 80 PSI
c. 3 31 to 50 PSI
d. 4 16 to 30 PSI
e. 5 0 to 15 PSI

7.2 Interference Fit—Greater interferences will require higher pressures to blow the hose off of the fitting (assuming no clamp). Proper hose to bead interference along with the proper clamp will give increased resistance to hose blow-off. Reinforcement type (i.e., braid, spiral, knit, etc.) and configuration (i.e., angle, loops-needles, etc.) are very important parameters in push-on forces required to install the hose.

7.2.1 INTERFERENCE FIT TO SHANK DIAMETER—See Figure 9.

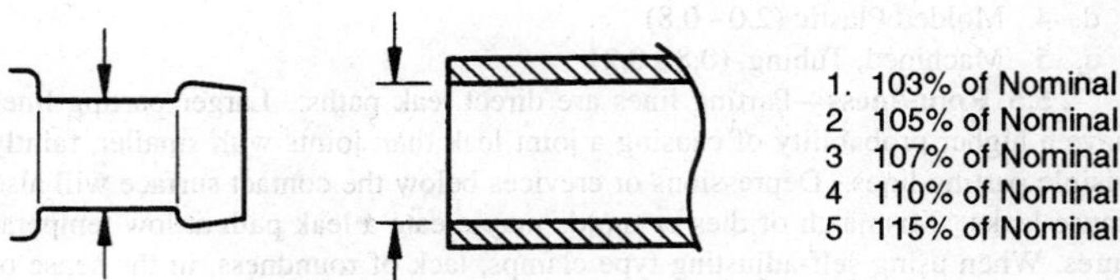

FIGURE 9—HOSE BLOW-OFF—INTERFERENCE FIT

7.3 Bead Diameter—Larger bead heights are better than smaller bead heights in resisting hose blow-off. However, as the bead height increases the force to assemble the joint also increases.

7.3.1 BEAD DIAMETER—See Figure 10.

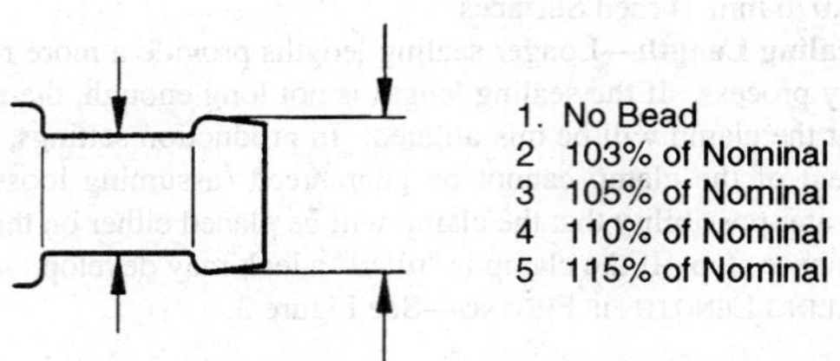

FIGURE 10—HOSE BLOW-OFF—BEAD DIAMETER

7.4 Bead Design (Back Angle)—See Figure 11.

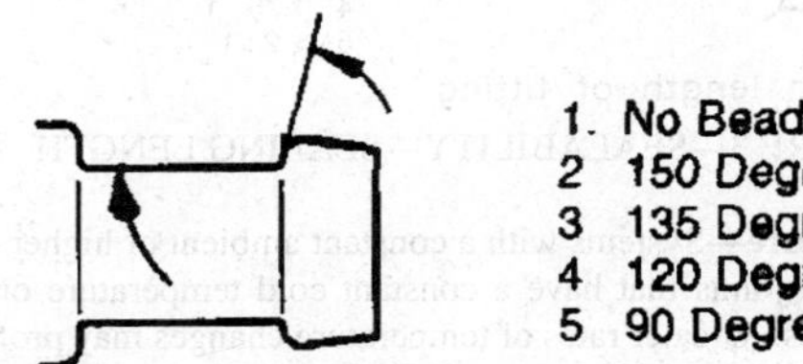

FIGURE 11—HOSE BLOW-OFF—BEAD DESIGN (BACK ANGLE)

7.5 Clamp Type—Fixed diameter clamps give the best resistance to hose blow-off. However, mechanically adjusted fixed diameter clamps will not compensate for the changing dynamics of a hose clamped joint nor will they respond to temperature fluctuations. Variable diameter clamps will not provide the blow-off resistance of fixed diameter clamps.

7.5.1 CLAMP TYPE

a. 1 No Clamp
b. 2 Compensating Diameter—Not manually adjustable
c. 3 Compensating Diameter—Manually adjustable
d. 4 Fixed Diameter—Not adjustable after installation
e. 5 Fixed Diameter—Adjustable after initial installation

7.6 Type of Assembly Lubrication—Lubrication aids in the assembly of the hose to the fitting in some cases. Typically lubricants are used because the interference between the hose and the fitting causes a high installation (push-on) force. Although interference is good for the seal of the joint, the related push-on forces must be kept manageable for production environments. Time and temperature will affect the dissipation of lubricants. Use of any type of nondissipating lubricant may increase the potential for hose blow-off.

7.7 Lubrication

a. 1 Non-Dissipating Lubricant
b. 2 Partially Dissipating Lubricant
c. 3 Water and Glycol
d. 4 Water
e. 5 None

8. Fastening and Assembly of Clamps Over Hose/Fitting

8.1 Number of Different Assembly Tools

a. 1 10 +
b. 2 6 to 10 tools
c. 3 3 to 5 tools
d. 4 2 to 3 tools
e. 5 1 tool

8.2 Operator Sensitivity

a. 1 Clamp position; tool; rpm; torque; >1 oper.
b. 2 Clamp position; tool; rpm; torque
c. 3 Clamp position; tool; rpm
d. 4 Clamp position; tool
e. 5 Clamp positioning or hose/clamp positioning only

8.3 Calibration of Tools—Tools that require calibration are sensitive to assembly variation.

a. 1 Recal., special tool, maintenance
b. 2 Recal. without special tool; not often
c. 3 Recal. with standard tool;
d. 4 No calibration but frequent adjustments
e. 5 No calibration; infrequent adjustments

8.4 Rpm of Air Tools (for screw clamps only)—High rpm tools are sources of assembly variation which may affect joint performance. The speed of the tightening tool will directly impact hose compression. High speed tools tend to shock the joint and fool the tool into shutting off before adequate hose compression is obtained. Lower rpm tools allow more time for the rubber to compress. Every air tool has a specific correlation between air pressure, rpm and torque. Variation in air pressure will cause variation in the dynamic torque reading. Setting the tool to a static torque specification is another source of variation. Static torque specifications for gasketed or soft joints often lead to frequent and unnecessary tool modifications.

a. 1 2500 +
b. 2 1500 to 2500 rpm
c. 3 1000 to 1499 rpm
d. 4 750 to 999 rpm
e. 5 < 750 rpm (enter 5 for nonscrew clamps)

8.5 Stray Assembly Lubricant (Slip Agents)—Assembly lubricants are necessary when interference fit designs are used. However, when stray lubricant comes in contact with the clamp, the joint performance can be compromised. Lubricants are intended to create a boundary layer between the hose and the fitting thus lowering the friction. Lower friction between the hose and the fitting translates directly into lower push-on forces. Problems are created specifically with screw clamps when stray assembly lubricant comes in contact with the screw. The lubricant will lower the friction coefficient between the screw and the band mechanism. The lower friction translates directly into higher forces for a given input torque. In some cases, the clamp will strip and in other cases, the hose will be damaged. Unless engineering specifically designed the joint with that lubricant on the screw clamp, the joint will be compressed differently. As the number of different slip lubricants used in the plant increases, the variation associated with clamping the joint also increases. Better joint designs limit the number of slip lubricants used on hose clamped joints and avoids contact with the clamp (specifically screw clamps).

a. 1 > 3 Slip Agents Used—100% contact
b. 2 2 Slip Agents—Occasional clamp contact
c. 3 2 Slip Agents—No clamp contact
d. 4 Only 1 Slip Agent—Occasional contact
e. 5 Only 1 Slip Agent—No clamp contact

9. Serviceability

9.1 Availability—Special tools will make any clamp or joint harder to service. Readily available tools will aid in the proper service of the joint.

a. 1 Special Order—Dealership
b. 2 Service Garage—Dealership
c. 3 Automotive Supply—Dealership
d. 4 Hardware Store—Dealership
e. 5 Grocery Store—Dealership

9.2 Clamp Reuse—Using different clamps may affect the performance of some joints, therefore using the same production clamp has some advantages.

a. 1 Not reusable
b. 2 Reusable but requires special care
c. 3 Reusable, if not initially damaged
d. 4 Reusable, if not damaged or rusted
e. 5 Very reusable; difficult to damage

9.3 Clamp Availability—Key to servicing a coolant carrying joint is the availability of similar if not identical replacement parts. Parts that can be easily obtained will lead to rapid joint repair.

a. 1 Special Order—Dealership
b. 2 Service Garage—Dealership
c. 3 Automotive Supply—Dealership
d. 4 Hardware Store—Dealership
e. 5 Grocery Store—Dealership

9.4 Clamp Adjustability—Clamps that are not reusable are typically destroyed when the joint requires servicing. In removing the clamp, there is a chance that the hose may be damaged (if the hose is not the reason the joint is being serviced).

Self-adjusting clamps work on the principle of spring rate. Once initially installed, the spring rate of the clamp keeps pressure on the joint after the joint has been thermal cycled and come to equilibrium. Some self-adjusting clamps have limited ranges and work for only very specific joint conditions (i.e., hose diameters, hose wall thickness, bead heights, etc.). By design, self-adjusting clamps are part of a "net joint design". Net joint design incorporates all necessary features to avoid in-process manual adjustments by production operators. Net joint design theory assumes that coolant leaks are caused by poor joint design, not poor component design.

Manually adjustable clamps can make up for joint deficiencies; however, they are very sensitive to proper fastening and assembly tooling. Typically the rate these clamps are adjusted directly impacts the residual pressure on the joint. Manually adjustable clamps, by their nature, are designed for joint repair in production and service repair in the field.

a. 1 Not manually or self-adjusting
b. 2 Adjustable Once Installed—Not reusable due to rust
c. 3 Self-Adjusting—No manual adjustment
d. 4 Self-Adjusting—Allows manual adjustment
e. 5 Manual adjustment

9.5 Clamp Corrosion—There are two primary types of corrosion: cosmetic and structural. Cosmetic corrosion will eventually lead to structural corrosion of carbon steel clamps if not properly protected with a corrosion protection finish. Typically corrosion is associated with poor quality and therefore is undesirable in a coolant joint design. Red rust on carbon steel clamps will make serviceability difficult and may require the clamp to be destroyed upon removal. Low carbon steel clamps that rust within a year (of the end user's driving environment) provide minimal corrosion protection and are poorly designed for clamp corrosion. Alternative corrosion protective finishes should be evaluated in this case.

Clamps that do not exhibit red rust with 10 years are considered excellent from a serviceability perspective. These clamps should be easy to remove if the joint needs to be serviced. All stainless steel clamps (300 series) have the best chance of meeting this requirement. Shipping, handling and assembly tools make it difficult for carbon steel clamps with corrosion protective finishes to meet this specification. If the finish is scratched or scrapped off, corrosion will begin.

a. 1 Red Rust within 1 year
b. 2 No Red Rust within 3 years
c. 3 No Red Rust within 5 years
d. 4 No Red Rust within 7 years
e. 5 No Red Rust within 10 years

TEST METHOD FOR EVALUATING THE SEALING CAPABILITY OF HOSE CONNECTIONS WITH A PVT TEST FACILITY—SAE J1610 JUN2001

SAE Recommended Practice

Report of the SAE Hose/Clamp Performance and Compatibility Subcommittee of the SAE Coolant Hose Committee approved June 1992, revised April 1993 and June 2001. Rationale statement available.

1. Scope—This test method provides a standardized procedure for evaluating the sealing capability of a hose connection or any of the individual components of the connection with a pressure, vibration, and temperature (PVT) test facility. This test method consists of a test procedure which includes vibration and coolant flow (#1) and a similar test procedure specified without vibration or coolant flow (#2). Any test parameters, other than those specified in this SAE Recommended Practice, are to be agreed to by the tester and the requestor.

2. References

2.1 Applicable Publications—The following publications form a part of this specification to the extent specified herein. Unless otherwise indicated, the latest issue of SAE publications shall apply.

2.1.1 SAE PUBLICATIONS—Available from SAE, 400 Commonwealth Drive, Warrendale, PA 15096-0001.

SAE J1231—Formed Tube Ends for Hose Connections and Hose Fittings
SAE J1508—Hose Clamps Specification

3. Materials and Equipment Required—Unless otherwise specified, the components for evaluating a hose connection should include:

3.1 Hose molded to consistent ID and OD and cut to a minimum length of 400 m (16 in).

3.2 Hose connectors per SAE J1231.

3.3 Series Type F hose clamps per SAE J1508.

3.4 PVT test facility.

3.5 An ethylene glycol/water (50/50 volume) mixture with appropriate inhibitors.

4. Preparation of Test Components

4.1 All pertinent information of the components (ID, OD, type of materials, etc.) should be documented before assembly.

4.2 The sealing surfaces should be cleaned of all foreign materials for the test.

4.3 An ethylene glycol/water (50/50 volume) mixture should be used as an assembly aid for the hose and connector unless another lubricant or no lubricant is specified for the test.

4.4 The Type F clamps should be torqued to 3.4 N·m (30 in-lb) unless otherwise specified in the requestor's test requirements.

4.5 After assembly, each hose connection should be evaluated by pressure testing to 345 kPa (50 psi) for a minimum of 60 s unless otherwise specified in the requestor's test requirements.

5. Test Procedure #1—With Vibration and Coolant Flow

5.1 Raise the temperature of the chamber from ambient to 121 °C (250 °F) at an approximate rate of 2 to 4 °C (3 to 7 °F) per minute.

5.1.1 Heat the coolant to 113 °C ± 8 °C (235 °F ± 15 °F).

5.1.2 Flow coolant through hose assembly at an approximate rate of 20 L/min (5 gal/min).

5.1.3 Vibrate one end of the hose assembly at an amplitude of 12.5 mm (0.5 in) and a total displacement of 25 mm (1 in) at 0.5 Hz.

5.1.4 Pressure cycle the hose assembly from 69 kPa ± 14 kPa to 193 kPa ± 14 kPa (10 psi ± 2 psi to 28 psi ± 2 psi) at a rate of 2 to 4 cycles per minute.

5.1.5 Estimated time—1 h.

5.2 Maintain the temperature of the assembly at 104 °C (220 °F) and continue the following test conditions for 1 h.

NOTE—The temperature of the hose assembly must be at a minimum of 104 °C (220 °F) for this 1 h period.

5.2.1 Continue flowing coolant through the hose assembly.

5.2.2 Continue vibrating the hose assembly.

5.2.3 Continue pressure cycling the hose assembly.

5.3 Reduce the chamber temperature to –40 °C (–40 °F) at an approximate rate of 2 to 4 °C (3 to 7 °F) per minute.

5.3.1 Coolant heaters should be off.

5.3.2 Flow of coolant should be off.

5.3.3 Vibration system should be off.

5.3.4 Pressure cycling should be off.

5.3.5 Estimated time—4.5 h.

5.4 Soak the hose assembly at a –40 °C (–40 °F) for 0.5 h.

NOTE—The temperature of the hose assembly must be –32 °C (–25 °F) or lower for this 0.5 h period. The thermocouple should be placed between the hose at interface of tube and fitting and the tube before the clamp.

5.4.1 Coolant heaters should be off.

5.4.2 Flow of coolant should be off.

5.4.3 Vibration system should be off.

5.4.4 Pressure cycling should be off.

5.5 At –40 °C (–40 °F), after the 0.5 h soak, start the following test sequence:

5.5.1 Heat the coolant to 24 °C (75 °F).

5.5.2 Flow coolant through the hose assembly at an approximate rate of 20 L/min max (5 gal/min).

5.5.3 Vibrate the hose assembly at an amplitude of 12.5 mm (0.5 in) and a displacement of 25 mm (1.0 in) at a frequency of 0.5 Hz.

5.5.4 Pressure cycle the hose assembly from 69 kPa ± 14 kPa to 193 kPa ± 14 kPa (10 psi ± 2 psi to 28 psi ± 2 psi) at a rate of 2 to 4 cycles per minute.

5.5.5 Estimated time—0.5 h.

5.6 Raise the chamber temperature from –40 °C (–40 °F) to ambient and repeat the test cycle.

5.6.1 Estimated time to return to ambient—0.5 h.

5.6.2 One test cycle is approximately 8 h.

5.6.3 The end of the testing is 15 complete test cycles, approximately 120 h.

6. Test Procedure #2—Without Vibration or Coolant Flow—The test procedure for this requirement does not include vibration or coolant flow. This procedure is similar to Test Procedure #1 except for the steps specified for flow and vibration.

7. Report—The test report should document the pertinent details of the entire test including the actual test conditions at the time of a failure, if experienced. The waveform used in the pressure cycle is optional and should be stated in the test report. The criteria for a failure should be any visible coolant leakage from the assembly unless otherwise specified in the requestor's test requirements. The reported data should include the date, time, number of hours, number of PVT test cycles, chamber temperature, coolant temperature, coolant pressure, and any related comments.

HOSE CLAMP SPECIFICATIONS—SAE J1508 AUG1997 SAE Standard

Report of the SAE Fasteners Committee approved June 1987. Completely revised by the SAE Hose/Clamp Subcommittee of the SAE Coolant Hose Committee May 1991, and revised June 1993. Completely revised by the SAE Hose/Hose Clamp Performance and Compatibility Committee August 1996, and revised August 1997.

TABLE OF CONTENTS

1. Scope—This SAE Standard covers thirty-two (32) types of clamps most commonly and suitably being used on OEM coolant, fuel, oil, vacuum, and emission systems.

1.1 Purpose—This document is compiled for the specific purpose of describing the basic characteristics and minimum performance requirements recommended by the manufacturers. No application recommendations are intended or implied.

1.1.1 For the benefit of the user in selecting appropriate products for their application, the committee has published ancillary documents that may assist you in this selection. The documents are SAE J1610, SAE J1697, and TMC RP 332.

2. References

2.1 Applicable Publications—The following publications form a part of this specification to the extent specified herein. Unless otherwise indicated, the latest issue of SAE publications shall apply.

2.1.1 SAE Publications—Available from SAE, 400 Commonwealth Drive, Warrendale, PA 15096-0001.

SAE J178—Music Steel Wire and Spring
SAE J402—SAE Numbering System for Wrought or Rolled Steel
SAE J478—Slotted and Recessed Head Screws
SAE J1086—Metals and Alloys in the Unified Numbering System
SAE J1610—Test Method for Evaluating the Sealing Capability of Hose Connections with a PVT Test Facility
SAE J1697—Recommended Practices for Design and Evaluation of Passenger and Light Truck Coolant Hose Clamped Joints

2.1.2 ANSI and IFI Publications—Available from ANSI, 11 West 42nd Street, New York, NY 10036-8002.

ANSI B1.1, 3M—Unified Inch Screw Thread
ANSI B1.3M—Screw Thread Gauging Systems for Dimensional Acceptability
IFI 112—High Performance Thread Rolling Screws

2.1.3 ASTM Publications—Available from ASTM, 100 Barr Harbor Drive, West Conshohocken, PA 19428-2959.

ASTM A 228—Standard Specification for Steel Wire, Music Spring Quality
ASTM A 525—Specification for General Requirements for Steel Sheet, Zinc-Coated (Galvanized) by the Hot-Dip Process
ASTM B 117—Standard Method of Salt Spray (Fog) Testing

2.1.4 Military Publications—Available from Commanding Officer, Naval Publications and Forms Center, 700 Robbins Avenue, Philadelphia, PA 19111.

MIL Std MS21044—Nut, Self-Locking, Hexagon, Regular Height, 250 °F, 125 ksi Ftu and 60 ksi Ftu
MIL Std MS21045—Nut, Self-Locking, Hexagon, Regular Height, 450 °F, 125 ksi Ftu
MIL Std MS39326—Clamp, Spring: Hose (Low Pressure) Type "E"

2.1.5 AISI Publication—Available from the American Iron and Steel Institute, 1101 17th N.W., Suite 1300, Washington, DC 20036.

NOTE—If specifications referred to in this document are no longer available through AISI, cross reference them to the SAE "J" standards in 2.2.1.

AISI—Material Standards

2.1.6 TMC Publications—Available from The Maintenance Council, 2200 Mill Road, Alexandria, VA 22314-5388.

TMC RP 332—Guidelines for Hose, Clamps, and Fittings for Cooling and Charge Air-Cooling Systems

2.2 Related Publications—The following publications are provided for information purposes only and are not a required part of this document.

2.2.1 SAE PUBLICATIONS—Available from SAE, 400 Commonwealth Drive, Warrendale, PA 15096-0001.

SAE J403—Chemical Composition of SAE Alloy Steels
SAE J404—Chemical Composition of SAE Carbon Steels
SAE J405—Chemical Composition of SAE Wrought Stainless Steels
SAE HS3500—Fuel, Oil, Emissions, and Coolant Systems Hose and Hose Clamp Standards Manual

3. Definitions

3.1 Free Torque—The torque value expressed in newton meters (pound inches) when the clamp is tightened four complete revolutions of the screw or nut, while in the free state. This value does not include any break-away effects due to staking or passage of the band ends beyond the screw head.

3.2 Durability Torque—The maximum torque value applied to a clamp without evidence of deformation or excessive wear when tightened once over a steel mandrel.

3.3 Installation Torque—The recommended torque for installation of the clamp. This is generally expressed in terms of 50% to 75% of the rated "Durability Torque" for specific clamps. Installation Torque is sometimes referred to as Application Torque.

3.4 Ultimate Torque—The torque value at which the clamp develops deformation to a degree that it cannot be reused or no longer achieves its intended use.

4. Classification—For ease of handling the various clamp designs and modifications thereof; clamps have been grouped by their basic design and functional characteristics:

4.1 Group #1 (Types "A," "AHH," "B," "D," "C," "F," "FEO," "FE," "HD," "I," "M," "MX," "TB," "SSC," and "G"—Clamps which require torquing a screw or nut for installation.

4.1.1 "A" AND "AHH"—Dual body wires utilizing a machine screw with trunnion nut for the tightening mechanism. Screw position tangential to the diameter. See Figure 1 and Tables 1A and 1B.

4.1.2 "B" AND "D"—Flat band body stock utilizing a machine screw and square nut for the tightening mechanism. Screw position tangential to the diameter. See Figures 2, 3A, and 3B and Tables 2 and 3A, and 3B.

4.1.3 "C"—Flat band body stock utilizing a bridge structure to position the machine screw and nut tightening mechanism perpendicular to the diameter. See Figure 4 and Tables 4A and 4B.

4.1.4 "F," "FEO," "FE," "HD," "I," "M," AND "MX"—A tangential worm drive screw engaging either pierced through slots or embossed threads. Those using pierced through slots are also available in extended band versions to protect soft hose compounds. See Figures 5 to 11 and Tables 5 to 14.

NOTE—"FE" means type "F," embossed slots; "FEO" means type "F," embossed slots with screw offset from centerline of the band.

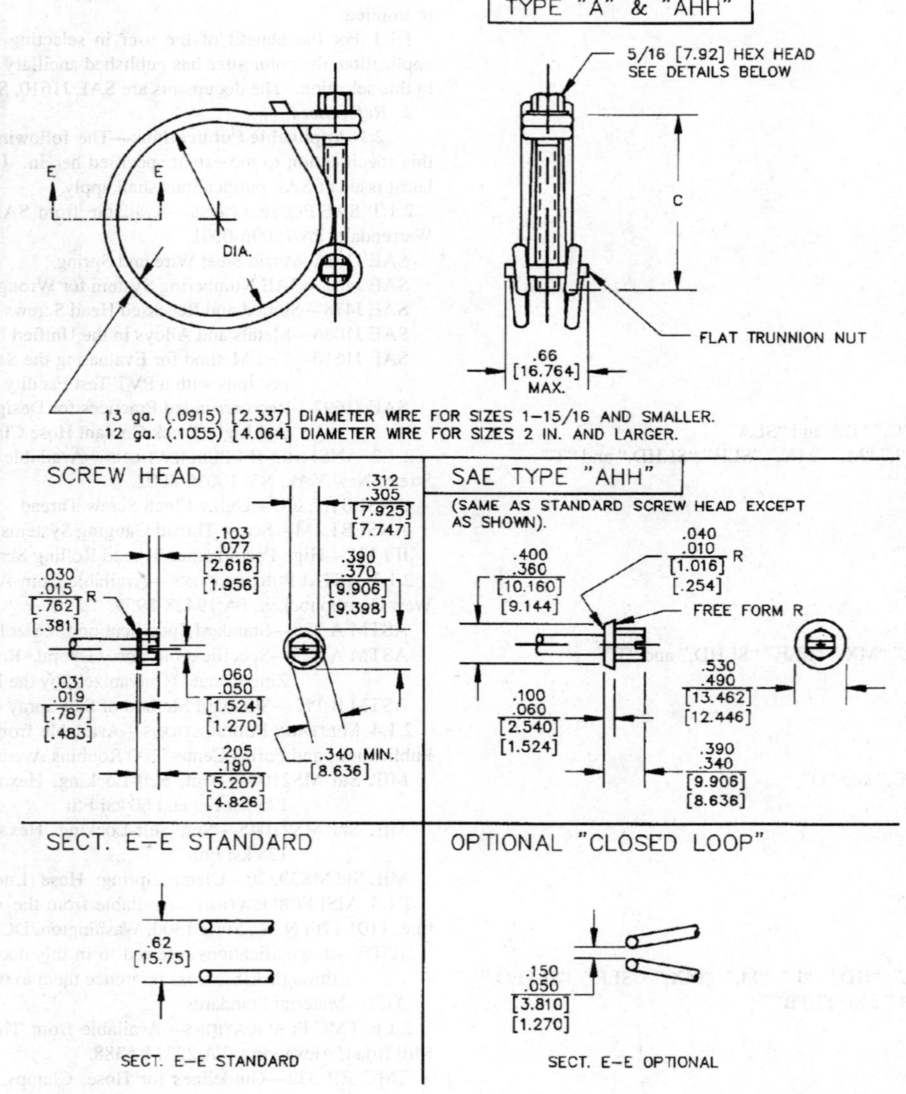

FIGURE 1—BASIC ENVELOPE DRAWING—inch (mm)

TABLE 1A—TYPE "A," "AHH," AND "SLA" (metric)

SAE Size No.	Open Dia. (mm)	Closed Dia. (mm)	Adjust Range (mm)	Screw Length (mm)	SAE Size No.	Open Dia. (mm)	Closed Dia. (mm)	Adjust Range (mm)	Screw Length (mm)
16	12.70	11.18	1.52	21.59		52.07	45.97	6.10	37.59
18	14.22	12.19	2.03	21.59	66	52.32	47.75	4.57	37.59
20	15.75	13.97	1.78	21.59	68	53.85	49.28	4.57	37.59
22	17.53	14.73	2.79	21.59		53.85	48.51	5.33	37.59
24	19.05	16.26	2.79	31.24		54.61	49.28	5.33	37.59
26	20.57	17.53	3.05	31.24	70	55.63	50.04	5.59	37.59
28	22.35	19.05	3.30	31.24		55.88	50.29	5.59	37.59
	23.11	19.81	3.30	31.24		55.88	49.53	6.35	43.94
30	23.88	20.57	3.30	31.24	72	57.15	51.56	5.59	37.59
	24.64	21.34	3.30	31.24		56.39	49.96	6.35	43.94
	25.15	21.34	3.81	31.24		56.39	50.29	6.10	37.59
32	25.40	22.35	3.05	31.24		57.15	51.56	5.69	37.59
	26.16	23.11	3.05	31.24		57.15	50.80	6.35	43.94
34	26.92	23.88	3.05	31.24	74	58.67	53.85	4.83	37.59
	27.69	24.38	3.30	31.24		58.67	52.32	6.35	43.94
	28.20	24.38	3.81	31.24		60.20	54.61	5.59	43.94
36	28.45	24.13	4.32	31.24	76	60.45	55.63	4.83	37.59
	28.96	25.65	3.30	31.24		60.96	55.37	5.59	37.59
	29.21	25.91	3.30	31.24	78	61.98	57.15	4.83	37.59
38	30.23	26.92	3.30	31.24	80	63.50	57.91	5.59	37.59
	30.48	27.18	3.30	31.24	82	65.02	59.44	5.59	37.59
	30.99	27.69	3.30	31.24	84	66.55	61.21	5.33	37.59
40	31.75	27.69	4.06	31.24	86	68.33	62.74	5.59	37.59
	32.51	27.94	4.57	37.59	88	69.85	64.26	5.59	37.59
42	33.27	29.46	3.81	31.24	90	71.37	65.79	5.59	37.59
44	35.05	30.23	4.83	31.24		72.14	66.55	5.59	37.59
46	36.58	31.75	4.83	31.24	92	73.15	67.56	5.59	37.59
48	38.10	33.27	4.83	31.24	94	74.68	69.09	5.59	37.59
50	39.62	35.05	4.57	31.24	96	76.20	70.61	5.59	37.59
	39.62	34.29	5.33	37.59	98	77.72	72.14	5.59	37.59
52	41.15	36.58	4.57	31.24	100	79.25	73.91	5.33	37.59
	41.66	35.31	6.35	37.59	102	81.03	75.44	5.59	37.59
	42.42	36.25	6.10	43.94	104	82.55	76.96	5.59	37.59
	42.67	36.32	6.35	43.94		83.31	77.72	5.59	37.59
54	42.93	38.10	4.83	31.24	106	84.07	78.49	5.59	37.59
	42.93	37.08	5.84	37.59	108	85.85	80.26	5.59	37.59
	43.18	37.34	5.84	37.59	110	87.38	81.79	5.59	37.59
	43.43	37.01	6.35	43.94	112	88.90	82.55	6.35	43.94
	43.69	38.10	5.59	37.59	114	90.42	84.07	6.35	43.94
	44.20	38.10	6.10	43.94	116	91.95	85.85	6.10	43.94
56	44.45	39.62	4.83	37.59	118	93.73	87.38	6.35	43.94
	44.45	38.86	5.59	37.59	120	95.25	88.90	6.35	43.94
	44.70	38.35	6.35	43.94	122	96.77	90.42	6.35	43.94
	45.72	39.62	6.10	37.59	124	98.55	91.95	6.35	43.94
58	45.97	41.15	4.83	37.59	126	100.08	93.73	6.35	43.94
	46.74	41.91	4.83	37.59	128	101.60	95.25	6.35	43.94
	46.74	41.15	5.59	37.59	130	103.12	96.77	6.35	43.94
	46.99	41.15	5.84	37.59	132	104.65	98.55	6.10	43.94
60	47,75	42.93	4.83	37.59	134	106.43	100.08	6.35	43.94
	47.75	41.40	6.35	43.94	136	107.95	101.60	6.35	43.94
	48.01	41.61	6.35	43.94	138	109.47	103.12	6.35	43.94
	48.51	43.69	4.83	37.59	140	111.25	104.65	6.60	43.94
	48.51	42.93	5.59	37.59	142	112.78	106.43	6.35	43.94
62	49.28	44.45	4.83	37.59	144	114.30	107.95	6.35	43.94
	49.28	43.69	5.59	37.59	146	115.82	109.47	6.35	43.94
	49.28	42.93	6.35	43.94	148	117.35	111.25	6.10	43.94
	49.78	43.31	6.35	43.94	150	119.13	112.78	6.35	43.94
	49.78	43.94	5.84	37.59	152	120.65	114.30	6.35	43.94
	50.29	43.94	6.35	43.94	154	122.17	115.82	6.35	43.94
64	50.80	45.97	4.83	37.59	156	123.95	117.35	6.60	43.94
	50.80	45.21	5.59	37.59	158	125.48	119.13	6.35	43.94
	50.80	44.45	6.35	43.94	160	127.00	120.65	6.35	43.94
	51.56	45.47	6.10	43.94					

TABLE 1B—TYPE "A," "AHH," AND "SLA" (English)

SAE Size No.	Open Dia. in	Closed Dia. in	Adjust Range in	Screw Length in
16	0.50	0.440	0.06	0.85
18	0.56	0.480	0.08	0.85
20	0.62	0.550	0.07	0.85
22	0.69	0.580	0.11	0.85
24	0.75	0.640	0.11	1.23
26	0.81	0.690	0.12	1.23
28	0.88	0.750	0.13	1.23
	0.91	0.780	0.13	1.23
30	0.94	0.810	0.13	1.23
	0.97	0.840	0.13	1.23
	0.99	0.840	0.15	1.23
32	1.00	0.880	0.12	1.23
	1.03	0.910	0.12	1.23
34	1.06	0.940	0.12	1.23
	1.09	0.960	0.13	1.23
	1.11	0.960	0.15	1.23
36	1.12	0.950	0.17	1.23
	1.14	1.010	0.13	1.23
	1.15	1.020	0.13	1.23
38	1.19	1.060	0.13	1.23
	1.20	1.070	0.13	1.23
	1.22	1.090	0.13	1.23
40	1.25	1.090	0.16	1.23
	1.28	1.100	0.18	1.48
42	1.31	1.160	0.15	1.23
44	1.38	1.190	0.19	1.23
46	1.44	1.250	0.19	1.23
48	1.50	1.310	0.19	1.23
50	1.56	1.380	0.18	1.23
	1.56	1.350	0.21	1.48
52	1.62	1.440	0.18	1.23
	1.64	1.390	0.25	1.48
	1.67	1.427	0.24	1.73
	1.68	1.430	0.25	1.73
54	1.69	1.500	0.19	1.23
	1.69	1.460	0.23	1.48
	1.70	1.470	0.23	1.48
	1.71	1.457	0.25	1.73
	1.72	1.500	0.22	1.48
	1.74	1.500	0.24	1.73
56	1.75	1.560	0.19	1.48
	1.75	1.530	0.22	1.48
	1.76	1.510	0.25	1.73
	1.80	1.560	0.24	1.48
58	1.81	1.620	0.19	1.48
	1.84	1.650	0.19	1.48
	1.84	1.620	0.22	1.48
	1.85	1.620	0.23	1.48
60	1.88	1.690	0.19	1.48
	1.88	1.630	0.25	1.73
	1.89	1.638	0.25	1.73
	1.91	1.720	0.19	1.48
	1.91	1.690	0.22	1.48
62	1.94	1.750	0.19	1.48
	1.94	1.720	0.22	1.48
	1.94	1.690	0.25	1.73
	1.96	1.705	0.25	1.73
	1.96	1.730	0.23	1.48
	1.98	1.730	0.25	1.73
64	2.00	1.810	0.19	1.48
	2.00	1.780	0.22	1.48
	2.00	1.750	0.25	1.73
	2.03	1.790	0.24	1.73

SAE Size in	Open Dia. in	Closed Dia. in	Adjust Range in	Screw Length in
	2.05	1.810	0.24	1.48
66	2.06	1.880	0.18	1.48
68	2.12	1.940	0.18	1.48
	2.12	1.910	0.21	1.48
	2.15	1.940	0.21	1.48
70	2.19	1.970	0.22	1.48
	2.20	1.980	0.22	1.48
	2.20	1.950	0.25	1.73
72	2.22	1.967	0.25	1.73
	2.22	1.980	0.24	1.48
	2.25	2.030	0.22	1.48
	2.25	2.030	0.22	1.48
	2.25	2.000	0.25	1.73
74	2.31	2.120	0.19	1.48
	2.31	2.060	0.25	1.73
	2.37	2.150	0.22	1.48
76	2.38	2.190	0.19	1.48
	2.40	2.180	0.22	1.48
78	2.44	2.250	0.19	1.48
80	2.50	2.280	0.22	1.48
82	2.56	2.340	0.22	1.48
84	2.62	2.410	0.21	1.48
86	2.69	2.470	0.22	1.48
88	2.75	2.530	0.22	1.48
90	2.81	2.590	0.22	1.48
	2.84	2.620	0.22	1.48
92	2.88	2.660	0.22	1.48
94	2.94	2.720	0.22	1.48
96	3.00	2.780	0.22	1.48
98	3.06	2.840	0.22	1.48
100	3.12	2.910	0.21	1.48
102	3.19	2.970	0.22	1.48
104	3.25	3.030	0.22	1.48
	3.28	3.060	0.22	1.48
106	3.31	3.090	0.22	1.48
108	3.38	3.160	0.22	1.48
110	3.44	3.220	0.22	1.48
112	3.50	3.250	0.25	1.73
114	3.56	3.310	0.25	1.73
116	3.62	3.380	0.24	1.73
118	3.69	3.440	0.25	1.73
120	3.75	3.500	0.25	1.73
122	3.81	3.560	0.25	1.73
124	3.88	3.620	0.26	1.73
126	3.94	3.690	0.25	1.73
128	4.00	3.750	0.25	1.73
130	4.06	3.810	0.25	1.73
132	4.12	3.880	0.24	1.73
134	4.19	3.940	0.25	1.73
136	4.25	4.000	0.25	1.73
138	4.31	4.060	0.25	1.73
140	4.38	4.120	0.26	1.73
142	4.44	4.190	0.25	1.73
144	4.50	4.250	0.25	1.73
146	4.56	4.310	0.25	1.73
148	4.62	4.380	0.24	1.73
150	4.69	4.440	0.25	1.73
152	4.75	4.500	0.25	1.73
154	4.81	4.560	0.25	1.73
156	4.88	4.620	0.26	1.73
158	4.94	4.690	0.25	1.73
160	5.00	4.750	0.25	1.73

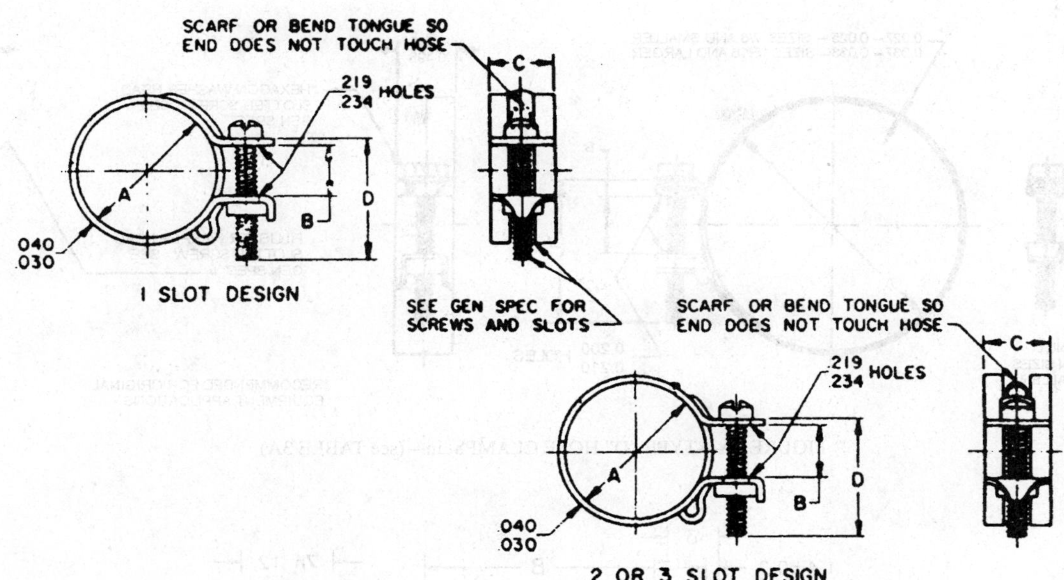

FIGURE 2—DIMENSIONS OF TYPE "B" HOSE CLAMPS

TABLE 2—DIMENSIONS OF TYPE "B" HOSE CLAMPS, in

SAE Size No.	A Dia. Nom	A Dia. Open	A Dia. Closed	B(1) Gap	C Band Width ±0.01	D Screw Length Min	SAE Size No.	A Dia. Nom	A Dia. Open	A Dia. Closed	B(1) Gap	C Band Width ±0.01	D Screw Length Min
18	0.50	0.58	0.44	0.38	0.50(2)	1.00	58	1.75	1.83	1.64	0.50	0.623	1.12
20	0.56	0.64	0.48	0.38	0.50(2)	1.00	60	1.81	1.89	1.70	0.50	0.623	1.12
22	0.62	0.70	0.55	0.38	0.50(2)	1.00	62	1.88	1.95	1.77	0.50	0.623	1.12
24	0.69	0.77	0.61	0.38	0.50(2)	1.00	64	1.94	2.02	1.83	0.50	0.623	1.12
26	0.75	0.83	0.67	0.38	0.50(2)	1.00	67	2.03	2.11	1.92	0.50	0.623	1.12
28	0.81	0.89	0.73	0.38	0.50(2)	1.00							
30	0.88	0.95	0.80	0.38	0.50(2)	1.00	70	2.12	2.20	2.02	0.50	0.623	1.12
32	0.94	1.02	0.86	0.38	0.50(2)	1.00	72	2.19	2.27	2.08	0.50	0.623	1.12
35	1.03	1.11	0.95	0.38	0.50(2)	1.00	75	2.28	2.36	2.17	0.50	0.623	1.12
36	1.06	1.14	0.98	0.38	0.50(2)	1.00	79	2.38	2.48	2.27	0.50	0.623	1.25
38	1.12	1.20	1.02	0.38	0.50(2)	1.12	83	2.50	2.61	2.39	0.50	0.623	1.25
40	1.19	1.27	1.08	0.50	0.50(2)	1.12	88	2.62	2.75	2.52	0.50	0.623	1.25
42	1.25	1.33	1.14	0.50	0.62(3)	1.12	92	2.75	2.88	2.64	0.50	0.623	1.25
44	1.31	1.39	1.20	0.50	0.62(3)	1.12	96	2.88	3.00	2.77	0.50	0.623	1.25
46	1.38	1.45	1.27	0.50	0.62(3)	1.12	100	3.00	3.12	2.89	0.50	0.62	1.25
48	1.44	1.52	1.33	0.50	0.62(3)	1.12	104	3.12	3.25	3.02	0.50	0.62	1.25
50	1.50	1.58	1.39	0.50	0.62(3)	1.12	108	3.25	3.38	3.14	0.50	0.62	1.25
52	1.56	1.64	1.45	0.50	0.62(3)	1.12	112	3.38	3.50	3.27	0.50	0.62	1.25
54	1.62	1.70	1.52	0.50	0.62(3)	1.12	122	3.56	3.81	3.42	0.62	0.75	1.38
56	1.69	1.77	1.58	0.50	0.62(3)	1.12							

1. Reference dimension. When gap is at value tabulated, clamp diameter shall approximate the nominal diameter.
2. 0.62 IN WIDTH OPTIONAL WITH USER.
3. 0.50 IN WIDTH OPTIONAL WITH USER.

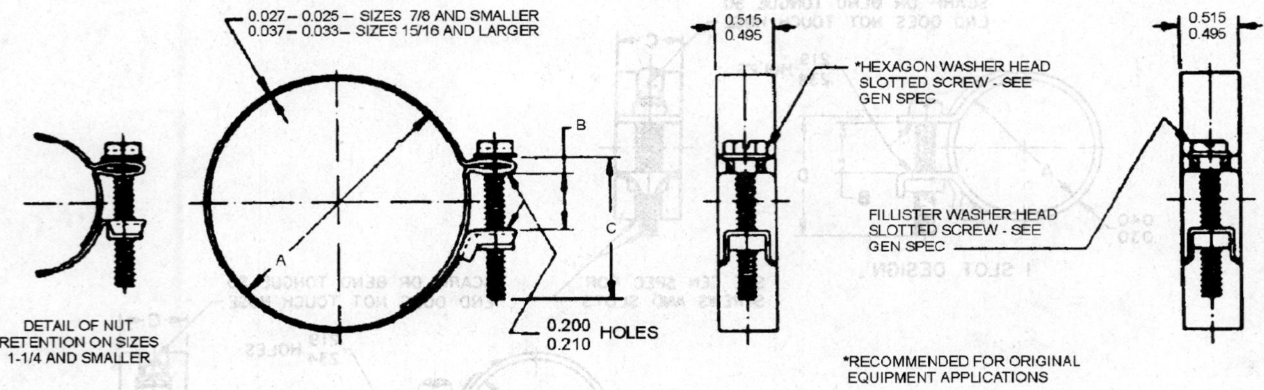

FIGURE 3A—TYPE "D" HOSE CLAMPS, in—(see TABLE 3A)

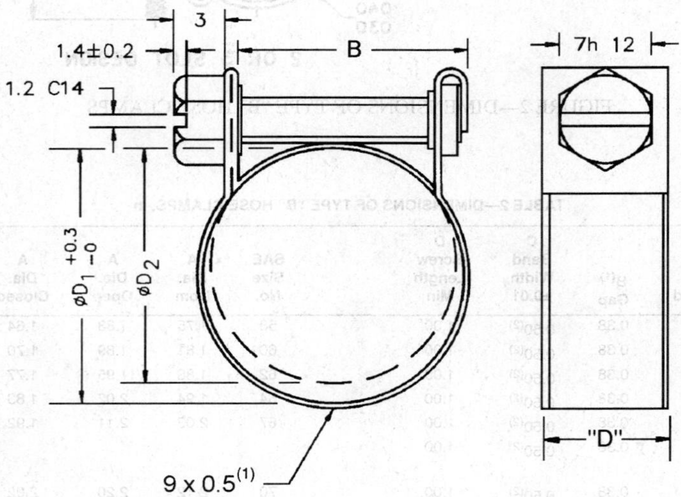

(1) t = BAND THICKNESS = [0.5 mm] 0.02 in

FIGURE 3B—TYPE "D"—(see TABLE 3B)

TABLE 3A—DIMENSIONS OF TYPE "D" HOSE CLAMPS, in—(See Figure 3A)

SAE Size No.	A Dia. Nom	A Dia. Open	A Dia. Closed	B Gap	C Screw Length Min	SAE Size No.	A Dia. Nom	A Dia. Open	A Dia. Closed	B Gap	C Screw Length Min
23	0.62	0.72	0.53	0.38	1.12	119	3.62	3.72	3.41	0.75	1.50
25	0.69	0.78	0.59	0.38	1.12	121	3.69	3.78	3.47	0.75	1.50
27	0.75	0.84	0.66	0.38	1.12	123	3.75	3.84	3.53	0.75	1.50
29	0.81	0.91	0.72	0.38	1.12	125	3.81	3.91	3.59	0.75	1.50
31	0.88	0.97	0.78	0.38	1.12	127	3.88	3.97	3.66	0.75	1.50
33	0.94	1.03	0.84	0.38	1.12	129	3.94	4.03	3.72	0.75	1.50
35	1.00	1.09	0.91	0.38	1.12	131	4.00	4.09	3.78	0.75	1.50
37	1.06	1.16	0.97	0.38	1.12	133	4.06	4.16	3.84	0.75	1.50
39	1.12	1.22	1.03	0.38	1.12	135	4.12	4.22	3.91	0.75	1.50
41	1.19	1.28	1.06	0.50	1.25	137	4.19	4.28	3.97	0.75	1.50
43	1.25	1.34	1.12	0.50	1.25	139	4.25	4.34	4.03	0.75	1.50
45	1.31	1.41	1.19	0.50	1.25	141	4.31	4.41	4.09	0.75	1.50
47	1.38	1.47	1.25	0.50	1.25	143	4.38	4.47	4.16	0.75	1.50
49	1.44	1.53	1.31	0.50	1.25	145	4.44	4.53	4.22	0.75	1.50
51	1.50	1.59	1.38	0.50	1.25	147	4.50	4.59	4.28	0.75	1.50
53	1.56	1.66	1.44	0.50	1.25	149	4.56	4.66	4.34	0.75	1.50
55	1.62	1.72	1.50	0.50	1.25	151	4.62	4.72	4.41	0.75	1.50
57	1.69	1.78	1.56	0.50	1.25	153	4.69	4.78	4.47	0.75	1.50

TABLE 3A—DIMENSIONS OF TYPE "D" HOSE CLAMPS, in—(See Figure 3A) (continued)

SAE Size No.	A Dia. Nom	A Dia. Open	A Dia. Closed	B Gap	C Screw Length Min	SAE Size No.	A Dia. Nom	A Dia. Open	A Dia. Closed	B Gap	C Screw Length Min
59	1.75	1.84	1.62	0.50	1.25	155	4.75	4.84	4.53	0.75	1.50
61	1.81	1.91	1.69	0.50	1.25	157	4.81	4.91	4.59	0.75	1.50
63	1.88	1.97	1.75	0.50	1.25	159	4.88	4.97	4.66	0.75	1.50
65	1.94	2.03	1.81	0.50	1.25	161	4.94	5.03	4.72	0.75	1.50
67	2.00	2.09	1.88	0.50	1.25	163	5.00	5.09	4.78	0.75	1.50
69	2.06	2.16	1.94	0.50	1.25	165	5.06	5.16	4.84	0.75	1.50
71	2.12	2.22	2.00	0.50	1.25	167	5.12	5.22	4.91	0.75	1.50
73	2.19	2.28	2.06	0.50	1.25	169	5.19	5.28	4.97	0.75	1.50
75	2.25	2.34	2.12	0.50	1.25	171	5.25	5.34	5.03	0.75	1.50
77	2.31	2.41	2.19	0.50	1.25	173	5.31	5.41	5.09	0.75	1.50
79	2.38	2.47	2.22	0.62	1.38	175	5.38	5.47	5.16	0.75	1.50
81	2.44	2.53	2.28	0.62	1.38	177	5.44	5.53	5.22	0.75	1.50
83	2.50	2.59	2.34	0.62	1.38	179	5.50	5.59	5.28	0.75	1.50
85	2.56	2.66	2.41	0.62	1.38	181	5.56	5.66	5.34	0.75	1.50
87	2.62	2.72	2.47	0.62	1.38	183	5.62	5.72	5.41	0.75	1.50
89	2.69	2.78	2.53	0.62	1.38	185	5.69	5.78	5.47	0.75	1.50
91	2.75	2.84	2.59	0.62	1.38	187	5.75	5.84	5.53	0.75	1.50
93	2.81	2.91	2.66	0.62	1.38	189	5.81	5.91	5.59	0.75	1.50
95	2.88	2.97	2.72	0.62	1.38	191	5.88	5.97	5.66	0.75	1.50
97	2.94	3.03	2.78	0.62	1.38	193	5.94	6.03	5.72	0.75	1.50
99	3.00	3.09	2.84	0.62	1.38	195	6.00	6.09	5.78	0.75	1.50
101	3.06	3.16	2.91	0.62	1.38						
103	3.12	3.22	2.97	0.62	1.38						
105	3.19	3.28	3.03	0.62	1.38						
107	3.25	3.34	3.09	0.62	1.38						
109	3.31	3.41	3.16	0.62	1.38						
111	3.38	3.47	3.22	0.62	1.38						
113	3.44	3.53	3.28	0.62	1.38						
115	3.50	3.59	3.34	0.62	1.38						
117	3.56	3.66	3.34	0.75	1.50						

TABLE 3B—TYPE "D"—(See Figure 3B)

Manufacturers Designation for SAE Size (1)	Diameter Supplied in mm	Diameter Supplied in in	Clamping Range mm	Clamping Range in	Clamping Range Decimals	B mm	B in	D mm	D in	Recommended Tightening Torque (N·m)
8	8.3	0.326	6.0 - 8.3	15/64 - 21/64	0.234 - 0.328	13.1	33/64	9.1	23/64	1.5
9	9.3	0.366	7.0 - 9.5	9/32 - 3/8	0.276 - 0.375	13.1	33/64	9.1	23/64	1.5
10	10.3	0.405	8.0 - 10.3	5/16 - 13.32	0.315 - 0.406	13.1	33/64	9.1	23/64	1.5
11	11.3	0.444	9.0 - 11.5	23/64 - 29/64	0.358 - 0.453	13.1	33/64	9.1	23/64	1.5
12	12.3	0.484	10.0 - 12.3	25/64 - 31/64	0.358 - 0.453	15.9	20/32	9.1	23/64	1.5
13	13.3	0.523	11.0 - 13.5	7/16 - 17/32	0.433 - 0.531	15.9	20/32	9.1	23/64	1.5
14	14.3	0.562	12.0 - 14.3	15/32 - 9/16	0.479 - 0.562	15.9	20/32	9.1	23/64	1.5
15	15.3	0.602	13.0 - 15.5	33/64 - 39/64	0.512 - 0.609	15.9	20/32	9.1	23/64	1.5
16	16.3	0.641	14.0 - 16.3	35/64 - 41/64	0.551 - 0.640	15.9	20/32	9.1	23/64	1.5
17	17.3	0.681	15.0 - 17.5	19/32 - 11/16	0.590 - 0.685	15.9	20/32	9.1	23/64	1.5

1. • = In the absence of an appropriate SAE size

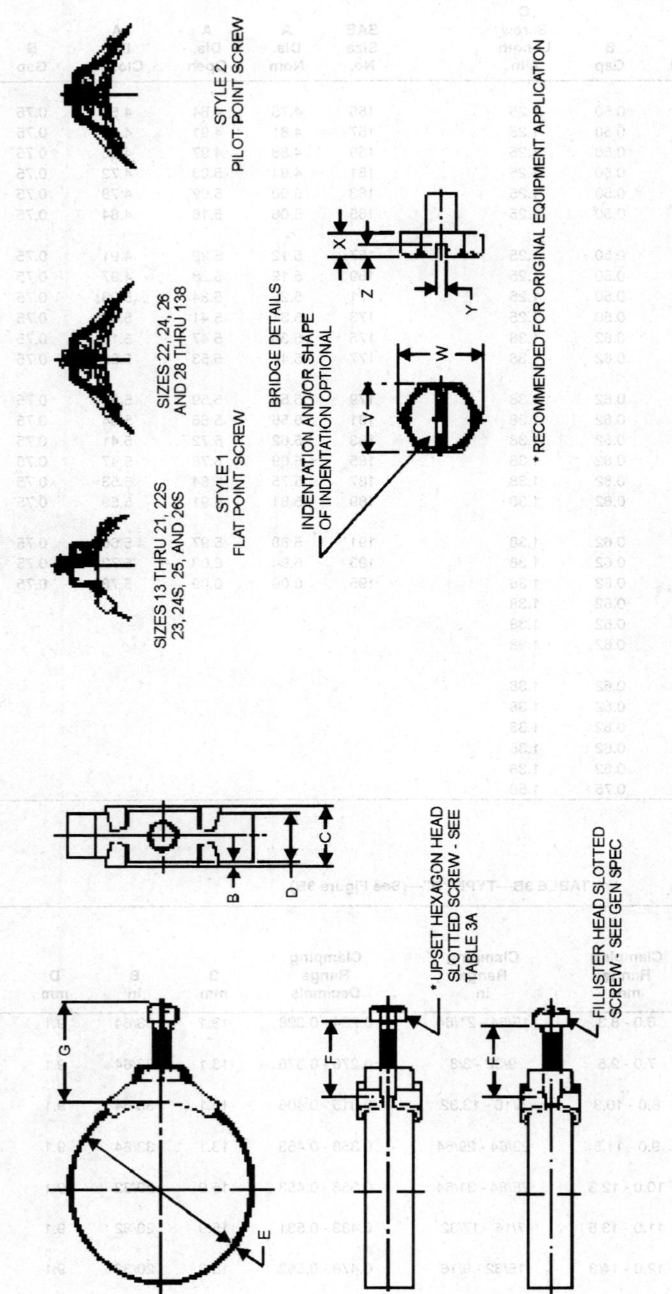

Torque required to draw band through bridge on free clamp shall not exceed 4 lb-in for sizes having 6-32 screws, 8 lb-in for sizes having 10-24 screws, and 10 lb-in for sizes having 12-24 screws.

It is recommended that Type "C" Clamps not be tightened beyond maximum torques of 9 lb-in for sizes having 6-32 screws, 22 lb-in for sizes having 10-24 screws, and 30 lb-in for sizes having 12-24 screws.

FIGURE 4—TYPE "C" HOSE CLAMPS

TABLE 4A—DIMENSIONS OF TYPE "C" HOSE CLAMPS, in

SAE Size No.[1]	A Diameter Open	A Diameter Closed	B Bridge Stock Thick-ness ±0.002	C[2] Bridge Width Max	D Band Width ±0.010	E[3] Band Thick-ness ±0.001	F Screw Size and Length	G[2] Height Over Screw Max
13	0.40	0.34	0.035	0.41	0.281	0.010	6-32 x 0.50	0.64
14	0.43	0.37	0.035	0.41	0.281	0.010	6-32 x 0.50	0.64
15	0.46	0.40	0.035	0.41	0.281	0.010	6-32 x 0.50	0.64
16	0.50	0.37	0.035	0.41	0.281	0.010	6-32 x 0.50	0.64
17	0.53	0.40	0.035	0.41	0.281	0.010	6-32 x 0.50	0.64
18	0.56	0.43	0.035	0.41	0.281	0.010	6-32 x 0.50	0.64
19	0.59	0.46	0.035	0.41	0.281	0.010	6-32 x 0.50	0.64
20	0.62	0.50	0.035	0.41	0.281	0.010	6-32 x 0.50	0.64
21	0.65	0.53	0.035	0.41	0.281	0.010	6-32 x 0.50	0.64
22	0.69	0.38	0.050	0.64	0.438	0.017	10-24 x 0.88	1.13
22N	0.69	0.56	0.035	0.41	0.281	0.010	6-32 x 0.50	0.64
23	0.71	0.59	0.035	0.41	0.281	0.010	6-32 x 0.50	0.64
24	0.75	0.44	0.050	0.64	0.438	0.017	10-24 x 0.88	1.13
24N	0.75	0.62	0.035	0.41	0.281	0.010	6-32 x 0.50	0.64
25	0.78	0.66	0.035	0.41	0.281	0.010	6-32 x 0.50	0.64
26	0.81	0.50	0.050	0.64	0.438	0.017	10-24 x 0.88	1.13
26N	0.81	0.69	0.035	0.41	0.281	0.010	6-32 x 0.50	0.64
28	0.88	0.56	0.050	0.64	0.438	0.017	10-24 x 0.88	1.13
30	0.94	0.62	0.050	0.72	0.505	0.017	12-24 x 0.88	1.13
30N	0.94	0.62	0.050	0.64	0.438	0.017	10-24 x 0.88	1.13
32	1.00	0.69	0.050	0.72	0.505	0.017	12-24 x 0.88	1.13
32N	1.00	0.69	0.050	0.64	0.438	0.017	10-24 x 0.88	1.13
34	1.06	0.75	0.050	0.72	0.505	0.020	12-24 x 0.88	1.13
34N	1.06	0.75	0.050	0.64	0.438	0.017	10-24 x 0.88	1.13
36	1.12	0.81	0.050	0.72	0.505	0.020	12-24 x 0.88	1.13
36N	1.12	0.81	0.050	0.64	0.438	0.017	10-24 x 0.88	1.13
38	1.19	0.88	0.062	0.72	0.505	0.020	12-24 x 0.88	1.13
38N	1.19	0.88	0.050	0.64	0.438	0.017	10-24 x 0.88	1.13
40	1.25	0.94	0.062	0.72	0.505	0.020	12-24 x 0.88	1.13
40N	1.25	0.94	0.050	0.64	0.438	0.017	10-24 x 0.88	1.13
42	1.31	1.00	0.062	0.72	0.505	0.020	12-24 x 0.88	1.13
42N	1.31	1.00	0.050	0.64	0.438	0.017	10-24 x 0.88	1.13
44	1.38	1.06	0.062	0.72	0.505	0.020	12-24 x 0.88	1.13
44N	1.38	1.06	0.050	0.64	0.438	0.017	10-24 x 0.88	1.13
46	1.44	1.12	0.062	0.72	0.505	0.020	12-24 x 0.88	1.13
46N	1.44	1.12	0.050	0.64	0.438	0.017	10-24 x 0.88	1.13
48	1.50	1.19	0.062	0.72	0.505	0.020	12-24 x 0.88	1.13
48N	1.50	1.19	0.050	0.64	0.438	0.017	10-24 x 0.88	1.13
50	1.56	1.25	0.062	0.72	0.505	0.020	12-24 x 0.88	1.13
52	1.62	1.31	0.062	0.72	0.505	0.020	12-24 x 0.88	1.13
54	1.69	1.38	0.62	0.72	0.505	0.020	12-24 x 1.00	1.13
56	1.75	1.44	0.62	0.72	0.505	0.020	12-24 x 1.00	1.13
58	1.81	1.50	0.62	0.72	0.505	0.020	12-24 x 1.00	1.13
60	1.88	1.56	0.62	0.72	0.505	0.020	12-24 x 1.00	1.13
62	1.94	1.62	0.62	0.72	0.505	0.020	12-24 x 1.00	1.13
64	2.00	1.69	0.62	0.72	0.505	0.020	12-24 x 0.88	1.13
66	2.06	1.69	0.62	0.72	0.505	0.020	12-24 x 0.88	1.25
68	2.12	1.75	0.62	0.72	0.505	0.020	12-24 x 0.88	1.25
70	2.19	1.81	0.62	0.72	0.505	0.020	12-24 x 0.88	1.25
72	2.25	1.88	0.62	0.72	0.505	0.020	12-24 x 0.88	1.25
74	2.31	1.94	0.62	0.72	0.505	0.020	12-24 x 0.88	1.25
76	2.38	2.00	0.62	0.72	0.505	0.020	12-24 x 1.00	1.25
78	2.44	2.06	0.62	0.72	0.505	0.020	12-24 x 1.00	1.25
80	2.50	2.12	0.62	0.72	0.505	0.020	12-24 x 1.00	1.25
82	2.56	2.19	0.62	0.72	0.505	0.020	12-24 x 1.00	1.25
84	2.62	2.25	0.62	0.72	0.505	0.020	12-24 x 1.00	1.25
86	2.69	2.31	0.62	0.72	0.505	0.020	12-24 x 1.00	1.25
88	2.75	2.38	0.62	0.72	0.505	0.020	12-24 x 1.00	1.25
90	2.81	2.44	0.62	0.72	0.505	0.020	12-24 x 1.00	1.25
92	2.88	2.50	0.62	0.72	0.505	0.020	12-24 x 1.00	1.25
94	2.94	2.56	0.62	0.72	0.505	0.020	12-24 x 1.00	1.25
96	3.00	2.62	0.62	0.72	0.505	0.020	12-24 x 1.00	1.25
100	3.12	2.75	0.62	0.72	0.505	0.020	12-24 x 1.00	1.25
104	3.25	2.88	0.62	0.72	0.505	0.020	12-24 x 1.00	1.25
110	3.44	3.06	0.62	0.72	0.505	0.020	12-24 x 1.00	1.25

TABLE 4A—DIMENSIONS OF TYPE "C" HOSE CLAMPS, in (continued)

SAE Size No.[(1)]	A Diameter Open	A Diameter Closed	B Bridge Stock Thick-ness ±0.002	C[(2)] Bridge Width Max	D Band Width ±0.010	E[(3)] Band Thick-ness ±0.001	F Screw Size and Length	G[(2)] Height Over Screw Max
114	3.56	3.19	0.62	0.72	0.505	0.020	12-24 x 1.00	1.25
118	3.69	3.31	0.62	0.72	0.505	0.020	12-24 x 1.00	1.25
138	4.31	3.94	0.62	0.72	0.505	0.020	12-24 x 1.00	1.25
54	1.69	1.38	0.62	0.72	0.505	0.020	12-24 x 1.00	1.13
56	1.75	1.44	0.62	0.72	0.505	0.020	12-24 x 1.00	1.13

1. The N suffix applied to SAE size numbers designates the smaller series clamp design where sizes overlap in two clamp designs.
2. Reference dimension for clearance purposes only.
3. For size numbers 30 – 138, clamps having 0.020 tabulated band thickness are also available with 0.018 – 0.016 and 0.027 – 0.025 band thickness where so specified by user.

TABLE 4B—DIMENSION OF HEXAGON SCREW HEADS, in

Screw Size	V Across Flats Max	V Across Flats Min	W Across Corners Mn	X Head Height Max	X Head Height Min	Y Slot Width Max	Y Slot Width Min	Z Slot Depth Max	Z Slot Depth Min
6	0.250	0.244	0.272	0.080	0.067	0.048	0.039	0.046	0.033
10	0.375	0.367	0.409	0.145	0.120	0.060	0.050	0.072	0.057
12	0.375	0.367	0.409	0.155	0.139	0.067	0.056	0.077	0.093

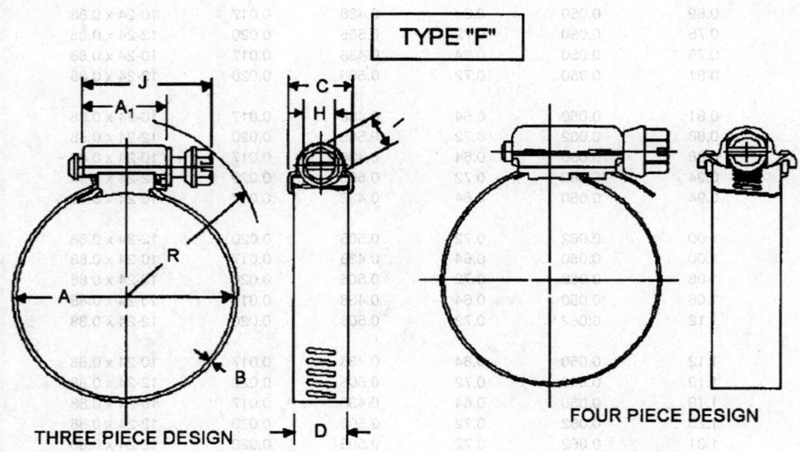

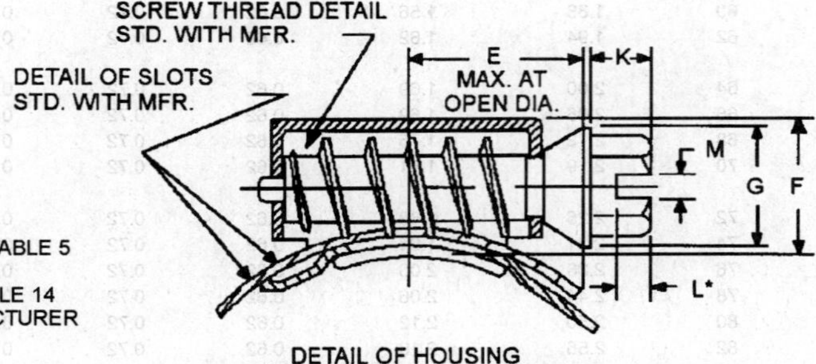

FOR DIMENSIONS RELATIVE TO THIS STYLE, REFER TO TABLE 5 TYPE "F," "I," AND "M"
FOR H.D. STYLE HOUSING DIMENSIONS, REFER TO TABLE 14
NOTE: SCREW HOUSING DESIGN MAY VARY BY MANUFACTURER

FIGURE 5—TYPE "F," "I," AND "M"

TABLE 5—DIMENSIONS OF TYPE "F," "I," AND "M" CLAMP

	Dimension	Type F mm	Type F in	Type I mm	Type I in	Type M mm	Type M in
A[(1)]	HSG Length (Ref.)	19.30	0.76	16.26	0.64	10.668	0.42
B	Thickness	0.533/0.787	0.021/0.031	0.483/0.762	0.019/0.030	0.483/0.660	0.019/0.026
C	HSG Width (Ref.)	20.570	0.81	13.462	0.53	15.240	0.60
D	Bandwidth	12.57/14.45	0.495/0.569	10.033/11.227	0.395/0.442	7.747/8.255	0.305/0.325
E	Max. at Open Diameter	19.050	0.75	12.700	0.50	11.176	0.44
F	Height (Ref.	14.450	0.56	10.16	0.40	9.652	0.38
G	Collar Diameter	9.398/10.79	0.370/0.425	7.493/9.525	0.295/0.375		(1)
H	Across Flats	7.747/7.925	0.305/0.312	6.198/6.350	0.244/0.250	6.198/6.350	0.244/0.250
I	Across Corners (Min.)	8.636	0.340	6.858	0.270	6.858	0.270
J	LG. of Screw (Max.)	34.29	1.35	28.702	1.13	20.32	0.80
K	Hex Height	3.556/6.350	0.140/0.250	3.556/4.445	0.140/0.175	3.810/4.699	0.150/0.185
L	Slot Depth	1.956/3.048	0.077/0.120	1.321/2.667	0.052/0.105	1.321/2.667	0.052/0.105
M	Slot Width	1.422/1.936	0.056/0.076	1.067/1.524	0.042/0.060	1.067/1.524	0.042/0.060

1. Type "M" clamps do not have collars as standard. See Style 6.

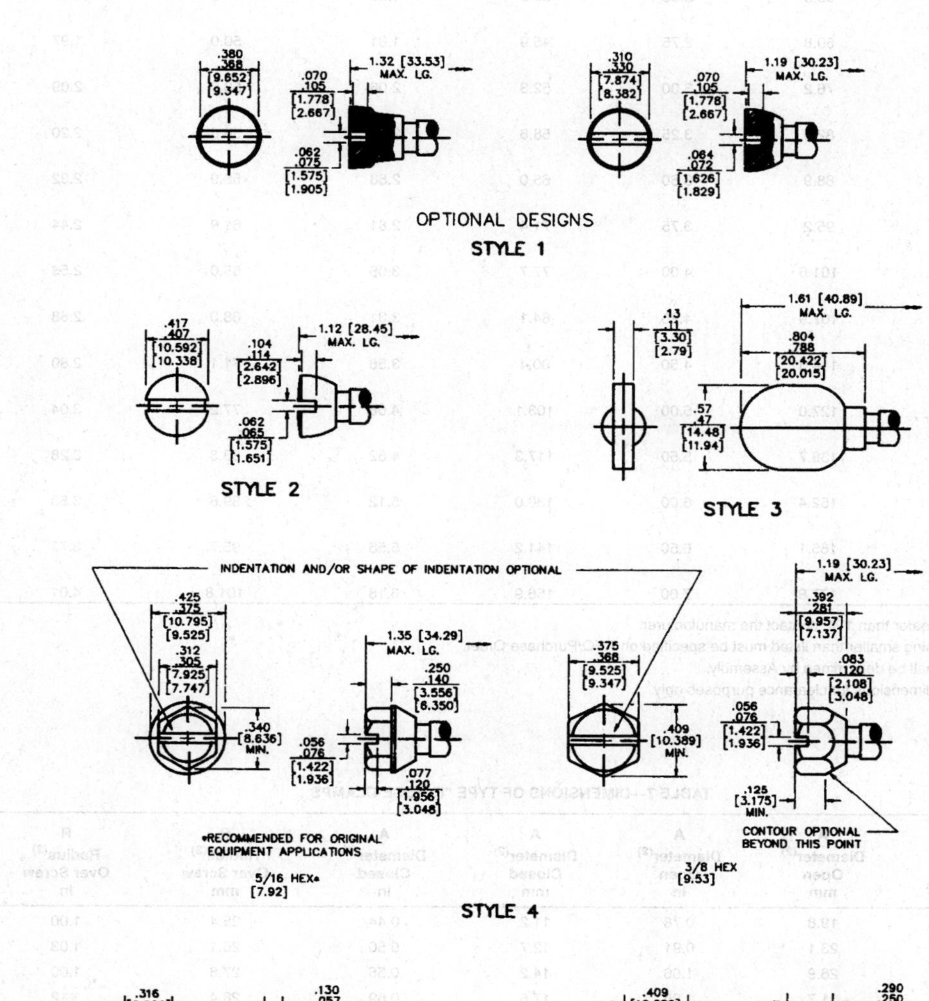

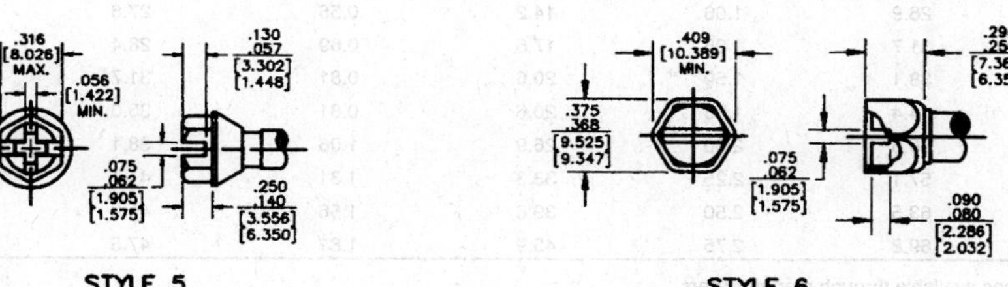

FIGURE 6—TYPE "F" HOSE CLAMPS

TABLE 6—DIMENSIONS OF TYPE "F" HOSE CLAMPS

SAE Size No.(1)(2)	A Diameter(3) Open mm	A Diameter(3) Open in	A Diameter(3) Closed mm	A Diameter(3) Closed in	R Radius(4) Over Screw mm	R Radius(4) Over Screw in
06	19.8	0.78	11.2	0.44	29.7	1.17
08	23.1	0.91	12.7	0.50	30.9	1.22
10	26.9	1.06	14.2	0.56	32.0	1.26
12	31.7	1.25	17.5	0.69	33.5	1.32
16	38.1	1.50	20.6	0.81	36.1	1.42
20	44.4	1.75	20.6	0.81	38.6	1.52
24	50.8	2.00	26.9	1.06	41.4	1.63
28	57.1	2.25	33.3	1.31	44.5	1.75
32	63.5	2.50	39.6	1.56	47.2	1.86
36	69.8	2.75	45.9	1.81	50.0	1.97
40	76.2	3.00	52.3	2.06	53.0	2.09
44	82.5	3.25	58.6	2.31	55.8	2.20
48	88.9	3.50	65.0	2.56	58.9	2.32
52	95.2	3.75	71.4	2.81	61.9	2.44
56	101.6	4.00	77.7	3.06	65.0	2.56
60	107.9	4.25	84.1	3.31	68.0	2.68
64	114.3	4.50	90.4	3.56	71.1	2.80
72	127.0	5.00	103.1	4.06	77.2	3.04
80	139.7	5.50	117.3	4.62	83.3	3.28
88	152.4	6.00	130.0	5.12	89.6	3.53
96	165.1	6.50	141.2	5.56	95.7	3.77
104	177.8	7.00	156.9	6.18	101.8	4.01

1. For sizes greater than 104, contact the manufacturer.
2. Clamps closing smaller than listed must be specified on RFQ/Purchase Order.
3. Diameter shall be determined by Assembly.
4. Reference dimensions for clearance purposes only.

TABLE 7—DIMENSIONS OF TYPE "I" HOSE CLAMPS

SAE Size No.(1)	A Diameter(2) Open mm	A Diameter(2) Open in	A Diameter(2) Closed mm	A Diameter(2) Closed in	R Radius(3) Over Screw mm	R Radius(3) Over Screw in
06	19.8	0.78	11.2	0.44	25.4	1.00
08	23.1	0.91	12.7	0.50	26.1	1.03
10	26.9	1.06	14.2	0.56	27.6	1.09
12	31.7	1.25	17.5	0.69	28.4	1.12
16	38.1	1.50	20.6	0.81	31.7	1.25
20	44.4	1.75	20.6	0.81	35.0	1.38
24	50.8	2.00	26.9	1.06	38.1	1.50
28	57.1	2.25	33.3	1.31	41.1	1.62
32	63.5	2.50	39.6	1.56	45.0	1.75
36	69.8	2.75	45.9	1.81	47.5	1.87

1. Larger size clamps available through manufacturers.
2. Diameter shall be determined by assembly over mandrels.
3. Reference dimensions for clearance purposes

TABLE 8—DIMENSIONS OF TYPE "M" HOSE CLAMPS

SAE Size No.[1]	A Diameter[2] Open mm	A Diameter[2] Open in	A Diameter[2] Closed mm	A Diameter[2] Closed in	R Radius[3] Over Screw mm	R Radius[3] Over Screw in
04	15.7	0.62	6.3	0.25	19.5	0.77
06	19.8	0.78	11.2	0.44	23.1	0.91
08	23.1	0.91	12.7	0.50	24.3	0.96
10	26.9	1.06	14.2	0.56	26.1	1.03
12	31.7	1.25	17.5	0.69	27.7	1.09

1. Larger size clamps available through manufacturers.
2. Diameter shall be determined by assembly over mandrels.
3. Reference dimensions for clearance purposes only.

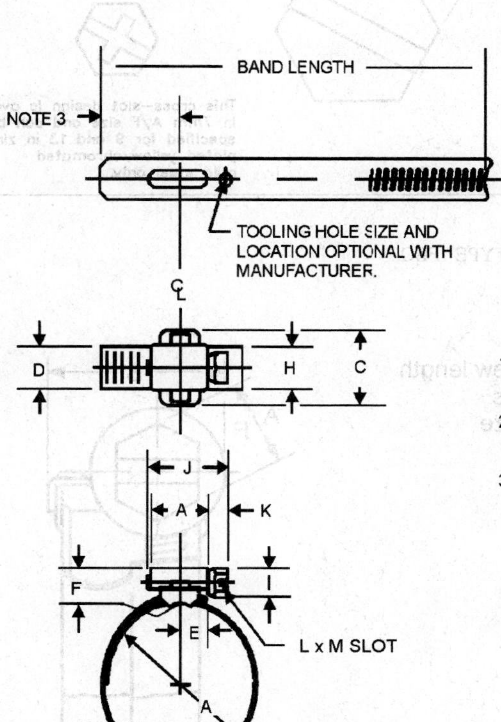

1. THREE SLOTS MAXIMUM, UNCOVERED BY LINER AT MAX. DIAMETER.
2. CLAMP SHAPE NEED NOT BE PERFECTLY ROUND AS LONG AS CLAMP WILL FREELY ACCEPT THE MAX. OPEN DIA. GAUGE.
3. BAND EXTENSION LENGTH OPTIONAL WITH MANUFACTURER FOR CONFORMANCE WITH NOTE 1.

FIGURE 7—TYPE "MX"

TABLE 9—TYPE "MX"

SAE Clamp Size	Old SAE Ref.	Clamp Diameter Open Metric	Clamp Diameter Open Inch	Clamp Diameter Close Metric	Clamp Diameter Close Inch
MX50		12.70	0.50	6.35	0.25
MX53		13.46	0.53	7.11	0.28
MX56		14.22	0.56	7.87	0.31
MX59		14.99	0.59	8.64	0.34
MX63	4	16.00	0.63	9.65	0.38
MX66		16.76	0.66	10.41	0.41
MX69		17.53	0.69	11.18	0.44
MX72		18.29	0.72	11.94	0.47
MX75		19.05	0.75	12.70	0.50
MX78	6	19.81	0.78	12.19	0.48
MX81		20.57	0.81	12.95	0.51
MX84		21.34	0.84	13.72	0.54

TABLE 9—TYPE "MX" (continued)

SAE Clamp Size	Old SAE Ref.	Clamp Diameter Open Metric	Clamp Diameter Open Inch	Clamp Diameter Close Metric	Clamp Diameter Close Inch
MX88		22.35	0.88	13.73	0.58
MX91	8	23.11	0.91	14.73	0.61
MX94		23.88	0.94	16.26	0.64
MX97		24.64	0.97	17.02	0.67
MX100		25.40	1.00	17.78	0.70
MX103		26.16	1.03	18.54	0.73
MX106	10	26.92	1.06	19.30	0.76
MX109		27.69	1.09	20.07	0.79
MX113		28.70	1.13	21.08	0.83
MX116		29.46	1.16	21.84	0.86
MX119		30.23	1.19	22.61	0.89
MX122		30.99	1.22	23.37	0.92
MX125	12	31.75	1.25	24.13	0.95

SPECIFICATIONS

Materials:

Both the 9mm and 13mm series are available in 5 different material types.

Material No.	
1	Zinc plated mild steel throughout. Can be yellow chromated for added corrosion protection.
2	Band and housing in stainless steel (430 SS) and zinc plated yellow chromated mild steel screw.
3	Stainless steel throughout. (430 SS)
4	Non magnetic stainless steel throughout. (304 SS)
5	High grade non magnetic stainless steel throughout. (316 SS)

Screwheads:

The standard head is hexagon with screwdriver slot and available in 2 different sizes, 6 and 7mm 'across flats'.

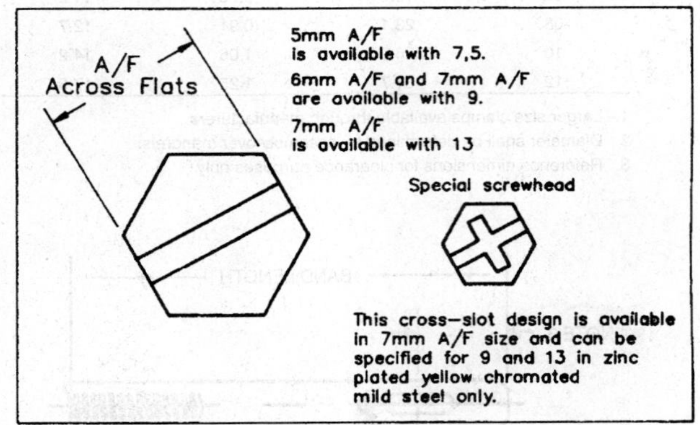
A/F
Across Flats
5mm A/F
is available with 7,5.
6mm A/F and 7mm A/F
are available with 9.
7mm A/F
is available with 13
Special screwhead
This cross-slot design is available in 7mm A/F size and can be specified for 9 and 13 in zinc plated yellow chromated mild steel only.

FIGURE 8—TYPE "FEO"

KEY:
b – Bandwidth
B – Housing width
h – Housing height
L – Housing + screw length
s – Band thickness
A/F – Screw head size

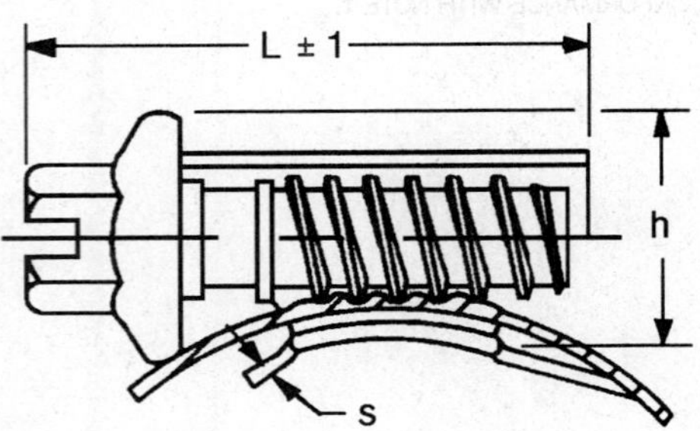
L ± 1
h
s

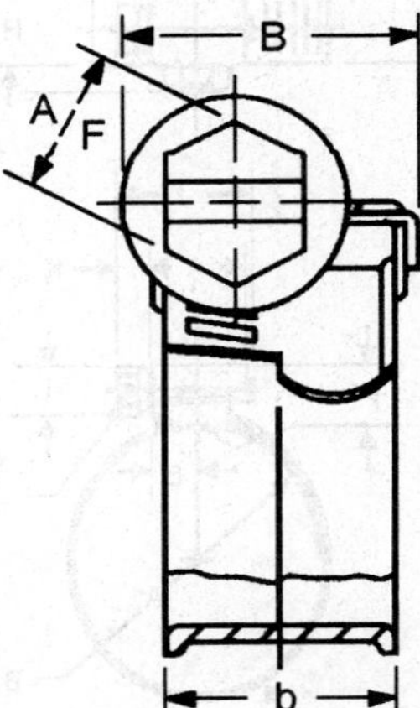
B
A/F
b

FIGURE 9—TYPE "FEO"

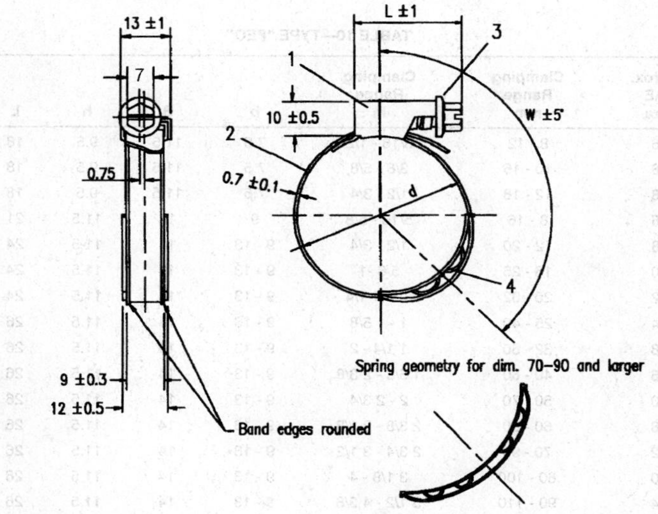

Material:

1 and 2	Band and housing	—Stainless steel AISI 430
3	Screw	—Stainless steel AISI 430
4	Spring	—SAE 1075 to Din 1.124B

part no. 4:

Surface Treatment: Double Deltotone/Deltoseal (zincferous)
Hardening: Austempered to HRC50 - 54

Clamp must withstand hand applied torque up to 5.0 N·m without failure

Application speed: 350 RPM (max.)

Item	L ± 1	Minimum Shipping Dia.	d	Ref W Angle
3	24	23	16 - 25	95 deg
5	24	30	20 - 32	103 deg
7	26	38	25 - 40	121 deg
8	26	43	30 - 45	120 deg
9	26	40	32 - 50	120 deg
10	26	50	40 - 60	129 deg
11	26	68	50 - 70	130 deg
12	26	78	60 - 68	130 deg
13	26	88	70 - 90	130 deg

FIGURE 10A—TYPE "SLFEO," mm

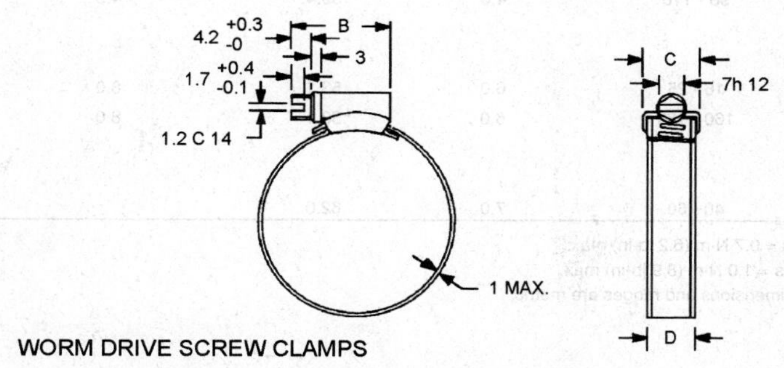

FIGURE 10B—TYPE "FE"—METRIC

TABLE 10—TYPE "FEO"

Approx. SAE Size	Clamping Range mm	Clamping Range in	b	B	h	L	S
06	8 - 12	5/16 - 1/2	7.5	11.5	9.5	18	0.6
08	10 - 16	3/8 - 5/8	7.5	11.5	9.5	18	0.6
08	12 - 18	1/2 - 3/4	7.5	11.5	9.5	18	0.6
06	8 - 16	5/16 - 5/8	9	14	11.5	21	0.6
08	12 - 20	1/2 - 3/4	9 - 13	14	11.5	24	0.7
10	16 - 25	5/8 -1	9 - 13	14	11.5	24	0.7
12	20 - 32	3/4 -1 1/4	9 - 13	14	11.5	24	0.7
24	25 - 40	1 - 1 5/8	9 - 13	14	11.5	26	0.7
28	32 - 50	1 1/4 - 2	9 - 13	14	11.5	26	0.7
36	40 - 60	1 5/8 - 2 3/8	9 - 13	14	11.5	26	0.7
40	50 - 70	2 - 2 3/4	9 - 13	14	11.5	26	0.7
48	60 - 80	2 3/8 - 3 1/8	9 - 13	14	11.5	26	0.7
52	70 - 90	2 3/4 - 3 1/2	9 - 13	14	11.5	26	0.7
60	80 - 100	3 1/8 - 4	9 - 13	14	11.5	26	0.7
64	90 - 110	3 1/2 - 4 3/8	9 - 13	14	11.5	26	0.7
72	100 - 120	4 - 4 3/4	9 - 13	14	11.5	26	0.7
80	110 - 130	4 3/8 - 5 1/8	9 - 13	14	11.5	26	0.7
80	120 - 140	4 3/4 - 5 1/2	9 - 13	14	11.5	26	0.7
88	130 - 150	5 1/8 - 5 7/8	9 - 13	14	11.5	26	0.7
96	140 - 160[1]	5 1/2 - 6 1/4	9 - 13	14	11.5	26	0.7

1. Larger sizes available.

NOTE—Unless otherwise noted, all dimensions and ranges are metric.

TABLE 11—TORQUE REQUIREMENTS FOR TYPE "FEO" CLAMPS[1]

Ultimate Torque Ref. SAE	Ultimate Torque Clamp Range	Torque by Material No. #1 N·m	Torque by Material No. #1 lb-in	Torque by Material No. #2 through #5 N·m	Torque by Material No. #2 through #5 lb-in
Clamps with 9 mm wide bands:					
6	8 - 16	2.5	22.2	3.0	26.6
8	12 - 20	4.0	35.4	4.5	39.8
64	90 - 110	4.0	35.4	4.5	39.8
Clamps with 13 mm wide bands:					
10	16 - 25	6.0	53.1	8.0	70.8
104	160 - 180	6.0	53.1	8.0	70.8
Except for:					
36	40 - 60	7.0	62.0		N/A

1. Free Torque for 9 mm clamps = 0.7 N·m (6.2 lb-in) max.
   Free torque for 13 mm clamps = 1.0 N·m (8.9 lb-in) max.
   Unless otherwise noted, all dimensions and ranges are metric.

TABLE 12—TYPE "FE"(1)

Approx. SAE Size	Clamping Range mm	Clamping Range in	Diameter Supplied mm	Diameter Supplied in	B mm	B in	C mm	C in	D mm	D in	Minimum Breaking Torque N·m
3	8 - 14	5/16 - 9/16	15	9/16	19.5	49/64	13	33/64	9	23/64	4.5
4	11 - 17	7/16 - 11/16	18	11/16	19.5	49/64	13	33/64	9	23/64	4.5
6	13 - 20	1/2 - 13/16	21	13/16	21.5	27/32	13	33/64	9	23/64	4.5
8	15 - 24	5/8 - 15/16	25		21.5	27/32	16	5/8	12.2	31/64	6.0
10	19 - 28	3/4 - 1 1/8	29	1 1/8	23.5	59/64	16	5/8	12.2	31/64	6.0
12	22 - 32	7/8 - 1 1/4	33	1 5/16	25.5	1	16	5/8	12.2	31/64	6.0
16	26 - 38	1 1/16 - 1 1/2	39	1 9/16	25.5	1	16	5/8	12.2	31/64	6.0
20	32 - 44	1 1/4 - 1 3/4	45	1 3/4	29,5	1 5/32	16	5/8	12.2	31/64	7.0
24	38 - 50	1 1/2 - 2	51	2	29.5	1 5/32	16	5/8	12.2	31/64	7.0
28	44 - 56	1 3/4 - 2 1/4	57	2 1/4	29.5	1 5/32	16	5/8	12.2	31/64	7.0
32	50 - 65	2 - 2 9/16	66	2 5/8	32.5	1 9/32	16	5/8	12.2	31/64	7.0
40	58 - 75	2 5/16 - 3	76	3	32.5	1 9/32	16	5/8	12.2	31/64	8.0
44	68 - 85	2 11/16 - 3 3/8	86	3 3/8	32.5	1 9/32	16	5/8	1212	31/64	8.0
52	77 - 95	3 - 3 3/4	96	3 13/16	32.5	1 9/32	16	5/8	12.2	31/64	8.0
64	87 - 112	3 7/16 - 4 7/16	113	4 7/16	32.5	1 9/32	16	5/8	12.2	31/64	8.0
80	104 - 138	4 1/8 - 5 7/16	139	5 1/2	32.5	1 9/32	16	5/8	12.2	31/64	8.0
96	130 - 165	5 1/8 - 6 1/2	166	6 9/16	32.5	1 9/32	16	5/8	12.2	31/64	8.0
104	150 - 180	5 7/8 - 7 1/8	181	7 1/8	32.5	1 9/32	16	5/8	12.2	31/64	8.0
122	175 - 205	6 7/8 - 8 1/8	206	8 1/8	32.5	1 9/32	16	5/8	12.2	31/64	8.0
138	200 - 231	7 7/8 - 9 1/8	232	9 1/8	32.5	1 9/32	16	5/8	12.2	31/64	8.0
154	226 - 256	8 7/8 - 10 1/16	257	10 1/8	32.5	1 9/32	16	5/8	12.2	31/64	8.0
170	251 - 282	9 7/8 - 11 1/8	283	11 1/8	32.5	1 9/32	16	5/8	12.2	31/64	8.0
186	277 - 307	10 7/8 - 12 1/8	308	12 1/8	32.5	1 9/32	16	5/8	12.2	31/64	8.0

1. t = Band thickness: 1 mm (0.04 in) max.
The free torque for A/M clamps: 1.0 N·m (8.9 lb-in) max.
The minimum torque above must be tested on a steel mandrel with the minimum diameter specified in the clamping range, i.e., 8, 11, 13, etc., as per above.

TABLE 13—TORQUE REQUIREMENTS FOR TYPE "FE" CLAMPS

Clamp Range mm	Minimum Ultimate N·m	Minimum Ultimate lb-in
8 – 14 to 13 – 20	4.5	39.8
15 – 24 to 26 – 38	6.0	53.1
32 – 44 to 50 – 65	7.0	62.0
58 – 75 to 277 – 307	8.0	70.8

TABLE 14—DIAMETER—STANDARD SIZE TYPE "HD," SLTF," AND "SLHD" CLAMPS

SAE No.(1)	Shipping mm	Shipping in	After Take Up mm	After Take Up in
212	53.98	2.125	31.75	1.25
262	66.68	2.625	44.45	1.75
312	79.38	3.125	57.15	2.25
362	92.08	3.625	69.85	2.75
412	104.78	4.125	82.55	3.25
462	117.48	4.625	95.25	3.75
512	130.18	5.125	107.95	4.25
562	142.88	5.625	120.65	4.75
612	155.60	6.126	133.35	5.25
662	168.28	6.625	146.05	5.75
712	180.98	7.125	158.75	6.25
762	193.68	7.625	171.45	6.75
812	206.38	8.125	184.15	7.25
862	219.08	8.625	196.85	7.75
912	231.78	9.125	209.55	8.25

1. Larger size clamps available through manufacturers.

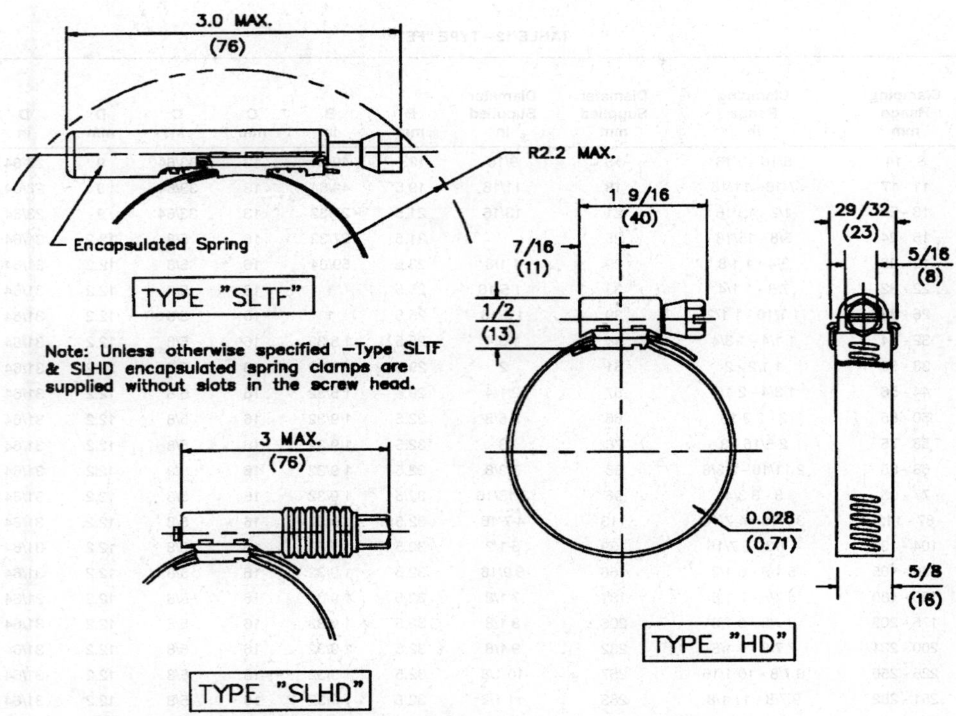

FIGURE 11—TYPE "HD," "SLTF," AND "SLHD"

4.1.5 "TB"—A fixed, tangential, T-bolt with a rotating locknut the turning of which draws both clamp ends together. Construction may employ either a floating bridge, tongue, or be of one piece (band) construction as standard. See Figures 12 and 13 and Tables 15 and 16.

4.1.6 "SSC"—Flat band body utilizing a machine screw and nuts for a closing mechanism. Screw position tangential to the band. See Figures 14A and 14B and Table 17.

4.1.7 TYPE "G"—Flat band clamp with rectangular perforations and machine screw. See Figures 15A and 15B and Table 18.

4.2 Group #2 (Types "E," "CTB," or "CTW")—Clamps which are either supplied in a locked, spring-loaded, full-open position or sprung open at installation and then released over the hose/fitting to create sealing due to the spring-like function.

4.2.1 "E"—Single round wire, heat-treated to spring temper. Ancillary specification MIL Std MS39326. See Figures 16 and 17 and Tables 19 and 20.

4.2.2 "CTB"—Flat band stock, heat-treated to spring temper. See Figure 18 and Table 21.

4.2.3 "CTW"—Dual rough pre-hardened spring wires, or wires heat-treated to spring temper. See Figure 19 and Tables 22 and 23.

4.3 Group #3 (Types "SLA," "SLF," "SLTF," "SLHD," "T," "SLTB," "SSPC," and "SLFEO")—Hybrid clamps which require torquing of a screw, or nut, for installation but which also incorporate a means of storing energy for the spring-like function.

4.3.1 "SLA"—Basic Type "A" clamp modified to incorporate a stack of spring washers for energy storage. See Figure 20.

4.3.2 "SLF"—Basic Type "F" clamp modified to incorporate a stack of conical spring washers for energy storage. See Figure 21.

4.3.3 "SLTF"—Basic Type "F" clamp modified to incorporate a coil spring encapsulated in the clamp housing. See Figure 11.

4.3.4 "SLHD"—Basic Type "HD" clamp modified to incorporate a stack of conical spring washers for energy storage. See Figure 11 and Table 14.

4.3.5 "T"—Basic Type "F" clamp utilizing a convoluted and heat-treated band for energy storage and a full, flanged inner shield. See Figures 22 and 23 and Table 24.

4.3.6 "SLTB"—Basic Type "TB" with a coil spring for energy storage. See Figures 12 and 13 and Table 15 and 16.

4.3.7 "SSPC"—Basic Type "SSC" modified to incorporate a coil spring for energy storage. See Figures 24A and 24B and Table 25.

4.3.8 "SLFEO"—Basic Type FEO modified to incorporate a convoluted and heat treated band for energy storage.

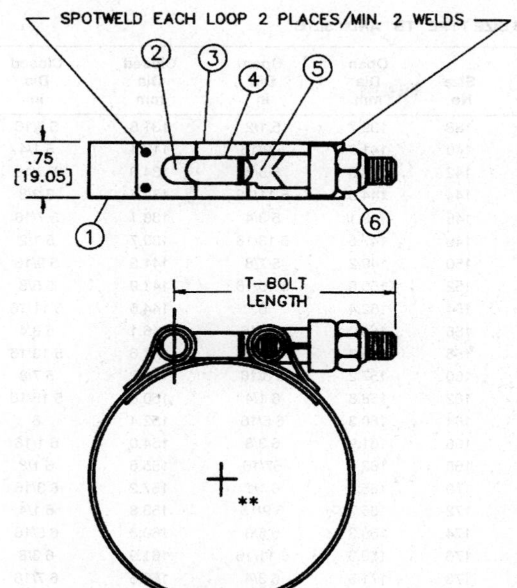

1. BAND
   AISI TYPE 201, 301, 302, 304 S.S
2. T-BOLT WRAPPER
3. TONGUE OR FLOATING BRIDGE, MFG'S OPTION
4. T-BOLT *
5. TRUNNION
6. NUT

* SEE 12.6.1 FOR DIMENSIONS

** FOR DIAMETER RANGE, SEE CHART DWG #23

NOTE: THESE ILLUSTRATIONS ARE FOR GRAPHIC PURPOSES ONLY. CONSTRUCTION MAY VARY ACCORDING TO MANUFACTURER.

FIGURE 12—TYPE "TB"

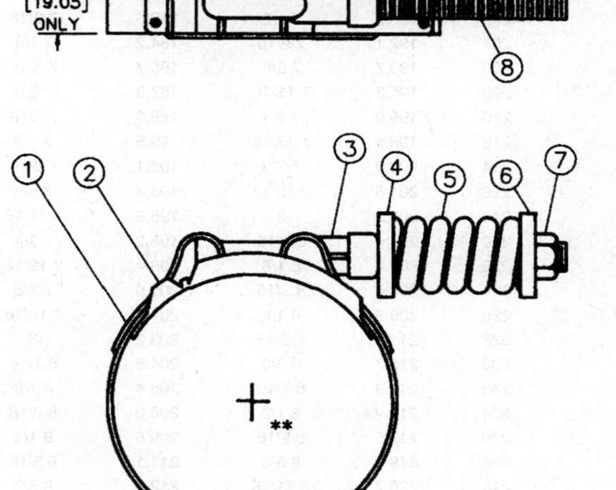

.250–28UNF – 2A OR 3A, MFG'S OPTION

1. BAND
   AISI TYPE 201, 301, 302 OR 304 CRES
   HALF HARD TEMPER
2. FLOATING BRIDGE OR TONGUE, MFG'S OPTION
   AISI TYPE 301, 302 OR 304 CRES
   ANNEALED TEMPER
3. TRUNNION
   C.Q. C.R.S. CAD OR ZINC PLATED
4. WASHER
   1.0 O.D. x .281 I.D. x .109 THICK (ANSI–B 27.2)
   STEEL – 0.20 CARBON MAX, COMM'L ZINC PLATED
5. COMPRESSION SPRING
   .187 DIA. MUSIC WIRE
   SAE J178 (ASTM A228)
   CAD OR ZINC PLATED
6. WASHER
   1.0 O.D. x .443 I.D. x .084 THICK
   STEEL – 0.20 CARBON MAX, COMM'L ZINC PLATED
7. T-NUT
   .250–28 UNF–2B
   CARBON STL 12L 14, COMM'L ZINC PLATED
8. T-BOLT
   .250–28 UNF–2A X OR 3A PERMISSIBLE
   C–1022–1038 STL, CAD OR ZINC PLATED

** FOR DIAMETER RANGE, SEE CHART DWG #23

NOTE: THESE ILLUSTRATIONS ARE FOR GRAPHIC PURPOSES ONLY. CONSTRUCTION MAY VARY ACCORDING TO MANUFACTURER.

FIGURE 13—TYPE "SLTB"

TABLE 15—DIAMETER—STANDARD SIZE TYPE "TB" AND "SLTB"

Size No.	Open Dia mm	Open Dia in	Closed Dia mm	Closed Dia in	Size No.	Open Dia mm	Open Dia in	Closed Dia mm	Closed Dia in
28	50.8	2	44.5	1 3/4	138	139.7	5 1/2	131.8	5 3/16
30	52.4	2 1/16	46.0	1 13/16	140	141.3	5 9/16	113.4	5 1/4
32	55.6	2 3/16	47.6	1 7/8	142	142.9	5 5/8	134.9	5 5/16
34	57.2	2 1/4	49.2	1 15/16	144	144.5	5 11/16	136.5	5 3/8
36	58.7	2 5/16	50.8	2	146	146.1	5 3/4	138.1	5 7/16
38	60.3	2 3/8	52.4	2 1/16	148	147.6	5 13/16	139.7	5 1/2
40	61.9	2 7/16	54.0	2 1/8	150	149.2	5 7/8	141.3	5 9/16
42	63.5	2 1/2	55.6	2 3/16	152	150.8	5 15/16	142.9	5 5/8
44	65.1	2 9/16	57.2	2 1/4	154	152.4	6	144.5	5 11/16
46	66.7	2 5/8	58.7	2 5/16	156	154.0	6 1/16	146.1	5 3/4
48	68.3	2 11/16	60.3	2 3/8	158	155.8	6 1/8	147.6	5 13/16
50	69.9	2 3/4	61.9	2 7/16	160	157.2	6 3/16	149.2	5 7/8
52	71.4	2 13/16	63.5	2 1/2	162	158.8	6 1/4	150.8	5 15/16
54	73.0	2 7/8	65.1	2 9/16	164	160.3	6 5/16	152.4	6
56	74.6	2 15/16	66.7	2 5/8	166	161.9	6 3/8	154.0	6 1/16
58	76.2	3	68.3	2 11/16	168	163.5	67/16	155.6	6 1/8
60	77.8	3 1/16	69.9	2 3/4	170	165.1	6 1/2	157.2	6 3/16
62	79.4	3 1/8	71.4	2 13/16	172	166.7	6 9/16	158.8	6 1/4
64	81.0	3 3/16	73.0	2 7/8	174	168.3	6 5/8	160.3	6 5/16
66	82.6	3 1/4	74.6	2 15/16	176	169.9	6 11/16	161.9	6 3/8
68	84.1	3 5/16	76.2	3	178	171.5	6 3/4	163.5	6 7/16
70	85.7	3 3/8	77.8	3 1/16	180	173.0	6 13/16	165.1	6 1/2
72	87.3	3 7/16	79.4	3 1/8	182	174.6	6 7/8	166.7	6 9/16
74	88.9	3 1/2	81.0	3 3/16	184	176.2	6 15/16	168.3	6 5/8
76	90.5	3 9/16	82.6	3 1/4	186	177.8	7	169.9	6 11/16
78	92.1	3 5/8	84.1	3 5/16	188	179.4	7 1/16	171.5	6 3/4
80	93.7	3 11/16	85.7	3 3/8	190	181.0	7 1/8	173.0	6 13/16
82	95.3	3 3/4	87.3	3 7/16	192	182.6	7 3/16	174.6	6 7/8
84	96.8	3 13/16	88.9	3 1/2	194	184.2	7 1/4	176.2	6 15/16
86	98.4	3 7/8	90.5	3 9/16	196	185.7	7 5/16	177.8	7
88	100.0	3 15/16	92.1	3 5/8	198	187.3	7 3/8	179.4	7 1/16
90	101.6	4	93.7	3 11/16	200	188.9	7 7/16	181.0	7 1/8
92	103.2	4 1/16	95.3	3 3/4	202	190.5	7 1/2	182.6	7 3/16
94	104.8	4 1/8	96.8	3 13/16	204	192.1	7 9/16	184.2	7 1/4
96	106.4	4 3/16	98.4	3 7/8	206	193.7	7 5/8	185.7	7 5/16
98	108.0	4 1/4	100.0	3 15/16	208	195.3	7 11/16	187.3	7 3/8
100	109.5	4 5/16	101.6	4	210	196.9	7 3/4	188.9	7 7/16
102	111.1	4 3/8	103.2	4 1/16	212	198.4	7 13/16	190.5	7 1/2
104	112.7	4 7/16	104.8	4 1/8	214	200.0	7 7/8	192.1	7 9/16
106	114.3	4 1/2	106.4	4 3/16	216	201.6	7 15/16	193.7	7 5/8
108	115.9	4 9/16	108.0	4 1/4	218	203.2	8	195.3	7 11/16
110	117.5	4 5/8	109.5	4 5/16	220	204.8	8 1/16	196.9	7 3/4
112	119.1	4 11/16	111.1	4 3/8	222	206.4	8 1/8	198.4	7 13/16
114	120.7	4 3/4	112.7	4 7/16	224	208.0	8 3/16	200.0	7 7/8
116	122.2	4 13/16	114.3	4 1/2	226	209.6	8 1/4	201.6	7 15/16
118	123.8	4 7/8	115.9	4 9/16	228	211.1	8 5/16	203.2	8
120	125.4	4 15/16	117.5	4 5/8	230	212.7	8 3/8	204.8	8 1/16
122	127.0	5	119.1	4 11/16	232	214.3	8 7/16	206.4	8 1/8
124	128.6	5 1/16	120.7	4 3/4	234	215.9	8 1/2	208.0	8 3/16
126	130.2	5 1/8	122.2	4 13/16	236	217.5	8 9/16	209.6	8 1/4
128	131.8	5 3/16	123.8	4 7/8	238	219.1	8 5/8	211.1	8 5/16
130	133.4	5 1/4	125.4	4 15/16	240	220.7	8 11/16	212.7	8 3/8
132	134.9	5 5/16	127.0	5	242	222.3	8 3/4	214.3	8 7/16
134	136.5	5 3/8	128.6	5 1/16	244	223.8	8 13/16	215.9	8 1/2
136	138.1	5 7/16	130.2	5 1/8	246	225.4	8 7/8	217.5	8 9/16
248	227.0	8 15/16	219.1	8 5/8	298	266.7	10 1/2	258.8	10 3/16
250	228.6	9	220.7	8 11/16	300	268.3	10 9/16	260.4	10 1/4
252	230.2	9 1/16	222.3	8 3/4	302	269.9	10 5/8	261.9	10 5/16
254	231.8	9 1/8	223.8	8 13/16	304	271.5	10 11/16	263.5	10 3/8
256	233.4	9 3/16	225.4	8 7/8	306	273.1	10 3/4	265.1	10 7/16
258	235.0	9 1/4	227.0	8 15/16	308	274.6	10 13/16	266.7	10 1/2
260	236.5	9 5/16	228.6	9	310	276.2	10 7/8	268.3	10 9/16
262	238.1	9 3/8	230.2	9 1/16	312	277.8	10 15/16	269.9	10 5/8
264	239.7	9 7/16	231.8	9 1/8	314	279.4	11	271.5	10 11/16
266	241.3	9 1/2	233.4	9 3/16	316	281.0	11 1/16	273.1	10 3/4
268	242.9	9 9/16	235.0	9 1/4	318	282.6	11 1/8	274.6	10 13/16
270	244.5	9 5/8	236.5	9 5/16	320	284.2	11 3/16	276.2	10 7/8
272	246.1	9 11/16	238.1	9 3/8	322	285.8	11 1/4	277.8	10 15/16

TABLE 15—DIAMETER—STANDARD SIZE TYPE "TB" AND "SLTB" (continued)

Size No.	Open Dia mm	Open Dia in	Closed Dia mm	Closed Dia in	Size No.	Open Dia mm	Open Dia in	Closed Dia mm	Closed Dia in
274	247.7	9 3/4	239.7	9 7/16	324	287.3	11 5/16	279.4	11
276	249.2	9 13/16	241.3	9 1/2	326	288.9	11 3/8	281.0	11 1/16
278	250.8	9 7/8	242.9	9 9/16	328	290.5	11 7/16	282.6	11 1/8
280	252.4	9 15/16	244.5	9 5/8	330	292.1	11 1/2	284.2	11 3/16
282	254.0	10	246.1	9 11/16	332	293.7	11 9/16	285.8	11 1/4
284	255.6	10 1/16	247.7	9 3/4	334	295.3	11 5/8	287.3	11 5/16
286	257.2	10 1/8	249.2	9 13/16	336	296.9	11 11/16	288.9	11 3/8
288	258.8	10 3/16	250.8	9 7/8	338	298.5	11 3/4	290.5	11 7/16
290	260.4	10 1/4	252.4	9 15/16	340	300.0	11 13/16	292.1	11 1/2
292	261.9	10 5/16	254.0	10	342	301.6	11 7/8	293.7	11 9/16
294	263.5	10 3/8	255.6	10 1/16	344	303.2	11 15/16	295.3	11 5/8
296	265.1	10 7/16	257.2	10 1/8	346	304.8	12	296.9	11 11/16

TABLE 16—TYPE "TB" AND "SLTB" COMPONENT DIMENSIONS AND TORQUE REQUIREMENTS

Type	B: Band Width mm (in)	Bolt Size	Hex Size	Recommended Installation Torque N·m	Recommended Installation Torque lb-in
TB	19.05 (0.75)	1/4-28 UNF	11.1 mm	9	75
		1/4-28 UNF	0.44 in	9	75
SLTB	13.72 (0.75)	M5x0.8-6g	8 mm	6	50
		10-32 UNF	0.38	6	50
	19.05 (0.75)	1/4 UNF	11.1 mm	9	75
		1/4-28 UNF	0.44 in	9	75

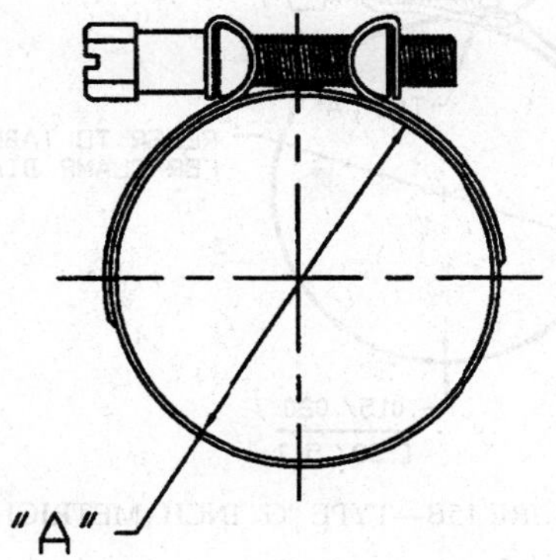

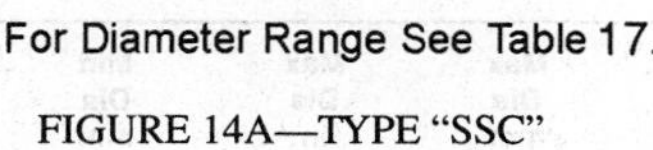

For Diameter Range See Table 17.

FIGURE 14A—TYPE "SSC"

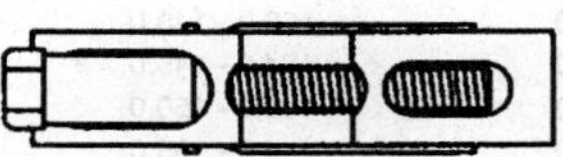

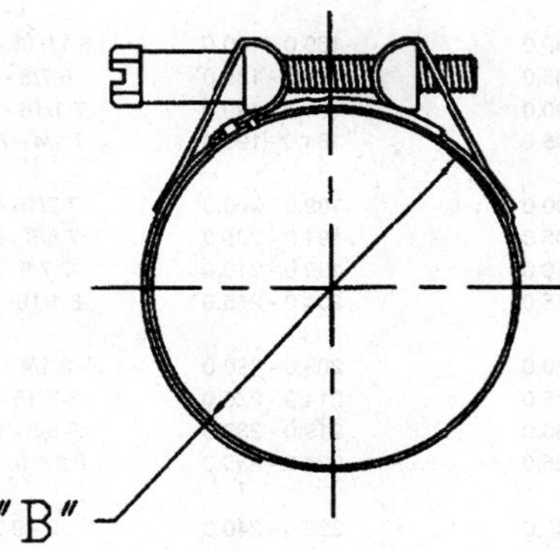

For Diameter Range See Table 17.

FIGURE 14B—TYPE "SSC"

TABLE 17—TYPE "SSC"

	Clamp Range mm	Clamp Range in
"A" Diameter		
24.0	18.0 - 24.0	11/16 - 15/16
26.0	20.0 - 26.0	13/16 - 1
28.0	22.0 - 28.0	7/8 -1 1/8
31.0	25.0 - 31.0	1 - 1 3/16
32.0	26.0 - 32.0	1 1/16 - 1 1/4
36.0	30.0 - 36.0	1 3/16 - 1 7/16
40.0	34.0 - 40.0	1 3/8 - 1 9/16
"B" Diameter		
45.0	37.5 - 45.0	1 1/2 - 1 3/4
50.0	42.5 - 50.0	1 11/16 - 1 15/16
55.0	47.5 - 55.0	1 7/8- 2 1/8
60.0	49.0 - 60.0	1 15/16 - 2 3/8
65.0	54.0 - 65.0	2 1/8 - 2 9/16
70.0	59.0 - 70.0	2 5/16 - 2 3/4
75.0	64.0 - 75.0	2 1/2 - 2 15/16
80.0	69.0 - 80.0	2 3/4 - 3 1/8
85.0	74.0 -85.0	2 15/16 - 3 5/16
90.0	79.0 - 90.0	3 1/8 - 3 1/2
95.0	84.0 - 95.0	3 5/16 - 3 3/4
100.0	89.0 - 100.0	3 1/2 - 3 15/16
105.0	94.0 - 105.0	3 11/16 - 4 1/8
110.0	99.0 - 110.0	3 7/8- 4 5/16
115.0	104.0 - 115.0	4 1/8 - 4 1/2
120.0	109.0 - 120.0	4 5/16 - 4 11/16
125.0	114.0 - 125.0	4 1/2 - 4 15/16
130.0	119.0 - 130.0	4 11/16 - 5 1/8
135.0	124.0 - 135.0	4 7/8- 5 5/16
140.0	129.0 - 140.0	5 1/16 - 5 1/2
145.0	134.0 - 145.0	5 1/4 - 5 11/16
150.0	139.0 - 150.0	5 1/2 - 5 7/8
155.0	144.0 - 155.0	5 11/16 - 6 1/16
160.0	149.0 - 160.0	5 7/8 - 6 5/16
165.0	154.0 - 165.0	6 1/16 - 6 1/2
170.0	159.0 - 170.0	6 1/4 - 6 11/16
175.0	164.0 - 175.0	6 1/2 - 6 7/8
180.0	169.0 - 180.0	6 11/16 - 7 1/16
185.0	174.0 - 185.0	6 7/8 - 7 1/4
190.0	179.0 - 190.0	7 1/16 - 7 7/16
195.0	184.0 - 195.0	7 1/4 - 7 11/16
200.0	189.0 - 200.0	7 7/16 - 7 7/8
205.0	194.0 - 205.0	7 5/8 - 8 1/16
210.0	199.0 - 210.0	7 7/8 - 8 1/4
215.0	204.0 - 215.0	8 1/16- 8 7/16
220.0	209.0 - 220.0	8 1/4 - 8 5/8
225.0	214.0 - 225.0	8 7/16 - 8 7/8
230.0	219.0 - 230.0	8 5/8 - 9 1/16
235.0	224.0 - 235.0	8 13/16 - 9 1/4
240.0	229.0 - 240.0	9 - 9 7/16
245.0	234.0 - 245.0	9 1/4 - 9 5/8
250.0	239.0 - 250.0	9 7/16 - 9 13/16
255.0	244.0 - 255.0	9 5/8 - 10

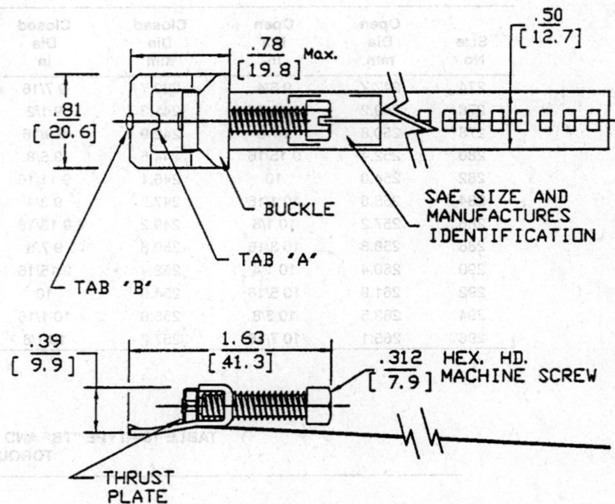

FIGURE 15A—TYPE "G" INCH (METRIC)

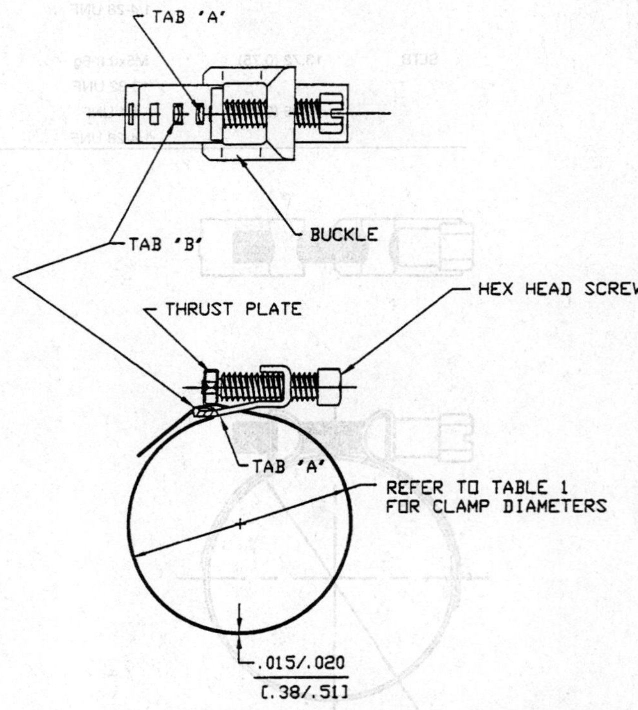

FIGURE 15B—TYPE "G" INCH (METRIC)

TABLE 18—TYPE "G"

SAE Size	Max Dia mm	Max Dia in	Min Dia mm	Min Dia in
12	32	1 1/4	17	11/16
20	44	1 3/4	17	11/16
32	67	2 5/8	17	11/16
72	127	5	44	1 3/4
104	178	7	102	4

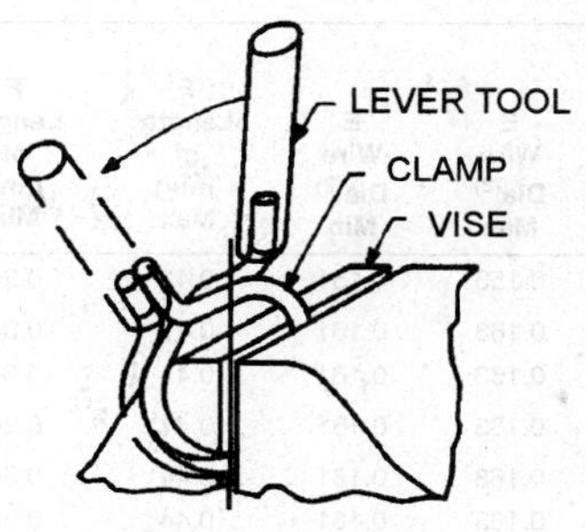

FIGURE 16—TYPE "E"

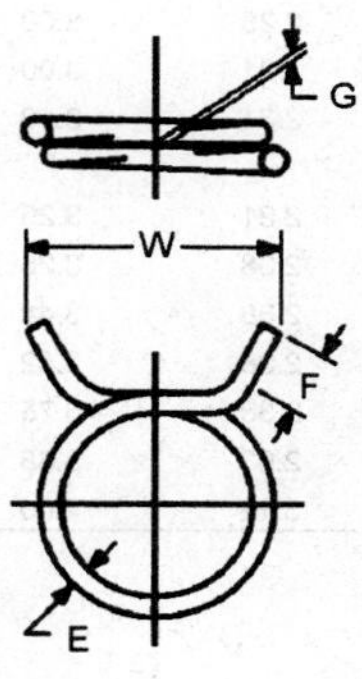

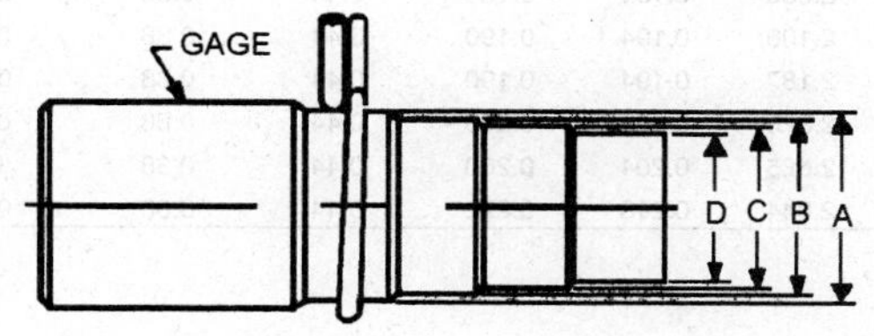

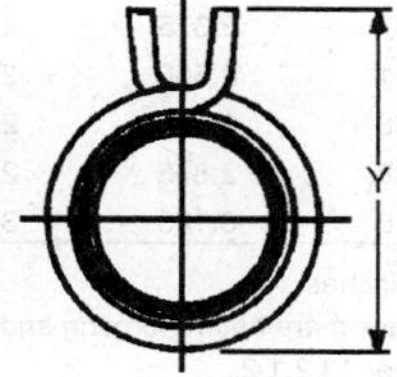

FIGURE 17—TYPE "E"

TABLE 19—TYPE "E"—CARBON, in

SAE Size no.	Effective Clamp Dia Range[1] A Maz	Effective Clamp Dia Range[1] B Nom	Effective Clamp Dia Range[1] C Min	D NO GO Gage Dia	E Wire Dia[2] Max	E Wire Dia[2] Min	F Length of Tang Max	F Length of Tang Min	G Clearance at Overlap Max	W Width Over Tangs Max	Y Over-all Height Ref	Z Gaging[3] Clear-ance Max
4[4]	0.253	0.250	0.247	0.233	0.063	0.061	0.38	0.34	0.010	0.75	0.88	0.003
5[5]	0.315	0.312	0.309	0.286	0.063	0.061	0.38	0.34	0.010	0.75	1.00	0.003
5.5[4]	0.345	0.342	0.339	0.320	0.063	0.061	0.38	0.34	0.101	0.75	1.00	0.003
6	0.380	0.375	0.370	0.350	0.083	0.081	0.38	0.34	0.015	0.88	1.06	0.005
7[4]	0.442	0.438	0.432	0.405	0.088	0.088	0.38	0.34	0.015	0.94	1.12	0.005
7.5	0.473	0.468	0.463	0.430	0.088	0.086	0.38	0.34	0.015	1.00	1.12	0.005
8[5]	0.510	0.500	0.490	0.462	0.093	0.091	0.38	0.34	0.025	1.00	1.19	0.005
8.5[4]	0.541	0.531	0.521	0.492	0.093	0.091	0.38	0.34	0.025	1.00	1.38	0.005
9	0.573	0.562	0.551	0.520	0.108	0.106	0.38	0.34	0.025	1.06	1.38	0.006
9.5[4]	0.604	0.593	0.582	0.550	0.108	0.106	0.38	0.34	0.025	1.06	1.38	0.006
10[4]	0.640	0.625	0.610	0.580	0.108	0.106	0.38	0.34	0.025	1.06	1.38	0.006
10.5	0.671	0.656	0.641	0.611	0.108	0.106	0.38	0.34	0.025	1.06	1.38	0.006
11[5]	0.703	0.688	0.671	0.635	0.113	0.111	0.38	0.34	0.025	1.12	1.50	0.006
12	0.770	0.750	0.730	0.690	0.113	0.111	0.38	0.34	0.031	1.19	1.50	0.008
13[4]	0.832	0.812	0.792	0.740	0.118	0.116	0.38	0.34	0.031	1.25	1.50	0.008
14[5]	0.900	0.875	0.850	0.800	0.123	0.121	0.38	0.34	0.031	1.25	1.62	0.008
15	0.968	0.938	0.906	0.855	0.123	0.121	0.38	0.34	0.062	1.25	1.69	0.008
16[4]	1.031	1.000	0.969	0.915	0.133	0.131	0.38	0.34	0.062	1.31	1.75	0.008
17[5]	1.090	1.062	1.034	0.960	0.143	0.141	0.41	0.34	0.062	1.50	1.88	0.010
17.5[5]	1.124	1.093	1.065	0.991	0.153	0.151	0.41	0.34	0.062	1.50	1.90	0.010
18	1.150	1.125	1.100	1.030	0.153	0.151	0.41	0.34	0.062	1.62	2.00	0.010
19[4]	1.218	1.188	1.156	1.095	0.153	0.151	0.41	0.34	0.062	1.62	2.02	0.010
19.5[5]	1.250	1.218	1.187	1.126	0.153	0.151	0.41	0.34	0.062	1.63	2.00	0.010

TABLE 19—TYPE "E"—CARBON, in (continued)

SAE Size no.	Effective Clamp Dia Range[1] A Maz	Effective Clamp Dia Range[1] B Nom	Effective Clamp Dia Range[1] C Min	D NO GO Gage Dia	E Wire Dia[2] Max	E Wire Dia[2] Min	F Length of Tang Max	F Length of Tang Min	G Clearance at Overlap Max	W Width Over Tangs Max	Y Over-all Height Ref	Z Gaging[3] Clear-ance Max
20[5]	1.280	1.250	1.219	1.145	0.153	0.151	0.41	0.34	0.062	1.75	2.00	0.010
21	1.344	1.312	1.281	1.210	0.163	0.161	0.41	0.34	0.062	1.75	2.31	0.010
22[4]	1.406	1.375	1.344	1.250	0.163	0.161	0.41	0.34	0.062	1.88	2.31	0.010
23[5]	1.468	1.437	1.406	1.300	0.163	0.161	0.41	0.34	0.62	1.88	2.31	0.010
24	1.531	1.500	1.469	1.350	0.163	0.161	0.44	0.38	0.062	1.88	2.40	0.010
25	1.592	1.561	1.530	1.411	0.163	0.161	0.44	0.38	0.62	1.88	2.53	0.010
26	1.672	1.625	1.578	1.455	0.174	0.170	0.44	0.38	0.062	2.00	2.69	0.010
28	1.797	1.750	1.703	1.550	0.174	0.170	0.44	0.38	0.062	2.12	2.75	0.010
30	1.937	1.875	1.812	1.675	0.179	0.175	0.44	0.38	0.093	2.25	2.88	0.010
31	2.000	1.938	1.875	1.720	0.179	0.175	0.44	0.38	0.093	2.25	3.00	0.010
32	2.061	2.000	1.939	1.750	0.179	0.175	0.44	0.38	0.093	2.31	3.00	0.010
34	2.187	2.125	2.062	1.860	0.184	0.180	0.44	0.38	0.093	2.31	3.19	0.010
35	2.250	2.188	2.125	1.925	0.184	0.180	0.44	0.38	0.093	2.31	3.25	0.010
36	2.312	2.250	2.187	2.000	0.184	0.180	0.44	0.38	0.093	2.38	3.25	0.010
38	2.437	2.375	2.312	2.100	0.194	0.190	0.44	0.38	0.093	2.38	3.44	0.010
40	2.581	2.500	2.439	2.187	0.194	0.190	0.44	0.38	0.093	2.38	3.62	0.010
42	2.688	2.625	2.562	2.320	0.204	0.200	0.44	0.38	0.093	2.38	3.75	0.010
46	2.938	2.875	2.812	2.625	0.204	0.200	0.44	0.38	0.93	2.63	3.88	0.012
50	3.218	3.125	3.032	2.844	0.218	0.222	0.44	0.38	0.125	3.12	4.00	0.022

1. All dimensions in inches.
2. Wire diameters shown are before forming and plating.
3. Gage clearance per 13.2.1.2.
4. These sizes shall be furnished with greenish hue. Optional when specified by purchaser.
5. These sizes shall be furnished with reddish hue. Optional when specified by purchaser.

TABLE 20—TYPE "E"—STAINLESS, in

SAE Size No.	Clamp Dia Range A Max	Clamp Dia Range B Nom	Clamp Dia Range C Min	D NO GO Gage Dia	E Wire Dia Max	E Wire Dia Min	F Tang Length Max	F Tang Length Min	G Clearance at Overlap Max	W Free Width Max	Y Height Ref	Z Gaging Clear-ance Max
S-4	0.253	0.250	0.247	0.235	0.039	0.041	0.38	0.34	0.015	0.75	0.68	0.004
S-5	0.315	0.312	0.309	0.292	0.052	0.050	0.38	0.34	0.015	0.81	0.68	0.004
S-6	0.380	0.375	0.370	0.360	0.067	0.065	0.38	0.34	0.015	0.88	1.06	0.004
S-7	0.442	0.438	0.432	0.415	0.077	0.075	0.38	0.34	0.015	0.94	1.12	0.004
S-8	0.510	0.500	0.490	0.472	0.083	0.081	0.38	0.34	0.025	1.00	1.19	0.005
S-9	0.573	0.562	0.551	0.530	0.093	0.091	0.38	0.34	0.025	1.06	1.38	0.006
S-10	0.640	0.625	0.610	0.,590	0.107	0.105	0.38	0.34	0.025	1.06	1.38	0.006
S-11	0.703	0.688	0.671	0.645	0.107	0.105	0.38	0.34	0.025	1.12	1.50	0.006
S-12	0.770	0.750	0.730	0.700	0.107	0.105	0.38	0.34	0.031	1.18	1.50	0.008
S-13	0.832	0.812	0.792	0.750	0.113	0.111	0.38	0.34	0.031	1.25	1.50	0.008
S-14	0.900	0.875	0.850	0.810	0.121	0.119	0.38	0.34	0.031	1.25	1.62	0.008
S-15	0.968	0.938	0.906	0.865	0.121	0.119	0.38	0.34	0.062	1.25	1.69	0.008
S-16	1.031	1.000	0.969	0.925	0.121	0.119	0.38	0.34	0.062	1.31	1.75	0.008
S-17	1.090	1.062	1.034	0.970	0.133	0.131	0.38	0.34	0.062	1.50	1.88	0.010
S-18	1.150	1.125	1.100	1.040	0.143	0.131	0.38	0.34	0.062	1.62	2.00	0.010

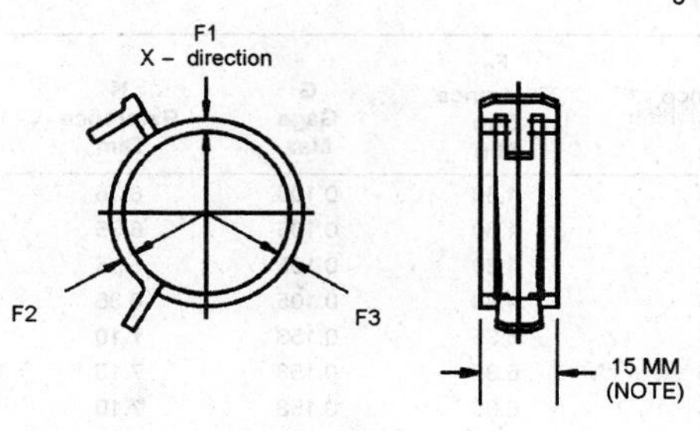

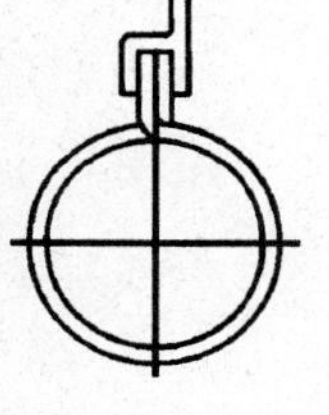

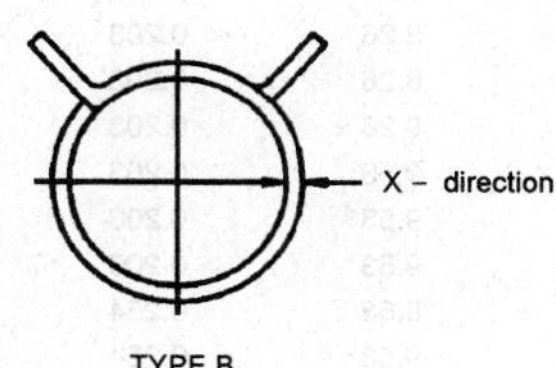

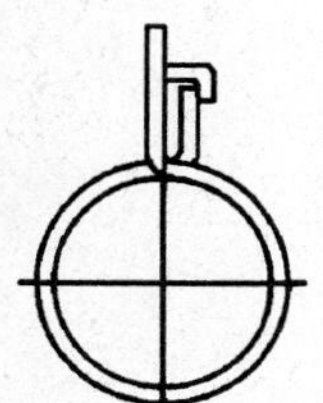

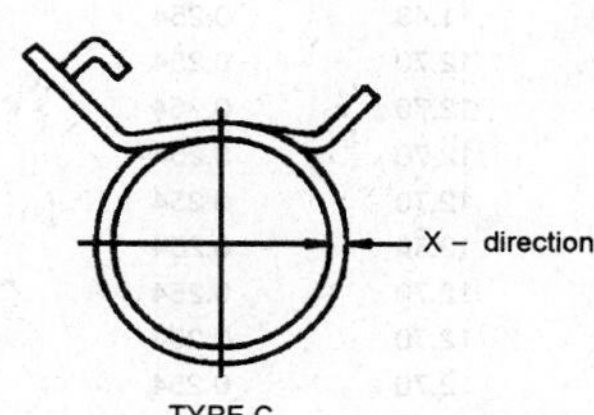

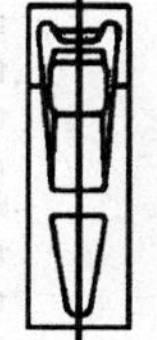

NOTE: FOR BAND WIDTHS OTHER THAN NOTED CONTACT MFG.

FIGURE 18—TYPE "CTB"

TABLE 21—TYPE "CTB"[(1)]

Nominal Size Code	Max Closed Diameter mm	Min Full Open Diameter mm
13	12.0	14.2
14	13.5	15.3
15	14.0	16.8
17	15.2	18.5
19	18.0	20.0
20	18.4	21.6
23	21.0	24.7
24	22.0	26.0
25	23.5	26.8
26	24.3	28.0
27	25.2	28.9
29	27.0	31.5
32	29.5	34.5
35	31.5	38.0
38	34.5	41.5
40	35.5	42.5
42	37.5	44.5
44	38.5	46.5
47	41.5	50.0
50	43.5	53.0
51	44.0	54.0
53	46.0	55.0
55	47.0	58.0
58	50.0	61.0

1. Table 1—Closed and full open diameters of most frequently used spring-type hose clamps.

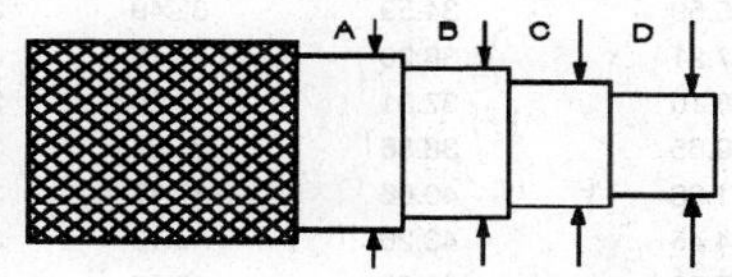

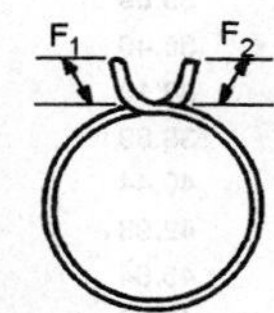

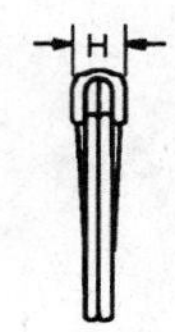

FIGURE 19—TYPE "CTW"

TABLE 22—TYPE "CTW"—METRIC[1]

A Clamp Diameters Max	B Clamp Diameters Nom	C Clamp Diameters Min	D No GO	E Wire Size	F_1 Reference Dim Max	F_2 Reference Dim Min	G Gage Max	H Reference Dim
7.47	7.26	6.96	6.73	1.00	6.35	4.80	0.105	6.35
7.80	7.60	7.30	7.10	1.00	6.35	4.80	0.105	6.35
8.80	8.70	8.60	8.10	1.00	6.35	4.80	0.105	6.35
9.65	9.50	9.40	8.90	1.00	6.35	4.80	0.105	6.35
10.57	10.39	10.19	9.68	1.50	9.65	6.35	0.153	7.10
11.25	11.13	11.00	10.28	1.50	9.65	6.35	0.153	7.10
13.00	12.55	12.50	11.73	1.50	9.65	6.35	0.153	7.10
14.10	13.73	13.36	12.36	1.50	9.65	6.35	0.153	7.10
14.58	14.31	14.00	13.75	1.70	10.80	6.35	0.153	8.25
15.93	15.60	15.11	14.10	1.70	10.80	6.35	0.153	8.25
16.26	15.88	15.49	14.73	1.70	10.80	6.35	0.153	8.25
16.81	16.41	15.93	14.88	1.70	10.80	6.35	0.153	8.25
17.86	17.48	17.04	16.13	1.98	12.70	8.26	0.203	9.14
18.69	18.19	17.70	16.51	1.98	12.70	8.26	0.203	9.14
19.50	19.00	18.50	17.50	1.98	12.70	8.26	0.203	9.14
20.62	20.19	19.61	18.25	1.98	12.70	8.26	0.203	9.14
21.13	20.62	20.12	18.80	1.98	12.70	8.26	0.203	9.14
22.75	22.13	21.50	20.25	2.19	13.97	9.53	0.203	10.16
23.57	23.09	22.40	20.98	2.19	13.97	9.53	0.203	10.16
24.59	23.83	23.01	21.72	2.19	13.97	9.53	0.203	10.16
26.29	25.50	24.61	23.24	2.49	14.22	9.53	0.254	11.43
27.68	26.97	26.26	24.38	2.49	14.22	9.53	0.254	11.43
28.12	27.48	26.67	24.99	2.49	14.22	9.53	0.254	11.43
29.21	28.58	27.94	26.16	2.49	14.22	9.53	0.254	11.43
30.94	30.18	29.36	27.81	2.80	16.76	11.43	0.254	12.19
32.00	31.29	30.38	28.37	2.80	16.76	11.43	0.254	12.19
32.51	31.75	30.96	29.08	2.80	16.76	11.43	0.254	12.19
34.14	33.32	32.54	30.73	2.80	16.76	11.43	0.254	12.19
35.69	34.98	33.91	32.00	3.00	19.00	12.70	0.254	13.72
36.40	35.59	34.59	32.49	3.00	19.00	12.70	0.254	13.72
38.10	37.21	36.20	33.78	3.00	19.00	12.70	0.254	13.72
38.89	38.10	37.31	34.29	3.20	19.00	12.70	0.254	14.22
40.44	39.65	38.86	35.84	3.20	19.00	12.70	0.254	14.22
42.98	41.28	40.08	37.47	3.20	19.00	12.70	0.254	14.22
45.64	44.45	43.26	40.13	3.20	19.00	12.70	0.254	14.22
49.20	47.63	46.02	43.69	3.20	19.00	12.70	0.254	14.22
50.80	49.23	47.63	45.19	3.50	20.32	13.97	0.254	14.99
52.35	50.80	49.25	46.48	3.50	20.32	13.97	0.254	14.99
55.55	53.98	52.37	49.43	3.50	20.32	13.97	0.254	14.99
57.15	55.55	53.98	50.17	3.50	20.32	13.97	0.254	14.99
58.42	57.15	55.55	50.80	3.50	20.32	13.97	0.254	14.99
71.00	69.85	60.00	63.00	3.80	21.60	13.97	0.508	17.02
78.50	76.20	74.00	69.50	3.80	21.60	13.97	0.508	17.02
85.00	82.55	80.00	75.00	4.00	21.60	13.97	0.560	18.03
91.70	88.90	86.20	81.00	4.00	21.60	13.97	0.560	18.03
98.20	95.25	92.30	87.00	4.00	21.60	13.97	0.560	18.03
104.77	101.60	98.50	92.50	4.00	21.60	13.97	0.560	18.03
111.40	107.95	104.50	98.00	4.20	21.60	13.97	0.609	19.05
118.00	114.30	110.50	103.80	4.20	21.60	13.97	0.609	19.05
124.68	120.65	116.50	109.35	4.20	21.60	13.97	0.609	19.05
131.50	127.00	122.50	115.00	4.20	21.60	13.97	0.609	19.05

1. For explanation, see 13.5.

TABLE 23—TYPE "CTW"—STANDARD, in

SAE Size No.	Effective Clamping Range A Max	Effective Clamping Range B Nom	Effective Clamping Range C Min	D No Go Gage Dia	E Nom. Wire Dia	F_1 Reference Dim. Max	F_2 Reference Dim. Min	G Gage Wire Max	H Width Reference Dim
4.5	0.294	0.286	0.274	0.265	0.039	0.250	0.190	0.004	0.250
5	0.306	0.301	0.285	0.280	0.039	0.250	0.190	0.004	0.250
5.5	0.345	0.342	0.339	0.320	0.039	0.250	0.190	0.004	0.250
6	0.380	0.375	0.370	0.350	0.039	0.250	0.190	0.004	0.250
6.5	0.416	0.409	0.401	0.381	0.059	0.380	0.250	0.006	0.280
7	0.442	0.438	0.432	0.405	0.059	0.380	0.250	0.006	0.280
8	0.510	0.500	0.490	0.462	0.059	0.380	0.250	0.006	0.280
8.5	0.555	0.539	0.524	0.484	0.059	0.380	0.250	0.006	0.280
9	0.573	0.562	0.551	0.520	0.070	0.425	0.250	0.006	0.325
9.5	0.627	0.614	0.595	0.555	0.070	0.425	0.250	0.006	0.325
10	0.640	0.625	0.610	0.580	0.070	0.425	0.250	0.006	0.325
10.5	0.662	0.646	0.627	0.586	0.070	0.425	0.250	0.006	0.325
11	0.703	0.688	0.671	0.635	0.078	0.500	0.325	0.008	0.360
11.5	0.736	0.716	0.697	0.650	0.078	0.500	0.325	0.008	0.360
12	0.770	0.750	0.730	0.690	0.078	0.500	0.325	0.008	0.360
12.5	0.812	0.795	0.772	0.720	0.078	0.500	0.325	0.008	0.360
13	0.832	0.812	0.792	0.740	0.078	0.500	0.325	0.008	0.360
14	0.900	0.875	0.850	0.800	0.086	0.550	0.375	0.008	0.400
14.5	0.928	0.909	0.882	0.826	0.086	0.550	0.375	0.008	0.400
15	0.968	0.938	0.906	0.855	0.086	0.550	0.375	0.008	0.400
16	1.031	1.000	0.969	0.915	0.098	0.560	0.375	0.008	0.450
17	1.090	1.062	1.034	0.960	0.098	0.560	0.375	0.008	0.450
17.5	1.107	1.082	1.050	0.984	0.098	0.560	0.375	0.008	0.450
18	1.150	1.125	1.100	1.030	0.098	0.560	0.375	0.008	0.450
19	1.218	1.188	1.156	1.095	0.110	0.660	0.450	0.010	0.480
19.5	1.260	1.232	1.196	1.117	0.110	0.660	0.450	0.010	0.480
20	1.280	1.250	1.219	1.145	0.110	0.660	0.450	0.010	0.480
21	1.344	1.312	1.281	1.210	0.110	0.660	0.450	0.010	0.480
22	1.405	1.377	1.335	1.260	0.118	0.750	0.500	0.010	0.540
22.5	1.433	1.401	1.362	1.279	0.118	0.750	0.500	0.010	0.540
23	1.500	1.465	1.425	1.330	0.118	0.750	0.500	0.010	0.540
24	1.531	1.500	1.469	1.350	0.126	0.750	0.500	0.010	0.560
25	1.592	1.561	1.530	1.411	0.126	0.750	0.500	0.010	0.560
26	1.692	1.625	1.578	1.475	0.126	0.750	0.500	0.010	0.560
27	1.745	1.688	1.640	1.528	0.126	0.750	0.500	0.010	0.560
28	1.797	1.750	1.703	1.580	0.126	0.750	0.500	0.010	0.560
30	1.937	1.875	1.812	1.720	0.126	0.750	0.500	0.010	0.560
31	2.000	1.938	1.875	1.799	0.137	0.800	0.550	0.010	0.590
32	2.061	2.000	1.939	1.830	0.137	0.800	0.550	0.010	0.590
34	2.187	2.125	2.062	1.946	0.137	0.800	0.550	0.010	0.590
35	2.250	2.187	2.125	1.975	0.137	0.800	0.550	0.010	0.590
36	2.300	2.250	2.187	2.000	0.137	0.800	0.550	0.010	0.590
44	2.795	2.750	2.638	2.480	0.150	0.850	0.550	0.020	0.670
48	3.090	3.000	2.913	2.736	0.150	0.850	0.550	0.020	0.670
52	3.346	3.250	3.150	2.953	0.158	0.850	0.550	0.022	0.710
56	3.610	3.500	3.394	3.189	0.158	0.850	0.550	0.022	0.710
60	3.866	3.750	3.634	3.425	0.158	0.850	0.550	0.022	0.710
64	4.125	4.000	3.878	3.642	0.158	0.850	0.550	0.022	0.710
68	4.386	4.250	4.114	3.858	0.165	0.850	0.550	0.024	0.750
72	4.645	4.500	4.350	4.087	0.165	0.850	0.550	0.024	0.750
76	4.909	4.750	4.587	4.305	0.165	0.850	0.550	0.024	0.750
80	5.177	5.000	4.823	4.528	0.165	0.850	0.550	0.024	0.750

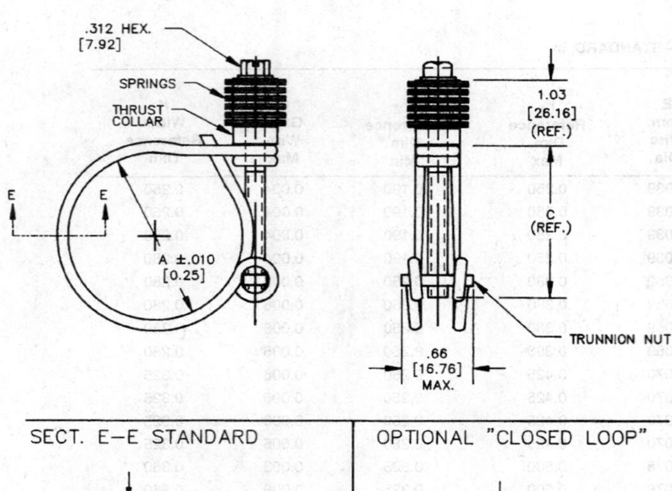

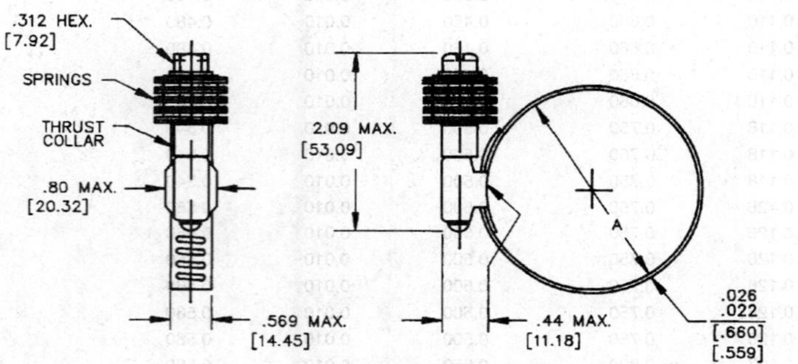

FIGURE 20—TYPE "SLA"—INCH (METRIC)

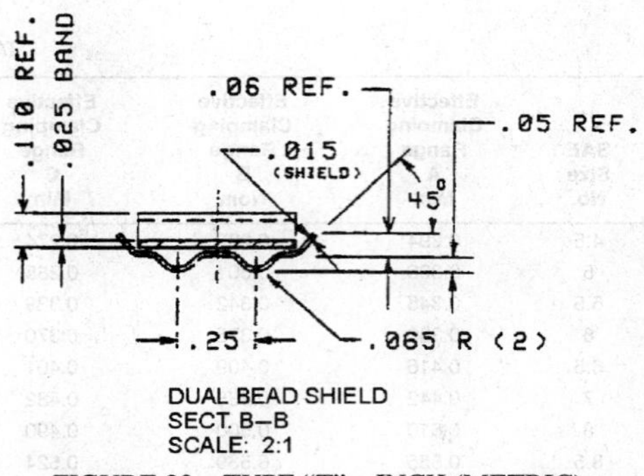

FIGURE 23—TYPE "T"—INCH (METRIC)

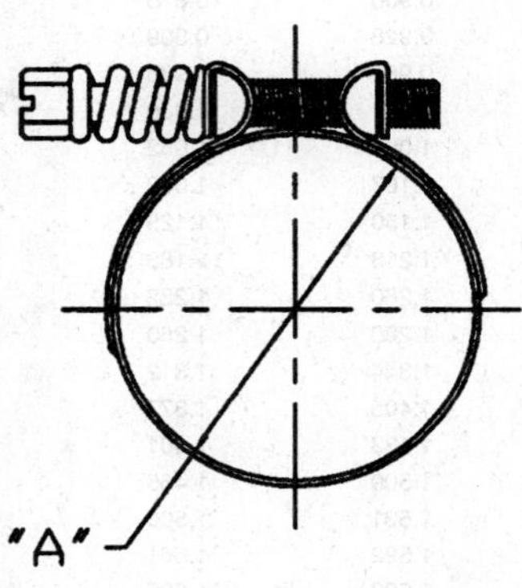

For Diameter Range See Table 25.

FIGURE 24A—TYPE "SSPC"

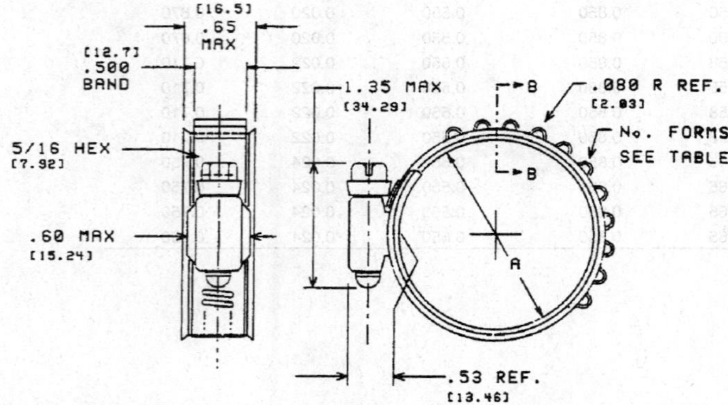

FIGURE 21—TYPE "SLF"—INCH (METRIC)

FIGURE 22—TYPE "T"

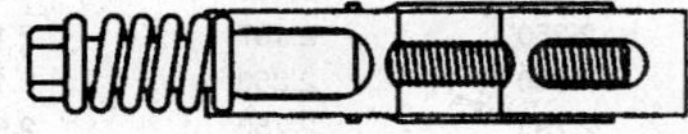

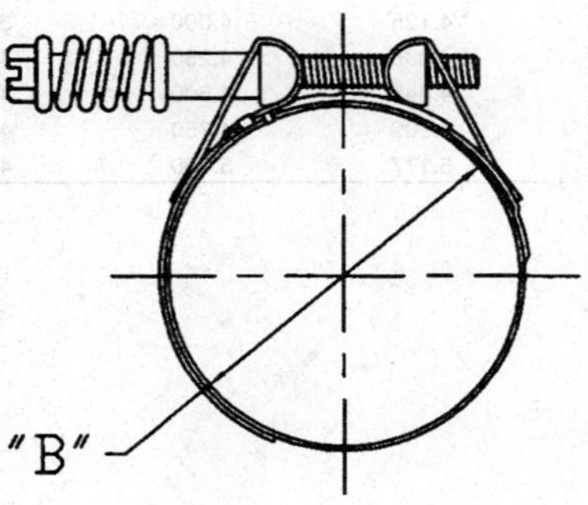

For Diameter Range See Table 25.

FIGURE 24B—TYPE "SSPC"

TABLE 24—TYPE "T"

SAE Size No.[1][2]	"A" Diameter Max mm	"A" Diameter Max in	"A" Diameter Min mm	"A" Diameter Min in	No. Slots	No. Forms
20	44.45	1.75	34.80	1.37	24	9
24	50.80	2.00	39.62	1.56	26	11
28	57.15	2.25	41.40	1.63	32	12
32	63.50	2.50	45.72	1.80	34	14
36	69.85	2.75	50.04	1.97	37	14
40	76.20	3.00	57.15	2.25	37	19
44	82.55	3.25	63.50	2.50	37	19
48	88.90	3.50	69.85	2.75	37	22
			64.26	2.53	48	
52	95.25	3.75	76.20	3.00	37	22
			67.06	2.64	48	
56	101.60	4.00	82.55	3.25	37	22
			73.41	2.89	48	
60	107.95	4.25	88.90	3.50	37	22
			79.76	3.14	48	
64	114.30	4.50	95.25	3.75	37	22
			86.11	3.39	48	
68	120.65	4.75	101.60	4.00	37	22
			92.46	3.64	48	
72	127.00	5.00	107.95	4.25	37	22
			124.21	3.89	48	
76	133.35	5.25	114.30	4.50	37	22
			105.16	4.14	48	
80	139.70	5.50	120.65	4.75	37	22
			111.51	4.39	48	
84	146.05	5.75	127.00	5.00	37	22
			117.86	4.64	48	
88	152.40	6.00	133.35	5.25	37	22
			124.21	4.89	48	
92	158.75	6.25	139.70	5.50	37	22
			130.56	5.14	48	
96	165.10	6.50	146.05	5.75	37	22
			136.91	5.39	48	
100	171.45	6.75	152.40	6.00	37	22
			143.26	5.64	48	
104	177.80	7.00	158.75	6.25	37	22
			175.01	5.89	48	
108	184.15	7.25	165.10	6.50	37	22
			155.96	6.14	48	
112	190.50	7.50	171.45	6.75	37	22
			162.31	6.39	48	
116	196.85	7.75	177.80	7.00	37	22
			168.66	6.64	48	
120	203.20	8.00	184.15	7.25	37	22
			175.01	6.89	48	

1. Sizes less than No. 20 are not available.
2. Other sizes available through manufacturers—Follow Type "F" for standard size increments.

TABLE 25—TYPE "SSPC"

	Clamp Range mm	Clamp Range in
"A" Diameter		
24.0	19.0 - 24.0	3/4 - 15/16
26.0	21.0 - 26.0	13/16 - 1
28.0	23.0 - 28.0	15/16 -1 1/8
31.0	26.0 - 31.0	1 - 1 3/16
32.0	27.0 - 32.0	1 1/16 - 1 1/4
36.0	31.0 - 36.0	1 3/16 - 1 7/16
40.0	35.0 - 40.0	1 3/8 - 1 9/16
"B" Diameter		
45.0	38.5 - 45.0	1 1/2 - 1 3/4
50.0	43.5 - 50.0	1 11/16 - 1 15/16
55.0	48.5 - 55.0	1 15/16 - 2 1/8
60.0	50.0 - 60.0	2 - 2 3/8
65.0	55.0 - 65.0	2 3/16 - 2 9/16
70.0	60.0 - 70.0	2 3/8 - 2 3/4
75.0	65.0 - 75.0	2 9/16 - 2 15/16
80.0	70.0 - 80.0	2 3/4 - 3 1/8
85.0	75.0 - 85.0	2 15/16 - 3 5/16
90.0	80.0 - 90.0	3 1/8 - 3 1/2
95.0	85.0 - 95.0	3 5/16 - 3 3/4
100.0	90.0 - 100.0	3 9/16 - 3 15/16
105.0	95.0 - 105.0	3 3/4 - 4 1/8
110.0	100.0 - 110.0	3 15/16 - 4 5/16
115.0	105.0 - 115.0	4 1/8 - 4 1/2
120.0	110.0 - 120.0	4 5/16 - 4 11/16
125.0	115.0 - 125.0	4 1/2 - 4 15/16
130.0	120.0 - 130.0	4 3/4 - 5 1/8
135.0	125.0 - 135.0	4 15/16 - 5 5/16
140.0	130.0 - 140.0	5 1/8 - 5 1/2

TABLE 25—TYPE "SSPC" (continued)

	Clamp Range mm	Clamp Range in
145.0	135.0 - 145.0	5 5/16 - 5 11/16
150.0	140.0 - 150.0	5 1/2 - 5 7/8
155.0	145.0 - 155.0	5 11/16 - 6 1/16
160.0	150.0 - 160.0	5 15/16 - 6 5/16
165.0	155.0 - 165.0	6 1/8 - 6 1/2
170.0	160.0 - 170.0	6 5/16 - 6 11/16
175.0	165.0 - 175.0	6 1/2 - 6 7/8
180.0	170.0 - 180.0	6 11/16 - 7 1/16
185.0	175.0 - 185.0	6 7/8 - 7 1/4
190.0	180.0 - 190.0	7 1/8 - 7 7/16
195.0	185.0 - 195.0	7 5/16 - 7 11/16
200.0	190.0 - 200.0	7 1/2 - 7 7/8
205.0	195.0 - 205.0	7 11/16 - 8 1/16
210.0	200.0 - 210.0	7 7/8 - 8 1/4
215.0	205.0 - 215.0	8 1/8 - 8 7/16
220.0	210.0 - 220.0	8 1/4 - 8 5/8
225.0	215.0 - 220.0	8 1/2 - 8 7/8
230.0	220.0 - 230.0	8 11/16 - 9 1/16
235.0	225.0 - 235.0	8 7/8 - 9 1/4
240.0	230.0 - 240.0	9 1/16 - 9 7/16
245.0	235.0 - 245.0	9 1/4 - 9 5/8
250.0	240.0 - 250.0	9 7/16 - 9 13/16
255.0	245.0 - 255.0	9 5/8 - 10

4.4 Group #4, (Types "J," "OES," "TE," "SEC")—Clamps which require the use of a special installation tool to deform and/or crimp tight a portion of the clamp specifically designed for said function.

4.4.1 "J"—Flat band clamp made with mechanical interlock or weld to secure band together. See Figure 25 and Table 26.

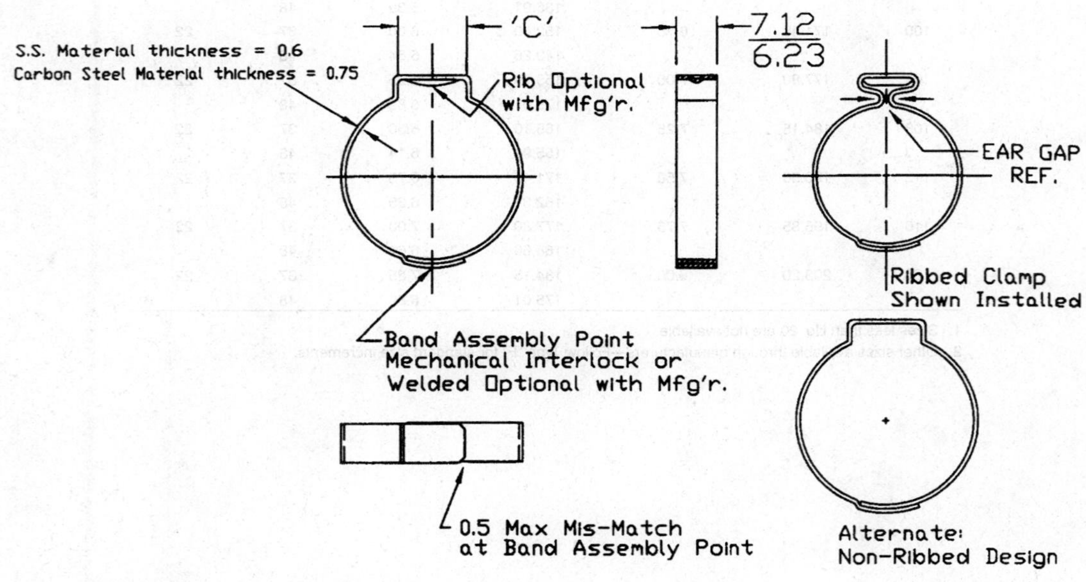

FIGURE 25—TYPE "J"

TABLE 26—TYPE "J"

SAE Size	Min "C" Dimension	Min Clamp Range mm	Min Clamp Range in	SAE Size	Min "C" Dimension	Min Clamp Range mm	Min Clamp Range in
101	5.0	8.5 - 10.1	0.335 - 0.397	515	10.0	48.4 - 51.5	1.905 - 2.027
105	5.0	8.9 - 10.5	0.350 - 0.413	530	10.0	49.9 - 53.0	1.964 - 2.086
113	5.0	9.7 - 11.3	0.381 - 0.444	535	10.0	50.3 - 53.5	1.980 - 2.106
123	6.0	10.4 - 12.3	0.409 - 0.484	540	10.0	50.8 - 54.0	2.001 - 2.125
133	6.0	11.4 - 13.3	0.448- 0.523	545	10.0	51.4 - 54.5	2.023 - 2.145
140	6.0	11.9 - 14.0	0.468 - 0.551	560	10.0	52.9 - 56.0	2.082 - 2.204
145	6.0	12.6 - 14.5	0.496 - 0.570	575	10.0	54.4 - 57.5	2.141 - 2.263
152	6.0	13.3 - 15.2	0.523 - 0.598	590	10.0	55.9 - 59.0	2.200 - 2.322
157	6.0	13.8 - 15.7	0.543 - 0.618	605	10.0	57.4 - 60.5	2.259 - 2.381
165	6.0	14.6 - 16.5	0.574 - 0.649	620	10.0	58.9 - 62.0	2.318 - 2.440
170	6.0	15.1 - 17.0	0.594 - 0.669	635	10.0	60.4 - 63.5	2.377- 2.500
180	9.0	15.1 - 18.0	0.594 - 0.708	650	10.0	61.9 - 65.0	2.437 - 2.559
185	9.0	15.7 - 18.5	0.618 - 0.728	665	10.0	63.4 - 66.5	2.496 - 2.618
198	9.0	17.0 - 19.8	0.669 - 0.779	680	10.0	64.9 - 68.0	2.555 - 2.677
210	9.0	18.2 - 21.0	0.716 - 0.826	695	10.0	66.4 - 69.5	2.614 - 2.736
226	9.0	19.8 - 22.6	0.779 - 0.889	710	10.0	67.9 - 71.0	2.673 - 2.795
241	9.0	21.3 - 24.1	0.838 - 0.948	725	10.0	69.4 - 72.5	2.732 - 2.854
256	9.0	22.8 - 25.6	0.897 - 1.007	740	10.0	70.9 - 74.0	2.791 - 2.913
271	10.0	24.0 - 27.1	0.944 - 1.066	755	10.0	72.4 - 75.5	2.850 - 2.972
286	10.0	25.5 - 28.6	1.003 - 1.125	770	10.0	73.9 - 77.0	2.909 - 3.031
301	10.0	27.0 - 30.1	1.062 - 1.185	785	10.0	75.4 -78.5	2.968 - 3.090
316	10.0	28.5 - 31.6	1.122 - 1.244	800	10.0	76.9 - 80.0	3.027 - 3.149
331	10.0	30.0 - 33.1	1.181 - 1.303	815	10.0	78.4 - 81.5	3.086 - 3.208
346	10.0	31.5 - 34.6	1.240 - 1.362	830	10.0	79.9 - 83.0	3.145 - 3.267
361	10.0	33.0 - 36.1	1.299 - 1.421	845	10.0	81.4 - 84.5	3.204 - 3.326
376	10.0	34.5 - 37.6	1.358 - 1.480	860	10.0	82.9 - 86.0	3.263 - 3.385
381	10.0	35.0 - 38.1	1.377 - 1.500	875	10.0	84.4 - 87.5	3.322 - 3.444
391	10.0	35.9 - 39.1	1.414 - 1.539	890	10.0	85.9 - 89.0	3.381 - 3.503
396	10.0	36.5 - 39.6	1.437 - 1.559	905	10.0	87.4 - 90.5	3.440 - 3.562
410	10.0	37.9 - 41.0	1.492 - 1.614	920	10.0	88.9 - 92.0	3.500 - 3.622
425	10.0	39.4 - 42.5	1.551 - 1.673	935	10.0	90.4 - 93.5	3.559 - 3.681
440	10.0	40.9 - 44.0	1.610 - 1.732	950	10.0	91.9 - 95.0	3.618 - 3.740
455	10.0	42.4 - 45.5	1.669 - 1.791	965	10.0	93.4 - 96.5	3.677 - 3.799
470	10.0	43.9 - 47.0	1.728 - 1.850	980	10.0	94.9 - 98.0	3.736 - 3.858
485	10.0	45.4 - 48.5	1.787 - 1.909	995	10.0	96.4 - 99.5	3.795 - 3.917
500	10.0	46.9 - 50.0	1.846 - 1.968				

4.4.2 "OES"—Flat band clamp made from spiral welded rings. See Figure 26 and Table 27.

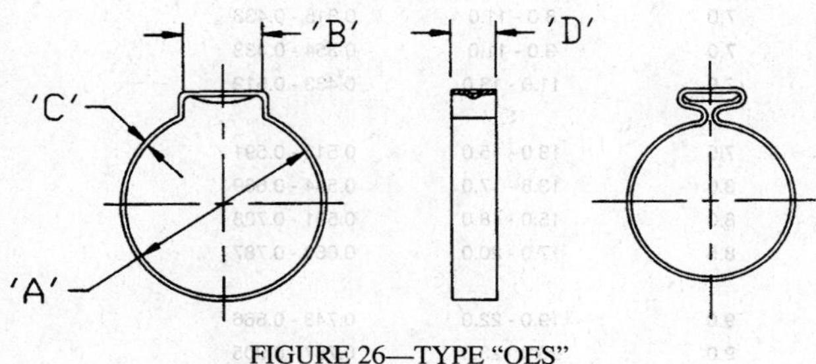

FIGURE 26—TYPE "OES"

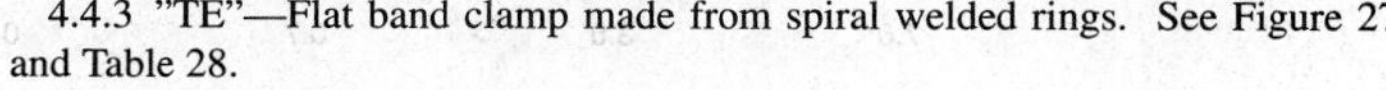

4.4.3 "TE"—Flat band clamp made from spiral welded rings. See Figure 27 and Table 28.

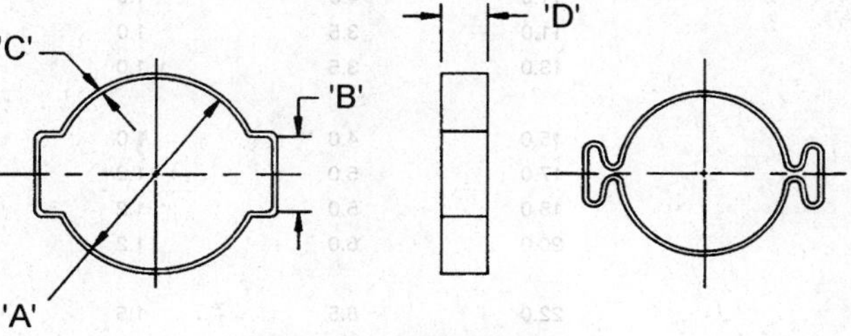

FIGURE 27—TYPE "TE"

TABLE 27—TYPE "OES"

A Diameter mm	B Dimension mm	C Dimension Zinc Pl Stl mm	C Dimension S.S mm	D Dimension mm	Clamp Range mm	Clamp Range in
3.3	1.4	0.5		3.0	2.9 - 3.3	0.114 - 0.130
3.5	1.4	0.5		3.0	3.0 - 3.5	0.118 - 0.138
4.1	2.5	0.5		4.0	3.3 - 4.1	0.130 - 0.161
5.1	3.2	0.5	0.5	4.0	4.1 - 5.1	0.161 - 0.201
6.1	3.2	0.5	0.5	4.0	5.1 - 6.1	0.201 - 0.240
6.6	3.2	0.5	0.5	4.0	5.6 - 6.6	0.220 - 0.260
7.0	3.0	0.5	0.5	5.0	6.1 - 7.0	0.240 - 0.276
8.0	4.0	0.5	0.5	5.0	6.8 - 8.0	0.268 - 0.315
8.7	4.0	0.8	0.5	5.0	7.5 - 8.7	0.295 - 0.343
9.5	5.0	1.0	0.7	6.0	7.9 - 9.5	0.311 - 0.374
10.0	5.0	0.7	0.7	6.0	8.5 - 10.0	0.335 - 0.394
10.5	5.0	0.7	0.7	6.0	8.9 - 10.5	0.357 - 0.413
11.0	5.0	0.7	0.7	6.0	9.4 - 11.0	0.370 - 0.433
11.3	5.5	0.7	0.7	6.0	9.6 - 11.3	0.376 - 0.445
11.8	5.5	0.7	0.7	6.0	10.1 - 11.8	0.398 - 0.465
12.0	6.0	1.0	0.7	6.0	10.1 - 12.0	0.398 - 0.472
12.3	6.5	0.8	0.7	6.0	10.3 - 12.3	0.406 - 0.484
12.8	6.5	0.8	0.7	6.0	10.8 - 12.8	0.425 - 0.504
13.3	6.0	1.0	0.8	6.0	11.4 - 13.3	0.448 - 0.524
14.0	6.0	1.0	0.8	6.0	12.1 - 14.0	0.476 - 0.551
14.5	6.5	1.0	0.8	6.0	12.5 - 14.5	0.492 - 0.571
16.0	6.0	1.0	0.8	6.0	14.1 - 16.0	0.555 - 0.630
17.5	7.5	1.0	0.8	6.0	15.3 - 17.5	0.602 - 0.689

TABLE 28—TYPE "TE"

A Diameter mm	B Dimension mm	C Dimension Zinc Pl Stl mm	C Dimension S.S mm	D Dimension mm	Clamp Range mm	Clamp Range in
4.1	1.5	0.5	0.5	3.5	3.1 - 4.1	0.122 - 0.161
4.5	1.5	0.6	0.5	3.5	3.5 - 4.5	0.138 - 0.177
5.0	2.5	0.7	0.5	5.0	3.0 - 5.0	0.118 - 0.197
7.0	3.0	0.7	0.5	6.0	5.0 - 7.0	0.197 - 0.276
9.0	3.2	1.0	0.8	7.0	7.0 - 9.0	0.276 - 0.354
11.0	4.5	1.0	0.8	7.0	8.0 - 11.0	0.315 - 0.433
11.0	3.5	1.0	0.8	7.0	9.0 - 11.0	0.354 - 0.433
13.0	3.5	1.0	0.8	7.0	11.0 - 13.0	0.433 - 0.512
15.0	4.0	1.0	0.8	7.5	13.0 - 15.0	0.512 - 0.591
17.0	5.0	1.2	0.8	8.0	13.8 - 17.0	0.544 - 0.669
18.0	5.0	1.2	0.8	8.0	15.0 - 18.0	0.591 - 0.708
20.0	6.0	1.2	1.0	8.5	17.0 - 20.0	0.669 - 0.787
22.0	6.5	1.5	1.0	9.0	19.0 - 22.0	0.748 - 0.866
23.0	6.5	1.5	1.0	9.0	20.0 - 23.0	0.787 - 0.905
25.0	6.5	1.5	1.0	10.0	22.0 - 25.0	0.866 - 0.984
27.0	7.0	1.5	1.0	10.0	23.0 - 27.0	0.905 - 1.063
28.0	6.5	1.5	1.0	10.0	25.0 - 28.0	0.984 - 1.102
31.0	7.5	1.5	1.0	10.0	27.0 - 31.0	1.063 - 1.220
31.0	6.5	1.5	1.0	10.0	28.0 - 31.0	1.102 - 1.220
34.0	7.5	1.5	1.0	10.0	31.0 - 34.0	1.220 - 1.339

4.4.4 "SEC"—Flat band clamp with mechanical interlock to secure bands together. See Figure 28 and Table 29.

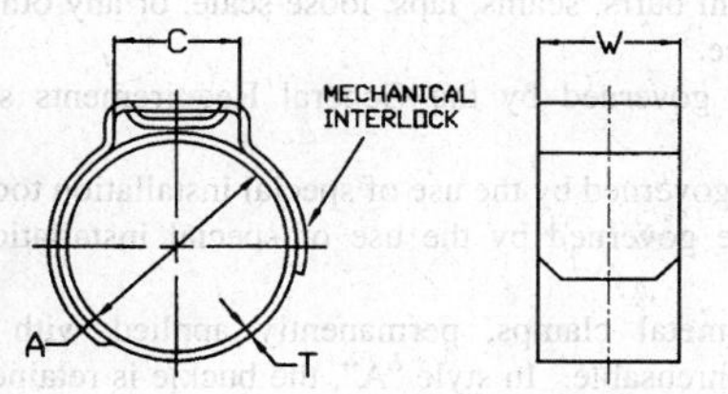

FIGURE 28—TYPE "SEC"

4.5 Group #5 (Type "LP")—Clamps which require a tool to close and engage hooks into windows.

4.5.1 "LP"—Flat band clamp which is reusable with the proper tool. See Figure 29 and Table 30.

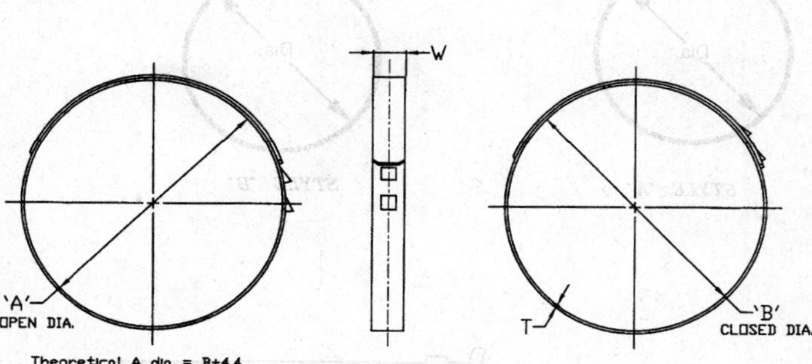

FIGURE 29—TYPE "LP"

TABLE 29—TYPE "SEC"—METRIC[1]

A Diameter	C Dimension	W 5.0	T 0.5	W 7.0	T 0.6	W 9.0	T 0.6	W 9.0	T 0.8	W 10	T 0.8	W 10	T 0.1
7.0	5.5	a	a										
8.0	5.5	a	a										
8.7	5.5	a	a										
9.5	5.5	a	a										
10.0	5.5	a	a										
10.5	5.5	a	a										
11.3	5.5	a	a										
11.8	5.5	a	a										
12.3	8.0			a	a								
13.3	8.0			a	a								
13.8	8.0			a	a								
14.0	8.0			a	a								
14.5	8.0			a	a								
15.7	8.0			a	a								
17.0	8.0			a	a								
>17.9	10.0			a	a								
>27.1	10.0			a	a	a	a	a	a	a	a		
>60.0	10.0			a	a	a	a	a	a	a	a	a	a

1. Legend:
a denotes available clamp sizes
W denotes material width
T denotes material thickness
NOTE: All sizes are in millimeters
Increments of 0.1 of a millimeter.

TABLE 30—TYPE "LP"—METRIC[1]

B Closed Diameter	W 5.0	T 0.5	W 7.0	T 0.6	W 9.0	T 0.6
>19.5	a	a				
>24.5			a	a	a	a

1. Legend:
a denotes available clamp sizes
W denotes material width
T denotes material thickness
NOTE: All sizes are in millimeters
Increments of 0.1 of a millimeter.

4.6 Group #6 (Type "H")—Permanent type fastening device.

4.6.1 APPLICATION—Double-wrapped clamps are used in pressure applications to clamp hoses to fittings. Both single- and double-wrapped clamps are used to clamp boots, heat shields, etc.

4.6.2 DESIGN—"H" type clamps are constructed of a piece of band and a separate buckle. The buckle is retained by a folded under band tab (Style "A") or a buckle nest formed into the band (Style "B"). Styles "A" and "B" are preformed and preassembled. Style "C" is purchased flat or made up by the user from bulk band and buckles to any size. See Figure 30 and Table 31.

5. General Requirements

5.1 Group #1—Clamps shall be supplied in the full open position. Those clamps using machine screws shall have the screws retained in the clamp by staking or other means agreeable to the user. Where so specified by the purchaser, types "B" and "D" clamps shall have provisions to retain the nut in base leg when axial pressure is applied to screw. All clamps shall close tight upon round steel mandrels of the sizes 4.1 indicated in the respective open and closed diameter charts. All clamps shall be free from burrs, seams, laps, loose scale, or any other defects that may affect their serviceability.

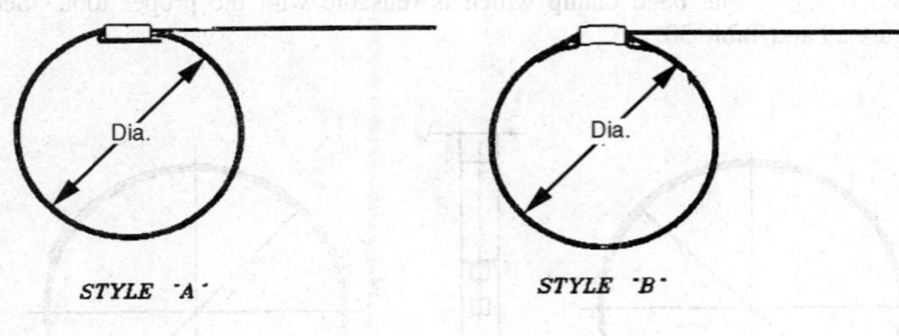

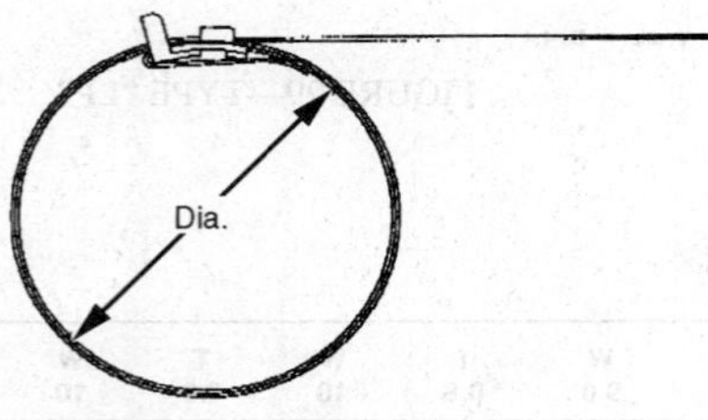

FIGURE 30—TYPE "H"—STYLES "A," "B," AND "C"

5.2 Group #2—Clamps type "E" and "CTW" shall be supplied in the free state, full-closed position. To assure that permanent deformation, resulting from opening the clamp at installation, does not occur—clamps shall be opened to a diameter no larger than that listed in column "A" (for each respective clamp type) and released to the free state at which point the clamps may not pass over a "NO-GO" size mandrel as listed in column "D," respectively. Clamps shall be free of burrs, heat-treat scale, and nicks that may affect their serviceability.

5.2.1 Type "CTB" clamps may be supplied in either the free-state (Table 21) or a locked, spring-loaded, full-opened position (Figure 18, b and c). The clamp shall be designed so as not to allow plastic deformation in the full-opened position. Clamps shall be free from burrs, seams, laps, loose scale, or any other defects that affect their performance.

5.3 Group #3—Clamps are governed by the General Requirements set forth for Group #1 clamps in 5.1.

5.4 Group #4—Clamps are governed by the use of special installation tool.

5.5 Group #5— Clamps are governed by the use of special installation tool.

5.6 Group #6—Preformed metal clamps, permanently applied with a specialized tool, nonadjustable, nonreusable. In style "A", the buckle is retained by a fold under of the band. Style "B" has a formed buckle nest.

5.6.1 Clamps are applied, tensioned, and locked with specialized manual or power tools capable of producing a permanent lock.

6. Materials—The materials listed in this section describe those which are currently being used by the clamp industry. It serves only as a reference for the user and in no way implies that the current manufacturers are required to use the listed materials. As raw material prices move and new technologies emerge, the clamp manufacturers reserve the right to change the raw materials and processes used in their products so long as they can demonstrate that overall clamp performance has not been impaired.

6.1 Materials—Group #1

6.1.1 Types "A" and "AHH"

6.1.1.1 Wire—UNS-G10080, AISI 1008—G10100, 1010 steel, 60 to 80 ksi typical.

6.1.1.2 Nut—UNS-G10100, AISI 1010 steel—UNS-G10200, AISI 1020 steel, HRB85-100.

6.1.1.3 Screw—UNS-G10200, AISI 1022, heat-treated HRC30-40.

6.1.2 Types "B" and "D"

6.1.2.1 Entire Clamp—UNS-G10100, AISI 1010 steel.

6.1.2.2 Entire Clamp—UNS-S30400, AISI 304 stainless (metric sizes per Figure 3A).

TABLE 31—TYPE "H" CLAMPS(1)

SAE Size	Diameter Dia mm	Diameter Dia in	Band Dimensions 1/4 x 0.020 6.4 x 0.50	Band Dimensions 3/8 x 0.025 9.50 x 0.64	Band Dimensions 1/2 x 0.030 12.7 x 0.75	Band Dimensions 5/8 x 0.030 15.9 x 0.75	Band Dimensions 3/4 x 0.030 19.1 x 0.75
12	19	0.75	a	a,b,c			
16	25	1.00	a,d,e	a,c	a,b,c		
20	32	1.25	a		a,b,c		
22	35	1.375	a	a,b,c			
24	38	1.50	a,d,e	a,c,e	a,c	a,b,c	
28	44	1.75		a,c	a,c	a,b,c	
32	51	2.00	a,d	a,b,c	a,b,c,e	a,b,c	a,b,c
36	57	2.25				a,b,c	
40	64	2.50	a,d,e	a,b,c	a,b,c	a,b,c,e	
44	70	2.75	a		a,c,		a,b,c
48	76	3.00	a,d	a,c	a,b,c		a,b,c,e
56	89	3.50	a,d,e	a,b,c	a,b,c		a,b,c
64	102	4.00	a	a,b,c	a,b,c,e		a,b,c
72	114	4.50	a,d,e				a,b,c
80	127	5.00					a,b,c,e
84	133	5.25					a,b,c
96	152	6.00		e			a,b,c
112	178	7.00					a,c,e
128	203	8.00				e	a,c
144	229	9.00					e
160	254	10.00				e	

1. Legend:
   a = Type 201 Stainless Steel, double wrapped STYLE "A" or "B."
   b = Type 316 Stainless Steel, double wrapped STYLE "A" or "B."
   c = Galvanized Carbon Steel, double wrapped STYLE "A" or "B."
   d = Type 201 Stainless Steel, single wrapped STYLE "B."
   e = Type 201 Stainless Steel, Free-End clamps, flat, STYLE "C."
   NOTE:
   Style "C" is supplied in flat configuration.
   Dia. = Maximum diameter for double wrap.

6.1.3 TYPE "C"

6.1.3.1 Band—UNS-G10100, AISI 1010 steel, except sizes #13 through #21, 22S, 23, 24S, 25, and 26S which are stainless steel grade.

6.1.3.2 Nut—Same as band (6.1.3.1) at manufacturer's option.

6.1.3.3 Screw—Same as band (6.1.3.11) at manufacturer's option.

6.1.3.4 Bridge—Same as band (6.1.3.1).

6.1.4 TYPES "F," "FEO," "FE," "HD," I," "M," AND "MX"

6.1.4.1 Band—UNS-S20100, AISI Austenitic stainless grades 201; S30100, 301; S30200, 302; S30400, 304; and S31600, 316; S43000, AISI Ferritic stainless grade 430; and heat-treated medium carbon steel.

6.1.4.2 Housing—Same as band, except unheat-treated carbon steel.

6.1.4.3 Saddle—Same as band, plus grade UNS-S30200, 302 stainless.

6.1.4.4 Screw—UNS-G10060, AISI 1006—G10180, 1018; and G10211 10B21 carbon steels; S41000, AISI grades 410; S43000, 430; S30200, 302; S30400, 304; S30550, 305; and S31600, 316 stainless steels.

6.1.5 TYPE "TB"

6.1.5.1 Band—UNS-S20100, AISI 201; S30100, 301; S30200, 302; or S30400, 304 stainless steel; half hard temper.

6.1.5.2 Bridge—UNS-S30100, AISI 301; S30200, 302; S30400, 304; stainless steel, annealed, 1/4 hard, or 1/2 hard temper.

6.1.5.3 Trunnion—Low carbon steel cadmium plated or stainless steel (same grades as for "bridge").

6.1.5.4 Nut—UNS-G10200, AISI 1020—G10500, 1050 steel, cadmium, or zinc plated. Reference to MS21044 and MS21045 where required.

6.1.5.5 T-Bolt

6.1.5.5.1 UNS-G40370, AISI 4037 alloy steel, heat-treated to 125 ksi minimum, cadmium or zinc plated.

6.1.5.5.2 UNS-S43100, AISI 431 stainless steel, heat-treated to 125 ksi minimum.

6.1.5.5.3 UNS-S66286, AISI A-286 stainless steel, 130 ksi minimum.

6.1.5.5.4 UNS-S30200, AISI 302; or S30500, 305 stainless steel, 95 ksi minimum.

6.1.5.5.5 UNS-G10220, AISI 1022; UNS-G10380, AISI 1038 steel, cadmium or zinc plated, 120 ksi minimum.

6.1.6 TYPE "G"

6.1.6.1 Band—UNS-S30100, AISI 304 stainless steel.

6.1.6.2 Buckle—UNS-30100, AISI 301 stainless steel.

6.1.6.3 Thrust Plate—UNS-S30100, AISI 301 stainless steel.

6.1.6.4 Screw—UNS-S30500, AISI 305 stainless steel.

6.1.6.5 Screw—UNS-S30200, AISI 302 stainless steel.

6.1.7 TYPE "SSC"

6.1.7.1 Band—UNS-S30400 AISI 304 Stainless Steel.

6.1.7.2 Nuts—Same as Band (6.1.7.1).

6.1.7.3 Spacer—Same as Band (6.1.7.1).

6.1.7.4 Bridge—Same as Band (6.1.7.1).

6.1.7.5 Screw—UNS-S30200, AISI 302 Stainless Steel.

6.2 Materials—Group #2

6.2.1 TYPE "E"—UNS-G10650–G10800, SAE 1065–1080 carbon steels; or S17700, AISI 17-7 PH stainless steel; the carbon steels heat treated to a minimum of Rockwell hardness RC50. Carbon steel and stainless steel clamps to meet the performance and ductility requirements specified in Section 12.

6.2.2 TYPE "CTB"—Carbon steel or alloyed spring steels, heat-treated to HRC47-53 (mean of HRC50) to meet the performance requirements specified in Section 13.

6.2.3 TYPE "CTW"—Carbon or stainless steel as follows:

6.2.3.1 UNS-G10700—UNS-G10700–G10850, SAE 1070–1085 carbon steel wire; pre-hardened to Rockwell RC50, then stress relieved after forming or UNS G10650–G10800, SAE 1065–1080 carbon steel wire formed and heat treated to Rockwell hardness RC50.

6.2.3.2 UNS-S17700—AISI 17-7PH stainless steel heat-treated to condition "C" by aging 1 h at 900 °F.

6.3 Materials—Group #3

6.3.1 TYPES "SLA," "SLF," "SLTF," "SLFEO," AND "SLHD"

6.3.1.1 Spring Washers

6.3.1.1.1 UNS-G10500-G10950—AISI 1050-1095 steel, heat-treated to HRC42-50.

6.3.1.1.2 UNS-G30100—AISI 301 steel, stainless, full hard.

6.3.1.2 Spacer—Steel, aluminum, stainless steel as supplied or furnished by manufacturer.

6.3.1.3 Remainder of Clamp—Same as Group #1—Types "A," "F," and "HD," respectively.

6.3.2 TYPE "T"

6.3.2.1 Band—AISI 450 stainless, heat-treated HRC40-46. (No UNS number.)

6.3.2.2 Shield—UNS-S20100, AISI 201 or S30100, 301 stainless steel.

6.3.2.3 Balance of Clamp—Same as Group #1—Type "F."

6.3.3 TYPE "SLTB"

6.3.3.1 Spring—Music wire per SAE J178 (ASTM A 228), diameter as recommended by manufacturer.

6.3.3.2 Washer—UNS-G10200, AISI 1006-1020 carbon steel.

6.3.3.3 Remainder of Clamp—Same as Group #1—Type "TB."

6.3.4 TYPE "SSPC"

6.3.4.1 Band—UNS-S30400, AISI 304 stainless steel.

6.3.4.2 Nuts—Same as band (6.3.4.1).

6.3.4.3 Spacer—Same as band (6.3.4.1).

6.3.4.4 Bridge—Same as band (6.3.4.1).

6.3.4.5 Screw—UNS-S30200, AISI 302 stainless steel.

6.3.4.6 Spring—AISI 17-7 pH stainless steel.

6.4 Materials—Group #4

6.4.1 TYPES "J," "OES," "TE," "SEC"

6.4.1.1 Entire clamp UNS-G10060—G10220 (AISI 1006-1022 carbon steel) or UNS-S30100, S30200, or S30400, (AISI 301, 302, or 304 stainless steel) or 6063 aluminum.

6.5 Material—Group #5

6.5.1 TYPE "LP"

6.5.1.1 Entire clamp UNS-S30400 AISI 304 stainless steel.

6.6 Materials—Group #6

6.6.1 TYPE "H"

6.6.1.1 Clamps are made of AISI 201 or 316 stainless steel, or AISI 1050 carbon steel, electro-galvanized.

*7. **Finishes***—General—Carbon steel components of clamps are normally supplied with rustproof finishes as specified by the purchaser. It is recommended that a reasonable latitude be allowed in the inspection of finishes on parts fabricated from precoated steel and the overlapping areas on clamps treated after assembly. All salt spray times (minimum hours) are per ASTM B 117.

NOTE—Magnitude of white corrosion and red rust permissible shall be determined between supplier and purchaser.

7.1 Finishes—Group #1

7.1.1 TYPES "A" AND "AHH"

7.1.1.1 Standard finish is 5 μm (0.0002 in) minimum zinc plate on all external surface areas. Rated time to red rust is 32 h (minimum).

7.1.1.2 Zinc plate plus yellow chromate, 72 h minimum to white corrosion, 168 h minimum to red rust. Iridescence is acceptable.

7.1.1.3 Zinc Phos/electrodeposited black paint with oil sealer, 168 h minimum to red rust.

CAUTION—High lubricity lowers the clamp ultimate torque capacity.

7.1.1.4 Optional—Aluminum base coat/organic plus lube, silver grey, and black color, 400 h minimum to red rust.

7.1.1.5 Optional—Phosphate/zinc flake/organic, silver grey color, 240 h minimum to red rust.

7.1.2 TYPES "B" AND "D"

7.1.2.1 Standard finish is 5 μm (0.0002 in) minimum zinc plate, 32 h minimum to red rust.

NOTE—For other finishes contact manufacturer.

7.1.3 TYPE "C"

7.1.3.1 Standard finish is 5 μm (0.0002 in) minimum zinc plate, 32 h minimum to red rust.

NOTE—For other finishes contact manufacturer.

7.1.4 TYPES "F," "FEO," "FE," "HD," "I," "M," "MX," AND "TB"

7.1.4.1 Band/Housing/Saddle/Bridge/Trunnion—Generally these items are made of stainless steel and therefore are supplied as manufactured. Optional finishes vary with the manufacturer but generally include the following: Passivation, black oxide, and color chromating of zinc-plated carbon steel parts.

7.1.4.2 Carbon Steel Screws/Nuts—Zinc plate plus chromate—thickness, chromate color and salt spray times vary, but are typically:

7.1.4.2.1 32 h minimum to red rust for 5 μm (0.0002 in) minimum zinc plus clear chromate.

7.1.4.2.2 72 h minimum to red rust for 5 μm (0.0002 in) minimum zinc plus yellow chromate.

7.1.4.3 Stainless steel screws do not receive plating. They can, however, be passivated, or black oxided along with the clamp assembly.

7.1.5 TYPE "FE"

7.1.5.1 Screw and Band—Bright galvanized plus clear chromate.

7.1.5.2 Housing—Multiple coats of alkyd enamel paint optional.

7.2 Finishes—Group #2

7.2.1 TYPES "E" AND "CTW"

7.2.1.1 Zinc plate or Aluminum Organic, 400 h minimum to red rust.

7.2.1.2 Mechanical or electroplated zinc 5 μm (0.0002 in) minimum plus chromate, 32 h minimum to red rust.

7.2.1.3 Stainless steel clamps are unfinished.

7.2.2 TYPE "CTB"

7.2.2.1 Zinc plate or Aluminum Organics, 400 h minimum to red rust. Other finishes available.

7.3 Finishes—Group #3

7.3.1 TYPE "SLA"

7.3.1.1 Wire, Screw, and Spacer—5 μm (0.0002 in) minimum zinc plate, 32 h minimum to red rust.

7.3.1.2 Spring Washers—5 μm (0.0002 in) minimum mechanical zinc plate plus clear chromate, 32 h minimum to red rust.

7.3.2 TYPE "SLF," "SLFEO," "SLTF," AND "SLHD"

7.3.2.1 Standard finish on carbon steel screw, spacer, and spring washers is 5 μm (0.0002 in) minimum zinc plate plus clear chromate, 32 h minimum to red rust.

7.3.2.2 For finish on stainless band and housing, see Type "F," "FEO," or "HD" stated previously.

7.3.3 TYPE "T"

7.3.3.1 Screws—See Type "F" in 7.1.4.

7.3.3.2 Band—Finish on 450 stainless steel band (Custom Grade—No UNS designation) is as heat-treated with heat-tint color (typically copper-blue).

7.3.3.3 Housing and Shield—Plain.

7.3.4 TYPE "SLTB"

7.3.4.1 Bolt and Nut—See Group #1 Type "TB" in 6.1.5.

7.3.4.2 Stainless steel band, bridge, and trunnion are plain, as manufactured.

7.3.5 TYPE "SSPC"

7.3.5.1 Spring—Painted for Identification.

7.3.5.2 Other stainless steel parts are supplied plain as manufactured.

7.4 Finishes—Group #4

7.4.1 TYPES "J," "OES," "TE," AND "SEC"

7.4.1.1 Stainless steel parts are supplied plain as manufactured.

7.4.1.2 Aluminum parts are supplied plain as manufactured.

7.4.1.3 Finish on carbon steel parts.

7.4.1.3.1 G90 Galvanized, ASTM A 525.

7.4.1.3.2 Zinc plated 5 μm (0.0002 in) minimum plus clear chromate or color chromate or other plating options contact manufacturer.

7.5 Finishes—Group #5

7.5.1 TYPE "LP"

7.5.1.1 Stainless steel clamps are supplied plain as manufactured.

7.6 Finish—Group #6

7.6.1 TYPE H

7.6.1.1 Galvanized Carbon Steel—Electroplated, lightly lubricated

7.6.1.2 Type 201 Stainless Steel—Bright annealed, lightly lubricated

7.6.1.3 Type 316 Stainless Steel—2B finish, lightly lubricated

8. Threads

8.1 Types "A," "AHH," "B," "C," "D," "G," and "SLA"—ANSI B1.1 Unified Inch Screw Threads Class 2A/2B, System 21 (ANSI B1.3M)—External and internal threads shall apply.

8.2 Types "F," "FEO," "HD," "I," "M," "MX," "SLF," "SLTF," "SLFEO," "SLHD," and "T"—Modified buttress thread standard with manufacturer.

8.3 Types "TB" and "SLTB"—ANSI B1.1 Unified Screw Threads, Class 3A/3B, System 21 (B1.3M)—External and internal threads shall apply.

8.4 Types "SSC" and "SSPC"—ANSI B1.13M Class 6H. External and internal threads shall apply.

9. Screws—Shall conform to the section on Machine Screws in SAE J478, except for special head and point details specified herein or unspecified detail specifically left to manufacturer's option.

9.1 Types "A," "AHH," and "SLA"—Use 10-24 UNC hexagon washer head slotted or special high hex washer slotted machine screws per the illustrations in the document. Thread-forming screws conforming to IFI-112 Type TT may be used.

9.2 Type "B"—Use 10-24 hexagon washer head slotted, 10-24 Fillister head slotted, 10-24 Fillister washer head slotted, 12-24 Fillister head slotted or 12-24 round head cross recess screws, as specified.

9.3 Type "C"—Use 6-32 hexagon head slotted machine screws, and 10-24 or 12-24 upset hexagon head slotted machine screws, or 10-24 or 12-24 Fillister head slotted machine screws, with flat or pilot point, as specified.

9.4 Type "D"—Use 10-24 hexagon washer head slotted or Fillister washer head slotted machine screws.

9.5 Types "F," "HD," "I," "M," "MX," "SLF," "SLTF," SLFEO," "SLHD," and "T"—Use screws conforming to Styles 1, 2, 3, 4, 5, or 6 on Figure 6 and as noted in the tables. Unspecified details are standard with the individual manufacturer.

9.6 Types "FEO" and "FE"—Use screws conforming to the manufacturer's specifications (see Figures 8 to 10B and Tables 10, 11, and 12).

9.7 Types "TB" and "SLTB"—Use 10-32 UNF, 1/4-28 UNF, 5/16-24 UNF "T"-Bolts depending upon the clamp width and/or clamp open diameter.

9.8 Types "SSPC" and "SSC"—Use 4 mm x 0.07 mm hexagon machine screw with combination of #2 Phillips and slotted.

10. Nuts

10.1 Types "A," "SLA," "B," "C," "G," and "D"—Use square or rectangular nuts as indicative, of a size to suit clamp design, except Types "A" and "SLA" clamps, which use a flat trunnion nut standard with the manufacturers.

10.2 Type "TB"—Uses commercial quality and size, hex nuts with nylon locking feature conforming to MIL Std MS21044. All steel plated locknuts are also available, conforming to MIL Std MS21045.

10.3 Type "SLTB"—May require special manufactured nuts depending upon the method used for captivating the coil spring.

10.4 Types "SSPC" and "SSC"—Use special manufactured nuts of a size to suit clamp design.

11. Identification

11.1 Types "A," "AHH," and "SLA" clamps are not marked for size identification due to the limited available flat surface area.

11.2 Types "B" and "C" clamps shall be marked with SAE size number or fractional equivalent thereof.

11.3 Type "E" clamps may be marked for size as indicated on Figures 16 and 17 and Tables 19 and 20; some sizes can be color chromated/painted when specified by the purchaser.

11.4 Types "F," "FE," "FEO," "HD," "I," "M," "MX," "SLF," "SLFEO," "SLHD," "SLTF," "T," "TB," and "SLTB"—clamps shall be identified by size number stamped on the band. At manufacturer's option, manufacturer's name or trademarks may appear adjacent to size identifications and/or on the housing.

11.5 Type "CTB"—Nominal clamp sizes as being distinguished by a number or letter code, stamped on the clamp. See Table 20.

11.6 Type "CTW"—Same as Type "E."

11.7 Type "G"—Type "G" clamps shall be marked with the SAE size number (see Table 18) or Metric range (English equivalent) and the identification/logo of the manufacturer.

11.8 Type "J," "OES," "TE," "SEC," "SSPC," and "SSC"—Are identified with the manufacturers name or abbreviation of name. Clamps are also stamped with open diameter in mm or English decimal equivalent.

11.8.1 TYPE "LP"—Same as 11.8 except clamps are stamped with closed diameter in millimeters.

12. Manufacturer's Notes

12.1 Type "B" clamps are normally manufactured with one slot in sizes up to and including No. 40; two slots in sizes No. 42 through No. 96 and three slots in sizes No. 100 and larger. Widths of slots and tongues shall not be greater than 40% of bandwidth and not less than 30% of bandwidth. Slots shall be centered in the bandwidth.

12.2 Type "CTW"—Working range is that difference between the "maximum" full open diameter (Dimension "A") and the "minimum" closed diameter (Dimension "C") of the clamp.

13. Clamp Performance, Acceptance Requirements, and Application Notes

13.1 Types "A," "AHH," and "SLA"

13.1.1 CLAMP DIAMETERS—The "standard SAE" sizes and the nonstandard sizes currently available are listed in Table 1A. Additional sizes can be made available with the standard incremental open diameter size being 0.25 mm (0.010 in). The closed diameter, being a function of usable screw length, will be in accordance with Table 32.

TABLE 32—CLAMP DIAMETERS mm (in)

Open Diameter mm	Open Diameter in	Maximum Range mm	Maximum Range in	Screw Length nominal mm	Screw Length nominal in
38.10 & up	1.50 & up	4.83	0.19	31.75	1.25
39.62 & up	1.56 & up	5.59	0.23	38.01	1.50
42.67 & up	1.69 & up	6.60	0.26	44.45	1.75

13.1.2 TOLERANCE ON DIAMETERS

13.1.2.1 Open diameter manufacturing tolerance will be either +0.51/-0.00 mm (+0.020/-0.000 in) or +0.76/-0.00 mm (+0.030/-0.000 in) depending upon the manufacturer.

13.1.2.2 Closed Diameter—All clamps shall close tight on a steel mandrel of the sizes listed in Table 32 without any significant air gaps.

13.1.3 MINIMUM ULTIMATE TORQUE—When tested on a round steel mandrel of the open diameter less 1.52 mm (0.06 in), the clamp must withstand the following hand applied torques without failure.

13.1.3.1 For standard zinc plated, optional zinc chromate, aluminum/organic, and zinc/organic finishes—5.65 N·m (50 lb-in) minimum.

13.1.3.2 For phosphate/paint/oil type finish and for other oil bearing finishes—2.03 N·m (18 lb-in) minimum.

13.1.4 FREE TORQUE—For all type finishes, the free running torque measured near the clamps open diameter size shall not exceed 0.45 N·m (4.0 lb-in) in four revolutions of the screw. The torque value does not include any break-away effects due to screw staking method and/or optional finishes.

13.1.5 APPLICATION TORQUE

13.1.5.1 2.82 to 3.39 N·m (25 to 30 lb-in) for zinc and zinc chromated clamps.

13.1.5.2 1.13 to 1.36 N·m (10 to 12 lb-in) for phosphate/paint/oil type finishes.

13.2 Type "E" Clamps—Acceptability of Type "E" clamps will be determined by the following tests and inspections:

13.2.1 EXPANSION AND PERMANENT SET—Expansion and permanent set of clamps shall be inspected by subjecting the clamps to the following tests and inspections in sequence:

13.2.1.1 Expand clamp to fit diameter "A" of gage.

NOTE—Care should be taken to avoid over-expansion during this operation.

13.2.1.2 Clamps shall be fitted respectively to gage diameter "B" and "C." When clamps are so fitted, a wire of "Z" diameter shall not pass between the gage and the clamp when inserted in a direction parallel to the axis of the gage.

13.2.1.3 In order to be sure that permanent set suffered by the material after assembly is within the prescribed limits for the best working range of the clamp and after being expanded to no greater than "A" diameter the clamp in the relaxed posture shall not fall off the "D" diameter gage.

13.2.2 BRITTLENESS (EMBRITTLEMENT)—Type "E" clamps subjected to corrosion preventive treatments which might produce hydrogen embrittlement shall be baked or otherwise treated to obviate such embrittlement and shall be capable of being expanded on a nominal diameter plug for a continuous 24 h period without signs of breaking or cracking.

13.2.3 DUCTILITY—Ductility of type "E" clamps shall be inspected by subjecting the clamps to the following tests:

13.2.3.1 The clamp shall be gripped in a vise in a manner such that the gripping edge of the vise will coincide with the clamp axis which bisects the angle between tangs as illustrated in Figures 16 and 17 and Tables 19 and 20. Clamp shall be expanded by moving the free tang as shown in Figures 16 and 17 and Tables 19 and 20 to a point where the free tang will position the stationary tang. There shall be no evidence of fracture during or after this test.

13.2.3.2 When clamp is expanded by movement of the free tang beyond the stationary tang to where the clamp fractures, the structure at the point of fracture shall show a fine grain and the clamp up to the instant of fracture shall deliver a tough springy reaction.

13.3 Types "F," "FE," "FEO," "HD," "I," "M," "MX," "SLF," "SLFEO," "SLHD," "SLTF," and "T" Clamps

13.3.1 DURABILITY TORQUE—Screw threads and slots in the band shall show no evidence of deformation or excessive wear when clamps are tightened once on a steel mandrel to the applied screw torques in Table 33.

TABLE 33—TORQUE N·m (lb-in) BY SCREW TYPE

Clamp Type	Carbon mm	Carbon in	410 ss mm	410 ss in	305 ss mm	305 ss in
"F"	5.65	50	6.78	60	6.78	60
"FEO," "SLFEO"			See Figure 10A and 10B	See Figure 10A and 10B		
"FE"			See Table 12	See Table 12		
"HD"	—	—	16.95	150	11.30	100
"I"	4.52	40	4.52	40	4.52	40
"M," "MX"	2.26	20	2.26	20	1.69	15
"SLF," "SLTF"	5.08	45	5.08	45	—	—
"SLHD," "SLTF"	—	—	14.12	125	—	—
"T"	8.47	75	8.47	75	8.47	75

13.3.2 FREE TORQUE—With the band fully engaging the screw, the torque required to turn the screw four turns shall not exceed the values in Table 34.

13.3.3 INSTALLATION TORQUE—The suggested installation torque for a particular application must be established by the supplier and the user, given due consideration to the physical configurations, properties of the materials involved, and assembly tools to be used.

13.3.3.1 Installation Torque—Good practice indicates that the clamp types listed in Tables 33 and 34 be installed at 50% to 70% of their rated "Durability Torque."

13.4 Type "CTB"

13.4.1 WORKING RANGE—That difference between the "minimum" full open diameter and the "maximum" closed diameter of the clamp.

13.4.2 The open diameter shall be measured by means of a step gage with 0.10 mm (0.0039 in) increments.

13.4.3 The closed diameter shall be measured in the "X" direction as shown by Figure 18.

TABLE 34—FREE TORQUE VALUES

Clamp Type	Max Free Torque N·m	Max Free Torque lb-in
"F"	4.5	4.0
"FEO," "SLFEO"—9 mm	0.70	6.2
"FEO," "SLFEO"—13 mm	1.01	8.9
"FE"	1.01	8.9
"HD," "SLHD," "SLTF"	0.68	6.0
"I"	0.45	4.0
"M," "MX"	0.45	4.0
"SLF," "SLTF"	0.45	4.0
"T"	0.45	4.0

13.4.4 A minimum clamping force may be specified by the purchaser. Said minimum clamping force shall be determined on a three segment load cell, simultaneously measuring 3 forces at 120-degree intervals around the clamp's inside diameter, when the clamp is at its "nominal" size.

13.5 Type "CTW"

13.5.1 Clamps may not fall off the "NO-GO" size mandrel.

13.5.2 DIMENSIONAL CONTROL—The following tests are to be made using plug gages for each of the following four diameters:

13.5.2.1 "A" Diameter—The clamp when opened to its maximum limit must pass over a gage of the "A" diameter.

13.5.2.2 "B" and "C" Diameters—After being expanded to no greater than "A" diameter the clamps must be round within "G" (gauging dimension) when installed on "B" and "C" diameter gages.

13.5.2.3 "D" Diameter—In order to be sure that permanent set suffered by the material after assembly is within prescribed limits for the best working of the clamp and after being expanded to no greater than "A" diameter the clamp in the relaxed posture shall not fall off the "D" diameter gage.

13.6 Type "TB"

13.6.1 CLAMP SIZES—"T-Bolt" band clamps are available in three basic bolt sizes. See Table 35.

13.6.2 T-BOLT SECTION—Criterion based upon: temperature, tensile strength, and installation torque. See Table 36.

13.7 Type "SLTB"

13.7.1 CLAMP SIZES—The "spring-loaded T-bolt" band clamps are also available with the 0.250-28UNF, 10-32UNF, or metric series thread size bolts.

13.7.2 MAXIMUM TORQUE—A maximum installation torque of 7.3 N·m (65 lb-in) is recommended for all clamp diameters.

13.7.3 TEMPERATURE—The type "SLTB" clamps are capable of 288 °C (550 °F) to 218 °C (450 °F) maximum service.

13.7.4 RECOMMENDED INSTALLATION TORQUE—See Table 16.

13.8 Types "J," "OES," "TE," and "SEC"

13.8.1 Correct size clamp has been selected when the ear gap measures 1.0 to 1.5 mm after closing. See Figure 22.

13.8.2 Clamps must be installed with hand or pneumatic tool that is recommended by manufacturer.

13.8.3 Welded clamp construction must be able to withstand a minimum shear load (across the band assembly point) of 1112 N (250 lb).

13.9 Types "SSPC" and "SSC"

13.9.1 Require a maximum of 2.0 N·m (18 lb-in) application torque for closure.

13.10 Type "G"—(See Figures 15A and 15B.)

13.10.1 EFFECTIVE CLAMPING DIAMETERS—See Tables 1A and 1B.

13.10.2 MAXIMUM OPEN DIAMETERS—See Tables 1A and 1B.

13.10.3 Band elongates upon tightening. No ultimate torque applicable.

13.10.4 Free torque not to exceed 0.226 N·m (2 lb-in).

13.10.5 Application torque

13.10.5.1 Approximately 2.83 to 4.51 N·m (25 to 40 lb-in).

13.10.6 INSTALLATION—TYPE "G."

13.10.6.1 With screw back out, insert band through buckle and pull firmly to engage one of the band slots into tab A, bend band another 90 degrees from buckle, away from the screw/thrust plate, and engage the locking tab B. See Figures 15A and 15B. Hold band down and tighten the screw to 2.83 to 4.51 N·m (25 to 40 lb-in) (approximately 8 turns). See Figures 15A and 15B.

TABLE 35—DIAMETRAL

Thread Size	T-Bolt Length mm	T-Bolt Length in	Min Clamp Dia. mm	Min Clamp Dia. in	Band Width Min/Max mm	Band Width Min/Max in	Adjust-ment ± mm	Adjust-ment ± in	Band Thickness(1) mm	Band Thickness(1) in
0.190-32	36.8 ± 1.52	1.75 ± 0.06	31.8	1.25	15.7/25.4	0.62/1.00	1.5/3.0	0.06/0.12	0.508 to 0.635	0.020 to 0.025
0.190-32	57.2 ± 1.52	2.25 ± 0.06	76.2	3.00	15.7/25.4	0.62/1.00	2.3/6.4	0.09/0.25	0.508 to 0.635	0.020 to 0.025
0.250-28	63.5 ± 69.9	2.50 ± 2.75	63.5	2.50	19.1/38.1	0.75/1.50	2.0/5.1	0.08/0.20	0.635	0.025
0.250-28	88.9 ± 1.52	3.50 ± 0.06	177.8	7.00	19.1/38.1	0.75/1.50	3.6/12.2	0.14/0.48	0.635	0.025
0.312-24	88.9 ± 1.52	3.50 ± 0.06	76.2	3.00	22.4/76.2	0.88/3.00	4.3/5.1	0.17/0.20	1.016	0.040
0.312-24	101.6 ± 1.52	4.00 ± 0.06	165.1	6.50	22.4/76.2	0.88/3.00	9.9/12.2	0.39/0.48	1.27	0.050

1. Thickness Tolerances:

Thickness	Tolerance
0.020 to 0.025	± 0.0381 (0.0015)
0.040	±0.0508 (0.002)
0.050	±0.0767 (0.003)

TABLE 36—T-BOLT SELECTION

T-Bolt Material	Rm. Temp. Max °C	Rm. Temp. Max °F	Tensile (ksi)	Maximum Installation Torque(1) N·m for Thread Sizes 0.190-32	Maximum Installation Torque(1) lb-in for Thread Sizes 0.190-32	Maximum Installation Torque(1) N·m for Thread Sizes 0.250-28	Maximum Installation Torque(1) lb-in for Thread Sizes 0.250-28	Maximum Installation Torque(1) N·m for Thread Sizes 0.312-24	Maximum Installation Torque(1) lb-in for Thread Sizes 0.312-24
AISI 4037	288	550	125	5.6	50	7.9	70	22.6	200
AISI 431	288	550	125	5.6	50	7.9	70	22.6	200
AISI 302/305	427	800	95	4.5	40	6.8	600	16.9	150
AISI A286	427	800	130	5.6	50	7.9	70	22.6	200
AISI 1022-1038	232	450	120	5.0	45	7.3	65	19.6	175

1. Maximum installation torque is that value recommended by the clamp manufacturer at which time the clamp shall achieve the intended purpose without destruction of the clamp or device it is applied to.

TYPE "F" CLAMPS FOR PLUMBING APPLICATIONS—SAE J1670 MAY1993

SAE Standard

Report of the SAE Hose/Clamp Subcommittee of the SAE Coolant Hose Committee approved May 1993.

Foreword—This Document has not changed other than to put it into the new SAE Technical Standards Board Format.

1. Scope—This SAE Standard covers complete dimensional and general specifications for worm gear/worm drive hose clamps for general use in the plumbing industry.

1.1 Purpose—To establish minimum functional guidelines for hose clamps intended for use in Plumbing application, herein referred to as Type "F" clamps.

2. References—There are no referenced publications specified herein.

3. General Description—Worm drive hose clamps for clamps with tangentially mounted buttress-like threaded screws, enclosed in a housing which is securely fastened to the band, which, in turn, is engaged with the screw. When the screw is rotated in a clockwise direction, the clamp becomes smaller and conversely a counterclockwise motion of the screw will eventually open the clamp.

4. General Dimensions—The following specifications tables and illustrations apply to Type "F" worm drive hose clamps.

4.1 Shipping Diameter—Type "F" clamps will be supplied in an "A" Diameter, full open, still engaged. See Table 1.

4.2 Identification—Clamps will be permanently marked with Country or Origin and/or manufacturer's identification.

4.2.1 The SAE clamp size number shall be clearly marked on the band.

5. Screws—The screws shall conform to the specifications designated as follows:

5.1 The screw head shall have an 8 mm (5/16 in) hex collar head screw as specified in Figure 1, Style 4, Slot optional.

5.1.1 Screw threads shall be modified buttress external thread standard with manufacturer.

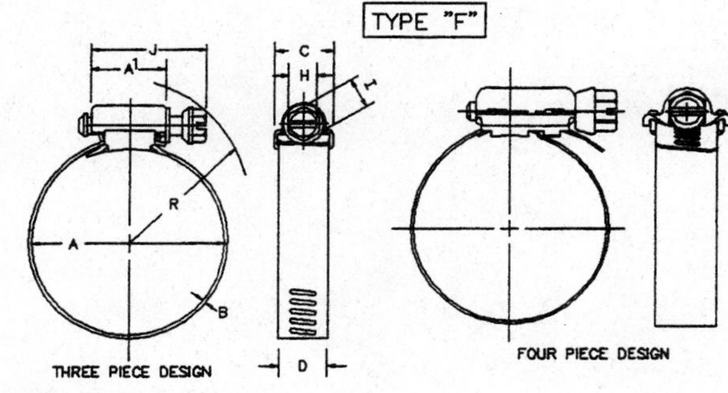

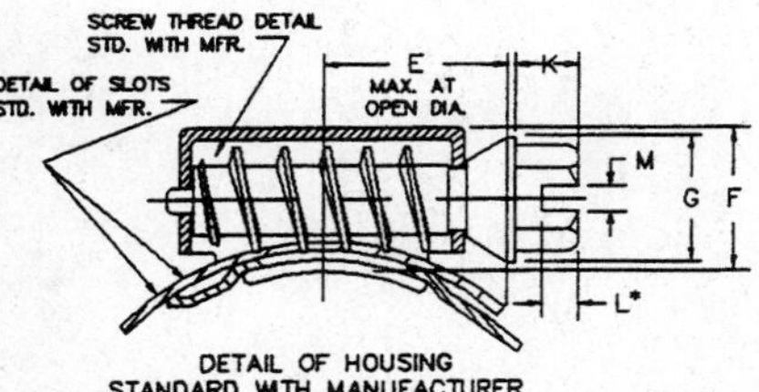

DIMENSIONS OF CLAMPS

Dimension	Type F mm	Type F in
A' HSG Length (Ref.)	19.30	0.76
B Thickness	0.533/0.787	0.021/0.031
C HSG Width (Ref.)	20.570	0.81
D Band Width	12.57/14.45	0.495/0.569
E Max. at Open Dia.	19.050	0.75
F Height (Ref.)	14.450	0.56
G Collar Diameter	9.398/10.79	0.370/0.425
H Across Flats	7.747/7.925	0.305/0.312
I Across Corners (Min.)	8.636	0.340
J Lg. of Screw (Max.)	34.29	1.35
K Hex Height	3.556/6.350	0.140/0.250
L Slot Depth (*Optional)	1.956/3.048	0.077/0.120
M Slot Width	1.422/1.936	0.056/0.076

* Slot optional
' Reference dimension only

FIGURE 1—STAINLESS STEEL HOSE CLAMPS

TABLE 1—DIMENSIONS OF TYPE F HOSE CLAMPS

SAE Size No.	A Dia.(1) Open mm	A Dia.(1) Open in	A Dia.(1) Closed mm	A Dia.(1) Closed in	R Radius(2) Over Screw mm	R Radius(2) Over Screw in
06	19.8	0.78	11.2	0.44	29.7	1.17
08	23.1	0.91	12.7	0.50	30.9	1.22
10	26.9	1.06	14.2	0.56	32.0	1.26
12	31.7	1.25	17.5	0.69	33.5	1.32
16	38.1	1.50	20.6	0.81	36.1	1.42
20	44.4	1.75	20.6	0.81	38.6	1.52
24	50.8	2.00	26.9	1.06	41.4	1.63
28	57.1	2.25	33.3	1.31	44.5	1.75
32	63.5	2.50	39.6	1.56	47.2	1.86
36	69.8	2.75	45.9	1.81	50.0	1.97
40	76.2	3.00	52.3	2.06	53.0	2.09
44	82.5	3.25	58.6	2.31	55.8	2.20
48	88.9	3.50	65.0	2.56	58.9	2.32
52	95.2	3.75	71.4	2.81	61.9	2.44
56	101.6	4.00	77.7	3.06	65.0	2.56
60	107.9	4.25	84.1	3.31	68.0	2.68
64	114.3	4.50	90.4	3.56	71.1	2.80
72	127.0	5.00	103.1	4.06	77.2	3.04
80	139.7	5.50	117.3	4.62	83.3	3.28
88	152.4	6.00	130.0	5.12	89.6	3.53
96	165.1	6.50	141.2	5.56	95.7	3.77
104	177.8	7.00	156.9	6.18	101.8	4.01

1. Diameter shall be determined by assembly over mandrels.
2. Reference dimensions for clearance purposes only.

NOTES—For sizes greater than 104 contact the manufacturer.
Clamps closing smaller than list must comply with 8.1

6. Materials—Screws, bands, and housing shall be fabricated from a minimum of 300 series stainless steel.

7. Workmanship—All clamps and components thereof shall be free of burrs, seams, loose scale, and other defects that might affect the performance.

8. Test and Performance Requirements—Clamp acceptability shall be determined by compliance with the following methods.

8.1 Clamping Diameter Range—Clamps shall assemble over and close tight upon round mandrels equal to the corresponding open and closed diameters listed in Table 1. Diameters smaller than the diameters shown are permissible. For diameters greater than listed, contact the manufacturers.

8.1.1 When tested for minimum and maximum open diameter, all threads must be fully engaged.

8.2 Free Running Torque

8.2.1 FREE TORQUE—The torque value expressed in newton meters (pound inches) when the clamp is tightened four complete revolutions of the screw or nut, while in the free state. This value does not include any break-away effects due to staking or passage of the band ends beyond the screw head.

8.3 Durability Torque—Clamps shall be tightened once, over a round steel mandrel of the specified open diameters less 1.52 mm (0.06 in) with hand-applied torque of 5.6 N·m (50 lb-in) There shall be no failure occurring in the clamp nor evidence of deformation of the threads on the screw and/or in the band. There shall be no deformation of the housing.

8.4 Ductility Tests—Bands shall be subjected to 180 degrees, bend around a 4.77 mm (0.188 in) diameter mandrel, at the perforated portion of the band and then restraightened. The band shall at no time during or after the test exhibit cracks, breaking, or other indications of failure.

9. Installation Torque—The suggested installation torque for a particular application must be established by the user.

9.1 Manufacturer's recommended installation torque for all size TYPE "F" worm drive clamp is:

TYPE "F" = 3.44 N·m (30 lb-in) for all size and materials.

9.2 Assembly Tools—It is advised that the use of power tools to install worm drive clamps be of the stall torque type. Use of clutch type or impact type assembly tools is not recommended.

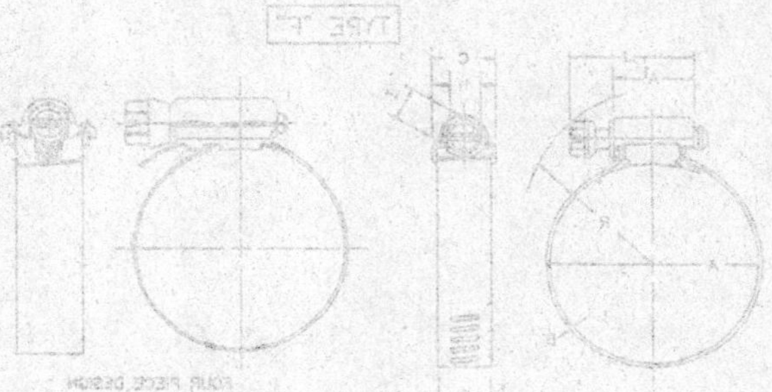

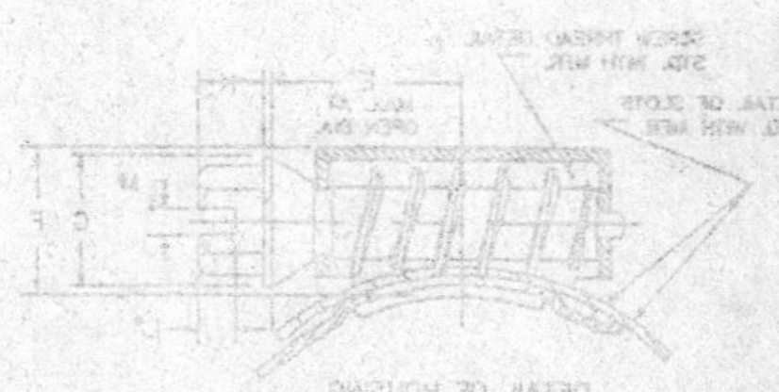

17 Ball Studs and Joints

STEERING BALL STUDS AND SOCKET ASSEMBLIES—SAE J491 NOV1987

SAE Recommended Practice

Report of the SAE Parts and Fittings Division approved August 1922 and revised by the SAE Steering and Suspension Ball Stud and Socket Committee November 1987.

Foreword—This Document has not changed other than to put it into the new SAE Technical Standards Board Format.

1. Scope—This SAE Recommended Practice has been established for the purpose of providing design criteria and suggested dimensional proportions which may be used for ball studs and ball stud socket assemblies as used on steering systems or control mechanisms of passenger vehicles, trucks and off-road equipment.

The recommended practice does not cover all applications. It is intended to provide assistance in obtaining functional satisfaction and interchangeability.

The inclusion of dimensional data in this report is not intended to imply that all the products described are stock production sizes. Consumers are requested to consult with manufacturers concerning stock production parts.

2. References

2.1 Applicable Publications—The following publications form a part of the specification to the extent specified herein. Unless otherwise indicated the lastest revision of SAE publications shall apply.

2.1.1 SAE Publication—Available from SAE, 400 Commonwealth Drive, Warrendale, PA 15096-0001.

SAE J485—Holes in Bolt and Capscrew Shanks and Slots in Nuts for Cotter Pins

2.1.2 ANSI Publication—Available from ANSI, 11 West 42nd Street, New York, NY 10036-8002.

ANSI B1.3M

3. Definitions

3.1 Master Gage—A taper gage that serves as a standard or base, designed to specific dimensions within blueprint specifications.

3.2 Blueing—A nondrying light paste with a pigment or die (such as "Prussian Blue") that colors a contacting surface. Blueing must be distributed evenly with minimum thickness on the taper surface of the master gage.

3.3 Blueing in a Master Gage—Blueing as applied to a master gage and gage forced onto a taper by hand pressure with a slight twisting motion followed by a rocking motion of the stud in the gage. (The gage should not rock.) Gage is removed for visual check of contact surface of taper.

ed. change

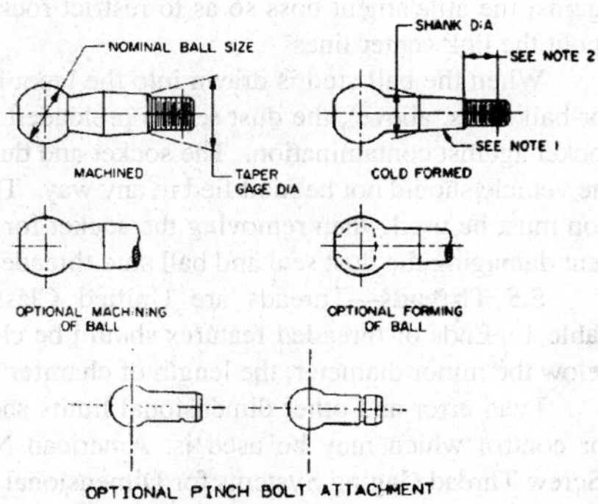

FIGURE 1—"FULL BALL" BALL STUDS

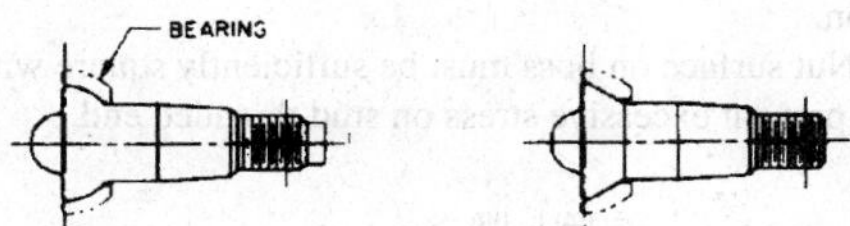

FIGURE 2—"HALF BALL" BALL STUDS FOR SEPARATE SPHERICAL BEARINGS

NOTE 1—Taper 1:8 on diameter unless other specified must show 60% minimum area of contact when blued in a master gage (See General Specifications).

NOTE 2—Cotter pin hole diameter should conform to SAE J485. The hole location is determined by the attachment eye and nut size. The hole should be located to provide a minimum of 50% engagement of the cotter pin with nut slot after allowing for draw-in at specified nut torque.

Cotter pin hole may be omitted and other than slotted nut used when application permits.

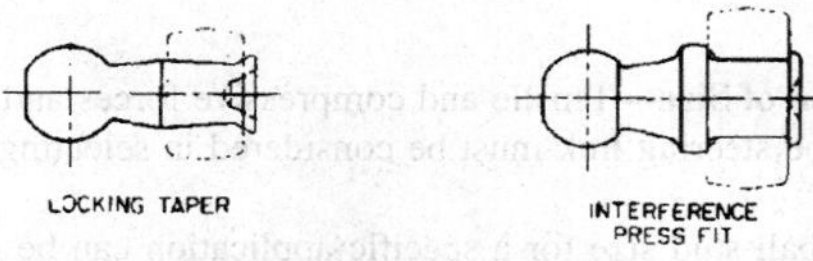

FIGURE 3—PERMANENTLY ATTACHED STUDS—RIVETED, WELDED, SPUN, OR STAKED

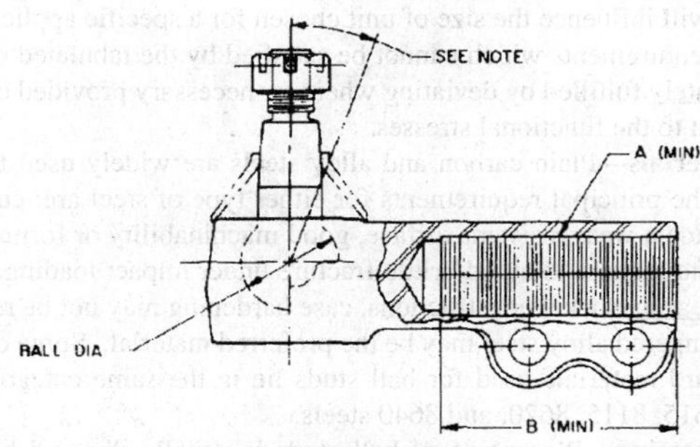

FIGURE 4—TYPICAL BALL STUD SOCKET ASSEMBLY WITH INTERNAL THREADED STEM

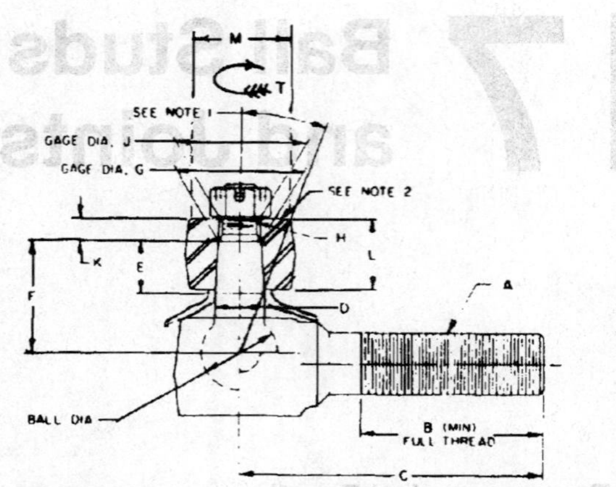

FIGURE 5—TYPICAL BALL STUD SOCKET ASSEMBLY WITH EXTERNAL THREADED STEM

NOTE 1—O - Angular travel determined as required for specific application.

NOTE 2—Nut surface on boss must be sufficiently square with tapered hole to prevent excessive stress on stud threaded end.

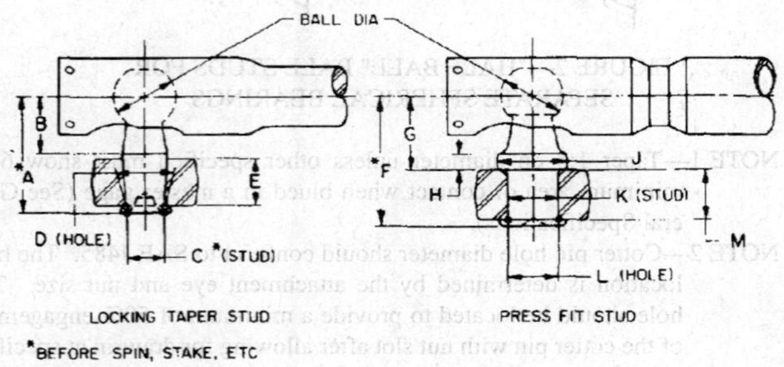

FIGURE 6—TYPICAL TUBULAR ("HORIZONTAL TYPE") SOCKET ASSEMBLY FOR RIVETED, SPUN, STAKED, WELDED, OR THREADED TAPER STUD ATTACHMENT. (FOR THREADED TAPER STUDS, USE TABLE 1 DIMENSIONS)

4. Ball Studs

4.1 Selection of Size—Tensile and compressive forces and functional load requirements of the steering link must be considered in selecting the proper ball stud size.

The proper ball stud size for a specific application can be reasonably well estimated by considering the stud as a cantilever beam supported at the junction with the mating boss, and loaded radially through the ball end by a force, or forces, the magnitude and direction of which have been previously determined. The type of loading, ball stud and bearing material, heat treatment, and load requirements will influence the size of unit chosen for a specific application.

Design requirements which cannot be satisfied by the tabulated dimensions may be adequately fulfilled by deviating wherever necessary provided due consideration is given to the functional stresses.

4.2 Materials—Plain carbon and alloy steels are widely used for all stud fabrication. The principal requirements for either type of steel are: case hardenability to provide a wear resistant surface, good machinability or formability, and adequate core toughness to avoid brittle fracture under impact loading. For plastic or rubber bearing socket constructions, case hardening may not be required. A quench and tempered alloy steel may be the preferred material. Some of the more popular standard materials used for ball studs lie in the same category as SAE 1019, 1541, 4615, 8115, 8620, and 8640 steels.

4.3 Processing—Processing of ball studs is usually dictated by the size, volume of production and equipment available. Ball studs used on passenger car and light truck steering systems are usually cold formed. Larger ball studs of relatively low production volume such as used on heavy duty trucks and off-road equipment are often fabricated as machined parts. Hot upset forging methods have also been used. The forming or machining is followed by total or selective hardening. Depending on the application and method of fabrication, it may be desirable to control the surface finish.

4.4 Attachment—The ball stud locking taper is usually used in conjunction with screw thread and nut attachment to allow for repair or replacement. The taper (usually 1:8) is designed to attach into mating parts made of steel; however, by proper design the ball studs can be adapted to mate with other materials for which different tapers may be desirable.

The nut selection should be determined by design requirements.

The specified nut torque or seating force may draw the stud locking taper into the mating arm significantly depending on several variables such as amount of taper, size of taper, material, heat treat and surface. When using a slotted nut, the nut is to be tightened to specification and then tightened further if necessary to align a slot with the cotter hole.

The amount of stud taper draw-in should be determined experimentally for each specific application.

The boss thickness and hole gage diameter at the nut face of the boss must be so related to the stud gage diameter as to provide sufficient unexposed threads to allow for draw-in at specified nut torque (reference Figure 5). To obtain the full stud cantilever strength, the face of the mounting boss should correspond nominally with the large end of the stud taper.

In addition to the screw thread and nut attachment method, locking pinch bolt type attachment may be used. permanent attachment means also may be used, such as riveting (upsetting), welding, spinning or staking. These methods may be used in conjunction with a locking taper or an interference press fit, in which case the stud is usually a straight shank end with a shoulder for locating purposes.

The permanently attached studs are used in conjunction with tubular ("horizontal type") sockets which can be assembled onto the stud (see Figure 6). The screw thread and nut tapered studs are usually preassembled into ball stud sockets, but can also be used with horizontal type sockets.

5. Sockets

5.1 Selection of Size—The socket size is generally dependent upon the ball stud size necessary for a specific application; however, the tensile and compressive forces and functional load requirements of the steering link must be considered in selecting the proper socket size.

5.2 Materials—Steering link sockets are often made of SAE 1030, 1038, 1040, and 1541 steels; however, a number of standard and special steels may be used to provide the desired mechanical properties for each application. Tubular ("horizontal type") sockets may also be made from seamless or welded tubing, frequently in SAE 1010, 1020 and 1025 steels.

5.3 Processing and Attachment—Steering link sockets are usually machined forgings with threaded stems for attaching to mating components. The stems may have external or internal threads. For internal threads, the socket may be forged with integral clamp ears that are machined to provide for locking the threads. Instead of clamp ears, lock nuts at the end of the internal threaded stem may also be used. Sockets may be forged into both ends of an integral link. In applications of sockets with threaded stems for attachment to tubular intermediaries or turnbuckles, a right-hand thread is usually paired with a left-hand thread to provide fast assembly and adjustment.

5.4 Socket Types & Dust Seals—In addition to sockets shown in Figure 4 and Figure 5, various other constructions are available. Selection depends on application. The sockets may have partial spherical surfaces under the dust seal area. Dust seals may be of the sliding type or boot seal type (which are attached to the socket). For limited angularity sockets, as may be used for some truck applications, the dust seal may be of dense resilient material to preload the socket against the attachment boss so as to restrict rocking motion of the steering links about the link center lines.

When the ball stud is drawn into the taper hole (as listed under Attachment for ball studs, above), the dust seal is preloaded to the proper amount to seal the socket against contamination. The socket and dust seal combination designed for the vehicle should not be modified in any way. The proper tools and extreme caution must be used when removing the socket for servicing attaching parts to prevent damaging the dust seal and ball stud threaded end.

5.5 Threads—Threads are Unified Class 2A of the size indicated in Table 1. Ends of threaded features should be chamfered approximately 0.02 in. below the minor diameter; the length of chamfer to be 1/2 to 1 1/2 threads.

Lead error and other dimensional limits should be controlled. A reference for control which may be used is: American National Standard ANSI B1.3M "Screw Thread Gaging Systems for Dimensional Acceptability."

In application of sockets with threaded stems, the length of engagement of stem threads with the attaching rod or sleeve depends on design and may vary, but should be approximately 2 1/2 times the thread diameter. Under extremes of adjustment, where the application permits, engagement may be as low as 1 1/2 times the thread diameter.

5.6 Lubrication—Lubrication fittings, if required, may be placed at any convenient location on the periphery or face of the socket provided the location does not create forging processing, assembly or functional complications.

5.7 Figures and Tables—The included Figures 4, 5, and 6 are intended to illustrate descriptions and table dimensions.

TABLE 1A—STEERING-BALL STUD SOCKET ASSEMBLY DIMENSIONS(1)
(DIMENSIONS IN UNITED STATES CUSTOMARY UNITS) SEE FIGURE 5.

	Socket Thread			Ball Stud					Attachment Arm				Stud Nut
Nominal Ball Dia	Size A	Length B	Socket Length C	Shank Dia D	Taper Length E	Gage Dia Location F	Gage Dia G	Thread Size H	Cage Dia J	Draw-in Clearance K(2)	Thickness L	Boss Dia M(3)	Tightening Torque T(4)
in	in	in	in	in	in	in	in	in	in	in	in	in	lb-ft0
5/8	1/2-20	1.74	2.62	0.469	0.41	1.06	0.418	3/8-24	0.402	0.128	0.50	1.25	15-30
3/4	9/16-18	1.94	2.94	0.547	0.45	1.20	0.490	7/16-20	0.473	0.136	0.56	1.38	30-45
7/8	11/16-18	2.06	3.12	0.625	0.52	1.36	0.560	1/2-20	0.543	0.136	0.62	1.50	35-55
1	11/16-18	2.21	3.38 0	0.703	0.72	1.62	0.613	9/16-18	0.590	0.184	0.88	1.75	55-80
1 1/8	7/8-18	2.75	3.88	0.781	0.84	1.88	0.675	5/8-18	0.652	0.184	1.00	1.88	80-110
1 1/4	1-16	3.19	4.25	0.875	0.94	2.03	0.758	5/8-18	0.731	0.216	1.12	2.00	80-110
1 1/2	1 1/8-12	3.75	4.88	1.031	1.12	2.44	0.890	3/4-16	0.863	0.216	1.31	2.25	100-140
1 3/4	1 1/4-12		5.75	1.250	1.28	2.81	1.074	7/8-14	1.043	0.248	1.50	2.75	120-170
2				1.350	1.50	3.22	1.166	1-12	1.131	0.280	1.75	3.00	140-220
2 1/4				1.510	1.78	3.72	1.285	1 1/8-12	1.250	0.280	2.00	3.25	180-270
2 1/2				1.700	2.06	4.34	1.441	1 1/4-12	1.406	0.280	2.25	3.50	230-320

1. These dimensions may be varied as required for specific applications. See General Specification.
2. Before tightening nut.
3. The boss diameter or "hoop size" was determined by using the recommended nut tightening torque to determine "hoop size" at recommended thickness "L" with the stress level below the yield strength of medium carbon steels forgings.
4. Ranges of tightening torque for 1:8 taper in medium carbon or alloy steel forgings. For other materials or tapers, these torque values must be adjusted. The torque values recommended are empirical values determined by combined experience of SAE Ball Stud and Tie Rod Socket Committee members.

TABLE 1B—STEERING-BALL STUD SOCKET ASSEMBLY DIMENSIONS
(DIMENSIONS IN SI UNITS) SEE FIGURE 5.

	Socket Thread			Ball Stud					Attachment Arm				Stud Nut
Nominal Ball Dia (1)	Size A	Length B	Socket Length C	Shank Dia D	Taper Length E	Gage Dia Location F	Gage Dia G	Thread Size H	Gage Dia J	Draw-in Clearance K(2)	Thickness L	Boss Dia M(3)	Tightening Torque T(4)
mm	mm	mm	mm	mm	mm	mm	mm	mm	mm	mm	mm	mm	N.m
16	M12×1.25	45	65	12	10.4	26	10.62	M10×1.25	10.21	3.3	13	32	24–40
20	M14×1.5	50	75	14	11.4	30	12.45	M12×1.25	12.01	3.5	14	35	40–60
22	M16×1.5	50	80	16	13.2	34	14.22	M12×1.25	13.79	3.5	16	38	40–60
25	M16×1.5	55	85	18	18.3	41	15.57	M14×1.5	14.99	4.7	22	44	75–110
28	M24×1.5	70	100	20	21.3	48	17.15	M16×1.5	16.56	4.7	25	48	110–150
32	M24×1.5	80	110	22	23.9	50	19.25	M16×1.5	18.57	5.5	28	50	110–150
38	M30×1.5	95	125	26	28.5	62	22.61	M20×1.5	21.92	5.5	33	58	140–190
44	M30×1.5		150	32	32.5	72	27.28	M24×1.5	26.49	6.3	38	70	180–230
50				34	38.1	82	29.62	M24×1.5	28.73	7.1	44	76	160–230
58				38	45.2	95	32.64	M30×1.5	31.75	7.1	50	82	240–370
64				44	52.3	110	36.6	M30x1.5	35.71	7.1	57	88	240-370

1. These dimensions may be varied as required for specific applications. See General Specification.
2. Before tightening nut.
3. The boss diameter or "hoop size" was determined by using the recommended nut tightening torque to determine "hoop size" at recommended thickness "L" with the stress level below the yield strength of medium carbon steel forgings.
4. Ranges of tightening torque for one unit per eight units of length taper in medium carbon or alloy steel forgings. For other materials or tapers, these torque values must be adjusted. The torque values recommended are empirical values determined by combined experience of SAE Ball Stud and Tie Rod Socket Committee members.

TABLE 2A—TYPICAL DIMENSIONS FOR TUBULAR SOCKET STUDS (DIMENSIONS IN UNITED STATES CUSTOMARY UNITS) SEE FIGURE 6.

Nominal Ball Dia	Locking Taper Studs					Press Fit Studs						
	A	B	C	D	E	F	G	H	J	K	L	M
in	in	in	in	in	in	in	in	in	in	in	in	in
5/8	1.31	0.68	0.387	0.402	0.50							
3/4	1.47	0.75	0.457	0.437	0.56	1.49	0.87	0.18	0.75	0.598	0.592	0.50
7/8	1.62	0.84	0.527	0.543	0.62	1.78	1.03	0.28	0.88	0.693	0.637	0.62
1	1.84	0.91	0.585	0.601	0.78	2.06	1.12	0.28	1.00	0.770	0.764	0.81
1 1/8	2.14	1.03	0.642	0.660	0.94	2.15	1.21	0.28	1.12	0.839	0.833	0.81
1 1/4	2.34	1.09	0.719	0.739	1.06							
1 1/2	2.72	1.31	0.855	0.879	1.19							
1 3/4	3.16	1.53	1.031	1.059	1.38							
2	3.50	1.72	1.131	1.162	1.50							
2 1/4	4.02	1.94	1.248	1.281	1.75							
2 1/2	4.69	2.28	1.399	1.437	2.00							

TABLE 2B—TYPICAL DIMENSIONS FOR TUBULAR SOCKET STUDS (DIMENSIONS IN SI UNITS) SEE FIGURE 6.

Nominal Ball Dia	Locking Taper Studs					Press Fit Studs						
	A	B	C	D	E	F	G	H	J	K	L	M
mm	mm	mm	mm	mm	mm	mm	mm	mm	mm	mm	mm	mm
16	33	17	10.0	10.4	13							
19	37	19	12.0	12.4	14	38.0	22.0	5	19	15.15	15.00	12.8
22	41	21	13.5	14.0	16	45.2	26.0	7	22	17.60	17.45	16.0
25	47	23	15.0	15.4	20	52.3	28.5	7	25	19.65	19.50	20.6
28	54	26	16.5	17.0	24	54.5	30.5	7	28	21.35	21.20	20.8
32	59	28	18.0	18.5	27							
38	70	33	22.0	22.6	30							
44	80	39	26.0	26.7	35							
50	90	44	29.0	29.8	38							
56	100	49	32.0	32.8	45							
64	120	58	35.5	36.5	50							

ROD ENDS AND CLEVIS PINS—SAE J493 JUN1961 SAE Standard

Report of the Miscellaneous Division approved January 1915 and last revised by the SAE Parts and Fittings Committee May 1959. Editorial change June 1961.

1. Scope

2. References

2.1 Applicable Publications—The following publications form a part of the specification to the extent specified herein. Unless otherwise indicated the latest revision of SAE publications shall apply.

2.1.1 SAE PUBLICATIONS—Available from SAE, 400 Commonwealth Drive, Warrendale, PA 15096-0001.

SAE J1010—Emission Control Hose

SAE J1111—Component Nomenclatue—Skidder-Grapple

3. General Specifications for Clevis Pins

3.1 Material—SAE 1010 or SAE 1111 steel or equivalent.

3.2 Heat Treatment—Clevis pins shall be supplied either soft or cyanide hardened as specified.

3.3 Defects—Clevis pins must be free from burrs, loose scale, sharp edges, and all other defects that might affect their serviceability.

3.4 Tolerances—General tolerances for all dimensions are ±0.010 unless otherwise specified.

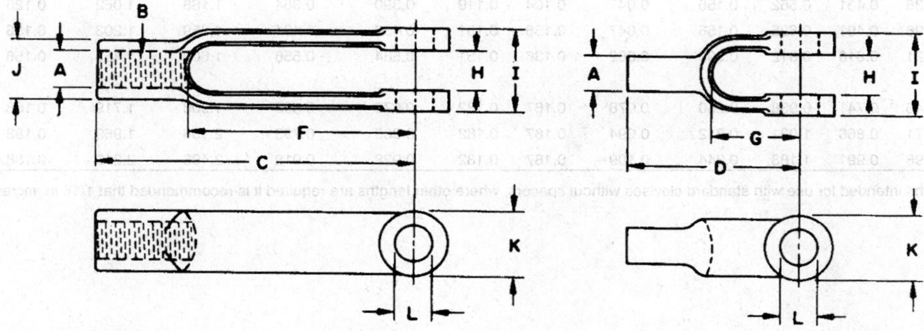

FIGURE 1—ADJUSTABLE AND PLAIN YOKES

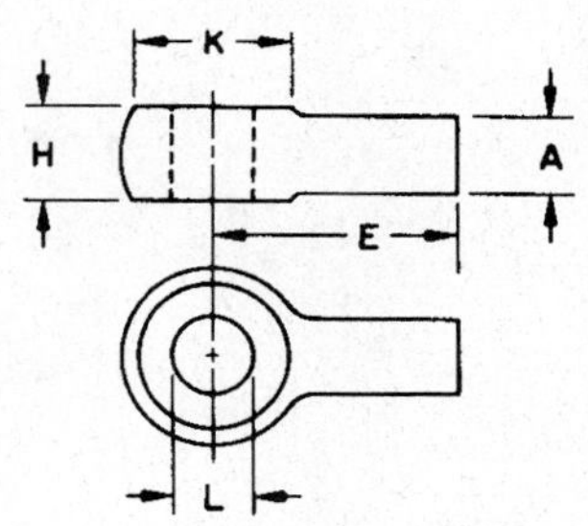

FIGURE 2—EYE

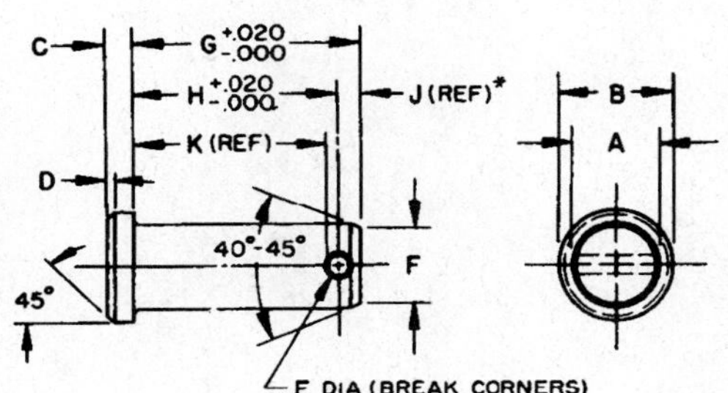

* THE "J" DIMENSION (DISTANCE FROM CENTERLINE OF HOLE TO END OF PIN) IS FOR CALCULATION ONLY. ON DETAIL DRAWINGS OF CLEVIS PINS, HOLE LOCATION WILL BE SHOWN AS THE DISTANCE FROM THE UNDERSIDE OF THE HEAD TO THE CENTERLINE OF THE HOLE

FIGURE 3—PIN

TABLE 1—ADJUSTABLE AND PLAIN YOKE AND EYE (SEE FIGURES 1 AND 2)

Series	A	Threads per In., B	C	D	E	F	G	H Fork ±0.010 Eye ± +0.000 –0.010	I ±0.010	J	K	L Nominal	L Tolerance Plus 0.001; Minus
	No. 10	32	1-9/16	1-1/4	1-1/4	1	7/16	3/16	7/16	5/16	3/8	3/16	0.001
	1/4	28	2	1-3/4	1-1/4	1-1/4	5/8	9/32	5/8	7/16	1/2	1/4	0.001
Light	5/16	24	2-1/4	2	1-3/8	1-7/16	3/4	11/32	3/4	1/2	19/32	5/16	0.001
	3/8	24	2-1/2	2-1/8	1-1/2	1-5/8	27/32	7/16	7/8	5/8	11/16	3/8	0.001
	7/16	20	2-7/8	2-1/4	1-1/2	1-7/8	1	1/2	1	23/32	13/16	7/16	0.001
	1/2	20	3	2-1/2	1-3/4	1-7/8	1-1/8	9/16	1-1/8	13/16	15/16	1/2	0.002
	1/2	20	4-3/16	2-1/2	1-3/4	3-1/16	1-1/8	9/16	1-1/8	13/16	15/16	1/2	0.002
	5/8	18	4-15/16	2-7/8	2	3-11/16	1-7/16	11/16	1-3/8	1-1/16	1-3/16	5/8	0.002
Heavy	3/4	16	6-1/16	3-5/8	2-3/8	4-9/16	1-11/16	13/16	1-5/8	1-1/4	1-7/16	3/4	0.002
	7/8	14	7-1/8	4	2-3/4	5-1/4	2	15/16	1-7/8	1-7/16	1-11/16	7/8	0.002
	1	14	8	4-1/2	3	6	2-1/2	1-1/16	2-1/8	1-5/8	1-15/16	1	0.002

TABLE 2—CLEVIS PINS, (SEE FIGURE 3)

Nominal Size	A Body Dia Max	A Body Dia Min	B Head Dia	C Head Height	D Head Chamfer	E Hole Dia Min	E Hole Dia Max	F Chamfer Dia Max	F Chamfer Dia Min	Length (H + J) Nom G(1)	H Under Head to Center of Hole	J Center of Hole to End Ref	K Under Head to Edge of Nom Hole Ref
3/16	0.186	0.181	0.312	0.062	0.016	0.073	0.088	0.152	0.147	0.578	0.484	0.094	0.445
1/4	0.248	0.243	0.375	0.094	0.031	0.073	0.088	0.214	0.209	0.766	0.672	0.094	0.633
5/16	0.311	0.306	0.438	0.094	0.031	0.104	0.119	0.265	0.259	0.938	0.812	0.125	0.757
3/8	0.373	0.368	0.500	0.125	0.031	0.104	0.119	0.327	0.321	1.062	0.938	0.125	0.883
7/16	0.436	0.431	0.562	0.156	0.047	0.104	0.119	0.390	0.384	1.188	1.062	0.125	1.008
1/2	0.496	0.491	0.625	0.156	0.047	0.136	0.151	0.439	0.431	1.359	1.203	0.156	1.133
5/8	0.621	0.616	0.812	0.203	0.062	0.136	0.151	0.564	0.556	1.609	1.453	0.156	1.383
3/4	0.746	0.741	0.938	0.250	0.078	0.167	0.182	0.678	0.668	1.906	1.719	0.188	1.633
7/8	0.871	0.866	1.031	0.312	0.094	0.167	0.182	0.803	0.793	2.156	1.969	0.188	1.883
1	0.996	0.991	1.188	0.344	0.109	0.167	0.182	0.928	0.918	2.406	2.219	0.188	2.133

1. Tabulated lengths intended for use with standard clevises without spacers, where other lengths are required it is recommended that 1/16 in. increments be used.

BALL STUD AND SOCKET ASSEMBLY—TEST PROCEDURES—SAE J193 JUN96

SAE Recommended Practice

Report of the SAE Ball Stud and Tie Rod Socket Committee approved August 1970. Completely revised by the SAE Steering and Suspension Ball Stud and Socket Committee February 1987. Reaffirmed by the SAE Materials, Parts, and Processes Division June 1996.

Foreword—This Document has not changed other than to put it into the new SAE Technical Standards Board Format.

1. ***Scope***—The test procedures describe a method to laboratory test suspension and steering system ball stud and/or socket assemblies for functional characteristics. This procedure is an extension of SAE J491b recommended practice on dimensional recommendations for ball studs towards a vehicle application. The tests are conducted either on ball studs individually or on complete integral assemblies representing the application.

1.1 Objective—To provide a uniform method of testing ball studs and ball stud and socket assemblies to ensure that the parts will meet functional requirements of the application.

2. ***References***

2.1 Applicable Publications—The following publications form a part of this specification to the extent specified herein. Unless otherwise specified, the latest issue of SAE publications shall apply.

2.1.1 SAE PUBLICATIONS—Available from SAE, 400 Commonwealth Drive, Warrendale, PA 15096-0001.

SAE J491—Steering Ball Studs and Socket Assemblies

SAE Paper #660102—Simulation of Field Loading in Fatigue Testing

3. ***Test Procedures***—The test procedures for suspension and steering components with few exceptions can be similar because all ball stud and socket assemblies are subject to axial, lateral, and longitudinal forces, differing only in the direction and magnitude of loading depending on the application.

The test procedures cover the following characteristics:

5.1 Ball Stud
5.1.1 Ball Stud Impact Strength
5.1.2 Ball Stud Yield
5.1.3 Ball Stud Tensile Load
5.2 Ball Stud and Socket
5.2.1 Ball Stud to Socket Rotating and Oscillating Torque
5.2.2 Ball Stud to Socket Axial End Movement
5.2.3 Ball Stud to Socket Cam-Out Strength
5.2.4 Ball Stud and Socket Assembly Fatigue and Heat Test
5.2.5 Ball Stud and Socket Pull-Out and Push-Out Strength
5.2.6 Ball Stud and Socket Angularity

4. ***Loading and Cycle Life***—The loading used in the test procedures should be as representative as possible in magnitude and direction with loads encountered in the design application. Recommended cycle life is provided where applicable with each procedure.

To determine preliminary loading magnitude and direction, a layout design model of the complete suspension and steering system, possibly computerized, should be utilized. A paper analysis can be made solving for the component loading by assuming maximum "G" forces at the wheel/ground contact.

Using a vehicle with a similar suspension and/or steering system design, a program loading procedure can be utilized to obtain a more realistic loading assessment. With this procedure, key load carrying components are strain gaged to measure the load magnitudes, direction, frequency of load application and phasing (timing of load application). The vehicle is driven over a circuit of road input events that simulate expected usage. From this data, histograms of loading magnitude versus cumulative load application cycles can be obtained that will establish the laboratory ultimate strength peak loads as well as a group of fatigue and wear test loads and associated cycles for a specific vehicle life.

Representative program loading procedures are described in many SAE reports (SAE Report #660102).

5. ***Objectives and Test Procedures***

5.1 Ball Stud—Tests conducted on individual ball studs.

5.1.1 BALL STUD IMPACT STRENGTH

5.1.1.1 Objective—To determine the impact strength of the ball stud.

5.1.1.2 Procedure—The test is applicable to either suspension or steering system studs. Mount the stud in a rigid fixture as shown in Figure 1. Lock stud in fixture by torquing the retaining nut to design specifications.

Apply an impact load to exceed the expected impact load in the vehicle application.

Increase the impact load incrementally until a separation occurs to determine the load capability. Only one impact per stud is permissible.

The stud must not fail by brittle fracture. Bending deflection must be 10 degrees minimum.

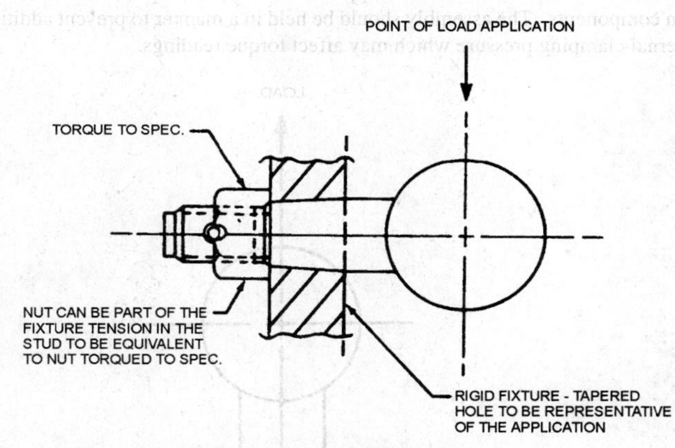

FIGURE 1—IMPACT TEST

5.1.2 BALL STUD YIELD

5.1.2.1 Objective—To determine at what load condition the ball stud will take a permanent set without fracture.

5.1.2.2 Procedure—The test is applicable to either suspension or steering system studs.

The test fixture is shown in Figure 2. Grind a small flat on the head of the stud for accuracy of reading, to receive the dial indicator or other measuring device.

Install the ball stud in the fixture with the mating taper hole in such a manner that a load can be applied to the stud at right angles to the stud centerline and opposite the flat ground on the stud. Lock stud in fixture by torquing the retaining nut to design specification.

Preload the stud. Set dial indicator or other measuring device to zero. Take deflection and set readings in desired increments to permanent set range.

Stud yield load is equal to load required to permanently set stud without surface cracks or failure and may be used to select stud application.

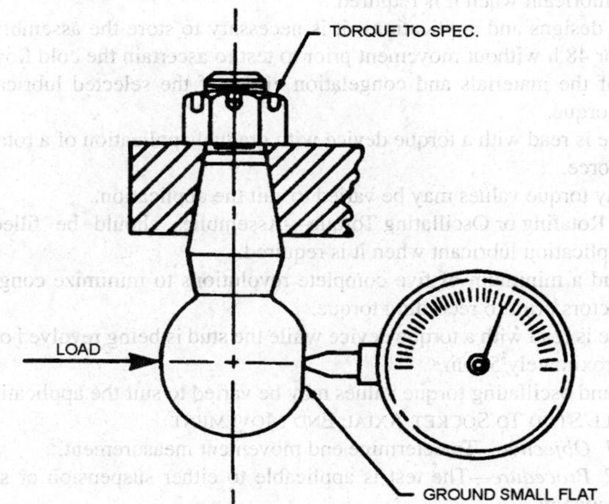

FIGURE 2—TEST FIXTURE

5.1.3 BALL STUD TENSILE LOAD

5.1.3.1 Objective—To determine the tensile load capability of the ball stud.

5.1.3.2 Procedure—The test is applicable to either suspension or steering system studies depending on the intended application, but generally would be appropriate for a suspension ball stud where the predominant loading would be in a tensile direction.

Mount the stud in a load/deflection testing machine as shown in Figure 3.

CAUTION—Use care to prevent eccentric loading. A typical tensile load application rate is 5 mm/min. Record load and mode of fracture for each sample tested.

5.2 Ball Stud and Socket—Tests conducted on complete ball stud and socket assemblies.

5.2.1 BALL STUD TO SOCKET ROTATING AND OSCILLATING TORQUE

5.2.1.1 Objective—To ensure desired rotating and oscillating torque is obtained.

5.2.1.2 Procedure—The test is applicable to either suspension or steering system components. The assembly should be held in a manner to prevent addition of external clamping pressure which may affect torque readings.

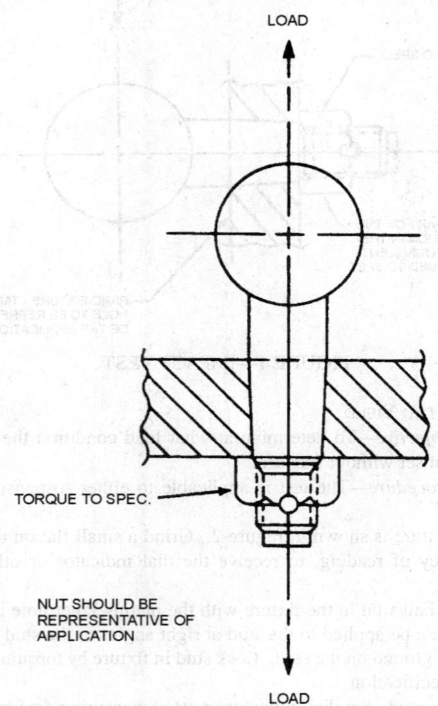

FIGURE 3—TENSILE TEST

5.2.1.2.1 Breakaway Torque—Assemblies should be filled with specified application lubricant when it is required.

For some designs and applications, it is necessary to store the assembly (with lubricant) for 48 h without movement prior to test to ascertain the cold flow characteristics of the materials and congelation effect of the selected lubricant and breakaway torque.

The torque is read with a torque device with gradual application of a rotating or oscillating force.

Breakaway torque values may be varied to suit the application.

5.2.1.2.2 Rotating or Oscillating Torque—Assemblies should be filled with specified application lubricant when it is required.

Rotate stud a minimum of five complete revolutions to minimize congelation and other factors prior to recording torque.

The torque is read with a torque device while the stud is being revolved or oscillated at approximately 5 rpm.

Rotating and oscillating torque values may be varied to suit the application.

5.2.2 BALL STUD TO SOCKET AXIAL END MOVEMENT

5.2.2.1 Objective—To determine end movement measurement.

5.2.2.2 Procedure—The test is applicable to either suspension or steering system components.

5.2.2.2.1 Spring Loaded Type—For axial movement, the following is commonly used. The stud should be set perpendicular to the socket. Socket should be supported on the bottom of assembly. A force is applied to the stud (less nut) and the axial movement of the stud is noted and recorded. (Figure 4A depicts typical fixture.)

NOTE—Ensure that the top of the stud is flat at the contact point of force (grind if necessary).

5.2.2.2.2 All Other Types of Socket Assemblies—With the shank of the socket assembly clamped to prevent squeezing of socket and stud, pull upward. After the movement of the stud is noted and recorded, the operation is repeated with a force pushing downward. (Figure 4B depicts a typical fixture for tie rod ends.)

5.2.3 BALL STUD TO SOCKET CAM-OUT STRENGTH

5.2.3.1 Objective—To determine retention of the ball stud in the socket at angular positions and to determine the angle of separation.

5.2.3.2 Procedure—The test is applicable to either suspension or steering system components. The ball stud and socket assemblies should be mounted in a tensile test machine with the test specimen stud held in a fixture which permits unrestricted angular travel. (Figure 5 depicts a typical fixture.)

A tensile load is applied to the assembly parallel to the normal load direction when the test stud is in full angular travel. The test is repeated with a new sample, using a compression load. The maximum load and angle induced prior to separating the stud from the socket is recorded.

5.2.4 BALL STUD AND SOCKET ASSEMBLY FATIGUE AND HEAT TEST

5.2.4.1 Objective—To determine fatigue and wear characteristics of ball stud and socket assemblies.

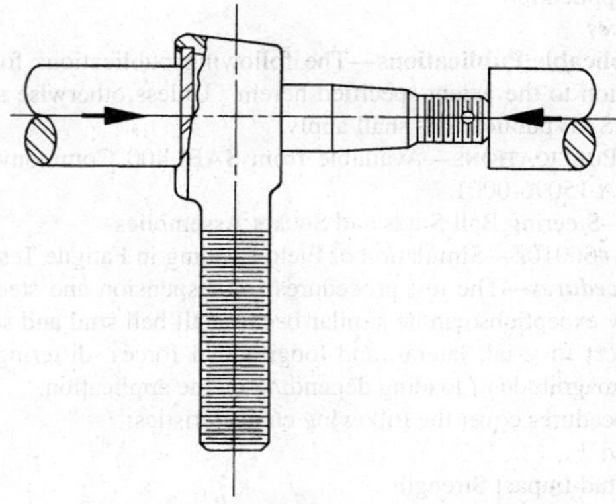

FIGURE 4A—BALL STUD TO SOCKET AXIAL END MOVEMENT—TYPICAL FIXTURE

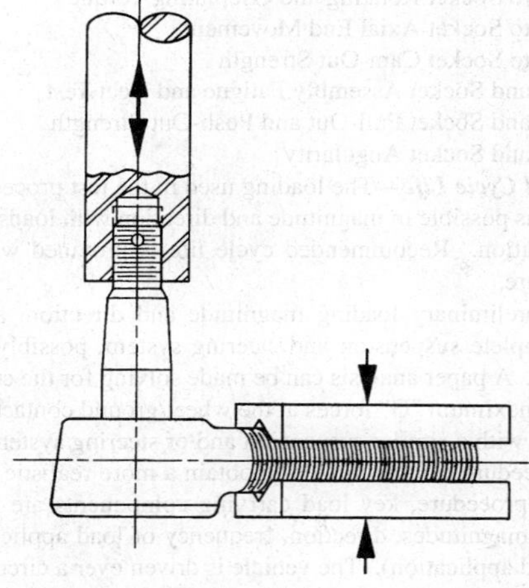

FIGURE 4B—BALL STUD SOCKET AXIAL END MOVEMENT—TYPICAL FIXTURE FOR TIE ROD ENDS

5.2.4.2 Procedure—This test is applicable to either suspension or steering system components. Use socket assemblies which have been tested according to 5.2.1, 5.2.2, and 5.2.6 and found acceptable. Socket assemblies should be filled with recommended lubricant when required in the application. Socket assemblies should be installed, with seals when required, in a fixture by placing the taper shank in the mating tapered hole with the retaining nut torqued to design specification. For each type to be tested, the ball stud and socket assemblies may be modified to suit the test machine providing the modifications do not affect test results. Securely clamp the link in a manner to achieve the required motions. The following are typical motions which may be used. (Refer to Figures 6A and 6B.)

a. Angular Oscillation—±20 degrees in a plan parallel to the link or 90 degrees to axis of suspension control arm pivot centerline. A typical rate is 60 cpm.

b. Angular Rotation—±40 degrees measured about the ball stud shank centerline. A typical rate is 32 cpm.

c. Load—Alternating designated horizontal tension and compression load for steering applications. Suspension ball stud and socket tests will also require vertical tension or compression loads. A typical rate is 60 cpm.

Load application angle may be varied to suit the application. The socket assemblies are then tested to required angles, frequencies, and load applications concurrently and completed in two phases. When actual use dictates, other application loads, angles, and frequencies may be substituted.

5.2.4.2.1 Phase I Test—Peak Load—To correlate the cycle life with the maximum operating load to which the assembly will be subjected in its actual application.

The cycle life varies for each type of application and environment; therefore, a program loading procedure for the specific application is required to establish load and cycle life required for this test.

In the absence of complete program loading data, and to provide a basis for standardized testing of the assembly, 7500 cycles is a reasonable cycle life for this test.

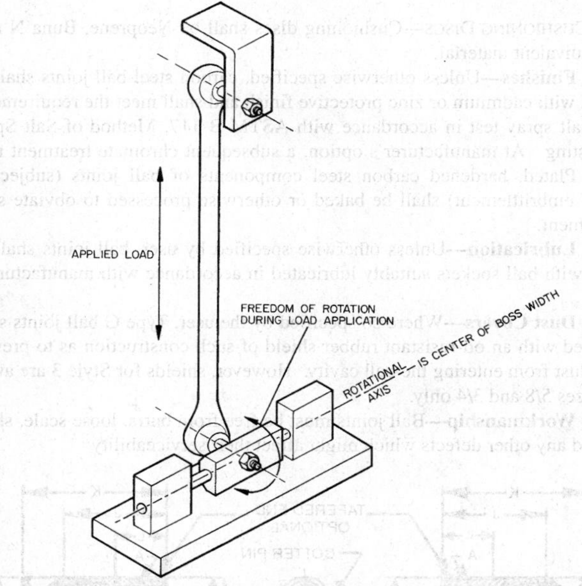

FIGURE 5—BALL STUD TO SOCKET CAM-OUT STRENGTH—TYPICAL FIXTURE

5.2.4.2.2 Phase II Test—Endurance Load—To correlate the cycle life of the assembly for the average load to which the assembly will be subjected in its application and environment, with life in actual use, and to establish the load which provides for extended fatigue and heat life.

The load and cycle life varies for each type of application and environment; therefore, a program loading procedure for the specific application is recommended to establish load and cycle life required for this test.

In the absence of complete program loading data and to provide a basis for standardized testing of the assembly, 250 000 cycles is reasonable life for this test.

During the Phase I and Phase II tests, artificial cooling may be used where deemed necessary to prevent heat build-up which would not be experienced in the application.

If the application of the ball stud and socket assembly includes environmental contamination, contaminants should be provided to correlate with these conditions in the test. This procedure will determine seal durability and effectiveness.

Typical test environments commonly used are:

a. Ozone atmosphere

b. Saline and dust, 4.0 L of water, 50% saturated solution of common salt at 21 °C to 24 °C, and 0.15 kg of SAE air cleaner test dust fine grade.

c. Steam

Conditions to be examined at completion of test to determine adequacy for the application:

The rotating and oscillating torque condition (See 5.2.1) (see 5.2.1).

The end movement (see 5.2.2)(See 5.2.2).

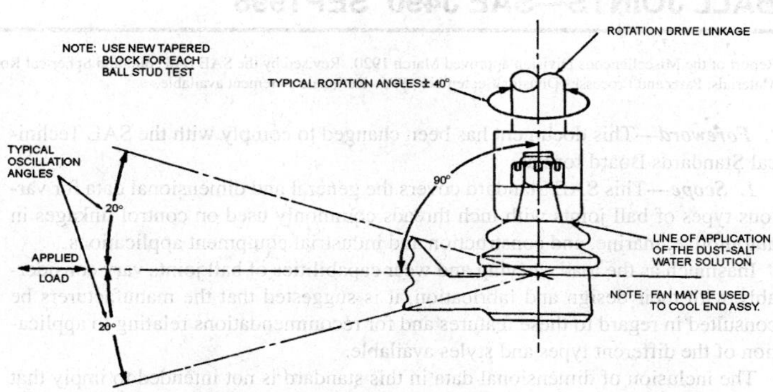

FIGURE 6A—TYPICAL STEERING LINKAGE BALL STUD AND SOCKET ASSEMBLY

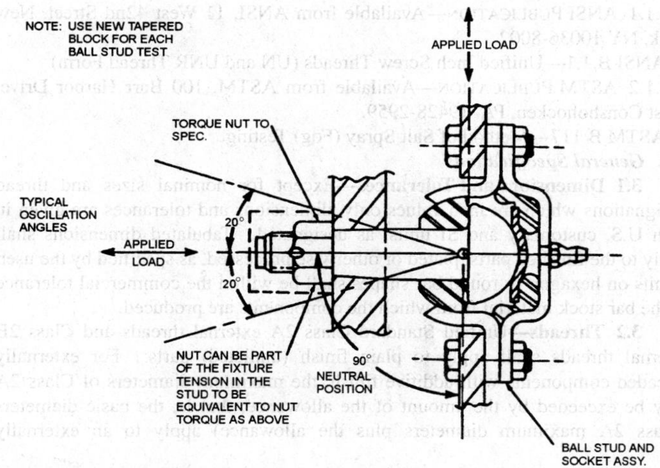

FIGURE 6B—TYPICAL SUSPENSION BALL STUD AND SOCKET ASSEMBLY

The ball stud should be examined for any surface cracks, determined by a dye check or approved equivalent.

The ball stud should be examined for any local yielding, determined by a dimension check.

The internal components should be examined for damage.

5.2.5 Ball Stud And Socket Pull-out And Push-out Strength

5.2.5.1 Objective—To determine the tension or compression loads which will separate the ball stud from the socket.

5.2.5.2 Procedure—This test is applicable to either suspension or steering system components. Assemble the ball stud and socket assembly in a load/deflection testing machine so that the load applied to the stud is perpendicular to the ball joint mounting surface.

Measure and record the stud tensile load required to separate the stud from the socket assembly. A typical load application rate is 5 mm/min. Repeat the test with another sample using a compressive load.

The acceptance criteria for stud pull– or push-out should be established from the calculated or measured loads based on the application.

5.2.6 Ball Stud And Socket Angularity

5.2.6.1 Objective—To determine if the socket throat is capable of providing the required stud angularity.

5.2.6.2 Procedure—This test is applicable to either suspension or steering system components. Assemble the ball stud and socket assembly into a rigid fixture simulating the assembly into a suspension arm or steering linkage.

Measure and record stud travel angularity both along the socket throat major axis and across the minor axis.

The acceptance criteria is based on the angularity requirements in the specific application adjusted to take into account the effect of dimensional variations and suspension/linkage compliance.

(R) BALL JOINTS—SAE J490 SEP1996 — SAE Standard

Report of the Miscellaneous Division approved March 1920. Revised by the SAE Ball Joint and Spherical Rod End Committee October 1981. Completely revised by the SAE Materials, Parts and Processes Division September 1996. Rationale statement available.

Foreword—This document has been changed to comply with the SAE Technical Standards Board format.

1. Scope—This SAE Standard covers the general and dimensional data for various types of ball joints with inch threads commonly used on control linkages in automotive, marine, and construction and industrial equipment applications.

Inasmuch as the load carrying and wear capabilities of ball joints vary considerably with their design and fabrication, it is suggested that the manufacturers be consulted in regard to these features and for recommendations relating to application of the different types and styles available.

The inclusion of dimensional data in this standard is not intended to imply that all the products described are stock production sizes. Consumers are requested to consult with manufacturers concerning availability of stock production parts.

2. References

2.1 Applicable Publications—The following publications form a part of this specification to the extent specified herein.

2.1.1 ANSI Publication—Available from ANSI, 11 West 42nd Street, New York, NY 10036-8002.

ANSI B.1.1—Unified Inch Screw Threads (UN and UNR Thread Form)

2.1.2 ASTM Publication—Available from ASTM, 100 Barr Harbor Drive, West Conshohocken, PA 19428-2959.

ASTM B 117—Method of Salt Spray (Fog) Testing.

3. General Specifications

3.1 Dimensions and Tolerances—Except for nominal sizes and thread designations which are inch values only, dimensions and tolerances are given in both U.S. customary and SI units, as designated. Tabulated dimensions shall apply to the finished parts, plated or otherwise processed, as specified by the user. Limits on hexagon or round bar shapes shall be within the commercial tolerance of the bar stock material from which the components are produced.

3.2 Threads—Unified Standard Class 2A external threads and Class 2B internal threads shall apply to plain finish (unplated) parts. For externally threaded components with additive finish, the maximum diameters of Class 2A may be exceeded by the amount of the allowance; that is, the basic diameters (Class 2A maximum diameters plus the allowance) apply to an externally threaded part after plating. For internally threaded components with additive finish, the Class 2B diameters apply after plating. See ANSI B 1.1.

3.2.1 External threads shall be chamfered to a diameter 0.01 in (0.3 mm) less than the minor diameter to produce a length of chamfered or partial thread equivalent to ¾ to 1¼ times the pitch (rounded to a three-place decimal).

3.2.2 Internal threads shall be countersunk 90 degrees included angle to a diameter 0.01 in (0.3 mm) greater than the major diameter of the thread (rounded to a two-place decimal).

3.3 Material

3.3.1 Ball Joints—Ball joints are normally made from low carbon free machining steel. The ball stud and mating plug components of Types A, AL, B, and C and the ball sockets on Type G, Styles 3 and 4, ball joints shall be case hardened unless otherwise specified. For special application, ball joints can be produced from alloy steel, corrosion resistant steel, brass, bronze, or other materials.

3.3.2 Cushioning Discs—Cushioning discs shall be Neoprene, Buna N rubber, or equivalent material.

3.4 Finishes—Unless otherwise specified, carbon steel ball joints shall be furnished with cadmium or zinc protective finish and shall meet the requirements of 32 h salt spray test in accordance with ASTM B 117, Method of Salt Spray (Fog) Testing. At manufacturer's option, a subsequent chromate treatment may be used. Plated, hardened carbon steel components of ball joints (subject to hydrogen embrittlement) shall be baked or otherwise processed to obviate such embrittlement.

3.5 Lubrication—Unless otherwise specified by user, ball joints shall be supplied with ball sockets suitably lubricated in accordance with manufacturer's practice.

3.6 Dust Covers—Where so specified by the user, Type G ball joints shall be supplied with an oil-resistant rubber shield of such construction as to prevent dirt and dust from entering the ball cavity. However, shields for Style 3 are available in sizes 5/8 and 3/4 only.

3.7 Workmanship—Ball joints must be free from burrs, loose scale, sharp edges, and any other defects which might affect their serviceability.

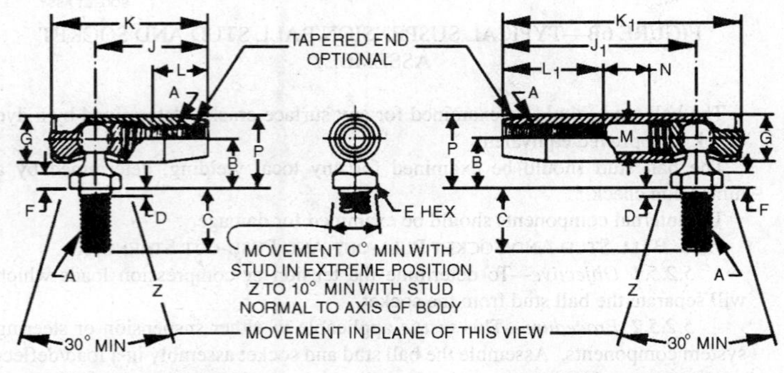

FIGURE 1—CRIMPED END PLUG WITH SPRING CONSTRUCTION—TYPE A

FIGURE 2—CRIMPED END PLUG WITH SPRING CONSTRUCTION—TYPE AL

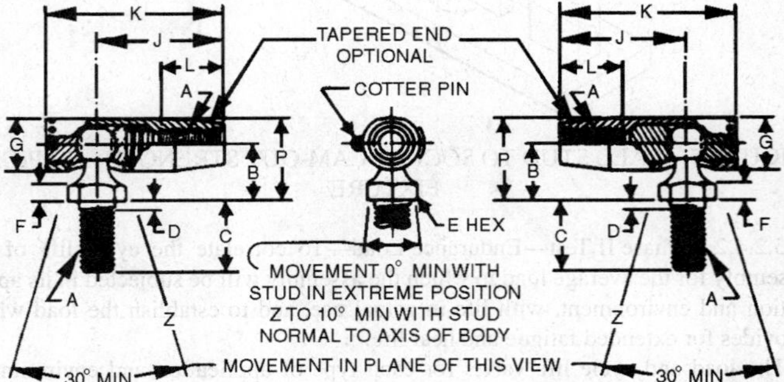

FIGURE 3—THREADED END PLUG WITH SPRING CONSTRUCTION—TYPE B

FIGURE 4—THREADED END PLUG WITHOUT SPRING CONSTRUCTION—TYPE C

TABLE 1A—DIMENSIONS OF TYPES A, B, C AND ALL BALL JOINTS—B THROUGH J_1 (FIGURES 1 TO 4)

Nominal Ball Joint Size and Thread Diameter, A, in		Threads per in	B in ±0.02	B mm ±0.5	C in ±0.02	C mm ±0.5	D max in	D Max mm	E Hex in	E Hex mm	F Min in	F Min mm	G Dia in	G Dia mm	J in ±0.03	J mm ±0.8	J_1 in ±0.03	J_1 mm ±0.8
No. 10	0.190	32	0.44	11.2	0.44	11.2	0.06	1.5	0.312	7.92	0.12	3.0	0.38	9.7	0.88	22.3	1.50	38.1
No. 12	0.216	32	0.44	11.2	0.44	11.2	0.06	1.5	0.312	7.92	0.12	3.0	0.38	9.7	0.88	22.3	1.50	38.1
1/4	0.250	28	0.47	11.9	0.56	14.2	0.09	2.3	0.375	9.52	0.12	3.0	0.44	11.2	0.97	24.6	1.81	46.0
5/16	0.3125	24	0.53	13.5	0.69	17.5	0.09	2.3	0.438	11.12	0.16	4.1	0.50	12.7	1.12	28.4	1.94	49.3
3/8	0.375	24	0.69	17.5	0.88	22.3	0.09	2.3	0.500	12.70	0.19	4.8	0.62	15.8	1.38	35.0	—	—
7/16	0.4375	20	0.88	22.3	1.12	28.4	0.12	3.0	0.625	15.88	0.25	6.4	0.75	19.0	1.94	49.3	—	—
1/2	0.500	20	0.88	22.3	1.12	28.4	0.12	3.0	0.625	15.88	0.25	6.4	0.75	19.0	1.94	49.3	—	—

TABLE 1B—DIMENSIONS OF TYPES A, B, C AND ALL BALL JOINTS—K THROUGH P (FIGURES 1 TO 4)

Nominal Ball Joint Size and Thread Diameter, A in		K in ±0.03	K mm ±0.8	K_1 in ±0.03	K_1 mm ±0.8	L Min Full Thread mm 0.44	L Min Full Thread mm 11.2	L_1 Min Full Thread in 0.56	L_1 Min Full Thread mm 14.2	M Dia in +0.01 -0.00	M Dia mm +0.3 -0.0	N(1) (Ref) in	N(1) (Ref) mm	P(1) Max (Ref) in	P(1) Max (Ref) mm	Stud Ball Dia (Ref)(1) Max in	Stud Ball Dia (Ref)(1) Max mm	Stud Ball Dia (Ref)(1) Min in	Stud Ball Dia (Ref)(1) Min mm
No. 10	0.190	1.25	31.8	1.81	46.0	0.44	11.2	0.56	14.2	0.20	5.1	0.50	12.7	0.65	16.5	0.255	6.48	0.250	6.35
No. 12	0.216	1.25	31.8	1.81	46.0	0.50	12.7	0.88	22.3	0.23	5.8	0.50	12.7	0.65	16.5	0.255	6.48	0.250	6.35
1/4	0.250	1.38	35.0	2.25	57.2	0.56	14.2	1.00	25.4	0.27	6.9	0.50	12.7	0.72	18.3	0.305	7.75	0.300	7.62
5/16	0.3125	1.56	39.6	2.38	60.5	0.75	19.0	—	—	0.33	8.4	0.50	12.7	0.81	20.6	0.350	8.89	0.345	8.76
3/8	0.375	1.94	49.3	—	—	1.00	25.4	—	—	—	—	—	—	1.03	26.2	0.424	10.77	0.419	10.64
7/16	0.4375	2.62	66.5	—	—	1.00	25.4	—	—	—	—	—	—	1.28	32.5	0.555	14.10	0.550	13.97
1/2	0.500	2.62	66.5	—	—	1.00	25.4	—	—	—	—	—	—	1.28	32.5	0.555	14.10	0.550	13.97

1. These dimensions are given for design purposes only and are not intended for inspection.

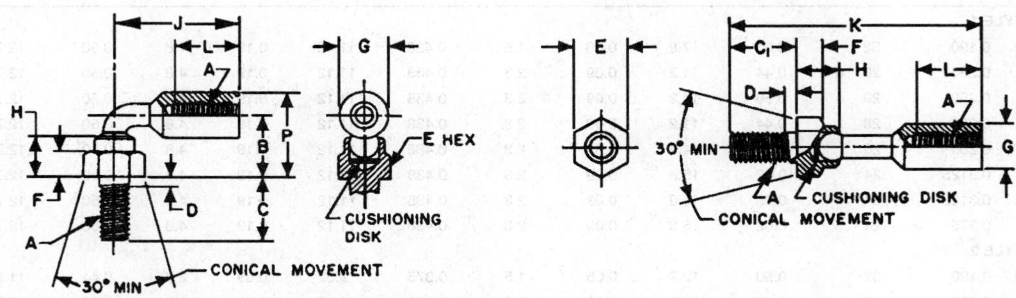

TYPES D AND DS ARE NOT RECOMMENDED FOR APPLICATIONS INVOLVING TENSION OR SEVERE VIBRATION.

FIGURE 5—CUSHIONED TWO-PIECE CONSTRUCTION—TYPE D*

FIGURE 6—CUSHIONED TWO-PIECE CONSTRUCTION—TYPE DS*

TABLE 2A—DIMENSIONS OF TYPES D AND DS BALL JOINTS—B THROUGH F (FIGURES 5 AND 6)

Nominal Ball Joint Size and Thread Diameter, A, in		Thds per in	B in ±0.03	B mm ±0.8	C in ±0.02	C mm ±0.5	C_1 in ±0.02	C_1 mm ±0.5	D Max in	D Max mm	E Hex in	E Hex mm	F Min in	F Min mm
No. 10	0.190	32	0.53	13.5	0.44	11.2	0.56	14.2	0.06	1.5	0.375	9.52	0.19	4.8
No. 10	0.190	32	0.53	13.5	0.44	11.2	—	—	0.06	1.5	0.375	9.52	0.19	4.8
No. 12	0.216	24	0.53	13.5	0.56	14.2	0.56	14.2	0.06	1.5	0.375	9.52	0.19	4.8
No. 12	0.216	32	0.53	13.5	0.56	14.2	0.56	14.2	0.06	1.5	0.375	9.52	0.19	4.8
1/4	0.250	28	0.56	14.2	0.56	14.2	0.56	14.2	0.06	1.5	0.438	11.12	0.19	4.8
5/16	0.3125	24	0.69	17.5	0.69	17.5	0.69	17.5	0.09	2.3	0.562	14.28	0.28	7.1

TABLE 2B—DIMENSIONS OF TYPES D AND DS BALL JOINTS—G THROUGH P_1 (FIGURES 5 AND 6)

Nominal Ball Joint Size and Thread Diameter, A, in		Thds per in	G Dia in	G Dia mm	H in ±0.03	H mm ±0.8	J in ±0.03	J mm ±0.8	K in ±0.03	K mm ±0.8	L Min Full Thread in	L Min-Full Thread mm	P(1) Max (Ref) in	P(1) Max (Ref) mm
No. 10	0.190	32	0.28	7.1	0.33	8.4	1.03	26.2	2.03	51.6	0.50	12.7	0.70	17.8
No. 10	0.190	32	0.28	7.1	0.33	8.4	0.78	19.8	—	—	0.38	9.7	0.70	17.8
No. 12	0.216	24	0.28	7.1	0.33	8.4	1.03	26.2	2.03	51.6	0.50	12.7	0.70	17.8
No. 12	0.216	32	0.28	7.1	0.33	8.4	1.03	26.2	2.03	51.6	0.50	12.7	0.70	17.8
1/4	0.250	28	0.31	7.9	0.35	8.9	1.06	26.9	2.09	53.1	0.56	14.2	0.75	19.0
5/16	0.3125	24	0.44	11.2	0.45	11.4	1.31	33.3	2.63	66.8	0.69	17.5	0.94	23.9

1. These dimensions are given for design purposes only and are not intended for inspection.

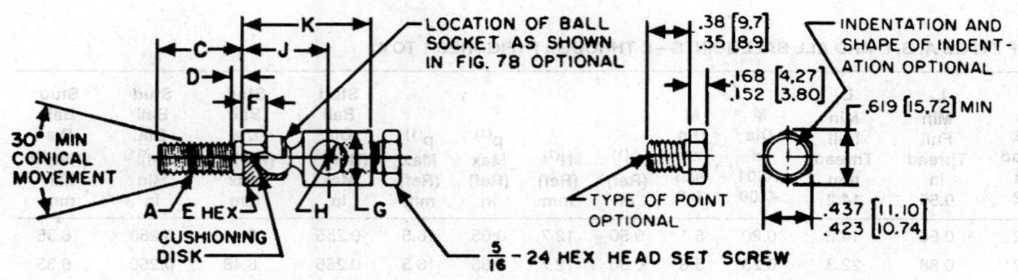

FIGURE 7A—TYPE DC—STYLE 1

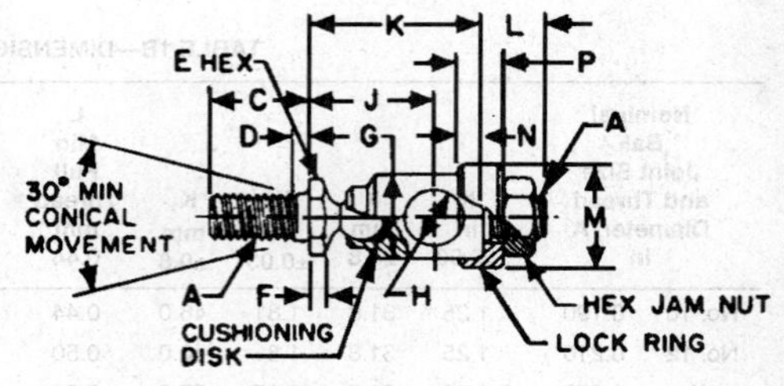

FIGURE 7B—TYPE DC—STYLE 2

TABLE 3A—DIMENSIONS OF TYPES DC BALL JOINTS—C THROUGH H (FIGURES 7A AND 7B)

Nominal Ball Joint Size and Thread Diameter, A, in		Thds per in	C in ±0.02	C mm ±0.5	D Max in	D Max mm	E Hex in	E Hex mm	F Min in	F Min mm	G Dia in	G Dia mm	H Dia in ±0.005	H Dia mm ±0.13
STYLE 1														
No. 10	0.190	32	0.31	7.9	0.06	1.5	0.438	11.12	0.19	4.8	0.50	12.7	0.323	8.20
1/4	0.250	20	0.44	11.2	0.09	2.3	0.438	11.12	0.19	4.8	0.50	12.7	0.323	8.20
1/4	0.250	20	0.56	14.2	0.09	2.3	0.438	11.12	0.19	4.8	0.50	12.7	0.323	8.20
1/4	0.250	28	0.44	11.2	0.09	2.3	0.438	11.12	0.19	4.8	0.50	12.7	0.323	8.20
1/4	0.250	28	0.56	14.2	0.09	2.3	0.438	11.12	0.19	4.8	0.50	12.7	0.323	8.20
5/16	0.3125	24	0.62	15.8	0.09	2.3	0.438	11.12	0.19	4.8	0.50	12.7	0.323	8.20
5/16	0.3125	24	0.75	19.0	0.09	2.3	0.438	11.12	0.19	4.8	0.50	12.7	0.323	8.20
3/8	0.375	24	0.62	15.8	0.09	2.3	0.438	11.12	0.19	4.8	0.50	12.7	0.323	8.20
STYLE 2														
No. 10	0.190	32	0.50	12.7	0.06	1.5	0.375	9.52	0.09	2.3	0.44	11.2	0.197	5.00
1/4	0.250	20	0.44	11.2	0.09	2.3	0.438	11.12	0.09	2.3	0.50	12.7	0.328	8.33
1/4	0.250	28	0.44	11.2	0.06	1.5	0.438	11.12	0.09	2.3	0.50	12.7	0.328	8.33
5/16	0.3125	24	0.62	15.8	0.09	2.3	0.438	11.12	0.11	2.8	0.56	14.2	0.380	9.65

TABLE 3B—DIMENSIONS OF TYPES DC BALL JOINTS—J THROUGH F (FIGURES 7A AND 7B)

Nominal Ball Joint Size and Thread Diameter, A, in		Thds per in	J in ±0.03	J in ±0.8	K in ±0.03	K mm ±0.8	L in ±0.2	L mm ±0.5	M Dia in	M Dia mm	N in ±0.01	N mm ±0.3	P in ±0.005	P mm ±0.13
STYLE 1														
No. 10	0.190	32	0.75	19.0	1.12	28.4	—	—	—	—	—	—	—	—
1/4	0.250	20	0.75	19.0	1.12	28.4	—	—	—	—	—	—	—	—
1/4	0.250	20	0.75	19.0	1.12	28.4	—	—	—	—	—	—	—	—
1/4	0.250	28	0.75	19.0	1.12	28.4	—	—	—	—	—	—	—	—
1/4	0.250	28	0.75	19.0	1.12	28.4	—	—	—	—	—	—	—	—
5/16	0.3125	24	0.75	19.0	1.12	28.4	—	—	—	—	—	—	—	—
5/16	0.3125	24	0.75	19.0	1.12	28.4	—	—	—	—	—	—	—	—
3/8	0.375	24	0.75	19.0	1.12	28.4	—	—	—	—	—	—	—	—
STYLE 2														
No. 10	0.190	32	0.62	15.8	0.78	19.8	0.40	10.2	0.56	14.2	0.12	3.0	0.250	6.35
1/4	0.250	20	0.78	19.8	1.02	25.9	0.34	8.6	0.62	15.8	0.12	3.0	0.250	6.35
1/4	0.250	28	0.78	19.8	1.02	25.9	0.34	8.6	0.62	15.8	0.12	3.0	0.250	6.35
5/16	0.3125	24	0.75	19.0	1.03	26.2	0.53	13.5	0.75	19.0	0.19	4.8	0.344	8.74

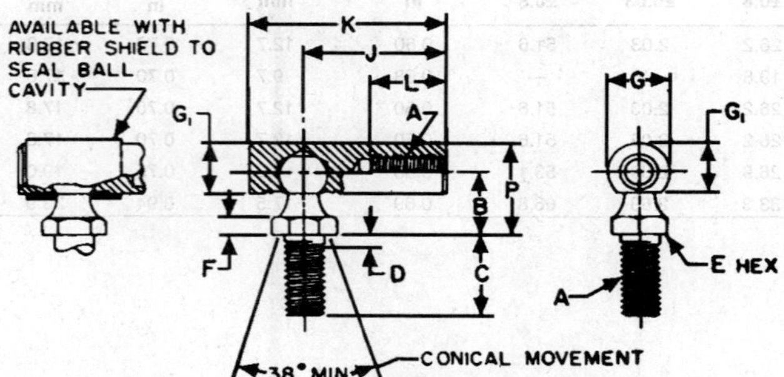

FIGURE 8A—TYPE G NONDETACHABLE CONSTRUCTION WITHOUT SPRING—STYLE 1

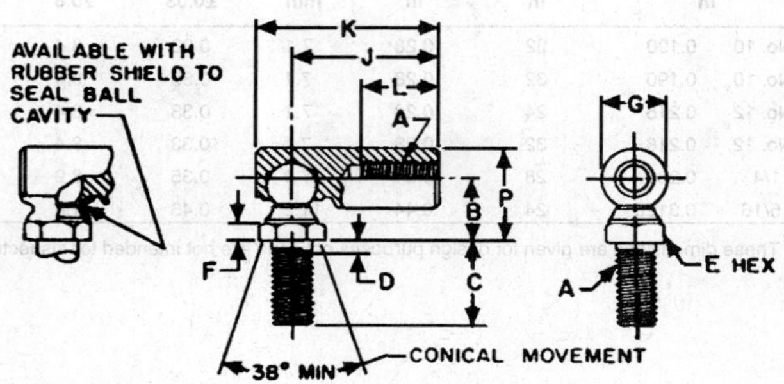

FIGURE 8B—TYPE G NONDETACHABLE CONSTRUCTION WITHOUT SPRING—STYLE 2

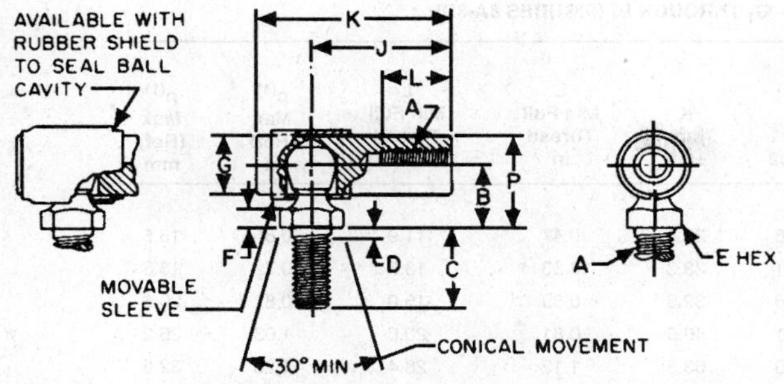

FIGURE 8C—TYPE G NONDETACHABLE CONSTRUCTION WITHOUT SPRING—STYLE 3[2]

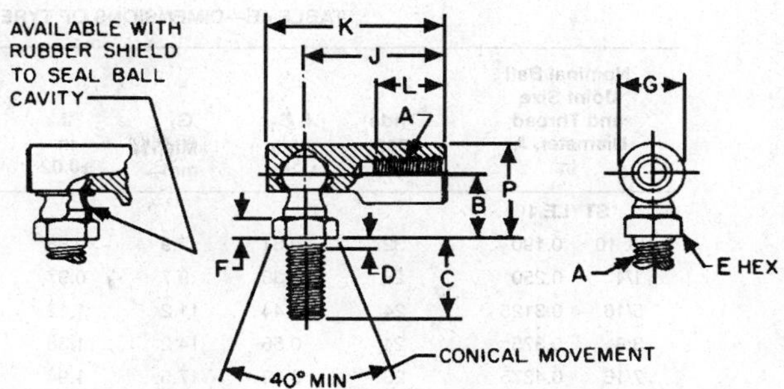

FIGURE 8D—TYPE G NONDETACHABLE CONSTRUCTION WITHOUT SPRING—STYLE 4[3]

TABLE 4A—DIMENSIONS OF TYPE G BALL JOINTS—B THROUGH G (FIGURES 8A-8D)

Nominal Ball Joint Size +and Thread Diameter, A, In		Thds per in	B in ±0.02	B mm ±0.5	C in ±0.02	C mm ±0.5	D Max in	D Max mm	E Hex in	E Hex mm	F Min in	F Min mm	G in	G mm
STYLE 1														
No. 10	0.190	32	0.44	11.2	0.44	11.2	0.06	1.5	0.312	7.92	0.12	3.0	0.38	9.7
1/4	0.250	28	0.47	11.9	0.56	14.2	0.06	1.5	0.375	9.52	0.12	3.0	0.44	11.2
5/16	0.3125	24	0.53	13.5	0.69	17.5	0.09	2.3	0.438	11.12	0.16	4.1	0.50	12.7
3/8	0.375	24	0.69	17.5	0.88	22.3	0.09	2.3	0.500	12.70	0.19	4.8	0.62	15.8
7/16	0.4375	20	0.88	22.3	1.12	28.4	0.12	3.0	0.625	15.88	0.25	6.4	0.75	19.0
1/2	0.500	20	0.88	22.3	1.12	28.4	0.12	3.0	0.625	15.88	0.25	6.4	0.75	19.0
STYLE 2														
No. 10	0.190	32	0.44	11.2	0.44	11.2	0.06	1.5	0.312	7.92	0.12	3.0	0.38	9.7
1/4	0.250	28	0.47	11.9	0.56	14.2	0.09	2.3	0.375	9.52	0.12	3.0	0.44	11.2
5/16	0.3125	24	0.53	13.5	0.69	17.5	0.09	2.3	0.438	11.12	0.16	4.1	0.50	12.7
3/8	0.375	24	0.69	17.5	0.88	22.3	0.09	2.3	0.500	12.70	0.19	4.8	0.62	15.8
7/16	0.4375	20	0.88	22.3	1.12	28.4	0.12	3.0	0.625	15.88	0.25	6.4	0.75	19.0
1/2	0.500	20	0.88	22.3	1.12	28.4	0.12	3.0	0.625	15.88	0.25	6.4	0.75	19.0
5/8	0.625	18	1.00	25.4	1.12	28.4	0.12	3.0	0.750	19.05	0.31	7.9	0.88	22.3
3/4	0.750	16	1.06	26.9	1.12	28.4	0.12	3.0	0.875	22.22	0.31	7.9	1.00	25.4
STYLE 3														
No. 10	0.190	32	0.44	11.2	0.44	11.2	0.06	1.5	0.312	7.92	0.12	3.0	0.38	9.7
1/4	0.250	28	0.47	11.9	0.56	14.2	0.06	1.5	0.375	9.52	0.12	3.0	0.44	11.2
5/16	0.3125	24	0.53	13.5	0.69	17.5	0.09	2.3	0.438	11.12	0.16	4.1	0.50	12.7
3/8	0.375	24	0.69	17.5	0.88	22.3	0.09	2.3	0.500	12.70	0.19	4.8	0.62	15.8
1/2	0.500	20	0.88	22.3	1.12	28.4	0.12	3.0	0.625	15.88	0.28	7.1	0.75	19.0
5/8	0.625	18	1.06	26.9	1.12	28.4	0.12	3.0	0.875	22.22	0.31	7.9	1.00	25.4
3/4	0.750	16	1.06	26.9	1.12	28.4	0.12	3.0	0.875	22.22	0.31	7.9	1.00	25.4
STYLE 4														
No. 10	0.190	32	0.47	11.9	0.44	11.2	0.06	1.5	0.375	9.52	0.12	3.0	0.44	11.2
1/4	0.250	28	0.47	11.9	0.56	14.2	0.09	2.3	0.375	9.52	0.12	3.0	0.44	11.2
5/16	0.3125	24	0.53	13.5	0.69	17.5	0.09	2.3	0.438	11.12	0.16	4.1	0.50	12.7
3/8	0.375	24	0.69	17.5	0.88	22.3	0.09	2.3	0.500	12.70	0.19	4.8	0.62	15.8
7/16	0.4375	20	0.88	22.3	1.12	28.4	0.12	3.0	0.625	15.88	0.25	6.4	0.75	19.0
1/2	0.500	20	0.88	22.3	1.12	28.4	0.12	3.0	0.625	15.88	0.25	6.4	0.75	19.0
5/8	0.625	18	1.00	25.4	1.12	28.4	0.12	3.0	0.750	19.05	0.31	7.9	0.88	22.3

TABLE 4B—DIMENSIONS OF TYPE G BALL JOINTS—G_1 THROUGH P_1 (FIGURES 8A-8D)

Nominal Ball Joint Size and Thread Diameter, A, in		Thds per in	G_1 Min in	G_1 Min mm	J in ±0.02	J mm ±0.5	K in ±0.02	K mm ±0.5	L Min Full Thread in	L Min Full Thread mm	P(1) Max (Ref) in	P(1) Max (Ref) mm
STYLE 1												
No. 10	0.190	32	0.31	7.9	0.88	22.3	1.16	29.5	0.47	11.9	0.65	16.5
1/4	0.250	28	0.38	9.7	0.97	24.6	1.31	33.3	0.53	13.5	0.72	18.3
5/16	0.3125	24	0.44	11.2	1.12	28.4	1.56	39.6	0.59	15.0	0.81	20.6
3/8	0.375	24	0.56	14.2	1.38	35.0	1.81	46.0	0.81	20.6	1.03	26.2
7/16	0.4375	20	0.69	17.5	1.94	49.3	2.50	63.5	1.12	28.4	1.28	32.5
1/2	0.500	20	0.69	17.5	1.94	49.3	2.50	63.5	1.12	28.4	1.28	32.5
STYLE 2												
No. 10	0.190	32	—	—	0.88	22.3	1.06	26.9	0.47	11.9	0.65	16.5
1/4	0.250	28	—	—	0.97	24.6	1.22	31.0	0.50	12.7	0.72	18.3
5/16	0.3125	24	—	—	1.12	28.4	1.41	35.8	0.56	14.2	0.81	20.6
3/8	0.375	24	—	—	1.38	35.0	1.69	42.9	0.75	19.0	1.03	26.2
7/16	0.4375	20	—	—	1.94	49.3	2.38	60.5	1.00	25.4	1.28	32.5
1/2	0.500	20	—	—	1.94	49.3	2.38	60.5	1.00	25.4	1.28	32.5
5/8	0.625	18	—	—	2.06	52.3	2.58	65.5	1.00	25.4	1.47	37.3
3/4	0.750	16	—	—	2.12	53.8	3.00	76.2	1.12	28.4	1.59	40.4
STYLE 3(2)												
No. 10	0.190	32	—	—	0.88	22.3	1.16	29.5	0.47	11.9	0.65	16.5
1/4	0.250	28	—	—	0.97	24.6	1.31	33.3	0.53	13.5	0.72	18.3
5/16	0.3125	24	—	—	1.12	28.4	1.56	39.6	0.59	15.0	0.81	20.6
3/8	0.375	24	—	—	1.38	35.0	1.81	46.0	0.81	20.6	1.03	26.2
1/2	0.500	20	—	—	1.94	49.3	2.62	66.5	1.12	28.4	1.28	32.5
5/8	0.625	18	—	—	2.12	53.8	3.00	76.2	1.12	28.4	1.59	40.4
3/4	0.750	16	—	—	2.12	53.8	3.00	76.2	1.12	28.4	1.59	40.4
STYLE 4(3)												
No. 10	0.190	32	—	—	0.97	24.6	1.22	31.0	0.44	11.2	0.72	18.3
1/4	0.250	28	—	—	0.97	24.6	1.22	31.0	0.50	12.7	0.72	18.3
5/16	0.3125	24	—	—	1.12	28.4	1.41	35.8	0.56	14.2	0.81	20.6
3/8	0.375	24	—	—	1.38	35.0	1.69	42.9	0.75	19.0	1.03	26.2
7/16	0.4375	20	—	—	1.94	49.3	2.38	60.5	1.00	25.4	1.28	32.5
1/2	0.500	20	—	—	1.94	49.3	2.38	60.5	1.00	25.4	1.28	32.5
5/8	0.625	18	—	—	2.06	52.3	2.58	65.5	1.00	25.4	1.47	37.3

1. These dimensions are given for design purposes only and are not intended for inspection.
2. Type G Style 3 ball joints are furnished with ball studs and ball cavities (ball stud only on 5/8 and 3/4 in sizes) hardened to assure longer wear.
3. Type G, Style 4 ball joints in all sizes are furnished with both ball studs and ball sockets hardened to assure longer wear.

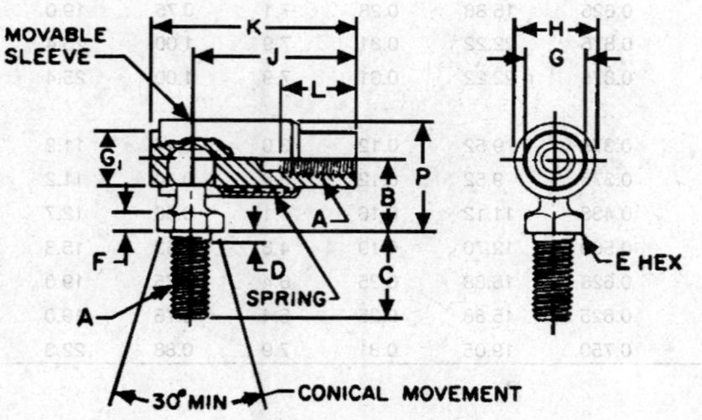

FIGURE 9A—TYPE S DETACHABLE CONSTRUCTION—STYLE 1

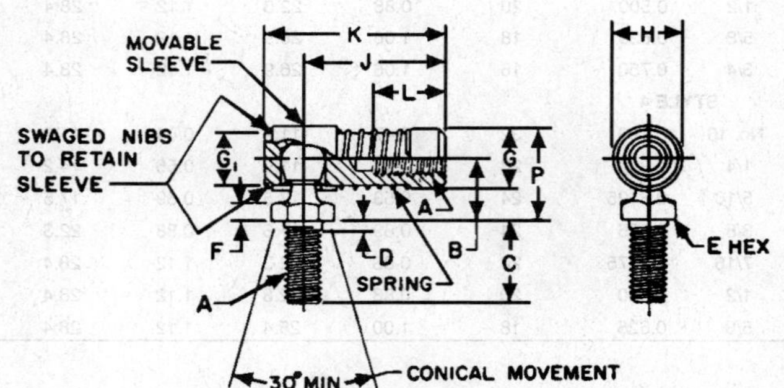

FIGURE 9B—TYPE S DETACHABLE CONSTRUCTION—STYLE 2

TABLE 5A—DIMENSIONS OF TYPE S BALL JOINTS—B THROUGH G (FIGURES 9A AND 9B)

Nominal Ball Joint Size and Thread Diameter, A, in		Thds per in	B in ±0.02	B mm ±0.5	C in ±0.02	C mm ±0.5	D Max in	D Max mm	E Hex in	E Hex mm	F Min in	F Min mm	G Dia in ±0.010
STYLE 1													
No. 10	0.190	32	0.47	11.9	0.44	11.2	0.06	1.5	0.312	7.92	0.12	3.0	0.312
No. 12	0.216	32	0.47	11.9	0.44	11.2	0.06	1.5	0.312	7.92	0.12	3.0	0.312
1/4	0.250	28	0.47	11.9	0.56	14.2	0.06	1.5	0.312	7.92	0.12	3.0	0.312
5/16	0.3125	24	0.59	15.0	0.69	17.5	0.09	2.3	0.438	11.12	0.16	4.1	0.438
3/8	0.375	24	0.72	18.2	0.88	22.3	0.09	2.3	0.500	12.70	0.19	4.8	0.562
7/16	0.4375	20	0.97	24.6	1.12	28.4	0.12	3.0	0.625	15.88	0.25	6.4	0.750
1/2	0.500	20	0.97	24.6	1.12	28.4	0.12	3.0	0.625	15.88	0.25	6.4	0.750
5/8	0.625	18	1.12	28.4	1.12	28.4	0.12	3.0	0.750	19.05	0.31	7.9	0.875
STYLE 2													
1/4	0.250	28	0.47	11.9	0.56	14.2	0.06	1.5	0.375	9.52	0.12	3.0	0.562
5/16	0.3125	24	0.53	13.5	0.69	17.5	0.09	2.3	0.438	11.12	0.16	4.1	0.625
3/8	0.375	24	0.69	17.5	0.88	22.3	0.09	2.3	0.500	12.70	0.19	4.8	0.750
1/2	0.500	20	0.88	22.3	1.12	28.4	0.12	3.0	0.625	15.88	0.28	7.1	0.938

TABLE 5B—DIMENSIONS OF TYPE S BALL JOINTS—G_1 THROUGH p[(1)] (FIGURES 9A AND 9B)

Nominal Bll Joint Size and Thread Diameter, A, in		Thds per in	G Dia mm ±0.25	G_1 Dia in ±0.010	G_1 Dia mm ±0.25	H Dia in ±0.01	H Dia mm ±0.3	J in ±0.02	J mm ±0.5	K in ±0.02	K mm ±0.5	L Min Full Thread in	L Min Full Thread mm	p[(1)] Max (Ref) in	p[(1)] Max (Ref) mm
STYLE 1															
No. 10	0.190	32	7.92	0.312	7.92	0.44	11.2	0.91	23.1	1.09	27.7	0.44	11.2	0.72	18.3
No. 12	0.216	32	7.92	0.312	7.92	0.44	11.2	0.91	23.1	1.09	27.7	0.44	11.2	0.72	18.3
1/4	0.250	28	7.92	0.312	7.92	0.44	11.2	0.91	23.1	1.09	27.7	0.50	12.7	0.72	18.3
5/16	0.3125	24	11.12	0.438	11.12	0.62	15.7	1.25	31.8	1.56	39.6	0.56	14.2	0.93	23.6
3/8	0.375	24	14.28	0.562	14.27	0.75	19.0	1.56	39.6	1.94	49.3	0.75	19.0	1.13	28.7
7/16	0.4375	20	12.70	0.750	19.05	1.00	25.4	2.03	51.6	2.53	64.3	1.00	25.4	1.50	38.1
1/2	0.500	20	12.70	0.750	19.05	1.00	25.4	2.03	51.6	2.53	64.3	1.00	25.4	1.50	38.1
5/8	0.625	18	22.22	0.875	22.22	1.12	28.4	2.31	58.7	2.88	73.2	1.00	25.4	1.71	43.4
STYLE 2															
1/4	0.250	28	14.28	0.438	11.12	0.53	13.5	0.97	24.6	1.25	31.8	0.53	13.5	0.78	19.8
5/16	0.3125	24	15.88	0.500	12.70	0.59	15.0	1.12	28.4	1.45	36.8	0.59	15.0	0.87	22.1
3/8	0.375	24	19.05	0.625	15.88	0.75	19.0	1.38	35.0	1.75	44.4	0.81	20.6	1.09	27.7
1/2	0.500	20	23.82	0.750	19.05	0.89	22.6	1.94	49.3	2.38	60.5	1.12	28.4	1.39	35.3

1. These dimensions are given for design purposes only and are not intended for inspection.

METRIC BALL JOINTS—SAE J2213 DEC1991 SAE Standard

Report of the SAE Ball Joint and Spherical Rod End Committee approved June 1991.

1. Scope

1.1 This SAE Standard covers the general and dimensional data for industrial quality ball joints commonly used on control linkages in metric automotive, marine, construction, and industrial equipment applications.

1.2 The ball joints described are available from several manufacturers within the range of the interchangeable specifications. The sliding contact self-aligning bearing members (ball and socket) are available in a variety of materials in the types shown. The load capacities and wear capabilities vary considerably with the design and fabrication. It is suggested that the manufacturers be consulted for recommendations for the type and design appropriate to particular applications.

1.3 The inclusion of dimensional data in the document is not intended to imply that all the products described are stock production sizes. Consumers are requested to consult with manufacturers concerning availability of stock production parts.

2. References

2.1 Applicable Publications—The following publications form a part of this specification to the extent specified herein. The latest issue of SAE Publications shall apply.

2.1.1 SAE PUBLICATION—Available from SAE, 400 Commonwealth Drive, Warrendale, PA 15096-0001.

SAE J490—Ball Joints

2.1.2 ANSI AND ISO PUBLICATIONS—Available from ANSI, 11 West 42nd Street, New York, NY 10036.

ANSI/ASME B1.13—Metric Screw Threads—M Profile

ISO 965-2—ISO general purpose metric screw threads—Tolerances—Part 2: Limits of sizes for general purpose bolt and nut threads—Medium quality

2.1.3 ASTM PUBLICATION—Available from ASTM, 100 Barr Harbor Drive, West Conshohocken, PA 19428-2959.

ASTM B 117—Method of Salt Spray (Fog) Testing

3. Dimensions

3.1 All dimensions and tolerances are in millimeters. See SAE J490 for the ball joint specification with unified threads.

3.2 Tabulated dimensions shall apply to the finished parts, plated or otherwise processed, as specified by the user. Limits on hexagon of round bar shapes shall be within the commercial tolerance of the bar stock material from which the components are produced.

3.3 Dimensions of ball joints are shown in Figures 1, 2, and 3.

3.4 Nominal Sizes—The ball joint sizes are specified by a number indicating the thread size (size 6 has M6 threads).

3.5 Threads

3.5.1 Thread form, diameter, and associated pitches are in accordance with ISO 965-2 and ANSI/ASME B1.13, tolerance class 6g external and 6H internal.

3.5.2 The threads shall be right hand unless otherwise specified. The threads must be chamfered to insure a clean start according to good industrial practice.

4. Material and Finishes

4.1 Ball joints are normally made from low carbon free machining steel. The ball stud and the ball sockets on Type A Style 2 ball joints shall be case hardened unless otherwise specified. For special application, ball joints can be produced from alloy steel, corrosion resistant steel, brass, bronze, or other materials.

4.2 Retainer clips shall be made of high carbon steel. Springs shall be stainless steel.

4.3 Unless otherwise specified, carbon steel ball joints shall be furnished with a zinc protective finish with subsequent chromate treatment and shall meet the requirements of 72 h salt spray test in accordance with ASTM B 117.

4.3.1 Plated, hardened carbon steel components of ball joints (subject to hydrogen embrittlement) shall be baked or otherwise processed to obviate such embrittlement.

5. Lubrication

5.1 Unless otherwise specified by the user, ball joints shall be supplied with ball sockets suitably lubricated in accordance with the manufacturer's practice.

6. Dust Covers

6.1 Where so specified by the user, Type G Style 1 ball joints shall be supplied with an oil resistant rubber shield of such construction as to prevent dirt and dust from entering the ball cavity.

7. Workmanship

7.1 Ball joints must be free from burrs, loose scale, sharp edges, and any other defects which might affect their serviceability.

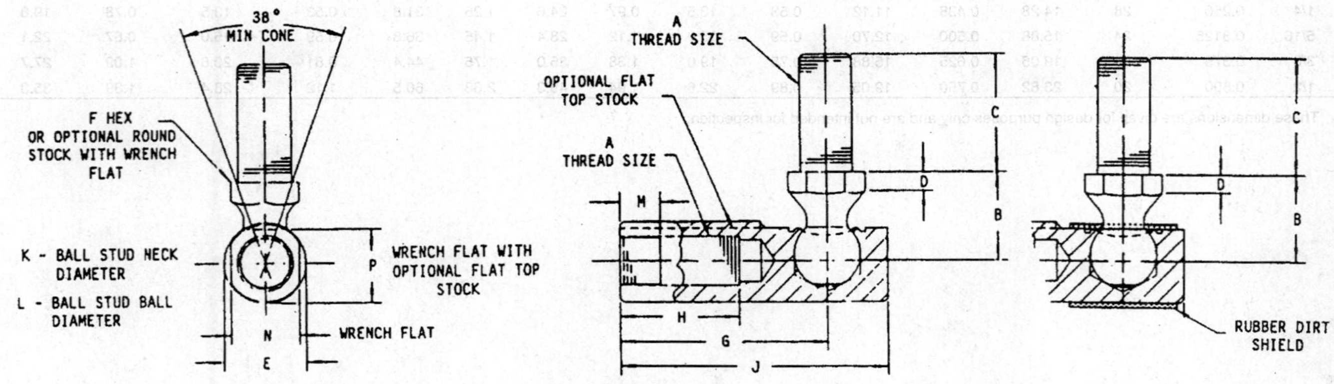

Size	A Thread Size	B ±0.5	C ±0.5	D MIN	D_1 MAX	E MAX	F MAX	G ±0.5	H MIN	J MAX	K MIN	L NOM	M ±0.5	N -0.25	P ±0.25
5	M5X0.8	9.0	11.0	2.4	3.0	10	8	22.0	12	30	4.25	7.60	6.5	8	8
6	M6X1	10.5	14.5	2.0	3.0	12	10	24.5	13	34	5.05	8.75	6.5	9	9
8	M8X1.25	12.5	17.5	2.4	3.5	13	13	28.5	15	40	6.10	10.25	7.0	11	11
10	M10X1.5	16.0	22.0	3.6	4.0	16	13	35.0	20	47	7.10	12.45	8.0	12	14
12	M12X1.75	20.5	28.5	4.4	4.5	20	16	49.0	28	64	9.45	15.60	9.5	16	16

FIGURE 1—DIMENSIONS OF TYPE A NONDETACHABLE BALL JOINT

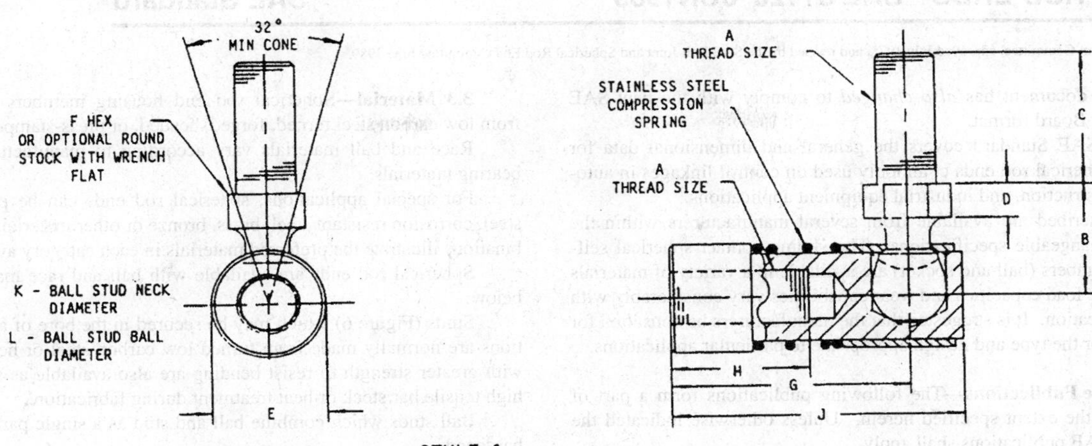

Size	A Thread Size	B ±0.5	C ±0.5	D MIN	D_1 MAX	E MAX	F MAX	G ±0.5	H MIN	J MAX	K MIN	L NOM
6	M6X1	12.0	14.5	2.8	3.0	15	10	24.5	13	33	4.65	8.75
8	M8X1.25	13.5	17.5	3.6	3.5	17	13	28.5	15	37	5.60	10.25
10	M10X1.5	17.5	22.0	4.4	4.0	20	13	35.0	20	45	6.70	12.45
12	M12X1.75	22.0	28.5	6.8	4.5	24	16	49.0	28	61	8.90	15.60

FIGURE 2—DIMENSIONS OF TYPE B DETACHABLE BALL JOINTS

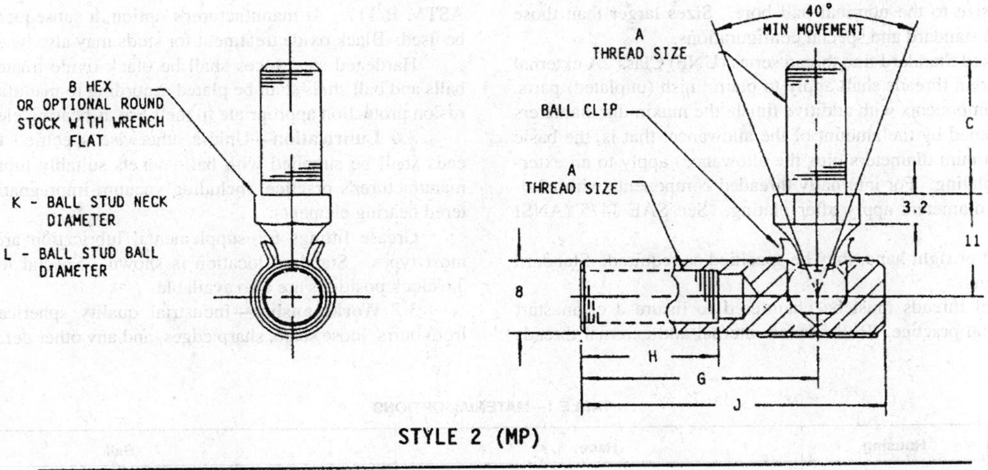

Size	A Thread Size	B ±0.5	C ±0.5	D MIN	D_1 MAX	F MAX	G ±0.5	H MIN	J MAX	K MIN	L ±0.15
5	M5X0.8	11.0	11.0	3.2	3	8	22.0	12	30	3.5	6.35
6	M6X1	11.0	14.5	3.2	3	8	24.5	13	33	3.5	6.35

FIGURE 3—DIMENSIONS OF TYPE B DETACHABLE BALL JOINTS—STYLE 2 (MP)

SPHERICAL ROD ENDS—SAE J1120 JUN1989 — SAE Standard

Report of the SAE Ball Joint Committee, approved July 1975, and revised by the SAE Ball Joint and Spherical Rod End Committee June 1989.

Foreword—This document has *also changed* to comply with the new SAE Technical Standards Board format.

1. Scope—This SAE Standard covers the general and dimensional data for industrial quality spherical rod ends commonly used on control linkages in automotive, marine, construction, and industrial equipment applications.

The rod ends described are available from several manufacturers within the range of the interchangeable specifications. The sliding contact spherical self-aligning bearing members (ball and socket) are available in a variety of materials in types shown. The load capacities and wear capabilities vary considerably with the design and fabrication. It is suggested that the manufacturers be consulted for recommendations for the type and design appropriate to particular applications.

2. References

2.1 Applicable Publications—The following publications form a part of the specification to the extent specified herein. Unless otherwise indicated the lastest revision of SAE publications shall apply.

2.1.1 SAE PUBLICATION—AVAILABLE FROM SAE, 400 COMMONWEALTH DRIVE, WARRENDALE, PA 15096-0001.

SAE J475—Screw Threads (ANSI/B 1.1-1974)

2.1.2 ASTM PUBLICATION—Available from ASTM, 100 Barr Harbor Drive, West Conshohocken, PA 19428-2959.

ASTM B 117—Method of Salt Spray (Fog) Testing

2.2 Related Publication—The following publication is provided for information purposes only and is not a required part of this document.

2.2.1 ANSI PUBLICATION—Available from ANSI, 11 West 42nd Street, New York, NY 10036-8002.

ANSI B 18.2.1-1972—Square and Hex Bolts and Screws—Inch Series

3. General Specification

3.1 Sizes—Spherical rod end sizes are normally specified by a number indicating the ball bore size in sixteenths of an inch (size 5 = 5/16 bore). The housing threads (external or internal) used for mounting, as well as the stud thread if required, are equal in size to the nominal ball bore. Sizes larger than those listed are available in both standard and special configurations.

3.2 Threads—Unified Standard fine thread series (UNF) Class 2A external threads and Class 2B internal threads shall apply to plain finish (unplated) parts. For externally threaded components with additive finish, the maximum diameters of Class 2A may be exceeded by the amount of the allowance: that is, the basic diameters (Class 2A maximum diameters plus the allowance) apply to an externally threaded part after plating. For internally threaded components with additive finish, the Class 2B diameters apply after plating. See SAE J475 (ANSI B1.1-1974).

Housing threads, left or right hand, may be specified as required. Standard studs are threaded right hand.

External and internal threads must be chamfered to insure a clean start according to good industrial practice. Roll formed internal and external threads are preferred.

3.3 Material—Spherical rod end housing members are normally made from low carbon steel turned, forged, headed, or press-stamped blanks.

Race and ball materials vary according to manufacturer's preference for bearing materials.

For special applications, spherical rod ends can be produced from alloy steel, corrosion resistant steel, brass, bronze or other materials. The charted combinations illustrate the preferred materials in each category available as standard.

Spherical rod ends are available with ball and race material options listed below:

Studs (Figure 6) which may be secured in the bore of any of the ball variations are normally made from turned low carbon steel or headed blanks. Studs with greater strength to resist bending are also available as standard, employing high tensile bar stock or heat treatment during fabrication.

Ball studs which combine ball and stud as a single part are mild steel case hardened.

3.4 Angle of Misalignment—If a spherical rod end is mounted between the legs of a fork or clevis, the total misalignment angle will be limited by the diameter of the housing head as it contacts the legs. This angle varies from 18 to 34 deg in race type spherical rod ends and from 12 to 30 deg in raceless construction. Specific information for a given size and type should be requested from the manufacturer if this is a critical element of the application. See illustration, Figure 1A.

If a spherical rod end is mounted on a shouldered shaft or with washers having a diameter equal to ball dimension "O", the shaft cone angle will vary from 25 to 34 deg. See illustration, Figure 1B.

The use of a stud for mounting increases the limit of total misalignment to a minimum of 50 deg. See illustration, Figure 1C.

3.5 Finishes—Unless otherwise specified, low carbon steel housings, races, and studs shall be furnished with cadmium or zinc protective finish and shall meet the requirements of 32 h Salt Spray Fog Testing in accordance with ASTM B 117. At manufacturer's option, a subsequent chromate treatment may be used. Black oxide treatment for studs may also be employed.

Hardened steel races shall be black oxide treated and oiled. Nonsintered balls and ball studs shall be plated according to manufacturer's preference for corrosion protection appropriate to their use as bearing elements.

3.6 Lubrication—Unless otherwise specified by the user, spherical rod ends shall be supplied with ball sockets suitably lubricated in accordance with manufacturer's practice, including vacuum impregnation of self-lubricating sintered bearing elements.

Grease fittings for supplemental lubrication are provided on request for most types. Standard location is shown. Special locations at 12 o'clock and 3 o'clock positions are also available.

3.7 Workmanship—Industrial quality spherical rod ends must be free from burrs, loose scale, sharp edges, and any other defects.

TABLE 1—MATERIAL OPTIONS

Rod End	Housing	Race	Ball
		Sintered Phosphor Bronze	Hardened Sintered Nickel Steel, Oil Impregnated
			Case Hardened Steel, Tin Nickel Plated
		Wrought Bronze, Brass	Hardened Sintered Steel
Type A (Figure 2)		Mild Steel, Cad Plated	Hardened 52100 Steel, Chrome Plated
			Hardened Sintered Steel
	Mild Steel, Alloy Steel, Stainless Steel, Hardened Steel, Aluminum Bronze, Brass	Hardened Steel	Hardened Sintered Nickel Steel, Oil Impregnated
			Sintered Bronze, Oil Impregnated
			Hardened 52100
		Nylon Reinforced, Detrin, TFE Lined	Case Hardened Steel, Cad or Tin Nickel Plated
Type B (Figure 3)			Hardened Sintered Nickel Steel, Oil Impregnated
			Hardened 52100
		None	Hardened 52100
Type C (Figure 4)			Hardened Sintered Iron, Oil Impregnated
			Case Hardened Steel, Tin Nickel Plated
Type D (Figure 5)		None	Mild Steel-Case Hardened,

3.8 Ball Bore Chamfer—Ball bores are chamfered at both faces to break the edge 0.005 in (0.13 mm) or up to a maximum of 0.03 in (0.8 mm) according to manufacturer's preference and method of fabrication. The user is cautioned against seating bolt heads against the ball face during mounting, because bolt fillets under the head may distort or crack the ball. This is especially true of hex bolts and screws meeting ANSI B 18.2.1-1972 specifications. The use of a washer or other suitable alternate is recommended.

Rod End Size	Min A	Min B
3	10°	34°
4	14°	34°
5	12°	28°
6	10°	30°
7	14°	32°
8	10°	32°
10	14°	30°
12	14°	25°

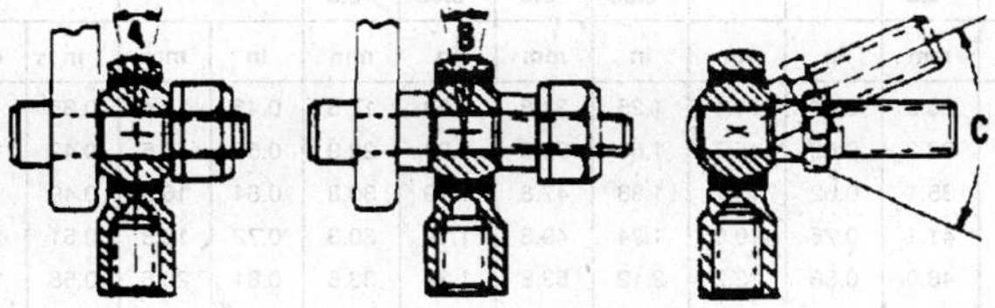

FIGURE 1—A-HOUSING STRIKES YOKE OR LEVER; B-WASHER OR SHOULDERED SHAFT WITH DIA "0" STRIKES RACE ID; C-STUD STRIKES RACE ID

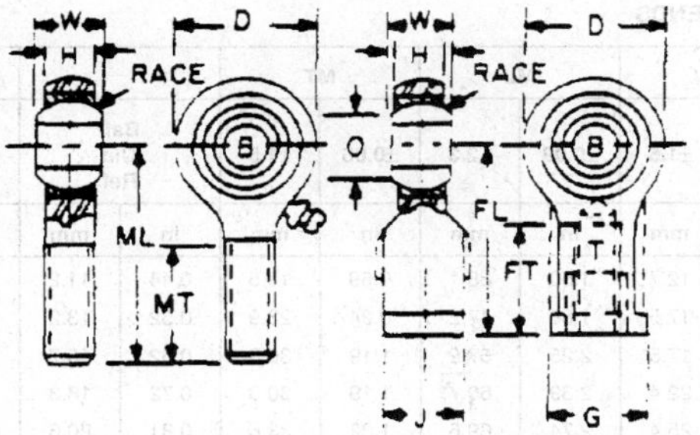

FIGURE 2—TYPE A METALLIC RACE

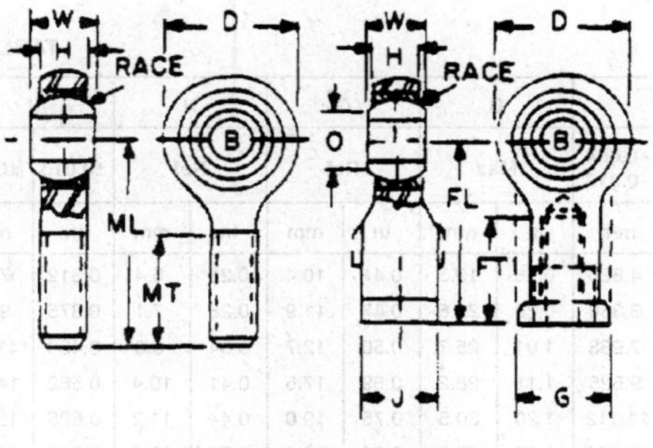

FIGURE 3—TYPE B MOLDED RACE

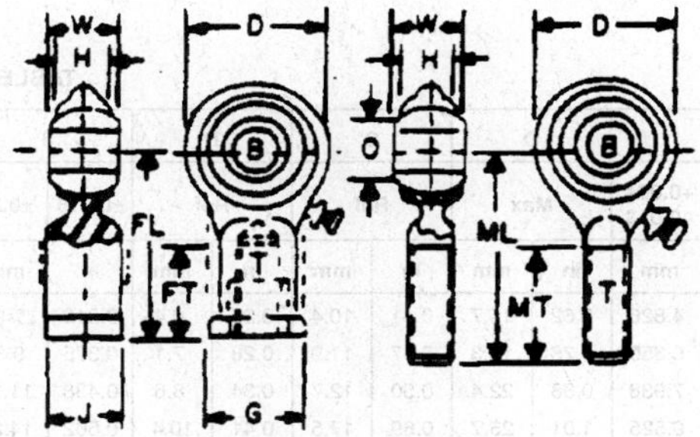

FIGURE 4—TYPE C RACELESS

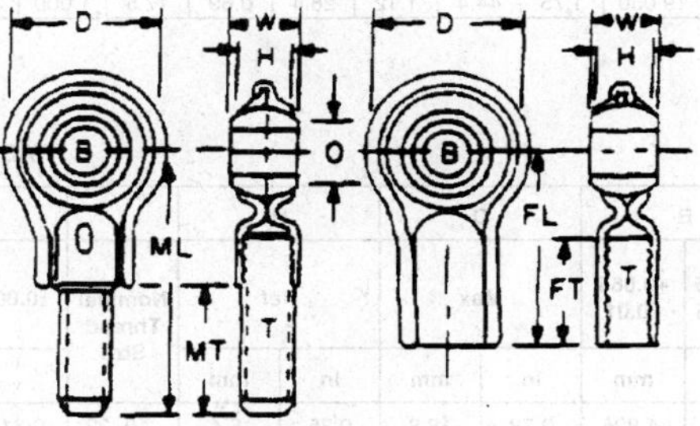

FIGURE 5—TYPE D RACELESS STAMPED HOUSING

TABLE 2—DIMENSIONS FOR TYPE A ROD ENDS

Rod End Size	B		D		G		H		J		T	W		FL		FT		ML		MT		Ball Dia Ref		O	
	+0.0025 −0.0005	+0.064 −0.013	Max.		Ref		Ref		±0.015	±0.38	Nominal Thread Size	±0.005	±0.13	+0.06 −0.03	+1.5 −0.8	±0.06	±1.5	+0.06 −0.03	+1.5 −0.8	±0.06	±1.5			Ref	
	in	mm	in	mm	in	mm	in	mm	in	mm		in	mm	in	mm	in	mm	in	mm	in	mm	in	mm	in	mm
3	0.1900	4.826	0.76	19.3	0.41	10.4	0.25	6.4	0.312	7.92	10–32	0.312	7.92	1.06	26.9	0.50	12.7	1.25	31.8	0.69	17.5	0.44	11.2	0.31	7.9
4	0.2500	6.350	0.89	22.6	0.47	11.9	0.28	7.1	0.375	9.52	1/4–28	0.375	9.52	1.31	33.3	0.69	17.5	1.56	39.6	0.94	23.9	0.51	13.0	0.35	8.9
5	0.3125	7.938	1.01	25.7	0.50	12.7	0.34	8.6	0.438	11.12	5/16–24	0.438	11.12	1.38	35.1	0.69	17.5	1.88	47.8	1.19	30.3	0.62	15.7	0.45	11.4
6	0.3750	9.525	1.11	28.2	0.69	17.5	0.41	10.4	0.562	14.27	3/8–24	0.500	12.70	1.62	41.1	0.88	22.4	1.94	49.3	1.19	30.3	0.72	18.3	0.52	13.2
7	0.4375	11.112	1.20	30.5	0.75	19.0	0.44	11.2	0.625	15.88	7/16–20	0.562	14.27	1.81	46.0	1.00	25.4	2.12	53.8	1.32	33.6	0.81	20.6	0.59	15.0
8	0.5000	12.700	1.39	35.3	0.88	22.4	0.50	12.7	0.750	19.05	1/2–20	0.625	15.88	2.12	53.8	1.13	28.7	2.44	62.0	1.44	36.6	0.94	23.9	0.70	17.8
10	0.6250	15.875	1.57	39.9	1.00	25.4	0.56	14.2	0.875	22.22	5/8–18	0.750	19.05	2.50	63.5	1.44	36.6	2.62	66.5	1.56	39.6	1.12	28.4	0.81	20.6
12	0.7500	19.050	1.82	46.2	1.12	28.4	0.69	17.5	1.000	25.40	3/4–16	0.875	22.22	2.88	73.2	1.69	42.9	2.88	73.2	1.69	42.9	1.32	33.5	1.02	25.9

TABLE 3—DIMENSIONS FOR TYPE B ROD ENDS

Rod End Size	B		D		G		H		J		T	W		FL		FT		ML		MT		Ball Dia Ref		O	
	+0.0025 −0.0005	+0.064 −0.013	Max		Ref		Ref		±0.015	±0.38	Nominal Thread Size	±0.005	±0.13	+0.06 −0.03	+1.5 −0.8	±0.06	±1.5	+0.06 −0.03	+1.5 −0.8	±0.06	±1.5				
	in	mm	in	mm	in	mm	in	mm	in	mm		in	mm	in	mm	in	mm	in	mm	in	mm	in	mm	in	mm
3	0.1900	4.826	0.76	19.3	0.41	10.4	0.25	6.4	0.312	7.92	10–32	0.312	7.92	1.06	26.9	0.50	12.7	1.25	31.8	0.69	17.5	0.44	11.2	0.31	7.9
4	0.2500	6.350	0.89	22.6	0.47	11.9	0.28	7.1	0.375	9.52	1/4–28	0.375	9.52	1.31	33.3	0.69	17.5	1.56	39.6	0.94	23.9	0.51	13.0	0.35	8.9
5	0.3125	7.938	1.01	25.7	0.50	12.7	0.34	8.6	0.438	11.12	5/16–24	0.438	11.12	1.38	35.1	0.69	17.5	1.88	47.8	1.19	30.3	0.62	15.7	0.45	11.4
6	0.3750	9.525	1.11	28.2	0.69	17.5	0.41	10.4	0.562	14.27	3/8–24	0.500	12.70	1.62	41.1	0.88	22.4	1.94	49.3	1.19	30.3	0.72	18.3	0.52	13.2
7	0.4375	11.112	1.20	30.5	0.75	19.0	0.44	11.2	0.625	15.88	7/16–20	0.562	14.27	1.81	46.0	1.00	25.4	2.12	53.8	1.32	33.6	0.81	20.6	0.59	15.0
8	0.5000	12.700	1.39	35.3	0.88	22.4	0.50	12.7	0.750	19.05	1/2–20	0.625	15.88	2.12	53.8	1.13	28.7	2.44	62.0	1.44	36.6	0.94	23.9	0.70	17.8
10	0.6250	15.875	1.51	38.4	1.00	25.4	0.56	14.2	0.875	22.22	5/8–18	0.750	19.05	2.50	63.5	1.44	36.6	2.62	66.5	1.56	39.6	1.12	28.4	0.81	20.6

TABLE 4—DIMENSIONS FOR TYPE A ROD ENDS

Rod End Size	B		D		G		H		J		T	W		FL		FT		ML		MT		Ball Dia Ref		O	
	+0.0025 −0.0005	+0.064 −0.013	Max		Ref		Ref		±0.015	±0.38	Nominal Thread Size	±0.005	±0.13	+0.06 −0.03	+1.5 −0.8	±0.06	±1.5	+0.06 −0.03	+1.5 −0.8	+0.06 −0.03	+1.5 −0.8			Ref	
	in	mm	in	mm	in	mm	in	mm	in	mm		in	mm	in	mm	in	mm	in	mm	in	mm	in	mm	in	mm
3	0.1900	4.826	0.62	15.7	0.41	10.4	0.25	6.4	0.312	7.92	10–32	0.312	7.92	1.06	26.9	0.44	11.1	1.25	31.8	0.69	17.5	0.45	11.4	0.35	8.9
4	0.2500	6.350	0.76	19.3	0.47	11.9	0.28	7.1	0.375	9.52	1/4–28	0.375	9.52	1.31	33.3	0.62	15.7	1.56	39.6	0.94	23.9	0.53	13.5	0.42	10.7
5	0.3125	7.938	0.88	22.4	0.50	12.7	0.34	8.6	0.438	11.12	5/16–24	0.438	11.12	1.38	35.1	0.62	15.7	1.88	47.8	1.19	30.3	0.64	16.3	0.49	12.4
6	0.3750	9.525	1.01	25.7	0.69	17.5	0.41	10.4	0.562	14.27	3/8–24	0.500	12.70	1.62	41.1	0.75	19.0	1.94	49.3	1.19	30.3	0.72	18.3	0.51	13.0
7	0.4375	11.112	1.12	28.4	0.75	19.0	0.44	11.2	0.625	15.88	7/16–20	0.562	14.27	1.81	46.0	0.88	22.2	2.12	53.8	1.32	33.6	0.81	20.6	0.58	14.7
8	0.5000	12.700	1.31	33.3	0.88	22.4	0.50	12.7	0.750	19.05	1/2–20	0.625	15.88	2.12	53.8	1.00	25.4	2.44	62.0	1.44	36.6	0.96	24.4	0.79	20.1
10	0.6250	15.875	1.50	38.1	1.00	25.4	0.56	14.2	0.875	22.22	5/8–18	0.750	19.05	2.50	63.5	1.32	33.3	2.62	66.5	1.56	39.6	1.16	29.5	0.92	23.4
12	0.7500	19.050	1.75	44.4	1.12	28.4	0.69	17.5	1.000	25.40	3/4–16	0.875	22.22	2.88	73.2	1.50	38.1	2.88	73.2	1.69	42.9	1.34	34.0	1.06	26.9

TABLE 5—DIMENSIONS FOR TYPE A ROD ENDS

Rod End Size	B		D		H		T	W		FL		FT		ML		MT		Ball Dia Ref		O	
	+0.0025 −0.0005	+0.064 −0.01	Max		Ref		Nominal Thread Size	±0.005	±0.13	±0.06	±1.5	±0.06	±1.5	±0.09	±2.3	±0.06	±1.5			Ref	
	in	mm	in	mm	in	mm				in	mm	in	mm	in	mm	in	mm	in	mm	in	mm
3	0.1900	4.826	0.78	18.8	0.25	6.4	10–32	0.312	7.92	1.06	26.9	0.50	12.7	1.50	38.1	0.69	17.5	0.44	11.2	0.31	7.9
4	0.2500	6.350	0.88	22.4	0.29	7.1	1/4–28	0.375	9.52	1.31	33.3	0.69	17.5	1.86	47.2	0.94	23.9	0.52	13.2	0.35	8.9
5	0.3125	7.938	1.05	26.7	0.31	7.9	5/16–24	0.438	11.12	1.38	35.1	0.69	17.5	2.25	57.2	1.19	30.3	0.62	15.7	0.45	11.4
6	0.3750	9.525	1.16	29.5	0.41	10.4	3/8–24	0.500	12.70	1.62	41.1	0.88	22.4	2.39	60.7	1.19	30.3	0.72	18.3	0.52	13.2
7	0.4375	11.112	1.37	34.8	0.44	11.2	7/16–20	0.562	14.27	1.91	48.5	1.00	25.4	2.74	69.6	1.32	33.6	0.81	20.6	0.59	15.0
8	0.5000	12.700	1.51	38.4	0.50	12.7	1/2–20	0.625	15.88	2.12	53.8	1.13	28.7	3.04	77.2	1.44	36.6	0.94	23.9	0.70	17.8

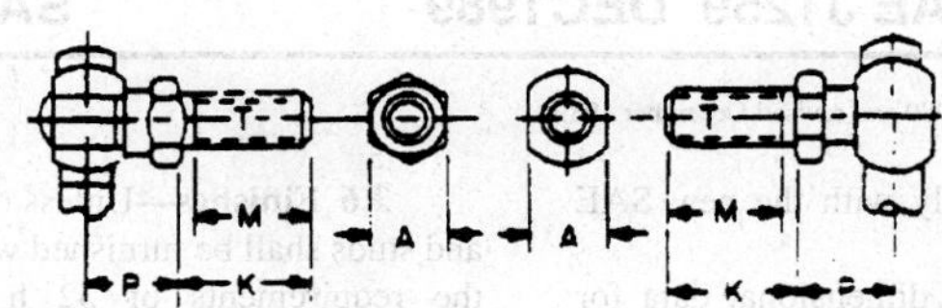

Rod End Size	A		K		M		P		T
	±0.010	0.25	±0.03	±0.8	±0.03	±0.8	±0.4	±1.0	Nominal Thread Size
	in	mm	in	mm	in	mm	in	mm	
3	0.312	7.92	0.50	12.7	0.44	11.2	0.48	12.2	10-32
4	0.375	9.52	0.56	14.2	0.50	12.7	0.48	12.2	1/4-28
5	0.437	11.10	0.69	17.5	0.59	15.0	0.54	13.7	5/16-24
6	0.500	12.70	0.89	22.6	0.81	20.6	0.65	16.5	3/8-24
7	0.625	15.88	1.09	27.7	0.97	24.6	0.84	21.3	7/16-20
8	0.625	15.88	1.12	28.4	1.00	25.4	0.88	22.4	1/2-20
10	0.750	19.05	1.50	38.1	1.38	35.1	1.00	25.4	5/8-18
12	1.000	25.40	1.81	46.0	1.63	41.4	1.19	30.2	3/4-16

FIGURE 6—STUD ASSEMBLED TO BALLS HAVING ANY STANDARD MATERIAL OPTIONS, ONE PIECE BALL STUD, LOW CARBON STEEL, CASE HARDENED

METRIC SPHERICAL ROD ENDS—SAE J1259 DEC1989 SAE Standard

Report of the SAE Ball Joint Spherical Rod End Committee, approved April 1980 and revised December 1989.

Foreword—This document has *also changed* to comply with the new SAE Technical Standards Board format.

1. Scope—This SAE Standard covers the general and dimensional data for industrial quality spherical rod ends commonly used on control linkages in metric automotive, marine, construction, and industrial equipment applications.

The rod ends described are available from several manufacturers within the range of the interchangeable specifications. The sliding contact spherical self-aligning bearing members (ball and socket) are available in a variety of materials in the types shown. The load capacities and wear capabilities vary considerably with the design and fabrication. It is suggested that the manufacturers be consulted for recommendations for the type and design appropriate to particular applications.

2. References

2.1 Applicable Publications—The following publications form a part of the specification to the extent specified herein. Unless otherwise indicated the lastest revision of SAE publications shall apply.

2.1.1 SAE PUBLICATIONS—Available from SAE, 400 Commonwealth Drive, Warrendale, PA 15096-0001.

SAE J1120 SEP79—Spherical Rod Ends

2.1.2 ANSI PUBLICATION—Available from ANSI, 11 West 42nd Street, New York, NY 10036-8002.

ANSI B1.13

2.1.3 ASTM PUBLICATION—Available from ASTM, 100 Barr Harbor Drive, West Conshohocken, PA 19428-2959.

ASTM B 117—Method of Salt Spray (Fog) Testing

2.1.4 ISO PUBLICATION—Available from SAE, 400 Commonwealth Drive, Warrendale,PA 15096-0001.

ISO 965/II

3. General Specifications

3.1 Dimensions—All dimensions are in millimeters. See SAE J1120 for the U.S. Customary unit specification for spherical rod ends.

3.2 Sizes—The spherical rod end sizes are normally specified by a number indicating the ball bore in millimeters (size 5 = 5 mm). The housing threads (external or internal) used for mounting, as well as the stud thread if required, are equal in size to the nominal ball bore. Sizes larger than those listed are available in both standard and special configurations.

3.3 Threads—Thread form, diameter, and associated pitches are in accordance with ISO 965/II and ANSI B1.13, tolerance class 6g external and 6H internal.

The threads shall be right hand unless otherwise specified. The threads must be chamfered to insure a clean start according to good industrial practice.

3.4 Material—The spherical rod end housing members are normally made from low-carbon steel turned, forged, or headed.

The race and ball materials vary according to the manufacturer's preference for bearing materials.

For special applications, spherical rod ends can be produced from alloy steel, corrosion resistant steel, brass, bronze, or other materials. The charted combinations illustrate the preferred materials in each category available as standard.

The spherical rod ends are available with the ball and race material options listed below:

The studs (Figure 5), which may be secured in the bore of any of the ball variations, are normally made from turned low-carbon steel or headed blanks. The studs with greater strength to resist bending are also available by agreement between the user and manufacturer.

The ball studs, which combine ball and stud as a single part, are mild steel case hardened.

3.5 Angle of Misalignment—If a spherical rod end is mounted between the legs of a fork or clevis, the total misalignment angle will be limited by that portion of the housing head that contacts the legs. This angle varies from 12–18 deg. Specific information for a given size and type should be requested from the manufacturer if this is a critical element of the application. See illustration, Figure 1A.

If a spherical rod end is mounted on a shouldered shaft or with washers having a diameter equal to ball dimension "O", the shaft cone angle will vary from 24–30 deg. See Illustration, Figure 1B.

The use of a stud for mounting increases the limit of total misalignment to a minimum of 44 deg. See illustration, Figure 1C.

3.6 Finishes—Unless otherwise specified, low-carbon steel housing, races, and studs shall be furnished with cadmium or zinc protective finish and shall meet the requirements of 32 h Salt Spray (Fog) Testing in accordance with ASTM B 117. At manufacturer's option, a subsequent chromate treatment may be used. A black oxide treatment for studs may also be employed.

Nonsintered balls and ball studs shall be plated according to the manufacturer's preference for corrosion protection appropriate to their use as bearing elements.

MATERIAL OPTIONS

Rod End	Housing	Race	Ball
Type A (Figure 2)	Mild Steel, Alloy Steel, Stainless Steel, Hardened Steel, Aluminum Bronze, Brass	Sintered Phosphor Bronze	Hardened Sintered Nickel Steel, Oil Impregnated Case Hardened Steel, Tin Nickel Plated
		Wrought Bronze, Brass	Hardened Sintered Steel
		Mild Steel, Cad Plated	Hardened 52100 Steel, Chrome Plated Hardened Sintered Steel
		Hardened Steel	Hardened Sintered Nickel Steel, Oil Impregnated Sintered Bronze, Oil Impregnated Hardened 52100
Type B (Figure 3)		Nylon Reinforced, Delrin, TFE Lined	Case Hardened Steel, Cad or Tin Nickel Plated Hardened Sintered Nickel Steel, Oil Impregnated Hardened 52100
Type C (Figure 4)		None	Hardened 52100 Hardened Sintered Iron, Oil Impregnated Case Hardened Steel, Tin Nickel Plated

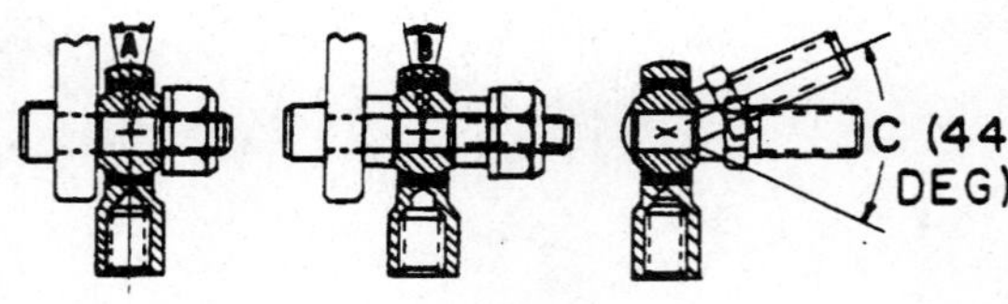

Rod End Size	Min A Deg	Min B Deg
5	13	24
6	12	24
8	14	26
10	14	26
12	14	26
14	18	30
16	17	30
20	17	28

FIGURE 1—A—HOUSING STRIKES YOKE OR LEVER;
B—WASHER OR SHOULDERED SHAFT WITH DIA "O" STRIKES RACE ID;
C—STUD STRIKES RACE ID

4. Lubrication—Unless otherwise specified by the user, spherical rod ends shall be supplied with ball sockets suitably lubricated in accordance with the manufacturer's practice, including vacuum impregnation of self-lubrication sintered bearing elements.

TABLE 1—DIMENSIONS FOR ROD ENDS - TYPE A (FIGURE 2), TYPE B (FIGURE 3), AND TYPE C (FIGURE 4)

Rod End Size	B +0.07 -0.00	D Max	G ±0.25	H ±0.15	J Ref	T Nominal Thread Size	W ±0.15	FL _1.5 -0.8	FT Min	ML ±1.5 -0.8	MT Min	Ball Dia Ref	O Ref
5	5	18	11	6.00	9.0	M5 × 0.80	8	26	9	32	19	11.1	7.7
6	6	22	13	6.75	10.0	M6 × 1.00	9	29	11	35	21	12.7	8.9
8	8	26	16	9.00	12.5	M8 × 1.25	12	35	15	41	24	15.8	10.4
10	10	30	19	10.50	15.0	M10 × 1.50	14	42	19	47	28	19.1	12.9
12	12	34	22	12.00	17.5	M12 × 1.75	16	49	21	54	32	22.2	15.4
14	14	38	25	13.50	20.0	M14 × 2.00	19	56	24	59	35	25.4	16.8
16	16	42	27	15.00	22.0	M16 × 2.00	21	63	27	65	39	28.6	19.3
20	20	50	34	18.00	27.5	M20 × 1.50	25	76	32	77	46	34.9	24.3

The grease fittings for supplemental lubrication are provided upon request for most types. The standard location is shown. Special locations at 12 o'clock and 3 o'clock positions are also available.

5. Workmanship—Industrial quality spherical rod ends must be free from burrs, loose scale, sharp edges, and any other defects.

6. Ball Bore Chamfer—The ball bores are chamfered at both faces to break the edge 0.13 mm or up to a maximum of 0.8 mm according to the manufacturer's preference and the method of fabrication. The user is cautioned against seating bolt heads against the ball face during mounting because bolt fillets under the head may distort or crack the ball. The use of a washer or other suitable alternate is recommended.

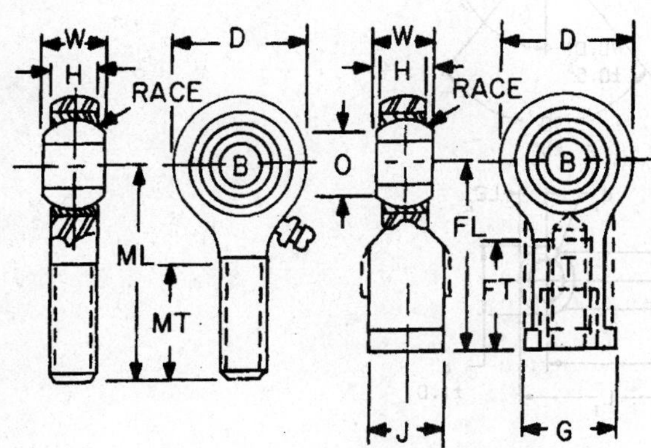

FIGURE 2—TYPE A - METALLIC RACE

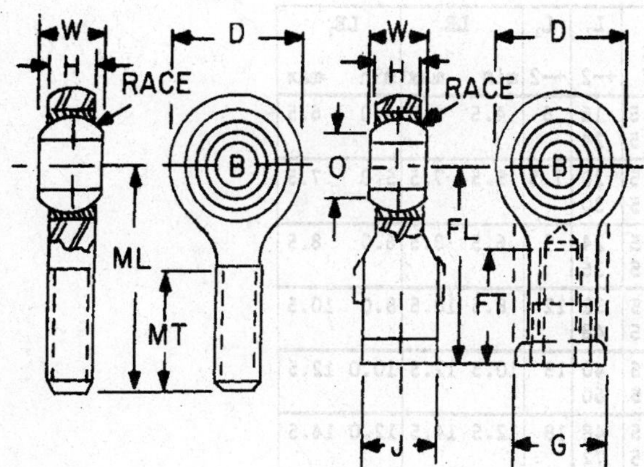

FIGURE 3—TYPE B - MOLDED RACE

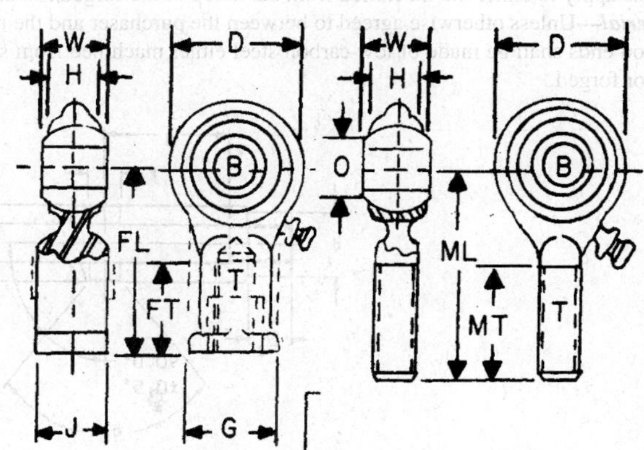

FIGURE 4—TYPE C - RACELESS

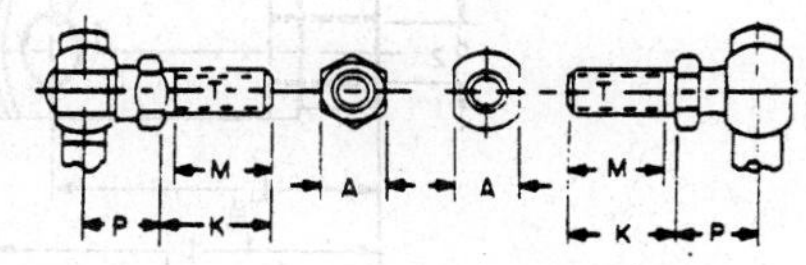

Rod End Size	A Ref	K ±0.25	M Min	P ±1	T Nominal Thread Size
5	8	13.0	10.0	9.0	M5 x 0.80
6	10	14.0	11.0	10.0	M6 x 1.00
8	12	17.5	14.0	12.0	M8 x 1.25
10	14	23.0	19.5	16.5	M10 x 1.50
12	16	28.5	24.5	19.5	M12 x 1.75
14	20	33.0	29.0	20.5	M14 x 2.00
16	22	38.0	34.0	24.0	M16 x 2.00
20	25	46.0	40.0	28.5	M20 x 1.50

FIGURE 5—STUDDED ASSEMBLIES

METRIC YOKE TYPE ROD ENDS—SAE J1651 FEB1994 SAE Standard

Report of the SAE Ball Joint Spherical Rod End Committee approved February 1994.

1. Scope—This SAE Standard provides dimensions, tolerances, material, and heat treatment for yoke type rod ends with metric threads and for use with metric size clevis pins.

2. References

2.1 Applicable Publication—The following publication forms a part of this specification to the extent specified herein.

2.1.1 ASME PUBLICATION—Available from ASME, 22 Law Drive, Fairfield, NJ 07007.

ASME B 18.8.8M—Headed Clevis Pins (Metric Series)

3. Dimensions—Figure 1 shows dimensions for the yoke type rod ends. Dimensions apply to either the machined from bar stock or the forged rod ends.

4. Material—Unless otherwise agreed to between the purchaser and the manufacturer, rod ends shall be made of low carbon steel either machined from square bar stock or forged.

5. Case Hardening—Unless otherwise specified, when case hardening is required the rod ends shall have a case depth of 0.05 to 0.20 mm and a hardness of Rockwell 15N 85.

6. Coating—Unless otherwise specified, rod ends shall be plated with a minimum of 0.0035 mm zinc with a dichromate conversion applied. Dimensions and tolerances apply after plating.

7. Workmanship—Yoke type ends shall be free from burrs, loose scale, sharp edges, and all other defects that affect their serviceability.

8. Clevis Pins—Clevis pins conforming to ASME B 18.8.8M are recommended for use with yoke type rod ends conforming to this document. Suggested lengths and some reference dimensions are shown in Figure 2.

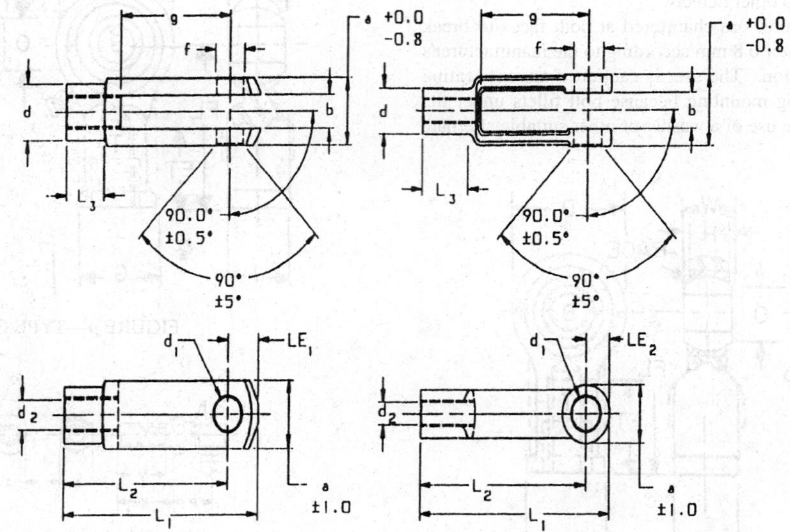

d_1 (H10*) -0.0	+	g min	a	b min	b max	d	d_3	f +- 0.5	L_1 max ref	L_2 +-2	L_3 +-2	LE_1 min	LE_1 max	LE_2 min	LE_2 max
4	0.05	8 16	8	4.10	4.40	M4x0.7	8	5	24.5 32.5	16 24	6	4.5	6.5	4.0	6.5
5	0.05	10 20	10	5.10	5.40	M5x0.8	9	6	29.5 39.5	20 30	7.5	5.5	7.5	5.0	7.5
6	0.05	12 24	12	6.10	6.40	M6x1	10	7	34.5 46.5	24 36	9	6.5	8.5	6.0	8.5
8	0.06	16 32	16	8.15	8.50	M8x1.25	14	9	44.5 60.5	32 48	12	8.5	10.5	8.0	10.5
10	0.07	20 40	20	10.15	10.50	M10x1.5	18	11	54.5 74.5	40 60	15	10.5	12.5	10.0	12.5
12	0.07	24 48	24	12.15	12.50	M12x1.75	20	13	64.5 88.5	48 72	18	12.5	14.5	12.0	14.5
16	0.07	32 64	32	16.15	16.50	M16x2	26	17	84.5 116.5	64 96	24	16.5	18.5	16.0	18.5
20	0.08	40 80	40	20.15	20.60	M20x2.5	34	21	106.0 146.0	80 120	30	21.0	24.0	20.0	24.0
24	0.08	48 96	48	25.15	25.60	M24x3	42	25	126.0 174.0	96 144	36	25.0	28.0	24.0	28.0
*ROUNDED															

FIGURE 1—YOKE TYPE ROD END DIMENSIONS (ALL DIMENSIONS IN MM)

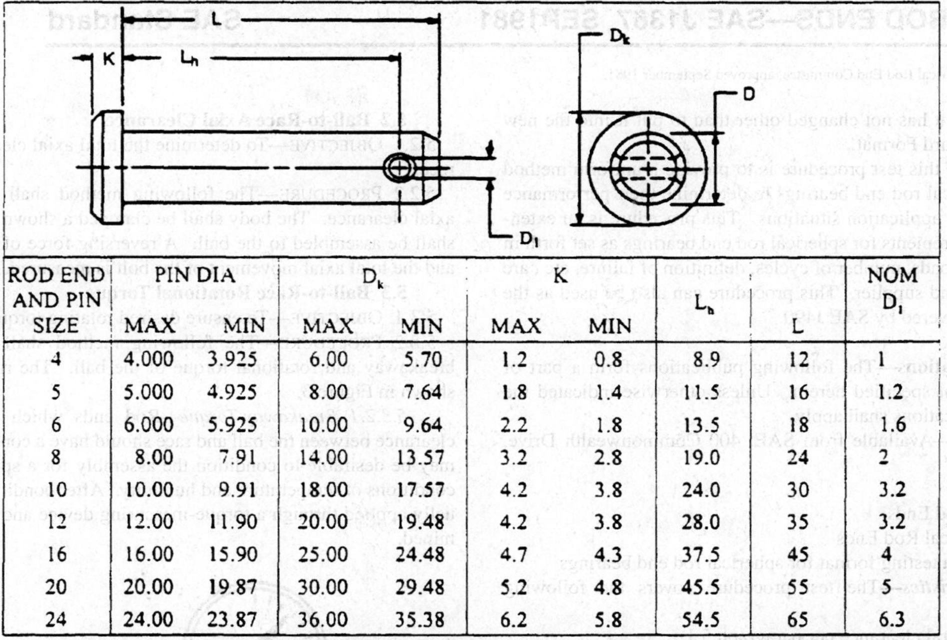

ROD END AND PIN SIZE	PIN DIA MAX	PIN DIA MIN	D_k MAX	D_k MIN	K MAX	K MIN	L_h	L	NOM D_1
4	4.000	3.925	6.00	5.70	1.2	0.8	8.9	12	1
5	5.000	4.925	8.00	7.64	1.8	1.4	11.5	16	1.2
6	6.000	5.925	10.00	9.64	2.2	1.8	13.5	18	1.6
8	8.00	7.91	14.00	13.57	3.2	2.8	19.0	24	2
10	10.00	9.91	18.00	17.57	4.2	3.8	24.0	30	3.2
12	12.00	11.90	20.00	19.48	4.2	3.8	28.0	35	3.2
16	16.00	15.90	25.00	24.48	4.7	4.3	37.5	45	4
20	20.00	19.87	30.00	29.48	5.2	4.8	45.5	55	5
24	24.00	23.87	36.00	35.38	6.2	5.8	54.5	65	6.3

FIGURE 2—DIMENSIONS OF RECOMMENDED CLEVIS PINS (ALL DIMENSIONS IN MM)

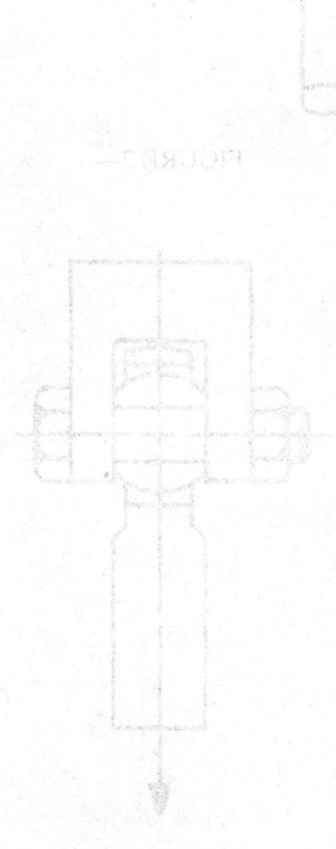

PERFORMANCE TEST PROCEDURE—BALL JOINTS AND SPHERICAL ROD ENDS—SAE J1367 SEP1981

SAE Standard

Report of the SAE Ball Joint And Spherical Rod End Committee, approved September 1981.

Foreword—This Document has not changed other than to put it into the new SAE Technical Standards Board Format.

*1. **Scope***—The purpose of this test procedure is to provide a uniform method of testing commercial spherical rod end bearings to determine their performance characteristics under specific application situations. This procedure is an extension of the dimensional requirements for spherical rod end bearings as set forth in SAE J1120 and J1259. The loads, number of cycles, definition of failure, etc., are to be agreed to by the user and supplier. This procedure can also be used as the basis for testing ball joints covered by SAE J490.

*2. **References***

2.1 Applicable Publications—The following publications form a part of the specification to the extent specified herein. Unless otherwise indicated the lastest revision of SAE publications shall apply.

2.1.1 SAE PUBLICATIONS—Available from SAE, 400 Commonwealth Drive, Warrendale, PA 15096-0001.

SAE J490—Ball Joints
SAE J1120—Spherical Rod Ends
SAE J259—Metric Shperical Rod Ends

*3. **Objective***—To provide a testing format for spherical rod end bearings.

*4. **Performance Characteristics***—The test procedure covers the following characteristics:

4.1 Ball-to-race diametral clearance per paragraph 5.1.
4.2 Ball-to-race axial clearance per paragraph 5.2.
4.3 Ball-to-race rotational torque per paragraph 5.3.
4.4 Radial static limit load per paragraph 5.4.
4.5 Axial static limit load per paragraph 5.5.
4.6 Fatigue and wear test per paragraph 5.6.

*5. **Test Objectives and Procedures***

5.1 Ball-to-Race Diametral Clearance

5.1.1 OBJECTIVE—To determine the total diametral clearance of the ball within the race.

5.1.2 PROCEDURE—The following method shall be used to determine total diametral clearance. The ball shall be fastened to the fixture as shown in Figure 1. A reversing force of 20 N is applied to the body and the total movement of the body is measured. The tightening torques shown in Figure 1 shall be used for all tests.

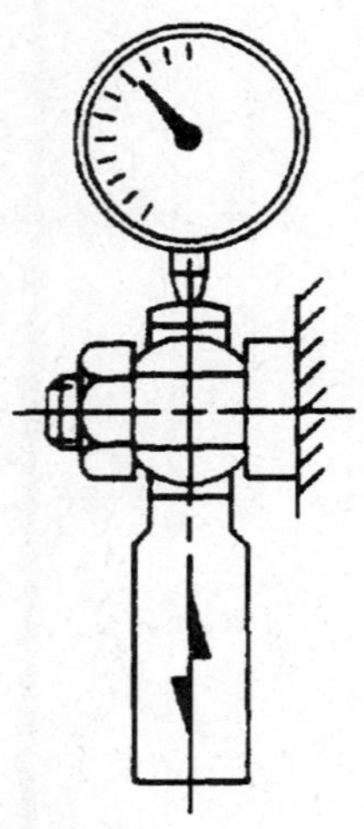

FIGURE 1—

Rod End Size		Nut Torque
SAE J1120	SAE J1259	N·m
3	5	0.9 ± 0.1
4	6	2.25 ± 0.25
5	8	3.4 ± 0.5
6	10	12 ± 4
7	12	25 ± 7
8	14	45 ± 7
10	16	100 ± 15
12	20	150 ± 20

5.2 Ball-to-Race Axial Clearance

5.2.1 OBJECTIVE—To determine the total axial clearance of the ball within the race.

5.2.2 PROCEDURE—The following method shall be used to determine total axial clearance. The body shall be clamped a shown in Figure 2. A nut and bolt shall be assembled to the ball. A reversing force of 20 N is applied to the bolt, and the total axial movement of the bolt is measured.

5.3 Ball-to-Race Rotational Torque

5.3.1 OBJECTIVE—To ensure desired rotating torque is obtained.

5.3.2 PROCEDURE—The following method shall be used to determine the breakaway and rotational torque of the ball. The rod end shall be mounted as shown in Figure 3.

5.3.2.1 Breakaway Torque—Rod ends which are designed to have zero clearance between the ball and race should have a control on breakaway torque. It may be desirable to condition the assembly for a specified period under certain conditions of temperature and humidity. After conditioning, torque shall be gradually applied through a torque-measuring device and the maximum torque determined.

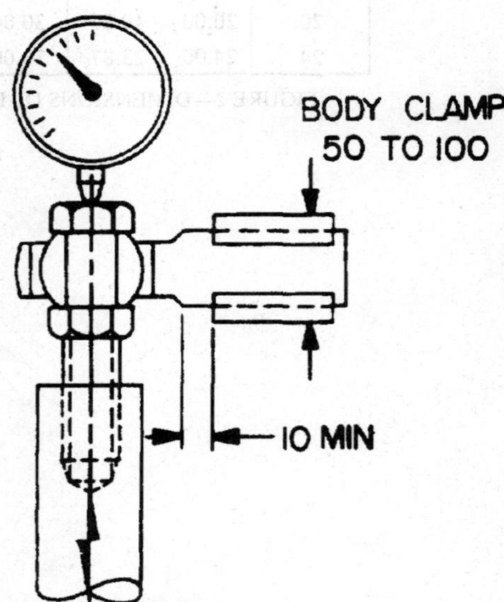

FIGURE 2—

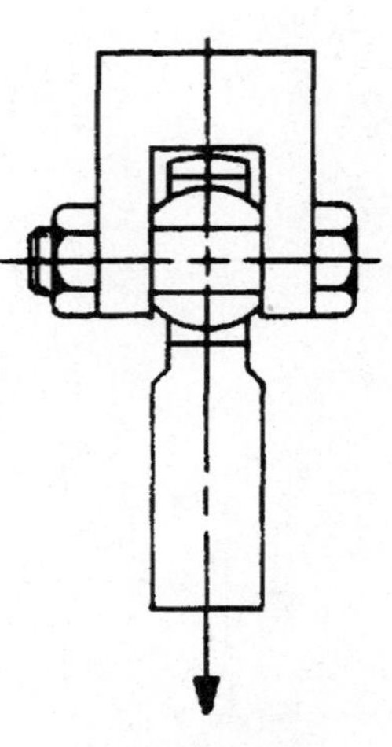

FIGURE 3—

5.3.2.2 No Load Rotational Torque—The ball should be rotated five revolutions prior to recording the torque. The torque is read with a torque-measuring device by the gradual application of a rotating force.

5.4 Radial Static Limit Load

5.4.1 OBJECTIVE—To check the operational radial static load and the radial static limit load capacity of the rod end. The operational radial static load is a load which can be applied a limited number of times to a rod end without impairing the operation.

5.4.2 PROCEDURE—The rod end shall be installed in a test fixture as shown in Figure 3 using a loose fit on the shaft. A tensile load shall be applied at the rate of 1%/s.

5.4.2.1 Operational Radial Static Load—Apply the load to the required operational radial static load. Hold for 30 s. Release the load. Repeat for a total of five cycles. The rod end ball shall still be free to rotate.

5.4.2.2 Ultimate Radial Static Load—Apply the load to the required ultimate radial static load. Hold for 30 s. The rod end body and other components shall remain intact.

5.5 Axial Static Limit Load

5.5.1 OBJECTIVE—To check the maximum axial load capacity of the rod end.

5.5.2 PROCEDURE—The rod end shall be mounted on a rigid fixture as shown in Figure 4, so that only the rod end body is supported. The axial static load shall be applied to the ball at the rate of 1%/s and maintained on the bearing for 3 s. No push-out of the bearing components shall occur when the axial load is applied.

5.6 Fatigue and Wear Test

5.6.1 OBJECTIVE—To determine fatigue and wear characteristics.

5.6.2 DISCUSSION—Rod end performance is a function of many variables. These include the bearing design, the characteristic of the materials from which the bearings are made, the way in which they are manufactured, as well as the many variables associated with their application. The only sure way to establish the satisfactory operation of a bearing selected for a specific application is by actual performance in the application. This is often impractical.

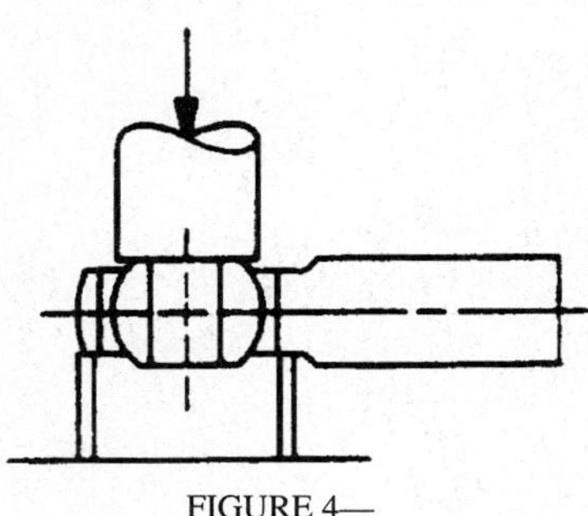

FIGURE 4—

When it is desirable to have an overall standard test, the test set-up shown in Figure 5 is recommended. This set-up results in a push/pull loading, ball rotation of ±30 degrees, and misalignment of approximately ±5 degrees.

5.6.3 PROCEDURE—Use rod ends which have been tested in accordance with paragraphs 5.1, 5.2, and 5.3 and found acceptable. Rod ends should be filled with recommended lubricant when required by the application. Assemblies should be securely fastened in the test machine in a manner to achieve the required motion. The load, cycle frequency, and required number of cycles shall be agreed upon between supplier and user.

5.6.4 EXAMINATION OF RESULTS—Upon completion of the cycle testing, the following features shall be determined. The user must determine the number of cycles and the maximum allowable wear for his particular application.

a. Diametral clearance,

b. Axial clearance,

c. Examination of rod end components for cracks and other signs of damage.

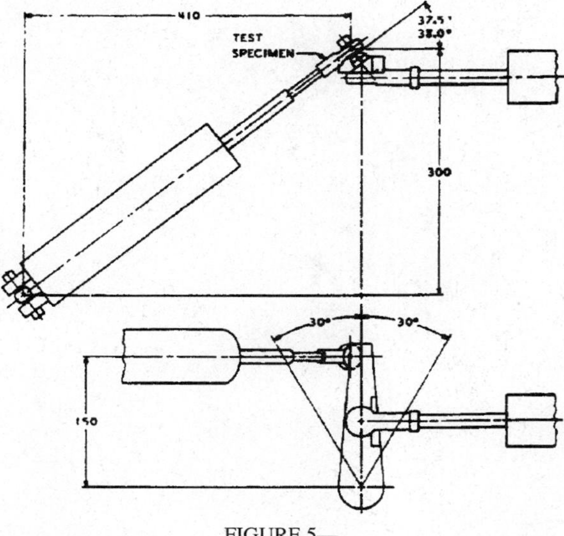

FIGURE 5—

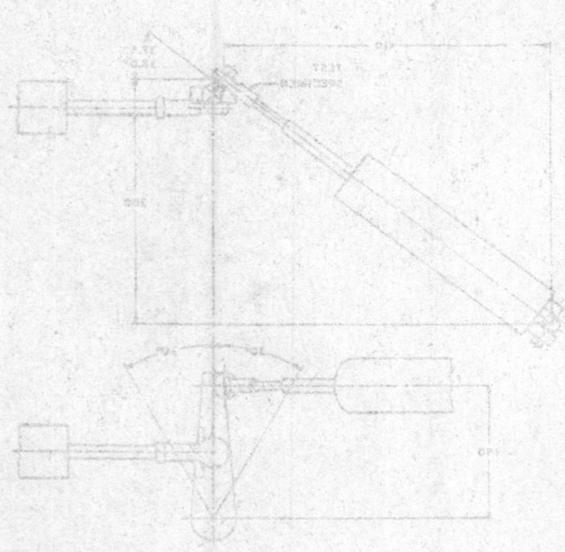

18 Splines

PARALLEL SIDE SPLINES FOR SOFT BROACHED HOLES IN FITTINGS—SAE J499a OCT1975

SAE Standard

Report of the SAE Broaches Division approved January 1914, revised by the SAE Shaft Fittings Division March 1920, and reviewed January 1936. Last revised by the ANSI B92 Committee—Involute Splines and Inspection—October 1975.

1. Scope—This Information Report along with SAE J500 and J501 is generally understood to be technically obsolete for the design of new applications. However, it is listed for those existing applications where it may be required. For the design of new applications, consult ANSI B92.1-1970—Involute Splines and Inspections Standard.

[The dimensions, given in inches, apply only to soft broached holes. The shaft dimensions depend upon the shape and material of the parts, their heat treatment, and methods of machining to give the required fit. The method and amount of "breaking" sharp corners and edges also depend upon the conditions and requirements of each application.

The formula for theoretical torque capacity (pressure on sides of spline) in inch-pounds per inch of bearing length (L) and at 1000 psi pressure is:

$$T = \text{Torque} = 1000 \times \text{No. of spines} \times \text{mean radius} \times h \times L \quad \text{(Eq. 1)}$$

The tolerances allowed are for good construction and may be readily maintained by usual broaching methods. The tolerances selected for the large and small diameters will depend upon whether the fit between the mating parts, as finally made, is on the large or the small diameter. The other diameter, being designed for clearance may have a wider manufacturing tolerance. If the final fit between the parts is on only the sides of the spline, wider tolerances may be permitted on both the large and small diameters.]

Radii on corners of splines are not to exceed 0.015 in.

Splines shall not be more than 0.006 in per ft out of parallel with respect to the axis of the shaft.

No allowance is made for radii on corners or for clearance. Dimensions are intended to apply to only the soft broached hole. Allowance must be made for machining.

For values of D, W, d, h, and T for four-, six-, ten-, and sixteen-spline fittings, Table 2, Table 3, Table 4 and Table 5, respectively.

TABLE 1—W, h, AND d, IN TERMS OF LARGE DIAMETER, D

No. of Splines	W For All Fits	A Permanent Fit		B To Slide when Not under Load		C To Slide under Load	
		h	d	h	d	h	d
4	0.241(1)	0.075	0.850	0.125	0.750	—	—
6	0.250	0.050	0.900	0.075	0.850	0.100	0.800
10	0.156	0.045	0.910	0.070	0.860	0.095	0.810
16	0.098	0.045	0.910	0.070	0.860	0.095	0.810

1. Four splines, for fits A and B only.

2. References

2.1 Applicable Publications—The following publications form a part of the specification to the extent specified herein. Unless otherwise indicated the lastest revision of SAE publications shall apply.

2.1.1 SAE PUBLICATIONS—Available from SAE, 400 Commonwealth Drive, Warrendale, PA 15096-0001.

SAE J500—Serrated Shaft Ends

SAE J501—Shaft Ends

2.1.2 ANSI PUBLICATION——Available from ANSI, 11 West 42nd Street, New York, NY 10036-8002.

ANSI B92.1-1970—Involute Splines and Inspections Standard

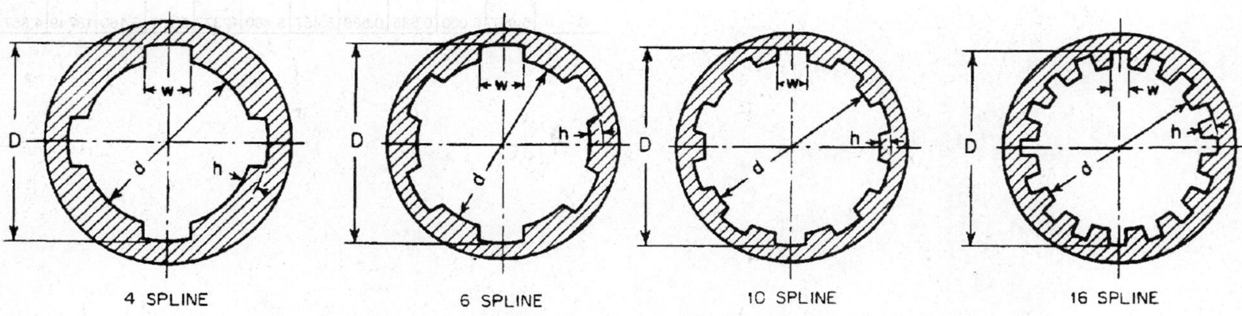

FIGURE 1—DIMENSIONS FOR 4, 6, 10, AND 16 SPLINE FITTINGS TABLE 1

TABLE 2—FOUR SPLINE FITTINGS

Nominal Dia	For All Fits				4A, Permanent Fit					4B, To Slide when Not under Load				
	D		W		d		h		T	d		h		T
	Min	Max	Min	Max	Min	Max	Min	Max		Min	Max	Min	Max	
3/4	0.749	0.750	0.179	0.181	0.636	0.637	0.055	0.056	78	0.561	0.562	0.093	0.094	123
7/8	0.874	0.875	0.209	0.211	0.743	0.744	0.065	0.066	107	0.655	0.656	0.108	0.109	167
1	0.999	1.000	0.239	0.241	0.849	0.850	0.074	0.075	139	0.749	0.750	0.124	0.125	219
1-1/8	1.124	1.125	0.269	0.271	0.955	0.956	0.083	0.084	175	0.843	0.844	0.140	0.141	277
1-1/4	1.249	1.250	0.299	0.301	1.061	1.062	0.093	0.094	217	0.936	0.937	0.155	0.156	341
1-3/8	1.374	1.375	0.329	0.331	1.168	1.169	0.102	0.103	262	1.030	1.031	0.171	0.172	414
1-1/2	1.499	1.500	0.359	0.361	1.274	1.275	0.111	0.112	311	1.124	1.125	0.186	0.187	491
1-5/8	1.624	1.625	0.389	0.391	1.380	1.381	0.121	0.122	367	1.218	1.219	0.202	0.203	577
1-3/4	1.749	1.750	0.420	0.422	1.486	1.487	0.130	0.131	424	1.311	1.312	0.218	0.219	670
2	1.998	2.000	0.479	0.482	1.698	1.700	0.148	0.150	555	1.498	1.500	0.248	0.250	875
2-1/4	2.248	2.250	0.539	0.542	1.910	1.912	0.167	0.169	703	1.685	1.687	0.279	0.281	1106
2-1/2	2.498	2.500	0.599	0.602	2.123	2.125	0.185	0.187	865	1.873	1.875	0.310	0.312	1365
3	2.998	3.000	0.720	0.723	2.548	2.550	0.223	0.225	1249	2.248	2.250	0.373	0.375	1969

TABLE 3—SIX SPLINE FITTINGS

Nominal Dia	For All Fits				6A, Permanent Fit			6B, To Slide when Not under Load			6C, To Slide when under Load		
	D		W		d		T	d		T	d		T
	Min	Max	Min	Max	Min	Max		Min	Max		Min	Max	
3/4	0.749	0.750	0.186	0.188	0.674	0.675	80	0.637	0.638	117	0.599	0.600	152
7/8	0.874	0.875	0.217	0.219	0.787	0.788	109	0.743	0.744	159	0.699	0.700	207
1	0.999	1.000	0.248	0.250	0.899	0.900	143	0.849	0.850	208	0.799	0.800	270
1-1/8	1.124	1.125	0.279	0.281	1.012	1.013	180	0.955	0.956	263	0.899	0.900	342
1-1/4	1.249	1.250	0.311	0.313	1.124	1.125	223	1.062	1.063	325	0.999	1.000	421
1-3/8	1.374	1.375	0.342	0.344	1.237	1.238	269	1.168	1.169	393	1.099	1.100	510
1-1/2	1.499	1.500	0.373	0.375	1.349	1.350	321	1.274	1.275	468	1.199	1.200	608
1-5/8	1.624	1.625	0.404	0.406	1.462	1.463	376	1.380	1.381	550	1.299	1.300	713
1-3/4	1.749	1.750	0.436	0.438	1.574	1.575	436	1.487	1.488	637	1.399	1.400	827
2	1.998	2.000	0.497	0.500	1.798	1.800	570	1.698	1.700	833	1.598	1.600	1080
2-1/4	2.248	2.250	0.560	0.563	2.023	2.025	721	1.911	1.913	1052	1.798	1.800	1367
2-1/2	2.498	2.500	0.622	0.625	2.248	2.250	891	2.123	2.125	1300	1.998	2.000	1688
3	2.998	3.000	0.747	0.750	2.698	2.700	1283	2.548	2.500	1873	2.398	2.400	2430

TABLE 4—TEN SPLINE FITTINGS

Nominal Dia	For All Fits				10A, Permanent Fit			10B, To Slide when Not under Load			10C, To Slide when under Load		
	D		W		d		T	d		T	d		T
	Min	Max	Min	Max	Min	Max		Max	Min				
3/4	0.749	0.750	0.115	0.117	0.682	0.683	120	0.644	0.645	183	0.607	0.608	241
7/8	0.874	0.875	0.135	0.137	0.795	0.796	165	0.752	0.753	248	0.708	0.709	329
1	0.999	1.000	0.154	0.156	0.909	0.910	215	0.859	0.860	326	0.809	0.810	430
1-1/8	1.124	1.125	0.174	0.176	1.023	1.024	271	0.967	0.968	412	0.910	0.911	545
1-1/4	1.249	1.250	0.193	0.195	1.137	1.138	336	1.074	1.075	508	1.012	1.013	672
1-3/8	1.374	1.375	0.213	0.215	1.250	1.251	406	1.182	1.183	614	1.113	1.114	813
1-1/2	1.499	1.500	0.232	0.234	1.364	1.365	483	1.289	1.290	732	1.214	1.215	967
1-5/8	1.624	1.625	0.252	0.254	1.478	1.479	566	1.397	1.398	860	1.315	1.316	1135
1-3/4	1.749	1.750	0.271	0.273	1.592	1.593	658	1.504	1.505	997	1.417	1.418	1316
2	1.998	2.000	0.309	0.312	1.818	1.820	860	1.718	1.720	1302	1.618	1.620	1720
2-1/4	2.248	2.250	0.348	0.351	2.046	2.048	1088	1.933	1.935	1647	1.821	1.823	2176
2-1/2	2.498	2.500	0.387	0.390	2.273	2.275	1343	2.148	2.150	2034	2.023	2.025	2688
3	2.998	3.000	0.465	0.468	2.728	2.730	1934	2.578	2.580	2929	2.428	2.430	3869
3-1/2	3.497	3.500	0.543	0.546	3.182	3.185	2632	3.007	3.010	3987	2.832	2.835	5266
4	3.997	4.000	0.621	0.624	3.637	3.640	3438	3.437	3.440	5208	3.237	3.240	6878
4-1/2	4.497	4.500	0.699	0.702	4.092	4.095	4351	3.867	3.870	6591	3.642	3.645	8705
5	4.997	5.000	0.777	0.780	4.547	4.550	5371	4.297	4.300	8137	4.047	4.050	10746
5-1/2	5.497	5.500	0.855	0.858	5.002	5.005	6500	4.727	4.730	9846	4.452	4.455	13003
6	5.997	6.000	0.933	0.936	5.457	5.460	7735	5.157	5.160	11718	4.857	4.860	15475

TABLE 5—SIXTEEN SPLINE FITTINGS

Nominal Dia	For All Fits				16A, Permanent Fit			16B, To Slide when Not under Load			16C, To Slide when under Load		
	D		W		d		T	d		T	d		T
	Min	Max	Min	Max	Min	Max		Min	Max		Min	Max	
2	1.997	2.000	0.193	0.196	1.817	1.820	1375	1.717	1.720	2083	1.617	1.620	2751
2-1/2	2.497	2.500	0.242	0.245	2.273	2.275	2149	2.147	2.150	3255	2.022	2.025	4299
3	2.997	3.000	0.291	0.294	2.727	2.730	3094	2.577	2.580	4687	2.427	2.430	6190
3-1/2	3.497	3.500	0.340	0.343	3.182	3.185	4212	3.007	3.010	6378	2.832	2.835	8426
4	3.997	4.000	0.389	0.392	3.637	3.640	5501	3.437	3.440	8333	3.237	3.240	11005
4-1/2	4.497	4.500	0.438	0.441	4.092	4.095	6962	3.867	3.870	10546	3.642	3.645	13928
5	4.997	5.000	0.487	0.490	4.547	4.550	8595	4.297	4.300	13020	4.047	4.050	17195
5-1/2	5.497	5.500	0.536	0.539	5.002	5.005	10395	4.727	4.730	15754	4.452	4.455	20806
6	5.997	6.000	0.585	0.588	5.457	5.460	12377	5.157	5.160	18749	4.857	4.860	24760

SHAFT ENDS—SAE J501 MAY1948 SAE Standard

Report of the SAE Broaches Division approved June 1914 and last revised by the SAE Parts and Fittings Committee May 1948.

1. Scope

2. References

2.1 Applicable Publication—The following publication forms a part of this specification to the extent specified herein. Unless otherwise indicated, the latest version of SAE publications shall apply.

2.1.1 SAE PUBLICATION—Available from SAE, 400 Commonwealth Drive, Warrendale, PA 15096-0001.

SAE J498—Involute Splines, Serrations, and Inspections

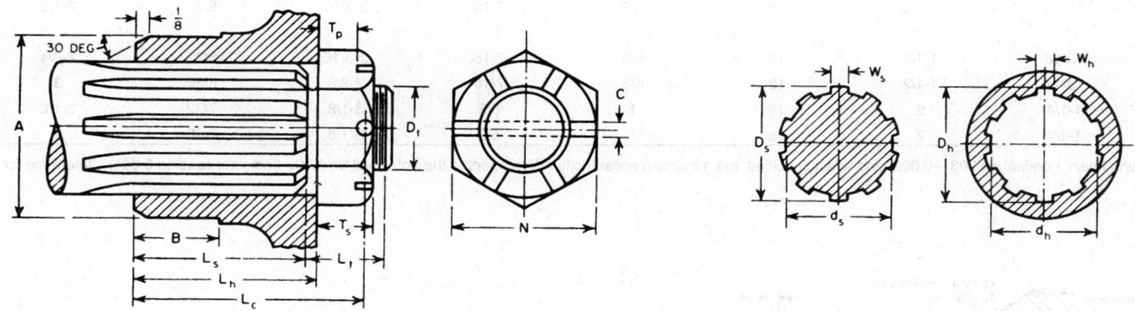

FIGURE 1—PERMANENT FIT SPLINE SHAFT ENDS (SEE TABLE 1)

TABLE 1A—PERMANENT FIT SPLINE SHAFT ENDS FOR UNIVERSAL JOINTS AND SIMILAR APPLICATIONS

Nominal Shaft Dia	10-Spline Shaft(1) D_8 +0.000 −0.001	10-Spline Shaft(1) W_8 +0.000 −0.0015	10-Spline Shaft(1) d_8 +0.000 −0.010	10-Spline Hole(1) D_h	10-Spline Hole(1) W_h +0.000 −0.0015	10-Spline Hole(1) d_h +0.010 −0.000	Hub Dimensions L_c	Hub Dimensions L_8	Hub Dimensions L_h
3/4	0.749	0.1170	0.632	0.751 0.749	0.1170	0.682	1-11/32	15/16	1
7/8	0.874	0.1370	0.745	0.876 0.874	0.1370	0.795	1-11/16	1-1/8	1-1/4
1	0.999	0.1560	0.859	1.001 0.999	0.1560	0.909	1-15/16	1-3/8	1-1/2
1-1/8	1.124	0.1760	0.973	1.126 1.124	0.1760	1.023	1-15/116	1-3/8	1-1/2
1-1/4	1.249	0.1950	1.087	1.251 1.249	0.1950	1.137	1-15/16	1-3/8	1-1/2
1-3/8	1.374	0.2150	1.200	1.376 1.374	0.2150	1.250	2-7/16	1-7/8	2
1-1/2	1.499	0.2340	1.304	1.501 1.499	0.2340	1.364	2-7/16	1-7/8	2
1-5/8	1.624	0.2540	1.347	1.627 1.624	0.2540	1.397	2-13/16	2-1/8	2-1/4
1-3/4	1.749	0.2730	1.454	1.752 1.749	0.2730	1.504	2-13/16	2-1/8	2-1/4
2	1.999	0.3120	1.668	2.002 1.999	0.3120	1.718	3-9/16	2-7/8	3
2-1/4	2.249	0.3510	1.883	2.252 2.249	0.3510	1.933	3-9/16	2-7/8	3
2-1/2	2.499	0.3900	2.098	2.502 2.499	0.3900	2.148	4-9/32	3-3/8	3-1/2
3	2.999	0.4680	2.528	3.002 2.999	0.4680	2.578	4-25/32	3-7/8	4

1. SAE Standard, Involute Splines, Serrations, and Inspection—SAE J498 optional.

TABLE 1B—PERMANENT FIT SPLINE SHAFT ENDS FOR UNIVERSAL JOINTS AND SIMILAR APPLICATIONS (Continued)

Nominal Shaft Dia	Hub Dimensions L_t	Hub Dimensions D_t	Hub Dimensions Threads per in.	Hub Dimensions T_8	Hub Dimensions T_p	Hub Dimensions N	C	A(1)	B
3/4	17/32	1/2	28	7/16	1/4	13/16	1/8	1-1/8	5/8
7/8	11/16	5/8	24	1/2	5/16	15/16	5/32	1-1/4	3/4
1	11/16	3/4	20	1/2	5/16	1-1/16	5/32	1-3/8	7/8
1-1/8	11/16	7/8	20	1/2	5/16	1-1/4	5/32	1-1/2	7/8

TABLE 1B—PERMANENT FIT SPLINE SHAFT ENDS FOR UNIVERSAL JOINTS AND SIMILAR APPLICATIONS (Continued)

Nominal Shaft Dia	Hub Dimensions L_t	Hub Dimensions D_t	Hub Dimensions Threads per in.	Hub Dimensions T_s	Hub Dimensions T_p	Hub Dimensions N	C	A[1]	B
1-1/4	11/16	1	20	1/2	5/16	1-7/16	5/32	1-3/4	7/8
1-3/8	11/16	1	20	1/2	5/16	1-7/16	5/32	2	1
1-1/2	13/16	1-1/4	18	5/8	7/16	1-13/16	5/32	2-1/4	1
1-5/8	13/16	1-1/4	18	5/8	7/16	1-13/16	5/32	2-3/8	1-1/4
1-3/4	13/16	1-1/4	18	5/8	7/16	2-3/16	5/32	2-1/2	1-1/4
2	13/16	1-1/4	18	5/8	7/16	2-3/16	5/32	2-3/4	1-1/2
2-1/4	13/16	1-1/2	18	5/8	7/16	2-3/8	5/32	3	1-1/2
2-1/2	1-1/4	2	16	1	5/8	3-1/8	7/32	3-1/2	1-3/4
3	1-1/4	2	16	1	5/8	3-1/8	7/32	4	2

1. Tolerance for ground finish, nominal +0.003, –0.002; and when specified, the maximum eccentricity with respect to the hole shall be 0.002 (indicator reading 0.004). Tolerance for lathe finish, nominal +1/32, –0.

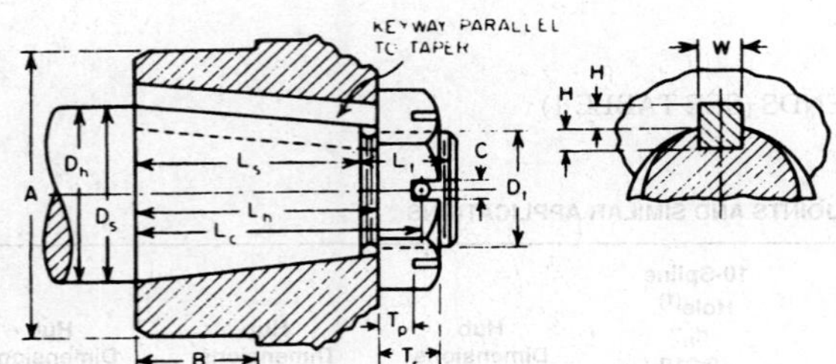

Taper per foot = 1.500 ± 0.002 in. Dimension H is measured normal to the key and at the large end of the taper.

C = cotter pin hole or slot. The centerline of the cotter pin hole shall be 90 deg from the position of the keyway, as shown in Fig. 2.

FIGURE 2—TAPER SHAFT END (SEE TABLE 2)

TABLE 2A—TAPER SHAFT END

Nominal Shaft Dia	D_s Shaft Diameter Max	D_s Shaft Diameter Min	D_h Hole Diameter Max	D_h Hole Diameter Min	L_c	L_s	L_h	L_t	D_t	Threads per in.
1/4	0.250	0.249	0.248	0.247	9/16	5/16	3/8	5/16	#10	40
3/8	0.375	0.374	0.373	0.372	47/64	7/16	1/2	23/64	5/16	32
1/2	0.500	0.499	0.498	0.497	63/64	11/16	3/4	23/64	5/16	32
5/8	0.625	0.624	0.623	0.622	1-3/32	11/16	3/4	17/32	1/2	28
3/4	0.750	0.749	0.748	0.747	1-11/32	15/16	1	17/32	1/2	28
7/8	0.875	0.874	0.873	0.872	1-11/16	1-1/8	1-1/4	11/16	5/8	24
1	1.001	0.999	0.997	0.995	1-15/16	1-3/8	1-1/2	11/16	3/4	20
1-1/8	1.126	1.124	1.122	1.120	1-15/16	1-3/8	1-1/2	11/16	7/8	20
1-1/4	1.251	1.249	1.247	1.245	1-15/16	1-3/8	1-1/2	11/16	1	20
1-3/8	1.376	1.374	1.372	1.370	2-7/16	1-7/8	2	11/16	1	20
1-1/2	1.501	1.499	1.497	1.495	2-7/16	1-7/8	2	11/16	1	20
1-5/8	1.626	1.624	1.622	1.620	2-13/16	2-1/8	2-1/4	13/16	1-1/4	18
1-3/4	1.751	1.749	1.747	1.745	2-13/16	2-1/8	2-1/4	13/16	1-1/4	18
1-7/8	1.876	1.874	1.872	1.870	3-1/16	2-3/8	2-1/2	13/16	1-1/4	18
2	2.001	1.999	1.997	1.995	3-9/16	2-7/8	3	13/16	1-1/4	18
2-1/4	2.252	2.248	2.245	2.242	3-9/16	2-7/8	3	13/16	1-1/2	18
2-1/2	2.502	2.498	2.495	2.492	4-9/32	3-3/8	3-1/2	1-1/4	2	16
2-3/4	2.752	2.748	2.745	2.742	4-9/32	3-3/8	3-1/2	1-1/4	2	16
3	3.002	2.998	2.995	2.992	4-25/32	3-7/8	4	1-1/4	2	16
3-1/4	3.252	3.248	3.245	3.242	5-1/32	4-1/8	4-1/4	1-1/4	2	16
3-1/2	3.502	3.498	3.495	3.492	5-7/16	4-3/8	4-1/2	1-3/8	2-1/2	16
4	4.002	3.998	3.995	3.992	6-7/16	5-3/8	5-1/2	1-3/8	2-1/2	16

TABLE 2B—TAPER SHAFT END (Continued)

Nominal Shaft Dia	T_8	T_p	Nut Width (Flats)	C	W Max	W Min	H +0.004 −0.000	Square Key Max	Square Key Min	A[1]	B
1/4	7/32	9/64	5/16	5/64	0.0625	0.0615	0.033	0.0635	0.0625	1/2	3/16
3/8	17/64	3/16	1/2	5/64	0.0937	0.0927	0.049	0.0947	0.0937	11/16	1/4
1/2	17/64	3/16	1/2	5/64	0.1250	0.1240	0.065	0.1260	0.1250	7/8	3/8
5/8	7/16	1/4	3/4	1/8	0.1562	0.1552	0.080	0.1572	0.1562	1-1/16	3/8
3/4	7/16	1/4	3/4	1/8	0.1875	0.1865	0.096	0.1885	0.1875	1-1/4	5/8
7/8	1/2	5/16	15/16	5/32	0.2500	0.2490	0.127	0.2510	0.2500	1-1/2	3/4
1	1/2	5/16	1-1/16	5/32	0.2500	0.2490	0.127	0.2510	0.2500	1-3/4	7/8
1-1/8	1/2	5/16	1-1/4	5/32	0.3125	0.3115	0.158	0.3135	0.3125	2	7/8
1-1/4	1/2	5/16	1-7/16	5/32	0.3125	0.3115	0.158	0.3135	0.3125	2-1/8	7/8
1-3/8	1/2	5/16	1-7/16	5/32	0.3750	0.3740	0.190	0.3760	0.3750	2-1/4	1
1-1/2	1/2	5/16	1-7/16	5/32	0.3750	0.3740	0.190	0.3760	0.3750	2-1/2	1
1-5/8	5/8	7/16	2-3/16	5/32	0.4375	0.4365	0.221	0.4385	0.4375	2-3/4	1-1/4
1-3/4	5/8	7/16	2-3/16	5/32	0.4375	0.4365	0.221	0.4385	0.4375	3	1-1/4
1-7/8	5/8	7/16	2-3/16	5/32	0.4375	0.4365	0.221	0.4385	0.4375	3-1/8	1-1/4
2	5/8	7/16	2-3/16	5/32	0.5000	0.4990	0.252	0.5010	0.5000	3-1/4	1-1/2
2-1/4	5/8	7/16	2-3/8	5/32	0.5625	0.5610	0.283	0.5640	0.5625	3-1/2	1-1/2
2-1/2	1	5/8	3-1/8	7/32	0.6250	0.6235	0.315	0.6265	0.6250	4	1-3/4
2-3/4	1	5/8	3-1/8	7/32	0.6875	0.6860	0.346	0.6890	0.6875	4-3/8	1-3/4
3	1	5/8	3-1/8	7/32	0.7500	0.7485	0.377	0.7515	0.7500	4-3/4	2
3-1/4	1	5/8	3-1/8	7/32	0.7500	0.7485	0.377	0.7515	0.7500	5	2-1/8
3-1/2	1-1/8	3/4	3-7/8	9/32	0.8750	0.8735	0.440	0.8765	0.8750	5-1/2	2-1/4
4	1-1/8	3/4	3-7/8	9/32	1.0000	0.9985	0.502	1.0015	1.0000	6-1/4	2-3/4

1. Tolerance for ground finish, nominal +0.003, −0.002; and when specified, the maximum eccentricity with respect to the hole shall be 0.002 (indicator reading 0.004). Tolerance for lathe finish, nominal +1/32, −0.

WOODRUFF KEYS—SAE J502 SEP1972

SAE Standard

Report of the SAE Parts and Fitting Division approved February 1928 and last revised by the SAE Parts and Fittings Committee January 1956. Editorial change September 1972.

1. Scope

2. References—There are no referenced publications specified herein.

3. Material—Keys are to be carbon steel or alloy heat treated steel as specified. Carbon steel keys are to be 0.30 carbon minimum, with hardness of Rockwell B 90 minimum. Alloy steel keys are to be SAE 2330 or 8630 steel, heat treated to a hardness of 40-50 RC; or other alloy steels having equal physical properties at the same hardness. Alloy heat treated keys are to be marked with depressions on the top to distinguish them from carbon steel keys.

4. Dimensions—Dimensions are to be as given in Tables 1A, 1B, and 2 and Figures 1, 2, and 3.

4.1 Width A (Shown in Illustrations Accompanying Tables)—Values shown were set with the maximum key slot width as that figure which will receive a key with the greatest amount of looseness consistent with assuring the key's sticking in the slot. Minimum key slot width is that figure permitting the largest shaft distortion acceptable when assembling maximum key in minimum key slot.

4.2 Dimensions A, B, C, and E—These dimensions are to be taken at the side intersection.

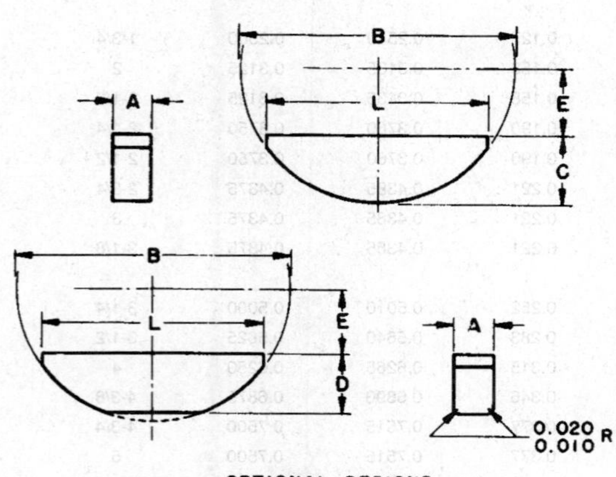

FIGURE 1—

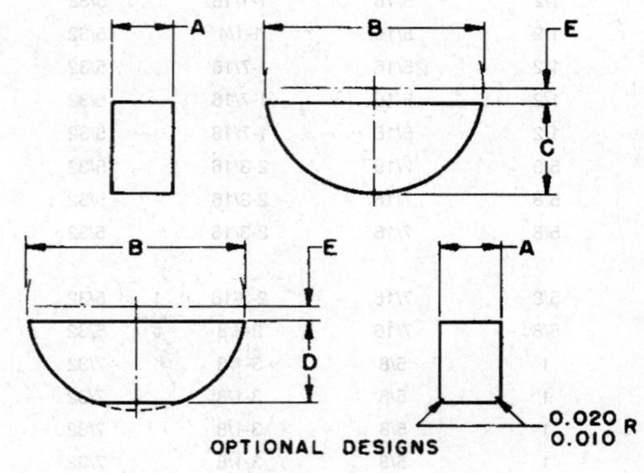

FIGURE 2—

TABLE 1A—KEY DIMENSIONS

Part No.	SAE Nominal Size	Width, A +0.001 −0.000	Dia, B +0.000 −0.010	Heights C +0.000 −0.006	Heights D +0.000 −0.006	Heights E Nominal	Key Area at Shear Line	Approximate Weight, Lb per 1000
201	1/16 x 1/4	0.0625	0.250	0.109	—	1/64	0.0145	0.6
206	1/16 x 5/16	0.0625	0.312	0.140	—	1/64	0.0184	0.7
207	3/32 x 5/16	0.0938	0.312	0.140	—	1/64	0.0264	0.9
211	1/16 x 3/8	0.0625	0.375	0.172	—	1/64	0.0225	0.9
212	3/32 x 3/8	0.0938	0.375	0.172	—	1/64	0.0328	1.3
213	1/8 x 3/8	0.1250	0.375	0.172	—	1/64	0.0420	1.5
1	1/16 x 1/2	0.0625	0.500	0.203	0.194	3/64	0.0296	1.3
2	3/32 x 1/2	0.0938	0.500	0.203	0.194	3/64	0.0434	1.9
3	1/8 x 1/2	0.1250	0.500	0.203	0.194	3/64	0.0512	2.5
4	3/32 x 5/8	0.0938	0.625	0.250	0.240	1/16	0.0523	3.0
5	1/8 x 5/8	0.1250	0.625	0.250	0.240	1/16	0.0716	3.9
6	5/32 x 5/8	0.1563	0.625	0.250	0.240	1/16	0.0871	4.9
61	3/16 x 5/8	0.1875	0.625	0.250	0.240	1/16	0.0105	5.8
7	1/8 x 3/4	0.1250	0.750	0.313	0.303	1/16	0.0884	6.1
8	5/32 x 3/4	0.1563	0.750	0.313	0.303	1/16	0.1086	7.5
9	3/16 x 3/4	0.1875	0.750	0.313	0.303	1/16	0.1279	9.0
91	1/4 x 3/4	0.2500	0.750	0.313	0.303	1/16	0.1623	12.0
10	5/32 x 7/8	0.1563	0.875	0.375	0.365	1/16	0.1294	11.0
11	3/16 x 7/8	0.1875	0.875	0.375	0.365	1/16	0.1531	13.0
12	7/32 x 7/8	0.2188	0.875	0.375	0.365	1/16	0.1813	14.9
A	1/4 x 7/8	0.2500	0.875	0.375	0.365	1/16	0.1976	17.0
13	3/16 x 1	0.1875	1.000	0.438	0.428	1/16	0.1781	17.0
14	7/32 x 1	0.2188	1.000	0.438	0.428	1/16	0.2100	20.1
15	1/4 x 1	0.2500	1.000	0.438	0.428	1/16	0.2320	23.0
B	5/16 x 1	0.3125	1.000	0.438	0.428	1/16	0.2811	29.0
16	3/16 x 1-1/8	0.1875	1.125	0.484	0.475	5/64	0.2007	22.0
17	7/32 x 1-1/8	0.2188	1.125	0.484	0.475	5/64	0.2320	25.0
18	1/4 x 1-1/8	0.2500	1.125	0.484	0.475	5/64	0.2622	29.0
C	5/16 x 1-1/8	0.3125	1.125	0.484	0.475	5/64	0.3193	36.0

TABLE 1A—KEY DIMENSIONS (continued)

Part No.	SAE Nominal Size	Width, A +0.001 −0.000	Dia, B +0.000 −0.010	Heights C +0.000 −0.006	Heights D +0.000 −0.006	Heights E Nominal	Key Area at Shear Line	Approximate Weight, Lb per 1000
19	3/16 x 1-1/4	0.1875	1.250	0.547	0.537	5/64	0.2284	27.1
20	7/32 x 1-1/4	0.2188	1.250	0.547	0.537	5/64	0.2608	31.8
21	1/4 x 1-1/4	0.2500	1.250	0.547	0.537	5/64	0.2955	36.0
D	5/16 x 1-1/4	0.3125	1.250	0.547	0.537	5/64	0.3621	45.0
E	3/8 x 1-1/4	0.3750	1.250	0.547	0.537	5/64	0.4243	54.0
22	1/4 x 1-3/8	0.2500	1.375	0.594	0.584	3/32	0.3259	43.0
23	5/16 x 1-3/8	0.3125	1.375	0.594	0.584	3/32	0.4003	54.0
F	3/8 x 1-3/8	0.3750	1.375	0.594	0.584	3/32	0.4705	65.0
24	1/4 x 1-1/2	0.2500	1.500	0.641	0.631	7/64	0.3562	50.0
25	5/16 x 1-1/2	0.3125	1.500	0.641	0.631	7/64	0.4384	63.0
G	3/8 x 1-1/2	0.3750	1.500	0.641	0.631	7/64	0.5166	75.0

TABLE 1B—KEY DIMENSIONS

Part No.	SAE Nominal Size	Width, A +0.001 -0.000	Dia, B +0.000 −0.010	Heights C +0.000 −0.005	Heights D +0.000 −0.006	Heights E Nominal	Length, L +0.000 −0.010	Key Area at Shear Line	Approximate Weight, Lb per 1000
126	3/16 x 2-1/8	0.1875	2.125	0.406	0.396	21/32	1.380	0.2578	23.4
127	1/4 x 2-1/8	0.2500	2.125	0.406	0.396	21/32	1.380	0.3437	31.2
128	5/16 x 2-1/8	0.3125	2.125	0.406	0.396	21/32	1.380	0.4296	39.3
129	3/8 x 2-1/8	0.3750	2.125	0.406	0.396	21/32	1.380	0.4833	47.2
26	3/16 x 2-1/8	0.1875	2.125	0.531	0.521	17/32	1.723	0.3222	36.3
27	1/4 x 2-1/8	0.2500	2.125	0.531	0.521	17/32	1.723	0.4178	48.2
28	5/16 x 2-1/8	0.3125	2.125	0.531	0.521	17/32	1.723	0.5062	60.1
29	3/8 x 2-1/8	0.3750	2.125	0.531	0.521	17/32	1.723	0.5868	72.3
Rx	1/4 x 2-3/4	0.2500	2.750	0.594	0.584	25/32	2.000	0.5000	64.8
Sx	5/16 x 2-3/4	0.3125	2.750	0.594	0.584	25/32	2.000	0.6286	80.8
Tx	3/8 x 2-3/4	0.3750	2.750	0.594	0.584	25/32	2.000	0.6943	96.6
Ux	7/16 x 2-3/4	0.4375	2.750	0.594	0.584	25/32	2.000	0.8253	112.9
Vx	1/2 x 2-3/4	0.5000	2.750	0.594	0.584	25/32	2.000	0.9094	129.3
R	1/4 x 2-3/4	0.2500	2.750	0.750	0.740	5/8	2.317	0.5718	91.6
S	5/16 x 2-3/4	0.3125	2.750	0.750	0.740	5/8	2.317	0.7071	114.2
T	3/8 x 2-3/4	0.3750	2.750	0.750	0.740	5/8	2.317	0.8319	136.6
U	7/16 x 2-3/4	0.4375	2.750	0.750	0.740	5/8	2.317	0.9499	159.2
V	1/2 x 2-3/4	0.5000	2.750	0.750	0.740	5/8	2.317	1.0606	191.8
30	3/8 x 3-1/2	0.3750	3.500	0.938	0.927	13/16	2.880	1.0781	216.0
31	7/16 x 3-1/2	0.4375	3.500	0.938	0.927	13/16	2.880	1.2371	252.0
32	1/2 x 3-1/2	0.5000	3.500	0.938	0.927	13/16	2.880	1.3905	288.0
33	9/16 x 3-1/2	0.5625	3.500	0.938	0.927	13/16	2.880	1.5368	325.0
34	5/8 x 3-1/2	0.6250	3.500	0.938	0.927	13/16	2.880	1.6755	359.0
35	11/16 x 3-1/2	0.6875	3.500	0.938	0.927	13/16	2.880	1.8062	399.0
36	3/4 x 3-1/2	0.7500	3.500	0.938	0.927	13/16	2.880	1.9281	435.0

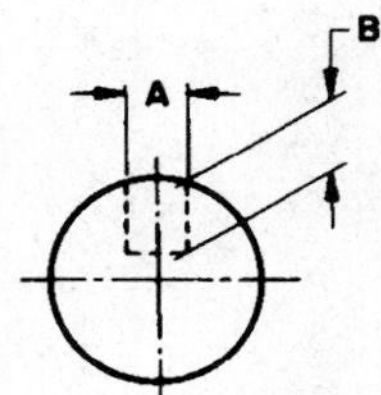

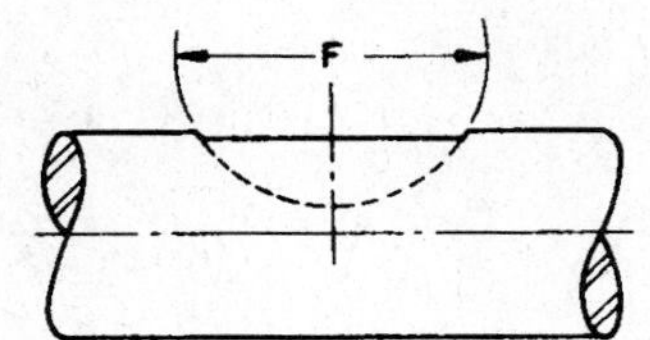

KEY SLOT

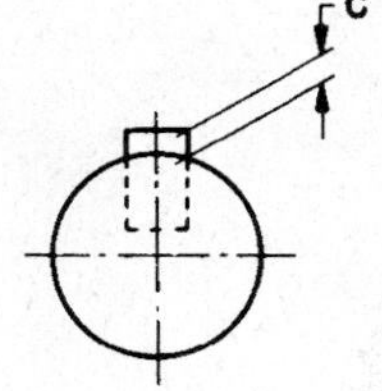

KEY ABOVE SHAFT

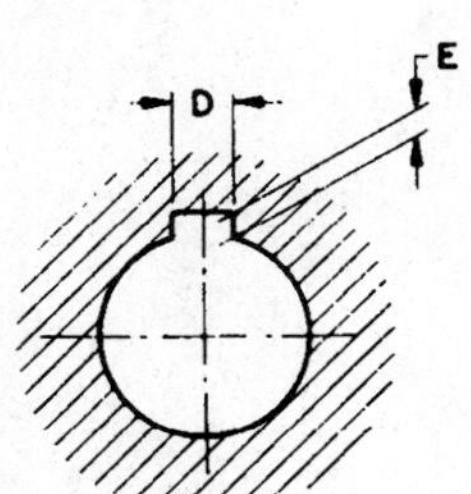

KEYWAY

FIGURE 3—

TABLE 2—KEY SLOT AND KEYWAY DIMENSIONS

Part No.	SAE Nominal Size	Key Slot Width, A Min	Key Slot Width A Max	Key Slot Depth, B +0.005 −0.000	Key Slot Dia, F Min	Key Slot Dia, F Max	Key above Shaft Height, C ±0.005	Key-way Width, D +0.002 −0.000	Key-way Depth, E +0.005 −0.000	Mfrs Part No.	SAE Nominal Size	Key Slot Width, A Min	Key Slot Width, A Max	Key Slot Depth, B +0.005 −0.000	Key Slot Dia, F Min	Key Slot Dia, F Max	Key above Shaft Height, C ±0.005	Key way Width, D +0.002 −0.000	Key way Depth, E +0.005 −0.000
201	1/16 x 1/4	0.0615	0.0630	0.0728	0.250	0.268	0.0312	0.0635	0.0372	E	3/8 x 1-1/4	0.3735	0.3755	0.3545	1.250	1.273	0.1875	0.3760	0.1935
206	1/16 x 5/16	0.0615	0.0630	0.1038	0.312	0.330	0.0312	0.0635	0.0372	22	1/4 x 1-3/8	0.2487	0.2505	0.4640	1.375	1.398	0.1250	0.2510	0.1310
207	3/32 x 5/16	0.0928	0.0943	0.0882	0.312	0.330	0.0469	0.0948	0.0529	23	5/16 x 1-3/8	0.3111	0.3130	0.4328	1.375	1.398	0.1562	0.3135	0.1622
211	1/16 x 3/8	0.0615	0.0630	0.1358	0.375	0.393	0.0312	0.0635	0.0372										
212	3/32 x 3/8	0.0928	0.0943	0.1202	0.375	0.393	0.0469	0.0948	0.0529	F	3/8 x 1-3/8	0.3735	0.3755	0.4015	1.375	1.398	0.1875	0.3760	0.1935
213	1/8 x 3/8	0.1240	0.1255	0.1045	0.375	0.393	0.0625	0.1260	0.0685	24	1/4 x 1-1/2	0.2487	0.2505	0.5110	1.500	1.523	0.1250	0.2510	0.1310
										25	5/16 x 1-1/2	0.3111	0.3130	0.4798	1.500	1.523	0.1562	0.3135	0.1622
1	1/16 x 1/2	0.0615	0.0630	0.1668	0.500	0.518	0.0312	0.0635	0.0372	G	3/8 x 1-1/2	0.3735	0.3755	0.4485	1.500	1.523	0.1875	0.3760	0.1935
2	3/32 x 1/2	0.0928	0.0943	0.1511	0.500	0.518	0.0469	0.0948	0.0529										
3	1/8 x 1/2	0.1240	0.1255	0.1355	0.500	0.518	0.0625	0.1260	0.0685	126	3/16 x 2-1/8	0.1863	0.1880	0.3073	2.125	2.160	0.0937	0.1885	0.0997
4	3/32 x 5/8	0.0928	0.0943	0.1981	0.625	0.643	0.0469	0.0948	0.0529	127	1/4 x 2-1/8	0.2487	0.2505	0.2760	2.125	2.160	0.1250	0.2510	0.1310
5	1/8 x 5/8	0.1240	0.1255	0.1825	0.625	0.643	0.0625	0.1260	0.0685	128	5/16 x 2-1/8	0.3111	0.3130	0.2448	2.125	2.160	0.1562	0.3135	0.1622
6	5/32 x 5/8	0.1553	0.1568	0.1669	0.625	0.643	0.0781	0.1573	0.0841	129	3/8 x 2-1/8	0.3735	0.3755	0.2135	2.125	2.160	0.1875	0.3760	0.1935
61	3/16 x 5/8	0.1863	0.1880	0.1513	0.625	0.643	0.0937	0.1885	0.0997	26	3/16 x 2-1/8	0.1863	0.1880	0.4323	2.125	2.160	0.0937	0.1885	0.0997
7	1/8 x 3/4	0.1240	0.1255	0.2455	0.750	0.768	0.0625	0.1260	0.0685	27	1/4 x 2-1/8	0.2487	0.2505	0.4010	2.125	2.160	0.1250	0.2510	0.1310
8	5/32 x 3/4	0.1553	0.1568	0.2299	0.750	0.768	0.0781	0.1573	0.0841	28	5/16 x 2-1/8	0.3111	0.3130	0.3698	2.125	2.160	0.1562	0.3135	0.1622
9	3/16 x 3/4	0.1863	0.1880	0.2143	0.750	0.768	0.0937	0.1885	0.0997	29	3/8 x 2-1/8	0.3735	0.3755	0.3385	2.125	2.160	0.1875	0.3760	0.1935
91	1/4 x 3/4	0.2487	0.2505	0.1830	0.750	0.768	0.1250	0.2510	0.1310										
10	5/32 x 7/8	0.1553	0.1568	0.2919	0.875	0.895	0.0781	0.1573	0.0841	Rx	1/4 x 2-3/4	0.2487	0.2505	0.4640	2.750	2.785	0.1250	0.2510	0.1310
										Sx	5/16 x 2-3/4	0.3111	0.3130	0.4328	2.750	2.785	0.1562	0.3135	0.1622
11	3/16 x 7/8	0.1863	0.1880	0.2763	0.875	0.895	0.0937	0.1885	0.0997	Tx	3/8 x 2-3/4	0.3735	0.3755	0.4015	2.750	2.785	0.1875	0.3760	0.1935
12	7/32 x 7/8	0.2175	0.2193	0.2607	0.875	0.895	0.1093	0.2198	0.1153	Ux	7/16 x 2-3/4	0.4360	0.4380	0.3703	2.750	2.785	0.2187	0.4385	0.2247
A	1/4 x 7/8	0.2487	0.2505	0.2450	0.875	0.895	0.1250	0.2510	0.1310	Vx	1/2 x 2-3/4	0.4985	0.5005	0.3390	2.750	2.785	0.2500	0.5010	0.2560
13	3/16 x 1	0.1863	0.1880	0.3393	1.000	1.020	0.0937	0.1885	0.0997										
14	7/32 x 1	0.2175	0.2193	0.3237	1.000	1.020	0.1093	0.2198	0.1153	R	1/4 x 2-3/4	0.2487	0.2505	0.6200	2.750	2.785	0.1250	0.2510	0.1310
15	1/4 x 1	0.2487	0.2505	0.3080	1.000	1.020	0.1250	0.2510	0.1310	S	5/16 x 2-3/4	0.3111	0.3130	0.5888	2.750	2.785	0.1562	0.3135	0.1622
										T	3/8 x 2-3/4	0.3735	0.3755	0.5575	2.750	2.785	0.1875	0.3760	0.1935
B	5/16 x 1	0.3111	0.3130	0.2768	1.000	1.020	0.1562	0.3135	0.1622	U	7/16 x 2-3/4	0.4360	0.4380	0.5263	2.750	2.785	0.2187	0.4385	0.2247
16	3/16 x 1-1/8	0.1863	0.1880	0.3853	1.125	1.145	0.0937	0.1885	0.0997	V	1/2 x 2-3/4	0.4985	0.5005	0.4950	2.750	2.785	0.2500	0.5010	0.2560
17	7/32 x 1-1/8	0.2175	0.2193	0.3697	1.125	1.145	0.1093	0.2198	0.1153										
18	1/4 x 1-1/8	0.2487	0.2505	0.3540	1.125	1.145	0.1250	0.2510	0.1310	30	3/8 x 3-1/2	0.3735	0.3755	0.7455	3.500	3.535	0.1875	0.3760	0.1935
C	5/16 x 1-1/8	0.3111	0.3130	0.3228	1.125	1.145	0.1562	0.3135	0.1622	31	7/16 x 3-1/2	0.4360	0.4380	0.7143	3.500	3.535	0.2187	0.4385	0.2247
19	3/16 x 1-1/4	0.1863	0.1880	0.4483	1.250	1.273	0.0937	0.1885	0.0997	32	1/2 x 3-1/2	0.4985	0.5005	0.6830	3.500	3.535	0.2500	0.5010	0.2560
										33	9/16 x 3-1/2	0.5610	0.5630	0.6518	3.500	3.535	0.2812	0.5635	0.2872
20	7/32 x 1-1/4	0.2175	0.2193	0.4327	1.250	1.273	0.1093	0.2198	0.1153	34	5/8 x 3-1/2	0.6235	0.6255	0.6205	3.500	3.535	0.3125	0.6260	0.3185
21	1/4 x 1-1/4	0.2487	0.2505	0.4170	1.250	1.273	0.1250	0.2510	0.1310	35	11/16 x 3-1/2	0.6860	0.6880	0.5893	3.500	3.535	0.3437	0.6885	0.3497
D	5/16 x 1-1/4	0.3111	0.3130	0.3858	1.250	1.273	0.1562	0.3135	0.1622	36	3/4 x 3-1/2	0.7485	0.7505	0.5580	3.500	3.535	0.3750	0.7510	0.3810

WOODRUFF KEY SLOTS AND KEYWAYS—SAE J503 MAY1959

SAE Information Report

Report of the SAE Parts and Fittings Division approved February 1928 and last revised by the SAE Parts and Fittings Committee January 1949. Editorial change May 1959.

Foreword—This Document has also changed to comply with the new SAE Technical Standards Board Format.

1. Scope

2. References—There are no referenced publications specified herein.

3. Shaft Diameter, L—Decimal equivalents are given to four places in Table 1. All figures are calculated from this basic dimension. Any change in the shaft diameter from basic will necessarily change all other figures; and, in this case, should accurate dimensions be required, the formula given below should be used.

4. Versed Sine, G—The versed sines specified are determined from the following formula:

$$G = \frac{L}{2} - \sqrt{\frac{L^2 - A^2}{4}} \qquad \text{(Eq. 1)}$$

where:

A is the minimum width of the key

5. Bottom of Key Slot to Opposite Side of Shaft, H—Obtain by subtracting the versed sine G, and depth of key slot, B, from the shaft diameter, L.

6. Top of Key to Opposite Side of Shaft, J—Obtain by subtracting the versed sine, G, from the shaft diameter, L, and then adding to this figure the height of key above shaft, C.

7. Bottom of Keyway to Opposite Side of Bore, K—Obtain by subtracting the versed sine, G, from the shaft diameter, L, and then adding to this figure the depth of keyway, E.

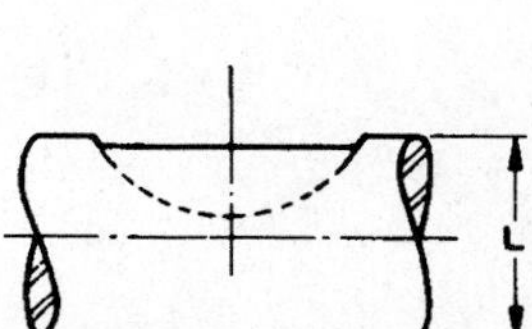

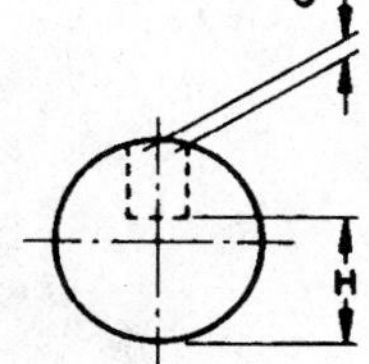

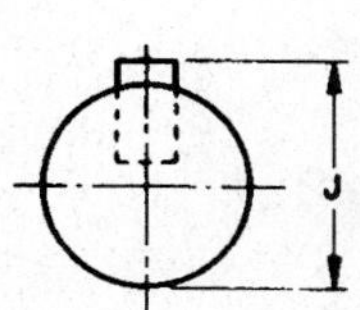

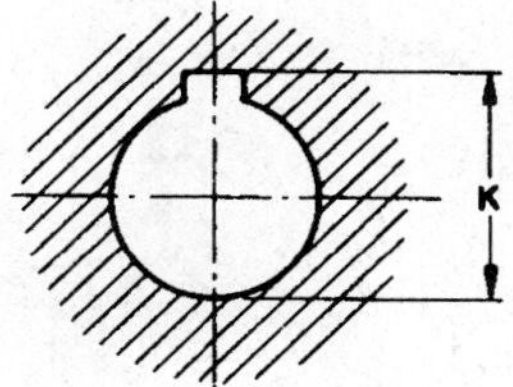

FIGURE 1—

TABLE 1—Versed Sine Dimension, G[(1)]

L Shaft Dia	Key Width 1/16	Key Width 3/32	Key Width 1/8	Key Width 5/32	Key Width 3/16	Key Width 7/32	Key Width 1/4	Key Width 5/16	Key Width 3/8	Key Width 7/16	Key Width 1/2	Key Width 9/16	Key Width 5/8	Key Width 11/16	Key Width 3/4
0.3125	0.0032	—	—	—	—	—	—	—	—	—	—	—	—	—	—
0.3437	0.0029	0.0065	—	—	—	—	—	—	—	—	—	—	—	—	—
0.3750	0.0026	0.0060	0.0107	—	—	—	—	—	—	—	—	—	—	—	—
0.4060	0.0024	0.0055	0.0099	—	—	—	—	—	—	—	—	—	—	—	—
0.4375	0.0022	0.0051	0.0091	—	—	—	—	—	—	—	—	—	—	—	—
0.4687	0.0021	0.0047	0.0085	0.0134	—	—	—	—	—	—	—	—	—	—	—
0.5000	0.0020	0.0044	0.0079	0.0125	—	—	—	—	—	—	—	—	—	—	—
0.5625	—	0.0039	0.0070	0.0111	0.0161	—	—	—	—	—	—	—	—	—	—
0.6250	—	0.0035	0.0063	0.0099	0.0144	0.0198	—	—	—	—	—	—	—	—	—
0.6875	—	0.0032	0.0057	0.0090	0.0130	0.0179	0.0235	—	—	—	—	—	—	—	—
0.7500	—	0.0029	0.0052	0.0082	0.0119	0.0163	0.0214	0.0341	—	—	—	—	—	—	—
0.8125	—	0.0027	0.0048	0.0076	0.0110	0.0150	0.0197	0.0312	—	—	—	—	—	—	—
0.8750	—	0.0025	0.0045	0.0070	0.0102	0.0139	0.0182	0.0288	—	—	—	—	—	—	—
0.9375	—	—	0.0042	0.0066	0.0095	0.0129	0.0170	0.0268	0.0391	—	—	—	—	—	—
1.0000	—	—	0.0039	0.0061	0.0089	0.0121	0.0159	0.0250	0.0365	—	—	—	—	—	—
1.0625	—	—	0.0037	0.0058	0.0083	0.0114	0.0149	0.0235	0.0342	—	—	—	—	—	—
1.1250	—	—	0.0035	0.0055	0.0079	0.0107	0.0141	0.0221	0.0322	0.0443	—	—	—	—	—
1.1875	—	—	0.0033	0.0052	0.0074	0.0102	0.0133	0.0209	0.0304	0.0418	—	—	—	—	—
1.2500	—	—	0.0031	0.0049	0.0071	0.0097	0.0126	0.0198	0.0288	0.0395	—	—	—	—	—
1.3750	—	—	—	0.0045	0.0064	0.0088	0.0115	0.0180	0.0261	0.0357	0.0471	—	—	—	—
1.5000	—	—	—	0.0041	0.0059	0.0080	0.0105	0.0165	0.0238	0.0326	0.0429	—	—	—	—
1.6250	—	—	—	0.0038	0.0054	0.0074	0.0097	0.0152	0.0219	0.0300	0.0394	0.0502	—	—	—
1.7500	—	—	—	—	0.0050	0.0069	0.0090	0.0141	0.0203	0.0278	0.0365	0.0464	—	—	—
1.8750	—	—	—	—	0.0047	0.0064	0.0084	0.0131	0.0189	0.0259	0.0340	0.0432	0.0536	—	—
2.0000	—	—	—	—	0.0044	0.0060	0.0078	0.0123	0.0177	0.0242	0.0318	0.0404	0.0501	—	—
2.1250	—	—	—	—	—	0.0056	0.0074	0.0116	0.0167	0.0228	0.0298	0.0379	0.0470	0.0572	0.0684
2.2500	—	—	—	—	—	—	0.0070	0.0109	0.0157	0.0215	0.0281	0.0357	0.0443	0.0538	0.0643
2.3750	—	—	—	—	—	—	—	0.0103	0.0149	0.0203	0.0266	0.0338	0.0419	0.0509	0.0608
2.5000	—	—	—	—	—	—	—	—	0.0141	0.0193	0.0253	0.0321	0.0397	0.0482	0.0576
2.6250	—	—	—	—	—	—	—	—	0.0135	0.0184	0.0240	0.0305	0.0377	0.0457	0.0547
2.7500	—	—	—	—	—	—	—	—	—	0.0175	0.0229	0.0291	0.0360	0.0437	0.0521
2.8750	—	—	—	—	—	—	—	—	—	0.0168	0.0219	0.0278	0.0344	0.0417	0.0498
3.0000	—	—	—	—	—	—	—	—	—	—	0.0210	0.0266	0.0329	0.0399	0.0476

1. Listed for the different shaft sizes and keyway widths for reference in checking dimensions H, J, and K.

19 V-Belts

V-BELTS AND PULLEYS—SAE J636 DEC2001

SAE Standard

Report of the SAE Miscellaneous Division approved August 1915, completely revised July 1977, editorial change January 1978 and reaffirmed by the SAE V-Belt Committee February 1987. Completely revised by the SAE Belt Drive Committee May 1992, reaffirmed August 1997, and December 2001. Rationale statement available.

Foreword——This Document has not changed other than to put it into the new SAE Technical Standards Board Format.

1. Scope—This specification covers standard dimensions, tolerances, and methods of measurement of V-belts and pulleys for automotive V-belt drives.

2. References—There are no referenced publications specified herein.

3. V-Belt Types—Automotive V-belts are produced in a variety of constructions in a basic trapezoidal shape. The inside circumference of the V-belt can be a plain straight line or corrugated by means of cogs or notches for the purpose of increasing the belt(s) flexibility for use with pulleys in the lower proposed diameter. Belts are to be dimensioned in such a way that they are functional in pulleys dimensioned as described in subsequent sections.

4. Pulleys—Pulleys are to conform to requirements of Figure 1 and Tables 1A, 1B, 2A, and 2B.

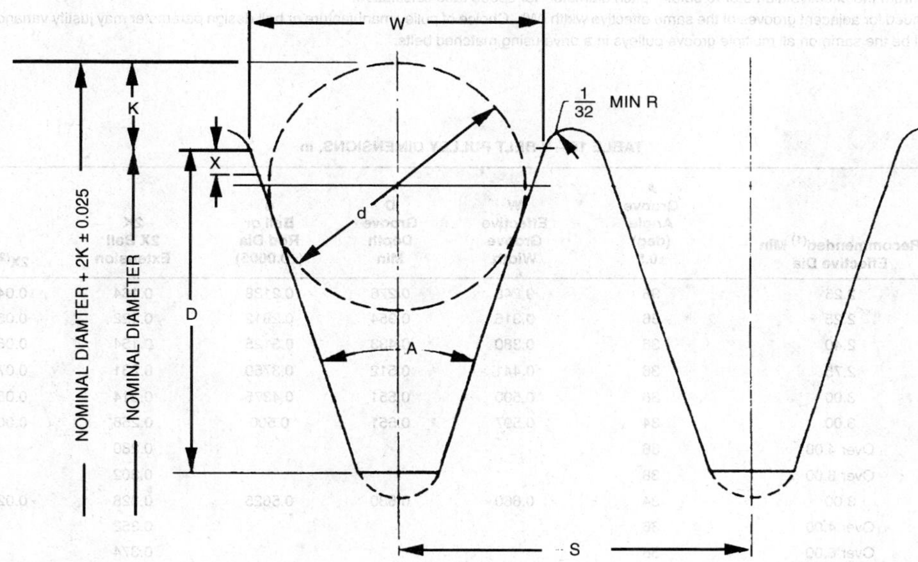

NOTES:

1. The sides of the groove are to be 3.2 µm (125 µin) A. A. maximum.
2. Radial runout is not to exceed 0.38 mm (0.015 in) full indicator movement (FIM). Axial runout is not to exceed 0.38 mm (0.015 in) FIM. Runout in the two directions is measured separately with a ball mounted under spring pressure to follow the groove as the pulley is rotated. Diameter, load, and overhang conditions may require or permit variations in the above-specified runout limits.
3. Bottom corner radii optional, but if used, it shall be below the depth, D.
4. In pulleys for use with belts in multiple on common centers, the diameters over the ball gages are not to vary from groove to groove in the same pulley more than 0.05 mm/25 mm (0.002 in/in) of diameter, with top limit of 0.30 mm (0.012 in) for diameters 152 mm (6 in) and above.
5. Centerline of groove is to be 90 degrees ± 2 degrees with pulley axis.
6. The X dimension is radial. 2X is to be subtracted from the effective diameter to obtain "pitch diameter" for speed ratio calculations.

FIGURE 1—V-BELT PULLEY DIMENSIONS

TABLE 1A—V-BELT PULLEY DIMENSIONS, mm

SAE Size	Recommended[1] Min Effective Dia	A Groove Angle (deg) ±0.5	W Effective Groove Width	D Groove Depth Min	d Ball or Rod Dia (±0.013)	2K 2X Ball[2] Extension	2X[3]	S Groove[4] Spacing (±0.38)
6A	57	36	6.3	7	5.558	4.16	1.0	8.00
8A	57	36	8.0	9	7.142	5.63	1.3	10.49
10A	61	36	9.7	11	7.938	3.77	1.5	13.74
11A	70	36	11.2	13	9.525	5.88	1.8	15.01
13A	76	36	12.7	14	11.113	7.99	2.0	16.79
15A	76	34				6.42		
	Over 102	36	15.2	14	12.700	7.02	0	19.76
	Over 152	38				7.56		
17A	76	34				8.21		
	Over 102	36	16.8	15	14.288	8.82	0.5	21.36
	Over 152	38				9.38		
20A	89	34				11.77		
	Over 114	36	20.0	18	17.463	12.42	1.0	24.54
	Over 152	38				13.02		
23A	102	34				15.67		
	Over 152	36	23.1	21	20.638	16.33	1.5	27.71
	Over 203	38				16.94		

1. Pulley effective diameters below those recommended should be used with caution, because power transmission and belt life may be reduced.
2. 2K dimensions are calculated in millimeters.
3. 2X is to be subtracted from the effective diameter to obtain "pitch diameter" for speed ratio calculation.
4. These values are intended for adjacent grooves of the same effective width (W). Choice of pulley manufacture or belt design parameter may justify variance from these values. The S dimension shall be the same on all multiple groove pulleys in a drive using matched belts.

TABLE 1B—V-BELT PULLEY DIMENSIONS, in

SAE Size	Recommended[1] Min Effective Dia	A Groove Angle (deg) ±0.5	W Effective Groove Width	D Groove Depth Min	d Ball or Rod Dia (±0.0005)	2K 2X Ball Extension	2X[2]	S Groove[3] Spacing (±0.015)
0.250	2.25	36	0.248	0.276	0.2188	0.164	0.04	0.315
0.315	2.25	36	0.315	0.354	0.2812	0.222	0.05	0.413
0.380	2.40	36	0.380	0.433	0.3125	0.154	0.06	0.541
0.440	2.75	36	0.441	0.512	0.3750	0.231	0.07	0.591
0.500	3.00	36	0.500	0.551	0.4375	0.314	0.08	0.661
11/16 (0.600)	3.00	34	0.597	0.551	0.500	0.258	0.00	0.778
	Over 4.00	36				0.280		
	Over 6.00	38				0.302		
3/4 (0.660)	3.00	34	0.660	0.630	0.5625	0.328	0.02	0.841
	Over 4.00	36				0.352		
	Over 6.00	38				0.374		
7/8 (0.790)	3.50	34	0.785	0.709	0.6875	0.472	0.04	0.966
	Over 4.50	36				0.496		
	Over 6.00	38				0.520		
1 (0.910)	4.00	34	0.910	0.827	0.8125	0.616	0.06	1.091
	Over 6.00	36				0.642		
	Over 8.00	38				0.666		

1. Pulley effective diameters below those recommended should be used with caution, because power transmission and belt life may be reduced.
2. 2X is to be subtracted from the effective diameter to obtain "pitch diameter" for speed ratio calculation.
3. These values are intended for adjacent grooves of the same effective width (W). Choice of pulley manufacture or belt design parameter may justify variance from these values. The S dimension shall be the same on all multiple groove pulleys in a drive using matched belts.

TABLE 2A—MEASURING PULLEY DIMENSIONS, mm

SAE Size	d_1 Effective Dia (±0.05)	Effective Pulley Circumference	A Groove Angle (deg) ±0.15	W Effective Groove Width	D Groove Depth Min	d Ball or Rod Dia (±0.013)	d_2 Dia(1) Over Balls or Rods (±0.05)
6A	97.03	304.8	36	6.3	7	5.558	101.18
8A	97.03	304.8	36	8.0	9	7.142	102.66
10A	97.03	304.8	36	9.7	11	7.938	100.80
11A	97.03	304.8	36	11.2	13	9.525	102.91
13A	97.03	304.8	36	12.7	14	11.113	105.02
15A	97.03	304.8	34	15.2	14	12.700	103.45
17A	97.03	304.8	34	16.8	16	14.288	105.24
20A	121.29	381.0	34	20.0	18	17.463	133.06
23A	121.29	381.0	34	23.1	21	20.638	136.96

1. d_2 dimensions are calculated in millimeters.

TABLE 2B—MEASURING PULLEY DIMENSIONS, in

SAE Size US	d_1 Effective Dia (±0.002)	Effective Pulley Circumference	A Groove Angle (deg) ±0.15	W Effective Groove Width	D Groove Depth Min	d Ball or Rod Dia (±0.0005)	d_2 Dia Over Balls or Rods (±0.002)
0.250	3.820	12.000	36	0.248	0.276	0.2188	3.984
0.315	3.820	12.000	36	0.315	0.354	0.2812	4.042
0.380	3.820	12.000	36	0.380	0.433	0.3125	3.974
0.440	3.820	12.000	36	0.441	0.512	0.3750	4.051
0.500	3.820	12.000	36	0.500	0.551	0.4375	4.134
11/16 (0.600)	3.820	12.000	34	0.597	0.551	0.5000	4.078
3/4 (0.660)	3.820	12.000	34	0.660	0.630	0.5625	4.148
7/8 (0.790)	4.775	15.000	34	0.785	0.709	0.6875	5.247
1 (0.910)	4.775	15.000	34	0.910	0.827	0.8125	5.391

5. V-Belt Measurement—Belt length and SAE size are defined by using effective length and rideout as measured in standard pulleys. These are determined by use of a measuring fixture comprised of two pulleys of equal diameter, a method of applying force, and a means of measuring the center distance between the two pulleys. One of the two pulleys is fixed in position while the other is movable along a graduated scale. The fixture is shown schematically in Figure 2. Specifications for measuring pulley dimensions are given in Tables 2A and 2B and Figure 3.

5.1 Length—To measure the length, the belt is placed on the measuring fixture at the force shown in Tables 3A and 3B, and rotated around the pulleys at least two revolutions of the belt to seat the belt properly in the pulley grooves and to divide the total force equally between the two strands of the belt. The midpoint of the center distance travel of the movable pulley defines the center distance and will be measured through one revolution of the belt minimum after the two seating revolutions. The belt effective length is equal to two times the center distance plus the effective pulley circumference. Standard belt center distance tolerances are shown in Tables 4A and 4B.

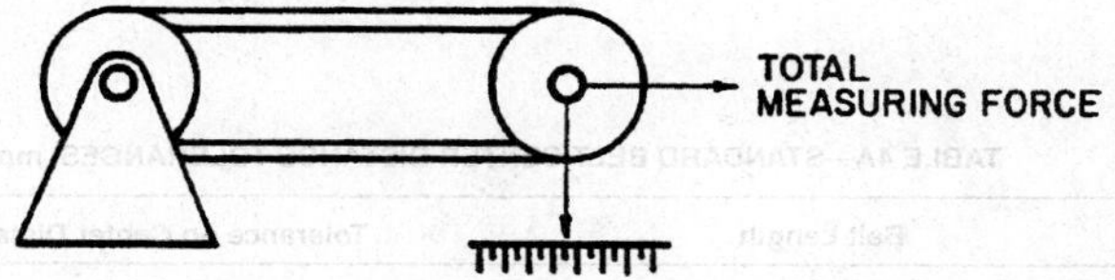

NOTE—The outside diameter and the effective diameter on the measuring pulley are one and the same.

FIGURE 2—DIAGRAM OF A FIXTURE FOR MEASURING V-BELTS

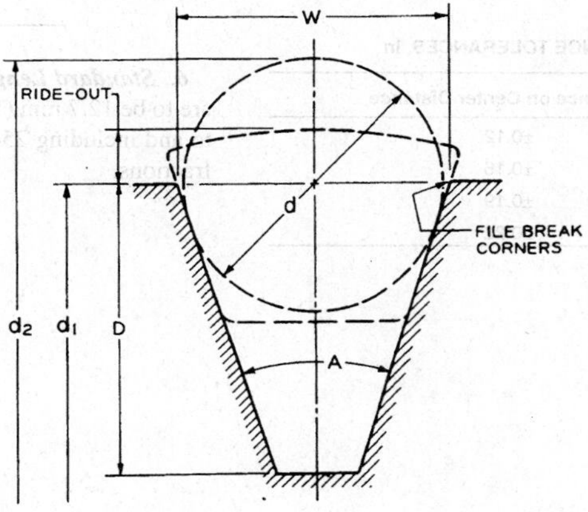

NOTE: The outside diameter and the effective diameter on the measuring pulley are one and the same.

FIGURE 3—MEASURING PULLEY DIMENSIONS

TABLE 3A—MEASURING CONDITIONS AND RIDEOUT, SI UNITS

SAE Size Metric	Total Measuring Force, N	Rideout(1) mm	Rideout(1) Tolerance mm
6A	222	0.8	±0.8
8A	222	0.8	±0.8
10A	267	1.5	±1.1
11A	267	1.0	±1.1
13A	267	1.5	±1.1
15A	267	2.3	±1.1
17A	356	2.3	±1.1
20A	445	2.3	±1.1
23A	534	2.3	±1.1

1. The belt rideout, as measured along the circumference of the belt, must fall within the specified tolerance at all points with the exception of measurements at points of dimension variations inherent to the manufacturing process or product such as material splices, belt identifications, etc.

TABLE 3B—MEASURING CONDITIONS AND RIDEOUT, U.S. CUSTOMARY UNITS

SAE Size in	Total Measuring Force, lb	Rideout(1) in	Rideout(1) Tolerance in
0.250	50	0.031	±0.031
0.315	50	0.031	±0.031
0.380	60	0.060	±0.045
0.440	60	0.040	±0.045
0.500	60	0.060	±0.045
11/16 (0.600)	60	0.090	±0.045
3/4 (0.660)	80	0.090	±0.045
7/8 (0.790)	100	0.090	±0.045
1 (0.910)	120	0.090	±0.045

1. The belt rideout, as measured along the circumference of the belt, must fall within the specified tolerance at all points with the exception of measurements at points of dimension variations inherent to the manufacturing process or product such as material splices, belt identifications, etc.

TABLE 4A—STANDARD BELT CENTER DISTANCE TOLERANCES, mm

Belt Length	Tolerance on Center Distance
1270 and less	±3.0
Over 1270–1524, incl.	±4.1
Over 1524–2032, incl.	±4.8
Over 2032–2540, incl.	±5.6

TABLE 4B—STANDARD BELT CENTER DISTANCE TOLERANCES, in

Belt Length	Tolerance on Center Distance
50 and less	±0.12
Over 50–60, incl.	±0.16
Over 60–80, incl.	±0.19
Over 80–100, incl.	±0.22

5.2 Rideout—The rideout standard and rideout tolerance are shown in Table 3. The rideout of a belt section is determined by measuring from a straight edge across the top of the belt to the rim of the measuring pulley, as shown in Figure 4.

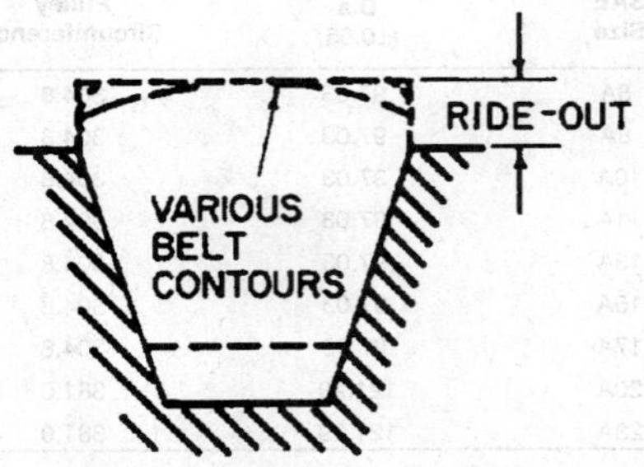

FIGURE 4—MEASURING BELT RIDE

5.3 Matched Belt Sets—For V-belts used in sets of two or more for a general application, the difference in center distance between the belts cannot exceed the values shown in Table 5.

TABLE 5A—MAXIMUM CENTER DISTANCE DIFFERENCE FOR BELTS IN A SET, mm

SAE Size	
6A	0.8
8A	0.8
10A	1.0
11A	1.0
13A	1.0
15A	1.5
17A	1.5
20A	1.5
23A	1.5

TABLE 5B—MAXIMUM CENTER DISTANCE DIFFERENCE FOR BELTS IN A SET, in

SAE Size	
0.250	0.03
0.315	0.03
0.380	0.04
0.440	0.04
0.500	0.04
11/16 (0.600)	0.06
3/4 (0.660)	0.06
7/8 (0.790)	0.06
1 (0.910)	0.06

6. Standard Lengths—Standard lengths up to and including 2032 mm (80 in) are to be 12.7 mm (1/2 in) increments. Standard lengths over 2032 mm (80 in) up to and including 2540 mm (100 in) are to be 25.4 mm (1 in) increments without fractions.

AUTOMOTIVE V-BELT DRIVES—SAE J637 DEC2001

SAE Recommended Practice

Report of the SAE Engine Committee approved January 1954 and completely revised by the SAE V-Belt Committee February 1989. Revised by the SAE Belt Drive Committee August 1997 and reaffirmed December 2001. Rationale statement available.

Foreword—Selection and specification of belts have been major problems due to the lack of a recognized industry standard for classifying V-belts according to performance and quality level.

From the very beginning of the use of V-belts on automotive drives, the automotive manufacturers and the V-belt manufacturers have employed laboratory tests on the products for such purposes as product development, source approval, and quality verification. This standard is the result of the combined effort of the users and suppliers.

1. Scope—The following information is intended as a guide to be used for evaluating belt construction, source approval, and quality audit. This recommendation has been prepared from existing literature, including standards, specifications, and data supplied by both producers and users.

These recommendations cover drive layout details and V-belt testing methods, including test layout, pulley diameters, torque loads, and guidance for interpreting test data. The application of these automotive V-belts is to power engine or vehicle accessories that are physically attached to the engine.

2. References

2.1 Applicable Publication—The following publication forms a part of this specification to the extent specified herein. Unless otherwise indicated, the latest version of SAE publications shall apply.

2.1.1 SAE PUBLICATION—Available from SAE, 400 Commonwealth Drive, Warrendale, PA 15096-0001.

SAE J636—V-Belts and Pulleys

2.1.2 RMA PUBLICATIONS—Available from Rubber Manufacturer's Association

IP-20—Classical Multi-V-Belts (A, B, C, and D) Belt Sections

IP-22—Narrow Multi-V-Belts (3 V , 5 V, and 8 V)

IP-23—Light Duty Single V-Belts (2 L, 3 L, 4 L, and 5 L)

2.1.3 ASAE PUBLICATION—Available from ASAE, 2950 Niles Road, St. Joseph, MI 49085-9569.

ASAE S211.4—V-Belt Drives for Farm Machines

3. General Drive Layout Considerations

3.1 Power Transmission—When the engine is used to drive an external unit equipped with industrial type pulleys and belts, it is recommended that the power takeoff pulley on the engine be grooved according to the appropriate industrial standard. There are four such standards. Three of these standards are published by the RMA-MPTA (Rubber Manufacturers Association-Mechanical Power Transmission Association) and include Classical Multi-V-Belt (A, B, C, and D belt sections), Narrow Multi-V-Belts (3 V, 5 V, and 8 V), and Single V-Belts (2 L, 3 L, 4 L, and 5 L). The fourth is published as an American Society of Agricultural Engineers standard, V-Belt Drives for Farm Machines.

The grooves in these four standards differ from each other in the reference dimensions. They are not interchangeable with SAE grooves which were standardized for engine accessory and other engine compartment drives.

3.2 Belt Speed—It is recommended that pulleys be as large as possible without continuously exceeding 35.6 m/s (7000 ft/min) belt speed. It is possible to have peak belt speeds of 43.2 m/s (8500 ft/min) but special pulleys may be needed. Consult the pulley manufacturer to verify the pulleys can handle the required rim speed.

3.3 Pulley Sizes—No pulley in the drive should be smaller than the recommended minimum effective diameters listed in SAE J636, Tables 1A and 1B.

3.4 Belt Length—Calculation of the belt effective length for a specific drive involves several design considerations, including provision for adequate installation and takeup.

To allow for belt installation and takeup, one pulley should be adjustable from its initial position with the mean length belt at installation tension. This formula gives the absolute minimum allowance for easy installation of the belt without prying it over the sides of the grooves.

3.4.1 Equation 1 can be used to calculate the recommended minimum belt effective length for installation:

$$\text{Min Belt EL} = (1.005)(L_1) + L_2 + C_I \qquad \text{(Eq. 1)}$$

where:

L_1 = Effective belt length (addition of span lengths and effective arc lengths on the pulleys) around the drive with the tensioning pulley in the minimum position. The 1.005 factor provides for length change from slack to measuring tension.

L_2 = 2 X negative belt manufacturing center distance tolerance. (SAE J636, Tables 4A and 4B)

C_I = Length to account for belt worked into groove. Installation constant (C_I) found in Table 3.

3.4.2 Select a belt to be used that has a nominal effective length equal to or greater than the recommended minimum EL.

3.4.3 Calculate the maximum required effective length around the drive to provide for take-up (see Equation 2):

$$\text{Maximum required belt path length} = (1.005)L_3 + L_4 + L_5 + L_6 \qquad \text{(Eq. 2)}$$

where:

L_3 = Nominal Belt EL as defined in 3.4.2. The 1.005 factor accounts for elongation from measuring to installation tension.

L_4 = (0.01) (EL) -- Allows 1% for tensile member growth and belt wear during service life.

L_5 = 2 X positive belt manufacturing center distance tolerance. (SAE J636, Tables 4a and 4B)

L_6 = Belt seating factor (9.6 mm, 0.38 in)

3.5 Pulley Misalignment—The recommended maximum misalignment between pulleys is 1.6 mm per 300 mm span length (1/16 in/ft of span length) or approximately 1/3 of 1 degree.

4. V-Belt Fatigue Test Method—The belt shall be mounted on a test layout as shown in Figure 1 with pulley diameters and speeds as given in Tables 1A, 1B, 2A, and 2B. The horsepower (kilowatts) to be absorbed at the driven pulley shall be compatible with the tension pulley diameter and belt length as shown in Tables 1A, 1B, 2A, and 2B.

The driver pulley speed (rpm) shall be used in the torque load calculation and the torque load shall be kept constant without compensation for loss of driven pulley rpm resulting from belt slippage and creep. See Equations 4 and 3.

$$\text{Torque, N·m} = \frac{\text{Specified kilowatts} \times 9549}{\text{Driver rpm}} \qquad \text{(Eq. 3)}$$

$$\text{Torque, lb·in} = \frac{\text{Specified horsepower} \times 63025}{\text{Driver rpm}} \qquad \text{(Eq. 4)}$$

Measurable parasitic loads due to bearing losses, lubricants, etc., shall be deducted from the specified horsepower (kilowatts) in the previous calculation.

The tension shall be applied by weights equal in number of pounds to 10 times the number of units of the specified horsepower (in number of Newtons to 60 times the number of units of the specified kilowatts).

4.1 The test procedure shall be as follows:

4.1.1 Condition the belt by running 5 min under the prescribed test details but without the dynamometer load. Maintain a constant tension during this period by operating with the tension pulley center position unlocked.

4.1.2 Stop the machine, allow to stand for a minimum of 10 min and lock the tension pulley center position midway of the limits of travel during belt rotation.

4.1.3 Restart with the dynamometer load and run until the slip reaches 8% or until the belt will no longer transmit the load uniformly because of breakage or rough running.

4.1.4 Whenever the slip reaches 8%, stop the machine, allow to stand for a minimum of 20 min, unlock the tension pulley center, restore the initial tension, relock, and restart the machine.

4.1.5 Record the number of hours run and the number of resets (exclusive of the 5 min run-in).

4.1.6 The ambient temperature shall be 27 to 32 °C (80 to 90 °F). An increase in internal belt temperature will reduce belt life. Internal belt temperature is dependent upon ambient temperature as well as other test conditions.

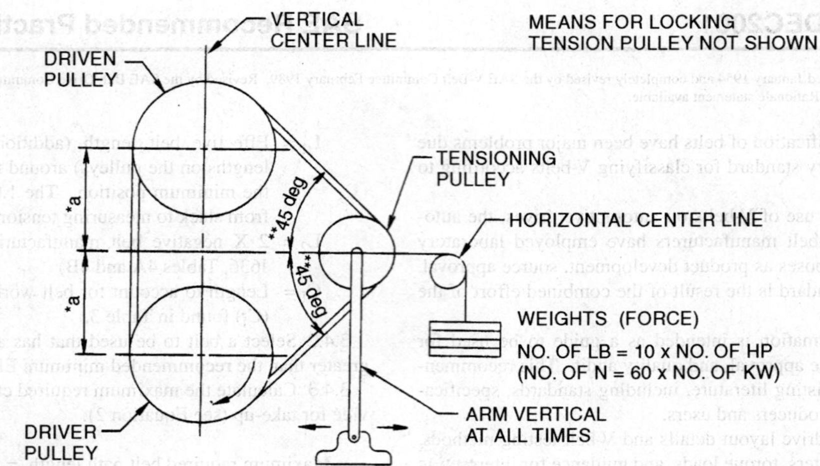

FIGURE 1—V-BELT FATIGUE TEST

5. Test Performance Guidelines—The test life which a belt must attain shall be according to agreement between user and manufacturer. However, typical curves of average test life versus belt length are shown in Figure 2. The typical curves of Figure 2 are constructed with the belt life varying as the 2.75 power of belt length for the test conditions given in Tables 1A, 1B, 2A, and 2B. The acceptable number of retensionings after the initial 5 min run-in shall be according to agreement between the manufacturer and user.

The belt manufacturer's test data on belts of a certain construction specification shall be considered valid for evaluation of all belts of the same construction specification regardless of the intended user. Belts shall be considered to be of the same construction specification when they are the same with respect to the manufacturer's cross section dimensions, material specifications, and method of manufacture.

In evaluating for part source approval and for production quality surveillance, test data for the entire length group containing a part in question shall be considered pertinent. The design of some test machines may not accommodate the shortest lengths shown in Figure 2. In such cases, test data on some longer belt(s) of the same construction specification and within the length group 710 to 1020 mm (28 to 40 in) shall be used. Similarly, test data on belt(s) within the length group 1420 to 1730 mm (56 to 68 in) shall be used for lengths beyond 1730 mm (68 in).

Whether testing is performed for part source approval or for production quality surveillance, a realistic statistical guide to acceptability would be "not more than 10% of test lives shall be permitted to fall below 50% of the specified average life."

For part source approval, test data of the immediately preceding three month period shall be considered pertinent. When such data are not sufficient for the statistical evaluation, the manufacturer may have the option of submitting data for source approval on a "sample" of the part under consideration or on samples of the same length group and construction specification. Because the data would be limited to this situation, a guide to approval could be to permit no test results to be below 50% of the specified average life.

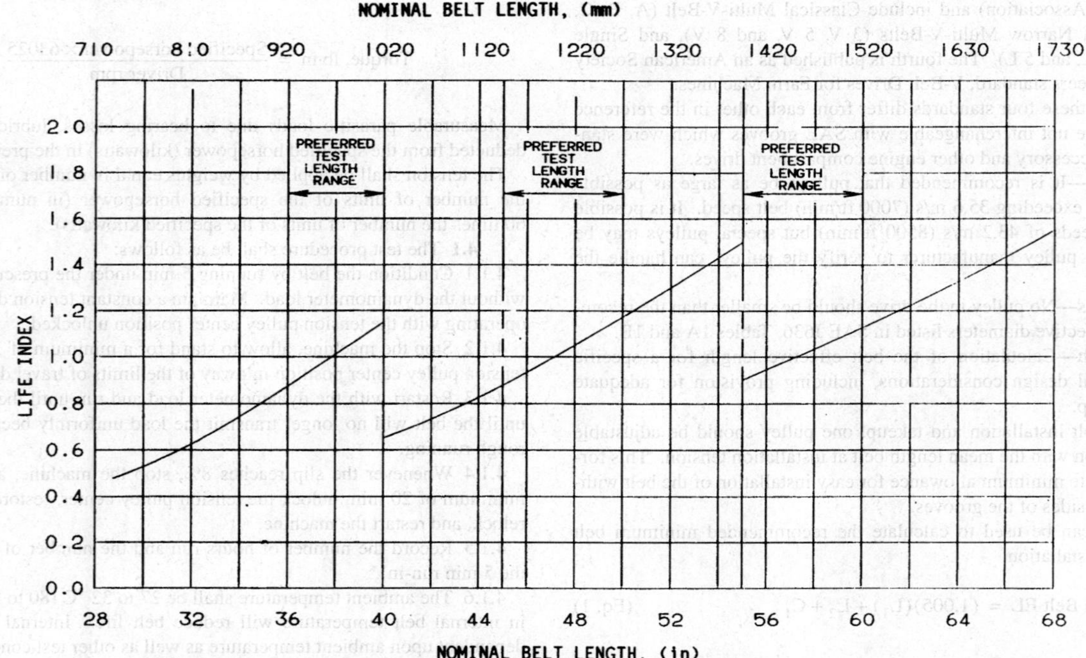

FIGURE 2—TYPICAL LIFE-LENGTH CURVES (FOR TEST CONDITIONS IN TABLES 1A, 1B, 2A, AND 2B)

TABLE 1A—TEST CONDITIONS[1] PLAIN SECTION BELTS, (mm)

SAE Belt Size	Standard Groove Width	Diameter Where Specified Groove Width Occurs (w/o Width Tol) DR & DN Pulley ±0.25	Diameter Where Specified Groove Width Occurs (w/o Width Tol) Tension Pulley ±0.25	Driver Pulley Speed RPM ±2%	Load kW	Length Range Total	Length Range Preferred
6A	6.3	120.65	57.15	4900	6.3	Under 1020	920 – 1020
					7.1	1020 – 1400	1140 – 1270
					(2)	Over 1400	1400 – 1520
8A	8.0	120.5	57.0	4900	6.9	Under 1020	920 – 1020
					7.6	1020 – 1400	1140 – 1270
					8.4	Over 1400	1400 – 1520
10A	9.7	120.5	63.5	4900	7.5	Under 1020	920 – 1020
					8.2	1020 – 1400	1140 – 1270
					8.9	Over 1400	1400 – 1520
11A	11.2	120.5	70.0	4900	8.0	Under 1020	920 – 1020
					8.8	1020 – 1400	1140 – 1270
					9.5	Over 1400	1400 – 1520
13A	12.7	127.0	76.0	4700	8.9	Under 1020	920 – 1020
					9.7	1020 – 1400	1140 – 1270
					10.4	Over 1400	1400 – 1520
15A	15.2	127.0	89.0	4700	9.7	Under 1020	920 – 1020
					10.4	1020 – 1400	1140 – 1270
					11.2	Over 1400	1400 – 1520
17A	16.8	127.0	92.0	4700	10.1	Under 1020	920 – 1020
					10.8	1020 – 1400	1140 – 1270
					11.6	Over 1400	1400 – 1520
20A	20.0	152.5	101.5	3900	(2)	(2)	(2)
23A	23.1	178.0	117.5	3350	(2)	(2)	(2)

1. Groove details as given in SAE J636, Table 1A, Figure 1
2. Values to be per agreement between user and manufacturer (insufficient usage for recommendations)

TABLE 1B—TEST CONDITIONS[1] PLAIN SECTION BELTS, (in)

SAE Belt Size	Standard Groove Width	Diameter Where Specified Groove Width Occurs (w/o Width Tol) DR & DN Pulleys ±0.010	Diameter Where Specified Groove Width Occurs (w/o Width Tol) Tension Pulley ±0.010	Driver Pulley Speed RPM ±2%	Load HP	Length Range Total	Length Range Preferred
0.250	0.248	4.750	2.250	4900	8.50	Under 40	36 – 40
					9.50	40 – 55	45 – 50
					(2)	Over 55	55 – 60
0.315	0.315	4.750	2.250	4900	9.25	Under 40	36 – 40
					10.25	40 – 55	45 – 50
					11.25	Over 55	55 – 60
0.380	0.380	4.750	2.500	4900	10.00	Under 40	36 – 40
					11.00	40 – 55	45 – 50
					12.00	Over 55	55 – 60
0.440	0.441	4.750	2.750	4900	10.75	Under 40	36 – 40
					11.75	40 – 55	45 – 50
					12.75	Over 55	55 – 60
0.500	0.500	5.000	3.000	4700	12.00	Under 40	36 – 40
					13.00	40 – 55	45 – 50
					14.00	Over 55	55 – 60
11/16 (0.600)	0.597	5.000	3.500	4700	13.00	Under 40	36 – 40
					14.00	40 – 55	45 – 50
					15.00	Over 55	55 – 60
3/4 (0.660)	0.660	5.000	3.625	4700	13.50	Under 40	36 – 40
					14.50	40 – 55	45 – 50
					15.50	Over 55	55 – 60
7/8 (0.790)	0.785	6.000	4.000	3900	(2)	(2)	(2)
1 (0.910)	0.910	7.000	4.625	3350	(2)	(2)	(2)

1. Groove details as given in SAE J636, Table 1B, Figure 1
2. Values to be per agreement between user and manufacturer (insufficient usage for recommendations)

TABLE 2A—TEST CONDITIONS[1] COG, OR NOTCHED BELTS, (mm)

SAE Belt Size	Standard Groove Width	Diameter Where Specified Groove Width Occurs (w/o Width Tol) DR & DN Pulleys ±0.010	Diameter Where Specified Groove Width Occurs (w/o Width Tol) Tension Pulley ±0.010	Driver Pulley Speed RPM ±2%	Load kW	Length Range Total	Length Range Preferred
6A	6.3	(2)	(2)	(2)	(2)	(2)	(2)
8A	8.0	(2)	(2)	(2)	(2)	(2)	(2)
10A	9.7	120.5	57.0	4900	7.5 8.2 8.9	Under 1020 1020 – 1400 Over 1400	920 – 1020 1140 – 1270 1400 – 1520
11A	11.2	120.5	63.5	4900	8.0 8.8 9.5	Under 1020 1020 – 1400 Over 1400	920 – 1020 1140 – 1270 1400 – 1520
13A	12.7	127.0	70.0	4700	8.9 9.7 10.4	Under 1020 1020 – 1400 Over 1400	920 – 1020 1140 – 1270 1400 – 1520
15A	15.2	127.0	82.5	4700	9.7 10.4 11.2	Under 1020 1020 – 1400 Over 1400	920 – 1020 1140 – 1270 1400 – 1520
17A	16.8	127.0	85.5	4700	10.1 10.8 11.6	Under 1020 1020 – 1400 Over 1400	920 – 1020 1140 – 1270 1400 – 1520
20A	20.0	152.5	95.0	3900	(2)	(2)	(2)
23A	23.1	178.0	111.0	3350	(2)	(2)	(2)

1. Groove details as given in SAE J636, Table 1A, Figure 1
2. Values to be per agreement between user and manufacturer (insufficient usage for recommendations)

TABLE 2B—TEST CONDITIONS[1] COG, OR NOTCHED BELTS, (in)

SAE Belt Size	Standard Groove Width	Diameter Where Specified Groove Width Occurs (w/o Width Tol) DR & DN Pulleys ±0.010	Diameter Where Specified Groove Width Occurs (w/o Width Tol) Tension Pulley ±0.010	Driver Pulley Speed RPM ±2%	Load HP	Length Range Total	Length Range Preferred
0.250	0.248	(2)	(2)	(2)	(2)	(2)	(2)
0.315	0.315	(2)	(2)	(2)	(2)	(2)	(2)
0.380	0.380	4.750	2.250	4900	10.00 11.00 12.00	Under 40 40 – 55 Over 55	36 – 40 45 – 50 55 – 60
0.440	0.441	4.750	2.500	4900	10.75 11.75 12.75	Under 40 40 – 55 Over 55	36 – 40 45 – 50 55 – 60
0.500	0.500	5.000	2.750	4700	12.00 13.00 14.00	Under 40 40 – 55 Over 55	36 – 40 45 – 50 55 – 60
11/16 (0.600)	0.597	5.000	3.250	4700	13.00 14.00 15.00	Under 40 40 – 55 Over 55	36 – 40 45 – 50 55 – 60
3/4 (0.660)	0.660	5.000	3.375	4700	13.50 14.50 15.50	Under 40 40 – 55 Over 55	36 – 40 45 – 50 55 – 60
7/8 (0.790)	0.785	6.000	3.750	3900	(2)	(2)	(2)
1 (0.910)	0.910	7.000	4.375	3350	(2)	(2)	(2)

1. Groove details as given in SAE J636, Table 1B, Figure 1
2. Values to be per agreement between user and manufacturer (insufficient usage for recommendations)

TABLE 3—CLEARANCE FACTOR FOR BELT INSTALLATION

SAE Size Metric	SAE Size English	C Metric Single	C Metric Multiple	C English Single	C English Multiple
6A	0.250	6.2	12.4	0.245	0.490
8A	0.315	6.1	12.2	0.240	0.480
10A	0.380	7.6	15.2	0.300	0.600
11A	0.440	7.6	15.2	0.300	0.600
13A	0.500	9.9	19.8	0.390	0.780
15A	11/16	8.9	17.8	0.350	0.700
17A	3/4	10.8	21.6	0.425	0.850
20a	7/8	12.3	24.6	0.485	0.970
23A	1	13.0	26.0	0.510	1.020

APPENDIX A
STANDARDIZED LABORATORY TESTING OF NONSTANDARDIZED AUTOMOTIVE V-BELTS

A.1 The following information is supplementary to the test conditions for the nine standard SAE top width belts shown in Tables 1A, 1B, 2A, and 2B.

"High ride" belts have been tried in a number of different standard SAE top width sheave grooves. At least one of these "high ride" belts has had sufficient usage to be recognized and test conditions specified for it. This "high ride" belt is defined as a belt that has a nominal rideout 2.7 mm (0.105 in) in an SAE 9.7 mm (0.380 in) pulley.

Considerations for the "high ride" belt in the standard 9.7 mm (0.380 in) groove are:

1. Improved belt life since the belt diameters are effectively larger, slightly increasing belt velocity and decreasing bending stress.
2. Decreased tension decay resulting from No. 1 previous, and a slight increase in belt tensile width.
3. Change in speed ratio with a reduced driven speed when used on such accessories as alternator drives.
4. Questions on belt stability.

The test conditions shown in Tables A1A and A1B are applicable to a "high ride" belt in SAE 9.7 mm (0.380 in) grooves.

TABLE A1A—TEST CONDITIONS, (mm)

Belt Type	Standard Groove Width	DR & DN Pulleys ±0.25	Tension Pulley ±0.25	Driver Speed rpm ±2%	Load kW	Length Range Total	Length Range Preferred
Plain Section	9.7	120.5	63.5	4900	8.2	Under 1020	920–1020
					9.4	1020–1400	1140–1270
					10.1	Over 1400	1400–1520
Notched or Cog	9.7	120.5	57.0	4900	8.2	Under 1020	920–1020
					9.4	1020–1400	1140–1270
					10.1	Over 1400	1400–1520

TABLE A1B—TEST CONDITIONS, (in)

Belt Type	Standard Groove Width	DR & DN Pulleys ±0.010	Tension Pulley ±0.010	Driver Speed rpm ±2%	Load hp	Length Range Total	Length Range Preferred
Plain Section	0.380	4.750	2.500	4900	11.0	Under 40	36–40
					12.5	40–55	45–50
					13.5	Over 55	55–60
Notched or Cog	0.380	4.750	2.250	4900	11.0	Under 40	36–40
					12.5	40–55	45–50
					13.5	Over 55	55–60

SI (METRIC) SYNCHRONOUS BELTS AND PULLEYS—SAE J1278 MAR1993

SAE Standard

Report of the SAE V-Belt Committee approved October 1980, reaffirmed without change June 1986. Reaffirmed by the SAE Belt Drive Committee March 1993.

Foreword—This reaffirmed document has been changed only to reflect the new SAE Technical Standards Board Format.

1. Scope—Synchronous belt drives consist of a toothed belt which mates with grooved pulleys to provide a precise Speed ratio between the driver and driven pulleys. This SAE Standard covers the synchronous belt and pulley sections currently in use in automotive applications such as camshaft, distributor, and other underhood drives that may require synchronization. It also provides for future sections to be added as usage develops. Table 1 lists the sections currently in use.

TABLE 1—PULLEY GENERATING TOOL RACK FORM DIMENSIONS (mm)

Pulley Section	Diameter Range (No. of Grooves)	P_b Pitch ± 0.003	± 0.25 deg	h_g + 0.05 −0.00	b_g + 0.05 −0.00	r_b ± 0.03	r_t ± 0.03	2α
ST	10 and over	9.525	40	2.13	3.10	0.86	0.53	0.762
SU	14 thru 19	12.700	40	2.59	4.24	1.47	1.04	1.372
SU	over 19	12.700	40	2.59	4.24	1.47	1.42	1.372
STA	19 and over	9.525	40	2.13	3.10	0.86	0.71	1.372

2. References—There are no referenced publications specified herein.

3. Belt and Pulley Sections—Synchronous belt and pulley sections are defined primarily by pitch, which is the linear distance between the axes of two consecutive teeth when the belt is loaded to the prescribed measuring force. Figure 1 and Figure 2 illustrate the location of the pitch line. A two- or three-letter designation is used to identify the standard sections. Two-letter designations identify a specific pitch, tooth form, and pitch line location. For example, an ST section has a pitch of 9.525 mm, while an SU section has a pitch of 12.700 mm. Since it is possible to have more than one section with the same pitch, a three-letter designation is used to identify a section that is a variation of a normal two-letter section. For example, an STA section has the same pitch as an ST section (9.525 mm) and the same tooth form as the ST section, but it utilizes the SU section pitch line location because of belt construction. As a result, STA section belts will not mesh properly with ST section pulleys even though the pitch and tooth forms are the same because it has a larger pitch line differential. Therefore, the STA section belt is a unique section and requires special pulleys designed for this particular section. Should another section with the ST (9.525 mm) pitch be standardized, it would have the section designation of STB.

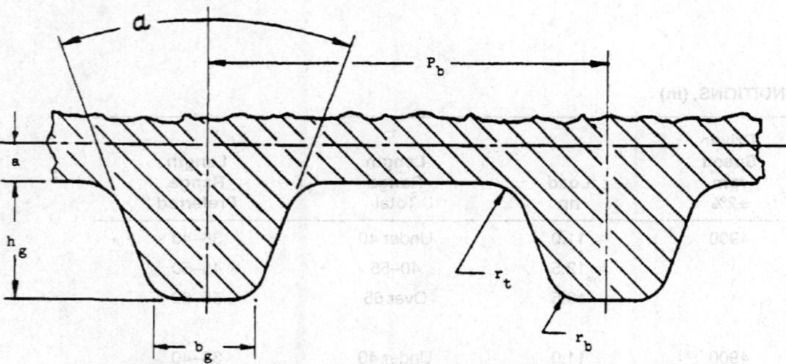

FIGURE 1—PULLEY GENERATING TOOL RACK FORM

4. Pulleys

4.1 Groove Profile—The groove profile is defined as the profile formed by the generating tool rack form described in Table 1 and Figure 1. The relationship of pitch diameter to outside diameter is illustrated in Figure 2.

4.2 Tolerances—Tolerances on pulleys shall conform to values shown in Table 2 and the accompanying footnotes.

4.3 Designation—Synchronous pulleys are identified by standard pulley numbers. The first digits in the number indicate the belt width the pulley is designed to accommodate. The letters indicate the section, and the numbers following the letters indicate the number of grooves in the pulley. (See Figure 3.)

TABLE 2—PULLEY TOLERANCES (mm)

Outside Diameter Range	Pitch to Pitch Tolerance Adjacent Grooves	Pitch to Pitch Tolerance Accumulative Over 90 deg
Up to 50, incl	± 0.03	± 0.09
Over 50 to 100, incl	± 0.03	± 0.11
Over 100 to 175, incl	± 0.03	± 0.13
Over 175 to 300, incl	± 0.03	± 0.15
Outside Diameter		**Tolerance**
Up to 50 mm, incl		+0.05 mm/−0.00 mm
For each additional 25 mm or portion thereof		+0.025 mm/−0.00 mm
Outside Diameter Runout[(1)]		0.08 mm (max)
Up to 75 mm, incl outside diameter		0.01 mm (max)
For each additional 25 mm or portion thereof		0.02 mm per 25 mm of diameter add 0.01 mm
Axial Runout[(1)] **(Side Wobble)**		
Up to 250 mm, incl outside diameter		
For each additional 25 mm outside diameter over 25 mm add 0.01 mm		
Diametrical Taper		
0.01 mm per 10 mm of face width		
Groove Helix		
0.01 mm per 10 mm of face width		

1. Full indicator movement

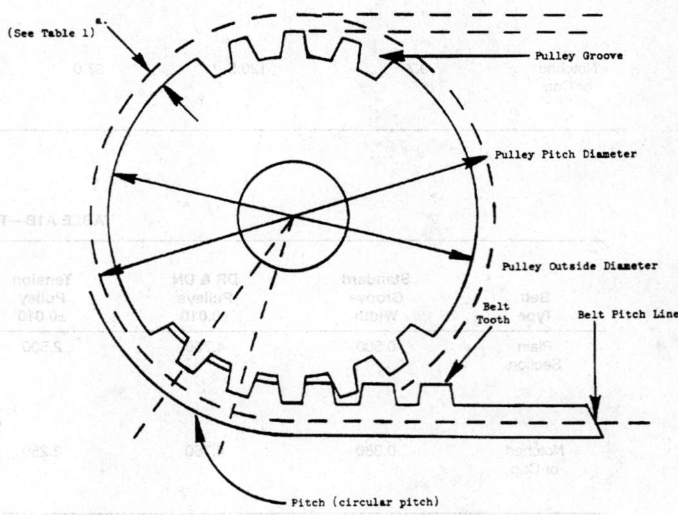

FIGURE 2—PULLEY DIMENSIONS

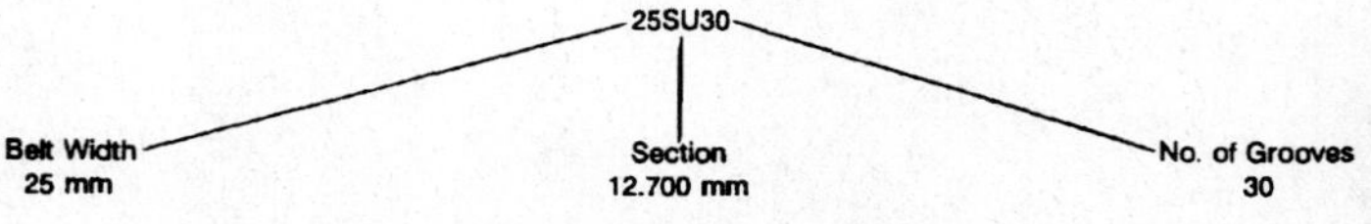

FIGURE 3—PULLEY DESIGNATION

5. *Belts*

5.1 Dimensions—Nominal dimensions of the synchronous belt sections are shown in Table 3 and Figure 4.

TABLE 3—NOMINAL BELT DIMENSIONS (mm)

Belt Section	Pitch	h_b	2 β deg	h_t	b_t	r_{bb}	r_{bt}
ST	9.525	3.6	40	1.9	3.2	0.5	0.5
SU	12.700	4.1	40	2.3	4.4	1.0	1.0
STA	9.525	4.1	40	1.9	3.2	0.5	0.5

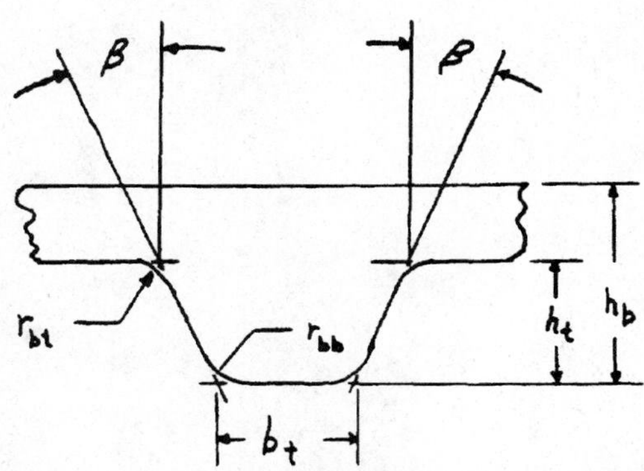

FIGURE 4—BELT SECTION

5.2 Tolerances—Tolerances on width shall conform to values shown in Table 4.

TABLE 4—BELT WIDTH TOLERANCES (mm)

Belt Width	Belt Length Range Up to 840, incl	Belt Length Range Over 840 to 1680, incl
Up to 40, incl	+0.6/–0.6	+0.6/–0.6
Over 40 to 50, incl	+0.8/–0.8	+1.0/–1.0

5.3 Designation—Belt sizes shall be identified by standard belt numbers. The first digits in the number indicate the belt width in millimeters. The letters indicate the belt section (pitch) designation, and the numbers following the letters indicate the pitch length in millimeters. For example, the number 25SU1500 indicates a belt 25 mm wide, SU section (pitch) of 12.7 mm, and a pitch length of 1500 mm. (See Figure 5.)

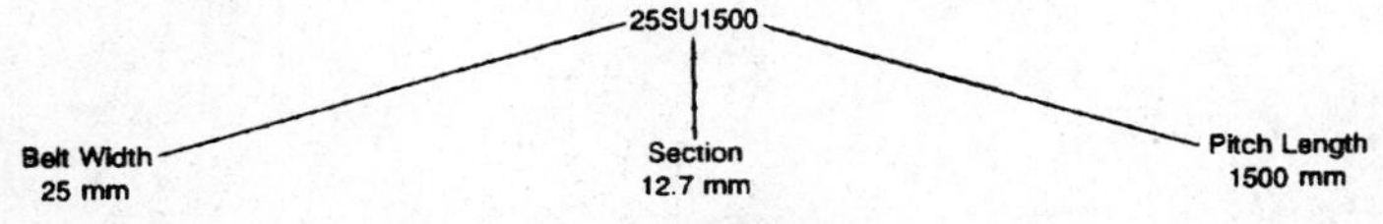

FIGURE 5—BELT DESIGNATION

5.4 Length Determination—The pitch length of a synchronous belt shall be determined by placing the belt on a measuring fixture comprised of two pulleys of equal pitch diameter, a method of applying force and a means of measuring the center distance between the two pulleys. One of the two pulleys is in a fixed location while the other is movable along a graduated scale. The fixture is shown schematically in Figure 6. Measuring pulley dimensions and measuring force are specified in Table 5, Table 6, and Figure 7.

TABLE 5—MEASURING PULLEY DIMENSIONS (mm)

Belt Section	No. of Grooves	Pitch Circumference	Outside Dia ±0.013	Outside Dia Runout FIM(1), max	Axial Runout (Side Wobble) FIM(1) max	Min Clearance(2)
ST	16	152.40	47.748	0.013	0.025	0.33
SU	20	254.00	79.479	0.013	0.025	0.38
STA	20	190.50	59.266	0.013	0.025	0.33

1. Full indicator movement
2. See Figure 7.

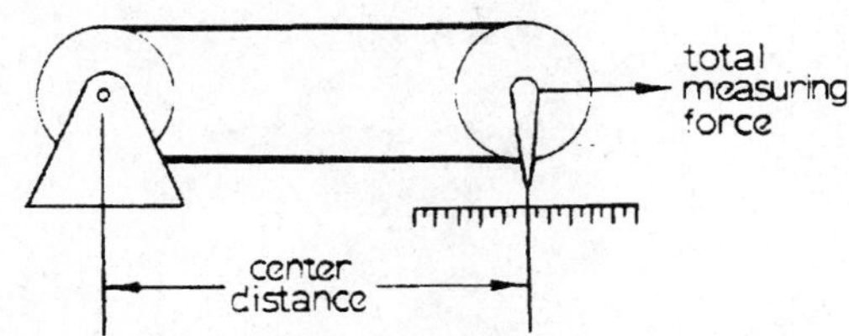

FIGURE 6—DIAGRAM OF FIXTURE FOR DETERMINING BELT PITCH LENGTH

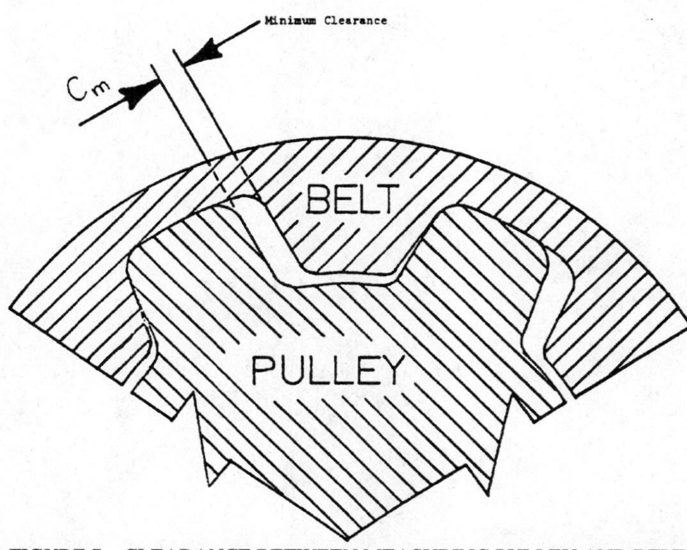

FIGURE 7—CLEARANCE BETWEEN MEASURING PULLEY AND BELT

In measuring the length of a synchronous belt, the belt should be rotated at least two revolutions of the belt in order to (a) seat the belt properly in the pulley grooves, (b) divide equally the total force between the two strands of the belt, and (c) determine the midpoint of the center distance travel of the movable pulley, which shall define the center distance. The pitch length shall be calculated by adding the pitch circumference of one of the measuring pulleys to twice the measured center distance between the two pulleys.

5.5 Length Tolerances—Belt length shall be within the limits specified in Table 7.

TABLE 6—TOTAL MEASURING FORCE (N)

Belt Section	Belt Width (mm)																
	8	10	12	14	16	18	19	20	22	25	28	30	33	35	40	45	50
ST	55	75	100	125	145	165	175	185	210	240	275	295	330	355	410	470	530
SU	—	—	245	300	370	420	445	475	530	610	700	750	840	900	1050	1200	1350
STA	—	—	245	300	370	420	445	475	530	610	700	750	840	900	1050	1200	1350

TABLE 7—BELT LENGTH TOLERANCES (mm)

Belt Length Range	Tolerance on Belt Pitch Length
Up to 400, incl	±0.46
Over 400 to 520, incl	±0.51
Over 520 to 770, incl	±0.61
Over 770 to 1020, incl	±0.66
Over 1020 to 1270, incl	±0.76
Over 1270 to 1525, incl	±0.81
Over 1525 to 1780, incl	±0.86
Over 1780 to 2040, incl	±0.91
Over 2040 to 2300, incl	±0.97
Over 2300 to 2560, incl	±1.02
Over 2560 to 3050, incl	±1.12

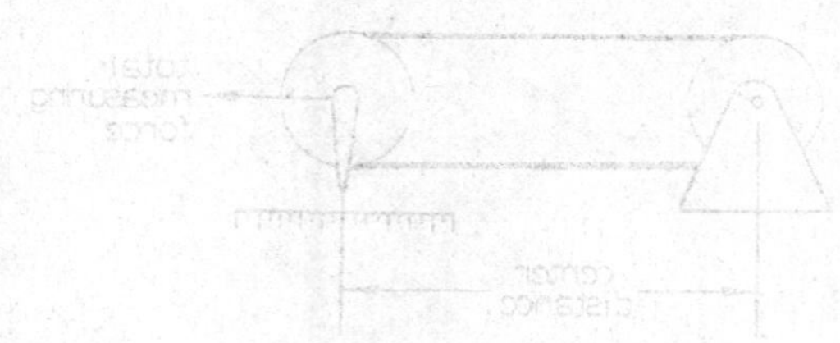

AUTOMOTIVE SYNCHRONOUS BELT DRIVES —SAE J1313 MAR1993

SAE Standard

Report of the SAE V-Belt Committee approved October 1980, reaffirmed without change June 1986. Reaffirmed by the SAE Belt Drive Committee March 1993.

Foreword—This Document has not changed other than to put it into the new SAE Technical Standards Board Format.

*1. **Scope***—The following information applies to automotive camshaft drives, distributor drives, or other underhood drives that may require synchronization. For other power transmission drives requiring synchronization, refer to Specifications for Drives using Synchronous Belts (MXL, XL, L, H, XH, and XXH belt sections) (IP 24/1978), published jointly by the Rubber Manufacturers Association (RMA), the Mechanical Power Transmission Association (MPTA), and the Rubber Association of Canada (RAC).

*2. **References***

2.1 Applicable Publications—The following publications form a part of this specification to the extent specified herein. The latest issue of SAE publications shall apply.

2.1.1 SAE PUBLICATION—Available from SAE, 400 Commonwealth Drive, Warrendale, PA 15096-0001.

SAE J1278—SI (Metric) Synchronous Belts and Pulleys

2.1.2 OTHER PUBLICATION

IP 24/1978—Published jointly by the Rubber Manufacturers Association (RMA), the Mechanical Power Transmission Association (MPTA), and the Rubber Association of Canada (RAC)

*3. **Pulleys***

3.1 Minimum Pulley Diameters—Minimum recommended pulley diameters are shown in Table 1.

TABLE 1—MINIMUM RECOMMENDED PULLEY DIAMETERS (mm)

Pulley Section	Pitch	Minimum Grooves	Minimum Pitch Diameter	Minimum Outside Diameter
ST	9.525	10	30.32	29.56
SU	12.700	14	56.60	55.23
STA	9.525	19	57.61	56.23

3.2 Minimum Pulley Width—The minimum pulley width between flanges (Figure 1) is determined by Equation 1:

$$1.5 \text{ (belt plus side tolerance)} + \text{nominal width} \qquad \text{(Eq. 1)}$$

NOTE—Stack up tolerances should be handled between pulley manufacturer and the user.

FIGURE 1—MINIMUM PULLEY WIDTH

3.3 Pulley Finish—A maximum surface finish of 2 µm Ra is normally satisfactory for standard drives. However, a maximum of 1 µm Ra finish is strongly recommended for crankshaft and other critical drive pulleys.

3.4 Flanging—Since a synchronous belt will have a tendency to ride to one side similar to a flat belt, it is necessary to contain it. Due to an inextensible tensile member, it is impossible to utilize a crown as is typical with flat belts. Therefore, flanges are used to guide the belt on the pulleys. The direction of track is controlled by the direction of rotation. (Any given belt will track opposite to its original track when the direction of rotation is reversed.) Since the direction of rotation is not usually furnished, and because of reversal applications, smaller driving pulleys are generally furnished with flanges on both sides.

3.5 Flanged Pulleys—Recommended flange dimensions are shown in Table 2 and Figure 2.

3.6 Selection of Flanged Pulleys—On all two-pulley drives, the minimum flanging requirements are: two flanges on one pulley, or one flange on each pulley on opposite sides.

TABLE 2—FLANGE DIMENSIONS (mm)

Pulley Section	Minimum Flange Thickness	Minimum Flange Height
ST	1.3	1.6
SU	1.3	2.0
STA	1.3	2.4

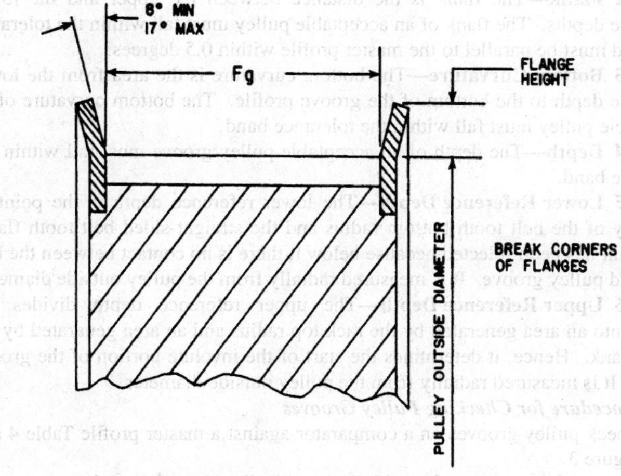

FIGURE 2—PULLEY FLANGES

On drives where the center distance is more than eight times the diameter of the small pulley, both pulleys should be flanged on both sides. On vertical shaft drives, it is usually advisable to flange the bottom side of the larger pulley as well as both sides of the smaller pulley. This is a function of center distance, speed ratio, and belt width, and will vary with respective applications.

On multipoint drives, the minimum flanging requirements are two flanges on every other pulley, or one flange on every pulley alternating sides around the system.

*4. **Recommended Use of Idlers***—The use of idlers should be restricted to those cases in which they are functionally necessary. The usual cases are:

a. As a means of applying tension when pulley centers are not adjustable.
b. To increase the number of teeth in mesh on the small pulley of relatively high ratio drives.

Idlers should be located on the slack side of the belt. For inside idlers, grooved pulleys are recommended up to 40 grooves. On larger diameters, flat uncrowned pulleys may be used. Outside idlers should be flat, uncrowned pulleys. Idler diameters should not be smaller than the smallest pulley diameter in the system.

Fixed idlers are recommended.

*5. **Belts***

5.1 Maximum Belt Width—Belt width should not exceed the small pulley diameter in order to avoid excessive belt side thrust.

*6. **Installation Tension***—Installation tension varies considerably with respective users. This is a result of other factors involved in the drive, such as guards, clearance areas, etc., as well as individual belt manufacturers' recommendations. The formulae in Table 3 are offered for general guidance covering belt widths from 5 to 50 mm:

TABLE 3—INSTALLATION TENSION FORMULAE

Section	Installation Tension (N) Min		Installation Tension (N) Max
ST	$5.5\,b_s$-17	≤ 1 ≤	$7.6\,b_s$-24
SU	$12\,b_s$-38	≤ 1 ≤	$20\,b_s$-62
STA			

where nominal belt width = b_s in millimeters

7. Master Profile—The master profile is generated by the nominal pulley generating tool rack form Table 1 of SAE J1278 at a specific number of grooves and nominal pulley OD. Master profiles can be obtained from belt manufacturers.

8. Tolerances—Pulley groove tolerances are applied separately to the four general areas of the profile: top curvature, flank, bottom curvature, and depth.

8.1 Top Curvature—The top curvature is the area from the outside diameter to the upper reference depth, start of the flank. The top curvature of an acceptable pulley must:

a. Fall within the tolerance band.
b. Have pulley top radius equal to or greater than the master profile, but not exceeding the maximum radius tolerance.
c. Have a top radius which blends smoothly into the flank no lower than the upper reference depth.
d. Have a top radius which blends smoothly into the outside diameter.

8.2 Flank—The flank is the distance between the upper and the lower reference depths. The flank of an acceptable pulley must fall within the tolerance band and must be parallel to the master profile within 0.5 degrees.

8.3 Bottom Curvature—The bottom curvature is the area from the lower reference depth to the bottom of the groove profile. The bottom curvature of an acceptable pulley must fall within the tolerance band.

8.4 Depth—The depth of an acceptable pulley groove must fall within the tolerance band.

8.5 Lower Reference Depth—The lower reference depth is the point of tangency of the belt tooth bottom radius and the straight-sided belt tooth flank. This point has been selected because below it there is no contact between the belt tooth and pulley groove. It is measured radially from the pulley outside diameter.

8.6 Upper Reference Depth—The upper reference depth divides the profile into an area generated by the rack top radius and an area generated by the cutter flank. Hence, it determines the start of the involute portion of the groove profile. It is measured radially from the pulley outside diameter.

9. Procedure for Checking Pulley Grooves

a. Check pulley grooves on a comparator against a master profile Table 4 and Figure 3.
b. Line up the master profile with the outside diameter of the pulley.
c. Determine if the subject profile falls within the tolerance bands in all four of the areas of the profile.
d. Check to see that the top radius is equal to or greater than the master profile top radius, but does not exceed the band width tolerance and maximum radius tolerance.
e. Check to see that all radii blend smoothly into the flank, groove bottom, and outside diameter.
f. Check angle of the flank against the master profile flank.

TABLE 4—PULLEY GROOVE TOLERANCES (mm)

Pulley Section	Top Curvature Band Width	Maximum Top Radius Tolerance	Flank Band Width	Bottom Curvature Band Width	Depth Band Width	Upper Reference Depth
ST	0.04	±0.1/–0.0	0.05	0.05	0.05	0.5
SU	0.04	±0.1/–0.0	0.05	0.05	0.05	0.8
STA	0.04	±0.1/–0.0	0.05	0.05	0.05	0.5

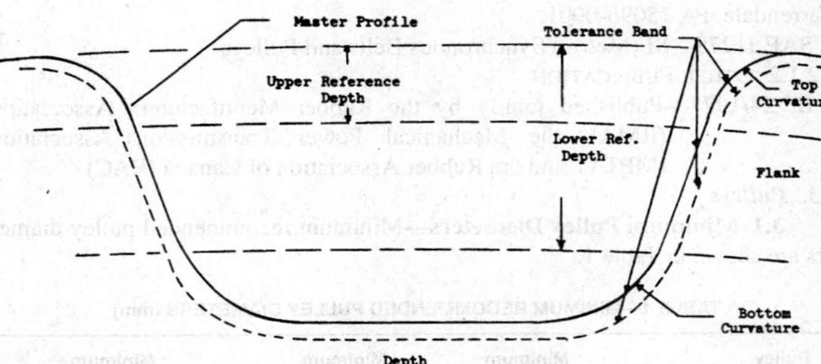

FIGURE 3—PULLEY GROOVE PROFILE

(R) V-RIBBED BELTS AND PULLEYS—SAE J1459 SEP2001 SAE Standard

Report of the SAE V-Belt Committee approved August 1984 and completely revised August 1988. Revised by the SAE Belt Drive Systems Committee August 1997 and completely revised September 2001. Rationale statement available.

1. Scope—This SAE Standard covers the dimensioning technique, tolerances, and methods of measurement of V-ribbed belts and mating pulleys for use on automotive accessory drives.

2. References—There are no referenced publications specified herein.

3. V-Ribbed Belts—Although several v-ribbed cross sections are available, this document shall be confined to "PK" (K) section belts which are used in automotive applications, including trucks at least up to Class 3. Belts shall conform to Figure 1.

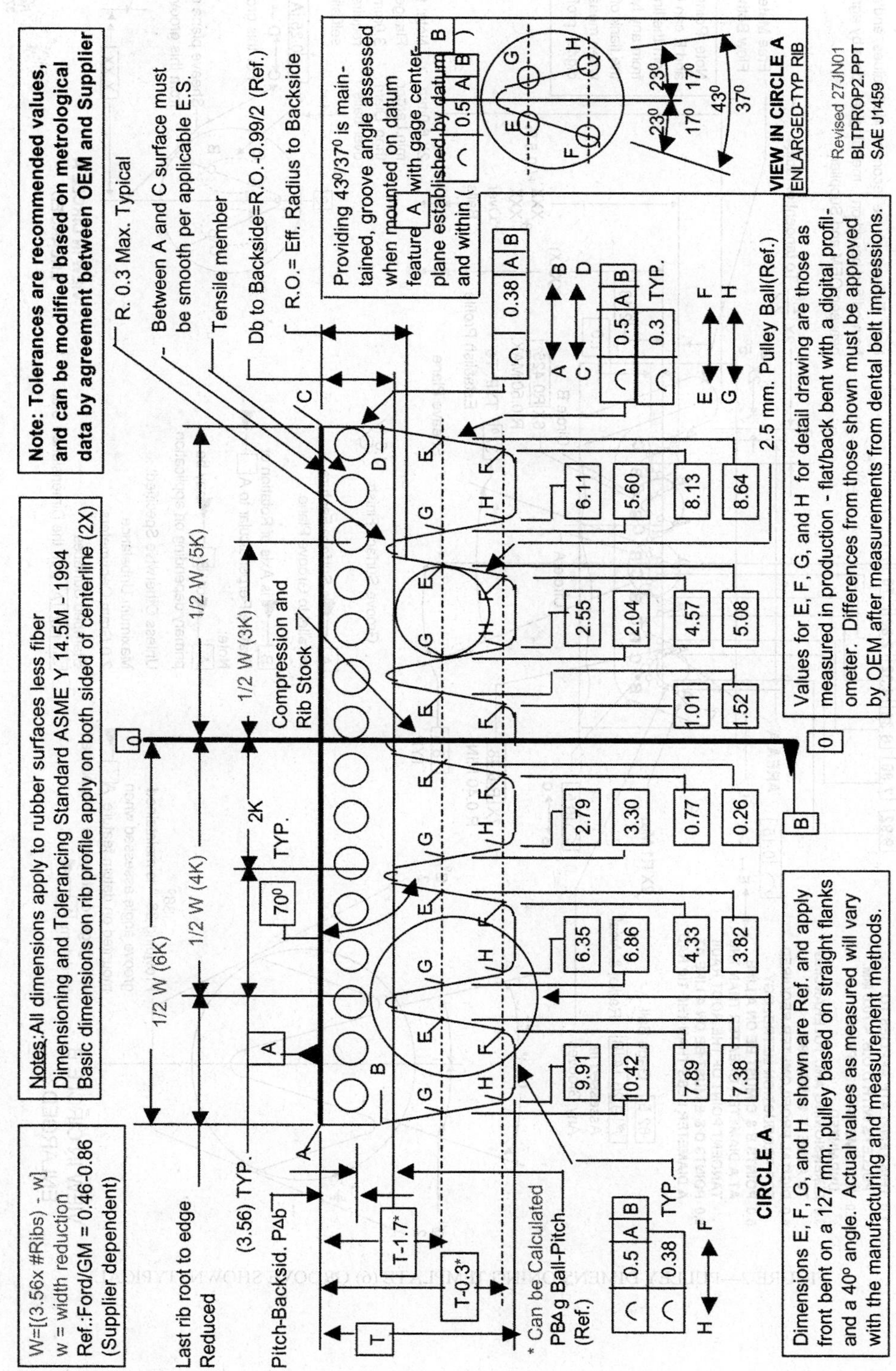

FIGURE 1—BELT DIMENSIONING TEMPLATE

4. Pulleys Mating with V-Ribbed Belts—It is the intention of this document to relate the belt profile to the pulley profile using the variables associated with the 2.50 mm ball used in measuring pulley diameters. Pulleys shall conform to Figure 2 for diameter over balls less than 70.00 mm and to Figure 3 for diameters of 70.00 mm or greater.

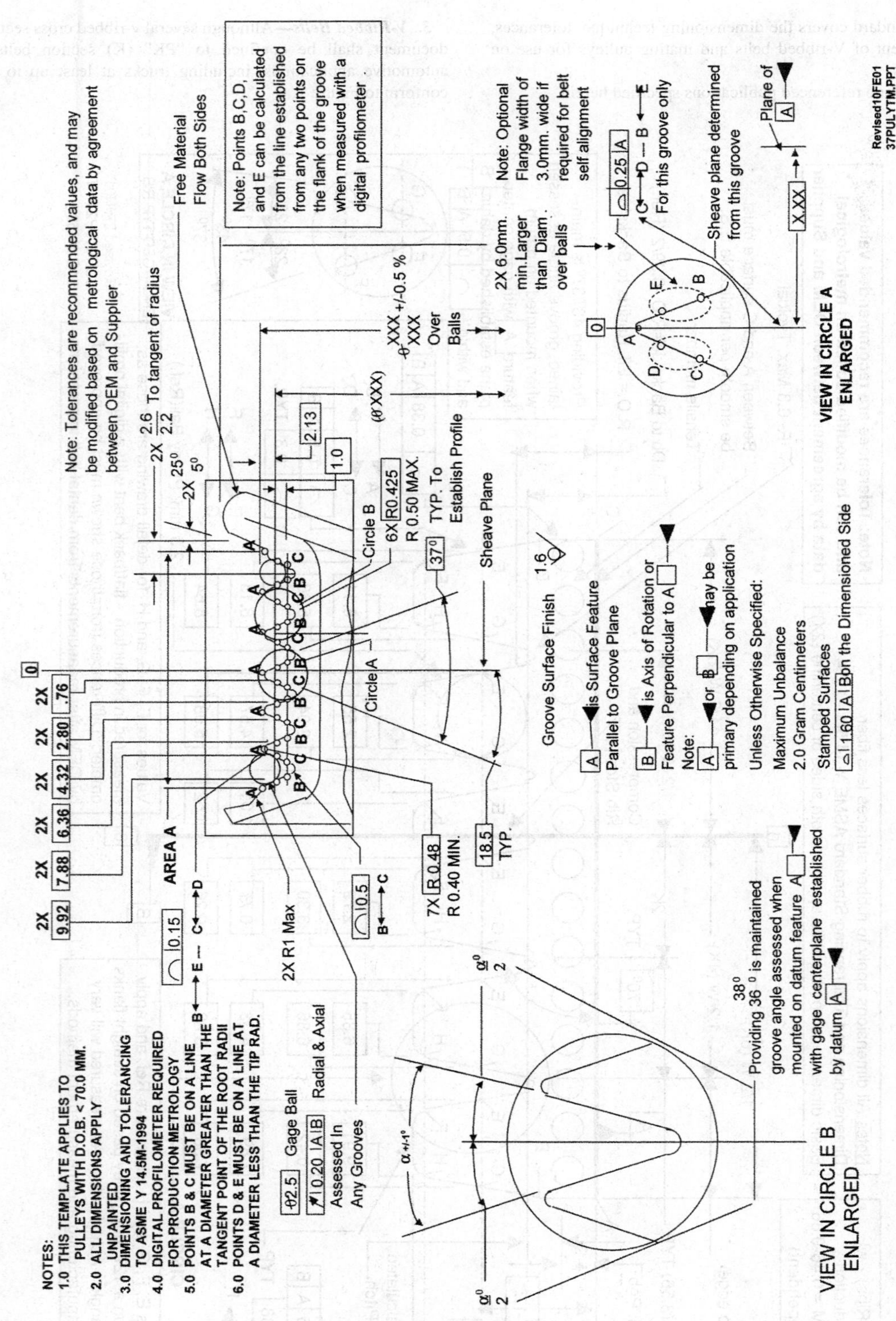

FIGURE 2—PULLEY DIMENSIONING TEMPLATE (6) GROOVE SHOWN (TYPICAL)

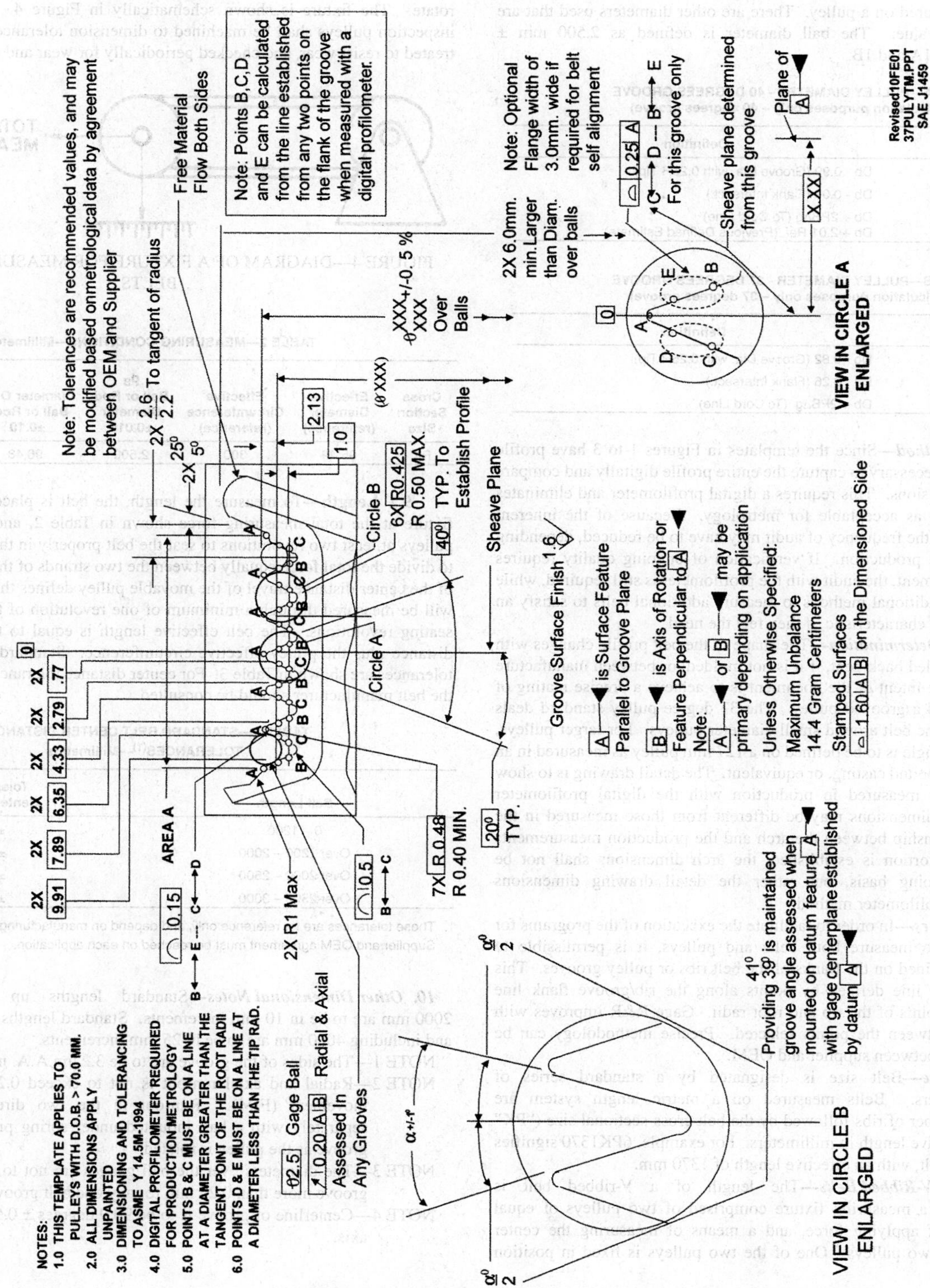

FIGURE 3—PULLEY DIMENSIONING TEMPLATE (6) GROOVE SHOWN (TYPICAL)

4.1 Pulley Diameter Definitions—The diameter over balls is the only diameter actually measured on a pulley. There are other diameters used that are calculated from this value. The ball diameter is defined as 2.500 mm ± 0.010 mm. See Tables 1A and 1B.

TABLE 1A—PULLEY DIAMETER - 40 DEGREES GROOVE
(for calculation purposes only – 40 degrees groove)

Diameter	Definition
Effective	Db - 0.99 (Groove Dia. with 0.25R Tip)
Apex	Db - 0.03 (Flank Intersect.)
Pitch	Db + 2PBΔg (To Cord Line) Db + 2.01 Ref. (Previous Defined Estimate)

TABLE 1B—PULLEY DIAMETER - 37 DEGREES GROOVE
(for calculation purposes only – 37 degrees groove)

Diameter	Definition
Effective	Db - 0.82 (Groove Dia. with 0.25R Tip)
Apex	Db - 0.26 (Flank Intersect.)
Pitch	Db + 2PBΔg (To Cord Line)

5. Measurement Method—Since the templates in Figures 1 to 3 have profile of a line callouts, it is necessary to capture the entire profile digitally and compare it to the drawing dimensions. This requires a digital profilometer and eliminates the optical comparator as acceptable for metrology. Because of the inherent speed of these devices, the frequency of audit may have to be reduced, depending on the process used in production. If verification of ongoing quality requires more frequent measurement, the audit with the profilometer is still required, while the supplier can use traditional methods to measure additional belts to satisfy an internal process control characteristic, if they feel the need.

6. Belt Dimension Determination—The shape of the belt profile changes with bending, either as profiled back bent, if it is not molded, or between manufacture and measurement. The intent of the document is to achieve a precise mating of the belt as bent around a grooved pulley. The 37 degree pulley standard deals with the distortion of the belt around small diameter pulleys. For larger pulleys, the 40 degree belt rib angle is to be defined on a 127 mm pulley as measured in an arch with a dental compound casting, or equivalent. The detail drawing is to show the rib dimensions as measured in production with the digital profilometer (usually flat). These dimensions may be different from those measured in the arch. Once the relationship between the arch and the production measurements due to the rubber distortion is established, the arch dimensions shall not be measured on an ongoing basis, but rather the detail drawing dimensions representing the flat profilometer method.

7. Metrological Issues—In order to facilitate the execution of the programs for digital profilometers to measure both belts and pulleys, it is permissible to calculate the points defined on the flanks of the belt ribs or pulley grooves. This can be done from the line defined by points along the rib/groove flank line between the tangent points of the tip and root radii. Gage R&R improves with increasing distance between the points selected. Precise methodology can be mutually agreed upon between supplier and OEM.

8. V-Ribbed Belt Size—Belt size is designated by a standard series of alphanumeric characters. Belts measured on a metric length system are designated by the number of ribs followed by the belt cross-sectional size ("PK" or "PL") and the effective length in millimeters. For example, 6PK1370 signifies a 6-rib "PK" section belt, with an effective length of 1370 mm.

9. Measurement of V-Ribbed Belts—The length of a V-ribbed belt is determined by use of a measuring fixture comprised of two pulleys of equal diameter, a method of applying force, and a means of measuring the center distance between the two pulleys. One of the two pulleys is fixed in position while the other is movable along a graduated scale. Both pulleys are allowed to rotate. The fixture is shown schematically in Figure 4. Grooves of master inspection pulleys shall be machined to dimension tolerances shown in Table 2, treated to resist wear, and checked periodically for wear and damage.

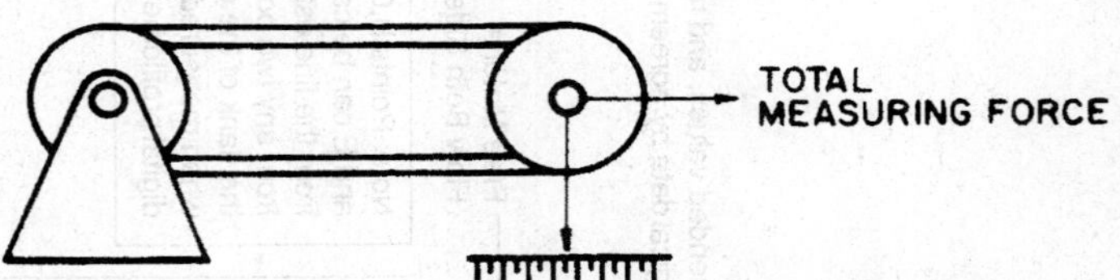

FIGURE 4—DIAGRAM OF A FIXTURE FOR MEASURING V-RIBBED BELTS

TABLE 2—MEASURING CONDITIONS—Millimeters

Cross Section Size	Effective Diameter (reference)	Effective Circumference (reference)	d_B Ball or Rod Diameter ±0.010	Diameter Over Ball or Rods ±0.10	Total Measuring Force Per Rib (N)
PK	95.49	300	2.500	96.48	100

9.1 Length—To measure the length, the belt is placed on the measuring fixture at the total measuring force shown in Table 2, and rotated around the pulleys at least two revolutions to seat the belt properly in the pulley grooves and to divide the total force equally between the two strands of the belt. The midpoint of the center distance travel of the movable pulley defines the center distance and will be measured through a minimum of one revolution of the belt after the two seating revolutions. The belt effective length is equal to two times the center distance plus the pulley effective circumference. Standard belt center distance tolerances are shown in Table 3. For center distance tolerances less than standard, the belt manufacturer should be consulted.

TABLE 3—STANDARD BELT CENTER DISTANCE TOLERANCES[(1)]—Millimeters

Belt Length	Tolerance on Center Distance
0 – 1200	± –4.0
Over 1200 – 2000	± –5.0
Over 2000 – 2500	± –6.0
Over 2500 – 3000	± –7.0

1. These tolerances are for reference only, and depend on manufacturing process as well as cost. Supplier and OEM agreement must be reached on each application.

10. Other Dimensional Notes—Standard lengths up to and including 2000 mm are to be in 10 mm increments. Standard lengths over 2000 mm up to and including 4000 mm are to be in 25 mm increments.

NOTE 1—The sides of the groove are to be 3.2 μm A.A. maximum.

NOTE 2—Radial and axial run-out is not to exceed 0.25 mm full indicator movement (FIM). Run-out in the two directions is measured separately with a ball mounted under spring pressure to follow the groove as the pulley is rotated.

NOTE 3—The diameters over the ball gauges are not to vary from groove to groove more than 0.25 mm for any one belt groove set in a pulley.

NOTE 4—Centerline of groove is to be 90.0 degrees ± 0.5 degrees with pulley axis.

PERFORMANCE TESTING OF PK SECTION V-RIBBED BELTS —SAE J2432 JAN2000

SAE Standard

Report of the SAE Belt Test Subcommittee of the SAE Belt System Committee approved January 2000.

1. Scope—The following information covers accessory drive belt testing methods and includes test configurations, pulley diameters, power loads, and guidance for interpreting test data. This information has been prepared from existing literature, including standards and data supplied by producers and users of V-ribbed belts.

1.1 Purpose—This SAE Standard is intended to provide methods to evaluate the performance, source approval, and/or quality audit of V-ribbed belt constructions.

1.2 Test Sample Size—The number of test samples should be statistically significant based on the requirements agreed to between each manufacturer and user.

1.3 Belt Test Lengths—The test belt range is 1200 mm ± 10 mm. Test data from belts of this length will be considered valid for all belt lengths of the same construction and specification.

1.4 Definition of Construction Specification—The belt manufacturers test data on belts of a certain construction shall be considered valid for evaluation of all belts, with respect to the manufacturer's cross section dimensions, material specifications, and method of manufacture.

1.5 Belt Temperature Rating—Belts shall be rated according to temperature capability. Belt types have been defined in 4.2 and 5.2. Belts capable of passing the extreme temperature tests shall be given a two letter designation, the first letter being the High Temperature capability and the second letter being the low temperature capability. For example, an 'AA' belt is rated for 121 °C to –43 °C, a 'BA' belt is for 107 °C to –43 °C.

1.6 Pulley Construction—Unless otherwise specified, all pulleys used on test fixtures should be machined steel pulleys, manufactured to SAE measurement pulley tolerances as shown in SAE J1459.

2. References

2.1 Applicable Publications—The following publications form a part of this specification to the extent specified herein. Unless otherwise indicated, the latest version of SAE publications shall apply.

2.1.1 SAE PUBLICATIONS—Available from SAE, 400 Commonwealth Drive, Warrendale, PA 15096-0001.

SAE J636—V-belts and Pulleys
SAE J1459—V-ribbed Belts and Pulleys
SAE J1596—Automotive V-ribbed Belt Drives and Test Methods

2.1.2 ASTM PUBLICATIONS—Available from ASTM, 100 Barr Harbor Drive, West Conshohocken, PA 19428-2959.

ASTM D 412—Test Methods for Rubber Properties in Tension
ASTM D 573—Test Method for Rubber—Deterioration in an Air Oven
ASTM D 575—Test Methods for Rubber Properties in Compression
ASTM D 1149-91—Test Method for Rubber Deterioration—Surface Ozone Cracking in a Chamber (Flat Specimens)

3. General Drive Layout Considerations—For general information on Accessory Drive Layout considerations, please refer to SAE J1596.

4. High Temperature, Constant Tension, Test

4.1 Purpose—To test the belt's durability under high temperature, high load conditions. This test was developed to reflect the increased use of automatic tensioners on automotive accessory drives. These systems have constant tension and therefore do not exhibit slip conditions resulting from loss of tension due to belt stretch.

Increased belt length will increase belt life on the test stand. Therefore, belt length has been limited to reduce test variability and provide comparable data from each manufacturer to the users.

4.2 Belt Type Designation—The belts for the High Temperature, Constant Tension Test are designated as follows:

Type A_{hot} Belt: 121 °C
Type B_{hot} Belt: 107 °C
Type C_{hot} Belt: 93 °C

4.3 Test Configuration—See Figure 1.

4.3.1 EQUIPMENT PARAMETERS

Driven Torque = 20 Nm ± 1 Nm
Belt Effective Length = 1200 mm ± 10 mm
Driver Speed = 4900 rpm ± 100 rpm
Number of Belt Ribs = 6
Grooved Pulley Diameters (across 2.50 mm gauge balls, all ±0.25 mm)
Driver (Pulley 1) = 121.6 mm
Driven (Pulley 3) = 121.6 mm
Idler (Pulley 2) = 61.0 mm
Backside Idler (Pulley 4) = 76.2 mm ± 0.25 mm (actual diameter)
Belt Tension = 629 N ± 31 N
Belt Hubload:
Option 1: Belt Horizontal Hubload W_1 = 904 N ± 44 N
Option 2: Belt Vertical Hubload at W_2 = 655 N ± 33 N

4.3.2 TEST CHAMBER TEMPERATURE

Type A_{hot} Belt: 121 °C ± 2 °C
Type B_{hot} Belt: 107 °C ± 2 °C
Type C_{hot} Belt: 93 °C ± 2 °C

Pulley	DIA	X	Y	Notes:
1	121.6 DOB	0.0	0.0	Driver Pulley
2	61.0 DOB	200.0	150.5	Idler Pulley
3	121.6 DOB	0.0	301.0	Driven Pulley
4	76.2	0.0	150.5	Idler Pulley
Effective Belt Length = 1200 mm				

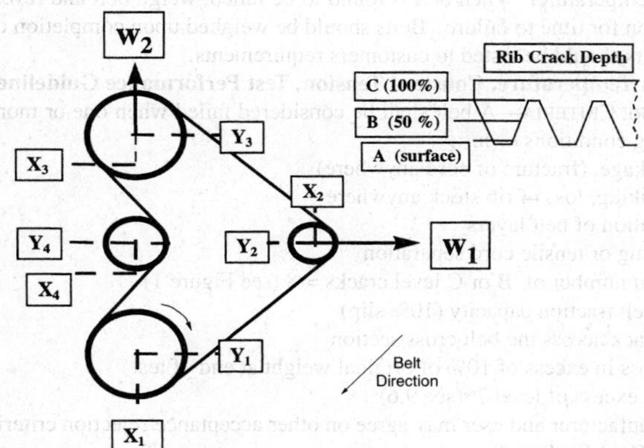

FIGURE 1—FOUR PULLEY DURABILITY TEST STAND CONFIGURATION

4.4 Test Fixture—The Four Pulley Hot Test stand is shown in Figure 1.

4.4.1 TENSION—The tension will be maintained either with a dead weight device or an automatic tensioner. If an automatic tensioner is used, the tension must be within ±5% at all times.

4.4.2 MOTOR—The life testing unit is driven by a motor sized to handle the sustained horsepower load plus system losses at the RPM indicated in 4.3.1. A torque recovery system may be used.

4.4.3 POWER ABSORBER—The driven pulley is to be attached to a power absorption unit capable of handling the torque indicated in 4.3.1.

4.4.4 TEMPERATURE CONTROL—The test stand should be mapped and proven to be capable of no more than ±2 °C variation throughout the test area, statically. Test stand must have at least one thermocouple centered on the horizontal centerline of the small pulleys (pulleys 2 and 4), midway between the centers of these pulleys for test stand control. It is recommended that stands be recertified when modified or annually if no modifications are performed.

4.4.5 MISCELLANEOUS—A governor capable of stopping the driver motor is to be mounted on the driven pulley. Test stand pulley misalignment should be less than 0.5 degree.

4.5 Test Load—The Torque (Nm) to be absorbed at the driven pulley shall be as shown in Table 1.

4.5.1 TORQUE CALCULATION—The driver pulley speed (rpm) shall be used in the torque load calculation, and the torque load shall be kept constant without compensation for loss of driven pulley rpm resulting from belt slippage.

$$\text{Torque, NM} = \frac{\text{Specified Kilowatts} \times 9549}{\text{Driver rpm}} \qquad \text{(Eq. 1)}$$

TABLE 1—TEST CONDITIONS—METRIC

SAE Belt Size	Belt Type	Test Temp. °C	Diameter Over Balls (mm) (Idler Is Actual Diameter) Driver and Driven Pulleys ±0.25	Diameter Over Balls (mm) (Idler Is Acutal Diameter) Tension Pulley ±0.25	Diameter Over Balls (mm) (Idler Is Acutal Diameter) Idler Pulley OD ±0.25	Driver Pulley Speed rpm ±2%	Load (NM)	Number of Ribs	Belt Length Range (mm) Length	Belt Length Range (mm) Tolerance
PK	Type A	121	121.6	61	76.2	4900	20	6	1200	±10
PK	Type B	107	121.6	61	76.2	4900	20	6	1200	±10
PK	Type C	93	121.6	61	76.2	4900	20	6	1200	±10

4.6 Test Procedure

4.6.1 Remove any grease, rubber, or other foreign material from the pulley grooves.

4.6.2 Weigh belt and install the belt on the test fixture and apply the required belt tension. The belt tension must be maintained constant throughout the life of the test. Tension tolerance is ±5% for the constant tension test.

4.6.3 START THE MACHINE—Adjust the torque to the proper setting. Adjust the torque to the proper setting, based on belt type chosen. Temperatures should be properly monitored to maintain constant temperature and reduce test variability.

4.6.4 Adjust the driven pulley governor to stop the machine when the driven pulley speed has dropped 10% from the target speed.

4.6.5 Inspect belts daily (minimum), recording test hours, chamber temperature, and belt temperature. When belt is found to be failed, weigh belt and revert to last inspection for time to failure. Belts should be weighed upon completion of all testing. Belts should be tested to customers requirements.

4.7 High Temperature, Constant Tension, Test Performance Guidelines

4.7.1 FAILURE CRITERIA—A belt shall be considered failed when one or more of the following conditions occur:

a. Belt breakage, (fracture of cord anywhere)
b. Belt chunking, loss of rib stock anywhere
c. Delamination of belt layers
d. Belt fraying or tensile cord separation
e. Maximum number of B or C level cracks = 8 (see Figure 1)
f. Loss of belt traction capacity (10% slip)
g. In-line crack across the belt cross section
h. Weight loss in excess of 10% of original weight at end of test
i. Pilling in excess of level 7 (see 9.6)

The belt manufacturer and user may agree on other acceptance/rejection criteria

5. Hot and Cold Cycling Test

5.1 Purpose—To test a belt's durability under high temperature, high load; and low temperature, no load conditions.

5.2 Belt Type Designation—Belt type designation for the Hot and Cold Cycling test is as follows:

5.2.1 HOT TEST

Type A_{hot} Belt: 121 °C
Type B_{hot} Belt: 107 °C
Type C_{hot} Belt: 93 °C

5.2.2 COLD TEST

Type A_{cold} Belt = –43 °C ± 1 °C
Type B_{cold} Belt = –35 °C ± 1 °C

5.3 Test Specification Summary

NOTE—The Hot and Cold Segments of this test use the same geometric configuration as shown in Figure 1.

5.3.1 EQUIPMENT PARAMETERS (HOT SEGMENT)

Driven Torque = 20 Nm ± 1 Nm
Belt Effective Length = 1200 mm ± 10 mm
Driver Speed = 4900 rpm ± 100 rpm
Number of Belt Ribs = 6
Grooved Pulley Diameters (across 2.50 mm gauge balls, all ±0.25 mm)
Driver (Pulley 1) = 121.6 mm
Driven (Pulley 3) = 121.6 mm
Idler (Pulley 2) = 61.0 mm
Backside Idler (Pulley 4) = 76.2 mm ± 0.25 mm
Test Chamber Temperature
Type A_{hot} Belt: 121 °C ± 2 °C
Type B_{hot} Belt: 107 °C ± 2°C
Type C_{hot} Belt: 93 °C ± 2 °C
Belt Tension = 629 N ± 31 N
Belt Hubload:
Option 1: Belt Horizontal Hubload W_1 = 904 N ± 44 N
Option 2: Belt Vertical Hubload at W_2 = 655 N ± 33 N

5.3.2 EQUIPMENT PARAMETERS (COLD SEGMENT)

Driver Speed = 100 rpm ± 4 rpm
Belt Effective Length = 1200 mm ± 10 mm
Number of Belt Ribs = 6
Test Chamber Temperature
Type A_{cold} = –43 °C ± 1 °C
Type B_{cold} = –35 °C ± 1 °C
Belt Tension = 267 N ± 13 N
Belt Hubload:
Horizontal Hubload at W_1 = 385 N ± 19 N
Vertical Hubload at W_2 = 378 N ± 19 N
No Torque Reaction Load is to be Applied

5.4 Test Fixture Setup

5.4.1 HOT FIXTURE SETUP—The four pulley stand is shown in Figure 1.

5.4.1.1 Tension—The tension will be maintained either with a dead weight device or an automatic tensioner. If an automatic tensioner is used, the tension must be within ±5% at all times, or the test must be started over with a new belt.

5.4.1.2 Power Absorber—The driven pulley is to be attached to a power absorption unit capable of handling the power indicated previously.

5.4.1.3 Motor—The life testing unit is driven by a motor sized to handle the sustained horsepower load plus system losses at the RPM indicated previously. A torque recovery system may be used.

5.4.1.4 Temperature Control—The test stand should be mapped and proven to be capable of no more than ±2 °C variation throughout the test area, statically. Test stand must have at least one thermocouple centered on the horizontal centerline of the small pulleys, midway between the centers of these pulleys for test stand control. It is recommended that stands be recertified when modified or annually if no modifications are performed.

5.4.1.5 Miscellaneous—A governor capable of stopping the driver motor is to be mounted on the driven pulley. Test stand pulley misalignment should be less than 0.5 degree.

5.4.2 COLD FIXTURE SETUP—The four pulley stand is shown in Figure 1.

5.4.2.1 Tension—The tension will be maintained either with a dead weight device or an automatic tensioner. If an automatic tensioner is used, the tension must be within ±5% at all times, or the test must be started over with a new belt.

5.4.2.2 Temperature Control—Thermocouples to be located at each of the 4 pulley interfaces. No greater than 2 °C variation among these 4 thermocouples at the end of the presoak will be allowed to assure the minimization of thermal gradients.

5.4.2.3 Motor—The life testing unit is driven by a motor sized to handle system losses at the RPM indicated previously.

5.4.2.4 Miscellaneous—A governor capable of stopping the driver motor is to be mounted on the driven pulley. Belt misalignment should be less than 0.5 degree.

5.5 Test Procedure

5.5.1 HOT TEST PROCEDURE

5.5.1.1 Remove any grease, rubber, or other foreign material from the pulley grooves.

5.5.1.2 Weigh belt and install the belt on the test fixture and apply the required belt tension. The belt tension must be maintained constant throughout the life of the test. Tension tolerance is ±5% for the constant tension test.

5.5.1.3 Set and maintain the driver pulley at speed.

5.5.1.4 Set the torque on the fixture motor by adjusting the power absorption unit. The driver pulley speed (rpm) shall be used in the torque load calculation, and the torque load shall be kept constant without compensation for loss of driven pulley rpm resulting from belt slippage.

5.5.1.5 Adjust the driven pulley governor to stop the machine when the driven pulley speed has dropped 10% from the target speed, and terminate the test, record as a failure.

5.5.1.6 Run for 48 h at the specified temperature and load condition.

5.5.1.7 Allow the belt to cool on the stand at ambient room temperature for 1/2 h. Note number of rib cracks if any and weigh belt. End test if failed.

5.5.2 COLD TEST PROCEDURE

5.5.2.1 Install the same belt on the cold chamber equipment.

5.5.2.2 Pre-cool the belt and stand until the specified temperature is reached at the belt and pulley interface. After the belt and pulley interfaces reach the specified temperature, soak the belt a minimum of one additional hour.

5.5.2.3 Run the driver pulley at 100 rpm for ten belt revolutions. 100 rpm must be achieved within 2 s.

5.5.2.4 Soak belt for 25 min at the specified temperature after cycling.

5.5.2.5 Rerun 5.5.2.3 through 5.5.2.4 nine times with the same belt and pulley at the specified temperature each time.

5.5.2.6 Note the number of rib cracks if any and record. End test if failed.

5.5.3 Remove belt and rerun steps 5.5.1 (Hot Test Procedure) and 5.5.2 (Cold Test Procedure). It is recommended that belts be able to pass a minimum of 2 cycles.

NOTE—One cycle is equal to one Hot Test Procedure (5.5.1) and One Cold Test Procedure (5.5.2).

5.6 Hot and Cold Cycling Test Guidelines

5.6.1 FAILURE CRITERIA—A belt shall be considered failed when one or more of the following conditions occur:

a. Belt breakage, (fracture of cord anywhere)
b. Belt chunking, loss of rib stock anywhere
c. Delamination of belt layers
d. Belt fraying or tensile cord separation
e. Maximum number of B or C level cracks = 8 (see Figure 1)
f. Loss of belt traction capacity (10% slip)
g. In-line crack across the belt cross section
h. Weight loss in excess of 10% of original weight
i. Pilling in excess of 7 (see 9.6)

The belt manufacturer and user may agree on other acceptance/rejection criteria.

6. Contamination Test

6.1 Purpose—To determine the effect of underhood fluids on the accessory drive belt.

6.2 Test Specification Summary—Use the identical test equipment specified in Section 4.

6.3 Fluid Requirements—Fluids that should be considered for this test should be those that may be spilled on the belt in the underhood environment. These include but are not limited to the following:

Antifreeze/Glycol
Motor Oil
P/S Fluid
Brake Fluid
Transmission Fluid
Washer Fluid

The belt manufacturer and the user should specify which fluids to use, based on the application.

CAUTION—Extreme care should be taken to avoid potential hazards of bringing the hot belt into contact with any potentially volatile and/or flammable fluid.

6.4 Test Procedure

6.4.1 Remove any grease, rubber, or other foreign material from the pulley grooves.

6.4.2 Weigh belt and install the belt on the test fixture and apply the required belt tension. The belt tension must be maintained constant throughout the life of the test. Tension tolerance is ±5% for the constant tension test.

6.4.3 Start the machine. Adjust the torque to the proper setting. Adjust the temperature to the proper setting. Temperatures should be properly monitored to maintain constant temperature and reduce test variability. Test stand must maintain specified temperature within ±2 °C throughout belt operating area.

6.4.4 Adjust the driven pulley governor to stop the machine when the driven pulley speed has dropped 10% from the target speed, and terminate the test, record as a failure.

6.4.5 Run belt for 48 h at the specified temperatures in Table 1.

6.4.6 Remove belt while hot, mark a 75 mm section on the side of the belt and dip the section of the belt in the underhood fluid agreed to by the supplier and OEM.

6.4.7 Hang belt for 5 min and then reinstall the belt on the stand in the same direction as when it was removed and restart the test as specified in steps 6.4.1 through 6.4.5.

6.4.8 Inspect belts daily (minimum), recording test hours, chamber temperature, and belt temperature. When belt is found to be failed, weigh belt and revert to last inspection for time to failure. Belts should be weighed upon completion of all testing. Belts should be tested to customers requirements.

6.5 Contamination Test Guidelines:

6.5.1 FAILURE CRITERIA—A belt shall be considered failed when one or more of the following conditions occur:

a. Belt breakage, (fracture of cord anywhere)
b. Belt chunking, loss of rib stock anywhere
c. Delamination of belt layers
d. Belt fraying or tensile cord separation
e. Maximum number of B or C level cracks = 8 (see Figure 1)
f. Loss of belt traction capacity (10% slip)
g. In-line crack across the belt cross section
h. Weight loss in excess of 10% of original weight at end of test
i. Pilling in excess of 7 (see 9.6)

The belt manufacturer and user may agree on other acceptance/rejection criteria

7. Five Pulley Flex Test

7.1 Purpose—To test the belt's flex durability under high-temperature, high-speed conditions.

7.2 Test Specification Summary—See Figure 2.

Belt Length = 1200 mm ± 10 mm
Driver Speed (D_1) = 3300 rpm
Optional Driver Speed (D_3) = 3900 rpm
Belt Speed = 10.4 m/s
Temperature = 100 °C to 130 °C
Belt Width = 6 ribs
Grooved Pulley Diameters (across 2.5 mm gauge balls, all ±0.25 mm)
D_1 = 60 mm
D_3 = 50 mm
D_4 = 50 mm
Backside Idler Pulley (D_2 and D_5) = 50 mm
Vertical Hubload = 800 N ± 40 N
Belt Tension = 400 N ± 20 N

7.3 Test Fixture—The Five Pulley Flex stand is shown in Figure 2.

7.3.1 TENSION—The tension will be maintained with a dead weight device or equivalent.

7.3.2 TEMPERATURE CONTROL—The test stand should be mapped and proven to be capable of no more than ±2 °C variation throughout the test area. Test stand must have at least one thermocouple for test stand control while running. The thermocouple shall be located on the vertical centerline, midway between the top pair of the grooved idler pulleys and the bottom pair of the backside idler pulleys. It is recommended that stands be recertified when modified or annually if no modifications are performed.

Pulley	DIA	X	Y	Description
1	60 DOB	0.0	0.0	Dead Weight/Driver
2	50 (Actual)	52.5	260.0	Idler Back Side
3	50 DOB	111.5	323.0	Optional Driver
4	50 DOB	-111.5	323.0	Idler
5	50 (Actual)	-52.5	260.0	Idler Back Side
F = 800 N			Belt Tension = 400.5 N	
Belt Effective Length = 1200 mm			Belt Speed = 10.4 m/sec	

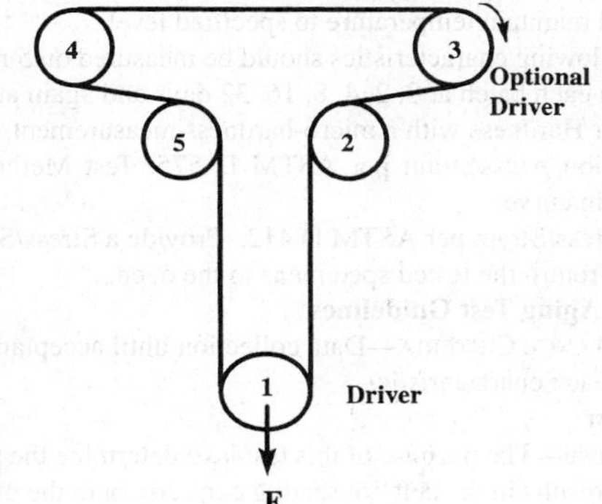

FIGURE 2—FIVE PULLEY FLEX TEST STAND CONFIGURATION

7.4 Test Procedure—Remove any grease, rubber, or other foreign material from the pulley grooves.

7.4.1 Set and maintain the temperature of the fixture box at 100 °C.

7.4.2 Weigh belt and install the belt on the test fixture noting the direction of installation. Set and maintain the driver pulley at speed.

7.4.3 After 50 h, stop the test and remove the belt.

7.4.4 Inspect and weigh the belt. If belt passes, repeat test with new belt and temperature in chamber increased by 5 °C

7.4.5 Repeat steps 7.4.2 through 7.4.5, increasing temperature by 5 °C until 130 °C is reached.

7.4.6 If belt passes 50 h at 130 °C, continue test until belt failure or agreed upon specified time with OEM.

7.5 Five Pulley Flex Test Guidelines

7.5.1 FAILURE CRITERIA—A belt shall be considered failed when one or more of the following conditions occur:

a. Belt breakage, (fracture of cord anywhere)
b. Belt chunking, loss of rib stock anywhere
c. Delamination of belt layers
d. Belt fraying or tensile cord separation
e. Maximum number of B or C level cracks = 8 (see Figure 1)
f. In-line crack across the belt cross section
g. Weight loss in excess of 10% of original weight at end of test
h. Pilling in excess of level 7 (see 9.6)

The belt manufacturer and user may agree on other acceptance/rejection criteria

8. Stationary Oven Test

8.1 Purpose—The purpose of this test is to determine the influence of elevated temperatures on the physical properties of vulcanized rubber. Rubber and rubber products must resist the deterioration of physical properties with time caused by oxidative and thermal aging. This test is intended to confirm that the retention of physical properties of production belts is adequate.

8.2 Test Specification Summary

Test Specimen = Dumbbell Shape Per ASTM D 412
Test Time = 1012 h
Test Chamber Temperature = 121 °C ± 2 °C

8.3 Test Fixture

8.3.1 OVEN—Test apparatus and measurement equipment should conform to those described in ASTM D 573, Section 5.

8.3.2 STRESS/STRAIN TEST FIXTURE—Fixture should be designed such that equal forces are maintained on the test specimen.

8.3.3 COMPRESSION FIXTURE—Per ASTM D 575, Test Method A.

8.4 Test Procedure—Test procedure should conform to those described in ASTM D 573 with the following exceptions:

8.4.1 Build two 1200 mm length belt sleeves from two separate batches with the production process. For compression testing, build slab using the production process per ASTM D 575.

8.4.2 Cure sleeves with production process.

8.4.3 After curing the sleeves, separate the cord layer from the rib stock by slicing. Lightly buff both sides of the rib stock and throw away the cord layer.

8.4.4 Randomly cut 35 dumbbell size specimens with correct fiber orientation, from each sleeve of rib stock per ASTM D 412. Label the specimens such that their build batch can easily be identified. From the slab to be used for the compression test, cut specimens per ASTM D 575 and label the specimens such that their build batch can easily be identified.

8.4.5 Hang dumbbells in test chamber. Place compression specimens in same test chamber to insure equal exposure to the heated environment.

8.4.6 Set and maintain temperature to specified level.

8.4.7 The following characteristics should be measured on 5 randomly selected specimens from each batch at 0, 2, 4, 8, 16, 32 days and again at 1000 to 1012 h:

a. Durometer Hardness with a micro-hardness measurement.
b. Compression stress/strain per ASTM D 575, Test Method A. Provide a stress/strain curve.
c. Tensile Stress/Strain per ASTM D 412. Provide a Stress/Strain curve.

8.4.8 Do not return the tested specimens to the oven.

8.5 Heat Aging Test Guidelines

8.5.1 ACCEPTANCE CRITERIA—Data collection until acceptance criteria can be established for each characteristic.

9. Pilling Test

9.1 Purpose—The purpose of this test is to determine the belts resistance to pilling. Pilling results in the belt not seating correctly onto the pulley which could result in belt noise if severe enough. Since pilling is a phenomenon associated with new belts, this test will not need to be run on aged belts.

CAUTION—Since the pulleys are not coated, this test will not identify pilling caused by the interaction between the belt and pulley coating. Test should be repeated and run with production intent coated pulleys.

9.2 Test Specification Summary

9.2.1 EQUIPMENT PARAMETERS

Driver Pulley Speed = 700 rpm ± 14 rpm
Torque Pulse Definition:
Amplitude = ±150 rpm (±7.5 rpm)
Frequency = 32 Hz ± 2 Hz
Wave Type: Sinusoidal
Belt Effective Length = 1200 mm ± 10 mm
Belt Width = 3 Ribs
Grooved Pulley Diameter = 76.2 mm DOB
Belt Hubload (F) = 667 N ± 33 N
Pulley Coating = None
Pulley Surface Finish = 3.2 μm RA max
Driven Inertia = 1.32 x 10^{-2} kg·m^2

9.3 Test Fixture—The Pilling Test Stand Configuration is shown in Figure 3.

9.3.1 TENSION—The tension will be set using a dead weight, pneumatic cylinder, or equivalent, rotated 3 revolutions of the belts and then locked for testing.

9.3.2 TEST EQUIPMENT—The test equipment must be capable of controlling the stand speed as defined previously. Torque pulses must be monitored to show that they meet the previous requirements.

9.3.3 TEST CHAMBER—Ambient room temperature, 21 °C or as specified.

Pulley	DIA	X	Y	Description
1	76.2 DOB	0.0	0.0	Driver Pulley
2	76.2 DOB	456.4	0.0	Tensioner Pulley
Belt Length = 1200 mm		Belt Tension = 334 N F = 668 N		
Torque Pulse Definition = ± 150 RPM @ 32 Hz				

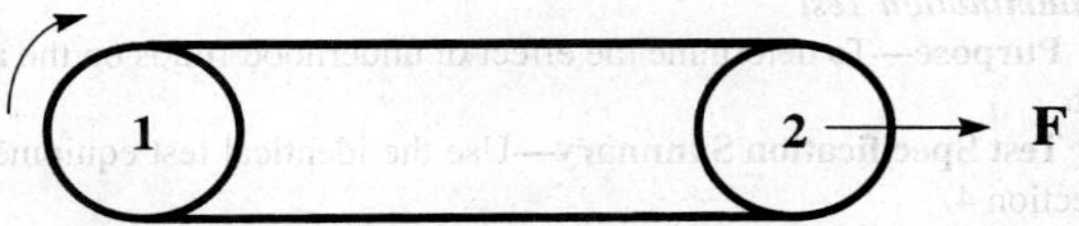

FIGURE 3—BELT PILLING TEST STAND CONFIGURATION

9.4 Test Procedure

9.4.1 Weigh belt to nearest gram. Belt should be weighed after soaking at 49 °C in a dry oven for 12 h.

9.4.2 Remove any grease, rubber, or other foreign materials from the pulley grooves.

9.4.3 Install belt on fixture and apply tension as specified in 9.3.1.

9.4.4 Run the belt for 20 min at the specified speed and torsional activities.

9.4.5 Stop the test and remove the belt from the stand.

9.4.6 Inspect the belt for signs of pilling. Record the pilling level as shown in 9.6.

9.4.7 Weigh the belt to the nearest gram. If the belt can not be weighed immediately, then belt should be weighed after soaking at 49 °C in a dry oven for 12 h.

9.5 Failure Criteria—After 20 min of testing, a belt shall be considered failed when one or more of the following conditions occur:

a. Belt breakage, (fracture of cord anywhere)
b. Belt chunking, loss of rib stock anywhere
c. Delamination of belt layers
d. Belt fraying or tensile cord separation
e. Maximum number of B or C level cracks = 8 (see Figure 1)
f. In-line crack across the belt cross section
g. Weight loss in excess of 10% of original weight at end of test
h. Pilling in excess of level 7 (see 9.6)

The belt manufacturer and user may agree on other acceptance/rejection criteria

9.6 Pilling Rating—See Figure 4.

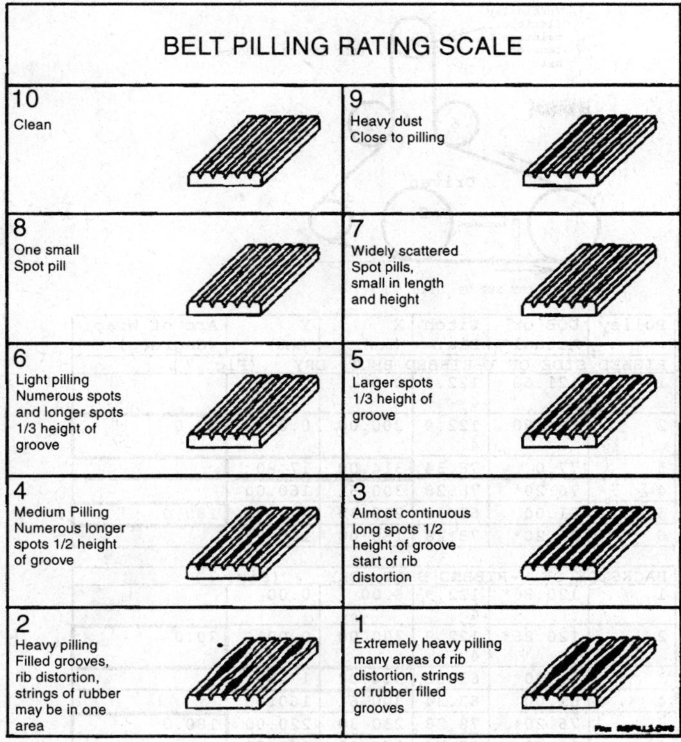

BELT PILLING RATING SCALE
10
Clean
9
Heavy dust
Close to pilling
8
One small
Spot pill
7
Widely scattered
Spot pills,
small in length
and height
6
Light pilling
Numerous spots
and longer spots
1/3 height of
groove
5
Larger spots
1/3 height of
groove
4
Medium Pilling
Numerous longer
spots 1/2 height
of groove
3
Almost continuous
long spots 1/2
height of groove
start of rib
distortion
2
Heavy pilling
Filled grooves,
rib distortion,
strings of rubber
may be in one
area
1
Extremely heavy pilling
many areas of rib
distortion, strings
of rubber filled
grooves

FIGURE 4—BELT PILLING RATING SCALE

10. Dynamic Ozone Testing

10.1 Purpose—The purpose of this test is to determine the belts capability to resist ozone aging. Ozone can be a major contributor to rubber compound degradation which may result in belt cracking.

10.2 Test Specification Summary

Procedure = ASTM D 3395 - Method B
Belt Length = 1200 mm ± 10 mm
Test Chamber Temperature = 40 °C ± 2 °C
Belt Width = 6 ribs
Pulley Diameters = 63.5 mm
Vertical Hubload = 178 N ± 9 N
Standard Ozone Partial Pressure = 200 mPa ± 5 mPa
Driver Pulley Speed = 62.5 rpm ± 3.0 rpm

10.3 Test Fixture—Test apparatus, measurement equipment, and ozone test chamber should conform to those described in ASTM D 3395, except entire belt to be installed rib side out, as shown in Figure 5.

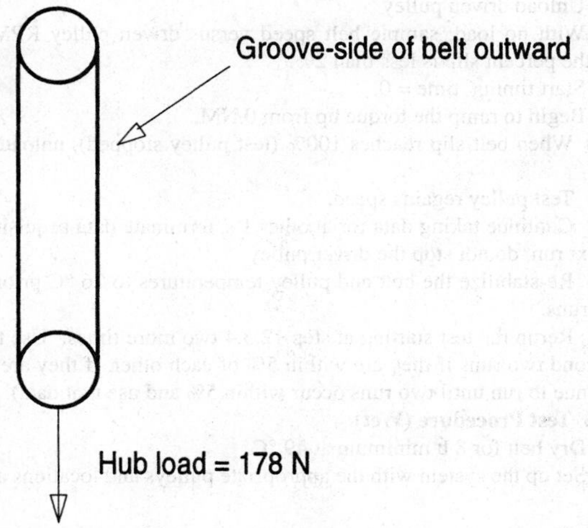

FIGURE 5—DYNAMIC OZONE TEST—BELT INSTALLATION

10.4 Test Procedure—Follow test procedure ASTM D 3395, Test Method B; except entire belt to be installed rib side out, as shown in Figure 5.

10.4.1 Set and stabilize the ozone partial pressure to 200 mPa.

10.4.2 Set and maintain chamber temperature as specified.

10.4.3 Start the belt and run at specified speed.

10.4.4 Inspect belt at 6 h, 24 h, and every 24 h thereafter until cracking is observed.

10.4.5 Record time of cracking and terminate test after 1st B/C level crack (Figure 1) has appeared. Terminate test after 150 h if no cracking has occurred.

10.5 Acceptance Criteria—Data acquisition only.

11. Belt Misalignment Noise Test

11.1 Purpose—The purpose of this test is to assess noise characteristics of the V-ribbed belt under various degrees of axial misalignment and environmental conditions.

11.2 Test Fixture—The Noise Test stand is shown in Figure 6.

Pulley	Pulley Material	DIA	X	Y	Description
1	303 Stainless Steel	101.0 DOB	0.0	0.0	Driver Pulley
2	303 Stainless Steel	61.0 DOB	-140.0	151.4	Adjustable Idler
3	Phenolic, Surface Finish = 0.8 μm RA Max	159.0 DOB	-301.0	0.0	Driven Pulley
4*	303 Stainless Steel	80.0 (Actual)	-155.0	20.0	Idler Pulley
Belt Effective Length = 1200 mm		Belt Tension = 267 N		T-Couple Location: X=-70.0, Y=72.5	

* Reference: Similar to Chrysler production pulley P/N 4536153

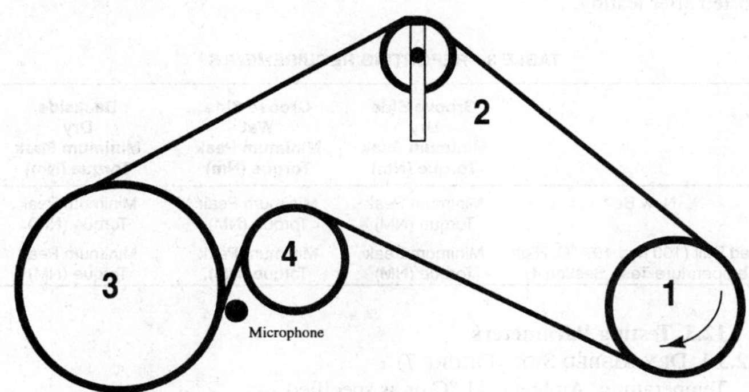

FIGURE 6—NOISE TEST STAND CONFIGURATION

11.2.1 TENSION—The tension will be maintained either with a dead weight device or an automatic tensioner. If an automatic tensioner is used, the tension must be within ±5% at all times.

11.2.2 TEMPERATURE CONTROL—The test stand should be mapped and proven to be capable of no more than ±2 °C variation throughout the test area. Test stand must have at least one thermocouple for test stand control while running and shall be located as specified in Figure 6. It is recommended that stands be recertified when modified or annually if no modifications are performed

11.2.3 ADJUSTABLE PULLEY—The stand must be designed so that the adjustable pulley alignment can be changed up to and including ±2.5 degrees while the stand is running.

11.3 Misalignment Noise Test Procedure—The noise test procedure will be run using the matrix shown in Table 2.

TABLE 2—NOISE TEST PROCEDURE MATRIX

Humidity	–5 °C	5 °C	15 °C	25 °C	35 °C	45 °C
50%		X	X	X	X	X
95% ± 5%		X	X	X	X	X

11.3.1 Set the stand and belt holding chamber temperature and humidity level to the Test Condition specified. For the –5 °C test point, it is difficult to control a specified humidity condition. For this reason, conduct testing at –5 °C temperature and the ambient humidity of the cold chamber.

11.3.2 Soak the belts on a belt rack in the holding chamber for 4 h prior to running the test.

11.3.3 Clean the pulleys with isopropyl alcohol or other nonresidue cleaner, before each test. Belts leave oils on the pulley surface which may have an effect on the noise test results.

11.3.4 Randomly select a belt, leaving the others in the holding chamber.

11.3.5 Install the belt on the noise test stand.

11.3.6 Set the offset of pulley 3, from the sheave line, so that $\tan^{-1}$(offset/span 3-4) = 1.5 degrees.

11.3.7 Run the test belt at 1700 rpm for 5 min at 1.5 degrees misalignment.

11.3.8 Reduce the speed to 750 rpm.

11.3.9 Measure the belt noise for 30 s with the microphone positioned 4 inches in front of, and aligned with, the entry span of the test pulley (see Figure 6). Record the maximum and average noise level (in dBA).

11.3.10 Remove the test belt from the stand and place back in the holding chamber.

11.3.11 Repeat steps 11.3.5 to 11.3.9 until all belts have been tested.

11.3.12 Repeat steps until each belt has been tested three times. Record the maximum and average noise level (in dBA).

11.3.13 Run belt for 24 h on the Hot test (4.4) and repeat noise test.

11.3.14 Repeat noise tests with individual belts that have run 100 h on the High Temperature, Constant Tension, Test (Section 4), 2 cycles of the Hot and Cold Cycling Test (Section 5), and 50 h of the Flex test at 121 °C (Section 7).

11.4 Acceptance Criteria—Belts must not exhibit objectionable noise such as "chirp," "pop," "squeal," etc., at specified test condition, new and aged at ±1.5 degrees misalignment.

12. Belt Torque Capacity Test

12.1 Purpose—To determine the torque carrying capacity of a K section V-Ribbed belt without damaging the belt.

12.2 Reporting Requirements—The information in Table 3 should be reported after testing:

TABLE 3—REPORTING REQUIREMENTS

	Groove Side Dry Minimum Peak Torque (Nm)	Groove Side Wet Minimum Peak Torque (Nm)	Backside Dry Minimum Peak Torque (Nm)
New Belt	Minimum Peak Torque (NM)	Minimum Peak Torque (NM)	Minimum Peak Torque (NM)
Aged Belt (100 h at 107 °C, High Temperature Test, Section 4)	Minimum Peak Torque (NM)	Minimum Peak Torque (NM)	Minimum Peak Torque (NM)

12.3 Testing Parameters

12.3.1 DRY RIBBED SIDE (FIGURE 7)

a. Temperature: Ambient, 21 °C or as specified
b. Belt Tension, Slack Side: 180 N applied at pulley 5
c. Test Pulley Speed: 400 rpm
d. Pulley Material: Stainless Steel (303 or 17-4PH - ASTM A 564 Type 630)
e. Pulley Surface Finish: 0.8 µm RA maximum
f. Load: Variable
g. Pulley Wrap: 20 degrees

12.3.2 DRY BACK SIDE (FIGURE 7)

a. Temperature: Ambient, or as specified
b. Belt Tension, Slack Side: 180 N applied at pulley 5
c. Test Pulley Speed: 400 rpm
d. Pulley Material: Stainless Steel 303
e. Pulley Surface Finish: 0.8 µm max.
f. Load: Variable
g. Initial Wrap: 20 degrees
h. Pulley Profile: flat within 0.1 mm profile, no crown

12.3.3 WET RIBBED SIDE (FIGURE 7)

a. Temperature: Ambient, or as specified
b. Belt Tension, slack side: 180 N applied at pulley 5
c. Test Pulley Speed: 800 rpm
d. Pulley material: Stainless Steel 303
e. Pulley Surface Finish: 0.8 µm RA maximum
f. Load: Variable from 0 to 20 Nm
g. Wrap: 45 degrees
h. Water Flow onto Grooves: 300 mL/min

12.4 Test Fixture

12.4.1 The test stand must be able to handle up to 40 Nm of driven and driver torque at 400 and 800 rpm.

12.4.2 Must be able to increase torque at a rate of 0.5 Nm per second.

12.4.3 Must take data at 40 samples per second (sample rate = 25 milliseconds)

12.4.4 Must be able to read the belt backside temperature surface before and during the test.

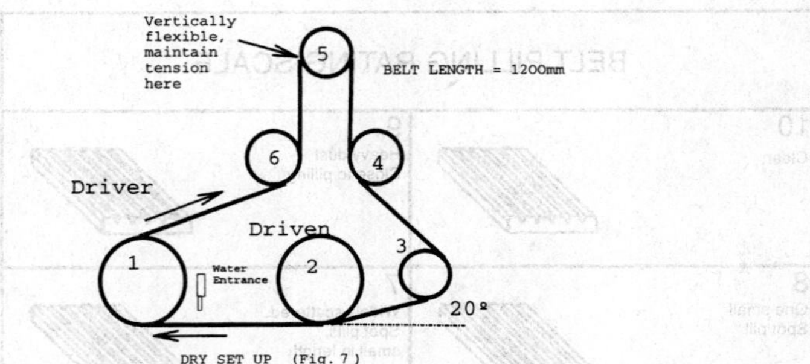

Pulley	DOB or Actual*	Pitch Dia.	X (mm)	Y (mm)	Arc of Wrap (degrees)
RIBBED SIDE OF V-RIBBED BELT, DRY (Fig. 7)					
1	121.60	122.94	0.00	0.00	
2	121.60	122.94	200.00	0.00	20.0
3	77.0	78.34	314.00	17.80	
4	76.20*	78.28	300.61	160.00	
5	61.00	62.34	230.30	225.00	180.0
6	76.20*	78.28	160.00	160.00	
BACKSIDE OF V-RIBBED BELT, DRY (Fig. 7)					
1	120.86*	122.94	0.00	0.00	
2	120.86*	122.94	200.00	0.00	20.0
3	76.20*	63.08	314.00	17.80	
4	61.00	62.34	300.61	160.00	
5	76.20*	78.28	230.30	220.00	180.0
6	61.00	62.34	160.00	160.00	

Wrap angles are for a belt with PBΔg = .67, and PΔb = 1.040.
*Indicates a backside pulley, and the actual diameter.

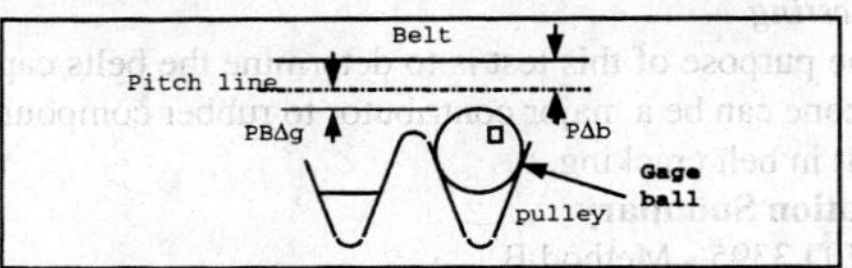

FIGURE 7—DRY SET UP

12.4.5 Must be able to maintain a constant slackside belt tension.

12.5 Test Procedure (Dry)

12.5.1 Dry belt for 8 h minimum at 49 °C.

12.5.2 Set up the system with the appropriate pulleys and locations as shown in Figure 6.

12.5.3 Clean pulleys with isopropyl alcohol first run only.

12.5.4 Install a belt on the stand (Figure 7).

12.5.5 Run for 2 min to break in at no torque load.

12.5.6 Unload driven pulley

12.5.7 With no load, sample belt speed versus driven pulley RPM, to make sure that the percent slip is less than 2%.

12.5.8 Start timing, time = 0.

12.5.9 Begin to ramp the torque up from 0 NM.

12.5.10 When belt slip reaches 100% (test pulley stopped), unload the driven pulley.

12.5.11 Test pulley regains speed.

12.5.12 Continue taking data for another 1 s, terminate data acquisition, set up for the next run, do not stop the driver pulley.

12.5.13 Re-stabilize the belt and pulley temperatures to 26 °C prior to second and third runs.

12.5.14 Rerun the test starting at step 12.5.4 two more times. Use the average of the second two runs if they are within 5% of each other. If they are not within 5%, continue to run until two runs occur within 5% and use that data).

12.6 Test Procedure (Wet)

12.6.1 Dry belt for 8 h minimum at 49 °C.

12.6.2 Set up the system with the appropriate pulleys and locations as shown in Figure 8.

12.6.3 Clean pulleys with isopropyl alcohol first run only.

12.6.4 Run for 2 min to break in at no torque load.

12.6.5 Unload driven pulley

12.6.6 With no load, sample belt speed versus driven pulley RPM, make sure that the percent slip is less than 2% but not less than 0.

12.6.7 Start the water flowing at the specified rate within 50 mm of the driven pulley entrance.

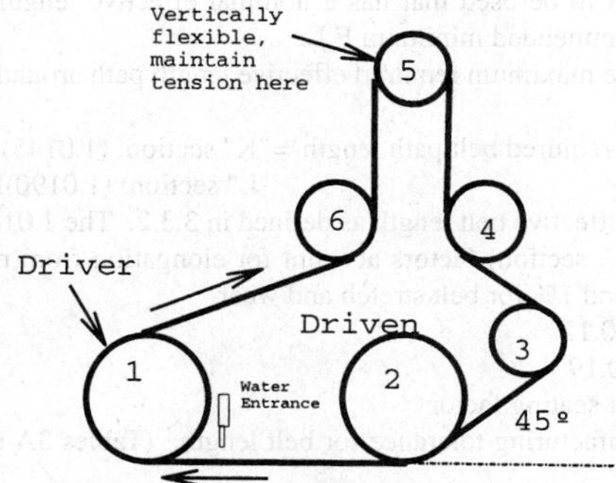

WET SET UP (Fig. 8)

RIBBED SIDE PULLEYS, WET (Fig. 8)					
1	121.6	122.94	0.00	0.00	
2	121.6	122.94	200.00	0.00	45.0
3	77.00	78.34	300.00	57.12	
4	76.20*	78.28	301.10	160	
5	61.00	62.34	230.1	230.3	180.0
6	76.20*	78.28	159.5	160	

Wrap angles are for a belt with PBΔg =.67, and PΔb = 1.040.
*Indicates a backside pulley, and the actual diameter.

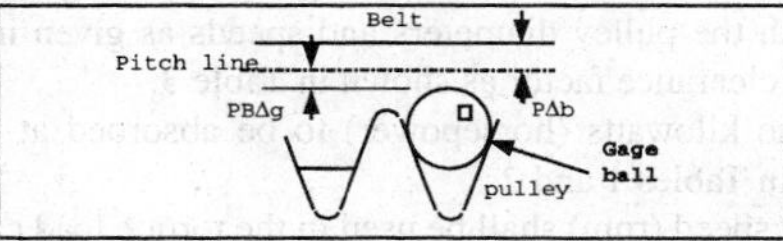

FIGURE 8—WET SET UP

12.6.8 Start taking data, time = 0, within 30 s of the water flow starting, begin to ramp the torque up from 0 NM.

12.6.9 When belt slip exceeds 100% (test pulley stopped), unload the driven pulley.

12.6.10 Test pulley regains speed.

12.6.11 Continue taking data for another 1 s, terminate data acquisition, set up for next run, do not stop the driver pulley, or the water flow.

12.6.12 Continue taking data for another 1 s, terminate data acquisition, quickly set up for next run, do not stop the driver pulley, or the water flow.

12.6.13 Wait until 1 min from start of last run, rerun starting at step 12.6.9.

12.6.14 Rerun the test 9 times for a total test time of 10 min.

12.6.15 Use the average of the last 4 min as the report out torque capacity of the belt.

12.7 Data Acquisition—Acquire the following information, every 25 milliseconds.

a. Driven pulley rpm
b. Idler No. 6 pulley speed in rpms
c. Torque being reacted
d. Belt friction surface temperature at driver pulley entrance

12.8 Data Calculation

a. Peak Torque
b. Peak Coefficient of friction

12.9 Plots to Generate (Optional)—Generate plots as shown in Figure 9.

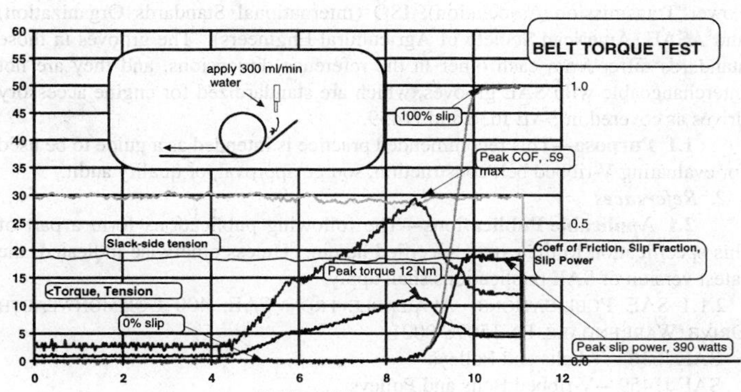

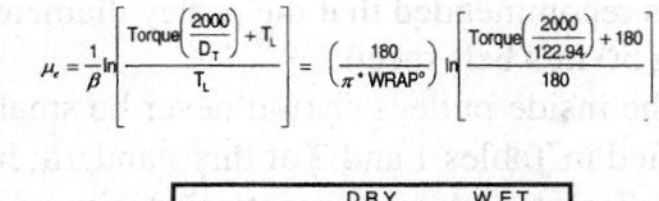

$$\mu_e = \frac{1}{\beta}\ln\left[\frac{\text{Torque}\left(\frac{2000}{D_T}\right) + T_L}{T_L}\right] = \left(\frac{180}{\pi * \text{WRAP}^\circ}\right)\ln\left[\frac{\text{Torque}\left(\frac{2000}{122.94}\right) + 180}{180}\right]$$

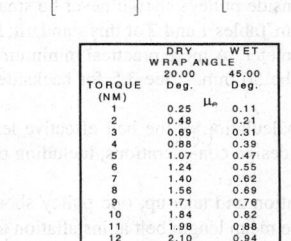

TORQUE (NM)	DRY WRAP ANGLE 20.00 Deg. μ_e	WET 45.00 Deg.
1	0.25	0.11
2	0.48	0.21
3	0.69	0.31
4	0.88	0.39
5	1.07	0.47
6	1.24	0.55
7	1.40	0.62
8	1.56	0.69
9	1.71	0.76
10	1.84	0.82
11	1.98	0.88
12	2.10	0.94
13	2.23	0.99
14	2.34	1.04
15	2.45	1.09
16	2.56	1.14
17	2.67	1.19
18	2.77	1.23

FIGURE 9—BELT TORQUE TEST

AUTOMOTIVE V-RIBBED BELT DRIVES AND TEST METHODS—SAE J1596 JUN1989

SAE Recommended Practice

Report of the SAE V-Belt Committee approved June 1989.

Foreword—This Document has not changed other than to put it into the new SAE Technical Standards Board Format.

1. Scope—The following information covers engine accessory drive layout details and testing methods and includes test configurations, pulley diameters, power loads, and guidance for interpreting test data. This information has been prepared from existing literature, including standards and data supplied by both producers and users of V-ribbed belts.

When the engine is used to drive an external unit equipped with industrial type V-pulleys and belts, it is recommended that the power takeoff pulley on the engine be grooved according to the appropriate industrial standard. These standards are published by RMA-MPTA (Rubber Manufacturers Association - Mechanical Power Transmission Association); ISO (International Standards Organization) and ASAE (American Society of Agricultural Engineers). The grooves in those standards differ from each other in the reference dimensions, and they are not interchangeable with SAE grooves, which are standardized for engine accessory drives as covered in SAE J636 and J1459.

1.1 Purpose—This recommended practice is intended as a guide to be used for evaluating V-ribbed belt construction, source approval, or quality audit.

2. References

2.1 Applicable Publications—The following publications form a part of this specification to the extent specified herein. Unless otherwise indicated, the latest version of SAE publications shall apply.

2.1.1 SAE PUBLICATIONS—AVAILABLE FROM SAE, 400 COMMONWEALTH DRIVE, WARRENDALE, PA 15096-0001.

SAE J636—V-belts and Pulleys

SAE J1459—V-ribbed Belts and Pulleys

3. General Drive Layout Considerations

3.1 Belt Speed—It is recommended that the pulley diameters be as large as possible without exceeding 50 m/s belt speed.

3.2 Pulley Sizes—The inside pulleys should never be smaller than the tension pulley diameter specified in Tables 1 and 2 of this standard; however, belt life is directly related to pulley diameter. A more practical minimum pulley diameter, for increased belt life, would be 50 mm. (See 3.5 for backside pulley diameter recommendations.)

3.3 Belt Length—The calculation of the belt effective length (E.L.) for a specific drive involves several design considerations, including provision for adequate installation and take-up.

To allow for belt installation and take-up, one pulley should be adjustable from its initial position with the mean length belt at installation tension. This formula gives the minimum allowance for easy installation of the belt without prying or otherwise forcing it over the sides of the grooves.

3.3.1 The following formula can be used to calculate the recommended minimum belt E.L. for installation:

"K" Section: Inside pulleys
Min. Belt E.L.= $1.003(L_1)+L_2+.77+6.28(h)$

"K" Section: Flat backside pulley
Min. Belt E.L. = $1.003(L_1)+L_2+6.28(h)$

"L" Section: Inside pulleys
Min. Belt E.L. = $1.005(L_1)+L_2+1.15+6.28(h)$

"L" Section: Flat backside pulley
Min. Belt E.L. = $1.005(L_1)+L_2+6.28(h)$

NOTE—The last pulley, over which the belt can be installed, should be considered and the appropriate belt installation formula used.

L_1 - The effective belt length (addition of span lengths and effective arc lengths on the pulleys) around the drive with the tensioning pulley in the minimum position. The 1.003 ("K" section) and 1.005 ("L" section) factors provide for length change from slack to measuring tension.

L_2 - The 2 X negative belt manufacturing center distance tolerance (Tables 3A and 3B, SAE J1459).

h - The flange height.

This formula also allows for full contact belt rib height for V-ribbed pulleys - 0.77 ("K" section) and 1.15 ("L" section).

The metric formulas are the same with the following exception:

"K" section - 0.77 value is 20

"L" section - 1.15 value is 29

The belt length, flange height, and manufacturing tolerance are in inches in the English system and millimeters in the metric system.

3.3.2 Select a belt to be used that has a nominal effective length equal to or greater than the recommended minimum E.L.

3.3.3 Calculate the maximum required effective length path around the drive to provide for take-up:

The maximum required belt path length = "K" section: $(1.0145)L_3+L_4+L_5$
"L" section: $(1.0190)L_3+L_4+L_5$

L_3 - The nominal effective belt length as defined in 3.3.2. The 1.0145 ("K" section) and 1.0190 ("L" section) factors account for elongation from measuring to installation tension and 1% for belt stretch and wear.

L_4 - "K" section - 0.12
"L" section - 0.19
Values for belt seating factor

L_5 - Positive manufacturing tolerance for belt length. (Tables 3A and 3B SAE J1459.)

The formulas are in English units with belt length in inches. The metric units will be belt length in millimeters and the following seating factor changes:

"K" section - 0.12 value is 3.0

"L" section - 0.19 value is 4.8

3.4 Pulley Misalignment—The recommended maximum misalignment between pulleys is 0.58 mm per 100 mm (0.069 in/ft) of span length or approximately 0.33 deg.

3.5 Backside Pulleys—The application design with backside pulleys is acceptable provided their minimum diameter is 90 mm (3.54 in) for PK (K) section, and 140 mm (5.5 in) for PL (L) section.

4. V-Ribbed Belt Fatigue Test Method

4.1 Test Configuration—The belt shall be mounted on a test fixture layout as shown in Figure 1 with the pulley diameters and speeds as given in Tables 1 and 2 and the installation clearance factor as shown in Table 3.

4.2 Test Load—The kilowatts (horsepower) to be absorbed at the driven pulley shall be as shown in Tables 1 and 2.

4.2.1 The driver pulley speed (rpm) shall be used in the torque load calculation, and the torque load shall be kept constant without compensation for loss of driven pulley rpm resulting from belt slippage.

$$\text{Torque, N}\cdot\text{m} = \frac{\text{Specified kilowatts}\times 9549}{\text{Driver rpm}} \quad \text{(Eq. 1)}$$

$$\text{Torque, lbf}\cdot\text{in} = \frac{\text{Specified horsepower}\times 63025}{\text{Driver rpm}}$$

4.2.2 The test equipment shall be maintained to minimize parasitic loads due to bearing losses, lubricants, etc.

4.2.3 The belt tensioning force shall be equal in the number of Newtons to sixty times the number of specified kilowatt units (in number of pounds to ten times the number of horsepower units).

4.3 Temperature—The ambient temperature of the test fixture shall be controlled to 80°C ± 3 (175° F ± 5) within a suitable enclosure.

4.4 Test Procedure—The test procedure shall be as follows:

4.4.1 Set the required torque load.

4.4.2 Install the belt on the test fixture and apply the required belt tension. Condition the belt by running it for 5 min without the dynomometer load. Maintain a constant tension during this period by operating with the tension pulley center position unlocked. Stop the machine, allow it to stand for a minimum of 10 min and lock the tension pulley center position midway of the limits of travel during belt rotation.

4.4.3 Start the machine. Adjust the torque to the proper setting. Adjust the temperature to the proper setting.

4.4.4 Whenever the slip reaches 8%, stop the machine, allow it to stand for a minimum of 20 min, unlock the tension pulley center, restore the initial tension per 4.2.3 relock, and restart the machine.

4.4.5 (Exclusive of the 5 min run-in)—Record the number of hours run and the number of re-tensions.

5. Test Performance Guidelines

5.1 Test Life—The test life, which a belt must attain, shall be according to agreement between the manufacturer and user.

5.2 Acceptable Number of Re-tensions—The acceptable number of re-tensions after the initial 5 min run-in shall be according to agreement between the manufacturer and user.

5.3 Failure Criteria—A belt shall be considered failed when it no longer transmits the specified power because of breakage or it exceeds the number of agreed re-tensions. The belt manufacturer and user may agree on other acceptance/rejection criteria.

5.4 Length vs. Life Relationship—Generally speaking, the belt test life is a function of the belt length. The relationship shall be according to agreement between the belt manufacturer and user.

5.5 Definition of Construction Specifications—The belt manufacturer's test data on belts of a certain construction specification shall be considered valid for evaluation of all belts of the same construction specification when they are the same with respect to the manufacturer's cross section dimensions, material specifications, and method of manufacture.

5.6 Belt Test Lengths—The test belt range will be: 1020–1400 mm (40-55) in) with recommended length being 1200 mm (47.24 in). When evaluating for part source approval and for production quality surveillance, the test data from one belt length will be representative of all belt lengths of the same construction.

5.7 Statistical Relationships—Whether testing is performed for part source approval or for production surveillance, a realistic statistical guide to acceptability would be "not more than 10% of the test lives shall be permitted to fall below 50% of the specified average life".

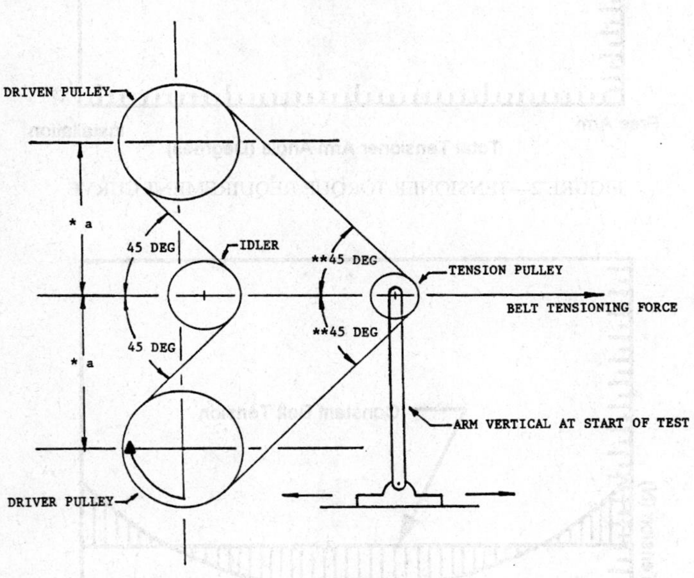

FIGURE 1—V-RIBBED BELT FATIGUE TEST

TABLE 1—TEST CONDITIONS - METRIC

SAE Belt Size	Effective Diameter			Driver Pulley Speed rpm ±2%	Load (KW)	Number of Ribs	Belt Length Range	
	Driver and Driven Pulleys ±0.25	Tension Pulley ±0.25	Idler Pulley ±0.25				Total	Preferred
PK	120.6	44.45	76.2	4900	10.4	3	1020–1400	1200
PL	b	b	b	b	b	b	1020–1400	1200

a = Groove details per SAE J1459

b = Not developed for Automotive belts

TABLE 2—TEST CONDITIONS - ENGLISH

SAE Belt Size	Effective Diameter			Driver Pulley Speed rpm ±2%	Load (HP)	Number of Ribs	Belt Length Range	
	Driver and Driven Pulleys ±0.010	Tension Pulley ±0.010	Idler Pulley ±0.010				Total	Preferred
K	4.750	1.750	3.000	4900	14	3	40.17–55.14	47.26
L	b	b	b	b	b	b	40.17–55.14	47.26

TABLE 3—CLEARANCE FACTOR FOR BELT INSTALLATION

SAE BELT SIZE		C VALUE	
Metric	English	mm	in
PK	K	3.07	0.12
PL	L	4.52	0.18

(R) GLOSSARY—AUTOMATIC BELT TENSIONER —SAE J2198 JUN2000

SAE Standard

Report of the SAE Bolt Drive Committee approved July 1992. Completely revised by the SAE Belt Committee June 2000.

1. Scope—This glossary was written to provide a consistent and uniform definition of terms used in describing an automatic belt tensioner as it applies to an automotive accessory drive system.

2. References

2.1 Related Publication—The following publication is for information purposes only and is not a required part of this document.

2.1.1 SAE PUBLICATION—Available from SAE, 400 Commonwealth Drive, Warrendale, PA 15096-0001.

SAE J2436—Accessory Drive Tensioner Test Standards (Mechanical Rotary Type)

3. System Related Tensioner Characteristics

3.1 Tensioner Torque Requirement Curve—The torque required to control belt tension in the tensioner range of travel. (See Figure 1.)

3.2 Positive/Negative Rate Geometry—A positive/negative slope resulting from the linear approximation of the tensioner torque requirement curve. (See Figure 2.)

3.3 Tension/Torque Error Curves—The tension/torque curves representing calculated tensioner output as compared to the tensioner torque requirement curve. (See Figures 1 and 3)

3.4 Tensioner Pivot Location—The x,y coordinates of the tensioner pivot as compared to the center of the driver pulley at (0,0). (See Figure 4.)

3.5 Hub Load Angle—The angle between a line from the center of the tensioner pivot to the center of the tensioner pulley and the hub load vector at the tensioner pulley.

3.6 Tensioner Belt "Take-Up"—The amount of belt length change a tensioner will accommodate as a function of tensioner arm displacement within the tensioner operation range. (See Figure 2.)

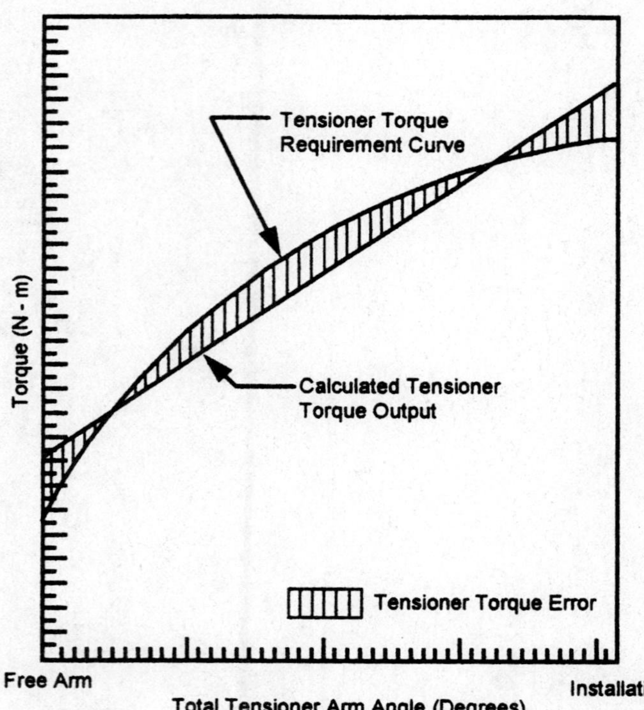

FIGURE 1—TENSIONER TORQUE ERROR CURVE

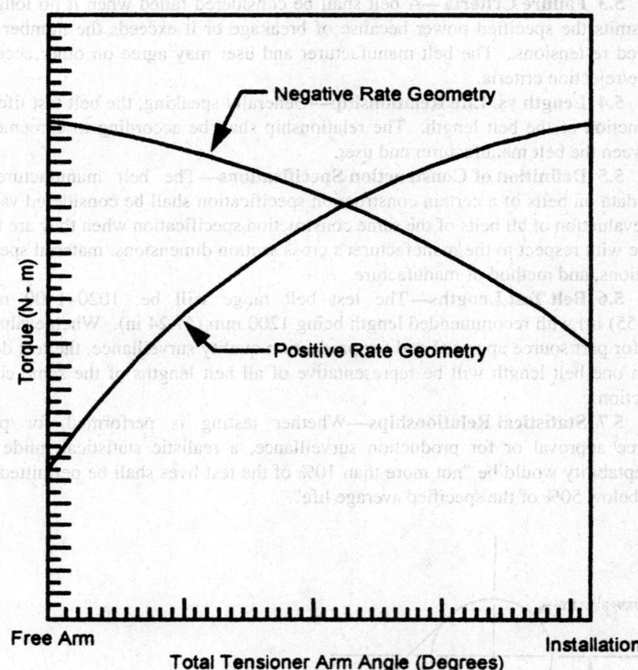

FIGURE 2—TENSIONER TORQUE REQUIREMENT CURVE

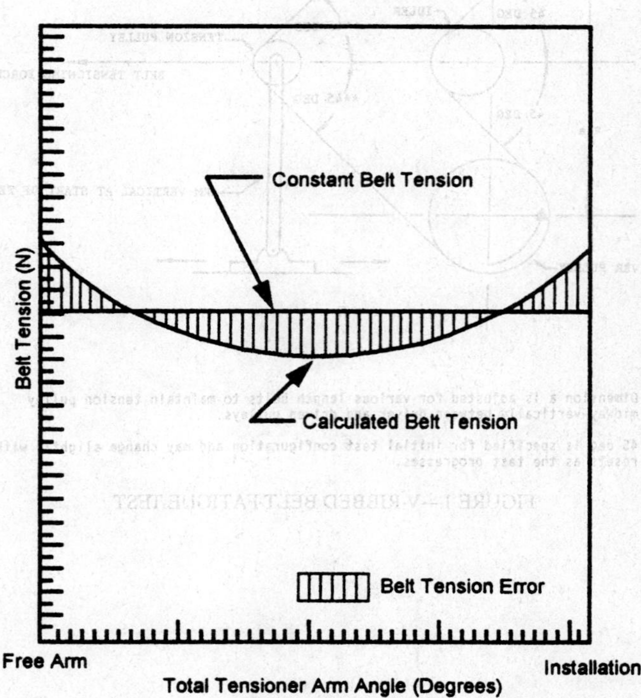

FIGURE 3—BELT TENSION ERROR CURVE

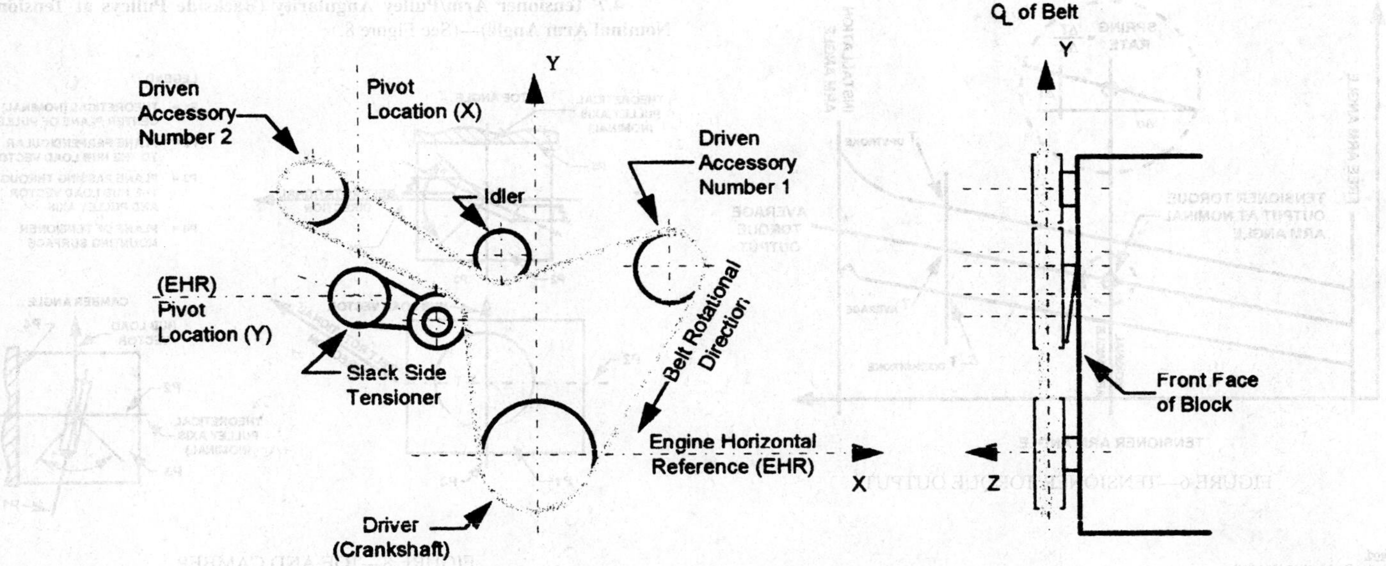

FIGURE 4—SYSTEM LAYOUT

3.7 Tensioner Arm Amplitude

3.7.1 MAXIMUM DYNAMIC TENSIONER ARM AMPLITUDE—Maximum Peak to Peak displacement at the pulley center of the tensioner arm in all dynamic (running) system conditions.

3.7.2 STEADY-STATE TENSIONER ARM AMPLITUDE—Maximum Peak to Peak arm amplitude at a constant engine speed. Various engine speeds and accessory load combinations except power steering should be evaluated to determine the worse case condition.

3.8 Slack Side Tensioner—The tensioner located between the driver pulley and the first load-carrying component in the direction of belt travel (routing idlers are not considered load-carrying components). (See Figure 4.)

3.9 Tight Side Tensioner—The tensioner located in any belt span other than the slack side of the driver pulley.

4. Tensioner Specific Design Characteristics

4.1 Tensioner Arm Angle—The angle of the line from the center of the tensioner pivot to the center of the tensioner pulley measured counter clockwise in accessory drive system polar coordinates where 0° = positive x-axis. (See Figures 4 and 5.)

4.1.1 TENSIONER NOMINAL ARM ANGLE—The tensioner arm angle which corresponds to the installed nominal length belt. (See β, Figure 5.)

4.1.2 TENSIONER FREE ARM ANGLE—The tensioner arm angle which corresponds to the free state of the tensioner, without the belt installed. (See α, Figure 5.)

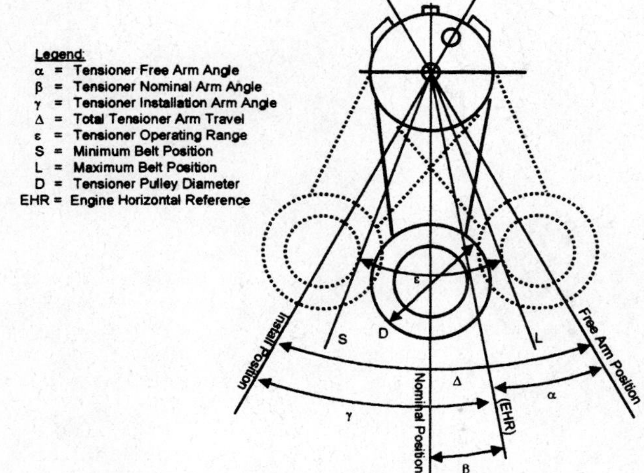

FIGURE 5—TENSIONER CHARACTERISTICS

4.1.3 TENSIONER INSTALLATION ARM ANGLE—The tensioner arm angle which corresponds to the stop feature of the tensioner arm to allow for belt installation. (See λ, Figure 5.)

4.1.4 TENSIONER MINIMUM NEW BELT ARM ANGLE—The tensioner arm angle which corresponds to an installed new minimum belt length used to ensure proper routing and belt length.

4.1.5 TENSIONER MAXIMUM NEW BELT ARM ANGLE—The tensioner arm angle which corresponds to an installed new maximum belt length used to ensure proper routing and belt length.

4.1.6 TENSIONER MAXIMUM ARM ANGLE—The tensioner arm angle at the longest belt length including stretch and wear.

4.2 Tensioner Arm Length—The distance between tensioner pivot location and tensioner pulley center. (See L, Figure 5.)

4.3 Tensioner Pulley Diameter—Diameter of the pulley attached to the tensioner arm as defined by SAE standard for groove side pulleys. SAE standard for backside pulleys is TBD. (See D, Figure 5.)

4.4 Tensioner Operation Range—The difference between the tensioner minimum new belt arm angle and the tensioner maximum arm angle. (See ε, Figure 5.)

4.5 Tensioner Torque Output Characteristics

4.5.1 TENSIONER TORQUE OUTPUT CURVE—Tensioner load output versus tensioner arm position (hysteresis curve). (See Figure 6.)

4.5.2 AVERAGE TORQUE OUTPUT—The average of tensioner up and down stroke torque values according to Equation 1 at each given arm position.

$$T_{average} = \frac{(T_{upstroke} - T_{downstroke})}{2} \quad \text{(Eq. 1)}$$

4.5.3 SPRING RATE—The rate of change in average torque output per degree of arm displacement.

4.5.4 SPRING SET—The change in tensioner torque output due to the initial stabilization of the various components in the tensioner assembly.

4.5.5 DAMPING (AT TENSIONER NOMINAL ARM ANGLE)—Hysteresis existing in the tensioner while operating at specified amplitude, frequency, and hub load angle. The procedure for calculating percent damping and work are shown in Equation 2 and 3 respectively.

$$\text{Percent Damping} = \frac{(T_{upstroke} - T_{average})}{T_{average}} \times 100 \quad \text{(Eq. 2)}$$

$$\text{Damping Work} = \int \frac{(T_{upstroke} - T_{downstroke})}{\text{Stroke}} \times 100 \quad \text{(Eq. 3)}$$

4.6 Tensioner Offset—The distance from tensioner mounting surface to theoretical centerline of belt. (See Figure 7.)

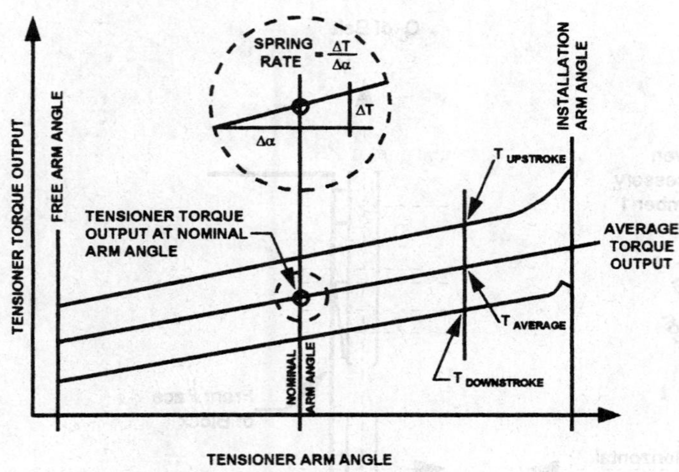

FIGURE 6—TENSIONER TORQUE OUTPUT

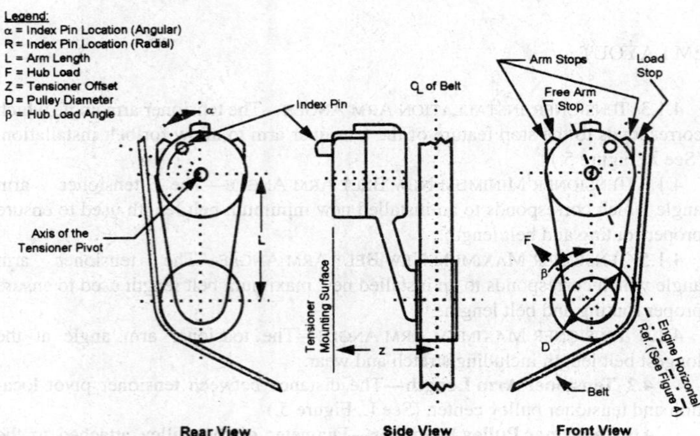

FIGURE 7—TENSIONER CHARACTERISTICS

4.6.1 Bearing Seat Height

4.7 Tensioner Arm/Pulley Angularity (Backside Pulleys at Tensioner Nominal Arm Angle)—(See Figure 8.)

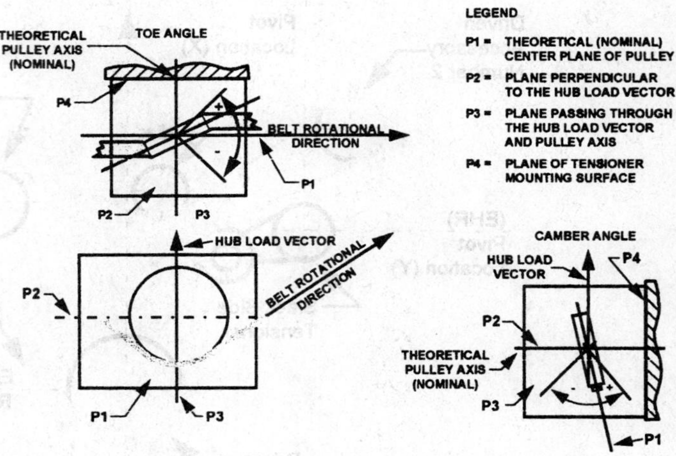

FIGURE 8—TOE AND CAMBER

4.7.1 Toe—The angle between the centerplane of the pulley and the plane of the tensioner mounting surface as measured in a plane perpendicular to the hub load vector as a rotation about the hub load axis (right hand rule with the thumb pointing in the direction of the hub load = positive direction). See Figure 8.

4.7.2 Camber—The angle between the centerplace of the pulley and the plane of the tensioner mounting surface measured in a place passing through the hub load vector and pulley axis as a rotation about the axis perpendicular to the hub load vector (right hand rule with the thumb pointing in the direction of belt motion in a clockwise rotating system). See Figure 8.

4.8 Bearing "Free Rock"—The total angular movement of the bearing outer race relative to the inner race.

4.9 Total Tensioner Arm Travel—The angular difference between the tensioner installation arm angle and the tensioner free arm angle. (stop to stop). (See Figure 5.)

ACCESSORY DRIVE TENSIONER TEST STANDARDS (MECHANICAL ROTARY TYPE)—SAE J2436 JUL1998

SAE Standard

Report of the SAE Belt Drive Committee approved July 1998.

1. Scope—To document test procedures and set-ups that address known failure modes for mechanical rotary tensioners and establish minimum acceptance criteria. This SAE Standard does not encompass the pulley or pulley bearing. The sample sizes should be determined by agreement between the original equipment manufacturer (OEM) and the supplier.

The failure modes to be addressed are:

a. Durability

Corrosion	Contamination
Structural	Wear
Temperature	Alignment

b. Functional

Clamp Load	Damping
Drop (Safety)	Lift Lugs
Load	Noise
Ozone	Snap

2. References

2.1 Applicable Publications—The following publications form a part of the specification to the extent specified herein. Unless otherwise indicated, the latest revision of SAE publications shall apply.

2.1.1 SAE Publication—Available from SAE, 400 Commonwealth Drive, Warrendale, PA 15096-0001.

SAE J2198—Glossary—Automatic Belt Tensioner (Measuring techniques for the acceptance criteria can be found in this paper.)

2.1.2 ASTM Publications—Available from ASTM, 100 Barr Harbor Drive, West Conshohocken, PA 19428-2959.

ASTM B 117-95—Method of Salt Spray (Fog) Testing

ASTM D 1149-91—Test Method for Rubber Deterioration—Surface Ozone Cracking in a Chamber (Flat Specimens)

3. General—Table 1 is based on a 100 mm arm length and is a general guideline for setting test parameters. It is for reference only since there are many factors that affect amplitude and frequency and should be specified by the OEM depending on the application. Peak-to-Peak refers to complete arm travel as measured at the pulley center. The frequency in the table refers to the drive excitation.

TABLE 1—GENERAL GUIDELINES

Damping	Engine Application
4 cylinder engine Application Frequency 25 Hz	
5%	8 mm peak-to-peak
10%	6 mm peak-to-peak
20%	4 mm peak-to-peak
40%	2 mm peak-to-peak
6 cylinder engine Application Frequency 30 Hz	
5%	6 mm peak-to-peak
10%	5 mm peak-to-peak
20%	2.5 mm peak-to-peak
40%	1.5 mm peak-to-peak
8 cylinder engine Application Frequency 40 Hz	
5%	4 mm peak-to-peak
10%	1.5 mm peak-to-peak
20%	1 mm peak-to-peak
40%	0.5 mm peak-to-peak

Figure 1 is an example of a belt driven test chamber. One of the pulleys must be eccentric to obtain the desired peak-to-peak arm travel of the tensioner. The production intent belt material should be used if possible. This test chamber is used for the cold test and the contamination test. It is more likely that the belt driven test chamber will seize the tensioner than the cable driven test chamber.

Figure 2 is an example of a cable driven test chamber. The center pulley is eccentric to obtain peak-to-peak arm travel. The specified cable diameter is 6 mm. This chamber is used for the corrosion test and the hot box test. This configuration is used to test durability by accelerating wear. This test stand must be capable of running at elevated temperatures.

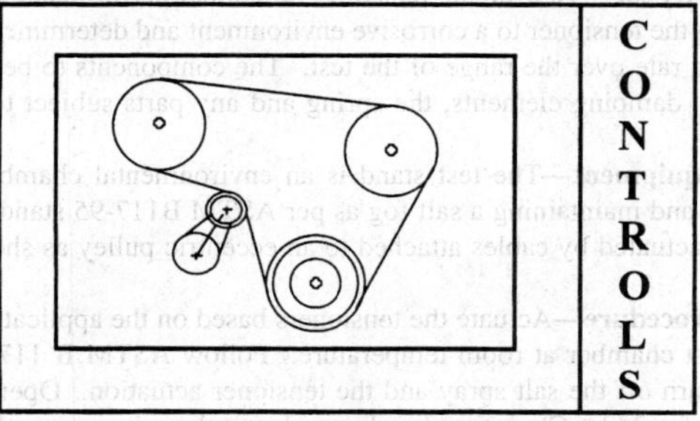

FIGURE 1—BELT DRIVEN TEST CHAMBER

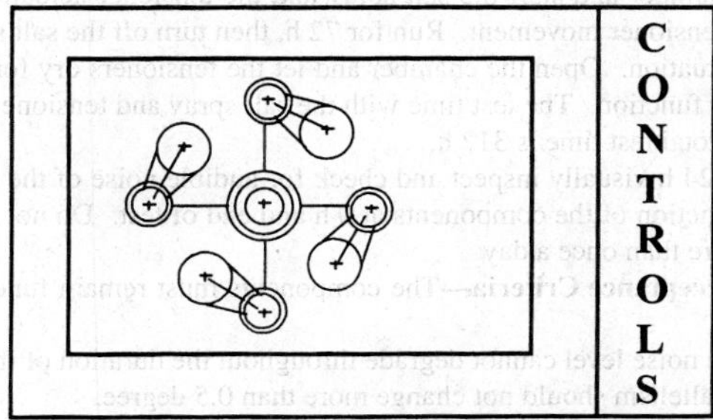

FIGURE 2—CABLE DRIVEN TEST CHAMBER

4. Contamination Test

4.1 Purpose—To evaluate tensioner lock up and durability by exposing the tensioner to a contaminated environment and to determine the effects on the damping rate over the range of the test. The components to be evaluated are the bushing, damping elements, the spring, and any parts subject to contamination. It is also possible to gain some preliminary knowledge of the sealing of the bearing if the production intent pulley, bearing, and dust shield are used.

4.2 Equipment—The test stand is an environmental chamber capable of operating at 70 °C ± 2 °C. The tensioners are to be installed in vehicle nominal position (to obtain correct hub load and gravity bias direction). The tensioners are to be actuated by a belt drive attached to an eccentric pulley, as shown in Figure 1. The belt should be production intent material. A squeeze bottle with a 1.8 mm nozzle should be used to apply the solution to the tensioner.

4.2.1 Contamination Solution:

a.	3.8 L	Water
b.	0.14 kg	SAE Course Test dust
c.	0.14 kg	#400 grit aluminum Oxide Grain
d.	0.05 kg	#150 grit aluminum Oxide Grain
e.	0.14 kg	Table salt
f.	0.005 L	Red food coloring

4.3 Procedure—Actuate the tensioners based on the application (see Table 1) in the test chamber at 70 °C ± 2 °C for 24 h with no contamination to run in the belt and tensioner. Reset the amplitude to the original displacement with the tensioner hot. Begin the test by actuating the tensioners in the test chamber at 70 °C ± 2 °C. Mix the previous ingredients into a solution and spray the tensioner in the 12, 3, 6, and 9 O'clock positions parallel to the mounting face and directly at the center of the front. Apply the solution for 2 s in each position completely wetting the tensioner 3 times a day. This test is to be run for 400 h with data collected at 0 h, 1 h 200 h, and 400 h.

4.4 Acceptance Criteria—The components must remain functional at the end of test.

a. The noise level cannot degrade throughout the duration of the test.
b. Parallelism should not change more than 0.5 degree.
c. The offset change should be no more than 0.80 mm.
d. The change in spring load should not be more than ±15%.
e. The damping must remain within the minimum and maximum design envelope established by application design parameters.

NOTE—Functional measurements of alignment and offset should be made at in vehicle geometry nominal position. If the damping changes and falls outside of the design specifications, the OEM may choose to continue the test at a higher amplitude to induce bushing failure which would be a secondary failure.

5. Corrosion Test

5.1 Purpose—To evaluate tensioner functional performance and durability by exposing the tensioner to a corrosive environment and determine the effects on the damping rate over the range of the test. The components to be evaluated are the bushing, damping elements, the spring and any parts subject to wear and/or corrosion.

5.2 Equipment—The test stand is an environmental chamber capable of introducing and maintaining a salt fog as per ASTM B117-95 standard. The tensioners are actuated by cables attached to an eccentric pulley as shown in Figure 2.

5.3 Procedure—Actuate the tensioners based on the application (see Table 1) in the test chamber at room temperature. Follow ASTM B 117-95. Run for 72 h, then turn off the salt spray and the tensioner actuation. Open the chamber and let it sit for 24 h. Close the chamber and start the salt spray and the tensioner actuation. Visually inspect the tensioner movement. Run for 96 h, then turn off the salt spray and the tensioner actuation. Open the chamber and let it sit for 24 h. Close the chamber and start the salt spray and the tensioner actuation. Visually inspect the tensioner movement. Run for 72 h, then turn off the salt spray and the tensioner actuation. Open the chamber and let the tensioners dry for 24 h before checking for function. The test time with the salt spray and tensioner actuation is 240 h. The total test time is 312 h.

Every 24 h visually inspect and check for audible noise of the components. Audit the function of the components at 0 h and end of test. Do not open the test chamber more than once a day.

5.4 Acceptance Criteria—The components must remain functional at the end of test.

a. The noise level cannot degrade throughout the duration of the test.
b. Parallelism should not change more than 0.5 degree.
c. The offset change should be no more than 0.80 mm.
d. The change in spring load should not be more than ±15%.
e. The damping must remain within the minimum and maximum design envelope established by application design parameters.

NOTE—Functional measurements of alignment and offset should be made at in vehicle geometry nominal position. If the damping changes and falls outside of the design specifications, the OEM may choose to continue the test at a higher amplitude to induce bushing failure which would be a secondary failure.

6. Hot/Cold Cycling Test

6.1 Purpose—To evaluate tensioner functional performance and durability by inducing wear on the components and to determine the effects of heat on the damping rate over the range of the test. The components to be evaluated are the bushing, damping elements, the spring, and any plastic parts.

6.2 Equipment

6.2.1 EQUIPMENT HOT CYCLE—The test stand for the hot cycle is an environmental chamber capable of maintaining a minimum of 100 °C ± 2 °C. The tensioners are actuated by cables attached to an eccentric pulley as shown in Figure 2.

6.2.2 EQUIPMENT COLD CYCLE—The test stand for the cold cycle must be capable of maintaining –40 °C ± 2 °C. The tensioners are actuated by a belt as shown in Figure 1 with the tensioner installed in vehicle position including belt wrap angle. The belt should be production intent material.

6.3 Procedure—Actuate the tensioners based on the application in the test chamber at 100 °C ± 2 °C for 1 h. Soak in cold box at –40 °C ± 2 °C for a minimum of 1 h. Cycle for 5 min with an acceleration rate of 100 rpm in the first 2 seconds, 750 rpm within 7 s, and the correct amplitude and frequency within 10 s. Return to hot box and run tensioners at 100 °C ± 2 °C for 100 h. Soak in cold box at –40 °C ± 2 °C for a minimum of 1 h. Cycle for 5 min with an acceleration rate of 100 rpm in the first 2 s, 750 rpm within 7 s, and the correct amplitude and frequency within 10 s. Return to hot box and run tensioners at 100 °C ± 2 °C for 100 h. Soak in cold box at –40 °C ± 2 °C for a minimum of 1 h. Cycle for 5 min with an acceleration rate of 100 rpm in the first 2 s, 750 rpm within 7 s, and the correct amplitude and frequency within 10 s. Total test time 201 h and 15 min.

Every 24 h inspect visually and check for audible noise of the components. Audit the function of the components at 0 h, 1 h, and end of test.

6.4 Acceptance Criteria—The components must remain functional at the end of test.

a. The noise level cannot degrade throughout the duration of the test.
b. Parallelism should not change more than 0.5 degree.
c. The offset change should be no more than 0.80 mm.
d. The change in spring load should not be more than ±15%.
e. The damping must remain within the minimum and maximum design envelope established by application design parameters.

NOTE—Functional measurements of alignment and offset should be made at in vehicle geometry nominal position. If the damping changes and falls outside of the design specifications, the OEM may choose to continue the test at a higher amplitude to induce bushing failure which would be a secondary failure.

7. Cold Box Test—Eliminated as a stand alone test. This test is to be run if the Hot/Cold Cycling Test was not passed. This will help identify if the failure was due to cold temperature.

7.1 Purpose—To evaluate tensioner functional performance and durability by inducing wear on the components. Determine the effects of cold on the damping rate over the range of the test. The components to be evaluated are the bushing, damping elements, the spring, and any plastic parts.

7.2 Equipment—The test stand must be capable of maintaining –40 °C ± 2 °C. The tensioners are actuated by a belt with the tensioner installed in vehicle position including belt wrap angle. The test chamber is shown in Figure 1.

7.3 Procedure—Actuate the tensioners based on the application in the test chamber at 100 °C ± 2 °C for 1 h. Soak in cold box at –40 °C ± 2 °C for a minimum of 1 h. Cycle for 5 min with an acceleration rate of 100 rpm in the first 2 s, 750 rpm within 7 s, and the correct amplitude and frequency within 10 s. Repeat the cold soak and 5 min cycle 3 times.

After each run inspect visually and check for audible noise of the components. Audit the function of the components at 0 h, 1 h, and end of test.

7.4 Acceptance Criteria—The components must remain functional at the end of test.

a. The noise level cannot degrade throughout the duration of the test.
b. Parallelism should not change more than 0.5 degree.
c. The offset change should be no more than 0.80 mm.
d. The change in spring load should not be more than ±15%.
e. The damping must remain within the minimum and maximum design envelope established by application design parameters.

NOTE—Functional measurements of alignment and offset should be made at in vehicle geometry nominal position. If the damping changes and falls outside of the design specifications, the OEM may choose to continue the test at a higher amplitude to induce bushing failure which would be a secondary failure.

8. Hot Box Test—Eliminated as a stand alone test. This test is to be run if the Hot/Cold Cycling Test was not passed. This will help identify if the failure was due to elevated temperature.

8.1 Purpose—To evaluate tensioner functional performance and durability by inducing wear on the components. Determine the effects of heat on the damping rate over the range of the test. The components to be evaluated are the bushing, damping elements, the spring, and any plastic parts.

8.2 Equipment—The test stand is an environmental chamber capable of maintaining a minimum of 100 °C ± 2 °C. The tensioners are actuated by cables attached to an eccentric pulley. The test chamber is shown in Figure 1.

8.3 Procedure—Actuate the tensioners based on the application and Table 1 in a test chamber shown in Figure 1 at 100 °C ± 2 °C for a minimum of 200 h. Every 24 h inspect visually and check for no audible noise of the components. Audit the function of the components at 0 h, 1 h, and 200 h.

8.4 Acceptance Criteria—The components must remain functional at the end of test.

a. The noise level cannot degrade throughout the duration of the test.
b. Parallelism should not change more than 0.5 degree.
c. The offset change should be no more than 0.80 mm.
d. The change in spring load should not be more than ±15%.
e. The damping must remain within the minimum and maximum design envelope established by application design parameters.

NOTE—Functional measurements of alignment and offset should be made at in vehicle geometry nominal position. If the damping changes and falls outside of the design specifications, the OEM may choose to continue the test at a higher amplitude to induce bushing failure which would be a secondary failure.

9. Lift Lug Test

9.1 Purpose—To test the affect of installing a belt on the tensioner arm for offset and parallelism. To determine the strength of the lifting feature of the tensioner.

9.2 Equipment—The fixture must be able to withstand the force necessary to break the lifting feature of the tensioner. Use a torque wrench capable of measuring and recording peak torque. OEM is to specify the torque wrench arm length.

9.3 Procedure—Install the tensioner assembly in the test fixture. Torque the tensioner mounting fasteners to the minimum torque specification. Lift the tensioner arm with the torque wrench as if the belt is being installed. Determine and record the amount of torque necessary to lift the arm to the belt install position (Load Stop). Using the torque wrench, lift the arm to the torque measured previously and continue to apply torque until the residual (break away) torque of the pulley bolt is reached. If the lifting feature is not a bolt, continue to apply torque until 2 times the measured torque as stated previously. Repeat the test 6 times per test part.

NOTE—The torque wrench should be oriented such that the wrench is along the axis of the tensioner to obtain the maximum force that can be applied (see Figure 3).

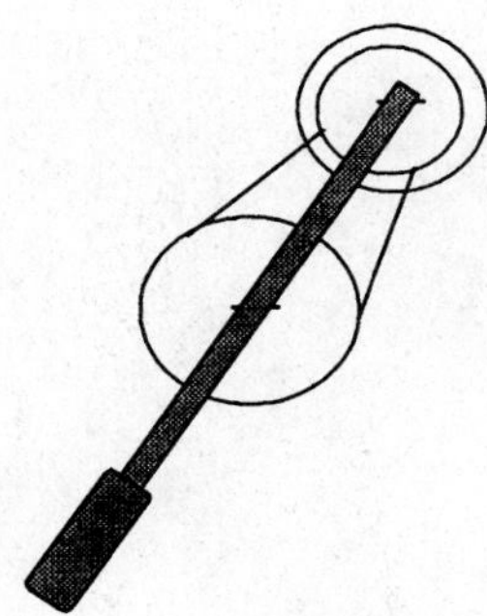

FIGURE 3—TORQUE WRENCH ORIENTATION

9.4 Acceptance Criteria—No failures allowed.

10. Ozone Test

10.1 Purpose—To test all exposed rubber for cracking resistance when subjected to a test chamber containing ozone.

10.2 Test Equipment—See ASTM D 1149-91

10.3 Procedure—See ASTM D 1149-91. Test duration is 70 h with an ozone concentration of 100 pphm.

10.4 Acceptance Criteria—No visible cracks to the unaided eye.

11. Safety Drop Test

11.1 Purpose—This test addresses safety issues by ensuring that the tensioner assembly remains intact after sustaining a drop from a specified height, simulating a possible assembly handling occurrence.

11.2 Test Equipment

a. Concrete Floor
b. Measuring Tape

11.3 Procedure—Holding the tensioner by the pulley, drop the tensioner on a concrete floor from a height of 1.5 m (lowest point of tensioner to floor). Drop same tensioner assembly 3 times.

Sample size—An amount to be agreed to by the supplier and OEM.

11.4 Acceptance Criteria—Basic structural components of the tensioner are to remain intact after sustaining 3 drops. Any retaining features (e.g., preload clip) must remain functional after the first drop.

NOTE—This excludes the pulley.

12. Snap Test

12.1 Purpose—To ensure that the tensioner assembly remains functional if during the belt installation the tensioner arm is suddenly released from the maximum travel position to the free arm position.

12.2 Equipment—The test fixture must be capable of holding the tensioner. A device must be present to rotate the tensioner to the maximum arm travel position and then instantaneously release the arm allowing it to "snap" to the free arm position.

12.3 Procedure—Install the tensioner assembly, including the pulley, in the test fixture. Rotate the tensioner to the maximum arm position (Load Stop) and hold to prevent rotation. Release the arm allowing it to "snap" to the free arm position. Each part should be tested 5 times.

12.4 Acceptance Criteria—No failures allowed.

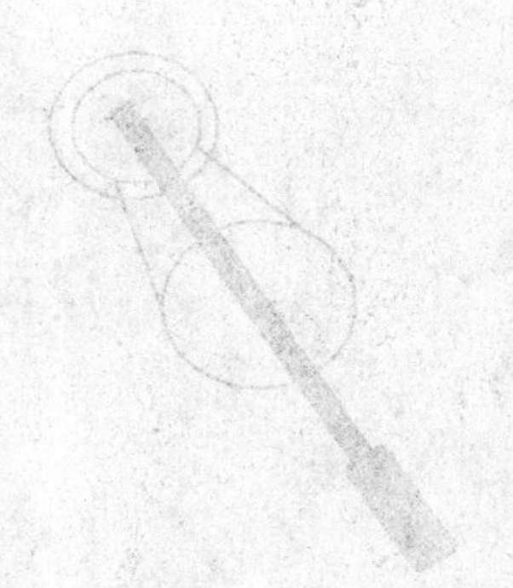

20 Springs

LEAF SPRINGS FOR MOTOR VEHICLE SUSPENSION —MADE TO METRIC UNITS—SAE J1123 NOV1992

SAE Standard

Report of the SAE Spring Committee, approved November 1975, second revision, SAE Leaf Spring Subcommittee, May 1985. Reaffirmed by the SAE Leaf Spring Subcommittee of the SAE Spring Committee November 1992.

Foreword—This reaffirmed document has been changed only to reflect the new SAE Technical Standards Board format.

1. Scope

NOTE—For leaf springs made to customary U.S. units, see SAE J510.

This SAE Standard is limited to concise specifications promoting an adequate understanding between spring maker and spring user on all practical requirements in the finished spring. The basic concepts for the spring design and for many of the details have been fully dealt with in HS-J788.

2. References

2.1 Applicable Publications—The following publications form a part of this specification to the extent specified herein. The latest issue of SAE publications shall apply.

2.1.1 SAE PUBLICATIONS—Available from SAE, 400 Commonwealth Drive, Warrendale, PA 15096-0001.

SAE J419—Methods of Measuring Decarburization

SAE J510—Leaf Springs for Motor Vehicle Suspension—Made to Customary U.S. Units

HS-J788—Manual on Design and Application of Leaf Springs

3. Bar Sizes and Tolerances—Round edge flat spring steel has been adopted as the SAE standard.

The bars shall be of flat rolled steel having two flat surfaces and two rounded (convex) edges. They are subject to the tolerances shown in Table 1. These cross-section tolerances permit the two flat surfaces to be slightly concave. When that occurs, the radii of the arcs of the two concave surfaces shall be of approximately equal length.

The rounding of the convex edges shall be an arc with a radius of curvature that may vary from 65 to 85% of the thickness of the bar.

Bars shall be substantially straight and free from physical characteristics known as "kinks" or "twists" which render them unsatisfactory for spring manufacturing purposes.

Distortions due to a bar being bent about either major axis of section shall be measured with the bar against a flat checking surface so as to make contact with this surface near both bar ends. Gaps between the bar and the checking surface shall not exceed 4.0 mm/1 m of bar length out of contact with the checking surface when this bar length is greater than 1 m. Also, a gap between the bar and a straight edge 1 m long applied along any portion of the surface or edge of the bar, shall not exceed 4.0 mm.

It is recommended that all leaf spring bars which have been cold straightened be identified by the steel mill so that the spring manufacturer can use them selectively.

The bars which are generally provided in alloy steel shall be specified and rolled as in Table 2:

4. Surface Decarburization—Surface decarburization may reduce the fatigue durability of the springs; therefore, it is important that surface decarburization be at a minimum.

Hot rolled steel bars as received from the mills have some decarb, at least of the minimum Type 3 (see SAE J419), where more than 50% of the base carbon content remains at the surface (that is, some partial, but not more than 50% loss of carbon).

If decarb is of Type 2, where 50% or less of the base carbon content remains at the surface (that is, appreciable partial, but not total loss of carbon), the decarb normally does not exceed a depth of 0.25 mm for steels of thicknesses 5.00 to 12.50 mm, nor a depth of 0.50 mm for steels of thicknesses over 12.50 to 37.50 mm.

With sections over 25.00 mm in thickness, some of the hot rolled steel bars may have decarb of Type 1, in which virtually carbon-free ferrite (that is, total loss of carbon) exists for a measurable distance below the surface.

The depth of decarb varies from mill to mill, from rolling to rolling, and from bar to bar. The extent to which the depth and type of the decarb can be acceptable will be subject to agreement between the steel producer and the spring manufacturer.

The edges of the bars are somewhat higher in decarb than the flat surfaces; decarb on both the edges and the flat surfaces usually has greater depth with increased bar thickness.

After forging and non-atmospheric controlled heat treating, the spring leaves will have greater decarb. Scaling of the steel in this processing reduces the thickness of the leaf. While some of the surface decarb is removed with the scale, the final depth of decarb is usually greater than it was in the steel bars as received from the mills.

5. Definitions, Dimensions, and Tolerances

5.1 Leaf Spring—A spring of full elliptic, semi-elliptic, or quarter-elliptic shape with one or more leaves. The term "multi-leaf" has generally applied to springs of constant width and with stepped leaves, each of constant thickness except where leaf ends may be tapered in thickness. More recently, the term has been extended to include an assembly of stacked "single" leaves, each of which is characterized by tapering either in width or in thickness, or by a combination of both. Examples of multi-leaf springs are shown in Figures 1 to 6. Figure 7 shows a single leaf spring.

The leaves of a multi-leaf spring are usually held together with a center bolt and prevented from lateral shifting by alignment clips. Prior to assembly, the leaves are formed (cambered) and heat-treated by heating, quenching, and tempering to the required hardness. Quench dies or fixtures are used to maintain the required camber within tolerances.

5.2 Datum Line—Reference line used with many of the subsequently defined terms. In Figure 1 (where the springs are shown inverted as in a machine for load and rate checking), it is shown as the line X-X. On springs with eyes, the datum line passes through the centers of the eyes. On other springs, it passes through the points where the load is applied near the ends of the spring. These points must be indicated on the drawing. When load and rate are checked, the spring ends shall be free to move in the direction of the datum line.

5.3 Seat Angle Base Line (see Figure 1)—Reference line drawn through the terminal points of the active spring length at each eye, taken along the tension surface of the main leaf. On springs without eyes, the seat angle base line is coincident with the datum line.

5.4 Loaded Length—Distance between spring eye centers when the spring is deflected to the specified load position. On springs without eyes, it is the distance between the lines where load is applied under the specified conditions. Tolerance, ±3.0 mm.

5.5 Loaded Fixed End Length—Distance from the center of the fixed end eye to the projection on the datum line of the point where the centerline of the center bolt intersects the spring surface in contact with the spring seat. Tolerance, ± 1.5 mm.

5.6 Straight Length—Distance between eye centers when the tension surface of the main leaf at the center bolt centerline is in the plane of the seat angle base line. The distance is measured parallel to the seat angle base line. Tolerance, ±3.0 mm.

5.7 Seat Length—Length of spring that is in actual engagement with the spring seat when installed on a vehicle at design height. It is always greater than the inactive length.

5.8 Inactive Length—Length of spring rendered inactive by the action of the U-bolts or clamping bolts.

5.9 Seat Angle (see Figure 1)—Angle between the tangent to the center of the spring seat and the seat angle base line. When the spring is viewed with the fixed end of the spring to the left as shown, and the load is applied to the shortest leaf from above, the seat angle may be specified as either positive (counterclockwise) or negative (clockwise), depending upon the angular direction in which the tangent to the center of the spring seat is disposed from the seat angle base line.

Consequently, with the spring in normal vehicle position so that the load is applied from below as shown in Figures 2, 4, 5, 6, and 7 and again with the fixed end of the spring to the left of the drawing, the seat angle is defined as positive when that tangent is disposed clockwise; and as negative when the tangent is disposed counterclockwise.

5.10 Finished Width—Width to which the spring leaves are ground or milled to give the edges a flat bearing surface. If the spring ends have a finished width, the required length of the finished edge must also be indicated. The usual tolerances for finished widths are as in Table 3.

5.11 Assembled Spring Width—Where more than one leaf constitutes a spring assembly, the overall width tolerance of the assembly within the spring seat length shall be as follows as in Table 4.

5.12 Stack Thickness—Aggregate of the nominal thicknesses of all leaves of the spring including any spacer plates which are part of the spring at the seat.

5.13 Leaf Ends—The leaf ends used most generally are:

a. Square as sheared
b. Trimmed to a shape
c. Taper rolled
d. Taper rolled; trimmed or forged to a shape or both

5.14 Surface Finish—Condition of the surface of the spring leaves after the steel has been heat treated and prior to coating.

5.14.1 "AS HEAT TREATED" FINISH—The surface of the spring leaves is in the condition as taken from the heat treating furnace where generally the leaves have a finish of oxide coating.

5.14.2 "SHOT PEENED" FINISH—The tension surface of the spring leaves has been exposed to the shot peening operation where the oxide coating and scale are removed and a matte luster finish is produced.

5.14.3 "GROUND OR POLISHED LEAF ENDS"—The bearing areas of leaves are ground or polished to produce a smooth surface for reduced friction. The distance or length to be ground or polished should be specified.

5.15 Protective Coating—Material added to surface of spring leaves or exposed areas of assembled springs. For additional information, see HS-J788.

5.16 Leaf Numbers (see Figure 1)—Leaves are designated by numbers, starting with the main leaf which is No. 1, the adjoining leaf is No. 2, and so on. If rebound leaves are used, the rebound leaf adjoining the main leaf is rebound leaf No. 1, the next one rebound leaf No. 2, and so on. (Rebound leaves are assembled adjacent to the side opposite the load bearing leaves.) Helper springs are considered as separate units.

5.17 Opening and Overall Height (see Figure 1)—Distance from the datum line to the point where the center bolt centerline intersects the surface of the spring that is in contact with the spring seat.

If the surface in contact with the seat is on the main leaf or a rebound leaf (as on underslung springs), this distance is called "opening."

If the surface in contact with the seat is on the shortest leaf (as on overslung springs), this distance is called "overall height."

"Opening" and "overall height" may be positive or negative (see Figure 1). They are specified dimensions not subject to a tolerance. (see 5.19) See 5.19 on Load.

TABLE 1—CROSS-SECTION TOLERANCES, mm

Width	Width Tolerance Minus 0.00	Tolerance in Thickness (±)(1) and in Flatness (–)(2) For Thickness 5.00–9.50	Tolerance in Thickness (±)(1) and in Flatness (–)(2) For Thickness 10.00–21.20	Tolerance in Thickness (±)(2) and in Flatness (–)(2) For Thickness 22.40–37.50	Maximum Difference in Thickness(3) For Thickness 5.00–9.50	Maximum Difference in Thickness(3) For Thickness 10.00–21.20	Maximum Difference in Thickness(3) For Thickness 22.40–37.50
40.0	+0.75	0.13	0.15	–	0.05	0.05	–
45.0	+0.75	0.13	0.15	–	0.05	0.05	–
50.0	+0.75	0.13	0.15	–	0.05	0.05	–
56.0	+0.75	0.13	0.15	–	0.05	0.05	–
63.0	+0.75	0.13	0.15	–	0.05	0.05	–
75.0	+1.15	0.15	0.20	0.30	0.08	0.10	0.15
90.0	+1.15	0.15	0.20	0.30	0.08	0.10	0.15
100.0	+1.15	0.15	0.20	0.30	0.08	0.10	0.15
125.0	+1.65	0.18	0.25	0.40	0.10	0.13	0.20
150.0	+2.30	–	0.30	0.50	–	0.15	0.25

1. Thickness measurements shall be taken at the edge of the bar where the flat surfaces intersect the rounded edge.
2. This tolerance represents the maximum amount by which the thickness at the center of the bar may be less than the thickness at the edges. Thickness at the center may never exceed the thickness at the edges.
3. Maximum difference in thickness between the two edges of each bar.

TABLE 2—SPECIFIED WIDTHS AND THICKNESSES OF ALLOY STEEL BARS, mm

Widths	Widths	Thicknesses	Thicknesses	Thicknesses	Thicknesses	Thicknesses	Thicknesses
40.0	75.0	5.00	7.10	10.00	14.00	20.00	28.00
45.0	90.0	5.30	7.50	10.60	15.00	21.20	30.00
50.0	100.0	5.60	8.00	11.20	16.00	22.40	31.50
56.0	125.0	6.00	8.50	11.80	17.00	23.60	33.50
63.0	150.0	6.30	9.00	12.50	18.00	25.00	35.50
		6.70	9.50	13.20	19.00	26.50	37.50

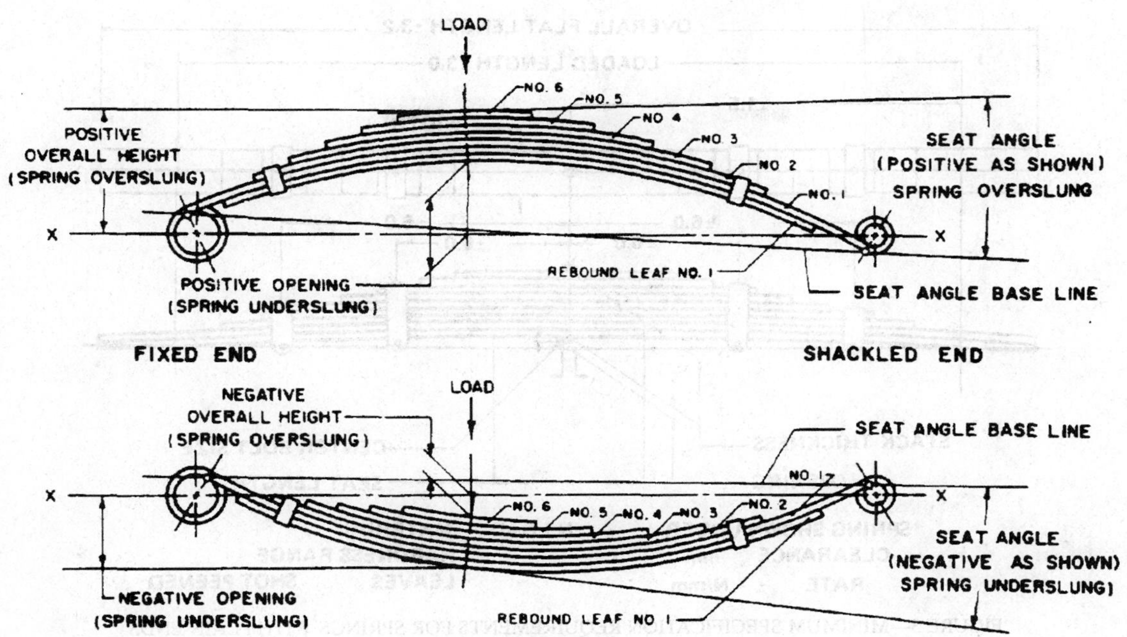

FIGURE 1—MEASUREMENT OF OPENING, OVERALL HEIGHT, AND SEAT ANGLE

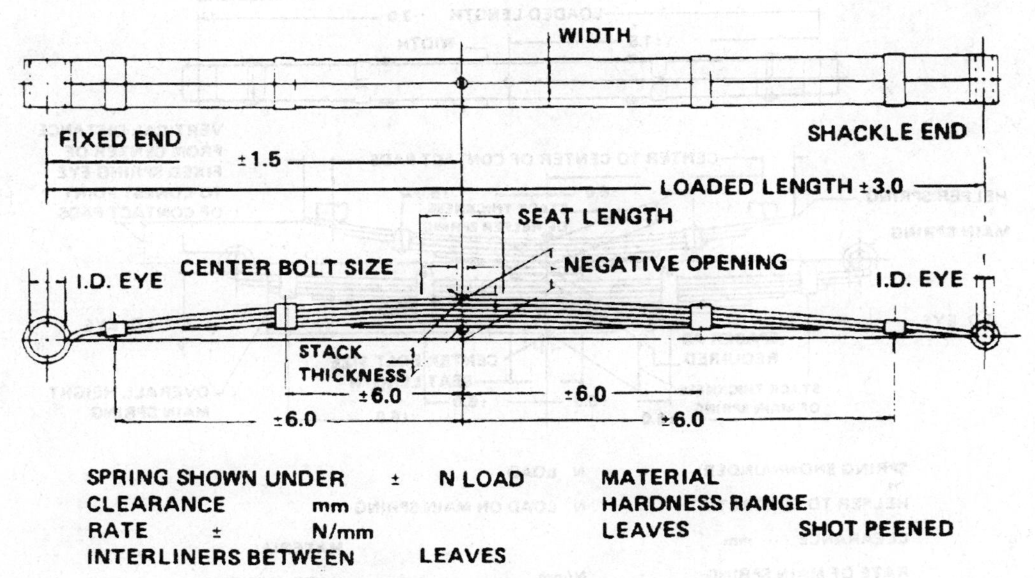

FIGURE 2—MINIMUM SPECIFICATION REQUIREMENTS FOR UNDERSLUNG SPRINGS WITH NEGATIVE OPENING

TABLE 3—TOLERANCES FOR FINISHED WIDTHS

Leaf Width Over	Leaf Width To and Including	Tolerance from Nominal Width +0.00
0	50	–0.25
50	63	–0.35
63	150	–0.50

TABLE 4—WIDTH TOLERANCE OF THE ASSEMBLY

Leaf Width Over	Leaf Width To and Including	Tolerance –0.000
0.0	63	+2.5
63	100	+3.0
100	125	+3.7
125	150	+4.4

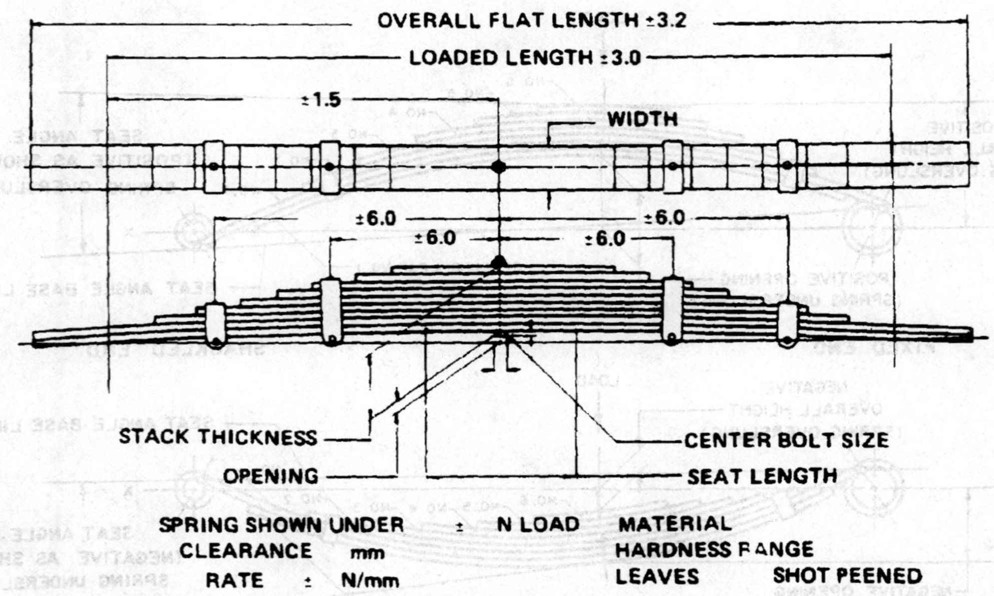

FIGURE 3—MINIMUM SPECIFICATION REQUIREMENTS FOR SPRINGS WITH PLAIN ENDS

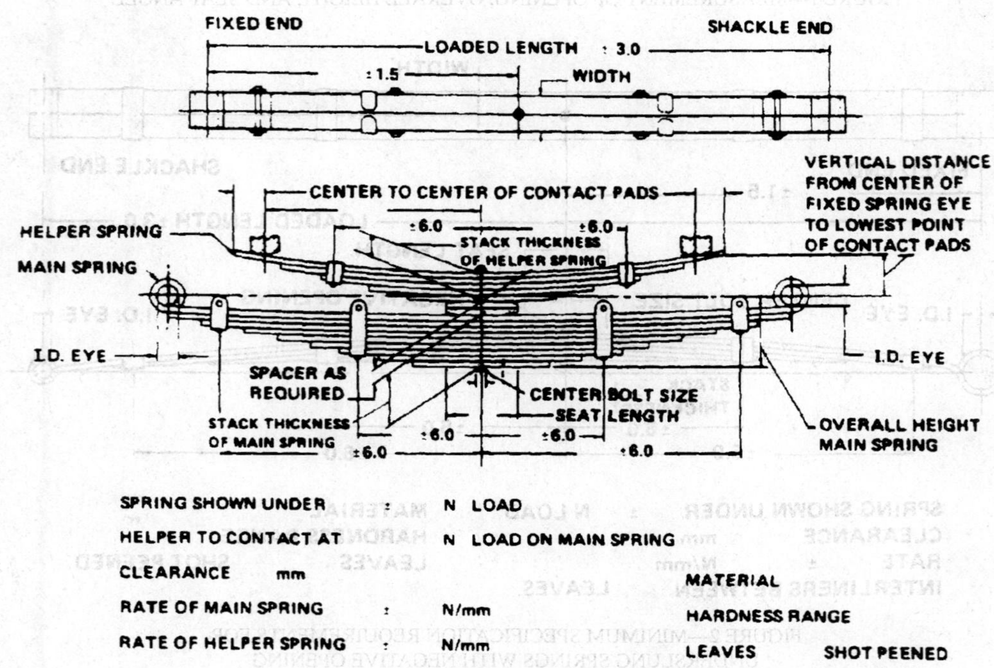

FIGURE 4—MINIMUM SPECIFICATION REQUIREMENTS FOR OVERSLUNG COMMERCIAL VEHICLE SPRINGS

5.18 Clearance—Difference in opening, or overall height, between the design load position and the extreme position (of maximum stress) to which the spring can be deflected on the vehicle.

5.19 Load—The force exerted by the spring at the specified opening or overall height. The total tolerance on load at the specified overall height or opening is usually expressed as a load range (N) which is equivalent to a deflection (mm) at the nominal rate (N/mm). This deflection may be as small as 6.0 mm for a passenger car spring and as large as 13.0 mm for a heavy truck spring.

5.20 Rate—The change of load per unit of spring deflection (N/mm). For leaf springs, it is determined as one fiftieth (2%) of the difference between the loads measured 25 mm above and 25 mm below the specified position, unless otherwise specified (see Figure 5). The tolerance is usually held within ± 5% on low rate springs and within ± 7% on high rate springs.

5.21 Load and Rate Checking—Load and rate are the terms usually employed to describe the basic characteristics of a leaf spring without center clamp and without shackles. They are, therefore, not the same as those of the installed spring.

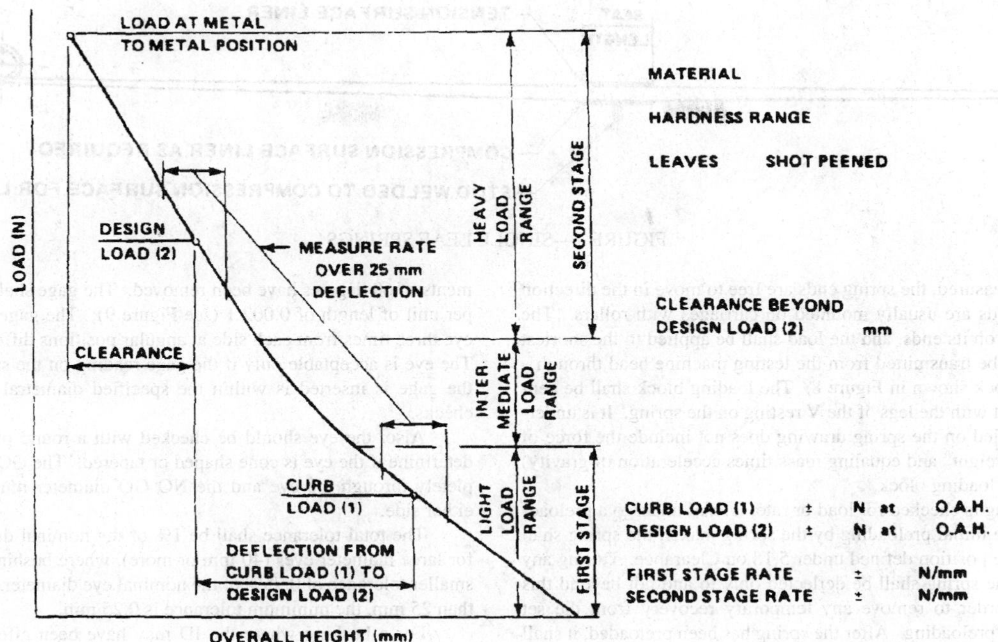

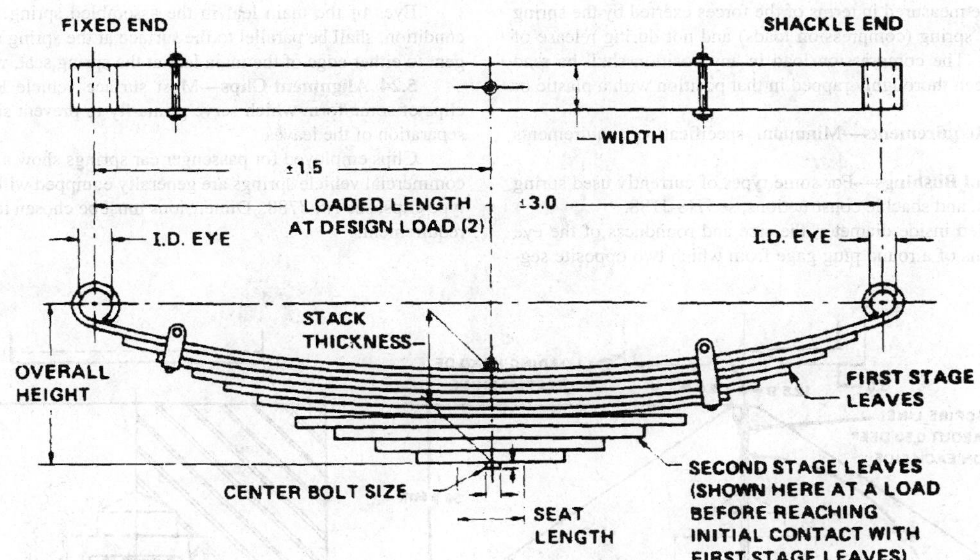

FIGURE 5—MINIMUM SPECIFICATION REQUIREMENTS FOR VARIABLE RATE OR PROGRESSIVE RATE SPRINGS (OVERSLUNG TYPE SHOWN)

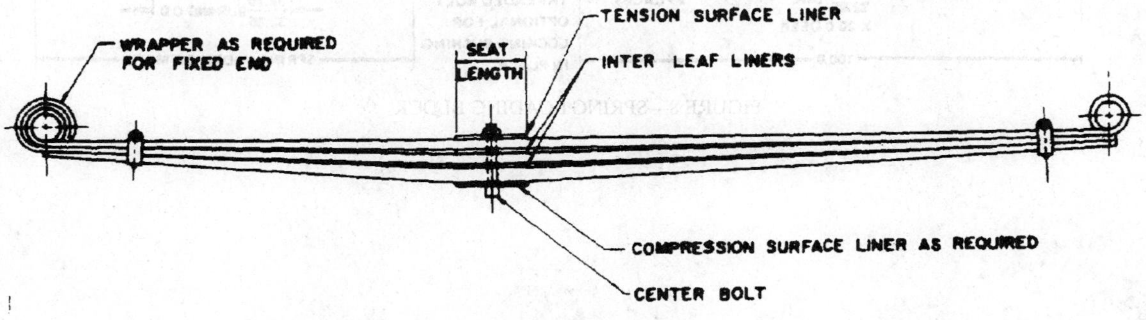

FIGURE 6—STACKED SINGLE LEAF SPRINGS

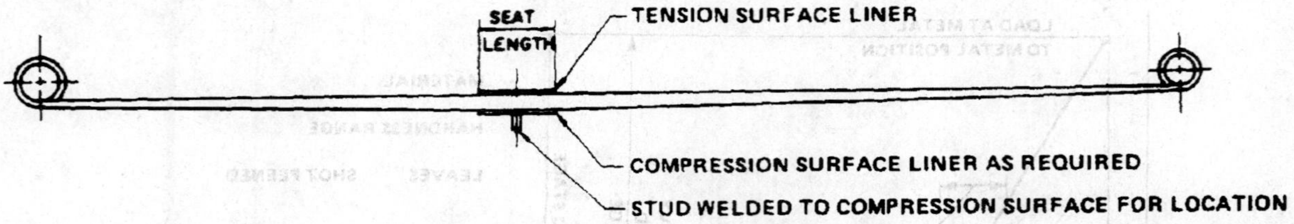

FIGURE 7—SINGLE LEAF SPRINGS

When the load is measured, the spring ends are free to move in the direction of the datum line; the ends are usually mounted on carriages with rollers. The spring shall be supported on its ends, and the load shall be applied to the shortest leaf from above. It shall be transmitted from the testing machine head through a standard SAE loading block shown in Figure 8. The loading block shall be centered above the center bolt with the legs of the V resting on the spring. It is understood that the load specified on the spring drawing does not include the force of gravity (usually called "weight" and equaling mass times acceleration of gravity) of either the spring or the loading block.

Just before the spring is checked for load or rate, it shall undergo a preloading operation. During the initial preloading by the spring maker, the spring shall be deflected at least to the position defined under 5.18 on Clearance. During any subsequent preloading, the spring shall be deflected only to and not beyond this "clearance position" in order to remove any temporary recovery from the set incurred during the initial preloading. After the spring has been preloaded, it shall be released to the free position before the load is applied for load and rate checking. For additional information on preloading, see HS-J788.

Load and rate shall be measured in terms of the forces exerted by the spring during compression of the spring (compression loads) and not during release of the spring (release loads). The compression load in any position shall be read only after the spring has been thoroughly rapped in that position with a plastic or soft metal hammer.

5.22 Specification Requirements—Minimum specification requirements are given in Figures 2 to 5.

5.23 Spring Eyes and Bushings—For some types of currently used spring eyes, spring ends, bushings, and shackle constructions, see HS-J788.

For eyes with specified inside diameter, the size and roundness of the eye should be checked by means of a round plug gage from which two opposite segments of 60 degrees have been removed. The gage shall have a taper on diameter per unit of length of 0.002:1 (see Figure 9). The gage shall be inserted into the eye three times from each side at angular positions differing by about 60 degrees. The eye is acceptable only if the gage reading on the side of the eye from which the gage is inserted is within the specified diametral limits at each of the six checks.

Also, the eye should be checked with a round plug, GO/NO GO gage, to determine if the eye is cone shaped or tapered. The GO diameter must pass completely through the eye and the NO GO diameter must not enter the eye from either side.

The total tolerance shall be 1% of the nominal diameter of the eye, except for large diameter eyes (40 mm or more), where bushing retention may require a smaller tolerance of 0.75% of the nominal eye diameter. For eye diameters of less than 25 mm, the minimum tolerance is 0.25 mm.

For a bushing where the ID may have been affected by pressing into the spring eye, it should be checked with a round plug gage. Total tolerance, 0.13 mm unless otherwise specified.

Eyes of the main leaf in the assembled spring, measured in the unloaded condition, shall be parallel to the surface at the spring seat, and square with a tangent to either edge of the main leaf at the spring seat, within ± 1 degree.

5.24 Alignment Clips—Most surface vehicle leaf springs are fitted with clips of some form which serve primarily to prevent sidewise spread and vertical separation of the leaves.

Clips employed for passenger car springs show a great variety in design, but commercial vehicle springs are generally equipped with either bolt-type or clinch-type clips, see HS-J788. Dimensions must be chosen to suit the individual service requirement.

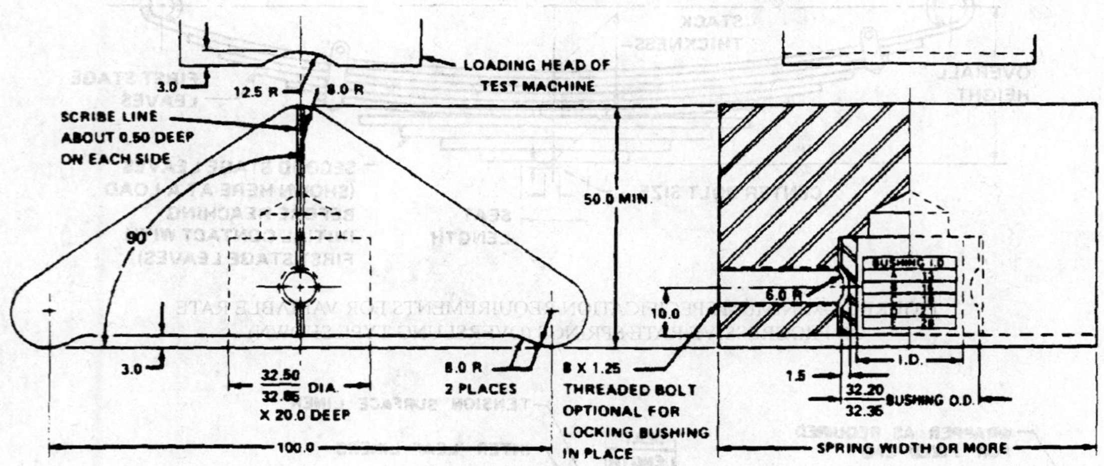

FIGURE 8—SPRING LOADING BLOCK

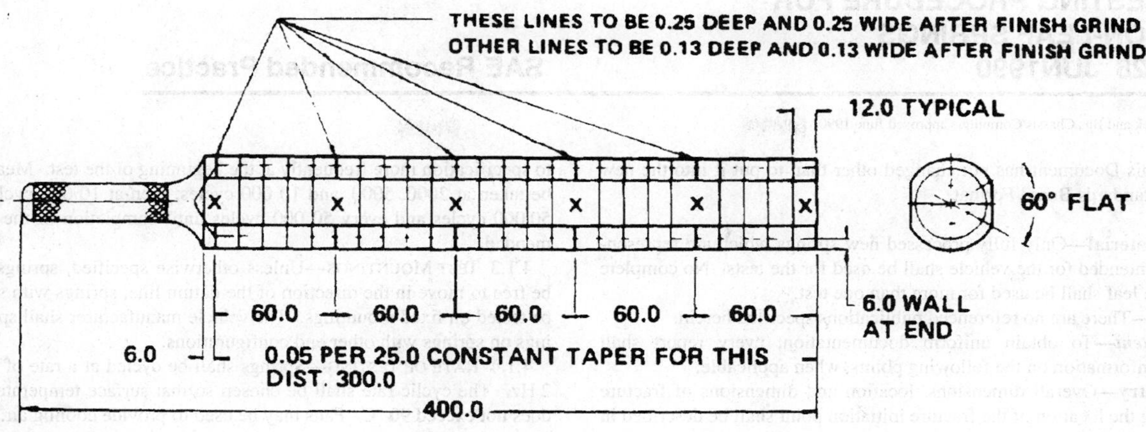

X-STAMP GAGE DIAMETERS AT THESE STATIONS

MATERIAL: STEEL UNS G40270 (SAE 4027) OR EQUIVALENT

PROCESS: CARBURIZED AND HARDENED; CASE DEPTH 0.50 MIN.
SURFACE HARDNESS: HRC 58 MIN.

FIGURE 9—GAGE—LEAF SPRING EYE PLUG

5.25 Center Bolt—The center bolt is required to hold the spring leaves together, and the center bolt head is used as a locating dowel during installation on the vehicle. For underslung springs, the head should be adjacent to the main leaf; for overslung springs, the head should be adjacent to the shortest leaf. The center bolt should not be depended upon to prevent the shifting of leaves due to driving and braking forces.

In most cases, center bolts are highly stressed in the handling of the springs and in service. Therefore, it is necessary to use bolts and nuts of high mechanical properties. See Table 5 for sizes.

TABLE 5—RECOMMENDED CENTER BOLT AND NUT DIMENSIONS (mm)

Nominal Bolt Diameter	Threads Pitch	Threads Minimum Length	Bolt Head Size Diameter	Bolt Head Size Height	Nut Size Style 1 Width Across Flats (Max)	Nut Size Style 1 Width Across Corners (Max)	Nut Size Style 1 Thickness (Max)
8	1.25	25	12.0	6.0	13.0	15.01	6.6
10	1.5	25	15.0	7.0	15.0	17.32	9.0
12	1.75	30	17.0	8.0	18.0	20.78	10.7
16	2	35	20.0	10.0	24.0	27.71	14.5

5.26 Cup Center—Cup centers are often used in heavy-duty springs which may not safely depend on clamps and center bolts to prevent a shifting of the spring on the axle seat due to driving and braking forces.

When the main leaf is assembled adjacent to the axle seat as in underslung springs, the cup is hot forged in the main leaf only (away from the No. 2 leaf). When the shortest leaf is mounted above the axle seat as in overslung springs, all the leaves must be cupped toward the shortest leaf.

This method of cupping locks the main leaf to the axle seat. The horizontal forces which are applied to the main leaf will be resisted by the cup rather than the clamp and the center bolt.

There are several types of cup centers in general use, one of which is shown in Figure 10. The cup dimensions are listed according to center bolt diameter; however, the cup diameter should not exceed one-half the leaf width, and the cup depth should not exceed one-half the leaf thickness.

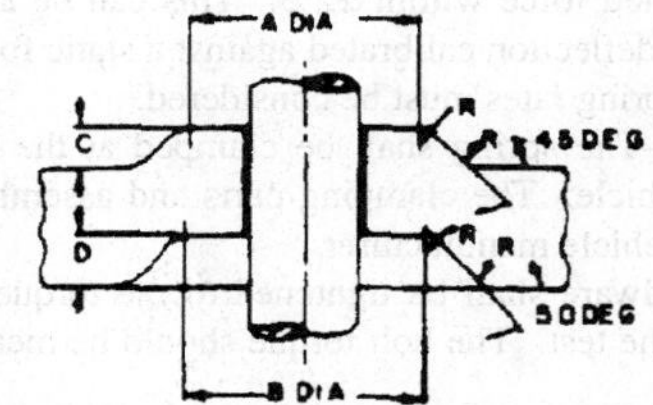

Dimension	Tolerance +0.0	For Use With Centerbolt Diameters 10, 12	16
Diameter A	−0.5	21.3	31.5
Diameter B	−0.5	22.4	33.0
Height C	−0.5	3.6	5.1
Depth D	−0.5	4.6	6.1
Radius R	−0.3	2.5	3.0

FIGURE 10—CUP CENTERS

FATIGUE TESTING PROCEDURE FOR SUSPENSION-LEAF SPRINGS —SAE J1528 JUN1990

SAE Recommended Practice

Report of the SAE Truck and Bus Chassis Committee approved June 1990.

Foreword—This Document has not changed other than to put it into the new SAE Technical Standards Board Format.

1. Scope

1.1 Test Material—Only fully processed new springs which are representative of springs intended for the vehicle shall be used for the tests. No complete spring or separate leaf shall be used for more than one test.

2. References—There are no referenced publications specified herein.

3. Report Content—To obtain uniform documentation, every report shall include detailed information on the following points, when applicable:

3.1 Geometry—Overall dimensions, location and dimensions of fracture sections including the location of the fracture initiation point shall be described in writing or by photographs.

3.2 Material and Manufacturing Process—The type of material, as well as essential steps in the manufacturing which may affect the test results, shall be specified. As examples, type of hardening, shot-peening under stress at given level, etc., can be mentioned.

The hardness shall be checked on critical surfaces, and the hardness distribution through the section shall be measured. Shot peen coverage and the microstructure shall be evaluated.

3.3 Fractography—Fracture surfaces shall be shown on photographs and the type of fracture discussed. The extension of fatigue fracture shall be measured and the crack starting points shall be examined.

3.4 Test Result Presentation—The individual test results may be clearly stated. Even noncritical events like cracks in secondary leaves must be recorded.

The results of the fatigue testing of a group of springs should be subjected to statistical analysis. The Weibull distribution is recommended. Also, it is recommended that minimum fatigue performance requirements be specified in terms of B10 life and population slope.

4. Vertical Loading Methods

4.1 General Directions

4.1.1 EQUIPMENT—The test machine shall be able to maintain the maximum and minimum specified force within ±2%. This can be accomplished by force control or control of deflection calibrated against a static force. In the latter case, dynamic and static spring rates must be considered.

4.1.2 CLAMPING—The spring shall be clamped at the center to simulate its installation in the vehicle. The clamping parts and assembly requirements must be specified by the vehicle manufacturer.

The clamping hardware shall be tightened to the torque values specified and verified throughout the test. The bolt torque should be measured and brought up to specification more frequently at the beginning of the test. Measurements are to be taken at 2000, 5000, and 10 000 cycles; then at 10 000 cycle intervals up to 50 000 cycles and every 50 000 cycles until completion of the tests are recommended.

4.1.3 TEST MOUNTINGS—Unless otherwise specified, springs with eyes shall be free to move in the direction of the datum line; springs with slipper ends shall be tested on fixed mountings. The vehicle manufacturer shall specify the mountings on springs with other end configurations.

4.1.4 RATE OF TESTING—Springs shall be cycled at a rate of between 0.5 and 2 Hz. The cyclic rate shall be chosen so that surface temperature on the spring does not exceed 90 °C. Fans may be used to provide cooling air.

4.2 Test Procedure

4.2.1 STATIC LOAD TEST—The spring shall be loaded from zero up to the prescribed maximum deflection and back to zero. It is acceptable to apply the load in steps.

The force shall be measured at the center clamp. The vertical deflection of the spring center shall also be measured. The relation between the force and the deflection during a full cycle may be plotted in a diagram.

4.2.2 FATIGUE TEST—The spring shall be loaded from 1/2 g (g = design load) to maximum load experienced under actual vehicle conditions, typically 2 g.

For validation, six springs for each design, shall be tested to failure or to the number of cycles specified.

Position limit switches shall be placed so that the test is terminated when the spring deflection has increased a prescribed distance (see 5.1).

In the case of a deflection controlled test, the spring rates shall be measured at uniform intervals during the test on at least one specimen in a test batch.

If the spring rate increased more than 5% during the test, the deflection should be corrected to keep the test peak forces constant. Regarding a corresponding decrease, see 5.1. If it is necessary to correct the deflection during the test as shown by the measurement of the spring rate, this shall be recorded and done in the same way, including the number of cycles, for all springs in the batch.

Measure the load at rated load position at 50 000 cycle intervals to determine load loss due to permanent set.

5. Fatigue Failure Criteria

5.1 Inability of Spring to Sustain Load—Normally, this is said to happen when deflection has increased 5 to 10% above the maximum total deflection at the test start or load loss at 50 000 cycles exceeds 5% of the load at test start.

5.2 Visible Crack in #1 Leaf or Visible Cracks in More Than Two Supporting Leaves.

LEAF SPRINGS FOR MOTOR VEHICLE SUSPENSION—MADE TO CUSTOMARY U.S. UNITS—SAE J510 NOV1992 SAE Standard

Report of the SAE Springs Division approved August 1951 and completely revised by the SAE Leaf Spring Subcommittee of the SAE Spring Committee May 1985. Reaffirmed by the SAE Spring Committee November 1992.

1. Scope

NOTE—For leaf springs made to metric units, see SAE J1123.

This SAE Standard is limited to concise specifications promoting an adequate understanding between spring maker and spring user on all practical requirements in the finished spring. The basic concepts for the spring design and for many of the details have been fully addressed in HS-J788, SAE Information Report, Manual on Design and Application of Leaf Springs, which is available from SAE Headquarters.

2. References

2.1 Applicable Publications—The following publications form a part of this specification to the extent specified herein. The latest issue of SAE publications shall apply.

2.1.1 SAE PUBLICATIONS—Available from SAE, 400 Commonwealth Drive, Warrendale, PA 15096-0001.

SAE J419—Methods of Measuring Decarburization

SAE HS-J788—Manual on Design and Application of Leaf Springs

SAE J1123—Leaf Springs for Motor Vehicle Suspension—Made to Metric Units

3. Bar Sizes and Tolerances—Round edge flat spring steel has been adopted as the SAE standard.

The bars shall be of flat rolled steel having two flat surfaces and two rounded (convex) edges. They are subject to the tolerances shown in Table 1. These cross-section tolerances permit the two flat surfaces to be slightly concave. When that occurs, the radii of the arcs of the two concave surfaces shall be of approximately equal length.

The rounding of the convex edges shall be an arc with a radius of curvature that may vary from 65 to 85% of the thickness of the bar.

Bars shall be substantially straight and free from physical characteristics known as kinks or twists which render them unsatisfactory for spring manufacturing purposes.

Distortions due to a bar being bent about either major axis of section shall be measured with the bar against a flat checking surface so as to make contact with this surface near both bar ends. Gaps between the bar and the checking surface shall not exceed 0.05 in/ft of bar length out of contact with the checking surface when this bar length is greater than 3 ft. Also, a gap between the bar and a straight edge, 3 ft long, applied along any portion of the surface or edge of the bar shall not exceed 0.15 in.

It is recommended that all leaf spring bars which have been cold straightened be identified by the steel mill so that the spring manufacturer can use them selectively.

Leaf spring bars are generally available in the following widths in inches: 1.75, 2.00, 2.25, 2.50, 3.00, 3.50, 4.00, 5.00, and 6.00.

Spring drawings shall specify steel of the following nominal thicknesses, in inches, to which all bars shall be rolled: 0.194, 0.204, 0.214, 0.225, 0.237, 0.249, 0.262, 0.276, 0.291, 0.307, 0.323, 0.341, 0.360, 0.380, 0.401, 0.423, 0.447, 0.473, 0.499, 0.527, 0.558, 0.590, 0.625, 0.662, 0.702, 0.744, 0.788, 0.836, 0.887, 0.941, 0.999, 1.061, 1.127, 1.197, 1.273, 1.354, and 1.440.

4. Surface Decarburization—Surface decarburization may reduce the fatigue durability of the springs; therefore, it is important that surface decarburization be at a minimum.

Hot-rolled steel bars as received from the mills have some decarb, at least of the minimum Type 3 (see SAE J419), where more than 50% of the base carbon content remains at the surface (i.e., some partial but not more than 50% loss of carbon).

If decarb is of Type 2, where 50% or less of the base carbon content remains at the surface (i.e., appreciable partial but not total loss of carbon), the decarb normally does not exceed a depth of 0.010 in for steels of thicknesses 0.194 to 0.499 in, nor a depth of 0.020 in for steels of thicknesses over 0.499 to 1.440 in.

With sections over 1.000 in thickness, some of the hot-rolled steel bars may have decarb of Type 1, in which virtually carbon-free ferrite (i.e., total loss of carbon) exists for a measurable distance below the surface.

The depth of decarb varies from mill to mill, from rolling to rolling, and from bar to bar. The extent to which the depth and type of the decarb can be acceptable will be subject to agreement between the steel producer and the spring manufacturer.

The edges of the bars are somewhat higher in decarb than the flat surfaces; decarb on both the edges and the flat surfaces usually has greater depth with increased bar thickness.

After forging and nonatmospheric controlled heat treating, the spring leaves will have greater decarb. Scaling of the steel in this processing reduces the thickness of the leaf. While some of the surface decarb is removed with the scale, the final depth of decarb is usually greater than it was in the steel bars as received from the mills.

5. Definitions, Dimensions, and Tolerances

5.1 Leaf Spring—A spring of full elliptic, semi-elliptic, or quarter-elliptic shape with one or more leaves. The term multi-leaf has generally applied to springs of constant width and with stepped leaves, each of constant thickness except where leaf ends may be tapered in thickness. More recently, the term has been extended to include an assembly of stacked single leaves, each of which is characterized by tapering either in width or in thickness or by a combination of both. Examples of multi-leaf springs are shown in Figures 1 to 6; Figure 7 shows a single leaf spring.

The leaves of a multi-leaf spring are usually held together with a center bolt and prevented from lateral shifting by alignment clips. Prior to assembly, the leaves are formed (cambered) and heat treated by heating, quenching, and tempering to the required hardness. Quench dies or fixtures are used to maintain the required camber within tolerances.

TABLE 1—CROSS-SECTION TOLERANCE, in

Nominal Width Over	Nominal Width To and Including	Tolerance in Width -0.00	For Thickness	Tolerance in Thickness (1) (±)	Tolerance in Flatness (2) (−)	Max Difference(3) in Thickness
0.00	2.50	+0.030	0.375 or under	0.005	0.005	0.002
			Over 0.375 to 0.875, incl	0.006	0.006	0.002
2.50	4.00	+0.045	0.375 or under	0.006	0.006	0.003
			Over 0.375 to 0.875, incl	0.008	0.008	0.004
			Over 0.875 to 1.500, incl	0.012	0.012	0.006
4.00	5.00	+0.065	0.375 or under	0.007	0.007	0.004
			Over 0.375 to 0.875, incl	0.010	0.010	0.005
			Over 0.875 to 1.500, incl	0.016	0.016	0.008
5.00	6.00	+0.090	Over 0.375 to 0.875, incl	0.012	0.012	0.006
			Over 0.875 to 1.500, incl	0.020	0.020	0.010

1. Thickness measurements shall be taken at the edge of the bar where the flat surfaces intersect the rounded edge.
2. This tolerance represents the maximum amount by which the thickness at the center of the bar may be less than the thickness of the edges. Thickness at the center may never exceed the thickness at the edges.
3. Maximum difference in thickness between the two edges of each bar.

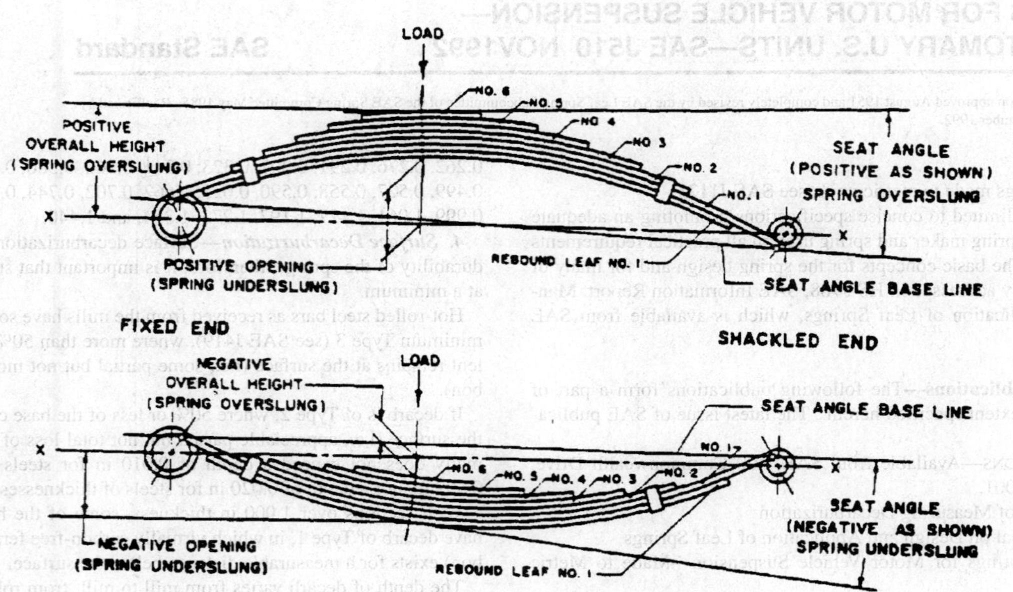

FIGURE 1—MEASUREMENT OF OPENING, OVERALL HEIGHT, AND SEAT ANGLE

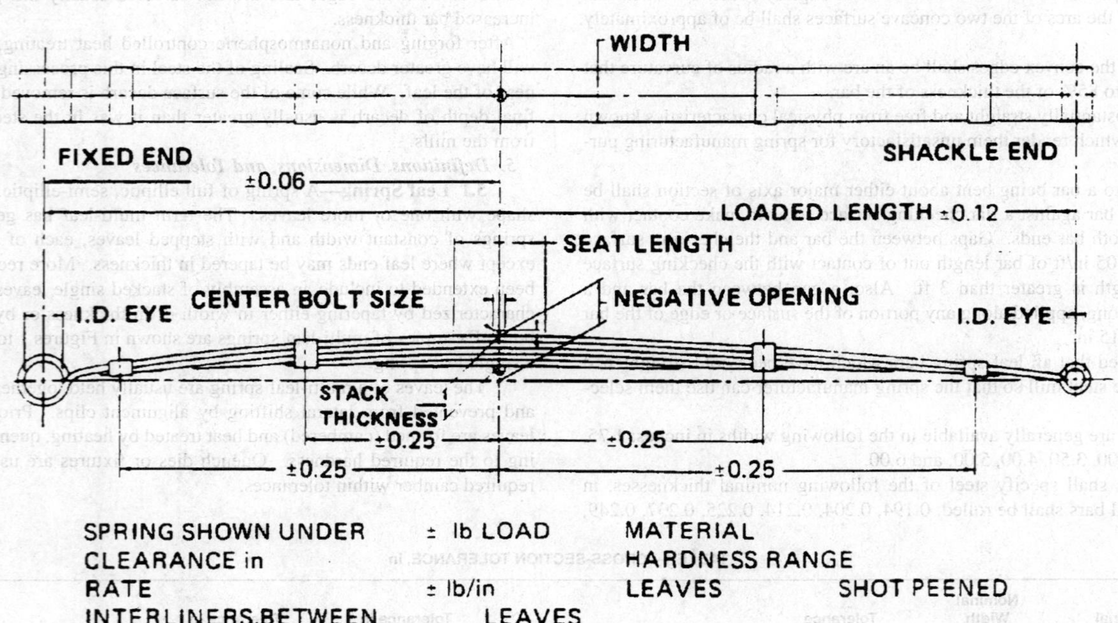

FIGURE 2—MINIMUM SPECIFICATION REQUIREMENTS FOR UNDERSLUNG SPRINGS WITH NEGATIVE OPENING

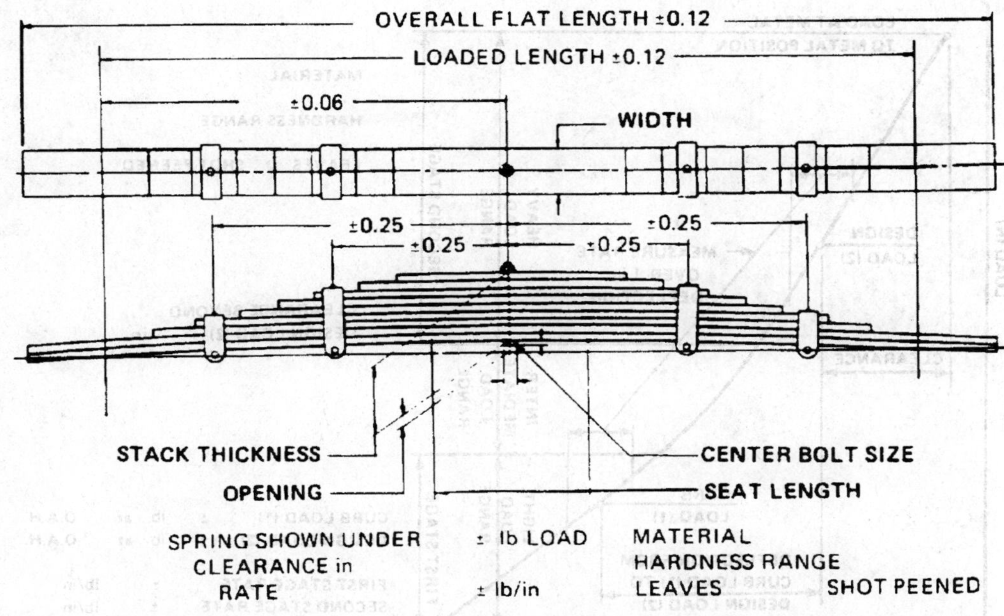

FIGURE 3—MINIMUM SPECIFICATION REQUIREMENTS FOR SPRINGS WITH PLAIN ENDS

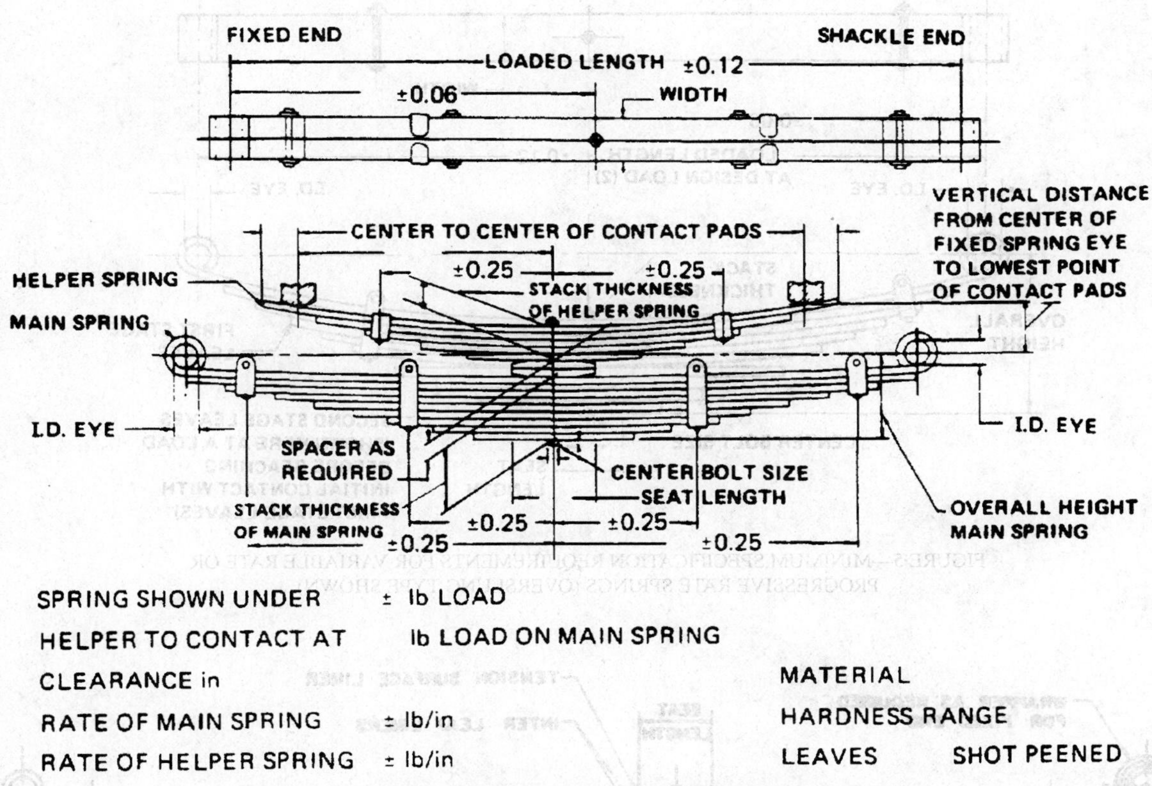

FIGURE 4—MINIMUM SPECIFICATION REQUIREMENTS FOR OVERSLUNG COMMERCIAL VEHICLE SPRINGS

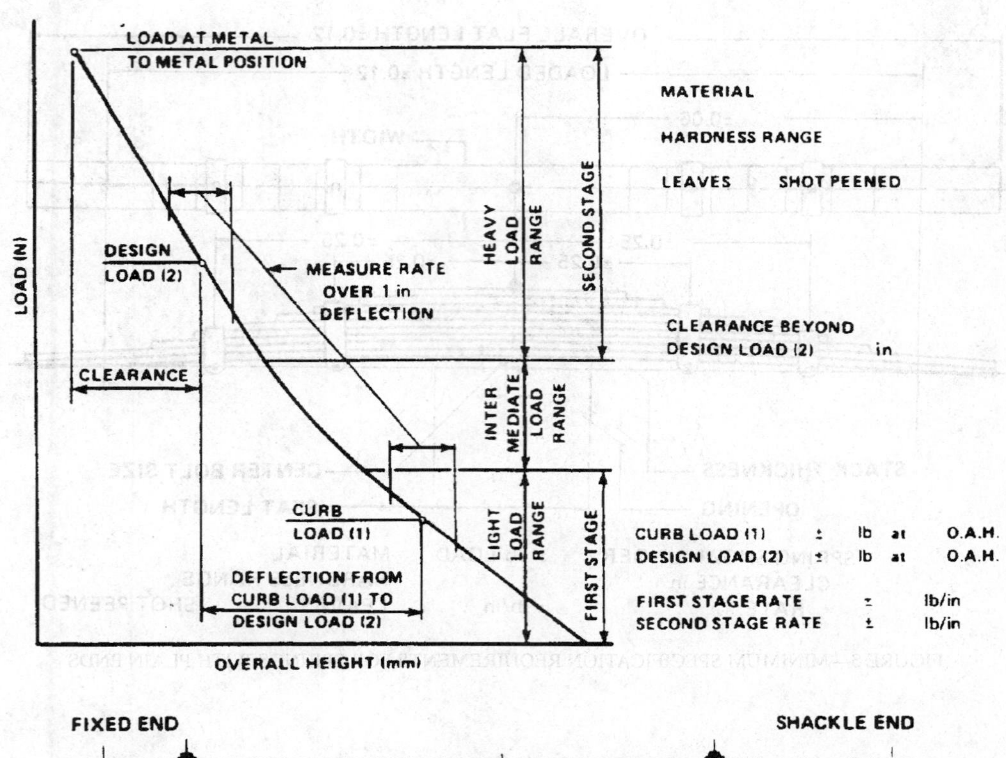

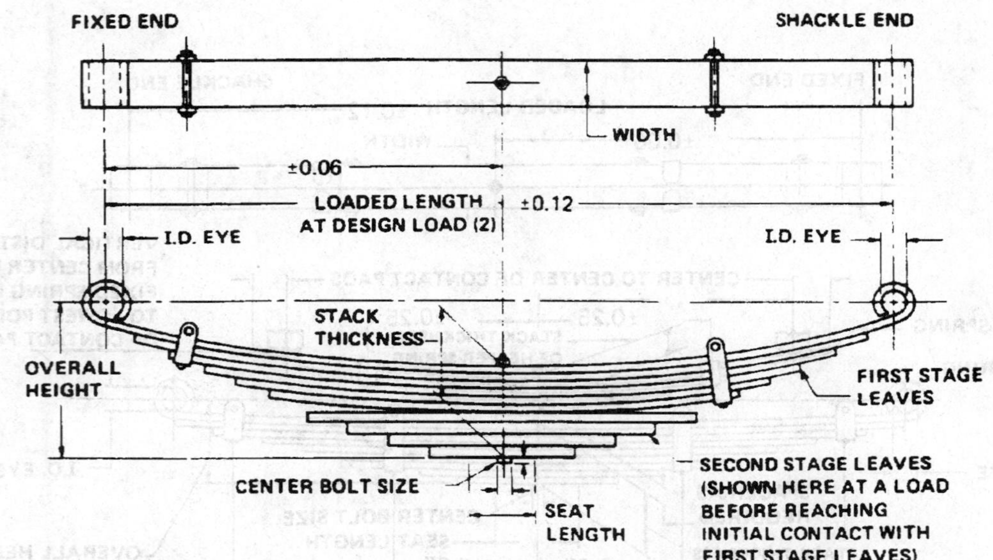

FIGURE 5—MINIMUM SPECIFICATION REQUIREMENTS FOR VARIABLE RATE OR PROGRESSIVE RATE SPRINGS (OVERSLUNG TYPE SHOWN)

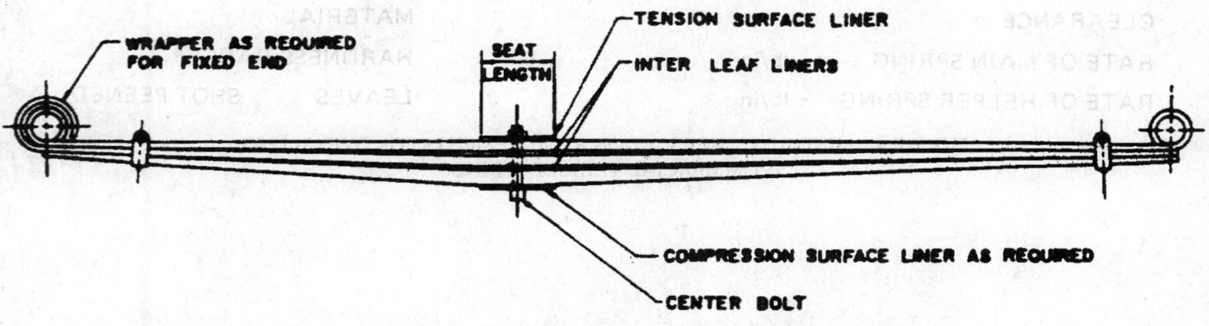

FIGURE 6—STACKED SINGLE LEAF SPRINGS

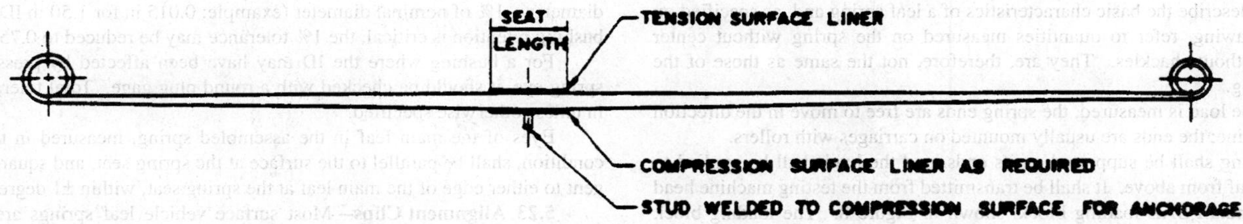

FIGURE 7—SINGLE LEAF SPRINGS

5.2 Datum Line—Reference line used with many of the subsequently defined terms. In Figure 1 (where the springs are shown inverted as in a machine for load and rate checking), it is shown as the line X-X. On springs with eyes, the datum line passes through the centers of the eyes. On other springs it passes through the points where the load is applied near the ends of the spring. These points must be indicated on the drawing. When load and rate are checked, the spring ends shall be free to move in the direction of the datum line.

5.3 Seat Angle Base Line (see Figure 1)—Reference line drawn through the terminal points of the active spring length at each eye, taken along the tension surface of the main leaf. On springs without eyes the seat angle base line is coincident with the datum line.

5.4 Loaded Length—Distance between spring eye centers when the spring is deflected to the specified load position. On springs without eyes, it is the distance between the lines where load is applied under the specified conditions. Tolerance, ± 0.12 in.

5.5 Loaded Fixed End Length—Distance from the center of the fixed end eye to the projection on the datum line of the point where the centerline of the center bolt intersects the spring surface in contact with the spring seat. Tolerance, ± 0.06 in.

5.6 Straight Length—Distance between eye centers when the tension surface of the main leaf at the center bolt centerline is in the plane of the seat angle base line. The distance is measured parallel to the seat angle base line. Tolerance, ± 0.12 in.

5.7 Seat Length—Length of spring that is in actual engagement with the spring seat when installed on a vehicle at design height. It is always greater than the inactive length.

5.8 Inactive Length—Length of spring rendered inactive by the action of the U-bolts or clamping bolts.

5.9 Seat Angle (see Figure 1)—Angle between the tangent to the center of the spring seat and the seat angle base line. When the spring is viewed with the fixed end of the spring to the left, as shown, and the load is applied to the shortest leaf from above, the seat angle may be specified as either positive (counterclockwise) or negative (clockwise), depending upon the angular direction in which the tangent to the center of the spring seat is disposed from the seat angle base line.

Consequently, with the spring in normal vehicle position so that the load is applied from below as shown in Figures 2, 4, 5, 6, 7, and again with the fixed end of the spring to the left of the drawing, the seat angle is defined as positive when that tangent is disposed clockwise; and as negative when the tangent is disposed counterclockwise.

5.10 Finished Width—Width to which the spring leaves are ground or milled to give the edges a flat bearing surface. If the spring ends have a finished width, the required length of the finished edge must also be indicated. The usual tolerances for finished widths are as indicated in Table 2.

TABLE 2—TOLERANCES FOR FINISHED WIDTHS

Leaf Width Over	Leaf Width To and Including	Tolerance from Nominal Width +0.000
0.00	2.00	–0.010
2.00	2.50	–0.015
2.50		–0.020

5.11 Assembled Spring Width—Where more than one leaf constitutes a spring assembly, the overall width tolerance of the assembly within the spring seat length shall be as follows in Table 3:

TABLE 3—WIDTH TOLERANCE OF THE ASSEMBLY

Leaf Width Over	Leaf Width To and Including	Tolerance -0.000
0.00	2.50	+0.100
2.50	4.00	+0.120
4.00	5.00	+0.145
5.00	6.00	+0.175

5.12 Stack Thickness—Aggregate of the nominal thicknesses of all leaves of the spring including any liners and spacer plates which are part of the spring at the seat.

5.13 Leaf Ends—The leaf ends used most generally are: square as sheared; trimmed to a shape; taper rolled; and taper rolled, trimmed or forged to a shape, or both.

5.14 Surface Finish—Condition of the surface of the spring leaves after the steel has been heat treated and prior to coating.

5.14.1 "AS HEAT-TREATED" FINISH—The surface of the spring leaves is in the condition as taken from the heat treating furnace where generally the leaves have a finish of oxide coating.

5.14.2 "SHOT-PEENED" FINISH—The tension surface of the spring leaves has been exposed to the shot peening operation where the oxide coating and scale are removed and a matte luster finish is produced.

5.14.3 GROUND OR POLISHED LEAF ENDS—The bearing areas of leaves are ground or polished to produce a smooth surface for reduced friction. The distance or length to be ground or polished should be specified.

5.15 Protective Coating—Material added to surface of spring leaves or exposed areas of assembled springs. For additional information, see HS-J788.

5.16 Leaf Numbers (see Figure 1)—Leaves are designated by numbers, starting with the main leaf which is No. 1. The adjoining leaf is No. 2 and so on. If rebound leaves are used, the rebound leaf adjoining the main leaf is rebound leaf No. 1, the next one rebound leaf No. 2, and so on. (Rebound leaves are assembled adjacent to the side opposite the load bearing leaves.) Helper springs are considered as separate units.

5.16.1 OPENING AND OVERALL HEIGHT (SEE FIGURE 1)—Distance from the datum line to the point where the center bolt centerline intersects the surface of the spring that is in contact with the spring seat.

If the surface in contact with the seat is on the main leaf or a rebound leaf (as on underslung springs), this distance is called opening.

If the surface in contact with the seat is on the shortest leaf (as on overslung springs), this distance is called overall height.

Opening and overall height may be positive or negative (see Figure 1). They are specified dimensions not subject to a tolerance. (see 5.18)See 5.18 on Load.

5.17 Clearance—Difference in opening or overall height between the design load position and the extreme position (of maximum stress) to which the spring can be deflected on the vehicle.

5.18 Load—The force exerted by the spring at the specified opening or overall height. The total tolerance on load at the specified overall height or opening is usually expressed as a load range (lb) which is equivalent to a deflection (in) at the nominal rate (lb/in). This deflection may be as small as 0.25 in for a passenger car spring and as large as 0.50 in for a heavy truck spring.

5.19 Rate—The change of load per unit of spring deflection (lb/in). For leaf springs it is determined as half of the difference between the loads measured 1 in above and 1 in below the specified load position, unless otherwise specified Figure 5. The tolerance is usually held within ± 5% on low rate springs and within ±7% on high rate springs.

5.20 Load and Rate Checking—Load and rate are the terms usually employed to describe the basic characteristics of a leaf spring and, as specified on the spring drawing, refer to quantities measured on the spring without center clamp and without shackles. They are, therefore, not the same as those of the installed spring.

When the load is measured, the spring ends are free to move in the direction of the datum line; the ends are usually mounted on carriages with rollers.

The spring shall be supported on its ends, and the load shall be applied to the shortest leaf from above. It shall be transmitted from the testing machine head through a standard SAE loading block, shown in Figure 8. The loading block shall be centered over the center bolt with the legs of the V resting on the spring. It is understood that the load specified on the spring drawing does not include either the weight of the spring or the weight of the loading block.

Just before the spring is checked for load or rate, it shall undergo a preloading operation. During the initial preloading by the spring maker, the spring shall be deflected at least to the position defined under 5.17 on Clearance. During any subsequent preloading, the spring shall be deflected only to and not beyond this clearance position in order to remove any temporary recovery from the set incurred during the initial preloading. After the spring has been preloaded, it shall be released to the free position before the load is applied for load and rate checking. For additional information on preloading, see HS-J788.

Load and rate shall be measured in terms of the forces exerted by the spring during compression of the spring (compression loads) and not during release of the spring (release loads). The compression load in any position shall be read only after the spring has been thoroughly rapped in that position with a plastic or soft metal hammer.

5.21 Specification Requirements—Minimum specification requirements are given in Figures 2 to 5.

5.22 Spring Eyes and Bushings—For some types of currently used spring eyes, spring ends, bushings, and shackle constructions, see HS-J788.

For eyes with specified inside diameter, the size and roundness of the eye should be checked by means of a round plug gage from which two opposite segments of 60 degrees have been removed. The gage shall have a taper on diameter per unit of length of 0.002:1 (see Figure 9). The gage shall be inserted into the eye three times from each side at angular positions differing by about 60 degrees. The eye is acceptable only if the gage reading on the side of the eye from which the gage is inserted is within the specified diametral limits at each of the six checks.

Also, the eye should be checked with a round plug, GO/NO GO gage, to determine if the eye is cone shaped or tapered. The GO diameter must pass completely through the eye and the NO GO diameter must not enter the eye from either side.

Total tolerance—For 1 in or less diameter—0.010 in; for larger than 1 in diameter—1% of nominal diameter (example: 0.015 in for 1.50 in ID eye); where bushing retention is critical, the 1% tolerance may be reduced to 0.75%.

For a bushing where the ID may have been affected by pressing into the spring eye, it should be checked with a round plug gage. Total tolerance—0.005 in unless otherwise specified.

Eyes of the main leaf in the assembled spring, measured in the unloaded condition, shall be parallel to the surface at the spring seat, and square with a tangent to either edge of the main leaf at the spring seat, within ±1 degree.

5.23 Alignment Clips—Most surface vehicle leaf springs are fitted with clips of some form which serve primarily to prevent sideways spread and vertical separation of the leaves.

Clips employed for passenger car springs show a great variety in design, but commercial vehicle springs are generally equipped with either bolt-type or clinch-type clips. (See HS-J788.) Dimensions must be chosen to suit the individual service requirement.

5.24 Center Bolt—The center bolt is required to hold the spring leaves together, and the center bolt head is used as a locating dowel during installation on the vehicle. For underslung springs, the head should be adjacent to the main leaf; for overslung springs, the head should be adjacent to the shortest leaf. The center bolt should not be depended upon to prevent the shifting of leaves due to driving and braking forces.

In most cases, center bolts are highly stressed in the handling of the springs and in service. Therefore, it is necessary to use bolts and nuts of high mechanical properties. (See Table 4 for sizes.)

TABLE 4—RECOMMENDED CENTER BOLT AND NUT DIMENSIONS, in

Bolt Diameter	Threads [1] Per Inch	Threads[1] Minimum Length	Head Size Nominal Diameter	Head Size Nominal Height	Nut Size Nominal Width Across Flats	Nut Size Nominal Thickness
5/16	24	1.00	1/2	1/4	1/2	17/64
3/8	24	1.00	9/16	5/16	9/16	21/64
7/16	20	1.25	5/8	3/8	11/16	3/8
1/2	20	1.25	3/4	7/16	3/4	7/16
5/8	18	1.50	7/8	9/16	15/16	35/64
3/4	16	1.75	1	5/8	1-1/8	41/64
7/8	14	2.00	1-1/8	11/16	1-5/16	3/4
1	12	2.25	1-5/16	25/32	1-1/2	55/64

1. Threads are Unified Standard Fine, Classes 2A and 2B.

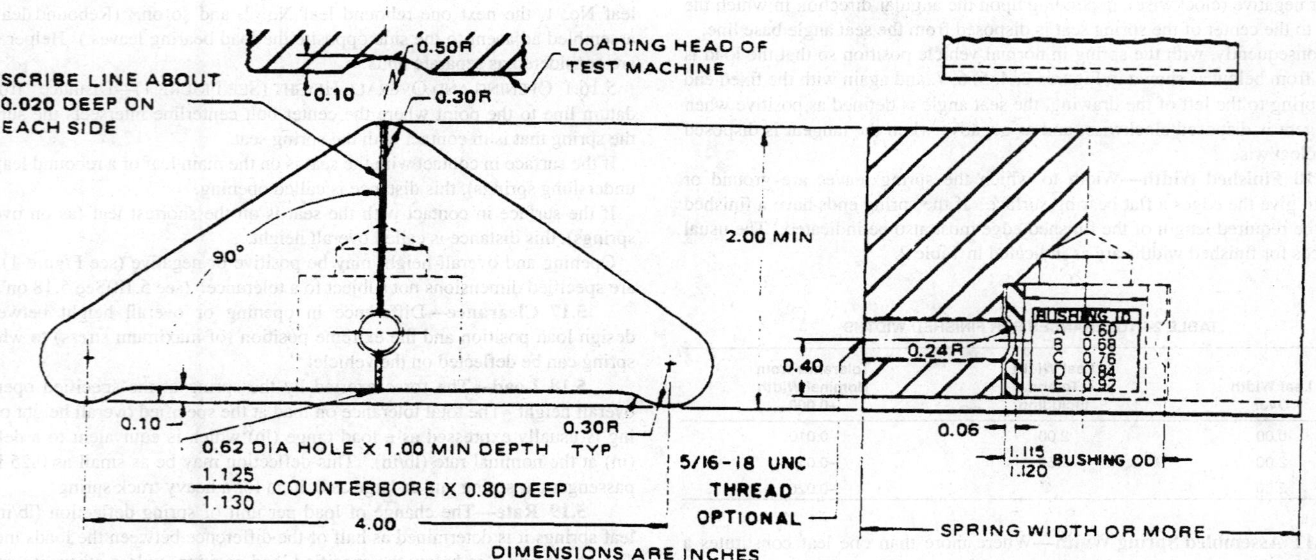

FIGURE 8—SPRING LOADING BLOCK

5.25 Cup Center—Cup centers are often used in heavy-duty springs which may not safely depend on clamps and center bolts to prevent a shifting of the spring on the axle seat due to driving and braking forces.

When the main leaf is assembled adjacent to the axle seat as in underslung springs, the cup is hot forged in the main leaf only (away from the No. 2 leaf); when the shortest leaf is mounted above the axle seat as in overslung springs, all the leaves must be cupped toward the shortest leaf.

This method of cupping locks the main leaf to the axle seat. The horizontal forces which are applied to the main leaf will be resisted by the cup rather than the clamp and the center bolt.

There are several types of cup centers in general use, one of which is shown in Figure 10. The cup dimensions are listed according to center bolt diameter; however, the cup diameter should not exceed one-half the leaf width, and the cup depth should not exceed one-half the leaf thickness.

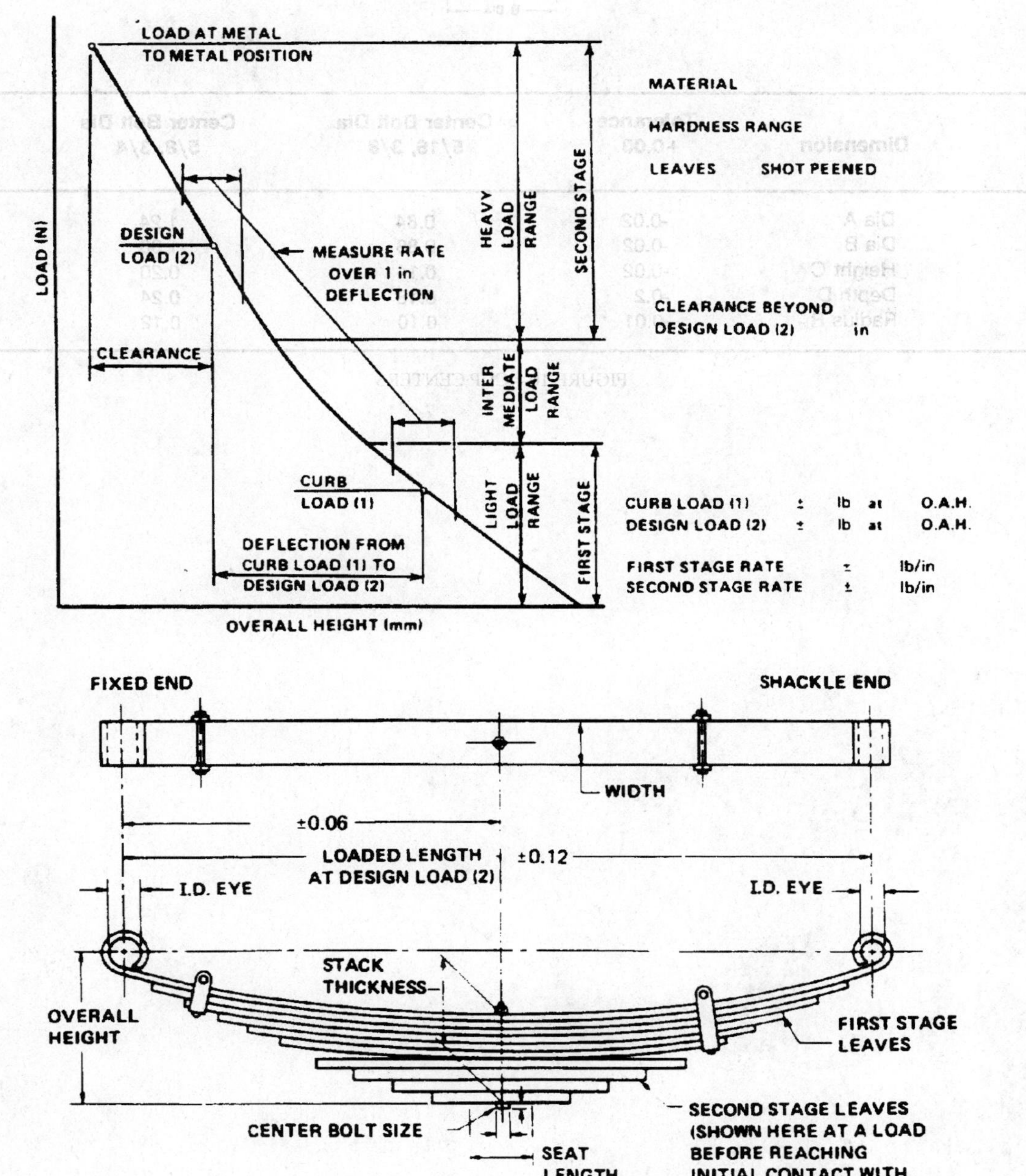

FIGURE 9—GAGE-LEAF SPRING EYE PLUG

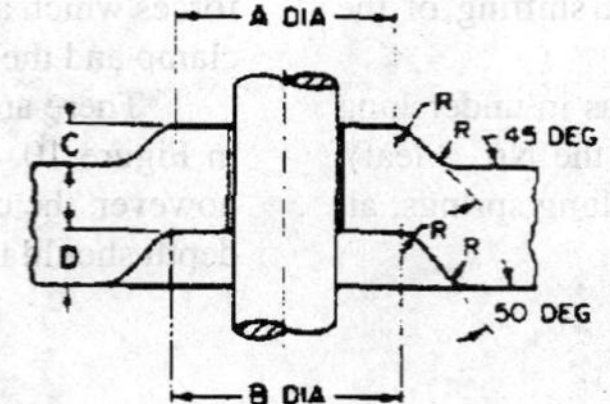

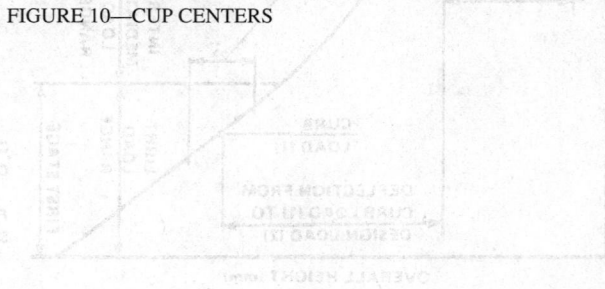

Dimension	Tolerance +0.00	Center Bolt Dia 5/16, 3/8	Center Bolt Dia 5/8, 3/4
Dia A	-0.02	0.84	1.24
Dia B	-0.02	0.88	1.30
Height C	-0.02	0.14	0.20
Depth D	-0.2	0.18	0.24
Radius R	-0.01	0.10	0.12

FIGURE 10—CUP CENTERS

PNEUMATIC SPRING TERMINOLOGY —SAE J511 JUN1989

SAE Information Report

Report of the SAE Spring Committee approved March 1960, last revised October 1970, and reaffirmed by the SAE Pneumatic Spring Terminology Committee June 1989.

Foreword—This Document has not been changed other than to put it into the new SAE Technical Standards Board Format.

*1. **Scope***—This pneumatic spring terminology has been developed to assist engineers and designers in the preparation of specifications and descriptive material relating to pneumatic springs and their components. It does not include gas supply or control systems.

*2. **References***—There are no referenced publications specified herein.

*3. **Pneumatic Spring***—A spring which utilizes the elasticity of a confined gas as the energy medium.

*4. **General Terms***

4.1 Flexible Member—The flexible portion of the pneumatic spring.

4.1.1 BEAD—That portion of the flexible member adjacent to any attachment part which provides an anchor and a gas seal.

NOTE—The bead can be classified as either mechaniclly fastened, which produces a seal through a positive clamping medium, or self-sealing, which produces a seal through gas pressure and/or bead displacement.

4.1.2 REINFORCEMENT—A structure of cord built into the flexible member to control its shape and strengthen its wall structure against internal gas pressure.

4.1.2.1 Cord Angle—The acute angle between a plane through the axial centerline of the flexible member and the centerline of any cord. This angle can pertain to the as-molded shape of the flexible member and will vary according to position of measurement and cross-sectional shape. It also can pertain to inflated shape and will vary according to position of measurement, cross-sectional shape, and inflation pressure.

NOTE—The cord angle is a determining factor of the inflated shape of the flexible member, and may affect the load-deflection characteristics of the assembly. Since it does not totally govern the load-deflection characteristics, cord angle is not usually specified.

4.1.3 COVER—The external layer of elastic substance which protects the reinforcement against abrasion, weathering, or other undesirable effects.

4.1.4 LINER—The internal layer of elastic substance which affords resistance to gas permeability and protects the reinforcement against aging or the effects of a harmful environment.

4.2 Piston (Internal Support)—The portion of the pneumatic spring which supports the smaller diameter of the flexible member and controls the inward movement of the flexible member during the working stroke, thereby affecting the shape of the load-deflection curve.

4.3 External Support—(See Figure 1, A, B, C, D.) A component of some pneumatic springs which controls the outside configuration of the flexible member, thereby affecting the shape of the load-deflection curve. The external support may be either fixed (A, B) or floating (C) in relation to one of the beads.

NOTE—Some pneumatic springs do not employ an external support, but rely on the self-restraining construction of the flexible member (D) to perform the functions of the external support.

*5. **Types Of Pneumatic Springs***

5.1 Piston Type—This type uses a piston which is attached to the inner bead of a reversible flexible member. See Figure 1.

5.1.1 REVERSIBLE DIAPHRAGM—In this type, the piston bead usually passes through the opposite bead of the flexible member. See Figure 1, A and B.

5.1.2 REVERSIBLE SLEEVE—In this type, the piston bead travels within the flexible member and does not pass through the opposite bead. See Figure 1, C and D.

5.2 Bellows Type—This type utilizes a nonreversible flexible member and relies upon its self-restraining characteristics to affect the load-deflection curve. See Figure 2.

NOTE—The flexible member (round or oblong in section) may consist of one or more convolutions. A girdle ring is usually used between the convolutions of the round section multiconvolution bellows type pneumatic spring.

5.3 Piston and Cylinder Type—This type uses a piston and cylinder, but does not require a flexible member. A gas-tight, sliding seal is provided between the piston and cylinder.

5.4 Bladder Type—This type utilizes no integral reinforcement. It relies on being contained with a restrictive structure, such as a coil spring, for its support.

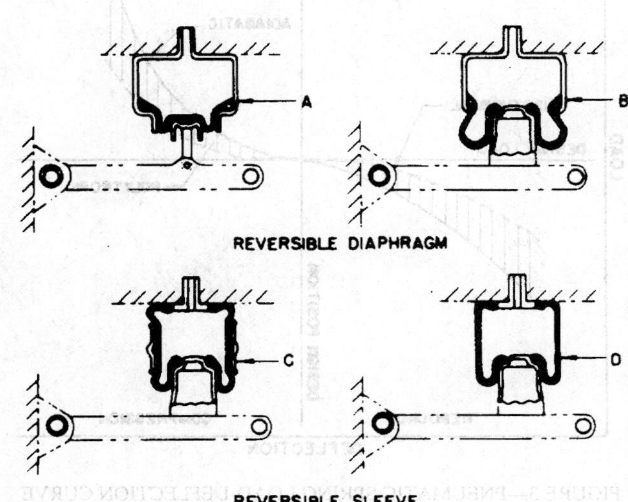

FIGURE 1—PISTON TYPE PNEUMATIC SPRINGS

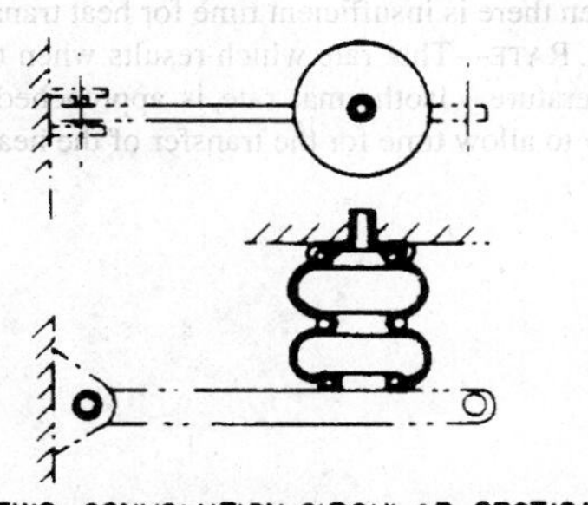

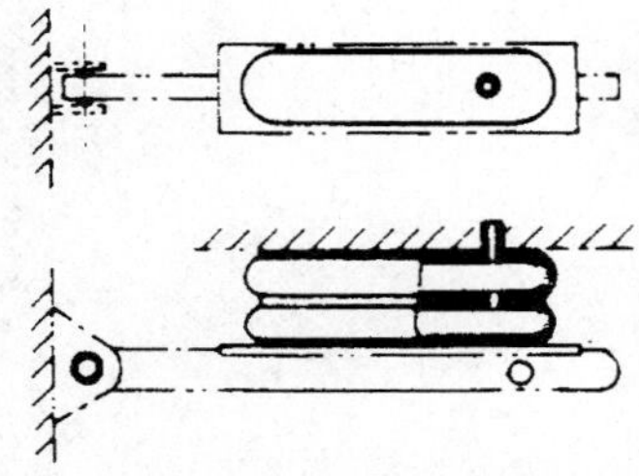

FIGURE 2—BELLOWS TYPE PNEUMATIC SPRINGS

5.5 Hydropneumatic Type—This type contains both liquid and gas. Spring characteristics are provided by the confined gas, while damping may be provided by forcing the liquid through a restriction.

*6. **Pneumatic Spring Characteristics***

6.1 Spring Rate—The change in load per unit of deflection.

NOTE—Figure 3 illustrates a typical load-deflection curve of a pneumatic spring which has a variable effective area versus spring deflection. (Spring supports and cord construction control the degree of variation of the effective area.) With such a pneumatic spring, the rate varies throughout the spring travel. Pneumatic spring rate also varies with the gas compression process, that is, adiabatic, isothermal, or polytropic. However, it is usually specified as the adiabatic rate at the design position.

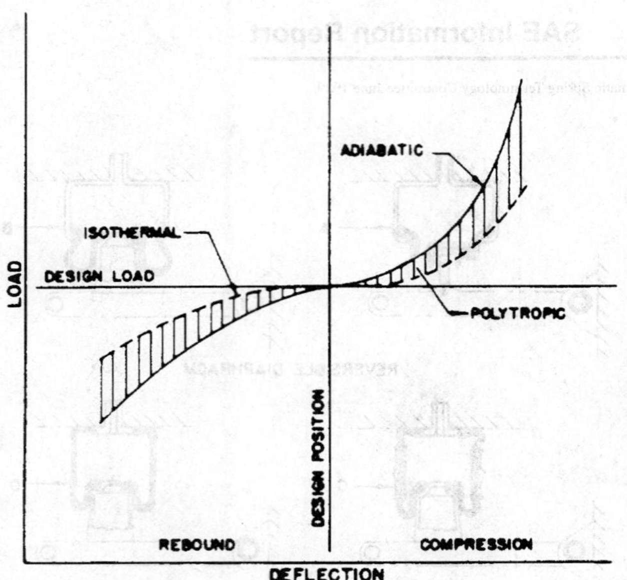

FIGURE 3—PNEUMATIC SPRING LOAD-DEFLECTION CURVE

6.1.1 Adiabatic Rate—That rate which results when there is no heat transfer to or from the gas during spring deflection. It is usually approached during rapid spring deflection when there is insufficient time for heat transfer.

6.1.2 Isothermal Rate—That rate which results when the spring deflects at a constant gas temperature. Isothermal rate is approached when the spring is deflected very slowly to allow time for the transfer of the heat.

6.1.3 Polytropic Rate—That rate which results when there is limited heat transfer to or from the gas during spring deflection. Polytropic rate results during spring deflections which produce neither adiabatic nor isothermal rate.

6.2 Working Volume—The confined gas volume of the pneumatic spring. It is usually specified at design position.

6.3 Design Position—The selected position of the pneumatic spring which satisfies the vehicle requirements. It is usually specified by a dimension between reference points on the fixed and movable parts of the pneumatic spring.

6.4 Total Spring Travel—The distance between the extremes of the spring position measured at the spring axis. It is designated as the total of the compression and rebound deflections from the design position.

6.5 Design Load—The pneumatic spring load at design position.

6.6 Design Pressure—The internal gas pressure required to support the design load at the design position.

6.6.1 Pressure Limits—The minimum and maximum permissible pressures at the design position which provide satisfactory pneumatic spring operation.

6.7 Effective Area—A nominal area found by dividing the load of the pneumatic spring by its gas pressure at any given spring position.

7. Color Coding To Identify Pneumatic Springs—Pneumatic springs may be color coded for specific properties and operational environments by placing permanent color markings at least 0.25 inch in diameter on a visible section of the flexible member. The recommended guide for normal capabilities is shown in Table 1.

TABLE 1—Identification Code

Color	Usage Characteristic	General Temperature Range, F
Yellow	Oil resistant	–20 to +150
Red	High temperature	–20 to +180
Green	Low temperature	–65 to +150
No color	General service	–20 to +150

These color codes may be used in combination. Other temperature ranges and usage characteristics are available with special materials.

(R) HELICAL COMPRESSION AND EXTENSION SPRING TERMINOLOGY—SAE J1121 JUL1988

SAE Recommended Practice

Report of the SAE Spring Committee approved November 1975 and completely revised by the SAE Coil Spring Subcommittee of the SAE Spring Committee July 1988.

Foreword—This document has *also been changed* to comply with the new SAE Technical Standards Board format.

1. Scope—The following recommended practice has been developed to assist engineers and designers in the preparation of specifications for the major types of helical compression and extension springs. It is restricted to a concise presentation of items which will promote an adequate understanding between spring manufacturer and spring user of the major practical requirements in the finished spring. Closer tolerances are obtainable where greater accuracy is required and the increased cost is justified.

For the basic concepts underlying the spring design and for many of the details, see the SAE Information Report MANUAL ON DESIGN AND APPLICATION OF HELICAL AND SPIRAL SPRINGS, SAE HS J795, which is available from SAE Headquarters in Warrendale, PA 15096. A uniform method for specifying design information is shown in the TYPICAL DESIGN CHECK LISTS FOR HELICAL SPRINGS, SAE J1122.

Two types of helical springs are considered:

a. Hot coiled compression springs for general automotive use as well as for motor vehicle suspensions.

b. Cold wound compression and extension springs for general automotive use.

This recommended practice uses SI (metric) units in accordance with the provisions of SAE J916 JUN82.

2. References

2.1 Applicable Publications—The following publications form a part of the specification to the extent specified herein. Unless otherwise indicated the latest revision of SAE publications shall apply.

2.1.1 SAE PUBLICATIONS—AVAILABLE FROM SAE, 400 COMMONWEALTH DRIVE, WARRENDALE, PA 15096-0001.

SAE HS 84—Manual on Shot Peening
SAE J113—Hard-Drawn Mechnical Spring Wire and Springs
SAE J132—Oil-Tempered Chromium-Vanadium Valve Spring Quality Wire and Springs
SAE J157—Oil-Tempered Chromium—Silicon Alloy Steel Wire and Springs
SAE J172—Hard Drawn Carbon Steel Valve Spring Quality Wire and Springs
SAE J178—Music Steel Spring Wire and Springs
SAE J217—Stainless Steel 17-7 PH Spring Wire and Springs
SAE J230—Stainless Steel, SAE 30302, Spring Wire and Springs
SAE J271—Special Quality High-Tensile, Hard-Drawn Mechnical Spring Wire and Springs
SAE J316—Oil-Tempered Carbon-Steel Spring Wire and Springs
SAE J351—Oil-Tempered Carbon-Steel Valve Spring Quality Wire and Springs
SAE J461—Wrought and Cast Copper Alloys
SAE HS J795—SAE Manual on Design and Application of Helical and Spiral Springs
SAE J808—Manual on Shot Peening
SAE J916—Rules for SAE Use of SAE (Metric) Units
SAE J1122—Helical Springs: Specification Check Lists

3. Hot Coiled Springs

3.1 Materials and Heat Treatment—Round spring steel bars are available in carbon and alloy analyses. The bars are generally used in the "as rolled" condition (either commercial hot rolled or precision hot rolled), but they may be centerless ground before coiling.

The heat treatment necessary to develop the required physical properties of the material may be accomplished by direct quench immediately after coiling, or by allowing the coiled spring to cool to a temperature below the critical, then reheating to the required temperature and quenching; the quench is followed by tempering to produce the specified hardness.

Table 1 lists available materials. Their hardenability limitations dictate maximum bar size. For tensile and torsional properties, see MANUAL, SAE HS J795, Chapter 2, Table 2.21.

3.2 Shot Peening—Shot peening is used to increase the fatigue life of springs. It consists of subjecting the spring to a stream of metallic shot moving at high velocity. The peening action of the shot reduces the effect of surface defects and sets up beneficial stresses in a thin surface layer. It also results in cold working this layer. To be effective, the peening must reach the area of highest stress which for helical compression springs is the inside diameter of the coil.

TABLE 1—MATERIALS FOR HOT COILED COMPRESSION SPRINGS

Materials	Specification	Max. Bar[(1)] Dia., mm
Carbon Steels	SAE 1085	10
	SAE 1095	10
Carbon Boron Steel	SAE 15B62H	25
Alloy Steels	SAE 5150 H	10
	SAE 5160 H	20
	SAE 9260 H	10
	SAE 51B60H	30
	SAE 4161 H	60
	SAE 6150 H	10

1. Based on a through hardened bar of 444 HB typical hardness ranges are 444 - 495 HB and 461 - 514 HB.

The fatigue life of hot coiled springs is greatly impaired when the bar surface is afflicted by such flaws as impurities, cracks, seams, or decarburization, but it can be increased by the peening operation in the order of 4 to 1. Even the much better fatigue life attainable in hot-coiled springs with nearly perfect bar surface will be improved by peening in the order of more than 2 to 1. For further details see MANUAL, SAE HS J795, Chapters 1 and 4, also SHOT PEENING MANUAL, SAE HS 84 J808.

3.3 Presetting—Presetting (also called scragging, cold setting, or bulldozing) is an operation during the manufacturing process in which the spring is compressed beyond the yield point of the heat treated material. In preparation for this, the spring is coiled to a free length in excess of the designated free length. The yielding in the surface layers of the bar which occurs during presetting produces beneficial residual stresses, thus increasing the elastic limit and thereby reducing the chances of settling in subsequent service. The yielding causes the spring to take a permanent set, thus bringing it down to the designated free length. See also Preset Length, 3.6.3.

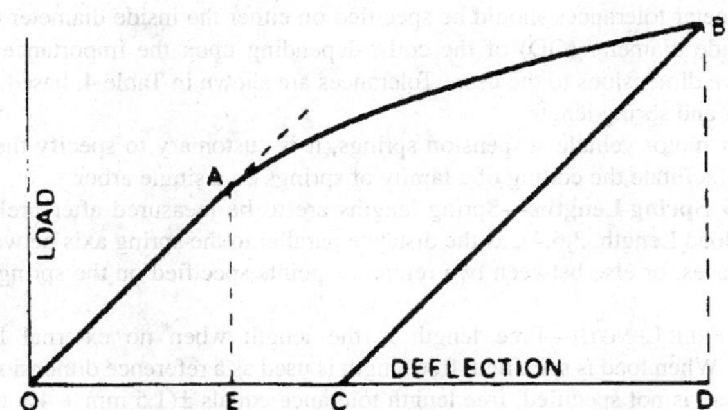

FIGURE 1—TYPICAL LOAD-DEFLECTION DIAGRAM OF HELICAL SPRING DURING PRESETTING

3.3.1 WARM SETTING—In order to reduce the "sag" of "settling" of helical suspension springs which occurs when they are subjected to vehicle loading over time, it has become common practice to warm set the spring at an elevated temperature (usually about 200 °C depending on the particular spring design). One theory holds that the major benefit of this operation results from an increase in the amount of strain hardening that occurs when the spring is stressed past the proportional limit (point "A" in Figure 1). Increasing the temperature lowers the proportional limit to some stress lower than point "A", and therefore if the spring is still stressed to point "B", the amount of strain hardening that occurs is greater. This increase in strain hardening will reduce the dynamic or static settling (load loss) that occurs over the useful life of the spring.

A second theory is that a more effective beneficial residual stress pattern is set up over the bar cross section, when a spring is warm set at elevated temperature.

It should be noted that a final (cold) presetting operation is still necessary.

In general, warm setting will decrease the load loss by more than 50%, depending on the working stress level.

3.4 Bar Diameter and Length—Round bars are hot rolled to any desired diameter between 9 and 100 mm. Table 2 shows the cross section tolerances for commercial hot rolled bars. Bars may be precision hot rolled with 50% of the tolerances in Table 2, or they may be centerless ground with 25% of the tolerances in Table 2.

Bars are commonly purchased in the exact length required to produce one spring. Tolerances for bar lengths are shown in Table 3.

TABLE 2—CROSS SECTION TOLERANCES FOR HOT ROLLED CARBON AND ALLOY STEEL ROUND BARS

Specified Diameter, mm Over	Specified Diameter, mm Thru	Tolerance, Plus and Minus, mm	Out of Round, mm
—	10	0.15	0.22
10	15	0.18	0.27
15	20	0.20	0.30
20	25	0.23	0.34
25	30	0.25	0.38
30	35	0.30	0.45
35	40	0.35	0.52
40	60	0.40	0.60
60	80	0.60	0.90
80	100	0.80	1.20

TABLE 3—LENGTH TOLERANCES FOR HOT ROLLED CARBON AND ALLOY ROUND STEEL BARS

Specified Diameter, mm Over	Specified Diameter, mm Thru	Length Tolerance, Plus Only, mm For Lengths, mm Over Thru	Length Tolerance, Plus Only, mm For Lengths, mm 1500 3000	Length Tolerance, Plus Only, mm For Lengths, mm 3000 —
—	25	12	20	
25	50	16	25	
50	100	25	40	

3.5 Coil Diameter—The coil diameter can be expressed in terms of the mean coil diameter (D) which is used in the rate and stress formulae. However, coil diameter tolerances should be specified on either the inside diameter (ID) or the outside diameter (OD) of the coils, depending upon the importance of the respective dimensions to the user. Tolerances are shown in Table 4, based on coil diameter and spring length.

For motor vehicle suspension springs, it is customary to specify the ID in order to facilitate the coiling of a family of springs on a single arbor.

3.6 Spring Lengths—Spring lengths are to be measured after preloading (see Preload Length, 3.6.4), as the distance parallel to the spring axis between the end surfaces, or else between two reference points specified on the spring drawing.

3.6.1 FREE LENGTH—Free length is the length when no external load is applied. When load is specified, free length is used as a reference dimension only. When load is not specified, free length tolerance equals ±(1.5 mm + 4% of free-to-solid deflection).

3.6.2 SOLID LENGTH (SEE ALSO NUMBER OF COILS, 3.7)—Solid length is the length when the spring is compressed with an applied load sufficient to bring all coils in contact; for practical purposes, this applied load is taken to equal approximately 150% of the load beyond which no appreciable deflection takes place.

3.6.3 PRESET LENGTH—In the presetting operation (see Presetting, 3.3), the spring is usually compressed solid. However, if the stress at solid length is so high that the spring would be excessively distorted, the presetting operation may only be carried to a specified preset length. If more than one preset compression is desired, this must be specified on the drawing. See Also MANUAL, SAE HS J795, Chapters 1 and 4.

3.6.4 PRELOAD LENGTH—Preloading is the operation of deflecting the spring to the preload length in order to remove temporary recovery of free length before the spring is checked for load and rate.

If the spring was preset during the manufacturing process to the solid length, the preloading may also be carried to the solid length, but it may be restricted to a preload length slightly greater than the solid length, provided the maximum deflection during subsequent service will not go below the preload length.

If the spring was preset to a specified preset length greater than the solid length, the preloading should be restricted to a preload length greater than the preset length.

However, the preload length must not exceed the minimum spring length possible in the mechanism for which the spring is designed. In suspensions, this is called the "length at metal-to-metal position." The metal-to-metal contact will occur in the suspension mechanism when rubber bumpers are disregarded. The spring deflection from the specified loaded length to the metal-to-metal position is called "clearance."

3.6.5 LOADED LENGTH—Loaded length is the length while the load is being measured; it is a fixed dimension, with the tolerance applied to the load.

3.7 Number of Coils—Total number of coils (N_t) are counted tip to tip, active number of coils (N) are specified as the number of working coils at free length. With increasing load, N may progressively decrease due to the "bottoming out" effect. If no appreciable bottoming out occurs, the relationships between N and N_t are as shown in Table 5 which also gives the formulae for nominal solid length.

Since nominal solid length may be exceeded somewhat by actual solid length due to manufacturing variations, a frequent practice is to specify nominal solid length together with a maximum solid length, as shown in Table 6.

3.8 Spring Ends—Four types of ends are used (Figure 2):

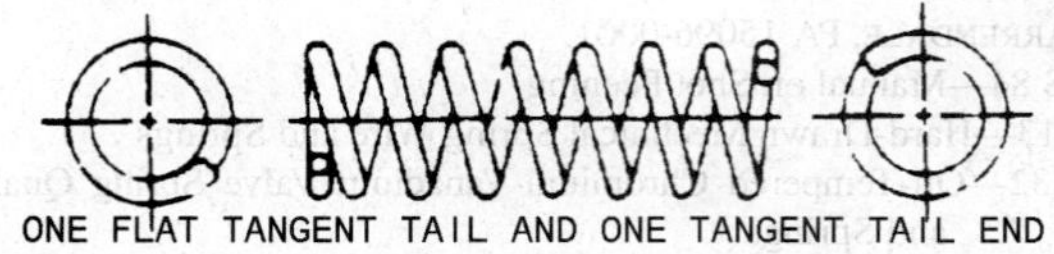

ONE FLAT TANGENT TAIL AND ONE TANGENT TAIL END

FIGURE 2—TYPICAL ENDS FOR HOT COILED COMPRESSION SPRINGS

1. A flat end formed from a tapered bar end. The bar end is usually tapered for a length equal to 2/3 coil and to a tip thickness of approximately 1/3 of the bar diameter. When the spring is coiled, the tip shall be in approximate contact with the adjacent coil and shall not protrude beyond the outside diameter by more than 20% of the bar diameter.

   When stipulated, the bearing surface of the spring end shall be ground perpendicular to the axis of the spring helix in order to produce a firm bearing. The actual ground bearing surface shall not be shorter than two-thirds of the mean coil circumference, nor narrower than half the width of the hot tapered surface of the bar. However, this grinding is usually not required if the tapering and coiling operations are performed adequately.
2. An untapered end coil formed substantially smaller than the central coils of the spring and in such a fashion as to have an outboard bearing surface perpendicular to the axis of the spring helix, the so-called "pigtail" end.
3. An untapered end coil formed as a helix having a pitch substantially equal to the bar diameter. To facilitate coiling, a straight end portion about 25 mm long is permitted to project tangent to the helix of this end construction, the so-called "tangent tail" end. The use of this type of end requires a spring seat formed at the same pitch of helix as that of the spring end.
4. An untapered end coil formed perpendicular to the axis of the spring helix for a circumference of at least 220 deg, the so-called "flat tangent tail" end. To facilitate coiling, a straight end portion about 25 mm long is permitted to project tangent to the outer circumference.

TABLE 4—COIL DIAMETER TOLERANCES

For Specified or ComputedOutside Diameter, mm	Inside or Outside Diameter Tolerance, Plus and Minus, mm For Free Spring Length, mm Up to 250	Inside or Outside Diameter Tolerance, Plus and Minus, mm For Free Spring Length, mm Over 250 thru 450	Inside or Outside Diameter Tolerance, Plus and Minus, mm For Free Spring Length, mm Over 450 thru 650	Inside or Outside Diameter Tolerance, Plus and Minus, mm For Free Spring Length, mm Over 650 thru 850	Inside or Outside Diameter Tolerance, Plus and Minus, mm For Free Spring Length, mm Over 850 thru 1050
75.0 thru 110.0	0.8	1.3	2.5	3.6	4.6
Over 110.0 thru 150.0	1.3	2.5	3.6	4.6	5.6
Over 150.0 thru 200.0	2.5	3.6	4.6	5.6	6.6
Over 200.0 thru 300.0	3.6	4.6	5.6	6.6	6.6

TABLE 5—FORMULAE FOR TOTAL COILS AND FOR NOMINAL SOLID LENGTH

End Configuration	Total Coils (N_t)	Nominal Solid Length (L_s)
Both ends taper rolled	N + 2	$1.01\ d\ (N_t - 1) + 2t$
Both ends with tangent tail	N + 1.33	$1.01\ d\ (N_t + 1)$
Both ends with pigtail	N + 1.50	$1.01\ d\ (N_t - 1.25)$
Taper rolled plus tangent tail	N + 1.67	$1.01\ d\ N_t + 1$
Taper rolled plus pigtail	N + 1.75	$1.01\ d\ (N_t - 1) + t$
Tangent tail plus pigtail	N + 1.42	$1.01\ d\ N_t$

where

d = bar diameter

t = tip thickness of taper rolled bar

1.01 = factor used to compensate for the cosine effect of the coil helix angle

The bracketed term in the solid length formula for springs with two pigtail ends may vary between (N_t – 0.90) and (N_t – 1.60), depending on the pigtail details.

TABLE 6—SPRING SOLID LENGTH TOLERANCES

Nominal Solid Length, mm Over	Nominal Solid Length, mm Thru	Maximum Deviation of Solid Length Above Nominal Solid Length, mm
—	175	1.5
175	250	2.5
250	325	3.0
325	400	4.0
400	475	4.8
475	550	5.5
550	625	6.5

Springs can be specified to have any combination of the four types of ends. The combination of two tangent tail ends may involve a complex arrangement for indexing the spring seats, unless the design of every spring is adjusted to an identical number of total coils. Springs for general automotive use generally have two flat tapered ends. Spring ends and seats are usually so formed as to render approximately two-thirds to one coil inactive at each end.

3.9 Squareness of Ends—Unless otherwise specified, the tapered ends of any spring having an outside diameter to bar diameter ratio of 4 or more, and a free length to outside diameter of 4 or less, shall not deviate more than 3 deg from the perpendicular to the spring axis, as determined by standing the spring on its end and measuring the angular deviation of the outer helix from a perpendicular to the plate on which the spring is standing. In the case of a tangent tail end, the spring must stand on a seat with matching helical ramp. Tolerances for springs outside these limits are subject to special agreement.

3.10 Load—Load is the force in newtons (N) measured on the load testing machine required to deflect the spring to the specified loaded length. It is to be measured during compression of the spring (compression load) and not during release of the spring (release load), unless otherwise specified.

With loaded length fixed, the usual tolerance for motor vehicle suspension springs is expressed in terms of load equivalent to a deflection of ±5 mm at the nominal rate. Where the demand for greater accuracy warrants the cost of additional presetting or other operations, the load tolerance may be specified as low as ±1.50 mm at the nominal rate.

In the springs for general automotive use, the load tolerance (with loaded length fixed) typically equals ±(1.50 mm + 3% of free-to-solid deflection) × nominal rate. This tolerance is limited to springs where the free length does not exceed 900 mm, does not exceed six times the free-to-solid deflection, and is not less than 0.8 times the OD.

3.11 Rate—Rate is the change of load per unit length of spring deflection (N/mm).

In the springs for motor vehicle suspension, the rate is expressed in terms of the load increase per 25 mm deflection (N/25 mm). It is therefore determined as one-half the difference between the loads measured 25 mm above and 25 mm below the specified loaded length. Tolerance is ±3% with centerless ground or with precision rolled bars, and ±4% when commercial hot rolled bars are used.

In the springs for general automotive use, the rate is determined between 20 and 60% of the total deflection unless otherwise defined. Typical tolerance is ±5%. In non-critical applications, this may be increased to ±10%.

3.12 Direction of Coiling—For most applications, the direction of coiling is unimportant; however, right hand coiling is preferred because most spring manufacturers are so equipped. When direction of coiling is important, as in the case of concentrically nested springs, it must be specified for each component spring, maintaining opposite directions for adjacent springs. For tangent tail springs, the direction of coiling must conform with the installation conditions.

3.13 Uniformity of Pitch—The pitch of coils in a compression spring must be sufficiently uniform so that when the spring is compressed, unsupported laterally, to a length representing a deflection of 80% of the nominal free-to-solid deflection, none of the coils must be in contact with one another, excluding the inactive end coils. This requirement does not apply when the design of the spring calls for variable pitch, or when it is such that the spring cannot be compressed to solid length without lateral support.

3.14 Shaped and Variable Rate Coils—Many newer motor vehicle applications require specially shaped suspension coil springs, or springs with variable output characteristics. The coils which are specially shaped usually exhibit a partially conical or barrel form in order to satisfy restricted height, tire clearance, or other suspension requirements. In some cases, the ends of the spring may be offset in order to provide off center loading for suspension strut applications.

With regard to variable output characteristics, some springs are designed to provide a variable rate and corresponding frequency change, for improved height control, ride and handling. The variable rate characteristic is achieved by designing and producing the spring with very specific coil spacing such that active coil segments "bottom out" against a spring seat or against each other as the spring is deflected, thereby decreasing the effective number of active coils and increasing the rate. This effect is achieved with the greatest material and space efficiency if the bar is conically tapered over the length of the coils which bottom out. It should be pointed out, however, that special equipment is required to conically taper the bars. Also, it is important to note that coil-to-coil or coil-to-seat contact can cause undesirable noise.

3.15 Concentricity of Coils—At free length, the center of all coils must be concentric with the spring axis within 1.5 mm. This axis is the straight line connecting the centers of the end coils.

4. Cold Wound Springs

4.1 Material—Round wire sizes and tolerances may be found in the individual wire specifications, such as:

Music Wire		SAE J176
Carbon Steel Spring Wire	- Oil Tempered	SAE J316
	- Hard Drawn	SAE J113
	- Special Quality High Tensile Hard Drawn	SAE J271
	- Valve Spring Quality Oil Tempered	SAE J351
	- Valve Spring Quality Hard Drawn	SAE J172
Chromium Vanadium Wire	- Valve Spring Quality	SAE J132
Chromium Silicon Alloy Steel Wire		SAE J157
Stainless Steel Wire, SAE 30302		SAE J230
Stainless Steel Wire, 17-7 PH		SAE J217
Phosphor-Bronze Wire, SAE CA510		SAE J461
Beryllium-Copper Wire, SAE CA172		SAE J461
Brass Wire, SAE CA260		SAE J461
Silicon-Bronze Wire, SAE CA655		SAE J461

4.2 Shot Peening—Shot peening is used to increase the fatigue life of springs. It consists of subjecting the spring to a stream of metallic shot moving at high velocity. The peening action of the shot reduces the effect of surface defects and sets up beneficial stresses in a thin surface layer. It also results in cold working this layer. To be effective, the peening must reach the area of highest stress which for helical compression and extension springs is the inside diameter of the coil.

Even when the wire surface is virtually flawless, the fatigue life of the cold-wound spring can be increased by peening in the order of more than 2 to 1. See MANUAL, SAE HS J795, Chapter 1, also SHOT PEENING MANUAL, SAE HS 84 J808.

4.3 Presetting—The need for presetting depends upon the design stresses, the application and its conditions and requirements. Then use of presetting is most beneficial when design stresses are at or near the yield point, and settling prevents the spring from performing as required.

Presetting is an operation that is performed during the manufacturing of helical compression springs in which the spring is compressed beyond the yield point of the material. The yielding of the surface layers of the wire which occurs during the presetting produces beneficial residual stresses, thus increasing the elestic limit of the spring and thereby reducing the chances of settling in subsequent service. The spring is coiled to a free length in excess of the designated free length. The yielding causes the spring to take a permanent set, thus bringing it down to the required free length.

The presetting operation may be performed at ambient temperature, called cold setting, or at some elevated temperature, called either heat setting or hot pressing. Heat setting consists of compressing the spring on a fixture, subjecting the compressed spring to a temperature higher than the desired operating temperature for a time suitable to insure complete penetration of the heat, and then cooling to room temperature before releasing.

Hot pressing consists of heating the spring in its free or relaxed position to some temperature for sufficient time to insure complete penetration; then, while the spring is at the temperature, it is compressed to some height below the installed or operating position and released.

4.4 Coil Diameter—Coil diameter tolerances can be specified on either the inside diameter (ID) or the outside diameter (OD) of the coils, depending upon the importance of the respective dimensions to the user. Tolerances are functions of the "Spring Index", which is the ratio of mean coil diameter (D) to wire diameter (d). They are to be considered as manufacturing tolerances and do not take into account the effects of changes in diameter due to applied loads. See Figures 3 and 4.

4.5 Spring Lengths—Spring lengths of compression springs are overall dimensions measured parallel to the axis of the spring.

Spring lengths of extension springs are measured inside to inside of the hooks (overall length minus two wire diameters).

4.5.1 FREE LENGTH—Free length is the length under no load. When load is specified, free length is used as a reference dimension only. When load is not specified, free length is specified for control and inspection purposes by using Figure 5 for compression springs and Figure 6 for extension springs.

The tolerances in Figure 3 are based on the number of active coils (N), the free length (L_o), and the spring index (D/d). With these parameters known, the N/L_o value is established on the abscissa, and the tolerance is found by multiplying the corresponding ordinate value by L_o. Round off the index to the nearest whole number and interpolate when this is an odd number. The tolerances shown in Figure 5 are for springs with ends closed and ground. For springs with the ends closed but not ground, multiply by 1.7.

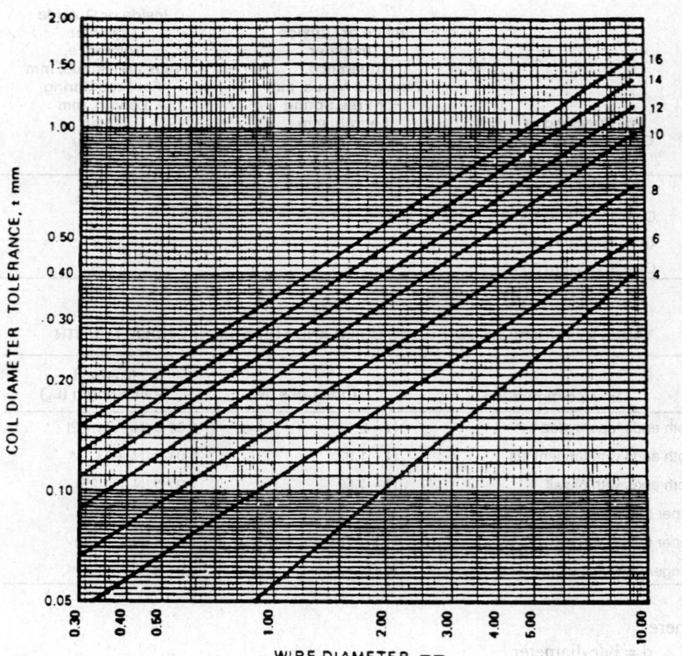

FIGURE 3—COIL DIAMETER TOLERANCE - COMPRESSION AND EXTENSION SPRINGS FOR WIRE SPRINGS FOR WIRE DIAMETERS 0.30 TO 9.50 mm. ROUND OFF INDEX TO NEAREST WHOLE NUMBER. INTERPOLATE WHEN THE ROUNDED-OFF VALUE IS AN ODD NUMBER. USE TOLERANCE FOR 0.30 mm WIRE DIAMETER WHEN WIRE DIAMETER IS LESS THAN 0.30 mm.

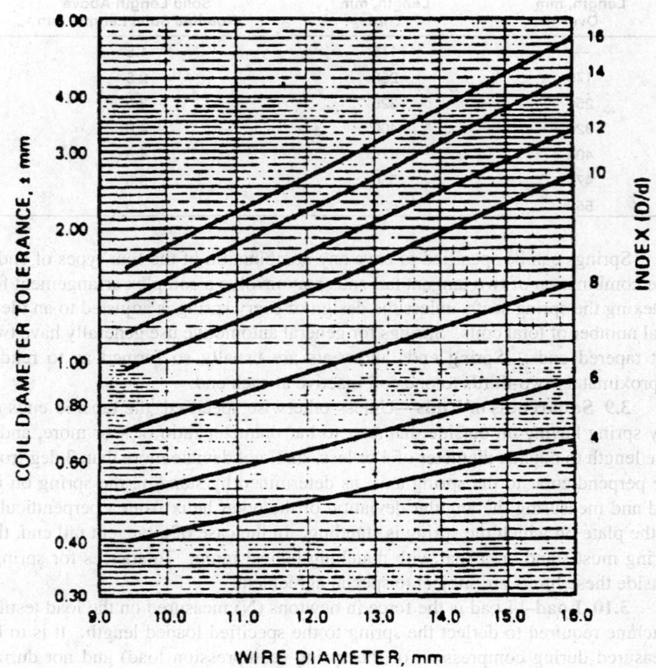

FIGURE 4—COIL DIAMETER TOLERANCE - COMPRESSION AND EXTENSION SPRINGS FOR WIRE DIAMETERS 9.5 TO 16.0 mm. ROUND OFF INDEX TO NEAREST WHOLE NUMBER. INTERPOLATE WHEN ROUNDED-OFF VALUE IS ODD NUMBER.

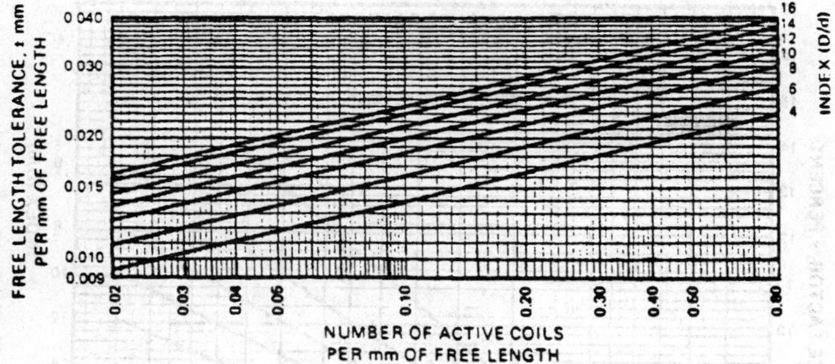

FIGURE 5—FREE LENGTH TOLERANCE - COMPRESSION SPRINGS. ROUND OFF INDEX TO NEAREST WHOLE NUMBER. INTERPOLATE WHEN ROUNDED-OFF VALUE IS ODD NUMBER. THESE ARE TOLERANCES FOR SPRINGS WITH ENDS CLOSED AND GROUND. FOR SPRINGS WITH ENDS CLOSED BUT NOT GROUND, MULTIPLY BY 1.7.

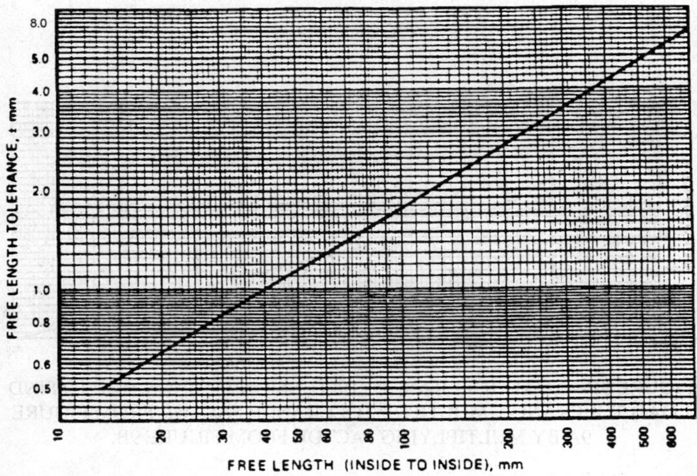

FIGURE 6—FREE LENGTH TOLERANCE - EXTENSION SPRINGS

4.5.2 SOLID LENGTH (SEE ALSO NUMBER OF COILS, 4.6)—In compression springs, this is the length with all active coils closed, to be specified as a maximum dimension allowing the manufacturer any tolerance required by the variations in wire size, total coils, and the amount of grind at the ends; platings and coatings increase the wire diameter and must be considered.

For springs with ground ends, the maximum solid length is the total number of coils times the wire diameter; for springs with ends not ground, the solid length is the total number of coils plus one, times the wire diameter.

4.5.3 PRESET LENGTH—After the compression spring has been coiled to a free length in excess of the designated free length, it is compressed solid or to a specified preset length; this produces yielding, which results in bringing the spring to the designated free length. If more than one preset compression is desired, it must be specified on the drawing. See also MANUAL, SAE HS J795, Chapters 1 and 4.

4.5.4 LOADED LENGTH—This is the length while the load is being measured. It is a fixed reference dimension, with the tolerance applied to the load.

4.5.5 MAXIMUM EXTENDED LENGTH—Extension springs normally do not have a definite stop to their deflection, therefore the drawing specifications should include a statement of the maximum extended length which must be attained without encountering permanent set.

4.6 Number of Coils—In compression springs, it is often necessary to vary the number of coils in order to meet the requirements on load, rate, free length, and solid length. Therefore, the number of coils should be specified as an approximate figure. For reference only, the tolerance for the number of coils is given in Table 7 compression springs and in Table 8 for extension springs. It is expressed in degrees as a function of the number of active coils.

TABLE 7—NUMBER OF COILS TOLERANCE OF COMPRESSION SPRINGS

Active Coils	Tolerance, ± deg
3 – 10	45
For each additional 10 coils, add	30

TABLE 8—NUMBER OF COILS TOLERANCE OF EXTENSION SPRINGS

Active Coils	Tolerance, ± deg Close Wound	Tolerance, ± deg Open Wound
3	30	90
4 – 10	45	90
For each additional 10 coils, add	15	30

In extension springs, either the number of coils in the body of the spring or the length over the coils may be specified, but only as an approximate figure. In computing the length over coils, it should be recognized that there is always one more wire diameter in the length than the number of coils in a close-wound spring.

4.7 Spring Ends—In compression springs, there are four typical end configurations (Figure 7):

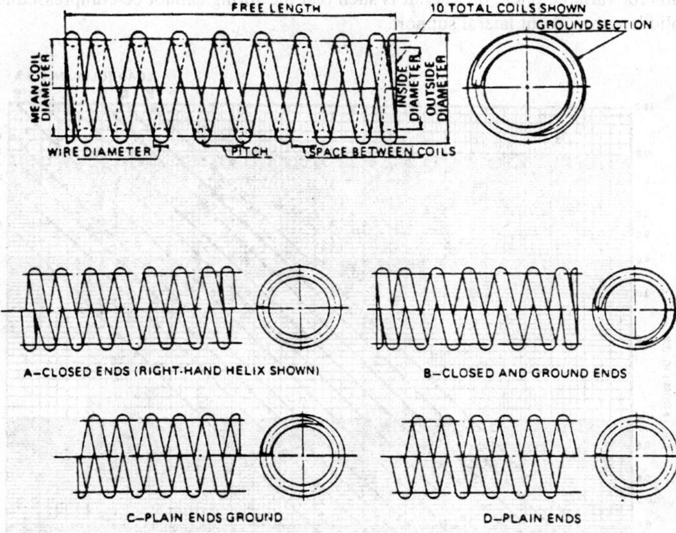

FIGURE 7—TYPICAL ENDS OF HELICAL COMPRESSION SPRINGS

1. Plain end (with the end coil having the same pitch as all other coils);
2. Plain end ground (the end surface being ground perpendicular to the spring axis);
3. Closed end (with the tip of the wire contacting the adjacent coil);
4. Closed and ground end (the closed end being ground perpendicular to the spring axis).

The unground ends may be used for reasons of economy, but they give eccentric loading with some increase in maximum spring wire stress and space required. The plain ends similarly produce eccentric loading and additionally present a handling problem due to springs tangling together.

In extension springs, many types of hooks, loops, eyes, etc. are used (see MANUAL, SAE HS J795, Figure 3.3). Details such as hook opening restraint of the loop within the body diameter should be specified on the drawing. The position of hooks relative to each other can be in line, at right angles, or at any other angular position as required. If this relative position is important, the spring drawing should emphasize the importance by a statement as well as by pictorial representation. Sharp bends in forming the end hooks should be avoided because they produce stress concentrations.

4.8 Squareness of Ends—In compression springs with closed and ground ends, the squareness of the ends, as measured in the unloaded position, is to be maintained within a limit of 3 deg with the axis of the spring.

4.9 Load—Load is the force in newtons (N) measured on the load testing machine required to deflect the spring to the specified loaded length.

For compression springs, the load is to be measured during compression of the spring (compression load) unless otherwise specified. Tolerances are shown in Figure 8 as functions of the nominal free length tolerance (Figure 5) and the deflection from free length to loaded length. Round off the percent load tolerance values to the next larger whole number. Interpolate when this is an odd number and when it is between 8 and 20%.

For extension springs, the load is to be measured during extension of the spring. Tolerances are computed as the product of the appropriate tolerance factor from Figure 9A and the appropriate multiplying factor from Figure 9B.

Cold coiled extension springs may be wound with tension between the coils so that a load must be applied to separate them, the so-called initial tension in the spring.

4.10 Rate—Rate is the change of load per unit length of spring deflection (N/mm). The rate is to be determined between 20 and 60% of the total deflection. Tolerances depending on the number of active coils are given in Figure 10.

4.11 Direction of Coiling—For most applications, the direction of coiling is unimportant; however, right hand coiling is preferred because most spring manufacturers are so equipped.

4.12 Uniformity of Pitch—The pitch of coils in a compression spring must be sufficiently uniform so that when the spring is compressed, unsupported laterally, to a length representing a deflection of 80% of the nominal free-to-solid deflection, none of the coils must be in contact with one another, excluding the inactive end coils. This requirement does not apply when the design of the spring calls for variable pitch, or when it is such that the spring cannot be compressed to solid length without lateral support.

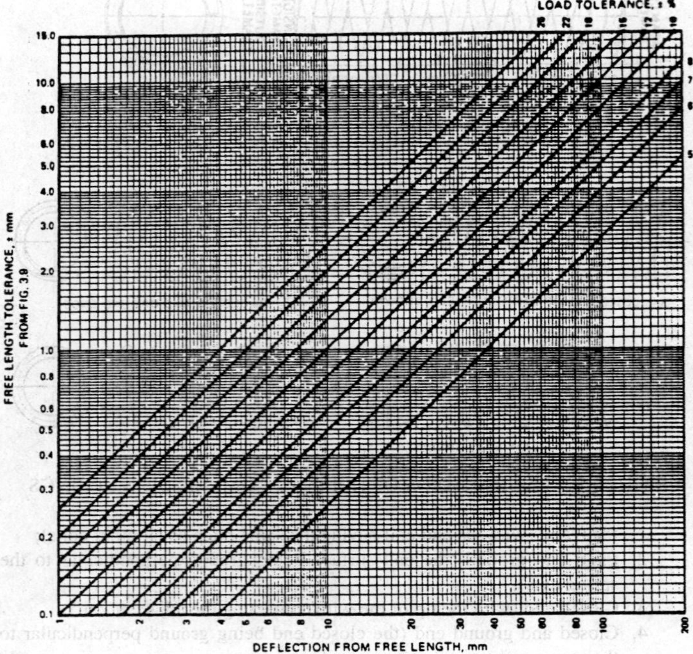

FIGURE 8—LOAD TOLERANCE - COMPRESSION SPRINGS, ±%. ENTER CHART FROM BOTTOM WITH DEFLECTION FROM FREE LENGTH TO LOADED LENGTH AND FROM LEFT WITH FREE LENGTH TOLERANCE OF FIGURE 4. ROUND OFF PERCENT LOAD TOLERANCE VALUES TO NEXT LARGER WHOLE NUMBER. INTERPOLATE WHEN ROUNDED-OFF VALUE IS ODD AND BETWEEN 8 AND 25%.

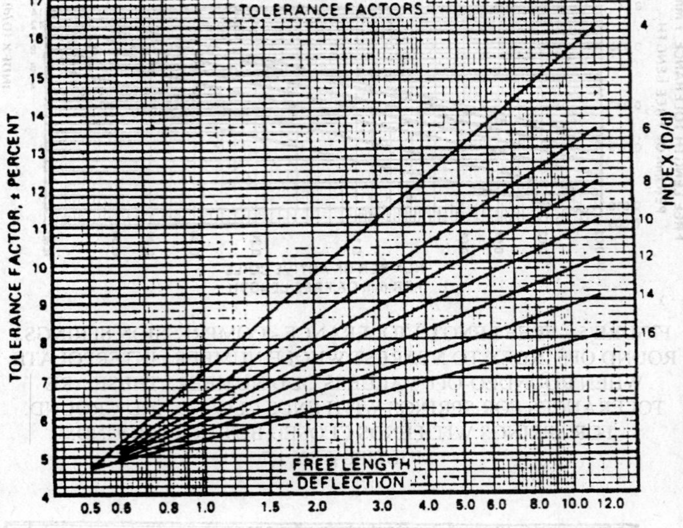

FIGURE 9A—

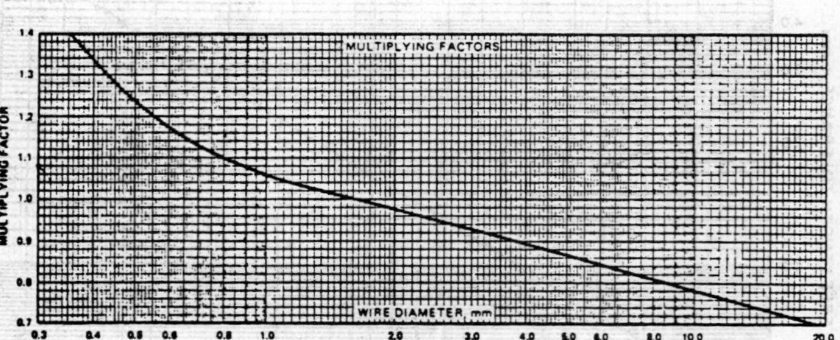

FIGURE 9B—LOAD TOLERANCE - EXTENSION SPRINGS, ±%. TO FIND LOAD TOLERANCE, MULTIPLY TOLERANCE FACTOR FROM FIGURE 9A BY MULTIPLYING FACTOR FROM FIGURE 9B.

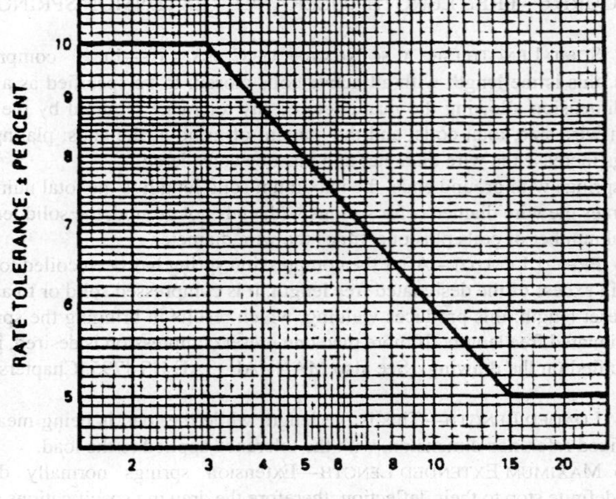

FIGURE 10—RATE TOLERANCE - COMPRESSION AND EXTENSION SPRINGS. RATE AND RATE TOLERANCE SHOULD BE SPECIFIED ONLY WHEN RATE IS FUNCTIONAL. WHEN RATE SPECIFICATION IS NECESSARY, RANGE OF DEFLECTION OVER WHICH IT IS TO APPLY MUST BE CLEARLY IDENTIFIED. DEFLECTION RANGES FOR RATE CONTROL SHOULD FALL WITHIN 20 - 60% LIMIT OF TOTAL DEFLECTION BECAUSE RATE IS LIKELY TO BE VARIABLE OUTSIDE THIS RANGE.

R) HELICAL SPRINGS: SPECIFICATION CHECK LISTS—SAE J1122 JUL1988

SAE Recommended Practice

Report the SAE Spring Committee approved February 1976 and completely revised by the SAE Coil Spring Subcommittee of the SAE Spring Committee July 1988.

Foreword—This Document has also changed to comply with the new SAE Technical Standards Board format.

1. Scope—The following SAE Recommended Practice furnishes sample forms for helical compression, extension and torsion springs to provide a uniform method for specifying design information. It is not necessary to fill in all the data, but sufficient information must be supplied to fully describe the part and to satisfy the requirements of its application. For detailed information, see "Design and Application of Helical and Spiral Springs - SAE HS J795 SEP82", also "Helical Compression and Extension Spring Terminology - SAE J1121 NOV75".

Both these documents use SI (metric) Units in accordance with the provisions of SAE J916 MAY85, and so does SAE J1122. Here, however, the U.S. Customary Units (in, lb, psi) have been added in parentheses after each SI Unit for the convenience of the user who must furnish specifications on a project where all requirements are listed in non-metric terms.

2. References

2.1 Applicable Publications—The following publications form a part of the specification to the extent specified herein. Unless otherwise indicated, the latest revision of SAE publications shall apply.

2.1.1 SAE PUBLICATIONS—Available from SAE, 400 Commonwealth Drive, Warrendale, PA 15096-0001.

SAE J916 JUN82—Rules for SAE Use of SI (Metric) Units
SAE J1121—Helical Compression and Extension Spring Terminology
SAE HS 795

TABLE 1—CONVERSION TABLE

To Convert from SI Unit to U.S. Customary Unit, Divide by the Factor

To Convert from U.S. Customary Unit to SI Unit, Multiply by the Factor

Quantity	SI Unit		Factor	U.S. Customary Unit	
Length	millimeter	mm	25.4 (Exactly)	inch	in
Area	square millimeter	mm^2	645.16 (Exactly)	square inch	in^2
Mass	kilogram	kg	0.453 592 4	pound-mass	lb_m
Force (or Load)	newton	N	4.448 222 (1)	pound-force	lb_f
Moment	newton millimeter	N.mm	112.984 8	pound inch	lb_f.in
Linear Spring Rate	newton per millimeter	N/mm	0.175 126 8	pound per inch	lb_f/in
Torsional Spring Rate	newton mm per degree	N.mm/deg	112.984 8	pound inch per degree	lb_f.in/deg
Stress	megapascal	MPa	0.006 894 757 (2)	pound per square inch	psi

1. 4.448 222 = 0.453 592 37 · 9.806 650
   where 9.806 650 = Acceleration of Gravity "g" adopted in 1901 by International Committee on Weights & Measures
2. 0.006 894 757 = 4.448 2216 · 0.000 645 16

A - HELICAL COMPRESSION SPRINGS Application ________

OD ________ mm (in) to work inside ________ mm (in) Dia Hole

ID ________ mm (in) to work over ________ mm (in) Dia Rod

Note: Specify only those diameters that are necessary for assembly and operation

Wire Dia ________ mm (in) Total Coils ________ Active Coils ________

Free Length ________ mm (in) approx

Direction of Coil Winding: Right Hand, Left Hand, or Optional

Type of Ends ________ Square with Axis within ________ deg

Max Solid Length ________ mm (in)

Load ________ N (lb) ± ________ N (lb) at ________ mm (in) length

Load ________ N (lb) ± ________ N (lb) at ________ mm (in) length

Rate ________ N/mm (lb/in) Ref

After being compressed to a length of ________ mm (in) for ________ hours at a temperature of ________ °C (°F) the spring must not show a load loss in excess of ________ N (lb) at a length of ________ mm (in)

Springn Index = Mean Coil Diameter/Wire Diameter (D/d) ________

Wahl Stress Correction Factor K_w ________

Stress at ________ mm (in) length: ________ MPa (psi) Corrected or Uncorrected ________

Stress at ________ mm (in) length: ________ MPa (psi) Corrected or Uncorrected ________

Material ________

Hardness or Tensile Strength ________

Surface Treatment/Finish ________

Identification ________

Remarks ________

B - HELICAL EXTENSION SPRINGS Application ____________

OD __________ mm (in) Wire Dia __________ mm (in)

Number of Coils __________

Direction of Coil Winding: Right Hand, Left Hand, or Optional ______

Free Length Inside Hooks __________ mm (in) approx

Type of Ends (use sketch if necessary) ____________________________

____

Load __________ N (lb) ± __________ N (lb) at __________ mm (in) length

Load __________ N (lb) ± __________ N (lb) at __________ mm (in) length

Initial Tension __________ N (lb) Ref

Rate __________ N/mm (lb/in) Ref

Stress at __________ mm (in) length: __________ MPa (psi) Corrected or Uncorrected __________

Stress at __________ mm (in) length: __________ MPa (psi) Corrected or Uncorrected __________

Max Extended Length without set __________ mm (in)

Stress at Max Extended Length __________ MPa (psi) Corrected or Uncorrected __________

Material ____

Hardness or Tensile Strength ______________________________________

Surface Treatment/Finish ____

Identification ____

Remarks ____

C - HELICAL TORSION SPRINGS   Application __________

OD __________ mm (in)

ID __________ mm (in) to work over __________ mm (in) Dia Shaft

Note: Specify only those diameters that are necessary for assembly and operation

Wire Dia __________ mm (in)   Number of Coils __________

Max Free Length __________ mm (in)

Direction of Coil Winding: Right Hand or Left Hand __________

Type of Ends (use sketch if necessary) ____________________

____

Moment __________ N mm (lb in) ± __________ N mm (lb mm) at __________ deg between ends

Moment __________ N mm (lb in) ± __________ N mm (lb mm) at __________ deg between ends

Rate __________ N mm/deg (lb in/deg) approx

Stress at __________ deg __________ MPa (psi)

Stress at __________ deg __________ MPa (psi)

Max Wound Position __________ deg

Stress at Max Wound Position __________ MPa (psi)

Material ____________________

Hardness or Tensile Strength ____________________

Surface Treatment/Finish ____________________

Identification ____________________

Remarks ____________________

RATED SUSPENSION SPRING CAPACITY—SAE J274 JUN1989

SAE Recommended Practice

Report of the SAE Spring Committee approved September 1972, completely revised June 1984, and reaffirmed June 1989.

Foreword—This Document has not changed other than to put it into the new SAE Technical Standards Board Format.

1. Scope—The Rated Suspension Spring Capacity definition has been developed to assist engineers and designers in the preparation of specifications and descriptive material and values relating thereto.

1.1 Purpose—The following definition of Rated Suspension Spring Capacity is applicable to all types of suspensions designed for vehicles used predominantly on the highway. This capacity provides a basis for comparison of spring load carrying abilities in a particular suspension application. This definition is intended to clarify a commonly used term which has heretofore been used indiscriminately.

2. References

2.1 Applicable Publication—The following publications form a part of the specification to the extent specified herein. Unless otherwise indicated the lastest revision of SAE publications shall apply.

2.1.1 SAE PUBLICATION—Available from SAE, 400 Commonwealth Drive, Warrendale, PA 15096-0001

HS J670

3. Definitions

3.1 Rated Suspension Spring Capacity—A load rating assigned to each spring installation and vehicle application which will provide adequate spring durability and vehicle stability under all intended load conditions. The value of the load rating must equal or exceed that portion of the maximum allowable force of gravity (usually called 'weight' and equaling mass times acceleration of gravity) at the ground which relates directly to the spring. Therefore, the load rating is based on the total of sprung and unsprung forces of gravity (usually called 'sprung weight' and 'unsprung weight') of the loaded vehicle

3.2 Spring—Includes all types of suspension springs (such as: leaf, coil, torsion bar, rubber, pneumatic, etc.).

3.3 Load Rating—Is expressed in the SI (metric) unit of load, the newton ($1N = 1\ kg \cdot 1\ m/s^2$), determined vertically with the vehicle on a horizontal plane. Here the acceleration in the equation is the 'acceleration of gravity' which, by International Agreement, is generally accepted as $9.806\ 650\ m/s^2$ on the surface of the earth. What is commonly called 'weight' is actually the force (or load) which requires an equal, but opposite force, to restrain the mass of a body against free fall. This 'force of gravity' (or 'gravitational pull') is proportional to the mass. Thus a body of

1 kg mass will 'weigh'

$1\ kg \cdot 9.806\ 650\ m/s^2 = 9.806\ 650\ N$.

3.4 Spring Installation—Any spring as used in a particular suspension.

3.5 Vehicle Application—The usage of the vehicle as intended by the vehicle manufacturer.

3.6 Adequate Spring Durability—The endurance life characteristics regarded as sufficient by the vehicle manufacturer to satisfy customer requirements.

3.7 Adequate Vehicle Stability—The ride and handling characteristics of the vehicle regarded by the vehicle manufacturer as sufficient for safe operation.

3.8 Intended Load Conditions—The various payloads and payload distribution applied to the vehicle within the prescribed limits of 'Gross Vehicle Weight (GVW)' or 'Vehicle Full Rated Load,' and component capacities as established by the vehicle manufacturer.

3.9 Sprung Weight and Unsprung Weight—Defined in 4.1.1 and 4.1.4 of SAE VEHICLE DYNAMICS TERMINOLOGY - HS J670, as published by SAE in 1978.

3.10 Loaded Vehicle—A vehicle which satisfies the conditions described in 4.7.

3.11 Maximum Allowable Force of Gravity (Weight) at the Ground—The Vehicle Full Rated Load or GVW acting at the ground.

3.12 Related Directly to the Spring—The load at the ground, which is transmitted through the suspension components to the spring and includes that portion of the unsprung weight.

The Rated Suspension Spring Capacity does not indicate spring payload capability, but rather the total of payload and vehicle weight. The assignment of a Rated Suspension Spring Capacity value is the responsibility of the vehicle manufacturer.

21 Speedometers and Tachometers

FACTORS AFFECTING ACCURACY OF MECHANICALLY DRIVEN AUTOMOTIVE SPEEDOMETER-ODOMETERS—SAE J862 JAN1989

SAE Information Report

Report of the SAE Speedometer and Tachometer Committee approved June 1963, third revision June 1981, and reaffirmed January 1989.

Foreword—This Document has not changed other than to put it into the new SAE Technical Standards Board Format.

1. Scope—This report is concerned with factors which affect accuracy of distance indication and speed indication of automotive type odometer speedometers. It is the intent to supply information regarding all items which affect the instrument.

2. References

2.1 Applicable Publications—The following publications form a part of the specification to the extent specified herein. Unless otherwise indicated the latest revision of SAE publications shall apply.

2.1.1 SAE PUBLICATIONS—Available from SAE, 400 Commonwealth Drive, Warrendale, PA 15096-0001.

SAE J678 JUN84—Speedometers and Tachometers-Automotive

SAE J1059 JUN84—Speedometer Test Procedure

3. Distance Indication—Distance traveled is indicated by a numbered set of wheels, called the odometer, normally viewed through a slot in the dial of the speedometer. The wheels incorporate gear teeth which engage a pinion interposed between each set of wheels. The odometer can then be said to be a set of gears with numerals on their outer surface. The odometer is driven by a system of reduction gearing within the speedometer instrument. This reduction gearing is, in turn, driven by the speedometer cable core. SAE J678 (JUN84) specifies that 1000 or 1001 revolutions of the speedometer cable core shall cause a 1 mile indication on the odometer (616 through 630 revolutions, depending on the odometer gear train drive, for 1 km) if driven from the transmission. In wheel driven speedometers, the nominal number of wheel revolutions per mile (kilometer) shall cause a 1 mile (km) indication on the odometer. Because of the positive gear driven mechanism, no slippage error occurs in the odometer.

4. Factors Affecting Odometer Accuracy

4.1 Overall Assembly in Vehicle—The ideal of achieving the exact nominal value of speedometer cable core revolutions in one unit of distance of vehicle travel can seldom be realized. This becomes apparent when consideration is given to the overall design problem.

4.1.1 The speedometer cable core is driven by a gear called the take off pinion gear which is driven by the worm drive gear connected to the transmission output shaft which, in turn, drives the wheels through the differential gears. The distance traveled is dependent on the number of tire revolutions in a mile (kilometer). By experimentation, a nominal figure of tire revolutions per unit of distance is determined for the vehicle. Knowing the differential ratio, it is possible to calculate the necessary ratio in the transmission and the take off pinion gear for the speedometer cable core to achieve 1000 or 1001 revolutions per mile or 616 through 630 revolutions per kilometer. In the case of an odometer/speedometer driven directly from a wheel, it is then necessary to calculate the proper gearing within the speedometer head itself to achieve nominal conditions.

4.1.2 The exact ratio frequently results in a fraction which must, of course, be rounded to a whole number of teeth for the take off pinion gear. This gear selection must be accurate enough to assure that the odometer records actual distances traveled within ±4% at 20, 40, and 55 mph (32.2, 64.4, and 88.5 km/h) [1].

4.1.3 Because of the different axle ratios used, it is necessary in any one line of automobiles to have a variety of take off pinion gears with different numbers of teeth. The number of teeth in the worm drive gear is not readily subject to change, since the gear is assembled within the transmission and is usually uniform for any transmission model.

4.2 Tires and Load—Tires are elastic members subject to variations from nominal size caused by manufacturing tolerances, temperature, inflation pressure, wear, speed, and loading. A tire will change size due to aging, after it is placed on a rim and inflated. These size variations, plus differences in construction material, and in the type of tread on tires from the same or different manufacturers, can result in a different number of tire revolutions per unit of distance. It is obvious that these variations from the nominal originally selected can directly affect distance indication.

4.3 Speed—A tire may experience as much as a 3% change in revolutions per unit of distance from a 30 mph (48.3 km/h) speed to a 90 mph (144.8 km/h) speed due to a change in rolling radius by centrifugal force.

4.4 Analysis and Summary—Figure 1 is a chart which demonstrates the magnitudes of error which might occur in odometer readings. The average individual effect will be less than the maximum indicated by the chart since some of the conditions tend to compensate for others. For instance, tire wear and aging growth are compensating factors. Tire wear has the effect of increasing odometer indication and the tire aging growth will decrease the indication. When reading the chart, however, it should be appreciated that the errors may be additive.

4.5 Corrective Measures

4.5.1 In the foregoing, it has been shown that there are factors present which cannot be economically reduced or controlled which will cause distance indication errors. Some of the factors, however, can, in some degree, be controlled by proper tire inflation and replacement of worn tires.

4.5.2 Inadvertent installation of an improper pinion gear for a particular axle ratio will, of course, result in considerable error in odometer reading. Such a condition is, however, easily remedied by installation of the correct take off pinion gear.

4.5.3 A vehicle operator, especially one who modified a standard vehicle, can determine his percentage of odometer error by driving an accurately known distance at approximately nominal operating conditions of speed, load, temperature, and proper tire inflation. The reading of the odometer shall be compared to the known distance traveled. A reading greater than the distance traveled indicates a plus error, conversely a reading less than the distance traveled, indicates a minus error. For example, if the odometer indicates 5.2 miles (km) as compared to a nominal 5.0 miles (km) distance traveled, an error of 0.2 divided by 5.0 or +4% exists. A grossly plus error may be compensated for by using a take off pinion gear with a greater number of teeth or a large minus error may be corrected with a take off pinion gear with less teeth.

1. See SAE J678 for specific state or local requirements.

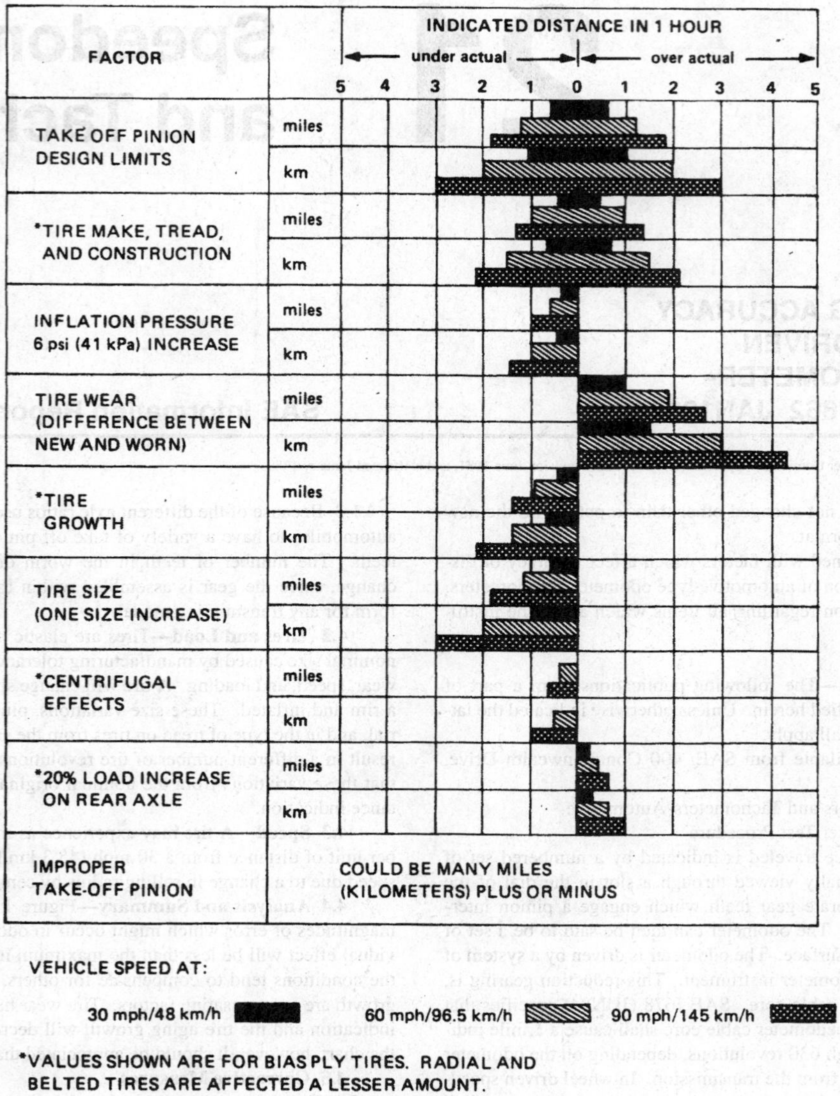

FACTOR		INDICATED DISTANCE IN 1 HOUR ← under actual | over actual → 5 4 3 2 1 0 1 2 3 4 5
TAKE OFF PINION DESIGN LIMITS	miles	
	km	
•TIRE MAKE, TREAD, AND CONSTRUCTION	miles	
	km	
INFLATION PRESSURE 6 psi (41 kPa) INCREASE	miles	
	km	
TIRE WEAR (DIFFERENCE BETWEEN NEW AND WORN)	miles	
	km	
•TIRE GROWTH	miles	
	km	
TIRE SIZE (ONE SIZE INCREASE)	miles	
	km	
•CENTRIFUGAL EFFECTS	miles	
	km	
•20% LOAD INCREASE ON REAR AXLE	miles	
	km	
IMPROPER TAKE-OFF PINION		COULD BE MANY MILES (KILOMETERS) PLUS OR MINUS

VEHICLE SPEED AT:

30 mph/48 km/h 60 mph/96.5 km/h 90 mph/145 km/h

•VALUES SHOWN ARE FOR BIAS PLY TIRES. RADIAL AND BELTED TIRES ARE AFFECTED A LESSER AMOUNT.

FIGURE 1—FACTORS WHICH AFFECT ODOMETER READINGS CROSS SECTION OF ALL U.S. MAKES

5. Speed Indication—Speed indication in an automotive speedometer is commonly accomplished through the use of a principle known as eddy current drive. The speedometer cable core drives a magnet shaft of the speedometer to which a permanent magnet is affixed. This magnet is located inside an aluminum or copper speed cup. The speed cup is attached to the same spindle on which the speedometer pointer is affixed. Also affixed to this spindle is a hairspring. A force applied to the speed cup results in a controlled reaction of the speedometer pointer. As the magnet rotates inside the speed cup, a force proportional to the speed of rotation is developed, thus providing measurement of speed indicated on the dial (Figure 2).

6. Speedometer Calibration—The speedometer is calibrated at room temperature 75°F (23.9°C) by the instrument manufacturer. See SAE J678 for the recommended calibration tolerances.

7. Factors Affecting Speedometer Accuracy

7.1 Drive Errors—Indication of speed is subject to the same errors as distance indication because the same speedometer cable core drives both the odometer and speed indicator. Some of the error may be compensated for by calibration of the speed indicator. Note should be taken that individual errors due to gearing, tire size, tire wear, tire pressure, speed, and load in the vehicle may be additive or subtractive to the speed indicator.

7.2 Temperature, Vibration, and Friction—The speed indication is affected by these factors. For information on the allowable variations due to these factors, see SAE J678 and SAE J1059.

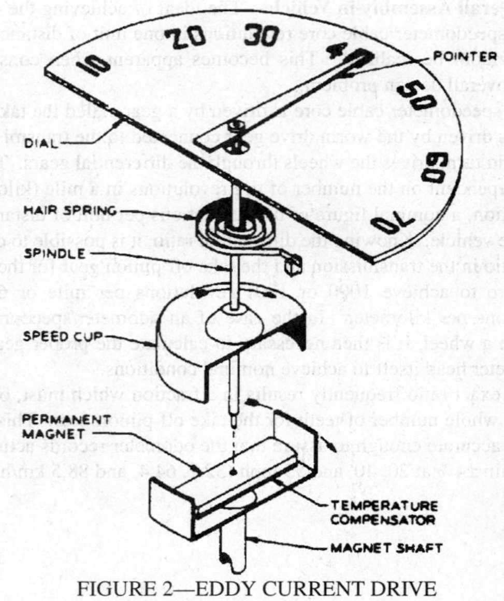

FIGURE 2—EDDY CURRENT DRIVE

SPEEDOMETERS AND TACHOMETERS - AUTOMOTIVE—SAE J678 DEC1988

SAE Recommended Practice

Report of the SAE Parts and Fittings Division approved January 1939, sixth revision, SAE Speedometer and Tachometer Committee, June 1984, reaffirmed December 1988.

Foreword—This Document has not changed other than to put it into the new SAE Technical Standards Board Format.

*1. **Scope***—This SAE Recommended Practice applies to speedometers, odometers, and speedometer drives typical of passenger vehicles, buses, and trucks used for personal or commercial purposes. The method of determining wheel revolutions per unit distance (3.1) and overall system design variation (3.3.3) are applicable to passenger cars only. Comparable recommendations for trucks and buses are under development. The data of tachometers is applicable to vehicular use, as previously described, and also to stationary and marine engines and special vehicles.

*2. **References***

2.1 Applicable Publications—The following publications form a part of this specification to the extent specified herein. Unless otherwise indicated, the latest version of SAE publications shall apply.

2.1.1 SAE PUBLICATIONS—Available from SAE, 400 Commonwealth Drive, Warrendale, PA 15096-0001.

SAE J862 JUN81—Factors Affecting Accuracy of Mechanically Driven Automotive Speedometer-Odometers

SAE J966 AUG66—Test Procedure for Measuring Passenger Car Tire Resolutions per Mile

2.1.2 NATIONAL BUREAU OF STANDARDS—National Institute of Standards and Technology (formerly National Bureau of Standards), U. S. Department of Commerce, Gaithersburg, MD 20899.

National Bureau of Standards Handbook 44

2.1.3 OTHER PUBLICATIONS

Australia D Regulation 1019
Japan Article 46
United Nations ECE R 39
European Economic Commission EEC 75/443

*3. **Speedometer***

3.1 Wheel Revolutions per Unit Distance[1]—The nominal number of vehicle wheel revolutions per mile (kilometer) is to be determined by the vehicle manufacturer and the information is to be used as a basis for design calculations of gearing and speedometer calibrations. Vehicle wheel revolutions shall be determined at 45 ± 2 mph (72.4 ± 3.2 km/h).[2] Tire inflation for measuring wheel revolutions is to be in accordance with the vehicle manufacturers' recommended pressure with tires at ambient test temperatures. This test is to be run immediately after a 5 mile (8 km) test run at 45 mph (72.4 km/h) to stabilize tire pressure, and with the vehicle at curb weight plus driver and one passenger [or 150 lb (68 kg)].

3.2 Types of Drive—The practice for cable-driven speedometers is to drive the system from either the transmission or the front wheel of the vehicle.

3.2.1 TRANSMISSION DRIVE—The design of a transmission drive for a speedometer requires that the vehicle manufacturer determine the nominal number of vehicle wheel revolutions per mile (kilometer). This information is then used as a basis for calculating the speedometer drive ratio. The number of teeth on the worm drive gear in the transmission and the number of teeth on the takeoff pinion gear (drive ratio) are selected to provide a proper odometer drive and speed indication, as defined in 3.3.1, 3.3.2, and 3.4.1. It is urged that those unfamiliar with conditions which affect vehicle wheel revolutions consult SAE J862 so that they may properly control conditions when determining the nominal value.

3.2.2 FRONT WHEEL DRIVE—This type of drive also requires that the nominal number of vehicle wheel revolutions be determined. The information is used to provide proper odometer drive gearing and for calibration purposes to achieve a proper speed indication.

3.3 Mileage Indication (Odometer)

3.3.1 INSTRUMENT DESIGN CONSIDERATION—Odometer tamper resistance should be considered when designing odometers for U.S. applications.

3.3.2 ALLOWABLE VARIATION WITHIN THE INSTRUMENT—The odometer shall indicate one mile for every 1000 or 1001 revolutions of the flexible shaft (one kilometer for every 616 thru 630 revolutions, depending on the odometer gear train drive) if driven from the transmission. The odometer of front wheel drive units shall indicate one mile (kilometer) when the flexible shaft is rotated a specified number of revolutions, as determined by the vehicle manufacturer.

1. See also SAE J966.
2. Direct metric conversions in parentheses.

3.3.3 OVERALL SYSTEM DESIGN VARIATION—The vehicle manufacturer shall specify odometer drive ratios that will produce one unit of distance indication within ±4% for each actual unit of distance travelled at 20, 40, and 55 mph (32.2, 64.4, and 88.5 km/h).[3] The design limits thus derived should not, however, be construed as absolute. Factors which cause variation from nominal wheel revolution per unit distance travelled under operating conditions are covered in SAE J862. It is recommended that SAE J862 be studied to determine probable effects on odometer accuracy under operating conditions.

3.4 Speed Indication

3.4.1 ALLOWABLE VARIATION WITHIN THE INSTRUMENT—Two philosophies exist in calibrating the instrument for overall vehicle system accuracy.

a. Calibrate the speedometer at the center of the graduations so that overall vehicle system accuracy will be within a specified amount, as established by the vehicle manufacturer. The intent is to have an instrument with no system bias. Generally ±4.0 mph (±6.4 km/h) is an acceptable limit for the vehicle system.
b. Bias the speedometer calibration high so that overall vehicle system calibration will be higher than true vehicle speed. Generally +6.0, –0.0 mph (+9.6, –0.0 km/h) is an acceptable limit for the vehicle system.

The specific calibration of the instrument relative to vehicle system limits should be determined by the instrument manufacturer and vehicle manufacturer.[4] The speedometer head should be calibrated in approximately the same angular position that it will have when mounted in the vehicle.

Factors influencing vehicle system accuracy are described in Figure 2 of SAE J862. In addition, the following factors also affect the speedometer head accuracy:

Temperature—The speed indication will vary with changes in temperature. Temperature affects the reaction between the speed cup and magnet - Refer to Figure 3 in SAE J862. To counteract this effect, an element called a temperature compensator is incorporated in all speedometers. Due to variations in materials which cannot be perfectly controlled, the change in indicated speed from temperature compensation may be as much as ±4% between temperatures of 20 and 130 °F (–7 to 55 °C).

Vibration—Another condition which affects speed indication is vibration. At 55 mph (88.5 km/h) an effect of 0.5 to 1 mph (0.8 to 1.6 km/h) may be noted.

Friction—A minor error which affects speed indication is frictional lag. This is a condition in which the speedometer will not read exactly the same under acceleration and deceleration. Investigations indicate that the error from frictional lag is less then 1 mph (1.6 km/h) at 55 mph (88.5 km/h).

3.5 Identification—Identification should appear on all speedometers. It should consist of a distinct marking of model number or part number on the instrument and the date of its manufacture. All kilometer speedometers should be identified by marking "Kilo" on the back of the speedometer case, unless identification of sufficient nature appears on the face dial or other suitable means of identification is applied, such as marking the speedometer head with a red dot. Drive ratio information shall appear on front-wheel drive instruments in an area readily visible when the instrument is removed.

*4. **Speedometer and Tachometer Drive***—Flexible shafts for driving mechanical speedometers and tachometers shall consist of a flexible casing and a flexible cable capable of transmitting motion from a suitable takeoff to operate the instrument. Recommended takeoff and instrument fittings are shown in the following illustrations.

In routing of flexible shafts, bends of less than 6 in (150 mm) radius should be avoided. Figures 1–5 and Table 1 give dimensions for SAE light, regular, square, and heavy-duty drive for speedometers and tachometers.

3. Some states and local regulations require an accuracy of ±3.75% under specified test conditions for vehicles introduced into rental or leasing markets. Test conditions are specified in the National Bureau of Standards Handbook 44.
4. The following regulatory requirements for speedometers should also be consulted:
Australia D Regulation 1019
Japan Article 46
United Nations ECE R 39
European Economic Comm. EEC 75/443

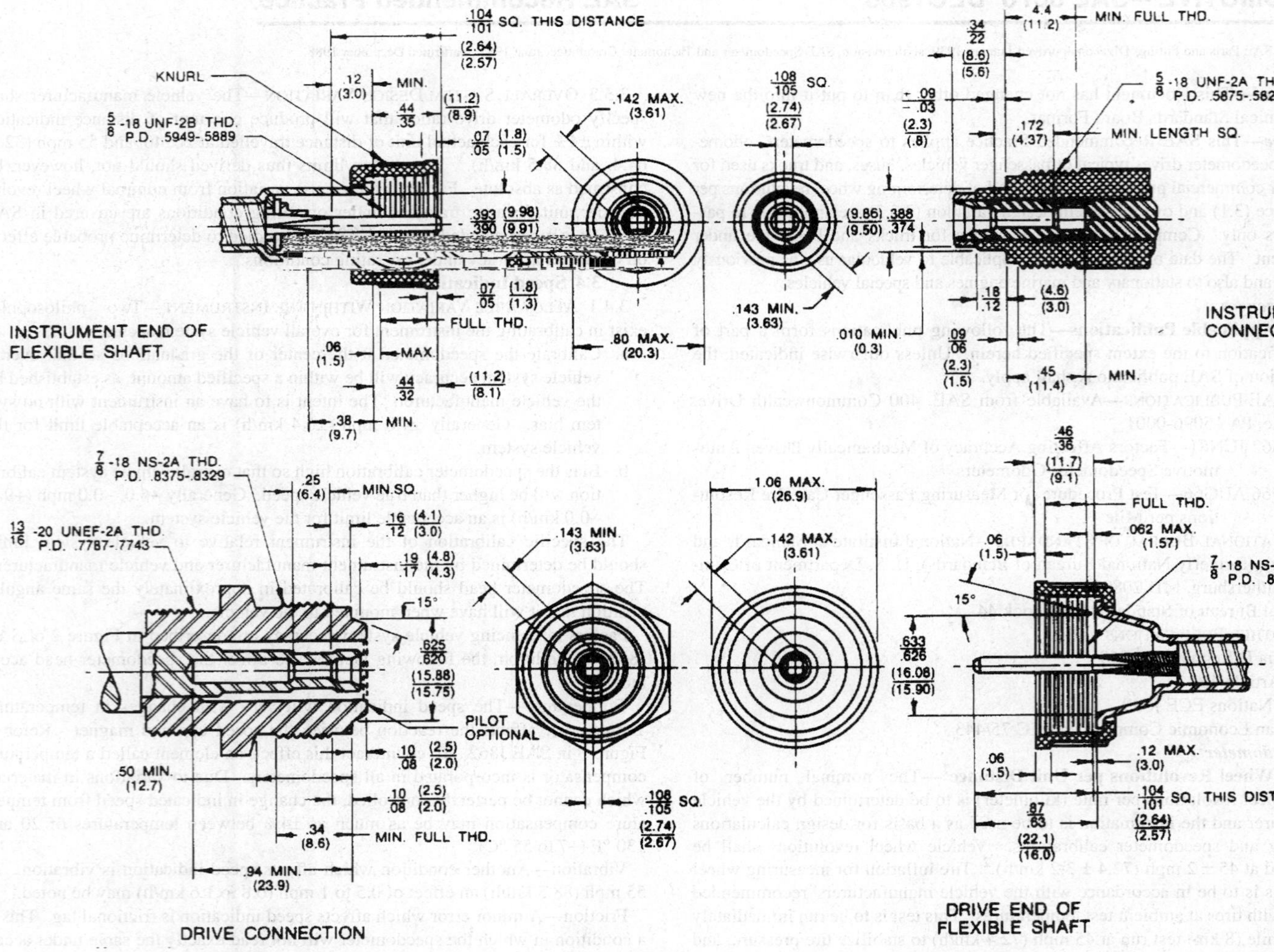

FIGURE 1—LIGHT-DUTY DRIVE (FOR USE WITH EDDY CURRENT TYPE INSTRUMENTS)

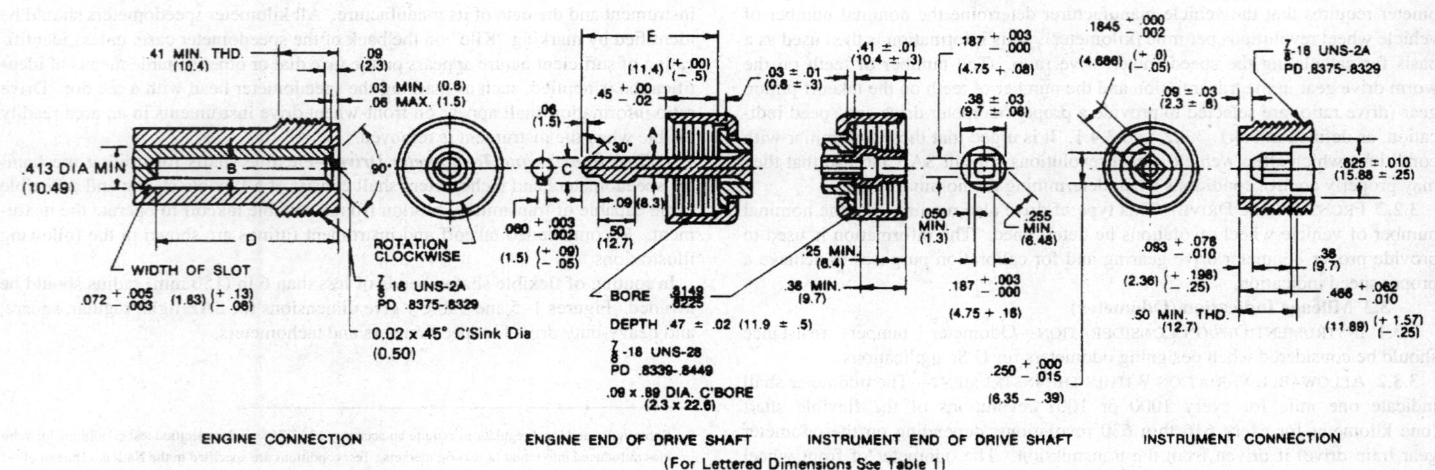

FIGURE 2—SAE REGULAR DRIVE FOR SPEEDOMETERS AND TACHOMETERS
(FOR LETTERED DIMENSIONS SEE TABLE 1)

13/16 -20 UNEF-2A THD.
P.D. .7787-.7743
7/8 -18 UNS-2A THD.
P.D. .8375-.8329
.105/.075 (2.67)/(1.90)
.25 MIN. SQ.
(6.4)
15°
.3105/.3090 (7.89)/(7.85)
.625/.620 (15.88)/(15.75)
PILOT
OPTIONAL
.10/.08
(2.5)/(2.0)
.18
(4.6)
.34
(8.6)
MIN. FULL THD.
.50
(12.7)
MIN.
.94
(23.9)
MIN.
DRIVE CONNECTION
.203 MIN.
(5.16)
.202 MAX.
(5.13)
.154/.151 SQ.
(3.91)/(3.84)
.150/.147 SQ.
(3.81)/(3.73)
.46/.36
(11.7)/(9.1)
FULL THD.
.062 MAX.
(1.57)
.06
(1.5)
7/8 -18 NS-2B THD.
P.D. .8389-.8449
"C" WASHER RECOMMENDED
ON ALL SHAFTS 80 INCHES (2 m)
OR LONGER TO RETAIN CABLE
15°
.633/.626 (16.08)/(15.90)
.06
(1.5)
.12 MAX.
(3.0)
.150/.147 SQ. THIS DISTANCE
(3.81)/(3.73)
.81/.62
(20.6)/(15.7)
DRIVE END OF FLEXIBLE SHAFT

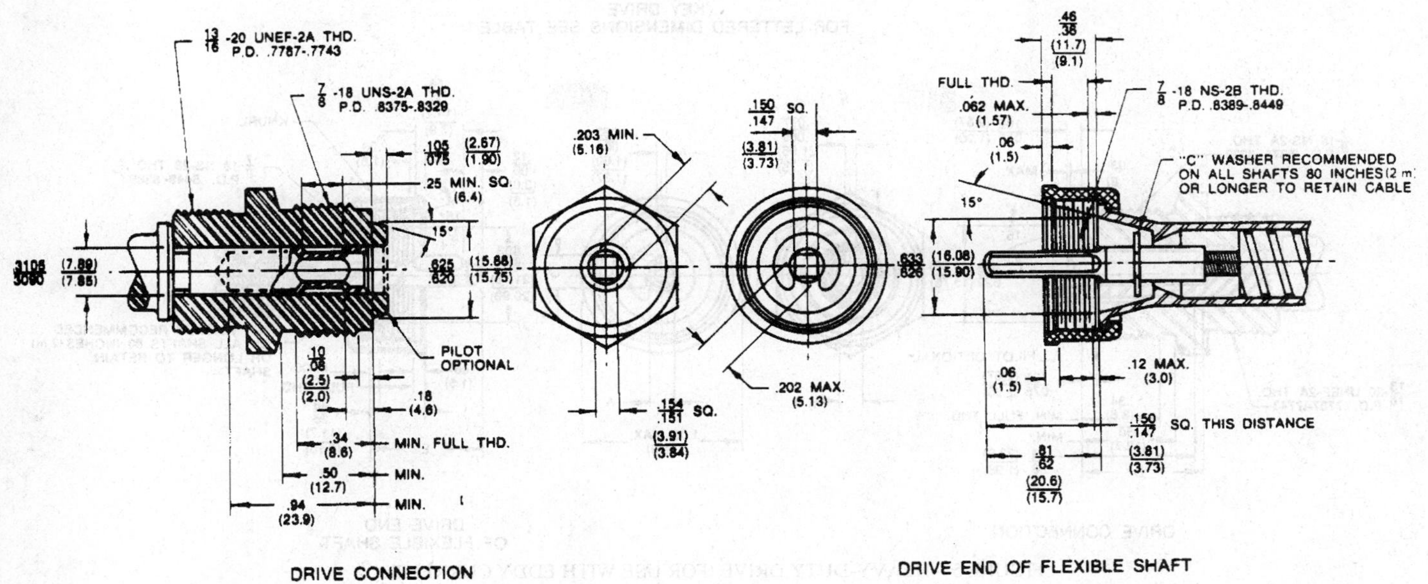

FIGURE 3—SQUARE DRIVE

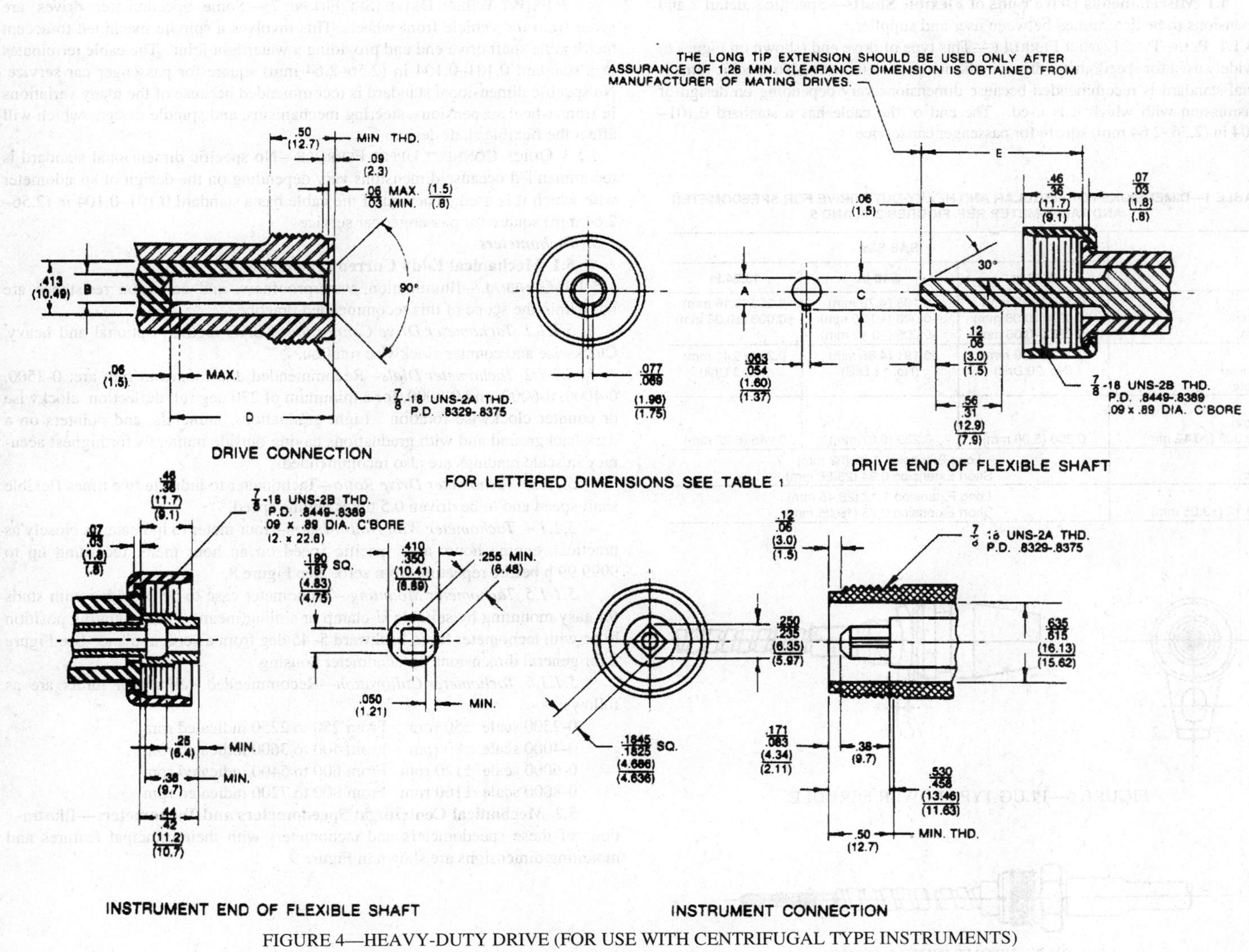

.50
(12.7)
MIN THD.
.09
(2.3)
.06 MAX. (1.5)
.03 MIN. (.8)
.413
(10.49)
B
90°
.06
(1.5)
MAX.
D
7/8 -18 UNS-2A THD.
P.D. .8329-.8375
.077/.069
(1.96)/(1.75)
DRIVE CONNECTION
FOR LETTERED DIMENSIONS SEE TABLE 1
THE LONG TIP EXTENSION SHOULD BE USED ONLY AFTER
ASSURANCE OF 1.26 MIN. CLEARANCE. DIMENSION IS OBTAINED FROM
MANUFACTURER OF MATING DRIVES.
E
.06
(1.5)
.46/.36
(11.7)/(9.1)
.07/.03
(1.8)/(.8)
30°
A
C
.12/.06
(3.0)/(1.5)
.063/.054
(1.60)/(1.37)
7/8 -18 UNS-2B THD.
P.D. .8449-.8389
.09 x .89 DIA. C'BORE
.56/.31
(12.9)/(7.9)
DRIVE END OF FLEXIBLE SHAFT
.46/.36
(11.7)/(9.1)
7/8 -18 UNS-2B THD.
P.D. .8449-.8389
.09 x .89 DIA. C'BORE
(2. x 22.6)
.07/.03
(1.8)/(.8)
.190/.187
(4.83)/(4.75)
.410/.350
(10.41)/(8.89)
.255 MIN.
(6.48)
.050
(1.21)
MIN.
.25
(6.4)
MIN.
.38
(9.7)
MIN.
.1845/.1825 SQ.
(4.686)/(4.636)
.44/.42
(11.2)/(10.7)
INSTRUMENT END OF FLEXIBLE SHAFT
.12/.06
(3.0)/(1.5)
7/8 -18 UNS-2A THD.
P.D. .8329-.8375
.250/.235
(6.35)/(5.97)
.635/.615
(16.13)/(15.62)
.171/.083
(4.34)/(2.11)
.38
(9.7)
.530/.458
(13.46)/(11.63)
.50
(12.7)
MIN. THD.
INSTRUMENT CONNECTION

FIGURE 4—HEAVY-DUTY DRIVE (FOR USE WITH CENTRIFUGAL TYPE INSTRUMENTS)

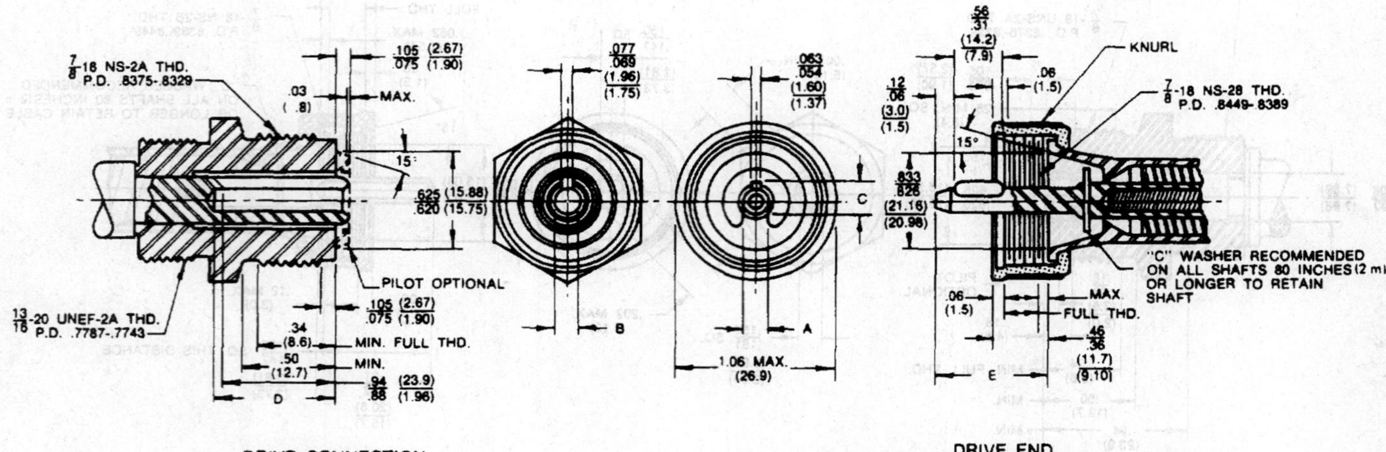

FIGURE 5—HEAVY-DUTY DRIVE (FOR USE WITH EDDY CURRENT TYPE INSTRUMENTS AND KEY DRIVE)

4.1 Miscellaneous Drive Ends of Flexible Shafts—Specific detail and dimensions to be determined between user and supplier.

4.1.1 PLUG TYPE LOWER FERRULE—This type of drive end (shown on Figure 6) is widely used for speedometer drives in the automotive industry. No specific dimensional standard is recommended because dimensions vary depending on design of transmission with which it is used. The end of the cable has a standard 0.101–0.104 in (2.56–2.64 mm) square for passenger car service.

TABLE 1—DIMENSIONS FOR REGULAR AND HEAVY-DUTY DRIVE FOR SPEEDOMETER AND TACHOMETER REF. FIGURES 2, 4, AND 5

	SAE Size		
	5/32 in	3/16 in	13/64 in
A Shaft Dia.	0.152 (3.86 mm) +0.003 (+0.08 mm) −0.002 (−0.06 mm)	0.188 (4.78 mm) +0.000 (+0.00 mm) −0.005 (−0.13 mm)	0.203 (5.16 mm) ±0.003 (±0.08 mm)
B Drilled Hole	0.161 (4.09 mm) (No. 20 Drill)	0.191 (4.85 mm) (No. 11 Drill)	0.213 (5.41 mm) (No. 3 Drill)
C Tang. ±0.005 (±0.12 mm)	0.200 (5.08 mm)	0.239 (6.07 mm)	0.245 (6.22 mm)
D Min.	Long Extension 1.26 (32 mm) Short Extension 0.94 (23.88 mm)		
E ±0.12 (±3.05 mm)	Long Extension 1.12 (28.45 mm) Short Extension 0.75 (19.05 mm)		

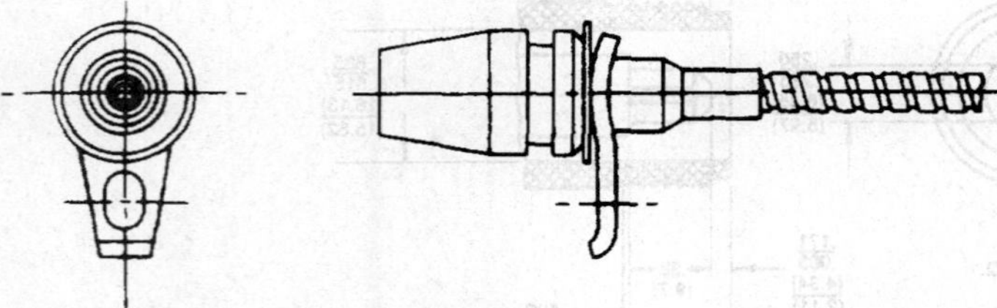

FIGURE 6—PLUG TYPE LOWER FERRULE

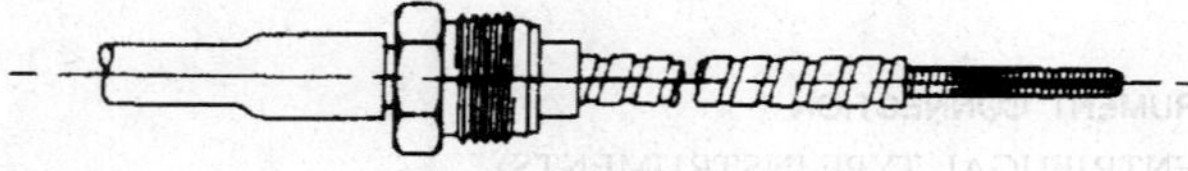

FIGURE 7—FRONT WHEEL DRIVE

4.1.2 FRONT-WHEEL DRIVE (SEE FIGURE 7)—Some speedometer drives are taken from the vehicle front wheel. This involves a spindle machined to accept the flexible shaft drive end and providing a watertight joint. The cable terminates in a standard 0.101–0.104 in (2.56–2.64 mm) square for passenger car service. No specific dimensional standard is recommended because of the many variations in front-wheel suspensions, steering mechanisms, and spindle designs which will affect the flexible shaft design.

4.1.3 QUICK CONNECT UPPER FERRULE—No specific dimensional standard is recommended because dimensions vary depending on the design of speedometer with which it is used. The end of the cable has a standard 0.101–0.104 in (2.56–2.64 mm) square for passenger car service.

5. Tachometers

5.1 Mechanical Eddy Current Tachometers

5.1.1 GENERAL—Illumination, waterproofness, and corrosion resistance are not within the scope of this recommended practice.

5.1.1.1 Tachometer Drive Connections—SAE regular, optional and heavy. Clockwise and counter clockwise rotation.

5.1.1.2 Tachometer Dials—Recommended dial ranges in rpm are: 0-2500, 0-4000, 0-6000, and 0-8000, for a minimum of 270 deg full deflection, clockwise or counter clockwise rotation. Light graduations, numerals, and pointers on a dark background and with graduations having outside numerals for highest accuracy in scale readings are also recommended.

5.1.1.3 Tachometer Drive Ratio—Tachometer to indicate two times flexible shaft speed and to be driven 0.5 times engine speed.

5.1.1.4 Tachometer With Hour Meter—Hour meter to indicate, as closely as practical, engine hours at a specific speed on an hour meter recording up to 9999.99 h before repeating from zero. See Figure 8.

5.1.1.5 Tachometer Mounting—Tachometer case to be provided with studs for easy mounting by suitable U-clamp or similar means. The mounting position to be with tachometer faced backward 5–45 deg from a vertical plane. See Figure 8 for general dimensions of tachometer housing.

5.1.1.6 Tachometer Calibration—Recommended calibration limits are as follows:

0-2500 scale	±50 rpm	From 250 to 2250 indicated rpm
0-4000 scale	±80 rpm	From 400 to 3600 indicated rpm
0-6000 scale	±120 rpm	From 600 to 5400 indicated rpm
0-8000 scale	±160 rpm	From 800 to 7200 indicated rpm

5.2 Mechanical Centrifugal Speedometers and Tachometers—Illustrations of these speedometers and tachometers with their principal features and mounting dimensions are shown in Figure 9.

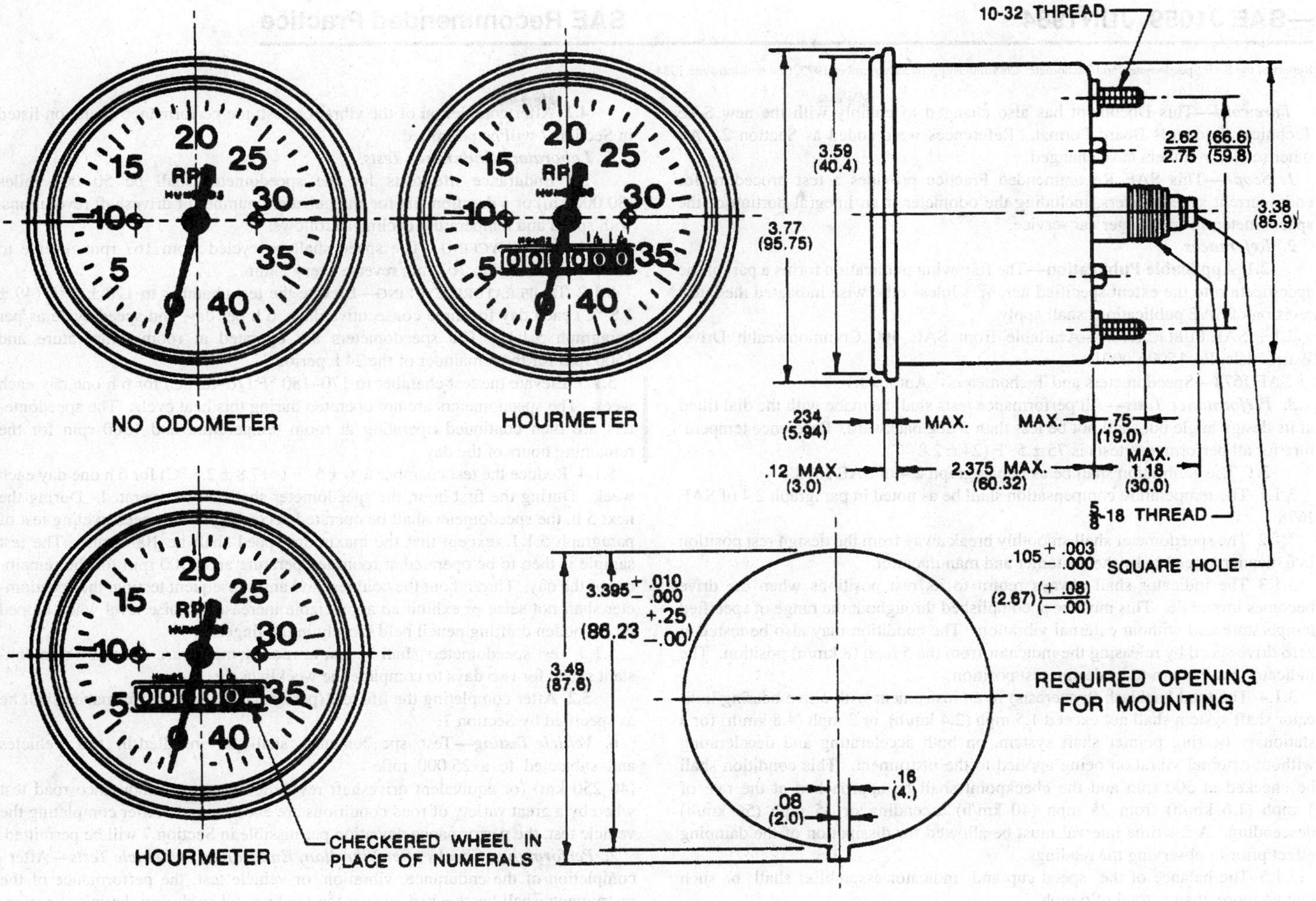

FIGURE 8—MECHANICAL EDDY CURRENT TACHOMETER

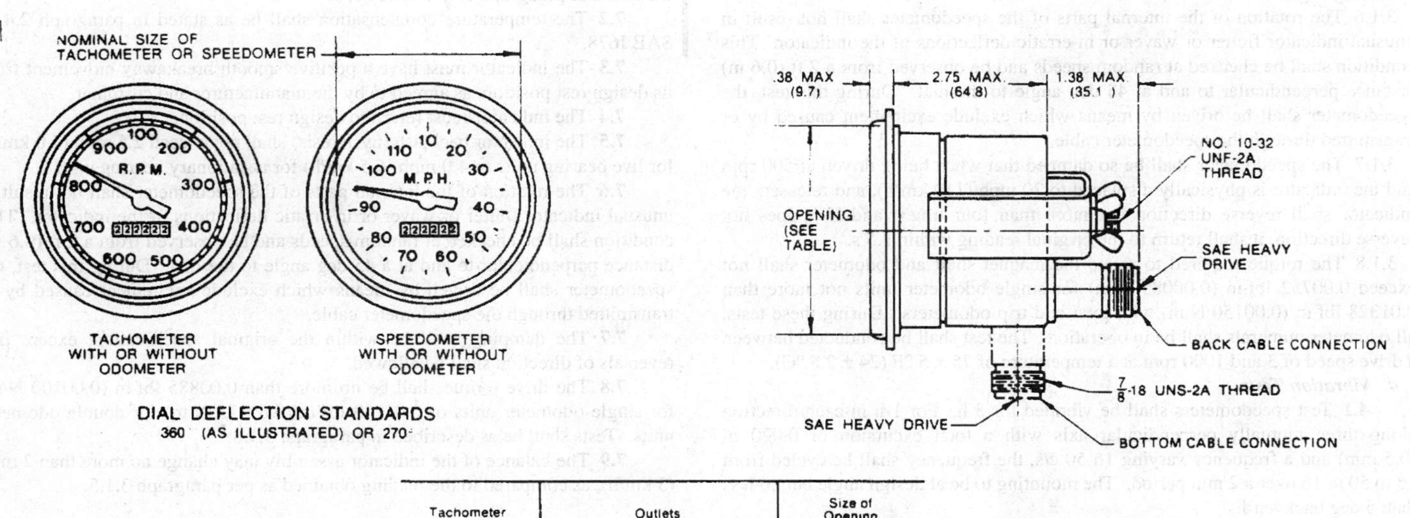

Tachometer or Speedometer Size, In.	Outlets		Size of Opening Required, Dia. −0.010 (−.25) −0.000 (−.000)
	Standard	Optional	
3	Back	Bottom	3.395 (86.23)
4	Bottom	Back	4.395 (111.63)
6 and over	Bottom	Back	5.250 (131.35)

FIGURE 9—MECHANICAL CENTRIFUGAL TACHOMETERS AND SPEEDOMETERS

SPEEDOMETER TEST PROCEDURE —SAE J1059 JUN1984

SAE Recommended Practice

Report of the SAE Speedometer and Tachometer Committee approved November 1973, first revision June 1984.

Foreword—This Document has also changed to comply with the new SAE Technical Standards Board Format. References were added as Section 2. All other section numbers have changed.

1. Scope—This SAE Recommended Practice provides a test procedure for eddy current speedometers, including the odometer if an integral portion of the speedometer, for passenger car service.

2. References

2.1 Applicable Publication—The following publication forms a part of the specification to the extent specified herein. Unless otherwise indicated the latest revision of SAE publications shall apply.

2.1.1 SAE PUBLICATION—Available from SAE 400 Commonwealth Drive, Warrendale, PA 15096-0001.

SAE J678—Speedometers and Tachometers—Automotive

3. Performance Tests—All performance tests shall be made with the dial tilted at its design angle but shall not be less than 5 deg backward. Reference temperature for all performance tests is 75 ± 5 °F (24 ± 2.8 °C).

3.1 The calibration shall be as in paragraph 2.4 of SAE J678.

3.1.1 The temperature compensation shall be as noted in paragraph 2.4 of SAE J678

3.1.2 The speedometer shall smoothly break away from the design rest position in a manner agreed to by the customer and manufacturer.

3.1.3 The indicator shall always return to its rest positions when the drive becomes immobile. This must be accomplished throughout the range of specified temperature and without external vibration. The condition may also be tested at zero drive speed by releasing the indicator from the 5 mph (8 km/h) position. The indicator must return to its design rest position.

3.1.4 The total backlash (hysteresis) in an instrument with a live bearing indicator shaft system shall not exceed 1.5 mph (2.4 km/h), or 3 mph (4.8 km/h) for a stationary bearing pointer shaft system, on both accelerating and decelerating without external vibration being applied to the instrument. This condition shall be checked at 500 rpm and the checkpoint shall be approached at the rate of 1 mph (1.6 km/h) from 25 mph (40 km/h) ascending or 35 mph (56 km/h) descending. A 2 s time interval must be allowed for dissipation of the damping effect prior to observing the readings.

3.1.5 The balance of the speed cup and indicator assemblies shall be such that no more than a total of 6 mph (10 km/h) change of indication occurs when the speedometer is driven at 500 rpm and the instrument is rotated 360 deg about the indicator axis and in the design mounting angle.

3.1.6 The rotation of the internal parts of the speedometer shall not result in unusual indicator flutter or waver or in erratic deflections of the indicator. This condition shall be checked at random speeds and be observed from a 2 ft (0.6 m) distance perpendicular to and at 45 deg angle to the dial. During this test, the speedometer shall be driven by means which exclude excitement caused by or transmitted through the speedometer cable.

3.1.7 The speedometer shall be so damped that when being driven at 500 rpm and the indicator is physically displaced to 70 mph (110 km/h), and released, the indicator shall reverse direction not more than four times; and if it does not reverse direction, it shall return to the original reading within 1.5 s.

3.1.8 The torque required to rotate the magnet shaft and odometer shall not exceed 0.00752 lbf·in (0.00085 N·m) for single odometer units not more than 0.01328 lbf·in (0.00150 N·m) with total and trip odometers. During these tests, all odometer numerals shall be in operation. The test shall be conducted between a drive speed of 3 and 1000 rpm at a temperature of 75 ± 5 °F (24 ± 2.8 °C).

4. Vibration Tests

4.1 Test speedometers shall be vibrated for 3 h. For 1 h in each direction along three mutually perpendicular axis with a total excursion of 0.020 in (0.5 mm) and a frequency varying 16-50 c/s, the frequency shall be cycled from 16 to 50 to 16 over a 2 min period. The mounting to be at design angle but no less than 5 deg backward.

4.2 After completion of the vibration test, the performance deviation listed in Section 7 will be permitted.

5. Laboratory Endurance Tests

5.1 Endurance life tests for the speedometer shall be 50 000 miles (80 000 km) or a duration test for an equivalent number of driveshaft revolutions, with speed and temperature cycling as follows:

5.1.1 SPEED CYCLING—The speed shall be cycled from 167 rpm reverse to 1500 rpm forward to 167 rpm reverse every 2 min.

5.1.2 TEMPERATURE CYCLING—Elevate the test chamber to 120 ± 5 °F (49 ± 2.8 °C) each day for three consecutive days, 6 h per day, and speed cycle as per paragraph 5.1.1. The speedometers are operated at room temperature and 1500 rpm for the remainder of the 24 h period.

5.1.3 Elevate the test chamber to 170–180 °F (76–82 °C) for 6 h one day each week. The speedometers are not operated during this heat cycle. The speedometers are then continued operating at room temperature and 1500 rpm for the remaining hours of the day.

5.1.4 Reduce the test chamber to 0 ± 5 °F (−17.8 ± 2.8 °C) for 6 h one day each week. During the first hour, the speedometer shall not be operated. During the next 5 h, the speedometer shall be operated according to the speed cycling test of paragraph 5.1.1., except that the maximum speed shall be 1000 rpm. The test sample is then to be operated at room temperature and 1500 rpm for the remainder of the day. Throughout the cold test and any subsequent testing, the speedometer shall not seize or exhibit an appreciable increase in noise level when tapped by a wooden drafting pencil held loosely in the fingers.

5.1.5 Test speedometers shall be run at room temperature and 1500 rpm constant speed for two days to complete the weekly cycle.

5.2 After completing the life test (paragraph 5.1), the performance shall be as specified by Section 7.

6. Vehicle Testing—Test speedometers shall be installed in test vehicles and subjected to a 25 000 mile (40 250 km) (or equivalent driveshaft revolutions) general endurance road test whereby a great variety of road conditions are encountered. After completing the vehicle test, the performance deviation permissible in Section 7 will be permitted.

7. Performance Checks after Vibration, Endurance, or Vehicle Tests—After completion of the endurance, vibration, or vehicle test, the performance of the instruments shall be checked against the readings taken during the initial performance check. Deviations are allowed as follows:

7.1 The calibration shall not deviate more than 3% of the test speed from the limits of paragraph 2.4 of SAE J678.

7.2 The temperature compensation shall be as stated in paragraph 2.4 of SAE J678.

7.3 The indicator must have a positive smooth breakaway movement from its design rest position, as agreed to by the manufacturer and customer.

7.4 The indicator must return to design rest position.

7.5 The indicator backlash (hysteresis) shall not exceed 2.5 mph (4.0 km/h) for live bearing units or 4.0 mph (6.5 km/h) for a stationary bearing unit.

7.6 The rotation of the internal parts of the speedometer shall not result in unusual indicator flutter or waver or in erratic deflections of the indicator. This condition shall be checked at random speeds and be observed from a 2 ft (0.6 m) distance perpendicular to and at a 45 deg angle to the dial. During this test, the speedometer shall be driven by means which exclude excitement caused by or transmitted through the speedometer cable.

7.7 The damping shall be within the original specification, except five reversals of direction shall be allowed.

7.8 The drive torque shall be no more than 0.00885 lbf·in (0.00100 N·m) for single odometer units or 0.01549 lbf·in (0.00175 N·m) for double odometer units. Tests shall be as described in paragraph 3.1.8.

7.9 The balance of the indicator assembly may change no more than 2 mph (3 km/h), as compared to the reading obtained as per paragraph 3.1.5.

ELECTRIC SPEEDOMETER SPECIFICATION ON ROAD—SAE J1226 FEB1983

SAE Recommended Practice

Report of the SAE Speeometer and Tachometer Committee approved February 1983.

Foreword—This Document has not changed other than to put it into the new SAE Technical Standards Board Format.

1. Scope—This SAE Recommended Practice covers electric speedometer systems for general on-road (passenger car, multi-purpose passenger vehicle, truck, and bus) applications.

1.1 Purpose—To recommend design practices and test procedures for electric speedometers used in an on-road vehicle environment using the methods of determining wheel revolutions per unit of distance specified in SAE J678,[1] paragraph 2.1, and SAE J966.

2. References

2.1 Applicable Publications—The following publications form a part of the specification to the extent specified herein. Unless otherwise indicated the latest revision of SAE publications shall apply.

2.1.1 SAE PUBLICATION—Available from SAE, 400 Commonwealth Drive, Warrendale, PA 15096-0001.

SAE J678—Speedometers and Tachometers—Automotive

SAE J862 JUN81—Factors Affecting Accuracy of Mechanically Driven Automotive Speedometer-Odometers

SAE J966 AUG66—Test Procedure for Measuring Passenger Car Tire Revolutions per Mile

2.1.2 ASTM DOCUMENT—Available from ASTM, 100 Barr Harbor Drive, West Conshohocken, PA 19428-2959.

ASTM B 117—Method of Salt (Fog) Spray

2.1.3 FEDERAL SPECIFICATION—Available from the Superintendent of Documents, U. S. Government Printing Office, Mail Stop: SSOP, Washington, DC 20402-9320.

FMVSS 127

3. Electric Speedometer System—A typical electric speedometer system consists of an indicating unit and sender unit with inter-connecting wiring. The indicating unit is made up of a speed indicator and distance indicator (odometer). In practice, the speed indicator is very similar to a conventional electric tachometer where the indication is proportional to the frequency of the input pulses. The distance indicator may utilize a counter such as described in SAE J862, paragraph 2, and may be driven by a stepping motor through a system of reduction gearing or by a solenoid. The stepping motor or solenoid in turn is driven by voltage pulses generated by an amplifier/divider circuit or from a switch in the sender. The divider circuit serves to reduce the frequency of the input pulses from the sender that are applied to the stepping motor or solenoid. The sender unit in most applications will be one of the following types: permanent magnet generator, magnetic switch, or magnetic sensor. Generally, they are either transmission or wheel mounted.

4. Factors Affecting Odometer System Accuracy

4.1 General—The overall accuracy of an electric speedometer distance indicator is subject to the same inaccuracies as those described in SAE J862. While the average effect shown in Figure 1 of SAE J862 may not be directly applicable to trucks, the effect of being either over or under is the same.

4.2 Transmission Driven Senders—Referring to Figure 1 of SAE J862, the factor "Take-Off Pinion Design Limits" is applicable to transmission driven senders only. Since the number of revolutions per unit distance for transmission driven senders is generally fixed at 1000 rpm at 60 mph (96.6 km/h), the accuracy of the odometer with respect to the rotation of the sender may be closely controlled by proper gearing or electrical division within the indicating unit itself.

4.3 Wheel Mounted Senders—Corrections for variations in rolling radius may be made by proper selection of the reduction gearing between the stepper motor and the odometer or of the sender excitation frequency. Where precise selection of the sender excitation frequency is possible, the overall odometer accuracy can be very high. However, rounding off of the reduction gearing and/or electrical division in the indicating unit can produce the same type of error that is obtained by rounding off any fractional number of teeth on the speedometer drive gear in the transmission.

1. When reference is made to existing SAE specifications, the latest revision shall apply.

5. Distance Indication (Allowable System Variation)

5.1 Overall Design Variation—The overall odometer accuracy shall be within –4% to +4% for each actual unit of distance of travel over the operating range of the instrument. The design limits should not, however, be construed as absolute under all operating conditions. Factors which cause variations from nominal wheel revolutions under operating conditions are covered in SAE J862. It is recommended that SAE J862 be studied to determine probable effects under service conditions.

5.1.1 ODOMETER INPUT—Inaccuracies contributed by the odometer and associated circuitry will be negligible with proper selection of the number of pulses per mile (kilometer) supplied to the unit. The actual number of sender pulses per mile (kilometer) can be negotiated between the user and the manufacturer.

5.2 Operating Range—The odometer shall meet the requirements of paragraphs 6.1 and 9.1.2 at any operating speed above 5 mph (8.05 km/h).

6. Distance Indication (Allowable Instrument Variation)

6.1 With nominal input frequency applied, the odometer shall indicate calculated mileage within ±0.3%.

6.2 For vehicles under 16 000 lb GVW, Federal Motor Vehicle Safety Standard 127 imposes certain requirements on the odometer and should be examined for the latest information.

7. Factors Affecting Speed Indication

7.1 Transmission Driven—The overall accuracy of speed indication is affected by the same errors as distance indication since the same sender drives both the odometer and speed indicator.

7.2 Wheel Driven—The speed indicator is calibrated for a nominal sender excitation frequency, therefore, the overall accuracy of speed indication is determined by the speed indicator calibration limits.

7.3 All Types—Speed indication may be affected by changes in ambient temperature and voltage.

8. Speed Indication (Allowable Instrument and Sender Variation)—The speed indicating unit shall be within the limits shown in Table 1 or Table 2 (consult speedometer vendor to determine proper table) when the sender is driven at the specified frequency at a temperature of 75 ± 5 °F (24 ± 3 °C) with nominal voltage applied. When analog displays are used, the spacing of the graduations on the speedometer dial may be non-linear to compensate for non-linearity in the system. It should be noted that variations in speedometer reading on the road may lie outside the limits of Table 1 due to the factors described in Figure 1 of SAE J862. All calibration of speedometers during manufacture shall be made with the instrument in approximately the same angular position that it will have when mounted in the vehicle. See Environmental Conditions for allowable variation within the instrument due to changes in ambient temperatures and voltage.

9. Effects Of Environmental Conditions

9.1 Temperature (Allowable System Variation)

9.1.1 SPEED INDICATION—With nominal voltage applied, the speed indication shall not vary more than ±2% of full scale from the reading determined in paragraph 8 while the indicating unit is operating over the range of +20 to +130 °F (–7 to +54 °C) and the sender is operating over the range of –40 to +280 °F (–40 to +138 °C). No permanent damage shall result from operating the indicating unit in a range of –40 to +180 °F (–40 to +82 °C). Internal lighting, if any, shall not be operating during this test.

9.1.2 DISTANCE INDICATION—With nominal voltage applied, the distance indication shall not vary more than ±0.3% from a reading obtained at 75 ± 5 °F (24 ± 3 °C) while the instrument is operating over the range of +20 to +130 °F (–7 to +54 °C) and the sender is operating over the range of –40 to +280 °F (–40 to +138 °C). No permanent damage shall result from operating the indicating unit in a range of –40 to +180 °F (–40 to +82 °C). Internal lighting, if any, shall not be operating during this test.

TABLE 1—SPEED INDICATION LIMITS FOR SPEEDOMETER FULL SCALE = 85 MPH (136.79 KM/H) BIASED

Actual Speed	mph	20	40	55
Indicated Speed	mph	18.9 – 22.4	39.5 – 43.0	55 – 58.4
Actual Speed	km/h	30	70	90
Indicated Speed	km/h	28.1 – 33.8	69.3 – 75.0	90 – 95.6

TABLE 2—SPEED INDICATION LIMITS FOR SPEEDOMETER FULL SCALE = 85 MPH (136.79 KM/H) NOT BIASED

Actual Speed	mph	20	40	55
Indicated Speed	mph	18.3 – 21.7	38.3 – 41.7	53.3 – 56.7
Actual Speed	km/h	30	70	90
Indicated Speed	km/h	27.2 – 32.8	67.2 – 72.8	87.2 – 92.8

NOTE—The speedometer accuracies are a percentage of full scale. If for example a 60 mph full scale is used, the speedometer accuracy will be ±1.2 mph. The total speedometer tolerance may be added to the actual speed to obtain the limits, as in Table 1, or may be split and added to and subtracted from the actual speed to obtain the limits, as in Table 2. Consult speedometer manufacturer to determine which method is used.

9.2 Temperature Extremes (Sender Only)—It will be necessary to evaluate the specific application to specify the allowable temperature extremes.

9.3 Storage (Indicating Unit Only)—A 4 h exposure of the indicating unit to a temperature of −40 to +185 °F (−40 to +85 °C) shall result in no more than ±1% of full scale permanent calibration change from the reading determined in paragraph 8. The rate of temperature change during this test shall not exceed 3.6 °F (2 °C) per minute.

9.4 Voltage Variation (Indicating Unit)

9.4.1 SPEED INDICATION—The indication shall not change more than ±1% of full scale indication from the reading determined in paragraph 8 within the following voltage ranges:

12 Volt System	24 Volt System
12 to 16 VDC	24 to 32 VDC

Twelve and 24 V indicating units shall not change more than ±3% of full scale indication from the reading obtained in paragraph 8 at 11 and 22 V respectively.

9.4.2 DISTANCE INDICATION—At 75 ± 5 °F (24 ± 3 °C) the distance indication shall not vary more than ±0.3% when operating within the voltage ranges given in paragraph 9.4.1.

9.5 Abnormal Voltage Conditions

9.5.1 TRANSIENT VOLTAGE PROTECTION—The indicating unit shall be capable of withstanding supply voltage transients without permanent damage and shall remain within the calibration specification of paragraphs 6.1 and 8 at the conclusion of this test.

The instrument shall be connected and operated for a total of 1 h with a means provided to impress upon the nominal battery voltage a repetitive rectangular voltage pulse of plus and minus six times nominal battery voltage with a duration of 300 μs and 1% duty cycle with a current of no more than 1.0 A.

For applications with transient voltages having a magnitude, duration, or duty cycle exceeding the above requirements, contact the instrument manufacturer for recommendations.

9.5.2 OVERVOLTAGE AND REVERSE POLARITY—Provisions for protection against booster starts with double battery voltage and/or reversed polarity must be negotiated between the user and the manufacturer.

9.6 Moisture Resistance

9.6.1 HUMIDITY (INDICATING UNIT)—Indicating unit shall withstand exposure to 95% relative humidity at 100 °F (38 °C) for 48 h.

9.6.2 SALT SPRAY (SENDER UNIT)—Sender units shall be corrosion resistant and shall withstand a salt spray (fog) test of 48 h duration with 5% salt solution (Reference ASTM B117-73).

9.6.3 PERFORMANCE DEGRADATION—Allowable degradation during humidity and salt spray tests (paragraphs 9.6.1 and 9.6.2) is negotiable between the user and the manufacturer.

9.7 Vibration Test (Indicating Unit)—The indicating unit shall be capable of withstanding without mechanical or electrical failure, 3 h of vibration, 1 h along each of the three mutually perpendicular axes. One axis is to be parallel to the indicator shaft. The vibration test shall be run at a double amplitude (peak to peak) of 0.030 in (0.76 mm) with the frequency varying from 10–30–10 Hz at intervals of 1 min. After completion of test, the calibration shall remain within tolerances as specified in paragraphs 8 and 6.1.

9.8 Vibration Test (Sender Only)

9.8.1 TRANSMISSION MOUNTED—The sender shall be capable of withstanding 6 h of vibration without mechanical or electrical failure, 2 h along each of the three mutually perpendicular axes. One axis is to be perpendicular to the mounting plane. The vibration test shall be run at a double amplitude (peak to peak) of 0.020 in (0.51 mm) with the frequency varying from 10-120-10 Hz at intervals of 1 min.

9.8.2 WHEEL MOUNTED SENDER—The sender shall be capable of withstanding 6 h of vibration without mechanical or electrical failure, 2 h along each of the three mutually perpendicular axes. One axis is to be perpendicular to the mounting plane. The vibration shall be run at a double amplitude (peak to peak) of 0.040 in (1.02 mm) with frequency varying from 10–120–10 Hz at intervals of 1 min.

9.9 Shock Test (Indicating Unit Only)—The indicating unit shall be capable of withstanding without mechanical or electrical failure the following series of shocks and still maintain the calibration tolerances specified in paragraphs 8 and 6.1. The indicating unit shall be subjected to one shock in each direction along each of three mutually perpendicular axes. One axis is to be parallel to the indicator shaft. Each shock shall have an amplitude of 23–27 g, half sine of 9–13 milliseconds duration.

9.10 Shock Test (All Senders)—The sender shall be capable of withstanding, without mechanical or electrical failure, six shocks of 44–55 g, half sine of 9–13 milliseconds duration in each direction along each of three mutually perpendicular axes. One axis is to be perpendicular to the mounting plane.

10. Design Detail Recommendations (Indicating Unit Only)

10.1 When analog displays are used, the display shall be accomplished by a pointer or other indicator traversing in a clockwise or left to right direction as applicable to register increasing speed over a suitable scale on the indicating unit dial. Consult FMVSS 127 for any requirements concerning dial specifications.

10.2 Graduations shall be designed for the best practical legibility and accuracy of reading.

10.3 Unless otherwise specified, pointers and dial printing shall be white, dial background shall be low gloss black, and visible portions of the indicating unit should exhibit low reflectivity. The distance indicator shall have white numerals on a low gloss black background except for the tenths indicator which shall have black numerals on a white background.

10.4 The indicating unit case shall be provided with studs for mounting by suitable U-clamps or similar means.

10.5 Typical envelope, mounting studs and terminal designations are displayed in Figures 1, 2, and 3.

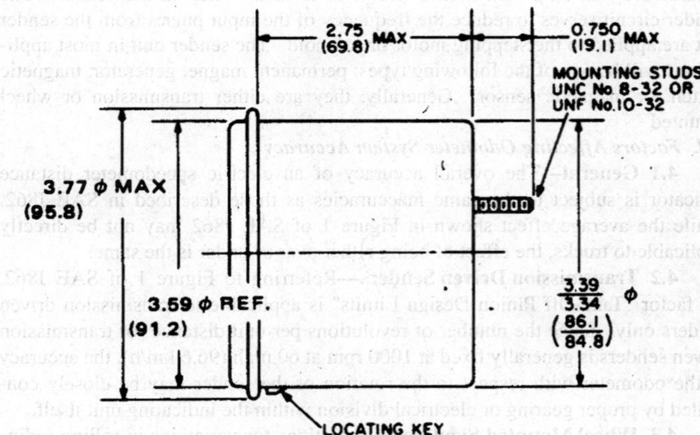

FIGURE 1—ENVELOPE AND MOUNTING STUDS

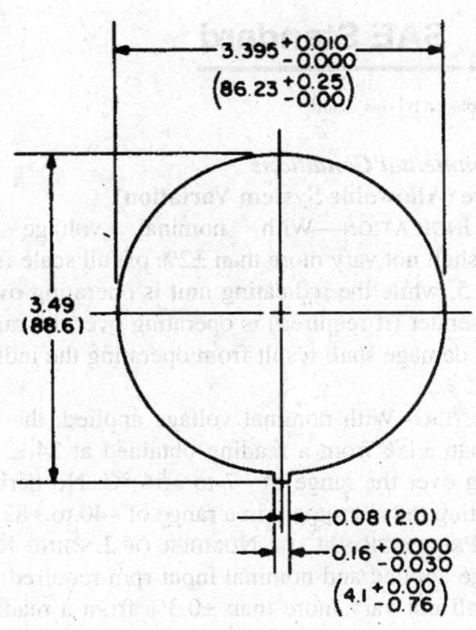

FIGURE 2—MOUNTING CUTOUT DETAIL

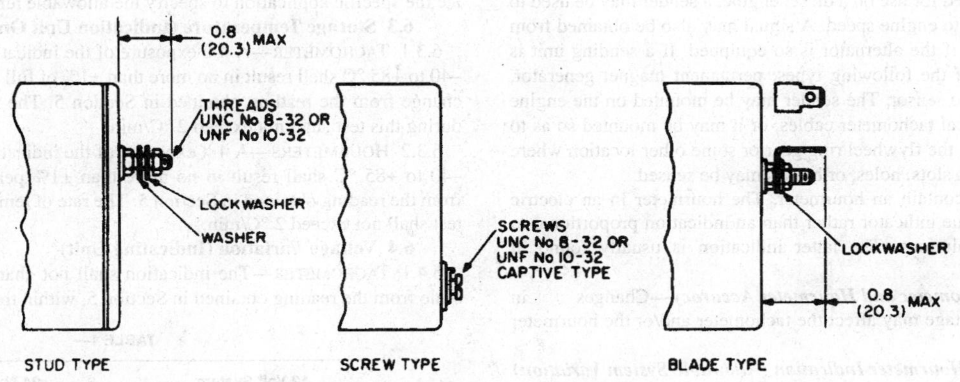

FIGURE 3—TERMINALS

11. Identification

11.1 Indicating Unit

11.1.1 To be legibly stamped on outside of case:

a. Manufacturer's or user's part number.
b. Manufacturer's or user's serial number and/or date of manufacture.

11.1.2 To be printed on dial and/or stamped on case: manufacturer's or user's name or trademark.

11.1.3 Electrical connections shall be clearly identified for proper wiring of instrument into circuit.

11.2 Sender—Sender identification is to be as agreed by the manufacturer and the user.

ELECTRIC TACHOMETER SPECIFICATION —SAE J1399 JUN1984

SAE Standard

Report of the SAE Speedometer and Tachometer Committee, Electric Subcommittee approved September 1982. SAE J196 and J197 have been replaced by this report.

Foreword—This Document has also changed to comply with the new SAE Technical Standards Board format.

1. Scope—This SAE Recommended Practice establishes minimum requirements for electric tachometer systems with and without hourmeter or revolution counter, for general applications as follows:

Class 1—Passenger Car
Class 2—Bus and Truck
Class 3—Off-Road Vehicles

2. References

2.1 Applicable Publication—The following publication forms a part of the specification to the extent specified herein. Unless otherwise indicated the latest revision of SAE publications shall apply.

2.1.1 ASTM Publication—Available from ASTM, 100 Barr Harbor Drive, West Conshohocken, PA 19428-2959.

ASTM B117-73

3. Electric Tachometer System—A typical electric tachometer system for engines using a Kettering ignition system or the newer electronic ignition systems, consists of an indicating unit that obtains a signal proportional to engine speed from the ignition system.

If the tachometer is intended for use on a diesel engine, a sender may be used to supply a signal proportional to engine speed. A signal may also be obtained from an a.c. tap on the alternator if the alternator is so equipped. If a sending unit is used, it will often be one of the following types: permanent magnet generator, magnetic switch, or magnetic sensor. The sender may be mounted on the engine outlet provided for mechanical tachometer cables, or it may be mounted so as to sense the number of teeth on the flywheel ring gear or some other location where a rotating element with teeth, slots, holes, or bosses may be sensed.

The indicating unit may contain an hourmeter. The hourmeter in an electric tachometer may be a true time indicator rather than an indication proportional to the number of engine revolutions. The latter indication is usually found in mechanical tachometers.

4. Factors Affecting Tachometer and Hourmeter Accuracy—Changes in ambient temperature and voltage may affect the tachometer and/or the hourmeter indication.

5. Tachometer and True Hourmeter Indication (Allowable System Variation)

5.1 Tachometers Driven by Signal from Ignition System or Alternator A.C. Tap—The tachometer indication shall be within ±2% of full scale with nominal voltage applied at a temperature of 24 ± 3 °C when the tachometer is driven with a signal from an ignition system or from an alternator a.c. tap, as applicable. If a calibrator is used, it must supply a signal having the same characteristics as that supplied by an ignition system or an alternator a.c. tap. Calibration of tachometers shall be made with the instrument in approximately the same angular position that it will have when mounted in the vehicle. See Environmental Conditions for allowable variation within the instrument due to changes in ambient temperatures and voltage.

5.1.1 Secondary Losses—The effect of the tachometer on the ignition system should not reduce the available secondary voltage by more than 4%. Testing is to be done with the exact ignition system to be used in actual practice. The distributor is to be run with the coil input voltage held constant at 14.0 V and the coil secondary open circuited. The exact test procedure for measurements shall be established by the supplier and consumer.

5.2 Sender Driven Units—The tachometer indication shall be within ±2% of full scale with nominal voltage applied at a temperature of 24 ± 3 °C, when the tachometer is driven with a signal from a sender either rotated or excited in a fashion simulating actual operation. If a calibrator is used, it must supply a signal having the same characteristics as the sender. Calibration of tachometers shall be made with the instrument in approximately the same angular position that it will have when mounted in the vehicle. See Environmental Conditions for allowable variation within the instrument due to changes in ambient temperatures and voltage.

5.3 True Hourmeter—The hourmeter indication shall be within ±2% of elapsed time with nominal voltage applied at a temperature of 24 ± 3 °C.

5.4 Hourmeter Proportional to Number of Engine Revolutions—The time indication shall be within ±0.3% with nominal voltage applied, nominal input rpm required to indicate I h and at a temperature of 24 ± 3 °C.

6. Effects of Environmental Conditions

6.1 Temperature (Allowable System Variation)

6.1.1 Tachometer Indication—With nominal voltage applied, the tachometer indication shall not vary more than ±2% of full scale from the reading determined in Section 5, while the indicating unit is operating over the range of –7 to +54 °C and the sender (if required) is operating over the range of –40 to + 138 °C. No permanent damage shall result from operating the indicating unit in a range of –40 to +82 °C.

6.1.2 True Hourmeter—With nominal voltage applied, the time indication shall not vary more than ±1% from a reading obtained at 24 ± 3 °C while the instrument is operating over the range of –7 to +54 °C. No permanent damage shall result from operating the instrument in a range of –40 to +82 °C.

6.1.3 Hourmeter Proportional to Number of Engine Revolutions—With nominal voltage applied and nominal input rpm required to indicate 1 h, the time indication shall not vary more than ±0.3% from a reading obtained in Section 5 while the instrument is operating over the range of –7 to +54 °C. No permanent damage shall result from operating the instrument in a range of –40 to +82 °C.

6.2 Temperature Extremes (Sender Only)—It will be necessary to evaluate the specific application to specify the allowable temperature extremes.

6.3 Storage Temperature (Indication Unit Only)

6.3.1 Tachometer—A 4 h exposure of the indicating unit to a temperature of –40 to +85 °C shall result in no more than ±1% of full scale permanent calibration change from the reading obtained in Section 5. The rate of temperature change during this test shall not exceed 2 °C/min.

6.3.2 Hourmeters—A 4 h exposure of the indicating unit to a temperature of –40 to +85 °C shall result in no more than ±1% permanent calibration change from the reading obtained in Section 5. The rate of temperature change during this test shall not exceed 2 °C/min.

6.4 Voltage Variation (Indicating Unit)

6.4.1 Tachometer—The indication shall not change more than ±1% of full scale from the reading obtained in Section 5, within the following voltage ranges.

TABLE 1—

12 Volt System	24 Volt System
12–16 VDC	24–32 VDC

Twelve and twenty-four volt tachometers shall not change more than ±3% of full scale, from the reading obtained in Section 5, at 11 and 22 V respectively.

6.4.2 True Hourmeter—The indication shall not change more than ±1% from the reading obtained in Section 5, within the following voltage ranges.

TABLE 2—

12 Volt System	24 Volt System
12–16 VDC	24–32 VDC

Twelve and twenty-four volt hourmeters shall not change more than ±3% from the reading obtained in Section 5, at 11 and 22 V respectively.

6.4.3 Hourmeter Proportional to Number of Engine Revolutions—At 24 ± 3 °C and with nominal input rpm required to indicate 1 h, the time indication shall not vary more than ±0.3% from a reading obtained in Section 5 when operating within the voltage ranges given in paragraph 6.4.2.

6.5 Abnormal Voltage Conditions—Tachometer and True Hourmeter

6.5.1 Transient Voltage Protection—The indicating unit shall be capable of withstanding supply voltage transients without permanent damage and shall remain within the calibration specification of Section 5 at the conclusion of this test. The instrument shall be connected and operated for a total of 1 h with a means provided to impress upon the nominal battery voltage a repetitive rectangular voltage pulse of plus and minus six times nominal battery voltage with a duration of 300 µs and 1% duty cycle with a current of no more than 1.0 A.

6.5.2 Overvoltage and Reverse Polarity—Provisions for protection against booster starts with double battery voltage and/or reversed polarity must be negotiated between the user and the manufacturer.

6.6 Moisture Resistance

6.6.1 HUMIDITY (INDICATING UNIT)—Indicating unit shall withstand exposure to 95% relative humidity at 38 °C for 48 h.

6.6.2 SALT SPRAY (SENDER UNIT)—Sender units shall be corrosion resistant and shall withstand a salt spray (fog) test of 48 h duration with 5% salt solution (Reference ASTM B 117-73).

6.7 Vibration Test (Indicating Unit)—The indicating unit shall be capable of withstanding without mechanical or electrical failure, 3 h of vibration, 1 h along each of the three mutually perpendicular axes. One of said axes is to be parallel to the indicator shaft. The vibration test shall be run at a double amplitude as specified in the table below with the frequency varying as shown in the table at intervals of I min. After completion of test, the calibration shall remain within tolerances as specified in Sections 5 and 6.

TABLE 3—

Class	Amplitude, DA (mm)	Frequency Range (Hz)	Max. Acceleration (g)
1	0.75	10–30–10	1.4 at 30 Hz
2	1.52	10–55–10	10 at 55 Hz
3	1.52	10–80–10	20 at 80 Hz

6.8 Vibration Test (Sender Only)

6.8.1 ENGINE MOUNTED—The sender shall be capable of withstanding 6 h of vibration without mechanical or electrical failure, 2 h along each of the three mutually perpendicular axes. One of said axes is to be parallel to the input shaft. The vibration test shall be run at a double amplitude of 0.50 mm with the frequency varying from 10-120-10 Hz at intervals of 1 min.

6.9 Shock Test (Indicating Unit Only)—The indicating unit shall be capable of withstanding without mechanical or electrical failure, the following series of shocks and still maintain the calibration tolerances specified in Sections 5 and 6. The indicating unit shall be subjected to an equal number of shocks in each direction along each of three mutually perpendicular axes. One of said axes is to be parallel to the indicator shaft. Each shock shall be half sine of 9–13 ms duration, the acceleration and total number of shocks per table below.

TABLE 4—

Class	Peak Acceleration (g)	Total Number
1	23–27	6
2	23–27	72
3	44–55	72

6.10 Shock Test (All Senders)—The sender shall be capable of withstanding, without mechanical or electrical failure, six shocks of 44–55 g, half sine of 9–13 ms duration in each direction along each of three mutually perpendicular axes. One of said axes is to be perpendicular to the mounting plane.

6.11 Design Detail Recommendations (Indicating Unit Only)

6.11.1 When analog displays are used, the display shall be accomplished by a pointer or other indicator traversing in a clockwise or left to right direction as applicable, to register increasing revolutions per minute over a suitable scale on the indicating unit dial.

6.11.2 Graduations shall be designed for the best practical legibility and accuracy of reading.

6.11.3 Unless otherwise specified: pointers and dial printing shall be white, dial background shall be low gloss black, and visible portions of the indicating unit should exhibit low reflectivity; the time or revolution indicator shall have white numerals on a low gloss black background except for the tenths indicator which shall have black numerals on a white background.

6.11.4 The indicating unit case shall be provided with studs for mounting by suitable U-clamps or similar means.

6.11.5 Typical envelope, mounting studs and terminal designations are displayed in Figures 1 - 3.

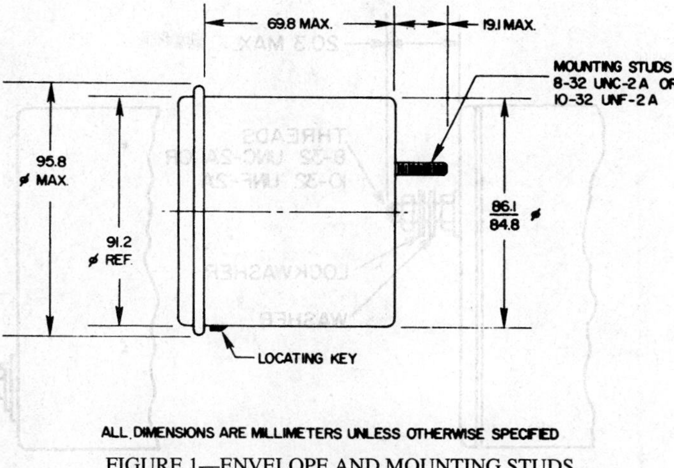

FIGURE 1—ENVELOPE AND MOUNTING STUDS

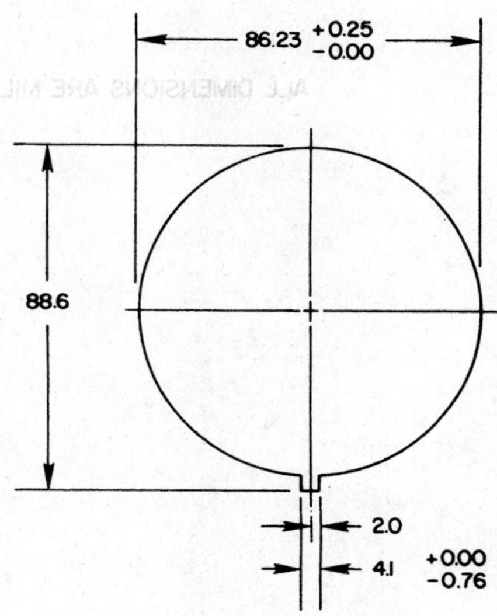

ALL DIMENSIONS ARE MILLIMETERS UNLESS OTHERWISE SPECIFIED

FIGURE 2—MOUNTING CUTOUT DETAIL

6.12 Identification

6.12.1 INDICATING UNIT

6.12.1.1 To be legibly indicated on outside of case:

a. Manufacturer's or user's part number.

b. Manufacturer's or user's serial number and/or date of manufacture.

6.12.1.2 To be printed on dial and/or indicated on case: Manufacturer's or user's name or trademark.

6.12.1.3 Electrical connections shall be clearly identified for proper wiring of instrument into circuit.

6.12.2 SENDER—Sender identification is to be used as agreed between manufacturer and user.

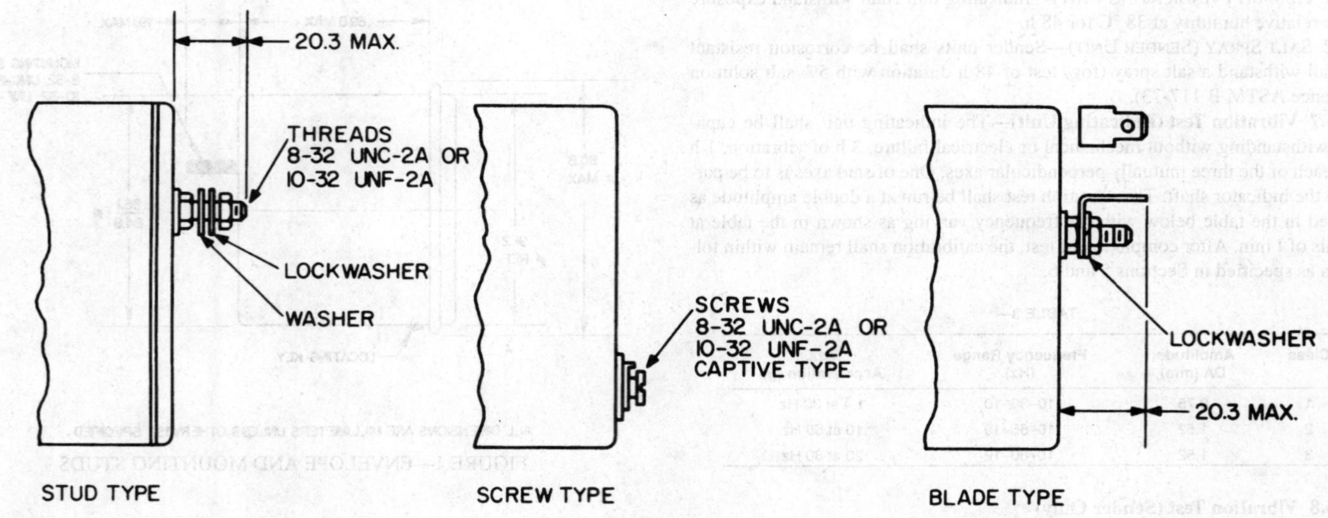
20.3 MAX.
THREADS
8-32 UNC-2A OR
10-32 UNF-2A
LOCKWASHER
WASHER
SCREWS
8-32 UNC-2A OR
10-32 UNF-2A
CAPTIVE TYPE
LOCKWASHER
20.3 MAX.
STUD TYPE
SCREW TYPE
BLADE TYPE
ALL DIMENSIONS ARE MILLIMETERS UNLESS OTHERWISE SPECIFIED

FIGURE 3—TERMINALS

ELECTRIC HOURMETER SPECIFICATION —SAE J1378 JUL1998

SAE Recommended Practice

Report of the SAE Speedometer and Tachometer Committee approved March 1983 and revised July 1998.

Foreword—This Document has also changed to comply with the new SAE Technical Standards Board format. In 5.3 and 5.6, μ was changed to m. References were added as Section 2. All other section numbers have changed.

1. Scope—This SAE Recommended Practice establishes minimum requirements for electric hourmeters for general vehicular applications.

2. References

2.1 Applicable Publication—The following publication forms a part of this specification to the extent specified herein. Unless otherwise indicated, the latest revision of SAE publications shall apply.

2.1.1 SAE PUBLICATION—Available from SAE, 400 Commonwealth Drive, Warrendale, PA 15096-0001.

SAE J1113—Electromagnetic Susceptibility Measurement Procedures for Vehicle Components (Except Aircraft)

NOTE—SAE J1113 is cancelled and is superseded by SAE J1113 Parts 1, 2, 3, 4, 11, 12, 13, 21, 22, 23, 25, 26, 27, 41, and 42.

3. Electric Hourmeter Description—A typical electric hourmeter is a true operating time indicator which functions when electrically energized. The hourmeter is a DC operated device. There are three basic electromechanical types among which are: Stepper Solenoids, Stepper Motors, and Electrically Operated Clocks.

4. Calibration—The hourmeter indication shall be within ±2% of the elapsed time or ±0.1 h, whichever is greater, with nominal voltage applied at a temperature of 24 °C ± 3 °C.

5. Effects of Environmental Conditions

5.1 Temperature

5.1.1 OPERATING—With nominal voltage applied, the time indication shall not vary more than ±1% of elapsed time in addition to the calibration error obtained in Section 4, while the unit is operating over the range of –7 to +54 °C. No permanent damage shall result from operating the unit in a range of –40 to +82 °C.

5.1.2 STORAGE—A 4-h exposure of the instrument to a temperature of –40 to +85 °C shall result in no more than an additional ±1% of elapsed time permanent change from calibration error obtained in Section 4. The rate of temperature change during this test shall not exceed 2 °C/min.

5.2 Voltage Variations—The time indication shall not change more than ±1% of elapsed time in addition to the calibration error obtained in Section 4 due to a voltage change of a nominal 12-V system from 12 to 16 VDC and a nominal 24-V system from 24 to 32 VDC. Twelve and 24-V hourmeters shall not change more than ±3% from the reading obtained in Section 4 at 11 and 22 V respectively.

5.3 Abnormal Voltage Conditions

5.3.1 TRANSIENT PROTECTION—The instrument shall be capable of withstanding supply voltage transients without permanent damage and shall remain within the calibration specification of Section 4 at the conclusion of this test. The instrument shall be connected and operated for a total of 1 h with a means provided to impress upon the nominal battery voltage a repetitive rectangular voltage pulse of plus and minus six times nominal battery voltage with a duration of 300 ms and 1% duty cycle with a current of no more than 1.0 A. For some applications which may have transient voltages having a magnitude, duration, or duty cycle exceeding the previous requirements, contact the instrument manufacturer for recommendations. Further information on transients may be found in SAE J1113.

5.3.2 OVERVOLTAGE AND REVERSE POLARITY—Provisions for protection against booster starts with double battery voltage and/or reversed polarity must be negotiated between the user and the manufacturer.

5.4 Humidity—Instrument shall not have its function impaired due to exposure to 95% relative humidity at 38 °C for 48 h.

5.5 Vibration Test—The electric hourmeter shall be capable of withstanding without mechanical or electrical failure 6 h of vibration, 2 h along each of the three mutually perpendicular axes, one axis to be perpendicular to mounting plane. The vibration tests shall be run at a double amplitude of 1.52 mm with the frequency varying from 10–80–10 Hz (20 g max) at intervals of 1 min. After completion of test, the calibration shall remain within tolerances as specified in Section 4.

5.6 Shock Test—The instrument shall be capable of withstanding without mechanical or electrical failure, the following series of shocks and still maintain the calibration tolerances specified in Section 4.

The unit shall be subjected to 12 shocks in each direction along each of the three mutually perpendicular axes (72 total shocks), one axis to be perpendicular to the mounting plane. Each shock shall have an amplitude of 44 to 55 g, half sine of 9 to 13 ms duration.

6. Design Detail Recommendations

6.1 Unless otherwise specified by user, dial printing shall be white, dial background shall be low gloss black, and visible portions of the instrument should exhibit low reflectivity; the indicating wheels or drums shall have white numerals on a low gloss black background, except for the tenths indicator, which shall have black numerals on a white background.

6.2 All exposed surfaces shall be corrosion resistant for limited exposure.

NOTE—If instruments are required for installations in extreme environments, contact manufacturer for recommendations.

6.3 Instruments shall be moisture and dust resistant. (See note in 6.2.)

6.4 The hourmeter case may be provided with studs for mounting by suitable U-clamps or similar means. Some hourmeters may have a flange for mounting.

6.5 Typical envelope, mounting studs, mounting flange, panel cutout, and terminal designations are displayed in Figures 1A to 4.

6.6 Identification (Unless Otherwise Specified)

6.6.1 To be legibly indicated on outside of case:

a. Manufacturer's or user's part number

b. Manufacturer's or user's serial number and/or date of manufacture

6.6.2 To be printed on dial and/or indicated on case: manufacturer's or user's name and/or trademark.

6.6.3 Electrical connections shall be clearly identified for proper wiring of instrument into circuit.

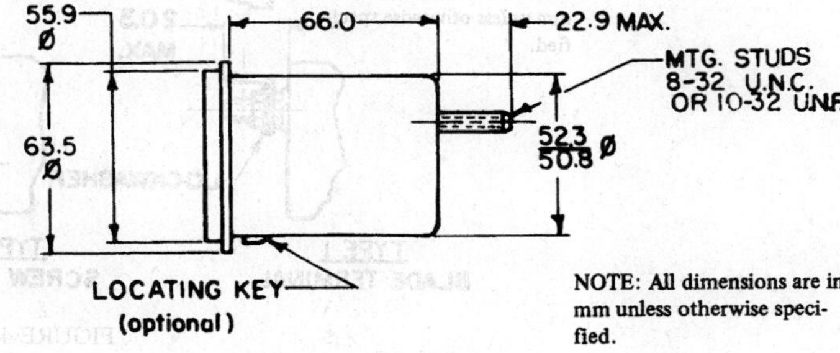

FIGURE 1A—(ENVELOPE) U-CLAMP MOUNT

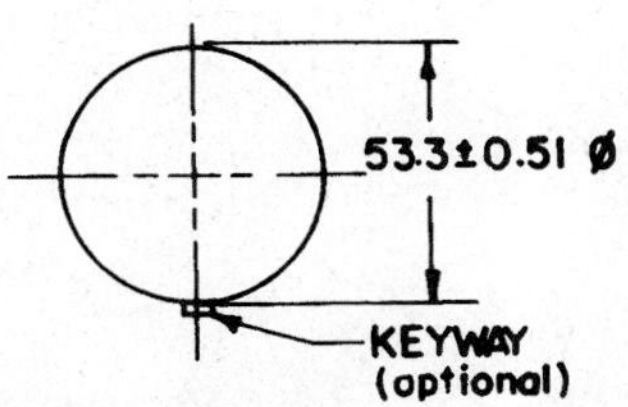

NOTE: All dimensions are in mm unless otherwise specified.

FIGURE 1B—PANEL CUTOUT

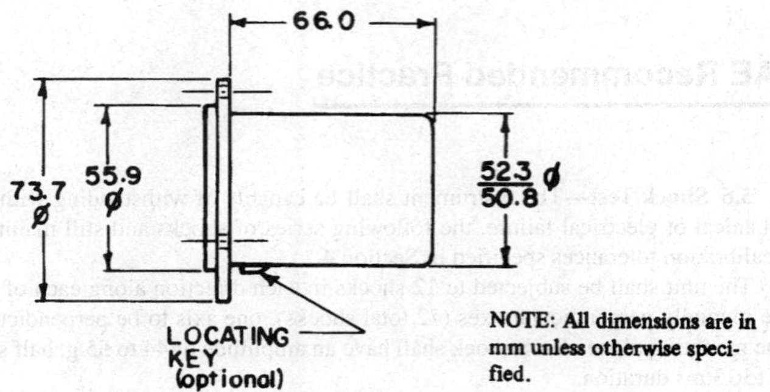

FIGURE 2A—(ENVELOPE) FLANGE MOUNT

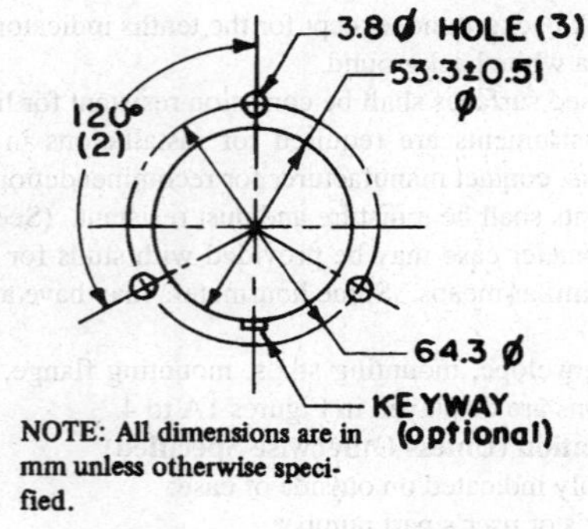

FIGURE 2B—PANEL CUTOUT

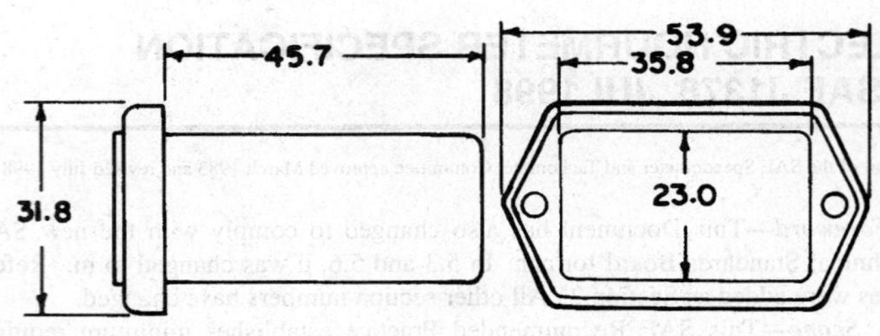

FIGURE 3A—(ENVELOPE) FLANGE MOUNT

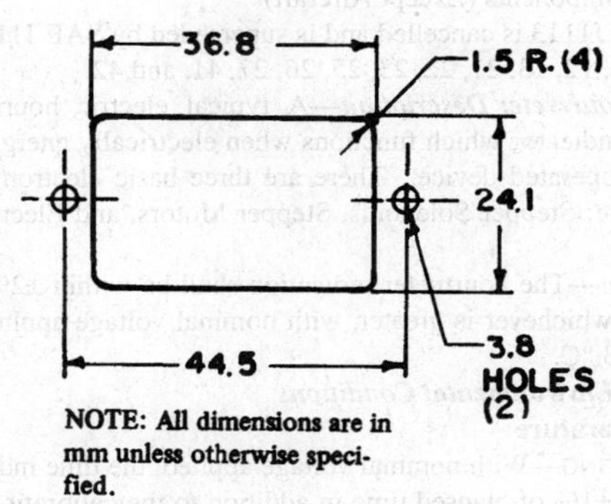

FIGURE 3B—PANEL CUTOUT

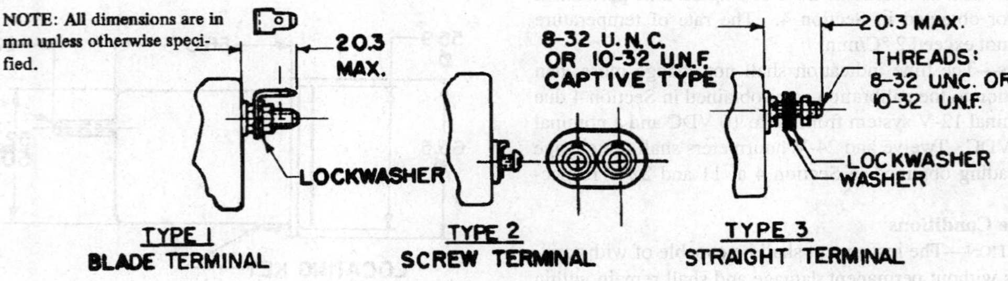

FIGURE 4—TERMINALS

AUTOMATIC VEHICLE SPEED CONTROL —MOTOR VEHICLES—SAE J195 DEC1988

SAE Recommended Practice

Report of SAE Automotive Safety Committee approved October 1970 and reaffirmed by the SAE Speedometer and Tachometer Committee December 1988.

Foreword—This Reaffirmed Document has been changed only to reflect the new SAE Technical Standards Board Format.

*1. **Scope***—This SAE Recommended Practice is intended to apply only to the design of an automatic vehicle speed control. It is not intended to encourage or discourage the installation of automatic vehicle speed controls on any class of vehicles, nor is it intended to influence the requirements of engine speed governors.

1.1 Purpose—The purpose of this SAE Recommended Practice is to provide a series of engineering guidelines for the design of an automatic vehicle speed control, and to define the minimum control performance which a device must provide in order to be classified an automatic vehicle speed control.

*2. **References***—There are no referenced publications specified herein.

*3. **Definitions***

3.1 Automatic Vehicle Speed Control—A device capable of maintaining selected vehicle speeds in the presence of changing road load conditions.

*4. **Design Recommendations***

4.1 The speed control shall require a deliberate action of the driver to cause activation and reactivation. Systems reactivated solely by the operation of the accelerator pedal shall include a signal to the driver to indicate reactivation.

4.2 The speed control shall be deactivated upon application of the service brakes (depressing the clutch pedal on manual clutch equipped vehicles shall also deactivate the speed control) and shall not reactivate without the deliberate action of the driver.

4.3 When deactivated, the speed control shall have no effect on vehicle operation.

4.4 If a speed signal source other than the drivetrain or a driving wheel is used, suitable precautions shall be provided to prevent runaway when a driving wheel loses traction.

4.5 An alternate hand-operated deactivation control within the reach of the driver, in addition to the brake, clutch (if so equipped), and ignition key, shall be provided.

4.6 The system shall be capable of deactivation or capable of being made inoperative by a control within the reach of the driver under the following conditions:

4.6.1 Failure of any power source to the device.

4.6.2 Failure of speed signal to the device.

4.6.3 Short circuit of electrical leads of the device.

4.6.4 Failure of other vehicle components upon which the device is dependent for function.

4.7 The device shall not be operable below 20 mph (32 km/h).

4.8 The speed control linkage shall be designed and installed to prevent inadvertent interference with normal accelerator control operation under all operating and environmental conditions consistent with the environmental capabilities of the vehicle upon which it is installed.

*5. **Performance Requirements***—The automatic vehicle speed control shall regulate the output power of the engine to provide a stable and essentially constant vehicle speed. The following test defines the minimum performance requirements of an automatic vehicle speed control.

5.1 Test Conditions—The performance evaluation shall be performed under the following conditions:

5.1.1 Ambient temperature of +30 °F–80 °F (–1 °C to +27 °C).

5.1.2 Altitude not to exceed 2500 ft (760 m) above sea level.

5.1.3 Component wind velocity in the direction of travel of the vehicle not to exceed 10 mph (16 km/h).

5.1.4 Selected vehicle speed of 40–70 mph (64–113 km/h).

5.1.5 Test road shall be hard surfaced and shall include a minimum of one 1/8 mile (200 m) (minimum) grade of –2% and one 1/8 mile (200 m) (minimum) grade of +2%, and shall be at least 5 miles (8 km) long.

5.2 Test Vehicle—The vehicle used for performance evaluation shall be capable of a level road 40–70 mph (64–113 km/h) acceleration time of not over 16 s. The vehicle qualification test shall be run in the highest available transmission gear or range. Downshifting is prohibited in meeting this requirement.

5.3 Performance Limits—Maximum vehicle speed variation shall not exceed ±3 mph (5 km/h).

TRANSMISSION MOUNTED VEHICLE SPEED SIGNAL ROTOR SPECIFICATION—SAE J1377 JAN1989

SAE Recommended Practice

Developed by the SAE Electric Speedometer and Tachometer Subcommittee, approved by the SAE Speedometer and Tachometer Committee June 1984 and reaffirmed January 1989.

Foreword—This Document has not changed other than to put it into the new SAE Technical Standards Board Format.

1. Scope—This SAE Recommended Practice covers the transmission output shaft mounted signal rotor and sensor mounting hole used for electronic speed sensing on Class 6, 7, and 8 highway vehicles.

1.1 Purpose—To standardize the number of discontinuities sensed (such as teeth or slots) per revolution of the transmission output shaft.

2. References

2.1 Applicable Publications—The following publications form a part of the specification to the extent specified herein. Unless otherwise indicated the lastest revision of SAE publications shall apply.

2.1.1 SAE PUBLICATIONS—Available from SAE, 400 Commonwealth Drive, Warrendale, PA 15096-0001.

SAE J514 APR80—Hydraulic Tube Fittings
SAE J515 JUN67—Hydraulic "O" Ring

3. Electronic Speed Sensing—A gear, stamping or milled disc with discontinuities that are sensed by a sensor, usually a magnetic sensor consisting of a coil of wire - suitably terminated - wound around a cylindrical magnet and encased in a metal housing, may be used as a vehicle speed signal source.

The vehicle speed signal may then be used to activate electronic speedometers, cruise controls, vehicle speed limiting devices, and other components requiring vehicle speed information.

4. Transmission Signal Rotor—The signal rotor shall have 16 teeth or discontinuities, and shall turn at the same speed as the transmission output shaft. The eccentricity of the sensed portion of the signal rotor shall not exceed 0.25 mm total indicated runout. When magnetic sensors are used, the signal rotor, gear, disc, or stamping in the transmission shall have teeth, slots, holes, and other discontinuities and shall be a low carbon, low remanence ferrous or magnetic material, such as cast iron or steel. The discontinuities shall be at least 3 mm deep. It is desirable for the discontinuities and the metal separating them to be of approximately equal size. The discontinuity size or rotor face width shall be no smaller than 3 mm wide.

5. Sensor Mounting Hole—The hole for the magnetic sensor shall be a 3/4 in 16 UNF thread. The axis of the hole shall be perpendicular to the sensed surface of the transmission gear, disc, or signal rotor, and shall be positioned so as to center the sensor over the discontinuities being sensed. The external surface around the speed sensor mounting hole shall be flat and smooth for a diameter sufficient to accommodate a locknut. The requirement for sealing in transmission lubricant should be negotiated between the user and the transmission and sensor suppliers. SAE Hydraulic Tube fitting O-ring seals are suggested. See SAE J514 and J515. (Reference nominal tube size 1/2 in.)

22 Tubing, Hose and Fittings

SAE HOSE MEASUREMENT STUDY—SAE J1759 OCT2000SAE Information Report

Report of the SAE Coolant Hose Committee approved October 2000. Rationale statement available.

1. Scope—The Measurement of Coolant Hose task group conducted a round-robin study to determine the measuring capability of automotive suppliers and users to measure Inside Diameter (ID), Outside Diameter (OD), Wall Thickness (Wall) and wall thickness variation of hose using traditional measuring devices and techniques. Seven companies (five suppliers and two end users) participated in this testing. Based upon the round-robin study this information report will detail procedures, test measuring devices, results and recommendations.

2. References

2.1 Applicable Publications—The following publication forms a part of this specification to the extent specified herein.

2.1.1 AIAG PUBLICATIONS—Available from Automotive Industry Action Group, Suite 200, 26200 Lahser Road, Southfield, MI 48034.

(MSA) Manual-Measurement Systems Analysis Manual

3. Procedure—The following procedures were employed in the round-robin study:

3.1 Two (2) sets of hoses were checked; there were 10 samples in each set.

3.2 One end of each hose was marked for measurement. The attribute was taken from 6.4 mm (0.250 in) to 25.4 mm (1.000 in) from the end of the hose.

NOTE—All measurements were made using inch measuring units due to the lack of adequate metric equipment).

3.3 Three (3) people repeated each measurement three (3) times at each testing location.

3.4 The data were recorded on forms supplied with the samples.

3.5 Hose samples and measuring devices were brought to equilibrium for 24 h in a controlled environment of 23 °C ± 2 °C and relative humidity of 50% +5%.

4. Attributes

4.1 Procedure—All of the samples and measuring devices were forwarded to the seven participants in order. The form for recording the measurements was also included. After taking the measurements, the data were sent to the chairman of the Measurement of Coolant Hose task group for analysis.

The attributes of ID, OD, Wall Thickness, and Wall thickness variation were measured as follows:

4.1.1 INSIDE DIAMETER—The ID of the sample hoses was measured with step gages. Two sets of gages were provided that were centered around the target of each of the hose ID's; one set included diameter steps in increments of 0.05 mm (0.002 in) and the other 0.1 mm (0.004 in). The gages were inserted dry with a steady rotating motion and not causing more than an increase of 0.13 mm (0.005 in) in the OD when measured with a pi tape.

4.1.2 OUTSIDE DIAMETER—The OD was measured by two methods:

4.1.2.1 Method 1—A plug which had an OD the same as the maximum specified ID of the hose to be measured was inserted into the hose. The OD was measured by means of pi tape. (The plug was provided for this test with diameter steps graduated in 0.25 mm (0.010 in) increments).

4.1.2.2 Method 2—The OD was measured by means of calipers. Find the largest OD and record; take another reading 90 degrees ± 15 degrees from the first and record. The average of the two readings was recorded and used as the OD of the hose.

(Calipers were provided for this test)

4.2 Wall Thickness—The wall thickness was measured with calipers. Four (4) readings were taken, starting with the thinnest spot on the hose and rotating 90 degrees for each of the following three (3) measurements. An average of the four (4) numbers was recorded as the wall thickness.

4.3 Wall Thickness Variation—The Wall Thickness Variation was calculated using the first wall thickness recorded in 4.2. A second measurement was taken at the thickest location of the wall measurement and recorded. The difference between the two readings was recorded as the Wall Thickness Variation.

5. Results—The Gage R & R calculation is based upon the Automotive Industry Action Group Measurement Systems Analysis (MSA) manual.

The Results of this study were as follows in Figures 1 to 17:

6. Recommendations—The results of this study have shown that traditional measuring devices and techniques are not capable of meeting the required 10% Gage R&R as suggested in the AIAG MSA automotive standards.

It is the consensus of the SAE Coolant Hose Committee that new gaging methods must be found and implemented before current hose measurement can be validated between companies. The SAE Coolant Hose Committee urges the membership jointly or individually to develop measuring devices and techniques which will conform to the AIAG MSA Automotive Gage R & R target of 10%.

5/13/92

MEDIAN VS AVERAGE TOLERANCE
FOR GAGE ERROR

CHARACTERISTIC	GAGE/METHOD	R&R MEDIAN	ACTUAL MEDIAN	R&R AVERAGE	ACTUAL AVERAGE
I.D.	.002 W/1.75	41.860	.013	67.730	.020
I.D.	.004 W/1.75	33.880	.010	44.457	.013
I.D.	.002 W/.725	16.190	.005	20.650	.006
I.D.	.004 W/.725	21.170	.006	26.375	.008
O.D.	PI TAPE W/1.75	62.310	.025	73.354	.029
O.D.	CALIPERS W/1.75	38.865	.016	43.437	.017
O.D.	PI TAPE W/.725	56.760	.023	66.834	.027
O.D.	CALIPERS W/.725	66.465	.027	67.470	.027
WALL	CALIPERS W/1.75	28.465	.011	42.418	.017
WALL	CALIPERS W/.725	44.440	.018	49.538	.020
CONCENTRICITY	CALIPERS W/1.75	61.200	.024	61.050	.024
CONCENTRICITY	CALIPERS W/.725	78.985	.032	75.088	.030

The characteristic "concentricity" is the wall variation

NOTE—1 in = 25.4 mm
1 lb/ft = 1.49 kg/m
1 psi = 6.9 kPa

FIGURE 1—MEDIAN VERSUS AVERAGE TOLERANCE FOR GAGE ERROR USING PLUG GAGE FOR ID, Pi TAPE AND CALIPERS FOR OD AND CALIPERSFOR WALL THICKNESS AND WALL VARIATION

5/13/92 SUMMARY SAE HOSES I.D.

COMPANY	DIM.	GAGE USED	REPEAT. % OF TOL.	ACTUAL TOL. USED	REPROD. % OF TOL.	ACTUAL TOL. USED	GAGE R & R	ACTUAL TOTAL TOL. USED	SPEC. TOL.
A-1	I.D.	.002 S/P 1.750	10.27	.003	22.35	.007	32.62	.010	.030
B-1	I.D.	.002 S/P 1.750	7.68	.002	7.62	.002	15.30	.005	.030
C-1	I.D.	.002 S/P 1.750	7.39	.002	97.17	.029	104.56	.031	.030
D-1	I.D.	.002 S/P 1.750	4.39	.001	37.47	.011	41.86	.013	.030
E-1	I.D.	.002 S/P 1.750	16.14	.005	1.64	.000	17.78	.005	.030
F-1	I.D.	.002 S/P 1.750	.29	.000	130.06	.039	130.34	.039	.030
G-1	I.D.	.002 S/P 1.750	.50	.000	131.15	.039	131.65	.039	.030
		AVERAGE:	6.666		61.066		67.730		
A-2	I.D.	.004 S/P 1.750	11.70	.004	1.02	.000	12.72	.004	.030
B-2	I.D.	.004 S/P 1.750	5.60	.002	15.42	.005	21.01	.006	.030
C-2	I.D.	.004 S/P 1.750	19.20	.006	50.57	.015	69.77	.021	.030
D-2	I.D.	.004 S/P 1.750	11.40	.003	22.48	.007	33.88	.010	.030
E-2	I.D.	.004 S/P 1.750	8.47	.003	2.17	.001	10.63	.003	.030
F-2	I.D.	.004 S/P 1.750	.88	.000	101.56	.030	102.44	.031	.030
G-2	I.D.	.004 S/P 1.750	1.48	.000	59.26	.018	60.75	.018	.030
		AVERAGE:	8.390		36.069		44.457		
A-1	I.D.	.002 S/P .725	6.38	.002	9.81	.003	16.19	.005	.030
B-1	I.D.	.002 S/P .725	5.76	.002	2.21	.001	7.97	.002	.030
C-1	I.D.	.002 S/P .725	10.28	.003	4.20	.001	14.48	.004	.030
D-1	I.D.	.002 S/P .725	5.02	.002	2.38	.001	7.41	.002	.030
E-1	I.D.	.002 S/P .725	14.38	.004	4.80	.001	19.18	.006	.030
F-1	I.D.	.002 S/P .725	.51	.000	43.55	.013	46.06	.014	.030
G-1	I.D.	.002 S/P .725	3.99	.001	29.27	.009	33.26	.010	.030
		AVERAGE:	6.617		13.746		20.650		
A-2	I.D.	.004 S/P .725	13.43	.004	3.13	.001	16.56	.005	.030
B-2	I.D.	.004 S/P .725	0.00	0.000	14.40	.004	14.40	.004	.030
C-2	I.D.	.004 S/P .725	19.54	.006	7.63	.002	21.17	.006	.030
D-2	I.D.	.004 S/P .725	7.44	.002	1.46	.000	8.89	.003	.030
E-2	I.D.	.004 S/P .725	14.54	.004	17.81	.005	32.35	.010	.030
F-2	I.D.	.004 S/P .725	1.89	.001	45.87	.014	47.75	.014	.030
G-2	I.D.	.004 S/P .725	2.71	.001	40.67	.012	43.38	.013	.030
		AVERAGE:	8.507		18.710		26.357		

NOTE—1 in = 25.4 mm
1 lb/ft = 1.49 kg/m
1 psi = 6.9 kPa

FIGURE 2—MEASUREMENT OF HOSE ID USING 0.05 mm (0.002 in) AND 0.1 mm (0.004 in) STEPPED PLUG GAGES

5/13/92

SUMMARY SAE HOSES O.D.

COMPANY	DIN.	GAGE USED	REPEAT. % OF TOL.	ACTUAL TOL. USED	REPROD. % OF TOL.	ACTUAL TOL. USED	GAGE R & R	ACTUAL TOTAL TOL. USED	SPEC. TOL.
A-1	O.D.	PI TAPE 1.750	23.60	.009	37.99	.015	61.59	.025	.040
B-1	O.D.	PI TAPE 1.750	7.61	.003	77.28	.031	84.89	.034	.040
C-1	O.D.	PI TAPE 1.750	35.95	.014	22.26	.009	58.22	.023	.040
D-1	O.D.	PI TAPE 1.750	31.75	.013	8.12	.003	39.88	.016	.040
E-1	O.D.	PI TAPE 1.750	37.43	.015	24.88	.010	62.31	.025	.040
F-1	O.D.	PI TAPE 1.750	2.36	.001	131.57	.053	133.94	.054	.040
G-1	O.D.	PI TAPE 1.750	69.71	.028	2.94	.001	72.65	.029	.040
		AVERAGE:	29.773		43.577		73.354		
A-2	O.D.	CALIPERS 1.750	22.60	.009	21.13	.008	43.73	.017	.040
B-2	O.D.	CALIPERS 1.750	31.99	.013	1.88	.001	33.87	.014	.040
C-2	O.D.	CALIPERS 1.750	34.74	.014	23.41	.009	58.16	.023	.040
D-2	O.D.	CALIPERS 1.750	17.94	.007	6.87	.003	24.81	.010	.040
E-2	O.D.	CALIPERS 1.750	33.61	.013	.38	.000	34.00	.014	.040
F-2	O.D.	CALIPERS 1.750							
G-2	O.D.	CALIPERS 1.750	62.12	.025	3.93	.002	66.05	.026	.040
		AVERAGE:	33.833		9.600		43.437		
A-1	O.D.	PI TAPE .725	10.06	.004	9.38	.004	19.43	.008	.040
B-1	O.D.	PI TAPE .725	5.82	.002	105.13	.042	110.95	.044	.040
C-1	O.D.	PI TAPE .725	24.24	.010	28.01	.011	52.25	.021	.040
D-1	O.D.	PI TAPE .725	87.15	.035	19.88	.008	107.30	.043	.040
E-1	O.D.	PI TAPE .725	52.46	.021	30.79	.012	83.25	.033	.040
F-1	O.D.	PI TAPE .725	24.54	.010	13.36	.005	37.90	.015	.040
G-1	O.D.	PI TAPE .725	30.99	.012	25.78	.010	56.76	.023	.040
		AVERAGE:	33.609		33.190		66.834		
A-2	O.D.	CALIPERS .725	34.33	.014	53.97	.022	88.29	.035	.040
B-2	O.D.	CALIPERS .725	22.99	.009	29.91	.012	52.90	.021	.040
C-2	O.D.	CALIPERS .725	57.56	.023	11.18	.004	68.74	.027	.040
D-2	O.D.	CALIPERS .725	43.75	.018	20.44	.008	64.19	.026	.040
E-2	O.D.	CALIPERS .725	38.22	.015	6.64	.003	44.86	.018	.040
F-2	O.D.	CALIPERS .725							
G-2	O.D.	CALIPERS .725	33.18	.013	52.66	.021	85.84	.034	.040
		AVERAGE:	38.338		29.133		67.470		

NOTE—1 in = 25.4 mm
1 lb/ft = 1.49 kg/m
1 psi = 6.9 kPa

FIGURE 3—MEASUREMENT OF HOSE OD USING Pi TAPE AND CALIPERS

5/13/92

SUMMARY SAE HOSES CONCENTRICITY

COMPANY	DIM.	GAGE USED	REPEAT. % OF TOL.	ACTUAL TOL. USED	REPROD. % OF TOL.	ACTUAL TOL. USED	GAGE R & R	ACTUAL TOTAL TOL. USED	SPEC. TOL
A	CONCEN.	CALIPERS 1.750	44.60	.018	27.62	.011	72.22	.029	.040
B	CONCEN.	CALIPERS 1.750	10.72	.004	32.82	.013	43.54	.017	.040
C	CONCEN.	CALIPERS 1.750	59.94	.024	3.18	.001	63.12	.025	.040
D	CONCEN.	CALIPERS 1.750	15.69	.006	43.61	.017	59.30	.024	.040
E	CONCEN.	CALIPERS 1.750	38.88	.016	1.03	.000	39.91	.016	.040
F	CONCEN.	CALIPERS 1.750							.040
G	CONCEN.	CALIPERS 1.750	86.22	.034	1.98	.001	88.21	.035	.040
		AVERAGE:	42.675		18.373		61.050		
A	CONCEN.	CALIPERS .725	42.05	.017	27.32	.011	69.37	.028	.040
B	CONCEN.	CALIPERS .725	18.87	.008	10.09	.004	28.97	.012	.040
C	CONCEN.	CALIPERS .725	48.17	.019	58.48	.023	106.65	.043	.040
D	CONCEN.	CALIPERS .725	82.97	.033	35.46	.014	118.43	.047	.040
E	CONCEN.	CALIPERS .725	36.99	.015	1.52	.001	38.51	.015	.040
F	CONCEN.	CALIPERS .725							.040
G	CONCEN.	CALIPERS .725	76.19	.030	12.41	.005	88.60	.035	.040
		AVERAGE:	50.873		24.213		75.088		

NOTE—1 in = 25.4 mm
1 lb/ft = 1.49 kg/m
1 psi = 6.9 kPa

FIGURE 4—MEASUREMENT OF HOSE CONCENTRICITY (WALL VARIATION) USING CALIPERS

5/13/92

SUMMARY SAE HOSES WALL

COMPANY	DIM.	GAGE USED	REPEAT. % OF TOL.	ACTUAL TOL. USED	REPROD. % OF TOL.	ACTUAL TOL. USED	GAGE R & R	ACTUAL TOTAL TOL. USED	SPEC. TOL.
A	WALL	CALIPERS 1.750	23.24	.009	3.46	.001	26.70	.011	.040
B	WALL	CALIPERS 1.750	9.56	.004	15.59	.006	25.15	.010	.040
C	WALL	CALIPERS 1.750	21.62	.009	8.61	.003	30.23	.012	.040
D	WALL	CALIPERS 1.750	18.41	.007	7.13	.003	25.55	.010	.040
E	WALL	CALIPERS 1.750	6.94	.003	99.39	.040	106.33	.043	.040
F	WALL	CALIPERS 1.750							
G	WALL	CALIPERS 1.750	31.10	.012	9.45	.004	40.55	.016	.040
		AVERAGE:	18.478		23.938		42.418		
A	WALL	CALIPERS .725	29.32	.012	10.96	.004	40.28	.016	.040
B	WALL	CALIPERS .725	6.63	.003	38.44	.015	45.07	.018	.040
C	WALL	CALIPERS .725	18.50	.007	25.31	.010	43.81	.018	.040
D	WALL	CALIPERS .725	11.39	.005	58.46	.023	69.85	.028	.040
E	WALL	CALIPERS .725	7.26	.003	55.68	.022	62.94	.025	.040
F	WALL	CALIPERS .725							
G	WALL	CALIPERS .725	34.72	.014	.57	.000	35.28	.014	.040
		AVERAGE:	17.970		31.570		49.538		

Number in parenthesis represents actual amount of tolerance attributed to gage and technique error.

10% gage error is maximum acceptable standard for most customers.

Repeatability: The variation in measurement obtained when one operator uses the same gage for measuring the identical characteristic of the same part.

Reproducibility: The variation in the average of measurements made by different operators using the same gage when measuring identical characteristics of the same parts.

NOTE—1 in = 25.4 mm
1 lb/ft = 1.49 kg/m
1 psi = 6.9 kPa

FIGURE 5—MEASUREMENT OF HOSE WALL THICKNESS USING CALIPERS

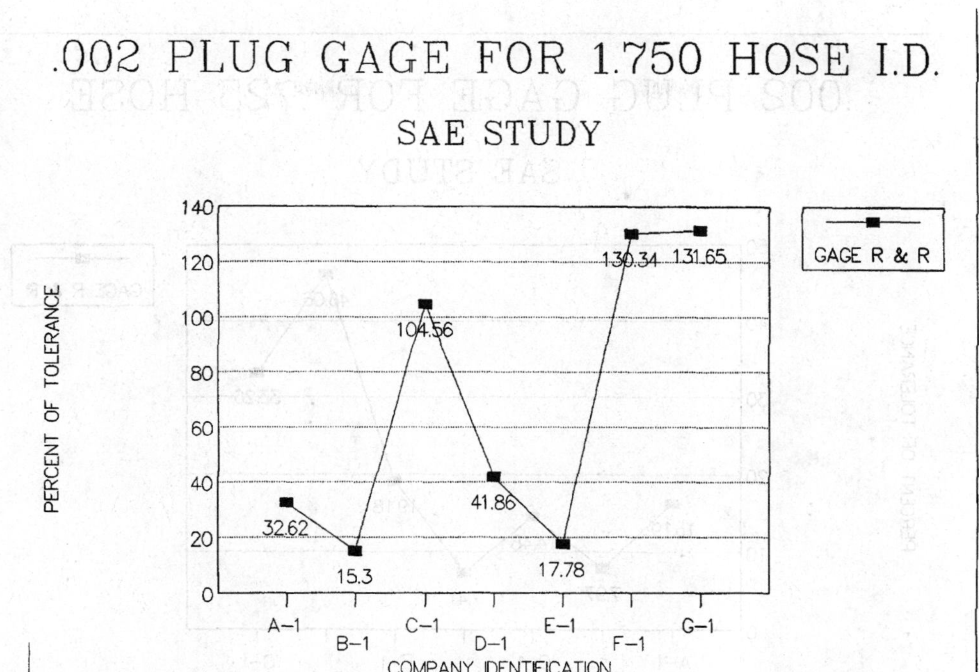

FIGURE 6—GRAPH OF 44.5 mm (1.75 in) HOSE ID GAGE R & R DATA FROM FIGURE 2 USING 0.05 mm (0.002 in) STEPPED PLUG GAGES

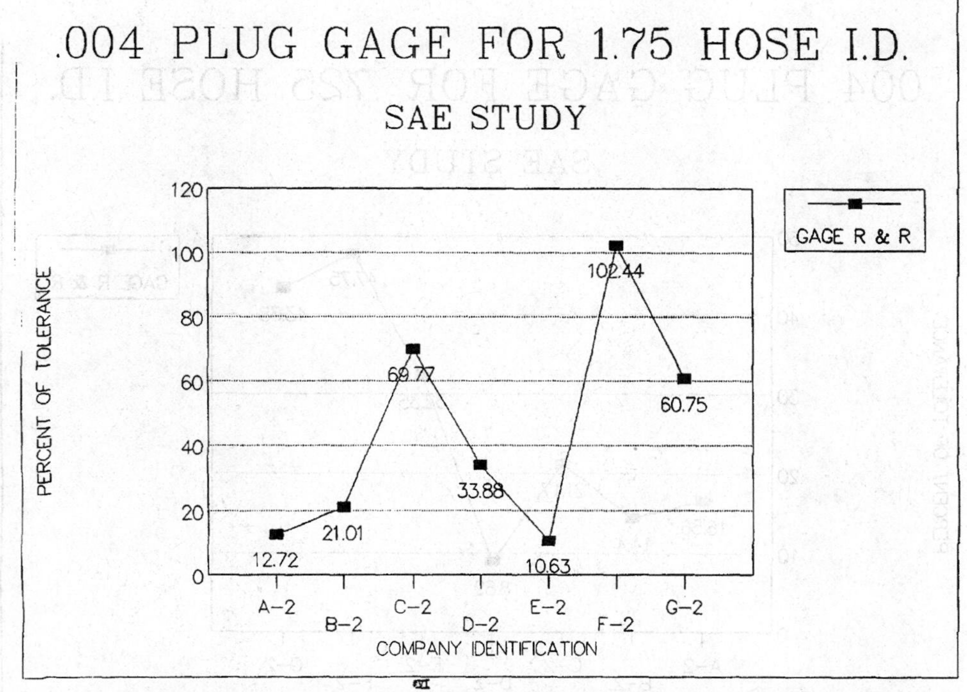

FIGURE 7—GRAPH OF 44.5 mm (1.75 in) HOSE ID GAGE R & R DATA FROM FIGURE 2 USING 0.10 mm (0.004 in) STEPPED PLUG GAGES

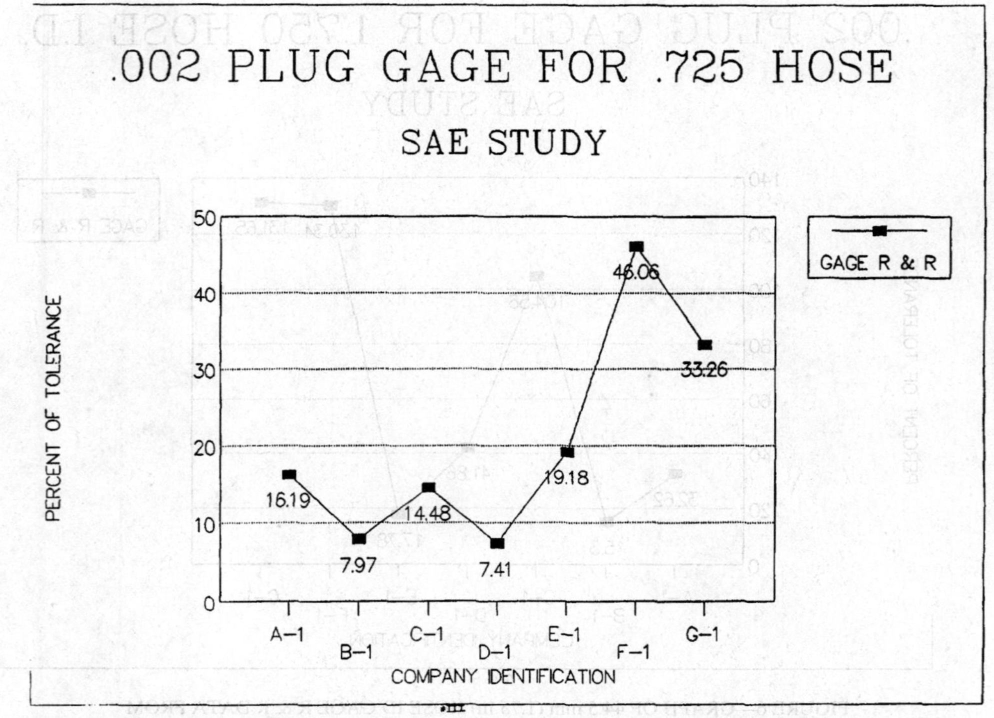

FIGURE 8—GRAPH OF 18.4 mm (0.725 in) HOSE ID GAGE R & R DATA FROM FIGURE 2 USING 0.05 mm (0.002 in) STEPPED PLUG GAGES

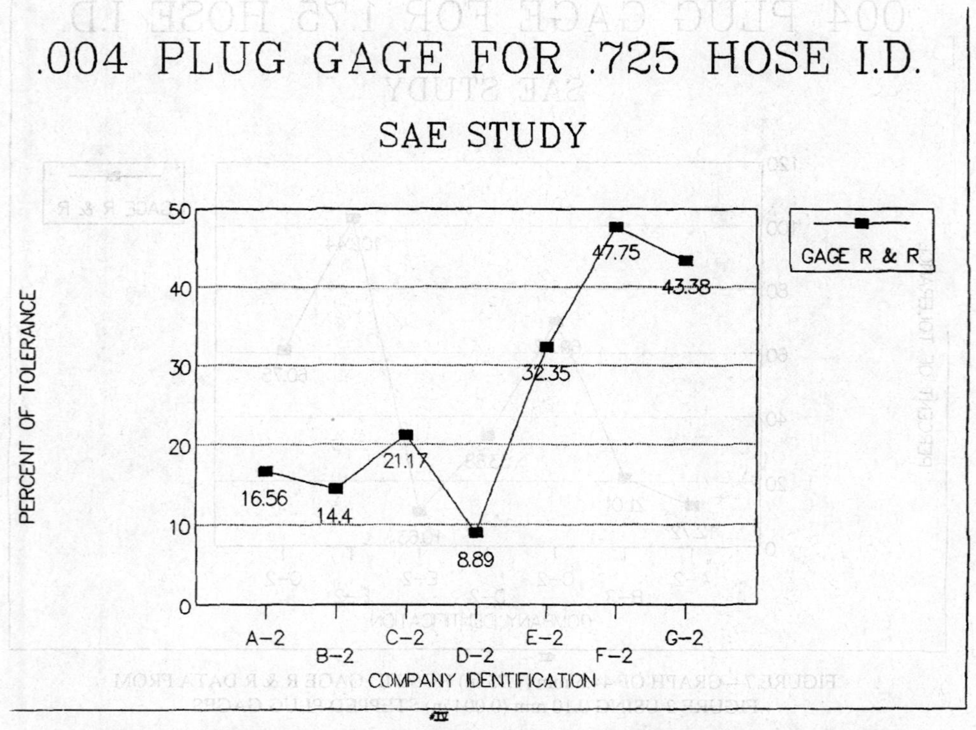

FIGURE 9—GRAPH OF 18.4 mm (0.725 in) HOSE ID GAGE R & R DATA FROM FIGURE 2 USING 0.1 mm (0.004 in) STEPPED PLUG GAGES

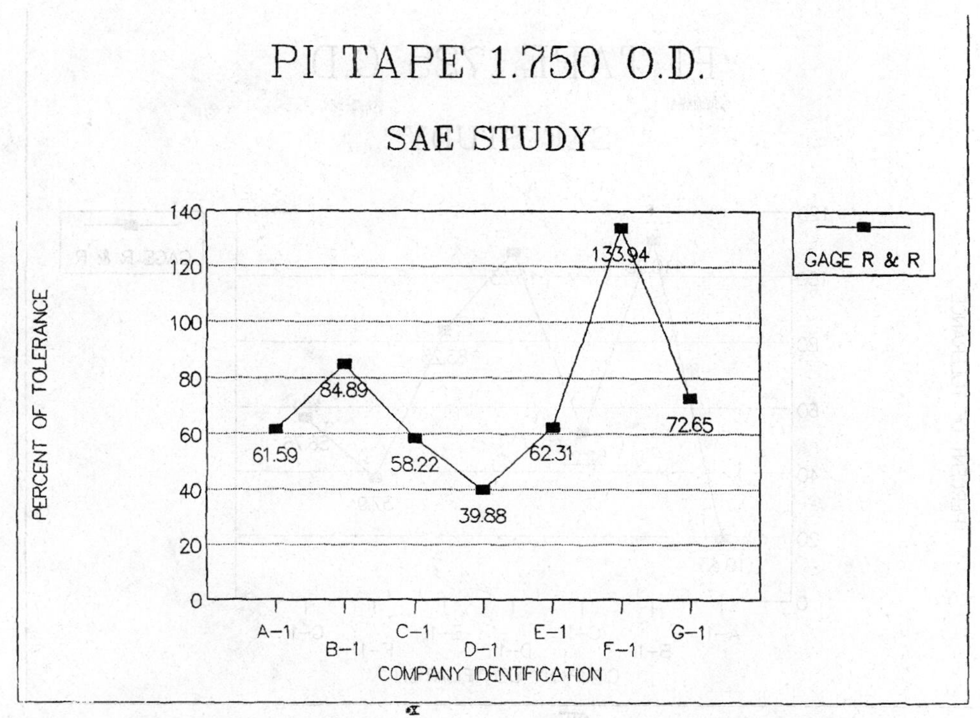

FIGURE 10—GRAPH OF 44.5 mm (1.75 in) HOSE OD GAGE R & R DATA FROM FIGURE 3 USING Pi TAPE

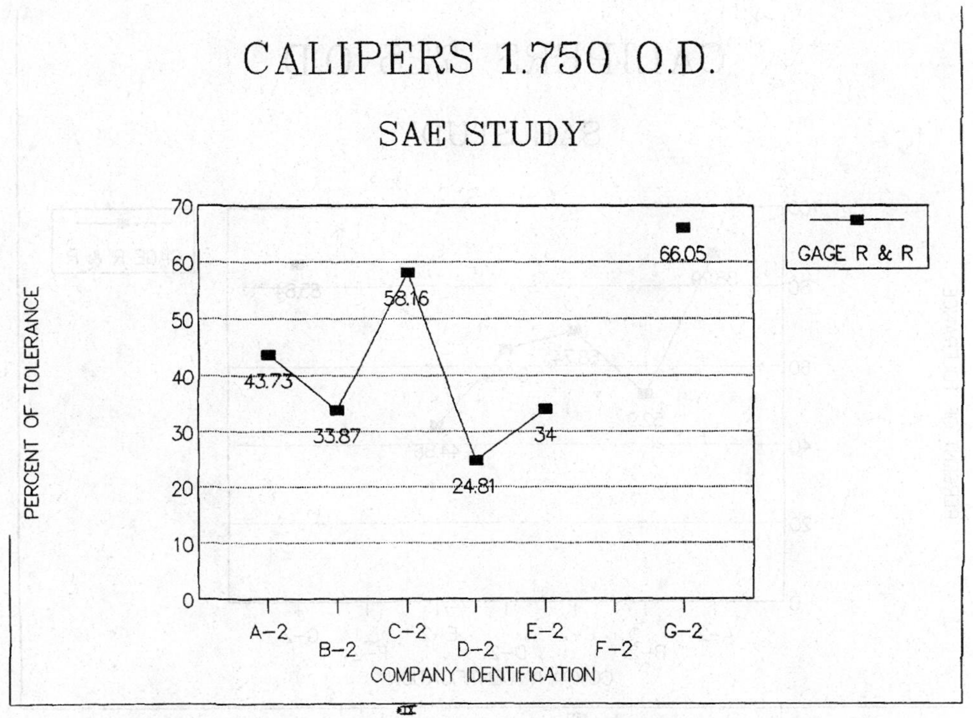

FIGURE 11—GRAPH OF 44.5 mm (1.75 in) HOSE OD GAGE R & R DATA FROM FIGURE 3 USING CALIPERS

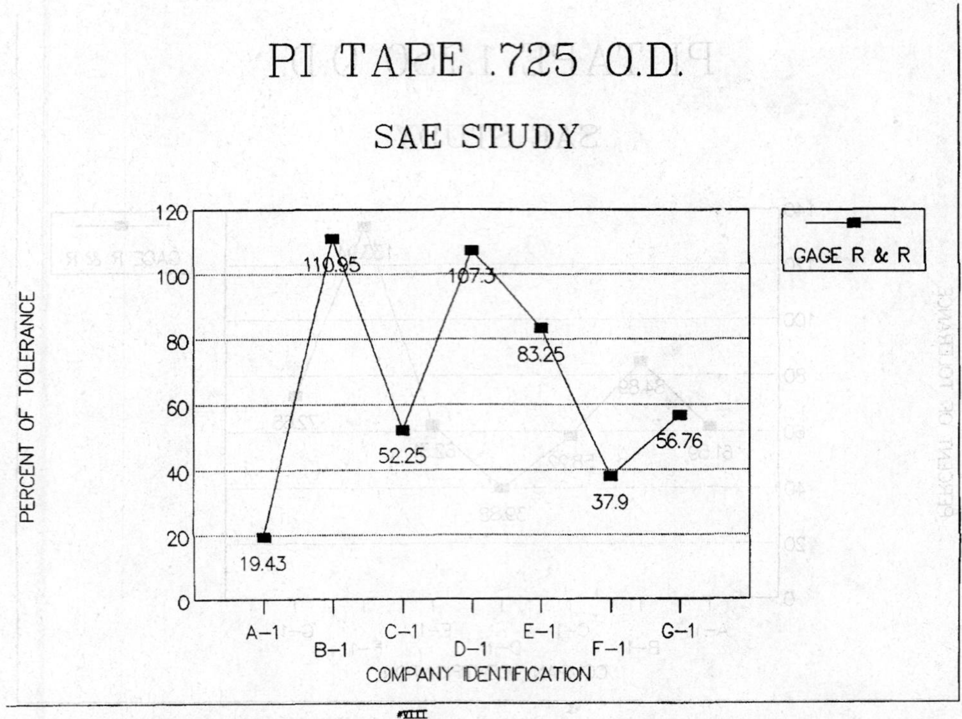

FIGURE 12—GRAPH OF 18.4 mm (0.725 in) HOSE OD GAGE R & R DATA FROM FIGURE 3 USING Pi TAPE

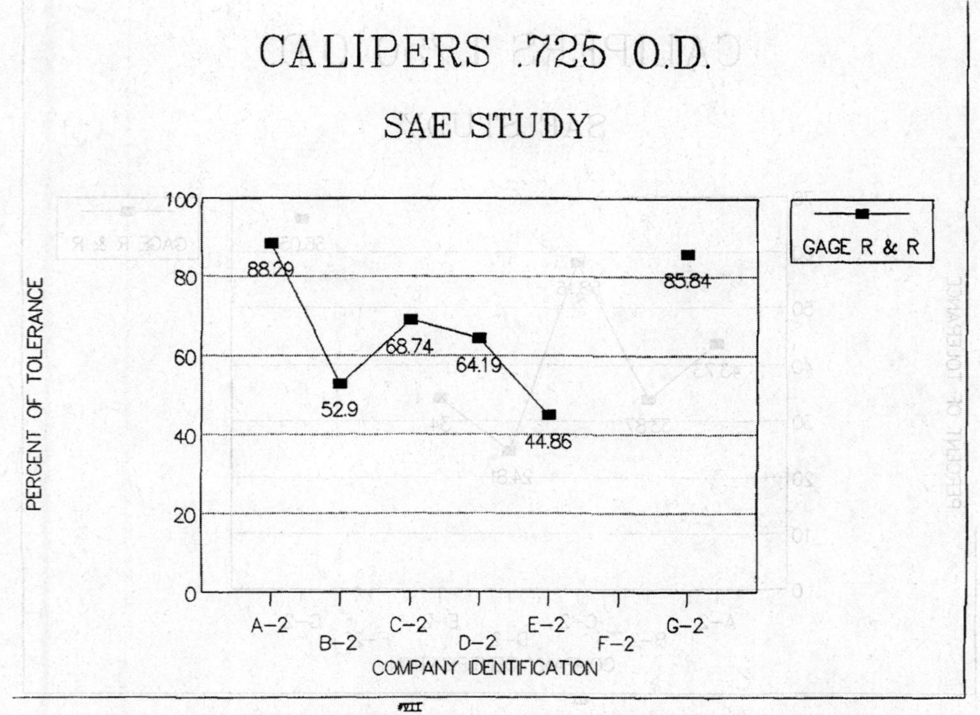

FIGURE 13—GRAPH OF 18.4 mm (0.725 in) HOSE OD GAGE R & R DATA FROM FIGURE 3 USING CALIPERS

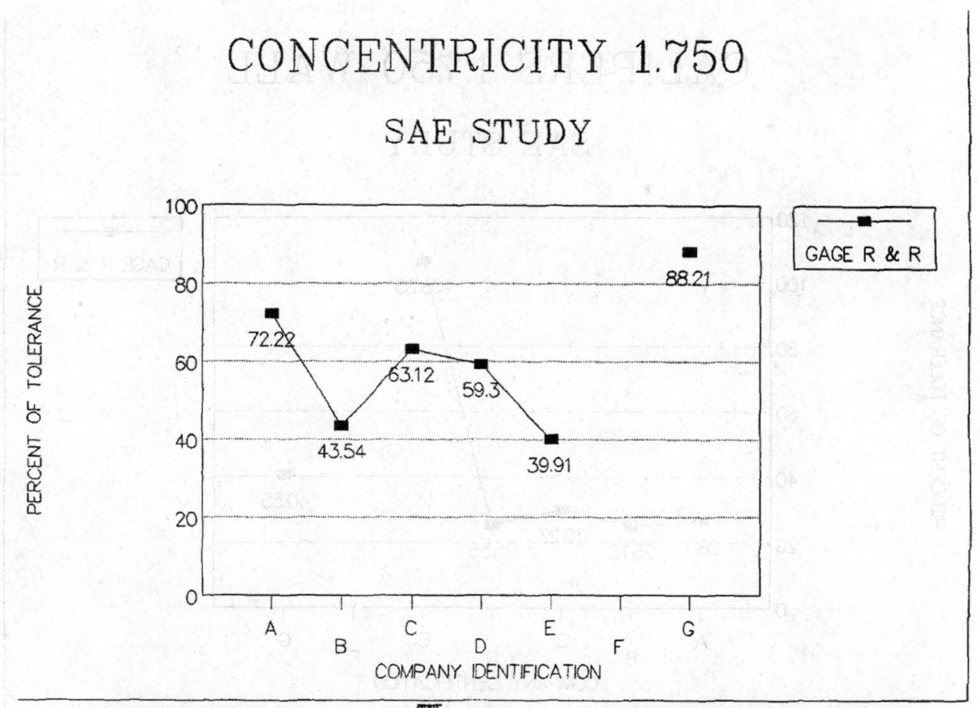

FIGURE 14—GRAPH OF 44.5 mm (1.75 in) HOSE CONCENTRICITY (WALL VARIATION) GAGE R & R DATA FROM FIGURE 4 USING CALIPERS

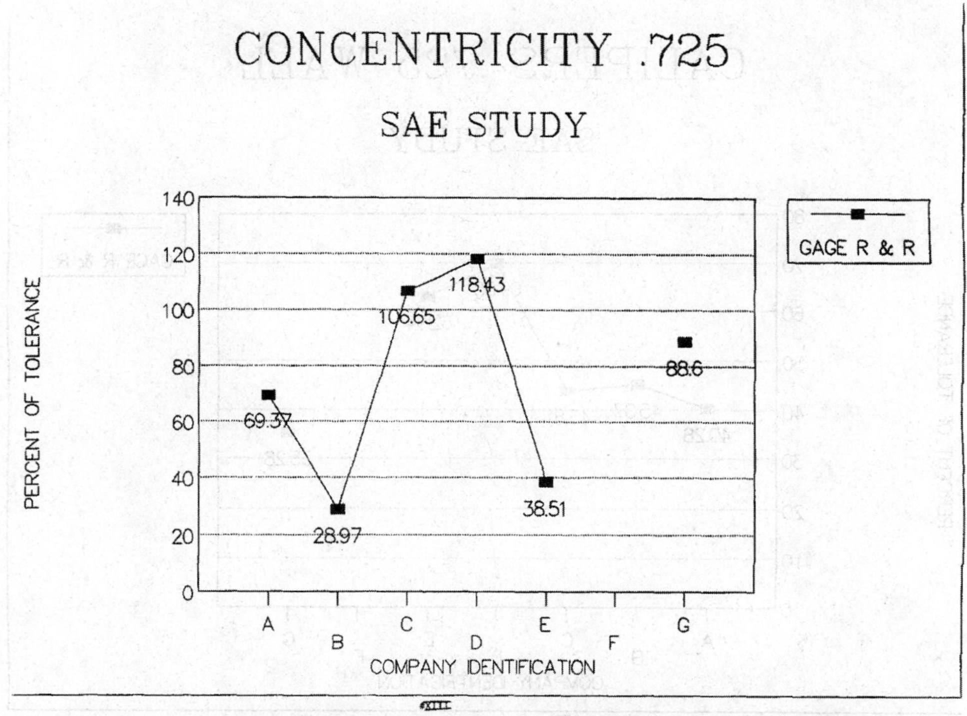

FIGURE 15—GRAPH OF 18.4 mm (0.725 in) HOSE CONCENTRICITY (WALL VARIATION) GAGE R & R DATA FROM FIGURE 4 USING CALIPERS

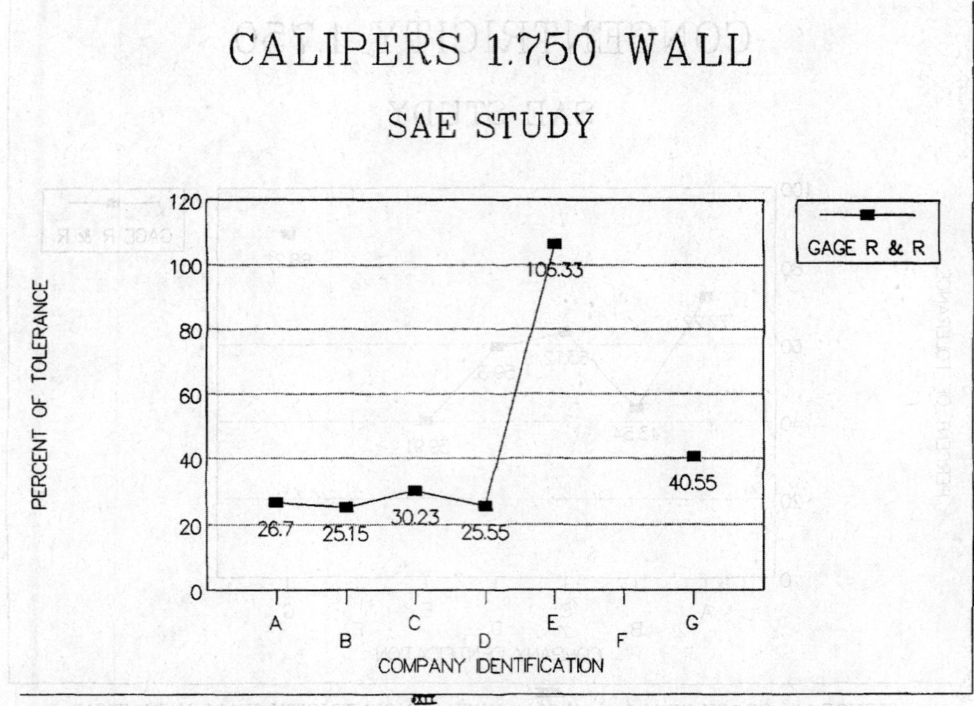

FIGURE 16—GRAPH OF 44.5 mm (1.75 in) HOSE WALL THICKNESS GAGE R & R DATA FROM FIGURE 5 USING CALIPERS

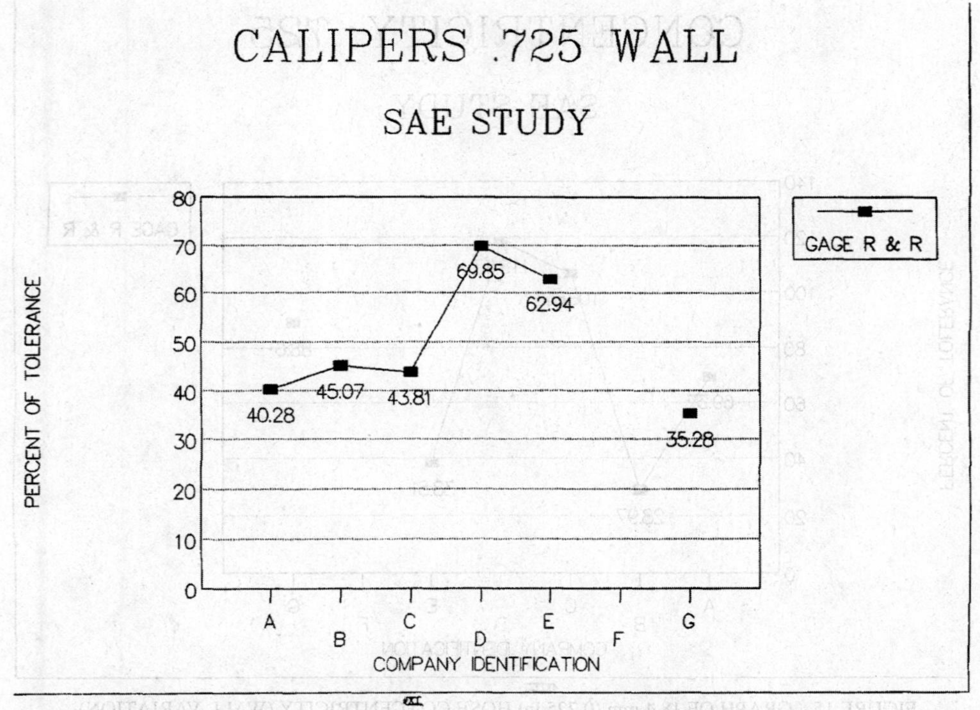

FIGURE 17—GRAPH OF 18.4 mm (0.725 in) HOSE WALL THICKNESS GAGE R & R DATA FROM FIGURE 5 USING CALIPERS

GENERAL REQUIREMENT FOR PREFORMED HOSES FOR AIR INDUCTION ON HEAVY-DUTY ENGINES—SAE J2140 JUL2000 SAE Standard

Report of the SAE Coolant Hose Committee approved July 2000. Rationale statement available.

1. Scope—This SAE Standard outlines the requirements for a preformed thermosetting hose intended for use in heavy-duty vehicle engines, such as air cleaner to carburetor hose, where it is exposed to normal heat and splash of motor oil.

2. References

2.1 Applicable Publications—The following publications form a part of this specification to the extent specified herein. Unless otherwise indicated, the latest issue of SAE publications shall apply.

2.1.1 SAE PUBLICATION—Available from SAE, 400 Commonwealth Drive, Warrendale, PA 15096-0001.

SAE J200—Classification System for Rubber Materials

2.1.2 ASTM PUBLICATIONS—Available from ASTM, 100 Barr Harbor Drive, West Conshohocken, PA 19428-2959.

ASTM D 395—Test Methods for Rubber Property—Compression Set
ASTM D 412—Test Methods for Rubber Properties in Tension
ASTM D 471—Test Method for Rubber Property—Effect of Liquids
ASTM D 573—Test Methods for Rubber-Deterioration in an Air Oven
ASTM D 1149—Test Method for Rubber Deterioration—Surface Ozone Cracking in a Chamber (Flat Specimens)
ASTM D 2137—Test Methods for Rubber Property—Brittleness Point of Flexible Polymers and Coated Fabrics
ASTM D 2240—Test Method for Rubber Property—Durometer Hardness

3. Physical Tests and Specifications—Physical tests and specifications shall be obtained from finished hoses where possible, or as agreed between manufacturer and user.

3.1 Hardness—Hardness, determined in accordance with the procedure in ASTM D 2240 Test Method. Standard durometer hardness for each polymer type shown in Section 5. If another hardness is needed, it should be specified by user.

3.2 Tensile Strength and Elongation at Break—Tensile strength and elongation at break, determined in accordance with the procedure in ASTM D 412 Test Method. Standard tensile and elongation specifications are shown in Section 5. If other tensile and elongation requirements are needed, they should be specified by user.

3.3 Change in Properties After Heat Aging—Heat aging shall be carried out in accordance with ASTM D 573 Test Method for 168 h at temperatures of 100 °C, 121 °C, 125 °C, 135 °C, 150 °C, or 200 °C. Test temperature should be specified by purchaser based on the application requirements. The change in hardness, tensile strength retention, and absolute elongation at break shall fall within the values shown in Table 1.

TABLE 1—MATERIAL REQUIREMENTS

Paragraph	Characteristic	Unit	Requirement
3.3	Accelerated Aging		
	Change in Hardness, max.	Points	±15
	Tensile Retained, min	%	70
	Absolute Elongation at Break, min	%	100
3.4	Low Temperature Flexibility		No cracks
3.5	Resistance to Oil IRM903		
	Volumetric Change, max		
	Grade A		Not required
	Grade B	%	≤80
	Grade C	%	≤20
3.6	Vacuum Resistance		Pass

NOTE—Not all combinations of the previous properties, 3.3 to 3.6, are available.

3.4 Low Temperature Flexibility—The test shall be carried out in accordance with ASTM D 2137 Method A Test Method. Immerse the specimens for 3.0 min ± 0.5 min at the test temperatures, –40 °C or –54 °C. Test temperature should be specified by purchaser based on the application requirements. After the test period, the specimen shall show no signs of cracks.

3.5 Resistance to Oil IRM903 (Replaces ASTM #3 oil)—Volumetric changes, when tested in accordance with ASTM D 471 Test Method, for 70 h at 100 °C shall not exceed the values shown in the Table 1.

Three grades are available; Grade A, B, and C, depending on the resistance to oil required. Grade should be specified by purchaser based on the application requirements.

3.6 Vacuum Resistance—The test shall be carried out at 8.4, 16.7, 33.3, or 66.7 kPa of negative pressure ±2%. The test temperature shall be selected from 3.3. The entire hose shall be kept in an air circulating oven at the specified temperature for 2 h ± 0.25 h. Vacuum shall be applied for a minimum of 15 s and a maximum of 30 s. The minimum outside diameter shall decrease by no more than 20%. The vacuum requirement should be specified by purchaser based on application requirements. Other vacuum requirements and temperatures may be decided between manufacturer and user.

4. Additional Requirements (optional)—See Table 2.

TABLE 2—ADDITIONAL REQUIREMENTS (OPTIONAL)

Property	Test Method
Compression Set	ASTM D 395
Ozone Resistance	ASTM D 1149, Method A
Adhesion (if multi-layered)	Test specified by procurer
Crush Resistance	Test specified by procurer
Fungus Resistance	Test specified by procurer
Pressure (burst) Resistance	Test specified by procurer
Bloom Resistance	No objectionable bloom

If required, other physical tests and specifications can be specified as agreed between manufacturer and user. SAE J200 call-outs may also be specified for specific properties not covered in 3.1 to Section 4.

5. Polymer Types and Properties Available—See Tables 3 and 4.

TABLE 3—POLYMER TYPES AND PROPERTIES AVAILABLE

	EPM EPDM	CM	NBR	ECO	MQ VMQ	CR	CSM	BIIR CIIR	NBR-PVC
High Temp	To 150 °C	To 135 °C	To 100 °C	To 135 °C	To 200 °C	To 100 °C	To 135 °C	To 135 °C	To 100 °C
Low Temp	–40 °C –54 °C	–40 °C	–40 °C	–40 °C	–54 °C	–40 °C –54 °C	–40 °C	–40 °C	–40 °C
Oil Swell IRM903	Not Recom-mended	≤80%	≤20%	≤20%	≤80%	≤80%	≤80%	Not Recom-mended	≤80% ≤20%
Minimum Tensile	6.9 MPa	6.9 MPa	6.9 MPa	6.9 MPa	5.5 MPa	6.9 MPa	6.9 MPa	6.9 MPa	6.9 MPa
Minimum Elongation	200%	200%	200%	200%	200%	200%	200%	200%	200%
Hardness Duro ±5	70	70	70	70	60	70	70	70	70

TABLE 4—ASTM CODES, POLYMER TYPES AND TRADE NAMES

ASTM Code	Polymer and (Trade Names)
EPM	Ethylene Propylene Copolymer
EPDM	Ethylene Propylene Diene Terpolymer
CM	Chloro-polyethylene
NBR	Acrylonitrile-Butadiene
ECO	Epichlorohydrin Copolymer
MQ	Silicone
VMQ	Silicone (Methyl, Vinyl)
CR	Chloroprene (Neoprene)
CSM	Chloro-sulfonyl-polyethylene
BIIR	Bromo-isobutene-isoprene (Bromobutyl)
CIIR	Chloro-isobutene-isoprene (Chlorobutyl)
NBR-PVC	Acrylonitrile-butadiene Polyvinyl Chloride blend

PUSH-TO-CONNECT TUBE FITTINGS FOR USE IN THE PIPING OF VEHICULAR AIR BRAKE—SAE J2494 MAY2000 SAE Standard

Report of the SAE Air Brake Tubing and Tube Fitting Subcommittee of the SAE Fluid Conductors and Connectors Committee approved May 2000. Rationale statement available.

1. Scope—This SAE Standard covers general and dimensional specifications for brass bodied reusable Push-to-Connect tube fittings for use in the piping of vehicular air brake systems. This type of fitting is intended for use with nylon tubing per SAE J844. Performance requirements for SAE J844 are covered in SAE J1131. See SAE J1131 for the Performance Requirements of Reusable (Push-to-Connect) Fittings Intended for Use in Automotive Air Brake Systems and U.S. Department of Transportation FMVSS 571.

2. References

2.1 Applicable Publications—The following publications form a part of this specification to the extend specified herein. Unless otherwise indicated, the latest issue of publication shall apply.

2.1.1 SAE PUBLICATIONS—Available from SAE, 400 Commonwealth Drive, Warrendale, PA 15096-0001.

SAE J476—Dryseal Pipe Threads
SAE J512—Automotive Tube Fittings
SAE J844—Nonmetallic Air Brake System Tubing
SAE J846—Coding Systems for Identification of Fluid Conductors and Connectors
SAE J1131—Performance Requirements for SAE J844 Nonmetallic Tubing and Fitting assemblies Used in Automotive Air Brake Systems

2.1.2 ANSI PUBLICATION—Available from ANSI, 11 West 42nd Street, New York, NY 10036-8002.

ANSI B 1.1—Unified Inch Screw Threads

2.1.3 FEDERAL PUBLICATIONS—Available from the Superintendent of Documents, U. S. Government Printing Office, Mail Stop: SSOP, Washington, DC 20402-9320.

FMVSS 571.106—Standard No. 106; Brake Hoses

2.1.4 ISO PUBLICATIONS—Available from ANSI, 11 West 42nd Street, New York, NY 10036-8002.

ISO 7-1—Pipe threads where pressure-tight joints are made on the threads—Part 1: Dimensions, tolerances and designation
ISO 228-1—Pipe threads where pressure-tight joints are not made on the threads
ISO 261—General purpose metric screw threads general plan

2.2 Related Publications—The following publications are for information purposes only.

2.2.1 ANSI PUBLICATIONS—Available from ANSI, 11 West 42nd Street, New York, NY 10036-8002.

ANSI B 1.20.3—Dryseal Pipe Threads
ANSI B 18.2.2—Square and Hex Nuts Inch Series

2.2.2 ASTM PUBLICATION—Available from ASTM, 100 Barr Harbor Drive, West Conshohocken, PA 19428-2959.

ASTM B 249—Specification for Wrought Copper and Copper Alloy Rod Bar and Shape

3. General Specifications—The following general specifications supplement the dimensional data contained in Tables 1A to with respect to all unspecified details.

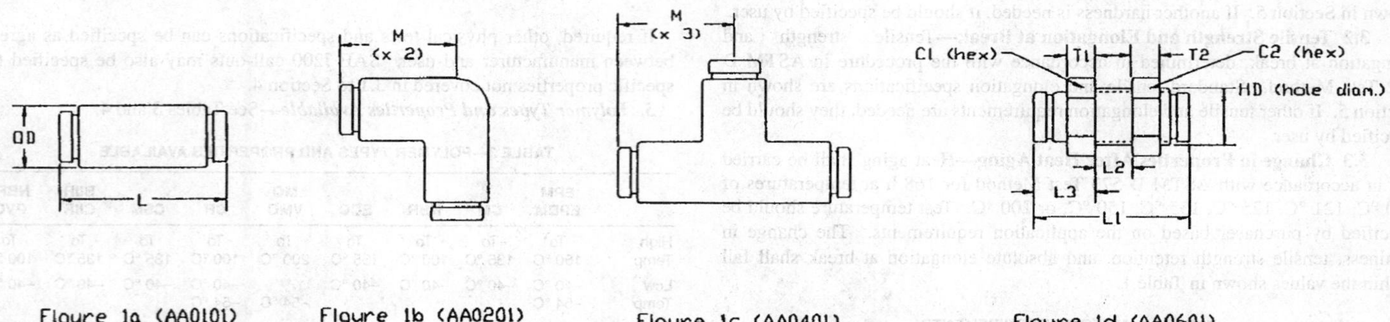

FIGURE 1—UNION CONNECTORS

TABLE 1A—DIMENSIONS OF UNION CONNECTORS(1) (FIGURE 1) - METRIC DIMENSIONS

Tube Size	C1, hex maximum	C2, hex maximum	HD maximum	L maximum	L1 maximum	L2 maximum	L3 maximum	M maximum	OD maximum	T1 maximum	T2 maximum
1/4	27.2	27.2	16.5	54.1	48.0	29.0	19.1	25.9	15.5	3.0	4.1
5/16	—	—	—	44.7	—	—	—	25.4	17.3	—	—
3/8	27.2	27.2	23.9	54.4	54.4	38.4	22.9	33.3	19.8	4.1	5.1
1/2	31.8	31.8	26.9	68.1	68.1	40.4	19.6	39.1	23.6	4.1	5.1
5/8	35.1	35.1	31.8	70.6	63.5	25.4	23.4	–	31.8	6.6	8.9

1. Dashes (—) in the table indicates dimensional data is unavailable for that fitting size and configuration.

TABLE 1B—DIMENSIONS OF UNION CONNECTORS(1) (FIGURE 1) - INCH DIMENSIONS

Tube Size	C1, hex maximum	C2, hex maximum	HD maximum	L maximum	L1 maximum	L2 maximum	L3 maximum	M maximum	OD maximum	T1 maximum	T2 maximum
1/4	1.07	1.07	0.65	2.13	1.89	1.14	0.75	1.02	0.61	0.12	0.16
5/16	–	—	—	1.76	—	—	—	1.00	0.68	—	—
3/8	1.07	1.07	0.94	2.14	2.14	1.51	0.90	1.31	0.78	0.16	0.20
1/2	1.25	1.25	1.06	2.68	2.68	1.59	0.77	1.54	0.93	0.16	0.20
5/8	1.38	1.38	1.25	2.78	2.50	1.00	0.92	—	1.25	0.26	0.35

1. Dashes (—) in the table indicate dimensional data is unavailable for that fitting size and configuration.

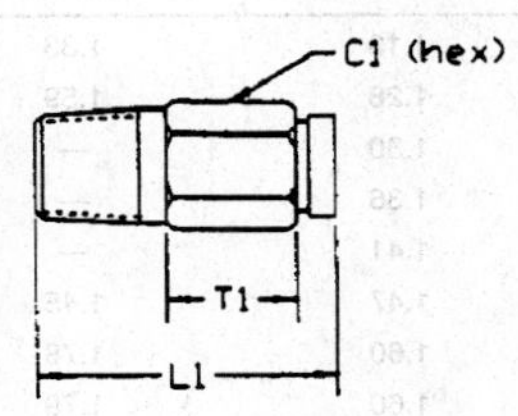

Figure 2a (AA0102)

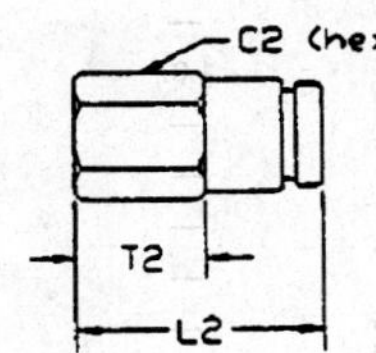

Figure 2b (AA0103)

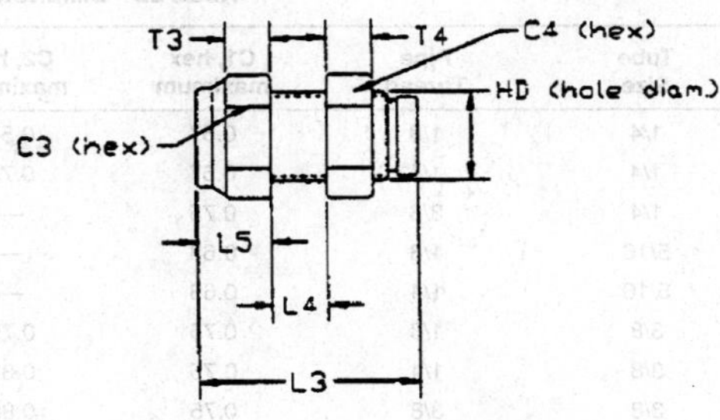

Figure 2c (AA0603)

FIGURE 2—STRAIGHT CONNECTORS

TABLE 2A—DIMENSIONS OF STRAIGHT CONNECTORS[(1)] (FIGURE 2) - METRIC DIMENSIONS

Tube Size	Pipe Thread	C1, hex maximum	C2, hex maximum	C3, hex maximum	C4, hex maximum	HD maximum	L1 maximum	L2 maximum
1/4	1/8	14.5	14.5	—	—	—	28.7	33.8
1/4	1/4	14.5	19.1	27.2	27.2	16.5	32.5	40.4
1/4	3/8	19.1	—	—	—	—	33.0	—
5/16	1/8	16.0	—	—	—	—	34.5	—
5/16	1/4	16.0	—	—	—	—	35.8	—
3/8	1/8	19.1	19.1	—	—	—	37.3	36.8
3/8	1/4	19.1	20.8	—	—	—	40.6	45.2
3/8	3/8	19.1	22.4	27.2	28.7	23.9	40.6	45.5
3/8	1/2	22.4	—	—	—	—	40.4	—
1/2	1/4	22.4	—	—	—	—	47.5	—
1/2	3/8	22.4	22.4	—	—	—	47.5	42.4
1/2	1/2	22.4	27.2	31.8	33.5	26.9	47.0	53.6
5/8	3/8	27.2	—	—	—	—	52.1	—
5/8	1/2	27.2	—	—	—	—	53.6	—
3/4	1/2	30.2	—	—	—	—	54.1	—

1. Dashes (—) in the table indicate dimensional data is unavailable for that fitting size and configuration.

TABLE 2A—DIMENSIONS OF STRAIGHT CONNECTORS — METRIC DIMENSIONS (continued)

Tube Size	Pipe Thread	L3 maximum	L4 maximum	L5 maximum	T1 minimum	T2 minimum	T3 minimum	T4 minimum
1/4	1/8	—	—	—	3.8	7.4	—	—
1/4	1/4	41.2	16.3	16.3	3.8	10.7	10.9	4.3
1/4	3/8	—	—	—	3.8	—	—	—
5/16	1/8	—	—	—	6.9	—	—	—
5/16	1/4	—	—	—	6.9	—	—	—
3/8	1/8	—	—	—	6.6	8.1	—	—
3/8	1/4	—	—	—	4.3	11.2	—	—
3/8	3/8	55.9	25.4	15.8	4.3	11.9	8.4	4.3
3/8	1/2	—	—	—	4.6	—	—	—
1/2	1/4	—	—	—	7.9	—	—	—
1/2	3/8	—	—	—	5.1	13.0	—	—
1/2	1/2	67.1	12.7	18.5	4.6	12.4	8.4	6.4
5/8	3/8	—	—	—	8.4	—	—	—
5/8	1/2	—	—	—	5.3	—	—	—
3/4	1/2	—	—	—	5.8	—	—	—

TABLE 2B—DIMENSIONS OF STRAIGHT CONNECTORS[(1)] (FIGURE 2) - INCH DIMENSIONS

Tube Size	Pipe Thread	C1, hex maximum	C2, hex maximum	C3, hex maximum	C4, hex maximum	HD maximum	L1 maximum	L2 maximum
1/4	1/8	0.57	0.57	—	—	—	1.13	1.33
1/4	1/4	0.57	0.75	1.07	1.07	0.65	1.28	1.59
1/4	3/8	0.75	—	—	—	—	1.30	—
5/16	1/8	0.63	—	—	—	—	1.36	—
5/16	1/4	0.63	—	—	—	—	1.41	—
3/8	1/8	0.75	0.75	—	—	—	1.47	1.45
3/8	1/4	0.75	0.82	—	—	—	1.60	1.78
3/8	3/8	0.75	0.88	1.07	1.13	0.94	1.60	1.79
3/8	1/2	0.88	—	—	—	—	1.59	—
1/2	1/4	0.88	—	—	—	—	1.87	—
1/2	3/8	0.88	0.88	—	—	—	1.87	1.67
1/2	1/2	0.88	1.07	1.25	1.32	1.06	1.85	2.11
5/8	3/8	1.07	—	—	—	—	2.05	—
5/8	1/2	1.07	—	—	—	—	2.11	—
3/4	1/2	1.19	—	—	—	—	2.13	—

1. Dashes (—) in the table indicate dimensional data is unavailable for that fitting size and configuration.

TABLE 2B—DIMENSIONS OF STRAIGHT CONNECTORS — INCH DIMENSIONS (continued)

Tube Size	Pipe Thread	L3 maximum	L4 maximum	L5 maximum	T1 minimum	T2 minimum	T3 minimum	T4 minimum
1/4	1/8	—	—	—	0.15	0.29	—	—
1/4	1/4	1.62	0.64	0.64	0.15	0.42	0.43	0.17
1/4	3/8	—	—	—	0.15	—	—	—
5/16	1/8	—	—		0.27	—	—	—
5/16	1/4	—	—	—	0.27	—	—	—
3/8	1/8	—	—	—	0.26	0.32	—	—
3/8	1/4	—	—	—	0.17	0.44	—	—
3/8	3/8	2.20	1.00	0.62	0.17	0.47	0.33	0.17
3/8	1/2	—	—	—	0.18	—	—	—
1/2	1/4	—	—		0.31			
1/2	3/8	—	—	—	0.20	0.51	—	—
1/2	1/2	2.64	0.50	0.73	0.18	0.49	0.33	0.25
5/8	3/8	—	—	—	0.33	—	—	—
5/8	1/2	—	—	—	0.21	—	—	—
3/4	1/2	—	—	—	0.23	—	—	—

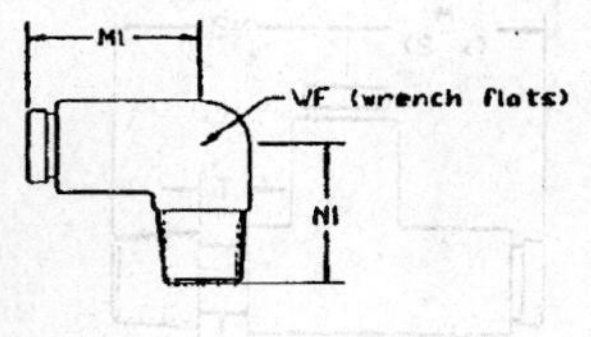

Figure 3a (AA0202)

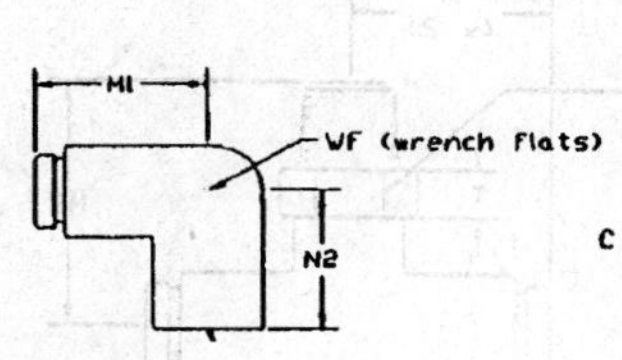

Figure 3b (AA0203)

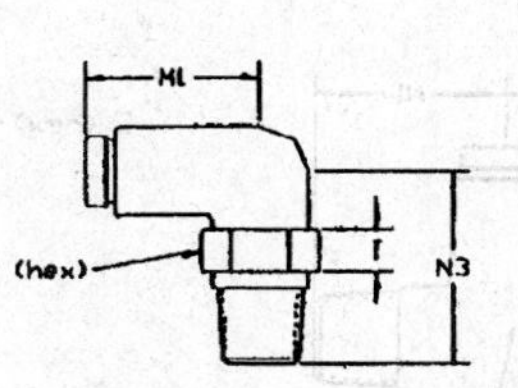

Figure 3c (AA02DD)

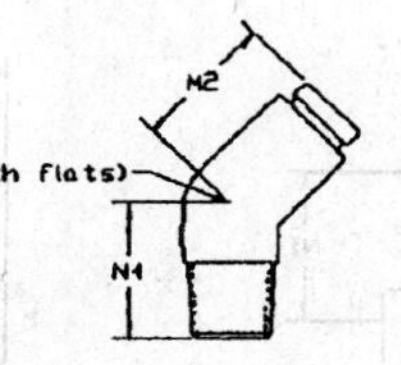

Figure 3d (AA0302)

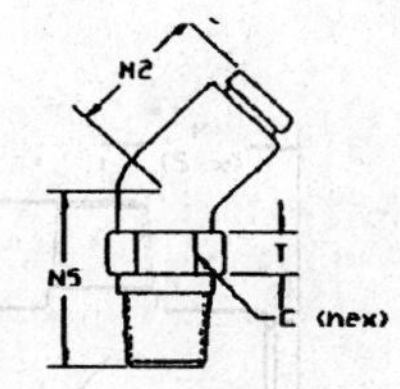

Figure 3e (AA03DD)

FIGURE 3—ELBOW CONNECTORS

TABLE 3A—DIMENSIONS OF ELBOW CONNECTORS(1) (FIGURE 3) — METRIC DIMENSIONS

Tube Size	Pipe Thread	C, hex maximum	M1 maximum	M2 maximum	N1 maximum	N2 maximum	N3 maximum	N4 maximum	N5 maximum	T minimum	WF maximum
1/4	1/8	11.2	26.2	25.1	20.1	22.9	32.3	22.1	31.5	2.5	17.5
1/4	1/4	14.5	28.7	25.1	26.2	26.2	39.6	25.1	37.1	4.1	19.1
1/4	3/8	19.1	27.9	—	28.2	—	39.6	—	—	5.8	22.1
3/8	1/8	16.0	33.3	30.5	22.9	—	35.8	28.2	36.6	2.5	19.1
3/8	1/4	19.1	32.5	30.5	26.2	27.7	40.1	28.2	40.9	4.1	20.8
3/8	3/8	19.1	33.3	30.5	28.2	—	40.4	33.0	40.9	4.1	22.1
3/8	1/2	22.4	30.7	33.0	35.1	—	45.5	33.0	—	5.1	24.1
1/2	1/4	22.1	39.1	32.5	29.2	—	43.9	33.0	—	5.1	22.4
1/2	3/8	22.1	33.0	32.5	29.2	—	46.0	28.7	45.2	4.1	24.1
1/2	1/2	22.4	39.1	33.0	35.1	—	49.8	33.0	49.0	4.1	24.1
5/8	3/8	22.4	37.1	—	31.0	—	51.6	—	—	5.8	25.4
5/8	1/2	—	39.1	37.1	36.1	—	—	37.1	—	—	30.2
3/4	1/2	—	46.0	38.6	37.6	—	—	38.6	—	—	33.5

1. Dashes (—) in the table indicate dimensional data is unavailable for that fitting size and configuration.

TABLE 3B—DIMENSIONS OF ELBOW CONNECTORS(1) (FIGURE 3) — METRIC DIMENSIONS

Tube Size	Pipe Thread	C, hex maximum	M1 maximum	M2 maximum	N1 maximum	N2 maximum	N3 maximum	N4 maximum	N5 maximum	T minimum	WF maximum
1/4	1/8	0.44	1.03	0.99	0.79	0.90	1.27	0.87	1.24	0.10	0.69
1/4	1/4	0.57	1.13	0.99	1.03	1.03	1.56	0.99	1.46	0.16	0.75
1/4	3/8	0.75	1.10	—	1.11	—	1.56	—	—	0.23	0.87
3/8	1/8	0.63	1.31	1.20	0.90	—	1.41	1.11	1.44	0.10	0.75
3/8	1/4	0.75	1.28	1.20	1.03	1.09	1.58	1.11	1.1	0.16	0.82
3/8	3/8	0.75	1.31	1.20	1.11	—	1.59	1.30	1.61	0.16	0.87
3/8	1/2	0.88	1.21	1.30	1.38	—	1.79	1.30	—	0.20	0.95
1/2	1/4	0.87	1.54	1.28	1.15	—	1.73	1.30	—	0.20	0.88
1/2	3/8	0.87	1.30	1.28	1.15	—	1.81	1.30	1.93	0.16	0.95
1/2	1/2	0.88	1.54	1.30	1.38	—	1.96	1.30	1.93	0.16	0.95
5/8	3/8	0.88	1.46	—	1.22	—	2.03	—	—	0.23	1.00
5/8	1/2	—	1.54	1.46	1.42	—	—	1.46	—	—	1.19
3/4	1/2	—	1.81	1.52	1.48	—	—	1.52	—	—	1.32

1. Dashes (—) in the table indicate dimensional data is unavailable for that fitting size and configuration.

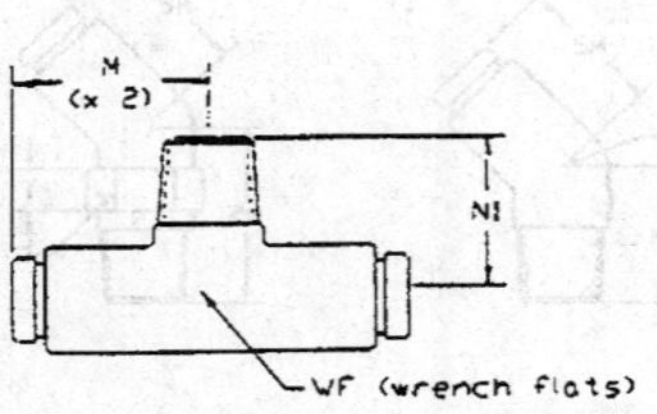

Figure 4a (AA0425)

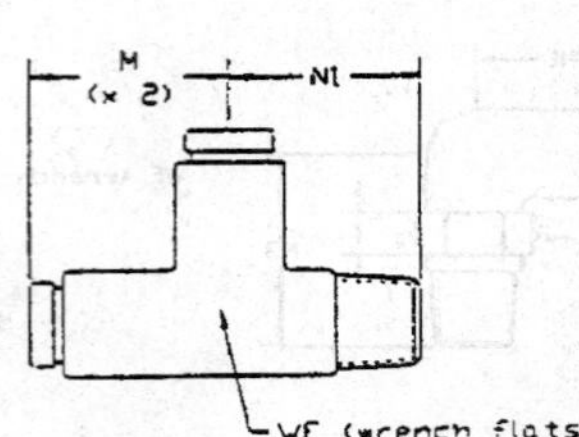

Figure 4b (AA0424)

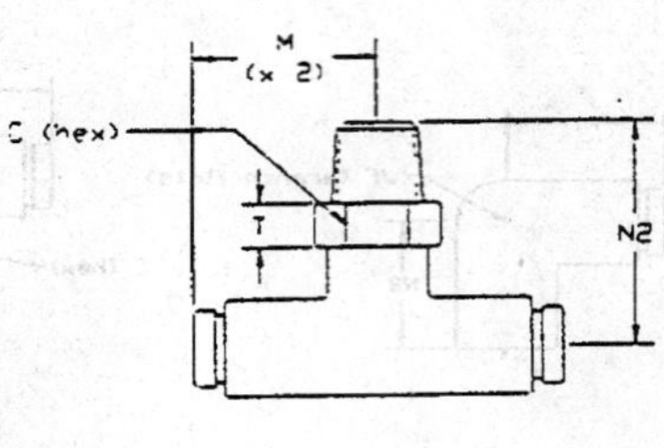

Figure 4c (AA 04FF)

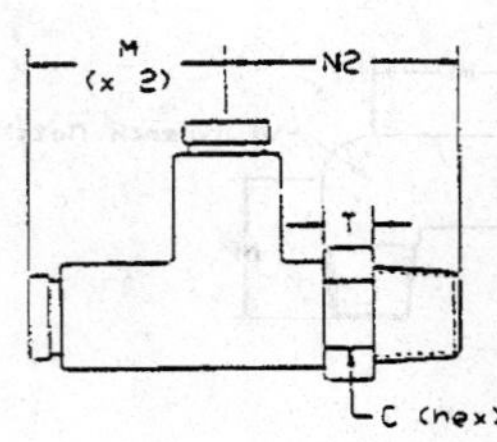

Figure 4d (AA04EE)

FIGURE 4—TEE CONNECTORS

TABLE 4A—DIMENSIONS OF TEE CONNECTORS(1) (FIGURE 4) — METRIC DIMENSIONS

Tube Size	Pipe Thread	C, hex maximum	M maximum	N1 maximum	N2 maximum	T minimum	WF maximum
1/4	1/8	11.2	25.9	20.1	31.8	2.5	14.5
1/4	1/4	14.5	25.9	24.6	37.6	4.1	18.0
3/8	1/8	14.5	31.0	—	42.2	2.5	—
3/8	1/4	19.1	31.0	25.4	46.5	4.1	19.1
3/8	3/8	19.1	33.3	28.2	46.5	4.1	22.1
1/2	1/4	22.1	34.0	—	43.9	4.1	—
1/2	3/8	22.1	34.0	36.1	46.5	4.1	24.1
1/2	1/2	22.4	39.1	36.1	50.5	4.1	24.1

1. Dashes (—) in the table indicate dimensional data is unavailable for that fitting size and configuration.

TABLE 4B—DIMENSIONS OF TEE CONNECTORS(1) (FIGURE 4) — INCH DIMENSIONS

Tube Size	Pipe Thread	C, hex maximum	M maximum	N1 maximum	N2 maximum	T minimum	WF maximum
1/4	1/8	0.44	1.02	0.79	1.25	0.10	0.57
1/4	1/4	0.57	1.20	0.97	1.48	0.16	0.71
3/8	1/8	0.57	1.22	—	1.66	0.10	—
3/8	1/4	0.75	1.22	1.00	1.83	0.16	0.75
3/8	3/8	0.75	1.36	1.11	1.83	0.16	0.87
1/2	1/4	0.87	1.34	—	1.73	0.16	—
1/2	3/8	0.87	1.34	1.42	1.83	0.16	0.95
1/2	1/2	0.88	1.54	1.42	1.99	0.16	0.95

1. Dashes (—) in the table indicate dimensional data is unavailable for that fitting size and configuration.

3.1 Identification—Any one component of the fitting shall be permanently and legibly marked according to the current U.S. Department of Transportation FMVSS 571.106 Regulation (NHTSA). The location of such markings shall be optional with manufacturer.

3.2 Size Designations—Fitting sizes are designated by the corresponding nominal outside diameter of the tubing for the various sizes of tube ends and by the corresponding standard nominal pipe size for pipe thread ends.

3.3 Dimensions and Tolerances—Except for nominal size and thread specifications, dimensions and tolerances are given in both SI units and U.S. customary as designated. Tabulated dimensions shall apply to the finished parts. The maximum and minimum across flat dimensions shall be within the commercial tolerance of bar or extruded stock from which the fittings are produced.

Angular tolerance on axis of ends of elbows and tees shall be ±2.50 degrees for sizes up to and including 3/8 in (8 mm), and ±1.50 degrees for sizes larger than 3/8 in (8 mm).

The minimum across corners dimensions of hexagons shall be 1.092 times the nominal width across flats, but shall not result in a side flat width less than 0.43 times the nominal width across flats.

Wrenching surfaces shall fit standard wrench openings. Where so illustrated, hexagon corners shall be chamfered 30 degrees ± 5 degrees to a diameter equal to the nominal width across flats, with a tolerance of –0.41 mm (–0.016 in); or, where design permits, corners may be chamfered to the diameter of the abutting surface, provided the length of chamfer does not exceed that produced by the 30 degree chamfer previously described.

Tabulated dimensions apply to measurements taken when the release mechanism is in the "in" position.

3.4 Passages—The minimum flow diameter through any section of the air brake fitting shall not be less than 66% of the nominal inside diameter of the air brake tubing.

Where passages in straight fittings are machined from opposite ends, the offset at the meeting point shall not exceed 0.38 mm (0.015 in). The cross-sectional area at the junction of passages in angle fittings shall not be less than that of the smallest passage. At manufacturer's option, all passages in a particular fitting may conform with the smallest diameter specified for that fitting. Where the passage is specified as tap drill diameter or less, the minimum shall be no less than the minimum diameter of the smallest passage in the fitting.

3.5 Wall Thickness—Unless otherwise designated, the wall thickness at any point on a fitting which may be subjected to internal fluid pressure shall not be less than the thickness established by the specified dimensions, tolerances, and eccentricities for inner and outer surfaces.

3.6 Contour—Details of contour shall be optional with manufacturer, provided the tabulated dimensions are maintained and serviceability of the fittings is not impaired. Wrench flat geometry on elbows and tees shall be optional. Where extruded and forged shapes are reduced to conserve material, the wall thickness, unless otherwise specified, shall not be less than the minimum values in Table 5.

TABLE 5—RECOMMENDED MINIMUM WALL THICKNESS FOR EXTRUDED AND FORGED SHAPES

Nominal Tube OD in	Wall Thickness Min mm	Wall Thickness Min in
1/4	1.0	0.04
5/16	1.3	0.05
3/8	1.3	0.05
1/2	1.5	0.06
5/8	2.0	0.08
3/4	2.0	0.08

3.7 Straight Threads—Unified straight threads shall be manufactured in accordance with ANSI B 1.1.

Unified standard Class 2A external and Class 2B internal threads shall apply to plain finish (un-plated) fittings of all types. For internally threaded parts with additive finish, the Class 2B diameters shall apply after plating.

Metric straight threads and British parallel pipe threads may be used and shall be manufactured in accordance with ISO 261 and ISO 228-1 respectively, however, this is not intended to preclude the use of other threads described in internationally accepted standards.

Where external threads are produced by roll threading and the body is not undercut, the unthreaded portion of body adjacent to the shoulder may be reduced to the minimum pitch diameter. (See Figure 5.)

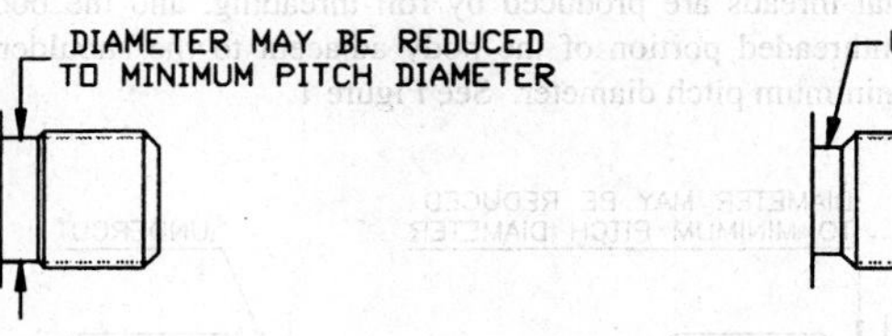

ROLLED STRAIGHT THREAD WITHOUT UNDERCUT

STRAIGHT THREAD WITH UNDERCUT

FIGURE 5—EXTERNAL ROLLED AND CUT STRAIGHT THREADS

External threads shall be suitably chamfered to allow for ease of assembly.

Internal threads shall be countersunk 90 degrees included angle to the diameters specified.

3.8 Thread Eccentricity Tolerances—The various thread elements of external and internal straight threads on tube fittings shall be concentric within the limitations specified in the General Specifications of SAE J512.

3.9 Pipe Threads—Taper pipe threads, unless there is specific authorization to the contrary, shall conform to the specifications found in SAE J476.

Where external pipe threads are produced by thread rolling, the diameter of the unthreaded portion of shank adjacent to shoulder may be reduced to the E2 basic pitch diameter. (See Figure 6.)

External pipe threads shall be suitably chamfered to allow for ease of assembly. Internal pipe threads shall be countersunk 90 degrees included angle, to the diameters tabulated in Table 6.

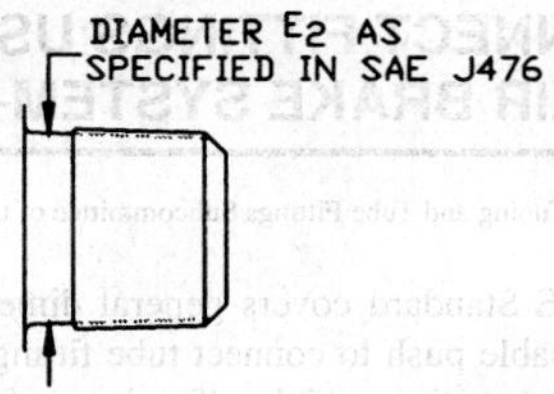

ROLLED TAPER PIPE THREAD WITHOUT UNDERCUT

FIGURE 6—ROLLED PIPE THREAD

TABLE 6—CHAMFER SPECIFICATIONS OF DRYSEAL PIPE THREADS

Nominal Pipe thread Size in	Internal Thread Countersink Diameter Max mm	Internal Thread Countersink Diameter Max in	Internal Thread Countersink Diameter Min mm	Internal Thread Countersink Diameter Min in
1/8	11.2	0.44	10.7	0.42
1/4	14.5	0.57	14.0	0.55
3/8	18.0	0.71	17.5	0.69
1/2	22.1	0.87	21.6	0.85
3/4	27.4	1.08	26.9	1.06
1	34.5	1.36	34.0	1.34

British pipe threads may be used and shall be manufactured in accordance with ISO 7-1.

3.10 Material and Manufacture—Fitting bodies shall be made from brass and may be machined from bar or forged. The bodies are to be made from one of the alloys shown in Table 7.

TABLE 7—ALLOWABLE BODY MATERIALS

Bar or Extruded Stock	Forge Stock
UNS C34500	UNS C37700
UNS C36000 (half hard)	ISO 426/2 CuZn40Pb2
UNS C35000	
ISO 426/2 CuZn 39Pb3	
JIS H3250 C3604B	

3.11 Workmanship—Workmanship shall conform to the best commercial practice to produce high-quality fittings. Fittings shall be free from all machining fluids, chips, hanging burrs, loose scale, and slivers which might become dislodged in usage and all other defects which might affect their serviceability.

3.12 Pipe Thread Sealant—Where it is not objectionable from a function or production standpoint, the use of a compatible lubricant or sealant may be desirable in assembling Dryseal pipe threads of tube fittings to minimize galling and effect a pressure-tight seal.

4. Part Ordering Information

4.1 SAE J846 Ordering Designation—By agreement between manufacturer and user, the ordering designation from SAE J846 may be used to abbreviate the ordering of connectors.

DIMENSIONAL SPECIFICATIONS FOR NON-METALLIC BODY PUSH-TO-CONNECT FITTINGS USED ON A VEHICULAR AIR BRAKE SYSTEM—SAE J2494-2 OCT2002

SAE Standard

Report of the SAE Air Brake Tubing and Tube Fittings Subcommittee of the SAE Fluid Conductors and Connectors Technical Committee approved October 2002.

1. Scope—This SAE Standard covers general dimensional specifications for non-metallic body reusable push to connect tube fittings for use in the piping of air brake systems on automotive vehicles. This type of fitting is intended for use with nylon tubing per SAE J844. It is not intended to restrict or preclude other designs of a tube fitting for use with SAE J844. Performance requirements for SAE J844 are covered in SAE J1131. See SAE J2494-3 for the performance requirements of Reusable (push-to-connect) fittings intended for use in Automotive Air Brake Systems and U.S. Department of Transportation FMVSS 571.106.

2. References

2.1 Applicable Publications—The following publications form a part of this specification to the extend specified herein. Unless otherwise specified, the latest issue of publication shall apply.

2.1.1 SAE PUBLICATIONS—Available from SAE, 400 Commonwealth Drive, Warrendale, PA 15096-0001.

SAE J476—Dryseal Pipe Threads

SAE J512—Automotive Tube Fittings

SAE 844—Nonmetallic Air Brake System Tubing

SAE J1131—Performance Requirements for SAE J844 Nonmetallic Tubing and Fitting Assemblies Used in Automotive Air Brake Systems

SAE 2494-3—Performance Requirements for SAE J844 Nonmetallic Air Brake Tubing and Push-To-Connect Fitting Assemblies used in Vehicular Air Brake Systems

2.1.2 ANSI PUBLICATIONS—Available from ANSI, 25 West 43rd Street, New York, NY 10036-8002.

ANSI B1.1—Unified Inch Screw Thread

2.1.3 ISO PUBLICATIONS—Available from ANSI, 25 West 43rd Street, New York, NY 10036-8002.

ISO 7-1—Pipe threads where pressure-tight joints are made on the threads—Part 1: Dimensions, tolerances and designation

ISO 228—Pipe threads where pressure-tight joints are not made on the threads.

ISO 261—General purpose metric screw threads—General plan

2.1.4 FEDERAL PUBLICATIONS—Available from the Superintendent of Documents, U.S. Printing Office, Washington, DC

FMVSS 571.106

2.2 Related Publications—The following publications are for information purposes only and are not a required part of this document.

2.2.1 ANSI PUBLICATIONS—Available from ANSI, 25 West 43rd Street, New York, NY 10036-8002

ANSI B1.20.3—Dryseal Pipe Threads

ANSI B18.2.2—Square and Hex Nuts Inch Series

2.2.2 ASTM PUBLICATION—Available from ASTM, 100 Barr Harbor Drive, West Conshohocken, PA 19428-2959.

ASTM B 249—Specification for Wrought Copper and Copper Alloy Rod Bar and Shape

3. Size Designations—Fitting sizes are designated by the corresponding nominal outside diameter of the tubing for the various sizes of the tube ends and by the corresponding standard nominal pipe size for pipe thread ends.

4. Fitting Identification—Any component of the fitting shall be permanently and legibly marked according to the current U.S. Department of Transportation FMVSS 571.106 Regulation (NHTSA). The location of such markings shall be optional with manufacturer.

5. Dimensions and Tolerances—Except for nominal size and thread specifications, dimensions and tolerances are given in both SI units and U.S. customary as designated.

Unless otherwise specified, tolerances on all dimensions shall be ± 0.4 mm [0.016 in]. Tabulated dimensions shall apply to the finish parts. Dimensions over external contour of fittings shown in Appendix A, Tables A1 through A10 reflect the maximum envelope of products available. Details of internal construction of the attaching portion of fittings are not specified and shall be optional with the manufacturer, providing the fittings, properly assembled onto the appropriate tube, will meet the requirements specified in SAE J2494-3.

Wrenching surfaces shall fit standard wrench size openings. The minimum across corners dimensions of external hexagon shall be 1.092 times the nominal width across flat, but shall not result in a side flat width of less than 0.43 times the nominal width across flats.

Tabulated dimensions apply to measurements taken when the release mechanism is in the "in" position

6. Passages—The minimum flow diameter through any section of the air brake fitting shall not be less than 66% of the nominal inside diameter of the air brake tubing.

Where passages in straight fittings are formed from opposite ends, the offset at the meeting point shall not exceed 0.38 mm (0.015 in). On angle fittings, the cross-sectional area at the junction of fluid passages shall not be less than that of the smallest passage. At manufacturer's option, all passages in a particular fitting may conform with the smallest diameter specified for that fitting.

7. Contour—Details of contour shall be optional with manufacturer, provided the dimensions Appendix A, Tables A1 through A10 are maintained and serviceability of the fitting is not impaired.

8. Straight Threads—Unified straight threads shall be manufactured in accordance with ANSI B1.1.

Unified standard Class 2A external and Class 2B internal threads shall apply to plain finish (unplated) fittings of all types. For internally threaded parts with additive finish, the Class 2B diameters shall apply after plating.

Metric straight threads may be used and shall be manufactured in accordance with ISO 261 or ISO 228; however, this is not intended to preclude the use of other threads described in internationally accepted standards.

Where external threads are produced by roll threading, and the body is not undercut, the unthreaded portion of the body adjacent to the shoulder may be reduced to the minimum pitch diameter. See Figure 1.

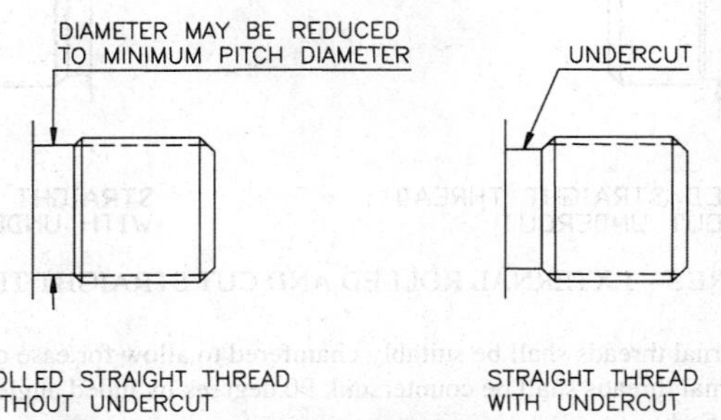

FIGURE 1—ROLLED STRAIGHT THREAD WITH OR WITHOUT UNDERCUT

External threads shall be suitably chamfered to allow for ease of assembly.

Internal threads shall be countersunk 90 degrees included angle to the diameters specified.

9. Thread Eccentricity Tolerances—The various thread elements of external and internal straight threads on tube fittings shall be concentric within the limitations specified in the General Specifications of SAE J512.

10. Pipe Threads—Taper pipe threads, unless there is specific authorization to the contrary, shall conform to the specifications found in SAE J476.

Where external pipe threads are produced by roll threading, the diameter of the unthreaded portion of shank adjacent to shoulder may be reduced to the E2 basic pitch diameter. See Figure 2.

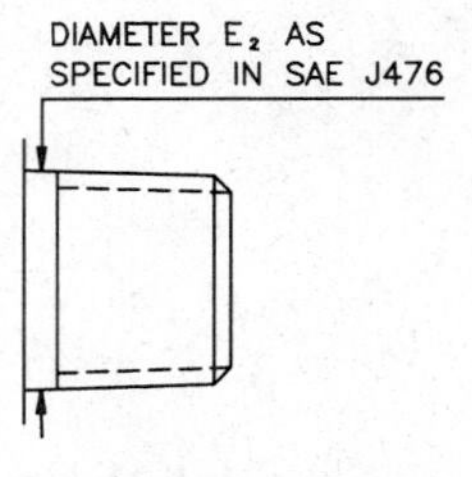

FIGURE 2—ROLLED TAPER PIPE THREAD WITHOUT UNDERCUT

External pipe threads shall be chamfered to allow ease of assembly. Internal pipe threads shall be countersunk 90 degrees included angle, to the diameters tabulated in Table 1.

TABLE 1—CHAMFER SPECIFICATION OF DRYSEAL PIPE THREAD

Nominal Pipe Thread Size in	Internal Thread Countersink Dia Max mm	Internal Thread Countersink Dia Max (in)	Internal Thread Countersink Dia Min mm	Internal Thread Countersink Dia Min (in)
1/8	11.2	0.44	10.7	0.42
1/4	14.5	0.57	14.0	0.55
3/8	18.0	0.71	17.5	0.69
1/2	22.1	0.87	21.6	0.85
3/4	27.4	1.08	26.9	1.06
1	34.5	1.36	34.0	1.34

British pipe threads may be used and shall be manufactured in accordance with ISO 7-1.

11. Materials—Fitting bodies shall be made from 100% virgin (no internal regrind) thermoplastic materials. Material shall be chosen such that the fitting will meet the performance requirements of SAE J2494-3.

For positionable threaded fitting, the base is to be made from one of the alloys shown as follows.

a. Allowable Base Materials
   UNS C34500
   UNS C35000
   ISO 426/2 CuZn $39Pb_3$
   JIS H3250 C3604B

12. Workmanship—Workmanship shall conform to the best commercial practice to produce high-quality fittings. Fittings shall be free from all processing materials, chips, hanging burrs, loose flash, and slivers which might become dislodged in usage and all other defects, which might affect their serviceability.

13. Pipe Thread Sealant—Where it is not objectionable from a function or production standpoint, the use of a compatible lubricant or sealant may be desirable in assembling Dryseal pipe threads on tube fittings to minimize galling and affect a pressure-tight seal.

APPENDIX A
FIGURES AND TABULATED DIMENSIONS FOR NON PUSH-METALLIC BODY PUSH TO CONNECT FITTINGS

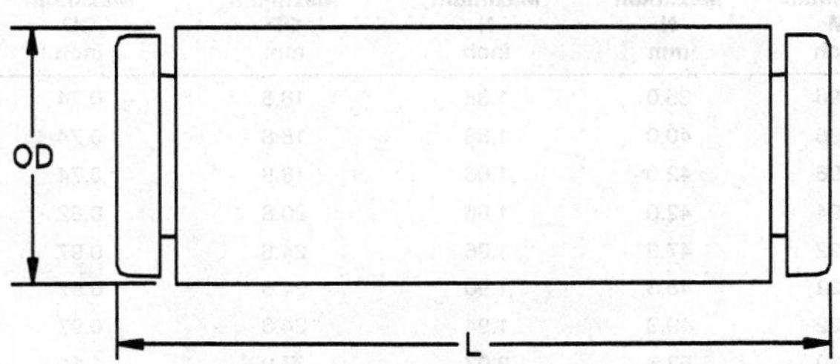

FIGURE A1—STRAIGHT EQUAL UNION (AA0101)
(Dimensions L and OD are listed in TABLE A1)

TABLE A1—DIMENSIONS FOR STRAIGHT EQUAL UNION

Tube Size	Maximum L mm	Maximum L inch	Maximum OD mm	Maximum OD inch
1/4	44.0	1.73	18.3	0.72
5/16	47.0	1.85	17.0	0.67
3/8	52.5	2.07	22.1	0.87
1/2	58.0	2.28	25.4	1.00

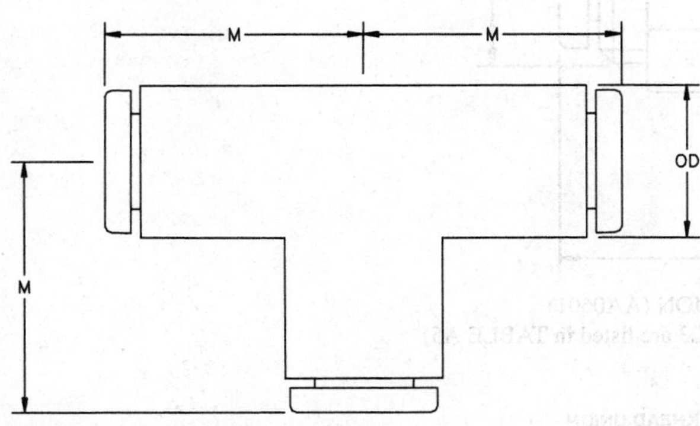

FIGURE A2—EQUAL TEE (AA0401)
(Dimensions M and OD are listed in TABLE A2)

TABLE A2—DIMENSIONS FOR EQUAL TEE

Tube Size	Maximum M mm	Maximum M Inch	Maximum OD mm	Maximum OD Inch
1/4	24.4	0.96	22.4	0.88
5/16	21.3	0.84	24.4	0.96
3/8	33.0	1.30	29.0	1.14
1/2	37.0	1.46	32.3	1.27

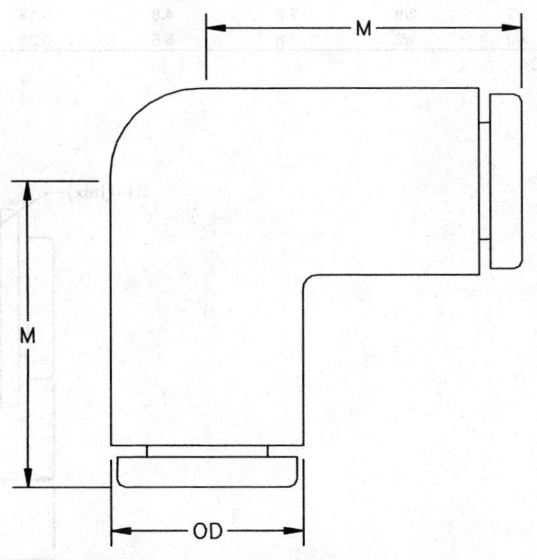

FIGURE A3—EQUAL ELBOW (AA0201)
(Dimensions M and OD are listed in TABLE A3)

TABLE A3—DIMENSIONS FOR EQUAL ELBOW

Tube Size	Maximum M mm	Maximum M inch	Maximum OD mm	Maximum OD inch
1/4	24.4	0.96	18.8	0.74
5/16	21.3	0.84	20.8	0.82
3/8	33.0	1.30	24.6	0.97
1/2	37.0	1.46	27.9	1.10

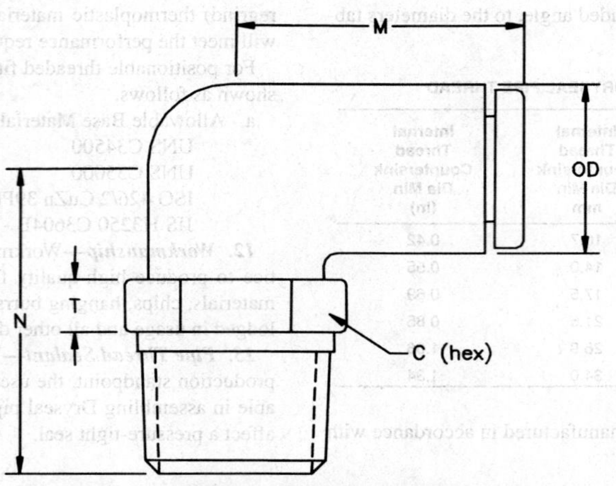

FIGURE A4—MALE ELBOW (POSITIONABLE) (AA02DD)
(Dimensions M, N, T, C, and OD are listed in TABLE A4)

TABLE A4—DIMENSIONS FOR MALE ELBOW

Tube Size	Pipe Thread	Maximum C Hex	Minimum T mm	Minimum T inch	Maximum M mm	Maximum M inch	Maximum N mm	Maximum N inch	Maximum OD mm	Maximum OD inch
1/4	1/8	5/8	2.8	0.11	24.3	0.96	35.0	1.38	18.8	0.74
1/4	1/4	5/8	3.8	0.15	24.3	0.96	40.0	1.58	18.8	0.74
1/4	3/8	11/16	4.5	0.18	24.3	0.96	42.0	1.66	18.8	0.74
5/16	1/4	9/16	3.8	0.15	23.9	0.94	42.0	1.66	20.8	0.82
3/8	1/4	3/4	3.8	0.15	31.0	1.22	47.3	1.86	24.6	0.97
3/8	3/8	11/16	4.8	0.19	31.0	1.22	48.3	1.90	24.6	0.97
3/8	1/2	7/8	5.0	0.20	31.0	1.22	49.3	1.94	24.6	0.97
1/2	1/4	7/8	3.8	0.15	33.0	1.30	52.6	2.07	27.9	1.10
1/2	3/8	7/8	4.8	0.19	33.0	1.30	53.4	2.10	27.9	1.10
1/2	1/2	7/8	5.8	0.23	33.0	1.30	58.4	2.30	27.9	1.10

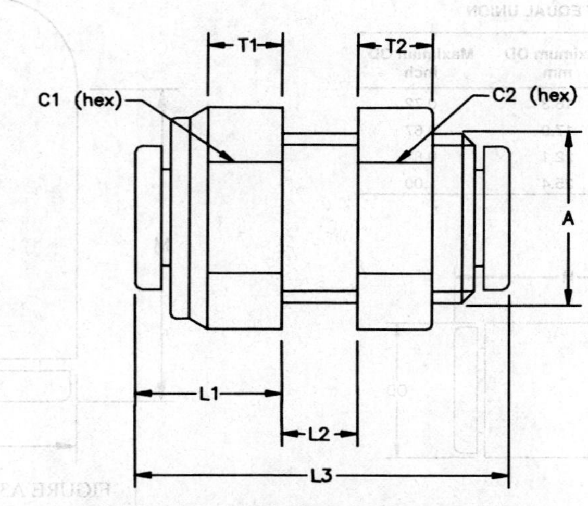

FIGURE A5—BULKHEAD UNION (AA0601)
(Dimensions T1, T2, C1, C2, A, L1, L2, and L3 are listed in TABLE A5)

TABLE A5—DIMENSIONS FOR BULKHEAD UNION

Tube Size	Thread A	Max. C1 Hex	Max. C2 Hex	Maximum L1 mm	Maximum L1 Inch	Maximum L3 mm	Maximum L3 Inch	Minimum Tl mm	Minimum T1 Inch	Minimum T2 mm	Minimum T2 Inch	Maximum L2 mm	Maximum L2 Inch
1/4	M12X1	15	15	10.5	0.41	29.5	1.16	6.5	0.26	6.5	0.26	9.5	0.37
5/16	M15X1	18	18	15.5	0.61	38.5	1.52	10.0	0.39	10.0	0.39	14.5	0.57
3/8	M18X1.5	22	22	15.5	0.61	44.0	1.73	10.0	0.39	10.0	0.39	14.5	0.57
1/2	M25X1.5	29	29	20.5	0.81	52.0	2.05	12.0	0.47	12.0	0.47	18.5	0.73

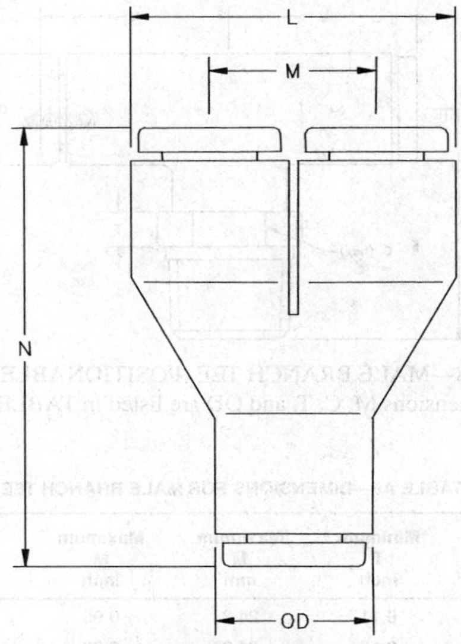

FIGURE A6—EQUAL Y
(Dimensions M, N, L, and OD are listed in TABLE A6)

TABLE A6—DIMENSIONS FOR EQUAL Y

Tube Size	Maximum L Length mm	Maximum L Length Inch	Maximum M Centerline mm	Maximum M Centerline Inch	Maximum N mm	Maximum N Inch	Maximum OD mm	Maximum OD Inch
1/4	48.8	1.92	17.0	0.67	38.9	1.53	24.1	0.95
5/16	37.8	1.49	18.0	0.71	30.7	1.21	25.4	1.00
3/8	58.9	2.32	24.0	0.94	43.5	1.71	27.4	1.08

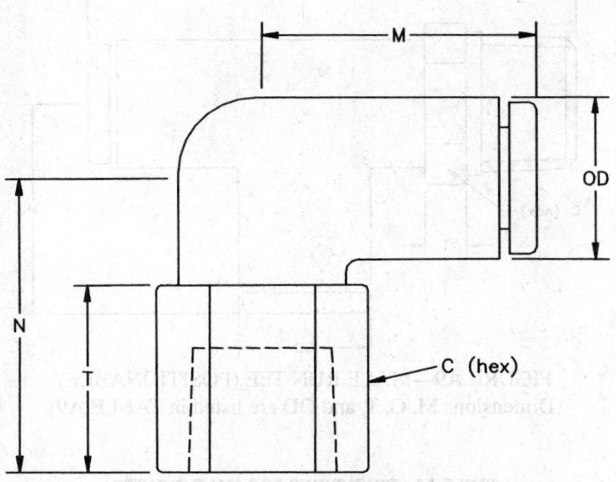

FIGURE A7—FEMALE ELBOW (POSITIONABLE)
(Dimensions M, N, T, C, and OD are listed in TABLE A7)

TABLE A7—DIMENSIONS FOR FEMALE ELBOW

Tube Size	Pipe Thread d	Maximum C Hex	T Min Hex Height mm	T Min Hex Height Inch	Maximum M Centerline mm	Maximum M Centerline Inch	Maximum N Centerline mm	Maximum H Centerline Inch	Maximum OD mm	Maximum OD Inch
1/4	1/8	5/8	9.4	0.37	24.3	0.96	29.7	1.17	18.8	0.74
1/4	1/4	3/4	10.5	0.41	24.3	0.96	34.8	1.37	18.8	0.74
5/16	1/4	3/4	10.5	0.41	21.3	0.84	34.8	1.37	20.8	0.82
3/8	1/4	3/4	13.0	0.51	31.1	1.23	40.3	1.59	24.6	0.97
1/2	3/8	7/8	13.4	0.53	29.0	1.14	43.1	1.70	27.9	1.10

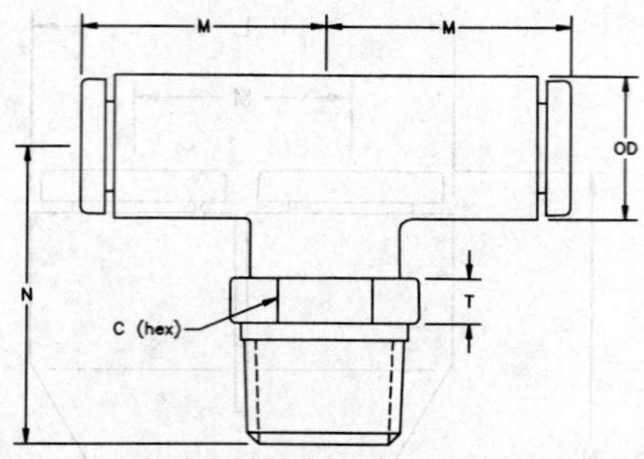

FIGURE A8—MALE BRANCH TEE (POSITIONABLE) (AA04FF)
(Dimensions M, C, T, and OD are listed in TABLE A8)

TABLE A8—DIMENSIONS FOR MALE BRANCH TEE

Tube Size	Pipe Thread	Maximum C Hex	Minimum T mm	Minimum T Inch	Maximum M mm	Maximum M Inch	Maximum N mm	Maximum N Inch	Maximum OD mm	Maximum OD Inch
1/4	1/8	5/8	2.8	0.11	24.3	0.96	35.0	1.38	22.4	0.88
1/4	1/4	5/8	3.8	0.15	24.3	0.96	40.0	1.58	22.4	0.88
1/4	3/8	11/16	4.0	0.16	24.3	0.96	42.0	1.66	22.4	0.88
5/16	1/8	1/2	2.8	0.11	21.3	0.84	32.5	1.28	24.4	0.96
5/16	1/4	9/16	3.8	0.15	21.3	0.84	37.1	1.46	24.4	0.96
3/8	1/8	11/16	3.8	0.15	31.0	1.22	43.1	1.70	29.0	1.14
3/8	1/4	3/4	3.8	0.15	31.0	1.22	47.3	1.86	29.0	1.14
3/8	3/8	3/4	4.8	0.19	31.0	1.22	48.3	1.90	29.0	1.14
3/8	1/2	7/8	5.0	0.20	31.0	1.22	49.3	1.94	29.0	1.14
1/2	1/4	7/8	3.8	0.15	33.0	1.30	52.6	2.07	31.5	1.24
1/2	3/8	7/8	4.8	0.19	33.0	1.30	53.5	2.11	31.5	1.24
1/2	1/2	7/8	5.8	0.23	33.0	1.30	58.4	2.30	31.5	1.24

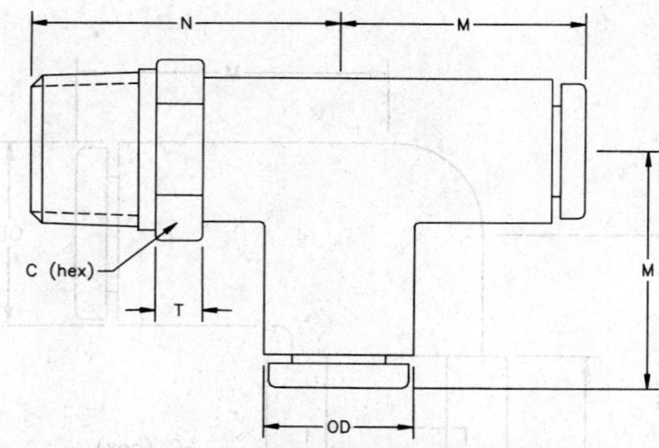

FIGURE A9—MALE RUN TEE (POSITIONABLE)
(Dimensions M, C, T, and OD are listed in TABLE A9)

TABLE A9—DIMENSIONS FOR MALE RUN TEE

Tube Size	Pipe Thread	Maximum C Hex	Minimum T Metric	Minimum T Inch	Maximum N Metric	Maximum N Inch	Maximum M Metric	Maximum M Inch	Maximum OD Metric	Maximum OD Inch
1/4	1/8	5/8	2.8	0.11	35.0	1.38	24.4	0.96	22.4	0.88
1/4	1/4	5/8	3.8	0.15	40.0	1.57	24.4	0.96	22.4	0.88
1/4	3/8	11/16	4.0	0.16	42.0	1.65	20.6	0.81	22.4	0.88
5/16	1/8	1/2	3.8	0.15	32.5	1.28	21.3	0.84	24.4	0.96
5/16	1/4	9/16	3.8	0.15	37.1	1.46	21.3	0.84	24.4	0.96
3/8	1/8	7/16	5.0	0.20	43.1	1.70	26.4	1.04	29.0	1.14
3/8	1/4	3/4	3.8	0.15	43.0	1.69	26.7	1.05	29.0	1.14
3/8	3/8	3/4	4.8	0.19	44.7	1.76	31.0	1.22	29.0	1.14
3/8	1/2	7/8	5.0	0.20	49.7	1.96	26.7	1.05	29.0	1.14
1/2	1/4	7/8	3.8	0.15	52.6	2.07	33.0	1.30	31.5	1.24
1/2	3/8	7/8	4.8	0.19	53.4	2.10	33.0	1.30	31.5	1.24
1/2	1/2	7/8	5.8	0.23	58.4	2.30	33.0	1.30	31.5	1.24

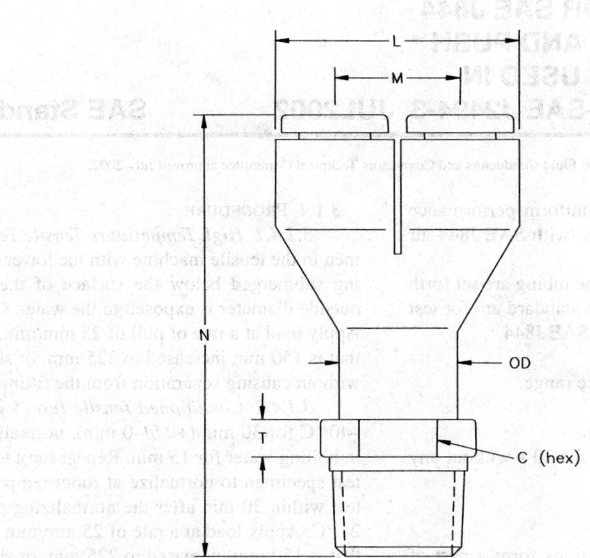

FIGURE A10—MALE Y (POSITIONABLE)
(Dimensions M, L, C, T, and OD are listed in TABLE A10)

TABLE A10—DIMENSIONS FOR MALE Y

Tube Size	Pipe Thread	Max C Hex	Minimum T mm	Minimum T Inch	Maximum M mm	Maximum M Inch	Maximum L mm	Maximum L Inch	Maximum OD mm	Maximum OD Inch	Maximum N mm	Maximum N Inch
1/4	1/4	5/8	3.2	0.13	17.0	0.67	38.9	1.53	24.1	0.95	57.7	2.27
1/4	3/8	11/16	4.0	0.16	17.0	0.67	33.5	1.32	24.1	0.95	54.6	2.15
5/16	1/4	9/16	3.8	0.15	18.0	0.71	30.7	1.21	25.4	1.00	53.3	2.10
5/16	3/8	11/16	4.0	0.16	18.0	0.71	30.7	1.21	25.4	1.00	51.8	2.04
3/8	1/4	3/4	4.8	0.19	22.0	0.87	43.5	1.71	27.4	1.08	63.5	2.50
3/8	3/8	3/4	5.0	0.20	22.0	0.87	49.0	1.93	27.4	1.08	70.4	2.77
3/8	1/2	7/8	5.0	0.20	22.0	0.87	43.5	1.71	27.4	1.08	68.3	2.69

PERFORMANCE REQUIREMENTS FOR SAE J844 NON-METALLIC AIR BRAKE TUBING AND PUSH TO CONNECT FITTING ASSEMBLIES USED IN VEHICULAR AIR BRAKE SYSTEMS—SAE J2494-3 JUL2002 SAE Standard

Report of the SAE Air Brake Tubing and Tube Fittings Subcommittee of the SAE Fluid Conductors and Connectors Technical Committee approved July 2002.

1. Scope—This SAE Standard is intended to establish uniform performance criteria and methods of testing push to connect tube fittings, with SAE J844 air brake tubing as used in vehicular air brake systems.

The specific tests and performance criteria applicable to the tubing are set forth in SAE J844. The test values contained in this performance standard are for test purposes only. For environmental and usage limitations, see SAE J844.

1.1 General Requirements

a. Test temperature shall use ±3 °C as the test tolerance range.
b. Dry Air shall be a minimum of –50 °C dew point
c. Tubing shall be cut square at 90 degrees ± 7 degrees
d. Precondition all test samples at 700 kPa ± 70 kPa for 30 s without any leakage.
e. New samples shall be used for all tests.

2. References

2.1 Applicable Publications—The following publications form a part of this specification to the extent specified herein. Unless otherwise indicated, the latest issue of SAE publications shall apply.

2.1.1 SAE PUBLICATIONS—Available from SAE, 400 Commonwealth Drive, Warrendale, PA 15096-0001.

SAE J844—Nonmetallic Air Brake Tubing

SAE J2024—Contaminants for Testing Air Brake Components and Auxiliary Pneumatic Devices

2.1.2 ASTM PUBLICATION—Available from ASTM, 100 Barr Harbor, West Conshohocken, PA 19428-2959.

ASTM B 117—Salt Spray (Fog) Testing

ASTM D 4329—Standard Practice for Fluorescent UV exposure of Plastics

ASTM G 53—Practice for Operating Light- and Water-Exposure Apparatus (Fluorescent UV- Condensation Type) for Exposure on Nonmetallic Materials

ASTM G 151—Standard Practice for Exposing Nonmetallic Materials in Accelerated Test Devices that Use Laboratory Light Sources

ASTM G 154—Practice for Operating Fluorescent Light Apparatus for UV Exposure of Nonmetallic Materials

2.2 Related Publications—The following publications are provided for information purposes only and are not a required part of this specification.

2.2.1 SAE PUBLICATION—Available from SAE, 400 Commonwealth Drive, Warrendale, PA 15096-0001.

SAE HS J806—SAE Oil Filter Procedure

2.2.2 FEDERAL PUBLICATION—Available from the Superintendent of Documents, U. S. Government Printing Office, Mail Stop: SSOP, Washington, DC 20402-9320.

DOT FMVSS 571.106 (49CFR 571.106) Brake Hoses

3. Requirements for Metallic and Non-metallic Fittings

3.1 Tensile Tests

3.1.1 DESCRIPTION—Both hot and cold tensile tests shall be conducted with different unaged assemblies (fittings attached within 30 days of test date). Tests consist of subjecting the assembly to increasing tensile load in a suitable testing machine until the specified force value or elongation percentage has been obtained.

3.1.2 APPARATUS—A tensile testing machine with suitable indicating device shall be used for the tensile test. The fixtures for holding the test specimens shall be arranged so the tubing and fittings have a straight centerline corresponding to the direction of the machine pull. The lower part of the fixture shall be equipped with a container of sufficient dimensions to submerge the required length of tubing in water. A means of heating the water to boiling shall be provided.

3.1.3 TEST SAMPLES—The tubing sample shall be obtained from current production stock and cut to a length sufficient to obtain 150 mm ± 6 mm of tubing between end fittings after assembly. Assemble fittings to the tubing using the manufacturer's recommendations.

3.1.4 PROCEDURE

3.1.4.1 High Temperature Tensile Test (5 samples)—Place the test specimen in the tensile machine with the lower fitting and 102 mm (+6/–0 mm) of tubing submerged below the surface of the boiling distilled water such that the outside diameter is exposed to the water. Continue boiling for 5 min (+5/–0 min.) Apply load at a rate of pull of 25 mm/min. The test specimen shall elongate 50%, that is 150 mm increased to 225 mm, or shall withstand the load listed in Table 1 without causing separation from the fitting.

3.1.4.2 Conditioned Tensile Test (5 samples)—Condition test specimen at –40 °C for 30 min (+0.5/–0 min), normalize at room temperature then submerge in boiling water for 15 min. Repeat for a total of four complete cycles. Allow the test specimen to normalize at room temperature for 30 min. Conduct the tensile test within 30 min after the normalizing period while at ambient temperature of 24 °C. Apply load at a rate of 25 mm/min. The test specimen shall elongate 50%, that is 150 mm increased to 225 mm, or shall withstand the load listed in Table 1 without causing separation from the fitting.

3.1.4.3 Water Absorption and Tensile Test (5 samples)—After immersion in distilled water at 24 °C for 70 h, conduct tensile test on the specimen by applying a load at the rate of 25 mm/min. The tube assembly shall withstand without separation of the tube and end fittings a tensile pull as listed in Table 1.

3.1.4.4 Acceptance Criteria

TABLE 1—TENSILE REQUIREMENTS

Nominal Tubing OD (in)	Tensile Load (Newtons)
5/32	225
3/16	225
1/4	225
5/16	335
3/8	670
1/2	900
5/8	1450
3/4	1560

3.2 Air Leakage (5 Samples)

3.2.1 DESCRIPTION—This test is designed to evaluate the effects of high and low system pressures on the fitting assembly at high and low temperatures.

3.2.2 APPARATUS—The equipment must be capable of controlling the ambient air temperature between –40 °C and 104 °C while applying 1035 kPa or 70 kPa dry air to the test lines. A mass flow meter capable of determining air leakage shall be provided.

3.2.3 TEST SAMPLES—Cut tubing sample to a length sufficient to obtain 460 mm between fittings after assembly. Assemble identical fittings to the tubing using the manufacturer's recommendation.

3.2.4 PROCEDURE—Place both ends of the test samples in temperature cycling cabinet and connect to a pressure source capable of 70 kPa ± 7 kPa and 1035 kPa ± 70 kPa pneumatic pressure. Pressure 4 c/h, alternating between 70 kPa ± 7 kPa and 1035 kPa ± 70 kPa. Subject the test samples while under pressure to 24 °C for 2 h, 104 °C for 12 h, 24 °C for 2 h, –40 °C for 2 h, and 24 °C again for 2 h in the order listed.

See Table 2 and Figure 1.

TABLE 2—AIR LEAKAGE TEST CONDITIONS

Time (hours)	Pressure (kPa)	Temperature (°C)
2	1035	24
14	1035	104
16	1035	24
18	1035	–40
20	1035	24

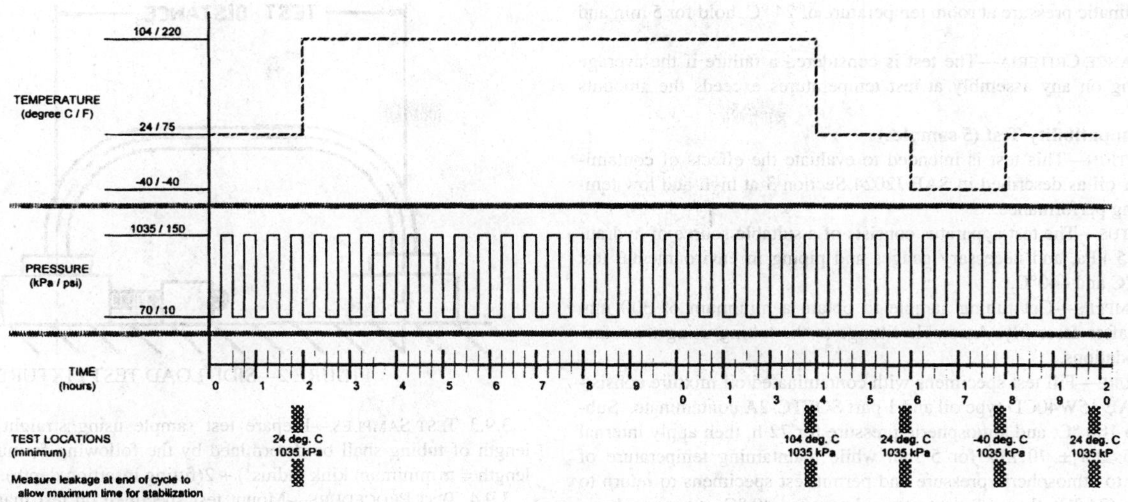

FIGURE 1—AIR LEAKAGE TEST CYCLE CHART

3.2.5 ACCEPTANCE CRITERIA—After the pressure in the assembly is allowed to stabilize, the test specimen is considered a failure if the average leakage per fitting on any assembly at specified test conditions in Table 2 exceeds the amounts listed in Table 3.

TABLE 3—LEAKAGE TEST REQUIREMENTS

Test Temperature (°C)	Maximum Leakage (Standard Cubic Centimeters/ minute)
104	3
24	5
–40	7

3.3 Vibration Test (5 samples)

3.3.1 DESCRIPTION—This test is designed to evaluate the effects of vibration on a tube and fitting assembly under varying internal pressures and ambient temperatures. Leakage rate is used to gauge acceptability.

3.3.2 APPARATUS—Equipment capable of vibrating one end of the test specimen at 600 c/min through 12 mm displacement in a plane perpendicular to the tube while the other end is held rigid. The distance between the static and vibrating head is to be such, that when the assembly is displaced 12 mm, no parallel pull to the longitudinal axis of the assembly will occur. The equipment must be capable of automatically adjusting the system pressure to compensate for fluctuating temperatures between –40 °C and 104 °C and associated air pressure of 830 kPa dry air during the test process. A mass flow meter capable of determining air leakage shall be provided.

3.3.3 TEST SAMPLES—Allowing 12.7 mm slack, cut tubing sample to a length sufficient to obtain 460 mm between fittings after assembly. Assemble identical fittings to the tubing using the manufacturer's recommendation.

3.3.4 PROCEDURE—Allowing 12 mm slack, mount the lines straight in the vibrating machine. Oscillate one end of the lines at 600 cycles/minute (±20 cpm) through a total stroke of 12 mm for a total of 1 000 000 cycles (+ 50 000/–0 cycles), while maintaining test conditions as shown in Table 4. Starting at 104 °C, vary the ambient air temperature from 104 °C to –40 °C at 250 000 vibration cycle intervals. Using a mass flow meter, observe for fitting leakage during and after the test.

TABLE 4—VIBRATION TEST REQUIREMENTS

Test Cycles	Test Pressure (kPa)	Test Temperature (°C)
0/250 000	0	104
250 001/500 000	0	–40
500 001/750 000	827	104
750 001/1 000 000	827	–40

3.3.5 ACCEPTANCE CRITERIA—The test is considered a failure if the average leakage per fitting on any assembly at test temperatures exceeds the amounts listed in Table 3.

3.4 Fitting Separation Pressure Test Requirements (5 samples)

3.4.1 DESCRIPTION—This test is intended to evaluate fitting retention at proof pressure of 2760 kPa ± 70 kPa and at minimum separation pressure.

3.4.2 APPARATUS—The test apparatus consists of a suitable source of hydraulic pressure and the necessary gauges and piping.

3.4.3 TEST SAMPLES—Cut tubing sample to obtain 300 mm between fittings after assembly. Assemble fittings to the tubing using the manufacturer's recommendations.

3.4.4 PROCEDURE—Plug one end of the test specimen and mount in the apparatus with the end unrestrained. Apply proof pressure at room temperature, 24 °C to the test specimen and hold for 30 s. Increase pressure at a constant rate so as to reach the specified minimum separation pressure within a time period of 3 to 15 s.

3.4.5 ACCEPTANCE CRITERIA—Fittings shall not separate from the tubing nor shall the assembly visibly leak at less than specified minimum separation pressure of 5500 kPa ± 70 kPa.

3.5 Frozen Water Retention Test (5 Samples)

3.5.1 DESCRIPTION—This test is intended to evaluate the effects of frozen water on fitting retention while assembly is pressurized to 2760 kPa ± 70 kPa.

3.5.2 APPARATUS—The test apparatus consists of a suitable source of pneumatic pressure and the necessary gauges and piping.

3.5.3 TEST SAMPLES—The tubing sample shall be obtained from current production stock and cut to a length sufficient to obtain 150 mm ± 6 mm of tubing between end fittings after assembly. Assemble fittings to the tubing using the manufacturer's recommendations.

3.5.4 PROCEDURE—Submerge one end of fitting assembly in water for 15 s, then remove the specimen from the water making sure the orientation of the fitting is such that no water is allowed to drain. Place test specimen in –10 °C air for a minimum of 1 h or until completely frozen. Conduct pressure test on the specimen while at –10 °C by applying 2760 kPa ± 70 kPa pneumatic pressure and hold for 5 min.

3.5.5 ACCEPTANCE CRITERIA—Fittings shall not separate from the tubing at the specified minimum test pressure of 2760 kPa.

3.6 Reassembly Test (5 samples)

3.6.1 DESCRIPTION—This test is intended to evaluate the effects of repeated assembly and disassembly of a tube and fitting. Leakage rate is used to gauge acceptability.

3.6.2 APPARATUS—The test apparatus consists of a suitable source of pneumatic pressure and the necessary gauges and piping. A mass flow meter capable of determining air leakage shall be provided.

3.6.3 TEST SAMPLES—Cut tubing sample to obtain 305 mm between fittings after assembly. Assemble fittings to the tubing using manufacturer's recommendations.

3.6.4 PROCEDURE—The tube and fitting connections shall be assembled, pressurized to 830 kPa ± 70 kPa pneumatic for 5 min, depressurized and disassembled five times. Tube end must not be trimmed between each assembly and disassembly cycle. Reassemble a sixth time and pressurize the test specimen to 830 kPa ± 70 kPa with pneumatic pressure at room temperature of 24 °C, hold for 5 min and check for leakage.

3.6.5 ACCEPTANCE CRITERIA—The test is considered a failure if the average leakage per fitting on any assembly at test temperatures exceeds the amounts listed in Table 3.

3.7 Oil Compatibility Test (5 samples)

3.7.1 DESCRIPTION—This test is intended to evaluate the effects of contaminated compressor oil as described in SAE J2024 Section 3 at high and low temperatures on fitting performance.

3.7.2 APPARATUS—The test apparatus consists of a suitable source of hydraulic pressure, 1035 kPa, and necessary gauges and piping in environmental test chambers at 100°C and –40°C.

3.7.3 TEST SAMPLES—Cut tubing sample to obtain a minimum of 300 mm between fittings after assembly. Assemble fittings to the tubing using manufacturer's recommendations.

3.7.4 PROCEDURE—Fill test specimens with contaminated oil mixture consisting of 11 parts SAE 15W40CD type oil and 1 part SOFTC-2A contaminate. Subject specimens to 100 °C, and atmospheric pressure for 72 h, then apply internal pressure of 1035 kPa ± 70 kPa for 5 min while maintaining temperature of 100 °C. Reduce to atmospheric pressure and permit test specimens to return to room temperature (24 °C); then subject test specimens to –40 °C and atmospheric pressure for 24 h. Then apply internal pressure of 1035 kPa ± 70 kPa for 5 min while maintaining a temperature of –40 °C.

3.7.5 ACCEPTANCE CRITERIA—Tubing shall not rupture or disconnect from the fittings.

3.8 Fitting Assembly Corrosion Resistance Test (5 samples)

3.8.1 DESCRIPTION—This test is designed to test the effects of salt spray corrosion on fitting assembly performance.

3.8.2 APPARATUS—Utilize the apparatus described in ASTM B 117 Salt Spray (Fog) Testing. Mix a salt solution five parts by weight of sodium chloride to 95 parts of distilled water, using sodium chloride substantially free of nickel and copper, and containing on a dry basis not more than 0.1% of sodium iodide and not more than 0.3 percent of total impurities. Ensure that the solution is free of suspended solids before the solution is atomized. After atomization at 35 °C, ensure that the collected solution is in the pH range of 6.5 to 7.2. Make the pH measurement at 25 °C. Maintain a compressed air supply to the nozzle or nozzles free of oil and dirt and between 70 and 170 kPa. The test sample shall be supported or suspended 30 degrees from the vertical and parallel to the principal direction of the horizontal flow of fog through the chamber. The test sample shall not have contact with any metallic material or any material capable of acting as a wick. Condensation that falls from the test sample shall not return to the solution reservoir for respraying. Condensation from any source shall not fall on the test sample or the solution collectors. Spray from the nozzles shall not be directed onto the test samples.

3.8.3 TEST SAMPLES—The test sample shall consist of two end fittings and a minimum of 200 mm of tubing between fittings.

3.8.4 TEST PROCEDURE—Subject the test samples to the salt spray continuously for 72 h. Regulate the mixture so that each collector will collect from 1 to 2 mL of solution per hour for each 80 cm^2 of horizontal collecting area. Maintain exposure zone temperature at 35 °C. Upon completion, remove the salt deposit from the surface of the tube assembly by washing gently or dipping in clean running water not warmer than 38 °C and then drying immediately. Allow the test assemblies to stabilize at 24 °C, then pressurize to 840 kPa ± 70 kPa pneumatic pressure for 5 min.

3.8.5 ACCEPTANCE CRITERIA—After 72 h exposure to salt spray, the fittings shall show no pit corrosion on the fitting surface. The average leakage per fitting on any assembly shall not exceed in amount listed in Table 3.

3.9 Side Load Leakage Test (5 samples)

3.9.1 DESCRIPTION—This test is designed to evaluate the leakage effects of maximum side loading on a tube and fitting assembly at room temperature 24 °C. Leakage rate is used to gauge acceptability.

3.9.2 APPARATUS—Equipment must be capable of controlling air pressure to 1035 kPa through a manifold consisting of a fixed and an adjustable block (see Figure 2). A mass flow meter capable of determining air leakage shall be provided.

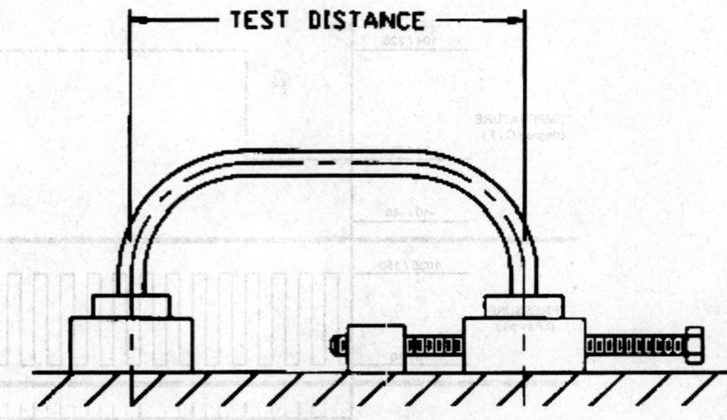

FIGURE 2—SIDE LOAD TEST FIXTURE

3.9.3 TEST SAMPLES—Prepare test sample using straight tube fittings. The length of tubing shall be determined by the following formula: Test specimen length = π(minimum kink radius[1]) + 2(fitting insertion depth).

3.9.4 TEST PROCEDURE—Mount test specimen on test manifold blocks using identical tube fittings as shown in Figure 1. Using the adjustable block, increase the distance between the centerlines of the test fittings to equal the test distance listed in Table 5. Pressurize the test specimen to 1035 kPa at 24 °C for a period of 5 min. If the tubing kinks during the test, the test shall be restarted using another sample of tubing.

TABLE 5—SIDE LOAD TEST REQUIREMENTS

Nominal Tubing OD (in)	Test Distance (mm)
5/32	30
3/16	50
1/4	65
5/16	80
3/8	95
1/2	127
5/8	160
3/4	180

3.9.5 ACCEPTANCE CRITERIA—After 5 min, the test is considered a failure if the average leakage per fitting on any assembly at test temperature exceeds the amount listed in Table 3.

4. Additional Requirements for Non-Metallic Fittings Only

4.1 Moisture Absorption (5 samples)

4.1.1 DESCRIPTION—This test is designed to evaluate the resistance of non-metallic fitting components to moisture absorption. Change in weight is used to gauge acceptability.

4.1.2 APPARATUS—Equipment must be capable of controlling air temperature within a temperature range of 24 °C to 110 °C and relative humidity of 100% at 24 °C.

4.1.3 TEST SAMPLES—Unassembled non-metallic fitting components.

4.1.4 TEST PROCEDURE—Expose all samples of non-metallic components for 24 h in a circulating air oven at 110 °C. Remove from oven, weigh immediately and expose for 100 h at 100% relative humidity and 24 °C. Within 5 min from humidity conditioning, remove surface moisture from both interior and exterior surfaces of the non-metallic components and re-weigh.

4.1.5 ACCEPTANCE CRITERIA—Moisture absorption of each non-metallic components shall not exceed 2% by weight.

4.2 Ultraviolet Resistance (5 samples)

4.2.1 DESCRIPTION—This test is designed to evaluate the resistance of non-metallic fittings to ultraviolet radiation exposure.

4.2.2 APPARATUS—A more complete description of the apparatus may be found in ASTM D 4329. Use fluorescent UV apparatus that conforms to the requirements defined in ASTM G 151 and G 154 is required to conform to this practice. Unless otherwise specified, the spectral power distribution of the fluorescent UV lamp shall conform to the requirements in ASTM G 154 for a UVA 340 lamp.

1. As listed in SAE J844 Table 3.

4.2.3 TEST SAMPLES—Cut tubing sample to obtain 300 mm between fittings after assembly. Assemble fittings to the tubing using the manufacturer's recommendations.

4.2.4 TEST PROCEDURE—Place samples of non-metallic fittings in the sample racks of a Q-Panel QUV test apparatus. Expose for 300 h minimum. If the test apparatus is equipped with a "Solar Eye", the bulbs need not be rotated and the irradiance should be set at 0.85, however all bulbs should be discarded after 4800 h maximum or if they fall below the 0.85 irradiance level, whichever occurs first. If the test apparatus is not equipped with a "Solar Eye", the bulbs must be rotated every 400 h maximum, as recommended by the manufacturer and ASTM G 53, this procedure will result in discarding lamps after 1600 h of use. Maintain test temperature of 45 °C ± 3 °C. The distance from the plate upon which the specimens are mounted and the light bulbs will be 51 mm maximum. The automatic humidity cycling must be turned off. Rotate the specimens according to ASTM D 4329 except the time interval should be each 96 h maximum, instead of weekly. Maintain and operate QUV tester in accordance with manufacturer instructions. Immediately following this exposure, stabilize the fitting for 0.5 to 3.0 h at 24 °C ± 3 °C and subject the fitting to a hydrostatic pressure test.

4.2.5 ACCEPTANCE CRITERIA—Fitting shall withstand a minimum internal pressure of 4400 kPa within a time period of 3 to 15 s.

4.3 Zinc Chloride Resistance (5 samples)

4.3.1 DESCRIPTION—This test is designed to evaluate the resistance of non-metallic fittings to Zinc Chloride. Visual evidence of cracking is used to gauge acceptability.

4.3.2 TEST PROCEDURE—Immerse non-metallic fitting in a 50% (by weight) aqueous solution of Zinc Chloride, pressurize assembly to 830 kPa ± 70 kPa for 200 h at 24°C ± 3° C. Remove from solution.

NOTE—Fresh, anhydrous zinc chloride should be used to make up a concentration of 50% (by weight) aqueous solution. (sg of 1.576 or a Baume rating of 53 degrees at 15.6 °C).

4.3.3 ACCEPTANCE CRITERIA—Fitting shall show no evidence of cracking on outside surfaces after pressurizing at 4400 kPa ± 70 kPa for 30s.

4.4 Methyl Alcohol Resistance (5 samples)

4.4.1 DESCRIPTION—This test is designed to evaluate the resistance of non-metallic fittings to Methyl Alcohol. Visual evidence of cracking is used to gauge acceptability.

4.4.2 TEST PROCEDURE—Immerse non-metallic fitting in 95% Methyl Alcohol for 200 h at 24 °C ± 3 °C. Remove from solution.

4.4.3 ACCEPTANCE CRITERIA—Fitting shall show no evidence of cracking on outside surfaces after pressurizing at 4400 kPa ± 70 kPa for 30 s.

4.5 Cold Temperature Impact (6 samples)

4.5.1 DESCRIPTION—This test is designed to evaluate the resistance of non-metallic fittings to Cold Temperature Impact. Leakage rate is used to gauge acceptability.

4.5.2 APPARATUS—Equipment must be capable of controlling air temperature within a temperature range of –40 °C to 110 °C. Impact apparatus as shown in Figure 3.

4.5.3 TEST SAMPLES—Cut tubing sample to obtain 300 mm between fittings after assembly. Assemble fittings to the tubing using the manufacturer's recommendations.

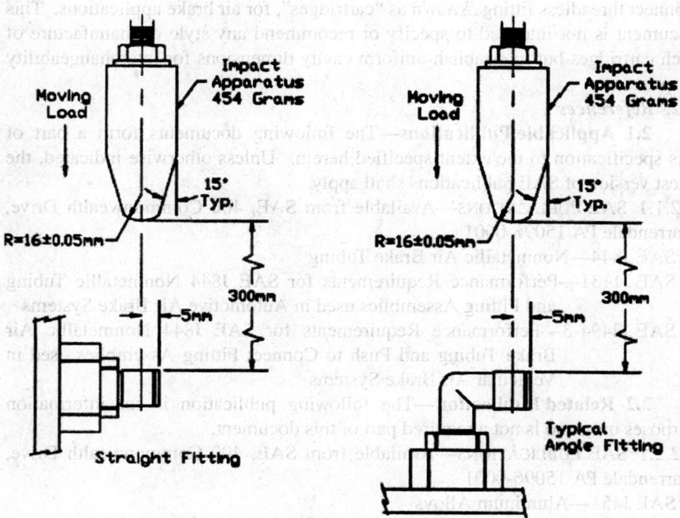

FIGURE 3—COLD IMPACT TEST FIXTURE

4.5.4 TEST PROCEDURE—Condition three samples for 24 h in a circulating air oven at 110 °C. Additionally, condition three samples in distilled boiling water for 2 h. Remove all samples from conditioning and allow to stabilize at 24 °C for 1 h. Expose all samples and impact test apparatus, shown in Figure 2, to –40 °C for 4 h. While fitting and test apparatus are at cold temperature (approximately –40 °C), subject fitting to impact by placing the fitting in the apparatus as shown in Figure 3 and allow the falling weight to free fall on the weakest zone of the fitting. The falling weight shall be mounted in a tubular housing or track in such a way as to permit free and unrestricted movement.

4.5.5 The distance between the bottom of the falling weight and the point of impact with the fitting shall be equal to 300 mm. After impact testing allow the fitting to stabilize at 24 °C. Within 30 min of stabilization, subject fitting to hydrostatic pressure of 4400 kPa within a time frame of 3 to 15 s.

4.5.6 ACCEPTANCE CRITERIA—Fittings shall not show any evidence of cracks or leakage.

CARTRIDGE CAVITY—SAE J2494-04 JUL2002 SAE Standard

Report of the SAE Air Brake and Tube Fittings Subcommittee of the SAE Fluid Conductors and Connectors Technical Committee approved July 2002. Rationale statement available.

1. Scope—This SAE Standard covers complete general and dimensional data for the manufacture of, T6061-T6 Aluminum cavities designed to receive Push To Connect threadless fittings known as "cartridges", for air brake applications. This document is not intended to specify or recommend any style or manufacture of such cartridges but to establish uniform cavity dimensions for interchangeability purposes.

2. References

2.1 Applicable Publications—The following documents form a part of this specification to the extent specified herein. Unless otherwise indicated, the latest version of SAE publications shall apply.

2.1.1 SAE PUBLICATIONS—Available from SAE, 400 Commonwealth Drive, Warrendale PA 15096-0001

SAE J844—Nonmetallic Air Brake Tubing

SAE J1131—Performance Requirements for SAE J844 Nonmetallic Tubing and Fitting Assemblies used in Automotive Air Brake Systems

SAE J2494-3—Performance Requirements for SAE J844 Nonmetallic Air Brake Tubing and Push to Connect Fitting Assemblies used in Vehicular Air Brake Systems

2.2 Related Publication—The following publication is for information purposes only and is not a required part of this document.

2.2.1 SAE PUBLICATIONS—Available from SAE, 400 Commonwealth Drive, Warrendale PA 15096-0001

SAE J451—Aluminum Alloys

3. General Requirements

3.1 Test Cavity material is to be T6061-T6 Aluminum

3.2 All dimensions unless specified differently are ±0.05 mm (±0.002 in).

3.3 All testing of subsequent assemblies must be performed with SAE J844 Air Brake Tubing

4. General Specifications

4.1 See Table 1 for cavity dimensions.

TABLE 1—CAVITY DIMENSIONS

Nominal Tubing OD	D1 mm	D1 in	K mm	K in	L1 (min) mm	L1 (min) in	R1 mm	R1 in
5/32	8.8	0.346	0.5	0.02	11.4	0.45	0.5	0.02
3/16	9.7	0.382	0.5	0.02	12.1	0.48	0.5	0.02
1/4	12.8	0.504	0.5	0.02	12.7	0.50	0.5	0.02
5/16	14.3	0.563	0.5	0.02	15.2	0.60	0.5	0.02
3/8	16.5	0.650	0.5	0.02	16.5	0.65	0.5	0.02
1/2	19.7	0.775	0.5	0.02	19.8	0.78	0.5	0.02
5/8	23.5	0.925	0.8	0.03	22.4	0.88	0.8	0.03
3/4	27.1	1.067	0.8	0.03	23.9	0.94	0.8	0.03

NOTE—Cavities made from materials other than T6061-T6 SHALL be adjusted dimensionally so that when installed; the tube/cartridge/cavity assembly will pass the applicable tests in SAE J1131 and SAE J2494-3.

4.2 Recommended Wall Thickness—Unless otherwise designated, the wall thickness at any point on a cartridge body, which may be subjected to internal pressure, is recommended to not be less than the thickness established by the specified dimensions and tolerances for inner and outer surfaces.

4.3 See Figure 1 for cavity detail and Table 2 for minimum wall thickness

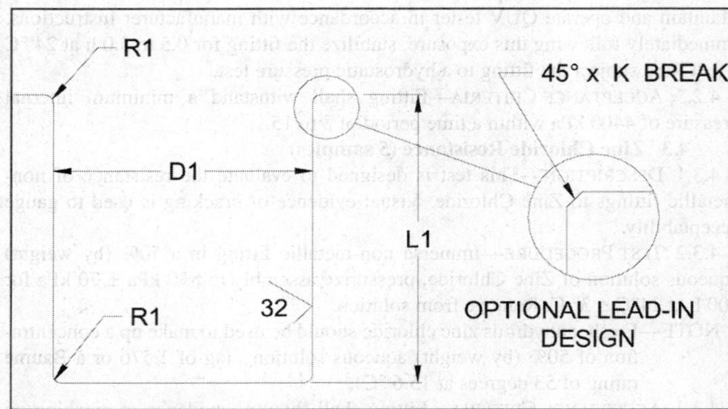

FIGURE 1—CAVITY DETAIL

TABLE 2—MINIMUM WALL THICKNESS

Nominal Tubing OD	Minimum Wall Thickness mm	Minimum Wall Thickness in
5/32	1.0	0.04
3/16	1.0	0.04
1/4	1.0	0.04
5/16	1.3	0.05
3/8	1.3	0.05
1/2	1.5	0.06
5/8	2.0	0.08
3/4	2.0	0.08

4.4 Workmanship—Workmanship shall conform to the best commercial practice to produce high quality cavities. Cavities shall be free from all machining fluids, chips, burrs, scale and slivers which either dislodge in usage or sever the external o-ring affecting serviceability.

TEST PROCEDURES FOR NON-SAE HYDRAULIC HOSES—SAE J2545 MAR2001

SAE Recommended Practice

Report of the SAE Fluid Conductors and Connectors Technical Committee S2—Hydraulic Hose and Hose Fittings approved March 2001. Rationale statement available.

1. Scope—This SAE Recommended Practice identifies test procedures and parameters which may be used to evaluate, qualify and inspect non-SAE hydraulic hoses or other hose constructions which do not conform to any established ISO or national standards defining hydraulic hoses. (Non-SAE hydraulic hoses are defined as those which do not conform to the categories listed in SAE J517.) It is not intended for evaluating fluoropolymer lined hose constructions or hose constructions with working pressures above 86 MPa.

2. References

2.1 Applicable Publications—The following publications form a part of this specification to the extent specified herein. Unless otherwise specified, the latest issue of SAE publications shall apply.

2.1.1 SAE PUBLICATIONS—Available from SAE, 400 Commonwealth Drive, Warrendale, PA 15096-0001.

SAE J343—Tests and Procedures for SAE 100R Series Hydraulic Hose and Hose Assemblies
SAE J516—Hydraulic Hose Fittings
SAE J517—Hydraulic Hose
SAE J1273—Recommended Practices for Hydraulic Hose Assemblies

2.2 Related Publications—The following publications are for information purposes only and are not a required part of this document.

2.2.1 SAE PUBLICATION—Available from SAE, 400 Commonwealth Drive, Warrendale, PA 15096-0001.

SAE J1401—Road Vehicle—Hydraulic Brake Hose Assemblies for Use with Nonpetroleum Base Hydraulic Fluids, Appendix A, Table A1 Hose Manufacturer Identification Code—Colored Yarn Assignments

2.2.2 FEDERAL STANDARD—Available from the Superintendent of Documents, U.S. Government Printing Office, Washington, DC 20402.

Federal Standard 595 Colors Used In Government Procurement

3. Connectors—The general and dimensional standards for hydraulic hose connectors are contained in SAE J516. It is recommended that connectors consistent with SAE J516 or ISO standards be used to conduct the following tests.

4. General Information—For information regarding Age Control, Application Factors, Size Designations, Identification, Offset, and Assembly Length, see sections 3 through 10 in SAE J517. Additional information regarding the selection, care, use and routing of hose can be found in SAE J1273.

5. Tests—Unless otherwise agreed upon between the manufacturer and purchaser, tests for evaluating conformance of product with specifications shall be on the basis of Qualification Tests and Inspection Tests set forth in this document. Tests may be conducted by the manufacturer, the purchaser, or independent lab, as decreed by the purchaser. All tests shall be conducted in accordance with the procedures in SAE J343.

5.1 Inspection Retests and Rejection—In the event of failure of one or more samples to meet any of the inspection tests specified, the product shall be resampled and retested for the test or tests in which it failed. Twice the number of samples designated under the initial test procedure shall be selected from the lot in question for such retests, and failure of any of the retested samples shall be cause for rejection of the entire lot.

5.2 Qualification Tests—For qualification, hose and/or hose assemblies made from the hose in question shall conform to the following tests and requirements. The values used in these tests shall be taken from the hose manufacturers specification and used as described herein.

5.2.1 DIMENSIONAL CHECK TEST (ALL SAMPLES)—Shall conform to the dimensions in the hose manufacturers specification. The inside diameter of hose shall be concentric with outside diameter of hose and the outer surface of the reinforcement within the limits of Table 1.

5.2.2 PROOF TEST (ALL SAMPLES)—Shall not leak at proof pressure which shall be twice the maximum working pressure of the hose.

5.2.3 CHANGE IN LENGTH TEST (ONE SAMPLE)—Shall not exceed the values shown in Table 2 when pressurized to maximum working pressure.

5.2.4 BURST TEST (ONE 460 mm FREE HOSE LENGTH ASSEMBLY)—Shall not leak or fail below the minimum burst pressure which shall be at least 4 times the working pressure.

TABLE 1—HOSE CONCENTRICITY

Type of Construction	Nominal Hose ID, mm	Concentricity, FIR ID to OD mm	Concentricity, FIR ID to Reinforcement mm
Rubber, Braided Reinforcement	Up to 6.3, incl	0.8	0.4
	Over 6.3 to 19, incl	1.0	0.7
	Over 19	1.3	0.9
Rubber, Spiral Wire Reinforcement	Up to 19, incl	1.0	0.7
	over 19	1.3	0.9
Thermoplastic	Up to 6.3, incl	0.8	—
	Over 6.3 to 19, incl	1.0	—
	Over 19	1.3	—

TABLE 2—LENGTH CHANGE

Type of Constuction	Allowable Length Change, %
Rubber, Braided Reinforcement	+2, –4
Rubber, Spiral Wire Reinforcement	±2
Thermoplastic	±3

5.2.5 LEAKAGE TEST (TWO 300 mm FREE HOSE LENGTH ASSEMBLIES)—Shall not leak or fail.

5.2.6 COLD BEND TEST (ONE ASSEMBLY)—Shall exhibit no cover cracks or leakage when tested at the low temperature limit of the hose. If no temperature is available use –40 °C.

5.2.7 OIL RESISTANCE TEST—After 70 h immersion at the upper temperature limit of the hose in IRM 903 oil, the volume change of hose inner tube and cover specimens shall be between 0% and +100%.

5.2.8 OZONE RESISTANCE TEST (TWO SAMPLES)—Specimens shall be subjected to an atmosphere comprised of air and ozone with an ozone partial pressure of 50 mPa (50 parts ozone per 100 million parts of air at standard atmospheric conditions) at an ambient temperature of 40°C. After 70 h exposure, specimens shall not show evidence of cracking or deterioration when viewed with seven-power magnification while still in a stressed condition.

5.2.9 IMPULSE TEST (FOUR UNAGED ASSEMBLIES)—The parameters for this test, oil temperature, pressure and number of cycles, shall be as determined by the manufacturer and the user. To aid in selecting these parameters the following table may be used. The values shown should be considered as minimum requirements and can be adjusted, as required, for each hose type being evaluated.

TABLE 3—IMPULSE TEST PARAMETERS

Type of Construction	Test Pressure (psi) as % of Working Pressure	Oil Test Temperature °C	Minimum Test Cycles
Fabric Braid	133%	100	200 000
Wire Braid	125% to 133%	100	200 000
Spiral Wire	120% to 133%	121	400 000
Thermoplastic	125% to 133%	93	200 000

5.2.10 VISUAL EXAMINATION (ALL SAMPLES)

5.2.11 ELECTRICAL CONDUCTIVITY TEST (THIS TEST APPLIES ONLY TO NON-CONDUCTIVE HOSES)—The maximum leakage shall not exceed 50 μA when subjected to 75 kV/305 mm (75 kV/ft) for 5 min.

This test shall not be applicable to hoses which contain pinpricked outer covers, metallic wire reinforcement, and static electricity dissipative materials.

5.3 Inspection Tests—Inspection tests listed as follows shall be performed on two samples representing each lot of 150 to 3000 m of bulk hose. Lots of less than 150 m of hose need not be subjected to these tests if a lot has been tested and met the requirements within the previous 12-month period. Requirements shall be the same as for corresponding Qualification Tests:

a. Dimensional Check Test (see 5.2.1)
b. Proof Test (see 5.2.2)
c. Change in Length Test (see 5.2.3)
d. Burst Test (see 5.2.4)

In addition, all hose and/or hose assemblies made therefrom shall be subjected to visual examination.

5.4 Hose Identification—Except for hose with a wire braided exterior, the entire length of hose shall be legibly marked with one or more stripes parallel to the longitudinal axis <u>if the manufacturing process permits</u>. Marking shall include, but is not limited to the following, and shall be repeated with the first letter of each repeat not more than 762 mm from the first letter of that preceding. <u>Marking may be in English or metric units as agreed upon by the user and manufacturer</u>.

Manufacturers Identification
Hose Dash Size Number
Hose ID in Fractions <u>or mm's</u>
Maximum Working Pressure (MPa preferred)
Date Code

No mention of the burst pressure or the design factor is allowed on the hose. This information could be misinterpreted by the user and result in a hose being used above its rated working pressure.

For additional hose identification information, see SAE J517, Section 8.

RECOMMENDED PRACTICES FOR FLUID CONDUCTOR METALLIC TUBING APPLICATIONS—SAE J2551 DEC2001

SAE Recommended Practice

Report of the SAE Metallic Tubing Subcommittee of the SAE Fluid Conductors and Connectors Technical Committee approved December 2001. Rationale statement available.

Foreword—The SAE Recommended Practice is intended as a guide to consider when designing and fabricating metallic tubes and tube assemblies for fluid power and general applications. It is subject to change to keep pace with experience and technical advances. Experienced designers and users skilled in achieving proper results, as well as the less experienced may use this outline as a list of considerations to keep in mind.

Fluid power systems are complex and require extensive knowledge of both the system requirements and the various types of tube. Therefore, all-inclusive, detailed, step-by-step instructions are not practical and are beyond the scope of this document. Less experienced designers and users who need more information may consult specialists such as experienced tube designers and fabricators. This guide may improve the communication process.

Following this document is highly recommended by the participating SAE/ISO organizations and their members. Adherence to these guidelines may assure the users they will create tube assemblies that can be efficiently manufactured, conveniently packaged/shipped, proficiently installed on their equipment, will perform adequately and safer to established industry standards and they will be using common practices and components that may be easily serviced anywhere globally.

Safety Considerations—These documents involve considerations to facilitate safer conditions when these products are in use; note these carefully during all phases of design and use of the tube assemblies. Improper selection, fabrication, installation, or maintenance of tube assemblies for fluid-power systems may result in serious personal injury or property damage. Adherence to these recommended practices could reduce the likelihood of component or system failure, thereby reducing the risk of injury or damage.

TABLE OF CONTENTS

1. Scope—These recommended practices provide general recommendations for designing and fabricating metallic tubes and tube assemblies for fluid power applications utilizing commonly available manufacturing methods and general guidelines for tube selection and application. These documents are primarily intended for mobile/stationary industrial equipment and automotive applications. Aircraft and Aerospace applications were not considered during the preparation of this document.

2. References

2.1 Applicable Publications—The following publications form a part of this specification to the extent specified herein. Unless otherwise specified, the latest issue of SAE publications shall apply.

2.1.1 SAE PUBLICATIONS—Available from SAE, 400 Commonwealth Drive, Warrendale, PA 15096-0001.

SAE J512—Automotive Tube Fittings

SAE J514—Hydraulic Tube Connections

SAE J518—Hydraulic Flanged Tube, Pipe, and Hose Connections. Four-Bolt Split Flange Type

SAE J533—Flares for Tubing

SAE J1065—Pressure Ratings for Hydraulic Tubing and Fittings

SAE J1231—Formed Tube Ends for Hose Connections and Hose Fittings

SAE J1453—Fitting—O-Ring Face Seal

2.1.2 ISO PUBLICATIONS—Available from ANSI, 25 West 43rd Street, New York, NY 10036-8002.

ISO 6162—Four-screw split-flange connections

ISO 8434—Metallic tube connections for fluid power and general use

ISO 10763—Plain-end, seamless and welded steel tubes—Dimensions and nominal working pressures

2.2 Related Publications—The following publications are for information purposes only and are not a required part of this document.

2.2.1 SAE PUBLICATIONS—Available from SAE, 400 Commonwealth Drive, Warrendale, PA 15096-0001.

SAE J246—Spherical and Flanged Sleeve (Compression) Tube Fittings

SAE J343—Tests and Test Procedures for SAE 100R Series Hydraulic Hose and Hose Assemblies

SAE J356—Welded Flash-Controlled Low-Carbon Steel Tubing Normalized for Bending, Double Flaring, and Beading

SAE J515—Specification for Hydraulic O-Ring Materials, Properties, and Sizes for Metric and Inch Stud Ends, Face Seal Fitting and Four-Screw Flange Tube Connections

SAE J524—Seamless Low-Carbon Steel Tubing Annealed for Bending and Flaring

SAE J525—Welded and Cold Drawn Low-Carbon Steel Tubing Annealed for Bending and Flaring

SAE J526—Welded Low-Carbon Steel Tubing

SAE J527—Brazed Double Wall Low-Carbon Steel Tubing

SAE J1273—Recommended Practices for Hydraulic Hose Assemblies

SAE J1290—Automotive Hydraulic Brake System—Metric Tube Connections

SAE J1677—Tests and Procedures for Low-Carbon Steel and Copper Nickel Tubing

SAE J1926-1—Connections for General Use and Fluid Power-Ports and Stud Ends with ISO 725 Threads and O-Ring Sealing—Part 1: Threaded Port with O-Ring Seal in Truncated Housing

SAE J1926-2—Connections for General Use and Fluid Power-Ports and Stud Ends with ISO 725 Threads and O-Ring Sealing—Part 2: Heavy-Duty (S Series) Stud Ends

SAE J1926-3—Connections for General Use and Fluid Power-Ports and Stud Ends with ISO 725 Threads and O-Ring Sealing—Part 3: Light-Duty (L Series) Stud Ends

SAE J2094—Vehicle and Control Modifications for Drivers with Physical Disabilities Terminology

SAE J2244-1—Connections for Fluid Power and General Use—Ports and Stud Ends with ISO 261 Threads and O-Ring Sealing—Part 1: Port with O-Ring Seal in Truncated Housing

SAE J2244-2—Connections for Fluid Power and General Use—Ports and Stud Ends with ISO 261 Threads and O-Ring Sealing—Part 2: Heavy-Duty (S Series) Stud Ends—Dimensions, Design, test Methods, and Requirements

SAE J2244-3—Connections for Fluid Power and General Use—Ports and Stud Ends with ISO 261 Threads and O-Ring Sealing—Part 3: Light-Duty (L Series) stud End—Dimensions, Design, Test Methods, and Requirements

SAE J2244-4—Connections for Fluid Power and General Use—Ports and Stud Ends with ISO 261 Threads and O-Ring Sealing—Part 4: Heavy-Duty (S Series) External Hex Port Plugs—Dimensions, Design, Test Methods, and Requirements

SAE J2435—Welded Flash Controlled, SAE 1021 Carbon Steel Tubing, Normalized for Bending, Double Flaring, and Beading

SAE J2467—Welded and Cold-Drawn, SAE 1021 Carbon Steel Tubing Normalized for Bending and Flaring

2.2.2 ISO PUBLICATIONS—Available from ANSI, 25 West 43rd Street, New York, NY 10036-8002.

ISO 272—Fasteners—Hexagon products—Widths across flats

ISO 273—Fasteners—Clearance holes for bolts and screws

ISO 2944—Fluid power systems and components—Nominal pressures

ISO 3304—Plain end seamless precision steel tubes—Technical conditions for delivery

ISO 3305—Plain end welded precision steel tubes—Technical conditions for delivery

ISO 3448—Industrial liquid lubricants—ISO viscosity classification

ISO 3457—Earth-moving machinery—Guards and shields—Definitions and specifications

ISO 3601—O-ring sealing devices for fluid carrier systems

ISO 4200—Plain end steel tubes, welded and seamless—General tables of dimensions and masses per unit length

ISO 4397—Connectors and associated components—Nominal outside diameters of tubes and nominal inside diameters of hoses

ISO 4399—Connectors and associated components—Nominal pressures

ISO 5598—Fluid power systems and components—Vocabulary

ISO 6072—Hydraulic fluid power—Compatibility between elastomeric materials and fluid

ISO 6149—Ports and stud ends with ISO 261 Metric threads and O-ring sealing

ISO 6150—Pneumatic fluid power—Cylindrical quick-action couplings

ISO 6163—Round flange, 8 and 12 screw connections

ISO 6164—Four-screw, one-piece square-flange connections
ISO 6605—Tests and test procedures
ISO 6743-4—Lubricants, industrial oils and related products (Class L)—Part 4: Family H (Hydraulic Systems)
ISO 7241—Quick action couplings
ISO 9974—Metric threaded ports and stud ends
ISO 10583—Test methods for tube connections
ISO 11926—Ports and stud ends with ISO 725 Inch threads and O-ring sealing
ISO 15171—Hydraulic couplings for diagnostic purposes
ISO 16028—Hydraulic flush face quick-action couplings

2.2.3 ASTM PUBLICATIONS—Available from ASTM, 100 Bar Harbor Drive, West Conshohocken, PA 19428-2959.

ASTM A 268/A 268M—Seamless and Welded Ferritis and Martensitic Stainless Steel Tubing
ASTM 269-96—Seamless and Welded Austenitic Stainless Steel Tubing for General Service
ASTM 312A/A312M—Seamless and Welded Austentic Stainless Steel Pipes
ASTM 316—Stainless Steel Tubing
ASTM A 450/A 450M-96a—General Requirements for Carbon, Ferritic Alloy and Austenitic Alloy Steel Tubing

3. Definitions—These explanations serve only to clarify this document and are not intended to stand alone. They are presented sequentially, with the former helping to explain the latter.

3.1 Arc—The curved portion of the bend.

3.2 Bend Die—A wheel-shaped die with a groove in the outer circumference that conforms to half the tube circumference. It will most often have a straight section used as half of the clamp set for holding the tube against the die. This type of die is used in rotary draw or compression bending to generate the bend radius.

3.3 Bend Radius—See Centerline radius

3.4 Bender (Tube)—A mechanical device capable of forming a bend in a straight length of material.

3.5 Boost—Device or system to apply a longitudinal positive force in the direction of the bend by either clamping or pushing on the end of the tube being bent. This force will reduce wall thinning of the outside wall and increase the compression and thickness of the inside wall.

3.6 Buckling—Definite folds, creases, or wrinkles formed on the surface of the tube during the bending operation.

3.7 Center to Center—The distance between the theoretical or calculated centers of adjoining bends. Also used for diametric measurement between the centerlines of two tangent points of a bend, (i.e., 180-degree bend for which the center to center distance will be equal to twice the centerline radius)

3.8 Centerline Diameter—The distance from the centerline axis of the tube across to the other centerline of a 180-degree bend.

3.9 Centerline Radius (CLR)—The distance on a bend forming tool from the center of curvature to a point corresponding to the centerline of the tubular shape when mounted in the bend-forming tool – nominal CLR.

3.10 Clamp Die—A tool used in rotary draw and compression bending to clamp the tube against the bend die to prevent the tube from slipping during bending.

3.11 Cold Bending—The bending of tube by cold working at ambient temperatures.

3.12 Compression—The forces that thicken the inside wall of the bend.

3.13 "D" of Bend—Centerline radius (CLR) divided by the tube diameter.

3.14 Degree of Bend (DOB)—The angle expressed in number of degrees, to which the bend is formed.

3.15 Distance Between Bends (DBB)—The actual length of the straight section between the tangent points of two adjoining bends.

3.16 Ductility—The ability of the material to deform plastically without fracture, as measured by elongation or reduction of area in a tensile test.

3.17 Elongation—The increase in length of a test specimen at failure in a tensile test, expressed as a percentage of the original length. The increase in length of material fiber during bending, expressed as a percentage of the original length.

3.18 Extrados—The outside arc of the bend.

3.19 Flat Plane—See Out-of-plane.

3.20 Flash—The excess material created at the weld joint when the tube was produced.

3.21 Flattening—See Ovality.

3.22 Fluid Power—Energy transmitted and controlled using pressurized hydraulic fluids or gases.

3.23 Follower Die—See Pressure die.

3.24 Hump—A rounded protrusion or bulge on the outside radius.

3.25 Hydraulic Pressure Spike—Rapid increase in system pressure that exceeds designed relief valve working pressure setting.

3.26 ID—The inside diameter of the tube.

3.27 Inner Radius—See Intrados.

3.28 Intrados—The inside arc of the bend.

3.29 Mandrel—A tool device used to provide internal support to the tube to prevent excessive flattening, collapse or wrinkling during rotary draw bending. The mandrel is supported by a mandrel rod that runs through the tube ID and is held in location at the bend die.

3.30 Minimum Wall Thickness—The wall thickness specified on the fabrication drawing or computed in accordance with the applicable specification as the minimum acceptable for the design criteria.

3.31 Neutral Axis—That portion of the tube that is neither in compression nor in tension.

3.32 Nominal—Used in reference to wall thickness, generally as a "mean" measurement.

3.33 Nominal OD—Usually refers to referenced pipe sizes, not actual OD.

3.34 Nominal Wall—The target measurement for the wall thickness.

3.35 OD—Outside diameter of the tube.

3.36 Out-of-Plane—The deviation of the horizontal plane of a single bend between its tangent points, based on the theoretical centerline of the bend.

3.37 Outside Radius—See Extrados.

3.38 Ovality—The distortion of the cross section of tube from its normal (round) shape usually expressed as a percentage of the difference between the major and minor axes of the starting material compared to the OD before bending.

3.39 Over Bend—The amount that a tube has to be bent past the desired bend angle to compensate for residual stresses in the bend. This allows the tube to return to the desired bend angle after all external support from clamping has been removed.

3.40 Plane of Bend (POB)—The plane of a bend in relation to the axis of the straight section preceding it. Used specifically for changes of plane in successive bends.

3.41 Press Die—See Ram die.

3.42 Pressure Die—A tool used in rotary draw bending that holds the tube against the die as the bend and clamp die rotate with the tube. Pressure dies can be of the static or follower type. Also used in compression bending to form the tube around the bend die.

3.43 Pressure Die Assist—A system that generates a longitudinal force on the tube during bending. The amount of force generated is dependent on the friction occurring in the interface of the pressure die and the tube.

3.44 Radial Growth—The difference between the actual CLR and the bend die CLR of a tubular shape after all external forces that restrained it are removed.

3.45 Radius—See Centerline radius.

3.46 Ram Die—A type of bend die used in a press or ram bender to form the bend.

3.47 Routing—The path or shape of the tube required to move fluid from one point to another point.

3.48 Shoe—See Wiper die.

3.49 Spring-back—The movement of the bent tube toward the original straight configuration after release of the bending moment.

3.50 Tangent—A straight section of material on either end to the arc of a bend.

3.51 Tangent Point—The theoretical point at which the bend is started or ended.

3.52 Tensile Strength—The point at which material stretched beyond its yield will rupture.

3.53 Tension—The force which thins the outside wall of the bend.

3.54 Throat Wall—The inner half of the tube or the half undergoing compression during bending. The thickness of tubular material usually expressed as "nominal" or "minimum".

3.55 Tube—The carbon steel fluid conductor to be formed.

3.56 Tube Assembly—Tube with fittings and other components attached.

3.57 Tube Failure—Occurrence in which the tube stops meeting system requirements.

3.58 Tube Fitting or Fitting—Connector which is attached to the tube.

3.59 Tube Service Life—Length of time tube meets system requirements without needing replacement.

3.60 Wall Factor—The ratio of the tube outside diameter (OD) to its wall thickness.

3.61 Wall Thickness—The thickness of the material usually stated as a decimal or "Gauge".

3.62 Wall Thinning—The amount of reduction from original wall thickness of tube to the amount of wall thickness remaining in the extrados of a bend after forming.

3.63 Wing Die—Tool used in press or ram bending that forms the tube around the ram or bend die.'

3.64 Wiper Die—A die mounted on the bender used in rotary draw bending. It is located on the compressive side of the bend, adjacent to the bend die centerline. It supports the intrados and helps prevent it from buckling during bending.

3.65 Wrinkles—See Buckling.

3.66 Yield Point—The point at which material permanently deforms during bending.

3.67 Yield Strength—The stress at which a material exhibits a specified deviation from proportionality as a result of stress and strain.

4. Tube Sizing, Tube Connection Selection, and Routings—A wide variety of interacting factors influence tube service life and the ability of each fluid-power system to operate satisfactorily, and the combined effects of these factors on service life are often unpredictable. Therefore, these documents should not be construed as design standards.

Metallic tubing is specified in either millimeter or inch size designations. Availability and cost of millimeter or inch sizes are largely determined by local factors. Selection of millimeter or inch size tubing affects the selection and availability of related bending, flaring, and forming tooling, as well as the connectors specified. Millimeter size tubing and metric connectors are recommended to provide eventual ISO global standards.

Unusual applications—Applications not addressed by the fabricator or by industry standards may require special testing prior to selecting metallic tubing.

Carefully analyze each system. Then design routings and select tube and related components to meet system performance, capacity and tube-service-life requirements, and to minimize the risks of personal injury and/or property damage. The following factors should be considered.

4.1 Sizing—Tube size should be determined by the proposed flow rate and pressure requirements of the fluid power system and the recommended design factors. Flow rate determines the fluid velocity in the system and is controlled by the outside diameter and wall thickness of the tube. Pressure determines the amount of force applied by the system fluids and the required strength of the tubing wall to conduct these pressures to the appropriate locations.

4.1.1 SYSTEM PRESSURE AND FLUID VELOCITY—Industry practice is a design factor of 4 to 1, burst pressure versus working pressure. See SAE J1065 and ISO 10763 for nominal reference working pressures for specific types of steel tubing and sizes.

Fluid velocity is a primary consideration when sizing tube for hydraulic systems. High fluid velocity can cause excess heat generation, turbulence and pressure drop in pressure lines. In suction lines, high velocity can lead to pump cavitation.

The following maximum fluid velocities are suggested initial design targets for hydraulic systems:

a. Pressure Line—7.62 m/s (25 ft/s)
b. Return Line—3.05 m/s (10 ft/s)
c. Suction Line—1.22 m/s (4 ft/s)

High velocities and line restrictions create heat and pump problems, which have an adverse effect on system performance. Computer modeling and very often, trial and error testing, are necessary to verify overall system performance and the determination of the need for coolers.

4.1.2 SEVERITY OF SERVICE—The recommended industry standard of 4 to 1 design factor, burst pressure versus working pressure, is adequate in systems with moderate mechanical and hydraulic shocks. When a system has known severe hydraulic shocks and mechanical strain, a design factor of 6 to 1, burst pressure versus working pressure, is recommended. In addition to hydraulic and mechanical shocks, high temperature also reduces the working pressure of the tube. When high operating temperatures are a system requirement, derating factors should be considered when calculating the working pressure of the tube. See tube manufacturer for derating factors.

4.2 Tube and End Connection Selection—When selecting tube and end connections for specific applications, refer to applicable Standards listed as follows.

4.2.1 TUBE SELECTION—Refer to the Related Publications 2.2 for various types of tubing. Refer to SAE J1065 and ISO 10763 for common tube OD'S, wall thickness and applicable nominal reference working pressure ratings for carbon steel tubing.

4.2.2 TUBE CONNECTION SELECTION—There are many types of hydraulic tube connections available for hydraulic systems. The type of connection used should be based on the following criteria:

a. System peak and working pressure
b. Number of potential leak paths or joints in the connection
c. Ease of assembly and repair

Connection types should be selected from the specifications shown in Figures 1 through 7. Specific maximum working pressures and performance capabilities are listed for most common connectors in each of the various specifications.

4.2.2.1 SAE J1453/ISO 8434 Part 3 - ORFS Connection—See Figure 1.

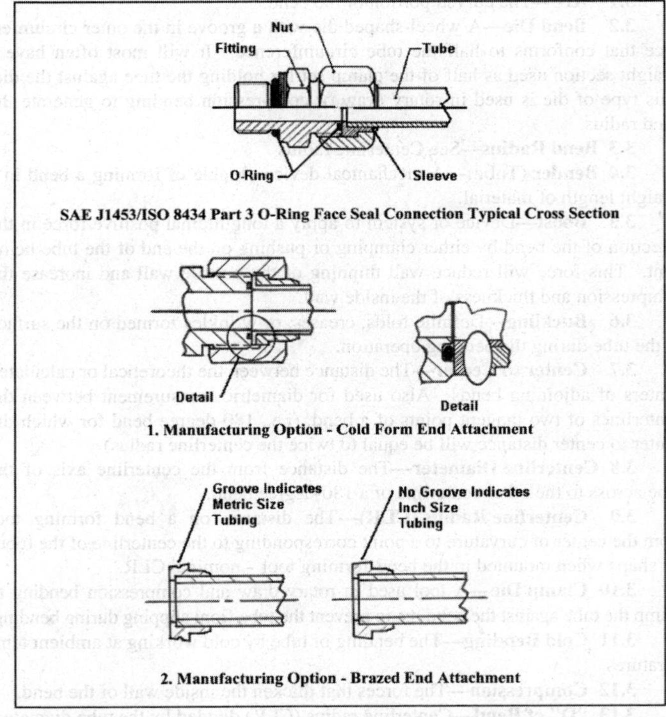

FIGURE 1—SAE J1453/ISO 8434 PART 3 O-RING FACE SEAL CONNECTION AND OPTIONAL MANUFACTURING METHODS. FOR USE IN SYSTEMS UP TO 63 MPA (9000 PSI), SEE ISO 8434 PART 3 FOR WORKING PRESSURES, O-RING SEAL INTERFACE HELPS PROVIDE LEAK FREE CONNECTIONS.

4.2.2.2 SAE J514/ISO 8434 Part 2 - 37 degree Flared Connections—See Figure 2.

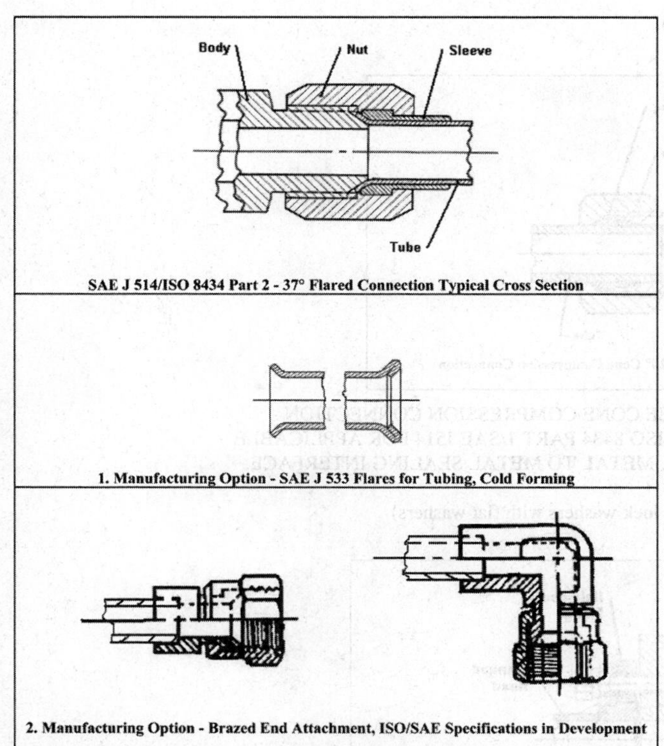

FIGURE 2—SAE J514/ISO 8434 PART 2 - 37 DEGREE FLARED CONNECTION AND OPTIONAL MANUFACTURING METHODS. FOR USE IN SYSTEMS UP TO 35 MPA (5000 PSI), SEE ISO/SAE J514/8434 PART 2 FOR APPLICABLE WORKING PRESSURES FOR VARIOUS TUBE SIZES, METAL TO METAL SEALING INTERFACE.

4.2.2.3 SAE J512 45 degree Inverted Flare Connections—See Figure 3.

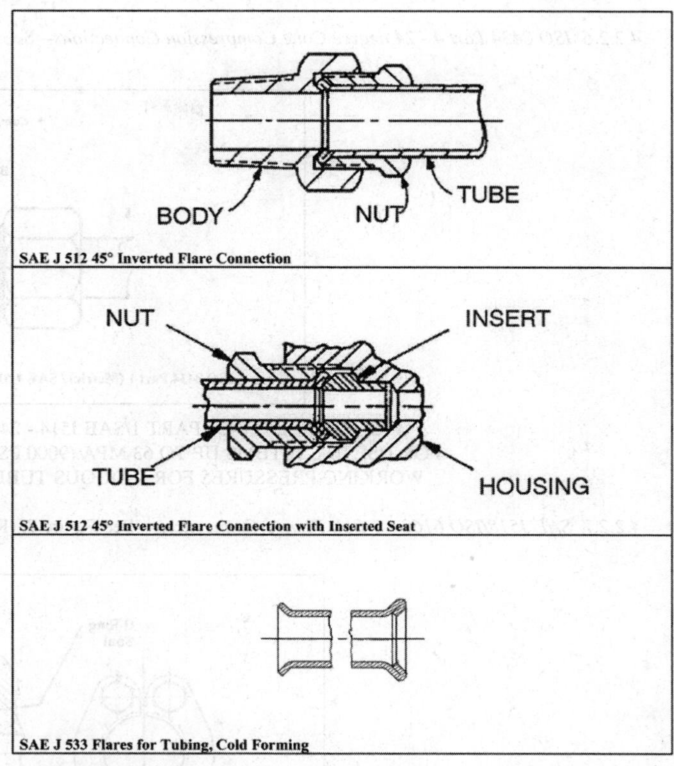

FIGURE 3—45 DEGREE FLARED CONNECTION TYPICALLY USED FOR AIR BRAKE SYSTEMS, CONTACT SUPPLIER FOR WORKING PRESSURE, METAL TO METAL SEALING INTERFACE.

4.2.2.4 SAE J1231 Formed Tube Ends for Hose Connections—See Figure 4.

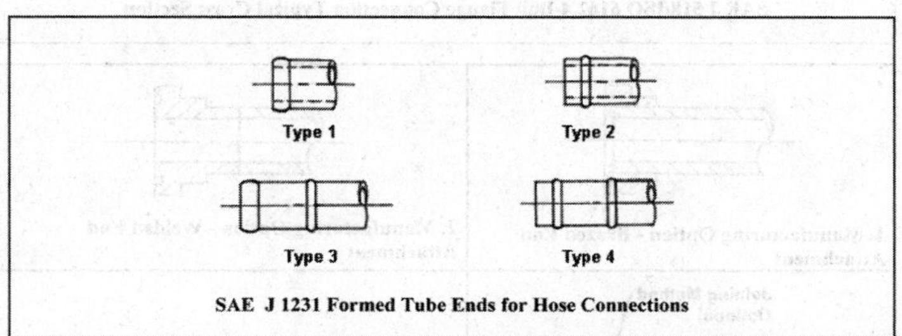

FIGURE 4—SAE J1231 FORMED BEADED TUBE ENDS TYPICALLY USED FOR SUCTION LINES, CONTACT SUPPLIER FOR PERFORMANCE REQUIREMENTS.

4.2.2.5 ISO 8434 Part 4 - 24 degree Cone Welded Nipple Connections—See Figure 5.

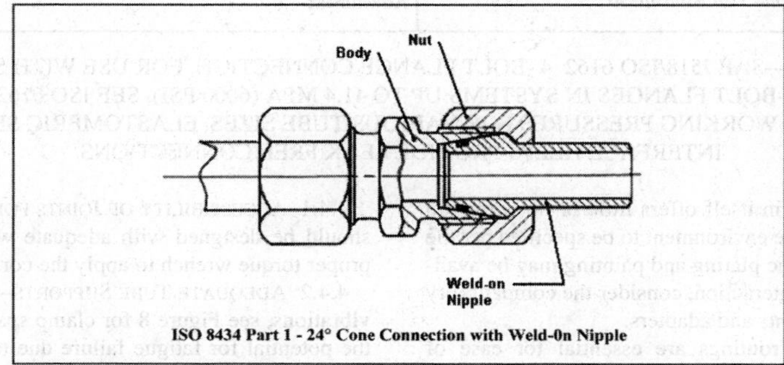

FIGURE 5—ISO 8434 PART 4 - 24 DEGREE CONE CONNECTION WITH WELD-ON NIPPLE FOR USE IN SYSTEMS UP TO 63 MPA (9000 PSI), SEE ISO 8434 PART 4 - FOR APPLICABLE WORKING PRESSURES FOR VARIOUS TUBE SIZES, METAL TO METAL AND ELASTOMERIC SEALING

INTERFACE HELP PROVIDE LEAK FREE CONNECTIONS.

4.2.2.6 ISO 8434 Part 4 - 24 degree Cone Compression Connections—See Figure 6.

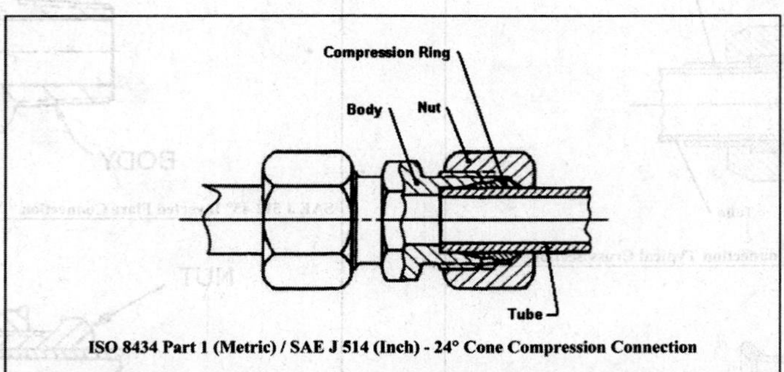

FIGURE 6—ISO 8434 PART 1/SAE J514 - 24 DEGREE CONE COMPRESSION CONNECTION - FOR USE IN SYSTEMS UP TO 63 MPA (9000 PSI), SEE ISO 8434 PART 1/SAE J514 FOR APPLICABLE WORKING PRESSURES FOR VARIOUS TUBE SIZES, METAL TO METAL SEALING INTERFACE.

4.2.2.7 SAE J518/ISO 6162 - 4-Bolt Flange Connections—See Figure 7. (Replaced lock washers with flat washers)

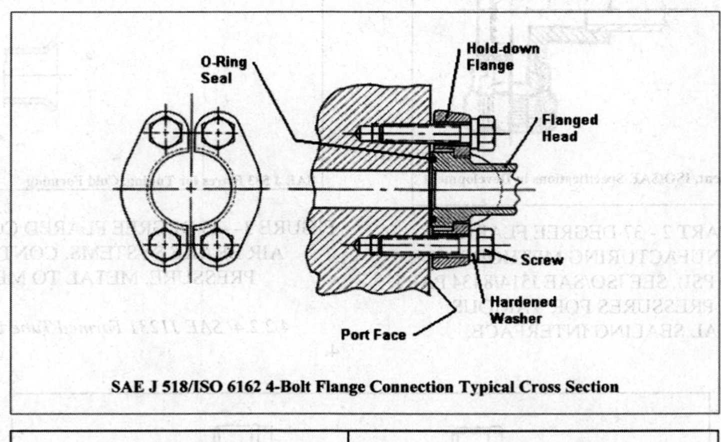

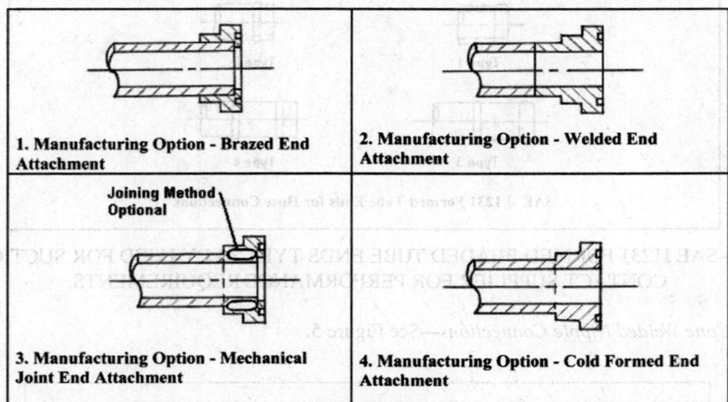

FIGURE 7—SAE J518/ISO 6162 4 -BOLT FLANGE CONNECTION, FOR USE WITH SPLIT OR CAPTIVE 4-BOLT FLANGES IN SYSTEMS UP TO 41.4 MPA (6000 PSI), SEE ISO 6162/SAE J518 FOR WORKING PRESSURES FOR VARIOUS TUBE SIZES. ELASTOMERIC SEAL INTERFACE HELPS PROVIDE LEAK FREE CONNECTIONS.

4.3 Environment—Carbon steel tube in itself offers little or no corrosion resistance. Appropriate coatings for the usage environment to be specified per the application. Coatings such as, phosphate, zinc plating and painting may be available. Because of the potential for galvanic interaction, consider the compatibility of the tube material and the related components and adapters.

4.4 Routings—Proper fluid carrier routings are essential for ease of assembly, overall efficiency, leak-free performance and general system appearance. After sizing the tube lines and selecting the style of fittings, consider the following in the design of the system.

4.4.1 ACCESSIBILITY OF JOINTS FOR ASSEMBLY—All joints in the system should be designed with adequate wrench clearance to provide the use of the proper torque wrench to apply the correct torque.

4.4.2 ADEQUATE TUBE SUPPORTS—Tube supports are mainly for dampening vibrations, see Figure 8 for clamp spacing guidelines. They reduce the noise and the potential for fatigue failure due to mechanical vibration. Tube line supports should only support the weight of the tubing. They should not support the weight of the valves, filters, regulators, etc. Valves should be mounted separately to prevent rotation of the valve body. When dynamic hoses are attached to tube assemblies, the tube should be clamped securely as near to the joint connection as possible to provide adequate support.

4.4.3 MAINTENANCE AND ACCESS CONSTRAINTS—Tube routings should not interfere with access doors, attaching bolts and other equipment that must have access for regular maintenance. In addition, the fluid carriers should remain clear of controls and not prohibit the operator's access to the controls

4.4.4 AREAS OF DYNAMIC MOVEMENT—Tube assemblies should be isolated from vibration stresses as much as possible. Flexible hose and dampening clamps should be used to isolate the tube assembly from vibratory stresses.

4.4.5 EXPANSION LOOPS—Expansion loops should be installed to prevent tension stresses and allow for temperature expansions. The use of "U" shapes instead of straight line runs between connections will increase the assemblies tolerance to expansion and contraction due to temperature changes and allow for motion under load, see Figure 9. Even some rigid systems do move when placed under a heavy load.

4.4.6 ROUTINGS BETWEEN FIXED POINTS—Tolerance build up should be considered when designing tube assemblies, see Figure 10. Adjustable brackets to allow the mating components to be properly located for correct joint interface alignment is recommended. Very often the ability to adjust the location of the mating components is very difficult, and the resultant is induced loads into the tube assembly after final assembly, which leads to early hour failure. Tube assembly design of this type should be avoided if adjustment can not be provided.

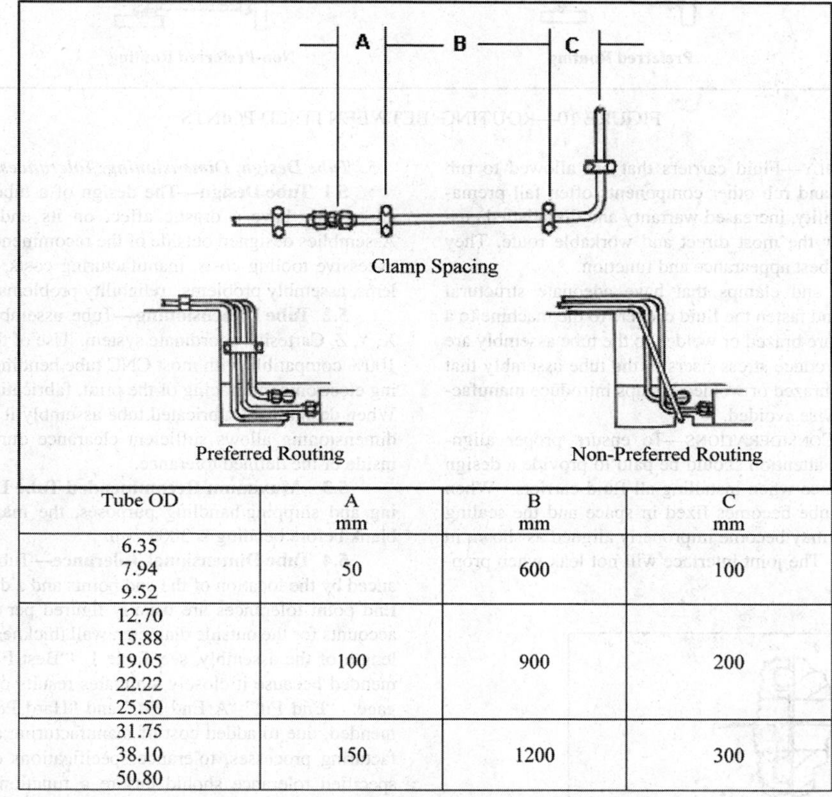

Tube OD	A mm	B mm	C mm
6.35 7.94 9.52	50	600	100
12.70 15.88 19.05 22.22 25.50	100	900	200
31.75 38.10 50.80	150	1200	300

FIGURE 8—ADEQUATE TUBE SUPPORTS AND CLAMP SPACING GUIDELINES TESTS SHOULD BE CONDUCTED TO EVALUATE THE OVERALL SYSTEM VIBRATION TO PREDICT ADEQUATE SERVICE LIFE.

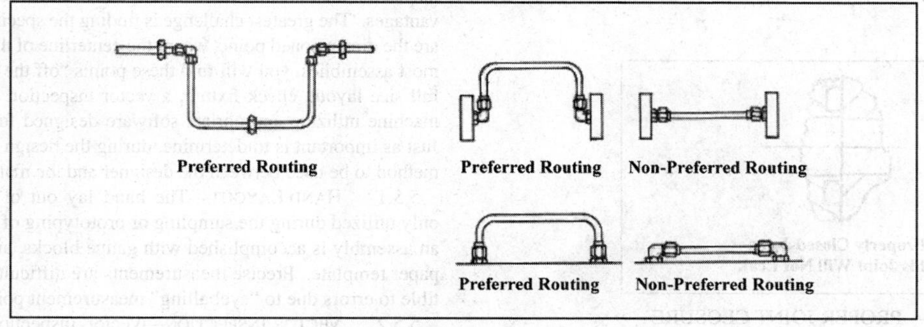

FIGURE 9—EXPANSION LOOPS

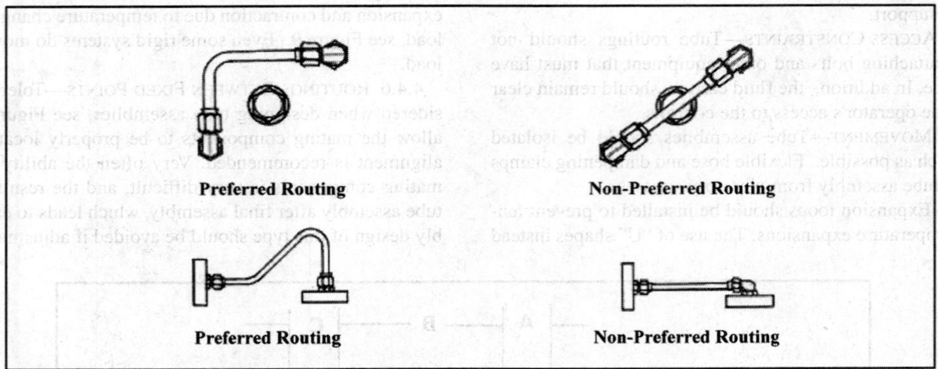

FIGURE 10—ROUTING BETWEEN FIXED POINTS

4.4.7 CONTACT AFTER ASSEMBLY—Fluid carriers that are allowed to rub sharp edges, criss-cross each other and rub other components often fail prematurely, which leads to reduced reliability, increased warranty and dissatisfied customers. Fluid carriers should follow the most direct and workable route. They should run parallel to each other for best appearance and function.

4.4.8 CLIPS AND CLAMPS—Clips and clamps that have adequate structural integrity should be used to support and fasten the fluid carriers to the machine to a rigid support location. Clamps that are brazed or welded to the tube assembly are not recommended because these introduce stress risers in the tube assembly that may reduce fatigue life. Also these brazed or welded clamps introduce manufacturing difficulties that may be otherwise avoided.

4.4.9 TIGHTENING SEQUENCE CONSIDERATIONS—To ensure proper alignment of the sealing interfaces, close attention should be paid to provide a design that allows correct tightening sequence when installing all fluid carriers. When the clamps are tightened first, the tube becomes fixed in space and the sealing interfaces at the tube assembly ends may become improperly aligned as shown in Figure 11, and will eventually leak. The joint interface will not leak when properly closed, as shown in Figure 12.

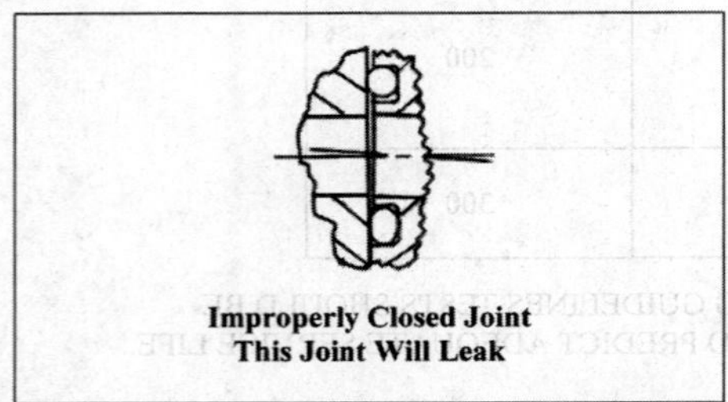

FIGURE 11—IMPROPER JOINT CLOSURE

FIGURE 12—PROPER JOINT CLOSURE

4.4.10 EXTERNAL PHYSICAL ABUSE—Fluid carriers should be guarded and located so they are not subject to damage from rocks/debris, or used as a step, platform or load holding device when removing or installing adjacent components.

4.4.11 HEAVY-DUTY APPLICATIONS—A heavy wall and larger OD tube may be required if the assembly may be regularly subjected to contact by foreign objects, such as, rocks, gravel. Stand off from uncoated surfaces should be at least 12 mm. Tube assemblies should be kept away from uncoated surfaces that may exhibit rust and corrosion over the life of the system.

5. Tube Design, Dimensioning, Tolerances, and Inspection

5.1 Tube Design—The design of a tube assembly and the required tolerances may have a drastic affect on its end use, manufacturability and cost. Assemblies designed outside of the recommendations of this document may drive excessive tooling costs, manufacturing costs, packaging/shipping/delivery problems, assembly problems, reliability problems, and quality issues.

5.2 Tube Dimensioning—Tube assemblies should be designed using the X, Y, Z, Cartesian coordinate system. Use of this system makes the dimensioning 100% compatible with most CNC tube bending and inspection equipment, allowing electronic interfacing of the print, fabrication, and inspection of the assembly. When designing a fabricated tube assembly it is very important to ensure that all dimensioning allows sufficient clearance during assembly of the finished part inside of the defined tolerance.

5.3 Maximum Recommended Tube Length—To facilitate manufacturing and shipping/handling purposes, the maximum recommended tube length blank before bending is 3000 mm.

5.4 Tube Dimensional Tolerance—Tube assemblies are typically toleranced by the location of the end points and a defined envelope of routing contour. End point tolerances are usually figured per assembly based on a formula that accounts for the outside diameter, wall thickness, number of bends, and developed length of the assembly, see Table 1. "Best Fit" method of inspection is recommended because it closely simulates results obtained with a standard inspection gage. "End Fit," "A End Fit," and "Hard Point" dimensioning are not recommended, due to added cost of manufacturing and inspection. As with all manufacturing processes, tolerance specifications can drive unnecessary costs. The specified tolerance should ensure a functional part that can be manufactured repeatedly, without excessive inspection and handling. Tight tolerance dimensioning should only be applied in specific applications where all other alternatives have been exhausted and the higher cost per assembly can be justified.

5.5 Types of Inspection Methods—There are several types of accepted inspection methods for tube assemblies. Each has it's unique advantages and disadvantages. The greatest challenge is finding the specified vertex points. These points are the dimensioned points where the centerline of the straight lengths intersect. On most assemblies, you will find these points "off the part," or hanging in mid air. A full size layout, check fixture, a vector inspection table or co-ordinate measuring machine utilizing appropriate software designed for this purpose should be used. Just as important is to determine, during the design process, the specific inspection method to be used between the designer and the manufacturer.

5.5.1 HAND LAYOUT—The hand lay out of a tube assembly is normally only utilized during the sampling or prototyping of a new design. Hand layout of an assembly is accomplished with gauge blocks, and usually, a full size Mylar or paper template. Precise measurements are difficult, time consuming, and susceptible to errors due to "eyeballing" measurement points.

5.5.2 VECTOR INSPECTION—Vector inspection tables usually consist of a measurement probe attached to an articulated arm to measure points on the assembly. The measurement data supplied by the operator is interpreted by a computer and compared to the print dimensions. Vector inspection tables are used to check for the tube contour and end point locations, although some newer machines have the ability to perform CMM measurements of attached components on the assembly. Checks on this type of machine can be made in 2 to 3 minutes and the machine may be electronically interfaced with the CNC bending machine. This interface allows for the automatic downloading of print characteristics and for machine adjustments after the part is checked.

5.5.3 Hard Point and Best Fit Inspection

5.5.3.1 Hard Point Inspection—The tube is supported at three defined points to obtain all of the tube dimensions relative to these points for the purpose of calculating the errors. The first two set up points should always be on or near one end of the tube. The third point should be as far possible from a straight line which connects the first two points. Otherwise, large errors can be expected when a tube is referenced to a support system which is significantly smaller than the overall size of the tube. Tube assemblies that require "hard point" inspection are not recommended.

5.5.3.2 Best Fit Inspection—The tube is supported on a holding device and the features are verified with an electronic detection system to fit inside of a mathematically calculated envelope established by the computer. This system allows the tube to float along the X, Y and Z axis and about the A, B and C roll axis to minimize or uniformly distribute the errors. Often, such as with the system "Supravision," the ends may be selected to have the ends of the tube held to a relatively closer fit than the intermediate portions. Tube assemblies that may be verified with this method of inspection are recommended. The vast majority of tube assemblies in the earth moving industry are of this type.

5.5.4 Advantages of Best Fit Inspection

5.5.4.1 Ideal Simulation—Ideally simulates the final installation conditions whereby errors are distributed and accommodated at many points.

5.5.4.2 Neutral Evolution—Allows neutral evolution from the hard gauge.

5.5.4.3 Non-Zero/Zero Accuracy—Does not require any one portion of the tube assembly to be "zero-zero" accurate.

5.5.5 Checking Fixtures—Check fixtures are used to perform attribute checks on the assembly. These fixtures may be used to check the tube contour, location of components, tube end points, and other attachments to the assembly. A check fixture may only check for a specific dimension or may be constructed to check the entire assembly. Check fixtures are good for random checking of parts by a process operator to ensure compliance to print dimensions and are especially effective during large-scale production runs of the same part. Check fixtures are recommended to inspect "hard point" designed tube assemblies.

6. Tube and Tube Assembly Fabrication

6.1 Tube Bending—This document is based on the utilization of automatic bending equipment. To minimize structural damage to the tube, the hardness and elongation characteristics of selected tube materials is very important to the ability to properly bend and cold form the tubing into the required configurations. Generally, harder materials with limited elongation, are very difficult to bend and cold form with satisfactory results. At the same time, the material should have proper structural integrity and grain structure to provide adequate fatigue life.

6.1.1 Minimum Bend Radii—The largest bend radius is the most cost effective; 3 times the tube OD is usually recommended, 2 times the tube OD is usual minimum. Generally, the smaller bend radii, the poorer the bend quality, therefore, the higher the scrap rate. The higher the scrap rate, the higher the cost.

6.1.2 Minimum Bend Angle—The preferred minimum bend angle is 10 degrees. Bend angles less than 10 degrees are difficult to set up for first piece approval due to the spring-back of the tube material. An accomplished bend requires the material to yield to the proper dimension during the bending operation, which is very difficult to accomplish with bends less than 10 degrees.

6.1.3 Maximum Bend Angle—Special tooling is required for bends over 180 degrees. Some tube end attached connectors are very difficult to remove from the bender when bent 150 degree to 180 degrees or more with remaining three times the tube OD straight length. The tube assembly supplier should be consulted before specifying 150 degree bends or larger.

6.1.4 Very Large Bend Radii—When a very large bend radius is needed, such as Excavator Boom Tubes, use a series of preferred bend radii with a series of short straight lengths between each bend.

6.2 Tube End Cold Forming—This process may be used to replace brazing and welding, generally as a manufacturing option, increasing shop throughput and improving repeatability. In most instances will reduce processing time and reduce pollutants into the atmosphere and water shed. To use the cold form process, materials with adequate elongation and hardness should be selected, consult your tube fabricator for guidance.

6.3 Recommended Clamp Lengths—To avoid the necessity of specialized clamp designs and bending equipment, and to minimize distortion and die marks near the bend areas, the following guidelines are recommended. Following these guidelines also generally allows the manufacturer to attach or form the tube ends while the tube is in the straight condition, which expedites processing, handling and loading the tube into the equipment.

6.3.1 Recommended End Clamp Length for Bending and End Cold Forming

a. Beginning end = 2 X Tube OD Plus the Connector

b. Opposite end = 3 X Tube OD, to allow for tolerance stack-up in the tube.

NOTE—The preferred bend radius should not be used in preference to a smaller radius if the resulting straight lengths are reduced to less than the minimum. Preferred straight lengths take precedence over preferred bend radius.

6.3.2 Recommended Straight Length Between Bends

a. 2 X Tube OD

NOTE—If the ratio of the bend radius to the tube OD is less than 2.0, it is recommended the clamp lengths should be made larger to distribute the higher loads required to bend the tube.

6.3.3 Compound Bends—The use of compound bends with little or no straight lengths is possible but requires special, dedicated equipment; therefore it is not recommended.

6.4 Ovality and Flattening—During the bending process, two different forces exert pressure on the tube material in the bend area. On the outside of the bend radius, the material may be stretched and thinned; on the inside of the radius, the material may be compressed. These opposing forces may alter the shape of the base material in the bend area. This alteration may extend a maximum distance of two times the outside diameter beyond the tangent of the radius. An internal mandrel may be used to support the tube from the inside during bending to limit the amount of flattening and ovality caused by the bending process. In hydraulic applications, excessive ovality may lead to early hour fatigue failure caused by wall movement when the pressure impulses. Consult your tube fabricator to determine the maximum allowable tube ovality. Endurance impulse testing for specific tube materials and size to be operated at specific high pressures, may be necessary to determine adequate product reliability.

6.5 Wall Thinning—During the bending process, the outside of the bend radius may stretch the tube. This may cause wall thinning in addition to the ovality distortion. Wall thinning should generally be held to 15% of the originally specified tube wall thickness. It is important to take this thinning into account when designing assemblies for high system pressures.

6.6 Buckling—Tubes may buckle when they are not sufficiently supported during bending. Buckling also may occur if the clamp and insert allow the tube to slip through the dies during bending. For hydraulic applications, the tube should not show evidence of buckling severe enough to exceed the recommended ovality and flattening requirements specified by the tube fabricator.

6.7 Marking—Marking, if required, should not affect the performance of the final assembly. Stamping, etching or laser marking the tube material may cause a thinned area in the tube wall, which may affect the performance or life of the finished product, especially in high pressure applications.

7. Tube Cleanliness—The inside and outside surfaces of the finished tubing should be commercially bright, clean, and free from grease, oxide scale, carbon deposits, and any other contamination that cannot readily be removed by cleaning agents normally used in manufacturing plants.

7.1 Compatibility of Process Coolants and Lubricants—Coolants and lubricants used during forming and fabricating should be compatible with the fluid power application or removed prior to assembly.

7.2 Cleaning Compatibility—Tube assemblies should be designed so cleaning operations can be completed prior to the forming process. Cleaning after forming is not as effective or efficient, due to fluids being trapped in the bend areas and the handling required to clean a bent configuration.

7.3 Contamination—Tube assemblies may be contaminated during fabrication. Clean tube assemblies to specified cleanliness levels. The cleanliness requirements of systems components, other than the tube, will determine the cleanliness requirements of the application. Consult the component manufacturer's cleanliness information for all components in the system. Tube assemblies vary in cleanliness levels; therefore, specify tube assemblies with adequate cleanliness for the system.

8. Unintended Uses—Tube assemblies are designed for the internal forces of conducted fluids. Tube is not to be used for purposes that may apply external forces for which the tube or fittings were not designed.

8.1 System Fluids Compatibility—System fluids should not be corrosive to carbon steels.

8.2 Serviceability Issues—To minimize serviceability problems, components not related to the fluid system should not be attached to or supported by the tube. Careful consideration should be made when designing the fluid carrier systems, to avoid causing service problems with adjoining systems.

8.3 Mechanical Load Carrying Applications—Tube fluid power applications should not be used for mechanical load carrying applications, as in the case with Excavator boom tubes, Bull Dozer lift cylinder tubes, Wheel Loader lift arms, etc.

TABLE 1—BENT TUBE SUGGESTED END POINT TOTAL ZONE TOLERANCES LISTED BY METRIC BLANK LENGTHS

Tube OD																
4.76	0-924	0-924	925-1188	925-1188	1189-1452	1189-1452	1453-1716	1453-1716	1717-1980	1717-1980	1981-2244	1981-2244	2245-2508	2245-2508	2509-2772	2509-2772
6.35	0-885	0-885	886-1138	886-1138	1139-1391	1139-1391	1392-1644	1392-1644	1645-1897	1645-1897	1898-2450	1898-2450	2151-2403	2151-2403	2404-2656	2404-2656
7.94	0-906	0-906	907-1165	907-1165	1166-1424	1166-1424	1425-1683	1425-1683	1684-1942	1684-1942	1943-2201	1943-2201	2202-2460	2202-2460	2461-2719	2461-2719
9.52	0-955	0-955	956-1228	956-1228	1229-1501	1229-1501	1502-1774	1502-1774	1775-2047	1775-2047	2048-2320	2048-2320	2321-2593	2321-2593	2594-3000	2594-3000
12.70	0-1099	0-1099	1100-1413	1100-1413	1414-1727	1414-1727	1728-2041	1728-2041	2042-2355	2042-2355	2356-2669	2356-2669	2670-3000	2670-3000		
15.88	0-1274	0-1274	1275-1638	1275-1638	1639-2002	1639-2002	2003-2366	2003-2366	2376-2730	2376-2730	2731-3000	2731-3000				
19.05	0-1463	0-1463	1464-1881	1464-1881	1882-2299	1882-2299	2300-2717	2300-2717	2718-3000	2718-3000						
22.22	0-1659	0-1659	1660-2133	1660-2133	2134-2607	2134-2607	2698-3000	2698-3000								
25.40	0-1862	0-1862	1863-2394	1863-2394	2395-2926	2395-2926										
28.58	0-2068	0-2068	2069-2659	2069-2659	2660-3000	2660-3000										
31.75	0-2278	0-2278	2279-2929	2279-2929												
38.10	0-2698	0-2698	2699-3000	2699-3000												
44.44	0-2848	0-2848	2849-3000	2849-3000												
50.80	0-3000	0-3000														
No. of Bends ⇒	1 - 5	6-10	1 - 5	6-10	1 - 5	6-10	1 - 5	6-10	1 - 5	6-10	1 - 5	6-10	1 - 5	6-10	1 - 5	6-10
Total True Position ⇒ Tolerance	6	8	8	10	10	12	12	14	14	16	16	18	18	20	20	22

CODING SYSTEMS FOR IDENTIFICATION OF FLUID CONDUCTORS AND CONNECTORS—SAE J846 FEB2003

SAE Recommended Practice

Report of the SAE Tube, Pipe, Hose and Lubrication Fittings Committee approved January 1963. Completely revised by the SAE Fluid Conductors and Connectors Technical Committee June 1989. Revised by the SAE Fluid Conductors and Connectors Technical Committee SC1—Automotive and Hydraulic Tube and Fittings, December 1993. Rationale statement available. Revised by the SAE Fluid Conductors and Connectors Technical Committee SC1—Automotive and Hydraulic Tube and Fittings, May 2001. Rationale statement available. Revised by the SAE Fluid Conductors and Connectors Technical Committee SC1—Automotive and Hydraulic Tube and Fittings February 2003. Rationale statement available.

Foreword—It should be noted that the code numbers assigned to the applicable standards covered by the coding system could possibly change. Therefore, it is recommended that for the purpose of transmitting technical or engineering information relating to the various tube, pipe, and hose fittings, the applicable code numbers, standard number, and revision letter be specified for proper identification.

Document is constantly under revision to include new codes/symbols.

1. Scope—This coding system is intended to provide a convenient means of identifying the various tube, pipe, and hose fittings, not intended for use in aircraft, and of transmitting technical or engineering information relating to them wherever drawings or other pictorial media may not be readily available. The code has been kept flexible to permit expansion to cover new fitting categories or styles and, if the need develops, the inclusion of materials. The system is also compatible with automatic data processing equipment.

It is not intended that this code should supersede established systems or means of identification. However, because the SAE code for automotive flare fittings shown in SAE J512 is also applicable to corresponding refrigeration fittings in SAE J513, both an SAE code and the existing code ANSI B70.1 are included throughout SAE J513. Therefore, it should be the prerogative of the user to apply that code which best satisfies his requirements.

2. References

2.1 Applicable Publications—The following publications form a part of the specification to the extent specified herein. Unless otherwise indicated, the latest revision of SAE publications shall apply.

2.1.1 SAE PUBLICATIONS—Available from SAE, 400 Commonwealth Drive, Warrendale, PA 15096-0001.

SAE J246—Spherical and Flanged Sleeve (Compression) Tube Fittings

SAE J512—Automotive Tube Fittings

SAE J513—Refrigeration Tube Fittings

SAE J514—Hydraulic Tube Fittings

SAE J515—Specification for Hydraulic O-Ring Materials, Properties, and Sizes for Metric and Inch Stud Ends Face Seal Fitting, and Four-Screw Flange Tube Connections

SAE J516—Hydraulic Hose Fittings

SAE J518—Hydraulic Flanged Tube, Pipe, and Hose Connectors, 4-Bolt Split Flange Type

SAE J530—Automotive Pipe Fittings

SAE J531—Automotive Pipe, Filler, and Drain Plugs

SAE J532—Automotive Straight Thread Filler and Drain Plugs

SAE J1231—Beaded Tube Hose Fittings

SAE J1453—Fitting-O-Ring Face Seal

SAE J1754-1—Hose Assemblies, Rubber, Hydraulic, Steel Wire Reinforced—Part 1: Procurement Document

SAE J1754-2—Hose Assemblies, Rubber, Hydraulic, Steel Wire Reinforced—Part 2: Ordering Information

SAE J1926-1—Connections for General Use and Fluid Power—Ports and Stud Ends with ISO 725 Threads and O-Ring Sealing—Part 1: Threaded Port with O-Ring Seal in Truncated Housing

SAE J1926-2—Connections for General Use and Fluid Power—Ports and Stud Ends with ISO 725 Threads and O-Ring Sealing—Part 2: Heavy-Duty (S Series) Stud Ends

SAE J1926-3—Connections for General use and Fluid Power—Ports and Stud Ends with ISO 725 Threads and O-Ring Sealing—Part 3: Light-Duty (L Series) Stud Ends

SAE J2244-1—Connections for Fluid Power and General Use—Ports and Stud Ends with ISO 261 Threads and O-Ring Sealing—Part 1: Port with O-Ring Seal in Truncated Housing

SAE J2244-2—Connections for Fluid Power and General Use—Ports and Stud Ends with ISO 261 Threads and O-Ring Sealing—Part 2: Heavy-Duty (S Series) Stud Ends—Dimensions, Design, Test Methods, and Requirements

SAE J2244-3—Connections for Fluid Power and General Use—Ports and Stud Ends with ISO 261 Threads and O-Ring Sealing—Part 3: Light-Duty (L Series) Stud End—Dimensions, Design, Test Methods, and Requirements

SAE J2494—Push-to-Connect Tube Fittings for Use in the Piping of Vehicular Air Brake Systems

SAE AMS-C-81562—Plating, Cadmium

2.1.2 ANSI PUBLICATION—Available from ANSI, 25 West 43rd Street, New York, NY 10036-8002.

ANSI B70.1—Refrigeration Flare Fittings

2.1.3 ASTM PUBLICATION—Available from ASTM, 100 Barr Harbor Drive, West Conshohocken, PA 19428-2959.

ASTM B 633—Specification for Electrodeposited Coatings of Zinc on Iron and Steel

2.1.4 ISO PUBLICATIONS—Available from ANSI, 25 West 43rd Street, New York, NY 10036-8002.

ISO 6149-1—Connections for fluid power and general use—Ports and stud ends with ISO 261 threads and O-ring sealing—Part 1: Ports with O-ring seal in truncated housing

ISO 6149-2—Connections for fluid power and general use—Ports and stud ends with ISO 261 threads and O-ring sealing—Part 2: Heavy-duty (S series) stud ends—Dimensions, design, test methods and requirements

ISO 6149-3—Connections for fluid power and general use—Ports and stud ends with ISO 261 threads and O-ring sealing—Part 3: Light-duty (L series) stud ends—Dimensions, design, test methods and requirements

ISO 8434-1—Metallic tube connections for fluid power and general use—Part 1: 24 degree compression fittings

ISO 11926-1—Connections for general use and fluid power—Ports and stud ends with ISO 725 threads and O-ring sealing—Part 1: Ports with O-ring seal in truncated housing

ISO 11926-2—Connections for general use and fluid power—Ports and stud ends with ISO 725 threads and O-ring sealing—Part 2: Heavy-duty (S series) stud ends

ISO 11926-3—Connections for general use and fluid power—Ports and stud ends with ISO 725 threads and O-ring sealing—Part 3: Light-duty (L series) stud ends

3. General Specifications

3.1 Part Identification Number (PIN) or Code—The PIN shall consist of the SAE 'J' standard number (when specified) followed by four-part code of numbers and/or letter(s): the first part, a group of numbers symbolizing the size identification; the second part, a group of numbers, sometimes combined with letters, symbolizing the fitting and hose identification; the third part, a letter symbolizing the material with finish, where applicable; and the fourth part, another letter symbolizing assembly, if applicable, as shown in Figure 1A. When ordering metric base fittings or components for metric tubing, see 3.1.1.6 and/or 3.1.2 for details.

EXAMPLE—A 37 degree flare tee for 1/2 in OD tubing made from corrosion protected carbon steel and assembled with sleeves and nuts is designated as shown in Figure 1A.

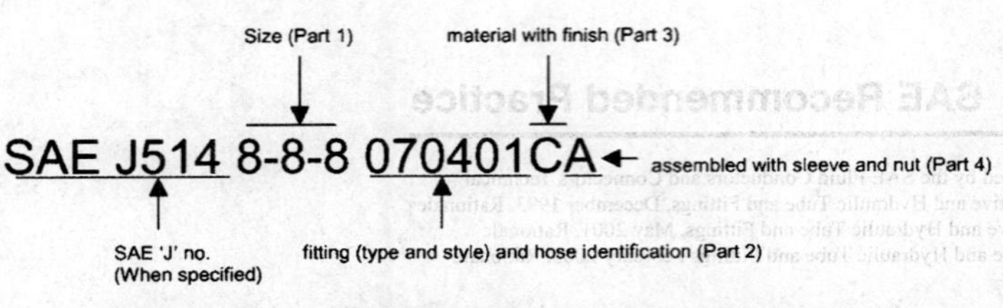

Note: All combinations of these codes may not be feasible or covered by an SAE standard. User needs to contact the manufacturer for availability.

FIGURE 1A—SAE PART IDENTIFICATION NUMBER (PIN) OR CODE SHOWING FOUR BASIC PARTS

3.1.1 Size Identification—The fitting size shall be identified by a series of dash numbers, each representing the size of the respective fitting ends. The size of the tube end shall precede the size of the pipe, hose, or other ends of the fitting. The dash shall be given in the sequence defined in Figure 1B:

When special size combinations of tube-to-tube fitting ends are specified, the largest tube size shall precede the smaller tube size for unions and union elbows. For tees, the (1) shall be the larger tube size of (1) and (2). For crosses, the (1) shall be the largest tube size of (1) and (2), and (3) shall be equal to or larger than (4). Male tube end shall precede female (swivel) tube end.

For stud fittings (tube to port connectors) the tube end shall precede the stud end.

For adapter unions shown in SAE J514, the order of thread designation shall be male pipe NPTF, female pipe NPTF, male O-ring and swivel female NPSM.

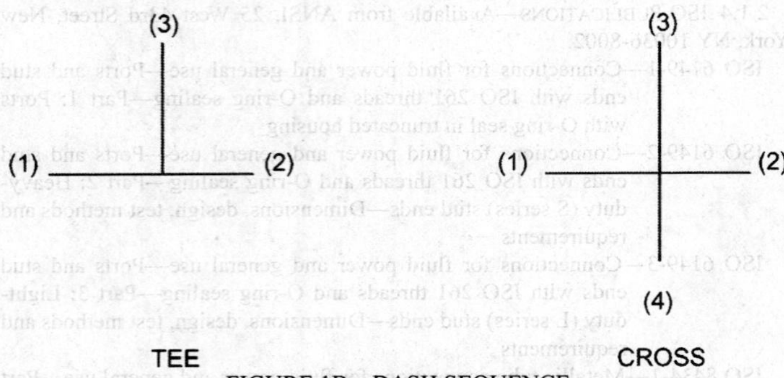

FIGURE 1B—DASH SEQUENCE

3.1.1.1 Tube and Straight Thread O-Ring Port Ends—The dash size code, applicable to all tube ends and straight thread O-ring port ends, shall consist of the number of sixteenth-inch increments contained in the outside diameter of the tubing (nominal tube OD) they are designed to be used with, as listed in Table 1.

3.1.1.2 Pipe Thread Ends—The dash size code for pipe thread ends shall be the number of sixteenth-inch increments contained in the nominal pipe thread size as listed in Table 2.

TABLE 1—DASH NUMBERS FOR TUBE AND STRAIGHT THREAD O-RING PORT ENDS

Nominal Tube OD, in	Dash Size Code	Nominal Tube OD, in	Dash Size Code	Nominal Tube OD, in	Dash Size Code
1/8	–2	3/8	–6	7/8	–14
5/32	–2.5[(1)]	7/16	–7[(1)]	1	–16
3/16	–3	1/2	–8	1-1/4	–20
1/4	–4	5/8	–10	1-1/2	–24
5/16	–5	3/4	–12	2	–32

1. For tube only, –2.5 and –7 Straight Thread O-ring Ports do not exist.

TABLE 2—DASH NUMBERS FOR PIPE THREAD ENDS

Nominal Pipe Thread Size, in	Dash Size Symbol	Nominal Pipe Thread Size, in	Dash Size Symbol	Nominal Pipe Thread Size, in	Dash Size Symbol
1/16	–1	3/8	–6	1	–16
1/8	–2	1/2	–8	1-1/4	–20
1/4	–4	3/4	–12	1-1/2	–24
				2	–32

A suffix "K" shall be added to the dash size code if the end has the optional 30 degree (60 degree included) seat, for sealing with an NPSM swivel end (Figures 47 to 49, SAE J514), as shown in Figure 1A of SAE J516.

EXAMPLE—A 37 degree flare male connector, with –8 tube end and –6 male pipe end with the optional 30 degree (60 degree included) seat, made from low carbon steel is called out as:

8 – 6K 070102C
└— 30° seat on –6 pipe end

The suffix is not required for hose fittings with male pipe ends where the 30 degree seat is mandatory (Figure 1, SAE J516).

3.1.1.3 Hose—The dash size code for hose shall be the number of sixteenth-inch increments contained in the inside diameter of the hose (nominal hose ID), except in the case of SAE 100R5 and 100R14 hose where it is equivalent to the number of sixteenth-inch increments in the outside diameter of tubing having approximately the same inside diameter as the hose. See Table 3 for respective hose types.

TABLE 3—DASH SIZE NUMBERS FOR 100R SERIES HOSES

Nominal Hose ID mm	Nominal Hose ID in	Hose Type 100R1	Hose Type 100R2	Hose Type 100R3	Hose Type 100R4	Hose Type 100R5	Hose Type 100R6	Hose Type 100R7	Hose Type 100R8	Hose Type 100R9	Hose Type 100R10	Hose Type 100R11	Hose Type 100R12	Hose Type 100R13	Hose Type 100R14	Hose Type 100R15	Hose Type 100R16	Hose Type 100R17	Hose Type 100R18
3.2	1/8	—	—	—	—	—	—	—	—	—	—	—	—	—	–3	—	—	—	—
5	3/16	–3	–3	–3	—	–4	–3	–3	–3	—	–3	–3	—	—	–4	—	—	—	–3
6.3	1/4	–4	–4	–4	—	–5	–4	–4	–4	—	–4	–4	—	—	–5	—	–4	–4	–4
8	5/16	–5	–5	–5	—	–6	–5	–5	—	—	—	—	—	—	–6	—	–5	–5	–5
10	3/8	–6	–6	–6	—	—	–6	–6	–6	–6	–6	–6	–6	—	–7	–6	–6	–6	–6
12	13/32	–6.5	—	—	—	–8	—	—	—	—	—	—	—	—	–8	—	—	—	—
12.5	1/2	–8	–8	–8	—	–10	–8	–8	–8	–8	–8	–8	–8	—	–10	–8	–8	–8	–8
16	5/8	–10	–10	–10	—	–12	–10	–10	–10	—	—	—	–10	—	–12	—	–10	–10	–10
19	3/4	–12	–12	–12	–12	—	–12	–12	–12	–12	–12	–12	–12	–12	–14	–12	–12	–12	–12
22	7/8	–14	–14	—	—	–16	—	—	—	—	—	—	—	—	–16	—	—	—	—
25	1	–16	–16	–16	–16	—	—	–16	–16	–16	–16	–16	–16	–16	–18	–16	–16	–16	–16
29	1-1/8	—	—	—	—	–20	—	—	—	—	—	—	—	—	–20	—	—	—	—
31.5	1-1/4	–20	–20	–20	–20	—	—	—	—	–20	–20	–20	–20	–20	—	–20	–20	—	—
35	1-3/8	—	—	—	—	–24	—	—	—	—	—	—	—	—	—	—	—	—	—
38	1-1/2	–24	–24	—	–24	—	—	—	—	–24	–24	–24	–24	–24	—	–24	—	—	—
46	1-13/16	—	—	—	—	–32	—	—	—	—	—	—	—	—	—	—	—	—	—
51	2	–32	–32	—	–32	—	—	—	—	–32	–32	–32	–32	–32	—	—	—	—	—
60	2-3/8	—	—	—	—	–40	—	—	—	—	—	—	—	—	—	—	—	—	—
63	2-1/2	—	–40	—	–40	—	—	—	—	—	—	–40	—	—	—	—	—	—	—

TABLE 3—DASH SIZE NUMBERS FOR 100R SERIES HOSES

Nominal Hose ID mm	Nominal Hose ID in	Hose Type 100R1	Hose Type 100R2	Hose Type 100R3	Hose Type 100R4	Hose Type 100R5	Hose Type 100R6	Hose Type 100R7	Hose Type 100R8	Hose Type 100R9	Hose Type 100R10	Hose Type 100R11	Hose Type 100R12	Hose Type 100R13	Hose Type 100R14	Hose Type 100R15	Hose Type 100R16	Hose Type 100R17	Hose Type 100R18
76	3	—	—		–48	–48	—		—	—	—	—		—	—		—	—	
89	3-1/2	—			–56		—	—	—	—		—	—	—	—	—	—	—	—
102	4	—	—	—	–64	—	—	—	—	—		—	—	—	—	—	—	—	—

3.1.1.4 Four Bolt Split Flange Connections—The dash size code for 4-bolt split flange O-ring connections shall be the number of sixteenth-inch increments contained in the nominal flange size as listed in Table 4.

TABLE 4—DASH SIZE CODES FOR 4-BOLT SPLIT FLANGE CONNECTIONS

Nominal Flange Size, in	Dash Size Code	Nominal Flange Size, in	Dash Size Code	Nominal Flange Size, in	Dash Size Code
1/2	–8	1-1/2	–24	3-1/2	–56
3/4	–12	2	–32	4	–64
1	–16	2-1/2	–40	5	–80
1-1/4	–20	3	–48		

3.1.1.5 Straight Thread Filler and Drain Plug Ends—The dash code for straight thread filler and drain plugs shall be the number of sixteenth-inch increments contained in the nominal straight thread size except in the case of metric sizes where the thread size shall be designated as the metric size code listed in Table 5A.

TABLE 5A—DASH SIZE CODES FOR STRAIGHT THREAD FILLER AND DRAIN PLUGS

Nominal Straight Thread Size, in	Dash Size Code	Nominal Metric Thread Size, mm	Metric Size Code
5/16	–5	M10 x 1	M10
3/8	–6	M14 x 1.25[(1)]	M14
1/2	–8	M18 x 1.5	M18
5/8	–10		
3/4	–12		
7/8	–14		
1	–16		
1-1/4	–20		
1-1/2	–24		
1-3/4	–28		
2	–32		

1. For all fittings other than drain plugs, code M14 signifies M14X1.5 thread size.

3.1.1.6 Tube and Port Ends for Metric Base Fittings—When ordering metric base fittings (those for use with metric tube and/or with hard metric hex and forging flat sizes), use metric tube sizes equivalent to the inch dash sizes as shown in Table 5B for size code, and replace the "–" (dash) with an "X" between the size codes, as shown in examples 1 and 3. When designating metric stud end size, the thread pitch is omitted as shown in Table 5B.

TABLE 5B—METRIC TUBE, PORT AND STUD END SIZE CODES

Inch Tube Dash Size	Equivalent Metric Tube Size Code	Nominal Metric Thread Size, mm	Port and Stud Size Codes
–2	4	M8X1	M8
–3	5	M10X1	M10
–4	6	M12X1.5	M12
–5	8	M14X1.5	M14
–6	10	M16X1.5	M16
–8	12	M18X1.5	M18
–10	16	M20X1.5	M20
–12	20	M22X1.5	M22
–14	22	M27X2	M27
–16	25	M30X2	M30
–20	30	M33X2	M33
–24	38	M42X2	M42
–32	50	M48X2	M48
		M60X2	M60

EXAMPLE 1—Metric O-ring Face Seal stud elbow with 20 mm (–12) face seal and M27X2 stud end per SAE J2244-2 (ISO 6149-2) made from low carbon steel is called out as:

SAE J1453-2* 20XM27 52M0287C

NOTE 2—'M' after the fitting type code '52' indicates metric forging flats per 3.1.2.

EXAMPLE 3—Style 'A' braze sleeve made from carbon steel for –8 or 12 mm size inch or metric base O-ring face seal fitting to mate with 1/2 in OD tube is called out as:

SAE J1453-3* 8-8 520115ACX (in inch base document)

SAE J1453-2* 8-8 520115ACX (in metric base document)

NOTE—"CX" indicates carbon steel with oil dip per 3.1.3.

EXAMPLE 4—Style 'B' braze sleeve for –8 or 12 mm size inch or metric base ORFS fitting to mate with 12 mm OD tube is called out as:

SAE J1453-3* 12X12 5201M15BCX (in inch base document)

SAE J1453-2* 12X12 5201M15BCX (in metric base document)

NOTE—Part number for a given sleeve in either document, in previous examples, is the same because the part is physically the same. Also, there is no 'M' after 52 because the sleeve has no hex, eliminating the need for 'Metric' hex designator. 'M' before 15 in example 3 indicates the sleeve is for metric tube.

EXAMPLE 4—A carbon steel braze connector with –10 or 16 mm ORFS end and braze socket for 3/4 in OD tube is called out as:

SAE J1453-3* 10-12 520104CX (in inch base document)

SAE J1453-2* 10-12 52M0104CX (in metric base document)

A similar connector for 20 mm OD metric tube is called out as:

SAE J1453-3* 16X20 5201M04CX (in inch base document)

SAE J1453-2* 16X20 52M01M04CX (in metric base document)

NOTE—*When specified and to be published.

3.1.1.7 Connection Ends for Metric 24 Degree Cone Hose Fittings—When ordering metric 24 degree cone hose fittings in accordance with ISO 8434-1, which are not presently listed under SAE J516, use metric tube sizes for the light-duty (L) and heavy-duty (S) connection ends as listed under the respective thread sizes in Table 5C.

TABLE 5C—METRIC 24 DEGREE CONE CONNECTOR END SIZE CODES

Light-Duty (L) Nominal Metric Thread Size, mm	Light-Duty (L) Metric Tube Size, mm	Heavy-Duty (S) Nominal Metric Thread Size, mm	Heavy-Duty (S) Metric Tube Size, mm
M12X1.5	6	M14X1.5	6
M14X1.5	8	M16X1.5	8
M16X1.5	10	M18X1.5	10
M18X1.5	12	M20X1.5	12
M22X1.5	15	M22X1.5	14
M26X1.5	18	M24X1.5	16

TABLE 5C—METRIC 24 DEGREE CONE CONNECTOR END SIZE CODES

Light-Duty (L) Nominal Metric Thread Size, mm	Light-Duty (L) Metric Tube Size, mm	Heavy-Duty (S) Nominal Metric Thread Size, mm	Heavy-Duty (S) Metric Tube Size, mm
M30X2	22	M30X2	20
M36X2	28	M36X2	25
M45X2	35	M42X2	30
M52X2	42	M52X2	38

3.1.2 Fitting Identification—The fitting identification shall consist of a basic six to eight digit alphanumeric code made up of three groups each symbolizing in sequence: (a) the fitting type, (b) the fitting shape, and (c) the fitting connecting ends. Each group may be modified with a prefix/suffix to signify features such as metric hex (example 2 as follows), metric tube (example 3 in 3.1.1.6), style of ferrule (example 3 as follows), etc.

EXAMPLE 1—

07 01 22
/a /b /c

/c — Per Table 8
/b — Per Table 7
/a — Per Table 6A and 6B

To identify a fitting made from a metric hex or with metric wrench flats, a suffix letter "M" shall be placed after the Fitting Type Codes (a) shown in Tables 6A and 6B.

EXAMPLE 2—**07M0122**
/Metric Hex or Wrench Flats

For assembled flareless fittings (SAE J514 - Section 2), suffix 'A' or 'B' after the fitting type code (08) shall be added to identify assembly with either type 'A' or type 'B' ferrule.

EXAMPLE 3—An assembled carbon steel flareless connector for 1/2 in OD tube with –8 SAE straight-thread end would be identified as:

SAE J514* 8-8 08A0120CA (with style 'A' ferrule)

SAE J514* 8-8 08B0120CA (with style 'B' ferrule)

NOTE—*When specified.

(For convenient reference, the fitting identification codes applicable to fittings appearing in SAE J246, J512, J513, J514, J516, J518, J530, J531, J532, J1453, J2494-1, and J2494-2 are shown in brackets adjacent to the respective figure numbers.) The identification codes for each of the three groups shall be as follows:

a. Fitting Type Identification—The two-digit codes applicable to the various fittings types and styles shall be as tabulated in Tables 6A and 6B.

TABLE 6A—FITTING TYPE CODES (ARRANGED NUMERICALLY)

Fitting Type Code	Fitting Type and Styles
01	45 degree flared, automotive - SAE J512
02	
03	
04	Inverted flared, automotive - SAE J512
05	
06	Tapered sleeve, automotive - SAE J512
07	37 degree flared, hydraulic - SAE J514
08	Flareless, hydraulic, unassembled - SAE J514
08A	Flareless, hydraulic, assembled with Type 'A' sleeve - SAE J514
08B	Flareless, hydraulic, assembled with Type 'B' sleeve - SAE J514
09	SAE O-ring boss, hydraulic - SAE J1926/ISO 11926 (previously part of SAE J514)
10	Flanged sleeve, nylon tube, automotive - SAE J246
11	4-bolt split flange O-ring, hydraulic - SAE J518
12	Spherical sleeve, copper tube, automotive - SAE J246
13	Pipe, automotive - SAE J530, SAE J531
14	Pipe, hydraulic - SAE J514

TABLE 6A—FITTING TYPE CODES (ARRANGED NUMERICALLY) (continued)

Fitting Type Code	Fitting Type and Styles
15	Male pipe, hose, permanently attached
16	Male pipe, hose, field attachable
17	Male pipe, hose, field attachable, segment clamp
18	SAE O-ring boss, hose, permanently attached
19	SAE O-ring boss, hose, field attachable
20	SAE O-ring boss, hose, field attachable, segment clamp
21	37 degree male flared, hose, permanently attached
22	37 degree male flared, hose, field attachable
23	37 degree male flared, hose, field attachable, segment clamp
24	37 degree female flared hose, permanently attached
25	37 degree female flared, hose, field attachable (2 piece)
26	37 degree female flared, hose, field attachable, segment clamp
27	37 degree female flared, hose, field attachable (3 piece)
28	45 degree male flared, hose, permanently attached
29	45 degree male flared, hose, field attachable
30	45 degree female flared, hose, permanently attached
31	45 degree female flared, hose, field attachable (2 piece)
32	45 degree female flared, hose, field attachable (3 piece)
33	Flareless, male, hose, permanently attached
34	Flareless, male, hose, field attachable
35	Flareless, male, hose, field attachable, segment clamp
36	Flareless, female, hose, permanently attached
37	Flareless, female, hose, field attachable
38	Flareless, female, hose, field attachable, segment clamp
39	Split flange, hose, standard pressure, permanently attached
40	Split flange, hose, standard pressure, field attachable
41	Split flange, hose, standard pressure, field attachable, segment clamp
42	Straight thread filler and drain plug - SAE J532
43	Beaded tube hose end - SAE J1231
45	Capillary, refrigeration - SAE J513
49	Split flange, hose, high pressure, permanently attached
50	Split flange, hose, high pressure, field attachable
51	Split flange, hose, high pressure, field attachable, segment clamp
52	O-ring face seal, hydraulic - SAE J1453
53	O-ring face seal, female, hose, permanently attached
54	O-ring face seal, female, hose, field attachable
55	O-ring face seal, male, hose, permanently attached
56	O-ring face seal, male, hose, field attachable
57	O-ring face seal, female, hose, field attachable, segment clamp
58	O-ring face seal, female, hose, field attachable, segment clamp
59	Female pipe, hose, permanently attached
60	Female pipe, hose, field attachable
61	Female pipe, hose, field attachable, segment clamp
62	Metric straight thread O-ring port - SAE J2244-1/ISO 6149-1
63	Push to connect, nylon tube, automotive - SAE J2494
64	Male pipe, hose, push-on
65	Female pipe, hose, push-on
66	45-degree male flared, hose, push-on
67	45-degree female flared, hose, push-on
68	37-degree male flared, hose, push-on
69	37-degree female flared, hose, push-on
70	Male pipe swivel, hose, push-on
71	Female NPSM pipe swivel, hose, push-on
72	45-degree female inverted flare, hose, push-on
73	Hose to hose, push-on
74	45-degree male inverted flare swivel, hose, push-on
75	Standpipe, hose, push-on
76	Metric 24 degree cone, light-duty (L), male, hose, permanently attached
77	Metric 24 degree cone, light-duty (L), female, hose, permanently attached
78	Metric 24 degree cone, heavy-duty (S), male, hose, permanently attached
79	Metric 24 degree cone, heavy-duty (S), female, hose, permanently attached
M[1]	Metric hex flats or metric wrench pads

1. The letter "M" shall be used to identify fittings with metric hex flats or metric wrench pads by placing it after the two-digit "Fitting Type Symbol" in Tables 6A and 6B (see example , 3.1.2).

TABLE 6B—FITTING TYPE CODES (ARRANGED BY TYPE)

Fitting Type or Style	Code
Tube Fittings and Adapters - Automotive	
Pipe, automotive - SAE J530, SAE J531	13
45-degree flared, automotive - SAE J512 (also refrigeration - SAE J513)	01
Inverted flare, automotive - SAE J512	04
Tapered sleeve, automotive - SAE J512	06
Flanged sleeve, nylon tube, automotive - SAE J246	10
Spherical sleeve, copper tube, automotive - SAE J246	12
Push to connect, nylon tube, automotive - SAE J2494	63
Straight thread filler and drain plug - SAE J532	42
Capillary, refrigeration - SAE J513	45
Tube Fittings and Adapters - Hydraulic	
Pipe, hydraulic - SAE J514	14
37 degree flared, hydraulic - SAE J514	07
Flareless, hydraulic, unassembled - SAE J514	08
Flareless, hydraulic, assembled with Type 'A' sleeve - SAE J514	08A
Flareless, hydraulic, assembled with Type 'B' sleeve - SAE J514	08B
SAE O-ring boss, hydraulic - SAE J1926/ISO 11926 (previously part of SAE J514)	09
4-bolt split flange O-ring, hydraulic - SAE J518	11
O-ring face seal, hydraulic - SAE J1453	52
Metric straight thread O-ring port, hydraulic - SAE J2244/ISO 6149-1	62
Hose Fittings - SAE J516	
Male pipe, hose, permanently attached	15
Male pipe, hose, field attachable	16
Male pipe, hose, field attachable, segment clamp	17
Male pipe, hose, push-on	64
Male pipe swivel, hose, push-on	70
Female pipe, hose, permanently attached	59
Female pipe, hose, field attachable	60
Female pipe, hose, field attachable, segment clamp	61
Female pipe, hose, push-on	65
Female NPSM pipe swivel, hose, push-on	71
45-degree male flared, hose, permanently attached	28
45-degree male flared, hose, field attachable	29
45-degree female flared, hose, permanently attached	30
45-degree male flared, hose, push-on	66
45-degree female flared, hose, field attachable (2 piece)	31
45-degree female flared, hose, field attachable (3 piece)	32
45-degree female flared, hose, push-on	67
37-degree male flared, hose, permanently attached	21
37-degree male flared, hose, field attachable	22
37-degree male flared, hose, field attachable, segment clamp	23
37-degree male flared, hose, push-on	68
37-degree female flared, hose, permanently attached	24
37-degree female flared, hose, field attachable (2 piece)	25
37-degree female flared, hose, field attachable, segment clamp	26
37-degree female flared, hose, field attachable (3 piece)	27
37-degree female flared, hose, push-on	69
Flareless, male, hose, permanently attached	33
Flareless, male, hose, field attachable	34
Flareless, male, hose, field attachable, segment clamp	35
Flareless, female, hose, field attachable	36
Flareless, female, hose, permanently attached	37
Flareless, female, hose, field attachable, segment clamp	38
SAE O-ring boss, hose, permanently attached	18
SAE O-ring boss, hose, field attachable	19
SAE O-ring boss, hose, field attachable, segment clamp	20
O-ring face seal, male, hose, permanently attached	55
O-ring face seal, male, hose, field attachable	56
O-ring face seal, male, hose, field attachable, segment clamp	58
O-ring face seal, female, hose, permanently attached	53
O-ring face seal, female, hose, field attachable	54
O-ring face seal, female, hose, field attachable, segment clamp	57
Split flange, standard pressure, hose, permanently attached	39

TABLE 6B—FITTING TYPE CODES (ARRANGED BY TYPE) (continued)

Fitting Type or Style	Code
Split flange, standard pressure, hose, field attachable	40
Split flange, standard pressure, hose, field attachable, segment clamp	41
Split flange, high pressure, hose, permanently attached	49
Split flange, high pressure, hose, field attachable	50
Split flange, high pressure, hose, field attachable, segment clamp	51
45-degree female inverted flare, hose, push-on	72
45-degree male inverted flare swivel, hose, push-on	74
Beaded tube hose end - SAE J1231	43
Hose to hose, push-on	73
Standpipe, hose, push-on	75
Metric 24 degree cone, light-duty (L), male, hose, permanently attached	76
Metric 24 degree cone, light-duty (L), female, hose permanently attached	77
Metric 24-degree cone, heavy-duty (S), male, hose permanently attached	78
Metric 24 degree cone, heavy-duty (S), female , hose, permanently attached	79

b. Fitting Shape Identification—The two-digit symbols applicable to the various shapes of fittings shall be as tabulated in Table 7.

TABLE 7—FITTING SHAPE CODES

Fitting Shape Code	Fitting Shape
01	Straight
02	90-degree elbow (not for use with hose fittings)
03	45-degree elbow
04	Tee
05	Cross
06	Straight bulkhead union
07	90-degree bulkhead elbow union
08	45-degree bulkhead elbow union
09	Bulkhead tee
10	22-1/2-degree elbow
11	30-degree elbow
12	60-degree elbow
13	67-1/2-degree elbow
14	90-degree elbow, short drop
15	90-degree elbow, long drop
16	90-degree elbow, extra long drop
17	Long straight, standard hex width
18	Long straight, long hex
19	45-degree elbow, long drop
20	90-degree elbow, medium drop
21	90-degree elbow, extra extra long drop

c. Fitting Connecting End Identification—The two-digit symbols applicable to the various threaded, hose, connecting ends, or combinations thereof, for the fittings covered shall be as tabulated in Table 8.

TABLE 8—FITTING CONNECTING END CODES

Fitting Connecting End Code	Connecting Ends, Hose, and Combinations
01	Tube, all ends
02	Tube to external pipe
03	Tube to internal pipe
04	Tube to solder connection, inch tube (also see 72)
M04	Tube to solder connection, metric tube (also see M72)
05	Internal flare to external flare - one piece reducer/expander
06	Internal flare to external pipe
07	Internal flare union
08	Swivel flare union internal, all ends
09	Plug (use suffix given in applicable document for the desired drive type)
09L	Plug, external hex, with lockwire provision
10	Short nut, tube
11	Long nut, tube
12	Cap

TABLE 8—FITTING CONNECTING END CODES (continued)

Fitting Connecting End Code	Connecting Ends, Hose, and Combinations
13	Flare gasket
14	Flare seal bonnet
15	Tube sleeve, inch tube
M15	Tube sleeve, metric tube
16	Reducing nut
17	Lock nut, SAE straight thread connection
18	Lock nut, bulkhead
19	Large hex union
20	Tube to SAE O-ring port stud end - SAE J1926/ISO 11926
21	Tube to SAE straight swivel connection (female swivel)
22	Open (previously connector, long - tube to SAE O-ring port stud end - See 17 in Table 7)
23	Reducer, seat to tube, without large end nut or nut and ferrule
23A	Reducer seat to tube, with large end nut or nut and ferrule
24	Tube to external pipe on run
25	Tube to external pipe on branch
26	Tube to internal pipe on run
27	Tube to internal pipe on branch
28	Tube to SAE O-ring port stud end on run - SAE J1926/ISO 11926
29	Tube to SAE O-ring port stud end on branch - SAE J1926/ISO 11926
30	Swivel straight pipe, NPSM to external pipe
31	Swivel straight pipe, NPSM to internal pipe
32	Tube to SAE straight swivel (female swivel) on run
33	Tube to SAE straight swivel (female swivel) on branch
34	Tube to internal pipe on run and external pipe on branch
35	Tube to external pipe on run and internal pipe on branch
36	SAE O-ring port stud end to port - SAE J1926/ISO 11926
37	External pipe to external pipe (nipple)
38	Internal pipe to internal pipe
39	Internal pipe to external pipe
40	Internal pipe inside external pipe, bushing
41	Seat insert - SAE J512
42	100R1 hose, Type A
43	100R2 hose, Types A and B
44	100R3 hose
45	100R4 hose
46	100R5 hose
47	100R6 hose
48	100R7 hose
49	100R8 hose
50	100R9 hose, Type A
51	100R10 hose, Type A
52	100R11 hose
53	100R1 hose, Type AT
54	100R2 hose, Types AT and BT
55	Push-on hose
56	Internal pipe to SAE O-ring port stud end - SAE J1926/ISO 11926
57	Swivel straight pipe NPSM to SAE O-ring port stud end - SAE J1926/ISO 11926
58	Tube to bulkhead on run
59	Tube to bulkhead on branch
60	Beaded tube to male pipe - SAE J1231
61	Split flange to flanged head, standard pressure series
62	Split flange to flanged head, high pressure series
63	Tube to pipe fusible - SAE J513
64	Plug, pipe, fusible - SAE J513
65	Tube to internal pipe, drum adapter - SAE J513
66	Nut, short, refrigeration
67	Nut, long, refrigeration
68	Nut, short, reducing, refrigeration

TABLE 8—FITTING CONNECTING END CODES (continued)

Fitting Connecting End Code	Connecting Ends, Hose, and Combinations
69	Nut, long, reducing, refrigeration
70	Swivel straight pipe NPSM to external pipe on branch
71	Swivel straight pipe NPSM to internal pipe on branch
72	Tube to braze connection, inch tubing
M72	Tube to braze connection, metric tube
73	Bulkhead to braze connection
74	SAE straight swivel (female swivel) to braze connection
75	100R9 hose, Type AT
76	100R10 hose, Type AT
77	100R12 hose
78	100R13 hose
79	100R14 hose, Type A
80	100R14 hose, Type B
81	SAE straight swivel (female swivel) to SAE O-ring port stud end
82	SAE straight swivel (female swivel) to butt weld (for weld sleeve), inch tube
83	Tube to braze on run, inch tube
M83	Tube to braze on run, metric tube
84	Tube to braze on branch, inch tube
M84	Tube to braze on branch, metric tube
85	Braze to tube on run, inch tube
M85	Braze to tube on run, metric tube
86	Braze to tube on branch, inch tube
M86	Braze to tube on branch, metric tube
87	Tube to metric O-ring port stud end - SAE J2244-2 or -3/ISO 6149-2 or -3
88	Tube to metric O-ring port stud end on run - SAE J2244-2 or -3/ISO 6149-2 or -3
89	Tube to metric O-ring port stud end on branch - SAE J2244-2 or -3/ISO 6149-2 or -3
90	100R15 hose
91	100R16 hose
92	Beaded tube to SAE O-ring port stud end
93	100R17 hose
94	100R18 hose
95	Open
96	Stud swivel, female swivel to metric O-ring port stud end - SAE J2244-2 or -3/ISO 6149-2 or -3
97	Beaded tube to metric O-ring port stud end - SAE J2244-2 or -3/ISO 6149-2 or -3
98	Tube to butt weld connection, inch tube
M98	Tube to butt weld connection, metric tube
A1	Tube to swivel external pipe
A2	Tube to swivel external pipe on run
A3	Tube to swivel external pipe on branch
A4	Tube to swivel internal pipe
A5	Open
A6	Tube to swivel internal pipe on branch
A7	Dual tube to external male pipe

3.1.3 MATERIAL IDENTIFICATION—The material identification shall consist of a letter code for the material with protective finish, where applicable, as shown in Table 9.

TABLE 9—MATERIAL IDENTIFICATION CODES(1)

Code	Material and Finish
B	Brass - no added finish treatment
C	Carbon steel - protected with appropriate finish for 72 h minimum salt spray protection, except cadmium(2).
CX	Carbon steel - oil dipped for brazing or welding
K	Composite material - non-metallic
S	300 series stainless steel - passivated

1. For additional material and finish requirements, see Appendix A.
2. Parts intended for industrial and commercial use shall not be cadmium plated.

If a user has a construction preference (i.e., cast, brazed, forged, extruded, etc.), it shall be specified on the drawing, the purchase order, or both. Otherwise, it is up to the manufacturers to meet the performance requirements with whatever manufacturing process they choose.

3.1.4 ASSEMBLED FITTING IDENTIFICATION—To designate assembly of multiple tube fitting components, supplied assembled rather than as separate pieces, code letter 'A' shall be placed after the material code (example 3 in 3.1.2). The suffix "A" does not signify, nor is it required, for fittings assembled with O-rings only (see 3.1.5). For convenient reference, this code is applicable to SAE J246, J512, J514, and J1453.

3.1.5 FITTING WITH O-RING IDENTIFICATION—To designate a fitting with O-rings on all applicable ends, in accordance with SAE J515, a letter code, as listed in Table 10, for the O-ring material shall be placed after the fitting material code or the assembly code letter 'A' (in case of assembled fittings.)

EXAMPLE 1—An O-ring Face Seal Stud Elbow with –12 face seal end and –16 stud end per SAE J1926-2 made from carbon steel and with 90 durometer Nitrile O-rings on both ends is called out as:

SAE J1453* 12 – 16 520220CN

Code for O-ring

EXAMPLE 2—A 37 degree flare stud elbow with –8 tube and –6 stud end per SAE J1926-3 assembled with the sleeve, nut and 90 durometer Nitrile O-ring on stud end is called out as:

SAE J514* 8 - 6 070220 CAN

NOTE—*When specified.

TABLE 10—O-RING IDENTIFICATION CODES (IN ACCORDANCE WITH SAE J515)(1)

Code	SAE J515 Material Type	Base Material and Shore 'A' Hardness
N	CH	Nitrile - 90 durometer
E	CA	Ethylene Propylene - 80 durometer
F	HK	Fluorocarbon - 90 durometer

1. If O-rings other than those specified in SAE J515 are required, they shall be specified on the drawing, the purchase order, or both.

4. Application of Code—The identification code shall be applied to the various fittings as depicted in the examples as follows:

4.1 Examples of Code Applied to Tube Fittings—The 45 degree flared tube connector made from brass for 1/8-in tube OD, shown in Figure 1A and Table 4 of SAE J512, would be coded as shown in Figure 2A:

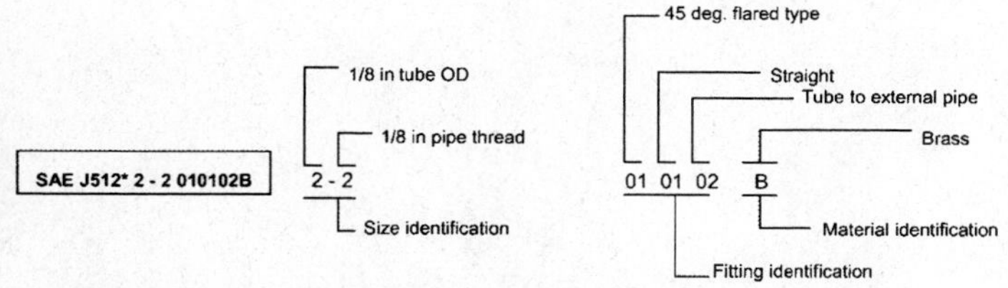

FIGURE 2A—EXAMPLE OF CODE APPLIED TO TUBE FITTINGS

The hydraulic flareless tube tee made from stainless steel and assembled with style 'A' ferrules and nuts, for 3/8 in tube OD, shown in Figure 22D and Table 9 of SAE J514, would be coded as shown in Figure 2B:

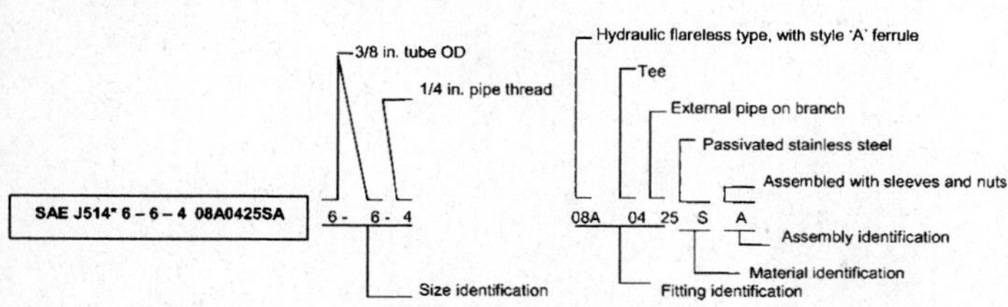

FIGURE 2B—EXAMPLE OF CODE APPLIED TO TUBE FITTINGS

4.2 Examples of Code Applied to Hose Fittings—The male 45 degree flared type permanently attached style hose fittings, made from carbon steel, for 1/4 in tube OD (–4 thread size) and 1/4 in ID SAE 100R1, type A hydraulic hose, shown in Figure 8A and Table 5A of SAE J516, would be coded as shown in Figure 3A:

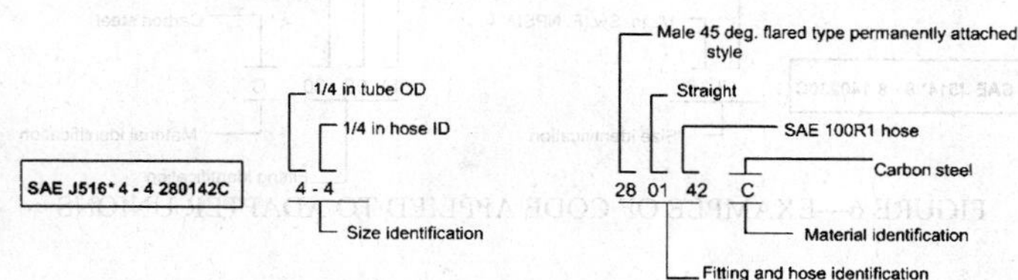

FIGURE 3A—EXAMPLE OF CODE APPLIED TO HOSE FITTINGS

The code 61 4-bolt split flange type field atttachable screw style 30 degree angle hose fitting, made from carbon steel, for 1/2 in flange size and 3/4 in ID SAE 100R2, type 'A' or 'B,' hydraulic hose, shown in Figure 17B and Table 9B of SAE J516, would be coded as shown in Figure 3B:

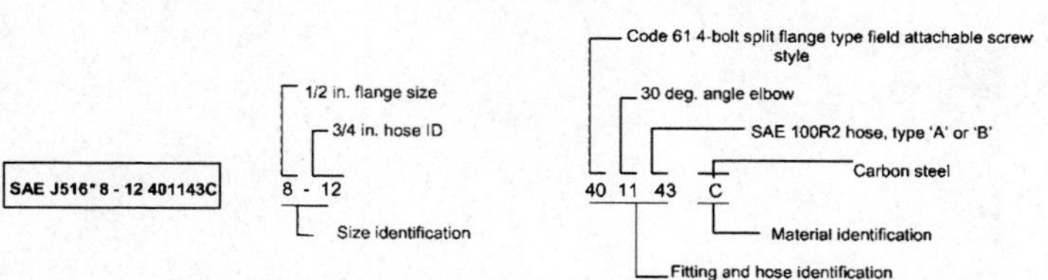

FIGURE 3B—EXAMPLE OF CODE APPLIED TO HOSE FITTINGS

4.3 Example of Code Applied to 4-Bolt Split Flange Connection—The 4-bolt split flange connection for the 1-1/4 in flange size and split flange to flanged head standard pressure series, made from carbon steel, shown in Figure 1 and Table 1 of SAE J518, would be coded as shown in Figure 4.

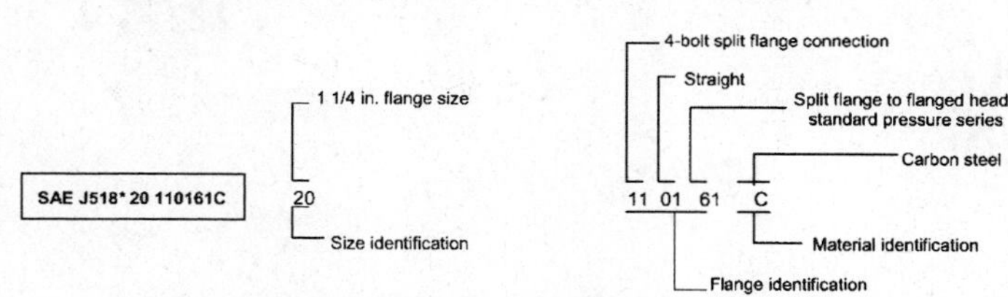

FIGURE 4—EXAMPLE OF CODE APPLIED TO 4-BOLT SPLIT FLANGE CONNECTIONS

4.4 Example of Code Applied to Assembled Tapered Sleeve, Automotive, Union—The tapered sleeve, automotive union assembly (of brass components) for 1/4 in tube OD, the union shown in Figure 12B and Table 10, the sleeve shown in Figure 15 and Table 11, and the nut shown in Figure 16 and Table 12 of SAE J512, would be coded as shown in Figure 5.

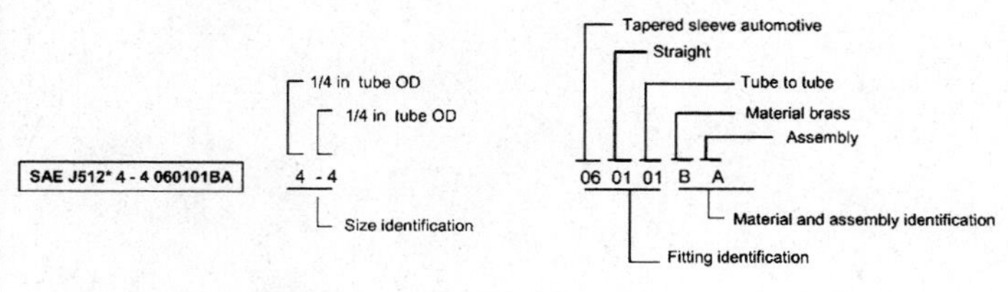

FIGURE 5—EXAMPLE OF CODE APPLIED TO ASSEMBLED TAPERED SLEEVE, AUTOMOTIVE, UNION

4.5 Example of Code Applied to Adapter Unions—The 90 degree adapter union, made from carbon steel in the 1/2 in size, shown in Figure 47C and Table 21 of SAE J514, would be coded as shown in Figure 6.

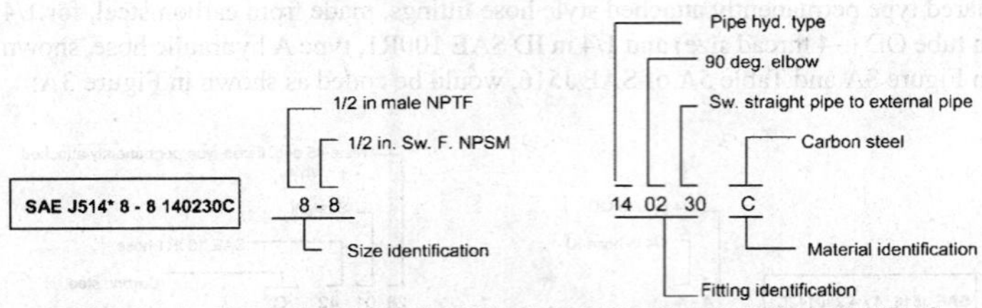

FIGURE 6—EXAMPLE OF CODE APPLIED TO ADAPTER UNIONS

NOTE—See 3.1.1 for the order of thread designation for adapter unions shown in SAE J514.
*Include SAE 'J' number in the part identification no. (PIN) when specified.

APPENDIX A
SPECIAL USER REQUIREMENTS

A.1 This appendix lists codes for special user requirements.

A.1.1 Material and Finish Identification—Following identification codes are for procuring special materials and finishes. They shall be applied to the PIN code the same way as the standard material codes of the main document.

TABLE A1—MATERIAL AND FINISH IDENTIFICATION CODES

Code	Material and Finish
D	Aluminum alloy 6061-T6, anodized
M	Monel, no additional finish
P	Low carbon steel with zinc phosphate finish per DOD-P-16232, Class 1
Q(1)	Carbon steel, cadmium plated per SAE-AMS-C-81562, type II, class 3 or QQ-P-416, type II, class 3
T	Titanium, passivated
Z	Low carbon steel, zinc plated per ASTM D 633, type II, Fe/Zn5 (sc1)

1. Cadmium plating is not preferred due to environmental reasons. FCCTC specifications do not allow cadmium for industrial and commercial uses. It shall be provided, when specified, for non-industrial and non-commercial uses only.

AUTOMOTIVE TUBE FITTINGS—SAE J512 APR1997

SAE Standard

Report1912-06 Rationale statement available.1997-04

1. Scope—This SAE Standard covers complete general and dimensional specifications for the various types of tube fittings intended for general application in the automotive, appliance, and allied fields. See SAE J1131 for the performance requirements of reusable (push to connect) fittings intended for use in automotive air brake systems.

Flare type fittings shall be as specified in Figures 1 to 4 and Tables 3 to 5.

NOTE—For sizes 3/16 to 3/8 and 1/2 to 3/4 the flare type fittings depicted in Figures 1A to 3C are identical with the corresponding refrigeration tube fittings specified in SAE J513. Special size combination fittings 3/16 to 3/8 and 1/2 to 3/4 shall be as specified in SAE J513.

Inverted flared type fittings shall be as specified in Figures 5 to 11 and Tables 3, 6, 7, 8, and 9. Gages and gaging procedures pertaining to inverted flared tube fittings are given in Appendix A.

NOTE—The seat dimensions specified in Table 6 are predicated on practical threading limitations in steel fittings and use of these fittings with double flared tubing. Therefore, wherever purchasers contemplate using these fittings with single flared tubing, it is recommended that the optional inverted flare nut (Figure 9A) be used.

Tapered sleeve compression type fittings intended for general use with annealed copper alloy tubings shall be as specified in Figures 12 to 17 and Tables 3, 10, 11, and 12. To assure satisfactory performance, spherical sleeve compression type fitting components (see SAE J246) should not be intermixed with tapered sleeve compression type fitting components when assembling connections in areas where both types are available.

Dimensions of single and double 45 degree flares on tubing to be used in conjunction with flared and inverted flared fittings are given in Figure 2 and Table 3 of SAE J533.

The following general specifications supplement the dimensional data for all types of fittings contained in Tables 3 to 13 with respect to all unspecified detail.

2. References

2.1 Applicable Publications—The following publications form a part of this specification to the extent specified herein. The latest issue of SAE publications shall apply.

2.1.1 SAE PUBLICATIONS—Available from SAE, 400 Commonwealth Drive, Warrendale, PA 15096-0001.

SAE J246—Spherical and Flanged Sleeve (Compression) Tube Fittings
SAE J476—Dryseal Pipe Threads
SAE J513—Refrigeration Tube Fittings
SAE J533—Flares for Tubing
SAE J846—Coding Systems for Identification of Fluid Conductors and Connectors

2.1.2 ANSI PUBLICATION—Available from ANSI, 11 West 42nd Street, New York, NY 10036-8002.

ANSI B1.1—Screw Threads

2.1.3 ASTM PUBLICATION—Available from ASTM, 1916 Race Street, Philadelphia, PA 19103-1187.

ASTM B 117—Method of Salt Spray (Fog) Testing

3. General Specifications

3.1 Size Designations—Fitting sizes are designated by the corresponding outside diameter of the tubing for the various types of tube ends and by the corresponding standard nominal pipe size for pipe thread ends.

3.2 Dimensions and Tolerances—Except for nominal sizes and thread specifications, dimensions and tolerances are given in both SI units and U.S. customary as designated. Tabulated dimensions shall apply to the finished parts, plated or otherwise processed, as specified by the purchaser. Unless otherwise specified, the maximum and minimum across flats dimensions shall be within the commercial tolerance of bar or extruded stock from which the fittings are produced. The minimum across corners dimensions of hexagons shall be 1.092 times the nominal width across flats, but shall not result in a side flat width less than 0.43 times the nominal width across flats.

Unless otherwise specified, tolerance on hole diameters designated drill in the dimensional tables shall be as tabulated in Table 1:

TABLE 1—DIMENSIONS AND TOLERANCES

Drill Size Range mm	Drill Size Range in	Tolerance on Hole Diameter Plus mm	Tolerance on Hole Diameter Plus in	Tolerance on Hole Diameter Minus mm	Tolerance on Hole Diameter Minus in
0.343 thru 4.699	0.0135 thru 0.1850	0.08	0.003	0.05	0.002
4.762 thru 6.299	0.1875 thru 0.2480	0.10	0.004	0.05	0.002
6.350 thru 19.050	0.2500 thru 0.7500	0.15	0.006	0.08	0.003
19.251 thru 25.400	0.7579 thru 1.0000	0.18	0.007	0.10	0.004

Tolerance on all dimensions not otherwise limited shall be 0.25 mm (±0.010 in). Angular tolerance on axis of ends on elbows, tees, and crosses shall be ±2.50 degrees for sizes up to and including 3/8 in, and ±1.50 degrees for sizes larger than 3/8 in.

Integral internal seats in inverted flared tube fittings shall be concentric with straight thread pitch diameters within 0.13 mm (0.005 in) full indicator reading (FIR). Unless otherwise specified, fitting seats shall be concentric with straight thread pitch diameters within 0.25 mm (0.010 in) full indicator reading (FIR).

Where so illustrated and not otherwise specified, hexagon corners shall be chamfered 30 degrees ± 5 degrees to a diameter equal to the nominal width across flats, with a tolerance of –0.41 mm (–0.016 in); or 0.41 where design permits, corners may be chamfered to the diameter of the abutting surface provided the length of chamfer does not exceed that produced by the 30 degree chamfer previously described.

3.3 Passages—Where passages in straight fittings are machined from opposite ends, the offset at the meeting point shall not exceed 0.38 mm (0.015 in). The cross-sectional area at the junction of passages in angle fittings shall not be less than that of the smallest passage. Where the passage is specified as a maximum, or as tap drill diameter or less, the minimum shall be no less than the minimum diameter of the smallest passage in the fitting.

3.4 Wall Thickness—Unless otherwise designated, the wall thickness at any point on fittings shall not be less than the thickness established by the specified dimensions, tolerances, and eccentricities for inner and outer surfaces.

3.5 Contour—Details of contour shall be optional with the manufacturer, provided the tabulated dimensions are maintained and serviceability of the fittings is not impaired. Wrench flats on elbows and tees shall be optional. Where extruded or forged shapes are reduced to conserve material, the wall thickness, unless otherwise specified, shall not be less than the respective minimum values tabulated in Table 2:

TABLE 2—WALL THICKNESS

Nom Tube OD in	Wall Thickness Min Extruded Shape(1) mm	Wall Thickness Min Extruded Shape(1) in	Wall Thickness Min Forged Shape mm	Wall Thickness Min Forged Shape in
1/8	1.0	0.04	1.52	0.060
3/16	1.0	0.04	1.78	0.070
1/4	1.0	0.04	1.90	0.075
5/16	1.3	0.05	1.90	0.075
3/8	1.3	0.05	2.29	0.090
7/16	1.5	0.06	2.29	0.090
1/2	1.5	0.06	2.29	0.090
9/16	1.5	0.06	2.29	0.090
5/8	2.0	0.08	2.54	0.100
3/4	2.0	0.08	2.54	0.100
7/8	2.0	0.08	3.05	0.120
1	2.0	0.08	3.05	0.120

1. Applies to reduction to one plane of shape only.

3.6 Straight Threads—Unified Standard Class 2A external threads and Class 2B internal threads with minor diameters, where specified, modified to Class 3B limits, shall apply to plain finish (unplated) fittings of all types. For externally threaded parts with additive finish, the maximum diameters of Class 2A may be exceeded by the amount of the allowance; that is, the basic diameters (Class 2A maximum diameters plus the allowance) shall apply to an externally threaded part after plating. For internally threaded parts with additive finish, the Class 2B diameters and modified minor diameters shall apply after plating.

The pitch diameter tolerance shall be the same as the corresponding diameter-pitch combination and the class of the Unified coarse and fine thread series or for special diameter-pitch combinations shall be based on diameter, pitch, and a length of engagement of 9 times the pitch. See ANSI B1.1.

Where external threads are produced by roll threading and the body is not undercut, the unthreaded portion of body adjacent to the shoulder may be reduced to the minimum pitch diameter.

External threads shall be chamfered to the diameter of abutting surfaces, or to the diameters specified, to produce a length of chamfered or partial thread equivalent to 3/4 to 1-1/4 times the pitch (rounded to a three-place decimal).

Internal threads shall be countersunk 90 degrees, included angle, to the diameters specified to the dimensional tables.

3.7 Thread Eccentricity Tolerances—The various thread elements of Class 2A external and Class 2B, modified, internal threads on tube fittings shall be concentric within the following limitations:

3.8 External Thread (Screw)

3.8.1 Where screw pitch diameter is maximum and screw major diameter is maximum, these two thread elements must be concentric. However, if the screw major diameter is out-of-round, undersize, these two thread elements may be eccentric at the point of out-of-roundness, a full indicator reading amount equal to the screw major diameter tolerance.

3.8.2 Where screw pitch diameter is minimum and screw major diameter is maximum, these two thread elements may be eccentric a full indicator reading amount equal to the screw pitch diameter tolerance.

3.8.3 Where screw pitch diameter is maximum and screw major diameter is minimum, these two thread elements may be eccentric a full indicator reading amount equal to the screw major diameter tolerance.

3.8.4 Where screw pitch diameter is minimum and screw major diameter is minimum, these two thread elements may be eccentric a full indicator reading amount equal to the sum of the screw pitch diameter tolerance and the screw major diameter tolerance.

3.9 Internal Thread (Nut)

3.9.1 Where nut pitch diameter is minimum and nut minor diameter is minimum, these two thread elements must be concentric. However, if the nut minor diameter is out-of-round, oversize, the two thread elements may be eccentric at the point of out-of-roundness, a full indicator reading amount equal to the nut minor diameter tolerance.

3.9.2 Where nut pitch diameter is maximum and nut minor diameter is minimum, these two thread elements may be eccentric a full indicator reading amount equal to the nut pitch diameter tolerance.

3.9.3 Where nut pitch diameter is minimum and nut minor diameter is maximum, these two thread elements may be eccentric a full indicator reading amount equal to the nut minor diameter tolerance.

3.9.4 Where nut pitch diameter is maximum and nut minor diameter is maximum, these two thread elements may be eccentric a full indicator reading amount equal to the sum of the nut pitch diameter tolerance and the nut minor diameter tolerance.

3.10 Pipe Threads—Pipe threads, unless there is specific authorization to the contrary, shall conform to the Dryseal American Standard Taper Pipe Thread (NPTF). At purchaser's option, the pipe thread on automotive tube fittings may be shortened in conformity with the SAE Short Dryseal Taper Pipe Thread (PTF-SAE Short). Specifications for pipe threads are given in detail in SAE J476.

The length of full form external thread shall not be shorter than L_2, plus one pitch (thread) for Dryseal NPTF and L_2, for Dryseal PTF-SAE Short, except that where thread is cut through into a relieved body or undercut on the fitting, the minimum full thread length may be reduced by one pitch (thread).

Where external pipe threads are produced by roll threading, the diameter of the unthreaded portion of shank adjacent to shoulder may be reduced to the E, basic diameter.

The tube fitting dimensions tabulated herein are based on length of the Dryseal American Standard Taper Pipe Thread (NPTF), it being the consensus of manufacturers and users that trouble-free assembly cannot be assured unless a full length is used. However, the tap drill depths and overall lengths specified in the tables for fittings with internal taper pipe threads are not consistent with the tap drill depths and overall thread lengths of the Dryseal American Standard Taper Pipe Threads (NPTF) given in Table A2, Appendix A, of SAE J476. The full length Dryseal American Standard Taper Pipe Taps specified in Table B2 of SAE J476 cannot be used, as the tap drill depths and overall lengths of the fittings have been reduced to the minimum required by bottoming taps to produce standard full length thread. The deviations described previously are peculiar to these tube fittings and as special tooling is required, caution should be exercised in specifying such deviations for any other products.

External pipe threads shall be chamfered from the diameters shown in Table 13 to produce the specified length of chamfered or partial thread. Internal pipe threads shall be countersunk 90 degrees, included angle, to the diameters shown in Table 13.

3.11 Material and Manufacture—All types of automotive tube fittings shall be made from brass or steel as specified by the purchaser and, at manufacturer's option and in accordance with his process of manufacture, may be milled from the bar or forged. Brass shall be UNS C36000 (half-hard), UNS C34500, or UNS C35000 for bar or extruded stock and UNS C37700 for forgings.

3.12 Finish—The external surfaces and threads of all carbon steel parts shall be plated or coated with a suitable material that passes a 72 h salt spray test in accordance with ASTM B 117. Any appearance of red rust during the 72 h salt spray test shall be considered failure, except for the following:

a. All internal fluid passages.
b. Edges such as hex points, serrations, and crests of threads where there may be mechanical deformation of the plating or coating typical of mass-produced parts or shipping effects.
c. Areas where there is mechanical deformation of the plating or coating caused by crimping, flaring, bending, and other post-plate metal forming operations.
d. Areas where the parts are suspended or affixed in the test chamber where condensate can accumulate.

NOTE—Cadmium plating is not preferred due to environmental reasons. Parts manufactured to this standard after January 1, 1997, shall not be cadmium plated. Internal fluid passages shall be protected from corrosion during storage. Changes in plating may affect assembly torques and require requalification, when applicable.

3.13 Workmanship—Workmanship shall conform to the best commercial practice to produce high-quality fittings. Fittings shall be free from all hanging burrs, loose scale, and slivers which might become dislodged in usage and all other defects which might affect their serviceability. All sealing surfaces must be smooth except that annular tool marks up to 2.5 mm (100 min) maximum shall be permissible.

3.14 Assembly Considerations—Where it is not objectionable from a function or production standpoint, the use of a compatible lubricant or sealant may be desirable in assembling Dryseal pipe threads on automotive tube fittings to minimize galling and effect a pressure-tight seal.

3.15 Wrenching Test—Steel nuts when assembled without tubing into mating brass fittings which are held securely by a suitable means, such as in a vise, shall be capable of being tightened by means of a standard open end wrench, having an opening as tabulated to the minimum torque values specified without failure (rounding) of the hexagon corner.

3.16 Inverted Flare Plugs—When assembling inverted flare plugs, it is recommended that a flare gasket (010113) be used to insure sealing. See SAE J513, Figure 38 for gasket details.

NOTE—The tabulated torque requirements should not in any case be misconstrued as being installation torques. They are intended solely for determining the adequacy of the hexagon corners. (See Table 8A.)

TABLE 3—STRAIGHT THREAD SPECIFICATION DATA, IN

Nominal Size	Series Designation	External Thread Pitch Diameter Max	External Thread Pitch Diameter Min	Internal Thread Pitch Diameter Max	Internal Thread Pitch Diameter Min[1]	Internal Thread Minor Diameter Max[2]	Internal Thread Minor Diameter Max[3]	Internal Thread Minor Diameter Max[4]
5/16-24	UNF	0.2843	0.2806	0.2902	0.2854	0.2754	0.277	0.267
5/16-28	UN	0.2883	0.2849	0.2937	0.2893	0.2807	0.282	0.274
3/8 -24	UNF	0.3468	0.3430	0.3528	0.3479	0.3372	0.340	0.330
7/16-20	UNF	0.4037	0.3995	0.4104	0.4050	0.3916	0.395	0.383
7/16-24	UNS	0.4093	0.4055	0.4153	0.4104	0.3994	0.402	0.392
1/2 -20	UNF	0.4662	0.4619	0.4731	0.4675	0.4537	0.457	0.446
1/2 -24	UNS	0.4717	0.4678	0.4780	0.4729	0.4619	0.465	0.455
9/16-24	UNEF	0.5342	0.5303	0.5354	0.5405	0.5244	0.527	0.517
5/8 -18	UNF	0.5875	0.5828	0.5949	0.5889	0.5730	0.578	0.565
5/8 -24	UNEF	0.5967	0.5927	0.6031	0.5979	0.5869	0.590	0.580
11/16-16	UN	0.6455	0.6407	0.6531	0.6469	0.6284	0.634	0.620
11/16-18	UNS	0.6500	0.6455	0.6573	0.6514	0.6335	0.640	0.627
11/16-20	UN	0.6537	0.6494	0.6606	0.6550	0.6412	0.645	0.633
3/4 -16	UNF	0.7079	0.7029	0.7159	0.7094	0.6908	0.696	0.682
3/4 -18	UNS	0.7125	0.7079	0.7199	0.7139	0.6980	0.703	0.690
13/16-18	UNS	0.7750	0.7704	0.7824	0.7764	0.7605	0.765	0.752
7/8 -14	UNF	0.8270	0.8216	0.8356	0.8286	0.8068	0.814	0.798
7/8 -18	UNS	0.8375	0.8239	0.8449	0.8389	0.8230	0.828	0.815
1 -18	UNS	0.9625	0.9578	0.9701	0.9639	0.9480	0.953	0.940
1- 1/16-14	UNS	1.0145	1.0092	1.0230	1.0161	0.9940	1.001	0.985
1- 1/16-16	UN	1.0204	1.0154	1.0284	1.0219	1.0033	1.009	0.995
1- 1/4 -12	UNF	1.1941	1.1879	1.2039	1.1959	1.1698	1.178	1.160
1- 3/8 -12	UNF	1.3127	1.3190	1.3291	1.3209	1.2948	1.303	1.285

1. These values are also the basic pitch diameter.
2. Class 3B maximum minor diameter limits shall apply where so designated in respective dimensional tables.
3. Class 2B minor diameter limits shall apply unless otherwise designated.

TABLE 4—DIMENSIONS OF CONNECTORS, UNIONS, ELBOWS, AND TEES (FIGURES 1A TO 3C)

Nom Tube OD in	B Dryseal Taper Thread NPTF[1] in	B Nom Thread Size in Class 2A Ext	C Nom in	C_1 Nom in	C_2 Nom in	D[5] Dia Drill mm	D[5] Dia Drill in
1/8	1/8	5/16-24	7/16	5/16	9/16	1.98	0.078
3/16	1/8	3/8 -24	7/16	3/8	9/16	3.18	0.125
1/4	1/8	7/16-20	7/16	7/16	9/16	4.78	0.188
5/16	1/8	1/2 -20	1/2	1/2	9/16	5.56	0.219
3/8	1/4	5/8 -18	5/8	5/8	11/16	7.14	0.281
7/16	1/4	11/16-16	11/16	11/16	11/16	7.92	0.312
1/2	3/8	3/4 -16	3/4	3/4	13/16	10.31	0.406
5/8	1/2	7/8 -14	7/8	7/8	1	12.70	0.500
3/4	1/2	1- 1/16-14	1- 1/16	1- 1/16	1- 1/16	15.88	0.625
7/8	3/4	1- 1/4 -12	1- 1/4	1- 1/4	1- 1/4	19.05	0.750
1	1	1- 3/8 -12	1- 3/8	1- 3/8	1- 1/2	22.22	0.875

Nom Tube OD in	D_1[5] Dia Drill mm	D_1[5] Dia Drill in	E Dia mm	E Dia in	F Dia mm	F Dia in	G[4] Dia mm +0.00 −0.25	G[4] Dia in +0.000 −0.010
3/16	5.56	0.219	3.96	0.156	7.54	0.297	—	—
1/4	5.56	0.219	5.56	0.219	8.74	0.344	—	—
5/16	5.56	0.219	6.35	0.250	10.31	0.406	—	—
3/8	7.92	0.312	7.92	0.312	13.49	0.531	—	—
7/16	7.92	0.312	8.74	0.344	14.63	0.578	15.14	0.596
1/2	10.31	0.406	11.13	0.438	16.28	0.641	16.74	0.659
5/8	14.27	0.562	13.49	0.531	19.05	0.750	19.56	0.770
3/4	14.27	0.562	18.26	0.719	23.83	0.938	24.33	0.958
7/8	19.05	0.750	20.24	0.797	28.58	1.125	28.65	1.128
1	23.82	0.938	23.83	0.938	31.75	1.250	31.83	1.253

TABLE 4—DIMENSIONS OF CONNECTORS, UNIONS, ELBOWS, AND TEES (FIGURES 1A TO 3C) (CONTINUED)

Nom Tube OD in	I mm	I in	J(4) Full Thread Min mm	J(4) Full Thread Min in	K mm	K in	L(2) mm ±0.08	L(2) in ±0.03
1/8	9.7	0.38	7.9	0.31	3.0	0.12	23.4	0.92
3/16	11.2	0.44	9.7	0.38	3.0	0.12	25.4	1.00
1/4	12.7	0.50	10.4	0.41	4.1	0.16	26.9	1.06
5/16	14.2	0.56	11.9	0.47	4.8	0.19	29.5	1.16
3/8	15.7	0.62	13.7	0.54	5.6	0.22	36.6	1.44
7/16	17.5	0.69	14.2	0.56	6.4	0.25	38.9	1.53
1/2	19.0	0.75	16.8	0.66	6.4	0.25	41.1	1.62
5/8	22.4	0.88	19.3	0.76	7.1	0.28	50.8	2.00
3/4	25.4	1.00	22.9	0.90	7.1	0.28	55.6	2.19
7/8	28.4	1.12	24.1	0.95	9.7	0.38	60.2	2.37
1	28.4	1.12	24.6	0.97	9.7	0.38	66.5	2.62

Nom Tube OD in	L_1 mm ±0.8	L_1 in ±0.03	L_2(2)(3) mm ±0.8	L_2(2)(3) in ±0.03	M mm ±0.8	M in ±0.03	M_1 mm ±0.8	M_1 in ±0.03
1/8	23.4	0.92	23.1	0.91	15.7	0.62	15.7	0.62
3/16	26.9	1.06	24.6	0.97	19.0	0.75	19.0	0.75
1/4	30.2	1.19	26.2	1.03	20.6	0.81	22.4	0.88
5/16	34.0	1.34	26.9	1.06	23.1	0.91	23.1	0.91
3/8	38.1	1.50	33.3	1.31	25.4	1.00	26.9	1.06
7/16	42.2	1.66	35.8	1.41	28.4	1.12	28.4	1.12
1/2	46.0	1.81	38.1	1.50	31.0	1.22	31.0	1.22
5/8	53.8	2.12	46.0	1.81	35.8	1.41	35.8	1.41
3/4	62.0	2.44	48.5	1.91	41.1	1.62	42.2	1.66
7/8	69.6	2.74	57.2	2.25	44.5	1.75	44.5	1.75
1	71.1	2.80	62.0	2.44	49.3	1.94	49.3	1.94

Nom Tube OD in	M_2 mm ±0.8	M_2 in ±0.03	M_3 mm ±0.8	M_3 in ±0.03	N(2) mm ±0.8	N(2) in ±0.03	N_1(2)(3) mm ±0.8	N_1(2)(3) in ±0.03
1/8	19.0	0.75	15.0	0.59	17.5	0.69	10.7	0.42
3/16	20.6	0.81	15.7	0.62	19.0	0.75	11.2	0.44
1/4	22.4	0.88	17.0	0.67	19.8	0.78	11.9	0.47
5/16	23.9	0.94	19.8	0.78	19.8	0.78	11.9	0.47
3/8	27.7	1.09	22.6	0.89	26.9	1.06	17.5	0.69
7/16	28.4	1.12	24.6	0.97	26.9	1.06	18.3	0.72
1/2	32.5	1.28	26.9	1.06	28.4	1.12	19.0	0.75
5/8	38.1	1.50	31.2	1.23	35.1	1.38	25.4	1.00
3/4	41.1	1.62	35.8	1.41	38.1	1.50	26.9	1.06
7/8	47.8	1.88	41.1	1.62	42.9	1.69	28.4	1.12
1	52.3	2.06	42.9	1.69	49.3	1.94	35.1	1.38

Nom Tube OD in	N_2(2) mm ±0.8	N_2(2) in ±0.03	P(2)(3) Min mm	P(2)(3) Min in	P_1(2)(3) mm	P_1(2)(3) in	S(2)(5) Max mm	S(2)(5) Max in	S_1(2)(5) Min mm	S_1(2)(5) Min in
1/8	13.2	0.52	9.7	0.38	9.7	0.38	11.7	0.46	19.6	0.77
3/16	13.2	0.52	9.7	0.38	9.7	0.38	12.2	0.48	21.6	0.85
1/4	16.3	0.64	9.7	0.38	9.7	0.38	12.2	0.48	23.4	0.92
5/16	16.3	0.64	9.7	0.38	9.7	0.38	—	—	—	—
3/8	21.8	0.86	14.2	0.56	14.2	0.56	17.5	0.69	31.5	1.24
7/16	21.8	0.86	14.2	0.56	14.2	0.56	—	—	—	—
1/2	24.1	0.95	14.2	0.56	14.2	0.56	—	—	—	—
5/8	29.7	1.17	19.0	0.75	19.1	0.75	23.9	0.94	42.4	1.67
3/4	30.5	1.20	19.0	0.75	19.1	0.75	31.0	1.22	51.3	2.02
7/8	32.2	1.27	19.0	0.75	19.1	0.75	—	—	—	—
1	37.6	1.48	23.9	0.94	23.9	0.94	31.0	1.22	61.5	2.42

TABLE 4—DIMENSIONS OF CONNECTORS, UNIONS, ELBOWS, AND TEES (FIGURES 1A TO 3C) (CONTINUED)

Nom Tube OD in	T(6) Ref mm	T(6) Ref in	T_1 Min mm	T_1 Min in	W(7) Dia mm +0.0 –0.5	W(7) Dia in +0.00 –0.02
1/8	3.8	0.15	5.3	0.21	14.2	0.56
3/16	4.6	0.18	5.3	0.21	14.2	0.56
1/4	4.6	0.18	6.1	0.24	14.2	0.56
5/16	5.3	0.21	6.1	0.24	14.2	0.56
3/8	6.1	0.24	7.6	0.30	17.5	0.69
7/16	6.9	0.27	7.6	0.30	17.5	0.69
1/2	7.6	0.30	9.4	0.37	20.6	0.81
5/8	9.4	0.37	10.9	0.43	25.4	1.00
3/4	10.9	0.43	12.4	0.49	26.9	1.06
7/8	12.4	0.49	13.2	0.52	31.8	1.25
1	14.0	0.55	14.7	0.58	38.1	1.50

1 Dryseal American Standard Taper Pipe Thread. See General Specifications.
2 Where SAE Short Pipe Thread is authorized by purchaser, dimensions L, L2, N, N1, P, S, and S1 are reduced in accordance with reduction of pipe thread length. See SAE J476 Tables 3 and 4.
3 Tap drill depths given require use of bottoming taps to produce standard full thread length. For increased tap clearance, see Internal Taper Pipe Threads in the General Specifications.
4 Where thread relief undercut is used, the last thread shall be chamfered 1/2 to 1 pitch long from G diameter and dimension 1 may be reduced by an amount equal to 1/2 pitch.
5 At manufacturers' option, through passages in fittings shown in Figures 1A and 3C may conform with the smaller diameter specified or be counterbored to the larger diameter from the appropriate end for depths S or S1, respectively.
6 Minimum design thickness, not subject to inspection.
7 Basic dimensions shown shall apply as minimum diameter or across flats for bosses. The –0.5 mm (–0.02 in) tolerance shall apply only to chamber diameter on full hexagon versions of fitting in Figure 1C.

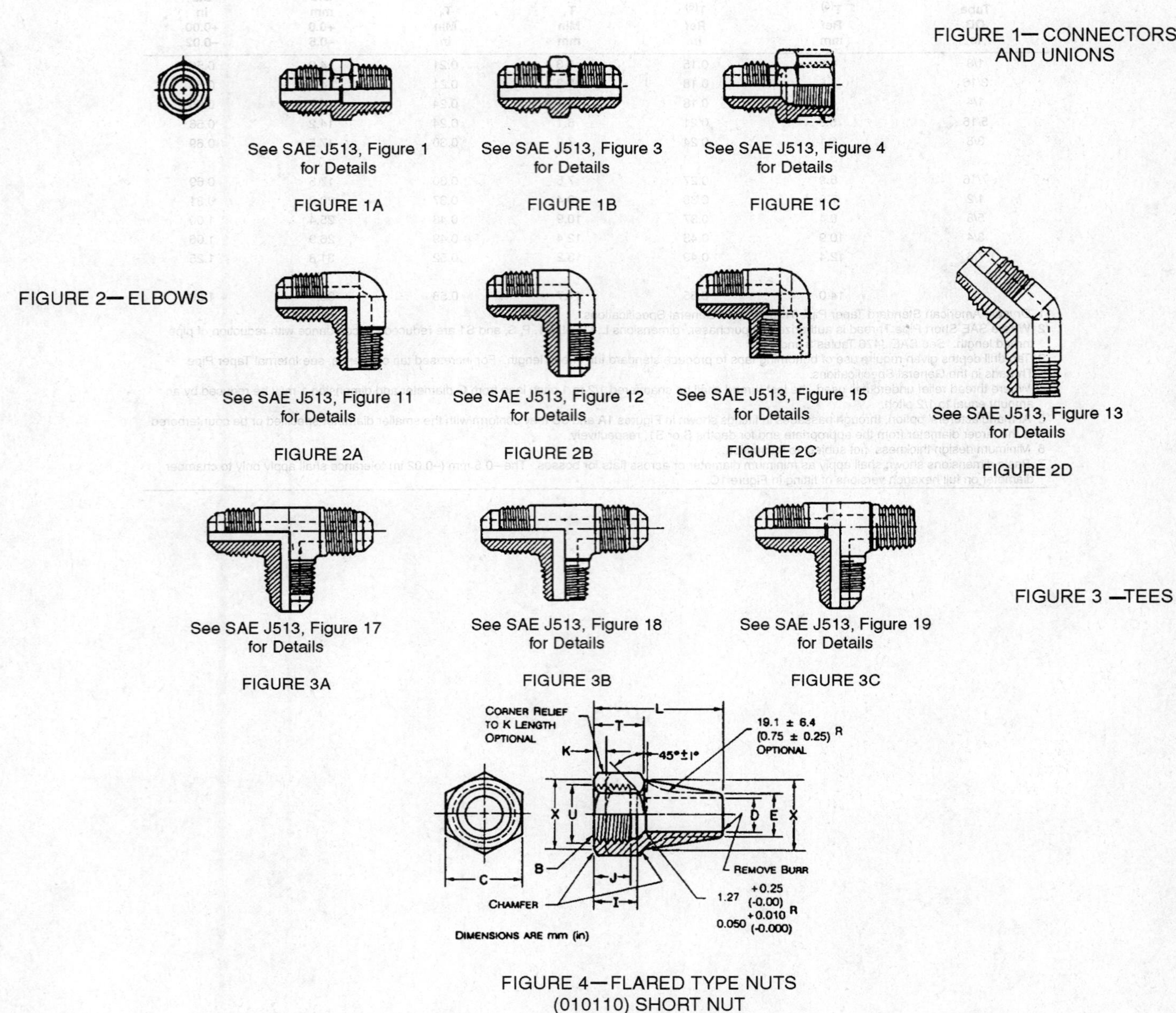

FIGURE 4—FLARED TYPE NUTS
(010110) SHORT NUT
(010111) LONG NUT

NOTES—UNSPECIFIED DETAIL WITH RESPECT TO DIMENSIONS, TOLERANCES, CONTOURS, MATERIAL, WORKMANSHIP, ETC., MUST CONFORM TO GENERAL SPECIFICATIONS FOR AUTOMOTIVE TUBE FITTINGS. THE DIMENSIONAL DESIGNATIONS ON THE FIRST FIGURE IN EACH GROUP SHALL APPLY TO ALL OTHER FIGURES IN THAT GROUP EXCEPT AS SHOWN OTHERWISE. CODES SHOWN IN BRACKETS ADJACENT TO FIGURE NUMBERS REPRESENT RESPECTIVE FITTING IDENTIFICATION IN ACCORDANCE WITH SAE J846.

TABLE 5—DIMENSIONS OF NUTS (FIGURE 4)

Nom Tube OD in	B Nom Thread Size in Class 2B int	C Nom in	D Dia mm +0.13 –0.00	D Dia in +0.005 –0.000	E Dia mm	E Dia in	I mm	I in
1/8	5/16-24	3/8	3.30	0.130	6.4	0.25	5.6	0.22
3/16	3/8 -24	7/16	4.88	0.192	7.9	0.31	7.1	0.28
1/4	7/16-20	9/16	6.48	0.255	9.7	0.38	8.6	0.34
5/16	1/2 -20	5/8	8.05	0.317	11.2	0.44	9.7	0.38
3/8	5/8 -18	3/4	9.65	0.380	12.7	0.50	11.2	0.44
7/16	11/16-16	13/16	11.23	0.442	14.2	0.56	11.9	0.47
1/2	3/4 -16	7/8	12.83	0.505	15.7	0.62	13.5	0.53
5/8	7/8 -14	1- 1/16	16.00	0.630	19.1	0.75	16.8	0.66
3/4	1- 1/16-14	1- 1/4	19.18	0.755	22.4	0.88	19.8	0.78
7/8	1- 1/4 -12	1- 1/2	22.35	0.880	26.9	1.06	19.8	0.78
1	1- 3/8 -12	1- 5/8	25.53	1.005	30.2	1.19	20.6	0.81

Nom Tube OD in	J Full Thread Min mm	J Full Thread Min in	K mm	K in	L Long mm	L Long in	L Short mm	L Short in
1/8	3.8	0.15	2.3	0.09	19.1	0.75	12.7	0.50
3/16	5.3	0.21	2.3	0.09	20.6	0.81	15.7	0.62
1/4	6.6	0.26	3.0	0.12	23.9	0.94	19.1	0.75
5/16	7.6	0.30	3.0	0.12	28.4	1.12	22.4	0.88
3/8	8.9	0.35	3.0	0.12	33.3	1.31	25.4	1.00
7/16	9.4	0.37	3.0	0.12	38.1	1.50	26.9	1.06
1/2	10.9	0.43	3.0	0.12	41.1	1.62	28.4	1.12
5/8	14.0	0.55	3.0	0.12	47.8	1.88	33.3	1.31
3/4	17.0	0.67	3.0	0.12	55.6	2.19	38.1	1.50
7/8	16.5	0.65	3.0	0.12	58.7	2.31	41.1	1.62
1	17.3	0.68	3.0	0.12	63.5	2.50	46.0	1.81

Nom Tube OD in	T mm	T in	U Dia Min mm	U Dia Min in	U Dia Max mm	U Dia Max in	X Dia mm	X Dia in
1/8	5.6	0.22	8.4	0.33	8.9	0.35	9.7	0.38
3/16	7.1	0.28	9.9	0.39	10.4	0.41	11.2	0.44
1/4	9.7	0.38	11.4	0.45	11.9	0.47	14.2	0.56
5/16	11.2	0.44	13.0	0.51	13.5	0.53	15.7	0.62
3/8	12.7	0.50	16.3	0.64	17.0	0.67	19.1	0.75
7/16	14.2	0.56	18.0	0.71	18.8	0.74	20.6	0.81
1/2	15.7	0.62	19.6	0.77	20.3	0.80	22.4	0.88
5/8	19.1	0.75	22.9	0.90	23.6	0.93	26.9	1.06
3/4	22.4	0.88	27.4	1.08	28.2	1.11	31.8	1.25
7/8	25.4	1.00	32.3	1.27	33.0	1.30	38.1	1.50
1	25.4	1.00	35.3	1.39	36.1	1.42	41.1	1.62

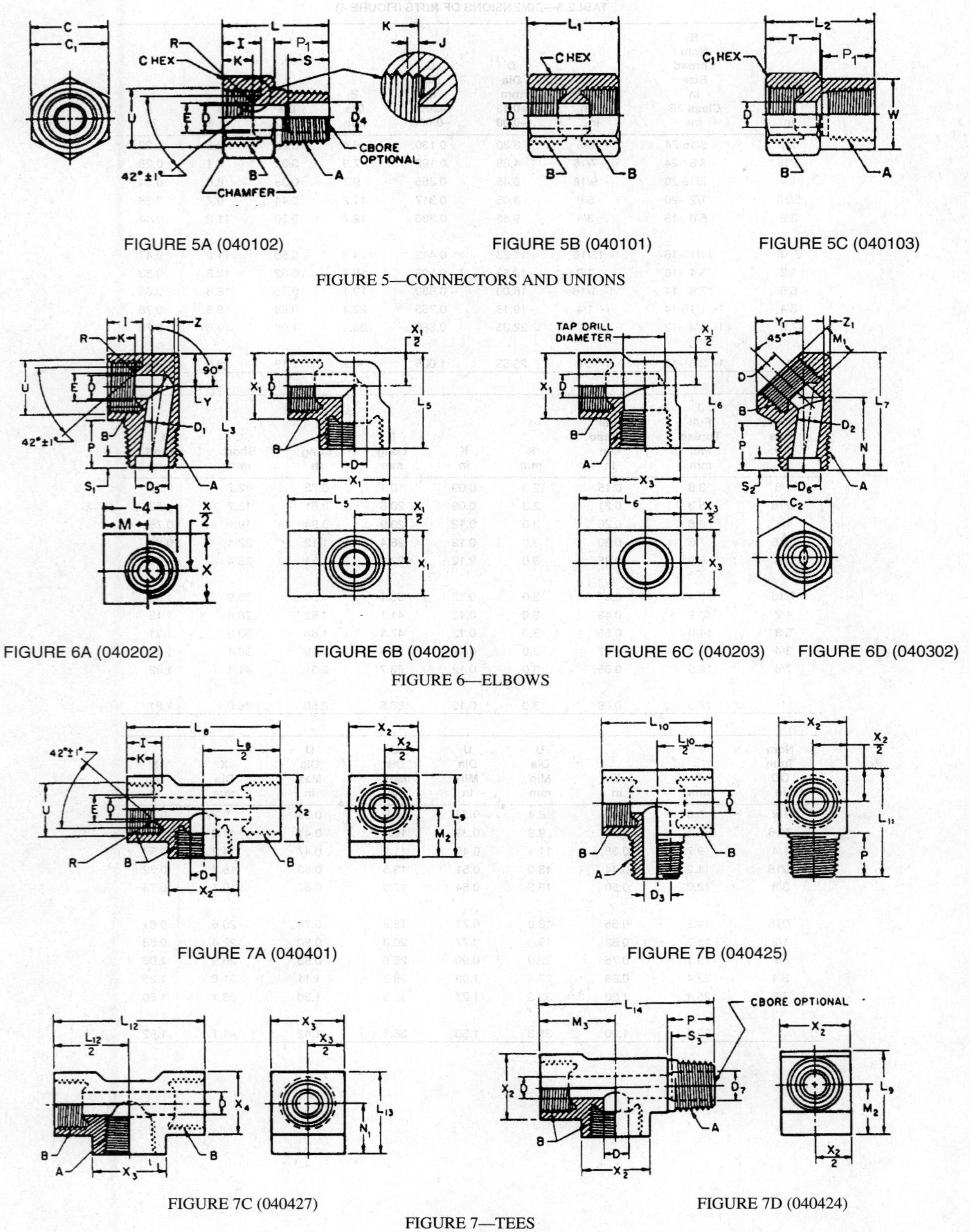

FIGURE 5A (040102)

FIGURE 5B (040101)

FIGURE 5C (040103)

FIGURE 5—CONNECTORS AND UNIONS

FIGURE 6A (040202)

FIGURE 6B (040201)

FIGURE 6C (040203)

FIGURE 6D (040302)

FIGURE 6—ELBOWS

FIGURE 7A (040401)

FIGURE 7B (040425)

FIGURE 7C (040427)

FIGURE 7D (040424)

FIGURE 7—TEES

NOTES—UNSPECIFIED DETAIL WITH RESPECT TO DIMENSIONS, TOLERANCES, CONTOURS, MATERIAL, WORKMANSHIP, ETC., MUST CONFORM TO GENERAL SPECIFICATIONS FOR AUTOMOTIVE TUBE FITTINGS. THE DIMENSIONAL DESIGNATIONS ON THE FIRST FIGURE IN EACH GROUP SHALL APPLY TO ALL OTHER FIGURES IN THAT GROUP EXCEPT AS SHOWN OTHERWISE. CODES SHOWN IN BRACKETS ADJACENT TO FIGURE NUMBERS REPRESENT RESPECTIVE FITTING IDENTIFICATION IN ACCORDANCE WITH SAE J846.

TABLE 6—DIMENSIONS OF CONNECTORS, UNIONS, ELBOWS, AND TEES (FIGURES 51 TO 7D)

Nom Tube OD in	A Dryseal Taper Thread NPTF[1] In	B Nom Thread Size in Class 2B Int[4]	C Nom in Brass	C Nom in Steel	C_1 Nom in Brass	C_1 Nom in Steel	C_2 Nom in Brass	C_2 Nom in Steel
1/8	1/8	5/16-28	13/32	7/16	1/2	1/2	1/2	1/2
3/16	1/8	3/8 -24	15/32	1/2	1/2	1/2	17/32	9/16
1/4	1/8	7/16-24	17/32	9/16	17/32	9/16	9/16	9/16
5/16	1/8	1/2 -20	19/32	5/8	19/32	5/8	5/8	5/8
5/16	1/4	1/2 -20	19/32	5/8	11/16	11/16	5/8	5/8
3/8	1/4	5/8 -18	3/4	3/4	3/4	3/4	25/32	13/16
7/16	1/4	11/16-18	13/16	13/16	13/16	13/16	13/16	13/16
1/2	3/8	3/4 -18	29/32	15/16	29/32	15/16	7/8	7/8
5/8	1/2	7/8 -18	1- 1/16	1- 1/16	1- 1/16	1- 1/16	1- 1/16	1- 1/16
3/4	3/4	1- 1/16-16	1- 1/4	1- 1/4	1- 1/4	1- 1/4	1- 5/16	1- 5/16

Nom Tube OD in	D Dia Drill mm	D Dia Drill in	D_1 Dia Drill mm	D_1 Dia Drill in	D_2 Dia Drill mm	D_2 Dia Drill in	D_3 Dia Drill mm	D_3 Dia Drill in
1/8	1.98	0.078	2.95	0.116	3.17	0.125	5.56	0.219
3/16	3.17	0.125	3.17	0.125	3.96	0.156	5.56	0.219
1/4	4.77	0.188	4.50	0.177	4.77	0.188	5.56	0.219
5/16	5.56	0.219	5.56	0.219	5.16	0.203	5.56	0.219
5/16	5.56	0.219	5.56	0.219	5.16	0.203	7.92	0.312
3/8	7.14	0.281	7.14	0.281	7.14	0.281	8.74	0.344
7/16	8.74	0.344	8.33	0.328	7.92	0.312	8.74	0.344
1/2	10.31	0.406	9.52	0.375	9.52	0.375	10.31	0.406
5/8	13.49	0.531	12.70	0.500	12.70	0.500	14.27	0.562
3/4	15.87	0.625	15.87	0.625	15.87	0.625	19.05	0.750

Nom Tube OD in	D_4 Dia Drill mm	D_4 Dia Drill in	D_5 Dia Drill mm	D_5 Dia Drill in	D_6 Dia Drill mm	D_6 Dia Drill in	D_7 Dia Drill mm	D_7 Dia Drill in
1/8	5.56	0.219	6.35	0.250	6.35	0.250	4.77	0.188
3/16	5.56	0.219	6.35	0.250	6.35	0.250	4.77	0.188
1/4	5.56	0.219	6.35	0.250	6.35	0.250	—	—
5/16	5.56	0.219	6.35	0.250	—	—	—	—
5/16	7.92	0.312	7.92	0.312	7.14	0.281	—	—
3/8	8.74	0.344	—	—	8.74	0.344	—	—
7/16	8.74	0.344	—	—	8.74	0.344	—	—
1/2	10.31	0.406	11.91	0.469	11.91	0.469	—	—
5/8	15.09	0.594	15.09	0.594	14.27	0.562	—	—
3/4	19.05	0.750	19.05	0.750	17.47	0.688	—	—

Nom Tube OD in	E Dia Min mm	E Dia Min in	E Dia Max mm	E Dia Max in	I Seat Depth mm +0.25 −0.13	I Seat Depth in +0.010 −0.005	J[5] End Full Thread Max mm	J[5] End Full Thread Max in
1/8	2.64	0.104	2.74	0.108	6.35	0.250	0.28	0.011
3/16	3.84	0.151	3.94	0.155	6.76	0.266	0.33	0.013
1/4	5.44	0.214	5.54	0.218	6.76	0.266	0.66	0.026
5/16	7.01	0.276	7.11	0.280	7.54	0.297	0.84	0.033
5/16	7.01	0.276	7.11	0.280	7.54	0.297	0.84	0.033
3/8	8.69	0.342	8.79	0.346	8.74	0.344	0.58	0.023
7/16	10.29	0.405	10.39	0.409	9.53	0.375	0.74	0.029
1/2	11.86	0.467	11.96	0.471	9.93	0.391	0.74	0.029
5/8	15.04	0.592	15.14	0.596	10.31	0.406	1.04	0.041
3/4	17.86	0.703	17.94	0.708	11.91	0.469	0.41	0.016

TABLE 6—DIMENSIONS OF CONNECTORS, UNIONS, ELBOWS, AND TEES (Figures 5a to 7d) (Continued)

Nom Tube OD in	K Seat Depth mm +0.25 −0.13	K Seat Depth in +0.010 −0.005	L(2) mm +0.8 −0.0	L(2) in +0.03 −0.00	L_1 mm +0.8 −0.0	L_1 in +0.03 −0.00	L_2(2)(3) mm +0.8 −0.0	L_2(2)(3) in +0.03 −0.00
1/8	4.75	0.187	15.7	0.62	15.0	0.59	18.3	0.72
3/16	5.16	0.203	17.5	0.69	15.7	0.62	19.1	0.75
1/4	5.16	0.203	18.5	0.73	15.7	0.62	19.1	0.75
5/16	5.94	0.234	19.8	0.78	17.8	0.70	19.8	0.78
5/16	5.94	0.234	24.6	0.97	—	—	25.4	1.00
3/8	6.76	0.266	25.9	1.02	20.3	0.80	26.2	1.03
7/16	7.52	0.296	26.7	1.05	22.4	0.88	26.9	1.06
1/2	7.93	0.312	26.9	1.06	23.1	0.91	27.7	1.09
5/8	8.33	0.328	33.3	1.31	24.6	0.97	33.3	1.31
3/4	9.12	0.359	35.1	1.38	28.4	1.12	38.1	1.50

Nom Tube OD in	L_3(2) mm +0.8 −0.0	L_3(2) in +0.03 −0.00	L_4 mm	L_4 in	L_5 mm +0.8 −0.0	L_5 in +0.03 −0.00	L_6(2)(3) mm +0.8 −0.0	L_6(2)(3) in +0.03 −0.00
1/8	19.8	0.78	12.4	0.49	17.8	0.70		
3/16	21.3	0.84	12.4	0.49	17.8	0.70	—	—
1/4	23.1	0.91	14.0	0.55	19.6	0.77	20.1	0.79
5/16	24.6	0.97	17.5	0.69	21.8	0.86	22.4	0.88
5/16	29.2	1.15	19.1	0.75	—	—	24.6	0.97
3/8	33.3	1.31	20.6	0.81	26.2	1.03	26.2	1.03
7/16	35.8	1.41	22.4	0.88	29.0	1.14	29.5	1.16
1/2	37.3	1.47	23.9	0.94	31.8	1.25	31.8	1.25
5/8	46.0	1.81	28.2	1.11	37.3	1.47	37.3	1.47
3/4	50.8	2.00	32.5	1.28	43.7	1.72	43.7	1.72

Nom Tube OD in	L_7(2) mm	L_7(2) in	L_8 mm +0.8 −0.0	L_8 in +0.03 −0.00	L_9 mm	L_9 in	L_{10} mm +0.8 −0.0	L_{10} in +0.03 −0.00
1/8	20.6	0.81	23.9	0.94	13.5	0.53	19.8	0.78
3/16	22.4	0.88	27.7	1.09	15.7	0.62	20.6	0.81
1/4	23.9	0.94	28.4	1.12	17.5	0.69	21.3	0.84
5/16	25.4	1.00	31.8	1.25	19.1	0.75	23.9	0.94
5/16	29.5	1.16	—	—	19.1	0.75	26.9	1.06
3/8	34.0	1.34	37.3	1.47	23.9	0.94	29.5	1.16
7/16	35.8	1.41	41.1	1.62	26.2	1.03	31.0	1.22
1/2	36.6	1.44	44.5	1.75	28.4	1.12	35.1	1.38
5/8	44.5	1.75	49.3	1.94	32.5	1.28	39.6	1.56
3/4	50.8	2.00	57.2	2.25	38.1	1.50	46.0	1.81

Nom Tube OD in	L_{11}(2) mm	L_{11}(2) in	L_{12} mm +0.8 −0.0	L_{12} in +0.03 −0.00	L_{13} mm	L_{13} in	L_{14}(2) mm	L_{14}(2) in
1/8	19.8	0.78	27.7	1.09	15.7	0.62	29.5	1.16
3/16	21.3	0.84	27.7	1.09	15.7	0.62	31.8	1.25
1/4	23.1	0.91	28.4	1.12	17.5	0.69	33.3	1.31
5/16	24.6	0.97	31.8	1.25	19.1	0.75	37.3	1.47
5/16	29.5	1.16	35.1	1.38	22.4	0.88	38.9	1.53
3/8	33.3	1.31	37.3	1.47	23.9	0.94	46.5	1.83
7/16	35.1	1.38	41.1	1.62	26.2	1.03	47.8	1.88
1/2	37.3	1.47	44.5	1.75	28.4	1.12	50.8	2.00
5/8	46.0	1.81	49.3	1.94	32.5	1.28	60.5	2.38
3/4	50.8	2.00	57.2	2.25	38.1	1.50	66.5	2.62

TABLE 6—DIMENSIONS OF CONNECTORS, UNIONS, ELBOWS, AND TEES (Figures 5a to 7d) (Continued)

Nom Tube OD in	M mm	M in	M_1 mm	M_1 in	M_2 mm	M_2 in	M_3 mm	M_3 in
1/8	6.9	0.27	5.6	0.22	8.4	0.33	11.9	0.47
3/16	6.9	0.27	6.4	0.25	9.9	0.39	13.5	0.53
1/4	8.4	0.33	6.9	0.27	10.7	0.42	14.2	0.56
5/16	11.9	0.47	8.6	0.34	11.4	0.45	15.7	0.62
5/16	11.4	0.45	5.8	0.23	11.4	0.45	15.7	0.62
3/8	13.5	0.53	9.7	0.38	14.2	0.56	19.1	0.75
7/16	15.0	0.59	10.4	0.41	15.7	0.62	20.6	0.81
1/2	15.0	0.59	9.6	0.38	17.0	0.67	22.4	0.88
5/8	17.0	0.67	11.4	0.45	19.1	0.75	24.6	0.97
3/4	19.1	0.75	12.7	0.50	22.4	0.88	28.4	1.12

Nom Tube OD in	N[(2)] mm	N[(2)] in	N_1 mm	N_1 in	P[(2)(3)] Min mm	P[(2)(3)] Min in	P_1[(2)(3)] mm	P_1[(2)(3)] in	R Radius Max mm	R Radius Max in
1/8	13.2	0.52	9.9	0.39	9.7	0.38	9.7	0.38	0.25	0.010
3/16	14.0	0.55	9.9	0.39	9.7	0.38	9.7	0.38	0.25	0.010
1/4	14.7	0.58	10.7	0.42	9.7	0.38	9.7	0.38	0.91	0.036
5/16	14.2	0.56	11.4	0.45	9.7	0.38	9.7	0.38	0.91	0.036
5/16	21.1	0.83	12.7	0.50	14.2	0.56	14.2	0.56	0.91	0.036
3/8	21.3	0.84	14.2	0.56	14.2	0.56	14.2	0.56	0.91	0.036
7/16	21.8	0.86	15.7	0.62	14.2	0.56	14.2	0.56	0.91	0.036
1/2	23.1	0.91	17.0	0.67	14.2	0.56	14.2	0.56	0.91	0.036
5/8	27.7	1.09	19.1	0.75	19.1	0.75	19.1	0.75	0.91	0.036
3/4	31.0	1.22	22.4	0.88	19.1	0.75	19.1	0.75	0.91	0.036

Nom Tube OD in	S[(2)] mm	S[(2)] in	S_1[(2)] mm	S_1[(2)] in	S_2[(2)] mm	S_2[(2)] in	S_3[(2)] mm	S_3[(2)] in
1/8	4.8	0.19	6.35	0.250	2.36	0.093	9.7	0.38
3/16	5.8	0.23	2.36	0.093	2.36	0.093	9.7	0.38
1/4	7.1	0.28	2.36	0.093	2.36	0.093	—	—
5/16	—	—	2.36	0.093	—	—	—	—
5/16	12.7	0.50	12.70	0.500	4.32	0.170	—	—
3/8	10.4	0.41	—	—	2.36	0.093	—	—
7/16	—	—	—	—	2.36	0.093	—	—
1/2	—	—	3.96	0.156	2.36	0.093	—	—
5/8	13.5	0.53	5.56	0.219	4.77	0.188	—	—
3/4	13.5	0.53	7.95	0.312	6.35	0.250	—	—

Nom Tube OD in	T mm	T in	U Dia Min mm	U Dia Min in	U Dia Max mm	U Dia Max in	W Dia mm +0.00 −0.25	W Dia in +0.00 −0.01
1/8	8.6	0.34	8.1	0.32	8.6	0.34	12.7	0.50
3/16	9.7	0.38	9.9	0.39	10.4	0.41	12.7	0.50
1/4	9.7	0.38	11.4	0.45	11.9	0.47	13.5	0.53
5/16	10.4	0.41	13.0	0.51	13.5	0.53	15.0	0.59
5/16	11.2	0.44	13.0	0.51	13.5	0.53	17.5	0.69
3/8	11.9	0.47	16.3	0.64	17.0	0.67	19.1	0.75
7/16	12.7	0.50	17.8	0.70	18.5	0.73	20.6	0.81
1/2	13.5	0.53	19.6	0.77	20.3	0.80	23.1	0.91
5/8	15.7	0.62	22.6	0.89	23.4	0.92	26.9	1.06
3/4	17.5	0.69	27.4	1.08	28.2	1.11	31.8	1.25

TABLE 6—DIMENSIONS OF CONNECTORS, UNIONS, ELBOWS, AND TEES (Figures 5A to 7D) (Continued)

Nom Tube OD in	X mm	X in	X_1 mm	X_1 in	X_2 mm	X_2 in	X_3 mm	X_3 in
1/8	11.2	0.44	10.4	0.41	10.4	0.41	12.7	0.50
3/16	11.9	0.47	11.9	0.47	11.9	0.47	12.7	0.50
1/4	13.5	0.53	13.5	0.53	13.5	0.53	13.5	0.53
5/16	15.0	0.59	15.0	0.59	15.0	0.59	15.0	0.59
5/16	15.0	0.59	15.0	0.59	15.0	0.59	17.5	0.69
3/8	19.1	0.75	18.3	0.72	19.1	0.75	19.1	0.75
7/16	21.3	0.84	19.8	0.78	20.6	0.81	20.6	0.81
1/2	23.1	0.91	22.4	0.88	23.1	0.91	23.1	0.91
5/8	26.9	1.06	26.9	1.06	26.9	1.06	26.9	1.06
3/4	31.8	1.25	31.8	1.25	31.8	1.25	31.8	1.25

Nom Tube OD in	X_4 mm	X_4 in	Y mm +0.25 −0.00	Y in +0.010 −0.000	Y_1[6] mm	Y_1[6] in	Z Min mm	Z Min in	Z_1 Min mm	Z_1 Min in
1/8	11.9	0.47	5.21	0.205	7.6	0.30	0.8	0.03	2.0	0.08
3/16	11.9	0.47	5.84	0.230	8.4	0.33	0.8	0.03	1.5	0.06
1/4	13.5	0.53	6.60	0.260	9.1	0.36	0.8	0.03	1.3	0.05
5/16	15.0	0.59	7.37	0.290	10.7	0.42	1.3	0.05	2.3	0.09
5/16	15.0	0.59	7.37	0.290	7.9	0.31	—	—	1.5	0.06
3/8	19.1	0.75	9.40	0.370	12.7	0.50	0.8	0.03	1.3	0.05
7/16	20.6	0.81	10.54	0.415	13.5	0.53	1.3	0.05	0.8	0.03
1/2	23.1	0.91	11.43	0.450	13.5	0.53	0.8	0.03	1.5	0.06
5/8	26.9	1.06	13.34	0.525	16.3	0.64	1.3	0.05	1.5	0.06
3/4	31.8	1.25	15.75	0.620	19.8	0.78	1.3	0.05	2.0	0.08

a Dryseal American Standard Taper Pipe Thread. See General Specifications.
b Where SAE Short Pipe Thread is authorized by purchaser, dimensions L, L2, L3, L5, L7, L11, L14, N, P, S, S1, S2, and S3 are reduced in accordance with reduction of pipe thread length. See SAE J476, Tables 3 and 4.
c Tap drill depths given require use of bottoming taps to produce standard full thread length. For increased tap clearance, see Internal Taper Pipe Threads in General Specifications.
d Class 3B minor diameter limits apply to copper alloy fittings and Class 2B minor diameter limits apply to steel fittings.
e End full thread is measured from face of cone seat to last full form thread of major diameter, see Appendix A. A minimum of 3/4 partial thread beyond the last full form thread is required.
f For steel parts, the Y1 dimension shall be 8.9 mm (0.35 in) for 3/16 in tube size and 13.2 mm (0.52 in) for 3/8 in tube size.

TABLE 6A—DIMENSIONS OF SPECIAL SIZE CONNECTORS (FIGURE 5A) AND ELBOWS (FIGURE 6A)

Nom Tube OD in	A Dryseal Taper Thread NPTF[1] in	B Nom Thread Size in Class 2B int[4]	C Nom in	D Dia Drill mm	D Dia Drill in	D_1 Dia Drill mm	D_1 Dia Drill in
1/4	1/4	7/16-24	9/16	4.78	0.188	4.78	0.188
3/8	1/8	5/8 -18	3/4	7.14	0.281	5.56	0.219
3/8	3/8	5/8 -18	3/4	7.14	0.281	7.92	0.312
1/2	1/4	3/4 -18	29/32	10.31	0.406	7.14	0.281
1/2	1/2	3/4 -18	29/32	10.31	0.406	10.31	0.406
5/8	3/8	7/8 -18	1- 1/16	13.49	0.531	11.10	0.437
3/4	1/2	1-1/16-16	1- 1/4	15.82	0.625	13.49	0.531

Nom Tube OD in	D_4 Dia Drill mm	D_4 Dia Drill in	D_5 Dia Drill mm	D_5 Dia Drill in	L[2] +0.8 −0.0 mm	L[2] +0.03 −0.00 in	L_3[2] +0.8 −0.0 mm	L_3[2] +0.03 −0.00 in
1/4	7.92	0.312	8.74	0.344	22.4	0.88	27.7	1.09
3/8	5.56	0.219	—	—	22.4	0.88	28.4	1.12
3/8	10.31	0.406	11.10	0.437	25.4	1.00	33.3	1.31
1/2	8.74	0.344	—	—	26.9	1.06	37.1	1.46
1/2	14.27	0.562	12.70	0.500	31.8	1.25	42.2	1.66
5/8	10.31	0.406	11.91	0.469	28.4	1.12	41.1	1.62
3/4	14.27	0.562	—	—	35.1	1.38	50.8	2.00

Nom Tube OD in	L_4 mm	L_4 in	M mm	M in	P(2)(3) mm	P(2)(3) in	P_1(2)(3) mm	P_1(2)(3) in	S(2)(7) mm	S(2)(7) in
1/4	14.2	0.56	7.1	0.28	14.2	0.56	14.2	0.56	11.2	0.44
3/8	19.1	0.75	13.5	0.53	9.7	0.38	9.7	0.38	9.7	0.38
3/8	21.3	0.84	12.7	0.50	14.2	0.56	14.2	0.56	10.4	0.41
1/2	22.4	0.88	15.0	0.59	14.2	0.56	14.2	0.56	11.2	0.44
1/2	27.7	1.09	16.8	0.66	19.0	0.75	19.1	0.75	15.7	0.62
5/8	28.2	1.11	19.0	0.75	14.2	0.56	14.2	0.56	11.2	0.44
3/4	33.0	1.30	21.6	0.85	19.0	0.75	19.1	0.75	11.9	0.47

Nom Tube OD in	S_1[2] mm	S_1[2] in	X mm	X in	Y +0.25 −0.00 mm	Y +0.010 −0.000 in	Z Min mm	Z Min in
1/4	6.10	0.240	14.2	0.56	6.98	0.275	0.8	0.03
3/8	—	—	19.0	0.75	9.40	0.370	—	—
3/8	11.10	0.437	19.0	0.75	9.40	0.370	1.3	0.05
1/2	—	—	23.1	0.91	11.43	0.450	—	—
1/2	15.88	0.625	23.1	0.91	11.43	0.450	—	—
5/8	3.96	0.156	26.9	1.06	13.34	0.525	1.3	0.05
3/4	—	—	31.8	1.25	15.75	0.620	—	—

a Dryseal American Standard Taper Pipe Thread. See General Specifications.
b Where SAE Short Pipe Thread is authorized by purchaser, dimensions L, L2, L3, L5, L7, L11, L14, N, P, S, S1, S2, and S3 are reduced in accordance with reduction of pipe thread length. See SAE J476, Tables 3 and 4.
c Tap drill depths given require use of bottoming taps to produce standard full thread length. For increased tap clearance, see Internal Taper Pipe Threads in General Specifications.
d Class 3B minor diameter limits apply to copper alloy fittings and Class 2B minor diameter limits apply to steel fittings.
e Measured from end containing the largest passage.

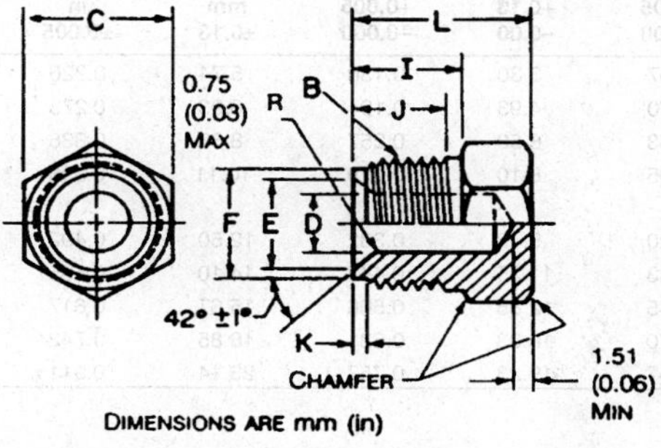

FIGURE 8—INVERTED FLARE PLUGS (040109)

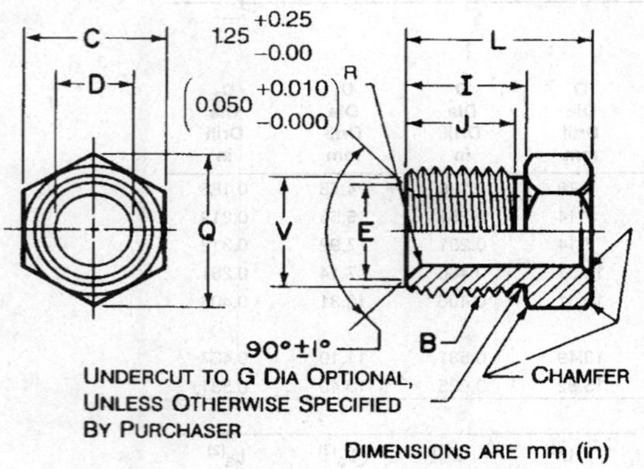

90°±1°
UNDERCUT TO G DIA OPTIONAL, UNLESS OTHERWISE SPECIFIED BY PURCHASER
CHAMFER
DIMENSIONS ARE mm (in)

FIGURE 9—INVERTED FLARE NUTS (040110)

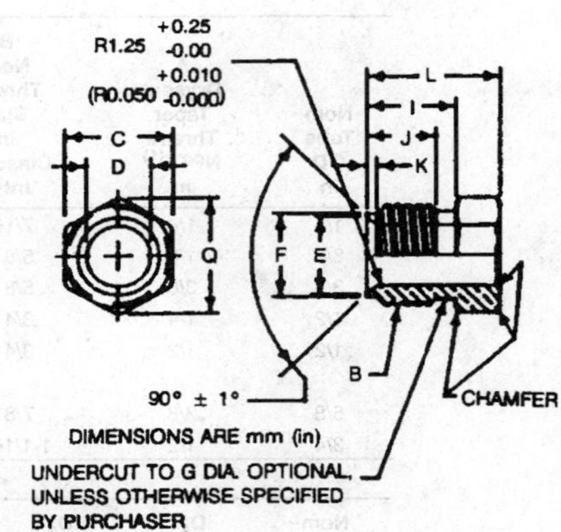

FIGURE 9A—INVERTED FLARE NUTS (040110) OPTIONAL FOR SINGLE FLARED TUBING

TABLE 7—DIMENSIONS OF PLUGS (FIGURE 8)

Nom Tube OD in	B Nom Thread Size in Class 2A Ext	C Hex Nom in	D Dia mm ±0.13	D Dia in ±0.005	E Dia mm ±0.13	E Dia in ±0.005	F Dia mm +0.00 –0.13	F Dia in +0.000 –0.005
3/16	3/8 -24	3/8	4.77	0.188	6.05	0.238	7.37	0.290
1/4	7/16-24	7/16	4.77	0.188	7.65	0.301	9.02	0.355
5/16	1/2 -20	1/2	6.35	0.250	9.22	0.363	10.59	0.417
3/8	5/8 -18	5/8	7.92	0.312	11.46	0.451	12.89	0.507
7/16	11/16-18	11/16	9.52	0.375	13.08	0.515	14.73	0.580
1/2	3/4 -18	3/4	11.10	0.437	14.63	0.576	16.26	0.640
5/8	7/8 -18	7/8	14.27	0.562	17.81	0.701	19.58	0.771
3/4	1- 1/16-16	1- 1/16	16.66	0.656	22.10	0.870	23.80	0.937

Nom Tube OD in	I mm	I in	J Full Thread Min mm	J Full Thread Min in	K mm	K in	L mm	L in
3/16	8.6	0.34	7.1	0.28	1.0	0.04	13.5	0.53
1/4	8.6	0.34	7.1	0.28	1.0	0.04	13.7	0.54
5/16	9.7	0.38	7.9	0.31	1.5	0.06	15.0	0.59
3/8	10.4	0.41	8.4	0.33	1.5	0.06	16.8	0.66
7/16	12.7	0.50	9.9	0.39	1.5	0.06	19.1	0.75
1/2	12.7	0.50	10.4	0.41	1.5	0.06	20.6	0.81
5/8	12.7	0.50	10.9	0.43	1.5	0.06	22.4	0.88
3/4	15.5	0.61	12.7	0.50	2.0	0.08	24.1	0.95

TABLE 8—DIMENSIONS OF NUTS (FIGURE 9)

Nom Tube OD in	B Nom Thread Size in Class 2A Ext	C[(2)] mm +0.13 –0.00	C[(2)] in +0.005 –0.000	D[(3)] Dia mm +0.13 –0.00	D[(3)] Dia in +0.005 –0.000	E Dia mm ±0.13	E Dia in ±0.005	F Dia mm +0.00 –0.13	F Dia in +0.000 –0.005	G Dia mm +0.00 –0.13	G Dia in +0.000 –0.005
1/8	5/16-28	7.80	0.307	3.30	0.130	5.74	0.226	6.60	0.260	6.58	0.259
3/16	3/8 -24	9.40	0.370	4.93	0.194	6.93	0.273	7.37	0.290	7.95	0.313
1/4	7/16-24	11.00	0.433	6.53	0.257	8.53	0.336	9.07	0.355	9.53	0.375
5/16	1/2 -20	12.57	0.495	8.10	0.319	10.11	0.398	10.59	0.417	10.85	0.427
1-3/8	5/8 -18	15.75	0.620	9.70	0.382	12.50	0.492	12.39	0.507	13.79	0.543
7/16	11/16-18	17.35	0.683	11.25	0.443	14.10	0.555	14.73	0.580	15.37	0.605
1/2	3/4 -18	18.92	0.745	12.85	0.506	15.67	0.617	16.26	0.640	16.97	0.668
5/8	7/8 -18	22.10	0.870	16.03	0.631	18.85	0.742	19.58	0.771	20.14	0.793
3/4	1- 1/16-16	26.85	1.057	19.23	0.757	23.14	0.911	23.80	0.937	24.66	0.971

TABLE 8—DIMENSIONS OF NUTS (FIGURE 9) (CONTINUED)

Nom Tube OD in	I mm	I in	J Full Thread Min mm	J Full Thread Min in	K mm	K in	L mm	L in	Q Min mm	Q Min in	V mm +0.00 −0.038	V in +0.000 −0.015
1/8	8.1	0.32	6.6	0.26	1.0	0.04	13.2	0.52	8.81	0.347	6.63	0.261
3/16	9.1	0.36	7.6	0.30	1.0	0.04	14.2	0.56	10.62	0.418	8.03	0.316
1/4	9.1	0.36	7.6	0.30	1.0	0.04	14.2	0.56	12.40	0.488	9.60	0.378
5/16	10.2	0.40	8.1	0.32	1.5	0.06	15.7	0.62	14.10	0.555	10.92	0.430
3/8	10.2	0.40	8.1	0.32	1.5	0.06	16.8	0.66	17.81	0.701	13.92	0.548
7/16	11.2	0.44	8.6	0.34	1.5	0.06	17.3	0.68	19.61	0.772	15.49	0.610
1/2	11.7	0.46	9.1	0.36	1.5	0.06	18.8	0.74	21.39	0.842	17.09	0.673
5/8	12.2	0.48	9.7	0.38	1.5	0.06	20.3	0.80	24.71	0.973	20.27	0.798
3/4	13.7	0.54	11.2	0.44	2.0	0.08	22.4	0.88	30.30	1.193	24.79	0.976

TABLE 8A—WRENCHING TEST REQUIREMENTS

Nom Tube OD in	Torque Requirements for Steel Nuts N-m	Torque Requirements for Steel Nuts lb-in	Wrench Opening Max mm	Wrench Opening Max in
1/8	6.8	60	8.18	0.322
3/16	13.6	120	9.75	0.384
1/4	16.9	150	11.33	0.446
5/16	20.3	180	12.95	0.510
3/8	23.7	210	16.15	0.636
7/16	33.9	300	17.76	0.699
1/2	45.2	400	19.38	0.763
5/8	56.5	500	22.56	0.888
3/4	73.4	650	27.36	1.077

TABLE 9A—DIMENSIONS OF TYPE A INVERTED FLARED TUBE SEAT INSERTS AND SEAT DETAIL[1] FIGURES 10 AND 11)

Nom Tube OD in	B Nom Thread Size in Class 2B Int.	D Dia Min mm	D Dia Min in	D Dia Max mm	D Dia Max in	D_1 Dia mm +0.08 −0.05	D_1 Dia in +0.003 −0.002	E Dia mm +0.00 −0.10	E Dia in +0.000 −0.004
1/8	5/16-28	1.91	0.075	2.06	0.081	4.09	0.161	2.74	0.108
3/16	3/8 -24	3.10	0.122	3.25	0.128	5.41	0.213	3.94	0.155
1/4	7/16-24	4.67	0.184	4.83	0.190	6.91	0.272	5.54	0.218
5/16	1/2 -20	5.46	0.215	5.61	0.221	7.67	0.302	7.11	0.280
3/8	5/8 -18	7.06	0.278	7.21	0.284	9.12	0.359	8.79	0.346
7/16	11/16-18	8.64	0.340	8.79	0.346	10.72	0.422	10.39	0.409
1/2	3/4 -18	10.24	0.403	10.39	0.409	12.29	0.484	11.96	0.471
5/8	7/8 -18	13.41	0.528	13.56	0.534	15.88	0.625	15.14	0.596
3/4	1- 1/16-16	15.77	0.621	15.98	0.629	19.05	0.750	17.98	0.708

Nom Tube OD in	F Dia mm +0.00 −0.13	F Dia in +0.000 −0.005	H Min mm	H Min in	H Max mm	H Max in	I mm +0.00 −0.10	I in +0.000 −0.004
1/8	6.71	0.264	0.38	0.015	0.51	0.020	3.71	0.146
3/16	8.15	0.321	0.38	0.015	0.51	0.020	3.84	0.151
1/4	9.73	0.383	0.38	0.015	0.51	0.020	3.84	0.151
5/16	11.05	0.435	0.64	0.025	0.76	0.030	4.22	0.166
3/8	14.10	0.554	0.76	0.030	0.89	0.035	5.00	0.197
7/16	16.65	0.616	0.76	0.030	0.89	0.035	5.00	0.197
1/2	17.25	0.679	0.89	0.035	1.14	0.045	5.49	0.216
5/8	29.42	0.804	0.89	0.035	1.14	0.045	5.99	0.236
3/4	24.97	0.983	1.14	0.045	1.40	0.055	7.24	0.285

TABLE 9A—DIMENSIONS OF TYPE A INVERTED FLARED TUBE SEAT INSERTS AND SEAT DETAILa (Continued)

Nom Tube OD in	J Full Thread Min mm	J Full Thread Min in	K Ref mm	K Ref in	L mm	L in	O Dia mm +0.00 −0.08	O Dia in +0.000 −0.003	P mm ±0.13	P in ±0.005
1/8	5.44	0.214	4.75	0.187	7.1	0.28	4.09	0.161	8.26	0.325
3/16	5.72	0.225	5.16	0.203	7.6	0.30	5.41	0.213	8.84	0.348
1/4	5.72	0.225	5.16	0.203	8.1	0.32	6.91	0.272	8.84	0.348
5/16	6.55	0.258	5.94	0.234	8.4	0.33	7.67	0.302	9.96	0.392
3/8	7.34	0.289	6.76	0.266	9.6	0.38	9.12	0.359	11.56	0.455
7/16	8.13	0.320	7.52	0.296	9.9	0.39	10.72	0.422	12.29	0.484
1/2	8.53	0.336	7.93	0.312	10.2	0.40	12.29	0.484	13.18	0.519
5/8	8.92	0.351	8.33	0.328	11.7	0.46	15.88	0.625	14.10	0.555
3/4	10.52	0.414	9.12	0.359	13.7	0.54	19.05	0.750	16.13	0.635

Nom Tube OD in	Q Dia mm +0.000 −0.064	Q Dia in +0.0000 −0.0025	R Radius mm	R Radius in	S Min mm	S Min in	U Dia Min mm	U Dia Min in	U Dia Max mm	U Dia Max in
1/8	4.242	0.1670	0.15	0.006	12.7	0.50	8.1	0.32	8.6	0.34
3/16	5.563	0.2190	0.15	0.006	13.7	0.54	9.9	0.39	10.4	0.41
1/4	7.061	0.2780	0.79	0.031	14.2	0.56	11.4	0.45	11.9	0.47
5/16	7.823	0.3080	0.79	0.031	15.0	0.59	13.0	0.51	13.5	0.53
3/8	9.271	0.3650	0.79	0.031	17.3	0.68	16.3	0.64	17.0	0.67
7/16	10.871	0.4280	0.79	0.031	18.3	0.72	17.8	0.70	18.5	0.73
1/2	12.446	0.4900	0.79	0.031	19.0	0.75	19.6	0.77	20.3	0.80
5/8	16.027	0.6310	0.79	0.031	20.8	0.82	22.6	0.89	23.4	0.92
3/4	19.202	0.7560	0.79	0.031	23.6	0.93	27.4	1.08	28.2	1.11

a Type A seat inserts are intended for general purpose applications in cast or malleable iron and steel. Where standard inserts are assembled into other materials, modifications of seat may be necessary to assure proper installation.

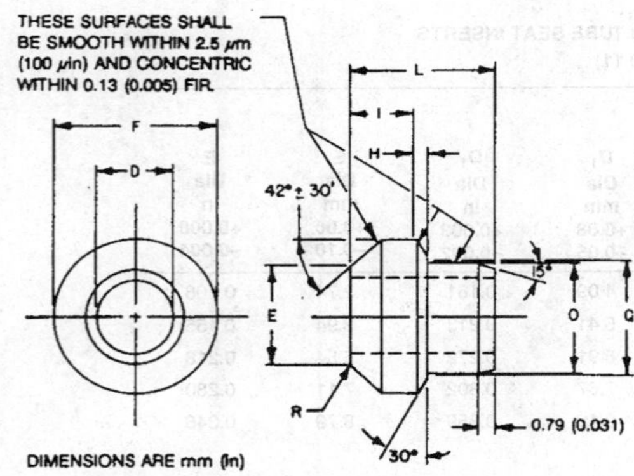

FIGURE 10—SEAT INSERT (040141)

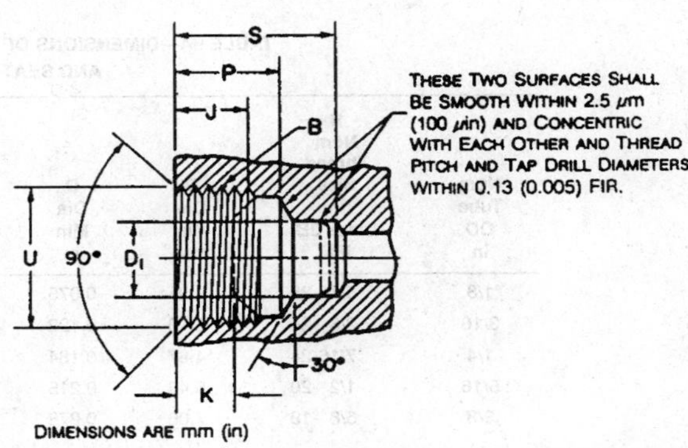

FIGURE 11—DETAIL OF SEAT ASSEMBLY

TABLE 9B—DIMENSIONS OF TYPE B INVERTED FLARED TUBE SEAT INSERTS AND SEAT DETAIL(1) (FIGURES 10 AND 11)

Nom Tube OD in	B Nom Thread Size in Class 2B Int.	D Dia mm +0.18 −0.00	D Dia in +0.007 −0.000	D_1 Dia mm ±0.03	D_1 Dia in ±0.001	E(2) Dia mm +0.00 ±0.10	E(2) Dia in +0.000 ±0.004	F Dia Max mm	F Dia Max in
3/16	3/8 -24	2.74	0.108	4.80	0.189	3.28	0.129	8.05	0.317
1/4	7/16-24	2.74	0.108	4.80	0.189	4.85	0.191	9.65	0.380

Nom Tube OD in	F Dia Min mm	F Dia Min in	H Dia mm +0.20 −0.00	H Dia in +0.008 −0.000	I mm +0.00 −0.00	I in +0.000 −0.004	J Full Thread Min mm	J Full Thread Min in
3/16	7.80	0.307	0.43	0.017	4.70	0.185	8.48	0.334
1/4	9.14	0.360	0.84	0.033	5.46	0.215	9.91	0.390

TABLE 9B—DIMENSIONS OF TYPE B INVERTED FLARED TUBE SEAT INSERTS AND SEAT DETAILa (Figures 10 and 11) (Continued)

Nom Tube OD in	K Max mm	K Max in	K Min mm	K Min in	L mm	L in	O Dia mm +0.00 –0.10	O Dia in +0.000 –0.004
3/16	6.20	0.244	5.69	0.224	8.6	0.34	4.85	0.191
1/4	6.60	0.260	5.84	0.230	9.9	0.39	4.85	0.191

Nom Tube OD in	P mm	P in	Q Dia mm +0.00 –0.05	Q Dia in +0.000 –0.002	R Radius mm ±0.03	R Radius in ±0.001	S Min mm	S Min in	U Dia Max mm	U Dia Max in
3/16	10.31	0.406	4.95	0.195	0.79	0.031	15.62	0.615	11.10	0.437
1/4	11.94	0.470	4.95	0.195	0.79	0.031	17.27	0.680	12.70	0.500

a Type B seat inserts are used extensively in cast or malleable iron and steel components of hydraulic brake systems. Where standard inserts are assembled into other materials, modifications of seat may be necessary to assure proper installation.
b On Type B inserts, E diameter defines center of R radius.

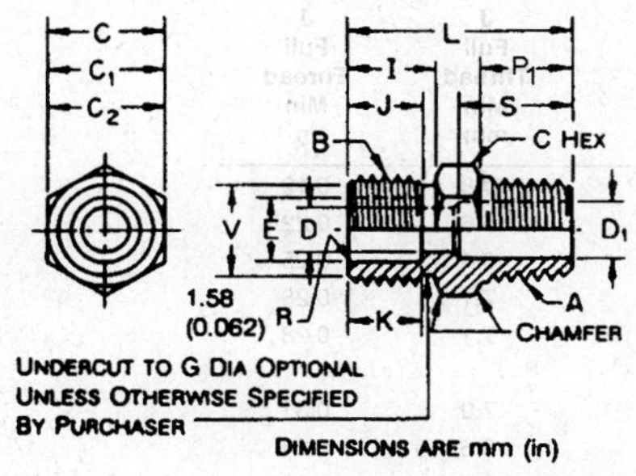

FIGURE 12A (060102)

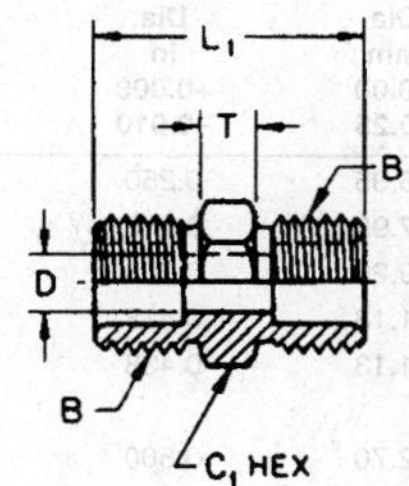

FIGURE 12B (060101)

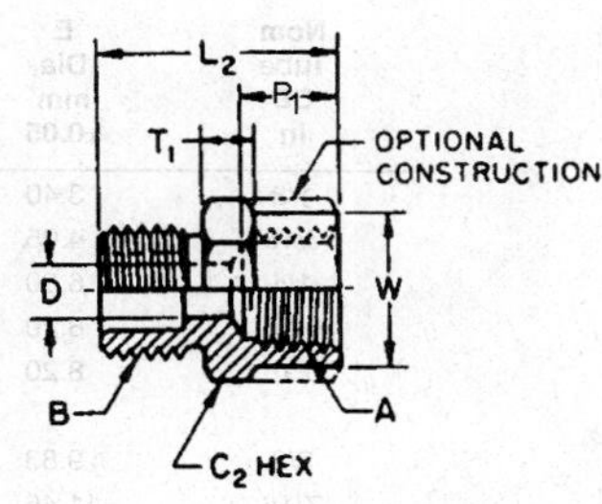

FIGURE 12C (060103)

FIGURE 12—CONNECTORS AND UNIONS

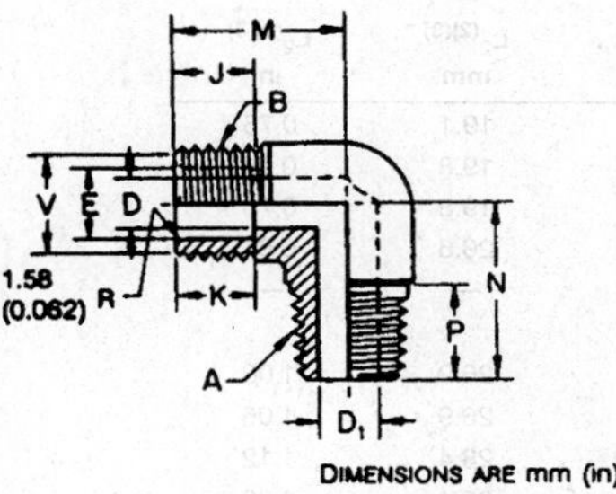

FIGURE 13A (060202)

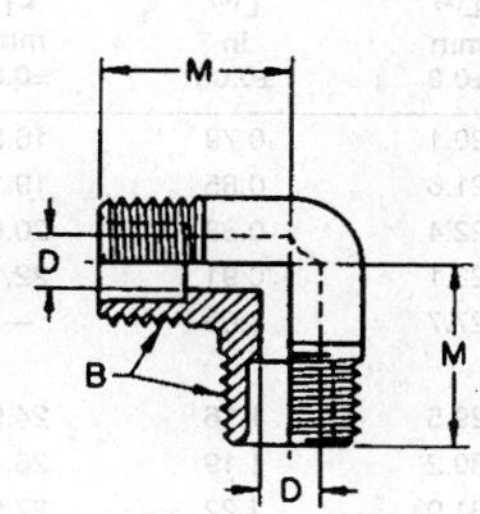

FIGURE 13B (060201)

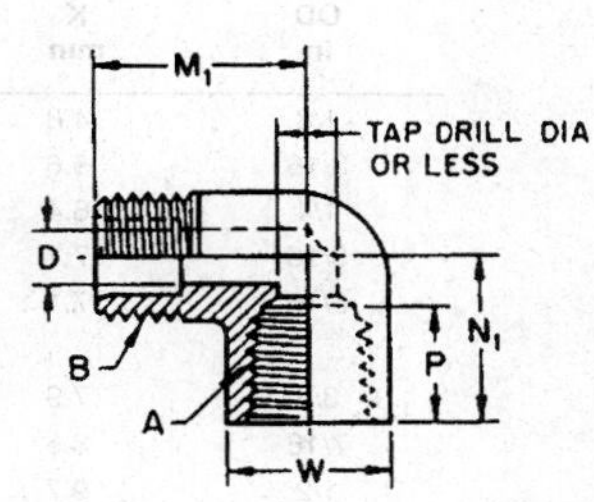

FIGURE 13C (060203)

FIGURE 13—ELBOWS

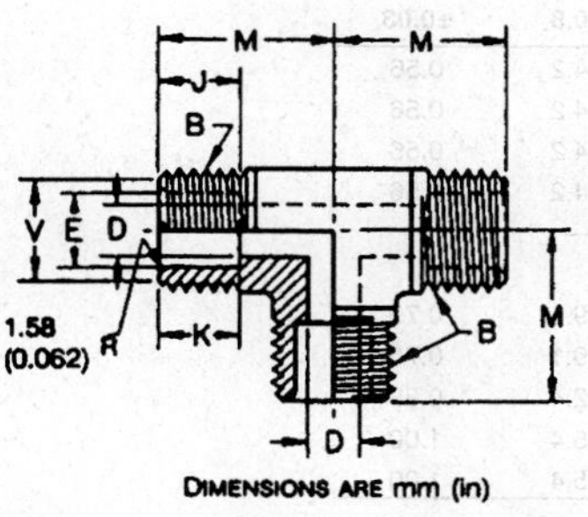

FIGURE 14A (060401)

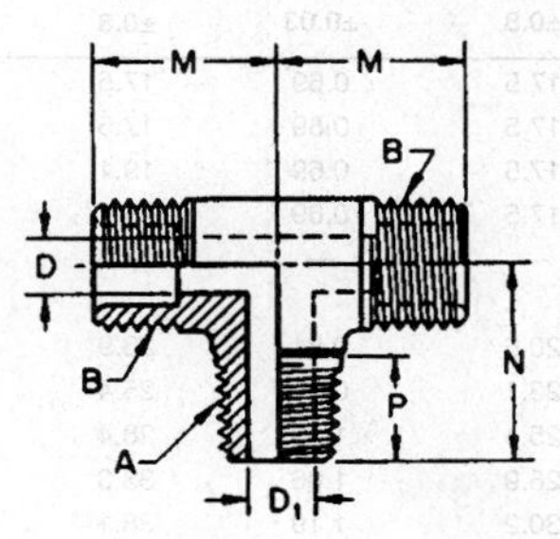

FIGURE 14B (060425)

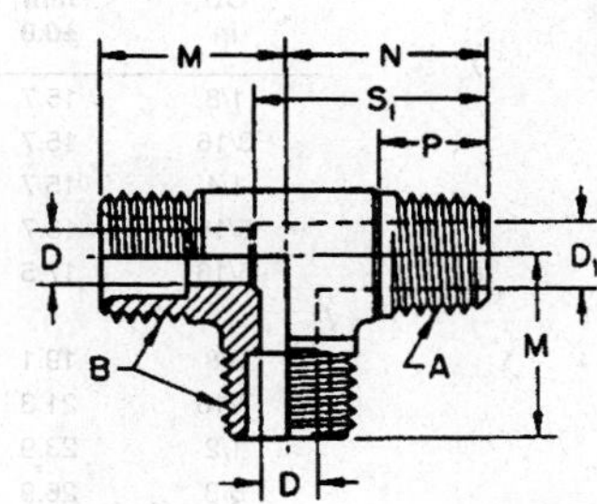

FIGURE 14C (060424)

FIGURE 14—TEES

NOTES—UNSPECIFIED DETAIL WITH RESPECT TO DIMENSIONS, TOLERANCES, CONTOURS, MATERIAL, WORKMANSHIP, ETC., MUST CONFORM TO GENERAL SPECIFICATIONS FOR AUTOMOTIVE TUBE FITTINGS. THE DIMENSIONAL DESIGNATIONS ON THE FIRST FIGURE IN EACH GROUP SHALL APPLY TO ALL OTHER FIGURES IN THAT GROUP EXCEPT AS SHOWN OTHERWISE. CODES SHOWN IN BRACKETS ADJACENT TO FIGURE NUMBERS REPRESENT RESPECTIVE FITTING IDENTIFICATION IN ACCORDANCE WITH SAE J846.

TABLE 10—DIMENSIONS OF CONNECTORS, UNIONS, ELBOWS, AND TEES (FIGURES 12A TO 14C)

Nom Tube OD in	A Dryseal Taper Thread NPTF(1) in	B Nom Thread Size in Class 2A Ext	C Nom in	C_1 Nom in	C_2 Nom in	D(5) Dia Drill mm	D(5) Dia Drill in	D_1(5) Dia Drill mm	D_1(5) Dia Drill in
3/16	1/8	3/8 -24	7/16	3/8	9/16	3.17	0.125	5.56	0.219
1/4	1/8	7/16-24	7/16	7/16	9/16	4.77	0.188	5.56	0.219
5/16	1/8	1/2 -24	1/2	1/2	9/16	6.35	0.250	5.94	0.234
5/16	1/4	1/2 -24	9/16	—	—	6.35	0.250	7.92	0.312
3/8	1/4	9/16-24	9/16	9/16	11/16	7.92	0.312	8.74	0.344
7/16	1/4	5/8 -24	5/8	5/8	11/16	7.92	0.312	8.74	0.344
1/2	3/8	11/16-20	11/16	11/16	13/16	10.31	0.406	10.31	0.406
5/8	1/2	13/16-18	7/8	13/16	1	12.70	0.500	14.27	0.562
3/4	1/2	1 -18	1	1	1	14.27	0.562	14.27	0.562

Nom Tube OD in	E Dia mm ±0.05	E Dia in ±0.002	G(4) Dia mm +0.00 −0.25	G(4) Dia in +0.000 −0.010	I mm	I in	J Full Thread Min mm	J Full Thread Min in
1/8	3.40	0.134	6.35	0.250	6.4	0.25	4.8	0.19
3/16	4.95	0.195	7.95	0.313	7.1	0.28	5.6	0.22
1/4	6.60	0.260	9.25	0.364	7.9	0.31	6.4	0.25
5/16	8.20	0.323	11.13	0.438	8.6	0.34	7.1	0.28
5/16	8.20	0.323	11.13	0.438	8.6	0.34	7.1	0.28
3/8	9.83	0.387	12.70	0.500	9.7	0.38	7.9	0.31
7/16	11.46	0.451	14.30	0.563	10.4	0.41	8.6	0.34
1/2	13.11	0.516	15.60	0.614	11.2	0.44	9.7	0.38
5/8	16.36	0.644	18.54	0.730	12.7	0.50	11.2	0.44
3/4	19.61	0.772	23.32	0.918	14.2	0.56	12.7	0.50

Nom Tube OD in	K mm	K in	L(2) mm ±0.8	L(2) in ±0.03	L_1 mm ±0.8	L_1 in ±0.03	L_2(2)(3) mm	L_2(2)(3) in
1/8	4.8	0.19	20.1	0.79	16.8	0.66	19.1	0.75
3/16	5.6	0.22	21.6	0.85	19.1	0.75	19.8	0.78
1/4	6.4	0.25	22.4	0.88	20.6	0.81	19.8	0.78
5/16	7.1	0.28	23.1	0.91	22.1	0.87	20.6	0.81
5/16	7.1	0.28	27.7	1.09	—	—	—	—
3/8	7.9	0.31	29.5	1.16	24.9	0.98	26.9	1.06
7/16	8.6	0.34	30.2	1.19	26.4	1.04	26.9	1.06
1/2	9.7	0.38	31.0	1.22	27.9	1.10	28.4	1.12
5/8	9.7	0.38	38.1	1.50	31.8	1.25	35.1	1.38
3/4	11.2	0.44	41.1	1.62	36.3	1.43	38.1	1.50

Nom Tube OD in	M mm ±0.8	M in ±0.03	M_1 mm ±0.8	M_1 in ±0.03	N(2) mm ±0.8	N(2) in ±0.03	N_1(2)(3) mm ±0.8	N_1(2)(3) in ±0.03
1/8	15.7	0.62	17.5	0.69	17.5	0.69	14.2	0.56
3/16	15.7	0.62	17.5	0.69	17.5	0.69	14.2	0.56
1/4	15.7	0.62	17.5	0.69	19.1	0.75	14.2	0.56
5/16	15.7	0.62	17.5	0.69	19.1	0.75	14.2	0.56
5/16	17.5	0.69	—	—	21.3	0.84	—	
3/8	19.1	0.75	20.6	0.81	23.9	0.94	19.1	0.75
7/16	21.3	0.84	23.1	0.91	25.4	1.00	19.1	0.75
1/2	23.9	0.94	25.4	1.00	28.4	1.12	22.4	0.88
5/8	26.9	1.06	26.9	1.06	33.3	1.31	25.4	1.00
3/4	30.2	1.19	30.2	1.19	38.1	1.50	25.4	1.00

TABLE 10—DIMENSIONS OF CONNECTORS, UNIONS, ELBOWS, AND TEES (FIGURES 12A TO 14C) (CONTINUED)

Nom Tube OD in	P[2][3] Min mm	P[2][3] Min in	P_1[2][3] mm	P_1[2][3] in	S[2][5] Max mm	S[2][5] Max in	S_1[2][5] Min mm	S_1[2][5] Min in	T[6] Ref mm	T[6] Ref in
1/8	9.7	0.38	9.7	0.38	11.7	0.46	19.8	0.78	3.8	0.15
3/16	9.7	0.38	9.7	0.38	12.2	0.48	20.1	0.79	4.6	0.18
1/4	9.7	0.38	9.7	0.38	12.2	0.48	22.6	0.89	4.6	0.18
5/16	9.7	0.38	9.7	0.38	10.7	0.42	20.1	0.79	4.6	0.18
5/16	14.2	0.56	14.2	0.56	16.8	0.66	25.6	1.01	4.6	0.18
3/8	14.2	0.56	14.2	0.56	17.0	0.67	29.0	1.14	5.3	0.21
7/16	14.2	0.56	14.2	0.56	17.0	0.67	30.5	1.20	5.3	0.21
1/2	14.2	0.56	14.2	0.56	—	—	—	—	5.3	0.21
5/8	19.1	0.75	19.1	0.75	22.4	0.88	40.6	1.60	6.1	0.24
3/4	19.1	0.75	19.1	0.75	—	—	—	—	7.6	0.30

Nom Tube OD in	T_1 Min mm	T_1 Min in	V Dia mm +0.0 −0.5	V Dia in +0.00 −0.02	W[7] mm +0.0 −0.5	W[7] in +0.00 −0.02
1/8	5.3	0.21	6.3	0.25	14.2	0.56
3/16	5.3	0.21	7.9	0.31	14.2	0.56
1/4	6.1	0.24	9.7	0.38	14.2	0.56
5/16	6.1	0.24	11.2	0.44	14.2	0.56
5/16	—	—	11.2	0.44	—	—
3/8	7.6	0.30	12.7	0.50	17.5	0.69
7/16	7.6	0.30	14.2	0.56	17.5	0.69
1/2	9.4	0.37	15.7	0.62	20.6	0.81
5/8	10.9	0.43	18.5	0.73	25.4	1.00
3/4	10.9	0.43	23.4	0.92	25.4	1.00

a Dryseal American Standard Taper Pipe Thread. See General Specifications.
b Where SAE Short Pipe Thread is authorized by purchaser, dimensions, L, L2, N, N1, P, S, and S1 are reduced in accordance with reduction of pipe thread length. See SAE J476, Tables 3 and 4.
c Tap drill depths given require use of bottoming taps to produce standard full thread length. For increased tap clearance, see Internal Taper Pipe Threads in General Specifications.
d Where thread relief undercut is used, the last thread shall be chamfered to 1/2 to 1 pitch long from G diameter.
e At manufacturer's option, through passages in fittings shown in Figures 12A and 14C may conform with smaller diameter specified or the appropriate end may be counterbored to larger diameter for depths defined by S or S1, respectively.
f Minimum design thickness, not subject to inspection.
g Basic dimensions shown shall apply as minimum diameter or across flats for bosses. The -0.5 mm (−0.02 in) tolerance shall apply only to chamfer diameter on full hexagon version of fitting in Figure 12C.

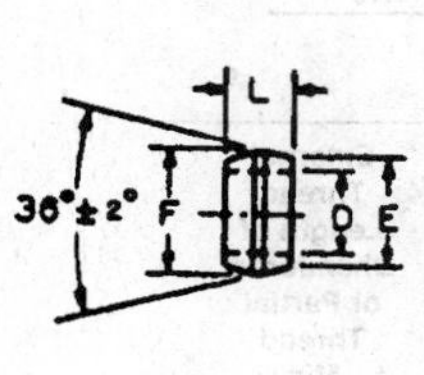

FIGURE 15—TAPERED SLEEVES (060115)

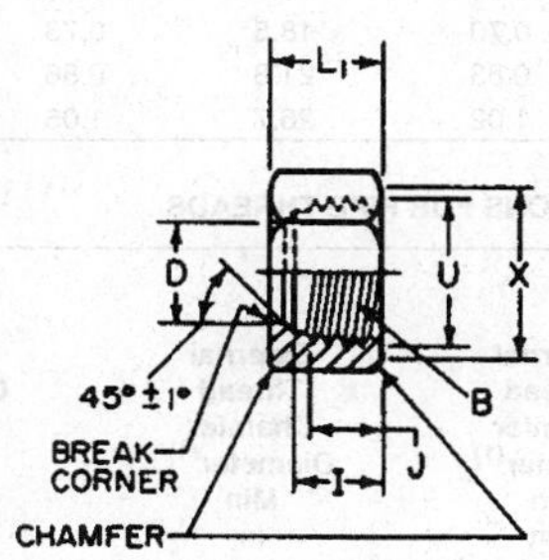

FIGURE 16—SHORT NUTS (060110)

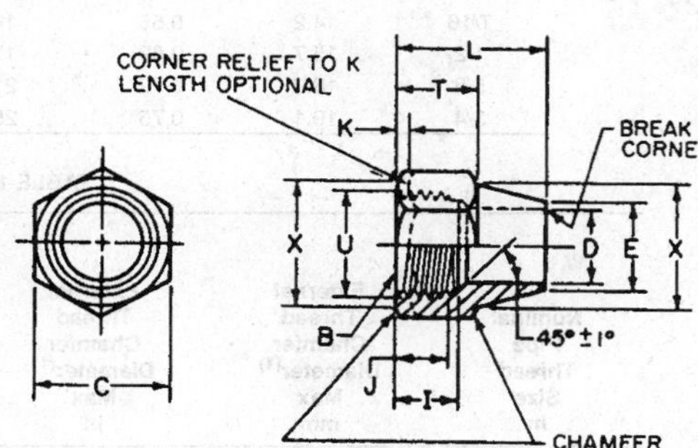

FIGURE 17—LONG NUTS (060111)

TABLE 11—DIMENSIONS OF TAPERED SLEEVES (FIGURE 15)

Nom Tube OD in	D Dia mm ±0.05	D Dia in ±0.002	E Dia mm ±0.08	E Dia in ±0.003	F Dia mm	F Dia in	L mm	L in
1/8	3.30	0.130	3.51	0.138	4.8	0.19	4.8	0.19
3/16	4.88	0.192	5.11	0.201	6.9	0.27	5.6	0.22
1/4	6.48	0.255	6.76	0.266	8.6	0.34	6.4	0.25
5/16	8.08	0.318	8.36	0.329	10.4	0.41	6.4	0.25
3/8	9.70	0.382	9.98	0.393	11.9	0.47	6.4	0.25
7/16	11.28	0.444	11.61	0.457	13.5	0.53	7.9	0.31
1/2	12.88	0.507	13.26	0.522	15.0	0.59	9.7	0.38
5/8	16.05	0.632	16.51	0.650	18.3	0.72	9.7	0.38
3/4	19.25	0.758	19.76	0.778	22.4	0.88	11.2	0.44

TABLE 12—DIMENSIONS OF SHORT AND LONG NUTS (FIGURES 16 AND 17)

Nom Tube OD in	B Straight Thread Nom Size in Class 2B Int	C Hex in Nom	D Dia mm ±0.05	D Dia in ±0.002	E Dia mm	E Dia in	I mm +0.00 −0.25	I in +0.000 −0.010
1/8	5/16-24	3/8	3.30	0.130	6.4	0.25	6.4	0.25
3/16	3/8 -24	7/16	4.88	0.192	7.9	0.31	7.1	0.28
1/4	7/16-24	1/2	6.48	0.255	9.7	0.38	7.9	0.31
5/16	1/2 -24	9/16	8.08	0.318	11.2	0.44	7.9	0.31
3/8	9/16-24	5/8	9.70	0.382	12.7	0.50	8.6	0.34
7/16	5/8 -24	11/16	11.28	0.444	14.2	0.56	9.4	0.37
1/2	11/16-20	13/16	12.88	0.507	15.7	0.62	12.4	0.49
5/8	13/16-18	15/16	16.05	0.632	19.1	0.75	12.7	0.50
3/4	1 -18	1- 3/16	19.25	0.758	22.4	0.88	13.5	0.53

Nom Tube OD in	J Full Thread Min mm	J Full Thread Min in	K mm	K in	L mm	L in	L_1 mm	L_1 in
1/8	4.6	0.18	2.3	0.09	12.7	0.50	9.7	0.38
3/16	5.3	0.21	2.3	0.09	15.7	0.62	10.4	0.41
1/4	5.8	0.23	3.0	0.12	19.1	0.75	11.2	0.44
5/16	5.8	0.23	3.0	0.12	21.3	0.84	11.2	0.44
3/8	6.4	0.25	3.0	0.12	24.6	0.97	11.9	0.47
7/16	6.9	0.27	3.0	0.12	26.2	1.03	12.7	0.50
1/2	9.9	0.39	3.0	0.12	26.9	1.06	15.7	0.62
5/8	9.9	0.39	3.0	0.12	30.2	1.19	15.7	0.62
3/4	10.7	0.42	3.0	0.12	35.1	1.38	17.5	0.69

Nom Tube OD in	T mm	T in	U Dia Min mm	U Dia Min in	U Dia Max mm	U Dia Max in	X Dia mm	X Dia in
1/8	6.4	0.25	8.4	0.33	8.9	0.35	9.7	0.38
3/16	7.1	0.28	9.9	0.39	10.4	0.41	11.2	0.44
1/4	9.7	0.38	11.4	0.45	11.9	0.47	12.7	0.50
5/16	11.2	0.44	13.0	0.51	13.5	0.53	14.2	0.56
3/8	12.7	0.50	14.7	0.58	15.2	0.60	15.7	0.62
7/16	14.2	0.56	16.3	0.64	16.8	0.66	17.5	0.69
1/2	15.7	0.62	17.8	0.70	18.5	0.73	20.6	0.81
5/8	18.3	0.72	21.1	0.83	21.8	0.86	23.9	0.94
3/4	19.1	0.75	25.9	1.02	26.7	1.05	30.2	1.19

TABLE 13—DIMENSIONS FOR PIPE THREADS

Nominal Pipe Thread Size in	External Thread Chamfer Diameter(1) Max mm	External Thread Chamfer Diameter(1) Max in	External Thread Chamfer Diameter(1) Min mm	External Thread Chamfer Diameter(1) Min in	External Thread Length of Chamfered or Partial Thread Min mm	External Thread Length of Chamfered or Partial Thread Min in
1/8	8.1	0.32	7.6	0.30	0.94	0.037
1/4	10.7	0.42	10.2	0.40	1.42	0.056
3/8	14.0	0.55	13.5	0.53	1.42	0.056
1/2	17.3	0.68	16.8	0.66	1.80	0.071
3/4	22.6	0.89	22.1	0.87	1.80	0.071
1	28.4	1.12	27.7	1.09	2.21	0.087

Nominal Pipe Thread Size in	External Thread Length of Chamfered or Partial Thread Max mm	External Thread Length of Chamfered or Partial Thread Max in	Internal Thread Countersink Diameter(1) Min mm	Internal Thread Countersink Diameter(1) Min in	Internal Thread Countersink Diameter(1) Min mm	Internal Thread Countersink Diameter(1) Min in
1/8	1.40	0.055	10.7	0.42	11.2	0.44
1/4	2.13	0.084	14.0	0.55	14.5	0.57
3/8	2.13	0.084	17.5	0.69	18.0	0.71
1/2	2.72	0.107	21.6	0.85	22.1	0.87
3/4	2.72	0.107	26.9	1.06	27.4	1.08
1	3.30	0.130	34.0	1.34	34.8	1.37

1. Tabulated diameters conform with Appendix A, SAE J476.

APPENDIX A
GAGES AND GAGING FOR INVERTED FLARED TYPE FITTINGS

A.1 General—The information contained herein is intended to provide and promote the use of uniform gaging practices for determining conformance of inverted flared type tube fittings with the specifications given in the standard.

Gaging of Cone Seats:

Depth of Face—Proper location of the face of the cone seat relative to the face of the fitting shall be determined by use of the step limit gage depicted in Figure A1. One-half of the top surface of body of this gage shall be machined and/or ground 0.38 mm (0.015 in) below the balance of surface to provide a low limit step. The gage pin shall have a minimum diameter equal to "E max" (see Table 4) and shall be of a length equivalent to the sum of the height of the high-limit side of gage body plus "K min" (see Table 4). The opposite faces of gage body and ends of gage pin shall be flat, smooth, parallel, and square with the axis of pin. The fit between gage pin and gage body shall be such that the pin alignment is maintained yet free to move, of its own weight, within the gage body. All gage components should be made from steel suitably hardened to assure adequate service life.

When this gage is placed on the face of fitting, in line with the axis of seat and with gage pin contacting face of seat, the top of gage pin must not protrude above the high limit nor be below the low limit top surfaces of the gage body for fitting to be acceptable.

Gaging of Internal Threads:

Size and Form—Conformance of internal threads with the dimensions specified shall be determined in accordance with standard thread gaging procedures.

Full Form Thread DepthæSuitability of the relationship between the last full form thread to the face of the cone seat shall be determined by use of the gage depicted in Figure A2. This gage shall have external threads, conforming in all respects with the corresponding GO thread plug gage for the respective thread size, of a minimum length equal to "K min" (see Table 4) plus one pitch (thread) and shall have the partial thread at starting end removed. Use of a thread relief undercut beyond a length equal to "K min" shall be permissible. The gage pin hole at starting end shall be suitably counterbored to clear the fitting cone seat to a depth equivalent to 1-1/2 pitches (threads). The length of the gage pin shall be equivalent to the overall length of the body of gage plus the difference between "J max" (see Table 4) and 1/2 pitch (thread). All other features of gage body, gage pin, fit, and material shall be as specified for the gage in Figure A1.

When this gage is assembled by hand into the fitting as far as the thread will permit, with pin contacting face of cone seat, the top of the gage pin must be flush with or protrude above the top surface of the gage body for fitting to be acceptable.

Concentricity Gage and Gaging:

Cone Seat Concentricity—Conformance with specified limitations on concentricity of cone seats with respect to thread pitch cylinder shall be checked by the use of functional gages of the type described herein and depicted in Figure A3, or equivalent means.

The gage consists of a body or frame providing a means for mounting a dial indicator gage in such a manner that it can be actuated through a rotating pin on the opposite end of which is a machined stylus designed to ride on the conical surface of the seat. The gage is centered on the threads of the fitting by means of an interchangeable male threaded gage insert. The threads on the insert shall conform in all respects with the corresponding GO thread plug gage for the respective thread size and the length of full form thread shall be equivalent to K min (see Table 3) plus one pitch (thread). The entering end of gage insert shall have a pilot of length equal to one pitch (thread) and diameter which will clear the minor diameter of the seat threads. The first thread beyond the pilot shall be chamfered or the partial portion shall be removed. Use of a thread relief undercut beyond a length equivalent to K min shall be permissible. The fit between the stylus extension pin and the hole through gage body and threaded gage insert shall be such that pin will move freely yet be retained in alignment. Fitting manufacturers may be consulted with regard to details of existing gages.

The fitting to be inspected shall be gaged in accordance with the following procedure:

1. The threaded end of gage shall be assembled by hand into the seat on the fitting as far as the thread will permit.
2. The indicator gage shall be zeroed and the stylus then rotated slowly through a complete 360 degree revolution by twisting the knurled collar through the finger notches in gage body.
3. The total runout indicated throughout the rotation of stylus shall be read and recorded. It shall not exceed 0.142 mm (0.0056 in) for the fitting to be acceptable. (The measured deviation is in a plane perpendicular to the plane of the cone seat. The concentricity variation, therefore, may be determined from Table A1, or by multiplying the dial indicator reading by the tangent of 42 degrees, or 0.90040.)

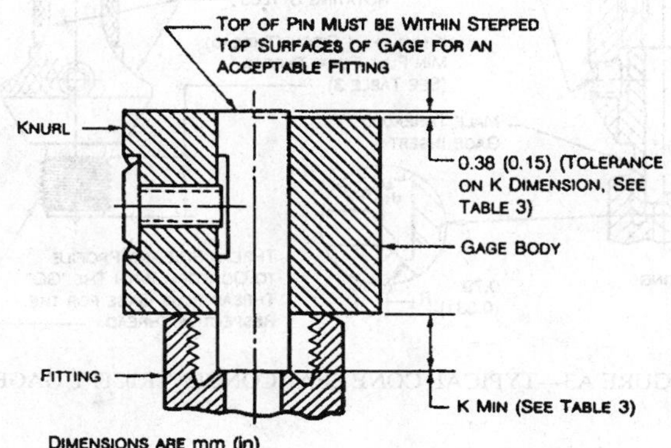

FIGURE A1—FLUSH PIN GAGE FOR CHECKING LOCATION OF FACE OF CONE SEAT

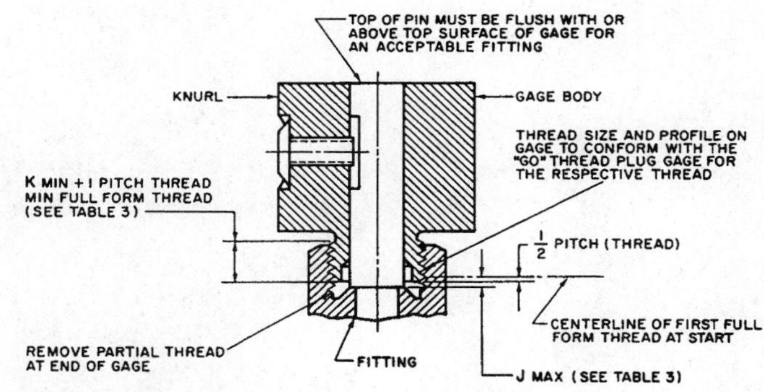

FIGURE A2—FLUSH PIN GAGE FOR CHECKING RELATION OF END OF FULL THREAD WITH FACE OF CONE SEAT

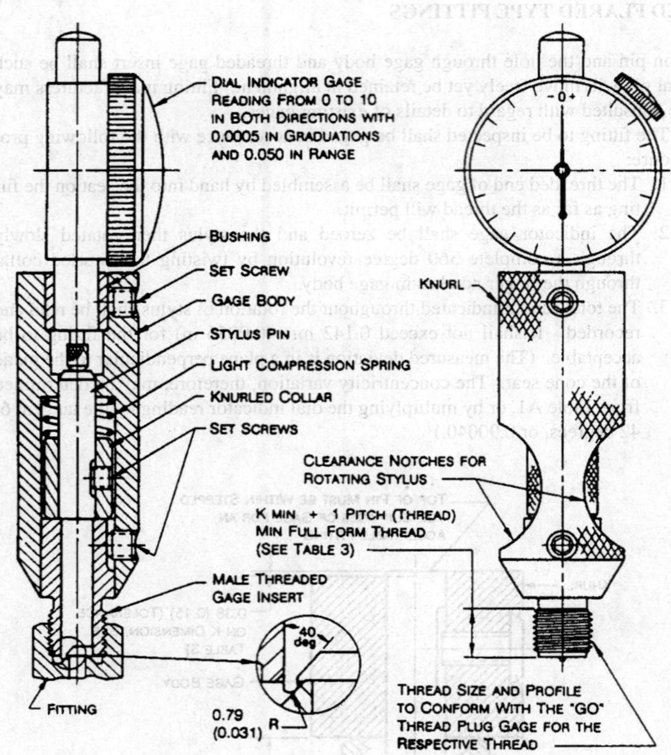

FIGURE A3—TYPICAL CONE SEAT CONCENTRICITY GAGE

TABLE A1—CONCENTRICITY

Dial Reading mm 3 Pl.	Dial Reading in	Concentricity mm 4 Pl.	Concentricity in
0.013	0.0005	0.0114	0.00045
0.025	0.0010	0.0229	0.00090
0.038	0.0015	0.0343	0.00135
0.051	0.0020	0.0457	0.00180
0.064	0.0025	0.0572	0.00225
0.076	0.0030	0.0686	0.00270
0.089	0.0035	0.0800	0.00315
0.102	0.0040	0.0914	0.00360
0.114	0.0045	0.1029	0.00405
0.127	0.0050	0.1143	0.00450
0.140	0.0055	0.1257	0.00495
0.152	0.0060	0.1372	0.00540

SPHERICAL AND FLANGED SLEEVE (COMPRESSION) TUBE FITTINGS—SAE J246 FEB2000

SAE Standard

Report of the SAE Tube, Pipe, Hose, and Lubrication Fittings Committee approved May 1971. Revised July 1977, editorial change March 1981. Completely revised by theSAE Fluid Conductors Technical Committee June 1990. Revised by the SAE Fluid Conductors and Connectors Technical Committee SC1—Automotive and Hydraulic Tube and Fittings April 1991 and June 1992. Revised by the SAE Fluid Conductors and Connectors Technical Committee June 1993. Rationale statement available. Revised by the SAE Fluid Conductors and Connectors Technical Committee May 1994, May 1995, January 1996, August 1997, and February 2000. Rationale statement available.

1. Scope—This SAE Standard covers complete general and dimensional specifications for tube fittings of the spherical and flanged sleeve compression types for use in the piping of air brake systems on automotive vehicles. The spherical sleeve compression type Figures 1A to 5 and Tables 1 to 3 is intended for use with annealed copper alloy tubing per SAE J1149, Type 1. The flanged sleeve compression type Figures 6A to 11 and Tables 4 to 6 is intended for use with nylon tubing per SAE J844. It is not intended to restrict or preclude other designs of a tube fitting for use with SAE J844, air brake tubing. Performance requirements for SAE J844 are covered in SAE J1131. See SAE J1131 for the Performance Requirements of Reusable (Push to Connect) Fittings Intended for Use in Automotive Air Brake Systems.

CAUTION—To assure satisfactory performance, tapered sleeve compression type fitting components (SAE J512) should not be intermixed with the spherical or flanged sleeve components, nor should the spherical sleeve compression type components be intermixed with the flanged sleeve compression type components when assembling connection in areas where the three types are available.

2. References

2.1 Applicable Publications—The following publications form a part of this specification to the extent specified herein. Unless otherwise indicated, the latest issue of SAE publications shall apply.

2.1.1 SAE PUBLICATIONS—Available from SAE, 400 Commonwealth Drive, Warrendale, PA 15096-0001.

SAE J476—Dryseal Pipe Threads
SAE J512—Automotive Tube Fittings
SAE J844—Nonmetallic Air Brake System Tubing
SAE J846—Coding Systems for Identification of Fluid Conductors and Connectors
SAE J1131—Performance Requirements for SAE J844 Nonmetallic Tubing and Fitting Assemblies Used in Automotive Air Brake Systems
SAE J1149—Metallic Air Brake System Tubing and Pipe

2.1.2 ANSI PUBLICATION—Available from ANSI, 11 West 42nd Street, New York, NY 10036-8002.

ANSI/ASME B1.1-1989—Unified Inch Screw Thread (UN and UNR)

2.1.3 ASTM PUBLICATIONS—Available from ASTM, 100 Barr Harbor Drive, West Conshohocken, PA 19428-2959.

ASTM B 117—Method of Salt Spray (Fog) Testing
FMVSS 106—Brake Hoses

3. General Specifications—The following general specifications supplement the dimensional data contained in Tables 1 to 8 with respect to all unspecified details.

3.1 Identification—At manufacturer's option, or where so specified by the purchaser, the fittings, except sleeves, may be permanently and legibly marked air brake. The nut shall be permanently and legibly marked according to the current U.S. Department of Transportation FMVSS 106 Regulation (NHTSA). The location of such markings shall be optional with manufacturer.

3.2 Size Designations—Fitting sizes are designated by the corresponding nominal outside diameter of the tubing for the various sizes of tube ends and by the corresponding standard nominal pipe size for pipe thread ends.

3.3 Dimensions and Tolerances—Except for nominal size and thread specifications, dimensions and tolerances are given in both SI units and U.S. customary as designated. Tabulated dimensions shall apply to the finished parts. The maximum and minimum across flat dimensions shall be within the commercial tolerance of bar or extruded stock from which the fittings are produced. The minimum across corners dimensions of hexagons shall be 1.092 times the nominal width across flats, but shall not result in a side flat width less than 0.43 times the nominal width across flats.

Unless otherwise specified, tolerance on hole diameters designated "drill" in the dimensional tables shall be as tabulated in Table 9.

Tolerance on all dimensions not otherwise specified shall be ±0.25 mm (±0.010 in). Tube seat diameters E shall be concentric with straight thread pitch diameters within 0.25 mm (0.010 in) full indicator reading (FIR). Large seat diameters F shall be concentric with tube seat diameters E within 0.13 mm (0.005 in) full indicator reading (FIR). The surface of tube stop at base of seat shall be flat and perpendicular to the axis of thread. Angular tolerance on axis of ends of elbows and tees shall be ±2.50 degrees for sizes up to and including 3/8 in, and ±1.50 degrees for sizes larger than 3/8 in.

Where so illustrated, hexagon corners shall be chamfered 30 degrees ± 5 degrees to a diameter equal to the nominal width across flats, with a tolerance of -0.41 mm (-0.016 in); or, where design permits, corners may be chamfered to the diameter of the abutting surface, provided the length of chamfer does not exceed that produced by the 30 degree chamfer previously described.

3.4 Passages—Where passages in straight fittings are machined from opposite ends, the offset at the meeting point shall not exceed 0.38 mm (0.015 in). The cross-sectional area at the junction of passages in angle fittings shall not be less than that of the smallest passage. At manufacturer's option, all passages in a particular fitting may conform with the smallest diameter specified for that fitting. Where the passage is specified as tap drill diameter or less, the minimum shall be no less than the minimum diameter of the smallest passage in the fitting.

3.5 Wall Thickness—Unless otherwise designated, the wall thickness at any point on fittings shall not be less than the thickness established by the specified dimensions, tolerances, and eccentricities for inner and outer surfaces.

3.6 Contour—Details of contour shall be optional with manufacturer, provided the tabulated dimensions are maintained and serviceability of the fittings is not impaired. Wrench flats on elbows and tees shall be optional. Where extruded and forged shapes are reduced to conserve material, the wall thickness, unless otherwise specified, shall not be less than the respective minimum values tabulated in Table 10.

3.7 Straight Threads—Unified standard Class 2A external and Class 2B internal threads shall apply to plain finish (unplated) fittings of all types. For internally threaded parts with additive finish, the Class 2B diameters shall apply after plating.

The pitch diameter tolerance shall be the same as the corresponding diameter-pitch combination and class of the Unified 18 and 20 thread series or for special diameter-pitch combinations shall be based on diameter, pitch, and a length of engagement of nine times the pitch. See ANSI B1.1.

For convenient reference, the data generally required to specify threads are given in Table 7. (Inasmuch as threads are normally produced and gaged with equipment made to the inch system of measurement, conversion of size designations and dimensions to SI units is considered unnecessary.)

Where external threads are produced by roll threading and the body is not undercut, the unthreaded portion of body adjacent to the shoulder may be reduced to the minimum pitch diameter.

External threads shall be chamfered to the diameters specified to produce a length of chamfered or partial thread equivalent to 1/4 to 1-1/4 times the pitch (rounded to a three-place decimal).

Internal threads shall be countersunk 90 degrees included angle to the diameters specified.

3.8 Thread Eccentricity Tolerances—The various thread elements of Class 2A external and Class 2B internal straight threads on tube fittings shall be concentric within the limitations specified in the General Specifications of SAE J512.

3.9 Pipe Threads—Taper pipe threads, unless there is specific authorization to the contrary, shall conform to the Dryseal American Standard Taper Pipe Thread (NPTF). Specifications for pipe threads are given in detail in SAE J476.

The length of full form external thread shall not be shorter than L2 plus one pitch (thread), except that where thread is cut through into a relieved body or undercut on the fitting, the minimum full threaded length may be reduced by one pitch (thread).

Where external pipe threads are produced by roll threading, the diameter of the unthreaded portion of shank adjacent to shoulder may be reduced to the E2 basic pitch diameter.

TABLE 1A—DIMENSIONS OF CONNECTORS, UNIONS, ELBOWS, AND TEES (FIGURES 1A TO 3E)

Nom Tube OD, in	Aa Dryseal Taper Thread in	B, Nom Thread Size, in Class 2A Ext.	C Nom, in	C_1 Nom, in	C_2 Nom, in	D Dia Drill mm	D Dia Drill in	D_1 Dia Drill mm	D_1 Dia Drill in	E Dia mm +0.10 −0.00	E Dia in +0.004 −0.000	F Dia mm +0.10 −0.00	F Dia in +0.004 −0.000	Gb Dia mm +0.00 −0.25	Gb Dia in +0.000 −0.010
1/4	1/8	7/16-24	7/16	7/16	9/16	4.78	0.188	4.78	0.188	6.45	0.254	7.90	0.311	9.96	0.392
5/16	1/8	1/2 -24	1/2	1/2	9/16	6.35	0.250	4.78	0.188	8.08	0.318	9.60	0.378	9.96	0.454
3/8	1/4	17/32-24	9/16	9/16	11/16	7.92	0.312	7.92	0.312	9.70	0.382	11.38	0.448	12.34	0.486
1/2	3/8	11/16-20	11/16	11/16	7/8	10.31	0.406	10.31	0.406	12.88	0.507	14.66	0.577	16.08	0.633
5/8	1/2	13/16-18	7/8	13/16	1- 1/16	13.49	0.531	13.49	0.531	16.05	0.632	18.01	0.709	19.10	0.752
3/4	1/2	1 -18	1	1	1- 1/16	16.66	0.656	13.49	0.531	19.25	0.758	21.59	0.850	23.85	0.939
3/4	3/4	1 -18	1- 1/16	1- 1/4	1- 1/4	16.66	0.656	19.05	0.750	19.25	0.758	21.59	0.850	23.85	0.939
1	1	1- 1/4 -16	1- 3/8	1- 1/4	1- 5/8	22.22	0.875	22.22	0.875	25.60	1.008	28.50	1.122	30.02	1.182

Nom Tube OD, in	Ic mm	Ic in	J Full Thread Min mm	J Full Thread Min in	K mm	K in	L mm ±0.8	L in ±0.03	L_1 mm ±0.8	L_1 in ±0.03	L_2 mm ±0.8	L_2 in ±0.03	M mm ±0.8	M in ±0.03	M_1 mm ±0.8	M_1 in ±0.03
1/4	8.4	0.33	6.9	0.27	6.4	0.25	22.9	0.90	21.6	0.85	21.6	0.85	16.0	0.63	17.8	0.70
5/16	8.6	0.34	7.1	0.28	7.1	0.28	23.9	0.94	22.9	0.90	21.8	0.86	17.0	0.67	17.8	0.70
3/8	11.2	0.44	9.7	0.38	7.9	0.31	31.0	1.22	27.9	1.10	30.2	1.19	20.3	0.80	22.9	0.90
1/2	13.5	0.53	11.2	0.44	11.2	0.44	34.0	1.34	33.3	1.31	32.5	1.28	23.9	0.94	26.4	1.04
5/8	15.0	0.59	12.7	0.50	11.2	0.44	40.4	1.59	36.3	1.43	38.4	1.51	27.9	1.10	30.5	1.20
3/4	16.8	0.66	13.5	0.53	14.2	0.56	42.9	1.69	40.6	1.60	40.1	1.58	30.5	1.20	31.2	1.23
3/4	16.8	0.66	13.5	0.53	14.2	0.56	43.7	1.72	—	—	41.4	1.63	32.5	1.28	34.5	1.36
1	18.3	0.72	15.0	0.59	19.8	0.78	50.8	2.00	45.2	1.78	48.5	1.91	36.6	1.44	40.4	1.59

Nom Tube OD, in	M_2 mm ±0.8	M_2 in ±0.03	M_3 mm ±0.8	M_3 in ±0.03	N mm ±0.8	N in ±0.03	N_1 mm ±0.8	N_1 in ±0.03	N_2 mm ±0.8	N_2 in ±0.03	P min mm	P min in	P_1 mm	P_1 in	S Max mm	S Max in
1/4	12.7	0.50	16.0	0.63	17.0	0.67	13.7	0.54	16.3	0.64	9.7	0.38	9.7	0.38	—	—
5/16	13.7	0.54	17.0	0.67	17.8	0.70	14.5	0.57	16.3	0.64	9.7	0.38	9.7	0.38	11.4	0.45
3/8	18.3	0.72	20.3	0.80	23.6	0.93	19.8	0.78	21.8	0.86	14.2	0.56	14.2	0.56	—	—
1/2	21.6	0.85	23.9	0.94	25.4	1.00	21.1	0.83	24.1	0.95	14.2	0.56	14.2	0.56	æ	—
5/8	23.9	0.94	27.9	1.10	31.8	1.25	27.4	1.08	29.7	1.17	19.1	0.75	19.1	0.75	—	—
3/4	28.4	1.12	31.8	1.25	34.0	1.34	29.0	1.14	30.5	1.20	19.1	0.75	19.1	0.75	20.3	0.80
3/4	30.5	1.20	—	—	34.0	1.34	29.0	1.14	30.5	1.20	19.1	0.75	19.1	0.75	21.8	0.86
1	32.3	1.27	36.6	1.44	42.2	1.66	36.6	1.44	37.6	1.48	23.9	0.94	23.9	0.94	—	—

Nom Tube OD, in	S_1 Min mm	S_1 Min in	T[d] Ref mm	T[d] Ref in	T_1 Min mm	T_1 Min in	V Dia Max mm	V Dia Max in	V Dia Min mm	V Dia Min in	W[e] Forged or Bar Min mm +0.0−0.5	W[e] Forged or Bar Min in +0.00 −0.02
1/4	—	—	4.6	0.18	4.6	0.18	9.7	0.38	9.1	0.36	14.2	0.56
5/16	19.8	0.78	5.3	0.21	5.3	0.21	11.2	0.44	10.7	0.42	14.2	0.56
3/8	—	—	5.3	0.21	5.3	0.21	12.2	0.48	11.7	0.46	17.5	0.69
1/2	—	—	6.1	0.24	6.1	0.24	15.7	0.62	15.5	0.61	20.6	0.81
5/8	—	—	6.1	0.24	6.1	0.24	18.5	0.73	18.3	0.72	25.4	1.00
3/4	38.1	1.50	6.9	0.27	6.9	0.27	23.4	0.92	22.9	0.90	25.4	1.00
3/4	43.7	1.72	7.6	0.30	7.6	0.30	23.4	0.92	22.9	0.90	31.8	1.25
1	—	—	8.4	0.33	8.4	0.33	29.5	1.16	29.0	1.14	38.1	1.50

a Dryseal American Standard Taper Pipe Thread, except as noted in General Specifications.
b Where thread relief undercut is used, last thread shall be chamfered 1/2 to 1 pitch long from G diameter. Thread marks on surface of undercut shall be permissible.
c For elbows and tees, the L dimensions shown shall apply to turned or finished length. Where body is relieved beyond thread, length of turned boss L may be reduced to the minimum full thread length J.
d Minimum design thickness, not subject to inspection.
e Basic dimensions shown shall apply as min dia or across flats for bosses. The -0.5 mm (-0.02 in) tolerance shall apply only to chamfer on full hexagon version in Figure 1C.

TABLE 1B—DIMENSIONS OF SPECIAL SIZE FITTINGS,[b]
CONNECTORS, ELBOWS, AND TEES (FIGURES 1A, 1C, 2A, 2C, 2D, 3B, 3C, 3D, AND 3E)

Nom Tube OD, In	A[a] Dryseal Taper Thread, in	A^a_1 Dryseal Taper Thread, in	B, Nom Thread Size, in Class 2A Ext.	C Nom, in	C_2 Nom, in	L mm ±0.8	L in ±0.03	L_2 mm ±0.8	L_2 in ±0.03	M mm ±0.8	M in ±0.03	M_1 mm ±0.8	M_1 in ±0.03
1/4	1/4		7/16-24	9/16	11/16	28.2	1.11	27.4	1.08	17.5	0.69	20.1	0.79
1/4	3/8	1/8	7/16-24	11/16	7/8	29.0	1.14	27.4	1.08	18.8	0.74	21.3	0.84
1/4	1/2		7/16-24	7/8	1- 1/16	33.8	1.33	31.8	1.25	21.3	0.84	23.9	0.94
5/16	1/4		1/2 -24	9/16	11/16	28.4	1.12	27.7	1.09	17.8	0.70	20.3	0.80
5/16	3/8	1/8	1/2 -24	11/16	7/8	29.2	1.15	27.7	1.09	19.0	0.75	26.6	0.85
5/16	1/2		1/2 -24	7/8	1- 1/16	34.0	1.34	32.0	1.26	21.6	0.85	24.1	0.95
3/8	1/8		17/32-24	9/16	9/16	26.4	1.04	25.7	1.01	18.5	0.73	21.3	0.84
3/8	3/8	1/4	17/32-24	11/16	7/8	31.8	1.22	30.2	1.19	21.6	0.85	24.1	0.95
3/8	1/4	1/4	17/32-24	9/16	9/16	31.0	1.22	30.2	1.19	20.3	0.80	22.9	0.90
3/8	1/2		17/32-24	7/8	1- 1/16	36.6	1.44	34.5	1.36	24.1	0.95	26.7	1.05
1/2	1/8		11/16-20	11/16	11/16	29.5	1.16	27.9	1.10	20.3	0.80	23.1	0.91
1/2	1/4		11/16-20	11/16	11/16	34.0	1.34	32.5	1.28	22.1	0.87	24.6	0.97
1/2	3/8	1/4	11/16-20	11/16	7/8	34.0	1.34	32.5	1.28	23.9	0.94	26.4	1.04
1/2	1/2	3/8	11/16-20	7/8	1- 1/16	38.9	1.53	36.8	1.45	26.4	1.04	29.0	1.14
1/2	3/4		11/16-20	1- 1/16	1- 1/4	40.4	1.59	38.1	1.50	29.2	1.15	31.2	1.23
1/2	1		11/16-20	1- 3/8	1- 5/8	46.0	1.81	43.7	1.72	31.8	1.25	35.6	1.40
5/8	1/4		13/16-18	13/16	13/16	35.6	1.40	33.5	1.32	24.1	0.95	26.4	1.04
5/8	3/8	1/2	13/16-18	13/16	7/8	35.6	1.40	33.5	1.32	25.7	1.01	27.9	1.10
5/8	3/4		13/16-18	1- 1/16	1- 1/4	41.9	1.65	39.6	1.56	30.7	1.21	32.8	1.29
5/8	1		13/16-18	1- 3/8	1- 5/8	47.5	1.87	45.2	1.78	33.3	1.31	37.1	1.46
3/4	1/4		1 -18	1	1	38.1	1.50	35.3	1.39	26.7	1.05	27.2	1.07
3/4	3/8		1 -18	1	1	38.1	1.50	35.3	1.39	27.9	1.10	28.7	1.13
3/4	1		1 -18	1- 3/8	1- 5/8	49.3	1.94	47.0	1.85	35.1	1.38	38.9	1.53
1	1/2	3/4	1- 1/4 -16	1- 1/4	1- 1/4	46.0	1.81	43.7	1.72	30.5	1.20	34.0	1.34
1	3/4		1- 1/4 -16	1- 1/4	1- 1/4	46.0	1.81	43.7	1.72	33.3	1.31	37.1	1.46

Nom Tube OD, in	M_2 mm ±0.8	M_2 in ±0.03	N mm ±0.8	N in ±0.03	N_1 mm ±0.8	N_1 in ±0.03	N_2 mm ±0.8	N_2 in ±0.03	N_3 mm ±0.8	N_3 in ±0.03	We mm +0.0 −0.5	We in +0.00 −0.02
1/4	15.5	0.61	22.4	0.88	18.3	0.72	21.8	0.86			17.5	0.69
1/4	16.5	0.65	22.1	0.87	18.3	0.72	24.1	0.95	23.9	0.94	20.6	0.81
1/4	17.3	0.68	26.9	1.06	23.1	0.91	29.7	1.17			25.4	1.00
5/16	15.7	0.62	23.1	0.91	19.0	0.75	21.8	0.86			17.5	0.69
5/16	16.8	0.66	23.1	0.91	19.0	0.75	24.1	0.95	23.9	0.94	20.6	0.81
5/16	17.5	0.69	27.7	1.09	23.9	0.94	29.7	1.17			25.4	1.00
3/8	18.3	0.72	19.0	0.75	15.2	0.60	17.3	0.68			14.2	0.56
3/8	19.3	0.76	23.4	0.92	19.8	0.78	24.1	0.95	25.4	1.00	20.6	0.81
3/8	18.3	0.72	23.6	0.93	19.8	0.78	21.8	0.86	23.6	0.93	17.5	0.69
3/8	20.1	0.79	28.2	1.11	24.6	0.97	29.7	1.17			25.4	1.00
1/2	21.6	0.85	20.8	0.82	16.5	0.65	19.6	0.77			14.2	0.56
1/2	21.6	0.85	25.4	1.00	21.1	0.83	24.1	0.95			17.5	0.69
1/2	21.6	0.85	25.4	1.00	21.1	0.83	24.1	0.95	25.4	1.00	20.6	0.81
1/2	22.4	0.88	30.2	1.19	25.9	1.02	29.7	1.17	31.8	1.25	25.4	1.00
1/2	27.2	1.07	30.0	1.18	25.7	1.01	30.5	1.20			31.8	1.25
1/2	27.4	1.08	35.1	1.38	30.7	1.21	37.6	1.48			38.1	1.50
5/8	23.9	0.94	26.9	1.06	22.6	0.89	24.8	0.98			17.5	0.69
5/8	23.9	0.94	26.9	1.06	22.6	0.89	24.8	0.98	34.0	1.34	20.6	0.81
5/8	28.7	1.13	31.8	1.25	27.4	1.08	30.5	1.20			31.8	1.25
5/8	29.0	1.14	36.6	1.44	32.3	1.27	37.6	1.48			38.1	1.50
3/4	28.4	1.12	29.2	1.15	24.1	0.95	25.7	1.01			17.5	0.69
3/4	28.4	1.12	29.2	1.15	24.1	0.95	25.7	1.01			20.6	0.81
3/4	30.7	1.21	38.9	1.53	33.8	1.33	37.6	1.48			38.1	1.50
1	32.3	1.27	37.3	1.47	31.8	1.25	32.8	1.29	37.3	1.47	25.4	1.00
1	32.3	1.27	37.3	1.47	31.8	1.25	32.8	1.29			31.8	1.25

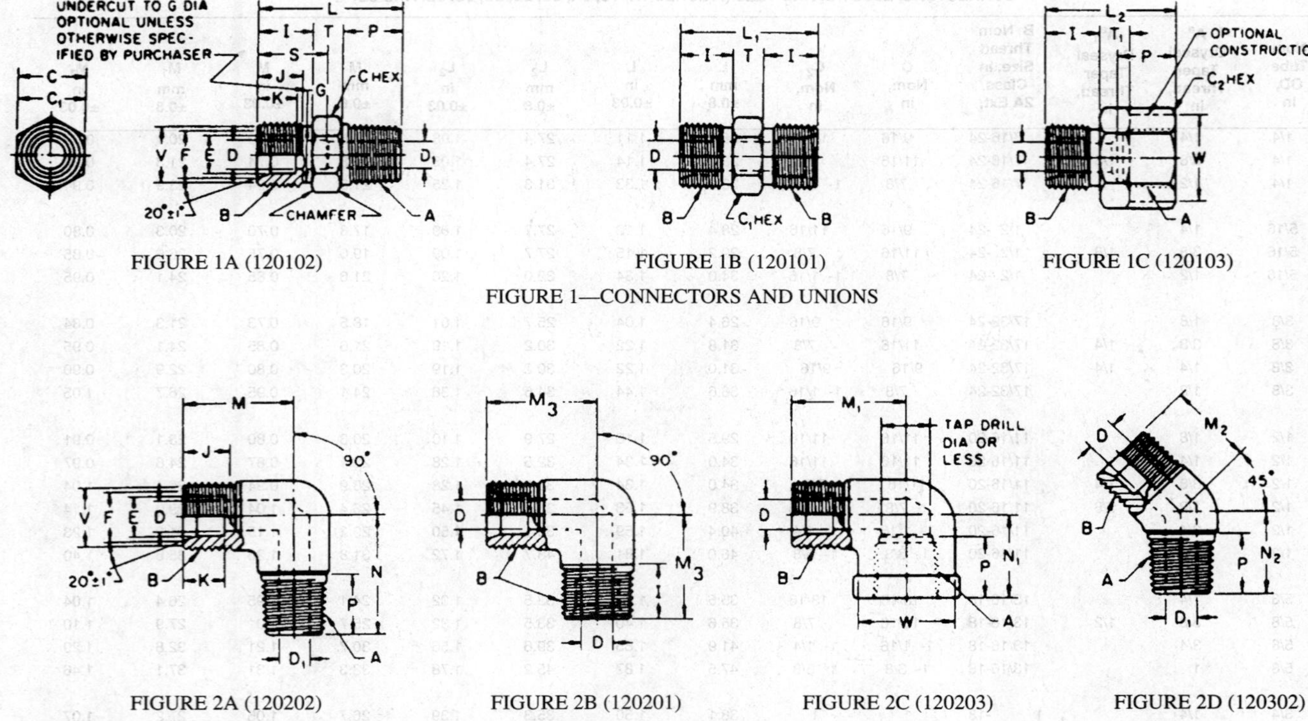

FIGURE 1A (120102)

FIGURE 1B (120101)

FIGURE 1C (120103)

FIGURE 1—CONNECTORS AND UNIONS

FIGURE 2A (120202)

FIGURE 2B (120201)

FIGURE 2C (120203)

FIGURE 2D (120302)

FIGURE 2—ELBOWS

NOTE—Unspecified detail with respect to dimensions, tolerances, contours, material, workmanship, etc., must conform to general specifications for spherical and flanged sleeve (compression) tube fittings. The dimensional designations on the first figure in each group shall apply to other figures in that group except as shown otherwise. Codes shown in brackets adjacent to figure numbers represent respective fitting identification in accordance with SAE J846.

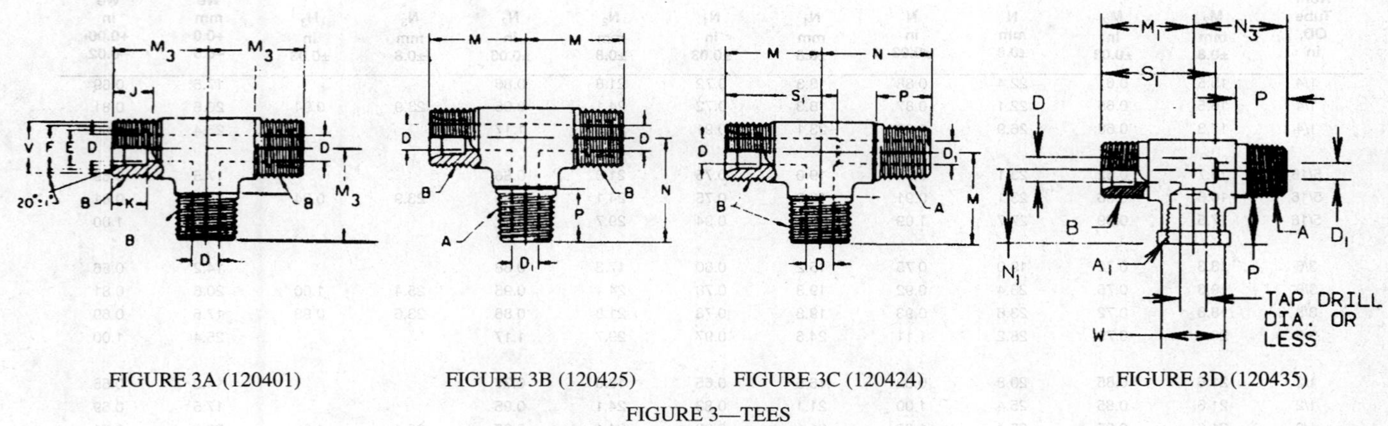

FIGURE 3A (120401)

FIGURE 3B (120425)

FIGURE 3C (120424)

FIGURE 3D (120435)

FIGURE 3—TEES

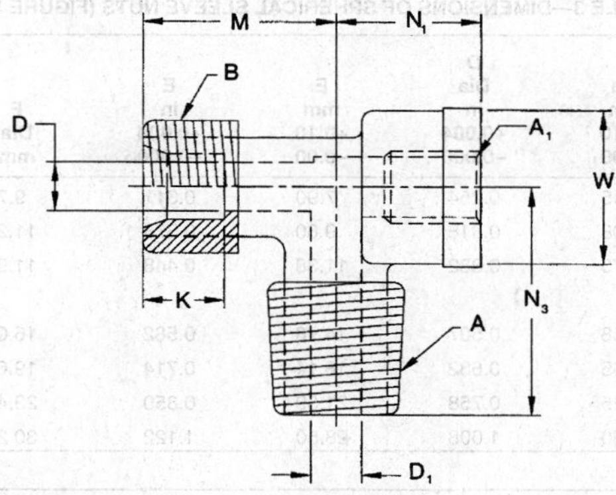

FIGURE 3E (120434)

NOTE—Unspecified detail with respect to dimensions, tolerances, contours, material, workmanship, etc., must conform to general specifications for spherical and flanged sleeve (compression) tube fittings. The dimensional designations on the first figure in each group shall apply to other figures in that group except as shown otherwise. Codes shown in brackets adjacent to figure numbers represent respective fitting identification in accordance with SAE J846.

FIGURES 1A THRU 3E

TABLE 2—DIMENSIONS OF SPHERICAL SLEEVES (FIGURE 4)

Nominal Tube OD, in	D Dia mm +0.10 –0.00	D Dia in +0.004 –0.000	F Dia mm +0.10 –0.00	F Dia in +0.004 –0.000	L mm ±0.13	L in ±0.005	R Radius mm +0.10 –0.00	R Radius in +0.004 –0.000
1/4	6.43	0.253	8.13	0.320	6.35	0.250	7.92	0.312
5/16	8.03	0.316	9.80	0.386	7.14	0.281	9.09	0.358
3/8	9.65	0.380	11.66	0.459	7.95	0.313	10.26	0.404
1/2	12.83	0.505	15.04	0.592	9.52	0.375	12.65	0.498
5/8	16.00	0.630	18.59	0.732	11.13	0.438	15.06	0.593
3/4	19.20	0.756	22.15	0.872	12.70	0.500	17.42	0.686
1	25.55	1.006	29.21	1.150	15.90	0.626	22.17	0.873

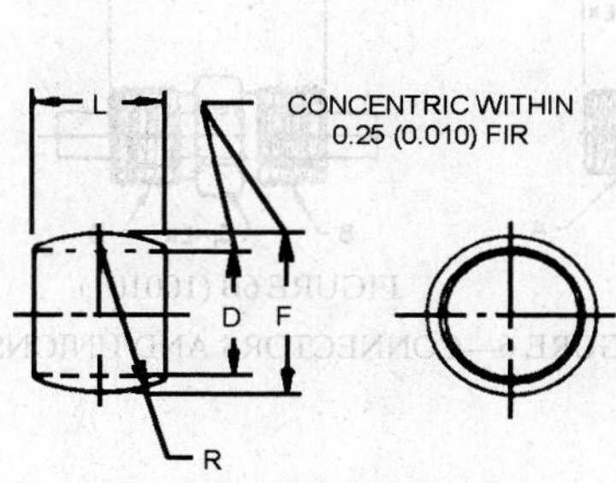

Note: Dimensions are mm (in)

NOTE—Unspecified detail with respect to dimensions, tolerances, contours, material, workmanship, etc., must conform to general specifications for spherical and flanged sleeve (compression) tube fittings. Codes shown in brackets adjacent to figure numbers represent respective fitting identification in accordance with SAE J846.

FIGURE 4—SPHERICAL SLEEVES (120115)

TABLE 3—DIMENSIONS OF SPHERICAL SLEEVE NUTS (FIGURE 5)

Nom Tube OD, in	B, Nom Thread Size, in Class 2B Int	C Nom, in	D Dia mm +0.10 −0.00	D Dia in +0.004 −0.000	E mm +0.10 −0.00	E in +0.004 −0.000	F Dia mm	F Dia in	I mm	I in
1/4	7/16-24	9/16	6.45	0.254	7.90	0.311	9.7	0.38	7.9	0.31
5/16	1/2 -24	5/8	8.08	0.318	9.60	0.378	11.2	0.44	7.9	0.31
3/8	17/32-24	5/8	9.70	0.382	11.38	0.448	11.9	0.47	10.4	0.41
1/2	11/16-20	13/16	12.88	0.507	14.78	0.582	16.0	0.63	12.7	0.50
5/8	13/16-18	15/16	16.05	0.632	18.14	0.714	19.6	0.77	14.2	0.56
3/4	1 -18	1- 1/8	19.25	0.758	21.59	0.850	23.4	0.92	15.7	0.62
1	1- 1/4 -16	1- 3/8	25.60	1.008	28.50	1.122	30.2	1.19	17.5	0.69

Nom Tube OD, in	J Full Thread Min mm	J Full Thread Min in	K mm	K in	L mm	L in	T mm	T in	U Dia mm +0.5 −0.0	U Dia in +0.02 −0.00	X Dia Min mm	X Dia Min in
1/4	6.4	0.25	3.3	0.13	19.0	0.75	9.7	0.38	11.4	0.45	13.5	0.53
5/16	6.4	0.25	3.3	0.13	22.4	0.88	12.7	0.50	13.0	0.51	15.0	0.59
3/8	8.9	0.35	3.3	0.13	28.7	1.13	13.5	0.53	13.7	0.54	15.5	0.61
1/2	10.7	0.42	3.3	0.13	31.8	1.25	16.0	0.63	17.8	0.70	19.8	0.78
5/8	12.2	0.48	4.8	0.19	35.1	1.38	18.3	0.72	21.1	0.83	23.1	0.91
3/4	13.7	0.54	4.8	0.19	39.6	1.56	19.0	0.75	25.9	1.02	27.7	1.09
1	15.2	0.60	4.8	0.19	42.9	1.69	23.9	0.94	32.3	1.27	34.0	1.34

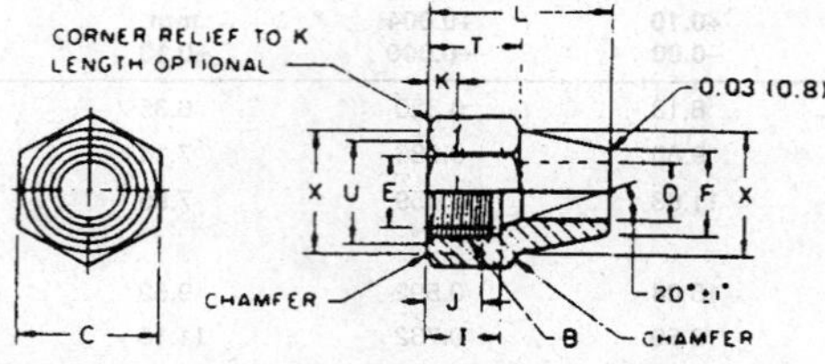

NOTE: Dimensions are mm (in)

FIGURE 5—SPHERICAL SLEEVE NUTS (120111)

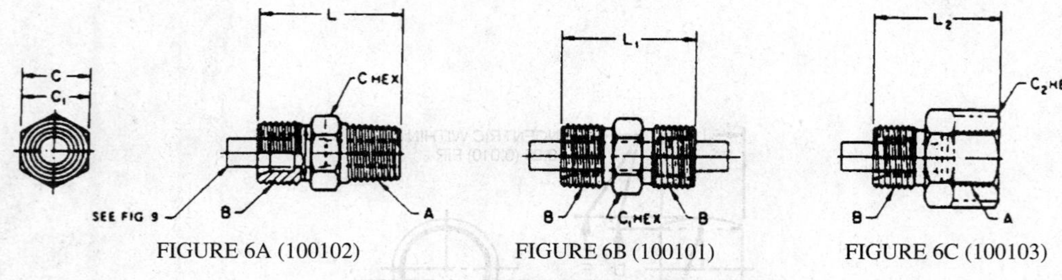

FIGURE 6A (100102) FIGURE 6B (100101) FIGURE 6C (100103)

FIGURE 6—CONNECTORS AND UNIONS

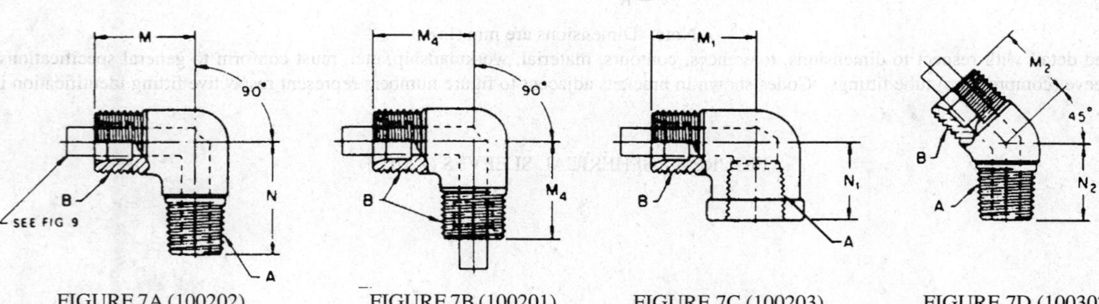

FIGURE 7A (100202) FIGURE 7B (100201) FIGURE 7C (100203) FIGURE 7D (100302)

FIGURE 7—ELBOWS

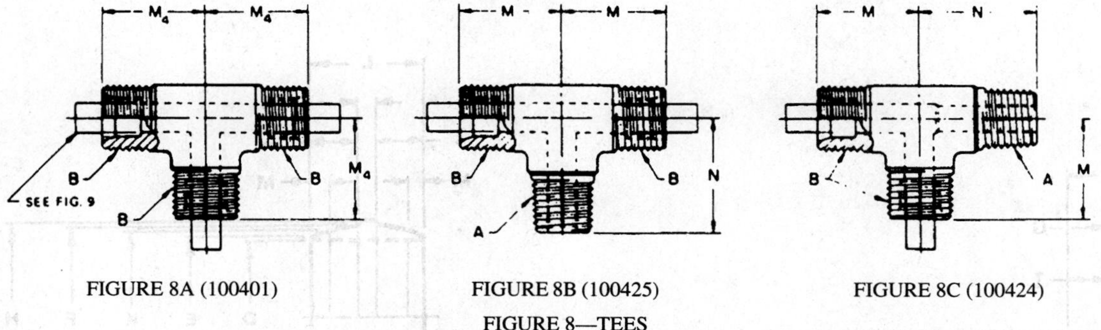

FIGURE 8A (100401) FIGURE 8B (100425) FIGURE 8C (100424)

FIGURE 8—TEES

NOTE—Flanged sleeve type fittings having tube support features (Figures 6A to 8C) are intended only for use with nylon tubing per SAE J844 in conjunction with flanged sleeve in Figure 10 and flanged sleeve nut in Figure 11.

Unspecified detail with respect to dimensions, tolerances, contours, materials, workmanship, etc., must conform to general specifications for spherical and flanged sleeve (compression) tube fittings. All dimensions for Figures 6A to 8C shall correspond with respective Figures 1A to 3C and Table 1A and 1B except for addition of the tube support shown in Figure 9 and Table 4. Codes shown in brackets adjacent to figure numbers represent respective fitting identification in accordance with SAE J846.

FIGURES 5 TO 8C

TABLE 4—DIMENSIONS OF TUBE SUPPORT (FIGURE 9)(1)

Nom Tube OD, in	D_2 Dia Min mm	D_2 Dia Min in	D_3 Dia Min mm	D_3 Dia Min in	D_3 Dia Max mm	D_3 Dia Max in	L_3 Min mm	L_3 Min in	O Min mm	O Min in	O Max mm	O Max in	Z Min mm	Z Min in	Z Max mm	Z Max in
1/4	3.12	0.123	4.09	0.161	4.19	0.165	11.4	0.45	6.1	0.24	7.6	0.30	0.30	0.012	0.43	0.017
3/8	5.21	0.205	6.17	0.243	6.27	0.247	14.5	0.57	7.4	0.29	8.9	0.35	0.33	0.013	0.43	0.017
1/2	8.28	0.326	9.35	0.368	9.45	0.372	19.0	0.75	8.6	0.34	10.2	0.40	0.33	0.013	0.48	0.019
5/8	9.75	0.384	10.97	0.432	11.07	0.436	20.1	0.79	10.2	0.40	11.7	0.46	0.41	0.016	0.56	0.022
3/4	12.73	0.501	14.15	0.557	14.25	0.561	24.6	0.97	11.7	0.46	13.2	0.52	0.41	0.016	0.66	0.026

1. For dimensions depicted on Figure 9 but not shown in Table 4, refer to Table 1A and 1B.

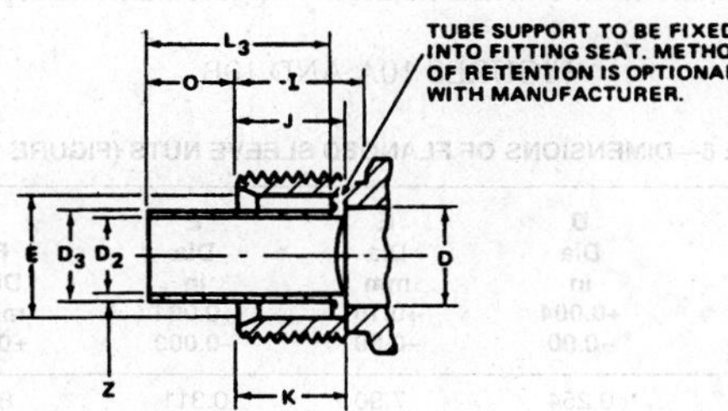

FIGURE 9—TUBE SUPPORT

TABLE 5—DIMENSIONS OF FLANGED SLEEVES (FIGURES 10A TO 10B)

Nom Tube OD, in	D Dia mm ±0.05	D Dia in ±0.002	E Dia mm ±0.05	E Dia in ±0.002	F Dia mm ±0.05	F Dia in ±0.002	G Ref mm	G Ref in	H Dia Max mm	H Dia Max in	H Dia Min mm	H Dia Min in
1/4	6.50	0.256	7.01	0.276	8.10	0.319	1.27	0.050	9.25	0.364	8.99	0.354
3/8	9.75	0.384	10.31	0.406	11.63	0.458	1.52	0.060	12.22	0.481	12.12	0.477
1/2	12.93	0.509	13.67	0.538	15.11	0.595	1.52	0.060	15.95	0.628	15.75	0.620
5/8	16.10	0.634	16.36	0.644	18.31	0.721	2.03	0.080	19.00	0.748	18.90	0.744
3/4	19.30	0.760	19.61	0.772	21.95	0.864	2.29	0.090	23.55	0.927	23.90	0.917

Nom Tube OD, in	I Max mm	I Max in	I Min mm	I Min in	K Dia mm ±0.05	K Dia in ±0.002	L mm ±0.13	L in ±0.005	M mm ±0.13	M in ±0.005
1/4	3.18	0.125	3.05	0.120	—	—	7.49	0.295	—	—
3/8	4.32	0.170	4.06	0.160	—	—	9.91	0.390	—	—
1/2	4.83	0.190	4.57	0.180	—	—	10.92	0.430	—	—
5/8	5.33	0.210	5.08	0.200	17.37	0.684	12.45	0.490	1.40	0.055
3/4	5.84	0.230	5.59	0.220	21.01	0.827	13.72	0.540	1.90	0.075

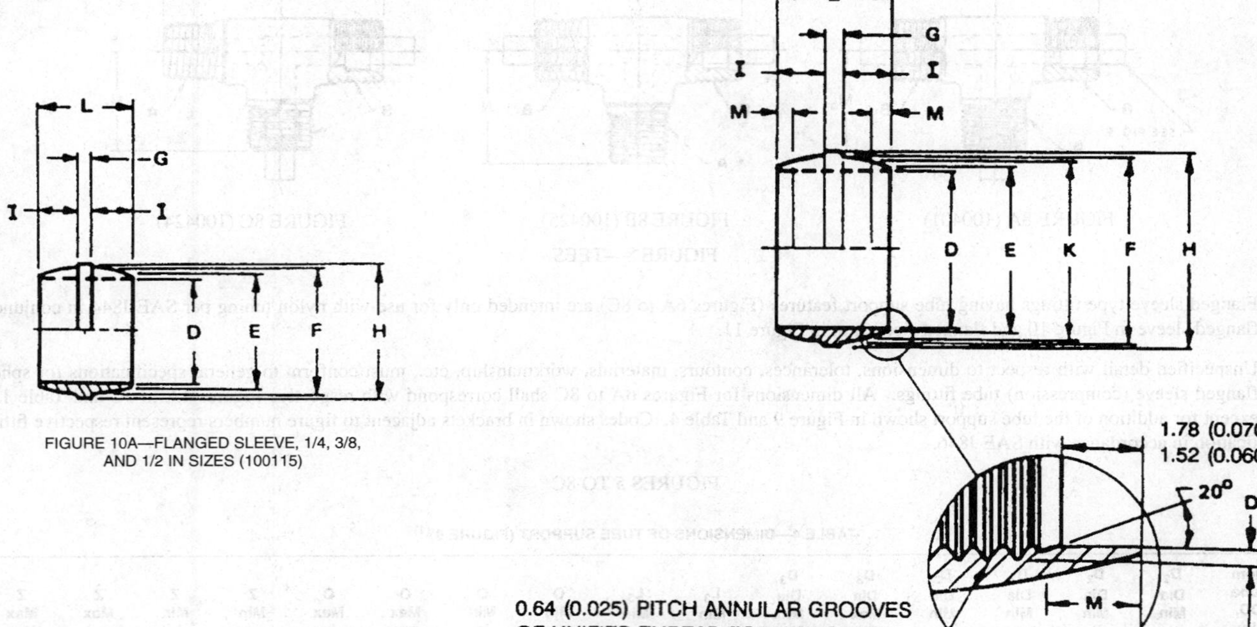

FIGURE 10A—FLANGED SLEEVE, 1/4, 3/8, AND 1/2 IN SIZES (100115)

FIGURE 10B—FLANGE SLEEVE 5/8 and 3/4 in Sizes (100115)

NOTE—Unspecified detail with respect to dimensions, tolerances, contours, material, workmanship, etc., must conform to general specifications for spherical and flanged sleeve (compression) tube fittings. Codes shown in brackets adjacent to figure numbers represent respective fitting identification in accordance with SAE J846.

FIGURES 10A AND 10B

TABLE 6—DIMENSIONS OF FLANGED SLEEVE NUTS (FIGURE 11)

Nom Tube OD, in	B_1 Nom Thread Size, in Class 2B Int	C Hex Nom in	D Dia mm +0.10 –0.00	D Dia in +0.004 –0.00	E Dia mm +0.10 –0.00	E Dia in +0.004 –0.000	F Dia mm ±0.5	F Dia in ±0.02	I mm	I in
1/4	7/16-24	9/16	6.45	0.254	7.90	0.311	8.6	0.34	7.9	0.31
3/8	17/32-24	5/8	9.70	0.382	11.38	0.448	11.9	0.47	11.2	0.44
1/2	11/16-20	13/16	12.88	0.507	14.78	0.582	15.5	0.61	13.0	0.51
5/8	13/16-18	15/16	16.05	0.632	18.14	0.714	18.8	0.74	14.7	0.58
3/4	1 -18	1- 1/8	19.25	0.758	21.59	0.850	22.4	0.88	15.7	0.62

Nom Tube OD, in	J Full Thd Min mm	J Full Thd Min in	K mm	K in	L mm	L in	U Dia mm +0.5 –0.0	U Dia in +0.02 –0.00	X Dia Min mm	X Dia Min in
1/4	6.4	0.25	3.3	0.13	11.4	0.45	11.4	0.45	13.5	0.53
3/8	9.7	0.38	3.3	0.13	16.0	0.63	13.7	0.54	15.5	0.61
1/2	11.2	0.44	3.3	0.13	18.3	0.72	17.8	0.70	19.8	0.78
5/8	12.7	0.50	4.8	0.19	19.6	0.77	21.1	0.83	23.1	0.91
3/4	13.7	0.54	4.8	0.19	20.6	0.81	25.9	1.02	27.7	1.09

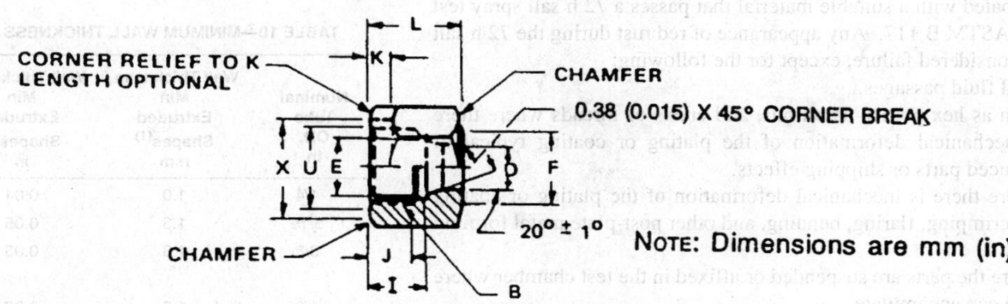

FIGURE 11—FLANGED SLEEVE NUTS (100110)

TABLE 7—STRAIGHT THREAD SPECIFICATION DATA, IN

Nominal Size	Series Designation	External Thread Pitch Diameter Max	External Thread Pitch Diameter Min	Internal Thread Pitch Diameter Max	Internal Thread Pitch Diameter Min[(1)]	Internal Thread Minor Diameter Max	Internal Thread Minor Diameter Min
7/16-24	UNS	0.4093	0.4055	0.4153	0.4104	0.402	0.392
1/2 -24	UNS	0.4717	0.4678	0.4780	0.4729	0.465	0.455
17/32-24	UNS	0.5030	0.4991	0.5092	0.5041	0.496	0.486
11/16-20	UN	0.6537	0.6494	0.6606	0.6550	0.645	0.633
13/16-18	UNS	0.7750	0.7704	0.7824	0.7764	0.765	0.752
1 -18	UNS	0.9625	0.9578	0.9701	0.9639	0.953	0.940
1 1/4 -16	UN	1.2079	1.2028	1.2160	1.2094	1.196	1.182

1. These values are also the basic pitch diameter.

TABLE 8—TOLERANCES FOR EXTERNAL AND INTERNAL THREADS

Nom Pipe Thread Size, in	External Thread chamfer Diameter[(1)] Max mm	External Thread Chamfer Diameter[(1)] Max in	External Thread Chamfer Diameter[(1)] Min mm	External Thread Chamfer Diameter[(1)] Min in	External Thread Length of Chamfered or Partial Thread Min mm	External Thread Length of Chamfered or Partial Thread Min in	External Thread Length of Chamfered or Partial Thread Max mm	External Thread Length of Chamfered or Partial Thread Max in	Internal Thread Countersink Diameter[(1)] Min mm	Internal Thread Countersink Diameter[(1)] Min in	Internal Thread Countersink Diameter[(1)] Max mm	Internal Thread Countersink Diameter[(1)] Max in
1/8	8.1	0.32	7.6	0.30	0.94	0.037	1.42	0.056	10.7	0.42	11.2	0.44
1/4	10.7	0.42	10.2	0.40	1.42	0.056	2.11	0.083	14.0	0.55	14.5	0.57
3/8	14.0	0.55	13.5	0.53	1.42	0.056	2.11	0.083	17.5	0.69	18.0	0.71
1/2	17.3	0.68	16.8	0.66	1.80	0.071	2.72	0.107	21.6	0.85	22.1	0.87
3/4	22.6	0.89	22.1	0.87	1.80	0.071	2.72	0.107	26.9	1.06	27.4	1.08
1	28.4	1.12	27.7	1.09	2.21	0.087	3.30	0.130	34.0	1.34	34.8	1.37

1. Tabulated diameters conform with Appendix A, SAE J476.

TABLE 9—TOLERANCE ON HOLD DIAMETERS

Drill Size Range mm	Drill Size Range in	Tolerance Plus mm	Tolerance Plus in	Tolerance Minus mm	Tolerance Minus in
0.343 thru 4.699	0.0135 thru 0.1850	0.08	0.003	0.05	0.002
4.762 thru 6.299	0.1875 thru 0.2480	0.10	0.004	0.05	0.002
6.350 thru 19.050	0.2500 thru 0.7500	0.15	0.006	0.08	0.003
19.251 thru 25.400	0.7579 thru 1.0000	0.18	0.007	0.10	0.004

The tube fitting dimensions tabulated herein are based on length of the Dryseal American Standard Taper Pipe Thread (NPTF), it being the consensus of manufacturers and users that trouble-free assembly cannot be assured unless a full length thread is used. However, the tap drill depths and overall lengths specified in the tables for fittings with internal taper pipe threads are not consistent with the tap drill depths and overall thread lengths of the Dryseal American Standard Taper Pipe Threads (NPTF) given in Table A2, Appendix A of SAE J476. The full length Dryseal American Standard Taper Pipe Taps specified in Table B2 of SAE J476 cannot be used, as the tap drill depths and overall lengths of the fittings have been reduced to the minimum required by bottoming taps to produce standard full thread length. The deviations described previously are peculiar to these tube fittings and as special tooling is required, caution should be exercised in specifying such deviations for any other products.

External pipe threads shall be chamfered from the diameters tabulated in Table 8 to produce the specified length of chamfered or partial thread. Internal pipe threads shall be countersink 90 degrees included angle, to the diameters tabulated in Table 8.

3.10 Material and Manufacture—Fittings shall be made from brass and, at manufacturer's option and in accordance with his process of manufacture, may be milled from the bar and forged. Brass shall be UNS C36000 (half-hard), UNS C34500, or UNS C35000 for bar or extruded stock and UNS C37700 for forgings. Sleeves shown in Figure 4 shall be made from UNS C36000 brass and annealed to a maximum hardness of Rockwell F70. Sleeves shown in Figure 10 shall be made from UNS C36000 brass. Tube supports shown in Figure 9 shall be made from UNS C26000 or 300 series stainless steel, according to manufacturer's process standard. Nuts may be made from steel when so specified by the purchaser.

3.11 Finish—The external surfaces and threads of all carbon steel parts shall be plated or coated with a suitable material that passes a 72 h salt spray test in accordance with ASTM B 117. Any appearance of red rust during the 72 h salt spray test shall be considered failure, except for the following:

a. All internal fluid passages.
b. Edges such as hex points, serrations, and crests of threads where there may be mechanical deformation of the plating or coating typical of mass-produced parts or shipping effects.
c. Areas where there is mechanical deformation of the plating or coating caused by crimping, flaring, bending, and other post-plate metal forming operations.
d. Areas where the parts are suspended or affixed in the test chamber where condensate can accumulate.

NOTE—Cadmium plating is not preferred due to environmental reasons. Parts manufactured to this Standard after January 1, 1997, shall not be cadmium plated. Internal fluid passages shall be protected from corrosion during storage. Changes in plating may affect assembly torques and require requalification, when applicable.

3.12 Workmanship—Workmanship shall conform to the best commercial practice to produce high-quality fittings. Fittings shall be free from all machining fluids, chips, hanging burrs, loose scale, and slivers which might become dislodged in usage and all other defects which might affect their serviceability. All seating surfaces for the spherical sleeve must be smooth except that annular tool marks up to 2.5 mm (100 min) maximum shall be permissible.

TABLE 10—MINIMUM WALL THICKNESS FOR EXTRUDED AND FORGED SHAPES

Nominal Tube OD, in	Wall Thickness, Min Extruded Shapes[(1)] mm	Wall Thickness, Min Extruded Shapes[(1)] in	Wall Thickness, Min Forged Shapes mm	Wall Thickness, Min Forged Shapes in
1/4	1.0	0.04	1.90	0.075
5/16	1.3	0.05	1.90	0.075
3/8	1.3	0.05	2.16	0.085
1/2	1.5	0.06	2.29	0.090
5/8	2.0	0.08	2.54	0.100
3/4	2.0	0.08	2.54	0.100
1	2.0	0.08	3.05	0.120

1. Applies to reduction to one plane of shape only.

3.13 Assembly Considerations—Where it is not objectionable from a function or production standpoint, the use of a compatible lubricant or sealant may be desirable in assembling Dryseal pipe threads on spherical and flanged sleeve (compression) tube fittings to minimize galling and effect a pressure-tight seal.

APPENDIX A
TABLES FOR CALCULATING DIMENSIONS ON SPECIAL SIZES

A.1 The tables in this Appendix present various factors to be used in determining the dimensions applicable to special size combination fittings not contained in SAE J246. (See Table 1A for calculated sizes.)

For any special size fitting, be it a connector, 45 or 90 degree elbow, tee, or cross, one end is always standard. Consider this end to be the largest on the fitting, it may then be used as the basis for establishing the stock size and the length (either overall or end to center) by deducting factors equivalent to the reduction in machining requirements from the appropriate standard lengths.

A.1.1 The factors applicable to the various end configurations and size reductions tabulated in Tables A1 to A9 were determined on the following basis:

a. Those pertaining to lengths were derived by maintaining the standard hexagon thickness for straight fittings and the standard centerline to machining start for shaped fittings.
b. Tables A1 and A2 were derived by subtracting the standard machining length required for the smaller end from that required for the larger end.
c. Table A3 factors are equal to one-half the difference in tube end thread diameters.
d. Table A4 factors are equal to one-half the difference in pipe end thread dimensions.
e. Table A5 factors are equal to one-half the difference in the tube end D drill diameter.
f. Table A6 factors are equal to one-half the difference in the pipe end W diameter or width.

A.1.2 Straight, Tube Size Reduced

L(L1, L2) special size = L(L1, L2) std size - factor from Table A2 (Eq. A1)

EXAMPLE—For a straight connector (Figures 1A and 1C) with 3/8 in tube and 3/8 in NPTF, the overall length would be determined as follows:

a. 34.0 mm (1.34 in) = L overall length for 1/2 tube to 3/8 NPTF from Table 7
b. 2.3 mm (0.09 in) = factor from Table A2 for 3/8 machining on 1/2 size fitting 31.8 mm (1.25 in) = overall length

The proper hex size will be the larger of the values for the tube size and external pipe size shown in Tables A7 and A8, respectively. The 3/8 in tube to 3/8 in NPTF fitting's hex size will (from Table A8) be 11/16 in.

A.1.3 Straight, Pipe Size Reduced

L(L1, L2) special size = L(L1, L2) std size - factor from Table A1 (Eq. A2)

A.1.4 Elbows with External Pipe Threads, Tube Size Reduced

M special size = M std size - factor from Table A2 (Eq. A3)

N special size = N std size - factor from Table A3 (Eq. A4)

EXAMPLE—For elbows and tees (Figures 2A, 3B, 3C) with 1/4 in tube and 1/4 in NPTF, the end to center length M would be derived as follows:

a. 20.3 mm (0.80 in) (M dimension for 3/8 tube to 1/4 NPTF from Table 1A) - 2.8 mm (0.11 in) (factor from Table A2 for 1/4 machined on 3/8 size fitting) = 17.5 mm (0.69 in) (end-to-center length)

The end to center length N would be derived as follows:

a. 23.6 mm (0.93 in) (N dimension for 3/8 tube to 1/4 NPTF from Table 1A) - 1.3 mm (0.05 in) (factor from Table A3 for 1/4 machined on 3/8 size fitting) = 22.3 mm (0.88 in) (end-to-center length)

The proper wrench pad width will be the larger value for the tube size and external pipe size shown in Tables A7 and A8, respectively. The wrench pad width for 1/4 in tube to 1/4 in NPTF fitting will (from Table A8) be 14.0 mm (0.55 in).

A.1.5 Elbows with External Pipe Thread, Pipe Size Reduced

M special size = M std size - factor from Table A4 (Eq. A5)

N special size = N std size - factor from Table A1 (Eq. A6)

A.1.6 Elbows, All Tube Ends

M4 reduced end = M4 std size - factor from Table A2 (Eq. A7)

M4 end not reduced = M4 std size - factor from Table A3 (Eq. A8)

A.1.7 Tees with External Pipe Thread, Tube Size Reduced—Figure as two elbows. Use larger of the two figures obtained for the branch centerline-to-end dimension.

A.1.8 Tees with External Pipe Thread, Pipe Size Reduced—Figure as two elbows. Use larger of the two figures obtained for the branch centerline-to-end dimension.

A.1.9 Tees, All Tube Ends—Figure as two elbows. Use larger of the two figures obtained for the branch centerline-to-end dimension.

A.1.10 Elbow with Internal Threads, Tube Size Reduced

M1 special size = M1 std size
- factor from Table A2 (Eq. A9)

N1 special size = N1 std size
- factor from Table A5 (Eq. A10)

A.1.11 Elbows with Internal Pipe Threads, Pipe Size Reduced

M1 special size = M1 std size
- factor from Table A6 (Eq. A11)

N1 special size = N1 std size
- factor from Table A1 (Eq. A12)

A.1.12 45 Degree Elbow, Tube Size Reduced

M2 special size = M2 std size
- factor from Table A2 (Eq. A13)

N2 special size = N2 std size (Eq. A14)

A.1.13 45 Degree Elbow, Pipe Size Reduced

M2 special size = M2 std size (Eq. A15)

N2 special size = N2 std size - factor from Table A1 (Eq. A16)

TABLE A1—LENGTH FACTORS STANDARD PIPE SIZE

	Nom Pipe Size, in	1/4 mm	1/4 in	3/8 mm	3/8 in	1/2 mm	1/2 in	3/4 mm	3/4 in	1 mm	1 in
Reduced Pipe Size	1/8	4.6	0.18	4.6	0.18	9.7	0.38	9.7	0.38	14.2	0.56
	1/4	—	—	0.0	0.00	4.8	0.19	4.8	0.19	9.7	0.38
	3/8	—	—	—	—	4.8	0.19	4.8	0.19	9.7	0.38
	1/2	—	—	—	—	—	—	0.0	0.00	4.8	0.19
	3/4	—	—	—	—	—	—	—	—	4.8	0.19

TABLE A2—LENGTH FACTORS STANDARD MACHINING SIZE

	Nom Tube OD, in	5/16 mm	5/16 in	3/8 mm	3/8 in	1/2 mm	1/2 in	5/8 mm	5/8 in	3/4 mm	3/4 in	1 mm	1 in
Reduced Tube Size	1/4	0.3	0.01	2.8	0.11	5.1	0.20	6.6	0.26	8.4	0.33	9.9	0.39
	5/16	—	—	2.5	0.10	4.8	0.19	6.4	0.25	8.1	0.32	9.7	0.38
	3/8	—	—	—	—	2.3	0.09	3.8	0.15	5.6	0.22	7.1	0.28
	1/2	—	—	—	—	—	—	1.5	0.06	3.3	0.13	4.8	0.19
	5/8	—	—	—	—	—	—	—	—	1.8	0.07	3.3	0.13
	3/4	—	—	—	—	—	—	—	—	—	—	1.5	0.06

TABLE A3—LENGTH FACTORS STANDARD MACHINING SIZE

	Nom Tube OD, in	5/16 mm	5/16 in	3/8 mm	3/8 in	1/2 mm	1/2 in	5/8 mm	5/8 in	3/4 mm	3/4 in	1 mm	1 in
Reduced Tube Size	1/4	0.8	0.03	1.3	0.05	3.3	0.13	4.8	0.19	7.1	0.28	10.4	1.41
	5/16	—	—	0.5	0.02	2.3	0.09	4.1	0.16	6.4	0.25	9.7	0.38
	3/8	—	—	—	—	2.0	0.08	3.6	0.14	5.8	0.23	9.1	0.36
	1/2	—	—	—	—	—	—	1.5	0.06	4.1	0.16	7.1	0.28
	5/8	—	—	—	—	—	—	—	—	2.3	0.09	5.6	0.22
	3/4	—	—	—	—	—	—	—	—	—	—	3.3	0.13

TABLE A4—LENGTH FACTORS STANDARD PIPE SIZE

	Nom Pipe Size, in	1/4 mm	1/4 in	3/8 mm	3/8 in	1/2 mm	1/2 in	3/4 mm	3/4 in	1 mm	1 in
Reduced	1/8	1.8	0.07	3.6	0.14	5.6	0.22	8.4	0.33	11.7	0.46
Pipe	1/4	—	—	1.8	0.07	3.8	0.15	7.1	0.28	9.9	0.39
Size	3/8	—	—	—	—	2.3	0.09	4.8	0.19	8.1	0.32
	1/2	—	—	—	—	—	—	2.8	0.11	6.1	0.24
	3/4	—	—	—	—	—	—	—	—	3.3	0.13

TABLE A5—LENGTH FACTORS STANDARD MACHINING SIZE

	Nom Tube OD, in	5/16 mm	5/16 in	3/8 mm	3/8 in	1/2 mm	1/2 in	5/8 mm	5/8 in	3/4 mm	3/4 in	1 mm	1 in
Reduced Tube Size	1/4	0.8	0.03	1.5	0.06	2.8	0.11	4.3	0.17	5.8	0.23	8.6	0.34
	5/16	—	—	0.8	0.03	2.0	0.08	3.6	0.14	5.1	0.20	7.9	0.31
	3/8	—	—	—	—	1.3	0.05	2.8	0.11	4.3	0.17	7.1	0.28
	1/2	—	—	—	—	—	—	1.5	0.06	3.3	0.13	5.8	0.23
	5/8	—	—	—	—	—	—	—	—	1.5	0.06	4.3	0.17
	3/4	—	—	—	—	—	—	—	—	—	—	2.8	0.11

TABLE A6—LENGTH FACTORS STANDARD PIPE SIZE

	Nom Pipe Size, in	1/4 mm	1/4 in	3/8 mm	3/8 in	1/2 mm	1/2 in	3/4 mm	3/4 in	1 mm	1 in
Reduced Pipe Size	1/8	1.5	0.06	3.3	0.13	5.6	0.22	8.9	0.35	11.9	0.47
	1/4	—	—	1.8	0.07	4.1	0.16	7.4	0.29	10.4	0.41
	3/8	—	—	—	—	2.5	0.10	5.6	0.22	8.9	0.35
	1/2	—	—	—	—	—	—	3.3	0.13	6.4	0.25
	3/4	—	—	—	—	—	—	—	—	3.3	0.13

TABLE A7—ALUMINUM STOCK SIZE FOR TUBE ENDS

Nom Tube OD, in	Hexagon Width, Min in	Width Over Wrench Pads, Min mm	Width Over Wrench Pads, Min in
1/4	7/16	11.2	0.44
5/16	1/2	12.7	0.50
3/8	9/16	13.5	0.53
1/2	11/16	17.5	0.69
5/8	13/16	20.6	0.81
3/4	1	25.4	1.00
1	1- 1/4	31.8	1.25

TABLE A8—MINIMUM STOCK SIZE FOR EXTERNAL PIPE ENDS

Nom Pipe Size, in	Hexagon Width, Min in	Width Over Wrench Pads, Min mm	Width Over Wrench Pads, Min in
1/8	7/16	10.4	0.41
1/4	9/16	14.0	0.55
3/8	11/16	17.5	0.69
1/2	7/8	21.6	0.85
3/4	1- 1/16	26.9	1.06
1	1- 3/8	33.8	1.33

TABLE A9—MINIMUM STOCK SIZE FOR INTERNAL PIPE ENDS

Nom Pipe Size, in	Hexagon Width, Min in	Width Over Wrench Pads, Min mm	Width Over Wrench Pads, Min in
1/8	9/16	14.2	0.56
1/4	11/16	17.5	0.69
3/8	7/8	20.6	0.81
1/2	1- 1/16	25.4	1.00
3/4	1- 1/4	31.8	1.25
1	1- 5/8	38.1	1.50

REFRIGERATION TUBE FITTINGS—GENERAL SPECIFICATIONS —SAE J513 JAN1999

SAE Standard

Report of the SAE Parts and Fittings Division approved January 1936. Ninth revision by the SAE Fluid Conductors and Connectors Technical Committee January 1999. Rationale statement available.

1. Scope—This SAE Standard covers complete general and dimensional specifications for refrigeration tube fittings of the flare type specified in Figures 1 to 42 and Tables 1 to 15. These fittings are intended for general use with flared annealed copper tubing in refrigeration applications.

Dimensions of single and double 45 degree flares on tubing to be used in conjunction with these fittings are given in Figure 2 and Table 1 of SAE J533.

The following general specifications supplement the dimensional data contained in Tables 1 to 15 with respect to all unspecified details.

2. References

2.1 Applicable Publications—The following publications form a part of this specification to the extent specified herein. The latest version of SAE publications shall apply.

2.1.1 SAE PUBLICATIONS—Available from SAE, 400 Commonwealth Drive, Warrendale, PA 15096-0001.

SAE J476—Dryseal Pipe Threads
SAE J512—Automotive Tube Fittings
SAE J528—Seamless Copper Tube
SAE J533—Flares for Tubing
SAE J846—Coding Systems for Identification of Fluid Conductors and Connectors

2.1.2 ANSI PUBLICATIONS—Available from ANSI, 11 West 42nd Street, New York, NY 10036-8002.

ANSI B1.1—Screw Threads
ANSI B2.1—Pipe Threads
ANSI B70.1—American Standard Refrigeration Flare Type Fittings

2.1.3 ASTM PUBLICATION—Available from ASTM, 100 Barr Harbor Drive, West Conshohocken, PA 19428-2959.

ASTM B 117—Method of Salt Spray (Fog) Testing

TABLE 1—STRAIGHT THREAD SPECIFICATION DATA, in

Nominal Size	Series Designation	External Thread Pitch Dia Max	External Thread Pitch Dia Min	Internal Thread Pitch Dia Max	Internal Thread Pitch Dia Min(1)	Internal Thread Minor Dia(2) Max	Internal Thread Minor Dia(2) Min
5/16-24	UNF	0.2843	0.2806	0.2902	0.2854	0.2754	0.2670
3/8 -24	UNF	0.3468	0.3430	0.3528	0.3479	0.3372	0.3300
7/16-20	UNF	0.4037	0.3995	0.4104	0.4050	0.3916	0.3830
1/2 -20	UNF	0.4662	0.4619	0.4731	0.4675	0.4537	0.4460
5/8 -18	UNF	0.5875	0.5828	0.5949	0.5889	0.5730	0.5650
3/4 -16	UNF	0.7079	0.7029	0.7159	0.7094	0.6908	0.6820
7/8 -14	UNF	0.8270	0.8216	0.8356	0.8286	0.8068	0.7980
1-1/16-14	UNS	1.0145	1.0092	1.0230	1.0161	0.9940	0.9850

1. These values are also the basic pitch diameter.
2. Class B minor diameter limits.

TABLE 2—PIPE THREAD SPECIFICATION DATA

Nominal Pipe Thread Size in	External Thread Chamfer Diameter(1) Max mm	External Thread Chamfer Diameter(1) Max in	External Thread Chamfer Diameter(1) Min mm	External Thread Chamfer Diameter(1) Min in	External Thread Length of Chamfered or Partial Thread Min mm	External Thread Length of Chamfered or Partial Thread Min in
1/8	8.1	0.32	7.6	0.30	0.90	0.037
1/4	10.7	0.42	10.2	0.40	1.42	0.056
3/8	14.0	0.55	13.5	0.53	1.42	0.056
1/2	17.3	0.68	16.8	0.66	1.80	0.071
3/4	22.6	0.89	22.1	0.87	1.80	0.071

Nominal Pipe Thread Size in	External Thread Length of Chamfered or Partial Thread Max mm	External Thread Length of Chamfered or Partial Thread Max in	Internal Thread Countersink Diameter(1) Min mm	Internal Thread Countersink Diameter(1) Min in	Internal Thread Countersink Diameter(1) Max mm	Internal Thread Countersink Diameter(1) Max in
1/8	1.41	0.056	10.7	0.42	11.2	0.44
1/4	2.12	0.083	14.0	0.55	14.5	0.57
3/8	2.12	0.083	17.5	0.69	18.0	0.71
1/2	2.72	0.107	21.6	0.85	22.1	0.87
3/4	2.72	0.107	26.9	1.06	27.4	1.08

1. Tabulated diameters conform with Appendix A, SAE J476.

* UNDERCUT TO G DIA OPTONAL ON FLARE SIZES 1/2 AND LARGER UNLESS OTHERWISE SPECIFIED BY PURCHASER

FIGURE 1—CONNECTOR (HALF UNION) (010102) (U1)

FIGURE 2—FUSIBLE CONNECTOR (HALF UNION) (010163) (FU)

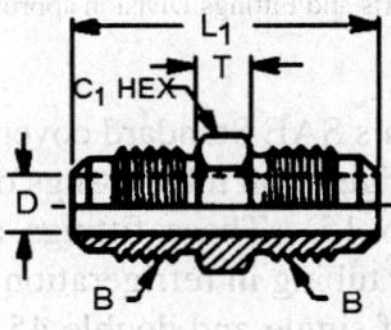

FIGURE 3—UNION (010101) (U2)

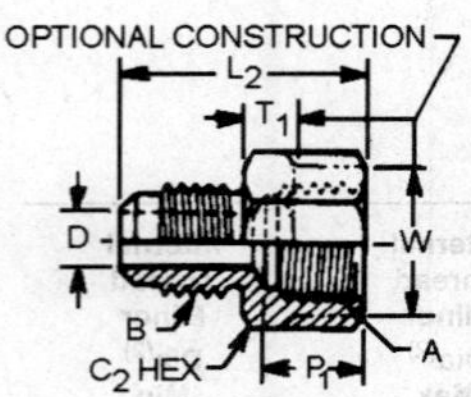

FIGURE 4—INTERNAL PIPE THREAD CONNECTOR (HALF UNION) (010103) (U3)

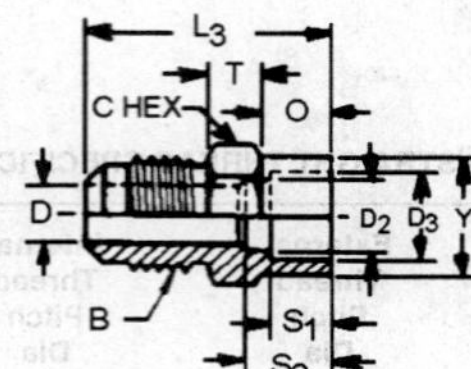

FIGURE 5—SOLDER CONNECTOR (HALF UNION) (010104) (US3)

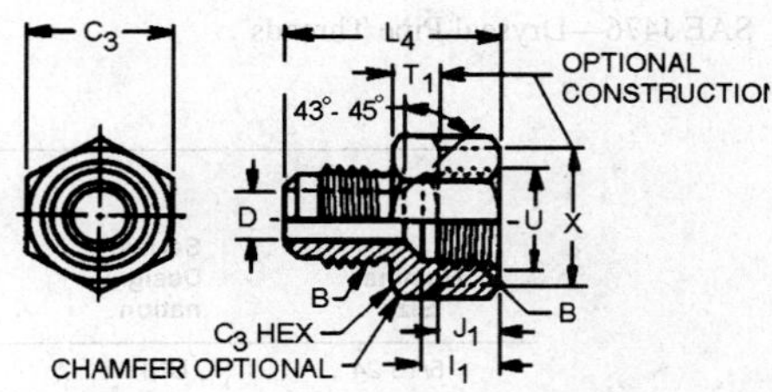

FIGURE 6—INTERNAL FLARE TO EXTERNAL FLARE ADAPTER (010105) (UR3)

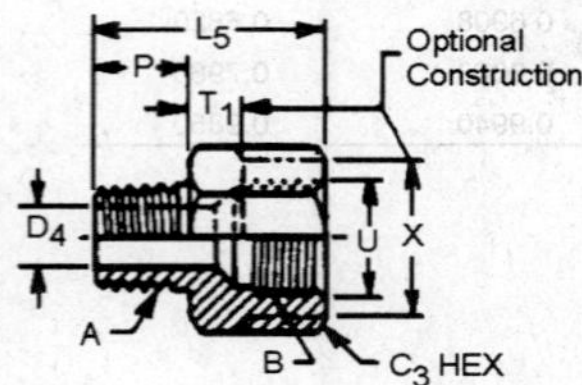

FIGURE 7—INTERNAL FLARE TO EXTERNAL PIPE ADAPTER (010106) (U5)

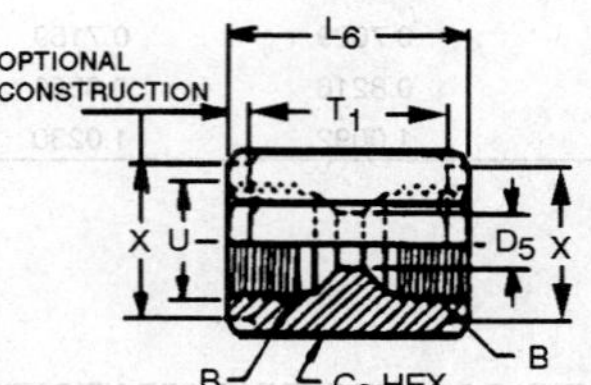

FIGURE 8—INTERNAL FLARE UNION (010107) (U4)

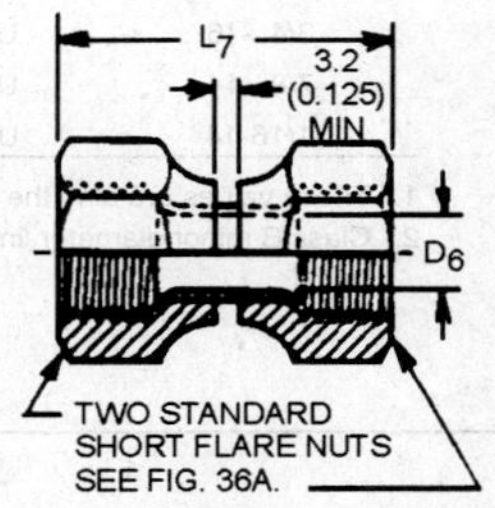

DIMENSIONS ARE mm (in)

FIGURE 9—INTERNAL FLARE SWIVEL UNION (010108) (US4)

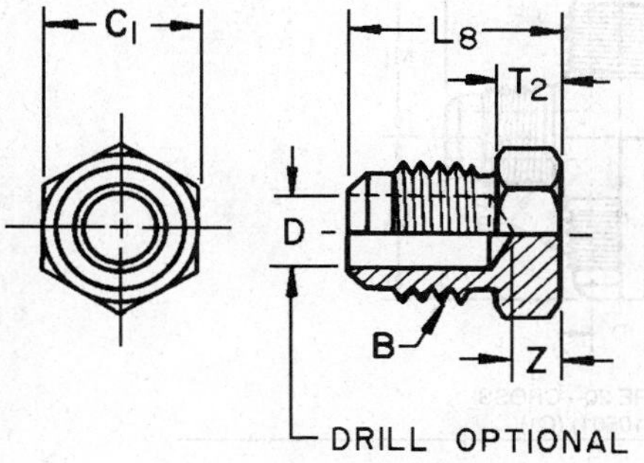

FIGURE 10—PLUG
(010109) (P2)

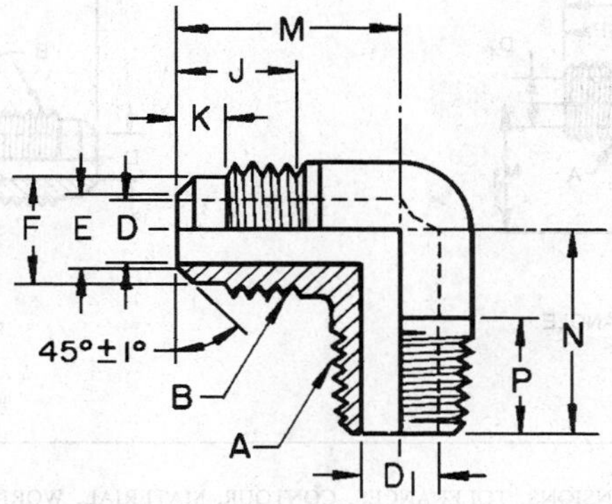

FIGURE 11—90 DEGREE ELBOW
(010202) (E1)

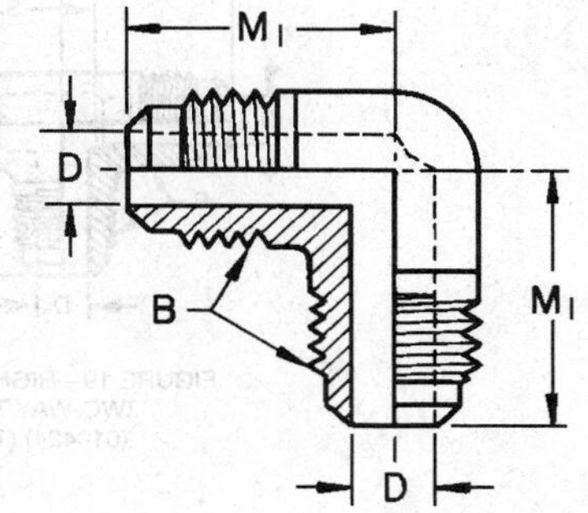

FIGURE 12—90 DEGREE
ELBOW UNION
(010201) (E2)

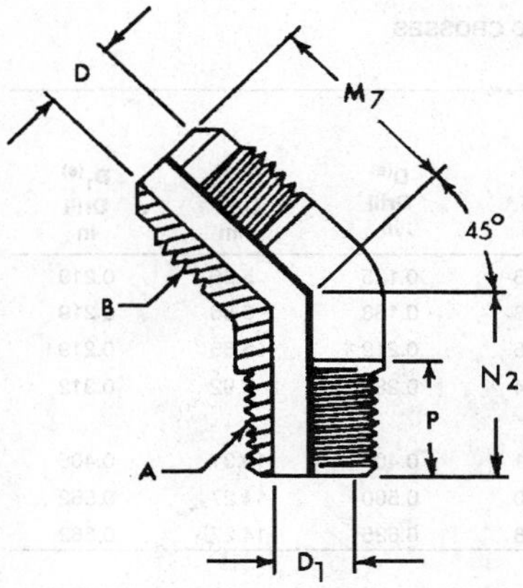

FIGURE 13—45 DEGREE
ELBOW
(010302) (E5)

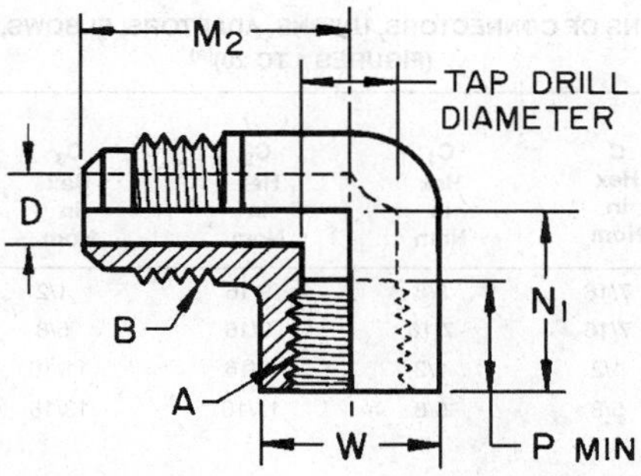

FIGURE 14—90 DEGREE
INTERNAL PIPE
THREAD ELBOW
(010203) (E3)

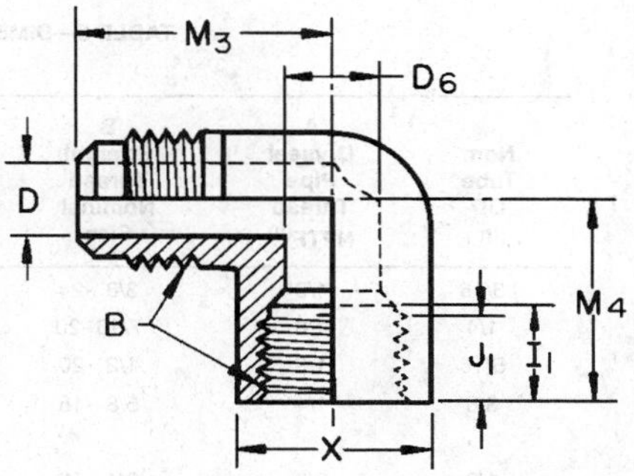

FIGURE 15—INTERNAL FLARE
TO EXTERNAL FLARE
90 DEGREE ELBOW
(010205) (E4)

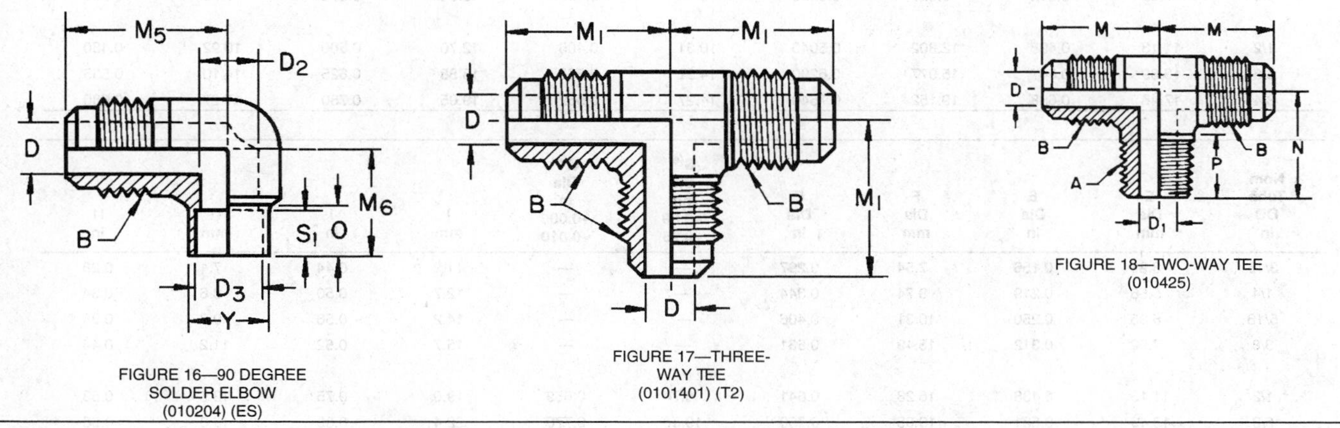

FIGURE 16—90 DEGREE
SOLDER ELBOW
(010204) (ES)

FIGURE 17—THREE-
WAY TEE
(0101401) (T2)

FIGURE 18—TWO-WAY TEE
(010425)

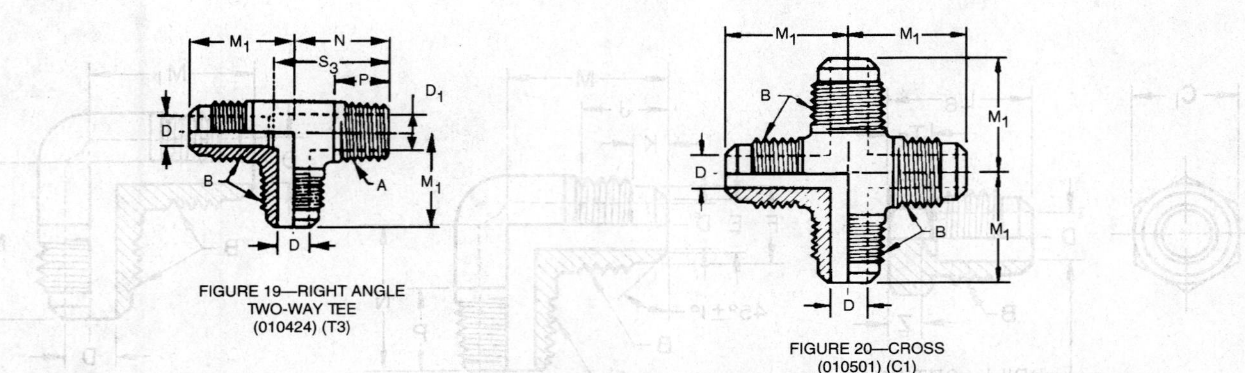

FIGURE 19—RIGHT ANGLE TWO-WAY TEE (010424) (T3)

FIGURE 20—CROSS (010501) (C1)

NOTE—UNSPECIFIED DETAIL WITH RESPECT TO DIMENSIONS, TOLERANCES, CONTOUR, MATERIAL, WORKMANSHIP, ETC., MUST CONFORM TO GENERAL SPECIFICATIONS FOR REFRIGERATION TUBE FITTINGS. THE DIMENSIONAL DESIGNATIONS IN FIGURES 1, 6, AND 11 AND THE FIRST FIGURE IN EACH GROUP SHALL APPLY TO CORRESPONDING FEATURES OF OTHER FIGURES ON THIS PAGE UNLESS SHOWN OTHERWISE. THE ILLUSTRATIONS ON THIS PAGE APPLY TO TABLE 3. CODES SHOWN IN BRACKETS ADJACENT TO FIGURE NUMBERS REPRESENT RESPECTIVE FITTING IDENTIFICATION IN ACCORDANCE WITH SAE J846 (FIRST NUMBER) AND ANSI B70.1 (SECOND NUMBER).

TABLE 3—DIMENSIONS OF CONNECTORS, UNIONS, ADAPTORS, ELBOWS, TEES, AND CROSSES (FIGURES 1 TO 20)[(a)]

Nom Tube OD in	A Dryseal Pipe Thread NPTF[(b)]	B Straight Thread Nominal Size	C Hex in Nom	C_1 Hex in Nom	C_2 Hex in Nom	C_3 Hex in Nom	D[(e)] Drill mm	D[(e)] Drill in	D_1[(e)] Drill mm	D_1[(e)] Drill in
3/16	1/8	3/8 -24	7/16	3/8	9/16	1/2	3.18	0.125	5.56	0.219
1/4	1/8	7/16 -20	7/16	7/16	9/16	5/8	4.78	0.188	5.56	0.219
5/16	1/8	1/2 -20	1/2	1/2	9/16	11/16	5.56	0.219	5.56	0.219
3/8	1/4	5/8 -18	5/8	5/8	11/16	13/16	7.14	0.281	7.92	0.312
1/2	3/8	3/4 -16	3/4	3/4	13/16	15/16	10.31	0.406	10.31	0.406
5/8	1/2	7/8 -14	7/8	7/8	1	1- 1/16	12.70	0.500	14.27	0.562
3/4	1/2	1-1/16-14	1-1/16	1-1/16	1-1/16	1- 5/16	15.88	0.625	14.27	0.562

Nom Tube OD in	D_2 Drill mm	D_2 Drill in	D_3[(h)] Dia mm ±0.025	D_3[(h)] Dia in ±0.0010	D_4 Drill mm	D_4 Drill in	D_5 Drill mm	D_5 Drill in	D_6[(j)] Tube ID mm	D_6[(j)] Tube ID in
3/16	3.96	0.156	4.864	0.1915	4.78	0.188	4.78	0.188	2.97	0.117
1/4	4.78	0.188	6.452	0.2540	5.56	0.219	6.35	0.250	4.57	0.180
5/16	6.35	0.250	8.039	0.3165	5.56	0.219	7.92	0.312	6.15	0.242
3/8	7.92	0.312	9.627	0.3790	8.74	0.344	9.52	0.375	7.75	0.305
1/2	11.13	0.438	12.802	0.5040	10.31	0.406	12.70	0.500	10.92	0.430
5/8	13.89	0.547	15.977	0.6290	14.27	0.562	15.88	0.625	14.10	0.555
3/4	17.48	0.688	19.152	0.7540	14.27	0.562	19.05	0.750	17.27	0.680

Nom Tube OD in	E Dia mm	E Dia in	F Dia mm	F Dia in	G[(e)] Dia mm +0.00 −0.25	G[(e)] Dia in +0.000 −0.010	I mm	I in	I1 mm	I1 in
3/16	3.96	0.156	7.54	0.297	—	—	11.2	0.44	7.1	0.28
1/4	5.56	0.219	8.74	0.344	—	—	12.7	0.50	8.6	0.34
5/16	6.35	0.250	10.31	0.406	—	—	14.2	0.56	9.7	0.38
3/8	7.92	0.312	13.49	0.531	—	—	15.7	0.62	11.2	0.44
1/2	11.13	0.438	16.28	0.641	16.74	0.659	19.0	0.75	13.5	0.53
5/8	13.49	0.531	19.05	0.750	19.56	0.770	22.4	0.88	16.8	0.66
3/4	18.26	0.719	23.83	0.938	24.33	0.958	25.4	1.00	19.8	0.78

TABLE 3—DIMENSIONS OF CONNECTORS, UNIONS, ADAPTORS, ELBOWS, TEES, AND CROSSES (FIGURES 1 TO 20) (CONTINUED)[a]

Nom Tube OD in	J[c] Full Thread Min mm	J[c] Full Thread Min in	J_1 Full Thread Min mm	J_1 Full Thread Min in	K mm	K in	L mm ±0.8	L in ±0.03	L_1 mm ±0.8	L_1 in ±0.03
3/16	9.4	0.37	5.3	0.21	3.0	0.12	25.4	1.00	26.9	1.06
1/4	10.4	0.41	6.6	0.26	4.1	0.16	26.9	1.06	30.2	1.19
5/16	11.9	0.47	7.6	0.30	4.8	0.19	29.5	1.16	34.0	1.34
3/8	13.5	0.53	8.6	0.34	5.6	0.22	36.6	1.44	38.1	1.50
1/2	16.5	0.65	5.4	0.43	6.4	0.25	41.1	1.62	46.0	1.81
5/8	19.3	0.76	13.7	0.54	7.1	0.28	50.8	2.00	53.8	2.12
3/4	23.4	0.88	16.8	0.66	7.1	0.28	55.6	2.19	62.0	2.44

Nom Tube OD in	L_2 mm ±0.8	L_2 in ±0.03	L_3 mm ±0.8	L_3 in ±0.03	L_4 mm ±0.8	L_4 in ±0.03	L_5 mm ±0.8	L_5 in ±0.03	L_6 mm ±0.8	L_6 in ±0.03
3/16	24.6	0.97	23.9	0.94	23.9	0.94	20.6	0.81	22.4	0.88
1/4	26.2	1.03	25.4	1.00	26.9	1.06	23.1	0.91	25.4	1.00
5/16	26.9	1.06	27.7	1.09	28.4	1.12	23.9	0.94	26.9	1.06
3/8	33.3	1.31	30.2	1.19	33.3	1.31	32.5	1.28	31.8	1.25
1/2	38.1	1.50	36.6	1.44	39.6	1.56	35.1	1.33	36.6	1.44
5/8	46.0	1.81	44.4	1.75	46.0	1.81	42.2	1.66	42.9	1.69
3/4	48.5	1.91	52.3	2.06	52.3	2.06	47.8	1.88	50.8	2.00

Nom Tube OD in	L_7 Min mm	L_7 Min in	L_8 mm ±0.8	L_8 in ±0.03	M mm ±0.8	M in ±0.03	M_1 mm ±0.8	M_1 in ±0.03	M_2 mm ±0.8	M_2 in ±0.03
3/16	33.3	1.31	15.0	0.59	19.0	0.75	19.0	0.75	20.6	0.81
1/4	33.3	1.31	17.5	0.69	20.6	0.81	22.4	0.88	22.4	0.88
5/16	35.1	1.38	19.8	0.78	23.1	0.91	23.1	0.91	23.9	0.94
3/8	38.1	1.50	22.4	0.88	25.4	1.00	26.9	1.06	27.7	1.09
1/2	44.4	1.75	26.9	1.06	31.0	1.22	31.0	1.22	32.5	1.28
5/8	50.8	2.00	30.2	1.19	35.8	1.41	35.8	1.41	38.1	1.50
3/4	60.5	2.38	33.3	1.31	41.1	1.62	42.2	1.66	41.1	1.62

Nom Tube OD in	M_3 mm ±0.8	M_3 in ±0.03	M_4 mm ±0.8	M_4 in ±0.03	M_5 mm ±0.8	M_5 in ±0.03	M_6 mm ±0.8	M_6 in ±0.03	M_7 mm ±0.8	M_7 in ±0.03
3/16	—	—	—	—	18.3	0.72	15.0	0.59	15.7	0.62
1/4	23.9	0.94	19.8	0.78	20.6	0.81	15.7	0.62	17.0	0.67
5/16	—	—	—	—	23.1	0.91	16.8	0.66	19.8	0.78
3/8	29.5	1.16	24.6	0.97	26.2	1.03	18.3	0.72	22.6	0.89
1/2	34.0	1.34	28.4	1.12	31.0	1.22	21.3	0.84	26.9	1.06
5/8	—	—	—	—	35.8	1.41	26.2	1.03	31.2	1.23
3/4	—	—	—	—	41.1	1.62	31.8	1.25	35.8	1.41

Nom Tube OD in	N mm ±0.8	N in ±0.03	N_1 mm ±0.8	N_1 in ±0.03	N_2 mm ±0.8	N_2 in ±0.03	O mm	O in	P Max mm	P Max in	P_1 mm	P_1 in
3/16	19.0	0.75	11.2	0.44	13.2	0.52	7.9	0.31	9.7	0.38	9.7	0.38
1/4	19.8	0.78	11.9	0.47	16.3	0.64	7.9	0.31	9.7	0.38	9.7	0.38
5/16	19.8	0.78	11.9	0.47	16.3	0.64	7.9	0.31	9.7	0.38	9.7	0.38
3/8	26.9	1.06	17.5	0.69	21.8	0.86	7.9	0.31	14.5	0.57	14.2	0.56
1/2	28.4	1.12	19.0	0.75	24.1	0.95	9.7	0.38	14.5	0.57	14.2	0.56
5/8	35.1	1.38	25.4	1.00	29.7	1.17	12.7	0.50	19.0	0.75	19.1	0.75
3/4	38.1	1.50	26.9	1.06	30.5	1.20	15.7	0.62	19.0	0.75	19.1	0.75

TABLE 3—DIMENSIONS OF CONNECTORS, UNIONS, ADAPTORS, ELBOWS, TEES, AND CROSSES (FIGURES 1 TO 20) (CONTINUED)[a]

Nom Tube OD in	Q[d] mm	Q[d] in	S[e] Max mm	S[e] Max in	S_1 mm	S_1 in	S_2[e] Max mm	S_2[e] Max in	S_3[e] Min mm	S_3[e] Min in
3/16	—	—	12.2	0.48	7.9	0.31	10.4	0.41	21.6	0.85
1/4	—	—	12.2	0.48	7.9	0.31	—	—	23.4	0.92
5/16	—	—	—	—	7.9	0.31	10.7	0.42	—	—
3/8	17.5	0.69	17.5	0.69	7.9	0.31	11.2	0.44	31.5	1.24
1/2	—	—	—	—	9.7	0.38	13.7	0.54	—	—
5/8	23.9	0.94	23.9	0.94	12.7	0.50	17.5	0.69	42.4	1.67
3/4	—	—	31.0	1.22	15.7	0.62	21.3	0.84	51.3	2.02

Nom Tube OD in	T[f] Ref mm	T[f] Ref in	T_1[f] Min mm	T_1[f] Min in	T_2[f] Ref mm	T_2[f] Ref in	U Dia Min mm	U Dia Min in	U Dia Max mm	U Dia Max in
3/16	4.6	0.18	5.3	0.21	3.8	0.15	9.9	0.39	10.4	0.41
1/4	4.6	0.18	6.1	0.24	4.6	0.18	11.4	0.45	11.9	0.47
5/16	5.3	0.21	6.1	0.24	5.3	0.21	13.0	0.51	13.5	0.53
3/8	6.1	0.24	7.6	0.30	6.1	0.24	16.3	0.64	17.0	0.67
1/2	7.6	0.30	9.4	0.37	7.6	0.30	19.6	0.77	20.3	0.80
5/8	9.4	0.37	10.9	0.43	7.6	0.30	22.9	0.90	23.6	0.93
3/4	10.9	0.43	12.4	0.49	7.6	0.30	27.4	1.08	28.2	1.11

Nom Tube OD in	W[g] Dia mm +0.00 −0.5	W[g] Dia in +0.00 −0.02	X[g] Dia mm +0.00 −0.5	X[g] Dia in +0.00 −0.02	Y Dia Min mm	Y Dia Min in	Z Min mm	Z Min in
3/16	14.2	0.56	12.7	0.50	7.1	0.28	1.5	0.06
1/4	14.2	0.56	15.7	0.62	8.6	0.34	1.3	0.05
5/16	14.2	0.56	17.5	0.69	10.2	0.40	1.5	0.06
3/8	17.5	0.69	20.6	0.81	12.2	0.48	1.5	0.06
1/2	20.6	0.81	23.9	0.94	15.2	0.60	2.0	0.08
5/8	25.4	1.00	26.9	1.06	18.8	0.74	2.5	0.10
3/4	26.9	1.06	33.3	1.31	21.8	0.86	2.5	0.10

a For reducing sizes of unions, internal flare to external flare adaptors, and 90 degree elbow unions, see Table 4; for reducing sizes of solder connectors and 90 degree solder elbows, see Table 5; for reducing sizes of connectors, internal pipe thread connectors, internal flare to external pipe adapters, 90 degree elbow, 45 degree elbow, and internal pipe thread 90 degree elbow, see Table 6; for reducing sizes of tees, see Tables 7 and 8.
b Dryseal American Standard Taper Pipe Thread.
c Where thread relief undercut is used, last thread shall be chamfered 1/2 to 1 pitch long from G diameter and dimension J may be reduced by an amount equal to 1/2 pitch.
d Available with three types of fusible alloys as specified in general specifications.
e At manufacturer's option through passages in fittings shown in Figures 1, 5, and 19 may conform with the smaller diameter specified or be counterbored to the larger diameter from the appropriate end for depths S, S2 or S3, respectively.
f Minimum design thickness, not subject to inspection.
g Basic dimensions shown shall apply as minimum diameter for bosses or across flats. The −0.5 mm (−0.02 in) tolerance shall apply only to chamfer diameters on full hexagon versions of fittings shown in Figures 4, 6 to 8.
h ID of solder cup shall not be out of round by more than 0.08 mm (0.0031 in).
j Refer to SAE J528, Table 1 for copper tube tolerances.

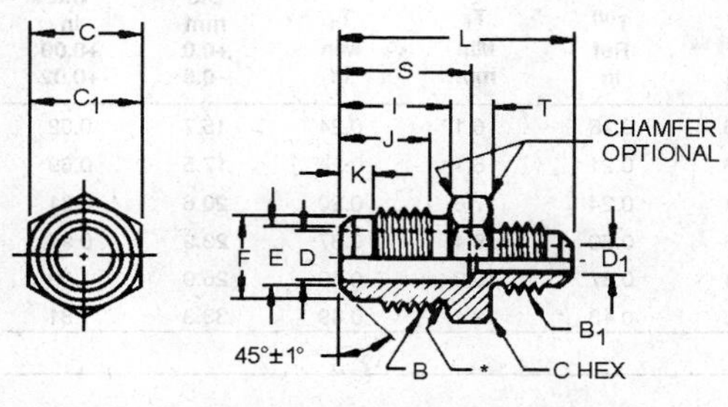

* UNDERCUT TO G DIA OPTIONAL ON FLARE SIZES 1/2 AND LARGER UNLESS OTHERWISE SPECIFIED BY PURCHASER (SEE FOOTNOTE C)

FIGURE 21—REDUCING UNION (010101) (UR2)

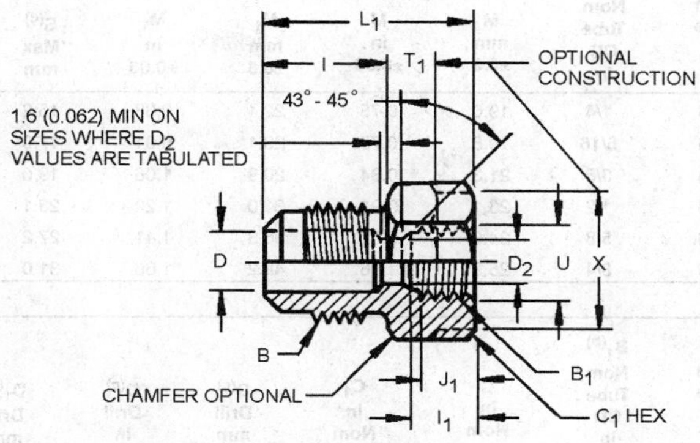

DIMENSIONS ARE mm (in)

FIGURE 22—INTERNAL FLARE TO EXTERNAL FLARE REDUCING ADAPTOR (1010105) (RO3)

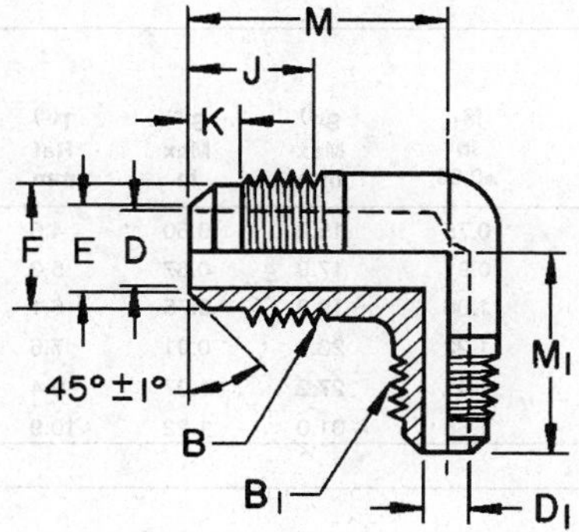

FIGURE 23—90 DEGREE REDUCING ELBOW UNION (010201) (ER2)

NOTE—UNSPECIFIED DETAIL WITH RESPECT TO DIMENSIONS, TOLERANCES, CONTOUR, MATERIAL, WORKMANSHIP, ETC., MUST CONFORM TO GENERAL SPECIFICATIONS FOR REFRIGERATION TUBE FITTINGS. THE ILLUSTRATIONS ON THIS PAGE APPLY TO TABLE 4. CODES SHOWN IN BRACKETS ADJACENT TO FIGURE NUMBERS REPRESENT RESPECTIVE FITTINGS IDENTIFICATION IN ACCORDANCE WITH SAE J846 (FIRST NUMBER) AND ANSI B70.1 (SECOND NUMBER).

TABLE 4—DIMENSIONS OF REDUCING UNIONS, REDUCING ADAPTERS, AND REDUCING ELBOW UNIONS (FIGURES 21 TO 23)[(a)]

B[(b)] Nom Tube OD in	B_1[(b)] Nom Tube OD in	C in Nom	C_1 in Nom	D[(c)] Drill mm	D[(C)] Drill in	D_1[(c)] Drill m	D_1[(c)] Drill in	D_2 Drill mm	D_2 Drill in	L mm ±0.8	L in ±0.03	L_1 mm ±0.8	L_1 in ±0.03
3/16	1/4	7/16	5/8	3.18	0.125	4.78	0.188	—	—	28.4	1.12	26.2	1.03
3/16	5/16	1/2	11/16	3.18	0.125	5.56	0.219	—	—	31.0	1.22	26.9	1.06
3/16	3/8	5/8	13/16	3.18	0.125	7.14	0.281	—	—	33.3	1.31	30.2	1.19
3/16	1/2	3/4	15/16	3.18	0.125	10.31	0.406	—	—	38.1	1.50	34.0	1.34
3/16	5/8	7/8	1- 1/16	3.18	0.125	12.70	0.500	—	—	42.9	1.69	38.9	1.53
3/16	3/4	1-1/16	1- 5/16	3.18	0.125	15.88	0.625	—	—	47.8	1.88	44.4	1.75

TABLE 4—DIMENSIONS OF REDUCING UNIONS, REDUCING ADAPTERS, AND REDUCING ELBOW UNIONS (FIGURES 21 TO 23)[(a)] (CONTINUED)

B[(b)] Nom Tube OD in	B_1[(b)] Nom Tube OD in	M mm ±0.8	M in ±0.03	M_1 mm ±0.8	M_1 in ±0.03	S[(c)] Max mm	S[(c)] Max in	T[(d)] Ref mm	T[(d)] Ref in	T_1 Min mm	T_1 Min in	X[(e)] Dia mm +0.0 −0.5	X[(e)] Dia in +0.00 +0.02
3/16	1/4	19.0	0.75	22.4	0.88	15.2	0.60	4.6	0.18	6.1	0.24	15.7	0.62
3/16	5/16	19.8	0.78	23.1	0.91	17.0	0.67	5.3	0.21	6.1	0.24	17.5	0.69
3/16	3/8	21.3	0.84	26.9	1.06	19.0	0.75	6.1	0.24	7.6	0.30	20.6	0.81
3/16	1/2	23.1	0.91	31.0	1.22	23.1	0.91	7.6	0.30	9.4	0.37	23.9	0.94
3/16	5/8	24.6	0.97	35.8	1.41	27.2	1.07	9.4	0.37	10.9	0.43	26.9	1.06
3/16	3/4	26.9	1.06	42.2	1.66	31.0	1.22	10.9	0.43	12.4	0.49	33.3	1.31

B[(b)] Nom Tube OD in	B_1[(b)] Nom Tube OD in	C in Nom	C_1 in Nom	D[(c)] Drill mm	D[(c)] Drill in	D_1[(c)] Drill mm	D_1[(c)] Drill in	D_2 Drill mm	D_2 Drill in	L mm ±0.8	L in ±0.03	L_1 mm ±0.8	L_1 in ±0.03
1/4	3/16	7/16	1/2	4.78	0.188	3.18	0.125	—	—	28.4	1.12	24.6	0.97
1/4	5/16	1/2	11/16	4.78	0.188	5.56	0.219	—	—	32.5	1.28	28.4	1.12
1/4	3/8	5/8	13/16	4.78	0.188	7.14	0.281	—	—	35.1	1.38	31.0	1.22
1/4	1/2	3/4	15/16	4.78	0.188	10.31	0.406	—	—	39.6	1.56	35.1	1.38
1/4	5/8	7/8	1- 1/16	4.78	0.188	12.70	0.500	—	—	44.4	1.75	39.6	1.56
1/4	3/4	1-1/16	1- 5/16	4.78	0.188	15.88	0.625	—	—	49.3	1.94	42.9	1.69

B[(b)] Nom Tube OD in	B_1[(b)] Nom Tube OD in	M mm ±0.8	M in ±0.03	M_1 mm ±0.8	M_1 in ±0.03	S[(c)] Max mm	S[(c)] Max in	T[(d)] Ref mm	T[(d)] Ref in	T_1 Min mm	T_1 Min in	X[(e)] Dia mm +00 −0.5	X[(e)] Dia in +0.00 +0.02
1/4	3/16	22.4	0.88	19.0	0.75	15.2	0.60	4.6	0.18	5.3	0.21	12.7	0.50
1/4	5/16	21.3	0.84	23.1	0.91	17.0	0.67	5.3	0.21	6.1	0.24	17.5	0.69
1/4	3/8	23.1	0.91	26.9	1.06	19.0	0.75	6.1	0.24	7.6	0.30	20.6	0.81
1/4	1/2	24.6	0.97	31.0	1.22	23.1	0.91	7.6	0.30	9.4	0.37	23.9	0.94
1/4	5/8	26.2	1.03	35.8	1.41	27.2	1.07	9.4	0.37	10.9	0.43	26.2	1.06
1/4	3/4	28.4	1.12	42.2	1.66	31.0	1.22	10.9	0.43	12.4	0.49	33.3	1.31

B[(b)] Nom Tube OD in	B1[(b)] Nom Tube OD in	C in Nom	C_1 in Nom	D[(c)] Drill mm	D[(c)] Drill in	D_1[(c)] Drill mm	D_1[(c)] Drill in	D_2 Drill mm	D_2 Drill in	L mm ±0.8	L in ±0.03	L_1 mm ±0.8	L_1 in ±0.03
5/16	3/16	1/2	1/2	5.56	0.219	3.18	0.125	4.78	0.188	31.0	1.22	25.4	1.00
5/16	1/4	1/2	5/8	5.56	0.219	4.78	0.188	—	—	32.5	1.28	27.7	1.09
5/16	3/8	5/8	13/16	5.56	0.219	7.14	0.281	—	—	36.6	1.44	31.8	1.25
5/16	1/2	3/4	15/16	5.56	0.219	10.31	0.406	—	—	41.1	1.62	35.8	1.41
5/16	5/8	7/8	1- 1/16	5.56	0.219	12.70	0.500	—	—	46.0	1.81	40.4	1.59
5/16	3/4	1-1/16	1- 5/16	5.56	0.219	15.88	0.625	—	—	50.8	2.00	46.0	1.81

B[(b)] Nom Tube OD in	B_1[(b)] Nom Tube OD in	M mm ±0.8	M in ±0.03	M_1 mm ±0.8	M_1 in ±0.03	S[(c)] Max mm	S[(c)] Max in	T[(d)] Ref mm	T[(d)] Ref in	T_1 Min mm	T_1 Min in	X[(e)] Dia mm +0.0 −0.5	X[(e)] Dia in +0.00 +0.02
5/16	3/16	23.1	0.91	19.8	0.78	17.0	0.67	5.3	0.21	5.3	0.21	12.7	0.50
5/16	1/4	23.1	0.91	21.3	0.84	17.0	0.67	5.3	0.21	6.1	0.24	15.7	0.62
5/16	3/8	24.6	0.97	26.9	1.06	19.0	0.75	6.1	0.24	7.6	0.30	20.6	0.81
5/16	1/2	26.2	1.03	31.0	1.22	23.1	0.91	7.6	0.30	9.4	0.37	23.9	0.94
5/16	5/8	27.7	1.09	35.8	1.41	27.2	1.07	9.4	0.37	10.9	0.43	26.9	1.06
5/16	3/4	30.2	1.19	42.2	1.66	31.0	1.22	10.9	0.43	12.4	0.49	33.3	1.31

TABLE 4—DIMENSIONS OF REDUCING UNIONS, REDUCING ADAPTERS, AND REDUCING ELBOW UNIONS (FIGURES 21 TO 23)[a] (CONTINUED)

B[b] Nom Tube OD in	B_1[b] Nom Tube OD in	C in Nom	C_1 in Nom	D[c] Drill mm	D[c] Drill in	D_1[c] Drill mm	D_1[c] Drill in	D_2 Drill mm	D_2 Drill in	L mm ±0.8	L in ±0.03	L_1 mm ±0.8	L_1 in ±0.03
3/8	3/16	5/8	5/8	7.14	0.281	3.18	0.125	4.78	0.188	33.3	1.31	26.2	1.03
3/8	1/4	5/8	5/8	7.14	0.281	4.78	0.188	6.35	0.250	35.1	1.38	28.4	1.12
3/8	5/16	5/8	11/16	7.14	0.281	5.56	0.219	—	—	36.6	1.44	30.2	1.19
3/8	1/2	3/4	15/16	7.14	0.281	10.31	0.406	—	—	42.9	1.69	36.6	1.44
3/8	5/8	7/8	1- 1/16	7.14	0.281	12.70	0.500	—	—	47.8	1.88	41.1	1.62
3/8	3/4	1-1/16	1- 5/16	7.14	0.281	15.89	0.625	—	—	52.3	2.06	46.7	1.84

B[b] Nom Tube OD in	B_1[b] Nom Tube OD in	M mm ±0.8	M in ±0.03	M_1 mm ±0.8	M_1 in ±0.03	S[c] Max mm	S[c] Max in	T[d] Ref mm	T[d] Ref in	T_1 Min mm	T_1 Min in	X[e] Dia mm +0.0 −0.5	X[e] Dia in +0.00 +0.02
3/8	3/16	26.9	1.06	21.3	0.84	19.0	0.75	6.1	0.24	6.1	0.24	15.7	0.62
3/8	1/4	26.9	1.06	23.1	0.91	19.0	0.75	6.1	0.24	6.1	0.24	15.7	0.62
3/8	5/16	26.9	1.06	24.6	0.97	19.0	0.75	6.1	0.24	6.1	0.24	17.5	0.69
3/8	1/2	27.7	1.09	31.0	1.22	23.1	0.91	7.6	0.30	9.4	0.37	23.9	0.94
3/8	5/8	29.5	1.16	35.8	1.41	27.2	1.07	9.4	0.37	10.9	0.43	26.9	1.06
3/8	3/4	31.8	1.25	42.2	1.66	31.0	1.22	10.9	0.43	12.4	0.49	33.3	1.31

B[b] Nom Tube OD in	B_1[b] Nom Tube OD in	C in Nom	C_1 in Nom	D[c] Drill mm	D[c] Drill in	D_1[c] Drill mm	D_1[c] Drill in	D_2 Drill mm	D_2 Drill in	L mm ±0.8	L in ±0.03	L_1 mm ±0.8	L_1 in ±0.03
1/2	3/16	3/4	3/4	10.31	0.406	3.18	0.125	4.78	0.188	38.1	1.50	29.5	1.16
1/2	1/4	3/4	3/4	10.31	0.406	4.78	0.188	6.35	0.250	39.6	1.56	31.8	1.25
1/2	5/16	3/4	3/4	10.31	0.406	5.56	0.219	7.92	0.312	41.1	1.62	32.5	1.28
1/2	3/8	3/4	13/16	10.31	0.406	7.14	0.281	9.52	0.375	42.9	1.69	35.8	1.41
1/2	5/8	7/8	1- 1/16	10.31	0.406	12.70	0.500	—	—	50.8	2.00	42.9	1.69
1/2	3/4	1-1/16	1- 5/16	10.31	0.406	15.88	0.625	—	—	55.6	2.19	48.5	1.91

B[b] Nom Tube OD in	B_1[b] Nom Tube OD in	M mm ±0.8	M in ±0.03	M_1 mm ±0.8	M_1 in ±0.03	S[c] Max mm	S[c] Max in	T[d] Ref mm	T[d] Ref in	T_1 Min mm	T_1 Min in	X[e] Dia mm +0.0 −0.5	X[e] Dia in +0.00 +0.02
1/2	3/16	31.0	1.22	23.1	0.91	23.1	0.91	7.6	0.30	7.6	0.30	19.0	0.75
1/2	1/4	31.0	1.22	24.6	0.97	23.1	0.91	7.6	0.30	7.6	0.30	19.0	0.75
1/2	5/16	31.0	1.22	26.2	1.03	23.1	0.91	7.6	0.30	7.6	0.30	19.0	0.75
1/2	3/8	31.0	1.22	27.7	1.09	23.1	0.91	7.6	0.30	7.6	0.30	20.6	0.81
1/2	5/8	32.5	1.28	35.8	1.41	27.2	1.07	9.4	0.37	10.9	0.43	26.9	1.06
1/2	3/4	35.1	1.38	42.2	1.66	31.0	1.22	10.9	0.43	12.4	0.49	33.3	1.31

B[b] Nom Tube OD in	B_1[b] Nom Tube OD in	C in Nom	C1 in Nom	D[c] Drill mm	D[c] Drill in	D_1[c] Drill mm	D_1[c] Drill in	D_2 Drill mm	D_2 Drill in	L mm ±0.8	L in ±0.03	L_1 mm ±0.8	L_1 in ±0.03
5/8	3/16	7/8	7/8	12.70	0.500	3.18	0.125	4.78	0.188	42.9	1.69	31.8	1.25
5/8	1/4	7/8	7/8	12.70	0.500	4.78	0.188	6.35	0.250	44.4	1.75	33.3	1.31
5/8	5/16	7/8	7/8	12.70	0.500	5.56	0.219	7.92	0.312	46.0	1.81	35.1	1.38
5/8	3/8	7/8	7/8	12.70	0.500	7.14	0.281	9.52	0.375	47.8	1.88	37.3	1.47
5/8	1/2	7/8	15/16	12.70	0.500	10.31	0.406	—	—	50.8	2.00	41.1	1.62
5/8	3/4	1-1/16	1- 5/16	12.70	0.500	15.88	0.625	—	—	58.7	2.31	50.0	1.97

TABLE 4—DIMENSIONS OF REDUCING UNIONS, REDUCING ADAPTERS, AND REDUCING ELBOW UNIONS (FIGURES 21 TO 23)[a] (CONTINUED)

B[b] Nom Tube OD in	B_1[b] Nom Tube OD in	M mm ±0.8	M in ±0.03	M_1 mm ±0.8	M_1 in ±0.03	S[c] Max mm	S[c] Max in	T[d] Ref mm	T[d] Ref in	T_1 Min mm	T_1 Min in	X[e] Dia mm +0.0 –0.5	X[e] Dia in +0.00 +0.02
5/8	3/16	35.8	1.41	24.6	0.97	27.2	1.07	9.4	0.37	9.4	0.37	22.4	0.88
5/8	1/4	35.8	1.41	26.2	1.03	27.2	1.07	9.4	0.37	9.4	0.37	22.4	0.88
5/8	5/16	35.8	1.41	27.7	1.09	27.2	1.07	9.4	0.37	9.4	0.37	22.4	0.88
5/8	3/8	35.8	1.41	29.5	1.16	27.2	1.07	9.4	0.37	9.4	0.37	22.4	0.88
5/8	1/2	35.8	1.41	32.5	1.28	27.2	1.07	9.4	0.37	9.4	0.37	23.9	0.94
5/8	3/4	38.1	1.50	42.2	1.66	31.0	1.22	10.9	0.43	12.4	0.49	33.3	1.31

B[b] Nom Tube OD in	B_1[b] Nom Tube OD in	C in Nom	C_1 in Nom	D[c] Drill mm	D[c] Drill in	D_1[c] Drill mm	D_1[c] Drill in	D_2 Drill mm	D_2 Drill in	L mm ±0.8	L in ±0.03	L_1 mm ±0.8	L_1 in ±0.03
3/4	3/16	1-1/16	1-1/16	15.88	0.625	3.18	0.125	4.78	0.188	47.8	1.88	36.6	1.44
3/4	1/4	1-1/16	1-1/16	15.88	0.625	4.78	0.188	6.35	0.250	49.3	1.94	36.6	1.44
3/4	5/16	1-1/16	1-1/16	15.88	0.625	5.56	0.219	7.92	0.312	50.8	2.00	36.6	1.44
3/4	3/8	1-1/16	1-1/16	15.88	0.625	7.14	0.281	9.52	0.375	52.3	2.06	38.9	1.53
3/4	1/2	1-1/16	1-1/16	15.88	0.625	10.31	0.406	12.70	0.500	55.6	2.19	42.9	1.69
3/4	5/8	1-1/16	1-1/16	15.88	0.625	12.70	0.500	—	—	58.7	2.31	47.8	1.88

B[b] Nom Tube OD in	B_1[b] Nom Tube OD in	M mm ±0.8	M in ±0.03	M_1 mm ±0.8	M_1 in ±0.03	S[c] Max mm	S[c] Max in	T[d] Ref mm	T[d] Ref in	T_1 Min mm	T_1 Min in	X[e] Dia mm +0.0 –0.5	X[e] Dia in +0.00 +0.02
3/4	3/16	42.2	1.66	26.9	1.06	31.0	1.22	10.9	0.43	10.9	0.43	26.9	1.06
3/4	1/4	42.2	1.66	28.4	1.12	31.0	1.22	10.9	0.43	10.9	0.43	26.9	1.06
3/4	5/16	42.2	1.66	30.2	1.19	31.0	1.22	10.9	0.43	10.9	0.43	26.9	1.06
3/4	3/8	42.2	1.66	31.8	1.25	31.0	1.22	10.9	0.43	10.9	0.43	26.9	1.06
3/4	1/2	42.2	1.66	35.1	1.38	31.0	1.22	10.9	0.43	10.9	0.43	26.9	1.06
3/4	5/8	42.2	1.66	38.1	1.50	31.0	1.22	10.9	0.43	10.9	0.43	26.9	1.06

a For flare dimensions shown on Figures 21 to 23 but not covered in Table 4, see corresponding dimensions for the specified Tube OD in Table 3.
b Where thread relief undercut is used last thread shall be chamfered 1/2 to 1 pitch long from G diameter and dimension J may be reduced by an amount equal to 1/2 pitch.
c At manufacturer's option through passages in fittings shown in Figure 21 may conform with the smaller diameter specified or be counterbored to the larger diameter from the appropriate end for depth S.
d Minimum design thickness, not subject to inspection.
e Basic dimensions shown shall apply as minimum for bosses. The –0.51 mm (–0.02 in) tolerance shall apply only to chamfer diameter on full hexagon version of fittings in Figure 22.

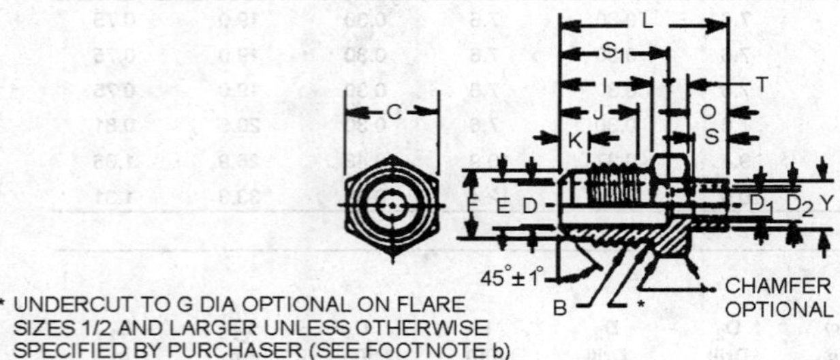

* UNDERCUT TO G DIA OPTIONAL ON FLARE SIZES 1/2 AND LARGER UNLESS OTHERWISE SPECIFIED BY PURCHASER (SEE FOOTNOTE b)

FIGURE 24—FLARE TO SOLDER REDUCING CONNECTOR (HALF UNION) (010104) (US3)

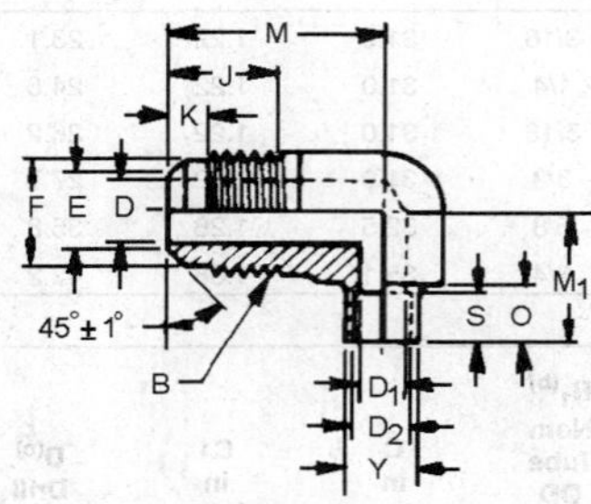

FIGURE 25—FLARE TO SOLDER 90 DEGREE REDUCING ELBOW (010204) (ES)

NOTE—UNSPECIFIED DETAIL WITH RESPECT TO DIMENSIONS, TOLERANCES, CONTOUR, MATERIAL, WORKMANSHIP, ETC., MUST CONFORM TO GENERAL SPECIFICATIONS FOR REFRIGERATION TUBE FITTINGS. THE ILLUSTRATIONS ON THIS PAGE APPLY TO TABLE 5. CODES SHOWN IN BRACKETS ADJACENT TO FIGURE NUMBERS REPRESENT RESPECTIVE FITTING IDENTIFICATION IN ACCORDANCE WITH SAE J846 (FIRST NUMBER) AND ANSI B70.1 (SECOND NUMBER).

TABLE 5—DIMENSIONS OF REDUCING SOLDER CONNECTORS AND REDUCING SOLDER ELBOWS (FIGURES 24 AND 25)[a]

B Nom Tube OD in	Solder Tube OD in	C Hex in Nom	D[c] Drill mm	D[c] Drill in	D_1[c] Drill mm	D_1[c] Drill in	D_2[e] Dia mm ±0.025	D_2[e] Dia in ±0.0010	L mm ±0.8	L in ±0.03	M mm ±0.8	M in ±0.03
3/16	1/8	3/8	3.18	0.125	2.39	0.094	3.277	0.1290	23.1	0.91	18.3	0.72
3/16	1/4	7/16	3.18	0.125	4.78	0.188	6.452	0.2540	23.9	0.94	18.3	0.72
3/16	5/16	7/16	3.18	0.125	6.35	0.250	8.039	0.3165	23.9	0.94	19.0	0.75
3/16	3/8	1/2	3.18	0.125	7.92	0.312	9.627	0.3790	23.9	0.94	19.8	0.78
3/16	1/2	5/8	3.18	0.125	11.13	0.438	12.802	0.5040	26.2	1.03	21.3	0.84
3/16	5/8	3/4	3.18	0.125	13.89	0.547	15.977	0.6290	30.2	1.19	23.1	0.91
3/16	3/4	7/8	3.18	0.125	17.48	0.688	19.152	0.7540	35.1	1.38	24.6	0.97
3/16	7/8	1	3.18	0.125	19.84	0.781	22.327	0.8790	39.6	1.56	26.9	1.06

B Nom Tube OD in	Solder Tube OD in	M_1 mm ±0.8	M_1 in ±0.03	O mm	O in	S mm	S in	S_1[c] Max mm	S_1[c] Max in	T[d] Ref mm	T[d] Ref in	Y Dia Min mm	Y Dia Min in
3/16	1/8	15.0	0.59	7.9	0.31	7.9	0.31	13.2	0.52	3.8	0.15	5.6	0.22
3/16	1/4	15.0	0.59	7.9	0.31	7.9	0.31	10.4	0.41	4.6	0.18	8.6	0.34
3/16	5/16	15.7	0.62	7.9	0.31	7.9	0.31	10.4	0.41	4.6	0.18	10.2	0.40
3/16	3/8	16.8	0.66	7.9	0.31	7.9	0.31	10.4	0.41	4.6	0.18	12.2	0.48
3/16	1/2	19.8	0.78	9.7	0.38	9.7	0.38	12.4	0.49	5.3	0.21	15.2	0.60
3/16	5/8	24.6	0.97	12.7	0.50	12.7	0.50	16.0	0.63	6.1	0.24	18.8	0.74
3/16	3/4	29.5	1.16	15.7	0.62	15.7	0.62	19.8	0.78	7.6	0.30	21.8	0.86
3/16	7/8	35.1	1.38	19.0	0.75	19.0	0.75	23.9	0.94	9.4	0.37	24.9	0.98

B Nom Tube OD in	Solder Tube OD in	C Hex in Nom	D[c] Drill mm	D[c] Drill in	D_1[c] Drill mm	D_1[c] Drill in	D_2[e] Dia mm ±0.025	D_2[e] Dia in ±0.0010	L mm ±0.8	L in ±0.03	M mm ±0.8	M in ±0.03
1/4	1/8	7/16	4.78	0.188	2.39	0.094	3.277	0.1290	25.4	1.00	20.6	0.81
1/4	3/16	7/16	4.78	0.188	4.78	0.188	4.864	0.1915	25.4	1.00	20.6	0.81
1/4	5/16	7/16	4.78	0.188	6.35	0.250	8.039	0.3165	25.4	1.00	20.6	0.81
1/4	3/8	1/2	4.78	0.188	7.92	0.312	9.627	0.3790	25.4	1.00	21.3	0.84
1/4	1/2	5/8	4.78	0.188	11.13	0.438	12.802	0.5040	27.7	1.09	23.1	0.91
1/4	5/8	3/4	4.78	0.188	13.89	0.547	15.977	0.6290	31.8	1.25	24.6	0.97
1/4	3/4	7/8	4.78	0.188	17.48	0.688	19.152	0.7540	36.6	1.44	26.2	1.03
1/4	7/8	1	4.78	0.188	19.84	0.781	22.327	0.8790	41.1	1.62	28.4	1.12

B Nom Tube OD in	Solder Tube OD in	M_1 mm ±0.8	M1 in ±0.03	O mm	O in	S mm	S in	S_1[c] Max mm	S_1[c] Max in	T[d] Ref mm	T[d] Ref in	Y Dia Min mm	Y Dia Min in
1/4	1/8	15.7	0.62	7.9	0.31	7.9	0.31	15.2	0.60	4.6	0.18	5.6	0.22
1/4	3/16	15.7	0.62	7.9	0.31	7.9	0.31	15.2	0.60	4.6	0.18	7.1	0.28
1/4	5/16	15.7	0.62	7.9	0.31	7.9	0.31	10.4	0.41	4.6	0.18	10.2	0.40
1/4	3/8	16.8	0.66	7.9	0.31	7.9	0.31	10.4	0.41	4.6	0.18	12.2	0.48
1/4	1/2	19.8	0.78	9.7	0.38	9.7	0.38	12.4	0.49	5.3	0.21	15.2	0.60
1/4	5/8	24.6	0.97	12.7	0.50	12.7	0.50	16.0	0.63	6.1	0.24	18.8	0.74
1/4	3/4	29.5	1.16	15.7	0.62	15.7	0.62	19.8	0.78	7.6	0.30	21.8	0.86
1/4	7/8	35.1	1.38	19.0	0.75	19.0	0.75	23.9	0.94	9.4	0.37	24.9	0.98

B Nom Tube OD in	Solder Tube OD in	C Hex in Nom	D[c] Drill mm	D[c] Drill in	D_1[c] Drill mm	D_1[c] Drill in	D_2[e] Dia mm ±0.025	D_2[e] Dia in ±0.0010	L mm ±0.8	L in ±0.03	M mm ±0.8	M in ±0.03
5/16	1/8	1/2	5.56	0.219	2.39	0.094	3.277	0.1290	27.7	1.09	23.1	0.91
5/16	3/16	1/2	5.56	0.219	3.96	0.156	4.864	0.1915	27.7	1.09	23.1	0.91
5/16	1/4	1/2	5.56	0.219	4.78	0.188	6.452	0.2540	27.7	1.09	23.1	0.91
5/16	3/8	1/2	5.56	0.219	7.92	0.312	9.627	0.3790	27.7	1.09	23.1	0.91
5/16	1/2	5/8	5.56	0.219	11.13	0.438	12.802	0.5040	29.5	1.16	24.6	0.97
5/16	5/8	3/4	5.56	0.219	13.89	0.547	15.977	0.6290	33.3	1.31	26.2	1.03
5/16	3/4	7/8	5.56	0.219	17.48	0.688	19.152	0.7540	38.1	1.50	27.7	1.09
5/16	7/8	1	5.56	0.219	19.84	0.781	22.327	0.8790	42.9	1.69	30.2	1.19

TABLE 5—DIMENSIONS OF REDUCING SOLDER CONNECTORS AND REDUCING SOLDER ELBOWS (FIGURES 24 AND 25)[a] (CONTINUED)

B Nom Tube OD in	Solder Tube OD in	M_1 mm ±0.8	M_1 in ±0.03	O mm	O in	S mm	S in	S_1[c] Max mm	S_1[c] Max in	T[d] Ref mm	T[d] Ref in	Y Dia Min mm	Y Dia Min in
5/16	1/8	16.8	0.66	7.9	0.31	7.9	0.31	17.0	0.67	5.3	0.21	5.6	0.22
5/16	3/16	16.8	0.66	7.9	0.31	7.9	0.31	17.0	0.67	5.3	0.21	7.1	0.28
5/16	1/4	16.8	0.66	7.9	0.31	7.9	0.31	17.0	0.67	5.3	0.21	8.6	0.34
5/16	3/8	16.8	0.66	7.9	0.31	7.9	0.31	10.7	0.42	5.3	0.21	12.2	0.48
5/16	1/2	19.8	0.78	9.7	0.38	9.7	0.38	12.4	0.49	5.3	0.21	15.2	0.60
5/16	5/8	24.6	0.97	12.7	0.50	12.7	0.50	16.0	0.63	6.1	0.24	18.8	0.74
5/16	3/4	29.5	1.16	15.7	0.62	15.7	0.62	19.8	0.78	7.6	0.30	21.8	0.86
5/16	7/8	35.1	1.38	19.0	0.75	19.0	0.75	23.9	0.94	9.4	0.37	24.9	0.98

B Nom Tube OD in	Solder Tube OD in	C Hex in Nom	D[c] Drill mm	D[c] Drill in	D_1[c] Drill mm	D_1[c] Drill in	D_2[e] Dia mm ±0.025	D_2[e] Dia in ±0.0010	L mm ±0.8	L in ±0.03	M mm ±0.8	M in ±0.03
3/8	1/8	5/8	7.14	0.281	2.39	0.094	3.277	0.1290	30.2	1.19	26.2	1.03
3/8	3/16	5/8	7.14	0.281	3.96	0.156	4.864	0.1915	30.2	1.19	26.2	1.03
3/8	1/4	5/8	7.14	0.281	4.78	0.188	6.452	0.2540	30.2	1.19	26.2	1.03
3/8	5/16	5/8	7.14	0.281	6.35	0.250	8.039	0.3165	30.2	1.19	26.2	1.03
3/8	1/2	5/8	7.14	0.281	11.13	0.438	12.802	0.5040	31.8	1.25	26.2	1.03
3/8	5/8	3/4	7.14	0.281	13.89	0.547	15.977	0.6290	35.1	1.38	27.7	1.09
3/8	3/4	7/8	7.14	0.281	17.48	0.688	19.152	0.7540	39.6	1.56	29.5	1.16
3/8	7/8	1	7.14	0.281	19.84	0.781	22.327	0.8790	44.4	1.75	31.8	1.25

B Nom Tube OD in	Solder Tube OD in	M_1 mm ±0.8	M_1 in ±0.03	O mm	O in	S mm	S in	S_1[c] Max mm	S_1[c] Max in	T[d] Ref mm	T[d] Ref in	Y Dia Min mm	Y Dia Min in
3/8	1/8	18.3	0.72	7.9	0.31	7.9	0.31	19.0	0.75	6.1	0.24	5.6	0.22
3/8	3/16	18.3	0.72	7.9	0.31	7.9	0.31	19.0	0.75	6.1	0.24	7.1	0.28
3/8	1/4	18.3	0.72	7.9	0.31	7.9	0.31	19.0	0.75	6.1	0.24	8.6	0.34
3/8	5/16	18.3	0.72	7.9	0.31	7.9	0.31	19.0	0.75	6.1	0.24	10.2	0.40
3/8	1/2	19.8	0.78	9.7	0.38	9.7	0.38	13.0	0.51	6.1	0.24	15.2	0.60
3/8	5/8	24.6	0.97	12.7	0.50	12.7	0.50	16.0	0.63	6.1	0.24	18.8	0.74
3/8	3/4	29.5	1.16	15.7	0.62	15.7	0.62	19.8	0.78	7.6	0.30	21.8	0.86
3/8	7/8	31.8	1.25	19.0	0.75	19.0	0.75	23.9	0.94	9.4	0.37	24.9	0.98

B Nom Tube OD in	Solder Tube OD in	C Hex in Nom	D[c] Drill mm	D[c] Drill in	D_1[c] Drill mm	D_1[c] Drill in	D_2[e] Dia mm ±0.025	D_2[e] Dia in ±0.0010	L mm ±0.8	L in ±0.03	M mm ±0.8	M in ±0.03
1/2	1/8	3/4	10.31	0.406	2.39	0.094	3.277	0.1290	35.1	1.38	31.0	1.22
1/2	3/16	3/4	10.31	0.406	3.96	0.156	4.864	0.1915	35.1	1.38	31.0	1.22
1/2	1/4	3/4	10.31	0.406	4.78	0.188	6.452	0.2540	35.1	1.38	31.0	1.22
1/2	5/16	3/4	10.31	0.406	6.35	0.250	8.039	0.3165	35.1	1.38	31.0	1.22
1/2	3/8	3/4	10.31	0.406	7.92	0.312	9.627	0.3790	35.1	1.38	31.0	1.22
1/2	5/8	3/4	10.31	0.406	13.89	0.547	15.977	0.6290	39.6	1.56	31.0	1.22
1/2	3/4	7/8	10.31	0.406	17.48	0.688	19.152	0.7540	42.9	1.69	32.5	1.28
1/2	7/8	1	10.31	0.406	19.84	0.781	22.327	0.8790	47.8	1.88	35.1	1.38

B Nom Tube OD in	Solder Tube OD in	M_1 mm ±0.8	M_1 in ±0.03	O mm	O in	S mm	S in	S_1[c] Max mm	S_1[c] Max in	T[d] Ref mm	T[d] Ref in	Y Dia Min mm	Y Dia Min in
1/2	1/8	19.8	0.78	7.9	0.31	7.9	0.31	23.1	0.91	7.6	0.30	5.6	0.22
1/2	3/16	19.8	0.78	7.9	0.31	7.9	0.31	23.1	0.91	7.6	0.30	7.1	0.28
1/2	1/4	19.8	0.78	7.9	0.31	7.9	0.31	23.1	0.91	7.6	0.30	8.6	0.34
1/2	5/16	19.8	0.78	7.9	0.31	7.9	0.31	23.1	0.91	7.6	0.30	10.2	0.40
1/2	3/8	19.8	0.78	7.9	0.31	7.9	0.31	23.1	0.91	7.6	0.30	12.2	0.48
1/2	5/8	24.6	0.97	12.7	0.50	12.7	0.50	16.8	0.66	7.6	0.30	18.8	0.74
1/2	3/4	29.5	1.16	15.7	0.62	15.7	0.62	19.8	0.78	7.6	0.30	21.8	0.86
1/2	7/8	35.1	1.38	19.0	0.75	19.0	0.75	23.9	0.94	9.4	0.37	24.9	0.98

TABLE 5—DIMENSIONS OF REDUCING SOLDER CONNECTORS AND REDUCING SOLDER ELBOWS (FIGURES 24 AND 25)[a] (CONTINUED)

Nom Tube OD in	Solder Tube OD in	C Hex in Nom	D[c] Drill mm	D[c] Drill in	D_1[c] Drill mm	D_1[c] Drill in	D_2[e] Dia mm ±0.025	D_2[e] Dia in ±0.0010	L mm ±0.8	L in ±0.03	M mm ±0.8	M in ±0.03
5/8	1/8	7/8	12.70	0.500	2.39	0.094	3.277	0.1290	39.6	1.56	35.8	1.41
5/8	3/16	7/8	12.70	0.500	3.96	0.156	4.864	0.1915	39.6	1.56	35.8	1.41
5/8	1/4	7/8	12.70	0.500	4.78	0.188	6.452	0.2540	39.6	1.56	35.8	1.41
5/8	5/16	7/8	12.70	0.500	6.35	0.250	8.039	0.3165	39.6	1.56	35.8	1.41
5/8	3/8	7/8	12.70	0.500	7.92	0.312	9.627	0.3790	39.6	1.56	35.8	1.41
5/8	1/2	7/8	12.70	0.500	11.13	0.438	12.802	0.5040	41.1	1.62	35.8	1.41
5/8	3/4	7/8	12.70	0.500	17.48	0.688	19.152	0.7540	47.8	1.88	35.8	1.41
5/8	7/8	1	12.70	0.500	19.84	0.781	22.327	0.8790	50.8	2.00	38.1	1.50

B Nom Tube OD in	Solder Tube OD in	M_1 mm ±0.8	M_1 in ±0.03	O mm	O in	S mm	S in	S_1[c] Max mm	S_1[c] Max in	T[d] Ref mm	T[d] Ref in	Y Dia Min mm	Y Dia Min in
5/8	1/8	21.3	0.84	7.9	0.31	7.9	0.31	27.2	1.07	9.4	0.37	5.6	0.22
5/8	3/16	21.3	0.84	7.9	0.31	7.9	0.31	27.2	1.07	9.4	0.37	7.1	0.28
5/8	1/4	21.3	0.84	7.9	0.31	7.9	0.31	27.2	1.07	9.4	0.37	8.6	0.34
5/8	5/16	21.3	0.84	7.9	0.31	7.9	0.31	27.2	1.07	9.4	0.37	10.2	0.40
5/8	3/8	21.3	0.84	7.9	0.31	7.9	0.31	27.2	1.07	9.4	0.37	12.2	0.48
5/8	1/2	23.1	0.91	9.7	0.38	9.7	0.38	27.2	1.07	9.4	0.37	15.2	0.60
5/8	3/4	29.5	1.16	15.7	0.62	15.7	0.62	20.6	0.81	9.4	0.37	21.8	0.86
5/8	7/8	35.1	1.38	19.0	0.75	19.0	0.75	23.9	0.94	9.4	0.37	24.9	0.98

B Nom Tube OD in	Solder Tube OD in	C Hex in Nom	D[c] Drill mm	D[c] Drill in	D_1[c] Drill mm	D_1[c] Drill in	D_2[e] Dia mm ±0.025	D_2[e] Dia in ±0.0010	L mm ±0.8	L in ±0.03	M mm ±0.8	M in ±0.03
3/4	1/8	1-1/16	15.88	0.625	2.39	0.094	3.277	0.1290	44.4	1.75	41.1	1.62
3/4	3/16	1-1/16	15.88	0.625	3.96	0.156	4.864	0.1915	44.4	1.75	41.1	1.62
3/4	1/4	1-1/16	15.88	0.625	4.76	0.188	6.452	0.2540	44.4	1.75	41.1	1.62
3/4	5/16	1-1/16	15.88	0.625	6.35	0.250	8.039	0.3165	44.4	1.75	41.1	1.62
3/4	3/8	1-1/16	15.88	0.625	7.92	0.312	9.627	0.3790	44.4	1.75	41.1	1.62
3/4	1/2	1-1/16	15.88	0.625	11.13	0.438	12.802	0.5040	46.0	1.81	41.1	1.62
3/4	5/8	1-1/16	15.88	0.625	13.89	0.547	15.977	0.6290	49.3	1.94	41.1	1.62
3/4	3/4	1-1/16	15.88	0.625	19.84	0.781	22.327	0.8790	55.6	2.19	41.1	1.62

B Nom Tube OD in	Solder Tube OD in	M_1 mm ±0.8	M_1 in ±0.03	O mm	O in	S mm	S in	S_1[c] Max mm	S_1[c] Max in	T[d] Ref mm	T[d] Ref in	Y Dia Min mm	Y Dia Min in
3/4	1/8	23.9	0.94	7.9	0.31	7.9	0.31	31.0	1.22	10.9	0.43	5.6	0.22
3/4	3/16	23.9	0.94	7.9	0.31	7.9	0.31	31.0	1.22	10.9	0.43	7.1	0.28
3/4	1/4	23.9	0.94	7.9	0.31	7.9	0.31	31.0	1.22	10.9	0.43	8.6	0.34
3/4	5/16	23.9	0.94	7.9	0.31	7.9	0.31	31.0	1.22	10.9	0.43	10.2	0.40
3/4	3/8	23.9	0.94	7.9	0.31	7.9	0.31	31.0	1.22	10.9	0.43	12.2	0.48
3/4	1/2	25.4	1.00	9.7	0.38	9.7	0.38	31.0	1.22	10.9	0.43	15.2	0.60
3/4	5/8	28.4	1.12	12.7	0.50	12.7	0.50	31.0	1.22	10.9	0.43	18.8	0.74
3/4	7/8	35.1	1.38	19.0	0.75	19.0	0.75	24.6	0.97	10.9	0.43	24.9	0.98

a For flare dimensions shown on Figures 24 and 25 but not covered in Table 5, see corresponding dimensions for the specified Tube OD in Table 3.
b Where thread relief undercut is used, last thread shall be chamfered 1/2 to 1 pitch long from G diameter and dimension J may be reduced by an amount equal to 1/2 pitch.
c At manufacturer's option through passages in fittings shown in Figure 24 may conform with the smaller diameter specified or be counterbored to the larger diameter from appropriate end for depth S_1.
d Minimum design thickness, not subject to inspection.
e ID of solder cup shall not be out of round by more than 0.08 (0.003 in).

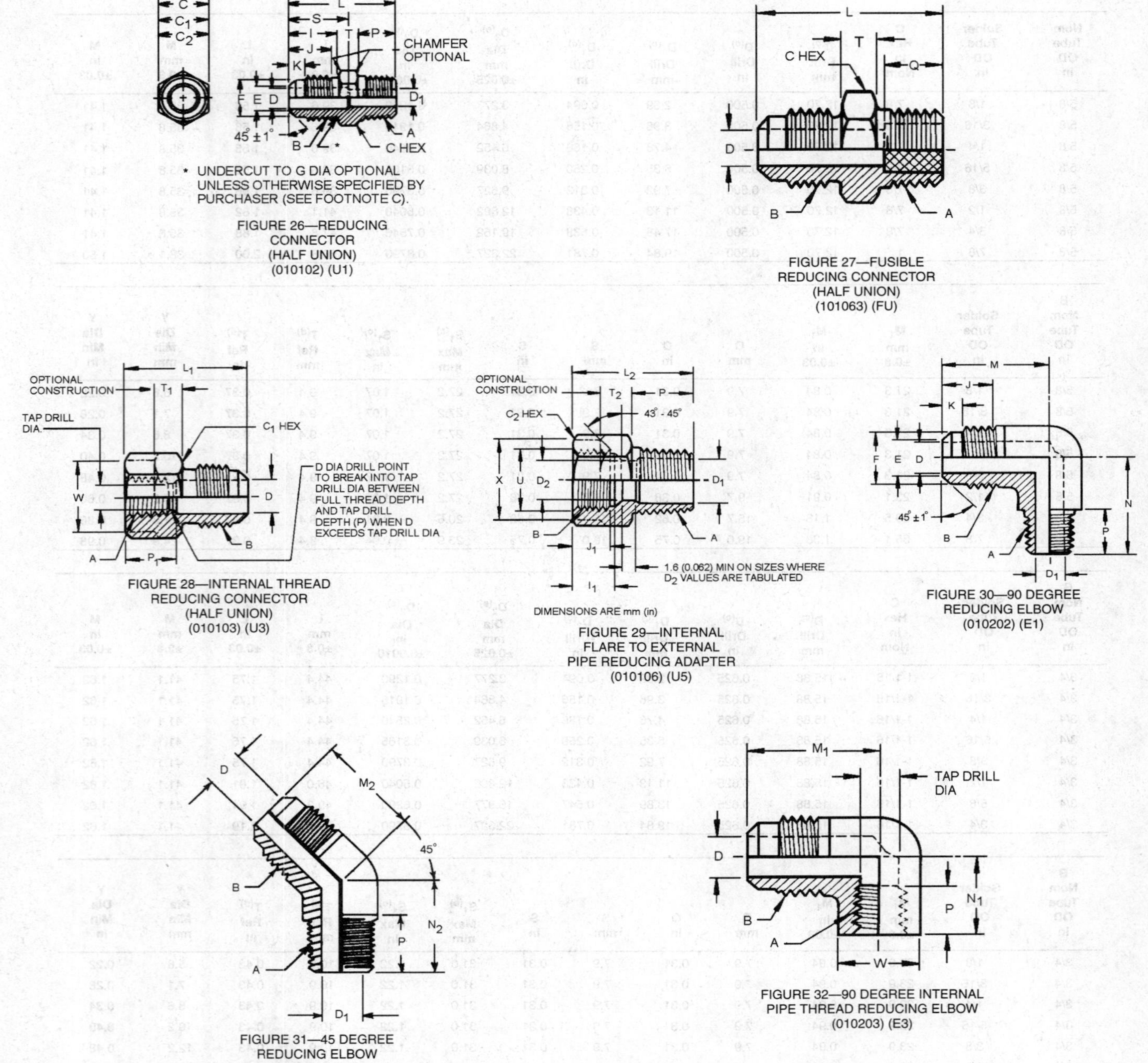

FIGURE 26—REDUCING CONNECTOR (HALF UNION) (010102) (U1)

FIGURE 27—FUSIBLE REDUCING CONNECTOR (HALF UNION) (101063) (FU)

FIGURE 28—INTERNAL THREAD REDUCING CONNECTOR (HALF UNION) (010103) (U3)

FIGURE 29—INTERNAL FLARE TO EXTERNAL PIPE REDUCING ADAPTER (010106) (U5)

FIGURE 30—90 DEGREE REDUCING ELBOW (010202) (E1)

FIGURE 31—45 DEGREE REDUCING ELBOW (010302) (E5)

FIGURE 32—90 DEGREE INTERNAL PIPE THREAD REDUCING ELBOW (010203) (E3)

NOTE—Unspecified detail with respect to dimensions, tolerances, contour, material, workmanship, etc., must conform to General Specifications for Refrigeration Tube Fittings. The dimensional designations in Figures 1 and 30 shall apply to corresponding features of other figures on this page unless shown otherwise. The illustrations on this page apply to Table 6. Codes shown in brackets adjacent to figure numbers represent respective fitting identification in accordance with SAE J846 (first number) and ANSI B70.1 (second number).

TABLE 6—DIMENSIONS OF REDUCING CONNECTORS, REDUCING ADAPTERS, AND REDUCING ELBOWS (FIGURES 26 TO 32)[a]

B Nom Tube OD in	A Dryseal Pipe Thread NPTF[b]	C Hex in Nom	C_1 Hex in Nom	C_2 Hex in Nom	D[d] Drill mm	D[d] Drill in	D_1[d] Drill mm	D_1[d] Drill in	D_2 Drill mm	D_2 Drill in	L mm ±0.8	L in ±0.03
3/16	1/4	9/16	11/16	9/16	3.18	0.125	7.92	0.312	4.78	0.188	30.2	1.19
3/16	3/8	11/16	13/16	11/16	3.18	0.125	10.31	0.406	4.78	0.188	31.8	1.22
3/16	1/2	7/8	1	7/8	3.18	0.125	14.27	0.562	4.78	0.188	38.1	1.44
3/16	3/4	1- 1/16	1- 1/4	1- 1/16	3.18	0.125	19.05	0.750	4.78	0.188	41.1	1.50

B Nom Tube OD in	L_1 mm ±0.8	L_1 in ±0.03	L_2 mm ±0.8	L_2 in ±0.03	M mm ±0.8	M in ±0.03	M_1 mm ±0.8	M_1 in ±0.03	M_2 mm ±0.8	M_2 in ±0.03	N mm ±0.8	N in ±0.03
3/16	30.2	1.19	23.9	0.94	20.6	0.81	23.1	0.91	18.0	0.71	24.6	0.97
3/16	31.0	1.22	21.3	0.84	22.4	0.88	24.6	0.97	19.0	0.75	25.4	1.00
3/16	36.6	1.44	26.9	1.06	24.6	0.97	26.9	1.06	20.3	0.80	32.5	1.28
3/16	38.1	1.50	30.2	1.19	26.9	1.06	31.0	1.22	21.3	0.84	35.1	1.38

B Nom Tube OD in	N_1 mm ±0.8	N_1 in ±0.03	N_2 mm ±0.8	N_2 in ±0.03	P Max mm	P Max in	Q[e] mm	Q[e] in	S[d] Max mm	S[d] Max in	T[f] Ref mm	T[f] Ref in
3/16	15.8	0.62	21.8	0.86	14.2	0.56	—	—	16.8	0.66	4.6	0.18
3/16	15.8	0.62	24.1	0.95	14.2	0.56	—	—	17.5	0.69	6.1	0.24
3/16	20.6	0.81	29.7	1.17	19.0	0.75	—	—	23.1	0.91	7.6	0.30
3/16	20.6	0.81	30.5	1.20	19.0	0.75	—	—	24.6	0.97	10.9	0.43

B Nom Tube OD in	T_1 Min mm	T_1 Min in	T_2 Min mm	T_2 Min in	W[g] mm +0.0 −0.5	W[g] in +0.00 −0.02	X[g] mm +0.0 −0.5	X[g] in +0.00 −0.02
3/16	6.1	0.24	5.3	0.21	17.5	0.69	14.2	0.56
3/16	7.6	0.30	6.1	0.24	20.6	0.81	17.5	0.69
3/16	9.4	0.37	7.6	0.30	25.4	1.00	22.4	0.88
3/16	12.4	0.49	10.9	0.43	31.8	1.25	26.9	1.06

B Nom Tube OD in	A Dryseal Pipe Thread NPTF[b]	C Hex in Nom	C_1 Hex in Nom	C_2 Hex in Nom	D[d] Drill mm	D[d] Drill in	D_1[d] Drill mm	D_1[d] Drill in	D_2 Drill mm	D_2 Drill in	L mm ±0.8	L in ±0.03
1/4	1/4	9/16	11/16	5/8	4.78	0.188	7.92	0.312	6.35	0.250	31.8	1.25
1/4	3/8	11/16	13/16	11/16	4.78	0.188	10.31	0.406	6.35	0.250	33.3	1.31
1/4	1/2	7/8	1	7/8	4.78	0.188	14.27	0.562	6.35	0.250	39.6	1.56
1/4	3/4	1- 1/16	1- 1/4	1- 1/16	4.78	0.188	19.05	0.750	6.35	0.250	42.9	1.69

B Nom Tube OD in	L_1 mm ±0.8	L_1 in ±0.03	L_2 mm ±0.8	L_2 in ±0.03	M mm ±0.8	M in ±0.03	M_1 mm ±0.8	M_1 in ±0.03	M_2 mm ±0.8	M_2 in ±0.03	N mm ±0.8	N in ±0.03
1/4	31.8	1.25	26.2	1.03	23.1	0.91	24.6	0.97	19.0	0.75	23.9	0.94
1/4	32.5	1.28	23.9	0.94	23.9	0.94	26.2	1.03	20.1	0.79	26.2	1.03
1/4	38.1	1.50	26.9	1.06	26.2	1.03	28.4	1.12	21.6	0.85	32.5	1.28
1/4	39.6	1.56	30.2	1.19	28.4	1.12	32.5	1.28	22.6	0.89	35.1	1.38

B Nom Tube OD in	N_1 mm ±0.8	N_1 in ±0.03	N_2 mm ±0.8	N_2 in ±0.03	P Min mm	P Min in	P_1 mm	P_1 in	Q[e] mm	Q[e] in	S[d] Max mm	S[d] Max in
1/4	16.8	0.66	24.1	0.95	14.2	0.56	14.2	0.56	17.5	0.69	17.5	0.69
1/4	21.3	0.84	29.7	1.17	19.0	0.75	14.2	0.56	—	—	23.1	0.91
1/4	21.3	0.84	30.5	1.20	19.0	0.75	19.1	0.75	—	—	24.6	0.97
1/4	21.3	0.84	30.5	1.20	19.0	0.75	19.1	0.75	—	—	24.6	0.97

TABLE 6—DIMENSIONS OF REDUCING CONNECTORS, REDUCING ADAPTERS, AND REDUCING ELBOWS (FIGURES 26 TO 32)[a] (CONTINUED)

B Nom Tube OD in	T[f] Ref mm	T[f] Ref in	T_1 Min mm	T_1 Min in	T_2 Min mm	T_2 Min in	W[g] mm +0.0 −0.5	W[g] in +0.00 −0.02	X[g] mm +0.0 −0.5	X[g] in +0.00 −0.02
1/4	4.6	0.18	6.1	0.24	6.1	0.24	17.5	0.69	15.7	0.62
1/4	6.1	0.24	7.6	0.30	6.1	0.24	20.6	0.81	17.5	0.69
1/4	7.6	0.30	9.4	0.37	7.6	0.30	25.4	1.00	22.4	0.88
1/4	10.9	0.43	12.4	0.49	10.9	0.43	31.8	1.25	26.9	1.06

B Nom Tube OD in	A Dryseal Pipe Thread NPTF[b]	C Hex in Nom	C_1 Hex in Nom	C_2 Hex in Nom	D[d] Drill mm	D[d] Drill in	D_1[d] Drill mm	D_1[d] Drill in	D_2 Drill mm	D_2 Drill in	L mm ±0.8	L in ±0.03
5/16	1/4	9/16	11/16	11/16	5.56	0.219	7.92	0.312	7.92	0.312	34.0	1.34
5/16	3/8	11/16	13/16	11/16	5.56	0.219	10.31	0.406	7.92	0.312	35.1	1.38
5/16	1/2	7/8	1	7/8	5.56	0.219	14.27	0.562	7.92	0.312	41.1	1.62
5/16	3/4	1- 1/16	1- 1/4	1- 1/16	5.56	0.219	19.05	0.750	7.92	0.312	44.4	1.75

B Nom Tube OD in	L_1 mm ±0.8	L_1 in ±0.03	L_2 mm ±0.8	L_2 in ±0.03	M mm ±0.8	M in ±0.03	M_1 mm ±0.8	M_1 in ±0.03	M_2 mm ±0.8	M_2 in ±0.03	N mm ±0.8	N in ±0.03
5/16	32.5	1.28	27.7	1.09	24.6	0.97	26.2	1.03	20.6	0.81	23.9	0.94
5/16	33.3	1.31	25.4	1.00	25.4	1.00	27.7	1.09	21.6	0.85	26.2	1.03
5/16	38.9	1.53	28.4	1.12	27.7	1.09	30.2	1.19	23.1	0.91	32.5	1.28
5/16	40.4	1.52	30.2	1.19	30.2	1.19	34.0	1.34	24.1	0.95	35.1	1.38

B Nom Tube OD in	N_1 mm ±0.8	N_1 in ±0.03	N_2 mm ±0.8	N_2 in ±0.03	P Min mm	P Min in	P_1 mm	P_1 in	Q[e] mm	Q[e] in	S[d] Max mm	S[d] Max in
5/16	16.8	0.66	21.8	0.86	14.2	0.56	14.2	0.56	—	—	17.0	0.67
5/16	16.8	0.66	24.1	0.95	14.2	0.56	14.2	0.56	—	—	17.5	0.69
5/16	21.3	0.84	29.7	1.17	19.0	0.75	19.1	0.75	—	—	23.1	0.91
5/16	21.3	0.84	30.5	1.20	19.0	0.75	19.1	0.75	—	—	24.6	0.97

B Nom Tube OD in	T[f] Ref mm	T[f] Ref in	T_1 Min mm	T_1 Min in	T_2 Min mm	T_2 Min in	W[g] mm +0.0 −0.5	W[g] in +0.00 −0.02	X[g] mm +0.0 −0.5	X[g] in +0.00 −0.02
5/16	5.3	0.21	6.1	0.24	6.1	0.24	17.5	0.69	17.5	0.69
5/16	6.1	0.24	7.6	0.30	6.1	0.24	20.6	0.81	17.5	0.69
5/16	7.6	0.30	9.4	0.37	7.6	0.30	25.4	1.00	22.4	0.88
5/16	10.9	0.43	12.4	0.49	10.9	0.43	31.8	1.25	26.9	1.06

B Nom Tube OD in	A Dryseal Pipe Thread NPTF[b]	C Hex in Nom	C_1 Hex in Nom	C_2 Hex in Nom	D[d] Drill mm	D[d] Drill in	D_1[d] Drill mm	D_1[d] Drill in	D_2 Drill mm	D_2 Drill in	L mm ±0.8	L in ±0.03
3/8	1/8	5/8	5/8	13/16	7.14	0.281	5.56	0.219	—	—	31.8	1.25
3/8	3/8	11/16	13/16	13/16	7.14	0.281	10.31	0.406	9.52	0.375	36.6	1.44
3/8	1/2	7/8	1	7/8	7.14	0.281	14.27	0.562	9.52	0.375	42.9	1.69
3/8	3/4	1- 1/16	1- 1/4	1- 1/16	7.14	0.281	19.05	0.750	9.52	0.375	46.0	1.81

B Nom Tube OD in	L_1 mm ±0.8	L_1 in ±0.03	L_2 mm ±0.8	L_2 in ±0.03	M mm ±0.8	M in ±0.03	M_1 mm ±0.8	M_1 in ±0.03	M_2 mm ±0.8	M_2 in ±0.03	N mm ±0.8	N in ±0.03
3/8	28.4	1.12	27.7	1.09	26.2	1.03	26.9	1.06	22.6	0.89	23.1	0.91
3/8	35.1	1.38	28.4	1.12	26.9	1.06	29.5	1.16	23.6	0.93	27.7	1.09
3/8	41.1	1.62	31.8	1.25	29.5	1.16	31.8	1.25	25.1	0.99	32.5	1.28
3/8	42.2	1.66	30.2	1.19	31.8	1.25	35.8	1.41	26.2	1.03	35.1	1.38

TABLE 6—DIMENSIONS OF REDUCING CONNECTORS, REDUCING ADAPTERS, AND REDUCING ELBOWS (FIGURES 26 TO 32)[a] (CONTINUED)

B Nom Tube OD in	N_1 mm ±0.8	N_1 in ±0.03	N_2 mm ±0.8	N_2 in ±0.03	P Min mm	P Min in	P_1 mm	P_1 in	Q[e] mm	Q[e] in	S[d] Max mm	S[d] Max in
3/8	12.7	0.50	17.0	0.67	9.7	0.38	9.7	0.38	—	—	19.0	0.75
3/8	17.5	0.69	24.1	0.95	14.2	0.56	14.2	0.56	17.5	0.69	17.5	0.69
3/8	22.4	0.88	29.7	1.17	19.0	0.75	19.1	0.75	—	—	23.1	0.91
3/8	22.4	0.88	30.5	1.20	19.0	0.75	19.1	0.75	—	—	24.6	0.97

B Nom Tube OD in	T[f] Ref mm	T[f] Ref in	T_1 Min mm	T_1 Min in	T_2 Min mm	T_2 Min in	W[g] mm +0.0 −0.5	W[g] in +0.00 −0.02	X[g] mm +0.0 −0.5	X[g] in +0.00 −0.02
3/8	6.1	0.24	6.1	0.24	7.6	0.30	15.7	0.62	20.6	0.81
3/8	6.1	0.24	7.6	0.30	7.6	0.30	20.6	0.81	20.6	0.81
3/8	7.6	0.30	9.4	0.37	7.6	0.30	25.4	1.00	22.4	0.88
3/8	10.9	0.43	12.4	0.49	10.9	0.43	31.8	1.25	26.9	1.06

B Nom Tube OD in	A Dryseal Pipe Thread NPTF[b]	C Hex in Nom	C_1 Hex in Nom	C_2 Hex in Nom	D[d] Drill mm	D[d] Drill in	D_1[d] Drill mm	D_1[d] Drill in	D_2 Drill mm	D_2 Drill in	L mm ±0.8	L in ±0.03
1/2	1/8	3/4	3/4	15/16	10.31	0.406	5.56	0.219	—	—	36.6	1.44
1/2	1/4	3/4	3/4	15/16	10.31	0.406	7.92	0.312	—	—	41.1	1.62
1/2	1/2	7/8	1	15/16	10.31	0.406	14.27	0.562	12.70	0.500	46.0	1.81
1/2	3/4	1-1/16	1-1/4	1- 1/16	10.31	0.406	19.05	0.750	12.70	0.500	49.3	1.94

B Nom Tube OD in	L_1 mm ±0.8	L_1 in ±0.03	L_2 mm ±0.8	L_2 in ±0.03	M mm ±0.8	M in ±0.03	M_1 mm ±0.8	M_1 in ±0.03	M_2 mm ±0.8	M_2 in ±0.03	N mm ±0.8	N in ±0.03
1/2	30.2	1.19	31.8	1.25	31.0	1.22	31.0	1.22	26.9	1.06	25.4	1.00
1/2	35.8	1.41	34.0	1.34	31.0	1.22	31.0	1.22	26.9	1.06	30.2	1.19
1/2	44.4	1.75	37.3	1.47	32.5	1.28	35.1	1.38	28.4	1.12	35.1	1.38
1/2	46.0	1.81	35.1	1.38	35.1	1.38	38.9	1.53	29.5	1.16	35.1	1.38

B Nom Tube OD in	N_1 mm ±0.8	N_1 in ±0.03	N_2 mm ±0.8	N_2 in ±0.03	P Min mm	P Min in	P_1 mm	P_1 in	Q[e] mm	Q[e] in	S[d] Max mm	S[d] Max in
1/2	14.2	0.56	19.3	0.76	9.7	0.38	9.7	0.38	—	—	23.1	0.91
1/2	19.0	0.75	24.1	0.95	14.2	0.56	14.2	0.56	—	—	23.1	0.91
1/2	23.9	0.94	29.7	1.17	19.0	0.75	19.1	0.75	—	—	23.1	0.91
1/2	23.9	0.94	30.5	1.20	19.0	0.75	19.1	0.75	—	—	24.6	0.97

B Nom Tube OD in	T[f] Ref mm	T[f] Ref in	T_1 Min mm	T_1 Min in	T_2 Min mm	T_2 Min in	W[g] mm +0.0 −0.5	W[g] in +0.00 −0.02	X[g] mm +0.0 −0.5	X[g] in +0.00 −0.02
1/2	7.6	0.30	7.6	0.30	9.4	0.37	19.0	0.75	23.9	0.94
1/2	7.6	0.30	7.6	0.30	9.4	0.37	19.0	0.75	23.9	0.94
1/2	7.6	0.30	9.4	0.37	9.4	0.37	25.4	1.00	23.9	0.94
1/2	10.9	0.43	12.4	0.49	10.9	0.43	31.8	1.25	26.9	1.06

B Nom Tube OD in	A Dryseal Pipe Thread NPTF[b]	C Hex in Nom	C_1 Hex in Nom	C_2 Hex in Nom	D[d] Drill mm	D[d] Drill in	D_1[d] Drill mm	D_1[d] Drill in	D_2 Drill mm	D_2 Drill in	L mm ±0.8	L in ±0.03
5/8	1/8	7/8	7/8	1-1/16	12.70	0.500	5.56	0.219	—	—	41.1	1.62
5/8	1/4	7/8	7/8	1-1/16	12.70	0.500	7.92	0.312	—	—	46.0	1.81
5/8	3/8	7/8	7/8	1-1/16	12.70	0.500	10.31	0.406	—	—	46.0	1.81
5/8	3/4	1-1/16	1-1/4	1-1/16	12.70	0.500	19.05	0.750	15.88	0.625	52.3	2.06

TABLE 6—DIMENSIONS OF REDUCING CONNECTORS, REDUCING ADAPTERS, AND REDUCING ELBOWS (FIGURES 26 TO 32)[a] (CONTINUED)

B Nom Tube OD in	L_1 mm ±0.8	L_1 in ±0.03	L_2 mm ±0.8	L_2 in ±0.03	M mm ±0.8	M in ±0.03	M_1 mm ±0.8	M_1 in ±0.03	M_2 mm ±0.8	M_2 in ±0.03	N mm ±0.8	N in ±0.03
5/8	32.5	1.28	35.8	1.41	35.8	1.41	35.8	1.41	31.2	1.23	26.9	1.06
5/8	38.1	1.50	38.9	1.53	35.8	1.41	35.8	1.41	31.2	1.23	31.8	1.25
5/8	40.4	1.59	39.6	1.56	35.8	1.41	35.8	1.41	31.2	1.23	31.8	1.25
5/8	48.5	1.91	42.2	1.66	36.6	1.44	42.2	1.66	32.3	1.27	38.1	1.50

B Nom Tube OD in	N_1 mm ±0.8	N_1 in ±0.03	N_2 mm ±0.8	N_2 in ±0.03	P Min mm	P Min in	P_1 mm	P_1 in	Q[e] mm	Q[e] in	S[d] Max mm	S[d] Max in
5/8	15.7	0.62	20.1	0.79	9.7	0.38	9.7	0.38	—	—	27.2	1.07
5/8	20.6	0.81	24.9	0.98	14.2	0.56	14.2	0.56	—	—	27.2	1.07
5/8	20.6	0.81	24.9	0.98	14.2	0.56	14.2	0.56	—	—	27.2	1.07
5/8	25.4	1.00	30.5	1.20	19.0	0.75	19.1	0.75	—	—	24.6	0.97

B Nom Tube OD in	T[f] Ref mm	T[f] Ref in	T_1 Min mm	T_1 Min in	T_2 Min mm	T_2 Min in	W[g] mm +0.0 −0.5	W[g] in +0.00 ±0.02	X[g] mm +0.0 −0.5	X[g] in +0.00 −0.02
5/8	9.4	0.37	9.4	0.37	10.9	0.43	22.4	0.88	26.9	1.06
5/8	9.4	0.37	9.4	0.37	10.9	0.43	22.4	0.88	26.9	1.06
5/8	9.4	0.37	9.4	0.37	10.9	0.43	22.4	0.88	26.9	1.06
5/8	10.9	0.43	12.4	0.49	10.9	0.43	31.8	1.25	26.9	1.06

B Nom Tube OD in	A Dryseal Pipe Thread NPTF[b]	C Hex in Nom	C_1 Hex in Nom	C_2 Hex in Nom	D[d] Drill mm	D[d] Drill in	D_1[d] Drill mm	D_1[d] Drill in	D_2 Drill mm	D_2 Drill in	L mm ±0.8	L in ±0.03
3/4	1/8	1-1/16	1-1/16	1-5/16	15.88	0.625	5.56	0.219	—	—	46.0	1.81
3/4	1/4	1-1/16	1-1/16	1-5/16	15.88	0.625	7.92	0.312	—	—	50.8	2.00
3/4	3/8	1-1/16	1-1/16	1-5/16	15.88	0.625	10.31	0.406	—	—	50.8	2.00
3/4	3/4	1-1/16	1-1/4	1-5/16	15.88	0.625	19.05	0.750	—	—	55.6	2.19

B Nom Tube OD in	L_1 mm ±0.8	L_1 in ±0.03	L_2 mm ±0.8	L_2 in ±0.03	M mm ±0.8	M in ±0.03	M_1 mm ±0.08	M_1 in ±0.03	M_2 mm ±0.8	M_2 in ±0.03	N mm ±0.8	N in ±0.03
3/4	35.1	1.38	41.1	1.62	41.1	1.62	40.4	1.59	35.8	1.41	31.0	1.22
3/4	39.6	1.56	44.4	1.75	41.1	1.62	40.4	1.59	35.8	1.41	35.8	1.41
3/4	42.2	1.66	45.2	1.78	41.1	1.62	40.4	1.59	35.8	1.41	35.8	1.41
3/4	50.0	1.97	45.2	1.78	40.4	1.59	45.2	1.78	35.8	1.41	41.1	1.62

B Nom Tube OD in	N_1 mm ±0.8	N_1 in ±0.03	N_2 mm ±0.8	N_2 in ±0.03	P Min mm	P Min in	P_1 mm	P_1 in	Q[e] mm	Q[e] in	S[d] Max mm	S[d] Max in
3/4	17.5	0.69	20.8	0.82	9.7	0.38	9.7	0.38	—	—	31.0	1.22
3/4	22.4	0.88	25.7	1.01	14.2	0.56	14.2	0.56	—	—	31.0	1.22
3/4	22.4	0.88	25.7	1.01	14.2	0.56	14.2	0.56	—	—	31.0	1.22
3/4	26.9	1.06	30.5	1.20	19.0	0.75	19.1	0.75	—	—	24.6	0.97

TABLE 6—DIMENSIONS OF REDUCING CONNECTORS, REDUCING ADAPTERS, AND REDUCING ELBOWS (FIGURES 26 TO 32)[(a)] (CONTINUED)

B Nom Tube OD in	T[(f)] Ref mm	T[(f)] Ref in	T_1 Min mm	T_1 Min in	T_2 Min mm	T_2 Min in	W[(g)] mm +0.0 –0.5	W[(g)] in +0.00 –0.02	X[(g)] mm +0.0 –0.5	X[(g)] in +0.00 –0.02
3/4	10.9	0.43	10.9	0.43	12.4	0.49	26.9	1.06	33.3	1.31
3/4	10.9	0.43	10.9	0.43	12.4	0.49	26.9	1.06	33.3	1.31
3/4	10.9	0.43	10.9	0.43	12.4	0.49	26.9	1.06	33.3	1.31
3/4	10.9	0.43	12.4	0.49	12.4	0.49	31.8	1.25	33.3	1.31

a For flare dimensions shown on Figures 26 to 32 but not given in Table 6, see corresponding dimensions for the specified Tube OD in Table 3.
b Dryseal American Standard Taper Pipe Thread.
c Where thread relief undercut is used, last thread shall be chamfered 1/2 to 1 pitch long from G diameter and dimension J may be reduced by an amount equal to 1/2 pitch.
d At manufacturer's option, through passages in fittings shown in Figure 26 may conform with the smaller diameter specified or be counterbored to the larger diameter from the appropriate end for depth S.
e Available with three types of fusible alloys as specified in General Specifications.
f Minimum design thickness, not subject to inspection.
g Basic dimensions shown shall apply as minimum for bosses. The –0.51 mm (–0.02 in) tolerance shall apply only to chamfer diameters on full hexagon versions of fittings shown in Figures 28 and 29.

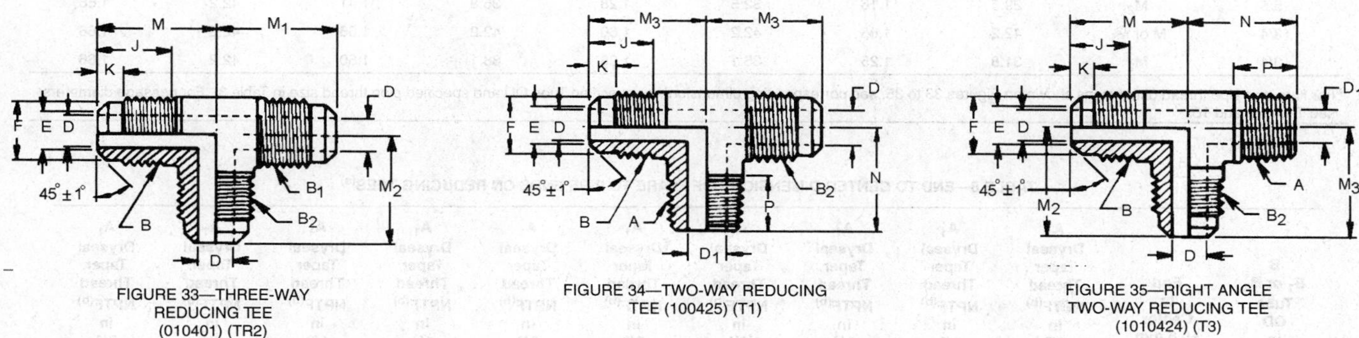

FIGURE 33—THREE-WAY REDUCING TEE (010401) (TR2)

FIGURE 34—TWO-WAY REDUCING TEE (100425) (T1)

FIGURE 35—RIGHT ANGLE TWO-WAY REDUCING TEE (1010424) (T3)

NOTE—Unspecified detail with respect to dimensions, tolerances, contour, material, workmanship, etc., must conform to General Specifications for Refrigeration Tube Fittings. The illustrations on this page apply to Tables 7 to 10. Codes shown in brackets adjacent to figure numbers represent respective fitting identification in accordance with SAE J846 (first number) and ANSI B70.1 (second number).

TABLE 7—END TO CENTER DIMENSIONS OF FLARE TO FLARE ENDS ON REDUCING TEES[(a)]

B and B_1 Tube OD of Run in	End to Center ±0.8 mm ±0.03 in	B_2 Nominal Flare Sizes of Branch in 3/16 mm	B_2 Nominal Flare Sizes of Branch in 3/16 in	B_2 Nominal Flare Sizes of Branch in 1/4 mm	B_2 Nominal Flare Sizes of Branch in 1/4 in	B_2 Nominal Flare Sizes of Branch in 5/16 mm	B_2 Nominal Flare Sizes of Branch in 5/16 in
3/16	M or M_1	19.0	0.75	19.0	0.75	19.8	0.78
3/16	M_2	19.0	0.75	22.4	0.88	23.1	0.91
1/4	M or M_1	22.4	0.88	22.4	0.88	21.3	0.84
1/4	M_2	19.0	0.75	22.4	0.88	23.1	0.91
5/16	M or M_1	23.1	0.91	23.1	0.91	23.1	0.91
5/16	M_2	19.8	0.78	21.3	0.84	23.1	0.91
3/8	M or M_1	26.9	1.06	26.9	1.06	26.9	1.06
3/8	M_2	21.3	0.84	23.1	0.91	24.6	0.97
1/2	M or M_1	31.0	1.22	31.0	1.22	31.0	1.22
1/2	M_2	23.1	0.91	24.6	0.97	26.2	1.03
5/8	M or M_1	35.8	1.41	35.8	1.41	35.8	1.41
5/8	M_2	24.6	0.97	26.2	1.03	27.7	1.09
3/4	M or M_1	42.2	1.66	42.2	1.66	42.2	1.66
3/4	M_2	26.9	1.06	28.4	1.12	30.2	1.19

TABLE 7—END TO CENTER DIMENSIONS OF FLARE TO FLARE ENDS ON REDUCING TEES[(a)] (CONTINUED)

B and B_1 Tube OD of Run in	End to Center ±0.8 mm ±0.03 in	B_2 Nominal Flare Sizes of Branch in 3/8 mm	B_2 Nominal Flare Sizes of Branch in 3/8 in	B_2 Nominal Flare Sizes of Branch in 1/2 mm	B_2 Nominal Flare Sizes of Branch in 1/2 in	B_2 Nominal Flare Sizes of Branch in 5/8 mm	B_2 Nominal Flare Sizes of Branch in 5/8 in	B_2 Nominal Flare Sizes of Branch in 3/4 mm	B_2 Nominal Flare Sizes of Branch in 3/4 in
3/16	M or M_1	21.3	0.84	23.1	0.91	24.6	0.97	26.9	1.06
3/16	M_2	26.9	1.06	31.0	1.22	35.8	1.41	42.2	1.66
1/4	M or M_1	23.1	0.91	24.6	0.97	26.2	1.03	28.4	1.12
1/4	M_2	26.9	1.06	31.0	1.22	35.8	1.41	42.2	1.66
5/16	M or M_1	24.6	0.97	26.2	1.03	27.7	1.09	30.2	1.19
5/16	M_2	26.9	1.06	31.0	1.22	35.8	1.41	42.2	1.66
3/8	M or M_1	26.9	1.06	27.7	1.09	29.5	1.16	31.8	1.25
3/8	M_2	26.9	1.06	31.0	1.22	35.8	1.41	42.2	1.66
1/2	M or M_1	31.0	1.22	31.0	1.22	32.5	1.28	35.1	1.38
1/2	M_2	27.7	1.09	31.0	1.22	35.8	1.41	42.2	1.66
5/8	M or M_1	35.8	1.41	35.8	1.41	35.8	1.41	38.1	1.50
5/8	M_2	29.5	1.16	32.5	1.28	35.8	1.41	42.2	1.66
3/4	M or M_1	42.2	1.66	42.2	1.66	42.2	1.66	42.2	1.66
3/4	M_2	31.8	1.25	35.1	1.38	38.1	1.50	42.2	1.66

[a]For flare and pipe thread dimensions shown on Figures 33 to 35, see corresponding dimensions for specified Tube OD and specified pipe thread size in Table 3. For passage diameters, see Tables 9 and 10.

TABLE 8—END TO CENTER DIMENSIONS OF FLARE TO PIPE ENDS ON REDUCING TEES[(a)]

B B_1 or B_2 Tube OD in	End to Center ±0.8 mm ±0.03 in	A_1 Dryseal Taper Thread NPTF[(b)] in 1/8 mm	A_1 Dryseal Taper Thread NPTF[(b)] in 1/8 in	A_1 Dryseal Taper Thread NPTF[(b)] in 1/4 mm	A_1 Dryseal Taper Thread NPTF[(b)] in 1/4 in	A_1 Dryseal Taper Thread NPTF[(b)] in 3/8 mm	A_1 Dryseal Taper Thread NPTF[(b)] in 3/8 in	A_1 Dryseal Taper Thread NPTF[(b)] in 1/2 mm	A_1 Dryseal Taper Thread NPTF[(b)] in 1/2 in	A_1 Dryseal Taper Thread NPTF[(b)] in 3/4 mm	A_1 Dryseal Taper Thread NPTF[(b)] in 3/4 in
3/16	M_3	19.0	0.75	20.6	0.81	22.4	0.88	24.6	0.97	26.9	1.06
3/16	N	19.0	0.75	24.6	0.97	25.4	1.00	32.5	1.28	35.1	1.38
1/4	M_3	20.6	0.81	23.1	0.91	23.9	0.94	26.2	1.03	28.4	1.12
1/4	N	19.8	0.78	23.9	0.94	26.2	1.03	32.5	1.23	35.1	1.38
5/16	M_3	23.1	0.91	24.6	0.97	25.4	1.00	27.7	1.09	30.2	1.19
5/16	N	19.8	0.78	23.9	0.94	26.2	1.03	32.5	1.28	35.1	1.38
3/8	M_3	26.2	1.03	25.4	1.00	26.9	1.06	29.5	1.16	31.8	1.25
3/8	N	23.1	0.91	26.9	1.06	27.7	1.09	32.5	1.28	35.1	1.38
1/2	M_3	31.0	1.22	31.0	1.22	31.0	1.22	32.5	1.28	35.1	1.38
1/2	N	25.4	1.00	30.2	1.19	28.4	1.12	35.1	1.38	35.1	1.38
5/8	M_3	35.8	1.41	35.8	1.41	35.8	1.41	35.8	1.41	36.6	1.44
5/8	N	26.9	1.06	31.8	1.25	31.8	1.25	35.1	1.38	38.1	1.50
3/4	M_3	41.1	1.62	41.1	1.62	41.1	1.62	41.1	1.62	40.4	1.59
3/4	N	31.0	1.22	35.8	1.41	35.8	1.41	38.1	1.50	41.1	1.62

a For flare and pipe thread dimensions shown on Figures 33 to 35, see corresponding dimensions for specified Tube OD and specified pipe thread size in Table 3. For passage diameters, see Tables 9 and 10.

b Dryseal American Standard Taper Pipe Thread.

TO DETERMINE CORRECT END TO CENTER LENGTHS ON TEES, EACH 90 DEGREES MUST BE FIGURED SEPARATELY AS AN ELBOW AND THE LARGER OF THE TWO BRANCH LENGTHS SHALL APPLY. SEE EXAMPLES BELOW.

Example: Find lengths for 5/8 x 1/2 x 3/8 in three-way reducing tee.

1. From Table 7 obtain values for each 90 degrees separately.
2. Use larger of two M_2 dimensions as found.

FROM TABLE 7

B Nominal Tube OD in	End to Center	B_2 3/8 mm	B_2 3/8 in
5/8	M	35.8	1.41
5/8	M_2	29.5	1.16

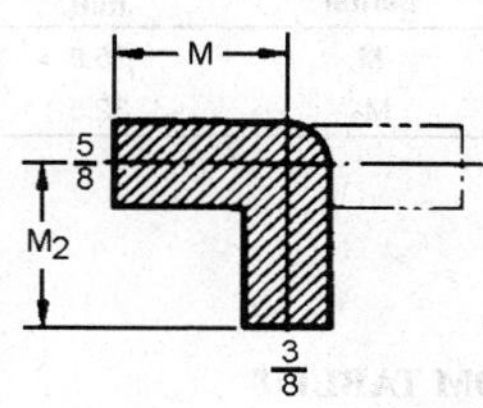

FROM TABLE 7

B_1 Nominal Tube OD in	End to Center	B_2 3/8 mm	B_2 3/8 in
1/2	M_1	31.0	1.22
1/2	M_2	27.7	1.09

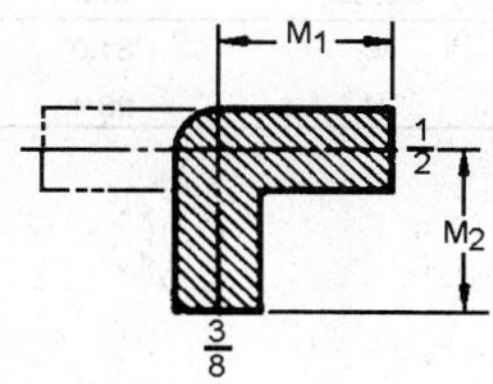

Result:

Dimension		mm	in
M	=	35.8	1.41
M_1	=	31.0	1.22
M_2	=	29.5	1.16

FIGURE 34A—THREE-WAY REDUCING TEE (010401) (TR2)

Example: Find lengths for 5/8 x 3/8 x 1/2 in right angle two-way tee.

1. From Tables 7 and 8 obtain values for each 90 degrees separately.
2. Use the larger dimension M_2 or M_3 as found.

FROM TABLE 7

B Nominal Tube OD in	End to Center	B_2 1/2 mm	B_2 1/2 in
5/8	M	35.8	1.41
5/8	M_2	32.5	1.28

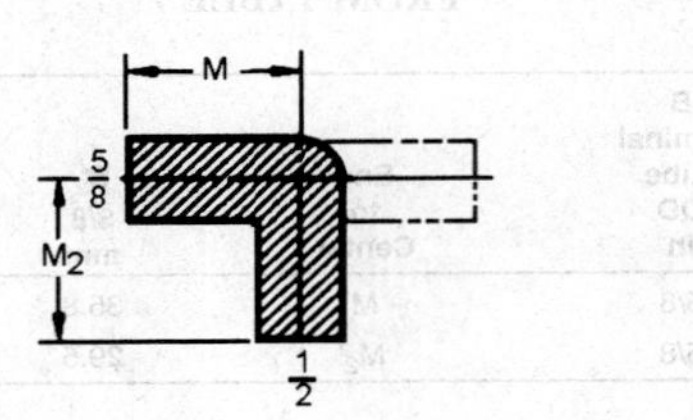

FROM TABLE 8

B Nominal Tube OD in	End to Center	A 3/8 mm	A 3/8 in
1/2	M_3	31.0	1.22
1/2	N	28.4	1.12

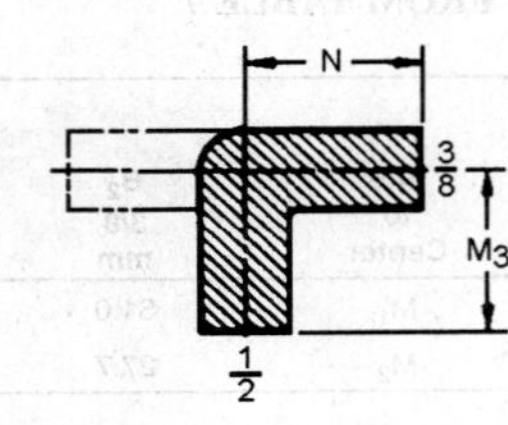

Result:

Dimension		mm	in
M	=	35.8	1.41
N	=	28.4	1.12
M_3	=	32.5	1.28

FIGURE 35A—RIGHT ANGLE TWO-WAY REDUCING TEE (01424) (T3)

NOTE—UNSPECIFIED DETAIL WITH RESPECT TO DIMENSIONS, TOLERANCES, CONTOUR, MATERIAL, WORKMANSHIP, ETC., MUST CONFORM TO GENERAL SPECIFICATIONS FOR REFRIGERATION TUBE FITTINGS. CODES SHOWN IN BRACKETS ADJACENT TO FIGURE NUMBERS REPRESENT RESPECTIVE FITTING IDENTIFICATION IN ACCORDANCE WITH SAE J846 (FIRST NUMBER) AND ANSI B70.1 (SECOND NUMBER).

TABLE 9—PASSAGE DIAMETERS THROUGH FLARE ENDS

Nom Tube OD in	D[1] Dia Drill mm	D[1] Dia Drill in
3/16	3.18	0.125
1/4	4.78	0.188
5/16	5.56	0.219
3/8	7.14	0.281
1/2	10.31	0.406
5/8	12.70	0.500
3/4	15.88	0.625

1. At manufacturer's option, through passages in tees shown in Figures 33 to 35 having varying diameters at opposite ends may conform to the smaller diameters specified or be counterbored to the larger diameter from the appropriate end for a minimum depth equivalent to the maximum end to center length of that end, plus 1/2 the maximum passage through brand plus 0.3 mm (0.01 in).

TABLE 10—PASSAGE DIAMETERS THROUGH PIPE THREAD ENDS

Nom Pipe Size in	D[1] Dia Drill mm	D[1] Dia Drill in
1/8	5.56	0.219
1/4	7.92	0.312
3/8	10.31	0.406
1/2	14.27	0.562
3/4	19.05	0.750

1. At manufacturer's option, through passages in tees shown in Figures 33 to 35 having varying diameters at opposite ends may conform to the smaller diameters specified or be counterbored to the larger diameter from the appropriate end for a minimum depth equivalent to the maximum end to center length of that end, plus 1/2 the maximum passage through branch plus 0.3 mm (0.01 in).

TABLE 11—DIMENSIONS FOR STANDARD SIZES OF SHORT AND LONG FLARE NUTS (FIGURES 36A AND 36B)

Nom Tube OD in	B Straight Thread Nom Size in	C Hex in Nom	D Dia mm +0.13 –0.00	D Dia in +0.005 –0.000	E Dia Min mm	E Dia Min in	I mm	I in	J Full Thread Min mm	J Full Thread Min in
3/16	3/8 -24	1/2	4.88	0.192	10.4	0.41	7.1	0.28	5.6	0.22
1/4	7/16-20	5/8	6.48	0.255	11.9	0.47	8.6	0.34	6.9	0.27
5/16	1/2 -20	11/16	8.05	0.317	11.9	0.47	9.7	0.38	7.6	0.30
3/8	5/8 -18	13/16	9.65	0.380	15.0	0.59	11.2	0.44	8.6	0.34
1/2	3/4 -16	15/16	12.83	0.505	19.0	0.75	13.5	0.53	11.2	0.44
5/8	7/8 -14	1- 1/16	16.00	0.630	23.9	0.94	16.8	0.66	14.0	0.55
3/4	1-1/16-14	1- 5/16	19.18	0.755	28.4	1.12	19.8	0.78	17.0	0.67

Nom Tube OD in	L mm ±0.8	L in ±0.03	L_1 mm +2.3 –0.0	L_1 in +0.09 –0.00	T mm ±0.8	T in ±0.03	U Dia Min mm	U Dia Min in	U Dia Max mm	U Dia Max in	X mm +0.0 –0.8	X in +0.00 –0.03
3/16	22.4	0.88	13.5	0.53	9.7	0.38	9.9	0.39	10.4	0.41	12.7	0.50
1/4	23.9	0.94	15.0	0.59	11.2	0.44	11.4	0.45	11.9	0.47	15.7	0.62
5/16	23.9	0.94	15.7	0.62	11.2	0.44	13.0	0.51	13.5	0.53	17.5	0.69
3/8	26.9	1.06	17.5	0.69	12.7	0.50	16.3	0.64	17.0	0.67	20.6	0.81
1/2	30.2	1.19	20.6	0.81	14.2	0.56	19.6	0.77	20.3	0.80	23.9	0.94
5/8	36.6	1.44	23.9	0.94	19.0	0.75	22.9	0.90	23.6	0.93	26.9	1.06
3/4	44.5	1.75	28.4	1.12	25.4	1.00	27.4	1.08	28.2	1.11	33.3	1.31

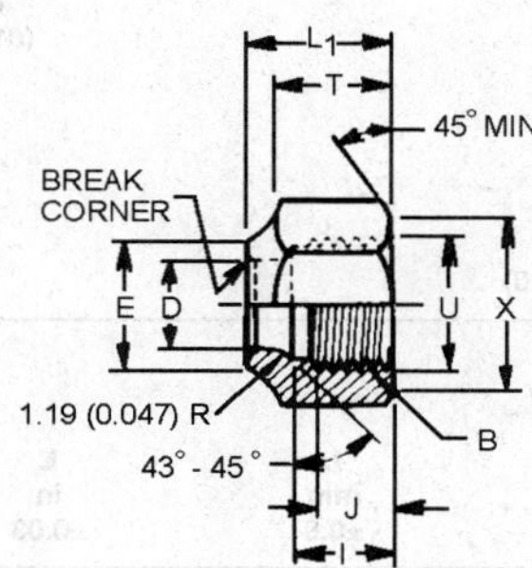

FIGURE 36A—SHORT NUTS (010166) (NS4)

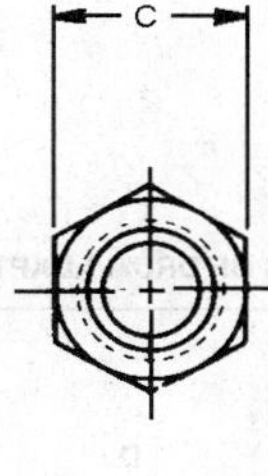

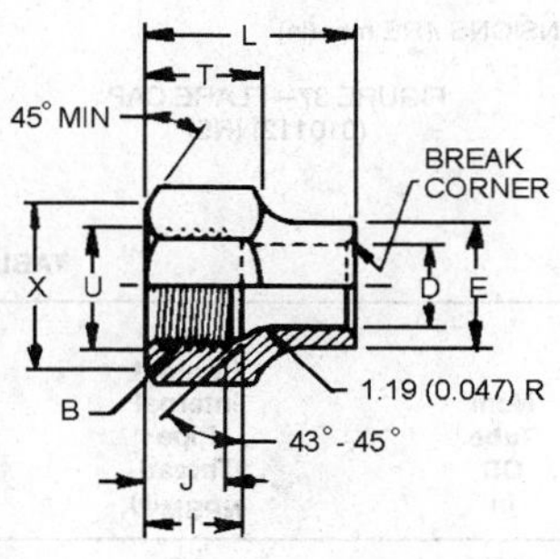

FIGURE 36B—LONG NUTS (010167) (N4)

FIGURE 36—FLARE NUTS

TABLE 12—DIMENSIONS OF FLARE CAP, FLARE GASKET, AND FLARE SEAL BONNET (FIGURES 37 TO 39)

Nom Tube OD in	B Straight Thread Nom Size Class 2B Int	C Hex in Nom	D Dia mm	D Dia in	I mm	I in	J Full Thread Min mm	J Full Thread Min in	L mm	L in	T Min mm	T Min in
3/16	3/8 -24	1/2	3.0	0.12	7.1	0.28	5.3	0.21	11.9	0.47	6.9	0.27
1/4	7/16-20	9/16	4.3	0.19	8.6	0.34	6.4	0.25	13.5	0.53	10.2	0.40
5/16	1/2 -20	5/8	5.6	0.22	9.7	0.38	7.4	0.29	15.7	0.62	10.2	0.40
3/8	5/8 -18	3/4	7.1	0.28	11.2	0.44	8.6	0.34	17.5	0.69	11.7	0.46
1/2	3/4 -16	7/8	10.4	0.41	13.5	0.53	10.9	0.43	21.3	0.84	13.2	0.52
5/8	7/8 -14	1-1/16	12.7	0.50	16.8	0.66	13.7	0.54	24.6	0.97	15.7	0.62
3/4	1-1/16-14	1-5/16	15.7	0.62	19.8	0.78	16.8	0.66	27.7	1.09	18.8	0.74

TABLE 12—DIMENSIONS OF FLARE CAP, FLARE GASKET, AND FLARE SEAL BONNET (FIGURES 37 TO 39) (CONTINUED)

Nom Tube OD in	U Dia Min mm	U Dia Min in	U Dia Max mm	U Dia Max in	V Dia mm ±0.8	V Dia in ±0.03	W Dia Max mm	W Dia Max in	X mm ±0.5	X in ±0.02	Y Min mm	Y Min in
3/16	9.9	0.39	10.4	0.41	3.0	0.12	7.9	0.31	4.1	0.16	4.1	0.16
1/4	11.4	0.45	11.9	0.47	4.8	0.19	9.1	0.36	5.6	0.22	5.6	0.22
5/16	13.0	0.51	13.5	0.53	5.6	0.22	10.7	0.42	7.1	0.28	7.1	0.28
3/8	16.3	0.64	17.0	0.67	7.1	0.28	14.0	0.55	9.1	0.36	8.6	0.34
1/2	19.6	0.77	20.3	0.80	10.4	0.41	16.8	0.66	11.9	0.47	10.4	0.41
5/8	22.9	0.90	23.6	0.93	12.7	0.50	19.6	0.77	15.5	0.61	11.2	0.44
3/4	27.4	1.08	28.2	1.11	15.7	0.62	24.1	0.95	18.3	0.72	14.2	0.56

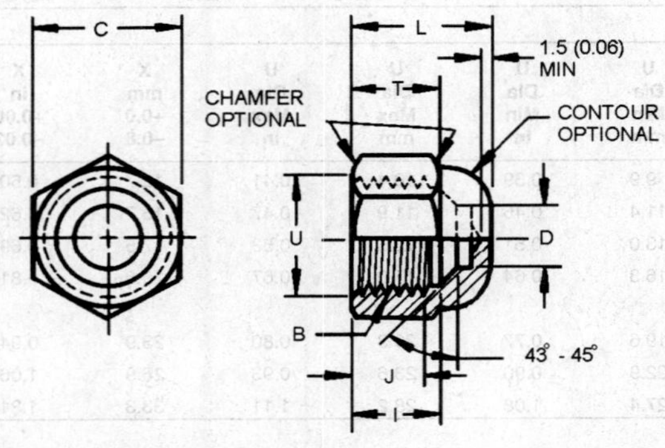

DIMENSIONS ARE mm (in)

FIGURE 37—FLARE CAP
(010112) (N5)

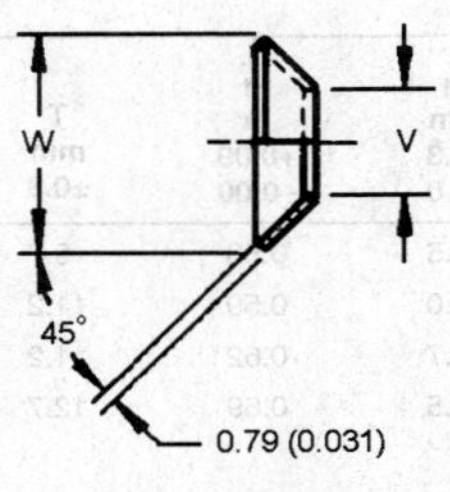

DIMENSIONS ARE mm (in)

FIGURE 38—FLARE GASKET
(010113) (B2)

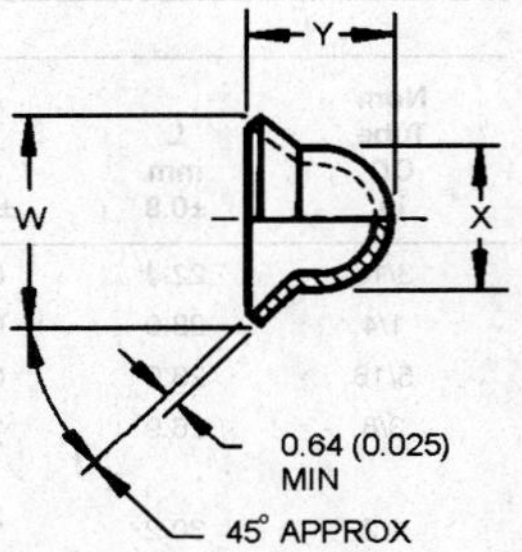

Y
X
W
0.64 (0.025) MIN
45° APPROX

DIMENSIONS ARE mm (in)

FIGURE 39—FLARE SEAL BONNET
(010114) (B1)

TABLE 13—DIMENSIONS OF DRUM ADAPTERS[(a)] (FIGURE 40)

Nom Tube OD in	A Straight Internal Pipe Thread NPSM[(b)]	C Hex in Nom	D Drill mm	D Drill in	L mm ±0.8	L in ±0.03
1/4	1/2	1-1/8	4.78	0.188	28.4	1.12
1/4	3/4	1-1/4	4.78	0.188	28.4	1.12
3/8	3/4	1-1/4	71.4	0.281	31.8	1.25
1/2	3/4	1-1/4	10.31	0.406	35.1	1.38

a For flare and dimensions shown on Figure 40 but not specified in Table 13, see corresponding dimensions for the specified Tube OD in Table 3. Drum adaptor fittings are normally supplied with seal gasket for pipe thread end.

b American Standard Straight Pipe Thread for Mechanical Joints.

c Where thread relief undercut is used, last thread shall be chamfered 1/2 to 1 pitch long from G diameter and dimension J may be reduced by an amount equal to 1/2 pitch.

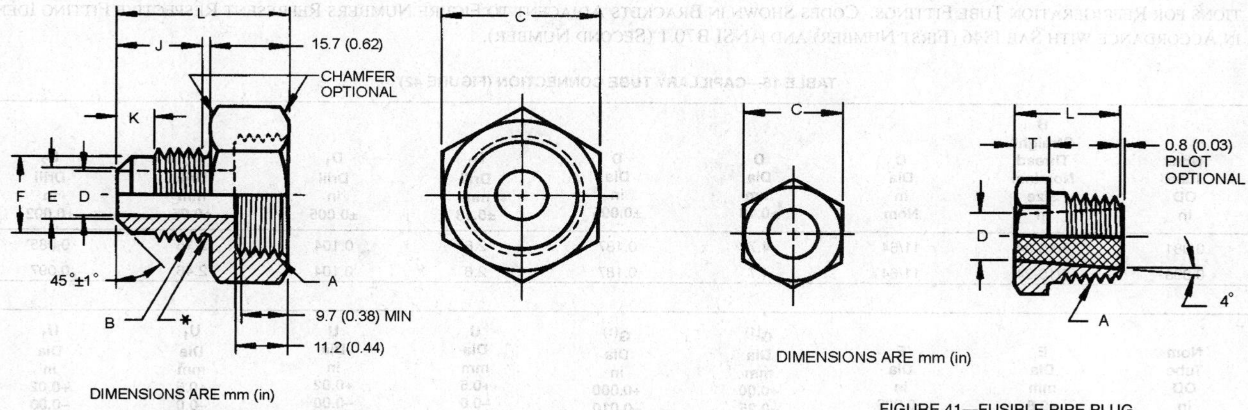

FIGURE 40—DRUM ADAPTOR (010165) (K)

FIGURE 41—FUSIBLE PIPE PLUG (010164) (FP)

NOTE—UNSPECIFIED DETAIL WITH RESPECT TO DIMENSIONS, TOLERANCES, CONTOUR, MATERIAL, WORKMANSHIP, ETC., MUST CONFORM TO GENERAL SPECIFICATIONS FOR REFRIGERATION TUBE FITTINGS. CODES SHOWN IN BRACKETS ADJACENT TO FIGURE NUMBERS REPRESENT RESPECTIVE FITTING IDENTIFICATION IN ACCORDANCE WITH SAE J846 (FIRST NUMBER) AND ANSI B70.1 (SECOND NUMBER).

TABLE 14—DIMENSIONS OF FUSIBLE PIPE PLUGS[a] (FIGURE 41)

A Dryseal Pipe Thread NPTF[b]	C Hex in Nom	D Dia mm	D Dia in	L mm	L in	T mm	T in
1/8	7/16	5.6	0.219	14.2	0.56	4.8	0.19
1/4	9/16	6.4	0.250	19.0	0.75	4.8	0.19
3/8	3/4	9.5	0.375	19.8	0.78	5.6	0.22

[a] Plugs are available with three types of fusible alloys as specified in general specifications.
[b] Dryseal American Standard Taper Pipe Thread.

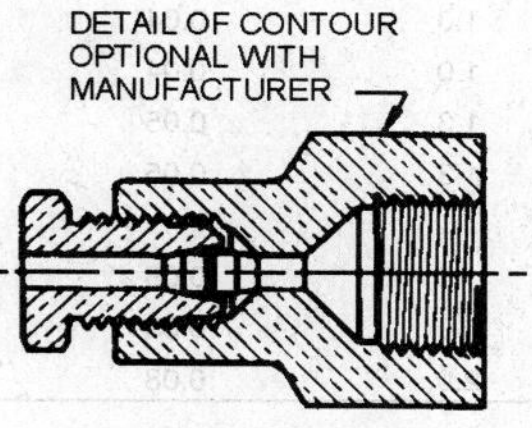

FIGURE 42A—CAPILLARY TUBE CONNECTION ASSEMBLY (450101BA)

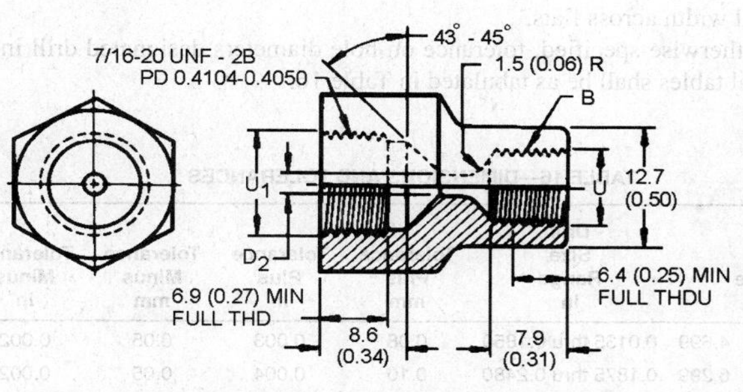

FIGURE 42B—CAPILLARY TUBE BODY (450101) (CTN)

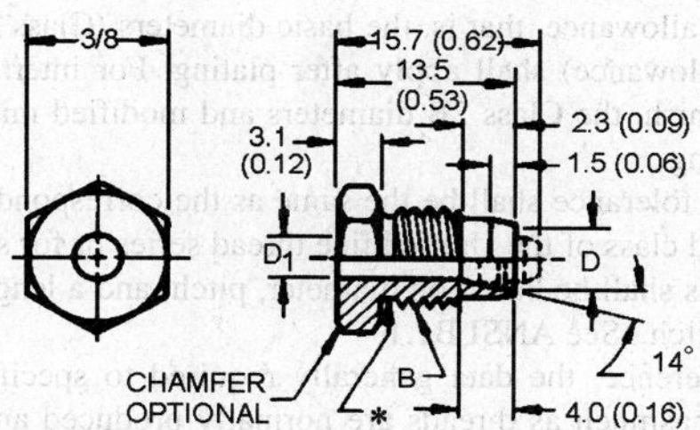

FIGURE 42C—CAPILLARY TUBE COMPRESSION SCREW (450110) (CTN)

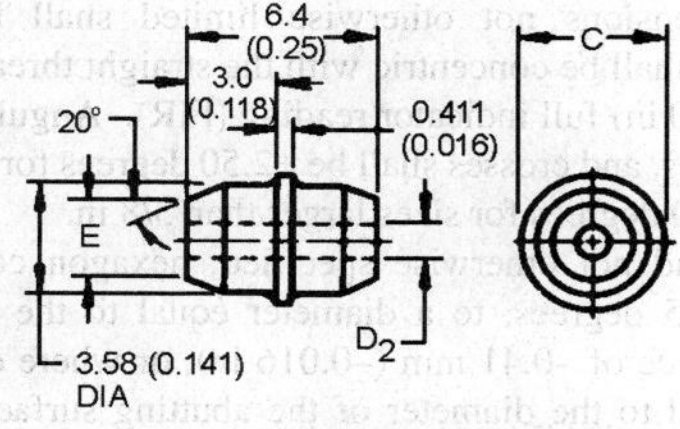

FIGURE 42D—CAPILLARY TUBE SLEEVE (450115) (CTN)

NOTE—Unspecified Detail with Respect to Dimensions, Tolerances, Contour, Material, Workmanship, Etc., Must Conform to General Specifications for Refrigeration Tube Fittings. Codes Shown in Brackets Adjacent to Figure Numbers Represent Respective Fitting Identification in Accordance with SAE J846 (First Number) and ANSI B70.1 (Second Number).

TABLE 15—CAPILLARY TUBE CONNECTION (FIGURE 42)

Nom Tube OD in	B Straight Thread Nominal Size in	C Dia in Nom	D Dia mm ±0.13	D Dia in ±0.005	D_1 Drill mm ±0.13	D_1 Drill in ±0.005	D_2 Drill mm ±0.05	D_2 Drill in ±0.002
0.081	5/16-24	11/64	4.7	0.187	2.6	0.104	2.16	0.085
0.093	5/16-24	11/64	4.7	0.187	2.6	0.104	2.46	0.097

Nom Tube OD in	E Dia mm ±0.8	E Dia in ±0.003	G[(1)] Dia mm +0.00 −0.25	G[(1)] Dia in +0.000 −0.010	U Dia mm +0.5 −0.0	U Dia in +0.02 −0.00	U_1 Dia mm +0.5 −0.0	U_1 Dia in +0.02 −0.00
0.081	2.67	0.105	6.35	0.250	8.4	0.33	11.4	0.45
0.093	2.67	0.105	6.35	0.250	8.4	0.33	11.4	0.45

1. Where thread relief undercut is used, the last thread shall be chamfered 1/2 to 1 pitch thread long from the G diameter.

3. Pressure Ratings and Service Limitations—Fittings covered by this document are satisfactory for operating pressures up to 3450 kPa (500 psi) and are suitable for use in systems conducting most fluorinated hydrocarbon refrigerants. Fitting manufacturers should be consulted for recommendations.

4. Size Designations—Fitting sizes throughout the dimensional tables are designated by the corresponding outside diameter of the tubing for flared type or solder type tube ends and by the corresponding standard nominal pipe size for pipe thread ends.

5. Dimensions and Tolerances—Except for nominal sizes and thread specifications, dimensions and tolerances are given in both SI and U.S. customary units as designated. Tabulated dimensions shall apply to the finished parts, plated or otherwise processed, as specified by the purchasers. Unless otherwise specified, the maximum and minimum across flat dimensions shall be within the commercial tolerance of bar or extruded stock from which the fittings are produced. The minimum across corners dimensions of hexagons shall be 1.092 times the nominal width across flats, but shall not result in a size flat width less than 0.43 times the nominal width across flats.

Unless otherwise specified, tolerance on hole diameters designated drill in the dimensional tables shall be as tabulated in Table 16.

TABLE 16—DIMENSIONS AND TOLERANCES

Drill Size Range mm	Drill Size Range in	Tolerance Plus mm	Tolerance Plus in	Tolerance Minus mm	Tolerance Minus in
0.343 thru 4.699	0.0135 thru 0.1850	0.08	0.003	0.05	0.002
4.762 thru 6.299	0.1875 thru 0.2480	0.10	0.004	0.05	0.002
6.350 thru 19.050	0.2500 thru 0.7500	0.15	0.006	0.08	0.003
19.25 thru 25.400	0.7579 thru 1.0000	0.18	0.007	0.10	0.004

Tolerance on all dimensions not otherwise limited shall be ±0.25 mm (±0.010 in). Fitting seats shall be concentric with the straight thread pitch diameters within 0.25 mm (0.010 in) full indicator reading (FIR). Angular tolerance on axis of ends on elbows, tees, and crosses shall be ±2.50 degrees for sizes up to and including 3/8 in, and ±1.50 degrees for sizes larger than 3/8 in.

Where so illustrated and not otherwise specified, hexagon corners shall be chamfered 30 degrees ± 5 degrees, to a diameter equal to the nominal width across flats, with a tolerance of –0.41 mm (–0.016 in); or where design permits, corners may be chamfered to the diameter of the abutting surface provided the length of chamfer does not exceed that produced by the 30 degree chamfer previously described.

6. Passages—Where passages in straight fittings are machined from opposite ends, the offset at the meeting point shall not exceed 0.38 mm (0.015 in). The cross-sectional area at the junction of passages in angle fittings shall not be less than that of the smallest passage. Where the passage is specified as a maximum or as tap drill diameter or less, the minimum shall be no less than the minimum diameter of the smallest passage in the fitting.

7. Wall Thickness—Unless otherwise designated, the wall thickness at any point on fittings shall not be less than the thickness established by the specified dimensions, tolerances, and eccentricities for inner and outer surfaces.

8. Contour—Details of contour shall be optional with the manufacturer, providing the tabulated dimensions are maintained and serviceability of the fittings is not impaired. Wrench flats on elbows and tees shall be optional. Where extruded or forged shapes are reduced to conserve material, the wall thickness, unless otherwise specified, shall not be less than the respective minimum values tabulated in Table 17.

TABLE 17—WALL THICKNESS

Nominal Tube OD in	Wall Thickness Min Extruded Shapes[(1)] mm	Wall Thickness Min Extruded Shapes[(1)] in	Wall Thickness Min Forged Shapes[(1)] mm	Wall Thickness Min Forged Shapes[(1)] in
3/16	1.0	0.04	1.52	0.060
1/4	1.0	0.04	1.90	0.075
5/16	1.3	0.05	1.90	0.075
3/8	1.3	0.05	2.16	0.085
1/2	1.5	0.06	2.29	0.090
5/8	2.0	0.08	2.54	0.100
3/4	2.0	0.08	2.54	0.100

1. Applies to reduction in one plane of shape only.

9. Straight Threads—Unified Standard Class 2A external and Class 2B internal threads with minor diameters, where specified, modified to Class 3B limits shall apply to plain finish (unplated) fittings of all types. For externally threaded parts with additive finish, the maximum diameters of Class 2A may be exceeded by the amount of the allowance, that is, the basic diameters (Class 2A maximum diameters plus the allowance) shall apply after plating. For internally threaded parts with additive finish, the Class 2B diameters and modified minor diameters shall apply after plating.

The pitch diameter tolerance shall be the same as the corresponding diameter-pitch combination and class of the Unified fine thread series or for special diameter-pitch combinations shall be based on diameter, pitch, and a length of engagement of 9 times the pitch. See ANSI B1.1.

For convenient reference, the data generally required to specify threads are given in Table 1. (Inasmuch as threads are normally produced and gaged with equipment made to the inch system of measurement, conversion of size designations and dimensions to SI units is considered unnecessary.)

Where external threads are produced by roll threading and the body is not undercut, the unthreaded portion of body adjacent to the shoulder may be reduced to the minimum pitch diameter.

External threads shall be chamfered to the diameter of abutting surfaces, or to the diameters specified, to produce a length of chamfered or partial thread equivalent to 3/4 to 1-1/4 times the pitch (rounded to a three-place decimal).

Internal threads shall be countersunk 90 degrees included angle to the diameters specified in the dimensional tables.

10. Thread Eccentricity Tolerances—The various thread elements of Class 2A external and Class 2B modified internal threads on tube fittings shall be concentric within the limitations specified in SAE J512.

11. Pipe Threads—Taper pipe threads, unless there is specific authorization to the contrary, shall conform to the Dryseal American Standard Taper Pipe Thread (NPTF). Specifications for pipe threads are given in detail in SAE J476.

The length of full form external thread shall not be shorter than L_2 plus one pitch (thread), except that where thread is cut through into a relieved body or undercut on the fitting, the minimum full thread length may be reduced by one pitch (thread).

Where external pipe threads are produced by roll threading, the diameter of the unthreaded portion of shank adjacent to shoulder may be reduced to the E_2 basic pitch diameter.

The tube fitting dimensions tabulated herein are based on length of the Dryseal American Standard Taper Pipe Thread (NPTF), it being the consensus of manufacturers and users that trouble-free assembly cannot be assured unless full length thread is used. However, the tap drill depths and overall lengths specified in the tables for fittings with internal taper pipe threads are not consistent with the tap drill depths and overall thread lengths of the Dryseal American Standard Taper Pipe Threads (NPTF) given in Table A2, Appendix A of SAE J476. The full length Dryseal American Standard Taper Pipe Taps specified in Table B2 of SAE J476 cannot be used, as the tap drill depths and overall lengths of the fittings have been reduced to the minimum required by bottoming taps to produce standard full thread length. The deviations described previously are peculiar to these tube fittings and as special tooling is required, caution should be exercised in specifying such deviations for any other products.

Straight pipe threads, where specified, shall conform to American Standard Straight Pipe Threads for Mechanical Joints (NPSM) in ANSI B2.1.

External pipe threads shall be chamfered from the diameters tabulated in Table 2 to produce the specified length of chamfered or partial thread. Internal pipe threads shall be countersunk 90 degrees included angle to the diameters tabulated in Table 2.

12. Material and Manufacture—Fittings shall be made from SAE CA360 brass (half-hard), CA345, or CA350 brass bar or extruded shapes or from SAE CA377 brass forgings in accordance with the manufacturer's processes. Nuts may be made from SAE CA377 brass forging, or steel as specified by the purchaser. Seal bonnets and gaskets shall be made from copper conforming to SAE CA102, CA110, or CA122. As specified by purchaser, fusible metal alloys shall be supplied for temperature ranges 70 to 74, 95 to 104, 135 to 143 °C (158 to 165, 203 to 219, or 275 to 290 °F).

13. Finish—The external surfaces and threads of all carbon steel parts shall be plated or coated with a suitable material that passes a 72 h salt spray test in accordance with ASTM B 117. Any appearance of red rust during the 72 h salt spray test shall be considered failure, except for the following:

a. All internal fluid passages.
b. Edges such as hex points, serrations, and crests of threads where there may be mechanical deformation of the plating or coating typical of mass-produced parts or shipping effects.
c. Areas where there is mechanical deformation of the plating or coating caused by crimping, flaring, bending, and other post-plate metal forming operations.
d. Areas where the parts are suspended or affixed in the test chamber where condensate can accumulate.

NOTE—Cadmium plating is not preferred due to environmental reasons. Parts manufactured to this standard after January 1, 1997, shall not be cadmium plated. Internal fluid passages shall be protected from corrosion during storage. Changes in plating may affect assembly torques and require requalification, when applicable.

14. Workmanship—Workmanship shall conform to the best commercial practice to produce high-quality fittings. Fittings shall be free from all hanging burrs, loose scale, and slivers which might become dislodged in usage and all other defects which might affect their serviceability. All sealing surfaces must be smooth except that annular tool marks up to 2.5 mm (100 min) maximum shall be permissible.

15. Assembly Considerations—Torque loads experienced during the assembly of the nut onto the flared ends of the fittings are variable due to the different metals used in the fittings and nuts, hardness of the tubing, manufacturing tolerances and conformance to the manufacturing recommendations. Therefore, it is recommended that flare nuts be assembled to the flared ends one quarter (1/4) turn past finger-tight. In the case of slight side loads which may exist during assembly, it may be necessary to "snug up" the mating parts with a wrench to achieve a finger-tight condition. The use of lubricants is not recommended.

16. Manufacturing Recommendations—Only circular tool marks concentric to the centerline of the sealing face will be permitted. Any such tool marks on the sealing face must be smooth within the limits of 2.5 mm (100 min).

Flare fittings should be handled, shipped, and stored in a manner that protects the sealing surface from damage.

HYDRAULIC TUBE FITTINGS—SAE J514 JUL2001 SAE Standard

Report of the SAE Construction and Industrial Machinery Technical Committee and the SAE Tube, Pipe, Hose and Lubrication Fittings Committee aproved May 1950. Completely revised by the SAE Fluid Conductors and Connectors Technical Committee May 1978, editorial change April 1980, and completely revised June 1990. Completely revised by the SAE Fluid Conductors and Connectors Technical Committee SC1—Automotive and Hydraulic Tube and Fittings, June 1991, and revised June 1992, June 1993, June 1994, June 1995, June 1996, June 1998, April 1999, and July 2001. Rationale statement available.

1. Scope—This SAE Standard covers complete general and dimensional specifications for 37 degree flared and flareless types of hydraulic tube fittings and O-ring plugs. Also included are pipe fittings and adapter unions for use in conjunction with these tube fittings. These fittings are intended for general application in hydraulic systems on industrial equipment and commercial products.

These fittings are capable of providing leakproof, full flow connections in hydraulic systems operating at working pressures as specified in Table 1 for respective sections.

Since many factors influence the pressure at which a hydraulic system will or will not perform satisfactorily, the values shown in SAE J1065 should not be construed as a guaranteed minimum.

For any application, it is recommended that sufficient testing be conducted and reviewed by both the user and fitting manufacturer to assure that performance levels will be safe and satisfactory.

TABLE 1—WORKING PRESSURE RATINGS[d] CAPABLE OF 4 TO 1 MINIMUM BURST

Nom SAE Dash Size	Nom Tube OD mm	Nom Tube OD in	Straight Thread Size	Nom Pipe Size	Rigid[a] SAE St. Threads Unions and Bulkheads MPa	Rigid[a] SAE St. Threads Unions and Bulkheads psi	Adjustable[b] SAE St. Threads and Female Swivels MPa	Adjustable[b] SAE St. Threads and Female Swivels psi	Fittings[c] With Pipe Threads MPa	Fittings[c] With Pipe Threads psi
2	3.18	0.125	5/16-24	1/8	34.5	5000	34.5	5000	34.5	5000
3	4.76	0.188	3/8 -24	1/8	34.5	5000	34.5	5000	34.5	5000
4	6.35	0.250	7/16-20	1/8	34.5	5000	31	4500	34.5	5000
5	7.94	0.313	1/2 -20	1/8	34.5	5000	27.5	4000	34.5	5000
6	9.52	0.375	9/16-18	1/4	34.5	5000	27.5	4000	27.5	4000
8	12.70	0.500	3/4 -16	3/8	31	4500	27.5	4000	21	3000
10	15.88	0.625	7/8 -14	1/2	24	3500	21	3000	21	3000
12	19.05	0.750	1-1/16-12	3/4	24	3500	21	3000	17	2500
14	22.22	0.875	1-3/16-12	3/4	21	3000	17	2500	17	2500
16	25.40	1.000	1-5/16-12	1	21	3000	17	2500	14	2000
20	31.75	1.250	1-5/8 -12	1-1/4	17	2500	14	2000	8	1150
24	38.10	1.500	1-7/8 -12	1-1/2	14	2000	10.5	1500	7	1000
32	50.80	2.000	2-1/2 -12	2	10.5	1500	8	1125	7	1000

(a) For fittings in Sections 1, 2, and 3.
(b) For fittings in Sections 1 and 2.
(c) For fittings in Sections 1, 2, and 4.
(d) Working pressures given are for low carbon steel fittings only. Consult the manufacturer for values for other materials.

The standard is divided into six sections as follows:

Section 1—37 Degree Flare Tube Fittings
Section 2—Flareless Tube Fittings
Section 3—O-ring Plugs (for O-ring Ports see SAE J1926)
Section 4—Hydraulic Pipe Fittings (formerly SAE J926)
Section 5—Adapter Unions (formerly in SAE J516)
Section 6—Tables for Calculating Dimensions on Special Sizes

2. References

2.1 Applicable Publications—The following publications form a part of this specification to the extent specified herein. The latest issue of SAE publications shall apply.

2.1.1 SAE PUBLICATIONS—Available from SAE, 400 Commonwealth Drive, Warrendale, PA 15096-0001.

SAE J343—Tests and Procedures for SAE 100R Series Hydraulic Hose and Hose Assemblies
SAE J405—Chemical Compositions of SAE Wrought Stainless Steels
SAE J476—Dryseal Pipe Threads
SAE J533—Flares for Tubing
SAE J1065—Pressure Ratings for Hydraulic Tubing and Fittings

2.1.2 ANSI PUBLICATION—Available from ANSI, 11 West 42nd Street, New York, NY 10036-8002.

ANSI B1.20.1—American Standard Straight Pipe Thread for Mechanical Joints
ANSI B1.20.3—Dryseal Pipe Threads (Inch)

2.1.3 ASTM PUBLICATION—Available from ASTM, 100 Barr Harbor Drive, West Conshohocken, PA 19428-2959.

ASTM B 117—Method of Salt Spray (Fog) Testing

3. General Specifications—The following general specifications supplement the dimensional data contained in Tables 3 to 21 with respect to all unspecified detail.

3.1 Size Designations—Fitting sizes are designated by the corresponding outside diameter of the tubing for the various types of tube ends and by the corresponding standard nominal pipe size for pipe thread ends.

See SAE J846 for proper coding and call-out.

3.2 Dimensions and Tolerances—Except for nominal sizes and thread specifications, dimensions and tolerances are given in both SI Units and U.S. Customary as designated. Tabulated dimensions shall apply to the finished parts, plated or otherwise processed, as specified by the purchasers. Hex tolerances across flats are listed in Table 1A. The minimum across-corners dimensions of hexagons shall be 1.092 times the nominal width across flats, but shall not result in a side-flat width less than 0.43 times the nominal width across flats. The minimum across-corners dimensions of external squares shall be 1.25 times the nominal width across flats, but shall not result in a side-flat width less than 0.75 times the nominal width across the flats.

TABLE 1A—HEX TOLERANCES

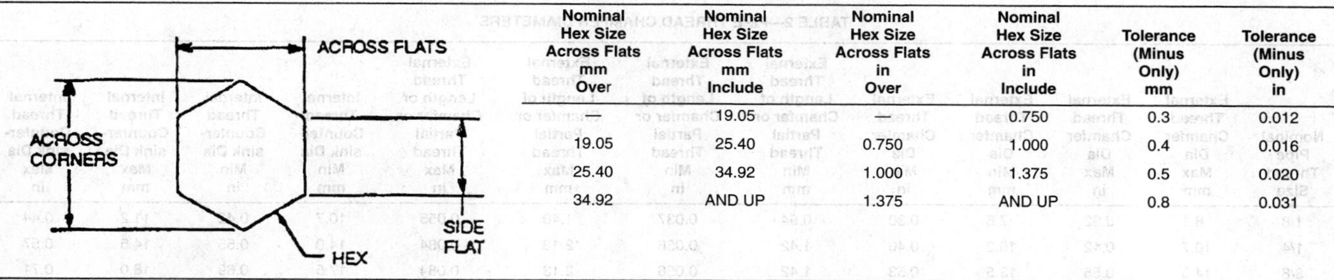

Nominal Hex Size Across Flats mm Over	Nominal Hex Size Across Flats mm Include	Nominal Hex Size Across Flats in Over	Nominal Hex Size Across Flats in Include	Tolerance (Minus Only) mm	Tolerance (Minus Only) in
—	19.05	—	0.750	0.3	0.012
19.05	25.40	0.750	1.000	0.4	0.016
25.40	34.92	1.000	1.375	0.5	0.020
34.92	AND UP	1.375	AND UP	0.8	0.031

Tolerance on all dimensions not otherwise limited shall be ±0.4 mm (±0.016 in). Fitting seats shall be concentric with straight thread pitch diameters within 0.25 mm (0.010 in) full indicator movement (FIM).

Unless otherwise specified, tolerance on hole diameters designated drill in the dimensional tables shall be as tabulated in Table 1B:

TABLE 1B—DRILL TOLERANCES

Drill Size Range mm	Drill Size Range in	Tolerance, mm Plus	Tolerance, mm Minus	Tolerance, in Plus	Tolerance, in Minus
0.35- 6.25	0.0135-0.246	0.08	0.08	0.003	0.003
6.35-12.70	0.250-0.500	0.10	0.10	0.004	0.004
13.10-19.05	0.516-0.750	0.13	0.13	0.005	0.005
19.40-25.40	0.765-1.000	0.18	0.13	0.007	0.005
25.80-38.10	1.016-1.500	0.20	0.13	0.008	0.005
38.50	1.516 and over	0.25	0.13	0.010	0.005

Angular tolerance on axis of ends on elbows, tees, and crosses shall be ±2.50 degrees for 1/8 to 3/8 in tube fittings or 1/8 and 1/4 pipe fittings; ±1.50 degrees for 1/2 to 2 in O.D. tube fittings or 3/8 to 2 in pipe fittings.

Where so illustrated and not otherwise specified, hexagon corners shall be chamfered 15 to 30 degrees to a diameter equal to the width across flats, with a minus tolerance of 0.4 mm (0.016 in); or where design permits, corners may be chamfered to the diameter of the abutting surface providing the length of chamfer does not exceed that produced by the 30 degree chamfer previously described.

Alternatively, on connections other than SAE straight thread, a 5 degree chamfer starting at the undercut diameter behind the threads or outside diameter of the threads shall be allowed, providing the hex width at corners is not reduced below that produced by the 30 degree chamfer previously described.

3.3 Passages—Where passages in straight fittings are machined from opposite ends, the offset at the meeting point shall not exceed 0.4 mm (0.016 in). The cross-sectional area at the junction of passages in angle fittings shall not be less than that of the smallest passage.

3.4 Wall Thickness—Unless otherwise designated, the wall thickness at any point on fittings shall not be less than the thickness established by the specified dimensions, tolerances, and eccentricities for inner and outer surfaces.

3.5 Contour—Details of contour shall be optional with manufacturer provided the tabulated dimensions are maintained and serviceability of the fittings is not impaired.

3.6 Straight Threads—Unified Standard Class 2A external and Class 2B internal threads with modified minor diameters, where specified, shall apply to plain finish (unplated) fittings of all types. For externally threaded parts with additive finish, the maximum diameters of Class 2A may be exceeded by the amount of the allowance, that is, the basic diameters (Class 2A maximum diameters plus the allowance) apply to an externally threaded part after plating. For internally threaded parts with additive finish, the Class 2B diameters and modified minor diameters apply after plating.

The pitch diameter tolerance shall be the same as the corresponding diameter-pitch combination and class of the Unified fine and 12 thread series. See SAE J475 (ISO R725).

Where external threads are produced by roll threading and body is not undercut, the unthreaded portion of body adjacent to the shoulder may be reduced to the minimum pitch diameter.

External threads shall be chamfered and internal threads shall be countersunk as specified in the dimensional tables.

3.7 Thread Eccentricity Tolerances—The various thread elements of Class 2A external and Class 2B, modified, internal threads on tube fittings shall be concentric within the following limitations:

3.7.1 External Thread (Screw)

a. Where screw pitch diameter is maximum and screw major diameter is maximum, these two thread elements must be concentric. However, if the screw major diameter is out-of-round, undersize, these two thread elements may be eccentric at the point of out-of-roundness, a full indicator reading amount equal to the screw major diameter tolerance.
b. Where screw pitch diameter is minimum and screw major diameter is maximum, these two thread elements may be eccentric a full indicator reading amount equal to the screw pitch diameter tolerance.
c. Where screw pitch diameter is maximum and screw major diameter is minimum, these two thread elements may be eccentric a full indicator reading amount equal to the screw major diameter tolerance.
d. Where screw pitch diameter is minimum and screw major diameter is minimum, these two thread elements may be eccentric a full indicator reading amount equal to the sum of the screw pitch diameter tolerance and the screw major diameter tolerance.

3.7.2 Internal Thread (Nut)

a. Where nut pitch diameter is minimum and nut minor diameter is minimum, these two thread elements must be concentric. However, if the nut minor diameter is out-of-round, oversize, the two thread elements may be eccentric at the point of out-of-roundness, a full indicator reading amount equal to the nut minor diameter tolerance.
b. Where nut pitch diameter is maximum and nut minor diameter is minimum, these two thread elements may be eccentric a full indicator reading amount equal to the nut pitch diameter tolerance.
c. Where nut pitch diameter is minimum and nut minor diameter is maximum, these two thread elements may be eccentric a full indicator reading amount equal to the nut minor diameter tolerance.
d. Where nut pitch diameter is maximum and nut minor diameter is maximum, these two thread elements may be eccentric a full indicator reading amount equal to the sum of the nut pitch diameter tolerance and the nut minor diameter tolerance.

3.8 Pipe Threads—Pipe threads, unless there is specific authorization to the contrary, shall conform to the Dryseal American Standard Taper Pipe Thread (NPTF). Specifications are given in detail in SAE J476 (ANSI B1.20.3).

The length of full form external thread shall not be shorter than L_2 plus one pitch (thread).

Where external pipe threads are produced by roll threading, the diameter of the unthreaded shank adjacent to shoulder may be reduced to the E_2 pitch diameter for brass fittings and to the root diameter on steel fittings.

External pipe threads shall be chamfered from the diameters tabulated below to produce the specified length of chamfer or partial thread. Internal pipe threads shall be countersunk 90 degrees, included angle, to the diameters tabulated in Table 2:

TABLE 2—PIPE THREAD CHAMFER DIAMETERS

Nominal Pipe Thread Size	External Thread Chamfer Dia Max mm	External Thread Chamfer Dia Max in	External Thread Chamfer Dia Min mm	External Thread Chamfer Dia Min in	External Thread Length of Chamfer or Partial Thread Min mm	External Thread Length of Chamfer or Partial Thread Min in	External Thread Length of Chamfer or Partial Thread Max mm	External Thread Length of Chamfer or Partial Thread Max in	Internal Thread Counter-sink Dia Min mm	Internal Thread Counter-sink Dia Min in	Internal Thread Counter-sink Dia Max mm	Internal Thread Counter-sink Dia Max in
1/8	8.1	0.32	7.6	0.30	0.94	0.037	1.40	0.055	10.7	0.42	11.2	0.44
1/4	10.7	0.42	10.2	0.40	1.42	0.056	2.13	0.084	14.0	0.55	14.5	0.57
3/8	14.0	0.55	13.5	0.53	1.42	0.056	2.13	0.084	17.5	0.69	18.0	0.71
1/2	17.3	0.68	16.8	0.66	1.80	0.071	2.72	0.107	21.6	0.85	22.1	0.87
3/4	22.6	0.89	22.1	0.87	1.80	0.071	2.72	0.107	26.9	1.06	27.4	1.08
1	28.4	1.12	27.7	1.09	2.21	0.087	3.30	0.130	34.0	1.34	34.8	1.37
1-1/4	37.1	1.46	36.3	1.43	2.21	0.087	3.30	0.130	42.7	1.68	43.4	1.71
1-1/2	43.2	1.70	42.4	1.67	2.21	0.087	3.30	0.130	48.8	1.92	49.5	1.95
2	55.1	2.17	54.4	2.14	2.21	0.087	3.30	0.130	60.7	2.39	61.5	2.42

Tabulated diameters conform with Appendix A of SAE J476.

3.9 Material—Unless otherwise specified, fittings and ferrules shall be made from carbon steel. Flareless type ferrules in Figures 28 and 29 shall be made from SAE 1010, 1112, 1113, 1213, 12L14, or 1215 steel and cyanide hardened to a depth of 0.03 to 0.05 mm (0.0010 to 0.0019 in).

Stainless steel fittings shall be made from AISI Type 300 Series stainless steel of good quality.[1] Flareless type ferrules in Figures 28 and 29 shall be made from stainless steel of such hardness as to be capable of biting, fully annealed type 304 stainless steel tubing. Unless otherwise specified by the purchaser, stainless steel fittings shall be passivated. Carbon steel and stainless steel fittings fabricated from multiple components must be bonded together with materials having a melting point of not less than 996 °C (1825 °F).

Thirty-seven degree flared type and pipe type brass fittings shall be made from C36000 (CA360) one-half hard barstock or extruded shapes or C37700 (CA377) forgings.

3.10 Finish—The external surfaces and threads of all carbon steel parts shall be plated or coated with a suitable material that passes a 72 h salt spray test in accordance with ASTM B 117. Any appearance of red rust during the 72 h salt spray test shall be considered failure, except for the following:

a. All internal fluid passages.
b. Edges such as hex points, serrations, and crests of threads where there may be mechanical deformation of the plating or coating typical of mass-produced parts or shipping effects.
c. Areas where there is mechanical deformation of the plating or coating caused by crimping, flaring, bending, and other post-plate metal forming operations.
d. Areas where the parts are suspended or affixed in the test chamber where condensate can accumulate.

NOTE—Cadmium plating is not preferred due to environmental reasons. Parts manufactured to this document after January 1, 1997, shall not be cadmium plated. Internal fluid passages shall be protected from corrosion during storage. Changes in plating may affect assembly torques and require requalification, when applicable.

3.11 Workmanship—Workmanship shall conform to the best commercial practice to produce high-quality fittings. Fittings shall be free from all hanging burrs, loose scale, and slivers which might become dislodged in usage and all other defects which might affect their serviceability. All sealing surfaces must be smooth except that annular tool marks up to 2.5 μm (100 μin) max A.A. shall be permissible.

3.12 Assembly Considerations—Use of a compatible lubricant is desirable in assembling dryseal pipe threads on hydraulic tube or pipe fittings to minimize galling and effect a pressure-tight seal.

The O-ring washer must be clinched to fitting with a tight slip fit to an interference fit. The slip fit shall be tight enough so that washer cannot be shaken loose to cause it to drop from its uppermost position by its own weight. The interference fit shall not require a locknut torque more than that indicated in Table 3 of SAE J1453. Position the washer farthest from the end of the fittings as shown in Figure 10A. Care must be taken not to clinch washer on the transition area between diameter Y and locknut thread which results in a loose washer when it is repositioned at assembly. Washer flatness allowance is given in Table 3 of SAE J1453. Any surface out of flatness must be uniform (not wavy) and concave with respect to the O-ring boss end of the fitting.

Torque values listed in Table 2A are for controlled testing to establish compliance to the performance requirements set forth in Table 1. Recommended assembly torques by manufacturers may vary from Table 2A.

Smaller sizes (–2 through –8) of 37 degree flare fittings are less tolerant to over torquing than the larger sizes. Over torquing in these sizes causes deformation of 37 degree cone of the male end. Excessive deformation of the cone results in loss of clamping force and, hence, loss of seal. It also reduces flow area.

Plating combination, surface finish, lubrication, etc., influence fittings' propensity for deformation when assembled to a given torque value. For this reason, many manufacturers recommend assembly to a given number of turns or flats of nut from finger tight position. This method circumvents the influence of variables listed previously, eliminating possibility of excess deformation of 37 degree cone. It is recommended that this method be followed wherever possible.

4. Performance Requirements—See Appendix B for minimum number of samples required for testing.

4.1 Working Pressure (For All Sections)—Working pressures for fittings shall be as listed in Table 1 or as specified in respective section. Proof pressures shall be twice the working pressures, and minimum burst pressures shall be four times the working pressures.

4.2 Proof Test (For All Sections)—All fittings for tubing and adapters shall be capable of withstanding proof pressure for a period of 1 min without failure or leakage.

4.3 Burst Test (For All Sections)—Burst test shall be conducted at minimum torque values or minimum number of turns from finger tight position specified in assembly procedure by manufacturer. For testing only, all adapter to hose fittings or tube fitting threads and contact surfaces shall be lubricated with SAE 10W hydraulic oil prior to assembly. Test blocks for burst testing shall be hardened to 45 to 55 HRC and left unplated. Adjustable fittings shall be backed out one full turn from finger tight position. The test shall be conducted as specified in SAE J343.

4.4 Cyclic Endurance (Impulse) Test (For All Sections)—All tube fittings and adapters shall pass a cyclic endurance test for one million cycles at 133% of corresponding working pressures as established per 4.1. The cycle test shall be conducted at minimum torque or number of turns from finger tight assembly. For testing only, all threads and contact surfaces shall be lubricated with SAE 10W hydraulic oil prior to assembly. Cycle rate shall be uniform at –5 to 1.3 Hz and shall conform in magnitude and frequency to the wave pattern shown in Figure 1 of SAE J343.

4.5 Hose Coupling Interface—Along with over torque test per 4.7, adapter interface and nut portion of hose stem assemblies shall meet proof, burst, and cyclic endurance requirements of hose to which they are attached.

4.6 O-ring—The standard O-ring used on SAE straight thread end for testing shall be nitrile (NBR) rubber with a durometer "A" hardness of 90.

4.7 Over Torque Test (For Fittings in Section 1)—Fitting swivel nuts shall be capable of withstanding the overtorque qualification test with no indication of failure. For testing only, all threads and contact surfaces shall be lubricated with SAE 10W hydraulic oil prior to applying torque listed in respective sections. Test adapters for torque testing shall be hardened to 40 to 50 HRC and left unplated. The fitting shall be restrained during test and the wrench shall be

1. See SAE J405.

located at the threaded end of the nut hex. Nuts that go through brazing in production shall be put through similar annealing cycle before testing.

Definition of failure after torque testing:

a. Nut cannot be removed by hand after breakaway.
b. Nut cannot swivel freely by hand.
c. Any visible cracks or severe deformation that would render nut unuseable.

4.8 Repeated Assembly (For Fittings in Section 1)—Three samples each of male flare shaped fittings assembled to tube flare (with sleeve and nut) and female swivel end shall be tested. Samples shall be assembled and disassembled ten times. Fittings shall be tightened, with threads lubricated with 10W hydraulic oil, to maximum torque values shown in Table 2A. Proof test per 4.2 shall be conducted following the first, fifth, and tenth assembly. There shall be no leakage and the fitting nut shall remain free to swivel by hand after the tenth disassembly.

TABLE 2A—QUALIFICATION TEST TORQUE[b] REQUIREMENTS

Nom SAE Dash Size	Nom Tube OD mm	Nom Tube OD in	Tube End and SAE O-Ring Port Thr'd Size	37 degree Flare End Swivel Nut Torque Nm	37 degree Flare End Swivel Nut Torque lb-ft	37 degree Flare End Swivel Nut Over Torque Nm	37 degree Flare End Swivel Nut Over Torque lb-ft	SAE O-Ring[a] Port End Torque Nm	SAE O-Ring[a] Port End Torque lb-ft
2	3.18	0.125	5/16-24	8- 9	6- 7	15	11	8- 9	6- 7
3	4.76	0.188	3/8 -24	11- 12	8- 9	19	14	11- 12	8- 9
4	6.35	0.250	7/16-20	15- 16	11- 12	24	18	18- 20	13- 15
5	7.94	0.313	1/2 -20	19- 21	14- 15	31	23	23- 26	17- 19
6	9.52	0.375	9/16-18	24- 28	18- 20	42	31	29- 33	22- 24
8	12.70	0.500	3/4 -16	49- 53	36- 39	80	59	49- 53	40- 43
10	15.88	0.625	7/8 -14	77- 85	57- 63	114	85	59- 64	43- 48
12	19.05	0.750	1-1/16-12	107-119	79- 88	160	118	93-102	68- 75
14	22.22	0.875	1-3/16-12	127-140	94-103	186	138	122-134	90- 99
16	25.40	1.000	1-5/16-12	147-154	108-113	214	158	151-166	112-123
20	31.75	1.250	1-5/8 -12	172-181	127-133	271	200	198-218	146-161
24	38.10	1.500	1-7/8 -12	215-226	158-167	339	250	209-231	154-170
32	50.80	2.000	2-1/2 -12	332-350	245-258	497	368	296-325	218-240

[a] This torque is applicable to fittings in Sections 1, 2, 3, and 5.
[b] Test torques given here are for low carbon steel fittings only. Consult the manufacturer for values for other materials.

5. Section 1—37 Degree Flare Tube Fittings—The 37 degree flared tube fittings shall be as shown in Figures 1 to 15 and Tables 3 to 7. Since the basic design of these fittings is derived from Air Force and Navy Standards for 37 degree flared fittings which meet a performance specification, any future changes should not be detrimental to the design or performance. Dimensions for double and single 37 degree flares on tubing to be used with these fittings are given in Figure 3 and Table 2 of SAE J533.

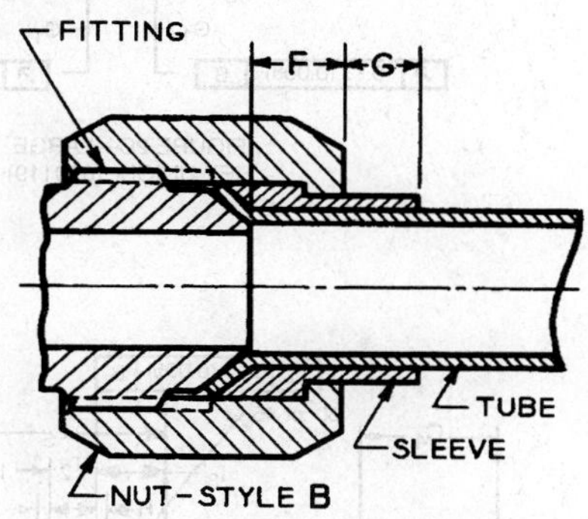

FIGURE 1A—THREE PIECE TUBE ASSEMBLY

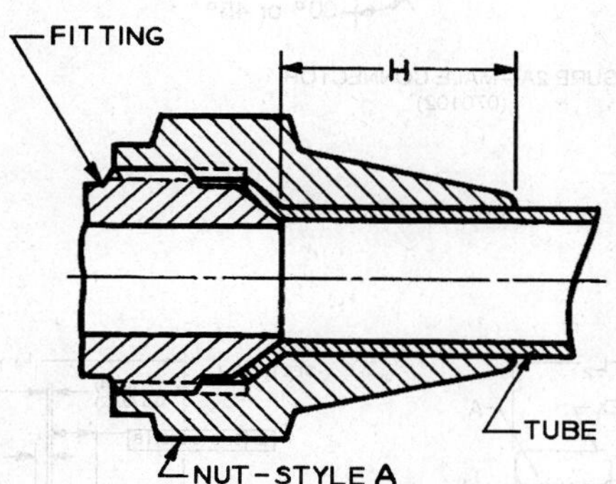

FIGURE 1B—TWO PIECE TUBE ASSEMBLY

FIGURE 1—DETAILS OF 37 DEGREE FLARED HYDRAULIC TUBE FITTING ASSEMBLIES (FIGURE 1)

TABLE 3—DIMENSIONS OF 37 DEGREE FLARED HYDRAULIC TUBE FITTING ASSEMBLIES (FIGURE 1)

Nominal Tube OD	F (Ref) mm	F (Ref) in	G (Ref) mm	G (Ref) in)	H (Ref) mm	H (Ref) in
1-1/8	4.8	0.19	3.0	0.12	12.2	0.48
3/16	6.4	0.25	3.0	0.12	14.2	0.56
1/4	4.8	0.19	4.3	0.17	15.0	0.59
5/16	7.6	0.30	2.8	0.11	16.8	0.66
3/8	7.1	0.28	4.8	0.19	17.5	0.69
1/2	7.9	0.31	4.8	0.19	20.6	0.81
5/8	9.7	0.38	6.9	0.27	23.9	0.94
3/4	9.1	0.36	6.4	0.25	26.2	1.03
7/8	9.7	0.38	7.9	0.31	30.2	1.19
1	8.6	0.34	10.4	0.41	33.3	1.31
1-1/4	8.6	0.34	9.9	0.39	38.1	1.50
1-1/2	12.7	0.50	14.0	0.55	38.9	1.53
2	14.0	0.55	13.5	0.53	44.4	1.75

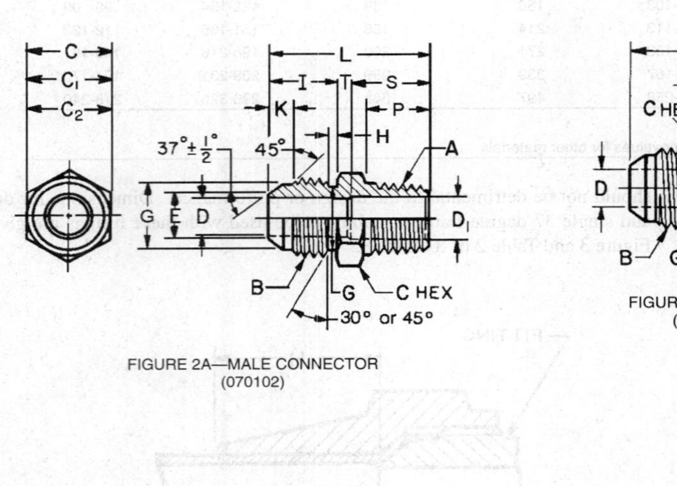

FIGURE 2A—MALE CONNECTOR
(070102)

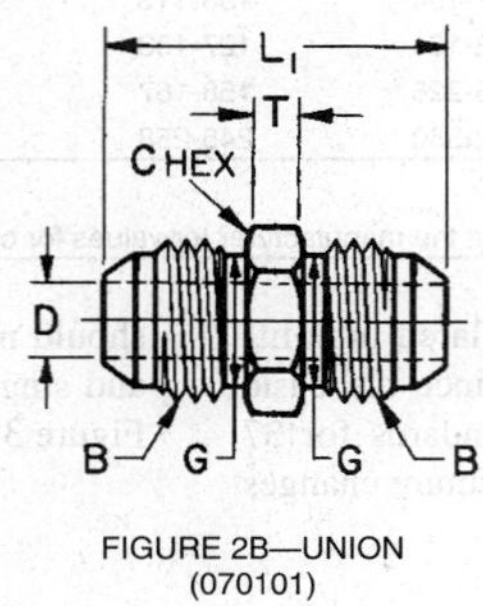

FIGURE 2B—UNION
(070101)

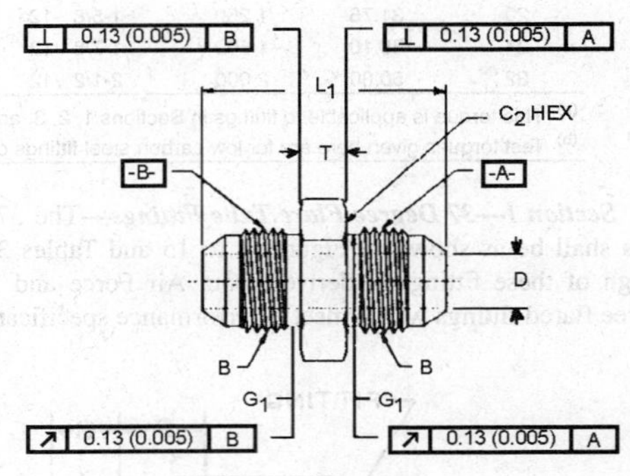

FIGURE 2C—LARGE
HEX UNION* (070119)

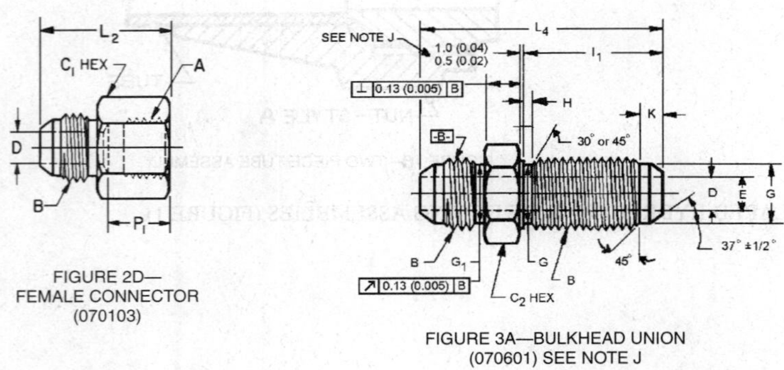

FIGURE 2D—
FEMALE CONNECTOR
(070103)

FIGURE 3A—BULKHEAD UNION
(070601) SEE NOTE J

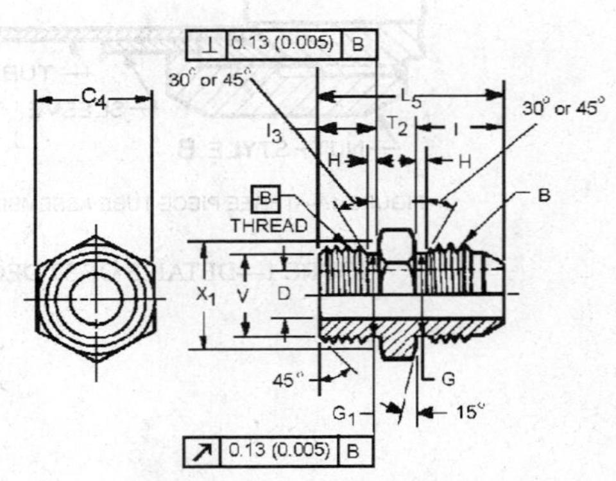

FIGURE 3B—STRAIGHT THREAD CONNECTOR SHORT* (070120)

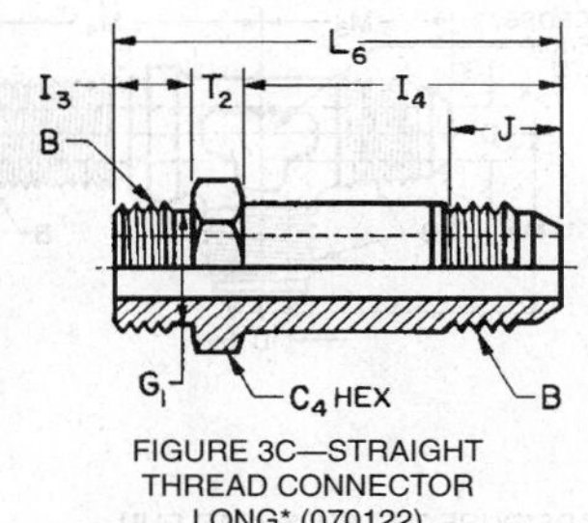

FIGURE 3C—STRAIGHT THREAD CONNECTOR LONG* (070122)

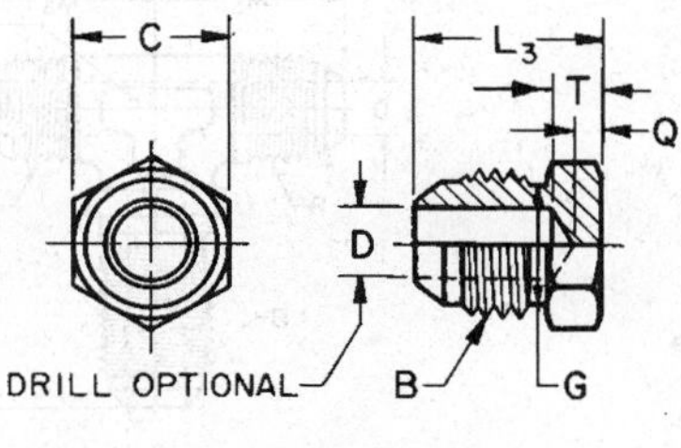

FIGURE 3D—PLUG (070109)

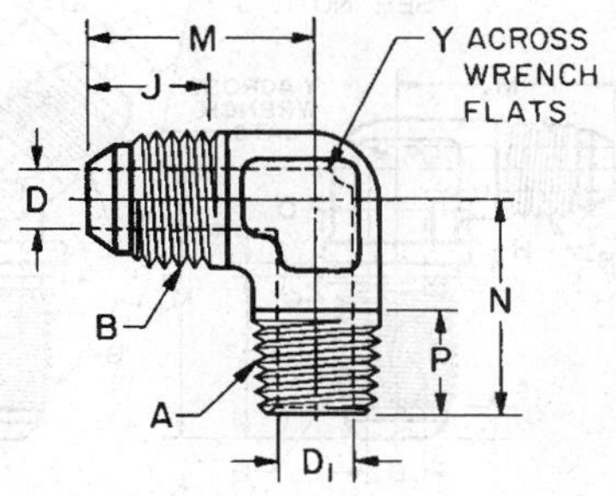

FIGURE 4A—90 DEGREE MALE ELBOW (070202)

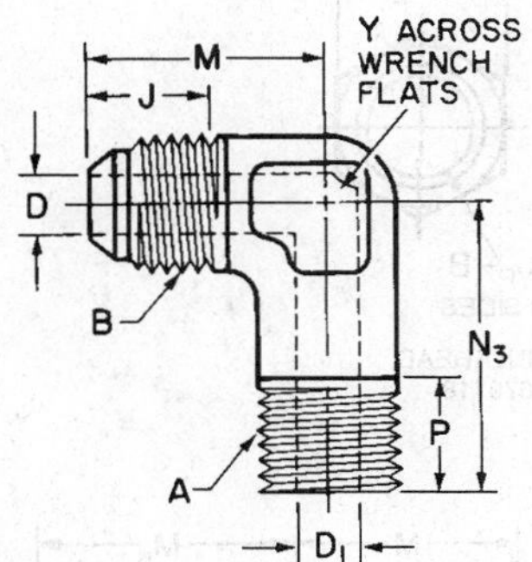

FIGURE 4B—90 DEGREE MALE LONG ELBOW (071502)

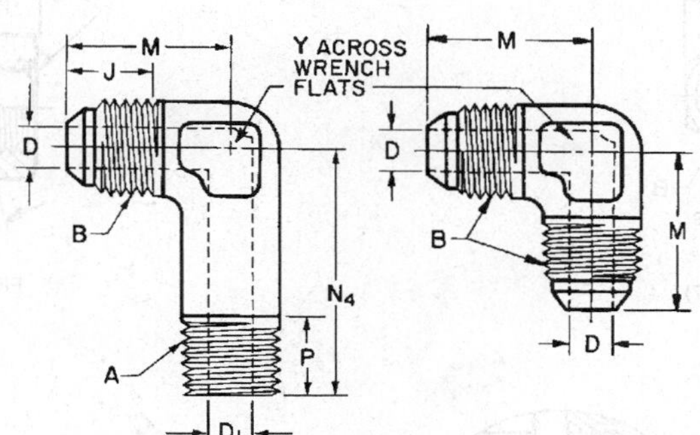

FIGURE 4C—90 DEGREE MALE EXTRA LONG ELBOW (071602)

FIGURE 4D—90 DEGREE UNION ELBOW (070201)

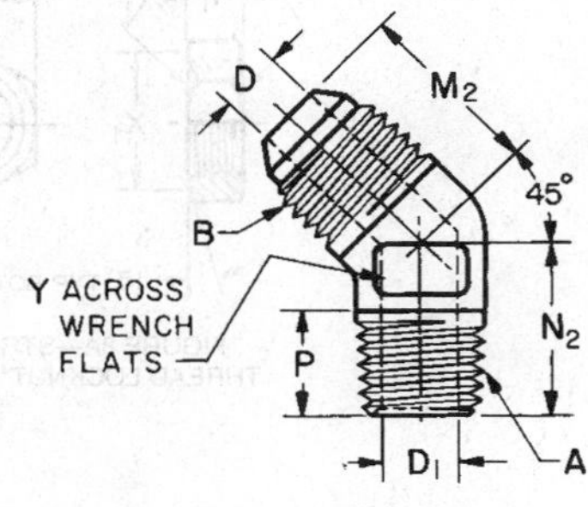

FIGURE 4E—45 DEGREE MALE ELBOW (070302)

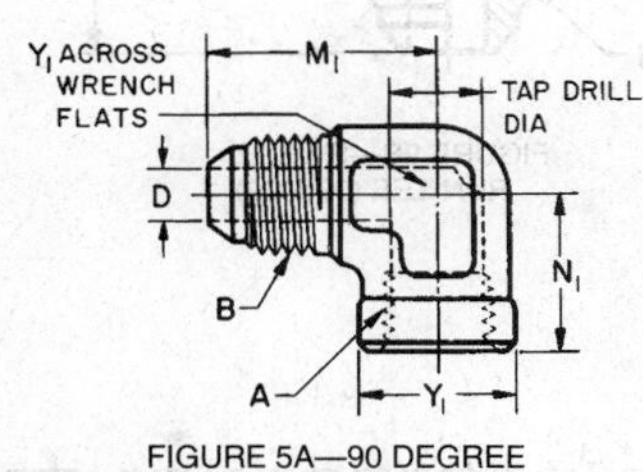

FIGURE 5A—90 DEGREE FEMALE ELBOW (070203)

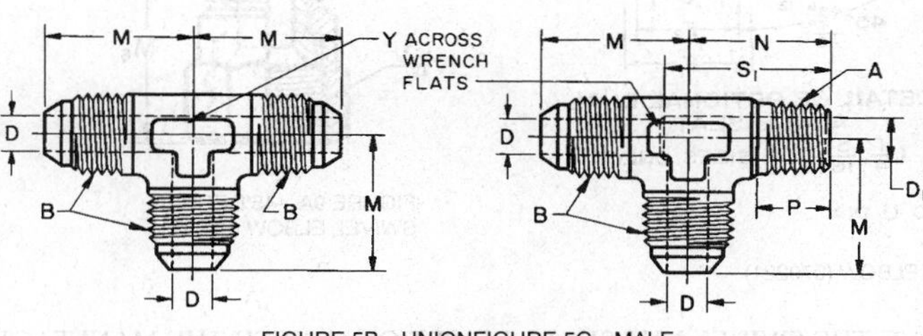

FIGURE 5B—UNION TEE (070401)

FIGURE 5C—MALE RUN TEE (070424)

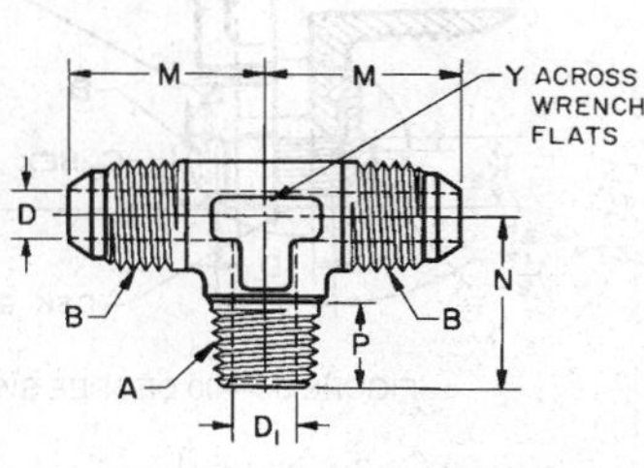

FIGURE 5D—MALE BRANCH TEE (070425)

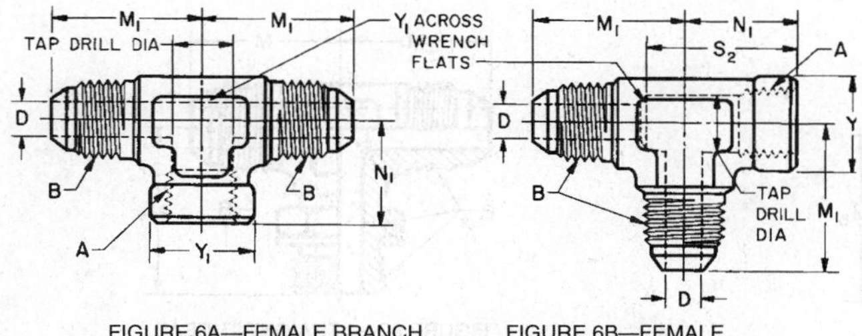

FIGURE 6A—FEMALE BRANCH TEE (070427)

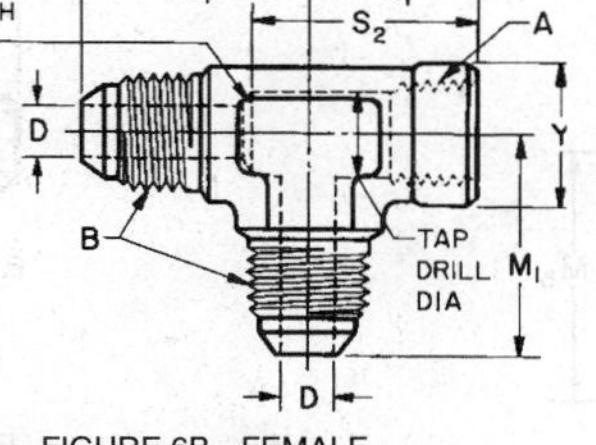

FIGURE 6B—FEMALE RUN TEE (070426)

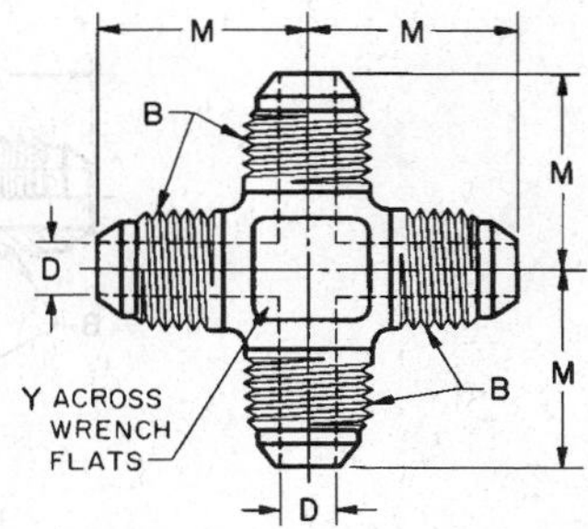

FIGURE 6C—CROSS (070501)

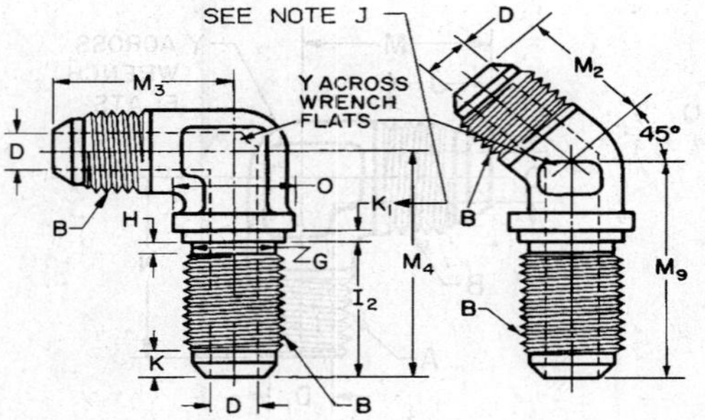

FIGURE 7A—90 DEGREE BULKHEAD ELBOW (070701)

FIGURE 7B—45 DEGREE BULKHEAD ELBOW (070801)

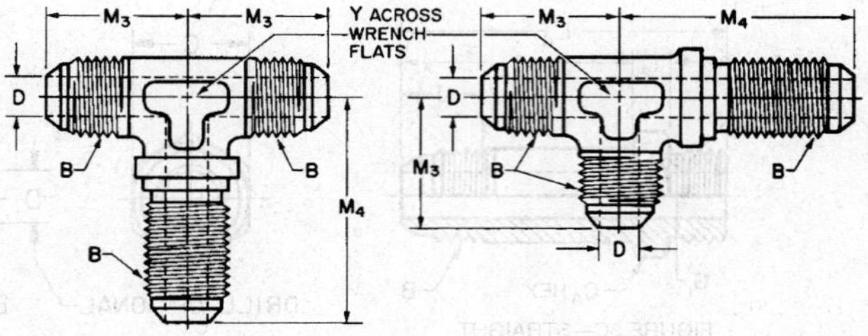

FIGURE 7C—BULKHEAD BRANCH TEE (070959)

FIGURE 7D—BULKHEAD RUN TEE (070958)

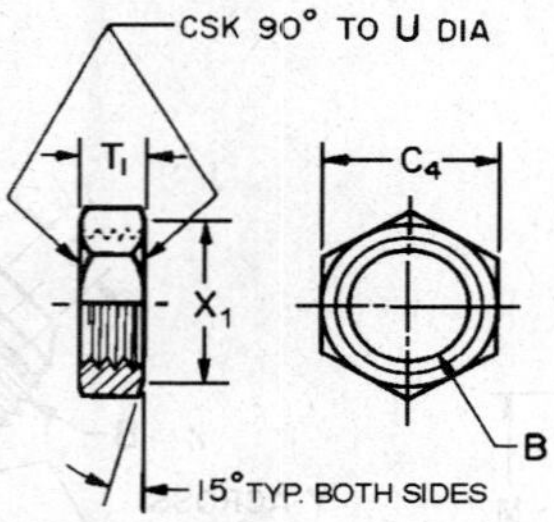

FIGURE 8A—STRAIGHT THREAD LOCKNUT* (070117)

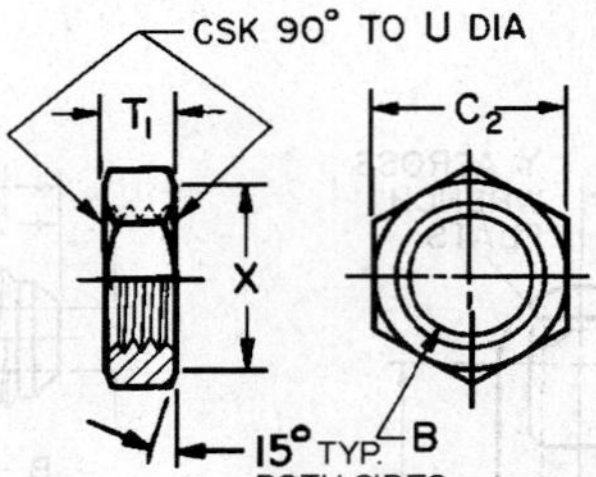

FIGURE 8B—BULKHEAD LOCKNUT (070118)

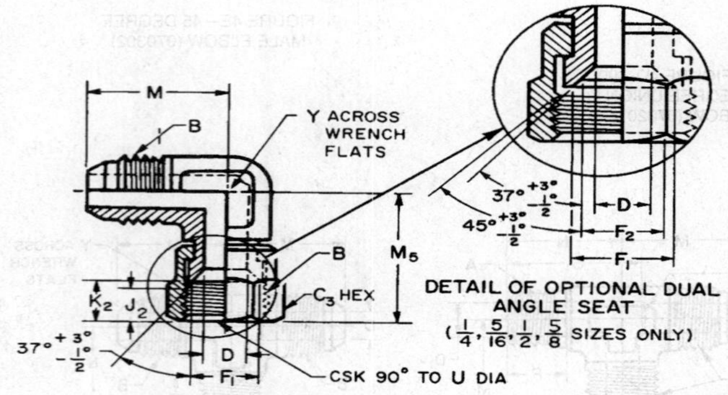

DETAIL OF OPTIONAL DUAL ANGLE SEAT ($\frac{1}{4}$, $\frac{5}{16}$, $\frac{1}{2}$, $\frac{5}{8}$ SIZES ONLY)

FIGURE 8C—90 DEGREE SWIVEL ELBOW (070221)

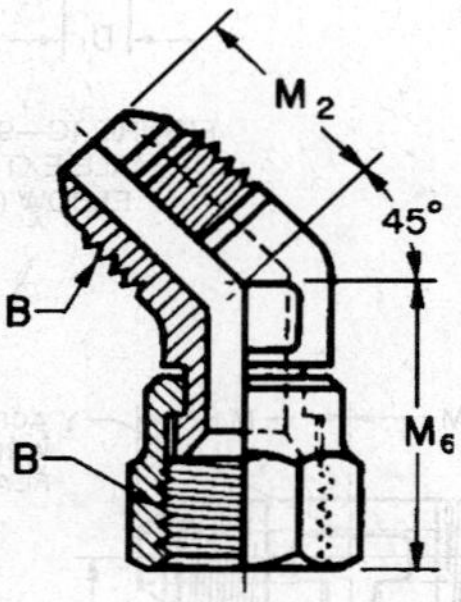

FIGURE 9A—45 DEGREE SWIVEL ELBOW (070321)

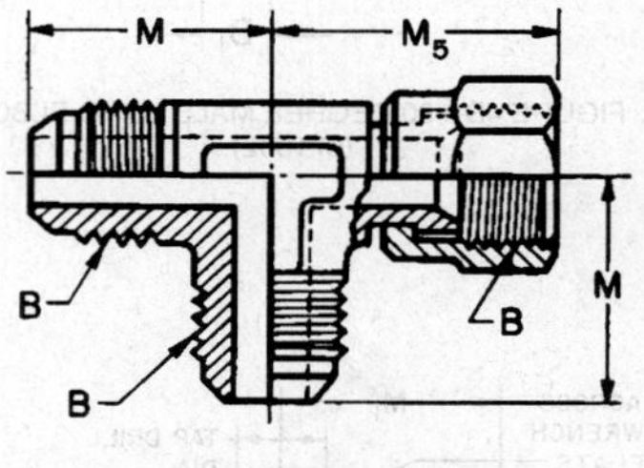

FIGURE 9B—SWIVEL RUN TEE (070432)

THE DESIGN AND METHOD OF ATTACHING THE SWIVEL NUT SHALL BE OPTIONAL WITH THE MANUFACTURER PROVIDING THE TABULATED DIMENSIONS ARE MAINTAINED AND THE NUT TURNS FREELY.

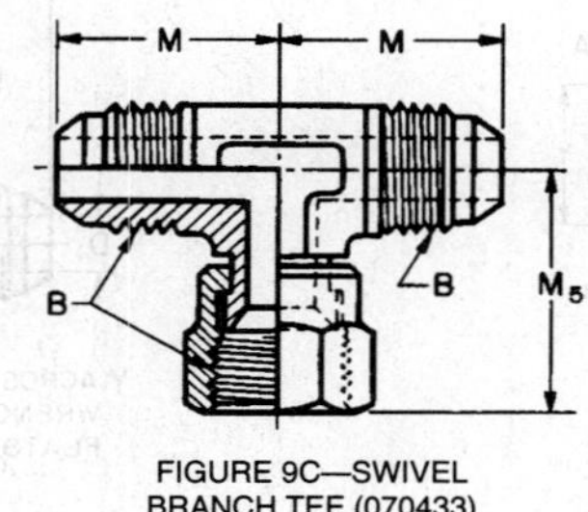

FIGURE 9C—SWIVEL BRANCH TEE (070433)

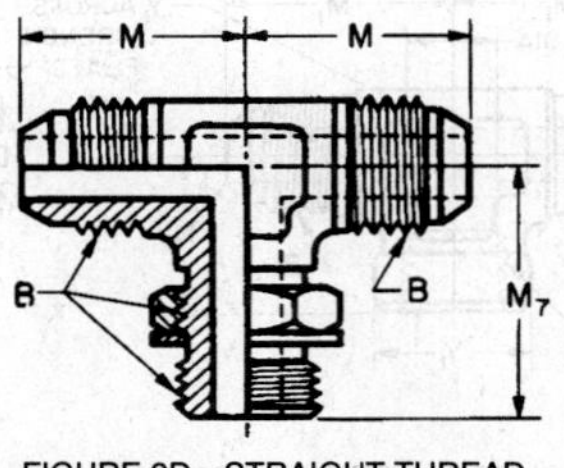

FIGURE 9D—STRAIGHT THREAD BRANCH TEE† (070429)

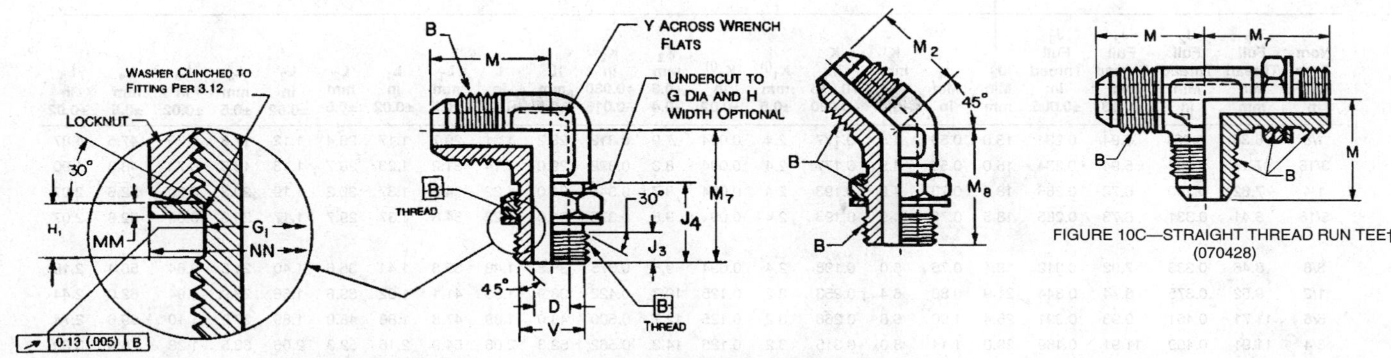

FIGURE 10A—90 DEGREE STRAIGHT THREAD ELBOW† (070220)

FIGURE 10B—45 DEGREE STRAIGHT THREAD ELBOW† (070320)

FIGURE 10C—STRAIGHT THREAD RUN TEE† (070428)

NOTES—UNSPECIFIED DETAIL WITH RESPECT TO DIMENSIONS, TOLERANCES, CONTOURS, MATERIAL, WORKMANSHIP, ETC., MUST CONFORM TO GENERAL SPECIFICATIONS FOR HYDRAULIC TUBE FITTINGS. THE DIMENSIONAL DESIGNATIONS FOR TUBE ENDS IN FIGURES 2A TO 10F, FOR SWIVEL ENDS IN FIGURES 8C TO 9C, FOR O-RING BOSS ENDS IN FIGURES 3B AND 3C, AND FOR ADJUSTABLE STRAIGHT THREAD ENDS IN FIGURES 9D TO 10F SHALL APPLY TO CORRESPONDING ENDS OF OTHER FIGURES ON THIS AND PRECEDING PAGE UNLESS SHOWN OTHERWISE. FIGURES 2A TO 10F ON THIS AND PRECEDING PAGE APPLY TO TABLE 4. CODES SHOWN IN BRACKETS ADJACENT TO FIGURE NUMBERS REPRESENT RESPECTIVE FITTING IDENTIFICATION IN ACCORDANCE WITH SAE J846.

*MODIFICATION OF 1/8-1 IN SIZES IN THESE TYPES OF FITTINGS FOR USE WITH MS 33649 (OR SUPERSEDED AND 10050) BOSSES IS SHOWN IN FIGURE 35 AND TABLE 15.

† IF DESIRED BY THE PURCHASER AND SO SPECIFIED, THESE FITTINGS MAY BE FURNISHED WITH LARGE HEXAGON LOCKNUT SHOWN IN FIGURE 8B.

TABLE 4—DIMENSIONS OF ALL BODIES AND LOCKNUTS (FIGURES 2A TO 10C)

Nom Tube OD, in	A Dryseal Pipe Thread SAE J476 (ANSI B1.20.3)	B[g] Thread Size, in SAE J425 (ISO R725) Class 2A Ext Class 2B Int	C[h] Hex Nom in	C_1[h] Hex Nom in	C_2[h] Hex Nom in	C_3[h] Hex Min in	C_4[h] Hex Nom in	D[i] Drill mm	D[i] Drill in	D_1[b][i] Drill mm	D_1[b][i] Drill in	E Dia mm ±0.08	E Dia in ±0.003	F_1 Dia mm ±0.25	F_1 Dia in ±0.010	F_2 Dia mm ±0.13	F_2 Dia in ±0.005
1/8	1/8-27	5/16-24	7/16	9/16	9/16	7/16	7/16	1.6	0.062	4.8	0.188	2.11	0.083	4.85	0.190	—	—
3/16	1/8-27	3/8-24	7/16	9/16	5/8	1/2	1/2	3.2	0.125	4.8	0.188	3.71	0.146	6.20	0.245	—	—
1/4	1/8-27	7/16-20	1/2	9/16	11/16	9/16	9/16	4.4	0.172	4.8	0.188	4.90	0.193	7.35	0.290	6.35	0.250
5/16	1/8-27	1/2-20	9/16	9/16	3/4	5/8	5/8	6.0	0.234	4.8	0.188	6.48	0.255	8.90	0.350	7.93	0.312
3/8	1/4-18	9/16-18	5/8	3/4	13/16	11/16	11/16	7.5	0.297	7.0	0.281	8.08	0.318	10.90	0.430	—	—
1/2	3/8-18	3/4-16	13/16	7/8	1	7/8	7/8	9.9	0.391	10.3	0.406	10.82	0.426	14.35	0.565	12.70	0.500
5/8	1/2-14	7/8-14	15/16	1-1/8	1-1/8	1	1	12.3	0.484	13.5	0.531	13.69	0.539	17.15	0.675	15.88	0.625
3/4	3/4-14	1-1/16-12	1-1/8	1-3/8	1-3/8	1-1/4	1-1/4	15.5	0.609	18.3	0.719	16.87	0.664	21.45	0.845	—	—
7/8	3/4-14	1-3/16-12	1-1/4	1-3/8	1-1/2	1-3/8	1-3/8	18.3	0.719	18.3	0.719	20.02	0.788	24.65	0.970	—	—
1	1-11-1/2	1-5/16-12	1-3/8	1-5/8	1-5/8	1-1/2	1-1/2	21.4	0.844	23.8	0.938	23.19	0.913	27.80	1.095	—	—
1-1/4	1-1/4-11-1/2	1-5/8-12	1-11/16	2	1-7/8	2	1-7/8	27.4	1.078	31.7	1.250	29.13	1.147	35.70	1.405	—	—
1-1/2	1-1/2-11-1/2	1-7/8-12	2	2-3/8	2-1/8	2-1/4	2-1/8	33.3	1.312	38.0	1.500	35.08	1.381	41.15	1.620	—	—
2	2-11-1/2	2-1/2-12	2-5/8	2-7/8	2-3/4	2-7/8	2-3/4	45.2	1.781	49.0	1.938	47.75	1.880	56.75	2.235	—	—

Nom Tube OD in	G Dia mm +0.05 −0.25	G Dia in +0.002 −0.010	G_1[a] Dia mm +0.05 −0.08	G_1[a] Dia in +0.002 −0.003	H mm +0.8 −0.0	H in +0.030 −0.000	H_1 mm +0.3 −0.0	H_1 in +0.010 −0.000	I mm ±0.4	I in ±0.016	I_1 mm ±0.5	I_1 in ±0.02	I_2 mm ±0.5	I_2 in ±0.02	I_3 mm ±0.13	I_3 in ±0.005	I_4 mm ±0.5	I_4 in ±0.02	J[k] Full Thread Min mm	J[k] Full Thread Min in
1/8	6.35	0.250	6.35	0.250	1.6	0.063	3.2	0.125	11.4	0.448	28.2	1.11	23.4	0.92	7.54	0.297	29.7	1.17	11.00	0.433
3/16	7.92	0.312	7.95	0.313	1.6	0.063	3.3	0.131	12.2	0.479	28.2	1.11	23.4	0.92	7.54	0.297	31.8	1.25	11.81	0.464
1/4	9.25	0.364	9.25	0.364	1.9	0.075	4.0	0.156	14.0	0.550	30.5	1.20	25.9	1.02	9.14	0.360	35.3	1.39	13.59	0.535
5/16	10.82	0.426	10.85	0.427	1.9	0.075	4.0	0.156	14.0	0.550	30.5	1.20	25.9	1.02	9.14	0.360	36.8	1.45	13.59	0.535
3/8	12.22	0.481	12.24	0.482	2.1	0.083	4.0	0.156	14.1	0.556	32.5	1.28	27.7	1.09	9.93	0.391	39.6	1.56	13.74	0.541
1/2	16.74	0.659	16.76	0.660	2.4	0.094	4.8	0.187	16.7	0.657	36.6	1.44	31.8	1.25	11.13	0.438	47.8	1.88	16.31	0.642
5/8	19.61	0.772	19.63	0.773	2.7	0.107	5.6	0.219	19.3	0.758	40.1	1.58	35.3	1.39	12.70	0.500	53.1	2.09	18.87	0.743
3/4	23.95	0.943	24.00	0.945	3.2	0.125	5.9	0.234	21.9	0.864	44.4	1.75	39.6	1.56	15.09	0.594	63.5	2.50	21.56	0.849
7/8	27.13	1.068	27.18	1.070	3.2	0.125	5.9	0.234	22.6	0.890	44.4	1.75	39.6	1.56	15.09	0.594	68.3	2.69	22.22	0.875
1	30.30	1.193	30.35	1.195	3.2	0.125	5.9	0.234	23.1	0.911	44.4	1.75	39.6	1.56	15.09	0.594	72.1	2.84	22.76	0.896
1-1/4	38.25	1.506	38.28	1.507	3.2	0.125	5.9	0.234	24.3	0.958	45.7	1.80	40.9	1.61	15.09	0.594	88.1	3.47	23.95	0.943
1-1/2	44.58	1.755	44.60	1.756	3.2	0.125	5.9	0.234	27.5	1.083	46.0	1.81	41.1	1.62	15.09	0.594	98.6	3.88	27.13	1.068
2	60.45	2.380	60.48	2.381	3.2	0.125	5.9	0.234	33.9	1.333	53.1	2.09	48.5	1.91	15.09	0.594	122.9	4.84	33.48	1.318

Continued on next page.

TABLE 4—DIMENSIONS OF ALL BODIES AND LOCKNUTS (FIGURES 2A TO 10C) (CONTINUED)

Nom Tube OD, in	J2 Full Thread Min mm	J2 Full Thread Min in	J3 Full Thread mm ±0.13	J3 Full Thread in ±0.005	J4 Min mm	J4 Min in	K mm +0.4 −0.0	K in +0.016 −0.000	K1[j] mm ±0.5	K1[j] in ±0.02	K2 mm +0.8 −0.4	K2 in +0.030 −0.016	L mm ±0.5	L in ±0.02	L1 mm ±0.5	L1 in ±0.02	L2 mm ±0.5	L2 in ±0.02	L3 mm ±0.5	L3 in ±0.02	L4 mm ±0.5	L4 in ±0.02
1/8	6.38	0.251	5.94	0.234	15.0	0.59	4.5	0.177	2.4	0.094	7.9	0.312	28.2	1.11	29.7	1.17	28.4	1.12	17.8	0.70	47.5	1.87
3/16	7.16	0.282	5.94	0.234	15.0	0.59	4.5	0.177	2.4	0.094	8.3	0.328	29.0	1.14	31.2	1.23	28.7	1.13	18.5	0.73	48.3	1.90
1/4	7.62	0.300	6.73	0.265	18.5	0.73	4.9	0.193	2.4	0.094	8.7	0.344	31.0	1.22	34.8	1.37	30.2	1.19	20.3	0.80	52.6	2.07
5/16	8.41	0.331	6.73	0.265	18.5	0.73	4.9	0.193	2.4	0.094	9.5	0.375	31.0	1.22	34.8	1.37	29.7	1.17	20.3	0.80	52.6	2.07
3/8	8.46	0.333	7.92	0.312	19.1	0.75	5.0	0.198	2.4	0.094	9.5	0.375	36.3	1.43	35.8	1.41	35.6	1.40	21.3	0.84	55.4	2.18
1/2	9.52	0.375	8.74	0.344	21.9	0.86	6.4	0.253	3.2	0.125	10.7	0.422	38.9	1.53	41.1	1.62	39.6	1.56	23.9	0.94	62.0	2.44
5/8	11.71	0.461	9.93	0.391	25.4	1.00	6.8	0.266	3.2	0.125	12.7	0.500	48.0	1.89	47.8	1.88	48.0	1.89	27.9	1.10	69.6	2.74
3/4	11.91	0.469	11.91	0.469	29.0	1.14	8.0	0.315	3.2	0.125	14.3	0.562	52.3	2.06	54.9	2.16	52.3	2.06	32.5	1.28	78.5	3.09
7/8	13.11	0.516	11.91	0.469	29.0	1.14	8.0	0.315	3.2	0.125	14.7	0.578	53.1	2.09	56.1	2.21	52.3	2.06	33.3	1.31	79.2	3.12
1	14.30	0.563	11.91	0.469	29.0	1.14	8.0	0.315	3.2	0.125	15.1	0.594	58.4	2.30	57.2	2.25	59.7	2.35	33.8	1.33	79.8	3.14
1-1/4	14.30	0.563	11.91	0.469	29.0	1.14	9.3	0.367	3.2	0.125	15.9	0.625	62.2	2.45	61.7	2.43	63.2	2.49	36.8	1.45	84.1	3.31
1-1/2	16.79	0.661	11.91	0.469	29.0	1.14	9.6	0.378	3.2	0.125	18.6	0.734	68.1	2.68	69.8	2.75	66.5	2.62	41.9	1.65	89.4	3.52
2	21.44	0.844	11.91	0.469	29.0	1.14	11.7	0.461	3.2	0.125	23.8	0.938	79.0	3.11	86.4	3.40	75.4	2.97	52.1	2.05	106.7	4.20

Nom Tube OD, in	L5 mm ±0.5	L5 in ±0.02	L6 mm ±0.5	L6 in ±0.02	M mm ±0.8	M in ±0.03	M1 mm ±0.8	M1 in ±0.03	M2 mm ±0.8	M2 in ±0.03	M3 mm ±0.8	M3 in ±0.03	M4 mm ±0.8	M4 in ±0.03	M5 mm ±1.5	M5 in ±0.06	M6 mm ±1.5	M6 in ±0.06	M7 mm ±0.8	M7 in ±0.03	M8 mm ±0.8	M8 in ±0.03	M9 mm ±0.8	M9 in ±0.03
1/8	26.9	1.06	45.5	1.79	19.6	0.77	25.4	1.00	17.5	0.69	22.4	0.88	38.1	1.50	24.6	0.97	23.9	0.94	23.9	0.94	22.4	0.88	36.1	1.42
3/16	27.9	1.10	47.5	1.87	21.1	0.83	26.2	1.03	17.5	0.69	23.9	0.94	38.1	1.50	25.4	1.00	23.9	0.94	23.9	0.94	22.4	0.88	36.1	1.42
1/4	31.2	1.23	52.8	2.08	22.6	0.89	27.4	1.08	18.3	0.72	24.6	0.97	40.4	1.59	25.4	1.00	23.9	0.94	26.2	1.03	26.7	1.05	38.9	1.53
5/16	31.2	1.23	54.4	2.14	24.1	0.95	27.4	1.08	19.6	0.77	26.9	1.06	43.7	1.72	26.9	1.06	25.4	1.00	28.7	1.13	26.7	1.05	42.2	1.66
3/8	33.0	1.30	58.7	2.31	26.9	1.06	31.2	1.23	21.1	0.83	27.7	1.09	46.0	1.81	31.8	1.25	28.4	1.12	31.8	1.25	29.0	1.14	42.4	1.67
1/2	37.6	1.48	68.6	2.70	31.8	1.25	36.1	1.42	24.9	0.98	34.5	1.36	53.6	2.11	35.1	1.38	32.5	1.28	36.8	1.45	33.0	1.30	49.3	1.94
5/8	43.2	1.70	77.2	3.04	36.8	1.45	41.7	1.64	28.2	1.11	39.6	1.56	60.7	2.39	41.1	1.62	36.6	1.44	43.2	1.70	38.6	1.52	55.1	2.17
3/4	50.0	1.97	91.7	3.61	42.2	1.66	48.0	1.89	32.5	1.28	45.2	1.78	67.8	2.67	44.4	1.75	38.1	1.50	49.3	1.94	43.9	1.73	62.0	2.44
7/8	50.5	1.99	96.5	3.80	45.7	1.80	47.2	1.86	36.8	1.45	48.8	1.92	71.1	2.80	45.2	1.78	41.1	1.62	50.8	2.00	47.2	1.86	63.5	2.50
1	51.8	2.04	101.1	3.98	46.0	1.81	55.1	2.17	37.3	1.47	49.3	1.94	71.1	2.80	50.8	2.00	44.4	1.75	52.1	2.05	47.2	1.86	65.0	2.56
1-1/4	55.1	2.17	119.1	4.69	52.3	2.06	59.2	2.33	40.4	1.59	55.1	2.17	79.2	3.12	58.7	2.31	51.6	2.03	57.2	2.25	48.5	1.91	67.3	2.65
1-1/2	60.2	2.37	131.3	5.17	59.2	2.33	73.4	2.89	45.2	1.78	59.4	2.34	86.9	3.42	65.8	2.59	57.2	2.25	60.7	2.39	48.5	1.91	67.8	2.67
2	70.6	2.78	159.8	6.29	77.7	3.06	83.8	3.30	56.4	2.22	73.4	2.89	104.4	4.11	85.9	3.38	73.9	2.91	73.4	2.89	47.2	1.86	73.9	2.91

Nom Tube OD, in	N mm ±0.8	N in ±0.03	N1 mm ±0.8	N1 in ±0.03	N2 mm ±0.8	N2 in ±0.03	N3 mm ±0.8	N3 in ±0.03	N4 mm ±0.8	N4 in ±0.03	O mm ±0.8	O in ±0.03	P Min mm	P Min in	P1 Max mm	P1 Max in	Q Min mm	Q Min in	S[b] Max mm	S[b] Max in	S1[b][c] Min mm	S1[b][c] Min in	S2[c] Min mm	S2[c] Min in
1/8	18.3	0.72	16.8	0.66	13.2	0.52	25.4	1.00	32.5	1.28	11.1	0.438	9.7	0.38	11.7	0.46	2.8	0.11	12.4	0.49	20.1	0.79	18.5	0.73
3/16	18.3	0.72	16.8	0.66	13.2	0.52	26.4	1.04	34.3	1.35	12.7	0.500	9.7	0.38	11.7	0.46	2.8	0.11	12.4	0.49	20.8	0.82	19.3	0.76
1/4	19.8	0.78	16.8	0.66	16.3	0.64	29.7	1.17	39.6	1.56	14.3	0.562	9.7	0.38	11.7	0.46	2.8	0.11	12.4	0.49	23.1	0.91	20.1	0.79
5/16	19.8	0.78	16.8	0.66	16.3	0.64	29.7	1.17	41.4	1.63	15.9	0.625	9.7	0.38	11.7	0.46	3.0	0.12	16.3	0.64	28.2	1.11	20.8	0.82
3/8	27.7	1.09	22.4	0.88	21.8	0.86	40.1	1.58	52.6	2.07	17.5	0.688	14.2	0.56	17.0	0.67	3.0	0.12	17.0	0.67	31.8	1.25	27.2	1.07
1/2	31.0	1.22	25.9	1.02	24.1	0.95	46.2	1.82	61.5	2.42	22.2	0.875	14.2	0.56	17.3	0.68	4.1	0.16	17.3	0.68	37.1	1.46	32.0	1.26
5/8	37.3	1.47	31.2	1.23	29.7	1.17	55.1	2.17	72.9	2.87	25.4	1.000	19.0	0.75	22.9	0.90	4.1	0.16	23.1	0.91	44.4	1.75	38.4	1.51
3/4	40.4	1.59	34.5	1.36	30.5	1.20	62.0	2.44	83.3	3.28	30.2	1.188	19.0	0.75	23.1	0.91	4.8	0.19	23.9	0.94	49.3	1.94	43.4	1.71
7/8	42.9	1.69	36.1	1.42	33.02	1.30	65.8	2.59	88.9	3.50	33.3	1.312	19.0	0.75	23.1	0.91	4.8	0.19	—	—	—	—	46.2	1.82
1	50.0	1.97	41.1	1.62	37.6	1.48	76.5	3.01	102.9	4.05	36.5	1.438	23.9	0.94	29.0	1.14	4.8	0.19	28.7	1.13	61.7	2.43	52.8	2.08
1-1/4	60.5	2.38	43.2	1.70	42.4	1.67	93.7	3.69	127.0	5.00	44.4	1.750	24.6	0.97	29.5	1.16	5.8	0.23	30.5	1.20	75.2	2.96	57.9	2.28
1-1/2	67.1	2.64	52.8	2.08	45.0	1.77	104.1	4.10	141.0	5.55	50.8	2.000	25.4	1.00	29.5	1.16	5.8	0.23	32.3	1.27	84.8	3.34	70.6	2.78
2	76.2	3.00	60.7	2.39	53.6	2.11	122.2	4.81	168.4	6.63	66.7	2.625	26.2	1.03	30.0	1.18	8.4	0.33	34.8	1.37	100.1	3.94	84.6	3.33

Continued on next page.

TABLE 4—DIMENSIONS OF ALL BODIES AND LOCKNUTS (FIGURES 2A TO 10C) (CONTINUED)

Nom Tube OD, in	T[d] Ref mm	T[d] Ref in	T_1 mm ±0.5	T_1 in ±002	T_2[d] Ref mm	T_2[d] Ref in	U Dia mm +0.4 −0.0	U Dia in +0.016 −0.000	V Dia mm ±0.25	V Dia in ±0.010	X Dia mm ±0.13	X Dia in ±0.005	X_1 Dia mm ±0.13	X_1 Dia in ±0.005
1/8	5.6	0.22	5.6	0.22	7.1	0.28	8.1	0.317	6.25	0.245	14.27	0.562	11.13	0.438
3/16	5.6	0.22	5.6	0.22	7.1	0.28	9.7	0.380	7.75	0.305	15.88	0.625	12.70	0.500
1/4	5.6	0.22	7.1	0.28	7.1	0.28	11.3	0.443	9.15	0.360	17.48	0.688	14.30	0.563
5/16	5.6	0.22	7.1	0.28	7.1	0.28	12.8	0.505	10.65	0.420	19.05	0.750	15.88	0.625
3/8	6.4	0.25	6.9	0.27	7.9	0.31	14.4	0.567	12.05	0.475	20.62	0.812	17.48	0.688
1/2	6.4	0.25	7.9	0.31	8.6	0.34	19.2	0.755	16.65	0.655	25.40	1.000	22.22	0.875
5/8	7.9	0.31	9.1	0.36	10.2	0.40	22.4	0.880	19.55	0.770	28.58	1.125	25.40	1.000
3/4	9.7	0.38	10.4	0.41	11.9	0.47	27.1	1.067	23.90	0.940	34.92	1.375	31.75	1.250
7/8	9.7	0.38	10.4	0.41	11.9	0.47	30.3	1.193	27.05	1.065	38.10	1.500	34.92	1.375
1	9.7	0.38	10.4	0.41	12.7	0.50	33.5	1.317	30.25	1.190	41.28	1.625	38.10	1.500
1-1/4	11.7	0.46	10.4	0.41	14.7	0.58	41.4	1.630	38.10	1.500	47.62	1.875	47.62	1.875
1-1/2	13.5	0.53	10.4	0.41	16.5	0.65	47.8	1.880	44.45	1.750	53.98	2.125	53.98	2.125
2	17.3	0.68	10.4	0.41	20.6	0.81	63.6	2.505	60.35	2.375	69.85	2.750	69.85	2.750

Nom Tube OD, in	Y Forging[f], mm +0.0	Y Forging[f], in +0.000	Y[f] Barstock Max mm	Y[f] Barstock Max in	Y_1[e][f] mm +0.0	Y_1[e][f] in +0.000	MM mm ±0.08	MM in ±0.003	NN Dia mm ±0.4	NN Dia in ±0.016	PP Dia mm ±0.25	PP Dia in ±0.010
1/8	11.1-0.8	0.438-0.030	—	—	14.3-0.8	0.562-0.030	0.76	0.030	12.8	0.504	6.25	0.245
3/16	11.1-0.8	0.438-0.030	—	—	14.3-0.8	0.562-0.030	0.76	0.030	14.6	0.575	7.75	0.305
1/4	11.1-0.8	0.438-0.030	14.3	0.562	14.3-0.8	0.562-0.030	0.89	0.035	16.5	0.650	9.15	0.360
5/16	14.3-0.8	0.562-0.030	15.9	0.625	14.3-0.8	0.562-0.030	0.89	0.035	18.3	0.722	10.65	0.420
3/8	14.3-0.8	0.562-0.030	20.6	0.812	19.0-0.8	0.750-0.030	0.89	0.035	20.2	0.794	12.05	0.475
1/2	19.0-0.8	0.750-0.030	22.2	0.875	22.2-0.8	0.875-0.030	1.04	0.041	25.7	1.010	16.65	0.655
5/8	22.2-0.8	0.875-0.030	28.6	1.125	27.0-0.8	1.062-0.030	1.27	0.050	29.3	1.155	19.55	0.770
3/4	27.0-1.0	1.062-0.040	34.9	1.375	33.3-1.0	1.312-0.040	1.27	0.050	36.7	1.444	23.90	0.940
7/8	33.3-1.0	1.312-0.040	38.1	1.500	33.3-1.0	1.312-0.040	1.27	0.050	40.4	1.589	27.05	1.065
1	33.3-1.0	1.312-0.040	41.3	1.625	41.3-1.0	1.625-0.040	1.27	0.050	44.0	1.732	30.25	1.190
1-1/4	41.3-1.0	1.625-0.040	54.0	2.125	47.6-1.0	1.875-0.040	1.27	0.050	55.0	2.165	38.10	1.500
1-1/2	47.6-1.0	1.875-0.040	57.2	2.250	65.1-1.0	2.562-0.040	1.27	0.050	62.3	2.454	44.45	1.750
2	63.5-1.0	2.500-0.040	82.6	3.250	71.4-1.0	2.812-0.040	1.27	0.050	80.3	3.160	—	—

a O-ring groove undercut must be smooth and free from tool marks.
b At manufacturer's option, through passages in Figures 2A and 5C may conform with the smaller diameter specified or the appropriate end may be counterbored to the larger diameter for depths S and S_1, respectively.
c Maximum depth shall be optional with manufacturer providing wall thickness is controlled with General Specifications.
d Minimum design thickness, not subject to inspection.
e The basic dimensions shown shall apply as minimum for boss diameters.
f For optional metric fitting flats see Appendix A.
g Unified class 2B thread shall apply to swivel nuts Figures 8C to 9C and with minor diameter modified to class 3B limits for locknuts Figures 8A and 8B.
h Across flat widths must fit standard wrench openings. See ANSI B18.2.2.
j Diameter of bulkhead pilot is the same as major thread diameter. Recommended pilot hole for bulkhead fittings is 0.4 mm (0.016 in) over major thread diameter.
k J full thread minimum with thread runout. If undercut to G diameter and H width. Length of thread and undercut must not be less than I.
l See Table 1A for tolerance.

TABLE 4A—ADDED VALUES FOR L, LL, AND LLL DROP LENGTHS (REF. FIGURES 10D (071520), 10E (071620), 10F (071720)

SAE Dash Size	M11 mm ±0.8	M11 in ±0.030	M12 mm ±0.8	M12 in ±0.030	M13 mm ±0.8	M13 in ±0.030
–2	33.27	1.31	37.34	1.47	51.56	2.03
–3	35.31	1.39	38.86	1.53	53.85	2.12
–4	39.12	1.54	43.94	1.73	61.98	2.44
–5	39.88	1.57	47.24	1.86	66.29	2.61
–6	42.16	1.66	52.83	2.08	73.91	2.91
–8	50.04	1.97	62.99	2.48	89.66	3.53
–10	57.40	2.26	73.41	2.89	102.87	4.05
–12	66.55	2.62	84.84	3.34	120.65	4.75
–14	70.10	2.76	90.42	3.56	129.29	5.09
–16	77.72	3.06	94.49	3.72	136.91	5.39
–20	88.39	3.48	112.01	4.41	166.62	6.56
–24	99.82	3.93	122.17	4.81	183.64	7.23
–32	113.28	4.46	151.89	5.98	230.63	9.08

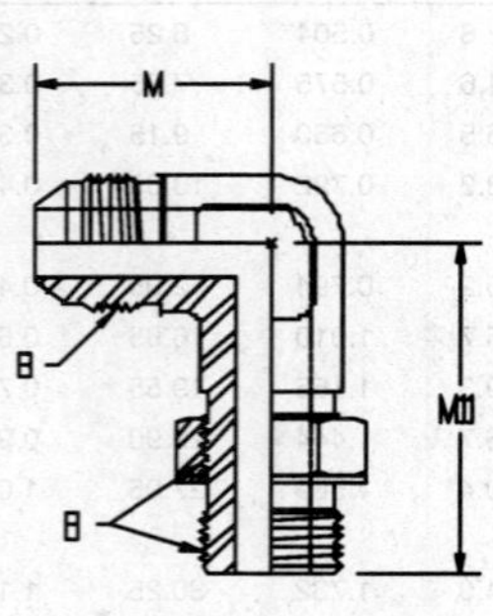

Figure 10D—90 Degree Straight Thread Elbow Long (071520)

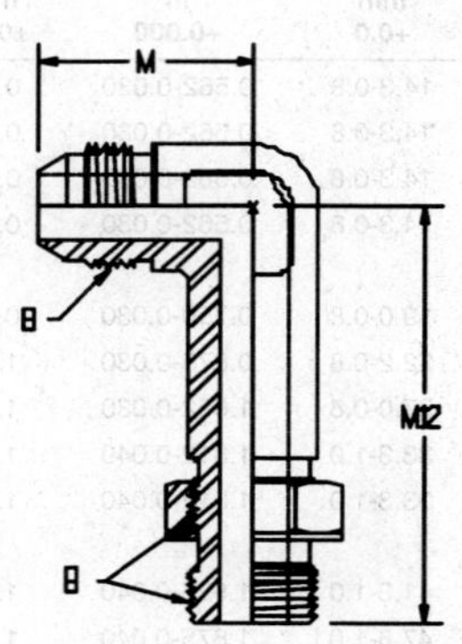

FIGURE 10E—90 Degree Straight Thread Elbow Extra Long (071620)

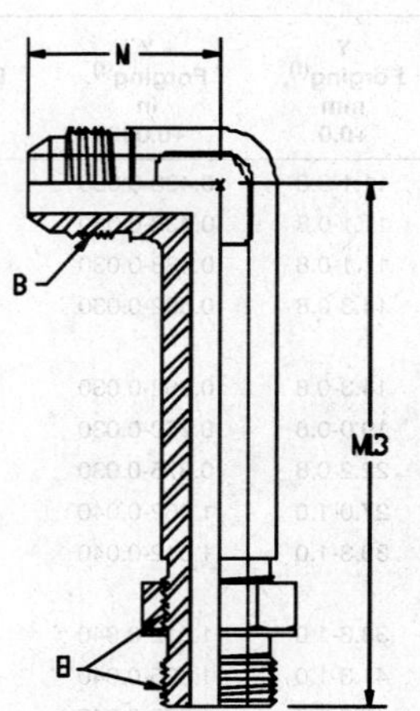

FIGURE 10F—90 Degree Straight Thread Elbow Extra Extra Long (071720)

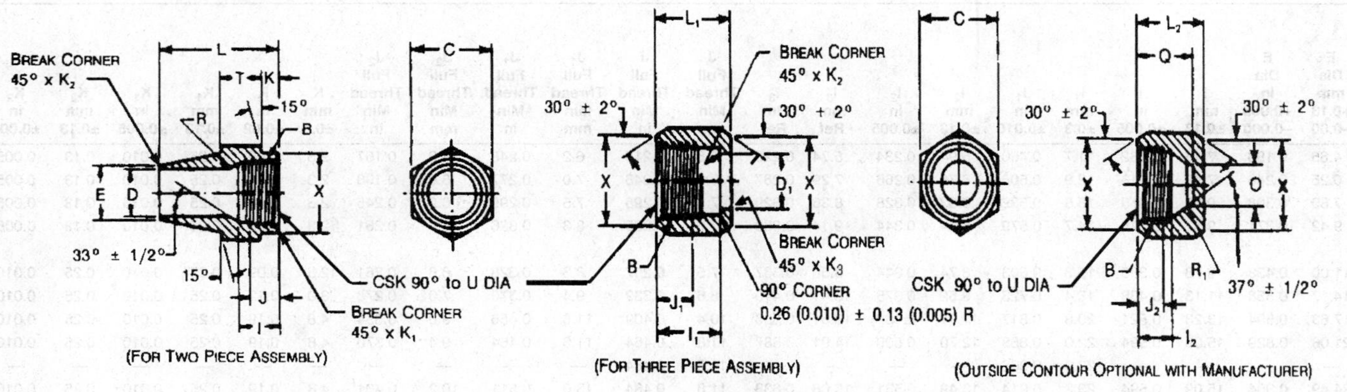

FIGURE 11—STYLE A NUT (070111)

FIGURE 12—STYLE B NUT (070110) FIGURE 13—CAP (070112)

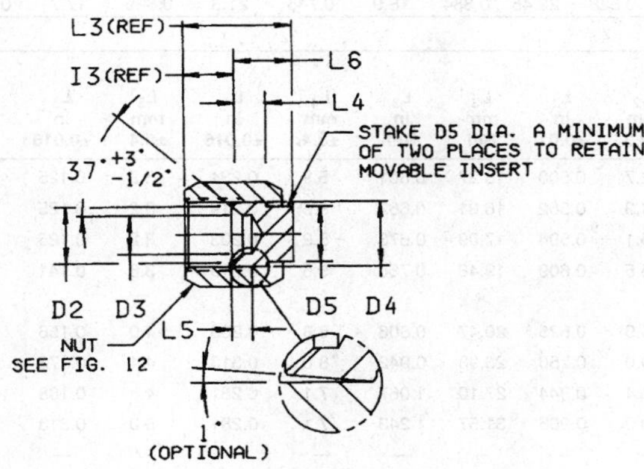

FIGURE 13A—CAP ASSEMBLY (MOVEABLE INSERT) (070112A)

TABLE 5—DIMENSIONS OF STYLE A AND B NUTS AND CAPS (FIGURES 11 TO 13A)

Nom Tube, OD in	B Thread Size, in SAE J475 (ISO R725) Class 2B Int	Thread[b] Minor Dia mm +0.13 −0.00	Thread[b] Minor Dia in +0.005 −0.000	C[a] Hex Min in	D Dia mm +0.8 −0.00	D Dia in +0.003 −0.000	D_1 Dia mm	D_1 Dia tol −0.00	D_1 Dia in	D_1 Dia tol −0.000	D_2 Dia mm 0.25	D_2 Dia in 0.01	D_3 Dia mm	D_3 Dia in	D_4 Dia mm +0.08 −0.00	D_4 Dia in +0.003 −0.000	D_5 Dia mm +0.13 −0.00	D_5 Dia in +0.005 −0.000
1/8	5/16-24	6.91	0.272	3/8	3.30	0.130	4.55	+0.10	0.179	+0.004	4.85	0.19	2.39	0.094	6.71	0.264	4.24	0.167
3/16	3/8-24	8.48	0.334	7/16	4.90	0.193	6.12	+0.10	0.241	+0.004	6.2	0.245	3.96	0.156	8.28	0.326	5.82	0.229
1/4	7/16-20	9.86	0.388	9/16	6.48	0.255	7.72	+0.10	0.304	+0.004	7.35	0.29	4.37	0.172	9.65	0.380	7.42	0.292
5/16	1/2-20	11.46	0.451	5/8	8.08	0.318	9.47	+0.10	0.373	+0.004	8.9	0.35	5.94	0.234	11.23	0.442	9.17	0.361
3/8	9/16-18	12.90	0.508	11/16	9.65	0.380	11.15	+0.10	0.439	+0.004	10.9	0.43	7.54	0.297	12.68	0.499	10.85	0.427
1/2	3/4-16	17.48	0.688	7/8	12.83	0.505	14.43	+0.13	0.568	+0.005	14.35	0.565	9.93	0.391	17.25	0.679	14.15	0.557
5/8	7/8-14	20.42	0.804	1	16.03	0.631	17.68	+0.13	0.696	+0.005	17.15	0.675	12.29	0.484	20.17	0.794	17.40	0.685
3/4	1-1/16-12	24.87	0.979	1-1/4	19.20	0.756	21.13	+0.13	0.832	+0.005	21.45	0.845	14.27	0.562	24.61	0.969	20.85	0.821
3/4[c] SPL	1-1/16-12	24.87	0.979	1-1/4	—	—	21.84	+0.13	0.860	+0.005	—	—	—	—	—	—	—	—
7/8	1-3/16-12	28.04	1.104	1-3/8	22.38	0.881	24.36	+0.13	0.959	+0.005	24.65	0.97	18.26	0.719	27.78	1.094	24.08	0.948
1	1-5/16-12	31.22	1.229	1-1/2	25.55	1.006	27.61	+0.13	1.087	+0.005	27.8	1.095	21.44	0.844	30.96	1.219	27.33	1.076
1-1/4	1- 5/8-12	39.14	1.541	2	32.00	1.260	34.14	+0.15	1.344	+0.006	35.7	1.405	27.38	1.078	38.88	1.531	33.88	1.334
1-1/2	1- 7/8-12	45.49	1.791	2-1/4	38.35	1.510	41.00	+0.15	1.614	+0.006	41.15	1.62	33.32	1.312	45.24	1.781	40.73	1.604
2	2- 1/2-12	61.37	2.416	2-7/8	51.16	2.014	54.97	+0.15	2.164	+0.006	56.75	2.235	45.23	1.781	61.11	2.406	54.71	2.154

Continued on next page.

TABLE 5—DIMENSIONS OF STYLE A AND B NUTS AND CAPS (FIGURES 11 TO 13A) (CONTINUED)

E Dia mm +0.13 −0.00	E Dia in +0.005 −0.000	I mm ±0.13	I in ±0.005	I_1 mm ±0.3	I_1 in ±0.010	I_2 mm ±0.13	I_2 in ±0.005	I_3 mm Ref	I_3 in Ref	J Full Thread Min mm	J Full Thread Min in	J_1 Full Thread Min mm	J_1 Full Thread Min in	J_2 Full Thread Min mm	J_2 Full Thread Min in	K mm ±0.5	K in ±0.02	K_1 mm ±0.13	K_1 in ±0.005	K_2 mm ±0.13	K_2 in ±0.005
4.65	0.183	7.16	0.282	11.7	0.460	5.94	0.234	5.74	0.226	5.5	0.215	6.2	0.246	4.2	0.167	2.3	0.09	0.25	0.010	0.13	0.005
6.25	0.246	7.95	0.313	12.9	0.506	6.76	0.266	7.29	0.287	6.2	0.246	7.0	0.277	5.0	0.198	2.3	0.09	0.25	0.010	0.13	0.005
7.82	0.308	9.52	0.375	13.5	0.532	8.33	0.328	8.36	0.329	7.5	0.295	7.5	0.295	6.2	0.245	2.3	0.09	0.25	0.010	0.13	0.005
9.42	0.371	9.52	0.375	14.7	0.579	8.74	0.344	9.14	0.360	7.5	0.295	8.3	0.326	6.6	0.261	2.3	0.09	0.25	0.010	0.13	0.005
11.00	0.433	9.78	0.385	15.3	0.603	8.74	0.344	8.56	0.337	7.5	0.297	8.3	0.328	6.6	0.261	2.3	0.09	0.25	0.010	0.25	0.010
14.17	0.558	11.13	0.438	18.4	0.723	9.52	0.375	10.41	0.410	8.6	0.339	9.4	0.370	7.0	0.276	3.0	0.12	0.25	0.010	0.25	0.010
17.63	0.694	13.23	0.521	20.8	0.817	11.91	0.469	13.61	0.536	10.4	0.409	11.6	0.456	9.0	0.354	4.8	0.19	0.25	0.010	0.25	0.010
21.06	0.829	15.09	0.594	22.0	0.868	12.70	0.500	14.91	0.587	11.8	0.464	11.8	0.464	9.4	0.370	4.8	0.19	0.25	0.010	0.25	0.010
—	—	—	—	22.0	0.868	—	—	—	—	11.8	0.464	—	—	—	—	—	—	—	—	—	—
24.49	0.964	15.09	0.594	23.2	0.914	13.49	0.531	16.08	0.633	11.8	0.464	13.0	0.511	10.2	0.401	4.8	0.19	0.25	0.010	0.25	0.010
27.91	1.099	15.88	0.625	24.4	0.962	14.30	0.563	16.89	0.665	12.6	0.495	14.2	0.558	11.0	0.433	4.8	0.19	0.25	0.010	0.25	0.010
34.37	1.353	15.88	0.625	25.8	1.017	14.30	0.563	16.31	0.642	12.6	0.495	14.2	0.558	11.0	0.433	6.4	0.25	0.25	0.010	0.25	0.010
40.72	1.603	17.98	0.708	29.7	1.170	16.66	0.656	19.41	0.764	14.7	0.578	16.7	0.656	13.4	0.526	6.4	0.25	0.25	0.010	0.25	0.010
54.03	2.127	22.22	0.875	37.1	1.462	21.03	0.828	22.45	0.884	18.9	0.745	21.3	0.839	17.7	0.698	7.9	0.31	0.38	0.015	0.38	0.015

K_3 mm Max	K_3 in Max	L mm ±0.5	L in ±0.02	L_1 mm ±0.5	L_1 in ±0.020	L_2 mm ±0.3	L_2 in ±0.01	L_3 mm Ref	L_3 in Ref	L_4 mm ±0.4	L_4 in ±0.016	L_5 mm ±0.4	L_5 in ±0.016	L_6 mm ±0.4	L_6 in ±0.016	O Dia mm ±0.13	O Dia in ±0.005	Q mm ±0.3	Q in ±0.010
0.5	0.020	21.3	0.84	14.0	0.550	12.7	0.500	15.27	0.601	5.9	0.234	3.2	0.125	9.5	0.375	1.57	0.062	11.1	0.438
0.5	0.020	23.9	0.94	15.5	0.610	14.3	0.562	16.81	0.662	5.6	0.219	3.2	0.125	9.5	0.375	3.18	0.125	12.7	0.500
0.5	0.020	25.4	1.00	15.8	0.620	15.1	0.594	17.09	0.673	5.2	0.203	3.2	0.125	8.7	0.344	4.37	0.172	13.5	0.531
0.5	0.020	26.9	1.06	17.3	0.680	15.5	0.609	19.46	0.766	5.6	0.219	3.6	0.141	10.3	0.406	5.94	0.234	13.9	0.547
0.5	0.020	27.7	1.09	18.5	0.730	15.9	0.625	20.47	0.806	6.8	0.266	4.0	0.156	11.9	0.469	7.54	0.297	14.3	0.562
0.5	0.020	32.5	1.28	21.6	0.850	19.0	0.750	23.93	0.942	8.0	0.313	4.4	0.172	13.5	0.531	9.93	0.391	15.9	0.625
1.0	0.040	37.6	1.48	24.9	0.980	21.4	0.844	27.10	1.067	7.1	0.281	4.8	0.188	13.5	0.531	12.29	0.484	18.3	0.719
1.0	0.040	42.2	1.66	26.2	1.030	23.0	0.906	31.57	1.243	7.1	0.281	8.0	0.313	16.7	0.656	15.47	0.609	19.8	0.781
1.0	0.040	—	—	26.2	1.030	—	—	—	—	—	—	—	—	—	—	—	—	—	—
1.0	0.040	46.0	1.81	27.7	1.090	24.6	0.969	31.95	1.258	7.1	0.281	6.4	0.250	15.9	0.625	18.26	0.719	21.4	0.844
1.0	0.40	49.3	1.94	28.7	1.130	25.8	1.016	32.76	1.290	7.6	0.297	5.6	0.219	15.9	0.625	21.44	0.844	21.8	0.859
1.0	0.40	55.6	2.19	31.2	1.230	27.0	1.062	35.35	1.392	9.5	0.375	7.1	0.281	19.1	0.750	27.38	1.078	23.0	0.906
1.0	0.40	58.7	2.31	36.1	1.420	30.2	1.188	43.20	1.701	10.3	0.406	9.5	0.375	23.8	0.938	33.32	1.312	26.2	1.031
1.0	0.40	69.8	2.75	44.5	1.750	36.5	1.438	52.60	2.071	14.7	0.578	10.3	0.406	30.1	1.188	45.24	1.781	32.5	1.281

Continued on next page.

TABLE 5—DIMENSIONS OF STYLE A AND B NUTS AND CAPS (FIGURES 11 TO 13A) (CONTINUED)

R Rad mm ±0.3	R Rad in ±0.01	R_1 Rad mm ±0.3	R_1 Rad in ±0.01	T mm ±0.5	T in ±0.02	U Dia mm +0.4 −0.0	U Dia in +0.016 −0.000	X mm ±0.3	X in ±0.01
0.8	0.03	0.8	0.03	6.4	0.25	8.05	0.317	9.1	0.36
0.8	0.03	0.8	0.03	6.9	0.27	9.65	0.380	10.7	0.42
0.8	0.03	0.8	0.03	8.4	0.33	11.25	0.443	13.7	0.54
0.8	0.03	0.8	0.03	8.4	0.33	12.83	0.505	15.2	0.60
1.3	0.05	1.5	0.06	8.6	0.34	14.40	0.567	17.0	0.67
1.5	0.06	1.5	0.06	11.4	0.45	19.18	0.755	21.8	0.86
1.5	0.06	1.5	0.06	13.2	0.52	22.35	0.880	24.9	0.98
2.0	0.08	1.5	0.06	16.3	0.64	27.10	1.067	31.5	1.24
2.3	0.09	1.5	0.06	17.5	0.69	30.30	1.193	34.5	1.36
—	—	—	—	—	—	30.30	1.193	34.5	1.36
2.3	0.09	1.5	0.06	18.5	0.73	33.45	1.317	37.6	1.48
2.3	0.09	1.5	0.06	18.5	0.73	41.40	1.630	50.3	1.98
2.8	0.11	1.5	0.06	21.1	0.83	47.75	1.880	56.9	2.24
2.8	0.11	1.5	0.06	23.4	0.92	63.63	2.505	72.6	2.86

a Across flat widths must fit standard wrench openings.
b Modified minor diameter.
c For use with 20 mm sleeve specified in Table 6A.

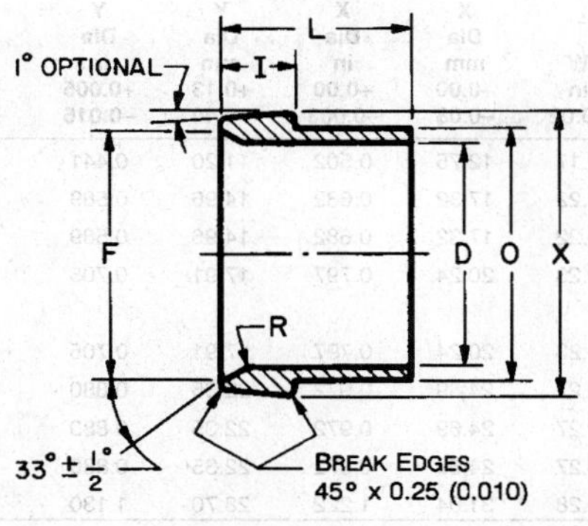

(FOR THREE PIECE ASSEMBLY)

FIGURE 14—SLEEVE (070115)

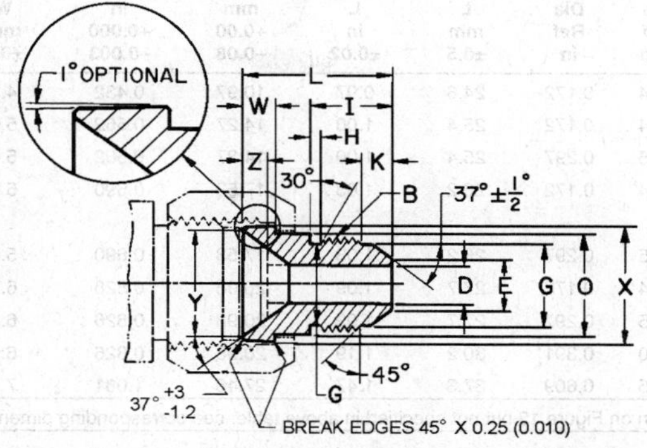

FIGURE 15—REDUCING ADAPTER (070123)

TABLE 6—DIMENSIONS FOR SLEEVES (FIGURE 14) FOR INCH TUBING

Nom Tube OD, in	D Dia mm +0.08 −0.00	D Dia in +0.003 −0.000	F Dia mm ±0.13	F Dia in ±0.005	I mm ±0.5	I in ±0.02	L mm ±0.5	L in ±0.02	O Dia mm +0.00 −0.08	O Dia in +0.000 −0.003	R Rad mm ±0.3	R Rad in ±0.01	X Dia mm +0.00 −0.08	X Dia in +0.000 −0.003
1/8	3.30	0.130	5.21	0.205	3.0	0.12	8.6	0.34	4.37	0.172	0.8	0.031	6.78	0.267
3/16	4.90	0.193	6.78	0.267	3.6	0.14	8.6	0.34	5.94	0.234	0.8	0.031	8.36	0.329
1/4	6.48	0.255	8.00	0.315	3.6	0.14	10.4	0.41	7.54	0.297	0.8	0.031	9.73	0.383
5/16	8.08	0.318	9.52	0.375	4.1	0.16	11.2	0.44	9.30	0.366	0.8	0.031	11.30	0.445
3/8	9.65	0.380	11.20	0.441	4.3	0.17	12.7	0.50	10.97	0.432	1.2	0.047	12.75	0.502
1/2	12.83	0.505	14.96	0.589	5.6	0.22	14.2	0.56	14.27	0.562	1.6	0.062	17.32	0.682
5/8	16.03	0.631	17.91	0.705	6.1	0.24	16.8	0.66	17.53	0.690	1.6	0.062	20.24	0.797
3/4	19.20	0.756	22.35	0.880	6.6	0.26	17.3	0.68	20.98	0.826	2.0	0.078	24.69	0.972
7/8	22.38	0.881	25.53	1.005	6.6	0.26	19.3	0.76	24.21	0.953	2.4	0.094	27.86	1.097
1	25.55	1.006	28.70	1.130	7.1	0.28	19.8	0.78	27.46	1.081	2.4	0.094	31.04	1.222
1-1/4	32.00	1.260	35.86	1.412	7.9	0.31	23.1	0.91	34.01	1.339	2.4	0.094	38.96	1.534
1-1/2	38.35	1.510	41.40	1.630	8.6	0.34	28.4	1.12	40.87	1.609	2.8	0.109	45.31	1.784
2	51.16	2.014	55.75	2.195	10.4	0.41	30.2	1.19	54.84	2.159	2.8	0.109	61.19	2.409

TABLE 6A—DIMENSIONS FOR SLEEVES (FIGURE 14) FOR METRIC TUBING[c]

Nom Tube OD, mm	D Dia mm 0.08 −0.00	D Dia in +0.003 −0.000	F Dia mm ±0.13	F Dia in ±0.005	I mm ±0.5	I in ±0.02	L mm ±0.5	L in ±0.02	O Dia mm +0.00 −0.08	O Dia in +0.000 −0.003	R Rad in ±0.30	R Rad in ±0.010	X Dia mm +0.00 −0.08	X Dia in +0.000 −0.003	In Size Body[a] and Nut
6	6.13	0.241	8.00	0.315	3.6	0.14	10.4	0.41	7.54	0.297	0.80	0.031	9.73	0.383	1/4
8	8.13	0.320	9.52	0.375	4.1	0.16	11.2	0.44	9.30	0.366	0.80	0.031	11.30	0.445	5/16
10	10.13	0.399	11.20	0.441	4.3	0.17	12.7	0.50	10.97	0.432	1.20	0.047	12.75	0.502	3/8
12	12.13	0.478	14.96	0.589	5.6	0.22	14.2	0.56	14.27	0.562	1.60	0.062	17.32	0.682	1/2
16	16.15	0.636	17.91	0.705	6.1	0.24	16.8	0.66	17.53	0.690	1.60	0.062	20.24	0.797	5/8
19[b]	19.20	0.756	22.35	0.880	6.6	0.26	17.3	0.68	20.98	0.826	2.00	0.078	24.69	0.972	3/4
20[d],[e]	20.15	0.793	22.6	0.886	6.6	0.26	17.3	0.68	21.64	0.852	2.00	0.078	24.69	0.972	3/4 SPL
20	20.15	0.793	25.53	1.005	6.6	0.26	19.3	0.76	24.21	0.953	2.40	0.094	27.86	1.097	7/8
25	25.15	0.990	28.70	1.130	7.1	0.28	19.8	0.78	27.46	1.081	2.40	0.094	31.04	1.222	1
32	32.25	1.270	35.86	1.412	7.9	0.31	23.1	0.91	34.01	1.339	2.40	0.094	38.96	1.534	1-1/4
38[b]	38.35	1.510	41.40	1.630	8.6	0.34	28.4	1.12	40.87	1.609	2.80	0.109	45.31	1.784	1-1/2
50	50.36	1.983	55.75	2.195	10.4	0.41	30.2	1.19	54.84	2.159	2.80	0.109	61.19	2.409	2

(a) With the exception of the 20 mm tube sleeve which requires use of the 3/4 SPL nut (footnote d), metric sleeves are used with standard Figure 12 (070110) tube nuts and standard fitting bodies shown in Figures 2a to 10c (Table 4) and Figure 15 (Table 7).

(b) 19 mm and 38 mm are shown only because they use the standard 3/4 and 1-1/2 size Figure 14 sleeve and there is aparent usage.

(c) In addition to plating, sleeves for metric tubing will be dyed blue for identification.

(d) Designed for use with a 3/4 SPL nut which is equivalent to the −12 nut shown in Figure 12, Table 5 with the D_1 diameter modified to 0.860 + 0.005/−0.000.

(e) Technically equivalent to the 20 mm tube sleeve specified in ISO 8434-2.

TABLE 7—DIMENSIONS[a] OF REDUCING ADAPTER (FIGURE 15)

Tube Reduction, in	D Dia Ref mm	D Dia Ref in	L mm ±0.5	L in ±0.02	O Dia mm +0.00 −0.08	O Dia in +0.000 −0.003	W mm ±0.5	W in ±0.02	X Dia mm +0.00 −0.08	X Dia in +0.00 −0.003	Y Dia mm +0.13 −0.40	Y Dia in +0.005 −0.016	Z mm ±0.5	Z in ±0.02
3/8 x 1/4	4.4	0.172	24.6	0.97	10.97	0.432	4.3	0.17	12.75	0.502	11.20	0.441	—	—
1/2 x 1/4	4.4	0.172	25.4	1.00	14.27	0.562	5.6	0.22	17.32	0.682	14.96	0.589	—	—
1/2 x 3/8	7.5	0.297	25.4	1.00	14.27	0.562	5.6	0.22	17.32	0.682	14.96	0.589	—	—
5/8 x 1/4	4.4	0.172	26.2	1.03	17.53	0.690	5.8	0.23	20.24	0.797	17.91	0.705	—	—
5/8 x 3/8	7.5	0.297	26.2	1.03	17.53	0.690	5.8	0.23	20.24	0.797	17.91	0.705	—	—
3/4 x 1/4	4.4	0.172	27.7	1.09	20.98	0.826	6.9	0.27	24.69	0.972	22.35	0.880	10.4	0.41
3/4 x 3/8	7.5	0.297	27.7	1.09	20.98	0.826	6.9	0.27	24.69	0.972	22.35	0.880	—	—
3/4 x 1/2	10.0	0.391	30.2	1.19	20.98	0.826	6.9	0.27	24.69	0.972	22.35	0.880	—	—
1 x 3/4	15.5	0.609	37.3	1.47	27.46	1.081	7.1	0.28	31.04	1.222	28.70	1.130	—	—

[a]For dimensions shown on Figure 15 but not specified in above table, see corresponding dimensions for the specified outside diameter in Table 4.

6. ***Section 2—Flareless Tube Fittings***—The flareless tube fittings shall be as shown in Figures 16 to 32 and Tables 8 to 12. The basic design of these fittings is derived from existing military standards.

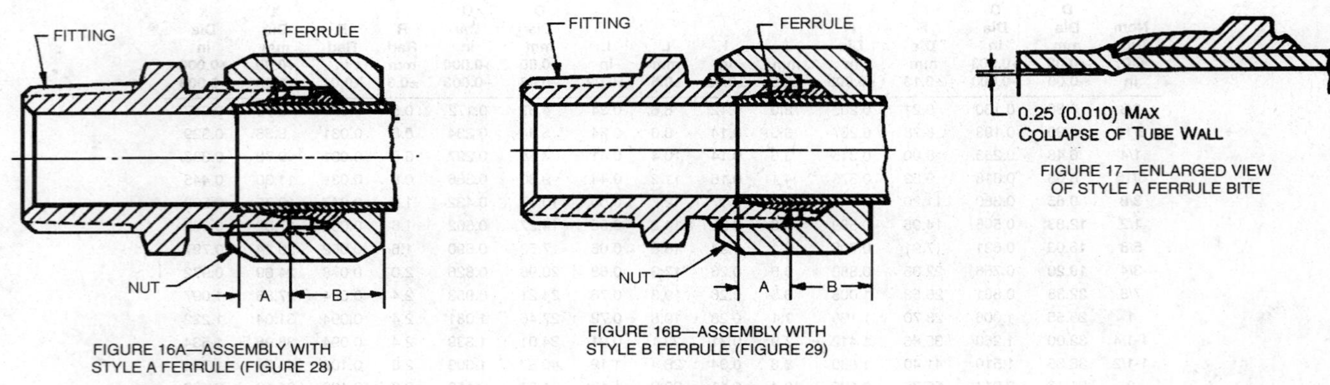

FIGURE 16A—ASSEMBLY WITH STYLE A FERRULE (FIGURE 28)

FIGURE 16B—ASSEMBLY WITH STYLE B FERRULE (FIGURE 29)

FIGURE 17—ENLARGED VIEW OF STYLE A FERRULE BITE

FIGURE 16—DETAILS OF FLARELESS HYDRAULIC TUBE FITTING ASSEMBLIES

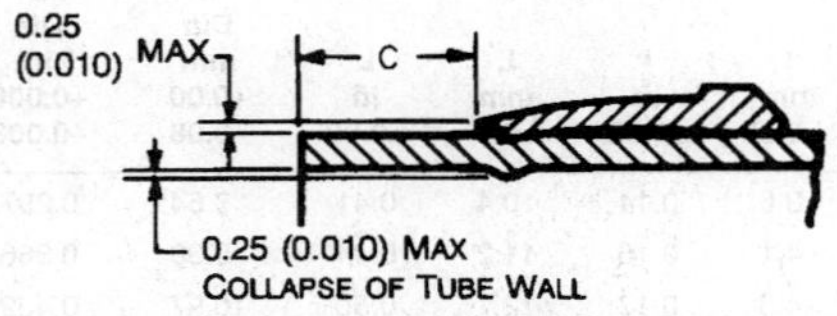

FIGURE 18—ENLARGED VIEW OF STYLE B FERRULE BITE

TABLE 8—DIMENSIONS OF FLARELESS HYDRAULIC TUBE FITTING ASSEMBLIES (FIGURES 16 AND 18)

Nominal Tube OD	A (Ref) mm	A (Ref) in	B (Ref) mm	B (Ref) in	C (Ref) mm	C (Ref) in
1/8	4.78	0.188	7.9	0.31	2.0	0.08
3/16	5.94	0.234	8.6	0.34	3.0	0.12
1/4	5.94	0.234	10.7	0.42	3.6	0.14
5/16	6.35	0.250	10.7	0.42	3.6	0.14
3/8	6.35	0.250	11.9	0.47	3.6	0.14
1/2	7.75	0.305	12.7	0.50	3.6	0.14
5/8	8.89	0.350	13.5	0.53	3.6	0.14
3/4	8.89	0.350	14.2	0.56	3.6	0.14
7/8	8.89	0.350	13.5	0.53	—	—
1	10.54	0.415	16.8	0.66	4.3	0.17
1-1/4	10.54	0.415	18.3	0.72	5.1	0.20
1-1/2	12.32	0.485	18.3	0.72	5.1	0.20
2	12.32	0.485	21.3	0.84	5.1	0.20

6.1 Assembly Instructions for Hydraulic Flareless Tube Fittings—These instructions apply to the assembly of hydraulic tube fittings of the flareless type given in Tables 9 to 12 and Figures 19 to 32.

The following instructions should be used to assure proper make-up of the fitting when assembled since the fitting depends on securing the ferrule to the tube by the cutting action of the ferrule into the tube.

6.1.1 Cut tube square and burr inside and outside corner (not excessive).

6.1.2 Assemble fitting by sliding nut over tubing with open end out. Slide ferrule on tubing with cutting edge out, the large head end should be inside of the nut. Lubricate the ferrule and the threads on the body and nut with oil or petrolatum. Insert tube into fitting.

6.1.3 Bottom the tube in the fitting, and tighten the nut until the ferrule just grips the tube. With a little experience, the mechanic can determine this point by feel. If the fittings are bench assembled, the gripping action can be determined by rotating the tube by hand as the nut is drawn down. When the tube can no longer be turned by hand, the ferrule has started to grip the tube.

6.1.4 After the ferrule grips the tube, tighten the nut one full turn. This may vary slightly with different tubing materials, but for general practice, it is a good rule for the mechanic to follow.

6.1.5 The fittings can now be disassembled for inspection. The two styles of ferrules differ somewhat in inspection even though their principles of makeup and application are similar.

a. For the ferrule in Figure 28, the bite or cut into the tube can be readily seen since it is on the lead edge of the ferrule. The bite into the tube should show a definite groove where the ferrule cuts into the tube and peels the metal over the lead edge of the ferrule. See Figure 17 for further detail.

b. For the ferrule in Figure 29, the pilot at the end of the ferrule should be contacting or be within 0.038 mm (0.0015 in) of the tube for hard material or not more than 0.13 mm (0.005 in) on soft material. See Figure 18 for further detail. This is an indication that the cutting edge has performed its function and has taken a secure bite in the tube. The sleeve should be slightly sprung or arched.

For both styles of ferrules, the rounded or lead edge should show a good seat in the fitting, and the head or shoulder end should be collapsed tight against the tube. The ferrules should have no end movement; however, the ferrule may be rotated on the tube due to spring back of the material. The performance of the fitting is not affected if the ferrule rotates.

6.1.6 In production, it may be preferable to use a threaded presetting tool to preform the ferrule onto the tubing. The presetting tool is a counterpart of the fitting hardened to provide good wearing properties for repeated usage. When using the presetting tool, the assembly instructions are the same, as the presetting tool takes the place of the fitting. Care should be taken to keep the cam surface of the presetting tool free of defects since they would transfer themselves to the ferrule, which would result in improper seating when the fitting is installed.

6.1.7 In some installations, it may be necessary to use a mandrel to support the inside of the tube when setting the ferrule. This is only necessary when the tube wall is so thin or so soft that it will not resist the biting action of the ferrule without collapsing. The mandrel in this instance supports the tube and allows the ferrule to bite into the tube without deforming or collapsing. Because the use of a mandrel allows very little give in the tubing, the setting of the ferrule may be made with slightly fewer turns than described previously.

6.2 Reassembly Instructions for Flareless Fittings—After disassembly of the fitting joint, the flareless fitting can be reassembled by assembling the tube and ferrule into the socket of the fitting and threading the nut onto the fitting.

The operation of assembly up to the point at which the ferrule seats itself in the fitting can usually be accomplished by hand or with the use of a small wrench. If a wrench is required, only low torques are necessary to seat the ferrule.

When the ferrule is seated, an increase in the torque will be quite evident. When this point is reached, draw the nut up approximately 1/6 of a turn minimum, but not more than 1/3 of a turn, to complete the tightening operation.

NOTE—Instructions for assembling adjustable and swivel style hydraulic fittings in straight thread O-ring bosses are given immediately following the table of dimensions of O-ring boss plugs.

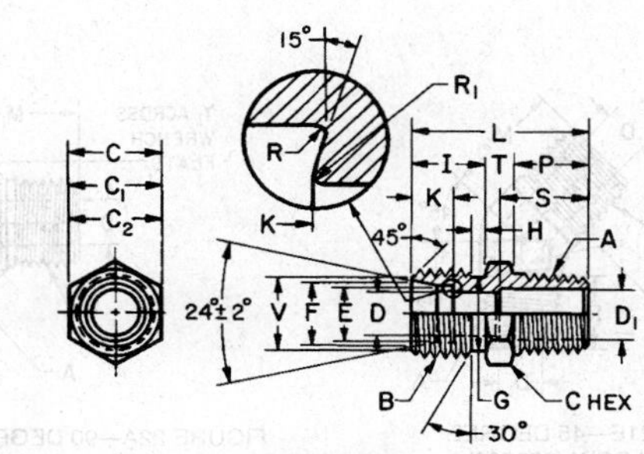

FIGURE 19A—MALE CONNECTOR (080102)

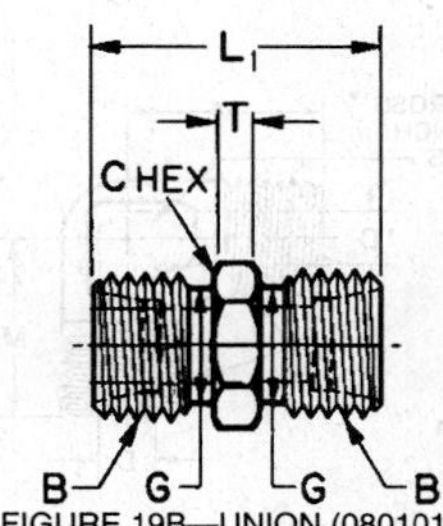

FIGURE 19B—UNION (080101)

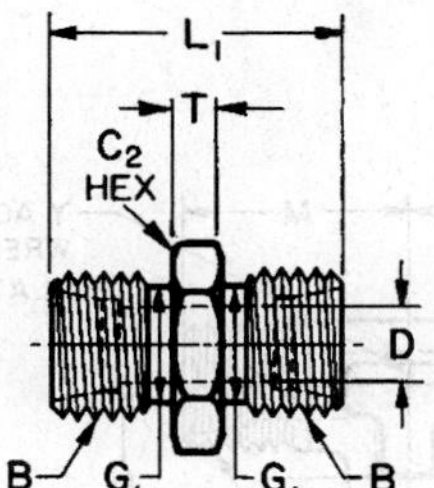

FIGURE 19C—LARGE HEX UNION* (080119)

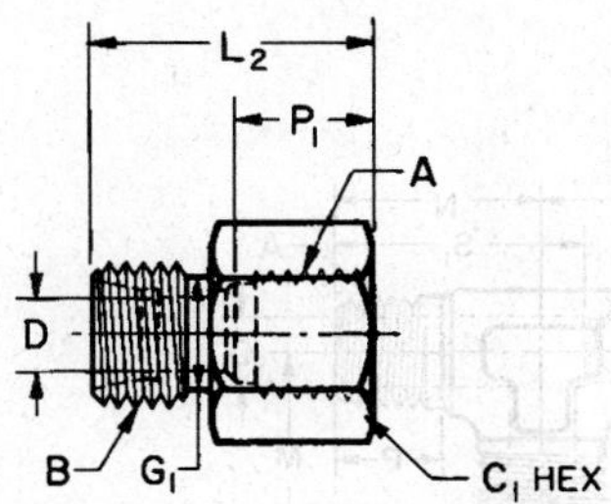

FIGURE 19D—FEMALE CONNECTOR (080103)

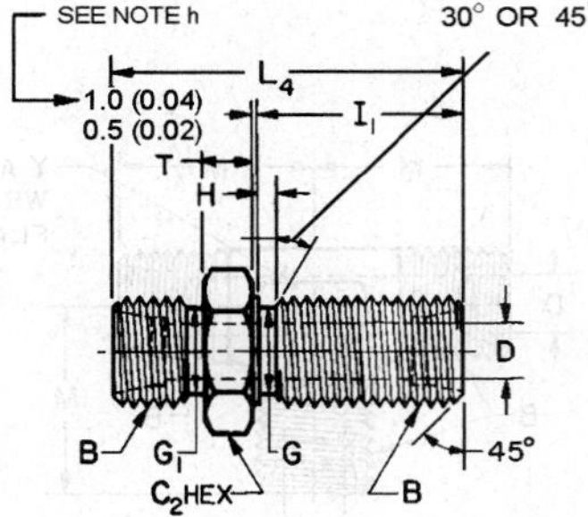

FIGURE 20A—BULKHEAD UNION (080601)

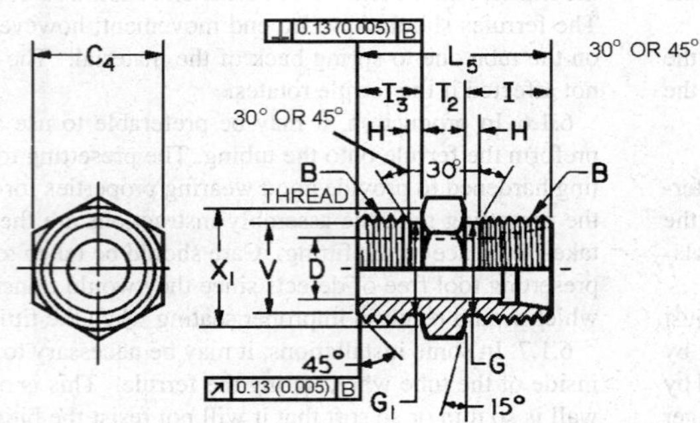

FIGURE 20B—STRAIGHT THREAD CONNECTOR SHORT* (080120)

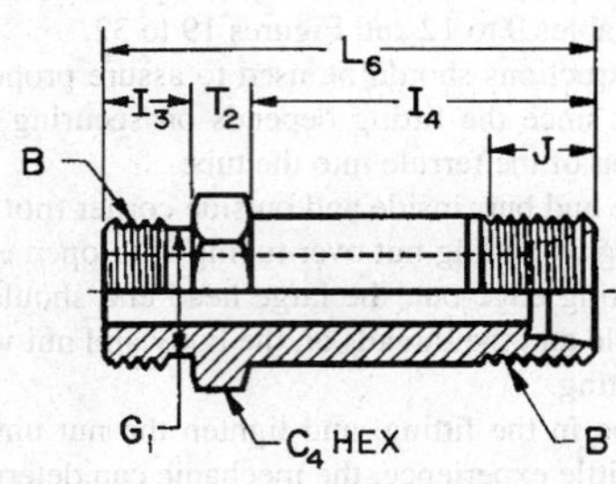

FIGURE 20C—STRAIGHT THREAD CONNECTOR LONG* (080122)

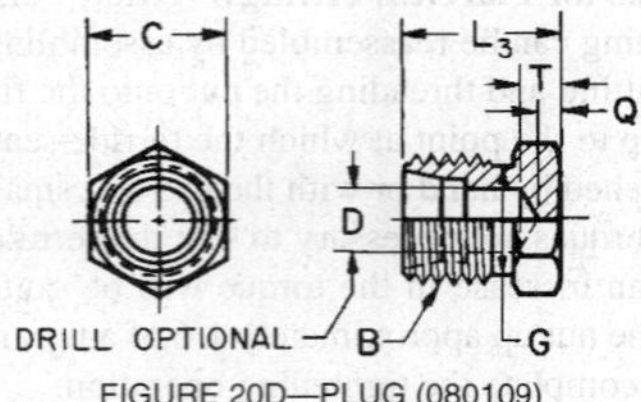

FIGURE 20D—PLUG (080109)

FIGURE 21A—90 DEGREE MALE ELBOW (080202)

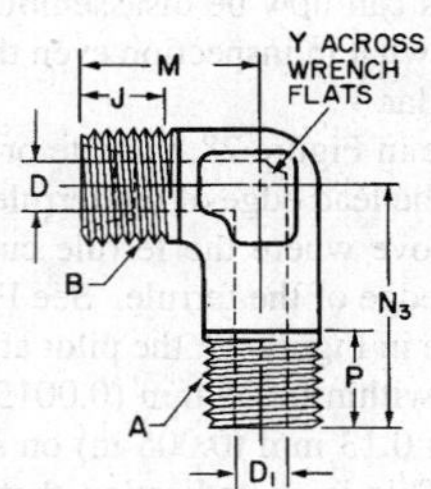

FIGURE 21B—90 DEGREE MALE LONG ELBOW (081502)

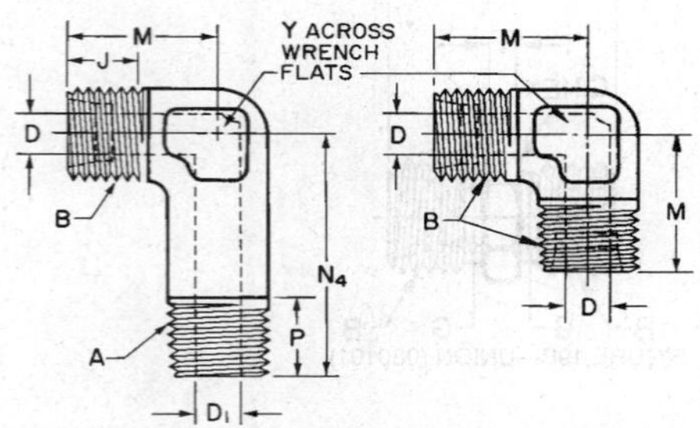

FIGURE 21C—90 DEGREE MALE EXTRA LONG ELBOW (081602)

FIGURE 21D—90 DEGREE UNION ELBOW (080201)

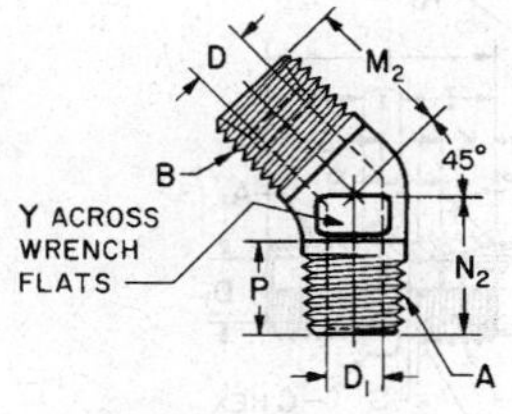

FIGURE 21E—45 DEGREE MALE ELBOW (080302)

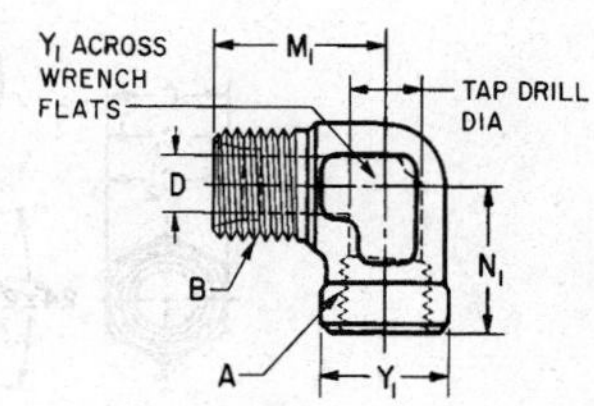

FIGURE 22A—90 DEGREE FEMALE ELBOW (080203)

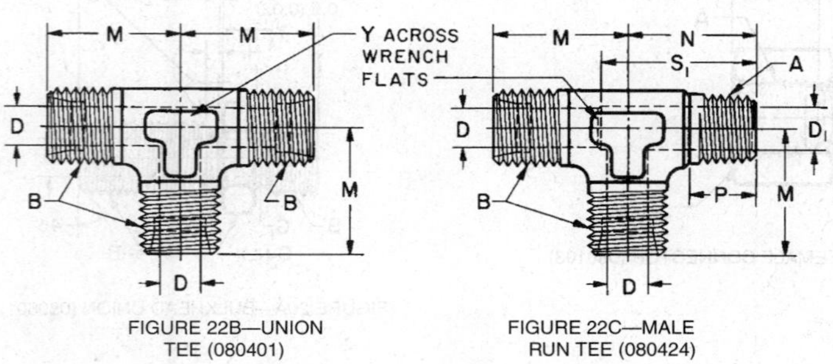

FIGURE 22B—UNION TEE (080401)

FIGURE 22C—MALE RUN TEE (080424)

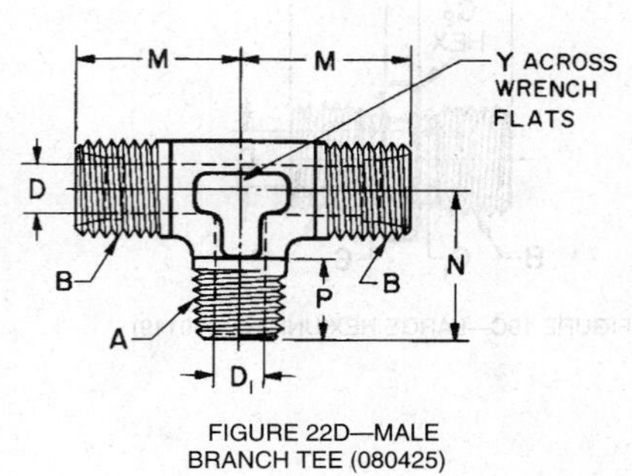

FIGURE 22D—MALE BRANCH TEE (080425)

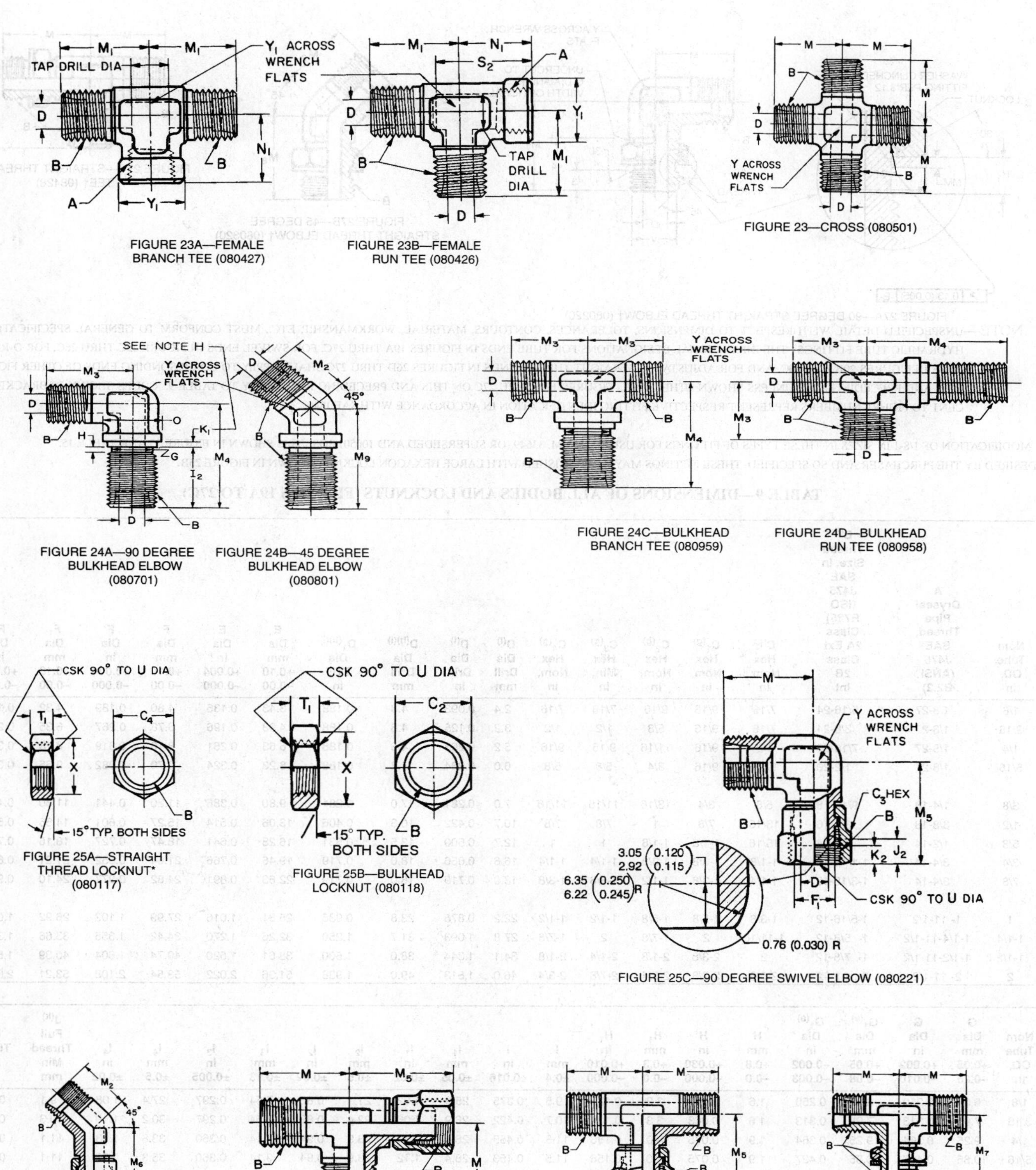

THE DESIGN AND METHOD OF ATTACHING THE SWIVEL NUT SHALL BE OPTIONAL WITH THE MANUFACTURER PROVIDING THE TABULATED DIMENSIONS ARE MAINTAINED AND THE NUT TURNS FREELY.

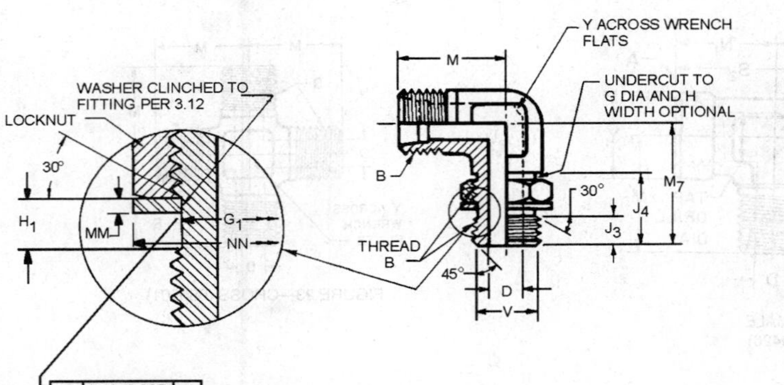

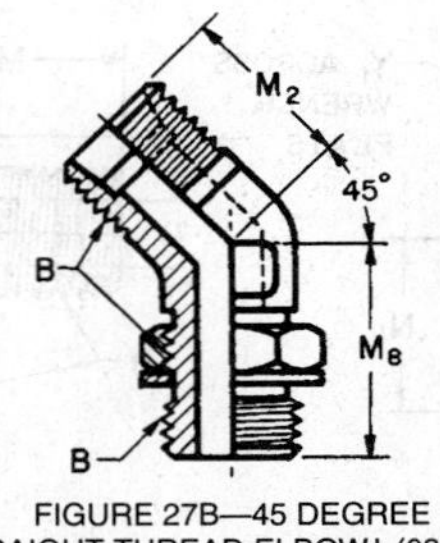

FIGURE 27B—45 DEGREE STRAIGHT THREAD ELBOW† (080320)

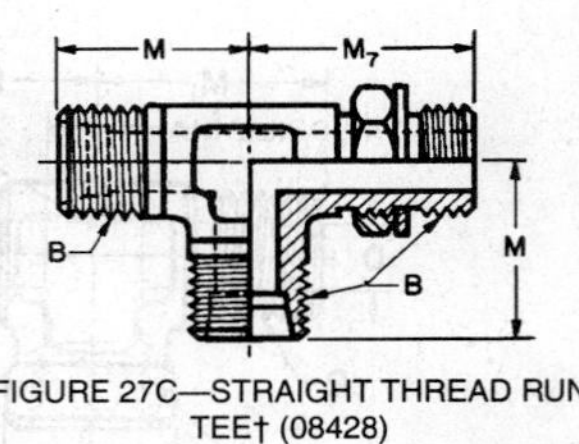

FIGURE 27C—STRAIGHT THREAD RUN TEE† (08428)

FIGURE 27A—90 DEGREE STRAIGHT THREAD ELBOW† (080220)

NOTE—UNSPECIFIED DETAIL WITH RESPECT TO DIMENSIONS, TOLERANCES, CONTOURS, MATERIAL, WORKMANSHIP, ETC., MUST CONFORM TO GENERAL SPECIFICATIONS FOR HYDRAULIC TUBE FITTINGS. THE DIMENSIONAL DESIGNATIONS FOR TUBE ENDS IN FIGURES 19A THRU 27C, FOR SWIVEL ENDS IN FIGURE 25C THRU 26C, FOR O-RING BOSS ENDS IN FIGURES 20B AND 20C, AND FOR ADJUSTABLE STRAIGHT THREAD ENDS IN FIGURES 26D THRU 27C SHALL APPLY TO CORRESONDING ENDS OF OTHER FIGURES ON THIS AND PRECEDING PAGE UNLESS SHOWN OTHERWISE. FIGURES 19A THRU 27C ON THIS AND PRECEDING PAGE APPLY TO TABLE 9. CODES SHOWN IN BRACKETS ADJACENT TO FIGURE NUMBERS REPRESENT RESPECTIVE FITTING IDENTIFICATION IN ACCORDANCE WITH SAE J846.

* MODIFICATION OF 1/8-1 IN SIZES IN THESE TYPES OF FITTINGS FOR USE WITH MM. 33649 (OR SUPERSEDED AND 10050) BOSSES IS SHOWN IN FIGURE 35 AND TABLE 15.

† IF DESIRED BY THE PURCHASER AND SO SPECIFIED, THESE FITTINGS MAY BE FURNISHED WITH LARGE HEXAGON LOCKNUT SHOWN IN FIGURE 25B.

TABLE 9—DIMENSIONS OF ALL BODIES AND LOCKNUTS (FIGURES 19A TO 27C)

Nom Tube OD, in	A Dryseal Pipe Thread, SAE J476 (ANSI B2.2)	B[f] Thread Size, in SAE J475 (ISO R725) Class 2A Ext Class 2B Int	C[g] Hex Nom, in	C_1[g] Hex Nom, in	C_2[g] Hex Nom, in	C_3[g] Hex Min, in	C_4[g] Hex Nom, in	D[l] Dia Drill mm	D[l] Dia Drill in	D[b][l] Dia Drill mm	D_1[b][l] Dia Drill in	E Dia mm +0.10 −0.00	E Dia in +0.004 −0.000	F Dia mm +0.10 −0.00	F Dia in +0.004 −0.000	F_1 Dia mm +0.13 −0.00	F_1 Dia in +0.005 −0.000
1/8	1/8-27	5/16-24	7/16	9/16	9/16	7/16	7/16	2.4	0.093	4.8	0.188	3.43	0.135	4.80	0.189	4.32	0.170
3/16	1/8-27	3/8-24	7/16	9/16	5/8	1/2	1/2	3.2	0.125	4.8	0.188	4.98	0.196	6.78	0.267	6.35	0.250
1/4	1/8-27	7/16-20	1/2	9/16	11/16	9/16	9/16	5.2	0.203	4.8	0.188	6.63	0.261	8.10	0.319	8.13	0.320
5/16	1/8-27	1/2-20	9/16	9/16	3/4	5/8	5/8	6.0	0.234	4.8	0.188	8.23	0.324	9.70	0.382	9.65	0.380
3/8	1/4-18	9/16-18	5/8	3/4	13/16	11/16	11/16	7.0	0.281	7.0	0.281	9.80	0.386	11.20	0.441	11.30	0.445
1/2	3/8-18	3/4-16	13/16	7/8	1	7/8	7/8	10.7	0.422	10.3	0.406	13.06	0.514	15.27	0.601	14.55	0.573
5/8	1/2-14	7/8-14	15/16	1-1/8	1-1/8	1	1	12.7	0.500	13.5	0.531	16.28	0.641	18.47	0.727	18.16	0.715
3/4	3/4-14	1-1/16-12	1-1/8	1-3/8	1-3/8	1-1/4	1-1/4	16.6	0.656	18.0	0.719	19.46	0.766	21.64	0.852	21.21	0.835
7/8	3/4-14	1-3/16-12	1-1/4	1-3/8	1-1/2	1-3/8	1-3/8	18.0	0.719	18.0	0.719	22.63	0.891	24.82	0.977	24.10	0.949
1	1- 11-1/2	1-5/16-12	1-3/8	1-5/8	1-5/8	1-1/2	1-1/2	22.2	0.875	23.8	0.938	25.81	1.016	27.99	1.102	26.92	1.060
1-1/4	1-1/4-11-1/2	1- 5/8-12	1-11/16	2	1-7/8	2	1-7/8	27.8	1.093	31.7	1.250	32.26	1.270	34.42	1.355	33.66	1.325
1-1/2	1-1/2-11-1/2	1- 7/8-12	2	2-3/8	2-1/8	2-1/4	2-1/8	34.1	1.344	38.0	1.500	38.61	1.520	40.74	1.604	40.39	1.590
2	2- 11-1/2	2- 1/2-12	2-5/8	2-7/8	2-3/4	2-7/8	2-3/4	46.0	1.813	49.0	1.938	51.36	2.022	53.54	2.108	53.21	2.095

Nom Tube OD, in	G Dia mm +0.05 −0.25	G Dia in +0.002 −0.010	G_1[a] Dia mm +0.05 −0.08	G_1[a] Dia in +0.002 −0.003	H mm +0.8 −0.0	H in +0.030 −0.000	H_1 mm +0.3 −0.0	H_1 in +0.010 −0.000	I mm ±0.4	I in ±0.016	I_1 mm ±0.05	I_1 in ±0.02	I_2 mm ±0.5	I_2 in ±0.02	I_3 mm ±0.13	I_3 in ±0.005	I_4 mm ±0.5	I_4 in ±0.02	J[k] Full Thread Min mm	J[k] Full Thread Min in
1/8	6.35	0.250	6.35	0.250	1.6	0.063	3.2	0.125	9.5	0.375	25.9	1.02	21.1	0.83	7.54	0.297	27.4	1.08	9.1	0.360
3/16	7.95	0.313	7.95	0.313	1.6	0.063	3.3	0.131	10.7	0.422	26.9	1.06	22.4	0.88	7.54	0.297	30.2	1.19	10.3	0.407
1/4	9.25	0.364	9.25	0.364	1.9	0.075	4.0	0.156	11.5	0.453	28.4	1.12	23.9	0.94	9.14	0.360	33.8	1.33	11.1	0.438
5/16	10.85	0.427	10.85	0.427	1.9	0.075	4.0	0.156	11.5	0.453	28.4	1.12	23.9	0.94	9.14	0.360	35.3	1.39	11.1	0.438
3/8	12.24	0.482	12.24	0.482	2.1	0.083	4.0	0.156	11.9	0.469	29.7	1.17	24.9	0.98	9.93	0.391	37.6	1.48	11.5	0.454
1/2	16.76	0.660	16.76	0.660	2.4	0.094	4.7	0.187	14.3	0.562	33.3	1.31	28.4	1.12	11.13	0.438	45.7	1.80	13.9	0.547
5/8	19.63	0.773	19.63	0.773	2.7	0.107	5.6	0.219	15.9	0.625	36.8	1.45	32.3	1.27	12.70	0.500	51.6	2.03	15.5	0.610
3/4	24.00	0.945	24.00	0.945	3.2	0.125	5.9	0.234	17.5	0.688	39.6	1.56	35.1	1.38	15.09	0.594	61.5	2.42	17.1	0.673
7/8	27.18	1.070	27.18	1.070	3.2	0.125	5.9	0.234	17.5	0.688	39.6	1.56	35.1	1.38	15.09	0.594	66.3	2.61	17.1	0.673
1	30.35	1.195	30.35	1.195	3.2	0.125	5.9	0.234	17.5	0.688	39.6	1.56	35.1	1.38	15.09	0.594	70.4	2.77	17.1	0.673
1-1/4	38.28	1.507	38.28	1.507	3.2	0.125	5.9	0.234	17.5	0.688	39.6	1.56	35.1	1.38	15.09	0.594	86.1	3.39	17.1	0.673
1-1/2	44.60	1.756	44.60	1.756	3.2	0.125	5.9	0.234	17.5	0.688	39.6	1.56	35.1	1.38	15.09	0.594	96.8	3.81	17.1	0.673
2	60.48	2.381	60.48	2.381	3.2	0.125	5.9	0.234	17.5	0.688	45.0	1.77	40.1	1.58	15.09	0.594	121.4	4.78	17.1	0.673

Continued on next page

TABLE 9—DIMENSIONS OF ALL BODIES AND LOCKNUTS (FIGURES 19A TO 27C) (CONTINUED)

Nom Tube OD, in	J_2 Full Thread Min mm	J_2 Full Thread Min in	J_3 Full Thread mm ±0.13	J_3 Full Thread in ±0.005	J_4 mm min	J_4 in min	K mm +0.40 −0.13	K in +0.016 −0.005	K_1[(h)] mm ±0.5	K_1[(h)] in ±0.02	K_2 mm +1.0 −0.5	K_2 in +0.04 −0.02	L mm ±0.5	L in ±0.02	L_1 mm ±0.5	L_1 in ±0.02	L_2 mm ±0.5	L_2 in ±0.02	L_3 mm ±0.5	L_3 in ±0.02
1/8	7.5	0.297	5.94	0.234	15.0	0.59	4.78	0.188	2.4	0.094	4.4	0.172	26.4	1.04	25.9	1.02	26.7	1.05	16.0	0.63
3/16	7.5	0.297	5.94	0.234	15.0	0.59	5.94	0.234	2.4	0.094	4.5	0.178	27.7	1.09	28.2	1.11	27.4	1.08	17.3	0.68
1/4	7.6	0.300	6.73	0.265	18.5	0.73	5.94	0.234	2.4	0.094	5.6	0.219	28.4	1.12	30.0	1.18	27.7	1.09	18.0	0.71
5/16	8.4	0.331	6.73	0.265	18.5	0.73	6.35	0.250	2.4	0.094	5.6	0.219	28.4	1.12	30.0	1.18	27.4	1.08	18.0	0.71
3/8	8.5	0.333	7.92	0.312	19.1	0.75	6.35	0.250	2.4	0.094	6.7	0.265	34.0	1.34	31.5	1.24	33.3	1.31	19.0	0.75
1/2	9.5	0.375	8.74	0.344	21.9	0.86	7.75	0.305	3.2	0.125	6.4	0.250	36.6	1.44	36.1	1.42	37.3	1.47	21.6	0.85
5/8	11.7	0.461	9.93	0.391	25.4	1.00	8.89	0.350	3.2	0.125	7.7	0.304	44.4	1.75	40.9	1.61	44.7	1.76	24.6	0.97
3/4	11.9	0.469	11.91	0.469	29.0	1.14	8.89	0.350	3.2	0.125	9.0	0.354	47.8	1.88	46.0	1.81	48.0	1.89	27.9	1.10
7/8	11.9	0.469	11.91	0.469	29.0	1.14	8.89	0.350	3.2	0.125	7.1	0.281	47.8	1.88	46.0	1.81	47.2	1.86	27.9	1.10
1	11.1	0.438	11.91	0.469	29.0	1.14	10.54	0.415	3.2	0.125	6.4	0.250	52.6	2.07	46.0	1.81	54.1	2.13	27.9	1.10
1-1/4	11.1	0.438	11.91	0.469	29.0	1.14	10.54	0.415	3.2	0.125	6.7	0.265	55.4	2.18	48.0	1.89	56.4	2.22	30.0	1.18
1-1/2	11.1	0.438	11.91	0.469	29.0	1.14	12.32	0.485	3.2	0.125	7.3	0.289	57.9	2.28	49.8	1.96	56.6	2.23	31.8	1.25
2	11.1	0.438	11.91	0.469	29.0	1.14	12.32	0.485	3.2	0.125	7.1	0.281	62.5	2.46	53.6	2.11	58.7	2.31	35.6	1.40

Nom Tube OD, in	L_4 mm ±0.5	L_4 in ±0.02	L_5 mm ±0.5	L_5 in ±0.02	L_6 mm ±0.5	L_6 in ±0.02	M mm ±0.8	M in ±0.03	M_1 mm ±0.8	M_1 in ±0.03	M_2 mm ±0.8	M_2 in ±0.03	M_3 mm ±0.8	M_3 in ±0.03	M_4 mm ±0.8	M_4 in ±0.03	M_5 mm ±1.5	M_5 in ±0.06	M_6 mm ±1	M_6 in ±0.06
1/8	43.4	1.71	25.1	0.99	43.2	1.70	19.6	0.77	21.1	0.83	16.3	0.64	20.3	0.80	34.5	1.36	24.9	0.98	24	0.95
3/16	45.7	1.80	26.4	1.04	46.0	1.81	21.1	0.83	21.1	0.83	16.3	0.64	23.9	0.94	36.6	1.44	25.9	1.02	24	0.95
1/4	48.0	1.89	28.7	1.13	51.3	2.02	22.6	0.89	22.6	0.89	17.8	0.70	24.1	0.95	38.6	1.52	26.7	1.05	24	0.98
5/16	48.0	1.89	28.7	1.13	52.8	2.08	24.1	0.95	24.1	0.95	19.1	0.75	26.7	1.05	42.2	1.66	29.0	1.14	26	1.05
3/8	50.3	1.98	30.7	1.21	56.6	2.23	26.7	1.05	26.7	1.05	21.1	0.83	27.4	1.08	43.2	1.70	32.5	1.28	30	1.20
1/2	56.4	2.22	35.1	1.38	66.5	2.62	31.8	1.25	31.2	1.23	24.9	0.98	33.8	1.33	50.0	1.97	37.3	1.47	33	1.33
5/8	63.0	2.48	39.9	1.57	75.7	2.98	36.1	1.42	36.1	1.42	27.4	1.08	38.6	1.52	57.7	2.27	40.9	1.61	37	1.48
3/4	69.1	2.72	45.5	1.79	89.7	3.53	40.1	1.58	40.1	1.58	32.3	1.27	41.7	1.64	63.0	2.48	45.0	1.77	40	1.61
7/8	69.1	2.72	45.5	1.79	94.5	3.72	42.2	1.66	41.1	1.62	34.0	1.34	43.2	1.70	64.8	2.55	45.7	1.80	40	1.58
1	69.1	2.72	46.2	1.82	99.3	3.91	43.9	1.73	43.9	1.73	34.5	1.36	43.9	1.73	66.3	2.61	47.2	1.86	43	1.70
1-1/4	71.1	2.80	48.3	1.90	117.1	4.61	48.0	1.89	52.8	2.08	36.8	1.45	51.3	2.02	73.4	2.89	52.8	2.08	45	1.80
1-1/2	72.9	2.87	50.0	1.97	129.5	5.10	51.3	2.02	65.5	2.58	38.6	1.52	55.9	2.20	80.5	3.17	55.9	2.20	48	1.92
2	82.0	3.23	54.1	2.13	158.2	6.23	62.2	2.45	67.1	2.64	46.5	1.83	60.7	2.39	95.8	3.77	64.0	2.52	52	2.05

Nom Tube OD, in	M_7 mm ±0.8	M_7 in ±0.03	M_8 mm ±0.8	M_8 in ±0.03	M_9 mm ±0.8	M_9 in ±0.03	N mm ±0.8	N in ±0.03	N_1 mm ±0.8	N_1 in ±0.03	N_2 mm ±0.8	N_2 in ±0.03	N_3 mm ±0.8	N_3 in ±0.03	N_4 mm ±0.8	N_4 in ±0.03	O mm ±0.5	O in ±0.02	P Min	P Min
1/8	23.1	0.91	22.4	0.88	32.5	1.28	18.3	0.72	16.8	0.66	13.2	0.52	25.4	1.00	32.5	1.28	11.1	0.438	9.7	0.38
3/16	23.9	0.94	22.4	0.88	33.8	1.33	18.3	0.72	16.8	0.66	13.2	0.52	26.4	1.04	34.3	1.35	12.7	0.500	9.7	0.38
1/4	26.2	1.03	26.7	1.05	36.8	1.45	19.8	0.78	16.8	0.66	16.3	0.64	29.7	1.17	39.6	1.56	14.3	0.562	9.7	0.38
5/16	28.7	1.13	26.7	1.05	36.8	1.45	20.6	0.81	16.8	0.66	16.3	0.64	29.7	1.17	41.4	1.63	15.9	0.625	9.7	0.38
3/8	31.8	1.25	29.0	1.14	39.6	1.56	27.7	1.09	22.4	0.88	21.8	0.86	40.1	1.58	52.6	2.07	17.5	0.688	14.2	0.56
1/2	36.8	1.45	33.0	1.30	46.0	1.81	31.0	1.22	25.9	1.02	24.1	0.95	46.2	1.82	61.5	2.42	22.2	0.875	14.2	0.56
5/8	43.2	1.70	38.6	1.52	52.1	2.05	37.3	1.47	31.2	1.23	29.7	1.17	55.1	2.17	72.9	2.87	25.4	1.000	19.0	0.75
3/4	49.3	1.94	43.9	1.73	57.2	2.25	40.4	1.59	34.5	1.36	30.5	1.20	62.0	2.44	83.3	3.28	30.2	1.188	19.0	0.75
7/8	50.8	2.00	45.7	1.80	58.7	2.31	42.9	1.69	36.1	1.42	33.0	1.30	65.8	2.59	88.9	3.50	33.3	1.312	19.0	0.75
1	52.1	2.05	47.2	1.86	60.5	2.38	50.0	1.97	41.1	1.62	37.6	1.48	76.5	3.01	102.9	4.05	36.5	1.438	23.9	0.94
1-1/4	57.2	2.25	48.5	1.91	61.2	2.41	60.5	2.38	43.2	1.70	42.4	1.67	93.7	3.69	127.0	5.00	44.4	1.750	24.6	0.97
1-1/2	60.7	2.39	48.5	1.91	61.5	2.42	67.1	2.64	52.8	2.08	45.0	1.77	104.1	4.10	141.0	5.55	50.8	2.000	25.4	1.00
2	73.4	2.89	47.2	1.86	65.5	2.58	76.2	3.00	60.7	2.39	53.6	2.11	122.2	4.81	168.4	6.63	66.7	2.625	26.2	1.03

Continued on next page.

TABLE 9—DIMENSIONS OF ALL BODIES AND LOCKNUTS (FIGURES 19A TO 27C) (CONTINUED)

Nom Tube OD, in	P_1 Max mm	P_1 Max in	Q Min mm	Q Min in	R Rad Max mm	R Rad Max in	R_1 Rad Max mm	R_1 Rad Max in	S[(b)] Max mm	S[(b)] Max in	S_1[(b)(c)] Min mm	S_1[(b)(c)] Min in	S_2[(c)] Min mm	S_2[(c)] Min in	T[(d)] Ref mm	T[(d)] Ref in	T_1 mm ±0.5	T_1 in ±0.02	T_2[(d)] Ref mm	T_2[(d)] Ref in
1/8	11.7	0.46	2.8	0.11	0.3	0.010	0.1	0.005	12.4	0.49	20.6	0.81	19.0	0.75	5.6	0.22	5.6	0.22	7.1	0.28
3/16	11.7	0.46	2.8	0.11	0.4	0.016	0.1	0.005	12.4	0.49	20.8	0.82	19.3	0.76	5.6	0.22	5.6	0.22	7.1	0.28
1/4	11.7	0.46	2.8	0.11	0.4	0.016	0.1	0.005	14.0	0.55	27.2	1.07	20.3	0.80	5.6	0.22	7.1	0.28	7.1	0.28
5/16	11.7	0.46	3.0	0.12	0.4	0.016	0.3	0.010	14.0	0.55	28.2	1.11	20.8	0.82	5.6	0.22	7.1	0.28	7.1	0.28
3/8	17.0	0.67	3.0	0.12	0.4	0.016	0.3	0.010	—	—	—	—	26.9	1.06	6.4	0.25	6.9	0.27	7.9	0.31
1/2	17.3	0.68	4.0	0.16	0.4	0.016	0.3	0.010	17.0	0.67	38.1	1.50	32.3	1.27	6.4	0.25	7.9	0.31	8.6	0.34
5/8	22.9	0.90	4.0	0.16	0.4	0.016	0.3	0.010	23.1	0.91	44.7	1.76	38.6	1.52	7.9	0.31	9.1	0.36	10.2	0.40
3/4	23.1	0.91	4.8	0.19	0.4	0.016	0.3	0.010	23.9	0.94	49.5	1.95	43.9	1.73	9.7	0.38	10.4	0.41	11.9	0.47
7/8	23.1	0.91	4.8	0.19	0.4	0.016	0.3	0.010	—	—	—	—	46.2	1.82	9.7	0.38	10.4	0.41	11.9	0.47
1	29.0	1.14	4.8	0.19	0.4	0.016	0.3	0.010	28.7	1.13	62.2	2.45	53.3	2.10	9.7	0.38	10.4	0.41	12.7	0.50
1-1/4	29.5	1.16	5.8	0.23	0.6	0.025	0.4	0.016	30.5	1.20	75.7	2.98	58.2	2.29	11.7	0.46	10.4	0.41	14.7	0.58
1-1/2	29.5	1.16	5.8	0.23	0.6	0.025	0.4	0.016	32.3	1.27	85.3	3.36	71.1	2.80	13.5	0.53	10.4	0.41	16.5	0.65
2	30.0	1.18	8.4	0.33	0.6	0.025	0.4	0.016	34.8	1.37	100.3	3.95	84.8	3.34	17.3	0.68	10.4	0.41	20.6	0.81

Nom Tube OD, in	U Dia mm +0.4 −0.0	U Dia in +0.016 −0.000	V Dia mm ±0.25	V Dia in ±0.010	X Dia mm ±0.13	X Dia in ±0.005	X_1 Dia mm ±0.13	X_1 Dia in ±0.005	Y[(m)] mm +0.0	Y[(m)] in +0.000	Y_1[(e)] mm +0.0	Y_1[(e)] in +0.000	MM mm ±0.08	MM in ±0.003	NN Dia mm ±0.4	NN Dia in ±0.016
1/8	8.1	0.317	6.25	0.245	14.27	0.562	11.13	0.438	11.1-0.8	0.438-0.030	14.3-0.8	0.562-0.030	0.76	0.030	12.8	0.504
3/16	9.7	0.380	7.75	0.305	15.88	0.625	12.70	0.500	11.1-0.8	0.438-0.030	14.3-0.8	0.562-0.030	0.76	0.030	14.6	0.575
1/4	11.3	0.443	9.15	0.360	17.48	0.688	14.30	0.563	11.1-0.8	0.438-0.030	14.3-0.8	0.562-0.030	0.89	0.035	16.5	0.650
5/16	12.8	0.505	10.65	0.420	19.05	0.750	15.88	0.625	14.3-0.8	0.562-0.030	14.3-0.8	0.562-0.030	0.89	0.035	18.3	0.722
3/8	14.4	0.567	12.05	0.475	20.62	0.812	17.48	0.688	14.3-0.8	0.562-0.030	19.0-0.8	0.750-0.030	0.89	0.035	20.2	0.794
1/2	19.2	0.755	16.65	0.655	25.40	1.000	22.22	0.875	19.0-0.8	0.750-0.030	22.2-0.8	0.875-0.030	1.04	0.041	25.7	1.010
5/8	22.4	0.880	19.55	0.770	28.58	1.125	25.40	1.000	22.2-0.8	0.875-0.030	27.0-0.8	1.062-0.030	1.27	0.050	29.3	1.155
3/4	27.1	1.067	23.90	0.940	34.92	1.375	31.75	1.250	27.0-1.0	1.062-0.040	33.3-1.0	1.312-0.040	1.27	0.050	36.7	1.444
7/8	30.3	1.193	27.05	1.065	38.10	1.500	34.92	1.375	33.3-1.0	1.312-0.040	33.3-1.0	1.312-0.040	1.27	0.050	40.4	1.589
1	33.5	1.317	30.25	1.190	41.28	1.625	38.10	1.500	33.3-1.0	1.312-0.040	41.3-1.0	1.625-0.040	1.27	0.050	44.0	1.732
1-1/4	41.4	1.630	38.10	1.500	47.62	1.875	47.62	1.875	41.3-1.0	1.625-0.040	47.6-1.0	1.875-0.040	1.27	0.050	55.0	2.165
1-1/2	47.8	1.880	44.45	1.750	53.98	2.125	53.98	2.125	47.6-1.0	1.875-0.040	65.1-1.0	2.562-0.040	1.27	0.050	62.3	2.454
2	63.6	2.505	60.35	2.375	69.85	2.750	69.85	2.750	63.5-1.0	2.500-0.040	71.4-1.0	2.812-0.040	1.27	0.050	80.3	3.160

(a) O-ring groove undercut must be smooth and free from tool marks.
(b) At manufacturer's option, through passages in Figures 19A and 22C may conform with the smaller diameter specified or the appropriate end may be counterbored to the larger diameter for depths S and S1, respectively.
(c) Maximum depth shall be optional with manufacturer providing wall thickness is controlled in compliance with General Specifications.
(d) Minimum design thickness, not subject to inspection.
(e) The basic dimensions shall apply as minimum for boss diameters.
(f) Unified class 2B thread shall apply to swivel nuts Figures 25C, 26A, 26B, and 26C and with minor diameter modified to class 3B limits for locknuts Figures 25A and 25B.
(g) Across flat widths must fit standard wrench openings. See ANSI B18.2.2.
(h) Diameter of bulkhead pilot is the same as major thread diameter. Recommended pilot hole for bulkhead fittings is 0.4 mm (0.016 in) over major thread diameter.
(k) J full thread minimum with thread runout. If undercut to G diameter and H width. Length of thread and undercut must not be less than i.
(l) See Table 1A for tolerance.
(m) For optional metric fitting flats see Appendix A.

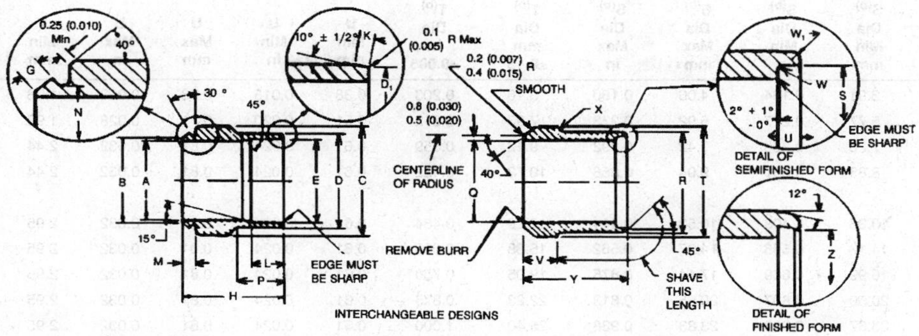

FIGURE 28—STYLE A FERRULE (080115A) FIGURE 29—STYLE B FERRULE (080115B)

NOTE— FIGURES 28 AND 29 APPLY TO TABLE 10. CODES SHOWN IN BRACKETS ADJACENT TO FIGURE NUMBERS REPRESENT RESPECTIVE FITTING IDENTIFICATiON IN ACCORDANCE WITH SAE J846.

TABLE 10—DIMENSIONS OF FERRULES (FIGURES 28 AND 29)

Nom Tube OD, in	A[(a)] Dia mm +0.08 −0.00	A[(a)] Dia in +0.003 −0.000	B Dia mm +0.00 −0.20	B Dia in +0.000 −0.008	C[(a)] Dia mm +0.13 −0.00	C[(a)] Dia in +0.005 −0.000	D[(a)] Dia mm +0.00 −0.08	D[(a)] Dia in +0.000 −0.003	D_1 Dia Ref mm	D_1 Dia Ref in	E[(a)] Dia mm +0.08 −0.00	E[(a)] Dia in +0.003 −0.000	G Ref mm	G Ref in	H mm ±0.08	H in ±0.003
1/8	3.30	0.130	3.81	0.150	6.02	0.237	4.52	0.178	4.3	0.171	3.56	0.140	0.69	0.027	7.32	0.288
3/16	4.90	0.193	5.38	0.212	7.80	0.307	6.32	0.249	6.1	0.242	5.21	0.205	0.69	0.027	8.36	0.329
1/4	6.48	0.255	6.98	0.275	9.32	0.367	7.92	0.312	7.7	0.303	6.81	0.268	0.69	0.027	9.22	0.363
5/16	8.08	0.318	8.59	0.338	10.92	0.430	9.52	0.375	9.3	0.366	8.38	0.330	0.69	0.027	9.32	0.367
3/8	9.65	0.380	10.16	0.400	12.50	0.492	11.18	0.440	10.9	0.431	9.98	0.393	0.74	0.029	9.98	0.393
1/2	12.83	0.505	13.59	0.535	16.84	0.663	14.91	0.587	14.7	0.577	13.23	0.521	1.12	0.044	10.90	0.429
5/8	16.03	0.631	16.79	0.661	19.81	0.780	18.11	0.713	17.9	0.703	16.43	0.647	1.07	0.042	11.23	0.442
3/4	19.20	0.756	19.96	0.786	23.50	0.925	21.29	0.838	21.0	0.828	19.61	0.772	1.27	0.050	12.06	0.475
7/8	22.38	0.881	23.14	0.911	26.42	1.040	24.46	0.963	24.2	0.953	22.78	0.897	1.32	0.052	12.06	0.475
1	25.55	1.006	26.31	1.036	30.15	1.187	27.64	1.088	27.4	1.078	25.96	1.022	1.37	0.054	12.06	0.475
1-1/4	32.00	1.260	32.74	1.289	36.73	1.446	32.06	1.341	33.8	1.331	32.38	1.275	1.57	0.062	12.06	0.475
1-1/2	38.35	1.510	39.09	1.539	43.03	1.694	40.39	1.590	40.1	1.580	38.71	1.524	1.57	0.062	12.06	0.475
2	51.16	2.014	51.79	2.039	56.13	2.210	53.19	2.094	52.9	2.084	51.46	2.026	1.78	0.070	12.93	0.509

Nom Tube OD, in	K mm +0.08 −0.05	K in +0.003 −0.002	L mm +0.40 −0.00	L in +0.016 −0.000	M mm +0.00 −0.15	M in +0.000 −0.006	N Dia mm +0.00 −0.13	N Dia in +0.000 −0.005	P Min mm	P Min in	P Max mm	P Max in	Q[(b)] Dia mm +0.08 −0.00	Q[(b)] Dia in +0.003 −0.000	R[(b)] Dia Min mm	R[(b)] Dia Min in
1/8	0.51	0.020	1.98	0.078	1.17	0.046	3.86	0.152	3.18	0.125	3.30	0.130	3.28	0.129	4.44	0.175
3/16	0.51	0.020	1.98	0.078	1.19	0.047	5.54	0.218	3.18	0.125	3.30	0.130	4.83	0.190	6.40	0.252
1/4	0.64	0.025	2.77	0.109	1.24	0.049	7.24	0.285	3.96	0.156	4.09	0.161	6.48	0.255	7.85	0.309
5/16	0.64	0.025	3.18	0.125	1.24	0.049	8.94	0.352	4.22	0.166	4.34	0.171	8.08	0.318	9.47	0.373
3/8	0.64	0.025	3.18	0.125	1.24	0.049	10.62	0.418	3.84	0.151	3.96	0.156	9.65	0.380	10.95	0.431
1/2	0.76	0.030	4.11	0.162	1.73	0.068	14.10	0.555	6.10	0.240	6.60	0.260	12.85	0.506	14.86	0.585
5/8	0.76	0.030	4.60	0.181	1.63	0.064	17.30	0.681	5.77	0.227	6.27	0.247	16.08	0.633	17.73	0.698
3/4	0.76	0.030	4.60	0.181	1.93	0.076	20.50	0.807	6.35	0.250	6.86	0.270	19.25	0.758	21.23	0.836
7/8	0.76	0.030	4.60	0.181	2.11	0.083	23.65	0.931	6.48	0.255	6.98	0.275	22.43	0.883	24.41	0.961
1	0.76	0.030	4.75	0.187	2.11	0.083	26.82	1.056	6.20	0.244	6.71	0.264	25.60	1.008	27.58	1.086
1-1/4	0.76	0.030	4.75	0.187	2.11	0.083	33.25	1.309	5.72	0.225	6.22	0.245	32.00	1.260	34.01	1.339
1-1/2	0.76	0.030	4.75	0.187	2.18	0.086	39.60	1.559	5.72	0.225	6.22	0.245	38.38	1.511	40.36	1.589
2	0.76	0.030	4.75	0.187	2.34	0.092	52.30	2.059	6.05	0.238	6.55	0.258	51.16	2.014	53.14	2.092

Continued on next page.

TABLE 10—DIMENSIONS OF FERRULES (FIGURES 28 AND 29) (CONTINUED)

Nom tube OD, in	R[b] Dia Max mm	R[b] Dia Max in	S[b] Dia Min mm	S[b] Dia Min in	S[b] Dia Max mm	S[b] Dia Max in	T[b] Dia mm ±0.13	T[b] Dia in ±0.005	U Min mm	U Min in	U Max mm	U Max in	V Min mm	V Min in	V Max mm	V Max in
1/8	4.52	0.178	3.91	0.154	4.06	0.160	5.16	0.203	0.38	0.015	0.58	0.023	1.98	0.078	2.13	0.084
3/16	6.50	0.256	5.77	0.227	5.92	0.233	7.93	0.312	0.51	0.020	0.71	0.028	1.98	0.078	2.13	0.084
1/4	7.95	0.313	7.26	0.286	7.42	0.292	9.12	0.359	0.61	0.024	0.81	0.032	2.44	0.096	2.59	0.102
5/16	9.58	0.377	8.89	0.350	9.04	0.356	10.72	0.422	0.61	0.024	0.81	0.032	2.44	0.096	2.59	0.102
3/8	11.05	0.435	10.36	0.408	10.52	0.414	12.29	0.484	0.61	0.024	0.81	0.032	2.95	0.116	3.10	0.122
1/2	14.96	0.589	14.12	0.556	14.27	0.562	15.88	0.625	0.61	0.024	0.81	0.032	2.95	0.116	3.10	0.122
5/8	17.83	0.702	16.99	0.669	17.14	0.675	19.05	0.750	0.61	0.024	0.81	0.032	2.95	0.116	3.10	0.122
3/4	21.34	0.840	20.50	0.807	20.65	0.813	22.23	0.875	0.61	0.024	0.81	0.032	2.95	0.116	3.10	0.122
7/8	24.51	0.965	23.67	0.932	23.83	0.938	25.40	1.000	0.61	0.024	0.81	0.032	2.95	0.116	3.10	0.122
1	27.69	1.090	26.85	1.057	27.00	1.063	28.58	1.125	0.61	0.024	0.81	0.032	2.95	0.116	3.10	0.122
1-1/4	34.11	1.343	33.27	1.310	33.43	1.316	35.71	1.406	0.61	0.024	0.81	0.032	2.95	0.116	3.10	0.122
1-1/2	40.46	1.593	39.62	1.560	39.78	1.566	42.06	1.656	0.61	0.024	0.81	0.032	2.95	0.116	3.10	0.122
2	53.24	2.096	52.40	2.063	52.55	2.069	55.58	2.188	0.61	0.024	0.81	0.032	3.89	0.153	4.04	0.159

Nom Tube OD, in	W Rad Min mm	W Rad Min in	W Rad Max mm	W Rad Max in	W_1 Rad mm	W_1 Rd in	X Rad mm	X Rad in	Y Min mm	Y Min in	Y Max mm	Y Max in	Z Dia Min mm	Z Dia Min in	Z Dia Max mm	Z Dia Max in
1/8	0.08	0.003	0.15	0.006	0.2	0.007	0.3	0.010	6.98	0.275	7.14	0.281	3.76	0.148	3.96	0.156
3/16	0.08	0.003	0.15	0.006	0.2	0.007	0.5	0.020	6.98	0.275	7.14	0.281	5.61	0.221	5.82	0.229
1/4	0.08	0.003	0.15	0.006	0.2	0.007	0.5	0.020	8.46	0.333	8.61	0.339	7.11	0.280	7.32	0.288
5/16	0.08	0.003	0.15	0.006	0.2	0.007	0.5	0.020	8.46	0.333	8.61	0.339	8.74	0.344	8.94	0.352
3/8	0.08	0.003	0.15	0.006	0.2	0.007	0.5	0.020	9.45	0.372	9.60	0.378	10.21	0.402	10.41	0.410
1/2	0.20	0.008	0.36	0.014	0.3	0.010	0.5	0.020	9.45	0.372	9.60	0.378	13.97	0.550	14.17	0.558
5/8	0.20	0.008	0.36	0.014	0.3	0.010	0.5	0.020	10.46	0.412	10.62	0.418	16.84	0.663	17.04	0.671
3/4	0.20	0.008	0.36	0.014	0.3	0.010	0.5	0.020	10.46	0.412	10.62	0.418	20.35	0.801	20.55	0.809
7/8	0.20	0.008	0.36	0.014	0.3	0.010	0.5	0.020	10.46	0.412	10.62	0.418	23.52	0.926	23.72	0.934
1	0.20	0.008	0.36	0.014	0.3	0.010	0.5	0.020	10.46	0.412	10.62	0.418	26.70	1.051	26.90	1.059
1-1/4	0.20	0.008	0.36	0.014	0.3	0.010	0.5	0.020	10.46	0.412	10.62	0.418	33.12	1.304	33.32	1.312
1-1/2	0.20	0.008	0.36	0.014	0.3	0.010	0.5	0.020	10.46	0.412	10.62	0.418	39.47	1.554	39.67	1.562
2	0.20	0.008	0.36	0.014	0.3	0.010	0.5	0.020	11.43	0.450	11.58	0.456	52.25	2.057	52.45	2.065

[a] These diameters, A, C, D, and E must be concentric with 0.13 mm (0.005 in).

[b] These diameters, Q, R, S, and T must be concentric wiht 0.13 mm (0.005 in).

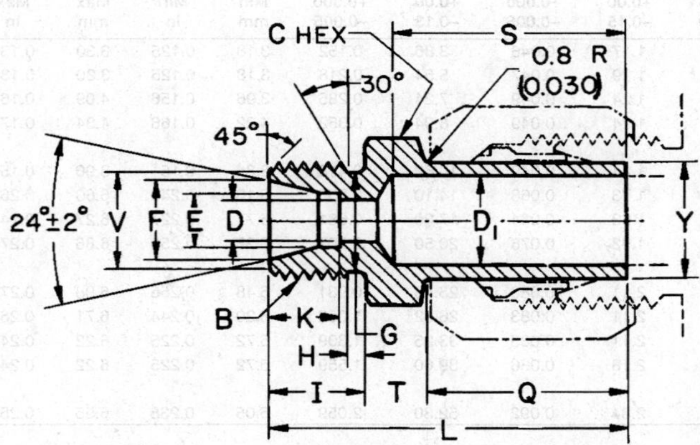

FIGURE 30—REDUCER (080123)

TABLE 11—DIMENSIONS[a] OF REDUCERS (FIGURE 30)

Tube Reduction in	B Thread Size, in SAE J475 (ISO R725) Class 2A Ext	C Hex Nom, in	D[c] Dia Drill mm	D[c] Dia Drill in	D_1[c] Dia Drill mm	D_1[c] Dia Drill in	L mm ±0.5	L in ±0.02	Q mm ±0.5	Q in ±0.02	S mm ±0.5	S in ±0.02	T[b] Ref mm	T[b] Ref in	Y Dia mm ±0.08	Y Dia in ±0.003
3/8 x 1/4	7/16-20	1/2	5.2	0.203	6.3	0.250	40.9	1.61	22.4	0.88	23.4	0.92	5.6	0.22	9.52	0.375
1/2 x 1/4	7/16-20	9/16	5.2	0.203	9.5	0.375	43.9	1.73	25.4	1.00	27.2	1.07	5.6	0.22	12.70	0.500
1/2 x 3/8	9/16-18	5/8	7.0	0.281	9.5	0.375	45.0	1.77	25.4	1.00	27.9	1.10	6.4	0.25	12.70	0.500
5/8 x 1/4	7/16-20	11/16	5.2	0.203	12.7	0.500	47.0	1.85	27.7	1.09	29.0	1.14	6.4	0.25	15.88	0.625
5/8 x 3/8	9/16-18	11/16	7.0	0.281	12.7	0.500	47.2	1.86	27.7	1.09	30.5	1.20	6.4	0.25	15.88	0.625
5/8 x 1/2	3/4-16	13/16	10.7	0.422	12.7	0.500	49.8	1.96	27.7	1.09	30.5	1.20	6.4	0.25	15.88	0.625
3/4 x 1/4	7/16-20	13/16	5.2	0.203	15.9	0.625	48.8	1.92	29.5	1.16	29.0	1.14	6.4	0.25	19.05	0.750
3/4 x 3/8	9/16-18	13/16	7.0	0.281	15.9	0.625	49.0	1.93	29.5	1.16	30.5	1.20	6.4	0.25	19.05	0.750
3/4 x 1/2	3/4-16	13/16	10.7	0.422	15.9	0.625	51.6	2.03	29.5	1.16	30.5	1.20	6.4	0.25	19.05	0.750
3/4 x 5/8	7/8-14	15/16	12.7	0.500	15.9	0.625	54.6	2.15	29.5	1.16	31.8	1.26	7.9	0.31	19.05	0.750
1 x 1/2	3/4-16	1-1/16	10.7	0.422	21.4	0.844	52.1	2.05	28.4	1.12	27.9	1.10	7.9	0.31	25.40	1.000
1 x 5/8	7/8-14	1-1/16	12.7	0.500	21.4	0.844	53.6	2.11	28.4	1.12	27.9	1.10	7.9	0.31	25.40	1.000
1 x 3/4	1-1/16-12	1-1/8	16.6	0.656	21.4	0.844	56.9	2.24	28.4	1.12	29.7	1.17	9.7	0.38	25.40	1.000
1-1/4 x 5/8	7/8-14	1-3/8	12.7	0.500	26.2	1.031	56.4	2.22	29.5	1.16	29.0	1.14	9.7	0.38	31.75	1.250
1-1/4 x 3/4	1-1/16-12	1-3/8	16.6	0.656	26.2	1.031	58.2	2.29	29.5	1.16	30.5	1.20	9.7	0.38	31.75	1.250
1-1/4 x 1	1-5/16-12	1-3/8	22.2	0.875	26.2	1.031	57.9	2.28	29.5	1.16	31.2	1.23	9.7	0.38	31.75	1.250

(a) For dimensions shown on Figure 30 but not specified in above table, see corresonding dimensions for the specified tube outside diameter in Table 9.
(b) Minimum design thickness, not subject to inspection.
(c) See Table 1 for tolerance.

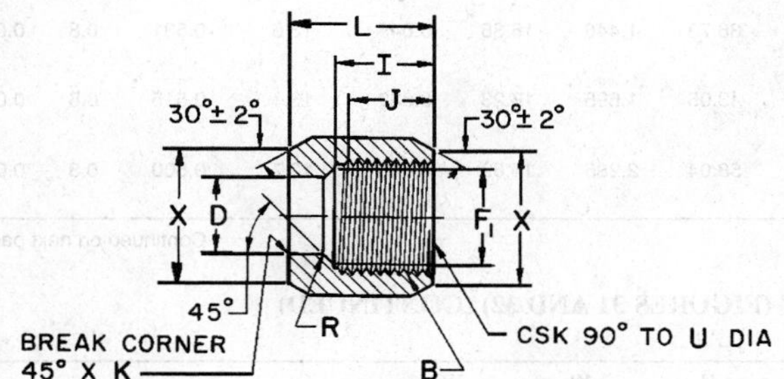

FIGURE 31—NUT (080110)

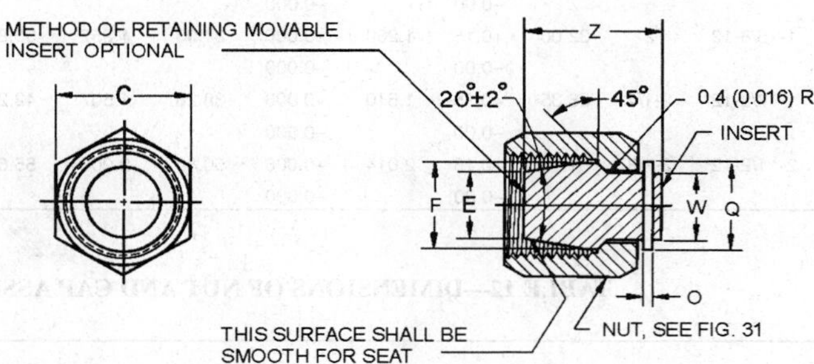

FIGURE 32—CAP ASSEMBLY (080112)

TABLE 12—DIMENSIONS OF NUT AND CAP ASSEMBLY (FIGURES 31 AND 32)

Nom tube OD, in	B Thread Size, in SAE J475 (ISO R725) Class 2B Int	C Hex Nom, in	D Dia mm	D Dia tol –0.00	D Dia in	D Dia tol –0.000	E Dia mm +0.13 –0.00	E Dia in +0.005 –0.000	F Dia mm ±0.5	F Dia in ±0.02	F_1 Dia mm ±0.13	F_1 Dia in ±0.005	I mm +0.40 –0.00	I in +0.016 –0.000	J Full Thread Min mm	J Full Thread Min in	K mm	K in
1/8	5/16-24	3/8	3.30	+0.10 –0.00	0.130	+0.004 –0.000	3.20	0.126	5.6	0.22		—	9.86	0.388	8.3	0.328	0.5	0.02
3/16	3/8-24	7/16	4.90	+0.10 –0.00	0.193	+0.004 –0.000	4.75	0.187	7.1	0.28	—	—	11.66	0.459	10.3	0.406	0.5	0.02
1/4	7/16-20	9/16	6.48	+0.10 –0.00	0.255	+0.004 –0.000	6.40	0.252	8.6	0.34	—	—	13.64	0.537	11.9	0.469	0.5	0.02
5/16	1/2-20	5/8	8.08	+0.10 –0.00	0.318	+0.004 –0.000	8.00	0.315	10.4	0.41	—	—	14.02	0.552	12.3	0.483	0.5	0.02
3/8	9/16-18	11/16	9.65	+0.10 –0.00	0.380	+0.004 –0.000	9.58	0.377	11.9	0.47	—	—	14.43	0.568	12.7	0.500	0.5	0.02
1/2	3/4-16	7/8	12.83	+0.13 –0.00	0.505	+0.005 –0.000	12.78	0.503	15.7	0.62	—	—	15.21	0.599	13.1	0.516	0.5	0.02
5/8	7/8-14	1	16.03	+0.13 –0.00	0.631	+0.005 –0.000	16.00	0.630	19.0	0.75	—	—	17.20	0.677	14.7	0.578	0.5	0.02
3/4	1-1/16-12	1-1/4	19.20	+0.13 –0.00	0.756	+0.005 –0.000	19.18	0.755	22.4	0.88	—	—	17.20	0.677	14.3	0.562	0.8	0.03
7/8	1-3/16-12	1-3/8	22.38	+0.13 –0.00	0.881	+0.005 –0.000	22.22	0.875	25.4	1.00	—	—	17.20	0.677	14.3	0.562	0.8	0.03
1	1-5/16-12	1-1/2	25.55	+0.13 –0.00	1.006	+0.005 –0.000	25.53	1.005	29.5	1.16	—	—	17.20	0.677	14.3	0.562	0.8	0.03
1-1/4	1- 5/8-12	2	32.00	+0.15 –0.00	1.260	+0.006 –0.000	31.93	1.257	35.8	1.41	36.73	1.446	16.38	0.645	13.5	0.531	0.8	0.03
1-1/2	1- 7/8-12	2-1/4	38.35	+0.15 –0.00	1.510	+0.006 –0.000	38.28	1.507	42.2	1.66	43.05	1.695	16.23	0.639	13.1	0.515	0.8	0.03
2	2- 1/2-12	2-7/8	51.16	+0.15 –0.00	2.014	+0.006 –0.000	50.80	2.000	55.6	2.19	58.04	2.285	15.62	0.615	12.7	0.500	0.8	0.03

Continued on next page.

TABLE 12—DIMENSIONS OF NUT AND CAP ASSEMBLY (FIGURES 31 AND 32) (CONTINUED)

Nom Tube OD, in	L mm ±0.5	L in ±0.02	O mm ±0.4	O in ±0.016	Q Max mm	Q Max in	R Rad mm	R Rad in	U Dia mm +0.4 –0.0	U Dia in +0.016 –0.000	W Dia mm +0.10 –0.00	W Dia in +0.004 –0.000	X Dia mm ±0.3	X Dia in ±0.01	Z Max mm	Z Max in
1/8	13.5	0.53	1.3	0.05	6.4	0.25	0.8	0.031	8.1	0.317	3.18	0.125	9.1	0.36	14.7	0.58
3/16	15.5	0.61	1.3	0.05	6.4	0.25	0.8	0.031	9.7	0.380	4.60	0.181	10.7	0.42	16.2	0.64
1/4	17.8	0.70	1.3	0.05	9.7	0.38	0.8	0.031	11.3	0.443	6.25	0.246	13.7	0.54	18.3	0.72
5/16	18.3	0.72	1.3	0.05	12.7	0.50	0.8	0.031	12.8	0.505	7.87	0.310	15.2	0.60	18.8	0.74
3/8	19.0	0.75	1.3	0.05	12.7	0.50	0.8	0.031	14.4	0.567	9.45	0.372	17.0	0.67	19.5	0.77
1/2	21.3	0.84	1.5	0.06	15.7	0.62	1.2	0.047	19.2	0.755	12.65	0.498	21.8	0.86	23.6	0.93
5/8	23.4	0.92	1.5	0.06	19.0	0.75	1.2	0.047	22.4	0.880	15.88	0.625	24.9	0.98	23.9	0.94
3/4	24.6	0.97	1.5	0.06	22.4	0.88	1.2	0.047	27.1	1.067	19.05	0.750	31.5	1.24	23.6	0.93
7/8	25.4	1.00	1.5	0.06	25.4	1.00	1.2	0.047	30.3	1.193	22.22	0.875	34.5	1.36	24.4	0.96
1	26.7	1.05	2.3	0.09	31.8	1.25	1.6	0.062	33.5	1.317	25.40	1.000	37.6	1.48	27.4	1.08
1-1/4	26.7	1.05	3.0	0.12	38.1	1.50	1.6	0.062	41.4	1.630	31.75	1.250	50.3	1.98	30.2	1.19
1-1/2	26.2	1.03	4.1	0.16	44.4	1.75	1.6	0.062	47.8	1.880	38.10	1.500	56.9	2.24	32.7	1.29
2	28.4	1.12	4.1	0.16	57.2	2.25	1.6	0.062	63.6	2.505	50.80	2.000	72.6	2.86	32.3	1.27

NOTE—Table 13 and Figure 33 have intentionally been deleted from this document. See SAE J1926, Specification for Straight Thread O-Ring Boss Port.

*7. **Section 3—O-Ring Plugs***—Specifications for straight thread O-ring port into which connector and adjustable styles of hydraulic tube fittings assemble are given in SAE J1926. O-ring boss plugs shall be as shown in Figure 34 and Table 14. Modification of hexagon chamfers on standard fittings when used in MS 33649 (or superseded AND 10050) type O-ring bosses is covered in Figure 35 and Table 15. For specifications of O-rings used in conjunction with these fittings, see SAE J515. Assembly instruction for O-ring fittings are shown in Figures 36 and 37.

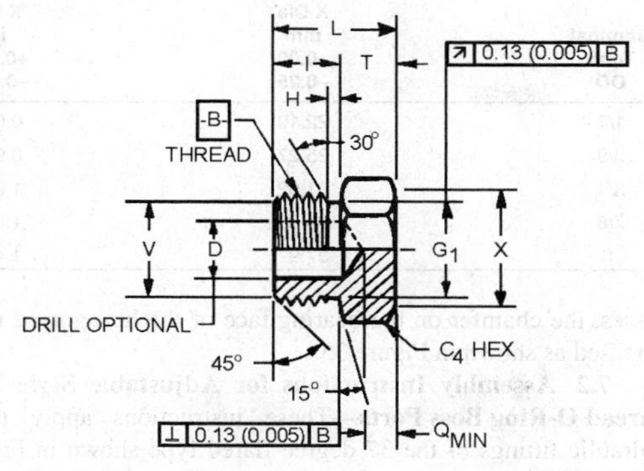

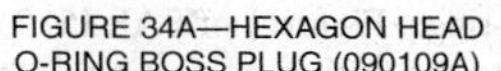

FIGURE 34A—HEXAGON HEAD O-RING BOSS PLUG (090109A)

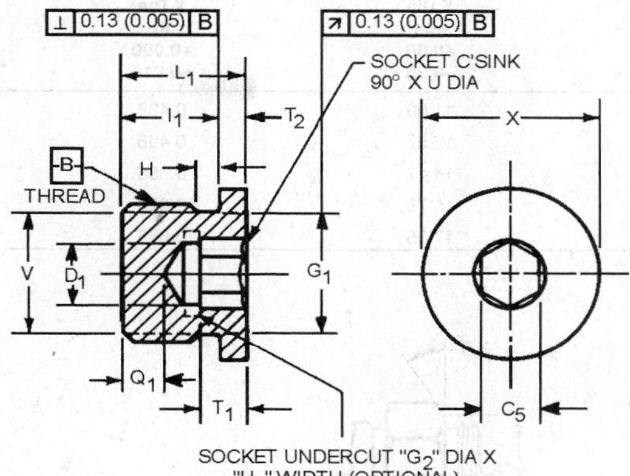

FIGURE 34B—HEXAGON SOCKET O-RING BOSS PLUG (090109B)

TABLE 14—DIMENSIONS[(a)] OF O-RING BOSS PLUS (FIGURES 34A TO 34B)

Nom tube OD, in	B Thread Size, in SAE J475 (ISO R725) Class 2A Ext. in	C_4 Hex Nom	C_5 Hex Socket mm +0.13 −0.00	C_4 Hex Socket in +0.005 −0.000	D[(d)] Drill mm	D[(d)] Drill in	D_1 Dia mm +0.13 −0.00	D_1 Dia in +0.005 −0.000	G_1[(b)] Dia mm +0.05 −0.08	G_1[(b)] Dia in +0.002 −0.003	G_2 Dia Optional mm +0.25 −0.00	G_2 Dia Optional in +0.010 −0.000	H mm +0.8 −0.0	H in +0.030 −0.000	H_1 Optional mm ±0.5	H_1 Optional in ±0.020
1/8	5/16-24	7/16	3.18	0.125	2.4	0.093	3.18	0.125	6.35	0.250	4.0	0.156	1.6	0.063	1.6	0.063
3/16	3/8-24	1/2	3.18	0.125	3.2	0.125	3.18	0.125	7.95	0.313	4.0	0.156	1.6	0.063	1.6	0.063
1/4	7/16-20	9/16	4.78	0.188	5.2	0.203	4.78	0.188	9.25	0.364	5.9	0.234	1.9	0.075	2.4	0.094
5/16	1/2-20	5/8	4.78	0.188	5.9	0.234	4.78	0.188	10.85	0.427	5.9	0.234	1.9	0.075	2.4	0.094
3/8	9/16-18	11/16	6.35	0.250	7.5	0.297	6.35	0.250	12.24	0.482	7.5	0.297	2.1	0.083	2.4	0.094
1/2	3/4-16	7/8	7.95	0.313	10.7	0.422	7.95	0.313	16.76	0.660	9.7	0.380	2.4	0.094	2.4	0.094
5/8	7/8-14	1	9.52	0.375	12.7	0.500	9.52	0.375	19.63	0.773	11.3	0.443	2.7	0.107	2.4	0.094
3/4	1-1/16-12	1-1/4	14.30	0.563	16.7	0.656	14.30	0.563	24.00	0.945	16.8	0.661	3.2	0.125	3.2	0.125
7/8	1-3/16-12	1-3/8	14.30	0.563	18.2	0.718	14.30	0.563	27.18	1.070	16.8	0.661	3.2	0.125	3.2	0.125
1	1-5/16-12	1-1/2	15.88	0.625	22.2	0.875	15.88	0.625	30.35	1.195	18.8	0.740	3.2	0.125	3.2	0.125
1-1/4	1- 5/8-12	1-7/8	19.05	0.750	27.8	1.093	19.05	0.750	38.28	1.507	22.2	0.875	3.2	0.125	3.2	0.125
1-1/2	1- 7/8-12	2-1/8	19.05	0.750	34.1	1.344	19.05	0.750	44.60	1.756	22.2	0.875	3.2	0.125	3.2	0.125
2	2- 1/2-12	2-3/4	19.05	0.750	46.1	1.813	19.05	0.750	60.48	2.381	22.2	0.875	3.2	0.125	3.2	0.125

Nom Tube OD, In	I_1 mm ±0.13	I_1 in ±0.005	L mm ±0.5	L in ±0.02	L_1 Ref mm	L_1 Ref in	Q Min mm	Q Min in	Q_1 Min mm	Q_1 Min in	T[(c)] Ref mm	T[(c)] Ref in	T_1 Min Hexa-gon Depth mm	T_1 Min Hexa-gon Depth in	T_2 mm +0.00 −0.25	T_2 in +0.000 −0.010	V Dia mm ±0.25	V Dia in ±0.010	X Dia mm ±0.13	X Dia in ±0.005	U Dia mm ±0.25	U Dia in ±0.010
1/8	7.54	0.297	15.2	0.60	10.2	0.40	1.5	0.06	2.8	0.11	7.1	0.28	3.18	0.125	2.74	0.108	6.25	0.245	11.13	0.438	4.0	0.156
3/16	7.54	0.297	15.2	0.60	10.2	0.40	2.0	0.08	2.8	0.11	7.1	0.28	3.18	0.125	2.74	0.108	7.75	0.305	12.70	0.500	4.0	0.156
1/4	9.14	0.360	17.0	0.67	11.9	0.47	2.5	0.10	3.0	0.12	7.1	0.28	3.96	0.156	2.92	0.115	9.15	0.360	14.30	0.563	5.6	0.219
5/16	9.14	0.360	17.0	0.67	11.9	0.47	3.0	0.12	3.0	0.12	7.1	0.28	3.96	0.156	2.92	0.115	10.65	0.420	15.88	0.625	5.6	0.219
3/8	9.93	0.391	18.5	0.73	12.7	0.50	4.1	0.16	3.0	0.12	7.9	0.31	4.77	0.188	2.92	0.115	12.05	0.475	17.48	0.688	7.5	0.297
1/2	11.13	0.438	20.3	0.80	14.7	0.58	5.6	0.22	3.8	0.15	8.6	0.34	4.77	0.188	3.73	0.147	16.65	0.655	22.23	0.875	9.5	0.375
5/8	12.70	0.500	23.6	0.93	16.5	0.65	6.4	0.25	3.8	0.15	10.4	0.41	6.35	0.250	3.94	0.155	19.55	0.770	25.40	1.000	11.1	0.438
3/4	15.09	0.594	27.7	1.09	19.5	0.77	6.4	0.25	3.8	0.15	11.9	0.47	7.95	0.313	4.60	0.181	23.90	0.940	31.75	1.250	16.7	0.656
7/8	15.09	0.594	27.7	1.09	19.5	0.77	6.4	0.25	3.8	0.15	11.9	0.47	7.95	0.313	4.60	0.181	27.05	1.065	34.93	1.375	16.7	0.656
1	15.09	0.594	28.4	1.12	19.5	0.77	6.4	0.25	4.8	0.19	12.7	0.50	9.52	0.375	4.60	0.181	30.25	1.190	38.10	1.500	18.6	0.734
1-1/4	15.09	0.594	30.5	1.20	19.5	0.77	6.4	0.25	4.8	0.19	14.7	0.58	9.52	0.375	4.60	0.181	38.10	1.500	47.63	1.875	23.0	0.906
1-1/2	15.09	0.594	32.3	1.27	19.5	0.77	6.4	0.25	6.4	0.25	16.5	0.65	9.52	0.375	4.60	0.181	44.45	1.750	53.98	2.125	23.0	0.906
2	15.09	0.594	36.3	1.43	19.5	0.77	7.6	0.30	6.4	0.25	20.6	0.81	9.52	0.375	4.60	0.181	60.35	2.375	69.85	2.750	23.0	0.906

(a) Modification of 1/8 to 1 in sizes for use with MS 33649 (or superseded AND 10050) bosses is shown in Figure 35 and Table 15.
(b) O-ring groove undercut must be smooth and free of tool marks.
(c) Minimum design thickness, not subject to inspection.
(d) See Table 1 for tolerance.

TABLE 15—DIMENSIONS OF MODIFIED CHAMFER (FIGURE 35)

Nominal Tube OD	X Dia mm +0.00 −0.25	X Dia in +0.000 −0.010	Nominal Tube OD	X Dia mm +0.00 −0.25	X Dia in +0.000 −0.010
1/8	11.00	0.433	1/2	22.10	0.870
3/16	12.57	0.495	5/8	25.27	0.995
1/4	14.17	0.558	3/4	31.62	1.245
5/16	15.75	0.620	7/8	34.80	1.370
3/8	17.35	0.683	1	37.97	1.495

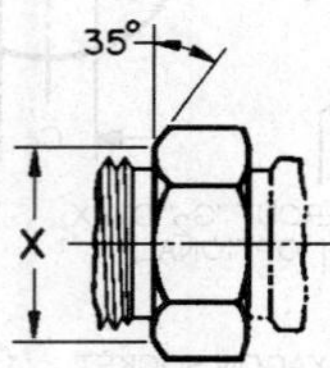

FIGURE 35—MODIFIED HEXAGON CHAMFER

7.1 Modification of Hexagons on Standard Fittings to Accommodate MS 33649 (or Superseded AND 10050) Bosses—When 37 degree flared fittings shown in Figures 3B and 3C, flareless fittings shown in Figures 20B and 20C, or O-ring boss plugs shown in Figure 34, in sizes from 1/8 to 1 in inclusive, are to be used with MS 33649 (or superseded AND 10050) type straight thread O-ring bosses, the chamfer on the bearing face of the hexagon of these fittings shall be modified as shown in Figure 35.

7.2 Assembly Instructions for Adjustable Style Fittings in Straight Thread O-Ring Boss Ports—These instructions apply to the assembly of hydraulic fittings of the 37 degree flared type shown in Figures 9D, 10A, 10B, 10C, and 8A, and flareless type shown in Figures 26D, 27A, 27B, 27C, and 25A, and hydraulic O-rings, Figure 1 of SAE J515.

7.2.1 Lubricate the O-ring by coating with a system compatible lubricant and install in the groove adjacent to the face of the metal back-up washer which is assembled at the extreme end of the groove as shown in Figure 36B.

7.2.2 Install the fitting into the SAE straight thread port (see SAE J1926) until the metal back-up washer contacts the face of the port as shown in Figure 36C.

7.2.3 Position the fitting by turning out (counterclockwise) up to a maximum of one turn. Holding the pad of the fitting with a wrench, tighten the locknut and washer against the face of the port as shown in Figure 36D.

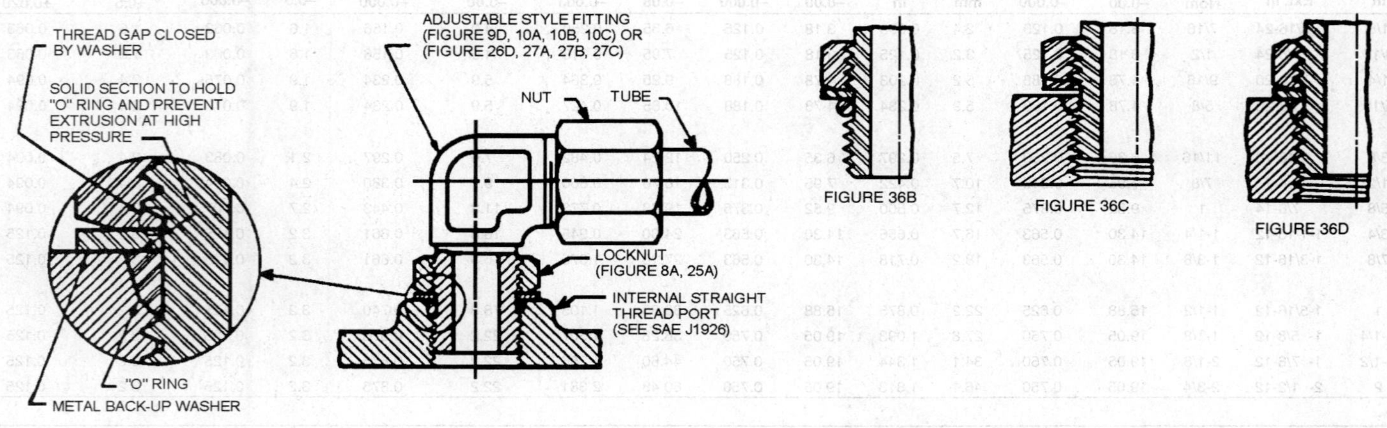

FIGURE 36—ADJUSTABLE STYLE FITTINGS

7.3 Assembly Instructions for Swivel Style and O-Ring Boss Fittings in Straight Thread O-Ring Ports—These instructions apply to the assembly of hydraulic fittings of the 37 degree flared type shown in Figures 3B and 3C, flareless type shown in Figures 20B and 20C, and O-ring boss plugs shown in Figure 34.

7.3.1 Lubricate O-ring by coating with a system compatible lubricant and install in the O-ring groove on the fitting.

7.3.2 Screw fitting into the straight thread port and tighten hexagon against the face of the port as shown in Figure 37C.

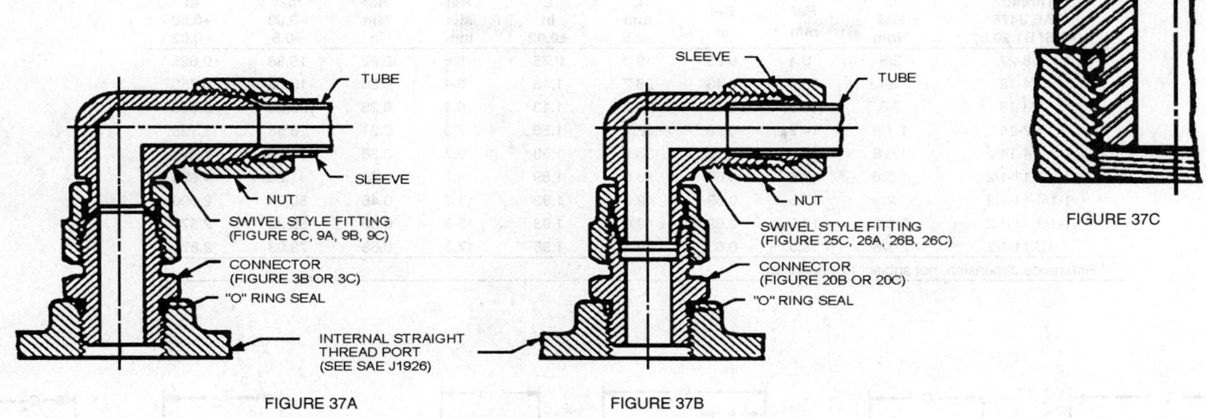

FIGURE 37A FIGURE 37B FIGURE 37C

FIGURE 37—SWIVEL STYLE FITTINGS

8. Section 4—Hydraulic Pipe Fittings—Hydraulic pipe fittings are shown in Figures 38 to 46 and Tables 16 to 19.

NOTE—UNSPECIFIED DETAIL WITH RESPECT TO DIMENSIONS, TOLERANCES, CONTOURS, MATERIAL, AND WORKMANSHIP MUST CONFORM TO GENERAL SPECIFICATIONS FOR HYDRAULIC PIPE FITTINGS. CODES SHOWN IN BRACKETS ADJACENT TO FIGURE NUMBERS REPRESENT RESPECTIVE FITTING IDENTIFICATION IN ACCORDANCE WITH SAE J846.

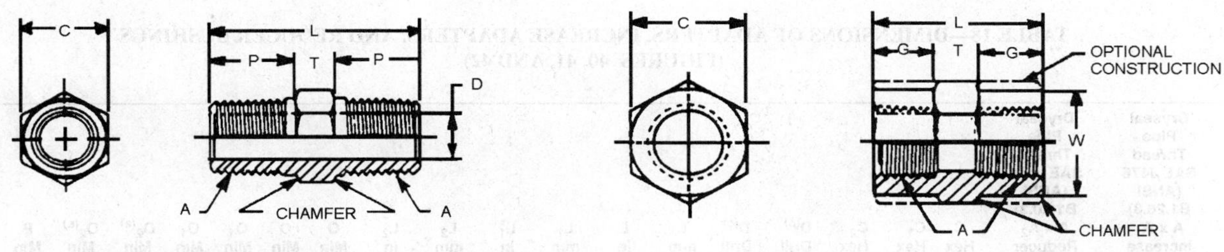

FIGURE 38—HEXAGON PIPE NIPPLE (140137)

FIGURE 39—HEXAGON PIPE COUPLING (140138)

TABLE 16—DIMENSIONS OF HEXAGON PIPE NIPPLES (FIGURE 38)

A Dryseal Pipe Thread SAE J476 (ANSI B1.20.3)	C Hex Nom	D[b] Drill mm	D[b] Drill in	L mm ±0.5	L in ±0.02	P Min mm	P Min in	T[a] Ref mm	T[a] Ref in
1/8-27	7/16	4.8	0.188	26.9	1.06	9.7	0.38	5.6	0.22
1/4-18	5/8	7.0	0.281	36.8	1.45	14.2	0.56	6.4	0.25
3/8-18	3/4	10.3	0.406	36.8	1.45	14.2	0.56	6.4	0.25
1/2-14	7/8	13.5	0.531	48.0	1.89	19.0	0.75	7.9	0.31
3/4-14	1-1/8	18.0	0.719	49.8	1.96	19.0	0.75	9.7	0.38
1-11-1/2	1-3/8	23.8	0.938	59.4	2.34	23.9	0.94	9.7	0.38
1-1/4-11-1/2	1-3/4	31.7	1.250	63.0	2.48	24.6	0.97	11.7	0.46
1-1/2-11-1/2	2	38.0	1.500	66.3	2.61	25.4	1.00	13.5	0.53
2-11-1/2	2-1/2	49.0	1.938	71.6	2.82	26.2	1.03	17.3	0.68

(a) Minimum design thickness, not subject to inspection.
(b) See Table 1 for tolerance.

TABLE 17—DIMENSIONS OF HEXAGON PIPE COUPLING (FIGURE 39)

A Dryseal Pipe Thread SAE J476 (ANSI B1.20.3)	C Hex Nom	G[a] Ref mm	G[a] Ref in	L mm ±0.5	L in ±0.02	T Ref Min mm	T Ref Min in	W Dia mm +0.00 −0.5	W Dia in +0.00 −0.02
1/8-27	5/8	6.4	0.25	19.0	0.75	5.6	0.22	15.88	0.625
1/4-18	3/4	10.9	0.43	28.7	1.13	6.4	0.25	19.05	0.750
3/8-18	7/8	10.9	0.43	28.7	1.13	6.4	0.25	22.22	0.875
1/2-14	1-1/8	14.2	0.56	38.1	1.50	7.9	0.31	28.58	1.125
3/4-14	1-3/8	14.2	0.56	38.9	1.53	9.7	0.38	34.92	1.375
1-11-1/2	1-5/8	17.5	0.69	48.0	1.89	9.7	0.38	41.28	1.625
1-1/4-11-1/2	2	17.5	0.69	49.0	1.93	11.7	0.46	50.80	2.000
1-1/2-11-1/2	2-3/8	17.5	0.69	49.0	1.93	13.5	0.53	60.32	2.375
2-11-1/2	2-7/8	16.0	0.63	49.8	1.96	17.3	0.68	73.03	2.875

[a] Reference dimension, not subject to inspection.

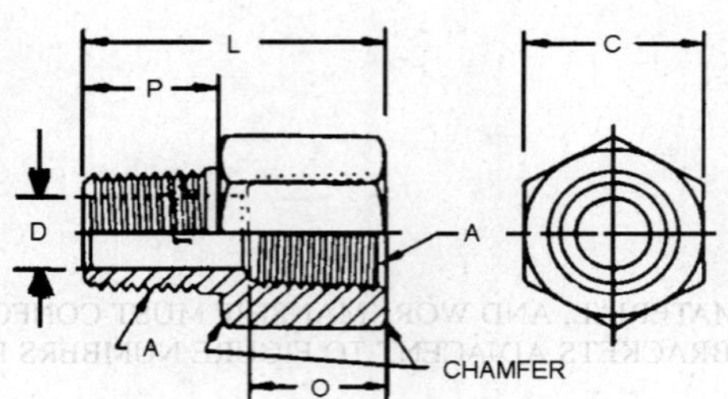

FIGURE 40—ADAPTER (140139)

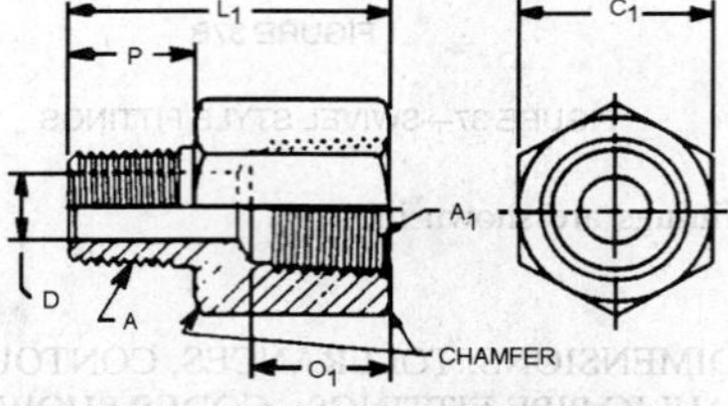

FIGURE 41—INCREASE ADAPTERS (140139)

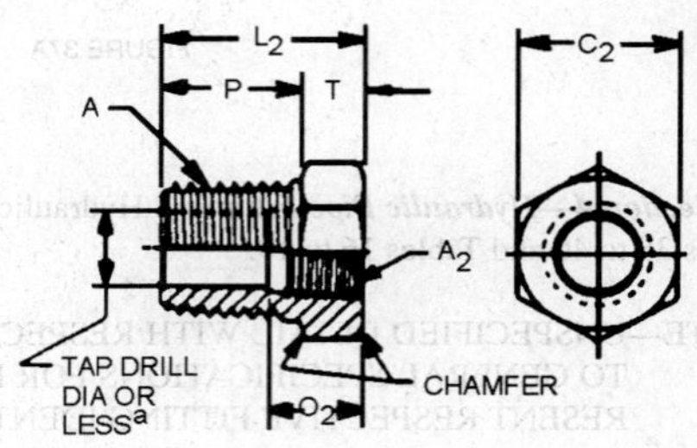

FIGURE 42—REDUCER BUSHINGS (140140)

TABLE 18—DIMENSIONS OF ADAPTERS, INCREASE ADAPTERS, AND REDUCER BUSHINGS (FIGURES 40, 41, AND 42)

Dryseal Pipe Thread SAE J476 (ANSI B1.20.3) A Adapter	Dryseal Pipe Thread SAE J476 (ANSI B1.20.3) A x A_1 Increase Adapter	Dryseal Pipe Thread SAE J476 (ANSI B1.20.3) A x A_2 Reducer Bushing	C Hex Nom	C_1 Hex Nom	C_2 Hex Nom	D[c] Drill mm	D[c] Drill in	L mm ±0.5	L in ±0.02	L_1 mm ±0.5	L_1 in ±0.02	L_2 mm ±0.5	L_2 in ±0.02	O Min mm	O Min in	O_1 Min mm	O_1 Min in	O_2[a] Min mm	O_2[a] Min in	P Min mm	P Min in	T[b] Ref mm	T[b] Ref in
1/8-27	1/8 x 1/4	—	5/8	3/4	—	4.8	0.188	26.4	1.04	30.7	1.21	—	—	9.7	0.38	14.2	0.56	—	—	9.7	0.38	—	—
1/4-18	1/4 x 3/8	1/4 x 1/8	3/4	7/8	5/8	7.0	0.281	35.3	1.39	36.6	1.44	21.6	0.85	14.2	0.56	14.7	0.58	9.7	0.38	14.2	0.56	6.4	0.25
3/8-18	3/8 x 1/2	3/8 x 1/4	7/8	1-1/8	3/4	10.3	0.406	36.6	1.44	42.7	1.68	21.6	0.85	14.7	0.58	19.0	0.75	14.2	0.56	14.2	0.56	6.4	0.25
1/2-14	1/2 x 3/4	1/2 x 3/8	1-1/8	1-3/8	7/8	13.5	0.531	47.5	1.87	49.0	1.93	27.9	1.10	19.0	0.75	19.6	0.77	14.7	0.58	19.0	0.75	7.9	0.31
3/4-14	3/4 x 1	3/4 x 1/2	1-3/8	1-5/8	1-1/8	18.0	0.719	49.0	1.93	55.4	2.18	29.7	1.17	19.6	0.77	23.9	0.94	19.0	0.75	19.0	0.75	9.7	0.38
1-11-1/2	1 x 1-1/4	1 x 1-3/4	1-5/8	2	1-3/8	23.8	0.938	60.2	2.37	62.5	2.46	34.5	1.36	23.9	0.94	23.9	0.94	19.6	0.77	23.9	0.94	9.7	0.38
1-1/4-11-1/2	1-1/4 x 1-1/2	1-1/4 x 1	2	2-3/8	1-3/4	31.7	1.250	63.2	2.49	63.5	2.50	37.3	1.47	23.9	0.94	23.9	0.94	23.9	0.94	24.6	0.97	11.7	0.46
1-1/2-11-1/2	1-1/2 x 2	1-1/2 x 1-1/4	2-3/8	2-7/8	2	38.0	1.500	64.3	2.53	66.8	2.63	39.9	1.57	23.9	0.94	24.6	0.97	23.9	0.94	25.4	1.00	13.5	0.53
2-11-1/2	—	2 x 1-1/2	2-7/8	—	2-1/2	49.0	1.938	67.6	2.66	—	—	44.5	1.75	24.6	0.97	—	—	23.9	0.94	26.2	1.03	17.3	0.68

[a] Beyond top drill depth O_2, hole may be reduced below tap drill diameter, but shall not be less than D diameter in corresponding external pipe size adapter.

[b] Minimum design thickness, not subject to inspection.

[c] See Table 1 for tolerance.

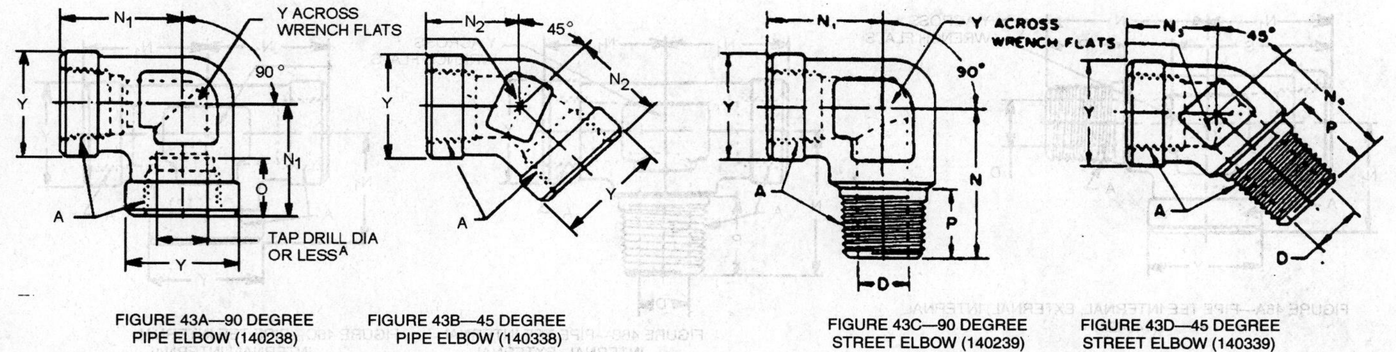

FIGURE 43A—90 DEGREE PIPE ELBOW (140238)

FIGURE 43B—45 DEGREE PIPE ELBOW (140338)

FIGURE 43C—90 DEGREE STREET ELBOW (140239)

FIGURE 43D—45 DEGREE STREET ELBOW (140339)

NOTE—FIGURES 43A TO 43D AND 46A TO 46C DEPICT FORGED CONSTRUCTION AND ARE OPTIONAL WITH SOLID OR FABRICATED BAR STOCK CONSTRUCTION DEPICTED IN FIGURES 44A to 45D.

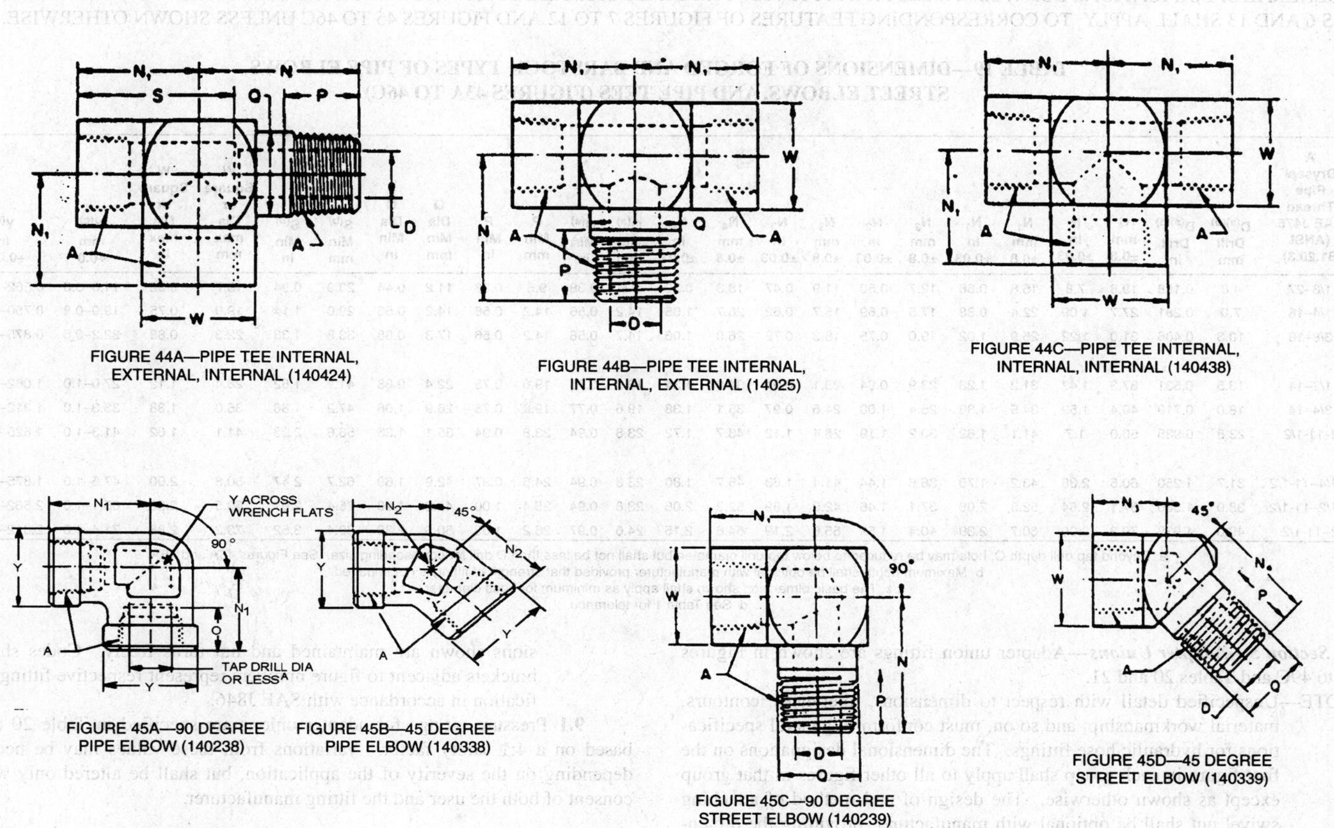

FIGURE 44A—PIPE TEE INTERNAL, EXTERNAL, INTERNAL (140424)

FIGURE 44B—PIPE TEE INTERNAL, INTERNAL, EXTERNAL (14025)

FIGURE 44C—PIPE TEE INTERNAL, INTERNAL, INTERNAL (140438)

FIGURE 45A—90 DEGREE PIPE ELBOW (140238)

FIGURE 45B—45 DEGREE PIPE ELBOW (140338)

FIGURE 45C—90 DEGREE STREET ELBOW (140239)

FIGURE 45D—45 DEGREE STREET ELBOW (140339)

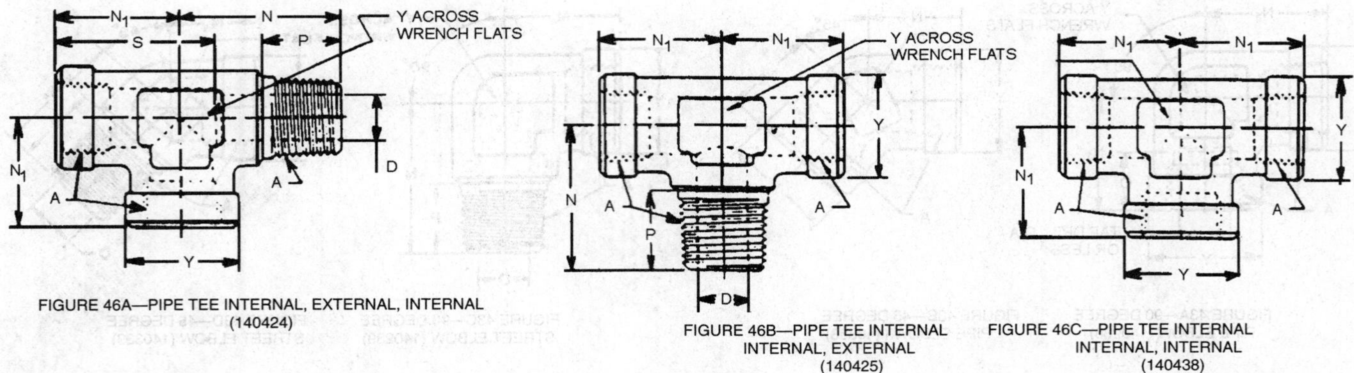

FIGURE 46A—PIPE TEE INTERNAL, EXTERNAL, INTERNAL (140424)

FIGURE 46B—PIPE TEE INTERNAL INTERNAL, EXTERNAL (140425)

FIGURE 46C—PIPE TEE INTERNAL INTERNAL, INTERNAL (140438)

NOTES—UNSPECIFIED DETAIL WITH RESPECT TO DIMENSIONS, TOLERANCES, CONTOURS, MATERIAL, AND WORKMANSHIP MUST CONFORM TO GENERAL SPECIFICATIONS FOR HYDRAULIC PIPE FITTINGS. THE DIMENSIONAL DESIGNATIONS FOR TAP DRILL AND NOTES SHOWN ON FIGURES 6 AND 13 SHALL APPLY TO CORRESPONDING FEATURES OF FIGURES 7 TO 12 AND FIGURES 45 TO 46C UNLESS SHOWN OTHERWISE.

TABLE 19—DIMENSIONS OF FORGED AND BARSTOCK TYPES OF PIPE ELBOWS, STREET ELBOWS, AND PIPE TEES (FIGURES 43A TO 46C)

A Dryseal Pipe Thread SAE J476 (ANSI B1.20.3)	D(a)(d) Drill mm	D(a)(d) Drill in	N mm ±0.8	N in ±0.03	N_1 mm ±0.8	N_1 in ±0.03	N_2 mm ±0.8	N_2 in ±0.03	N_3 mm ±0.8	N_3 in ±0.03	N_4 mm ±0.8	N_4 in ±0.03	O(a) Min mm	O(a) Min in	P Min mm	P Min in	Q Dia Min mm	Q Dia Min in	S(b) Min mm	S(b) Min in	W Square or Dia max mm	W Square or Dia max in	Y(c) mm +0.0	Y(c) in +0.000
1/8–27	4.8	0.188	19.8	7.8	16.8	0.66	12.7	0.50	11.9	0.47	18.3	0.72	9.6	0.38	9.6	0.38	11.2	0.44	23.9	0.94	15.7	0.62	14.3–0.8	0.562–0.030
1/4–18	7.0	0.281	27.7	1.09	22.4	0.88	17.5	0.69	15.7	0.62	26.7	1.05	14.2	0.56	14.2	0.56	14.2	0.56	29.0	1.14	19.0	0.75	19.0–0.8	0.750–0.030
3/8–18	10.3	0.406	31.0	1.22	25.9	1.02	19.0	0.75	18.3	0.72	26.9	1.06	14.7	0.58	14.2	0.56	17.3	0.68	33.8	1.33	22.3	0.88	22.2–0.8	0.875–0.030
1/2–14	13.5	0.531	37.3	1.47	31.2	1.23	23.9	0.94	23.1	0.91	34.0	1.34	19.0	0.75	19.0	0.75	22.4	0.88	41.1	1.62	28.4	1.12	27.0–1.0	1.062–0.040
3/4–14	18.0	0.719	40.4	1.59	34.5	1.36	25.4	1.00	24.6	0.97	35.1	1.38	19.6	0.77	19.0	0.75	26.9	1.06	47.2	1.86	35.0	1.38	33.3–1.0	1.312–0.040
1-11-1/2	23.8	0.938	50.0	1.7	41.1	1.62	30.2	1.19	28.4	1.12	43.7	1.72	23.8	0.94	23.8	0.94	35.1	1.38	56.6	2.23	41.1	1.62	41.3–1.0	1.625–0.040
1-1/4–11-1/2	31.7	1.250	60.5	2.38	43.2	1.70	36.6	1.44	41.4	1.63	45.7	1.80	23.8	0.94	24.6	0.97	42.9	1.69	62.7	2.47	50.8	2.00	47.6–1.0	1.875–0.040
1-1/2–11-1/2	38.0	1.500	67.1	2.64	52.8	2.08	37.1	1.46	42.9	1.69	52.3	2.06	23.8	0.94	25.4	1.00	48.3	1.90	75.4	2.97	60.5	2.38	65.1–1.0	2.562–0.040
2–11-1/2	49.0	1.938	76.2	3.00	60.7	2.39	40.4	1.59	55.6	2.19	54.6	2.15	24.6	0.97	26.2	1.03	60.5	2.38	89.4	3.52	73.2	2.88	71.4–1.0	2.812–0.040

a Beyond tap drill depth O, hole may be reduced to below tap drill diameter, but shall not be less than D drill for corresonding size. See Figures 43A and 45A.
b Maximum depth shall be optional with manufacturer provided that strength of fitting is not impaired.
c The basic dimension shown shall apply as minimum for boss diameter.
d See Table 1 for tolerance.

9. Section 5—Adapter Unions—Adapter union fittings are shown in Figures 47A to 49C and Tables 20 and 21.

NOTE—Unspecified detail with respect to dimensions, tolerances, contours, material workmanship, and so on, must conform to general specifications for hydraulic hose fittings. The dimensional designations on the first figure in each group shall apply to all other figures in that group except as shown otherwise. The design of and method of attaching swivel nut shall be optional with manufacturer, providing the dimensions shown are maintained and nut turns freely. Codes shown in brackets adjacent to figure numbers represent respective fitting identification in accordance with SAE J846.

9.1 Pressure ratings for adapter unions are specified in Table 20 and are based on a 4:1 safety factor. Variations from these values may be necessary, depending on the severity of the application, but shall be altered only with the consent of both the user and the fitting manufacturer.

TABLE 20—PRESSURE RATINGS OF ADAPTER UNIONS

A_1 Straight Pipe Thread (NPSM) d	Max Operating Pressure[(a)] MPa	Max Operating Pressure[(a)] psi
–2	34.5	5000
–4	34.5	5000
–6	27.6	4000
–8	24.1	3500
–12	15.5	2250
–16	13.8	2000
–20	11.2	1625
–24	8.6	1250
–32	7.8	1125

(a) Pressure ratings shown are the pressure ratings for the fitting and are not necessarily the pressure ratings applicable in an assembly with hydraulic hose. The applicable pressure rating for an assembly with hydraulic hose is the lower value specified for the hose and the fitting unless otherwise agreed to by the supplier and user.

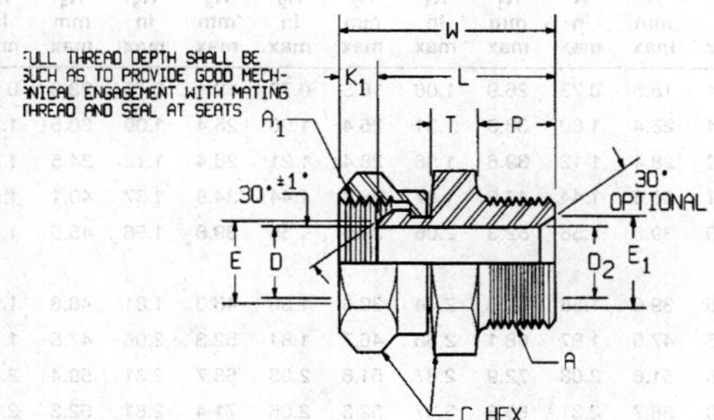

FIGURE 47A—FEMALE ADAPTER UNION TO MALE PIPE (140130)

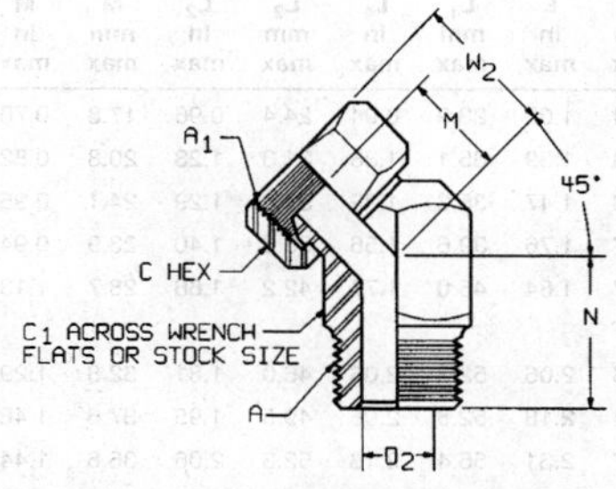

FIGURE 47B—45° FEMALE ADAPTER UNION TO MALE PIPE (140330)

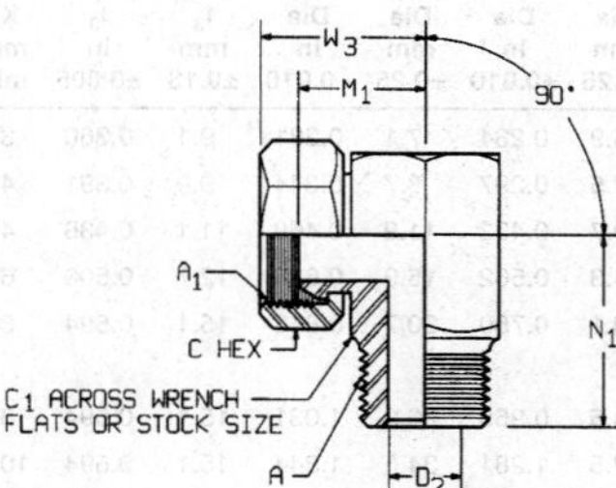

FIGURE 47C—90° FEMALE ADAPTER UNION TO MALE PIPE (140230)

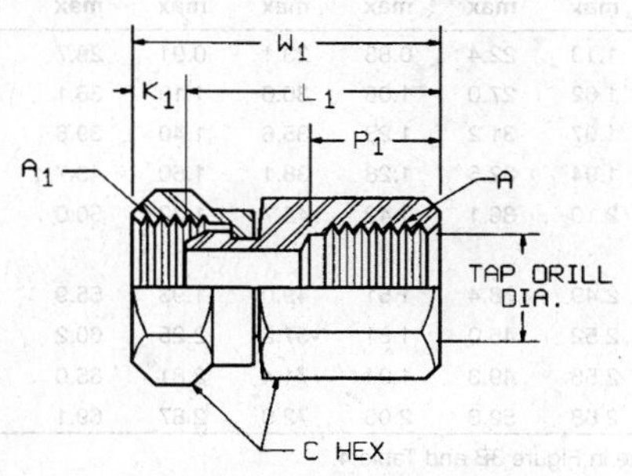

FIGURE 48A—FEMALE ADAPTER UNION TO FEMALE PIPE (140131)

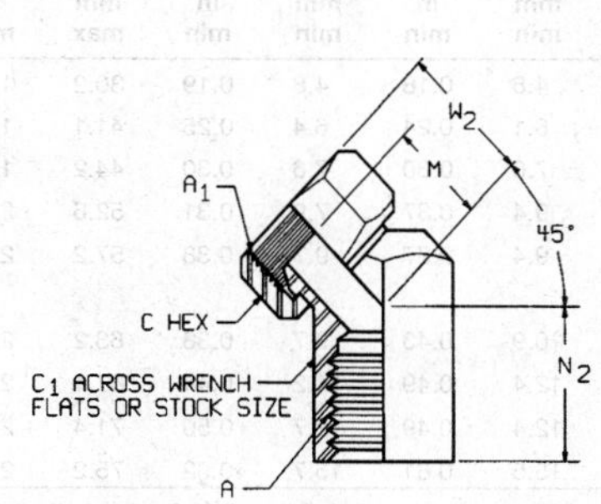

FIGURE 48B—45° FEMALE ADAPTER UNION TO FEMALE PIPE (140331)

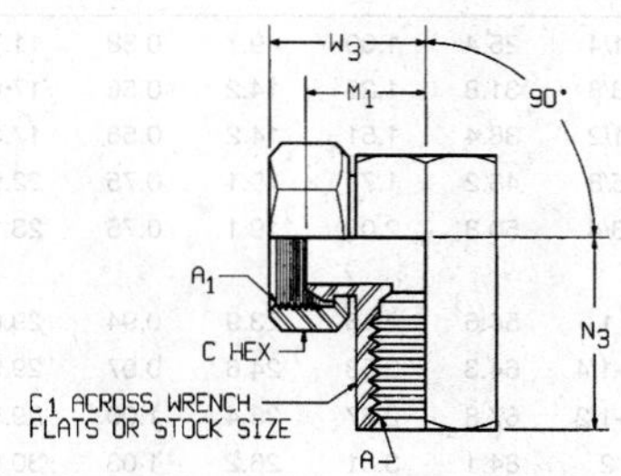

FIGURE 48—90° FEMALE ADAPTER UNION TO FEMALE PIPE (140231)

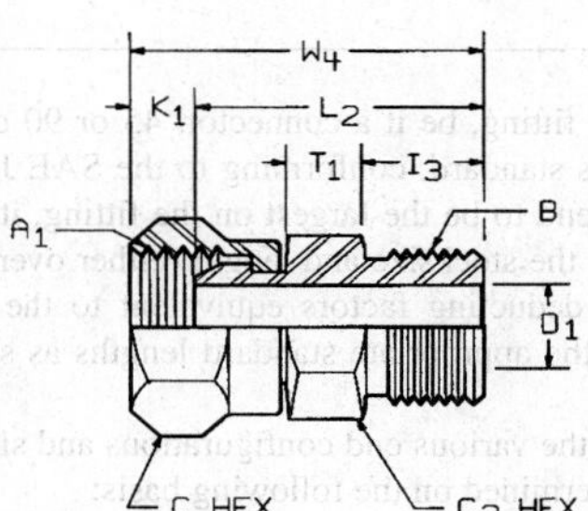

FIGURE 49A—FEMALE ADAPTER UNION TO MALE STRAIGHT THREAD (140157)

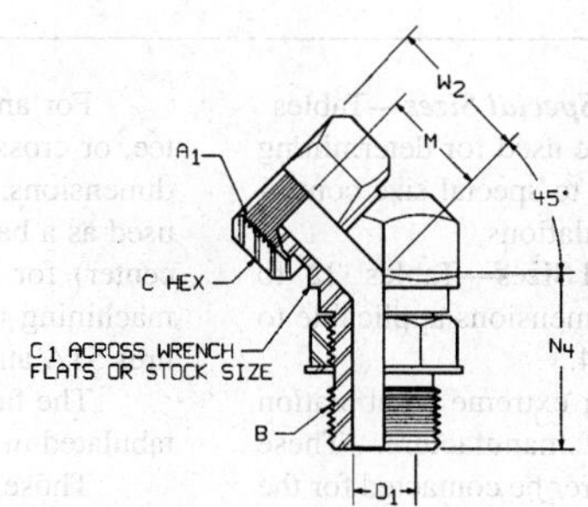

FIGURE 49B—45° FEMALE ADAPTER UNION TO ADJ. MALE STRAIGHT THREAD (140357)

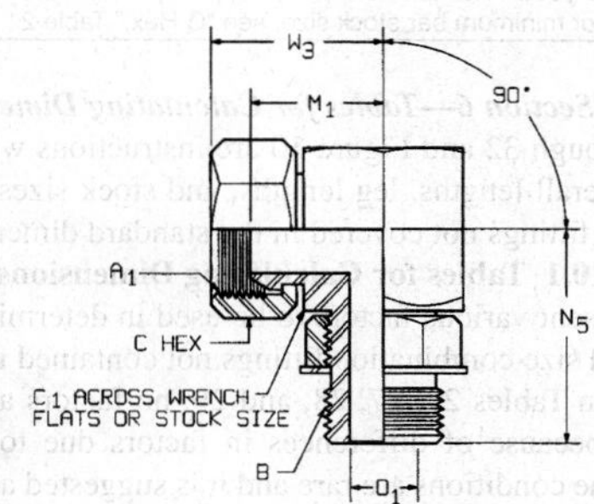

FIGURE 49C—90° FEMALE ADAPTER UNION TO ADJ. MALE STRAIGHT THREAD (140257)

TABLE 21—DIMENSIONS OF ADAPTER UNIONS (FIGURES 47A TO 49C)

Nominal Tube Size	Pipe Thread Dash Size	A Dryseal Pipe Thread (NPTF) (SAE J476[e]) (ANSI B1.20.3)	A_1 Straight Pipe Thread NPSM[d]	B Thread Size, In (ISO R725) SAE J475 Class 2A, Int Class 2B, Ext	C Hex Nom	C_1 Forging mm	C_1 Forging in	C_1 Bar Stock mm max	C_1[f] Bar Stock in max	C_2 Hex Nom	D Dia min mm	D Dia min in	D Dia max mm	D Dia max in	D_1 Min Dia mm	D_1 Min Dia in	D_2 Min Dia mm	D_2 Min Dia in
1/4	–2	1/8-27	1/8-27	7/16-20	9/16	11.1	0.44	14.3	0.56	9/16	2.8	0.11	4.8	0.19	2.8	0.11	3.3	0.13
3/8	–4	1/4-18	1/4-18	9/16-18	11/16	12.7	0.50	20.6	0.81	11/16	5.3	0.21	5.8	0.23	5.3	0.21	5.6	0.22
1/2	–6	3/8-18	3/8-18	3/4-16	7/8	19.1	0.75	22.4	0.88	7/8	8.1	0.32	9.1	0.36	8.4	0.33	8.4	0.33
5/8	–8	1/2-14	1/2-14	7/8-14	1	22.4	0.88	28.7	1.13	1	11.2	0.44	12.2	0.48	11.4	0.45	11.9	0.47
3/4	–12	3/4-14	3/4-14	1-1/16-12	1-1/4	33.3	1.31	35.1	1.38	1-1/4	15.5	0.61	16.8	0.66	15.2	0.60	16.5	0.65
1	–16	1-11-1/2	1-11-1/2	1-5/16-12	1-1/2	33.3	1.31	41.4	1.63	1-1/2	19.8	0.78	22.4	0.88	21.1	0.83	21.1	0.83
1-1/4	–20	1-1/4-11-1/2	1-1/4-11-1/2	1 -5/8-12	1-7/8	41.4	1.63	54.1	2.13	1-7/8	25.7	1.01	29.5	1.16	27.2	1.07	28.4	1.12
1-1/2	–24	1-1/2-11-1/2	1-1/2-11-1/2	1- 7/8-12	2-1/8	47.8	1.88	57.2	2.25	2-1/8	31.8	1.25	35.0	1.38	33.0	1.30	34.5	1.36
2	–32	2-11-1/2	2-11-1/2	2- 1/2-12	2-5/8	63.5	2.50	82.3	3.25	2-3/4	43.7	1.72	47.7	1.88	45.0	1.77	45.5	1.79

Nominal Tube Size	E Dia mm ±0.25	E Dia in ±0.010	E_1 Dia mm ±0.25	E_1 Dia in ±0.010	I_3 mm ±0.13	I_3 in ±0.005	K_1 mm min	K_1 in min	L mm max	L in max	L_1 mm max	L_1 in max	L_2 mm max	L_2 in max	M mm max	M in max	M_1 mm max	M_1 in max	N mm max	N in max	N_1 mm max	N_1 in max	N_2 mm max	N_2 in max	N_3 mm max	N_3 in max	N_4 mm max	N_4 in max
1/4	5.9	0.234	7.1	0.281	9.1	0.360	3.0	0.12	25.4	1.00	23.9	0.94	24.4	0.96	17.8	0.70	18.8	0.74	18.5	0.73	26.9	1.06	18.5	0.73	19.1	0.75	23.9	0.94
3/8	7.5	0.297	8.7	0.344	9.9	0.391	4.3	0.17	35.3	1.39	35.1	1.38	31.3	1.23	20.8	0.82	23.9	0.94	25.4	1.00	33.3	1.31	25.4	1.00	25.4	1.00	30.5	1.20
1/2	10.7	0.422	11.9	0.469	11.1	0.438	4.8	0.19	37.3	1.47	35.3	1.39	32.8	1.29	24.1	0.95	28.4	1.12	28.4	1.12	39.6	1.56	28.4	1.21	28.4	1.12	34.5	1.36
5/8	14.3	0.562	15.9	0.625	12.7	0.500	6.6	0.26	44.7	1.76	39.6	1.56	35.6	1.40	23.9	0.94	28.2	1.11	36.6	1.44	47.5	1.87	36.6	1.44	34.8	1.37	40.1	1.58
3/4	19.1	0.750	20.7	0.813	15.1	0.594	8.4	0.33	46.7	1.84	45.0	1.77	42.2	1.66	28.7	1.13	35.3	1.39	39.6	1.56	52.3	2.06	39.6	1.56	39.6	1.56	45.5	1.79
1	24.6	0.969	26.2	1.031	15.1	0.594	8.4	0.33	52.3	2.06	52.3	2.06	46.0	1.81	32.8	1.29	39.6	1.56	39.6	1.56	62.0	2.44	39.6	1.56	46.0	1.81	48.8	1.92
1-1/4	32.5	1.281	34.1	1.344	15.1	0.594	10.2	0.40	55.4	2.18	52.3	2.06	49.5	1.95	37.6	1.48	47.0	1.85	47.5	1.87	68.1	2.68	46.7	1.84	52.3	2.06	47.5	1.87
1-1/2	38.1	1.500	41.3	1.625	15.1	0.594	10.2	0.40	58.7	2.31	55.4	2.18	52.3	2.06	36.6	1.44	52.1	2.05	51.6	2.03	72.9	2.87	51.6	2.03	58.7	2.31	59.4	2.34
2	50.8	2.000	52.4	2.063	15.1	0.594	10.2	0.40	62.5	2.46	68.1	2.68	56.4	2.22	39.6	1.56	61.0	2.40	58.7	2.31	85.6	3.37	52.3	2.06	71.4	2.81	52.3	2.06

Nominal Tube Size	N_5 mm max	N_5 in max	P mm min	P in min	P_1 mm max	P_1 in max	T[c] mm min	T[c] in min	T_1[c] mm min	T_1[c] in min	W mm max	W in max	W_1 mm max	W_1 in max	W_2 mm max	W_2 in max	W_3 mm max	W_3 in max	W_4 mm max	W_4 in max
1/4	25.4	1.00	9.7	0.38	11.7	0.46	4.6	0.18	4.8	0.19	30.2	1.19	28.7	1.13	22.4	0.88	23.1	0.91	28.7	1.13
3/8	31.8	1.25	14.2	0.56	17.0	0.67	6.1	0.24	6.4	0.25	41.1	1.62	41.1	1.62	27.0	1.06	30.0	1.18	36.1	1.42
1/2	38.4	1.51	14.2	0.56	17.3	0.68	7.6	0.30	7.6	0.30	44.2	1.74	42.4	1.67	31.2	1.23	35.6	1.40	39.6	1.56
5/8	43.2	1.70	19.1	0.75	22.9	0.90	9.4	0.37	7.9	0.31	52.6	2.07	49.3	1.94	32.5	1.28	38.1	1.50	43.7	1.72
3/4	50.8	2.00	19.1	0.75	23.1	0.91	9.4	0.37	9.7	0.38	57.2	2.25	53.3	2.10	36.1	1.42	43.7	1.72	50.0	1.97
1	54.6	2.15	23.9	0.94	29.0	1.14	10.9	0.43	9.7	0.38	63.2	2.49	63.2	2.49	38.4	1.51	49.0	1.93	55.9	2.20
1-1/4	64.3	2.53	24.6	0.97	29.5	1.16	12.4	0.49	11.2	0.44	67.1	2.64	64.0	2.52	46.0	1.81	57.2	2.25	60.2	2.37
1-1/2	67.8	2.67	25.4	1.00	29.5	1.16	12.4	0.49	12.7	0.50	71.4	2.81	65.0	2.56	49.3	1.94	71.4	2.81	65.0	2.56
2	84.1	3.31	26.2	1.03	30.0	1.18	15.5	0.61	15.7	0.62	75.2	2.96	68.1	2.68	52.3	2.06	72.9	2.87	69.1	2.72

(a) For dimensions shown in Figure 49A but not specified in Table 21, see corresponding dimensions for respective straight thread size in Figure 3B and Table 4. For dimensions of mating bosses, see Figure 1 and Table 1 of SAE J1926.
(b) For dimensions shown in Figure 49B and 49C, but not specified in Table 21, see corresponding dimensions for respective straight thread size in Figure 10A and Table 4.
(c) Minimum design thickness, not subject to inspection.
(d) American Standard Straight Pipe Thread for Mechanical Joints.
(e) Dryseal American Standard Taper Pipe Thread.
(f) For minimum bar stock size, see "C Hex," Table 21.

10. Section 6—Tables for Calculating Dimensions on Special Sizes—Tables 22 through 32 and Figure 50 are instructions which may be used for determining the overall lengths, leg lengths, and stock sizes applicable to special size combination fittings not covered in the standard dimensional tabulations.

10.1 Tables for Calculating Dimensions on Special Sizes—Tables 22 to 32 present various factors to be used in determining the dimensions applicable to special size combination fittings not contained in SAE J514.

In Tables 23, 27, 28, and 29, no factors are given for extreme combination sizes because of differences in factors due to method of manufacture. These extreme conditions are rare and it is suggested a manufacturer be contacted for the proper dimension.

No factors are given for bulkhead or swivel ends as combinations are not generally specified for these fittings.

Tables 30 to 32 present the minimum stock size acceptable for the various machine ends. Minimum stock sizes specified in Tables 31 and 32 do not apply to adapter unions, Figures 47A to 49C.

For any nonstandard size fitting, be it a connector, 45 or 90 degree elbow, tee, or cross, one end is always standard, conforming to the SAE J514 tables of dimensions. Considering this end to be the largest on the fitting, it may then be used as a basis for establishing the stocksize and length (either over-all or end to center) for all other parts by deducting factors equivalent to the reduction in machining requirements from the appropriate standard lengths as shown in Figures 51A and 51B.

The factors applicable to the various end configurations and size reductions tabulated in the tables were determined on the following basis:

Those pertaining to lengths were derived by maintaining the standard hexagon thickness for straight fittings and the standard centerline to machining start for shaped fittings.

The factors shown in Tables 22, 24, 26, 28, and 29 were derived by subtracting the standard machining length required for the smaller end from that required for the larger standard end and rounding the result to a two-place decimal.

The factors given in Tables 23, 25, and 27 were derived by subtracting the standard machining length plus an allowance of 1-1/2 pitches (threads) for imperfect thread length required for the smaller end from the same value required for the larger end and rounding the result to a two-place decimal.

The minimum allowable stock size for the various types of ends are also tabulated for reference purposes.

10.1.1 DRILL PASSAGES—At manufacturer's option, drill through passages in straight special size (jump) fittings may conform to the smaller diameter specified for up to two step size difference, or conform to one of the following for any size difference:

a. The appropriate end may be countersunk to the larger diameter, or

b. The appropriate end may be drilled to the larger diameter up to the middle of the hex.

10.2 Examples

10.2.1 For a 37 degree flared male connector (Figure 2A) with 1/2 tube OD and 3/4 NPTF, the overall length would be determined as follows:

2.06 = L overall length for 3/4 tube to 3/4 NPTF from Table 2
<u>-0.21</u> = Factor from Table 22 for 1/2 machining on 3/4 size fitting
1.85 = Overall length for the nonstandard male connector

Since the 3/4 NPTF is the larger machining, the hexagon width of 1-1/8 from Table 31 would apply.

TABLE 22—FACTORS FOR 37 DEGREE FLARED END ON STRAIGHT FITTINGS (FIGURES 2A TO 2D, 3A TO 3C, AND 15)

Reduced Maching Size — Nominal Tube OD	Standard Matching Size — 3/16 mm	3/16 in	1/4 mm	1/4 in	5/16 mm	5/16 in	3/8 mm	3/8 in	1/2 mm	1/2 in	5/8 mm	5/8 in	3/4 mm	3/4 in	7/8 mm	7/8 in	1 mm	1 in	1-1/4 mm	1-1/4 in	1-1/2 mm	1-1/2 in	2 mm	2 in	Nominal Tube OD
1/8	0.8	0.03	2.5	0.10	2.5	0.10	2.8	0.11	5.3	0.21	7.9	0.31	10.7	0.42	11.2	0.44	11.7	0.46	13.0	0.51	16.3	0.64	22.6	0.89	1/8
3/16	—	—	1.8	0.07	1.8	0.07	2.0	0.08	4.6	0.18	7.1	0.28	9.9	0.39	10.4	0.41	10.9	0.43	12.2	0.48	15.2	0.60	21.6	0.85	3/16
1/4	—	—	—	—	0.0	0.00	0.3	0.01	2.8	0.11	5.3	0.21	7.9	0.31	8.6	0.34	9.1	0.36	10.4	0.41	13.5	0.53	19.8	0.78	1/4
5/16	—	—	—	—	—	—	0.3	0.01	2.8	0.11	5.3	0.21	7.9	0.31	8.6	0.34	9.1	0.36	10.4	0.41	13.5	0.53	19.8	0.78	5/16
3/8	—	—	—	—	—	—	—	—	2.5	0.10	5.1	0.20	7.9	0.31	8.4	0.33	9.1	0.36	10.2	0.40	13.5	0.53	19.8	0.78	3/8
1/2	—	—	—	—	—	—	—	—	—	—	2.5	0.10	5.3	0.21	5.8	0.23	6.4	0.25	7.6	0.30	10.9	0.43	17.3	0.68	1/2
5/8	—	—	—	—	—	—	—	—	—	—	—	—	2.8	0.11	3.3	0.13	3.8	0.15	5.1	0.20	8.4	0.33	14.7	0.58	5/8
3/4	—	—	—	—	—	—	—	—	—	—	—	—	—	—	0.8	0.03	1.3	0.05	2.3	0.09	5.6	0.22	11.9	0.47	3/4
7/8	—	—	—	—	—	—	—	—	—	—	—	—	—	—	—	—	0.5	0.02	1.8	0.07	4.8	0.19	11.2	0.44	7/8
1	—	—	—	—	—	—	—	—	—	—	—	—	—	—	—	—	—	—	1.3	0.05	4.3	0.17	10.7	0.42	1
1-1/4	—	—	—	—	—	—	—	—	—	—	—	—	—	—	—	—	—	—	—	—	3.3	0.13	9.7	0.38	1-1/4
1-1/2	—	—	—	—	—	—	—	—	—	—	—	—	—	—	—	—	—	—	—	—	—	—	6.4	0.25	1-1/2

10.2.2 For a 37 degree flared 90 degree male elbow (Figure 4A) with 1/2 OD tube and 3/4 NPTF, the end to center length M would be derived as follows:

1.66 = M dimension for standard 3/4 37 degree end
<u>-0.24</u> = Factor from Table 23 for 1/2 machining on 3/4 size fitting
1.42 = End to center length

Since the 3/4 NPTF is the standard end, the N end-to-center dimension would remain 1.59 as shown in Table 4. The wrench flat size would be as shown by the Y column in Table 4 for the 3/4 tube OD.

10.3 Tolerances—The following tolerances apply to nonstandard sizes:

Overall length of straight fittings = ±0.5 mm (±0.02 in)
Centerline to end on shaped fittings = ±1.5 mm (±0.06 in)

TABLE 23—FACTORS FOR 37 DEGREE FLARED END ON SHAPE FITTINGS (FIGURES 4A TO 4E, 5A TO 5D, 6A TO 6C, 7A TO 7D, 8C, 9A TO 9D, AND 10A TO 10C)

Reduced Maching Size — Nominal Tube OD	Standard Matching Size — 3/16 mm	3/16 in	1/4 mm	1/4 in	5/16 mm	5/16 in	3/8 mm	3/8 in	1/2 mm	1/2 in	5/8 mm	5/8 in	3/4 mm	3/4 in	7/8 mm	7/8 in	1 mm	1 in	1-1/4 mm	1-1/4 in	1-1/2 mm	1-1/2 in	2 mm	2 in	Nominal Tube OD
1/8	0.8	0.03	2.8	0.11	2.8	0.11	3.3	0.13	—	—	—	—	—	—	—	—	—	—	—	—	—	—	—	—	1/8
3/16	—	—	2.0	0.08	2.0	0.08	2.5	0.10	5.3	0.21	—	—	—	—	—	—	—	—	—	—	—	—	—	—	3/16
1/4	—	—	—	—	0.0	0.00	0.3	0.01	3.3	0.13	6.1	0.24	—	—	—	—	—	—	—	—	—	—	—	—	1/4
5/16	—	—	—	—	—	—	0.3	0.01	3.3	0.13	6.1	0.24	9.1	0.36	—	—	—	—	—	—	—	—	—	—	5/16
3/8	—	—	—	—	—	—	—	—	2.8	0.11	5.8	0.23	8.9	0.35	9.7	0.38	—	—	—	—	—	—	—	—	3/8
1/2	—	—	—	—	—	—	—	—	—	—	3.0	0.12	6.1	0.24	6.9	0.27	7.4	0.29	—	—	—	—	—	—	1/2
5/8	—	—	—	—	—	—	—	—	—	—	—	—	3.0	0.12	3.8	0.15	4.3	0.17	5.6	0.22	—	—	—	—	5/8
3/4	—	—	—	—	—	—	—	—	—	—	—	—	—	—	0.8	0.03	1.3	0.05	2.3	0.09	5.5	0.22	—	—	3/4
7/8	—	—	—	—	—	—	—	—	—	—	—	—	—	—	—	—	0.5	0.02	1.8	0.07	4.8	0.19	11.2	0.44	7/8
1	—	—	—	—	—	—	—	—	—	—	—	—	—	—	—	—	—	—	1.3	0.05	4.3	0.17	10.7	0.42	1
1-1/4	—	—	—	—	—	—	—	—	—	—	—	—	—	—	—	—	—	—	—	—	3.3	0.13	9.7	0.38	1-1/4
1-1/2	—	—	—	—	—	—	—	—	—	—	—	—	—	—	—	—	—	—	—	—	—	—	6.4	0.25	1-1/2

TABLE 24—FACTORS FOR FLARELESS STRAIGHT FITTINGS (FIGURES 19A TO 19D, 20A TO 20C, AND 30)

		Standard Machining Size													
	Nominal Tube OD	3/16 mm	3/16 in	1/4 mm	1/4 in	5/16 mm	5/16 in	3/8 mm	3/8 in	1/2 mm	1/2 in	5/8 mm	5/8 in	3/4 thru 2 mm	3/4 thru 2 in
Reduced Maching Size	1/8	1.3	0.05	2.0	0.08	2.0	0.08	2.5	0.10	4.8	0.19	6.4	0.25	7.9	0.31
	3/16	—	—	0.8	0.03	0.8	0.03	1.3	0.05	3.6	0.14	5.1	0.20	6.6	0.26
	1/4	—	—	—	—	0.0	0.00	0.5	0.02	2.8	0.11	4.3	0.17	5.8	0.23
	5/16	—	—	—	—	—	—	0.5	0.02	2.8	0.11	4.3	0.17	5.8	0.23
	3/8	—	—	—	—	—	—	—	—	2.3	0.09	3.8	0.15	5.3	0.21
	1/2	—	—	—	—	—	—	—	—	—	—	1.5	0.06	3.0	0.12
	5/8	—	—	—	—	—	—	—	—	—	—	—	—	1.5	0.06
	3/4 to 1-1/2	—	—	—	—	—	—	—	—	—	—	—	—	0.0	0.00

TABLE 25—FACTORS FOR FLARELESS SHAPE FITTINGS (FIGURES 21A TO 21E, 22A TO 22D, 23A TO 23C, 24A TO 24D, 25C, 26A TO 26D, AND 27A TO 27C)

		Standard Machining Size													
	Nominal Tube OD	3/16 mm	3/16 in	1/4 mm	1/4 in	5/16 mm	5/16 in	3/8 mm	3/8 in	1/2 mm	1/2 in	5/8 mm	5/8 in	3/4 thru 2 mm	3/4 thru 2 in
Reduced Maching Size	1/8	1.3	0.05	2.5	0.10	2.5	0.10	3.0	0.12	5.8	0.23	7.6	0.30	9.7	0.38
	3/16	—	—	1.3	0.05	1.3	0.05	1.8	0.07	4.6	0.18	6.4	0.25	8.4	0.33
	1/4	—	—	—	—	0.0	0.00	0.5	0.02	3.3	0.13	5.1	0.20	7.1	0.28
	5/16	—	—	—	—	—	—	0.5	0.02	3.3	0.13	5.1	0.20	7.1	0.28
	3/8	—	—	—	—	—	—	—	—	2.8	0.11	4.6	0.18	6.6	0.26
	1/2	—	—	—	—	—	—	—	—	—	—	1.8	0.07	3.8	0.15
	5/8	—	—	—	—	—	—	—	—	—	—	—	—	2.0	0.08
	3/4 to 1-1/2	—	—	—	—	—	—	—	—	—	—	—	—	0.0	0.00

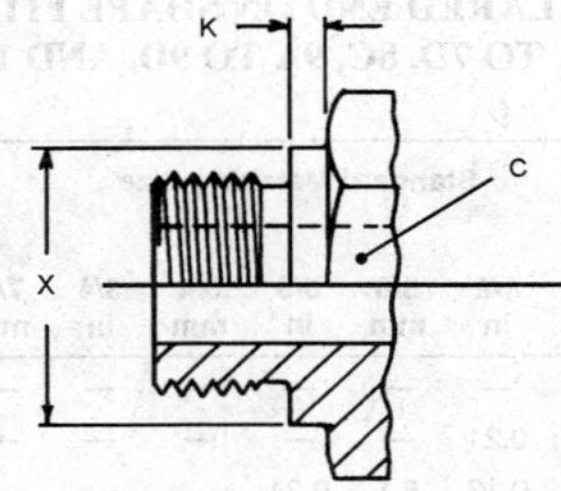

FIGURE 50—SMALLER NONADJUSTABLE STRAIGHT THREAD END

TABLE 26—FACTORS FOR NONADJUSTABLE STRAIGHT THREAD ENDS (FIGURES 3B, 3C, 20B, 20C)

Standard Matching Size

Reduced Maching Size: Nominal Tube OD	3/16 mm	3/16 in	1/4 mm	1/4 in	5/16 mm	5/16 in	3/8 mm	3/8 in	1/2 mm	1/2 in	5/8 mm	5/8 in	3/4 mm	3/4 in	7/8 mm	7/8 in	1 mm	1 in	1-1/4 mm	1-1/4 in	1-1/2 mm	1-1/2 in
1/8	0.0	0.00	−1.5	−0.06	+0.8	+0.03	0.0	0.00	−1.3	−0.05	−2.8	−0.11	−5.3	−0.21	−5.3	−0.21	−5.3	−0.21	−5.3	−0.21	−5.3	−0.21
3/16	—	—	−1.5	−0.06	−1.5	−0.06	0.0	0.00	−1.3	−0.05	−2.8	−0.11	−5.3	−0.21	−5.3	−0.21	−5.3	−0.21	−5.3	−0.21	−5.3	−0.21
1/4	—	—	—	—	0.0	0.00	−0.8	−0.03	+0.3	+0.01	−1.3	−0.05	−3.6	−0.14	−3.6	−0.14	−3.6	−0.14	−3.6	-0.14	−3.6	−0.14
5/16	—	—	—	—	—	—	−0.8	−0.03	+0.3	+0.01	−1.3	−0.05	−3.6	−0.14	−3.6	−0.14	−3.6	−0.14	−3.6	-0.14	−3.6	−0.14
3/8	—	—	—	—	—	—	—	—	−1.0	−0.04	+0.3	+0.01	−2.8	−0.11	−2.8	−0.11	−2.8	−0.11	−2.8	−0.11	−2.8	−0.11
1/2	—	—	—	—	—	—	—	—	—	—	−1.5	−0.06	−0.8	−0.03	−0.8	−0.03	−0.8	−0.03	−0.8	−0.03	−0.8	−0.03
5/8	—	—	—	—	—	—	—	—	—	—	—	—	−2.3	−0.09	+0.8	+0.03	+0.8	+0.03	+0.8	+0.03	+0.8	+0.03
3/4	—	—	—	—	—	—	—	—	—	—	—	—	—	—	0.0	0.00	0.0	0.00	+3.3	+0.13	+3.3	+0.13
7/8	—	—	—	—	—	—	—	—	—	—	—	—	—	—	—	—	0.0	0.00	+3.3	+0.13	+3.3	+0.13
1	—	—	—	—	—	—	—	—	—	—	—	—	—	—	—	—	—	—	+4.1	+0.16	+4.1	+0.16
1-1/4	—	—	—	—	—	—	—	—	—	—	—	—	—	—	—	—	—	—	—	—	+4.1	+0.16
1-1/2	—	—	—	—	—	—	—	—	—	—	—	—	—	—	—	—	—	—	—	—	—	—

[(a)] Fittings involving hex sizes larger than "C" shall include a turned shoulder of diameter "X" and thickness "K" as shown in Figure 50. This turned shoulder permits the reduced straight thread end to seat in a standard port spotface.
For some combinations, additional length will be required to accommodate this feature. Therefore, all factors designated as plus in above table should be added to standard length dimensions to obtain applicable values.

Reduced Maching Size: Nominal Tube OD	2 mm	2 in	Nominal Tube OD	X Dia mm ±0.3	X Dia in ±0.01	K mm ±0.5	K in ±0.02	C[(a)] Hex mm	C[(a)] Hex in
1/8	−5.3	−0.21	1/8	12.7	0.50	2.3	0.09	14.27	9/16
3/16	−5.3	−0.21	3/16	14.2	0.56	2.3	0.09	15.88	5/8
1/4	−3.6	−0.14	1/4	16.0	0.63	2.3	0.09	17.48	11/16
5/16	−3.6	−0.14	5/16	17.5	0.69	2.3	0.09	19.05	3/4
3/8	−2.8	−0.11	3/8	19.0	0.75	2.3	0.09	20.64	13/16
1/2	−0.8	−0.03	1/2	23.9	0.94	3.3	0.13	25.40	1
5/8	+0.8	+0.03	5/8	26.9	1.06	3.3	0.13	28.58	1-1/8
3/4	+3.3	+0.13	3/4	33.3	1.31	3.3	0.13	31.92	1-3/8
7/8	+3.3	+0.13	7/8	36.6	1.44	3.3	0.13	38.10	1-1/2
1	+4.1	+0.16	1	39.6	1.56	4.1	0.16	41.28	1-5/8
1-1/4	+4.1	+0.16	1-1/4	47.7	1.88	4.1	0.16	49.22	1-15/16
1-1/2	+4.1	+0.16	1-1/2	54.1	2.13	4.1	0.16	55.58	2-3/16

TABLE 27—FACTORS FOR ADJUSTABLE STRAIGHT THREAD ENDS (FIGURES 9D, 10A TO 10C, 26D, AND 27A TO 27C)

Standard Machining Size

Reduced Maching Size: Nominal Tube OD	3/16 mm	3/16 in	1/4 mm	1/4 in	5/16 mm	5/16 in	3/8 mm	3/8 in	1/2 mm	1/2 in	5/8 mm	5/8 in	3/4 thru 2 mm	3/4 thru 2 in
3/16	—	—	2.8	0.11	2.8	0.11	4.3	0.17	7.6	0.30	—	—	—	—
1/4	—	—	—	—	0.0	0.00	1.5	0.06	4.8	0.19	8.9	0.35	—	—
5/16	—	—	—	—	—	—	1.5	0.06	4.8	0.19	8.9	0.35	—	—
3/8	—	—	—	—	—	—	—	—	3.3	0.13	7.4	0.29	11.4	0.45
1/2	—	—	—	—	—	—	—	—	—	—	4.1	0.16	8.1	0.32
5/8	—	—	—	—	—	—	—	—	—	—	—	—	4.1	0.16
3/4 to 1-1/2	—	—	—	—	—	—	—	—	—	—	—	—	0.0	0.00

TABLE 28—FACTORS FOR ALL MALE PIPE ENDS (FIGURES 2A, 4A TO 4C, 4E, 5C, 5D, 19A, 21A TO 21C, 21E, 22C AND 22D)

	Standard Pipe Size																
	Nominal Pipe Size	1/4 mm	1/4 in	3/8 mm	3/8 in	1/2 mm	1/2 in	3/4 mm	3/4 in	1 mm	1 in	1-1/4 mm	1-1/4 in	1-1/2 mm	1-1/2 in	2 mm	2 in
Reduced Pipe Size	1/8	4.8	0.19	4.8	0.19	9.7	0.38	9.7	0.38	—	—	—	—	—	—	—	—
	1/4	—	—	0.0	0.00	4.8	0.19	4.8	0.19	9.7	0.38	—	—	—	—	—	—
	3/8	—	—	—	—	4.8	0.19	4.8	0.19	9.7	0.38	10.4	0.41	—	—	—	—
	1/2	—	—	—	—	—	—	0.0	0.00	4.8	0.19	5.6	0.22	6.4	0.25	—	—
	3/4	—	—	—	—	—	—	—	—	4.8	0.19	5.6	0.22	6.4	0.25	7.1	0.28
	1	—	—	—	—	—	—	—	—	—	—	0.8	0.03	1.5	0.06	2.3	0.09
	1-1/4	—	—	—	—	—	—	—	—	—	—	—	—	0.8	0.03	1.5	0.06
	1-1/2	—	—	—	—	—	—	—	—	—	—	—	—	—	—	0.8	0.03

TABLE 29—FACTORS FOR ALL FEMALE PIPE ENDS (FIGURES 2D, 5A, 6A, 6B, 19D, 22A, 23A, AND 23B)

	Standard Pipe Size																
	Nominal Pipe Size	1/4 mm	1/4 in	3/8 mm	3/8 in	1/2 mm	1/2 in	3/4 mm	3/4 in	1 mm	1 in	1-1/4 mm	1-1/4 in	1-1/2 mm	1-1/2 in	2 mm	2 in
Reduced Pipe Size	1/8	5.3	0.21	5.6	0.22	11.2	0.44	11.4	0.45	—	—	—	—	—	—	—	—
	1/4	—	—	0.3	0.01	5.8	0.23	6.1	0.24	11.9	0.47	—	—	—	—	—	—
	3/8	—	—	—	—	5.6	0.22	5.8	0.23	11.7	0.46	12.2	0.48	—	—	—	—
	1/2	—	—	—	—	—	—	0.3	0.01	6.1	0.24	6.6	0.26	6.6	0.26	—	—
	3/4	—	—	—	—	—	—	—	—	5.8	0.23	6.4	0.25	6.4	0.25	6.9	0.27
	1	—	—	—	—	—	—	—	—	—	—	0.5	0.02	0.5	0.02	1.0	0.04
	1-1/4	—	—	—	—	—	—	—	—	—	—	—	—	0.0	0.00	0.5	0.02
	1-1/2	—	—	—	—	—	—	—	—	—	—	—	—	—	—	0.5	0.02

TABLE 30—MINIMUM STOCK SIZE FOR TUBE ENDS

Nominal Tube OD	Hexagon Width Minimum	Width Over Forged Pads Minimum
1/8	3/8	0.31
3/16	7/16	0.38
1/4	1/2	0.44
5/16	9/16	0.50
3/8	5/8	0.56
1/2	13/16	0.75
5/8	15/16	0.88
3/4	1-1/8	1.06
7/8	1-1/4	1.19
1	1-3/8	1.31
1-1/4	1-11/16	1.62
1-1/2	2	1.88
2	2-5/8	2.50

TABLE 31—MINIMUM STOCK SIZE FOR FEMALE PIPE ENDS (EXCEPT ADAPTER UNIONS, FIGURES 48A TO 48C

Nominal Pipe Size	Hexagon Width Minimum	Width Over Forged Pads Minimum
1/8	9/16	0.56
1/4	3/4	0.75
3/8	7/8	0.88
1/2	1-1/8	1.06
3/4	1-3/8	1.31
1	1-5/8	1.62
1-1/4	2	1.88
1-1/2	2-3/8	2.50
2	2-7/8	2.81

TABLE 32—MINIMUM STOCK SIZE FOR MALE PIPE ENDS (EXCEPT ADAPTER UNIONS, FIGURES 47A TO 47C)

Nominal Pipe Size	Hexagon Width Minimum	Width Over Forged Pads Minimum
1/8	7/16	0.44
1/4	9/16	0.56
3/8	3/4	0.75
1/2	7/8	0.88
3/4	1-1/8	1.06
1	1-3/8	1.31
1-1/4	1-11/16	1.62
1-1/2	2	1.88
2	2-1/2	2.50

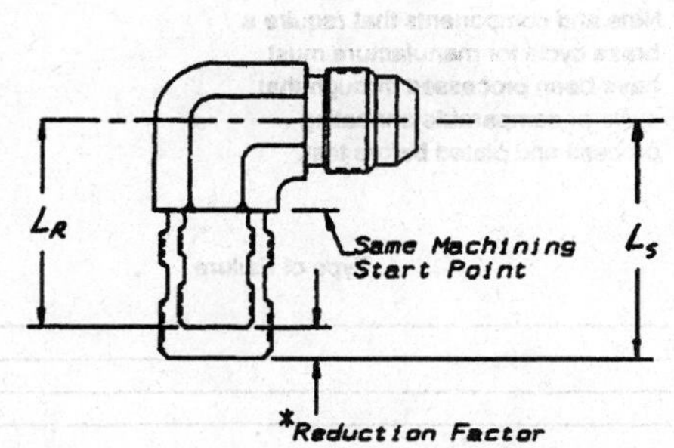

FIGURE 51A—JUMP SIZE CALCULATIONS—PORT SIZE

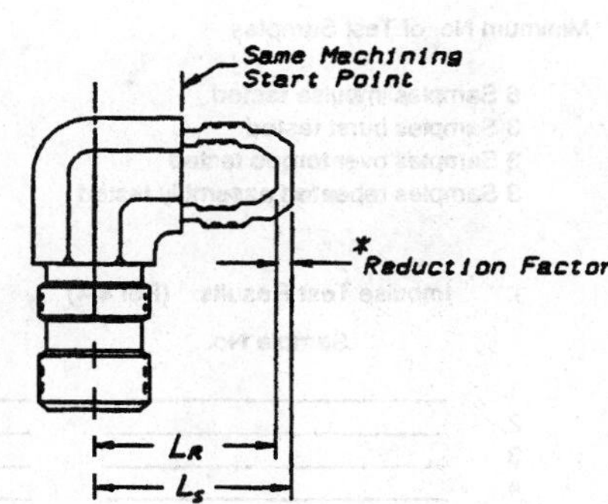

FIGURE 51B—JUMP SIZE CALCULATIONS—TUBE SIDE

APPENDIX A
OPTIONAL METRIC FITTING FLAT DIMENSIONS

By agreement between user and supplier, the metric flat sizes in Table B1, shall be used in lieu of inch sizes.

TABLE A1—OPTIONAL METRIC FITTING FLAT DIMENSIONS

Size	Y Forging	Y Barstock Max	Y_1 Forging
–3	12.00/–0.8		14.00/–0.8
–4	12.00/–0.8	14	14.00/–0.8
–5	14.00/–0.8	17	14.00/–0.8
–6	14.00/–0.8	22	19.00/–0.8
–8	19.00/–0.8	22	22.00/–0.8
–10	22.00/–0.8	32	27.00/–1.0
–12	27.00/–1.0	36	32.00/–1.0
–14	32.00/–1.0	41	32.00/–1.0
–16	32.00/–1.0	41	41.00/–1.0
–20	41.00/–1.0	55	50.00/–1.0
–24	50.00/–1.0	60	65.00/–1.0
–32	65.00/–1.0	80	70.00/–1.0

APPENDIX B
TEST DATA SHEET FOR HYDRAULIC TUBE FITTINGS

Manufacturer ____________ Part No. ____________ SAE Fitting Code ____________

Fitting Size ____________ Type f Construction (Per 3.9) ____________

Fitting Type ____________ Minimum Material Tensile Strength ____________ MPa (______ psi)

Working Pressure Rating (Per Table 1) ______ MPa (______ psi) Oil Temperature ______ °C (______ °F)

Test Pressure (= 133% W.P.) ______ MPa (______ psi) Impulse Cycle Rate (Per 4.4 ______ cpm)

Impulse Cycle Goal for Fitting 1 000 000 Cycles (Per 4.4)

Minimum Burst Pressure (= 4 x W.P. ______ MPa (______ psi) - Per 4.3 - See Table ____)

Proof Test all Samples (= 2 x W.P. ______ MPa (______ psi) - Per 4.2 - See Table ____)

Qualification Test Assembly Torque ______ Nm (______ lb-ft) - Per Table ____

Minimum No. of Test Samples

6 Samples impulse tested
3 Samples burst tested
3 Samples over torque tested
3 Samples repeated assembly tested

* Note: Nuts and components that require a braze cycle for manufacture must have been processed through that cycle or comparable annealing process and plated before test.

I. Impulse Test Results: (Per 4.4)

Sample No.	Cycles @ Failure	Type of Failure
1.		
2.		
3.		
4.		
5.		
6.		

II Burst Test Results: Per 4.3 - see Table ___)

Sample No.	*Nut Hardness	Pressure @ Failure	Type of Failure
1.	RB/RC	MPa (psi)	
2.	RB/RC	MPa (psi)	
3.	RB/RC	MPa (psi)	

III. Over Torque Test Results: (Per 4.7 - see Table ___)

Nut No.	*Nut Hardness	Pressure @ Failure	Type of Failure
1.	RB/RC	Nm (lb-ft)	
2.	RB/RC	Nm (lb-ft)	
3.	RB/RC	Nm (lb-ft)	

IV. Repeated Assembly Test Results: (Per 4.8)

Sample No.	Type of Failure
1.	
2.	

V. Conclusions: ____________

VI. Dimensions: List Any Exception ____________

NOTE: The above test should be conducted on each of the following types and sizes of fittings to ensure overall performance of all configurations: Figure 12 (070110), Figure 10A (070220), Figure 3B (070120), Figure 8C (070221), and Figure 14 (070115) for Section 1 and applicable figures for other sections.

HYDRAULIC HOSE FITTINGS—SAE J516 JAN2001 SAE Standard

Report of the SAE Construction and Industrial Machinery Technical Committee, Nometallic Materials Committee, and Tube, Pipe, Hose and Lubrication Fittings Committee approved January 1952. Thirteenth revision by the SAE Fluid Conductors and Connectors Technical Committee SC2—Hydraulic Hose and Hose Fittings February 1999. Revised by the SAE Fluid Conductors and Connectors Technical Committee SC2—Hydraulic Hose and Hose Fittings January 2001. Rationale statement available.

1. Scope—This SAE Standard provides general and dimensional specifications for the most common hose fittings used in conjunction with hydraulic hoses specified in SAE J517 and utilized in hydraulic systems on mobile and stationary equipment.

The general specifications contained in Sections 1 through 15 are applicable to all hydraulic hose fittings and supplement the detailed specifications for the 100R-series fittings contained in the later sections of this document.

This document shall be utilized as a procurement document only to the extent agreed upon by the manufacturer and user.

Refer to SAE J517 for specifications of hose and information on hose assemblies. SAE J1273 contains information on application factors affecting hose fittings, hose, and hose assemblies.

THE RATED WORKING PRESSURE OF A HOSE ASSEMBLY COMPRISING SAE J516 FITTINGS AND SAE J517 HOSE SHALL NOT EXCEED THE LOWER OF THE TWO WORKING PRESSURE RATED VALUES.

The following are hose fitting types contained in this document:

a. Male dryseal pipe thread type hose fittings shall be as shown in Figures 1A to 1C for the respective styles, and in Tables 1A to 1M for the applicable hoses and sizes.
b. Male straight thread O-ring boss type hose fittings shall be as shown in Figures 2A and 2B for the respective styles, and in Tables 2A to 2H for the applicable hoses and sizes.
c. Male 37-degree flared type hose fittings shall be as shown in Figures 3B to 3C for the respective styles, and in Tables 3A to 3L for the applicable hoses and sizes.
d. Female 37-degree flared type hose fittings shall be as shown in Figures 4A to 7B for the respective styles and shapes, and in Tables 4A to 4M for the applicable hoses and sizes.
e. Male 45-degree flared type hose fittings shall be as shown in Figures 8A and 8B for the respective styles, and in Tables 5A to 5E for the applicable hoses and sizes.
f. Female 45-degree flared type hose fittings shall be as shown in Figures 9A to 12B for the respective styles and shapes, and in Tables 6A to 6E for the applicable hoses and sizes.
g. Male flareless type hose fittings shall be as shown in Figures 13A and 13B for the respective styles, and in Tables 7A and 7B for the applicable hoses and sizes.
h. Female flareless type hose fittings shall be as shown in Figures 14A to 14C for the respective styles, and in Tables 8A and 8B for the applicable hoses and sizes.
i. 4-bolt split flange type hose fittings shall be as shown in Figures 15A to 21C for the respective styles and shapes, and in Tables 9A to 9I2 for the applicable hoses and sizes.
j. Female O-ring face seal hose fittings shall be as shown in Figures 22A to 25B for the respective styles, and Tables 10A to 10L for the applicable hoses and sizes.

It is recommended that where step sizes or additional types of fittings are required, they be designed to conform with the specifications of this document insofar as they may apply. The following general specifications shall supplement the dimensional data contained in the tables with respect to all unspecified detail.

2. References

2.1 Applicable Publications—The following publications form a part of the specification to the extent specified herein. Unless otherwise indicated, the latest revision of SAE publications shall apply.

2.1.1 SAE PUBLICATIONS—Available from SAE, 400 Commonwealth Drive, Warrendale, PA 15096-0001.

SAE J475—Screw Threads
SAE J476—Dryseal Pipe Threads
SAE J512—Automotive Tube Fittings
SAE J514—Hydraulic Tube Fittings
SAE J517—Hydraulic Hose
SAE J518—Hydraulic Flanged Tube, Pipe, and Hose Connections, 4-Bolt Split Flange Type
SAE J533—Flares for Tubing
SAE J846—Coding Systems for Identification of Fluid Conductors and Connectors
SAE J1273—Selection, Installation, and Maintenance of Hose and Hose Assemblies
SAE J1402—Automotive Air Brake Hose and Hose Assemblies
SAE J1453—Fitting—O-Ring Face Seal
SAE J1453-1—Specification for O-Ring Face Seal Fittings—Part 1: Tube Connection Details and Common Requirements for Performance and Tests
SAE J1926—Specification for Straight Thread O-Ring Boss Port

2.1.2 ANSI PUBLICATION—Available from ANSI, 11 West 42nd Street, New York, NY 10036-8002.

ANSI/ASME B1.20.1-1983—General Purpose Pipe Threads

2.1.3 ASTM PUBLICATION—Available from ASTM, 100 Barr Harbor Drive, West Conshohocken, PA 19428-2959.

ASTM B 117—Method of Salt Spray (Fog) Testing

2.1.4 FMVSS PUBLICATION—Available from the Superintendent of Documents, U. S. Government Printing Office, Mail Stop: SSOP, Washington, DC 20402-9320.

FMVSS 106

3. Size Designations—The hose fitting size is generally designated by the fractional inch nominal hose inside diameter together with the nominal pipe or straight thread size or nominal split flange size for the respective fitting types. However, these sizes may also be designated by their dash sizes as follows:

3.1 The hose dash size is equivalent to the number of sixteenth inch increments in the hose inside diameter, except in the case of SAE 100R5 and 100R14 hose where it is equivalent to the number of sixteenth inch increments in the outside diameter of tubing having approximately the same inside diameter as the hose.

3.2 The pipe thread dash size is the number of sixteenth inch increments in the nominal pipe thread size.

3.3 The O-ring boss, 37-degree and 45-degree flared, and flareless type thread dash sizes correspond to the number of sixteenth inch increments in the outside diameter of the tubing with which they are designed to be used.

3.4 The 4-bolt split flange dash size is the number of sixteenth inch increments in the nominal flange size.

4. Fitting Identification—Permanently attached style fittings that are not assembled to hose by fitting manufacturers and all field attachable styles of hose fittings shall be permanently and legibly marked to identify the hose size and type on which they are designed to be used.

5. Dimensions and Tolerances—Tabulated dimensions shall apply to the finished parts, plated or otherwise processed, as specified by the purchaser. Dimensions over external contour of shell portion of fittings shown in the tables reflect the maximum envelope of products available. Dimensions W and Z are indicative of the minimum diameter hole through which the hose fitting will pass. Details of internal construction of the attaching portion of fittings are not specified and shall be optional with the manufacturer, providing the fittings, properly assembled onto the appropriate hose, will not be the point of failure when the assemblies are subjected to the various tests specified in SAE J517. In the case of field attachable styles of fittings, this requirement shall apply to a minimum of one reuse as well.

The maximum and minimum across flat dimensions shall be within the commercial tolerance of bar stock from which the fittings are produced. Formed or upset hexagon contours shall fit standard wrench size openings. The minimum across corners dimensions of external hexagons shall be 1.092 times the nominal width across flats, but shall not result in a side flat width of less than 0.43 times the nominal width across flats.

Tolerance on all dimensions not otherwise limited shall be ±0.016 in. Fitting seats shall be concentric with straight thread pitch diameters within 0.010 in full indicator reading (FIR).

6. Passages—The tabulated D dimensions reflect the minimum bore at any point through the fitting prior to assembly to the hose. The after assembly bore reduction will be a maximum of 10% starting at size 5/16[1] to 2 in. The 1/4 in and smaller D dimension is the minimum for after assembly bore. The reduction must be in the general shape of a venturi. Where passages in straight fittings are machined from opposite ends, the offset at the meeting point shall not exceed 0.015 in. On angle fittings, the cross-sectional area at the junction of fluid passages shall not be less than that of the smallest passage. This assembly passage definition does not apply to bent tubes.

7. Contour—Details of contour shall be optional with the manufacturer, providing the tabulated dimensions are maintained and serviceability of fittings is not impaired. The wrench clearance dimension Y, where specified, represents the width of the fitting hexagon T plus sufficient clearance in the shell portion of fitting adjacent to the hexagon to provide adequate space for application of a standard wrench to the hexagon without interfering with mating components during assembly.

8. Straight Threads—Unified Standard Class 2A external and Class 2B internal threads shall apply to plain finish (unplated) fittings having straight threads designated B. For externally threaded parts with additive finish, the maximum diameters of Class 2A may be exceeded by the amount of the allowance, that is, the basic diameters (Class 2A maximum diameters plus the allowance) shall apply to an externally threaded part after plating. For internally threaded parts with additive finish, the Class 2B diameters apply after plating.

The pitch diameter tolerance shall be the same as the corresponding diameter-pitch combination and class of the Unified fine and 12-thread series. See SAE J475.

Where external threads are produced by roll threading and the body is not undercut, the unthreaded portion adjacent to the shoulder may be reduced to the minimum pitch diameter.

External threads shall be chamfered and internal threads shall be countersunk as specified in the illustrations and dimensional tables.

9. Thread Eccentricity Tolerances—The various thread elements of Class 2A external and Class 2B internal threads on hose fittings shall be concentric within the limitations specified under General Specifications in SAE J512.

10. Pipe Threads—Taper pipe threads designated A in the illustrations and dimensional tables shall conform to the Dryseal American Standard Taper Pipe Thread (NPTF). Specifications are given in detail in SAE J476.

The length of full form external thread shall not be shorter than L_2 plus one pitch (thread).

Where external pipe threads are produced by roll threading, the diameter of the unthreaded shank adjacent to shoulder may be reduced to the E_2 pitch diameter.

Straight internal pipe threads designated A1 in the illustrations and tables shall conform with free fitting American Standard Straight Pipe Threads for Mechanical Joints (NPSM) as specified in USA Standard, ANSI/ASME B1.20.1-1983 of latest issue.

External pipe threads shall be chamfered from the diameters tabulated in Table 1 to produce the specified length of chamfered or partial thread. Internal pipe threads shall be countersunk 90 degrees, included angle, to the diameters specified in Table 1:

11. Material—Fittings shall be made from materials of good quality, capable of withstanding the stresses resulting from hydraulic pressures equal to the minimum burst pressure of the applicable hose size and type to which they are assembled without failure.

1. Hose I.D.

TABLE 1—PIPE THREAD DIMENSIONS

Nominal Pipe Thread Size in	External Chamfer Dia(1) Max mm	External Chamfer Dia(1) Min mm	Thread Length of Chamfered or Partial Thread Max mm	Thread Length of Chamfered or Partial Thread Min mm	Internal Thread Countersink Dia(1) Max mm	Internal Thread Countersink Dia(1) Min mm
1/8	8.1	7.6	1.40	0.94	11.2	10.7
1/4	10.7	10.2	2.13	1.42	14.5	14.0
3/8	14.0	13.4	2.13	1.42	18.0	17.5
1/2	17.3	16.8	2.72	1.80	22.1	21.6
3/4	22.6	22.1	2.72	1.80	27.4	26.9
1	28.4	27.7	3.30	2.21	34.8	34.0
1–1/4	37.1	36.3	3.30	2.21	43.4	42.7
1–1/2	43.2	42.4	3.30	2.21	49.5	48.8
2	55.1	54.4	3.30	2.21	61.2	60.7

1. Tabulated diameters conform with Appendix A, SAE J476.

12. Finish—The external surfaces and threads of all carbon steel parts shall be plated or coated with a suitable material that passes a 72 h salt spray test in accordance with ASTM B 117. Any appearance of red rust during the 72 h salt spray test shall be considered failure, except for the following:

a. All internal fluid passages.
b. Edges such as hex points, serrations, and crests of threads where there may be mechanical deformation of the plating or coating typical of mass-produced parts or shipping effects.
c. Areas where there is mechanical deformation of the plating or coating caused by crimping, flaring, bending, and other post-plate metal forming operations.
d. Areas where the parts are suspended or affixed in the test chamber where condensate can accumulate.

NOTE—Cadmium plating is not preferred due to environmental reasons. Parts manufactured to this standard after January 1, 1997, shall not be cadmium plated. Internal fluid passages shall be protected from corrosion during storage. Changes in plating may affect assembly torques and require requalification, when applicable.

13. Workmanship—Workmanship shall conform to the best commercial practice to produce high-quality fittings. Fittings shall be free from all hanging burrs, loose scales, and slivers which might become dislodged in usage, sharp edges, and all other defects that might affect their serviceability. All sealing surfaces must be smooth except that annular tool marks up to 100 µin maximum, unless specified otherwise, shall be permissible.

14. Assembly Considerations—Use of a compatible lubricant in assembling dryseal pipe threads on hose fittings may be desirable to minimize galling and effect a pressure-tight seal.

15. Pressure Ratings—Some hose pressure ratings in SAE J517 exceed the pressure ratings for the connection (threads, flanges, etc.) of certain types of hose fittings shown in SAE J516. SAE J518 and J1453 specify pressure ratings for 4-bolt split flange and O-ring face seal type hose fittings, respectively. For all other types of hose fitting connections consult the fitting manufacturer for pressure ratings. The pressure rating of a hose assembly comprising SAE J516 fittings and SAE J517 hose shall not exceed the lower of the two pressure rating values.

MALE DRYSEAL PIPE THREAD TYPE

NOTE—UNSPECIFIED DETAIL WITH RESPECT TO DIMENSIONS, TOLERANCES, CONTOURS, MATERIAL, WORKMANSHIP, AND SO ON, MUST CONFORM TO GENERAL SPECIFICATIONS FOR HYDRAULIC HOSE FITTINGS. THE DIMENSIONAL DESIGNATIONS ON THE FIRST FIGURE IN EACH GROUP SHALL APPLY TO ALL OTHER FIGURES IN THAT GROUP EXCEPT AS SHOWN OTHERWISE. CODES SHOWN IN BRACKETS ADJACENT TO FIGURE NUMBERS REPRESENT RESPECTIVE FITTING IDENTIFICATION, WITH XX SUBSTITUTED FOR THE HOSE TYPE CODE DEPICTED IN BRACKETS AT END OF RESPECTIVE TABLE TITLES, IN ACCORDANCE WITH SAE J846.

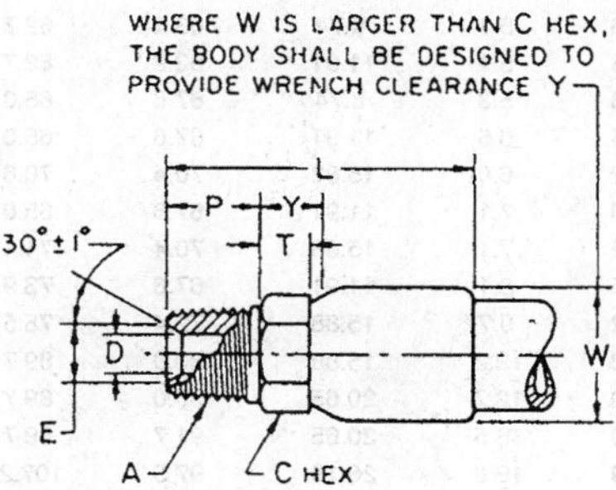

FIGURE 1A—PERMANENTLY ATTACHED STYLE (1501XX)

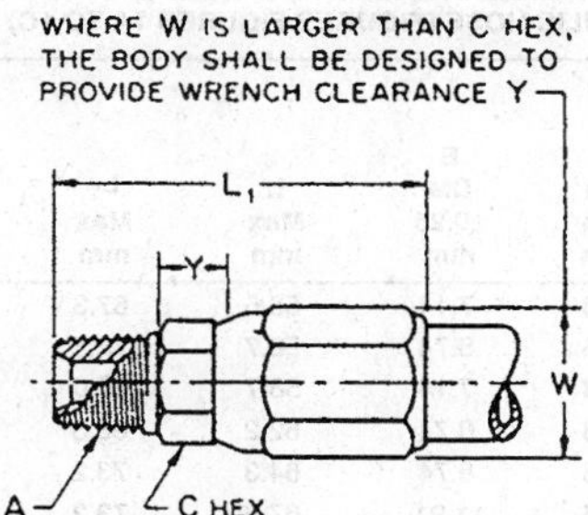

FIGURE 1B—FIELD ATTACHABLE SCREW STYLE (1601XX)

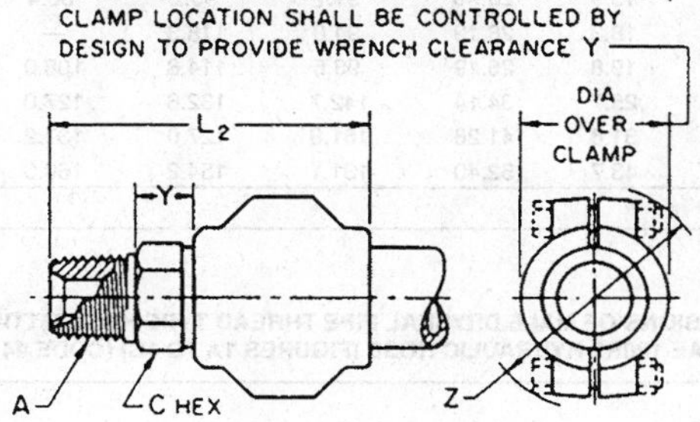

FIGURE 1C—FIELD ATTACHABLE SEGMENT CLAMP STYLE (1701XX)

FIGURE 1—MALE DRYSEAL PIPE THREAD TYPE HOSE FITTINGS

TABLE 1A—DIMENSIONS OF MALE DRYSEAL PIPE THREAD TYPE HOSE FITTINGS FOR USE ON SAE 100R1 HYDRAULIC HOSE (FIGURES 1A TO 1C) (CODES 42 AND 53)

Nominal SAE 100R1 Hose ID mm	Hose Dash Size	A Dryseal Taper Thread[(a)] NPTF	Pipe Thread Dash Size	C Min mm	D Dia Min mm	E Dia ±0.25 mm	L Max mm	L_1 Max mm	L_2 Max mm	P Min mm	T Min mm	W Max mm	Y Min mm	Z Max mm
4.8	∠3	1/8	∠2	11.1	2.3	7.14	54.9	54.9	—	9.7	4.8	19.0	9.4	—
4.8	∠3	1/4	∠4	14.3	2.3	8.74	57.2	60.5	—	14.2	5.6	19.0	10.4	—
6.4	∠4	1/8	∠2	11.1	2.8	7.14	58.7	56.9	—	9.7	4.8	22.1	9.4	—
6.4	∠4	1/4	∠4	14.3	2.8	8.74	63.2	61.5	—	14.2	5.6	22.1	10.4	—
7.9	∠5	1/4	∠4	14.3	5.1	8.74	63.2	62.7	—	14.2	5.6	23.9	10.4	—
7.9	∠5	3/8	∠6	17.5	5.1	11.91	63.2	62.7	—	14.2	6.4	23.9	12.7	—
9.5	∠6	1/4	∠4	14.3	5.3	8.74	67.6	65.0	—	14.2	5.6	27.7	10.4	—
9.5	∠6	3/8	∠6	17.5	6.6	11.91	67.6	65.0	—	14.2	6.4	27.7	12.7	—
9.5	∠6	1/2	∠8	22.2	6.6	15.88	70.4	70.6	—	19.0	7.9	27.7	14.2	—
10.3	–6.5	3/8	∠6	17.5	7.1	11.91	67.6	65.0	—	14.2	6.4	29.5	12.7	—
10.3	–6.5	1/2	∠8	22.2	7.1	15.88	70.4	71.4	—	19.0	7.9	29.5	14.2	—
12.7	∠8	3/8	∠6	17.5	8.1	11.91	67.6	73.9	—	14.2	6.4	31.2	12.7	—
12.7	∠8	1/2	∠8	22.2	9.7	15.88	72.4	78.5	78.5	19.0	7.9	31.2	14.2	63.5
15.9	10	1/2	∠8	22.2	12.2	15.88	80.0	89.7	—	19.0	7.9	34.8	14.2	—
15.9	10	3/4	∠12	27.0	12.7	20.65	80.0	89.7	—	19.0	9.7	34.8	15.5	—
19.0	12	3/4	∠12	27.0	15.5	20.65	91.7	89.7	86.4	19.0	9.7	40.4	15.5	76.2
25.4	16	1	∠16	34.9	19.8	26.19	97.5	107.2	100.8	23.9	9.7	51.3	15.5	91.2
31.8	20	1–1/4	∠20	42.9	25.7	34.14	109.5	119.4	111.3	24.6	11.2	62.5	23.9	101.6
38.1	24	1–1/2	∠24	50.8	31.8	41.28	116.6	127.0	118.9	25.4	12.7	69.6	23.9	114.3
50.8	32	2	∠32	61.9	44.2	52.40	131.1	139.7	139.7	26.2	17.5	88.1	28.4	130.0

(a) Dryseal American Standard Taper Pipe Thread.

TABLE 1B—DIMENSIONS OF MALE DRYSEAL PIPE THREAD TYPE HOSE FITTINGS FOR USE ON SAE 100R2 HYDRAULIC HOSE (FIGURES FIGURES 1A TO 1C) (CODES 43 AND 54)

Nominal SAE 100R2 Hose ID mm	Hose Dash Size	A Dryseal Taper Thread[(a)] NPTF	Pipe Thread Dash Size	C Min mm	D Dia Min mm	E Dia ±0.25 mm	L Max mm	L_1 Max mm	L_2 Max mm	P Min mm	T Min mm	W Max mm	Y Min mm	Z Max mm
4.8	–3	1/8	–2	11.1	2.3	7.14	55.6	67.3	—	9.7	4.8	22.9	9.4	—
4.8	–3	1/4	–4	14.3	2.3	8.74	58.7	72.1	—	14.2	5.6	22.9	10.4	—
6.4	–4	1/8	–2	11.1	2.8	7.14	58.7	62.0	—	9.7	4.8	25.4	9.4	—
6.4	–4	1/4	–4	14.3	2.8	8.74	62.2	68.3	63.5	14.2	5.6	25.4	10.4	54.1
9.5	–6	1/4	–4	14.3	5.3	8.74	64.3	73.2	—	14.2	5.6	30.2	10.4	—
9.5	–6	3/8	–6	17.5	6.6	11.91	67.6	73.2	66.8	14.2	6.4	30.2	12.7	62.7
9.5	–6	1/2	–8	22.2	6.6	15.88	70.4	78.0	—	19.1	7.9	30.2	14.2	—
12.7	–8	3/8	–6	17.5	8.1	11.91	69.3	76.2	—	14.2	6.4	35.1	12.7	—
12.7	–8	1/2	–8	22.2	9.7	15.88	73.9	81.8	78.7	19.0	7.9	35.1	14.2	62.7
15.9	–10	1/2	–8	22.2	12.2	15.88	81.0	95.2	—	19.0	7.9	39.6	14.2	—
15.9	–10	3/4	–12	27.0	12.7	20.65	81.0	95.2	86.4	19.0	9.7	39.6	15.5	73.2
19.0	–12	3/4	–12	27.0	15.5	20.65	91.7	95.2	86.4	19.0	9.7	44.4	15.5	76.2
22.2	–14	1	–16	34.9	18.3	26.19	94.0	113.3	—	23.9	9.7	46.0	15.5	—
25.4	–16	1	–16	34.9	19.8	26.19	93.5	114.8	108.0	23.9	9.7	52.3	15.5	91.4
31.8	–20	1–1/4	–20	42.9	25.7	34.14	142.7	132.6	127.0	24.6	11.2	66.8	23.9	114.3
38.1	–24	1–1/2	–24	50.8	31.8	41.28	161.8	127.0	137.2	25.4	12.7	74.7	23.9	127.0
50.8	–32	2	–32	61.9	43.7	52.40	131.1	154.2	160.0	26.2	17.5	88.9	28.4	133.4

(a) Dryseal American Standard Taper Pipe Thread.

TABLE 1C—DIMENSIONS OF MALE DRYSEAL PIPE THREAD TYPE HOSE FITTINGS FOR USE ON SAE 100R3 HYDRAULIC HOSE (FIGURES 1A TO 1C) (CODE 44)

Nominal SAE 100R3 Hose ID mm	Hose Dash Size	A Dryseal Taper Thread[(a)] NPTF	Pipe Thread Dash Size	C Min mm	D Dia Min mm	E Dia ±0.25 mm	L Max mm	L_1 Max mm	L_2 Max mm	P Min mm	T Min mm	W Max mm	Y Min mm	Z Max mm
6.4	–4	1/8	–2	11.1	2.8	7.14	58.7	55.4	—	9.7	4.8	22.4	9.4	—
6.4	–4	1/4	–4	14.3	2.8	8.74	63.2	60.5	—	14.2	4.8	22.4	9.4	—
9.5	–6	1/4	–4	14.3	6.6	8.74	64.0	65.0	—	14.2	5.6	26.9	10.4	—
9.5	–6	3/8	–6	17.5	6.6	11.91	64.0	65.0	—	14.2	5.6	26.9	10.4	—
12.7	–8	3/8	–6	17.5	9.1	11.91	66.8	65.0	—	14.2	6.4	33.3	12.7	—
12.7	–8	1/2	–8	22.2	9.7	15.88	73.2	77.0	66.8	19.0	7.9	33.3	14.2	63.5
19.0	–12	3/4	–12	27.0	15.5	20.65	91.7	79.2	73.2	19.0	7.9	42.2	15.5	76.2
25.4	–16	1	–16	34.9	19.8	26.19	97.5	94.0	85.9	23.9	7.9	51.3	15.5	82.6
31.8	–20	1–1/4	–20	42.9	25.7	34.14	103.6	—	101.6	24.6	9.7	51.3	23.9	100.1

(a) Dryseal American Standard Taper Pipe Thread.

TABLE 1D—DIMENSIONS OF MALE DRYSEAL PIPE THREAD TYPE HOSE FITTINGS FOR USE ON SAE 100R4 HYDRAULIC HOSE (FIGURES 1A TO 1C) (CODE 45)

Nominal SAE 100R4 Hose ID mm	Hose Dash Size	A Dryseal Taper Thread[a] NPTF	Pipe Thread Dash Size	C Min mm	D Dia Min mm	E Dia ±0.25 mm	L Max mm	L_2 Max mm	P Min mm	T Min mm	W Max mm	Y Min mm	Z Max mm
19.0	–12	3/4	–12	27.0	15.5	20.65	66.8	91.7	19.0	7.9	43.9	15.5	76.2
25.4	–16	1	–16	35.0	19.8	26.19	73.2	97.5	23.9	7.9	51.1	15.5	82.6
31.8	–20	1–1/4	–20	42.9	25.7	34.14	77.0	104.6	24.6	9.7	58.7	23.9	100.1
38.1	–24	1–1/2	–24	50.8	31.8	41.28	90.4	114.3	25.4	12.7	66.0	23.9	110.2
50.8	–32	2	–32	61.9	43.7	52.40	101.6	124.0	26.2	14.2	80.8	28.4	125.5

[a] Dryseal American Standard Taper Pipe Thread.

TABLE 1E—DIMENSIONS OF MALE DRYSEAL PIPE THREAD TYPE HOSE FITTINGS FOR USE ON SAE 100R5 HYDRAULIC HOSE (FIGURES 1A TO 1B) (CODE 46)

Nominal SAE 100R5 Hose ID mm	Hose Dash Size	A Dryseal Taper Thread[a] NPTF	Pipe Thread Dash Size	C Min mm	D Dia Min mm	E Dia ±0.25 mm	L Max mm	L_1 Max mm	P Min mm	T Min mm	W Max mm	Y Min mm
4.8	–4	1/8	–2	11.1	2.3	7.14	46.2	45.7	9.7	4.8	20.1	9.4
4.8	–4	1/4	–4	14.3	2.3	8.74	50.8	52.3	14.2	4.8	20.1	10.4
6.4	–5	1/4	–4	14.3	2.8	8.74	51.8	52.3	14.2	4.8	22.1	10.4
7.9	–6	1/4	–4	14.3	5.1	8.74	52.6	55.6	14.2	4.8	23.9	10.4
10.3	–8	3/8	–6	17.5	7.1	11.91	54.9	64.5	14.2	6.4	27.4	12.7
12.7	–10	1/2	–8	22.2	9.7	15.88	61.0	74.7	19.0	7.9	33.3	14.2
15.9	–12	3/4	–12	27.0	12.7	20.65	62.0	83.8	19.0	9.7	38.6	15.5
22.2	–16	3/4	–12	27.0	18.3	20.65	68.6	77.7	19.0	9.7	43.9	15.5
22.2	–16	1	–16	34.9	18.3	26.19	73.4	81.0	23.9	9.7	43.9	15.5
28.6	–20	1–1/4	–20	42.9	23.9	34.14	77.2	88.1	24.6	11.2	51.3	23.9
34.9	–24	1–1/2	–24	50.8	29.5	41.28	85.9	90.2	25.4	12.7	58.7	23.9
46.0	–32	2	–32	61.9	40.9	52.40	96.3	104.1	26.2	17.5	73.4	28.4

[a] Dryseal American Standard Taper Pipe Thread.

NOTE— For SAE J1402 and DOT FMVSS 106 air brake applications, couplings used on 100R5 hose shall have a minimum assembled orifice no less than 66% of the nominal hose I.D.

TABLE 1F—DIMENSIONS OF MALE DRYSEAL PIPE THREAD TYPE HOSE FITTINGS FOR USE ON SAE 100R6 HYDRAULIC HOSE (FIGURES 1A TO 1B) (CODE 47)

Nominal SAE 100R6 Hose ID mm	Hose Dash Size	A Dryseal Taper Thread[a] NPTF	Pipe Thread Dash Size	C Min mm	D Dia Min mm	E Dia ±0.25 mm	L Max mm	L_1 Max mm	P Min mm	T Min mm	W Max mm	Y Min mm
4.8	–3	1/8	–2	11.1	2.3	7.14	58.7	29.2	9.7	3.0	16.0	9.4
4.8	–3	1/4	–4	14.3	2.3	8.74	63.5	35.3	14.2	4.3	16.0	10.4
6.4	–4	1/8	–2	11.1	2.8	7.14	58.7	31.8	9.7	3.0	19.0	9.4
6.4	–4	1/4	–4	14.3	2.8	8.74	63.5	36.8	14.2	4.3	19.0	10.4
6.4	–4	3/8	–6	17.5	2.8	11.91	64.3	—	14.2	6.4	19.0	12.7
7.9	–5	1/4	–4	14.3	5.1	8.74	65.0	36.8	14.2	3.0	20.6	10.4
7.9	–5	3/8	–6	17.5	5.1	11.91	68.1	38.6	14.2	6.4	20.6	12.7
9.5	–6	1/4	–4	14.3	5.3	8.74	68.1	39.1	14.2	3.0	25.4	10.4
9.5	–6	3/8	–6	17.5	6.6	11.91	74.7	39.1	14.2	6.4	25.4	12.7
12.7	–8	3/8	–6	17.5	9.1	11.91	74.7	41.4	14.2	6.4	28.4	12.7
12.7	–8	1/2	–8	22.2	9.7	15.88	79.0	47.8	19.0	7.9	28.4	14.2
15.9	–10	1/2	–8	22.2	12.2	15.88	81.3	—	19.0	7.9	26.9	14.2
15.9	–10	3/4	–12	27.0	12.7	20.65	89.4	—	19.0	9.7	26.9	15.5
19.0	–12	3/4	–12	27.0	14.5	20.65	101.6	79.5	19.0	7.9	36.8	15.5

[a] Dryseal American Standard Taper Pipe Thread

TABLE 1G—DIMENSIONS OF MALE DRYSEAL PIPE THREAD TYPE HOSE FITTINGS FOR USE ON SAE 100R7 HYDRAULIC HOSE (FIGURES 1A TO 1B) (CODE 48)

Nominal SAE 100R7 Hose ID mm	Hose Dash Size	A Dryseal Taper Thread[(a)] NPTF	Pipe Thread Dash Size	C Min mm	D Dia Min mm	E Dia ±0.25 mm	L Max mm	L_1 Max mm	P Min mm	T Min mm	W Max mm	Y Min mm
4.8	–3	1/8	–2	11.1	2.3	7.14	58.7	50.8	9.7	4.8	19.0	9.4
4.8	–3	1/4	–4	14.3	2.3	8.74	63.5	52.6	14.2	5.6	19.0	10.4
6.4	–4	1/8	–2	11.1	2.8	7.14	58.7	52.6	9.7	4.8	20.6	9.4
6.4	–4	1/4	–4	14.3	2.8	8.74	63.5	57.2	14.2	5.6	20.6	10.4
7.9	–5	1/4	–4	14.3	5.1	8.74	64.3	60.5	14.2	5.6	22.4	10.4
7.9	–5	3/8	–6	17.5	5.1	11.9	65.0	60.5	14.2	5.8	22.4	12.7
9.5	–6	1/4	–4	14.3	5.3	8.74	68.1	66.8	14.2	5.6	25.7	10.4
9.5	–6	3/8	–6	17.5	6.6	11.9	68.1	66.8	14.2	5.8	25.7	12.7
9.5	–6	1/2	–8	22.2	6.6	15.9	74.7	71.6	19.0	7.9	25.7	14.2
12.7	–8	3/8	–6	17.5	8.1	11.9	74.7	74.4	14.2	5.8	31.2	12.7
12.7	–8	1/2	–8	22.2	9.1	15.9	79.0	79.5	19.0	7.9	31.2	14.2
15.9	–10	1/2	–8	22.2	12.2	15.9	81.3	—	19.0	7.9	34.8	14.2
19.0	–12	3/4	–12	27.0	14.5	20.7	89.4	88.9	19.0	8.4	40.4	15.5
25.4	–16	1	–16	34.9	19.8	26.2	101.6	101.6	23.9	9.1	49.5	15.5

(a) Dryseal American Standard Taper Pipe Thread

TABLE 1H—DIMENSIONS OF MALE DRYSEAL PIPE THREAD TYPE HOSE FITTINGS FOR USE ON SAE 100R8 HYDRAULIC HOSE (FIGURE 1A) (CODE 49)

Nominal SAE 100R8 Hose ID mm	Hose Dash Size	A Dryseal Taper Thread[(a)] NPTF	Pipe Thread Dash Size	C Min mm	D Dia Min mm	E Dia ±0.25 mm	L Max mm	P Min mm	T Min mm	W Max mm	Y Min mm
4.8	–3	1/8	–2	11.1	2.3	7.14	58.7	9.7	4.8	19.0	9.4
4.8	–3	1/4	–4	14.3	2.3	8.74	63.5	14.2	5.6	19.0	10.4
6.4	–4	1/8	–2	11.1	2.8	7.14	58.7	9.7	4.8	20.6	9.4
6.4	–4	1/4	–4	14.3	2.8	8.74	63.5	14.2	5.6	20.6	10.4
9.5	–6	1/4	–4	14.3	5.3	8.74	68.1	14.2	5.6	25.7	10.4
9.5	–6	3/8	–6	17.5	6.6	11.91	68.1	14.2	5.8	25.7	12.7
9.5	–6	1/2	–8	22.2	6.6	15.88	74.7	19.0	7.9	25.7	14.2
12.7	–8	3/8	–6	17.5	8.1	11.91	74.7	14.2	5.8	31.2	12.7
12.7	–8	1/2	–8	22.2	9.7	15.88	79.0	19.0	7.9	31.2	14.2
15.9	–10	1/2	–8	22.2	12.2	15.88	81.3	19.0	7.9	36.8	14.2
19.0	–12	3/4	–12	27.0	14.5	20.65	89.4	19.0	8.4	40.4	15.5
25.4	–16	1	–16	34.9	19.8	26.19	101.6	23.9	9.1	49.5	15.5

(a) Dryseal American Standard Taper Pipe Thread

TABLE 1I—DIMENSIONS OF MALE DRYSEAL PIPE THREAD TYPE HOSE FITTINGS FOR USE ON SAE 100R9 HYDRAULIC HOSE (FIGURES 1A TO 1B) (CODES 50 AND 75)

Nominal SAE 100R9 Hose ID mm	Hose Dash Size	A Dryseal Taper Thread[(a)] NPTF	Pipe Thread Dash Size	C Min mm	D Dia Min mm	E Dia ±0.25 mm	L Max mm	L_1 Max mm	P Min mm	T Min mm	W Max mm	Y Min mm
9.5	–6	3/8	–6	17.5	6.6	11.91	77.2	73.2	14.2	6.35	30.2	12.7
12.7	–8	1/2	–8	22.2	9.7	15.88	85.6	81.8	19.0	7.87	35.1	14.2
19.0	–12	3/4	–12	27.0	15.5	20.65	95.5	95.2	19.0	9.65	44.5	15.5
25.4	–16	1	–16	34.9	19.8	26.19	102.1	114.8	23.9	9.65	52.3	15.5
31.8	–20	1-1/4	–20	42.9	25.7	34.14	142.7	—	24.6	11.2	66.8	23.9
38.1	–24	1-1/2	–24	50.8	31.8	41.28	161.8	—	25.4	12.7	74.7	23.9
50.8	–32	2	–32	61.9	43.7	52.40	154.2	—	26.2	17.5	88.9	28.4

(a) Dryseal American Standard Taper Pipe Thread

TABLE 1J—DIMENSIONS OF MALE DRYSEAL PIPE THREAD TYPE HOSE FITTINGS FOR USE ON SAE 100R10 HYDRAULIC HOSE (FIGURES 1A TO 1C) (CODES 51 AND 76)

Nominal SAE 100R10 Hose ID mm	Hose Dash Size	A Dryseal Taper Thread[(a)] NPTF	Pipe Thread Dash Size	C Min mm	D Dia Min mm	E Dia ±0.25 mm	L Max mm	L_1 Max mm	L_2 Max mm	P Min mm	T Min mm	W Max mm	Y Min mm	Z Max mm
6.4	–4	1/4	–4	14.3	2.8	8.74	75.7	76.2	63.5	14.2	5.6	28.7	10.4	54.1
9.5	–6	3/8	–6	17.5	5.6	11.91	83.3	82.6	66.8	14.2	6.4	28.7	12.7	62.7
12.7	–8	1/2	–8	22.2	8.6	15.88	101.1	101.6	78.7	19.0	7.9	31.8	14.2	62.7
19.0	–12	3/4	–12	27.0	12.7	20.65	112.5	114.3	86.4	19.0	9.7	42.9	15.5	79.2
25.4	–16	1	–16	34.9	17.3	26.19	131.8	133.4	103.6	23.9	9.7	50.8	15.5	107.2
31.8	–20	1–1/4	–20	42.9	22.1	34.14	153.7	152.4	116.6	24.6	11.2	62.2	17.8	126.0
38.1	–24	1–1/2	–24	50.8	27.7	41.28	166.4	171.4	139.4	25.4	12.7	76.2	19.3	133.1
50.8	–32	2	–32	63.5	39.6	52.40	195.6	203.2	169.7	26.2	17.5	81.8	28.4	166.6

(a) Dryseal American Standard Taper Pipe Thread

TABLE 1K—DIMENSIONS OF MALE DRYSEAL PIPE THREAD TYPE HOSE FITTINGS FOR USE ON SAE 100R11 HYDRAULIC HOSE (FIGURE 1A) (CODE 52)

Nominal SAE 100R11 Hose ID mm	Hose Dash Size	A Dryseal Taper Thread[(a)] NPTF	Pipe Thread Dash Size	C Min mm	D Dia Min mm	E Dia ±0.25 mm	L Max mm	P Min mm	T Min mm	W Max mm	Y Min mm
25.4	–16	1	–16	34.9	18.5	26.19	133.9	23.9	9.7	55.9	15.5
31.8	–20	1–1/4	–20	42.9	24.1	34.14	147.3	24.6	11.2	66.8	18.5
38.1	–24	1–1/2	–24	50.8	30.5	41.28	170.7	25.4	12.7	74.7	20.1
50.8	–32	2	–32	61.9	41.9	52.40	195.6	26.2	17.5	88.9	21.8

(a) Dryseal American Standard Taper Pipe Thread

TABLE 1L—DIMENSIONS OF MALE DRYSEAL PIPE THREAD TYPE HOSE FITTINGS FOR USE ON SAE 100R12 HYDRAULIC HOSE (FIGURE 1A) (CODE 77)

Nominal SAE 100R12 Hose ID mm	Hose Dash Size	A Dryseal Taper Thread[(a)] NPTF	Pipe Thread Dash Size	C Min mm	D Dia Min mm	E Dia ± 0.25 mm	L Max mm	P Min mm	T Min mm	W Max mm	Y Min mm
9.5	–6	3/8	–6	17.5	5.6	11.91	83.3	14.2	6.4	28.7	12.7
12.7	–8	1/2	–8	22.2	8.6	15.88	101.1	19.0	7.9	31.8	14.2
15.9	–10	3/4	–12	27.0	10.0	20.65	101.6	19.0	9.7	38.0	14.2
19.0	–12	3/4	–12	27.0	12.7	20.65	114.3	19.0	9.7	42.9	14.2
25.4	–16	1	–16	34.9	17.3	26.19	131.8	23.9	9.7	50.8	15.5
31.8	–20	1–1/4	–20	42.9	22.1	34.14	153.7	24.6	11.2	60.5	17.8
38.1	–24	1–1/2	–24	50.8	27.7	41.28	166.4	25.4	12.7	67.8	18.8
50.8	–32	2	–32	61.9	39.6	52.40	195.6	26.2	17.5	81.8	28.4

(a) Dryseal American Standard Taper Pipe Thread

TABLE 1M—DIMENSIONS OF MALE DRYSEAL PIPE THREAD TYPE HOSE FITTINGS FOR USE ON SAE 100R13 HYDRAULIC HOSE (FIGURE 1A) (CODE 78)

Nominal SAE 100R13 Hose ID mm	Hose Dash Size	A Dryseal Taper Thread[(a)] NPTF	Pipe Thread Dash Size	C Min mm	D Dia Min mm	E Dia ±0.25 mm	L Max mm	P Min mm	T Min mm	W Max mm	Y Min mm
19.0	–12	3/4	–12	27.0	12.7	20.65	114.3	19.0	9.7	43.7	14.2
25.4	–16	1	–16	34.9	17.5	26.19	119.4	23.9	9.7	50.8	15.7
31.8	–20	1–1/4	–20	42.9	22.4	34.14	143.8	24.6	11.2	63.5	19.0
38.1	–24	1–1/2	–24	50.8	27.7	41.28	156.7	25.4	12.7	71.1	18.8
50.8	–32	2	–32	61.9	38.1	52.40	216.4	26.2	17.5	88.9	21.6

(a) Dryseal American Standard Taper Pipe Thread

MALE STRAIGHT THREAD O-RING BOSS TYPE

NOTE—UNSPECIFIED DETAIL WITH RESPECT TO DIMENSIONS, TOLERANCES, CONTOURS, MATERIAL, WORKMANSHIP, AND SO ON, MUST CONFORM TO GENERAL SPECIFICATIONS FOR HYDRAULIC HOSE FITTINGS. THE DIMENSIONAL DESIGNATIONS ON THE FIRST FIGURE IN EACH GROUP SHALL APPLY TO ALL OTHER FIGURES IN THAT GROUP EXCEPT AS SHOWN OTHERWISE. CODES SHOWN IN BRACKETS ADJACENT TO FIGURE NUMBERS REPRESENT RESPECTIVE FITTING IDENTIFICATION, WITH XX SUBSTITUTED FOR THE HOSE TYPE CODE DEPICTED IN BRACKETS AT END OF RESPECTIVE TABLE TITLES, IN ACCORDANCE WITH SAE J846.

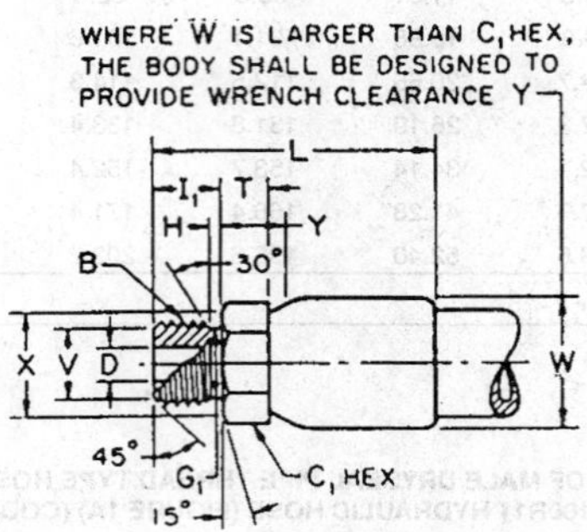

FIGURE 2A—PERMANENTLY ATTACHED STYLE (1801XX)

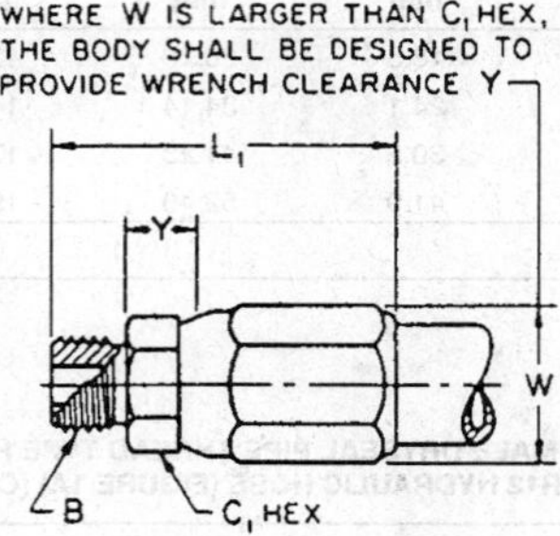

FIGURE 2B—FIELD ATTACHABLE SCREW STYLE (1901XX)

FIGURE 2—MALE STRAIGHT THREAD O-RING BOSS TYPE HOSE FITTINGS

TABLE 2A—DIMENSIONS OF MALE STRAIGHT THREAD O-RING BOSS TYPE HOSE FITTINGS FOR USE ON SAE 100R1 HYDRAULIC HOSE[(a)] (FIGURES 2A TO 2B) (CODES 42 AND 53)

Nominal SAE 100R1 Hose ID mm	Hose Dash Size	B Nominal Straight Thread Size	Thread Dash Size	C_1 Min mm	D Dia Min mm	L Max mm	L_1 Max mm	T Min mm	W Max mm	Y Min mm
7.9	–5	9/16–18	–6	17.5	5.1	62.7	62.7	7.9	23.9	10.4
9.5	–6	9/16–18	–6	17.5	6.6	64.5	64.5	7.9	27.7	10.4
9.5	–6	3/4–16	–8	22.2	6.6	68.3	68.3	8.6	27.7	12.7
10.3	–6.5	3/4–16	–8	22.2	6.6	68.3	68.3	8.6	29.5	12.7
12.7	–8	3/4–16	–8	22.2	9.7	70.1	76.2	8.6	31.2	14.2
12.7	–8	7/8–14	–10	25.4	9.7	72.6	78.7	7.9	31.2	14.2
15.9	–10	7/8–14	–10	25.4	12.2	77.7	86.9	7.9	34.8	14.2
15.9	–10	1–1/16–12	–12	31.8	12.7	81.3	90.9	9.7	34.8	17.5
19.0	–12	7/8–14	–10	25.4	12.2	81.3	90.9	9.7	40.4	14.2
19.0	–12	1–1/16–12	–12	31.8	14.5	81.3	90.9	9.7	40.4	17.5
19.0	–12	1–3/16–12	–14	34.9	15.5	84.1	93.7	9.7	40.4	17.5
25.4	–16	1–5/16–12	–16	38.1	19.8	94.5	107.7	12.7	51.3	19.0

(a) For dimensions shown in Figure 2A, but not specified in Table 2A, see corresponding dimensions for respective straight thread size in Figure 34A and Table 12 of SAE J514. For dimensions of mating boss ports, see Figure 1 and Table 1 of SAE J1926.

TABLE 2B—DIMENSIONS OF MALE STRAIGHT THREAD O-RING BOSS TYPE HOSE FITTINGS FOR USE ON SAE 100R2 HYDRAULIC HOSE[(a)] (FIGURE 2A) (CODES 43 AND 54)

Nominal SAE 100R2 Hose ID mm	Hose Dash Size	B Nominal Straight Thread Size	Thread Dash Size	C_1 Min mm	D Dia Min mm	L Max mm	T Min mm	W Max mm	Y Min mm
9.5	–6	9/16–18	–6	17.5	6.6	64.5	7.9	30.2	10.4
9.5	–6	3/4–16	–8	22.2	6.6	68.3	7.9	30.2	12.7
12.7	–8	3/4–16	–8	22.2	9.7	70.1	6.4	35.1	12.7
12.7	–8	7/8–14	–10	25.4	9.7	72.6	7.9	35.1	14.2
15.9	–10	7/8–14	–10	25.4	12.2	77.7	7.9	39.6	14.2
15.9	–10	1-1/16–12	–12	31.8	12.7	81.3	9.7	39.6	17.5
19.0	–12	7/8–14	–10	25.4	12.2	88.9	9.7	44.5	14.2
19.0	–12	1-1/16–12	–12	31.8	14.5	88.9	9.7	44.5	17.5
19.0	–12	1-3/16–12	–14	34.9	15.5	88.9	9.7	44.5	17.5
22.2	–14	1-3/16–12	–14	34.9	18.3	93.2	9.7	46.0	17.5
22.2	–14	1-5/16–12	–16	38.1	18.3	94.5	12.7	46.0	19.0
25.4	–16	1-5/16–12	–16	38.1	19.8	101.6	9.4	52.3	19.0
31.8	–20	1-5/8–12	–20	47.6	25.7	133.4	9.4	66.8	23.9

[(a)] For dimensions shown in Figure 2A, but not specified in Table 2B, see corresponding dimensions for respective straight thread size in Figure 34A and Table 12 of SAE J514. For dimensions of mating boss ports, see Figure 1 and Table 1 of SAE J1926.

TABLE 2C—DIMENSIONS OF MALE STRAIGHT THREAD O-RING BOSS TYPE HOSE FITTINGS FOR USE ON SAE 100R5 HYDRAULIC HOSE[(a)] (FIGURES 2A TO 2B) (CODE 46)

Nominal SAE 100R5 Hose ID mm	Hose Dash Size	B Nominal Straight Thread Size	Thread Dash Size	C_1 Min mm	D Dia Min mm	L Max mm	L_1 Max mm	T Min mm	W Max mm	Y Min mm
4.8	–4	7/16–20	–4	14.3	2.3	47.5	45.2	4.3	20.1	9.4
6.4	–5	1/2–20	–5	15.9	2.8	48.3	48.3	4.3	22.1	10.4
7.9	–6	9/16–18	–6	17.5	5.1	49.8	53.1	6.1	23.9	10.4
10.3	–8	3/4–16	–8	22.2	7.1	53.3	63.2	6.4	27.4	12.7
12.7	–10	7/8–14	–10	25.4	9.7	56.1	70.1	7.9	31.5	14.2
15.9	–12	1-1/16–12	–12	31.8	12.7	58.4	79.2	9.7	38.6	17.5
22.2	–16	1-1/16–12	–16	38.1	18.3	64.5	70.6	9.7	43.9	17.5
28.6	–20	1-5/8–12	–20	47.6	23.9	67.6	74.2	11.9	51.3	17.5

[(a)] For dimensions shown in Figure 2A, but not specified in Table 2C, see corresponding dimensions for respective straight thread size in Figure 34A and Table 12 of SAE J514. For dimensions of mating boss ports, see Figure 1 and Table 1 of SAE J1926.

NOTE— For SAE J1402 and DOT FMVSS 106 air brake applications, couplings used on 100R5 hose shall have a minimum assembled orifice no less than 66% of the nominal hose I.D.

TABLE 2D—DIMENSIONS OF MALE STRAIGHT THREAD O-RING BOSS TYPE HOSE FITTINGS FOR USE ON SAE 100R7 HYDRAULIC HOSE[(a)] (FIGURE 2A) (CODE 48)

Nominal SAE 100R7 Hose ID mm	Hose Dash Size	B Nominal Straight Thread Size	Thread Dash Size	C_1 Min mm	D Dia Min mm	L Max mm	T Min mm	W Max mm	Y Min mm
4.8	–3	7/16–20	–4	14.3	2.3	58.4	4.8	19.1	9.4
6.4	–4	7/16–20	–4	14.3	2.8	58.4	5.6	20.6	10.4
7.9	–5	9/16–18	–6	17.5	5.1	59.9	5.6	22.4	10.4
9.5	–6	9/16–18	–6	17.5	6.6	66.8	6.6	25.7	10.4
9.5	–6	3/4–16	–8	22.2	6.6	66.8	6.6	25.7	12.7
12.7	–8	3/4–16	–8	22.2	9.1	71.6	8.6	31.2	12.7
12.7	–8	7/8–14	–10	25.4	9.1	73.2	8.6	31.2	14.2
15.9	–10	7/8–14	–10	25.4	12.2	77.7	8.6	34.8	14.2
19.0	–12	1-1/16–12	–12	31.8	14.5	85.1	9.1	40.4	17.5
19.0	–12	1-3/16–12	–14	34.9	14.5	85.1	9.7	40.4	17.5
25.4	–16	1-5/16–12	–16	38.1	19.8	90.7	12.7	49.5	19.1

[(a)] For dimensions shown in Figure 2A, but not specified in Table 2D, see corresponding dimensions for respective straight thread size in Figure 34A and Table 12 of SAE J514. For dimensions of mating boss ports, see Figure 1 and Table 1 of SAE J1926.

TABLE 2E—DIMENSIONS OF MALE STRAIGHT THREAD O-RING BOSS TYPE HOSE FITTINGS FOR USE ON SAE 100R8 HYDRAULIC HOSE[(a)] (FIGURE 2A) (CODE 49)

Nominal SAE 100R8 Hose ID mm	Hose Dash Size	B Nominal Straight Thread Size	Thread Dash Size	C_1 Min mm	D Dia Min mm	L Max mm	T Min mm	W Max mm	Y Min mm
4.8	–3	7/16–20	–4	14.3	2.3	58.4	4.8	19.0	9.4
6.4	–4	7/16–20	–4	14.3	2.8	57.4	5.6	20.6	10.4
9.5	–6	9/16–18	–6	17.5	6.6	66.8	6.6	25.7	10.4
9.5	–6	3/4–16	–8	22.2	6.6	66.8	6.6	25.7	12.7
12.7	–8	3/4–16	–8	22.2	9.7	71.6	8.6	31.2	12.7
12.7	–8	7/8–14	–10	25.4	9.7	73.2	8.6	31.2	14.2
15.9	–10	7/8–14	–10	25.4	12.2	77.7	8.6	36.8	14.2
19.0	–12	1-1/16–12	–12	31.8	14.5	85.1	9.1	40.4	17.5
19.0	–12	1-3/16–12	–14	34.9	14.5	85.1	9.7	40.4	17.5
25.4	–16	1-5/16–12	–16	38.1	19.8	90.7	12.7	49.5	19.0

(a) For dimensions shown in Figure 2A, but not specified in Table 2E, see corresponding dimensions for respective straight thread size in Figure 34A and Table 12 of SAE J514. For dimensions of mating boss ports, see Figure 1 and Table 1 of SAE J1926.

TABLE 2F—DIMENSIONS OF MALE STRAIGHT THREAD O-RING BOSS TYPE HOSE FITTINGS FOR USE ON SAE 100R9 HYDRAULIC HOSE[(a)] (FIGURE 2A) (CODES 50 AND 75)

Nominal SAE 100R9 Hose ID mm	Hose Dash Size	B Nominal Straight Thread Size	Thread Dash Size	C_1 Min mm	D Dia Min mm	L Max mm	T Min mm	W Max mm	Y Min mm
9.5	–6	9/16–18	–6	17.5	6.6	70.4	7.9	30.2	10.4
12.7	–8	3/4–16	–8	22.2	9.7	70.6	8.6	35.1	12.7
19.0	–12	1-1/16–12	–12	31.8	14.5	90.9	9.7	44.5	17.5
25.4	–16	1-5/16–12	–16	38.1	19.8	101.6	12.7	52.3	19.0

(a) For dimensions shown in Figure 2A, but not specified in Table 2F, see corresponding dimensions for respective straight thread size in Figure 34A and Table 12 of SAE J514. For dimensions of mating boss ports, see Figure 1 and Table 1 of SAE J1926.

TABLE 2G—DIMENSIONS OF MALE STRAIGHT THREAD O-RING BOSS TYPE HOSE FITTINGS FOR USE ON SAE 100R10 HYDRAULIC HOSE[(a)] (FIGURES 2A TO 2B) (CODES 50 AND 76)

Nominal SAE 100R10 Hose ID mm	Hose Dash Size	B Nominal Straight Thread Size	Thread Dash Size	C Min mm	D Dia Min mm	L Max mm	L_1 Max mm	T Min mm	W Max mm	Y Min mm
6.4	–4	7/16–20	–4	14.3	2.8	70.6	63.5	5.6	28.7	10.4
9.5	–6	9/16–18	–6	17.5	5.6	79.5	63.5	6.4	28.7	12.7
12.7	–8	3/4–16	–8	22.2	8.6	92.2	69.8	7.9	31.8	12.7
19.0	–12	1–1/16–12	–12	31.8	12.7	107.4	104.1	9.7	42.9	13.0
25.4	–16	1–5/16–12	–16	38.1	17.3	120.1	120.6	9.7	50.8	14.5
31.8	–20	1–5/8–12	–20	47.6	22.1	131.1	133.4	11.2	62.2	23.9
38.1	–24	1–7/8–12	–24	54.0	27.7	142.2	146.0	12.7	76.2	23.9
50.8	–32	2–1/2–12	–32	69.8	39.6	163.1	165.1	17.6	81.8	28.4

(a) For dimensions shown in Figure 2A, but not specified in Table 2G, see corresponding dimensions for respective straight thread size in Figure 34A and Table 12 of SAE J514. For dimensions of mating boss ports, see Figure 1 and Table 1 of SAE J1926.

TABLE 2H—DIMENSIONS OF MALE STRAIGHT THREAD O-RING BOSS TYPE HOSE FITTINGS FOR USE ON SAE 100R12 HYDRAULIC HOSE[(a)] (FIGURE 2A) (CODE 77)

Nominal SAE 100R12 Hose ID mm	Hose Dash Size	B Nominal Straight Thread Size	Thread Dash Size	C Min mm	D Dia Min mm	L Max mm	T Min mm	W Max mm	Y Min mm
9.5	–6	9/16–18	–6	17.5	5.6	79.5	6.4	28.7	12.7
12.7	–8	3/4–16	–8	22.2	8.6	92.2	7.9	31.8	12.7
15.9	–10	7/8–14	–10	25.4	10.0	99.0	8.0	38.0	13.0
19.0	–12	1–1/16–12	–12	31.8	12.7	107.4	9.7	42.9	13.0
25.4	–16	1–5/16–12	–16	38.1	17.3	120.1	9.7	50.8	14.5
31.8	–20	1–5/8–12	–20	47.6	22.1	131.1	11.0	60.5	23.9
38.1	–24	1–7/8–12	–24	54.0	27.7	142.2	12.7	67.8	23.9
50.8	–32	2–1/2–12	–32	69.8	39.6	163.1	17.5	81.8	28.4

(a) For dimensions shown in Figure 2A, but not specified in Table 2H, see corresponding dimensions for respective straight thread size in Figure 34A and Table 12 of SAE J514. For dimensions of mating boss ports, see Figure 1 and Table 1 of SAE J1926.

MALE 37-DEGREE FLARED TYPE

NOTE—UNSPECIFIED DETAIL WITH RESPECT TO DIMENSIONS, TOLERANCES, CONTOURS, MATERIAL, WORKMANSHIP, AND SO ON, MUST CONFORM TO GENERAL SPECIFICATIONS FOR HYDRAULIC HOSE FITTINGS. THE DIMENSIONAL DESIGNATIONS ON THE FIRST FIGURE IN EACH GROUP SHALL APPLY TO ALL OTHER FIGURES IN THAT GROUP EXCEPT AS SHOWN OTHERWISE. CODES SHOWN IN BRACKETS ADJACENT TO FIGURE NUMBERS REPRESENT RESPECTIVE FITTING IDENTIFICATION, WITH XX SUBSTITUTED FOR THE HOSE TYPE CODE DEPICTED IN BRACKETS AT END OF RESPECTIVE TABLE TITLES, IN ACCORDANCE WITH SAE J846.

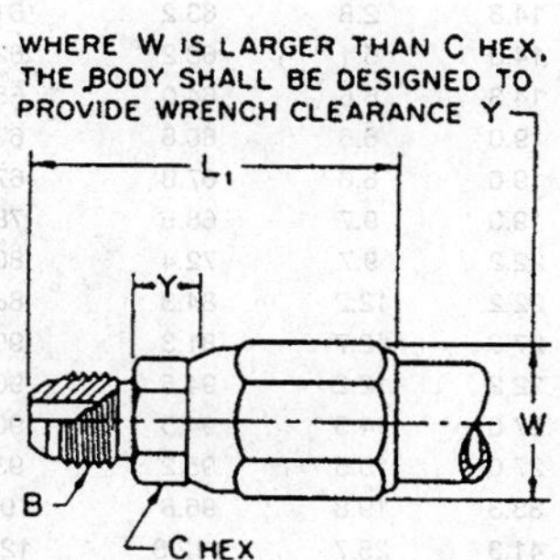

FIGURE 3A—FIELD ATTACHABLE SCREW STYLE (2201XX)

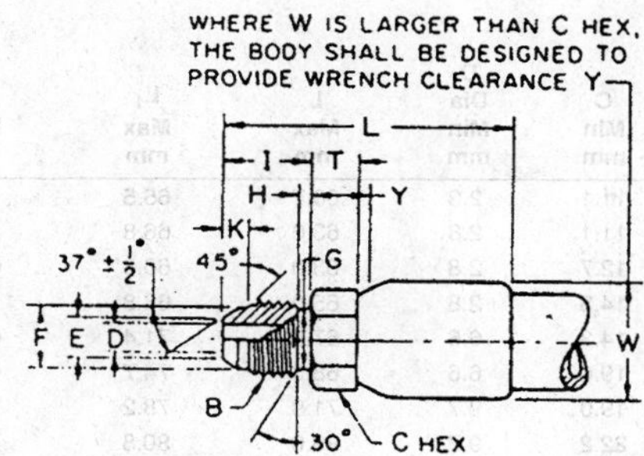

FIGURE 3B—PERMANENTLY ATTACHED STYLE (2101XX)

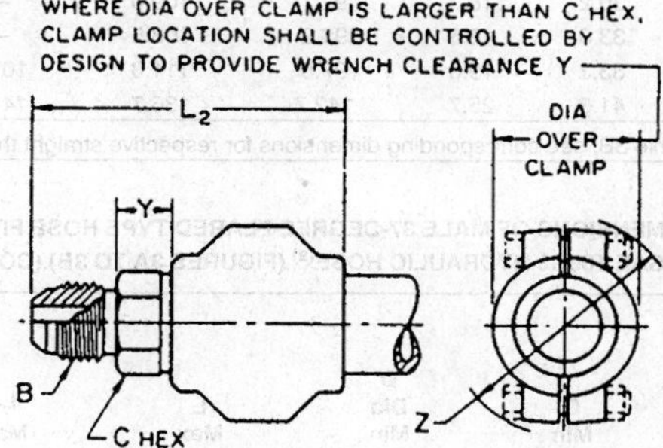

FIGURE 3C—FIELD ATTACHABLE SEGMENT CLAMP STYLE (2301XX)

FIGURE 3—MALE 37-DEGREE FLARED TYPE HOSE FITTINGS

TABLE 3A—DIMENSIONS OF MALE 37-DEGREE FLARED TYPE HOSE FITTINGS FOR USE ON SAE 100R1 HYDRAULIC HOSE[(a)] (FIGURES 3A TO 3C) (CODES 42 AND 53)

Nominal SAE 100R1 Hose ID mm	Hose Dash Size	B Nominal Straight Thread Size	Thread Dash Size	C Min mm	D Dia Min mm	L Max mm	L_1 Max mm	L_2 Max mm	T Min mm	W Max mm	Y Min mm	Z Max mm
4.8	–3	7/16–20	–4	11.1	2.3	59.2	59.2	—	5.6	19.0	9.4	—
6.4	–4	7/16–20	–4	11.1	2.8	63.0	61.2	—	5.6	22.1	9.4	—
6.4	–4	1/2–20	–5	12.7	2.8	63.0	61.2	—	5.6	22.1	10.4	—
6.4	–4	9/16–18	–6	14.3	2.8	63.2	61.2	—	5.6	22.1	10.4	—
7.9	–5	9/16–18	–6	14.3	5.1	63.2	62.0	—	5.6	23.9	10.4	—
9.5	–6	9/16–18	–6	14.3	6.6	64.0	65.0	—	5.6	27.7	10.4	—
9.5	–6	3/4–16	–8	19.0	6.6	66.8	67.6	—	6.4	27.7	12.7	—
10.3	–6.5	3/4–16	–8	19.0	6.6	67.8	67.6	—	6.4	29.5	12.7	—
12.7	–8	3/4–16	–8	19.0	9.7	68.6	78.2	—	6.4	31.2	12.7	—
12.7	–8	7/8–14	–10	22.2	9.7	72.4	80.8	80.8	6.4	31.2	14.2	63.5
15.9	–10	7/8–14	–10	22.2	12.2	84.3	86.9	—	6.4	34.8	14.2	—
15.9	–10	1-1/16–12	–12	27.0	12.7	81.3	90.9	—	7.9	34.8	15.5	—
15.9	–10	7/8–14	–10	22.2	12.2	94.5	90.9	—	7.9	40.4	14.2	—
19.0	–12	1-1/16–12	–12	27.0	14.5	94.5	90.9	87.6	7.9	40.4	15.5	76.2
19.0	–12	1-3/16–12	–14	27.0	15.5	95.2	93.2	89.9	9.7	40.4	15.5	76.2
25.4	–16	1-5/16–12	–16	33.3	19.8	96.8	106.4	95.2	9.7	51.3	17.5	92.2
31.8	–20	1-5/8–12	–20	41.3	25.7	112.8	120.1	112.0	11.7	62.5	21.3	101.6

(a) For dimensions shown in Figure 3B, but not specified in Table 3A, see corresponding dimensions for respective straight thread size in Figure 2A and Table 4 of SAE J514.

TABLE 3B—DIMENSIONS OF MALE 37-DEGREE FLARED TYPE HOSE FITTINGS FOR USE ON SAE 100R2 HYDRAULIC HOSE[(a)] (FIGURES 3A TO 3C)

Nominal SAE 100R2 Hose ID mm	Hose Dash Size	B Nominal Straight Thread Size	Thread Dash Size	C Min mm	D Dia Min mm	L Max mm	L_1 Max mm	L_2 Max mm	T Min mm	W Max mm	Y Min mm	Z Max mm
4.8	–3	7/16–20	–4	11.1	2.3	60.7	65.5	—	4.8	22.9	9.4	—
6.4	–4	7/16–20	–4	11.1	2.8	63.0	66.8	—	4.8	25.4	9.4	—
6.4	–4	1/2–20	–5	12.7	2.8	63.0	66.8	63.2	4.8	25.4	10.4	54.1
6.4	–4	9/16–18	–6	14.3	2.8	65.0	66.8	—	5.6	25.4	10.4	—
9.5	–6	9/16–18	–6	14.3	6.6	67.6	71.4	66.0	5.6	30.2	10.4	62.7
9.5	–6	3/4–16	–8	19.0	6.6	68.3	74.7	69.3	6.4	30.2	12.7	62.7
12.7	–8	3/4–16	–8	19.0	9.7	71.9	78.2	—	6.4	35.1	12.7	—
12.7	–8	7/8–14	–10	22.2	9.7	99.6	80.8	77.5	6.4	35.1	14.2	62.7
15.9	–10	7/8–14	–10	22.2	12.2	84.3	92.5	—	6.4	39.6	14.2	—
15.9	–10	1-1/16–12	–12	27.0	12.7	83.6	96.5	—	7.9	39.6	15.5	—
19.0	–12	7/8–14	–10	22.2	12.2	94.5	96.5	—	7.9	44.5	14.2	—
19.0	–12	1-1/16–12	–12	27.0	14.5	94.5	96.5	87.6	7.9	44.5	15.5	76.2
19.0	–12	1-3/16–12	–14	30.2	15.5	95.2	98.8	—	9.7	44.5	15.5	—
22.2	–14	1-3/16–12	–14	30.2	18.3	92.7	109.0	—	9.7	46.0	15.5	—
22.2	–14	1-5/16–12	–16	33.3	18.3	93.2	108.5	—	9.7	46.0	17.5	—
25.4	–16	1-5/16–12	–16	33.3	19.8	97.5	111.3	107.2	9.7	52.3	17.5	91.4
31.8	–20	1-5/8–12	–20	41.3	25.7	142.7	136.7	141.7	11.7	66.8	21.3	114.3

(a) For dimensions shown in Figure 3A, but not specified in Table 3B, see corresponding dimensions for respective straight thread size in Figure 2A and Table 4 of SAE J514.

TABLE 3C—DIMENSIONS OF MALE 37-DEGREE FLARED TYPE HOSE FITTINGS FOR USE ON SAE 100R3 HYDRAULIC HOSE[(a)] (FIGURES 3A TO 3B) (CODE 44)

Nominal SAE 100R3 Hose ID mm	Hose Dash Size	B Nominal Straight Thread Size	Thread Dash Size	C Min mm	D Dia Min mm	L Max mm	L_1 Max mm	T Min mm	W Max mm	Y Min mm
6.4	–4	7/16–20	–4	11.1	2.8	63.0	60.5	5.6	22.4	9.4
6.4	–4	1/2–20	–5	12.7	2.8	63.0	60.5	5.6	22.4	10.4
9.5	–6	9/16–18	–6	14.3	6.6	64.0	65.0	5.6	26.9	10.4
9.5	–6	3/4–16	–8	19.0	6.6	66.56	66.8	6.4	26.9	12.7
12.7	–8	3/4–16	–8	19.0	8.9	69.3	76.2	6.4	33.3	12.7
12.7	–8	7/8–14	–10	22.2	8.9	73.4	77.7	6.4	33.3	14.2
15.9	–10	7/8–14	–10	22.2	12.2	83.8	84.3	6.4	38.1	14.2
19.0	–12	7/8–14	–10	22.2	12.2	94.5	85.3	7.9	41.4	14.2
19.0	–12	1-1/16–12	–12	27.0	14.5	94.5	85.3	7.9	41.4	15.5
25.4	–16	1-5/16–12	–16	33.3	19.8	96.8	103.1	9.7	50.8	17.5

(a) For dimensions shown in Figure 3B, but not specified in Table 3C, see corresponding dimensions for respective straight thread size in Figure 2A and Table 4 of SAE J514.

TABLE 3D—DIMENSIONS OF MALE 37-DEGREE FLARED TYPE HOSE FITTINGS FOR USE ON SAE 100R4 HYDRAULIC HOSE[(a)] (FIGURE 3A) (CODE 45)

Nominal SAE 100R4 Hose ID mm	Hose Dash Size	B Nominal Straight Thread Size	Thread Dash Size	C Min mm	D Dia Min mm	L Max mm	T Min mm	W Max mm	Y Min mm
19.0	–12	1-1/16–12	–12	27.0	14.5	94.5	7.9	43.9	15.5
25.4	–16	1-5/16–12	–16	33.3	19.8	96.8	7.9	51.1	17.5
31.8	–20	1-5/8–12	–20	41.3	25.7	106.7	7.9	58.7	21.3

(a) For dimensions shown in Figure 3B, but not specified in Table 3D, see corresponding dimensions for respective straight thread size in Figure 2A and Table 4 of SAE J514.

TABLE 3E—DIMENSIONS OF MALE 37-DEGREE FLARED TYPE HOSE FITTINGS FOR USE ON SAE 100R5 HYDRAULIC HOSE[(a)] (FIGURES 3A TO 3B) (CODED 46)

Nominal SAE 100R5 Hose ID mm	Hose Dash Size	B Nominal Straight Thread Size	Thread Dash Size	C Min mm	D Dia Min mm	L Max mm	L_1 Max mm	T Min mm	W Max mm	Y Min mm
4.8	–4	7/16–20	–4	11.1	2.3	47.5	52.3	4.8	20.1	9.4
6.4	–5	1/2–20	–5	12.7	2.8	48.3	52.3	4.8	22.1	10.4
7.9	–6	9/16–18	–6	14.3	5.6	49.3	55.4	5.6	23.9	10.4
10.3	–8	3/4–16	–8	19.0	7.1	54.4	66.8	6.4	27.4	12.7
22.7	–10	7/8–14	–10	22.2	9.7	58.2	74.7	6.4	31.5	14.2
15.9	–12	1–1/16–12	–12	27.0	12.7	63.5	86.6	7.9	38.6	15.5
22.2	–16	1–5/16–12	–16	33.3	18.3	70.0	80.3	9.7	43.9	17.5
28.6	–20	1–5/8–12	–20	41.3	23.9	73.9	83.3	11.7	51.3	21.3
34.9	–24	1–7/8–12	–24	47.6	29.5	85.1	91.9	12.7	58.7	25.4
46.0	–32	2–1/2–12	–32	63.5	40.9	101.1	111.8	15.7	73.4	28.7

(a) For dimensions shown in Figure 3B, but not specified in Table 3E, see corresponding dimensions for respective straight thread size in Figure 2A and Table 4 of SAE J514.
NOTE— For SAE J1402 and DOT FMVSS 106 air brake applications, couplings used on 100R5 hose shall have a minimum assembled orifice no less than 66% of the nominal hose I.D.

TABLE 3F—DIMENSIONS OF MALE 37-DEGREE FLARED TYPE HOSE FITTINGS FOR USE ON SAE 100R6 HYDRAULIC HOSE[(a)] (FIGURE 3A) (CODE 47)

Nominal SAE 100R6 Hose ID mm	Hose Dash Size	B Nominal Straight Thread Size	Thread Dash Size	C Min mm	D Dia Min mm	L Max mm	T Min mm	W Max mm	Y Min mm
6.4	–4	7/16–20	–4	11.1	2.8	35.1	4.8	19.0	9.4
6.4	–4	1/2–20	–5	12.7	2.8	35.1	4.8	19.0	10.4
9.5	–6	9/16–18	–6	14.3	6.6	41.1	5.6	25.4	10.4
9.5	–6	3/4–16	–8	19.0	6.6	43.7	6.4	25.4	12.7
12.7	–8	3/4–16	–8	19.0	9.7	44.4	6.4	28.4	12.7
15.9	–10	7/8–14	–10	22.2	12.2	50.8	6.4	30.2	14.2
19.0	–12	1–1/16–12	–12	27.0	14.5	85.9	7.9	36.8	15.5

(a) For dimensions shown in Figure 3B, but not specified in Table 3F, see corresponding dimensions for respective straight thread size in Figure 2A and Table 4 of SAE J514.

TABLE 3G—DIMENSIONS OF MALE 37-DEGREE FLARED TYPE HOSE FITTINGS FOR USE ON SAE 100R7 HYDRAULIC HOSE[(a)] (FIGURE 3A) (CODE 48)

Nominal SAE 100R7 Hose ID mm	Hose Dash Size	B Nominal Straight Thread Size	Thread Dash Size	C Min mm	D Dia Min mm	L Max mm	T Min mm	W Max mm	Y Min mm
4.8	–3	7/16–20	–4	11.1	2.3	63.2	4.8	19.0	9.4
6.4	–4	7/16–20	–4	11.1	2.8	63.2	4.8	20.6	9.4
6.4	–4	1/2–20	–5	12.7	2.8	63.8	4.8	20.6	10.4
6.4	–4	9/16–18	–6	14.3	2.8	63.8	5.6	20.6	10.4
7.9	–5	9/16–18	–6	14.3	5.1	64.3	5.6	22.4	10.4
9.5	–6	9/16–18	–6	14.3	6.6	68.6	5.6	25.7	10.4
9.5	–6	3/4–16	–8	19.0	6.6	68.6	6.4	25.7	12.7
12.7	–8	3/4–16	–8	19.0	9.1	77.2	6.4	31.2	12.7
12.7	–8	7/8–14	–10	22.2	9.1	78.0	6.4	31.2	14.2
15.9	–10	7/8–14	–10	22.2	12.2	84.3	6.4	34.8	14.2
19.0	–12	1-1/16–12	–12	27.0	14.5	90.2	7.9	40.4	15.5
19.0	–12	1-3/16–12	–14	30.2	14.5	92.7	9.7	40.4	15.5
25.4	–16	1-5/16–12	–16	33.3	19.8	104.1	9.7	40.4	17.5

(a) For dimensions shown in Figure 3B, but not specified in Table 3G, see corresponding dimensions for respective straight thread size in Figure 2A and Table 4 of SAE J514.

TABLE 3H—DIMENSIONS OF MALE 37-DEGREE FLARED TYPE HOSE FITTINGS FOR USE ON SAE 100R8 HYDRAULIC HOSE[(a)] (CODE 49)

Nominal SAE 100R8 Hose ID mm	Hose Dash Size	B Nominal Straight Thread Size	Thread Dash Size	C Min mm	D Dia Min mm	L Max mm	T Min mm	W Max mm	Y Min mm
4.8	–3	7/16–20	–4	11.1	2.3	63.2	4.8	19.0	9.4
6.4	–4	7/16–20	–4	11.1	2.8	63.2	4.8	20.6	9.4
6.4	–4	1/2–20	–5	12.7	2.8	63.8	4.8	20.6	10.4
6.4	–4	9/16–18	–6	14.3	2.8	63.8	5.6	20.6	10.4
9.5	–6	9/16–18	–6	14.3	6.6	68.6	5.6	25.7	10.4
9.5	–6	3/4–16	–8	19.0	6.6	68.6	6.4	25.7	12.7
12.7	–8	3/4–16	–8	19.0	9.1	77.2	6.4	31.2	12.7
12.7	–8	7/8–14	–10	22.2	9.1	78.0	6.4	31.2	14.2
15.9	–10	7/8–14	–10	22.2	12.2	84.3	6.4	36.8	14.2
19.0	–12	1-1/16–12	–12	27.0	14.5	90.2	7.9	40.4	15.5
19.0	–12	1-3/16–12	–14	30.2	14.5	92.7	9.7	40.4	15.5
25.4	–16	1-5/16–12	–16	33.3	19.8	104.1	9.7	49.5	17.5

(a) For dimensions shown in Figure 3B, but not specified in Table 3H, see corresponding dimensions for respective straight thread size in Figure 2A and Table 4 of SAE J514.

TABLE 3I—DIMENSIONS OF MALE 37-DEGREE FLARED TYPE HOSE FITTINGS FOR USE ON SAE 100R9 HYDRAULIC HOSE[(a)] (FIGURES 3A TO 3B) (CODES 50 AND 75)

Nominal SAE 100R9 Hose ID mm	Hose Dash Size	B Nominal Straight Thread Size	Thread Dash Size	C Min mm	D Dia Min mm	L Max mm	L_1 Max mm	T Min mm	W Max mm	Y Min mm
9.5	–6	9/16–18	–6	14.3	6.6	74.4	71.4	5.6	30.2	10.4
12.7	–8	3/4–16	–8	19.0	9.7	76.2	78.2	6.4	35.1	12.7
19.0	–12	1-1/16–12	–12	27.0	14.5	98.3	98.8	7.9	44.5	15.5
25.4	–16	1-5/16–12	–16	33.3	19.8	101.3	111.3	9.7	52.3	17.5
31.8	–20	1-5/8–12	–20	41.3	25.7	142.7	—	11.7	66.8	21.3

(a) For dimensions shown in Figure 3B, but not specified in Table 3I, see corresponding dimensions for respective straight thread size in Figure 2A and Table 4 of SAE J514.

TABLE 3J—DIMENSIONS OF MALE 37-DEGREE FLARED TYPE HOSE FITTINGS FOR USE ON SAE 100R10 HYDRAULIC HOSE[(a)] (FIGURES 3A TO 3C) (CODES 51 TO 76)

Nominal SAE 100R10 Hose ID mm	Hose Dash Size	B Nominal Straight Thread Size	Thread Dash Size	C Min mm	D Dia Min mm	L Max mm	L_1 Max mm	L_2 Max mm	T Min mm	W Max mm	Y Min mm	Z Max mm
6.4	–4	7/16–20	–4	11.1	2.8	75.4	61.2	63.5	5.6	28.7	9.4	54.1
9.5	–6	9/16–18	–6	14.3	5.6	83.3	78.0	79.2	5.6	28.7	10.4	62.7
12.7	–8	3/4–16	–8	19.0	8.6	98.8	78.2	82.6	6.4	31.8	12.7	62.7
19.0	–12	1-1/16–12	–12	27.0	12.7	115.6	94.5	87.6	7.9	42.9	14.5	79.2
25.4	–16	1-5/16–12	–16	33.3	17.3	132.8	111.3	102.9	9.7	50.8	17.5	107.2
31.8	–20	1-5/8–12	–20	41.3	22.1	142.0	137.9	116.3	11.7	62.2	17.8	126.0
38.1	–24	1-7/8–12	–24	47.6	27.7	160.0	148.6	133.4	12.7	76.2	19.3	133.1
50.8	–32	2-1/2–12	–32	63.5	39.6	186.2	196.8	190.5	17.5	81.8	28.4	166.6

(a) For dimensions shown in Figure 3B, but not specified in Table 3J, see corresponding dimensions for respective straight thread size in Figure 2A and Table 4 of SAE J514.

TABLE 3K—DIMENSIONS OF MALE 37-DEGREE FLARED TYPE HOSE FITTINGS FOR USE ON SAE 100R12 HYDRAULIC HOSE[(a)] (FIGURE 3A) (CODE 77)

Nominal SAE 100R12 Hose ID mm	Hose Dash Size	B Nominal Straight Thread Size	Thread Dash Size	C Min mm	D Dia Min mm	L Max mm	T Min mm	W Max mm	Y Min mm
9.5	–6	9/16–18	–6	14.3	5.6	83.3	5.6	28.7	10.4
12.7	–8	3/4–16	–8	19.0	8.6	98.8	6.4	31.8	12.7
15.9	–10	7/8–14	–10	22.2	10.0	108.0	7.9	38.0	14.5
19.0	–12	1-1/16–12	–12	27.0	12.7	117.3	7.9	42.9	14.5
25.4	–16	1-5/16–12	–16	33.3	17.3	132.8	9.7	50.8	15.7
31.8	–20	1-5/8–12	–20	41.3	22.1	143.5	11.2	60.5	17.5
38.1	–24	1-7/8–12	–24	47.6	27.7	160.0	12.7	67.8	18.8
50.8	–32	2-1/2–12	–32	63.5	39.6	186.2	15.7	81.8	22.4

(a) For dimensions shown in Figure 3B, but not specified in Table 3K, see corresponding dimensions for respective straight thread size in Figure 2A and Table 4 of SAE J514.

TABLE 3L—DIMENSIONS OF MALE 37-DEGREE FLARED TYPE HOSE FITTINGS FOR USE ON SAE 100R13 HYDRAULIC HOSE[(a)] (FIGURE 3A) (CODE 78)

Nominal SAE 100R13 Hose ID mm	Hose Dash Size	B Nominal Straight Thread Size	Thread Dash Size	C Min mm	D Dia Min mm	L Max mm	T Min mm	W Max mm	Y Min mm
19.0	–12	1-1/16–12	–12	27.0	12.7	117.3	7.9	43.7	15.7
25.4	–16	1-5/16–12	–16	33.3	17.5	127.0	9.7	50.8	15.7
31.8	–20	1-5/8–12	–20	41.3	22.4	143.5	11.2	63.5	17.5
38.1	–24	1-7/8–12	–24	47.6	27.7	159.0	12.7	71.1	18.8
50.8	–32	2-1/2–12	–32	63.5	38.1	224.3	15.7	88.9	22.4

(a) For dimensions shown in Figure 3B, but not specified in Table 3L, see corresponding dimensions for respective straight thread size in Figure 2A and Table 4 of SAE J514.

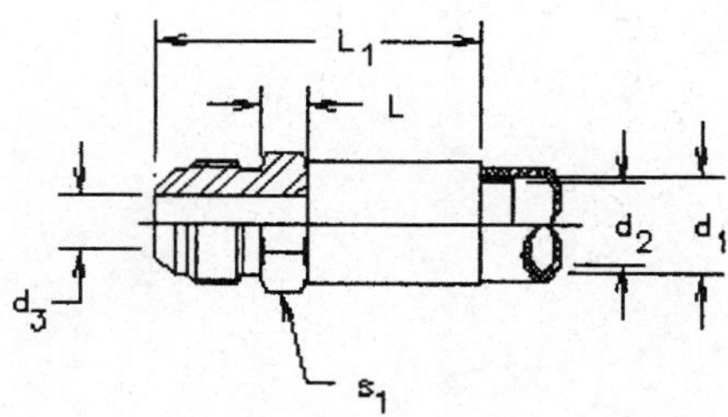

NOTES
1 Connection details in accordance with ISO 8434-2.
2 Method of attachment of fitting to hose is optional.

FIGURE 3D—STRAIGHT MALE HOSE FITTING (S)—2101XX

TABLE 3M—DIMENSIONS OF STRAIGHT MALE HOSE FITTINGS (S)
DIMENSIONS IN MILLIMETERS

Fitting Size	SAE Dash Size	Thread[(1)]	Nominal Connection Size	d_1 (nominal Inside diameter of hose)	d_2[(2)] min	d_3[(3)] max	L min	L_1[(4)] max	S_1 Std	S_1[(5)] Optional
6 x 6.3	4–4	7/16-20 UNF	6	6.3	3	4.6	7	75	12	11.1
8 x 8	5–5	1/2-20 UNF	8	8	5	6.2	7	80	14	12.7
10 x 10	6–6	9/16-18 UNF	10	10	6	7.7	8	85	17	14.3
12 x 12.5	8–8	3/4-16 UNF	12	12.5	8	10.1	8	100	19	—
16 x 16	10–10	7/8-14 UNF	16	16	11	12.6	10	110	24	22.2
20 x 19	12–12	1 1/16-12 UN	20	19	14	15.8	11	120	27	—
25 x 25	16–16	1 5/16-12 UN	25	25	19	21.8	11	135	36	33.3
32 x 31.5	20–20	1 5/8-12 UN	32	31.5	25	27.8	13	145	46	41.3
38 x 38	24–24	1 7/8-12 UN	38	38	30	33.4	15	160	50	47.6
50 x 51	32–32	2 1/2-12 UN	50	51	40	45.4	18	225	65	63.5

1. In accordance with ISO 725 and ISO 5864, class 2A.
2. Minimum diameter at any point through the fitting prior to assembly to the hose. The diameter after assembly shall not be less than $0.9d_2$.
3. Dimenison d_3 is in accordance with ISO 8434-2, except the minimum diameter for d_3 shall not be less than d_2. Transition between diameters d_2 (hose nipple through diameter) and d_3 (through diameter of the 37 degree flared end) shall be located to minimize stress concentration.
4. Dimension L_1 is measured after assembly.
5. Based on available inch hex sizes.

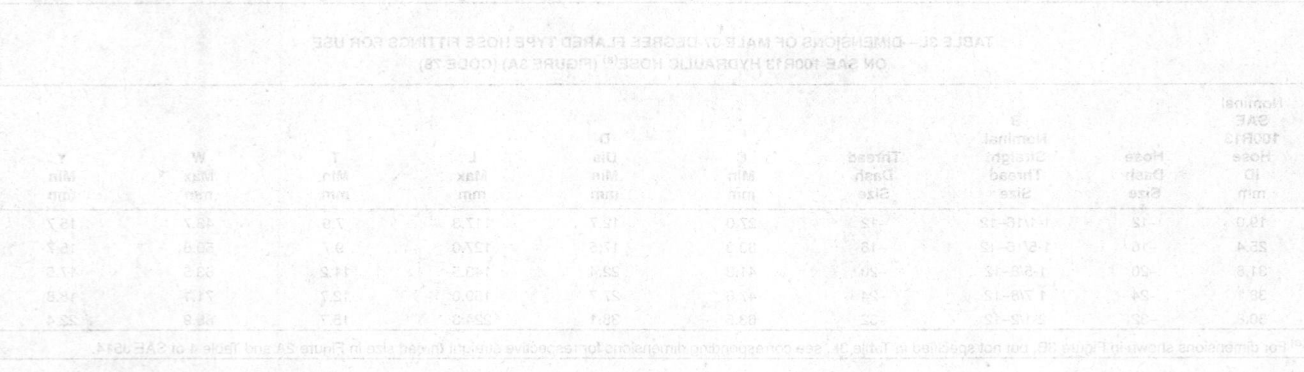

NOTE—UNSPECIFIED DETAIL WITH RESPECT TO DIMENSIONS, TOLERANCES, CONTOURS, MATERIAL, WORKMANSHIP, AND SO ON, MUST CONFORM TO GENERAL SPECIFICATIONS FOR HYDRAULIC HOSE FITTINGS. THE DIMENSIONAL DESIGNATIONS ON THE FIRST FIGURE IN EACH GROUP SHALL APPLY TO ALL OTHER FIGURES IN THAT GROUP EXCEPT AS SHOWN OTHERWISE. CODES SHOWN IN BRACKETS ADJACENT TO FIGURE NUMBERS REPRESENT RESPECTIVE FITTING IDENTIFICATION, WITH XX SUBSTITUTED FOR THE HOSE TYPE CODE DEPICTED IN BRACKETS AT END OF RESPECTIVE TABLE TITLES, IN ACCORDANCE WITH SAE J846.

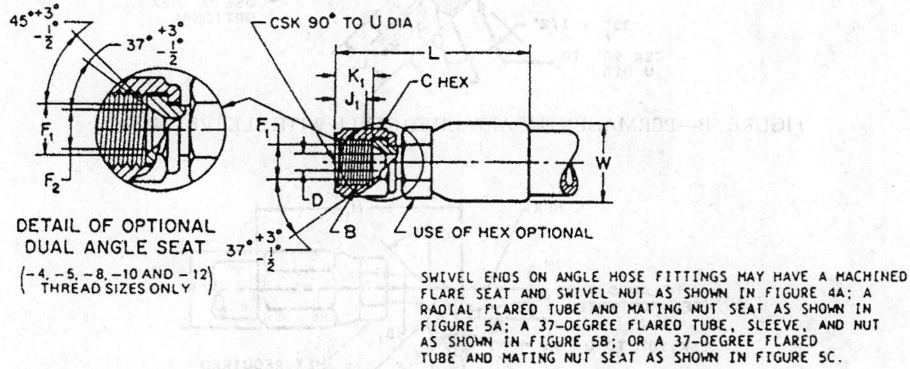

FIGURE 4A—PERMANENTLY ATTACHED STYLE (2401XX)

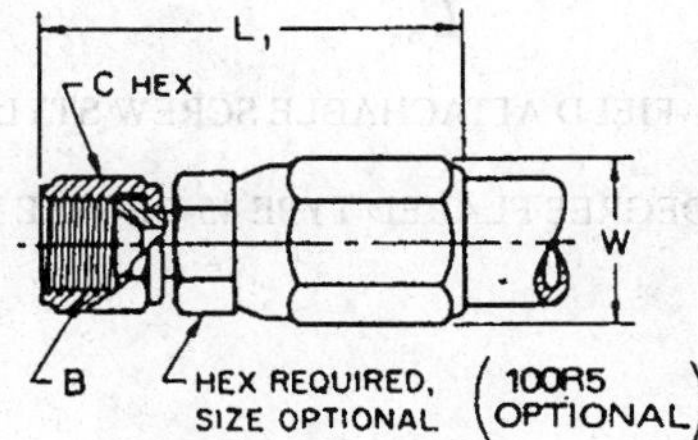

FIGURE 4B—FIELD ATTACHABLE SCREW STYLE (2501XX)

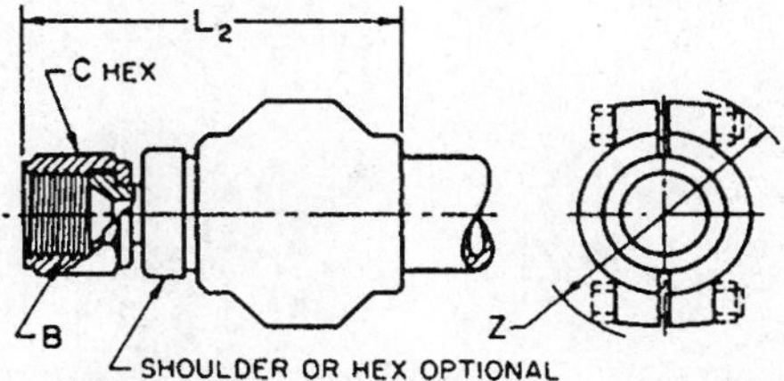

FIGURE 4C—FIELD ATTACHABLE SEGMENT CLAMP STYLE (2601XX)

FIGURE 4—FEMALE 37-DEGREE FLARED TYPE HOSE FITTINGS

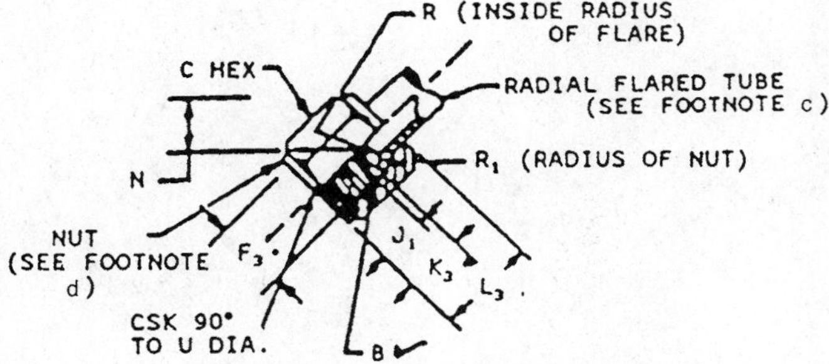

FIGURE 5A—OPTIONAL 37-DEGREE RADIAL FLARE SWIVEL END

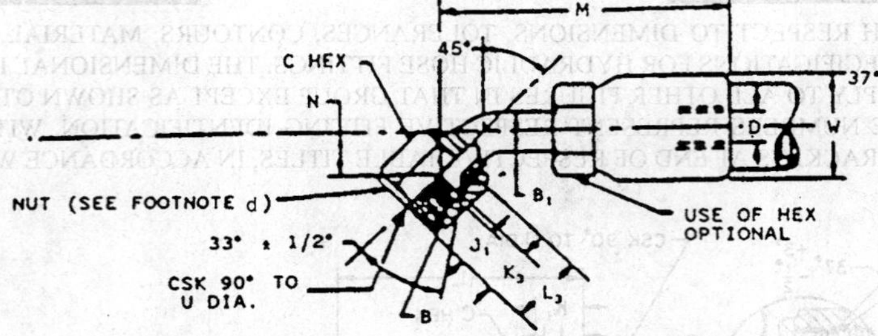

FIGURE 5B—PERMANENTLY ATTACHED STYLE WITH SLEEVE (2403XX)

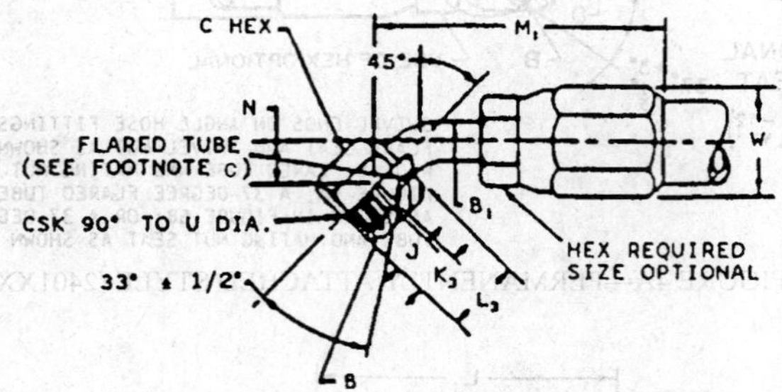

FIGURE 5C—FIELD ATTACHABLE SCREW STYLE (2503XX)

FIGURE 5—FEMALE 37-DEGREE FLARED TYPE 45-DEGREE ANGLE HOSE FITTINGS

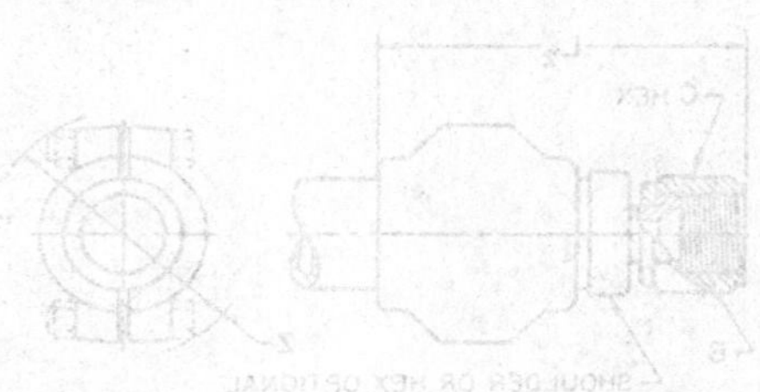

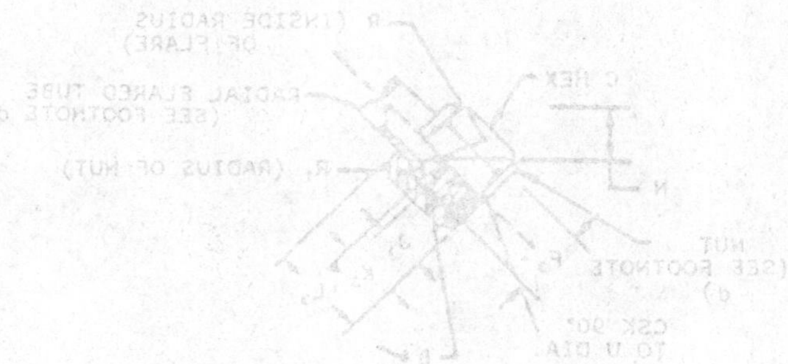

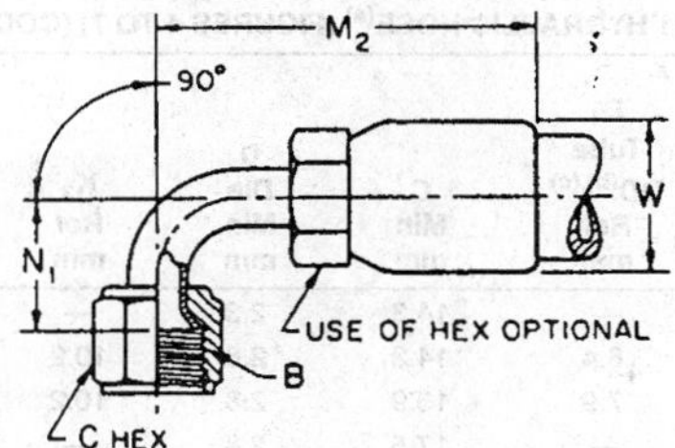

FIGURE 6A—PERMANENTLY ATTACHED STYLE (2414XX)

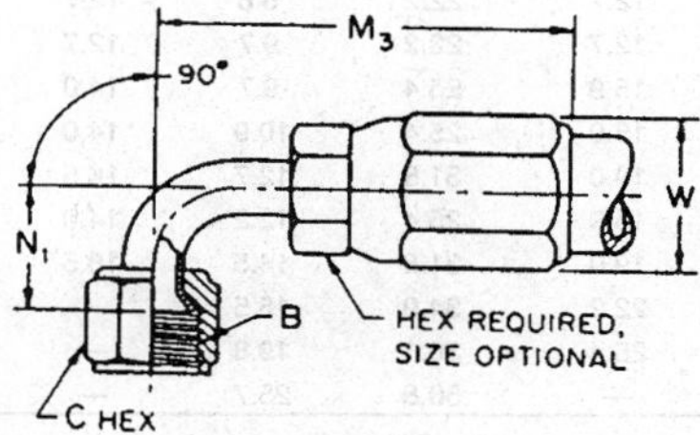

FIGURE 6B—FIELD ATTACHABLE SCREW STYLE (2514XX)

FIGURE 6—FEMALE 37-DEGREE FLARED TYPE 90-DEGREE ANGLE SHORT DROP HOSE FITTINGS

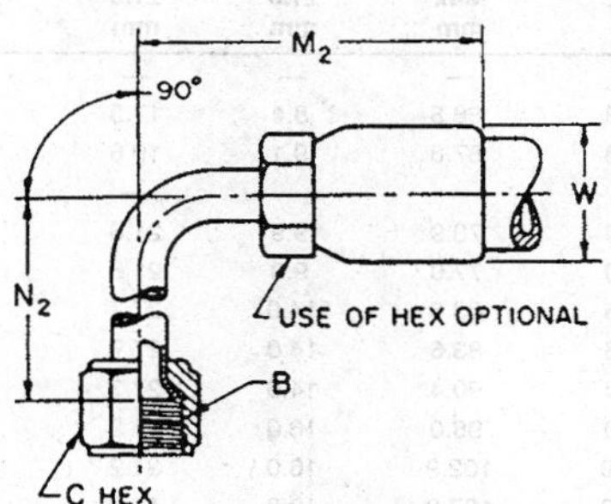

FIGURE 7A—PERMANENTLY ATTACHED STYLE (2415XX)

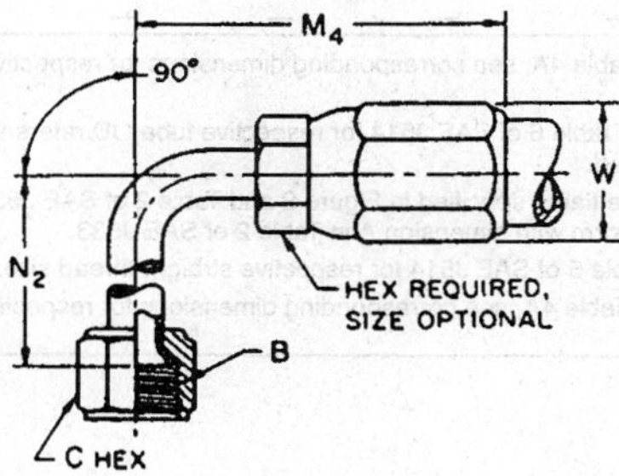

FIGURE 7B—FIELD ATTACHABLE SCREW STYLE (2515XX)

FIGURE 7—FEMALE 37-DEGREE FLARED TYPE 90-DEGREE ANGLE LONG DROP HOSE FITTINGS

TABLE 4A—DIMENSIONS OF FEMALE 37-DEGREE FLARED TYPE HOSE FITTINGS FOR USE ON SAE 100R1 HYDRAULIC HOSE[a] (FIGURES 4 TO 7) (CODES 42 AND 53)

Nominal SAE 100R1 Hose ID mm	Hose Dash Size	B Nominal Straight Thread Size[e]	Thread and Tube Dash Size	B_1 Tube OD[b],[c] Ref mm	C Min mm	D Dia Min mm	K_3 Ref mm	L Max mm	L_1 Max mm	L_2 Max mm	L_3 ±0.3 mm	M Max mm
4.8	-3	7/16–20	-4	—	14.3	2.3	—	60.5	65.0	—	—	—
6.4	-4	7/16–20	-4	6.4	14.3	2.8	10.2	66.3	66.5	—	15.5	67.6
6.4	-4	1/2–20	-5	7.9	15.9	2.8	10.2	67.8	66.5	—	15.7	68.8
6.4	-4	9/16–18	-6	—	17.5	2.8	10.2	68.1	67.6	—	—	—
7.9	-5	9/16–18	-6	9.5	17.5	5.1	10.2	68.1	67.6	—	16.8	74.7
9.5	-6	9/16–18	-6	9.5	17.5	6.6	10.2	68.8	70.6	—	16.8	76.2
9.5	-6	3/4–16	-8	12.7	22.2	6.6	12.7	71.4	73.9	—	16.8	85.9
10.3	-6.5	3/4–16	-8	12.7	22.2	6.6	12.7	71.4	73.9	—	16.8	85.9
12.7	-8	3/4–16	-8	12.7	22.2	9.7	12.7	73.2	82.3	—	17.3	85.9
12.7	-8	7/8–14	-10	15.9	25.4	9.7	14.0	78.0	83.1	81.8	23.6	92.2
15.9	-10	7/8–14	-10	15.9	25.4	10.9	14.0	89.7	88.4	—	23.6	102.6
15.9	-10	1-1/16–12	-12	19.0	31.8	12.7	16.5	88.4	93.5	—	28.4	106.4
19.0	-12	7/8–14	-10	15.9	25.4	12.2	14.0	98.0	95.8	—	23.6	116.1
19.0	-12	1-1/16–12	-12	19.0	31.8	14.5	16.5	98.0	93.5	88.9	28.4	116.1
19.0	-12	1-3/16–12	-14	22.2	34.9	15.5	—	102.6	96.8	93.5	—	114.3
25.4	-16	1-5/16–12	-16	25.4	38.1	19.8	—	102.6	108.7	108.7	—	123.2
31.8	-20	1-5/8–12	-20	—	50.8	25.7	—	115.8	126.0	—	—	—

TABLE 4A—DIMENSIONS OF FEMALE 37-DEGREE FLARED TYPE HOSE FITTINGS FOR USE ON SAE 100R1 HYDRAULIC HOSE[a] (FIGURES 4 TO 7) (CODES 42 AND 53) (CONTINUED)

Nominal SAE 100R1 Hose ID mm	Thread and Tube Dash Size	M_1 Max mm	M_2 Max mm	M_3 Max mm	M_4 Max mm	N ±1.5 mm	N_1 ±1.5 mm	N_2 ±1.5 mm	R Ref mm	R_1 ±0.13 mm	W Max mm	Z Max mm
4.8	-4	—	—	—	—	—	—	—	—	—	19.0	—
6.4	-4	74.2	64.5	66.8	66.8	8.4	17.3	45.7	5.21	3.2	22.1	—
6.4	-5	75.4	64.5	67.8	67.8	9.1	19.6	45.7	6.02	3.2	22.1	—
6.4	-6	—	—	—	—	—	—	—	—	—	22.1	—
7.9	-6	82.8	68.3	73.9	73.9	9.9	21.6	55.4	5.44	3.2	23.9	—
9.5	-6	84.6	69.9	77.0	77.0	9.9	21.6	55.4	5.44	3.2	27.7	—
9.5	-8	90.2	77.7	83.6	83.6	14.0	27.7	61.7	5.23	3.2	27.7	—
10.3	-8	90.2	77.7	83.6	83.6	14.0	27.7	61.7	5.23	3.2	29.5	—
12.7	-8	97.8	77.7	90.4	90.4	14.0	27.7	61.7	5.23	3.2	30.5	—
12.7	-10	104.6	82.6	96.0	96.0	16.0	31.2	65.3	7.77	4.8	30.5	63.5
15.9	-10	113.0	108.0	102.9	102.9	16.0	31.2	65.3	7.77	4.8	34.8	—
15.9	-12	115.1	96.5	107.2	107.2	19.8	46.2	94.7	6.60	3.8	34.8	—
19.0	-10	115.1	114.8	108.7	108.7	16.0	31.2	65.3	7.77	4.8	40.4	—
19.0	-12	115.1	114.8	108.7	108.7	19.8	46.2	94.7	6.60	3.8	40.4	76.2
19.0	-14	125.0	104.9	115.6	115.6	21.3	50.8	99.8	—	—	40.4	76.2
25.4	-16	146.8	122.9	132.1	132.1	22.6	54.4	110.0	—	—	51.3	91.2
31.8	-20	—	—	—	—	—	—	—	—	—	62.5	—

(a) For dimensions shown in Figures 4 to 7, but not specified in Table 4A, see corresponding dimensions for respective straight thread size in Figure 8C andTable 4 of SAE J514.

(b) Sleeves shown in Figure 5B shall conform with Figure 14 and Table 6 of SAE J514 for respective tube OD referenced above except on some sizes and shapes where sleeve length must be shortened.

(c) 37-degree flares shall conform with single or double 37-degree flares specified in Figure 2 and Table 2 of SAE J533 for respective tube OD referencedabove. Dimension F3 of radial flares shall conform with dimension A in Table 2 of SAE J533.

(d) Nuts shown in Figure 5B shall conform with Figure 12 and Table 5 of SAE J514 for respective straight thread size.

(e) For dimensions shown in Figures 5 to 7, but not specified in Table 4A, see corresponding dimensions for respective straight thread size in Figures 11 and 13, and Table 5 of SAE J514.

TABLE 4B—DIMENSIONS OF FEMALE 37-DEGREE FLARED TYPE HOSE FITTINGS FOR USE ON SAE 100R2 HYDRAULIC HOSE[(a)] (FIGURES 4 TO 7) (CODES 43 AND 54)

Nominal SAE 100R2 Hose ID mm	Hose Dash Size	B Nominal Straight Thread Size[(e)] mm	Thread and Tube Dash Size	B_1 Tube OD[(b), (c)] Ref mm	C Min mm	D Dia Min mm	K_3 Ref mm	L Max mm	L_1 Max mm	L_2 Max mm	L_3 ±0.3 mm	M Max mm
4.8	–3	7/16–20	–4	—	14.3	2.3	—	62.0	67.8	—	—	—
6.4	–4	7/16–20	–4	6.4	14.3	2.8	10.2	66.3	73.2	—	15.5	71.1
6.4	–4	1/2–20	–5	7.9	15.9	2.8	10.2	67.8	74.7	66.0	15.7	73.7
6.4	–4	9/16–18	–6	—	17.5	2.8	—	68.1	74.7	—	—	—
9.5	–6	9/16–18	–6	9.5	17.5	6.6	10.2	69.1	80.3	70.9	16.8	79.2
9.5	–6	3/4–16	–8	12.7	22.2	6.6	12.7	74.4	80.3	71.4	16.8	88.1
12.7	–8	3/4–16	–8	12.7	22.2	9.7	12.7	76.7	84.6	—	16.8	93.5
12.7	–8	7/8–14	–10	15.9	25.4	9.7	14.0	78.5	85.9	84.3	23.6	102.1
15.9	–10	7/8–14	–10	15.9	25.4	10.9	14.0	89.7	94.7	—	23.6	108.5
15.9	–10	1–1/16–12	–12	19.0	31.8	12.7	16.5	88.4	103.6	—	28.4	114.8
19.0	–12	7/8–14	–10	15.9	25.4	12.2	14.0	98.0	103.6	—	23.6	117.3
19.0	–12	1–1/16–12	–12	19.0	31.8	14.5	16.5	98.0	103.6	94.7	28.4	117.3
19.0	–12	1–3/16–12	–14	22.2	34.9	15.5	—	102.6	105.2	—	—	120.9
22.2	–14	1–3/16–12	–14	22.2	34.9	18.3	—	99.1	114.3	—	—	114.3
22.2	–14	1–5/16–12	–16	25.4	38.1	18.3	—	100.1	115.3	—	—	120.7
25.4	–16	1–5/16–12	–16	25.4	38.1	19.8	—	106.4	115.3	114.0	—	140.2
31.8	–20	1–5/8–12	–20	—	50.8	25.7	—	166.6	138.9	133.4	—	—
38.1	–24	1–7/8–12	–24	—	57.2	31.8	—	170.7	148.6	146.0	—	—
50.8	–32	2–1/2–12	–32	—	73.0	43.7	—	177.8	165.9	171.7	—	—

Continued on next page.

TABLE 4B—DIMENSIONS OF FEMALE 37-DEGREE FLARED TYPE HOSE FITTINGS FOR USE ON SAE 100R2 HYDRAULIC HOSE[(a)] (FIGURES 4 TO 7) (CODES 43 AND 54) (CONTINUED)

Nominal SAE 100R2 Hose ID mm	Thread and Tube Dash Size	M_1 Max mm	M_2 Max mm	M_3 Max mm	M_4 Max mm	N ±1.5 mm	N_1 ±1.5 mm	N_2 ±1.5 mm	R Ref mm	R_1 ±0.13 mm	W Max mm	Z Max mm
4.8	–4	—	—	—	—	—	—	—	—	—	22.9	—
6.4	–4	79.0	64.5	76.2	76.2	8.4	17.3	45.7	5.21	3.2	22.6	—
6.4	–5	77.2	66.5	71.1	71.1	9.1	19.6	45.7	6.02	3.2	25.4	54.1
6.4	–6	—	—	—	—	—	—	—	—	—	25.4	—
9.5	–6	86.9	71.9	84.3	84.3	9.9	21.6	55.4	5.44	3.2	30.2	62.7
9.5	–8	90.7	80.3	85.9	90.7	14.0	27.7	61.7	5.23	3.2	30.2	62.7
12.7	–8	100.3	85.6	92.7	92.7	14.0	27.7	61.7	5.23	3.2	31.5	—
12.7	–10	106.9	92.2	98.3	98.3	16.0	31.2	65.3	7.77	4.8	31.5	62.7
15.9	–10	113.0	108.0	105.2	105.2	16.0	31.2	65.3	7.77	4.8	39.6	—
15.9	–12	114.6	104.9	112.0	112.0	19.8	46.2	94.7	6.60	3.8	39.6	—
19.0	–10	122.2	114.8	112.0	120.9	16.0	31.2	65.3	7.77	4.8	44.4	—
19.0	–12	122.2	114.8	112.0	120.9	19.8	46.2	94.7	6.60	3.8	44.4	76.2
19.0	–14	129.5	108.0	120.1	120.1	21.3	50.8	99.8	—	—	44.4	—
22.2	–14	129.5	108.0	125.7	125.7	21.3	50.8	99.8	—	—	45.5	—
22.2	–16	146.8	114.3	132.1	132.1	22.6	54.4	110.0	—	—	45.5	—
25.4	–16	146.8	133.4	134.9	139.7	22.6	54.4	110.0	—	—	52.1	91.4
31.8	–20	—	—	—	—	—	—	—	—	—	66.8	114.3
38.1	–24	—	—	—	—	—	—	—	—	—	74.7	127.0
50.8	–32	—	—	—	—	—	—	—	—	—	88.9	133.4

(a) For dimensions shown in Figures 4 to 7, but not specified in Table 4B, see corresponding dimensions for respective straight thread size in Figure 8C and Table 4 of SAE J514.

(b) Sleeves shown in Figure 5B shall conform with Figure 14 and Table 6 of SAE J514 for respective tube OD referenced above except on some sizes and shapes where sleeve length must be shortened.

(c) 37-degree flares shall conform with single or double 37-degree flares specified in Figure 2 and Table 2 of SAE J533 for respective tube OD referenced above. Dimension F3 of radial flares shall conform with dimension A in Table 2 of SAE J533.

(d) Nuts shown in Figure 5B shall conform with Figure 12 and Table 5 of SAE J514 for respective straight thread size.

(e) For dimensions shown in Figures 5 to 7, but not specified in Table 4B, see corresponding dimensions for respective straight thread size in Figures 11 and 13, and Table 5 of SAE J514.

TABLE 4C—DIMENSIONS OF FEMALE 37-DEGREE FLARED TYPE HOSE FITTINGS FOR USE ON SAE 100R3 HYDRAULIC HOSE[(a)] (FIGURES 4 TO 7) (CODE 44)

Nominal SAE 100R3 Hose ID mm	Hose Dash Size	B Nominal Straight Thread Size	Thread Dash Size	C Min mm	D Dia Min mm	L Max mm	L_1 Max mm	L_2 Min mm	W Max mm	Z Min mm
6.4	–4	7/16–20	–4	14.3	2.8	66.3	63.5	—	22.4	—
6.4	–4	1/2–20	–5	15.9	2.8	67.8	63.5	—	22.4	—
9.5	–6	9/16–18	–6	17.5	6.6	70.6	70.4	—	26.9	—
9.5	–6	3/4–16	–8	22.2	6.6	70.9	69.8	—	26.9	—
12.7	–8	3/4–16	–8	22.2	9.7	74.4	78.7	—	33.3	—
12.7	–8	7/8–14	–10	25.4	9.7	77.2	82.6	—	33.3	—
15.9	–10	7/8–14	–10	25.4	10.9	89.7	83.8	—	38.1	—
19.0	–12	7/8–14	–10	25.4	12.2	98.0	85.9	—	41.4	—
19.0	–12	1-1/16–12	–12	31.8	14.5	98.0	85.9	—	42.2	—
25.4	–16	1-15/16–12	–16	38.1	19.8	102.6	95.2	93.5	50.8	82.6

(a) For dimensions shown in Figures 4 to 7, but not specified in Table 4C, see corresponding dimensions for respective straight thread size in Figure 8C and Table 4 of SAE J514.

TABLE 4D—DIMENSIONS OF FEMALE 37-DEGREE FLARED TYPE HOSE FITTINGS FOR USE ON SAE 100R4 HYDRAULIC HOSE[(a)] (FIGURES 4 TO 7) (CODE 45)

Nominal SAE 100R4 Hose ID mm	Hose Dash Size	B Nominal Straight Thread Size	Thread Dash Size	C Min mm	D Dia Min mm	L Max mm	W Max mm
19.0	–12	1-1/16–12	–12	31.8	14.5	98.0	43.9
25.4	–16	1-5/16–12	–16	38.1	19.8	102.6	51.1
31.8	–20	1-5/8–12	–20	50.8	25.7	106.7	58.7

(a) For dimensions shown in Figures 4 to 7, but not specified in Table 4D, see corresponding dimensions for respective straight thread size in Figure 8C and Table 4 of SAE J514.

TABLE 4E—DIMENSIONS OF FEMALE 37-DEGREE FLARED TYPE HOSE FITTINGS FOR USE ON SAE 100R5 HYDRAULIC HOSE[(a)] (FIGURES 4 TO 7) (CODE 46)

Nominal SAE 100R5 Hose ID mm	Hose Dash Size	B Nominal Straight Thread Size[(e)]	Thread and Tube Dash Size	B_1 Tube OD[(b),(c)] Ref mm	C Min mm	D Dia Min mm	K_3 Ref mm	L Max mm	L_1 Max mm	L_3 mm	M_1 Max mm	M_3 Max mm	M_4 Max mm	N ±1.5 mm	N_1 ±1.5 mm	N_2 ±1.5 mm	R Ref mm	R_1 mm	W Max mm
4.8	–4	7/16–20	–4	6.4	14.3	2.3	10.2	53.1	53.8	15.5	62.2	59.7	59.7	8.4	17.3	45.7	5.21	3.18	20.1
6.4	–5	1/2–20	–5	7.9	15.9	2.8	10.2	56.1	55.4	15.7	66.0	64.5	64.5	9.1	19.6	45.7	6.02	3.18	22.1
7.9	–6	9/16–18	–6	9.7	17.5	5.1	10.2	57.9	60.7	16.8	69.8	67.3	67.3	9.9	21.6	55.4	5.44	3.18	23.9
10.3	–8	3/4–16	–8	12.7	22.2	7.1	12.7	64.0	73.2	16.8	84.8	81.0	81.0	14.0	27.7	61.7	5.23	3.18	27.4
12.7	–10	7/8–14	–10	15.9	25.4	9.7	14.0	67.6	80.3	23.6	93.0	88.1	88.1	16.0	31.2	65.3	7.77	4.78	31.8
15.9	–12	1-1/16–12	–12	19.0	31.8	12.7	16.5	70.4	91.9	28.4	84.8	109.1	109.0	19.8	46.2	94.7	6.60	3.81	38.6
22.2	–16	1-5/16–12	–16	25.4	38.1	18.3	—	80.8	88.9	—	105.7	103.6	103.6	22.6	54.4	110.0	—	—	43.9
28.6	–20	1-5/8–12	–20	31.8	50.8	23.9	—	84.3	98.6	—	105.4	103.6	103.6	27.9	65.5	134.1	—	—	51.3
34.9	–24	1-7/8–12	–24	—	57.2	29.5	—	96.6	101.1	—	—	—	—	—	—	—	—	—	58.7
46.0	–32	2-1/2–12	–32	—	73.0	40.9	—	114.3	120.9	—	—	—	—	—	—	—	—	—	73.4

(a) For dimensions shown in Figures 4 to 7, but not specified in Table 4E, see corresponding dimensions for respective straight thread size in Figure 8C and Table 2 of SAE J514.

(b) Sleeves shown in Figure 5B shall conform with Figure 14 and Table 6 of SAE J514 for respective tube OD referenced above except on some sizes and shapes where sleeve length must be shortened.

(c) 37-degree flares shall conform with single or double 37-degree flares specified in Figure 2 and Table 2 of SAE J533 for respective tube OD referenced above. Dimension F3 of radial flares shall conform with dimension A in Table 2 of SAE J533.

(d) Nuts shown in Figure 5B shall conform with Figure 12 and Table 5 of SAE J514 for respective straight thread size.

(e) For dimensions shown in Figures 5 to 7, but not specified in Table 4E, see corresponding dimensions for respective straight thread size in Figures 11 and 13, and Table 5 of SAE J514.

NOTE—For SAE J1402 and DOT FMVSS 106 air brake applications, couplings used in 100R5 hose shall have a minimum assembled orifice no less than 66% of the nominal hose I.D.

TABLE 4F—DIMENSIONS OF FEMALE 37-DEGREE FLARED TYPE HOSE FITTINGS FOR USE ON SAE 100R6 HYDRAULIC HOSE[a] (FIGURES 4 TO 7) (CODE 47)

Nominal SAE 100R6 Hose ID mm	Hose Dash Size	B Nominal Straight Thread Size	Thread Dash Size	C Min mm	D Dia Min mm	L Max mm	L_1 Max mm	W Max mm
6.4	–4	7/16–20	–4	14.3	2.8	38.1	39.6	19.0
6.4	–4	1/2–20	–5	15.9	2.8	38.1	39.6	19.0
7.9	–5	1/2–20	–5	15.9	5.1	40.1	42.9	22.4
7.9	–5	9/16–18	–6	17.5	5.1	40.1	37.1	22.4
9.5	–6	9/16–18	–6	17.5	6.6	45.2	46.7	25.4
9.5	–6	3/4–16	–8	22.2	6.6	46.0	46.7	25.4
12.7	–8	3/4–16	–8	22.2	9.7	46.0	47.8	28.4
12.7	–8	7/8–14	–10	25.4	9.7	48.5	—	28.4
15.9	–10	7/8–14	–10	25.4	12.2	57.4	58.9	30.2
19.0	–12	1-1/16–12	–12	31.8	14.5	85.9	83.8	36.8

[a] For dimensions shown in Figures 4 to 7, but not specified in Table 4F, see corresponding dimensions for respective straight thread size in Figure 8C and Table 4 of SAE J514.

TABLE 4G—DIMENSIONS OF FEMALE 37-DEGREE FLARED TYPE HOSE FITTINGS FOR USE ON SAE 100R7 HYDRAULIC HOSE[a] (FIGURES 4 TO 7) (CODE 48)

Nominal SAE 100R7 Hose ID mm	Hose Dash Size	B Nominal Straight Thread Size	Thread and Tube Dash Size[e]	B_1 Tube OD Ref mm	C Min mm	D Dia Min mm	L Max mm	L_1 Max mm	M Max mm	M_2 Max mm	N ± 1.5 mm	N_1 ± 1.5 mm	N_2 ± 1.5 mm	W Max mm
4.8	–3	7/16–20	–4	—	14.3	2.3	66.3	51.3	76.2	72.4	8.4	17.3	45.7	19.0
6.4	–4	7/16–20	–4	6.14	14.3	2.8	66.3	56.4	87.6	82.0	8.4	17.3	45.7	20.6
6.4	–4	1/2–20	–5	7.9	15.9	2.8	66.5	56.4	88.9	83.3	9.1	19.6	45.7	20.6
6.4	–4	9/16–18	–6	—	17.5	2.8	67.1	56.4	—	—	—	—	—	20.6
7.9	–5	9/16–18	–6	9.5	17.5	5.1	67.8	64.3	90.2	84.1	9.9	21.6	55.4	22.4
9.5	–6	9/16–18	–6	9.5	17.5	6.6	74.2	70.4	94.7	88.9	9.9	21.6	55.4	25.7
9.5	–6	3/4–16	–8	12.7	22.2	6.6	76.2	70.4	103.6	96.8	14.0	27.7	61.7	25.7
12.7	–8	3/4–16	–8	12.7	22.2	9.1	80.8	79.2	107.2	100.1	14.0	27.7	61.7	31.2
12.7	–8	7/8–14	–10	15.9	25.4	9.1	83.6	79.2	115.8	106.7	16.0	31.2	65.3	31.2
15.9	–10	7/8–14	–10	15.9	25.4	10.9	89.7	—	118.4	111.8	16.0	31.2	65.3	34.8
19.0	–12	1-1/16–12	–12	19.0	31.8	14.5	91.7	88.4	120.9	117.1	19.8	46.2	94.7	40.4
19.0	–12	1-3/16–12	–14	22.2	34.9	14.5	92.2	82.8	—	—	—	—	—	40.4
25.4	–16	1-5/16–12	–16	25.4	38.1	19.8	105.7	94.5	140.2	133.4	22.6	54.4	110.0	49.5

[a] For dimensions shown in Figures 4 to 7, but not specified in Table 4G, see corresponding dimensions for respective straight thread size in Figure 8C and Table 4 of SAE J514.

[b] Sleeves shown in Figure 5B shall conform with Figure 14 and Table 6 of SAE J514 for respective tube OD referenced above except on some sizes and shapes where sleeve length must be shortened.

[c] Flares shall conform with single or double 37-degree flares specified in Figure 2 and Table 2 of SAE J533 for respective tube OD referenced above.

[d] Nuts shown in Figure 5B shall conform with Figure 12 and Table 3 of SAE J514 for respective straight thread size.

[e] For dimensions shown in Figures 5 to 7, but not specified in Table 4G, see corresponding dimensions for respective straight thread size in Figures 11 and 13,and Table 5 of SAE J514.

TABLE 4H—DIMENSIONS OF FEMALE 37-DEGREE FLARED TYPE HOSE FITTINGS FOR USE ON SAE 100R8 HYDRAULIC HOSE[a] (FIGURES 4 TO 7) (CODE 49)

Nominal SAE 100R8 Hose ID mm	Hose Dash Size	B Nominal Straight Thread Size[e]	Thread and Tube Dash Size	B_1 Tube OD Ref mm	C Min mm	D Dia mm	L Max mm	L_1 Max mm	M Min mm	M_1 Max mm	M_2 Min mm	M_3 Max mm	M_4 Max mm	N ±1.5 mm	N_1 ±1.5 mm	N_2 ±1.5 mm	W Max mm
4.8	−3	7/16−20	−4	—	14.3	2.3	66.3	—	76.2	—	72.4	—	—	8.4	17.3	45.7	19.0
6.4	−4	7/16−20	−4	6.4	14.3	2.8	66.3	—	87.6	—	82.0	—	—	8.4	17.3	45.7	20.6
6.4	−4	1/2−20	−5	7.9	15.9	2.8	66.5	—	88.9	—	83.3	—	—	9.1	19.6	45.7	20.6
6.4	−4	9/16−18	−6	—	17.5	2.8	67.1	—	—	—	—	—	—	—	—	—	—
9.5	−6	9/16−18	−6	9.5	17.5	6.6	72.9	—	94.7	—	88.9	—	—	9.9	21.6	55.4	25.7
9.5	−6	3/4−16	−8	12.7	22.2	6.6	75.9	—	103.6	—	96.8	—	—	14.0	27.7	61.7	25.7
12.7	−8	3/4−16	−8	12.7	22.2	9.7	80.8	—	107.2	—	100.1	—	—	14.0	27.7	61.7	31.2
12.7	−8	7/8−14	−10	15.9	25.4	9.7	83.6	—	115.8	—	106.7	—	—	16.0	31.2	65.3	31.2
15.9	−10	7/8−14	−10	15.9	25.4	10.9	89.7	—	118.4	—	111.8	—	—	16.0	31.2	65.3	36.8
19.0	−12	1-1/16−12	−12	19.0	31.8	14.5	91.7	—	120.9	—	117.1	—	—	19.8	46.2	94.7	40.4
19.0	−12	1-3/16−12	−14	22.2	34.9	14.5	92.2	—	—	—	—	—	—	—	—	—	40.4
25.4	−16	1-5/16−12	−16	25.4	38.1	19.8	105.7	—	140.2	—	133.4	—	—	22.6	54.4	110.0	49.5

(a) For dimensions shown in Figures 4 to 7, but not specified in Table 4H, see corresponding dimensions for respective straight thread size in Figure 8C and Table 4 of SAE J514.

(b) Sleeves shown in Figure 5B shall conform with Figure 14 and Table 6 of SAE J514 for respective tube OD referenced above except on some sizes and shapes where sleeve length must be shortened.

(c) Flares shall conform with single or double 37-degree flares specified in Figure 2 and Table 2 of SAE J533 for respective tube OD referenced above.

(d) Nuts shown in Figure 5B shall conform with Figure 12 and Table 5 of SAE J514 for respective straight thread size.

(e) For dimensions shown in Figures 5 to 7, but not specified in Table 4H, see corresponding dimensions for respective straight thread size in Figures 11 and 13, and Table 5 of SAE J514.

TABLE 4I—DIMENSIONS OF FEMALE 37-DEGREE FLARED TYPE HOSE FITTINGS FOR USE ON SAE 100R9 HYDRAULIC HOSE[a] (FIGURES 4 TO 7) (CODES 50 AND 75)

Nominal SAE 100R9 Hose ID mm	Hose Dash Size	B Nominal Straight Thread Size[e]	Thread and Tube Dash Size	B_1 Tube OD[b],[c] Ref mm	C Min mm	D Dia Min mm	L Max mm	L_1 Max mm	M Max mm	M_1 Max mm	M_2 Max mm	M_3 Min mm	N ±3.0 mm	N_1 ±3.0 mm	W Max mm
9.5	−6	9/16-18	−6	9.5	17.5	6.6	80.0	80.3	79.2	86.9	71.9	84.3	9.9	21.6	30.2
12.7	−8	3/4-16	−8	12.7	22.2	9.7	85.9	84.6	93.5	100.3	91.4	92.7	14.0	27.7	31.5
19.0	−12	1-1/16-12	−12	19.0	31.8	14.5	98.0	103.6	117.3	122.2	114.8	112.0	19.8	46.2	44.5
25.4	−16	1-5/16-12	−16	25.4	38.1	19.8	109.0	115.3	140.2	146.8	133.4	134.9	22.6	54.4	52.1
31.8	−20	1-5/8-12	−20	—	50.8	25.7	159.0	—	—	—	—	—	—	—	66.8
38.1	−24	1-7/8-12	−24	—	57.2	31.8	170.7	—	—	—	—	—	—	—	74.7
50.8	−32	2-1/2-12	−32	—	73.0	43.7	177.8	—	—	—	—	—	—	—	88.9

(a) For dimensions shown in Figures 4 to 7, but not specified in Table 4I, see corresponding dimensions for respective straight thread size in Figure 8C and Table 4 of SAE J514.

(b) Sleeves shown in Figure 5B shall conform with Figure 14 and Table 6 of SAE J514 for respective tube OD referenced above except on some sizes and shapes where sleeve length must be shortened.

(c) Flares shall conform with single or double 37-degree flares specified in Figure 2 and Table 2 of SAE J533 for respective tube OD referenced above.

(d) Nuts shown in Figure 5B shall conform with Figure 12 and Table 5 of SAE J514 for respective straight thread size.

(e) For dimensions shown in Figures 5 to 7, but not specified in Table 4I, see corresponding dimensions for respective straight thread size in Figures 11 and 13, and Table 5 of SAE J514.

TABLE 4J—DIMENSIONS OF FEMALE 37-DEGREE FLARED TYPE HOSE FITTINGS FOR USE ON SAE 100R10 HYDRAULIC HOSE[a] (FIGURES 4 TO 7) (CODES 51 AND 76)

Nominal SAE 100R10 Hose ID mm	Hose Dash Size	B Nominal Straight Thread Size[e]	Thread and Tube Dash Size	B_1 Tube OD[b], [c] Ref mm	C Min mm	D Dia Min mm	L Max mm	L_1 Max mm	L_2 Max mm	M Max mm
6.4	−4	7/16-20	−4	6.4	14.3	2.8	66.3	66.5	67.3	73.7
9.5	−6	9/16-18	−6	9.5	17.5	5.6	81.3	83.8	71.1	87.4
12.7	−8	3/4-16	−8	12.7	22.2	8.6	98.0	82.3	82.6	103.6
19.0	−12	1-1/16-12	−12	19.0	31.8	12.7	114.0	98.0	95.2	130.6
25.4	−16	1-5/16-12	−16	25.4	38.1	17.3	135.6	113.8	109.0	142.7
31.8	−20	1-5/8-12	−20	31.8	50.8	22.1	158.2	143.3	121.2	169.2
38.1	−24	1-7/8-12	−24	38.1	57.2	27.7	173.5	171.4	136.9	189.7
50.8	−32	2-1/2-12	−32	50.8	73.0	39.6	207.8	203.2	178.6	254.0

Continued on next page.

TABLE 4J—DIMENSIONS OF FEMALE 37-DEGREE FLARED TYPE HOSE FITTINGS FOR USE ON SAE 100R10 HYDRAULIC HOSE[a] (FIGURE 4 TO 7) (CODES 51 AND 76) (Continued)

Nominal SAE 100R10 Hose ID mm	Thread and Tube Dash Size	M_1 Max mm	M_2 Max mm	M_3 Max mm	M_4 Max mm	N ±1.5 mm	N_1 ±1.5 mm	N_2 ±1.5 mm	W Max mm	Z Max mm
6.4	–4	74.2	69.6	66.8	66.8	8.4	17.3	45.7	28.7	54.1
9.5	–6	84.6	82.8	77.0	77.0	9.9	21.6	55.4	28.7	62.7
12.7	–8	97.8	99.6	90.4	90.4	14.0	27.7	61.7	31.8	62.7
19.0	–12	115.1	134.4	113.0	113.0	19.8	46.2	94.7	42.9	79.2
25.4	–16	146.8	160.0	139.7	139.7	22.6	54.4	110.0	50.8	107.2
31.8	–20	188.5	172.2	171.4	171.4	43.2	86.4	134.1	62.2	126.0
38.1	–24	212.9	195.1	191.0	191.0	50.8	100.3	157.2	76.2	133.1
50.8	–32	285.8	285.8	285.8	285.8	69.8	139.7	222.2	81.8	166.6

(a) For dimensions shown in Figures 4 to 7, but not specified in Table 4J, see corresponding dimensions for respective straight thread size in Figure 8C and Table 4 of SAE J514.

(b) Sleeves shown in Figure 5B shall conform with Figure 14 and Table 6 of SAE J514 for respective tube OD referenced above except on some sizes and shapes where sleeve length must be shortened.

(c) Flares shall conform with single or double 37-degree flares specified in Figure 2 and Table 2 of SAE J533 for respective tube OD referenced above.

(d) Nuts shown in Figure 5B shall conform with Figure 12 and Table 5 of SAE J514 for respective straight thread size.

(e) For dimensions shown in Figures 5 to 7, but not specified in Table 4J, see corresponding dimensions for respective straight thread size in Figures 11 and 13, and Table 5 of SAE J514.

TABLE 4K—kDIMENSIONS OF FEMALE 37-DEGREE FLARED TYPE HOSE FITTINGS FOR USE ON SAE 100R11 HYDRAULIC HOSE[a] (Figure 4A) (CODE 52)

Nominal SAE 100R11 Hose ID mm	Hose Dash Size	B Nominal Straight Thread Size	Thread and Tube Dash Size	C Nom mm	D Dia Min mm	L Max mm	W Max mm
19.0	–12	1–1/16–12	–12	31.8	13.5	115.8	46.2
25.4	–16	1–5/16–12	–16	38.1	18.5	140.7	55.9
31.8	–20	1–5/8–12	–20	50.8	24.1	153.7	66.8
38.1	–24	1–7/8–12	–24	57.2	30.5	171.2	74.7
50.8	–32	2–1/2–12	–32	73.0	41.9	207.0	88.9

(a) For dimensions shown in Figures 4 to 7, but not specified in Table 4K, see corresponding dimensions for respective straight thread size in Figure 8C and Table 4 of SAE J514.

TABLE 4L—DIMENSIONS OF FEMALE 37-DEGREE FLARED TYPE HOSE FITTINGS FOR USE ON SAE 100R12 HYDRAULIC HOSE[a] (Figures 4A, 5A, 5B, AND 6A) (CODE 77)

Nominal SAE 100R12 Hose ID mm	Hose Dash Size	B Nominal Straight Thread Size[e]	Thread and Tube Dash Size	C Nom mm	D Dia Min mm	L Max mm	M Max mm	M_2 Max mm	N mm	N_1 mm	W Max mm
9.5	–6	9/16–18	–6	17.5	5.6	81.3	87.4	82.8	9.9	21.6	28.7
12.7	–8	3/4–16	–8	22.2	8.6	98.0	109.5	99.6	14.0	27.7	31.8
15.9	–10	7/8–14	–10	25.4	10.0	101.6	—	—	—	—	38.0
19.0	–12	1–1/16–12	–12	31.8	12.7	114.0	136.4	136.7	30.5	61.0	42.9
25.4	–16	1–5/16–12	–16	38.1	17.3	135.6	159.0	160.0	38.9	76.2	50.8
31.8	–20	1–5/8–12	–20	50.8	22.1	158.5	207.0	173.5	43.2	88.9	60.5
38.1	–24	1–7/8–12	–24	57.2	27.7	173.5	232.9	209.6	50.8	101.6	67.8
50.8	–32	2–1/2–12	–32	73.0	39.6	207.8	274.8	248.4	69.8	139.7	81.8

(a) For dimensions shown in Figures 4 to 7, but not specified in Table 4L, see corresponding dimensions for respective straight thread size in Figure 8C and Table 4 of SAE J514.

TABLE 4M—DIMENSIONS OF FEMALE 37-DEGREE FLARED TYPE HOSE FITTINGS FOR USE ON SAE 100R13 HYDRAULIC HOSE[(a)] (FIGURES 4 AND 6) (CODE 78)

Nominal SAE 100R13 Hose ID mm	Hose Dash Size	B Nominal Straight Thread Size	Thread and Tube Dash Size	C Min mm	D Dia Min mm	L Max mm	M Max mm	M_2 Max mm	N ±3.3 mm	N_1 ±5.0 mm	W Max mm
19.0	−12	1–1/16–12	−12	31.8	12.7	113.5	171.2	136.7	30.5	61.0	43.7
25.4	−16	1–5/16–12	−16	38.1	17.5	126.2	153.7	153.9	38.9	76.2	50.8
31.8	−20	1–5/8–12	−20	50.8	22.4	158.5	190.5	173.5	43.2	88.9	63.5
38.1	−24	1–7/8–12	−24	57.2	27.7	160.0	232.9	209.6	50.8	101.6	71.1
50.8	−32	2–1/2–12	−32	73.0	38.1	198.6	274.8	248.4	69.8	139.7	88.9

(a) For dimensions shown in Figures 4 to 7, but not specified in Table 4M, see corresponding dimensions for respective straight thread size in Figure 8C and Table 4 of SAE J514.

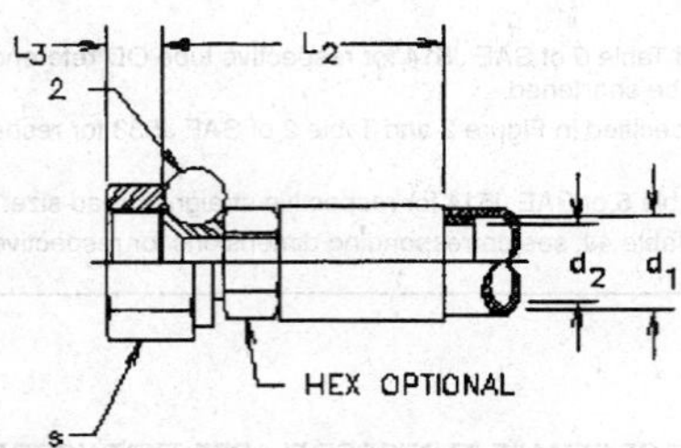

NOTES

1 Connection details in accordance with ISO 8434-2.
2 Method of attachment of swivel nut is as chosen by the manufacturer.
3 Method of attachment of fitting to hose is optional.

FIGURE 7C—STRAIGHT FEMALE SWIVEL HOSE FITTING (SWS)—2401XX

TABLE 4N—DIMENSIONS OF STRAIGHT FEMALE SWIVEL HOSE FITTING (SWS) DIMENSIONS IN MILLIMETERS

Fitting Size	SAE Dash Size	Thread[(1)]	Nominal Connection Size	d_1 (nominal inside diameter of hose)	d_2[(2)] min	L_2[(3)] max	L_3 ref	S[(4)] Std	S[(4)] Optional[(5)]
6 x 6.3	4–4	7/16-20 UNF	6	6.3	3	75	8.7	14	14.3
8 x 8	5–5	1/2-20 UNF	8	8	5	80	9.5	17	15.9
10 x 10	6–6	9/16-18 UNF	10	10	6	85	9.5	19	17.5
12 x 12.5	8–8	3/4-16 UNF	12	12.5	8	100	10.7	22	22.2
16 x 16	10–10	7/8-14 UNF	16	16	11	110	12.7	27	25.4
20 x 19	12–12	1 1/16-12 UN	20	19	14	115	14.3	32	31.8
25 x 25	16–16	1 5/16-12 UN	25	25	19	140	15.1	41	38.1
32 x 31.5	20–20	1 5/8-12 UN	32	31.5	25	160	15.9	50	50.8
38 x 38	24–24	1 7/8-12 UN	38	38	30	175	18.6	65	57.2
50 x 51	32–32	2 1/2-12 UN	50	51	40	210	23.8	75	73.0

1. In accordance with ISO 725 and ISO 5864, class 2B.
2. Minimum diameter at any point through the fitting prior to assembly to the hose. The diameter after assembly shall not be less than $0.9d_2$.
3. Dimension L_2 is measured after assembly
4. In accordance wiht ISO 4759, product grade C.
5. Based on available inch hex sizes.

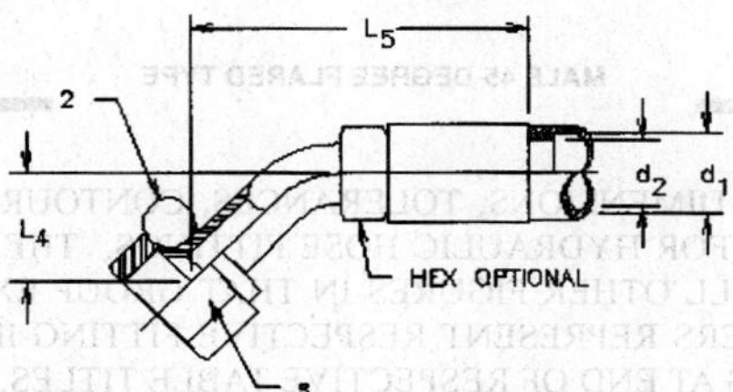

NOTES
1 Connection details in accordance with ISO 8434-2.
2 Method of attachment of swivel nut is as chosen by the manufacturer.
3 Method of attachment of fitting to hose is optional.

FIGURE 7D—45 DEGREE ELBOW FEMALE SWIVEL HOSE FITTING (SWE45)—2403XX

TABLE 4O—DIMENSIONS OF 45 DEGREE ELBOW FEMALE SWIVEL HOSE FITTING (SDE) DIMENSIONS IN MILLIMETERS

Fitting Size	SAE Dash Size	Thread(1)	Nominal Connection Size	d_1 (nominal inside diameter of hose)	d_2(2) min	L_4 ±1.5	L_5(3) max	S(4) Std	S(4) Optional(5)
6 x 6.3	4–4	7/16-20 UNF	6	6.3	3	10	90	14	14.3
8 x 8	5–5	1/2-20 UNF	8	8	5	10	90	17	15.9
10 x 10	6–6	9/16-18 UNF	10	10	6	11	95	19	17.5
12 x 12.5	8–8	3/4-16 UNF	12	12.5	8	15	110	22	22.2
16 x 16	10–10	7/8-14 UNF	16	16	11	16	120	27	25.4
20 x 19	12–12	1 1/16-12 UN	20	19	14	21	145	32	31.8
25 x 25	16–16	1 5/16-12 UN	25	25	19	24	175	41	38.1
32 x 31.5	20–20	1 5/8-12 UN	32	31.5	25	25	200	50	50.8
38 x 38	24–24	1 7/8-12 UN	38	38	30	27	240	60	57.2
50 x 51	32–32	2 1/2-12 UN	50	51	40	34	290	75	73.0

1. In accordance with ISO 725 and ISO 5864, class 2B.
2. Minimum diameter at any point through the fitting prior to bending and/or assembly to the hose. The diameter after bending and/or assembly shall not be less than $0.9d_2$.
3. Dimension L_5 is measured after assembly.
4. In accordance with ISO 4759, product grade C.
5. Based on available inch hex sizes.

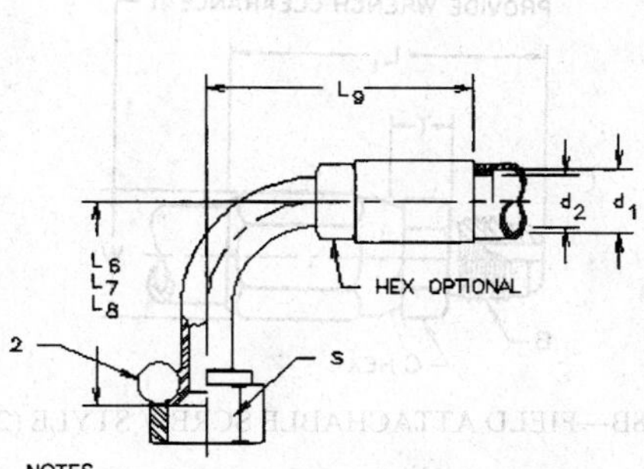

NOTES
1 Connection details in accordance with ISO 8434-2.
2 Method of attachment of swivel nut is as chosen by the manufacturer.
3 Method of attachment of fitting to hose is optional.

FIGURE 7E—90 DEGREE ELBOW FEMALE SWIVEL HOSE FITTINGS [SHORT (SWES), MEDIUM (SWEM) AND LONG (SWEL)]—2414XX

TABLE 4P—DIMENSIONS OF 90 DEGREE ELBOW FEMALE SWIVEL HOSE FITTINGS [SHORT (SWS), MEDIUM (SWEM), AND LONG (SWEL)] DIMENSIONS IN MILLIMETERS

Fitting Size	SAE Dash Size	Thread(1)	Nominal Connection Size	d_1 (nominal Inside diameter of hose)	d_2(2) min	L_6(3) ±1.5 SWES	L_7(4) ±1.5 SWEM	L_8(5) ±1.5 SWEL	L_9(6) max	S(7) Std	S Optional(8)
6 x 6.3	4–4	7/16-20 UNF	6	6.3	3	21	46	46	85	14	14.3
8 x 8	5–5	1/2-20 UNF	8	8	5	21	46	46	85	17	15.9
10 x 10	6–6	9/16-18 UNF	10	10	6	23	54	54	90	19	17.5
12 x 12.5	8–8	3/4-16 UNF	12	12.5	8	29	64	64	100	22	22.2
16 x 16	10–10	7/8-14 UNF	16	16	11	32	70	70	110	27	25.4
20 x 19	12–12	1 1/16-12 UN	20	19	14	48	96	96	140	32	31.8
25 x 25	16–16	1 5/16-12 UN	25	25	19	56	114	114	170	41	38.1
32 x 31.5	20–20	1 5/8-12 UN	32	31.5	25	64	129	129	200	50	50.8
38 x 38	24–24	1 7/8-12 UN	38	38	30	69	141	141	230	60	57.2
50 x 51	32–32	2 1/2-12 UN	50	51	40	88	222	222	280	75	73.0

1. In accordance with ISO 725 and ISO 5864, class 2B.
2. Minimum diameter at any point through the fitting prior to bending and/or assembly to the hose. The diameter after bending and/or assembly shall not be less than $0.9d_2$.
3. Short drop (SWES) dimensions. See Appendix A.
4. Medium drop (SWEM) dimensions. Medium drop hose fittings will clear 90 degrees adjustable stud elbow (SDE) per ISO 8434-2, Figure 15. See Appendix A.
5. Long drop (SWEL) dimensions. Long drop hose fittings will clear short drop (SWES) hose fittings. See Appendix A.
6. Dimension L_9 is measured after assembly.
7. In accordance with ISO 4759, product grade C.
8. Based on available inch hex sizes.

MALE 45-DEGREE FLARED TYPE

NOTE—UNSPECIFIED DETAIL WITH RESPECT TO DIMENSIONS, TOLERANCES, CONTOURS, MATERIAL, WORKMANSHIP, AND SO ON, MUST CONFORM TO GENERAL SPECIFICATIONS FOR HYDRAULIC HOSE FITTINGS. THE DIMENSIONAL DESIGNATIONS ON THE FIRST FIGURE IN EACH GROUP SHALL APPLY TO ALL OTHER FIGURES IN THAT GROUP EXCEPT AS SHOWN OTHERWISE. CODES SHOWN IN BRACKETS ADJACENT TO FIGURE NUMBERS REPRESENT RESPECTIVE FITTING IDENTIFICATION, WITH XX SUBSTITUTED FOR THE HOSE TYPE CODE DEPICTED IN BRACKETS AT END OF RESPECTIVE TABLE TITLES, IN ACCORDANCE WITH SAE J846.

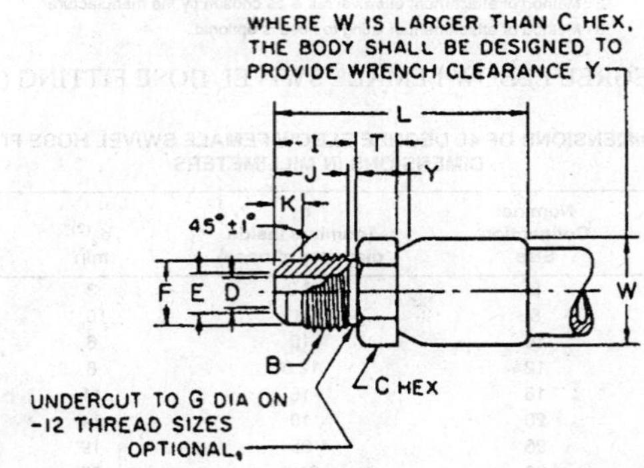

FIGURE 8A—PERMANENTLY ATTACHED STYLE (2801XX)

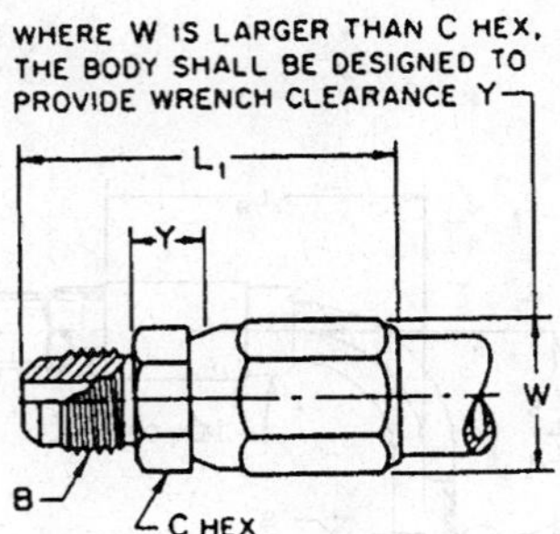

FIGURE 8B—FIELD ATTACHABLE SCREW STYLE (2901XX)

FIGURE 8—MALE 45-DEGREE FLARED TYPE HOSE FITTINGS

TABLE 5A—DIMENSIONS OF MALE 45-DEGREE FLARED TYPE HOSE FITTINGS FOR USE ON SAE 100R1 HYDRAULIC HOSE[(a)] (FIGURES 8A AND 8B) (CODES 42 AND 53)

Nominal SAE 100R1 Hose ID mm	Hose Dash Size	B Nominal Straight Thread Size	Thread Dash Size	C Min mm	D Dia Min mm	L Max mm	L_1 Max mm	T Max mm	W Max mm	Y Min mm
6.4	–4	7/16–20	–4	11.1	2.8	60.2	60.2	5.6	22.1	9.4
6.4	–4	1/2–20	–5	12.7	2.8	60.2	61.5	5.6	22.1	10.4
7.9	–5	9/16–18	–6	15.9	5.1	62.0	64.0	5.6	23.9	10.4
9.5	–6	9/16–18	–6	15.9	6.6	63.5	66.8	5.6	27.7	10.4
9.5	–6	3/4–16	–8	19.0	6.6	72.4	66.8	6.4	27.7	12.7
10.3	–6.5	3/4–16	–8	19.0	6.6	72.4	69.8	6.4	29.5	12.7
12.7	–8	3/4–16	–8	19.0	9.7	72.4	78.2	6.4	31.2	12.7
12.7	–8	7/8–14	–10	22.2	9.7	75.2	81.3	6.4	31.2	14.2
15.9	–10	7/8–14	–10	22.2	12.7	86.9	90.4	6.4	34.8	14.2
15.9	–10	1–1/16–12	–12	27.0	12.7	81.3	91.4	7.9	34.8	15.5
19.0	–12	7/8–14	–10	22.2	12.2	81.3	91.4	7.9	40.4	14.2
19.0	–12	1–1/16–12	–12	27.0	14.5	81.3	91.4	7.9	40.4	15.5

(a) For dimensions shown in Figure 8A, but not specified in Table 5A, see corresponding dimensions for respective straight thread size in Figure 1A and Table 4 of SAE J512.

TABLE 5B—DIMENSIONS OF MALE 45-DEGREE FLARED TYPE HOSE FITTINGS FOR USE ON SAE 100R3 HYDRAULIC HOSE[(a)] (FIGURE 8A) (CODE 44)

Nominal SAE 100R3 Hose ID mm	Hose Dash Size	B Nominal Straight Thread Size	Thread Dash Size	C Min mm	D Dia Min mm	L Max mm	T Min mm	W Max mm	Y Min mm
6.4	–4	7/16–20	–4	11.1	2.8	47.8	5.6	22.4	9.4
6.4	–4	1/2–20	–5	12.7	2.8	47.8	5.6	22.4	10.4
9.5	–6	9/16–18	–6	15.9	6.6	58.7	5.6	26.9	10.4
9.5	–6	3/4–16	–8	19.0	6.6	60.5	6.4	26.9	12.7
12.7	–8	3/4–16	–8	19.0	9.7	63.5	6.4	33.3	12.7
12.7	–8	7/8–14	–10	22.2	9.7	66.8	6.4	33.3	14.2
15.9	–10	7/8–14	–10	22.2	12.2	86.9	6.4	36.8	14.2
19.0	–12	7/8–14	–10	22.2	12.2	71.4	7.9	42.2	14.2
19.0	–12	1-1/16–12	–12	27.0	14.5	71.4	7.9	42.2	15.5

(a) For dimensions shown in Figure 8A, but not specified in Table 5B, see corresponding dimensions for respective straight thread size in Figure 1A and Table 4 of SAE J512.

TABLE 5C—DIMENSIONS OF MALE 45-DEGREE FLARED TYPE HOSE FITTINGS FOR USE ON SAE 100R5 HYDRAULIC HOSE[(a)] (FIGURES 8A TO 8B) (CODE 46)

Nominal SAE 100R5 Hose ID mm	Hose Dash Size	B Nominal Straight Thread Size	Thread Dash Size	C Min mm	D Dia Min mm	L Max mm	L_1 Max mm	T Min mm	W Max mm	Y Min mm
4.8	–4	7/16–20	–4	11.1	2.3	46.2	50.8	4.8	20.1	9.4
6.4	–5	1/2–20	–5	12.7	2.8	48.5	52.3	4.8	22.1	10.4
7.9	–6	5/8–18	–6	15.9	5.1	51.1	57.2	5.6	23.9	10.4
10.3	–8	3/4–16	–8	19.0	7.1	56.6	69.1	6.4	27.4	12.7
12.7	–10	7/8–14	–10	22.2	9.7	61.2	77.7	6.4	31.5	14.2
15.9	–12	1-1/16–14	–12	27.0	12.7	65.3	90.2	7.9	38.6	15.5

(a) For dimensions shown in Figure 8A, but not specified in Table 5C, see corresponding dimensions for respective straight thread size in Figure 1A and Table 4 of SAE J512.
NOTE— For SAE J1402 and DOT FMVSS 106 air brake applications, couplings used in 100R5 hose shall have a minimum assembled orifice no less than 66% of the nominal hose I.D.

TABLE 5D—DIMENSIONS OF MALE 45-DEGREE FLARED TYPE HOSE FITTINGS FOR USE ON SAE 100R6 HYDRAULIC HOSE[(a)] (FIGURE 8A) (CODE 47)

Nominal SAE 100R6 Hose ID mm	Hose Dash Size	B Nominal Straight Thread Size	Thread Dash Size	C Min mm	D Dia Min mm	L Max mm	T Min mm	W Max mm	Y Min mm
4.8	–3	3/8–24	–3	9.5	2.3	31.8	3.8	16.0	8.9
4.8	–3	7/16–20	–4	11.1	2.3	31.8	3.8	16.0	8.9
6.4	–4	3/8–24	–3	9.5	2.8	34.3	3.8	19.0	8.9
6.4	–4	7/16–20	–4	11.1	2.8	35.1	3.8	19.0	8.9
6.4	–4	1/2–20	–5	12.7	2.8	35.1	3.8	19.0	8.9
7.9	–5	1/2–20	–5	12.7	5.1	35.6	3.8	22.4	8.9
7.9	–5	5/8–18	–6	15.9	5.1	37.3	4.8	22.4	10.2
9.5	–6	5/8–18	–6	15.9	6.6	40.6	4.8	25.4	10.2
9.5	–6	3/4–16	–8	19.0	6.6	43.7	4.8	25.4	10.9
12.7	–8	3/4–16	–8	19.0	9.7	45.2	4.8	28.4	10.9
15.9	–10	7/8–14	–10	22.2	12.2	50.8	6.4	30.2	12.7
19.0	–12	1-1/16–14	–12	27.0	14.5	88.9	7.9	36.8	15.5

(a) For dimensions shown in Figure 8A, but not specified in Table 5D, see corresponding dimensions for respective straight thread size in Figure 1A and Table 4 of SAE J512.

TABLE 5E—DIMENSIONS OF MALE 45-DEGREE FLARED TYPE HOSE FITTINGS FOR USE ON SAE 100R7 HYDRAULIC HOSE[(a)] (FIGURE 8A) (CODE 48)

Nominal SAE 100R7 Hose ID mm	Hose Dash Size	B Nominal Straight Thread Size	Thread Dash Size	C Min mm	D Dia Min mm	L Max mm	T Min mm	W Max mm	Y Min mm
4.8	–3	7/16–20	–4	11.1	2.3	61.7	5.6	19.0	9.4
6.4	–4	7/16–20	–4	11.1	2.8	61.7	5.6	20.6	9.4
6.4	–4	1/2–20	–5	12.7	2.8	63.5	5.6	20.6	10.4
7.9	–5	5/8–18	–6	15.9	5.1	66.0	5.6	22.4	10.4
9.5	–6	5/8–18	–6	15.9	6.6	69.6	5.6	25.7	10.4
9.5	–6	3/4–16	–8	19.0	6.6	71.1	6.4	25.7	12.7
12.7	–8	3/4–16	–8	19.0	9.1	79.2	6.4	31.2	12.7
12.7	–8	7/8–14	–10	22.2	9.4	79.2	6.4	31.2	14.2
15.9	–10	7/8–14	–10	22.2	12.2	86.9	6.4	34.8	14.2
19.0	–12	1-1/16–14	–12	27.0	14.5	93.2	7.9	40.4	15.5

(a) For dimensions shown in Figure 8A, but not specified in Table 5E, see corresponding dimensions for respective straight thread size in Figure 1A and Table 4 of SAE J512.

FEMALE 45-DEGREE FLARED TYPE

NOTE—UNSPECIFIED DETAIL WITH RESPECT TO DIMENSIONS, TOLERANCES, CONTOURS, MATERIAL, WORKMANSHIP, AND SO ON, MUST CONFORM TO GENERAL SPECIFICATIONS FOR HYDRAULIC HOSE FITTINGS. THE DIMENSIONAL DESIGNATIONS ON THE FIRST FIGURE IN EACH GROUP SHALL APPLY TO ALL OTHER FIGURES IN THAT GROUP EXCEPT AS SHOWN OTHERWISE. THE DESIGN OF AND METHOD OF ATTACHING SWIVEL NUT SHALL BE OPTIONAL WITH MANUFACTURER PROVIDING THE DIMENSIONS SHOWN ARE MAINTAINED AND NUT TURNS FREELY. CODES SHOWN IN BRACKETS ADJACENT TO FIGURE NUMBERS REPRESENT RESPECTIVE FITTING IDENTIFICATION, WITH XX SUBSTITUTED FOR THE HOSE TYPE CODE DEPICTED IN BRACKETS AT END OF RESPECTIVE TABLE TITLES, IN ACCORDANCE WITH SAE J846.

SWIVEL ENDS ON ANGLE FITTINGS MAY HAVE A MACHINED FLARE SEAT AND SWIVEL NUT AS SHOWN IN FIGURE 9A, A RADIAL FLARED TUBE AND MATING NUT SEAT AS SHOWN IN FIGURE 10A, OR A 45-DEGREE FLARED TUBE AND MATING NUT SEAT AS SHOWN IN FIGURE 10B.

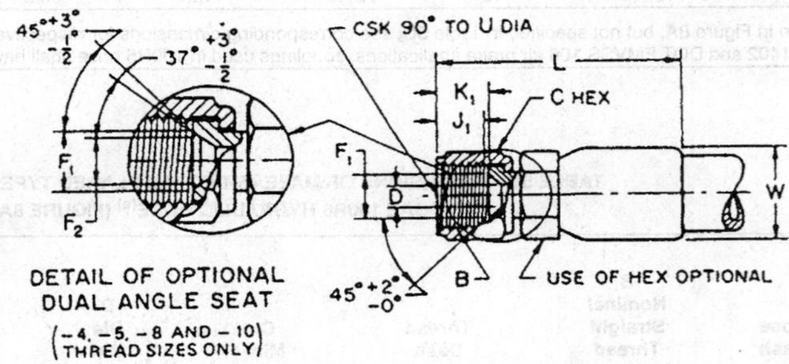

FIGURE 9A—PERMANENTLY ATTACHED STYLE (3001XX)

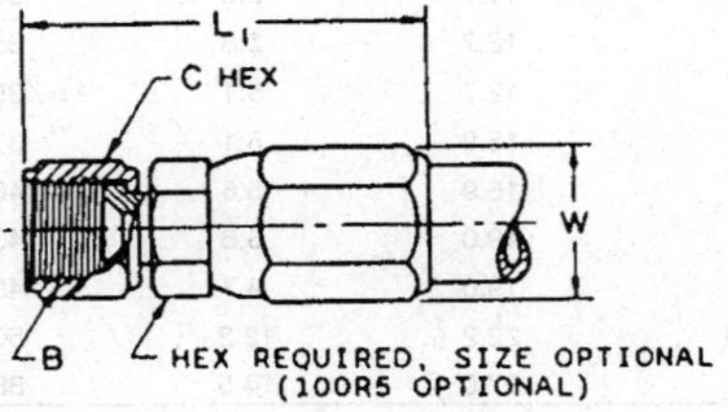

FIGURE 9B—FIELD ATTACHABLE SCREW STYLE (3101XX)

FIGURE 9—FEMALE 45-DEGREE FLARED TYPE HOSE FITTINGS

SWIVEL ENDS ON ANGLE FITTINGS MAY HAVE A MACHINED FLARE SEAT AND SWIVEL NUT AS SHOWN IN FIG. 9A, OR A 45-DEG FLARED TUBE AND MATING NUT SEAT AS SHOWN IN FIG. 10A.

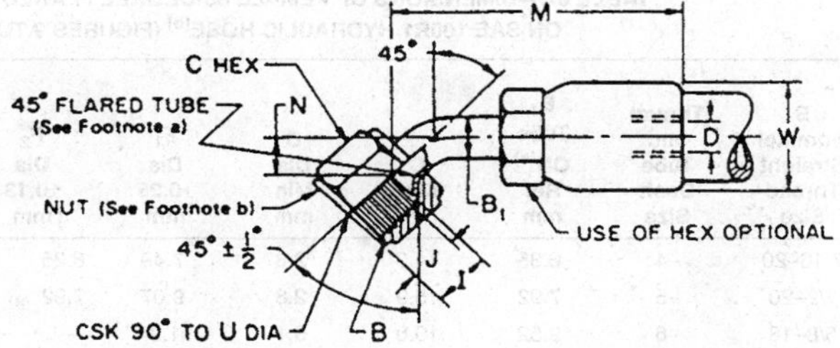

FIGURE 10A—PERMANENTLY ATTACHED STYLE (3003XX)

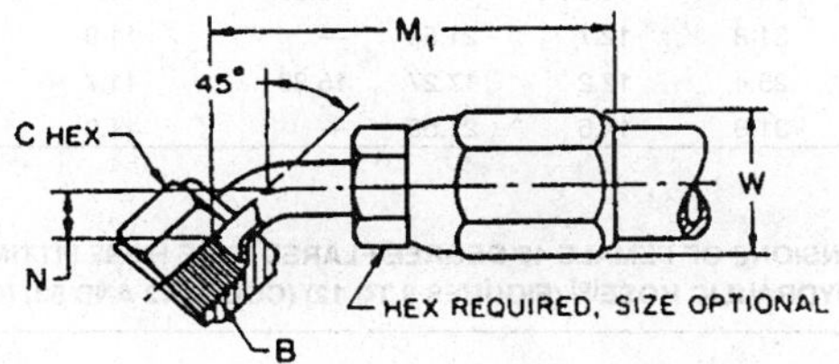

FIGURE 10B—FIELD ATTACHABLE SCREW STYLE (3103XX)

FIGURE 10—FEMALE 45-DEGREE FLARED TYPE 45-DEGREE ANGLE HOSE FITTINGS

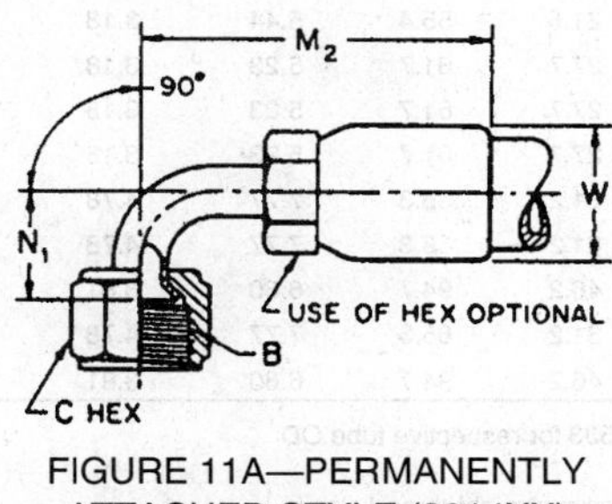

FIGURE 11A—PERMANENTLY ATTACHED STYLE (3014XX)

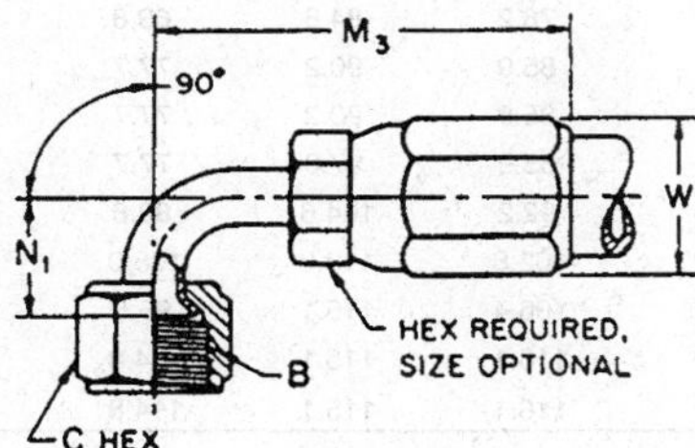

FIGURE 11B—FIELD ATTACHABLE SCREW STYLE (3114XX)

FIGURE 11—FEMALE 45-DEGREE FLARED TYPE 90-DEGREE ANGLE SHORT DROP HOSE FITTINGS

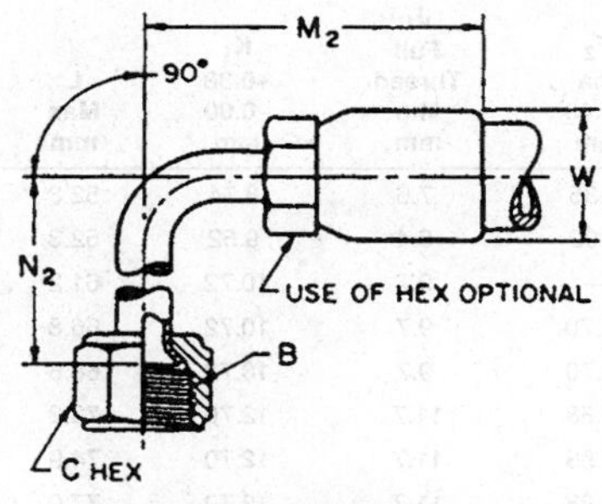

FIGURE 12A—PERMANENTLY ATTACHED STYLE (3015XX)

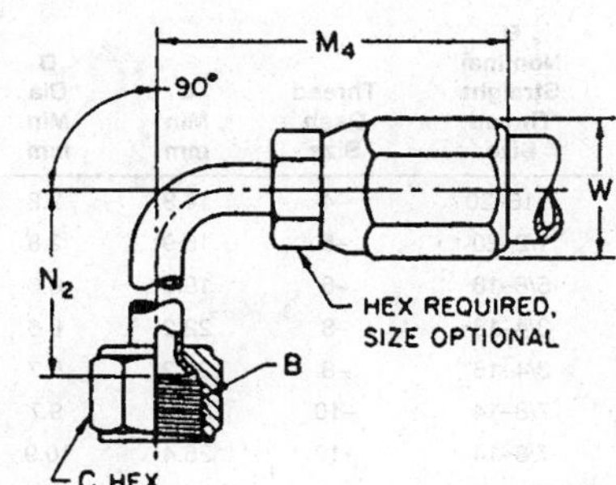

FIGURE 12B—FIELD ATTACHABLE SCREW STYLE (3115XX)

FIGURE 12—FEMALE 45-DEGREE FLARED TYPE 90-DEGREE ANGLE LONG DROP HOSE FITTINGS

TABLE 6A—DIMENSIONS OF FEMALE 45-DEGREE FLARED TYPE HOSE FITTINGS FOR USE ON SAE 100R1 HYDRAULIC HOSE[(b)] (FIGURES 9 TO 12) (CODES 42 AND 53)

Nominal SAE 100R1 Hose ID mm	Hose Dash Size	B Nominal Straight Thread Size	Thread and Tube Dash Size	B_1 Tube OD[(a)] Ref mm	C Min mm	D Dia Min mm	F_1 Dia ±0.25 mm	F_2 Dia ±0.13 mm	J_1 Full Thread Min mm	K_1 +0.38 −0.00 mm	K_4 Ref mm	L Max mm	L_1 Max mm	L_4 ±0.03 mm
6.4	−4	7/16–20	−4	6.35	14.3	2.8	7.49	6.35	7.6	8.74	10.2	66.3	66.5	15.5
6.4	−4	1/2–20	−5	7.92	15.9	2.8	9.07	7.92	8.4	9.52	10.2	67.8	66.5	15.7
7.9	−5	5/8–18	−6	9.52	19.0	5.1	11.94	—	9.1	10.72	9.7	65.3	67.6	18.5
9.5	−6	5/8–18	−6	9.52	19.0	6.6	11.94	—	9.1	10.72	9.7	68.3	70.6	18.5
9.5	−6	3/4–16	−8	12.70	22.2	6.6	14.53	12.70	9.7	10.72	12.7	71.4	72.4	20.8
10.3	−6.5	3/4–16	−8	12.70	22.2	6.6	14.53	12.70	9.7	10.72	12.7	71.4	73.9	20.8
12.7	−8	3/4–16	−8	12.70	22.2	9.7	14.53	12.70	9.7	10.72	12.7	73.2	79.5	20.8
12.7	−8	7/8–14	−10	15.88	25.4	9.7	17.27	15.88	11.7	12.70	14.0	78.0	83.1	23.6
15.9	−10	7/8–14	−10	15.88	25.4	10.9	17.27	15.88	11.7	12.70	14.0	83.3	88.4	23.6
15.9	−10	1-1/16-14	−12	19.05	31.8	12.7	21.59	—	11.9	14.27	17.5	88.4	93.5	33.0
19.0	−12	7/8–14	−10	15.88	25.4	12.2	17.27	15.88	11.7	12.70	14.0	98.0	93.5	23.6
19.0	−12	1-1/16-14	−12	19.05	31.8	14.5	21.59	—	11.9	14.27	17.5	98.0	93.5	33.0

TABLE 6A—DIMENSIONS OF FEMALE 45-DEGREE FLARED TYPE HOSE FITTINGS FOR USE ON SAE 100R1 HYDRAULIC HOSE[(b)] (FIGURES 9 TO 12) (CODES 42 AND 53) (CONTINUED)

Nominal SAE 100R1 Hose ID mm	Thread and Tube Dash Size	M Max mm	M_1 Max mm	M_2 Max mm	M_3 Max mm	M_4 Max mm	N ±1.5 mm	N_1 ±1.5 mm	N_2 ±1.5 mm	R Ref mm	R_1 ±1.13 mm	U Dia +0.38 −0.00 mm	W Max mm
6.4	−4	67.6	74.2	64.5	66.8	66.8	8.4	17.3	45.7	5.21	3.18	11.25	22.1
6.4	−5	68.8	75.4	64.5	67.8	67.8	9.1	19.6	45.7	6.02	3.18	12.83	22.1
7.9	−6	74.7	82.8	68.3	73.9	73.9	9.9	21.6	55.4	5.44	3.18	16.00	23.9
9.5	−6	76.2	84.6	69.8	77.0	77.0	9.9	21.6	55.4	5.44	3.18	16.00	27.7
9.5	−8	85.9	90.2	77.7	83.6	83.6	14.0	27.7	61.7	5.23	3.18	19.18	27.7
10.3	−8	85.9	90.2	77.7	83.6	83.6	14.0	27.7	61.7	5.23	3.18	19.18	29.5
12.7	−8	85.9	97.8	77.7	90.4	90.4	14.0	27.7	61.7	5.23	3.18	19.18	31.2
12.7	−10	92.2	104.6	82.6	96.0	96.0	16.0	31.2	65.3	7.77	4.78	22.35	31.2
15.9	−10	102.6	113.0	108.0	102.9	102.9	16.0	31.2	65.3	7.77	4.78	22.35	34.8
15.9	−12	106.4	115.1	96.5	107.2	107.0	19.8	46.2	94.7	6.60	3.81	27.10	34.8
19.0	−10	116.1	115.1	114.8	108.7	108.7	16.0	31.2	65.3	7.77	4.78	22.35	40.4
19.0	−12	116.1	115.1	114.8	108.7	108.7	19.8	46.2	94.7	6.60	3.81	27.10	40.4

(a) 45-degree flares shall conform with single or double 45-degree flares specified in Figure 1 and Table 1 of SAE J533 for respective tube OD referenced above. Dimensions F3 of radial flares shall conform with dimension A in Table 1 of SAE J533.

(b) For dimensions shown in Figures 9 to 12, but not specified in Table 6A, see corresponding dimensions for respective straight thread size in Figure 4 and Table 5 of SAE J512.

TABLE 6B—DIMENSIONS OF FEMALE 45-DEGREE FLARED TYPE HOSE FITTINGS FOR USE ON SAE 100R3 HYDRAULIC HOSE[(b)] (FIGURES 9 TO 12) (CODE 44)

Nominal SAE 100R3 Hose ID mm	Hose Dash Size	B Nominal Straight Thread Size	Thread Dash Size	C Min mm	D Dia Min mm	F_1 Dia ±0.25 mm	F_2 Dia ±0.13 mm	J_1 Full Thread Min mm	K_1 +0.38 −0.00 mm	L Max mm	U Dia +0.38 −0.00 mm	W Max mm
6.4	−4	7/16–20	−4	14.3	2.8	7.49	6.35	7.6	8.74	52.3	11.25	22.4
6.4	−4	1/2–20	−5	15.9	2.8	9.07	7.92	8.4	9.52	52.3	12.83	22.4
9.5	−6	5/8–18	−6	19.0	6.6	11.94	—	9.7	10.72	61.2	16.00	26.9
9.5	−6	3/4–16	−8	22.2	6.6	14.53	12.70	9.7	10.72	66.8	19.18	26.9
12.7	−8	3/4–16	−8	22.2	9.7	14.53	12.70	9.7	10.72	68.6	19.18	33.3
12.7	−8	7/8–14	−10	25.4	9.7	17.27	15.88	11.7	12.70	73.2	22.35	33.3
15.9	−10	7/8–14	−10	25.4	10.9	17.27	15.88	11.7	12.70	74.9	22.35	38.1
19.0	−12	7/8–14	−10	25.4	12.2	17.27	15.88	11.7	12.70	77.0	22.35	42.2
19.0	−12	1-1/16–14	−12	31.8	14.5	21.59	—	11.9	14.27	77.0	27.10	42.2

a 45-degree flares shall conform with single or double 45-degree flares specified in Figure 1 and Table 1 of SAE J533 for respective tube OD referenced above. Dimension F3 of radial flares shall conform with dimension A in Table 1 of SAE J533.

b For dimensions shown in Figure 9 to 12, but not specified in Table 6B, see corresponding dimensions for respective straight thread size in Figure 5 and Table 5 of SAE J512.

TABLE 6C—DIMENSIONS OF FEMALE 45-DEGREE FLARED TYPE HOSE FITTINGS FOR USE ON SAE 100R5 HYDRAULIC HOSE (FIGURES 9 TO 12) (CODE 46)

Nominal SAE 100R5 Hose ID mm	Hose Dash Size	B Nominal Straight Thread Size	Thread and Tube Dash Size	B_1 Tube OD[(a)] Ref mm	C Min mm	D Dia Min mm	F_1 Dia ±0.25 mm	F_2 Dia ±0.13 mm	J_1 Full Thread Min mm	K_1 +0.38 −0.00 mm	K_4 Ref mm	L Max mm	L_1 Max mm	L_4 ±0.3 mm
4.8	−4	7/16–20	−4	6.35	14.3	2.3	7.49	6.35	7.6	8.74	10.2	53.1	53.8	15.5
6.4	−5	1/2–20	−5	7.92	15.9	2.8	9.07	7.92	8.4	9.52	10.2	56.1	55.4	15.7
7.9	−6	5/8–18	−6	9.52	19.0	5.1	11.94	—	9.7	10.72	9.7	57.9	60.5	18.5
10.3	−8	3/4–16	−8	12.70	22.2	7.1	14.53	12.70	9.7	10.72	12.7	64.0	73.2	20.8
12.7	−10	7/8–14	−10	15.88	25.4	9.7	17.27	15.88	11.7	12.70	14.0	67.6	80.3	23.6
15.9	−12	1-1/16-14	−12	19.05	31.8	12.7	21.59	—	11.9	14.27	17.5	70.4	90.9	33.0

[a] 45-degree flares shall conform with single or double 45-degree flares specified in Figure 1 and Table 1 of SAE J533 for respective tube OD referenced above. Dimension F3 of radial flares shall conform with dimension A in Table 1 of SAE J533.

[b] For dimensions shown in Figure 9 to 12, but not specified in Table 6B, see corresponding dimensions for respective straight thread size in Figure 5 and Table 5 of SAE J512.

NOTE—For SAE J1402 and DOT FMVSS 106 air brake applications, couplings used on 100R5 hose shall have a minimum assembled orifice no less than 66% of the nominal hose I.D.

TABLE 6C—TDIMENSIONS OF FEMALE 45-DEGREE FLARED TYPE HOSE FITTINGS FOR USE ON SAE 100R5 HYDRAULIC HOSE[(b)] (FIGURES 9 TO 12) (CODE 46) (CONTINUED)

Nominal SAE 100R5 Hose ID mm	Thread Dash Size	M_1 Max mm	M_3 Max mm	M_4 Max mm	N ± 1.5 mm	N_1 ± 1.5 mm	N_2 ± 1.5 mm	R Ref mm	R_1 ±0.13 mm	U Dia +0.38 −0.15 mm	W Max mm
4.8	−4	62.2	59.7	74.9	8.4	17.3	45.7	5.21	3.18	11.25	20.1
6.4	−5	66.0	64.5	64.5	9.1	19.6	48.0	6.02	3.18	12.83	22.1
7.9	−6	69.0	68.3	68.3	9.9	21.6	55.4	5.44	3.18	16.00	23.9
10.3	−8	84.8	81.0	81.0	14.0	25.4	61.7	5.23	3.18	19.18	27.4
12.7	−10	93.0	88.1	88.1	16.0	31.2	65.3	7.77	4.78	22.35	31.5
15.9	−12	110.2	109.0	109.0	19.8	46.2	94.7	6.60	3.81	27.10	38.6

[a] 45-degree flares shall conform with single or double 45-degree flares specified in Figure 1 and Table 1 of SAE J533 for respective tube OD referenced above. Dimension F3 of radial flares shall conform with dimension A in Table 1 of SAE J533.

[b] For dimensions shown in Figure 9 to 12, but not specified in Table 6C, see corresponding dimensions for respective straight thread size in Figure 5 and Table 5 of SAE J512.

NOTE—For SAE J1402 and DOT FMVSS 106 air brake applications, couplings used on 100R5 hose shall have a minimum assembled orifice no less than 66% of the nominal hose I.D.

TABLE 6D—DIMENSIONS OF FEMALE 45-DEGREE FLARED TYPE HOSE FITTINGS FOR USE ON SAE 100R6 HYDRAULIC HOSE[(b)] (FIGURES 9 TO 12) (CODE 47)

Nominal SAE 100R6 Hose ID mm	Hose Dash Size	B Nominal Straight Thread Size	Thread Dash Size	C Min mm	D Dia Min mm	F_1 Dia ±0.013 mm	F_2 Dia ±0.013 mm	J_1 Full Thread Min mm	K_1 +0.38 −0.00 mm	L Max mm	L_1 Max mm	U Dia +0.38 −0.00 mm	W Max mm
4.8	−3	7/16-20	−4	14.3	2.3	7.49	6.35	7.6	8.74	36.1	—	11.25	16.0
6.4	−4	7/16-20	−4	14.3	2.8	7.49	6.35	7.6	8.74	38.1	39.6	11.25	19.0
6.4	−4	1/2-20	−5	15.9	2.8	9.07	7.92	8.4	9.52	38.1	—	12.83	19.0
7.9	−5	1/2-20	−5	15.9	2.8	9.07	7.92	8.4	9.52	40.1	42.9	12.83	22.4
7.9	−5	5/8-18	−6	19.0	5.1	11.94	—	9.7	10.72	40.6	—	16.00	22.4
9.5	−6	5/8-18	−6	19.0	6.6	11.94	—	9.7	10.72	45.2	46.7	16.00	25.4
12.7	−8	3/4-16	−8	22.2	9.7	14.53	12.70	9.7	10.72	46.7	47.8	19.18	28.4
15.9	−10	7/8-14	−10	25.4	12.2	17.27	15.88	11.7	12.70	56.6	59.9	22.35	30.2
19.0	−12	1-1/16-14	−12	31.8	14.5	21.59	—	11.9	14.27	90.4	88.1	27.10	36.8

[a] 45-degree flares shall conform with single or double 45-degree flares specified in Figure 1 and Table 1 of SAE J533 for respective tube OD referenced above. Dimension F3 of radial flares shall conform with dimension A in Table 1 of SAE J533.

[b] For dimensions shown in Figure 9 to 12, but not specified in Table 6D, see corresponding dimensions for respective straight thread size in Figure 4 and Table 5 of SAE J512

TABLE 6E—DIMENSIONS OF FEMALE 45-DEGREE FLARED HOSE FITTINGS FOR USE ON SAE 100R7 HYDRAULIC HOSE[b] (FIGURES 9 TO 12) (CODE 48)

Nominal SAE 100R7 Hose ID mm	Hose Dash Size	B Nominal Straight Thread Size	Thread and Tube Dash Size	B_1 Tube OD[a] Ref mm	C Min mm	D Dia Min mm	F_1 Dia mm	F_2 Dia mm	J_1 Full Thread Min mm	K_1 mm	L Max mm	M Max mm	M_2 Max mm	N ±1.5 mm	N_1 ±1.5 mm	N_2 ±1.5 mm	U Dia mm	W Max mm
6.4	–4	7/16–20	–4	6.35	14.3	2.8	7.49	6.35	7.6	8.74	66.	87.6	82.0	8.4	17.3	45.7	11.25	20.6
6.4	–4	1/2–20	–5	7.92	15.9	2.8	9.07	7.92	8.4	9.52	66.5	88.9	83.3	9.1	19.6	45.7	12.83	20.6
7.9	–5	5/8–18	–6	9.52	19.0	5.1	11.94	—	9.1	10.72	68.6	90.2	84.1	9.9	21.6	55.4	16.00	22.4
9.5	–6	5/8–18	–6	9.52	19.0	6.6	11.94	—	9.1	10.72	74.2	94.7	88.9	9.9	21.6	55.4	16.00	25.7
9.5	–6	3/4–16	–8	12.70	22.2	6.6	14.53	12.70	9.7	10.72	76.2	103.6	96.8	14.0	27.7	61.7	19.18	25.7
12.7	–8	3/4–16	–8	12.70	22.2	9.1	14.53	12.70	9.7	10.72	80.8	107.2	100.1	14.0	27.7	61.7	19.18	31.2
12.7	–8	7/8–14	–10	15.88	25.4	9.1	17.27	15.88	11.7	12.70	83.6	115.8	106.7	16.	31.2	65.3	22.35	31.2
15.9	–10	7/8–14	–10	15.88	25.4	10.9	17.27	15.88	11.7	12.70	86.4	118.4	111.8	16.0	31.2	65.3	22.35	34.8
19.0	–12	1-1/16–14	–12	19.05	31.8	14.5	21.59	—	11.9	14.27	91.7	120.9	117.1	19.8	46.2	94.7	27.10	40.4

[a] Flares shall conform with single or double 45-degree flares specified in Figure 1 and Table 1 of SAE J533 for respective tube OD referenced above.

[b] For dimensions shown in Figures 10 to 12, but not specified in Table 6E, see corresponding dimensions for respective straight thread size in Figure 4 and Table 5 of SAE J512.

MALE FLARELESS TYPE

NOTE—UNSPECIFIED DETAIL WITH RESPECT TO DIMENSIONS, TOLERANCES, CONTOURS, MATERIAL, WORKMANSHIP, AND SO ON, MUST CONFORM TO GENERAL SPECIFICATIONS FOR HYDRAULIC HOSE FITTINGS. THE DIMENSIONAL DESIGNATIONS ON THE FIRST FIGURE IN EACH GROUP SHALL APPLY TO ALL OTHER FIGURES IN THAT GROUP EXCEPT AS SHOWN OTHERWISE. CODES SHOWN IN BRACKETS ADJACENT TO FIGURE NUMBERS REPRESENT RESPECTIVE FITTING IDENTIFICATION, WITH XX SUBSTITUTED FOR THE HOSE TYPE CODE DEPICTED IN BRACKETS AT END OF RESPECTIVE TABLE TITLES, IN ACCORDANCE WITH SAE J846.

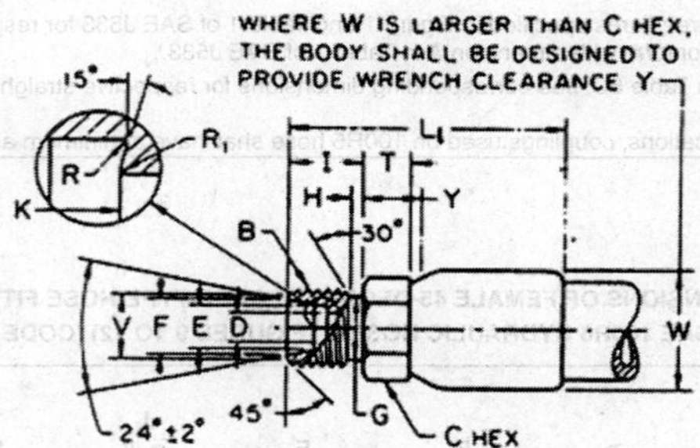

FIGURE 13A—PERMANENTLY ATTACHED STYLE (3301XX)

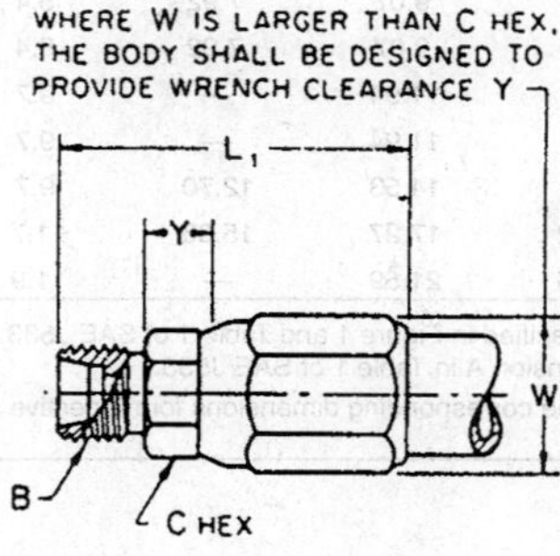

FIGURE 13B—FIELD ATTACHABLE SCREW STYLE (3401XX)

FIGURE 13—MALE FLARELESS TYPE HOSE FITTINGS

TABLE 7A—DIMENSIONS OF MALE FLARELESS TYPE HOSE FITTINGS FOR USE ON SAE 100R1 HYDRAULIC HOSE[(a)] (FIGURE 13) (CODES 42 AND 53)

Nominal SAE 100R1 Hose ID mm	Hose Dash Size	B Nominal Straight Thread Size	Thread Dash Size	C Min mm	D Dia Min mm	L Max mm	L_1 Max mm	T Min mm	W Max mm	Y Min mm
6.4	–4	7/16–20	–4	11.1	2.8	60.5	57.9	5.6	22.1	9.4
7.9	–5	9/16–18	–6	14.3	5.1	59.9	59.9	5.6	23.9	10.4
9.5	–6	9/16–18	–6	14.3	6.6	61.7	61.5	5.6	27.7	10.4
9.5	–6	3/4–16	–8	19.0	6.6	64.5	64.5	6.4	27.7	12.7
10.3	–6.5	3/4–16	–8	19.0	6.6	64.5	64.5	6.4	29.5	12.7
12.7	–8	3/4–16	–8	19.0	9.7	66.3	73.9	6.4	31.2	12.7
12.7	–8	7/8–14	–10	22.2	9.7	67.8	75.4	6.4	31.2	14.2
15.9	–10	7/8–14	–10	22.2	12.2	77.2	82.3	6.4	34.8	14.2
15.9	–10	1-1/16–12	–12	31.8	12.7	77.0	88.1	7.9	34.8	15.5
19.0	–12	7/8–14	–10	22.2	12.2	90.2	88.1	7.9	40.4	14.2
19.0	–12	1-1/16–12	–12	31.8	14.5	90.2	88.1	7.9	40.4	15.5
25.4	–16	1-5/16–12	–16	38.1	19.8	91.2	101.6	9.7	51.3	17.5

(a) For dimensions shown in Figure 13A, but not specified in Table 7A, see corresponding dimensions for respective straight thread size in Figure 19A and Table 9 of SAE J514.

TABLE 7B—DIMENSIONS OF MALE FLARELESS TYPE HOSE FITTINGS FOR USE ON SAE 100R2 HYDRAULIC HOSE[(a)] (FIGURE 13) (CODES 43 AND 54)

Nominal SAE 100R2 Hose ID mm	Hose Dash Size	B Nominal Straight Thread Size	Thread Dash Size	C Min mm	D Dia Min mm	L Max mm	L_1 Max mm	T Min mm	W Max mm	Y Min mm
6.4	–4	7/16–20	–4	11.1	2.8	60.5	64.3	4.8	25.4	9.4
9.5	–6	9/16–18	–6	14.3	6.6	61.7	69.1	5.6	30.2	10.4
9.5	–6	3/4–16	–8	19.0	6.6	64.5	72.4	6.4	30.2	12.7
12.7	–8	3/4–16	–8	19.0	9.7	66.3	75.2	6.4	35.1	12.7
12.7	–8	7/8–14	–10	22.2	9.7	67.8	76.7	6.4	35.1	14.2
15.9	–10	7/8–14	–10	22.2	12.2	77.2	84.6	6.4	39.6	14.2
15.9	–10	1-1/16–12	–12	31.8	12.7	77.0	92.2	7.9	39.6	15.5
19.0	–12	7/8–14	–10	22.2	12.2	90.2	92.2	7.9	44.4	14.2
19.0	–12	1-1/16–12	–12	31.8	14.5	90.2	92.2	7.9	44.4	15.5
25.4	–16	1-5/16–12	–16	38.1	19.8	91.2	105.4	9.7	52.3	17.5

(a) For dimensions shown in Figure 13A, but not specified in Table 7B, see corresponding dimensions for respective straight thread size in Figure 19A and Table 9 of SAE J514.

FEMALE FLARELESS TYPE

NOTE—UNSPECIFIED DETAIL WITH RESPECT TO DIMENSIONS, TOLERANCES, CONTOURS, MATERIAL, WORKMANSHIP, AND SO ON, MUST CONFORM TO GENERAL SPECIFICATIONS FOR HYDRAULIC HOSE FITTINGS. THE DIMENSIONAL DESIGNATIONS ON THE FIRST FIGURE IN EACH GROUP SHALL APPLY TO ALL OTHER FIGURES IN THAT GROUP EXCEPT AS SHOWN OTHERWISE. CODES SHOWN IN BRACKETS ADJACENT TO FIGURE NUMBERS REPRESENT RESPECTIVE FITTING IDENTIFICATION, WITH XX SUBSTITUTED FOR THE HOSE TYPE CODE DEPICTED IN BRACKETS AT END OF RESPECTIVE TABLE TITLES, IN ACCORDANCE WITH SAE J846.

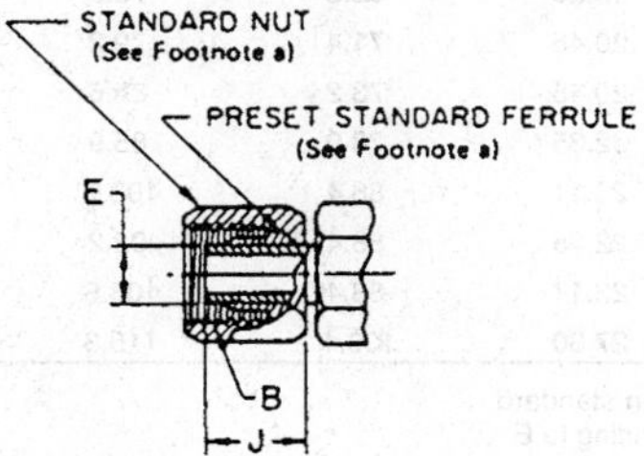

FIGURE 14A—OPTIONAL PRESET FERRULE END CONSTRUCTION

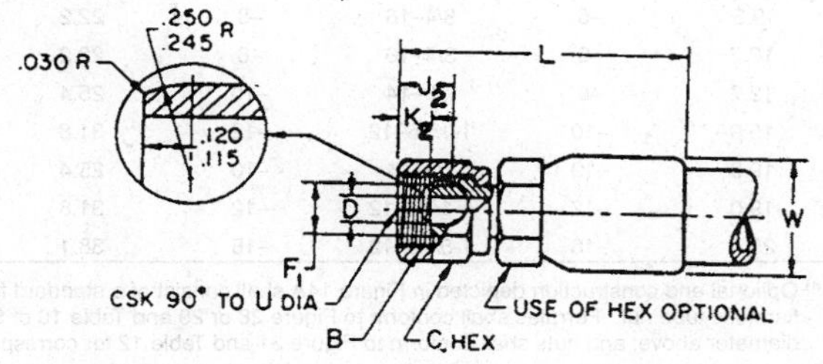

FIGURE 14B—PERMANENTLY ATTACHED STYLE (3601XX)

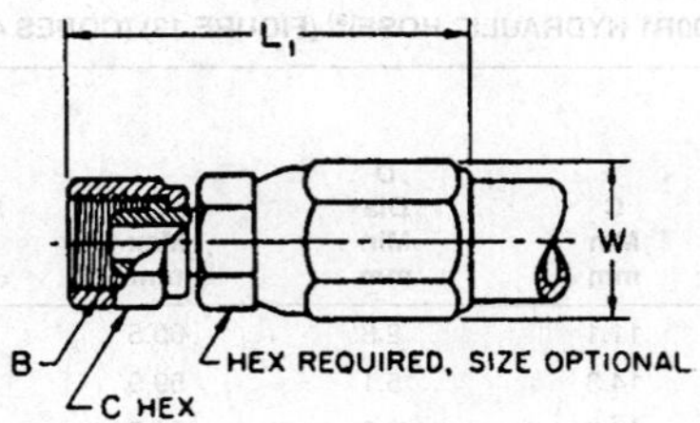

FIGURE 14C—FIELD ATTACHABLE SCREW STYLE (3701XX)

FIGURE 14—FEMALE FLARELESS TYPE HOSE FITTINGS

TABLE 8A—DIMENSIONS OF FEMALE TYPE HOSE FITTINGS FOR USE ON SAE 100R1 HYDRAULIC HOSE[b] (FIGURE 14) (CODES 42 AND 53)

Nominal SAE 100R1 Hose ID mm	Hose Dash Size	B Nominal Straight Thread Size	Thread Dash Size	C Min mm	D Dia Min mm	E Dia mm	J Ref mm	L Max mm	L_1 Max mm	W Max mm
6.4	–4	7/16–20	–4	14.3	2.8	6.35	16.61	61.5	66.5	22.1
7.9	–5	9/16–18	–6	17.5	5.1	9.52	18.29	62.3	67.6	23.9
9.5	–6	9/16–18	–6	17.5	6.6	9.52	18.29	68.3	70.6	27.7
9.5	–6	3/4–16	–8	22.2	6.6	12.70	20.45	71.4	73.9	27.7
10.3	–6.5	3/4–16	–8	22.2	6.6	12.70	20.45	71.4	73.9	29.5
12.7	–8	3/4–16	–8	22.2	9.7	12.70	20.45	73.2	82.3	31.2
12.7	–8	7/8–14	–10	25.4	9.7	15.88	22.35	78.0	83.1	31.2
15.9	–10	7/8–14	–10	25.4	12.2	15.88	22.35	89.4	87.6	34.8
15.9	–10	1-1/16–12	–12	31.8	12.7	19.05	23.11	88.4	92.2	34.8
19.0	–12	7/8–14	–10	25.4	12.2	15.88	22.35	88.4	92.2	40.4
19.0	–12	1-1/16–12	–12	31.8	14.5	19.05	23.11	88.4	92.2	40.4
25.4	–16	1-5/16–12	–16	38.1	19.8	25.40	27.30	100.1	108.7	51.3

[a] Optional end construction depicted in Figure 14A shall consist of a standard ferrule preset into a tubular nipple to retain standard flareless tube nut. Ferrules shall conform to Figure 28 or 29 and Table 10 of SAE J514 for nominal tube OD corresponding to E diameter above; and nuts shall conform to Figure 31 and Table 12 for corresponding straight thread size.

[b] For dimensions shown in Figure 14B, but not specified in Table 8A, see corresponding dimensions for respective straight thread size in Figure 25C and Table 9 of SAE J514.

TABLE 8B—DIMENSIONS OF FEMALE FLARELESS TYPE HOSE FITTINGS FOR USE ON SAE 100R2 HYDRAULIC HOSE[b] (FIGURE 14) (CODES 43 AND 54)

Nominal SAE 100R2 Hose ID mm	Hose Dash Size	B Nominal Straight Thread Size	Thread Dash Size	C Min mm	D Dia Min mm	E Dia mm	J Ref mm	L Max mm	L_1 Max mm	W Max mm
6.4	–4	7/16–20	–4	14.3	2.8	6.35	16.61	63.0	67.8	25.4
9.5	–6	9/16–18	–6	17.5	6.6	9.52	18.29	68.3	76.2	30.2
9.5	–6	3/4–16	–8	22.2	6.6	12.70	20.45	71.4	79.2	30.2
12.7	–8	3/4–16	–8	22.2	9.7	12.70	20.45	73.2	84.6	35.1
12.7	–8	7/8–14	–10	25.4	9.7	15.88	22.35	78.0	85.9	35.1
15.9	–10	1-1/16–12	–12	31.8	12.7	19.05	23.11	88.4	103.6	39.6
19.0	–12	7/8–14	–10	25.4	12.2	15.88	22.35	88.4	92.2	44.4
19.0	–12	1-1/16–12	–12	31.8	14.5	19.05	23.11	88.4	103.6	44.4
25.4	–16	1-5/16–12	–16	38.1	19.8	25.40	27.30	100.1	115.3	52.3

[a] Optional end construction depicted in Figure 14A shall consist of a standard ferrule preset into a tubular nipple to retain standard flareless tube nut. Ferrules shall conform to Figure 28 or 29 and Table 10 of SAE J514 for nominal tube OD corresponding to E diameter above; and nuts shall conform to Figure 31 and Table 12 for corresponding straight thread size.

[b] For dimensions shown in Figure 14B, but not specified in Table 8B, see corresponding dimensions for respective straight thread size in Figure 25C and Table 9 of SAE J514.

4-BOLT SPLIT FLANGE TYPE

NOTE—UNSPECIFIED DETAIL WITH RESPECT TO DIMENSIONS, TOLERANCES, CONTOURS, MATERIAL, WORKMANSHIP, AND SO ON, MUST CONFORM TO GENERAL SPECIFICATIONS FOR HYDRAULIC HOSE FITTINGS. THE DIMENSIONAL DESIGNATIONS ON THE FIRST FIGURE IN EACH GROUP SHALL APPLY TO ALL OTHER FIGURES IN THAT GROUP EXCEPT AS SHOWN OTHERWISE. CODES SHOWN IN BRACKETS ADJACENT TO FIGURE NUMBERS REPRESENT RESPECTIVE FITTING IDENTIFICATION, WITH XX SUBSTITUTED FOR THE HOSE TYPE CODE DEPICTED IN BRACKETS AT END OF RESPECTIVE TABLE TITLES, IN ACCORDANCE WITH SAE J846.

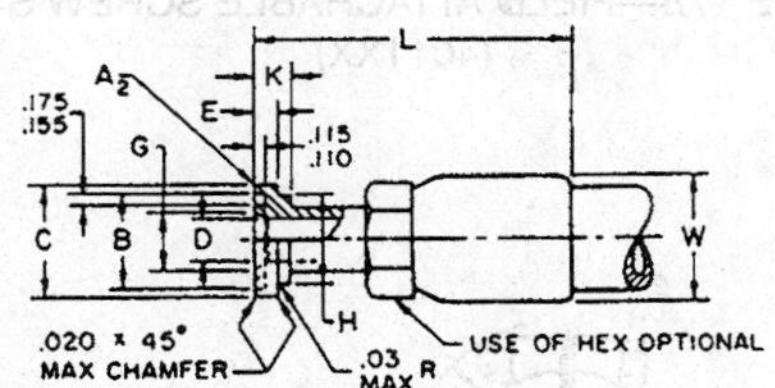

FIGURE 15A—PERMANENT ATTACHED STYLE (3901XX)

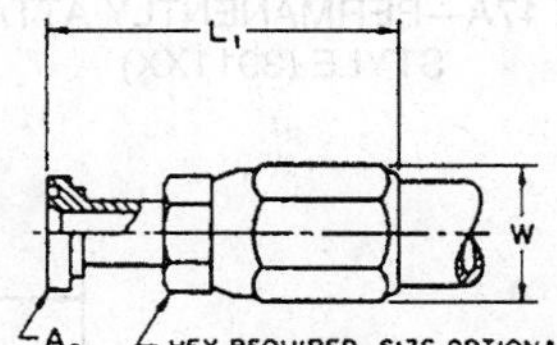

FIGURE 15B—FIELD ATTACHABLE SCREW STYLE (4001XX)

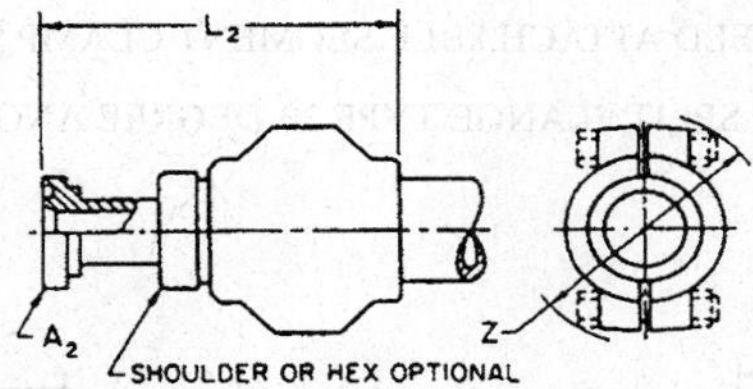

FIGURE 15C—FIELD ATTACHABLE SEGMENT CLAMP STYLE (4101xx)

FIGURE 15—4-BOLT SPLIT FLANGE TYPE HOSE FITTINGS

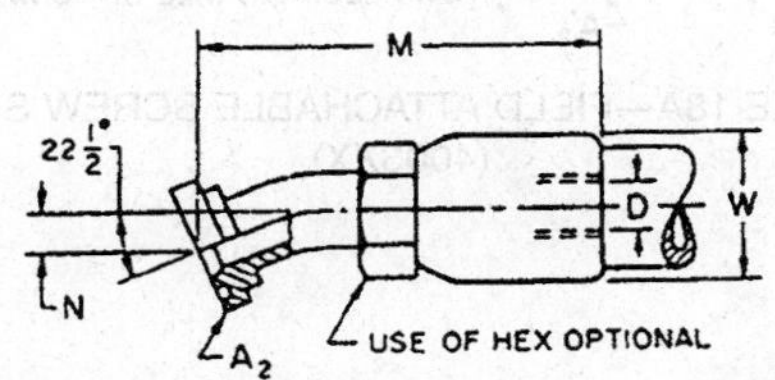

FIGURE 16A—PERMANENTLY ATTACHED STYLE (3910XX)

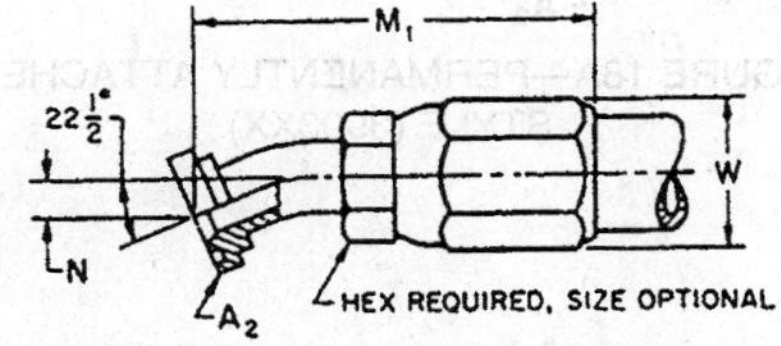

FIGURE 16B—FIELD ATTACHABLE SCREW STYLE (4010XX)

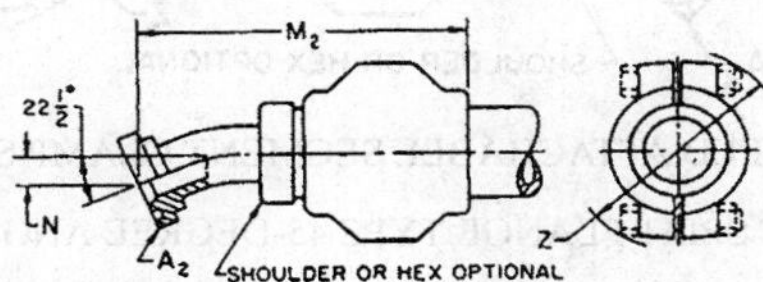

FIGURE 16C—FIELD ATTACHABLE SEGMENT CLAMP STYLE (4110XX)

FIGURE 16—4-BOLT SPLIT FLANGE TYPE 22 1/2-DEGREE ANGLE HOSE FITTINGS

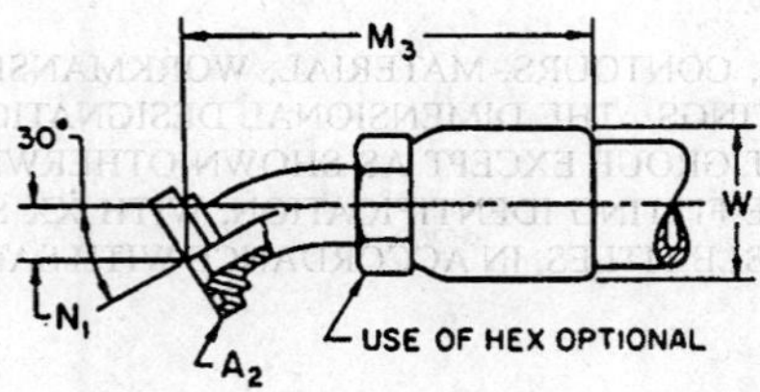

FIGURE 17A—PERMANENTLY ATTACHED STYLE (3911XX)

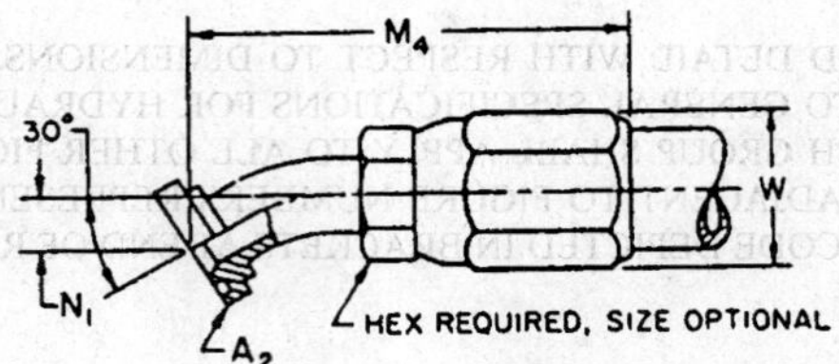

FIGURE 17B—FIELD ATTACHABLE SCREW STYLE (4011XX)

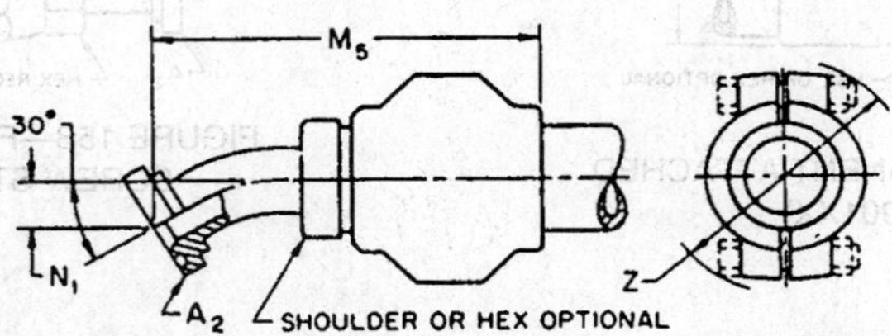

FIGURE 17C—FIELD ATTACHABLE SEGMENT CLAMP STYLE (4111XX)

FIGURE 17—4-BOLT SPLIT FLANGE TYPE 30-DEGREE ANGLE HOSE FITTINGS

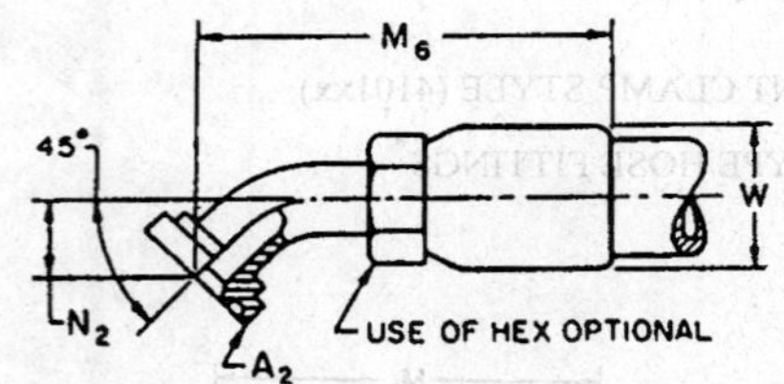

FIGURE 18A—PERMANENTLY ATTACHED STYLE (3903XX)

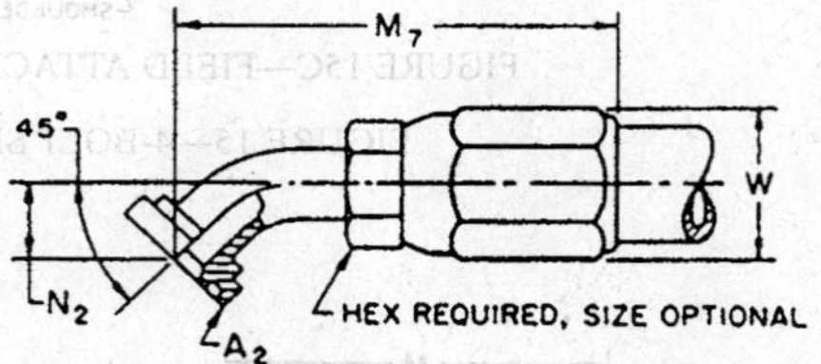

FIGURE 18A—FIELD ATTACHABLE SCREW STYLE (4003XX)

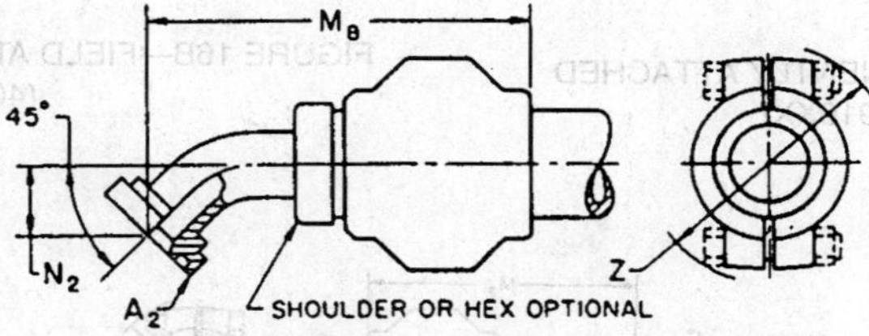

FIGURE 18C—FIELD ATTACHABLE SEGMENT CLAMP STYLE (4103XX)

FIGURE 18—4-BOLT SPLIT FLANGE TYPE 45-DEGREE ANGLE HOSE FITTINGS

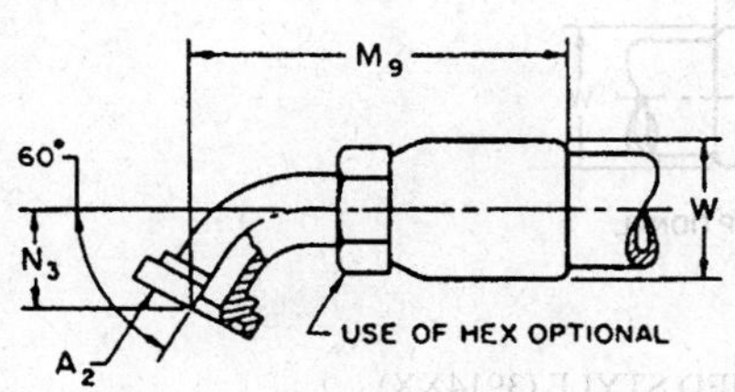

FIGURE 19A—PERMANENTLY ATTACHED STYLE (3912XX)

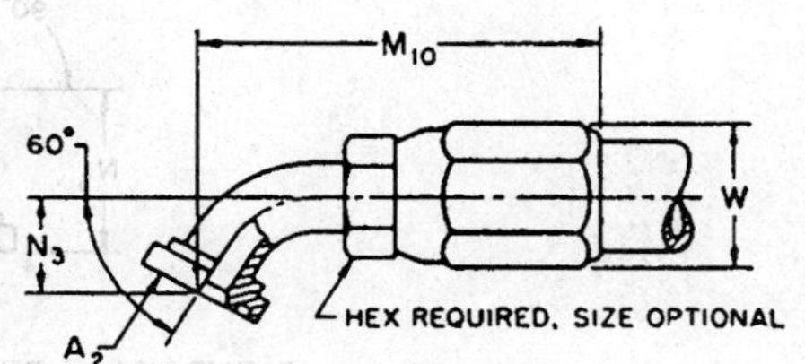

FIGURE 19B—FIELD ATTACHABLE SCREW STYLE (4012XX)

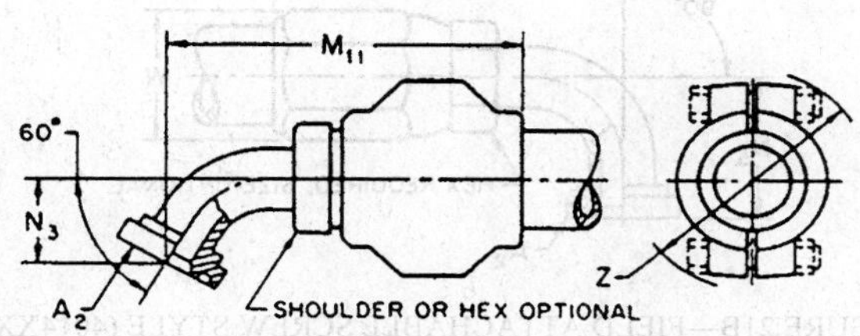

FIGURE 19C—FIELD ATTACHABLE SEGMENT CLAMP STYLE (4112XX)

FIGURE 19—4-BOLT SPLIT FLANGE TYPE 60-DEGREE ANGLE HOSE FITTINGS

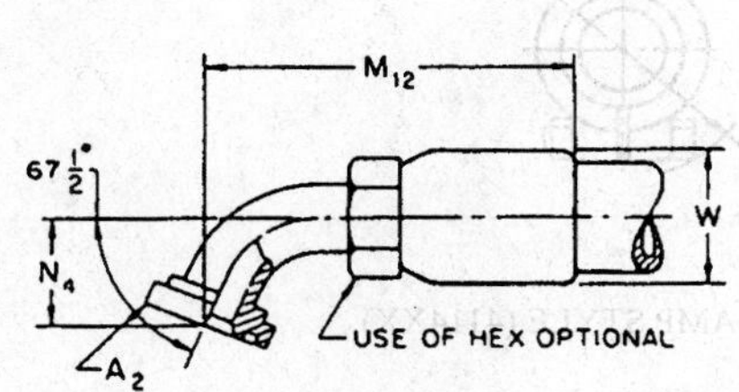

FIGURE 20A—PERMANENTLY ATTACHED STYLE (3913XX)

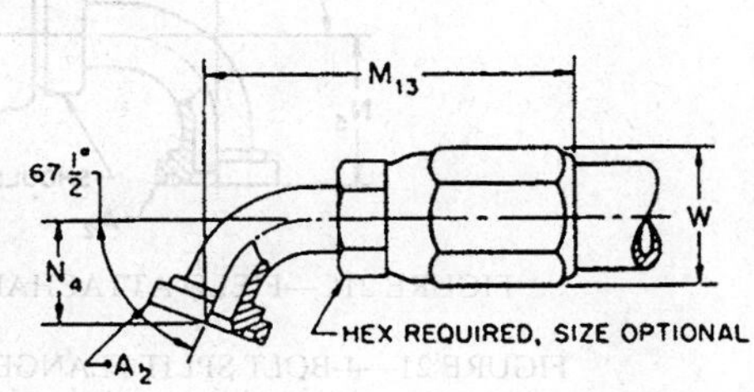

FIGURE 20A—FIELD ATTACHABLE SCREW STYLE (4013XX)

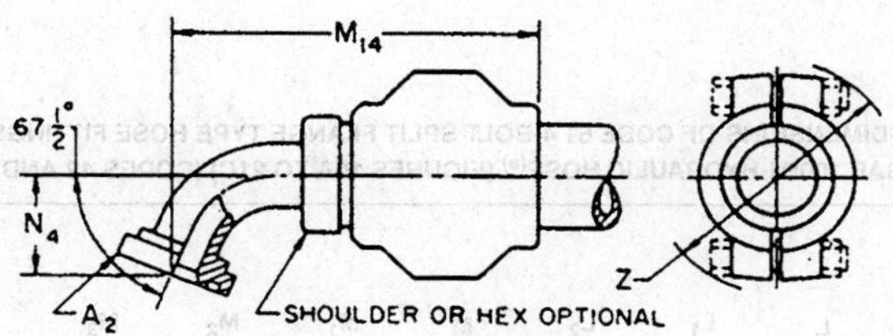

FIGURE 20C—FIELD ATTACHABLE SEGMENT CLAMP STYLE (4113XX)

FIGURE 20—4-BOLT SPLIT FLANGE TYPE 67 1/2-DEGREE ANGLE HOSE FITTINGS

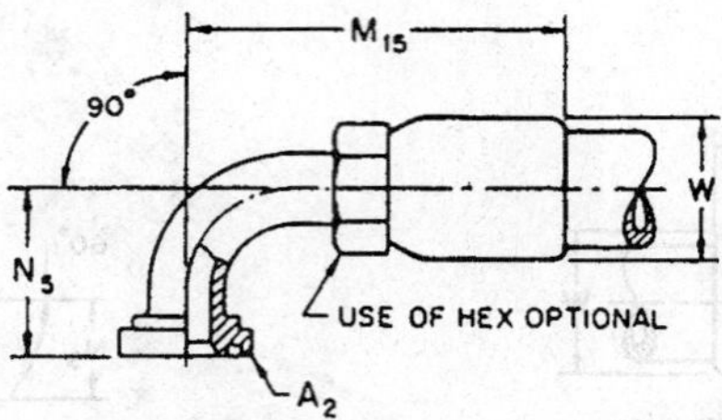

FIGURE 21A—PERMANENTLY ATTACHED STYLE (3914XX)

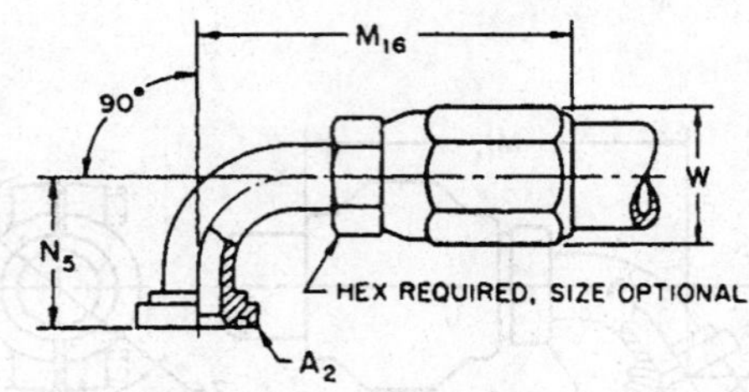

FIGURE 21B—FIELD ATTACHABLE SCREW STYLE (4014XX)

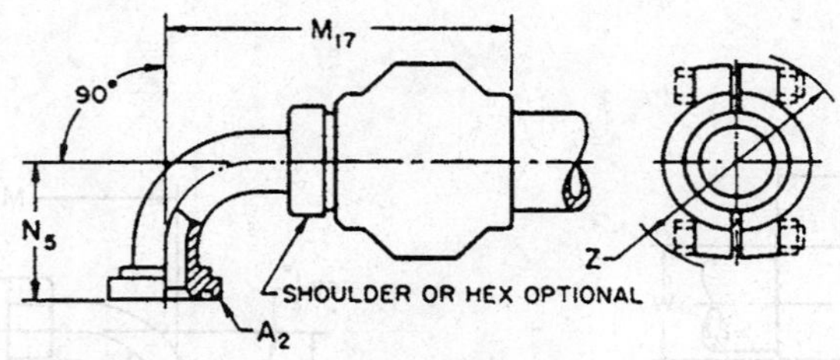

FIGURE 21C—FIELD ATTACHABLE SEGMENT CLAMP STYLE (4114XX)

FIGURE 21—4-BOLT SPLIT FLANGE TYPE 90-DEGREE ANGLE HOSE FITTINGS

NOTE—The Code Identification numbers shown in Figures 15A through 21C are Standard Pressure (Code 61) Split Flanges. For High Pressure (Code 62) flanges, replace the first 2 digits with the numbers shown below:

49 replaces 39 for permanently attached
50 replaces 40 for field reusables
51 replaces 41 for segment clamp cplgs.
Ref: See SAE J846

TABLE 9A—DIMENSIONS OF CODE 61 4-BOLT SPLIT FLANGE TYPE HOSE FITTINGS FOR USE ON SAE 100R1 HYDRAULIC HOSE[(a)] (FIGURES 15A TO 21C) (CODES 42 AND 53)

Nominal SAE 100R1 Hose ID mm	Hose Dash Size	A_2 Nominal Flange Size mm	Flange Dash Size	D Dia Min mm	L Max mm	L_1 Max mm	L_2 Max mm	M Max mm	M_1 Max mm	M_2 Max mm	M_3 Max mm	M_4 Max mm	M_5 Max mm	M_6 Max mm	M_7 Max mm	M_8 Max mm	M_9 Max mm
12.7	–8	12.7	–8	9.7	76.2	93.5	85.9	85.3	—	—	86.1	—	85.3	86.1	99.3	86.1	85.3
15.9	–10	19.0	–12	12.7	88.9	—	—	100.1	100.1	—	100.1	100.1	—	103.1	—	—	97.5
19.0	–12	19.0	–12	14.5	88.9	100.8	101.6	100.1	100.1	100.1	100.1	100.1	100.1	103.1	118.9	103.1	97.5
25.4	–16	25.4	–16	19.8	88.9	108.7	111.3	106.7	118.4	118.4	106.7	118.4	118.4	110.2	140.0	122.2	111.3
31.8	–20	31.8	–20	25.7	106.2	108.7	111.3	111.8	130.3	130.3	122.4	130.3	130.3	127.0	138.2	138.2	119.1
38.1	–24	38.1	–24	31.8	114.3	120.6	111.3	145.3	145.3	145.3	145.3	145.3	145.3	151.6	151.6	151.6	155.7
50.8	–32	50.8	–32	43.7	136.7	128.5	127.0	171.4	189.0	189.0	171.4	189.0	189.0	193.0	196.8	196.8	204.0

TABLE 9B—DIMENSIONS OF CODE 61 4-BOLT SPLIT FLANGE TYPE HOSE FITTINGS FOR USE ON SAE 100R1 HYDRAULIC HOSE[(a)] (FIGURES 15A TO 21C) (CODES 42 AND 53) (CONTINUED)

Nominal SAE 100R1 Hose ID mm	Flange Dash Size	M_{10} Max mm	M_{11} Max mm	M_{12} Max mm	M_{13} Max mm	M_{14} Max mm	M_{15} Max mm	M_{16} Max mm	M_{17} Max mm	N ±3.0 mm	N_1 ±3.0 mm	N_2 3.0 mm	N_3 ±3.0 mm	N_4 ±3.0 mm	N_5 ±3.0 mm	W Max mm	Z Max mm
12.7	–8	—	85.3	85.3	—	85.3	83.8	90.4	83.8	9.7	12.7	19.8	26.7	31.8	41.4	31.2	63.5
15.9	–12	103.9	—	97.5	103.9	—	93.7	100.1	—	9.7	13.5	21.3	29.5	33.3	54.1	34.8	—
19.0	–12	103.9	103.9	97.5	103.9	103.9	93.7	108.7	100.1	11.2	14.7	25.4	35.8	40.6	54.1	40.4	76.2
25.4	–16	124.0	124.0	111.3	124.0	124.0	108.0	132.1	120.6	11.2	15.7	26.9	38.1	44.4	60.5	51.3	91.2
31.8	–20	144.5	144.5	119.1	144.5	144.5	122.2	135.6	135.6	12.7	18.3	29.2	42.2	48.3	66.5	62.5	101.6
38.1	–24	161.0	161.0	155.7	161.0	161.0	155.7	152.4	152.4	16.0	22.4	35.8	50.8	50.8	79.2	69.5	114.3
50.8	–32	209.6	158.8	204.0	209.6	209.6	193.8	203.2	203.2	22.4	31.8	50.8	73.2	82.6	114.3	88.1	130.0

(a) For dimensions of flanged head shown in Figure 15A, but not specified in Table 9A, see corresponding dimensions for respective nominal flange size in Figure 3 and Table 1A of SAE J518.

TABLE 9C—DIMENSIONS OF CODE 61 4-BOLT SPLIT FLANGE TYPE HOSE FITTINGS FOR USE ON SAE 100R2 HYDRAULIC HOSE[(a)] (FIGURES 15A TO 21C)) (CODES 43 AND 54)

Nominal SAE 100R2 Hose ID mm	Hose Dash Size	A_2 Nominal Flange Size mm	Flange Dash Size	D Dia Min mm	L Max mm	L_1 Max mm	L_2 Max mm	M Max mm	M_1 Max mm	M_2 Max mm	M_3 Max mm	M_4 Max mm	M_5 Max mm	M_6 Max mm	M_7 Max mm	M_8 Max mm	M_9 Max mm
12.7	–8	12.7	–8	9.7	91.7	96.0	88.9	88.9	96.0	87.9	88.9	—	90.4	91.9	101.6	91.2	91.9
12.7	–8	19.0	–12	9.7	82.6	98.6	88.9	90.4	—	90.4	90.4	—	91.9	91.9	—	92.7	91.9
15.9	–10	19.0	–12	12.7	70.6	—	—	111.3	—		113.8	—	—	116.1	—	—	116.8
19.0	–12	19.0	–12	14.5	96.8	108.0	93.0	101.6	112.8	102.6	104.6	115.3	105.2	106.7	118.9	108.7	108.0
19.0	–12	25.4	–16	14.5	86.6	108.0	93.0	101.6	116.8	106.7	104.6	119.4	109.2	106.7	121.9	111.8	108.0
22.2	–14	25.4	–16	18.3	82.6	—	—	—	—	—	—	—	—	—	—	—	—
25.4	–16	25.4	–16	19.8	108.7	120.4	102.4	111.8	123.4	117.9	115.3	121.9	121.9	119.9	138.4	125.5	120.6
25.4	–16	31.8	–20	19.8	110.2	120.4	109.7	113.3	123.4	120.9	117.3	125.0	125.0	120.6	138.4	128.0	121.4
31.8	–20	31.8	–20	25.7	136.7	135.9	130.3	153.9	142.7	142.7	158.8	154.4	148.3	166.6	164.3	151.9	171.4
31.8	–20	38.1	–24	25.7	136.7	135.9	130.3	153.9	—	144.3	158.8	—	148.3	166.6	—	151.9	171.4
38.1	–24	38.1	–24	31.8	155.4	142.5	134.9	177.3	165.6	165.6	180.3	172.7	172.7	186.2	177.8	177.8	187.5
38.1	–24	50.8	–32	31.8	155.4	142.5	134.9	177.3	—	165.6	180.3	—	172.7	186.2	—	177.8	187.5
50.8	–32	50.8	–32	43.7	138.2	161.8	162.6	185.9	206.2	165.6	193.0	213.4	221.0	198.1	218.4	226.1	210.3

TABLE 9B—DIMENSIONS OF CODE 61 4-BOLT SPLIT FLANGE TYPE HOSE FITTINGS FOR USE ON SAE 100R2 HYDRAULIC HOSE[(a)] (FIGURES 15A TO 21C) (CODES 43 AND 543) (CONTINUED)

Nominal SAE 100R2 Hose ID mm	Flange Dash Size	M_{10} Max mm	M_{11} Max mm	M_{12} Max mm	M_{13} Max mm	M_{14} Max mm	M_{15} Max mm	M_{16} Max mm	M_{17} Max mm	N ±3.0 mm	N_1 ±3.0 mm	N_2 3.0 mm	N_3 ±3.0 mm	N_4 ±3.0 mm	N_5 ±3.0 mm	W Max mm	Z Max mm
12.7	–8	93.0	91.9	89.4	93.0	90.4	85.9	92.7	88.9	9.7	12.7	19.8	26.7	31.8	41.4	35.1	66.6
12.7	–12	—	92.7	90.4		91.2	85.9		88.9	9.7	13.5	21.3	29.5	33.3	42.9	35.1	66.6
15.9	–12	—	—	115.8	—	—	113.0	—	—	9.7	13.5	21.3	29.5	33.3	54.1	39.6	—
19.0	–12	118.9	108.7	106.4	118.1	108.0	103.1	111.8	101.6	11.2	14.7	25.4	35.8	40.6	54.1	44.4	79.2
19.0	–16	121.9	111.8	106.4	120.6	110.5	103.1	114.3	104.1	11.2	14.7	25.4	35.8	40.6	54.1	44.4	79.2
22.2	–16	—	—	—	—	—	—	—	—	—	—	—	—	—	—	46.0	—
25.4	–16	132.1	129.3	122.9	129.6	128.6	117.3	130.6	124.5	11.2	15.7	26.9	38.1	44.4	60.5	52.3	91.4
25.4	–20	132.1	130.0	122.9	129.6	129.3	117.3	130.6	127.0	11.9	16.8	27.7	39.6	46.0	60.5	52.3	91.4
31.8	–20	154.9	154.9	171.4	152.4	152.4	165.1	160.8	152.4	12.7	18.3	29.2	42.2	48.3	66.5	66.8	114.3
31.8	–24	—	154.9	171.4	—	153.2	165.1	160.8	152.4	13.5	19.0	31.0	44.4	50.8	68.3	66.8	114.3
38.1	–24	179.3	179.3	185.9	176.8	176.8	185.4	178.1	175.3	16.0	22.4	35.8	50.8	50.8	79.2	74.7	127.0
38.1	–32		179.3	185.9	—	176.8	185.4	—	175.3	16.0	22.4	35.8	50.8	57.2	79.2	74.7	127.0
50.8	–32	230.6	238.3	207.8	228.1	235.7	198.1	218.9	226.1	22.4	31.8	50.8	73.2	82.6	114.3	88.9	149.4

(a) For dimensions of flanged head shown in Figure 15A, but not specified in Table 9B, see corresponding dimensions for respective nominal flange size in Figure 3 and Table 1A of SAE J518.

TABLE 9C—DIMENSIONS OF CODE 61 4-BOLT SPLIT FLANGE TYPE HOSE FITTINGS FOR USE ON SAE 100R4 HYDRAULIC HOSE[(a)] (FIGURES 15A, 15C, 16A, 16C, 17A, 18A, 18C, 19A, 19C, 20A, 20C, 21A, AND 21C) (CODE 45)

Nominal SAE 100R4 Hose ID mm	Hose Dash Size	A_2 Nominal Flange Size mm	Flange Dash Size	D_1 Dia Min mm	L Min mm	L_2 Max mm	M Max mm	M_2 Max mm	M_3 Max mm	M_5 Max mm	M_6 Max mm	M_8 Max mm	M_9 Max mm
19.0	–12	19.0	–12	14.5	82.3	76.2	84.1	86.6	86.6	88.9	89.7	92.2	90.4
25.4	–16	25.4	–16	19.8	89.7	82.6	93.7	104.9	96.8	108.0	103.1	112.0	103.1
31.8	–20	31.8	–20	25.7	111.3	96.8	101.6	118.9	104.9	124.0	114.3	131.8	115.8
38.1	–24	38.1	–24	31.8	127.5	104.9	131.8	131.8	138.2	139.7	142.7	146.0	143.8
50.8	–32	50.8	–32	42.9	136.7	122.4	163.6	177.8	169.9	182.6	178.6	190.5	190.2
63.5	–40	63.5	–40	57.2	127.0	125.5	139.7	152.4	148.3	162.1	165.9	178.6	176.3
76.2	–48	76.2	–48	68.3	155.4	139.7	184.2	173.0	194.6	185.7	215.9	204.7	228.6

TABLE 9C—DIMENSIONS OF CODE 61 4-BOLT SPLIT FLANGE TYPE HOSE FITTINGS FOR USE ON SAE 100R4 HYDRAULIC HOSE[(a)] (FIGURES 15A, 15C, 16A, 16C, 17A, 18A, 18C, 19A, 19C, 20A, 20C, 21A, AND 21C) (CODES 45) (CONTINUED)

Nominal SAE 100R4 Hose ID mm	Flange Dash Size	M_{11} Max mm	M_{12} Max mm	M_{14} Max mm	M_{15} Max mm	M_{17} Max mm	N ±3.0 mm	N_1 ±3.0 mm	N_2 ±3.0 mm	N_3 ±3.0 mm	N_4 ±3.0 mm	N_5 ±3.0 mm	W Max mm	Z Max mm
19.0	–12	93.5	89.7	92.2	86.6	88.9	11.2	14.7	25.4	35.8	40.6	54.1	43.9	76.2
25.4	–16	114.3	102.4	112.8	100.1	111.3	11.2	15.7	26.9	38.1	44.4	60.5	51.1	82.6
31.8	–20	138.2	115.1	131.8	120.6	129.3	12.7	18.3	29.2	42.2	48.3	66.5	58.7	100.1
38.1	–24	155.7	144.3	152.4	134.1	146.0	16.0	22.4	35.8	50.8	50.8	79.2	66.0	110.2
50.8	–32	203.2	189.0	203.2	190.5	196.8	22.4	31.8	50.8	50.8	82.6	114.3	80.8	125.5
63.5	–40	189.0	179.3	192.0	177.8	190.5	15.7	23.9	43.7	66.5	79.2	117.3	99.8	139.7
76.2	–48	217.4	231.6	223.8	230.9	221.0	18.3	28.4	51.6	79.2	94.5	139.7	113.3	157.2

(a) For dimensions of flanged head shown on Figure 15A, but not specified in Table 9C, see corresponding dimensions for respective nominal flange size in Figure 3 and Table 1A of SAE J518.

TABLE 9D—DIMENSIONS OF CODE 61 4-BOLT SPLIT FLANGE TYPE HOSE FITTINGS FOR USE ON SAE 100R5 HYDRAULIC HOSE[(a)] (FIGURES 15B, 16B, 17B, 18B, 19B, AND 21B) (CODE 46),

Nominal SAE 100R5 Hose ID mm	Hose Dash Size	A_2 Nominal Flange Size mm	Flange Dash Size	D Dia Min mm	L_1 Max mm	M_1 Max mm	M_4 Max mm	M_7 Min mm	M_{10} Max mm	M_{16} Min mm	N ±3.0 mm	N_1 ±3.0 mm	N_2 ±3.0 mm	N_3 ±3.0 mm	N_5 ±3.0 mm	W Max mm
10.3	–8	12.7	–8	7.1	71.6	90.2	—	88.9	—	74.7	12.7	—	25.4	—	41.1	27.4
15.9	–12	19.0	–12	12.7	81.8	101.3	103.6	103.4	106.9	96.5	12.7	17.5	25.4	41.1	53.8	38.6
22.2	–16	25.4	–16	18.3	71.9	91.7	85.9	98.0	99.6	91.7	12.7	12.7	28.4	41.7	60.5	43.9
28.6	–20	31.8	–20	23.9	92.5	98.6	113.8	105.7	108.7	103.6	12.7	24.4	28.4	41.7	63.5	51.3
34.9	–24	38.1	–24	29.5	103.4	103.6	102.1	112.8	121.7	113.8	12.7	14.7	28.7	50.8	69.8	58.7
46.0	–32	50.8	–32	40.9	126.5	117.9	120.4	133.1	—	138.4	12.7	16.5	31.8	—	82.6	73.4

(a) For dimensions of flanged head shown in Figure 15A, but not specified in Table 9D, see corresponding dimensions for respective nominal flange size in Figure 3 and Table 1A of SAE J518.
NOTE—For SAE J1402 and DOT FMVSS 106 air brake applications, couplings used on 100R5 hose shall have a minimum assembled orifice no less than 66% of the nominal hose I.D.

TABLE 9E—DIMENSIONS OF CODE 61 4-BOLT SPLIT FLANGE TYPE HOSE FITTINGS FOR USE ON SAE 100R9 HYDRAULIC HOSE[(a)] (FIGURES 15A TO 21C) (CODES 50 AND 75)

Nominal SAE 100R9 Hose ID mm	Hose Dash Size	A_2 Nominal flange Size mm	Flange Dash Size	D_1 Dia Min mm	L Max mm	L_1 Max mm	M Max mm	M_1 Max mm	M_3 Max mm	M_4 Max mm	M_6 Max mm	M_7 Max mm	M_9 Max mm
12.7	–8	12.7	–8	9.7	98.0	96.0	102.1	96.0	104.4	—	104.4	101.6	104.4
19.0	–12	19.0	–12	14.5	111.3	108.0	120.6	112.8	122.7	115.3	127.0	118.9	127.0
25.4	–16	25.4	–16	19.8	123.2	120.4	132.6	123.4	134.6	121.9	137.4	138.4	137.7
31.8	–20	31.8	–20	25.7	142.2	—	164.1	—	169.2	—	166.6	—	171.4
38.1	–24	38.1	–24	31.8	155.4	—	178.1	—	180.3	—	186.2	—	187.5
50.8	–32	50.8	–32	43.7	189.7	—	210.3	—	216.4	—	216.4	—	227.1

TABLE 9E—DIMENSIONS OF CODE 61 4-BOLT SPLIT FLANGE TYPE HOSE FITTINGS FOR USE ON SAE 100R9 HYDRAULIC HOSE[(a)] (FIGURES 15A TO 21C) (CODES 50 AND 75) (CONTINUED)

Nominal SAE 100R9 Hose ID mm	Flange Dash Size	M_{10} Max mm	M_{12} Max mm	M_{13} Max mm	M_{15} Max mm	M_{16} Max mm	N ±4.8 mm	N_1 ±4.8 mm	N_2 ±4.8 mm	N_3 ±4.8 mm	N_4 ±4.8 mm	N_5 ±4.8 mm
12.7	−8	93.0	103.6	93.0	97.3	92.7	9.7	13.5	24.6	28.4	34.8	41.9
19.0	−12	118.9	120.4	118.1	127.0	111.8	12.4	17.0	26.7	39.6	42.7	57.2
25.4	−16	132.1	136.1	129.5	131.8	130.6	13.7	16.0	29.2	42.4	47.2	63.8
31.8	−20	—	159.5	—	165.1	—	14.0	21.3	30.5	43.7	50.5	69.1
38.1	−24	—	185.9	—	185.4	—	18.3	22.9	37.3	55.6	63.5	85.9
50.8	−32	—	225.8	—	214.1	—	23.9	34.0	53.3	79.2	88.4	123.7

(a) For dimensions of flanged head shown in Figure 15A, but not specified in Table 9E, see corresponding dimensions for respective nominal flange size in Figure 3 and Table 1A of SAE J518.

TABLE 9F1—DIMENSIONS OF CODE 61 4-BOLT SPLIT FLANGE TYPE HOSE FITTINGS FOR USE ON SAE 100R10 HYDRAULIC HOSE[(a)] (FIGURES 15A TO 21C) (CODES 51 AND 76)

Nominal SAE 100R10 Hose ID mm	Hose Dash Size	A_2 Nominal Flange Size mm	Flange Dash Size	D Dia Min mm	L Max mm	L_2 Max mm	M Max mm	M_2 Max mm	M_3 Max mm	M_5 Max mm	M_6 Max mm	M_8 Max mm
19.0	−12	19.0	−12	12.7	133.4	133.4	133.4	133.4	134.1	134.1	141.5	141.5
25.4	−16	25.4	−16	17.3	144.0	144.0	166.6	166.6	165.1	165.1	162.6	162.6
31.8	−20	31.8	−20	22.1	166.4	166.4	183.9	183.9	182.4	182.4	188.0	188.0
38.1	−24	38.1	−24	27.7	177.5	177.5	190.2	190.2	183.9	183.9	209.3	209.3
50.8	−32	50.8	−32	39.6	207.5	207.5	241.8	241.8	227.6	227.6	269.2	269.2

TABLE 9F1—DIMENSIONS OF CODE 61 4-BOLT SPLIT FLANGE TYPE HOSE FITTINGS FOR USE ON SAE 100R10 HYDRAULIC HOSE(a) (FIGURES 15A TO 21C) (CODES 51 AND 76) (CONTINUED)

Nominal SAE 100R10 Hose ID mm	Flange Dash Size	M_9 Max mm	M_{11} Max mm	M_{12} Max mm	M_{14} Max mm	M_{15} Max mm	M_{17} Max mm	N ±3.3 mm	N_1 ±3.3 mm	N_2 ±3.3 mm	N_3 ±3.3 mm	N_4 ±3.3 mm	N_5 ±3.3 mm	W Max mm	Z Max mm
19.0	−12	139.2	139.2	138.2	138.2	127.0	127.0	12.2	16.8	26.7	38.4	42.9	55.6	42.9	79.2
25.4	−16	179.8	179.8	174.0	174.0	160.0	160.0	12.7	16.8	27.9	40.9	47.2	62.0	50.8	107.2
31.8	−20	200.4	200.4	194.8	194.8	199.1	199.1	14.5	19.3	31.8	44.7	50.8	68.1	62.2	126.0
38.1	−24	202.7	202.7	195.6	195.6	200.4	200.4	17.0	23.1	36.6	52.8	61.0	80.8	76.2	133.1
50.8	−32	259.1	259.1	231.9	231.9	259.1	259.1	23.9	33.3	52.8	76.2	86.4	114.3	81.8	166.6

(a) For dimensions of flanged head shown in Figure 15A, but not specified in Table 9F1, see corresponding dimensions for respective nominal flange size in Figure 3 and Table 1A of SAE J518.

TABLE 9F2—DIMENSIONS OF CODE 62 4-BOLT SPLIT FLANGE TYPE HOSE FITTINGS FOR USE ON SAE 100R10 HYDRAULIC HOSE[(a)] (FIGURES 15 TO 21) (CODES 51 AND 76)

Nominal SAE 100R10 Hose ID mm	Hose Dash Size	A_2 Nominal Flange Size mm	Flange Dash Size	D Dia Min mm	L Max mm	L_2 Max mm	M_6 Max mm	M_8 Max mm	M_{15} Max mm	M_{17} Max mm	N_2 ±3.3 mm	N_5 ±3.3 mm	W Max mm	Z Max mm
19.0	−12	19.0	−12	12.7	133.4	133.4	141.5	141.5	134.4	134.4	25.4	54.1	42.9	79.2
25.4	−16	25.4	−16	17.3	149.9	149.9	164.3	164.3	160.0	160.0	30.2	68.6	50.8	107.2
31.8	−20	31.8	−20	22.1	166.4	166.4	191.5	191.5	181.4	181.4	35.8	76.5	62.2	126.0
38.1	−24	38.1	−24	27.7	193.0	193.0	217.7	217.7	200.4	200.4	45.0	91.2	76.2	133.1
50.8	−32	50.8	−32	39.6	219.7	219.7	281.4	281.4	259.1	259.1	63.8	131.6	81.8	166.6

(a) For dimensions of flanged head shown in Figure 15A, but not specified in Table 9F2, see corresponding dimensions for respective nominal flange size in Figure 3 and Table 1B of SAE J518.

TABLE 9G—DIMENSIONS OF CODE 61 4-BOLT SPLIT FLANGE TYPE HOSE FITTINGS FOR USE ON SAE 100R11 HYDRAULIC HOSE[(a)] (FIGURES 15 TO 21) (CODES 52 AND 76)

Nominal SAE 100R11 Hose ID mm	Hose Dash Size	A_2 Nominal Flange Size mm	Flange Dash Size	D Dia Min mm	L Max mm	M Max mm	M_3 Max mm	M_6 Max mm	M_9 Max mm	M_{12} Max mm	M_{15} Max mm	N ±3.3 mm	N_1 ±3.3 mm	N_2 ±3.3 mm	N_3 ±4.8 mm	N_4 ±4.8 mm	N_5 ±4.8 mm	W Max mm
25.4	–16	25.4	–16	18.5	162.1	165.1	168.1	171.4	173.0	171.4	168.1	12.7	17.8	28.7	41.4	47.0	63.5	55.9
31.8	–20	31.8	–20	24.1	74.2	179.1	185.9	182.4	187.5	188.0	184.7	12.7	19.0	30.2	44.4	50.8	69.1	67.3
38.1	–24	38.1	–24	30.5	196.8	200.7	207.8	212.1	216.7	215.9	212.3	16.5	23.6	38.1	53.3	58.7	82.6	74.7
50.8	–32	50.8	–32	41.9	238.8	254.0	264.2	270.5	275.3	276.4	269.2	22.9	33.0	53.3	76.2	85.9	119.1	88.9

(a) For dimensions of flanged head shown in Figure 15A, but not specified in Table 9G, see corresponding dimensions for respective nominal flange size in Figure 3 and Table 1A of SAE J518.

TABLE 9H1—DIMENSIONS OF CODE 61 4-BOLT SPLIT FLANGE TYPE HOSE FITTINGS FOR USE ON SAE 100R12 HYDRAULIC HOSE[(a)] (FIGURES 15A, 16A, 17A, 18A, 19A, 20A, AND 21A) (CODE 77)

Nominal SAE 100R12 Hose ID mm	Hose Dash Size	A2 Nominal Flange Size mm	Flange Dash Size mm	D Dia Min mm	L Max mm	M Max mm	M3 Max mm	M6 Max mm	M9 Max mm	M12 Max mm	M15 Max mm	N ±3.3 mm	N1 ±4.1 mm	N2 ±6.4 mm	N3 ±6.4 mm	N4 ±6.4 mm	N5 ±8.9 mm
12.7	–8	12.7	–8	8.9	108.2	110.0	110.0	110.5	110.5	110.5	110.5	9.7	12.7	19.8	26.7	31.8	41.4
15.9	–10	19.0	–12	10.0	120.7	120.7	120.7	127.0	139.2	138.2	127.0	12.2	16.8	26.7	38.4	42.9	55.9
19.0	–12	19.0	–12	12.7	133.4	133.4	133.4	141.5	139.2	138.2	127.0	12.2	16.8	26.7	38.4	42.9	55.9
25.4	–16	25.4	–16	17.3	144.0	166.6	165.1	162.6	179.8	174.0	160.0	12.7	16.8	27.9	40.6	47.0	62.0
31.8	–20	31.8	–20	22.0	166.4	183.9	182.4	188.0	200.4	194.8	199.1	14.5	19.3	31.8	44.7	50.8	68.1
38.1	–24	38.1	–24	27.7	177.5	190.2	183.9	209.3	202.7	195.6	200.4	17.0	23.1	36.6	52.8	61.0	79.2
50.8	–32	50.8	–32	38.0	207.5	241.8	227.6	269.2	259.1	231.9	259.1	23.9	33.3	52.8	76.2	86.4	118.0

(a) For dimensions of flanged head shown in Figure 15A, but not specified in Table 9H1, see corresponding dimensions for respective nominal flange size in Figure 3 and Table 1A of SAE J518.

TABLE 9H2—DIMENSIONS OF CODE 62 4-BOLT SPLIT FLANGE TYPE HOSE FITTINGS FOR USE ON SAE 100R12 HYDRAULIC HOSE[(a)] (FIGURES 15A, 16A, 17A, 18A, 19A, 20A, AND 21A) (CODE 77)

Nominal SAE 100R12 Hose ID mm	Hose Dash Size	A2 Nominal Flange Size mm	Flange Dash Size	D Dia Min mm	L Max mm	M Max mm	M3 Max mm	M6 Max mm	M9 Max mm	M12 Max mm	M15 Max mm	N ±3.3 mm	N_1 ±4.1 mm	N2 ±6.4 mm	N3 ±6.4 mm	N4 ±6.4 mm	N5 ±8.9 mm
15.9	–10	19.0	–12	10.0	137.9	134.9	142.5	145.3	144.8	143.8	136.7	12.7	16.3	28.7	37.6	42.9	57.9
19.0	–12	19.0	–12	12.7	137.9	134.9	142.5	145.3	144.8	143.8	136.7	12.7	16.3	28.7	37.6	42.9	57.9
25.4	–16	25.4	–16	17.3	149.9	167.6	165.9	164.3	179.8	174.0	160.0	12.7	18.3	30.0	40.6	47.0	66.3
31.8	–20	31.8	–20	22.0	166.4	205.0	198.1	197.1	202.4	197.1	190.8	14.0	20.3	32.3	46.0	52.3	71.4
38.1	–24	38.1	–24	27.7	193.0	231.9	230.9	220.7	240.3	218.4	209.3	17.8	25.4	41.1	56.9	63.5	86.6
50.8	–32	50.8	–32	38.0	219.7	294.9	290.6	281.4	279.4	269.2	259.1	25.4	35.8	57.2	82.6	86.4	122.9

(a) For dimensions of flanged head shown in Figure 15A, but not specified in Table 9H2, see corresponding dimensions for respective nominal flange size in Figure 3 and Table 1B of SAE J518.

TABLE 9I2—DIMENSIONS OF CODE 62 4-BOLT SPLIT FLANGE TYPE HOSE FITTINGS FOR USE ON SAE 100R13 HYDRAULIC HOSE[(a)] (FIGURES 15A TO 21A) (CODE 78)

Nominal SAE 100R13 Hose ID mm	Hose Dash Size	A2 Nominal Flange Size mm	Flange Dash Size	D Dia Min mm	L Max mm	M Max mm	M3 Max mm	M6 Max mm	M9 Max mm	M12 Max mm	M15 Max mm	N ±3.3 mm	N1 ±4.1 mm	N2 ±6.4 mm	N3 ±6.4 mm	N4 ±6.4 mm	N5 ±8.9 mm	W Max mm
19.0	–12	19.0	–12	12.7	137.9	134.9	142.5	145.3	144.8	143.8	136.7	12.7	16.3	28.7	37.6	42.9	57.9	43.7
25.4	–16	25.4	–16	17.5	148.6	167.6	165.9	160.3	166.6	174.0	156.7	12.7	18.3	30.0	40.6	47.0	66.3	50.8
31.8	–20	31.8	–20	22.4	163.3	205.0	198.1	197.1	202.4	197.1	190.8	14.0	20.3	32.3	46.0	52.3	71.4	63.5
38.1	–24	38.1	–24	27.7	191.8	231.9	230.9	220.7	240.3	218.4	209.3	17.8	25.4	41.1	56.9	63.5	86.6	71.1
50.8	–32	50.8	–32	38.1	234.2	302.5	298.2	288.8	300.5	290.6	280.9	25.4	35.8	57.2	82.6	86.4	122.9	88.9

(a) For dimensions of flanged head shown in Figure 15A, but not specified in Table 9I2, see corresponding dimensions for respective nominal flange size in Figure 3 and Table 1B of SAE J518.

FEMALE 0-RING FACE SEAL TYPE

NOTE—UNSPECIFIED DETAIL WITH RESPECT TO DIMENSIONS, TOLERANCES, CONTOURS, MATERIAL, WORKMANSHIP, AND SO ON, MUST CONFORM TO GENERAL SPECIFICATIONS FOR HYDRAULIC HOSE FITTINGS. THE DIMENSIONAL DESIGNATORS ON THE FIRST FIGURE SHALL APPLY TO ALL OTHER FIGURES EXCEPT AS SHOWN OTHERWISE. THE DESIGN AND METHOD OF ATTACHING THE SWIVEL NUT SHALL BE OPTIONAL WITH MANUFACTURER PROVIDING (1) THE DIMENSIONS SHOWN ARE MAINTAINED, (2) THE NUT TURNS FREELY, (3) THE NUT IS CAPABLE OF MEETING THE MAXIMUM TORQUE REQUIREMENTS OF SAE J1453, PARAGRAPH 8.9 AND TABLE 5 AND (4) THE FITTING, WHEN PROPERLY ASSEMBLED ON THE APPROPRIATE HOSE, MEETS THE VARIOUS PERFORMANCE REQUIREMENTS OF SAE J517. CODES SHOWN IN BRACKETS ADJACENT TO FIGURE NUMBERS REPRESENT RESPECTIVE FITTING IDENTIFICATION, WITH XX SUBSTITUTED FOR THE HOSE TYPE CODE DEPICTED IN BRACKETS AT END OF RESPECTIVE TABLE TITLES, IN ACCORDANCE WITH SAE J846.

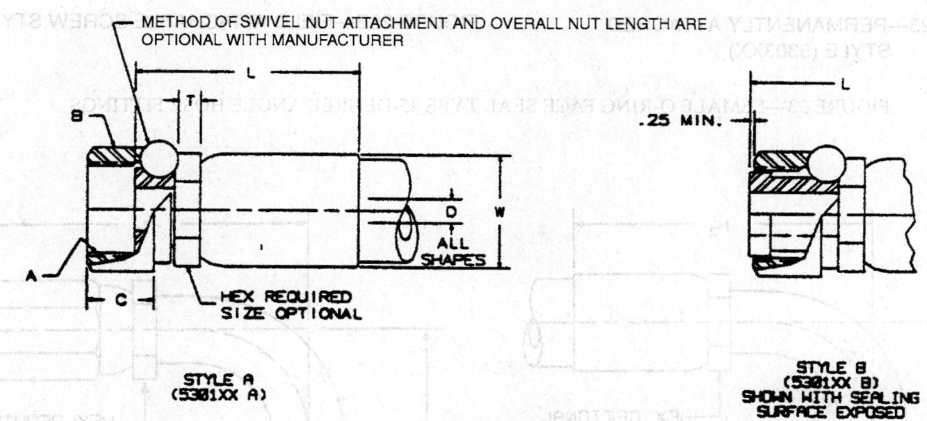

FIGURE 22A—PERMANENTLY ATTACHED STYLES (5301XX)

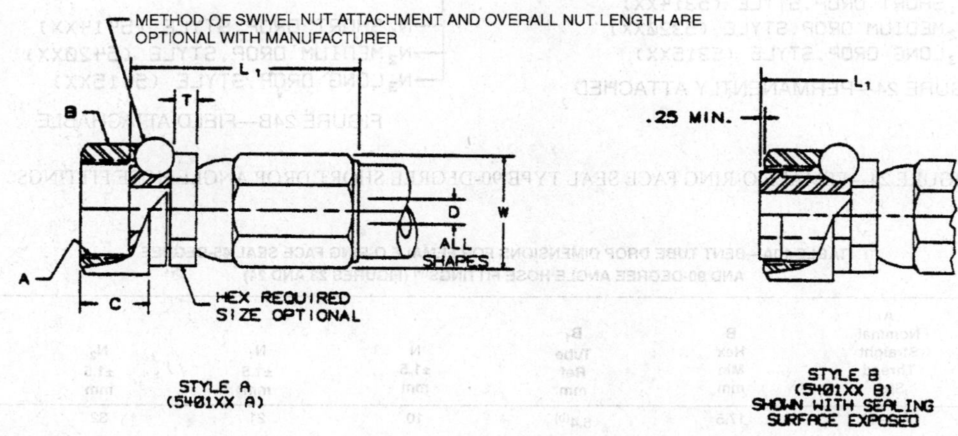

FIGURE 22B—FIELD ATTACHABLE SCREW STYLES (5401XX)

FIGURE 22—FEMALE 0-RING FACE SEAL TYPE HOSE FITTINGS

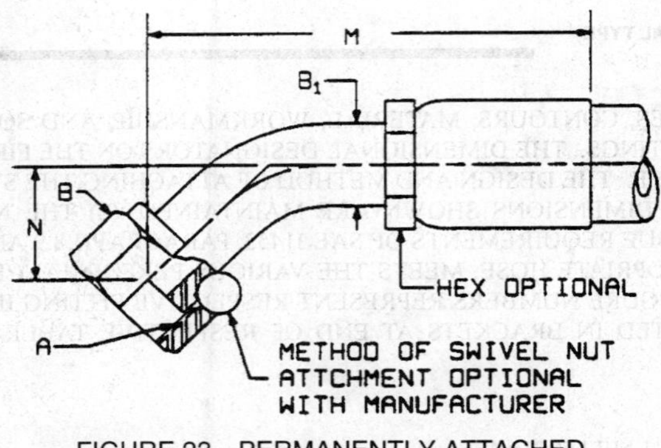

FIGURE 23—PERMANENTLY ATTACHED STYLE (5303XX)

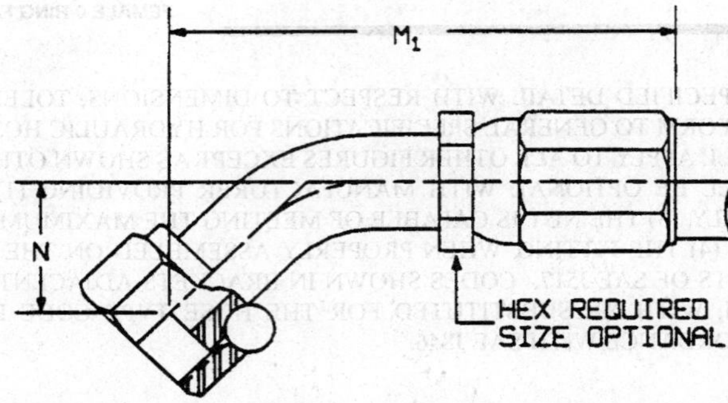

FIGURE 23B—FIELD ATTACHABLE SCREW STYLE (5403XX)

FIGURE 23—FEMALE O-RING FACE SEAL TYPE 45-DEGREE ANGLE HOSE FITTINGS

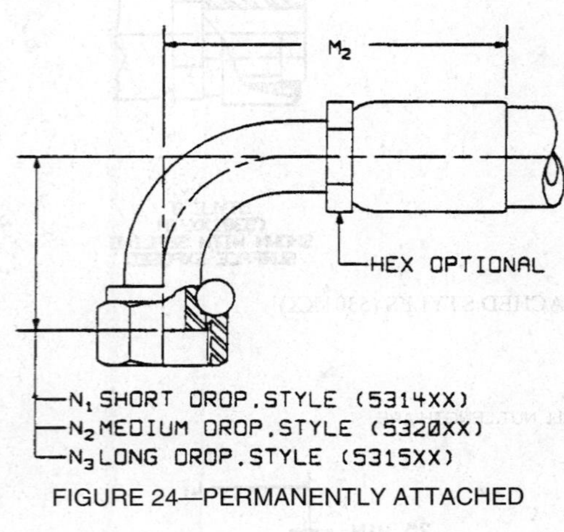

FIGURE 24—PERMANENTLY ATTACHED

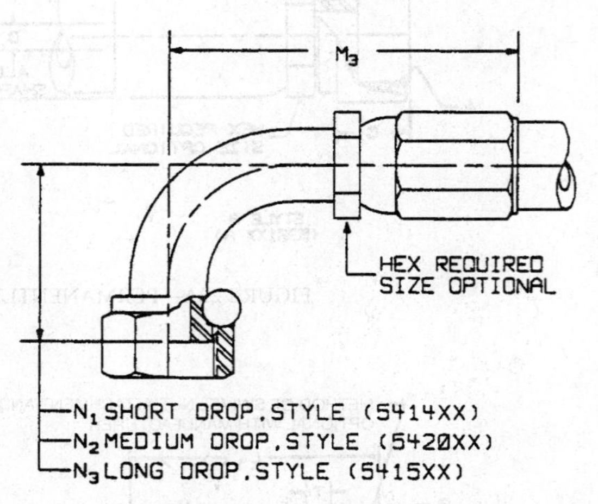

FIGURE 24B—FIELD ATTACHABLE

FIGURE 24—FEMALE O-RING FACE SEAL TYPE 90-DEGREE SHORT DROP ANGLE HOSE FITTINGS

TABLE 10A—BENT TUBE DROP DIMENSIONS FOR FEMALE O-RING FACE SEAL 45-DEGREE AND 90-DEGREE ANGLE HOSE FITTINGS[(a)] (FIGURES 23 AND 24)

Thread Dash Size	A Nominal Straight Thread Size	B Hex Min mm	B_1 Tube Ref mm	N ±1.5 mm	N_1 ±1.5 mm	N_2 ±1.5 mm	N_3 ±1.5 mm
–4	9/16–18	17.5	6.4[(b)]	10	21	32	46
–6	11/16–16	20.6	9.5	11	23	38	54
–8	13/16–16	23.8	12.7	15	29	41	64
–10	1–14	28.6	15.9	16	32	47	70
–12	1-3/16–12	34.9	19	21	48	58	96
–16	1-7/16–12	41.3	25.4	24	56	71	114
–20	1-11/16–12	47.6	31.8	25	64	78	129
–24	2–12	57.2	38.1	27	69	86	141

(a) For dimensions not specified in Tables 10A to 10M, refer to Figures 4, 6, and 10 of SAE J1453-1.

(b) 5/16 tube is acceptable for this size.

TABLE 10B—DIMENSIONS OF FEMALE O-RING FACE SEAL TYPE HOSE FITTINGS FOR USE ON SAE 100R1 HYDRAULIC HOSE[(a)] (FIGURES 22 TO 24) (CODES 42 AND 53)

Nominal SAE 100R1 Hose ID mm	Hose Dash Size	A Nominal Straight Thread Size	Thread Dash Size	B Hex Min mm	C Min mm	D Dia Min mm	L Style A Max mm	L Style B Max mm	L_1 Style A Max mm	L_1 Style B Max mm	M Max mm	M_1 Max mm	M_2 Max mm	M_3 Max mm	T Min mm	W Max mm
6.4	–4	9/16–18	–4	17.5	6.5	2.8	67	74	67	74	82	83	78	77	6	23
9.5	–6	11/16–16	–6	20.6	6.5	6.6	75	83	76	84	87	96	80	93	6	28
12.7	–8	13/16–16	–8	23.8	8	8.5	79	89	76	86	109	106	92	98	6	32
15.9	–10	1–14	–10	28.6	9.5	10.9	84	96	81	93	112	119	98	103	6	35
19	–12	1–3/16–12	–12	34.9	9.5	14.5	94	107	89	102	122	119	120	116	7	41
25.4	–16	1–7/16–12	–16	41.3	11	19.8	97	110	105	118	135	143	134	142	8	52
31.8	–20	1–11/16–12	–20	47.6	12.5	25.7	107	120	121	135	163	178	163	177	9	63
38.1	–24	2–12	–24	57.2	15.5	31.8	119	133	111	125	183	177	185	189	9	70

(a) For dimensions not specified in Tables10A to 10M, refer to Figures 4, 6, and 10 of SAE J1453-1.

TABLE 10C—DIMENSIONS OF FEMALE O-RING FACE SEAL TYPE HOSE FITTINGS FOR USE ON SAE 100R2 HYDRAULIC HOSE[(a)] (FIGURES 22 TO 24) (CODES 43 AND 53)

Nominal SAE 100R2 Hose ID mm	Hose Dash Size	A Nominal Straight Thread Size	Thread Dash Size	B Hex Min mm	C Min mm	D Dia Min mm	L Style A Max mm	L Style B Max mm	L_1 Style A Max mm	L_1 Style B Max mm	M Max mm	M_1 Max mm	M_2 Max mm	M_3 Max mm	T Min mm	W Max mm
6.4	–4	9/16–18	–4	17.5	6.5	2.8	67	74	67	74	82	83	78	77	6	26
9.5	–6	11/16–16	–6	20.6	6.5	6.6	75	83	76	84	87	96	80	93	6	31
12.7	–8	13/16–16	–8	23.8	8	8.5	79	89	78	88	109	106	92	98	6	36
15.9	–10	1–14	–10	28.6	9.5	10.9	84	96	81	93	112	119	98	103	6	40
19	–12	1–3/16–12	–12	34.9	9.5	14.5	94	107	92	105	122	119	120	116	7	45
25.4	–16	1–7/16–12	–16	41.3	11	19.8	97	110	109	122	135	143	134	142	8	53
31.8	–20	1–11/16–12	–20	47.6	12.5	25.7	106	120	123	137	163	145	163	177	9	67
38.1	–24	2–12	–24	57.2	15.5	31.8	119	133	123	137	183	148	185	189	9	75

(a) For dimensions not specified in Tables 10A to 10M, refer to Figures 4, 6, and 10 of SAE J1453-1.

TABLE 10D—DIMENSIONS OF FEMALE O-RING FACE SEAL TYPE HOSE FITTINGS FOR USE SAE 100R3 HYDRAULIC HOSE[(a)] (FIGURES 22 TO 24) (CODE 44)

Nominal SAE 100R3 Hose ID mm	Hose Dash Size	A Nominal Straight Thread Size	Thread Dash Size	B Hex Min mm	C Min mm	D Dia Min mm	L Style A Max mm	L Style B Max mm	M Max mm	M_2 Max mm	T Min mm	W Max mm
6.4	–4	9/16–18	–4	17.5	6.5	2.8	67	74	82	78	6	26
9.5	–6	11/16–16	–6	20.6	6.5	6.6	75	83	87	80	6	31
12.7	–8	13/16–16	–8	23.8	8	8.5	79	89	109	92	6	36
15.9	–10	1–14	–10	28.6	9.5	10.9	84	96	112	98	6	40
19	–12	1–3/16–12	–12	34.9	9.5	14.5	94	107	122	120	7	45
25.4	–16	1–7/16–12	–16	41.3	11	19.8	97	110	143	134	8	53

(a) For dimensions not specified in Tables 10A to 10M, refer to Figures 4, 6, and 10 of SAE J1453-1.

TABLE 10E—DIMENSIONS OF FEMALE O-RING FACE SEAL TYPE HOSE FITTINGS FOR USE ON SAE 100R4 HYDRAULIC HOSE[(a)] (FIGURES 22 TO 24) (CODE 45)

Nominal SAE 100R4 Hose ID mm	Hose Dash Size	A Nominal Straight Thread Size	Thread Dash Size	B Hex Min mm	C Min mm	D Dia Min mm	L Style A Max mm	L Style B Max mm	M Max mm	M_2 Max mm	T Min mm	W Max mm
19	–12	1–3/16–12	–12	34.9	9.5	14.5	94	107	122	120	7	45
25.4	–16	1–7/16–12	–16	41.3	11	19.8	97	110	135	134	8	52
31.8	–20	1–11/16–12	–20	47.6	12.5	25.7	106	120	163	163	9	59

(a) For dimensions not specified in Tables 10A to 10M, refer to Figures 4, 6, and 10 of SAE J1453-1.

TABLE 10F—DIMENSIONS OF FEMALE O-RING FACE SEAL TYPE HOSE FITTINGS FOR USE ON SAE 100R5 HYDRAULIC HOSE[(a)] (FIGURES 22 TO 24) (CODE 46)

Nominal SAE 100R5 Hose Id mm	Hose Dash Size	A Nominal Straight Thread Size	Thread Dash Size	B Hex Min mm	C Min mm	D Dia Min mm	L Style A Max mm	L Style B Max mm	L_1 Style A MAX mm	L_1 Style B Max mm	M Max mm	M_1 Max mm	M_2 Max mm	M_3 Max mm	T Min mm	W Max mm
4.8	–4	9/16–18	–4	17.5	6.5	2.3	48	55	57	64	82	67	78	60	6	21
7.9	–6	11/16–16	–6	20.6	6.5	5.1	61	99	66	74	87	74	80	71	6	24
10.3	–8	13/16–16	–8	23.8	8	7.1	63	73	76	86	109	95	92	87	6	28
12.7	–10	1–14	–10	28.6	9.5	8.5	68	80	80	92	112	97	98	91	6	33
15.9	–12	1-3/16–12	–12	34.9	9.5	12.7	71	84	88	101	122	116	120	114	7	41
22.2	–16	1-7/16–12	–16	41.3	11	18.3	74	87	82	95	135	116	134	114	8	48
28.6	–20	1-11/16–12	–20	47.6	12.5	23.9	78	92	85	99	163	139	163	139	9	56
34.9	–24	2–12	–24	57.2	15.5	29.5	99	113	91	105	183	177	185	160	9	66

(a) For dimensions not specified in Tables 10A to 10M, refer to Figures 4, 6, and 10 of SAE J1453-1.
For SAE J1402 and DOT FMVSS 106 air brake applications, couplings used on 100R5 hose shall have a minimum assembled orifice no less than 66% of the nominal hose I.D.

TABLE 10G—DIMENSIONS OF FEMALE O-RING FACE SEAL TYPE HOSE FITTINGS FOR USE ON SAE 100R6 HYDRAULIC HOSE[(a)] (FIGURES 22 TO 24) (CODE 47)

Nominal SAE 100R6 Hose ID mm	Hose Dash Size	A Nominal Straight Thread Size	Thread Dash Size	B Hex Min mm	C Min mm	D Dia Min mm	L Style A Max mm	L Style B Max mm	T Min mm	W Max mm
6.4	–4	9/16–18	–4	17.5	6.5	2.8	67	74	6	26
9.5	–6	11/16–16	–6	20.6	6.5	6.6	75	83	6	31
12.7	–8	13/16–16	–8	23.8	8	8.5	79	89	6	36
15.9	–10	1–14	–10	28.6	9.5	12.2	84	96	6	40

(a) For dimensions not specified in Tables 10A to 10M, refer to Figures 4, 6, and 10 of SAE J1453-1.

TABLE 10H—DIMENSIONS OF FEMALE O-RING FACE SEAL TYPE HOSE FITTINGS FOR USE ON SAE 100R7 HYDRAULIC HOSE[(a)] (FIGURES 22 TO 24) (CODE 48)

Nominal SAE 100R7 Hose Id mm	Hose Dash Size	A Nominal Straight Thread Size	Thread Dash Size	B Hex Min mm	C Min mm	D Dia Min mm	L Style A Max mm	L Style B Max mm	M Max mm	M_2 Max mm	T Min mm	W Max mm
6.4	–4	9/16–18	–4	17.5	6.5	2.8	66	73	90	88	6	22
9.5	–6	11/16–16	–6	20.6	6.5	6.6	75	83	96	89	6	26
12.7	–8	13/16–16	–8	23.8	8	8.5	78	88	109	101	6	30
15.9	–10	1–14	–10	28.6	9.5	10.9	83	95	114	115	6	40
19	–12	1-3/16–12	–12	34.9	9.5	14.5	83	96	127	118	7	41
25.4	–16	1-7/16–12	–16	41.3	11	19.8	101	114	147	147	8	52

(a) For dimensions not specified in Tables 10A to 10M, refer to Figures 4, 6, and 10 of SAE J1453-1.

TABLE 10I—DIMENSIONS OF FEMALE O-RING FACE SEAL TYPE HOSE FITTINGS FOR USE ON SAE 100R8 HYDRAULIC HOSE[(a)] (FIGURES 22 TO 24) (CODE 49)

Nominal SAE 100R8 Hose ID mm	Hose Dash Size	A Nominal Straight Thread Size	Thread Dash Size	B Hex Min mm	C Min mm	D Dia Min mm	L Style A Max mm	L Style B Max mm	M Max mm	M_2 Max mm	T Min mm	W Max mm
6.4	–4	9/16–18	–4	17.5	6.5	2.8	66	73	90	88	6	22
9.5	–6	11/16–16	–6	20.6	6.5	6.6	75	83	96	89	6	26
12.7	–8	13/16–16	–8	23.8	8	8.5	78	88	109	101	6	30
15.9	–10	1–14	–10	28.6	9.5	10.9	83	95	112	107	6	40
19	–12	1-3/16–12	–12	34.9	9.5	14.5	83	96	124	118	7	41
25.4	–16	1-7/16–12	–16	41.3	11	19.8	101	114	147	147	8	52

(a) For dimensions not specified in Tables 10A to 10M, refer to Figures 4, 6, and 10 of SAE J1453-1.

TABLE 10J—DIMENSIONS OF FEMALE O-RING FACE SEAL TYPE HOSE FITTINGS FOR USE ON SAE 100R9 HYDRAULIC HOSE[a] (FIGURES 22 TO 24) (CODES 50 AND 75)

Nominal SAE 100R9 Hose Id mm	Hose Dash Size	A Nominal Straight Thread Size	Thread Dash Size	B Hex Min mm	C Min mm	D Dia Min mm	L Style A Max mm	L Style B Max mm	L_1 Style A Max mm	L_1 Style B Max mm	M Max mm	M_1 Max mm	M_2 Max mm	M_3 Max mm	T Min mm	W Max mm
9.5	−6	11/16–16	−6	20.6	6.5	6.6	77	85	76	84	81	96	87	77	6	28
12.7	−8	13/16–16	−8	23.8	8	8.5	75	85	78	88	96	106	92	91	6	32
19	−12	1–3/16–12	−12	34.9	9.5	14.5	84	97	92	105	112	119	115	109	7	41
25.4	−16	1–7/16–12	−16	41.3	11	19.8	94	107	109	122	129	143	134	133	8	52
31.8	−20	1–11/16–12	−20	47.6	12.5	25.7	103	117	123	137	153	178	163	145	9	63

(a) For dimensions not specified in Tables 10A to 10M, refer to Figures 4, 6, and 10 of SAE J1453-1.

TABLE 10K—DIMENSIONS OF FEMALE O-RING FACE SEAL TYPE HOSE FITTINGS FOR USE ON SAE 100R10 HYDRAULIC HOSE[a] (FIGURES 22 TO 24) (CODES 51 AND 76)

Nominal SAE 100R10 Hose ID mm	Hose Dash Size	A Nominal Straight Thread Size	Thread Dash Size	B Hex Min mm	C Min mm	D Dia Min mm	L Style A Max mm	L Style B Max mm	M Max mm	M_2 Max mm	T MIN mm	W Max mm
9.5[b]	−6	11/16–16	−6	20.6	6.5	5.8	79	87	86	82	6	33
12.7[b]	−8	13/16–16	−8	23.8	8	8.5	92	102	105	99	6	42
19	−12	1–3/16–12	−12	34.9	9.5	14	115	128	154	152	7	51
25.4	−16	1–7/16–12	−16	41.3	11	19.8	133	146	206	180	8	60
31.8	−20	1–11/16–12	−20	47.6	12.5	25.7	149	163	207	207	9	70
38.1	−24	2–12	−24	57.2	15.5	31.8	161	175	229	237	9	85

(a) For dimensions not specified in Tables 10A to 10M, refer to Figures 4, 6, and 10 of SAE J1453-1.
(b) Hose pressure rating exceeds O-ring face seal fitting rating in noted sizes.

TABLE 10L—DIMENSIONS OF FEMALE O-RING FACE SEAL TYPE HOSE FITTINGS FOR USE ON SAE 100R11 HYDRAULIC HOSE[a] (FIGURES 22 TO 24) (CODE 52)

Nominal SAE 100R11 Hose ID mm	Hose Dash Size	A Nominal Straight Thread Size	Thread Dash Size	B Hex Min mm	C Min mm	D Dia Min mm	L Style A Max mm	L Style B Max mm	M Max mm	M_2 Max mm	T Min mm	W Max mm
19.0[b]	−12	1–3/16–12	−12	34.9	9.5	13.7	115	128	154	152	7	44
25.4[b]	−16	1–7/16–12	−16	41.3	11	19.8	133	146	206	180	8	56
31.8	−20	1–11/16–12	−20	47.6	12.5	25.7	149	163	207	207	9	59
38.1	−24	2–12	−24	57.2	15.5	31.8	161	175	229	237	9	75

(a) For dimensions not specified in Table 10A to 10M, refer to Figures 4, 6, and 10 of SAE J1453-1.
(b) Hose pressure rating exceeds O-ring face seal fitting rating in noted sizes.

TABLE 10M—DIMENSIONS OF FEMALE O-RING FACE SEAL TYPE HOSE FITTINGS FOR USE ON SAE 100R12 HYDRAULIC HOSE[a] (FIGURES 22 TO 24) (CODE 77)

Nominal SAE 100R12 Hose ID mm	Hose Dash Size	A Nominal Straight Thread Size	Thread Dash Size	B Hex Min mm	C Min mm	D Dia Min mm	L Style A Max mm	L Style B Max mm	M Max mm	M_2 Max mm	T Min mm	W Max mm
9.5	−6	11/16–16	−6	20.6	6.5	6.6	78	86	96	87	6	33
12.7	−8	13/16–16	−8	23.8	8	8.1	82	92	112	105	6	42
19	−12	1–3/16–12	−12	34.9	9.5	13.7	102	115	127	127	7	51
25.4	−16	1–7/16–12	−16	41.3	11	19.8	114	127	148	153	8	60
31.8	−20	1–11/16–12	−20	47.6	12.5	25.7	126	140	176	178	9	70
38.1	−24	2–12	−24	57.2	15.5	31.8	139	153	186	204	9	85

(a) For dimensions not specified in Tables 10A to 10M, refer to Figures 4, 6, and 10 of SAE J1453-1.

(R) HOSE ASSEMBLIES, RUBBER, HYDRAULIC, STEEL WIRE REINFORCED—PART 1: PROCUREMENT DOCUMENT—SAE J1754-1 DEC2001

SAE Standard

Report of the SAE Fluid Conductors and Connectors Technical Committee SC2—Hydraulic Hose and Hose Fittings approved June 1996 and completely revised December 2001. Rationale statement available.

1. Scope—This SAE Standard covers steel wire reinforced rubber hose assemblies using connectors specified in SAE J516 for use in hydraulic systems using petroleum based hydraulic fluids with maximum working pressures of 1.7 to 42 MPa. See SAE J1754-2, Table 8 for hose operating temperature ranges and identification codes.

NOTE—Working pressure is defined as maximum system pressure.

2. References

2.1 Applicable Publications—The following publications form a part of this specification to the extent specified herein. Unless otherwise indicated, the latest issue of the publications shall apply.

2.1.1 SAE PUBLICATIONS—Available from SAE, 400 Commonwealth Drive, Warrendale, PA 15096-0001.

SAE J343—Test and Procedures Hydraulic Hose Assemblies and Hose
SAE J516—Hydraulic Hose Fittings
SAE J517—Hydraulic Hose
SAE J1176—External Leakage Classifications for Hydraulic Systems
SAE J1273—Recommended Practices for Hydraulic Hose Assemblies
SAE J1405—Optional Impulse Test Procedures for Hydraulic Hose Assemblies
SAE J1754-2—Hose Assemblies, Rubber, Hydraulic, Steel Wire Reinforced—Part 2: Ordering Information

2.1.2 ASTM PUBLICATIONS—Available from ASTM, 100 Barr Harbor Drive, West Conshohocken, PA 19428-2959.

ASTM B 117—Standard Test Method of Salt Spray (Fog) Testing
ASTM D 380—Methods of Testing Rubber Hose
ASTM D 471—Test Method for Rubber Property - Effect of Liquids

2.1.3 ISO PUBLICATIONS—Available from ANSI, 11 West 42nd Street, New York, NY 10036.

ISO 4397—Fluid power systems and components—Connectors and associated components—Nominal outside diameters of tubes and nominal inside diameters of hoses
ISO 4406—Hydraulic fluid power—Fluids—Method of coding level of contamination by solid particles

2.2 Related Publications—The following publications are for information purposes only and are not a required part of this document.

2.2.1 SAE PUBLICATION—Available from SAE, 400 Commonwealth Drive, Warrendale, PA 15096-0001.

SAE J846—Coding Systems for Identification of Fluid Conductors and Connectors

2.2.2 ISO PUBLICATION—Available from ANSI, 11 West 42nd Street, New York, NY 10036.

ISO 3448—Industrial liquid lubricants—ISO viscosity classification
ISO 12151-1—Connections for hydraulic fluid power and general use—Hose fittings—Part 1: Hose fittings with ISO 8434-3 o-ring face seal ends
ISO 12151-2—Connections for hydraulic fluid power and general use—Hose fittings—Part 2: Hose fittings with ISO 8434-1 24° cone ends
ISO 12151-3—Connections for hydraulic fluid power and general use—Hose fittings—Part 3: Hose fittings with ISO 6162 flange ends
ISO 12151-4—Connections for hydraulic fluid power and general use—Hose fittings—Part 4: Hose fittings with ISO 6149 metric stud ends
ISO 12151-5—Connections for hydraulic fluid power and general use—Hose fittings—Part 5: Hose fittings with ISO 8434-2 37° flare ends
ISO 12151-6—Connections for hydraulic fluid power and general use—Hose fittings—Part 6: Hose fittings with ISO 8434-6 60° cone ends

3. Requirements

3.1 Hose Assembly Construction—Hose used in assemblies shall have an elastomeric, oil resistant tube; wire reinforcement; and an elastomeric oil and weather resistant black cover, unless otherwise specified by the purchaser. Connectors shall be permanent and shall be capable of meeting the performance requirements of this standard. For connector material, see SAE J1754-2.

3.2 Dimensions—Hose shall conform to all the dimensions in Tables 1 to 10. Hose concentricity shall be in accordance with Table 11. Connector dimensions shall be per SAE J516. Hose assemblies shall conform to the applicable part standard or engineering drawing. Double bent tube (double elbow) assemblies are not recommended and are considered non-standard due to the detrimental effects of twist on the hose.

TABLE 1—1.7 MPa PRESSURE RATING

Metric Size[1]	SAE Dash Size[2]	Maximum Hose Outside Diameter[3] mm	Minimum Burst Pressure (MPa)	Proof Pressure (MPa)	Maximum Working Pressure (MPa)	Minimum Bend Radius[4] mm
19	–12	31	6.8	3.4	1.7	240
25	–16	40	6.8	3.4	1.7	305
51	–32	72	6.8	3.4	1.7	635
63	–40	98	6.8	3.4	1.7	760

1. Metric hose size in mm per ISO 4397.
2. SAE hose dash size is equal to hose ID expressed in 1/16's of an inch.
3. Hose OD listed is largest OD of the approved hose materials. If the OD is critical (hose clamping), the OD shall be specified.
4. If a smaller bend radius is required, the bend radius shall be specified.

See Appendix A for rationalized pressure ratings and SAE J1754-2, Table 1 for maximum working pressure identification codes.

TABLE 2—2.8 MPa PRESSURE RATING

Metric Size[1]	SAE Dash Size[2]	Maximum Hose Outside Diameter[3] mm	Minimum Burst Pressure MPa	Proof Pressure MPa	Maximum Working Pressure MPa	MinimumBend Radius[4] mm
6.3	–04	17	11.2	5.6	2.8	75
10	–06	21	11.2	5.6	2.8	100
12.5	–08	25	11.2	5.6	2.8	125
19	–12	33	11.2	5.6	2.8	240
25	–16	40	11.2	5.6	2.8	305
31.5	–20	48	11.2	5.6	2.8	420
38	–24	54	11.2	5.6	2.8	510
51	–32	69	11.2	5.6	2.8	635

1. Metric hose size in mm per ISO 4397.
2. SAE hose dash size is equal to hose ID expressed in 1/16's of an inch.
3. Hose OD listed is largest OD of the approved hose materials. If the OD is critical (hose clamping), the OD shall be specified.
4. If a smaller bend radius is required, the bend radius shall be specified.

See Appendix A for rationalized pressure ratings and SAE J1754-2 Table 1 for maximum working pressure identification codes.

TABLE 3—7 MPa PRESSURE RATING

Metric Size(1)	SAE Dash Size(2)	Maximum Hose Outside Diameter(3) mm	Minimum Burst Pressure MPa	Proof Pressure MPa	Maximum Working Pressure MPa	Minimum Bend Radius(4) mm
12.5	–08	24	28	14	7	180
16	–10	27	28	14	7	200
19	–12	31	28	14	7	240
25	–16	40	28	14	7	305
31.5	–20	53	28	14	7	420
38	–24	59	28	14	7	510
51	–32	72	28	14	7	635
63	–40	98	28	14	7	760

1. Metric hose size in mm per ISO 4397.
2. SAE hose dash size is equal to hose ID expressed in 1/16's of an inch.
3. Hose OD listed is largest OD of the approved hose materials. If the OD is critical (hose clamping), the OD shall be specified.
4. If a smaller bend radius is required, the bend radius shall be specified.

See Appendix A for rationalized pressure ratings and SAE J1754-2, Table 1 for maximum working pressure identification codes.

TABLE 4—14 MPa PRESSURE RATING

Metric Size(1)	SAE Dash Size(2)	Maximum Hose Outside Diameter(3) mm	Minimum Burst Pressure MPa	Proof Pressure MPa	Maximum Working Pressure MPa	Minimum Bend Radius(4) mm
10	–06	21	56	28	14	125
12.5	–08	24	56	28	14	180
16	–10	29	56	28	14	200
19	–12	33	56	28	14	240
25	–16	41	56	28	14	305
31.5	–20	53	56	28	14	420
38	–24	59	56	28	14	510
51	–32	74	56	28	14	660

1. Metric hose size in mm per ISO 4397.
2. SAE hose dash size is equal to hose ID expressed in 1/16's of an inch.
3. Hose OD listed is largest OD of the approved hose materials. If the OD is critical (hose clamping), the OD shall be specified.
4. If a smaller bend radius is required, the bend radius shall be specified.

See Appendix A for rationalized pressure ratings and SAE J1754-2, Table 1 for maximum working pressure identification codes.

TABLE 5—17.5 MPa PRESSURE RATING

Metric Size(1)	SAE Dash Size(2)	Maximum Hose Outside Diameter(3) mm	Minimum Burst Pressure MPa	Proof Pressure MPa	Maximum Working Pressure MPa	Minimum Bend Radius(4) mm
6.3	–04	17	70	35	17.5	100
10	–06	23	70	35	17.5	125
12.5	–08	26	70	35	17.5	180
16	–10	29	70	35	17.5	240
19	–12	33	70	35	17.5	280
25	–16	41	70	35	17.5	360
31.5	–20	54	70	35	17.5	420
38	–24	63	70	35	17.5	560
51	–32	77	70	35	17.5	660

1. Metric hose size in mm per ISO 4397.
2. SAE hose dash size is equal to hose ID expressed in 1/16's of an inch.
3. Hose OD listed is largest OD of the approved hose materials. If the OD is critical (hose clamping), the OD shall be specified.
4. If a smaller bend radius is required, the bend radius shall be specified.

See Appendix A for rationalized pressure ratings and SAE J1754-2, Table 1 for maximum working pressure identification codes.

TABLE 6—21 MPa PRESSURE RATING

Metric Size(1)	SAE Dash Size(2)	Maximum Hose Outside Diameter(3) mm	Minimum Burst Pressure MPa	Proof Pressure MPa	Maximum Working Pressure MPa	Minimum Bend Radius(4) mm
5	–03	14	84	42	21	90
6.3	–04	19	84	42	21	100
10	–06	23	84	42	21	125
12.5	–08	26	84	42	21	180
16	–10	29	84	42	21	240
19	–12	33	84	42	21	300
25	–16	41	84	42	21	420
31.5	–20	57	84	42	21	460
38	–24	63	84	42	21	510
51	–32	75	84	42	21	635

1. Metric hose size in mm per ISO 4397.
2. SAE hose dash size is equal to hose ID expressed in 1/16's of an inch.
3. Hose OD listed is largest OD of the approved hose materials. If the OD is critical (hose clamping), the OD shall be specified.
4. If a smaller bend radius is required, the bend radius shall be specified.

See Appendix A for rationalized pressure ratings and SAE J1754-2, Table 1 for maximum working pressure identification codes.

TABLE 7—24.5 MPa PRESSURE RATING

Metric Size[(1)]	SAE Dash Size[(2)]	Maximum Hose Outside Diameter[(3)] mm	Minimum Burst Pressure MPa	Proof Pressure MPa	Maximum Working Pressure MPa	Minimum Bend Radius[(4)] mm
5	–03	17	98	49	24.5	90
6.3	–04	19	98	49	24.5	100
10	–06	23	98	49	24.5	125
12.5	–08	26	98	49	24.5	180
16	–10	29	98	49	24.5	240
19	–12	38	98	49	24.5	280
25	–16	50	98	49	24.5	360
31.5	–20	52	98	49	24.5	420
38	–24	59	98	49	24.5	510
51	–32	73	98	49	24.5	700

1. Metric hose size in mm per ISO 4397.
2. SAE hose dash size is equal to hose ID expressed in 1/16's of an inch.
3. Hose OD listed is largest OD of the approved hose materials. If the OD is critical (hose clamping), the OD shall be specified.
4. If a smaller bend radius is required, the bend radius shall be specified.

See Appendix A for rationalized pressure ratings and SAE J1754-2, Table 1 for maximum working pressure identification codes.

TABLE 8—28 MPa PRESSURE RATING

Metric Size[(1)]	SAE Dash Size[(2)]	Maximum Hose Outside Diameter[(3)] mm	Minimum Burst Pressure MPa	Proof Pressure MPa	Maximum Working Pressure MPa	Minimum Bend Radius[(4)] mm
5	–03	17	112	56	28	90
6.3	–04	19	112	56	28	100
10	–06	23	112	56	28	125
12.5	–08	26	112	56	28	180
16	–10	29	112	56	28	240
19	–12	38	112	56	28	280
25	–16	50	112	56	28	360
31.5	–20	52	112	56	28	460
38	–24	59	112	56	28	560
51	–32	73	112	56	28	635

1. Metric hose size in mm per ISO 4397.
2. SAE hose dash size is equal to hose ID expressed in 1/16's of an inch.
3. Hose OD listed is largest OD of the approved hose materials. If the OD is critical (hose clamping), the OD shall be specified.
4. If a smaller bend radius is required, the bend radius shall be specified.

See Appendix A for rationalized pressure ratings and SAE J1754-2, Table 1 for maximum working pressure identification codes.

TABLE 9—35 MPa PRESSURE RATING

Metric Size[(1)]	SAE Dash Size[(2)]	Maximum Hose Outside Diameter[(3)] mm	Minimum Burst Pressure MPa	Proof Pressure MPa	Maximum Working Pressure MPa	Minimum Bend Radius[(4)] mm
5	–03	17	140	70	35	90
6.3	–04	19	140	70	35	150
10	–06	22	140	70	35	180
12.5	–08	25	140	70	35	230
16	–10	29	140	70	35	250
19	–12	38	140	70	35	310
25	–16	50	140	70	35	360
31.5	–20	52	140	70	35	420
38	–24	59	140	70	35	510
51	–32	73	140	70	35	635

1. Metric hose size in mm per ISO 4397.
2. SAE hose dash size is equal to hose ID expressed in 1/16's of an inch.
3. Hose OD listed is largest OD of the approved hose materials. If the OD is critical (hose clamping), the OD shall be specified.
4. If a smaller bend radius is required, the bend radius shall be specified.

See Appendix A for rationalized pressure ratings and SAE J1754-2, Table 1 for maximum working pressure identification codes.

TABLE 10—42 MPa PRESSURE RATING

Metric Size(1)	SAE Dash Size(2)	Maximum Hose Outside Diameter(3) mm	Minimum Burst Pressure MPa	Proof Pressure MPa	Maximum Working Pressure MPa	Minimum Bend Radius(4) mm
10	–06	26	168	84	42	180
12.5	–08	32	168	84	42	230
16	–10	29	168	84	42	240
19	–12	41	168	84	42	280
25	–16	50	168	84	42	360
31.5	–20	52	168	84	42	445
38	–24	59	168	84	42	530

1. Metric hose size in mm per ISO 4397.
2. SAE hose dash size is equal to hose ID expressed in 1/16's of an inch.
3. Hose OD listed is largest OD of the approved hose materials. If the OD is critical (hose clamping), the OD shall be specified.
4. If a smaller bend radius is required, the bend radius shall be specified.

See Appendix A for rationalized pressure ratings and SAE J1754-2, Table 1 for maximum working pressure identification codes.

TABLE 11—HOSE CONCENTRICITY

Metric Size(1)	SAE Dash Size(2)	I.D. to Reinforcement Concentricity, FIR (mm)	I.D. to O.D. Concentricity, FIR (mm)
Up to 6.3 included	Up to –04 included	0.5	0.8
Over 6.3 through 19 included	Over –04 through –12 included	0.7	1.0
Over 19	Over –12	0.9	1.3

1. Metric hose size in mm per ISO 4397.
2. SAE hose dash size is equal to hose ID expressed in 1/16's of an inch.

3.3 Hose Classifications—Two classifications of hose are established: Class A and Class B. See Table 12.

Class of hose is determined by type of application, duty cycle, working pressure, pressure surges (spikes) above nominal system pressure, flow velocity, flexing and/or the environment in which it is used. If the hose classification is not obvious (i.e., Class A or Class B) select Class A. See SAE J1273 for more details and consult hose assembly manufacturer for specific applications.

3.3.1 CLASS A—High frequency or severity of flexing and/or pressure impulse cycles. See 4.3.7 for details.

3.3.2 CLASS B—Low frequency or severity of flexing and/or pressure impulse cycles. See 4.3.7 for details.

3.4 Performance—Hose assemblies shall satisfy the performance requirements in 4.3.

3.5 Application Factors—Hydraulic hose assemblies have a finite life. Only careful selection, installation and maintenance will insure the desired service life. Always design hydraulic systems to match hose capabilities (pressure, flow, temperature, flex, etc.) and do not specify unique hose materials unless needed for very special applications. See SAE J1273 Recommended Practices for Hydraulic Hose Assemblies for additional information on application factors.

Among factors to be avoided shall be:

a. Flexing the hose tighter than the specified minimum bend radius.
b. Not to be used for vacuum applications.
c. Twisting, pulling, kinking, or crushing the hose.
d. Operating above maximum and below minimum temperature.
e. Exposing the hose to surge pressures above the maximum working pressure.
f. High fluid velocity in pressure lines generates heat, turbulence, pressure loss, noise, and inner tube erosion. There are no physical benefits from high fluid velocities.
g. Intermixing hose, connectors or assembly equipment not recommended by the manufacturer or not following the manufacturer's instructions for fabricating hose assemblies.

NOTE—Surge pressures are rapid and transient rises in pressure, and the hose working pressure should allow for these pressure surges (spikes). Surge pressures will not be indicated on many common pressure gages and can best be identified on electronic measuring instruments with a high-frequency response.

3.6 First Time Suppliers—When required by the purchaser, first time suppliers of each hose assembly size may need to supply documentation that products meet the requirements of 4.3.1 through 4.3.9 of this document.

3.7 Age Control—Shelf life of rubber hose in bulk form or in hose assemblies passing visual inspection and proof test is forty quarters (ten years) from the date of vulcanization. Bulk hose and hose assemblies shall be protected from the detrimental effects of ozone, heat, ultra-violet light, moisture or swelling agents such as fuel, solvents or corrosive vapors. Suppliers who assemble from bulk hose and connectors and do not manufacture from raw products shall show proof of compliance to the requirements of this paragraph. Refer to SAE J517 and SAE J1273 for additional information on age control.

3.8 Marking

3.8.1 Each hose assembly shall have the following information permanently and clearly marked on the connector or on a tag permanently attached to the assembly:

a. Hose assembly manufacturer's name or trademark
b. Maximum working pressure of the hose assembly
c. Date of manufacture of the hose assembly.

3.8.2 The following information shall be permanently marked on the hose lay line of each assembly per SAE J517 Section 8, if applicable:

a. Manufacturer's name or trademark
b. Manufacturer's hose part number
c. Manufacturer's maximum working pressure of the hose
d. Date of hose manufacture (as a minimum must identify the quarter and the year that the hose was manufactured)

NOTE—No mention of the burst pressure or design factor shall be marked on the hose.

3.9 Workmanship—Workmanship shall be of the quality necessary to produce hose assemblies free from all defects that will affect proper form, fit and function in service.

3.10 Cleanliness—Hose assemblies shall meet the cleanliness ISO 4406 Code Number 19 / 16 requirement or cleanliness requirement specified by the purchaser.

4. Tests—SAE J343 unless otherwise specified.

4.1 Responsibility for Tests—Unless otherwise specified in the contract or purchase order, the supplier of the hose assembly is responsible for the performance of all test requirements as specified herein. The supplier of the hose assembly may use his own or any other facilities suitable for the performance of the test requirements unless disapproved by the customer. The customer reserves the right to perform any of the tests specified to assure supplies and services conform to the standard requirements.

4.2 Classification of Tests—Requirements are classified as follows:

a. Qualification Tests. Consist of the tests in 4.3.
b. Quality Conformance Tests. Consist of the tests in 4.4.

4.2.1 Unless otherwise stated, test quantities shall be in accordance with Table 13 or as specified in the contract or order.

4.2.2 After completion of qualification in accordance with 4.3, subsequent production of hose assemblies of the same dash size produced of the same materials and procedures shall be tested in accordance with 4.4. It is recommended that a complete qualification be accomplished at 3 year intervals.

4.3 Qualification Tests—When specified (see Section 7) the qualification tests within this standard are mandatory.

4.3.1 PROOF TEST—All unaged hose assemblies to be used for qualification tests shall be proof tested in accordance with SAE J343 at the specified proof pressure in Tables 1 to 10. There shall be no indication of failure or leakage.

4.3.2 CHANGE IN LENGTH TEST—Two unaged hose assemblies of at least 500 mm in length of free hose between hose connectors shall be tested for change in length in accordance with SAE J343 at the specified maximum working pressure in Tables 1 to 10. The hose assembly shall not exceed +2% to –4% change in length for braided hoses and ±2% for spiral hoses.

4.3.3 BURST TEST—Two unaged hose assemblies of at least 500 mm in length of free hose between hose connectors shall be burst tested in accordance with SAE J343. There shall be no leakage, hose burst or other indication of failure below the specified minimum burst pressure in Tables 1 to 10.

NOTE—Burst Test is a destructive test. Assemblies which have been subjected to this test shall be destroyed.

4.3.4 COLD BEND TEST—Two unaged hose assemblies shall be cold bend tested in accordance with SAE J343 at –40 °C or colder, when specified. Reject any samples with visible cracks or leakage.

NOTE—Cold Bend Test is a destructive test. Assemblies which have been subjected to this test shall be destroyed.

4.3.5 OIL RESISTANCE TEST—The tube and cover shall be tested in accordance with ASTM D 471. Immersions shall be for 70 h in IRM 903 oil at the maximum working temperature of the hose. The volume change of specimens taken from the hose inner tube and cover shall be between 0 and 100%.

4.3.6 OZONE RESISTANCE TEST—Hose shall be tested for resistance of the cover compound to ozone in accordance with the latest issue of ASTM D 380, except that the mandrel shall be a diameter twice the minimum bend radius specified in Tables 1 to 10 and the cover shall be examined at the completion of the test under 7X magnification. Reject any samples with visible cracks.

4.3.7 IMPULSE TEST—Four unaged hose assemblies shall be impulse tested in accordance with SAE J343, and at the percentage stated in Table 12 of the maximum working (operating) pressure in Tables 1 to 10.

TABLE 12—HOSE CLASSIFICATIONS

Hose Classifications	Class A	Class B(1)
Test Pressure	150% of maximum working pressure	133% of maximum working pressure
Impulse Cycles	300 000 without failures or leakage	200 000 without failures or leakage

1. Class B classification is the most commonly used for industry hose assembly duty cycles, but if hose classification is not obvious select Class A.

4.3.7.1 Class A—A cool down test shall also be conducted during the impulse test on Class A hose assemblies in accordance with SAE J1405 Option III. SAE J1176 Class 0 leakage shall be required for Class A hose assemblies.

NOTE—Impulse Test is a destructive test. Assemblies which have been subjected to this test shall be destroyed.

4.3.8 LEAKAGE TEST—Two unaged hose assemblies of at least 500 mm in length of free hose between hose connectors shall be subjected to the leakage test in accordance with SAE J343. There shall be no leakage or evidence of failure.

NOTE—Leakage Test is a destructive test. Assemblies which have been subjected to this test shall be destroyed.

4.3.9 CORROSION RESISTANCE TEST—Two hose connector ends shall be subjected to the salt spray test of ASTM B 117 for 96 h. Any appearance of red rust during the 96 h salt spray test shall be considered failure, except for the following:

a. All internal fluid passages.
b. Edges such as hex points, serration's and crests of threads where there may be mechanical deformation of the plating or coating typical of mass-produced parts or shipping effects.
c. Areas where there is mechanical deformation of the plating or coating caused by crimping, flaring, bending and other post-plate metal forming operations.
d. Areas where the parts are suspended or affixed in the test chamber where condensate can accumulate.

NOTE—Parts manufactured to this standard shall not be cadmium plated. Internal fluid passages shall be protected from corrosion during storage and shipping. Changes in plating may affect torque and require re-qualification, when applicable.

4.4 Quality Conformance Tests

4.4.1 EXAMINATION OF PRODUCT—Each hose assembly shall be examined visually to determine conformance to this standard and the appropriate associated standard parts sheet with respect to the following:

a. Workmanship
b. Dimensions
c. Thread Size
d. Material
e. Marking

4.4.2 TEST OF PRODUCT—If required by the purchaser, samples shall be selected at random as specified in Table 13.

Manufacturer of the hose assemblies if required by the customer, will provide certification that the testing has been conducted and the product meets the requirements of 4.4.2. Any nonconformance to 4.4.2 or other customer required testing, must be reviewed and the agreed action implemented in compliance with the customer policy.

a. Proof Test (see 4.3.1)
b. Change in Length Test (see 4.3.2)
c. Burst Test (see 4.3.3)

TABLE 13—SAMPLES IF REQUIRED

PRODUCTION SIZE	NUMBER OF SAMPLES
1 to 10	1
11 to 100	2
101 to 500	3
501 to 1000	4
Greater than 1000	One additional sample shall be selected for each additional 1000 hose assemblies manufactured

4.4.3 OVERALL LENGTH—Unless otherwise specified, assembly length shall be the overall length measured from the extreme end of one fitting to the extreme end of the other, except for O-Ring face seal type and four bolt flange connectors which shall be measured from sealing face. Where elbow connectors are used, measurement shall be to the centerline of the sealing surface of the elbow end. The sealing surface of female flared elbow connectors shall be the centerline of the outer end of the cone seat (see SAE J517 Figure 3). Tolerances on assembly length shall be as in Table 14.

5. Product Approval—See SAEJ1754-2 for agreement between purchaser and supplier.

6. Packaging—Packaging shall be as specified in the contract or purchase order, or as agreed upon between the purchaser and supplier.

7. Ordering Data—The following data shall be required when ordering per this standard:

a. Title and date of this document.
b. Applicable design parts standard and/or engineering drawing.
c. Connector material.
d. Quantity.
e. When qualification testing is required per 3.6 and 4.3.
f. When performance tests are specified per 4.4.2.
g. Type of packaging required.

TABLE 14—TOLERANCES ON ASSEMBLY LENGTH

HOSE ASSEMBLY LENGTH (mm)	TOLERANCE (mm)
Up to 300 mm included	±3
Over 300 mm through 450 mm included	±5
Over 450 mm through 900 mm included	±7
Over 900 mm	±1%(1)

1. Measured to the nearest whole millimeter.

APPENDIX A
MPa TO psi CONVERSION TABLE

A.1 Table A1 gives rationalized conversion pressures from MPa to psi. These converted equivalent pressures allow for minimum deviation from the mathematically correct conversion, while allowing for the use of the most common available pressures. The conversions were also rationalized to allow the burst pressures to be a minimum of 4 times the maximum working pressures.

TABLE A1—MPa TO psi CONVERSION TABLE

MPa	psi	MPa	psi	MPa	psi	MPa	psi	MPa	psi
350	50 000	78	11 250	29.5	4 250	9.8	1 400	2.1	300
315	45 000	77	11 000	28	4 000	8.7	1 250	1.7	250
280	40 000	70	10 000	24.5	3 500	8.4	1 200	1.6	225
245	35 000	63	9 000	22.7	3 250	7.8	1 125	1.4	200
210	30 000	61	8 750	22.4	3 200	7	1000	1.25	180
175	25 000	59.5	8 500	21	3 000	6.1	875	1.05	150
168	24 000	56	8 000	20	2 900	5.6	800	1	140
160	23 200	52.5	7 500	19.2	2 750	5.2	750	0.85	125
157	22 500	49	7 000	17.5	2 500	5	725	0.8	112
140	20 000	45.5	6 500	16.8	2 400	4.9	700	0.7	100
122	17 500	43.5	6 250	15.7	2 250	4.3	625	0.6	90
119	17 000	42	6 000	14	2 000	4.2	600	0.5	70
112	16 000	40	5 800	12.2	1 750	3.9	565	0.4	62
98	14 000	38.5	5 500	11.3	1 625	3.5	500	0.4	56
87	12 500	35	5 000	11.2	1 600	2.8	400	0.35	50
84	12 000	33.5	4 800	10.5	1 500	2.6	375	0.3	45
80	11 600	31.5	4 500	10	1 450	2.4	350	0.25	35

(R) HOSE ASSEMBLIES, RUBBER, HYDRAULIC, STEEL WIRE REINFORCED—PART 2: ORDERING INFORMATION—SAE J1754-2 DEC2001

SAE Standard

Report of the SAE Fluid Conductors and Connectors Technical Committee approved June 1996. Completely revised by the SAE Fluid Conductors and Connectors Technical Committee SC2—Hydraulic Hose and Hose Fittings December 2001. Rationale statement available.

1. Scope—This SAE Standard covers ordering information for steel wire reinforced rubber hose assemblies using connectors specified in SAE J516 for use in hydraulic systems using petroleum based hydraulic fluids with maximum working pressures of 1.7 to 42 MPa. See SAE J1754-2, Table 8 for hose operating temperature ranges and identification codes.

NOTE—Working pressure is defined as maximum system pressure.

2. References

2.1 Applicable Publications—The following publications form a part of this specification to the extent specified herein. Unless otherwise indicated, the latest issue of the publications shall apply.

2.1.1 SAE PUBLICATIONS—Available from SAE, 400 Commonwealth Drive, Warrendale, PA 15096-0001.

SAE J343—Test and Procedures Hydraulic Hose Assemblies & Hose
SAE J516—Hydraulic Hose Fittings
SAE J517—Hydraulic Hose
SAE J846—Coding Systems for Identification of Fluid Conductors & Connectors
SAE J1176—External Leakage Classifications for Hydraulic Systems
SAE J1273—Recommended Practices for Hydraulic Hose Assemblies
SAE J1405—Optional Impulse Test Procedures for Hydraulic Hose Assemblies
SAE J1754-1—Hose Assemblies, Rubber, Hydraulic, Steel Wire Reinforced—Part 1: Procurement Document

2.1.2 ASTM PUBLICATIONS—Available from ASTM, 100 Barr Harbor Drive, West Conshohocken, PA 19428-2959.

ASTM B 117—Standard Test Method of Salt Spray (Fog) Testing
ASTM D 380—Methods of Testing Rubber Hose
ASTM D 471—Test Method for Rubber Property - Effect of Liquids

2.1.3 ISO PUBLICATIONS—Available from ANSI, 11 West 42nd Street, New York, NY 10036.

ISO 3448—Industrial liquid lubricants—ISO viscosity classification
ISO 4397—Fluid power systems and components—Connectors and associated components—Nominal outside diameters of tubes and nominal inside diameters of hoses
ISO 4406—Hydraulic fluid power—Fluids—Method of coding level of contamination by solid particles
ISO 12151-1—Connections for hydraulic fluid power and general use—Hose fittings—Part 1: Hose fittings with ISO 8434-3 O-Ring Face Seal Ends
ISO 12151-2—Connections for hydraulic fluid power and general use—Hose fittings—Part 2: Hose fittings with ISO 8434-1 24° cone ends
ISO 12151-3—Connections for hydraulic fluid power and general use—Hose fittings—Part 3: Hose fittings with ISO 6162 flange ends
ISO 12151-4—Connections for hydraulic fluid power and general use—Hose fittings—Part 4: Hose fittings with ISO 6149 metric stud ends
ISO 12151-5—Connections for hydraulic fluid power and general use—Hose fittings—Part 5: Hose fittings with ISO 8434-2 37° flare ends
ISO 12151-6—Connections for hydraulic fluid power and general use—Hose fittings—Part 6: Hose fittings with ISO 8434-6 60° cone ends

3. Requirements

3.1 Hose Assembly Identification—Hose assemblies shall be identified using Tables 1 to 7 and either Appendix A or Appendix B.

3.2 Construction and Performance—Hose assemblies shall be qualified in accordance with the requirements in SAE J1754-1. Users of this document are advised to control source approval, as required.

TABLE 1—MAXIMUM OPERATING PRESSURE RANGE RATING CODES

TABLES(1)	1	2	3	4	5	6	7	8	9	10	----
PRESSURE RATING - MPa (1)	1.7	2.8	7	14	17.5	21	24.5	28	35	42	(2)
LETTER DESIGNATION	C	D	E	F	G	H	J	K	M	N	X

1. See SAE J2174-1 - Tables 1 to 10 for outside diameter, proof pressure, burst pressure, and minimum bend radius.
2. See drawing for operating pressure rating.

TABLE 2—HOSE COVER TYPE CODES

Standard synthetic rubber cover	Intermediate (medium abrasion) cover	High abrasion cover
1(1)	2(1)	3(1)

1. Hose cover type material per purchasers approved material specification.

TABLE 3A—HOSE SIZE IDENTIFICATION CODES

SAE HOSE DASH SIZE(1)	03	04	05	06	08	10	12	—	16	20	24	32	40
ISO HOSE SIZE(2)	5	6.3	8	10	12.5	16	19	—	25	31.5	38	51	63
LETTER DESIGNATION	D	E	F	G	H	J	K	—	N	P	R	T	U

1. Hose dash size is based on inches, with each dash size equal to 1/16 inch.
2. ISO hose size is based on the equivalent SAE J517 inch hose sizes per ISO 4397.

NOTE—Hose size columns in Table 3A line up with the appropriate standard connector end size in Table 3B.

TABLE 3B—CONNECTOR SIZE IDENTIFICATION CODES

SAE CONNECTOR DASH SIZE[1]	CODE	03	04	05	06	08	10	12	14	16	20	24	32	40
ISO 12151-1 CONNECTOR SIZE[2]	S		6	8	10	12	16	20	---	25	30	38	---	---
ISO 12151-2 CONNECTOR SIZE-L[3]	L		6	8	10	12	15	18	22	28	35	42	---	---
ISO 12151-2 CONNECTOR SIZE-S[4]	S	---	8	10	12	12	16	20	25	30	38	---	---	---
ISO 12151-3 CONNECTOR SIZE-L[3]	L	---	---	---	---	---	13	---	19	25	32	38	51	---
ISO 12151-3 CONNECTOR SIZE-S [4]	S	---	---	---	---	---	13	---	19	25	32	38	51	---
ISO 12151-4 CONNECTOR SIZE-L [3]	L	---	---	6	8	10	12	16	20	25	30	38	51	---
ISO 12151-4 CONNECTOR SIZE-S [4]	S		---	6	8	10	12	16	20	25	30	38	51	---
ISO 12151-5 CONNECTOR SIZE[5]	L	---	---	6	8	10	12	16	20	25	32	38	50	---
ISO 12151-6 CONNECTOR SIZE[5]	L	---	2	4	6	8	10	12	16	20	24	32	---	---
LETTER DESIGNATION		D	E	F	G	H	J	K	M	N	P	R	T	U

1. Connector dash size is based on inch tubing, with each dash size equal to 1/16 inch.
2. ISO connector size is based on ISO 12151-1 with S (Heavy-duty series) only.
3. ISO connector size is based on ISO 12151-2, 3, and 4 with L (Light duty series).
4. ISO connector size is based on ISO 12151-2, 3 and 4 with S (Heavy duty series).
5. ISO connector size is based on ISO 12151-5 & 6 with L (Light duty series) only.

NOTE 1—In Appendix A, B, and Figure 1 the hose assembly end connection description and shape codes are found in SAE J846, Table 6B and Table 7.

NOTE 2—In Appendix B drawing, the end sizes will need to be filled in the blank space, due to the different end sizes in each of the ISO 12151 standards for each letter code. Example: If a 12151-1 end connection with a 13/16-16 UN thread is used, the size and code would be 12 / H.

TABLE 4—SLEEVE CODES[1]

Code	Description
A	Flat Armor Guard
B	Round Spring Guard
C	Polyurethane Sleeve
D	Polyamide Sleeve
E	Fire Sleeve
W	None
X	See Drawing

1. Full length sleeve over entire hose is assumed on hose assembly. If partial length sleeve is required on hose assembly, place an "X" to see drawing.

TABLE 5—HOSE CURVATURE ORIENTATION CODES[1]

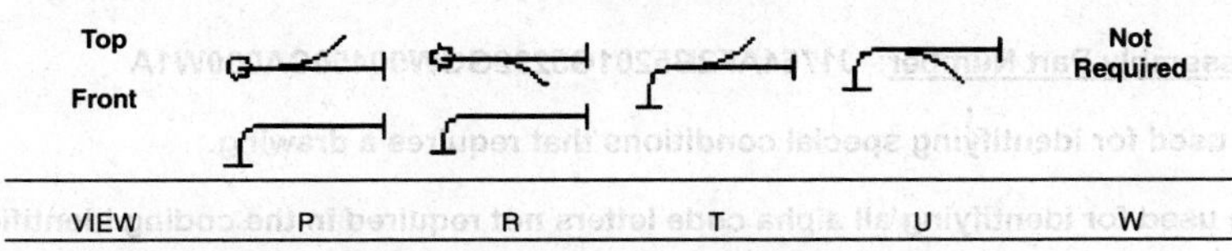

VIEW	P	R	T	U	W

1. Hose curvature orientation to be used when required for ease of assembly.

TABLE 6—NUMBER OF WIRE REINFORCEMENT LAYERS CODE

Code	Description
W	Not Specified
1	One Wire Braid
2	Two Wire Braid
4	Four Wire Spiral
6	Six Wire Spiral
X	See Drawing

TABLE 7—HOSE OPERATING TEMPERATUE RANGE CODES

Code	Temperatures
A	–40°C minimum to +100 °C maximum
B	–40°C minimum to +121 °C maximum
X	See drawing for hose temperature rating

3.3 Part Identification Numbers

EXAMPLE—See Figure 1.

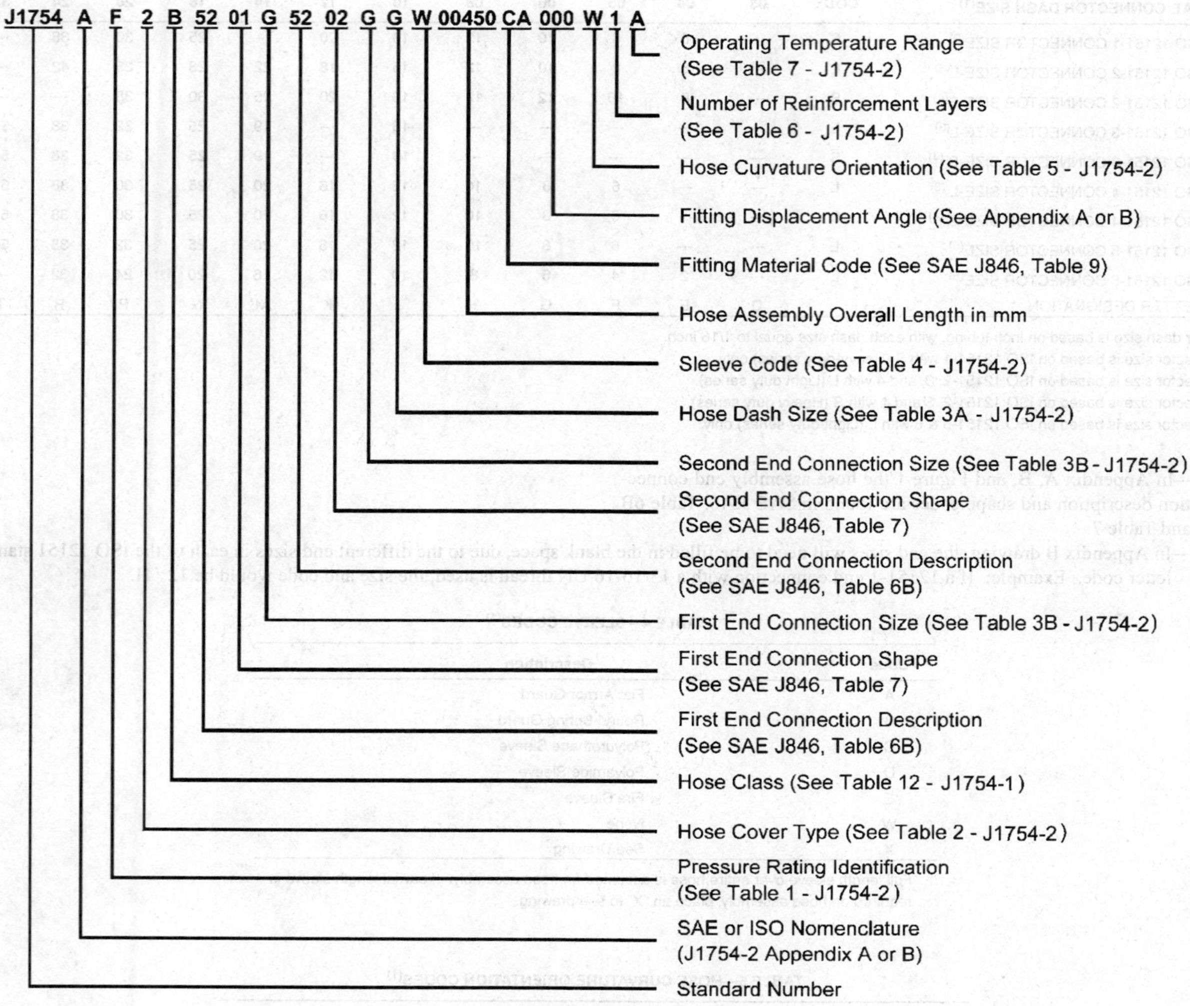

Example of Hose Assembly Part Number: J1754AF2B5201G5202GGW00450CA000W1A

NOTE 1: "X" To be used for identifying special conditions that requires a drawing.

NOTE 2: "W" To be used for identifying all alpha code letters not required in the coding identification.

NOTE 3: "0" To be used for identifying all numerical numbers not used in the coding identification.

FIGURE 1—EXAMPLE OF HOSE ASSEMBLY PART NUMBER

APPENDIX A
SAE HOSE ASSEMBLY DRAWING

End 1 — Hose Assembly Overall Length ________ mm — End 2

Connector 1 Information

Hex: Inch
End: Male ☐ Female ☐
Straight ☐ Angle ____°
Drop: Short: ☐ Medium: ☐ Long: ☐

SAE J516

Hose Connector End Type:
☐ O-Ring Face Seal
☐ Code 61 Flange
☐ Code 62 Flange
☐ JIC (37°) Flare
☐ NPTF Pipe
☐ Male O-Ring Stud-Light Duty
☐ Male O-Ring Stud-Heavy Duty
☐ OTHER________

Dash Size/Code: ☐ -03 / D ☐ -04 / E ☐ -05 / F ☐ -06 / G ☐ -08 / H ☐ -10 / J ☐ -12 / K ☐ -14 / M ☐ -16 / N ☐ -20 / P ☐ -24 / R ☐ -32 / T ☐ -40 / U

Cover Type: ☐ 1, ☐ 2, or ☐ 3

Hose Class: ☐ Class A ☐ Class B

Working Pressure / Code: ☐ 1.7 MPa / C ☐ 2.8 MPa / D ☐ 7 MPa / E ☐ 14 MPa / F ☐ 17.5 MPa / G ☐ 21 MPa / H ☐ 24.5 MPa / J ☐ 28 MPa / K ☐ 35 MPa / M ☐ 42 MPa / N ☐ __ MPa / X

SAE Hose Dash Size/Code: ☐ -03 / D ☐ -04 / E ☐ -05 / F ☐ -06 / G ☐ -08 / H ☐ -10 / J ☐ -12 / K ☐ -16 / N ☐ -20 / P ☐ -24 / R ☐ -32 / T ☐ -40 / U

Connector 2 Information

Hex: Inch
End: Male ☐ Female ☐
Straight ☐ Angle ____°
Drop: Short: ☐ Medium: ☐ Long: ☐

SAE J516

Hose Connector End Type:
☐ O-Ring Face Seal
☐ Code 61 Flange
☐ Code 62 Flange
☐ JIC (37°) Flare
☐ NPTF Pipe
☐ Male O-Ring Stud-Light Duty
☐ Male O-Ring Stud-Heavy Duty
☐ OTHER________

Dash Size/Code: ☐ -03 / D ☐ -04 / E ☐ -05 / F ☐ -06 / G ☐ -08 / H ☐ -10 / J ☐ -12 / K ☐ -14 / M ☐ -16 / N ☐ -20 / P ☐ -24 / R ☐ -32 / T ☐ -40 / U

Wire Reinforcement Layer Code: ☐ 1, ☐ 2, ☐ 4 or ☐ 6

Hose Assembly Operating Temperature Range (Code): ☐ -40° to +100°C (A), ☐ -40° to +121°C (B) or ________°C (X).

Displacement Angle: ________ ± 3°

180° / ANGLE / 270° / 90° / NEAR END / 0°

Front connector down.
Point assembly away from you.
Measure counter-clockwise.

Accessories: Sleeve Type / Code	Type of Sleeve	Full Length	Partial Length	From End Of Connector
☐ Steel Flat Armor Guard / A		☐	______ mm	______
☐ Round Spring Guard / B		☐	______ mm	______
☐ Polyamide Sleeve / C		☐	______ mm	______
☐ Plastic Flat Armor Guard / D		☐	______ mm	______
☐ Fire Sleeve / E		☐	______ mm	______
☐ Other / X:________		☐	______ mm	______

Cleanliness Requirements: ISO 4406 CODE NUMBER 19 / 16

Inside Area: ____________ m^2
Max Weight: ____________ mg
Max Particle Size: ______ X ______ X ______ cm^2

Hose Curvature Orientation: _____

Top / Front					Not Required
VIEW	P	R	T	U	W

SAE Hose Assembly Part Number:

J1754AF2B5201G5202GGW00450CA000W1A

SAE — The Engineering Society For Advancing Mobility Land Sea Air and Space — 400 COMMONWEALTH DRIVE, WARRENDALE, PA 15096	J1754-2
REV.:	DATED:
SUPPLIER PART #:	
CUSTOMER PART #:	
TITLE:	HOSE ASSEMBLY, HYDRAULIC
SCALE =	(DO NOT SCALE DRAWING)

FIGURE A1—SAE HOSE ASSEMBLY DRAWING

APPENDIX B
ISO HOSE ASSEMBLY DRAWING

End 1 |◄— Hose Assembly Overall Length ____ mm —►| End 2

Connector 1 Information **Cover Type:** ☐ 1, ☐ 2, or ☐ 3 **Connector 2 Information**

Hex: Metric
End: Male ☐ Female ☐
Straight ☐ Angle ____
Drop: Short: ☐ Medium: ☐ Long: ☐
ISO 12151
Hose Connector End Type: **Size/Code:**
☐ Part 1 - Face Seal - Code S ☐ __ / E
☐ Part 2 - 24° Cone - Code L ☐ __ / F
☐ Part 2 - 24° Cone - Code S ☐ __ / G
☐ Part 3 - Flange - Code L ☐ __ / H
☐ Part 3 - Flange - Code S ☐ __ / J
☐ Part 4 - Stud End - Code L ☐ __ / K
☐ Part 4 - Stud End - Code S ☐ __ / M
☐ Part 5 - 37° Flare - Code L ☐ __ / N
☐ Part 6 - 60° Cone - Code L ☐ __ / P
☐ OTHER____________ ☐ __ / R
☐ __ / T

Hose Class: **ISO Metric Hose Size/Code:**
☐ Class A ☐ 5 / D
☐ Class B ☐ 6.3 / E
Working Pressure / Code: ☐ 8 / F
☐ 1.7 MPa / C ☐ 10 / G
☐ 2.8 MPa / D ☐ 12.5 / H
☐ 7 MPa / E ☐ 16 / J
☐ 14 MPa / F ☐ 19 / K
☐ 17.5 MPa / G ☐ 25 / N
☐ 21 MPa / H ☐ 31.5 / P
☐ 24.5 MPa / J ☐ 38 / R
☐ 28 MPa / K ☐ 51 / T
☐ 35 MPa / M ☐ 63 / U
☐ 42 MPa / N
☐ __ MPa / X

Hex: Metric
End: Male ☐ Female ☐
Straight ☐ Angle ____
Drop: Short: ☐ Medium: ☐ Long: ☐
ISO 12151
Hose Connector End Type: **Size/Code:**
☐ Part 1 - Face Seal - Code S ☐ __ / E
☐ Part 2 - 24° Cone - Code L ☐ __ / F
☐ Part 2 - 24° Cone - Code S ☐ __ / G
☐ Part 3 - Flange - Code L ☐ __ / H
☐ Part 3 - Flange - Code S ☐ __ / J
☐ Part 4 - Stud End - Code L ☐ __ / K
☐ Part 4 - Stud End - Code S ☐ __ / M
☐ Part 5 - 37° Flare - Code L ☐ __ / N
☐ Part 6 - 60° Cone - Code L ☐ __ / P
☐ OTHER____________ ☐ __ / R
☐ __ / T

Wire Reinforcement Layer Code: ☐ 1, ☐ 2, ☐ 4 or ☐ 6

Hose Assembly Operating Temperature Range (Code): ☐ -40° to +100°C (A), ☐ -40° to +121°C (B) or __________°C (X).

Displacement Angle: ______ ± 3°

180° ANGLE 270° 90° NEAR END 0°

Front connector down.
Point assembly away from you.
Measure counter-clockwise.

Accessories: Sleeve Type / Code	Type of Sleeve	Full Length	Partial Length	From End Of Connector
☐ Steel Flat Armor Guard / A		☐	______ mm	______
☐ Round Spring Guard / B		☐	______ mm	______
☐ Polyamide Sleeve / C		☐	______ mm	______
☐ Plastic Flat Armor Guard / D		☐	______ mm	______
☐ Fire Sleeve / E		☐	______ mm	______
☐ Other / X:________		☐	______ mm	______

Cleanliness Requirements: ISO 4406 CODE NUMBER 19 / 16
Inside Area: __________ m^2
Max Weight: __________ mg
Max Particle Size: ______ X ______ X ______ cm^2

Hose Curvature Orientation: ____

Top / Front VIEW	P	R	T	U	Not Required W

SAE Hose Assembly Part Number:

J1754BF2B5201G5202GGW00450CA000W1A

SAE The Engineering Society For Advancing Mobility Land Sea Air and Space
400 COMMONWEALTH DRIVE, WARRENDALE, PA 15096

J1754-2

REV.:	DATED:
SUPPLIER PART #:	
CUSTOMER PART #:	
TITLE:	HOSE ASSEMBLY, HYDRAULIC
SCALE =	(DO NOT SCALE DRAWING)

FIGURE B1—ISO HOSE ASSEMBLY DRAWING

HOSE AND HOSE ASSEMBLIES FOR MARINE APPLICATIONS—SAE J1942 NOV2002

SAE Standard

Report of the SAE Fluid Conductors and Connectors Technical Committee approved March 1989. Completely revised by the SAE Fluid Conductors and Connectors Technical Committee SC2—Hydraulic Hose and Hose Fittings May 1992, and revised June 1993, May 1995, May 1997, and November 2002. Rationale statement available.

1. Scope—SAE J1942, developed through the cooperative efforts of the U.S. Coast Guard and SAE, became effective August 28, 1991[1], as the official document for nonmetallic flexible hose assemblies for commercial marine use.

This SAE Standard covers specific requirements for several styles of hose and/or hose assemblies in systems on board commercial vessels inspected and certificated by the U.S. Coast Guard. It is intended that this document establish hose constructions and performance levels that are essential to safe operations in the marine environment. Refer to SAE J1273 for selection, installation, and maintenance of hose and hose assemblies.

Refer to SAE J1527 Marine Fuel Hose for hose to convey gasoline or diesel fuel aboard small craft, including pleasure craft and related small commercial craft regulated directly or by reference under 33 CFR 183 Subpart J, and boats and yachts meeting American Boat and Yacht Council standards.

SAE J1942-1—Qualified Hoses for Marine Applications is a listing of the products which have been certified for use in the applications described in SAE J1942, Table 1—HOSE APPLICATION/CONSTRUCTION, for Fluid Power, Fuel Oil, Lube Oil, Water, and Pneumatic systems.

SAE J1942-1 is updated yearly and is available from SAE as a single copy document.

2. References

2.1 Applicable Publications—The following publications form a part of the specification to the extent specified herein. Unless otherwise indicated, the latest revision of SAE publications shall apply.

2.1.1 SAE PUBLICATIONS—Available from SAE, 400 Commonwealth Drive, Warrendale, PA 15096-0001.

SAE J343—Test and Procedures for SAE 100 R Series Hydraulic Hose and Hose Assemblies
SAE J517—Hydraulic Hose
SAE J1273—Selection, Installation, and Maintenance of Hose and Hose Assemblies
SAE J1475—Hydraulic Hose Fittings for Marine Applications
SAE J1527—Marine Fuel Hoses
SAE J1942-1—Qualified Hoses for Marine Applications

2.1.2 ASTM PUBLICATIONS—Available from ASTM, 100 Barr Harbor Drive, West Conshohocken, PA 19428-2959.

ASTM D 1141-52—Specification for Substitute Ocean Water

2.1.3 MSHA PUBLICATIONS

MSHA 30 CFR 18.65—Conservation of Power and Water Resources—Subchapter B—Regulations Under the Federal Power Act

3. Hose Application/Construction—Hose construction and performance shall conform to Table 1.

4. Fittings—Fittings shall conform to SAE J1475 where applicable; only hose and fitting combinations that have been tested and passed the requirements of this document as hose assemblies are acceptable. Push-on fittings, quick disconnect couplings, and fittings with a single worm-gear clamp or a single band around the hose, are unacceptable.

5. Qualification Tests—For qualification to this document, hose and/or assemblies made therefrom shall conform to the tests and requirements specified in Table 1 for each hose application.

Testing shall conform to SAE J343 except as noted.

Manufacturers wishing to have their hose assemblies listed in SAE J1942-1 shall:

a. Successfully test their hose to the requirements of Table 1.
b. Submit a letter of certification to the SAE J1942 test requirements for each specific type of hose tested. All sizes should be included in the same letter which must also include all of the information necessary to make a SAE J1942-1 listing.
c. The SAE will review the letter and may, at their discretion, request to see some or all of the test results. A copy of the submittal letter marked "Accepted For Listing" will be returned to the applicant and a duplicate copy sent to the USCG.
d. The cutoff date for inclusion of a hose listing in the annual SAE Handbook is April 30 of the preceding year. However, listed hoses may be used on vessels as soon as the "Accepted For Listing" letter is issued by the SAE.

6. Immersion-Burst Test—One 450 mm assembly, uncapped, shall be completely immersed in a nonpressurized, closed container filled with synthetic sea water conforming to ASTM D 1141-52 for 48 h ± 1 h at 70 °C ± 1 °C. The assembly shall then be removed and held for 48 h ± 1 h in air at room temperature 21 °C ± 2.5 °C. Following this aging, the assembly shall be subjected to the burst test specified in SAE J343.

Burst shall not occur at a pressure less than four times the rated hose working pressure. Within 0.5 h following the burst test, the hose shall be cut apart and the reinforcement examined for signs of corrosion and/or deterioration. The wire of wire-reinforced hose shall not show red rust.

7. Flame Resistance—The hose cover shall pass the MSHA (Mine Safety Health Administration) flame resistance requirements of 30 CFR 18.65. In lieu of testing the hose cover, it may be protected by a fire sleeve of suitable material that conforms to the flame resistance criteria of 30 CFR 18.65.

1. Ref. Federal Register/Vol. 56, No. 145/Monday, July 29, 1991/Rules and Regulations

TABLE 1—HOSE APPLICATION/CONSTRUCTION

Code	Application	Maximum Service Pressure	Hose Reinforcement/ Construction	Requirements	Notes
HF	All Services	(1) (2)	Plies or braids of steel wire with or without textile(3)	Sections 6, 7, 8, 9, 10, 11 (SAE J517 may be substituted for Section 9)	Acceptable for Codes H, VW, NVW, and F applications(2)
H	Fluid Power (Hydraulic Systems)	(1)	Plies or braids of steel wire or textile(2)	Sections 6, 7, 9, 10, 11 (SAE J517 may be substituted for Section 9)	Acceptable for Codes H, VW, and NVW applications
F	Lube Oil and Fuel Systems	(1)	Plies or braids of steel wire with or without textile(2)	Sections 6, 7, 8, 9, (impulse per 9E not required) 10, 11	Acceptable for Codes F, VW, and NVW applications
VW	Vital and Nonvital Fresh and Salt Water	(1)	Plies or braids of steel wire or textile(2)	Sections 6, 7, 10, 11	Acceptable for Codes VW and NVW applications
NVW	Nonvital Water and Pneumatic	0.34 MPa	Optional	Sections 6, 7, 10, 11	Acceptable for Code NVW application only

1. As rated by SAE J517 or as rated by manufacturer.
2. Maximum service pressure for lube oil and fuel systems applications (Code F) may be less than maximum service pressure for other systems applications, e.g., Code H. Refer to manufacturer's catalog and Hose Assemblies List, SAE J1942-1.
3. Wire helix construction may be used on suction and return lines i conjunction with a textile reinforcement.

8. 2.5 Min Fire Test—For hose 51 mm inside diameter and smaller, three assemblies are to be consecutively tested for fire resistance. For hoses larger than 51 mm inside diameter, one hose assembly shall be tested. Free hose length measured between the fittings shall be 400 to 600 mm. At least one end fitting shall be positioned to be engulfed in the flame. The hose shall be positioned 230 mm above the top edge of an open pan the size of 215 x 355 x 13 mm. Sufficient heptane shall be added to the pan to provide for a 2.5 min burn.

Thermocouples shall be mounted so as to sense the flame temperature in the same plane and elevation as the hose assembly. The assembly shall be pressurized with water to the maximum working pressure and maintained during the burning portion of the test. Following ignition of the heptane, timing shall begin and the temperature shall be monitored. The temperature shall reach a minimum of 650 °C but shall not exceed 730 °C. (If 650 °C is not reached, the test must be repeated with a new sample. If 730 °C is exceeded, results may be discarded and the test repeated.)

At the end of 2.5 min of fire exposure, the flame shall be extinguished and pressure relieved. Water from a 915 mm height shall flow through the assembly. Failure to achieve free flow shall constitute failure. With free flow established, the assembly shall be pressurized to the maximum working pressure for 30 s. Leakage during the fire exposure or subsequent pressure test shall constitute failure. Reference Figures 1 and 2 for fire test set-up and test chamber.

NOTE—Hose assemblies may use protective fire sleeves.

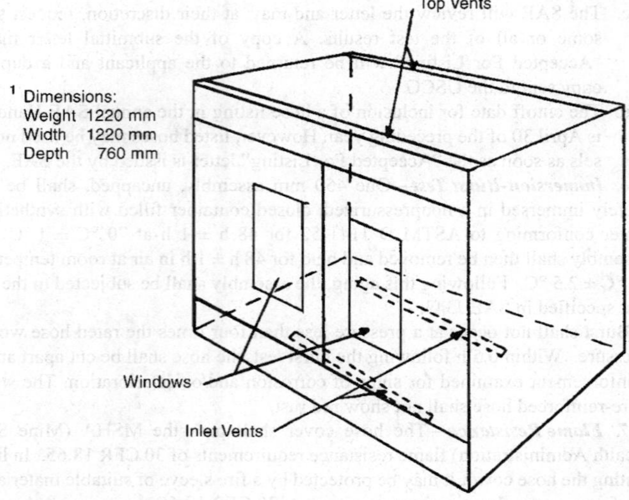

FIGURE 1—FIRE TEST CABINET

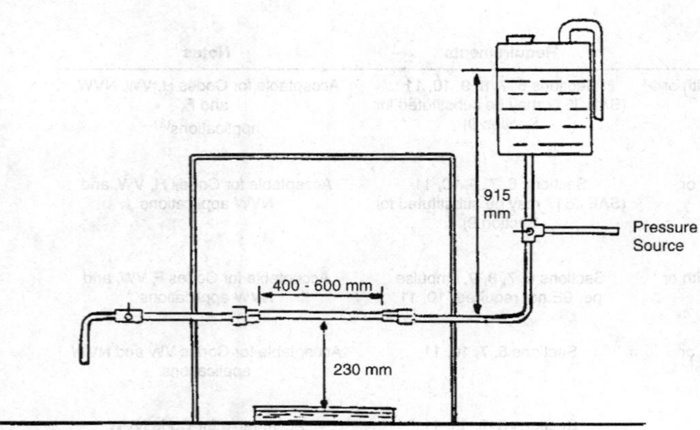

FIGURE 2—TEST SET-UP

9. Non-SAE J517 Hose/Hose Assemblies—Products not conforming to SAE J517 shall meet the following:

a. Proof test per SAE J343, no leakage allowed.
b. Change in length per SAE J343, not to exceed +2 and –4% (does not apply to wire helix type hose).
c. Burst test per SAE J343, minimum burst shall be at least four times the rated hose working pressure.
d. Cold bend test per SAE J343, no cracking or leakage allowed. Testing to be done at the manufacturer's minimum recommended temperature.
e. Impulse test per SAE J343. Conduct test at 125% of rated hose working pressure for 200 000 cycles at a fluid temperature of 100 °C. No leakage or other malfunction is allowed. (Impulse not required on wire helix type hose.)

10. Inspection Tests—The tests required in Table 1 shall be repeated at least every 3 years except for the 2.5 min fire test (Section 8) which does not need to be rerun unless there is a change in the construction or material of the listed hose.

All test results shall be maintained on file, for review, for a period of 6 years; except that test results of the 2.5 min fire test shall be maintained for at least 5 years after termination of hose production.

Test reports may be requested for inspection, at any time, by the U.S. Coast Guard.

11. Marking—Hose meeting SAE J517 is to be identified in accordance with SAE J517. Non-SAE J517 hose shall contain, as a minimum, the following information: manufacturer's name and part number, hose size, maximum working pressure, and the date of manufacture, repeated with the first letter of each repeat not more than 762 mm (30 in) from the first letter of that preceding.

No mention of the burst pressure or the design factor is allowed on the hose. This information could be misinterpreted by the user and result in a hose being used above its rated working pressure.

Working pressures may be shown on a hose in numerous ways and is not limited to the following examples:

EXAMPLE—XXXX MAX. W.P.
XXXX Maximum W.P
XXXX Max. Working Pressure

In addition, as an option to expedite U.S. Coast Guard inspection, hoses may be marked with the propeller symbol ✤ as shown in Figure 3, followed by the appropriate alphabetical code from Table 1. Examples of hose markings, with the optional propeller symbol, are shown in Figure 4.

FIGURE 3—HOSE MARKING PROPELLER SYMBOL

SAE J517 Hose—Good for all Service Applications

ABC Co. MT12 3/4" I.D. SAE 100R2AT 2250 PSI Max W.P. FEB89 ✤ HF

NON-SAE J517 Hose—Good for Fuel & Lube Oil Service

ABC Co. JK08 1/2" I.D. 3.4 MPa Max Working Pressure FEB89 ✤ F

FIGURE 4—EXAMPLES OF HOSE MARKINGS WITH THE OPTIONAL PROPELLER SYMBOL

The manufacturer's catalog and the Hose Assemblies List, SAE J1942-1, shall be consulted prior to final selection and installation of all marine hose assemblies to ensure that they are adequate for the intended service application.

QUALIFIED HOSES FOR MARINE APPLICATIONS—SAE J1942-1 DEC2003

SAE Information Report

Report of the SAE Fluid Conductors and Connectors Technical Committee SC2—Hydraulic Hose and Hose Fittings approved June 1993, revised May 1994, May 1995, May 1996, May 1997, May 1998, June 1999, April 2001, May 2002, May 2003 and December 2003. Rationale statement available.

1. Scope—Effective August 28, 1991, the SAE replaced the USCG as the listing agency for Marine Hose Assemblies. The previous USCG list was discontinued as of December 31, 1992, and is being replaced by this SAE listing, J1942-1.

All products appearing on the USCG list as of December 31, 1992, may be carried over to the SAE J1942-1 provided they meet the new test requirements listed in SAE J1942.

If your products comply, you may retain your listings with no additional testing. (Please note that the USCG has the authority to request and inspect your test results at their discretion.)

The following list consists of hose data provided as of December 2003, and is for convenience in determining acceptability of nonmetallic flexible hose assemblies intended for usage under 46 CFR 56.60-25. Where the maximum allowable working pressure (MAWP) or type of fitting is not specified, use the manufacturer's recommended MAWP or type of fitting. This list has been compiled by SAE Staff from information provided by the manufacturers whose product listings appear in this document.

Manufacturers wishing to list their products in this document shall:

a. Successfully test their hose to the requirements of SAE J1942, Table 1.
b. Submit a letter of certification to the SAE J1942 test requirements for each specific type of hose tested. All sizes should be included in the same letter which must also include all of the information necessary to make a SAE J1942-1 listing.
c. The SAE will review the letter and may, at their discretion, request to see some, or all, of the test results. A copy of the submittal letter marked "Accepted For Listing" will be returned to the applicant and a duplicate copy sent to the USCG.
d. The cutoff date for inclusion of a hose listing in the annual SAE Handbook is April 30, of the preceding year. However, listed hoses may be used on vessels as soon as the "Accepted For Listing" letter is issued by the SAE.

Next publication of this listing is scheduled to take place in May 2004. If you wish to include additional hoses in the 2004 publication of this list, please submit your Certified List to SAE Headquarters by March 2004.

2. References

2.1 Applicable Publication—The following publication forms a part of the specification to the extent specified herein. Unless otherwise indicated the lastest revision of SAE publications shall apply.

2.1.1 SAE PUBLICATION—Available from SAE, 400 Commonwealth Drive, Warrendale, PA 15096-0001

SAE J1942—Hose and Hose Assemblies for Marine Applications

3. Listing Instructions—(Refer to Table 1 in SAE J1942 and the attached Sample Listing Page (see Table 1).

3.1 Column 1—Hose Number—List each complete hose supplier catalog number, including the size (one line listing for a series of hoses will no longer be acceptable.)

3.2 Column 2—Application Code—Will show an HF, F, H, VW, or NVW, nothing more!

Hoses with an F and H rating, at the **same working pressure**, should be rated HF, good for all services.

If a hose is qualified for use in both an F and H application, but **at different working pressures**, or requires a fire sleeve for either application, it must be listed twice, once for F and once for H, with the appropriate information for each listing.

Hoses listed as F can be used for VW and NVW applications and **do not** require a separate listing for VW and NVW.

Hoses listed as H can also be used for VW and NVW applications and do not require a separate listing for VW and NVW.

Hoses listed as VW can also be used for NVW applications (at 50 psi). NVW listings are for NVW listings only (refer to Table 1).

Because of the multiple uses for F, H, and VW hoses, no hose has to be listed more than twice.

3.3 Column 3—Hose I.D.—The actual hose I.D. shall be shown in fractions.

3.4 Column 4—Maximum Allowable Working Pressure—Shall be shown in PSI. VW applications can use F and H hoses at the pressures shown in the listing or their own listed pressure. NVW applications are all rated at 50 psi maximum.

3.5 Column 5—Fittings—Shall show the catalog number of each fitting style used on each hose size.

3.6 Column 6—Fire Sleeve—Show the number of the appropriate fire sleeve if one is required.

3.7 Column 7—Listing Date—For all hoses now on the USCG list, this date will be the date that SAE J1942-1 is printed. (The USCG letter date will be dropped.) Future listings will be the date the hose is added to the list by SAE.

3.8 Column 8—Notes—Will be removed. With the individual listing of each hose size, this column will no longer be required.

TABLE 1—SAMPLE LISTING PAGE

1 Hose Number	2 Applic. Code	3 Hose ID	4 MAWP (PSI)	5 Fittings	6 Fire Sleeve	7 Listing Date
E704	H	1/4	3000	HF,EA,CH	—	4JAN93
E705	H	5/16	2750	HU,EA,CH	—	4JAN93
E706	H	3/8	2500	HU,EA,CH	—	4JAN93
E708	H	1/2	2250	HU,CH	—	4JAN93
M716	H	1	4000	HW	—	4JAN93
M720	H	1-1/4	3000	HW	—	4JAN93
M724	H	1-1/4	2500	HW	—	4JAN93
G104	HF	1/4	3000	GL,EC	—	4JAN93
G105	HF	5/16	2500	GL,EC	—	4JAN93
G106	HF	3/8	2500	GL,EC	—	4JAN93
G108	HF	1/2	2250	GL,EC	—	4JAN93
Y904	H	3/16	3000	BC,BN	—	4JAN93
Y905	H	1/4	3000	BC,BN	—	4JAN93
Y906	H	5/16	2250	BC,BN	—	4JAN93
Y910	H	1/2	1750	BC,BN	—	4JAN93
Y904	F	3/16	300	BC,BN	14372	4JAN93
Y905	F	1/4	300	BC,BN	14372	4JAN93
Y906	F	5/16	300	BC,BN	14372	4JAN93
N256-2	VW	2	400	H-620	—	4JAN93
N256-3	VW	3	400	H-630	—	4JAN93
N256-4	VW	4	400	H-640	—	4JAN93
N-1401-12	NVW	3/4	50	H-132	—	4JAN93
N-1401-16	NVW	1	50	H-140	—	4JAN93
N-1401-20	NVW	1-1/4	50	H-146	—	4JAN93

4. Aeroquip Corporation
Aeroquip Industrial Americas Group
Technical Center
1660 Indian Wood Circle
Maumee, OH 43537-4069
Ph: (419) 891-7600
Fax: (419) 891-7790

TABLE 2—AEROQUIP CORPORATION LISTING

Hose Number	Applic. Code	Hose ID	MAWP (PSI)	Fittings	Fire Sleeve	Listing Date
1503-4	HF	3/16	3000	400 Type,4400 Type	624-11	20NOV97
1503-5	HF	1/4	3000	400 Type,4400 Type	624-11	20NOV97
1503-6	HF	5/16	2250	400 Type,4400 Type	624-14	20NOV97
1503-8	HF	13/32	2000	400 Type,4400 Type	624-16	20NOV97
1503-10	HF	1/2	1750	400 Type,4400 Type	624-18	20NOV97
1503-12	HF	5/8	1500	400 Type,4400 Type	624-20	20NOV97
1503-16	HF	7/8	800	400 Type,4400 Type	624-24	20NOV97
1503-20	HF	1-1/8	625	400 Type,4400 Type	624-30	20NOV97
1503-24	HF	1-3/8	500	400 Type,4400 Type	624-32	20NOV97
1503-32	HF	1-13/16	350	400 Type,4400 Type	624-38	20NOV97
1509-4	F	1/4	5000	4700 Type, 1SA Type	624-14	6APR95
1509-4	H	1/4	5000	4700 Type, 1SA Type	N.R.	6APR95
1509-6	F	3/8	4000	4700 Type, 1SA Type	624-16	6APR95
1509-6	H	3/8	4000	4700 Type, 1SA Type	N.R.	6APR95
1509-8	F	1/2	4000	4700 Type, 1SA Type	624-18	6APR95
1509-8	H	1/2	4000	4700 Type, 1SA Type	N.R.	6APR95
1509-10	HF	5/8	2750	4700 Type, 1SA Type	N.R.	6APR95
1509-12	HF	3/4	2250	4700 Type, 1SA Type	N.R.	6APR95
1509-16	HF	1	2000	4700 Type, 1SA Type	N.R.	6APR95
1509-20	HF	1-1/4	1625	4700 Type, 1SA Type	N.R.	6APR95
1509-24	HF	1-1/2	1250	4700 Type, 1SA Type	N.R.	6APR95
1509-32	HF	2	1125	4700 Type, 1SA Type	N.R.	6APR95
1529-4	VW	1/4	5000	4700 or 1SB Type	N.R.	17OCT95
1529-6	VW	3/8	4000	4700 or 1SB Type	N.R	17OCT95
1529-8	VW	1/2	3500	4700 or 1SB Type	N.R	17OCT95
1529-10	VW	5/8	2750	4700 or 1SB Type	N.R	17OCT95
1529-12	VW	3/4	2250	4700 or 1SB Type	N.R	17OCT95
1529-16	VW	1	2000	4700 or 1SB Type	N.R	17OCT95
1529-20	VW	1-1/4	1625	4700 or 1SB Type	N.R	17OCT95
1529-24	VW	1-1/2	1250	4700 or 1SB Type	N.R	17OCT95
1529-32	VW	2	1125	4700 or 1SB Type	N.R	17OCT95
2580-4	H	3/16	1000	400 Type,4400 Type	N.R.	6APR95
2580-5	H	1/4	800	400 Type,4400 Type	N.R	6APR95
2580-6	H	5/16	650	400 Type,4400 Type	N.R	6APR95
2580-8	H	13/32	625	400 Type,4400 Type	N.R	6APR95
2580-10	H	1/2	600	400 Type,4400 Type	N.R	6APR95
2580-12	H	5/8	550	400 Type,4400 Type	N.R	6APR95
2580-16	H	7/8	500	400 Type,4400 Type	N.R	6APR95
2580-20	H	1-1/8	450	400 Type,4400 Type	N.R	6APR95
2580-24	H	1-3/8	400	400 Type,4400 Type	N.R	6APR95
2580-32	H	1-13/16	350	400 Type,4400 Type	N.R	6APR95
2651-4	F	3/16	3000	400 Type,4400 Type	624-11	6APR95
2651-4	H	3/16	3000	400 Type,4400 Type	N.R.	6APR95
2651-5	F	1/4	3000	400 Type,4400 Type	624-12	6APR95
2651-5	H	1/4	3000	400 Type,4400 Type	N.R	6APR95
2651-6	F	5/16	2250	400 Type,4400 Type	624-14	6APR95
2651-6	H	5/16	2250	400 Type,4400 Type	N.R	6APR95
2651-8	F	13/32	2000	400 Type,4400 Type	624-16	6APR95
2651-8	H	13/32	2000	400 Type,4400 Type	N.R	6APR95
2651-10	F	1/2	1750	400 Type,4400 Type	624-18	6APR95
2651-10	H	1/2	1750	400 Type,4400 Type	N.R	6APR95
2651-12	HF	5/8	1500	400 Type,4400 Type	N.R	6APR95
2651-16	HF	7/8	800	400 Type,4400 Type	N.R	6APR95
2651-20	HF	1-1/8	625	400 Type,4400 Type	N.R	6APR95

TABLE 2—AEROQUIP CORPORATION LISTING (continued)

Hose Number	Applic. Code	Hose ID	MAWP (PSI)	Fittings	Fire Sleeve	Listing Date
2651-24	HF	1-3/8	500	400 Type,4400 Type	N.R	6APR95
2651-32	HF	1-13/16	350	400 Type,4400 Type	N.R	6APR95
2651-40	HF	2-3/8	350	400 Type,4400 Type	N.R	6APR95
2652-40	H	2-1/2	600	400 Type	N.R	6APR95
2652-48	H	3	450	400 Type	N.R	6APR95
2661-12	HF	3/4	300	FC9000 Type,1AA Type	N.R.	6APR95
2661-16	HF	1	250	FC9000 Type,1AA Type	N.R	6APR95
2661-20	HF	1-1/4	200	FC9000 Type,1AA Type	N.R	6APR95
2661-24	HF	1-1/2	150	FC9000 Type,1AA Type	N.R	6APR95
2661-32	HF	2	100	FC9000 Type,1AA Type	N.R	6APR95
2661-40	HF	2-1/2	62	FC9000 Type	N.R	6APR95
2661-48	HF	3	56	FC9000 type	N.R	6APR95
2681-3	F	3/16	4000	1SA Type	624-11	6APR95
2681-3	H	3/16	4000	1SA Type	N.R.	6APR95
2681-4	F	1/4	3250	1SA Type	624-12	6APR95
2681-4	H	1/4	3250	1SA Type	N.R.	6APR95
2681-5	F	5/16	3250	1SA Type	624-14	6APR95
2681-5	H	5/16	3250	1SA Type	N.R.	6APR95
2681-6	F	3/8	3000	1SA Type	624-18	6APR95
2681-6	H	3/8	3000	1SA Type	N.R.	6APR95
2681-8	F	1/2	2500	1SA Type	624-20	6APR95
2681-8	H	1/2	2500	1SA Type	N.R.	6APR95
2681-10	HF	5/8	2000	1SA Type	N.R.	6APR95
2681-12	HF	3/4	1750	1SA Type	N.R.	6APR95
2681-16	HF	1	1250	1SA Type	N.R.	6APR95
2681-20	HF	1-1/4	900	1SA Type	N.R.	6APR95
2681-24	HF	1-1/2	700	1SA Type	N.R.	6APR95
2681-32	HF	2	500	1SA Type	N.R.	6APR95
2781-4	F	1/4	5750	4700 Type, 1SA Type	624-14	6APR95
2781-4	H	1/4	5750	4700 Type, 1SA Type	N.R.	6APR95
2781-6	F	3/8	5000	4700 Type, 1SA Type	624-16	6APR95
2781-6	H	3/8	5000	4700 Type, 1SA Type	N.R.	6APR95
2781-8	F	1/2	4250	4700 Type, 1SA Type	624-18	6APR95
2781-8	H	1/2	4250	4700 Type, 1SA Type	N.R.	6APR95
2781-10	HF	5/8	3250	4700 Type, 1SA Type	N.R.	6APR95
2781-12	HF	3/4	3000	4700 Type, 1SA Type	N.R.	6APR95
2781-16	HF	1	2500	4700 Type, 1SA Type	N.R.	6APR95
2781-20	HF	1-1/4	2250	4700 Type, 1SA Type	N.R.	6APR95
2781-32	HF	1-1/2	1750	4700 Type, 1SA Type	N.R.	6APR95
2781-32	HF	2	1500	4700 Type, 1SA Type	N.R.	6APR95
2807-3	F	9/64	3000	1906 Type, FC9000 Type	624-17	6APR95
2807-3	H	9/64	3000	1906 Type, FC9000 Type	N.R.	6APR95
2807-4	F	3/16	3000	1906 Type, FC9000 Type	624-8	6APR95
2807-4	H	3/16	3000	1906 Type, FC9000 Type	N.R.	6APR95
2807-5	F	1/4	3000	1906 Type, FC9000 Type	624-9	6APR95
2807-5	H	1/4	3000	1906 Type, FC9000 Type	N.R.	6APR95
2807-6	F	5/16	2500	1906 Type, FC9000 Type	624-10	6APR95
2807-6	H	5/16	2500	1906 Type, FC9000 Type	N.R.	6APR95
2807-8	F	13/32	2000	1906 Type, FC9000 Type	624-12	6APR95
2807-8	H	13/32	2000	1906 Type, FC9000 Type	N.R.	6APR95
2807-10	F	1/2	1500	1906 Type, FC9000 Type	624-14	6APR95
2807-10	H	1/2	1500	1906 Type, FC9000 Type	N.R.	6APR95
2807-12	F	5/8	1200	1906 Type, FC9000 Type	624-16	6APR95
2807-12	H	5/8	1200	1906 Type, FC9000 Type	N.R.	6APR95
2807-16	F	7/8	1000	1906 Type, FC9000 Type	624-20	6APR95
2807-16	H	7/8	1000	1906 Type, FC9000 Type	N.R.	6APR95
2807-20	F	1-1/8	625	1906 Type	624-24	6APR95
2807-20	H	1-1/8	625	1906 Type	N.R.	6APR95
2808-8	F	13/32	2750	1905 Type	624-16	6APR95
2808-8	H	13/32	2750	1905 Type	N.R.	6APR95

TABLE 2—AEROQUIP CORPORATION LISTING (continued)

Hose Number	Applic. Code	Hose ID	MAWP (PSI)	Fittings	Fire Sleeve	Listing Date
2808-10	F	1/2	2500	1905 Type	624-18	6APR95
2808-10	H	1/2	2500	1905 Type	N.R.	6APR95
2808-12	F	5/8	1750	1905 Type	624-20	6APR95
2808-12	H	5/8	1750	1905 Type	N.R.	6APR95
2808-16	F	7/8	1500	1905 Type	624-26	6APR95
2808-16	H	7/8	1500	1905 Type	N.R.	6APR95
2808-20	F	1-1/8	1125	1905 Type	624-32	6APR95
2808-20	H	1-1/8	1125	1905 Type	N.R.	6APR95
2808-24	F	1-3/8	800	1905 Type	624-38	6APR95
2808-24	H	1-3/8	800	1905 Type	N.R.	6APR95
150901-40	HF	2-1/2	1200	1907 Type	N.R.	6APR95
150901-48	HF	3	900	1907 Type	N.R.	6APR95
150901-64	HF	4	600	1907 Type	N.R.	6APR95
AE369-4	F	3/16	3000	411, 4411	624-11	3APR96
AE369-5	F	1/4	3000	411, 4411	624-12	3APR96
AE369-6	F	5/16	2250	411, 4411	624-14	3APR96
AE369-8	F	13/32	2000	411, 4411	624-16	3APR96
AE369-10	F	1/2	1750	411, 4411	624-18	3APR96
AE369-12	F	5/8	1500	411, 4411.	N.R.	3APR96
AE369-16	F	7/8	800	411, 4411	N.R.	3APR96
AE369-20	F	1-1/8	625	411, 4411	N.R.	3APR96
AE369-24	F	1-3/8	500	411, 4411	N.R.	3APR96
AE369-32	F	1-13-16	350	411, 4411	N.R.	3APR96
AE369-40	F	2-3/8	350	411, 4411	N.R.	3APR96
AE370-40	H	2-1/2	600	190767	—	3APR96
AE370-40	H	3	450	411, 190767	—	3APR96
AE371-4	VW	1/4	5000	4721	—	3APR96
AE371-6	VW	3/8	4000	4721	—	3APR96
AE371-8	VW	1/2	3500	4721	—	3APR96
AE371-10	VW	5/8	2750	4721	—	3APR96
AE371-12	VW	3/4	2250	4721	—	3APR96
AE371-16	VW	1	2000	4721	—	3APR96
AE371-20	VW	1-1/4	1625	4721	—	3APR96
AE371-24	VW	1-1/2	1250	4721	—	3APR96
AE371-32	VW	2	1125	4721	—	3APR96
AE372-4	HF	3/16	3000	411, 4411	624-11	3APR96
AE372-5	HF	1/4	3000	411, 4411	624-12	3APR96
AE372-6	HF	5/16	2250	411, 4411	624-14	3APR96
AE372-8	HF	13/32	2000	411, 4411	624-16	3APR96
AE372-10	HF	1/2	1750	411, 4411	624-18	3APR96
AE372-12	HF	5/8	1500	411, 4411	624-20	3APR96
AE372-16	HF	7/8	800	411, 4411	624-24	3APR96
AE372-20	HF	1-1/8	625	411, 4411	624-30	3APR96
AE372-24	HF	1-3/8	500	411, 4411	624-32	3APR96
AE372-32	HF	1-13/16	300	411, 4411	624-38	3APR96
AE372-40	HF	2-3/8	300	411, 4411	N.R.	3APR96
AE373-4	HF	1/4	5750	4721	624-14	3APR96
AE373-6	HF	3/8	5000	4721	624-16	3APR96
AE373-8	HF	1/2	4250	4721	624-18	3APR96
AE373-10	HF	5/8	3250	4721	N.R.	3APR96
AE373-12	HF	3/4	3000	4721	N.R	3APR96
AE373-16	HF	1	2550	4721	N.R	3APR96
AE373-20	HF	1-1/4	2250	4721	N.R	3APR96
AE373-24	HF	1-1/2	1750	4721	N.R	3APR96
AE373-32	HF	2	1250	4721	N.R	3APR96
AE374-16	H	1	5000	FJ9000	—	3APR96
AE374-20	H	1-1/4	4000	FJ9364	—	3APR96
AE374-24	H	1-1/2	3000	FJ9364	—	3APR96
AE374-32	H	2	3000	FJ9364	—	3APR96

TABLE 2—AEROQUIP CORPORATION LISTING (continued)

Hose Number	Applic. Code	Hose ID	MAWP (PSI)	Fittings	Fire Sleeve	Listing Date
FC132-40	VW	2-1/2	1000	FC9500 Type	—	6APR95
FC132-48	VW	3	900	FC9500 Type	—	6APR95
FC132-64	VW	4	600	FC9500 Type	—	6APR95
FC133-06	VW	3/8	2000	FC7100 Type	—	6APR95
FC133-08	VW	1/2	2000	FC7100 Type	—	6APR95
FC133-12	VW	3/4	1500	FC7100 Type	—	6APR95
FC133-16	VW	1	1400	FC7100 Type	—	6APR95
FC133-20	VW	1-1/4	1000	FC7100 Type	—	6APR95
FC133-24	VW	1-1/2	1000	FC7100 Type	—	6APR95
FC133-32	VW	2	900	FC7100 Type	—	6APR95
FC136-06	H	3/8	5500	19000 Type,FC9500 Type	—	6APR95
FC136-08	H	1/2	5000	19000 Type,FC9500 Type	—	6APR95
FC136-10	H	5/8	5000	19000 Type,FC9500 Type	—	6APR95
FC136-12	H	3/4	4000	19000 Type,FC9500 Type	—	6APR95
FC136-16	H	1	4000	19000 Type,FC9500 Type	—	6APR95
FC136-20	H	1-1/4	3000	19000 Type,FC9500 Type	—	6APR95
FC136-24	H	1-1/2	2500	19000 Type,FC9500 Type	—	6APR95
FC136-32	H	2	2500	19000 Type,FC9500 Type	—	6APR95
FC186-04	F	3/16	1000	1906 Type,FC9000 Type	624-8	6APR95
FC186-04	H	3/16	1000	1906 Type,FC9000 Type	N.R.	6APR95
FC186-05	F	1/4	1000	1906 Type,FC9000 Type	624-9	6APR95
FC186-05	H	1/4	1000	1906 Type,FC9000 Type	N.R.	6APR95
FC186-06	F	5/16	1000	1906 Type,FC9000 Type	624-10	6APR95
FC186-06	H	5/16	1000	1906 Type,FC9000 Type	N.R.	6APR95
FC186-08	F	13/32	750	1906 Type,FC9000 Type	624-12	6APR95
FC186-08	H	13/32	750	1906 Type,FC9000 Type	N.R.	6APR95
FC186-10	F	1/2	600	1906 Type,FC9000 Type	624-14	6APR95
FC186-10	H	1/2	600	1906 Type,FC9000 Type	N.R.	6APR95
FC186-12	F	5/8	600	1906 Type,FC9000 Type	624-16	6APR95
FC186-12	H	5/8	600	1906 Type,FC9000 Type	N.R.	6APR95
FC194-04	F	1/4	3250	1SA Type	624-12	6APR95
FC194-04	H	1/4	3250	1SA Type	N.R.	6APR95
FC194-06	F	3/8	3000	1SA Type	624-18	6APR95
FC194-06	H	3/8	3000	1SA Type	N.R.	6APR95
FC194-08	F	1/2	2500	1SA Type	624-20	6APR95
FC194-08	H	1/2	2500	1SA Type	N.R.	6APR95
FC194-12	HF	3/4	1750	1SA Type	N.R.	6APR95
FC194-16	HF	1	1250	1SA Type	N.R.	6APR95
FC194-20	HF	1-1/4	900	1SA Type	N.R.	6APR95
FC195-04	F	1/4	5750	4700 Type, 1SA Type	624-14	6APR95
FC195-04	H	1/4	5750	4700 Type, 1SA Type	N.R.	6APR95
FC195-06	F	3/8	5000	4700 Type, 1SA Type	624-16	6APR95
FC195-06	H	3/8	5000	4700 Type, 1SA Type	N.R.	6APR95
FC195-08	F	1/2	4250	4700 Type, 1SA Type	624-18	6APR95
FC195-08	H	1/2	4250	4700 Type, 1SA Type	N.R.	6APR95
FC195-10	HF	5/8	3250	4700 Type, 1SA Type	N.R.	6APR95
FC195-12	HF	3/4	3000	4700 Type, 1SA Type	N.R.	6APR95
FC195-16	HF	1	2500	4700 Type, 1SA Type	N.R.	6APR95
FC195-20	HF	1-1/4	2250	4700 Type, 1SA Type	N.R.	6APR95
FC195-24	HF	1-1/2	1750	4700 Type, 1SA Type	N.R.	6APR95
FC195-32	HF	2	1500	4700 Type, 1SA Type	N.R.	6APR95
FC211-04	F	1/4	2750	1AA Type,1SA Type	624-11	6APR95
FC211-04	H	1/4	2750	1AA Type,1SA Type	N.R.	6APR95
FC211-06	F	3/8	2250	1AA Type,1SA Type	624-14	6APR95
FC211-06	H	3/8	2250	1AA Type,1SA Type	N.R.	6APR95
FC211-08	F	1/2	2000	1AA Type,1SA Type	624-16	6APR95
FC211-08	H	1/2	2000	1AA Type,1SA Type	N.R.	6APR95
FC211-12	F	3/4	1250	1AA Type,1SA Type	624-24	6APR95
FC211-12	H	3/4	1250	1AA Type,1SA Type	N.R.	6APR95

TABLE 2—AEROQUIP CORPORATION LISTING (continued)

Hose Number	Applic. Code	Hose ID	MAWP (PSI)	Fittings	Fire Sleeve	Listing Date
FC211-16	HF	1	1000	1AA Type,1SA Type	N.R.	6APR95
FC212-04	F	1/4	5000	1AA Type	624-11	6APR95
FC212-04	H	1/4	5000	1AA Type	N.R.	6APR95
FC212-06	F	3/8	4000	1AA Type	624-14	6APR95
FC212-06	H	3/8	4000	1AA Type	N.R.	6APR95
FC212-08	F	1/2	3500	1AA Type	624-16	6APR95
FC212-08	H	1/2	3500	1AA Type	N.R.	6APR95
FC212-12	HF	3/4	2250	1AA Type	N.R.	6APR95
FC212-16	HF	1	2000	1AA Type	N.R.	6APR95
FC212-20	HF	1-1/4	1625	1AA Type	N.R.	6APR95
FC212-24	HF	1-1/2	1250	1AA Type	N.R.	6APR95
FC212-32	HF	2	1125	1AA Type	N.R.	6APR95
FC234-05	F	1/4	400	400 Type,4400 Type	N.R.	6APR95
FC234-05	H	1/4	1500	400 Type,4400 Type	N.R.	6APR95
FC234-06	F	5/16	1500	400 Type,4400 Type	N.R.	6APR95
FC234-08	F	13/32	1250	400 Type,4400 Type.	N.R.	6APR95
FC234-10	F	1/2	400	400 Type,4400 Type	N.R.	6APR95
FC234-10	H	1/2	1250	400 Type,4400 Type	N.R.	6APR95
FC234-12	F	5/8	750	400 Type,4400 Type.	N.R.	6APR95
FC234-16	F	7/8	400	400 Type,4400 Type	N.R.	6APR95
FC254-08	H	1/2	7500	FC5000 Type	—	6APR95
FC254-12	H	3/4	6250	FC5000 Type,FJ9200 Type	—	6APR95
FC254-16	H	1	5000	FC5000 Type,FJ9200 Type	—	6APR95
FC254-20	H	1-1/4	4000	FC5000 Type,FJ9200 Type	—	6APR95
FC254-24	H	1-1/2	3000	FC5000 Type,FJ9200 Type	—	6APR95
FC254-32	H	2	3000	FC5000 Type	—	6APR95
FC273-12	H	3/4	5000	FC5300 Type	—	6APR95
FC273-16	H	1	5000	FC5300 Type	—	6APR95
FC273-20	H	1-1/4	5000	FC5300 Type	—	6APR95
FC273-24	H	1-1/2	5000	FC5300 Type	—	6APR95
FC273-26	H	2	5000	FC5300 Type	—	6APR95
FC279-04	F	1/4	150	1SA Type	N.R.	20APR95
FC279-04	H	1/4	2750	1SA Type	N.R.	20APR95
FC279-06	F	3/8	150	1SA Type	N.R.	20APR95
FC279-06	H	3/8	2250	1SA Type	N.R.	20APR95
FC279-08	F	1/2	150	1SA Type	N.R.	20APR95
FC279-08	H	1/2	2000	1SA Type	N.R.	20APR95
FC279-12	F	3/4	150	1SA Type	N.R.	20APR95
FC279-12	H	3/4	1250	1SA Type	N.R.	20APR95
FC279-16	F	1	150	1SA Type	N.R.	20APR95
FC279-16	H	1	1000	1SA Type	N.R.	20APR95
FC279-20	F	1-1/4	150	1SA Type	N.R.	20APR95
FC279-20	H	1-1/4	625	1SA Type	N.R.	20APR95
FC300-04	HF	3/16	3000	400 Type,4400 Type	624-11	20NOV97
FC300-05	HF	1/4	3000	400 Type,4400 Type	624-12	20NOV97
FC300-06	HF	5/16	2250	400 Type,4400 Type	624-14	20NOV97
FC300-08	HF	13/32	2000	400 Type,4400 Type	624-16	20NOV97
FC300-10	HF	1/2	1750	400 Type,4400 Type	624-18	20NOV97
FC300-12	HF	5/8	1500	400 Type,4400 Type	624-20	20NOV97
FC300-16	HF	7/8	800	400 Type,4400 Type	624-24	20NOV97
FC300-20	HF	1-1/8	625	400 Type,4400 Type	624-30	20NOV97
FC300-24	HF	1-3/8	500	400 Type,4400 Type	624-32	20NOV97
FC300-32	HF	1-13/16	300	400 Type,4400 Type	624-38	20NOV97
FC300-40	H	2-3/8	300	400 Type,4400 Type	624-42	20NOV97
FC310-04	H	1/4	5000	FC5100 Type,1AA Type	—	6APR95
FC310-06	H	3/8	4000	FC5100 Type,1AA Type	—	6APR95
FC310-08	H	1/2	3500	FC5100 Type,1AA Type	—	6APR95
FC310-10	H	5/8	2750	FC5100 Type,1AA Type	—	6APR95
FC310-12	H	3/4	2250	FC5100 Type,1AA Type	—	6APR95

TABLE 2—AEROQUIP CORPORATION LISTING (continued)

Hose Number	Applic. Code	Hose ID	MAWP (PSI)	Fittings	Fire Sleeve	Listing Date
FC310-16	H	1	2000	FC5100 Type,1AA Type	—	6APR95
FC310-20	H	1-1/4	1625	FC5100 Type,1AA Type	—	6APR95
FC323-12	H	3/4	3000	FJ9700 Type,FC5000 Type	—	6APR95
FC323-16	H	1	3000	FJ9700 Type,FC5000 Type	—	6APR95
FC323-20	H	1-1/4	3000	FJ9700 Type,FC5000 Type	—	6APR95
FC323-24	H	1-1/2	3000	FJ9700 Type,FC5000 Type	—	6APR95
FC323-32	H	2	3000	FC5000 Type	—	6APR95
FC324-08	H	1/2	4000	FJ9700 Type	—	6APR95
FC324-12	H	3/4	4000	FJ9700 Type	—	6APR95
FC324-16	H	1	4000	FJ9700 Type	—	6APR95
FC325-12	H	3/4	5000	FC5300 Type	—	6APR95
FC325-16	H	1	5000	FC5300 Type	—	6APR95
FC350-04	HF	3/16	2000	400 Type,4400 Type	624-11	20NOV97
FC350-05	HF	1/4	1500	400 Type,4400 Type	624-12	20NOV97
FC350-06	HF	5/16	1500	400 Type,4400 Type	624-14	20NOV97
FC350-08	HF	13/32	1250	400 Type,4400 Type	624-16	20NOV97
FC350-10	HF	1/2	1250	400 Type,4400 Type	624-18	20NOV97
FC350-12	HF	5/8	750	400 Type,4400 Type	624-20	20NOV97
FC350-16	HF	7/8	400	400 Type,4400 Type	624-24	20NOV97
FC350-20	HF	1-1/8	300	400 Type,4400 Type	624-30	20NOV97
FC350-24	HF	1-3/8	250	400 Type,4400 Type	624-32	20NOV97
FC363-08	F	1/2	1250	FJ9500 Type	624-14	6APR95
FC363-12	F	3/4	1100	FJ9500 Type	624-14	6APR95
FC363-16	F	1	1000	FJ9500 Type	624-22	6APR95
FC363-20	F	1-1/4	1000	FJ9500 Type	624-26	6APR95
FC363-24	F	1-1/2	750	FJ9500 Type	624-30	6APR95
FC363-32	F	2	500	FJ9500 Type	624-42	6APR95
FC510-04	H	1/4	5000	FC5100 Type	—	6APR95
FC510-06	H	3/8	4000	FC5100 Type	—	6APR95
FC510-08	H	1/2	3500	FC5100 Type	—	6APR95
FC510-10	H	5/8	2750	FC5100 Type	—	6APR95
FC510-12	H	3/4	2250	FC5100 Type	—	6APR95
FC510-16	H	1	2000	FC5100 Type	—	6APR95
FC510-20	H	1-1/4	1625	1AA Type	—	6APR95
FC659-06	H	3/8	4000	1B Type	N.R.	28APR03
FC659-08	H	1/2	4000	1B Type	N.R.	28APR03
FC659-10	H	5/8	4000	1B Type	N.R.	28APR03
FC659-12	H	3/4	4000	1B Type	N.R.	28APR03
FC659-16	H	1	4000	1B Type	N.R.	28APR03
FC659-20	H	1-1/4	3000	1B Type	N.R.	28APR03
FC659-24	H	1-1/2	2500	1B Type	N.R.	28APR03
FC659-32	H	2	2500	1B Type	N.R.	28APR03
FBA0400	F	3/16	1000	FBM Type	624-9	6APR95
FBA0600	F	5/16	1000	FBM Type	624-11	6APR95
FBA0800	F	13/32	1000	FBM Type	624-12	6APR95
FBA1000	F	1/2	1000	FBM Type	N.R.	6APR95
FBA1200	F	5/8	1000	FBM Type	N.R.	6APR95
FBA1600	F	7/8	750	FBM Type	N.R.	6APR95
FBA2000	F	1-1/8	500	FBM Type	N.R.	6APR95
GH195-04	F	1/4	5750	1AA Type	624-13	23FEB01
GH195-04	H	1/4	5750	1AA Type	N.R.	23FEB01
GH195-06	F	3/8	5000	1AA Type	624-16	23FEB01
GH195-06	H	3/8	5000	1AA Type	N.R.	23FEB01
GH195-08	HF	1/2	4250	1AA Type	N.R.	23FEB01
GH195-10	HF	5/8	3250	1AA Type	N.R.	23FEB01
GH195-12	HF	3/4	3000	1AA Type	N.R.	23FEB01
GH195-16	HF	1	2500	1AA Type	N.R.	23FEB01

TABLE 2—AEROQUIP CORPORATION LISTING (continued)

Hose Number	Applic. Code	Hose ID	MAWP (PSI)	Fittings	Fire Sleeve	Listing Date
GH195-20	HF	1-1/4	2250	1AA Type	N.R.	23FEB01
GH195-24	HF	1-1/2	1750	1AA Type	N.R.	23FEB01
GH195-32	HF	2	1500	1AA Type	N.R.	23FEB01
GH493-6	H	3/8	4000	1BA Type	—	6APR95
GH493-8	H	1/2	4000	1BA Type	—	6APR95
GH493-10	H	5/8	4000	1BA Type	—	6APR95
GH493-12	H	3/4	4000	1BA Type	—	6APR95
GH493-16	H	1	4000	1BA Type	—	6APR95
GH493-20	H	1-1/4	3000	1BA Type	—	6APR95
GH493-24	H	1-1/2	2000	1BA Type	—	6APR95
GH663-4	F	1/4	3250	FC7900 Type,1AA Type	624-11	6APR95
GH663-4	H	1/4	3250	FC7900 Type,1AA Type	N.R.	6APR95
GH663-6	F	3/8	3000	FC7900 Type,1AA Type	624-14	6APR95
GH663-6	H	3/8	3000	FC7900 Type,1AA Type	N.R.	6APR95
GH663-8	HF	1/2	2500	FC7900 Type,1AA Type	N.R.	6APR95
GH663-12	HF	3/4	1800	FC7900 Type,1AA Type	N.R.	6APR95
GH663-16	HF	1	1300	FC7900 Type,1AA Type	N.R.	6APR95
GH781-4	F	1/4	5750	1AA Type,1SA Type	624-12	6APR95
GH781-4	H	1/4	5750	1AA Type,1SA Type	N.R.	6APR95
GH781-6	F	3/8	5000	1AA Type,1SA Type	624-14	6APR95
GH781-6	H	3/8	5000	1AA Type,1SA Type	N.R.	6APR95
GH781-8	F	1/2	4250	1AA Type,1SA Type	624-16	6APR95
GH781-8	H	1/2	4250	1AA Type,1SA Type	N.R.	6APR95
GH781-10	F	5/8	3625	1AA Type,1SA Type	624-18	6APR95
GH781-10	H	5/8	3625	1AA Type,1SA Type	N.R.	6APR95
GH781-12	HF	3/4	3125	1AA Type,1SA Type	N.R.	6APR95
GH781-16	HF	1	2500	1AA Type,1SA Type	N.R.	6APR95
GH781-20	HF	1-1/4	2500	1AV Type,1SA Type	N.R.	6APR95
GH793-4	F	1/4	5750	FC5900 Type,1AA Type	624-12	6APR95
GH793-4	H	1/4	5750	FC5900 Type,1AA Type	N.R.	6APR95
GH793-6	F	3/8	5000	FC5900 Type,1AA Type	624-14	6APR95
GH793-6	H	3/8	5000	FC5900 Type,1AA Type	N.R.	6APR95
GH793-8	F	1/2	4250	FC5900 Type,1AA Type	624-18	6APR95
GH793-8	H	1/2	4250	FC5900 Type,1AA Type	N.R.	6APR95
GH793-10	F	5/8	3625	1AA Type	N.R.	6APR95
GH793-10	H	5/8	3625	1AA Type	N.R.	17OCT95
GH793-12	F	3/4	3125	FC5900 Type,1AA Type	N.R.	6APR95
GH793-12	H	3/4	3125	FC5900 Type,1AA Type	N.R.	17OCT95
GH793-16	F	1	2500	FC5900 Type,1AA Type	N.R.	6APR95
GH793-16	H	1	2500	FC5900 Type,1AA Type	N.R.	17OCT95
GH793-20	F	1-1/4	2250	1AA Type	N.R.	6APR95
GH793-20	H	1-1/4	2250	1AA Type	N.R.	17OCT95

5. Anchor Coupling Inc.
5520 13th Street
Menominee, MI 49858
Ph: (906) 863-2671
Fax: (906) 863-3242

TABLE 3—ANCHOR COUPLING INC. LISTING

Hose Number	Applic. Code	Hose ID	MAWP (PSI)	Fittings	Fire Sleeve	Listing Date
4 FND	H	1/4	2750	MN	—	28APR03
6 FND	H	3/8	2250	MN	—	28APR03
8 FND	H	1/2	2000	MN	—	28APR03
10 FND	H	5/8	1500	MN	—	28APR03
12 FND	H	3/4	1250	MN	—	28APR03
16 FND	H	1	1000	MN	—	28APR03
20 FND	H	1-1/4	625	MN	—	28APR03

TABLE 3—ANCHOR COUPLING INC. LISTING (continued)

Hose Number	Applic. Code	Hose ID	MAWP (PSI)	Fittings	Fire Sleeve	Listing Date
24 FND	H	1-1/2	500	MN	—	28APR03
32 FND	H	2	375	MN	—	28APR03
4 CAT 716	H	1/4	2750	MN	—	28APR03
6 CAT 716	H	3/8	2250	MN	—	28APR03
8 CAT 716	H	1/2	2000	MN	—	28APR03
10 CAT 716	H	5/8	1500	MN	—	28APR03
12 CAT 716	H	3/4	1250	MN	—	28APR03
16 CAT 716	H	1	1000	MN	—	28APR03
20 CAT 716	H	1-1/4	625	MN	—	28APR03
24 CAT 716	H	1-1/2	500	MN	—	28APR03
32 CAT 716	H	2	375	MN	—	28APR03
4 FND	F	1/4	825	MN	—	28APR03
6 FND	F	3/8	675	MN	—	28APR03
8 FND	F	1/2	600	MN	—	28APR03
10 FND	F	5/8	450	MN	—	28APR03
12 FND	F	3/4	375	MN	—	28APR03
16 FND	F	1	300	MN	—	28APR03
20 FND	F	1-1/4	188	MN	—	28APR03
24 FND	F	1-1/2	150	MN	—	28APR03
32 FND	F	2	113	MN	—	28APR03
4 CAT 716	F	1/4	825	MN	—	28APR03
6 CAT 716	F	3/8	675	MN	—	28APR03
8 CAT 716	F	1/2	600	MN	—	28APR03
10 CAT 716	F	5/8	450	MN	—	28APR03
12 CAT 716	F	3/4	375	MN	—	28APR03
16 CAT 716	F	1	300	MN	—	28APR03
20 CAT 716	F	1-1/4	188	MN	—	28APR03
24 CAT 716	F	1-1/2	150	MN	—	28APR03
32 CAT 716	F	2	113	MN	—	28APR03
4 CND	H	1/4	5000	MN	—	28APR03
6 CND	H	3/8	4000	MN	—	28APR03
8 CND	H	1/2	3500	MN	—	28APR03
10 CND	H	5/8	2750	MN	—	28APR03
12 CND	H	3/4	2250	MN	—	28APR03
16 CND	H	1	2000	MN	—	28APR03
20 CND	H	1-1/4	1625	MN	—	28APR03
24 CND	H	1-1/2	1250	MN	—	28APR03
32 CND	H	2	1125	MN	—	28APR03
4 CAT 294	H	1/4	5000	MN	—	28APR03
6 CAT 294	H	3/8	4000	MN	—	28APR03
8 CAT 294	H	1/2	3500	MN	—	28APR03
10 CAT 294	H	5/8	2750	MN	—	28APR03
12 CAT 294	H	3/4	2250	MN	—	28APR03
16 CAT 294	H	1	2000	MN	—	28APR03
20 CAT 294	H	1-1/4	1625	MN	—	28APR03
24 CAT 294	H	1-1/2	1250	MN	—	28APR03
32 CAT 294	H	2	1125	MN	—	28APR03
12 SWH	VW	3/4	50	MN	—	28APR03
16 SWH	VW	1	50	MN	—	28APR03
20 SWH	VW	1-1/4	50	MN	—	28APR03
24 SWH	VW	1-1/2	50	MN	—	28APR03
32 SWH	VW	2	50	MN	—	28APR03
12 CAT 844	VW	3/4	50	MN	—	28APR03
16 CAT 844	VW	1	50	MN	—	28APR03
20 CAT 844	VW	1-1/4	50	MN	—	28APR03
24 CAT 844	VW	1-1/2	50	MN	—	28APR03
32 CAT 844	VW	2	50	MN	—	28APR03

6. Dana Corporation
Boston Weatherhead Division
1621 Service Merchandise Boulevard
Brentwood, TN 37027
Ph: (615) 377-6700
Fax: (615) 377-1005

TABLE 4—DANA CORPORATION LISTING

Hose Number	Applic. Code	Hose ID	MAWP (PSI)	Fittings	Fire Sleeve	Listing Date
H009	H	1/4	400	009H		13APR95
H009	H	5/16	400	E, 009H	—	13APR95
H009	H	3/8	400	E, 009H	—	13APR95
H009	H	1/2	400	E, 009H	—	13APR95
H017	H	1/4	1250	U	—	1JAN93
H017	H	3/8	1125	U	—	1JAN93
H017	H	1/2	1000	U	—	1JAN93
H017	H	3/4	750	U	—	1JAN93
H017	H	1	560	U	—	1JAN93
H017	H	1-1/4	375	U	—	1JAN93
H039	H	3/4	300	U,S	—	13APR95
H039	H	1	250	U,S	—	13APR95
H039	H	1-1/4	200	U,S	—	13APR95
H039	H	1-1/2	150	430E, 430U	—	23APR01
H039	H	2	100	430E, 430U	—	23APR01
H059	F	3/16	500	069E, 229P, 247N	—	23NOV98
H059	F	1/4	500	069E, 247N	—	23NOV98
H059	F	5/16	500	069E, 229P, 247N	—	23NOV98
H059	F	13/32	500	069E, 229P, 247N	—	23NOV98
H059	F	1/2	500	069E, 229P, 247N	—	23NOV98
H059	F	5/8	500	069E, 247N	—	23NOV98
H059	F	7/8	500	069E, 247N	—	23NOV98
H104	H	1/4	2750	U, 104N, S	—	13APR95
H104	H	3/8	2250	U, 104N, S	—	13APR95
H104	H	1/2	2000	U, 104N, S	—	13APR95
H104	H	5/8	1500	U	—	1JAN93
H104	H	3/4	1250	U, 104N, S	—	13APR95
H104	H	1	1000	U, 104N, S	—	13APR95
H104	H	1-1/4	625	U, S	—	1JAN93
H104	F	1/4	500	U, 104N, S	A6912	13APR95
H104	F	3/8	500	U, 104N, S	A6914	13APR95
H104	F	1/2	500	U, 104N, S	A6916	13APR95
H104	F	5/8	500	U	—	13APR95
H104	F	3/4	500	U, 104N, S	—	13APR95
H104	F	1	500	U, 104N, S	—	13APR95
H104	F	1-1/4	500	U, S	—	13APR95
H145	H	1/4	3000	U, S, M	—	23APR01
H145	H	3/8	3000	U, S, M	—	23APR01
H145	H	1/2	3000	U, S, M	—	23APR01
H145	H	5/8	3000	U, M	—	07JUL02
H145	H	3/4	3000	U, S	—	23APR01
H145	H	1	3000	430U, S	—	23APR01
H179	H	5/16	2250	17906	—	23NOV98
H245	H	1/4	5000	U, S, M	—	23APR01
H245	H	3/8	4000	U, S, M	—	23APR01
H245	H	1/2	3500	U, S, M	—	23APR01
H245	H	5/8	2750	U, M	—	23APR01
H245	H	3/4	2250	430U, U, S	—	23APR01
H245	H	1	2000	430U, U, S	—	23APR01
H245	H	1-1/4	1625	430U , U, S	—	13APR95

TABLE 4—DANA CORPORATION LISTING (continued)

Hose Number	Applic. Code	Hose ID	MAWP (PSI)	Fittings	Fire Sleeve	Listing Date
H245	F	1/4	500	U, S	A6912	13APR95
H245	F	3/8	500	U, S	A6914	13APR95
H245	F	1/2	500	U, S	A6916	13APR95
H245	F	5/8	500	U	A6920	13APR95
H245	F	3/4	500	U, S	A6924	13APR95
H245	F	1	500	U, S	A6928	13APR95
H245	F	1-1/4	500	U, S	A6936	13APR95
H425	H	1/4	5000	U, S	—	1JAN93
H425	H	3/8	4000	U, S, 425N	—	1JAN93
H425	H	1/2	3500	U, S, 425N	—	13APR95
H425	H	5/8	2750	U	—	13APR95
H425	H	3/4	2250	430E, 430U, U, S, 425N	—	23APR01
H425	H	1	2000	430E, 430U, U, S, 425N	—	23APR01
H425	H	1-1/4	1625	430E, 430U, U, S, 425N	—	23APR01
H425	H	1-1/2	1250	430E, 430U	—	1JAN93
H425	H	2	1125	430E, 430U, 430N	—	1JAN93
H425	F	1/4	500	U, S, 425N	A6912	13APR95
H425	F	3/8	500	U, S, 425N	A6916	13APR95
H425	F	1/2	500	U, S, 425N	A6920	13APR95
H425	F	5/8	500	U	A6920	13APR95
H425	F	3/4	500	U, S, 425N, 430E	A6924	13APR95
H425	F	1	500	U, S, 425N, 430E	A6928	13APR95
H425	F	1-1/4	500	U, S, 425N, 430E	—	13APR95
H430	H	1/2	4000	430E	—	13APR95
H430	H	3/4	4000	430E, 430U	—	1JAN93
H430	H	1	4000	430E, 430U	—	1JAN93
H430	H	1-1/4	3000	430E, 430U	—	1JAN93
H430	H	1-1/2	2500	430E, 430U	—	13APR95
H430	H	2	2500	430E, 430U	—	13APR95
H439	H	1/2	4000	430E, 430U	—	13APR95
H439	H	3/4	4000	430E, 430U	—	1JAN93
H439	H	1	4000	430E, 430U	—	1JAN93
H439	H	1-1/4	3000	430E, 430U	—	1JAN93
H439	H	1-1/2	2500	430E, 430U	—	13APR95
H439	H	2	2500	430E, 430U	—	13APR95
H470	H	3/4	5000	470E	—	1JAN93
H470	H	1	5000	470E	—	1JAN93
H470	H	1-1/4	5000	470E	—	1JAN93
H569	H	3/16	3000	069E	—	31JUL02
H569	H	5/16	2250	069E, 247N	—	23APR01
H569	H	13/32	2000	069E, 247N	—	23APR01
H569	H	1/2	1750	069E, 247N	—	23APR01
H569	H	5/8	1500	069E, 247N	—	23APR01
H569	H	7/8	800	069E	—	23APR01
H569	H	1-1/8	625	069E	—	23APR01

7. Dayco Products, Inc./Imperial Eastman
(Purchased by Parker Hannifin Corp.)
Springfield Technical Center
P.O. Box 3258
Springfield, MO 65808-3258
Ph: (417) 881-7440
Fax: (417) 888-5434

TABLE 5—DAYCO PRODUCTS, INC. LISTING

Hose Number	Applic. Code	Hose ID	MAWP (PSI)	Fittings	Fire Sleeve	Listing Date
A604	H	1/4	400	HY	—	14MAY02
A606	H	3/8	400	HY	—	14MAY02
A608	H	1/2	400	HY	—	14MAY02

TABLE 5—DAYCO PRODUCTS, INC. LISTING (continued)

Hose Number	Applic. Code	Hose ID	MAWP (PSI)	Fittings	Fire Sleeve	Listing Date
A610	H	5/8	350	HF, HY	—	14MAY02
A612	H	3/4	300	HY	—	14MAY02
AM04	H	1/4	3000	HY	—	14MAY02
AM06	H	3/8	3000	HY	—	14MAY02
AM08	H	1/2	3000	HY	—	14MAY02
AM10	H	5/8	3000	HF/HY	—	14MAY02
AM12	H	3/4	3000	BW/HY	—	14MAY02
AM16	H	1	3000	BW/HY	—	14MAY02
AX04	H	1/4	3000	HY	—	14MAY02
AX06	H	3/8	3000	HY	—	14MAY02
AX08	H	1/2	3000	HY	—	14MAY02
AX10	H	5/8	1500	HY	—	14MAY02
AX12	H	3/4	1250	HY	—	14MAY02
AX16	H	1	1000	HY	—	14MAY02
BA04	H	1/4	5000	BC, BW	—	14MAY02
BA06	H	3/8	4000	BC, BW	—	14MAY02
BA08	H	1/2	3500	BC, BW	—	14MAY02
BA10	H	5/8	2750	BC	—	14MAY02
BA12	H	3/4	2250	BC, BW	—	14MAY02
BA16	H	1	2000	BC, BW	—	14MAY02
BA20	H	1-1/4	1625	BC, BW	—	14MAY02
BA24	H	1-1/2	1250	BC, BW	—	14MAY02
BA32	H	2	1125	BC, BW	—	14MAY02
BXX04	H	1/4	5000	BC, BW, HY	—	14MAY02
BXX06	H	3/8	4000	BC, BW, HY	—	14MAY02
BXX08	H	1/2	3500	BC, BW, HY	—	14MAY02
BXX10	H	5/8	2750	BC, BW, HY	—	14MAY02
BXX12	H	3/4	2250	BC, BW, HY	—	14MAY02
BXX16	H	1	2000	BC, BW, HY	—	14MAY02
BXX20	H	1-1/4	1625	BC, BW, HY	—	14MAY02
BXX24	H	1-1/2	1250	BC, BW	—	14MAY02
BXX32	H	2	1125	BC, BW	—	14MAY02
C12	H	3/4	300	BW, HY	—	14MAY02
C16	H	1	250	BW, HY	—	14MAY02
C20	H	1-1/4	200	BW, HY	—	14MAY02
C24	H	1-1/2	150	BW, HR	—	14MAY02
C32	H	2	100	BW, HR	—	14MAY02
C40	H	2-1/2	62	HR	—	14MAY02
C48	H	3	56	HR	—	14MAY02
CET06	H	3/8	4000	BW, JJ	—	14MAY02
CET08	H	1/2	4000	BW, JJ	—	14MAY02
CE12	H	3/4	4000	BW, JJ	—	14MAY02
CE16	H	1	4000	BW, JJ	—	14MAY02
CE20	H	1-1/4	3000	BW, JJ	—	14MAY02
CE24	H	1-1/2	2500	BW, JJ	—	14MAY02
CE32	H	2	2500	BW, JJ	—	14MAY02
CN20	H	1-1/4	4000	BW, JJ	—	14MAY02
CN24	H	1-1/2	3000	BW, JJ	—	14MAY02
CN32	H	2	3000	BW, JJ	—	14MAY02
D104	H	1/4	1250	HY	—	14MAY02
D106	H	3/8	1125	HY	—	14MAY02
D108	H	1/2	1000	HY	—	14MAY02
D112	H	3/4	750	HY	—	14MAY02
D116	H	1	565	HY	—	14MAY02
D120	H	1-1/4	375	BC, HY	—	14MAY02
D803	H	3/16	3000	CH, EA	—	14MAY02

TABLE 5—DAYCO PRODUCTS, INC. LISTING (continued)

Hose Number	Applic. Code	Hose ID	MAWP (PSI)	Fittings	Fire Sleeve	Listing Date
D804	H	1/4	2750	BW, CH, EA	—	14MAY02
D805	H	5/16	2500	CH, EA	—	14MAY02
D806	H	3/8	2250	BW, CH, EA	—	14MAY02
D808	H	1/2	2000	BW, CH, EA	—	14MAY02
D810	H	5/8	1500	EA, HF	—	14MAY02
D812	H	3/4	1250	BW, CH	—	14MAY02
D816	H	1	1000	BW, CH, HY	—	14MAY02
DT06	HF	3/8	4000	BW, HY	—	14MAY02
DT08	HF	1/2	3500	BW, HY	—	14MAY02
DT12	HF	3/4	2250	BW, HY	—	14MAY02
DT16	HF	1	2000	BW, HY	—	14MAY02
FX04	H	1/4	5000	BC, HY	—	14MAY02
FX06	H	3/8	4000	BC, HY	—	14MAY02
FX08	H	1/2	3500	BC, BW, HY	—	14MAY02
FX10	H	5/8	2750	BC, BW, HY	—	14MAY02
FX12	H	3/4	2250	BC, BW, HY	—	14MAY02
FX16	H	1	2000	BC, BW, HY	—	14MAY02
FX20	H	1-1/4	1625	BC, BW, HY	—	14MAY02
GL04	HF	3/16	1500	GL, HF	IJ10 or Equal	14MAY02
GL05	HF	1/4	1500	GL, HY	IJ11 or Equal	14MAY02
GL06	HF	5/16	1500	GL, HY	IJ12 or Equal	14MAY02
GL08	HF	13/32	1250	GL, HY	IJ14 or Equal	14MAY02
GL10	HF	1/2	1000	GL, HY	IJ16 or Equal	14MAY02
GL12	HF	5/8	750	GL, HY	IJ18 or Equal	14MAY02
GL16	HF	7/8	400	GL, HY	IJ22 or Equal	14MAY02
GL20	HF	1-1/8	300	GL, HY	IJ26 or Equal	14MAY02
HFS/HR1C04	H	1/4	3000	CH, EA, HY	—	14MAY02
HFS05	H	5/16	3000	CH, HY	—	14MAY02
HFS/HR1C06	H	3/8	2500	CH, EA, HY	—	14MAY02
HFS/HR1C08	H	1/2	2500	CH, EA, HY	—	14MAY02
HFS12	H	3/4	1500	HY	—	14MAY02
HFS16	H	1	1250	HY	—	14MAY02
HFS204	H	1/4	5000	BW, CH, HY	—	14MAY02
HFS206	H	3/8	4000	CH, EA, HY	—	14MAY02
HFS208	H	1/2	3500	BW, CH, EA, HY	—	14MAY02
HFS210	H	5/8	2750	EA, HF, HY	—	14MAY02
HFS212	H	3/4	2250	BW, CH, HY	—	14MAY02
HFS216	H	1	2000	BW, CH, HY	—	14MAY02
HTB04	H	1/4	7000	BW, HY	—	14MAY02
HTB06	H	3/8	5500	BW, HY, JJ	—	14MAY02
HTB08	H	1/2	5000	BW, HY, JJ	—	14MAY02
HTB10	H	5/8	4000	BW, HY, JJ	—	14MAY02
HTB12	H	3/4	4000	BW, HY, JJ	—	14MAY02
HTB16	H	1	3500	BW, HY, JJ	—	14MAY02
J420	H	1-1/4	1625	BW, JJ	—	14MAY02
J424	H	1-1/2	1250	BW, JJ	—	14MAY02
J432	H	2	1125	BW, JJ	—	14MAY02
L106	H	3/8	4500	BW, HY	—	14MAY02
L108	H	1/2	4000	BW, HY	—	14MAY02
L112	H	3/4	3000	BW, HY, JJ	—	14MAY02
L116	H	1	3000	BW, HY, JJ	—	14MAY02
L120	H	1-1/4	2500	BW, JJ	—	14MAY02
M03	H	3/16	3000	BC, GFC	—	14MAY02
M04	H	1/4	2750	BC, BW	—	14MAY02
M06	H	3/8	2250	BC, BW	—	14MAY02
M08	H	1/2	2000	BC, BW	—	14MAY02
M10	H	5/8	1500	BC, BW	—	14MAY02

TABLE 5—DAYCO PRODUCTS, INC. LISTING (continued)

Hose Number	Applic. Code	Hose ID	MAWP (PSI)	Fittings	Fire Sleeve	Listing Date
M12	H	3/4	1250	BC, BW	—	14MAY02
M16	H	1	1000	BC, BW	—	14MAY02
M20	H	1-1/4	625	BC, BW	—	14MAY02
M24	H	1-1/2	500	BC, BW	—	14MAY02
M32	H	2	375	BC, BW	—	14MAY02
M706	H	3/8	4000	BW, JJ	—	14MAY02
M708	H	1/2	4000	BW, JJ	—	14MAY02
M710	H	5/8	4000	BW, JJ	—	14MAY02
M712	H	3/4	4000	BW, JJ	—	14MAY02
M716	H	1	4000	BW, JJ	—	14MAY02
M720	H	1-1/4	3000	BW, JJ	—	14MAY02
M724	H	1-1/2	2500	BW, JJ	—	14MAY02
M732	H	2	2500	BW, JJ	—	14MAY02
MX03	H	3/16	3000	BC, HF	—	14MAY02
MX04	H	1/4	2750	BC, BW, HY	—	14MAY02
MX06	H	3/8	2250	BC, BW, HY	—	14MAY02
MX08	H	1/2	2000	BC, BW, HY	—	14MAY02
MX12	H	3/4	1250	BC, BW, HY	—	14MAY02
MX16	H	1	1000	BC, BW, HY	—	14MAY02
MX20	H	1-1/4	625	BC, BW, HY	—	14MAY02
N306	H	3/8	6400	JJ	—	14MAY02
N308	H	1/2	6000	JJ	—	14MAY02
N310	H	5/8	6000	BW, JJ	—	14MAY02
N312	H	3/4	6000	JJ	—	14MAY02
N316	H	1	5500	JJ	—	14MAY02
N320	H	1-1/4	5000	JJ	—	14MAY02
N324	H	1-1/2	4200	JJ	—	14MAY02
N612	H	3/4	5000	BW, JJ	—	14MAY02
N616	H	1	5000	BW, JJ	—	14MAY02
N620	H	1-1/4	5000	BW, JJ	—	14MAY02
N624	H	1-1/2	5000	BW, JJ	—	14MAY02
N632	H	2	5000	JJ	—	14MAY02
NH12	H	3/4	5000	BW, JJ	—	14MAY02
NH16	H	1	5000	BW, JJ	—	14MAY02
NH20	H	1-1/4	5000	JJ, NB	—	14MAY02
NH24	H	1-1/2	5000	NB	—	14MAY02
NH32	H	2	5000	NB	—	14MAY02
QX06	H	3/8	4500	BW	—	14MAY02
QX08	H	1/2	4000	BW	—	14MAY02
QX12	H	3/4	3000	BW	—	14MAY02
QX16	H	1	3000	BW	—	14MAY02
QX20	H	1-1/4	2500	BW	—	14MAY02
QX24	H	1-1/2	2000	BW	—	14MAY02
QX32	H	2	2000	BW	—	14MAY02
ST04	HF	1/4	2750	BW, HY	—	14MAY02
ST06	HF	3/8	2250	BW, HY	—	14MAY02
ST08	HF	1/2	2000	BW, HY	—	14MAY02
ST12	HF	3/4	1250	BW, HY	—	14MAY02
ST16	HF	1	1000	BW, HY	—	14MAY02
U412	H	3/4	300	BW, HY	—	14MAY02
U416	H	1	250	BW, HY	—	14MAY02
U420	H	1-1/4	200	BW, HY	—	14MAY02
U424	H	1-1/2	150	BW, HR	—	14MAY02
U432	H	2	100	BW, HR	—	14MAY02
U440	H	2-1/2	62	HR	—	14MAY02
U448	H	3	56	HR	—	14MAY02
Y904	HF	3/16	3000	BN, HF	618982 or Equal	14MAY02
Y905	HF	1/4	3000	BN, HY	618982 or Equal	14MAY02
Y906	HF	5/16	2250	BN, HY	618982 or Equal	14MAY02
Y908	HF	13/32	2000	BN, HY	618982 or Equal	14MAY02
Y910	HF	1/2	1750	BN, HY	618982 or Equal	14MAY02
Y912	HF	5/8	1500	BN, HY	618982 or Equal	14MAY02
Y916	HF	7/8	800	BN, HY	618982 or Equal	14MAY02
Y920	HF	1-1/8	625	BQ, HY	618982 or Equal	14MAY02
Y924	HF	1-3/8	500	BQ, HY	618982 or Equal	14MAY02
Y932	HF	1-13/16	350	BQ, HY	618982 or Equal	14MAY02

8. Eaton Aeroquip
Industrial Division
Technical Center
1660 Indian Wood Circle
Maumee, OH 43537
Ph: (419) 891-7705
Fax: (419) 891-7790

TABLE 6—THE EATON AEROQUIP LISTING

Hose Number	Applic. Code	Hose ID	MAWP (PSI)	Fittings	Fire Sleeve	Listing Date
FCC849-04	H	1/4	4000	1AA Type	N.R.	23JUL03
FCC849-06	H	3/8	4000	1AA Type, 1SA Type	N.R.	23JUL03
FCC849-08	H	1/2	4000	1AA Type, 1SA Type	N.R.	23JUL03
FCC849-10	H	5/8	4000	1AA Type, 1SA Type	N.R.	23JUL03
FCC849-12	H	3/4	4000	1AA Type, 1SA Type	N.R.	23JUL03

9. The Gates Rubber Company
Hose/Connector Operations
P.O. Box 1196
Galesburg, IL 61402-1196
Ph: (309) 345-5471
Fax: (309) 345-5423

TABLE 7—THE GATES RUBBER COMPANY LISTING

Hose Number	Applic. Code	Hose ID	MAWP (PSI)	Fittings	Fire Sleeve	Listing Date
4C1A	F	1/4	500	PC SERIES	—	26JUN72
5C1A	F	5/16	750	PC SERIES	—	26JUN72
6C1A	F	3/8	1000	PC SERIES	—	26JUN72
8C1A	F	1/2	1000	PC SERIES	—	26JUN72
10C1A	F	5/8	1000	PC SERIES	—	26JUN72
12C1A	F	3/4	1000	PC SERIES	—	26JUN72
16C1A	F	1	1000	PC SERIES	—	26JUN72
20C1A	F	1-1/4	1000	PC SERIES	—	26JUN72
3C1A	H	3/16	3625	PC SERIES	—	7FEB96
4C1A	H	1/4	3275	PC SERIES	—	20APR95
5C1A	H	5/16	3125	PC SERIES	—	7FEB96
6C1A	H	3/8	2600	PC SERIES	—	20APR95
8C1A	H	1/2	2325	PC SERIES	—	20APR95
10C1A	H	5/8	1900	PC SERIES	—	20APR95
12C1A	H	3/4	1525	PC SERIES	—	20APR95
16C1A	H	1	1275	PC SERIES	—	20APR95
20C1A	H	1-1/4	925	PC SERIES	—	20APR95
24C1A	H	1-1/2	725	PC SERIES	—	20APR95
32C1A	H	2	600	PC SERIES	—	20APR95
3G1	H	3/16	3625	PC	—	14MAY02
4G1	H	1/4	3275	PC, G	—	14MAY02
5G1	H	5/16	3125	PC	—	14MAY02
6G1	H	3/8	2600	PC, G	—	14MAY02
8G1	H	1/2	2325	PC, G	—	14MAY02
10G1	H	5/8	1900	PC	—	14MAY02
12G1	H	3/4	1525	PC, G	—	14MAY02
16G1	H	1	1275	PC, G	—	14MAY02
20G1	H	1-1/4	925	PC	—	14MAY02
24G1	H	1-1/2	725	PC	—	14MAY02

TABLE 7—THE GATES RUBBER COMPANY LISTING (continued)

Hose Number	Applic. Code	Hose ID	MAWP (PSI)	Fittings	Fire Sleeve	Listing Date
32G1	H	2	600	PC	—	14MAY02
4G1H	F	1/4	500	PC SERIES	—	14MAY02
6G1H	F	3/8	750	PC SERIES	—	14MAY02
8G1H	F	1/2	1000	PC SERIES	—	14MAY02
12G1H	F	3/4	1000	PC SERIES	—	14MAY02
16G1H	F	1	1000	PC SERIES	—	14MAY02
4C2A	F	1/4	500	PC SERIES	—	23JAN73
6C2A	F	3/8	750	PC SERIES	—	23JAN73
8C2A	F	1/2	1000	PC SERIES	—	23JAN73
10C2A	F	5/8	1000	PC SERIES	—	23JAN73
12C2A	F	3/4	1000	PC SERIES	—	23JAN73
16C2A	F	1	1000	PC SERIES	—	23JAN73
20C2A	F	1-1/4	1000	PC SERIES	—	23JAN73
24C2A	F	1-1/2	1000	PC SERIES	—	23JAN73
32C2A	F	2	1000	PC SERIES	—	23JAN73
3C2A	H	3/16	5000	PC SERIES	—	20APR95
4C2A	H	1/4	5800	PC SERIES	—	20APR95
5C2A	H	5/16	4250	PC SERIES	—	20APR95
6C2A	H	3/8	4800	PC SERIES	—	20APR95
8C2A	H	1/2	4000	PC SERIES	—	20APR95
10C2A	H	5/8	3625	PC SERIES	—	20APR95
12C2A	H	3/4	3100	PC SERIES	—	20APR95
16C2A	H	1	2400	PC SERIES	—	20APR95
20C2A	H	1-1/4	1825	PC SERIES	—	20APR95
24C2A	H	1-1/2	1300	PC SERIES	—	20APR95
32C2A	H	2	1175	PC SERIES	—	20APR95
4C2AH	H	1/4	5000	PC SERIES	—	27JUL73
6C2AH	H	3/8	4000	PC SERIES	—	27JUL73
8C2AH	H	1/2	3500	PC SERIES	—	27JUL73
3G2	H	3/16	5000	PC	—	14MAY02
4G2	H	1/4	5800	PC, G	—	14MAY02
6G2	H	3/8	4800	PC, G	—	14MAY02
8G2	H	1/2	4000	PC, G	—	14MAY02
10G2	H	5/8	3625	PC	—	14MAY02
12G2	H	3/4	3100	PC, G	—	14MAY02
16G2	H	1	2400	PC, G	—	14MAY02
20G2	H	1-1/4	1825	PC	—	14MAY02
24G2	H	1-1/2	1300		—	14MAY02
32G2	H	2	1175		—	14MAY02
24G2H	H	1-1/2	1250	PC SERIES	—	14MAY02
32G2H	H	2	1125	PC SERIES	—	14MAY02
20G2H	F	1-1/4	1000	PC SERIES	—	14MAY02
24G2H	F	1-1/2	1000	PC SERIES	—	14MAY02
32G2H	F	2	1000	PC SERIES	—	14MAY02
6C5M	F	5/16	350	C5	—	7FEB96
8C5M	F	13/32	500	C5	—	7FEB96
8C5M	F	13/32	350	PC-S.S.	—	7FEB96
10C5M	F	1/2	500	C5, PC-S.S.	—	7FEB96
12C5M	F	5/8	500	C5, PC-S.S.	—	7FEB96
16C5M	F	1	500	C5, PC-S.S.	—	7FEB96
8G2AT-HMP	H	1/2	4250	PC SERIES	—	16DEC85
10G2AT-HMP	H	5/8	3500	PC SERIES	—	16DEC85
12G2AT-HMP	H	3/4	3000	PC SERIES	—	16DEC85
16G2AT-HMP	H	1	2500	PC SERIES	—	16DEC85

TABLE 7—THE GATES RUBBER COMPANY LISTING (continued)

Hose Number	Applic. Code	Hose ID	MAWP (PSI)	Fittings	Fire Sleeve	Listing Date
4M2T	H	1/4	5000	PC SERIES	—	16DEC85
6M2T	H	3/8	4000	PC SERIES	—	16DEC85
8M2T	H	1/2	3500	PC SERIES	—	16DEC85
10M2T	H	5/8	2750	PC SERIES	—	16DEC85
12M2T	H	3/4	2250	PC SERIES	—	16DEC85
16M2T	H	1	2000	PC SERIES	—	16DEC85
6C12	H	3/8	4000	PCS	—	1DEC92
8C12	H	1/2	4000	PCS	—	1DEC92
12C12	H	3/4	4000	PCH,PCS	—	05AUG85
12C12M	H	3/4	4000	PCS SERIES	—	17MAY95
16C12	H	1	4000	PCH,PCS	—	05AUG85
16C12M	H	1	4000	PCS SERIES	—	17MAY95
20C12	H	1-1/4	3000	PCH,PCS	—	05AUG85
20C12M	H	1-1/4	3000	PCS SERIES	—	17MAY95
24C12	H	1-1/2	2500	PCH,PCS	—	05AUG85
32C12	H	2	2500	PCH,PCS	—	05AUG85
12C13	H	3/4	5000	PCM	—	1DEC92
16C13	H	1	5000	PCM	—	16DEC85
20C13	H	1-1/4	5000	PCM	—	16DEC85
24C13	H	1-1/2	5000	PCM	—	16DEC85
32C13	H	2	5000	PCM	—	16DEC85
16G6K	H	1	6000	PCM	—	1DEC92
16G4H	H	1	200	PC	—	1DEC92
20G4H	H	1-1/4	200	C4,PC	—	1DEC92
24GMV	H	1-1/2	162	C4,PC	—	14MAY02
32GMV	H	2	112	C4,PC	—	14MAY02
40GMV	H	2-1/2	68	C4	—	14MAY02
48GMV	H	3	62	C4	—	14MAY02
56GMV	H	3-1/2	56	C4	—	14MAY02
64GMV	H	4	56	C4	—	14MAY02
4M3K	H	1/4	3000	PC	—	1DEC92
6M3K	H	3/8	3000	PC	—	1DEC92
8M3K	H	1/2	3000	PC	—	1DEC92
10M3K	H	5/8	3000	PC	—	1DEC92
12M3K	F	3/4	500	PC	—	7FEB96
12M3K	H	3/4	3000	PC	—	1DEC92
16M3K	F	1	1000	PC	—	7FEB96
16M3K	H	1	3000	PC	—	1DEC92
4C5R	H	3/16	3000	PC,C5	—	1DEC92
5C5R	H	1/4	3000	PC,C5	—	1DEC92
6C5R	H	5/16	2250	PC,C5	—	1DEC92
8C5R	H	13/32	2000	PC,C5	—	1DEC92
10C5R	H	1/2	1750	PC,C5	—	1DEC92
12C5R	H	5/8	1500	PC,C5	—	1DEC92
16C5R	H	7/8	800	C5	—	1DEC92
20C5R	H	1-1/8	625	C5	—	1DEC92
24C5R	H	1-3/8	500	C5	—	1DEC92
32C5R	H	1-13/16	350	C5	—	1DEC92
24G3K	H	1-1/2	3000	PSC	—	14MAY02
32G3K	H	2	3000	PSC	—	14MAY02

10. Parker ITR S.r.l.
Via G. B. Pirelli, 6
IT- 22070 Veniano (CO) Italy
Ph: 39 031 936111
Fax: 39 031 936664

TABLE 8—PARKER ITR S.r.l. LISTING

Hose Number	Applic. Code	Hose ID	MAWP (PSI)	Fittings	Fire Sleeve	Listing Date
53705000	H	3/16	3000	2NBF/1445	—	14FEB01
53706000	H	1/4	2750	2NBF/1445	—	14FEB01
53708000	H	5/16	2500	2NBF/1445	—	14FEB01
53709000	H	3/8	2250	2NBF/1445	—	14FEB01
53713000	H	1/2	2000	2NBF/1445	—	14FEB01
53716000	H	5/8	1500	2NBF/1445	—	14FEB01
53719000	H	3/4	1250	2NBF/1445	—	14FEB01
53725000	H	1	1000	2NBF/1445	—	14FEB01
53732000	H	1-1/4	650	2NBF/1445	—	14FEB01
53738000	H	1-1/2	500	2NBF/1419	—	14FEB01
53735100	H	2	375	2NBF/1419	—	14FEB01
50305000	H	3/16	3000	2NBF/1445	—	14FEB01
50306000	H	1/4	2750	2NBF/1445	—	14FEB01
50308000	H	5/16	2500	2NBF/1445	—	14FEB01
50309000	H	3/8	2250	2NBF/1445	—	14FEB01
50313000	H	1/2	2000	2NBF/1445	—	14FEB01
50316000	H	5/8	1500	2NBF/1445	—	14FEB01
50319000	H	3/4	1250	2NBF/1445	—	14FEB01
50325000	H	1	1000	2NBF/1445	—	14FEB01
50332000	H	1-1/4	650	2NBF/1445	—	14FEB01
50338000	H	1-1/2	500	2NBF/1419	—	14FEB01
50351000	H	2	375	2NBF/1419	—	14FEB01
53805000	H	3/16	5000	2NBF/1442/1419	—	14FEB01
53806000	H	1/4	5000	2NBF/1442/1419	—	14FEB01
53808000	H	5/16	4250	2NBF/1442/1419	—	14FEB01
53809000	H	3/8	4000	2NBF/1442/1419	—	14FEB01
53813000	H	1/2	3500	2NBF/1442/1419	—	14FEB01
53816000	H	5/8	2750	2NBF/1442/1419	—	14FEB01
53819000		3/4	2250	2NBF/1442/1419		
53825000	H	1	2000	2NBF/1442/1419	—	14FEB01
53832000	H	1-1/4	1625	2NBF/1442/1419	—	14FEB01
53838000	H	1-1/2	1250	2NBF/1419	—	14FEB01
53851000	H	2	1125	2NBF/1419	—	14FEB01
50605000	H	3/16	5000	2NBF/1419	—	14FEB01
50606000	H	1/4	5000	2NBF/1419	—	14FEB01
50608000	H	5/16	4250	2NBF/1419	—	14FEB01
50609000	H	3/8	4000	2NBF/1419	—	14FEB01
50613000	H	1/2	3500	2NBF/1419	—	14FEB01
50616000	H	5/8	2750	2NBF/1419	—	14FEB01
50619000	H	3/4	2250	2NBF/1419	—	14FEB01
50625000	H	1	2000	2NBF/1419	—	14FEB01
50632000	H	1-1/4	1625	2NBF/1419	—	14FEB01
50638000	H	1-1/2	1250	2NBF/1419	—	14FEB01
50651000	H	2	1125	2NBF/1419	—	14FEB01
54106000	H	1/4	5000	2NBF/1445/1446	—	14FEB01
54108000	H	5/16	4300	2NBF/1445/1446	—	14FEB01
54109000	H	3/8	4000	2NBF/1445/1446		14FEB01
54113000	H	1/2	3500	2NBF/1445/1446	—	14FEB01
54116000	H	5/8	2750	2NBF/1445/1446	—	14FEB01
54116000	H	3/4	2250	2NBF/1445/1446	—	14FEB01
54125000	H	1	2050	2NBF/1445/1446	—	14FEB01
54132000	H	1-1/4	1600	2NBF/1446	—	14FEB01
54606000	H	1/4	5800	2NBF/1445/1446	—	14FEB01
54608000	H	5/16	5450	2NBF/1445/1446	—	14FEB01
54609000	H	3/8	5100	2NBF/1445/1446	—	14FEB01

TABLE 8—PARKER ITR S.r.l. LISTING (continued)

Hose Number	Applic. Code	Hose ID	MAWP (PSI)	Fittings	Fire Sleeve	Listing Date
54613000	H	1/2	4350	2NBF/1445/1446	—	14FEB01
54616000	H	5/8	4000	2NBF/1445/1446	—	14FEB01
54619000	H	3/4	3400	2NBF/1445/1446	—	14FEB01
54625000	H	1	2700	2NBF/1445/1446	—	14FEB01
54632000	H	1-1/4	2400	2NBF/1445/1446	—	14FEB01
53309000	H	3/8	4000	4SPR/1409/1437	—	14FEB01
53313000	H	1/2	4000	4SPR/1409/1437	—	14FEB01
53319000	H	3/4	4000	4SPR/1409/1437	—	14FEB01
53325000	H	1	4000	4SPR/1409/1437	—	14FEB01
53332000	H	1-1/4	3000	4SPR/1409/1437	—	14FEB01
53338000	H	1-1/2	2500	4SPR/1409/1437	—	14FEB01
53351000	H	2	2500	4SPR/1409/1437	—	14FEB01
58213000	H	1/2	7500	4SPR/1440	—	14FEB01
58219000	H	3/4	5000	4SPR/1437	—	14FEB001
58225000	H	1	5000	4SPR/1437	—	14FEB01
58232000	H	1-1/4	5000	4SPR/1444	—	14FEB01
58238000	H	1-1/2	5000	4SPR/1444	—	14FEB01
58251000	H	2	5000	4SPR/1444	—	14FEB01
50409000	H	3/8	6000	4SPR/1437	—	14FEB01
50413000	H	1/2	6000	4SPR/1437	—	14FEB01
50419000	H	3/4	6000	4SPR/1437	—	14FEB01
50425000	H	1	6000	4SPR/1437	—	14FEB01
50432000	H	1-1/4	6000	4SPR/1452	—	14FEB01
50438000	H	1-1/2	6000	4SPR/1452	—	14FEB01
50451000	H	2	6000	6SPH	—	14FEB01
PCH 25-4	H	1/4	3500	PC 35 series	—	23SEPT03
PCH 25-5	H	5/16	3500	PC 35 series	—	23SEPT03
PCH 25-6	H	3/8	3500	PC 35 series	—	23SEPT03
PCH 25-8	H	1/2	3500	PC 35 series	—	23SEPT03
PCH 25-10	H	5/8	3500	PC 35 series	—	23SEPT03
PCH 25-12	H	3/4	3500	PC 35 series	—	23SEPT03
PCH 25-16	H	1	3500	PC 35 series	—	23SEPT03
PCH 25-20	H	1-1/4	1800	PC 25 series	—	23SEPT03
PCH 25-24	H	1-1/2	1300	PC 25 series	—	23SEPT03
PCH 25-32	H	2	1150	PC 25 series	—	23SEPT03
PCH 35-4	H	1/4	5000	PC 35 series	—	23SEPT03
PCH 35-5	H	5/16	5000	PC 35 series	—	23SEPT03
PCH 35-6	H	3/8	5000	PC 35 series	—	23SEPT03
PCH 35-8	H	1/2	5000	PC 35 series	—	23SEPT03
PCH 35-10	H	5/8	5000	PC 35 series	—	23SEPT03
PCH 35-12	H	3/4	5000	PC 35 series	—	23SEPT03
PCH 35-12S	H	3/4	5000	PC 35 series	—	23SEPT03
PCH 35-16	H	1	5000	PC 35 series	—	23SEPT03
PCH 35-16S	H	1	5000	PC 35 series	—	23SEPT03
PCH 35-20	H	1-1/4	5000	PC 35 series	—	23SEPT03
PCH 35-24	H	1-1/2	5000	PC 35 series	—	23SEPT03
PCH 35-32	H	2	5000	PC 35 series	—	23SEPT03
PCH 42-4	H	1/4	6000	PC 35 series	—	23SEPT03
PCH 42-6	H	3/8	6000	PC 42 series	—	23SEPT03
PCH 42-8	H	1/2	6000	PC 42 series	—	23SEPT03
PCH 42-10	H	5/8	6000	PC 42 series	—	23SEPT03
PCH 42-12	H	3/4	6000	PC 42 series	—	23SEPT03
PCH 42-16	H	1	6000	PC 42 series	—	23SEPT03
PCH 42-20	H	1-1/4	6000	PC 42 series	—	23SEPT03
PCH 42-24	H	1-1/2	6000	PC 42 series	—	23SEPT03
PCH 42-32	H	2	6000	PC 42 series	—	23SEPT03
PFMU25-4	H	1/4	3500	PC 35 series	—	9AUG03
PFMU25-5	H	5/16	3500	PC 35 series	—	9AUG03
PFMU25-6	H	3/8	3500	PC 35 series	—	9AUG03

TABLE 8—PARKER ITR S.r.l. LISTING (continued)

Hose Number	Applic. Code	Hose ID	MAWP (PSI)	Fittings	Fire Sleeve	Listing Date
PFMU25-8	H	1/2	3500	PC 35 series	—	9AUG03
PFMU25-10	H	5/8	3500	PC 35 series	—	9AUG03
PFMU25-12	H	3/4	3500	PC 35 series	—	9AUG03
PFMU25-16	H	1	3500	PC 35 series	—	9AUG03
SAE 100 R2AT-20	H	1-1/4	1800	PC 35 series	—	9AUG03
SAE 100 R2AT-24	H	1-1/2	1300	PC 35 series	—	9AUG03
SAE 100 R2AT-32	H	2	1150	PC 35 series	—	9AUG03
PFMU35-4	H	1/4	5000	PC 35 series	—	9AUG03
PFMU35-5	H	5/16	5000	PC 35 series	—	9AUG03
PFMU35-6	H	3/8	5000	PC 35 series	—	9AUG03
PFMU35-8	H	1/2	5000	PC 35 series	—	9AUG03
PFMU35-10	H	5/8	5000	PC 35 series	—	9AUG03
PFMU35-12	H	3/4	5000	PC 35 series	—	9AUG03
PFMU35S-12	H	3/4	5000	PC 35 series	—	9AUG03
PFMU35-16	H	1	5000	PC 35 series	—	9AUG03
PFMU35S-16	H	1	5000	PC 35 series	—	9AUG03
PFMU35S-20	H	1-1/4	5000	PC 35 series	—	9AUG03
PFMU35S-24	H	1-1/2	5000	PC 35 series	—	9AUG03
PFMU35S-32	H	2	5000	PC 35 series	—	9AUG03
PFMU42-4	H	1/4	6000	PC 35 series	—	9AUG03
PFMU42-6	H	3/8	6000	PC 42 series	—	9AUG03
PFMU42-8	H	1/2	6000	PC 42 series	—	9AUG03
PFMU42-10	H	5/8	6000	PC 42 series	—	9AUG03
PFMU42-12	H	3/4	6000	PC 42 series	—	9AUG03
PFMU42-16	H	1	6000	PC 42 series	—	9AUG03
PFMU42-20	H	1-1/4	6000	PC 42 series	—	9AUG03
PFMU42-24	H	1-1/2	6000	PC 42 series	—	9AUG03
PFMU42-32	H	2	6000	PC 42 series	—	9AUG03

11. Parker Hannifin Corporation
Hose Products Division
30240 Lakeland Boulevard
Wickliffe, OH 44092
Ph: (440) 943-5700
Fax: (440) 943-3129

TABLE 9—PARKER HANNIFIN CORPORATION LISTING

Hose Number	Applic. Code	Hose ID	MAWP (PSI)	Fittings	Fire Sleeve	Listing Date
42CHT-4	HF	1/4	2750	43	—	31MAY95
42CHT-6	HF	3/8	2250	43	—	31MAY95
42CHT-8	HF	1/2	2000	43	—	31MAY95
42CHT-10	HF	5/8	1500	43	—	31MAY95
42CHT-12	HF	3/4	1250	43	—	31MAY95
42CHT-16	HF	1	1000	43	—	31MAY95
42CHT-20	HF	1-1/4	625	43	—	31MAY95
77C-6	H	3/8	4000	71	—	4JAN93
77C-8	H	1/2	4000	71	—	4JAN93
77C-10	H	5/8	4000	71	—	4JAN93
77C-12	H	3/4	4000	71	—	4JAN93
77C-16	H	1	4000	71	—	4JAN93
77C-20	H	1-1/4	3000	71	—	4JAN93
77C-24	H	1-1/2	2500	71	—	4JAN93
77C-32	H	2	2500	71	—	4JAN93
78C-12	H	3/4	5000	78	—	4JAN93
78C-16	H	1	5000	78	—	4JAN93
78C-20	H	1-1/4	5000	78	—	4JAN93
78C-24	H	1-1/2	5000	78	—	4JAN93
78C-32	H	2	5000	78	—	4JAN93
212-4	H	1/4	5000	60XX	—	4JAN93
212-6	H	3/8	4000	60XX	—	4JAN93

TABLE 9—PARKER HANNIFIN CORPORATION LISTING (continued)

Hose Number	Applic. Code	Hose ID	MAWP (PSI)	Fittings	Fire Sleeve	Listing Date
212-8	H	1/2	3500	60XX	—	4JAN93
212-10	H	5/8	2750	60XX	—	4JAN93
212-12	H	3/4	2250	60XX	—	4JAN93
212-16	H	1	2000	60XX	—	4JAN93
212-20	H	1-1/4	1625	60XX	—	4JAN93
212-24	H	1-1/2	1250	60XX	—	4JAN93
212-32	H	2	1125	60XX	—	4JAN93
212-4	F	1/4	700	60XX	—	4JAN93
212-6	F	3/8	700	60XX	—	4JAN93
212-8	F	1/2	700	60XX	—	4JAN93
212-10	F	5/8	500	60XX	—	4JAN93
212-12	F	3/4	500	60XX	—	4JAN93
212-16	F	1	200	60XX	—	4JAN93
212-20	F	1-1/4	200	60XX	—	4JAN93
212-24	F	1-1/2	200	60XX	—	4JAN93
212-32	F	2	200	60XX	—	4JAN93
215-3	H	3/16	4000	60XX	—	4JAN93
215-4	H	1/4	3250	60XX	—	4JAN93
215-5	H	5/16	3250	60XX	—	4JAN93
215-6	H	3/8	3000	60XX	—	4JAN93
215-8	H	1/2	2500	60XX	—	4JAN93
215-10	H	5/8	2000	60XX	—	4JAN93
215-12	H	3/4	1750	60XX	—	4JAN93
215-16	H	1	1250	60XX	—	4JAN93
215-20	H	1-1/4	900	60XX	—	4JAN93
215-24	H	1-1/2	700	60XX	—	4JAN93
215-32	H	2	500	60XX	—	4JAN93
215-4	F	1/4	250	60XX	—	4JAN93
215-6	F	3/8	250	60XX	—	4JAN93
215-8	F	1/2	250	60XX	—	4JAN93
215-10	F	5/8	250	60XX	—	4JAN93
215-12	F	3/4	250	60XX	—	4JAN93
215-16	F	1	250	60XX	—	4JAN93
215-20	F	1-1/4	250	60XX	—	4JAN93
215-24	F	1-1/2	250	60XX	—	4JAN93
215-32	F	2	250	60XX	—	4JAN93
221FR-5	HF	1/4	500	20,22,26	—	1DEC00
221FR-6	HF	5/16	500	20,22,26	—	1DEC00
221FR-8	HF	13/32	500	20,22,26	—	1DEC00
221FR-10	HF	1/2	500	20,22,26	—	1DEC00
221FR-12	HF	5/8	500	20,22,26	—	1DEC00
221FR-16	HF	7/8	500	20,22,26	—	1DEC00
225-4	H	3/16	3000	20,22	—	4JAN93
225-5	H	1/4	3000	20,22	—	4JAN93
225-6	H	5/16	2250	20,22	—	4JAN93
225-8	H	13/32	2000	20,22	—	4JAN93
225-10	H	1/2	1750	20,22	—	4JAN93
225-12	H	5/8	1500	20,22	—	4JAN93
225-16	H	7/8	800	20,22	—	4JAN93
225-20	H	1-1/8	525	20,22	—	4JAN93
225-4	F	3/16	100	20,22	—	4JAN93
225-5	F	1/4	150	20,22	—	4JAN93
225-6	F	5/16	400	20,22	—	4JAN93
225-8	F	13/32	500	20,22	—	4JAN93
225-10	F	1/2	500	20,22	—	4JAN93
225-12	F	5/8	500	20,22	—	4JAN93
225-16	F	7/8	500	20,22	—	4JAN93
225-20	F	1-1/8	500	20,22	—	4JAN93
225-24	HF	1-3/8	500	20,22	—	4JAN93
225-32	HF	1-13/16	350	20,22	—	4JAN93

TABLE 9—PARKER HANNIFIN CORPORATION LISTING (continued)

Hose Number	Applic. Code	Hose ID	MAWP (PSI)	Fittings	Fire Sleeve	Listing Date
226-6	H	5/16	1500	20,22	—	4JAN93
226-6	F	5/16	750	20,22	—	4JAN93
226-8	HF	13/32	1250	20,22	—	4JAN93
226-12	HF	5/8	750	20,22	—	4JAN93
301-4	HF	1/4	5000	30,31,43	—	4JAN93
301-5	HF	5/16	4250	43	—	4JAN93
301-6	HF	3/8	4000	30,31,43	—	4JAN93
301-8	HF	1/2	3500	30,31,43	—	4JAN93
301-10	HF	5/8	2750	30,31,43	—	4JAN93
301-12	HF	3/4	2250	30,31,43	—	4JAN93
301-16	HF	1	2000	30,31,43	—	4JAN93
301-20	HF	1-1/4	1625	30,43	—	4JAN93
301-24	HF	1-1/2	1250	30,43	—	4JAN93
301-32	HF	2	1125	30,43	—	4JAN93
301LT-4	H	1/4	5000	43	—	26SEP95
301LT-6	H	3/8	4000	43	—	26SEP95
301LT-8	H	1/2	3500	43	—	26SEP95
301LT-12	H	3/4	2250	43	—	26SEP95
301LT-16	H	1	2000	43	—	26SEP95
341-6	HF	3/8	4500	31,34,43	—	4JAN93
341-8	HF	1/2	4000	31,34,43	—	4JAN93
341-12	HF	3/4	3000	31,34,43	—	4JAN93
341-16	HF	1	3000	31,34,43	—	4JAN93
381-4	H	1/4	5800	30,31,43	—	4JAN93
381-5	H	5/16	5250	43	—	4JAN93
381-6	H	3/8	5000	30,31,43	—	4JAN93
381-8	H	1/2	4250	30,31,43	—	4JAN93
381-10	H	5/8	3600	30,31,43	—	4JAN93
381-12	H	3/4	3100	30,31,43	—	4JAN93
381-16	H	1	2500	30,31,43	—	4JAN93
381-20	H	1-1/4	2250	30,43	—	4JAN93
381-24	H	1-1/2	1750	30,43	—	4JAN93
381-32	H	2	1250	30,43	—	4JAN93
421-4	H	1/4	2750	31,42,43	—	4JAN93
421-6	H	3/8	2250	42	—	4JAN93
421-4	F	1/4	2000	31,42,43	—	4JAN93
421-5	HF	5/16	2500	42,43	—	4JAN93
421-6	F	3/8	2000	42	—	4JAN93
421-6	HF	3/8	2250	31,41,43	—	4JAN93
421-8	HF	1/2	2000	31,41,42,43	—	4JAN93
421-10	HF	5/8	1500	31,42,43	—	4JAN93
421-12	HF	3/4	1250	31,41,42,43	—	4JAN93
421-16	HF	1	1000	31,41,42,43	—	4JAN93
421-20	HF	1-1/4	625	43	—	4JAN93
421-24	HF	1-1/2	500	43	—	4JAN93
421-32	HF	2	375	43	—	4JAN93
421HT-4	HF	1/4	2750	43	—	4JAN93
421HT-5	HF	5/16	2500	43	—	4JAN93
421HT-6	HF	3/8	2250	43	—	4JAN93
421HT-8	HF	1/2	2000	43	—	4JAN93
421HT-10	HF	5/8	1500	43	—	4JAN93
421HT-12	HF	3/4	1250	43	—	4JAN93
421HT-16	HF	1	1000	43	—	4JAN93
421HT-20	HF	1-1/4	625	43	—	4JAN93
421HT-24	HF	1-1/2	500	43	—	4JAN93
421HT-32	HF	2	375	43	—	4JAN93
431-4	H	1/4	5000	31,43	—	4JAN93

TABLE 9—PARKER HANNIFIN CORPORATION LISTING (continued)

Hose Number	Applic. Code	Hose ID	MAWP (PSI)	Fittings	Fire Sleeve	Listing Date
431-5	H	5/16	4250	43	—	4JAN93
431-6	H	3/8	4000	31,42,43	—	4JAN93
431-8	H	1/2	3500	31,42,43	—	4JAN93
431-10	H	5/8	2750	31,42,43	—	4JAN93
431-12	H	3/4	2250	31,42,43	—	4JAN93
431-16	H	1	2000	31,42,43	—	4JAN93
436-6	H	3/8	4000	42,43	—	4JAN93
436-8	H	1/2	3500	42,43	—	4JAN93
436-10	H	5/8	2750	42,43	—	4JAN93
436-12	H	3/4	2250	42,43	—	4JAN93
436-16	H	1	2000	42,43	—	4JAN93
441-6	H	3/8	4000	43	—	9JAN98
441-8	H	1/2	3500	43	—	9JAN98
441-10	H	5/8	2750	43	—	9JAN98
441-12	H	3/4	2250	43	—	9JAN98
451TC-4	H	1/4	3000	43	—	15JUL97
451TC-6	H	3/8	3000	43	—	15JUL97
451TC-8	H	1/2	3000	43	—	15JUL97
451TC-10	H	5/8	3000	43	—	15JUL97
451TC-12	H	3/4	3000	43	—	15JUL97
451TC-16	H	1	3000	43	—	15JUL97
471-4	H	1/4	5800	43	—	9JAN98
471-6	H	3/8	5000	43	—	9JAN98
471-8	H	1/2	4250	43	—	9JAN98
471-10	H	5/8	3600	43	—	9JAN98
471-12	H	3/4	3100	43	—	9JAN98
471-16	H	1	2500	43	—	9JAN98
471-20	H	1-1/4	2250	43	—	9JAN98
481-4	H	1/4	3250	31,42,43	—	4JAN93
481-5	H	5/16	3250	43	—	4JAN93
481-6	H	3/8	3000	31,42,43	—	4JAN93
481-8	H	1/2	2500	31,42,43	—	4JAN93
481-10	H	5/8	2000	31,42,43	—	4JAN93
481-12	H	3/4	1750	31,42,43	—	4JAN93
481-16	H	1	1250	31,42,43	—	4JAN93
601-4	H	1/4	1250	43	—	4JAN93
601-6	H	3/8	1125	43	—	4JAN93
601-8	H	1/2	1000	43	—	4JAN93
601-12	H	3/4	750	43	—	4JAN93
601-16	H	7/8	565	43	—	4JAN93
701-6	H	3/8	6500	70	—	26SEP95
701-8	H	1/2	6000	70	—	26SEP95
701-10	H	5/8	5000	70	—	26SEP95
731-12	H	3/4	6000	73	—	28MAR95
731-16	H	1	5500	73	—	28MAR95
731-20	H	1-1/4	4700	73	—	28MAR95
731-24	H	1-1/2	4200	73	—	28MAR95
731-32	H	2	3600	73	—	28MAR95
772-8	H	1/2	4000	71	—	9AUG95
772-10	H	5/8	4000	71	—	9AUG95
772-12	H	3/4	4000	71	—	26SEP95
772-16	H	1	4000	71	—	26SEP95
772-20	H	1-1/4	3000	71	—	26SEP95
772-24	H	1-1/2	2500	71	—	26SEP95
772-32	H	2	2500	71	—	26SEP95
782-12	H	3/4	5000	78	—	3APR98

TABLE 9—PARKER HANNIFIN CORPORATION LISTING (continued)

Hose Number	Applic. Code	Hose ID	MAWP (PSI)	Fittings	Fire Sleeve	Listing Date
782-16	H	1	5000	78	—	3APR98
782-20	H	1-1/4	5000	78	—	3APR98
792-12	H	3/4	6000	79	—	15JUL97
792-16	H	1	6000	79	—	15JUL97
792-20	H	1-1/4	6000	79	—	15JUL97
881-12	H	3/4	300	43,81,88DB	—	4JAN93
881-16	H	1	250	43,81,88DB	—	4JAN93
881-20	H	1-1/4	200	43,81,88DB	—	4JAN93
881-24	H	1-1/2	150	43,71,81,88DB	—	4JAN93
881-32	H	2	100	43,71,81,88DB	—	4JAN93
881HT-12	H	3/4	300	43,81,88DB	—	4JAN93
881HT-16	H	1	250	43,81,88DB	—	4JAN93
881HT-20	H	1-1/4	200	43,81,88DB	—	4JAN93
881HT-24	H	1-1/2	150	43,71,81,88DB	—	4JAN93
881HT-32	H	2	100	43,71,81,88DB	—	4JAN93
3212-4	H	1/4	5750	60XX	—	4JAN93
3212-6	H	3/8	5000	60XX	—	4JAN93
3212-8	H	1/2	4250	60XX	—	4JAN93
3212-10	H	5/8	3250	60XX	—	4JAN93
3212-12	H	3/4	3000	60XX	—	4JAN93
3212-16	H	1	2500	60XX	—	4JAN93
3212-20	H	1-1/4	2250	60XX	—	4JAN93
3212-24	H	1-1/2	1750	60XX	—	4JAN93
3212-32	H	2	1500	60XX	—	4JAN93
3270-6	H	3/8	4000	60XX	—	4JAN93
3270-8	H	1/2	4000	60XX	—	4JAN93
3270-12	H	3/4	4000	337XX	—	4JAN93
3270-16	H	1	4000	337XX	—	4JAN93
3270-20	H	1-1/4	3000	337XX	—	4JAN93
3270-24	H	1-1/2	2500	337XX	—	4JAN93
3270-32	H	2	2500	337XX	—	4JAN93
4240-12	H	3/4	5000	337XX	—	4JAN93
4240-16	H	1	5000	337XX	—	4JAN93
4240-20	H	1-1/4	5000	367XX	—	4JAN93
4240-24	H	1-1/2	5000	367XX	—	4JAN93
4240-32	H	2	5000	368XX	—	4JAN93
5219-5	H	1/4	1500	20,22	—	4JAN93
5219-6	H	5/16	1500	20,22	—	4JAN93
5219-8	H	13/32	1250	20,22	—	4JAN93
5219-10	H	1/2	1250	20,22	—	4JAN93
5219-12	H	5/8	750	20,22	—	4JAN93
5219-5	F	1/4	500	20,22	—	4JAN93
5219-6	F	5/16	500	20,22	—	4JAN93
5219-8	F	13/32	1000	20,22	—	4JAN93
5219-10	F	1/2	700	20,22	—	4JAN93
5219-12	F	5/8	500	20,22	—	4JAN93
5219-16	HF	1	400	20,22	—	4JAN93

12. RYCO Hydraulics Inc
19 Whitehall Street
Footscray, Melbourne 3011
Australia

RYCO Hydraulics Inc
1610 Greens Road
Suite 100
Houston, TX 77031 USA

TABLE 10—RYCO HYDRAULICS INC LISTING

Hose Number	Applic. Code	Hose ID	MAWP (PSI)	Fittings	Fire Sleeve	Listing Date
RQP24	HF	1/4	5800	T200	—	18FEB02
RQP26	HF	3/8	5100	T200 & T700	—	18FEB02
RQP28	HF	1/2	4350	T200 & T700	—	18FEB02
RQP210	HF	5/8	3600	T200	—	18FEB02
RQP212	HF	3/4	3100	T200 & T700	—	18FEB02
RQP216	HF	1	2420	T200 & T700	—	18FEB02
RQP220	HF	1-1/4	2175	T700	—	18FEB02
RQP224	HF	1-1/2	1450	T700	—	18FEB02
RQP232	HF	2	1300	T700	—	18FEB02
T24A	H	1/4	5800	T200	—	18FEB02
T26A	H	3/8	4800	T200 & T700	—	18FEB02
T28A	H	1/2	4000	T200 & T700	—	18FEB02
T210A	H	5/8	3600	T200	—	18FEB02
T212A	H	3/4	3100	T200 & T700	—	18FEB02
T216A	H	1	2400	T700	—	18FEB02
T220A	H	1-1/4	1800	T700	—	18FEB02
RQP54	H	3/16	3000	V series & 5RT200	FS1072	16MAY03
RQP54	F	3/16	1750	V series & 5RT200	FS1072	16MAY03
RQP55	H	1/4	3000	V series & T400 series	FS1072	16MAY03
RQP55	F	1/4	1750	V series & T400 series	FS1072	16MAY03
RQP56	H	5/16	2250	V series & T400 series	FS1072	16MAY03
RQP56	F	5/16	1750	V series & T400 series	FS1072	16MAY03
RQP58	H	13/32	2000	V series & T400 series	FS1072	16MAY03
RQP58	F	13/32	1750	V series & T400 series	FS1072	16MAY03
RQP510	HF	1/2	1750	V series & T400 series	FS1072	16MAY03
RQP512	HF	5/8	1500	V series & T400 series	FS1072	16MAY03
T54	H	3/16	3000	V series & 5RT200	FS1072	16MAY03
T54	F	3/16	1750	V series & 5RT200	FS1072	16MAY03
T55	H	1/4	3000	V series & T400 series	FS1072	16MAY03
T55	F	1/4	1750	V series & T400 series	FS1072	16MAY03
T56	H	5/16	2250	V series & T400 series	FS1072	16MAY03
T56	F	5/16	1750	V series & T400 series	FS1072	16MAY03
T58	H	13/32	2000	V series & T400 series	FS1072	16MAY03
T58	F	13/32	1750	V series & T400 series	FS1072	16MAY03
T510	HF	1/2	1750	V series & T400 series	FS1072	16MAY03
T512	HF	5/8	1500	V series & T400 series	FS1072	16MAY03
T24D	H	1/4	5800	T200	—	30APR97
T26D	H	3/8	5100	T200 & T700	—	30APR97
T28D	H	1/2	5100	T200 & T700	—	30APR97
T210D	H	5/8	3600	T200	—	30APR97
T212D	H	3/4	3100	T200 & T700	—	30APR97
T216D	H	1	2540	T700	—	30APR97
T220D	H	1-1/4	2175	T700	—	18FEB02
T224D	H	1-1/2	1450	T700	—	18FEB02
T232D	H	2	1300	T700	—	18FEB02
T240D	H	2-1/2	1000	T700	—	18FEB02
RQP14	H	1/4	3250	T200	—	18FEB02
RQP16	H	3/8	2600	T200 & T700	—	18FEB02
RQP18	H	1/2	1890	T200 & T700	—	18FEB02
RQP110	H	5/8	1890	T200	—	18FEB02
RQP112	H	3/4	1740	T200 & T700	—	18FEB02
T14A	H	1/4	2600	T200	—	18FEB02
T16A	H	3/8	2600	T200 & T700	—	18FEB02
T18A	H	1/2	2300	T200 & T700	—	18FEB02
T110A	H	5/8	1890	T200	—	18FEB02
T112A	H	3/4	1500	T200 & T700	—	18FEB02
T116A	H	1	1300	T700	—	18FEB02
T120A	H	1-1/4	945	T700	—	18FEB02

TABLE 10—RYCO HYDRAULICS INC LISTING (continued)

Hose Number	Applic. Code	Hose ID	MAWP (PSI)	Fittings	Fire Sleeve	Listing Date
T14D	H	1/4	3250	T200	—	18FEB02
T16D	H	3/8	2600	T200 & T700	—	18FEB02
T18D	H	1/2	2300	T200 & T700	—	18FEB02
T110D	H	5/8	1900	T200	—	18FEB02
T112D	H	3/4	1740	T200 & T700	—	18FEB02
T116D	H	1	1300	T700	—	18FEB02
T120D	H	1-1/4	1160	T700	—	18FEB02
T124D	H	1-1/2	940	T700	—	18FEB02
T132D	H	2	800	T700	—	18FEB02
H1206A	H	3/8	4000	T700	—	18FEB02
H1208A	H	1/2	4000	T700	—	18FEB02
H1212A	H	3/4	4000	T700	—	18FEB02
H1216A	H	1	4000	T700	—	18FEB02
H1220A	H	1-1/4	3000	T700	—	18FEB02
H1224A	H	1-1/2	2500	T700	—	18FEB02
H1232A	H	2	2500	T700	—	18FEB02
H1206D	H	3/8	4000	T700	—	18FEB02
H1208D	H	1/2	4000	T700	—	18FEB02
H1212D	H	3/4	4000	T700	—	18FEB02
H1216D	H	1	4000	T700	—	18FEB02
H1220D	H	1-1/4	3000	T700	—	18FEB02
H1224D	H	1-1/2	2500	T700	—	18FEB02
H1232D	H	2	2500	T700	—	18FEB02
H1312A	H	3/4	5000	T900	—	18FEB02
H1316A	H	1	5000	T900	—	18FEB02
H1320A	H	1-1/4	5000	T900	—	18FEB02
H1324A	H	1-1/2	5000	T900	—	18FEB02
H1332A	H	2	5000	T900	—	18FEB02
H1312D	H	3/4	5000	T900	—	18FEB02
H1316D	H	1	5000	T900	—	18FEB02
H1320D	H	1-1/4	5000	T900	—	18FEB02
H1324D	H	1-1/2	5000	T900	—	18FEB02
H1332D	H	2	5000	T900	—	18FEB02

13. Specma Dunlop Hydraulic AB
Attn: Jörn Jensen
Technical Manager
Box 164
S-401 23 Göteburg
Sweden
Ph: 46 (31) 89 17 00
Fax: 46 (31) 45 77 65

TABLE 11—SPECMA DUNLOP HYDRAULIC AB LISTING

Hose Number	Applic. Code	Hose ID	MAWP (PSI)	Fittings	Fire Sleeve	Listing Date
811-04	H	1/4	4060	P	—	30APR97
811-06	H	3/8	3265	P	—	30APR97
811-08	H	1/2	2755	P	—	30APR97
811-12	H	3/4	2175	P	—	30APR97
811-16	H	1	1595	P	—	30APR97
821-04	H	1/4	6525	P	—	30APR97
821-06	H	3/8	5075	P	—	30APR97
821-08	H	1/2	4495	P	—	30APR97
821-10	H	5/8	4060	P	—	30APR97
821-12	H	3/4	4060	P	—	30APR97
821-16	H	1	3262	P	—	30APR97
833-06	H	3/8	7252	P	—	30APR97
833-08	H	1/2	6815	P	—	30APR97
833-10	H	5/8	5947	P	—	30APR97

TABLE 11—SPECMA DUNLOP HYDRAULIC AB LISTING (continued)

Hose Number	Applic. Code	Hose ID	MAWP (PSI)	Fittings	Fire Sleeve	Listing Date
833-12	H	3/4	5435	P,M	—	30APR97
833-16	H	1	4742	P,M	—	30APR97
833-20	H	1-1/4	3481	P,M	—	30APR97
755-24	H	1-1/2	4206	IL	—	30APR97
766-32	H	2	4713	WLS	—	30APR97

14. Teleflex Fluid Systems
One Firestone Drive
Suffield, CT 06078
Ph: (860) 668-1285
Fax: (860) 668-2353

TABLE 12—TELEFLEX FLUID SYSTEMS LISTING

Hose Number	Applic. Code	Hose ID	MAWP (PSI)	Fittings	Fire Sleeve	Listing Date
T1167-03	F	3/16	3000	100xxx, 1002xx, 110xxx, 1102xx, 116xxx, 130xxx, 131xxx, I1004xx, I1005xx	AS1072-05	30APR97
T1167-03	H	3/16	3000	100xxx, 1002xx, 110xxx, 1102xx, 116xxx, 130xxx, 131xxx, I1004xx, I1005xx	N.R.	30APR97
T1167-04	F	1/4	3000	100xxx, 1002xx, 110xxx, 1102xx, 116xxx, 130xxx, 131xxx, I1004xx, I1005xx	AS1072-06	30APR97
T1167-04	H	1/4	3000	100xxx, 1002xx, 110xxx, 1102xx, 116xxx, 130xxx, 131xxx, I1004xx, I1005xx	N.R.	30APR97
T1167-05	F	5/16	3000	100xxx, 1002xx, 110xxx, 1102xx, 116xxx, 130xxx, 131xxx, I1004xx, I1005xx	AS1072-07	30APR97
T1167-05	H	5/16	3000	100xxx, 1002xx, 110xxx, 1102xx, 116xxx, 130xxx, 131xxx, I1004xx, I1005xx	N.R.	30APR97
T1167-06	F	3/8	2500	100xxx, 1002xx, 110xxx, 1102xx, 116xxx, 130xxx, 131xxx, I1004xx, I1005xx	AS1072-08	30APR97
T1167-06	H	3/8	2500	100xxx, 1002xx, 110xxx, 1102xx, 116xxx, 130xxx, 131xxx, I1004xx, I1005xx	N.R.	30APR97
T1167-08	F	1/2	2000	100xxx, 1002xx, 110xxx, 1102xx, 116xxx, 130xxx, 131xxx, I1004xx, I1005xx	AS1072-10	30APR97
T1167-08	H	1/2	2000	100xxx, 1002xx, 110xxx, 1102xx, 116xxx, 130xxx, 131xxx, I1004xx, I1005xx	N.R.	30APR97
T1167-10	F	5/8	1500	100xxx, 1002xx, 110xxx, 1102xx, 116xxx, 130xxx, 131xxx, I1004xx, I1005xx	AS1072-12	30APR97
T1167-10	H	5/8	1500	100xxx, 1002xx, 110xxx, 1102xx, 116xxx, 130xxx, 131xxx, I1004xx, I1005xx	N.R.	30APR97
T1167-12	F	3/4	1200	100xxx, 1002xx, 110xxx, 1102xx, 116xxx, 130xxx, 131xxx, I1004xx, I1005xx	AS1072-14	30APR97
T1167-12	H	3/4	1200	100xxx, 1002xx, 110xxx, 1102xx, 116xxx, 130xxx, 131xxx, I1004xx, I1005xx	N.R.	30APR97
T1167-16	F	1	1000	100xxx, 1002xx, 110xxx, 1102xx, 116xxx, 130xxx, 131xxx, I1004xx, I1005xx	AS1072-20	30APR97
T1167-16	H	1	1000	100xxx, 1002xx, 110xxx, 1102xx, 116xxx, 130xxx, 131xxx, I1004xx, I1005xx	N.R.	30APR97
T1170-03	F	3/16	3000	100xxx, 1002xx, 110xxx, 1102xx, 116xxx, 130xxx, 131xxx, I1004xx, I1005xx	AS1072-05	30APR97
T1170-03	H	3/16	3000	100xxx, 1002xx, 110xxx, 1102xx, 116xxx, 130xxx, 131xxx, I1004xx, I1005xx	N.R.	30APR97
T1170-04	F	1/4	3000	100xxx, 1002xx, 110xxx, 1102xx, 116xxx, 130xxx, 131xxx, I1004xx, I1005xx	AS1072-06	30APR97
T1170-04	H	1/4	3000	100xxx, 1002xx, 110xxx, 1102xx, 116xxx, 130xxx, 131xxx, I1004xx, I1005xx	N.R.	30APR97

TABLE 12—TELEFLEX FLUID SYSTEMS LISTING (continued)

Hose Number	Applic. Code	Hose ID	MAWP (PSI)	Fittings	Fire Sleeve	Listing Date
T1170-05	F	5/16	3000	100xxx, 1002xx, 110xxx, 1102xx, 116xxx, 130xxx, 131xxx, I1004xx, I1005xx	AS1072-07	30APR97
T1170-05	H	5/16	3000	100xxx, 1002xx, 110xxx, 1102xx, 116xxx, 130xxx, 131xxx, I1004xx, I1005xx	N.R.	30APR97
T1170-06	F	3/8	2500	100xxx, 1002xx, 110xxx, 1102xx, 116xxx, 130xxx, 131xxx, I1004xx, I1005xx	AS1072-08	30APR97
T1170-06	H	3/8	2500	100xxx, 1002xx, 110xxx, 1102xx, 116xxx, 130xxx, 131xxx, I1004xx, I1005xx	N.R.	30APR97
T1170-08	F	1/2	2000	100xxx, 1002xx, 110xxx, 1102xx, 116xxx, 130xxx, 131xxx, I1004xx, I1005xx	AS1072-10	30APR97
T1170-08	H	1/2	2000	100xxx, 1002xx, 110xxx, 1102xx, 116xxx, 130xxx, 131xxx, I1004xx, I1005xx	N.R.	30APR97
T1170-10	F	5/8	1500	100xxx, 1002xx, 110xxx, 1102xx, 116xxx, 130xxx, 131xxx, I1004xx, I1005xx	AS1072-12	30APR97
T1170-10	H	5/8	1500	100xxx, 1002xx, 110xxx, 1102xx, 116xxx, 130xxx, 131xxx, I1004xx, I1005xx	N.R.	30APR97
T1170-12	F	3/4	1200	100xxx, 1002xx, 110xxx, 1102xx, 116xxx, 130xxx, 131xxx, I1004xx, I1005xx	AS1072-14	30APR97
T1170-12	H	3/4	1200	100xxx, 1002xx, 110xxx, 1102xx, 116xxx, 130xxx, 131xxx, I1004xx, I1005xx	N.R.	30APR97
T1170-16	F	1	1000	100xxx, 1002xx, 110xxx, 1102xx, 116xxx, 130xxx, 131xxx, I1004xx, I1005xx	AS1072-20	30APR97
T1170-16	H	1	1000	100xxx, 1002xx, 110xxx, 1102xx, 116xxx, 130xxx, 131xxx, I1004xx, I1005xx	N.R.	30APR97
T1764-04	F	1/4	4000	TFX100xxx, TFX1002xx, TFX110xxx, TFX1102xx, TFX116xxx, TFX130xxx, TFX131xxx, TFXI1004xx, TFXI1005xx	AS1072-08	30APR97
T1764-04	H	1/4	4000	TFX100xxx, TFX1002xx, TFX110xxx, TFX1102xx, TFX116xxx, TFX130xxx, TFX131xxx, TFXI1004xx, TFXI1005xx	N.R.	30APR97
T1764-06	F	3/8	3500	TFX100xxx, TFX1002xx, TFX110xxx, TFX1102xx, TFX116xxx, TFX130xxx, TFX131xxx, TFXI1004xx, TFXI1005xx	AS1072-10	30APR97
T1764-06	H	3/8	3500	TFX100xxx, TFX1002xx, TFX110xxx, TFX1102xx, TFX116xxx, TFX130xxx, TFX131xxx, TFXI1004xx, TFXI1005xx	N.R.	30APR97
T1764-08	F	1/2	2500	TFX100xxx, TFX1002xx, TFX110xxx, TFX1102xx, TFX116xxx, TFX130xxx, TFX131xxx, TFXI1004xx, TFXI1005xx	AS1072-12	30APR97
T1764-08	H	1/2	2500	TFX100xxx, TFX1002xx, TFX110xxx, TFX1102xx, TFX116xxx, TFX130xxx, TFX131xxx, TFXI1004xx, TFXI1005xx	N.R.	30APR97
T1764-10	F	5/8	1800	TFX100xxx, TFX1002xx, TFX110xxx, TFX1102xx, TFX116xxx, TFX130xxx, TFX131xxx, TFXI1004xx, TFXI1005xx	AS1072-13	30APR97
T1764-10	H	5/8	1800	TFX100xxx, TFX1002xx, TFX110xxx, TFX1102xx, TFX116xxx, TFX130xxx, TFX131xxx, TFXI1004xx, TFXI1005xx	N.R.	30APR97
T1764-12	F	3/4	1500	TFX100xxx, TFX1002xx, TFX110xxx, TFX1102xx, TFX116xxx, TFX130xxx, TFX131xxx, TFXI1004xx, TFXI1005xx	AS1072-16	30APR97

TABLE 12—TELEFLEX FLUID SYSTEMS LISTING (continued)

Hose Number	Applic. Code	Hose ID	MAWP (PSI)	Fittings	Fire Sleeve	Listing Date
T1764-12	H	3/4	1500	TFX100xxx, TFX1002xx, TFX110xxx, TFX1102xx, TFX116xxx, TFX130xxx, TFX131xxx, TFXI1004xx, TFXI1005xx	N.R.	30APR97
T1764-16	F	1	1100	TFX100xxx, TFX1002xx, TFX110xxx, TFX1102xx, TFX116xxx, TFX130xxx, TFX131xxx, TFXI1004xx, TFXI1005xx	AS1072-22	30APR97
T1764-16	H	1	1100	TFX100xxx, TFX1002xx, TFX110xxx, TFX1102xx, TFX116xxx, TFX130xxx, TFX131xxx, TFXI1004xx, TFXI1005xx	N.R.	30APR97
T1765-04	F	1/4	4000	TFX100xxx, TFX1002xx, TFX110xxx, TFX1102xx, TFX116xxx, TFX130xxx, TFX131xxx, TFXI1004xx, TFXI1005xx	AS1072-08	30APR97
T1765-04	H	1/4	4000	TFX100xxx, TFX1002xx, TFX110xxx, TFX1102xx, TFX116xxx, TFX130xxx, TFX131xxx, TFXI1004xx, TFXI1005xx	N.R.	30APR97
T1765-06	F	3/8	3500	TFX100xxx, TFX1002xx, TFX110xxx, TFX1102xx, TFX116xxx, TFX130xxx, TFX131xxx, TFXI1004xx, TFXI1005xx	AS1072-10	30APR97
T1765-06	H	3/8	3500	TFX100xxx, TFX1002xx, TFX110xxx, TFX1102xx, TFX116xxx, TFX130xxx, TFX131xxx, TFXI1004xx, TFXI1005xx	N.R.	30APR97
T1765-08	F	1/2	2500	TFX100xxx, TFX1002xx, TFX110xxx, TFX1102xx, TFX116xxx, TFX130xxx, TFX131xxx, TFXI1004xx, TFXI1005xx	AS1072-12	30APR97
T1765-08	H	1/2	2500	TFX100xxx, TFX1002xx, TFX110xxx, TFX1102xx, TFX116xxx, TFX130xxx, TFX131xxx, TFXI1004xx, TFXI1005xx	N.R.	30APR97
T1765-10	F	5/8	1800	TFX100xxx, TFX1002xx, TFX110xxx, TFX1102xx, TFX116xxx, TFX130xxx, TFX131xxx, TFXI1004xx, TFXI1005xx	AS1072-13	30APR97
T1765-10	H	5/8	1800	TFX100xxx, TFX1002xx, TFX110xxx, TFX1102xx, TFX116xxx, TFX130xxx, TFX131xxx, TFXI1004xx, TFXI1005xx	N.R.	30APR97
T1765-12	F	3/4	1500	TFX100xxx, TFX1002xx, TFX110xxx, TFX1102xx, TFX116xxx, TFX130xxx, TFX131xxx, TFXI1004xx, TFXI1005xx	AS1072-16	30APR97
T1765-12	H	3/4	1500	TFX100xxx, TFX1002xx, TFX110xxx, TFX1102xx, TFX116xxx, TFX130xxx, TFX131xxx, TFXI1004xx, TFXI1005xx	N.R.	30APR97
T1765-16	F	1	1100	TFX100xxx, TFX1002xx, TFX110xxx, TFX1102xx, TFX116xxx, TFX130xxx, TFX131xxx, TFXI1004xx, TFXI1005xx	AS1072-22	30APR97
T1765-16	H	1	1100	TFX100xxx, TFX1002xx, TFX110xxx, TFX1102xx, TFX116xxx, TFX130xxx, TFX131xxx, TFXI1004xx, TFXI1005xx	N.R.	30APR97
T1820-6	F	5/16	200	PD3630	N.R.	24JUL03

FORMED TUBE ENDS FOR HOSE CONNECTIONS AND HOSE FITTINGS—SAE J1231 JAN2001

SAE Standard

Report of the SAE Fluid Conductors and Connectors Committee approved May 1978 and revised October 1988. Completely revised by the SAE Fluid Conductors and Connectors Committee SC2—Hydraulic Hose and Hose Fittings Subcommittee June 1992, revised June 1993, completely revised March 1997, and revised July 1998, May 1999, and January 2001. Rationale statement available. Revised by the SAE Fluid Conductors and Connectors Technical Committee SC2—Hydraulic Hose and Hose Fittings, January 2001. Rationale statement available.

1. Scope—This SAE standard provides general and dimensional specifications for formed tube ends and hose fittings. These connections are intended for general applications in low pressure automotive and hydraulic systems on automotive, industrial, and commercial products. The fittings shown in Figures 2 and 3 are intended to be retained by hose clamps as specified in SAE J1508.

It is recommended that where step sizes or additional types of fittings are required, they be designed to conform with the specifications of this document insofar as they may apply. The following general specifications shall supplement the dimensional data contained in the tables with respect to all unspecified detail.

2. References

2.1 Applicable Publications—The following publications form a part of this specification to the extent specified herein. The latest issue of SAE publications shall apply.

2.1.1 SAE PUBLICATIONS—Available from SAE, 400 Commonwealth Drive, Warrendale, PA 15096-0001.

SAE J475—Screw Threads
SAE J476—Dryseal Pipe Threads
SAE J512—Automotive Tube Fittings
SAE J514—Hydraulic Tube Fittings
SAE J846—Coding Systems for Identification of Fluid Conductors and Connectors
SAE J1508—Hose Clamp Specifications

2.1.2 ASTM PUBLICATION—Available from ASTM, 100 Barr Harbor Drive, West Conshohocken, PA 19428.

ASTM B 117—Method of Salt Spray (Fog) Testing

2.2 Related Publications—The following publications are provided for information purposes only and are not a required part of this document.

2.2.1 SAE PUBLICATIONS—Available from SAE, 400 Commonwealth Drive, Warrendale, PA 15096-0001.

SAE J516—Hydraulic Hose Fittings
SAE J1273—Selection, Installation, and Maintenance of Hose and Hose Assemblies

2.2.2 ANSI PUBLICATION—Available from ANSI,11 West 42nd Street, New York, NY 10036-8002.

ANSI/ASME B1.20.1-1983—General Purpose Pipe Threads

3. Size Designations—The hose fitting size is generally designated by the fractional inch nominal hose inside diameter together with the nominal pipe or straight thread size. However, these sizes may also be designated by their dash sizes as follows:

3.1 The hose dash size is equivalent to the number of sixteenth inch increments in the hose inside diameter.

3.2 The pipe thread dash size is the number of sixteenth inch increments in the nominal pipe thread size.

3.3 The O-ring boss thread dash sizes correspond to the number of sixteenth inch increments in the outside diameter of the tubing with which they are designed to be used.

4. Dimensions and Tolerances—Tabulated dimensions shall apply to the finished parts, plated or otherwise processed, as specified by the purchaser. Details of internal construction of fittings are not specified and shall be optional with the manufacturer.

Where applicable, the maximum and minimum flat dimensions shall be within the commercial tolerance of bar stock from which the fittings are produced. Formed or upset contours shall fit standard wrench openings. The minimum across corners dimensions of external hexagons shall be 1.092 times the nominal width across flats, but shall not result in a side flat width of less than 0.43 times the nominal width across flats.

Except for nominal sizes and thread specifications, dimensions and tolerances are given in SI units. Tolerance on all dimensions not otherwise limited shall be ±0.25 mm. Angular tolerance on axis of ends on elbows shall be ±2.50 degrees for sizes up to and including 9.52 mm and ±1.50 degrees for sizes larger than 9.52 mm.

Unless otherwise specified, tolerances on hole diameters designated as a drill in the dimensional tables (Tables 3, 4, and 5) shall conform to Table 1:

TABLE 1—TOLERANCES ON DRILLED HOLES

Drill Size Range, mm	Tolerance on Hole Diameter, mm Plus	Tolerance on Hole Diameter, mm Minus
0.35-6.25	0.08	0.08
6.35-12.70	0.10	0.10
13.10-19.05	0.13	0.13
19.40-25.40	0.18	0.13
25.80-38.10	0.20	0.13
38.50 and up	0.25	0.13

5. Passages—Where passages in straight fittings are machined from opposite ends, the offset at the meeting point shall not exceed 0.40 mm. The cross-sectional area at the junction of fluid passages shall not be less than that of the smallest passage. This assembly passage definition does not apply to bent tubes.

6. Contour—Details of contour shall be optional with manufacturer provided the tabulated dimensions are maintained and serviceability of the fittings is not impaired. Wrench flats on elbows shall be optional.

7. Straight Threads—Unified Standard Class 2A external and Class 2B internal threads shall apply to plain finish (unplated) fittings having straight threads designated A1 in Figure 3 and Table 5. For externally threaded parts with additive finish, the maximum diameters of Class 2A may be exceeded by the amount of the allowance, that is, the basic diameters (Class 2A maximum diameters plus the allowance) shall apply to an externally threaded part after plating. For internally threaded parts with additive finish, the Class 2B diameters apply after plating.

The pitch diameter tolerance shall be the same as the corresponding diameter-pitch combination and class of the Unified fine and 12-thread series. See SAE J475.

Where external threads are produced by roll threading and the body is not undercut, the unthreaded portion adjacent to the shoulder may be reduced to the minimum pitch diameter.

External threads shall be chamfered and internal threads shall be countersunk as specified in the illustrations and dimensional tables.

8. Thread Eccentricity Tolerances—The various thread elements of Class 2A external and Class 2B internal threads on hose fittings shall be concentric within the limitations specified under General Specifications in SAE J512.

9. Pipe Threads—Taper pipe threads designated A in Figure 2 and Table 4 shall conform to the Dryseal American Standard Taper Pipe Thread (NPTF). Specifications are given in detail in SAE J476. At purchaser's option, the pipe thread may be shortened in conformity with the SAE Short Dryseal Taper Pipe Thread (PTF-SAE Short).

The length of a full-form external thread shall not be shorter than L plus one pitch (thread) for Dryseal NPTF and L for Dryseal PTF-SAE Short; except where the thread is cut through into a relieved body or undercut on the fitting, then the minimum full thread length may be reduced by one pitch (thread).

External pipe threads shall be chamfered from the diameters shown in Table 2 to produce the specified length of chamfered or partial thread.

10. Materials and Manufacture—Formed tube hose fittings shall be made from brass, steel, or other materials listed in SAE J846, and specified by the purchaser.

Brass shall be SAE UNS C36000 (half hard), SAE UNS C34500, or SAE UNS C35000 for bar or extruded stock and SAE UNS C37700 for forgings. Steel tubing shall be SAE standard single wall intended for general applications in low pressure automotive and hydraulic systems. When steel tubing is used for a formed tube connection, the wall thickness shall be the manufacturer's option unless specified by the purchaser. Dimension D Nominal I.D. in Table 3 does not apply to steel tubing. However, the D dimension shall be the same as the nominal tubing I.D.

At the manufacturer's option, parts may be machined or milled from bar, forged, or of multiple component design.

Fittings made from multiple components shall be capable of withstanding 100 psi (minimum) without leakage or failure.

TABLE 2—DIMENSIONS OF CHAMFERS ON EXTERNAL PIPE THREADS

External Nominal Pipe Thread in	Chamfer Dia[(1)] maximum mm	Chamfer Dia[(1)] minimum mm	Length of Chamfered or Partial Thread maximum mm	Length of Chamfered or Partial Thread minimum mm
1/8	8.1	7.6	1.40	0.94
1/4	10.7	10.2	2.13	1.42
3/8	14.0	13.4	2.13	1.42
1/2	17.3	16.8	2.72	1.80
3/4	22.6	22.1	2.72	1.80
1	28.4	27.7	3.30	2.21
1 1/4	37.1	36.3	3.30	2.21
1 1/2	43.2	42.4	3.30	2.21
2	55.1	54.4	3.30	2.21

1. Tabulated diameters conform with Appendix A, SAE J476.

TABLE 3—DIMENSIONS OF FORMED TUBE CONNECTIONS (Reference Figure 1)

Hose Dash Size	Tube OD Nominal mm	Tube OD Nominal in	A ±0.25 mm	B ±0.07 mm	C Reference mm	D Nominal Drill mm
–3	4.76	3/16	5.58	0.41	2.0	3.2
–4	6.35	1/4	7.37	0.51	2.5	4.8
–5	7.94	5/16	9.16	0.61	2.5	6.4
–6	9.52	3/8	10.95	0.71	2.5	7.5
–7	11.11	7/16	12.45	0.71	2.5	9.1
–8	12.7	1/2	14.22	0.76	3.0	10.3
–9	14.29	9/16	15.75	0.76	3.0	11.1
–10	15.88	5/8	17.55	0.84	3.0	12.7
–12	19.05	3/4	20.83	0.89	3.0	15.9
–16	25.4	1	28.09	1.35	3.0	21.4
–20	31.75	1-1/4	34.44	1.35		27.8
–24	38.1	1-1/2	41.25	1.57		34.1
–32	50.8	2	54.51	1.85		46.8

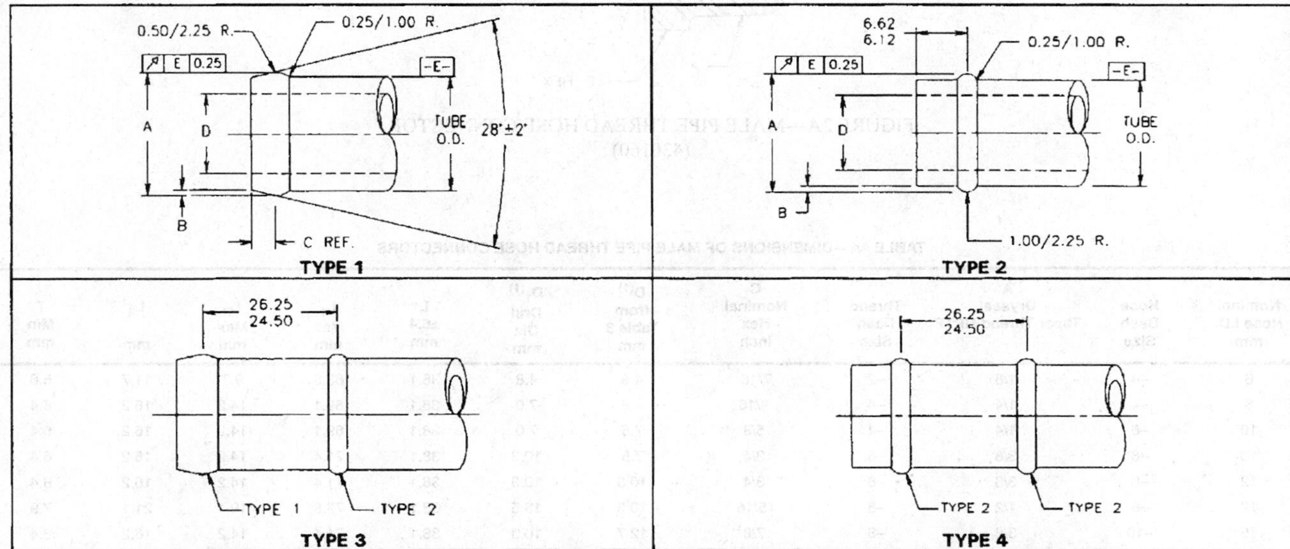

FIGURE 1—FORMED TUBE CONNECTION STYLES

*11. **Finish***—The external surfaces and threads of all carbon steel parts shall be plated or coated with a suitable material that passes a 72 h salt spray test in accordance with ASTM B 117. Any appearance of red rust during the 72 h salt spray test shall be considered failure, except for the following:

a. All internal fluid passages.
b. Edges such as hex points, serrations, and crests of threads where there may be mechanical deformation of the plating or coating typical of mass produced parts or shipping effects.
c. Areas where there is mechanical deformation of the plating or coating caused by crimping, flaring, bending, and other post-plate metal forming operations.
d. Areas where the parts are suspended or affixed in the test chamber where condensate can accumulate.

NOTE—Cadmium plating is not preferred due to environmental reasons. Parts manufactured to this document after January 1, 1997, shall not be Cadmium plated. Internal fluid passages shall be protected from corrosion during storage. Changes in plating may affect assembly torques and require re-qualification, when applicable.

*12. **Workmanship***—Workmanship shall conform to the best commercial practice to produce high quality fittings. Fittings shall be free from all hanging burrs, loose scale, and all other defects that might affect serviceability. All sealing surfaces must be smooth except that annular tool marks up to 2.5 μm maximum, unless otherwise specified, shall be permissible.

*13. **Assembly Considerations***—Use of a compatible lubricant or sealant in assembling Dryseal pipe threads may be desirable to minimize galling and effect a tight seal.

*14. **Formed Tube Connections***—Formed tube connections may be shaped to either of four styles. Type 2 shall be supplied unless agreed to by the purchaser and the manufacturer.

*15. **Hose Fittings***—Two types of hose fittings are defined. Male Dryseal Pipe Thread (Figure 2, Table 4) and Male Straight Thread O-Ring Boss (Figure 3, Table 5). Type 2 connections shall be supplied unless agreed to by the purchaser and the manufacturer.

MALE DRYSEAL PIPE THREAD TYPE

UNSPECIFIED DETAIL WITH RESPECT TO DIMENSIONS, TOLERANCES, CONTOURS, MATERIAL, WORKMANSHIP, AND SO ON, MUST CONFORM TO GENERAL SPECIFICATIONS FOR HYDRAULIC TUBE FITTINGS PER SAE J514 FIGURE 2A. THE DIMENSIONAL DESIGNATIONS ON THE FIRST FIGURE IN EACH GROUP SHALL APPLY TO ALL OTHER FIGURES IN THAT GROUP EXCEPT AS SHOWN OTHERWISE. CODES SHOWN IN BRACKETS ADJACENT TO FIGURE NUMBERS REPRESENT RESPECTIVE FITTING IDENTIFICATION, IN ACCORDANCE WITH SAE J846.

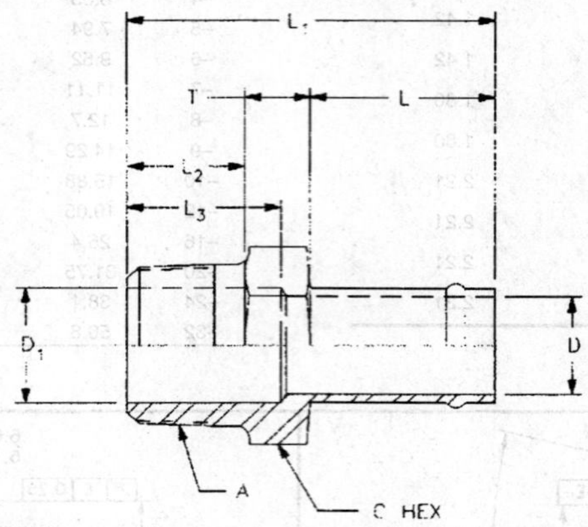

FIGURE 2A—MALE PIPE THREAD HOSE CONNECTOR
(430160)

TABLE 4A—DIMENSIONS OF MALE PIPE THREAD HOSE CONNECTORS

Nominal Hose I.D. mm	Hose Dash Size	A Dryseal Taper Thread NPTF	Thread Dash Size	C Nominal Hex inch	D[(1)] from Table 3 mm	D_1[(1)] Drill Dia mm	L ±6.4 mm	L_1 Max mm	L_2 Max mm	L_3 mm	T Min mm
6	–4	1/8	–2	7/16	4.8	4.8	38.1	63.6	9.7	11.7	5.6
6	–4	1/4	–4	9/16	4.8	7.0	38.1	69.1	14.2	16.2	6.4
10	–6	1/4	–4	5/8	7.5	7.0	38.1	69.1	14.2	16.2	6.4
10	–6	3/8	–6	3/4	7.5	10.3	38.1	71.4	14.2	16.2	6.4
12	–8	3/8	–6	3/4	10.3	10.3	38.1	71.4	14.2	16.2	6.4
12	–8	1/2	–8	15/16	10.3	13.5	38.1	77.8	19.1	21.1	7.9
16	–10	3/8	–6	7/8	12.7	10.3	38.1	71.4	14.2	16.2	6.4
16	–10	1/2	–8	15/16	12.7	13.5	38.1	77.8	19.1	21.2	7.9
20	–12	3/8	–6	1	15.9	10.3	38.1	71.4	14.2	16.2	6.4
20	–12	1/2	–8	1	15.9	13.5	38.1	77.8	19.1	21.2	7.9
20	–12	3/4	–12	1-1/8	15.9	18.0	38.1	79.1	19.1	21.2	9.7
25	–16	3/4	–12	1-1/4	21.4	18.0	38.1	79.1	19.1	21.2	9.7
25	–16	1	–16	1-3/8	21.4	23.8	38.1	83.9	23.9	25.9	9.7
30	–20	1	–16	1-1/2	27.8	23.8	38.1	83.9	23.9	25.9	9.7
30	–20	1-1/4	–20	1-3/4	27.8	31.7	38.1	93.0	24.6	26.6	11.2
30	–20	1-1/2	–24	2	27.8	38.0	38.1	93.8	25.4	27.4	12.7
38	–24	1-1/4	–20	1-3/4	34.1	31.7	38.1	93.0	24.6	26.6	11.2
38	–24	1-1/2	–24	2	34.1	38.0	38.1	93.8	25.4	27.4	12.7
50	–32	1-1/2	–24	2-1/4	46.8	38.0	38.1	93.8	25.4	27.4	12.7
50	–32	2	–32	2-5/8	46.8	49.0	38.1	99.1	26.2	28.2	17.5

1. At the manufacturer's option, the through passage in Figure 2A may conform with the smaller diameter specified or the appropriate end may be counterbored to the larger diameter.

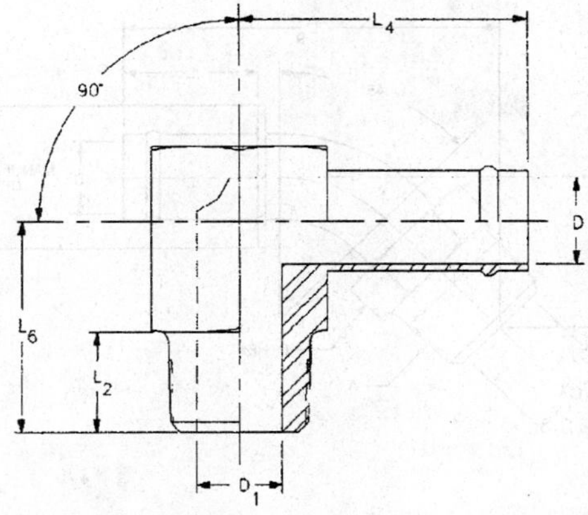

FIGURE 2B—90-DEGREE MALE PIPE HOSE FITTING

(431460)

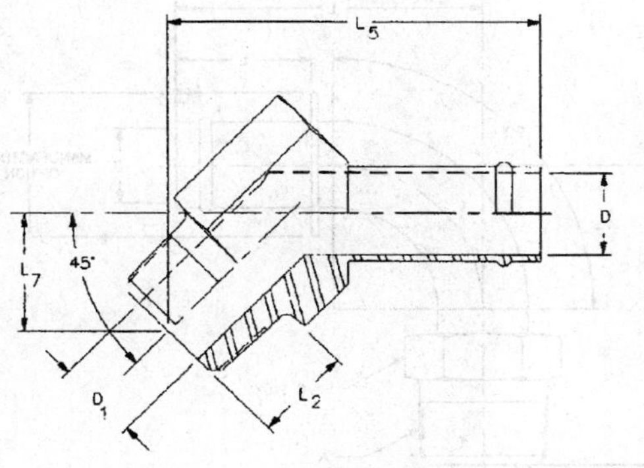

FIGURE 2C—45-DEGREE MALE PIPE HOSE FITTING

(430360)

TABLE 4B—DIMENSIONS OF 90-DEGREE AND 45-DEGREE MALE PIPE HOSE FITTINGS

Nominal Hose I.D. mm	Hose Dash Size	A Dryseal Taper Thread NPTF	Thread Dash Size	Minimum Stock Size[1] inch	D from Table 3 mm	D_1 Drill Dia mm	L_2 Min mm	L_4 Max mm	L_5 Max mm	L_6 ±1.5 mm	L_7 ±1.5 mm
6	–4	1/8	–2	1/2	4.8	4.8	9.7	58.7	70.1	19.1	11.4
6	–4	1/4	–4	5/8	4.8	7.0	14.2	61.9	74.1	27.8	15.4
6	–4	3/8	–6	3/4	4.8	10.3	14.2	66.7	75.8	31.0	17.1
8	–5	1/8	–2	1/2	6.4	4.8	9.7	58.7	70.1	18.3	11.4
8	–5	1/4	–4	5/8	6.4	7.0	14.2	61.9	74.2	27.8	15.5
10	–6	1/4	–4	5/8	7.5	7.0	14.2	61.9	74.2	27.8	15.5
10	–6	3/8	–6	3/4	7.5	10.3	14.2	66.7	75.8	31.0	17.1
10	–6	1/2	–8	15/16	7.5	13.5	19.1	69.9	79.8	37.3	21.1
12	–8	1/4	–4	3/4	10.3	7.0	14.2	61.9	74.2	28.6	15.5
12	–8	3/8	–6	13/16	10.3	10.3	14.2	66.7	75.7	31.0	17.0
12	–8	1/2	–8	15/16	10.3	13.5	19.1	69.9	79.8	37.3	21.1
12	–8	3/4	–12	1-1/8	10.3	18.0	19.1	76.2	80.3	40.5	21.6
16	–10	1/2	–8	15/16	12.7	13.5	19.1	69.9	79.8	37.3	21.1
16	–10	3/4	–12	1-1/8	12.7	18.0	19.1	76.2	80.3	40.5	21.6
20	–12	1/2	–8	1-1/8	15.9	13.5	19.1	69.9	79.8	39.7	21.1
20	–12	3/4	–12	1-1/8	15.9	18.0	19.1	76.2	80.6	40.5	21.9
20	–12	1	–16	1-3/8	15.9	23.8	23.9	82.6	85.1	50.0	26.4
25	–16	3/4	–12	1-1/8	21.4	18.0	19.1	76.2	80.3	40.5	21.6
25	–16	1	–16	1-3/8	21.4	23.8	23.9	82.6	85.1	50.0	26.4
25	–16	1-1/4	–20	1-3/4	21.4	31.7	24.6	90.5	88.7	60.3	30.0
30	–20	1	–16	1-3/8	27.8	23.8	23.9	82.6	85.4	50.0	26.7
30	–20	1-1/4	–20	1-3/4	27.8	31.7	24.6	90.5	88.7	60.3	30.0
30	–20	1-1/2	–24	2	27.8	38.0	25.4	101.6	90.5	66.7	31.8
38	–24	1-1/4	–20	1-3/4	34.1	31.7	24.6	90.5	88.7	60.3	30.0
38	–24	1-1/2	–24	2	34.1	38.0	25.4	101.6	90.5	66.7	31.8
50	–32	2	–32	2-5/8	46.8	49.0	26.2	114.3	96.5	76.2	37.8

1. Forging, square, or hex form is at the manufacturer's option.

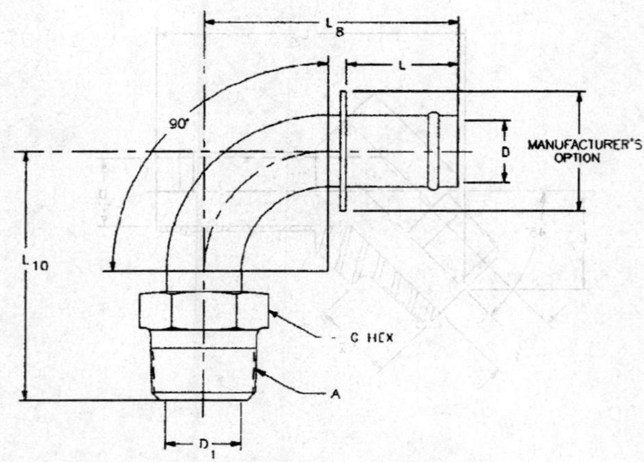

FIGURE 2D—90-DEGREE LONG DROP MALE PIPE HOSE FITTING

(431560)

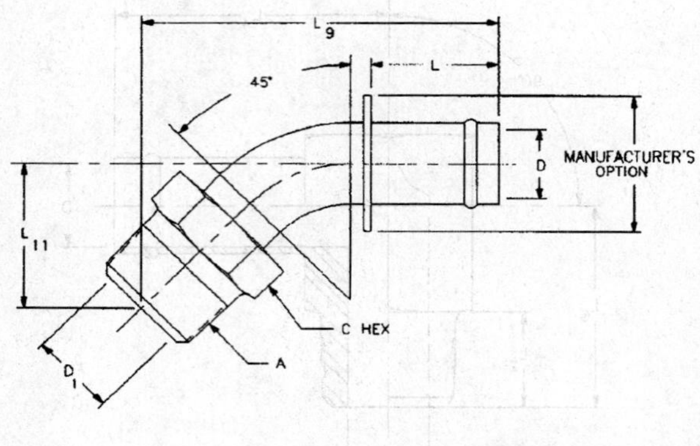

FIGURE 2E—45-DEGREE LONG DROP MALE PIPE HOSE FITTING

(431960)

TABLE 4C—DIMENSIONS OF 90-DEGREE AND 45-DEGREE LONG DROP MALE HOSE FITTINGS[1]

Nominal Hose I.D. mm	Hose Dash Size	A Dryseal Taper Thread NPTF	Thread Dash Size	C Nominal Hex inch	D from Table 3 mm	D1 Drill Dia mm	L ±6.4 mm	L_8 ±1.5 mm	L_9 ±1.5 mm	L_{10} ±1.5 mm	L_{11} ±1.5 mm
12	–8	1/2	–8	7/8	10.3	13.5	38.1	58.7	73.9	55.6	30.2
20	–12	1/2	–8	1	15.9	13.5	38.1	65.0	81.0	67.6	34.0
20	–12	3/4	–12	1-1/8	15.9	18.0	38.1	65.0	80.3	66.8	33.8
20	–12	1	–16	1-3/8	15.9	23.8	38.1	65.0	84.8	73.2	38.1
25	–16	3/4	–12	1-1/4	21.4	18.0	38.1	74.7	89.4	74.7	36.8
25	–16	1	–16	1-3/8	21.4	23.8	38.1	74.7	91.7	77.7	39.4
30	–20	1	–16	1-1/2	27.8	23.8	38.1	90.4	104.4	85.9	43.7
30	–20	1-1/4	–20	1-3/4	27.8	31.7	38.1	90.4	103.9	84.8	43.2
30	–20	1-1/2	–24	2	27.8	38.0	38.1	90.4	106.7	88.9	46.0
38	–24	1-1/4	–20	1-3/4	34.1	31.7	38.1	103.1	119.1	97.5	49.3
38	–24	1-1/2	–24	2	34.1	38.0	38.1	103.1	120.7	100.1	51.3
50	–32	2	–32	2-5/8	46.8	49.0	38.1	122.2	145.5	141.2	68.3

1. The use of a collar is optional and may be omitted if agreed to by the purchaser and the manufacturer.

MALE STRAIGHT THREAD O-RING BOSS TYPE

UNSPECIFIED DETAIL WITH RESPECT TO DIMENSIONS, TOLERANCES, CONTOURS, MATERIAL, WORKMANSHIP, AND SO ON, MUST CONFORM TO GENERAL SPECIFICATIONS FOR HYDRAULIC TUBE FITTINGS PER SAE J514 FIGURES 3B AND 10A. THE DIMENSIONAL DESIGNATIONS ON THE FIRST FIGURE IN EACH GROUP SHALL APPLY TO ALL OTHER FIGURES IN THAT GROUP EXCEPT AS SHOWN OTHERWISE. CODES SHOWN IN BRACKETS ADJACENT TO FIGURE NUMBERS REPRESENT RESPECTIVE FITTING IDENTIFICATION, IN ACCORDANCE WITH SAE J846.

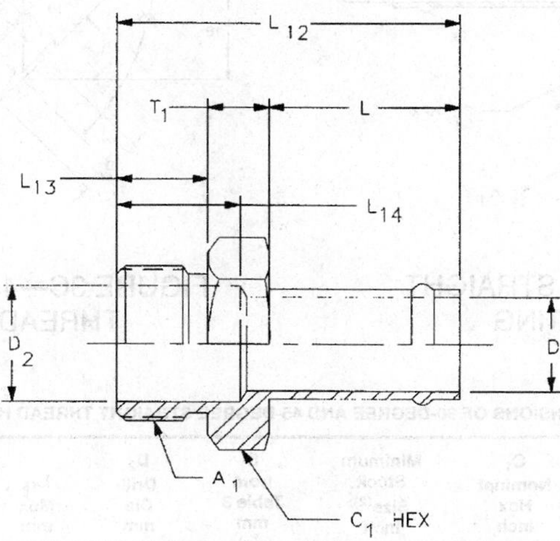

FIGURE 3A—MALE STRAIGHT THREAD HOSE CONNECTOR (430192)

TABLE 5A—DIMENSIONS OF MALE STRAIGHT THREAD HOSE CONNECTORS

Nominal Hose I.D. mm	Hose Dash Size	A_1 Nominal Straight Thread Size	Thread Dash Size	C_1 Nominal Hex Inch	D[(1)] from Table 3 mm	D_2[(1)] Drill Dia mm	L ±6.4 mm	L_{12} Max mm	L_{13} Min mm	L_{14} Max mm	T_1 Min mm
6	–4	7/16-20	–4	9/16	4.8	4.4	38.1	64.0	9.14	11.4	7.1
10	–6	9/16-18	–6	11/16	7.5	7.5	38.1	67.1	9.93	11.93	7.9
12	–8	3/4-16	–8	7/8	10.3	9.9	38.1	69.8	11.13	13.13	8.6
12	–8	7/8-14	–10	1	10.3	12.3	38.1	71.4	12.70	14.70	10.2
16	–10	7/8-14	–10	1	12.7	12.3	38.1	71.4	12.70	14.70	10.2
20	–12	7/8-14	–10	1	15.9	12.3	38.1	71.4	12.70	14.70	10.2
20	–12	1-1/16x12	–12	1-1/4	15.9	15.5	38.1	75.1	15.09	17.09	11.9
25	–16	1-1/16x12	–12	1-1/4	21.4	15.5	38.1	75.1	15.09	17.09	11.9
25	–16	1-5/16x12	–16	1-1/2	21.4	21.5	38.1	75.1	15.09	17.09	11.9
25	–16	1-5/8x12	–20	1-7/8	21.4	27.5	38.1	83.5	15.09	17.09	14.7
30	–20	1-5/8x12	–20	1-7/8	27.8	27.5	38.1	83.5	15.09	17.09	14.7
30	–20	1-7/8x12	–24	2-1/8	27.8	33.0	38.1	83.5	15.09	17.09	16.5
38	–24	1-5/8x12	–20	1-7/8	34.1	27.5	38.1	83.5	15.09	17.09	14.7
38	–24	1-7/8x12	–24	2-1/8	34.1	33.0	38.1	83.5	15.09	17.09	16.5
50	–32	2-1/2x12	–32	2-3/4	46.8	45.0	38.1	88.0	15.09	17.09	20.6

1. At the manufacturer's option, the through passage in Figure 3A may conform with the smaller diameter specified or the appropriate end may be counterbored to the larger diameter.

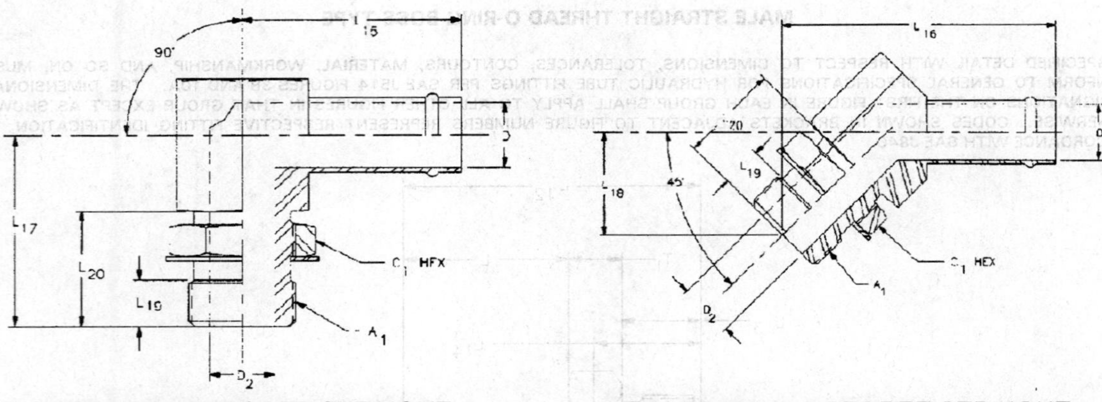

FIGURE 3B—90-DEGREE STRAIGHT THREAD HOSE FITTING
(431492)

FIGURE 3C—45-DEGREE STRAIGHT THREAD HOSE FITTING
(430392)

TABLE 5B—DIMENSIONS OF 90-DEGREE AND 45-DEGREE STRAIGHT THREAD HOSE FITTINGS[1]

Nominal Hose I.D. mm	Hose Dash Size	A_1 Nominal Straight Thread Size	Thread Dash Size	C_1 Nominal Hex Inch	Minimum Stock Size[2] Inch	D from Table 3 mm	D_2 Drill Dia mm	L_{15} Max mm	L_{16} Max mm	L_{17} ±1.5 mm	L_{18} ±1.5 mm	L_{19} Min mm	L_{20} Min mm
6	–4	7/16-20	–4	9/16	1/2	4.76	4.37	60.3	77.5	26.2	18.8	7.6	17.8
10	–6	9/16-18	–6	11/16	5/8	7.54	7.54	63.5	79.3	31.5	20.6	7.6	20.3
10	–6	3/4-16	–8	7/8	13/16	7.54	9.93	68.3	82.3	36.6	23.6	7.6	22.9
12	–8	9/16-18	–6	11/16	5/8	10.32	7.54	63.5	79.3	31.2	20.6	7.6	20.3
12	–8	3/4-16	–8	7/8	13/16	10.32	9.93	68.3	82.1	36.8	23.4	7.6	22.9
12	–8	7/8-14	–10	1	15/16	10.32	12.29	71.4	85.9	42.9	27.2	10.2	25.4
12	–8	1-1/16x12	–12	1-1/4	1-1/8	10.32	15.47	76.2	89.7	49.0	31.0	12.7	27.9
16	–10	3/4-16	–8	7/8	13/16	12.70	9.93	68.3	82.3	36.6	23.6	7.6	22.9
16	–10	7/8-14	–10	1	15/16	12.70	12.29	71.4	85.9	43.2	27.2	10.2	25.4
16	–10	1-1/16x12	–12	1-1/4	1-1/8	12.70	15.47	76.2	89.7	48.8	31.0	12.7	27.9
20	–12	7/8-14	–10	1	15/16	15.88	12.29	71.4	85.9	42.9	27.2	10.2	25.4
20	–12	1-1/16x12	–12	1-1/4	1-1/8	15.88	15.47	76.2	89.7	49.0	31.0	12.7	27.9
20	–12	1-3/16x12	–14	1-3/8	1-1/8	15.88	18.26	76.2	91.0	50.3	32.3	12.7	27.9
20	–12	1-5/16x12	–16	1-1/2	1-3/8	15.88	21.44	82.6	91.7	51.6	33.0	12.7	27.9
25	–16	1-1/16x12	–12	1-1/4	1-1/8	21.43	15.47	76.2	89.7	48.8	31.0	12.7	27.9
25	–16	1-3/16x12	–14	1-3/8	1-1/8	21.43	18.26	76.2	91.0	50.3	32.3	12.7	27.9
25	–16	1-5/16x12	–16	1-1/2	1-3/8	21.43	21.44	82.6	92.0	51.8	33.3	12.7	27.9
25	–16	1-5/8x12	–20	1-7/8	1-11/16	21.43	27.38	90.5	92.7	56.6	34.0	12.7	27.9
30	–20	1-5/16x12	–16	1-1/2	1-3/8	27.78	21.44	82.6	91.7	51.6	33.0	12.7	27.9
30	–20	1-5/8x12	–20	1-7/8	1-11/16	27.78	27.38	90.5	92.7	56.9	34.0	12.7	27.9
30	–20	1-7/8x12	–24	2-1/8	2	27.78	33.27	101.6	93.0	60.5	34.3	12.7	27.9
38	–24	1-5/8x12	–20	1-7/8	1-11/16	34.13	27.38	90.5	92.7	56.6	34.0	12.7	27.9
38	–24	1-7/8x12	–24	2-1/8	2	34.13	33.27	101.6	93.0	60.5	34.3	12.7	27.9
38	–24	2-1/2x12	–32	2-3/4	2-5/8	34.13	45.21	117.5	92.5	73.2	33.8	12.7	27.9
50	–32	2-1/2x12	–32	2-3/4	2-5/8	46.83	45.21	117.5	92.2	73.2	33.5	12.7	27.9

1. If specified by the purchaser, the fittings in Figure 3 may be furnished with the larger hexagon locknut shown in SAE J514 Figure 8B.
2. Forging, square, or hex form is at the manufacturer's option.

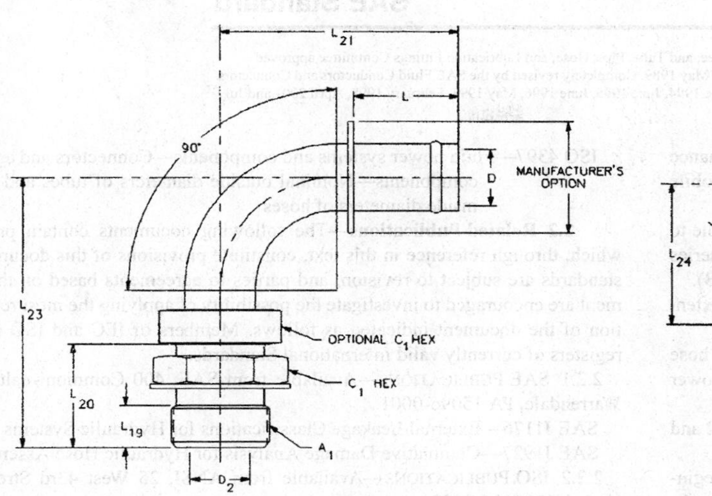

FIGURE 3D—90-DEGREE LONG DROP STRAIGHT THREAD HOSE FITTING

(431592)

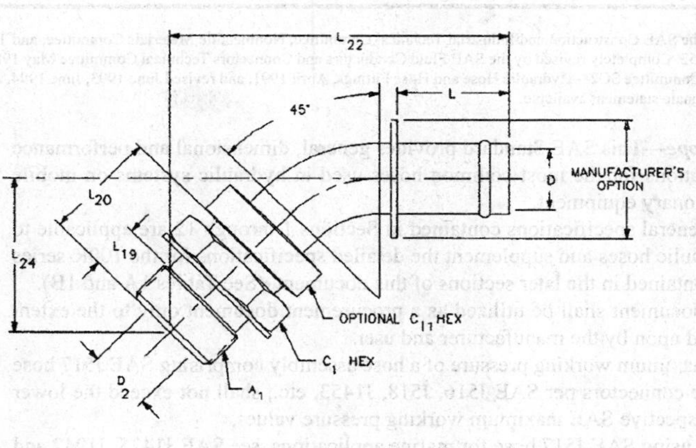

FIGURE 3E—45-DEGREE LONG DROP STRAIGHT THREAD HOSE FITTING

(431992)

TABLE 5C—DIMENSIONS 90-DEGREE AND 45-DEGREE LONG DROP STRAIGHT THREAD HOSE FITTINGS(1)

Nominal Hose I.D. mm	Hose Dash Size	A_1 Nominal Straight Thread Size	Thread Dash Size	C_1 Nominal Hex Inch	D from Table 3 mm	D_2 Drill Dia mm	L ±6.4 mm	L_{19} Min mm	L_{20} Min mm	L_{21} ±1.5 mm	L_{22} ±1.5 mm	L_{23} ±1.5 mm	L_{24} ±1.5 mm
12	–8	3/4-16	–8	7/8	10.3	9.9	38.1	7.6	22.9	58.7	77.0	60.5	33.3
12	–8	1-1/16x12	–12	1-1/4	10.3	15.5	38.1	12.7	27.9	58.7	83.8	69.9	40.1
20	–12	1-1/16x12	–12	1-1/4	15.9	15.5	38.1	12.7	27.9	65.0	89.7	80.3	43.2
20	–12	1-5/16x12	–16	1-1/2	15.9	21.5	38.1	12.7	27.9	65.0	90.9	81.8	44.5
25	–16	1-1/16x12	–12	1-1/4	21.4	15.5	38.1	12.7	27.9	74.7	97.3	85.9	45.0
25	–16	1-5/16x12	–16	1-1/2	21.4	21.5	38.1	12.7	27.9	74.7	97.3	85.9	45.0
25	–16	1-5/8x12	–20	1-7/8	21.4	27.5	38.1	12.7	27.9	74.7	97.3	85.9	45.0
30	–20	1-5/16x12	–16	1-1/2	27.8	21.5	38.1	12.7	27.9	90.4	108.7	92.2	48.5
30	–20	1-5/8x12	–20	1-7/8	27.8	27.5	38.1	12.7	27.9	90.4	108.7	92.2	48.5
30	–20	1-7/8x12	–24	2-1/8	27.8	33.0	38.1	12.7	27.9	90.4	108.7	92.2	48.5
38	–24	1-5/8x12	–20	1-7/8	34.1	27.5	38.1	12.7	27.9	103.1	122.9	103.1	53.1
38	–24	1-7/8x12	–24	2-1/8	34.1	33.0	38.1	12.7	27.9	103.1	122.9	103.1	53.1
38	–24	2-1/2x12	–32	2-3/4	34.1	45.0	38.1	12.7	27.9	103.1	122.9	103.1	53.1
50	–32	2-1/2x12	–32	2-3/4	46.8	45.0	38.1	12.7	27.9	122.2	143.3	138.2	65.8

1. The use of a collar is optional and may be omitted if agreed to by the purchaser and the manufacturer. If specified by the purchaser, the fittings in Figure 3 may be furnished with the larger hexagon locknut shown in SAE J514 Figure 8B.

16. Part Identification Number (PIN)—Hose fittings to this document shall be identified by a part identification number consisting of the following:

a. The SAE standard number J1231
b. The connection dash size followed by the hose dash size
c. The style designation code from SAE J1231
d. The material designation per SAE J846[1]

1. Table 9 and appendix.

For example, to designate a 90-degree long drop male pipe thread hose fitting with a 3/4 NPTF thread for use with –8 size hose, made from carbon steel:

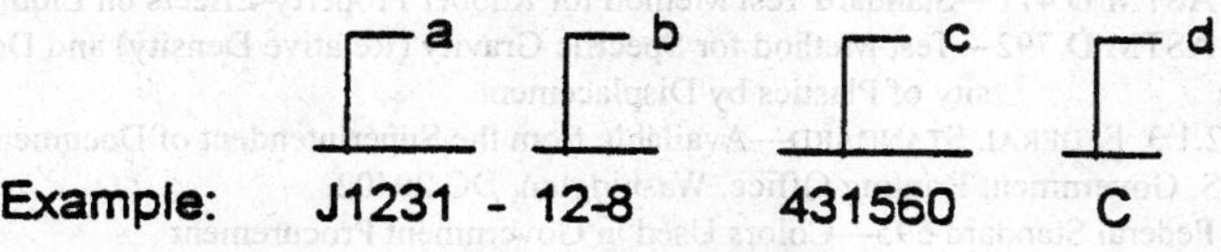

FIGURE 4—EXAMPLE PIN

HYDRAULIC HOSE—SAE J517 JUL2003 SAE Standard

Report of the SAE Construction and Industrial Technical Committee, Nonmetallic Materials Committee, and Tube, Pipe, Hose, and Lubrication Fittings Committee approved January 1952. Completely revised by the SAE Fluid Conductors and Connectors Technical Committee May 1989. Completely revised by the SAE Fluid Conductors and Connectors Technical Committee SC2—Hydraulic Hose and Hose Fittings, April 1991, and revised June 1993, June 1994, June 1995, June 1996, May 1997, February 1998, April 2001 and July 2003. Rationale statement available.

1. Scope—This SAE Standard provides general, dimensional and performance specifications for the most common hoses used in hydraulic systems on mobile and stationary equipment.

The general specifications contained in Sections 1 through 12 are applicable to all hydraulic hoses and supplement the detailed specifications for the 100R-series hoses contained in the later sections of this document. (See Tables 1A and 1B).

This document shall be utilized as a procurement document only to the extent as agreed upon by the manufacturer and user.

The maximum working pressure of a hose assembly comprising SAE J517 hose and hose connectors per SAE J516, J518, J1453, etc., shall not exceed the lower of the respective SAE maximum working pressure values.

When using SAE J517 hose for marine applications, see SAE J1475, J1942 and J1942-1.

The SAE J517 100R9, 100R10 and 100R11 hoses will be discontinued beginning with the year 2005, due to lack of demand.

The SAE J517 100R1A, 100R2A, 100R2B and 100R2BT will be discontinued beginning with the year 2005 due to lack of demand. For DOD orders after 2004, use 100R1AT and 100R2AT to replace 100R1A and 100R2A.

The SAE J517 100R2AT maximum working pressures will be replaced by the type S maximum working pressures beginning with the year 2006, eliminating the need to label 100R2 as type S.

The SAE J517 100R16 maximum working pressures will be replaced by the type S maximum working pressures with the year 2008, eliminating the need to label 100R16 as type S.

2. References

2.1 Applicable Publications—The following publications form a part of this specification to the extent specified herein. Unless otherwise indicated, the latest issue of the publications shall apply.

2.1.1 SAE PUBLICATIONS—Available from SAE, 400 Commonwealth Drive, Warrendale, PA 15096-0001.

SAE J343—Test and Test Procedures for SAE 100R Series Hydraulic Hose and Hose Assemblies

SAE J516—Hydraulic Hose Fittings

SAE J518—Hydraulic Flanged Tube, Pipe and Hose Connections, Four-Bolt Split Flange Type

SAE J846—Coding Systems for Identification of Fluid Conductors and Connectors

SAE J1273—Recommended Practices for Hydraulic Hose Assemblies

SAE J1401—Road Vehicle—Hydraulic Brake Hose Assemblies for Use with Nonpetroleum-Base Hydraulic Fluids (Appendix A, Table A1, Hose Manufacturers Identification Code—Colored Yarn Assignments)

SAE J1453—Fitting—O-Ring Face Seal

SAE J1475—Hydraulic Hose Fittings for Marine Applications

SAE J1942—Hose and Hose Assemblies for Marine Applications

SAE J1942-1—Qualified Hoses for Marine Applications

2.1.2 ASTM PUBLICATIONS—Available from ASTM, 100 Barr Harbor Drive, West Conshohocken, PA 19428-2959.

ASTM D 380—Standard Test Methods for Rubber Hose

ASTM D 471—Standard Test Method for Rubber Property-Effects on Liquids

ASTM D 792—Test Method for Specific Gravity (Relative Density) and Density of Plastics by Displacement

2.1.3 FEDERAL STANDARD—Available from the Superintendent of Documents, U.S. Government Printing Office, Washington, DC 20402.

Federal Standard 595—Colors Used in Government Procurement

2.1.4 MILITARY PUBLICATIONS—Available from Naval Publications and Forms Center, 700 Robbins Avenue, Philadelphia, PA 19111.

MIL-PRF-83282—Hydraulic Fluid, Fire Resistant Synthetic Hydrocarbon Base, NATO Code Number H-537

MIL-H-8446—Hydraulic Fluid, Nonpetroleum Base, Aircraft

MIL-PRF-7808—Lubricating Oil, Aircraft Turbine Engine, Synthetic Base

2.1.5 ISO PUBLICATIONS—Available from ANSI, 25 West 43rd Street, New York, NY 10036-8002.

ISO 4397—Fluid power systems and components—Connectors and associated components—Nominal outside diameters of tubes and nominal inside diameters of hoses

2.2 Related Publications—The following documents contain provisions which, through reference in this text, constitute provisions of this document. All standards are subject to revision, and parties to agreements based on this document are encouraged to investigate the possibility of applying the most recent edition of the document indicated as follows. Members of IEC and ISO maintain registers of currently valid International Standards.

2.2.1 SAE PUBLICATIONS—Available from SAE, 400 Commonwealth Drive, Warrendale, PA 15096-0001.

SAE J1176—External Leakage Classifications for Hydraulic Systems

SAE J1927—Cumulative Damage Analysis for Hydraulic Hose Assemblies

2.2.2 ISO PUBLICATIONS—Available from ANSI, 25 West 43rd Street, New York, NY 10036-8002.

ISO 1402—Rubber and plastics hoses and hose assemblies—Hydrostatic testing

ISO 1436-1—Rubber hoses and hose assemblies—Wire reinforced hydraulic type—Specification

ISO 1817—Rubber vulcanized—Determination of the effect of liquids

ISO 3862-1—Rubber hoses and hose assemblies—Rubber-covered, spiral wire reinforced, hydraulic type—Specification

ISO 3949—Plastics hoses and hose assemblies—Thermoplastics, textile-reinforced, hydraulic type—Specification

ISO 4079—Rubber hoses and hose assemblies—Textile-reinforced hydraulic type—Specification

ISO 4671—Rubber and plastic hoses and hose assemblies—Methods of measurement of dimensions

ISO 6803—Rubber or plastic hoses and hose assemblies—Hydraulic pressure impulse test without flexing

ISO 6945—Rubber hoses—Determination of abrasion resistance of the outer cover

ISO 11237-1—Rubber hoses and hose assemblies—Rubber covered, wire braid compact design, hydraulic type specification

3. Age Control—Age control of rubber hose is a method for designating a period of time, following manufacture, during which it is reasonable to expect that this product retains full capabilities for rendering the intended service, provided it has been stored as prescribed in SAE J1273.

Hose and hose assemblies are affected by exposure to ozone, oxygen, heat, sunlight, rain, and other similar environmental factors. Storage of bulk hose and hose assemblies should be in such a manner that exposure to these environmental factors is controlled as much as possible. (See SAE J1273 for selection, installation and maintenance of hose and hose assemblies).

Hose and hose assemblies should be stored, handled, shipped and used in such a manner as to facilitate first-in first-out usages based on manufacturing date on hose or hose assembly.

Hose, in bulk form or in hose assemblies passing visual inspection and proof test, shall be acceptable for use up to and including 40 quarters (10 years) from the date of manufacture. Shelf life of thermoplastic and polytetrafluoroethylene hose is considered to be unlimited.

4. Hose Connectors—Hydraulic hose is rarely used without connectors. Hose with connectors attached are commonly referred to as hose assemblies. The general and dimensional standards for hydraulic hose connectors are contained in SAE J516. SAE J516 connectors are identified by a code system as specified in SAE J846. The hose code, in accordance with SAE J846, for use with their respective connectors is shown in Appendix B.

SAE J1475 covers general and performance specifications for hydraulic hose connectors when used in marine applications.

5. Hose Assemblies—Hose assemblies may be fabricated by the manufacturer, an agent for or customer of the manufacturer, or by the user. Fabrication of permanently attached connectors to hydraulic hose requires specialized assembly equipment. Field attachable connectors (screw style and segment clamp style) can usually be assembled without specialized equipment although many manufacturers provide equipment to assist in this operation.

TABLE 1A—SUMMARY OF SAE J517 100R-SERIES HOSE MAXIMUM WORKING PRESSURES (MPa)[1]
Metric Size[2] (SAE Dash Size)

Hose Type	5 (–3)	6.3 (–4)	8 (–5)	10 (–6)	12.5 (–8)	16 (–10)	19 (–12)	25 (16)	31.5 (–20)	38 (–24)	51 (–32)	63 (–40)	78 (–48)	89 (–56)	102 (–64)
100R1	21	19.2	17.5	15.7	14	10.5	8.7	7	4.3	3.5	2.6				
100R1S[3]	25	22.5	21.5	18	16	13	10.5	8.8	6.3	5	4				
100R2	35	35	29.7	28	24.5	19.2	15.7	14	11.3	8.7	7.8	7			
100R2S[3]	41.5	40	35	33	27.5	25	21.5	16.5	12.5	9	8	7			
100R3	10.5	8.7	8.4	7.8	7	6.1	5.2	3.9	2.6						
100R4							2.1	1.7	1.4	1.05	0.7	0.4	0.4	0.3	0.25
100R6	3.5	2.8	2.8	2.8	2.8	2.4	2.1								
100R7	21	19.2	17.5	15.7	14	10.5	8.7	7							
100R8	35	35		28	24.5	19.2	15.7	14							
100R9				31.5	28		21	21	17.5	14	14				
100R10	70	61		52.5	43.5		35	28	21	17.5	17.5				
100R11	87	78		70	52.5		43.5	35	24.5	21	21	17.5			
100R12				28	28	28	28	28	21	17.5	17.5				
100R13							35	35	35	35	35				
100R15				42	42		42	42	42	42					
100R16		35	29.7	28	24.5	19.2	15.7	14	11.3						
100R16S[4]	41.5	40	35	33	27.5	25	21.5	16.5	12.5						
100R17		21	21	21	21	21	21	21							
100R18	21	21	21	21	21	21	21	21							

NOTE—Minimum burst pressure of 100R hoses is at least 4 times maximum working pressure.

1. See Appendix A for conversion table from MPa to psi.
2. Metric Size is in mm (Ref. ISO 4397).
3. Type S pressures match ISO 1436 for types 1SN, 2SN.
4. Type S pressures match ISO 11237 for type 2SC.

TABLE 1B—SUMMARY OF SAE J517 100R-SERIES HOSE MAXIMUM WORKING PRESSURES (MPa)[1]
Metric Size[2] (SAE Dash Size)

Hose Type	3.2 (–3)	5 (–4)	6.3 (–5)	8 (–6)	10 (–7)	11 (–8)	12.5 (–10)	16 (–12)	19 (–14)	22 (–16)	25 (–18)	29 (–20)	35 (–24)	46 (–32)	60 (–40)	76 (–48)
100R5		21	21	15.7		14	12.2	10.5		5.6		4.3	3.5	2.4	2.4	1.4
100R14	10.5	10.5	10.5	10.5	10.5	7	5.6	5.6	5.6	5.6	5.6	4.2				

NOTE—Minimum burst pressure of 100R hoses is at least 4 times maximum working pressure.

1. See Appendix A for conversion table from MPa to psi.
2. Metric Size is in mm (Ref. ISO 4397).

SAE J517 hose from one manufacturer is usually not compatible with SAE J516 connectors supplied by another manufacturer. It is the responsibility of the fabricator to consult the manufacturer's written assembly instructions or the manufacturers directly before intermixing hose and connectors from two manufacturers. Similarly, assembly equipment from one manufacturer is usually not interchangeable with that of another manufacturer. It is the responsibility of the fabricator to consult the manufacturer's written instructions or the manufacturer directly for proper assembly equipment. Always follow the manufacturer's instructions for proper preparation and fabrication of hose assemblies.

6. Application Factors—Hydraulic hose assemblies have a finite life and factors which will reduce life include:

a. Flexing the hose to less than the specified minimum bend radius
b. Twisting, pulling, kinking, crushing, or abrading the hose
c. Operating above maximum and below minimum temperature
d. Exposing the hose to surge pressures above the maximum working pressure
e. Intermixing hose, connectors, or assembly equipment not recommended by the manufacturer or not following the manufacturer's instructions for fabricating hose assemblies

Surge pressures, noted in item d, are rapid and transient rises in pressure. Surge pressures will not be indicated on many common pressure gauges and can best be identified on electronic measuring instruments with a high-frequency response.

Refer to SAE J1273 for additional information on application factors.

The test requirements for each 100R-series hose is detailed in this document. Specific procedures for conducting each test are contained in SAE J343. The specified tests provide a baseline for performance capability of a hose assembly under controlled laboratory conditions. It is recognized that hydraulic systems will seldom duplicate these test parameters precisely. The hydraulic designer must consider the system demands on the hose assembly and correlate those demands with the specified requirements, with particular concern for the frequency and amplitude of pressure fluctuations. Rapid pressure cycling with a return to zero accelerates fatigue failures.

7. Size Designations—Hose sizes are normally designated by the nominal hose inside diameter expressed in millimeters (mm) or by the SAE dash size which, except for SAE 100R5 and 100R14, represents the number of sixteenth inch increments in the hose inside diameter. For these exceptions, the SAE dash size represents the number of sixteenth inch increments in the outside diameter of tubing having approximately the same inside diameter as that of the hose. See dimensional tables for the respective hoses.

8. Hose Identification—Except for hose with a wire braided exterior, the entire length of hose shall be legibly marked with one or more stripes parallel to the longitudinal axis. Marking shall include, but is not limited to, the SAE hose specification number, including type designation where applicable, the hose dash size number, the fractional (in) nominal hose inside diameter, the maximum working pressure of the hose and the date of manufacture, repeated with the first letter of each repeat not more than 760 mm from the first letter of that preceding.

No mention of the burst pressure or the design factor is allowed on the hose. This information could be misinterpreted and result in a hose being used above its maximum working pressure.

Working pressures may be shown on a hose in numerous ways and is not limited to the following examples:

EXAMPLES: XXXX MAX. W.P.
XXXX Maximum W.P.
XXXX Max. Working Pressure

Electrically nonconductive 100R7, 100R8 and 100R18 thermoplastic hoses shall have an orange-colored cover. (Reference color, chip #22510, Federal Standard 595). Also, in addition to the information required previously, the word nonconductive or electrically nonconductive shall appear in each marking repeat.

The date of manufacture may be expressed as month, day, and year (2/19/88), month and year (2/88), or quarter and year (1Q88) at the option of the manufacturer.

Date of manufacture is optional with the manufacturer on SAE 100R7, 100R8 and 100R18.

SAE J517 hoses are referenced by listing, in sequence, the 100R number (100R1, 100R7, etc.), the hose type letters (A, AT, B, or BT) where applicable, and the hose dash size number (–4, –16, –24, etc.).

EXAMPLES:	100R2AT-8	12.5 mm ID, 2 Wire, Type AT
	100R2S-8	12.5 mm I.D., 2 Wire, Type S thin cover, ISO working pressure
	100R4-32	51 mm ID, Suction Hose
	100R14B-16	22 mm ID, Electrically Conductive PTFE Hose

For hose with a wire braided exterior, information shall be incorporated on a tag or tape applied to each coil or length of bulk hose. Additionally, except for 100R14, a colored yarn shall be incorporated into the wall of the hose, identifying the manufacturer. The color shall be as designated by the Rubber Manufacturers Association. (See SAE J1401, Appendix A, Table A1).

*9. **Orientation of Offset Elbow Ends in a Hose Assembly***—For double elbow assemblies, it is imperative that the method of description and measurement provide the desired displacement rather than its mirror image. To achieve this, either end may be selected as the reference point, provided angle displacement is determined appropriately (clockwise or counterclockwise) for the reference selected.

As shown in Figure 1, with the centerline of the near end as a base reference, angular displacement is measured counterclockwise to the centerline of the far end.

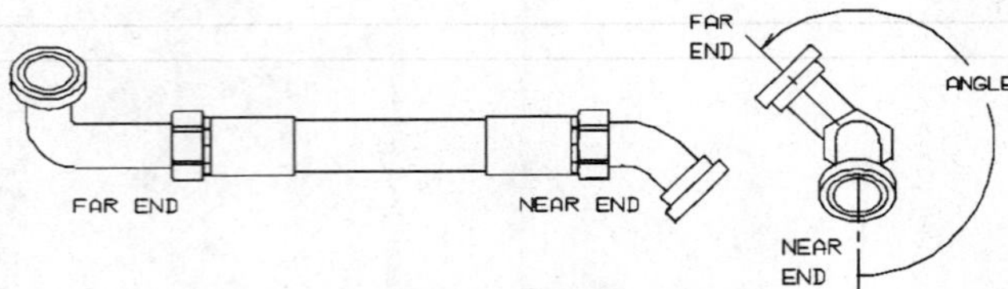

FIGURE 1—NEAR END REFERENCE—MEASURED COUNTER-CLOCKWISE

As shown in Figure 2, with the centerline of the far end as a base reference, angular displacement is measured clockwise to the centerline of the near end.

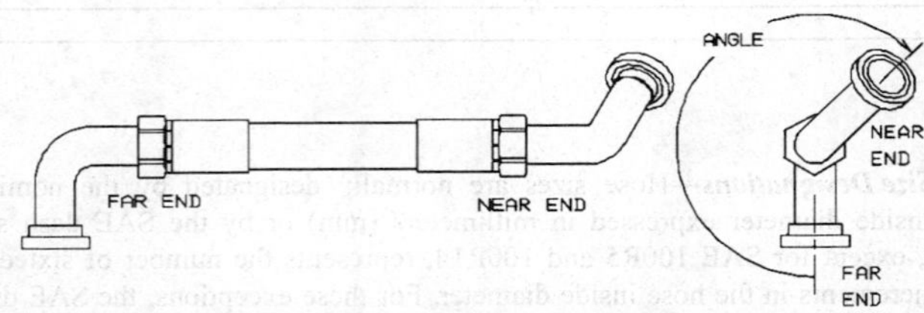

FIGURE 2—FAR END REFERENCE—MEASURED CLOCKWISE

Displacement angle may have any value up to 360 degrees. Please note that making the angle determination in the wrong direction will result in an unacceptable part.

Unless otherwise specified, a tolerance of ±3 degrees is acceptable for assembly lengths up to 610 mm inclusive, and ±5 degrees for assembly lengths over 610 mm.

Try to avoid use of double elbow hose assemblies. Twisting of the hose during installation may occur. The relative location of the natural curvature in the hose may induce a twist during pressure cycling. Twisted hose may reduce the life of the hose assembly.

*10. **Assembly Length***—Unless otherwise specified, assembly length shall be the overall length measured from the extreme end of one connector to the extreme end of the other, except for O-ring face seal type connectors which shall be measured from the sealing face. Where elbow connectors are used, measurement shall be to the centerline of the sealing surface of the elbow end (The sealing surface of female flared elbow connectors shall be the centerline of the outer end of the cone seat). See Figure 3.

Method of measurement should be specified. Tolerances on assembly length shall be as in Table 2.

*11. **Tests***—Unless otherwise agreed upon between the manufacturer and purchaser, tests for evaluating conformance of product with specifications shall be on the basis of Qualification Tests and Inspection Tests set forth in this document. Tests may be conducted by the manufacturer, the purchaser, or both, as decreed by the purchaser. The tests, sampling, and criteria applicable to both test classifications are given in Table 3 and the detailed specifications and tables for each hose. All tests shall be conducted in accordance with the procedures in SAE J343.

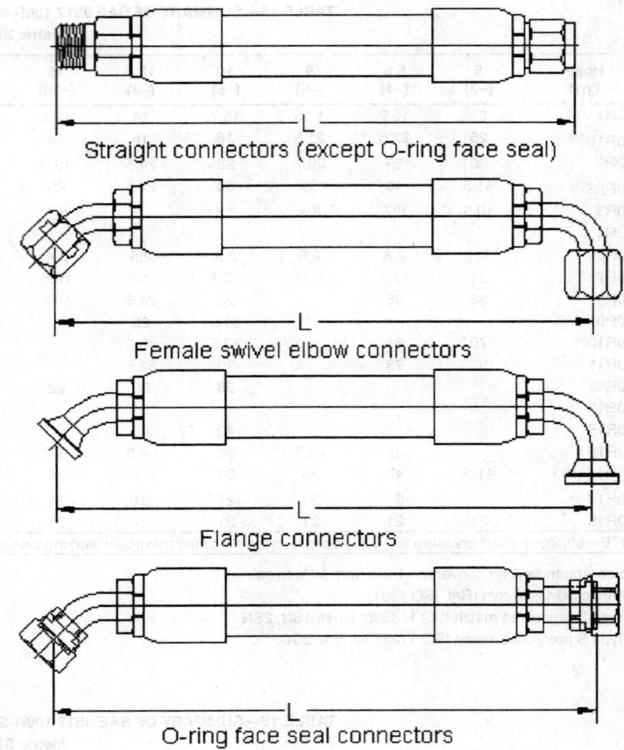

FIGURE 3—ASSEMBLY LENGTH MEASUREMENT

TABLE 2—TOLERANCES ON ASSEMBLY LENGTH

Length	Tolerance (Plus or Minus) mm
Up to 300 mm, included	3
Over 300 mm through 450 mm, included	5
Over 450 mm through 900 mm, included	7
Over 900 mm	1%(1)

1. Measured to nearest whole millimeter.

11.1 Qualification Tests—The following are tests required for qualification of various 100R-series hoses specified in SAE J517. Some of these tests do not apply to certain 100R-series hose types. See Table 3 to determine which of these qualification tests are specified for each 100R-series hose type. Table 3 also provides specific requirements for each hose type where temperatures, percent length change and impulse requirements vary by hose type. Some hose types like 100R1, R5, R9 and R14 have added special impulse requirements which are specified in J517 immediately after the hose construction for these hose types. For such hose types, Table 3 states "See 100R1" or "See 100R5", etc., for impulse requirements. Some other hose types like 100R7, R8, R14 and R18 have specialized conductivity tests and Table 3 again states "See 100R7" or "See 100R8", etc. for the specific test requirements.

11.1.1 Dimensional Check Test (All Samples)—Shall conform to the dimensions in the respective table for that 100R-series hose type and these detailed specifications.

11.1.2 Proof Test (All Samples)—Shall not leak at a proof pressure equal to 2X the maximum working pressure for that type and size of hose. The exception is 100R14, use the proof pressure listed for the hose type and size.

11.1.3 Change in Length Test (One Sample)—When pressurized to the maximum working pressure, shall not exceed the percentage change listed in Table 3 for that 100R-series type of hose.

11.1.4 Burst Test (One 460 mm Free Hose Length Assembly)—Shall not leak or fail below the minimum burst pressure equal to 4X the maximum working pressure for that type and size of hose. The exception is 100R14, use the minimum burst pressure listed for the hose type and size.

11.1.5 LEAKAGE TEST (TWO 300 mm FREE HOSE LENGTH ASSEMBLIES)—Shall not leak or fail at the leakage pressure stipulated in SAE J343 for that type and size of hose.

11.1.6 COLD BEND TEST (ONE ASSEMBLY)—Shall exhibit no cover cracks or leakage. Exposure shall be at the temperature listed in Table 3 for that 100R-series type of hose.

11.1.7 OIL RESISTANCE TEST (ONE SAMPLE EACH OF HOSE INNER TUBE AND COVER)—Tube and cover samples shall be prepared in accordance with ASTM D 380, and tested in accordance with ASTM D 471. After 70 h immersion in ASTM IRM 903 oil at the temperature specified in Table 3 for that type of hose, the volume change of the inner tube and cover shall be between the limits listed for that type of hose in Table 3.

11.1.8 OZONE RESISTANCE TEST (TWO SAMPLES)—Specimens shall be subjected to an atmosphere comprised of air and ozone with an ozone partial pressure of 50 mPa (50 parts of ozone per 100 million parts of air) at standard atmospheric conditions at an ambient temperature of 40 °C. After 70 h exposure, specimens shall not show evidence of cracking or deterioration when viewed with seven-power magnification while still in a stressed condition.

11.1.9 IMPULSE TEST (FOUR UNAGED ASSEMBLIES)—When tested with circulating petroleum-base hydraulic fluid at the percentage of maximum working pressure and temperature listed in Table 3, hose assemblies shall withstand the minimum number of cycles specified in Table 3 for that type of hose, without leakage or other malfunction.

11.1.10 RESISTANCE TO VACUUM TEST (ONE SAMPLE)—After 5 min at the absolute pressure specified in Table 3 for that type of hose, there shall be no evidence of hose blistering or collapse.

11.1.11 VISUAL EXAMINATION (ALL SAMPLES)

11.2 Inspection Tests—Inspection tests listed as follows shall be performed on two samples representing each lot of 150 to 3000 m of bulk hose. Lots of less than 150 m of hose need not be subjected to these tests if a lot has been tested and met the requirements within the previous 12-month period. Requirements shall be same as for corresponding Qualification Tests (see 11.1):

a. Dimensional Check Test
b. Proof Test
c. Change in Length Test
d. Burst Test

Visual Examination is required for all hose and/or hose assemblies.

Hose manufacturing facilities that are ISO 9000 or ISO/TS 16949 certified with a quality management system, which undergoes routine assessments by an accredited third party registrar, may use their documented inspection test procedures in lieu of the inspection test requirements listed above.

12. Inspection Retests and Rejection—In the event of failure of one or more samples to meet any of the Inspection Tests specified, the product shall be resampled and retested for the test or tests in which it failed. Twice the number of samples designated under the initial test procedure shall be selected from the lot in question for such retests, and failure of any of the retested samples shall be cause for rejection of the entire lot.

13. Steel Wire Reinforced, Rubber Covered Hydraulic Hose (SAE 100R1)—This section covers hose for use with petroleum base hydraulic fluids within a temperature range of –40 to +100 °C and with water base hydraulic fluids within the temperature ranges agreed upon by the manufacturers of both the hose and the fluid. Operating temperatures in excess of +100 °C with petroleum base hydraulic fluids may materially reduce the life of the hose. Maximum working pressure and minimum bend radius are specified in Table 4.

It should be noted that the detailed specifications which follow shall be supplemented by the general specifications given at the beginning of this document.

13.1 Dimensions—Dimensions and tolerances applicable to this hose are given in Table 4. The inside diameter of the hose shall be concentric with the outside diameter of the hose and the outer surface of the reinforcement within the limits in Table 5.

13.2 Hose Construction

13.2.1 TYPE A—This hose shall consist of an inner tube of oil resistant synthetic rubber, a single steel wire braid reinforcement, and an oil and weather resistant synthetic rubber cover. A ply or braid of suitable material may be used over the inner tube and/or over the wire reinforcement to anchor the synthetic rubber to the wire.

13.2.2 TYPE AT—This hose shall be of the same construction as Type A, except having a cover designed to assemble with fittings which do not require removal of the cover or a portion thereof.

13.2.3 TYPE S—This hose shall have the same construction as Type AT and working pressures of ISO 1436-1, Type 1SN.

13.3 Qualification—For qualification to this section, hose and/or hose assemblies made therefrom shall comply with the following test and the tests specified in Table 3, and conform to the requirements of 11.1.

13.3.1 IMPULSE TEST (FOUR UNAGED ASSEMBLIES)—Hose assemblies, when tested at 125% of the maximum working pressure for hose sizes 25 mm (–16) and smaller and 100% of the maximum working pressure for hose sizes 31.5 mm (-20) and larger, with 100 °C circulating petroleum-base test fluid, shall withstand a minimum of 150 000 cycles without leakage or other malfunction.

13.4 Inspection Tests—Inspection tests specified in 11.2 for bulk hose shall be performed.

TABLE 3—SAE J517 QUALIFICATION TEST REQUIREMENTS

Type of Test	100R1	100R2	100R3	100R4	100R5	100R6	100R7	100R8	100R9	100R10	100R11	100R12	100R13	100R14	100R15	100R16	100R17	100R18
Dimensional Check	X	X	X	X	X	X	X	X	X	X	X	X	X	X	X	X	X	X
Proof	X	X	X	X	X	X	X	X	X	X	X	X	X	X	X	X	X	X
Change in Length (%)	+2 / –4	+2 / –4	+2 / –4	+2 / –4	+2 / –4	+2 / –4	+3 / –3	+3 / –3	+2 / –4	+2 / –4	+2 / –4	+2 / –2	+2 / –2	+2 / –4	+2 / –2	+2 / –4	+2 / –4	+3 / –3
Burst	X	X	X	X	X	X	X	X	X	X	X	X	X	X	X	X	X	X
Leakage	X	X	X	X	X	X	X	X	X	X	X	X	X	X	X	X	X	X
Cold Bend (°C)	–40	–40	–40	–40	–40	–40	–40	–40	–40	–40	–40	–40	–40	–54	–40	–40	–40	–40
Volume Change at +100 °C Tube and Cover –0 / 100%	X	X	X	X	X	X			X	X	X					X	X	
Volume Change at +100 °C Tube and Cover –15 / 35%							X	X										X
Volume Change at +121 °C Tube –0 / 100%												X	X		X			
Volume Change at +121 °C Cover –0 /125%												X	X		X			
Ozone Resistance 70 Hours at +40 °C	X	X	X	X	X	X	X	X	X	X	X	X	X		X	X	X	X
Impulse Test Temperature (°C)	+100	+100	+100		+100		+93	+93	+100	+100	+100	+121	+121	+204	+121	+100	+100	+93
Impulse Test % of Working Pressure	See 100R1	133	133		See 100R5		125	133	133	133	133	133	120	See 100R14	120	133	133	133
Impulse Test Minimum Cycles	See 100R1	200 000	200 000		See 100R5		150 000	200 000	See 100R9	400 000	400 000	500 000	500 000	150 000	500 000	200 000	200 000	200 000
Vacuum Resistance at Absolute Pressure				17 kPa														
Electrical Conductivity (For Thermoplastic Only)							See 100R7	See 100R8										See 100R18
Electrical Conductivity (For PTFE Only)														See 100R14				
Specific Gravity (PTFE Tube)														See 100R14				
Visual Examination	X	X	X	X	X	X	X	X	X	X	X	X	X	X	X	X	X	X

TABLE 4—DIMENSIONS AND SPECIFICATIONS FOR SAE 100R1 HOSE
Dimensions are in Millimeters

Metric Size(1)	SAE Dash Size(2)	ID Min	ID Max	Reinforce-ment Dia Min	Reinforce-ment Dia Max	OD Type A Min	OD Type A Max	OD Type AT Max	Cover Thickness(3) Type AT Min	Cover Thickness(3) Type AT Max	Max Working Pressure MPa	Max Working Pressure Type S(4) MPa	Min Burst and Proof Pressure have	Min Bend Radius(5)
5	–3	4.6	5.4	8.9	10.1	11.9	13.5	12.5	0.8	1.5	21	25.0	been	90
6.3	–4	6.2	7.0	10.6	11.7	15.1	16.7	14.1	0.8	1.5	19.2	22.5	deleted	100
8	–5	7.7	8.5	12.1	13.3	16.7	18.3	15.7	0.8	1.5	17.5	21.5	from	115
10	–6	9.3	10.1	14.5	15.7	19.0	20.6	18.1	0.8	1.5	15.7	18.0	this table	125
12.5	–8	12.3	13.5	17.5	19.0	22.2	23.8	21.5	0.8	1.5	14	16.0	See para	180
16	–10	15.5	16.7	20.6	22.2	25.4	27.0	24.7	0.8	1.5	10.5	13.0	11.1.2,	205
19	–12	18.6	19.8	24.6	26.2	29.4	31.0	28.6	0.8	1.5	8.7	10.5	11.1.4	240
25	–16	25.0	26.4	32.5	34.1	36.9	39.3	36.6	0.8	1.5	7	8.7		300
31.5	–20	31.4	33.0	39.3	41.7	44.4	47.6	44.8	1.0	2.0	4.3	6.2		420
38	–24	37.7	39.3	45.6	48.0	50.8	54.0	52.0	1.3	2.5	3.5	5.0		500
51	–32	50.4	52.0	58.7	61.9	65.1	68.3	65.9	1.3	2.5	2.6	4.0		630

1. Metric Size is in mm (Ref. ISO 4397).
2. SAE Dash Size is equal to the hose ID, expressed in 1/16's of an inch.
3. Cover thickness shall be measured by means of a dial indicator depth gage having a rounded foot placed parallel to the hose, bridging a groove obtained by stripping a 12.5 to 25 mm width of cover from the hose. A mandrel should be placed in the hose bore to insure freedom from misalignment.
4. Type S pressures are the same as ISO 1436-1, 1SN.
5. Bend radius measured at inside of bend.

TABLE 5—HOSE CONCENTRICITY (100R1)
Dimensions are in Millimeters

Hose Size	Concentricity, FIR ID to OD	Concentricity, FIR ID to Reinforcement
Up to 6.3 mm (–4), included	0.8	0.4
Over 6.3 mm (–4) to 19 mm (–12), included	1.0	0.6
Over 19 mm (–12)	1.3	0.8

14. High Pressure, Steel Wire Reinforced, Rubber Covered Hydraulic Hose (SAE 100R2)—This section covers hose for use with petroleum base hydraulic fluids within a temperature range of –40 to +100 °C and with water base hydraulic fluids within the temperature ranges agreed upon by the manufacturers of both the hose and the fluid. Operating temperatures in excess of +100 °C with petroleum base hydraulic fluids may materially reduce the life of the hose. Maximum working pressure and minimum bend radius are specified in Table 6.

It should be noted that the detailed specifications which follow shall be supplemented by the general specifications given at the beginning of this document.

14.1 Dimensions—Dimensions and tolerances applicable to this hose are given in Table 6. The inside diameter of the hose shall be concentric with the outside diameter of the hose and the outer surface of the reinforcement within the limits in Table 7.

14.2 Hose Construction—This hose shall consist of an inner tube of oil resistant synthetic rubber, steel wire reinforcement according to the hose type detailed in 14.2.1 through 14.2.4 and an oil and weather resistant synthetic rubber cover. A ply or braid of suitable material may be used over the inner tube and/or over the wire reinforcement to anchor the synthetic rubber to the wire.

14.2.1 TYPE A—This hose shall have two braids of steel wire reinforcement.

14.2.2 TYPE B—This hose shall have two spiral plies and one braid of steel wire reinforcement.

14.2.3 TYPE AT—This hose shall be of the same construction as Type A, except having a cover designed to assemble with fittings which do not require removal of the cover or a portion thereof.

14.2.4 TYPE BT—This hose shall be of the same construction as Type B, except having a cover designed to assemble with fittings which do not require removal of the cover or a portion thereof.

14.2.5 TYPE S—This hose is the same construction as Type AT and working pressures of ISO 1436-1 Type 2SN.

14.3 Qualification—For qualification to this section, hose and/or hose assemblies made therefrom shall comply with the tests specified in Table 3, and conform to the requirements of 11.1.

14.4 Inspection Tests—Inspection tests specified in 11.2 for bulk hose shall be performed.

15. Double Fiber Braid (Nonmetallic), Rubber Covered Hydraulic Hose (SAE 100R3)—This section covers hose for use with petroleum base hydraulic fluids within a temperature range of –40 to +100 °C and with water base hydraulic fluids within the temperature ranges agreed upon by the manufacturers of both the hose and the fluid. Operating temperatures in excess of +100 °C with petroleum base hydraulic fluids may materially reduce the life of the hose. Maximum working pressure and minimum bend radius are specified in Table 8.

It should be noted that the detailed specifications which follow shall be supplemented by the general specifications given at the beginning of this document.

15.1 Dimensions—Dimensions and tolerances applicable to this hose are given in Table 8. The inside diameter and outside diameter of the hose shall be concentric within the limits in Table 9.

15.2 Hose Construction—This hose shall consist of an inner tube of oil resistant synthetic rubber, two braids of suitable fiber, and an oil and weather resistant synthetic rubber cover.

15.3 Qualification—For qualification to this section, hose and/or hose assemblies made therefrom shall comply with the tests specified in Table 3, and conform to the requirements of 11.1.

15.4 Inspection Tests—Inspection tests specified in 11.2 for bulk hose shall be performed.

TABLE 6—DIMENSIONS AND SPECIFICATIONS FOR SAE 100R2 HOSE
Dimensions are in Millimeters

Metric Size(1)	SAE Dash Size(2)	ID Min	ID Max	Reinforcement Dia Min	Reinforcement Dia Max	OD Type A and D Min	OD Type A and D Max	OD Type AT and DT Max	Cover Thickness(3) Type AT and DT Min	Cover Thickness(3) Type AT and DT Max	Max Working Pressure MPa	Max Working Pressure Type S(4) MPa	Min Burst and Proof Pressure have	Min Bend Radius(5)
5	–3	4.6	5.4	10.6	11.7	15.1	16.7	14.1	0.8	1.5	35	41.5	been	90
6.3	–4	6.2	7.0	12.1	13.3	16.7	18.3	15.7	0.8	1.5	35	40.0	deleted	100
8	–5	7.7	8.5	13.7	14.9	18.3	19.8	17.3	0.8	1.5	29.7	35.0	from	115
10	–6	9.3	10.1	16.1	17.3	20.6	22.2	19.7	0.8	1.5	28	33.0	this	125
													table	
12.5	–8	12.3	13.5	19.0	20.6	23.8	25.4	23.1	0.8	1.5	24.5	27.5	See	180
16	–10	15.5	16.7	22.2	23.8	27.0	28.6	26.3	0.8	1.5	19.2	25.0	para	205
19	–12	18.6	19.8	26.2	27.8	31.0	32.5	30.2	0.8	1.5	15.7	21.5	11.1.2	240
25	–16	25.0	26.4	34.1	35.7	38.5	40.9	38.9	1.0	2.0	14	16.5	and	300
													11.1.4	
31.5	–20	31.4	33.0	43.2	45.6	49.2	52.4	49.6	1.3	2.5	11.3	12.5		420
38	–24	37.7	39.3	49.6	52.0	55.6	58.7	56.0	1.3	2.5	8.7	9.0		500
51	–32	50.4	52.0	62.3	64.7	68.3	71.4	68.6	1.3	2.5	7.8	8.0		630
63	–40	63.1	65.1	74.6	77.8	80.9	84.1	—	—	—	7	7.0		760

1. Metric Size is in mm (Ref. ISO 4397).
2. SAE Dash Size is equal to the hose ID, expressed in 1/16's of an inch.
3. Cover thickness shall be measured by means of a dial indicator depth gage having a rounded foot placed parallel to the hose, bridging a groove obtained by stripping a 12.5 to 25 mm width of cover from the hose. A mandrel should be placed in the hose bore to insure freedom from misalignment.
4. Type S hose has the same working pressures as ISO 1436-1, 2SN.
5. Bend radius measured at inside of bend.

TABLE 7—HOSE CONCENTRICITY (100R2)
Dimensions are in Millimeters

Hose Size	Concentricity, FIR ID to OD	Concentricity, FIR ID to Reinforcement
Up to 6.3 mm (–4), included	0.8	0.5
Over 6.3 mm (–4) to 19 mm (–12), included	1.0	0.7
Over 19 mm (–12)	1.3	0.9

TABLE 8—DIMENSIONS AND SPECIFICATIONS FOR SAE 100R3 HOSE
Dimensions are in Millimeters

Metric Size(1)	SAE Dash Size(2)	ID Min	ID Max	OD Min	OD Max	Max Working Pressure MPa	Min Burst and Proof	Min Bend Radius(3)
5	–3	4.5	5.4	11.9	13.5	10.5	Pressure	75
6.3	–4	6.1	7.0	13.5	15.1	8.7	have	75
8	–5	7.6	8.5	16.7	18.3	8.4	been	100
10	–6	9.2	10.1	18.3	19.8	7.8	deleted	100
							from	
12.5	–8	12.4	13.5	23.0	24.6	7	this	125
16	–10	15.6	16.7	26.2	27.8	6.1	table	140
19	–12	18.7	19.8	31.0	32.5	5.2	See para	150
25	–16	25.1	26.2	36.9	39.3	3.9	11.1.2	205
31.5	–20	31.4	32.9	42.9	46.0	2.6	and 11.1.4	250

1. Metric Size is in mm (Ref. ISO 4397).
2. SAE Dash Size is equal to the hose ID, expressed in 1/16's of an inch.
3. Bend radius measured at inside of bend.

TABLE 9—HOSE CONCENTRICITY (100R3)
Dimensions are in Millimeters

Hose Size	Concentricity, FIR ID to OD
Up to 6.3 mm (–4), included	0.8
Over 6.3 mm (–4) to 19 mm (–12), included	1.0
Over 19 mm (–12)	1.3

16. Wire Inserted Hydraulic Suction Hose (SAE 100R4)—This section covers hose for use in low pressure and vacuum applications with petroleum base hydraulic fluids within a temperature range of –40 to +100 °C and with water base hydraulic fluids within the temperature ranges agreed upon by the manufacturers of both the hose and the fluid. Operating temperatures in excess of +100 °C with petroleum base hydraulic fluids may materially reduce the life of the hose. Maximum working pressure, minimum bend radius and other performance data are specified in Table 10.

It should be noted that the detailed specifications which follow shall be supplemented by the general specifications given at the beginning of this document.

16.1 Dimensions—Dimensions and tolerances applicable to this hose are given in Table 10.

16.2 Hose Construction—This hose shall consist of an inner tube of oil resistant synthetic rubber, a reinforcement consisting of a ply or plies of woven or braided textile fibers with a suitable spiral of body steel wire, and an oil and weather resistant synthetic rubber cover.

16.3 Qualification—For qualification to this section, hose and/or hose assemblies made therefrom shall comply with the tests specified in Table 3, and conform to the requirements of 11.1.

16.4 Inspection Tests—Inspection tests specified in 11.2 for bulk hose shall be performed.

TABLE 10—DIMENSIONS AND SPECIFICATIONS FOR SAE 100R4 HOSE
Dimensions are in Millimeters

Metric Size[1]	SAE Dash Size[2]	ID Min	ID Max	OD Max	Max Working Pressure MPa	Min Burst and Proof	Min Bend Radius[3]
19	–12	18.2	19.8	34.9	2.1	Pressure	125
25	–16	24.6	26.2	41.3	1.7	have	150
31.5	–20	30.6	33.0	50.8	1.4	been	200
38	–24	36.9	39.3	57.2	1.05	deleted	255
						from	
51	–32	49.2	52.4	69.9	0.7	this	300
63	–40	61.9	65.1	82.6	0.4	table	355
76	–48	74.6	77.8	95.3	0.4	See para	460
89	–56	87.3	90.5	107.9	0.3	11.1.2	530
102	–64	100.0	103.2	120.7	0.25	and 11.1.4	610

1. Metric Size is in mm (Ref. ISO 4397).
2. SAE Dash Size is equal to the hose ID, expressed in 1/16's of an inch.
3. Bend radius measured at inside of bend.

17. Single Wire Braid, Textile Covered Hydraulic Hose (SAE 100R5)—This section covers hose for use with petroleum base hydraulic fluids within a temperature range of –40 to +100 °C and with water base hydraulic fluids within the temperature ranges agreed upon by the manufacturers of both the hose and the fluid. Operating temperatures in excess of +100 °C with petroleum base hydraulic fluids may materially reduce the life of the hose. Maximum working pressure and minimum bend radius are specified in Table 11.

It should be noted that the detailed specifications which follow shall be supplemented by the general specifications given at the beginning of this document.

17.1 Dimensions—Dimensions and tolerances applicable to this hose are given in Table 11. The inside diameter and outside diameter of the hose shall be concentric within the limits in Table 12.

17.2 Hose Construction—This hose shall consist of an inner tube of oil resistant synthetic rubber, a single wire braid reinforcement and a fiber braided cover. A braid or fabric of suitable material may be used over the inner tube to anchor the synthetic rubber to the wire. All braids and fabrics shall be oil and mildew resistant.

17.3 Qualification—For qualification to this section, hose and/or hose assemblies made therefrom shall comply with the following test and the tests specified in Table 3, and conform to the requirements of 11.1.

17.3.1 IMPULSE TEST (FOUR UNAGED ASSEMBLIES)—Hose assemblies, when tested at 125% of the maximum working pressure for hose sizes 22 mm (–16) and smaller and 100% of the maximum working pressure for hose sizes 29 mm (–20) and larger, with 100 °C circulating petroleum-base test fluid, shall withstand a minimum of 150 000 cycles for hose sizes 22 mm (–16) and smaller and 100 000 cycles for hose sizes 29 mm (–20) and larger, without leakage or other malfunction. Hose sizes 29 mm (–20) and larger shall be tested straight.

17.4 Inspection Tests—Inspection tests specified in 11.2 for bulk hose shall be performed.

TABLE 11—DIMENSIONS AND SPECIFICATIONS FOR SAE 100R5 HOSE
Dimensions are in Millimeters

Metric Size[1]	SAE Dash Size[2]	ID Min	ID Max	OD Min	OD Max	Max Working Pressure MPa	Min Burst and Proof	Min Bend Radius[3]
5	–4	4.8	5.5	12.7	13.7	21	Pressure	75
6.3	–5	6.4	7.2	14.3	15.3	21	have	85
8	–6	7.9	8.7	16.7	17.6	15.7	been	100
11	–8	10.3	11.1	18.9	20.0	14	deleted	115
							from	
12.5	–10	12.7	13.7	22.8	24.0	12.2	this	140
16	–12	15.9	17.0	26.8	28.0	10.5	table	165
22	–16	22.2	23.3	30.6	32.2	5.6	See para	185
29	–20	28.6	29.8	37.3	38.9	4.3	11.1.2	230
							and 11.1.4	
35	–24	34.9	36.1	43.7	45.2	3.5		265
46	–32	46.0	47.2	55.2	57.6	2.4		335
60	–40	60.3	61.9	71.8	74.2	2.4		610
76	–48	76.2	77.8	89.3	91.7	1.4		840

1. Metric Size is in mm (Ref. ISO 4397).
2. SAE Dash Size is the same as the OD of tubing having approximately the same ID as the hose, expressed in 1/16's of an inch.
3. Bend radius measured at inside of bend.

TABLE 12—HOSE CONCENTRICITY (100R5)
Dimensions are in Millimeters

Hose Size	Concentricity, FIR ID to OD
Up to 11 mm (–8), included	0.6
Over 11 mm (–8)	0.8

18. Single Fiber Braid (Nonmetallic), Rubber Covered Hydraulic Hose (SAE 100R6)—This section covers hose for use with petroleum base hydraulic fluids within a temperature range of –40 to +100 °C and with water base hydraulic fluids within the temperature ranges agreed upon by the manufacturers of both the hose and the fluid. Operating temperatures in excess of +100 °C with petroleum base hydraulic fluids may materially reduce the life of the hose. Maximum working pressure and minimum bend radius are specified in Table 13.

It should be noted that the detailed specifications which follow shall be supplemented by the general specifications given at the beginning of this document.

18.1 Dimensions—Dimensions and tolerances applicable to this hose are given in Table 13. The inside diameter and outside diameter of the hose shall be concentric within the limits in Table 14.

18.2 Hose Construction—This hose shall consist of an inner tube of oil resistant synthetic rubber, one braid of suitable fiber, and an oil and weather resistant synthetic rubber cover.

18.3 Qualification—For qualification to this section, hose and/or hose assemblies made therefrom shall comply with the tests specified in Table 3, and conform to the requirements of 11.1.

18.4 Inspection Tests—Inspection tests specified in 11.2 for bulk hose shall be performed.

TABLE 13—DIMENSIONS AND SPECIFICATIONS FOR SAE 100R6 HOSE
Dimensions are in Millimeters

Metric Size(1)	SAE Dash Size(2)	ID Min	ID Max	OD Min	OD Max	Max Working Pressure MPa	Min Burst and Proof	Min Bend Radius(3)
5	–3	4.5	5.4	10.3	11.9	3.5	Pressure	50
6.3	–4	6.1	7.0	11.9	13.5	2.8	have been	65
8	–5	7.6	8.5	13.5	15.1	2.8	deleted	75
10	–6	9.2	10.1	15.1	16.7	2.8	from this table	75
12.5	–8	12.4	13.5	19.0	20.6	2.8	See para	100
16	–10	15.6	16.7	22.2	23.8	2.4	11.1.2	125
19	–12	18.7	19.8	25.4	27.8	2.1	and 11.1.4	150

1. Metric Size is in mm (Ref. ISO 4397).
2. SAE Dash Size is equal to the hose ID, expressed in 1/16's of an inch.
3. Bend radius measured at inside of bend.

TABLE 14—HOSE CONCENTRICITY (100R6)
Dimensions are in Millimeters

Hose Size	Concentricity, FIR ID to OD
Up to 6.3 mm (–4), included	0.8
Over 6.3 mm (–4)	1.0

19. Thermoplastic Hydraulic Hose (SAE 100R7)—This section covers thermoplastic hose for use with petroleum base and synthetic hydraulic fluids within a temperature range of –40 to +93 °C, and with water base hydraulic fluids within the temperature ranges agreed upon by the manufacturers of both the hose and the fluid. Operating temperatures in excess of +93 °C with petroleum base hydraulic fluids may materially reduce the life of the hose. Maximum working pressure and minimum bend radius are specified in Table 15.

Electrically nonconductive 100R7 hose is available for use in applications where there is potential of contact with high voltage sources. To be classified as nonconductive, a hose must pass the Electrical Conductivity Test described in 19.4.1. Nonconductive hose is identified by its orange cover and layline.

It should be noted that the detailed specifications which follow shall be supplemented by the general specifications given at the beginning of this document.

19.1 Dimensions—Dimensions and tolerances applicable to this hose are given in Table 15. The inside diameter of the hose shall be concentric with the outside diameter of the hose within the limits in Table 16.

19.2 Hose Construction—This hose shall consist of a thermoplastic inner tube resistant to hydraulic fluids with suitable synthetic fiber reinforcement, and a hydraulic fluid and weather resistant thermoplastic cover.

Nonconductive 100R7 hose shall be identified with an orange cover and appropriate layline. (Reference color, orange chip #22510, Federal Standard 595).

19.3 Connector Compatibility—Connectors for thermoplastic hose may not be interchangeable. Therefore, it is recommended that connectors and hose be properly matched. Connector and/or hose manufacturers shall be consulted for recommendations.

19.4 Qualification—For qualification to this section, hose and/or hose assemblies made therefrom shall comply with the following test and the tests specified in Table 3, and conform to the requirements of 11.1.

19.4.1 ELECTRICAL CONDUCTIVITY TEST (TWO 152 mm FREE HOSE LENGTH CONDITIONED ASSEMBLIES)—The maximum electrical leakage shall not exceed 50 µA when subjected to 37.5 kV for 5 min. This test shall not be applicable to hose with a pinpricked cover.

19.5 Inspection Tests—Inspection tests specified in 11.2 for bulk hose shall be performed.

TABLE 15—DIMENSIONS AND SPECIFICATIONS FOR SAE 100R7
Dimensions are in Millimeters

Metric Size(1)	SAE Dash Size(2)	ID Min	ID Max	OD Max	Max Working Pressure MPa	Min Burst and Proof	Min Bend Radius(3)
5	–3	4.6	5.4	11.4	21	Pressure	90
6.3	–4	6.2	7.0	13.7	19.2	have been	100
8	–5	7.7	8.5	15.6	17.5	deleted	115
10	–6	9.3	10.3	18.4	15.7	from this table	125
12.5	–8	12.3	13.5	22.5	14	See para	180
16	–10	15.5	16.7	25.8	10.5	11.1.2	205
19	–12	18.6	19.8	28.6	8.7	and 11.1.4	240
25	–16	25.0	26.4	36.7	7		300

1. Metric Size is in mm (Ref. ISO 4397).
2. SAE Dash Size is equal to the hose ID, expressed in 1/16's of an inch.
3. Bend radius measured at inside of bend.

TABLE 16—HOSE CONCENTRICITY (100R7)
Dimensions are in Millimeters

Hose Size	Concentricity, FIR ID to OD
Up to 6.3 mm (–4), included	0.8
Over 6.3 mm (–4) to 19 mm (–12), included	1.0
Over 19 mm (-12)	1.3

20. High Pressure Thermoplastic Hydraulic Hose (SAE 100R8)—This section covers thermoplastic hose for use with petroleum base and synthetic hydraulic fluids within a temperature range of –40 to +93 °C, and with water base hydraulic fluids within the temperature ranges agreed upon by the manufacturers of both the hose and the fluid. Operating temperatures in excess of +93 °C with petroleum base hydraulic fluids may materially reduce the life of the hose. Maximum working pressure and minimum bend radius are specified in Table 17.

Electrically nonconductive 100R8 hose is available for use in applications where there is potential of contact with high voltage sources. To be classified as nonconductive, a hose must pass the Electrical Conductivity Test described in 20.4.1. Nonconductive hose is identified by its orange cover and layline.

It should be noted that the detailed specifications which follow shall be supplemented by the general specifications given at the beginning of this document.

20.1 Dimensions—Dimensions and tolerances applicable to this hose are given in Table 17. The inside diameter of the hose shall be concentric with the outside diameter of the hose within the limits in Table 18.

20.2 Hose Construction—This hose shall consist of a thermoplastic inner tube resistant to hydraulic fluids with suitable synthetic fiber reinforcement, and a hydraulic fluid and weather resistant thermoplastic cover.

Nonconductive 100R8 hose shall be identified with an orange cover and appropriate layline. (Reference color, orange chip #22510, Federal Standard 595).

20.3 Connector Compatibility—Connectors for thermoplastic hose may not be interchangeable. Therefore, it is recommended that connectors and hose be properly matched. Connector and/or hose manufacturers shall be consulted for recommendations.

20.4 Qualification—For qualification to this section, hose and/or hose assemblies made therefrom shall comply with the following test and the tests specified in Table 3, and conform to the requirements of 11.1.

20.4.1 ELECTRICAL CONDUCTIVITY TEST (TWO 152 mm FREE HOSE LENGTH CONDITIONED ASSEMBLIES)—The maximum electrical leakage shall not exceed 50 µA when subjected to 37.5 kV for 5 min. This test shall not be applicable to hose with a pinpricked cover.

20.5 Inspection Tests—Inspection tests specified in 11.2 for bulk hose shall be performed.

TABLE 17—DIMENSIONS AND SPECIFICATIONS FOR SAE 100R8 HOSE
Dimensions are in Millimeters

Metric Size(1)	SAE Dash Size(2)	ID Min	ID Max	OD Max	Max Working Pressure MPa	Min Burst and Proof	Min Bend Radius(3)
5	–3	4.6	5.4	14.6	35	Pressure	90
6.3	–4	6.2	7.0	16.8	35	have been	100
10	–6	9.3	10.3	20.3	28	deleted	125
						from this	
12.5	–8	12.3	13.5	24.6	24.5	table	180
16	–10	15.5	16.7	29.8	19.2	See para	205
19	–12	18.6	19.8	33.0	15.7	11.1.2	240
25	–16	25.0	26.4	38.6	14	and 11.1.4	300

1. Metric Size is in mm (Ref. ISO 4397).
2. SAE Dash Size is equal to the hose ID, expressed in 1/16's of an inch.
3. Bend radius measured at inside of bend.

TABLE 18—HOSE CONCENTRICITY (100R8)
Dimensions are in Millimeters

Hose Size	Concentricity, FIR ID to OD
Up to 6.3 mm (–4), included	0.8
Over 6.3 mm (–4) to 19 mm (–12), included	1.0
Over 19 mm (–12)	1.3

21. High Pressure, Four Spiral Steel Wire Reinforced, Rubber Covered Hydraulic Hose (SAE 100R9)—This section covers hose for use with petroleum base hydraulic fluids within a temperature range of –40 to +100 °C and with water base hydraulic fluids within the temperature ranges agreed upon by the manufacturers of both the hose and the fluid. Operating temperatures in excess of +100 °C with petroleum base hydraulic fluids may materially reduce the life of the hose. Maximum working pressure and minimum bend radius are specified in Table 19.

It should be noted that the detailed specifications which follow shall be supplemented by the general specifications given at the beginning of this document.

21.1 Dimensions—Dimensions and tolerances applicable to this hose are given in Table 19. The inside diameter of the hose shall be concentric with the outside diameter of the hose and the outer surface of the reinforcement within the limits in Table 20.

21.2 Hose Construction

21.2.1 TYPE A—This hose shall consist of an inner tube of oil resistant synthetic rubber, four spiral plies of steel wire wrapped in alternating directions, and an oil and weather resistant synthetic rubber cover. A ply or braid of suitable material may be used over the inner tube and/or over the wire reinforcement to anchor the synthetic rubber to the wire.

21.2.2 TYPE AT—This hose shall be of the same construction as Type A, except having a cover designed to assemble with fittings which do not require removal of the cover or a portion thereof.

21.3 Qualification—For qualification to this section, hose and/or hose assemblies made therefrom shall comply with the following test and the tests specified in Table 3, and conform to the requirements of 11.1.

21.3.1 IMPULSE TEST (FOUR UNAGED ASSEMBLIES)—Hose assemblies, when tested at 133% of the maximum working pressure with 100 °C circulating petroleum-base test fluid, shall withstand a minimum of 200 000 cycles for hose sizes 10 mm (–6) and 12.5 mm (–8) and 300 000 cycles for all other sizes, without leakage or other malfunction.

21.4 Inspection Tests—Inspection tests specified in 11.2 for bulk hose shall be performed.

TABLE 19—DIMENSIONS AND SPECIFICATIONS FOR SAE 100R9 HOSE
Dimensions are in Millimeters

Metric Size(1)	SAE Dash Size(2)	ID Min	ID Max	Reinforcement Dia Min	Reinforcement Dia Max	OD Type A Min	OD Type A Max	OD Type AT Max	Cover Thickness(3) Type AT Min	Cover Thickness(3) Type AT Max	Max Working Pressure MPa	Min Burst and Proof Pressure have	Min Bend Radius(4)
10	–6	9.3	10.1	16.9	18.0	20.6	22.2	21.1	0.8	1.6	31.5	been	125
12.5	–8	12.3	13.5	19.4	21.0	23.8	25.4	24.3	1.0	2.0	28	deleted	180
19	–12	18.6	19.8	26.6	28.2	30.6	32.2	31.9	1.0	2.0	21	from	240
25	–16	25.0	26.4	34.5	36.1	38.5	40.9	40.5	1.1	2.4	21	this	300
												table	
31.5	–20	31.4	33.0	43.3	45.6	49.2	52.4	50.7	1.3	2.8	17.5	See para	420
38	–24	37.7	39.3	49.6	52.0	55.6	58.7	—	—	—	14	11.1.2	500
51	–32	50.4	52.0	63.9	66.2	69.9	73.0	—	—	—	14	and 11.1.4	660

1. Metric Size is in mm (Ref. ISO 4397).
2. SAE Dash Size is equal to the hose ID, expressed in 1/16's of an inch.
3. Cover thickness shall be measured by means of a dial indicator depth gage having a rounded foot placed parallel to the hose, bridging a groove obtained by stripping a 12.5 to 25 mm width of cover from the hose. A mandrel shall be placed in the hose bore to insure freedom from misalignment.
4. Bend radius measured at inside of bend.

TABLE 20—HOSE CONCENTRICITY (100R9)
Dimensions are in Millimeters

Hose Size	Concentricity, FIR ID to OD	Concentricity, FIR ID to Reinforcement
Up to 19 mm (–12), included	1.0	0.7
Over 19 mm (–12)	1.3	0.9

22. Heavy Duty, Four Spiral Steel Wire Reinforced, Rubber Covered Hydraulic Hose (SAE 100R10)—This section covers hose for use with petroleum base hydraulic fluids within a temperature range of –40 to +100 °C and with water base hydraulic fluids within the temperature ranges agreed upon by the manufacturers of both the hose and the fluid. Operating temperatures in excess of +100 °C with petroleum base hydraulic fluids may materially reduce the life of the hose. Maximum working pressure and minimum bend radius are specified in Table 21.

It should be noted that the detailed specifications which follow shall be supplemented by the general specifications given at the beginning of this document.

22.1 Dimensions—Dimensions and tolerances applicable to this hose are given in Table 21. The inside diameter of the hose shall be concentric with the outside diameter of the hose and the outer surface of the reinforcement within the limits in Table 22.

22.2 Hose Construction

22.2.1 TYPE A—This hose shall consist of an inner tube of oil resistant synthetic rubber, four spiral plies of heavy steel wire wrapped in alternating directions, and an oil and weather resistant synthetic rubber cover. A ply or braid of suitable material may be used over the inner tube and/or over the wire reinforcement to anchor the synthetic rubber to the wire.

22.2.2 TYPE AT—This hose shall be of the same construction as Type A, except having a cover designed to assemble with fittings which do not require removal of the cover or a portion thereof.

22.3 Qualification—For qualification to this section, hose and/or hose assemblies made therefrom shall comply with the tests specified in Table 3, and conform to the requirements of 11.1.

22.4 Inspection Tests—Inspection tests specified in 11.2 for bulk hose shall be performed.

TABLE 21—DIMENSIONS AND SPECIFICATIONS FOR SAE 100R10 HOSE
Dimensions are in Millimeters

Metric Size(1)	SAE Dash Size(2)	ID Min	ID Max	Reinforcement Dia Min	Reinforcement Dia Max	OD Type A Min	OD Type A Max	OD Type AT Max	Cover Thickness(3) Type AT Min	Cover Thickness(3) Type AT Max	Max Working Pressure MPa	Min Burst and Proof Pressure have	Min Bend Radius(4)
5	–3	4.6	5.4	14.3	15.9	18.3	19.8	—	—	—	70	been	100
6.3	–4	6.2	7.0	15.8	17.4	19.8	21.4	—	—	—	61	deleted	125
10	–6	9.3	10.1	19.0	20.6	23.0	24.6	—	—	—	52.5	from	150
12.5	–8	12.5	13.7	23.0	24.6	27.0	28.6	—	—	—	43.5	this	200
19	–12	19.0	20.2	30.9	32.5	35.7	37.3	36.8	1.0	2.0	35	table	280
												See para	
25	–16	25.4	27.0	38.9	40.5	43.3	45.6	45.5	1.2	2.4	28	11.1.2	360
31.5	–20	31.8	33.4	44.8	47.2	49.2	52.4	52.3	1.4	2.8	21	and	460
38	–24	38.1	39.7	51.1	53.6	55.6	58.7	58.7	1.4	2.8	17.5	11.1.4	560
51	–32	50.8	52.6	64.6	67.1	69.1	72.2	72.1	1.4	2.8	17.5		710

1. Metric Size is in mm (Ref. ISO 4397).
2. SAE Dash Size is equal to the hose ID, expressed in 1/16's of an inch.
3. Cover thickness shall be measured by means of a dial indicator depth gage having a rounded foot placed parallel to the hose, bridging a groove obtained by stripping a 12.5 to 25 mm width of cover from the hose. A mandrel should be placed in the hose bore to insure freedom from misalignment.
4. Bend radius measured at inside of bend.

TABLE 22—HOSE CONCENTRICITY (100R10)
Dimensions are in Millimeters

Hose Size	Concentricity, FIR ID to OD	Concentricity, FIR ID to Reinforcement
Up to 6.3 mm (-4), included	0.8	0.5
Over 6.3 mm (–4) to 19 mm (–12), included	1.0	0.7
Over 19 mm (–12)	1.3	0.9

23. Heavy Duty, Six Spiral Steel Wire Reinforced, Rubber Covered Hydraulic Hose (SAE 100R11)—This section covers hose for use with petroleum base hydraulic fluids within a temperature range of –40 to +100 °C and with water base hydraulic fluids within the temperature ranges agreed upon by the manufacturers of both the hose and the fluid. Operating temperatures in excess of +100 °C with petroleum base hydraulic fluids may materially reduce the life of the hose. Maximum working pressure and minimum bend radius are specified in Table 23.

It should be noted that the detailed specifications which follow shall be supplemented by the general specifications given at the beginning of this document.

23.1 Dimensions—Dimensions and tolerances applicable to this hose are given in Table 23. The inside diameter of the hose shall be concentric with the outside diameter of the hose and the outer surface of the reinforcement within the limits in Table 24.

23.2 Hose Construction—This hose shall consist of an inner tube of oil resistant synthetic rubber, six spiral plies of steel wire wrapped in alternating directions, and an oil and weather resistant synthetic rubber cover. A ply or braid of suitable material may be used over the inner tube and/or over the wire reinforcement to anchor the synthetic rubber to the wire.

23.3 Qualification—For qualification to this section, hose and/or hose assemblies made therefrom shall comply with the tests specified in Table 3, and conform to the requirements of 11.1.

23.4 Inspection Tests—Inspection tests specified in 11.2 for bulk hose shall be performed.

24. Heavy Duty, High Impulse, Four Spiral Steel Wire Reinforced, Rubber Covered Hydraulic Hose (SAE 100R12)—This section covers hose for use with petroleum base hydraulic fluids within a temperature range of –40 to +121 °C and with water base hydraulic fluids within the temperature ranges agreed upon by the manufacturers of both the hose and the fluid. Operating temperatures in excess of +121 °C with petroleum base hydraulic fluids may materially reduce the life of the hose. Maximum working pressure and minimum bend radius are specified in Table 25.

It should be noted that the detailed specifications which follow shall be supplemented by the general specifications given at the beginning of this document.

24.1 Dimensions—Dimensions and tolerances applicable to this hose are given in Table 25. The inside diameter of the hose shall be concentric with the outside diameter of the hose and the outer surface of the reinforcement within the limits in Table 26.

24.2 Hose Construction—This hose shall consist of an inner tube of oil resistant synthetic rubber, four spiral plies of steel wire wrapped in alternating directions, and an oil and weather resistant synthetic rubber cover. A ply or braid of suitable material may be used over or within the inner tube and/or over the wire reinforcement to anchor the synthetic rubber to the wire.

24.3 Qualification—For qualification to this section, hose and/or hose assemblies made therefrom shall comply with the tests specified in Table 3, and conform to the requirements of 11.1.

24.4 Inspection Tests—Inspection tests specified in 11.2 for bulk hose shall be performed.

TABLE 23—DIMENSIONS AND SPECIFICATIONS FOR SAE 100R11 HOSE
Dimensions are in Millimeters

Metric Size(1)	SAE Dash Size(2)	ID Min	ID Max	Reinforce-ment Dia Min	Reinforce-ment Dia Max	OD Min	OD Max	Max Working Pressure MPa	Min Burst and Proof Pressure	Min Bend Radius(3)
5	−3	4.6	5.4	17.5	19.1	21.4	23.0	87	have	100
6.3	−4	6.2	7.0	19.1	20.6	23.0	24.6	78	been	125
10	−6	9.3	10.1	22.2	23.8	26.2	27.8	70	deleted	150
12.5	−8	12.5	13.7	26.2	27.8	30.2	31.8	52.5	from	200
19	−12	19.0	20.2	34.1	35.7	38.9	40.5	43.5	this	280
									table	
25	−16	25.4	27.0	41.7	44.0	47.2	49.6	35	See para	360
31.5	−20	31.8	33.4	48.0	50.4	53.2	56.4	24.5	11.1.2	460
38	−24	38.1	39.7	54.4	56.7	59.5	62.7	21	and	560
51	−32	50.8	52.6	68.6	71.0	73.8	77.0	21	11.1.4	710
63	−40	63.5	65.3	83.5	86.3	89.7	92.9	17.5		920

1. Metric Size is in mm (Ref. ISO 4397).
2. SAE Dash Size is equal to the hose ID, expressed in 1/16's of an inch.
3. Bend radius measured at inside of bend.

TABLE 24—HOSE CONCENTRICITY (100R11)
Dimensions are in Millimeters

Hose Size	Concentricity, FIR ID to OD	Concentricity, FIR ID to Reinforcement
Up to 6.3 mm (−4), included	0.8	0.5
Over 6.3 mm (−4) to 19 mm (−12), included	1.0	0.7
Over 19 mm (−12)	1.3	0.9

TABLE 25—DIMENSIONS AND SPECIFICATIONS FOR SAE 100R12 HOSE
Dimensions are in Millimeters

Metric Size(1)	SAE Dash Size(2)	ID Min	ID Max	Reinforce-ment Dia Min	Reinforce-ment Dia Max	OD Min	OD Max	Max Working Pressure MPa	Min Burst and Proof Pressure	Min Bend Radius(3)
10	−6	9.3	10.1	16.6	17.8	19.5	21.0	28	have	125
12.5	−8	12.3	13.5	19.9	21.5	23.0	24.6	28	been	180
16	−10	15.5	16.7	23.8	25.4	26.6	28.2	28	deleted	200
19	−12	18.6	19.8	26.9	28.7	29.9	31.7	28	from	240
									this	
25	−16	25.0	26.4	34.1	36.0	36.8	39.4	28	table	300
31.5	−20	31.4	33.0	42.7	45.1	45.4	48.6	21	See para	420
38	−24	37.7	39.3	49.2	51.6	51.9	55.0	17.5	11.1.2	500
51	−32	50.8	52.0	62.5	64.8	65.1	68.3	17.5	and 11.1.4	640

1. Metric Size is in mm (Ref. ISO 4397).
2. SAE Dash Size is equal to the hose ID, expressed in 1/16's of an inch.
3. Bend radius measured at inside of bend.

TABLE 26—HOSE CONCENTRICITY (100R12)
Dimensions are in millimeters

Hose Size	Concentricity, FIR ID to OD	Concentricity, FIR ID to Reinforcement
Up to 19 mm (−12), included	1.0	0.7
Over 19 mm (−12)	1.3	0.9

25. Heavy Duty, High Impulse, Multiple Spiral Steel Wire Reinforced, Rubber Covered Hydraulic Hose (SAE 100R13)—This section covers hose for use with petroleum base hydraulic fluids within a temperature range of −40 to +121 °C and with water base hydraulic fluids within the temperature ranges agreed upon by the manufacturers of both the hose and the fluid. Operating temperatures in excess of +121 °C with petroleum base hydraulic fluids may materially reduce the life of the hose. Maximum working pressure and minimum bend radius are specified in Table 27.

It should be noted that the detailed specifications which follow shall be supplemented by the general specifications given at the beginning of this document.

25.1 Dimensions—Dimensions and tolerances applicable to this hose are given in Table 27. The inside diameter of the hose shall be concentric with the outside diameter of the hose and the outer surface of the reinforcement within the limits in Table 28.

25.2 Hose Construction—This hose shall consist of an inner tube of oil resistant synthetic rubber, multiple spiral plies of heavy steel wire wrapped in alternating directions, and an oil and weather resistant synthetic rubber cover. A ply or braid of suitable material may be used over or within the inner tube and/or over the wire reinforcement to anchor the synthetic rubber to the wire.

25.3 Qualification—For qualification to this section, hose and/or hose assemblies made therefrom shall comply with the tests specified in Table 3, and conform to the requirements of 11.1.

25.4 Inspection Tests—Inspection tests specified in 11.2 for bulk hose shall be performed.

TABLE 27—DIMENSIONS AND SPECIFICATIONS FOR SAE 100R13 HOSE
Dimensions are in Millimeters

Metric Size(1)	SAE Dash Size(2)	ID Min	ID Max	Reinforcement Dia Min	Reinforcement Dia Max	OD Min	OD Max	Max Working Pressure MPa	Min Burst and Proof Pressure have been deleted	Min Bend Radius(3)
19	–12	18.6	19.8	28.2	29.8	31.0	33.2	35	from this	240
25	–16	25.0	26.4	34.9	36.4	37.6	39.8	35	table	300
31.5	–20	31.4	33.0	45.6	48.0	48.3	51.3	35	See para	420
38	–24	37.7	39.3	53.1	55.5	55.8	58.8	35	11.1.2	500
51	–32	50.4	52.0	66.9	69.3	69.5	72.7	35	and 11.1.4	640

1. Metric Size is in mm (Ref. ISO 4397).
2. SAE Dash Size is equal to the hose ID, expressed in 1/16's of an inch.
3. Bend radius measured at inside of bend.

TABLE 28—HOSE CONCENTRICITY (100R13)
Dimensions are in Millimeters

Hose Size	Concentricity, FIR ID to OD	Concentricity, FIR ID to Reinforcement
19 mm (–12)	1.0	0.7
Over 19 mm (–12)	1.3	0.9

26. PTFE Lined Hydraulic Hose (SAE 100R14)—This section covers hose for use with petroleum base and synthetic base hydraulic fluids within a temperature range of –54 to +204 °C, and with water base hydraulic fluids within the temperature ranges agreed upon by the manufacturers of both the hose and the fluid. Operating temperatures in excess of +204 °C with petroleum base hydraulic fluids may materially reduce the life of the hose. Maximum working pressure, minimum bend radius and other performance data are specified in Table 29. This does not exclude utilization of the hose in a multiplicity of applications for which PTFE is suitable. For such applications consult the manufacturer.

It should be noted that the detailed specifications which follow shall be supplemented by the general specifications given at the beginning of this document.

26.1 Dimensions—Dimensions and tolerances applicable to this hose are given in Table 29. Hose tube dimensions and concentricity requirements are given in Table 30.

26.2 Hose Construction

26.2.1 TYPE A—This hose shall consist of an inner tube of polytetrafluoroethylene (PTFE), reinforced with a single braid of 303XX series stainless steel wire.

26.2.2 TYPE B—This hose shall be of the same construction as Type A, but shall have the additional feature of an electrically conductive inner surface so as to preclude buildup of an electrostatic charge.

26.3 Connector Compatibility—Connectors for PTFE lined hose may not be interchangeable. Therefore, it is recommended that connectors and hose be properly matched. Connector and/or hose manufacturers shall be consulted for recommendations.

26.4 Qualification—For qualification to this section, hose and/or hose assemblies made therefrom shall comply with the following tests and the tests specified in Table 3, and conform to the requirements of 11.1.

26.4.1 IMPULSE TEST (FOUR UNAGED ASSEMBLIES)—Hose assemblies, when tested at 125% of the maximum working pressure for hose sizes 22 mm (–16) and smaller and 100% of the maximum working pressure for hose sizes 25 mm (–18) and larger, with 204 °C synthetic-base test fluid, shall withstand a minimum of 150 000 cycles without leakage or other malfunction. Test fluid shall conform to MIL-PRF-83282, MIL-H-8446 or MIL-PRF-7808.

26.4.2 SPECIFIC GRAVITY TEST (ONE TUBE SAMPLE)—Shall be within 2.12 and 2.21 at 25 °C ± 1 °C using ASTM D 792, Method A-1. Two drops of a wetting agent shall be added to the water.

26.4.3 CONDUCTIVITY TEST (ONE 330 MM CUT LENGTH SAMPLE)—Type B hose only. Size 11 mm (–8) and smaller shall be capable of conducting a direct current of 6 µA or greater, and size 12.5 mm (–10) and larger, 12 µA or greater, with 1000 V applied between the electrodes (see SAE J343 Figure 3).

26.5 Inspection Tests—Inspection tests specified in 11.2 for bulk hose shall be performed.

TABLE 29—DIMENSIONS AND SPECIFICATIONS FOR SAE 100R14 HOSE
Dimensions are in Millimeters

Metric Size(1)	SAE Dash Size(2)	ID Min	ID Max	OD Min	OD Max	Max Working Pressure MPa	Proof Pressure MPa	Min Burst Pressure MPa	Min Bend Radius(3)
3.2	–3	2.8	3.8	5.3	6.8	10.5	42	84	40
5	–4	4.4	5.2	7.1	8.2	10.5	35	70	50
6.3	–5	6.0	6.9	8.9	10.1	10.5	31.5	63	75
8	–6	7.5	8.4	10.4	11.6	10.5	28	56	100
10	–7	9.1	10.0	12.2	13.4	10.5	24.5	49	125
11	–8	9.9	10.9	12.9	14.3	7	21	42	135
12.5	–10	12.3	13.3	15.3	16.8	5.6	21	42	165
16	–12	15.3	16.5	18.6	20.1	5.6	17.5	35	200
19	–14	18.4	19.6	21.3	23.3	5.6	14	28	230
22	–16	21.4	23.0	24.6	26.9	5.6	12.2	24.5	230
25	–18	24.6	26.2	27.8	29.8	5.6	12.2	24.5	300
29	–20	27.8	29.4	31.9	33.5	4.2	8.7	17.5	410

1. Metric Size is in mm (Ref. ISO 4397).
2. SAE Dash Size is the same as the OD of tubing having approximately the same ID as the hose, expressed in 1/16's of an inch.
3. Bend radius measured at inside of bend.

TABLE 30—HOSE TUBE DIMENSIONS AND CONCENTRICITY (100R14)
Dimensions are in Millimeters

Hose Size	Tube Thickness Max	Tube Thickness Min	Concentricity, FIR ID to OD
3.2 mm (–3) to 12.7 mm (–10)	0.9	0.7	0.3
16 mm (–12)	1.1	0.7	0.3
19 mm (–14) to 25 mm (–18)	1.2	0.8	0.3
29 mm (–20)	1.3	0.9	0.3

27. Heavy Duty, High Impulse, Multiple Spiral Steel Wire Reinforced, Rubber Covered Hydraulic Hose (SAE 100R15)—This section covers hose for use with petroleum base hydraulic fluids within a temperature range of –40 to +121 °C. Operating temperatures in excess of +121 °C with petroleum base hydraulic fluids may materially reduce the life of the hose. Maximum working pressure and minimum bend radius are specified in Table 31.

It should be noted that the detailed specifications which follow shall be supplemented by the general specifications given at the beginning of this document.

27.1 Dimensions—Dimensions and tolerances applicable to this hose are given in Table 31. The inside diameter of the hose shall be concentric with the outside diameter of the hose and the outer surface of the reinforcement within the limits in Table 32.

27.2 Hose Construction—This hose shall consist of an inner tube of oil resistant synthetic rubber, multiple spiral plies of heavy steel wire wrapped in alternating directions, and an oil and weather resistant synthetic rubber cover. A ply or braid of suitable material may be used over or within the inner tube and/or over the wire reinforcement to anchor the synthetic rubber to the wire.

27.3 Qualification—For qualification to this section, hose and/or hose assemblies made therefrom shall comply with the tests specified in Table 3, and conform to the requirements of 11.1.

27.4 Inspection Tests—Inspection tests specified in 11.2 for bulk hose shall be performed.

TABLE 31—DIMENSIONS AND SPECIFICATIONS FOR SAE 100R15
Dimensions are in Millimeters

Metric Size(1)	SAE Dash Size(2)	ID Min	ID Max	Reinforcement Dia Max	OD Max	Max Working Pressure MPa	Min Burst and Proof Pressure	Min Bend Radius(3)
10	–6	9.3	10.1	20.3	23.3	42	have been	150
12.5	–8	12.3	13.5	24.0	26.8	42	deleted from	200
19	–12	18.6	19.8	32.9	36.1	42	this table	265
25	–16	25.0	26.4	38.9	42.9	42	See para	330
31.5	–20	31.4	33.0	48.4	51.5	42	11.1.2	445
38	–24	37.7	39.3	56.3	59.6	42	and 11.1.4	530

1. Metric Size is in mm (Ref. ISO 4397).
2. SAE Dash Size is equal to the hose ID, expressed in 1/16's of an inch.
3. Bend radius measured at inside of bend.

TABLE 32—HOSE CONCENTRICITY (100R15)
Dimensions are in Millimeters

Hose Size	Concentricity, FIR ID to OD	Concentricity, FIR ID to Reinforcement
Up to 19 mm (–12), included	1.0	0.7
Over 19 mm (–12)	1.3	0.9

28. Compact, High Pressure, One and Two Steel Wire Reinforced, Rubber Covered Hydraulic Hose (SAE 100R16)—This section covers hose for use with petroleum base hydraulic fluids within a temperature range of –40 to +100 °C and with water base hydraulic fluids within the temperature ranges agreed upon by the manufacturers of both the hose and the fluid. Operating temperatures in excess of +100 °C with petroleum base hydraulic fluids may materially reduce the life of the hose. Maximum working pressure and minimum bend radius are specified in Table 33.

This hose is not suitable for use with castor oil based and ester based fluids.

It should be noted that the detailed specifications which follow shall be supplemented by the general specifications given at the beginning of this document.

28.1 Foreword—Compact wire braided hydraulic hoses have been increasingly used over the recent years and it is considered that their status in the hydraulic hose field merits the development of an SAE standard.

Hoses of this type are smaller in diameter than two wire braided hoses with similar performance characteristics specified in SAE 100R2, which gives them the ability to operate at smaller bend radii. They are also lighter in weight and their compactness offers advantages when minimal space is available in installations. This hose can be manufactured as either a one wire braid or a two wire braid design and the hose shall be identified as to the number of braids.

28.2 Dimensions—Dimensions and tolerances applicable to this hose are given in Table 33 The inside diameter of the hose shall be concentric with the outside diameter of the hose and the outer surface of the reinforcement within the limits in Table 34.

28.3 Hose Construction—This hose shall consist of an inner tube of oil resistant synthetic rubber, steel wire reinforcement according to hose design (one or two braids), and an oil and weather resistant synthetic rubber cover. A ply or braid of suitable material may be used over the inner tube and/or over the wire reinforcement to anchor the synthetic rubber to the wire.

28.4 Qualification—For qualification to this section, hose and/or hose assemblies made therefrom shall comply with the tests specified in Table 3, and conform to the requirements of 11.1.

28.5 Inspection Tests—Inspection tests specified in 11.2 for bulk hose shall be performed.

29. Compact, 21 MPa Maximum Working Pressure, One and Two Steel Wire Reinforced, Rubber Covered Hydraulic Hose (SAE 100R17)—This section covers hose for use with petroleum base hydraulic fluids within a temperature range of –40 to +100 °C and with water base hydraulic fluids within the temperature ranges agreed upon by the manufacturers of both the hose and the fluid. Operating temperatures in excess of +100 °C with petroleum base hydraulic fluids may materially reduce the life of the hose. Maximum working pressure and minimum bend radius are specified in Table 35.

This hose is not suitable for use with castor oil based and ester based fluids.

29.1 Foreword—Compact wire braided hydraulic hoses have been increasingly used over the recent years and it is considered that their status in the hydraulic hose field merits the development of an SAE standard.

Hoses of this type are smaller in diameter than one and two wire braided hoses with similar performance characteristics specified in SAE 100R1 and SAE 100R2, which gives them the ability to operate at smaller bend radii. They are also lighter in weight and their compactness offers advantages when minimal space is available in installations. This hose can be manufactured as either a one wire braid or a two wire braid design and the hose shall be identified as to the number of braids.

29.2 Dimensions—Dimensions and tolerances applicable to this hose are given in Table 35. The inside diameter of the hose shall be concentric with the outside diameter of the hose and the outer surface of the reinforcement within the limits in Table 36.

29.3 Hose Construction—This hose shall consist of an inner tube of oil resistant synthetic rubber, steel wire reinforcement according to hose design (one or two braids), and an oil and weather resistant synthetic rubber cover. A ply or braid of suitable material may be used over the inner tube and/or over the wire reinforcement to anchor the synthetic rubber to the wire.

29.4 Qualification—For qualification to this section, hose and/or hose assemblies made therefrom shall comply with the tests specified in Table 3, and conform to the requirements of 11.1.

29.5 Inspection Tests—Inspection tests specified in 11.2 for bulk hose shall be performed.

TABLE 33—DIMENSIONS AND SPECIFICATIONS FOR SAE 100R16 HOSE
Dimensions are in Millimeters

Metric Size(1)	SAE Dash Size(2)	ID Min	ID Max	Reinforcement Dia Max	OD Max	Cover Thickness(3) Min	Cover Thickness(3) Max	Max Working Pressure MPa	Max Working Pressure Typs S(4) MPa	Min Burst and Proof Pressure have	Min Bend Radius(5)
6.3	–4	6.2	7.0	12.3	14.5	0.8	1.5	35	40.0	been	50
8	–5	7.7	8.5	13.3	15.7	0.8	1.5	29.7	35.0	deleted	55
10	–6	9.3	10.1	15.9	18.8	0.8	1.5	28	33.0	from	65
12.5	–8	12.3	13.5	19.0	22.0	0.8	1.5	24.5	27.5	this table	90
16	–10	15.5	16.7	22.5	25.4	0.8	1.5	19.2	25.0	See para	100
19	–12	18.6	19.8	26.3	29.0	0.8	1.5	15.7	21.5	11.1.2	120
25	–16	25.0	26.4	34.0	36.6	0.8	1.5	14	16.5	and 11.1.4	150
31.5	–20	31.4	33.0	41.9	44.3	1.0	2.0	11.3	12.5		210

1. Metric Size is in mm (Ref. ISO 4397).
2. SAE Dash Size is equal to the hose ID, expressed in 1/16's of an inch.
3. Cover thickness shall be measured by means of a dial indicator depth gage having a rounded foot placed parallel to the hose, bridging a groove obtained by stripping a 12.5 to 25 mm width of cover from the hose. A mandrel should be placed in the hose bore to insure freedom from misalignment.
4. Type S hose has the same working pressures as ISO 11237-1 Type 2SC.
5. Bend radius measured at inside of bend.

TABLE 34—HOSE CONCENTRICITY (100R16)
Dimensions are in Millimeters

Hose Size	Concentricity, FIR ID to OD	Concentricity, FIR ID to Reinforcement
Up to 6.3 mm (–4), included	0.8	0.5
Over 6.3 mm (–4) to 19 mm (–12), included	1.0	0.7
Over 19 mm (–12)	1.3	0.9

TABLE 35—DIMENSIONS AND SPECIFICATIONS FOR SAE 100R17 HOSE
Dimensions are in Millimeters

Metric Size(1)	SAE Dash Size(2)	ID Min	ID Max	Reinforcement Dia Max	OD Max	Cover Thickness(3) Min	Cover Thickness(3) Max	Max Working Pressure MPa	Min Burst and Proof Pressure	Min Bend Radius(4)
5	–3	4.6	5.4	10.1	11.6	0.8	1.5	21	have been	45
6.3	-4	6.2	7.0	11.0	13.2	0.8	1.5	21	deleted	50
8	–5	7.7	8.5	13.0	15.0	0.8	1.5	21	from this	55
10	–6	9.3	10.1	15.0	17.0	0.8	1.5	21	table	65
12.5	–8	12.3	13.5	18.8	21.1	0.8	1.5	21	See para 11.1.2	90
16	–10	15.5	16.7	23.6	25.9	0.8	1.5	21	and 11.1.4	100
19	–12	18.6	19.8	27.7	30.3	0.8	1.5	21		120
25	–16	25.0	26.4	35.6	38.6	0.8	2.2	21		150

1. Metric Size is in mm (Ref. ISO 4397).
2. SAE Dash Size is equal to the hose ID, expressed in 1/16's of an inch.
3. Cover thickness shall be measured by means of a dial indicator depth gage having a rounded foot placed parallel to the hose, bridging a groove obtained by stripping a 12.5 to 25 mm width of cover from the hose. A mandrel should be placed in the hose bore to insure freedom from misalignment.
4. Bend Radius measured at inside of bend.

TABLE 36—HOSE CONCENTRICITY (100R17)
Dimensions are in Millimeters

Hose Size	Concentricity, FIR ID to OD	Concentricity, FIR ID to Reinforcement
6.3 mm (–4)	0.8	0.4
Over 6.3 mm (–4) to 19 mm (–12), included	1.0	0.7
Over 19 mm (–12)	1.3	0.9

30. 21 MPa Thermoplastic Hydraulic Hose (SAE 100R18)—This section covers thermoplastic hose for use with petroleum base and synthetic hydraulic fluids within a temperature range of –40 to +93 °C, and with water base hydraulic fluids within the temperature ranges agreed upon by the manufacturers of both the hose and the fluid. Operating temperatures in excess of +93 °C with petroleum base hydraulic fluids may materially reduce the life of the hose. Maximum working pressure and minimum bend radius are specified in Table 37.

Electrically nonconductive 100R18 hose is available for use in applications where there is potential of contact with high voltage sources. To be classified as nonconductive, a hose must pass the Electrical Conductivity Test described in 30.4.1. Nonconductive hose is identified by its orange cover and layline.

It should be noted that the detailed specifications which follow shall be supplemented by the general specifications given at the beginning of this document.

30.1 Dimensions—Dimensions and tolerances applicable to this hose are given in Table 37. The inside diameter of the hose shall be concentric with the outside diameter of the hose within the limits in Table 38.

30.2 Hose Construction—This hose shall consist of a thermoplastic inner tube resistant to hydraulic fluids with suitable synthetic fiber reinforcement, and a hydraulic fluid and weather resistant thermoplastic cover.

Nonconductive 100R18 hose shall be identified with an orange cover and appropriate layline. (Reference color, orange chip #22510, Federal Standard 595).

30.3 Connector Compatibility—Connectors for thermoplastic hose may not be interchangeable. Therefore, it is recommended that connectors and hose be properly matched. Connector and/or hose manufacturers shall be consulted for recommendations.

30.4 Qualification—For qualification to this section, hose and/or hose assemblies made therefrom shall comply with the following test and the tests specified in Table 3, and conform to the requirements of 11.1.

30.4.1 ELECTRICAL CONDUCTIVITY TEST (TWO 152 mm FREE HOSE LENGTH CONDITIONED ASSEMBLIES)—The maximum electrical leakage shall not exceed 50 µA when subjected to 37.5 kV for 5 min. This test shall not be applicable to hose with a pinpricked cover.

30.5 Inspection Tests—Inspection tests specified in 11.2 for bulk hose shall be performed.

TABLE 37—DIMENSIONS AND SPECIFICATIONS FOR SAE 100R18 HOSE
Dimensions are in Millimeters

Metric Size(1)	SAE Dash Size(2)	ID Min	ID Max	OD Max	Max Working Pressure MPa	Min Burst and Proof	Min Bend Radius(3)
5	–3	4.6	5.4	10.8	21	Pressure	30
6.3	–4	6.2	7.0	13.5	21	have been	45
8	–5	7.7	8.5	16.6	21	deleted	50
10	–6	9.3	10.3	18.4	21	from this table	75
12.5	–8	12.3	13.5	22.8	21	See para	90
16	–10	15.5	16.8	27.2	21	11.1.2	125
19	–12	18.6	19.8	31.5	21	and 11.1.4	165
25	–16	25.0	26.4	40.4	21		250

1. Metric Size is in mm (Ref. ISO 4397).
2. SAE Dash Size is equal to the hose ID, expressed in 1/16's of an inch.
3. Bend radius measured at inside of bend.

TABLE 38—HOSE CONCENTRICITY (100R18)
Dimensions are in Millimeters

Hose Size	Concentricity, FIR ID to OD
Up to 6.3 mm (–4), included	0.8
Over 6.3 mm (–4) to 19 mm (–12), included	1.0
Over 19 mm (–12)	1.3

APPENDIX A

A.1 Table A1 gives rationalized conversion pressures from MPa to psi. These converted equivalent pressures allow for minimum deviation from the mathematically correct conversion, while allowing for the use of the most common available pressures. The conversions were also rationalized to allow the burst pressures to be a minimum of 4 times the maximum working pressures.

TABLE A1—MPa TO PSI CONVERSION TABLE

MPa	psi	MPa	psi	MPa	psi	MPa	psi	MPa	psi
350	50 000	78	11 250	29.7	4 250	9.8	1 400	2.1	300
315	45 000	77	11 000	28	4 000	8.7	1 250	1.7	250
280	40 000	70	10 000	24.5	3 500	8.4	1 200	1.6	225
245	35 000	63	9 000	22.7	3 250	7.8	1 125	1.4	200
210	30 000	61	8 750	22.4	3 200	7	1000	1.25	180
175	25 000	59.5	8 500	21	3 000	6.1	875	1.05	150
168	24 000	56	8 000	20	2 900	5.6	800	1	140
160	23 200	52.5	7 500	19.2	2 750	5.2	750	0.85	125
157	22 500	49	7 000	17.5	2 500	5	725	0.8	112
140	20 000	45.5	6 500	16.8	2 400	4.9	700	0.7	100
122	17 500	43.5	6 250	15.7	2 250	4.3	625	0.6	90
119	17 000	42	6 000	14	2 000	4.2	600	0.5	70
112	16 000	40	5 800	12.2	1 750	3.9	565	0.4	62
98	14 000	38.5	5 500	11.3	1 625	3.5	500	0.4	56
87	12 500	35	5 000	11.2	1 600	2.8	400	0.35	50
84	12 000	33.5	4 800	10.5	1 500	2.6	375	0.3	45
80	11 600	31.5	4 500	10	1 450	2.4	350	0.25	35

APPENDIX B

B.1 Table B1 gives the SAE J517 100R hose codes in accordance with SAE J846.

TABLE B1—HOSE CODES

SAE J517 Hose	Hose Code
100R1 Type A	42
100R1 Type AT	53
100R1 Type S	new
100R2 Type A and B	43
100R2 Type AT and BT	54
100R2 Type S	new
100R3	44
100R4	45
100R5	46
100R6	47
100R7	48
100R8	49
100R9 Type A	50
100R9 Type AT	75
100R10 Type A	51
100R10 Type AT	76
100R11	52
100R12	77
100R13	78
100R14 Type A	79
100R14 Type B	80
100R15	90
100R16	91
100R16 Type S	new
100R17	93
100R18	94

CUMULATIVE DAMAGE ANALYSIS FOR HYDRAULIC HOSE ASSEMBLIES—SAE J1927 MAR2001

SAE Information Report

Report of the SAE Materials, Processes, and Parts Division approved October 1988. Reaffirmed by the SAE Fluid Conductors and Connectors Technical Committee S2—Hydraulic Hose and Hose Fittings July 1993 and revised MAR2001. Rationale statement available.

Foreword—This document has also changed to reflect the new SAE Technical Standards Board format. Equations are all numbered and are in order.

WARNING—**Hydraulic hose assemblies have a finite life and the exposure to surge pressures above the maximum working pressure will substantially reduce their service life. This analysis is intended to show the loss of hose working life due to elevated hydraulic pressures. Use of this SAE Information report is intended for those individuals that can produce a recorded history of pressure peaks and the frequency of the peaks. Under no circumstances should cumulative damage analysis be used unless recorded pressure history can be verified before implementing the design. Without proper documentation of the system pressure history, the application of any hose assembly above the rated working pressure is not recommended by hose manufacturers and will substantially decrease the working life of the hose. The user/installing company is accountable for the analysis and application of results.**

1. Scope—This SAE Information Report is intended to provide the hydraulic system analyst with a procedure which will assist in the selection and use of high-pressure wire reinforced hydraulic hose assemblies. Many construction, agricultural, industrial, or commercial equipment systems utilize hydraulic hose assemblies that are subjected to irregular cyclic pressure variations (cannot be approximated by a constant amplitude pressure cycle). This document relates damage done by pressure cycles with the pressure-life performance curve for the hose assembly being evaluated, using a linear damage rule to predict fatigue life similar to that used for predicting metal fatigue life. More detailed information on the subject may be found in SAE Paper No. 880713. The accuracy of cumulative damage calculations is directly related to proper measurement of the service pressure history and pressure-life performance for the hose assembly being evaluated. Final selection of a hose assembly must also consider installation and maintenance as noted in SAE J1273.

1.1 Background—In the current SAE J517 for hydraulic hose, each style and size hose is assigned a maximum operating pressure rating to assure the user reasonable service life in a wide variety of applications. (See Appendix A for further explanation of nomenclature used in this document.) This rating is based on assessment of many factors, including repeated pressure cycling under controlled laboratory conditions at a pressure equal to or greater than the assigned maximum operating pressure. This standard test procedure, as detailed in SAE J343 minimizes variables so as to provide a baseline for performance capability. SAE J517 takes note that actual pressure cycling in a hydraulic system will seldom duplicate those test parameters precisely. It provides basic hose construction details; SAE J343 establishes standard test procedures—which may be utilized to develop data at pressures other than the established test value for any hose assembly. SAE J1273 provides a guide for selection, installation, and maintenance for hose and hose assemblies.

Many hydraulic systems will be subjected to variable amplitude pressure cycles, and in some of these the highest surge peaks will occur only a few times. Strict interpretation of SAE J517 indicates the use of hose assemblies with a maximum operating pressure equal to or greater than the highest peak—even if that peak should occur only once in the life of the system. If this were done, the hose would have more reinforcement, larger outside diameter, less flexibility, and higher cost than might be needed. It should not be necessary to use a hose that has over a million cycle capability at a pressure which is likely to occur only a few times in the application. What is needed, then, is a design verification procedure that assures adequate fatigue life for applications with variable amplitude pressure usage where the highest surge peaks are between 100 and 200% of rated pressure.

1.1.1 Cumulative damage of hydraulic hose is in many ways comparable to cumulative damage of metal components. The design verification of metal components is done in two ways depending on whether loading is of constant amplitude or variable amplitude:

a. Size the part cross section so the constant amplitude (maximum) load will not produce a stress at the highest stressed area in excess of the material "endurance limit stress." This is a stress that will not cause failure in a million cycles of loading.

b. Do a cumulative damage analysis on the variable amplitude load or strain history to predict fatigue life as is normally done to evaluate prototype machines in the ground vehicle industry.

1.1.2 In a similar manner, hydraulic hose design verification should be done in two ways:

a. Select a hose assembly so the constant amplitude (maximum) pressure during service is less than the SAE J517 rated pressure.

b. Do a cumulative damage analysis with the variable amplitude pressure history to determine if the fatigue life will meet the design life of the product. The block diagram in Figure 1 illustrates how both the pressure history and the P-N curve information are the essential inputs for this procedure.

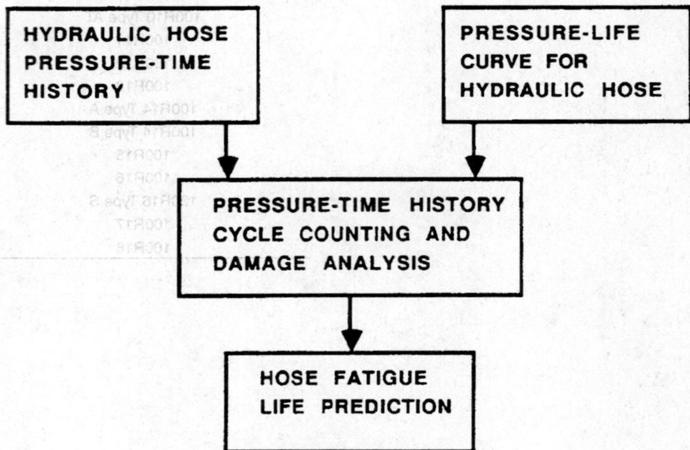

FIGURE 1—BLOCK DIAGRAM FOR HOSE FATIGUE ANALYSIS

For both metal parts and hydraulic hose assemblies, the first method is appropriate when the load (pressure) is known to be a large number of cyclic applications of nearly constant amplitude. However, if the load (pressure) involves infrequent cycling or includes only a few large peaks, then the first method may lead to designs that are heavy, bulky, inflexible, and more costly than need be. For variable amplitude loads or pressure applications, it is logical to do a cumulative damage analysis to judge the adequacy of the design.

Other factors, such as internal temperature, ambient temperature, and ozone exposure, for all intents and purposes, have not been considered in this cumulative damage analysis procedure. Long-term exposure to extreme limits or high levels of these elements could affect the overall hose assembly life.

2. References

2.1 Applicable Publications—The following publications form a part of this specification to the extent specified herein. Unless otherwise indicated, the latest version of SAE publications shall apply.

2.1.1 SAE Publications—Available from SAE, 400 Commonwealth Drive, Warrendale, PA 15096-0001.

SAE J343—Tests and Procedures for SAE 100R Series Hydraulic Hose and Hose Assemblies

SAE J517—Hydraulic Hose

SAE J1273—Selection, Installation, and Maintenance of Hose and Hose Assemblies

SAE 880713—SAE Test Program on Cumulative Damage for Hydraulic Hose Assemblies

3. Use of P-N Curves in Design—A cumulative damage analysis is needed for a hydraulic system subjected to variable amplitude pressure cycles if system pressures in excess of rated pressure are to be in the design consideration. An approach for this analysis is to use the Reference P-N curve as defined in the previously mentioned reference paper and shown in Figure 2. Verification that the actual hose assemblies have a P-N curve in excess of the Reference P-N curve is essential. The equation for the Reference P-N curve in Figure 2 is:

$$P_a = P_b(N)^s \quad \text{(Eq. 1)}$$

where:

P_a = Zero-to-Max amplitude of pressure cycle
N = Cycles to failure at pressure amplitude P_a
P_b = Burst pressure (one cycle life)
s = Slope of curve on log-log plot

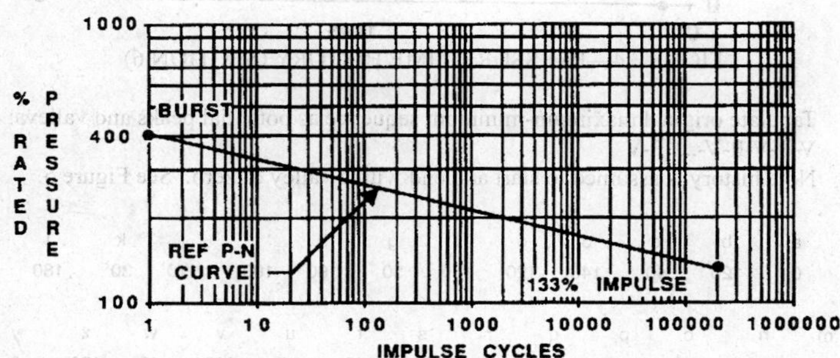

FIGURE 2—HYDRAULIC HOSE PRESSURE-LIFE PERFORMANCE CURVE (SECTION 3)

WARNING—This figure is here to show the concept of Equation 1. This should be used for conceptual purposes only. The user is responsible for the actual graph. The user's graph needs to be based on actual history of tested data.

By using two known points on this line:

- 1 cycle at 400% (Burst Point)
- 200 000 cycles at 133% (Impulse Point)

the values of P_b and s can be found:

$$P_b = 400 \text{ and } s = -0.0902 \quad \text{(Eq. 2)}$$

and

$$P_a = 400(N)^{-0.0902} \quad \text{(Eq. 3)}$$

Rearranged to a more useful form to solve for N cycles at any pressure P_a this becomes:

$$N = \left[\frac{400}{P_a}\right]^{11.086} \quad \text{(Eq. 4)}$$

If a different impulse point (for example 500 000 cycles at 133%) were used, this would result in a different slope for the P-N curve. The Hydraulic Design Analyst has the option of using other Reference P-N curves in the analysis as long as there are data to demonstrate the actual P-N curve is in excess of the Reference P-N curve. In addition, the analyst can increase statistical confidence by requiring a low percentage failure P-N curve (for example, a B_{10} Curve) for test data for the hose assembly being considered to be in excess of the Reference P-N curve used in the analysis. (This is explained in greater detail in SAE Paper No. 880713.)

In order to use this prediction procedure, a sample pressure history has to be available. The cycle counting procedure for a pressure history is explained in more detail in the next section. The fundamental theory for damage accumulation uses zero-to-max pressure cycles since the P-N curve is determined from zero-to-max test pressure cycles. This is slightly different than for stress-life or strain-life curves for metal where there are fully reversed loads (zero mean stress). It is appropriate to resolve pressure cycles to zero-to-max cycles (mean pressure equals one-half of the maximum) since any possible negative pressure must be very small compared to the "high pressures" generally used in wire reinforced hydraulic hose assemblies. The damage is accumulated in a linear manner as is done for metal fatigue (see Equation 5):

$$D = \sum_{i=1}^{J} \frac{n_i}{N_i} \quad \text{(Eq. 5)}$$

where:

D = Damage done (D = 1 assumes failure)
n_i = Number of cycles in the history at amplitude i
N_i = Number of cycles to cause failure at amplitude i
j = Number of different amplitudes in the history

This equation and the P-N curve illustrates that when subjected to repeated constant amplitude pressure cycles above a given level, a hose assembly will eventually fail. The higher this constant amplitude pressure, the shorter the life. If the pressure is large enough, then failure can occur in one cycle. This is a burst test and is represented by the one cycle pressure value at the left end of the P-N curve and is analogous to the ultimate strength of metal parts. Damage due to a variable amplitude pressure history (which has been resolved to zero-to-max cycles) is then simply the sum of the n_i/N_i for all the different amplitudes in the history. When this summation equals one, failure is predicted.

If a typical pressure history of a given length of time (t) (time factor is machine operation time, not calendar time) is analyzed, Equation 4 will give a decimal fraction for the damage done. Then the fatigue life prediction is as in Equation 5:

$$\text{Life}(L) = t(1/D) \quad \text{(Eq. 6)}$$

For example, if D = 0.01, one one-hundredth of damage has been done in t units of time and the total expected life would be one hundred times t units of time for the total life.

The procedure will work with either constant or variable amplitude pressure histories. Figure 1 illustrates how the P-N curve and the pressure history are the two necessary inputs for the procedure. If the user of the procedure has test data to demonstrate that the actual P-N curve is in excess of the reference P-N curve, then life predictions will be conservative for the sample pressure history that is used in the analysis.

*4. **Pressure History Cycle Counting***—Typical hydraulic hose pressure histories are variable amplitude and are almost totally positive pressure. Depending on the hydraulic component that the hose may be connected to, it is sometimes possible to have a partial vacuum in a hose. In the worst possible case, this could never be more than one atmosphere, which is small compared to the maximum that "high pressure" hoses normally experience, but should be avoided in system design as the impact on useful life is far greater than a numerical relationship would suggest. For cycle counting, pressure cycle histories will be considered to be all positive pressures. As indicated in the previous section, the cycle counting procedure needs to be designed to resolve the pressure history into zero-to-maximum pressure cycles since this is the type of pressure cycle used to determine the P-N curves.

A cycle counting procedure is discussed in detail in SAE Paper No. 880713 and suggests the following three steps:

a. Tabulate the pressure peaks from the history and assume each is followed by a minimum pressure value of zero.
b. A pressure peak is defined as a maximum value that is preceded and followed by pressure minimums of a specified lower magnitude (threshold). A pressure maximum that does not meet this requirement is not counted.
c. Threshold must be selected based on engineering judgment of the analyst.

As a result of the previous steps, all cycles that are counted will be zero-to-max cycles and can be used directly in the damage Equation 5. The threshold value needs to be at least 35 to 50% of the hose rated pressure to avoid counting cycles that are small pressure undulations and not pressure cycles that cause significant fatigue damage. Engineering judgment must be used to select the threshold to make an appropriate cycle count. This cycle counting procedure assumes the pressure minimums following significant maximums are zero. This was done to keep the procedure simple, practical, and conservative but not ultraconservative when only a few large pressure cycles are in the history. If, however, the service history does have a large number of cycles at the largest value, this evaluation procedure will still give the appropriate cycle count and life prediction. It will work with constant amplitude histories just as well as with variable amplitude histories.

An important part of the cycle counting is the ability to determine when a maximum should be kept as a peak. Figure 3 shows the four possible cases that can occur. Only case one is considered a valid peak and kept for the cycle counting. From Figure 3:

a. Case I
  R1 > T and R2 > T
  Count P_1
b. Case II
  R1 > T and R2 ≤ T
  Discard P1 and V2
  Keep V1 as Valley
  Consider next Peak and Valley

c. Case III
   R1 ≤ T and R2 > T
   Discard P1 and V1
   Keep V2 as Valley
   Consider next Peak and Valley

d. Case IV
   R1 ≤ T and R2 ≤ T
   Discard P1 and highest Valley
   Keep lower Valley
   Consider next Peak and Valley

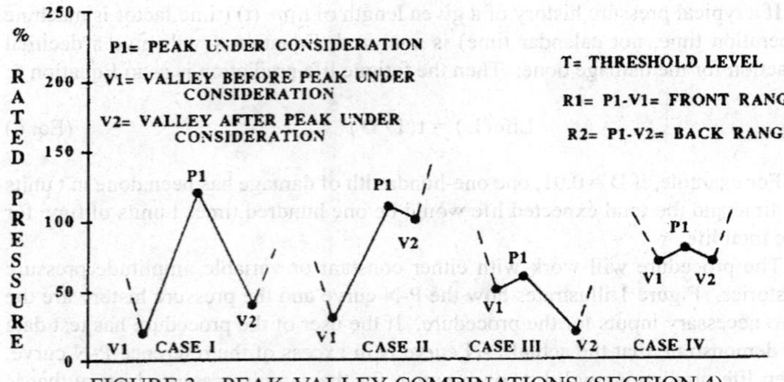

FIGURE 3—PEAK-VALLEY COMBINATIONS (SECTION 4)

5. *Summary of Procedure to Predict Hose Assembly Life*

5.1 The analyst must have data to demonstrate that the actual P-N curve for the hose assembly under consideration falls above and to the right of the Reference P-N curve.

$$P_a = P_b(N)^s \quad \text{(Eq. 7)}$$

For a burst of 400% of rated pressure and a 200 000 cycle life at 133% of rated pressure this is:

$$P_a = 400(N)^{-0.0902} \quad \text{rearranged } N = \left[\frac{400}{P_a}\right]^{11.086} \quad \text{(Eq. 8)}$$

5.2 Establish a sample pressure history for the system for a known time.

5.3 Determine valid "peaks" and count the number of occurrences (n_i) for each peak value (amplitude) in the sample pressure history.

5.4 For each peak value, calculate cycles to failure (N_i) from the Reference P-N curve (step 5.1).

5.5 For each peak value, calculate the ratio of counted cycles (n_i) and the projected number to failure (N_i) to determine the fraction of damage for each peak value.

5.6 Total all fractions of damage from (step 5.5) for total damage (D) due to the sample pressure history.

5.7 Project the fatigue life (L) as the ratio of system operation time (t) for the sample pressure history divided by the total of all damage incurred during that time.

$$L = t(1/D) \quad \text{(Eq. 9)}$$

6. *Sample Problem for Cumulative Damage*—This simple example is used to illustrate the complete cumulative damage procedure. It shows how to cycle count a sample pressure history, Figure 4, and then calculate the damage done and predict the life of the hose for the sample pressure history. The example is done "by hand" since it is only a few peaks and valleys. "Real" histories would be much longer and would logically be done with a computer program that has been programmed to consider the various special cases of cycle counting and choice of threshold.

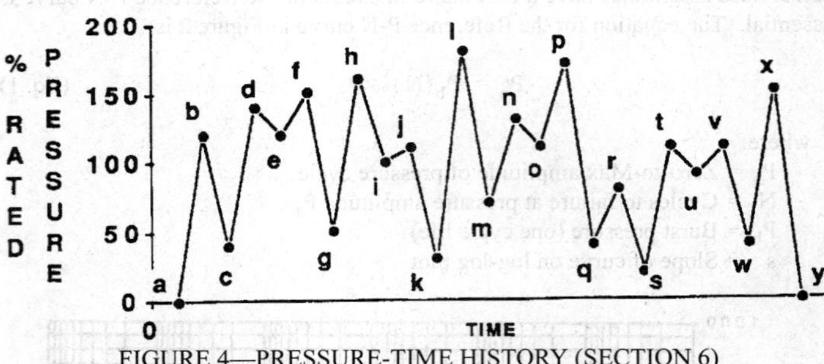

FIGURE 4—PRESSURE-TIME HISTORY (SECTION 6)

Tabulate original maximum-minimum sequence as potential peaks and valleys: V-P-V-P-V-.....P-V

Note history is assumed to start and end with a valley of zero. See Figure 5.

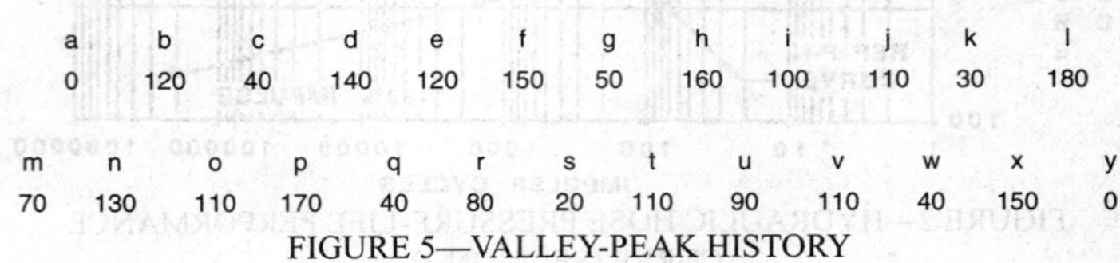

FIGURE 5—VALLEY-PEAK HISTORY

Follow procedure in the previous section and Figure 3 to determine which potential peaks will be counted.

For this example assume threshold is 35%.

Counted peaks which result are shown in Figure 6:

b	f	h	l	p	r	t	x
120	150	160	180	170	80	110	150

FIGURE 6—COUNTED PEAKS

Then for a hose assembly that has a P-N curve in excess of Reference P-N curve, use Equation 4 to calculate N_i for each P_a. Table 1 shows the tabulated results for the sample pressure history.

TABLE 1—TABULATED DATA

Pressure as a % of Rated Pressure Pn	Calculated Cycles to Cause Failure at Pressure i Ni	Counted Cycles in History at Pressure i ni	Degree of Damage Effected by ni ni/Ni
80	56×10^6	1	0.178×10^{-7}
110	16.4×10^5	1	6.09×10^{-7}
120	62.6×10^4	1	16.0×10^{-7}
150	52.8×10^3	2	3.79×10^{-5}
160	25.8×10^3	1	3.87×10^{-5}
170	13.2×10^3	1	7.59×10^{-5}
180	6.99×10^3	1	14.3×10^{-5}

Using Equation 5:

$$\sum \frac{n_i}{N_i} = 29.8 \times 10^{-5} \quad \text{(Eq. 10)}$$

Assume pressure history is for 0.5 h. Then from Equation 6:

$$\text{Life(L)} = \frac{0.5}{29.8 \times 10^{-5}} = 1679 \text{ h} \quad \text{(Eq. 11)}$$

APPENDIX A

A.1 Nomenclature—To facilitate understanding of the concept and life calculation procedure used in this document and in related documents, the following nomenclature is used.

A.1.1 Pressure History—The time oriented variations of internal pressure in a hydraulic system (hose assembly). This may be tabulated by listing a sequence of relative maximums and minimums from recorded pressure versus time data. Significant maximums and minimums are called peaks and valleys. (See section on cycle counting). A peak is defined as a maximum both preceded and followed by a minimum less than the peak by a specified amount or threshold (differential pressure). A valley is defined as the smallest minimum between significant peaks. Note that it is possible for peaks to be lower than valleys in cases where they are not adjacent. Likewise, valleys could be greater than nonadjacent peaks.

A.1.2 Threshold (Differential Pressure)—The magnitude of pressure difference (differential pressure) between a maximum and adjacent minimum in a pressure history that is considered significant by the hydraulic design analyst. This threshold (differential pressure) must be chosen by the analyst and is usually at least 35% of the hose rated pressure. If both the differential pressure before and after a maximum are equal to or greater than the threshold, then that maximum is defined to be a significant peak in the pressure history. (See Figure 3.)

A.1.3 Sample Pressure History—A representative recording for a given length of time of the pressure history for a hydraulic hose. Generally, a sequence of peaks and valleys for a given length of time, requiring a choice of threshold to disregard insignificant pressure variations.

A.1.4 Constant Amplitude Pressure History—A pressure history where all the peaks are of similar magnitude with the valleys near zero.

A.1.5 Variable Amplitude Pressure History—A pressure history where the peaks and valleys are irregular.

A.1.6 Rated Pressure—The reference pressure or "nominal design pressure" for a hose assembly from which other pressures are based.

A.1.7 Operating Pressure—(Used in SAE J517) Same as rated pressure.

A.1.8 Maximum Operating Pressure—(Used in SAE J517) Same as rated pressure.

A.1.9 Minimum Burst Pressure—Defined as 400% of rated pressure.

A.1.10 Burst Pressure—The actual pressure at which a hose assembly fails when subjected to slowly increasing hydrostatic pressure (see SAE J343).

A.1.11 Surge Pressure—(Used in SAE J517 and J1273.) A rapid and transient rise in pressure in a pressure history.

A.1.12 Impulse Test Pressure—A laboratory test pressure level to which a hose assembly is repeatedly subjected with near zero valleys between peaks. (See SAE J343). Generally given in percent of rated pressure and is usually greater than 100%.

A.1.13 Impulse Life—The number of cycles to failure for a hose assembly when subjected to cyclic testing for a given impulse test pressure.

A.1.14 Fatigue Life—The predicted time to failure (length of operational service) for a hose assembly in a working hydraulic system, based on a sample pressure history and cumulative damage calculations.

A.1.15 Cumulative Damage Calculation—A procedure to calculate fatigue life of a hose assembly by relating pressure cycles and fatigue damage for a sample pressure history with a given P-N curve.

A.1.16 Pressure-Life (P-N) Curve—The relationship between impulse test pressure, P, and impulse life, N, for a given type and size of hose. Can be plotted as a line on a log-log chart of percent of rated pressure and cycles to failure.

A.1.17 Reference P-N Curve—A straight line relation on a P-N plot connecting one cycle at 400% (minimum burst) with the impulse test point (for example 200 000 cycles at 133%). In this form (percent of rated pressure versus life), hoses with different rated pressure all plot with the same Reference P-N curve. P-N curves can also be plotted with pressure units rather than percent of rated pressure. In this form, a "family" of parallel P-N curves result for different rated pressures.

A.1.18 10% P-N Curve-B_{10} Curve—A P-N curve for test data where 10% failure of a population of hoses would occur. Can be used to increase the statistical confidence of life prediction (see reference paper #880713).

RECOMMENDED PRACTICES FOR HYDRAULIC HOSE ASSEMBLIES—SAE J1273 DEC2002

SAE Recommended Practice

Report of the SAE Fluid Conductors and Connectors Technical Committee approved September 1979 and reaffirmed May 1986. Completely revised by the SAE Fluid Conductors and Connectors Technical Committee SC2—Hydraulic Hose and Hose Fittings November 1991. Rationale statement available. Completely revised by the SAE Fluid Conductors and Connectors Technical Committee SC3—Training and Education Subcommittee October 1996 and reaffirmed March 2001. Rationale statement available. Revised by the SAE Fluid Conductors and Connectors Technical Committee SC3—Training and Education Subcommittee December 2002. Rationale statement available.

Foreword—This SAE Recommended Practice is intended as a guide to consider when selecting, routing, fabricating, installing, replacing, maintaining, and storing hose for fluid-power systems. It is subject to change to keep pace with experience and technical advances. For those new to hose use in fluid-power systems, this guide outlines practices to note during each phase of system design and use. Experienced designers and users skilled in achieving proper results, as well as the less experienced, can use this outline as a list of considerations to keep in mind.

Fluid power systems are complex and require extensive knowledge of both the system requirements and the various types of hose. Therefore, all-inclusive, detailed, step-by-step instructions are not practical and are beyond the scope of this document. Less experienced designers and users who need more information can consult specialists such as hose suppliers and manufacturers. This guide can improve the communication process.

Safety Considerations—These recommended practices involve safety considerations; note these carefully during all phases of design and use of hose systems. Improper selection, fabrication, installation, or maintenance of hose and hose assemblies for fluid-power systems may result in serious personal injury or property damage. These recommended practices can reduce the likelihood of component or system failure, thereby reducing the risk of injury or damage.

TABLE OF CONTENTS

1. Scope—SAE J1273 provides guidelines for selection, routing, fabrication, installation, replacement, maintenance, and storage of hose and hose assemblies for fluid-power systems. Many of these SAE Recommended Practices also may be suitable for other hoses and systems.

2. References

2.1 Applicable Publications—The following publications form a part of this specification to the extent specified herein. Unless otherwise specified, the latest issue of SAE publications shall apply.

2.1.1 SAE PUBLICATIONS—Available from SAE, 400 Commonwealth Drive, Warrendale, PA 15096-0001.

SAE J343—Test and Procedures for SAE 100 R Series Hydraulic Hose and Hose Assemblies

SAE J514—Hydraulic Tube Fittings

SAE J517—Hydraulic Hose

SAE J1927—Cumulative Damage Analysis for Hydraulic Hose Assemblies

2.1.2 ISO PUBLICATION—Available from ANSI, 25 West 43rd Street, New York, NY 10036-8002.

ISO 3457—Earth moving machinery—Guards and shields—Definitions and specifications

3. Definitions—These explanations serve only to clarify this document and are not intended to stand alone. They are presented sequentially, with the former helping to explain the latter.

3.1 Fluid Power—Energy transmitted and controlled using pressurized hydraulic fluids or compressed air.

3.2 Hose—Flexible conductor. In this document, the term hose also may refer to a hose assembly with related accessories used in fluid power applications.

3.3 Hose Fitting or Fitting—Connector which can be attached to the end of a hose.

3.4 Hose Assembly—Hose with hose fittings attached.

3.5 Hose Failure—Occurrence in which a hose stops meeting system requirements.

3.6 Hose Service Life—Length of time a hose meets system requirements without needing replacement.

4. Safety Considerations—Listed in 4.1 to 4.7 are some potential conditions and situations that may lead to personal injury and/or property damage. This list is not necessarily all inclusive. Consider reasonable and feasible means, including those described in this section, to reduce the risk of injuries or property damage.

Training, including the information in this document, for operators, maintenance personnel, and other individuals working with hoses under pressure is encouraged.

4.1 Fluid Injections—Fine streams of escaping pressurized fluid can penetrate skin and enter a human body. These fluid injections may cause severe tissue damage and loss of limb.

Consider various means to reduce the risk of fluid injections, particularly in areas normally occupied by operators. Consider careful routing, adjacent components, warnings, guards, shields, and training programs.

Relieve pressure before disconnecting hydraulic or other lines. Tighten all connections before applying pressure.

Avoid contact with escaping fluids. Treat all leaks as though pressurized and hot enough to burn skin. Never use any part of your body to check a hose for leaks.

If a fluid-injection accident occurs, see a doctor immediately. **DO NOT DELAY OR TREAT AS A SIMPLE CUT!** Any fluid injected into the skin must be surgically removed *within a few hours* or gangrene may result. Doctors unfamiliar with this type of injury should consult a knowledgeable medical source.

4.2 Whipping Hose—If a pressurized hose assembly blows apart, the fittings can be thrown off at high speed, and the loose hose can flail or whip with great force. This is particularly true in compressible-fluid systems.

When this risk exists, consider guards and restraints to protect against injury.

4.3 Burns from Conveyed Fluids—Fluid-power media may reach temperatures that can burn human skin. If there is risk of burns from escaping fluid, consider guards and shields to prevent injury, particularly in areas normally occupied by operators.

4.4 Fire and Explosions from Conveyed Fluids—Most fluid-power media, including fire-resistant hydraulic fluids, will burn under certain conditions. Fluids which escape from pressurized systems may form a mist or fine spray which can flash or explode upon contact with an ignition source.

Consider selecting, guarding, and routing hose to minimize the risk of combustion (see Section 5 and ISO 3457).

4.5 Fire and Explosions from Static-Electric Discharge—Fluid passing through hose can generate static electricity, resulting in static-electric discharge. This may create sparks that can ignite system fluids or gases in the surrounding atmosphere.

When this potential exists, select hose specifically designed to carry the static-electric charge to ground.

4.6 Electrical Shock—Electrocution could occur if hose conducts electricity through a person. Most hoses are conductive. Many contain metal or have metal fittings. Even nonconductive hoses can be conduits for electricity if they carry conductive fluids.

Be aware of routing or using hose near electrical sources. When this cannot be avoided, select appropriate hose. Nonconductive hoses should be considered. SAE J517—100R7 and 100R8 hoses, with orange covers marked "Nonconductive" are available for applications requiring nonconductive hose.

4.7 Mechanisms Controlled by Fluid Power—Mechanisms controlled by fluids in hoses can become hazardous when a hose fails. For example, when a hose bursts, objects supported by fluid pressure may fall, or vehicles or machines may lose their brakes or steering.

If mechanisms are controlled by fluid power, consider safe modes of failure that minimize risks of injury or damage.

5. Hose Selection and Routing—A wide variety of interacting factors influence hose service life and the ability of each fluid-power system to operate satisfactorily, and the combined effects of these factors on service life are often unpredictable. Therefore, these documents should not be construed as design standards. For applications outside the specifications in SAE J517, SAE J514, or other relevant design standards, performance of hose assemblies should be determined by appropriate testing.

Carefully analyze each system. Then design routings and select hose and related components to meet the system-performance and hose-service-life requirements, and to minimize the risks of personal injury and/or property damage. Consider the following factors:

5.1 System Pressures—Excessive pressure can accelerate hose assembly failure. Analyze the steady-state pressures, and the frequency and amplitude of pressure surges, such as pulses and spikes. These are rapid and transient rises in pressure which may not be indicated on many common pressure gages and can be identified best on high-frequency-response electronic measuring instruments.

For maximum hose service life, hose selection should be based on a system pressure, including surges, that is less than the hose maximum working pressure. Hose may be used above its maximum working pressure where reduced life expectancy is acceptable. SAE J1927 provides one method to help predict wire-reinforced hose service life for a given hydraulic application, where the surge pressure peaks vary, and/or the highest pressure peaks occur infrequently.

5.2 Suction—For suction applications, such as inlet flow to pumps, select hose to withstand both the negative and positive pressures the system imposes on the hose.

5.3 External Pressure—In certain applications, such as in autoclaves or under water, the external environmental pressures may exceed the fluid pressure inside the hose. In these applications, consider the external pressures, and if necessary, consult the manufacturers.

5.4 Temperature—Exceeding hose temperature ratings may significantly reduce hose life. Select hose so the fluid and ambient temperatures, both static and transient, fall within the hose ratings. The effects of external heat sources should not raise the temperature of the hose above its maximum operating temperature. Select hose, heat shields, sleeving, and other methods for these requirements, and route or shield hose to avoid hose damage from external heat sources.

5.5 Permeation—Permeation, or effusion, is seepage of fluid through the hose. Certain materials in hose construction are more permeable than others. Consider the effects of permeation when selecting hose, especially with gaseous fluids. Consult the hose and fluid manufacturers for permeability information.

5.6 Hose-Material Compatibility—Variables that can affect compatibility of system fluids with hose materials include, but are not limited to:

a. Fluid pressure
b. Temperature
c. Concentration
d. Duration of exposure

Because of permeation (see 5.5), consider compatibility of system fluids with the hose, tube, cover, reinforcement, and fittings. Consult the fluid and hose manufacturers for compatibility information.

NOTE—Many fluid/elastomer compatibility tables in manufacturers' catalogs show ratings based on fluids at 21 °C, room temperature. These ratings may change at other temperatures. Carefully read the notes on the compatibility tables, and if in doubt, consult the manufacturer.

5.7 Environment—Environmental conditions can cause hose and fitting degradation. Conditions to evaluate include, but are not limited to:

a. Ultraviolet light
b. Salt water
c. Air pollutants
d. Temperature (see 5.4)
e. Ozone
f. Chemicals
g. Electricity
h. Abrasion

If necessary, consult the manufacturers for more information.

5.8 Static-Electric Discharge—Fluid passing through hose can generate static electricity resulting in static-electric discharge. This may create sparks that can puncture hose. If this potential exists, select hose with sufficient conductivity to carry the static-electric charge to ground.

5.9 Sizing—The power transmitted by pressurized fluid varies with pressure and rate of flow. Select hose with adequate size to minimize pressure loss, and to avoid hose damage from heat generation or excessive velocity. Conduct calculations, or consult the manufacturers for sizing at flow velocities.

5.10 Unintended Uses—Hose assemblies are designed for the internal forces of conducted fluids. Do not pull hose or use it for purposes that may apply external forces for which the hose or fittings were not designed.

5.11 Specifications and Standards—When selecting hose and fittings for specific applications, refer to applicable government, industry, and manufacturer's specifications and standards.

5.12 Unusual Applications—Applications not addressed by the manufacturer or by industry standards may require special testing prior to selecting hose.

5.13 Hose Cleanliness—The cleanliness requirements of system components, other than hose, will determine the cleanliness requirements of the application. Consult the component manufacturers' cleanliness information for all components in the system. Hose assemblies vary in cleanliness levels; therefore, specify hose assemblies with adequate cleanliness for the system.

5.14 Hose Fittings—Selection of the proper hose fittings for the hose and application is essential for proper operation and safe use of hose and related assembly equipment. Hose fittings are qualified with the hose. Therefore, select only hose fittings compatible with the hose for the applications.

Improper selection of hose fittings or related assembly equipment for the application can result in injury or damage from leaks, or from hose assemblies blowing apart (see 4.2, 6.2, 6.3, and 6.4).

5.15 Vibration—Vibration can reduce hose service life. If required, conduct tests to evaluate the frequency and amplitude of system vibration. Clamps or other means may be used to reduce the effects of vibration. Consider the vibration requirements when selecting hose and predicting service life.

5.16 Hose Cover Protection—Protect the hose cover from abrasion, erosion, snagging, and cutting. Special abrasion-resistant hoses and hose guards are available for additional protection. Route hose to reduce abrasion from hose rubbing other hose or objects that may abrade it. (See Figure 1)

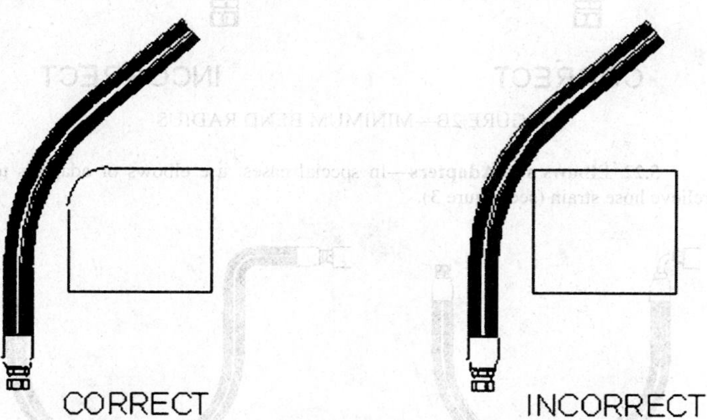

FIGURE 1—PREVENTION OF EXTERNAL DAMAGE

5.17 External Physical Abuse—Route hose to avoid:

a. Tensile loads
b. Side loads
c. Flattening
d. Thread damage
e. Kinking
f. Damage to sealing surfaces
g. Abrasion
h. Twisting

5.18 Swivel-Type Adapters—Swivel-type fittings or adapters do not transfer torque to hose while being tightened. Use these as needed to prevent twisting during installation.

5.19 Live Swivels—If two components in the system are rotating in relation to each other, live swivels may be necessary. These connectors reduce the torque transmitted to the hose.

5.20 Slings and Clamps—Use slings and clamps to support heavy or long hose and to keep it away from moving parts. Use clamps that prevent hose movement that will cause abrasion.

5.21 Minimum Bend Radius—The minimum bend radius is defined in SAE J343 and is specified in other SAE standards and hose manufacturer's product literature. Routing at less than minimum bend radius may reduce hose life. Sharp bending at the hose/fitting juncture may result in leaking, hose rupturing, or the hose assembly blowing apart (see 4.2 and Figures 2A and 2B).

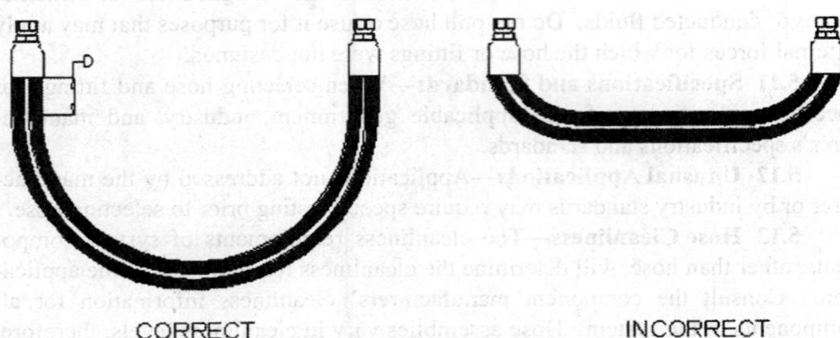

FIGURE 2A—MINIMUM BEND RADIUS

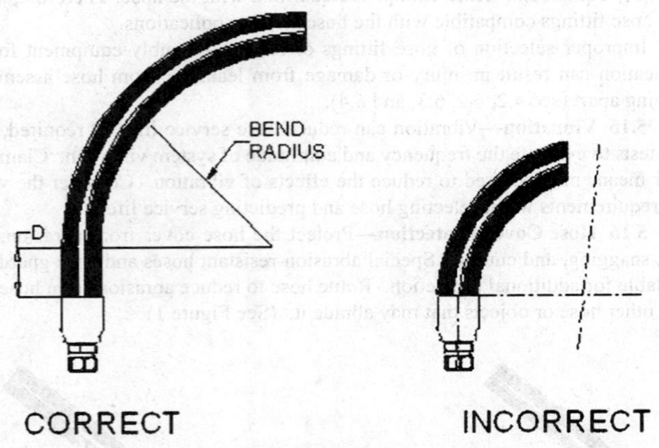

FIGURE 2B—MINIMUM BEND RADIUS

5.22 Elbows and Adapters—In special cases, use elbows or adapters to relieve hose strain (see Figure 3).

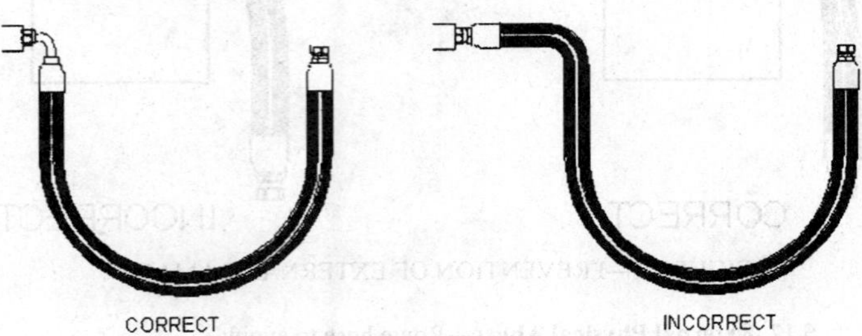

FIGURE 3—ELBOWS AND ADAPTERS

5.23 Lengths—Unnecessarily long hose can increase pressure drop and affect system performance. When pressurized, hose that is too short may pull loose from its fittings, or stress the fitting connections, causing premature metallic or seal failures. When establishing hose length, refer to Figures 4, 5, and 6; and use the following practices:

5.23.1 Motion Absorption—Provide adequate hose length to distribute movement and prevent bends smaller than the minimum bend radius.

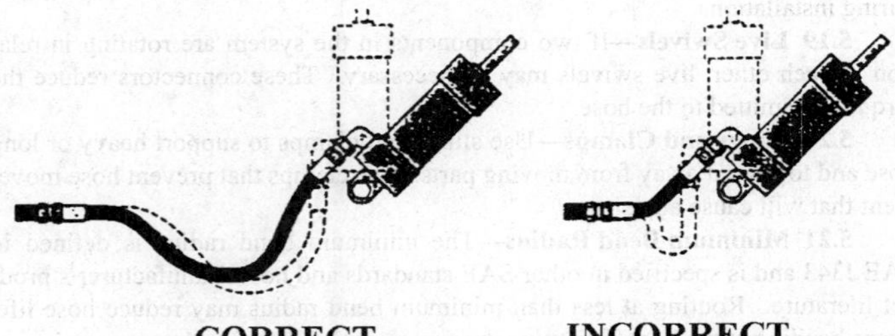

FIGURE 4—MOTION ABSORPTION

5.23.2 Hose and Machine Tolerances—Design hose to allow for changes in length due to machine motion and tolerances.

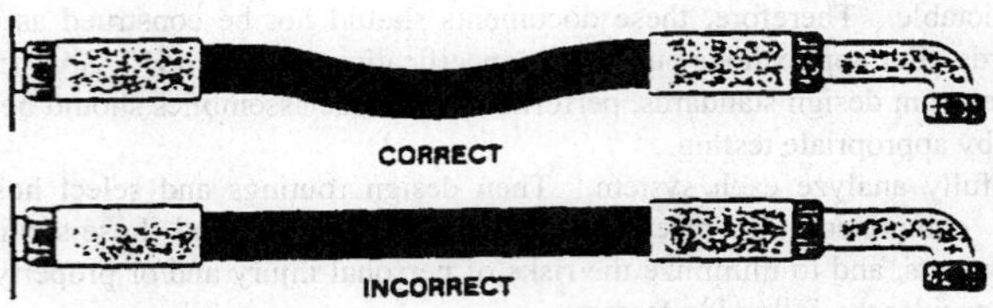

FIGURE 5—HOSE AND MACHINE TOLERANCES

5.23.3 Hose Length Change Due to Pressure—Design hose to accommodate length changes from changing pressures. Do not cross or clamp together high- and low-pressure hoses. The difference in length changes could wear the hose covers.

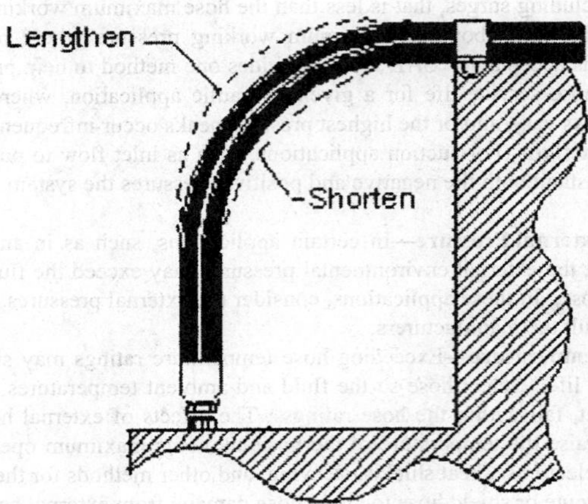

FIGURE 6—HOSE LENGTH CHANGE DUE TO PRESSURE

5.24 Hose Movement and Bending—Hose allows relative motion between system components. Analyze this motion when designing hose systems. The number of cycles per day may significantly affect hose life. Also avoid multiple planes of motion and twisting motion. Consider the motion of the hose when selecting hose and predicting service life. In applications that require hose to move or bend, refer to Figures 7A, 7B, and 8; and use these practices:

5.24.1 Bend in Only One Plane to Avoid Twisting

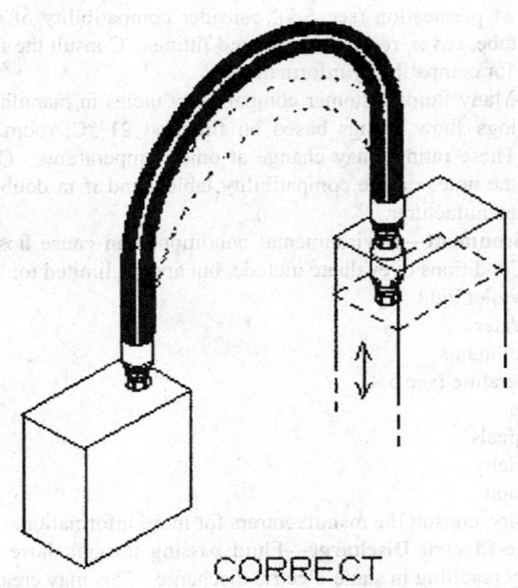

FIGURE 7A—BEND IN ONLY ONE PLANE TO AVOID TWISTING

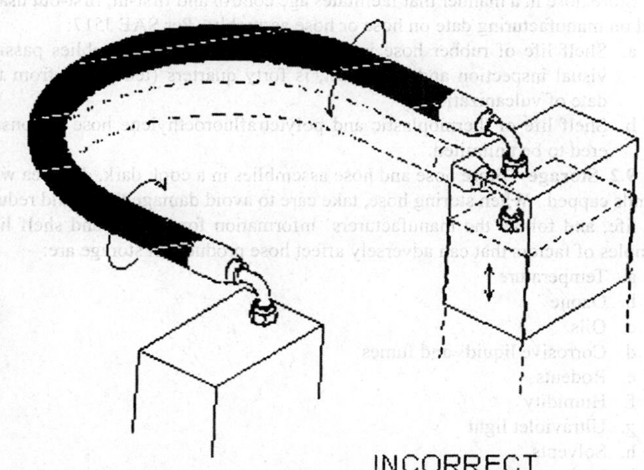

FIGURE 7B—BEND IN ONLY ONE PLANE TO AVOID TWISTING

5.24.2 PREVENT HOSE BENDING IN MORE THAN ONE PLANE—If hose follows a compound bend, couple it into separate segments, or clamp it into segments that flex in only one plane.

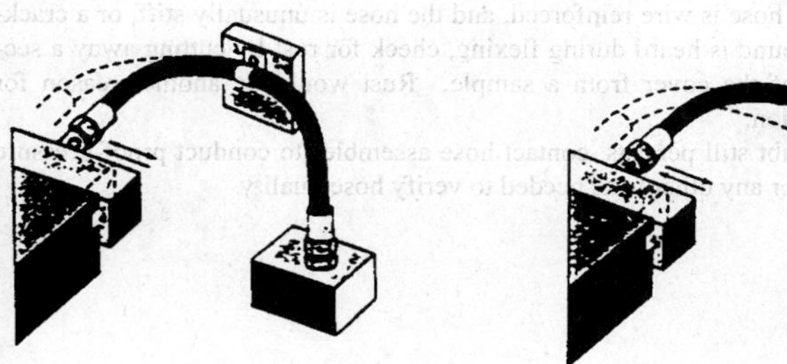

FIGURE 8—PREVENT HOSE BENDING IN MORE THAN ONE PLANE

6. Hose-Assembly Fabrication—Persons fabricating hose assemblies should be trained in the proper use of equipment and materials. The manufacturers' instructions and the practices listed as follows must be followed. Properly assembled fittings are vital to the integrity of a hose assembly. Improperly assembled fittings can separate from the hose and may cause serious injury or property damage from whipping hose, or from fire or explosion of vapor expelled from the hose.

6.1 Component Inspection—Prior to assembly, examine components for:

a. Style or type
b. Cleanliness
c. Loose covers
d. Nicks
e. Size
f. Inside obstructions
g. Visible defects
h. Damage
i. Length
j. Blisters
k. Burrs

6.2 Hose Fittings—Hose fitting components from one manufacturer are not usually compatible with fitting components supplied by another manufacturer. For example, do not use a hose fitting nipple from one manufacturer with a hose socket from another manufacturer.

It is the responsibility of the fabricator to consult the manufacturer's written instructions or the manufacturer directly for information on proper fitting components.

6.3 Hose and Fitting Compatibility—Care must be taken to determine proper compatibility between the hose and fitting. Base selection on the manufacturers' recommendations substantiated by testing to industry standards such as SAE J517. Hose from one manufacturer is not usually compatible with fittings from another. Do not intermix hose and fittings from two manufacturers without approval from both manufacturers.

6.4 Hose Assembly Equipment—Assembly equipment from one manufacturer is usually not interchangeable with that from another manufacturer. Hoses and fittings from one manufacturer should not generally be assembled with the equipment of another manufacturer.

6.5 Safety Equipment—During fabrication, use proper safety equipment, including eye protection, breathing apparatus, and adequate ventilation.

6.6 Reuse of Hose and Fittings—When fabricating hose assemblies, do **not** reuse:

a. Field-attachable fittings that have blown or pulled off hose
b. Any part of hose fittings that were permanently crimped or swaged to hose
c. Hose that has been in service after system checkout (see 7.7)

6.7 Cleanliness of Hose Assemblies—Hose assemblies may be contaminated during fabrication. Clean hoses to specified cleanliness levels (see 5.13).

7. Hose Installation and Replacement—Use the following practices when installing hose assemblies in new systems or replacing hose assemblies in existing systems:

7.1 Pre-Installation Inspection—Before installing hose assemblies, examine:

a. Hose length and routing for compliance with original design
b. Assemblies for correct style, size, length, and visible nonconformities
c. Fitting sealing surfaces for burrs, nicks, or other damage

NOTE—When replacing hose assemblies in existing systems, verify that the replacement is of equal quality to the original assembly.

7.2 Handling During Installation—Handle hose with care during installation. Kinking hose, or bending at less than minimum bend radius may reduce hose life. Avoid sharp bending at the hose/fitting juncture (see 5.21).

7.3 Twist Angle and Orientation—Pressure applied to a twisted hose may shorten the life of the hose or loosen the connections. To avoid twisting, use the hose lay line or marking as a reference (see Figure 9).

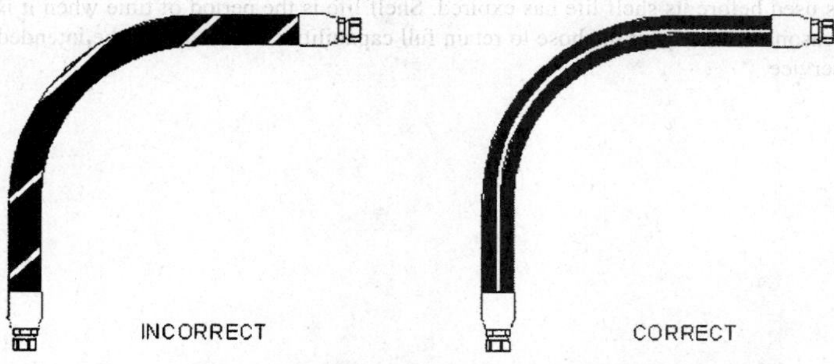

FIGURE 9—TWIST ANGLE AND ORIENTATION

7.4 Securement and Protection—Install necessary restraints and protective devices. Determine that such devices do not create additional stress or wear points.

7.5 Routing—Review proper routing practices provided in Section 5 and make appropriate corrections to obtain optimum performance.

7.6 Assembly Torque—The connection end of a hose fitting is normally threaded to obtain a tight pressure seal when attached to a port, an adapter, or another fitting. Sometimes bolts or screws provide the threaded connection. Each size and type of connection requires different torque values, and these may vary due to type of material or exterior coating.

Follow appropriate torquing instructions to obtain a proper pressure seal without over-torquing. A properly calibrated torque wrench should be used to tighten each connection, except when the manufacturer specifies tightening a specified number of hex flat turns beyond finger tight to obtain a seal.

7.7 System Checkouts—In hydraulic or other liquid systems, eliminate all air entrapment after completing the installation. Follow manufacturers' instructions to test the system for possible malfunctions and leaks.

7.7.1 To avoid injury during system checkouts:

a. Do not touch any part of the system when checking for leaks (see 4.1).
b. Stay out of potentially hazardous areas while testing hose systems (see Section 4).
c. Relieve system pressure before tightening connections.

8. Maintenance Inspection—A hose and fitting maintenance program may reduce equipment downtime, maintain peak operating performance, and reduce the risk of personal injury and/or property damage. The user should design and implement a maintenance program that suits the specific application and each specific hose in that application.

8.1 Inspection Frequency—Evaluate factors such as the nature and severity of the application, past history, and manufacturers' information to establish the frequency of visual inspections and functional tests.

8.2 Visual Inspection (Hose and Fittings)—Visually inspect hose and fittings for:

a. Leaks at hose fitting or in hose
b. Damaged, cut, or abraded cover
c. Exposed reinforcement
d. Kinked, crushed, flattened, or twisted hose
e. Hard, stiff, heat cracked, or charred hose
f. Blistered, soft, degraded, or loose cover
g. Cracked, damaged, or badly corroded fittings
h. Fitting slippage on hose
i. Other signs of significant deterioration

If any of these conditions exist, evaluate the hose assemblies for correction or replacement.

8.3 Visual Inspection (All Other Components)—When visually inspecting hose and fittings, inspect for related items including:

a. Leaking ports
b. Damaged or missing hose clamps, guards, or shields
c. Excessive dirt and debris around hose
d. System fluid: level, type, contamination, condition, and air entrainment

If any of these are found, address them appropriately.

8.4 Functional Test—Functional tests determine if systems with hose are leak free and operating properly. Carry out functional tests per information from equipment manufacturers.

9. Hose Storage—Age control and the manner of storage can affect hose life. Use the following practices when storing hose.

9.1 Age Control—Maintain a system of age control to determine that hose is used before its shelf life has expired. Shelf life is the period of time when it is reasonable to expect the hose to retain full capabilities for rendering the intended service.

Store hose in a manner that facilitates age control and first-in, first-out usage based on manufacturing date on hose or hose assembly. Per SAE J517:

a. Shelf life of rubber hose in bulk form, or in hose assemblies passing visual inspection and proof test, is forty quarters (ten years) from the date of vulcanization.
b. Shelf life of thermoplastic and polytetrafluoroethylene hose is considered to be unlimited.

9.2 Storage—Store hose and hose assemblies in a cool, dark, dry area with the ends capped. When storing hose, take care to avoid damage that could reduce hose life, and follow the manufacturers' information for storage and shelf life. Examples of factors that can adversely affect hose products in storage are:

a. Temperature
b. Ozone
c. Oils
d. Corrosive liquids and fumes
e. Rodents
f. Humidity
g. Ultraviolet light
h. Solvents
i. Insects
j. Radioactive materials

If there are questions regarding the quality or usability of hose or hose assemblies, evaluate appropriately:

a. Flex the hose to the minimum bend radius and compare it with new hose. After flexing, examine the cover and tube for cracks. If any appear, no matter how small, reject the hose.
b. If the hose is wire reinforced, and the hose is unusually stiff, or a cracking sound is heard during flexing, check for rust by cutting away a section of the cover from a sample. Rust would be another reason for rejection.
c. If doubt still persists, contact hose assembler to conduct proof-pressure tests or any other tests needed to verify hose quality.

TEST AND TEST PROCEDURES FOR SAE 100R SERIES HYDRAULIC HOSE AND HOSE ASSEMBLIES—SAE J343 JUL2001

SAE Standard

Report of the SAE Tube, Pipe, Hose, and Lubrication Fittings Committee approved June 1968. Revised by the SAE Fluid Conductors and Connectors Technical Committee May 1989, and completely revised May 1990. Revised by the SAE Fluid Conductors and Connectors Technical Committee SC2—Hydraulic Hose and Hose Fittings April 1991 and June 1993. Completely revised November 1995, and revised March 1999 and July 2001. Rationale statement available.

This document is technically equivalent to ISO 6605 except as noted in the Foreword.

Foreword—SAE J343 has been revised to be technically equivalent to ISO 6605, except that additional tests in paragraphs 4.9 to 4.14 were included.

1. Scope—This SAE Standard gives methods for testing and evaluating performance of the SAE 100R series of hydraulic hose and hose assemblies (hose and attached end fittings) used in hydraulic fluid power systems.

Specific tests and performance criteria for evaluating hose assemblies used in hydraulic service are in accordance with the requirements for hose in the respective specifications of SAE J517.

This document further establishes a uniform means of testing and evaluating performance of hydraulic hose assemblies.

2. References

2.1 Applicable Publications—The following publications form a part of the specification to the extent specified herein. Unless otherwise indicated, the latest revision of SAE publications shall apply.

2.1.1 SAE PUBLICATION—Available from SAE, 400 Commonwealth Drive, Warrendale, PA 15096-0001.

SAE J517—Hydraulic Hose

2.1.2 ASTM PUBLICATIONS—Available from ASTM, 100 Barr Harbor Drive, West Conshohocken, PA 19428-2959.

ASTM D 380—Standard Methods of Testing Rubber Hose

2.1.3 ISO PUBLICATIONS—Available from ANSI, 11 West 42nd Street, New York, NY 10036-8002.

ISO 3448—Industrial liquid lubricants—ISO viscosity classification

ISO 6605—Hydraulic fluid power—Hose assemblies—Method of test

3. Test Procedures—The test procedures described in the current issue of ASTM D 380 shall be followed. However, in cases of conflict between the ASTM specifications and those described as follows, the latter shall take precedence. Unless otherwise specified in this document, or other SAE standards, tests shall be conducted at the prevailing ambient temperature of the testing facility.

4. Standard Tests

Water or another liquid suitable for the hose under test shall be used as the test medium. The use of air and other gaseous materials as testing media should be avoided because of the risk to operators. In special cases where such media are required for the tests, strict safety measures are imperative. Furthermore, it is stressed that when a liquid is used as the test medium, it is essential that all air is expelled from the test piece because of the risk of injury to the operator due to the sudden expansion of trapped air released when the hose bursts.

4.1 Dimensional Check Test—The hose shall be inspected for conformity to all dimensions tabulated in the applicable specification.

Determine finished outside diameters and reinforcement diameters, where required, by calculation from measurement of the respective circumference.

As an alternative, use a flexible tape graduated to read the diameter directly.

Measure the inside diameter by means of a suitable expanding ball or telescoping gage.

Measure concentricity over both the reinforcement and the finished outside diameters using either a dial indicator gage or a micrometer.

Round the foot of the measuring instrument to conform to the inside diameter of the hose.

Take readings at 90 degree intervals around the hose

NOTE—Acceptability is based on the total variation between the high and the low readings.

Take inside and outside diameter measurements at a minimum of 25 mm from the hose ends and concentricity measurements at a minimum of 13 mm from the hose ends.

4.2 Proof Test—Test the hose assemblies hydrostatically to the specified proof pressure for a period of not less than 30 s nor more than 60 s.

There shall be no indication of failure or leakage.

4.3 Change in Length Test—Conduct measurements for the determination of elongation or contraction on a previously untested, unaged hose assembly having at least 600 mm length of free hose between hose fittings.

Attach the hose assembly to the pressure source in an unrestricted straight position. If the hose is not straight due to its natural curvature, it may be fastened laterally to achieve a straight position. Pressurize to the specified operating pressure for a period of 30 s, then release the pressure.

Place accurate reference marks 500 mm apart on the outer cover of the hose, midway between fittings, after allowing the hose assembly to restabilize for a period of 30 s following pressure release.

Repressurize the hose assembly to the specified operating pressure for a period of 30 s.

Measure the final length while the hose is pressurized. The final length is the distance between reference marks while the hose is pressurized.

Complete the determination of the change in length using Equation 1:

$$\Delta l = \frac{l_1 - l_0}{l_0} \times 100 \quad \text{(Eq. 1)}$$

where:

l_0 is the distance between the reference marks when the hose was not pressurized following the initial pressurization;

l_1 is the distance between the reference marks under pressure;

$\Delta\lambda$ is the percentage change in length, which will be positive (+) in the case of an increase in length and negative (–) in the case of a decrease in length.

4.4 Burst Test—Subject unaged hose assemblies, on which the end fittings have been attached for not more than 30 days, to a hydrostatic pressure, increased at a constant rate so as to attain the specified minimum burst pressure within a period of not less than 15 s nor more than 60 s.

Reject hose assemblies showing leakage, hose burst or indication of failure below the specified minimum burst pressure.

NOTE—This is a destructive test. Assemblies which have been subjected to this test shall be destroyed.

4.5 Cold Bend Test—Subject hose assemblies to the specified temperature in a straight position for 24 h.

Then, while still at the specified temperature, the samples shall be evenly and uniformly bent once over a mandrel having a diameter equal to twice the specified minimum bend radius. Bending shall be accomplished within a period of not less than 8 s nor more than 12 s.

In the case of hose sizes up to and including 22 mm nominal inside diameter, bend them through 180 degrees over the mandrel; in the case of hose sizes larger than 22 mm nominal inside diameter, bend them through 90 degrees over the mandrel.

After bending, allow the sample to warm to room temperature, visually examine it for cover cracks and subject it to the proof test. There shall be no cover cracks or leakage. (In lieu of the bending test, hoses larger than 22 mm nominal inside diameter may be considered acceptable if samples of tube and cover pass the Low Temperature Test on Tube and Cover of ASTM D 380.)

Reject any samples with visible cracks or leakage.

NOTE—This is a destructive test. Assemblies which have been subjected to this test shall be destroyed.

4.6 Impulse Test—Test four unaged hose assemblies with end fittings which have been attached for not more than 30 days. Where the individual standard requires, also test aged hose assemblies.

Apply a pulsating pressure internally to the hose assemblies at a rate between 0.5 and 1.3 Hz; record the frequency used. The pressure cycle shall fall within the shaded area of Figure 1 and conform as closely as possible to the curve shown.

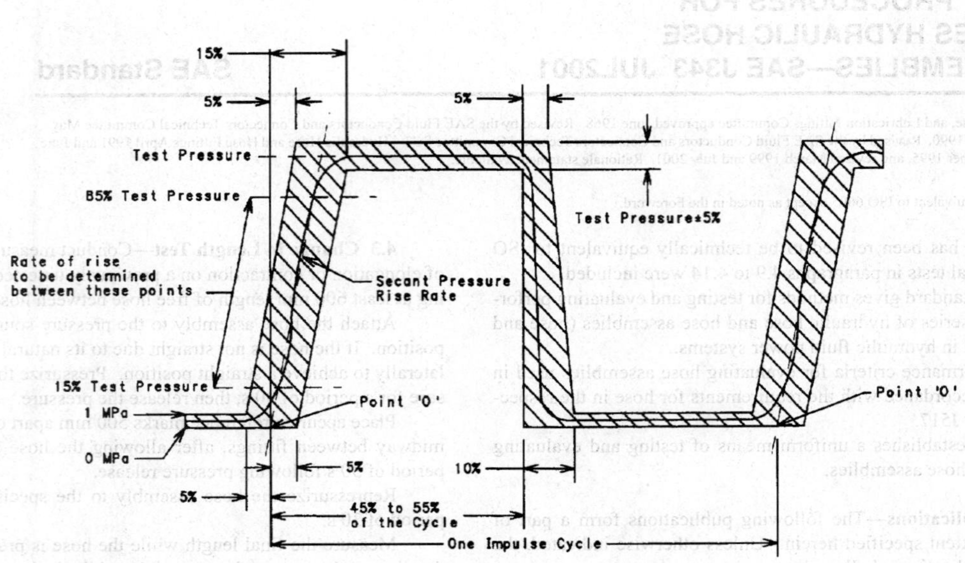

NOTES:
1. Secant pressure rise is the straight line drawn through two points on the pressure rise curve; one point at 15% of the test pressure and the other at 85% of the test pressure
2. Point '0' is the intersection of the secant pressure rise with 0 pressure.
3. Pressure rise rate is the slope of the secant pressure rise expressed in MPa/s.
4. Cycle rate shall be uniform at 0.5 to 1.3 Hz.
5. The nominal rate of pressure rise shall be equal to:
   R = f (10p − k)
   where: R = rate of pressure rise in MPa/s
   f = frequency in Hz
   p = nominal impulse test pressure in MPa
   k = 5 MPa

FIGURE 1—PRESSURE-IMPULSE CYCLE METHOD OF DETERMINATION OF RATE OF PRESSURE RISE IN IMPULSE TEST

The nominal rate of pressure rise shall be equal to that shown in Equation 2:

$$R = f(10p - k) \quad \text{(Eq. 2)}$$

where:

R = rate of pressure rise in MPa/s
f = frequency in Hz
p = nominal impulse test pressure in MPa
k = 5 MPa

The actual rate of pressure rise shall be determined as shown on Figure 1, and shall be within a tolerance of ±10% of the calculated nominal value.

Select a test fluid which complies with the requirements of ISO VG 46 ± 4.6 at 40 °C per ISO 3448, and circulate it at a rate sufficient to maintain a uniform fluid temperature within the hose assemblies. Other fluids may be used as agreed upon between the customer and the manufacturer.

Calculate the free (exposed) length of hose under test, shown on Figure 2, as follows:

a. Hose sizes up to and including 22 mm nominal inside diameter (see Equation 3):

$$\text{180 degrees bend free length} = \pi(r + d/2) + 2d \quad \text{(Eq. 3)}$$

b. Hose sizes larger than 22 mm nominal inside diameter (see Equation 4):

$$\text{90 degrees bend free length} = \pi/2(r + d/2) + 2d \quad \text{(Eq. 4)}$$

where:

r = minimum bend radius
d = hose outside diameter

Connect the test pieces to the apparatus. The test pieces shall be installed according to Figure 2. Test pieces of hose of nominal inside diameter up to and including 22 mm shall be bent through 180 degrees and hoses of nominal inside diameter larger than 22 mm shall be bent through 90 degrees.

Test the hose at the impulse test pressure indicated in the individual specification. The test fluid shall be circulated through the assemblies at the specified temperature with a tolerance of ±3 °C. Cooling or heating of the test chamber shall not be permitted, except when individual standards require testing with synthetic base test fluids at a temperature higher than 150 °C. When such higher temperatures are required, the impulse test fluid need not be circulated if both the fluid and the assemblies are externally heated in the test chamber, at the specified temperature with a tolerance of ±5 °C.

Determine the duration of the impulse test in total number of cycles by the individual standard for the hose assemblies. Where aged samples are required, refer to the individual standards.

It is recommended the test fluid be changed frequently to prevent breakdown.

NOTE—This is a destructive test. Assemblies which have been subjected to this test shall be destroyed.

4.7 Leakage Test—Subject unaged hose assemblies, on which the end fittings have been attached for not more than 30 days, to a hydrostatic pressure of 70% of the specified minimum burst pressure for a period of between 5.0 to 5.5 min.

Reduce the fluid pressure to 0 MPa.

Re-apply the 70% of minimum burst hydrostatic pressure for another 5.0 to 5.5 min period.

Reject assemblies showing leakage or failure.

NOTE—This is a destructive test. Assemblies which have been subjected to this test shall be destroyed.

4.8 Visual Examination of Product—All bulk hose shall be visually inspected to see that the hose identification has been properly applied and all assemblies shall be inspected to determine that the correct fittings are properly installed.

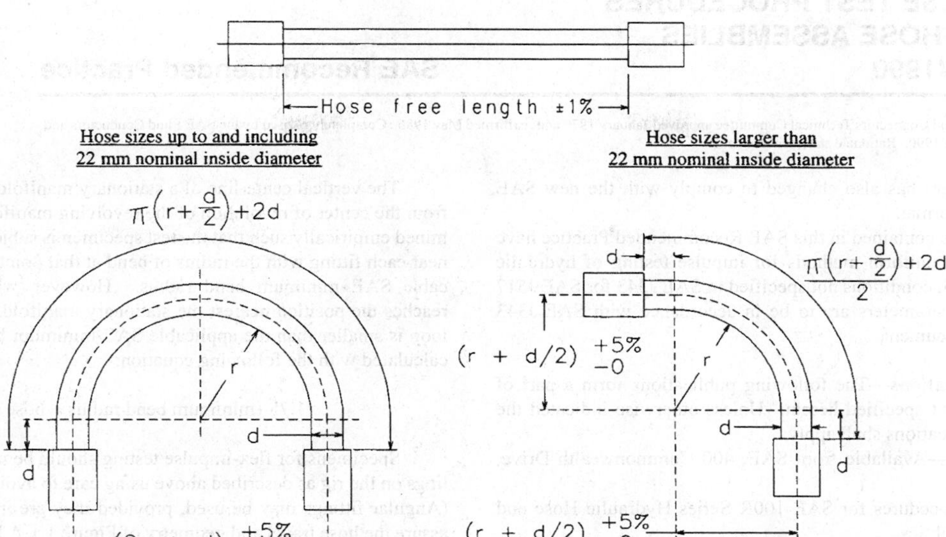

FIGURE 2—TEST SPECIMEN FOR PRESSURE IMPULSE TEST

4.9 Oil Resistance Test—After 70 h immersion in ASTM Emergency Standard Practice IRM903 oil at the designated temperature, the volume change of specimens taken from the hose inner tube and cover shall be within the specified limits.

4.10 Ozone Resistance Test—Hydraulic hose shall be tested for resistance of the cover compound to ozone in accordance with the latest issue of ASTM D 380, except that the mandrel shall be a diameter twice the minimum bend radius specified in the individual hose standard, and the cover shall be examined at the completion of the test under 7X magnification.

4.11 Electrical Conductivity Test (for thermoplastic hose only)—Hose assemblies having a free length of 152 mm ± 13 mm without fluid and capped to prevent entry of moisture shall be exposed to a minimum of 85% relative humidity at 24 °C ± 3 °C for a period of 168 h. Surface moisture shall be removed prior to testing.

Conditioned assemblies shall have one end fitting attached to the lead from a source of 60 Hz sinusoidal, 37.5 kV (rms) electricity. This lead shall be suspended by dry fabric strings so that the hose hangs free, at least 600 mm from any extraneous objects. The lower end of the hose shall be connected to ground through a 1000 to 1 000 000 Ω resistor, keeping the resistor near the end of the hose. A suitable AC voltmeter shall be connected across the resistor, using a fully shielded cable with the shielding well grounded. Thirty-seven and one-half kV shall be applied to the specimen for 5 min and a current reading taken. This current shall not exceed the value specified.

4.12 Electrical Conductivity Test (PTFE hose only)—Test specimen shall be a 330 mm ± 10 mm cut length of hose with fitting attached to one end and the reinforcing braid flared away from the PTFE tube on the opposite end to prevent contact with the free end of the tube. The inner surface of the tube shall be cleaned, first with naphtha dry cleaning fluid or Stoddard solvent, and then with isopropyl alcohol to remove surface contamination, followed by thorough drying at room temperature.

Relative humidity shall be kept below 70% and room temperature between 16 °C and 32 °C.

The specimen shall be mounted in a vertical position as shown in Figure 3. The adapter at the base is simply a convenient means of assuring proper electrical contact if a swivel female fitting is chosen, and may be omitted if a male fitting is used. In either case, the electrode must be insulated from ground.

A mercury or salt water solution electrode shall be provided at the upper end as shown, by inserting a nonmetallic plug with an O-ring seal to a distance of 75 mm from the end of the tubing, thus providing an average test length of 255 mm. Mercury or salt water solution shall then be added to a level 25 mm above the plug. Any suitable conductor to this electrode may be used, including a threaded end attached to the plug if so desired. Concentration of salt water, if used, shall be 450 g NaCl per liter of H_2O.

1000 V DC shall be applied between the upper electrode and the lower electrode (adapter or male fitting hex). The current shall be measured with an instrument with a sensitivity of at least 1 μA (1×10^{-6} A).

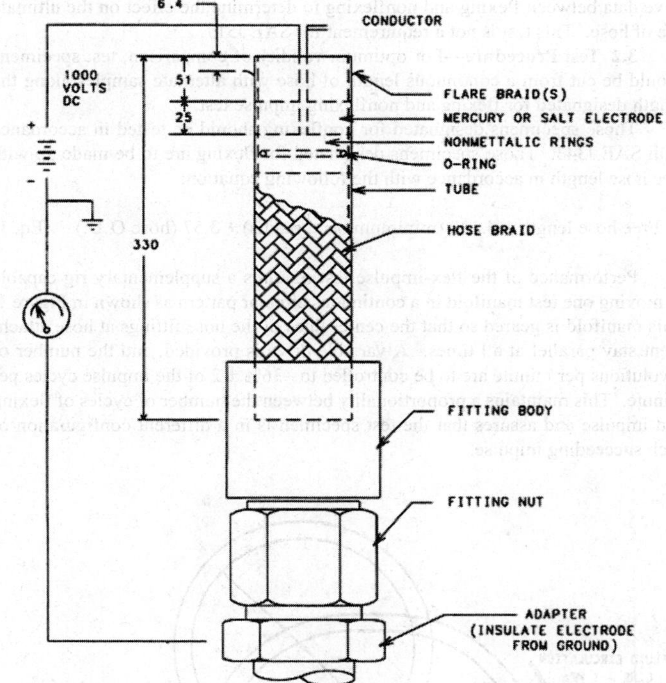

FIGURE 3—CONDUCTIVITY TEST DIAGRAM

4.13 Resistance to Vacuum Test—The hose shall not blister nor show any other indication of failure when subjected to the specified vacuum for a period of 5 min. Where practicable, one end of the hose shall be equipped with a transparent cap and electric light to permit visual examination for failure. Where the length or size of the hose precludes visual examination, failure shall be determined by inability to pass through the hose a ball or cylinder 6.5 mm less in diameter than the bore of hoses of 12.5 mm nominal inside diameter and larger. For hoses under 12.5 mm nominal inside diameter, a ball or cylinder 3.0 mm smaller in diameter than the bore shall be used.

4.14 Volumetric Expansion Test—Volumetric expansion tests shall be run in accordance with the current issue of ASTM D 380.

(R) OPTIONAL IMPULSE TEST PROCEDURES FOR HYDRAULIC HOSE ASSEMBLIES —SAE J1405 JUN1990

SAE Recommended Practice

Report of the SAE Fluid Conductors and Connectors Technical Committee approved January 1979 and reaffirmed May 1986. Completely revised by the SAE Fluid Conductors and Connectors Technical Committee June 1990. Rationale statement available.

Foreword—This Document has also changed to comply with the new SAE Technical Standards Board format.

1. Scope—The procedures contained in this SAE Recommended Practice have been developed to establish uniform methods for impulse testing of hydraulic hose assemblies under special conditions not specified in SAE J343 for SAE J517 hoses. Basic impulse test parameters are to be in accordance with SAE J343 except as modified in this document.

2. References

2.1 Applicable Publications—The following publications form a part of the specification to the extent specified herein. Unless otherwise indicated the lastest revision of SAE publications shall apply.

2.1.1 SAE PUBLICATIONS—Available from SAE, 400 Commonwealth Drive, Warrendale, PA 15096-0001.

SAE J343—Tests and Procedures for SAE 100R Series Hydraulic Hose and Hose Assemblies
SAE J517—Hydraulicc Hose
SAE J1176—External Leakage Classifications for Hydraulic Systems

3. Option I - Comparative Flex Impulse Procedure

3.1 Purpose—To generate comparative impulse test data, with and without flexing. This test procedure minimizes impulse test variables to provide comparative data between flexing and nonflexing to determine the effect on the ultimate life of hose. This test is not a requirement for SAE J517.

3.2 Test Procedure—For optimum validity of comparison, test specimens should be cut from a continuous length of hose with alternate samples along the length designated for flexing and nonflexing impulse test.

Those specimens designated for nonflexing should be tested in accordance with SAE J343. Those specimens designated for flexing are to be made up with free hose length in accordance with the following equation:

$$\text{Free hose length} = 4.142 \text{ (minimum bend radius)} + 3.57 \text{ (hose O.D.)} \quad \text{(Eq. 1)}$$

Performance of the flex-impulse test requires a supplementary rig capable of moving one test manifold in a continuous circular pattern as shown in Figure 1. This manifold is geared so that the center lines of the hose fittings at hose attachment stay parallel at all times. A variable drive is provided, and the number of revolutions per minute are to be controlled to –36% ± 2 of the impulse cycles per minute. This maintains a proportionality between the number of cycles of flexing and impulse and assures that the test specimen is in a different configuration of each succeeding impulse.

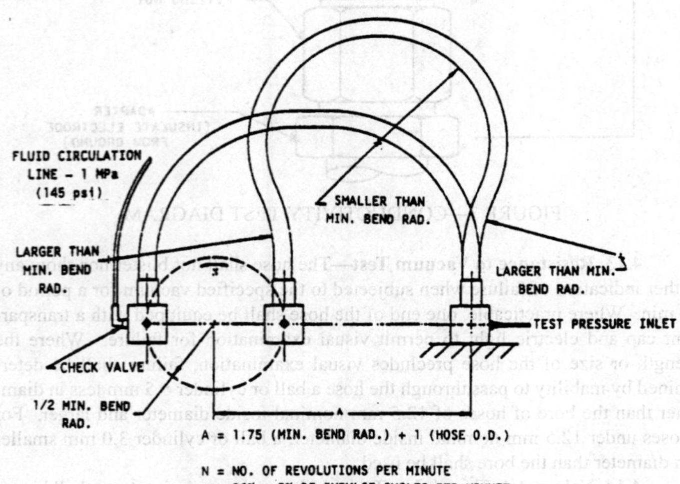

FIGURE 1—FLEX IMPULSE TEST HOSE GEOMETRY

The vertical centerline of a stationary manifold is positioned a distance "A" from the center of revolution of the revolving manifold. This distance was determined empirically such that the test specimen is subjected to back bending motion near each fitting with the radius of bend at that point being greater than the applicable SAE minimum bend radius. However, when the revolving manifold reaches the position nearest the stationary manifold, the bend [1] radius inside the loop is smaller than the applicable SAE minimum bend radius. Distance "A" is calculated with the following equation:

$$1.75 \text{ (minimum bend radius + hose O.D.)} \quad \text{(Eq. 2)}$$

Specimens for flex-impulse testing should be mounted with straight end fittings on the rig as described above using care to avoid imparting twist to the hose. (Angular fittings may be used, provided they are installed in such a position to assure the hose travel and geometry of Figure 1.) A like number of samples, preferably not less than three, should be tested simultaneously and should be run to failure.

To accelerate completion of the test for comparative purposes, a pressure based on actual burst values of the hose is recommended, with flexing and nonflexing specimens to be tested at the same pressure. Suggested procedure is to first determine the average burst strength for the test length of hose and from this calculate the impulse test pressure as 35% of average burst. If this test procedure does not produce failures within the desired range, a higher or lower percentage may be used.

4. Option II - Flex Impulse Test

4.1 Purpose—To establish requirements for impulse testing with the addition of flexing. This is a specialized test which is not a requirement of SAE J517, nor is it specified in SAE J343. It is intended to provide a standard method to flex-impulse hose assemblies when flexing is deemed necessary.

4.2 Test Procedure—Four unaged hose assemblies for flexing are to be made up with free hose length in accordance with the following equation:

$$\text{Free hose length} = 4.142 \text{ (minimum bend radius)} + 3.57 \text{ (hose O.D.)} \quad \text{(Eq. 3)}$$

Performance of the flex-impulse test requires a supplementary rig capable of moving one test manifold in a continuous circular pattern as shown in Figure 1. This manifold is geared so that the center lines of the hose fittings at hose attachment stay parallel at all times. A variable drive is provided, and the number of revolutions per minute are to be controlled to 36% ± 2 of the impulse cycles per minute. This maintains a proportionality between the number of cycles of flexing and impulse and assures that the test specimen is in a different configuration on each succeeding impulse.

The vertical centerline of a stationary manifold is positioned a distance "A" from the center of revolution of the revolving manifold. This distance was determined empirically such that the test specimen is subjected to back bending motion near each fitting with the radius of bend at that point being greater than the applicable SAE minimum bend radius. However, when the revolving manifold reaches the position nearest the stationary manifold, the bend radius inside the loop is smaller than the applicable SAE minimum bend radius. [2] Distance "A" is calculated with the following equation:

$$1.75 \text{ (minimum bend radius)} + \text{hose O.D.} \quad \text{(Eq. 4)}$$

Specimens for flex-impulse testing should be mounted with straight end fittings on the rig as described above using care to avoid imparting twist to the hose. (Angular fittings may be used provided they are installed in such a position to assure the hose travel and geometry of Figure 1.)

1. Violation of the minimum bend radius for this test does not imply that such violation is recommended in applications.
2. Violation of the minimum bend radius for this test does not imply that such violation is recommended in applications.

4.3 Test Requirements—The hose assemblies shall be tested at the impulse pressures, temperatures and minimum bend radii, for the minimum number of impulse cycles, as specified in SAE J517 for 100R series hoses. Other test parameters, as agreed upon by the supplier and/or user may be used.

5. Option III - Cool Down Leakage Test

5.1 Purpose—To establish requirements for performing a cold start leakage test to be used in conjunction with both flexing or nonflexing impulse tests.

5.2 Test Procedure—The impulse test unit shall be shut down at 40% ± 10 and 90% ± 10 of the required number of impulse cycles and allowed to cool until the test oil and hose assemblies reach a temperature of 30 °C ± 3 (85 °F ± 5). Accelerated cool down procedures, i.e. fans, heat exchangers, etc., may be used to speed the cooling process. Check test assemblies to assure they are clean and dry. With oil heater turned off, resume the test and observe and note leakage for 1000 impulse cycles. The acceptable rate of leakage shall be as agreed upon by the supplier and/or user. (See SAE J1176 for leakage classes.)

After completing the 1000 impulse cycles, turn on oil heater and continue the impulse test.

If leakage is noted during the cool down cycle, notation shall also be made as to whether or not a seal-off was effected as the temperature came back up. Results are applicable only to the specific hose construction and size, hose fitting design and size, and fitting assembly technique.

(R) TESTS AND PROCEDURES FOR HIGH TEMPERATURE TRANSMISSION OIL HOSE, ENGINE LUBRICATING OIL HOSE, AND HOSE ASSEMBLIES—SAE J1019 JUN1990

SAE Standard

Report of the SAE Tube, Pipe, Hose, and Lubrication Fittings Committee approved April 1973 and reaffirmed by the SAE Fluid Conductors and Connectors Technical Committee, May 1986. Completely revised by the SAE Fluid Conductors and Connectors Technical Committee June 1990.

1. Scope—This SAE Standard is intended to establish uniform methods for testing and evaluation of hose and hose assemblies for use in high temperature transmission oil systems and high temperature lubricating oil systems using petroleum base oils within a temperature range of –40 ° to 150 °C (–40 ° to 302 °F) and a maximum working pressure of 1.5 MPa (217 psi). Hose construction, dimensions, identification, and hose fitting configurations shall be agreed upon by the supplier and user.

2. References

2.1 Applicable Publications—The following publications form a part of the specification to the extent specified herein. Unless otherwise indicated the lastest revision of SAE publications shall apply.

2.1.1 ASTM PUBLICATIONS—Available from ASTM, 100 Barr Harbor Drive, West Conshohocken, PA 19428-2959.

ASTM D 380—Methods of Testing Rubber Hose

ASTM D 518—Test Method for Rubber Deterioration—Surface Cracking

ASTM D 622—Methods of Testing Rubber Hose for Automotive Air and Vacuum Brake System

ASTM D 1149—Test Method for Rubber Deterioration—Surface Ozone Cracking in a Chamber (Flat Specimens)

3. Performance Tests

3.1 Preconditioning—The test hose or hose assemblies shall be conditioned at room temperature a minimum of 24 h prior to testing.

3.2 Qualification Tests—For qualification to this document, hose and hose assemblies made therefrom shall conform to the following tests and requirements:

3.2.1 PROOF TEST—Hose and hose assemblies shall be hydrostatically tested to 3 MPa (435 psi) for a period of not less than 30 s nor more than 60 s. There shall be no indication of failure or leakage.

3.2.2 LEAKAGE TEST—Two previously untested unaged hose assemblies having 300 mm ± 3 (12 in ± 1/8) length of free hose between fittings, on which the hose fittings have been attached for not over 30 days, shall be subjected to a hydrostatic pressure of 4.2 MPa (609 psi) for a period of 5 to 5.5 min and then reduced to zero after which 4.2 MPa (609 psi) shall be reapplied for another 5 to 5.5 min. There shall be no leakage or other evidence of failure. This shall be considered a destructive test and the samples shall be destroyed.

3.2.3 CHANGE IN LENGTH TEST—Measurements for the determination of elongation or contraction shall be conducted on two previously untested, unaged hose assemblies having at least 300 mm (12 in) length of free hose between hose fittings. The hose assemblies shall be attached to the pressure source and pressurized to 1.5 MPa (217 psi) for a period of 30 s, after which time the pressure shall be released. After allowing the hose to restabilize for a period of 30 s following pressure release, reference marks 254 mm (10 in) apart shall be accurately placed upon the hose outer cover, midway between the hose fittings. This length shall be the "original length".

The hose assemblies shall then be repressurized to 1.5 MPa (217 psi) for a period of 30 s, after which time, while the hose is pressurized, the distance between the reference marks shall be measured. This length shall be the "final length". Change in length shall be computed using the following equation:

$$\text{Percent change} = \frac{(\text{Final Length} - \text{Original Length}) \times 100}{\text{Original Length}} \quad \text{(Eq. 1)}$$

(Minus percent) Change = Contraction

(Plus percent) Change = Elongation

The percent change shall be within the agreed limits.

3.2.4 BURST TEST—Two unaged hose assemblies having at least 300 mm (12 in) length of free hose between fittings, on which the hose fittings have been attached for not over 30 days, shall be subjected to a hydrostatic pressure increasing at a constant rate so as to attain 6 MPa (870 psi) within a period of not less than 15 s nor more than 30 s. There shall be no leakage, hose burst, or other indication of failure below 6 MPa (870 psi). This shall be considered a destructive test and the sample shall be destroyed.

3.2.5 TENSILE TEST—Two hose assemblies having at least 300 mm (12 in) length of free hose between fittings shall be tested. The rate of separation of the head of the testing machine shall be 0.42 mm/s ± 0.04 (1 in/min ± 0.1). The minimum force required to separate the hose from a hose fitting shall be 1 kN (225 lbs). This shall be considered a destructive test and the samples shall be destroyed.

3.2.6 COLD FLEXIBILITY TEST—Two hose assemblies shall be subjected to –40 °C ± 2 (–40 °F ± 3.6) for 24 h in a straight position. After this time and while still at the specified temperature, each hose assembly shall be evenly and uniformly bent over a mandrel equal to 8 times the nominal hose outside diameter (or twice the minimum bend radius, if specified). Bending shall be accomplished within a period of not less than 8 s and no more than 12 s. Hoses of less than 25 mm (1 in) nominal inside diameter shall be bent 180 degrees over the mandrel and hoses of 25 mm (1 in) nominal inside diameter and larger shall be bent 90 degrees over the mandrel.

After flexing, each sample shall be allowed to warm to room temperature, then visually examined for cover cracks and subjected to the Proof Test (3.2.1). There shall be no leakage, or cracks on the cover. In lieu of the flexing test, hoses of 25 mm (1 in) nominal inside diameter and larger shall be considered acceptable if samples of tube and cover pass the Low Temperature Test on Tube and Cover, Section 25 of ASTM D 380 of latest revision.

3.2.7 TEMPERATURE CYCLING TEST—Four hose assemblies having not less than 300 mm (12 in) nor more than 1000 mm (39 in) length of free hose between hose fittings shall be tested. Two shall be filled with transmission Type F fluid and two with oil conforming to MIL-L-2104, and lightly capped. The hose assemblies shall be placed in a circulating air oven at 150 °C ± 2 (302 °F ± 3.6) for 2 h, removed from the air oven, and allowed to stabilize to room temperature for 1 h minimum; then placed in a cold box at –40 °C ± 2 (–40 °F ± 3.6) for 2 h, removed from the cold box, and allowed to stabilize to room temperature for 1 h minimum. Ten such cycles shall be conducted, after which the hose assemblies shall be stabilized to room temperature for 1 h minimum and subjected to the Proof Test (3.2.1). There shall be no leakage or failure. This shall be considered a destructive test and the samples shall be destroyed.

3.2.8 OZONE TEST—Two samples of the cover compound shall be tested in accordance with the latest issue of ASTM D 622, procedure 9, and ASTM D 1149. Where space limitations prohibit use of a hose, specimen cover stock tested in accordance with ASTM D 518, procedure B, may be substituted. After 70 h exposure in an atmosphere comprised of air and ozone with an ozone partial pressure of 50 mPa (50 parts ozone per 100 million parts of air at standard atmospheric conditions) at ambient temperature of 40 °C (104 °F), specimens shall show no evidence of cracks or deterioration when viewed with 7 power magnification while still in a stressed condition. This shall be considered a destructive test and the samples shall be destroyed.

3.2.9 HIGH TEMPERATURE CIRCULATION TEST—A minimum of two hose assemblies having at least 355 mm (14 in) length of free hose between hose fittings shall be mounted on a circulating oil test unit in a straight configuration. The ambient temperature shall be 93 °C ± 11 (200 °F ± 20) and the oil temperature 150 °C ± 2 (302 °F ± 3.6) between inlet and outlet. Oil conforming to MIL-L-2104 shall be circulated through the hose assemblies at a pressure between 0.35 and 0.69 MPa (50 to 100 psi). Entrained air in the oil must be kept to a minimum and caution must be exercised so that the hose assemblies do not come into contact with the heating elements and are located to permit good air circulation. The test fluid shall be changed every 375 h ± 25. Tests are to be run continuously except for oil change and addition or removal of samples. All shutdown time is to be recorded. After 750 h ± 5, the test assemblies shall be removed, the oil drained, and allowed to cool for a minimum of 4 h. The samples shall then be bent around a mandrel having a diameter of 12 times the inside diameter of the hose. The time required to bend the hose around the mandrel shall be between 8 and 12 s. Rubber covered hose shall be examined visually for cover cracks. No cracks are permitted. The assemblies shall then be subjected to Proof Test (3.2.1), with the hoses in the straight position. There shall be no failure or leakage through the hose or at hose fitting juncture. All tests are to be completed within 24 h of removal of samples from the circulating oil test unit. This shall be considered a destructive test and the samples shall be destroyed.

4. Inspection Test—Inspection tests and lot sizes for inspection shall be negotiated between user and seller.

HYDRAULIC FLANGED TUBE, PIPE, AND HOSE CONNECTIONS FOUR-BOLT SPLIT FLANGE TYPE—SAE J518 JUN1993

SAE Standard

Report of the SAE Construction and Industrial Machinery Technical Committee and SAE Tube, Pipe, Hose, and Lubrication Fittings Committee approved February 1952, revised by the SAE Tube, Pipe, Hose,and Lubrication Fittings Committee May 1972, and reaffirmed by the SAE Fluid Conductors and Connectors Technical Committee December 1987. Completely revised by the SAE Fluid Conductors and Connectors Technical Committee SC2—Hydraulic Hose and Hose Fittings April 1991, and revised June 1993. Rationale statement available.

Foreword—This Reaffirmed Document has been changed only to reflect the new SAE Technical Standards Board Format.

1. Scope—This SAE Standard covers complete general and dimensional specifications for the flanged heads and split flange clamp halves applicable to four-bolt split flange type tube, pipe, and hose connections with appropriate references to the O-ring seals and attaching components used in their assembly. (See Figures 1 and 2.) Also included are recommended port dimensions and port design considerations.

The flanged heads specified are incorporated into fittings having suitable means for attachment of tubes, pipes, or hoses to provide connection ends. These connections are intended for application in hydraulic systems, on industrial and commercial products, where it is desired to avoid the use of threaded connections.

THE RATED WORKING PRESSURE OF A HOSE ASSEMBLY COMPRISING SAE J518 HOSE CONNECTIONS AND SAE J517 HOSE SHALL NOT EXCEED THE LOWER OF THE TWO WORKING PRESSURE RATED VALUES.

Flanged heads shall be as specified in Figure 3 and Table 1. Split flange clamp halves shall be as specified in Figure 4 and Table 1. Port dimensions and spacing shall be as specified in Figure 5 and Table 2.

O-ring seals, having nominal dimensions as indicated in Table 1, are used in conjunction with these connections. They shall conform to the seals specified in SAE J120, Table on Dimensions and Tolerances.

Bolts for use with these connections shall be of the sizes and lengths indicated in Table 1. They shall be of SAE Grade 5 material or better as specified in SAE J429. Socket head cap screws of SAE Grade 5 material or better are acceptable.

Lock washers, if used, shall be in accordance with the light spring lock washers specified in SAE J489, Dimensions of Light, Medium, Heavy, Extra Heavy, and Hi Collar Spring Lock Washers, and of sizes applicable to the corresponding bolts.

The following general specifications supplement the dimensional data contained in Table 1 with respect to all unspecified detail.

2. References

2.1 Applicable Publications—The following publications form a part of this specification to the extent specified herein. The latest issue of SAE publications shall apply.

2.1.1 SAE PUBLICATIONS—Available from SAE, 400 Commonwealth Drive, Warrendale, PA 15096-0001.

SAE J120—Rubber Rings for Automotive Applications
SAE J429—Mechanical and Material Requirements for Externally Threaded Fasteners
SAE J489—Lock Washers
SAE J517—Hydraulic Hose
SAE J846—Coding Systems for Identification of Fluid Conductors and Connectors

2.1.2 ASTM PUBLICATION—Available from ASTM, 100 Barr Harbor Drive, West Conshohocken, PA 19428-2959.

ASTM B 117—Method of Salt Spray (Fog) Testing

3. Size Designation—Four-bolt split flange connection sizes are designated by the nominal flange size which corresponds to the maximum inside diameter of the hole through the flanged head.

NOTE—UNSPECIFIED DETAIL WITH RESPECT TO DIMENSIONS, TOLERANCES, CONTOURS, MATERIAL, WORKMANSHIP, ETC., MUST CONFORM TO GENERAL SPECIFICATIONS OF HYDRAULIC FLANGED TUBE, PIPE, AND HOSE CONNECTIONS, 4-BOLT SPLIT FLANGE TYPE. DIMENSIONS IN FIGURES 1 TO 4 APPLY TO TABLE 1. CODES SHOWN IN PARENTHESES ADJACENT TO FIGURE NUMBERS REPRESENT RESPECTIVE FLANGED CONNECTION IDENTIFICATION, WITH XX SUBSTITUTED FOR THE PRESSURE RATING CODE DEPICTED IN RESPECTIVE SUBHEADINGS OF TABLE 1. IN ACCORDANCE WITH SAE J846.

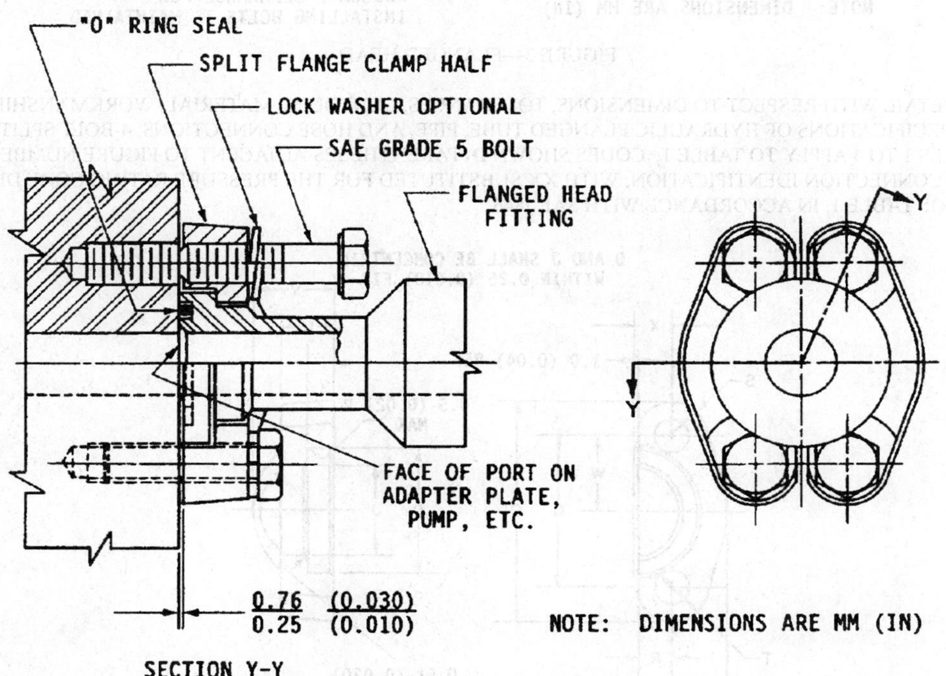

FIGURE 1—ASSEMBLED SPLIT FLANGED CONNECTION

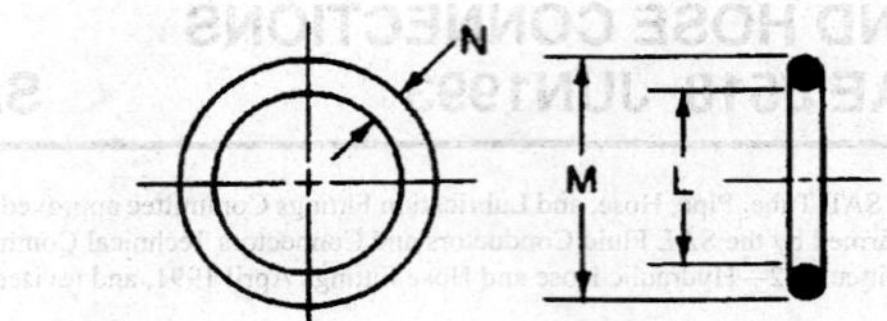

BASIC "O" RING DIMENSIONS ARE SHOWN FOR REFERENCE ONLY

FIGURE 2—O-RING SEAL

NOTE—UNSPECIFIED DETAIL WITH RESPECT TO DIMENSIONS, TOLERANCES, CONTOURS, MATERIAL, WORKMANSHIP, ETC., MUST CONFORM TO GENERAL SPECIFICATIONS OF HYDRAULIC FLANGED TUBE, PIPE, AND HOSE CONNECTIONS, 4-BOLT SPLIT FLANGE TYPE. DIMENSIONS IN FIGURES 1 TO 4 APPLY TO TABLE 1. CODES SHOWN IN PARENTHESES ADJACENT TO FIGURE NUMBERS REPRESENT RESPECTIVE FLANGED CONNECTION IDENTIFICATION, WITH XX SUBSTITUTED FOR THE PRESSURE RATING CODE DEPICTED IN RESPECTIVE SUBHEADINGS OF TABLE 1. IN ACCORDANCE WITH SAE J846.

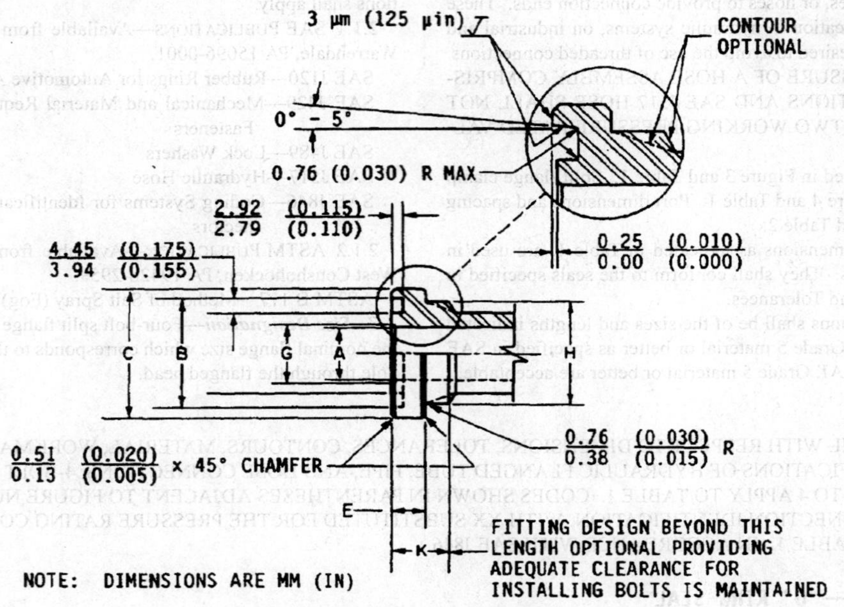

FIGURE 3—FLANGED HEAD

NOTE—UNSPECIFIED DETAIL WITH RESPECT TO DIMENSIONS, TOLERANCES, CONTOURS, MATERIAL, WORKMANSHIP, ETC., MUST CONFORM TO GENERAL SPECIFICATIONS OF HYDRAULIC FLANGED TUBE, PIPE, AND HOSE CONNECTIONS, 4-BOLT SPLIT FLANGE TYPE. DIMENSIONS IN FIGURES 1 TO 4 APPLY TO TABLE 1. CODES SHOWN IN PARENTHESES ADJACENT TO FIGURE NUMBERS REPRESENT RESPECTIVE FLANGED CONNECTION IDENTIFICATION, WITH XX SUBSTITUTED FOR THE PRESSURE RATING CODE DEPICTED IN RESPECTIVE SUBHEADINGS OF TABLE 1, IN ACCORDANCE WITH SAE J846.

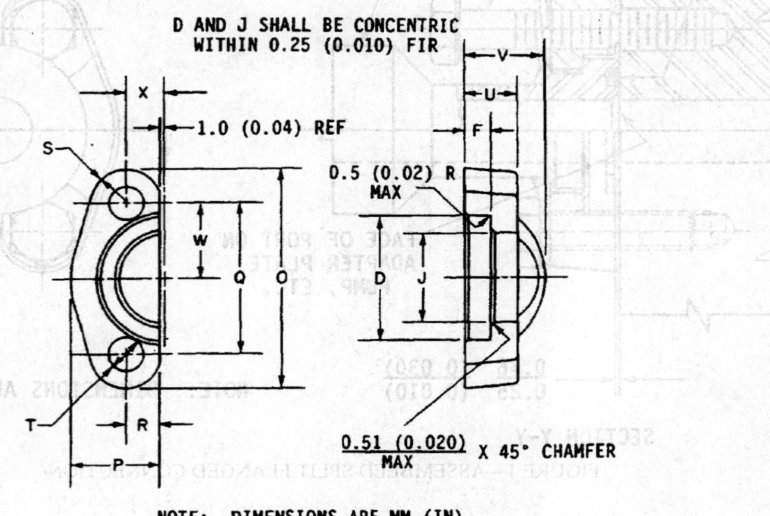

FIGURE 4—SPLIT FLANGE CLAMP HALF (1101XX)

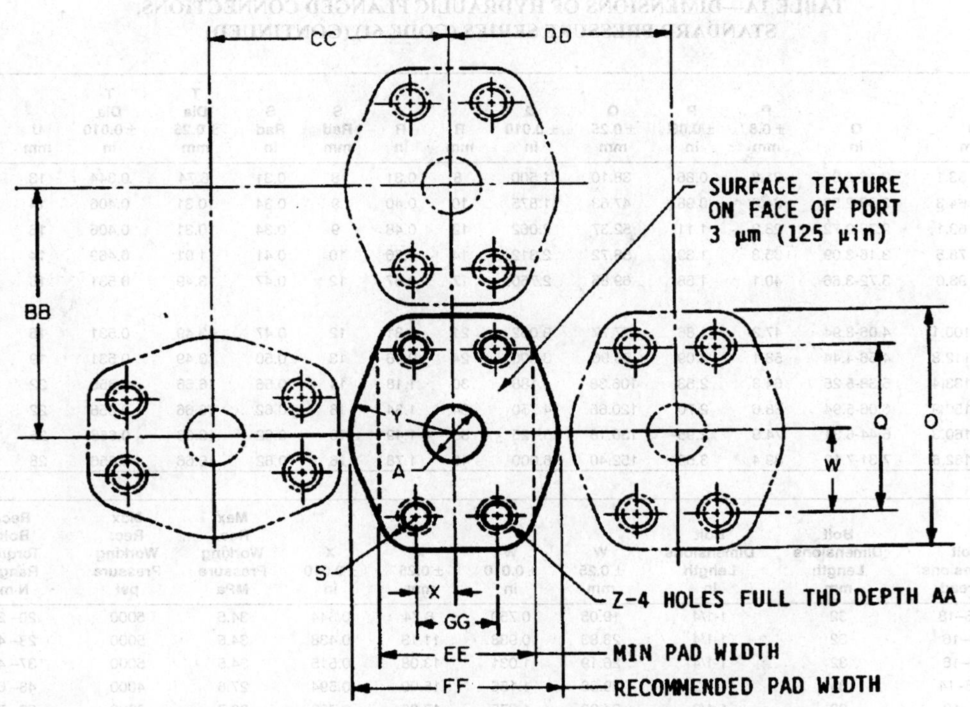

FIGURE 5—PORT DIMENSIONS FOR HYDRAULIC FLANGED, TUBE, PIPE, AND HOSE CONNECTIONS, FOUR-BOLT SPLIT FLANGE TYPE

TABLE 1A— DIMENSIONS OF HYDRAULIC FLANGED CONNECTIONS, STANDARD PRESSURE SERIES (CODE 61)

Nominal Flange Size, in	Flange Dash Size	A Dia Max mm	A Dia Max in	B Dia mm	B Dia in	C Dia ± 0.25 mm	C Dia ± 0.010 in	D Dia ± 0.25 mm	D Dia ± 0.010 in	E ± 0.13 mm	E ± 0.005 in	F ± 0.13 mm	F ± 0.005 in
1/2	–8	13	0.50	25.53- 25.40	1.005-1.000	30.18	1.188	30.96	1.219	6.73	0.265	6.22	0.245
3/4	–12	19	0.75	31.88- 31.75	1.255-1.250	38.10	1.500	38.89	1.531	6.73	0.265	6.22	0.245
1	–16	25	1.00	39.75- 39.62	1.565-1.560	44.45	1.750	45.24	1.781	8.00	0.315	7.49	0.295
1-1/4	–20	32	1.25	44.58- 44.45	1.755-1.750	50.80	2.000	51.59	2.031	8.00	0.315	7.49	0.295
1-1/2	–24	38	1.50	53.98- 53.72	2.125-2.115	60.33	2.375	61.09	2.406	8.00	0.315	7.49	0.295
2	–32	51	2.00	63.50- 63.25	2.500-2.490	71.42	2.812	72.24	2.844	9.53	0.375	9.02	0.355
2-1/2	–40	64	2.50	76.33- 76.07	3.005-2.995	84.12	3.312	84.94	3.344	9.53	0.375	9.02	0.355
3	–48	76	3.00	92.08- 91.82	3.625-3.615	101.60	4.000	102.39	4.031	9.53	0.375	9.02	0.355
3-1/2	–56	89	3.50	104.52-104.01	4.115-4.095	114.30	4.500	115.09	4.531	11.23	0.422	10.72	0.422
4	–64	102	4.00	117.22-116.71	4.615-4.595	127.00	5.000	127.79	5.031	11.23	0.442	10.72	0.422
5	–80	127	5.00	142.62-142.11	5.615-5.595	152.40	6.000	153.19	6.031	11.23	0.442	10.72	0.422

Nominal Flange Size, in	G Dia Max mm	G Dia Max in	H Dia Max mm	H Dia Max in	J Dia ± 0.25 mm	J Dia ± 0.010 in	K Ref mm	K Ref in	L ID Ref mm	L ID Ref in	M OD Ref mm	M OD Ref in	N Dia Ref mm	N Dia Ref in	O-Ring Size No.
1/2	14	0.56	24	0.94	24.26	0.955	13	0.50	18.64	0.734	25.70	1.012	3.53	0.139	210
3/4	21	0.81	32	1.25	32.13	1.265	14	0.56	24.99	0.984	32.05	1.262	3.53	0.139	214
1	27	1.06	38	1.50	38.48	1.515	14	0.56	32.92	1.296	39.98	1.574	3.53	0.139	219
1-1/4	33	1.31	43	1.70	43.69	1.720	14	0.56	37.69	1.484	44.75	1.762	3.53	0.139	222
1-1/2	40	1.56	50	1.98	50.80	2.000	16	0.62	47.22	1.859	54.28	2.137	3.53	0.139	225
2	52	2.06	62	2.45	62.74	2.470	16	0.62	56.74	2.234	63.80	2.512	3.53	0.139	228
2-1/2	65	2.56	74	2.92	74.93	2.950	18	0.69	69.44	2.734	76.50	3.012	3.53	0.139	232
3	78	3.06	90	3.55	90.93	3.580	19	0.75	85.32	3.359	92.38	3.637	3.53	0.139	237
3-1/2	90	3.56	102	4.00	102.36	4.030	22	0.88	98.02	3.859	105.08	4.137	3.53	0.139	241
4	103	4.06	114	4.50	115.06	4.530	25	1.00	110.72	4.359	117.78	4.637	3.53	0.139	245
5	129	5.06	140	5.50	140.46	5.530	28	1.12	136.12	5.359	143.18	5.637	3.53	0.139	253

TABLE 1A—DIMENSIONS OF HYDRAULIC FLANGED CONNECTIONS, STANDARD PRESSURE SERIES (CODE 61) (CONTINUED)

Nominal Flange Size, in	O mm	O in	P ± 0.8 mm	P ± 0.03 in	Q ± 0.25 mm	Q ± 0.010 in	R mm	R in	S Rad mm	S Rad in	T Dia ± 0.25 mm	T Dia ± 0.010 in	U mm	U in	V mm	V in
1/2	54.9- 53.1	2.16-2.09	21.8	0.86	38.10	1.500	8	0.31	8	0.31	8.74	0.344	13	0.50	19	0.75
3/4	65.8- 64.3	2.59-2.53	24.9	0.98	47.63	1.875	10	0.40	9	0.34	10.31	0.406	14	0.56	22	0.78
1	70.6- 69.1	2.78-2.72	28.2	1.11	52.37	2.062	12	0.48	9	0.34	10.31	0.406	16	0.62	24	0.94
1-1/4	80.3- 78.5	3.16-3.09	35.3	1.39	58.72	2.312	14	0.56	10	0.41	11.91	0.469	14	0.56	22	0.88
1-1/2	94.5- 93.0	3.72-3.66	40.1	1.58	69.85	2.750	17	0.67	12	0.47	13.49	0.531	16	0.62	25	1.00
2	103.1-100.1	4.06-3.94	47.2	1.86	77.77	3.062	21	0.81	12	0.47	13.49	0.531	16	0.62	26	1.03
2-1/2	115.8-112.8	4.56-4.44	53.1	2.09	88.90	3.500	24	0.96	13	0.50	13.49	0.531	19	0.75	38	1.50
3	136.7-133.4	5.38-5.25	64.3	2.53	106.38	4.188	30	1.18	14	0.56	16.66	0.656	22	0.88	41	1.62
3-1/2	153.9-150.9	6.06-5.94	68.6	2.70	120.65	4.750	34	1.34	16	0.62	16.66	0.656	22	0.88	28	1.12
4	163.6-160.3	6.44-6.31	74.9	2.95	130.18	5.125	38	1.49	16	0.62	16.66	0.656	25	1.00	35	1.38
5	185.7-182.6	7.31-7.19	89.4	3.52	152.40	6.000	45	1.78	16	0.62	16.66	0.656	28	1.12	41	1.62

Nominal Flange Size, in	Bolt Dimensions Thread	Bolt Dimensions Length mm	Bolt Dimensions Length in	W ± 0.25 mm	W ± 0.010 in	X ± 0.25 mm	X ± 0.010 in	Max Rec. Working Pressure MPa	Max Rec. Working Pressure psi	Rec. Bolt Torque Range N·m	Rec. Bolt Torque Range lb-in
1/2	5/16–18	32	1-1/4	19.05	0.750	8.74	0.344	34.5	5000	20– 25	175– 225
3/4	3/8–16	32	1-1/4	23.83	0.938	11.13	0.438	34.5	5000	28– 40	250– 350
1	3/8–16	32	1-1/4	26.19	1.031	13.08	0.515	34.5	5000	37– 48	325– 425
1-1/4	7/16–14	38	1-1/2	29.36	1.156	15.09	0.594	27.6	4000	48– 62	425– 550
1-1/2	1/2–13	38	1-1/2	34.93	1.375	17.86	0.703	20.7	3000	62– 79	550– 700
2	1/2–13	38	1-1/2	38.89	1.531	21.44	0.844	20.7	3000	73– 90	650– 800
2-1/2	1/2–13	44	1-3/4	44.45	1.750	25.40	1.000	17.2	2500	107–124	950–1100
3	5/8–11	44	1-3/4	53.19	2.094	30.96	1.219	13.8	2000	186–203	1650–1800
3-1/2	5/8–11	51	2	60.33	2.375	34.93	1.375	3.4	500	158–181	1400–1600
4	5/8–11	51	2	65.07	2.562	38.89	1.531	3.4	500	158–181	1400–1600
5	5/8–11	57	2-1/4	76.20	3.000	46.02	1.812	3.4	500	158–181	1400–1600

TABLE 1B—DIMENSIONS OF HYDRAULIC FLANGED CONNECTIONS, High PRESSURE SERIES (CODE 62)

Nominal Flange Size, in	Flange Dash Size	A Dia Max mm	A Dia Max in	B Dia mm	B Dia in	C Dia ± 0.25 mm	C Dia ± 0.010 in	D Dia ± 0.25 mm	D Dia ± 0.010 in	E ± 0.13 mm	E ± 0.005 in	F ± 0.13 mm	F ± 0.005 in
1/2	–8	13	0.50	25.53–25.40	1.005-1.000	31.75	1.250	32.54	1.281	7.75	0.305	7.24	0.285
3/4	–12	19	0.75	31.88-31.75	1.255-1.250	41.28	1.625	42.06	1.656	8.76	0.345	8.26	0.325
1	–16	25	1.00	39.75-39.62	1.565-1.560	47.63	1.875	48.41	1.906	9.53	0.375	9.02	0.355
1-1/4	–20	32	1.25	44.58-44.45	1.755-1.750	53.98	2.125	54.76	2.156	10.29	0.405	9.78	0.385
1-1/2	–24	38	1.50	53.98-53.72	2.125-2.115	63.50	2.500	64.29	2.531	12.57	0.495	12.07	0.475
2	–32	51	2.00	63.50-63.25	2.500-2.490	79.38	3.125	80.16	3.156	12.57	0.495	12.07	0.475

Nominal Flange Size, in	G Dia Max mm	G Dia Max in	H Dia Max mm	H Dia Max in	J Dia ± 0.25 mm	J Dia ± 0.010 in	K Ref mm	K Ref in	L ID Ref mm	L ID Ref in	M OD Ref mm	M OD Ref in	N Dia Ref mm	N Dia Ref in	O-Ring Size No.
1/2	14	0.56	24	0.94	24.64	0.970	14	0.56	18.64	0.734	25.70	1.012	3.53	0.139	210
3/4	21	0.81	32	1.25	32.51	1.280	18	0.69	24.99	0.984	32.05	1.262	3.53	0.139	214
1	27	1.06	38	1.50	38.86	1.530	21	0.81	32.92	1.296	39.98	1.574	3.53	0.139	219
1-1/4	33	1.31	44	1.72	44.45	1.750	25	1.00	37.69	1.484	44.75	1.762	3.53	0.139	222
1-1/2	40	1.56	51	2.00	51.56	2.030	30	1.19	47.22	1.859	54.28	2.137	3.53	0.139	225
2	52	2.06	67	2.62	67.56	2.660	38	1.50	56.74	2.234	63.80	2.512	3.53	0.139	228

Nominal Flange Size, in	O mm	O in	P ± 0.8 mm	P ± 0.03 in	Q ± 0.25 mm	Q ± 0.010 in	R mm	R in	S Rad mm	S Rad in	T Dia ± 0.25 mm	T Dia ± 0.010 in	U mm	U in	V mm	V in
1/2	57.2- 55.6	2.25-2.19	22.6	0.89	40.49	1.594	8	0.32	8	0.31	8.74	0.344	16	0.62	22	0.88
3/4	72.1- 70.6	2.84-2.78	29.0	1.14	50.80	2.000	11	0.43	10	0.41	10.31	0.406	19	0.75	28	1.12
1	81.8- 80.3	3.22-3.16	33.8	1.33	57.15	2.250	13	0.51	12	0.47	11.91	0.469	24	0.94	33	1.31
1-1/4	96.0- 94.5	3.78-3.72	37.6	1.48	66.68	2.625	15	0.59	14	0.56	13.49	0.531	27	1.06	38	1.50
1-1/2	114.3-111.3	4.50-4.38	46.5	1.83	79.38	3.125	17	0.68	17	0.66	16.66	0.656	30	1.19	43	1.69
2	134.9-131.8	5.31-5.19	55.9	2.20	96.82	3.812	21	0.84	18	0.72	19.84	0.781	37	1.44	52	2.06

TABLE 1B—DIMENSIONS OF HYDRAULIC FLANGED CONNECTIONS, HIGH PRESSURE SERIES (CODE 62) (CONTINUED)

Nominal Flange Size, in	Bolt Dimensions Thread	Bolt Dimensions Length mm	Bolt Dimensions Length in	W ± 0.25 mm	W ±0.010 in	X ±0.25 mm	X ±0.010 in	Max Rec. Working Pressure MPa	Max Rec. Working Pressure psi	Rec. Bolt Torque Range N-m	Rec. Bolt Torque Range lb-in
1/2	5/16–18	32	1-1/4	20.24	0.797	9.12	0.359	41.4	6000	20 –25	175 –225
3/4	3/8–16	38	1-1/2	25.40	1.000	11.91	0.469	41.4	6000	34 –45	300 –400
1	7/16-14	44	1-3/4	28.58	1.125	13.89	0.547	41.4	6000	56– 68	500– 600
1-1/4	1/2–13	44	1-3/4	33.32	1.312	15.88	0.625	41.4	6000	85–102	750– 900
1-1/2	5/8–11	57	2-1/4	39.67	1.562	18.26	0.719	41.4	6000	158–181	1400–1600
2	3/4–10	70	2-3/4	48.41	1.906	22.23	0.875	41.4	6000	271–294	2400–2600

TABLE 2A—PORT DIMENSIONS FOR BOLTED FLANGE CONNECTIONS, STANDARD PRESSURE SERIES

Nominal Flange Size, in	Flange Dash Size	A Dia + 0.0 –1.5 mm	A Dia + 0.00 –0.06 in	O mm	O in	FF mm	FF in	Q ± 0.25 mm	Q ± 0.010 in	GG ± 0.25 mm	GG ± 0.010 in	S Rad mm	S Rad in	W mm	W in
1/2	–8	12.7	0.50	54	2.12	46	1.81	38.10	1.500	17.48	0.688	8	0.31	19	0.75
3/4	–12	19.1	0.75	65	2.56	52	2.06	47.63	1.875	22.23	0.875	9	0.34	24	0.94
1	–16	25.4	1.00	70	2.75	59	2.31	52.37	2.062	26.19	1.031	9	0.34	26	1.03
1-1/4	–20	31.8	1.25	79	3.12	73	2.88	58.72	2.312	30.18	1.188	10	0.41	29	1.16
1-1/2	–24	38.1	1.50	94	3.69	83	3.25	69.85	2.750	35.71	1.406	12	0.47	35	1.38
2	–32	50.8	2.00	102	4.00	97	3.81	77.77	3.062	42.88	1.688	12	0.47	39	1.53
2-1/2	–40	63.5	2.50	114	4.50	109	4.28	88.90	3.500	50.80	2.000	13	0.50	44	1.75
3	–48	76.2	3.00	135	5.31	131	5.16	106.38	4.188	61.93	2.438	14	0.56	53	2.09
3-1/2	–56	88.9	3.50	152	6.00	140	5.50	120.65	4.750	69.85	2.750	16	0.62	60	2.38
4	–64	101.6	4.00	162	6.38	152	6.00	130.18	5.125	77.77	3.062	16	0.62	65	2.56
5	–80	127.0	5.00	184	7.25	181	7.12	152.40	6.000	92.08	3.625	16	0.62	76	3.00

Nominal Flange Size, in	X mm	X in	Y Rad mm	Y Rad mm	Z Thread UNC-2B	AA Min mm	AA Min mm	BB (1) Min mm	BB[1] Min in	CC[1] Min mm	CC[1] Min in	DD[1] Min mm	DD[1] Min in	EE Min mm	EE Min in
1/2	9	0.34	23	0.91	5/16–18	24	0.94	56	2.22	52	2.06	49	1.91	33	1.31
3/4	11	0.44	26	1.03	3/8–16	22	0.88	68	2.66	61	2.41	55	2.16	41	1.62
1	13	0.52	29	1.16	3/8–16	22	0.88	72	2.84	67	2.62	61	2.41	48	1.88
1-1/4	15	0.59	37	1.44	7/16-14	28	1.12	82	3.22	78	3.09	75	2.97	54	2.12
1-1/2	18	0.70	41	1.62	1/2-13	27	1.06	96	3.78	90	3.56	85	3.34	64	2.50
2	21	0.84	49	1.91	1/2–13	27	1.06	104	4.09	102	4.00	99	3.91	76	3.00
2-1/2	25	1.00	54	2.14	1/2–13	30	1.19	117	4.59	114	4.50	111	4.38	89	3.50
3	31	1.22	66	2.58	5/8–11	30	1.19	137	5.41	136	5.34	133	5.25	106	4.19
3-1/2	35	1.38	70	2.75	5/8–11	33	1.31	155	6.09	148	5.84	142	5.59	119	4.69
4	39	1.53	76	3.00	5/8–11	30	1.19	164	6.47	160	6.28	155	6.09	132	5.19
5	46	1.81	90	3.56	5/8–11	33	1.31	186	7.34	185	7.28	183	7.22	151	6.19

1. Dimensions BB, CC, and DD provide 1.5 mm (0.06 in) clearance between flanges, dimensionally on the high limit, when, the same size flanges are used on adjacent ports. These dimensions do not apply when more than one size of flanges are used on adjacent ports.

TABLE 3A—PORT DIMENSIONS FOR BOLTED FLANGE CONNECTIONS, HIGH PRESSURE SERIES

Nominal Flange Size, in	Flange Dash Size	A Dia + 0.0 −1.5 mm	A Dia + 0.00 −0.06 in	O mm	O in	FF mm	FF in	Q ± 0.25 mm	Q ± 0.010 in	GG ± 0.25 mm	GG ± 0.010 in	S Rad mm	S Rad in	W mm	W in
1/2	−8	12.7	0.50	56	2.22	48	1.88	40.49	1.594	18.24	0.718	8	0.31	20	0.80
3/4	−12	19.1	0.75	71	2.81	60	2.38	50.80	2.000	23.80	0.937	10	0.41	25	1.00
1	−16	25.4	1.00	81	3.19	70	2.75	57.15	2.250	27.76	1.093	12	0.47	28	1.12
1−1/4	−20	31.8	1.25	95	3.75	78	3.06	66.68	2.625	31.75	1.250	14	0.56	33	1.31
1−1/2	−24	38.1	1.50	113	4.44	95	3.75	79.38	3.125	36.50	1.437	17	0.66	40	1.56
2	−32	50.8	2.00	133	5.25	114	4.50	96.82	3.812	44.45	1.750	18	0.72	49	1.91

Nominal Flange Size, in	X mm	X in	Y Rad mm	Y Rad in	Z Thread UNC-2B	AA Min mm	AA Min in	BB (1) Min mm	BB[1] Min in	CC[1] Min mm	CC[1] Min in	DD[1] Min mm	DD[1] Min in	EE Min mm	EE Min in
1/2	9	0.36	24	0.94	5/16–18	21	0.81	59	2.34	56	2.22	53	2.09	38	1.50
3/4	12	0.47	30	1.19	3/8–16	24	0.94	75	2.94	70	2.75	66	2.59	48	1.88
1	14	0.55	35	1.38	7/16–14	27	1.06	84	3.31	80	3.16	75	2.97	54	2.12
1−1/4	16	0.62	39	1.53	1/2–13	25	1.00	99	3.88	90	3.56	83	3.25	60	2.38
1−1/2	18	0.72	48	1.88	5/8–11	35	1.38	116	4.56	108	4.25	101	3.97	70	2.75
2	22	0.88	57	2.25	3/4–10	38	1.50	137	5.38	128	5.03	120	4.72	86	3.38

1. Dimensions BB, CC, and DD provide 1.5 mm (0.06 in) clearance between flanges, dimensionally on the high limit, when the same size flanges are used on adjacent ports. These dimensions do not apply when more than one size of flanges are used on adjacent ports.

TABLE 4—MATERIAL PROPERTIES

Standard series — 1/2 in (–8) size	Minimum yield, 221 MPa (32 000 psi)
	Minimum elongation, 3%
All other sizes	Minimum yield, 414 MPa (60 000 psi)
	Minimum elongation, 3%
High pressure series — all sizes	Minimum yield, 331 MPa (48 000 psi)
	Minimum elongation, 3%

*4. **Dimensions and Tolerances***—Tabulated dimensions and tolerances shall apply to the finished parts, plated or otherwise processed, as specified by the purchaser. Tolerances on all dimensions for flanged heads, split flange clamp halves, and ports not otherwise limited shall be ±0.4 mm (0.016 in).

*5. **Material***—Flanged heads shall be made of steel. Split flange clamp halves shall be made from a material with the properties in Table 3.

*6. **Finish***—The external surfaces and threads of all carbon steel parts shall be plated or coated with a suitable material that passes a 72 h salt spray test in accordance with ASTM B 117. Any appearance of red rust during the 72 h salt spray test shall be considered failure, except for the following:

a. All internal fluid passages.
b. Edges such as hex points, serrations, and crests of threads where there may be mechanical deformation of the plating or coating typical of mass-produced parts or shipping effects.
c. Areas where there is mechanical deformation of the plating or coating caused by crimping, flaring, bending, and other post-plate metal forming operations.
d. Areas where the parts are suspended or affixed in the test chamber where condensate can accumulate.

NOTE—Cadmium plating is not preferred due to environmental reasons. Parts manufactured to this Standard after January 1, 1997, shall not be cadmium plated. Internal fluid passages shall be protected from corrosion during storage. Changes in plating may affect assembly torques and require requalification, when applicable.

Bolts shall be finished with a suitable coating that meet the previous requirements after a 16 h salt spray test in accordance with ASTM B 117. Lock washers may have a plain (natural) finish or a suitable coating.

*7. **Workmanship***—Workmanship shall conform to the best commercial practice to produce high-quality connection components. Connection components shall be free from all hanging burrs, loose scale, and slivers which might become dislodged in usage and all other defects which might affect their serviceability. All sealing surfaces must be smooth except that annular tool marks up to 3 μm (100 μin) max, unless specified otherwise, shall be permissible.

R) CLIP FASTENER FITTING—SAE J1467 JUN1993 SAE Standard

Report of the SAE Fluid Conductors and Connectors Technical Committee approved December 1988 and completely revised June 1993. Rationale statement available.

Foreword—This Document has also changed to comply with the new SAE Technical Standards Board format.

1. Scope—This SAE Standard covers material and dimensional requirements of steel clip fastener fittings. These fittings are intended for use in hydraulic systems on industrial equipment primarily in mining applications.

2. References

2.1 Applicable Publication—The following publication forms a part of this specification to the extent specified herein.

2.1.1 ASTM PUBLICATION—Available from ASTM, 100 Barr Harbor Drive, West Conshohocken, PA 19428-2959.

ASTM B 117—Method of Salt Spray (Fog) Testing

3. Size Designation—Fitting sizes are designated by the corresponding nominal inside diameter of hose. See Table 1.

TABLE 1—NOMINAL SIZE DESIGNATIONS

Nominal SAE Dash Size	Nominal Hose I.D. mm
–4	6.35
–6	9.52
–8	12.70
–12	19.05
–16	25.40
–20	31.75
–24	38.10
–32	50.80

4. Material and Manufacture

4.1 Material

4.1.1 MALE AND FEMALE—The material used in the manufacture of the male and female components shall be steel such as AISI 12L14, 1137, 1141, or other free cutting steels having a minimum yield strength of 193 MPa and a minimum tensile strength of 345 MPa. See Figure 1 and Figure 2.

4.1.2 O-RING—The standard clip fastener O-ring shall be manufactured from an elastomeric material that is compatible with the fluid being conveyed. Suitable materials include nitrile (NBR) rubber or viton having a minimum Shore 'A' hardness of 80 durometer. See Figure 3.

4.1.3 BACK-UP RING—The clip fastener back-up ring shall be manufactured from a material that is compatible with the fluid being conveyed. Suitable materials include acetal homopolymers, polyamide, or Teflon (PTFE). See Figure 3.

4.1.4 STAPLES—The clip fastener staple (clip) shall be manufactured from corrosion-resistant steel or spring steel. Contour and details of staple are optional with manufacturer providing that interchangeability of the male and female is not affected. See Figure 4.

4.2 Finish—The external surfaces and threads of all carbon steel parts shall be plated or coated with a suitable material that passes a 72 h salt spray test in accordance with ASTM B 117. Any appearance of red rust during the 72 h salt spray test shall be considered failure, except for the following:

a. All internal fluid passages.
b. Edges such as hex points, serrations, and crests of threads where there may be mechanical deformation of the plating or coating typical of mass-produced parts or shipping effects.
c. Areas where there is mechanical deformation of the plating or coating caused by crimping, flaring, bending, and other post-plate metal forming operations.
d. Areas where the parts are suspended or affixed in the test chamber where condensate can accumulate.

NOTE—Cadmium plating is not preferred due to environmental reasons. Parts manufactured to this document after January 1, 1977, shall not be cadmium plated. Internal fluid passages shall be protected from corrosion during storage. Changes in plating may affect assembly torques and require requalification, when applicable.

4.3 Workmanship—Workmanship shall conform to the best commercial practice to produce high-quality fittings. Fittings must be free from visual contaminants, all hanging burrs, loose scale, and slivers which might be dislodged in usage, and any other defects that might affect the function of the parts.

4.4 Construction—Fittings may be made by forging, cold heading, or machined from bar stock. Carbon steel fittings fabricated from multiple components may be bonded together by copper brazing, silver brazing, welding, or other suitable processes.

4.5 Dimensions—The dimensions for the components shown in Figure 5 shall be in accordance with Figures 1 through 4.

NOTE—The alternate methods of fabricating the female may be used providing the envelope dimensions are not affected to the extent that interchangeability becomes a problem. See Figure 5.

5. Protection—Sealing surfaces and threads (both internal and external) shall be protected by the manufacturer from nicks, scratches, or any damage that is detrimental to their function.

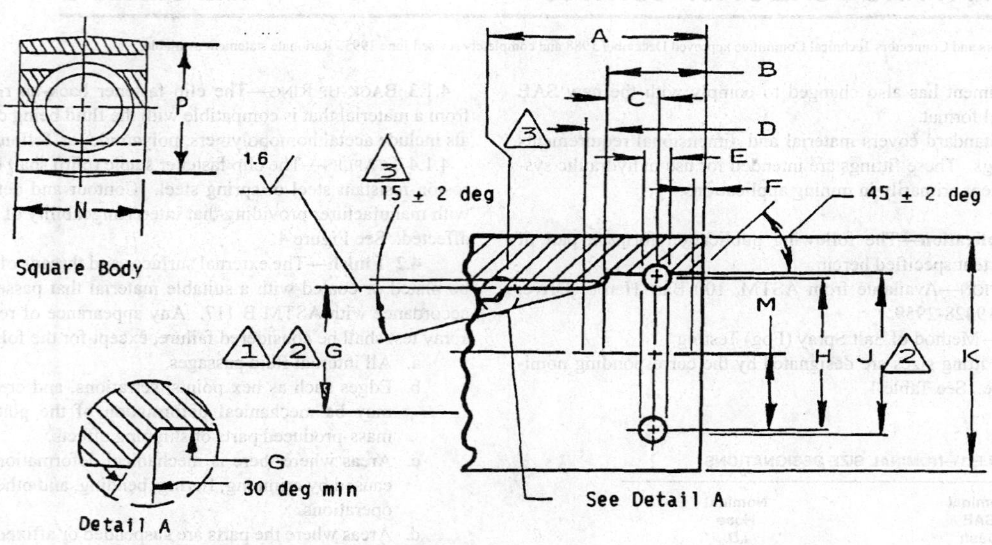

Nominal SAE Dash Size	A min mm	B ±0.5 mm	C	D ±0.10 mm	E mm	F max mm	G ±0.025 mm	H mm	J ±0.08 mm	K dia mm	M ±0.13 mm	N ±0.5 mm	P ±0.5 mm
-4	27.43	15.5	7.7 7.0	2.0	6.15 5.89	1.1	10.03	13.3 12.8	15.16	27.2 23.0	6.50	21.0	22.3
-6	27.43	15.5	7.7 7.0	2.0	6.15 5.89	1.1	14.02	18.3 17.8	20.17	32.0 30.0	9.02	26.0	30.0
-8	27.43	15.5	7.7 7.0	2.0	6.15 5.89	1.1	18.03	22.3 21.8	24.16	36.6 34.9	11.0	30.0	35.0
-12	27.43	15.5	7.7 7.0	2.0	6.15 5.89	1.1	24.03	27.3 26.8	29.16	45.2 41.0	13.51	35.0	41.0
-16	32.51	20.5	9.7 9.0	2.0	8.69 8.30	1.1	31.01	36.3 35.7	39.12	55.1 52.4	18.0	48.0	53.0
-20	32.51	20.5	9.7 9.0	2.0	8.69 8.30	1.1	38.02	43.4 42.8	46.15	65.3 60.0	21.50	55.0	60.0
-24	34.54	20.5	11.7 11.0	2.0	9.19 8.30	1.1	47.02	52.4 51.6	55.22	73.0 70.0	26.0	--	--
-32	34.54	20.5	11.7 11.0	2.0	9.19 8.30	1.1	56.00	61.4 60.6	64.21	82.6 80.0	30.50	--	--

4 The female body can be manufactured as a swivel type where the design and method of attachment shall be optional with the manufacturer (see Figure 5).

3 Optional Design: 1.0 (1.5) x 30° ± 2°

2 These diameters must be concentric within 0.05 TIR.

1 "G" diameter to run to the full depth of "A" dimension.

FIGURE 1—FEMALE CLIP FASTENER BODY

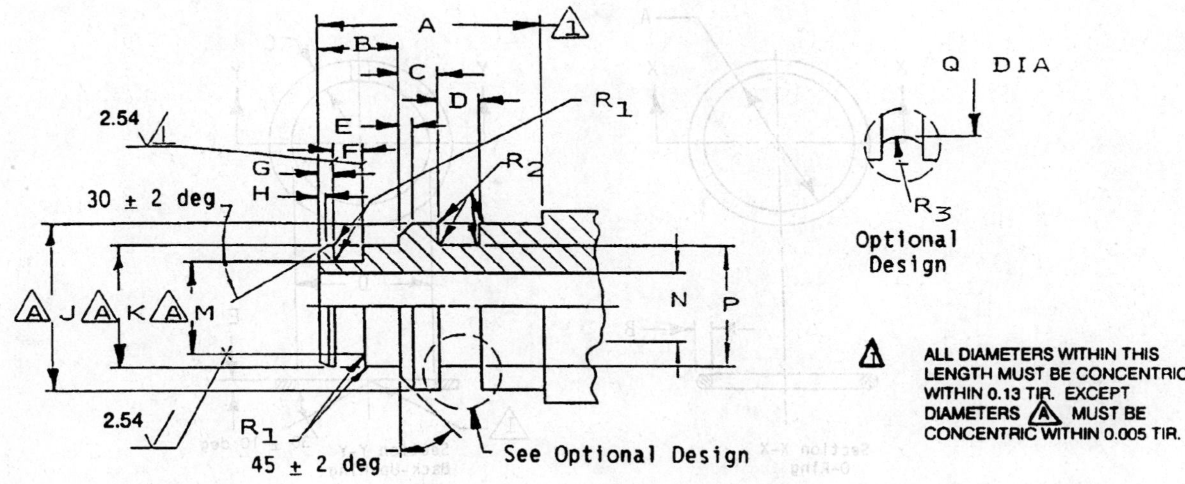

Nominal SAE Dash Size	A min mm	B mm	C ±0.1 mm	D ±0.1 mm	E ±0.2 mm	F ±0.010 mm	G mm	H ±0.25 mm	J ±0.08 mm	K +0.05 -0.08	M mm	N mm	P ±0.1 mm	Q ±0.1 mm	R_1 max mm	R_2 max mm	R_3 ref mm
-4	27.74	11.25 10.74	4.9	5.1	1.5	3.1	3.1 2.6	1.0	14.90	9.90	6.86 6.73	4.7 2.8	8.40	7.42	0.5	0.7	3.4
-6	27.74	11.25 10.74	4.9	5.1	1.5	3.1	3.1 2.6	1.0	19.90	13.90	10.85 10.72	8.2 6.6	13.40	12.40	0.5	0.7	3.4
-8	27.74	11.25 10.74	4.9	5.1	1.5	3.6	3.1 2.6	1.0	23.90	17.90	14.05 13.92	11.4 9.7	17.40	16.40	0.5	0.7	3.4
-12	27.74	11.25 10.74	4.9	5.1	1.5	3.6	3.1 2.6	1.0	28.90	23.90	20.04 19.91	17.0 15.4	22.40	21.39	0.5	0.7	3.4
-16	32.90	11.25 10.74	5.9	7.1	1.5	3.6	3.1 2.6	1.0	38.80	30.90	27.05 26.92	23.0 19.8	29.90	28.78	0.5	0.7	5.3
-20	32.90	11.25 10.74	5.9	7.1	1.5	3.6	3.1 2.6	1.0	45.90	37.90	34.04 33.91	30.0 24.8	36.90	35.79	0.5	0.7	5.3
-24	36.30	13.28 12.78	7.9	7.1	1.5	5.1	3.1 2.6	1.0	54.90	46.90	42.00 41.90	35.8 30.0	45.90	44.78	0.6	0.7	5.3
-32	36.30	13.28 12.78	7.9	7.1	1.5	5.1	3.1 2.6	1.0	63.90	55.90	51.00 50.90	45.0 40.0	54.90	53.77	0.6	0.7	5.3

FIGURE 2—MALE CLIP FASTENER BODY

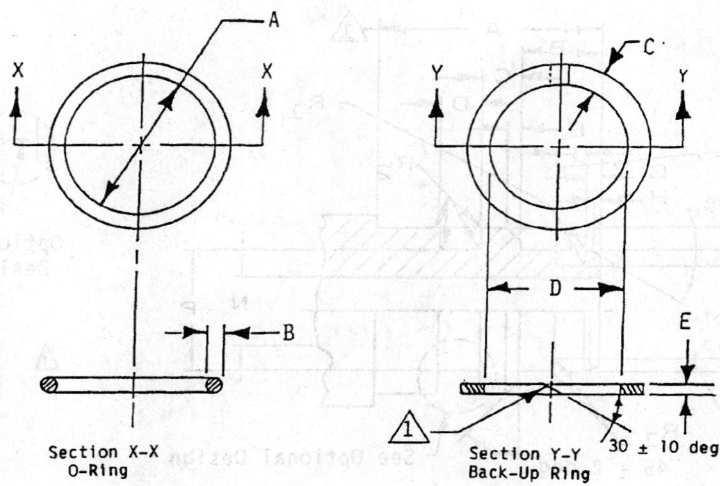

Nominal SAE Dash Size	A Dia mm	B Dia mm	C mm	D Dia mm	E mm
-4	6.16 5.84	2.08 1.92	1.65 1.55	6.96 6.86	.90 .70
-6	10.20 9.80	2.08 1.92	1.65 1.55	10.95 10.85	.90 .70
-8	13.25 12.75	2.59 2.41	2.06 1.96	14.15 14.05	.90 .70
-12	19.40 18.60	2.59 2.41	2.06 1.96	20.14 20.04	.90 .70
-16	25.40 24.60	2.59 2.41	2.06 1.96	27.15 27.05	.90 .70
-20	33.40 32.60	2.59 2.41	2.06 1.96	34.14 34.04	.90 .70
-24	40.50 39.50	3.10 2.90	2.57 2.46	42.11 42.01	1.85 1.40
-32	50.50 49.50	3.10 2.90	2.57 2.46	51.10 51.00	1.85 1.40

2 All surfaces must be smooth and free from irregularities.

⚠1 Cut must be clean and sharp.

FIGURE 3—O-RING SEAL AND BACK-UP RING

Nominal SAE Dash Size	Cross Section Type Square L Length mm	Cross Section Type Round D Diameter mm
-4	4.07 3.93	4.78 4.72
-6	4.07 3.93	4.78 4.72
-8	4.07 3.93	4.78 4.72
-12	4.07 3.93	4.78 4.72
-16	6.08 5.92	6.40 6.35
-20	6.08 5.92	6.40 6.35
-24	6.08 5.92	6.40 6.35
-32	6.08 5.92	6.40 6.35

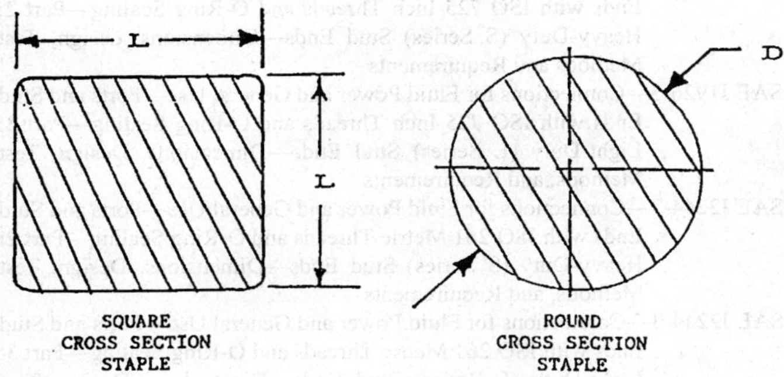

FIGURE 4—STAPLE CROSS SECTIONS

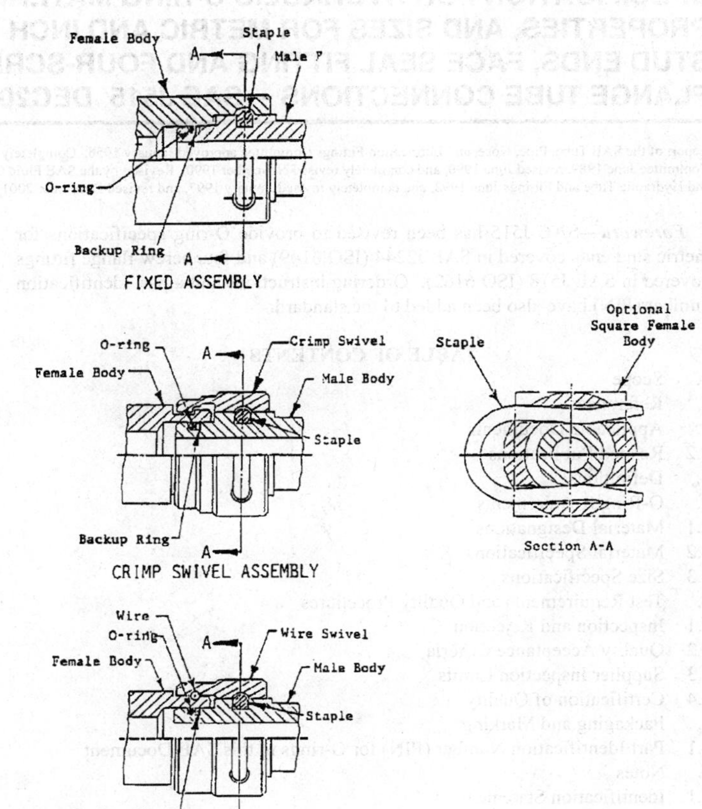

FIGURE 5—TYPICAL ASSEMBLIES OF SWIVEL AND FIXED CONNECTIONS

SPECIFICATION FOR HYDRAULIC O-RING MATERIALS, PROPERTIES, AND SIZES FOR METRIC AND INCH STUD ENDS, FACE SEAL FITTING AND FOUR-SCREW FLANGE TUBE CONNECTIONS —SAE J515 DEC2001

SAE Standard

Report of the SAE Tube, Pipe, Hose, and Lubrication Fittings Committee approved January 1956. Completely revised by the SAE Fluid Conductors and Connectors Technical Committee June 1989, revised June 1990, and completely revised November 1990. Revised by the SAE Fluid Conductors and Connectors Technical Committee SC1—Automotive and Hydraulic Tube and Fittings June 1992, and completely revised January 1997, and revised December 2001. Rationale statement available.

Foreword—SAE J515 has been revised to provide O-ring specifications for metric stud ends covered in SAE J2244 (ISO 6149) and four screw flange fittings covered in SAE J518 (ISO 6162). Ordering instructions and a part identification number (PIN) have also been added to the standard.

TABLE OF CONTENTS

1. Scope—SAE J515 covers the specification for hydraulic O-ring material and properties and sizes applicable to face seal fittings, metric and inch stud ends, and four-bolt flange fittings. The standard includes a size code to allow industry and government agencies to order O-ring with a coded part number.

2. References

2.1 Applicable Publications—The following standards contain provisions which, through reference in this text, constitute provisions of this document. At the time of publication, the editions indicated were valid. All standards are subject to revision, and parties to agreements based on this document are encouraged to investigate the possibility of applying the most recent edition of the standards indicated as follows.

2.1.1 SAE PUBLICATIONS—Available from SAE, 400 Commonwealth Drive, Warrendale, PA 15096-0001.

SAE AS568A—Aerospace Size Standard for O-Rings
SAE J120—Rubber Rings for Automotive Applications
SAE J200—Classification System for Rubber Materials
SAE J518—Hydraulic Flanged Tube, Pipe, and Hose Connections, 4-Bolt Split Flange Type
SAE J1453-2[1]—Specification for O-Ring Face Seal Fittings—Part 2: Fittings with SAE J1926/2 (ISO 11926-2), Inch Stud Ends
SAE J1453-3[2]—Specification for O-Ring Face Seal Fittings—Part 3: Fittings with SAE J2244-2 (ISO 6149-2), Metric Stud Ends
SAE J1926-2—Connections for Fluid Power and General Use—Ports and Stud Ends with ISO 725 Inch Threads and O-Ring Sealing—Part 2: Heavy-Duty (S Series) Stud Ends—Dimensions, design, Test Methods and Requirements
SAE J1926-3—Connections for Fluid Power and General Use—Ports and Stud Ends with ISO 725 Inch Threads and O-Ring Sealing—Part 3: Light-Duty (L Series) Stud Ends—Dimensions, Design, Test Methods, and Requirements
SAE J2244-2—Connections for Fluid Power and General Use—Ports and Stud Ends with ISO 261 Metric Threads and O-Ring Sealing—Part 2: Heavy-Duty (S Series) Stud Ends—Dimensions, Design, Test Methods, and Requirements
SAE J2244-3—Connections for Fluid Power and General Use—Ports and Stud Ends with ISO 261 Metric Threads and O-Ring Sealing—Part 3: Light-Duty (L Series) Stud Ends—Dimensions, Design, Test Methods, and Requirements

2.1.2 ISO PUBLICATIONS—Available from ANSI, 25 West 43rd Street, New York, NY 10036-8002.

ISO 3601-3:1987—Fluid systems—Sealing devices—O-rings—Part 3: Quality acceptance criteria
ISO 5598:1985—Fluid power systems and components—Vocabulary
ISO 6149-2—Connections for fluid power and general use—Ports and stud ends with ISO 261 metric threads and O-ring sealing—Part 2: Heavy duty (S series) stud ends—Dimensions, design, test methods and requirements
ISO 6149-3—Connections for fluid power and general use—Ports and stud ends with ISO 261 threads and O-ring sealing—Part 3: Light duty (L series) stud ends—Dimensions, design, test methods and requirements
ISO 6162—Hydraulic fluid power—Four-screw split-flange connections for use at pressures of 2.5 MPa to 40 MPa—Type I inch series and type II metric series
ISO 8434-3—Metallic tube connections for fluid power and general use—Part 3: O-ring face seal fitting
ISO 11926-2—Connections for fluid power and general use—Ports and stud ends with ISO 725 threads and O-ring sealing—Part 2: Heavy duty (S series) stud ends—Dimensions, design, test methods, and requirements
ISO 11926-3—Connections for fluid power and general use—Ports and stud ends with ISO 725 threads and O-ring sealing—Part 3: Light duty (L series) stud ends—Dimensions, design, test methods, and requirements

2.1.3 ASTM PUBLICATION—Available from ASTM, 100 Barr Harbor Drive, West Conshohocken, PA 19428-2959.

ASTM D 2000—Classification System for Rubber Materials in Automotive Applications

1. To be published, see SAE J1453.
2. To be published, see SAE J1453.

2.2 Related Publications—The following publications are provided for information purposes only and are not a required part of this document.

2.2.1 SAE PUBLICATION—Available from SAE, 400 Commonwealth Drive, Warrendale, PA 15096-0001.

SAE AS871—Manufacturing and Inspection Standards for Preformed Packings (O-Rings)

2.2.2 ASTM PUBLICATIONS—Available from ASTM, 100 Barr Harbor Drive, West Conshohocken, PA 19428-2959.

ASTM D 395—Test Methods for Rubber Property—Compression Set
ASTM D 412—Test Methods for Rubber Properties in Tension
ASTM D 471—Test Method for Rubber Property—Effect of Liquids
ASTM D 624—Test Method for Rubber Property—Tear Resistance
ASTM D 865—Test Method for Rubber—Deterioration by Heating in Air (Test Tube Enclosure)
ASTM D 1329—Method for Evaluating Rubber Property—Retraction at Lower Temperatures (TR Test)
ASTM D 1414—Methods of Testing Rubber O-Rings
ASTM D 1415—Test Method for Rubber Property—International Hardness
ASTM D 2137—Standard Test Methods for Nonvolatile Matter in Halogenated Organic Solvents and Their Admixtures
ASTM D 2240—Test Method for Rubber Property—Durometer Hardness

2.2.3 DIN PUBLICATION—Available from Deutsches Institut Fur Normung E V, Burggratestr. 6, D-10787, Berlin, Germany.

DIN 3771-3—Fluid Systems: O-Rings; Materials, Field of Application

2.2.4 ISO PUBLICATIONS—Available from ANSI, 25 West 43rd Street, New York, NY 10036-8002.

ISO 48:1979—Vulcanized rubbers—Determination of hardness (Hardness between 30 and 85 IRHD)
ISO 1101: 1983—Technical drawings—Tolerancing of form, orientation, location and run-out—Generalities, definitions, symbols, indications on drawings
ISO 1302:1978—Technical drawings—Method of indicating surface texture on drawings
ISO 3448:1975—Industrial liquid lubricants—ISO viscosity classification
ISO 3601-1:1987—Fluid systems—O-rings—Part 1: Inside diameters, cross sections, tolerances, and size identification

2.2.5 MILITARY PUBLICATIONS—Available from DODSSP, Subscription Service Desk, 700 Robbins Avenue, Building 4D, Philadelphia, PA 19111-5094.

MIL-STD-413—Visual Inspection Guide for Elastomeric O-Rings
MIL-R-83248C:1994—Rubber, Fluorocarbon Elastomer, High Temperature, Fluid, and Compression Set Resistant

*3. **Definitions***—For the purposes of this document, the definitions given in ISO 5598 shall apply.

*4. **O-Ring Requirements***

4.1 Material Designations—Designations and descriptions for O-ring materials are shown in Table 1. ASTM/SAE Type and Class are from ASTM D 2000 and SAE J200.

TABLE 1—DESIGNATIONS AND DESCRIPTIONS FOR O-RING MATERIALS

ASTM/SAE[1] Type and Class	Description
CH	Nitrile Elastomer, 90 Durometer Hardness, Good for temperature range of –30 °C to 125 °C for petroleum-based fluids
CA	EPDM Elastomer, 80 Durometer Hardness, Good for temperature range of –40 °C to 125 °C for water-based hydraulic or nonpetroleum-based fluids
HK	Fluorocarbon Elastomer, 90 Durometer Hardness, Good for temperature range of –15 °C to maximum temperature of 275 °C for petroleum or nonpetroleum-based fluids

1. SAE Type CH was SAE Type 1: Type CA was SAE Type 2 and Type HK was SAE Type 3.

4.2 Material Specifications—O-rings shall conform to the specifications in Table 2.

4.3 Size Specifications—O-rings shall conform to the dimensions given in Figures 1 to 5 and Tables 3 to 7.

TABLE 2—O-RING MATERIAL SPECIFICATIONS[1]

Specification	SAE/ASTM TypeCH	SAE/ASTM TypeCA	SAE/ASTM TypeHK
Description	Petroleum-base and nonflammable water-base hydraulic fluids	Nonflammable phosphate ester base hydraulic fluids	High temperature for hydraulic fluids
General Service	High-pressure applications of pneumatics, water-base hydraulic fluids, lubricating oils, hydraulic oils, and gasoline	High-pressure applications of nonflammable hydraulic fluids of phosphate ester base type	High-pressure, high-temperature applications of pneumatic, water base hydraulic fluids, lubricating oils, hydraulic oils, and fuels
Temperature	–30 °C to 125 °C	–40 °C to 125 °C	–15 °C to 275 °C
Shore Hardness	90 pts ± 5 pts	80 pts ± 5 pts	90 pts ± 5 pts
Elongation	100% min	150% min	100% min
Tensile	10 MPa min	10 MPa min	10 MPa min
Compound	Nitrile (Buna N) to ASTM D 2000 or SAE J200 M4CH910B14E015E035Z1 Z1 = TR 10 temperature –21 °C or lower. Alternate Low Temperature Product Test, 5 hours at –30 °C, rings compressed 25% of ID, no cracks.	EPDM to ASTM D 2000 or SAE J200 M7CA810A25B35F17	Fluorocarbon to ASTM D 2000 or SAE J200 M7HK910A1–11B38EF31E088Z1 Z1 = TR 10 temperature –15 °C or lower (similar to MIL-R-83248 Type 1, Class 2)
Lubrication	When assembling Type CH O-rings with O-ring style fittings, the O-ring shall be coated with the fluid used or petrolatum before assembly to ease installation.	When assembling Type CA O-rings with O-ring style fittings, lubricate the O-ring with the fluid used in the system. Do not use a petroleum-based lubricant.	When assembling Type HK O-rings with O-ring style fittings, the O-ring shall be coated with fluid used or petrolatum before assembly to ease installation.

1. For special applications, consult manufacturer for alternate material compounds.

O–ring Size Specifications –

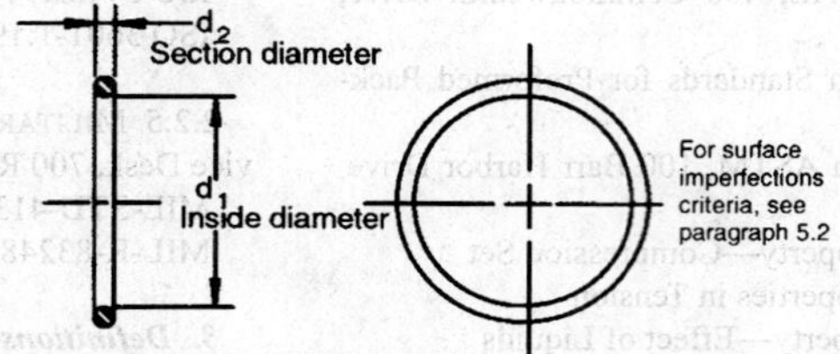

FIGURE 1—O-RING DETAIL FOR STANDARD O-RINGS

TABLE 3—O-RING SIZE SPECIFICATIONS FOR SAE J1926-2 AND SAE J1926-3 (ISO 11926-2 AND ISO 11926-3) INCH STUD ENDS DIMENSIONS ARE IN MILLIMETERS

Nominal Tube OD or Hose ID Inch Tubing DashSize[1]	Nominal Tube OD or Hose ID Inch Tubing mm	Nominal Tube OD or Hose ID Metric Tubing mm	Inch, SAE J1926-2 & SAE J1926-3 (ISO 11926-2 & ISO 11926-3) Thread in	Inch SAE J1926-2 & SAE J1926-3 (ISO 11926-2 & ISO 11926-3) O-ring DashSize[2]	ID d_1	ID d_1 tol, ±	Cross-Section d_2	Cross-Section, d_2 tol, ±	SAE J515O-ring SizeOrdering Code[3]
– 2	3.18	4	5/16–24	902	6.07	0.13	1.63	0.08	163x0060H
– 3	4.76	5	3/8-24	903	7.65	0.13	1.63	0.08	163x0076H
– 4	6.35	6	7/16–20	904	8.92	0.13	1.83	0.08	183x0089H
– 5	7.94	8	1/2–20	905	10.52	0.13	1.83	0.08	183x0105H
– 6	9.52	10	9/16–18	906	11.89	0.13	1.98	0.08	198x0118H
– 8	12.70	12	3/4–16	908	16.36	0.23	2.21	0.08	221x0163H
–10	15.88	16	7/8–14	910	19.18	0.23	2.46	0.08	246x0191H
–12	19.05	20	1–1/16–12	912	23.47	0.23	2.95	0.10	295x0234H
–14	22.22	22	1–3/16–12	914	26.62	0.25	2.95	0.10	295x0266H
–16	25.40	25	1–5/16–12	916	29.74	0.25	2.95	0.10	295x0297H
–20	31.75	30	1–5/8–12	920	37.47	0.36	3.00	0.10	300x0374H
–24	38.10	38	1–7/8–12	924	43.69	0.36	3.00	0.10	300x0436H
–32	50.80	50	2–1/2–12	932	59.36	0.46	3.00	0.10	300x0593H

1. The dash size symbol applicable to all tube ends and straight thread O-ring boss ends shall consist of the number of sixteenth inch increments contained in the outside diameter of the tubing (nominal OD or inside diameter of the hose nominal hose ID) for which they are assembled.
2. Dash size numbers are per SAE AS568A. Note the number includes the dash size.
3. Ordering size code gives basic size of O-ring without tolerance, the cross-section is given first (Y.YY) followed by the inside diameter (YYY.Y). See Section 6.

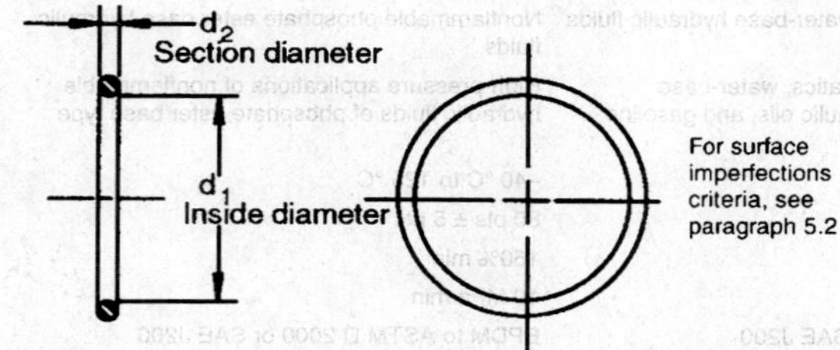

FIGURE 2—O-RING DETAIL FOR STANDARD O-RINGS

TABLE 4—O-RING SIZE SPECIFICATIONS FOR SAE J2244-2 AND SAE J2244-3 (ISO 6149-2 AND ISO 6149-3) METRIC STUD ENDS DIMENSIONS ARE IN MILLIMETERS

Nominal Tube OD or Hose ID Inch Tubing Dash Size[1]	Nominal Tube OD or Hose ID Inch Tubing mm	Nominal Tube OD or Hose ID Metric Tubing mm	Thread mm	ID d_1	ID d_1 tol, ±	Cross-Section d_2	Cross-Section, d_2 tol, ±	SAE J515 O-ring Size Ordering Code[2]
– 2	3.18	4	M8x1	6.1	0.20	1.6	0.08	160x0061H
– 3	4.76	5	M10x1	8.1	0.20	1.6	0.08	160x0081H
– 4	6.35	6	M12x1.5	9.3	0.20	2.2	0.08	220x0093H
– 5	7.94	8	M14x1.5	11.3	0.20	2.2	0.08	220x0113H
– 6	9.52	10	M16x1.5	13.3	0.20	2.2	0.08	220x0133H
– 8	12.70	12	M18x1.5	15.3	0.20	2.2	0.08	220x0153H
			M20x1.5	17.3	0.22	2.2	0.08	220x0173H
–10	15.88	16	M22x1.5	19.3	0.22	2.2	0.08	220x0193H
–12	19.05	20	M27x2	23.6	0.24	2.9	0.09	290x0236H
–14	22.22	22	M30x2	26.6	0.26	2.9	0.09	290x0266H
–16	25.40	25	M33x2	29.6	0.29	2.9	0.09	290x0296H
–20	31.75	30	M42x2	38.6	0.37	2.9	0.09	290x0386H
–24	38.10	38	M48x2	44.6	0.43	2.9	0.09	290x0446H
–32	50.80	50	M60x2	56.6	0.51	2.9	0.09	290x0566H

1. The dash size symbol applicable to all tube ends and straight thread O-ring boss ends shall consist of the number of sixteenth inch increments contained in the outside diameter of the tubing (nominal OD or inside diameter of the hose nominal hose ID) for which they are assembled.
2. Ordering size code gives basic size of O-ring without tolerance, the cross-section is given first (Y.YY) followed by the inside diameter (YYY.Y). See Section 6.

d2
Section diameter
d1
Inside diameter
For surface imperfections criteria, see paragraph 5.2

FIGURE 3—O-RING DETAIL FOR STANDARD O-RINGS

TABLE 5—O-RING SIZE SPECIFICATIONS FOR SAE J518 (ISO 6162)
FOUR SCREW FLANGE CONNECTIONS
DIMENSIONS ARE IN MILLIMETERS

SAE J518 Inch Nominal Tubing Dash Size[1]	SAE J518 Inch Nominal Tubing mm	DN ISO 6162.2 Flange Size	O-ring Dash Size[2]	ID d_1	ID d_1 tol, ±	Cross-Section d_2	Cross-Section, d_2 tol, ±	SAE J515 O-ring Size Ordering Code[3]
– 8	12.70	13	210	18.64	0.15	3.53	0.10	353x0186H
–12	19.05	19	214	24.99	0.15	3.53	0.10	353x0249H
–16	25.40	25	219	32.92	0.15	3.53	0.10	353x0329H
–20	31.75	32	222	37.69	0.15	3.53	0.10	353x0376H
–24	38.10	38	225	47.22	0.25	3.53	0.10	353x0472H
–32	50.80	51	228	56.74	0.25	3.53	0.10	353x0567H
–40	63.5	64	232	69.44	0.38	3.53	0.10	353x0694H
–48	76.2	76	237	85.32	0.38	3.53	0.10	353x0853H
–56	88.9	89	241	98.02	0.38	3.53	0.10	353x0980H
–64	101.6	102	245	110.72	0.38	3.53	0.10	353x1107H
–80	127	127	253	136.12	0.58	3.53	0.10	353x1361H

1. The dash size symbol shall consist of the number of sixteenth inch increments contained in the outside diameter of the tubing (nominal OD or inside diameter of the hose nominal hose ID) for which they are assembled.
2. Dash sizes are per SAE AS568A, but the ID tolerances are the same as SAE J120, which are much tighter tolerances than AS568A.
3. Ordering size code gives basic size of O-ring without tolerance, the cross-section is given first (Y.YY) followed by the inside diameter (YYY.Y). See Section 6.

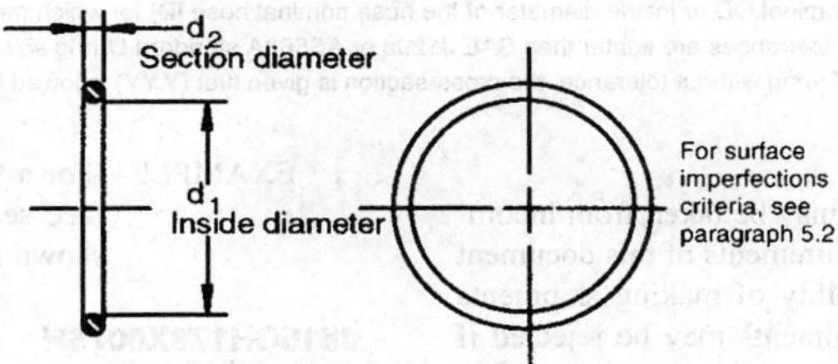

FIGURE 4—O-RING DETAIL FOR STANDARD O-RINGS

TABLE 6—O-RING SIZE SPECIFICATIONS FOR SAE J1453-2[1] (ISO 8434-3)
AND SAE J1453-3[1] FACE SEAL TUBE CONNECTIONS
DIMENSIONS ARE IN MILLIMETERS

Nominal Tube OD or Hose ID Inch Tubing Dash Size[2]	Nominal Tube OD or Hose ID Inch Tubing mm	Nominal Tube OD or Hose ID Metric Tubing mm	Thread in	O-ring Dash Size[3]	ID d_1	ID d_1 tol, ±	Cross-Section d_2	Cross-Section, d_2 tol, ±	SAE J515 O-ring Size Ordering Code[4]
– 2	3.18	4	—	—					
– 3	4.76	5	9/16–18	011	7.65	0.13	1.78	0.08	178x0076H
– 4	6.35	6	9/16–18	011	7.65	0.13	1.78	0.08	178x0076H
– 5	7.94	8	9/16–18	011	7.65	0.13	1.78	0.08	178x0076H
– 6	9.52	10	11/16–16	012	9.25	0.13	1.78	0.08	178x0092H
– 8	12.70	12	13/16–16	014	12.42	0.13	1.78	0.08	178x0124H
–10	15.88	16	1–14	016	15.60	0.13	1.78	0.08	178x0156H
–12	19.05	20	1-3/16–12	018	18.77	0.13	1.78	0.08	178x0187H
–14	22.22	22	1-3/16–12	018	18.77	0.13	1.78	0.08	178x0187H
–16	25.40	25	1-7/16–12	021	23.52	0.15	1.78	0.08	178x0235H
–20	31.75	30	1-11/16–12	025	29.87	0.15	1.78	0.08	178x0298H
–24	38.10	38	2–12	029	37.82	0.25	1.78	0.08	178x0378H
–32	50.80	50	—	—	—	—	—	—	—

1. To be published, see SAE J1453.
2. The dash size symbol applicable to all tube ends and straight thread O-ring boss ends shall consist of the number of sixteenth inch increments contained in the outside diameter of the tubing (nominal OD or inside diameter of the hose nominal hose ID) for which they are assembled.
3. Dash size numbers are per SAE AS568A.
4. Ordering size code gives basic size of O-ring without tolerance, the cross-section is given first (Y.YY) followed by the inside diameter (YYY.Y). See Section 6.

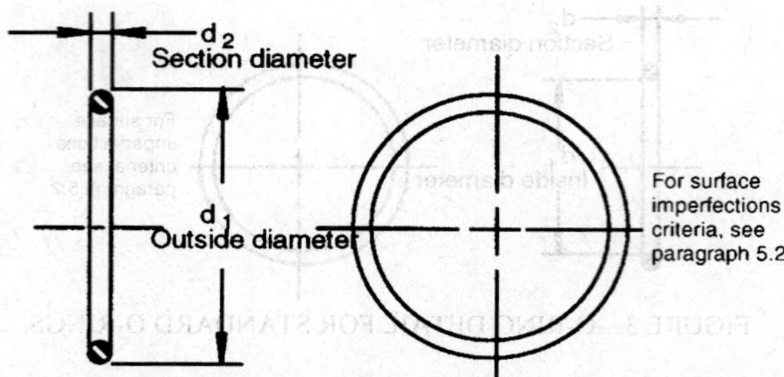

FIGURE 5—O-RINGS DETAIL FOR OD DIMENSIONED O-RINGS (SPECIAL)

TABLE 7—OPTIONAL OD TOLERANCED O-RING SIZE SPECIFICATIONS FOR SAE J1453-2(1) AND SAE J1453-3(1) FACE SEAL FITTINGS(2)
NOTE—DIMENSIONS DO NOT CONFORM TO SAE J120A OR AS568A
DIMENSIONS ARE IN MILLIMETERS

Nominal Tube OD or Hose ID Inch Tubing DashSize(3)	Nominal Tube OD or Hose ID Inch Tubing mm	Nominal Tube OD or Hose ID Metric Tubing mm	Thread in	Outside Diameter(4) ID d_1	ID d_1 tol, ±	Cross-Section d_2 ±0.08	SAE J515O-ring Size Ordering Code(5)
– 4	6.35	6	9/16–18	11.23	0.13	1.78	178x0112Y
– 5	7.94	8	9/16–18	11.23	0.13	1.78	178x0112Y
– 6	9.52	10	11/16–16	12.83	0.13	1.78	178x0128Y
– 8	12.70	12	13/16–16	16.03	0.13	1.78	178x0160Y
–10	15.88	16	1–14	19.28	0.13	1.78	178x0192Y
–12	19.05	20	1–3/16–12	22.50	0.13	1.78	178x0225Y
–14	22.22	22	1–3/16–12	22.50	0.13	1.78	178x0225Y
–16	25.40	25	1–7/16–12	27.22	0.15	1.78	178x0272Y
–20	31.75	30	1–11/16–12	33.57	0.15	1.78	178x0335Y
–24	38.10	38	2–12	41.54	0.25	1.78	178x0415Y

1. To be published, see SAE J1453.
2. Dimensions for special OD toleranced O-rings for use with SAE J1453 fittings to improve assembly performance associated with O-ring fallout.
3. The dash size symbol applicable to all tube ends and straight thread O-ring boss ends shall consist of the number of sixteenth inch increments contained in the outside diameter of the tubing (nominal OD or inside diameter of the hose nominal hose ID) for which they are assembled.
4. Dimensions do not conform to, and the tolerances are tighter than SAE J120a or AS568A standard O-ring sizes.
5. Ordering size code gives basic size of O-ring without tolerance, the cross-section is given first (Y.YY) followed by the inside diameter (YYY.Y). See Section 6.

5. *Test Requirements and Quality Assurance*

5.1 Inspection and Rejection—While samples may be taken from incoming shipments and checked for conformance to the requirements of this document by the buyer, the supplier shall accept the responsibility of making shipments which meet the appropriate specification limits. Shipments may be rejected if they do not meet specifications.

5.2 Quality Acceptance Criteria—Surface imperfections shall meet the requirements outlined in ISO 3601-3 for offset, combined flash, offset and parting line projection, backrind, trimming, flow marks, non-fills, and indentations.

5.3 Supplier Inspection Limits—Inspection limits that fall within the general specification limits for SAE J515 O-rings may be established for individual compounds approved under this document. Shipments may be rejected if they do not meet these supplier inspection limits.

5.4 Certification of Quality—Individual companies may establish certification requirements for O-rings manufactured from SAE J515 materials.

6. *Packing and Marking*

6.1 Part Identification Number (PIN) for O-Rings to this SAE Document—O-rings to this SAE document shall be identified by a part identification number consisting of the following:

a. The standard, J515
b. The ASTM/SAE material type (see 4.1 and Table 1)
c. The size designation code

EXAMPLE—For a 90 durometer nitrile O-ring for a –4 (6 mm) tube end face seal fitting, the ordering code information would be as shown in Figure 6.

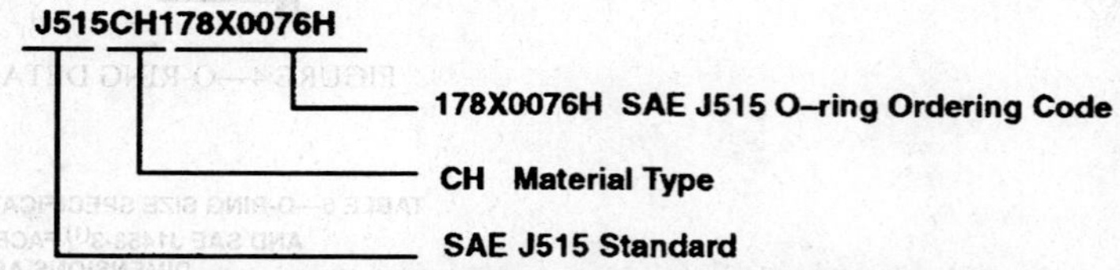

FIGURE 6—PART IDENTIFICATION NUMBER (PIN) EXAMPLE

7. *Notes*

7.1 Identification Statement—Use the following statement in test reports, catalogues and sales literature when electing to comply with this part of SAE J515:

O-rings conform to SAE J515, Specification for Hydraulic O-ring materials properties and sizes for inch and metric stud ends, face seal fittings, and four screw connections.

7.2 Key Words—Dimensions, designation, test methods, metric, O-ring seal, material specifications, face seal fittings, four-bolt flange fittings, metric stud ends, inch stud ends, requirements, nitrile, fluorocarbon, EPDM, elastomer.

APPENDIX A
HYDRAULIC O-RINGS LISTED BY SIZE

A.1 Hydraulic O-Rings Listed by Size—See Figures A1 and A2 and Tables A1 and A2.

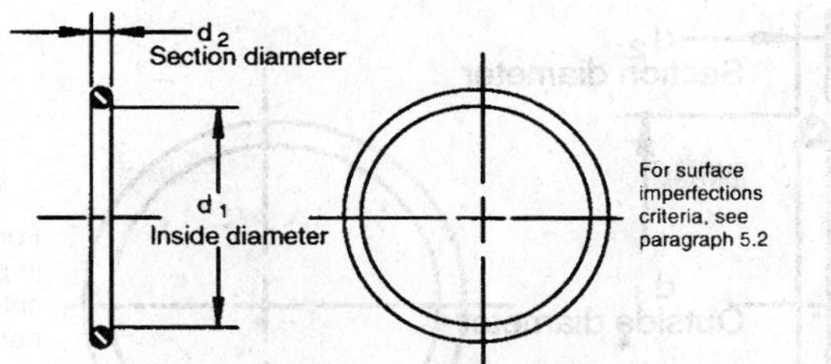

FIGURE A1—O-RING DETAIL FOR STANDARD O-RING

TABLE A1—DIMENSIONS OF O-RINGS FOR USE WITH SAE AND ISO HYDRAULIC FITTINGS AND STUD-ENDS BY SIZE CODE (H SERIES) DIMENSIONS ARE IN MILLIMETERS

SAE J515 O-Ring Size Ordering Code	ID d_1	tol, ±	Applicable Standard and Size of Thread or Tube OD	
Cross Section, d_2 1.6 ± 0.08				
160x0061H	6.1	0.20	SAE J2244-2, ISO 6149-2 and ISO 6149-3	M8X1
160x0081H	8.1	0.20	SAE J2244-2, ISO 6149-2 and ISO 6149-3	M10x1
Cross Section, d_2 1.63 ± 0.08				
163x0060H	6.07	0.13	SAE J1926-2 and SAE J1926-3	5/16–24
163x0076H	7.65	0.13	SAE J1926-2 and SAE J1926-3, ISO 11926-2 and ISO 11926-3	3/8–24
Cross Section, d_2 1.78 ± 0.08				
178x0076H	7.65	0.13	SAE J1453-2[1] and SAE J1453-3[1], ISO 8434-3	9/16–18
178x0092H	9.25	0.13	SAE J1453-2[1] and SAE J1453-3[1], ISO 8434–3	11/16–16
178x0124H	12.42	0.13	SAE J1453-2[1] and SAE J1453-3[1], ISO 8434-3	13/16–16
178x0156H	15.6	0.13	SAE J1453-2[1] and SAE J1453-3[1], ISO 8434-3	1–14
178x0187H	18.77	0.13	SAE J1453-2[1] and SAE J1453-3[1], ISO 8434-3	1–3/16–12
178x0235H	23.52	0.15	SAE J1453-2[1] and SAE J1453-3[1], ISO 8434-3	1–7/16–12
178x0298H	29.87	0.15	SAE J1453-2[1] and SAE J1453-/3[1], ISO 8434-3	1–11/16–12
178x0378H	37.82	0.25	SAE J1453-2[1] and SAE J1453-3[1], ISO 8434-3	2–12
Cross Section, d_2 1.83 ± 0.08				
183x0089H	8.92	0.13	SAE J1926-2 and SAE J1926-3, ISO 11926-2 and ISO 11926-3	7/16–20
183x0105H	10.52	0.13	SAE J1926-2 and SAE J1926-3, ISO 11926-2 and ISO 19926-3	1/2–20
Cross Section, d_2 1.98 ± 0.08				
198x0118H	11.89	0.13	SAE J1926-2 and SAE J1926-3, ISO 11926-2 and ISO 11926-3	9/16–18
Cross Section, d_2 2.2 ± 0.08				
220x0093H	9.3	0.20	SAE J2244-2, ISO 6149-2 and ISO 6149-3	M12x1.5
220x0113H	11.3	0.20	SAE J2244-2, ISO 6149-2 and ISO 6149-3	M14x1.5
220x0133H	13.3	0.20	SAE J2244-2, ISO 6149-2 and ISO 6149-3	M16x1.5
220x0153H	15.3	0.20	SAE J2244- 2, ISO 6149-2 and ISO 6149-3	M18x1.5
220x0173H	17.3	0.22	SAE J2244-2, ISO 6149-2 and ISO 6149-3	M20x1.5
220x0193H	19.3	0.22	SAE J2244-2, ISO 6149-2 and ISO 6149-3	M22x1.5
Cross Section, d_2 2.21 ± 0.08				
221x0163H	16.36	0.23	SAE J1926-2 and SAE J1926-3, ISO 11926-2 and ISO 11926-3	3/4–16
Cross Section, d_2 2.46 ± 0.08				
246x0191H	19.18	0.23	SAE J1926-2 and SAE J1926-3, ISO 11926-2 and ISO 11926-3	7/8–14
Cross Section, d_2 2.9 ± 0.08				
290x0236H	23.6	0.24	SAE J2244-2, ISO 6149-2 and ISO 6149-3	M27x2
290x0266H	26.6	0.26	SAE J2244-2, ISO 6149-2 and ISO 6149-3	M30x2
290x0296H	29.6	0.29	SAE J2244-2, ISO 6149-2 and ISO 6149-3	M33x2
290x0386H	38.6	0.37	SAE J2244-2, ISO 6149-2 and ISO 6149-3	M42x2
290x0446H	44.6	0.43	SAE J2244-2, ISO 6149-2 and ISO 6149-3	M48x2
290x0566H	56.6	0.51	SAE J2244-2, ISO 6149-2 and ISO 6149-3	M60x2
Cross Section, d_2 2.95 ± 0.08				
295x0234H	23.47	0.23	SAE J1926 -2 and SAE J1926-3, ISO 11926-2 and ISO 11926-3	1–1/16–12
295x0266H	26.62	0.25	SAE J1926- 2 and SAE J1926-3, ISO 11926-2 and ISO 11926-3	1–3/16–12
295x0297H	29.74	0.25	SAE J1926-2 and SAE J1926-3, ISO 11926-2 and ISO 11926-3	1–5/16–12
Cross Section, d_2 3 ± 0.08				
300x0374H	37.47	0.36	SAE J1926-2 and SAE J1926-3, ISO 11926-2 and ISO 11926-3	1–5/8–12
300x0436H	43.69	0.36	SAE J1926- 2 and SAE J1926-3, ISO 11926-2 and ISO 11926-3	1–7/8–12
300x0593H	59.36	0.46	SAE J1926-2 and SAE J1926-3, ISO 11926-2 and ISO 11926-3	2–1/2–12
Cross Section, d_2 3.53 ± 0.08				
353x0186H	18.64	0.15	SAE J518, ISO 6162	DN 13
353x0249H	24.99	0.15	SAE J518, ISO 6162	DN 19
353x0329H	32.92	0.15	SAE J518, ISO 6162	DN 25
353x0376H	37.69	0.15	SAE J518, ISO 6162	DN 32
353x0472H	47.22	0.25	SAE J518, ISO 6162	DN 38
353x0567H	56.74	0.25	SAE J518, ISO 6162	DN 51
353x0694H	69.44	0.38	SAE J518, ISO 6162	DN 64
353x0853H	85.32	0.38	SAE J518, ISO 6162	DN 76
353x0980H	98.02	0.38	SAE J518, ISO 6162	DN 89
353x1107H	110.72	0.38	SAE J518, ISO 6162	DN 102
353x1361H	136.12	0.58	SAE J518, ISO 6162	DN 127

1. To be published, see SAE J1453.

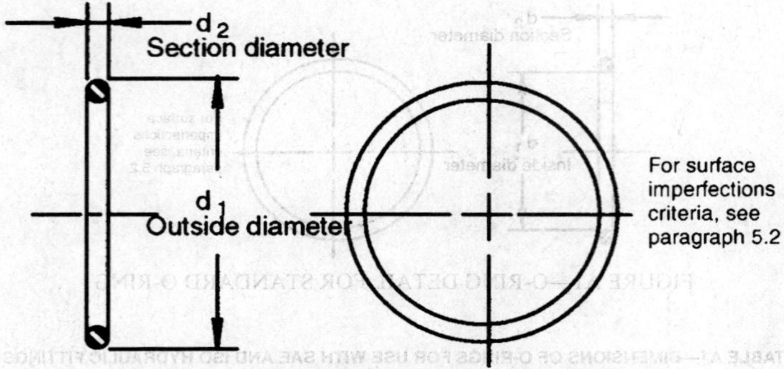

FIGURE A2—O-RING DETAIL FOR OD DIMENSIONED O-RINGS (SPECIAL)

TABLE A2—DIMENSIONS OF O-RING SIZES SPECIFIED BY OUTSIDE DIAMETER FOR OPTIONAL USE WITH FACE SEAL FITTINGS BY SIZE CODE (Y SERIES)

SAE J515 O-Ring Size Ordering Code	OD d_1	tol, ±	Applicable Standard(s) and Size of Thread or Tube OD	
Cross Section, d_2 1.78 ± 0.08				
178x0112Y	11.23	0.15	SAE J1453, ISO 8434-3	9/16–18
178x0128Y	12.83	0.15	SAE J1453, ISO 8434-3	11/16–16
178x0160Y	16.03	0.18	SAE J1453, ISO 8434-3	13/16–16
178x0192Y	19.28	0.20	SAE J1453, ISO 8434-3	1–14
178x0225Y	22.50	0.23	SAE J1453, ISO 8434-3	1-3/16–12
178x0272Y	27.22	0.25	SAE J1453, ISO 8434-3	1-7/16–12
178x0335Y	33.57	0.30	SAE J1453, ISO 8434-3	1-11/16–12
178x0415Y	41.54	0.34	SAE J1453, ISO 8434-3	2–12

FLARES FOR TUBING—SAE J533 DEC1999 SAE Standard

Report of the SAE Parts and Fittings Technical Committee approved February 1947. Revised by the SAE Tube, Pipe, Hose, and Lubrication Fittings Committee January 1972. Completely revised by the SAE Fluid Conductors and Connectors Technical Committee SC1—Automotive and Hydraulic Tube and Fitting June 1992 and August 1996. Rationale statement available. Revised by the SAE Fluid Conductors and Connectors Technical Committee S1—Automotive and Hydraulic Tube and Fittings, December 1999. Rationale statement available.

1. Scope—This SAE Standard covers specifications for 37-degree and 45-degree single and double flares for tube ends intended for use with 37-degree flared tube fittings and 45-degree flared or inverted flared tube fittings, respectively.

2. References

2.1 Applicable Publications—The following publications form a part of this specification to the extent specified herein. Unless otherwise indicated, the latest issue of SAE publications shall apply.

2.1.1 SAE PUBLICATIONS—Available from SAE, 400 Commonwealth Drive, Warrendale, PA 15096-0001.

SAE J514—Hydraulic Tube Fittings
SAE TSB 003—Rules for Use of SI (Metric) Units

3. General Specifications

3.1 Dimensions—Dimensions in this document are based on and, unless designated otherwise, are specified in metric units.

3.1.1 Single and double 45-degree flares shall conform to the dimensions specified in Figure 1 and Table 1.

3.1.2 Single and double 37-degree flares shall conform to the dimensions specified in Figure 2 and Table 2.

3.1.3 Optional configurations for single 37-degree flares are specified in Figure 3 and Table 2. These configurations provide extended length of seal contact surface and are recommended for tube wall thickness exceeding "E-Table 2."

3.1.4 The following general specifications supplement the dimensional data with respect to unspecified detail and apply to both 37-degree and 45-degree flares for tubing.

3.2 Deburring Prior to Flaring—To assure producing satisfactory flares, it may be necessary to perform deburring operations on the tube end prior to flaring. Smoothly breaking the inside corner before single flaring ferrous, and some nonferrous tubing is normally required to eliminate the cutoff burr which might otherwise create leakage paths across a substantial portion of the flare. Smoothly breaking the outside corner prior to single flaring, or both outside and inside corners prior to double flaring, shall be permissible on any tube material to minimize splitting.

3.2.1 Recommended OD chamfers for optional 37-degree single flares are specified in Figure 3 and Table 2.

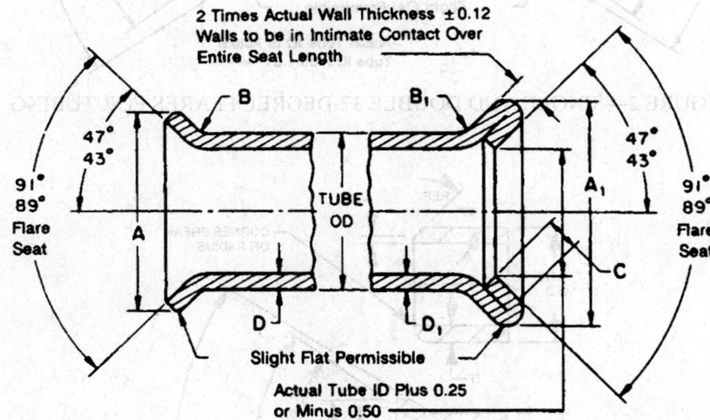

FIGURE 1—SINGLE AND DOUBLE 45-DEGREE FLARES FOR TUBING

TABLE 1—DIMENSIONS OF SINGLE AND DOUBLE 45-DEGREE FLARES FOR TUBING(1) (FIGURE 1)

Nominal Tube OD mm	Nominal Tube OD in	A Single Flare Diameter mm Max	A Single Flare Diameter mm Min	A_1 Double Flare Diameter mm Max	A_1 Double Flare Diameter mm Min	B Single Flare Radius mm ±0.25	B_1 Double Flare Radius mm ±0.25	C Double Flare Coined Seat Length mm Min	D(2) Single Flare Wall Thickness mm Max	D_1(2) Double Flare Wall Thickness mm Max
3.18	0.13	4.59	4.35	5.41	5.03	0.51	1.02	1.02	0.88	0.63
4.76	0.19	6.32	6.08	7.11	6.74	0.51	1.02	1.02	0.88	0.71
6.35	0.25	8.25	8.01	9.14	8.77	0.51	1.02	1.02	1.24	0.83
7.94	0.31	10.26	9.86	10.79	10.42	0.51	1.02	1.57	1.24	0.88
9.52	0.38	12.36	11.97	12.70	12.32	0.51	1.02	1.57	1.65	1.24
11.11	0.44	14.24	13.85	14.47	14.10	0.51	1.02	1.57	1.65	1.24
12.70	0.50	15.82	15.42	16.25	15.88	0.51	1.02	1.57	2.10	1.24
14.29	0.56	17.17	16.77	18.08	17.71	0.51	1.02	1.57	2.10	1.24
15.88	0.63	18.99	18.60	19.60	19.23	0.51	1.02	1.57	2.41	1.24
19.05	0.75	23.26	22.86	23.16	22.79	0.51	1.02	1.57	2.76	1.24
22.22	0.88	26.44	26.04	—	—	0.51	—	—	2.76	—
25.40	1.00	29.38	28.99	—	—	0.51	—	—	3.04	—

1. It is not the intent of this document to define the appropriateness of fittings to be used in conjunction with the flares specified. Considerations such as the effects of wall thickness on working pressures, length of thread engagements, etc., shall be the responsibility of the user. See SAE J514.
2. Recommended maximum nominal wall thickness of tubing normally considered suitable for flaring to the above specifications.

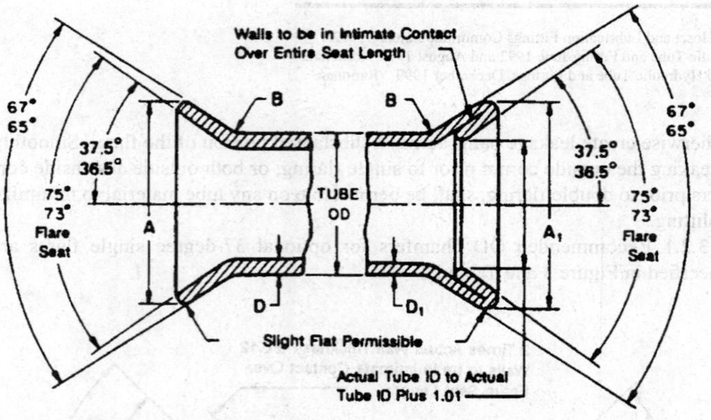

FIGURE 2—SINGLE AND DOUBLE 37-DEGREE FLARES FOR TUBING

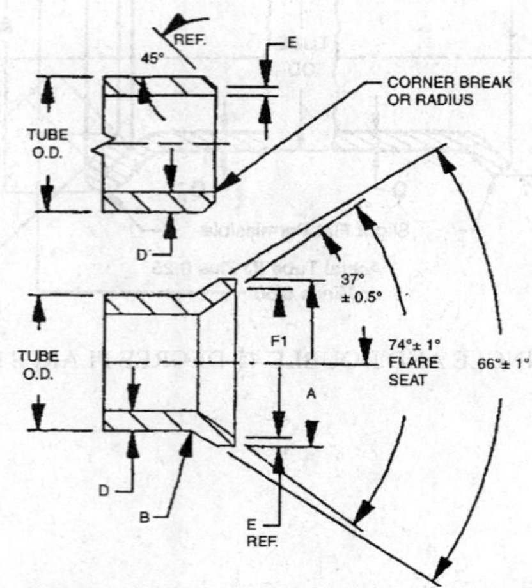

FIGURE 3—OPTIONAL TUBE PREPARATION AND

3.2.2 Inasmuch as the specified dimensions shall prevail, whether or not the corners are broken, the quality of the finished flare shall be the only criterion applied to the burring operation.

3.3 Concentricity—Flare seat shall be concentric with tube outside diameter within 0.38 mm full indicator reading (FIR). To promote uniformity in checking concentricity of flare seat to the tube outside diameter, it is recommended the gaging method depicted in Figure 4 and the following procedure, or equivalent means, be used.

3.3.1 Mount tube in precision collet, dividing head, or equivalent rotational centering and clamping device with the rear of flare not more than 3 mm ahead of the collet. A minimum straight length of tube behind the flare of 25.4 mm, or twice the tube outside diameter, whichever is greater, must be available for mounting purposes.

3.3.2 Place stylus of indicator gage on the coined portion of flare seat.

3.3.3 Rotate the mounted tube through full 360 degree revolution.

3.3.4 Read full indicator reading occurring over the 360 degrees of rotation.

3.4 Workmanship—Flares shall be free from loose scale, burrs, slivers, and cracks. Seating surfaces shall be smooth and free from nicks, pit marks, and any other defects that prevent sealing.

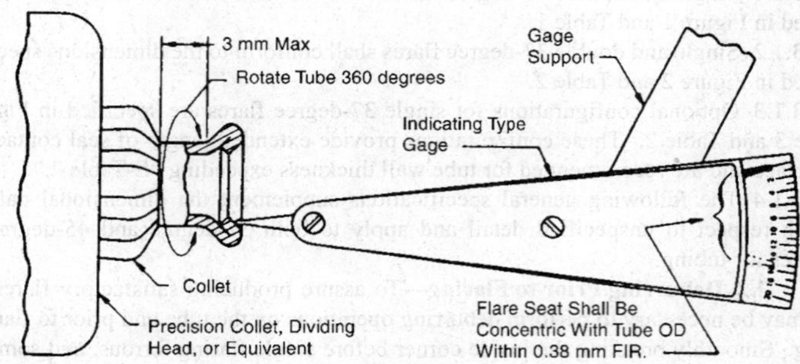

FIGURE 4—TYPICAL FLARE CONCENTRICITY GAGE

TABLE 2—DIMENSIONS OF SINGLE AND DOUBLE 37-DEGREE FLARES FOR TUBING[1] (FIGURES 2 and 3)

Nominal Tube OD mm	Nominal Tube OD in	A Single Flare Diameter mm Max	A Single Flare Diameter mm Min	A_1 Double Flare Diameter mm Max	A_1 Double Flare Diameter mm Min	B Radius mm ±0.5	D[2] Single Flare Wall Thickness mm Max	D_1[2] Double Flare Wall Thickness mm Max	E Optional Tube Chamfer Face Width mm	F_1 Dia mm ±0.25
3.18	0.13	5.08	4.58	5.08	4.58	0.80	0.88	0.63	0.5 ± 0.12	4.85
4.76	0.19	7.11	6.61	7.11	6.61	0.80	0.88	0.71	0.5 ± 0.12	6.20
6.35	0.25	9.14	8.64	9.14	8.64	0.80	1.65	0.88	0.75 ± 0.12	7.35
7.94	0.31	10.92	10.16	10.92	10.16	0.80	1.65	0.88	0.75 ± 0.12	8.90
9.52	0.38	12.44	11.69	12.44	11.69	1.00	1.65	1.24	0.75 ± 0.12	10.90
12.70	0.50	16.76	16.01	16.76	16.01	1.50	2.10	1.24	1.25 ± 0.25	14.35
15.88	0.63	20.06	19.31	20.06	19.31	1.50	2.41	1.24	1.25 ± 0.25	17.15
19.05	0.75	24.13	23.37	24.13	23.37	2.00	2.76	1.24	1.25 ± 0.25	21.45
22.22	0.88	27.17	26.42	27.17	26.42	2.00	2.76	1.65	1.25 ± 0.25	24.65
25.40	1.00	30.48	29.72	30.48	29.72	2.30	3.04	1.65	1.25 ± 0.25	27.80
28.58	1.13	35.05	34.29	35.05	34.29	2.30	3.04	1.65	1.25 ± 0.25	—
31.75	1.25	38.35	37.60	38.35	37.60	2.30	3.04	1.65	1.25 ± 0.25	35.70
38.10	1.50	43.94	43.18	43.94	43.18	2.80	3.04	1.65	1.25 ± 0.25	41.15
44.45	1.75	53.59	52.84	53.59	52.84	2.80	3.04	1.65	1.50 ± 0.25	—
50.80	2.00	59.94	59.19	59.94	59.19	2.80	3.40	1.65	1.50 ± 0.25	56.75

1. It is not the intent of this document to define the appropriateness of fittings to be used in conjunction with the flares specified. Considerations such as the effects of wall thickness on working pressures, length of thread engagements, etc., shall be the responsibility of the user. See SAE J514.
2. Recommended maximum nominal wall thickness of tubing normally considered suitable for flaring to the above specifications.

WELDED FLASH CONTROLLED, HIGH STRENGTH LOW ALLOY STEEL HYDRAULIC TUBING, SUB-CRITICALLY ANNEALED FOR BENDING, DOUBLE FLARING, AND BENDING—SAE J2613 OCT2002

SAE Standard

Report of the SAE Metallic Tubing Subcommittee of the SAE Fluid Conductors and Connectors Technical Committee approved October 2002.

1. Scope—This SAE Standard covers sub-critically annealed electric resistance welded flash controlled single-wall high strength low alloy steel tubing intended for use in hydraulic pressure lines and in other applications requiring tubing of a quality suitable for bending, double flaring, cold forming, welding and brazing. Material produced to this specification is not intended to be used for single flare applications due to the potential leak path that would be caused by the ID weld bead.

The grade of material produced to this specification is of micro-alloy content and is considerably stronger and intended to service higher pressure applications than like sizes of the grades of material specified in SAE J356 and SAE J2435. Due to the alloy content of the material, the forming characteristics of the finished tube are equal to or better, when compared to SAE J356 and SAE J2435. Nominal reference working pressures for this tubing are listed in SAE J1065.

2. References

2.1 Applicable Publications—The following publications form a part of this specification to extent specified herein. Unless other specified, the latest issue of the SAE publications shall apply.

2.1.1 SAE PUBLICATIONS—Available from SAE, 400 Commonwealth Drive, Warrendale, PA 15096-0001.

SAE J356—Welded Flash-Controlled Low-Carbon Steel Tubing Normalized for Bending, Double Flaring, and Beading

SAE J409—Product Analysis—Permissible Variations from Specified Chemical Analysis of a Heat or Cast of Steel

SAE J533—Flares for Tubing

SAE J1065—Pressure Rating for Hydraulic Tubing and Fittings

SAE J1677—Tests and Procedures for SAE Low-Carbon Steel and Copper Nickel Tubing

SAE J2435—Welded Flash Controlled, SAE 1021 Carbon Steel Tubing, Normalized for Bending, Flaring, and Beading

2.2 Related Publications—The following publications are provided for informational purposes only and are not a required part of this document.

2.2.1 SAE PUBLICATIONS—Available from SAE, 400 Commonwealth Drive, Warrendale, PA 15096-0001.

SAE J514—Hydraulic Tube Fittings

SAE J518—Hydraulic Flanged Tube, Pipe and Hose Connections; 4-Bolt Type

SAE J1453—Fitting - O-Ring Face Seal

SAE J2551—Recommended Practices for Fluid Conductor Metallic Tubing Applications

2.2.2 ISO PUBLICATIONS—Available from ANSI, 25 West 43rd Street, New York, NY 10036-8002.

ISO 3304—Plain end seamless precision steel tubes - Technical conditions for delivery

ISO 3305—Plain end welded precision steel tubes - Technical conditions for delivery

ISO 4200—Plain end steel tubes, welded and seamless - General tables of dimensions and masses per unit length

ISO 4397—Connectors and associated components - Nominal outside diameters of tubes and nominal inside diameters of hoses

ISO 4399—Connectors and associated components - Nominal pressures

ISO 5598—Fluid power systems and components - Vocabulary

ISO 6162—Four-screw split-flange connections

ISO 6163—Round flange, 8 and 12 screw connections

ISO 6164—Four-screw, one-piece square-flange connections

ISO 6605—Tests and test procedures

ISO 8434—Metallic tube connections for fluid power and general use

ISO 10583—Test methods for tube connections

ISO 10763—Plain-end, seamless and welded steel tubes - Dimensions and nominal working pressures

2.2.3 DIN PUBLICATIONS—Available from ANSI, 25 West 43rd Street, New York, NY 10036-8002.

DIN 17120—Welded Circular Steel Tubing

DIN 17121—Seamless Circular Steel Tubing

3. Manufacture—The tubing shall be made from a single strip of steel shaped into a tubular shape, the edges of which are joined and fused by electric resistance welding. After forming and welding, the outside flash shall be removed to provide a smooth surface. The inside flash shall be of uniform contour, free from saw-tooth peaks and controlled in height by seam-welding techniques or by cutting, not by hammering or rolling. The inside flash height shall conform to the following as in Table 1.

The tubing shall be sub-critically annealed via a controlled method to produce a finished product, which will meet all requirements of this document.

Sub-critically anneal - An annealing treatment in which steel is heated to below the A1 temperature, then slowly cooled to room temperature. A1 temperature is the critical transformation temperature depending on steel classification.

TABLE 1—INSIDE FLASH HEIGHT

Nominal Wall Thickness mm	Maximum Flash Height(1)(2) Through 25.4 mm OD mm	Maximum Flash Height Over 25.4 mm OD mm
Less than 0.90	0.13	0.25
0.90 through 1.65	0.20	0.25
Greater than 1.65	0.25	0.25

1. For tubes having an ID greater than 8 mm, the height of the inside weld flash shall be measure with a ball micrometer having a 3.96 mm ± 0.41 mm radius from the anvil or ballpoint. For tubes having an ID 8 mm or less, screw thread micrometers shall be used. The height of the flash shall be the difference between the thickness of the tube wall at the point of maximum height of the flash and the average of the wall thickness measured at points adjacent to both sides of the flash.
2. Tubing with an ID that is smaller than the producer's capability to scarf the ID weld bead, shall be produced as "flash in" tubing. Seam welding techniques may be applied to control the ID flash height. The maximum ID flash height, however, will be determined by agreement between the producer and the purchaser.

4. Dimensions and Tolerances—The tolerances applicable to tubing outside diameter are shown in Table 2. The tolerances applicable to tubing wall thickness are shown in Table 3. Particular attention shall be given to areas adjacent to the weld to insure against thin spots and/or sharp indentations.

TABLE 2—TUBING OUTSIDE DIAMETER TOLERANCE

Nominal Tubing OD(1)(2) mm	Tube OD and ID Tolerance ±mm
Up to 9.50	0.06
Over 9.50 to 15.88	0.08
Over 15.88 to 28.57	0.09
Over 28.57 to 50.80	0.13
Over 50.80 to 63.50	0.15
Over 63.50 to 76.20	0.20
Over 76.20 to 88.90	0.23
Over 88.90 to 101.60	0.25

1. OD measurements shall be taken at least 50 mm from the end of tubing.
2. For nominal tubing OD's to be used in conjunction with this tubing, refer to the various fluid carrier connector standards and SAE J533 for recommended maximum nominal wall thickness for double flaring.

TABLE 3—TUBING WALL THICKNESS TOLERANCES

Nominal Wall Thickness[(1)] mm	Nominal Tubing Outside Diameter Through 22 mm ±mm[(2)]	Nominal Tubing Outside Diameter Over 22 mm Through 48 mm ±mm[(2)]	Nominal Tubing Outside Diameter Over 48 mm Through 101.60 ±mm[(2)]
0.71	0.05/0.08	0.05/0.08	0.05/0.08
0.89	0.05/0.10	0.05/0.10	0.05/0.10
1.00	0.05/0.10	0.05/0.10	0.05/0.10
1.24	0.10/0.13	0.08/0.13	0.10/0.20
1.25	0.10/0.13	0.08/0.13	0.10/0.20
1.50	0.15/0.15	0.10/0.20	0.10/0.20
1.65	0.15/0.15	0.10/0.20	0.10/0.20
2.00	0.15/0/25	0.15/0.25	0.15/0.25
2.11	0.15/0/25	0.15/0.25	0.15/0.25
2.41	0.15/0/25	0.15/0.25	0.15/0.25
2.50	0.15/0/25	0.15/0.25	0.15/0.25
2.77	0.15/0/25	0.15/0.25	0.15/0.25
3.00	0.15/0/25	0.15/0.25	0.15/0.25
3.05	0.15/0/25	0.15/0.25	0.15/0.25
3.40	0.15/0/25	0.15/0.25	0.15/0.25
3.75	---	0.18/0.28	0.18/0.28
3.76	---	0.18/0.28	0.18/0.28
3.96	---	0.18/0.28	0.18/0.28
4.00	---	0.18/0.28	0.18/0.28
4.19	---	0.18/0.28	0.18/0.28
4.57	---	0.18/0.28	0.18/0.28
4.76	---	0.18/0.28	0.18/0.28
5.00	---	0.20/0.30	0.20/0.30
5.16	---	0.20/0.30	0.20/0.30
5.59	---	0.20/0.30	0.20/0.30
6.00	---	0.36/0.46	0.36/0.46
6.05	---	0.36/0.46	0.36/0.46
6.35	---	0.36/0.46	0.36/0.46
6.58	---	0.36/0.51	0.36/0.51

1. For intermediate wall thickness, the tolerance for the next heavier wall thickness shall apply.
2. Plus tolerances include allowance for crown on flat-rolled steel.

5. Manufacturing Standards

5.1 Straightness—Tubing shall be straightened to a tolerance of 0.8 mm in 1000 mm. Straightness tolerances shall be measured by placing a 915 mm straight edge against the tube while lying on it's neutral axis. The point of maximum deflection of the tube from the straight edge should not be more than allowed by the specification when measured with a feeler gauge.

5.2 Tubing End Condition—The tubing will be produced using normal mill cut off practices. This shall include, but not limited to, punch-cut ends, double-cut ends and rotary-cut ends. Care shall be taken to minimize the distortion of the tube ends. Distortion of the tube must not affect the normal re-cutting processes that will be performed by the end user. Ends that require further processing will be addressed by agreement between the producer and the tube purchaser.

5.3 Finish—The outside surface finish of the tube is critical to prevent possible leak paths on double flare connections, mechanical formed connections or applications where the outside surface of the tube becomes the sealing surface of the finished connection. The outside surface finish of the tube shall be free of excessive roll marks, score marks, chatter marks or other surface imperfections that may be considered detrimental to the function of the finished tube.

5.4 Thermal Treatment—The tubing is to be sub-critically annealed by heating to a temperature below the transformation point and then slowly cooled to room temperature. Special attention to the mechanical properties, especially the Rockwell B85 Hardness Target, should be made to produce tubing suitable for bending and forming for hydraulic pressure applications. However, to obtain acceptable hardness characteristics, the yield strength and the tensile strength shall not be compromised and 30% minimum elongation shall be maintained.

6. Material—The tubing shall be made from alloy steel strip conforming to the chemical composition in Table 4. The steel shall be made by the open-hearth basic oxygen or electric furnace process. A ladle analysis of each heat shall be made to determine the percentages of the elements specified. The chemical composition thus determined shall be reported to the purchaser or purchaser's representative, if requested, and shall be conform to the requirements specified. If a check analysis is required, the tolerances shall be as specified in SAE J409, Table 3.

TABLE 4—CHEMICAL REQUIREMENTS

Element	Cast or Heat Analysis, Weight %
Carbon	0.18 Max
Manganese	1.50 Max
Sulfur	0.035 Max
Phosphorus	0.035 Max
Silicon	0.35 Max
Aluminum	0.020 Min
Micro Alloying Elements	0.15 Max

7. Mechanical Properties—The finished tubing shall have mechanical properties as shown in Table 5.

TABLE 5—MECHANICAL PROPERTIES

Properties	Values
Yield Strength, Minimum	345 MPa
Tensile Strength, Minimum	500 MPa
Elongation in 50 mm, Minimum	30% Minimum
Hardness, Target	Rockwell B85[(1)]
Hardness, Maximum	Rockwell B90[1]

1. The hardness test shall not be required on tubing with a nominal wall thickness of less than 1.65 mm. Such tubing shall meet all other mechanical properties and performance requirements.

8. Performance Requirements—The finished tubing shall satisfactorily meet the following performance tests. All tests are to be conducted in accordance with the procedures in SAE J1677.

8.1 Flattening Test—See SAE J1677.

8.2 Flaring Test—See SAE J1677.

8.3 Reverse Flattening Test—See SAE J1677.

8.4 Expansion Test—See SAE J1677.

8.5 Hardness Test—See SAE J1677.

8.6 Tensile Test—See SAE J1677.

8.7 Elongation Test—See SAE J1677.

8.8 Pressure Proof Test—See SAE J1677.

8.9 Nondestructive Electronic—See SAE J1677. The tests referenced in SAE J1677, paragraph 5.9, are to be conducted after all cold-working tube manufacturing operations are performed on the tubing.

9. Test Certificates—A certificate of compliance to the performance requirements shall be furnished to the purchaser by the producer if requested in the purchase agreement. The tube producer shall be able to certify that each heat lot of the material used to produce the tubing complies with the performance requirements.

10. Cleanliness—The inside and outside surfaces of the finished tubing shall be commercially bright, clean and free from grease, oxide scale, carbon deposits, and any other contamination that can not readily be removed by cleaning agents normally used in manufacturing plants.

11. Corrosion Protection—The inside and outside surfaces of the finished tubing shall be protected against corrosion during shipment and normal storage. If a corrosion preventive compound is applied, it shall be such that after normal periods, it can be readily removed by cleaning agents normally used in manufacturing plants.

12. Packaging—The tubing is to be packaged in such a way to allow it to be transported and stored, with normal care, without being damaged. Any special packaging shall be by agreement between the producer and the purchaser.

(R) SEAMLESS LOW-CARBON STEEL TUBING ANNEALED FOR BENDING AND FLARING—SAE J524 FEB1996 SAE Standard

Report of the SAE Tube, Pipe, Hose, and Lubrication Fittings Committee approved January 1954. Reaffirmed by the SAE Fluid Conductors and Connectors Technical Committee May 1986. Completely revised by the SAE Fluid Conductors and Connectors Technical Committee SC1—Automotive and Hydraulic Tube and Fittings, June 1991 and February 1996.

1. Scope—This SAE Standard covers cold drawn and annealed seamless low-carbon steel pressure tubing intended for use as hydraulic lines and in other applications requiring tubing of a quality suitable for flaring and bending.

2. References

2.1 Applicable Publications—The following publications form a part of this specification to the extent specified herein. Unless otherwise specified, the latest issue of SAE publications shall apply.

2.1.1 SAE PUBLICATIONS—Available from SAE, 400 Commonwealth Drive, Warrendale, PA 15096-0001.

SAE J409—Product Analysis—Permissible Variations from Specified Chemical Analysis of a Heat or Cast of Steel

SAE J514—Hydraulic Tube Fittings

SAE J1677—Tests and Procedures for SAE Low-Carbon Steel and Copper Nickel Tubing

2.2 Related Publication—The following publication is provided for information purposes only and is not a required part of this document.

2.2.1 SAE PUBLICATION—Available from SAE, 400 Commonwealth Drive, Warrendale, PA 15096-0001.

SAE J533—Flares for Tubing

3. Manufacture—The tubing shall be cold drawn to size and after forming shall be annealed in such a manner as to produce a finished product which will meet all requirements of this document.

4. Dimensions and Tolerances—The tolerances applicable to tubing outside diameter are shown in Table 1. The wall thickness shall not vary more than ±10% for tubing having 12.7 mm or larger, nominal inside diameter nor more than ±15% for tubing having a smaller nominal inside diameter. Tubing outside diameter and wall thickness shall be as specified by purchaser.

TABLE 1—TUBING OUTSIDE DIAMETER TOLERANCES

Nominal Tubing OD(1)(2) mm	OD Tolerance ± mm
Up to 25.4	0.10
Over 25.4 to 38.1 inclusive	0.15
Over 38.1 to 50.8 inclusive	0.20
Over 50.8 to 88.9 inclusive	0.25

1. The actual outside diameter shall be the average of the maximum and minimum outside diameters as determined at any one cross section through the tubing.
2. Refer to SAE J514 for nominal tubing outside diameters to be used in conjunction with standard hydraulic tube fittings.

5. Quality—Lengths of finished tubing shall be reasonably straight and have smooth ends free from burrs. Tubing shall be free from scale and injurious defects and have a workmanlike finish. Surface imperfections such as handling marks, die marks, or shallow pits shall not be considered injurious defects provided the imperfections are within the tolerances specified for diameter and wall thickness. The removal of such surface imperfections is not required.

6. Material—Tubing shall be made from low-carbon steel conforming to the following chemical composition as shown in Table 2.

TABLE 2—CHEMICAL REQUIREMENTS

Element	Cast or Heat Analysis(1) % by Weight
Carbon	0.18 max
Manganese	0.30 to 0.60
Phosphorus	0.040 max
Sulfur	0.050 max

1. Check analysis tolerance shall be as specified in SAE J409, Table 1.

7. Mechanical Properties—The finished tubing shall have mechanical properties as tabulated in Table 3:

TABLE 3—MECHANICAL PROPERTIES

Properties	Values
Yield Strength, min	170 MPa
Ultimate Strength, min	310 MPa
Elongation in 50 mm, min	35%(1)
Hardness (Rockwell B), max	65(2)

1. For tubing having nominal outside diameter of 9.5 mm or less, and/or wall thicknesses of 0.9 mm or less, a minimum elongation of 25% is permissible.
2. The hardness test shall not be required on tubing with a nominal wall thickness of less than 1.65 mm. Such tubing shall meet all other mechanical properties and performance requirements.

8. Performance Requirements—The finished tubing shall satisfactorily meet the following performance tests. All tests are to be conducted in accordance with the procedures in SAE J1677. (The section listed in the parentheses is for the SAE J1677 document.)

8.1 Flattening Test (5.1)

8.2 Flaring Test—As Required(Double Flare 5.5.1) (Single Flare 5.5.3)

8.3 Expansion Test (5.4)

8.4 Pressure Proof Test (5.8)—Where allowable unit stress of material(s) = 140 MPa.

8.5 Nondestructive Electronic Test (5.9)

9. Test Certificates—A certificate of compliance to the performance requirements shall be furnished to the purchaser by the producer if requested in the purchase agreement.

10. Cleanliness—The inside of tubing shall be clean and free from any contamination that cannot be readily removed by cleaning agents normally used in manufacturing.

11. Corrosion Protection—The inside and outside of the finished tubing shall be protected against corrosion during shipment and normal storage. If a corrosion preventive compound is applied, it shall be such that after normal storage periods it can readily be removed by cleaning agents normally used in manufacturing.

Extended corrosion resistance coatings, such as tern coating, galvanizing, epoxy paint, etc., are available and can be supplied at the request of the user.

(R) WELDED AND COLD DRAWN LOW-CARBON STEEL TUBING ANNEALED FOR BENDING AND FLARING—SAE J525 MAY1999 SAE Standard

Report of the SAE Pipe, Hose, and Lubrication Fittings Committee approved April 1958. Reaffirmed by the SAE Fluid Conductors and Connectors Technical Committee May 1986. Completely revised by the SAE Fluid Conductors and Connectors Technical Committee SC1—Automotive and Hydraulic Tube and Fittings, June 1991 and February 1996. Completely revised by the SAE Fluid Conductors and Connectors Technical Committee SC5—Metallic Tubing, May 1999. Rationale statement available.

1. Scope—This SAE Standard covers normalized electric-resistance welded, cold-drawn, single-wall, low-carbon steel pressure tubing intended for use as pressure lines and in other applications requiring tubing of a quality suitable for bending, flaring, forming, and brazing.

2. References

2.1 Applicable Publications—The following publications form a part of this specification to the extent specified herein. Unless otherwise specified, the latest issue of SAE publications shall apply.

2.1.1 SAE PUBLICATIONS—Available from SAE, 400 Commonwealth Drive, Warrendale, PA 15096-0001.

SAE J409—Product Analysis—Permissible Variations from Specified Chemical Analysis of a Heat or Cast of Steel
SAE J514—Hydraulic Tube Fittings
SAE J533—Flares for Tubing
SAE J1677—Tests and Procedures for SAE Low-Carbon Steel and Copper Nickel Tubing

2.2 Related Publication—The following publication is provided for information purposes only and is not a required part of this document.

2.2.1 SAE PUBLICATION—Available from SAE, 400 Commonwealth Drive, Warrendale, PA 15096-0001.

SAE J1065—Pressure Rating for Hydraulic Tubing and Fittings
SAE J1453—Fitting—O-Ring Face Seal

3. Manufacture—The tubing shall be made from flat-rolled steel shaped into a tubular form, the edges of which are joined and fused together by electric-resistance welding. After forming and welding, the tubing shall be normalized and subjected to a cold-drawing operation that shall result in a 15% minimum reduction in cross-sectional area, of which 8% shall consist in a reduction in wall thickness. Subsequent to cold working, the tubing shall be normalized via an atmospherically controlled method to produce a finished product that will meet all requirements of this document.

4. Dimensions and Tolerances—The tolerances applicable to the tubing outside diameter and inside diameter are shown in Table 1. The tolerances applicable to tubing wall thickness are shown in Table 2. Dimensional tolerances can only apply to two of the three tubing dimensions (OD, ID, or wall). Unless otherwise agreed upon between the purchaser and tube producer, dimensional tolerances shall apply to the tube OD and wall dimension.

TABLE 1—TUBING OUTSIDE DIAMETER TOLERANCE

Nominal Tubing OD(1)(2) mm	Tube Tolerance OD ±mm	Tube Tolerance ID ±mm
Up to 9.50	0.05	0.05
Over 9.50 to 15.88 inclusive	0.06	0.06
Over 15.88 to 50.80 inclusive	0.08	0.08
Over 50.80 to 63.50 inclusive	0.10	0.10
Over 63.50 to 76.20 inclusive	0.13	0.13
Over 76.20 to 100.00 inclusive	0.15	0.15

1. OD measurements shall be taken at least 50 mm from the end of the tubing.
2. Refer to SAE J514 for nominal tubing OD to be used in conjunction with standard hydraulic tube fittings and SAE J533 for recommended maximum nominal wall thickness for double flaring.

5. Manufacturing Standards

5.1 Straightness—Tubing shall be straightened to a tolerance of 0.8 mm in 1000 mm. Straightness tolerances shall be measured by placing a 1000 mm straight edge against the tube while lying on its neutral axis. The point of maximum deflection of the tube from the straight edge should not be more than allowed by the specification when measured with a feeler gauge.

TABLE 2—TUBING WALL THICKNESS TOLERANCES

Nominal Wall Thickness(1)	Nominal Tubing Outside Diameter Through 22 mm +/– mm	Nominal Tubing Outside Diameter Over 22mm Through 48 mm +/– mm	Nominal Tubing Outside Diameter Over 48 mm Through 100 mm +/– mm
0.89	0.05/0.05	0.05/0.05	0.05/0.05
1.00	0.05/0.05	0.05/0.08	0.05/0.08
1.25	0.05/0.05	0.05/0.08	0/05/0.08
1.50	0.05/0.05	0.05/0/08	0.05/0.08
1.65	0.05/0.05	0.05/0/08	0.05/0.08
2.00	0.05/0.05	0.05/0.08	0.08/0.08
2.11	0.05/0.05	0.05/0.08	0.08/0.08
2.41	0.05/0.05	0.05/0.08	0.08/0.08
2.50	0.05/0.08	0.05/0.10	0.08/0.08
2.77	0.05/0.08	0.05/0.10	0.08/0.08
3.00	0.08/0.08	0.05/0.10	0.08/0.08
3.05	0.08/0.08	0.05/0.10	0.08/0.08
3.40	—	0.05/0.10	0.08/0.08
3.75	—	0.05/0.10	0.08/0.08
4.00	—	0.08/0.10	0.08/0.10
4.19	—	0.08/0.10	0.08/0.10
4.57	—	0.10/0.10	0.08/0.13
5.00	—	0.10/0.13	0.10/0.13
5.16	—	0.10/0.13	0.10/0.13
5.59	—	0.10/0.15	0.10/0.15
6.00	—	0.13/0.15	0.13/0.15
6.05	—	0.13/0.15	0.13/0.15
6.58	—	0.13/0.15	0.13/0.15

1. For intermediate wall thickness, the tolerance for the next heavier wall thickness shall apply.

5.2 Tubing End Condition—The tubing will be produced using normal mill cut-off practices. This will include, but is not limited to double-cut ends, saw-cut, and rotary-cut ends. Care will be taken to minimize the distortion of the tube ends. Distortion of the tube ends must not affect the normal re-cutting processes that will be performed by the end user. Ends that require further processing will be by agreement between the producer and tube purchaser.

5.3 Surface Finish—The outside and inside surface finish of the tube are critical in order to prevent possible leak paths on flared fittings, mechanical form fittings, or other applications where the surface of the tube becomes the sealing surface. The surface of the tube shall be free of excessive roll marks, score marks, chatter marks, or other surface imperfections that would be considered detrimental to the function of the tubing.

5.4 Thermal Treatment—The tubing is to be heated to a temperature above the upper transformation point via an atmospherically controlled method, and then cooled in a protective atmosphere.

6. Material—Tubing shall be made from low-carbon flat-rolled steel conforming to the chemical composition in Table 3. The steel shall be made by the open-hearth, basic oxygen, or electric furnace process. A ladle analysis of each heat shall be made to determine the percentages of the elements specified. The chemical composition thus determined shall be reported to the purchaser or his representative, if requested, and shall conform to the requirements specified. If a check analysis is required, the tolerances shall be as specified in SAE J409, Table 3.

TABLE 3—CHEMICAL REQUIREMENTS

Element	Cast or Heat Analysis, Weight %
Carbon	0.06 min/0.18 max
Manganese	0.30 through 0.60
Phosphorus	0.04 max
Sulfur	0.05 max

7. Mechanical Properties—The finished tubing shall have mechanical properties as tabulated in Table 4:

TABLE 4—MECHANICAL PROPERTIES

Properties	Values
Yield Strength, min	170 MPa
Ultimate Strength, min	310 MPa
Elongation in 50 mm, min	35%[(1)]
Hardness (Rockwell B), max	65[(2)]

1. For tubing having nominal outside diameter of 9.5 mm or less, and/or wall thickness of 0.9 mm or less, a minimum elongation of 25% is permissible.
2. The hardness test shall not be required on tubing with a nominal wall thickness of less than 1.65 mm. Such tubing shall meet all other mechanical properties and performance requirements.

8. Performance Requirements—The finished tubing shall satisfactorily meet the following performance tests. All tests are to be conducted in accordance with the procedures in SAE J1677.

8.1 Flattening Test—SAE J1677, paragraph 5.1.

8.2 Flaring Test—SAE J1677, paragraph 5.5.1.

8.3 Reverse Flattening Test—SAE J1677, paragraph 5.2.

8.4 Expansion Test—SAE J1677, paragraph 5.4.

8.5 Hardness Test—SAE J1677, paragraph 5.6.

8.6 Tensile Test—SAE J1677, paragraph 5.7.

8.7 Pressure Proof Test—SAE J1677, paragraph 5.8, performed when agreed upon between the purchaser and the producer (where allowable unit stress of material(s) = 140 MPa (80% of minimum yield strength).)

8.8 Nondestructive Electronic Test—SAEJ1677, paragraph 5.9. The tests that are referenced in 5.9 of SAE J1677 are to be conducted after all cold-working operations are performed on the tubing.

9. Test Certificates—A certificate of compliance to the performance requirements shall be furnished to the purchaser by the producer, if requested in the purchase agreement. The tube producer must be able to certify that each heat lot used to produce the tubing complies with the performance requirement.

10. Cleanliness—The inside and outside surfaces of the finished tubing shall be commercially bright, clean, and free from grease, oxide scale, carbon deposits, and any other contamination that cannot be readily removed by cleaning agents normally used in manufacturing plants.

11. Corrosion Protection—The inside and outside of the finished tubing shall be protected against corrosion during shipment and normal storage. If a corrosion preventive compound is applied, it shall be such that after normal storage periods, it can readily be removed by cleaning agents normally used in manufacturing.

12. Packaging—The tubing is to be packaged in such a way to allow it to be transported and stored, with normal care, without being damaged. Any special packaging will be by agreement between the producer and purchaser.

WELDED LOW-CARBON STEEL TUBING—SAE J526 JAN2000 SAE Standard

Report of the SAE Tube, Pipe, Hose, and Lubrication Fittings Committee approved January 1952. Reaffirmed by the SAE Fluid Conductors and Connectors Technical Committee May 1986, and completely revised June 1990. Revised by the SAE Fluid Conductors and Connectors Technical Committee SC1—Automotive and Hydraulic Tube and Fittings, June 1991 and June 1995, and completely revised February 1996. Rationale statement available. Revised by the SAE Fluid Conductors and Connectors Technical Committee SC5—Metallic Tubing January 2000. Rationale statement available.1

1. Scope—SAE J526 Standard covers welded single-wall low-carbon steel tubing intended for general automotive, refrigeration, hydraulic, and other similar applications requiring tubing of a quality suitable for bending, flaring, beading, forming, and brazing.

2. References

2.1 Applicable Publication—The following publication forms a part of this specification to the extent specified herein. Unless otherwise indicated, the latest issue of SAE publications shall apply.

2.1.1 SAE PUBLICATION—Available from SAE, 400 Commonwealth Drive, Warrendale, PA 15096-0001.

SAE J1677—Tests and Procedures for SAE Low-Carbon Steel and Copper Nickel Tubing

2.2 Related Publication—The following publication is provided for information purposes only and is not a required part of this document.

2.2.1 SAE PUBLICATION—Available from SAE, 400 Commonwealth Drive, Warrendale, PA 15096-0001.

SAE J409—Product Analysis-Permissible Variations from Specified Chemical Analysis of a Heat or Cast of Steel
SAE J514—Hydraulic Tube Fittings
SAE J516—Hydraulic Hose Fittings
SAE J533—Flares for Tubing
SAE J1065—Pressure Ratings for Hydraulic Tubing and Fittings
SAE J1290—Automotive Hydraulic Brake System—Metric Tube Connection
SAE J1453—O-Ring Face Seal

3. Manufacture—The tubing shall be made from a single strip of steel shaped into a tubular form, the edges of which are joined and sealed by a suitable welding process. After welding, the bead shall be removed from the outside to provide a smooth round surface and the tubing shall be processed in such a manner as to produce a finished product which will meet all requirements of this document. Typically this type of tubing is available in both coiled and straight condition. Straightness requirements should be agreed upon between supplier and purchaser.

4. Dimensions and Tolerances—The standard nominal diameters and the applicable dimensions and tolerances are shown in Table 1.

TABLE 1—TUBING DIMENSIONS AND TOLERANCES(1)

Dash Size	Nominal Tubing OD mm	Outside Diameter(2) Basic mm	Outside Diameter(2) Tolerance ±mm	Wall Thickness(3)(4) basic mm	Wall Thickness(3) Tolerance ±mm
–2	3.18	3.18	0.05	0.64	0.13
–3	4.76	4.78	0.08	0.71	0.13
–4	6.35	6.35	0.08	0.71	0.08
–5	7.94	7.92	0.08	0.71	0.08
–6	9.53	9.53	0.08	0.71	0.08
–7	11.11	11.13	0.10	0.76	0.08
–8	12.70	12.70	0.10	0.76	0.08
–8	12.70	12.70	0.10	0.89	0.09
–9	14.29	14.27	0.10	0.76	0.08
–10	15.88	15.88	0.10	0.89	0.09

1. Other sizes may be specified by agreement between the supplier and the user.
2. The actual outside diameter shall be the average of the maximum and minimum outside diameters as determined at any one cross section through the tubing.
3. The tolerances listed represent the maximum permissible deviation at any point.
4. For intermediate wall thickness, the tolerance for the next heavier wall thickness shall apply.

5. Manufacturing Standards

5.1 Tubing End Condition—The tubing will be produced using normal mill cut-off practices. This will include, but is not limited to single-cut ends, double-cut ends, saw-cut, and rotary-cut ends. Care will be taken to minimize the distortion of the tube ends. Ends that require further processing will be by agreement between the producer and tube purchaser.

5.2 Surface Finish—Surface imperfections such as handling marks, die marks, or shallow pits shall not be considered injurious defects provided such imperfections are not detrimental to the function of the tubing and these imperfections are within the tolerances specified for diameter and wall thickness. The removal of such surface imperfections is not required. A slight weld bead and splatter on the inside surface shall be permissible but must be held to the minimum consistent with good welding practice. Special weld bead requirements must be agreed upon at time of purchase.

6. Material—Tubing shall be made from low-carbon steel, such as UNS G10080 or UNS G10100.

7. Mechanical Properties—The finished tubing shall have mechanical properties as tabulated in Table 2.

TABLE 2—MECHANICAL REQUIREMENTS

Properties	Values
Yield Strength, min (0.2% offset)	170 MPa
Tensile Strength, min	290 MPa
Elongation in 50 mm	14% min
Hardness (Rockwell 30 T scale), max	65

8. Performance Requirements—The finished tubing shall satisfactorily meet the following performance tests. All tests are to be conducted in accordance with the procedures in SAE J1677.

8.1 Flaring Test—SAE J1677–(5.5.1 Double Flare)
(5.5.3 Single Flare)

8.2 Hardness Test—SAE J1677— 5.6

8.3 Bending Test—SAE J1677—5.3

8.4 Pressure Proof Test—SAE J1677—5.8

8.5 Nondestructive Electric Test—SAE J1677—5.9

8.6 Flattening Test—SAE J1677—5.1

8.7 Expansion Test—SAE J1677—5.4

8.8 Tensile Test—SAE J1677—5.7

9. Test Certificates—A certificate of compliance to the performance requirements shall be furnished to the purchaser by the producer if requested in the purchase agreement.

10. Cleanliness—The inside of tubing shall be clean and free from any contamination which will impair the processing or serviceability of the tubing.

11. Corrosion Protection—The inside and outside of the finished tubing shall be protected against corrosion during shipment and normal storage. If a corrosion preventive compound is applied, it shall be such that after normal storage periods it can readily be removed by cleaning agents normally used in manufacturing. Extended corrosion resistance coatings, such as tern coating, galvanizing, epoxy paint, etc., may be available.

12. Packaging—The tubing is to be packaged in such a way to allow it to be transported and stored, with normal care, without being damaged. Any special packaging will be by agreement between the producer and the purchaser.

(R) BRAZED DOUBLE WALL LOW-CARBON STEEL TUBING—SAE J527 NOV2000

SAE Standard

Report of the SAE Tube, Pipe, Hose, and Lubrication Fittings Committee approved January 1952. Fourth revision by the SAE Fluid Conductors and Connectors Technical Committee January 1983 and completely revised June 1990. Revised by the SAE Fluid Conductors and Connectors Technical Committee SC1—Automotive and Hydraulic Tube and Fittings, June 1991, and completely revised February 1996. Completely revised by the SAE Fluid Conductors and Connectors Technical Committee SC5—Automotive and Hydraulic Tube and Fittings November 2001. Rationale statement available.

1. Scope—This SAE Standard covers brazed double wall low-carbon steel tubing intended for general automotive, refrigeration, hydraulic, and other similar applications requiring tubing of a suitable quality for bending, flaring, beading, forming, and brazing.

2. References

2.1 Applicable Publications—The following publications form a part of this specification to the extent specified herein. Unless otherwise specified, the latest issue of SAE publications shall apply.

2.1.1 SAE PUBLICATION—Available from SAE, 400 Commonwealth Drive, Warrendale, PA 15096-0001.

SAE J1677—Tests and Procedures for SAE Low-Carbon Steel and Copper Nickel Tubing

2.1.2 ASTM PUBLICATION—Available from ASTM, 100 Barr Harbor Drive, West Conshohocken, PA 19428-2959.

ASTM A 254—Standard Specification for Copper Brazed Steel Tubing

2.2 Related Publications—The following publications are provided for information purposes only and are not a required part of this document.

2.2.1 SAE PUBLICATION—Available from SAE, 400 Commonwealth Drive, Warrendale, PA 15096-0001.

SAE J409—Product Analysis-Permissible Variations from Specified Chemical Analysis of a Heat or Cast of Steel
SAE J512—Automotive Tube Fittings
SAE J513—Refrigeration Tube Fittings-General Specifications
SAE J514—Hydraulic Tube Fittings
SAE J516—Hydraulic Hose Fittings
SAE J533—Flares for Tubing
SAE J1065—Pressure Ratings for Hydraulic Tubing and Fittings
SAE J1290—Automotive Hydraulic Brake System—Metric Tube Connection
SAE J1453—O-Ring Face Seal

3. Manufacture—The tubing shall be made from a single or double strip of steel shaped into the form of a double-wall tubing, the walls of which are secured and sealed by copper brazing in a controlled atmosphere. The braze shall be uniform with no evidence of a bead on either the inside or outside of the tubing. Typically this type of tubing is available in both coiled and straight condition. Straightness requirements should be agreed upon between supplier and purchaser.

4. Dimensions and Tolerances—The standard nominal diameters and the applicable dimensions and tolerances are shown in Table 1.

TABLE 1—TUBING DIMENSIONS AND TOLERANCES(1)

Dash Size	Nominal Tubing OD mm	Outside Diameter(1) Basic mm	Outside Diameter(1) Tolerance ±mm	Wall Thickness Basic mm	Wall Thickness Tolerance (2)(3)(4) ±mm
–2	3.18	3.18	0.05	0.64	0.13
–3	4.76	4.78	0.08	0.71	0.08
–4	6.35	6.35	0.08	0.71	0.08
–5	7.94	7.92	0.08	0.71	0.08
–6	9.53	9.53	0.08	0.71	0.08
–7	11.11	11.13	0.10	0.76	0.08
–8	12.70	12.70	0.10	0.89	0.09
–9	14.29	14.27	0.10	0.89	0.09
–10	15.88	15.88	0.10	0.89	0.09

1. The actual outside diameter shall be the average of the maximum and minimum outside diameters at any one cross section through the tubing.
2. The tolerances listed represent the maximum permissible deviation at any point.
3. Other sizes may be specified by agreement between the supplier and the user.
4. For intermediate wall thickness, the tolerance for the next heavier wall thickness shall apply.

5. Manufacturing Standards

5.1 Tubing End Condition—The tubing will be produced using normal mill cut-off practices. This will include, but is not limited to single-cut ends, double-cut ends, saw-cut ends, and rotary cut ends. Care will be taken to minimize the distortion of the tube ends. Ends that require further processing will be by agreement between the producer and purchaser.

5.2 Surface Finish—Surface imperfections such as handling marks, die marks, or shallow pits shall not be considered injurious defects provided such imperfections are not detrimental to the function of the tubing, and these imperfections are within the tolerances specified for diameter and wall thickness. The removal of such surface imperfections is not required. A slight seam lift or separation on the outside bevel edge of the outside wall on double wall tubing is not considered an injurious defect during end forming operations, provided that the seam condition doesn't effect the sealing area of the end form. Sealing surfaces shall be smooth and free from nicks, pit marks, and any other defects that prevent sealing.

6. Material—Tubing shall be made from low carbon steel, such as UNS G10080 or UNS G10100.

7. Mechanical Properties—The finished tubing shall have mechanical properties as tabulated in Table 2:

TABLE 2—MECHANICAL PROPERTIES

Properties	Values
Yield Strength, min (0.2% offset)	170 MPa
Tensile Strength, min	290 MPa
Elongation in 50 mm	14% min
Hardness (Rockwell 30 T scale), max	65

8. Performance Requirements—The finished tubing shall satisfactorily meet the following performance tests. All tests are to be conducted in accordance with the procedures in SAE J1677 or ASTM A 254 as designated.

8.1 Bending Test —SAE J1677 JAN1996 (Section 5.3)

8.2 Flaring Test —SAE J1677 JAN1996 (Section 5.5.2)

8.3 Pressure Proof Test —SAE J1677 JAN1996 (Section 5.8). Performed by agreement between purchaser and producer, (where allowable unit stress of material(s) = 140 MPa (80% of minimum yield strength).

8.4 Nondestructive Electronic Test—SAE J1677 JAN1996 (Section 5.9)

8.5 Hardness Test—SAE J1677 JAN1996 (Section 5.6)

8.6 Flattening Test—SAE J1677 JAN1996 (Section 5.1)

8.7 Tensile Test—SAE J1677 JAN1996 (Section 5.7)

8.8 Inside Surface Cleanliness—ASTM A 254 March 1997(Section 8)

9. Test Certificates—A certificate of compliance to the performance requirements shall be furnished to the purchaser by the producer if requested in the purchase agreement.

10. Corrosion Protection—The inside and outside of the finished tubing shall be protected against corrosion during shipment and normal storage. If a corrosion preventive compound is applied, it shall be such that after normal storage periods it can readily be removed by cleaning agents normally used in manufacturing.

Extended corrosion resistance coatings, such as tern coating, galvanizing, epoxy paint, etc., are available and can be supplied at the request of the user.

11. Packaging—The tubing is to be packaged in such a way to allow it to be transported and stored with normal care, without being damaged. Any special packaging will be by agreement between the producer and the purchaser.

(R)SEAMLESS COPPER-NICKEL 90-10 TUBING —SAE J1650 OCT1997

SAE Standard

Report of the SAE Fluid Conductors and Connectors Technical Committee S1—Automotive and Hydraulic Tube and Fittings approved March 1993, revised June 1994, and completely revised October 1997.

1. Scope—This SAE Standard covers seamless copper-nickel tubing for use in hydraulic brake pressure conductors, general automotive applications, and other similar uses.

2. References

2.1 Applicable Publication—The following publication forms a part of the specification to the extent specified herein. Unless otherwise indicated the latest revision of SAE publications shall apply.

2.1.1 SAE PUBLICATION—Available from SAE, 400 Commonwealth Drive, Warrendale, PA 15096-0001.

SAE J533—Flares for Tubing

SAE J1677—Tests and Procedures for SAE Low Carbon Steel and Copper Nickel Tubing

2.2 Related Publication—The following publication is provided for information purposes only and is not a required part of this document.

2.2.1 ASTM PUBLICATION—Available from ASTM, 100 Barr Harbor Drive, West Conshohocken, PA 19428-2959.

ASTM B 466M—Seamless Copper-Nickel Pipe and Tube (METRIC)

3. Manufacture—This tubing shall be made from 90-10 copper-nickel and cold drawn to size. It shall then be annealed in such a manner as to produce product which will meet all of the requirements in this document.

4. Dimensions and Tolerances—The standard nominal diameters and the applicable dimensions and tolerances are shown in Table 1.

5. Quality—Finished tubing shall be clean, smooth, and round, both inside and outside, and shall be free from scale and harmful imperfections. Surface imperfections such as handling marks, die marks, or shallow pits shall not be considered harmful provided such imperfections are within the tolerances specified for diameter and wall thickness and do not affect the servicability of the tube.

6. Material—Tubing shall be made from copper-nickel alloy UNS 70600.

7. Mechanical Properties—The finished tubing shall have mechanical properties as tabulated in Table 2.

8. Performance Requirements—The tubing shall satisfactorily meet the following performance tests. All tests are to be conducted in accordance with the procedures in SAE J1677.

8.1 Flaring Test—(See 5.5.2 of SAE J1677.)

8.2 Hardness Test—(See 5.6 of SAE J1677.)

8.3 Bending Test—(See 5.3 of SAE J1677.)

8.4 Pressure Proof Test—(See 5.8 of SAE J1677.) Where allowable fiber stress of material = 72 MPa.

8.5 Nondestructive Electric Test—(See 5.9 of SAE J1677.)

9. Test Certificates—A certificate of compliance to the performance requirements shall be furnished to the purchaser by the producer if requested in the purchase agreement.

10. Cleanliness—The inside of the tubing shall be clean and free from any contamination which will impair the processing or serviceability of the tubing.

11. Corrosion Protection—The inside and outside of the finished tubing shall be protected against corrosion during shipment and normal storage. If a corrosion preventive compound is applied, it shall be such that after normal storage periods, it can readily be removed by cleaning agents normally used in manufacturing.

TABLE 1—TUBING DIMENSIONS AND TOLERANCES(1)

Dash Size	Nominal Tubing OD mm	Outside Diameter(1) Basic mm	Outside Diameter(1) Tolerance ±mm	Wall Thickness Basic mm	Wall Thickness Tolerance(2)
–2	3.18	3.18	0.05	0.64	0.13
–3	4.76	4.78	0.08	0.71	0.08
–4	6.35	6.35	0.08	0.71	0.08
–5	7.94	7.92	0.08	0.71	0.08
–6	9.53	9.53	0.08	0.71	0.08
–7	11.11	11.13	0.10	0.76	0.08
–8	12.70	12.70	0.10	0.89	0.09
–9	14.29	14.27	0.10	0.89	0.09
–10	15.88	15.88	0.10	0.89	0.09

1. The actual outside diameter shall be the average of the maximum and minimum outside diameters as determined at any one cross section through the tubing.
2. The tolerances listed represent the maximum permissible deviation at any point.

TABLE 2—MECHANICAL PROPERTIES

Properties	Values
Yield Strength, min (0.2% offset)	105 MPa
Tensile Strength, min	275 MPa
Elongation in 50 mm	14%
Hardness (Rockwell 30t scale), max	65

(R) WELDED FLASH-CONTROLLED LOW-CARBON STEEL TUBING NORMALIZED FOR BENDING, DOUBLE FLARING, AND BEADING—SAE J356 MAY1999

SAE Standard

Report of the SAE Tube, Pipe, Hose, and Lubricants Fittings Committee approved July 1968. Reaffirmed by the Fluid Conductors and Connectors Technical Committee May 1986. Completely revised by the SAE Fluid Conductors and Connectors Technical Committee SC1—Automotive and Hydraulic Tube and Fittings, June 1991 and February 1996. Completely revised by the SAE Fluid Conductors and Connectors Technical Committee SC5—Metallic Tubing May 1999. Rationale statement available.

1. Scope—The SAE Standard covers normalized electric-resistance welded flash-controlled single-wall, low-carbon steel pressure tubing intended for use as pressure lines and in other applications requiring tubing of a quality suitable for bending, double flaring, beading, forming, and brazing. Material produced to this specification is not intended to be used for single flare applications due to the potential leak path that would be caused by the ID weld bead.

This specification also covers SAE J356 Type-A tubing. The mechanical properties and performance requirements of standard SAE J356 and SAE J356 Type-A are the same. Therefore, the designated differences of Type-A tubing are not meant to imply that Type-A tubing is in anyway inferior to standard SAE J356. The Type-A designation is only meant to address the unique manufacturing differences of the small diameter, light wall sizes (typically 15.88 mm OD x 1.24 mm wall and smaller.) The primary differences between SAE J356 and SAE J356 Type-A are described in the following paragraph.

Type-A tubing is heat treated in-line to relieve stresses and is generally produced in coiled form. When Type-A tubing is produced in coil form, straight lengths of Type-A are only available through a secondary straightening and cut-to-length operation. Standard SAE J356 is produced as straight lengths and then receives a secondary normalizing operation. All standard SAE J356 requirements apply to Type-A tubing unless the specific requirement is noted with a "Type-A" designation. Standard SAE J356 is also available in the same sizes as Type-A, in which case all the standard SAE J356 specifications apply.

2. References

2.1 Applicable Publications—The following publications form a part of this specification to the extent specified herein. Unless otherwise specified, the latest issue of SAE publications shall apply.

2.1.1 SAE PUBLICATIONS—Available from SAE, 400 Commonwealth Drive, Warrendale, PA 15096-0001.

SAE J409—Product Analysis—Permissible Variations from Specified Chemical Analysis of a Heat or Cast of Steel
SAE J514—Hydraulic Tube Fittings
SAE J533—Flares for Tubing
SAE J1677—Tests and Procedures for SAE Low-Carbon Steel and Copper Nickel Tubing

2.2 Related Publications—The following publications are provided for information purposes only and are not a required part of this document.

2.2.1 SAE PUBLICATIONS—Available from SAE, 400 Commonwealth Drive, Warrendale, PA 15096-0001.

SAE J1065—Pressure Ratings for Hydraulic Tubing and Fittings
SAE J1453—Fitting—O-Ring Face Seal

3. Manufacture—The tubing shall be made from flat-rolled steel shaped into a tubular form, the edges of which are joined and fused together by electric-resistance welding. After forming and welding, the outside flash shall be removed to provide a smooth surface. The inside flash shall be of uniform contour, free from saw-tooth peaks, and controlled in height by seam-welding techniques or by cutting, but not by hammering or rolling. The inside flash height shall conform to the following as in Table 1.

The tubing shall be normalized via an atmospherically controlled method to produce a finished product which will meet all requirements of this document.

3.1 Type-A—The tubing shall be heat treated to relieve stresses via an atmospherically controlled method to produce a finished product which will meet all requirements of this document.

4. Dimensions and Tolerances—The tolerances applicable to tubing outside diameter are shown in Table 2. The tolerances applicable to tubing wall thickness are shown in Table 3. Particular attention shall be given to areas adjacent to the weld to insure against thin spots and/or sharp indentations.

5. Manufacturing Standards

5.1 Straightness—Tubing shall be straightened to a tolerance of 0.8 mm in 1000 mm. Straightness tolerances shall be measured by placing a 1000 mm straight edge against the tube while lying on its neutral axis. The point of maximum deflection of the tube from the straight edge should not be more than allowed by the specification when measured with a feeler gauge. The aforementioned straightness tolerance may be waived if agreed upon between producer and purchaser, and will not apply to Type-A tubing that is coil form.

TABLE 1—INSIDE FLASH HEIGHT

Nominal Wall Thickness mm	Maximum Flash Height(1)(2) Thru 25.4 mm OD mm	Maximum Flash Height(1)(2) Over 25.4 mm OD mm
less than 0.90	0.13	0.25
0.90 through 1.65	0.20	0.25
greater than 1.65	0.25	0.25

1. For tubes having an ID greater than 8 mm, the height of the inside weld flash shall be measured with a ball micrometer having a 3.96 mm ± 0.41 mm radius on the anvil or ball point. For tubes having an ID 8 mm or less, screw thread micrometers shall be used. The height of the flash shall be the difference between the thickness of the tubing wall at the point of maximum height of the flash and the average of the wall thickness measured at points adjacent to both sides of the flash.
2. Tubing with an ID that is smaller than the producer's capability to scarf the ID weld bead shall be produced as a "flash in" tube. Seam welding techniques may be applied in order to control the ID flash height. The maximum ID flash height, however, will be determined by agreement between the producer and the purchaser.

TABLE 2—TUBING OUTSIDE DIAMETER TOLERANCE

Nominal Tubing OD(1)(2) mm	Tube OD Tolerance ±mm
Up to 9.50	0.06
Over 9.50 to 15.88	0.08
Over 15.88 to 28.57	0.09
Over 28.57 to 50.80	0.13
Over 50.80 to 63.50	0.15
Over 63.50 to 76.20	0.20
Over 76.20 to 88.90	0.23
Over 88.90 to 101.60	0.25

1. OD measurements shall be taken at least 50 mm from the end of the tubing.
2. Refer to SAE J514 for nominal tubing OD to be used in conjunction with standard hydraulic tube fittings and SAE J533 for recommended maximum nominal wall thickness for double flaring.

5.2 Tubing End Condition—The tubing will be produced using normal mill cut-off practices. This will include, but is not limited to, punch-cut ends, double-cut ends, and rotary-cut ends. Care will be taken to minimize the distortion of the tube ends. Distortion of the tube ends must not affect the normal recutting processes that will be performed by the end user. Ends that require further processing will be by agreement between the producer and tube purchaser.

5.3 Finish—The outside surface finish of the tube is critical in order to prevent possible leak paths on double flare fittings, mechanical form fittings, or other applications where the outside surface of the tube becomes the sealing surface. The outside surface of the tube shall be free of excessive roll marks, score marks, chatter marks, or other surface imperfections that would be considered detrimental to the function of the tubing.

5.4 Thermal Treatment—The tubing is to be heated to a temperature above the upper transformation point via an atmospherically controlled method, and then cooled in a protective atmosphere.

5.4.1 TYPE-A—The tubing shall be heat treated to relieve stresses via an atmospherically controlled method.

6. Material—Tubing shall be made from low-carbon, flat-rolled steel conforming to the chemical composition in Table 4. The steel shall be made by the open hearth basic oxygen or electric furnace process. A ladle analysis of each heat shall be made to determine the percentages of the elements specified. The chemical composition thus determined shall be reported to the purchaser, or his representative, if requested, and shall conform to the requirements specified. If a check analysis is required, the tolerances shall be as specified in SAE J409, Table 3.

TABLE 3—TUBING WALL THICKNESS TOLERANCES

Nominal Wall Thickness(1) mm	Nominal Tubing Outside Diameter Thru 25 mm Plus(2)/Minus mm	Nominal Tubing Outside Diameter Over 25 mm Thru 50 mm Plus(2)/Minus mm	Nominal Tubing Outside Diameter Over 50 mm Thru 100 mm Plus(2)/Minus mm
0.71	0.05/0.08	0.08/0.08	0.08/0.08
0.89	0.05/0.10	0.05/0.10	0.05/0.10
1.00	0.05/0.10	0.05/0.10	0.05/0.13
1.25	0.10/0.13	0.08/0.13	0.10/0.20
1.50	0.15/0.15	0.10/0.20	0.10/0.20
1.65	0.15/0.15	0.10/0.20	0.10/0.20
2.00	0.15/0.25	0.15/0.25	0.15/0.25
2.11	0.15/0.25	0.15/0.25	0.15/0.25
2.41	0.15/0.25	0.15/0.25	0.15/0.25
2.50	0.15/0.25	0.15/0.25	0.15/0.25
2.77	0.15/0.25	0.15/0.25	0.15/0.25
3.00	0.15/0.25	0.15/0.25	0.15/0.25
3.05	0.15/0.25	0.15/0.25	0.15/0.25
3.40	0.15/0.25	0.15/0.25	0.15/0.25
3.75	—	0.18/0.28	0.18/0.28
4.00	—	0.18/0.28	0.18/0.28
4.19	—	0.18/0.28	0.18/0.28
4.57	—	0.18/0.28	0.18/0.28
5.00	—	0.20/0.30	0.20/0.30
5.16	—	0.20/0.30	0.20/0.30
5.59	—	0.20/0.30	0.20/0.30
6.00	—	0.36/0.46	0.36/0.46
6.05	—	0.36/0.46	0.36/0.46
6.58	—	0.36/0.51	0.36/0.51

1. For intermediate wall thicknesses, the tolerance for the next heavier wall thickness shall apply.
2. Plus tolerances include allowance for crown on flat-rolled steel.

TABLE 4—CHEMICAL REQUIREMENTS

Element	Cast or Heat Analysis, Weight %
Carbon	0.06 min/ 0.18 max
Manganese	0.30 thru 0.60
Phosphorus	0.04 max
Sulfur	0.05 max
Type-A	
Carbon	0.02 min/0.18 max
Manganese	0.10 thru 0.60
Phosphorus	0.04 max
Sulfur	0.05 max

7. Mechanical Properties—The finished tubing shall have mechanical properties as tabulated in Table 5.

TABLE 5—MECHANICAL PROPERTIES

Properties	Values
Yield Strength, min	170 MPa
Ultimate Strength, min	310 MPa
Elongation in 50 mm, min	35%(1)
Hardness (Rockwell B), max	65(2)

1. For tubing having nominal outside diameter of 9.5 mm or less, and/or wall thicknesses of 0.9 mm or less, a minimum elongation of 25% is permissible.
2. The hardness test shall not be required on tubing with a nominal wall thickness of less than 1.65 mm. Such tubing shall meet all other mechanical properties and performance requirements.

8. Performance Requirements—The finished tubing shall satisfactorily meet the following performance tests. All tests are to be conducted in accordance with the procedures in SAE J1677.

8.1 Flattening Test—SAE J1677, paragraph 5.1.

8.2 Flaring Test—SAE J1677, paragraph 5.5.1.

8.3 Reverse Flattening Test—SAE J1677, paragraph 5.2.

8.4 Expansion Test—SAE J1677, paragraph 5.4.

8.5 Hardness Test—SAEJ1677, paragraph 5.6.

8.6 Tensile Test—SAE J1677, paragraph 5.7.

8.7 Pressure Proof Test—SAE J1677, paragraph 5.8, performed when agreed upon between the purchaser and the producer (where allowable unit stress of material(s) = 140 MPa (80% of minimum yield strength).

8.8 Nondestructive Electronic Test—SAE J1677, paragraph 5.9. The tests that are referenced in 5.9 of SAE J1677 are to be conducted after all cold-working tube manufacturing operations are performed on the tubing.

9. Test Certificates—A certificate of compliance to the performance requirements shall be furnished to the purchaser by the producer if requested in the purchase agreement. The tube producer must be able to certify that each heat lot used to produce the tubing complies with the performance requirement.

10. Cleanliness—The inside and outside surfaces of the finished tubing shall be commercially bright, clean, and free from grease, oxide scale, carbon deposits, and any other contamination that cannot be readily removed by cleaning agents normally used in manufacturing plants.

11. Corrosion Protection—The inside and outside surfaces of the finished tubing shall be protected against corrosion during shipment and normal storage. If a corrosion preventive compound is applied, it shall be such that after normal storage periods it can readily be removed by cleaning agents normally used in manufacturing.

Extended corrosion resistance coatings, such as tern coating, galvanizing, epoxy paint, etc., may be available and may be supplied at the request of the purchaser.

12. Packaging—The tubing is to be packaged in such a way to allow it to be transported and stored, with normal care, without being damaged. Any special packaging will be by agreement between the producer and purchaser.

WELDED AND COLD-DRAWN, SAE 1021 CARBON STEEL TUBING NORMALIZED FOR BENDING AND FLARING—SAE J2467 APR1999 SAE Standard

Report of the SAE Fluid Conductors and Connectors Technical Committee S5—Metallic Tubing, approved April 1999.

1. Scope—The SAE Standard covers normalized electric resistance welded, cold-drawn, single-wall, SAE 1021 carbon steel pressure tubing intended for use as pressure lines and in other applications requiring tubing of a quality suitable for bending, flaring, forming, and brazing.

The grade of material produced to this specification is higher in carbon content and manganese content than the grade of material specified in SAE J525. The material produced to this specification is intended to service higher pressure applications than like sizes of SAE J525. Due to the higher carbon and manganese content, however, the forming characteristics of the finished tube is diminished somewhat when compared to SAE J525. Special attention to the overall forming requirements of the finished assembly should be taken into consideration when utilizing material produced to this specification.

2. References

2.1 Applicable Publications—The following publications form a part of this specification to the extent specified herein. Unless otherwise specified, the latest issue of SAE publications shall apply.

2.1.1 SAE PUBLICATIONS—Available from SAE, 400 Commonwealth Drive, Warrendale, PA 15096-0001.

SAE J409—Product Analysis—Permissible Variations from Specified Chemical Analysis of a Heat or Cast of steel
SAE J514—Hydraulic Tube Fittings
SAE J525—Welded and Cold Drawn Low-Carbon Steel Tubing Annealed for Bending and Flaring
SAE J533—Flares for Tubing
SAE J1677—Tests and Procedures for SAE Low-Carbon Steel and Copper Nickel Tubing

2.2 Related Publications—The following publications are provided for information purposes only and are not a required part of this document.

2.2.1 SAE PUBLICATIONS—Available from SAE, 400 Commonwealth Drive, Warrendale, PA 15096-0001.

SAE J1065—Pressure Ratings for Hydraulic Tubing and Fittings
SAE J1453—Fitting—O-Ring Face Seal

3. Manufacture—The tubing shall be made from flat rolled steel shaped into a tubular form, the edges of which are joined and fused together by electric resistance welding. After forming and welding, the tubing shall be normalized and subjected to a cold drawing operation that shall result in a 15% minimum reduction in cross sectional area, of which 8% shall consist in a reduction of wall thickness. Subsequent to cold drawing, the tubing shall be *normalized* via an atmospherically controlled method to produce a finished product that will meet all requirements of this document.

4. Dimensions and Tolerances—The tolerances applicable to the tubing outside diameter and inside diameter are shown in Table 1. The tolerances applicable to tubing wall thickness are shown in Table 2. Dimensional tolerances can only apply to two of the three tubing dimensions (OD, ID, or wall). Unless otherwise agreed upon between the purchaser and tube producer, dimensional tolerances shall apply to the tube *OD* and *wall* dimension.

5. Manufacturing Standards

5.1 Straightness—Tubing shall be straightened to a tolerance of 0.8 mm in 1000 mm. Straightness tolerances shall be measured by placing a 915 mm straight edge against the tube while lying on its neutral axis. The point of maximum deflection of the tube from the straight edge should not be more than allowed by the specification when measured with a feeler gauge.

TABLE 1—TUBING DIAMETER TOLERANCES

Nominal Tubing OD(1)(2) mm	Tube OD Tolerance ±mm	TUBE ID Tolerance ±mm
Up to 9.50	0.05	0.05
Over 9.50 to 15.88	0.06	0.06
Over 15.88 to 50.80	0.08	0.08
Over 50.80 to 63.50	0.10	0.10
Over 63.50 to 76.20	0.13	0.13
Over 76.20 to 100.00	0.15	0.15

1. OD measurements shall be taken at least 50 mm from the end of the tubing.
2. Refer to SAE J514 for nominal tubing OD to be used in conjunction with standard hydraulic tube fittings and SAE J533 for recommended maximum nominal wall thickness for double flaring.

TABLE 2—TUBING WALL THICKNESS TOLERANCES

Nominal Wall Thickness(1)	Nominal Tubing Outside Diameter Through 22 mm +/– mm	Nominal Tubing Outside Diameter Over 22 mm Through 48 mm +/– mm	Nominal Tubing Outside Diameter Over 48 mm Through 100 mm +/– mm
0.89	0.05/0.05	0.05/0.05	0.05/0.05
1.00	0.05/0.05	0.05/0.08	0.05/0.08
1.25	0.05/0.05	0.05/0.08	0.05/0.08
1.50	0.05/0.05	0.05/0.08	0.05/0.08
1.65	0.05/0.05	0.05/0.08	0.05/0.08
2.00	0.05/0.05	0.05/0.08	0.08/0.08
2.11	0.05/0.05	0.05/0.08	0.08/0.08
2.41	0.05/0.05	0.05/0.08	0.08/0.08
2.50	0.05/0.08	0.05/0.10	0.08/0.08
2.77	0.05/0.08	0.05/0.10	0.08/0.08
3.00	0.08/0.08	0.05/0.10	0.08/0.08
3.05	0.08/0.08	0.05/0.10	0.08/0.08
3.40	—	0.05/0.10	0.08/0.08
3.75	—	0.05/0.10	0.08/0.08
4.00	—	0.08/0.10	0.08/0.10
4.19	—	0.08/0.10	0.08/0.10
4.57	—	0.10/0.10	0.08/0.13
5.00	—	0.10/0.13	0.10/0.13
5.16	—	0.10/0.13	0.10/0.13
5.59	—	0.10/0.15	0.10/0.15
6.00	—	0.13/0.15	0.13/0.15
6.05	—	0.13/0.15	0.13/0.15
6.58	—	0.13/0.15	0.13/0.15

1. For intermediate wall thickness, the tolerance for the next heavier wall thickness shall apply.

5.2 Tubing End Condition—The tubing will be produced using normal mill cut-off practices. This will include, but is not limited to double-cut ends, saw-cut, and rotary-cut ends. Care will be taken to minimize the distortion of the tube ends. Distortion of the tube ends must not affect the normal re-cutting processes that will be performed by the end user. Ends that require further processing will be by agreement between the producer and tube purchaser.

5.3 Surface Finish—The outside and inside surface finish of the tube are critical in order to prevent possible leak paths on flared fittings, mechanical form fittings, or other applications where the surface of the tube becomes the sealing surface. The surface of the tube shall be free of excessive roll marks, score marks, chatter marks, or other surface imperfections that would be considered detrimental to the function of the tubing.

5.4 Thermal Treatment—The tubing is to be heated to a temperature above the upper transformation point via an atmospherically controlled method, and then cooled in a protective atmosphere.

6. Material—Tubing shall be made from low-carbon, flat rolled steel conforming to the chemical composition in Table 3. The steel shall be made by the open-hearth, basic oxygen, or electric furnace process. A ladle analysis of each heat shall be made to determine the percentages of the elements specified. The chemical composition thus determined shall be reported to the purchaser, or his representative, if requested, and shall conform to the requirements specified. If a check analysis is required, the tolerances shall be as specified in SAE J409, Table 3.

TABLE 3—CHEMICAL REQUIREMENTS

Element	Cast or Heat Analysis, Weight %
Carbon	0.17 min/0.23 max
Manganese	0.60 through 0.90
Phosphorus	0.04 max
Sulfur	0.05 max

7. Mechanical Properties—The finished tubing shall have mechanical properties as tabulated in Table 4.

TABLE 4—MECHANICAL PROPERTIES

Properties	Values
Yield Strength, min	275 MPa
Ultimate Strength, min	415 MPa
Elongation in 50 mm, min	25%
Hardness (Rockwell B), max	75(1)

1. The hardness test shall not be required on tubing with a nominal wall thickness of less than 1.65 mm. Such tubing shall meet all other mechanical properties and performance requirements.

8. Performance Requirements—The finished tubing shall satisfactorily meet the following performance tests. All tests are to be conducted in accordance with the procedures in SAE J1677.

8.1 Flattening Test—SAE J1677 - paragraph 5.1

8.2 Flaring Test—SAE J1677 - paragraphs 5.5.1 and 5.5.3

8.3 Reverse Flattening Test—SAE J1677 - paragraph 5.2

8.4 Expansion Test—SAE J1677 - paragraph 5.4

8.5 Hardness Test—SAE J1677 - paragraph 5.6

8.6 Tensile Test—SAE J1677 - paragraph 5.7

8.7 Pressure Proof Test—SAE J1677 - paragraph 5.8, performed when agreed upon between the purchaser and the producer (where allowable unit stress of material(s) = 220 MPa (80% of minimum yield strength).)

8.8 Nondestructive Electronic Test—SAE J1677 - paragraph 5.9. The tests that are referenced in paragraph 5.9 of SAE J1677 are to be conducted after all cold-working operations are performed on the tubing.

9. Test Certificates—A certificate of compliance to the performance requirements shall be furnished to the purchaser by the producer, if requested in the purchase agreement. The tube producer must be able to certify that each heat lot used to produce the tubing complies with the performance requirement.

10. Cleanliness—The inside and outside surfaces of the finished tubing shall be commercially bright, clean, and free from grease, oxide scale, carbon deposits, and any other contamination that cannot readily be removed by cleaning agents normally used in manufacturing plants.

11. Corrosion Protection—The inside and outside surfaces of the finished tubing shall be protected against corrosion during shipment and normal storage. If a corrosion preventive compound is applied, it shall be such that after normal storage periods it can readily be removed by cleaning agents normally used in manufacturing.

12. Packaging—The tubing is to be packaged in such a way to allow it to be transported and stored, with normal care, without being damaged. Any special packaging will be by agreement between the producer and purchaser.

WELDED FLASH CONTROLLED, SAE 1021 CARBON STEEL TUBING, NORMALIZED FOR BENDING, DOUBLE FLARING, AND BEADING—SAE J2435 APR1999

SAE Standard

Report of the SAE Fluid Conductors and Connectors Technical Committee S5—Metallic Tubing approved April 1999.

1. Scope—The SAE Standard covers normalized electric resistance welded flash controlled single-wall, SAE 1021 carbon steel pressure tubing intended for use as pressure lines and in other applications requiring tubing of a quality suitable for bending, double flaring, beading, and brazing. Material produced to this specification is not intended to be used for single flare applications due to the potential leak path that would be caused by the ID weld bead.

The grade of material produced to this specification is higher in carbon content and manganese content than the grade of material specified in SAE J356. The material produced to this specification is intended to service higher pressure applications than like sizes of SAE J356. Due to the higher carbon and manganese content, however, the forming characteristics of the finished tube is diminished somewhat when compared to SAE J356. Special attention to the overall forming requirements of the finished assembly should be taken into consideration when utilizing material produced to this specification.

2. References

2.1 Applicable Publications—The following publications form a part of this specification to the extent specified herein. Unless otherwise indicated, the latest version of SAE publications shall apply.

2.1.1 SAE PUBLICATIONS—Available from SAE, 400 Commonwealth Drive, Warrendale, PA 15096-0001.

SAE J356—Welded Flash Controlled Low-Carbon Steel Tubing Normalized for Bending, Double Flaring, and Beading
SAE J409—Product Analysis—Permissible Variations from Specified Chemical Analysis of a Heat or Cast of steel
SAE J514—Hydraulic Tube Fittings
SAE J533—Flares for Tubing
SAE J1677—Tests and Procedures for SAE Low-Carbon Steel and Copper Nickel Tubing

2.2 Related Publications—The following publications are provided for information purposes only and are not a required part of this document.

SAE J1065—Pressure Ratings For Hydraulic Tubing and Fittings
SAE J1453—Fitting - O-Ring Face Seal

3. Manufacture—The tubing shall be made from a single strip of steel shaped into a tubular form, the edges of which are joined and fused by electric resistance welding. After forming and welding, the outside flash shall be removed to provide a smooth surface. The inside flash shall be of uniform contour, free from saw-tooth peaks, and controlled in height by seam-welding techniques or by cutting, but not by hammering or rolling. The inside flash height shall conform to the following as in Table 1.

The tubing shall be *normalized* via an atmospherically controlled method to produce a finished product, which will meet all requirements of this document.

TABLE 1—INSIDE FLASH HEIGHT

Nominal Wall Thickness mm	Maximum Flash Height(1)(2) Through 25.4 mm OD mm	Maximum Flash Height Over 25.4 mm OD mm
Less than 0.90	0.13	0.25
0.90 through 1.65	0.20	0.25
Greater than 1.65	0.25	0.25

1. For tubes having an ID greater than 8 mm, the height of the inside weld flash shall be measured with a ball micrometer having a 3.96 mm ± 0.41 mm radius on the anvil or ballpoint. For tubes having an ID 8 mm or less, screw thread micrometers shall be used. The height of the flash shall be the difference between the thickness of the tubing wall at the point of maximum height of the flash and the average of the wall thickness measured at points adjacent to both sides of the flash.
2. Tubing with an ID that is smaller than the producer's capability to scarf the ID weld bead shall be produced as a "flash in" tube. Seam welding techniques may be applied in order to control the ID flash height. The maximum ID flash height, however, will be determined by agreement between the producer and the purchaser.

4. Dimensions and Tolerances—The tolerances applicable to tubing outside diameter are shown in Table 2. The tolerances applicable to tubing wall thickness are shown in Table 3. Particular attention shall be given to areas adjacent to the weld to insure against thin spots and/or sharp indentations.

TABLE 2—TUBING OUTSIDE DIAMETER TOLERANCE

Nominal Tubing OD(1)(2) mm	Tube OD Tolerance ± mm
Up to 9.50	0.06
Over 9.50 to 15.88	0.08
Over 15.88 to 28.57	0.09
Over 28.57 to 50.80	0.13
Over 50.80 to 63.50	0.15
Over 63.50 to 76.20	0.20
Over 76.20 to 88.90	0.23
Over 88.90 to 101.60	0.25

1. OD measurements shall be taken at least 50 mm from the end of the tubing.
2. Refer to SAE J514 for nominal tubing OD to be used in conjunction with standard hydraulic tube fittings and SAE J533 for recommended maximum nominal wall thickness for double flaring.

TABLE 3—TUBING WALL THICKNESS TOLERANCES

Nominal Wall Thickness(1) mm	Nominal Tubing Outside Diameter Through 25 mm +/–(2) mm	Nominal Tubing Outside Diameter Through 50 mm +/–(2) mm	Nominal Tubing Outside Diameter Over 50 mm Through 100 mm +/–(2) mm
0.71	0.05/0.08	0.08/0.08	0.08/0.08
0.89	0.05/0.10	0.05/0.10	0.05/0.10
1.00	0.05/0.10	0.05/0.10	0.05/0.10
1.25	0.10/0.13	0.08/0.13	0.10/0.20
1.50	0.15/0.15	0.10/0.20	0.10/0.20
1.65	0.15/0.15	0.10/0.20	0.10/0.20
2.00	0.15/0.25	0.15/0.25	0.15/0.25
2.11	0.15/0.25	0.15/0.25	0.15/0.25
2.41	0.15/0.25	0.15/0.25	0.15/0.25
2.50	0.15/0.25	0.15/0.25	0.15/0.25
2.77	0.15/0.25	0.15/0.25	0.15/0.25
3.00	0.15/0.25	0.15/0.25	0.15/0.25
3.05	0.15/0.25	0.15/0.25	0.15/0.25
3.40	0.15/0.25	0.15/0.25	0.15/0.25
3.75	—	0.18/0.28	0.18/0.28
4.00	—	0.18/0.28	0.18/0.28
4.19	—	0.18/0.28	0.18/0.28
4.57	—	0.18/0.28	0.18/0.28
5.00	—	0.20/0.30	0.20/0.30
5.16	—	0.20/0.30	0.20/0.30
5.59	—	0.20/0.30	0.20/0.30
6.00	—	0.36/0.46	0.36/0.46
6.05	—	0.36/0.46	0.36/0.46
6.58	—	0.36/0.51	0.36/0.51

1. For intermediate wall thickness, the tolerance for the next heavier wall thickness shall apply.
2. Plus tolerances include allowance for crown on flat-rolled steel.

5. Manufacturing Standards

5.1 Straightness—Tubing shall be straightened to a tolerance of 0.8 mm in 1000 mm. Straightness tolerances shall be measured by placing a 915 mm straight edge against the tube while lying on its neutral axis. The point of maximum deflection of the tube from the straight edge should not be more than allowed by the specification when measured with a feeler gauge.

5.2 Tubing End Condition—The tubing will be produced using normal mill cut-off practices. This will include, but is not limited to, punch-cut ends, double-cut ends, and rotary-cut ends. Care will be taken to minimize the distortion of the tube ends. Distortion of the tube ends must not affect the normal re-cutting processes that will be performed by the end user. Ends that require further processing will be by agreement between the producer and tube purchaser.

5.3 Finish—The outside surface finish of the tube is critical in order to prevent possible leak paths on double flare fittings, mechanical form fittings, or other applications where the outside surface of the tube becomes the sealing surface. The outside surface of the tube shall be free of excessive roll marks, score marks, chatter marks, or other surface imperfections that would be considered detrimental to the function of the tubing.

5.4 Thermal Treatment—The tubing is to be heated to a temperature above the upper transformation point in an atmospherically controlled furnace, and then cooled in a protective atmosphere.

6. Material—Tubing shall be made from low-carbon, hot- or cold-rolled steel conforming to the chemical composition in Table 4. If rimmed steel is used, it shall be single strand. The steel shall be made by the open-hearth basic oxygen or electric furnace process. A ladle analysis of each heat shall be made to determine the percentages of the elements specified. The chemical composition thus determined shall be reported to the purchaser, or his representative, if requested, and shall conform to the requirements specified. If a check analysis is required, the tolerances shall be as specified in SAE J409, Table 3.

TABLE 4—CHEMICAL REQUIREMENTS

Element	Cast or Heat Analysis, Weight %
Carbon	0.17 min/0.23 max
Manganese	0.60 through 0.90
Phosphorus	0.04 max
Sulfur	0.05 max

7. Mechanical Properties—The finished tubing shall have mechanical properties as tabulated in Table 5.

TABLE 5—MECHANICAL PROPERTIES

Properties	Values
Yield Strength, min	275 MPa
Ultimate Strength, min	415 MPa
Elongation in 50 mm, min	25%
Hardness(Rockwell B), max	78[(1)]

1. The hardness test shall not be required on tubing with a nominal wall thickness of less than 1.65 mm. Such tubing shall meet all other mechanical properties and performance requirements.

8. Performance Requirements—The finished tubing shall satisfactorily meet the following performance tests. All tests are to be conducted in accordance with the procedures in SAE J1677.

8.1 Flattening Test—SAE J1677 - paragraph 5.1

8.2 Flaring Test—SAE J1677 as required (Double Flare 5.5.1)

8.3 Reverse Flattening Test—SAE J1677 - paragraph 5.2

8.4 Expansion Test—SAE J1677 - paragraph 5.4

8.5 Hardness Test—SAE J1677 - paragraph 5.6

8.6 Tensile Test—SAE J1677 - paragraph 5.7

8.7 Pressure Proof Test—SAE J1677 - paragraph 5.8 performed when agreed upon between the purchaser and the producer (where allowable unit stress of material(s) = 220 MPa (80% of minimum yield strength).)

8.8 Nondestructive Electronic Test (5.9)—SAE J1677 - paragraph 5.9. The tests that are referenced in paragraph 5.9 of SAE J1677 are to be conducted after all cold-working tube manufacturing operations are performed on the tubing.

9. Test Certificates—A certificate of compliance to the performance requirements shall be furnished to the purchaser by the producer if requested in the purchase agreement. The tube producer must be able to certify that each heat lot used to produce the tubing complies with the performance requirement.

10. Cleanliness—The inside and outside surfaces of the finished tubing shall be commercially bright, clean, and free from grease, oxide scale, carbon deposits, and any other contamination that cannot readily be removed by cleaning agents normally used in manufacturing plants.

11. Corrosion Protection—The inside and outside surfaces of the finished tubing shall be protected against corrosion during shipment and normal storage. If a corrosion preventive compound is applied, it shall be such that after normal storage periods it can readily be removed by cleaning agents normally used in manufacturing.

12. Packaging—The tubing is to be packaged in such a way to allow it to be transported and stored, with normal care, without being damaged. Any special packaging will be by agreement between the producer and purchaser.

R) NOMINAL REFERENCE WORKING PRESSURES FOR STEEL HYDRAULIC TUBING—SAE J1065 FEB2003 SAE Information Report

Report of the SAE Tube, Pipe, Hose and Lubrication Fittings Committee approved January 1974. Completely revised by the SAE Fluid Conductors and Connectors Technical Committee S1—Automotive and Hydraulic Tube and Fittings, March 1992, and revised July 1995. Rationale statement available. Completely revised by the SAE Fluid Conductors and Connectors Technical Committee SC5—Metallic Tubing Subcommittee of the SAE Fluid Conductors and Connectors Technical Committee February 2003. Rationale statement available.

1. Scope—This SAE Information Report is intended to provide design guidance in the selection of steel tubing and related tube fittings for general hydraulic system applications. The information presented herein is based on tubing products which conform to SAE standards listed in the reference section.

1.1 Purpose—The purpose of this document is to provide nominal reference working pressures for selecting tube material, OD size and wall thickness for given hydraulic system working pressures based on desired 4 to 1 design factor of the applicable burst pressure rating.

1.2 Information Report—Since many factors influence the pressure at which a hydraulic system will or will not perform satisfactorily, this document should not be used as a "standard" nor a "specification," and the values shown herein should not be construed as "guaranteed" minimum or absolutes. This document is an information report only. See SAE J2551 for information concerning designing, bending, fabrication and routing of fluid conductor metallic tube assemblies.

1.3 Minimum Tensile Strength—Within the fluid power industry, many criteria are used for determining the pressure capability of steel tubing. In this document, consideration is given to specified minimum tensile strength of the materials to calculate the nominal minimum burst pressure of the specified steel tubing. The actual tensile strength of the material can be easily determined by common methods of testing.

1.4 Straight Tube Sections—The nominal reference working pressures listed in this document are for straight tube sections of the listed tubing materials only. Factors such as the thinning of tube walls due to forming operations, shock loads, and vibration characteristics of the system should also be considered when designing all hydraulic tubes and tube assemblies, especially in high pressure applications.

1.5 Operating at 100% of the Reference Working Pressures—When designing systems that operate at 100% of the charted reference working pressure, in conjunction with the materials being subjected to bending, cold forming, wall thinning, brazing, welding, side loads, shock loads and extreme vibrations, the maximum yield strength of the material may be compromised and may cause premature failure of the tube material. Therefore, a good recommended practice is to design hydraulic systems to operate at a level less than the calculated maximum reference working pressures of the materials used. This diminished level may vary from application to application, depending on the operating conditions, pressure spikes and designer discretion, 90% is commonly used.

1.6 Endurance Testing—It is impractical to specify in this report guaranteed allowable working pressures that will satisfy all design criteria for every hydraulic system. Therefore, endurance testing in accordance with SAE J343 and/or ISO 6605 is recommended.

2. References

2.1 Applicable Publications—The following publications form a part of this specification to the extent specified herein. Unless otherwise indicated, the latest issue of SAE publications shall apply.

2.1.1 SAE PUBLICATIONS—Available from SAE, 400 Commonwealth Drive, Warrendale, PA 15096-0001.

SAE J343—Test and Test Procedures for SAE 100R Series Hydraulic Hose and Hose Assemblies
SAE J356—Welded Flash-Controlled Low-Carbon Steel Tubing Normalized for Bending, Double Flaring, and Beading
SAE J524—Seamless Low-Carbon Steel Tubing Annealed for Bending and Flaring
SAE J525—Welded and Cold Drawn for Low-Carbon Steel Tubing Annealed for Bending and Flaring
SAE J526—Welded Low-Carbon Steel Tubing
SAE J527—Brazed Double Wall Low-Carbon Steel Tubing
SAE J533—Flares for Tubing
SAE J2435—Welded Flash Controlled, SAE 1021 Carbon Steel Tubing, Normalized for Bending, Double Flaring, and Beading
SAE J2467—Welded and Cold-Drawn, SAE 1021 Carbon Steel Tubing Normalized for Bending and Flaring
SAE J2551—Recommended Practices for Fluid Conductor Metallic Tubing Applications
SAE J2613—Welded Flash Controlled High Strength Low Alloy Steel Hydraulic Tubing, Sub-Critically Annealed for Bending, Flaring and Beading
SAE J2614—Welded and Cold Drawn High Strength Low Alloy Steel Hydraulic Tubing, Sub-Critically Annealed for Bending and Flaring

2.1.2 ISO PUBLICATIONS—Available from ANSI, 25 West 43rd Street, New York, NY 10036-8002.

ISO 6605—Tests and test procedures

2.2 Related Publications—The following publications are provided for informational purposes only and are not a required part of this document.

2.2.1 SAE PUBLICATIONS—Available from SAE, 400 Commonwealth Drive, Warrendale, PA 15096-0001.

SAE J246—Spherical and Flanged Sleeve (Compression) Tube Fittings
SAE J514—Hydraulic Tube Fittings
SAE J515—Specification for Hydraulic O-Ring Materials, Properties, and Sizes for Metric and inch Stud Ends, Face Seal Fitting and Four-Screw Flange Tube Connections
SAE J518—Hydraulic Flanged Tube, Pipe, and Hose Connections, Four-Bolt Split Flange Type
SAE J1231—Formed Tube Ends for Hose Connections and Hose Fittings
SAE J1273—Recommended Practices for Hydraulic Hose Assemblies
SAE J1290—Automotive Hydraulic Brake System—Metric Tube Connections
SAE J1453—Fitting—O-Ring Face Seal
SAE J1644—Metallic Tube Connections for Fluid Power and General Use—Test Methods for Threaded Hydraulic Fluid Power Connectors
SAE J1677—Tests and Procedures for SAE Low-Carbon Steel and Copper-Nickel Tubing

2.2.2 ISO PUBLICATIONS—Available from ANSI, 25 West 43rd Street, New York, NY 10036-8002.

ISO 2944—Fluid power systems and components - Nominal pressures
ISO 3304—Plain end seamless precision steel tubes - Technical conditions for delivery
ISO 3305—Plain end welded precision steel tubes - Technical conditions for delivery
ISO 4397—Connectors and associated components - Nominal outside diameters of tubes and nominal inside diameters of hoses
ISO 4399—Connectors and associated components - Nominal pressures
ISO 5598—Fluid power systems and components - Vocabulary
ISO 6162—Four-screw split-flange connections
ISO 6163—Round Flange, 8 and 12 screw connections
ISO 6164—Four-screw, one-piece square-flange connections
ISO 8434—Metallic tube connections for fluid power and general Use
ISO 10583—Test Methods for tube connections
ISO 10763—Plain-end, seamless and welded steel tubes - Dimensions and nominal working pressures

2.2.3 DIN PUBLICATIONS—Available from ANSI, 25 West 43rd Street, New York, NY 10036-8002.

DIN 17120—Welded Circular Steel Tubing
DIN 17121—Seamless Circular Steel Tubing

3. Tube Selection—Tube material, size and wall thickness may be selected from Tables 1 through 4.

4. *Nominal Pressures*—See Tables 1 through 4 for nominal reference working pressures. The nominal reference working pressures listed are based on a design factor ratio of 4 to 1 between the calculated nominal static reference burst pressure and the calculated nominal reference working pressure using the following formulas:

$$\text{Burst Pressure -- Pb} = \text{Rm, min}\left(\ln\frac{D}{d}\right) \quad \text{(Eq. 1)}$$

$$\text{Working Pressure -- Pw} = \frac{\text{Pb}}{4} \quad \text{(Eq. 2)}$$

where:

- Pb is the nominal static reference burst pressure in MPa (megapascals)
- Pw is the nominal reference working pressure in MPa (megapascals)
- Rm, min is the minimum tensile strength in MPa (megapascals)
- ln is the natural logarithm, also referred to as log e
- D is the nominal tube outside diameter in millimeters
- d is the nominal tube inside diameter in millimeters

NOTE—These formulae and the derived nominal reference working pressures are only applicable to the listed tube materials, of which, all have at least a 50% ratio of the minimum yield strength to the minimum tensile strength. When calculating nominal reference pressures for tube materials where this ratio falls below a 50% ratio, formulae listed in "Appendix A" should be used.

TABLE 1—NOMINAL REFERENCE WORKING PRESSURES IN MPa (MPa X 145 = PSI), FOR SAE J526 AND SAE J527 HYDRAULIC STEEL HYDRAULIC TUBING AT 4 TO 1 DESIGN FACTOR, MATERIAL STRENGTH = 290 MPa MINIMUM TENSILE

Inch Size Tubing Nom SAE Dash Size	Inch Size Tubing Nom Tube OD mm	Inch Size Tubing Nom Tube OD Inch	Nominal Wall Thickness in mm 0.71	Nominal Wall Thickness in mm 0.89	Nominal Wall Thickness in mm 1.24	Nominal Wall Thickness in mm 1.65	Nominal Wall Thickness in mm 2.11	Nominal Wall Thickness in mm 2.41	Nominal Wall Thickness in mm 2.77	Nominal Wall Thickness in mm 3.05	Nominal Wall Thickness in mm 3.40	Nominal Wall Thickness in mm 3.76	Nominal Wall Thickness in mm 3.96	Nominal Wall Thickness in mm 4.76	Nominal Wall Thickness in mm 6.35
–2	3.18	0.125	42.9	59.5											
–3	4.76	0.188	25.4	33.7	53.0										
–4	6.35	0.250	18.3	23.8	35.9	53.1									
–5	7.94	0.312	14.5	18.6	27.4	39.2	55.3								
–6	9.52	0.375	11.7	15.0	21.8	32.0	42.4	51.1							
–8	12.70	0.500		10.9	15.7	21.8	29.2	34.6	41.5	47.4					
–10	15.88	0.625		8.6	12.3	16.8	22.4	26.2	31.1	35.1	40.5	46.5			
–12	19.05	0.750		7.1	10.1	13.8	18.1	21.1	24.9	28.0	32.0	36.4	39.0		
–14	22.23	0.875		6.0	8.5	11.6	15.2	17.7	20.7	23.2	26.4	29.9	31.9	40.5	
–16	25.40	1.000		5.2	7.4	10.1	13.1	15.2	17.8	19.9	22.6	25.4	27.1	34.0	50.2
–18	28.58	1.125			6.6	8.9	11.6	13.4	15.6	17.4	19.7	22.1	23.5	29.4	42.6
–20	31.75	1.250			5.9	7.9	10.3	11.9	13.9	15.5	17.4	19.6	20.8	25.8	37.0
–24	38.10	1.500				6.5	8.5	9.8	11.4	12.6	14.2	15.9	16.9	20.8	29.4
–28	44.45	1.750				5.6	7.2	8.3	9.6	10.7	12.0	13.4	14.2	17.4	24.4
–32	50.80	2.000				4.9	6.3	7.2	8.3	9.3	10.4	11.6	12.3	15.0	20.8
–36	57.15	2.250				4.3	5.5	6.4	7.4	8.2	9.2	10.2	10.8	13.2	18.2
–40	63.50	2.500				3.9	5.0	5.7	6.6	7.3	8.2	9.1	9.6	11.8	16.2
–48	76.20	3.000				3.2	4.1	4.7	5.5	6.0	6.8	7.5	8.0	9.7	13.2

NOTE—Tube sizes for pressures shown to the right of the bold line are not considered suitable for flaring to SAE J533.

TABLE 2—NOMINAL REFERENCE WORKING PRESSURES IN MPa (MPa X 145 = PSI), fOR SAE J356, SAE J524, AND SAE J525 LOW CARBON STEEL HYDRAULIC TUBING AT 4 TO 1 DESIGN FACTOR, MATERIAL STRENGTH = 310 MPa MINIMUM TENSILE

Inch Size Tubing Nom SAE Dash Size	Inch Size Tubing Nom Tube OD mm	Inch Size Tubing Nom Tube OD Inch	Nominal Wall Thickness in mm 0.71	Nominal Wall Thickness in mm 0.89	Nominal Wall Thickness in mm 1.24	Nominal Wall Thickness in mm 1.65	Nominal Wall Thickness in mm 2.11	Nominal Wall Thickness in mm 2.41	Nominal Wall Thickness in mm 2.77	Nominal Wall Thickness in mm 3.05	Nominal Wall Thickness in mm 3.40	Nominal Wall Thickness in mm 3.76	Nominal Wall Thickness in mm 3.96	Nominal Wall Thickness in mm 4.76	Nominal Wall Thickness in mm 6.35
–2	3.18	0.125	45.8	63.6											
–3	4.76	0.188	27.4	36.2	56.9										
–4	6.35	0.250	19.6	25.5	38.4	56.8									
–5	7.94	0.312	15.3	19.7	29.1	41.8	60.0								
–6	9.52	0.375	12.5	16.0	23.4	33.0	45.4	54.7							
–8	12.70	0.500		11.7	16.8	23.3	31.3	37.0	44.4	50.7					
–10	15.88	0.625		9.2	13.2	18.1	23.9	28.0	33.3	37.6	43.3	49.7			
–12	19.05	0.750		7.6	10.8	14.7	19.4	22.6	26.6	29.9	34.2	38.9	41.7		
–14	22.23	0.875		6.5	9.2	12.5	16.3	18.9	22.2	24.9	28.3	32.0	34.1	43.3	
–16	25.40	1.000		5.6	8.0	10.8	14.1	16.3	19.1	21.3	24.2	27.2	29.0	36.4	53.7
–18	28.58	1.125			7.0	9.5	12.4	14.3	16.7	18.6	21.1	23.7	25.1	31.4	45.5
–20	31.75	1.250			6.3	8.5	11.1	12.8	14.9	16.5	18.7	20.9	22.2	27.6	39.6
–24	38.10	1.500				7.0	9.1	10.5	12.2	13.5	15.2	17.0	18.1	22.3	31.4
–28	44.45	1.750				6.0	7.7	8.9	10.3	11.4	12.9	14.4	15.2	18.7	26.1
–32	50.80	2.000				5.2	6.7	7.7	8.9	9.9	11.1	12.4	13.1	16.1	22.3
–36	57.15	2.250				4.6	5.9	6.8	7.9	8.7	9.8	10.9	11.6	14.1	19.5
–40	63.50	2.500				4.1	5.3	6.1	7.1	7.8	9.2	9.8	10.3	12.6	17.3
–48	76.20	3.000				3.4	4.4	5.1	5.8	6.5	7.2	8.1	8.5	10.3	14.1

NOTE—Tube sizes for pressures shown to the right of the bold line are not considered suitable for flaring to SAE J533.

TABLE 3—NOMINAL REFERENCE WORKING PRESSURES IN MPa (MPa X 145 = PSI), FOR SAE J2435 AND SAE J2467 MEDIUM CARBON STEEL HYDRAULIC TUBING AT 4 TO 1 DESIGN FACTOR, MATERIAL STRENGTH = 415 MPa MINIMUM TENSILE

Inch Size Tubing Nom SAE Dash Size	Inch Size Tubing Nom Tube OD mm	Inch Size Tubing Nom Tube OD Inch	Nominal Wall Thick-ness in mm 0.71	Nominal Wall Thick-ness in mm 0.89	Nominal Wall Thick-ness in mm 1.24	Nominal Wall Thick-ness in mm 1.65	Nominal Wall Thick-ness in mm 2.11	Nominal Wall Thick-ness in mm 2.41	Nominal Wall Thick-ness in mm 2.77	Nominal Wall Thick-ness in mm 3.05	Nominal Wall Thick-ness in mm 3.40	Nominal Wall Thick-ness in mm 3.76	Nominal Wall Thick-ness in mm 3.96	Nominal Wall Thick-ness in mm 4.76	Nominal Wall Thick-ness in mm 6.35
–2	3.18	0.125	61.4	104											
–3	4.76	0.188	36.7	48.5	76.1										
–4	6.35	0.250	26.3	34.1	51.4	76.1									
–5	7.94	0.312	20.5	26.4	39.0	55.9	79.0								
–6	9.52	0.375	16.8	21.5	31.3	44.2	60.8	73.2							
–8	12.70	0.500		15.7	22.5	31.1	41.9	49.5	59.5	67.9					
–10	15.88	0.625		12.3	17.6	24.2	32.0	37.5	44.5	50.3	58.0	66.5			
–12	19.05	0.750		10.2	14.5	19.7	26.0	30.3	35.7	40.0	45.8	52.1	55.8		
–14	22.23	0.875		8.7	12.3	16.7	21.8	25.4	29.7	33.3	37.9	42.8	45.7	58.0	
–16	25.40	1.000		7.5	10.7	14.4	18.9	21.8	25.5	28.5	32.3	36.4	38.8	48.7	71.9
–18	28.58	1.125			9.4	12.7	16.6	19.2	22.4	24.9	28.2	31.7	33.7	42.0	61.0
–20	31.75	1.250			8.4	11.4	14.8	17.1	19.9	22.1	25.0	28.0	29.8	37.0	53.0
–24	38.10	1.500				9.4	12.2	14.0	16.3	18.1	20.4	22.8	24.2	29.8	42.1
–28	44.45	1.750				8.0	10.3	11.9	13.8	15.3	17.2	19.2	20.4	25.0	34.9
–32	50.80	2.000				7.0	9.0	10.3	12.0	13.3	14.9	16.6	17.6	21.5	29.8
–36	57.15	2.250				6.2	8.0	9.1	10.6	11.7	13.1	14.6	15.5	18.9	26.1
–40	63.50	2.500				5.5	7.1	8.2	9.5	10.5	11.8	13.1	13.8	16.9	23.2
–48	76.20	3.000				4.6	5.9	6.8	7.8	8.7	9.7	10.8	11.4	13.8	18.9

NOTE—Tube sizes for pressures shown to the right of the bold line are not considered suitable for flaring to SAE J533.

TABLE 4—NOMINAL REFERENCE WORKING PRESSURES IN MPa (MPa X 145 = PSI), FOR SAE J2613 AND SAE J2614 ALLOY STEEL HYDRAULIC TUBING AT 4 TO 1 DESIGN FACTOR, MATERIAL STRENGTH = 500 MPa MINIMUM TENSILE

Inch Size Tubing Nom SAE Dash Size	Inch Size Tubing Nom Tube OD mm	Inch Size Tubing Nom Tube OD Inch	Nominal Wall Thick-ness in mm 0.71	Nominal Wall Thick-ness in mm 0.89	Nominal Wall Thick-ness in mm 1.24	Nominal Wall Thick-ness in mm 1.65	Nominal Wall Thick-ness in mm 2.11	Nominal Wall Thick-ness in mm 2.41	Nominal Wall Thick-ness in mm 2.77	Nominal Wall Thick-ness in mm 3.05	Nominal Wall Thick-ness in mm 3.40	Nominal Wall Thick-ness in mm 3.76	Nominal Wall Thick-ness in mm 3.96	Nominal Wall Thick-ness in mm 4.76	Nominal Wall Thick-ness in mm 6.35
–2	3.18	0.125	73.9	102											
–3	4.76	0.188	43.9	58.1	91.4										
–4	6.35	0.250	31.6	41.1	61.9	91.6									
–5	7.94	0.312	24.7	31.8	46.9	67.3	95.1								
–6	9.52	0.375	20.2	25.8	37.7	53.2	73.2	88.2							
–8	12.70	0.500		18.9	27.2	37.6	50.5	59.7	71.6	81.8					
–10	15.88	0.625		14.8	21.2	29.1	38.6	45.2	53.6	60.6	69.8	80.2			
–12	19.05	0.750		12.2	17.4	23.8	31.3	36.4	42.9	48.2	55.2	62.7	67.2		
–14	22.23	0.875		10.4	14.8	20.1	26.3	30.5	35.8	40.1	45.6	51.6	55.0	69.9	
–16	25.40	1.000		9.1	12.8	17.4	22.7	26.3	30.7	34.3	38.9	43.9	46.7	58.7	86.6
–18	28.58	1.125			11.3	15.3	20.0	23.1	26.9	30.0	34.0	38.1	40.5	50.6	73.4
–20	31.75	1.250			10.1	13.7	17.8	20.6	24.0	26.7	30.1	33.8	35.9	44.5	63.8
–24	38.10	1.500				11.3	14.7	16.9	19.6	21.8	24.6	27.5	29.1	35.9	50.7
–28	44.45	1.750				9.6	12.5	14.3	16.6	18.4	20.7	23.2	24.5	30.1	42.0
–32	50.80	2.000				8.4	10.8	12.5	14.4	16.0	18.0	20.0	21.2	25.9	36.0
–36	57.15	2.250				7.4	9.6	11.0	12.7	14.1	15.8	17.6	18.6	22.8	31.4
–40	63.50	2.500				6.7	8.6	9.9	11.4	12.6	14.1	15.7	16.6	20.3	27.9
–48	76.20	3.000				5.5	7.1	8.2	9.4	10.4	11.7	13.0	13.7	16.7	22.8

NOTE—Tube sizes for pressures shown to the right of the bold line are not considered suitable for flaring to SAE J533.

APPENDIX A

A.1 Formerly Accepted Formulae—When calculating nominal reference pressures for tube materials where the ratio of the minimum yield strength to the minimum tensile strength falls below a 50% ratio, formulae listed in this annex should be used.

A.1.1 Formulae

A.1.1.1 THE BARLOW FORMULA

$$P = \frac{2ST}{D} \quad \text{(Eq. A1)}$$

A.1.1.2 THE BOARDMAN FORMULA

$$P = \frac{2ST}{D - 0.8T} \quad \text{(Eq. A2)}$$

A.1.1.3 THE LAME FORMULA

$$P = S\left(\frac{D^2 - d^2}{D^2 + d^2}\right) \quad \text{(Eq. A3)}$$

where:

D = Nominal Outside Diameter of Tubing, mm
d = Nominal Inside Diameter of Tubing, mm
P = Hydrostatic Working Pressure, MPa
T = Nominal Wall Thickness of Tubing, mm
S = Allowable Fiber Stress of Material, MPa
Use 86 MPa Fiber Stress for 4 to 1 Design Factor (Burst Pressure to Working Pressure)
Use 117 MPa Fiber Stress for 3 to 1 Design Factor (Burst Pressure to Working Pressure)

(R) SEAMLESS COPPER TUBE—SAE J528 JUN1991 **SAE Standard**

Report of the SAE Tube, Pipe, Hose, and Lubrication Fittings Committee approved January 1953, reaffirmed by the SAE Fluid Conductors and Connectors Technical Committee, May 1986. Completely revised by the SAE Fluid Conductors and Connectors Technical Committee SC1—Automotive and Hydraulic Tube and Fittings June 1991.

1. Scope—This SAE Standard covers minimum requirements for soft (061) annealed seamless copper tube intended for automotive and general purposes. (Comparable specification is ASTM B 75. Other copper tube is covered in SAE J463.)

2. References

2.1 Applicable Publications—The following publications form a part of this specification to the extent specified herein. The latest issue of SAE publications shall apply.

2.1.1 SAE PUBLICATION—Available from SAE, 400 Commonwealth Drive, Warrendale, PA 15096-0001.

SAE J463—Wrought Copper and Copper Alloys

2.1.2 ASTM PUBLICATION—Available from ASTM, 100 Barr Harbor Drive, West Conshohocken, PA 19428-2959.

ASTM B 75—Specification for Seamless Copper Tube

3. Manufacture—The tube shall be cold drawn to size and after forming shall be annealed in such a manner as to produce a finished product which will meet all requirements of this document.

4. Dimensions and Tolerances—Tube furnished to this standard shall conform to the dimensional tolerances shown in Table 1 for the size of tube specified by the purchaser. (Standard nominal sizes are listed.)

5. Quality—The finished tube shall be clean, smooth, and round, free from internal and external mechanical imperfections, and shall have a bright appearance.

6. Material—Unless otherwise specified by purchaser, tube shall be made from any one of the materials listed in Table 2. (UNS C12200 is most commonly used.) Average grain size of the tube shall be 0.040 mm, minimum.

7. Mechanical Properties—Tube shall conform to Table 3:

8. Expansion Test—Samples of tube (selected from sections which have not been subjected to cold working after anneal of the finished sized tube) shall be cut square and deburred. These shall be expanded on a hardened and ground tapered steel pin having an included angle of 60 degrees until the outside diameter is increased 40%. Care should be taken to keep the axes of the pin and the tube in line during the expansion operation. The test may be made in a die to restrict the expansion to 40%. The expanded tube shall show no cracking or rupture visible to the unaided eye.

9. Hydrostatic Test—Unless otherwise specified, tube shall show no evidence of weakness or defects when subjected to an internal hydrostatic pressure sufficient to subject the material to a hoop (circumferential) fiber stress of 40 MPa (6000 psi) determined by the following formula for thin, hollow cylinders under pressure. The tube need not be tested at a hydrostatic pressure of over 7 MPa (1000 psi) unless so specified.

$$P = \frac{2St}{D - 0.8t} \quad \text{(Eq. 1)}$$

where:

P = hydrostatic pressure, MPa (psi)
t = minimum thickness of tube wall, mm (in)
D = basic outside diameter of tube, mm (in)
S = allowable stress of the material = 40 MPa (6000 psi)

10. Embrittlement Test—The tube is expected to pass the following test although the actual performance of the test is not required under this specification unless specifically stipulated by the purchaser:

a. Heat the cleaned or degreased specimens for 20 min minimum at a temperature of 850 °C ± 25 (1562 °F ± 45) in a furnace in which the atmosphere is at least 10% of hydrogen by volume. Then quench the specimens immediately and rapidly in water or in the same atmosphere with minimum contact with air.
b. Polish and etch if desired, cross-sectional test specimens taken transverse to, and bounded by, an original surface of the material. Examine the prepared surface microscopically under illumination at a magnification of 75 to 200 diameters inclusive. Specimens shall show no passing or open grain structure characteristic of embrittlement.

TABLE 1—TUBING DIMENSIONS AND TOLERANCES

Nominal Tubing OD		Outside Diameter[1] Basic		Outside Diameter[2] Tolerance		Wall Thickness Basic		Wall Thickness[2] Tolerance	
mm	in	mm	in	± mm	± in	mm	in	± mm	± in
3.18	1/8	3.18	0.125	0.05	0.0020	0.76	0.030	0.08	0.0030
4.76	3/16	4.78	0.188	0.05	0.0020	0.76	0.030	0.063	0.0025
6.35	1/4	6.35	0.250	0.05	0.0020	0.76	0.030	0.063	0.0025
7.94	5/16	7.92	0.312	0.05	0.0020	0.81	0.032	0.063	0.0025
9.53	3/8	9.53	0.375	0.05	0.0020	0.81	0.032	0.063	0.0025
12.70	1/2	12.70	0.500	0.05	0.0020	0.81	0.032	0.063	0.0025
15.88	5/8	15.88	0.625	0.05	0.0020	0.89	0.035	0.063	0.0025
19.05	3/4	19.05	0.750	0.063	0.0025	0.89	0.035	0.063	0.0025

1. The actual outside diameter shall be the average of the maximum and minimum outside diameters as described at any one cross section through the tubing.
2. The tolerances listed represent the maximum permissible deviation at any point.

TABLE 2—CHEMICAL COMPOSITION, WEIGHT %

SAE Alloy No.[1]	UNS No.[2]	Similar ASTM Copper No. [3]	Copper, min	Phosphorus	Arsenic
CA102	C10200	102 (was OF)	99.95	—	—
CA120	C12000	120 (was DLP)	99.90	0.004–0.012	—
CA122	C12200	122 (was DHP)	99.90	0.015–0.040	—
—	—	142 (was DPA)	99.40	0.015–0.040	0.15–0.50

1. SAE J463.
2. Unified Numbering System.
3. ASTM B 75.

TABLE 3—MECHANICAL PROPERTIES

Ultimate Strength (Tensile), min	205 MPa (30 000 psi)
Yield Strength (Tensile), min [1]	62.0 MPa (9 000 psi)

1. At 0.5% extension under load.

TESTS AND PROCEDURES FOR SAE LOW-CARBON STEEL AND COPPER NICKEL TUBING—SAE J1677 JAN1996

SAE Standard

Report of the SAE Fluid Conductors and Connectors Technical Committee SC1—Automotive and Hydraulic Tube and Fittings approved January 1996.

1. Scope—This SAE Standard is intended to establish uniform methods for the testing and performance evaluation of certain types of steel and copper nickel tubing. The specific test and performance criteria applicable to each variety of tubing are set forth in the respective SAE J-Specifications.

2. References

2.1 Applicable Publications—The following publications form a part of this specification to the extent specified herein. Unless otherwise specified, the latest issue of SAE publications shall apply.

2.1.1 SAE PUBLICATION—Available from SAE, 400 Commonwealth Drive, Warrendale, PA 15096-0001.

SAE J533—Flares for Tubing

2.1.2 ASTM PUBLICATION—Available from ASTM, 100 Barr Harbor Drive, West Conshohocken, PA 19428-2959.

ASTM A 370—Methods and Definitions for Mechanical Testing of Steel Products

2.2 Related Publications—The following publications are provided for information purposes only and are not a required part of this document.

2.2.1 SAE PUBLICATIONS—Available from SAE, 400 Commonwealth Drive, Warrendale, PA 15096-0001.

SAE J356—Welded Flash Controlled Low-Carbon Steel Tubing Normalized for Bending, Double Flaring and Beading

SAE J524—Seamless Low-Carbon Steel Tubing Annealed for Bending and Flaring

SAE J525—Welded and Cold-Drawn Low-Carbon Steel Tubing Annealed for Bending and Flaring

SAE J526—Welded Low-Carbon Steel Tubing

SAE J527—Brazed Double Wall Low-Carbon Steel Tubing

SAE J1650—Seamless Copper Nickel 90-10 Tubing

3. Test Procedures—The test procedures described in the current issue of ASTM D 370 shall be followed. However, in cases of conflict between the ASTM specifications and those described herein, the latter shall take precedence.

3.1 Test Frequency—There are many factors which can effect the required frequency of these tests, including:

a. Tube size
b. Production run quantity
c. Type of production equipment
d. Production methods
e. End use
f. Material

Therefore, it shall be the responsibility of the manufacturer and user to establish a test frequency that will produce tubing which conforms to the SAE Standards as well as the needs and requirements of the user.

4. Test Specimens—Test specimens for mechanical tests shall be smooth on the ends and free from flaws. If any test specimen exhibits burrs, flaws, or defective machining before testing, it may be discarded and another specimen may be selected. Test specimens shall be taken from tubing which has not been subjected to cold working after the anneal of the finished sized tubing. All tests shall be conducted at room temperature using finished tubing.

5. Performance Tests—Test specimens shall be taken from tubing which has not been subjected to cold working after the final processing of the finished sized tubing.

5.1 Flattening Test—Test specimens approximately 75 mm in length shall not crack or show any flaws when flattened between parallel plates to a distance equal to three times the wall thickness of the section under test. For welded tubing, the weld shall be placed at 90 degrees from the direction of applied force. Superficial ruptures resulting from minor surface imperfections shall not be considered cause for rejection.

5.2 Reverse Flattening Test—Test specimens shall be split longitudinally 90 degrees on each side of the weld. The section containing the weld shall be opened and flattened with the weld at the point of maximum bend. There shall be no evidence of cracks or metal flaking, or lack of weld penetration or overlaps resulting from flash control or flash removal in the weld.

5.3 Bending Test—If a bend test is required, the customer shall specify a suitable test method at time of purchase.

5.4 Expansion Test—Test specimens shall be subjected to expansion over a hardened tapered plug having a slope of 0.1:1.0, until the outside diameter has been expanded 25% without evidence of cracking or flaws.

5.5 Flaring Test

5.5.1 DOUBLE FLARE—METHOD A—Test sections having squared and deburred ends shall withstand being double flared at one end to the dimensions shown in SAE J533. The test section shall be held firmly and squarely in the die and the punch, while being forced down, shall be guided parallel to the axis of the tubing. The flare shall exhibit no evidence of splitting or flaws in area A (Figure 1).

a. Area B—The flare seat, defined as the surface within the included angle. Conical surface shall be smooth and free from cracks or other irregularities which could cause leaks after assembly.
b. Area C—The surface beyond the length of the double thickness created by the flare.

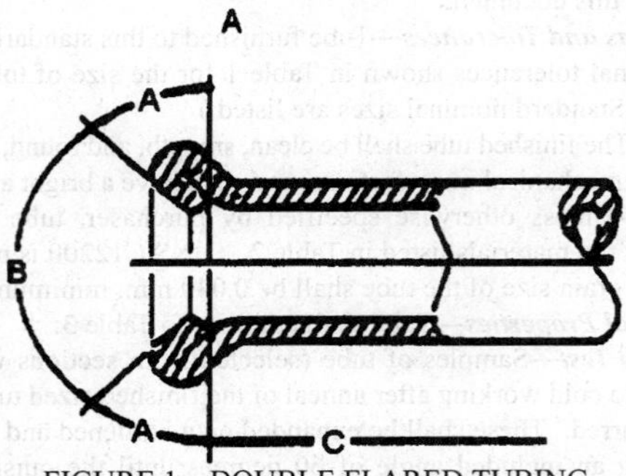

FIGURE 1—DOUBLE FLARED TUBING

5.5.2 DOUBLE FLARE—METHOD B—Test sections having squared and deburred ends shall withstand being double flared at one end to the dimensions shown in SAE J533. The test section shall be held firmly and squarely in the die and the punch, while being forced down, shall be guided parallel to the axis of the tubing. The flare shall exhibit no evidence of splitting or flaws except that a separation of the outer lap joint with area A (Figure 2) shall be permissible providing it does not exceed 3.1 mm in length and is confined to the outer thickness only. Seam separation shall not be permissible in the following areas:

a. Area B—The flare seat, defined as the surface within the included angle. Conical surface shall be smooth and free from cracks or other irregularities which could cause leaks after assembly.
b. Area C—The surface beyond the length of the double thickness created by the flare.

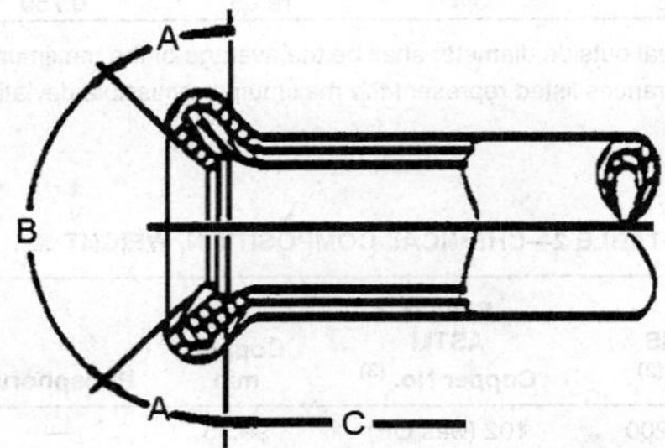

FIGURE 2—DOUBLE FLARED, DOUBLE WALL TUBING

5.5.3 SINGLE FLARE—Test sections having squared and deburred ends shall withstand being single flared at one end to the dimensions shown in SAE J533. The test section shall be held firmly and squarely in the die and the punch, while being forced down, shall be guided parallel to the axis of the tubing. The flare shall exhibit no evidence of splitting or flaws in area A (Figure 3).

a. Area B—The flare seat, defined as the surface within the included angle. Conical surface shall be smooth and free from cracks or other irregularities which could cause leaks after assembly.

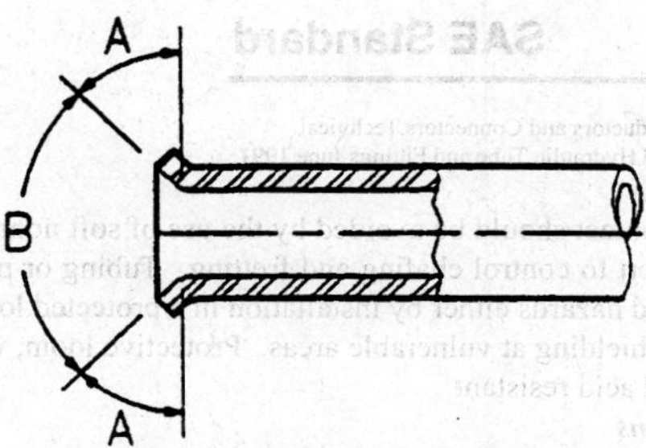

FIGURE 3—SINGLE FLARED TUBING

5.6 Hardness Test—Hardness tests shall be made on the inside surfaces of test specimens. This test is not required on tubing with a nominal wall thickness less than 1.7 mm. Such tubing shall meet all other mechanical properties and performance requirements.

5.7 Tensile Test—If the percentage of elongation of the test specimen is less than that specified and/or any part of the fracture is more than 19 mm from the center of the gage length, as indicated by scribe marks on the specimen before testing, a retest shall be allowed.

5.8 Proof Pressure Test—Tubing shall be tested hydrostatically, with no evidence of failure, at a pressure which will subject the material to the appropriate fiber stress. Test pressures shall be as determined by Barlow's formula for thin hollow cylinders under pressure:

$$P = \frac{2TS}{D} \qquad \text{(Eq. 1)}$$

where:

D = outside diameter of tubing, mm
P = hydrostatic pressure, MPa
S = allowable unit stress of material from applicable tubing specification, MPa
T = minimum wall thickness of tubing, mm

No tube shall be tested beyond a hydrostatic pressure of 35 MPa unless so specified and mutually agreed upon by supplier and customer.

5.9 Nondestructive Electronic Test—In lieu of the hydrostatic test, where mutually agreed upon by the purchaser and manufacturer, all tubing shall be tested by passing it through a nondestructive electronic test (such as eddy current, flux leakage, or ultrasonic) which is capable of detecting defects that would prevent the tubing from passing the hydrostatic pressure proof test.

(R) METALLIC AIR BRAKE SYSTEM TUBING AND PIPE—SAE J1149 JUN1991

SAE Standard

This standard was formerly designated SAE J844 approved June 1963, completely revised July 1976, and reaffirmed by the SAE Fluid Conductors and Connectors Technical Committee December 1987. Completely revised by the SAE Fluid Conductors and Connectors Technical Committee SC1—Automotive and Hydraulic Tube and Fittings June 1991.

Foreword—This Document has also changed to comply with the new SAE Technical Standards Board format.

1. Scope—This SAE Standard covers minimum requirements for two types of metallic tubing and pipe as used in automotive air brake systems. It includes material and performance specifications, corrosion precautions, and installation recommendations. Copper tubing is designated Type 1, and galvanized steel pipe Type 2.

2. References

2.1 Applicable Publications—The following publications form a part of this specification to the extent specified herein. Unless otherwise indicated, the latest version of SAE publications shall apply.

2.1.1 SAE PUBLICATIONS—Available from SAE, 400 Commonwealth Drive, Warrendale, PA 15096-0001.

SAE J463—Wrought Copper and Copper Alloys

SAE J476—Dryseal Pipe Threads

2.1.2 ASTM PUBLICATIONS—Available from ASTM, 100 Barr Harbor Drive, West Conshohocken, PA 19428-2959.

ASTM A 120—Specification for Black and Hot-Dipped Zinc-Coated (Galvanized) Welded and Seamless Steel Pipe for Ordinary Uses

ASTM A 370—Methods and Definitions for Mechanical Testing of Steel Products

ASTM E 8—Methods of Tension Testing of Metallic Materials

ASTM E 62—Method of Test for Antimony in Copper and Copper Base Alloys

ASTM E 79—Methods for Estimating the Average Grain Size of Wrought Copper and Copper Base Alloys

3. Corrosion Precautions—In the design and selection of air brake system components, adequate provision shall be made to control corrosion due to galvanic coupling of widely dissimilar metals and alloys when such materials used for tubing, pipe, fittings, and attaching or supporting parts are in intimate contact with each other. Also, adequate provision shall be made to protect the tubing, pipe, and fittings from oxygen concentration cell type of corrosion. Where soft nonmetallic cushions are used to prevent metal-to-metal contact between supporting components and tubing, pipe, and fittings, the cushioning material shall be such that it will not absorb and retain significant amounts of water.

4. Installation Recommendations—The tubing or pipe installed in air brake systems shall be supported in such a manner as to minimize fatigue conditions. Metal-to-metal contact should be avoided by the use of soft nonmetallic cushions at points of support to control chafing and fretting. Tubing or pipe shall be protected against road hazards either by installation in a protected location or by providing adequate shielding at vulnerable areas. Protective loom, where used, shall be both water and acid resistant.

5. Specifications

5.1 Type 1—Copper Tubing—This material specification covers the minimum requirements for seamless annealed copper tubing that shall be used for automotive air brake lines.

5.1.1 MANUFACTURE—The tubing shall be seamless cold drawn to size and bright annealed as a final operation in such a manner as to produce a finished product which will meet all requirements of this document.

5.1.2 DIMENSIONS AND TOLERANCES—The finished tubing shall conform to the dimensions and tolerances shown in Table 1, for the nominal diameter specified by the purchaser.

5.1.3 QUALITY—The finished tubing shall be clean, smooth, and round, free from internal and external mechanical imperfections, corrosion, scale, seams, and cracks.

5.1.4 MATERIAL—The tubing shall be made from phosphorized, low residual phosphorus copper conforming to SAE J463, UNS C12200 which has the chemical composition as in Table 2:

5.1.5 MECHANICAL PROPERTIES—The finished tubing shall have mechanical properties as tabulated in Table 3:

5.1.6 GRAIN SIZE—The tubing shall be furnished in either of two temper conditions with grain size as tabulated in Table 4:

5.1.7 PERFORMANCE REQUIREMENTS—The finished tubing shall satisfactorily meet the following performance tests. Test specimens shall be taken from tubing which has not been subjected to cold working after the anneal of the finished sized tubing.

5.1.8 FLARING TEST—A test section cut from the finished tubing, having squared and deburred ends, shall withstand being flared at one end over a polished tapered mandrel of 60 degrees included angle until the actual average outside diameter is increased 40% without evidence of splitting or flaws. The axis of the mandrel and axis of the tubing shall be kept parallel during the flaring process and the test may be made in a die to restrict the expansion to 40%.

TABLE 1—DIMENSIONS AND TOLERANCES OF AIR BRAKE TUBING

Nominal Tubing OD (in)	Outside Diameter[1] Specified mm	Outside Diameter[1] Specified in	Outside Diameter[1] Tolerance± mm	Outside Diameter[1] Tolerance± in	Wall Thickness (min) mm	Wall Thickness (min) in
1/4	6.35	0.250	0.05	0.002	0.75	0.0295
5/16	7.92	0.312	0.05	0.002	0.75	0.0295
3/8	9.53	0.375	0.05	0.002	0.75	0.0295
7/16	11.10	0.437	0.05	0.002	1.160	0.0455
1/2	12.70	0.500	0.05	0.002	1.160	0.0455
5/8	15.88	0.625	0.05	0.002	1.160	0.0455
3/4	19.05	0.750	0.06	0.0025	1.160	0.0455
1	25.40	1.000	0.06	0.0025	1.160	0.0455

1. The actual outside diameter shall be the average of the maximum and minimum outside diameters as determined at any one cross section through the tubing.

TABLE 2—CHEMICAL REQUIREMENTS

Element	Ladle Analysis % by Weight
Copper	99.90 min
Phosphorus	0.015-0.040

TABLE 3—MECHANICAL PROPERTIES, COPPER TUBING

Yield Strength MPa (psi) min[1]	Tensile Strength MPa (psi) min	Elongation in 50 mm (2 in), % min Tubing OD 19 mm (3/4 in) and smaller	Elongation in 50 mm (2 in), % min Tubing OD Over 19 mm (3/4 in)
62 (9000)	210 (30 000)	30	40

1. At 0.5% extension under load

TABLE 4—GRAIN SIZE

Temper	Grain Size, mm
Light Annealed	0.015-0.040
Soft Annealed	0.040 min

5.1.9 PRESSURE PROOF TEST—Unless otherwise specified, tubing supplied under this document shall withstand, with no evidence of failure, a hydrostatic proof test at a pressure equivalent to a hoop (circumferential) stress of 62 MPa (9000 psi). The test pressure shall be as determined from Barlow's formula for thin hollow cylinders under pressure:

$$P = \frac{2TS}{D} \quad \text{(Eq. 1)}$$

where:

D = outside diameter of tubing, mm (in)
P = hydrostatic pressure, MPa (psi)
S = allowable unit stress of material = 62 MPa (9000 psi)
T = minimum wall thickness of tubing, mm (in)

The test pressure at a yield strength of 62 MPa (9000 psi) for the minimum wall thicknesses allowed are given in Table 5.

5.1.10 AIR PRESSURE TEST—Each length of finished tubing shall be tested at the maximum operating air pressure, as specified by the purchaser. The tubing shall show no leakage at the test pressure. An electric eddy current test may be substituted for the air pressure test, providing the rejection limits are such that the hydrostatic and air pressure requirements can be guaranteed.

5.1.11 IDENTIFICATION—Tubing shall be permanently and legibly marked at intervals not greater than 381 mm (15 in) with the words Air Brake.

TABLE 5—HYDROSTATIC TEST PRESSURES FOR AIR BRAKE TUBING

Nominal Tubing OD, in	Hydrostatic Test Pressure MPa	Hydrostatic Test Pressure psi	Nominal Tubing OD, in	Hydrostatic Test Procedure MPa	Hydrostatic Test Procedure psi
1/4	1.450	2100	1/2	11.00	1600
5/16	11.70	1700	5/8	8.95	1300
3/8	9.65	1400	3/4	6.90	1000
7/16	12.40	1800	1	5.50	800

5.1.12 METHODS OF TEST—All tests to determine conformance with the foregoing specifications shall be conducted in accordance with the following ASTM Standards:

5.1.12.1 Chemical Analysis—See ASTM E 62.

5.1.12.2 Grain Size—See ASTM E 79.

5.1.12.3 Tensile—See ASTM E 8.

5.2 Type 2—Galvanized Steel Pipe—This material specification covers the minimum requirements for pipe that shall be used in automotive air brake lines.

5.2.1 SPECIFICATIONS—Welded or seamless steel pipe shall be Schedule 40, Zinc Coated, (galvanized by the hot dip process), and manufactured in accordance with ASTM A 120.

5.2.2 DIMENSIONS AND TOLERANCES—The finished pipe shall conform to the dimensions and tolerances listed for several nominal sizes in Tables 6A and 6B.

5.2.3 PIPE THREADS—Both ends of lengths of pipe shall be threaded after coating, unless there is specific authorization to the contrary, to conform to Dryseal American Standard Taper Thread (NPTF). Specifications for pipe threads are given in detail in SAE J476.

5.2.4 MECHANICAL PROPERTIES—The steel in the finished pipe, including the weld, shall have mechanical properties as tabulated in Table 7.

TABLE 6A—DIMENSIONS AND TOLERANCES OF PIPE FOR AIR BRAKE USE, mm

Nominal Pipe Size	Outside Diameter Specified mm	Outside Diameter Tolerance min	Outside Diameter Tolerance max	Inside Diameter (Ref)	Wall Thickness Specified	Wall Thickness min	Threads per in	Nominal Weight Plain ends kg/m ± 5%
1/8	10.29	9.50	10.67	6.83	1.73	1.52	27	0.36
1/4	13.72	12.93	14.10	9.25	2.24	1.96	18	0.63
3/8	17.14	16.36	17.53	12.53	2.31	2.03	18	0.85
1/2	21.34	20.55	21.72	15.80	2.77	2.41	14	1.27
3/4	26.67	25.88	27.05	20.93	2.87	2.51	14	1.68
1	33.40	32.61	33.78	26.64	3.38	2.95	11.5	2.50

TABLE 6B—DIMENSIONS AND TOLERANCES OF PIPE FOR AIR BRAKE USE, in

Nominal Pipe Size	Outside Diameter Specified mm	Outside Diameter Tolerance Plus	Outside Diameter Tolerance Minus	Inside Diameter (Ref)	Wall Thickness Specified	Wall Thickness min	Threads per in	Weight Per ft,[1] lb ± 5%
1/8	0.405	0.016	0.031	0.269	0.068	0.060	27	0.24
1/4	0.540	0.016	0.031	0.364	0.088	0.077	18	0.42
3/8	0.675	0.016	0.031	0.493	0.091	0.080	18	0.57
1/2	0.840	0.016	0.031	0.622	0.109	0.095	14	0.85
3/4	1.050	0.016	0.031	0.824	0.113	0.099	14	1.13
1	1.315	0.016	0.031	1.049	0.133	0.116	11.5	1.68

1. Nominal Weight Plain Ends.

TABLE 7—MECHANICAL PROPERTIES, GALVANIZED STEEL PIPE

Yield Strength, MPa (psi), min	Elongation in 50 mm (2 in), %
170 (25 000)	14-40

5.2.5 PRESSURE PROOF TESTS PER TEST METHOD ASTM A 370, SUPPLEMENT II

5.2.5.1 Hydrostatic Test—Unless otherwise specified, each length of pipe shall be tested at the mill to a hydrostatic pressure of 4850 kPa (700 psi). For nominal sizes over 25.4 mm (1 in) dia see ASTM A 120.

5.2.5.2 Nondestructive Electric Test—In lieu of the hydrostatic test, if mutually agreeable to purchaser and the manufacturer, each pipe may be tested by passing it through an electric eddy current tester which is capable of detecting defects 1.57 mm (0.062 in) in length and one-half the wall thickness, or defects of any length completely penetrating the wall. Such tests shall be made on the welded seam and the adjacent metal affected thereby.

5.2.5.3 Corrosion Protection—The inside and outside surface of the pipe shall be coated with zinc by the hot dip process. The coating shall weight at least 610 g/m^2 (2.0 oz/ft^2) of total surface. Tests to determine whether product meets this requirement shall be conducted in accordance with ASTM A 120.

5.2.5.4 Bending—Pipe shall be used for essentially straight runs; however, generous curves having a radius in excess of 20 times the outside diameter shall be permitted. In no case, shall heat be used to facilitate bending of pipe.

NONMETALLIC AIR BRAKE SYSTEM TUBING—SAE J844 JUN1998

SAE Standard

Report of the SAE Tube, Pipe, Hose, and Lubrication Fittings Committee approved June 1963. Completely revised by the SAE Fluid Conductors and Connectors Technical Committee October 1988 and June 1990. Revised by the SAE Fluid Conductors and Connectors Technical Committee SC4—Air Brake Tubing and Fitting October 1994, May 1997, and June 1998.

1. Scope[1]— This SAE Standard covers the minimum requirements for nonmetallic tubing as manufactured for use in air brake systems. Nonreinforced products are designated type A and reinforced products type B. It is not intended to cover tubing for any portion of the system which operates below –40 °C (–40 °F), above +93 °C (+200 °F), above a maximum working gage pressure of 1030 kPa (150 psi), or in an area subject to attack by battery acid. This tubing is intended for use in the brake system for connections which maintain a basically fixed relationship between components during vehicle operation. Coiled tube assemblies required for those installations where flexing occurs are covered by this document and SAE J1131 to the extent of setting minimum requirements on the essentially straight tube and tube fitting connections which are used in the construction of such assemblies[2].

2. References

2.1 Applicable Publications—The following publications form a part of this specification to the extent specified herein. Unless otherwise specified, the latest issue of SAE publications shall apply.

2.1.1 SAE PUBLICATIONS—Available from SAE, 400 Commonwealth Drive, Warrendale, PA 15096-0001.

SAE J246—Spherical and Flanged Sleeve (Compression) Tube Fittings

SAE J1131—Performance Requirements for SAE J844 Nonmetallic Tubing and Fitting Assemblies Used in Automotive Air Brake Systems

SAE J1149—Metallic Air Brake System Tubing and Pipe

2.1.2 ASTM PUBLICATIONS—Available from ASTM, 100 Barr Harbor Drive, West Conshohocken, PA 19428-2959.

ASTM D 4329—Practice for Operating Light- and Water-Exposure Apparatus (Fluorescent UV-Condensation Type) for Exposure of Plastics

ASTM G 53—Recommended Practice for Operating Light- and Water-Exposure Apparatus (Fluorescent U-Condensation Type) for Exposure of Nonmetallic Materials

2.1.3 FEDERAL REGULATIONS—Available from The Superintendent of Documents, U.S. Government Printing Office, Washington, DC 20402.

49CFR393.45—Brake Tubing and Hose Adequacy

49CFR571.106—Brake Hoses

3. Installation and Assembly Recommendations

3.1 End Fittings—End fittings are to be assembled to the tubing in accordance with the fitting manufacturer's recommendations. The fitting may be of the design shown in SAE J246, or any other design suitable for use with nonmetallic air brake tubing. Performance test requirements for nonmetallic air brake assemblies are covered in SAE J1131.

3.2 Noncoiled Tubing—Noncoiled tubing should not be used in flexing applications such as frame to axle.

3.3 Support and Routing—When installed in a vehicle this tubing shall be routed and supported so as to:

a. Eliminate chafing, abrasion, kinking, or other mechanical damage
b. Minimize fatigue conditions
c. Be protected against road hazards by installation in a protected location or by providing adequate shielding at vulnerable areas
d. Not to be exposed to temperatures, internal or external, over +93 °C (+200 °F) or below –40 °C (–40 °F)
e. Not to be exposed to attack by battery acid
f. Avoid excessive sag

4. Identification—Air brake tubing shall be labeled in a contrasting color with the legend repeated every 380 mm (15 in) or less along the entire length of tubing in legible block capital letters.

The following minimum information, in the order listed, is required. Additional information and/or another lay line may be added, if necessary.

a. Air brake
b. SAE J844
c. Type, A or B
d. Nominal, tubing OD in fractions of 6.4, 9.5, 12.7 mm (1/4, 3/8, 1/2 in), etc.
e. Tubing manufacturer's identification

5. Manufacture—The tubing shall be manufactured to comply with the requirements outlined in this document.

6. Construction—Type A tubing shall consist of a single wall extrusion of 100% virgin nylon (polyamide) containing additives which provide heat and light resistance. Type B tubing shall consist of a core extrusion of 100% virgin nylon (polyamide) containing additives which provide heat resistance. This core shall be reinforced with polyester braid or equivalent, and covered with a protective jacket of 100% virgin nylon (polyamide) containing additives which provide heat and light resistance. The protective covering shall be bonded to the core through the interstices of the braid. The inner core and outer jacket shall be of contrasting colors.

7. Dimensions and Tolerances—The tubing shall conform to dimensions shown in Table 1 under all conditions of moisture. Conformance with this requirement shall be determined on samples which have been subjected to 110 °C (230 °F)[3] for 4 h[4] in a circulating air oven, and on separate samples which have been immersed in boiling water for 2 h. Dimensional tests shall be made after samples have been returned to room temperature for 1/2 to 3 h.

8. Mechanical Properties—The tubing shall conform to the mechanical properties shown in Table 2, when tested according to the methods outlined in this document.

1. See SAE J1149 for Metallic Air Brake System Tubing and Pipe.
2. Federal regulations covering designed requirements and accepted applications for coiled tube assemblies are set forth in 49CFR393.45. Conformance to SAE J844 does not imply compliance with Federal regulations for air brake tubing. Sizes 3.97 mm (5/32 in) and below may not meet 49CFR571.106 requirements for air brake systems.
3. All test temperatures specified may vary by ±3 °C (±5 °F).
4. All times are minimum unless otherwise specified.

TABLE 1—DIMENSIONS AND TOLERANCES

Type of Tubing	Nominal Tubing OD	Outside Diameter max mm	Outside Diameter max in	Outside Diameter min mm	Outside Diameter min in	Inside Diameter Basic mm	Inside Diameter Basic in	Wall Thickness Basic mm	Wall Thickness Basic in	Wall Thickness Tolerances mm	Wall Thickness Tolerances in
A	1/8	3.25	0.128	3.10	0.122	2.01	0.079	0.58	0.023	±0.08	±0.003
A	5/32	4.04	0.159	3.89	0.153	2.34	0.092	0.81	0.032	±0.08	±0.003
A	3/16	4.83	0.190	4.67	0.184	2.97	0.117	0.89	0.035	±0.08	±0.003
A	1/4	6.43	0.253	6.27	0.247	4.32	0.170	1.02	0.040	±0.08	±0.003
A	5/16	8.03	0.316	7.82	0.308	5.89	0.232	1.02	0.040	±0.10	±0.004
B	3/8	9.63	0.379	9.42	0.371	6.38	0.251	1.57	0.062	±0.10	±0.004
B	1/2	12.83	0.505	12.57	0.495	9.55	0.376	1.57	0.062	±0.10	±0.004
B	5/8	16.00	0.630	15.75	0.620	11.20	0.441	2.34	0.092	±0.13	±0.005
B	3/4	19.18	0.755	18.92	0.745	14.38	0.566	2.34	0.092	±0.13	±0.005

TABLE 2—MECHANICAL PROPERTIES

Type of Tubing	Nominal Tubing OD	Minimum Burst Pressure at 24 °C (75 °F)(1) kPa	Minimum Burst Pressure at 24 °C (75 °F)(1) psi	Test Bend Radius(2) mm	Test Bend Radius(2) in	Maximum Stiffness N	Maximum Stiffness lbf
A	1/8	6900	1000	9.4	0.37	4.4	1
A	5/32	8300	1200	12.7	0.50	4.4	1
A	3/16	8300	1200	19.1	0.75	4.4	1
A	1/4	8300	1200	25.4	1.00	8.9	2
A	5/16	6900	1000	31.8	1.25	27.0	6
B	3/8	9700	1400	38.1	1.50	36.0	8
B	1/2	6600	950	50.8	2.00	89.0	20
B	5/8	6200	900	63.5	2.50	222.0	50
B	3/4	5500	800	76.2	3.00	356.0	80

1. With moisture content of tubing 0.06% maximum.
2. For test purpose only.

9. Performance Requirements—The tubing shall satisfactorily meet the following performance tests (see footnotes 3, 4, 5, 6, 7, and 8).

9.1 Leak Test[5]—The tubing manufacturer shall subject each continuous length of tubing to test at a gage pressure of 200 psi +50, –0 (1380 kPa +350, –0) with an appropriate gas for a period of time (minimum 30 s) sufficient to determine the presence of any leaks. Defective sections shall be cut off and scrapped. The remaining tubing shall be recoupled at the points where defective sections were removed and again subjected to the 200 psi +50, –0 (1380 kPa +350, –0) pressure test. The procedure shall be repeated until all sections of tubing designated for distribution to users have successfully withstood the test.

9.2 Moisture Absorption[6]—Expose sample of tubing for 24 h in a circulating air oven at 110 °C (230 °F). Remove from oven, weigh immediately and expose for 100 h at 100% relative humidity and 24 °C (75 °F). Within 5 min from humidity conditioning, wipe surface moisture from both the interior and exterior surfaces of the tubing and reweigh. Moisture absorption shall not exceed 2% by weight.

9.3 Ultraviolet Resistance[6]—Place samples of tubing in the sample racks of a Q-Panel QUV test apparatus* equipped with Phillips bulbs, type UVA-340. Expose for 300 h minimum. If the test apparatus is equipped with a "Solar Eye," the bulbs need not be rotated and the irradiance should be set at 0.85, however all bulbs should be discarded after 4800 h maximum, or if they fall below the 0.85 irradiance level, whichever occurs first. If the test apparatus is not equipped with a "Solar Eye," the bulbs must be rotated every 400 h maximum, as recommended by the manufacturer and ASTM G 53, this procedure will result in discarding lamps after 1600 h of use. Control the temperature of the appartus to 45 °C ± 3 °C. The distance from the plate upon which the specimens are mounted and the light bulbs will be 51 mm (2 in) maximum. The automatic humidity cycling must be turned off. Rotate the specimens according to ASTM D 4329 except the time interval should be each 96 hours maximum instead of weekly. Maintain and operate the QUV tester in accordance with the manufacturers instructions. Immediately following this exposure, subject the tubing to the impact test shown in Figure 1. Subject tubing to room temperature burst as specified in 9.10. Tubing shall withstand no less than 80% of the burst pressure shown in Table 2.

* The Q-Panel QUV Accelerated Weathering Tester is available from:

The Q-Panel Company
26200 First Street
Cleveland, OH 44145
(216) 835-8700

9.4 Cold Temperature Flexibility[6]—Expose sample of tubing for 24 h in a circulating air oven at 110 °C (230 °F). Remove from oven and within 30 min expose for 4 h at –40 °C (–40 °F). Also expose a mandrel at –40 °C (–40 °F) having a diameter equal to 12 times the nominal diameter of the tubing. (In order to obtain uniform temperatures, the tubing and mandrel may be supported by a nonmetallic surface during the entire period of test.) Immediately following this exposure, bend tubing 180 degrees over the mandrel, accomplishing the bending motion within a period of 4 to 8 s. The tubing shall show no evidence of fracture.

9.5 Heat Aging[7]—Three separate heat aging tests shall be conducted; each phase shall be run on separate tubing samples. Subject tubing to room temperature burst test as specified in 9.10. Tubing shall withstand 80% of the burst pressure shown in Table 2.

a. Phase 1—Bend samples of tubing 180 degrees around a mandrel having a diameter equivalent to twice the test bend radius specified in Table 2. While in this position, expose tubing and mandrel for 72 h in a circulating air oven at 110 °C (230 °F). Remove from oven and permit tubing to return to 24 °C (75 °F) while still on the mandrel. Within 30 min after stabilization at 24 °C (75 °F), return the tubing to a straight position in a minimum of 4 s, then rebend (against the set) 180 degrees around the mandrel, accomplishing the bending motion within a period of 4 to 8 s.
b. Phase 2—Expose samples of tubing for 72 h in a circulating air oven at 110 °C (230 °F). Remove from oven and permit tubing to return to 24 °C (75 °F). Within 30 min after stabilization at 24 °C (75 °F), subject tubing to the impact test shown in Figure 1.
c. Phase 3—Immerse samples of tubing in boiling water for 2 h. Remove from water and permit to return to 24 °C (75 °F). Within 30 min after stabilization at 24 °C (75 °F), subject tubing to the impact test shown in Figure 1.

9.6 Resistance to Zinc Chloride[7]—Bend tubing to the test bend radius shown in Table 2. While in this position, immerse in a 50% (by weight) aqueous solution of zinc chloride for 200 h at 24 °C (75 °F). Remove from solution. Tubing shall show no evidence of cracking on the outside diameter.

NOTE—Fresh, anhydrous zinc chloride should be used to make up a concentration of 50% (by weight) aqueous solution (specific gravity of 1.576 or a Baume rating of 53 degrees at 16 °C (61 °F)).

9.7 Resistance to Methyl Alcohol[7]—Bend tubing to the test bend radius shown in Table 2. While in this position, immerse in 95% methyl alcohol for 200 h at 24 °C (75 °F). Remove from solution. Tubing shall show no evidence of cracking.

9.8 Stiffness[7]—Use samples 280 mm (11 in) long. Insert a rod of suitable size into the tubing to maintain a straight position within 3.2 mm (±0.125 in). Expose tubing and rod for 24 h in a circulating air oven at 110 °C (230 °F). Remove from oven and permit tubing and rod to return to 24 °C (75 °F). Within 30 min after stabilization at 24 °C (75 °F), remove rod and subject tubing to stiffness test shown in Figure 2. Tubing shall require no more force than specified in Table 2 to deflect 51 mm (2 in).

9.9 Boiling Water Stabilization and Burst Test[7]—Immerse tubing in boiling water for 2 h. Remove from water and subject to the room temperature burst test as specified in 9.10. Tubing shall withstand no less than 80% of the burst pressure shown in Table 2.

9.10 Room Temperature Burst Test[8]—Tubing shall be stabilized for 0.5 to 3.0 h at 24 °C (75 °F) and tested by increasing pressure at a constant rate to reach the specified minimum burst pressure in Table 2 within a time period of 3 to 15 s. Tubing that bursts below the pressure specified in Table 2 shall be rejected.

5. Normally an Inspection Test conducted on each lot of tubing, and where a lot is defined as "the output of one production shift of one size and color of tubing."
6. A Qualification Test.
7. A Qualification Test.
8. Normally an Inspection Test conducted on each lot of tubing, and where a lot is defined as "the output of one production shift of one size and color of tubing."

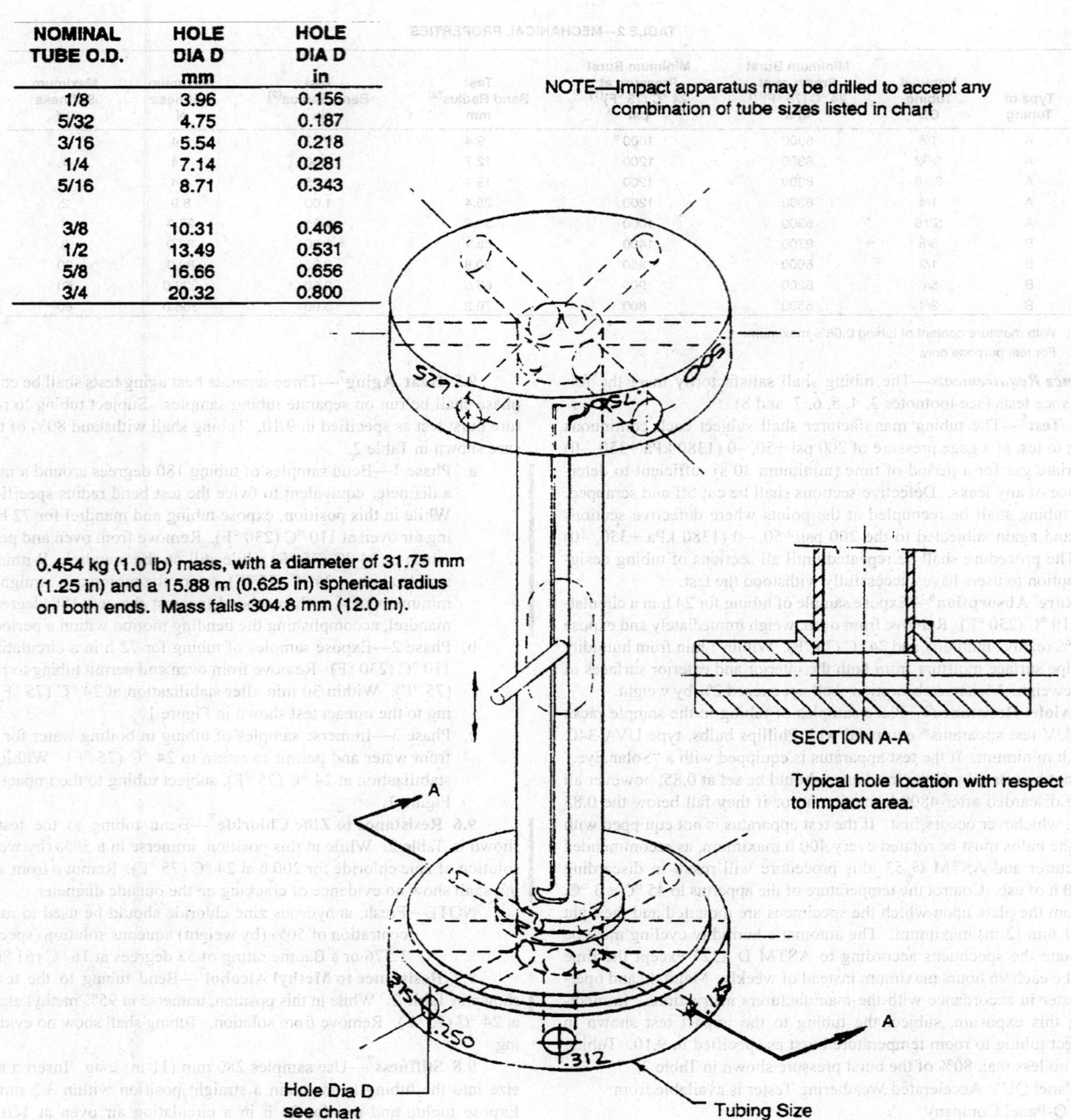

NOMINAL TUBE O.D.	HOLE DIA D mm	HOLE DIA D in
1/8	3.96	0.156
5/32	4.75	0.187
3/16	5.54	0.218
1/4	7.14	0.281
5/16	8.71	0.343
3/8	10.31	0.406
1/2	13.49	0.531
5/8	16.66	0.656
3/4	20.32	0.800

NOTE—Impact apparatus may be drilled to accept any combination of tube sizes listed in chart
0.454 kg (1.0 lb) mass, with a diameter of 31.75 mm (1.25 in) and a 15.88 m (0.625 in) spherical radius on both ends. Mass falls 304.8 mm (12.0 in).
SECTION A-A
Typical hole location with respect to impact area.
A
A
Hole Dia D see chart
Tubing Size
.250
.312

FIGURE 1—TYPICAL NYLON TUBING IMPACT APPARATUS

9.11 Cold Temperature Impact[9]—Condition tubing by exposing one half the samples for 24 h at 110 °C (230 °F) in a circulating air oven, and one half the samples in boiling water for 2 h; then expose all the samples to –40 °C (–40 °F) for 4 h. Also, expose impact test apparatus, shown in Figure 1, to –40 °C (–40 °F). While tubing and apparatus are at this cold temperature (approximately –40 °C (–40 °F), subject tubing to impact as specified. The tubing shall show no evidence of cracks. After impact testing, permit tubing to return to 24 °C (75 °F). Within 30 min after stabilization at 24 °C (75 °F), subject tubing to room temperature burst test as specified in 9.10. Tubing shall withstand at least 80% of the burst pressure shown in Table 2. Sample size shall be 10 specimens per lot. In the event of any failures, a second sample from the same lot consisting of 20 specimens shall be tested. If another failure occurs, the lot shall be rejected.

9.12 Adhesion Test[9]

9.12.1 This test applies only to the reinforced products, Type B.

9.12.2 CONDITION—This test shall be conducted at 24 °C (75 °F) ambient temperature.

9. Normally an Inspection Test conducted on each lot of tubing, and where a lot is defined as "the output of one production shift of one size and color of tubing."

TABLE 3—DIMENSIONS AND TOLERANCES OF AIR BRAKE TUBING

Nominal Tubing OD (in)	Outside Diameter(1) Specified mm	Outside Diameter(1) Specified in	Outside Diameter(1) Tolerance± mm	Outside Diameter(1) Tolerance± in	Wall Thickness (min) mm	Wall Thickness (min) in
1/4	6.35	0.250	0.05	0.002	0.75	0.0295
5/16	7.92	0.312	0.05	0.002	0.75	0.0295
3/8	9.53	0.375	0.05	0.002	0.75	0.0295
7/16	11.10	0.437	0.05	0.002	1.160	0.0455
1/2	12.70	0.500	0.05	0.002	1.160	0.0455
5/8	15.88	0.625	0.05	0.002	1.160	0.0455
3/4	19.05	0.750	0.06	0.0025	1.160	0.0455
1	25.40	1.000	0.06	0.0025	1.160	0.0455

1. The actual outside diameter shall be the average of the maximum and minimum outside diameters as determined at any one cross section through the tubing.

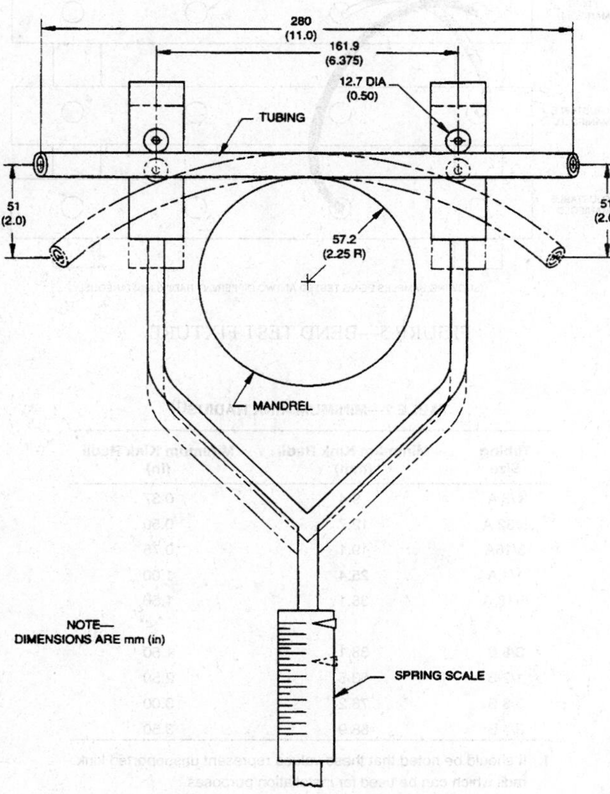

FIGURE 2—STIFFNESS TEST APPARATUS

TABLE 4—CHEMICAL REQUIREMENTS

Element	Ladle Analysis % by Weight
Copper	99.90 min
Phosphorus	0.015-0.040

TABLE 5—MECHANICAL PROPERTIES, COPPER TUBING

Yield Strength MPa (psi) min(1)	Tensile Strength MPa (psi) min	Elongation in 50 mm (2 in), % min Tubing OD 19 mm (3/4 in) and smaller	Elongation in 50 mm (2 in), % min Tubing OD Over 19 mm (3/4 in)
62 (9000)	210 (30 000)	30	40

1. At 0.5% extension under load

TABLE 6—GRAIN SIZE

Temper	Grain Size, mm
Light Annealed	0.015-0.040
Soft Annealed	0.040 min

9.12.3 PROCEDURE AND REQUIREMENTS—Cut a strip of tubing into a 6.0 mm (0.25 in) wide helical coil equal in length to five times the circumference of the tubing. Bend the helical coil in reverse of coiling so as to expose the braid gap between the outer jacket and core tube section. Start by working a sharp knife blade into the braid gap to initiate separation, and then attempt to separate the outer jacket from the core tube at the braid interstices. The bonded surface (excluding the braided area) between the outer jacket and core section shall be inseparable for the entire test sample length.

9.13 Heat Aging Adhesion Test[10]

9.13.1 PROCEDURE—Subject samples to Phase 1 of the heat aging test procedure per 9.5.

9.13.2 REQUIREMENTS—After completion of the Phase 1 procedure, the tubing shall meet the requirements of 9.12.

9.14 Collapse Resistance Test Procedure[10]

9.14.1 GENERAL—All tests are to be conducted at room temperature 93 °C (75 °F)[11] unless otherwise specified.

9.14.2 PREPARATION OF TEST SAMPLES—Three samples shall be prepared for testing. The free tube length of the samples shall be as follows:

3.14 x (min kink radius) + 10 x (tube OD) + 2 x (length of supporting pin)

9.14.3 TEST PROCEDURE—Place a reference mark at the middle of each sample and measure the cross section diameter (Minor Diameter [unbent]) at this point and record.

NOTE—See Figures 4 and 3 for location of minor diameters.

9.14.4 Carefully install the samples on a bend test fixture (as shown in Figure 5) in a 180-degree bend condition. The tube shall be bent in the direction of the natural curvature of the tube. Samples prepared per 9.14.2 shall be bent to a radius equal to the minimum kink radius called out in Table 7.

9.14.5 Age samples on test fixture at 93 °C (200 °F)[12] for 24 h[13]. Allow the samples to cool to room temperature. While the samples are on the test fixture, measure the minor diameter (bent). Collapse of greater than 20% is considered a failure (see Equation 1).

$$\text{Percent Collapse} = \frac{\text{Minor OD [unbent]} - \text{Minor OD [bent]}}{\text{Minor OD [unbent]}} \times 100 \qquad \text{(Eq. 1)}$$

10. A Qualification Test.

11. All test temperatures specified may vary by ±3 °C (±5 °F).

12. All test temperatures specified may vary by ±3 °C (±5 °F).

13. All times are minimum unless otherwise specified.

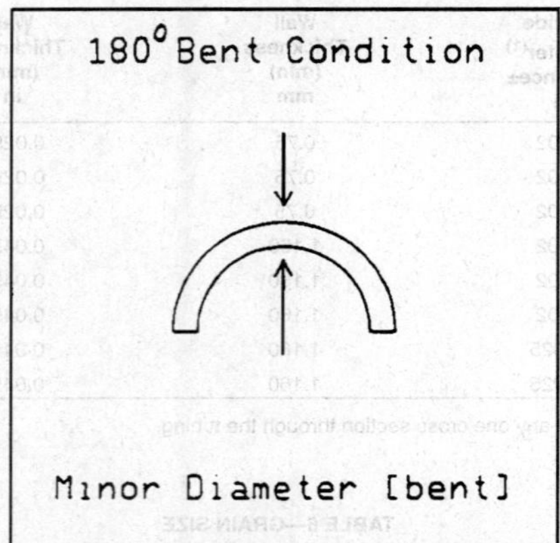

FIGURE 3—MINOR DIAMETER (BENT)

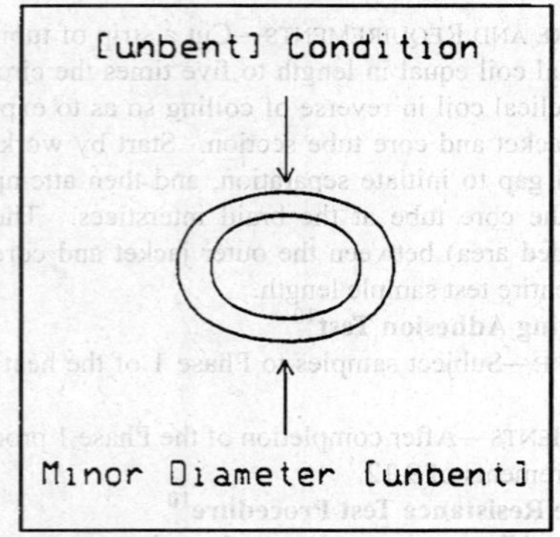

FIGURE 4—MINOR DIAMETER (UNBENT)

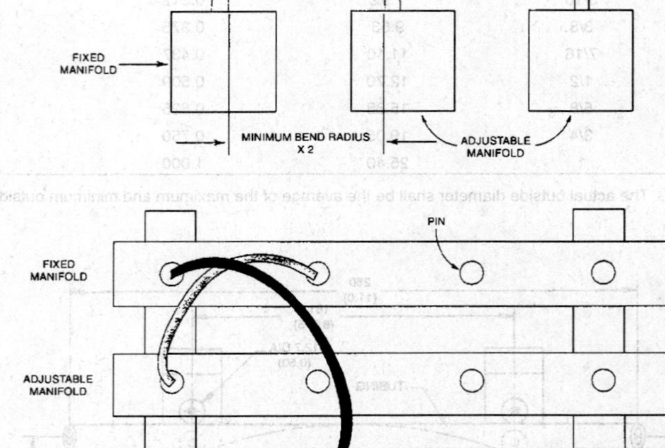

FIGURE 5—BEND TEST FIXTURE

TABLE 7—MINIMUM KINK RADIUS[(1)]

Tubing Size	Minimum Kink Radii (mm)	Minimum Kink Radii (in)
1/8 A	9.4	0.37
5/32 A	12.7	0.50
3/16A	19.1	0.75
1/4 A	25.4	1.00
5/16 A	38.1	1.50
3/8 B	38.1	1.50
1/2 B	63.5	2.50
5/8 B	76.2	3.00
3/4 B	88.9	3.50

1. It should be noted that these values represent unsupported kink radii which can be used for installation purposes.

METRIC NONMETALLIC AIR BRAKE SYSTEM TUBING[1] —SAE J1394 APR2000

SAE Standard

Report of the SAE Fluid Conductors and Connectors Technical Committee, approved April 1983 and revised May 1989. Completely revised by the SAE Fluid Conductors and Connectors Technical Committee S4—Air Brake Tubing and Tube Fittings Subcommittee April 1981, revised June 1998 and revised April 2000. Rationale statement available.

1. Scope—This SAE Standard covers the minimum requirements for metric sizes of nonmetallic tubing as manufactured for use in air brake systems. Nonreinforced products are designated type A and reinforced products type B. It is not intended to cover tubing for any portion of the system that operates below –40 °C (–40 °F), above +93 °C (+200 °F), above a maximum working gage pressure of 1.0 MPa (150 psi), or in an area subject to attack by battery acid. This tubing is intended for use in the brake system for connections that maintain a basically fixed relationship between components during vehicle operation. Coiled tube assemblies required for those installations where flexing occurs are covered by this standard and SAE J1131 to the extent of setting minimum requirements on the essentially straight tube and tube fitting connections, which are used in the construction of such assemblies.[2]

2. References

2.1 Applicable Publications—The following publications form a part of the specification to the extent specified herein. Unless otherwise indicated, the latest revision of SAE publications shall apply.

2.1.1 SAE PUBLICATIONS—Available from SAE, 400 Commonwealth Drive, Warrendale, PA 15096-0001.

SAE J246—Spherical and Flanged Sleeve (Compression) Tube Fittings
SAE J844—Nonmetallic Air Brake System Tubing
SAE J1131—Performance Requirements for SAE J844 Nonmetallic Tubing and Fittings Assemblies Used in Automotive Air Brake Systems
SAE J1149—Metallic Air Brake System Tubing and Pipe

2.1.2 GOVERNMENT PUBLICATIONS—Available from the Superintendent of Documents, U. S. Government Printing Office, Mail Stop: SSOP, Washington, DC 20402-9320.

49 CFR 393.45—Brake Tubing and Hose, Adequacy
49 CFR 571.106—Brake Hoses

2.1.3 ASTM PUBLICATIONS—Available from ASTM, 100 Barr Harbor Drive, West Conshohocken, PA 19428-2959.

ASTM D 4329—Practice for Operating Light- and Water-Exposure Apparatus (Fluorescent UV-Condensation Type) for Exposure of Plastics
ASTM G 53—Recommended Practice for Operating Light- and Water-Exposure Apparatus (Fluorescent UV-Condensation Type) for Exposure of Nonmetallic Materials

3. Installation and Assembly Recommendations

3.1 End Fittings—End fittings are to be assembled to the tubing in accordance with the fitting manufacturer's recommendations. The fitting may be of the design shown in the proposed metric version of SAE J246, or any other design suitable for use with metric size nonmetallic air brake tubing. Performance test requirements for nonmetallic air brake assemblies are covered in SAE J1131.

3.2 Noncoiled Tubing—Noncoiled tubing should not be used in flexing applications such as frame to axle.

3.3 Support and Routing—When installed in a vehicle, this tubing shall be routed and supported so as to:

a. Eliminate chafing, abrasion, kinking, or other mechanical damage.
b. Minimize fatigue conditions.
c. Be protected against road hazards by installation in a protected location or by providing adequate shielding at vulnerable areas.
d. Not be exposed to temperatures, internal or external, over +93 °C (+200 °F) or below –40 °C (–40 °F).
e. Not be exposed to attack by battery acid.
f. Avoid excessive sag.

4. Identification—Air brake tubing shall be labeled in contrasting color with the legend repeated every 380 mm (15 in) or less along the entire length of tubing in legible block capital letters.

The following minimum information, in the order listed, is required. Additional information and/or another lay line may be added, if necessary.

a. Metric airbrake
b. SAE J1394
c. Type A or B
d. Nominal tubing OD in mm—6, 8, 10, 12, or 16
e. Tubing manufacturer's identification

5. Manufacture—The tubing shall be manufactured to comply with the requirements outlined in this document.

6. Construction—Type A tubing shall consist of a single wall extrusion of 100% virgin nylon (polyamide) containing additives that provide heat and light resistance. Type B tubing shall consist of a core extrusion of 100% virgin nylon (polyamide) containing additives that provide heat resistance. This core shall be reinforced with polyester braid or equivalent and covered with a protective jacket of 100% virgin nylon (polyamide) containing additives that provide heat and light resistance. The protective covering shall be bonded to the core through the interstices of the braid. The inner core and outer jacket shall be of contrasting colors.

7. Dimensions and Tolerances—The tubing shall conform to dimensions shown in Table 1 under all conditions of moisture. Conformance with this requirement shall be determined on samples that have been subjected to 110 °C (230 °F)[3] for 4 h[4] in a circulating air oven, and on separate samples that have been immersed in boiling water for 2 h. Dimensional tests shall be made after samples have been returned to room temperature for 0.5 to 3.0 h.

8. Mechanical Properties—The tubing shall conform to the mechanical properties shown in Table 2, when tested according to the method outlined in this document.

9. Performance Requirements—The tubing shall satisfactorily meet the following performance tests (see Footnotes 3, 4, 5, and 6).

9.1 Leak Test[5]—The tubing manufacturer shall subject each continuous length of tubing to test at a gage pressure of 1.4 MPa + 0.35, –0 (200 psi + 50, –0) with an appropriate gas for a period of time (minimum 30 s) sufficient to determine the presence of any leaks. Defective sections shall be cut off and scrapped. The remaining tubing shall be recoupled at the points where defective sections were removed and again subjected to the 1.4 MPa + 0.35, –0 (200 psi + 50, –0) pressure test. The procedure shall be repeated until all sections of tubing designated for distribution to users have successfully withstood the test.

9.2 Moisture Absorption[6]—Expose sample of tubing for 24 h in a circulating air oven at 110 °C (230 °F). Remove from oven, weigh immediately, and expose for 100 h at 100% relative humidity and 24 °C (75 °F). Within 5 min from humidity conditioning, wipe surface moisture from both the interior and exterior surfaces of the tubing and reweigh. Moisture absorption shall not exceed 2% by weight.

9.3 Ultraviolet Resistance[6]—Place samples of tubing in the sample racks of a Q-Panel QUV test apparatus* equipped with Phillips bulbs, type UVA-340. Expose for 300 h minimum. If the test apparatus is equipped with a "Solar Eye," the bulbs need not be rotated and the irradiance should be set at 0.85, however all bulbs should be discarded after 4800 h maximum, or if they fall below the 0.85 irradiance level, which ever occurs first. If the test apparatus is not equipped with a "Solar Eye," the bulbs must be rotated every 400 h maximum, as recommended by the manufacturer and ASTM G 53, this procedure will result in discarding lamps after 1600 h of use. Control the temperate of the apparatus to 45 °C ± 3 °C. The distance from the plate upon which the specimens are mounted and the light bulbs will be 51 mm maximum. The automatic humidity cycling must be turned off. Rotate the specimens according to ASTM D 4329 except the time interval should be each 96 h maximum instead of weekly. Maintain and operate the QUV tester in accordance with the manufacturers instructions. Immediately following this exposure, subject the tubing to the impact test shown in Figure 1. Subject tubing to room temperature burst as specified in 9.10. Tubing shall withstand no less than 80% of the burst pressure shown in Table 2.

---

1. The metric values contained herein are to be regarded as standard; the in-lb values in parentheses may only be approximate. See SAE J844 for nonmetallic air brake system tubing (inch-dimensioned) and SAE J1149 for metallic air brake system tubing and pipe.
2. Federal regulations covering designed requirements and accepted applications for coiled tube assemblies are set forth in 49CFR393.45.
3. All test temperatures specified may vary by ±3 °C (±5 °F).
4. All times are minimum unless otherwise specified.
5. An inspection test conducted on each lot of tubing and where a lot is defined as "the output of one production shift of one size and color of tubing."
6. A qualification test.

TABLE 1—DIMENSIONS AND TOLERANCES

Tubing Type	Tubing Size OD mm	Tubing Size OD in	Tubing Size ID mm	Tubing Size ID in	Minimum Wall Thickness mm	Minimum Wall Thickness in	OD Tolerances mm	OD Tolerances in	ID Tolerances mm	ID Tolerances in
A	6.0	0.236	4.0	0.157	0.9	0.035	±0.1	±0.004	±0.1	±0.004
A	8.0	0.315	6.0	0.236	0.9	0.035	±0.1	±0.004	±0.1	±0.004
B	10.0	0.393	7.0	0.275	1.35	0.053	±0.15	±0.006	±0.15	±0.006
B	12.0	0.472	9.0	0.354	1.35	0.053	±0.15	±0.006	±0.15	±0.006
B	16.0	0.629	12.0	0.472	1.8	0.071	±0.15	±0.006	±0.15	±0.006

TABLE 2—MECHANICAL PROPERTIES

Tubing Type	Nominal Tubing OD mm	Minimum Burst Pressure at 24 °C (75 °F)(1) MPa	Minimum Burst Pressure at 24 °C (75 °F)(1) psi	Test Bend Radius(2) mm	Test Bend Radius(2) in	Maximum Stiffness N	Maximum Stiffness lbf
A	6	7.6	1100	20	0.75	9	2
A	8	6.2	900	32	1.25	27	6
B	10	8.2	1200	38	1.50	36	8
B	12	6.9	1000	45	1.75	90	20
B	16	6.0	875	70	2.75	225	50

1. With moisture content of tubing 0.06% max.
2. For test purposes only.

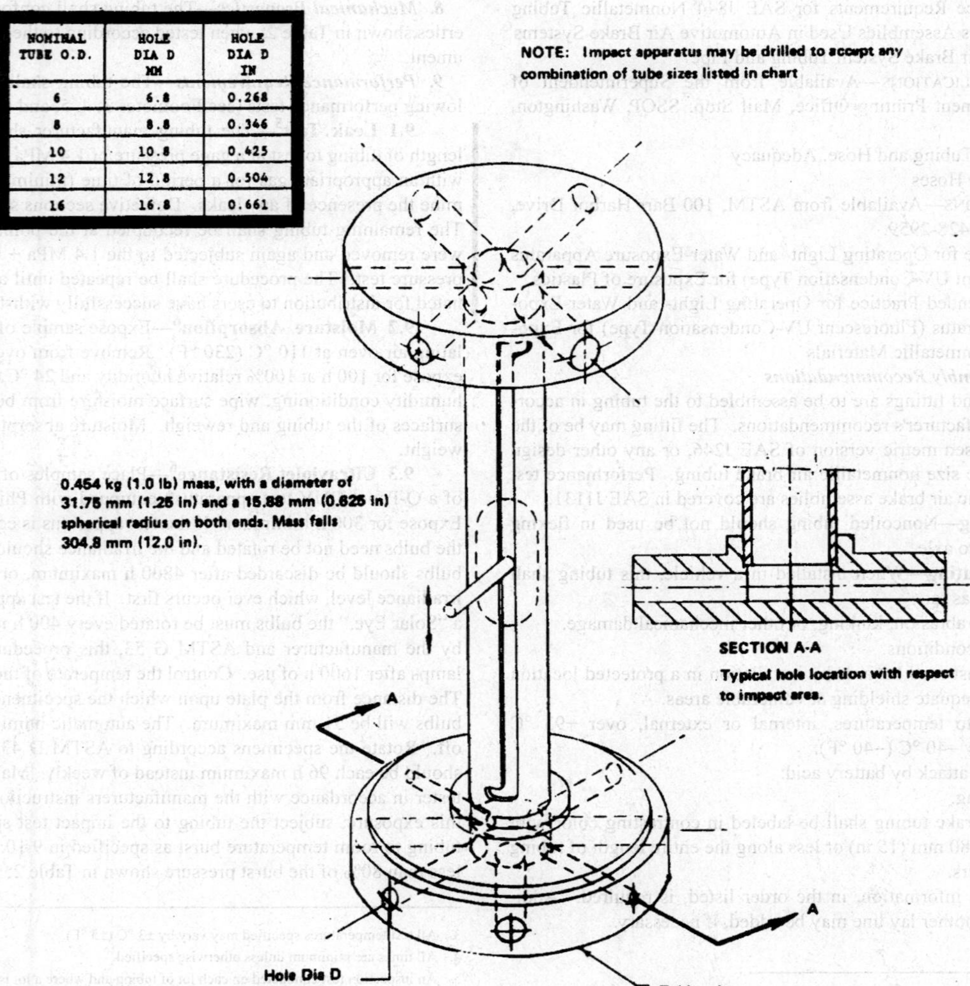

NOMINAL TUBE O.D.	HOLE DIA D MM	HOLE DIA D IN
6	6.8	0.268
8	8.8	0.346
10	10.8	0.425
12	12.8	0.504
16	16.8	0.661

NOTE: Impact apparatus may be drilled to accept any combination of tube sizes listed in chart
0.454 kg (1.0 lb) mass, with a diameter of 31.75 mm (1.25 in) and a 15.88 mm (0.625 in) spherical radius on both ends. Mass falls 304.8 mm (12.0 in).
A
A
SECTION A-A
Typical hole location with respect to impact area.
Hole Dia D see chart
Tubing size

FIGURE 1—TYPICAL NYLON TUBING IMPACT APPARATUS

*The Q-Panel QUV Accelerated Weathering Tester is available from:
The Q-Panel Company
26200 First Street
Cleveland, OH 44145
(216) 835-8700

9.4 Cold Temperature Flexibility[6]—Expose sample of tubing for 24 h in a circulating air oven at 110 °C (230 °F). Remove from oven and within 30 min expose for 4 h at –40 °C (–40 °F). Also expose a mandrel at –40 °C (–40 °F) having a diameter equal to twelve times the nominal diameter of the tubing. (In order to obtain uniform temperatures, the tubing and mandrel may be supported by a nonmetallic surface during the entire period of test.) Immediately following this exposure, bend tubing 180 degrees over the mandrel, accomplishing the bending motion within a period of 4 to 8 s. The tubing shall show no evidence of fracture.

9.5 Heat Aging[6]—Three separate heat aging tests shall be conducted; each phase shall be run on separate tubing samples. Subject tubing to room temperature burst test as specified in 9.10. Tubing shall withstand 80% of the burst pressure shown in Table 2.

9.5.1 PHASE 1—Bend samples of tubing 180 degrees around a mandrel having a diameter equivalent to twice the bend radius specified in Table 2. While in this position, expose tubing and mandrel for 72 h in an circulating air oven at 110 °C (230 °F). Remove from oven and permit tubing to return to 24 °C (75 °F) while still on the mandrel. Within 30 min after stabilization at 24 °C (75 °F), return the tubing to a straight position in a minimum of 4 s, then rebend (against the set) 180 degrees around the mandrel, accomplishing the bending motion within a period of 4 to 8 s.

9.5.2 PHASE 2—Expose samples of tubing for 72 h in a circulating air oven at 110 °C (230 °F). Remove from oven and permit tubing to return to 24 °C (75 °F). Within 30 min after stabilization at 24 °C (75 °F), subject tubing to the impact test shown in Figure 1.

9.5.3 PHASE 3—Immerse samples of tubing in boiling water for 2 h. Remove from water and permit to return to 24 °C (75 °F). Within 30 min after stabilization at 24 °C (75 °F), subject tubing to the impact test shown in Figure 1.

9.6 Resistance to Zinc Chloride[7]—Bend tubing to the bend radius shown in Table 2. While in this position, immerse in a 50% (by weight) aqueous solution of zinc chloride for 200 h at 24 °C (75 °F). Remove from solution. Tubing shall show no evidence of cracking on the outside diameter.

NOTE—Fresh, anhydrous zinc chloride should be used to make a concentration of 50% (by weight) aqueous solution (specific gravity of 1.576 or a Baume rating of 53 degrees at 16 °C [61 °F]).

9.7 Resistance to Methyl Alcohol[7]—Bend tubing to the bend radius shown in Table 2. While in this position, immerse in 95% methyl alcohol for 200 h at 24 °C (75 °F). Remove from solution. Tubing shall show no evidence of cracking.

9.8 Stiffness[8]— Use samples 280 mm (11 in) long. Insert a rod of suitable size into the tubing to maintain a straight position within ±3 mm (0.120 in). Expose tubing and rod for 24 h in a circulating air oven at 110 °C (230 °F). Remove from oven and permit tubing and rod to return to 24 °C (75 °F). Within 30 min after stabilization at 24 °C (75 °F), remove rod and subject tubing to the stiffness test shown in Figure 2. Tubing shall require no more force than specified in Table 2 to deflect 50 mm (1.97 in).

9.9 Boiling Water Stabilization and Burst Test[9]—Immerse tubing in boiling water for 2 h. Remove from water and subject to the room temperature burst test as specified in 9.10. Tubing shall withstand no less than 80% of the burst pressure shown in Table 2.

9.10 Room Temperature Burst Test[9]—Tubing shall be stabilized 0.5 to 3.0 h at 24 °C (75 °F) and tested by increasing pressure at a constant rate to reach the specified minimum burst pressure in Table 2 within a time period of 3 to 15 s. Tubing that bursts below the pressure specified in Table 2 shall be rejected.

9.11 Cold Temperature Impact[10]—Condition tubing by exposing one half of the samples for 24 h at 110 °C (230 °F) in a circulating air oven and one half of the samples in boiling water for 2 h; then expose all the samples to –40 °C (–40 °F) for 4 h. Also, expose impact test apparatus, shown in Figure 1, to –40 °C (–40 °F). While tubing and apparatus are at this cold temperature (approximately –40 °C), subject tubing to impact as specified. The tubing shall show no evidence of cracks. After impact testing, permit tubing to return to 24 °C (75 °F). Within 30 min after stabilization at 24 °C (75 °F), subject tubing to room temperature burst test as specified in 9.10. Tubing shall withstand at least 80% of the burst pressure shown in Table 2. Sample size shall be 10 specimens per lot. In the event of any failures, a second sample from the same lot consisting of 20 specimens shall be tested. If another failure occurs, the lot shall be rejected.

9.12 Adhesion Test[10]

9.12.1 This test applies only to the reinforced products, Type B.

9.12.2 CONDITION—This test shall be conducted at 24 °C (75 °F) ambient temperature.

9.12.3 PROCEDURE AND REQUIREMENTS—Cut a strip of tubing into a 6.0 mm (0.25 in) wide helical coil equal in length to five times the circumference of the tubing. Bend the helical coil in reverse of coiling so as to expose the braid gap between the outer jacket and the core tube section. Start by working a sharp knife blade into the braid gap to initiate separation, and then attempt to separate the outer jacket from the core tube at the braid interstices. The bonded surface (excluding the braided area) between the outer jacket and core section shall be inseparable for the entire test sample length.

9.13 Heat Aging Adhesion Test[11]

9.13.1 PROCEDURE—Subject samples to Phase 1 of the heat aging test procedure per 9.5.

9.13.2 REQUIREMENTS—After completion of the Phase 1 procedure, the tubing shall meet the requirements of 9.12.

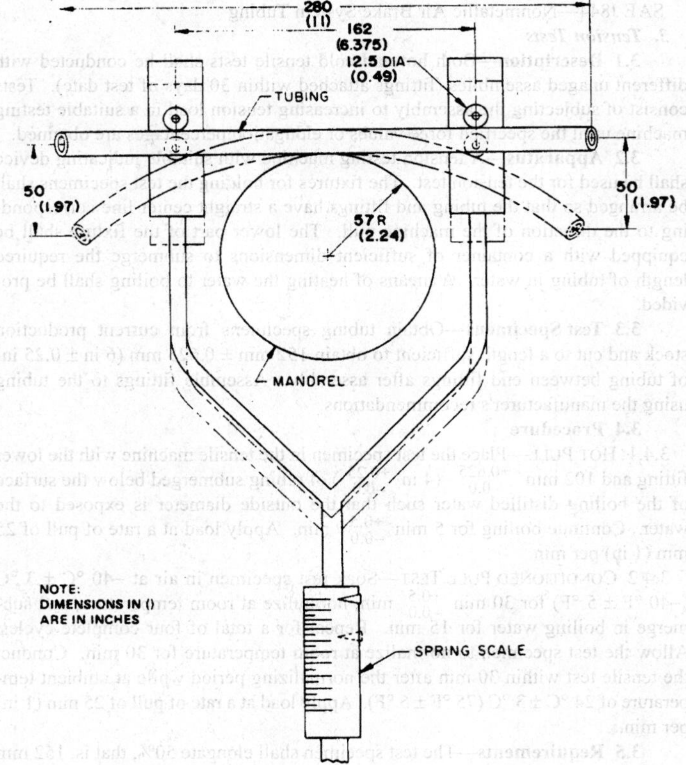

FIGURE 2—STIFFNESS TEST APPARATUS

7. A qualification test.
8. A qualification test.
9. An inspection test conducted on each lot of tubing and where a lot is defined as "the output of one production shift of one size and color of tubing."
10. An inspection test conducted on each lot of tubing and where a lot is defined as "the output of one product shift of one size and color of tubing."
11. A qualification test.

PERFORMANCE REQUIREMENTS FOR SAE J844 NONMETALLIC TUBING AND FITTING ASSEMBLIES USED IN AUTOMOTIVE AIR BRAKE SYSTEMS —SAE J1131 AUG1998

SAE Standard

Report of the SAE Tube, Pipe, Hose, and Lubrication Fittings Committee approved January 1976. Reaffirmed by the SAE Fluid Conductors and Connectors Technical Committee December 1987. Completely revised by the SAE Fluid Conductors and Connectors Technical Committee SC4—Air Brake Tubing and Tube Fittings March 1997, and revised August 1998. Rationale statement available.

1. Scope—This SAE Standard is intended to establish uniform methods of testing SAE J844 tubing and fitting assemblies as used in automotive air brake systems.

This document also establishes minimum qualifications for tensile and pressure capabilities, vibrational durability under cyclic temperatures, serviceability, and fitting compatibility requirements. The specific tests and performance criteria applicable to the tubing are set forth in SAE J844.

NOTE—The test values contained in this document are for test purposes only. For environmental and usage limitations see SAE J844. Fittings—A type of fitting for use with SAE J844 nonmetallic tubing is included in SAE J246; however, it is not intended to restrict or preclude the use of other designs of fittings that comply with this document.

2. References

2.1 Applicable Publications—The following publications form a part of this specification to the extent specified herein. Unless otherwise indicated, the latest issue of SAE publications shall apply.

2.1.1 SAE PUBLICATIONS—Available from SAE, 400 Commonwealth Drive, Warrendale, PA 15096-0001.

SAE J246—Spherical and Flanged Sleeve (Compression) Tube Fittings
SAE J844—Nonmetallic Air Brake System Tubing

3. Tension Tests

3.1 Description—Both hot and cold tensile tests shall be conducted with different unaged assemblies (fittings attached within 30 days of test date). Tests consist of subjecting the assembly to increasing tension load in a suitable testing machine until the specified force values or elongation percentages are obtained.

3.2 Apparatus—A tension testing machine with suitable indicating device shall be used for the tension test. The fixtures for holding the test specimens shall be arranged so that the tubing and fittings have a straight center line corresponding to the direction of the machine pull. The lower part of the fixture shall be equipped with a container of sufficient dimensions to submerge the required length of tubing in water. A means of heating the water to boiling shall be provided.

3.3 Test Specimens—Obtain tubing specimens from current production stock and cut to a length sufficient to obtain 152 mm ± 0.625 mm (6 in ± 0.25 in) of tubing between end fittings after assembly. Assemble fittings to the tubing using the manufacturer's recommendations.

3.4 Procedure

3.4.1 HOT PULL—Place the test specimen in the tensile machine with the lower fitting and 102 mm $^{+0.625}_{-0.0}$ (4 in $^{+0.25}_{-0.0}$) of tubing submerged below the surface of the boiling distilled water such that the outside diameter is exposed to the water. Continue boiling for 5 min $^{+0.5}_{-0.0}$ min. Apply load at a rate of pull of 25 mm (1 in) per min.

3.4.2 CONDITIONED PULL TEST—Soak test specimen in air at −40 °C ± 3 °C (−40 °F ± 5 °F) for 30 min $^{+0.5}_{-0.0}$ min, normalize at room temperature, and submerge in boiling water for 15 min. Repeat for a total of four complete cycles. Allow the test specimen to normalize at room temperature for 30 min. Conduct the tensile test within 30 min after the normalizing period while at ambient temperature of 24 °C ± 3 °C (75 °F ± 5 °F). Apply load at a rate of pull of 25 mm (1 in) per min.

3.5 Requirements—The test specimen shall elongate 50%, that is, 152 mm (6 in) increased to 229 mm (9 in), or shall withstand the load shown in Table 1, without causing separation from the fitting.

4. Vibration Test

4.1 Description—This test is designed to evaluate the effects of vibration under varying ambient temperatures on a tubing and fitting assembly. Leakage rate is used to gage acceptability.

4.2 Apparatus—Equipment capable of vibrating one end of the test specimen at 600 cpm through 12.7 mm (0.5 in) displacement in a plane perpendicular to the tube while the other end is held rigid. The distance between the static and vibrating heads is to be such that when the assembly is displaced 0.5 in, no parallel pull to the longitudinal axis of the assembly will occur. The equipment must be capable of controlling the ambient air temperature between −40 °C ± 3 °C (−40 °F ± 5 °F) and 104 °C ± 3 °C (220 °F ± 5 °F) and of applying 827 kPa ± 69 kPa (120 psig ± 10 psig) dry air to the test lines. A mass flow meter capable of determining air leakage shall be provided.

4.3 Test Specimens—Cut tubing specimens to a length sufficient to obtain 457 mm (18 in) between fittings after assembly. Assemble identical fittings to the tubing using the manufacturer's recommendations. Fitting attaching nuts are not permitted to be retightened during the test.

4.4 Procedure—Allowing 12.7 mm (0.5 in) slack, mount the lines straight in the vibration machine. Oscillate one end of the lines at 600 cycles per min ± 20 cycles per min through a total stroke of 12.7 mm (0.5 in) for a total of 1 000 000 $^{+50\,000}_{-0.0}$ cycles, while maintaining an internal pressure of 827 kPa ± 69 kPa (120 psig ± 10 psig) using dry air. Starting at 104 °C ± 3 °C (220 °F ± 5 °F), vary the ambient air temperature from 104 °C ± 3 °C (220 °F ± 5 °F) to −40 °C ± 3 °C (−40 °F ± 5 °F) at 250 000 vibration cycle intervals approximately 7 h intervals). Using a mass flow meter observe for fitting leakage during and after the test. Check nut tightness after completing the test.

4.5 Requirements—The test specimen is considered a failure if leakage exceeds 50 cm^3/min at −40 °C ± 3 °C (−40 °F ± 5 °F) or 25 cm^3/min at 21 °C ± 3 °C (70 °F ± 5 °F). The fitting is considered a failure if the attaching nut becomes loose. This is defined as follows:

1. Record the initial tightening torque.
2. At the conclusion of the test, attempt to tighten the nut further by applying 20% of the initial tightening torque in the tightening direction. Do not apply a higher torque and do not apply any torque or force in the loosening direction.
3. If the nut moves at all under the 20% torque, it shall be defined as a loose nut and failure of the test. Record the movement in degrees to reach 20%.

TABLE 1—REQUIREMENTS

Nominal Tubing OD mm[(1)]	Nominal Tubing OD in	Tensile Load N	Tensile Load lb
3.2	1/8	67	15
4.0	5/32	178	40
4.8	3/16	178	40
6.4	1/4	222	50
7.9	5/16	334	75
9.5	3/8	667	150
12.7	1/2	890	200
15.9	5/8	1446	325
19.0	3/4	1557	350

1. For reference only.

5. Proof and Burst Pressure Test

5.1 Description—This test is intended to evaluate fitting retention at proof pressure (50% of minimum burst) and at minimum burst pressure as listed in the latest issue of SAE J844.

5.2 Apparatus—The test apparatus consists of a suitable source of hydraulic pressure and the necessary gages and piping.

5.3 Test Specimen—Cut tubing specimens to obtain 305 mm (12 in) between fittings after assembly. Assemble fittings to the tubing using the manufacturer's recommendations.

5.4 Procedure—Plug one end of the test specimen and mount in the apparatus with the end unrestrained. Apply proof pressure at room temperature, 24 °C ± 3 °C (75 °F ± 5 °F) to the test specimen and hold for 30 s. Increase pressure at a constant rate so as to reach the specified minimum burst pressure within a time period of 3 to 15 s.

5.5 Requirements—Fittings shall not separate from the tubing nor shall the assembly visibly leak at less than specified minimum burst pressure.

6. Serviceability Test

6.1 Description—This test is intended to evaluate the effects of repeated assembly and disassembly of a tubing and fitting assembly. Leakage rate is used to gage acceptability.

6.2 Apparatus—The test apparatus consists of a suitable source of pneumatic pressure and the necessary gages and piping. A mass flow meter capable of determining air leakage shall be provided.

6.3 Test Specimens—Cut tubing specimens to obtain 305 mm (12 in) between fittings after assembly. Assemble fittings to the tubing using manufacturer's recommendations.

6.4 Procedure—The tubing and fitting connections shall be disassembled and reassembled for a minimum of five times. After the fifth reassembly, pressurize the test specimens with air to 827 kPa ± 69 kPa (120 psig ± 10 psig) at room temperature, 24 °C ± 3 °C (75 °F ± 5 °F), and check for leakage.

6.5 Requirements—Leakage rate must not exceed 25 cm^3/min.

7. Fitting Compatibility Test

7.1 Description—This test is intended to evaluate the effects of high and low temperatures on fitting performance.

7.2 Apparatus—The test apparatus consists of a suitable source of hydraulic pressure, 3103 kPa ± 69 kPa (450 psig ± 10 psig), and necessary gages and piping in environmental test chambers at 93 °C ± 3 °C (200 °F ± 5 °F) and –40 °C ± 3 °C (–40 °F ± 5 °F).

7.3 Test Specimens—Cut tubing specimens to obtain 305 mm (12 in) between fittings after assembly. Assemble fittings to the tubing using manufacturer's recommendations.

7.4 Procedure—Fill test specimens with hydraulic fluid and subject to 93 °C ± 3 °C (200 °F ± 5 °F) and atmospheric pressure for 24 h $^{+1}_{-0.0}$ h then apply internal pressure of 3103 kPa ± 69 kPa (450 psig ± 10 psig) for 5 min while maintaining temperature of 93 °C ± 3 °C (200 °F ± 5 °F). Reduce to atmospheric pressure and permit test specimens to return to room temperature; then subject test specimens to –40 °C ± 3 °C (–40 °F ± 5 °F) and atmospheric pressure for 24 h. Apply internal pressure of 3103 kPa ± 69 kPa (450 psig ± 10 psig) for 5 min $^{+0.5}_{-0.0}$ min while maintaining temperature of –40 °C ± 3 °C (–40 °F ± 5 °F).

7.5 Requirements—Tubing shall not rupture or disconnect from the fittings.

AUTOMOTIVE PIPE FITTINGS—SAE J530 MAY1995 SAE Standard

Report of the SAE Parts and Fittings Committee approved February 1948, revised by the SAE Tube, Pipe, Hose, and Lubrication Fittings Committee December 1973, editorial change January 1981. Revised by the SAE Fluid Conductors and Connectors Technical Committee SC1—Automotive and Hydraulic Tube and Fittings June 1992. Rationale statement available. Revised by the SAE Fluid Conductors and Connectors Technical Committee SC1—Automotive and Hydraulic Tube and Fittings June 1993, May 1994, and May 1995. Rationale statement available.

Foreword—This Reaffirmed Document has been changed only to reflect the new SAE Technical Standards Board Format.

1. Scope—This SAE Standard includes complete general and dimensional specifications for those types of pipe fittings commonly used in the automotive and other mass production industries where the use of lubricants or sealers is objectionable. The automotive pipe fittings shown in Figures 1 to 17 and Tables 1 to 6 are intended for general automotive and similar applications involving low or medium pressures or in conjunction with automotive tube fittings in piping systems.

2. References

2.1 Applicable Publications—The following publications form a part of this specification to the extent specified herein. The latest issue of SAE publications shall apply.

2.1.1 SAE PUBLICATIONS—Available from SAE, 400 Commonwealth Drive, Warrendale, PA 15096-0001.

SAE J476—Dryseal Pipe Threads
SAE J846—Coding Systems for Identification of Fluid Conductors and Connectors
SAE J1615—Thread Sealants

2.1.2 ASTM PUBLICATION—Available from ASTM, 100 Barr Harbor Drive, West Conshohocken, PA 19428-2959.

ASTM B 117—Method of Salt Spray (Fog) Testing

2.1.3 AUTOMOTIVE PIPE FITTINGS

NOTE—Unspecified Detail With Respect To Dimensions, Tolerances, Contours, Material, Workmanship, Etc., Must Conform To General Specifications For Automotive Pipe Fittings. Codes Shown In Brackets Adjacent To Figure Numbers Represent Respective Fitting Identification In Accordance With Sae J846 (February, 1979).

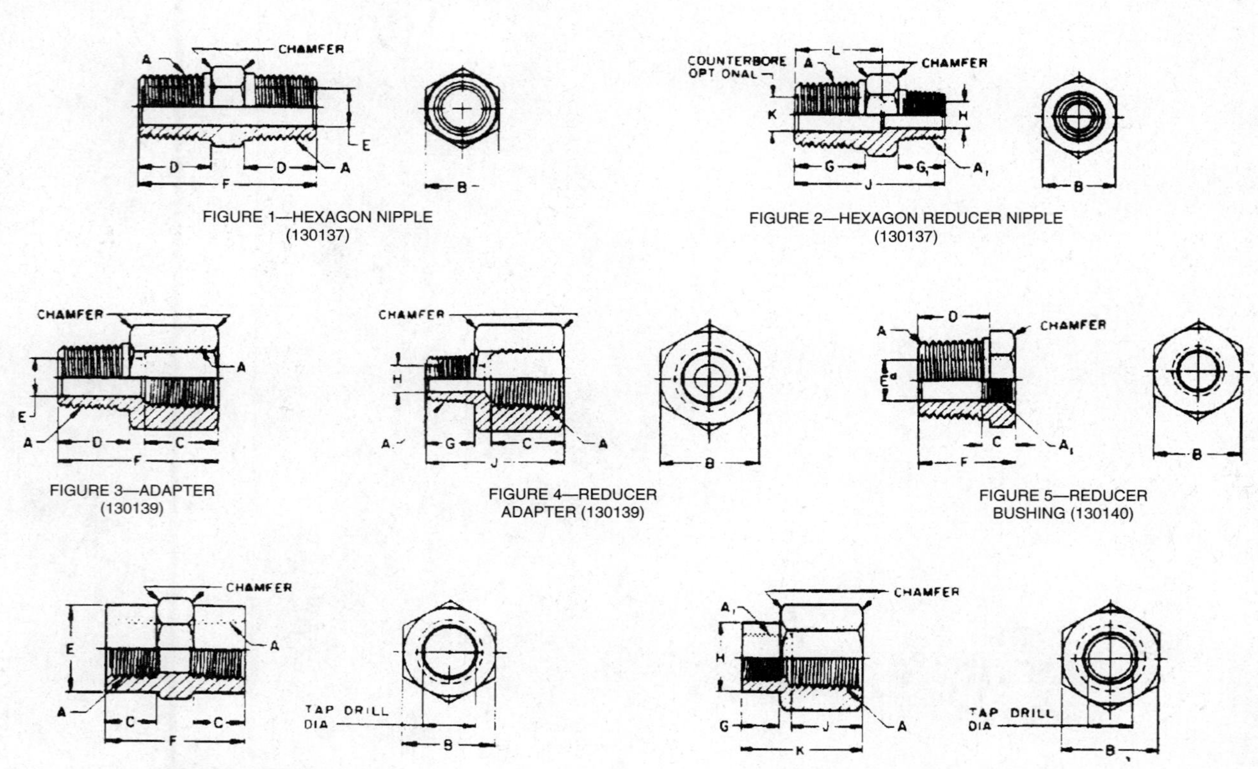

FIGURE 1—HEXAGON NIPPLE (130137)

FIGURE 2—HEXAGON REDUCER NIPPLE (130137)

FIGURE 3—ADAPTER (130139)

FIGURE 4—REDUCER ADAPTER (130139)

FIGURE 5—REDUCER BUSHING (130140)

FIGURE 6—COUPLING (130138)

FIGURE 7—REDUCER COUPLING (130138)

TABLE 1—DIMENSIONS OF HEXAGON NIPPLES AND REDUCER NIPPLES (FIGURES 1 AND 2)

Dryseal Taper Thread NPTF(1) in A Hexagon Nipples	Dryseal Taper Thread NPTF(1) in A x A_1 Hexagon Reducer Nipples	All Nipples B Hexagon Width Max mm	All Nipples B Hexagon Width Max in	All Nipples B Hexagon Width Min mm	All Nipples B Hexagon Width Min in	Nipples D Shoulder Length(2) mm	Nipples D Shoulder Length(2) in	Nipples E Drill Dia mm	Nipples E Drill Dia in	Nipples F Overall Length(2) mm	Nipples F Overall Length(2) in
1/16–27	—	8.03	0.316	7.87	0.310	9.7	0.38	3.58	0.141	23.9	0.94
1/8–27	1/8 x 1/16	11.18	0.440	11.02	0.434	9.7	0.38	5.56	0.219	24.6	0.97
1/4–18	1/4 x 1/8	14.38	0.566	14.17	0.558	14.2	0.56	7.92	0.312	35.1	1.38
3/8–18	3/8 x 1/8	17.58	0.692	17.37	0.684	14.2	0.56	11.13	0.438	35.8	1.41
—	3/8 x 1/4	17.58	0.692	17.37	0.684	—	—	—	—	—	—
1/2–14	1/2 x 3/8	22.33	0.879	22.12	0.871	19.0	0.75	14.27	0.562	46.0	1.81 0

Dryseal Taper Thread NPTF(1) in A x A_1 Hexagon Reducer Nipples	Reducer Nipples G Shoulder Length(2) Min mm	Reducer Nipples G Shoulder Length(2) Min in	Reducer Nipples G_1 Shoulder Length(2) Min mm	Reducer Nipples G_1 Shoulder Length(2) Min in	Reducer Nipples H Drill Dia (3) mm	Reducer Nipples H Drill Dia(3) in	Reducer Nipples J Overall Length(2) mm	Reducer Nipples J Overall Length(2) in	Reducer Nipples Counterbore K Max Dia(3) mm	Reducer Nipples Counterbore K Max Dia(3) in	Reducer Nipples Counterbore L Max Depth(2),(3) mm	Reducer Nipples Counterbore L Max Depth(2),(3) in
1/8 x 1/16	9.7	0.38	9.7	0.38	3.58	0.141	24.6	0.97	5.66	0.223	11.9	0.47
1/4 x 1/8	14.2	0.56	9.7	0.38	5.56	0.219	30.2	1.19	8.08	0.310	17.5	0.69
3/8 x 1/8	14.2	0.56	9.7	0.38	5.56	0.219	31.0	1.22	11.28	0.444	17.5	0.69
3/8 x 1/4	14.2	0.56	14.2	0.56	7.92	0.312	35.8	1.41	11.28	0.444	17.5	0.69
1/2 x 3/8	19.0	0.75	14.2	0.56	11.13	0.438	41.1	1.62	14.43	0.568	23.1	0.91

1. Dryseal American Standard Taper Pipe Thread. See General Specifications.
2. Where SAE Short Pipe Thread is authorized by purchaser, dimensions D, F, G, G_1, J, and L are reduced in accordance with reduction of pipe thread length. See General Specifications.
3. At manufacturer's option, through passages may conform with the smaller diameter specified or be counterbored to the larger diameter for the depth specified.

TABLE 2—DIMENSIONS OF ADAPTERS AND REDUCER ADAPTERS (FIGURES 3 AND 4)

Dryseal Taper Thread NPTF(1) in A Adapters	Dryseal Taper Thread NPTF(1) in A x A_1 Reducer Adapters	All Adapters B Hexagon Width Max mm	All Adapters B Hexagon Width Max in	All Adapters B Hexagon Width Min mm	All Adapters B Hexagon Width Min in	All Adapters C Tap Drill Depth(2),(3) Min mm	All Adapters C Tap Drill Depth(2),(3) Min in	Adapters D Shoulder Length(2) Min mm	Adapters D Shoulder Length(2) Min in	Adapters E Dia Drill mm	Adapters E Dia Drill in
1/16–27	—	11.18	0.440	11.02	0.434	9.7	0.38	9.7	0.38	3.58	0.141
1/8–27	1/8 x 1/16	14.38	0.566	14.17	0.558	9.7	0.38	9.7	0.38	5.56	0.219
1/4–18	1/4 x 1/8	19.15	0.754	18.95	0.746	14.2	0.56	14.2	0.56	7.92	0.312
3/8–18	3/8 x 1/4	22.33	0.879	22.12	0.871	14.2	0.56	14.2	0.56	11.13	0.438
1/2–14	1/2 x 3/8	27.13	1.068	26.87	1.058	19.0	0.75	19.0	0.75	14.27	0.562
3/4–14	3/4 x 1/2	35.05	1.380	34.80	1.370	19.0	0.75	19.0	0.75	19.05	0.750
1–11-1/2	1 x 3/4	41.40	1.630	41.15	1.620	23.9	0.94	23.9	0.94	23.82	0.938

Dryseal Taper Thread NPTF(1) in A Adapters	Dryseal Taper Thread NPTF(1) in A x A_1 Reducer Adapters	Adapters F Overall Length(2)(3) mm	Adapters F Overall Length(2) in	Reducer Adapters G Shoulder Length(2) Min mm	Reducer Adapters G Shoulder Length(2) Min in	Reducer Adapters H Dia Drill mm	Reducer Adapters H Dia Drill in	Reducer Adapters J Overall Length(2) mm	Reducer Adapters J Overall Length(2) in
1/16–27	—	21.3	0.84	—	—	—	—	—	—
1/8–27	1/8 x 1/16	22.4	0.88	9.7	0.38	3.58	0.141	21.3	0.84
1/4–18	1/4 x 1/8	31.8	1.25	9.7	0.38	5.56	0.219	26.9	1.06
3/8–18	3/8 x 1/4	31.8	1.28	14.2	0.56	77.92	0.312	31.8	1.25
1/2–14	1/2 x 3/8	42.2	1.66	14.2	0.56	11.13	0.438	37.3	1.47
3/4–14	3/4 x 1/2	42.9	1.69	19.0	0.75	14.27	0.562	42.9	1.69
1–11-1/2	1 x 3/4	52.3	2.06	19.0	0.75	19.05	0.750	47.8	1.88

1. Dryseal American Standard Taper Pipe Thread. See General Specifications.
2. Where SAE SHort Pipe Thread is authorized by purchaser, dimensions C, F, G, and J are reduced in accordance with reduction of pipe thread length. See General Specifications.
3. Tap drill depths given require use of bottoming taps to produce standard full thread lengths. See General Specifications.

2.1.4 Automotive Pipe Fittings—Cast Type

NOTE—UNSPECIFIED DETAIL WITH RESPECT TO DIMENSIONS, TOLERANCES, CONTOURS, MATERIAL, WORKMANSHIP, ETC., MUST CONFORM TO GENERAL SPECIFICATIONS FOR AUTOMOTIVE PIPE FITTINGS. THE DIMENSIONAL DESIGNATIONS ON THE FIRST FIGURE IN EACH GROUP SHALL APPLY TO ALL OTHER FIGURES IN THAT GROUP EXCEPT AS SHOWN OTHERWISE. CODES SHOWN IN BRACKETS ADJACENT TO FIGURE NUMBERS REPRESENT RESPECTIVE FITTING IDENTIFICATION IN ACCORDANCE, WITH SAE J846 (FEBRUARY, 1979).

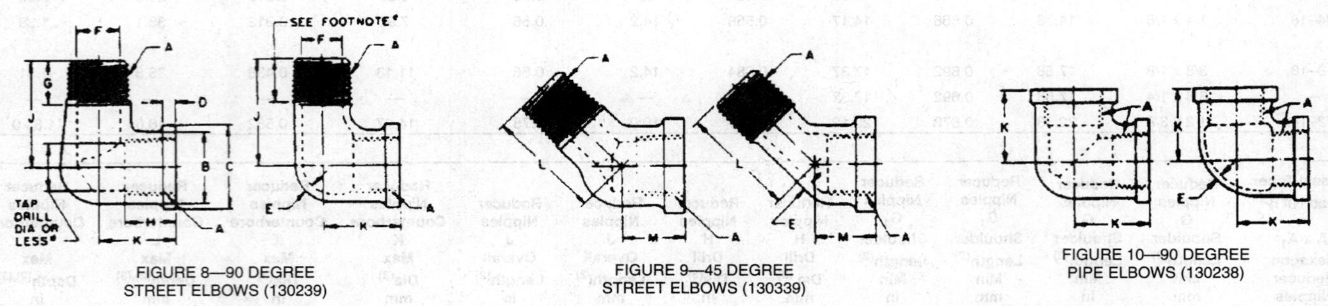

FIGURE 8—90 DEGREE STREET ELBOWS (130239)

FIGURE 9—45 DEGREE STREET ELBOWS (130339)

FIGURE 10—90 DEGREE PIPE ELBOWS (130238)

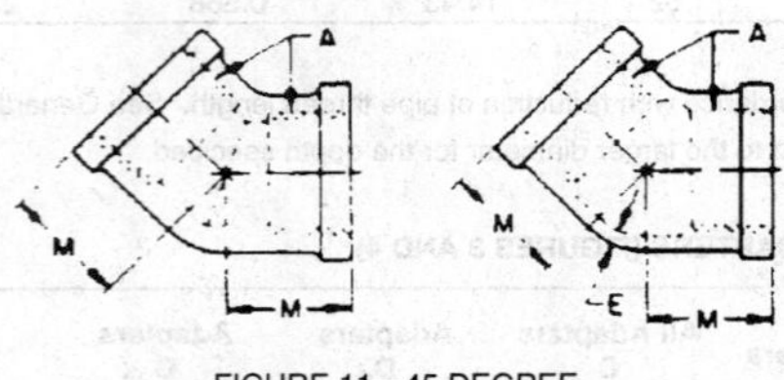

FIGURE 11—45 DEGREE PIPE ELBOWS (130338)

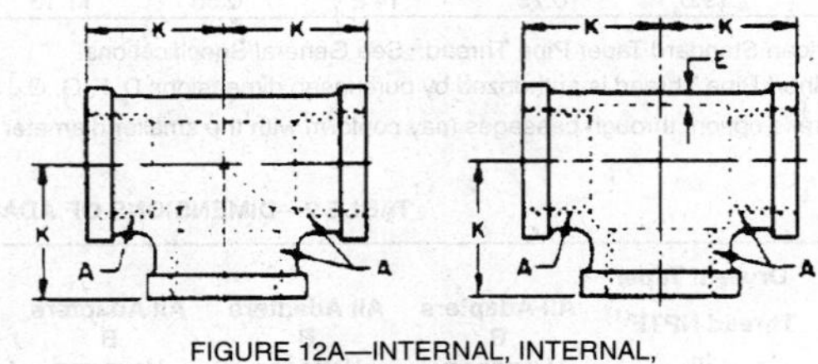

FIGURE 12A—INTERNAL, INTERNAL, INTERNAL TEES (130438)

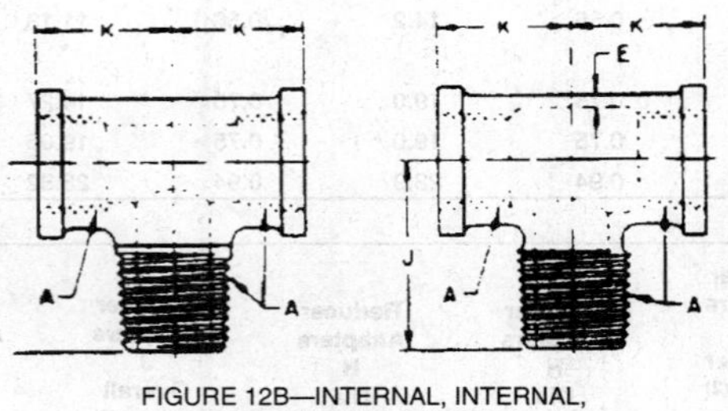

FIGURE 12B—INTERNAL, INTERNAL, EXTERNAL TEES (130425)

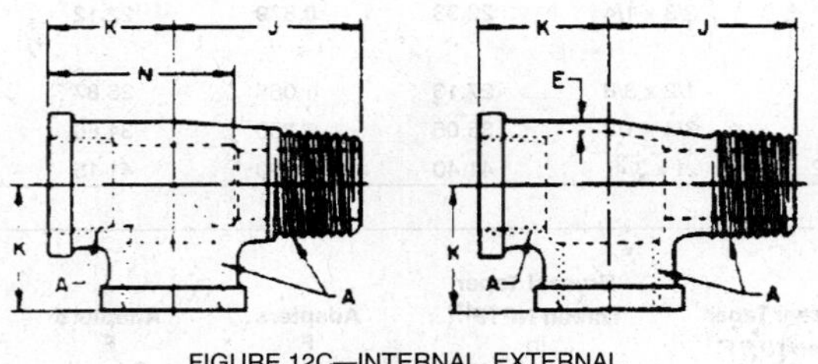

FIGURE 12C—INTERNAL, EXTERNAL, INTERNAL TEES (130424)

TABLE 3—DIMENSIONS OF REDUCER BUSHINGS (FIGURE 5)

Dryseal Taper Thread NPTF[1], in A x A_1	B Hexagon Width Max mm	B Hexagon Width Max in	B Hexagon Width Min mm	B Hexagon Width Min in	C Tap Drill Depth[2],[3] Min mm	C Tap Drill Depth[2],[3] Min in	D Shoulder Length[2] Min mm	D Shoulder Length[2] Min in	E Hole Dia[4] Min mm	E Hole Dia[4] Min in	F Overall Length[2] mm	F Overall Length[2] in
1/8 x 1/16	11.18	0.440	11.02	0.434	9.7	0.38	9.7	0.38	3.53	0.139	14.2	0.56
1/4 x 1/8	14.38	0.566	14.17	0.558	9.7	0.38	14.2	0.56	5.51	0.217	19.0	0.75
3/8 x 1/8	17.58	0.692	17.37	0.684	9.7	0.38	14.2	0.56	5.51	0.217	19.0	0.75
3/8 x 1/4	19.15	0.754	18.95	0.746	14.2	0.56	14.2	0.56	7.85	0.309	19.0	0.75
1/2 x 1/8	22.33	0.879	22.12	0.871	9.6	0.38	19.0	0.75	5.51	0.217	25.4	1.00
1/2 x 1/4	22.33	0.879	22.12	0.871	14.2	0.56	19.0	0.75	7.85	0.309	25.4	1.00
1/2 x 3/8	22.33	0.879	22.12	0.871	14.2	0.56	19.0	0.75	11.05	0.435	25.4	1.00
3/4 x 1/4	28.70	1.130	28.45	1.120	14.2	0.56	19.0	0.75	7.85	0.309	25.4	1.00
3/4 x 3/8	28.70	1.130	28.45	1.120	14.2	0.56	19.0	0.75	11.05	0.435	25.4	1.00
3/4 x 1/2	28.70	1.130	28.45	1.120	19.0	0.75	19.0	0.75	14.20	0.559	25.4	1.00
1 x 1/2	36.63	1.442	36.37	1.432	19.0	0.75	23.9	0.94	14.20	0.559	33.3	1.31
1 x 3/4	36.63	1.442	36.37	1.432	19.0	0.75	23.9	0.94	18.98	0.747	33.3	1.31

1. Dryseal American Standard Pipe Thread. See General Specifications.
2. Where SAE Short Pipe Thread is authorized by purchaser, dimensions C, D, and F are reduced in accordance with reduction of pipe thread length. See General Specifications.
3. Tap drill depths given require use of bottoming taps to produce standard full thread lengths. See General Specifications.
4. At manufacturer's option, hole may conform to tap drill diameter or may be reduced beyond tap drill depth C, but in no case shall it be smaller than E diameter specified.

2.1.5 Automotive Pipe Fittings—Extruded Or Bar Stock Type

NOTE—UNSPECIFIED DETAIL WITH RESPECT TO DIMENSIONS, TOLERANCES, CONTOURS, MATERIAL, WORKMANSHIP, ETC., MUST CONFORM TO GENERAL SPECIFICATIONS FOR AUTOMOTIVE PIPE FITTINGS. THE DIMENSIONAL DESIGNATIONS ON THE FIRST FIGURE IN EACH GROUP SHALL APPLY TO ALL OTHER FIGURES IN THAT GROUP EXCEPT AS SHOWN OTHERWISE. CODES SHOWN IN BRACKETS ADJACENT TO FIGURE NUMBERS REPRESENT RESPECTIVE FITTING IDENTIFICATION IN ACCORDANCE WITH SAE J846 (FEBRUARY, 1979).

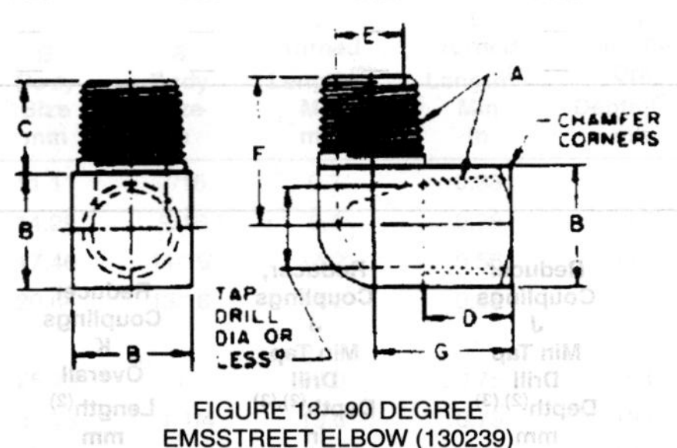

FIGURE 13—90 DEGREE EMSSTREET ELBOW (130239)

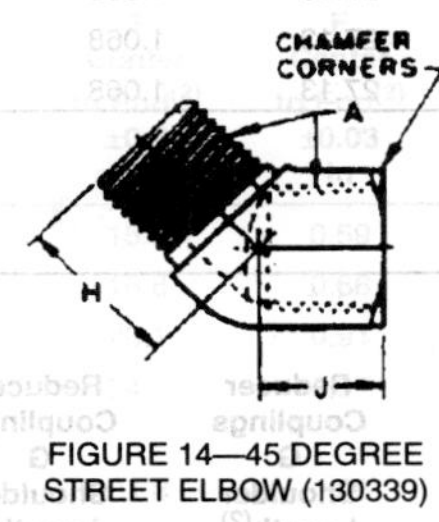

FIGURE 14—45 DEGREE STREET ELBOW (130339)

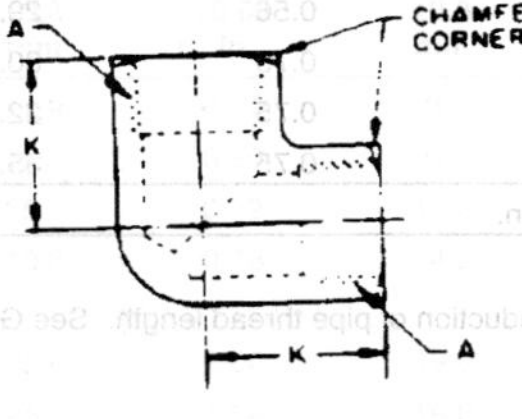

FIGURE 15—90 DEGREE EMSPIPE ELBOW (130238)

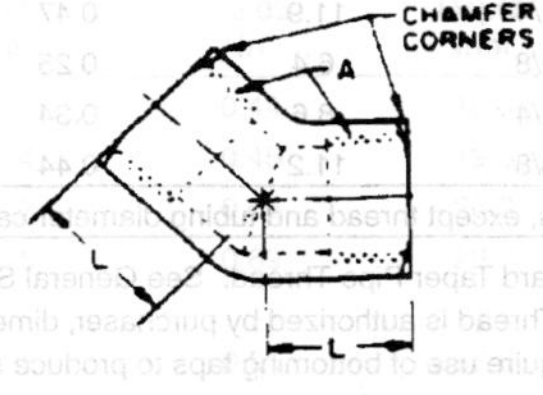

FIGURE 16—45 DEGREE, PIPE ELBOW (130338)

3. *General Specifications*

3.1 Dimensions and Tolerances—Except for nominal sizes and thread specifications, dimensions and tolerances are given in both SI and U.S. customary units as designated. Tabulated dimensions shall apply to the finished fittings, plated or otherwise processed, as specified by the purchaser. Unless otherwise specified, maximum and minimum across flats dimensions shall be within the commercial tolerance of bar or extruded stock from which the fittings are produced. The minimum across corner dimensions of external hexagons shall be 1.092 times the nominal width across flats, but shall not result in a side flat width less than 0.43 times the nominal width across flats. The minimum across corner dimensions of external squares shall be 1.25 times the nominal width across flats, but shall not result in a side flat width less than 0.75 times the nominal width across flats. Unless otherwise specified, tolerance on hole diameters designated drill in the dimensional tables shall be as tabulated in Table 7.

TABLE 7—DRILL TOLERANCES

Drill Size Range mm	Drill Size Range in	Tolerance on Hole Diameter Plus mm	Tolerance on Hole Diameter Plus in	Tolerance on Hole Diameter Minus mm	Tolerance on Hole Diameter Minus in
0.343 thru 4.699	0.0135 thru 0.1850	0.08	0.003	0.05	0.002
4.762 thru 6.299	0.1875 thru 0.2480	0.10	0.004	0.05	0.002
6.350 thru 19.050	0.2500 thru 0.7500	0.15	0.006	0.08	0.003
19.25 thru 25.400	0.7579 thru 1.0000	0.18	0.007	0.10	0.004

Tolerance on all dimensions not otherwise limited shall be ±0.25 mm (±0.010 in). Angular tolerance on axis of ends on elbows and tees shall be ±2.50 degrees for sizes up to and including 3/8 in, and ±1.50 degrees for sizes larger than 3/8 in.

3.2 Wall Thickness—Unless otherwise designated, the wall thickness at any point on fittings shall not be less than the thickness established by the specified dimensions, tolerances, and eccentricities for inner and outer surfaces.

3.3 Contour—Details of contour shall be optional with the manufacturer provided the tabulated dimensions are maintained and serviceability of the fittings is not impaired. Wrench flats on elbows and tees shall be optional. Where extruded or forged shapes are reduced to conserve material, the wall thickness, unless otherwise specified, shall not be less than the respective minimum values tabulated in Table 8.

3.4 Passages—Where passages in straight fittings are machined from opposite ends, the offset at the meeting point shall not exceed 0.38 mm (0.015 in). The cross-sectional area at the junction of passages in angle fittings shall not be less than that of the smaller passage.

TABLE 8—MINIMUM WALL THICKNESS

Nominal Pipe Thread Size, in	Wall Thickness Min[1] mm	Wall Thickness Min[1] in
1/16	1.0	0.04
1/8	1.0	0.04
1/4	1.3	0.05
3/8	1.5	0.06
1/2	2.0	0.08
3/4	2.0	0.08
1	2.0	0.08

1. Applies to reduction to one plane only on extruded shapes.

3.5 Pipe Threads—The pipe threads, unless there is specific authorization to the contrary, shall conform with the Dryseal American Standard Taper Pipe Thread (NPTF). At purchaser's option, the pipe thread may be shortened in conformity with the SAE Short Dryseal Taper Pipe Thread (PTF-SAE Short). Specifications for pipe threads are given in detail in SAE J476 (June, 1961). The pipe fitting dimensions tabulated herein are based on length of the Dryseal American Standard Taper Pipe Thread (NPTF), it being the consensus of manufacturers and users that trouble-free assembly and pressure-tight joints without lubricant or sealer cannot be assured (per SAE J1615.)

However, the tap drill depths and the overall lengths specified in the tables for fittings with internal taper pipe threads are not consistent with the tap drill depths and the overall thread lengths of the Dryseal American Standard Taper Pipe Threads (NPTF) specified in Table A2, Appendix A of SAE J476. The full-length Dryseal American Standard Taper Pipe Taps specified in Table B2, Appendix B of SAE J476 cannot be used as the tap drill depths, and overall lengths of the fittings have been reduced to the minimum required by bottoming taps to produce standard full thread length. The deviations described herein are peculiar to automotive pipe fittings. As special tooling is required, caution should be exercised in specifying the deviations for any other products. External pipe threads shall be chamfered from the diameters tabulated in Table 9 to produce the specified length of chamfered or partial thread. Internal pipe threads shall be countersunk 90 degrees included angle, to the diameters shown in Table 9.

3.6 Material and Manufacture—Pipe fittings may be made from cast iron, malleable iron, steel, stainless steel, brass, or aluminum alloy as specified by the purchaser, by casting, forging, milling from the bar, or upsetting from a grade of material free from defects which will affect their serviceability. However, all varieties and sizes of pipe fittings may not be currently available in the aforementioned materials. Nipples, adapters, bushings, and couplings are generally available in brass and steel. Cast elbows and tees are generally available in malleable iron for sizes 1/4 in and over and in brass. Extruded and forged elbows and tees are generally available in brass and steel.

3.7 Finish—The external surfaces and threads of all carbon steel parts shall be plated or coated with a suitable material that passes a 72 h salt spray test in accordance with ASTM B 117. Any appearance of red rust during the 72 h salt spray test shall be considered failure, except for the following:

a. All internal fluid passages.
b. Edges such as hex points, serrations, and crests of threads where there may be mechanical deformation of the plating or coating typical of mass-produced parts or shipping effects.
c. Areas where there is mechanical deformation of the plating or coating caused by crimping, flaring, bending, and other post-plate metal forming operations.
d. Areas where the parts are suspended or affixed in the test chamber where condensate can accumulate.

NOTE—Cadmium plating is not preferred due to environmental reasons. Parts manufactured to this standard after January 1, 1997, shall not be cadmium plated. Internal fluid passages shall be protected from corrosion during storage. Changes in plating may affect assembly torques and require requalification, when applicable.

3.8 Workmanship—Workmanship shall conform to the best commercial practice to produce high-quality fittings. Fittings shall be free from all hanging burrs, loose scale, and slivers which might become dislodged in usage and all other defects which might affect serviceability.

TABLE 9—PIPE THREAD CHAMFER DIAMETERS

Nominal Pipe Thread Size in	External Thread Chamfer Diameter[1] Max mm	External Thread Chamfer Diameter[1] Max in	External Thread Chamfer Diameter[1] Min mm	External Thread Chamfer Diameter[1] Min in	External Thread Length of Chamfered of Partial Thread Min mm	External Thread Length of Chamfered of Partial Thread Min in	External Thread Length of Chamfered or Partial Thread Max mm	External Thread Length of Chamfered or Partial Thread Max in	Internal Thread Countersink Diameter[1] Min mm	Internal Thread Countersink Diameter[1] Min in	Internal Thread Countersink Diameter[1] Max mm	Internal Thread Countersink Diameter[1] Max in
1/16	5.8	0.23	5.3	0.21	0.94	0.037	1.42	0.056	8.4	0.33	8.9	0.35
1/8	8.1	0.32	7.6	0.30	0.94	0.037	1.42	0.056	10.7	0.42	11.2	0.44
1/4	10.7	0.42	10.2	0.40	1.42	0.056	2.11	0.083	14.0	0.55	14.5	0.57
3/8	14.0	0.55	13.5	0.53	1.42	0.056	2.11	0.083	17.5	0.69	18.0	0.71
1/2	17.3	0.68	16.8	0.66	1.80	0.071	2.72	0.107	21.6	0.85	22.1	0.87
3/4	22.6	0.89	22.1	0.87	1.80	0.071	2.72	0.107	26.9	1.06	27.4	1.08
1	28.4	1.12	27.7	1.09	2.21	0.087	3.30	0.130	34.0	1.34	34.8	1.37

1. Tabulated diameters conform with Appendix A, SAE J476 (June, 1961).

THREAD SEALANTS—SAE J1615 AUG2001 SAE Recommended Practice

Report of the SAE Fluid Conductors and Connectors Technical Committee SC1—Automotive and Hydraulic Tube and Fittings approved June 1993 and reaffirmed August 2001. Rationale statement available.

1. Scope—Male pipe threads, including male dryseal pipe threads, when made into assemblies or installed into ports, will generally leak if not covered with a sealant.

This SAE Recommended Practice is intended as a guide to assist designers and/or users in the selection and application of various types of thread sealants. The designers and users must make a systematic review of each type and application and then select the sealant to fulfill the requirements of the application. The following are general guidelines and are not necessarily a complete list.

2. References—There are no referenced publications specified herein.

3. Types of Sealant

3.1 PTFE tape applied as joints are assembled.

3.2 Pre-applied paste.

3.3 Paste applied as joints are assembled.

4. Application of PTFE Tape

4.1 Inspect threads to be sure they are not damaged nor contain slivers, burrs, dirt, or other contaminants.

4.2 Looking from the leading end of the male thread, wrap the tape clockwise circumferentially around the thread. Overlap each spiral wrap of tape approximately 1/2 the width of the tape so that no more than two plies are applied. Be careful to leave the first 1/2 to 1-1/2 threads bare. Each wrap should be wound so that the tape is tight on the threads.

4.3 When assembling, each taped threaded end should be put together two full turns past finger tight on sizes up to 1/2 in male pipe thread. On larger sizes, each threaded end should be put together 1-1/2 to 2-1/2 full turns past finger tight. (Caution—During assembly, shredding of the tape can occur with consequent contamination of the system.)

4.4 Each taped threaded end must be able to pass the test requirements detailed in 7.1 and 8.1. PTFE tape is not recommended for repositioning or reassembly.

5. Application of Pre-Applied Paste

5.1 Inspect threads to be sure they are not damaged nor contain slivers, burrs, dirt, or other contaminants.

5.2 Apply paste evenly, without air pockets, around the circumference of the threaded area, leaving the first 1/2 to 1-1/2 threads unpasted and then extending to completely cover a minimum of the next three threads.

5.3 For recommended weights of sealant, if that method is used or specified, follow manufacturer's recommendation or submit parts to the acceptance test detailed in Section 7 or 8.

5.4 See manufacturer's recommendation for drying times and temperatures. Before use of a threaded part in an assembly, coatings should be firm without being tacky.

5.5 When assembling, each prepasted end should be put together two full turns past finger tight on sizes up to 1/2 in male pipe thread. On larger sizes, each threaded end should be put together 1-1/2 to 2-1/2 full turns past finger tight.

5.6 Each prepasted end must be able to pass the test requirements detailed in Section 7 or 8.

6. Application of Paste at Time of Assembly

6.1 Inspect threads to be sure they are not damaged nor contain slivers, burrs, dirt, or other contaminants.

6.2 Apply paste evenly around the circumference over the first four or five male pipe threads, being careful to avoid air pockets.

6.3 When assembling, each pasted end should be put together two full turns past finger tight on sizes up to 1/2 in male pipe thread. On larger sizes, each threaded end should be put together 1-1/2 to 2-1/2 full turns past finger tight.

6.4 Each pasted end must be able to pass the test requirements detailed in Section 7 or 8.

7. Functional Tests for Pneumatic Applications (When Using Brass or Aluminum Fittings)

7.1 Leakage After Initial Installation—Male pipe threads, sealed and assembled into a female pipe thread in accordance with this document, shall not leak when subjected to 0.8 MPa (120 psig) air.

7.2 Leakage After Reuse—After 24 h have elapsed, remove the samples used in 7.1 and reassemble them two full turns past finger tight. Subject them to 0.8 MPa (120 psig) air. To pass, no leakage is allowed.

7.3 Repeat 7.2 three additional times, each at 24 h intervals. To pass, no leakage is allowed.

8. Functional Tests for Pneumatic Applications (When Using Steel Fittings)

8.1 Leakage After Initial Installation—Male pipe threads, sealed and assembled into a female pipe thread in accordance with this document, shall not leak when subjected to air at the working pressure of the hose or tubing used in the assembly.

8.2 Leakage After Reuse—After 24 h have elapsed, remove the samples used in 8.1 and reassemble them two full turns past finger tight. Subject them to air at the working pressure of the hose or tubing used in the assembly. To pass, no leakage is allowed.

8.3 Repeat 8.2 three additional times, each at 24 h intervals. To pass, no leakage is allowed.

9. Assembly Recommendations

9.1 To minimize the possibility of a leaking threaded joint after assembling male to female pipe threads, neither end should be backed out (loosened) once the assembly has been made.

9.2 If positioning of a shaped part like an elbow or a tee must be accomplished, thread the shaped part in approximately 1 to 1-1/2 turns past finger tight and tighten further to the desired position.

AUTOMOTIVE PIPE, FILLER, AND DRAIN PLUGS —SAE J531 MAY1995

SAE Standard

Report of the SAE Parts and Fittings Committee approved February 1948, revised by the SAE Tube, Pipe, Hose, and Lubrication Fittings Committee December 1973, editorial change January 1981. Reaffirmed by the SAE Fluid Conductors and Connectors Technical Committee S1—Automotive and Hydraulic Tube and Fittings February 1992, and revised June 1993 and May 1995. Rationale statement available.

1. Scope—This SAE Standard includes complete general and dimensional specifications for those types of pipe, filler, and drain plugs (shown in Figures 1 to 6 and Tables 1 to 4) commonly used in automotive and related industrial applications.

2. References

2.1 Applicable Publications—The following publications form a part of the specification to the extent specified herein. Unless otherwise indicated the latest revision of SAE publications shall apply.

2.1.1 SAE PUBLICATIONS—Available from SAE, 400 Commonwealth Drive, Warrendale PA 15096-0001.

SAE J476—Dryseal Pipe Threads

SAE J846—Coding Systems for Identification of Fluid Conductors and Connectors

2.1.2 ASTM PUBLICATION—Available from ASTM, 100 Barr Harbor Drive, West Conshohocken, PA 19428-2959.

ASTM B 117—Method of Salt Spray (Fog) Testing

3. General Specifications

3.1 Dimensions and Tolerances—Except for nominal sizes and thread specifications, dimensions and tolerances are given in both SI and U.S. customary units as designated. Tabulated dimensions shall apply to the finished plugs, plated, hardened, or otherwise processed, as specified by the purchaser. The minimum across corner dimensions of external hexagons shall be 1.092 times the nominal width across flats. The minimum across corner dimensions of external squares shall be 1.25 times the nominal width across flats, but shall not result in a side flat width less than 0.75 times the nominal width across flats. At maximum material condition, the radii at corners of hexagon and square sockets in broached and upset plugs shall not exceed 0.13 mm (0.005 in). Tolerance on dimensions not otherwise limited shall be ±0.25 mm (±0.010 in).

3.2 Pipe Threads—The pipe threads on automotive pipe plugs, unless there is specific authorization to the contrary, shall conform with the Dryseal American Standard Taper Pipe Thread (NPTF) and be gaged accordingly. The automotive pipe plug dimensions are based on the length of the NPTF thread and are intended for assembly with all types of Dryseal taper and straight internal threads. It is the consensus of manufacturers and users that trouble-free assembly and pressure-tight joints without lubricant or sealer cannot be assured.

The pipe threads on automotive filler and drain plugs, unless there is specific authorization to the contrary, shall conform with the Dryseal SAE Short Taper Pipe Thread (PTF-SAE Short) and be gaged accordingly. The automotive filler and drain plug dimensions are based on the length of the (PTF-SAE Short) thread and are primarily intended for assembly with Dryseal American Standard Taper (NPTF) or Dryseal American Standard Intermediate Straight (NPSI) internal pipe threads in installations where it is desirable to limit the entry of the small end of the plug. Limitations on other applications of this thread are explained in SAE J476.

External pipe threads shall be chamfered or rounded from the diameters tabulated in Table 1 to produce a length of chamfered or partial thread as specified. The threads on countersunk headless types of plugs shall be chamfered on both ends to the dimensions shown.

Related specifications covering blank sizes, dies, chasers, and gages are shown in SAE J476.

3.3 Material and Manufacture—Plugs may be made from low carbon steel, cast iron, malleable iron, brass, bronze, or aluminum alloy as specified by purchaser, by casting, milling from the bar, or upsetting from a grade of material free of defects which will affect their serviceability.

TABLE 1—CHAMFER DIMENSIONS

Nominal Dryseal Pipe Thread Size in	Chamfer Dia at Small End of Plugs of All Types[1] Max mm	Chamfer Dia at Small End of Plugs of All Type[1] Max in	Chamfer Dia at Small End of Plugs of All Types[1] Min mm	Chamfer Dia at Small End of Plugs of All Types[1] Min in	Chamfer Dia at Large End of Countersunk Headless Plugs Max mm	Chamfer Dia at Large End of Countersunk Headless Plugs Max in
1/16	5.8	0.23	5.3	0.21	6.4	0.25
1/8	8.1	0.32	7.6	0.30	8.6	0.34
1/4	10.7	0.42	10.2	0.40	11.4	0.45
3/8	14.0	0.55	13.5	0.53	14.7	0.58
1/2	17.3	0.68	16.8	0.66	18.3	0.72
3/4	22.6	0.89	22.1	0.87	23.6	0.93
1	28.4	1.12	27.7	1.09	29.7	1.17

1. Tabulated diameters conform with Appendix A, SAE J476.(Continued)

Nominal Dryseal Pipe Thread Size in	Chamfer Dia at Large End of Countersunk Headless Plugs Min mm	Chamfer Dia At Large End of Countersunk Headless Plugs Min in	Length of Chamfer or Partial Thread Max mm	Length of Chamfer or Partial Thread Max in	Length of Chamfer or Partial Thread Min mm	Length of Chamfer or Partial Thread Min in
1/16	5.8	0.23	1.42	0.056	0.94	0.037
1/8	8.1	0.32	1.42	0.056	0.94	0.037
1/4	10.9	0.43	2.11	0.083	1.42	0.056
3/8	14.2	0.56	2.11	0.083	1.42	0.056
1/2	17.8	0.70	2.72	0.107	1.80	0.071
3/4	23.1	0.91	2.72	0.107	1.80	0.071
1	29.0	1.14	3.30	0.130	2.21	0.087

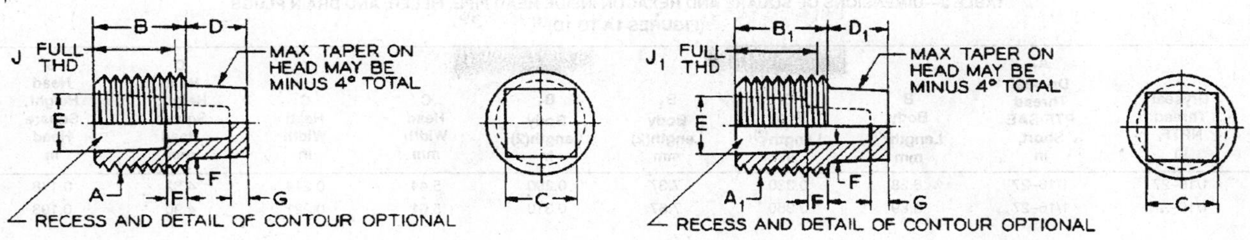

FIGURE 1A—SQUARE INSIDE HEAD PIPE PLUGS (130109A)

FIGURE 1B—SQUARE INSIDE HEAD FILLER AND DRAIN PLUGS[a] (130109B)

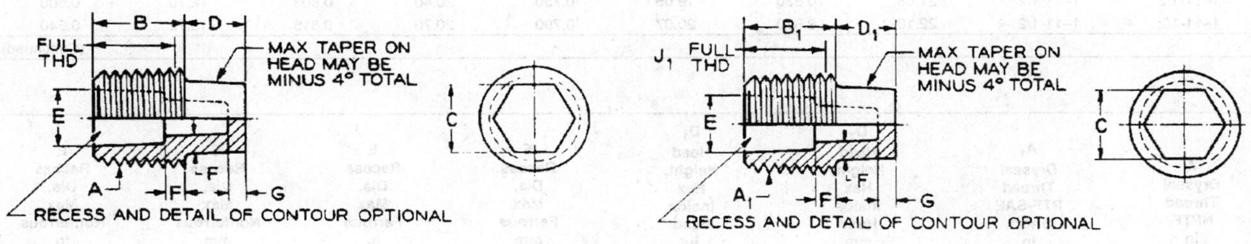

FIGURE 1C—HEXAGON INSIDE HEAD PIPE PLUGS (130109C)

FIGURE 1D—HEXAGON INSIDE HEAD FILLER AND DRAIN PLUGS[a] (130109D)

FIGURE 1—SQUARE AND HEXAGON INSIDE HEAD PLUGS

CODES SHOWN IN BRACKETS ADJACENT TO FIGURE NUMBERS REPRESENT RESPECTIVE FITTING IDENTIFICATION IN ACCORDANCE TO SAE J846.

3.4 Finish—The external surfaces and threads of all carbon steel parts shall be plated or coated with a suitable material that passes a 72 h salt spray test in accordance with ASTM B 117. Any appearance of red rust during the 72 h salt spray test shall be considered failure, except for the following:

a. All internal fluid passages.
b. Edges such as hex points, serrations, and crests of threads where there may be mechanical deformation of the plating or coating typical of mass-produced parts or shipping effects.
c. Areas where there is mechanical deformation of the plating or coating caused by crimping, flaring, bending, and other post-plate metal forming operations.
d. Areas where the parts are suspended or affixed in the test chamber where condensate can accumulate.

NOTE—Cadmium plating is not preferred due to environmental reasons. Parts manufactured to this standard after January 1, 1997, shall not be cadmium plated. Internal fluid passages shall be protected from corrosion during storage. Changes in plating may affect assembly torques and require requalification, when applicable.

3.5 Workmanship—Workmanship shall conform to the best commercial practice to produce high-quality parts. Plugs shall be free from all hanging burrs, loose scale, and slivers which might become dislodged in usage and all other defects which might affect their serviceability.

TABLE 2—DIMENSIONS OF SQUARE AND HEXAGON INSIDE HEAD PIPE, FILLER, AND DRAIN PLUGS (FIGURES 1A TO 1D)[1]

A Dryseal Thread NPTF, in	A_1 Dryseal Thread PTF-SAE Short, in	B Body Length[2] mm	B Body Length[2] in	B_1 Body Length(2) mm	B_1 Body Length(2) in	C Head Width mm	C Head Width in	D Head Height, Square Head mm	D Head Height, Square Head in
1/16–27	1/16–27	8.38	0.330	7.37	0.290	5.44	0.214	4.52	0.178
1/16–27	1/16–27	8.89	0.350	7.87	0.310	5.61	0.221	4.90	0.193
1/8–27	1/8–27	8.38	0.330	7.37	0.290	7.01	0.276	6.10	0.240
1/8–27	1/8–27	8.89	0.350	7.87	0.310	7.19	0.283	6.48	0.255
1/4–18	1/4–18	12.57	0.495	11.30	0.445	9.40	0.370	7.11	0.280
1/4–18	1/4–18	13.34	0.525	12.06	0.475	9.58	0.377	7.62	0.300
3/8–18	3/8–18	12.57	0.495	11.30	0.445	10.87	0.428	7.87	0.310
3/8–18	3/8–18	13.34	0.525	12.06	0.475	11.18	0.440	8.51	0.335
1/2–14	1/2–14	16.76	0.660	14.99	0.590	14.05	0.533	9.65	0.380
1/2–14	1/2–14	17.78	0.700	16.00	0.630	14.35	0.565	10.41	0.410
3/4–14	3/4–14	17.02	0.670	15.24	0.600	15.62	0.615	11.18	0.440
3/4–14	3/4–14	18.03	0.710	16.26	0.640	15.93	0.627	11.94	0.470
1–11-1/2	1–11-1/2	21.08	0.830	19.05	0.750	20.40	0.803	12.70	0.500
1–11-1/2	1–11-1/2	22.10	0.870	20.07	0.790	20.70	0.815	13.72	0.540

(Continued)

A Dryseal Thread NPTF, in	A_1 Dryseal Thread PTF-SAE Short, in	D_1 Head Height, Hex Inside Head mm	D_1 Head Height, Hex Inside head in	E Recess Dia, Max Ferrous mm	E Recess Dia, Max Ferrous in	E Recess Dia, Max Nonferrous mm	E Recess Dia, Max Nonferrous in
1/16–27	1/16–27	4.14	0.163	—	—	—	—
1/16–27	1/16–27	4.52	0.178				
1/8–27	1/8–27	5.72	0.225	—	—	—	—
1/8–27	1/8–27	6.10	0.240				
1/4–18	1/4–18	6.60	0.260	—	—	—	—
1/4–18	1/4–18	7.11	0.280				
3/8–18	3/8–18	7.24	0.285	7.9	0.31	9.1	0.36
3/8–18	3/8–18	7.87	0.310				
1/2–14	1/2–14	8.89	0.350	9.7	0.38	13.5	0.53
1/2–14	1/2–14	9.65	0.380				
3/4–14	3/4–14	10.41	0.410	14.2	0.56	18.3	0.72
3/4–14	3/4–14	11.18	0.440				
1–11-1/2	1–11-1/2	11.68	0.460	19.0	0.75	23.6	0.93
1–11-1/2	1–11-1/2	12.70	0.500				

(Continued on next page)

A Dryseal Thread NPTF, in	A_1 Dryseal Thread PTF-SAE Short in	Wall Thickness Min F Ferrous mm	Wall Thickness Min F Ferrous in	Wall Thickness Min F Nonferrous mm	Wall Thickness Min F Nonferrous in	Wall Thickness Min G Ferrous mm	Wall Thickness Min G Ferrous in
1/16–27	1/16–27	—	—	—	—	—	—
1/8–27	1/8–27	—	—	—	—	—	—
1/4–18	1/4–18	—	—	—	—	—	—
3/8–18	3/8–18	3.3	0.13	2.8	0.11	3.3	0.13
1/2–14	1/2–14	4.1	0.16	3.0	0.12	4.1	0.16
3/4–14	3/4–14	4.6	0.18	3.3	0.13	4.6	0.18
1–11-1/2	1–11-1/2	5.1	0.20	3.6	0.14	5.1	0.20

(Continued)

TABLE 2—DIMENSIONS OF SQUARE AND HEXAGON INSIDE HEAD PIPE, FILLER, AND DRAIN PLUGS (Figures 1A to 1D)[(1)] (Continued)

A Dryseal Thread NPTF, in	A_1 Dryseal Thread PTF-SAE Short in	Wall Thickness Min G Nonferrous mm	Wall Thickness Min G Nonferrous in	J Full Thread Length mm	J Full Thread Length in	J_1 Full Thread Length mm	J_1 Full Thread Length in
1/16–27	1/16–27	—	—	7.6	0.30	6.6	0.26
1/8–27	1/8–27	—	—	7.6	0.30	6.9	0.27
1/4–18	1/4–18	—	—	11.7	0.46	10.4	0.41
3/8–18	3/8–18	2.0	0.08	11.7	0.46	10.4	0.41
1/2–14	1/2–14	2.3	0.09	15.5	0.61	13.5	0.53
3/4–14	3/4–14	2.5	0.10	15.7	0.62	14.0	0.55
1–11-1/2	1–11-1/2	2.8	0.11	19.6	0.77	17.5	0.69

1. WARNING—AUTOMOTIVE FILLER AND DRAIN PLUGS ARE PRIMARILY INTENDED FOR INSTALLATION WHERE IT IS DESIRABLE TO LIMIT THE ENTRY OF THE SMALL END OF THE PLUG. SEE GENERAL SPECIFICATIONS.
2. Length B may be reduced one (p) thread if the thread is cut through at head corners.

HEXAGON OUTSIDE HEAD

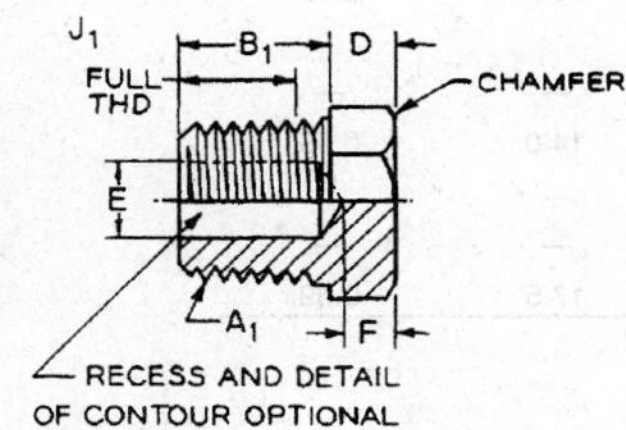

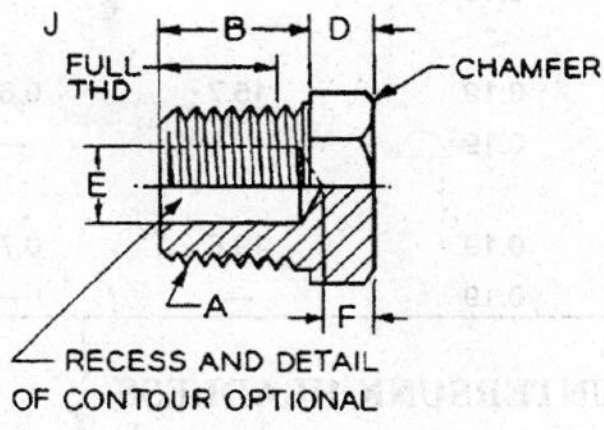

FIGURE 2A—HEXAGON OUTSIDE HEAD PIPE PLUGS (130109E)

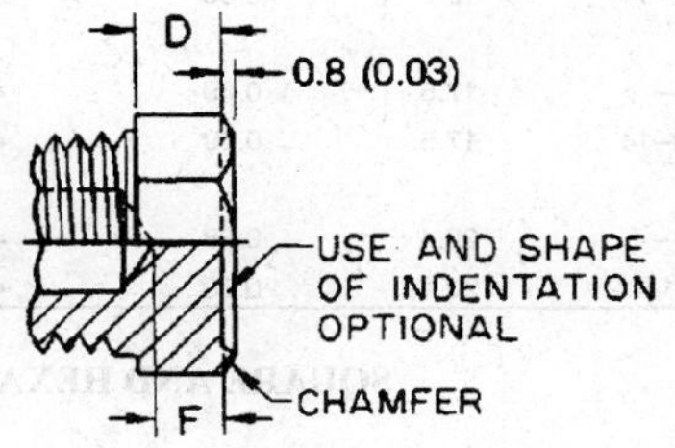

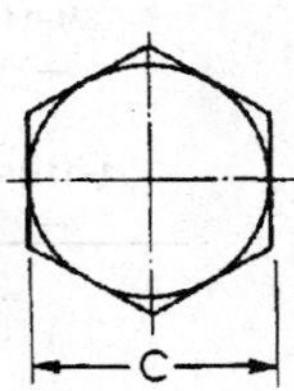

NOTE - DIMENSIONS ARE mm (in)

FIGURE 2B—HEXAGON OUTSIDE HEAD FILLER AND DRAIN PIPE PLUGS[1] (130109F)

CODES SHOWN IN BRACKETS ADJACENT TO FIGURE NUMBERS REPRESENT RESPECTIVE FITTING IDENTIFICATION IN ACCORDANCE TO SAE J846.

TABLE 3—DIMENSIONS OF HEXAGON OUTSIDE HEAD PIPE, FILLER, AND DRAIN PLUGS[(1)] (Figures 2A and 2B)

A Dryseal Thread NPTF, in	A_1 Dryseal Thread PTF-SAE Short, in	B Shoulder Length[(2)] mm	B Shoulder Length[(2)] in	B_1 Shoulder Length[(2)] mm	B_1 Shoulder Length[(2)] in	C Hex (Nom) in	D Head Height mm	D Head Height in
1/16–27	—	9.7	0.38	—	—	5/16	3.84	0.151
—	1/16–27	—	—	8.1	0.32	5/16	4.11	0.162
1/8–27	—	9.7	0.38	—	—	7/16	4.60	0.181
—	1/8–27	—	—	8.1	0.32	7/16	4.93	0.194
1/4–18	—	14.2	0.56	—	—	9/16	4.60	0.181
—	1/4–18	—	—	12.4	0.49	9/16	4.93	0.194
3/8–18	—	14.2	0.56	—	—	11/16	5.38	0.212
—	3/8–18	—	—	12.4	0.49	11/16	5.77	0.227
1/2–14	—	19.0	0.75	—	—	7/8	5.38	0.212
—	1/2–14	—	—	16.3	0.64	7/8	5.77	0.227
3/4–14	—	19.0	0.75	—	—	1-1/16	7.72	0.304
—	3/4–14	—	—	16.5	0.65	1-1/16	8.20	0.323
1–11-1/2	—	23.9	0.94	—	—	1-5/16	7.72	0.304
—	1–11-1/2	—	—	20.6	0.81	1-5/16	8.20	0.323

1. WARNING—AUTOMOTIVE FILLER AND DRAIN PLUGS ARE PRIMARILY INTENDED FOR INSTALLATION WHERE IT IS DESIRABLE TO LIMIT THE ENTRY OF THE SMALL END OF THE PLUG. SEE GENERAL SPECIFICATIONS.
2. Length B may be reduced one (p) thread if thread is cut through at head corners.

TABLE 3—DIMENSIONS OF HEXAGON OUTSIDE HEAD PIPE, FILLER, AND DRAIN PLUGS[(1)] (Figures 3 to 6) (Continued)

A Dryseal Thread NPTF, in	A_1 Dryseal Thread PTF-SAE Short, in	E Recess Dia, Max mm	E Recess Dia, Max in	F Wall Thickness Min mm	F Wall Thickness Min in	J Full Thread mm	J Full Thread in	J_1 Full Thread mm	J_1 Full Thread in
1/16–27	—	2.5	0.010	2.3	0.09	7.6	0.30	—	—
—	1/16–27	2.5	0.010	2.3	0.09	—	—	6.6	0.26
1/8–27	—	4.1	0.16	3.0	0.12	7.6	0.30	—	—
—	1/8–27	4.1	0.16	3.0	0.12	—	—	6.9	0.27
1/4–18	—	6.4	0.25	3.0	0.12	11.7	0.46	—	—
—	1/4–18	6.4	0.25	3.0	0.12	—	—	10.4	0.41
3/8–18	—	9.7	0.38	4.1	0.16	11.7	0.46	—	—
—	3/8–18	9.7	0.38	4.1	0.16	—	—	10.4	0.41
1/2–14	—	12.7	0.50	4.1	0.16	15.5	0.61	—	—
—	1/2–14	12.7	0.50	4.1	0.16	—	—	13.5	0.53
3/4–14	—	17.5	0.69	4.8	0.19	15.7	0.62	—	—
—	3/4–14	17.5	0.69	4.8	0.19	—	—	14.0	0.55
1-11-1/2	—	22.4	0.88	4.8	0.19	19.6	0.77	—	—
—	1-11-1/2	22.4	0.88	4.8	0.19	—	—	17.5	0.69

SQUARE AND HEXAGON COUNTERSUNK HEADLESS

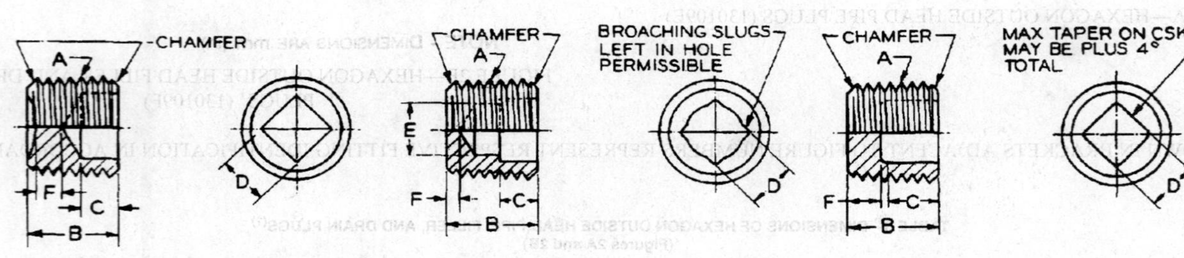

FIGURE 3A—UPSET (130109G)　**FIGURE 3B—BROACHED (130109H)**　**FIGURE 3C—E CAST (130109J)**

FIGURE 3—SQUARE COUNTERSUNK HEADLESS PIPE PLUGS (NPTF)

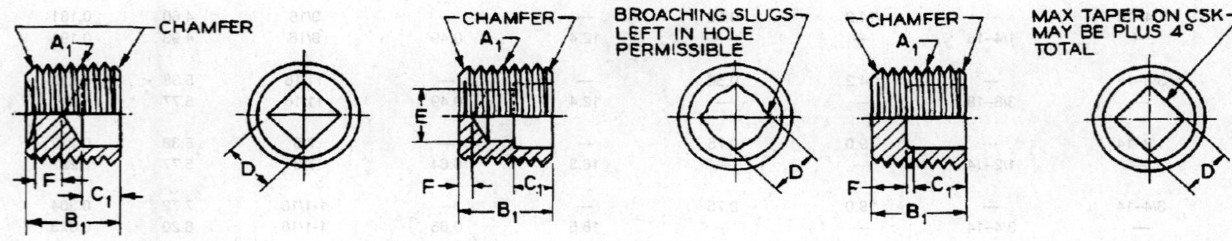

FIGURE 4A—UPSET (130109K)　**FIGURE 4B—BROACHED (130109L)**　**FIGURE 4C—CAST (130109M)**

FIGURE 4—SQUARE COUNTERSUNK HEADLESS FILLER AND DRAIN PLUGS (PTF)[1]

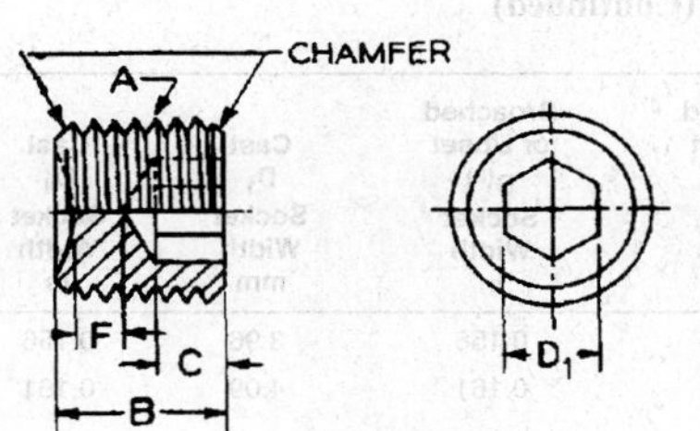

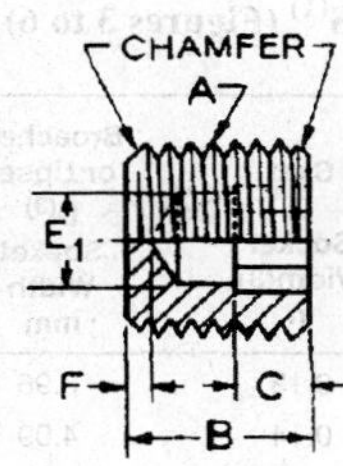

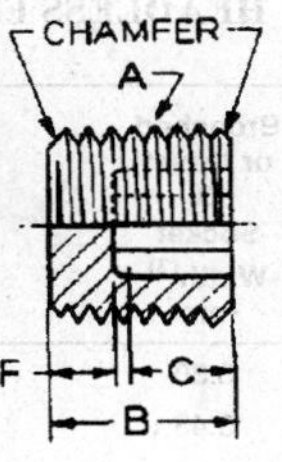

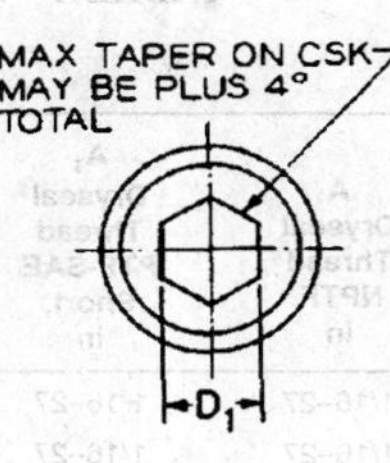

FIGURE 5A—UPSET (130109N)   FIGURE 5B—BROACHED (130109P)   FIGURE 5C—CAST (130109R)

FIGURE 5—HEXAGON COUNTERSUNK HEADLESS PIPE PLUGS (NPTF)

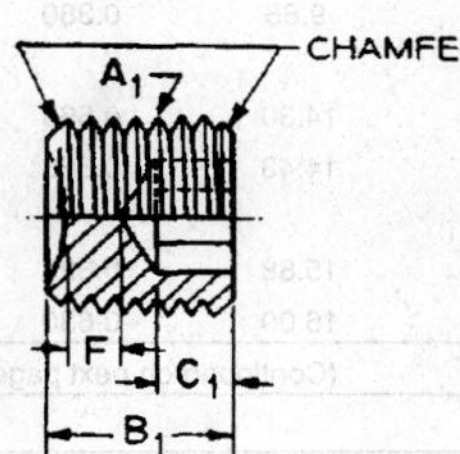

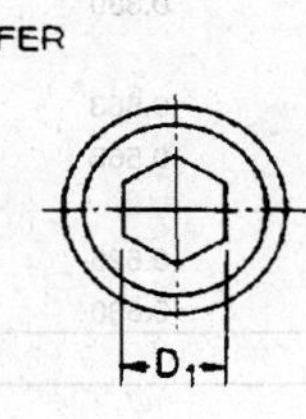

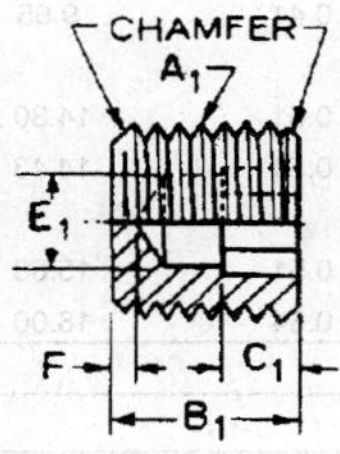

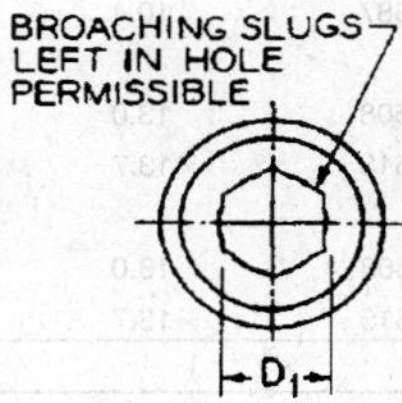

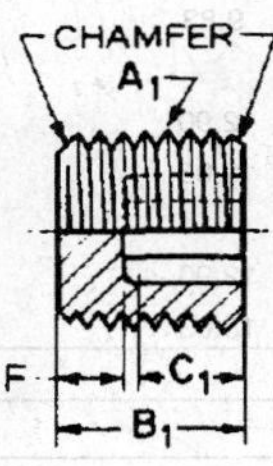

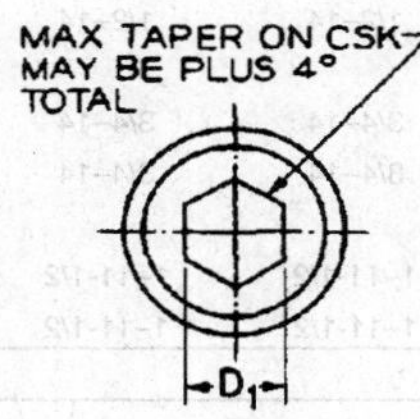

FIGURE 6A—UPSET (130109S)   FIGURE 6B—BROACHED (130109T)   FIGURE 6C—CAST (130109U)

FIGURE 6—HEXAGON COUNTERSUNK HEADLESS FILLER AND DRAIN PLUGS (PTF)[1]

TABLE 4—DIMENSIONS OF SQUARE AND HEXAGON COUNTERSUNK HEADLESS PIPE PLUGS AND HEADLESS FILLER AND DRAIN PLUGS[(1)] (Figures 3 to 6)

A Dryseal Thread NPTF, in	A_1 Dryseal Thread PTF-SAE Short, in	B Body Length[(2)] mm	B Body Length[(2)] in	B_1 Body Length(2) mm	B_1 Body Length[(2)] in	C Socket Depth, Min mm	C Socket Depth, Min in	C_1 Socket Depth, Min mm	C_1 Socket Depth Min in
1/16–27	1/16–27	7.37	0.290	6.35	0.250	3.0	0.12	2.3	0.09
1/16–27	1/16–27	7.87	0.310	6.86	0.270	—	—	—	—
1/8–27	1/8–27	7.37	0.290	6.60	0.260	3.0	012	2.3	0.09
1/8–27	1/8–27	7.87	0.310	7.11	0.280	—	—	—	—
1/4–18	1/4–18	11.30	0.445	10.03	0.395	4.8	0.19	4.1	0.16
1/4–18	1/4–18	12.06	0.475	10.80	0.425	—	—	—	—
3/8–18	3/8–18	11.30	0.445	10.03	0.395	4.8	0.19	4.1	0.16
3/8–18	3/8–18	12.06	0.475	10.80	0.425				
1/2–14	1/2–14	14.99	0.590	13.21	0.520	6.4	0.25	4.8	0.19
1/2–14	1/2–14	16.00	0.630	14.22	0.560	—	—	—	—
3/4–14	3/4–14	15.24	0.600	13.46	0.530	7.9	0.31	4.8	0.19
3/4–14	3/4–14	16.26	0.640	14.48	0.570	—	—	—	—
1–11-1/2	1–11-1/2	19.05	0.750	17.02	0.670	9.7	0.38	6.4	0.25
1–11-1/2	1–11-1/2	20.07	0.790	18.03	0.710	—	—	—	—

(Continued)

TABLE 4—DIMENSIONS OF SQUARE AND HEXAGON COUNTERSUNK HEADLESS PIPE PLUGS AND HEADLESS FILLER AND DRAIN PLUGS(1) (Figures 3 to 6) (Continued)

A Dryseal Thread NPTF, in	A_1 Dryseal Thread PTF-SAE Short, in	Broached or Upset D Socket Width(3) mm	Broached or Upset D Socket Width(3) in	Cast D Socket Width(3) mm	Cast D Socket Width(3) in	Broached or Upset D(3) Socket Width mm	Broached or Upset D(3) Socket Width in	Cast D_1 Socket Width mm	Cast D_1 Socket Width in
1/16–27	1/16–27	3.30	0.130	3.3	0.13	3.96	0.156	3.96	0.156
1/16–27	1/16–27	3.43	0.135	3.6	0.14	4.09	0.161	4.09	0.161
1/8–27	1/8–27	4.88	0.192	4.8	0.19	4.78	0.188	4.78	0.188
1/8–27	1/8–27	5.00	0.197	5.3	0.21	4.90	0.193	4.90	0.193
1/4–18	1/4–18	6.48	0.255	6.6	0.26	6.35	0.250	6.35	0.250
1/4–18	1/4–18	6.60	0.260	7.1	0.28	6.48	0.255	6.48	0.255
3/8–18	3/8–18	8.10	0.319	8.1	0.32	7.95	0.313	7.95	0.313
3/8–18	3/8–18	8.23	0.324	8.9	0.35	8.08	0.318	8.08	0.318
1/2–14	1/2–14	9.70	0.382	9.7	0.38	9.53	0.375	9.52	0.375
1/2–14	1/2–14	9.83	0.387	10.4	0.41	9.65	0.380	9.65	0.380
3/4–14	3/4–14	12.90	0.508	13.0	0.51	14.30	0.563	14.30	0.563
3/4–14	3/4–14	13.03	0.513	13.7	0.54	14.43	0.568	14.43	0.568
1–11-1/2	1–11-1/2	12.90	0.508	13.0	0.51	15.88	0.625	15.88	0.625
1–11-1/2	1–11-1/2	13.03	0.513	13.7	0.54	16.00	0.630	16.00	0.630

(Continued on next page)

A Dryseal Thread NPTF, in	A_1 Dryseal Thread PTF-SAE Short, in	Broached or Upset E Hole Dia Max mm	Broached or Upset E Hole Dia Max mm	Broached or Upset E Hole Dia Max in	Broached or Upset E_1 Hole Dia Steel Max mm	Broached or Upset E_1 Hole Dia Steel Max in	Broached or Upset E_1 Hole Dia Nonferrous Max mm
1/16–27	1/16–27	3.63	0.143	4.09	0.161	4.09	0.161
1/8–27	1/8–27	5.31	0.209	4.90	0.193	4.90	0.193
1/4–18	1/4–18	7.06	0.278	6.48	0.255	6.63	0.261
3/8–18	3/8–18	8.76	0.345	8.08	0.318	8.20	0.323
1/2–14	1/2–14	10.41	0.410	9.68	0.381	9.80	0.386
3/4–14	3/4–14	14.05	0.553	14.48	0.570	14.48	0.570
1–11-1/2	1–11-1/2	14.05	0.553	16.08	0.633	16.08	0.633

(Continued)

A Dryseal Thread NPTF, in	A_1 Dryseal Thread PTF-SAE Short, in	Broached or Upset F Wall Thickness Min mm	Broached or Upset F Wall Thickness Min in	Cast F Wall Thickness Ferrous Min mm	Cast F Wall Thickness Ferrous Min in	Cast F Wall Thickness Nonferrous Min mm	Cast F Wall Thickness Nonferrous Min in
1/16–27	1/16–27	1.5	0.06	1.5	0.06	1.5	0.06
1/8–27	1/8–27	1.5	0.06	2.0	0.08	1.5	0.06
1/4–18	1/4–18	1.5	0.06	2.5	0.10	1.8	0.07
3/8–18	3/8–18	1.5	0.06	3.3	0.13	2.0	0.08
1/2–14	1/2–14	2.3	0.09	4.1	0.16	2.3	0.09
3/4–14	3/4–14	2.3	0.09	4.6	0.18	2.5	0.10
1–11-1/2	1–11-1/2	3.0	0.12	5.1	0.20	2.8	0.11

1. WARNING—AUTOMOTIVE FILLER AND DRAIN PLUGS ARE PRIMARILY INTENDED FOR INSTALLATION WHERE ITIS DESIRABLE TO LIMIT THE ENTRY OF THE SMALL END OF THE PLUG. SEE GENERAL SPECIFICATIONS.
2. Thread must be full or complete thread for length B and B1.
3. Tabulated limits shall be maintained for a distance equal to one-half the specified socket depth. Width at top and bottom portions of the socket may slightly exceed maximum.

R) AUTOMOTIVE STRAIGHT THREAD FILLER AND DRAIN PLUGS—SAE J532 JUN1993

SAE Standard

Report of the SAE Parts and Fittings Committee approved February 1918. Revised by the SAE Tube, Pipe, Hose, and Lubrication Fittings Committee December 1973, editorial change January 1981. Completely revised by the SAE Fluid Conductors and Connectors Technical Committee June 1993. Rationale statement available.

Foreword—This Document has also changed to comply with the new SAE Technical Standards Board format.

*1. **Scope***—This SAE Standard includes complete general and dimensional specifications for those types of filler and drain plugs (shown in Figures 1 to 7 and Tables 1 to 3) having straight threads which are commonly used with gaskets or seals in automotive and related industrial applications.

*2. **References***

2.1 Applicable Publications—The following publications form a part of this specification to the extent specified herein. The latest issue of SAE publications shall apply.

2.1.1 SAE PUBLICATIONS—Available from SAE, 400 Commonwealth Drive, Warrendale, PA 15096-0001.

SAE J548/1—Spark Plugs
SAE J548/2—Spark Plug Installation Sockets

2.1.2 ANSI PUBLICATION—Available from ANSI, 11 West 42nd Street, New York, NY 10036-8002.

ANSI/SAE J475—Screw Threads (ANSI B1.1)

2.1.3 ASTM PUBLICATION—Available from ASTM, 100 Barr Harbor Drive, West Conshohocken, PA 19428-2959.

ASTM B 117—Method of Salt Spray (Fog) Testing

*3. **General Specifications***

3.1 Dimensions and Tolerances—Except for nominal sizes and thread specifications, dimensions and tolerances are given in both SI units and U.S. customary as designated. Tabulated dimensions shall apply to the finished plugs, plated, hardened, or otherwise processed, as specified by the purchaser. The minimum across corner dimensions of external hexagons shall be 1.092 times the nominal width across flats, but shall not result in a side flat width less than 0.43 times the nominal width across flats. The minimum across corner dimensions of external squares shall be 1.25 times the nominal width across flats, but shall not result in a side flat width less than 0.75 times the nominal width across flats. The diameter of the washer face on hexagon outside head plugs shall be equal to 95% of the maximum width across flats within a tolerance of ±5%. At maximum material condition, the radii at corners of hexagon and square sockets in broached or upset plugs shall not exceed 0.13 mm (0.005 in).

Tolerance on dimensions not otherwise limited shall be ±0.25 mm (±0.010 in).

3.2 Straight Threads—Unified standard Class 2A external and Class 2B internal threads shall apply to inch sizes of plain finish (unplated) plugs and holes into which they assemble. For externally threaded parts with additive finish, the maximum diameters of Class 2A may be exceeded by the amount of the allowance, that is, the basic diameters (Class 2A maximum diameter plus the allowance) shall apply after plating. The pitch diameter tolerance for special diameter-pitch combinations shall be based on diameter, pitch, and a length of engagement of 9 times the pitch. See SAE J475.

For metric sizes of plugs and mating holes, threads shall conform with SAE J548.

For convenient reference, the data generally required to specify threads is given in Table 1 for both the plugs and mating holes. (Inasmuch as threads are normally produced and gaged with equipment made to the respective measurement system, conversion of size designations and dimensions to other measurement systems is considered unnecessary.)

External threads shall be chamfered or rounded from the diameters tabulated in Table 4 to produce a length of chamfered or partial thread as specified.

3.3 Material and Manufacture—Plugs may be made from low carbon steel, cast iron, malleable iron, brass, bronze, or aluminum alloy as specified by purchaser, by casting, milling from the bar, or upsetting from a grade of material free of defects which will affect their serviceability.

3.4 Finish—The external surfaces and threads of all carbon steel parts shall be plated or coated with a suitable material that passes a 72 h salt spray test in accordance with ASTM B 117. Any appearance of red rust during the 72 h salt spray test shall be considered failure, except for the following:

a. All internal fluid passages.
b. Edges such as hex points, serrations, and crests of threads where there may be mechanical deformation of the plating or coating typical of mass-produced parts or shipping effects.
c. Areas where there is mechanical deformation of the plating or coating caused by crimping, flaring, bending, and other post-plate metal forming operations.
d. Areas where the parts are suspended or affixed in the test chamber where condensate can accumulate.

NOTE—Cadmium plating is not preferred due to environmental reasons. Parts manufactured to this Standard after January 1, 1997, shall not be cadmium plated. Internal fluid passages shall be protected from corrosion during storage. Changes in plating may affect assembly torques and require requalification, when applicable.

3.5 Workmanship—Workmanship shall conform to the best commercial practice to produce high-quality parts. Plugs shall be free from all hanging burrs, loose scale, and slivers which might become dislodged in usage and all other defects which might affect their serviceability.

TABLE 1—STRAIGHT THREAD SIZES (EXTERNAL AND INTERNAL) (FIGURES 1 TO 7)

Nom Size, in	Series Designation	External Thread Pitch Diameter Max mm	External Thread Pitch Diameter Max in	External Thread Pitch Diameter Min mm	External Thread Pitch Diameter Min in	Internal Thread Pitch Diameter Max mm	Internal Thread Pitch Diameter Max in	Internal Thread Pitch Diameter Min mm	Internal Thread Pitch Diameter Min in	Internal Thread Minor Diameter Max mm	Internal Thread Minor Diameter Max in	Internal Thread Minor Diameter Min mm	Internal Thread Minor Diameter Min in
5/16–24	UNF		0.2843		0.2806		0.2902		0.2854		0.277		0.267
3/8–24	UNF		0.3468		0.3430		0.3528		0.3479		0.340		0.330
1/2–20	UNF		0.4662		0.4619		0.4731		0.4675		0.457		0.446
5/8–18	UNF		0.5875		0.5828		0.5949		0.5889		0.578		0.565
3/4–16	UNF		0.7079		0.7029		0.7159		0.7094		0.696		0.682
7/8–18	UNS		0.8375		0.8329		0.8449		0.8389		0.828		0.815
1–18	UNS		0.9625		0.9578		0.9701		0.9639		0.953		0.940
1-1/4–18	UNEF		1.2124		1.2075		1.2202		1.2139		1.203		1.190
1-1/2–18	UNEF		1.4624		1.4574		1.4704		1.4639		1.452		1.440
1-3/4–16	UN		1.7078		1.7025		1.7163		1.7094		1.696		1.682
2–16	UN		1.9578		1.9524		1.9664		1.9594		1.946		1.932
Metric Thread Sizes													
10 x 1	—	9.335		9.238		9.446		9.350		8.954		8.844	
14 x 1.25	—	13.155		13.048		13.297		13.188		12.962		12.499	
18 x 1.5	—	16.980		16.853		17.153		17.026		16.426		16.266	

SQUARE AND HEXAGON HEAD

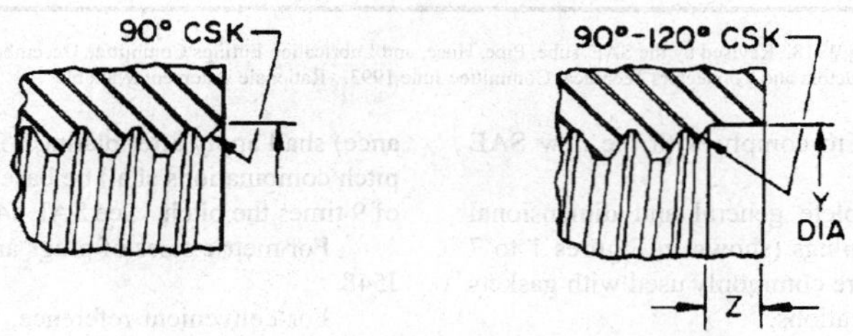

FIGURE 1—RECOMMENDED HOLE DATA

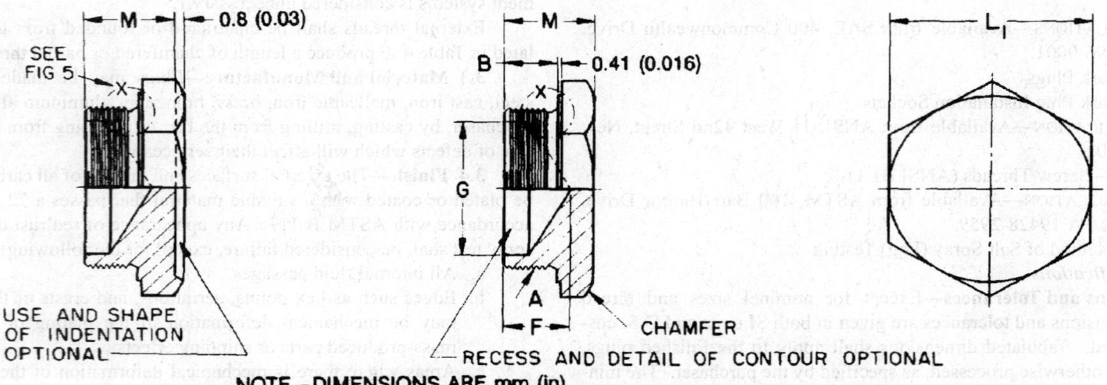

FIGURE 2—HEXAGON OUTSIDE HEAD PLUG (420109A)

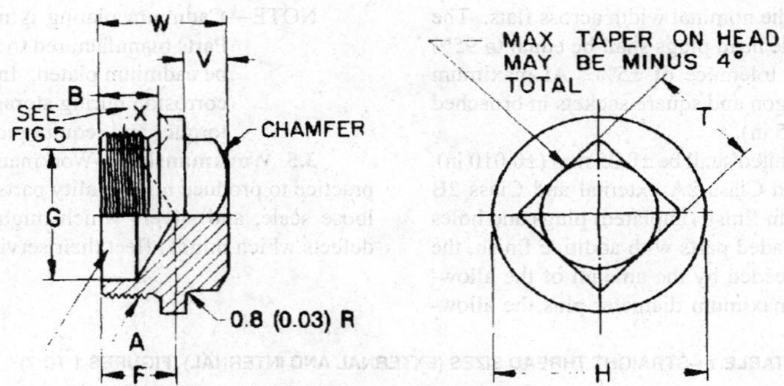

FIGURE 3—SQUARE HEAD PLUG (420109B)

CODES SHOWN IN BRACKETS ADJACENT TO FIGURE NUMBERS REPRESENT RESPECTIVE FITTING IDENTIFICATION IN ACCORDANCE WITH SAE J846.

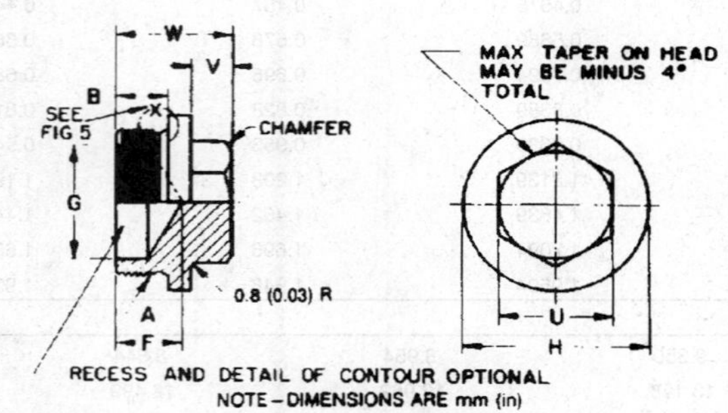

FIGURE 4—HEXAGON INSIDE HEAD PLUG (420109C)

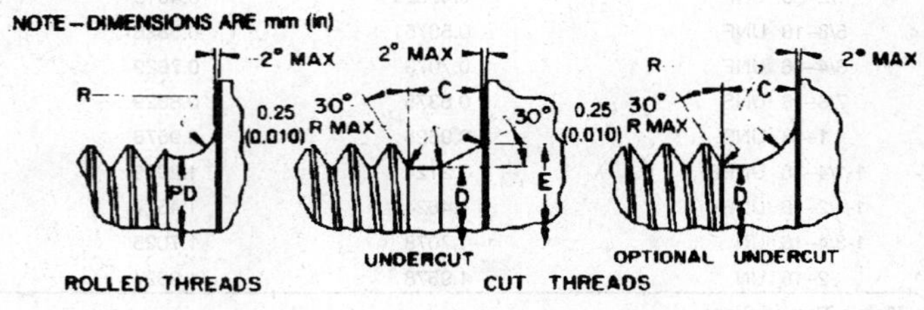

FIGURE 5—DETAIL X ENLARGED

TABLE 2A—DIMENSIONS OF HEXAGON OUTSIDE HEAD AND SQUARE, AND HEXAGON INSIDE HEAD FILLER AND DRAIN PLUGS (FIGURES 2 TO 5)

Nom Size, in	B Shoulder Length mm	B Shoulder Length in	C Relief Width mm	C Relief Width in	D Relief Dia mm	D Relief Dia in	E Pilot Dia mm	E Pilot Dia in	F Recess Depth mm	F Recess Depth in	G Recess Dia, Max mm	G Recess Dia, Max in	H Flange Dia mm	H Flange Dia in	R Fillet Radius [1] Approx mm	R Fillet Radius[1] Approx in
5/16	7.9	0.31	2.3	0.09	6.40 6.22	0.252 0.245	8.33 8.15	0.328 0.321	—	—	—	—	14.2	0.56	1.07	0.042
3/8	7.9	0.31	2.3	0.09	7.98 7.80	0.314 0.307	9.93 9.75	0.391 0.384	—	—	—	—	15.7	0.62	1.07	0.042
1/2	8.6	0.34	2.3	0.09	10.87 10.69	0.428 0.421	13.11 12.93	0.516 0.509	10.4	0.41	6.4	0.25	19.0	0.75	1.27	0.050
5/8	9.7	0.38	3.0	0.12	13.84 13.64	0.545 0.537	16.28 16.08	0.641 0.633	11.9	0.47	9.7	0.38	22.4	0.88	1.42	0.056
3/4	9.7	0.38	3.0	0.12	16.76 16.54	0.660 0.651	19.46 19.23	0.766 0.757	11.9	0.47	12.7	0.50	25.4	1.00	1.57	0.062
7/8	10.4	0.41	3.0	0.12	20.14 19.94	0.793 0.785	22.63 22.43	0.891 0.883	12.7	0.50	14.2	0.56	28.4	1.12	1.42	0.056
1	11.2	0.44	3.0	0.12	23.32 23.11	0.918 0.910	25.81 25.60	0.016 1.008	14.2	0.56	17.5	0.69	31.8	1.25	1.42	0.056
1-1/4	11.9	0.47	3.0	0.12	29.64 29.44	1.167 1.159	32.16 31.95	1.266 1.258	15.0	0.59	23.9	0.94	38.1	1.50	1.42	0.056
1-1/2	12.7	0.50	3.0	0.12	35.99 35.79	1.417 1.409	38.51 38.30	1.516 1.508	17.5	0.69	28.4	1.12	44.4	1.75	1.42	0.056
1-3/4	14.2	0.56	3.0	0.12	42.09 41.86	1.657 1.648	44.86 44.63	1.766 1.757	19.0	0.75	35.1	1.38	50.8	2.00	1.57	0.062
2	14.2	0.56	3.0	0.12	48.44 48.21	1.907 1.898	51.21 50.98	2.016 2.007	19.0	0.75	41.1	1.62	57.2	2.25	1.57	0.062
Metric Thread Sizes																
10	7.9	0.31	2.3	0.09	8.53 8.36	0.336 0.329	10.41 10.24	0.410 0.403	—	—	—	—	15.7	0.62	1.00	0.039
14	8.6	0.34	2.3	0.09	12.19 12.01	0.480 0.473	14.40 14.22	0.567 0.560	10.4	0.41	7.9	0.31	20.6	0.81	1.25	0.049
18	9.7	0.38	3.0	0.12	15.82 15.60	0.623 0.614	18.39 18.16	0.724 0.715	11.9	0.47	11.2	0.44	23.9	0.94	1.50	0.059

1. See detail X in Figure 5.

TABLE 2B—DIMENSIONS OF HEXAGON OUTSIDE HEAD AND SQUARE, AND HEXAGON INSIDE HEAD FILLER AND DRAIN PLUGS (FIGURES 2 TO 5)

Nom Size, in	R_1 Fillet Radius [1] Approx mm	R_1 Fillet Radius[1] Approx in	Hex Outside Head L Hex Width mm	Hex Outside Head L Hex Width in	Hex Outside Head M Overall Length mm	Hex Outside Head M Overall Length in	Square and Hexagon Inside Head T Square Size mm	Square and Hexagon Inside Head T Square Size in	Square and Hexagon Inside Head U Hex Size mm	Square and Hexagon Inside Head U Hex Size in	Square and Hexagon Inside Head V Square and Hex Height mm	Square and Hexagon Inside Head V Square and Hex Height in	Square and Hexagon Inside Head W Overall Length mm	Square and Hexagon Inside Head W Overall Length in
5/16	1.57	0.062	14.35 14.00	0.565 0.551	12.7	0.50	5.61 5.44	0.221 0.214	7.19 7.01	0.283 0.276	5.6	0.22	16.8	0.66
3/8	1.57	0.062	15.93 15.54	0.627 0.612	12.7	0.50	7.19 7.01	0.283 0.276	8.00 7.72	0.315 0.304	6.4	0.25	17.5	0.69
1/2	1.90	0.075	19.10 18.72	0.752 0.737	13.5	0.53	9.58 9.40	0.377 0.370	11.18 10.87	0.440 0.428	6.4	0.25	18.3	0.72
5/8	2.11	0.083	22.28 21.84	0.877 0.860	15.7	0.62	11.18 10.87	0.440 0.428	12.75 12.42	0.502 0.489	7.1	0.28	19.8	0.78
3/4	2.39	0.094	25.45 24.97	1.002 0.983	15.7	0.62	12.75 12.45	0.502 0.490	14.35 14.00	0.565 0.551	7.1	0.28	20.6	0.81
7/8	2.11	0.083	28.63 28.09	1.127 1.106	16.8	0.66	14.35 14.05	0.565 0.553	15.93 15.54	0.627 0.612	7.9	0.31	22.4	0.88
1	2.11	0.083	31.80 31.24	1.252 1.230	19.0	0.75	15.93 15.62	0.627 0.615	20.70 20.27	0.815 0.798	7.9	0.31	23.1	0.91
1-1/4	2.11	0.083	38.15 37.52	1.502 1.477	19.8	0.78	20.70 20.40	0.815 0.803	25.45 24.97	1.002 0.983	8.6	0.34	25.4	1.00

TABLE 2B—DIMENSIONS OF HEXAGON OUTSIDE HEAD AND SQUARE, AND HEXAGON INSIDE HEAD FILLER AND DRAIN PLUGS (FIGURES 2 TO 5) (continued)

Nom Size, in	R_1 Fillet Radius (1) Approx mm	R_1 Fillet Radius (1) Approx in	Hex Outside Head L Hex Width mm	Hex Outside Head L Hex Width in	Hex Outside Head M Overall Length mm	Hex Outside Head M Overall Length in	Square and Hexagon Inside Head T Square Size mm	Square and Hexagon Inside Head T Square Size in	Square and Hexagon Inside Head U Hex Size mm	Square and Hexagon Inside Head U Hex Size in	Square and Hexagon Inside Head V Square and Hex Height mm	Square and Hexagon Inside Head V Square and Hex Height in	Square and Hexagon Inside Head W Overall Length mm	Square and Hexagon Inside Head W Overall Length in
1-1/2	2.11	0.083	44.50 43.82	1.752 1.725	22.4	0.88	23.88 23.57	0.940 0.928	28.63 28.09	1.127 1.106	9.7	0.38	28.4	1.12
1-3/4	2.39	0.094	50.85 50.14	2.002 1.974	23.9	0.94	28.63 28.32	1.127 1.115	31.80 31.24	1.252 1.230	11.2	0.44	31.8	1.25
2	2.39	0.094	57.20 56.69	2.252 2.232	23.9	0.94	33.40 33.07	1.315 1.302	38.15 37.52	1.502 1.477	11.2	0.44	33.3	1.31
Metric Thread Sizes														
10	1.50	0.059	15.93 15.54	0.627 0.612	12.7	0.50	7.19 7.01	0.283 0.276	8.00 7.72	0.315 0.304	6.4	0.25	17.5	0.69
14	1.88	0.074	20.68 20.29	0.814 0.799	13.5	0.53	9.58 9.40	0.377 0.370	11.18 10.87	0.440 0.428	6.4	0.25	18.3	0.72
18	2.25	0.089	23.88 23.39	0.940 0.921	15.7	0.62	12.75 12.45	0.502 0.490	14.35 14.00	0.565 0.551	7.1	0.28	20.6	0.81

1. See detail X in Figure 5.

SQUARE AND HEXAGON SOCKET HEAD

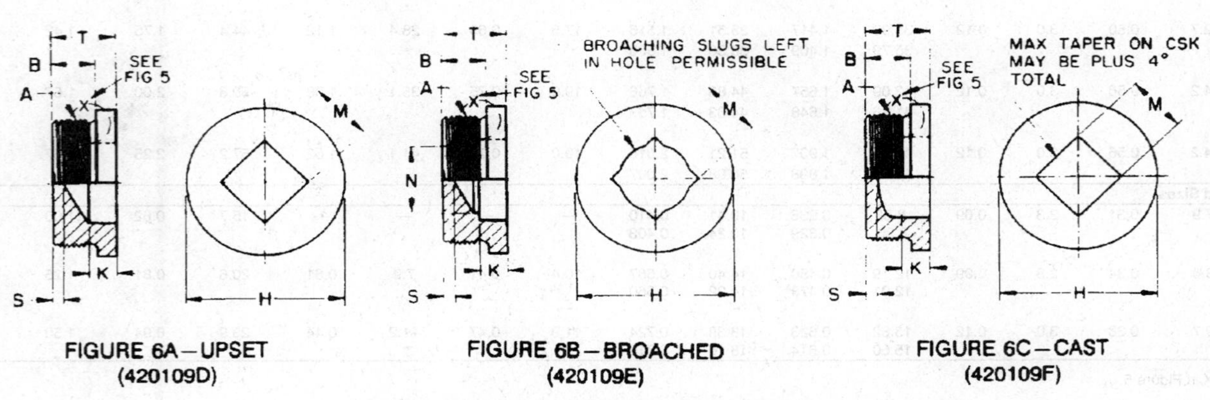

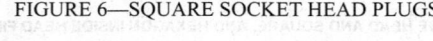

FIGURE 6—SQUARE SOCKET HEAD PLUGS

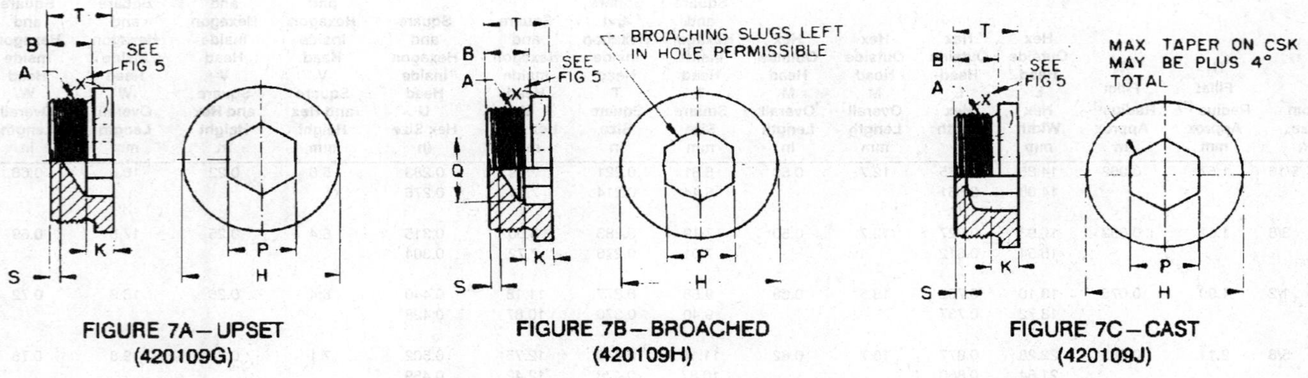

FIGURE 7—HEXAGON SOCKET HEAD PLUGS

TABLE 3A—DIMENSIONS OF SQUARE AND HEXAGON SOCKET HEAD FILLER AND DRAIN PLUGS (FIGURES 5 TO 7)

Nom Size, in	B Shoulder Length mm	B Shoulder Length in	C Relief Width mm	C Relief Width in	D Relief Dia mm	D Relief Dia in	E Pilot Dia mm	E Pilot Dia in	H Flange Dia mm	H Flange Dia in	K Socket Depth, Min mm	K Socket Depth, Min in	S Wall Thickness, Min mm	S Wall Thickness, Min in	T Overall Length mm	T Overall Length in
5/16	7.9	0.31	2.3	0.09	6.40	0.252	8.33	0.328	14.2	0.56	3.0	0.12	3.0	0.12	11.2	0.44
					6.22	0.245	8.15	0.321								
3/8	7.9	0.31	2.3	0.09	7.98	0.314	9.93	0.391	15.7	0.62	3.0	0.12	3.0	0.12	11.2	0.44
					7.80	0.307	9.75	0.384								
1/2	8.6	0.34	2.3	0.09	10.87	0.428	13.11	0.516	19.0	0.75	4.8	0.19	3.0	0.12	11.9	0.47
					10.69	0.421	12.93	0.509								
5/8	9.7	0.38	3.0	0.12	13.84	0.545	16.28	0.641	22.4	0.88	4.8	0.19	3.0	0.12	12.7	0.50
					13.64	0.537	16.08	0.633								
3/4	9.7	0.38	3.0	0.12	16.76	0.660	19.46	0.766	25.4	1.00	6.4	0.25	3.0	0.12	13.2	0.52
					16.54	0.651	19.23	0.757								
7/8	10.4	0.41	3.0	0.12	20.14	0.793	22.63	0.891	28.4	1.12	6.4	0.25	3.0	0.12	14.2	0.56
					19.94	0.785	22.43	0.883								
1	11.2	0.44	3.0	0.12	23.32	0.918	25.81	1.016	31.8	1.25	6.4	0.25	3.0	0.12	15.0	0.59
					23.11	0.910	25.60	1.008								
1-1/4	11.9	0.47	3.0	0.12	29.64	1.167	32.16	1.266	38.1	1.50	7.9	0.31	3.0	0.12	16.8	0.66
					29.44	1.159	31.95	1.258								
1-1/2	12.7	0.50	3.0	0.12	35.99	1.417	38.51	1.516	44.4	1.75	9.7	0.38	3.0	0.12	19.0	0.75
					35.79	1.409	38.30	1.508								
1-3/4	14.2	0.56	3.0	0.12	42.09	1.657	44.86	1.766	50.8	2.00	9.7	0.38	3.0	0.12	20.6	0.81
					41.86	1.648	44.63	1.757								
2	14.2	0.56	3.0	0.12	48.44	1.907	51.21	2.016	57.2	2.25	9.7	0.38	3.0	0.12	22.4	0.88
					48.21	1.898	50.98	2.007								
MetricThreadSizes																
10	7.9	0.31	2.3	0.09	8.53	0.336	10.41	0.410	15.7	0.62	3.0	0.12	3.0	0.12	11.2	0.44
					8.36	0.329	10.24	0.403								
14	8.6	0.34	2.3	0.09	12.19	0.480	14.40	0.567	20.6	0.81	4.8	0.19	3.0	0.12	11.9	0.47
					12.01	0.473	14.22	0.560								
18	9.7	0.38	3.0	0.12	15.82	0.623	18.39	0.724	23.9	0.94	6.4	0.25	3.0	0.12	13.5	0.53
					15.60	0.614	18.16	0.715								

[1] See detail X in Figure 5.

TABLE 3B—DIMENSIONS OF SQUARE AND HEXAGON SOCKET HEAD FILLER AND DRAIN PLUGS (FIGURES 5 TO 7)

Nom Size, in	R Fillet Radius[(1)] Approx mm	R Fillet Radius[(1)] Approx in	R_1 Fillet Radius[(1)] Approx mm	R_1 Fillet Radius[(1)] Approx in	Square Socket Broached or Upset M[(1)] Socket Width mm	Square Socket Broached or Upset M[(1)] Socket Width in	Square Socket Broached or Upset N Hole Dia Max mm	Square Socket Broached or Upset N Hole Dia Max in	Square Socket Cast M Socket Width mm	Square Socket Cast M Socket Width in	Hexagon Socket Broached or Upset P[(1)] Socket Width mm	Hexagon Socket Broached or Upset P[(1)] Socket Width in	Hexagon Socket Broached or Upset Q Hole Dia Max mm	Hexagon Socket Broached or Upset Q Hole Dia Max in	Hexagon Socket Cast P Socket Width mm	Hexago n Socket Cast P Socket Width in
5/16	1.07	0.042	1.57	0.062	3.30	0.130	3.63	0.143	3.3	0.13	3.96	0.156	4.09	0.161	3.96	0.156
					3.43	0.135			3.6	0.14	4.09	0.161			4.09	0.161
3/8	1.07	0.042	1.57	0.062	4.88	0.192	5.31	0.209	4.8	0.19	4.78	0.188	4.90	0.193	4.78	0.188
					5.00	0.197			5.3	0.21	4.90	0.193			4.90	0.193
1/2	1.27	0.500	1.90	0.075	6.48	0.255	7.06	0.278	6.6	0.26	6.35	0.250	6.48	0.255	6.35	0.250
					6.60	0.260			7.1	0.28	6.48	0.255			6.48	0.255
5/8	1.42	0.056	2.11	0.083	8.10	0.319	8.76	0.345	8.1	0.32	7.95	0.313	8.08	0.318	7.95	0.313
					8.23	0.324			8.9	0.35	8.08	0.318			8.08	0.318
3/4	1.57	0.062	2.39	0.094	9.70	0.382	10.41	0.410	9.7	0.38	9.53	0.375	9.68	0.381	9.53	0.375
					9.83	0.387			10.4	0.41	9.65	0.380			9.65	0.380
7/8	1.42	0.056	2.11	0.083	10.49	0.413	11.25	0.443	10.4	0.41	12.70	0.500	12.85	0.506	12.70	0.500
					10.62	0.418			11.2	0.44	12.83	0.505			12.83	0.505

TABLE 3B—DIMENSIONS OF SQUARE AND HEXAGON SOCKET HEAD FILLER AND DRAIN PLUGS (FIGURES 5 TO 7) (continued)

Nom Size, in	R Fillet Radius[1] Approx mm	R Fillet Radius[1] Approx in	R_1 Fillet Radius[1] Approx mm	R_1 Fillet Radius[1] Approx in	Square Socket Broached or Upset M[1] Socket Width mm	Square Socket Broached or Upset M[1] Socket Width in	Square Socket Broached or Upset N Hole Dia Max mm	Square Socket Broached or Upset N Hole Dia Max in	Square Socket Cast M Socket Width mm	Square Socket Cast M Socket Width in	Hexagon Socket Broached or Upset P[1] Socket Width mm	Hexagon Socket Broached or Upset P[1] Socket Width in	Hexagon Socket Broached or Upset Q Hole Dia Max mm	Hexagon Socket Broached or Upset Q Hole Dia Max in	Hexagon Socket Cast P Socket Width mm	Hexago n Socket Cast P Socket Width in
1	1.42	0.056	2.11	0.083	10.49	0.413	11.25	0.443	10.4	0.41	14.30	0.563	14.48	0.570	14.30	0.563
					10.62	0.418			11.2	0.44	14.43	0.568			14.43	0.568
1-1/4	1.42	0.056	2.11	0.083	12.90	0.508	14.05	0.553	13.0	0.51	15.88	0.625	16.08	0.633	15.88	0.625
					13.03	0.513			13.7	0.54	16.00	0.630			16.00	0.630
1-1/2	1.42	0.056	2.11	0.083	16.05	0.632	17.25	0.679	16.0	0.63	19.05	0.750	19.23	0.757	19.05	0.750
					16.18	0.637			16.8	0.66	19.18	0.755			19.30	0.760
1-3/4	1.57	0.062	2.39	0.094	19.28	0.759	20.83	0.820	19.3	0.76	22.23	0.875	22.43	0.883	22.23	0.875
					19.41	0.764			20.3	0.80	22.35	0.880			22.48	0.885
2	1.57	0.062	2.39	0.094	22.45	0.884	24.00	0.945	22.6	0.89	28.58	1.125	28.80	1.134	28.58	1.125
					22.58	0.889			23.6	0.93	28.70	1.130			28.83	1.135
MetricThreadSizes																
10	1.00	0.039	1.50	0.059	4.88	0.192	5.31	0.209	4.8	0.19	4.78	0.188	4.90	0.193	4.78	0.188
					5.00	0.197			5.3	0.21	4.90	0.193			4.90	0.193
14	1.25	0.049	1.88	0.074	6.48	0.255	7.06	0.278	6.6	0.26	6.35	0.250	6.48	0.255	6.35	0.250
					6.60	0.260			7.1	0.28	6.48	0.255			6.48	0.255
18	1.50	0.059	2.25	0.089	9.70	0.382	10.41	0.410	9.7	0.38	9.53	0.375	9.68	0.381	9.53	0.375
					9.83	0.387			10.4	0.41	9.65	0.380			9.65	0.380

1. See detail X in Figure 5.

TABLE 4—(FIGURE 1)

Nom Size, in	Series Desig- nation	External Thread Chamfer Dia Max mm	External Thread Chamfer Dia Max in	External Thread Chamfer Dia Min mm	External Thread Chamfer Dia Min in	External Thread Length of Chamfer or Partial Thread Max mm	External Thread Length of Chamfer or Partial Thread Max in	External Thread Length of Chamfer or Partial Thread Min mm	External Thread Length of Chamfer or Partial Thread Min in	Internal Thread Y CSK or C'Bore Dia Basic mm	Internal Thread Y CSK or C'Bore Dia Basic in	Internal Thread Z C'Bore Depth Basic mm	Internal Thread Z C'Bore Depth Basic in
5/16-24	UNF	6.4	0.25	6.1	0.24	1.32	0.052	0.79	0.031	8.6	0.34	1.07	0.042
3/8-24	UNF	7.9	0.31	7.6	0.30	1.32	0.052	0.79	0.031	10.2	0.40	1.07	0.042
1/2-20	UNF	10.9	0.43	10.7	0.42	1.57	0.062	0.97	0.038	13.5	0.53	1.27	0.050
5/8-18	UNF	13.7	0.54	13.2	0.52	1.75	0.069	1.07	0.042	16.8	0.66	1.42	0.056
3/4-16	UNF	16.8	0.66	16.3	0.64	1.98	0.078	1.19	0.047	19.8	0.78	1.57	0.062
7/8-18	UNS	20.1	0.79	19.6	0.77	1.75	0.069	1.07	0.042	23.1	0.91	1.42	0.056
1-18	UNS	23.4	0.92	22.9	0.90	1.75	0.069	1.07	0.042	26.2	1.03	1.42	0.056
1-1/4-18	UNEF	29.7	1.17	29.2	1.15	1.75	0.069	1.07	0.042	32.5	1.28	1.42	0.056
1-1/2-18	UNEF	36.1	1.42	35.6	1.40	1.75	0.069	1.07	0.042	38.9	1.53	1.42	0.056
1-3/4-16	UN	42.2	1.66	41.7	1.64	1.98	0.078	1.19	0.047	45.2	1.78	1.57	0.062
2-16	UN	48.5	1.91	48.0	1.89	1.98	0.078	1.19	0.047	51.6	2.03	1.57	0.062
MetricThreadSizes													
10 x 1	–	8.4	0.33	8.1	0.32	1.25	0.049	0.75	0.030	10.8	0.42	1.00	0.039
14 x 1.25	–	12.2	0.48	11.9	0.47	1.56	0.061	0.94	0.037	14.8	0.58	1.25	0.049
18 x 1.5	–	15.7	0.62	15.2	0.60	1.88	0.074	1.12	0.044	18.8	0.74	1.50	0.059

LUBRICATION FITTINGS—SAE J534 JUL1998 SAE Standard

Report of the SAE Parts and Fittings Committee approved January 1949. Revised by the SAE Tube, Pipe, Hose, and Lubrication Fittings Committee October 1973. Editorial change January 1981. Revised by the SAE Fluid Conductors and Connectors Technical Committee June 1993, August 1996, and July 1998. Rationale statement available.

1. Scope—This SAE Standard covers complete general and dimensional specifications for the various types of lubrication fittings and related threaded components intended for general application in the automotive and allied fields.

2. References

2.1 Applicable Publication—The following publication forms a part of this specification to the extent specified herein. The latest issue of SAE publications shall apply.

2.1.1 SAE PUBLICATION—Available from SAE, 400 Commonwealth Drive, Warrendale, PA 15096-0001.

SAE J476a—Dryseal Pipe Threads

2.1.2 ASTM PUBLICATION—Available from ASTM, 1916 Race Street, Philadelphia, PA 19103-1187.

ASTM B 117—Method of Salt Spray (Fog) Testing

3. General Specifications

3.1 Designations—Lubrication fittings are designated by the type and size of the threaded ends and the configuration of the fitting (Figures 1a, 1b, c).

3.2 Dimensions and Tolerances—Except for nominal sizes and thread designations, dimensions and tolerances are given in both SI units and U.S. customary, as designated in Table 1. Tabulated dimensions shall apply to the finished parts, plated or otherwise processed, as specified by the purchaser. Tolerance on all dimensions not otherwise limited shall be ±0.3 mm. The maximum and minimum across flats dimensions shall be within the commercial tolerance of bar or extruded stock from which the fittings are produced. The minimum across corners dimensions of hexagons shall be 1.092 times the nominal width across flats, but shall not result in a side flat width less than 0.43 times the nominal width across flats.

3.3 Check Valve—All the standard hydraulic lubrication fittings contained herein are supplied with ball check valves. Fittings without valves are not recommended by the lubrication fitting industry.

3.4 Contour—Details of contour shall be optional with the manufacturer, provided the tabulated dimensions are maintained and serviceability of the fittings is not impaired.

3.5 Pipe Threads—The pipe threads on fittings, unless there is specific authorization to the contrary, shall conform with the specifications given in detail in SAE J476 for the designated thread series, except that external thread crests may have greater maximum truncation due to manufacturing practices. Experience has shown that the crest of the threads on lubrication fittings, intended for use with grease, does not have to conform to Dryseal American Standard Form to function satisfactorily. The deviations from standard Dryseal practice are peculiar to lubrication fittings and as special considerations are involved, it is not advisable to use them in any other application of pipe thread practice.

External pipe threads shall be chamfered from a diameter (rounded to a two-place decimal) obtained by subtracting 0.41 mm from the minimum minor diameter at the small end, with a minus tolerance on the diameter of 0.5 mm, to produce a length of chamfered or partial thread equivalent to 1 to 1-1/2 times pitch (rounded to a three-place decimal). See Appendix A of SAE J476.

Internal pipe threads shall be countersunk 90 degrees included angle to a diameter (rounded to a two-place decimal) obtained by adding 0.41 mm to the maximum major diameter at the large end with a plus tolerance on the diameter of 0.5 mm. See Appendix A of SAE J476.

Recommended assembly considerations for the various combinations of Dryseal pipe threads are given under the respective standard thread series and the paragraph headed Limitation of Assembly, Appendix D, in SAE J476.

3.6 1/4-28 Taper Thread—External taper threads designated SAE-LT shall be Unified Standard Form 1/4-28 with 19.0 mm ± 1.5 mm, diametral taper per 304.8 mm of length. The pitch diameter measured at start of thread on small end shall be 5.733 to 5.649 mm.

Threads shall be chamfered 0.91 to 1.37 mm long from a diameter of 5.1 mm with a tolerance of –0.5 mm.

It is recommended that SAE-LT taper threads be assembled into 1/4-28 UNF, Class 3B, straight threaded holes having a modified maximum minor diameter of 5.466 mm to insure 75% minimum thread height.

3.7 Special Thread Forming Threads—The 1/4-28 special taper thread forming thread and the 1/8-27 pipe special thread forming thread, where specified, shall conform to the dimensions specified in Figure 4 and Table 2. Fittings employing these threads may be driven or spun into unthreaded holes of diameters recommended and they are generally either marked or colored to provide ready identification.

3.8 Material and Manufacture—Unless otherwise specified, fittings shall be made from steel standard with the manufacturer. At the manufacturer's option, caps for water pump fittings may be made from brass, steel, or aluminum.

The greasing end of fittings shall be hardened. They shall have a case depth of 0.13 to 0.23 mm and minimum hardness of 83 on the Rockwell 15N scale. The threaded end on special thread forming fittings shall also be hardened.

3.9 Finish—Steel fittings shall have a minimum plating thickness of 0.005 mm (0.0002 in) of cadmium or zinc. Zinc plated fittings shall have a supplementary treatment other than organic coating and both cadmium and zinc plated fittings shall withstand a minimum 50 h salt spray test in accordance with ASTM B 117, Method of Salt Spray (Fog) Testing, before showing red rust on external surfaces.

3.10 Related Fittings—Figures 5, 6, 7a and 7b designate special adapters used in conjunction with lubrication fittings.

3.11 Workmanship—Fittings shall be free from burrs, loose scale, sharp edges, and all other defects that might affect their serviceability.

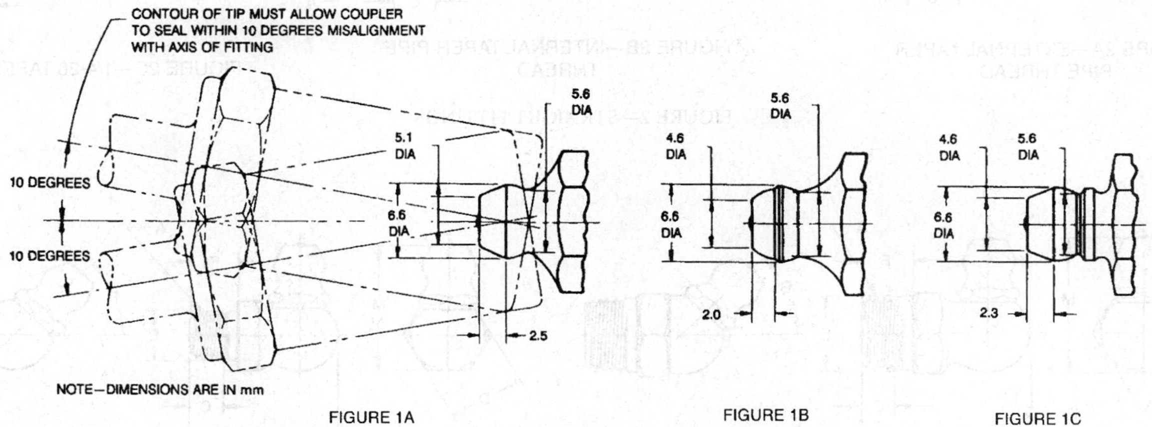

FIGURE 1—OPTIONAL TIPS FOR LUBRICATION FITTINGS

TABLE 1—DIMENSIONS OF STRAIGHT AND ELBOW FITTINGS (FIGURES 2 AND 3)

Type	A Thread	B Angle, ± 3 deg	C Effective Thread Length, min mm	D Hex Width Across Flats, Nom, in	E Shank Dia mm	F Shank Length mm ± 0.8	L Overall Length mm ± 1.0	M Overall Height mm ± 1.0
Straight Fittings	1/8–27 Dryseal-PTF special extra short	---	4.6	7/16	10.2	7.1	16.8	---
	1/8–27 Dryseal-PTF special short	---	5.6	7/16	10.2	19.3	32.0	---
	1/8–27 Dryseal-PTF special short	---	5.6	7/16	10.2	32.5	44.7	---
	1/8–27 Dryseal-PTF special short	---	5.6	7/16	10.2	55.4	66.5	---
	1/8 pipe special thread forming	---	3.6	7/16	10.2	6.1	15.7	---
	1/8–27 Dryseal-NPTF internal thread	---	7.1	1/2	12.2	8.1	25.4	---
	1/4–28 taper thread (SAE-LT)	---	2.5	5/16	6.6	4.6	13.7	---
	1/4–28 taper thread (SAE-LT)	---	5.1	5/16	6.6	8.6	17.3	---
	1/4–28 taper thread (SAE-LT)	---	5.1	5/16	6.6	15.7	23.9	---
	1/4–28 special taper thread forming	---	2.5	5/16	6.50	5.1	14.0	---
Elbow Fittings	1/8–27 Dryseal-PTF special short	30	5.6	7/16	10.2	7.6	22.9	14.2
	1/8–27 Dryseal-PTF special short	30	5.6	7/16	10.2	32.0	53.3	14.2
	1/8 pipe special thread forming	30	3.6	7/16	10.2	5.1	21.8	14.2
	1/8–27 Dryseal-PTF special short	45	5.6	7/16	10.2	7.6	21.8	16.3
	1/4–28 taper thread (SAE-LT)	45	2.5	3/8	6.6	5.1	20.8	14.7
	1/4–28 taper thread (SAE-LT)	45	5.1	3/8	6.6	7.6	23.9	14.7
	1/4–28 special taper thread forming	45	2.5	3/8	6.50	4.8	20.3	14.7
	1/8–27 Dryseal-PTF special short	65	5.6	7/16	10.2	7.6	21.8	18.3
	1/8–27 Dryseal-PTF special short	65	5.6	7/16	10.2	14.2	30.0	18.3
	1/8 pipe special shread forming	65	3.6	7/16	10.2	5.1	19.8	18.3
	1/8–27 Dryseal-PTF special short	90	5.6	7/16	10.2	7.6	21.3	18.3
	1/8–27 Dryseal-PTF special short	90	5.6	7/16	10.2	32.0	46.2	18.3
	1/8 pipe special thread forming	90	3.6	7/16	10.2	5.1	19.3	18.3
	1/4–28 taper thread (SAE-LT)	90	2.5	3/8	6.6	5.1	19.3	16.8
	1/4–28 special taper thread forming	90	2.5	3/8	6.50	4.8	19.3	16.8
	1/8–27 Dryseal-PTF special short	105	5.6	7/16	10.2	7.6	26.9	19.3

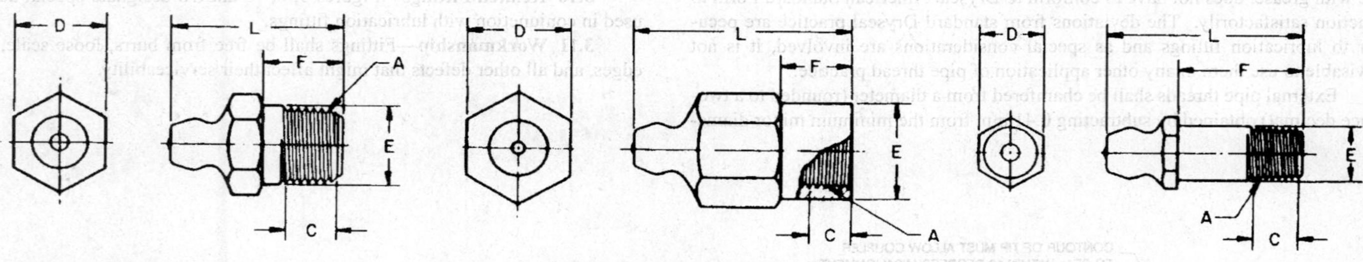

FIGURE 2A—EXTERNAL TAPER PIPE THREAD

FIGURE 2B—INTERNAL TAPER PIPE THREAD

FIGURE 2C—1/4-28 TAPER THREAD

FIGURE 2—STRAIGHT FITTINGS

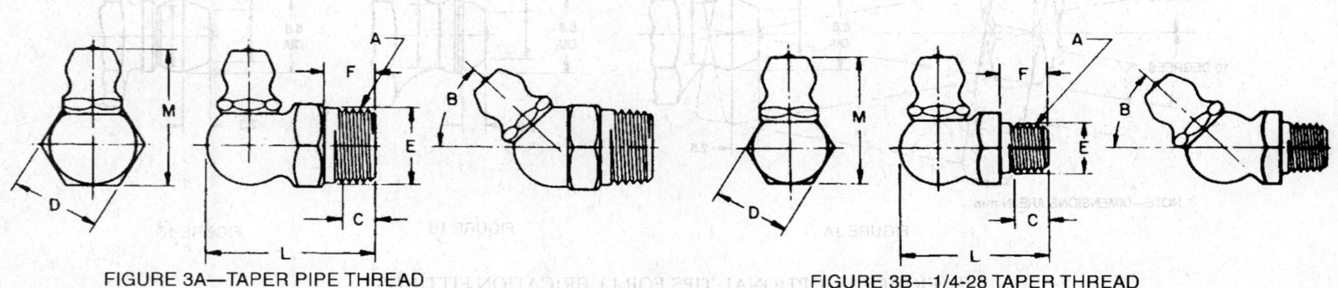

FIGURE 3A—TAPER PIPE THREAD

FIGURE 3B—1/4-28 TAPER THREAD

FIGURE 3—ELBOW FITTINGS

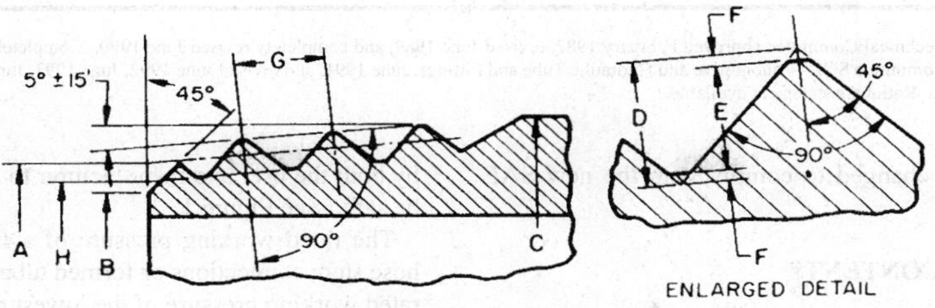

FIGURE 4—SPECIAL THREAD FORMING THREADS

TABLE 2—DIMENSIONS OF SPECIAL THREAD FORMING THREADS (FIGURE 4)

Nominal Thread Size	A Pitch Dia at Small End mm	B Chamfer Dia mm	C Shank Dia mm	D Height of Sharp V Thread mm	E Height of Truncated Thread mm	F Height of Truncated at Crest and Root mm	G Pitch mm	H Root Dia at Small End mm	Recommended Hole Dia[1] mm
1/4–28	5.654	5.1	6.58	0.452	0.427	0.069	0.907	5.28	5.97
Spl Taper	5.476	4.6	6.43		0.315	0.013		5.11	5.84
1/8–27	9.070	8.4	10.24	0.470	0.445	0.074	0.940	8.69	9.65
Spl Pipe	8.892	7.9	10.06		0.323	0.013		8.51	9.47

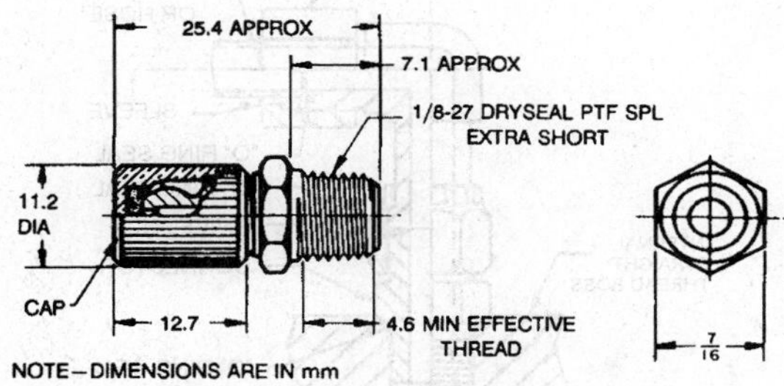

FIGURE 5—WATER PUMP FITTING

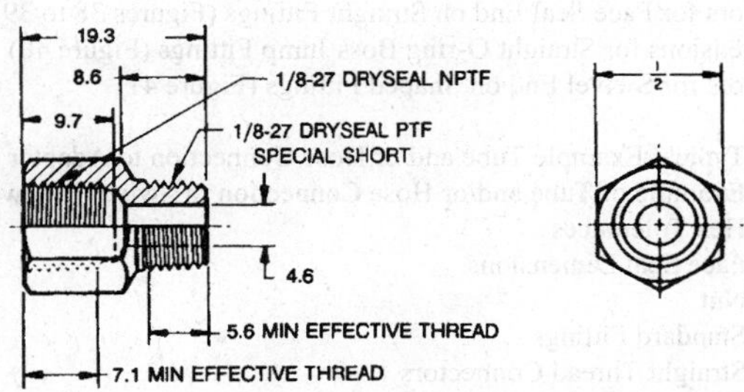

FIGURE 6—EXTENSION

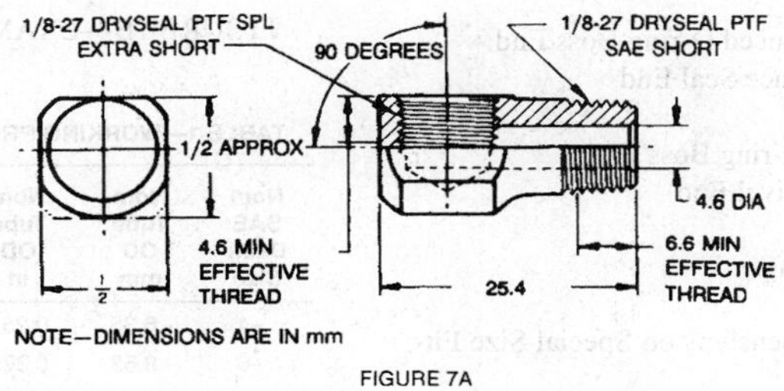

FIGURE 7A

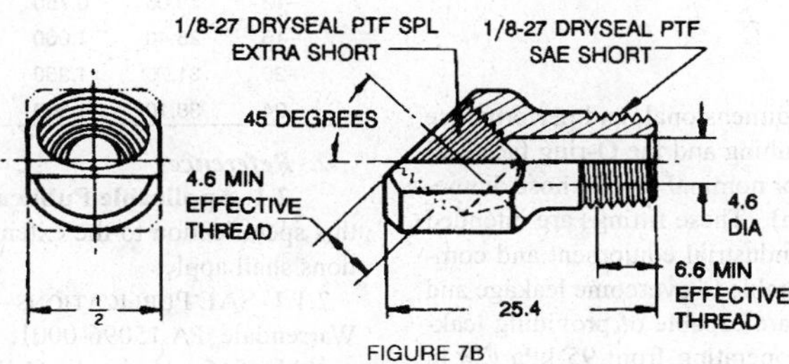

FIGURE 7B

FIGURE 7—ELBOW ADAPTERS

NOTE—UNSPECIFIED DETAIL WITH RESPECT TO DIMENSIONS, TOLERANCES, CONTOURS, MATERIAL, WORKMANSHIP, ETC., MUST CONFORM TO GENERAL SPECIFICATIONS FOR LUBRICATION FITTINGS.

FITTING—O-RING FACE SEAL—SAE J1453 JUN2002 SAE Standard

Report of the SAE Fluid Conductors and Connectors Technical Committee approved February 1987, revised June 1989, and completely revised June 1990. Completely revised by the SAE Fluid Conductors and Connectors Technical Committee SC1—Automotive and Hydraulic Tube and Fittings, June 1991, and revised June 1992, June 1993, June 1994, May 1995, June 1996, May 1997, June 1998, and June 2002. Rationale statement available.

Foreword—This Document has also changed to comply with the new SAE Technical Standards Board Format.

TABLE OF CONTENTS

1. Scope—This SAE Standard covers material, dimensional, and performance requirements of steel O-ring face seal fittings for tubing and the O-ring face seal interface and nut portion of hose stem assemblies for nominal tube or hose diameters 6.35 mm (0.250 in) through 38.1 mm (1.500 in). These fittings are intended for general application and hydraulic systems on industrial equipment and commercial products, where elastomeric seals are acceptable to overcome leakage and variations in assembly procedures. These fittings are capable of providing leakproof full flow connections in hydraulic systems operating from 95 kPa (28 in Hg) vacuum to working pressures shown in Table 1. Since many factors influence the pressure at which a hydraulic system will or will not perform satisfactorily, these values should not be construed as guaranteed minimums. For any application, it is recommended that sufficient testing be conducted and reviewed by both the user and manufacturer to assure that required performance levels will be safe. See Figure 1.

The rated working pressure of a fluid conductor assembly using SAE J1453 hose stem connections or formed tube connection per Figure 32a, shall not exceed rated working pressure of the lowest rated component thereof.

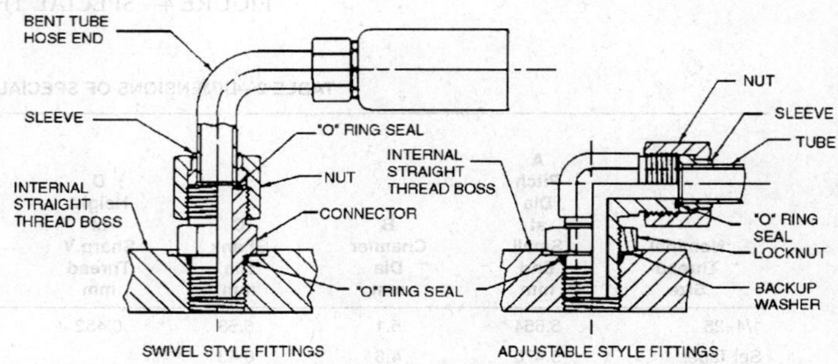

FIGURE 1A—TYPICAL EXAMPLE OF TUBE AND/OR HOSE CONNECTION TO ADAPTER

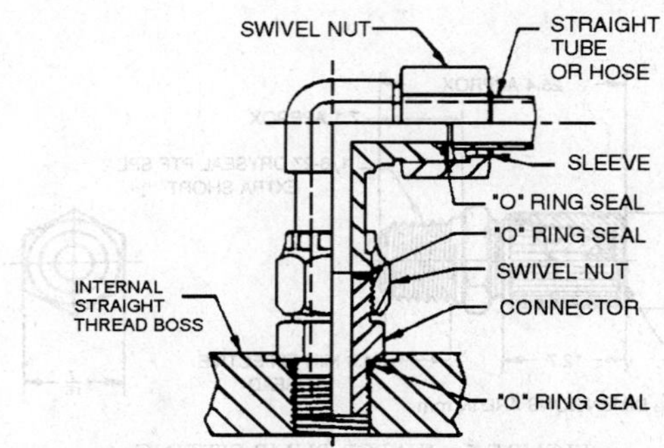

OPTIONAL CONFIGURATION FOR FULL PERFORMANCE RATING.
FOR –16 AT 41.3 MPa (6000 PSI)
FOR –24 AT 27.5 MPa (4000 PSI)

FIGURE 1B—EXAMPLE OF TUBE AND/OR HOSE CONNECTION TO SWIVEL ELBOW

TABLE 1—WORKING PRESSURE RATINGS CAPABLE OF 4 TO 1 MINIMUM BURST

Nom SAE Dash Size	Nom Tube OD mm	Nom Tube OD in	Straight Fittings MPa	Straight Fittings psi	Adjustable Style Fittings MPa	Adjustable Style Fittings psi
–4	6.35	0.250	41.3	6000	41.3	6000
–6	9.52	0.375	41.3	6000	41.3	6000
–8	12.70	0.500	41.3	6000	41.3	6000
–10	15.88	0.625	41.3	6000	41.3	6000
–12	19.05	0.750	41.3	6000	41.3	6000
–16	25.40	1.000	41.3	6000	34.5	5000
–20	31.75	1.250	27.5	4000	27.5	4000
–24	38.10	1.500	27.5	4000	20.7	3000

2. References

2.1 Applicable Publications—The following publications form a part of this specification to the extent specified herein. The latest issue of SAE publications shall apply.

2.1.1 SAE Publications—Available from SAE, 400 Commonwealth Drive, Warrendale, PA 15096-0001.

SAE J515—Hydraulic O-Rings

SAE J343—Tests and Procedures for SAE 100R Series Hydraulic Hose and Hose Assemblies

SAE J846—Coding Systems for Identification of Fluid Conductors and Connectors

2.1.2 ASTM PUBLICATION—Available from ASTM, 100 Barr Harbor Drive, West Conshohocken, PA 19428-2959.

ASTM B 117—Method of Salt Spray (Fog) Testing

2.1.3 ANSI PUBLICATIONS—Available from ANSI, 11 West 42nd Street, New York, NY 10036-8002.

ANSI B1.1—Screw Thread

ANSI B46.1—Surface Texture

3. Size Designation

3.1 Fitting sizes are designated by the nominal outside diameter of the tubing or nominal inside diameter of hose. (See SAE J846.)

4. Material and Manufacture

4.1 Material—Fittings shall be made from manufacturer's standard steel that will fulfill the performance requirements in Section 9.

4.2 Finish—The external surfaces and threads of all carbon steel parts shall be plated or coated with a suitable material that passes a 72 h salt spray test in accordance with ASTM B 117. Any appearance of red rust during the 72 h salt spray test shall be considered failure, except for the following:

a. All internal fluid passages.

b. Edges such as hex points, serrations, and crests of threads where there may be mechanical deformation of the plating or coating typical of mass-produced parts or shipping effects.

c. Areas where there is mechanical deformation of the plating or coating caused by crimping, flaring, bending, and other post-plate metal forming operations.

d. Areas where the parts are suspended or affixed in the test chamber where condensate can accumulate.

NOTE—Cadmium plating is not preferred due to environmental reasons. Parts manufactured to this standard after January 1, 1997, shall not be cadmium plated. Internal fluid passages shall be protected from corrosion during storage. Changes in plating may affect assembly torques and require requalification, when applicable.

Braze-on type fittings and style "B" nut (520110) shall be protected from corrosion by an oil film or other corrosion protection coating, but do not need to meet the 72 h salt spray test requirement.

4.3 Workmanship—Workmanship shall conform to the best commercial practice to produce high-quality fittings. Fittings must be free from visual contaminants, all hanging burrs, loose scale, and slivers which might be dislodged in usage, and any other defects that might affect the function of the parts.

4.4 Construction—Fittings may be made by forging, cold heading, formed tubing, or machined from bar stock. Carbon steel fittings fabricated from multiple components must be bonded together with materials having a melting point of not less than 996 °C (1825 °F).

4.5 Fitting bodies and tube nuts must be permanently marked with individual supplier's trademark or code identifier, unless otherwise agreed upon by user and manufacturer.

5. Dimensions and Tolerances

5.1 Dimensions specified apply to finished parts. Tolerances on all untoleranced dimensions are ±0.4 mm (±0.016 in). Special nonstandard fittings may have additional tolerance. On nonstandard size fittings, the larger end is considered standard and is the basis for dimensions and tolerances (overall, end to center, stock size, etc.). The tolerance on centerline to end of nonstandard shaped fittings will be ±1.5 mm (±0.06 in). See Tables 7, 8, 9, 10, and 11 for factors on how to calculate jump size and reduced sized fittings.

5.2 Hex tolerances across flats are listed in Figure 2. Minimum across corner hex dimensions are 1.092 times the nominal width across flats. The minimum side flat is 0.43 times the nominal width across flats (see Figure 2). Unless otherwise specified or shown, hex corners are chamfered 15 to 30 degrees to a diameter equal to the width across flats, with a tolerance of +0.0 mm +0.000 in

−0.4 −0.016

Alternatively, on connections other than SAE straight thread, a 5 degree chamfer starting at the undercut diameter behind the threads or outside diameter of the threads shall be allowed, providing the hex width at corners is not reduced below that produced by the 30 degree chamfer previously described.

5.3 The across flat dimensions of elbows, tees, bulkhead, and swivel fittings shown as "JJ forging" or "JJ barstock" in Table 6 are intended to be for nominal inch wrench sizes with a minus tolerance only. The basic forging size may be increased up to the maximum size shown for barstock, but the size selected must be a nominal inch wrench size across flats with minus tolerance only.

NOTE—For optional metric stock sizes, see Appendix D.

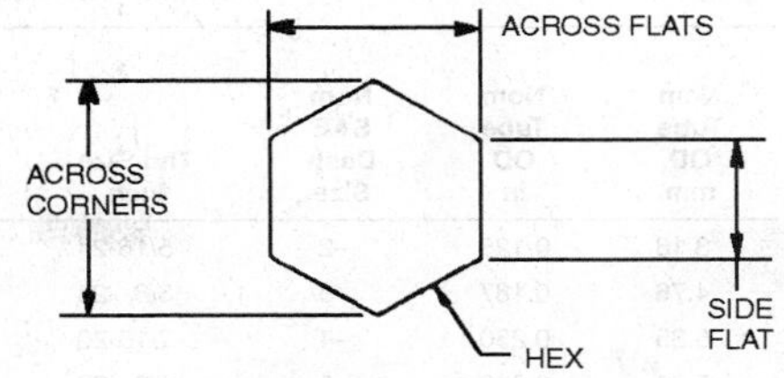

Nominal Hex Size Across Flats mm Over	Nominal Hex Size Across Flats mm Include	Nominal Hex Size Across Flats in Over	Nominal Hex Size Across Flats in Include	Tolerance (Minus Only) mm	Tolerance (Minus Only) in
—	19.05	—	0.750	0.3	0.012
19.05	25.40	0.750	1.000	0.4	0.016
25.40	34.92	1.000	1.375	0.5	0.020
34.92	AND UP	1.375	AND UP	0.8	0.031

FIGURE 2—HEX TOLERANCES

5.4 Where passages in straight fittings are machined from opposite ends, the offset at the meeting point shall not exceed 0.4 mm (0.016 in). No cross-sectional area at a junction of passages shall be less than that of the smallest passage.

5.5 Angular tolerance on axis of ends on elbows, tees, and crosses is ±2.5 degrees for sizes up to 9.52 mm (0.375 in) and ±1.5 degrees for all larger sizes.

5.6 Details of contour are optional with the manufacturer, providing the tabulated dimensions are maintained. Wrench flats on elbows and tees must meet the tabulated dimensions. Abrupt reduction of a section must be avoided. Junctions of small external sections and adjoining relatively heavy sections must be blended by means of ample fillets.

5.7 Tolerances on hole diameters designated as drill diameter in other dimensional tables shall be as shown in Table 2.

TABLE 2—DRILL TOLERANCES

Drill Size Range mm	Drill Size Range in	Tolerance Plus mm	Tolerance Minus mm	Tolerance Plus in	Tolerance Minus in
0.35- 6.25	0.0135-0.246	0.08	0.08	0.003	0.003
6.35-12.70	0.250-0.500	0.10	0.10	0.004	0.004
13.10-19.05	0.516-0.750	0.13	0.13	0.005	0.005
19.40-25.40	0.765-1.000	0.18	0.13	0.007	0.005
25.80-38.10	1.016-1.500	0.20	0.13	0.008	0.005
38.50 and up	1.516 and up	0.25	0.13	0.010	0.005

5.8 The O-ring washer must be clinched to fitting with a tight slip fit to an interference fit. The slip fit shall be tight enough so that washer cannot be shaken loose to cause it to drop from its uppermost position by its own weight. The interference fit shall not require a locknut torque more than that indicated in Table 3. Position the washer farthest from the end of the fittings as shown in Figure 9. Care must be taken not to clinch washer on the transition area between diameter Y and locknut thread which results in a loose washer when it is repositioned at assembly. Washer flatness allowance is given in Table 3. Any surface out of flatness must be uniform (not wavy) and concave with respect to the O-ring boss end of the fitting. Maximum torque to move washer is shown in Table 3.

6. Threads

6.1 Straight threads must be class 2A or 2B in accordance with ANSI B1.1 screw thread specification, except for internal thread minor diameter (see Figure 4, Note C). External class 2A threads which are plated or coated may exceed 2A diameters but shall not exceed maximum 3A diameters. Internal threads of all classes must be within specified limits after plating or coating.

6.2 When external threads are produced by thread rolling and the body is not undercut, the unthreaded area adjacent to the shoulder may be reduced to the minimum pitch diameter.

TABLE 3—MAXIMUM TORQUE TO MOVE WASHER AND WASHER FLATNESS

Nom Tube OD mm	Nom Tube OD in	Nom SAE Dash Size	Thd Size Inch	Nom Hex Size mm	Nom Hex Size in	Maximum Torque To Move Washer N·m	Maximum Torque To Move Washer lb·in	Washer Flatness Allowance mm	Washer Flatness Allowance in
3.18	0.125	–2	5/16-24	12.70	0.500	1	9	0.25	0.010
4.76	0.187	–3	3/8 -24	14.29	0.562	3	26	0.25	0.010
6.35	0.250	–4	7/16-20	15.88	0.625	4	35	0.25	0.010
7.94	0.312	–5	1/2 -20	17.46	0.687	5	44	0.25	0.010
9.52	0.375	–6	9/16-18	19.05	0.750	7	62	0.25	0.010
12.70	0.500	–8	3/4 -16	23.81	0.937	10	88	0.25	0.010
15.88	0.625	–10	7/8 -14	26.99	1.062	12	106	0.25	0.010
19.05	0.750	–12	1-1/16-12	34.92	1.375	15	133	0.40	0.016
22.22	0.875	–14	1-3/16-12	38.10	1.500	18	159	0.40	0.016
25.40	1.000	–16	1-5/16-12	41.28	1.625	20	177	0.40	0.016
31.75	1.250	–20	1-5/8 -12	47.62	1.875	25	221	0.50	0.020
38.10	1.500	–24	1-7/8 -12	53.98	2.125	30	265	0.50	0.020
50.80	2.000	–32	2-1/2 -12	69.85	2.750	40	353	0.50	0.020

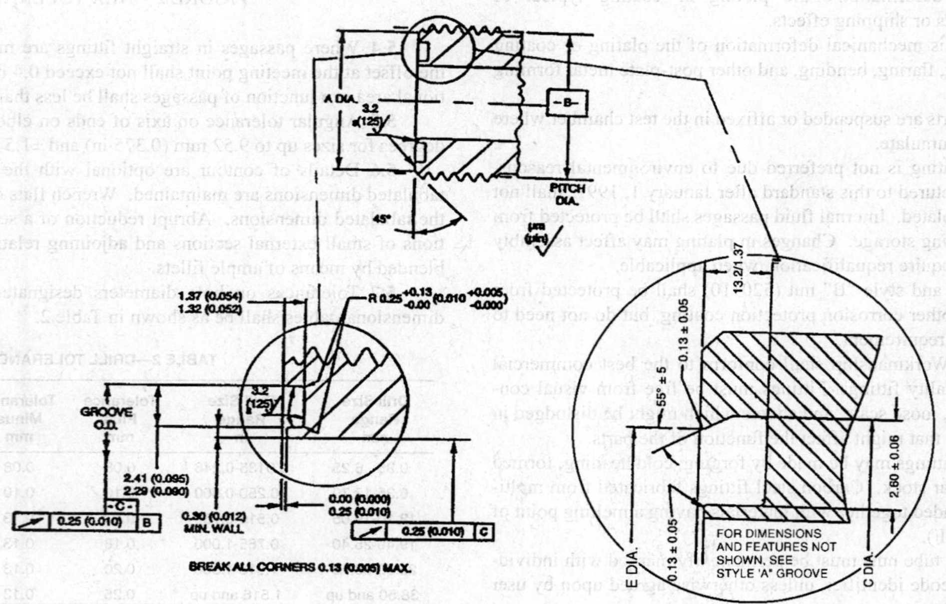

Nom SAE Dash Size	Nom Tube Dia mm	A Chamfer Dia mm	Style 'A' C Groove OD mm	Style 'B' C Groove OD mm	E Retention Ledge Dia ±0.15	O-Ring Seal SAE J515 Seal Size (90 Durometer, Shore A)
–4	6.35	12.27 ± 0.15	11.00 ± 0.08	11.00 ± 0.08	10.65	–011
–6	9.52	15.10 ± 0.25	12.60 ± 0.08	12.80 ± 0.08	12.25	–012
–8	12.70	18.25 ± 0.25	15.77 ± 0.08	15.97 ± 0.08	15.40	–014
–10	15.88	22.60 ± 0.40	19.00 ± 0.08	19.20 ± 0.08	18.50	–016
–12	19.05	27.00 ± 0.40	22.17 ± 0.10	22.37 ± 0.10	21.65	–018
–16	25.40	33.35 ± 0.40	26.87 ± 0.10	27.10 ± 0.13	26.40	–021
–20	31.75	39.75 ± 0.40	33.25 ± 0.13	33.45 ± 0.13	32.75	–025
–24	38.10	47.65 ± 0.40	41.17 ± 0.13	41.37 ± 0.13	40.65	–029

NOTE—See Appendix A for details on surface finish requirements.

FIGURE 3—FACE SEAL DIMENSIONS

*7. **Fitting Seat***

7.1 The face seal end dimensions shall conform to Figure 3. Surface finish of O-ring groove, and mating surfaces, shall be as shown in Figure 3 in accordance with ANSI B46.1.

7.2 O-ring—See J515 for O-ring details.

*8. **Protection***

8.1 By agreement between purchaser and supplier, the face of O-ring fittings and threads (both internal and external) must be protected by the manufacturer from nicks and scratches detrimental to their function. All passages must be securely covered to prevent entrance of dirt or other contaminants prior to assembly and for parts distribution, handling, and storage. Paper caps and plugs are not permitted.

8.2 Braze-on type fittings require protection on sealing face and threaded end only.

8.3 Nuts and sleeves furnished separately must be protected from rust but do not require capping.

*9. **Performance Requirements***—See Appendix B for minimum number of samples required for testing.

9.1 The working, proof, and minimum burst pressures are shown for straight and adjustable fittings in Table 4.

TABLE 4—WORKING, PROOF, AND MINIMUM BURST PRESSURES

Nom SAE Dash Size	Straight Fittings Working MPa	Straight Fittings Working psi	Straight Fittings Proof MPa	Straight Fittings Proof psi	Straight Fittings Min Burst MPa	Straight Fittings Min Burst psi	Adjustable Fittings Working MPa	Adjustable Fittings Working psi	Adjustable Fittings Proof MPa	Adjustable Fittings Proof psi	Adjustable Fittings Min Burst MPa	Adjustable Fittings Min Burst psi
–3	41.3	6000	82.5	12 000	165.0	24 000	41.3	6000	82.5	12 000	165.0	24 000
–4	41.3	6000	82.5	12 000	165.0	24 000	41.3	6000	82.5	12 000	165.0	24 000
–5	41.3	6000	82.5	12 000	165.0	24 000	41.3	6000	82.5	12 000	165.0	24 000
–6	41.3	6000	82.5	12 000	165.0	24 000	41.3	6000	82.5	12 000	165.0	24 000
–8	41.3	6000	82.5	12 000	165.0	24 000	41.3	6000	82.5	12 000	165.0	24 000
–10	41.3	6000	82.5	12 000	165.0	24 000	41.3	6000	82.5	12 000	165.0	24 000
–12	41.3	6000	82.5	12 000	165.0	24 000	41.3	6000	82.5	12 000	165.0	24 000
–14	41.3	6000	82.5	12 000	165.0	24 000	34.5	5000	69.0	10 000	138.0	20 000
–16	41.3	6000	82.5	12 000	165.0	24 000	34.5	5000	69.0	10 000	138.0	20 000
–20	27.5	4000	55.0	8 000	110.0	16 000	27.5	4000	55.0	8 000	110.0	16 000
–24	27.5	4000	55.0	8 000	110.0	16 000	20.7	3000	41.3	6 000	82.5	12 000

9.2 All O-ring face seal fittings for tubing and adapters must be capable of withstanding proof pressure for a period of 1 min without failure or leakage.

9.3 Burst test shall be conducted at minimum torque values shown in Table 5. For testing only, all adapter to hose fittings or tube fitting threads and contact surfaces shall be lubricated with SAE 10W hydraulic oil prior to application of torque shown in Table 5. Test blocks for burst testing must be unplated and hardened to Rockwell C50-55. Adjustable fittings must be backed out one full turn from finger-tight position to correctly test possible actual assembly conditions. Burst test at a rate not to exceed 138 000 kPa (20 000 psi) per minute.

TABLE 5—QUALIFICATION TEST TORQUE REQUIREMENTS

Nom SAE Dash Size	Nominal Tube OD mm	Nominal Tube OD in	O-ring Face Seal End Thread Size in	O-ring Face Seal End Swivel Nut Torque N·m	O-ring Face Seal End Swivel Nut Torque lb·ft	Over Torque N·m	Over Torque lb·ft	SAE O-ring Boss End Thread Size in	SAE O-ring Boss End Straight Fitting or Locknut Torque N·m	SAE O-ring Boss End Straight Fitting or Locknut Torque lb·ft
–3	4.76	0.188	(a)	(a)	(a)	(a)	(a)	3/8 -24	11- 13	8- 10
–4	6.35	0.250	9/16-18	14- 16	10- 12	32	24	7/16-20	20- 22	14- 16
–5	7.94	0.312	(a)	(a)	(a)	(a)	(a)	1/2 -20	24- 27	18- 20
–6	9.52	0.375	11/16-16	24- 27	18- 20	54	40	9/16-18	33- 35	24- 26
–8	12.70	0.500	13/16-16	43- 47	32- 35	81	60	3/4 -16	68- 78	50- 60
–10	15.88	0.625	1-14	60- 68	46- 50	136	100	7/8 -14	98-110	72- 80
–12	19.05	0.750	1- 3/16-12	90- 95	65- 70	180	140	1-1/16-12	170-183	125-135
–14	22.22	0.875	1- 3/16-12	90- 95	65- 70	180	140	1-3/16-12	230-260	170-190
–16	25.40	1.000	1- 7/16-12	125-135	92-100	270	200	1-5/16-12	270-300	200-220
–20	31.75	1.250	1-11/16-12	170-190	125-140	380	280	1-5/8 -12	285-380	210-280
–24	38.10	1.500	2-12	200-225	150-165	450	330	1-7/8 -12	370-490	270-360

(a)O-ring face seal type end not defined for this tube size.

9.4 All tube fittings and adapters must pass a cyclic endurance test for one million cycles at 133% of corresponding working pressures for straight and adjustable fittings per Table 4. Cycle test to be conducted at minimum torque values shown in Table 5. For testing only, all adapter to hose fittings or tube fitting threads and contact surfaces shall be lubricated with SAE 10W hydraulic oil prior to application of torque shown in Table 5. Cycle rate shall be uniform at 30 to 75 cpm and shall conform to magnitude and frequency to the wave pattern shown in Figure 1 of SAE J343.

9.5 Components that require brazing to assemble and all style "B" 520110 nuts must be processed through a copper braze cycle of 996 to 1150 °C, with the cycle time sufficiently long to permit parts to reach above temperature and then be cooled in a protective atmosphere to prevent scaling. After annealing and before burst, cyclic endurance, or torque testing, the nuts must be plated per 4.2.

9.6 Fitting shall be capable of withstanding 95 kPa (28 in Hg) vacuum without leakage for 5 min.

9.7 The standard face seal O-ring used for test shall be nitrile (NBR) rubber with a durometer "A" hardness of 90. (See Figure 3.)

9.8 Fitting swivel nuts shall be capable of withstanding the over torque qualification test with no indication of failure. For testing only, fitting threads and contact surfaces shall be lubricated with SAE 10W hydraulic oil prior to application of over torque specified in Table 5. For torque testing, use an unplated steel mandrel hardened to Rockwell C40-45. Fittings shall be restrained during test and the wrench shall be located at the threaded end of the nut hex.

Definition of failure after torque testing.

a. The nut cannot be removed by hand after breakaway.
b. The nut cannot swivel freely by hand.
c. The nut will not retract to its original position by hand.
d. Any visible cracks or severe deformation that would render nut unusable.

9.9 Parts which pass burst test or over torque test must not be tested further, used, or returned to stock.

9.10 Parts which pass burst test or over torque test must not be tested further, used, or returned to stock.

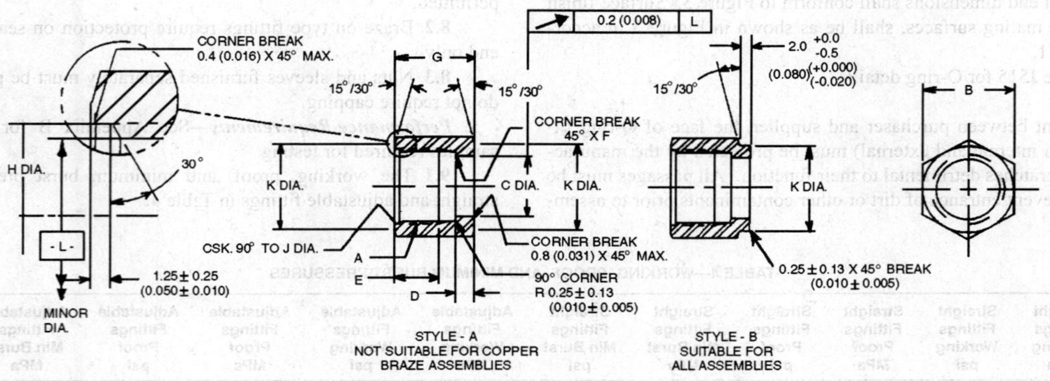

Nom Tube OD mm	Nom Tube OD in	A Thread Size in	Thread Minor Dia[c] mm min	Thread Minor Dia[c] mm max	Thread Minor Dia[c] in min	Thread Minor Dia[c] in max	B Hex[a] mm	B Hex[a] in	C Dia mm ±0.08	C Dia in ±0.003	D LG mm ±0.25	D LG in ±0.010
6.35	0.250	9/16-18	12.90	13.08	0.508	0.515	17.46	0.687	10.46	0.412	2.50	0.098
9.52	0.375	11/16-16	15.90	16.10	0.626	0.634	20.64	0.812	13.51	0.532	3.00	0.118
12.70	0.500	13/16-16	19.08	19.28	0.751	0.759	23.81	0.938	16.56	0.652	5.00	0.197
15.88	0.625	1-14	23.60	23.83	0.929	0.938	28.58	1.125	21.06	0.829	4.00	0.157
19.05	0.750	1- 3/16-12	28.02	28.32	1.103	1.115	34.92	1.375	24.13	0.950	5.00	0.197
22.22[b]	0.875	1- 3/16-12	28.02	28.32	1.103	1.115	34.92	1.375	25.04	0.986	5.00	0.197
25.40	1.000	1- 7/16-12	34.37	34.67	1.353	1.365	41.28	1.625	29.06	1.144	6.00	0.236
31.75	1.250	1-11/16-12	40.72	41.02	1.603	1.615	47.62	1.875	35.94	1.415	6.00	0.236
38.10	1.500	2-12	48.67	48.97	1.916	1.928	57.15	2.250	43.89	1.728	6.00	0.236

Nom Tube OD mm	Nom Tube OD in	E Min Full Thread mm min	E Min Full Thread in min	F Chamfer mm ±0.13	F Chamfer in ±0.005	G LG mm ±0.25	G LG in ±0.010	H Dia mm ±0.25	H Dia in ±0.010	J Dia mm +0.4 −0.0	J Dia in +0.016 −0.000	K Dia mm ±0.3	K Dia in ±0.01
6.35	0.250	9.0	0.35	0.13	0.005	14.70	0.580	—	—	14.4	0.567	17.0	0.67
9.52	0.375	10.3	0.41	0.13	0.005	17.00	0.670	—	—	17.6	0.693	20.3	0.80
12.70	0.500	11.9	0.47	0.13	0.005	21.00	0.827	—	—	20.8	0.819	23.5	0.92
15.88	0.625	14.5	0.57	0.25	0.010	23.50	0.925	25.91	1.020	—	—	28.2	1.11
19.05	0.750	15.5	0.61	0.25	0.010	26.00	1.024	30.68	1.208	—	—	34.6	1.36
22.22[b]	0.875	15.5	0.61	0.25	0.010	30.86	1.215	30.68	1.208	—	—	34.6	1.36
25.40	1.000	16.0	0.63	0.38	0.015	27.80	1.095	37.03	1.458	—	—	41.0	1.61
31.75	1.250	16.0	0.63	0.38	0.015	27.80	1.095	43.38	1.708	—	—	47.2	1.86
38.10	1.500	16.0	0.63	0.38	0.015	27.80	1.095	51.31	2.020	—	—	56.9	2.24

(a) For hex tolerance, see 5.2 and Figure 2).

(b) For use with expanding sleeve 91.05 to 22.22, see Figure 34.)

(c) Modified minor dia (not the minor dia listed in ANSI B1.1)

FIGURE 4—NUT (520110)

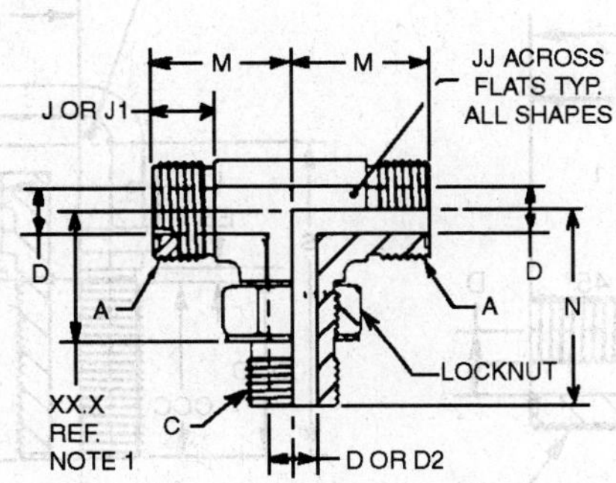

FIGURE 5—STRAIGHT THREAD BRANCH TEE (520429)

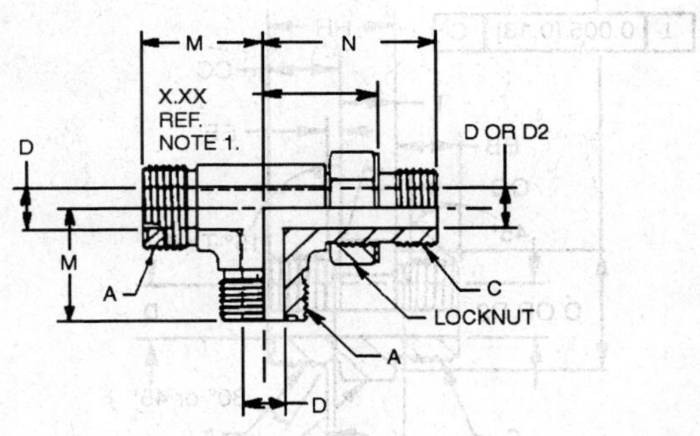

FIGURE 6—STRAIGHT THREAD RUN TEE (520428)

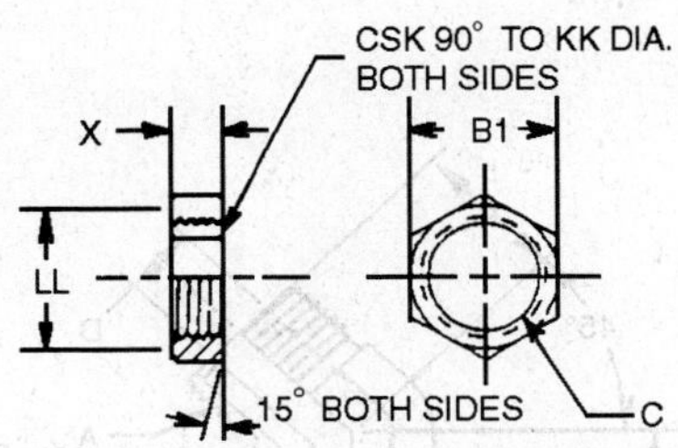

FIGURE 7—STRAIGHT THREAD LOCKNUT (520117)

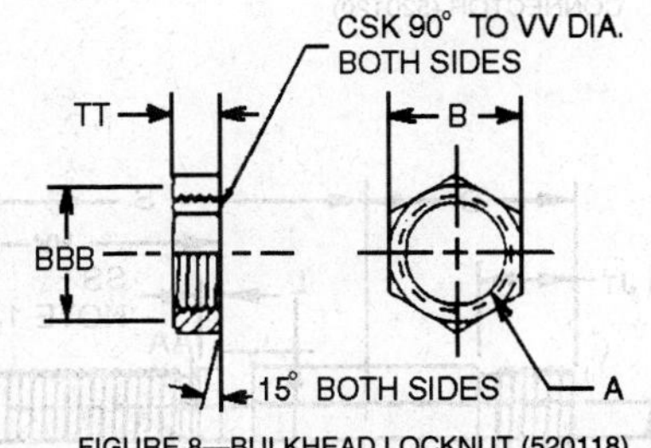

FIGURE 8—BULKHEAD LOCKNUT (520118)

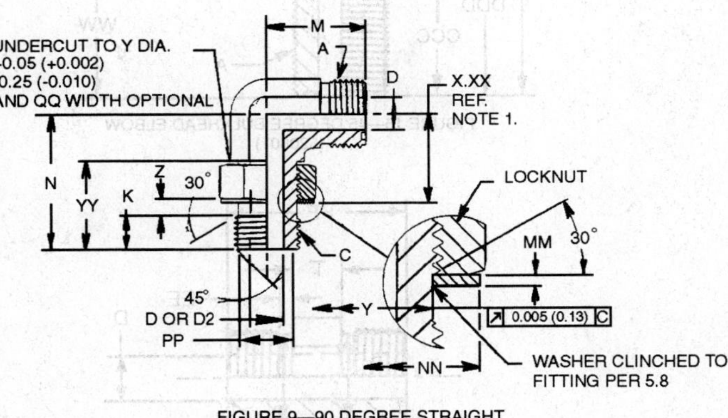

FIGURE 9—90 DEGREE STRAIGHT THREAD ELBOW (520220)

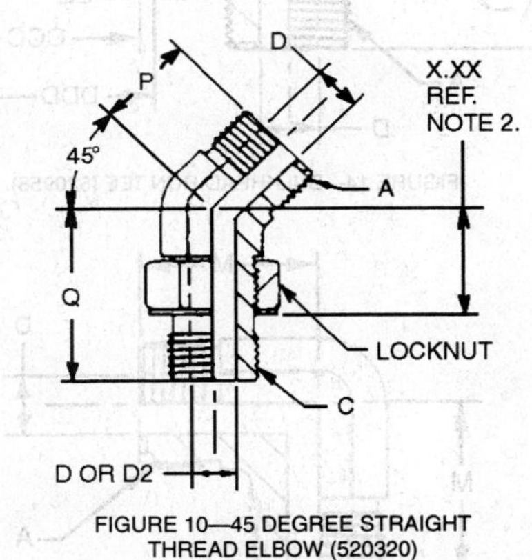

FIGURE 10—45 DEGREE STRAIGHT THREAD ELBOW (520320)

NOTE 1—Ref dim. calculated by formula ref = N – (K+Z–MM).
NOTE 2—Ref dim. calculated by formula ref = Q – (K+Z–MM).

For O-ring groove dimensions and thread chamfer diameter, see Figure 3.

FIGURES 5 TO 25—FITTINGS

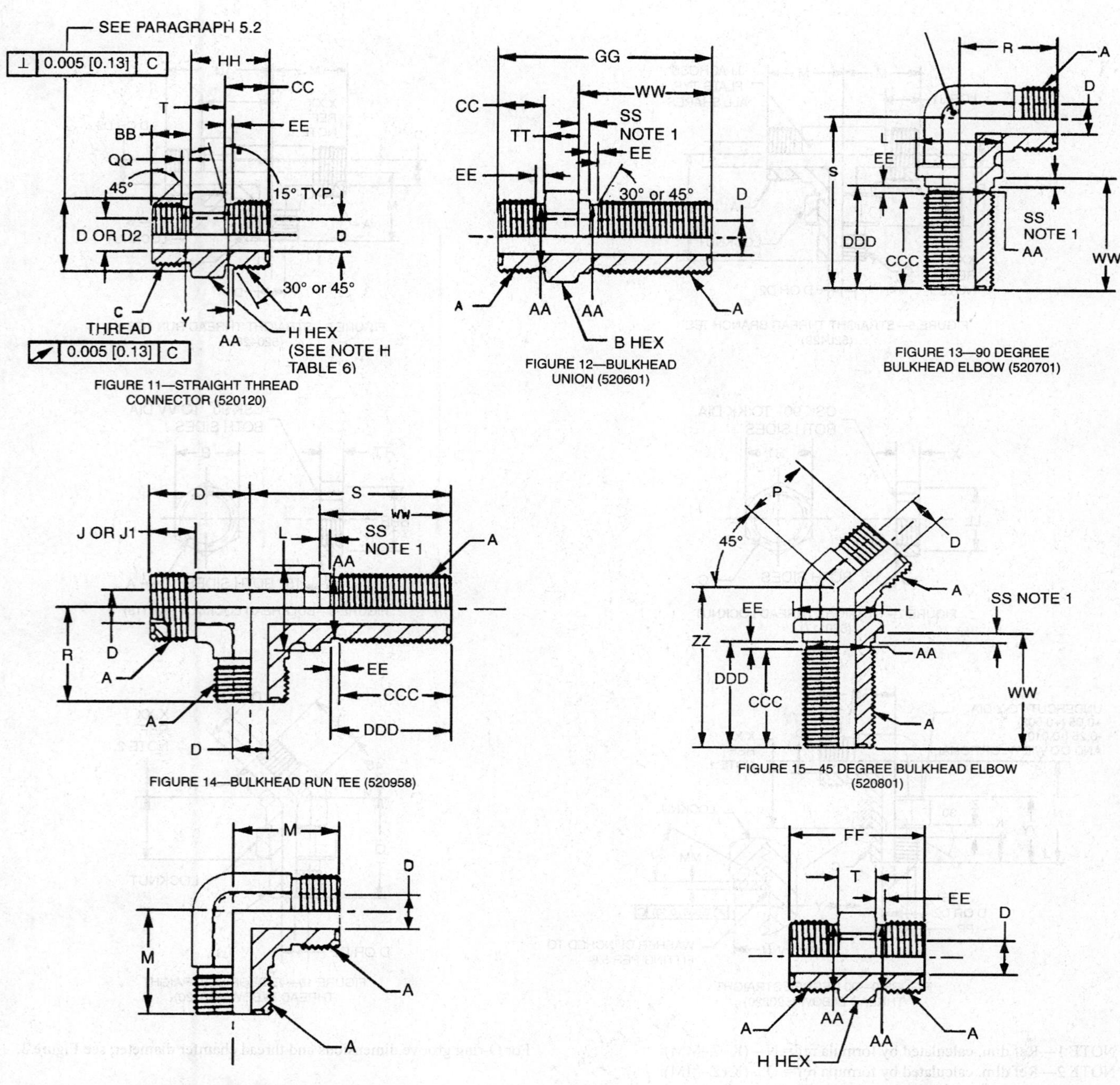

FIGURE 11—STRAIGHT THREAD CONNECTOR (520120)

FIGURE 12—BULKHEAD UNION (520601)

FIGURE 13—90 DEGREE BULKHEAD ELBOW (520701)

FIGURE 14—BULKHEAD RUN TEE (520958)

FIGURE 15—45 DEGREE BULKHEAD ELBOW (520801)

FIGURE 16—90 DEGREE UNION ELBOW (520201)

FIGURE 17—UNION (520101)

NOTE 1—Recommended clearance hole for bulkhead fittings is 0.4 (0.015) over major thread diameter. Diameter of SS pilot is same as major thread diameter.

For O-Ring groove dimensions and thread chamfer diameter, see Figure 3.

FIGURES 5 TO 25—(CONTINUED)

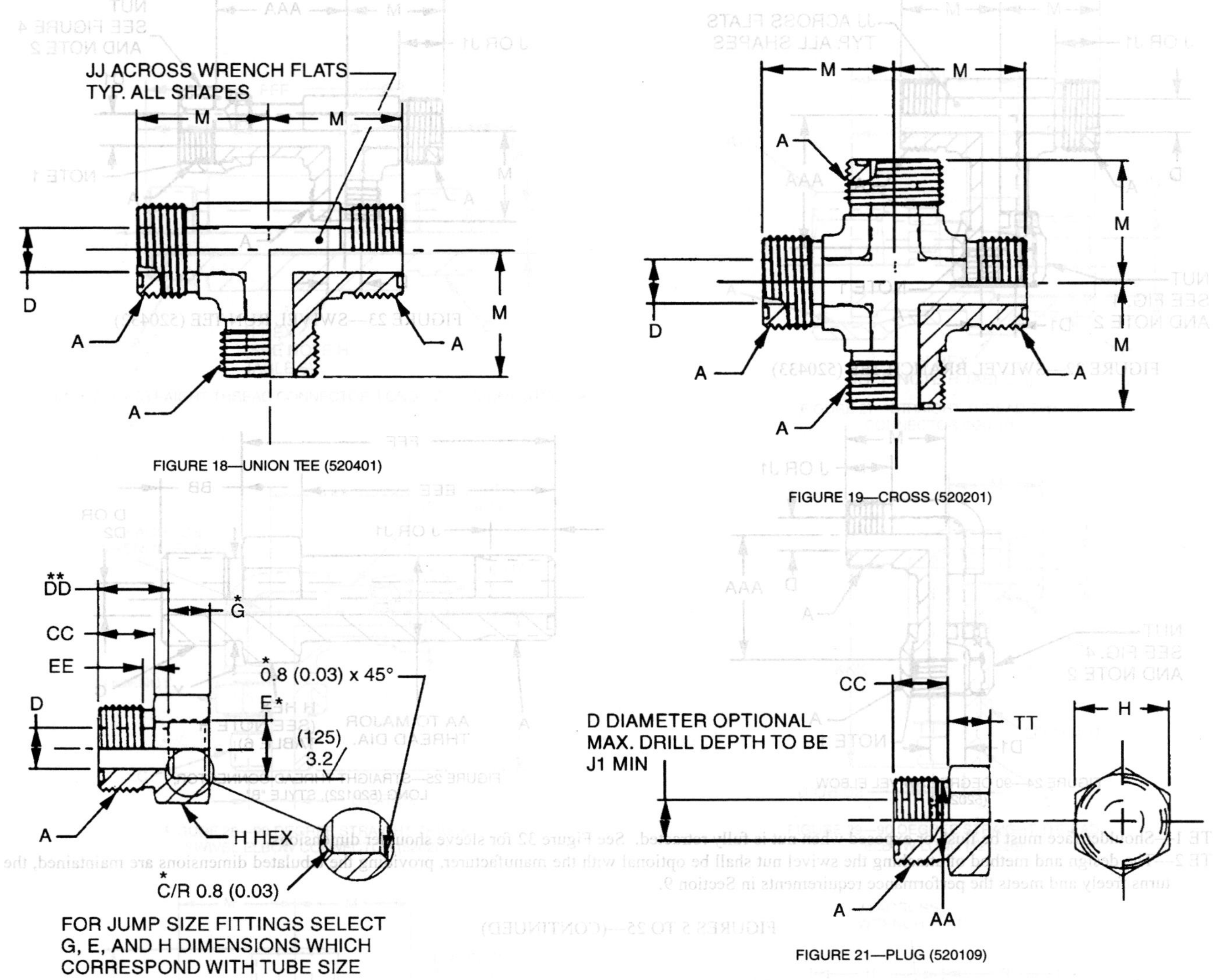

FIGURE 18—UNION TEE (520401)

FIGURE 19—CROSS (520201)

FIGURE 20—MALE CONNECTOR (520104)

FIGURE 21—PLUG (520109)

* Dimensions are for silver brazing. Other dimensions may apply for other joining methods.
** DD dimensions remains constant for jump size fittings.
For O-ring groove dimensions and thread chamfer diameter, see Figure 3.

FIGURES 5 TO 25—(CONTINUED)

TABLE 6*—FITTING DIMENSIONS (FIGURES 5 TO 31)[(n)] (CONTINUED)

Nom Tube OD mm	Nom Tube OD in	YY mm min	YY in min	ZZ mm ±0.8	ZZ in ±0.03	AAA mm ±1.5	AAA in ±0.06	BBB Dia mm ±0.25	BBB Dia in ±0.010	Ref CCC Full Thd[(m)] mm min	Ref CCC Full Thd[(m)] in min	DDD Full Thd[(l)] mm min	DDD Full Thd[(l)] in min
3.18	0.125	18.2	0.72	—	—	—	—	—	—	—	—	—	—
4.76	0.187	18.8	0.72	—	—	—	—	—	—	—	—	—	—
6.35	0.250	20.5	0.81	44.0	1.73	26.4	1.04	20.64	0.812	27.9	1.10	29.0	1.14
7.94	0.312	22.4	0.88	—	—	—	—	—	—	—	—	—	—
9.52	0.375	22.4	0.88	48.5	1.91	29.2	1.15	25.40	1.000	29.1	1.15	31.5	1.24
12.70	0.500	26.1	1.03	51.0	2.01	37.9	1.49	28.58	1.125	31.1	1.22	33.5	1.32
15.88	0.625	30.2	1.19	56.6	2.23	41.2	1.62	33.34	1.312	34.9	1.37	37.6	1.48
19.05	0.750	33.8	1.33	60.7	2.39	46.3	1.82	38.10	1.500	35.5	1.40	38.7	1.52
22.22	0.875	33.8	1.33	—	—	—	—	—	—	—	—	—	—
25.40	1.000	34.6	1.36	65.2	2.57	53.3	2.10	44.45	1.750	36.0	1.42	39.2	1.54
31.75	1.250	34.6	1.36	67.0	2.64	58.2	2.29	50.80	2.000	36.0	1.42	39.2	1.54
38.10	1.500	34.6	1.36	67.0	2.64	61.2	2.41	60.33	2.375	36.0	1.42	39.2	1.54

Nom Tube OD mm	Nom Tube OD in	EEE mm ±0.5	EEE in ±0.02	FFF mm ±0.5	FFF in ±0.02	GGG mm ±1.5	GGG in ±0.06	HHH mm +1.5 −0.0	HHH in +0.06 −0.00	KKK mm ±0.8	KKK in ±0.03
3.18	0.125	—	—	—	—	—	—	—	—	—	—
4.76	0.187	—	—	—	—	—	—	—	—	—	—
6.35	0.250	33.8	1.33	41.7	1.64	15.0	0.59	26.2	1.03	56.6	2.23
7.94	0.312	—	—	—	—	—	—	—	—	—	—
9.52	0.375	37.0	1.46	45.7	1.80	17.3	0.68	28.2	1.11	66.3	2.61
12.70	0.500	44.5	1.75	53.8	2.12	21.3	0.84	35.3	1.39	74.9	2.95
15.88	0.625	52.6	2.07	63.5	2.50	23.9	0.94	37.8	1.49	89.2	3.51
19.05	0.750	64.0	2.52	77.0	3.03	26.2	1.03	41.2	1.62	100.8	3.97
22.22	0.875	—	—	—	—	—	—	—	—	—	—
25.40	1.000	72.9	2.87	86.6	3.41	28.2	1.11	49.0	1.93	114.6	4.51
31.75	1.250	86.6	3.41	102.4	4.03	28.2	1.11	49.0	1.93	126.5	4.98
38.10	1.500	97.0	3.82	115.1	4.53	28.2	1.11	49.0	1.93	139.2	5.48

a Nominal design thickness, not subject to inspection.
b O-ring groove has a surface texture of 3.2 mm.
c See Table 2 for tolerance.
d For hex tolerance, see 5.2 and Figure 2.
e J full THD min with thread runout.
f J1 full THD min with undercut to AA dia. Length of THD and undercut width must not be less than CC minimum.
g See 5.3.
h For 31.75 mm (1.250 in) NOM tube OD, use 47.62 mm (1.875 in) hex for (520120 and 520181) connectors.
i When purchased, assembled as part of a fitting, only minimum thickness applies to inspection.
j Actual bore size depends on joining process. (Dimensions given are for silver braze.)
k Actual length of engagement depends on joining process. (Dimensions given are for silver braze.)
l DOD full THD min with thread runout.
m CCC full THD min with undercut and AA dia. Length of THD and undercut width must not be less than DDD minimum.
n See Tables 7, 8, 9, 10, or 11 for "Jump Fitting" length factors.
p Standard fittings not defined for 3.18 mm, 4.76 mm, 7.94 mm, and 22.22 mm. All fittings are jump sizes, therefore, hex size will vary. See Tables 7 or 8.

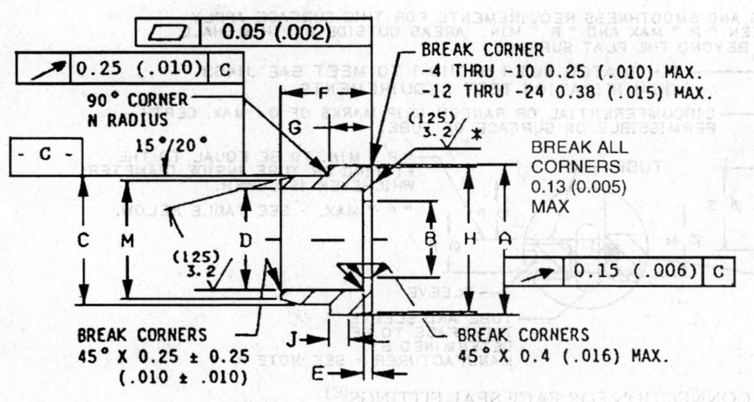

FIGURE 32—STANDARD SLEEVE (520115)

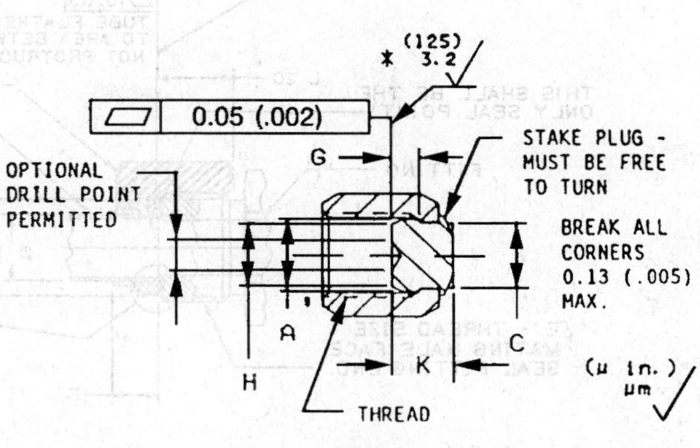

FIGURE 32a—CAP ASSEMBLY (520112)

Nom Tube OD mm	Nom Tube OD in	Metric Tube(d) mm	A Dia mm +0.00 −0.00	A Dia in +0.000 −0.005	B Drill Dia(a) Nom mm	B Drill Dia(a) Nom in	C Dia mm ±0.08	C Dia in ±0.003	D Dia(b) mm ±0.05	D Dia(b) in ±0.002	E mm ±0.13	E in ±0.005
6.35	0.250	6	12.75	0.502	4.4	0.172	10.21	0.402	6.50	0.256	1.00	0.040
9.52	0.375	10	15.75	0.620	6.7	0.264	13.26	0.522	9.68	0.381	1.00	0.040
12.70	0.500	12	18.92	0.745	9.6	0.378	16.31	0.642	12.85	0.506	1.00	0.040
15.88	0.625	16	23.44	0.923	12.3	0.484	20.75	0.817	16.03	0.631	1.50	0.060
19.05	0.750	19	27.86	1.097	15.5	0.609	23.77	0.936	19.23	0.757	1.50	0.060
25.40	1.000	25	34.21	1.347	20.6	0.811	28.70	1.130	25.58	1.007	1.50	0.060
31.75	1.250	32	40.56	1.597	26.0	1.024	35.59	1.401	31.93	1.257	1.50	0.060
38.10	1.500	38	48.51	1.910	32.0	1.260	43.54	1.714	38.28	1.507	1.50	0.060

Nom Tube OD mm	Nom Tube OD in	F(c) mm ±0.13	F(c) in ±0.012	G mm ±0.13	G in ±0.005	H Dia mm ±0.13	H Dia in ±0.005	J mm ±0.5	J in ±0.02	K mm ±0.5	K in ±0.02	L Dia mm max	L Dia in max	M Dia mm ±0.13	M Dia in ±0.005	N Corner Radius mm +0.13 −0.00	N Corner Radius in +0.005 −0.000
6.35	0.250	9.5	0.374	4.00	0.157	—	—	—	—	8.5	0.34	4.0	0.157	8.51	0.335	0.13	0.005
9.52	0.375	9.5	0.374	4.50	0.177	—	—	—	—	9.5	0.37	5.0	0.197	11.81	0.465	0.13	0.005
12.70	0.500	9.5	0.374	5.00	0.197	—	—	—	—	12.0	0.47	8.0	0.315	15.11	0.595	0.13	0.005
15.88	0.625	10.5	0.413	6.00	0.236	22.61	0.890	1.3	0.05	12.0	0.47	10.0	0.394	19.18	0.755	0.25	0.010
19.05	0.750	14.0	0.551	6.50	0.256	27.00	1.063	1.3	0.05	13.5	0.53	10.0	0.394	22.10	0.870	0.25	0.010
25.40	1.000	15.5	0.610	7.00	0.276	33.35	1.313	1.3	0.05	15.0	0.59	15.0	0.591	28.07	1.105	0.50	0.020
31.75	1.250	15.5	0.610	7.00	0.276	39.73	1.564	1.3	0.05	15.0	0.59	15.0	0.591	34.04	1.340	0.50	0.020
38.10	1.500	15.5	0.610	7.00	0.276	47.65	1.876	1.3	0.05	15.0	0.59	15.0	0.591	41.91	1.650	0.50	0.020

(a) See Table 2 for tolerance. When purchased assembled, hole diameter may be reduced to tube ID.
(b) Actual bore size depends on joining process. (Dimensions given are for silver braze of inch tube.)
(c) Actual length of sleeve depends on joining process. (Dimensions given are for silver braze of inch tube.)
(d) Sleeve may be used to adapt to metric tube

NOTE—See Appendix A for details on surface finish requirements.

FIGURES 32 TO 32A—STANDARD SLEEVE AND CAP ASSEMBLY

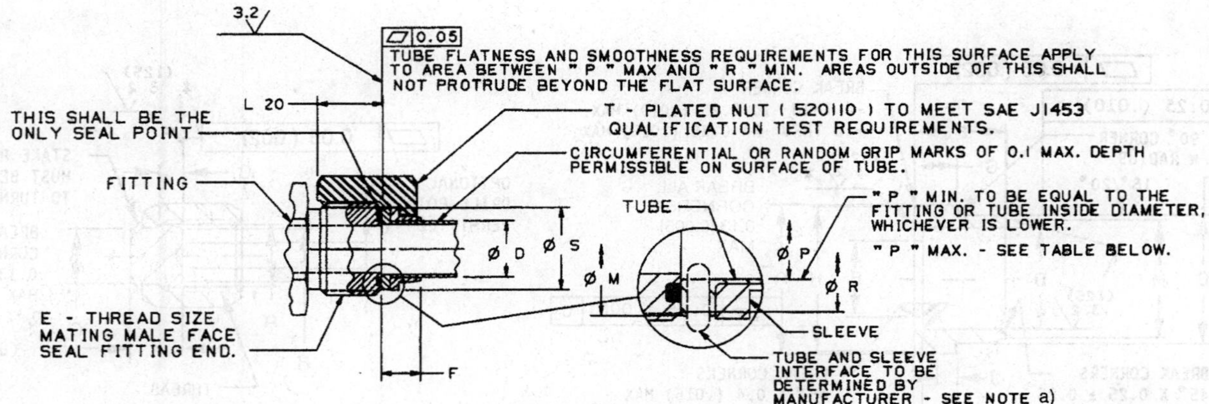

FIGURE 33—FORMED TUBE CONNECTION FOR FACE SEAL FITTINGS[C]

D Nominal Tube OD Inch Tubing Dash Size	D Nominal Tube OD Inch Tubing Inch	D Nominal Tube OD Metric Tubing mm	E Thread Size inch	F min/max mm	L20 min/max	M min/max Formed OD
–4	1/4	6	9/16–18 UNF	6.6/12.5	6.6/9.0	12.10/12.75
–6	3/8	10	11/16-16 UN	7.9/13.0	7.0/10.3	14.85/15.75
–8	1/2	12	13/16–16 UN	9.4/17.0	8.6/11.9	18.00/18.90
–10	5/8	16	1-14 UNS	10.3/17.0	11.5/14.5	22.20/23.45
–12	3/4	20	1 3/16–12 UN	11.9/18.5	12.6/15.5	26.60/27.85
–16	1	25	1 7/16–12 UN	12.7/19.0	12.5/16.0	32.95/34.20
–20	1-1/4	30	1 11/16–12 UN	12.7/19.0	12.5/16.0	39.35/40.55
–24	1-1/2	38	2 –12 UN	12.7/19.0	12.5/16.0	47.25/48.50

D Nominal Tube OD Inch Tubing Dash Size	D Nominal Tube OD Inch Tubing Inch	D Nominal Tube OD Metric Tubing mm	P Max Dia mm	R Min. Dia. mm	S Min/max OD mm	T Hex Size Inch[b] Nut
–4	1/4	6	7.3	12.1	12.6/12.75	11/16
–6	3/8	10	8.9	14.3	15.6/15.75	13/16
–8	1/2	12	12.1	17.4	18.75/18.9	15/16
–10	5/8	16	15.3	21.2	23.3/23.45	1-1/8
–12	3/4	20	18.5	24.8	27.7/27.85	1-3/8
–16	1	25	23.2	30.6	34.05/34.2	1-5/8
–20	1-1/4	30	29.5	36.9	40.4/40.55	1-7/8
–24	1-1/2	38	37.4	44.9	48.35/48.5	2-1/4

a.
a. Formed tube end shall provide a sealing surface that can be assembled with a standard SAE J1453 fitting and nut and meet performance requirements for a working pressure equivalent to that of the fluid conductor.
b. See Figure 4 for tube nut dimensions.
c. For detailed explanation of various dimensions, see Appendix F.

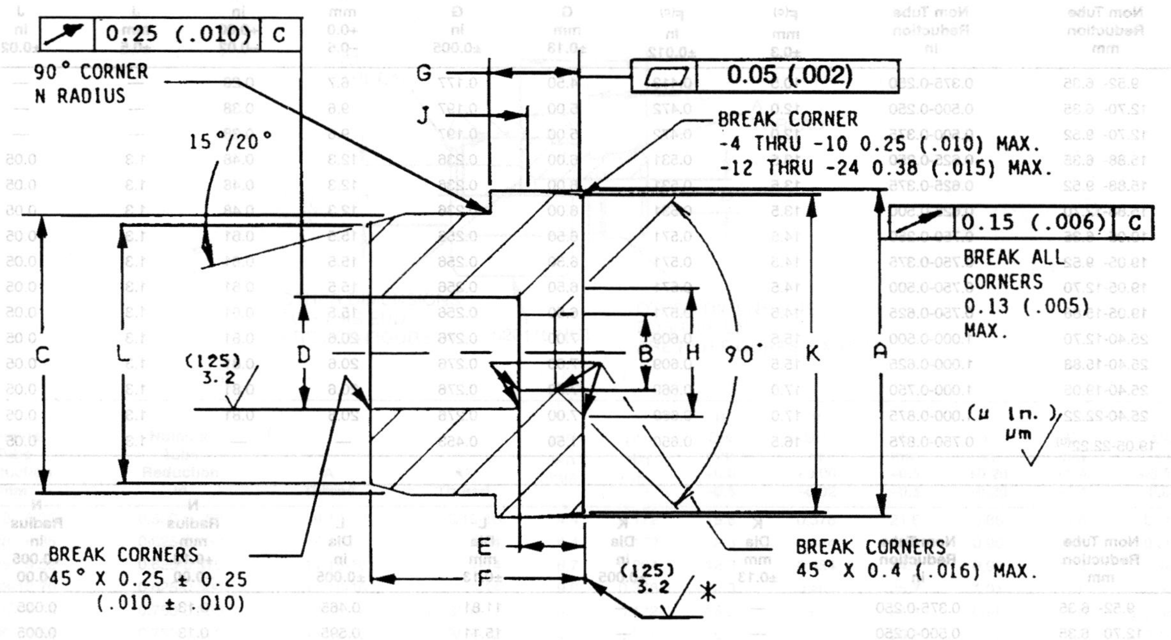

FIGURE 34—REDUCING AND EXPANDING SLEEVES

Nom Tube Reduction mm	Nom Tube Reduction in	A Dia mm +0.00 –0.13	A Dia in +0.000 –0.005	B Drill Dia[a] Nom mm	B Drill Dia[a] Nom in	C Dia mm ±0.08	C Dia in ±0.003	D Dia[b] mm ±0.05	D Dia[b] in ±0.002	E mm ±0.13	E in ±0.005
9.52- 6.35	0.375-0.250	15.75	0.620	4.4	0.172	13.26	0.522	6.50	0.256	2.00	0.079
12.70- 6.35	0.500-0.250	18.92	0.745	4.4	0.172	16.31	0.642	6.50	0.256	3.50	0.138
12.70- 9.52	0.500-0.375	18.92	0.745	6.7	0.264	16.31	0.642	9.68	0.381	3.50	0.138
15.88- 6.35	0.625-0.250	23.44	0.923	4.4	0.172	20.75	0.817	6.50	0.256	5.00	0.197
15.88- 9.52	0.625-0.375	23.44	0.923	6.7	0.264	20.75	0.817	9.68	0.381	5.00	0.197
15.88-12.70	0.625-0.500	23.44	0.923	9.6	0.378	20.75	0.817	12.85	0.506	5.00	0.197
19.05- 6.35	0.750-0.250	27.86	1.097	4.4	0.172	23.77	0.936	6.50	0.256	6.00	0.236
19.05- 9.52	0.750-0.375	27.86	1.097	6.7	0.264	23.77	0.936	9.68	0.381	6.00	0.236
19.05-12.70	0.750-0.500	27.86	1.097	9.6	0.378	23.77	0.936	12.85	0.506	6.00	0.236
19.05-15.88	0.750-0.625	27.86	1.097	12.3	0.484	23.77	0.936	16.03	0.631	6.00	0.236
25.40-12.70	1.000-0.500	34.21	1.347	9.6	0.378	28.70	1.130	12.85	0.506	7.00	0.276
25.40-15.88	1.000-0.625	34.21	1.347	12.3	0.484	28.70	1.130	16.03	0.631	7.00	0.276
25.40-19.05	1.000-0.750	34.21	1.347	15.5	0.609	28.70	1.130	19.23	0.757	4.50	0.177
25.40-22.22	1.000-0.875	34.21	1.347	18.0	0.709	28.70	1.130	22.40	0.882	3.00	0.118
19.05-22.22[d]	0.750-0.875	27.86	1.097	15.5	0.609	24.69	0.972	22.40	0.882	1.50	0.060

* See end of Table for notes.

*NOTE—See Appendix A for details on surface finish requirements.

FIGURE 34—REDUCING SLEEVE (520115)

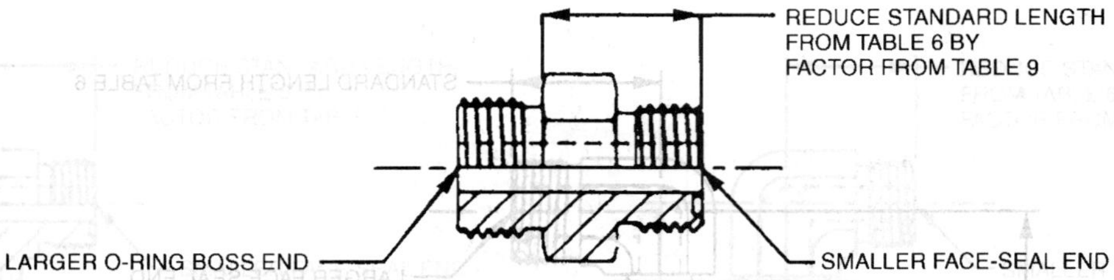

REDUCE STANDARD LENGTH FROM TABLE 6 BY FACTOR FROM TABLE 9

LARGER O-RING BOSS END

SMALLER FACE-SEAL END

FIGURE 38—STRAIGHT THREAD CONNECTOR WITH REDUCED FACE SEAL END

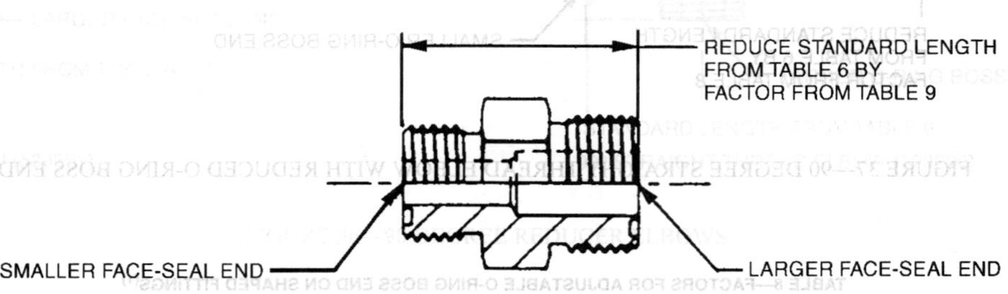

FIGURE 39—REDUCER UNION

TABLE 9—FACTORS FOR FACE SEAL END ON STRAIGHT FITTINGS(1) (FIGURES 38 TO 39)

			STANDARD MACHINING SIZE (LARGEST END OF FITTING)													
Dash Size	Nominal Tube OD mm	Nominal Tube OD in	−6 mm 9.52	−6 in 0.375	−8 mm 12.70	−8 in 0.500	−10 mm 15.88	−10 in 0.625	−12 mm 19.05	−12 in 0.750	−16 mm 25.40	−16 in 1.000	−20 mm 31.75	−20 in 1.250	−24 mm 38.10	−24 in 1.500
−4	6.35	0.250	1.4	0.05	3.0	0.12	5.6	0.22	7.2	0.28	7.7	0.30	7.7	0.30	7.7	0.30
−6	9.52	0.375	—	—	1.5	0.06	4.3	0.17	5.8	0.23	6.3	0.25	6.3	0.25	6.3	0.25
−8	12.70	0.500	—	—	—	—	2.7	0.11	4.2	0.17	4.7	0.19	4.7	0.19	4.7	0.19
−10	15.88	0.625	—	—	—	—	—	—	1.5	0.06	2.0	0.08	2.0	0.08	2.0	0.08
−12	19.05	0.750	—	—	SEE NOTE (2)		—	—	—	—	0.5	0.02	0.5	0.02	0.5	0.02
−16	25.40	1.000	—	—	—	—	—	—	—	—	—	—	0.0	0.00	0.0	0.00
−20	31.75	12.50	—	—	—	—	—	—	—	—	—	—	—	—	0.0	0.00
		MIN														
		HEX	17.46	0.688	22.22	0.875	25.40	1.000	31.75	1.250	38.10	1.500	47.62	1.875	53.98	2.125

1. To be used when nominal tube OD of one face seal end or O-ring boss end is larger than the nominal tube OD of the other end.
2. No factor required for fittings with same end sizes. For fittings with face seal end larger than other end, use Table 10.

NOTES:

For any nonstandard size fitting, one end, the largest, is always standard. It may then be used as a basis of establishing the stocksize and length (either overall or end to center) for all other ends by deducting the above factors equivalent to the reduction in machining requirements from the appropriate standard length in Table 6. See Figures 38 and 39.

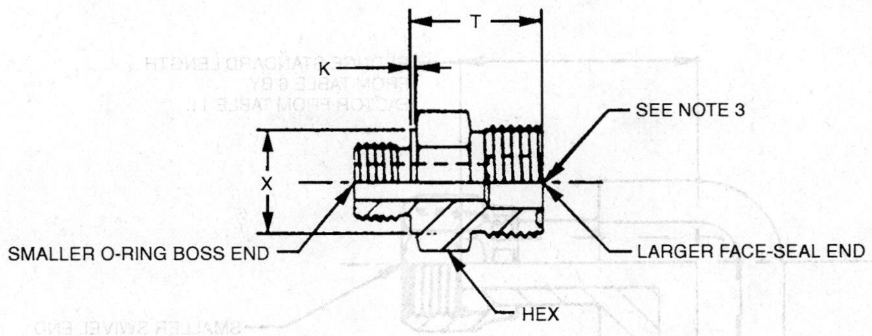

FIGURE 40—STRAIGHT THREAD CONNECTOR WITH REDUCED O-RING BOSS END

TABLE 10A—DIMENSIONS FOR STRAIGHT O-RING BOSS JUMP FITTINGS(1) (FIGURE 40)

			FACE SEAL END SIZE, T													
Dash Size	**Nominal Tube OD mm**	**Nominal Tube OD in**	**–4 mm 6.35**	**–4 in 0.250**	**–6 nn 9.52**	**–6 in 0.375**	**–8 mm 12.70**	**–8 in 0.500**	**–10 mm 15.88**	**–10 in 0.625**	**–12 mm 19.05**	**–12 in 0.750**	**–16 mm 25.4**	**–16 in 1.000**	**–20 mm 31.75**	**–20 in 1.250**
–2	3.18	0.125	21.0	0.83	23.1	0.91	25.5	1.00	29.7	1.17	33.0	1.30	34.3	1.35	36.3	1.43
–3	4.76	0.188	17.7	0.70	23.1	0.91	25.5	1.00	29.7	1.17	33.0	1.30	34.3	1.35	36.3	1.43
–4	6.35	0.250	—	—	23.1	0.91	25.5	1.00	29.7	1.17	33.0	1.30	34.3	1.35	36.3	1.43
–5	7.94	0.312	—	—	19.8	0.78	25.5	1.00	29.7	1.17	33.0	1.30	34.3	1.35	36.3	1.43
–6	9.52	0.375	—	—	—	—	25.5	1.00	29.7	1.17	33.0	1.30	34.3	1.35	36.3	1.43
–8	12.70	0.500	—	—	—	—	—	—	31.2	1.23	34.5	1.36	35.8	1.41	37.8	1.49
–10	15.88	0.625	—	—	—	—	—	—	—	—	34.5	1.36	35.8	1.41	37.8	1.49
–12	19.05	0.750	—	—	SEE NOTE (2)						—	—	35.8	1.41	37.8	1.49
–14	22.22	0.875	—	—	—	—	—	—	—	—	—	—	31.0	1.22	37.8	1.49
–16	25.40	1.000	—	—	—	—	—	—	—	—	—	—	—	—	39.3	1.55
–20	31.75	1.250	—	—	—	—	—	—	—	—	—	—	—	—	—	—
	HEX		15.86	0.625	19.05	0.750	22.22	0.875	26.99	1.062	31.75	1.250	38.10	1.500	44.45	1.750
			T (SEE FIGURE 33)													

1. To be used when nominal tube OD of O-ring boss end is smaller than nominal tube OD of the face seal end.
2. No shoulder required for these sizes. For fittings with face seal end smaller than O-ring boss end, use Table 9.
3. Optional Drill permitted on this end to size and depth illustrated in Figure 21 plug.

TABLE 10B—DIMENSIONS FOR STRAIGHT O-RING BOSS JUMP FITTINGS(1) (FIGURE 40) (CONTINUED)

			FACE SEAL END SIZE, SEE FIGURE 40					
Dash Size	**Nominal Tube OD mm**	**Nominal Tube OD in**	**–24 mm 38.10**	**–24 in 1.500**	**K mm ±0.5**	**K in ±0.02**	**X Dia mm ±0.3**	**X Dia in ±0.01**
-2	3.18	0.125	38.1	1.50	4.1	0.16	12.7	0.50
-3	4.76	0.188	38.1	1.50	4.1	0.16	14.2	0.56
-4	6.35	0.250	38.1	1.50	4.1	0.16	16.0	0.63
-5	7.94	0.312	38.1	1.50	4.1	0.16	17.5	0.69
-6	9.52	0.375	38.1	1.50	4.1	0.16	19.0	0.75
-8	12.70	0.500	39.6	1.56	5.6	0.22	23.9	0.94
-10	15.88	0.625	39.6	1.56	5.6	0.22	26.9	1.06
-12	19.05	0.750	39.6	1.56	5.6	0.22	33.3	1.31
-14	22.22	0.875	39.6	1.56	5.6	0.22	36.6	1.44
-16	25.40	1.000	41.1	1.62	7.1	0.28	39.6	1.56
-20	31.75	1.250	41.1	1.62	7.1	0.28	47.7	1.88
	HEX		53.98	2.125	—	—	—	—

NOTE—

(1) To be used when nominal tube OD of O-ring boss end is smaller than nominal tube OD of the face seal end.
(2) No shoulder required for these sizes. For fittings with face seal end smaller than O-ring boss end, use Table 9.
(3) Optional Drill permitted on this end to size and depth illustrated in Figure 21 plug.

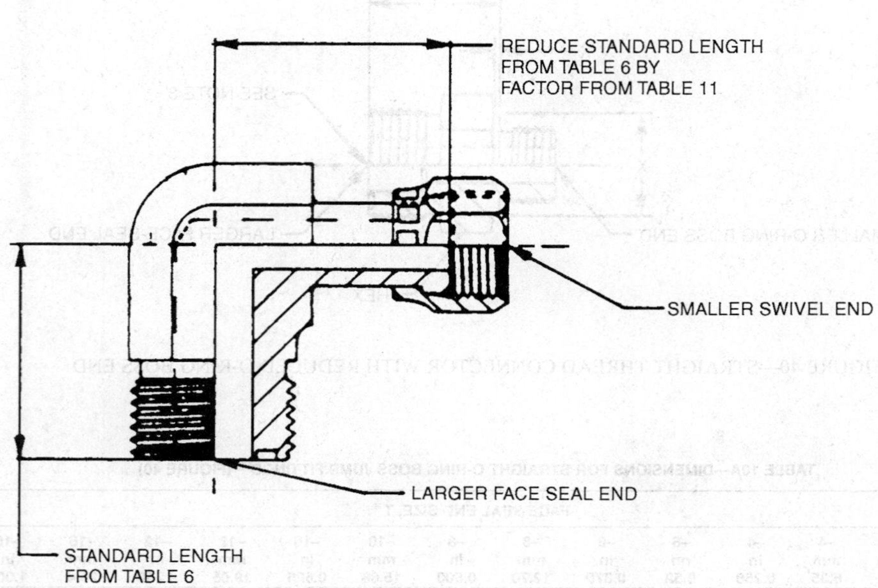

FIGURE 41—90 DEGREE SWIVEL ELBOW WITH REDUCED SWIVEL END

TABLE 11—FACTORS FOR SWIVEL END ON SHAPED FITTINGS[1] (FIGURE 41)

			STANDARD MACHINING SIZE (LARGEST END OF FITTING)													
Dash Size	Nominal Tube OD mm	Nominal Tube OD in	–6 mm 9.52	–6 in 0.375	–8 mm 12.70	–8 in 0.500	–10 mm 15.88	–10 in 0.625	–12 mm 19.05	–12 in 0.750	–16 mm 25.40	–16 in 1.000	–20 mm 31.75	–20 in 1.250	–24 mm 38.10	–24 in 1.500
–4	6.35	0.250	2.3	0.09	6.4	0.25	8.6	0.34	11.1	0.44	13.2	0.52	13.2	0.52	13.2	0.52
											SEE NOTE [3]					
–6	9.52	0.375	—	—	4.1	0.16	6.6	0.26	8.9	0.35	10.7	0.42	10.7	0.42	10.7	0.42
–8	12.70	0.500	—	—	—	—	2.5	0.10	5.1	0.20	6.8	0.27	6.8	0.27	6.8	0.27
–10	15.88	0.625	—	—	—	—	—	—	2.5	0.10	4.3	0.17	4.3	0.17	4.3	0.17
–12	19.05	0.750	—	—	—	—	SEE NOTE [2]		—	—	1.8	0.07	1.8	0.07	1.8	0.07
–16	25.40	1.000	—	—	—	—	—	—	—	—	—	—	0.0	0.00	0.0	0.00
–20	31.75	1.250	—	—	—	—	—	—	—	—	—	—	0.0	0.00	0.0	0.00

NOTE:

For any nonstandard size fitting, be it a connector, 45 or 90 degree elbow, tee, or cross, one end is always standard. Considering this end to be the largest on the fitting, it may then be used as a basis of establishing the stocksize and length (either overall or end to center) for all other ends by deducting the above factors equivalent to the reduction in machining requirements from the appropriate standard lengths in Table 6 of SAE J1453.

(1) To be used when nominal tube OD of at least one shoulder end is smaller than the nominal tube OD of the standard end.
(2) No factor required for fittings with the same end sizes. For fittings with swivel end larger than other end, use Table 7 of SAE J1453.
(3) Multiple jump fittings are not recommended.

APPENDIX A
SURFACE ACCEPTANCE CRITERIA FOR FACE SEAL FITTINGS

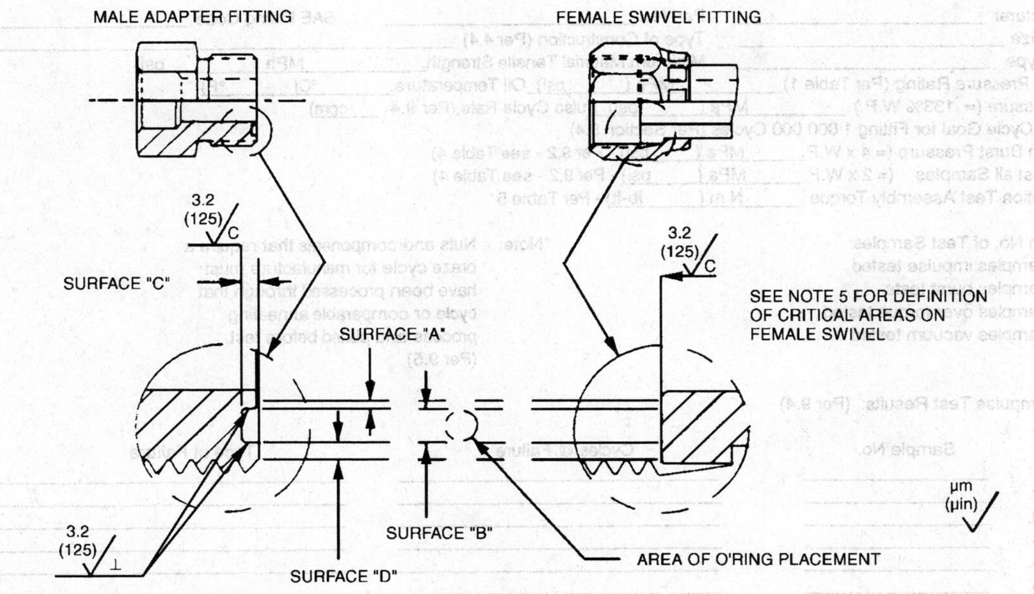

THE ENLARGED DETAIL ILLUSTRATIONS ABOVE ARE ALIGNED TO REPRESENT THE APPROXIMATE POSITION OF THE MALE FITTING WITH THE FEMALE SWIVEL FITTING WHEN CONNECTED. SURFACES DESIGNATED APPLY TO BOTH MALE AND FEMALE SURFACES.

Notes:

1. Surface Roughness—3.2 µm (125 µin) maximum arithmetical average on surfaces in Figure A1.
2. Raised extrusions are not permitted on sealing surfaces "B" and "C" above.
3. Annular (Circumferential) tool marks up to 3.2 µm (125 µin) Ra maximum are acceptable. Scratches with a width greater than 0.13 mm (0.005 in) running perpendicular, radial, or spiral to the fitting I.D. on surface "B" are not acceptable. Surface mars with no depth or height are acceptable.
4. On surfaces "A" and "D," surface imperfections are allowed providing they do not inhibit assembly of fittings.
5. For clarification of the female swivel fitting which does not have the three distinct surfaces present, Table A1 defines this surface location. The surface I.D. and O.D. dimensions represent the total female face area contacted by the O-Ring in each male fitting O-ring groove.

FIGURE A1—SURFACE ACCEPTANCE CRITERIA FOR FACE SEAL FITTINGS

TABLE A1—DIMENSIONS FOR SURFACE ACCEPTANCE CRITERIA

Nom Tube OD mm	Nom Tube OD in	Nom Dash Size Ref	Male Face Seal Fitting Thread Size Ref	Surface "B" Minimum OD mm	Surface "B" Minimum OD in	Surface "B" Maximum ID mm	Surface "B" Maximum ID in
6.35	0.250	–4	9/16-18	11.08	0.436	6.10	0.240
9.52	0.375	–6	11/16-16	12.68	0.499	7.70	0.303
12.70	0.500	–8	13/16-16	15.85	0.624	10.87	0.428
15.88	0.625	–10	1-14	19.08	0.751	14.10	0.555
19.05	0.750	–12	1- 3/16-12	22.27	0.877	17.25	0.679
25.40	1.000	–16	1- 7/16-12	26.97	1.062	21.95	0.864
31.75	1.250	–20	1-11/16-12	33.38	1.314	28.30	1.114
38.10	1.500	–24	2-12	41.30	1.626	36.22	1.426

APPENDIX B
TEST DATA SHEET FOR O-RING FACE SEAL FITTINGS

Manufacturer ________ Part No. ________ SAE Fitting Code ________
Fitting Size ________ Type of Construction (Per 4.4) ________
Fitting Type ________ Minimum Material Tensile Strength. ____ MPa (____ psi)
Working Pressure Rating (Per Table 1) ____ MPa (____ psi) Oil Temperature. ____ °C(____ °F)
Test Pressure (= 133% W.P.) ____ MPa (____ psi) Pulse Cycle Rate (Per 9.4 ____ cpm)
Impulse Cycle Goal for Fitting 1 000 000 Cycles (Per Section 9.4)
Minimum Burst Pressure (= 4 x W.P. ____ MPa (____ psi) - Per 9.2 - see Table 4)
Proof Test all Samples (= 2 x W.P. ____ MPa (____ psi) - Per 9.2 - see Table 4)
Qualification Test Assembly Torque ____ N·m (____ lb-ft) - Per Table 5

Minimum No. of Test Samples:
6 Samples impulse tested
3 Samples burst tests
3 Samples over torque tested
2 Samples vacuum tested

*Note: Nuts and components that require a braze cycle for manufacture must have been processed through that cycle or comparable annealing process and plated before test. (Per 9.5)

I. Impulse Test Results: (Per 9.4)

Sample No.	Cycles @ Failure	Type of Failure
1.		
2.		
3.		
4.		
5.		
6.		

II. Burst Test Results: (Per 9.3 - see Tables 4 and 5)

Sample No.	*Nut Hardness	Pressure @ Failure	Type of Failure
1.	RB/RC	MPa (psi)	
2.	RB/RC	MPa (psi)	
3.	RB/RC	MPa (psi)	

III. Over Torque Test Results: (Per 9.9 - see Table 5)

Nut Type	*Nut Hardness	Torque @ Failure	Type of Failure
1.	RB/RC	N·m (psi)	
2.	RB/RC	N·m (psi)	
3.	RB/RC	N·m (psi)	

IV. Vacuum Test Results (Per 9.6)

Sample No.	Temperature	Test Pressure	Type of Failure
1.	°C(°F)	In Hg	
2.	°C (°F)	In Hg	

V. Conclusions: ________

VI. Dimensions: List Any Exception: ________

NOTE—The above test should be conducted on each of the following types and sizes of fittings to ensure overall performance of all configurations: Figure 4 (520110), Figure 9 (520220), Figure 11 (520120), Figure 24 (520221), Figure 32 (520115) and Figure 33.

FIGURE B1—TEST DATA SHEET FOR O-RING FACE SEAL FITTINGS

APPENDIX C
INSTRUCTIONS AND EXAMPLES FOR CALCULATING DIMENSIONS ON SPECIAL SIZE FITTINGS

C.1 Tables 7, 8, 9, 10, and 11 present various factors to be used in determining the dimensions applicable to special size combination fittings not contained in SAE J1453.

Tables 7 and 8 for Note 3 conditions have no factors for extreme conditions due to methods of manufacture. These extreme conditions are rare and it is suggested a manufacturer be contacted for the proper dimensions.

For any nonstandard size fitting (a fitting where the tube ends are not the same size, e.g., -6, -6, -6) be it connector, 45 or 90 degree elbow, tee, or cross, one end is always standard conforming to SAE J1453 table of dimensions. Considering this to be the largest on the fitting, it may then be used as a basis for establishing the stock size and length (either overall or end to center) for all other ports by deducting factors equivalent to the reduction in machining requirements from the appropriate standard lengths.

Drill Passages—At manufacturer's option, drill through passages in straight special size (jump) fittings may conform to the smaller diameter specified for up to two step size difference, or conform to one of the following for any size difference:

a. The appropriate end may be countersunk to the larger diameter, or
b. The appropriate end may be drilled to the larger diameter up to the middle of the hex

The factors applicable to the various end configurations and size reductions tabulated in the tables were determined on the following basis:

a. Length dimensions were derived by maintaining the standard hexagon thickness for straight fittings, and the standard centerline to machining start for shaped fittings.
b. Factors given in Tables 7 and 8 were derived by subtracting the standard machining length plus an allowance of 1-1/2 pitches (threads) for imperfect thread length required for the smaller end from the same value required for the larger end and rounding the result to a two-place decimal.
c. Factors given in Tables 9, 10, and 11 were derived by subtracting the standard machining length required for the smaller end from that required for the larger standard end and rounding the result to a two-place decimal.

NOTE—See Figures C1a and C1b.

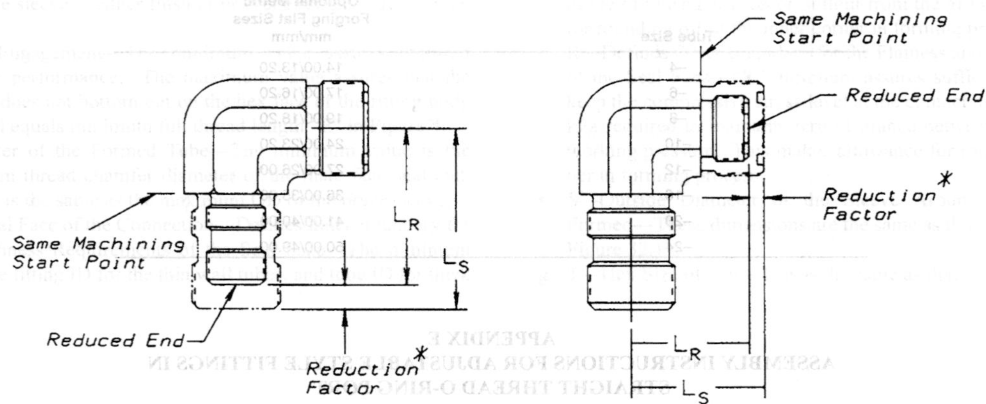

L_S - Standard Size

L_R = (Ls-Reduction Factor)

FIGURE C1A—PORT SIDE

L_S - Standard Size

L_R = (Ls-Reduction Factor)

FIGURE C1B—TUBE SIDE

* Reduction Factor Equals:

(MIN. PERF. THRD. Length + 1 1/2 Pitches of Standard Size.) – (MIN. PERF. THRD. Length + 1 1/2 Pitches of Smaller Size.)

FIGURE C1—JUMP SIZE CALCULATIONS

EXAMPLE—Straight Thread Connector Short, Figure 11 (520120)

3 Situations—

1. Even Sizes, –8 ORFS and –8 O-ring end sizes. Read data from Table 6.
2. ORFS end > O-ring end—Use with Figure 40.

EXAMPLE— –10 ORFS and –8 O-ring

Read "T" in Table 10 for –10 = 31.2 mm (1.23 in) and Read Hex from Table 6 = 26.99 mm (1.062 in).

Also note a shoulder is required. Read K and X dimensions from Table 10, K = 5.6 mm (0.22 in) and X = 23.9 mm (0.94 in).

All remaining dimensions are from Table 6.

3. O-ring end > ORFS end—Use with Figure 38.

EXAMPLE— –10 O-ring and –8 ORFS

Read dimensions given for –10 ORFS in Table 6 even though the ORFS end is –8, –10 is the largest end.

Read HH from Table 6 for –10 = 27.1 mm (1.07 in).

Since the fitting is a –8 ORFS, using Table 9 subtract 2.7 mm (0.11 in) from 27.1 mm (1.07 in) and HH = 24.4 mm (0.96 in).

All remaining dimensions come from Table 6.

EXAMPLE—45 Degree Straight Thread, Figure 10 (520320)

3 Situations—

1. Even Sizes, –8 ORFS and –8 O-ring end sizes. Read data from Table 6.
2. ORFS end > O-ring end—Use with Figure 37.

EXAMPLE— –10 ORFS and –8 O-ring

Read Q = 44.7 mm (1.76 in) from Table 6 for –10 ORFS. From Table 8 subtract 4.3 mm (0.17 in) from the 44.7 mm (1.76 in) length, thus the drop length Q = 40.4 mm (1.59 in).

All other dimensions come from Table 6.

3. O-ring end > ORFS end—Use with Figure 36.

EXAMPLE— –16 O-ring and –8 ORFS

The O-ring end is considered the largest end of the fitting and Q for –16 = 52.3 mm (2.06 in).

Reference dimension under washer = Q – (K + Z – MM)

- in millimeters: = 52.3 – (13.80 + 5.9 – 1.27) = 33.87 mm
- in inches: = 2.06 – (0.543 + 0.234 – 0.05) = 1.33 in

P dimension must be adjusted since it is a –8 end. Read P for –16 = 30.0 mm (1.18 in) and from Table 7 read the deduction length of 4.3 mm (0.17 in).

- in millimeters: P = 30.0 – 4.3 = 25.7 mm
- in inches: P = 1.18 – 0.17 = 1.01 in

All other dimensions come from Table 6.

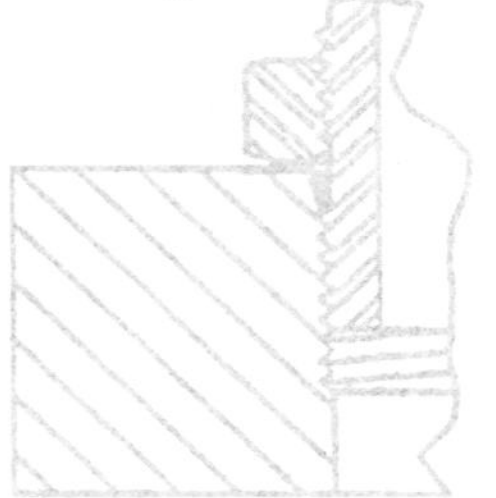

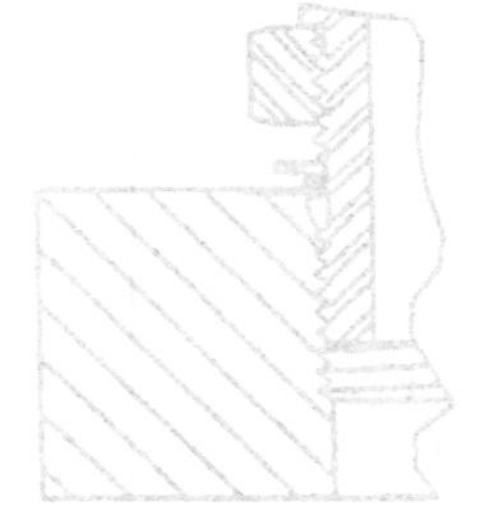

ISO 11926-3:-[1]—Connections for fluid power and general use—Ports and stud ends with ISO 725 threads and O-ring sealing—Part 3: Light duty (L series) stud end

2.2 Other Publications—U.S. References Identical to ISO References

2.2.1 ANSI PUBLICATIONS—Available from ANSI, 11 West 42nd Street, New York, NY 10036-8002.

ANSI/ASME B1.13M—83, Metric Screw Threads—M Profile

2.2.2 SAE PUBLICATIONS—Available from SAE, 400 Commonwealth Drive, Warrendale, PA 15096-0001.

SAE J343 APR91—Test and Procedures for SAE 100R Series Hydraulic Hose and Hose Assemblies

SAE J1926 AUG88—Specifications for Straight Thread O-ring Boss Port

SAE J2244/1/ISO 6149-1:DEC91—Connections for Fluid Power and General Use—Ports and Stud Ends With ISO 261 Threads and O-ring Sealing—Part 1: Port With O-ring Seal in Truncated Housing

3. Definitions—For the purposes of this part of SAE J2244, the definitions given in ISO 5598 and the following definitions shall apply:

3.1 Adjustable Stud End—A stud end that allows for orientation before final tightening of the connection.

3.2 Nonadjustable Stud End—A stud end that does not allow for orientation before final tightening of the connection.

4. Stud End Size—The stud ends shall be specified by SAE J2244/2 and the thread size, separated by a colon, for example, SAE J2244/2:M18 x 1.5.

5. Requirements

5.1 Dimensions—Heavy-duty (S series) stud ends shall conform to the dimensions given in Figures 1A and 1B and Table 1. Hex tolerances across flats shall be according to ISO 4759-1, product grade C.

5.2 Working Pressure—Heavy-duty (S series) stud ends made of carbon steel shall be designed for use at the working pressures given in Table 2.

5.3 Performance—Heavy-duty (S series) stud ends made of carbon steel shall meet or exceed the burst and impulse pressures given in Table 2, when tested according to Section 7.

5.4 Identification—Heavy-duty (S series) stud ends shall be identified according to the detail shown in Figures 1A and 1B and the dimensions given in Table 1. Nonadjustable (straight) stud ends shall be identified by a turn diameter, d_2, and a notch on the turn diameter. Adjustable stud ends shall be identified by only a turn diameter, d_2, on the locknut. In addition to this identification, for both the nonadjustable and adjustable stud ends, the manufacturer may mark the stud end with the word "metric."

5.5 Adjustable Stud End Washer Fit and Flatness—The washer shall be clinched to the stud end with a tight slip fit to an interference fit. The slip fit shall be tight enough so that the washer cannot be shaken loose to cause it to drop from its uppermost position by its own weight. The locknut torque needed to move the washer at the maximum washer interference fit shall not exceed the torques given in Table 3.

Any washer surface that is out of flatness shall be uniform (i.e., not wavy) and concave with respect to the stud end and shall conform to the allowance given in Table 3.

6. O-rings—O-rings for use with heavy-duty (S series) stud ends shall conform to the dimensions given in Figure 2 and Table 4.

7. Test Methods

NOTE—Parts used for cyclic endurance or burst test shall not be tested further, used, or returned to stock.

7.1 Burst Pressure Test

7.1.1 PRINCIPLE—Three samples of both adjustable and nonadjustable shall be tested to confirm that heavy-duty (S series) stud ends meet or exceed a ratio of 4:1 between the burst and working pressures.

7.1.2 MATERIALS

7.1.2.1 Test Block and Stud Ends—Test blocks shall be unplated and hardened to 45-55 HRC. Stud ends shall be made from carbon steel and plated.

7.1.2.2 Test O-rings—Unless otherwise specified, O-rings shall be made from nitrile (NBR) rubber with a hardness of 85 +10/-0 IRHD when measured per ISO 48. O-rings shall conform to the dimensions given in Table 4 and shall meet or exceed the quality requirement grade N in ISO 3601-3.

7.1.3 PROCEDURES

7.1.3.1 Thread Lubrication—For testing only, threads and contact surfaces shall be lubricated with hydraulic oil with a viscosity of VG 32 per ISO 3448 prior to the application of torque.

7.1.3.2 Stud End Torque—Stud ends shall be tested after application of the torques given in Table 5. Adjustable stud locknut torques shall be applied after the stud end has been backed out one full turn from finger tight position, to correctly test the worst possible actual assembly conditions.

7.1.3.3 Pressure Rise Rate—During the burst test, the rate of pressure rise shall not exceed 138 MPa per minute.

7.1.4 TEST REPORT—Test results and conditions shall be reported on the test data form in Appendix A.

7.2 Cyclic Endurance (Impulse) Test

7.2.1 PRINCIPLE—Six samples of both adjustable and nonadjustable stud ends, when tested at their respective impulse pressures, shall pass a cyclic endurance test of 1 000 000 cycles.

7.2.2 MATERIALS—Use the same materials as per 7.1.2.

7.2.3 PROCEDURES

7.2.3.1 Thread Lubrication—Apply lubricant per 7.1.3.1.

7.2.3.2 Stud End Torques—Apply torque per 7.1.3.2.

7.2.3.3 Cycle and Pressure Rise Rate—Cycle rate shall be uniform at 0.5 to 1.3 Hz and shall conform to the wave pattern shown in SAE J343 (ISO 6803).

7.2.4 TEST REPORT—Test results and conditions shall be reported on the test data form in Appendix A.

8. Identification Statement—Use the following statement, except for M30 x 2,[3] in test reports, catalogues, and sales literature when electing to comply with this part of SAE J2244 (ISO 6149-2): Heavy-duty (S series) stud end conforms to SAE J2244/2 (ISO 6149-2), Connections for Fluid Power and General Use—Ports and Stud Ends with ISO 261 Threads and O-ring Sealing—Part 2: Heavy-duty (S series) Stud Ends—Dimensions, Design, Test Methods, and Requirements.

9. Key Words—fluid power, pipe fittings, standard connection, standard coupling, pipe joints, ports, stud ends, specifications, design, operating requirements, dimensions, designation, test methods, metric, straight thread, O-ring seal, high pressure

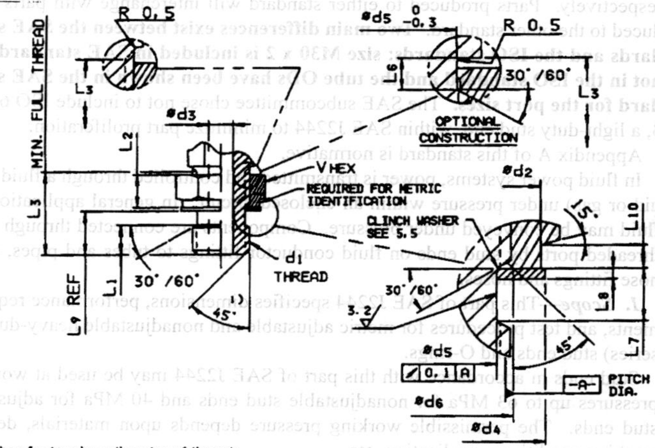

1) Chamfer to minor diameter of threads

FIGURE 1A—ADJUSTABLE SAE J2244/2 HEAVY-DUTY (S SERIES) STUD END DETAIL

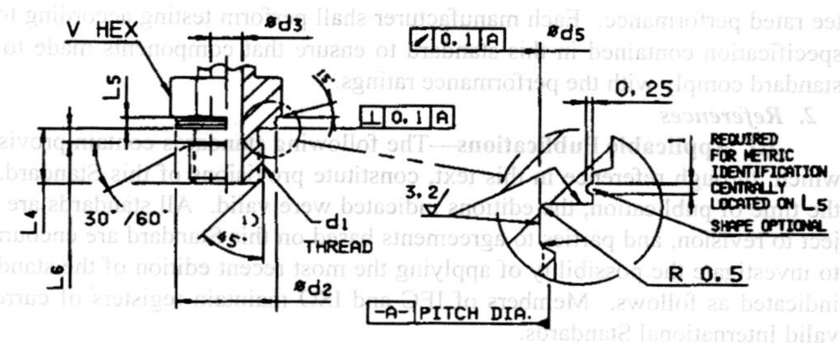

1) Chamfer to minor diameter of threads

FIGURE 1B—NONADJUSTABLE SAE J2244/2 HEAVY-DUTY (S SERIES) STUD END DETAIL

3. Not included in ISO 6149.

TABLE 1—SAE J2244/2—HEAVY-DUTY (S SERIES) STUD AND DIMENSIONS

Dimensions in Millimeters

Tube OD	Inch Nominal Tube Dash Size	Inch Nominal Tube OD mm	Inch Nominal Tube OD in	d_1[1]	d_2 ±0.2	d_3	d_4 ±0.4	d_5 0 −0.1	d_6 +0.4 0	L_1 ±0.2	L_2 ±0.2	L_3 Min	L_4 ±0.2	L_5 ±0.1	L_6 ±0.3 0	L_7 ±0.1	L_8 ±0.08 0	L_9 Ref.	L_{10} ±0.1	V Hex
4	−2	3.18	0.125	M8 x 1	11.8	2 + 0.14/0	12.5	6.4	8.1	6.5	7	18	9.5	2.5	2	4	0.9	9.6	1.5	12
5	−3	4.76	0.188	M10 x 1	13.8	3 + 0.14/0	14.5	8.4	10.1	6.5	7	18	9.5	2.5	2	4	0.9	9.6	1.5	14
6	−4	6.35	0.250	M12 x 1.5	16.8	4 + 0.18/0	17.5	9.7	12.1	7.5	8.5	21	11	2.5	3	4.5	0.9	11.1	2	17
8	−5	7.94	0.312	M14 x 1.5[2]	18.8	6 + 0.18/0	19.5	11.7	14.1	7.5	8.5	21	11	2.5	3	4.5	0.9	11.1	2	19
10	−6	9.52	0.375	M16 x 1.5	21.8	7 + 0.22/0	22.5	13.7	16.1	9	9	23	12.5	2.5	3	4.5	0.9	12.6	2	22
12	−8	12.7	0.500	M18 x 1.5	23.8	9 + 0.22/0	24.5	15.7	18.1	10.5	10.5	26	14	2.5	3	4.5	0.9	14.1	2.5	24
16	−10	15.88	0.625	M22 x 1.5	26.8	12 + 0.27/0	27.5	19.7	22.1	11	11	27.5	15	2.5	3	5	1.25	14.8	2.5	27
20	−12	19.05	0.750	M27 x 2	31.8	15 + 0.27/0	32.5	24	27.1	13.5	13.5	33.5	18.5	2.5	4	6	1.25	18.3	2.5	32
22	−14	22.22	0.875	M30 x 2[3]	35.8	18 + 0.33/0	36.5	27	30.1	13.5	13.5	33.5	18.5	2.5	4	6	1.25	18.3	2.5	36
25	−16	25.4	1.000	M33 x 2	40.8	20 + 0.33/0	41.5	30	33.1	13.5	13.5	33.5	18.5	3	4	6	1.25	18.3	3	41
30	−20	31.75	1.250	M42 x 2	49.8	26 + 0.33/0	50.5	39	42.1	14	14	34.5	19	3	4	6	1.25	18.8	3	50
38	−24	38.10	1.500	M48 x 2	54.8	32 + 0.39/0	55.5	45	48.1	16.5	15	38	21.5	3	4	6	1.25	21.3	3	55
50	−32	50.80	2.000	M60 x 2	64.8	40 + 0.39/0	65.5	57	60.1	19	17	42.5	24	3	4	6	1.25	23.8	3	65
				M20 x 1.5[4]	26.8			17.7					14	2.5	3				2.5	

1. Thread Class 6 g per ISO 261.
2. Preferred for diagnostic port applications.
3. Not included in ISO 6149.
4. For plug for cartridge cavity only. (See ISO 7789.)

TABLE 2—SAE J2244/2 HEAVY-DUTY (S SERIES) STUD END PRESSURE[1]

Units in Megapascals[2]

Tube OD	Thread Size	Stud End Style Nonadjustable Working[1] Pressure	Stud End Style Nonadjustable Test Pressure Burst	Stud End Style Nonadjustable Test Pressure Impulse[3]	Stud End Style Adjustable Working[1] Pressure	Stud End Style Adjustable Test Pressure Burst	Stud End Style Adjustable Test Pressure Impulse[3]
4	M8 x 1	63	252	83.8	40	160	53.2
5	M10 x 1	63	252	83.8	40	160	53.2
6	M12 x 1.5	63	252	83.8	40	160	53.2
8	M14 x 1.5	63	252	83.8	40	160	53.2
10	M16 x 1.5	63	252	83.8	40	160	53.2
12	M18 x 1.5	63	252	83.8	40	160	53.2
16	M22 x 1.5	63	252	83.8	40	160	53.2
20	M27 x 2	40	160	53.2	40	160	53.2
22	M30 x 2	40	160	53.2	40	160	53.2
25	M33 x 2	40	160	53.2	31.5	126	41.9
30	M42 x 2	25	100	33.2	25	100	33.2
38	M48 x 2	25	100	33.2	20	80	26.6
50	M60 x 2	25	100	33.2	16	64	21.3
	For plug for cartridge valve cavity only (See ISO 7789)						
	M20 x 1.5	40	160	53.2	—	—	—

1. These pressures were established using fittings made of carbon steel when tested in accordance with Section 7.
2. To convert from MPa to bar multiply by 10. (10 bar/MPa)
3. Cyclic endurance test pressure.

TABLE 3—ADJUSTABLE STUD END WASHER TORQUE AND FLATNESS ALLOWANCE

Thread Size	Maximum Nut Torque to Move Washer N·m	Maximum Washer Flatness Allowance mm
M8 x 1	1	0.25
M10 x 1	3	0.25
M12 x 1.5	4	0.25
M14 x 1.5	5	0.25
M16 x 1.5	7	0.25
M18 x 1.5	10	0.25
M22 x 1.5	12	0.25
M27 x 2	15	0.40
M30 x 2	18	0.40
M33 x 2	20	0.40
M42 x 2	25	0.50
M48 x 2	30	0.50
M60 x 2	40	0.50

FIGURE 2—O-RING DETAIL

TABLE 4—SAE J2244/2 STUD END O-RING DIMENSIONS

Dimensions in Millimeters

Thread Size	Inside Diameter d_8	Inside Diameter d_8 tol. ±	Cross Section Diameter d_9	Cross Section Diameter d_9 tol ±
M8 x 1	6.1	0.20	1.6	0.08
M10 x 1	8.1	0.20	1.6	0.08
M12 x 1.5	9.3	0.20	2.2	0.08
M14 x 1.5	11.3	0.20	2.2	0.08
M16 x 1.5	13.3	0.20	2.2	0.08
M18 x 1.5	15.3	0.20	2.2	0.08
M22 x 1.5	19.3	0.22	2.2	0.08
M27 x 2	23.6	0.24	2.9	0.09
M30 x 2[1]	26.6	0.26	2.9	0.09
M33 x 2	29.6	0.29	2.9	0.09
M42 x 2	38.6	0.37	2.9	0.09
M48 x 2	44.6	0.43	2.9	0.09
M60 x 2	56.6	0.51	2.9	0.09
M20 x 1.5[2]	17.3	0.22	2.2	0.08

1. Not included in ISO 6149.
2. For plug for cartridge valve cavity only. (See ISO 7789.)

TABLE 5—TORQUE REQUIREMENTS FOR STUD END QUALIFICATION TEST

Thread Size	Torque +10% N·m −0
M8 x 1	10
M10 x 1	20
M12 x 1.5	35
M14 x 1.5	45
M16 x 1.5	55
M18 x 1.5	70
M22 x 1.5	100
M27 x 2	170
M30 x 2	215
M33 x 2	310
M42 x 2	330
M48 x 2	420
M60 x 2	500
M20 x 1.5[1]	80

1. For plug for cartridge valve cavity only. (See ISO 7789.)

APPENDIX A
(NORMATIVE)

A.1 See Figure A1.

SAE J2244/2 PORT AND STUD END TEST DATA FORM

Stud end specification:

Manufacturer ____________ **Test Facility** ____________

Stud End Type ____________ **Size** ____________

Minimum Material Tensile Strength ____________ **MPa**

Stud End Working Pressure (Table 2) ____________ **MPa**

Stud End Impulse Test Pressure (Table 2) ____________ **MPa**

Stud End Burst Test Pressure (Table 2) ____________ **MPa**

Qualification Test Assembly Torque (Table 3) ____________ **N·m**

Burst Test Results: (Three samples minimum burst tested)

Sample No.	Pressure @ Failure	Torque	Hardness	Type of Failure
1.	MPa	N·m		
2.	MPa	N·m		
3.	MPa	N·m		

Cyclic endurance test results: (Six samples minimum impulse tested)

Sample No.	Cycles @ Failure	Torque	Hardness	Type of Failure
1.		N·m		
2.		N·m		
3.		N·m		
4.		N·m		
5.		N·m		
6.		N·m		

Conclusions: Pass/fail and why- ____________

Dimensions/ List any exception: ____________

Name (printed/typed) and signature of person certifying report: ____________

Date: ____________

FIGURE A1—SAE J2244/2 PORT AND STUD END TEST DATA FORM

CONNECTIONS FOR FLUID POWER AND GENERAL USE—PORTS AND STUD ENDS WITH ISO 261 METRIC THREADS AND O-RING SEALING, PART 3: LIGHT-DUTY (L SERIES) STUD ENDS—DIMENSIONS, DESIGN, TEST METHODS, AND REQUIREMENTS —SAE J2244-3 JUN1998

SAE Standard

Report of the SAE Fluid Conductors and Connectors Technical Committee SC1—Automotive and Hydraulic Tube and Fitting approved April 1996 and revised June 1998. Rationale statement available.

This document is technically equivalent to ISO 6149-3.

Foreword—SAE J2244/ISO 6149 was prepared by SAE FCCTC-SC1, Automotive and Hydraulic Tube and Fitting Subcommittee and ISO/TC 131, Fluid power systems. SAE J2244 consists of the following parts under the general title: Connections for Fluid Power and General Use—Ports and Stud Ends with ISO 261 Threads and O-ring Sealing—

Part 1: Port with O-ring Seal in Truncated Housing

Part 2: Heavy-duty (S series) Stud Ends—Dimensions, Design, Test Methods, and Requirements

Part 3: Light-duty (L series) Stud Ends—Dimensions, Design, Test Methods, and Requirements

The three parts of SAE J2244 constitute a revision of ISO 6149:1980. This part defines performance requirements, dimensions, and designs for light-duty (L series) stud ends. SAE J2244-2 (ISO 6149-2) applies to fittings detailed in ISO 8434-3 and SAE J2244-3 applies to fittings detailed in SAE J514 (ISO 8434-2).

SAE J2244 Parts 1, 2, and 3 are technically equivalent to ISO 6149 parts 1, 2, and 3, respectively. Parts produced to either standard will interchange with parts produced to the other standard. **The main difference between this SAE standard and the ISO standard is the test requirements have been referenced to SAE J1644. SAE J1644 test requirements are identical to those in ISO 6149-3.**

Appendix A of this standard is normative.

In fluid power systems, power is transmitted and controlled through a fluid (liquid or gas) under pressure within an enclosed circuit. In general applications, a fluid may be conveyed under pressure. Components are connected through their threaded ports by stud ends on fluid conductor fittings to tubes and pipes or to hose fittings and hoses.

1. Scope—This part of SAE J2244 specifies dimensions, performance requirements, and test procedures for metric adjustable and nonadjustable light-duty (L series) stud ends and O-rings.

Stud ends in accordance with this part of SAE J2244 may be used at working pressures up to 40 MPa for nonadjustable stud ends and 31.5 MPa for adjustable stud ends. The permissible working pressure depends upon materials, design, working conditions, applications, etc.

For threaded ports and stud ends for use in new designs in hydraulic fluid power applications, only SAE J2244 shall be used. Threaded ports and stud ends in accordance with ISO 1179, ISO 9974, and SAE J1926 (ISO 11926) shall not be used in new designs in hydraulic fluid power applications.

Conformance to the dimensional information in this SAE Standard does not guarantee rated performance. Each manufacturer shall perform testing according to the specification contained in this document to ensure that components made to this document comply with the performance ratings.

2. References

2.1 Applicable Publications—The following standards contain provisions which, through reference in this text, constitute provisions of this document. All standards are subject to revision, and parties to agreements based on this document shall apply the most recent edition of the standards. Members of IEC and ISO maintain registers of currently valid International Standards.

2.1.1 SAE PUBLICATIONS—Available from SAE, 400 Commonwealth Drive, Warrendale, PA 15096-0001.

SAE J1644—Metallic Tube Connections for Fluid Power and General Use—Test Methods for Threaded Hydraulic Fluid Power Connectors

SAE J1926-2—Connections for General Use and Fluid Power—Ports and Stud Ends with ISO 725 Threads and O-ring Sealing—Part 2: Heavy-duty (S Series) Stud Ends

SAE J2244/ISO 6149-1—Connections for Fluid Power and General Use—Ports and Stud Ends With ISO 261 Threads and O-ring Sealing—Part 1: Port With O-ring Seal in Truncated Housing

SAE J2244-2/ISO 6149-2—Connections for Fluid Power and General Use—Ports and Stud Ends with ISO 261 Threads and O-ring Sealing—Part 2: Heavy-duty (S Series) Stud Ends—Dimensions, Design, Test Methods, and Requirements

2.1.2 ISO PUBLICATIONS—Available from ANSI, 11 West 42nd Street, New York, NY 10036-8002.

ISO 261—ISO general purpose metric screw threads—General plan

ISO 1179-1—Connections for fluid power and general use—Ports and stud ends with ISO 228-1 threads with elastomeric and metal-to-metal sealing—Part 1: Threaded port

ISO 1179-2—Connections for fluid power and general use—Ports and stud ends with ISO 228-1 threads with elastomeric and metal-to-metal sealing—Part 2: Heavy duty (S series) and light duty (L series) stud ends with elastomeric sealing (type E)

ISO 1179-3—Connections for fluid power and general use—Ports and stud ends with ISO 228-1 threads with elastomeric and metal-to-metal sealing—Part 3: Light duty (L series) stud ends with sealing by O-ring with retaining ring (types G and H)

ISO 1179-4—Connections for fluid power and general use—Ports and stud ends with ISO 228-1 threads with elastomeric and metal-to-metal sealing—Part 4: Stud end for general use only with metal-to-metal sealing (type B)

ISO 4759-1—Tolerances for fasteners—Part 1: Bolts, screws and nuts with thread diameters between 1.6 (inclusive) and 150 mm (inclusive) and product grades A, B and C

ISO 5598—Fluid power systems and components—Terminology

ISO 6149-2—Connections for fluid power and general use—Ports and stud ends with ISO 261 threads and O-ring sealing—Part 2: Heavy duty (S series) stud ends—Dimensions, design, test methods and requirements

ISO 6149-3—Connections for fluid power and general use—Ports and stud ends with ISO 261 threads and O-ring sealing—Part 3: Light duty (L series) stud ends—Dimensions, design, test methods and requirements

ISO 8434-2—Metallic tube connections for fluid power and general use—Part 2: 37× flared fittings

ISO 8434-3—Metallic tube connections for fluid power and general use—Part 3: O-ring face seal fittings

ISO 9974-1—Connections for fluid power and general use—Ports and stud ends with ISO 261 threads and elastomeric sealing ring and metal-to-metal sealing—Part 1: Threaded port

ISO 9974-2—Connections for fluid power and general use—Ports and stud ends with ISO 261 threads and elastomeric sealing ring and metal-to-metal sealing—Part 2: Stud end with elastomeric sealing (type E)

ISO 9974-3—Connections for fluid power and general use—Ports and stud ends with ISO 261 threads and elastomeric sealing ring and metal-to-metal sealing—Part 3: Stud end with metal-to-metal sealing (type B)

ISO 11926-1—Connections for fluid power and general use—Ports and stud ends with ISO 725 threads and O-ring sealing—Part 1: Threaded port

ISO 11926-2—Connections for fluid power and general use—Ports and stud ends with ISO 725 threads and O-ring sealing—Part 2: Heavy duty (S series) stud end

ISO 11926-3—Connections for fluid power and general use—Ports and stud ends with ISO 725 threads and O-ring sealing—Part 3: Light duty (L series) stud end

2.2 Related Publications—The following publications form a part of this specification to the extent specified herein. Unless otherwise specified, the latest issue of SAE publications shall apply.

2.2.1 SAE PUBLICATIONS—Available from SAE, 400 Commonwealth Drive, Warrendale, PA 15096-0001.

SAE J343—Test and Procedures for SAE 100R Series Hydraulic Hose and Hose Assemblies

SAE J514—Hydraulic Tube Fittings

SAE J515—Hydraulic O-Ring

SAE J1926-1—Connections for General Use and Fluid Power—Ports and Stud Ends with ISO 725 Threads and O-ring Sealing—Part 1: Threaded Port with O-ring Seal in Truncated Housing

2.2.2 ANSI PUBLICATION—Available from ANSI, 11 West 42nd Street, New York, NY 10036-8002.

ANSI/ASME B1.13M-83—Metric Screw Threads—M Profile

2.2.3 ISO PUBLICATIONS—Available from ANSI, 11 West 42nd Street, New York, NY 10036-8002.

ISO 48—Vulcanized rubbers—Determination of hardness (Hardness between 30 and 85 IRHD)

ISO 1302—Technical drawings—Method of indicating surface texture on drawings

ISO 3448—Industrial liquid lubricants—ISO viscosity classification

ISO 3601-3—Fluid systems—Sealing devices—O-rings—Part 3: Quality acceptance criteria

ISO 6149-1—Connections for fluid power and general use—Ports and stud ends with ISO 261 threads and O-ring sealing—Part 1: Port with O-ring seal in truncated housing

ISO 6803—Rubber or plastic hoses and hose assemblies—Hydraulic pressure impulse test without flexing

ISO 7789—Hydraulic fluid power—Two, three- and four-port screw-in cartridge valve cavities

3. Definitions—For the purposes of this part of SAE J2244, the definitions given in ISO 5598 and the following definitions shall apply:

3.1 Adjustable Stud End—Stud end connector that allows for fitting orientation through final tightening of the locknut to complete the connection. This type of stud end is typically used on shape fittings (e.g., tees, crosses, and elbows).

3.2 Nonadjustable Stud End—Stud end connector that does not require specific orientation before final tightening of the connection because it is only used on straight fittings.

4. Stud End Size—The stud ends shall be specified by SAE J2244-3 and the thread size, separated by a colon, for example,

SAE J2244-3:M18 x 1.5

5. Requirements

5.1 Dimensions—Light-duty (L series) stud ends shall conform to the dimensions given in Figures 1A and 1B and Table 1. Hex tolerances across flats shall be according to ISO 4759-1, product grade C.

5.2 Working Pressure—Light-duty (L series) stud ends made of carbon steel shall be designed for use at the working pressures given inTable 2.

5.3 Performance—Light-duty (L series) stud ends made of carbon steel shall meet or exceed the burst and impulse pressures given in Table 2, when tested according to Section 7.

5.4 Identification—Light-duty (L series) stud ends shall be identified according to the detail shown in Figures 1A and 1B and the dimensions given in Table 1. Nonadjustable (straight) stud ends shall be identified by a turn diameter, d2, and a notch on the turn diameter. Adjustable stud ends shall be identified by only a turn diameter, d2, on the locknut. In addition to this identification, for both the nonadjustable and adjustable stud ends, the manufacturer may mark the stud end with the word "metric."

5.5 Adjustable Stud End Washer Fit and Flatness—The washer shall be clinched to the stud end with a tight slip fit to an interference fit. The slip fit shall be tight enough so that the washer cannot be shaken loose to cause it to drop from its uppermost position by its own weight. The locknut torque needed to move the washer at the maximum washer interference fit shall not exceed the torques given in Table 3.

Any washer surface that is out of flatness shall be uniform (i.e., not wavy) and concave with respect to the stud end and shall conform to the allowance given in Table 3.

6. O-rings—O-rings for use with light-duty (L series) stud ends shall conform to the dimensions given in Figure 2 and Table 4.

7. Test Methods

NOTE—Parts used for cyclic endurance or burst test shall not be tested further, used, or returned to stock.

7.1 Performance Tests

7.1.1 Parts shall be tested according to SAE J1644 for burst and cyclic endurance (impulse).

7.2 Test O-rings

7.2.1 Test O-rings shall meet the requirements of SAE/ASTM Type CH according to SAE J515 and shall conform to the dimensions specified in Table 4.

8. Identification Statement—Use the following statement in test reports, catalogues, and sales literature when electing to comply with this part of SAE J2244-3 (ISO 6149-3):

Light-duty (L series) stud end conforms to SAE J2244-3 (ISO 6149-3), Connections for Fluid Power and General Use—Ports and Stud Ends with ISO 261 Threads and O-ring Sealing—Part 3: Light-duty (L series) Stud Ends—Dimensions, Design, Test Methods, and Requirements.

9. Key Words—Fluid power, pipe fittings, standard connection, standard coupling, pipe joints, ports, stud ends, specifications, design, operating requirements, dimensions, designation, test methods, metric, straight thread, O-ring seal, high pressure

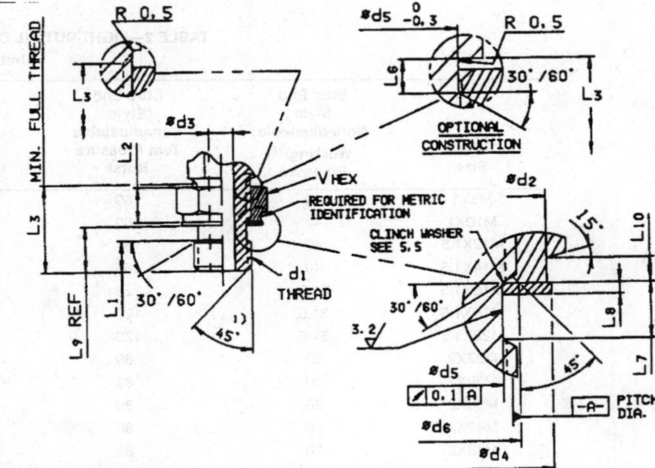

1) Chamfer to minor diameter of threads

FIGURE 1A—ADJUSTABLE (L SERIES) STUD DETAIL

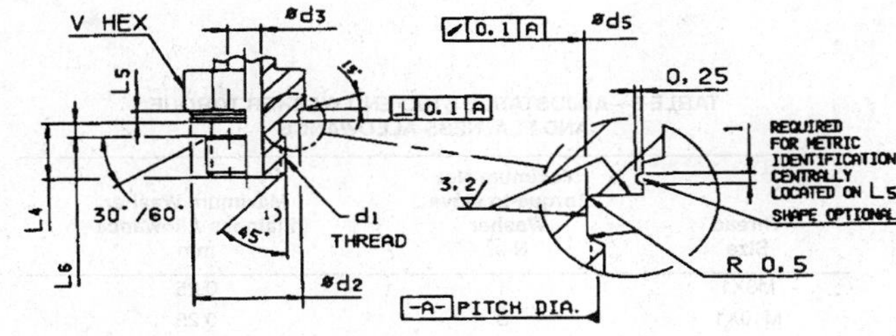

1) Chamfer to minor diameter of threads

FIGURE 1B—NONADJUSTABLE (L SERIES) STUD DETAIL

TABLE 1—METRIC LIGHT-DUTY (L SERIES) STUD DIMENSIONS

d_1[1]	d_2 ±0.2	d_3	d_4 ±0.4	d_5 0 −0.1	d_6 +0.4 0	L_1 ±0.2	L_2 ±0.2	L_3 Min	L_4[2] ±0.2	L_5 ±0.1	L_6 +0.3 0	L_7 ±0.1	L_8 ±0.08	L_9 Ref	L_{10} ±0.1	V Hex
M8X1	11.8	3 +0.14/0	12.5	6.4	8.1	5.5	6	16	8.5	2.5	2	4	0.9	8.6	1.5	12
M10X1	13.8	4.5+0.18/0	14.5	8.4	10.1	5.5	6	16	8.5	2.5	2	4	0.9	8.6	1.5	14
M12X1.5	16.8	6 +0.18/0	17.5	9.7	12.1	7.5	7.5	20	11	2.5	3	4.5	0.9	11.1	2	17
M14X1.5[3]	18.8	7.5+0.22/0	19.5	11.7	14.1	7.5	7.5	20	11	2.5	3	4.5	0.9	11.1	2	19
M16X1.5	21.8	9 +0.22/0	22.5	13.7	16.1	8	7.5	20.5	11.5	2.5	3	4.5	0.9	11.6	2	22
M18X1.5	23.8	11 +0.27/0	24.5	15.7	18.1	9	7.5	21.5	12.5	2.5	3	4.5	0.9	12.6	2.5	24
M22X1.5	26.8	14 +0.27/0	27.5	19.7	22.1	9	8	22.5	13	2.5	3	5	1.25	12.8	2.5	27
M27X2	31.8	18 +0.27/0	32.5	24	27.1	11	10	27.5	16	2.5	4	6	1.25	15.8	2.5	32
M30X2	35.8	21 +0.33/0	36.5	27	30.1	11	10	27.5	16	2.5	4	6	1.25	15.8	2.5	36
M33X2	40.8	23 +0.33/0	41.5	30	33.1	11	10	27.5	16	3	4	6	1.25	15.8	3	41
M42X2	49.8	30 +0.33/0	50.5	39	42.1	11	10	27.5	16	3	4	6	1.25	15.8	3	50
M48X2	54.8	36 +0.39/0	55.5	45	48.1	12.5	10	29	17.5	3	4	6	1.25	17.3	3	55
M60X2	64.8	44 +0.39/0	65.5	57	60.1	12.5	10	29	17.5	3	4	6	1.25	17.3	3	65

1. Thread class 6g per ISO 261.
2. Optional length L_4 in accordance with SAE J2244-2.
3. Preferred for diagnostic port applications.

TABLE 2—LIGHT-DUTY (L SERIES) STUD END PRESSURE RATINGS[1]
Units in megapascals[2]

Thread Size	Stud End Style Nonadjustable Working[1] Pressure	Stud End Style Nonadjustable Test Pressure Burst	Stud End Style Nonadjustable Test Pressure Impulse[3]	Stud End Style Adjustable Working[1] Pressure	Stud End Style Adjustable Test Pressure Burst	Stud End Style Adjustable Test Pressure Impulse[3]
M8X1	40	160	53.2	31.5	126	41.9
M10X1	40	160	53.2	31.5	126	41.9
M12X1.5	40	160	53.2	31.5	126	41.9
M14X1.5	40	160	53.2	31.5	126	41.9
M16X1.5	31.5	126	41.9	25	100	33.2
M18X1.5	31.5	126	41.9	25	100	33.2
M22X1.5	31.5	126	41.9	25	100	33.2
M27X2	20	80	26.6	16	64	21.3
M30X2	20	80	26.6	16	64	21.3
M33X2	20	80	26.6	16	64	21.3
M42X2	20	80	26.6	16	64	21.3
M48X2	20	80	26.6	16	64	21.3
M60X2	16	64	21.3	10	40	13.3

1. These pressure ratings were established using fittings made of low carbon steel and O-rings per 7.2.1.
2. To convert from MPa to bar multiply by 10 (10 bar/MPa).
3. Cyclic endurance test pressure.

TABLE 3—ADJUSTABLE STUD END WASHER TORQUE AND FLATNESS ALLOWANCE

Thread Size	Maximum Nut Torque to Move Washer N·m	Maximum Washer Flatness Allowance mm
M8X1	1	0.25
M10X1	3	0.25
M12X1.5	4	0.25
M14X1.5	5	0.25
M16X1.5	7	0.25
M18X1.5	10	0.25
M22X1.5	12	0.25
M27X2	15	0.40
M30X2	18	0.40
M33X2	20	0.40
M42X2	25	0.50
M48X2	30	0.50
M60X2	40	0.50

TABLE 4—STUD O-RING DIMENSIONS
Dimensions in millimeters

Thread Size	d_8 Inside Diameter	d_9 Section Diameter
M8X1	6.1 ± 0.20	1.6 ± 0.08
M10X1	8.1 ± 0.20	1.6 ± 0.08
M12X1.5	9.3 ± 0.20	2.2 ± 0.08
M14X1.5	11.3 ± 0.20	2.2 ± 0.08
M16X1.5	13.3 ± 0.20	2.2 ± 0.08
M18X1.5	15.3 ± 0.20	2.2 ± 0.08
M22X1.5	19.3 ± 0.22	2.2 ± 0.08
M27X2	23.6 ± 0.24	2.9 ± 0.09
M30X2	26.6 ± 0.26	2.9 ± 0.09
M33X2	29.6 ± 0.29	2.9 ± 0.09
M42X2	38.6 ± 0.37	2.9 ± 0.09
M48X2	44.6 ± 0.43	2.9 ± 0.09
M60X2	56.6 ± 0.51	2.9 ± 0.09

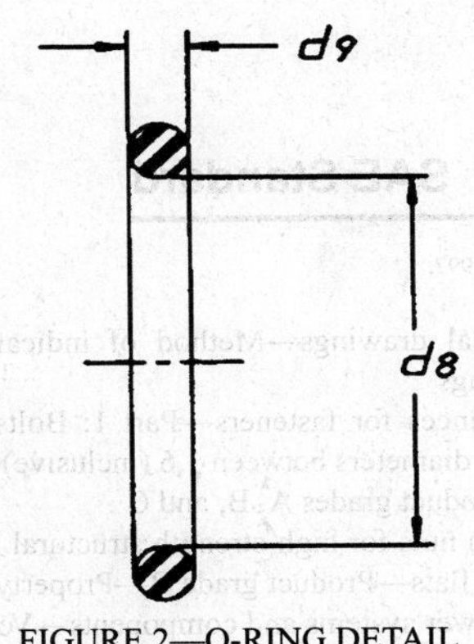

FIGURE 2—O-RING DETAIL

TABLE 5—STUD QUALIFICATION TEST TORQUE REQUIREMENTS

Thread Size	Torque +10% N·m 0
M8X1	8
M10X1	15
M12X1.5	25
M14X1.5	35
M16X1.5	40
M18X1.5	45
M22X1.5	60
M27X2	100
M30X2	130
M33X2	160
M42X2	210
M48X2	260
M60X2	315

APPENDIX A
(NORMATIVE)

SAE J2244/2 PORT AND STUD END TEST DATA FORM

Stud end specification:

Manufacturer ____________________ **Test Facility** ____________________

Stud End Type ____________________ **Size** ____________________

Minimum Material Tensile Strength ____________________ **MPa**

Stud End Working Pressure (Table 2) ____________________ **MPa**

Stud End Impulse Test Pressure (Table 2) ____________________ **MPa**

Stud End Burst Test Pressure (Table 2) ____________________ **MPa**

Qualification Test Assembly Torque (Table 3) ____________________ **N·m**

Burst Test Results: (Three samples minimum burst tested)

Sample No.	Pressure @ Failure	Torque	Hardness	Type of Failure
1. ______	______ MPa	______ N·m	______	______
2. ______	______ MPa	______ N·m	______	______
3. ______	______ MPa	______ N·m	______	______

Cyclic endurance test results: (Six samples minimum impulse tested)

Sample No.	Cycles @ Failure	Torque	Hardness	Type of Failure
1. ______	______	______ N·m	______	______
2. ______	______	______ N·m	______	______
3. ______	______	______ N·m	______	______
4. ______	______	______ N·m	______	______
5. ______	______	______ N·m	______	______
6. ______	______	______ N·m	______	______

Conclusions: Pass/fail and why- ____________________

____

Dimensions/ List any exception: ____________________

____

____

Name (printed/typed) and signature of person certifying report:

____________________ **Date:** ____________________

FIGURE A1—METRIC PORT AND STUD TEST DATA FORM

CONNECTIONS FOR FLUID POWER AND GENERAL USE —PORTS AND STUD ENDS WITH ISO 261 THREADS AND O-RING SEALING—PART 4: HEAVY-DUTY (S SERIES) EXTERNAL HEX PORT PLUGS—DIMENSIONS, DESIGN, TEST METHODS, AND REQUIREMENTS—SAE J2244-4 JAN1997 SAE Standard

Report of the SAE Fluid Conductors and Connectors Technical Committee SC1—Automotive and Hydraulic Tube and Fittings approved January 1997.

Foreword—SAE J2244 was prepared by the SAE FCCTC-SC1, Automotive and Hydraulic Tube and Fitting Subcommittee and ISO/TC 131, Fluid power systems. SAE J2244 consists of the following parts under the general title: Connections for Fluid Power and General Use—Ports and Stud Ends with ISO 261 Threads and O-ring Sealing:

Part 1: Port with O-Ring Seal in Truncated Housing

Part 2: Heavy-Duty (S Series) Stud Ends—Dimensions, Design, Test Methods, and Requirements

Part 3: Light-Duty (L Series) Stud Ends—Dimensions, Design, Test Methods, and Requirements

Part 4: Heavy-Duty (S-Series) External Hex Port Plugs—Dimensions, Design, Test Methods, and Requirements

The four parts of SAE J2244 constitute a revision of ISO 6149:1980. This part defines performance requirements, dimensions, and designs for 13 port plugs. Significant testing was conducted to confirm the performance requirements of stud ends made from carbon steel. SAE J2244-2 (ISO 6149-2) applies to fittings detailed in SAE J1453-2 (ISO 8434 parts 1, 3, and 4), and SAE J2244-3 (ISO 6149-3) applies to fittings in SAE J514 (ISO 8434-2).

SAE J2244 Parts 1, 2, and 3 are technically equivalent to ISO 6149 parts 1, 2, and 3, respectively. Parts produced to either standard will interchange with parts produced to the other standard. Two main differences exist between the SAE standards and the ISO standards: size M30 x 2 is included in the SAE standard but not in the ISO standard and the tube ODs have been shown in the SAE standard for the stud ends.

In fluid power systems, power is transmitted and controlled through a fluid (liquid or gas) under pressure within an enclosed circuit. In general applications, a fluid may be conveyed under pressure. Components are connected through their threaded ports by stud ends on fluid conductor fittings to tubes and pipes or to hose fittings and hoses.

1. Scope—This part of SAE J2244 specifies dimensions, performance requirements, and test procedures for metric external hex O-rings port plugs.

Port plugs in accordance with this part of SAE J2244 may be used at working pressures up to 63 MPa. The permissible working pressure depends upon materials, design, working conditions, applications, etc.

For threaded ports and stud ends for use in new designs in hydraulic fluid power applications, only SAE J2244 shall be used. Threaded ports and stud ends in accordance with ISO 1179, ISO 9974, and SAE J1926 (ISO 11926) shall not be used in new designs in hydraulic fluid power applications.

Conformance to the dimensional information in this document does not guarantee rated performance. Each manufacturer shall perform testing according to the specification contained in this document to ensure that components made to this document comply with the performance ratings.

2. References

2.1 Applicable Publications—The following standards contain provisions which through reference in this text, constitute provisions of this document. At the time of publication, the editions indicated were valid. All standards are subject to revision, and parties to agreements based on this document are encouraged to investigate the possibility of applying the most recent editions of the standards indicated as follows.

2.1.1 SAE PUBLICATIONS—Available from SAE, 400 Commonwealth Drive, Warrendale, PA 15096-0001.

SAE J515—Hydraulic O-Rings

SAE J1644—Metallic Tube Connections for Fluid Power and General Use—Test Methods for Threaded Hydraulic Fluid Power Connectors

SAE J2244-3—Connections for Fluid Power and General Use—Ports and Stud Ends with ISO 261 Threads and O-Ring Sealing—Part 3: Light-Duty (L Series) Stud Ends—Dimensions, Design, Test Methods, and Requirements

2.1.2 ISO PUBLICATIONS—Available from ANSI, 11 West 42nd Street, New York, NY 10036-8002.

ISO 261—ISO general-purpose metric screw threads—General plan

ISO 965-1—ISO general purpose metric screw threads—Tolerances—Part 1: Principles and basic data

ISO 1302—Technical drawings—Method of indicating surface texture on drawings

ISO 4579-1—Tolerances for fasteners—Part 1: Bolts, screws and nuts with thread diameters between 1,6 (inclusive) and 150 mm (inclusive) and product grades A, B, and C

ISO 4755—Hexagon nuts for high-strength structural bolting with large width across flats—Product grade B—Property classes 8 and 10

ISO 5598—Fluid power systems and components—Vocabulary

ISO 6149-3—Connections for fluid power and general use—Ports and stud ends with ISO 261 threads and O-ring sealing—Part 3: Light-duty (L) series stud ends—Dimensions, design, test methods and requirements

ISO 7789—Hydraulic fluid power—Two–, three– and four–port screw-in cartridge valve cavaties

ISO 9227—Corrosion tests in artificial atmosphere—Salt spray tests

2.1.3 ASME PUBLICATION—Available from the American Society of Mechanical Engineers, 345 East 47th Street, New York, NY 10017-2330.

ASME B46.1—Surface Texture (Surface Roughness, Waviness and Lay)

2.1.4 ASTM PUBLICATIONS—Available from ASTM, 100 Barr Harbor Drive, West Conshohocken, PA 19428-2959.

ASTM B 633—Standard Specifications for Electrodeposited Coatings of Zinc on Iron and Steel

ASTM B 117—Method of Salt Spray (Fog) Test

3. Definitions—For the purposes of this document, the definitions given in ISO 5598 and the following definitions apply.

3.1 Plug—A stud end with no through hole for fluid passage, used to contain hydraulic fluid.

4. Requirements

4.1 Performance—Plugs shall meet the following performance requirements when tested per Section 5.

4.1.1 APPLICATION TEMPERATURE—Carbon steel plugs shall meet the working pressures when used at temperatures between –40 °C and +121 °C. For pressures or temperatures outside these ranges, the manufacturer shall be consulted.

4.1.2 WORKING PRESSURE—External hex and internal hex plugs made of low carbon steel shall be designated for use at the working pressures given in Table 1.

TABLE 1—PRESSURES FOR EXTERNAL HEX, (S SERIES) PORT PLUGS
Units in Megapascals(1)

Thread	Port Plug Style External Hex Working Pressure(2)	Port Plug Style External Hex Test Pressure Burst	Port Plug Style External Hex Test Pressure Impulse(3)
M8x1	63	252	83.8
M10x1	63	252	83.8
M12x1.5	63	252	83.8
M14x1.5	63	252	83.8
M16x1.5	63	252	83.8
M18x1.5	63	252	83.8
M20x1.5(4)	40	160	53.2
M22x1.5	63	252	83.8
M27x2	40	160	53.2
M30x2	40	160	53.2
M33x2	40	160	53.2
M42x2	25	100	33.2
M48x2	25	100	33.2
M60x2	25	100	33.2

1. 10^5 N/m^2 = 10^5 Pa = 0.1 MPa = 14.5 psi. (To convert from MPa to psi multiply by 145, for example, 63 MPa = 9135 psi.)
2. These pressures were established using plugs made of low carbon steel when tested in accordance with Section 5.
3. Cyclic endurance test pressure.
4. For plug for cartridge valve cavity only. (See ISO 7789.)

4.1.3 CYCLIC ENDURANCE (IMPULSE) TEST—Plugs shall exceed one million impulse cycles when tested at 133% of the working pressure shown in Table 1 to verify the minimum fatigue strength of the fitting.

4.1.4 PROOF TEST—Plugs shall meet the minimum required proof pressures to verify a minimum of a 2:1 Proof to Working pressure ratio.

4.1.5 BURST TEST—Plugs shall meet the minimum required burst pressures to verify a minimum of a 4:1 Burst to Working pressure ratio to determine the minimum ultimate strength of the plug.

4.1.6 VACUUM TEST—Plugs shall be capable of withstanding a vacuum of 95 kPa (0.95 bar) negative pressure for 5 min without leakage.

4.1.7 TEST METHODS—Port plug tests shall be conducted in accordance with SAE J1644 for burst, cyclic endurance (impulse) and vacuum. Test results are to be reported on the form in SAE J1644.

4.2 Design

4.2.1 PLUG DIMENSIONS—Heavy-duty external hex (S series) plugs shall conform to the dimensions shown in Figure 1 and Table 2.

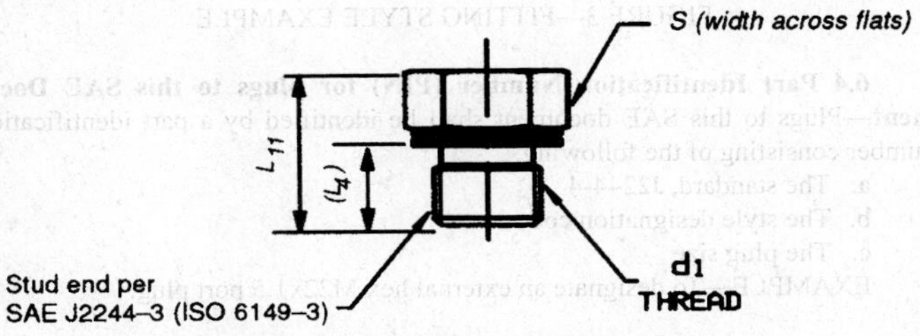

FIGURE 1—HEAVY-DUTY (S SERIES) PORT PLUG

TABLE 2—DIMENSIONS OF HEAVY-DUTY EXTERNAL (S SERIES) PORT PLUGS

Tube OD	d_1[(1)]	L_{11} ±0.5	(L_4)[(2)]	S[(3)] Hex
4	M8x1	16.2	8.5	12
5	M10x1	16.2	8.5	14
6	M12x1.5	18.5	11	17
8	M14x1.5	19.5	11	19
10	M16x1.5	21.5	11.5	22
12	M18x1.5	23.5	12.5	24
14	M20x1.5	24	12.5	27
16	M22x1.5	25.5	13	27
20	M27x2	32	16	32
22	M30x2	32	16	36
25	M33x2	32	16	41
30	M42x2	34	16	50
38	M48x2	35.5	17.5	55
50	M60x2	33	17.5	65

1. Thread class 6g per ISO 261.
2. L_4 dimension for M30x2 is the specification for the stud length since it isn't given in either the SAE or ISO standards; the tolerance is ±0.2 mm.
3. See Section 5 for tolerance.

4.2.2 HEX TOLERANCES—Hex tolerances across flats shall be in accordance with ISO 4759-1, product grade B. Minimum across corner dimensions are 1.092 times the nominal width across flats. The minimum side flat is 0.43 times the nominal width across flats. Unless otherwise specified or shown, hex corners shall be chamfered 15 to 30 degrees to a diameter equal the width across flats, with a tolerance of 0/–0.4 min.

4.2.3 SCREW THREADS—The screw threads on the plug shall be metric screw threads to ISO 261 class 6g.

4.2.4 METRIC IDENTIFICATION—Port plugs shall be identified according to SAE J2244-3. In addition to this identification, the manufacturer may mark the plug screw with the word "metric."

4.3 Manufacture

4.3.1 CONSTRUCTION—Plugs may be made from low carbon steel forging, cold forming, or machined from bar stock.

4.3.2 WORKMANSHIP—Workmanship shall conform to the best commercial practice to produce high-quality plugs. Plugs shall be free from visual contaminants, all hanging burrs, loose scale and slivers which might be dislodged in use, and any other defects that might affect the function of the parts.

4.3.3 SURFACE FINISH—Unless otherwise specified, surface finish on all surfaces shall be R_a £ 6.3 μm.

4.3.4 PLATING—The external surfaces and threads of all carbon steel parts shall be plated or coated with a suitable material that passes a 72 h salt spray test in accordance with ASTM B 117 (ISO 9227). Any appearance of red rust during the 72 h salt spray test shall be considered failure.

NOTE—CADMIUM PLATING—Cadmium plating is not preferred due to environmental reasons. Parts manufactured to this document after January 1, 1997, shall not be Cadmium plated. Changes in plating may affect assembly torques and require requalification, where applicable.

4.3.4.1 Exceptions—The following exceptions to the plating requirement apply:

a. Edges such as hex points, serrations, and crests of threads where there may be mechanical deformation of the plating or coating typical of mass-produced parts or shipping effects.
b. Areas where there is mechanical deformation of the plating or coating caused by crimping, flaring, bending or other post-plate metal forming operations.
c. Areas where the parts are suspended or affixed in the test chamber where condensate can accumulate. Corrosion protection requirements do not apply to corners or edges such as hex points, serrations and the crest of threads.

5. *Test Requirements and Quality Procedures*

5.1 Test Procedures—Port plugs shall be tested per SAE J1644.

5.2 Test Frequency—Qualification testing shall be required when there is a change in design, material, or process.

5.3 O-rings—O-rings for testing shall conform to SAE J515 Type 1 (90 durometer nitrile) and the size given in SAE J515. See Figure 2 and Table 3.

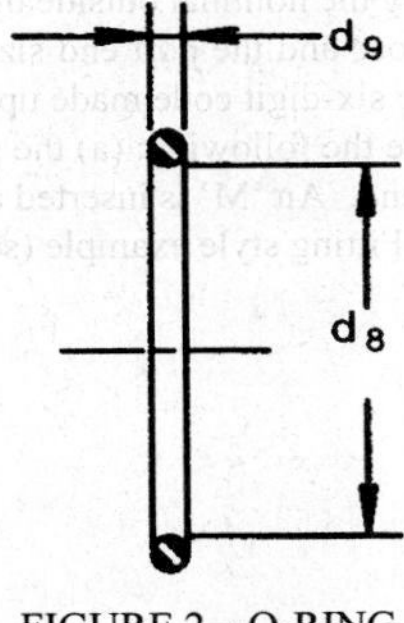

FIGURE 2—O-RING

TABLE 3—DIMENSIONS OF O-RING
Dimensions in millimeters

Thread	Inside Diameter d_8 nom.	Inside Diameter d_8 tol.	Cross-Section Diameter d_9 nom.	Cross-Section Diameter d_9 tol.
M8x1	6.1	±0.2	1.6	±0.08
M10x1	8.1	±0.2	1.6	±0.08
M12x1.5	9.3	±0.2	2.2	±0.08
M14x1.5	11.3	±0.2	2.2	±0.08
M16x1.5	13.3	±0.2	2.2	±0.08
M18x1.5	15.3	±0.2	2.2	±0.08
M20x1.5	17.3	±0.22	2.2	±0.08
M22x1.5	19.3	±0.22	2.2	±0.08
M27x2	23.6	±0.24	2.9	±0.09
M30x2	26.6	±0.26	2.9	±0.09
M33x2	29.6	±0.29	2.9	±0.09
M42x2	38.6	±0.37	2.9	±0.09
M48x2	44.6	±0.43	2.9	±0.09
M60x2	56.6	±0.51	2.9	±0.09

5.4 Test Torque—Plugs shall be tested per Table 4 values.

TABLE 4—TORQUES FOR HEAVY-DUTY (S SERIES) EXTERNAL HEX PLUG SCREWS

Port or Plug Thread Size	Torque (N•m) +10/–0%
M8x1	10
M10x1	20
M12x1.5	35
M14x1.5	45
M16x1.5	55
M18x1.5	70
M20x1.5	80
M22x1.5	100
M27x2	170
M30x2	215
M33x2	310
M42x2	330
M48x2	420
M60x2	500

6. Packaging and Marking

6.1 Marking—Plugs shall be permanently marked with the individual supplier's trademark or code identifier, unless otherwise agreed upon by the user and manufacturer.

6.2 Plug Protection—By a method agreed between manufacturer and user, the face of the port plug, threads shall be protected by the manufacturer from nicks and scratches which would be detrimental to the fitting's function. Paper caps and plugs are not permitted.

6.3 Size and Style Designation—Plugs are designated according to SAE J846. The size is indicated by the nominal outside diameter of the tubing or nominal inside diameter of the hose and the port end size for stud fittings. The style designation consist of a basic six-digit code made up of three groups of two digits each symbolizing in sequence the following: (a) the plug type, (b) the plug shape, and (c) the plug connecting end. An 'M' is inserted after the plug type to indicate a metric hex or wrench flat. Fitting style example (see Figure 3):

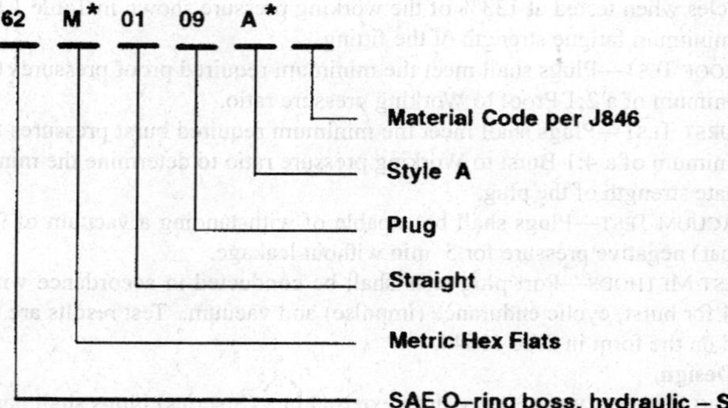

FIGURE 3—FITTING STYLE EXAMPLE

6.4 Part Identification Number (PIN) for plugs to this SAE Document—Plugs to this SAE document shall be identified by a part identification number consisting of the following:

a. The standard, J2244-4
b. The style designation code
c. The plug size

EXAMPLE—To designate an external hex M22x1.5 port plug:

Example: J2244-4 62M0109A M22

6.5 Procurement Information—The following minimum information should be supplied by the purchaser when making an inquiry or placing an order:

a. Description of plug (using designation per Section 6)
b. Material of plug
c. Fluid to be conveyed
d. Pressure rating
e. Working temperature

7. Notes

7.1 Identification Statement—Use the following statement in test reports, catalogues, and sales literature when electing to comply with this document.

"Heavy-duty (S series) port plugs conform to SAE J2244-4, Connections for fluid power and general use—Ports and stud ends with ISO 261 threads and O-ring sealing—Parts 4: Heavy-duty (S series) external hex port plugs—Dimensions, design, test methods, and requirements."

WELDED AND COLD-DRAWN, HIGH STRENGTH LOW ALLOY STEEL HYDRAULIC TUBING, SUB-CRITICALLY ANNEALED FOR BENDING AND FLARING —SAE J2614 JAN2003

SAE Standard

Report of the SAE Metallic Tubing Subcommittee SC5 of the SAE Fluid Conductors and Connectors Technical Committee approved January 2003.

1. Scope—This specification covers sub-critically annealed electric resistance welded and cold-drawn single-wall high strength low alloy steel tubing intended for use in hydraulic pressure lines and in other applications requiring tubing of a quality suitable for bending, flaring, cold forming, welding and brazing.

The grade of material produced to this specification is of micro-alloy content and is considerably stronger and intended to service higher pressure applications than like sizes of the grades of material specified in SAE J525 and SAE J2467. Due to the alloy content of the material, the forming characteristics of the finished tube are equal to or better, when compared to SAE J525 and SAE J2467. Nominal reference working pressures for this tubing are listed in SAE J1065.

2. References

2.1 Applicable Publications—The following publications form a part of this specification to extent specified herein. Unless other specified, the latest issue of the SAE publications shall apply.

2.1.1 SAE PUBLICATIONS—Available from SAE, 400 Commonwealth Drive, Warrendale, PA 15096-0001

SAE J409—Product Analysis—Permissible Variations from Specified Chemical Analysis of a Heat or Cast of Steel

SAE J525—Welded and Cold Drawn Low Carbon Steel Tubing Annealed for Bending and Flaring

SAE J533—Flares for Tubing

SAE J1065—Pressure Ratings for Hydraulic Tubing and Fittings

SAE J1677—Tests and Procedures for SAE Low Carbon Steel and Copper-Nickel Tubing

SAE J2467—Welded and Cold Drawn, SAE 1021 Carbon Steel Tubing, Normalized for Bending and Flaring

2.2 Related Publications—The following publications are provided for informational purposes only and are not a required part of this document.

2.2.1 SAE PUBLICATIONS—Available from SAE, 400 Commonwealth Drive, Warrendale, PA 15096-0001

SAE J514—Hydraulic Tube Connections

SAE J518—Hydraulic Flanged Tube, Pipe and Hose Connections, Four-Bolt Split Flange Type

SAE J1453—Fitting - O-Ring Face Seal

SAE J1392—Steel, High Strength, Hot Rolled Sheet and Strip, Cold Rolled Sheet and Coated Sheet

SAE J2551—Recommended Practices for Fluid Conductor Metallic Tubing Applications

2.2.2 ISO PUBLICATIONS—Available from ANSI, 25 West 43rd Street, New York, NY 10036-8002.

ISO 3304—Plain end seamless precision steel tubes - Technical conditions for delivery

ISO 3305—Plain end welded precision steel tubes - Technical conditions for delivery

ISO 4200—Plain end steel tubes, welded and seamless - General tables of dimensions and masses per unit length

ISO 4397—Connectors and associated components - Nominal outside diameters of tubes and nominal inside diameters of hoses

ISO 4399—Connectors and associated components - Nominal pressures

ISO 5598—Fluid power systems and components - Vocabulary

ISO 6162—Four-screw Split-Flange Connections

ISO 6163—Round Flange, 8 and 12 Screw Connections

ISO 6164—Four-screw, one-piece Square-Flange Connections

ISO 6605—Tests and Test Procedures

ISO 8434—Metallic Tube Connections for Fluid Power and General Use

ISO 10583—Test Methods for Tube Connections

ISO 10763—Plain-end, Seamless and Welded Steel Tubes - Dimensions and Nominal Working Pressures

2.2.3 DIN PUBLICATIONS—Available from ANSI, 25 West 43rd Street, New York, NY 10036-8002.

DIN 17120—Welded Circular Steel Tubing

DIN 17121—Seamless Circular Steel Tubing

3. Manufacture—The tubing shall be made from a single strip of steel shaped into a tubular shape, the edges of which are joined and fused by electric resistance welding.

The tubing shall be sub-critically annealed via a controlled method to produce a finished product, which will meet all requirements of this document.

3.1 Sub-Critically Anneal—An annealing treatment in which steel is heated to below the A1 temperature, then slowly cooled to room temperature. A1 temperature is the critical transformation temperature depending on steel classification.

4. Dimensions and Tolerances—The tolerances applicable to tubing outside diameter are shown in Table 1. The tolerances applicable to tubing wall thickness are shown in Table 2. Particular attention shall be given to areas adjacent to the weld to insure against thin spots and/or sharp indentations.

TABLE 1—TUBING OUTSIDE DIAMETER TOLERANCE

Nominal Tubing OD(1)(2) mm	Tube OD and ID Tolerance ± mm
Up to 9.50	0.05
Over 9.50 to 15.88	0.06
Over 15.88 to 50.80	0.08
Over 50.80 to 63.50	0.10
Over 63.50 to 76.20	0.13
Over 76.20 to 101.60	0.15

1. OD measurements shall be taken at least 50 mm from the end of tubing.
2. For nominal tubing OD's to be used in conjunction with this tubing, refer to the various fluid carrier connector standards and SAE J533 for recommended maximum nominal wall thickness for double flaring.

5. Manufacturing Standards

5.1 Straightness—Tubing shall be straightened to a tolerance of 0.8 mm in 1000 mm. Straightness tolerances shall be measured by placing a 1000 mm straight edge against the tube while lying on it's neutral axis. The point of maximum deflection of the tube from the straight edge should not be more than allowed by the specification when measured with a feeler gauge.

5.2 Tubing End Condition—The tubing will be produced using normal mill cut off practices. This shall include, but not limited to, punch-cut ends, double-cut ends and rotary-cut ends. Care shall be taken to minimize the distortion of the tube ends. Distortion of the tube must not affect the normal re-cutting processes that will be performed by the end user. Ends that require further processing will be addressed by agreement between the producer and the tube purchaser.

5.3 Finish—The outside surface finish of the tube is critical to prevent possible leak paths on double flare connections, mechanical formed connections or applications where the outside surface of the tube becomes the sealing surface of the finished connection. The outside surface finish of the tube shall be free of excessive roll marks, score marks, chatter marks or other surface imperfections that may be considered detrimental to the function of the finished tube.

5.4 Thermal Treatment—The tubing is to be sub-critically annealed by heating to a temperature below the transformation point and then slowly cooled to room temperature. Special attention to the mechanical properties, especially the Rockwell B85 Hardness Target, should be made to produce tubing suitable for bending and forming for hydraulic pressure applications. However, to obtain acceptable hardness characteristics, the yield strength and the tensile strength shall not be compromised and 30% minimum elongation shall be maintained.

TABLE 2—TUBING WALL THICKNESS TOLERANCES

Nominal Wall Thickness[(1)] mm	For Nominal Tubing Outside Diameter Through 22 mm[(2)] +/- mm	For Nominal tubing Outside Diameter Over 22 mm Through 48 mm [(2)] +/- mm	For Nominal Tubing Outside Diameter Over 48 mm Through 101.60[(2)] +/- mm
0.71	0.05/0.05	0.05/0.05	0.05/0.05
0.89	0.05/0.05	0.05/0.08	0.05/0.08
1.00	0.05/0.05	0.05/0.08	0.05/0.08
1.24	0.05/0.05	0.05/0.08	0.05/0.08
1.25	0.05/0.05	0.05/0.08	0.05/0.08
1.50	0.05/0.05	0.05/0.08	0.05/0.08
1.65	0.05/0.05	0.05/0.08	0.05/0.08
2.00	0.05/0.05	0.05/0.08	0.08/0.08
2.11	0.05/0.05	0.05/0.08	0.08/0.08
2.41	0.05/0.05	0.05/0.08	0.08/0.08
2.50	0.05/0.08	0.05/0.10	0.08/0.08
2.77	0.05/0.08	0.05/0.10	0.08/0.08
3.00	0.08/0.08	0.05/0.10	0.08/0.08
3.05	0.08/0.08	0.05/0.10	0.08/0.08
3.40	—	0.05/0.10	0.08/0.08
3.75	—	0.05/0.10	0.08/0.08
3.76	—	0.08/0.10	0.08/0.10
3.96	—	0.08/0.10	0.08/0.10
4.00	—	0.08/0.10	0.08/0.10
4.19	—	0.08/0.10	0.08/0.10
4.57	—	0.10/0.10	0.08/0.13
4.76	—	0.10/0.13	0.08/0.13
5.00	—	0.10/0.13	0.10/0.13
5.16	—	0.10/0.13	0.10/0.13
5.59	—	0.10/0.15	0.10/0.15
6.00	—	0.13/0.15	0.13/0.15
6.05	—	0.13/0.15	0.13/0.15
6.35	—	0.13/0.15	0.13/0.15
6.58	—	0.13/0.15	0.13/0.15

1. For intermediate wall thickness, the tolerance for the next heavier wall thickness shall apply.
2. Plus tolerances include allowance for crown on flat-rolled steel.

6. ***Material***—The tubing shall be made from alloy steel strip conforming to the chemical composition in Table 3. The steel shall be made by the open-hearth basic oxygen or electric furnace process. A ladle analysis of each heat shall be made to determine the percentages of the elements specified. The chemical composition thus determined shall be reported to the purchaser or purchaser's representative, if requested, and shall be conform to the requirements specified. If a check analysis is required, the tolerances shall be as specified in SAE J409, Table 3.

TABLE 3—CHEMICAL REQUIREMENTS

Element	Cast or Heat Analysis, Weight %
Carbon	0.18 Max
Manganese	1.50 Max
Sulfur	0.035 Max
Phosphorus	0.035 Max
Silicon	0.35 Max
Aluminum	0.020 Min
Micro Alloying Elements	0.15 Max

7. ***Mechanical Properties***—The finished tubing shall have mechanical properties as shown in Table 4.

8. ***Performance Requirements***—The finished tubing shall satisfactorily meet the following performance tests. All tests are to be conducted in accordance with the procedures in SAE J1677.

8.1 Flattening Test—See SAE J1677.

8.2 Flaring Test—See SAE J1677.

8.3 Reverse Flattening Test—See SAE J1677.

8.4 Expansion Test—See SAE J1677.

8.5 Hardness Test—See SAE J1677.

8.6 Tensile Test—See SAE J1677.

8.7 Elongation Test—See SAE J1677.

8.8 Pressure Proof Test—See SAE J1677.

TABLE 4—MECHANICAL PROPERTIES

Properties	Values
Yield Strength, Minimum	345 MPa
Tensile Strength, Minimum	500 MPa
Elongation in 50 mm, Minimum	30% Minimum
Hardness Target	Rockwell B85 [(1)]
Hardness Maximum	Rockwell B90[(1)]

1. The hardness test shall not be required on tubing with a nominal wall thickness of less than 1.65 mm. Such tubing shall meet all other mechanical properties and performance requirements

8.9 Nondestructive Electronic—See SAE J1677. The tests referenced in SAE J1677, paragraph 5.9, are to be conducted after all cold-working tube manufacturing operations are performed on the tubing.

9. ***Test Certificates***—A certificate of compliance to the performance requirements shall be furnished to the purchaser by the producer if requested in the purchase agreement. The tube producer shall be able to certify that each heat lot of the material used to produce the tubing complies with the performance requirements.

10. ***Cleanliness***—The inside and outside surfaces of the finished tubing shall be commercially bright, clean and free from grease, oxide scale, carbon deposits and any other contamination that can not readily be removed by cleaning agents normally used in manufacturing plants.

11. ***Corrosion Protection***—The inside and outside surfaces of the finished tubing shall be protected against corrosion during shipment and normal storage. If a corrosion preventive compound is applied, it shall be such that after normal periods, it can be readily removed by cleaning agents normally used in manufacturing plants.

12. ***Packaging***—The tubing is to be packaged in such a way to allow it to be transported and stored, with normal care, without being damaged. Any special packaging shall be by agreement between the producer and the purchaser.

METALLIC TUBE CONDUCTOR ASSEMBLIES FOR FLUID POWER AND GENERAL USE—TEST METHODS FOR HYDRAULIC FLUID POWER METALLIC TUBE ASSEMBLIES—SAE J2658 JUL2003

SAE Recommended Practice

Report of the SAE Fluid Conductors and Connectors Technical Committee SC5—Metallic Tubing Subcommittee approved July 2003.

Foreword—In fluid power systems, power is transmitted and controlled through a fluid (liquid or gas) under pressure within an enclosed circuit. Metallic tube conductor assemblies must be designed to meet these requirements under varying conditions. Testing of metallic tube conductor assemblies to meet performance requirements provides users a basis of assurance for determining design application and for checking compliance with their stated requirements. This standard also provides a means to evaluate functional requirements of new metallic tube conductor materials and end configuration manufacturing processes. This standard is primarily intended for mobile/stationary industrial equipment applications. Aircraft, Automotive and Aerospace applications were not considered during the preparation of this document.

TABLE OF CONTENTS

1. Scope—This SAE standard specifies uniform methods for various types of tests to evaluate functional performance requirements for metallic tube conductor assemblies for hydraulic fluid power applications made from both standard and non-standard metallic tubing and components. See the appropriate listed SAE or ISO tubing and connector standard for chemical, mechanical and dimensional requirements for standard tubing, end components and tube end joint configurations for the standard tube assemblies being tested. See SAE J1065 and ISO 10763 for listed nominal reference working pressures and/or reference formula that may be used to calculate reference working pressures for standard and non-standard metallic tube conductors.

1.1 Application—This standard is to be used to qualify metallic hydraulic tube assemblies manufactured with various standard and non-standard tubing materials, tube end components and tube end joining processes, primarily intended for mobile/stationary industrial equipment applications. Aircraft, Automotive and Aerospace applications were not considered during the preparation of this document.

2. References

2.1 Applicable Publications—The following standards contain provisions which, through reference in this text, constitute provisions of this document. At the time of publication, the editions indicated were valid. All standards are subject to revision, and parties to agreements based on this document are encouraged to investigate the possibility of applying the most recent edition of the standards indicated as follows. Members of IEC and ISO maintain registers of currently valid International Standards.

2.1.1 SAE PUBLICATIONS—Available from SAE, 400 Commonwealth Drive, Warrendale, PA 15096-0001.

SAE J514—Hydraulic Tube Fittings
SAE J518—Hydraulic Flanged Tube, Pipe and Hose Connections; 4-Bolt Type
SAE J533—Flares for Tubes
SAE J1065—Nominal Reference Working Pressures for Hydraulic Steel Tubing
SAE J1453—Fitting- O-Ring Face Seal

2.1.2 ISO PUBLICATIONS—Available from ANSI, 25 West 43rd Street, New York, NY 10036-8002.

ISO 6162—Hydraulic Fluid Power - Flange connectors with split or one-piece flange clamps and metric or inch screws
ISO 8434-1—Metallic tube connections for fluid power and general use - Part 1: 24 degree compression connectors
ISO 8434-2—Metallic tube connections for fluid power and general use - Part 2: 37 degree flared connectors
ISO 8434-3—Metallic tube connections for fluid power and general use - Part 3: O-ring face seal connectors
ISO 8434-4—Metallic tube connections for fluid power and general use - Part 4: 24 degree cone connectors with o-ring weld-on nipples
ISO 8434-5—Metallic tube connections for fluid power and general use - Part 5: method of testing threaded hydraulic connections
ISO 8434-6—Metallic tube connections for fluid power and general use - Part 6: 60 degree cone connectors and weld-on nipples
ISO 10763—Hydraulic fluid power - Plain-end, seamless and welded steel tubes - dimensions and nominal working pressures

2.2 Related Publications—The following publications are for information purposes only and are not a required part of this document.

2.2.1 SAE PUBLICATIONS—Available from SAE, 400 Commonwealth Drive, Warrendale, PA 15096-0001.

SAE J343—Tests and Test Procedures for SAE 100R Series Hydraulic Hose and Hose Assemblies
SAE J356—Welded Flash Controlled Low Carbon Steel Tubing Normalized for Bending, Double Flaring, and Beading
SAE J515—Specifications for Hydraulic O-Ring Materials, Properties and Size for Metric and Inch Stud Ends, Face Seal Connections and Four-Screw Flange Connections
SAE J524—Seamless Low Carbon Steel Tubing Annealed for Bending and Flaring
SAE J525—Welded and Cold Drawn Low Carbon Steel Tubing Annealed for Bending and Flaring
SAE J526—Welded Low Carbon Steel Tubing
SAE J527—Brazed Double Wall Low Carbon Steel Tubing
SAE J1615—Thread Sealants
SAE J1644—Metallic Tube Connections for Fluid Power and General Use - Test Methods for Threaded Hydraulic Fluid Power Connectors
SAE J1677—Tests and Procedures for Low Carbon Steel and Copper-Nickel Tubing
SAE J1926/1—Part 1, Inch Ports and Stud End Connections for Fluid Power and General Use, Threaded Port with O-Ring seal in Truncated Housing
SAE J1926/2—Part 2, Connections for General use and Fluid Power-Ports and Stud Ends with ISO 725 Threads and O-Ring Sealing, Heavy-Duty (S Series) Stud Ends
SAE J1926/3—Part 3, Connections for General use and Fluid Power-Ports and Stud Ends with ISO 725 Threads and O-Ring Sealing, Light-Duty (L Series) Stud Ends

SAE J2244/1—Part 1, Connections for Fluid Power and General Use - Ports and Stud Ends with ISO 261 Threads and O-Ring Sealing, Port with O-Ring Seal in Truncated Housing

SAE J2244/2—Part 2, Connections for Fluid Power and General Use - Ports and Stud ends with ISO 261 Threads and O-Ring Sealing, Heavy-Duty (S Series) Stud Ends - Dimensions, Design, Test Methods, and Requirements

SAE J2244/3—Part 3, Connections for Fluid Power and General Use - Ports and Stud Ends with ISO 261 Threads and O-Ring Sealing, Light-Duty (L Series) Stud End - Dimensions, Design, Test Methods, and Requirement

SAE J2244/4—Part 4, Connections for Fluid Power and General Use - Ports and Stud Ends With ISO 261 Threads and O-Ring Sealing, Heavy-Duty (S Series) External Hex Port Plugs--Dimensions, Design, Test Methods, and Requirements

SAE J2435—Welded Flash Controlled, SAE 1021 Carbon Steel Tubing, Normalized for Bending, Flaring, and Beading

SAE J2467—Welded and Cold Drawn, SAE 1021 Carbon Steel Tubing Normalized for Bending, Flaring and Beading

SAE J2551—Recommended Practices For Hydraulic Tube Assemblies

SAE J2613—Welded Flash Controlled High Strength Low Alloy Steel Hydraulic Tubing, Sub-Critically Annealed for Bending, Flaring & Beading

SAE J2614—Welded and Cold Drawn High Strength Low Alloy Steel Hydraulic Tubing, Sub-Critically Annealed for Bending & Flaring

2.2.2 ISO PUBLICATIONS—Available from ANSI, 25 West 43rd Street, New York, NY 10036-8002

ISO 48—Vulcanized rubbers - Determination of hardness (hardness between 30 and 85 IRHD)

ISO 3304—Plain end seamless precision steel tubes - Technical conditions for delivery

ISO 3305—Plain end welded precision steel tubes - Technical conditions for delivery

ISO 3448—Industrial liquid lubricants - ISO viscosity classification - First edition

ISO 3601-3—Fluid systems - Sealing devices - O-rings - Part 3: quality acceptance criteria

ISO 5598—Fluid power systems and components - Vocabulary

ISO 6149—Fluid power systems and components - Metric ports - Dimensions and design

ISO 6508—Metallic materials - Hardness test - Rockwell test (scales A-B-C-D-E-F-G-H-K)

ISO 6605—Hydraulic fluid power - Hose assemblies - Methods of test

ISO 9974—Connections for general use and fluid power - Port and stud ends with ISO 261 threads with elastomeric or metal-to-metal sealing

ISO 10583—Test methods for tube connections

ISO 11926-1—Connections for general use and fluid power - Ports and stud ends with ISO 725 inch threads and O-ring sealing - Part 1: ports with O-ring seal in truncated housing

ISO 11926-2—Connections for general use and fluid power - Ports and stud ends with ISO 725 inch threads and O-ring sealing - Part 2: heavy-duty (S Series) stud ends

ISO 11926-3—Connections for general use and fluid power - Ports and stud ends with ISO 725 inch threads and O-ring sealing - Part 3: light-duty (L Series) stud ends

ISO 19879—Metallic tube connections for fluid power and general Use - Method of testing hydraulic connectors

2.2.3 EUROPEAN AND JAPANESE PUBLICATIONS—Available from ANSI, 25 West 43rd Street, New York, NY 100360-8002

DIN 17120—Welded Circular Steel Tubing

DIN 17121—Seamless Circular Steel Tubing

EN 10210-1—Hot Finished Structural Hollow Sections of Non-Alloy and Fine Grain Structural Steels

JIS 4502—Seamless

3. Definitions—For the purpose of this document, the definitions given in ISO 5598 shall apply.

4. General Requirements for Qualification of Tube Assemblies

4.1 Standard Tests—WARNING—Some of the tests described in this document are considered hazardous; it is therefore essential that, in conducting these tests, all appropriate safety precautions are strictly adhered to. Attention is drawn to the danger of fine jets of high pressure hydraulic fluid which can penetrate the skin. To reduce the hazard to energy release, bleed air out of test specimens prior to pressure testing. Tests shall be set-up and performed by properly trained personnel. Also safety equipment such as safety glasses, hearing protection and metatarsal safety shoes, should be used when working around and on hydraulic test laboratories and equipment.

4.2 Materials of Components for Testing Purposes

4.2.1 TEST BLOCK—Test blocks shall be unplated and hardened to 45 to 55 Rockwell "C".

4.2.2 TEST SEALS (IF APPLICABLE)—Unless otherwise specified, seals shall be nitrile (NBR) rubber with a hardness of 85, +10/0 IHRD in accordance with SAE J515.

4.3 Typical Tube Assembly Samples—See Figure 1 for typical tube assembly samples, test configurations and test cabinet set up.

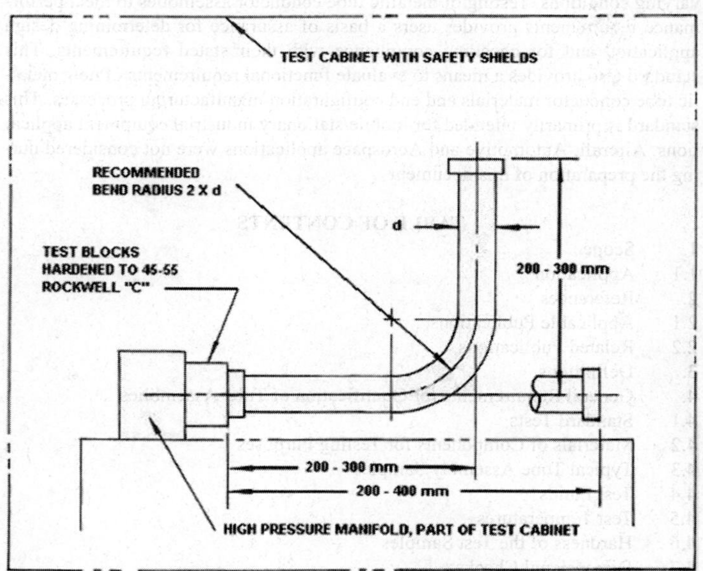

FIGURE 1—TYPICAL TUBE ASSEMBLY SAMPLES, TEST CONFIGURATIONS AND TEST CABINET SET UP

4.4 Test Fluids—Select a hydraulic fluid suitable for most hydraulic systems. Test fluids must be used as agreed upon between the customer and the manufacturer. It is recommended the test fluid be changed frequently to prevent breakdown.

4.5 Test Temperatures—Test temperature (ambient and fluid) shall be 15 to 35 °C unless otherwise specified in the controlling SAE or ISO standard.

4.6 Hardness of the Test Samples—The tube material hardness on the Rockwell "B" scale shall be checked and recorded on the test data form for all test samples.

4.7 Dimensional Checks—The tube assembly shall be inspected for conformity to all dimensions tabulated in the applicable tube specification. Determine finished outside diameter and wall thickness. Take readings at 90 degree intervals around the tube to determine acceptable ovality and wall thickness uniformity. Out of limits dimensions will lead to premature failure of the tubing and cause the test to be unsuccessful. Acceptability of the tubing to be used is based on the total variation between the high and low readings of the applicable SAE/ISO dimensional requirements.

4.8 Thread Lubrication—Lubricate the o-ring and threads with a light coat of system fluid or compatible oil.

4.9 Assembly of Test Samples and Assembly Torque—Tube connections shall be tested as assembled with the required minimum test torques shown in the following conductor and connector standards. Otherwise test at the minimum torque values supplied by the manufacturer. See Figure 1 for the connection of typical tube assembly test samples to a test apparatus.

SAE J514—Hydraulic Tube Connectors (37 Degree Flared, Flareless Type and O-Ring Plugs)

SAE J518—Hydraulic Flanged Tube, Pipe and Hose Connections; 4-Bolt Type

SAE J533—Flares for Tubing; 37 Degree and 45 Degree

SAE J1453—Specifications for O-Ring Face Seal Connectors for Fluid Power

ISO 6162—Hydraulic fluid power - Flange connectors with split or one-piece flange clamps and metric or inch screws

ISO 8434-1—Metallic tube connections for fluid power and general use - Part 1: 24 degree compression connectors

ISO 8434-2—Metallic tube connections for fluid power and general use - Part 2: 37 degree flared connectors

ISO 8434-3—Metallic tube connections for fluid power and general use - Part 3: O-ring face seal connectors

ISO 8434-4—Metallic tube connections for fluid power and general use - Part 4: 24 degree cone connectors with o-ring weld-on nipples

4.10 Reuse of Tube Assembly Samples—Tube assembly samples which pass these tests shall not be tested further, used, or returned to stock.

5. Qualification Tests—See SAE J1065 and ISO 10763 for the applicable rated reference working pressure as it pertains to the reference tube OD, wall thickness and material to be tested. For tube materials, OD's and wall sizes not listed in SAE J1065 and ISO 10763, use the nominal reference working pressure formula to calculate the target pressures for testing purposes. The type of tests selected from Appendix A, timeliness, frequency and configuration of the test samples will be determined by the tube assembly manufacturer and/or agreement between the tube assembly manufacturer and the customer. All tube assembly samples shall be tested in the final form, as the customer would receive a typical part.

See Appendix A for summary work sheet for applicable qualification tests for various metallic tube conductor assembly end connection configuration standards. This work sheet can also be used to qualify non-standard tube assemblies and tube end joining methods.

See Appendix B for the tube assembly test data form. Test results and test conditions shall be reported on this test data form.

5.1 Burst Test—Three samples shall be tested to confirm that the specified conductor(s) shall be capable of withstanding an internal hydrostatic pressure to a minimum of four times the intended working pressure without failure. The rate of pressure rise shall be constant and chosen to reach the final pressure between 30 and 60 seconds.

NOTE—This is a destructive test. Assemblies which have been subjected to this test shall be destroyed.

5.2 Proof Pressure Test—Three samples shall not leak when subjected to an internal hydrostatic pressure equal to two times the specified reference working pressure for 30 to 60 seconds.

5.3 Cyclic Endurance Impulse Test

5.3.1 Six samples, when tested at the respective impulse pressure at 133% of the rated reference working pressure, shall pass a cyclic endurance test for 1 000 000 cycles without leakage or failure of the conductor. Apply a pulsating pressure internally to the hose assemblies at a rate between 0.5 and 1.3 Hz; record the frequency used on the test data sheet in Appendix B. The pressure cycle shall fall within the shaded area of Figure 1 and conform as closely as possible to the curve shown.

NOTE—This is a destructive test. Assemblies which have been subjected to this test shall be destroyed.

5.3.2 The pressure rise rate nominal slope shall be calculated using Equation 1.

$$R = f(10P - k) \quad \text{(Eq. 1)}$$

where:

R = Rate of rise (MPa/s)
f = Frequency in Hz
P = Nominal Cyclic Endurance Impulse Test Pressure in Megapascals
k = 5 MPa

The actual rate of pressure rise and pressure drop shall be measured with an oscilloscope or equivalent device and shall be determined to be as close as possible to the pictorial shown on Figure 2, and shall be within a tolerance of ±10% of the calculated nominal value.

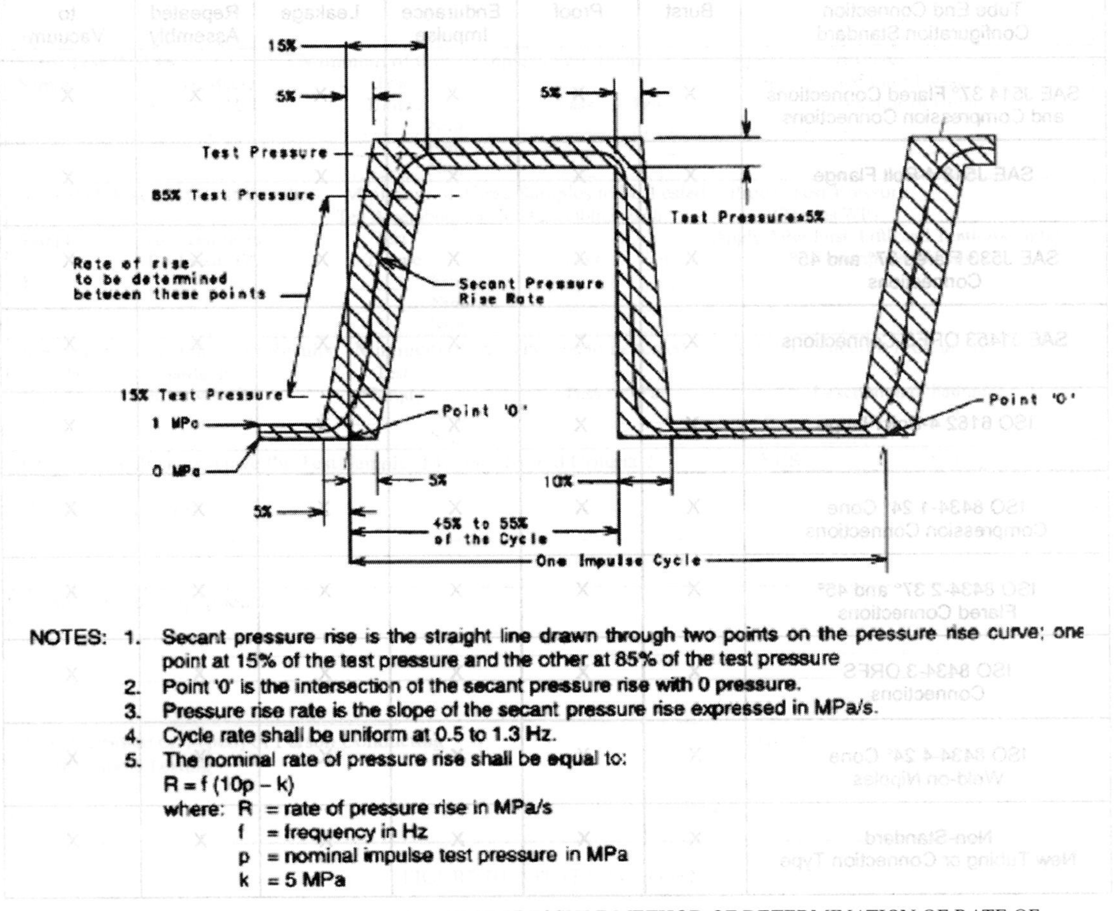

15%
5%
5%
Test Pressure
85% Test Pressure
Test Pressure±5%
Rate of rise to be determined between these points
Secant Pressure Rise Rate
15% Test Pressure
1 MPa
0 MPa
Point '0'
Point '0'
5%
5%
10%
45% to 55% of the Cycle
One Impulse Cycle
NOTES: 1. Secant pressure rise is the straight line drawn through two points on the pressure rise curve; one point at 15% of the test pressure and the other at 85% of the test pressure
2. Point '0' is the intersection of the secant pressure rise with 0 pressure.
3. Pressure rise rate is the slope of the secant pressure rise expressed in MPa/s.
4. Cycle rate shall be uniform at 0.5 to 1.3 Hz.
5. The nominal rate of pressure rise shall be equal to:
R = f (10p – k)
where: R = rate of pressure rise in MPa/s
f = frequency in Hz
p = nominal impulse test pressure in MPa
k = 5 MPa

FIGURE 2—CYCLIC ENDURANCE IMPULSE PRESSURE METHOD OF DETERMINATION OF RATE OF PRESSURE RISE IN IMPULSE TEST

5.5.2 Research reports need not be in the format outlined in Section 7. However, they shall have at least the following content:

5.5.3 A statement of Scope indicating the nature of the report.

6. Numbering of SAE Technical Reports

6.1 Number Assignment—Prior to the submission of a new (as opposed to revised) technical report to an appropriate Council/Division, SAE staff will assign an identifying number to the report (i.e., J4500 or AS4704).

6.2 Revisions

6.2.1 When a J report is revised, the year digits shall be changed to reflect the year that the revision was approved. The J-number shall not be changed. The revised date suffix shall be shown in all indexes, and should be used as appropriate in all references.

6.2.2 When an Air and Space report is revised, the revisions shall be indicated by a Gothic letter following the document number; e.g., AS9999A. The first revision shall be marked with the letter "A" and succeeding revisions shall be indicated by the other letters in alphabetical sequence, except that the letters I, O, Q, S, X, and Z shall not be used.

6.3 Integrity of SAE Document Numbers—Changes to an SAE technical report that will alter it sufficiently to affect its interchangeability or interchangeable application shall require a new number. The superseded number shall continue to exist unless the report is canceled. When a report is canceled, its number shall continue to be listed in the appropriate index with its suffix, classification, cross-reference to any superseding number, and an indication of its last date and method of publication.

7. Format of Technical Reports—The following recommendations for the content and sequence of items to be included in SAE Technical Reports are all-inclusive. Accordingly, all items may not be required for every type of report. Requirements for standard parts drawings are covered in the SAE Style Manual for Technical Reports. To assist in the electronic capture of all other SAE technical reports, 7.1.1, 7.2.1, 7.2.2, and 7.2.7 shall be included in all SAE Technical Reports.

This format corresponds to an international standards format issued by the International Standards Organization (ISO). Its usage for SAE technical reports can facilitate International acceptance.

7.1 Front Matter

7.1.1 TITLE—Each report shall have a title that does not duplicate an existing title. The title will appear in the title block on SAE format paper. Reference to equivalent ISO standards will also be made in the title block separate and distinct from the title. If more room is required than is available in the title block, a footnote shall reference the appropriate paragraph in the NOTES section.

7.1.2 CLASSIFICATION—See Section 5 of this report.

7.1.3 APPROVAL NOTE—Includes original approval date and date of the last revision or reaffirmation. A statement indicating what this revision supersedes is also included here.

7.1.4 FOREWORD

7.1.5 TABLE OF CONTENTS

7.2 Body of the Report

7.2.1 SECTION 1—SCOPE—Can include subsections describing scope, purpose, and application of the report.

7.2.2 SECTION 2—REFERENCES—Section 2 shall be titled References if this section contains Related Publications (as in a Bibliography), Definitions, Symbols, and/or Abbreviations as described in 7.2.2.2 and 7.2.2.3. If this section contains only Applicable Documents, the title of this section shall be Applicable Documents.

7.2.2.1 Paragraph 2.1—Applicable Documents—Lists the publications referenced in the report.

7.2.2.2 Paragraph 2.2—Definitions—Includes definitions used in the report. May also include systems of classification, designation, and/or coding of products or processes.

7.2.2.3 Paragraph 2.3—Symbols and Abbreviations—Lists symbols and abbreviations used in the report.

7.2.3 SECTION 3—REQUIREMENTS—Can include subsections on requirements, materials, design, performance, and manufacturing.

7.2.4 SECTION 4—QUALITY ASSURANCE PROVISIONS—Can include subsections covering quality assurance sampling quantities and procedures.

7.2.5 SECTION 5—TEST METHODS—Can include subsections covering test equipment, environment, and procedures.

7.2.6 SECTION 6—LABELING, MARKING, AND PACKAGING—Can include subsections covering marking (e.g., manufacturer's trademark or model number), and requirements for labeling and packaging of product.

7.2.7 SECTION 7—NOTES—Can include subsections covering explanatory or general information, installation guidelines, health and safety warnings, rationale statements, etc. Key Words shall be provided in this section.

7.3 Back Matter—Can include, as appropriate, appendices, index, rationale statement, explanation of relationship to ISO standards as referenced in title block, etc.

7.4 Table 1 summarizes the recommended and required sectional arrangement for SAE Technical Reports.

8. Preparation of SAE Technical Reports

8.1 Paragraph Numbering—A decimal numbering system shall be used in numbering sections of a report. Decimals shall be used to indicate successive subheadings, e.g.:

1 Section Heading

1.1 Primary Paragraph

1.1.1 Sub(s)paragraph (Numbering of paragraphs beyond x.x.x is not recommended)

1.1.1.1 Sub-subparagraph (If this level is essential)

TABLE 1—SECTIONAL ARRANGEMENT

Element	Status
Foreword	Optional
Table of Contents	Optional
1. Scope	Required
1.1 Purpose	Required in AMS; optional in others
1.2 Field of Application	Required in AMS; optional in others
1.3 Product Classification	Required in AMS; optional in others
1.4 Form	Required in AMS; optional in others
2. References	Required
2.1 Applicable Documents	As applicable
2.2 Other Applicable References	As applicable
2.3 Related Publications	As applicable
3. Definitions(1)	As applicable
3.1 Symbols(1)	As applicable
3.2 Terminology(1)	As applicable
4 XXXXXXXXXXXXXX	To be determined by the preparing committee; for technical requirements of specific document types, refer to the SAE Style Manual for Technical Reports
x. XXXXXXXXXXXXXX	Subsequent sections as determined by the preparing committee
y. Notes	Required; the last numbered section of all documents shall be Notes:
y.1 Marginal Indicia	As required
y.x XXXXXXXXXXXXXXXXXX	As determined by the preparing committee
y.x Key Words	Required; the last numbered paragraph of all documents shall be Key Words

1. These paragraphs may be combined at the discretion of the preparing committee.

8.2 Draft Reports—Drafts of new reports and major revisions of existing reports shall be double spaced.

NOTE—Minor revisions are best handled by marking up the most recent version of the document. New or completely revised reports may be submitted on floppy discs for publication. A hard copy of the report shall also be provided. Floppy discs should adhere to the following guidelines:

a. "3-1/2" disks are preferred (regular or high-density)
b. ASCII file version, "generic" file version, or Word Perfect Version 5.0 or 5.1
c. If submitting an ASCII or generic file, include a copy of your original word processing file and identify the software used; this will enable translation attempts.

8.3 Submission of Draft on Computer Disc—When preparing a disc for submission, all text should be typed flush left. Indents, tabs, etc. will be put in at SAE.

Artwork submitted on a disc should be stored as either a .PCX or .TIF file. Hard copy original artwork should accompany the disc.

8.4 Artwork

8.4.1 CAMERA-READINESS—All artwork shall be prepared by the committee or the sponsor. It is recommended that artwork meet the requirements for readability of AIIM MS 35. The art preparation must be readable down to 64% reduction. Clear, sharp glossy prints of specified original artwork are acceptable if originals must be kept in committee's files.

8.4.2 All figures shall be numbered (Arabic) consecutively in order of mention and shall have a title.

8.4.3 LETTERING—Typewriter lettering and pencil drawings are unacceptable as both fade and drop out in the reproduction process. Please use black ink.

All lettering to be capitals unless lower case letters are necessary for a specific term. Lettering shall be vertical except for quantity symbols which shall be in italics. Use only Roman alphabet, except where letters are recognized standard symbols.

8.4.4 NUMBERS IN ARTWORK—Align column of numbers on decimal point.

8.5 Tables—Tables shall be numbered in Arabic numbers consecutively throughout the report, and shall be referred to in the text. Each table shall be titled.

8.5.1 Concise descriptions, measurement units, and letter symbols shall be used in column headings.

8.5.2 Explanatory notes shall be located at the bottom of the table, with distinct reference symbols.

8.5.3 Numerical ranges should be concise. Do not overlap ranges or leave gaps in ranges. An example of good practice is:

0.75 through 1.25 mm
Over 1.25 through 2.00 mm
Over 2.00 through 3.25 mm

8.6 Dimensioning—Dimensions and units of measurement in new and revised SAE technical reports shall be expressed in SI (metric) units (See Section 10). Nominal sizes shall be expressed as determined by their design basis or historical use. Where these considerations are not decisive, decimal nominal sizes shall be used. (See SAE TSB 003.)

8.6.1 SIGNIFICANCY—The number of significant digits used in a dimension should relate to the precision of the quantity stated. This is particularly important in decimalizing dimensions previously expressed as fractions. A dimension of 1-3/16 with an intended precision of about ±0.01 shall be decimalized as 1.19, not as 1.1875. For further information, consult SAE TSB 003.

8.6.2 ROUNDING OFF—When it is necessary to reduce the number of decimals by rounding off, the method shown in SAE TSB 003 shall be used.

8.6.3 ZEROS—Where decimal values less than 1 appear, a zero shall be placed to the left of the decimal point. Parts or Design Standards, however, that comply with ANSI Y14.5 shall follow the format specified.

8.6.4 LARGE NUMBERS—To facilitate the reading of numbers having five or more digits, the digits shall be placed in groups of three separated by a space instead of a comma, counting both to the left and to the right of the decimal point. In the case of four digits, the space is optional. This style avoids confusion caused by the use of the comma to express the decimal marker in some countries.

For example, use:

1 532 or 1532 instead of 1,532
132 541 816 instead of 132,541,816
983 769.788 16 instead of 983,769.78816

8.7 Cross References—As necessary, reports by other SAE committees or other organizations may be referenced.

8.7.1 Reference shall be made to other reports by the name of the organization, the number of the report, and in the Reference list, the date of issuance; e.g., SAE J848 NOV84, ASTM 2649-83. If the date is included, it must be assumed that a specific report is being referenced, even though it may have been canceled.

8.7.2 If the SAE technical report corresponds to but is not identical to the report of another organization (i.e., ISO or ANSI) it shall be indicated in the approval note; e.g., "This report conforms essentially to American National Standard B 32.3."

8.7.3 Joint development of a report with another committee or organization shall be indicated in the approval note; e.g., "This is a joint report of SAE and ASTM."

9. Use of Basic Terms

9.1 Surface Vehicle or Machine - The words "surface vehicle" or "machine" are preferred to "automotive" for use in identifying technical reports that do not apply to aerospace technology.

9.1.1 VEHICLE—Pertains to self-propelled devices for carrying passengers, goods, or equipment; e.g., a car, bus, or truck.

9.1.2 MACHINE—Pertains to self-propelled or mobile devices designed to alter or transmit energy and force for the performance of useful work; e.g., tractor, loader, ditcher, combine, etc.

9.2 Mechanical Properties—Those properties of a material that pertain to its elastic and plastic behavior when force is applied; e.g., yield strength, ultimate strength, elongation, hardness, etc.

9.3 Physical Properties—Those properties other than mechanical properties that pertain to the physics of a material; e.g., density, electrical conductivity, thermal expansion, etc. This term is often improperly used to express mechanical properties.

9.4 "Shall" or "Should"—The use of "shall" or "should" has no bearing on the voluntary nature of SAE technical reports. Inclusion of or reference to an SAE report in a document, standard, or contract by a company or agency is a voluntary act. When a report is so cited, the report becomes a requirement within the limitations set forth by the document, standard, or contract. The following shall apply to the use of "shall" or "should" in SAE reports:

9.4.1 SHALL—Is to be used wherever the criterion for conformance with the specific recommendations requires that there shall be no deviation. Its use shall not be avoided on the grounds that compliance with the report is considered voluntary.

9.4.2 SHOULD—Is to be used wherever noncompliance with a specific recommendation is permissible. "Should" shall not be substituted for "shall" on the grounds that compliance with the report is voluntary.

9.5 "Safe" and "Safety"—The words "safe" and "safety" shall be used in SAE technical reports only when they are in whole or in part commonly used engineering terms, such as: failsafe, factor of safety, safety glazing, etc. To preclude misuse of "safe" and "safety" more descriptive phrases shall be used, such as:

"lock wiring" rather than "safety wiring"
"lock nut" rather than "safety nut"
"relief valve" rather than "safety valve"
"integrity of the painted surface" rather than "safety of the painted surface"

If circumstances arise which strongly indicate the need for using "safe" or "safety", SAE staff should be consulted.

10. Metrication—The SAE Technical Standards Board has mandated that only SI (metric) units shall be used in SAE Technical Reports unless an exception is provided for by the operating board. Guidance in the use of SI units can be found in SAE TSB 003.

11. Notes

11.1 Indicating Revisions

11.1.1 TECHNICAL REVISIONS—In drafts of revisions to existing Technical Reports, the symbol "(R)" is used to indicate technical changes. If the entire document is revised, the (R) shall be placed before the title. All changes require a change in the suffix of the report number; e.g., JXXXX NOV87 to JXXXXX JAN90 or AMS 1234A to AMS 1234B. This indication of change shall be put on the draft revision at the earliest circulation.

11.1.1.1 The revision symbol "(R)" is always placed in the left margin for single column copy and in the left-or-right hand margin, respectively, for double column copy (e.g., J Handbook). It is used to indicate technical changes in text, tables, or figures. In the case of text, a separate symbol is used for each revised paragraph. In the case of tables or figures, the symbol is used once for each revised table or figure.

11.1.1.2 The revision symbol shall be carried in the revised published document. If the document is again revised, old symbols are deleted and appropriate new ones are added.

RULES FOR SAE USE OF SI (METRIC) UNITS —SAE TSB 003 MAY1999

SAE Standard

Report of the SAE Publication Policy Committee approved June 1965, sixth revision May 1985. Revised by the SAE Editorial Advisory Committee May 1991 and June 1992. Rationale statements available. Revised by the SAE Metric Advisory Committee May 1999. Rationale statement available.

Foreword—SI denotes The International System of Units (*Le Système International d'Unités*). SI was established in 1960, under the Treaty of the Meter, by Resolutions and Recommendations of the General Conference on Weights and Measures (*Conférence Générale des Poids et Mesures, CGPM*) and the International Committee for Weights and Measures (*Comité International des Poids et Mesures, CIPM*) on The International System of Units. The abbreviation "SI" is used in all languages.

In 1969, the SAE Board of Directors issued a directive that "SAE will include SI units in SAE Standards and other technical reports." During the ensuing several decades, SAE metric policy evolved and implementation progressed. The SAE's current metric policy is, "Operating Boards shall not use any weights and measures system other than metric (SI), except when conversion is not practical, or where a conflicting world industry practice exists."

Principal driving forces for SAE metrication were: worldwide movement to metric units; enactment of United States Federal metric legislation and the resultant national metrication activity; the international trend in industry and business throughout the world, and the growing international scope of SAE. Currently, the widespread, strong support for international standards harmonization is another key motivating factor in the global metrication movement.

TSB 003 (formerly SAE J916) has been updated periodically, to reflect SAE metric policy evolution—as well as developments in the specific, formal content of SI; and in the correct, consistent usage and application of SI...which sometimes is referred to as "the modern version of the metric measurement system."

The content of TSB 003 is consistent with international and U.S. national authoritative resource documents for SI—such as: NIST SP 330; IEEE/ASTM/ANSI SI 10; the U.S. Federal Register Notice, "Metric System of Measurement"; and ISO 1000. For additional information on SI, see Section 2 of this document.

Throughout this document, SI is intended to include recognized SI units, as established by CGPM, and a limited number of other units that, formally, are not SI units. The reason is that: SI forms the foundation of international standardization; but it is recognized worldwide that certain exceptions are required. For example, the degree (of plane angle), the minute, and the hour, are non-SI units. It is the purpose of this document to provide guidance and further references on SI metric practice for SAE use; and, also, to give guidance concerning acceptable use of non-SI units in SAE practice.

TABLE OF CONTENTS

1. Scope

1.1 This SAE Standard provides information on the International System of Units (abbreviated SI in all languages), and its application in measurement unit usage.

1.2 The purpose is to provide information on SI and guidance on SI's correct, uniform usage in application to land, sea, and aerospace design, engineering, and manufacturing practices and technical communications.

1.3 This document and the referenced IEEE/ASTM/ANSI SI 10 Standard, establish rules for the use of SI units in SAE technical reports, including Standards, Recommended Practices, and Information Reports, as well as technical papers, publications, etc. This TSB 003 document is designated as applicable for goverance of SI metric practice in all SAE operations, internal and external communications, products, and services.

1.4 Throughout this document, SI is intended to include recognized SI units, as established by the General Conference on Weights and Measures (CGPM), and a limited number of other units that, formally, are not SI units.

SI forms the foundation of international metric standardization. But it is recognized, worldwide, that certain exceptions are required. For example: the degree (of plane angle), the minute, and the hour, are non-SI units. The decibel is another example.

This document provides guidance and authoritative references for acceptable use of certain non-SI units within the SAE's operations, practices, services, and products.

2. References

2.1 Applicable Publications—The following publications form a part of the specification to the extent specified herein. Unless otherwise indicated, the latest revision of SAE publications shall apply.

2.1.1 SAE PUBLICATION—Available from SAE, 400 Commonwealth Drive, Warrendale, PA 15096-0001.

In the SAE Strategic Plan, January 1, 1997, under the Technical Standards Board's implementation of the Vision "To provide world-class standards-related products and services to the global mobility industry," the SAE Vision/Ends Strategies include "H. Encourage and promote the use of metric weights and measures by adopting the system of SI Metrics."

2.1.2 ANSI PUBLICATIONS—Available from ANSI, 11 West 42nd Street, New York, NY 10036-8002.

The SAE Metric Advisory Committee adopted (Feb. 1997) the ANSI (American National Standards Institute) American National Standard; IEEE/ASTM SI 10-1997 "Standard for Use of the International System of Units (SI): The Modern Metric System"—as the SAE's primary reference for SI. The SI 10 document is the formally designated primary American National Standard for use of the International System of Units.

2.1.3 U.S. GOVERNMENT PUBLICATIONS—Available from U.S. Government Printing Office, Washington, DC 20402.

NIST Special Publication 330—The International System of Units (SI)—1991

U.S. Federal Register Notice, Metric System of Measurement; Interpretation of the International System of Units for the United States, July 28, 1998 (see Appendix C)

2.1.4 ISO PUBLICATION—Available from ANSI, 11 West 42nd Street, New York, NY 10036-8002.

ISO 1000—SI Units and Recommendations for the use of their multiples and of certain other units, 1992

2.2 Related Publications—The following publications are provided for information purposes only and are not a required part of this document.

2.2.1 SAE PUBLICATIONS—Available from SAE, 400 Commonwealth Drive, Warrendale, PA 15096-0001.

SAE Paper No. 850218—SI Metric for the Practicing Mechanical Engineer, S. R. Jakuba

SAE Book—Metric (SI) in Everyday Science and Engineering, Stan Jakuba, 1993

SAE & ANMC Book—Metrication for the Manager, John T. Benedict, 1992

SAE J390—Dual Dimensioning—1982

2.2.2 U.S. GOVERNMENT PUBLICATIONS—Available from U. S. Government, DOD SSP, Subscription Service Division, Building 4D, 700 Robbins Avenue, Philadelphia, PA 19111-5094

NIST Special Publication 304—SI Chart, The Modernized Metric System, 1997

NIST Special Publication SP330—The International System of Units (SI), 1991

NIST Special Publication 811—Guide for the Use of the International System of Units, (SI), 1995

NIST Special Publication 814—Interpretation of the SI for the United States and Metric Conversion Policy for Federal Agencies, 1991

GSA (General Services Administration)—Federal Standard 376B—Preferred Metric Units for General Use by the Federal Government, 1993

U.S. Government Printing Office—Style Manual—1984
U.S. Dept. of Defense Production & Logistics Office—SD-10 Guide for Identification and Development of Metric Standards, 1990

3. Definitions—To facilitate application of SI ("The Modern Version of the Metric Measurement System"), and to ensure consistent, reliable conversion and rounding practices, an understanding of related terms is helpful. Definitions and explanations for various terms are given in Annex B1 Terminology, page 50, of the primary reference document: IEEE/ASTM SI 10-1997. Following, are definitions for some additional relevant terms.

3.1 Base Units—SI is built upon seven base units, which are regarded as independent. The base units are: meter, kilogram, second, ampere, kelvin, mole, and candela.

3.2 Capacity Rating—The capacity rating of a crane, a truck, a bridge, etc., is intended to define the mass that can be supported safely. Such a rating is expressed in a mass unit rather than a force unit, thus in kilograms or metric tons, as appropriate, rather than newtons.

3.3 Coherent System of Units—A system of units of measurement in which a small number of base units, defined as dimensionally independent, are used to derive all other units in the system by rules of multiplication and division with no numerical factors other than unity. The SI base units and derived units form a coherent set.

3.4 Conversion-Hard—A hard conversion is the process of changing a measurement from inch-pound units to nonequivalent metric units, which necessitates physical configuration changes of the item outside those permitted by established measurement tolerances. "Hard conversion" often is a concomitant of international standardization.

3.5 Conversion-Soft—A soft conversion is the process of changing a measurement from inch-pound to equivalent metric units within acceptable measurement tolerances, without changing the physical configuration of the item.

3.6 Derived Units—Derived units are formed by combining base units according to the algebraic relations linking the corresponding quantities. Symbols for derived units are obtained by means of mathematical signs for multiplication, division, and the use of exponents. For example, the SI unit for speed is the meter per second (m/s or $m{\cdot}s^{-1}$) and that for density is kilogram per cubic meter (kg/m^3 or $kg{\cdot}m^{-3}$). Most derived units have only their composite names, such as meter per second for speed or velocity. Others have special names, such as newton (N), joule (J), watt (W), and pascal (Pa), given to SI units of force, energy, power, and pressure (or stress), respectively.

3.7 Inch-Pound Units—Formally, the U.S. Customary Measurement System. Units based upon the yard and the pound commonly used in the United States of America and defined by the National Institute of Standards and Technology. Note that units having the same names in other countries may differ in magnitude.

3.8 Load—The term "load" in mechanics means either mass, force, or pressure, depending on its use. A load that produces a vertical downward force because of the influence of gravity acting on a mass may be expressed in mass units, e.g., kilograms. A load that produces a force from anything other than the influence of gravity is expressed in force units, i.e., newtons, although the pressure unit, pascal, is used in some cases. For example, a wind, snow, or roof load may be a pressure and may be expressed in newtons per square meter (N/m^2), that is, pascals (Pa). Floor loading in a building, however, may properly be expressed in mass units, e.g., in kilograms or kilograms per square meter.

3.9 Metrication—Any act tending to increase the use of the metric system (SI), whether it be increased use of metric units or of engineering standards that are based on such units.

3.10 SI—SI denotes The International System of Units (*Le Système International d' Unités*). SI consists of two classes of units: base units and derived units (coherent units derived from the base units.) Since 1995, the radian and steradian are deemed derived units (the supplementary units classification was eliminated). SI is defined (formally; authoritatively) in such documents as: the U.S. Federal Register, SI Notice; NIST SP330; IEEE/ASTM SI 10; ISO 1000.

3.11 Units for Mass, Weight, and Force—Mass units, such as kilogram, pound, and ounce, have often been used for units of both mass and force. This has led to serious confusion. In SI this confusion is eliminated because the unit of mass is the kilogram, and the unit of force is the newton. The kilogram-force (from which the suffix "force" in practice has often been erroneously dropped) is not used. Derived units that include force are formed using the newton.

3.12 Weight—The weight of a body in a particular reference frame is defined as the force that provides the body an acceleration equal to the local acceleration of free fall in that reference frame. Thus the SI unit of weight is the newton (N).

In commercial and everyday use, the term "weight" is often used as a synonym for mass, for which the SI unit is the kilogram. The verb "to weigh" means "to determine the mass of" or "to have a mass of." Nevertheless, in scientific and technical practice, the term "weight" should not be used to mean mass.

3.13 Work, Heat, Energy—The joule (N·m) is work done when the point of application of a force of one newton is displaced a distance of one meter in the direction of the force. The SI unit of energy is the joule, which is equal to newton meter or watt second. The kilowatt hour is accepted as a unit of electrical energy only.

4. SAE Metric Policy

4.1 Statement—The following statement of Metric Policy was approved by the SAE Board of Directors on March 4, 1993:

4.1.1 SAE METRIC POLICY—Operating Boards shall <u>not</u> use any weights and measures system other than metric (SI), except when conversion is not practical, or where a conflicting world industry practice exists..."

5. Measurement Units Approved for SAE Use

5.1 As noted above, SAE has endorsed and adopted as its primary SI Reference, the ANSI/IEEE/ASTM SI 10-1997 document, which is the primary American National Standard for SI. SAE Reports and other documents must utilize, as applicable, the metric units of SI and other allowable units given in the SI 10-1997 Standard and in Appendix C.

5.2 The liter, which the General Conference established as a special name for the cubic decimeter, is approved for SAE use. The only prefixed use allowed is mL. SAE preference should be to use cubic centimeter (cm^3), rather than milliliter (mL); and cubic decimeter (dm^3) rather than liter (L).

5.3 In regard to <u>time</u>, committees should use the second and its multiples, except where minutes or hours units are warranted.

EXAMPLE—km/h for velocity.

5.4 Additional examples of approved non-SI units.

5.4.1 The unit metric ton (exactly 1 Mg) is in wide use, but should be limited to commercial description of vehicle mass, or freight mass; and no prefix is permitted.

5.4.2 The unit hectare (exactly 1 h m^2) is restricted to land and water area measurement.

5.4.3 In acoustics, the bel is retained as a unit for measuring the loudness of sounds, in its prefixed form, decibel (dB).

5.5 Some expressions for derived SI units are valid. For example: The SI unit for electric field strength is V/m; however, field strength also is expressed in terms of base units as $kg{\cdot}m/(s^3{\cdot}A)$ or $kg{\cdot}m{\cdot}s^{-3}{\cdot}A^{-1}$. Likewise, torque and bending moment (N·m) may also be expressed as $kg{\cdot}m^2/s^2$ or $kg{\cdot}m^2{\cdot}s^{-2}$

6. Units Not Approved for Use

6.1 Gravimetric units such as kilogram-force for force and kilogram-force per square millimeter or centimeter for pressure or stress, which have been commonly used in some countries, must not be used in SAE metric practice. Similarly: calorie, bar, angstrom, and dyne are not SI units, and are not approved for general use. Numerous examples of units that are not to be used, are listed in Table 8, pp.10-11, of the primary referenced Standard, IEEE/ASTM SI 10.

7. Rules for Use of SI Units

7.1 Requirements of this document establish the use of SI units in SAE practice, in one of the following manners:

7.1.1 Exclusively as regular (primary) units.

7.1.2 As regular units followed by other units in parentheses.

7.1.3 Under special circumstances it is permissible to deviate from these rules. See Appendix A.

7.2 SI units must be those shown in Appendices B and C, or their decimal multiples or units derived from approved units. For example: use kg/s for mass per unit time. In case of need for other units, the Metric Advisory Committee of the SAE Technical Standards Board should be consulted. If units for <u>quantities</u> not included in Appendix B are required, the above committee should be contacted for guidance.

An apparent anomaly exists in the use of the joule for work (J = N·m) and the use of N·m for torque or bending moment. These are, however, entirely different units. In the former, the unit of work results from unit force moving through unit distance. In the latter, there is no implication of movement, and unit force acts at right angles to the lever arm of unit length. This would be readily seen if vectors were incorporated in the unit symbols. For these reasons, it is important to express work and other energy in joules. Moment of force, torque and bending moment are expressed in newton meters, not joules.

7.3 Symbols and Abbreviations

7.3.1 DISTINCTION—The distinction between unit symbols and unit abbreviations is not always recognized, particularly with certain U.S. inch-pound units of measure. There are, however, several distinctions between unit symbols and conventional abbreviations. Unit symbols are standardized forms, the same in all languages. They have the same form in singular and plural; they may be handled mathematically (for example, ft/s, cm^3); they are not followed by periods. Conventional abbreviations and acronyms are language-dependent (for example, cfm for cubic foot per minute), shortened presentations of words or names in a particular language. The symbols for some U.S. units are also abbreviations (ft, in, yd). In many cases the unit symbol and the abbreviation are not the same (such as unit symbol ft^3/min and abbreviation cfm; unit symbol A and abbreviation amp; unit symbol in^3 and abbreviation cu in); see Table 1.

7.3.2 USAGE—Use symbols and technical abbreviations only where necessary to save time and space and only where their meaning is unquestionably clear to the intended reader. Unit symbols are to be used in place of conventional abbreviations for units. Units used with specific numbers (for example, 3.7 m) are abbreviated or designated by symbol, except where a potential exists for misinterpretation; in which case the units should be spelled out, such as unit symbol "in" should be spelled out as "inch" or "inches."

TABLE 1—ABBREVIATIONS AND SYMBOLS FOR UNITS OTHER THAN SI

Unit Name	Symbol	Abbreviation	Unit Name	Symbol	Abbreviation
brake horsepower		bhp	inch pound-force	in·lbf	
Brinell hardness number		Bhn	kilocycle per second	kc/s	
British thermal unit	Btu		kilogram-force	kgf	
calorie	cal		mile	mile	
candlepower		cp	mile per hour	mi/h	mph
cubic foot per minute	ft^3/min	cfm	minute (angle)		min
cubic foot per second	$ft^{3/s}$	cfs	ounce	oz	
cycle per minute	c/min	cpm	ounce-force	ozf	
cycle per second	c/s	cps	part per gallon		ppg
cycle	c		pint	pt	
degree Fahrenheit	°F		pound	lb	
degree Rankine	°R		poundal	pdl	
dram	dr		pound-force	lbf	
foot	ft		pound-force per		
footcandle	fc		square inch	lbf/in^2	psi
foot per minute	ft/min		pound-force per		
foot per second	ft/s		square inch absolute		psia
foot pound-force	ft · lbf		pound-force per		
friction horsepower		fhp	square inch gage		psig
gallon	gal		quart	qt	
gallon per minute	gal/min	gpm	revolution per minute	r/min	rpm
gallon per second	gal/s	gps	revolution per second	r/s	rps
horsepower	hp		Saybolt universal second		SUS
inch	in		second (angle)	"	sec
inch of mercury	inHg		minute (angle)	'	min
inch of water	inH_2O		yard	yd	yd

7.3.3 UNIT SYMBOL COMPOSITION—Unit symbols are letters or groups of letters predominantly from the Latin alphabet representing the units in which physical quantities are measured (m for meter, W·h for watt hour). Non-English alphabet unit symbols are (Ω) for ohm, (°) for the plane angle degree or used with the Celsius (°C) temperature scale, and (μ) for the prefix micro. All unit symbols are printed in Roman (upright) type. The symbol °C for degree Celsius is treated as an entity; the two components ° and C are not to be separated.

7.3.4 UNIT SYMBOL STYLE[1]—Unit symbols, in general, use lower case letters. If, however, the symbol is derived from a proper name, it or the first letter (where more than one) is an upper case letter (Hz, Wb, Pa). An exception to the above permits the upper case (L) to represent the unit liter because of the confusion that can occur between the lower case unit symbol (l) and the number one (1).

The letter style must be followed for SI unit symbols and prefixes even in applications where all other lettering is upper case (such as technical drawings). The only exception allowed is for computer and machine displays with limited character sets. For symbols for use in systems with limited character sets, refer to ANSI/IEEE Std. 260. The symbols for limited character sets must not be used when the available character set permits the use of the proper symbols as given herein.

7.3.5 QUANTITY SYMBOLS—Quantity symbols must not be confused with unit symbols. Quantity symbols are single letters representing physical quantities (*I* for electric current, *e* for charge of an electron). The established symbol must always be maintained (*f*-frequency, *F*-force, *m*-mass, *M*-moment of force).

Quantity symbols are single letters of the English (Latin) or Greek alphabet, and are printed in italic (slanting) type.

7.3.6 ABBREVIATIONS—Abbreviations are shortened forms of words or phrases formed in various ways that have been approved (ANSI/ASME Y1.1—1989). They are generally letters from the word being abbreviated, except where the abbreviation is taken from another language (no for number, lb for pound). Abbreviations are never to be used when a mathematical operation sign is involved, unless the abbreviation is also the symbol.

7.3.7 SYMBOLIZED COMPOUND (DERIVED) UNITS[2]—Compound (derived) units constitute a mathematical expression. Where compound units include the solidus (/), it must not be repeated in the same expression. In complicated cases, negative powers or parentheses should be used. For example, write: m/s^2 or $m \cdot s^{-2}$ but not m/s/s; or write $kg \cdot m/(s^3 \cdot A)$ or $kg \cdot m \cdot s^{-3} \cdot A^{-1}$ but not $kg \cdot m/s^3/A$.

7.3.8 PLURAL—The form of symbols and abbreviations is the same for singular or plural (1 in, 10 in, 1 s, 27 s).

7.3.9 Periods are not used after symbols or abbreviations. The same abbreviation is used for related nouns, verb, adverb, etc., (inclusion, include, inclusive are all abbreviated incl). When these rules would cause confusion, spell out the word. Words of four letters or less are not abbreviated.

7.3.10 When writing a quantity, a space is left between the numerical value and a unit symbol. For example, write: 35 mm, not 35mm; write 20 °C, not 20°C.

Exception: No space is left between numerical values and symbols for degree, minute, and second of plane angle. Example: 45°. However in SAE Practice, the ° symbol is not used for plane angle. The word degree is spelled out.

7.4 Mass, Force, and Weight

7.4.1 The principal departure of SI from the gravimetric system of metric engineering units is the use of distinct units for mass and force. In SI, the name kilogram is restricted to the unit of mass, and the kilogram-force (from which the suffix force was in practice often erroneously dropped) should not be used. In its place the SI unit of force, the newton (N) is used. Likewise, the newton rather than the kilogram-force is used to form derived units that include force, for example, pressure or stress (N/m^2 = Pa), energy (N·m = J), and power (N·m/s = W).

7.4.2 Considerable confusion exists in the use of the term weight as a quantity to mean either force or mass. In commercial and everyday use, the term weight

1. Handling of Unit Names—Names of units are not capitalized except at the beginning of sentences or in titles. (Modifiers used in unit names are capitalized if proper names; for example, degree Fahrenheit.) Compound unit names are formed with a space for product and the word "per" for quotient. Prefixes become part of the word: ampere (A), milliampere (mA), ampere second (A·s), meter per second (m/s).

2. See footnote 1.

nearly always means mass; thus, when one speaks of a person's weight, the quantity referred to is mass. This nontechnical use of the term weight in everyday life will probably persist. In science and technology, the term weight of a body usually meant the force that, if applied to the body, would give it an acceleration equal to the local acceleration of free fall. The adjective "local" in the phrase "local acceleration of free fall" usually meant a location on the surface of the earth. In this context, the "local acceleration of free fall" has the symbol g (commonly referred to as "acceleration of gravity"). Values of g differing by over 0.57 at various points on the earth's surface have been observed.[1] In a technical context, the use of force of gravity (mass times acceleration of gravity), instead of weight with this meaning is recommended. Because the term weight is ambiguous, care should be taken to assure that the intended meaning is clear.

7.4.3 Many units for rates are not shown in Appendix B, but should be derived from approved units. For example: the proper unit for mass per unit time is kg/s; (see 7.2).

7.5 Temperature Conversion—The SI unit for thermodynamic temperature is the kelvin. The SI unit degree Celsius will be used for commonly expressed temperatures.

The Celsius degree is related to the kelvin degree as follows:
One degree Celsius equals one kelvin exactly. Celsius temperature ($t_{°C}$) is related to kelvin temperature (T_K) as follows:

$$T_K = 273.15 + t_{°C} \qquad \text{(Eq. 1)}$$

The Celsius degree is related to the Fahrenheit degree as follows:
One degree Celsius equals 9/5 of a degree Fahrenheit, exactly. Celsius temperature ($t_{°C}$) is related to Fahrenheit temperature ($t_{°F}$) as follows:

$$t_{°C} = 5/9(t_{°F} - 32) \qquad \text{(Eq. 2)}$$

General guidance for converting tolerances from degrees Fahrenheit to kelvins or degrees Celsius is given in Table 2.

TABLE 2—CONVERSION OF TEMPERATURE TOLERANCE REQUIREMENTS

Tolerance, K or °C (±)	Tolerance, °F (±)
0.5	1
1	2
3	5
5.5	10
8.5	15
11	20
14	25

1. The standard value of g = 9.806 650 m/s^2 was adopted in 1913 by the CGPM. This value is used on earth whenever it is determined that the local differing value may be disregarded.

Normally, temperatures expressed in a whole number of degrees Fahrenheit should be converted to the nearest 0.5 kelvin (or degree Celsius). As with other quantities, the number of significant digits to retain will depend upon implied accuracy of the original dimension. For example:

a. 100 °F ± 5 °F—implied accuracy estimated to be 2 °F
37.7777 °C ± 2.7777 °C rounds to 38 °C ± 3 °C

b. 1000 °F ± 50 °F—implied accuracy estimated to be 20 °F
537.7777 °C ± 27.7777 °C rounds to 540 °C ± 30 °C

7.6 Miscellaneous

7.6.1 With nominal sizes that are not measurements but are names for items, no conversion should be made. For example: 1/4-20 UNC thread, 1 in pipe, 2 x 4 lumber.

7.6.2 The decimal marker used by SAE is the dot on the line (.) for quantities in either U.S. customary or SI units.

To facilitate the reading of numbers having five or more digits, the digit should be placed in groups of three separated by a space instead of a comma, counting both to the left and to the right of the decimal point. In the case of four digits, the spacing is optional. This style also avoids confusion caused by the use elsewhere of the comma to express the decimal marker.

For example, use:
1 532 or 1532 instead of 1,532
132 541 816 instead of 132,541,816
983 769.788 16 instead of 983,769.78816

7.6.3 Surface roughness expressed in microinches should be converted to micrometers (µm); the term "micron" shall not be used.

7.6.4 Linear dimensions on engineering drawings related to SAE committee documentation will customarily be given in millimeters, regardless of length.

7.6.5 Expressions that can be stated as a ratio of the same unit, such as 0.006 inch per inch, should be changed to a designation of a ratio such as 0.006:1. Where an expression might be shown in two different units one of which is a multiple of the other, reduce the expression to a common unit and show it as a ratio.

EXAMPLE—1.50 in per ft = 0.125 ft per ft. Express as a ratio 0.125:1.

7.6.6 It has been internationally recommended that pressure units themselves should not be modified to indicate whether the pressure is absolute (that is, above zero) or gage (that is, above atmospheric pressure). If, therefore, the context leaves any doubt to which is meant, the word pressure must be qualified appropriately.

For example:
"... at a gage pressure of 200 kPa" or
"... at an absolute pressure of 95 kPa" or
"... reached an absolute pressure of 95 kPa," etc.

8. Notes

8.1 Historical Note—When tracing the background/history of TSB 003, it is necessary to know... that ... this SAE Standard was renumbered in 1992. At that time, it was put into a new class of TSB (Technical Standards Board) documents and designated TSB 003. As stated in the Foreword (paragraph 4), prior to 1992, it was SAE J916. The SAE J916 number was used from the inception of *Rules for SAE Use of SI (Metric) Units*, in 1965, through various revisions, including the 1991 version of J916.

APPENDIX A
METHODS FOR APPLYING SI IN TABLES AND GRAPHS

Preface—As covered in 7.1, SI units are required in SAE reports. To assist committees in carrying out this requirement in special circumstances, some qualifying rules are covered here.

A.1 In standards that have alternate or optional procedures based on apparatus calibrated in either U.S. inch-pound or SI units, converted values need not be included. If optional procedures or dimensions produce equally acceptable results, the options may be shown by using the word "or" rather than parentheses. For example: in a 2-in gage length metal tension test specimen, the gage length may be shown as "50 mm or 2 in."

A.2 A specific equivalent, for example 25.4 mm (1.00 in), need be inserted only the first time it occurs in each paragraph.

A.3 Special instructions cover the use of tabular material.

A.3.1 Case 1—Limited Tabular Material—Provide SI equivalents in tables in parentheses or in separate columns (see Table A1).

TABLE A1—FASTENERS FOR GRINDERS

H	L mm	L in	R
3/8-24 UNF-2A	28.58	1-1/8	
1/2-13 UNC-2A	44.45	1-3/4	Governed by thickness
5/8-11 UNC-2A	53.98	2-1/8	of wheel used
5/8-11 UNC-2A	79.38	3-1/8	
3/4-10 UNC-2A	82.55	3-1/4	

A.3.2 Case 2—One or Two Large Tables—When the size of a table and limitations of space (on the printed page) make it impractical to expand the table to include SI equivalents, the table should be duplicated in U.S. inch-pound units and in SI units (see Tables A2 and A3).

A.3.2.1 If Cases 1 and 2 would still result in major increase in the size of the standard document, consideration must be given to other methods. SAE staff should first be consulted on techniques of arranging column spacing, etc., to accomplish addition of SI as shown in Cases 1 and 2.

Cases 3 and 4 are two approaches to reduce the number of pages involved in adding SI to reports with extensive tabular data. They should be used only in extreme cases since they do not accomplish the intent of SAE policy. Also, these approaches should not be considered when the users of the report are judged to need SI units for its use.

A.3.3 Case 3—Extensive Tabular Material—When the tabulated data are extensive and the above procedures would require an impractical addition to the standard, a summary appendix may be prepared listing all of the values appearing in the tables, along with the conversion of each, as in Tables A4, A5, A6, and A7.

A.3.4 Case 4—In extreme cases when all the above approaches do not apply because of the size and number of tables, conversion factors may be placed in a footnote under each table, as in the example in Table A8. It should be noted that usage of inch-pound oriented material such as this is an exception to the SAE Policy and is expected to decline as the metric transition progresses with the phase-in of the SI metric oriented technical data.

TABLE A2—DIMENSIONS IN SI UNITS

Chain No.	H60	H74	H75	H78	H82	H124
P (mm)	58.62	66.27	66.27	66.27	78.10	101.60
A (mm)	7.92	9.52	7.92	12.70	11.27	19.05
F (mm)	18.5	25.4	19.0	28.4	31.75	39.62
H (mm)	18.5	22.3	18.3	22.3	30.2	36.6
Proof test load (kN)						
Class M	12.50	17.80	12.50	28.50	35.60	53.40
Class P	15.60	22.20	15.60	35.60	44.50	66.80
No. of pitches per nominal						
3048 mm strand	52	46	46	46	39	30
Theoretical length of nominal						
3048 mm strand	3048.5	3048.2	3048.2	3048.2	3046.0	3048.0
Measuring load (N)	850	1200	850	580	2270	3600

TABLE A3—DIMENSIONS IN U.S. INCH-POUND UNITS

Chain No.	H60	H74	H75	H78	H82	H124
P (in)	2.308	2.609	2.609	2.609	3.075	4.000
A (in)	0.312	0.375	0.312	0.500	0.562	0.750
F (in)	0.73	1.00	0.75	1.12	1.25	1.56
H (in)	0.75	0.88	0.72	0.88	1.19	1.44
Proof test load (lbf)						
Class M	2 800	4 000	2 800	6 400	8 000	12 000
Class P	3 500	5 000	3 500	8 000	10 000	15 000
No. of pitches per nominal						
120 in strand	52	46	46	46	39	30
Theoretical length of nominal						
120 in strand	120.02	120.01	120.01	120.01	119.92	120.00
Measuring load (lbf)	190	270	190	130	510	810

A.4 Graphs and charts may be handled in several ways depending on the circumstances. In adding SI units to a graphic presentation of data, the practice of specific addition of metric conversions to existing ordinate or abscissa values should be avoided (see Figure A1).

TABLE A4—SI EQUIVALENTS—MILLIMETERS TO INCHES

mm	in	mm	in	mm	in
0.38	0.015	8.89	0.350	25.07	0.987
0.51	0.020	9.52	0.375	25.40	1.000
0.71	0.028	9.73	0.383	28.65	1.128
0.97	0.038	10.95	0.431	29.92	1.178
1.12	0.044	11.10	0.437	32.26	1.270
1.27	0.050	12.37	0.487	35.81	1.410
1.42	0.056	12.70	0.500	39.90	1.571
1.63	0.064	13.72	0.540	49.86	1.963
1.80	0.071	15.55	0.612	59.84	2.356
3.63	0.143	15.88	0.625	69.82	2.749
4.85	0.191	17.78	0.700	79.81	3.142
6.07	0.239	19.05	0.750	90.02	3.544
6.65	0.262	20.07	0.790	101.35	3.990
7.26	0.286	22.22	0.875	112.52	4.430
8.48	0.334	22.58	0.889		

TABLE A5—SI EQUIVALENTS—SQUARE INCHES TO SQUARE CENTIMETERS

cm^2	in^2	cm^2	in^2	cm^2	in^2
0.71	0.11	2.84	0.44	6.45	1.00
1.29	0.20	3.87	0.60	8.19	1.27
2.00	0.31	5.10	0.79	10.06	1.56

TABLE A6—SI EQUIVALENTS—POUNDS PER FOOT TO KILOGRAMS PER METER

kg/m	lb/ft	kg/m	lb/ft	kg/m	lb/ft
0.560	0.376	2.235	1.502	4.96	3.33
0.994	0.668	3.042	2.044	6.403	4.303
1.552	1.043	3.973	2.670	7.906	5.313

TABLE A7—SI EQUIVALENTS—POUNDS-FORCE PER SQUARE INCH TO MEGAPASCALS

MPa	psi	MPa	psi
345	50 000	550	80 000
415	60 000	620	90 000

TABLE A8—LARGE TABLE WITH CONVERSION FACTORS AS FOOTNOTES

Nominal Size, in	Outside Diameter, in[(1)]	Wall Thickness, in[(1)]	Nominal Mass per ft. Plain End, lb/ft[(2)]	Weight Class	Schedule No.	Test Pressure,[(3)] Butt-Welded	Test Pressure,[(3)] Grade A	Test Pressure,[(3)] Grade B
20	20.000	0.250	52.73	—	10	—	450	500
		0.281	59.18	—	—	—	500	600
		0.312	65.60	—	—	—	550	650
		0.344	72.21	—	—	—	600	700
		0.375	78.60	STD	20	—	700	800
		0.406	84.96	—	—	—	750	850
		0.438	91.51	—	—	—	800	900
		0.469	97.83	—	—	—	850	950
		0.500	104.13	XS	30	—	900	1000
		0.594	123.11	—	40	—	1100	1200
		0.812	166.40	—	60	—	1500	1700
		1.031	208.87	—	80	—	1900	2200
		1.281	256.10	—	100	—	2300	2700
		1.500	296.37	—	120	—	2700	2800
		1.750	341.10	—	140	—	2800	2800
		1.969	379.17	—	160	—	2800	2800
24	24.000	0.250	63.41	—	10	—	400	450
		0.281	71.18	—	—	—	400	500
		0.312	78.93	—	—	—	450	550
		0.344	86.91	—	—	—	500	600
		0.375	94.62	STD	20	—	550	650
		0.406	102.31	—	—	—	600	700
		0.438	110.22	—	—	—	650	750
		0.469	117.86	—	—	—	700	825
		0.500	125.49	XS	—	—	750	900
		0.562	140.68	—	30	—	850	1000
		0.688	171.29	—	40	—	1000	1200
		0.938	231.03	—	—	—	1400	1600
		0.969	238.85	—	60	—	1500	1700
		1.219	296.58	—	90	—	1800	2100
		1.531	367.39	—	100	—	2300	2700
		1.812	429.39	—	120	—	2700	2800
		2.062	483.12	—	140	—	2800	2800
		2.344	542.14	—	160	—	2800	2800
26	26.000	0.250	68.75	—	—	—	50	400
		0.281	77.18	—	—	—	390	450
		0.312	85.60	—	10	—	430	500
		0.344	94.26	—	—	—	480	560
		0.375	102.63	STD	—	—	520	610
		0.406	110.98	—	—	—	560	660
		0.438	119.57	—	—	—	610	710
		0.469	127.88	—	—	—	650	760
		0.500	136.17	XS	20	—	690	810
		0.562	152.68	—	—	—	780	910

1. 1 in = 25.4 mm
2. 1 lb/ft = 1.49 kg/m
3. 1 psi = 6.9 kPa

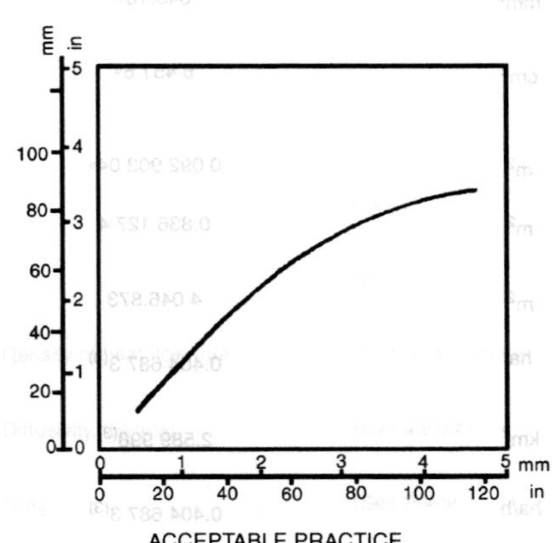

ACCEPTABLE PRACTICE

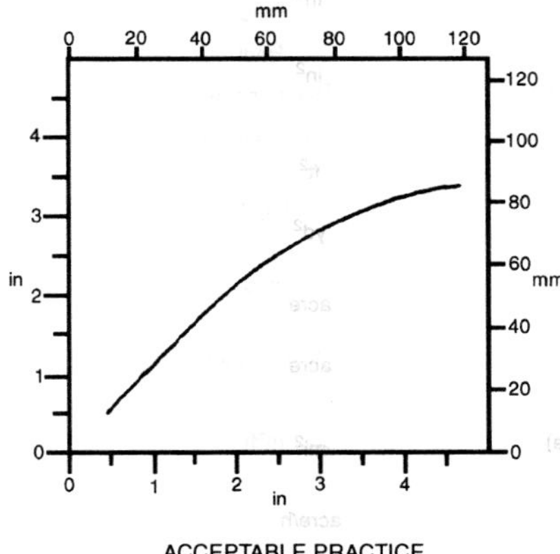

ACCEPTABLE PRACTICE

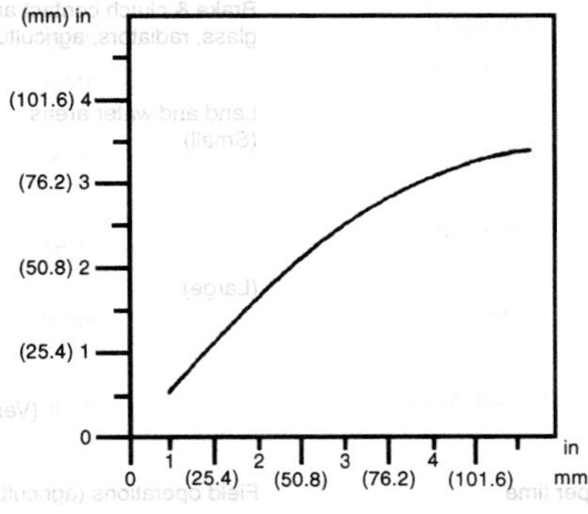

UNACCEPTABLE PRACTICE

FIGURE A1—GRAPHS AND CHARTS

APPENDIX C
FEDERAL REGISTER NOTICE, JULY 28, 1998
METRIC SYSTEM OF MEASUREMENT: INTERPRETATION OF THE INTERNATIONAL SYSTEM OF UNITS FOR THE UNITED STATES

Preface—Appendix C is an SAE adaptation of Federal Register Notice, July 28, 1998—Metric System of Measurement: Interpretation of the International System of Units for the United States, which consists only of reformatting the FEDERAL REGISTER NOTICE of JULY 28, 1998 into SAEs format.

C.1 FEDERAL REGISTER NOTICE, July 28, 1998—Metric System of Measurement: Interpretation of the International System of Units for the United States—DEPARTMENT OF COMMERCE

National Institute of Standards and Technology

[Docket No. 980430113-8113-01]

Metric System of Measurement: Interpretation of the International System of Units for the United States

AGENCY: National Institute of Standards and Technology, Commerce.

ACTION: Notice.

C.1.1 Summary—This notice restates the intepretation of the International System of Units (SI) for the United States by the Department of Commerce. This interpretation was last published by the Department of Commerce in the **Federal Register** on December 20, 1990 (55 FR 52242-52245). Since the publication of that notice, the international bodies that are responsible for the SI have made some changes to it. It has therefore become necessary to set forth a new interpretation of the SI for the United States that reflects these changes.

C.1.2 For Futher Information Contact—For information regarding the International System of Units, contact Dr. Barry N. Taylor, Building 225, Room B161, National Institute of Standards and Technology, Gaithersburg, MD 20899-0001, telephone number (301) 975-4220. For information regarding the Federal Government's efforts to coordinate the transition of the United States to the International System of Units, contact Mr. James B. McCracken, Metric Program, Building 820, Room 306, National Institute of Standards and Technology, Gaithersburg, MD 20899-0001, telephone number (301) 975-3690, email: metric_prg@nist.gov.

C.1.3 Supplementary Information—Section 5164 of Public Law 100–418, the Omnibus Trade and Competitiveness Act of 1988, amended Public Law 94–168, the Metric Conversion Act of 1975. In particular, section 3 of the Metric Conversion Act (codified as amended 15 U.S.C. 205b) reads as follows:

"Sec. 3. It is therefore the declared policy of the United States—

1. to designate the metric system of measurement as the preferred system of weights and measures for United States trade and commerce;
2. to require that each Federal agency, by a date certain and to the extent economically feasible by the end of the fiscal year 1992, use the metric system of measurement in its procurements, grants, and other business related activities, except to the extent that such use is impractical or is likely to cause significant inefficiencies or loss of markets to United States firms, such as when foreign competitors are producing competing products in non-metric units;
3. to seek out ways to increase understanding of the metric system of measurement through educational information and guidance and in Government publications; and
4. to permit the continued use of traditional systems of weights and measures in nonbusiness activities."

In the Metric Conversion Act of 1975, the 'metric system of measurement' is defined as the International System of Units as established in 1960 by the General Conference of Weights and Measures (abbreviated CGPM after the French *Conférence Général des Poids et Mesures*) and interpreted or modified for the United States by the Secretary of Commerce (15 U.S.C. 205c). The Secretary has delegated this authority to the Director of the National Institute of Standards and Technology. In implementation of this authority, tables and associated text were published in the **Federal Register** of December 20, 1990 (55 FR 52242-52245), setting forth the interpretation for the United States of the International System of Units (abbreviated SI in all languages after the French *Systéme International d'Unités*).

The CGPM is an intergovernmental organization established by the Meter Convention (*Convention du Métre*), which was signed by the United States and 16 other countries in Paris in 1875 (nearly 50 countries are now members of the Convention). One of the responsibilities of the CGPM is to ensure that the SI reflects the latest advances in science and tehcnology. Since the publication of the 1990 **Federal Register** notice, the CGPM has made two significant changes to the SI. These are (1) the addition of four new SI prefixes to form decimal multiples and submultiples of SI units; and (2) the elimination of the class of supplementary units (the radian and the steradian) as a separate class in the SI. Further, the International Committee for Weights and Measures (abbreviated CIPM after the French *Comité International des Poids et Mesures*), which comes under the authority of the CGPM, has made some new recommendations regarding units not part of the SI that may be used with the SI. It is therefore necessary to issue new tables and associated text that reflect these changes and which set forth a new interpretation of the SI for the United States. Thus this **Federal Register** notice supersedes the previous interpretation published in the **Federal Register** on December 20, 1990 (55 FR 52242-52245).

C.1.4 Classes of SI Units—There are now only two classes of units in the International System of Units: *base units* and *derived units*. The units of these two classes form a *coherent* set of units and are designated by the name "SI units." Here, the term coherent is used to mean a unit system where all derived units are obtained from the base units by the rules of multiplication and division with no numerical factor other than the number 1 ever occurring in the expressions for the derived units in terms of the base units. The SI also includes *prefixes* to form decimal multiples and submultiples of SI units. Because units formed with SI prefixes are not coherent with SI units, the units so formed are designated by their complete name "decimal multiples and submultiples of SI units" in order to make a distinction between them and the coherent set of SI units proper. The SI units and their decimal multiples and submultiples together are often called "units of the SI."

C.1.5 SI Base Units—The SI is founded on seven SI *base units* for seven *base quantities* assumed to be mutually independent. These units and quantities are given in Table C1.

TABLE C1—SI BASE UNITS

Base Quantity	SI Derived Unit Name	SI Derived Unit Symbol
length	meter	m
mass[1]	kilogram	kg
time	second	s
electric current	ampere	A
thermodynamic temperature	kelvin	K
amount of substance	mole	mol
luminous intensity	candela	cd

1. "Weight" in common parlance is often used to mean mass.

C.1.6 SI Derived Units—Other quantities, called *derived quantities*, are defined in terms of these seven base quantities through a system of quantity equations. Si *derived units* for these derived quantities are obtained from this system of equations and the seven SI base units in a coherent manner, which means, in keeping with the above discussion of the term coherent, that they are formed as products of powers (both positive and negative) of the SI base units corresponding to the base quantities concerned without numerical factors. Table C2 gives some examples of SI derived units.

C.1.7 Quantities of Dimension 1—The last entry of Table C2, mass fraction, is an example of certain derived quantities that are defined as the ratio of two mutually comparable quantities, that is, two quantities of the same kind. Since the coherent SI derived unit of such a derived quantity is the ratio of two identical SI units, that unit may also be expressed by the number one, symbol 1. Such quantities are called *quantities of dimension 1*, or *dimensionless quantities*, and the SI unit of all such quantities is the number 1. Examples of other derived quantities of dimension 1, and thus with a coherent SI derived unit that may be expressed by the number 1, are relative permeability, dynamic friction factor, refractive index, characteristic numbers such as the Mach number, and numbers that represent a count, such as a number of molecules. However, the number 1 is generally not explicitly shown in the expression for the value of a quantity of dimension 1. For example, the value of the refractive index of a given medium is expressed as $n = 1.51$ rather than as $n = 1.51 \times 1$. In a few cases a special name and symbol are given to the number 1 to aid understanding. The radian, unit symbol rad, and steradian, unit symbol sr, which are given in Table C3 and are discussed in connection with Table C4, are two such examples.

TABLE C2—EXAMPLES OF SI DERIVED UNITS

Derived Quantity	SI Derived Unit Name	SI Derived Unit Symbol
area	square meter	m^2
volume	cubic meter	m^3
speed, velocity	meter per second	m/s
acceleration	meter per second squared	m/s^2
wave number	reciprocal meter	m^{-1}
mass density (density)	kilogram per cubic meter	kg/m^3
specific volume	cubic meter per kilogram	m^3/kg
current density	ampere per square meter	A/m^2
magnetic field strength	ampere per meter	A/m
amount-of-substance concentration (concentration)	mole per cubic meter	mol/m^3
luminance	candela per square meter	cd/m^2
mass fraction	kilogram per kilogram, which may be represented by the number 1	kg/kg = 1

C.1.8 SI Derived Units With Special Names and Symbols—For ease of understanding and convenience, 21 SI derived units have been given special names and symbols. These are listed in Table C3, where it should be noted that the last three units of Table C3, the becquerel, unit symbol Bq, the gray, unit symbol Gy, and the sievert, unit symbol Sv, were specifically introduced by the CGPM with a view to safeguarding human health.

C.1.9 Degree Celsius—The derived unit in Table C3 with special name degree Celsius and special symbol °C deserves comment. Because of the way temperature scales used to be defined, it remains common practice to express a thermodynamic temperature, symbol T, in terms of its difference from the reference temperature T_o = 273.15 K, the ice point. This temperature difference is called Celsius temperature, symbol t, and is defined by the quantity equation $t = T - T_o$. The unit of Celsius temperature is the degree Celsius, symbol °C. The numerical value of a Celsius temperature t expressed in degrees Celsius is given by

$$\frac{t}{°C} = \frac{T}{K} - 273.15 \quad \text{(Eq. C1)}$$

It follows from the definition of t that the degree Celsius is equal in magnitude to the kelvin, which in turn implies that the numerical value of a given temperature difference or temperature interval whose value is expressed in the unit degree Celsius (°C) is equal to the numerical value of the same difference or interval when its value is expressed in the unit kelvin (K). Thus temperature differences or temperature intervals may be expressed in either the degree Celsius or the kelvin using the same numerical value. For example, the Celsius temperature difference Δt and the thermodynamic temperature difference ΔT between the melting point of gallium and the triple point of water may be written as Δt = 29.7546 °C = ΔT = 29.7546 K. (Note that the centigrade temperature scale is obsolete; the unit name degree centigrade should no longer be used.)

TABLE C3—SI DERIVED UNITS WITH SPECIAL NAMES AND SYMBOLS

Derived Quantity	SI Derived Unit Special Name	SI Derived Unit Special Symbol	SI Derived Unit Expression in Terms of Other SI Units	SI Derived Unit Expression in Terms of SI Base Units
plane angle	radian	rad		$m \cdot m^{-1} = 1$
solid angle	steradian	sr		$m^2 \cdot m^{-2} = 1$
frequency	hertz	Hz		s^{-1}
force	newton	N		$m\ kg \cdot s^{-2}$
pressure, stress	pascal	Pa	N/m^2	$m^{-1} \cdot kg \cdot s^{-2}$
energy, work, quantity of heat	joule	J	$N \cdot m$	$m^2 \cdot kg \cdot s^{-2}$
power, radiant flux	watt	W	J/s	$m^2 \cdot kg \cdot s^{-3}$
electric charge, quantity of electricity	coulomb	C		$s \cdot A$
electric potential difference, electromotive force	volt	V	W/A	$m^2 \cdot kg \cdot s^{-3} \cdot A^{-1}$
capacitance	farad	F	C/V	$m^{-2} \cdot kg^{-1} \cdot s^4 \cdot A^2$
electric resistance	ohm	Ω	V/A	$m^2 \cdot kg \cdot s^{-3} \cdot A^{-2}$
electric conductance	siemens	S	A/V	$m^{-2} \cdot kg^{-1} \cdot s^3 \cdot A^2$
magnetic flux	weber	Wb	$V \cdot s$	$m^2 \cdot kg \cdot s^{-2} \cdot A^{-1}$
magnetic flux density	tesla	T	Wb/m^2	$kg \cdot s^{-2} \cdot A^{-1}$
inductance	henry	H	Wb/A	$m^2 \cdot kg \cdot s^{-2} \cdot A^{-2}$
Celsius temperature	degree Celsius	°C		K
luminous flux	lumen	lm	$cd \cdot sr$	$m^2 \cdot m^{-2} \cdot cd = cd$
illuminance	lux	lx	lm/m^2	$m^2 \cdot m^{-4} \cdot cd = m^{-2} \cdot cd$
activity (of a radionuclide)	becquerel	Bq		s^{-1}
absorbed dose, specific energy (imparted), kerma	gray	Gy	J/kg	$m^2 \cdot s^{-2}$
dose equivalent, ambient dose equivalent, directional dose equivalent, personal dose equivalent, equivalent dose	sievert	SV	J/kg	$m^2 \cdot s^{-2}$

C.1.10 Use of SI Derived Units With Special Names and Symbols—The special names and symbols of the 21 SI derived units with special names and symbols given in Table C3 may themselves be included in the names and symbols of other SI derived units. This use is shown in Table C4. All of the SI derived units in Table C4, like those in Table C3, have been obtained from the SI base units in the same coherent manner discussed above.

C.1.11 Radian and Steradian—As indicated in Table C3, the radian, unit symbol rad, and steradian, unit symbol sr, are the special names and symbols for the derived units of plane angle and solid angle, respectively. These units may be used or not in expressions for derived units as is convenient in order to distinguish between derived quantities that are not of the same kind but are of the same dimension (that is, derived quantities whose units when expressed in SI base units are the same). Table C4 includes some examples of derived units that use the radian and steradian.

C.1.12 SI Prefixes—Table C5 gives the 20 SI prefixes used to form decimal multiples and submultiples of SI units. It is important to note that the kilogram is the only SI unit with a prefix as part of its name and symbol. Because multiple prefixes may not be used, in the case of the kilogram the prefix names of Table C5 are used with the unit name "gram" and the prefix symbols are used with the unit symbol "g." With this exception, any SI prefix may be used with any SI unit, including the degree Celsius and its symbol °C.

Because the SI prefixes strictly represent powers of 10, it is inappropriate to use them to represent powers of 2. Thus 1 kbit = 10^3 bit = 1000 bit and *not* 2^{10} = 1024 bit, where 1 kbit is one kilobit.

C.1.13 Units Outside the SI—Certain units are not part of the International System of Units, that is, they are outside the SI, but are important and widely used. Consistent with the recommendations of the CIPM, the units in this category that are accepted for use in the United States with the SI are given in Tables C6 and C7.

C.1.14 Liter and Metric Ton—The units liter and metric ton in Table C6 deserve comment. The liter and its symbol l were adopted by the CIPM in 1879. The alternative symbol for the liter, L, was adopted by the CGPM in 1979 in order to avoid the risk of confusion between the letter l and the number 1. Thus, although *both* l and L are internationally accepted symbols for the liter, to avoid this risk the preferred symbol for use in the United States is L. Neither a lowercase script letter l nor an uppercase script letter l are approved symbols for the liter. With regard to the metric ton, this is the name to be used in the United States for the unit with symbol t and defined according to 1 t = 10^3 kg. (The name "metric ton" is also used in some other English speaking countries, but the name "tonne" is used in many countries.)

C.1.15 Other Units Outside the SI—Other units outside the SI that are currently accepted for use with the SI in the United States are given in Table C8. These units, which are subject to future review by the NIST Director on behalf of the Secretary of Commerce, should be defined in relation to the SI in every document in which they are used; their continued use is not encouraged. The CIPM currently accepts the use of all of the units given in Table C8 with the SI except for the curie, roentgen, rad, and rem. Because of the continued wide use of these units in the United States, especially in regulatory documents dealing with health and safety, this interpretation of the SI for the United States accepts their use with the SI. Nevertheless, use of the corresponding SI units is encouraged whenever possible, with values given in terms of the older units in parentheses if necessary.

TABLE C4—EXAMPLES OF SI DERIVED UNITS WHOSE NAMES AND SYMBOLS INCLUDE SI DERIVED UNITS WITH SPECIAL NAMES AND SYMBOLS

Derived Quantity	SI Derived Unit Name	SI Derived Unit Symbol	SI Derived Unit Expression in Terms of SI Base Units
dynamic viscosity	pascal second	Pa · s	$m^{-1}\cdot kg\cdot s^{-1}$
moment of force	newton meter	N · m	$m^2\cdot kg\cdot s^{-2}$
surface tension	newton per meter	N/m	$kg\cdot s^{-2}$
angular velocity	radian per second	rad/s	$m\cdot m^{-1}\cdot s^{-1} = s^{-1}$
angular acceleration	radian per second squared	rad/s^2	$m\cdot m^{-1}\cdot s^{-2} = s^{-2}$
heat flux density, irradiance	watt per square meter	W/m^2	$kg\cdot s^{-3}$
heat capacity, entropy	joule per kelvin	J/K	$m^2\cdot kg\cdot s^{-2}\cdot K^{-1}$
specific heat capacity, specific entropy	joule per kilogram kelvin	J/(kg·K)	$m^2\cdot s^{-2}\cdot K^{-1}$
specific energy	joule per kilogram	J/kg	$m^2\cdot s^{-2}$
thermal conductivity	watt per meter kelvin	W/(m·K)	$m\cdot kg\cdot s^{-3}\cdot K^{-1}$
energy density	joule per cubic meter	J/m^3	$m^{-1}\cdot kg\cdot s^{-2}$
electric field strength	volt per meter	V/m	$m\cdot kg\cdot s^{-3}\cdot A^{-1}$
electric charge density	coulomb per cubic meter	C/m^3	$m^{-3}\cdot s\cdot A$
electric flux density	coulomb per square meter	C/m^2	$m^{-2}\cdot s\cdot A$
permittivity	farad per meter	F/m	$m^{-3}\cdot kg^{-1}\cdot s^4\cdot A^2$
permeability	henry per meter	H/m	$m\cdot kg\cdot s^{-2}\cdot A^{-2}$
molar energy	joule per mole	J/mol	$m^2\cdot kg\cdot s^{-2}\cdot mol^{-1}$
molar entropy, molar heat capacity	joule per mole kelvin	J/(mol·K)	$m^2\cdot kg\cdot s^{-2}\cdot K^{-1}\cdot mol^{-1}$
exposure (x and γ rays)	coulomb per kilogram	C/kg	$kg^{-1}\cdot s\cdot A$
absorbed dose rate	gray per second	Gy/s	$m^2\cdot s^{-3}$
radiant intensity	watt per steradian	W/sr	$m^4\cdot m^{-2}\cdot kg\cdot s^{-3} = m^2\cdot kg\cdot s^{-3}$
radiance	watt per square meter steradian	$W/(m^2\cdot sr)$	$m^2\cdot m^{-2}\ kg\cdot s^{-3} = kg\cdot s^{-3}$

TABLE C5—SI PREFIXES

Factor	Name	Symbol	Factor	Name	Symbol
$10^{24}=(10^3)^8$	yotta	Y	10^{-1}	deci	d
$10^{21}=(10^3)^7$	zetta	Z	10^{-2}	centi	c
$10^{18}=(10^3)^6$	exa	E	$10^{-3}=(10^3)^{-1}$	milli	m
$10^{15}=(10^3)^5$	peta	P	$10^{-6}=(10^3)^{-2}$	micro	µ
$10^{12}=(10^3)^4$	tera	T	$10^{-9}=(10^3)^{-3}$	nano	n
$10^9=(10^3)^3$	giga	G	$10^{-12}=(10^3)^{-4}$	pico	p
$10^6=(10^3)^2$	mega	M	$10^{-15}=(10^3)^{-5}$	femto	f
$10^3=(10^3)^1$	kilo	k	$10^{-18}=(10^3)^{-6}$	atto	a
10^2	hecto	h	$10^{-21}=(10^3)^{-7}$	zepto	z
10^1	deka	da	$10^{-24}=(10^3)^{-8}$	yocto	y

TABLE C6—UNITS OUTSIDE THE SI THAT ARE ACCEPTED FOR USE WITH THE SI

Name		Symbol	Value in SI Units
minute }		min	1 min=60 s
hour	time	h	1 h=60 min = 3600 s
day		d	1 d=24 h = 86 400 s
degree }		°	1°=(π/180) rad
minute	plane angle	′	1′=(1/60)° = (π/10 800) rad
second		ð	1ð=(1/60)′ = (π/648 000) rad
liter		L	1 L=1 dm³ = 10⁻³ m³
metric ton		t	1 t=10³ kg
neper		Np	1 Np=1
bel		B	1 B=(1/2) ln 10 NP(1)

1. Although the neper is coherent with SI units and is accepted by the CIPM, it has not been adopted by the CGPM and is thus not an SI unit.

TABLE C7—UNITS OUTSIDE THE SI THAT ARE ACCEPTED FOR USE WITH THE SI, BUT WHOSE VALUES IN SI UNITS ARE OBTAINED EXPERIMENTALLY

Name	Symbol	Value in SI Units(1)
electronvolt(2)	eV	1 eV=1.602 177 33(49) x 10^{-19} J
unified atomic mass unit(3)	u	1 u=1.660 540 2(10) x 10^{-27} kg
astronomical unit(4)	ua	1 ua=1.495 978 70(30) x 10^{11} m

1. The combined standard uncertainty (that is, estimated standard deviation) of the last two figures is shown in parentheses.
2. The electronvolt is the kinetic energy acquired by an electron in passing through a potential difference of 1 V in vacuum.
3. The unified atomic mass unit is equal to 1/12 of the mass of an unbound atom of the nuclide ^{12}C at rest and in its ground state.
4. The astronomical unit is a unit of length approximately equal to the mean Earth-Sun distance. Its value is such that, when used to describe the motion of bodies in the solar system, the heliocentric gravitation constant is $(0.017\ 202\ 098\ 95)^2$ ua^3·d^{-2}.

TABLE C8—OTHER UNITS OUTSIDE THE SI THAT ARE CURRENTLY ACCEPTED FOR USE WITH THE SI, SUBJECT TO FUTURE REVIEW

Name	Symbol	Value in SI Units
nautical mile		1 nautical mile = 1852 m
knot		1 nautical mile per hour = (1852/3600) m/s
arc(1)	a	1 a = 1 dam² = 10² m²
hectare(1)	ha	1 ha = 1 hm² = 10⁴ m²
bar	bar	1 bar = 0.1 MPa = 1 kPa = 1000 hPa = 10⁵ Pa
ångström	Å	1 Å = 0.1 nm = 10^{-10} m
barn	b	1 b = 100 fm² = 10^{-28} m²
curie	Ci	1 Ci = 3.7 x 10^{10} Bq
roentgen	R	1 R = 2.58 x 10^{-4} C/kg
rad	rad(2)	1 rad = 1 cGy = 10^{-2} Gy
rem	rem	1 rem = 1 cSv = 10^{-2} Sv

1. This unit and its symbol are used to express areas of land.
2. When there is risk of confusion with the symbol for the radian, rd may be used as the symbol for rad.

C.1.16 Use of SI Prefixes WIth Units Outside the SI—Some SI prefixes are used with some of the units given in Tables C6, C7, and C8. For example, prefixes for both positive and negative powers of ten are used with the liter, the electronvolt, the unified atomic mass unit, the bar, and the barn. Prefixes for positive powers of ten are used with the metric ton, and prefixes for negative powers of ten are used with the neper and the bel, although the bel is most commonly used in the form of the decibel:

1dB = 0.1 B.

C.1.17 Rules and Style Conventions—A number of rules and style conventions have been adopted internationally for the use of the SI to ensure that scientific and technical communication is not hindered by ambiguity. The most important of these are as follows:

1. Unit symbols are printed in roman (upright) type regardless of the type used in the surrounding text.
2. Unit symbols are printed in lowercase letters except that:
   a. the symbol or the first letter of the symbol is an uppercase letter when the name of the unit is derived from the name of a person; and
   b. the preferred symbol for the liter in the United States is L.
3. When the name of a unit is spelled out, it is always written with a lowercase initial letter unless it begins a sentence.
4. Unit symbols are unaltered in the plural.
5. Unit symbols are not followed by a period unless at the end of a sentence.
6. Symbols for units formed from other units by multiplication are indicated by means of a half-high (that is, centered) dot or space.

EXAMPLE—N·m or N m

7. Symbols for units formed from other units by division are indicated by means of solidus (oblique stroke,/), a horizontal line, or negative exponents.

EXAMPLE—m/s, $\frac{m}{s}$, or m · s^{-1}

However, to avoid ambiguity, the solidus must not be repeated on the same line unless parentheses are used.

EXAMPLES—

m/s² or m·s^{-2} *but not*: m/s/s

m·kg/(s³·A) or m·kg·s^{-3}·A^{-1} *but not*: m·kg/s³/A

Negative exponents should be used in complicated cases.

8. Prefix symbols are printed in roman (upright) type regardless of the type used in the surrounding text, and are attached to unit symbols without a space between the prefix symbol and the unit symbol. This last rule also applies to prefix names attached to unit names.

EXAMPLES—

1 mL (one milliliter)
1 pm (one picometer)
1 GΩ (one gigaohm)
1 THz (one terahertz)

9. The grouping formed by a prefix symbol attached to a unit symbol constitutes a new inseparable symbol (forming a multiple or submultiple of the unit concerned) which can be raised to a positive or negative power and which can be combined with other unit symbols to form compound unit symbols.

EXAMPLES—

2.3 cm³ = 2.3 (cm)³ = 2.3 (10^{-2} m)³ = 2.3 x 10^{-6} m³
1 cm^{-1} = 1 (cm)$^{-1}$ = 1 (10^{-2} m)$^{-1}$ = 10² m^{-1}
5000 µs^{-1} = 5000 (µs)$^{-1}$
= 5000 (10^{-6} s)$^{-1}$
= 5000 x 10^{6} s^{-1} = 5 x 10^{9} s^{-1}

Prefix names are also inseparable from the unit names to which they are attached. Thus, for example, millimeter, micropascal, and meganewton are single words.

10. Compound prefix symbols, that is, prefix symbols formed by the juxtaposition of two or more prefix symbols, are not permitted. This rule also applies to compound prefix names.

EXAMPLE—1 nm (one nanometer) *but not*: 1 mµm (one millimicrometer)

11. An SI prefix symbol (and name) cannot stand alone, but must always be attached to a unit symbol (or name).

EXAMPLE—5 x 10^6/m³ *but not*: 5 M/m³

12. In the expression for the value of a quantity, the unit symbol is placed after the numerical value and a space is left between the numerical value and the unit symbol. The only exceptions to this rule are for the unit symbols for degree, minute, and second for plane angle: °, ′, ð, respectively (see Table C6), in which case no space is left between the numerical value and the unit symbol.

EXAMPLE—α = 30°22′8ð

This rule means that:

a. The symbol °C for the degree Celsius is preceded by a space when one expresses the values of Celsius temperatures.

EXAMPLE—*t* = 30.2 °C *but not*: *t* = 30.2°C or *t* = 30.2° C

b. Even when the value of a quantity is used in an adjectival sense, a space is left between the numerical value and the unit symbol. (This rule recognizes that unit symbols are not like ordinary words or abbreviations but are mathematical entities, and that the value of a quantity should be expressed in a way that is as independent of language as possible.)

EXAMPLES—

a 1 m end gauge *but not*: a 1-m end gage
a 10 kΩ resistance *but not*: a 10-kΩ resistance

However, if there is any ambiguity, the words should be rearranged accordingly. For example, the statement "the samples were placed in 22 mL vials" should be replaced with the statement "the samples were placed in vials of volume 22 mL," or "the samples were placed in 22 vials of volume 1 mL," whichever was meant.

NOTE—When unit names are spelled out as is often the case in nontechnical writing, the normal rules of English apply. Thus, for example, "a roll of 35-millimeter film" is acceptable.

C.1.18 Obsolete Units—As stated in the 1990 **Federal Register** notice, metric units, symbols, and terms that are not in accordance with the foregoing interpretation are not accepted for continued use in the United States with the International System of Units. Accordingly, the following units and terms listed in the table of metric units in section 2 of the Act of July 28, 1866 (15 U.S.C. 205) that legalized the metric system of weights and measures in the United States are not accepted for use in the United States.

myriameter
stere
millier or tonneau
quintal
myriagram
kilo (for kilogram).

C.1.19 Additional Information on the SI—Additional information on the SI may be found in NIST Special Publication (SP) 811, *Guide for the Use of the International System of Units (SI)*, by Barry N. Taylor. This publication is for sale by the Superintendent of Documents, but is also available online (as will be this notice) at URL http://physics.nist.gov/cuu. (Although the 1995 edition of SP 811 is the edition currently available in print and online, a new edition that fully reflects the contents of this notice is under preparation and will replace the 1995 edition.)

Although there is no formal comment period, public comments are welcome on a continuing basis. Comments should be submitted to Dr. Barry N. Taylor at the above address.

Dated: June 19, 1998.
Robert E. Hebner,
Acting Deputy Director.
[FR Doc. 98-16965 Filed 7-27-98; 8;45 am]
Billing Code 3510-13-M

TECHNICAL COMMITTEE GUIDELINES —SAE TSB 004 JUL1998

SAE Recommended Practice

Report of the SA Publications Advisory Committee, approved August 1979. Completely revised by the SAE Staff for the Technical Standards Board June 1992 and revised July 1998.

1. Scope

1.1 These Guidelines were written to provide information needed by SAE technical committee members. Subject matter covers relations of technical committees to the SAE organization and, in broad terms, committee operating procedures.

1.2 The Guidelines are the outgrowth of the principles and policies of the Society, and they reflect the philosophies, traditions, and methodology that have emerged from years of successful operations of SAE technical committees.

1.3 These Guidelines are necessarily brief and presented in an outline form. For additional information, refer to the latest issue of the SAE Technical Standards Board Governance Policy and appropriate Council Operating Practices.

2. References

2.1 Applicable Publications—The following publications form a part of the specification to the extent specified herein. Unless otherwise indicated, the latest revision of SAE publications shall apply.

2.1.1 SAE PUBLICATIONS—Available from Technical Division, SAE, 400 Commonwealth Drive, Warrendale, PA 15096-0001.

TSB 002—Preparation of SAE Technical Reports—Surface Vehicles and Machines: Standards, Recommended Practices, and Information Reports (formerly J1159)
TSB 003—Rules for SAE Use of SI (Metric) Units (formerly J916)
SAE AMS Editorial Procedure and Form
SAE Committee Guidelines Manual
SAE Technical Standards Board Governance Policy

3. SAE Objective

3.1 The objective of the Society is to promote the Arts, Sciences, Standards, and Engineering Practices connected with the design, construction, and utilization of self-propelled mechanisms, prime movers, components thereof, and related equipment. SAE serves its members and the General Public through meetings and programs developed by its various Engineering Activities and Sections, through its Placement Committee, and through its publications; *it serves industry, government, and the public through the development of technical reports*[1] *including engineering standards and recommended practices, and distributing these documents.*

4. SAE Technical Standards Board

4.1 Organization—The SAE Technical Standards Board is the agent of the SAE Board of Directors with authority to direct and supervise services to government and industry, including standardization, research, and the participation in technical committee activity of other organizations. Figure 1 shows the organizational structure of the Technical Standards Board.

4.2 Philosophies

4.2.1 The SAE Technical Standards Board will consider those projects for which industry, government, the public, or other responsible agencies have expressed a need and which lend themselves to cooperative solution. Within their own operations, technical committees frequently generate projects meeting the previously noted criteria.

4.2.2 The SAE Technical Standards Board expects its councils/divisions to set up their own organizations, procedures, and programs within their scopes and the limits of the SAE Technical Standards Board's Governance Policy.

4.3 Recognition of Achievements—Annually, the Board awards a maximum of 30 *Certificates of Appreciation* to technical committee members and to individuals representing SAE in other organizations. Nominations for awards are submitted through the councils to the Technical Standards Board Awards Committee by the various technical committees. Supporting data outlining the basis for nomination is required.

5. Councils/Divisions of the SAE Technical Standards Board

5.1 The SAE Technical Standards Board delegates to its councils/divisions the authority to direct and approve (see 8.4) SAE Standards, Recommended Practices, Information Reports, Draft Technical Reports, and Technical Data Reports (subject to the right of anyone to appeal a decision to the Board). The councils are authorized to establish committees that may be needed to accomplish this assignment.

1. The term "technical reports" as used in these Guideposts standards for the end product of a committee's efforts and may consist of an SAE Standard, Recommended Practice, Information Report, or Aerospace Material Specification.

5.2 Committee Sponsor—The chairperson of each council appoint annually council members to act as sponsors for committees functioning directly under the council. The council chairperson may appoint the council technical committee chairpersons as members of the council and as sponsors for their committees. The committee sponsor shall represent the committee to the council, and serve as liaison between the committee and the council. During periods when a committee is without a sponsor, the council chairperson will perform such functions.

6. SAE Technical Committees

6.1 Objectives—The objectives of a technical committee are to coordinate and utilize the knowledge, experience, and skill of engineers and other qualified individuals on technical problems within the scope of its activities to:

a. Conduct necessary investigations and develop technical reports.
b. Review technical reports periodically, revise as necessary, and maintain content abreast of latest technology.
c. Advise, consult, and cooperate with industry, government, educational institutions, the public, other standardizing bodies, and other SAE committees and members.
d. Assist committees of the SAE Engineering Meetings Board in the preparation and presentation of papers at national meetings and specialty conferences.

6.2 Principles—The end products of the committee's work are offered as the best judgment of a group technically competent to deal with the problems covered and do not represent an industry-trade position. Employers of committee members are not committed by an action of an SAE committee. Over many years, the extensive use of SAE technical reports clearly indicates that committee members, working as individuals, do produce results that are practical and useful to industry, government, and the public.

Technical Standards Board

Strategic Planning
- Research Executive Committee
- Metric Advisory Committee
- International Harmonization Committee

Governance Policy/By-Laws
- Regulatory Relations
- Performance Metrics
- Awards
- Appeals
- Finance

Executive Product Council
- Professional Development
- Standards Development Process
- Training
- Products/Services
- Councils/Divisions
  - Aerospace Council
  - Construction Agricultural & Off-Road Machinery Council
  - Fuels & Lubricants Division
  - Intelligent Transportation Systems Division
  - Manufacturing Division
  - Materials, Processes & Parts Division
  - Motor Vehicle Council
  - Reliability, Maintainability, Supportability & Logistics Division
  - Specialized Vehicle & Equipment Division
  - Truck & Bus Council
  - Vehicle Service Development Division

FIGURE 1—SAE TECHNICAL STANDARDS BOARD ORGANIZATION

6.3 Scope—A technical committee shall be responsible for a field of endeavor, as defined by its scope. In cases where projects overlap areas of interest of another council's/division's committee, the originating committee shall submit the project(s) for review and approval to the other concerned committee and its council prior to issuance. A committee is established when a new major project area is to be undertaken and no existing committee is available. A committee is discharged when the assigned work is completed and there is not further need for its services. The councils/divisions retain responsibility for periodic review of technical reports developed by their disbanded committees.

6.4 Membership

6.4.1 QUALIFICATIONS—All participants are appointed to SAE technical committees by the committee chairperson on the basis of their individual qualifications which enable them to contribute to the work of these committees. Overall, committee membership should attain an equitable balance of representation by knowledgeable *parties at interest*. All relevant points of view should be invited to participate. SAE membership is not a prerequisite for committee membership.

6.4.2 SAE policy dictates that SAE technical committee members act as *individuals* and not as agents or representatives of their employers. Their actions are accepted as personal actions based on sound technical judgement and do not necessarily represent their employer's attitudes or view.

6.4.3 GRADES—Committee participants shall be classified as *member, liaison member, and consultant member*, or committee officer. *Liaison and consultant members* are appointed by the chairperson on the basis of need for their particular services. *Liaison members* relay information to and from paralleling activities of other committees and organizations. *Consultant members* supply advice on the specific program for which they have been appointed. *Liaison and consultant members* are not eligible to vote on committee actions except at the request of the committee chairperson.

6.4.4 Governmental agency employees may be appointed as *members, liaison members, or consultant members* of the committee with aforementioned responsibilities and privileges.

6.4.5 BALANCE—Overall Technical Committee membership shall attempt to attain an equitable balance of representation by knowledgeable persons at interest so as to provide a competent and authoritative committee. In considering the equitable balance of a committee, the individual's point of view as a producer, user, consumer, or regulator shall be considered. The number of members on a technical committee may vary depending on the specific needs.

6.5 Organization—Typical organization patterns are shown in Figure 2.

6.6 Officers—The committee shall always have a chairperson and may have a vice-chairperson and secretary.

6.6.1 The chairperson and vice-chairperson of a newly-formed committee shall be appointed by the council/division chairperson with advice of council members. Existing committees shall nominate a chairperson and vice-chairperson annually for council approval. The chairperson may become a member of a council by appointment by the council chairperson.

6.6.2 The secretary shall be appointed annually by the committee chairperson.

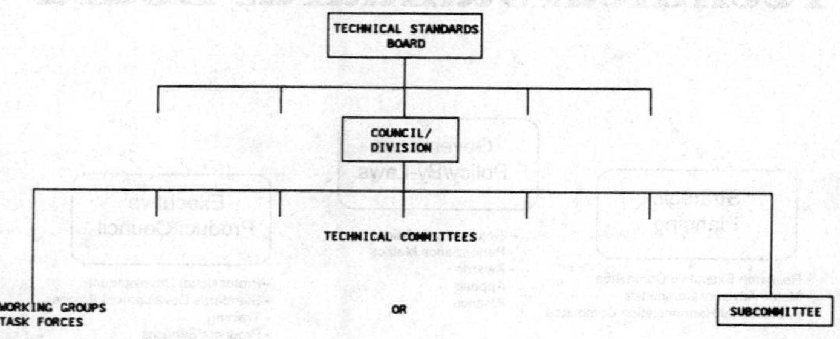

FIGURE 2—EXAMPLE OF EXECUTIVE COMMITTEE OF LARGE TECHNICAL COMMITTEE

6.6.3 Reasonably frequent rotation of committee chairperson, is encouraged, for example 2 or 3 year terms. However, renominations of chairperson who have served five or more consecutive years shall be reviewed and approved by the council.

6.6.4 It is the duty of the chairperson to:

a. Plan and conduct meetings.
b. Establish subcommittees, appoint their chairperson, and supervise their operation.
c. Establish working panels, including appointment of their chairperson and/or individual member work assignments, and supervise their operation.
d. Assign projects so as to balance and expedite the committee's work.
e. Act for the committee between meetings, subject to confirmation at the next meeting.
f. Supervise and report voting on all committee reports.
g. Review the membership annually to maintain an active and balanced committee.
h. Recommend revisions of committee procedures as needed.
i. Arrange for the nomination of candidates for the SAE Technical Standards Board Certificate of Appreciation Award. Candidates must be nominated by August 1.
j. Serve as chairperson of the steering committee (or executive committee), if applicable.

6.7 Executive Committees—When a technical committee has numerous subcommittees, projects, or is so large as to make meetings of the entire group impractical, an executive committee may be established to organize and manage the affairs of the committee. The executive committee shall include all committee officers, and may include all subcommittee chairperson and such additional members as may be desirable to form an efficient working group. The technical committee officers shall be the officers of the executive committee.

6.8 Subordinate Structure

6.8.1 Subcommittees, working groups, or task forces are organized to carry out specific continuing technical segments of the committee's scope. The original chairperson shall be appointed by the parent technical committee chairperson; thereafter, the chairperson may be nominated by the group, subject to review and approval by the parent technical committee chairperson. It is desirable that the subcommittee chairperson be a member of the parent committee.

The original membership will be appointed by either the parent committee chairperson or by the subcommittee chairperson. Thereafter, membership matters are handled by the subcommittee chairperson.

Duties of subcommittee officers in relation to their subcommittees are the same as those of the technical committee officers in relation to the technical committee, except as outlined in the SAE Technical Standards Board Governance Policy.

6.8.2 WORKING TECHNICAL PANELS (FIGURE 2)—When a committee or subcommittee wishes to have several of its members work together in preparation of a draft technical report, a temporary (ad hoc) working panel may be formed. After completion of its task, responsibility for review and maintenance of resulting technical reports reverts to the committee or subcommittee, and the panel is discharged.

6.9 SAE Staff Representative—An SAE Staff representative will advise the committee officers on procedures and assist the committee in its organization and operation, attend meetings, and assure that meeting minutes are prepared and properly distributed.[2] SAE staff representative performs tally of committee voting and disseminates results of balloting.

7. Relationships with Other SAE and Non-SAE Groups

7.1 Intra-SAE Relationships—As a primary principle, each SAE technical report should be reasonably self-contained or cross-reference other SAE documents. Development of a draft technical report will often require use of data which falls within the scope of another SAE committee. In these instances, liaison should be established by formation of a joint subgroup, by membership on or from that committee, or through the SAE staff. In any event, comments and/or approval by the consultant committee should be solicited by the committee preparing the draft technical report. Adherence to this principle will avoid duplication of effort and will insure against conflicts and ambiguities. Because of his/her intimate knowledge of SAE activities, the SAE staff representative can help the technical committee in its relationships with other Society groups. See 6.6 in SAE TSB 002.

7.2 Liaison with Other Organizations—Technical committees should coordinate their efforts with parallel activities in other organizations such as the American National Standards Institute, American Society for Testing and Materials, American Iron and Steel Institute, American Petroleum Institute, and the Aerospace Industries Association. To maintain this liaison, the SAE Technical Standards Board appoints individuals to represent the Society. It is the duty of the representatives to report developments to the appropriate SAE committee, and to present SAE views which are the consensus of the concerned SAE committee(s) to these organizations.

7.2.1 Representatives of SAE on American National Standards committees or standards committees of other standards writing organizations shall be appointed by the Chairperson of the SAE Technical Standards Board.

7.2.2 Representatives of SAE on non-SAE standards committees shall report to a technical committee or, if none exists, to the appropriate council.

7.2.3 Representatives of SAE shall, where feasible, develop SAE positions regarding draft technical reports developed by such non-SAE committees through consultation with the appropriate SAE technical committee or council.

2. When the chairperson or the appointed secretary records the minutes, a copy (or copies, as appropriate) should be forwarded to the SAE office where they will be reviewed and distributed. They will be maintained for five years and made available for inspection and for distribution as appropriate.

7.2.4 The representative of SAE shall report activities of the non-SAE committee annually and shall advise the technical committee or council of the SAE vote on approval or disapproval of standards or other substantive matters coming before the non-SAE committee. The SAE representative may seek additional SAE support in backing up the SAE position through the appropriate SAE committees and councils.

7.3 American National Standards Institute

7.3.1 Approval of American National Standards by American National Standards Institute (ANS) committees for which SAE is sponsor, cosponsor, or secretariat shall be by the appropriate SAE council on either recommendation of the appropriate SAE committee or the SAE representatives on the American National Standards Committee.

7.3.2 Upon approval by SAE of an ANS for which SAE is *sponsor, cosponsor, or secretariat*, the subject standard shall be considered an approved SAE Standard. In the event that SAE is not the publisher of the subject standard as an ANS, but does provide coverage of the subject matter contained in the standard in the SAE Handbook or other SAE publications, such SAE publications will be revised as soon as possible after SAE approval of the ANS but not later than one year after such approval. When SAE coverage of the subject matter is approved in advance of a revision to the ANS, the Society will immediately initiate a revision of the ANS.

7.4 Joint Sponsorship with Other Organizations—SAE joint sponsorship of committees with outside organizations is discouraged, unless such joint sponsorship is of direct benefit to SAE committees. Where possible, SAE should perform its standardization and cooperative engineering functions without the establishment of jointly sponsored groups.

7.4.1 In cases where SAE technical committee work or technical projects are of major interest outside of SAE (for example, splines and screw threads), cooperation is encouraged in established SAE sponsored organizations such as the American National Standards Institute (ANSI) and the Coordinating Research Council (CRC).

7.4.2 Where joint sponsorship of a project with an outside organization is proposed, specific SAE Technical Standards Board approval is required.

7.4.3 Any technical reports resulting from such cooperative activity will be subject to normal SAE review and approval procedures. In such technical reports, recognition of the participation of outside groups is appropriate.

7.5 Cooperation with Government Agencies—Technical committee cooperation with government agencies in developing technical reports of mutual interest is encouraged. Such technical reports will be identified by normal SAE numbering systems when published by the SAE, and appropriately cross-referenced when issued in some other manner.

7.5.1 Where there is a divergence of technical opinion on a proposed technical report between a committee and interested governmental agency, the committee may offer the government its technical opinion in the form of comments upon a proposed government prepared specification or standard. If the committee so chooses, and with review and approval by the appropriate council, the committee's technical opinion can be published in the form of an SAE technical report.

7.6 SAE Participation in International Standards

7.6.1 SAE may serve as the U.S. technical secretariat for ANSI in International Organization for Standards (ISO) and International Electro-Technical Commission (IEC) technical committees, subcommittees, and working groups only when approved by the SAE Technical Standards Board.

7.6.2 In administering such ISO and IEC technical secretariats, SAE shall form a U.S. Technical Advisory Group (TAG) consistent with procedures of the American National Standards Institute. Membership on the TAG shall follow the rules governing membership on SAE technical committees. Appointments to the TAG shall be subject to confirmation by the appropriate SAE council. The TAG will call upon cognizant SAE technical committees and outside activities, if appropriate, to assist in developing U.S. positions on proposed ISO or IEC standards and in the development of draft standards.

7.6.3 SAE shall follow the provisions of the "ANSI Procedures for U.S. Participation in the International Standards Activities of the ISO/IEC."

*8. **Technical Committee Technical Reports***—The major effort of technical committee activity is the development of technical reports for publication by the SAE.

8.1 Development—The initial work on a draft technical report is usually handled by a task force which presents its work to a parent group, preferably well in advance of a meeting date. Corrections to the proposal are officially recognized at the meeting of the parent group and documented in the minutes. Depending on procedures established for each group, mailing or draft technical reports may be handled directly by the chairperson, the SAE staff representative, or by a delegated member.

8.2 Guides for Preparation of Technical Reports—Annually, a large number of documents are developed by the technical committee for publication. It is not practical for the SAE staff to restyle them.

8.2.1 Technical committees will use the following SAE publications:

a. SAE TSB 002—*Preparation of SAE Technical Reports—Surface Vehicles and Machines: Standards, Recommended Practices, Information Reports*
b. SAE TSB 003—*Rules for SAE Use of SI (Metric) Units—establishes the rules for the use of Systeme International (SI) units in SAE documents including specifications and standards.*
c. *AMS Editorial Procedure and Form* for the preparation of Aerospace Material Specifications (AMS) and other Aerospace Material Documents
d. *Aerospace Council's Organization and Operating Guide for Aerospace Cooperative Engineering Program* for the preparation of Aerospace Standards, Military Standards, Aerospace Recommended Practices, and Aerospace Information Reports.
e. Technical Standards Board *Governance Policy*

8.3 Committee Correspondence—It is required that all correspondence within and between committees be classified by subject so that it may be readily identified. Copies of committee correspondence should be sent to the chairperson and SAE staff representative. Committees shall use technical committee correspondence forms which are available, upon request, from the SAE staff representative. Committees shall not use stationery with a company or business letterhead.

8.4 Approval

8.4.1 Draft technical reports, submitted to a council for approval, in general, should have the unanimous approval of the committee making such a submittal. Where unanimous approval cannot be achieved, draft technical reports shall have the approval of at least 66% of the responding committee members who have voted approval or disapproval, provided that such approvals and disapprovals constitute at least 50% of all members responding. Dissenting views, including those of liaison and consulting members shall accompany draft technical reports when they are circulated to the council for final review and approval prior to publication. The committee's reasons for not accepting the dissenting views should be included.

8.4.2 Committee draft technical reports shall normally require confirmation by letter ballot, except when they are submitted for final voice vote approval. In such instances, the draft technical reports shall be distributed to the members of the voting group at least two weeks prior to the meeting. Where a single draft technical report is a joint project of two committees reporting to separate councils, it shall be submitted to both councils for review and approval.

8.4.3 The SAE Technical Standards Board retains the authority for final review and approval when dissenting views cannot be reconciled.

8.5 Publication and Timing—After approval by the council, the technical report will be published at the earliest opportunity by SAE Staff.

8.5.1 The preparation of technical reports intended for publication in the SAE Handbook should be scheduled so that council approval can be obtained prior to the closing date set by the Publications Committee. At least four weeks should be allowed for circulating drafts to the councils. Timing on technical reports which are to be released in individual form is not as critical with respect to publication date. The SAE staff representative should be consulted as required, to determine target dates.

8.5.2 DISTRIBUTION AND USE—A basic tenet of SAE technical committee operating policy is that technical reports produced by technical committees are advisory in nature. The use of such technical reports by industry, government, or other responsible agencies is entirely voluntary.

8.5.3 Early recognition by the SAE membership of new or revised technical reports is highly desirable. This provides better service for members, government, and the public, and may result in beneficial comment leading to further improvement. For these reasons, information should be submitted by the technical committee chairperson to *SAE AUTOMOTIVE ENGINEERING* or *AEROSPACE ENGINEERING* as a news item, or, if the technical report has wide appeal, it may be given more extensive treatment. With a view to providing increased service, notice of all new and revised technical reports will appear as soon as possible after council approval in the *AUTOMOTIVE ENGINEERING* or *AEROSPACE ENGINEERING* magazine.

8.6 Review—Each technical report shall be reviewed at least every five years. The staff advisor shall initiate such reviews. At such reviews, the technical report may be reaffirmed, revised, or canceled. If reaffirmed, no formal ballot of the affected council is needed, but the council should be informed of the action. Regular balloting of the council is required for a revision or cancellation.

8.7 Metric Unit Policy

a. All new technical reports including standards, recommended practices, and information reports, will be expressed in metric units (SI) effective December 31, 1990.

b. Each council and division reporting to the Technical Standards Board will develop and adopt a plan by which existing technical reports can be converted to SI units.

9. Some General Considerations for Technical Reports—SAE technical reports are to be limited to technical and engineering considerations. They are not to include provisions that are of a commercial nature such as prices, warranties, allocation of risk or loss or conditions of acceptance or rejection, nor are such considerations to be a basis for SAE documents.

9.1 Minimum Requirements—SAE technical reports should be written in terms of performance rather than design so as not to exclude any technically adequate equipment, product, design, material, or process. Where technical requirements are established to achieve a state purpose, such requirements should be the minimum required to achieve such purpose. In terms of standardization or interchangeability of products, only that portion of the product necessary to accomplish such standard or interchangeability should be specified in the document. When a specific product, design, material, or the like is known not to conform to the requirements or conditions of an SAE technical report applicable to the same class of products, designs, materials, or the like, the reasons (in terms of performance characteristics) for such failure are to be set forth in the minutes or files of the appropriate SAE committee together with all data supporting the conclusions of the committee.

9.2 Source of Supply—It is desirable that technical reports not contain a reference to sources of supply of parts or products, or the identity of manufacturers. Where a committee finds it necessary to specify a particular brand of product, such specification is to be accompanied by the statement *or equivalent*.

9.3 Other Society or Association Product Listings—An SAE technical report may reference a list of products that has been developed by other recognized organizations; however, in such case, the source of the list is to be clearly identified. A statement is to be made that the listing is included only for the convenience of the user and does not indicate either approval by SAE or the technical committee or its fitness for purposes specified.

9.4 Test Materials—A particular product or material may be identified by name when it is essential to uniformity in testing. In such cases, an *or equivalent* statement should be added to the company product or material referenced.

9.5 Patents and Copyrights—The committees in developing a technical report are not to consider whether the subject matter set forth is patented or copyrighted. However, if the committee is aware of any copyrights applicable to published material then such material shall not be used in the technical report. In the event it is known by the committee that following the teachings of a technical report will probably result in the infringement of a patent, the committee is to set forth criteria which will permit the user to conform to the technical report without infringing such patent.

9.6 Notice on all Technical Reports—Every approved technical report shall carry the following statements: *This report is published by SAE to advance the state of technical and engineering sciences. The use of this report is entirely voluntary, and its applicability and suitability for any particular use, including any patent infringement arising therefrom, is the sole responsibility of the user.*

9.7 Interpretation of Technical Reports—No member or participant of a technical committee, council/division or Board or SAE staff representative shall make any interpretation of a Technical Report in the name of SAE. A request for interpretation or clarification of a technical report shall be made in writing to the Secretary of the Technical Standards Board who will review the request and, if determined to be appropriate for further review, promptly forward it to the Chairperson of the technical committee, who determines that the report requires clarification, then the technical committee shall initiate a revision of the report in accordance with Section 2.1.5 of the Technical Standards Board Governance Policy. The requestor shall be notified of the decision to revise such report. If either the Chairperson or Secretary determines that no clarification or further review is required, the Secretary shall notify the requestor of such determination in writing.

10. Appeals—Any person may file an appeal of an action or refusal to act by any council/division. See Technical Standards Board Governance Policy, Section 2.20 or contact SAE Staff for procedures.

11. Records—The records of the Board, its councils/divisions, and its committees, shall be maintained for a reasonable time in the offices of the SAE where they will be available for inspection by members of the SAE and public, except as the board or the SAE Legal Counsel (in the case of classified material) directs otherwise. All documents which provide a basis for a Technical Report, including minutes, shall be maintained by SAE for a period of five years. Such documents shall be in sufficient detail so as to enable one to understand what transpired in the development, revision, or repeal of Technical Report, except that the individual ballots shall not be maintained.

GUIDELINES FOR DEVELOPING AND REVISION SAE NOMENCLATURE AND DEFINITIONS—SAE J1115 FEB1976

SAE Information Report

Report of SAE Nomenclature Advisory Committee of SAE Automotive Council approved June 1975. Editorial change February 1976.

Foreword—This Document has not changed other than to put it into the new SAE Technical Standards Board Format.

1. Scope—Historically SAE has been concerned with nomenclature as an integral part of the standards development process. Guidelines for automotive nomenclature were written in 1916, were last revised in 1941, and were included in the SAE Handbook until 1962. The present diversity of groups working on nomenclature in the various ground vehicle committees led to the organization of the Nomenclature Advisory Committee under SAE Automotive Council.

1.1 Objective—The objective of the Committee is to promote understandable and precise communication relating to the engineering aspects of on-highway vehicles, their components, their design, and their evaluation. In order to reach this objective, the Committee is primarily concerned with the definition or redefinition of needed terms considering (a) current usage, (b) changing needs, and (c) the interactive use of a particular term by various SAE Committees, government agencies, and other national and international organizations. In order to facilitate and encourage the use of generally accepted terminology by SAE committees and other organizations, the Nomenclature Advisory Committee plans to prepare and maintain a glossary of terms appearing in SAE technical reports.

2. References

2.1 Applicable Publications—The following publications form a part of the specification to the extent specified herein. Unless otherwise indicated the latest revision of SAE publications shall apply.

2.1.1 SAE PUBLICATIONS—Available from SAE, 400 Commonwealth Drive, Warrendale, PA 15096-0001.

SAE J670d—Vehicle Dynamics Terminology
SAE J782a—Seating Manual
SAE J1100a—Motor Vehicle Dimensions
Recommendations for Writing SAE Technical Reports
SAE Handbook
49 CFR 571.3 and appropriate FMVSS

3. Guidelines—Since the basic approach of the Committee is one of advice and coordination, the following guidelines for developing and revising SAE nomenclature and definitions are recommended.

3.1 Before developing and revising nomenclature, check for similar terms already defined in existing SAE Standards, Recommended Practices, and Information Reports and in Federal motor vehicle standards, in order to minimize duplication, to avoid conflict, and to achieve uniformity of format. In addition to the SAE Handbook, consult the following SAE and DOT reports:

Vehicle Dynamics Terminology, SAE J670d
Seating Manual, SAE J782A
Motor Vehicle Dimensions, SAE J1100a
Recommendations for Writing SAE Technical Reports
49 CFR 571.3 and appropriate FMVSS

3.2 If dictionary definitions of common generic terms can be used, they need not be included in nomenclature listings; for example, "Acceleration."

3.3 Develop general definitions for general terms; for example, define "Fully Latched" generically and not specifically as applied to doors, hoods or trunk lids. General definitions must be valid for all possible situations or contingencies, not just for the situation under immediate consideration.

3.4 Specific concepts or components should be identified by correspondingly specific terms when defined in a document, so that these terms can stand alone when extracted from that document and integrated with other terms in a glossary. For example, use "Tire Valve Core" rather than "Core" alone, so that the term will not be confused with another type of core, such as "Radiator Core."

3.5 The abbreviation for a defined term, when included, should follow it and be placed in parentheses; for example, "Decibel (dB)."

3.6 Terminology should follow normal word order; for example, use "Lighting Device," not "Device, Lighting," and "Brake Cylinder," not "Cylinder (Brake)." The glossary will index the defined term under each significant word in that term. For example, "Accelerator Heel Point" will appear in the index in the following permuted forms:

Accelerator Heel Point
Heel Point, Accelerator
Point, Accelerator Heel

3.7 Term definitions should be directed at concise statements of the items being defined, rather than at specifications, performance requirements, or test procedures. As an example, the following description includes both a definition and a test procedure.

Windshield Slope Angle—The angle between the vertical reference line and a chord of the windshield arc running from the lower DLO to the upper DLO at the car centerline, when such chord is no longer than 18.0 in. If the windshield is no longer than 18.0 in, the angle to be measured will be formed by a chord 18.0 in long, drawn from the lower DLO to the intersecting point on the windshield.

3.8 The opposite of a term already defined within a document need not also be defined; for example, the definition of "Asymmetrical Beam" is implied by the definition of "Symmetrical Beam."

3.9 Nomenclature which refers to a diagram should have a sufficient written definition to make the term understandable without the diagram.

3.10 Explanatory or historical notes should be stated separately from and should follow the base definition and be so identified. The following example illustrates this usage:

Static Loaded Tire Radius—The loaded radius of a stationary tire inflated to normal recommended pressure.

NOTE—In general, the static loaded radius is different from the radius of a slowly rolling tire; and the static radius of a tire rolled into position may be different from that of a tire loaded without being rolled.

3.11 When two or more terms have the same definition and are used interchangeably, a preferred term should be chosen and defined. Synonymous terms may also be listed but with only a reference to the preferred item term.

Example:
Barrel Gasket—The cylindrical sleeve of rubber-like material, etc.
Barrel Seal—Use Barrel Gasket.

3.12 Definitions should be clear and useful to all who use the SAE Handbook as an engineering or technical reference.

(R) DUAL DIMENSIONING ENGINEERING DRAWINGS—SAE J390 MAY1999

SAE Standard

Report of the Drawing Standards Committee and Metric Advisory Committee, approved July 1970, first revision prepared by the Metric Advisory Committee June 1982. Completely revised by the SAE Drawing Standards Committee and Metric Advisory May 1999. Formerly HS J390.

Foreword—This Document also changed to comply with the new SAE Technical Standards Board format. Scope is Section 1, References, Section 2. All other section numbers have changed accordingly.

1. Scope—This document covers a dual dimensioning practice that provides both U.S. customary inch-pound units and SI metric units for all dimensions on the field of the drawing. The scope does not include the various methods by which computer programs are used for dual dimensioning. In one method that has had some usage, drawings are dimensioned in SI (metric) units, with conversions to U.S. customary inch-pound units provided in a computer-generated chart on the drawing.

1.1 Purpose—The purpose of this document is to provide an authoritative guide for uniform application of dual dimensioning on engineering drawings. SAE recognizes that a decision regarding measurement units is an individual judgment based on needs and circumstances. While providing this information, SAE takes no official position concerning dual dimensioning. Issuance of this publication should not be construed as advocacy.

1.2 General—Introduction—This document establishes a uniform method of combining inch-pound units and metric units of measure on the same engineering drawing. In this document "metric units" means the International System of Units (abbreviated SI) as described in SAE TSB 003. Herein is guidance for converting from one system to the other while maintaining functional interchangeability.

2. References

2.1 Applicable Publications—The following publications form a part of the specification to the extent specified herein. Unless otherwise indicated, the latest revision of SAE publications shall apply.

2.1.1 SAE PUBLICATIONS—Available from SAE, 400 Commonwealth Drive, Warrendale, PA 15096-0001.

SAE TSB 003—Rules for SAE Use of SI (Metric) Units

2.1.2 ANSI PUBLICATION—Available from ANSI, 11 West 42nd Street, New York, NY 10036-8002.

ANSI Y14.5

IEEE/ASTM SI 10—Standard for Use of the International System of Units (SI): The Modern Metric System

NOTE—This American National Standard is available from ANSI and also from:

IEEE, 445 Hoes Lane, P.O. Box 1331, Piscataway, NJ 08855-1331.

ASTM, 100 Barr Harbor Drive, West Conshohocken, PA 19428-2959.

3. Standard Units

3.1 Inch-Pound Units—The inch-pound unit for linear dimensions is the inch with decimal dimensioning preferred. (One inch equals 25.4 mm, exactly.)

3.2 Metric Units—The metric unit, on engineering drawings, for linear dimensions is the millimeter.

3.3 Identification of Units—The inch and millimeter dimensions must be identified, one from the other as follows:

3.3.1 ALTERNATIVE METHODS—It is permissible to use one of the following methods of identification:

a. Dimensions may be identified by relative position with the millimeter dimension above or to the left of the inch dimensions.

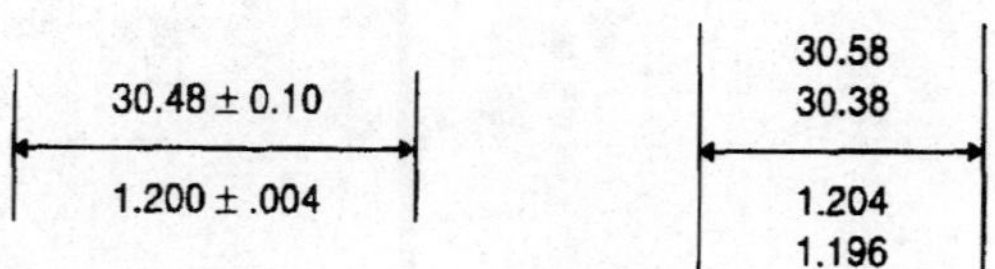

30.48 ± 0.10/1.200 ± .004

FIGURE 1—ALTERNATIVE METHODS FOR DUAL DIMENSIONING

b. Position method as in (a) except with inch dimension above or to the left of the millimeter dimension.

c. Square brackets [ ] surrounding the millimeter dimensions, placed adjacent to the inch dimensions (position optional).

d. Square brackets [ ] surrounding the inch dimensions, placed adjacent to the millimeter dimensions (position optional).

3.3.2 Only one of the previous methods of identification of units shall be used throughout a single drawing. Each drawing shall illustrate how to identify the inch and millimeter dimensions, by a note adjacent to or within the title block, such as:

$$\frac{\text{MILLIMETER}}{\text{INCH}}\text{; MILLIMETER/INCH,}$$

$$\frac{\text{INCH}}{\text{[MILLIMETER]}}\text{; INCH [MILLIMETER], etc.}$$

FIGURE 2—ENGINEERING DRAWING TITLE BLOCK NOTE FOR DUAL DIMENSIONING

or by reference to a drawing interpretation specification.

3.3.3 In converting existing drawings to dual-dimensioning, space limitations may sometimes make it impractical to locate dimensions as required for identification by position. In these cases, it is permissible to show the converted dimension in a nearby associated location identified with the symbol mm or IN.

3.3.4 Units other than linear and all units used for other than normal drawing dimensions (e.g., notes or text) shall be identified with the appropriate symbol.

EXAMPLE—13.6 N·m/10 lbf·ft

OVERHANG LIMITED TO 12.7 mm/.50 in

3.4 Common Units—Some units can be stated so that the call-out will satisfy the units of both systems. That is, .06 inch per inch or 0.06 millimeter per millimeter can both be expressed simply as a ratio, 0.06:1, or in a note, such as TAPER 0.06:1.

3.5 Angles—Angular dimensions need no conversion. Angles stated in degrees and decimals of a degree, or in degrees, minutes, and seconds are common to the inch-pound and metric systems of measurement.

3.6 Nominal Designations—Nominal designations such as thread sizes and tire sizes will not be converted.

4. Principles

4.1 Millimeter Dimensioning Practices

4.1.1 A zero precedes a decimal point in a millimeter value of less than one;

EXAMPLE—0.13

4.1.2 Where unilateral tolerancing is used and either the plus or minus value is nil, this value shall be expressed by a single zero only.

EXAMPLE—

$$32^{\ 0}_{-0.02} \qquad 32^{+0.02}_{\ 0}$$

4.1.3 Nonsignificant zeros are not shown after the decimal point, in the composition of a millimeter value, except as follows:

a. Where limit dimensioning is used and either the maximum or minimum dimension has digits following the decimal point, the other value shall have zeros added for uniformity.

EXAMPLE—

$$\begin{matrix}25.00\\25.45\end{matrix} \cdot \text{not} \cdot \begin{matrix}25\\25.45\end{matrix}$$

b. Where bilateral tolerancing is used, both the plus and minus values shall have the same number of decimal places, using zeros where necessary.

EXAMPLE—

$$32^{+0.25}_{-0.10} \text{ not } 32^{+0.25}_{-0.1}$$

4.1.4 The symbol ϕ and the abbreviation DIA are synonymous, defining a feature as diametral. Either may be used on a dual dimension drawing; however, both shall not be used on the same drawing. The application of either the symbol ϕ or DIA is self explanatory. The symbol ϕ may either precede or follow the dimension:

EXAMPLE—

$$\phi\frac{25.4}{1.00} \text{ or } \frac{25.4}{1.00}\phi$$

4.1.5 The decimal sign for metric values shall be the same as that used for the inch decimal dimension, a dot (.).

4.1.6 Commas and spaces shall not be used to denote thousands in either inch or metric values.

EXAMPLE—32541 not 32,541 nor 32 541

5. Application

5.1 New Drawings—Dual dimensioning of new drawings is facilitated if all dimensions are shown in decimals.

5.2 General Tolerances—General tolerances usually expressed on a drawing as part of the format or as a general note shall be dual dimensioned.

5.3 Symbols—Geometric characteristic symbols for form and position and the related tolerancing procedure are recommended to be used on dual dimensioned drawings. See ANSI Y14.5.

5.3.1 Dual dimensioned drawings shall specify, by the ISO symbol as shown in Figure 3, the angle of projection used. Although first angle projection is commonly used in many countries where the metric measurement system is standard, it is recommended that third angle projection be used on dual dimensioned drawings that follow this document.

*6. **Interchangeability***—Interchangeability of parts, functionally, physically, or both, is dependent upon the degree of round-off accuracy used in converting an inch value to a metric value or a metric value to an inch value with the resultant placed on a drawing. For conversion principles, see ANSI IEEE/ASTM SI 10, Standard for Use of the International System of Units (SI): The Modern Metric System, and SAE TSB 003, Rules for SAE Use of SI (Metric) Units. Where considered necessary, dual dimensioned drawings should identify the referee dimensional units to assure acceptability of product and repeatability of inspection practices.

*7. **Drawing Application***—With the addition of a title block and applicable notes, Figure 3 illustrates a typical dual dimensioned drawing.

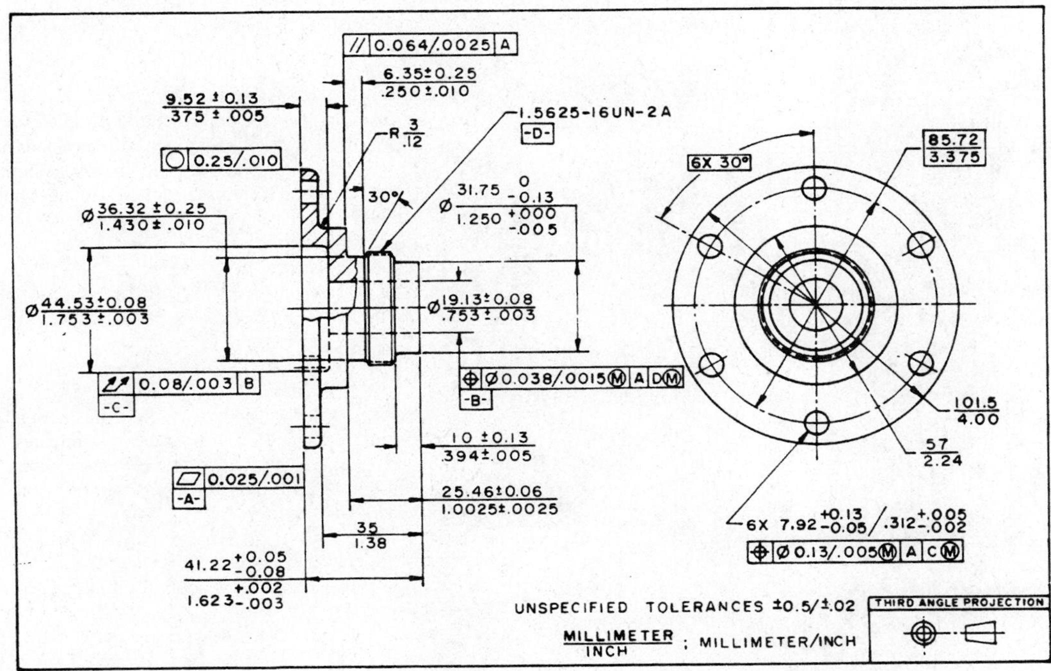

FIGURE 3—ANGLE OF PROJECTION SYMBOL ON DUAL DIMENSIONED DRAWINGS

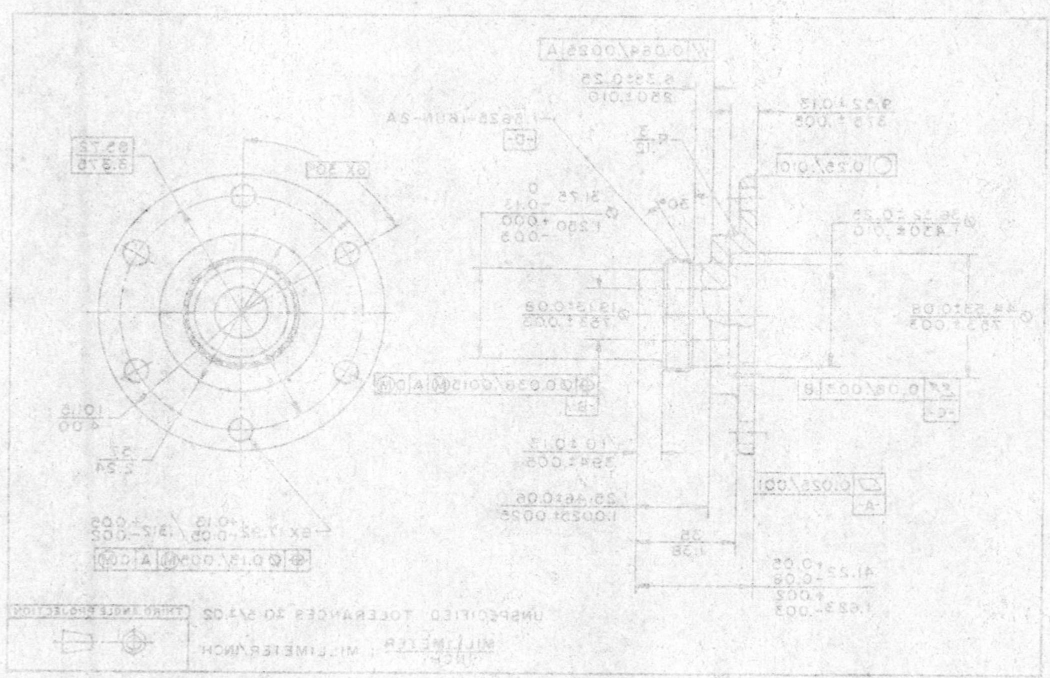